Stanley Gibbons

SIMPLIFIED CATALOGUE

Stamps of the World

2005 Edition

IN COLOUR

An illustrated and priced four-volume guide to the postage stamps of the whole world, excluding changes of paper, perforation, shade and watermark

VOLUME 3

COUNTRIES K–R

STANLEY GIBBONS LTD
London and Ringwood

By Appointment to
Her Majesty the Queen
Stanley Gibbons Limited
London
Philatelists

70th Edition

Published in Great Britain by
Stanley Gibbons Ltd
Publications Editorial, Sales Offices and Distribution Centre
Parkside, Christchurch Road,
Ringwood, Hampshire BH24 3SH
Telephone 01425 472363

ISBN: 085259-571-9

Published as Stanley Gibbons Simplified Stamp Catalogue from 1934 to 1970, renamed Stamps of the World in 1971, and produced in two (1982-88), three (1989-2001) or four (from 2002) volumes as Stanley Gibbons Simplified Catalogue of Stamps of the World.
This volume published October 2004

S.G. Item No. 2883 (05)

Printed in Great Britain by CPI Bath Press, Somerset

Stanley Gibbons
SIMPLIFIED CATALOGUE

Stamps of the World

This popular catalogue is a straightforward listing of the stamps that have been issued everywhere in the world since the very first–Great Britain's famous Penny Black in 1840.

This edition, in which both the text and the illustrations have been captured electronically, is arranged completely alphabetically in a four-volume format. Volume 1 (Countries A–D), Volume 2 (Countries E–J), Volume 3 (Countries K–R) and Volume 4 (Countries S–Z).

Readers are reminded that the Catalogue Supplements, published in each issue of **Gibbons Stamp Monthly**, can be used to update the listings in **Stamps of the World** as well as our 22-part standard catalogue. To make the supplement even more useful the Type numbers given to the illustrations are the same in the Stamps of the World as in the standard catalogues. The first Catalogue Supplement to this Volume appeared in the September 2004 issue of **Gibbons Stamp Monthly**.

Gibbons Stamp Monthly can be obtained through newsagents or on postal subscription from Stanley Gibbons Publications, Parkside, Christchurch Road, Ringwood, Hants BH24 3SH.

The catalogue has many important features:

- The vast majority of illustrations are now in full colour to aid stamp identification.
- All Commonwealth and all Western Europe miniature sheets are now included.
- As an indication of current values virtually every stamp is priced. Thousands of alterations have been made since the last edition.
- By being set out on a simplified basis that excludes changes of paper, perforation, shade, watermark, gum or printer's and date imprints it is particularly easy to use. (For its exact scope see "Information for users" pages following.)
- The thousands of colour illustrations and helpful descriptions of stamp designs make it of maximum appeal to collectors with thematic interests.
- Its catalogue numbers are the world-recognised Stanley Gibbons numbers throughout.
- Helpful introductory notes for the collector are included, backed by much historical, geographical and currency information.
- A very detailed index gives instant location of countries in this volume, and a cross-reference to those included in the other volumes.

Over 2,510 stamps and miniature sheets and 935 new illustrations have been added to the listings in this volume. This year's four-volumes now contain over 417,545 stamps and 100,767 illustrations.

The listings in this edition are based on the standard catalogues: Part 1, Commonwealth & British Empire Stamps 1840–1952, Part 2 (Austria & Hungary) (6th edition), Part 3 (Balkans) (4th edition), Part 4 (Benelux) (5th edition), Part 5 (Czechoslovakia & Poland) (6th edition), Part 6 (France) (5th edition), Part 7 (Germany) (6th edition), Part 8 (Italy & Switzerland) (6th edition), Part 9 (Portugal & Spain) (4th edition), Part 10 (Russia) (5th edition), Part 11 (Scandinavia) (5th edition), Part 12 (Africa since Independence A-E) (2nd edition), Part 13 (Africa since Independence F-M) (1st edition), Part 14 (Africa since Independence N-Z) (1st edition), Part 15 (Central America) (2nd edition), Part 16 (Central Asia) (3rd edition), Part 17 (China) (6th edition), Part 18 (Japan & Korea) (4th edition), Part 19 (Middle East) (5th edition), Part 20 (South America) (3rd edition), Part 21 (South-East Asia) (4th edition) and Part 22 (United States) (5th edition).

This edition includes major repricing for some Western Europe countries in addition to the changes for South-East Asia Part 21.

Acknowledgements

A wide-ranging revision of prices for Western European countries has been undertaken for this edition with the intention that the catalogue should be more accurate to reflect the market for foreign issues.

Many dealers in both Great Britain and overseas have participated in this scheme by supplying copies of their retail price lists on which the research has been based.

We would like to acknowledge the assistance of the following for this edition:

ALMAZ CO
of Brooklyn, U.S.A.

AMATEUR COLLECTOR LTD, THE
of London, England

E. ANGELOPOULOS
of Thessaloniki, Greece

AVION THEMATICS
of Nottingham, England

J BAREFOOT LTD
of York, England

BELGIAN PHILATELIC SPECIALISTS INC
of Larchmont, U.S.A.

Sir CHARLES BLOMEFIELD
of Chipping Camden, England

T. BRAY
of Shipley, West Yorks, England

CENTRAL PHILATELIQUE
of Brussels, Belgium

JEAN-PIERRE DELMONTE
of Paris, France

EUROPEAN & FOREIGN STAMPS
of Pontypridd, Wales

FILATELIA LLACH SL
of Barcelona, Spain

FILATELIA RIVA RENO
of Bologna, Italy

FILATELIA TORI
of Barcelona, Spain

FORMOSA STAMP COMPANY, THE
of Koahsiung, Taiwan

FORSTAMPS
of Battle, England

ANTHONY GRAINGER
of Leeds, England

HOLMGREN STAMPS
of Bollnas, Sweden

INDIGO
of Orewa, New Zealand

ALEC JACQUES
of Selby, England

M. JANKOWSKI
of Warsaw, Poland

D.J.M. KERR
of Earlston, England

H. M. NIELSEN
of Vejle, Denmark

LEO BARESCH LTD
of Hassocks, England

LORIEN STAMPS
of Chesterfield, England

MANDARIN TRADING CO
of Alhambra, U.S.A.

MICHAEL ROGERS INC
of Winter Park, U.S.A.

PHILATELIC SUPPLIES
of Letchworth, England

PHIL-INDEX
of Eastbourne, England

PHILTRADE A/S
of Copenhagen, Denmark

PITTERI SA
of Chiasso, Switzerland

KEVIN RIGLER
of Shifnal, England

ROLF GUMMESSON AB
of Stockholm, Sweden

R. D. TOLSON
of Undercliffe, England

JAY SMITH
of Snow Camp, U.S.A.

R. SCHNEIDER
of Belleville, U.S.A.

ROBSTINE STAMPS
of Hampshire, England

SOUTHERN MAIL
of Eastbourne, England

STAMP CENTER
of Reykjavik, Iceland

REX WHITE
of Winchester, England

Some Western European countries have been repriced this year in Stamps of the World and where there is no up-to-date specialised foreign volume in a country these will be the new Stanley Gibbons prices.

It is hoped that this improved pricing scheme will be extended to other foreign countries and thematic issues as information is consolidated.

Information for users

Aim

The aim of this catalogue is to provide a straightforward illustrated and priced guide to the postage stamps of the whole world to help you to enjoy the greatest hobby of the present day.

Arrangement

The catalogue lists countries in alphabetical order and there is a complete index at the end of each volume. For ease of reference country names are also printed at the head of each page.

Within each country, postage stamps are listed first. They are followed by separate sections for such other categories as postage due stamps, parcel post stamps, express stamps, official stamps, etc.

All catalogue lists are set out according to dates of issue of the stamps, starting from the earliest and working through to the most recent.

Scope of the Catalogue

The *Simplified Catalogue of Stamps of the World* contains listings of postage stamps only. Apart from the ordinary definitive, commemorative and airmail stamps of each country – which appear first in each list – there are sections for the following where appropriate:

- postage due stamps
- parcel post stamps
- official stamps
- express and special delivery stamps
- charity and compulsory tax stamps
- newspaper and journal stamps
- printed matter stamps
- registration stamps
- acknowledgement of receipt stamps
- late fee and too late stamps
- military post stamps
- recorded message stamps
- personal delivery stamps

We receive numerous enquiries from collectors about other items which do not fall within the categories set out above and which consequently do not appear in the catalogue lists. It may be helpful, therefore, to summarise the other kinds of stamp that exist but which we deliberately exclude from this postage stamp catalogue.

We do *not* list the following:

Fiscal or revenue stamps: stamps used solely in collecting taxes or fees for non-postal purposes. Examples would be stamps which pay a tax on a receipt, represent the stamp duty on a contract or frank a customs document. Common inscriptions found include: Documentary, Proprietary, Inter. Revenue, Contract Note.

Local stamps: postage stamps whose validity and use are limited in area, say to a single town or city, though in some cases they provided, with official sanction, services in parts of countries not covered by the respective government.

Local carriage labels and Private local issues: many labels exist ostensibly to cover the cost of ferrying mail from one of Great Britain's offshore islands to the nearest mainland post office. They are not recognised as valid for national or international mail. Examples: Calf of Man, Davaar, Herm, Lundy, Pabay, Stroma. Items from some other places have only the status of tourist souvenir labels.

Telegraph stamps: stamps intended solely for the prepayment of telegraphic communication.

Bogus or "phantom" stamps: labels from mythical places or non-existent administrations. Examples in the classical period were Sedang, Counani, Clipperton Island and in modern times Thomond and Monte Bello Islands. Numerous labels have also appeared since the War from dissident groups as propaganda for their claims and without authority from the home governments. Common examples are labels for "Free Albania", "Free Rumania" and "Free Croatia" and numerous issues for Nagaland, Indonesia and the South Moluccas ("Republik Maluku Selatan").

Railway letter fee stamps: special stamps issued by railway companies for the conveyance of letters by rail. Example: Talyllyn Railway. Similar services are now offered by some bus companies and the labels they issue likewise do not qualify for inclusion in the catalogue.

Perfins ("perforated initials"): numerous postage stamps may be found with initial letters or designs punctured through them by tiny holes. These are applied by private and public concerns as a precaution against theft and do not qualify for separate mention.

Information for users

Labels: innumerable items exist resembling stamps but – as they do not prepay postage – they are classified as labels. The commonest categories are:

- propaganda and publicity labels: designed to further a cause or campaign;
- exhibition labels: particularly souvenirs from philatelic events;
- testing labels: stamp-size labels used in testing stamp-vending machines;
- Post Office training school stamps: British stamps overprinted with two thick vertical bars or SCHOOL SPECIMEN are produced by the Post Office for training purposes;
- seals and stickers: numerous charities produce stamp-like labels, particularly at Christmas and Easter, as a means of raising funds and these have no postal validity.

Cut-outs: items of postal stationery, such as envelopes, cards and wrappers, often have stamps impressed or imprinted on them. They may usually be cut out and affixed to envelopes, etc., for postal use if desired, but such items are not listed in this catalogue.

Collectors wanting further information about exact definitions are referred to *Philatelic Terms Illustrated,* published by Stanley Gibbons and containing many illustrations in colour.

There is also a priced listing of the postal fiscals of Great Britain in our *Commonwealth & British Empire Stamps 1840–1952* Catalogue and in Volume 1 of the *Great Britain Specialised* Catalogue (5th and later editions).

Prices are shown as follows:

10 means 10p (10 pence);
1.50 means £1.50 (1 pound and 50 pence);
For £100 and above, prices are in whole pounds.

Our prices are for stamps in fine condition, and in issues where condition varies we may ask more for the superb and less for the sub-standard.

The minimum catalogue price quoted is 10p. For individual stamps prices between 10p and 45p are provided as a guide for catalogue users. The lowest price charged for individual stamps purchased from Stanley Gibbons is 50p.

The prices quoted are generally for the cheapest variety of stamps but it is worth noting that differences of watermark, perforation, or other details, outside the scope of this catalogue, may often increase the value of the stamp.

Prices quoted for mint issues are for single examples. Those in se-tenant pairs, strips, blocks or sheets may be worth more.

Where prices are not given in either column it is either because the stamps are not known to exist in that particular condition, or, more usually, because there is no reliable information as to value.

All prices are subject to change without prior notice and we give no guarantee to supply all stamps priced. Prices quoted for albums, publications, etc. advertised in this catalogue are also subject to change without prior notice.

Due to different production methods it is sometimes possible for new editions of Parts 2 to 22 to appear showing revised prices which are not included in that year's *Stamps of the World.*

Catalogue Numbers

Stanley Gibbons catalogue numbers are recognised universally and any individual stamp can be identified by quoting the catalogue number (the one at the left of the column) prefixed by the name of the country and the letters "S.G.". Do not confuse the catalogue number with the type numbers which refer to illustrations.

Prices

Prices in the left-hand column are for unused stamps and those in the right-hand column for used. Prices are given in pence and pounds:

100 pence (p) 1 pound (£1).

Unused Stamps

In the case of stamps from *Great Britain* and the *Commonwealth,* prices for unused stamps of Queen Victoria to King George V are for lightly hinged examples; unused prices of King Edward VIII to Queen Elizabeth II issues are for unmounted mint. The prices of unused Foreign stamps are for lightly hinged examples for those issued before 1946, thereafter for examples unmounted mint.

Used Stamps

Prices for used stamps generally refer to fine postally used examples, though for certain issues they are for cancelled-to-order.

Information for users

Guarantee

All stamps supplied by us are guaranteed originals in the following terms:

If not as described, and returned by the purchaser, we undertake to refund the price paid to us in the original transaction. If any stamp is certified as genuine by the Expert Committee of the Royal Philatelic Society, London, or by B.P.A. Expertising Ltd., the purchaser shall not be entitled to make any claim against us for any error, omission or mistake in such certificate.

Consumers' statutory rights are not affected by the above guarantee.

Currency

At the beginning of each country brief details give the currencies in which the values of the stamps are expressed. The dates, where given, are those of the earliest stamp issues in the particular currency. Where the currency is obvious, e.g. where the colony has the same currency as the mother country, no details are given.

Illustrations

Illustrations of any surcharges and overprints which are shown and not described are actual size; stamp illustrations are reduced to $\frac{3}{4}$ linear, *unless otherwise stated.*

"Key-Types"

A number of standard designs occur so frequently in the stamps of the French, German, Portuguese and Spanish colonies that it would be a waste of space to repeat them. Instead these are all illustrated on page xiv together with the descriptive names and letters by which they are referred to in the lists.

Type Numbers

These are the bold figures found below each illustration. References to "Type **6**", for example, in the lists of a country should therefore be understood to refer to the illustration below which the number **"6"** appears. These type numbers are also given in the second column of figures alongside each list of stamps, thus indicating clearly the design of each stamp. In the case of Key-Types – see above – letters take the place of the type numbers.

Where an issue comprises stamps of similar design, represented in this catalogue by one illustration, the corresponding type numbers should be taken as indicating this general design.

Where there are blanks in the type number column it means that the type of the corresponding stamps is that shown by the last number above in the type column of the same issue.

A dash (–) in the type column means that no illustration of the stamp is shown.

Where type numbers refer to stamps of another country, e.g. where stamps of one country are overprinted for use in another, this is always made clear in the text.

Stamp Designs

Brief descriptions of the subjects of the stamp designs are given either below or beside the illustrations, at the foot of the list of the issue concerned, or in the actual lists. Where a particular subject, e.g. the portrait of a well-known monarch, recurs frequently the description is not repeated, nor are obvious designs described.

Generally, the unillustrated designs are in the same shape and size as the one illustrated, except where otherwise indicated.

Surcharges and Overprints

Surcharges and overprints are usually described in the headings to the issues concerned. Where the actual wording of a surcharge or overprint is given it is shown in bold type.

Some stamps are described as being "Surcharged in words", e.g. **TWO CENTS**, and others "Surcharged in figures and words", e.g. **20 CENTS**, although of course many surcharges are in foreign languages and combinations of words and figures are numerous. There are often bars, etc., obliterating old values or inscriptions but in general these are only mentioned where it is necessary to avoid confusion.

No attention is paid in this catalogue to colours of overprints and surcharges so that stamps with the same overprints in different colours are not listed separately.

Numbers in brackets after the descriptions of overprinted or surcharged stamps are the catalogue numbers of the unoverprinted stamps.

Note – the words "inscribed" or "inscription" always refer to wording incorporated in the design of a stamp and not surcharges or overprints.

Coloured Papers

Where stamps are printed on coloured paper the description is given as e.g. "4 c. black on blue" – a stamp printed in black on blue paper. No attention is paid in this catalogue to difference in the texture of paper, e.g. laid, wove.

Information for users

Watermarks

Stamps having different watermarks, but otherwise the same, are not listed separately. No reference is therefore made to watermarks in this volume.

Stamp Colours

Colour names are only required for the identification of stamps, therefore they have been made as simple as possible. Thus "scarlet", "vermilion", "carmine" are all usually called red. Qualifying colour names have been introduced only where necessary for the sake of clearness.

Where stamps are printed in two or more colours the central portion of the design is in the first colour given, unless otherwise stated.

Perforations

All stamps are perforated unless otherwise stated. No distinction is made between the various gauges of perforation but early stamp issues which exist both imperforate and perforated are usually listed separately.

Where a heading states "Imperf. or perf". or "Perf. or rouletted" this does not necessarily mean that all values of the issue are found in both conditions.

Dates of Issue

The date given at the head of each issue is that of the appearance of the earliest stamp in the series. As stamps of the same design or issue are usually grouped together a list of King George VI stamps, for example, headed "1938" may include stamps issued from 1938 to the end of the reign.

Se-tenant Pairs

Many modern issues are printed in sheets containing different designs or face values. Such pairs, blocks, strips or sheets are described as being "se-tenant" and they are outside the scope of this catalogue, although reference to them may occur in instances where they form a composite design.

Miniature Sheets

As an increasing number of stamps are now only found in miniature sheets, Stamps of the World will, in future, list these items. This edition lists all Commonwealth countries' miniature sheets, plus those of all non-Commonwealth countries which have appeared in the catalogue supplement during the past year. Earlier miniature sheets of non-Commonwealth countries will be listed in future editions.

"Appendix" Countries

We regret that, since 1968, it has been necessary to establish an Appendix (at the end of each country as appropriate) to which numerous stamps have had to be consigned. Several countries imagine that by issuing huge quantities of unnecessary stamps they will have a ready source of income from stamp collectors – and particularly from the less-experienced ones. Stanley Gibbons refuse to encourage this exploitation of the hobby and we do not stock the stamps concerned.

Two kinds of stamp are therefore given the briefest of mentions in the Appendix, purely for the sake of record. Administrations issuing stamps greatly in excess of true postal needs have the offending issues placed there. Likewise it contains stamps which have not fulfilled all the normal conditions for full catalogue listing.

These conditions are that the stamps must be issued by a legitimate postal authority, recognised by the government concerned, and are adhesives, valid for proper postal use in the class of service for which they are inscribed. Stamps, with the exception of such categories as postage dues and officials, must be available to the general public at face value with no artificial restrictions being imposed on their distribution.

The publishers of this catalogue have observed, with concern, the proliferation of 'artificial' stamp-issuing territories. On several occasions this has resulted in separately inscribed issues for various component parts of otherwise united states or territories.

Stanley Gibbons Publications have decided that where such circumstances occur, they will not, in the future, list these items in the SG catalogue without first satisfying themselves that the stamps represent a genuine political, historical or postal division within the country concerned. Any such issues which do not fulfil this stipulation will be recorded in the Catalogue Appendix only.

Stamps in the Appendix are kept under review in the light of any newly acquired information about them. If we are satisfied that a stamp qualifies for proper listing in the body of the catalogue it is moved there.

Information for users

"Undesirable Issues"

The rules governing many competitive exhibitions are set by the Federation Internationale de Philatelie and stipulate a downgrading of marks for stamps classed as "undesirable issues".

This catalogue can be taken as a guide to status. All stamps in the main listings and Addenda are acceptable. Stamps in the Appendix should not be entered for competition as these are the "undesirable issues".

Particular care is advised with Aden Protectorate States, Ajman, Bhutan, Chad, Fujeira, Khor Fakkan, Manama, Ras al Khaima, Sharjah, Umm al Qiwain and Yemen. Totally bogus stamps exist (as explained in Appendix notes) and these are to be avoided also for competition. As distinct from "undesirable stamps" certain categories are not covered in this catalogue purely by reason of its scope (see page viii). Consult the particular competition rules to see if such are admissable even though not listed by us.

Where to Look for More Detailed Listings

The present work deliberately omits details of paper, perforation, shade and watermark. But as you become more absorbed in stamp collecting and wish to get greater enjoyment from the hobby you may well want to study these matters.

All the information you require about any particular postage stamp will be found in the main Stanley Gibbons Catalogues.

Commonwealth countries before 1952 are covered by the Commonwealth & British Empire Stamps 1840–1952 published annually.

For foreign countries you can easily find which catalogue to consult by looking at the country headings in the present book.

To the right of each country name are code letters specifying which volume of our main catalogues contains that country's listing.

The code letters are as follows:

Pt. 2 Part 2

Pt. 3 Part 3 etc.

(See page xiii for complete list of Parts.)

So, for example, if you want to know more about Chinese stamps than is contained in the *Simplified Catalogue of Stamps of the World* the reference to

CHINA Pt. 17

guides you to the Gibbons Part 17 *(China)* Catalogue listing for the details you require.

New editions of Parts 2 to 22 appear at irregular intervals.

Correspondence

Whilst we welcome information and suggestions we must ask correspondents to include the cost of postage for the return of any stamps submitted plus registration where appropriate. Letters should be addressed to The Catalogue Editor at Ringwood.

Where information is solicited purely for the benefit of the enquirer we regret we cannot undertake to reply.

Identification of Stamps

We regret we do not give opinions as to the genuineness of stamps, nor do we identify stamps or number them by our Catalogue.

Users of this catalogue are referred to our companion booklet entitled *Stamp Collecting – How to Identify Stamps.* It explains how to look up stamps in this catalogue, contains a full checklist of stamp inscriptions and gives help in dealing with unfamiliar scripts.

Stanley Gibbons would like to complement your collection

At Stanley Gibbons we offer a range of services which are designed to complement your collection.

Our modern stamp shop, the largest in Europe, together with our rare stamp department has one of the most comprehensive stocks of Great Britain in the world, so whether you are a beginner or an experienced philatelist you are certain to find something to suit your special requirements.

Alternatively, through our Mail Order services you can control the growth of your collection from the comfort of your own home. Our Postal Sales Department regularly sends out mailings of Special Offers. We can also help with your wants list—so why not ask us for those elusive items?

Why not take advantage of the many services we have to offer? Visit our premises in the Strand or, for more information, write to the appropriate address on page x.

The Stanley Gibbons Group Addresses

Stanley Gibbons Limited,
Stanley Gibbons Auctions

339 Strand, London WC2R 0LX
Telephone 020 7836 8444, Fax 020 7836 7342,
E-mail: enquiries@stanleygibbons.co.uk
Internet: www.stanleygibbons.com for all departments.

Auction Room and Specialist Stamp Departments.
Open Monday–Friday 9.30 a.m. to 5 p.m.

Shop. Open Monday–Friday 9 a.m. to 5.30 p.m. and Saturday 9.30 a.m. to 5.30 p.m.

Stanley Gibbons Publications

Parkside, Christchurch Road, Ringwood, Hants BH24 3SH.
Telephone 01425 472363 (24 hour answer phone service), Fax 01425 470247,
E-mail: info@stanleygibbons.co.uk

Publications Mail Order. FREEPHONE 0800 611622
Monday–Friday 8.30 a.m. to 5 p.m.

Fraser's
(a division of Stanley Gibbons Ltd)

399 Strand, London WC2R 0LX
Autographs, photographs, letters and documents

Telephone 020 7836 8444, Fax 020 7836 7342,
E-mail: info@frasersautographs.co.uk
Internet: www.frasersautographs.com

Monday–Friday 9 a.m. to 5.30 p.m. and Saturday 10 a.m. to 4 p.m.

Stanley Gibbons Publications Overseas Representation

Stanley Gibbons Publications are represented overseas by the following sole distributors (*), distributors (**) or licensees (***).

Australia
Lighthouse Philatelic (Aust.) Pty. Ltd.*
Locked Bag 5900 Botany DC, New South Wales, 2019 Australia.

Stanley Gibbons (Australia) Pty. Ltd.***
Level 6, 36 Clarence Street, Sydney, New South Wales 2000, Australia.

Belgium and Luxembourg**
Davo c/o Philac, Rue du Midi 48, Bruxelles, 1000 Belgium.

Canada*
Lighthouse Publications (Canada) Ltd., 255 Duke Street, Montreal Quebec, Canada H3C 2M2.

Denmark**
Samlerforum/Davo, Ostergade 3, DK 7470 Karup, Denmark.

Finland**
Davo c/o Kapylan Merkkiky Pohjolankatu 1 00610 Helsinki, Finland.

France*
Davo France (Casteilla), 10, Rue Leon Foucault, 78184 St. Quentin Yvelines Cesex, France.

Hong Kong**
Po-on Stamp Service, GPO Box 2498, Hong Kong.

Israel**
Capital Stamps, P.O. Box 3769, Jerusalem 91036, Israel.

Italy*
Ernesto Marini Srl, Via Struppa 300, I-16165, Genova GE, Italy.

Japan**
Japan Philatelic Co. Ltd., P.O. Box 2, Suginami-Minami, Tokyo, Japan.

Netherlands*
Davo Publications, P.O. Box 411, 7400 AK Deventer, Netherlands.

New Zealand***
Mowbray Collectables.
P.O. Box 80, Wellington, New Zealand.

Norway**
Davo Norge A/S, P.O. Box 738 Sentrum, N-0105, Oslo, Norway.

Singapore**
Stamp Inc Collectibles Pte Ltd., 10 Ubi Cresent, #01-43 Ubi Tech Park, Singapore 408564.

Sweden*
Chr Winther Soerensen AB, Box 43, S-310 Knaered, Sweden.

Switzerland**
Phila Service, Burgstrasse 160, CH 4125, Riehen, Switzerland.

Abbreviations

Anniv.	denotes	Anniversary
Assn.	,,	Association
Bis.	,,	Bistre
Bl.	,,	Blue
Bldg.	,,	Building
Blk.	,,	Black
Br.	,,	British or Bridge
Brn.	,,	Brown
B.W.I.	,,	British West Indies
C.A.R.I.F.T.A.	,,	Caribbean Free Trade Area
Cent.	,,	Centenary
Chest.	,,	Chestnut
Choc.	,,	Chocolate
Clar.	,,	Claret
Coll.	,,	College
Commem.	,,	Commemoration
Conf.	,,	Conference
Diag.	,,	Diagonally
E.C.A.F.E.	,,	Economic Commission for Asia and Far East
Emer.	,,	Emerald
E.P.T. Conference	,,	European Postal and Telecommunications Conference
Exn.		Exhibition
F.A.O.	,,	Food and Agriculture Organization
Fig.	,,	Figure
G.A.T.T.	,,	General Agreement on Tariffs and Trade
G.B.	,,	Great Britain
Gen.	,,	General
Govt.	,,	Government
Grn.	,,	Green
Horiz.	,,	Horizontal
H.Q.	,,	Headquarters
Imperf.	,,	Imperforate
Inaug.	,,	Inauguration
Ind.	,,	Indigo
Inscr.	,,	Inscribed or inscription
Int.	,,	International
I.A.T.A.	,,	International Air Transport Association
I.C.A.O.	,,	International Civil Aviation Organization
I.C.Y.	,,	International Co-operation Year
I.G.Y.	,,	International Geophysical Year
I.L.O.	,,	International Labour Office (or later, Organization)
I.M.C.O.	,,	Inter-Governmental Maritime Consultative Organization
I.T.U.	,,	International Telecommunication Union
Is.	,,	Islands
Lav.	,,	Lavender
Mar.	,,	Maroon
mm.	,,	Millimetres
Mult.	,,	Multicoloured
Mve.	denotes	Mauve
Nat.	,,	National
N.A.T.O.	,,	North Atlantic Treaty Organization
O.D.E.C.A.	,,	Organization of Central American States
Ol.	,,	Olive
Optd.	,,	Overprinted
Orge. or oran.	,,	Orange
P.A.T.A.	,,	Pacific Area Travel Association
Perf.	,,	Perforated
Post.	,,	Postage
Pres.	,,	President
P.U.	,,	Postal Union
Pur.	,,	Purple
R.	,,	River
R.S.A.	,,	Republic of South Africa
Roul.	,,	Rouletted
Sep.	,,	Sepia
S.E.A.T.O.	,,	South East Asia Treaty Organization
Surch.	,,	Surcharged
T.	,,	Type
T.U.C.	,,	Trades Union Congress
Turq.	,,	Turquoise
Ultram.	,,	Ultramarine
U.N.E.S.C.O.	,,	United Nations Educational, Scientific Cultural Organization
U.N.I.C.E.F.	,,	United Nations Children's Fund
U.N.O.	,,	United Nations Organization
U.N.R.W.A.	,,	United Nations Relief and Works Agency for Palestine Refugees in the Near East
U.N.T.E.A.	,,	United Nations Temporary Executive Authority
U.N.R.R.A.	,,	United Nations Relief and Rehabilitation Administration
U.P.U.	,,	Universal Postal Union
Verm.	,,	Vermilion
Vert.	,,	Vertical
Vio.	,,	Violet
W.F.T.U.	,,	World Federation of Trade Unions
W.H.O.	,,	World Health Organization
Yell.	,,	Yellow

Arabic Numerals

As in the case of European figures, the details of the Arabic numerals vary in different stamp designs, but they should be readily recognised with the aid of this illustration:

٠	١	٢	٣	٤
0	1	2	3	4
٥	٦	٧	٨	٩
5	6	7	8	9

Stanley Gibbons Stamp Catalogue
Complete List of Parts

1 **Commonwealth & British Empire Stamps 1840–1952** (Annual)

Foreign Countries

2 **Austria & Hungary** (6th edition, 2002)
Austria · U.N. (Vienna) · Hungary

3 **Balkans** (4th edition, 1998)
Albania · Bosnia & Herzegovina · Bulgaria · Croatia · Greece & Islands · Macedonia · Rumania · Slovenia · Yugoslavia

4 **Benelux** (5th edition, 2003)
Belgium & Colonies · Luxembourg · Netherlands & Colonies

5 **Czechoslovakia & Poland** (6th edition, 2002)
Czechoslovakia · Czech Republic · Slovakia · Poland

6 **France** (5th edition, 2001)
France · Colonies · Post Offices · Andorra · Monaco

7 **Germany** (6th edition, 2002)
Germany · States · Colonies · Post Offices

8 **Italy & Switzerland** (6th edition, 2003)
Italy & Colonies · Liechtenstein · San Marino · Switzerland · U.N. (Geneva) · Vatican City

9 **Portugal & Spain** (4th edition, 1996)
Andorra · Portugal & Colonies · Spain & Colonies

10 **Russia** (5th edition, 1999)
Russia · Armenia · Azerbaijan · Belarus · Estonia · Georgia · Kazakhstan · Kyrgyzstan · Latvia · Lithuania · Moldova · Tajikistan · Turkmenistan · Ukraine · Uzbekistan · Mongolia

11 **Scandinavia** (5th edition, 2001)
Aland Islands · Denmark · Faroe Islands · Finland · Greenland · Iceland · Norway · Sweden

12 **Africa since Independence A-E** (2nd edition, 1983)
Algeria · Angola · Benin · Burundi · Cameroun · Cape Verdi · Central African Republic · Chad · Comoro Islands · Congo · Djibouti · Equatorial Guinea · Ethiopia

13 **Africa since Independence F-M** (1st edition, 1981)
Gabon · Guinea · Guinea-Bissau · Ivory Coast · Liberia · Libya · Malagasy Republic · Mali · Mauritania · Morocco · Mozambique

14 **Africa since Independence N-Z** (1st edition, 1981)
Niger Republic · Rwanda · St. Thomas & Prince · Senegal · Somalia · Sudan · Togo · Tunisia · Upper Volta · Zaire

15 **Central America** (2nd edition, 1984)
Costa Rica · Cuba · Dominican Republic · El Salvador · Guatemala · Haiti · Honduras · Mexico · Nicaragua · Panama

16 **Central Asia** (3rd edition, 1992)
Afghanistan · Iran · Turkey

17 **China** (6th edition,1998)
China · Taiwan · Tibet · Foreign P.O.s · Hong Kong · Macao

18 **Japan & Korea** (4th edition, 1997)
Japan · Korean Empire · South Korea · North Korea

19 **Middle East** (5th edition, 1996)
Bahrain · Egypt · Iraq · Israel · Jordan · Kuwait · Lebanon · Oman · Qatar · Saudi Arabia · Syria · U.A.E. · Yemen

20 **South America** (3rd edition, 1989)
Argentina · Bolivia · Brazil · Chile · Colombia · Ecuador · Paraguay · Peru · Surinam · Uruguay · Venezuela

21 **South-East Asia** (4th edition, 2004)
Bhutan · Burma · Indonesia · Kampuchea · Laos · Nepal · Philippines · Thailand · Vietnam

22 **United States** (5th edition, 2000)
U.S. & Possessions · Marshall Islands · Micronesia · Palau · U.N. (New York, Geneva, Vienna)

Thematic Catalogues

Stanley Gibbons Catalogues for use with **Stamps of the World.**
Collect Aircraft on Stamps (out of print)
Collect Birds on Stamps (5th edition, 2003)
Collect Chess on Stamps (2nd edition, 1999)
Collect Fish on Stamps (1st edition, 1999)
Collect Fungi on Stamps (2nd edition, 1997)
Collect Motor Vehicles on Stamps (1st edition, 2004)
Collect Railways on Stamps (3rd edition, 1999)
Collect Shells on Stamps (1st edition, 1995)
Collect Ships on Stamps (3rd edition, 2001)

Key-Types

(see note on page vii)

French Group

A. "Blanc."

B. "Mouchon."

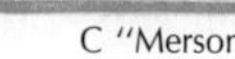

C "Merson."

D. "Tablet."

E.

F.

G.

H.

"International Colonial Exhibition."

I. "Faidherbe."

J. "Palms."

K. "Balay."

L. "Natives."

M. "Figure."

German Group

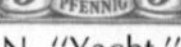
N. "Yacht."

O. "Yacht."

Spanish Group

X. "Alfonso XII."

Y. "Baby."

Z. "Curly Head"

Portuguese Group

P. "Crown."

Q. "Embossed."

R. "Figures."

S. "Carlos."

T. "Manoel."

U. "Ceres."

V. "Newspaper."

W. "Due."

STANLEY GIBBONS SIMPLIFIED CATALOGUE OF STAMPS OF THE WORLD—VOLUME 3 COUNTRIES K–R

KAMPUCHEA Pt. 21

Following the fall of the Khmer Rouge government, which had terminated the Khmer Republic, the People's Republic of Kampuchea was proclaimed on 10 January 1979.

Kampuchea was renamed Cambodia in 1989.

100 cents = 1 riel.

105 Soldiers with Flag and Independence Monument, Phnom Penh

106 Moscow Kremlin and Globe

1980. Multicoloured. Without gum.

402	0.1r. Type **105**	4·50	4·50
403	0.2r. Khmer people and flag	7·25	7·25
404	0.5r. Fisherman pulling in nets	11·00	11·00
405	1r. Armed forces and Kampuchean flag	18·00	18·00

1982. 60th Anniv of U.S.S.R. Multicoloured.

406	50c. Type **106**	35	20
407	1r. Industrial complex and map of U.S.S.R.	55	25

107 Arms of Kampuchea

1983. 4th Anniv of People's Republic of Kampuchea. Multicoloured.

408	50c. Type **107**	55	10
409	1r. Open book illustrating national flag and arms (horiz)	90	20
410	3r. Stylized figures and map	2·50	65

108 Runner with Olympic Torch

109 Orange Tiger

1983. Olympic Games, Los Angeles (1984) (1st issue). Multicoloured.

412	20c. Type **108**	25	10
413	50c. Javelin throwing	35	10
414	80c. Pole vaulting	45	10
415	1r. Discus throwing	55	10
416	1r.50 Relay (horiz)	90	20
417	2r. Swimming (horiz)	1·30	20
418	3r. Basketball	2·00	20

See also Nos. 526/32.

1983. Butterflies. Multicoloured.

420	20c. Type **109**	20	10
421	50c. "Euploea althaea"	25	10
422	80c. "Byasa polyeuctes" (horiz)	35	10
423	1r. "Stichophthalma howqua" (horiz)	55	10
424	1r.50 Leaf butterfly	1·20	20
425	2r. Blue argus	1·30	20
426	3r. Lemon migrant	2·00	20

110 Srah Srang

1983. Khmer Culture. Multicoloured.

427	20c. Type **110**	20	10
428	50c. Bakong	25	10
429	80c. Ta Som (vert)	35	10
430	1r. North gate, Angkor Thom (vert)	55	20
431	1r.50 Kennora (winged figures) (vert)	1·20	25
432	2r. Apsara (carved figures), Angkor (vert)	1·30	35
433	3r. Banteai Srei (goddess), Tevoda (vert)	2·00	55

111 Dancers with Castanets

1983. Folklore. Multicoloured.

434	50c. Type **111**	25	20
435	1r. Dancers with grass headdresses	90	25
436	3r. Dancers with scarves	2·00	65

112 Detail of Fresco

1983. 500th Birth Anniv of Raphael (artist).

438 **112**	20c. multicoloured	20	10
439 –	50c. multicoloured	25	10
440 –	80c. multicoloured	35	10
441 –	1r. multicoloured	80	20
442 –	1r.50 multicoloured	1·30	25
443 –	2r. multicoloured	1·60	35
444 –	3r. multicoloured	2·20	55

DESIGNS: Nos. 439/44, different details of frescoes by Raphael.

113 Montgolfier Balloon

1983. Bicentenary of Manned Flight. Mult.

446	20c. Type **113**	20	10
447	30c. "La Ville d'Orleans", 1870	25	10
448	50c. Charles's hydrogen balloon	35	10
449	1r. Blanchard and Jeffries crossing Channel, 1785	65	20
450	1r.50 Salomon Andree's balloon flight over Arctic	90	25
451	2r. Auguste Piccard's stratosphere balloon "F.N.R.S."	1·30	35
452	3r. Hot-air balloon race	1·80	70

114 Cobra

116 Sunflower

115 Rainbow Lory

1983. Reptiles. Multicoloured.

454	20c. Crested lizard (horiz)	20	10
455	30c. Type **114**	25	20
456	80c. Trionyx turtle (horiz)	45	20
457	1r. Chameleon	70	25
458	1r.50 Boa constrictor	1·30	45
459	2r. Crocodile (horiz)	1·60	65
460	3r. Turtle (horiz)	2·10	90

1983. Birds. Multicoloured.

461	20c. Type **115**	20	10
462	50c. Barn swallow	25	10
463	80c. Golden eagle (horiz)	45	10
464	1r. Griffon vulture (horiz)	90	10
465	1r.50 Javanese collared dove (horiz)	1·60	20
466	2r. Black-billed magpie	2·00	20
467	3r. Great Indian hornbill	3·50	20

1983. Flowers. Multicoloured.

468	20c. Type **116**	20	10
469	50c. "Caprifoliaceae"	25	10
470	80c. "Bougainvillea"	35	10
471	1r. "Ranunculaceae"	65	20
472	1r.50 "Nyctagynaeceae"	1·30	20
473	2r. Cockscomb	1·60	25
474	3r. Roses	2·00	45

117 Luge

1983. Winter Olympic Games, Sarajevo (1984) (1st issue). Multicoloured.

475	1r. Type **117**	65	10
476	2r. Biathlon	1·40	20
477	4r. Ski-jumping	2·75	25
478	5r. Two-man bobsleigh	3·25	35
479	7r. Ice hockey	4·75	45

See also Nos. 496/502.

118 Cyprinid

1983. Fishes. Multicoloured.

481	20c. Type **118**	20	10
482	50c. Loach	25	10
483	80c. Bubblebee catfish	35	10
484	1r. Spiny eel	70	10
485	1r.50 Cyprinid (different)	1·30	10
486	2r. Cyprinid (different)	1·80	20
487	3r. Aberrant fish	2·20	20

119 Factory and Gearwheel

1983. Festival of Rebirth. Multicoloured.

488	50c. Type **119**	25	20
489	1r. Tractor and cow (horiz)	90	20
490	3r. Bulk carrier, diesel locomotive, car and bridge	2·00	55

120 Red Cross and Sailing Ship

1984. 5th Anniv of Liberation. Multicoloured.

492	50c. Type **120**	25	20
493	1r. Three soldiers, flags and temple	65	20
494	3r. Crowd surrounding temple	1·80	55

121 Speed Skating

122 Ilyushin Il-62M Jet over Angkor Vat

1984. Winter Olympic Games, Sarajevo (2nd issue). Multicoloured.

496	20c. Type **121**	20	10
497	50c. Ice hockey	25	10
498	80c. Skiing	35	10
499	1r. Ski jumping	65	20
500	1r.50 Skiing (different)	1·30	20
501	2r. Cross-country skiing	1·60	25
502	3r. Ice skating (pairs)	2·00	45

1984. Air.

504 **122**	5r. multicoloured	4·00	20
505	10r. multicoloured	7·50	35
506	15r. multicoloured	11·00	45
507	25r. multicoloured	18·00	80

For design as Type **122** but inscribed "R.P. DU KAMPUCHEA", see Nos. 695/8.

123 Cattle Egret

124 Doves and Globe

1984. Birds. Multicoloured.

508	10c. Type **123**	20	10
509	40c. Black-headed shrike	65	10
510	80c. Slaty-headed parakeet	1·20	20
511	1r. Golden-fronted leafbird	1·60	20
512	1r.20 Red-winged crested cuckoo	1·80	25

513 2r. Grey wagtail 3·50 35
514 2r.50 Forest wagtail 3·75 45

1984. International Peace in South-East Asia Forum, Phnom Penh. Mult, background colour given.
515 **124** 50c. green 25 20
516 1r. blue 65 20
517 3r. violet 1·80 55

125 "Luna 2"

1984. Space Research. Multicoloured.
518 10c. "Luna 1" 20 10
519 40c. Type **125** 25 10
520 80c. "Luna 3" 35 10
521 1r. "Soyuz 6" and cosmonauts (vert) 65 10
522 1r.20 "Soyuz 7" and cosmonauts (vert) 90 20
523 2r. "Soyuz 8" and cosmonauts (vert) 1·30 20
524 2r.50 Book, rocket and S. P. Korolev (Russian spaceship designer) (vert) 1·80 20

126 Throwing the Discus

1984. Olympic Games, Los Angeles (2nd issue). Multicoloured.
526 20c. Type **126** 20 10
527 50c. Long jumping 25 10
528 80c. Hurdling 35 10
529 1r. Relay 90 20
530 1r.50 Pole vaulting 1·20 20
531 2r. Throwing the javelin 1·40 25
532 3r. High jumping 2·00 45

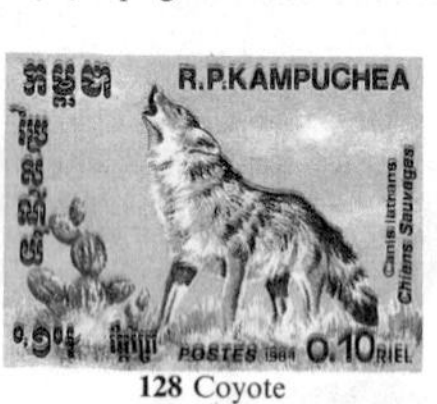
128 Coyote

1984. Dog Family. Multicoloured.
535 10c. Type **128** 20 10
536 40c. Dingo 25 10
537 80c. Hunting dog 45 10
538 1r. Golden jackal 90 10
539 1r.20 Red fox 1·10 20
540 2r. Maned wolf (vert) 2·00 20
541 2r.50 Wolf 3·00 20

129 Class BB 1002 Diesel Locomotive, 1966, France

1984. Railway Locomotives. Multicoloured.
542 10c. Type **129** 20 10
543 40c. Class BB 1052 diesel locomotive, 1966, France 25 10
544 80c. Franco-Belgian-built steam locomotive, 1945, France 35 10
545 1r. Steam locomotive No. 231-505, 1929, France 80 10
546 1r.20 Class 803 diesel railcar, 1968, Germany 1·30 20
547 2r. Class BDE-405 diesel locomotive, 1957, France 1·60 20
548 2r.50 Class DS-01 diesel railcar, 1925, France 2·75 20

130 Magnolia

1984. Flowers. Multicoloured.
549 10c. Type **130** 20 10
550 40c. "Plumeria"
551 80c. "Himenoballis" sp. 45 10
552 1r. "Peltophorum roxburghii" 1·10 20
553 1r.20 "Couroupita guianensis" 1·30 20
554 2r. "Lagerstroemia" sp. 2·20 20
555 2r.50 "Thevetia perubiana" 3·50 25

131 Mercedes Benz

1984. Cars. Multicoloured.
556 20c. Type **131** 20 10
557 50c. Bugatti 25 20
558 80c. Alfa Romeo 45 20
559 1r. Franklin 1·00 25
560 1r.50 Hispano-Suiza 1·40 35
561 2r. Rolls Royce 2·00 45
562 3r. Tatra 2·75 70

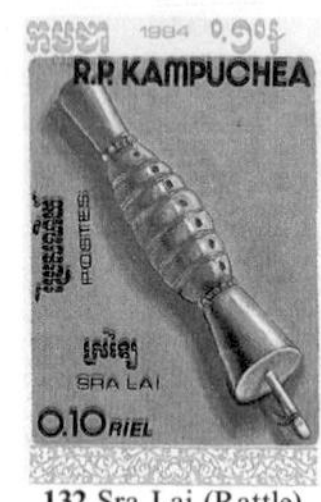
132 Sra Lai (Rattle)

133 Gazelle

1984. Musical Instruments. Multicoloured.
564 10c. Type **132** 20 10
565 40c. Skor drum (horiz) 25 10
566 80c. Skor drums (different) 35 10
567 1r. Thro khmer (stringed instrument) (horiz) 65 20
568 1r.20 Raneat ek (xylophone) (horiz) 1·30 35
569 2r. Raneat kong (bells) (horiz) 1·40 35
570 2r.50 Thro khe (stringed instrument) (horiz) 2·20 65

1984. Mammals. Multicoloured.
571 10c. Type **133** 20 10
572 40c. Roe deer 25 10
573 80c. Hare (horiz) 35 10
574 1r. Red deer 65 20
575 1r.20 Indian elephant 1·30 20
576 2r. Genet (horiz) 1·40 20
577 2r.50 Kouprey (horiz) 2·20 25

134 "Madonna and Child"

1984. 450th Death Anniv of Correggio (artist). Multicoloured.
578 20c. Type **134** 20 10
579 50c. Detail showing man striking monk 25 10
580 80c. "Madonna and Child" (different) 35 10
581 1r. "Madonna and Child" (different) 70 20
582 1r.50 "Mystical Marriage of St. Catherine" 1·30 20
583 2r. "Pieta" 1·50 20
584 3r. Detail showing man descending ladder 2·00 25

135 Bullock Cart

1985. National Festival (6th Anniv of People's Republic). Multicoloured.
586 50c. Type **135** 45 20
587 1r. Horse-drawn passenger cart 90 25
588 3r. Elephants 2·75 45

136 Footballers

138 Glistening Ink Cap

137 Eska-Mofa Motor Cycle, 1939

1985. World Cup Football Championship, Mexico (1986) (1st issue). Designs showing footballers.
590 **136** 20c. multicoloured 20 10
591 – 50c. multicoloured 25 10
592 – 80c. multicoloured 35 10
593 – 1r. multicoloured (horiz) 65 20
594 – 1r.50 mult (horiz) 1·10 20
595 – 2r. multicoloured 1·30 20
596 – 3r. multicoloured 2·00 25
See also Nos. 680/6.

1985. Centenary of Motor Cycle. Multicoloured.
598 20c. Type **137** 20 10
599 50c. Wanderer, 1939 25 10
600 80c. Premier, 1929 35 20
601 1r. Ardie, 1939 70 25
602 1r.50 Jawa, 1932 1·30 45
603 2r. Simson, 1983 1·50 70
604 3r. "CZ 125", 1984 2·00 90

1985. Fungi. Multicoloured.
606 20c. "Gymnophilus spectabilis" (horiz) 20 10
607 50c. Type **138** 35 10
608 80c. Panther cap 70 10
609 1r. Fairy cake mushroom 1·00 10
610 1r.50 Fly agaric 2·00 20
611 2r. Shaggy ink cap 2·75 20
612 3r. Caesar's mushroom 3·00 20

139 "Sputnik 1"

1985. Space Exploration. Multicoloured.
613 20c. Type **139** 20 10
614 50c. "Soyuz" rocket on transporter and Yuri Gagarin (first man in space) 25 20
615 80c. "Vostok 6" and Valentina Tereshkova (first woman in space) 35 20
616 1r. Space walker 65 25
617 1r.50 "Salyut"–"Soyuz" link 1·10 35
618 2r. "Lunokhod 1" (lunar vehicle) 1·30 45
619 3r. "Venera" (Venus probe) 2·00 70

140 Absara Dancer

140a Captured Nazi Standards, Red Square, Moscow

1985. Traditional Dances. Multicoloured.
621 50c. Absara group (horiz) 45 10
622 1r. Tepmonorom dance (horiz) 90 25
623 3r. Type **140** 1·80 70

1985. 40th Anniv of End of Second World War. Multicoloured.
623a 50c. Rejoicing soldiers in Berlin 35 10
623b 1r. Type **140a** 80 25
623c 3r. Tank battle 2·40 70

141 Tortoiseshell Cat

142 "Black Dragon" Lily

1985. Domestic Cats. Multicoloured.
624 20c. Type **141** 20 10
625 50c. Tortoiseshell (different) 25 20
626 80c. Tabby 45 20
627 1r. Long-haired Siamese 1·00 25
628 1t.50 Sealpoint Siamese 1·40 35
629 2r. Grey cat 2·00 45
630 3r. Black cat 2·75 70

1985. Flowers. Multicoloured.
631 20c. Type **142** 20 10
632 50c. "Iris delavayi" 25 10
633 80c. "Crocus aureus" 35 10
634 1r. "Cyclamen persicum" 70 20
635 1r.50 Fairy primrose 1·30 25
636 2r. Pansy "Ullswater" 1·80 35
637 3r. "Crocus purpureus grandiflorus" 2·10 55

143 "Per Italiani" (Antoine Watteau)

144 Lenin and Arms

1985. International Music Year. Multicoloured.
638 20c. Type **143** 20 10
639 50c. "St. Cecilia" (Carlos Saraceni) 25 10
640 80c. "Still Life with Violin" (Jean Baptiste Oudry) (horiz) 55 10
641 1r. "Three Musicians" (Fernand Leger) 65 20
642 1r.50 Orchestra 90 25
643 2r. "St. Cecilia" (Bartholomeo Schedoni) 1·30 35
644 3r. "Harlequin with Violin" (Christian Caillard) 1·80 55

1985. 115th Birth Anniv of Lenin. Multicoloured.
646 1r. Type **144** 1·10 35
647 3r. Lenin on balcony and map 2·10 70

145 Saffron-cowled Blackbird

1985. "Argentina '85" International Stamp Exhibition, Buenos Aires. Birds. Multicoloured.
648 20c. Type **145** 20 10
649 50c. Saffron finch (vert) 25 10
650 80c. Blue and yellow tanager (vert) 35 10
651 1r. Scarlet-headed blackbird 70 20
652 1r.50 Amazon kingfisher (vert) 1·30 25
653 2r. Toco toucan (vert) 1·80 35
654 3r. Rufous-bellied thrush 2·10 55

146 River Launch, Cambodia, 1942

1985. Water Craft. Multicoloured.
655 10c. Type **146** 20 10
656 40c. River launch, Cambodia, 1948 25 10
657 80c. Tug, Japan, 1913 35 10
658 1r. Dredger, Holland 65 20
659 1r.20 Tug, U.S.A. 90 25
660 2r. River freighter 1·30 35
661 2r.50 River tanker, Panama 1·80 55

147 "The Flood" (Michelangelo)

148 Son Ngoc Minh

1985. "Italia '85" International Stamp Exhibition, Rome. Paintings. Multicoloured.

No.	Description		
662	20r. Type **147**	20	10
663	50r. "The Virgin of St. Marguerite" (Mazzola)	25	10
664	80r. "The Martyrdom of St. Peter" (Zampieri Domenichino)	35	10
665	1r. "Allegory of Spring" (detail) (Sandro Botticelli)	70	10
666	1r.50 "The Sacrifice of Abraham" (Caliari)	1·30	20
667	2r. "The Meeting of Joachim and Anne" (Giotto)	1·80	20
668	3r. "Bacchus" (Michel Angelo Carravaggio)	2·10	20

1985. Festival of Rebirth.

No.	Description		
670 **148**	50c. multicoloured	35	20
671	1r. multicoloured	55	25
672	3r. multicoloured	1·30	45

149 Tiger Barbs

1985. Fishes. Multicoloured.

No.	Description		
673	20c. Type **149**	20	10
674	50c. Giant snakehead	25	10
675	80c. Veil-tailed goldfish	35	10
676	1r. Pearl gourami	65	20
677	1r.50 Six-banded tiger barbs	1·10	25
678	2r. Siamese fighting fish	1·30	35
679	3r. Siamese tigerfish	2·00	55

150 Footballers

152 "Mir" Space Station and Spacecraft

151 Cob

1986. World Cup Football Championship, Mexico (2nd issue).

No.	Description		
680 **150**	20c. multicoloured	20	10
681 –	50c. multicoloured	25	10
682 –	80c. multicoloured	35	10
683 –	1r. multicoloured	65	20
684 –	1r.50 multicoloured	90	25
685 –	2r. multicoloured	1·30	35
686 –	3r. multicoloured	1·80	55

DESIGNS: 50c. to 3r. Various footballing scenes.

1986. Horses. Multicoloured.

No.	Description		
688	20c. Type **151**	20	10
689	50c. Arab	25	10
690	80c. Australian pony	35	10
691	1r. Appaloosa	70	20
692	1r.50 Quarter horse	1·30	20
693	2r. Vladimir heavy draught horse	1·50	20
694	3r. Andalusian	2·00	25

1986. 27th Russian Communist Party Congress. Multicoloured.

No.	Description		
694a	50c. Type **152**	25	10
694b	1r. Lenin	80	35
694c	5r. Statue and launch of space rocket	3·00	65

1986. Air. As Nos. 504/7 but inscr "R.P. DU KAMPUCHEA".

No.	Description		
695 **122**	5r. multicoloured	3·50	20
696	10r. multicoloured	7·25	35
697	15r. multicoloured	9·00	45
698	25r. multicoloured	16·00	80

153 Edaphosaurus (⅔-size illustration)

1986. Prehistoric Animals. Multicoloured.

No.	Description		
699	20c. Type **153**	35	10
700	50c. Sauroctonus	45	10
701	80c. Mastodonsaurus	90	10
702	1r. Rhamphorhynchus (vert)	1·60	20
703	1r.50 "Brachiosaurus brancai" (vert)	2·50	25
704	2r. "Tarbosaurus bataar" (vert)	3·25	35
705	3r. Indricotherium (vert)	4·50	70

154 "Luna 16"

1986. 25th Anniv of First Man in Space. Multicoloured.

No.	Description		
706	10c. Type **154**	20	10
707	40c. "Luna 3"	25	10
708	80c. "Vostok"	35	10
709	1r. Cosmonaut Leonov on space walk	65	20
710	1r.20 "Apollo" and "Soyuz" preparing to dock	1·10	20
711	2r. "Soyuz" docking with "Salyut" space station	1·30	20
712	2r.50 Yuri Gagarin (first man in space) and spacecraft	2·00	25

155 Baksei Chmkrong Temple, 920

1986. Khmer Culture. Multicoloured.

No.	Description		
713	20c. Type **155**	20	10
714	50c. Buddha's head	25	10
715	80c. Prea Vihear monastery, Dangrek	35	10
716	1r. Fan with design of man and woman	45	20
717	1r.50 Fan with design of men fighting	65	25
718	2r. Fan with design of dancer	1·10	35
719	3r. Fan with design of dragon-drawn chariot	1·50	70

156 Tricar, 1885

1986. Centenary (1985) of Motor Car. Mercedes Benz Models. Multicoloured.

No.	Description		
720	20c. Type **156**	20	10
721	50c. Limousine, 1935	25	10
722	80c. Open tourer, 1907	35	10
723	1r. Light touring car, 1920	65	20
724	1r.50 Cabriolet, 1932	1·10	25
725	2r. "SKK" tourer, 1938	1·30	35
726	3r. "190", 1985	2·00	70

157 Orange Tiger

159 Solar System, Copernicus, Galileo and Tycho Brahe (astronomers)

158 English Kogge of Richard II's Reign

1986. Butterflies. Multicoloured.

No.	Description		
727	20c. Type **157**	20	10
728	50c. Five-bar swallowtail	25	10
729	80c. Chequered swallowtail	35	10
730	1r. Chestnut tiger	70	20
731	1r.50 "Idea blanchardi"	1·30	25
732	2r. Common mormon	1·50	35
733	3r. "Dabasa payeni"	2·00	55

1986. Medieval Ships.

No.	Description		
734	20c. Type **158**	20	10
735	50c. Kogge	25	10
736	80c. Knarr	35	10
737	1r. Galley	65	20
738	1r.50 Norman ship	90	25
739	2r. Mediterranean usciere	1·30	35
740	3r. French kogge	1·80	55

1986. Appearance of Halley's Comet. Multicoloured.

No.	Description		
741	10c. Type **159**	20	10
742	20c. "Nativity" (Giotto) and comet from Bayeux Tapestry	20	10
743	50c. Comet, 1910, and Mt. Palomar observatory, U.S.A.	25	10
744	80c. Edmond Halley and "Planet A" space probe	45	20
745	1r.20 Diagram of comet's trajectory and "Giotto" space probe	70	25
746	1r.50 "Vega" space probe and camera	90	35
747	2r. Thermal pictures of comet	1·30	55

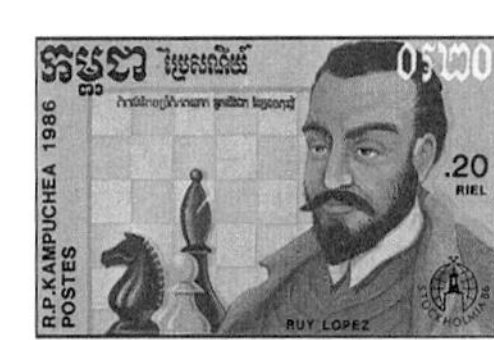

160 Ruy Lopez

1986. "Stockholmia 86" International Stamp Exhibition. Chess. Multicoloured.

No.	Description		
749	20c. Type **160**	20	10
750	50c. Francois-Andre Philidor	25	10
751	80c. Karl Anderssen and Houses of Parliament, London	35	10
752	1r. Wilhelm Steinitz and Charles Bridge, Prague	70	20
753	1r.50 Emanuel Lasker and medieval knight	1·30	25
754	2r. Jose Raul Capablanca and Morro Castle, Cuba	1·80	35
755	3r. Aleksandr Alekhine	2·10	70

161 "Parodia maassii"

162 Bananas

1986. Cacti. Multicoloured.

No.	Description		
757	20c. Type **161**	20	10
758	50c. "Rebutia marsoneri"	25	10
759	80c. "Melocactus evae"	35	10
760	1r. "Gymnocalycium valnicekianum"	70	20
761	1r.50 "Discocactus silichromus"	1·30	25
762	2r. "Neochilenia simulans"	1·50	35
763	3r. "Weingartia chiquichuquensis"	2·00	55

1986. Fruit. Multicoloured.

No.	Description		
764	10c. Type **162**	20	10
765	40c. Papaya	25	20
766	80c. Mangoes	35	20
767	1r. Breadfruit	45	20
768	1r.20 Lychees	65	35
769	2r. Pineapple	1·10	55
770	2r.50 Grapefruit (horiz)	1·50	70

163 Concorde (⅔-size illustration)

1986. Aircraft. Multicoloured.

No.	Description		
771	20c. Type **163** (wrongly inscr "Concord")	20	10
772	50c. Douglas DC-10	25	10
773	80c. Boeing 747SP	35	10
774	1r. Ilyushin Il-62M	65	20
775	1r.50 Ilyushin Il-86	90	25
776	2r. Antonov An-24 (wrongly inscr "AN-124")	1·30	35
777	3r. Airbus Industrie A300	1·80	70

164 Elephant and Silver Containers on Tray

1986. Festival of Rebirth. Silverware. Mult.

No.	Description		
778	50c. Type **164**	35	20
779	1r. Tureen	70	25
780	3r. Dish on stand	2·10	45

165 Kouprey

1986. Endangered Animals. Cattle. Mult.

No.	Description		
781	20c. Type **165**	1·10	20
782	20c. Gaur	1·60	25
783	80c. Bateng cow and calf	4·00	35
784	1r.50 Asiatic water buffalo	6·75	55

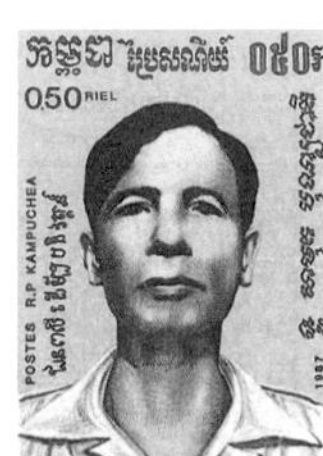

166 Tou Samuth (revolutionary)

1987. National Festival. 8th Anniv of People's Republic.

No.	Description		
785 **166**	50c. multicoloured	25	20
786	1r. multicoloured	45	25
787	3r. multicoloured	1·10	45

167 Biathlon

1987. Winter Olympic Games, Calgary (1988) (1st issue). Multicoloured.

No.	Description		
788	20c. Type **167**	20	10
789	50c. Figure skating	25	10
790	80c. Speed skating	35	10
791	1r. Ice hockey	65	20
792	1r.50 Two-man luge	90	25
793	2r. Two-man bobsleigh	1·30	35
794	3r. Cross-country skiing	1·80	70

See also Nos. 864/70.

168 Weightlifting

1987. Olympic Games, Seoul (1988) (1st issue). Designs showing ancient Greek and modern athletes. Multicoloured.
796 20c. Type **168** 20 10
797 50c. Archery (horiz) 25 10
798 80c. Fencing (horiz) 35 20
799 1r. Gymnastics 65 20
800 1r.50 Throwing the discus (horiz) 90 20
801 2r. Throwing the javelin . . . 1·30 25
802 3r. Hurdling . . . . 1·80 35
See also Nos. 875/81.

169 Papillon

1987. Dogs. Multicoloured.
804 20c. Type **169** 20 10
805 50c. Greyhound 25 10
806 80c. Great Dane 35 10
807 1r. Dobermann 70 20
808 1r.50 Samoyed . . . . 1·30 25
809 2r. Borzoi . . . . 1·80 35
810 3r. Rough collie . . . . . . 2·10 55

170 "Sputnik 1" **171** Flask

1987. Space Exploration. Multicoloured.
811 20c. Type **170** 20 10
812 50c. "Soyuz 10" 25 10
813 80c. "Proton" 35 10
814 1r. "Vostok 1" 65 20
815 1r.50 "Elektron 2" 90 25
816 2r. "Kosmos" . . . . 1·30 35
817 3r. "Luna 2" . . . . 1·80 70

1987. Metalwork. Multicoloured.
819 50c. Type **171** 25 20
820 1r. Repousse box (horiz) . . 70 25
821 1r.50 Teapot and cups on tray (horiz) . . . . 1·10 35
822 3r. Ornamental sword . . . 2·00 55

172 Carmine Bee Eater

1987. "Capex'87" International Stamp Exhibition, Toronto. Birds. Multicoloured.
823 20c. Type **172** 20 10
824 50c. Hoopoe (vert) 25 10
825 80c. South African crowned crane (vert) 35 10
826 1r. Barn owl (vert) 65 20
827 1r.50 Grey-headed kingfisher (vert) . . . . 1·10 25
828 2r. Red-whiskered bulbul . . 1·30 35
829 3r. Purple heron (vert) . . . 2·00 55

173 Horatio Phillip's "Multiplane" Model, 1893

1987. Experimental Aircraft Designs. Mult.
831 20c. Type **173** 20 10
832 50c. John Stringfellow's steam-powered model, 1848 25 10
833 80c. Thomas Moy's model "Aerial Steamer", 1875 . . 35 10
834 1r. Leonardo da Vinci's "ornithopter", 1490 . . . 65 20
835 1r.50 Sir George Cayley's "convertiplane", 1843 . . . 1·10 20
836 2r. Sir Hiram Maxim's "Flying Test Rig", 1894 . . 1·30 20
837 3r. William Henson's "Aerial Steam Carriage", 1842 . . 2·00 25

174 Giant Tortoise

1987. Reptiles. Multicoloured.
839 20c. Type **174** 20 10
840 50c. African spiny-tailed lizard 25 10
841 80c. Iguana 35 10
842 1r. Coast horned lizard . . . 65 20
843 1r.50 Northern chuckwalla 90 25
844 2r. Glass lizard . . . . . . 1·30 35
845 3r. Common garter snake . . 1·80 55

175 Kamov Ka-15

1987. "Hafnia 87" International Stamp Exhibition, Copenhagen. Helicopters. Multicoloured.
846 20c. Type **175** 20 10
847 50c. Kamov Ka-18 . . . . . 25 10
848 80c. Westland Lynx 35 10
849 1r. Sud Aviation Gazelle . . 65 20
850 1r.50 Sud Aviation SA 330E Puma 90 20
851 2r. Boeing-Vertol CH-47 Chinook . . . . 1·30 20
852 3r. Boeing UTTAS . . . . . 1·80 25

176 Revolutionaries **178** Earth Station Dish Aerial

177 Magirus-Deutz No. 21

1987. 70th Anniv of Russian October Revolution. Multicoloured.
853a 2r. Revolutionaries on street corner (horiz) . . . . . 1·10 20
853b 3r. Type **176** . . . . 1·30 45
853c 5r. Lenin receiving ticker-tape message (horiz) . . . 3·00 70

1987. Fire Engines. Multicoloured.
854 20c. Type **177** 20 10
855 50c. "SIL-131" rescue vehicle 25 10
856 80c. "Cas-25" fire pump . . 35 10
857 1r. Sirmac Saab "424" . . . 70 20
858 1r.50 Rosenbaum-Falcon . . 1·30 25
859 2r. Tatra "815-PRZ" . . . . 1·80 35
860 3r. Chubbfire "C-44-20" . . 2·10 55

1987. Telecommunications. Multicoloured.
861 50c. Type **178** 35 20
862 1r. Technological building with radio microwave aerial (27 × 44 mm) 70 25
863 3r. Intersputnik programme earth station (44 × 27 mm) 1·60 65

179 Speed Skating

1988. Winter Olympic Games, Calgary (2nd issue). Multicoloured.
864 20c. Type **179** 20 10
865 50c. Ice hockey 25 10
866 80c. Slalom 35 10
867 1r. Ski jumping 65 10
868 1r.50 Biathlon 90 20
869 2r. Ice dancing . . . . . . 1·30 20
870 3r. Cross-country skiing . . . 1·80 20

180 Irrigation Canal Bed

1988. Irrigation Projects. Multicoloured.
872 50c. Type **180** 35 20
873 1r. Dam construction 70 25
874 3r. Dam and bridge . . . . 1·60 45

181 Beam Exercise

1988. Olympic Games, Seoul (2nd issue). Women's Gymnastics. Multicoloured.
875 20c. Type **181** 20 10
876 50c. Bar exercise (horiz) . . . 25 10
877 80c. Ribbon exercise 35 10
878 1r. Hoop exercise 55 10
879 1r.50 Baton exercise 70 20
880 2r. Ball exercise (horiz) . . . 1·20 20
881 3r. Floor exercise (horiz) . . 1·60 20

182 Abyssinian

1988. "Juvalux 88" 9th Youth Philately Exhibition, Luxembourg. Cats. Multicoloured.
883 20c. White long-haired (horiz) 20 10
884 50c. Type **182** 25 10
885 80c. Ginger and white long-haired 35 10
886 1r. Tortoiseshell queen and kitten (horiz) 65 20
887 1r.50 Brown cat . . . . . . 1·10 25
888 2r. Black long-haired cat . . 1·30 35
889 3r. Grey cat . . . . 2·00 55

183 "Emerald Seas" (liner)

1988. "Essen 88" International Stamp Fair. Ships. Multicoloured.
891 20c. Type **183** 20 10
892 50c. Car ferry 25 10
893 80c. "Mutsu" (nuclear-powered freighter) 35 10
894 1r. "Kosmonavt Yury Gagarin" (research ship) 65 20
895 1r.50 Tanker . . . . 1·10 25
896 2r. Hydrofoil . . . . 1·30 35
897 3r. Hovercraft . . . . 2·00 55

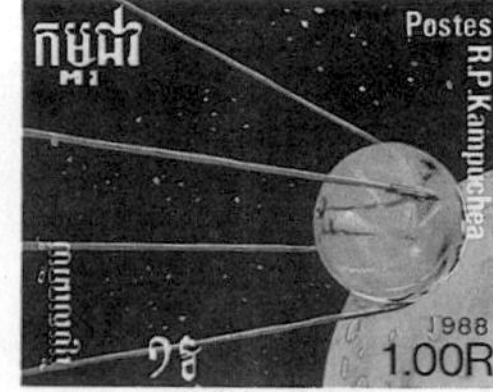

184 Satellite

1988. Space Exploration. Designs showing different satellites.
899 – 20c. multicoloured (vert) 20 10
900 – 50c. multicoloured (vert) 25 10
901 – 80c. multicoloured (vert) 35 10
902 **184** 1r. multicoloured 55 10
903 – 1r.50 multicoloured . . . 80 20
904 – 2r. multicoloured . . . . 1·20 20
905 – 3r. multicoloured . . . . 1·60 20

185 Swordtail

1988. "Finlandia 88" International Stamp Exhibition, Helsinki. Tropical Fish. Multicoloured.
907 20c. Type **185** 20 10
908 50c. Head-and-taillight tetra 25 10
909 80c. Paradise fish 35 20
910 1r. Black moor goldfish . . . 65 20
911 1r.50 Cardinal tetra . . . . 1·10 20
912 2r. Sword-tailed characin . . 1·30 25
913 3r. Sail-finned molly . . . . 2·00 35

186 Flowery Helicostyla **188** "Cattleya aclandiae"

187 Seven-spotted Ladybird

1988. Sea Shells. Multicoloured.
915 20c. Type **186** 20 10
916 50c. Changing helicostyla . . 25 10
917 80c. Shining helicostyla . . . 35 10
918 1r. Marinduque helicostyla 65 10
919 1r.50 Siren chlorena . . . . 1·10 20
920 2r. Miraculous helicostyla . . 1·30 20
921 3r. "Helicostyla limansauensis" . . . . . 2·00 20

1988. Insects. Multicoloured.
922 20c. Type **187** 20 10
923 50c. "Zonabride geminata" (blister beetle) 25 10
924 80c. "Carabus auronitens" (ground beetle) 35 10
925 1r. Honey bee 65 10
926 1r.50 Praying mantis . . . . 1·10 20
927 2r. Dragonfly . . . . 1·30 20
928 3r. Soft-winged flower beetle 2·00 20

1988. Orchids. Multicoloured.
929 20c. Type **188** 20 10
930 50c. "Odontoglossum" "Royal Sovereign" 25 10
931 80c. "Cattleya labiata" . . . 35 10
932 1r. Bee orchid 65 10
933 1r.50 "Laelia anceps" 90 20
934 2r. "Laelia pumila" . . . . . 1·30 20
935 3r. "Stanhopea tigrina" (horiz) . . . . 1·80 20

189 Egyptian Banded Cobra

190 Walking Dance

1988. Reptiles. Multicoloured.
936 20c. Type **189** 20 10
937 50c. Common iguana 25 10
938 80c. Long-nosed vine snake (horiz) 35 10
939 1r. Common box turtle (horiz) 65 10
940 1r.50 Iguana (horiz) 1·10 20
941 2r. Viper (horiz) 1·30 20
942 3r. Common cobra 2·00 20

1988. Festival of Rebirth. Khmer Culture. Multicoloured.
943 50c. Type **190** 35 20
944 1r. Peacock dance (horiz) 80 25
945 3r. Kantere dance (horiz) 2·00 65

191 Bridge

1989. Multicoloured.
946 50c. Type **191** 25 10
947 1r. More distant view of bridge 65 35
948 3r. Closer view of bridge 1·60 90

192 Cement Works

1989. National Festival. 10th Anniv of People's Republic of Kampuchea. Multicoloured.
949 3r. Bayon Earth Station (horiz) 25 10
950 12r. Electricity generating station 4 (horiz) 70 35
951 30r. Type **192** 2·00 90

193 Footballers

1989. World Cup Football Championship, Italy (1990).
952 **193** 2r. multicoloured 20 10
953 – 3r. multicoloured 25 10
954 – 5r. multicoloured 35 10
955 – 10r. multicoloured 80 10
956 – 15r. multicoloured 1·20 20
957 – 20r. multicoloured 1·60 20
958 – 35r. multicoloured 2·75 20
DESIGNS: 3r. to 35r. Various footballing scenes.

194 Tram

1989. Trams and Trains. Multicoloured.
960 2r. Type **194** 25 10
961 3r. ETR 401 Pendolino express train, 1976, Italy 35 10
962 5r. High speed train, Germany 45 10
963 10r. Theme park monorail train 80 10
964 15r. German Trans Europe Express (TEE) train 1·20 20
965 20r. "Hikari" express train, Sanyo Shinkansenline, Japan 1·60 20
966 35r. TGV express train, France 3·00 20

195 Fidel Castro

196 Scarlet Macaw

1989. 30th Anniv of Cuban Revolution.
968 **195** 12r. multicoloured 1·10 55

1989. Parrots. Multicoloured.
969 20c. Type **196** 20 10
970 80c. Sulphur-crested cockatoo 25 10
971 3r. Rose-ringed parakeet 35 10
972 6r. Blue and yellow macaw 70 10
973 10r. Brown-necked parrot 90 20
974 15r. Blue-fronted amazon 1·40 20
975 25r. White-capped parrot (horiz) 2·00 20

197 Skiing

1989. Winter Olympic Games, Albertville (1992). Multicoloured.
977 2r. Type **197** 20 10
978 3r. Biathlon 25 10
979 5r. Cross-country skiing 35 10
980 10r. Ski jumping 80 10
981 15r. Speed skating 1·10 20
982 20r. Ice hockey 1·30 20
983 35r. Two-man bobsleighing 2·75 20

198 "Nymphaea capensis" (pink)

1989. Water Lilies. Multicoloured.
985 20c. Type **198** 20 10
986 80c. "Nymphaea capensis" (mauve) 20 10
987 3r. "Nymphaea lotus dentata" 25 10
988 6r. "Dir. Geo. T. Moore" 45 10
989 10r. "Sunrise" 65 20
990 15r. "Escarboncle" 1·30 20
991 25r. "Cladstoniana" 2·00 20

199 Wrestling

1989. Olympic Games, Barcelona (1992). Multicoloured.
993 2r. Type **199** 20 10
994 3r. Gymnastics (vert) 25 10
995 5r. Putting the shot 35 10
996 10r. Running (vert) 70 10
997 15r. Fencing 1·10 20
998 20r. Canoeing (vert) 1·30 20
999 35r. Hurdling (vert) 2·75 20

200 Downy Boletus

1989. Fungi. Multicoloured.
1001 20c. Type **200** 20 10
1002 80c. Red-staining inocybe 25 10
1003 3r. Honey fungus 35 10
1004 6r. Field mushroom 70 10
1005 10r. Brown roll-rim 90 20
1006 15r. Shaggy ink cap 1·40 20
1007 25r. Parasol mushroom 2·00 20

201 Shire Horse

1989. Horses. Multicoloured.
1008 2r. Type **201** 20 10
1009 3r. Brabant 25 10
1010 5r. Bolounais 35 10
1011 10r. Breton 80 10
1012 15r. Vladimir heavy draught horse 1·20 20
1013 20r. Italian heavy draught horse 1·60 20
1014 35r. Freiberger 2·75 20

KATANGA Pt. 14

The following stamps were issued by Mr. Tshombe's Government for independent Katanga. In 1963 Katanga was reunited with the Central Government of Congo.

1960. Various stamps of Belgian Congo optd **KATANGA** and bar or surch also. (a) Masks issue of 1948.
1 1f.50 on 1f.25 mauve and blue 80 20
2 3f.50 on 2f.50 green and brown 80 25
3 20f. purple and red 2·75 85
4 50f. black and brown 6·50 3·00
5 100f. black and red 48·00 21·00

(b) Flowers issue of 1952. Flowers in natural colours; colours given are of backgrounds and inscriptions.
6 10c. yellow and purple 20 20
7 15c. green and red 20 20
8 20c. grey and green 35 25
9 25c. orange and green 35 25
10 40c. salmon and green 35 25
11 50c. turquoise and red 45 35
12 60c. purple and green 35 25
13 75c. grey and lake 45 35
14 1f. lemon and red 55 45
15 2f. buff and olive 65 55
16 3f. pink and green 90 65
17 4f. lavender and sepia 1·25 95
18 5f. green and purple 1·25 95
19 6f.50 lilac and red 1·25 85
20 7f. brown and green 1·75 1·25
21 8f. yellow and green 1·75 1·25
22 10f. olive and purple 28·00 17·00

(c) Wild animals issue of 1959.
23 10c. brown, sepia and blue 20 10
24 20c. blue and red 1·60 80
25 40c. brown and blue 20 10
26 50c. multicoloured 20 10
27 1f. black, green and brown 6·75 4·00
28 1f.50 black and yellow 11·00 7·50
29 2f. black, brown and red 50 10
30 3f. black, purple and slate 4·25 3·00
31 5f. brown, green and sepia 75 30
32 6f.50 brown, yellow and blue 95 30
33 8f. bistre, violet and brown 1·40 35
34 10f. multicoloured 2·10 50

(d) Madonna.
35 **102** 50c. brown, ochre & chest 15 15
36 1f. brown, violet and blue 15 15
37 2f. brown, blue and slate 20 20

(e) African Technical Co-operation Commission. Inscr in French or Flemish.
38 **103** 3f. salmon and slate 7·00 7·00
39 3f.50 on 3f. salmon & slate 2·10 2·10

1960. Independence. Independence issue of Congo optd **11 JUILLET DE L'ETAT DU KATANGA**.
40 **106** 20c. bistre 10 10
41 50c. red 10 10
42 1f. green 10 10
43 1f.50 brown 10 10
44 2f. mauve 10 10
45 3f.50 violet 15 10
46 5f. blue 15 10
47 6f.50 black 15 10
48 10f. orange 25 20
49 20f. blue 45 30

5

1961. Katanga Art.
50 **5** 10c. green 10 10
51 20c. violet 10 10
52 50c. blue 10 10
53 1f.50 green 10 10
54 2f. brown 10 10
55 – 3f.50 blue 10 10
56 – 5f. turquoise 10 10
57 – 6f. brown 10 10
58 – 6f.50 blue 10 10
59 – 8f. purple 15 10
60 – 10f. brown 15 10
61 – 20f. myrtle 25 20
62 – 50f. brown 50 40
63 – 100f. turquoise 85 70
DESIGNS: 3f.50 to 8f. "Preparing food"; 10f. to 100f. "Family circle".

6 Pres. Tshombe

1961. 1st Anniv of Independence. Portrait in brown.
64 **6** 6f.50+5f. red, green & gold 1·25 1·00
65 8f.+5f. red, green and gold 1·25 1·00
66 10f.+5f. red, green and gold 1·25 1·00

7 "Tree"

8 Early Aircraft, Steam Train and Safari

1961. Katanga International Fair. Vert symbolic designs as T **7**.
67 **7** 50c. red, green and black 10 10
68 – 1f. black and blue 10 10
69 – 2f.50 black and yellow 15 15
70 **7** 3f.50 red, brown and black 15 15
71 – 5f. black and violet 25 25
72 – 6f.50 black and yellow 30 30

1961. Air.
73 **8** 3f.50 multicoloured 3·00 3·25
74 – 6f.50 multicoloured 65 65
75 **8** 8f. multicoloured 3·00 3·25
76 – 10f. multicoloured 65 65
DESIGNS: 6f.50, 10f. Tail of Boeing 707.

9 Gendarme in armoured Vehicle

1962. Katanga Gendarmerie.
77 **9** 6f. multicoloured 2·25 2·25
78 8f. multicoloured 35 35
79 10f. multicoloured 45 45

POSTAGE DUE STAMPS

1960. Postage Due stamps of Belgian Congo handstamped **KATANGA**. (a) On Nos. D270/4.
D50 **D 86** 10c. olive 80 80
D51 20c. blue 80 80
D52 50c. green 1·00 1·00
D53 1f. brown
D54 2f. orange

(b) On Nos. D330/6.
D55 **D 99** 10c. brown 3·25 3·25
D56 20c. purple 3·25 3·25
D57 50c. green 3·25 3·25
D58 1f. blue 1·00 1·00
D59 2f. red 2·00 2·00
D60 4f. violet 2·75 2·75
D61 6f. blue 3·25 3·25

KATHIRI STATE OF SEIYUN Pt. 1

The stamps of Aden were used in Kathiri State of Seiyun from 22 May 1937 until 1942.

1937. 16 annas = 1 rupee.
1951. 100 cents = 1 shilling.
1966. 1000 fils = 1 dinar.

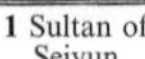

1 Sultan of Seiyun

2 Seiyun

1942.

1	**1**	½a. green	20	60
2		¾a. brown	40	1·00
3		1a. blue	70	60
4	**2**	1½a. red	70	80
5	–	2a. brown	40	80
6	–	2½a. blue	1·25	1·00
7	–	3a. brown and red	1·75	2·25
8	–	8a. red	1·25	50
9	–	1r. green	3·75	1·75
10	–	2r. blue and purple	7·00	10·00
11	–	5r. brown and green	22·00	17·00

DESIGNS—VERT: 2a. Tarim; 2½a. Mosque at Seiyun; 1r. South Gate, Tarim; 5r. Mosque entrance, Tarim. HORIZ: 3a. Fortress at Tarim; 8a. Mosque at Seiyun; 2r. A Kathiri house.

1946. Victory. Optd **VICTORY ISSUE 8TH JUNE 1946**.

12	**2**	1½a. red	10	65
13	–	2½a. blue (No. 6)	10	10

1949. Royal Silver Wedding. As T **4b/c** of Pitcairn Islands.

14	1½a. red	30	2·00
15	5r. green	16·00	9·00

1949. 75th Anniv of U.P.U. As T **4d/g** of Pitcairn Islands surch with new values.

16	2½a. on 20c. blue	15	50
17	3a. on 30c. red	1·25	1·00
18	8a. on 50c. orange	25	1·00
19	1r. on 1s. blue	30	1·00

1951. 1942 stamps surch in cents or shillings.

20	**1**	5c. on 1a. blue	15	80
21	–	10c. on 2a. brown	30	60
22	–	15c. on 2½a. blue	15	1·00
23	–	20c. on 3a. brown and red	20	1·75
24	–	50c. on 8a. red	20	60
25	–	1s. on 1r. green	50	2·00
26	–	2s. on 2r. blue and purple	3·25	24·00
27	–	5s. on 5r. brown and green	20·00	35·00

1953. Coronation. As T **4h** of Pitcairn Islands.

28	15c. black and green	30	1·75

14 Sultan Hussein

29 "Telstar"

1954. As 1942 issue and new designs, but with portrait of Sultan Hussein as in T **14**.

29	**14**	5c. brown	10	10
30		10c. blue	15	10
31	**2**	15c. green	15	10
32	–	25c. red	15	10
33	–	35c. blue	15	10
34	–	50c. brown and red	15	10
39	–	70c. black	2·00	1·00
35	–	1s. orange	15	10
40	–	1s.25 green	2·00	7·50
41	–	1s.50 violet	2·00	7·50
36	–	2s. green	4·00	2·25
37	–	5s. blue and violet	7·50	6·50
38	–	10s. brown and violet	7·50	6·50

DESIGNS—VERT: 35c. Mosque at Seiyun; 70c. Qarn Adh Dhabi; 2s. South Gate, Tarim; 10s. Mosque entrance, Tarim. HORIZ: 50c. Fortress at Tarim; 1s. Mosque at Seiyun; 1s.25, Seiyun; 1s.50, Gheil Omer; 5s. Kathiri house.

1966. Nos. 29 etc surch **SOUTH ARABIA** in English and Arabic, with value and bar.

42	**14**	5f. on 5c.	15	10
43		5f. on 10c.	15	50
44	**2**	10f. on 15c.	15	50
45	–	15f. on 25c.	20	60
46	–	20f. on 35c.	15	30
47	–	25f. on 50c.	15	75
61	–	35f. on 70c.	2·00	80
49	–	50f. on 1s.	20	20
50	–	65f. on 1s.25	20	20
51	–	75f. on 1s.50	20	30
65	–	100f. on 2s.	3·25	2·50
53	–	250f. on 5s.	1·40	3·75
54	–	500f. on 10s.	1·75	3·75

Each value has two similar surcharges.

1966. Nos. 57, 59, 61/7 variously optd as given below, together with Olympic "rings".

68	10f. on 15c. (**LOS ANGELES 1932**)	35	35
69	20f. on 35c. (**BERLIN 1936**)	45	45
70	35f. on 70c. (**INTERNATIONAL COOPERATION**, etc)	45	45
71	50f. on 1s. (**LONDON 1948**)	50	55
72	65f. on 1s.25 (**HELSINKI 1952**)	50	1·00
73	75f. on 1s.50 (**MELBOURNE 1956**)	60	1·50
74	100f. on 2s. (**ROME 1960**)	70	1·75
75	250f. on 5s. (**TOKYO 1964**)	1·00	3·50
76	500f. on 10s. (**MEXICO CITY 1968**)	1·25	4·00

1966. World Cup Football Championship. Nos. 57, 59, 61/2, 65/7 optd **CHAMPIONS ENGLAND** (10f., 50f. and 250f.) or **FOOTBALL 1966** (others). Both with football symbol.

77	10f. on 15c.	70	30
78	20f. on 35c.	90	40
79	35f. on 70c.	1·25	40
80	50f. on 1s.	1·40	40
81	100f. on 2s.	3·75	2·00
82	250f. on 5s.	7·50	5·00
83	500f. on 10s.	9·50	8·00

1966. Centenary of I.T.U. (1965).

84	**29**	5f. green, black and violet	1·25	15
85	–	10f. purple, black and green	1·40	20
86	–	15f. blue, black and orange	1·75	20
87	**29**	25f. green, black and red	2·50	20
88	–	35f. purple, black and yellow	2·75	20
89	–	50f. blue, black and brown	3·25	25
90	**29**	65f. green, black and yellow	3·75	30

DESIGNS: 10, 35f. "Relay"; 15, 50f. "Ranger".

32 Churchill at Easel

1966. Sir Winston Churchill's Paintings. Mult.

91	5f. Type **32**	1·75	15
92	10f. "Antibes"	2·00	15
93	15f. "Flowers" (vert)	2·00	20
94	20f. "Tapestries"	2·00	35
95	25f. "Village, Lake Lugano"	2·00	35
96	35f. "Church, Lake Como" (vert)	2·00	40
97	50f. "Flowers at Chartwell" (vert)	2·25	65
98	65f. Type **32**	2·75	90

1967. "World Peace". Nos. 57, 59, 61/7 optd **WORLD PEACE** and names as given below.

99	10f. on 15c. (**PANDIT NEHRU**)	1·25	1·00
100	20f. on 35c. (**WINSTON CHURCHILL**)	4·50	2·25
101	35f. on 70c. (**DAG HAMMARSKJOLD**)	50	80
102	50f. on 1s. (**JOHN F. KENNEDY**)	60	90
103	65f. on 1s.25 (**LUDWIG ERHARD**)	70	1·10
104	75f. on 1s.50 (**LYNDON JOHNSON**)	80	1·25
105	100f. on 2s. (**ELEANOR ROOSEVELT**)	1·00	2·00
106	250f. on 5s. (**WINSTON CHURCHILL**)	13·00	10·00
107	500f. on 10s. (**JOHN F. KENNEDY**)	5·00	11·00

40 "Master Crewe as Henry VIII" (Sir Joshua Reynolds)

1967. Paintings. Multicoloured.

108	5f. Type **40**	30	25
109	10f. "The Dancer" (Degas)	35	30
110	15f. "The Fifer" (Manet)	40	35
111	20f. "Stag at Sharkey's" (boxing match, G. Bellows)	45	40
112	25f. "Don Manuel Osorio" (Goya)	50	45
113	35f. "St. Martin distributing his Cloak" (A. van Dyck)	70	65
114	50f. "The Blue Boy" (Gainsborough)	85	75
115	65f. "The White Horse" (Gauguin)	1·10	1·00
116	75f. "Mona Lisa" (Da Vinci) (45 × 62 mm)	1·40	1·25

1967. American Astronauts. Nos. 57, 59, 61/2 and 65/6 optd as below, all with space capsule.

117	10f. on 15c. (**ALAN SHEPARD JR.**)	55	1·25
118	20f. on 35c. (**VIRGIL GRISSOM**)	70	1·25
119	35f. on 70c. (**JOHN GLENN JR.**)	95	1·50
120	50f. on 1s. (**SCOTT CARPENTER**)	95	1·50
121	100f. on 2s. (**WALTER SCHIRRA JR.**)	2·25	3·75
122	250f. on 5s. (**GORDON COOPER JR.**)	3·50	7·00

50 Churchill Crown

1967. Churchill Commemoration.

123	**50**	75f. multicoloured	9·00	6·50

APPENDIX

The following stamps have either been issued in excess of postal needs or have not been made available to the public in reasonable quantities at face value.

1967.

Hunting. 20f.

Olympic Games, Grenoble. Postage 10, 25, 35, 50, 75f.; Air 100, 200f.

Scout Jamboree, Idaho. Air 150f.

Paintings—Renoir. Postage 10, 35, 50, 65, 75f.; Air 100, 200, 250f.

Paintings—Toulouse-Lautrec. Postage 10, 35, 50, 65, 75f.; Air 100, 200, 250f.

The National Liberation Front is said to have taken control of Kathiri State of Seiyun on 1 October 1967.

KAZAKHSTAN Pt. 10

Formerly a constituent republic of the Soviet Union, Kazakhstan declared its independence on 16 December 1991.

1992. 100 kopeks = 1 rouble.
1994. 100 tyin (ty.) = 1 tenge (t.).

1 "Golden Warrior"

КАЗАКСТАН
(2)

1992. "Golden Warrior" (from 5th-century B.C. tomb).

1	**1**	50k. multicoloured	15	15

1992. Nos. 6079/80 of Russia optd as T **2**, in Cyrillic (2, 4) or English (3, 5) capitals.

2	12k. purple	2·75	2·25
3	12k. purple	2·75	2·25
4	13k. violet	2·75	2·25
5	13k. violet	2·75	2·25

(3)

4 Saiga

1992. Russian–French Space Flight. Nos. 6072/4 of Russia surch as T **3**.

6	30k. on 2k. brown	50	20
7	75k. on 3k. green	35	35
8	1r. on 1k. brown	45	45

1992.

9	**4**	75k. multicoloured	15	15

5 "Turksib" (E. K. Kasteev)

1992. Kazakh Art.

10	**5**	1r. multicoloured	25	25

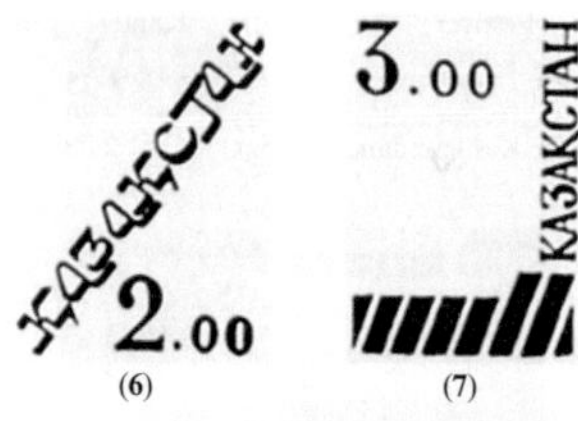

(6) (7)

(8)

9 National Flag and Arms

1992. Various stamps of Russia surch as T **6** (11/12), **7** (13/14) or **8** (15/16).

11	1r.50 on 1k. brown (No. 5940)	15	10
12	2r. on 2k. brown (No. 6073)	40	20
13	3r. on 6k. blue (No. 4673)	25	20
14	5r. on 6k. blue (No. 4673)	25	20
15	10r. on 1k. brown (No. 5940)	40	30
16	24r.50 on 1k. brown (No. 5940)	40	30

1992. Republic Day.

17	**9**	5r. multicoloured	25	15

10 Rocket Launch

11 National Flag

1993.

18	**10**	1r. green	10	10
19		3r. red	10	10
20		10r. bistre	15	10
21		25r. violet	30	15
22	**11**	50r. yellow, blue and deep blue	60	30

See also Nos. 45 etc.

12 Rocket and Earth

1993. Space Mail.

23	**12**	100r. multicoloured	35	30

13 Cock

1993. New Year. Year of the Cock.

24	**13**	60r. black, red and yellow	35	30

14 Space Station

1993. Cosmonautics Day.
25 **14** 90r. multicoloured 35 30

15 Nazarbaev and Flag on Map

1993. President Nursultan Nazarbaev (1st series).
26 **15** 50r. multicoloured 35 25
See also No. 28.

16 Kalkaman-Uly

1993. 325th Birth Anniv of Bukar Zhyrau Kalkaman-Uly (poet).
27 **16** 15r. multicoloured 35 25

17 Arms, Flag on Map and Nazarbaev

1993. President Nursultan Nazarbaev (2nd series).
28 **17** 100r. multicoloured 35 25

18 Desert Dormouse

1993. Mammals. Multicoloured.
29 5r. Type **18** 10 10
30 10r. Porcupine 10 10
31 15r. Marbled polecat 20 10
32 20r. Asiatic wild ass 25 15
33 25r. Mouflon 30 15
34 30r. Cheetah 35 20

19 Ice Hockey
20 Skiers

1994. Winter Olympic Games, Lillehammer, Norway (1st issue). Multicoloured.
35 15t. Type **19** 10 10
36 25t. Skiing 10 10
37 90t. Ski jumping 35 15
38 150t. Speed skating 60 30

1994. Winter Olympic Games, Lillehammer, Norway (2nd issue). Multicoloured.
39 2t. Type **20** 20 10
40 6t.80 Vladimir Smirnov (Kazakh skier) 55 20
See also No. 42.

21 Dog
22 Smirnov

1994. New Year. Year of the Dog.
41 **21** 30t. black, blue and green 25 10

1994. Vladimir Smirnov, Winter Olympic Games Medals Winner. As No. 40 but face value changed and with additional inscription in Kazakh.
42 **22** 12t. multicoloured 75 35

23 Launch of "Soyuz TM16" at Baikonur

1994. Cosmonautics Day.
43 **23** 2t. multicoloured 25 10

24 Space Shuttle *Buran* on Baikonur Launch Pad and Toktar Aubakrirov

1994. 1st Space Flight of Kazakh Cosmonaut. Sheet 107 × 66 mm.
MS44 **24** 4 × 6t.80 multicoloured 1·10 1·10

1994.
45 **10** 15ty. blue 10 10
76 20ty. orange 10 10
77 25ty. yellow 10 10
78 50ty. grey 10 10
46 80ty. purple 15 10
79 1t. green 20 10
80 2t. blue 35 15
81 4t. mauve 60 25
82 6t. green 90 40
83 12t. mauve . . . . 1·90 90

25 Mt. Abay

1994. 5th "Asia Dauysy" International Music Festival, Almaty. Multicoloured.
47 10t. Type **25** 50 25
48 15t. Medeo Ice Stadium, Almaty 85 45

26 Horsfield's Tortoises

1994. Reptiles. Multicoloured.
49 1t. Type **26** 10 10
50 1t.20 Toad-headed agamas . . 10 10
51 2t. Halys vipers 10 10
52 3t. Turkestan plate-tailed geckos 15 10
53 5t. Steppe agamas 25 15
54 7t. Glass lizards 35 20
MS55 93 × 73 mm. 10t. Transcaspian desert monitor (*Varanus griseus*) 50 50

27 National Arms

1994. Republic Day.
56 **27** 2t. multicoloured 15 10

28 "Why does the Swallow have a Forked Tail?" (dir. Amen Khaidorov)

1994. Children's Fund. Kazakh Children's Films. Multicoloured.
57 1t.+30ty. Type **28** 10 10
58 1t.+30ty. "The Calf and Hare seek a Better Life" (E. Abdrakhmanov) 10 10
59 1t.+30ty. Asses ("Lame Kulan" dir. Amen Khaidarov) 10 10

29 Entelodon

1994. Prehistoric Animals. Multicoloured.
60 1t. Type **29** 10 10
61 1t.20 Saurolophus 10 10
62 2t. Plesiosaurus 10 10
63 3t. "Sordes pilosus" 15 10
64 5t. Mosasaurus 25 15
65 7t. "Megaloceros giganteum" 35 20
MS66 92 × 72 mm. 10t. *Koelodonta antiquitatis* 50 50

1995. Nos. 45/6 surch.
67 **24** 1t. on 15ty. blue 10 10
68 2t. on 15ty. blue 15 10
69 3t. on 80ty. purple 25 10
70 4t. on 80ty. purple 35 15
71 6t. on 80ty. purple 45 20
72 8t. on 80ty. purple 50 25
73 12t. on 80ty. purple . . . . 1·10 50
74 20t. on 80ty. purple . . . . 2·10 85

31 Pig
32 Kunanbaev

1995. New Year. Year of the Pig.
75 **31** 10t. blue, black and light blue 50 50

1995. 150th Birth Anniv of Abai Kunanbaev (writer). Multicoloured.
86 4t. Type **32** 25 25
87 9t. Kunanbaev holding pen and book 50 50

33 Flight Path of "Soyuz" Spacecraft

1995. Cosmonautics Day. Multicoloured.
88 2t. Type **33** 80 40
89 10t. Yuri Malenchenko, Talgat Musabaev and Ulf Merbold (cosmonauts) . . . . . . 7·50 7·50

34 Manshuk Mametova and Battle Scene

1995. 50th Anniv of End of Second World War. Multicoloured.
90 1t. Type **34** 35 20
91 3t. Aliya Moldafulova and tank . . . . 1·00 75
92 5t. Wheat field, dove and eternal flame . . . . 3·75 3·25

35 "Spring" (S. Membeev)

1995. Paintings. Multicoloured.
93 4t. Type **35** 50 50
94 9t. "Mountains" (Zh. Shardenov) . . . . 1·00 1·00
95 15t. "Kulash Baiseitova in role of Kyz Zhibek" (G. Ismailova) (vert) . . . . 2·00 2·00
96 28t. "Kokpar" (K. Telzhanov) 4·00 4·00

1995. "Asia Dauysy" International Music Festival, Almaty. Nos. 47/8 optd **KAZAKSTAN '95 1995**.
97 10t. multicoloured . . . . . . 1·00 80
98 15t. multicoloured . . . . . . 1·50 1·25

37 Dauletkerei

1995. 175th Birth Anniv of Dauletkerei (composer and poet).
99 **37** 2t. multicoloured 35 25
100 28t. multicoloured . . . . 4·25 3·75

38 Gandhi, Temple and Spinning Wheel

1995. 125th Birth Anniv (1994) of Mahatma Gandhi.
101 **38** 9t. red and black . . . . . 1·00 80
102 22t. red and black . . . . 4·00 3·50

39 Anniversary Emblem
40 Cathedral of the Ascension

1995. 50th Anniv of U.N.O.
103 **39** 10t. gold and blue . . . . 1·00 80
104 36t. gold and blue . . . . 4·00 3·50

1995. Buildings in Almaty.
105 **40** 1t. green 15 15
106 – 2t. blue 20 10
107 – 3t. red 30 15
108 – 48t. brown . . . . 5·50 5·50
DESIGNS: 2t. Culture Palace; 3t. Opera and Ballet House; 48t. Theatre.
See also Nos. 124/5.

41 White-tailed Sea Eagle

1995. Birds of Prey. Multicoloured.
109 1t. Type **41** 10 10
110 3t. Osprey 20 10
111 5t. Lammergeier 35 15
112 6t. Himalayan griffon 40 20
113 30t. Saker falcon . . . . . . 2·10 1·00
114 50t. Golden eagle . . . . . 3·50 1·75

42 Rat and Lunar Cycle
43 Baikonur Launch Pad highlighted on Globe

1996. Chinese New Year. Year of the Rat.
115 **42** 25t. red, black and lilac . . 1·40 1·00

1996. Cosmonautics Day. Multicoloured.
116 6t. Type **43** 80 60
117 15t. Yuri Gagarin . . . . . 1·90 1·50
118 20t. Proposed "Alpha" space station . . . . 3·00 2·50

44 Carancal (*Felis caracal*)

1996. "Save the Aral Sea". Sheet 128 × 108 mm containing T **44** and similar horiz designs. Multicoloured.
MS119 20t. Type **44**; 20t. Aral trout (*Salmo trutta aralensis*); 20t. Striped hyena (*Hyaena hyaena*); 20t. Kaufmann's shovelnose (*Pseudoscaphirhynchus kaufmanni*); 20t. Pike asp (*Aspiolucius esocinus*) . . . . . 3·00 2·00

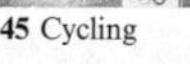
45 Cycling

46 Zhabaev (after embroidery by G. Atknin)

1996. Olympic Games, Atlanta. Multicoloured.
120 4t. Type **45** 35 20
121 6t. Wrestling 55 25
122 30t. Boxing . . . . 2·75 1·40
MS123 92 × 69 mm. 50t. Hurdling (45 × 27 *mm*) . . . . 1·75 1·25

1996. As T **40** but smaller, size 24 × 19 mm.
124 1t. green 10 10
125 6t. green 20 10
DESIGNS: 1t. Circus; 6t. Academy of Sciences (50th anniv).

1996. 150th Birth Anniv of Zhambil Zhabaev (writer).
126 **46** 12t. multicoloured 70 50

47 Tomb, Dombauyl

1996. Ancient Buildings. Multicoloured.
127 1t. Type **47** 20 10
128 3t. Mausoleum, Aisha Biy . . 50 30
129 6t. Mausoleum, Syrly Tam 2·50 2·00
MS130 90 × 60 mm. 30t. Kozha Ahmet Yasavi Mausoleum, Turkestan . . . . 1·10 75

48 "Soyuz TM-13" docked with "Mir" Space Station

49 Map of Kazakhstan and Dove with Letter

1996. 5th Anniv of Toktar Aubakirov's (cosmonaut) Service on "Mir". Multicoloured.
131 46t. Type **48** . . . . 1·90 1·50
132 46t. Aubakirov . . . . . . 1·90 1·50
Nos. 131/2 were issued together, se-tenant, forming a composite design.

1996. World Post Day.
133 **49** 9t. blue 35 20
134 – 40t. orange . . . . 3·50 3·00
DESIGN: 40t. Dove with letter and Universal Postal Union emblem.

1996. Republic Day. No. 56 surch **KAZAKSTAN 1. 1996.**
135 **27** 21t. on 2t. multicoloured 1·00 75

51 "Saturnia schenki"

1996. Butterflies. Multicoloured.
136 4t. Type **51** 15 10
137 6t. "Parnassius patricius" . . 20 10
138 12t. "Parnasssius ariadne" . . 40 20
139 46t. "Colias draconis" . . . 1·50 1·10

52 Borzois giving Chase

1996. Hunting Dogs.
140 **52** 5t. multicoloured 20 10
MS141 95 × 70 mm. **52** 100t. multicoloured . . . . 2·50 1·75

53 Bride before Yurte

54 Writing Materials and Books

1996. Traditional Costumes and Dwelling. Multicoloured.
142 10t. Type **53** 20 10
143 16t. Bridegroom before yurte 45 25
144 45t. Yurte interior . . . . . 1·25 65
Nos. 142/4 were issued together, se-tenant, Nos. 142/3 forming a composite design.

1996. Bicentenary of National Archive.
145 **54** 4t. brown 15 10
146 – 68t. violet . . . . 2·50 2·10
DESIGN: 68t. Book and documents.

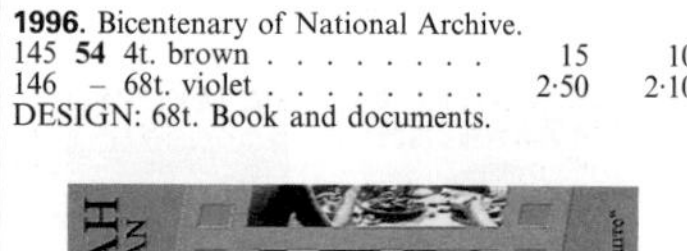
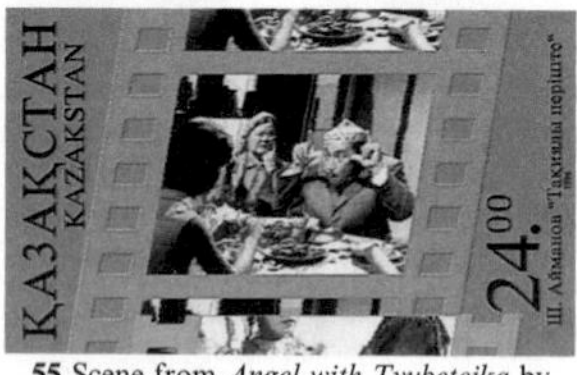

55 Scene from *Angel with Tyubetejka* by Shaken Aimanov

1996. Centenary (1995) of Motion Pictures. Sheet 135 × 148 mm containing T **55** and similar horiz designs. Multicoloured.
MS147 24t. Type **55**; 24t. *The Zhibek Girl* (S. Kozhykov); 24t. *His Time will Come* (M. Begalin); 24t. *My Name is Kozha* (A. Karsakbaev) 2·25 1·50

56 Head

1997. The Marbled Polecat. Multicoloured.
148 6t. Type **56** 15 10
149 10t. Adult with tail down . . 25 15
150 32t. Two polecats 80 45
151 46t. Adult with tail raised . . 1·10 70

57 Ox

58 Aries

1997. New Year. Year of the Ox.
152 **57** 40t. brown, black and green . . . . 1·00 70

1997. Star Signs. Each violet and purple.
153 1t. Type **58** 10 10
154 2t. Taurus 10 10
155 3t. Gemini 10 10
156 4t. Cancer 10 10
157 5t. Leo 10 10
158 6t. Virgo 10 10
159 7t. Libra 10 10
160 8t. Scorpio 10 10
161 9t. Sagittarius 10 10
162 10t. Capricorn 10 10
163 12t. Aquarius 25 20
164 20t. Pisces 40 30
MS165 109 × 164 mm. Nos. 153/64 1·50 1·50

59 Saturn and Automatic Transfer Vehicle

60 Emblem

1997. Cosmonautics Day. Multicoloured.
166 10t. Type **59** 25 20
167 10t. Space shuttle and "Mir" space station 25 20
168 10t. "Sputnik 1" and Earth 25 20
Nos. 166/8 were issued together, se-tenant, forming a composite design.

1997. World Book and Copyright Day.
169 **60** 15t. yellow and green . . . 30 20
170 60t. yellow and green . . . 1·10 85

61 Auezov Museum, Almaty

1997. Birth Centenary of Mukhtar Auezov (philologist). Multicoloured.
171 25t. Type **61** 45 35
172 40t. Auezov at table (after Shcherkassky) 80 55

62 Order of Bravery

63 "Tulipa alberti"

1997. Orders and Medals. Multicoloured.
173 15t. Type **62** 30 20
174 15t. Medal of Honour . . . 30 20
175 20t. Order of Victory 40 30
176 30t. National Order of Merit 55 40

1997. Tulips. Multicoloured.
177 15t. "Tulipa regelii" 30 20
178 35t. Type **63** 70 45
179 35t. "Tulipa greigii" 70 45

64 "Shepherd" (Sh. Sariev)

65 Moss Agate

1997. Paintings. Multicoloured.
180 25t. Type **64** 45 35
181 25t. "Fantastic Still Life" (S. Kalmykov) 45 35
182 25t. "Capturing Horse" (M. Kenbaev) (horiz) . . . 45 35

1997. Minerals. Multicoloured.
183 15t. Type **65** 30 20
184 15t. Chalcedony 30 20
185 20t. Azurite 40 30
186 20t. Malachite 40 30
MS187 110 × 99 mm. Nos. 182/5 2·25 2·25

66 "Gylippus rickmersi"

67 Argali

1997. Arachnidae. Multicoloured.
188 30t. Type **66** 60 40
189 30t. "Latrodectus pallidus" 60 40
190 30t. "Oculicosa supermirabilis" 60 40
191 30t. "Anomalobuthus rickmersi" 60 40

1997. Karkaraly Nature Park. Sheet 114 × 148 mm containing T **67** and similar vert designs. Multicoloured.
MS192 30t. Type **67**; 30t. Common juniper; 30t. Cudgel stone . . . 1·90 1·50

68 Horse Race

1997. National Sports. Multicoloured.
193 20t. Type **68** 40 30
194 20t. Tearing goatskin ("Koknar") 40 30
195 20t. Wrestling 40 30
196 20t. Two-horse race 40 30

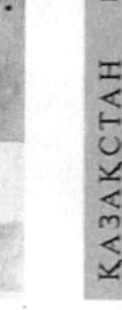

69 Ice Dancing

70 "Little Girl" (A. Ashkiyazara)

1998. Winter Sports. Multicoloured.
197 15t. Type **69** 30 20
198 30t. Biathlon 55 40

1998. Children's Paintings. Multicoloured.
199 15t. Type **70** 30 20
200 15t. "My House" (M. Tarakara) (horiz) . . . 30 20

71 Tiger and Lunar Cycle

72 Kurmangazy

1998. New Year. Year of the Tiger.
201 **71** 30t. brown, black and yellow 55 40

1998. 175th Birth Anniv of Kurmangazy (composer).
202 **72** 30t. yellow, brown & black 55 40

73 Baitursynov

75 "Apollo 8" Spacecraft and Moon

74 Winged and Horned Beasts, Issyk Kurgan

1998. 125th Birth Anniv of Akhmet Baitursynov (writer).
203 **73** 30t. light brown, brown and black 55 40

1998. Archaeological Finds. Multicoloured.
204 15t. Type **74** 35 25
205 30t. Pendants, Aktasty (vert) 70 50
206 40t. Gold and jewel-studded open-work ornament depicting animals, Kargaly 95 65

1998. Cosmonautics Day. Multicoloured.
207 30t. Type **75** 55 40
208 30t. "Apollo 8", Earth and Moon 55 40
209 50t. "Vostok 6" orbiting Earth 90 60

Nos. 207/8 were issued together, se-tenant, forming a composite design.

76 Mosque　**77** State Arms

1998. Astana. New Capital of Kazakhstan.

No.	Type	Description	Mint	Used
210	**76**	10t. brown	20	15
211	–	15t. blue (inscr "Akmola")	30	20
212	–	15t. blue (inscr "Astana")	1·00	90
213	–	20t. blue	40	30
214	–	25t. violet	30	20
MS215		99 × 73 mm. 100t. multicoloured	2·40	1·60

DESIGNS—VERT: 15t. Petroleum Ministry; 20t. Parliament. HORIZ: 25k. Presidents Palace. 43 × 25 mm.—100t. Presidents Palace.

1998.

No.	Type	Description	Mint	Used
216	**77**	1t. green	10	10
217		2t. blue	10	10
218		3t. red	10	10
219		4t. purple	10	10
220		5t. yellow	10	10
221		8t. orange	10	10
225		20t. orange	15	10
229		50t. blue	25	15

78 Climber fixing Tent

1998. Kazakhstan Expedition to Mt. Everest. Sheet 85 × 67 mm.

No.	Type	Description	Mint	Used
MS230	**78**	100t. multicoloured	2·40	1·60

79 Black Stork

1998. Birds. Multicoloured.

No.	Description	Mint	Used
231	15t. Type **79**	30	20
232	30t. Greater flamingoes	55	40
233	50t. Great white crane	90	60

80 Lynx　**82** Stamp and U.P.U. Emblem

81 Dove and Emblem

1998. Wild Cats. Multicoloured.

No.	Description	Mint	Used
234	15t. Type **80**	30	20
235	30t. Sand dune cat	55	40
236	50t. Snow leopard	90	60

1998. Admission of Kazakhstan to Universal Postal Union. Sheet 104 × 84 mm.

No.	Type	Description	Mint	Used
MS237	**81**	50t. multicoloured	1·25	85

1998. World Post Day.

No.	Type	Description	Mint	Used
238	**82**	30t. bistre	35	25

83 Anniversary Emblem　**84** Warrior with Sword

1998. 5th Anniv of the Tenge (currency unit).

No.	Type	Description	Mint	Used
239	**83**	40t. orange	50	30

1998. Kazakh Horsemen. Multicoloured.

No.	Description	Mint	Used
240	20t. Type **84**	25	20
241	30t. Using bow and arrow	35	25
242	40t. With spear and shield	65	50

85 Rock Formation in Lake

1998. Environmental Protection. Buradai National Park. Sheet 110 × 98 mm containing T **85** and similar vert design. Multicoloured.

No.	Description	Mint	Used
MS243	30t. Type **85**; 30t. View over lake	1·50	1·00

86 Family (census)　**87** Rabbit and Lunar Cycle

1999.

No.	Type	Description	Mint	Used
244	**86**	1t. green	10	10
245	–	3t. red	10	10
246	–	9t. green	10	10
247	–	15t. red	25	15
248	–	20t. brown	30	20
249	–	30t. brown	40	25

DESIGNS—HORIZ: 15t. Kanyish Sambaev (geologist and President of Academy of Sciences, birth centenary) and book; 20t. Sambaev and Academy of Sciences. VERT: 3, 9, 30t. Dish aerial and "Intelsat" satellite.

1999. New Year. Year of the Rabbit.

No.	Type	Description	Mint	Used
250	**87**	40t. green, black and yellow	50	30

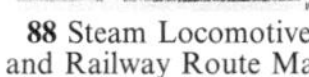

88 Steam Locomotive and Railway Route Map　**89** Satellite

1999. Railway Locomotives. Multicoloured.

No.	Description	Mint	Used
251	40t. Type **88**	50	30
252	50t. Electric locomotive	60	55
253	60t. Diesel railcar	75	50
254	80t. Electric locomotive (different)	1·00	90

1999. Cosmonautics Day. Multicoloured.

No.	Description	Mint	Used
255	50t. Type **89**	60	40
256	90t. Astronaut on Moon (30th anniv of first manned Moon landing) (horiz)	1·00	70

90 "Pseudoeremostachys severzowii"　**91** Scene from *Turksib* (1929)

1999. Flowers. Multicoloured.

No.	Description	Mint	Used
257	20t. Type **90**	25	20
258	30t. "Rhaphidophyton regelii"	35	25
259	90t. "Niedzwedzkia semiretschenskia"	1·00	70

1999. 70th Anniv of Kazak Cinema. Multicoloured.

No.	Description	Mint	Used
260	15t. Type **91**	15	10
261	20t. M. Berkovich (director) and scenes from *Jambul's Youth* (1997) and *Wolf Cub among People* (1998)	20	15
262	30t. Scenes from *The Devil Paths* (1935), *Our Dear Doctor* (1957) and *Amangeldy* (1938)	30	20
263	35t. Scenes from *Zama-ay* (1997), *Biography of a Young Accordionist* (1994) and *Who are you Rider?* (1989)	35	25
264	50t. Alfred Hitchcock (director) and scene from *The Birds*	50	35
265	60t. Sergei Eisenstein (director)	60	40

92 Red Fox　**93** Magnifying Glass and Stamps

1999. Endangered Species. Foxes. Multicoloured.

No.	Description	Mint	Used
266	20t. Type **92**	20	15
267	30t. Dhole	30	20
268	90t. Corsac fox	90	60

1999. 125th Anniv of Universal Postal Union.

No.	Type	Description	Mint	Used
269	**93**	10t. violet	10	10

94 Mushroom Cloud

1999. Environmental Protection Sheet 130 × 108, containing T **94** and similar horiz designs. Multicoloured.

No.	Description	Mint	Used
MS270	15t. Type **94** (tenth Anniv of cessation of nuclear testing at Semipalatinsk); 45t. Emblem (International Day for Protection of the Ozone Layer); 60t. Butterflies and landscape	1·30	1·30

95 Flower　**96** T. Musabayev

1999. Endangered Flora (1st series).

No.	Type	Description	Mint	Used
271	**95**	4t. mauve	10	10
272		30t. green	30	20

See also Nos. 296/8, 310/11 and 357/63.

1999. Cosmonauts. Multicoloured.

No.	Description	Mint	Used
273	40t. Type **96**	40	25
274	50t. T. Aubakirov (first Kazakhstan cosmonaut) (vert)	50	35

97 Ice Hockey Match

1999. Sports. Multicoloured.

No.	Description	Mint	Used
275	20t. Type **97**	20	15
276	30t. Ice hockey team	30	20
277	40t. G. Kosanov (athlete)	40	25

99 Oil Rig

2000. Centenary of Oil Extraction in Kazakhstan.

No.	Type	Description	Mint	Used
279	**99**	7t. red	10	10

100 Yurt, Horse racing and Artifacts　**101** Millennium Emblem

2000. Navruz Bayram Festival. Imperf.

No.	Type	Description	Mint	Used
280	**100**	20t. multicoloured	15	10

2000. New Millennium.

No.	Type	Description	Mint	Used
281	**101**	30t. blue, deep blue and orange	25	15

102 28th Guardsman-Panfilovs Memorial and Eternal Flame, Alma-Ata　**103** "Stride into the Bright Future" (painting, Kostya Balakirev)

2000. 55th Anniv of End of Second World War.

No.	Type	Description	Mint	Used
282	**102**	3t. brown and red	10	10

2000. International Children's Day. New Millennium. Sheet 127 × 106 mm.

No.	Type	Description	Mint	Used
MS283	**103**	70t. multicoloured	60	60

104 Koumiss (fermented mare's milk) Flask

2000. Joint issue with People's Republic of China. Pots. Multicoloured.

No.	Description	Mint	Used
284	15t. Type **104**	10	10
285	50t. He-pot (Chinese wine vessel)	40	25

105 Mukanov　**106** Dulati

2000. Birth Centenary of Sabit Mukanov (writer).

No.	Type	Description	Mint	Used
286	**105**	1t. green	10	10

2000. 500th Birth Anniv of Mukhammed Khaidar Dulti (historian) (1999).

No.	Type	Description	Mint	Used
287	**106**	8t. blue	10	10

107 Canoeing　**108** "Echo" Telecommunications Satellite

2000. Olympics Games, Sydney. Multicoloured.

No.	Description	Mint	Used
288	35t. Type **107**	30	20
289	40t. Gymnastics	35	20
290	40t. Taekwondo	35	20
291	50t. Triathlon	40	25

2000.

No.	Type	Description	Mint	Used
292	**108**	5t. orange	10	10
293		15t. blue	10	10
294		20t. blue	15	10

109 Arystan Bab's Mausoleum

2000. 1500th Anniv of Turkestan (town). Sheet 160 × 140 mm containing T **109** and similar horiz designs. Multicoloured.

No.	Description	Mint	Used
MS295	50t. Type **109**; 50t. Rabiy Sultan Begim's and Karashash Ana's mausolea; 70t. Kozhah Akhmet Yassauy's mausoleum	1·40	1·40

Stamps of a similar design were issued by Turkey.

110 Flower

111 Momysh-Uly and Gold Star of Hero of Soviet Union Medal

2000. Endangered Flora (2nd series).
296 **110** 1t. green 10 10
297 2t. blue 10 10
298 50t. blue 20 15

2000. 90th Birth Anniv of Baurdzhan Momyush-Uly (Soviet military leader).
299 **111** 4t. brown and black . . . 10 10

2001. Nos. 57/9 surch **2001 10.00.**
300 10t. on 1t. +30ty. multicoloured 10 10
301 10t. on 1t. +30ty. multicoloured 10 10
302 10t. on 1t. +30ty. multicoloured 10 10

113 Snail and Lunar Cycle

2001. New Year. Year of the Snail.
303 **113** 40t. black, blue and yellow 35 20

114 Rocket, Yuri Gagarin and Dogs

2001. Cosmonautics Day (2000). Multicoloured.
304 40t. Type **114** (40th anniv of space flight by Belka and Strelka (dogs)) 35 20
305 70t. Rocket launch (45th anniv of Baikonur cosmodrome) (vert) 60 30

115 Snake and Lunar Cycle

2001. New Year. Year of the Snake.
306 **115** 40t. black, brown and green 35 20

116 Dove, Globe and Transport

2001. 10th Anniv of Ministry of Transportation and Communication. Sheet 100 × 70 mm.
MS307 **116** 100t. multicoloured 85 85

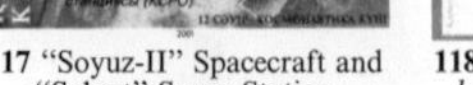

117 "Soyuz-II" Spacecraft and "Salyut" Space Station

118 *Aquilegia karatavica*

2001. Cosmonautics Day. Multicoloured.
308 45t. Type **117** 35 20
309 70t. Yuri Gagarin and earth (40th anniv of first manned space flight) 60 30

2001. Endangered Flora (3rd series).
310 **118** 3t. green 10 10
311 10t. green 10 10

119 Abulkhair-Khan (1693–1748)

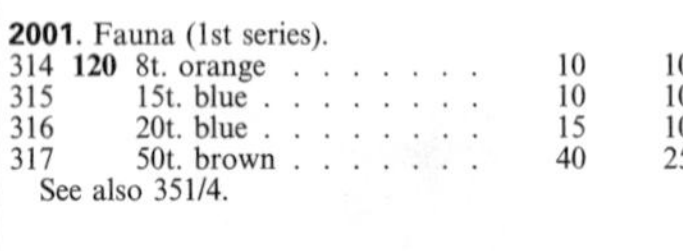

120 Roborovski Hamster (*Phodopus roborovskii*)

2001. Khans (feudal rulers). Multicoloured.
312 50t. Type **119** 40 25
313 60t. Abylai-Khan (1711–1781) 50 30

2001. Fauna (1st series).
314 **120** 8t. orange 10 10
315 15t. blue 10 10
316 20t. blue 15 10
317 50t. brown 40 25
See also 351/4.

121 Northern Eagle Owl (*Bubo bubo*)

2001. Owls. Multicoloured.
318 30t. Type **121** 25 15
319 40t. Long-eared owl (*Asio otis*) 35 20
320 50t. Hawk owl (*Surnia ulula*) 40 25

122 Winged Lion and Fibre Optic Cable

123 Red Deer (*Cervus elaphus*)

2001. National Development Plan. Communications.
321 **122** 40t. multicoloured 35 20

2001. Fauna of Lake Markakol (national park). Sheet 110 × 98 mm containing T **123** and similar vert designs. Multicoloured.
MS322 Type **123**; 30t. Brown bear (*Ursus arctos*); 30t. Lenok (*Brachymystax lenok*) 70 70

124 Bobak Marmot (*Marmota bobak*)

2001. Flora and Fauna. Sheet 215 × 102 mm containing T **124** and similar horiz designs. Multicoloured.
MS323 Type **124**; 12t. Great bustard (*Otis tarda*); 25t. Relict gull (*Larus relictus*); 60t. African wildcat (*Felis silvestris libyca*); 90t. Water lily (*Nymphaea alba*); 100t. Dalmatian pelican (*Pelecanus crispus*) . . 3·00 3·00

125 Druzhba Station Facade

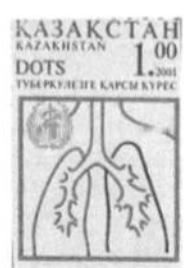

126 Lungs and United Nations Emblem

2001. Anniversaries. Sheet 105 × 74 mm containing T **125** and similar horiz designs. Multicoloured.
MS324 Type **125** (10th anniv of Kazakhstan–China railway); 20t. Steam locomotive (70th anniv of Turkestan–Siberia railway); 50t. Workmen (opening of Aksu–Delegen railway) 70 70

2001. Health.
325 **126** 1t. green, blue and black 10 10
326 – 5t. red, grey and black . . 10 10
DESIGNS: Type **126** (tuberculosis prevention campaign); 5t. Ribbon and book (AIDS prevention campaign).

127 River Charyn Cliffs

2001. International Year of Mountains. Multicoloured.
327 35t. Type **127** 30 15
328 60t. Mt. Khan Tegri 50 25

128 Alexej Leonov

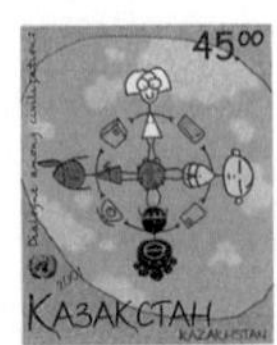

129 Children encircling Globe

2001. Space Anniversaries. Mlticoloured.
329 50t. Type **128** (35th anniv of 1st space walk) 40 20
330 70t. *Soyuz* and *Apollo* space craft (25th anniv of joint USSR–USA space flight) (horiz) 55 25

2001. United Nations Year of Dialogue among Civilizations.
331 **129** 45t. multicoloured 35 15

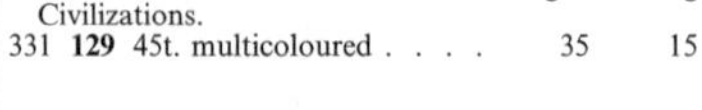

130 Wild Ass

2001. Endangered Species. Asiatic Wild Ass (*Equus heminus kulan*). Multicoloured.
332 9t. Type **130** 10 10
333 12t. Galloping 10 10
334 25t. Fighting 10 10
335 50t. Mare and foal 40 20

131 School Palace, Alma Ata

132 Union Emblem

2001. Architecture.
336 **131** 7t. mauve 10 10
337 – 30t. green 25 10
DESIGN: 30t. School Palace, Alma Ata (different).

2001. 10th Anniv of Union of Independent States.
338 **132** 40t. multicoloured 30 30

133 Pres. Nursultan Nazarbaev and Pope John Paul II

2001. Visit of Pope John Paul II to Kazakhstan. Multicoloured.
339 20t. Type **133** 15 10
340 50t. Pres. Nazarbaev and Pope John Paul II (different) 40 20

134 Independence Monument, Almaty

135 Celebration Emblem and Map

2001. 10th Anniv of Independence (1st issue). Sheet 110 × 96 mm containing T **134** and similar vert designs. Multicoloured.
MS341 Type **134**; 25t. Parliament House, Astana; 35t. Pres. Nursultan Nazarbaev 60 60
See also No. 342.

2001. 10th Anniv of Independence (2nd issue).
342 **135** 40t. yellow, blue and black 30 15

136 Man's Costume

138 Horse and Lunar Cycle

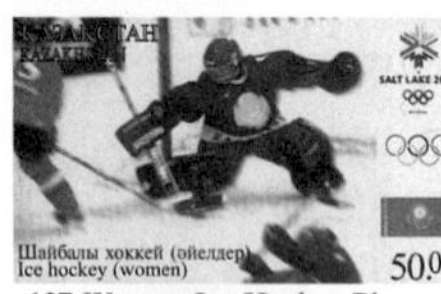

137 Women Ice Hockey Players

2001. Traditional Costumes. Multicoloured.
343 25t. Type **136** 20 10
344 35t. Woman's costume . . . 30 15
Nos. 343/4 were issued together, se-tenant, forming a composite design.

2002. Winter Olympic Games, Salt Lake City, USA. Multicoloured.
345 50t. Type **137** 40 20
346 150t. Freestyle ski jump . . . 1·20 1·20

2002. New Year. Year of the Horse.
347 **138** 50t. black, ochre and stone 40 20

139 Chestnut Horse

2002. Horses. Multicoloured.
348 9t. Type **139** 10 10
349 25t. Dark chestnut, two legs raised 20 10
350 60t. Grey 50 25

140 Pallid Pygmy Jerboa (*Salpingotus pallidus*)

142 *Pterygostemon spathulatus*

141 Denis Tito (passenger), Talgat Musabaev and Yury Baturin (crew of Soyuz TM-32)

2002. Fauna (2nd series).
351 **140** 5t. purple 10 10
352 15t. blue 10 10
353 40t. brown 30 15
354 50t. sepia 40 20

2002. Cosmonautics Day. Multicoloured.
355 30t. Type **141** 25 10
356 70t. Flags of USA, Kazakhstan and Russia . . 55 25

2002. Endangered Flora (4th series).
357 **142** 1t. green 10 10
358 2t. blue 10 10
359 3t. green 10 10
360 10t. violet 10 10
361 12t. mauve 10 10
362 25t. violet 20 10
363 35t. olive 30 15

143 Two Players

2002. World Cup Football Championships, Japan and South Korea. Multicoloured.
364 10t. Type **143** 10 10
365 10t. Player heading ball 10 10

144 Globe
145 *Leontopodium fedtschenkoanum* (flower)

2002. TRANSEURASIA 2002 International Conference.
366 **144** 30t. blue, black and yellow 25 10

2002. Alatau National Park. Sheet 115 × 110 mm containing T **145** and similar vert designs. Multicoloured.
MS367 30t. × 3, Type **145**; Ermine (*Mustela erminea*); Aport Alexander apples 70 70

146 Trading House
147 "Kazakh Composition" (E. Sidorkin)

2002. 250th Anniv of Petropavlovsk.
368 **146** 6t. red 10 10
369 – 7t. purple 10 10
370 – 8t. orange (vert) 10 10
371 – 23t. blue (vert) 15 10
DESIGNS: 7t. No. 368; 8t. Karasai and Agyntai (heroes) monument; 23t. No. 371.

2002. Art.
372 **147** 8t. brown, bistre and black 10 10
373 – 9t. black and drab 10 10
374 – 60t. sepia, bistre and black 50 25
DESIGNS: 9t. "Makhambet" (M. Kisametdinov); 60t. "Batyr" (E. Sidorkin).

148 Great Black-headed Gull (Pallas' Gull) (*Larus ichthyaetus Pallas*)

2002. Endangered Species. Birds. Multicoloured.
375 10t. Type **148** 10 10
376 15t. Demoiselle crane (*Anthropoides virgo*) 10 10
Stamps of the same design were issued by Russia.

149 *Huso huso ponticus* (fish)

2002. Endangered Species. Marine Animals. Multicoloured.
377 20t. Type **149** 15 10
378 35t. Caspian seal (*Phoca caspica*) 30 15
Stamps of the same design were issued by Ukraine.

150 Mosque

2002. Bimillenary of Taraz. Sheet 115 × 80 mm.
MS379 **150** 70t. multicoloured 55 55

151 Altau Mountains
152 Gabiden Mustaphin

2002. International Year of Mountains. Sheet 90 × 70 mm.
MS380 **151** 50t. multicoloured 40 40

2002. Birth Centenary of Gabiden Mustaphin (writer).
381 **152** 10t. blue 10 10

153 Gani Muratbaev
154 Gabit Musrepov

2002. Birth Centenary of Gani Muratbaev (politician).
382 **153** 3t. brown 10 10

2002. Birth Centenary of Gabit Musrepov (writer).
383 **154** 20t. multicoloured 15 10

155 Ilyushin IL-86 over Almaty Airport

2002. Aircraft. Multicoloured.
384 20t. Type **155** 15 10
385 40t. Tupelov TU-144 (25th Anniv of flight from Russia to Almaty) 35 15

KEDAH Pt. 1

A state of the Federation of Malaya, incorporated in Malaysia in 1963.

100 cents = 1 dollar (Straits or Malayan).

1 Sheaf of Rice
2 Malay ploughing

1912.
1 **1** 1c. black and green 60 25
26 1c. brown 70 20
52 1c. black 1·00 10
27 2c. green 1·50 20
2 3c. black and red 4·50 30
19 3c. purple 65 1·00
53 3c. green 2·25 90
3 4c. red and grey 10·00 25
20 4c. red 3·75 20
54 4c. violet 1·00 10
4 5c. green and brown 2·25 3·00
55 5c. yellow 1·50 10
56 6c. red 1·75 65
5 8c. black and blue 3·75 3·50
57 8c. black 12·00 10
6 **2** 10c. blue and brown 2·25 90
58 12c. black and blue 4·00 4·00
31 20c. black and green 4·00 2·00
32 21c. mauve and purple 2·00 13·00
33 25c. blue and purple 2·25 8·50
34 30c. black and pink 3·00 10·00
59 35c. purple 8·00 28·00
9 40c. black and purple 3·50 14·00
36 50c. brown and blue 2·50 14·00
37w – $1 black and red on yellow 6·50 9·00
38 – $2 green and brown 13·00 95·00
39 – $3 black and blue on blue 65·00 95·00
40 – $5 black and red 75·00 £150
DESIGN—As Type **2**: $1 to $5, Council Chamber.

1919. Surch in words.
24 50c. on $2 green and brown 70·00 75·00
25 $1 on $3 black and blue on blue 20·00 90·00

1922. Optd **MALAYA-BORNEO EXHIBITION**.
45 **1** 1c. brown 3·00 16·00
41 2c. green 3·50 24·00
46 3c. purple 3·00 42·00
47 4c. red 3·00 25·00
48 **2** 10c. blue and sepia 4·50 45·00
42 21c. purple 27·00 80·00
43 25c. blue and purple 27·00 80·00
44 50c. brown and blue 27·00 95·00

6 Sultan Abdul Hamid Halimshah

1937.
60 **6** 10c. blue and brown 4·25 1·25
61 12c. black and violet 38·00 9·00
62 25c. blue and purple 7·50 4·50
63 30c. green and red 8·00 10·00
64 40c. black and purple 4·00 16·00
65 50c. brown and blue 6·50 4·50
66 $1 black and green 4·00 10·00
67 $2 green and brown £120 75·00
68 $5 black and red 32·00 £160

1948. Silver Wedding. As T **4b/c** of Pitcairn Islands.
70 10c. violet 20 30
71 $5 red 27·00 32·00

1949. U.P.U. As T **4d/g** of Pitcairn Islands.
72 10c. purple 25 75
73 15c. blue 1·75 1·50
74 25c. orange 65 1·50
75 50c. black 1·00 2·75

7 Sheaf of Rice
8 Sultan Badlishah

1950.
76 **7** 1c. black 50 30
77 2c. orange 50 15
78 3c. green 2·00 1·00
79 4c. brown 75 10
79ab 5c. purple 1·75 1·00
80 6c. grey 70 15
81 8c. red 1·75 2·50
81a 8c. green 1·00 1·75
82 10c. mauve 70 10
82a 12c. red 1·00 2·50
83 15c. blue 1·25 35
84 20c. black and green 1·25 2·50
84a 20c. blue 1·00 10
85 **8** 25c. purple and orange 1·50 30
85a 30c. red and purple 2·50 1·25
85b 35c. red and purple 1·00 1·50
86 40c. red and purple 2·75 6·00
87 50c. black and blue 2·25 35
88 $1 blue and purple 3·00 4·25
89 $2 green and red 20·00 23·00
90 $5 green and brown 42·00 42·00

1953. Coronation. As T **4h** of Pitcairn Islands.
91 10c. black and purple 1·25 60

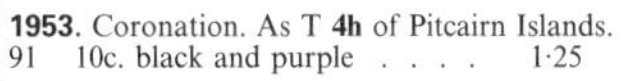

15 Fishing Craft
20 Sultan Abdul Halim Mu' Adzam Shah

1957. Inset portrait of Sultan Badlishah.
92 – 1c. black 10 60
93 – 2c. red 10 1·75
94 – 4c. sepia 10 1·00
95 – 5c. lake 10 75
96 – 8c. green 2·00 8·00
97 – 10c. sepia 65 40
98 **15** 20c. blue 2·75 2·50
99 – 50c. black and blue 2·50 3·50
100 – $1 blue and purple 5·50 12·00
101 – $2 green and red 25·00 32·00
102 – $5 brown and green 40·00 35·00
DESIGNS—HORIZ: 1c. Copra; 2c. Pineapples; 4c. Ricefield; 5c. Masjid Alwi Mosque, Kangar; 8c. East Coast Railway "Golden Blowpipe" Express; $1 Govt Offices; $2 Bersilat (form of wrestling); $5 Weaving. VERT: 10c. Tiger; 50c. Aborigines with blowpipe.

1959. Installation of Sultan.
103 **20** 10c. yellow, brown and blue 10 10

21 Sultan Abdul Halim Shah

1959. As Nos. 92/102 but with inset portrait of Sultan Abdul Halim Shah as in T **21**.
104 1c. black 10 75
105 2c. red 10 2·00
106 4c. sepia 10 75
107 5c. lake 10 10
108 8c. green 3·50 3·50
109 10c. sepia 1·00 10
109a 10c. purple 5·00 40
110 20c. blue 1·00 1·00
111a 50c. black and blue 30 60
112 $1 blue and purple 1·75 2·25
113 $2 green and red 13·00 18·00
114 $5 brown and green 16·00 19·00

22 "Vanda hookeriana"

1965. Flowers. Multicoloured.
115 1c. Type **22** 10 1·25
116 2c. "Arundina graminifolia" 10 1·75
117 5c. "Paphiopedilum niveum" 10 10
118 6c. "Spathoglottis plicata" 15 60
119 10c. "Arachnis flos-aeris" 30 10
120 15c. "Rhyncostylis retusa" 1·50 10
121 20c. "Phalaenopsis violacea" 1·75 1·00
The higher values used in Kedah were Nos. 20/7 of Malaysia.

23 "Danaus melanippus"

1971. Butterflies. Multicoloured.
124 1c. "Delias ninus" 30 1·75
125 2c. Type **23** 50 1·75
126 5c. "Parthenos sylvia" 1·25 40
127 6c. "Papilio demoleus" 1·25 2·00
128 10c. "Hebomoia glaucippe" 1·25 10
129 15c. "Precis orithya" 1·25 10
130 20c. "Valeria valeria" 1·50 70
The higher values in use with this issue were Nos. 64/71 of Malaysia.

24 "Pterocarpus indicus"

1979. Flowers. Multicoloured.
135 1c. "Rafflesia hasseltii" 10 90
136 2c. Type **24** 10 90
137 5c. "Lagerstroemia speciosa" 10 60
138 10c. "Durio zibethinus" 15 10
139 15c. "Hibiscus rosa-sinensis" 15 10
140 20c. "Rhododendron scortechinii" 20 10
141 25c. "Etlingera elatior" (inscr "Phaeomeria speciosa") 40 20

25 Sultan Abdul Halim Shah
26 Cocoa

1983. Silver Jubilee of Sultan's Installation. Multicoloured.
142 20c. Type **25** 70 30
143 40c. Paddy fields (horiz) 1·75 1·75
144 60c. Paddy fields and Mount Jerai (horiz) 2·50 4·75

1986. Agricultural Products of Malaysia. Mult.
152 1c. Coffee 10 10
153 2c. Coconuts 10 10
154 5c. Type **26** 15 10
155 10c. Black pepper 15 10
156 15c. Rubber 25 10
157 20c. Oil palm 25 15
158 30c. Rice 30 15

KELANTAN Pt. 1

A state in the Federation of Malaya, incorporated in Malaysia in 1963.

100 cents = 1 dollar (Straits or Malayan).

1 3 Sultan Ismail

1911.

1a 1 1c. green . . . . 4·75 30
15 1c. black . . . . 1·00 50
16 2c. brown . . . . 7·00 3·75
16a 2c. green . . . . 3·50 40
2 3c. red . . . . 4·25 15
16b 3c. brown . . . . 4·50 1·00
17 4c. black and red . . . . . 2·50 10
18 5c. green and red on yellow 1·50 10
19 6c. purple . . . . 3·25 1·50
19a 6c. red . . . . 4·00 5·50
5 8c. blue . . . . 5·50 1·00
20 10c. black and mauve . . . 3·00 10
21 30c. purple and red . . . . 4·00 5·50
8 50c. black and orange . . . 8·00 2·50
9 $1 green . . . . 48·00 48·00
9a $1 green and brown . . . . 48·00 2·00
10 $2 green and red . . . . . 1·50 4·00
11 $5 green and blue . . . . . 4·00 7·50
12 $25 green and orange . . . 42·00 80·00

1922. Optd **MALAYA BORNEO EXHIBITION**.
37 1 1c. green . . . . 3·50 48·00
30 4c. black and red . . . . . 5·00 48·00
31 5c. green and red on yellow 6·00 48·00
38 10c. black and mauve . . . . 6·00 60·00
32 30c. purple and red . . . . 6·00 65·00
33 50c. black and orange . . . 8·50 70·00
34 $1 green and brown . . . . 27·00 90·00
35 $2 green and red . . . . . . 65·00 £170
36 $5 green and blue £160 £350

1928.
40 3 1c. olive and yellow 50 55
41 2c. green . . . . 4·00 20
42 4c. red . . . . 5·50 1·00
43 5c. brown . . . . 4·75 10
44 6c. red . . . . 11·00 8·00
45 8c. olive . . . . 4·75 10
46 10c. purple . . . . 22·00 2·75
47 12c. blue . . . . 3·50 6·00
48 25c. red and purple . . . . . 5·00 3·50
49 30c. violet and red . . . . . 40·00 20·00
50 40c. orange and green . . . . 8·50 26·00
51 50c. olive and orange . . . . 65·00 5·50
39 $1 blue . . . . 14·00 80·00
52 $1 violet and green . . . . . 48·00 13·00
53 $2 red £225 £180
54 $5 red £375 £475
All except No. 39 are larger than T 3.

1948. Silver Wedding. As T **4b/c** of Pitcairn Islands.
55 10c. violet . . . . 75 2·75
56 $5 red . . . . 26·00 48·00

1949. U.P.U. As T **4d/g** of Pitcairn Islands.
57 10c. purple 25 30
58 15c. blue . . . . 2·00 1·00
59 25c. orange . . . . 40 2·75
40 50c. black . . . . 70 2·50

5 Sultan Ibrahim

6 Sultan Yahya Petra and Crest of Kelantan

1951.
61 5 1c. black 50 30
62 2c. orange . . . . 1·25 35
63 3c. green . . . . 4·00 1·25
64 4c. brown 75 15
65 5c. purple . . . . 1·25 50
66 6c. grey 75 20
67 8c. red . . . . 2·00 3·50
68 8c. green . . . . 1·25 1·75
69 10c. mauve 50 10
70 12c. red . . . . 2·50 2·25
71 15c. blue . . . . 4·25 60
72 20c. black and green . . . . 80 6·00
73 20c. blue . . . . 1·00 25
74 25c. purple and orange . . . 1·50 55
75 30c. red and purple . . . . . 1·25 2·00
76 35c. red and purple . . . . . 1·25 1·50
77 40c. red and purple . . . . . 9·00 13·00
78 50c. black and blue . . . . . 3·75 40
79 $1 blue and purple . . . . . 7·50 5·00
80 $2 green and red . . . . . . 27·00 27·00
81 $5 green and brown . . . . 48·00 40·00

1953. Coronation. As T **4h** of Pitcairn Islands.
82 10c. black and purple . . . . 1·25 1·40

1957. As Nos. 92/102 of Kedah but inset portrait of Sultan Ibrahim.
83 1c. black 10 30
84 2c. red . . . . 75 1·50
85 4c. sepia 40 10
86 5c. lake 40 10
87 8c. green . . . . 1·00 3·00
88 10c. sepia . . . . 2·25 10
89 10c. purple . . . . 8·00 7·00
90 20c. blue . . . . 2·25 30
91 50c. black and blue 50 50
92 $1 blue and purple . . . . . 6·00 1·50
93 $2 green and red . . . . . . 12·00 6·00
94 $5 brown and green . . . . . 15·00 12·00

1961. Coronation of the Sultan.
95 6 10c. multicoloured 40 30

7 Sultan Yahya Petra

8 "Vanda hookeriana"

1961. As Nos. 83, etc, but with inset portrait of Sultan Yahya Petra as in T **7**.
96 1c. black . . . . 10 2·00
97 2c. red . . . . 10 2·00
98 4c. sepia . . . . 80 1·25
99 5c. lake 60 20
100 8c. green . . . . 8·00 10·00
101 10c. purple . . . . 1·75 25
102 20c. blue . . . . 4·75 1·50

1965. As Nos. 115/21 of Kedah but with inset portrait of Sultan Yahya Petra as in T **8**.
103 8 1c. multicoloured . . . . . 10 1·00
104 – 2c. multicoloured . . . . . 10 1·75
105 – 5c. multicoloured 15 30
106 – 6c. multicoloured . . . . . 70 2·25
107 – 10c. multicoloured 30 25
108 – 15c. multicoloured . . . . . 1·50 25
109 – 20c. multicoloured . . . . . 1·50 1·50
The higher values used in Kelantan were Nos. 20/7 of Malaysia (National Issues).

9 "Parthenos sylvia"

1971. Butterflies. As Nos. 124/30 of Kedah but with portrait of Sultan Yahya Petra as in T **9**.
112 – 1c. multicoloured . . . . . 30 2·25
113 – 2c. multicoloured . . . . . 40 2·25
114 9 5c. multicoloured . . . . . 1·50 60
115 – 6c. multicoloured . . . . . 1·50 2·50
116 – 10c. multicoloured . . . . . 1·50 30
117 – 15c. multicoloured . . . . . 1·50 10
118 – 20c. multicoloured . . . . . 2·00 1·50
The higher values in use with this series were Nos. 64/71 of Malaysia (National Issues).

10 "Lagerstroemia speciosa"

1979. Flowers. As Nos. 135/41 of Kedah but with portrait of Sultan Yahya Petra as in T **10**.
123 1c. "Rafflesia hasseltii" . . . 10 1·00
124 2c. "Pterocarpus indicus" . . 10 1·00
125 5c. Type **10** 10 80
126 10c. "Durio zibethinus" . . . 15 10
127 15c. "Hibiscus rosa-sinensis" 15 10
128 20c. "Rhododendron scortechinii" 20 10
129 25c. "Etlingera elatior" (inscr "Phaeomeria speciosa") . . 40 50

11 Sultan Tengku Ismail Petra

12 Black Pepper

1980. Coronation of Sultan Tengku Ismail Petra.
130 11 10c. multicoloured 40 75
131 15c. multicoloured 40 15
132 50c. multicoloured . . . . 90 2·75

1986. Agricultural Products of Malaysia. Mult.
140 1c. Coffee 10 30
141 2c. Coconuts 10 30
142 5c. Cocoa 50 10
143 10c. Type **12** 20 10
144 15c. Rubber 30 10
145 20c. Oil palm 20 15
146 30c. Rice 40 15

KENYA Pt. 1

Formerly part of Kenya, Uganda and Tanganyika (q.v.). Became independent in 1963 and a Republic in 1964.

100 cents = 1 shilling.

1 Cattle Ranching **4** Cockerel

3 National Assembly

1963. Independence.
1 1 5c. multicoloured 10 55
2 – 10c. brown 10 10
3 – 15c. mauve . . . . 1·00 10
4 – 20c. black and green 15 10
5 – 30c. black and yellow 15 10
6 – 40c. brown and blue 15 30
7 – 50c. red, black and green . . 15 10
8 – 65c. turquoise and yellow . . 55 65
9 3 1s. multicoloured 20 10
10 – 1s.30 brown, black & green 4·50 30
11 – 2s. multicoloured . . . . . . 1·25 40
12 – 5s. brown, blue and green . . 1·25 50
13 – 10s. brown and blue . . . . 8·50 3·00
14 – 20s. black and red . . . . . 4·00 8·50
DESIGNS—As Type **1**: 10c. Wood-carving; 15c. Heavy industry; 20c. Timber industry; 30c. Jomo Kenyatta facing Mt. Kenya; 40c. Fishing industry; 50c. Kenya flag; 65c. Pyrethrum industry. As Type **3**: 1s.30, Tourism (Treetops hotel); 2s. Coffee industry; 5s. Tea industry; 10s. Mombasa Port; 20s. Royal College, Nairobi.

1964. Inauguration of Republic. Multicoloured.
15 15c. Type **4** 15 15
16 30c. Pres. Kenyatta 15 10
17 50c. African lion 15 10
18 1s.30 Hartlaub's turaco . . . 3·00 50
19 2s.50 Nandi flame . . . . . . 40 3·75

5 Thomson's Gazelle

7 Greater Kudu

1966.
20 5 5c. orange, black and sepia 20 20
21 – 10c. black and green 10 10
22 – 15c. black and orange . . . 10 10
23 – 20c. ochre, black and blue . . 10 15
24 – 30c. indigo, blue and black 20 10
25 – 40c. black and brown 60 30
26 – 50c. black and orange . . . 60 10
27 – 65c. black and green . . . . 1·25 2·00
28 – 70c. black and red . . . . . 5·00 1·50
29 7 1s. brown, black and blue . . 30 10
30 – 1s.30 blue, green and black 4·00 20
31 – 1s.50 black, brown and green 3·00 2·25
32 – 2s.50 yellow, black & brown 3·25 1·25
33 – 5s. yellow, black and green 75 70
34 – 10s. ochre, black and brown 1·75 3·50
35 – 20s. multicoloured . . . . . 5·50 13·00
DESIGNS—As Type **5**: 10c. Sable antelope; 15c. Aardvark ("Ant Bear"); 20c. Lesser bushbaby; 30c. Warthog; 40c. Common zebra; 50c. African buffalo; 65c. Black rhinoceros; 70c. Ostrich. As Type **7**: 1s.30, African elephant; 1s.50, Bat-eared fox; 2s.50, Cheetah; 5s. Savanna monkey ("Vervet Monkey"); 10s. Giant ground pangolin; 20s. Lion.

8 Perna Tellin

9 Ramose Murex

1971. Sea Shells. Multicoloured.
36 5c. Type **8** 10 30
37 10c. Episcopal mitre 15 10
38 15c. Purplish clanculus . . . 15 20
39 20c. Humpback cowrie . . . 15 20
40 30c. Variable abalone 20 10
41 40c. Flame top shell 20 10
42 50c. Common purple janthina 30 20
43 50c. Common purple janthina 11·00 3·00
44 60c. Bullmouth helmet . . . 30 1·75
45 70c. Chambered or pearly nautilus . . . . 45 1·50
46 70c. Chambered or pearly nautilus . . . . 10·00 6·00
47a 1s. Type **9** 20 10
48 1s.50 Trumpet triton . . . . 1·00 10
49 2s.50 Trapezium horse conch 1·00 10
50a 5s. Great green turban . . . 1·00 10
51 10s. Textile or cloth of gold cone . . . . 1·50 15
52a 20s. Scorpion conch . . . . 1·50 25
INSCRIPTIONS: No. 42, "Janthina globosa"; 43, "Janthina janthina"; 45, "Nautilus pompileus"; 46, "Nautilus pompilius".
Nos. 47/52 are larger, as Type **9**.

1975. Nos. 48/9 and 52a surch.
53 2s. on 1s.50 Trumpet triton . . 6·00 5·00
54 3s. on 2s.50 Trapezium horse conch . . . . 9·50 20·00
55 40s. on 20s. Scorpion conch 6·00 14·00

11 Microwave Tower

1976. Telecommunications Development. Mult.
56 50c. Type **11** 10 10
57 1s. Cordless switchboard (horiz) 10 10
58 2s. Telephones 20 30
59 3s. Message switching centre (horiz) 25 45
MS60 120 × 120 mm. Nos. 56/9. Imperf . . . . 1·10 2·50

12 Akii Bua, Ugandan Hurdler

1976. Olympic Games, Montreal. Multicoloured.
61 50c. Type **12** 10 10
62 1s. Filbert Bayi, Tanzanian runner 15 10
63 2s. Steve Muchoki, Kenyan boxer 45 35
64 3s. Olympic flame and East African flags 90 50
MS65 129 × 154 mm. Nos. 61/4 6·00 7·50

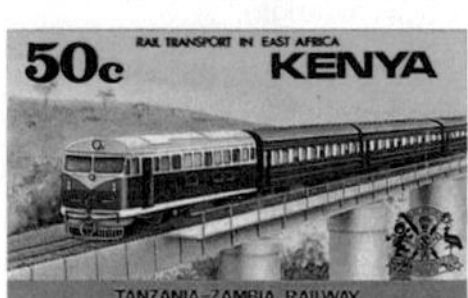

13 Diesel-hydraulic Train, Tanzania–Zambia Railway

1976. Railway Transport. Multicoloured.
66 50c. Type **13** 35 10
67 1s. Nile Bridge, Uganda . . . 60 15
68 2s. Nakuru Station, Kenya . . 1·50 1·00
69 3s. Uganda Railway Class A steam locomotive, 1896 . . 1·50 1·50
MS70 154 × 103 mm. Nos. 66/9 8·00 8·00

14 Nile Perch

1977. Game Fish of East Africa. Multicoloured.
71 50c. Type **14** 25 10
72 1s. Nile mouthbrooder ("Tilapia") 35 10
73 3s. Sailfish 75 60
74 5s. Black marlin 90 80
MS75 153 × 129 mm. Nos. 71/4 7·50 4·00

15 Maasai Manyatta (village), Kenya

1977. 2nd World Black and African Festival of Arts and Culture, Nigeria. Multicoloured.
76 50c. Type **15** 15 10
77 1s. "Heartbeat of Africa" (Ugandan dancers) 15 10
78 2s. Makonde sculpture, Tanzania . . . . 60 1·25
79 3s. "Early man and technology" (skinning hippopotamus) . . . . . . 75 2·00
MS80 132 × 109 mm. Nos. 76/9 4·00 5·50

16 Rally Car and Villagers

1977. 25th Anniv of Safari Rally. Multicoloured.
81 50c. Type **16** 15 10
82 1s. Pres. Kenyatta starting rally 15 10
83 2s. Car fording river 50 60
84 5s. Car and elephants . . . . 1·40 1·50
MS85 126 × 93 mm. Nos. 81/4 . . 3·75 6·50

17 Canon Kivebulaya

1977. Centenary of Ugandan Church. Multicoloured.
86 50c. Type **17** 10 10
87 1s. Modern Namirembe Cathedral 10 10
88 2s. The first Cathedral 30 55
89 5s. Early congregation, Kigezi 50 1·25
MS90 126 × 94 mm. Nos. 86/9 . . 1·40 2·50

18 Sagana Royal Lodge, Nyeri, 1952

1977. Silver Jubilee. Multicoloured.
91 2s. Type **18** 15 15
92 5s. Treetops Hotel (vert) . . . 20 35
93 10s. Queen Elizabeth and Pres. Kenyatta 30 60
94 15s. Royal visit, 1972 . . . . 45 1·00
MS95 Two sheets. (a) 140 × 60 mm. No. 94. (b) 152 × 127 mm. 50s. Queen and Prince Philip in Treetops Hotel Set of 2 sheets 2·00 1·40

19 Pancake Tortoise

1977. Endangered Species. Multicoloured.
96 50c. Type **19** 30 10
97 1s. Nile crocodile 40 10
98 2s. Hunter's hartebeest . . . 1·60 40
99 3s. Red colobus monkey . . 1·75 50
100 5s. Dugong . . . . 2·00 75
MS101 127 × 101 mm. Nos. 97/100 7·00 8·50

20 Kenya-Ethiopia Border Point

1977. Nairobi–Addis Ababa Highway. Mult.
102 50c. Type **20** 15 10
103 1s. Archer's Post 15 10
104 2s. Thika Flyover 30 25
105 5s. Marsabit Game Lodge . . 50 75
MS106 144 × 91 mm. Nos. 102/5 2·25 3·50

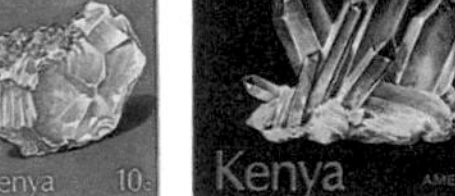

21 Gypsum **22** Amethyst

1977. Minerals. Multicoloured.
107 10c. Type **21** . . . . 1·25 20
108 20c. Trona . . . . 2·00 20
109 30c. Kyanite . . . . 2·00 20
110 40c. Amazonite . . . . . . 1·40 10
111 50c. Galena . . . . 1·40 10
112 70c. Silicified wood . . . . . 7·50 1·00
113 80c. Fluorite . . . . 7·50 60
114 1s. Type **22** . . . . 1·40 10
115 1s.50 Agate . . . . 1·50 30
116 2s. Tourmaline . . . . 1·50 20
117 3s. Aquamarine . . . . . . 1·75 55
118 5s. Rhodolite garnet . . . . 1·75 1·10
119 10s. Sapphire . . . . 1·75 1·50
120 20s. Ruby . . . . 4·50 2·50
121 40s. Green grossular garnet 18·00 19·00

23 Joe Kadenge (Kenya) and Forwards

1978. World Cup Football Championship, Argentina. Multicoloured.
122 50c. Type **23** 10 10
123 1s. Mohamed Chuma (Tanzania) and cup presentation 10 10
124 2s. Omari Kidevu (Zanzibar) and goalmouth scene . . . 30 70
125 3s. Polly Ouma (Uganda) and three forwards 40 95
MS126 136 × 81 mm. Nos. 122/5 3·75 3·50

24 Boxing

1978. Commonwealth Games, Edmonton. Mult.
127 50c. Type **24** 15 10
128 1s. Welcoming the Olympic Games Team, 1968 . . . . 15 10
129 3s. Javelin throwing . . . . 50 1·00
130 5s. Pres. Kenyatta admiring boxer's trophy . . . . . . 60 1·60

25 "Overloading is Dangerous"

1978. Road Safety. Multicoloured.
131 50c. Type **25** 50 10
132 1s. "Speed does not pay" . . 70 20
133 1s.50 "Ignoring Traffic Signs may cause death" 85 55
134 2s. "Slow down at School Crossing" . . . . 1·25 1·00
135 3s. "Never cross a continuous line" . . . . 1·40 2·50
136 5s. "Approach Railway Level Crossing with extreme caution" . . . . 2·00 3·50

26 Pres. Kenyatta at Mass Rally, 1963

1978. Kenyatta Day. Multicoloured.
137 50c. "Harambee Water Project" 15 10
138 1s. Handing over of Independence Instruments, 1963 . . . . 15 10
139 2s. Type **26** 30 35
140 3s. "Harambee, 15 Great Years" . . . . 60 1·00
141 5s. "Struggle for Independence, 1952" . . . 80 2·00

27 Freedom Fighters, Namibia

1978. International Anti-Apartheid Year.
142 **27** 50c. multicoloured 15 10
143 – 1s. black and blue 15 10
144 – 2s. multicoloured 30 30
145 – 3s. multicoloured 50 65
146 – 5s. multicoloured . . . . . 55 1·00
DESIGNS: 1s. International seminar on apartheid; 2s. Steve Biko's tombstone; 3s. Nelson Mandela; 5s. Bishop Lamont.

28 Children Playing

1979. International Year of the Child. Multicoloured.
147 50c. Type **28** 15 10
148 2s. Boy fishing 40 60
149 3s. Children singing and dancing . . . . 55 1·10
150 5s. Children with camels . . 1·00 2·00

29 "The Lion and the Jewel"

1979. Kenya National Theatre. Multicoloured.
151 50c. Type **29** 15 10
152 1s. "Utisi" 15 10
153 2s. Theatre programmes . . . 25 30
154 3s. Kenya National Theatre 35 45
155 5s. "Genesis" 50 75

30 Blind Telephone Operator **31** "Father of the Nation" (Kenyatta's funeral procession)

1979. 50th Anniv of Salvation Army Social Services.
156 50c. Type **30** 30 10
157 1s. Care for the aged 30 10
158 3s. Village polytechnic (horiz) 60 1·50
159 5s. Vocational training (horiz) 1·00 2·50

1979. 1st Death Anniv of President Kenyatta. Multicoloured.
160 50c. Type **31** 10 10
161 1s. "First President of Kenya" (Kenyatta receiving independence) . . 10 10
162 3s. "Kenyatta the politician" (speaking at rally) 30 50
163 5s. "A true son of Kenya" (Kenyatta as a boy carpenter) 40 95

32 British East Africa Company 1890 1a. Stamp

1979. Death Centenary of Sir Rowland Hill.
164 **32** 50c. multicoloured 15 10
165 – 1s. multicoloured 15 10
166 – 2s. black, red and brown 20 40
167 – 5s. multicoloured . . . . . 35 1·00
DESIGNS: 1s. Kenya, Uganda and Tanganyika 1935 1s. stamp; 2s. Penny Black; 5s. 1964 2s.50 Inauguration of Republic commemorative.

33 Roads, Globe and Conference Emblem

1980. International Road Federation. African Highway Conference, Nairobi. Multicoloured.
168 50c. Type **33** 15 10
169 1s. New weighbridge, Athi River 15 10
170 3s. New Nyali Bridge, Mombasa 40 85
171 5s. Highway to Jomo Kenyatta International Airport . . . . 50 2·00

34 Mobile Unit in action in Masailand

1980. Flying Doctor Service. Multicoloured.
172 50c. Type **34** 10 10
173 1s. Donkey transport to Turkana airstrip (vert) . . 20 10
174 3s. Surgical team in action at outstation (vert) . . . . . 65 1·00
175 5s. Emergency airlift from North Eastern Province . . 90 1·60
MS176 146 × 133 mm. Nos. 172/5 1·60 2·50

35 Statue of Sir Rowland Hill **37** Blue-spotted Stingray

36 Pope John Paul II

1980. "London 1980" International Stamp Exhibition.
177 **35** 25s. multicoloured . . . . 1·00 2·50
MS178 114 × 101 mm. No. 177 1·00 2·75

1980. Papal Visit. Multicoloured.
179 50c. Type **36** 40 10
180 1s. Pope, arms and cathedral (vert) 40 10
181 5s. Pope, flags and dove (vert) 75 85
182 10s. Pope, President Moi and map of Africa . . . . . . 1·25 1·75

1980. Marine Life. Multicoloured.
183 50c. Type **37** 30 10
184 2s. Allard's anemonefish . . 1·00 80
185 3s. Four-coloured nudibranch 1·25 1·75
186 5s. "Eretmochelys imbricata" 1·75 2·75

38 National Archives

1980. Historic Buildings. Multicoloured.
187 50c. Type **38** 10 10
188 1s. Provincial Commissioner's Office, Nairobi 15 10
189 1s.50 Nairobi House 20 20
190 2s. Norfolk Hotel 25 50
191 3s. McMillan Library 35 95
192 5s. Kipande House . . . . . 55 1·60

39 "Disabled enjoys Affection"

1981. Int Year for Disabled Persons. Mult.

193	50c. Type **39**	15	10
194	1s. President Moi presenting flag to Disabled Olympic Games team captain	15	10
195	3s. Blind people climbing Mount Kenya, 1975	55	65
196	5s. Disabled artist at work	70	1·00

40 Longonot Complex

1981. Satellite Communications. Multicoloured.

197	50c. Type **40**	15	10
198	2s. "Intelsat V"	40	35
199	3s. "Longonot I"	45	55
200	5s. "Longonot II"	60	85

41 Kenyatta Conference Centre

1981. O.A.U. (Organization of African Unity) Summit Conference, Nairobi.

201 **41**	50c. multicoloured	15	10
202 –	1s. black, yellow and blue	15	10
203 –	3s. multicoloured	40	40
204 –	5s. multicoloured	70	65
205 –	10s. multicoloured	80	1·00
MS206	110 × 110 mm. No. 205	1·10	1·50

DESIGNS: 1s. "Panaftel" earth stations; 3s. Parliament Building; 5s. Jomo Kenyatta International Airport; 10s. O.A.U. flag.

42 St. Paul's Cathedral **43** Giraffe

1981. Royal Wedding. Multicoloured.

207	50c. Prince Charles and President Daniel Arap Moi	10	10
208	3s. Type **42**	15	20
209	5s. Royal Yacht "Britannia"	25	30
210	10s. Prince Charles on safari in Kenya	40	55
MS211	85 × 102 mm. 25s. Prince Charles and Lady Diana Spencer	75	80

1981. Rare Animals. Multicoloured.

212	50c. Type **43**	15	10
213	2s. Bongo	25	25
214	5s. Roan antelope	40	1·00
215	10s. Agile mangabey	60	2·25

44 "Technical Development" **45** Kamba

1981. World Food Day. Multicoloured.

216	50c. Type **44**	10	10
217	1s. "Mwea rice projects"	15	10
218	2s. "Irrigation schemes"	30	55
219	5s. "Breeding livestock"	60	1·75

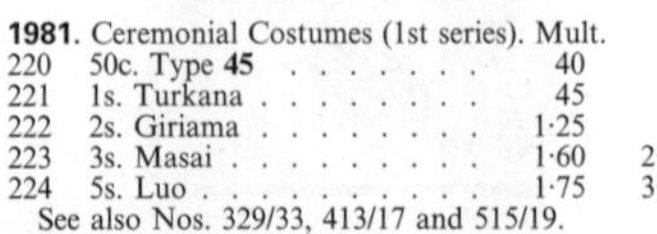

1981. Ceremonial Costumes (1st series). Mult.

220	50c. Type **45**	40	10
221	1s. Turkana	45	10
222	2s. Giriama	1·25	85
223	3s. Masai	1·60	2·25
224	5s. Luo	1·75	3·50

See also Nos. 329/33, 413/17 and 515/19.

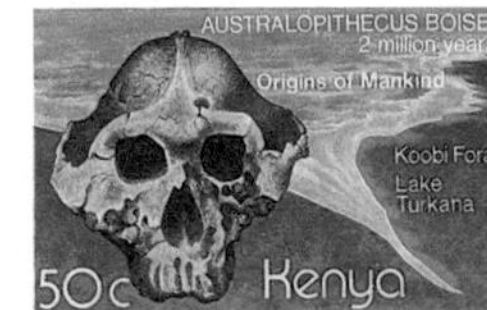

46 "Australopithecus boisei"

1982. "Origins of Mankind". Skulls. Multicoloured.

225	50c. Type **46**	1·75	30
226	2s. "Homo erectus"	3·25	1·50
227	3s. "Homo habilis"	3·25	3·75
228	5s. "Proconsul africanus"	3·75	5·00

47 Tree-planting

1982. 75th Anniv of Boy Scout Movement (Nos. 229, 231, 233 and 235) and 60th Anniv of Girl Guide Movement (Nos. 230, 232, 234 and 236). Multicoloured.

229	70c. Type **47**	50	80
230	70c. Paying homage	50	80
231	3s.50 "Be Prepared"	1·25	2·00
232	3s.50 "International Friendship"	1·25	2·00
233	5s. Helping disabled	1·50	2·50
234	5s. Community service	1·50	2·50
235	6s.50 Paxtu Cottage (Lord Baden-Powell's home)	1·50	2·75
236	6s.50 Lady Baden-Powell	1·50	2·75
MS237	112 × 112 mm. Nos. 229, 231, 233 and 235	3·75	3·00

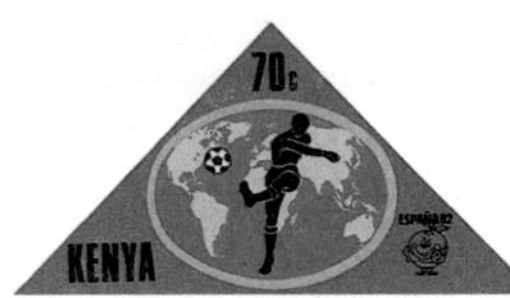

48 Footballer displaying Shooting Skill

1982. World Cup Football Championship, Spain. Footballers silhouetted against Map of World. Multicoloured.

238	70c. Type **48**	1·50	65
239	3s.50 Heading	2·75	2·75
240	5s. Goalkeeping	3·75	4·25
241	10s. Dribbling	5·50	8·00
MS242	101 × 76 mm. 20s. Tackling	5·50	4·00

49 Cattle Judging **50** Micro-wave Radio System

1982. 80th Anniv of Agricultural Society of Kenya. Multicoloured.

243	70c. Type **49**	50	10
244	2s.50 Farm machinery	1·25	1·25
245	3s.50 Musical ride	1·50	2·50
246	6s.50 Agricultural Society emblem	2·00	4·25

1982. I.T.U. Plenipotentiary Conference, Nairobi. Multicoloured.

247	70c. Type **50**	50	10
248	3s.50 Sea-to-shore service link	1·75	1·75
249	5s. Rural telecommunications system	2·25	3·75
250	6s.50 I.T.U. emblem	2·50	4·50

1982. No. 113 surch **70c.**

251	70c. on 80c. Fluorite	1·00	1·25

52 Container Cranes

1983. 5th Anniv of Kenya Ports Authority. Mult.

252	70c. Type **52**	85	10
253	2s. Port by night	1·75	1·90
254	3s.50 Container cranes (different)	2·50	3·50
255	5s. Map of Mombasa Port	3·25	4·50
MS256	125 × 85 mm. Nos. 252/5	7·50	9·00

53 Shada Zambarau **54** Waridi Kikuba

1983. Flowers. Multicoloured.

257	10c. Type **53**	40	40
258	20c. Kilua Kingulima	55	40
259	30c. Mwalika Mwiya	55	40
260	40c. Ziyungi Buluu	55	40
261	50c. Kilua Habashia	55	30
262	70c. Chanuo Kato	60	20
262a	80c. As 40c.	4·50	4·50
262b	1s. Waridi Kikuba	4·50	80
263	1s. Type **54**	65	20
264	1s.50 Mshomoro Mtambazi	1·75	60
265	2s. Papatuo Boti	1·75	60
266	2s.50 Tumba Mboni	1·75	60
266a	3s. Mkuku Mrembo	13·00	8·50
267	3s.50 Mtongo Mbeja	1·50	1·50
267b	4s. Mnukia Muuma	4·75	7·00
268	5s. Nyungu Chepuo	1·50	1·50
268a	7s. Mlua Miba	6·50	10·00
269	10s. Muafunili	1·50	1·50
270	20s. Mbake Nyanza	1·50	2·50
271	40s. Njuga Pagwa	2·25	8·00

The 1s.50 to 40s. are in the same format as T **54**.

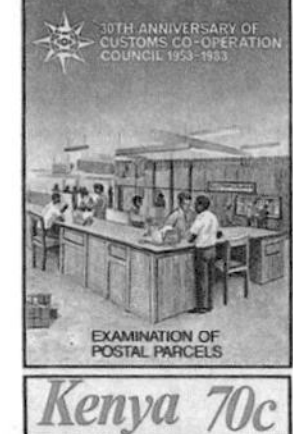

55 Coffee Plucking **56** Examining Parcels

1983. Commonwealth Day. Multicoloured.

272	70c. Type **55**	10	10
273	2s. President Daniel Arap Moi	15	20
274	5s. Satellite view of Earth (horiz)	35	45
275	10s. Masai dance (horiz)	65	1·00

1983. 30th Anniv of Customs Co-operation Council. Multicoloured.

276	70c. Type **56**	25	10
277	2s.50 Customs Headquarters, Mombasa	65	30
278	3s.50 Customs Council Headquarters, Brussels	75	40
279	10s. Customs patrol boat	2·40	2·50

57 Communications via Satellite

1983. World Communications Year. Multicoloured.

280	70c. Type **57**	60	10
281	2s.50 "Telephone and Postal Services"	1·50	1·75
282	3s.50 Communications by sea and air (horiz)	2·00	3·00
283	5s. Road and rail communications (horiz)	2·50	4·00

58 "Craftsman" (freighter) in Kilindini Harbour

1983. 25th Anniv of Intergovernmental Maritime Organization. Multicoloured.

284	70c. Type **58**	95	10
285	2s.50 Life-saving devices	2·00	1·75
286	3s.50 Mombasa container terminal	2·50	3·00
287	10s. Marine park	3·50	7·00

59 President Moi signing Visitors' Book

1983. 29th Commonwealth Parliamentary Conference. Multicoloured.

288	70c. Type **59**	25	10
289	2s.50 Parliament building, Nairobi (vert)	90	1·25
290	5s. State opening of Parliament (vert)	1·60	3·00
MS291	122 × 141 mm. Nos. 288/90	2·50	6·00

60 Kenyan and British Flags

1983. Royal Visit. Multicoloured.

292	70c. Type **60**	50	10
293	3s.50 Sagana State Lodge	2·00	1·50
294	5s. Treetops Hotel	2·25	2·75
295	10s. Queen Elizabeth II and President Moi	3·50	7·00
MS296	126 × 100 mm. 25s. Designs as Nos. 292/5, but without face values. Imperf	4·50	7·50

61 President Moi

1983. 20th Anniv of Independence. Mult.

297	70c. Type **61**	10	10
298	2s. President Moi planting tree	15	20
299	3s.50 Kenyan flag and emblem	25	35
300	5s. School milk scheme	40	50
301	10s. People of Kenya	75	1·10
MS302	126 × 93 mm. 25s. Designs as Nos. 297 and 299/301, but without face values. Imperf	1·50	2·75

62 White-backed Night Heron **63** Radar Tower

1984. Rare Birds of Kenya. Multicoloured.

303	70c. Type **62**	1·75	30
304	2s.50 Quail plover	3·00	2·50
305	3s.50 Taita olive thrush	3·75	3·75
306	5s. Mufumbiri shrike	4·25	4·25
307	10s. White-winged apalis	5·50	7·00

1984. 40th Anniv of International Civil Aviation Organization. Multicoloured.

308	70c. Type **63**	15	10
309	2s.50 Kenya School of Aviation (horiz)	45	60
310	3s.50 Boeing 707 taking off from Moi airport (horiz)	65	1·25
311	5s. Air traffic control centre	95	1·60

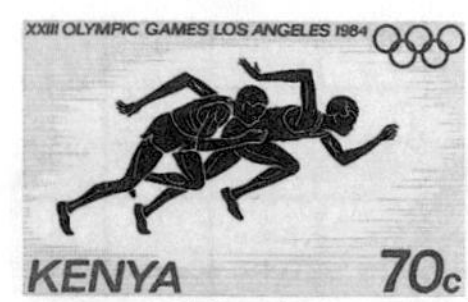

64 Running

1984. Olympic Games, Los Angeles.

312 **64**	70c. black, green & dp green	30	10
313 –	2s.50 black, purple & violet	60	70
314 –	5s. black, blue & deep blue	1·50	2·50
315 –	10s. black, yellow & brown	3·50	6·00
MS316	130 × 121 mm. 25s. Designs as Nos. 312/15, but without face values. Imperf	3·25	3·25

DESIGNS: 2s.50, Hurdling; 5s. Boxing; 10s. Hockey.

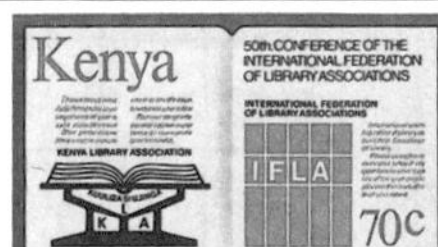

65 Conference and Kenya Library Association Logos

1984. 50th Conference of the International Federation of Library Associations. Multicoloured.
317 70c. Type **65** 10 10
318 3s.50 Mobile library 50 60
319 5s. Adult library 65 1·25
320 10s. Children's library 1·00 3·25

66 Doves and Cross **67** Export Year Logo

1984. 4th World Conference on Religion and Peace. As T **66**, each design showing a different central symbol. Multicoloured.
321 70c. Type **66** 30 10
322 2s.50 Arabic inscription 1·25 1·50
323 3s.50 Peace emblem 1·60 2·50
324 6s.50 Star and Crescent 2·00 4·00

1984. Kenya Export Year. Multicoloured.
325 70c. Type **67** 30 10
326 3s.50 Forklift truck with air cargo (horiz) 1·75 2·00
327 5s. Loading ship's cargo 2·50 3·00
328 10s. Kenyan products (horiz) 3·75 6·50

1984. Ceremonial Costumes (2nd series). As T **45**. Multicoloured.
329 70c. Luhya 80 15
330 2s. Kikuyu 2·00 1·75
331 3s.50 Pokomo 2·50 2·25
332 5s. Nandi 3·00 3·00
333 10s. Rendile 4·00 6·50

68 Staunton Knight and Nyayo National Stadium

1984. 60th Anniv of International Chess Federation. Multicoloured.
334 70c. Type **68** 2·25 40
335 2s.50 Staunton rook and Fort Jesus 3·25 1·75
336 3s.50 Staunton bishop and National Monument 3·75 2·00
337 5s. Staunton queen and Parliament Building 4·00 3·75
338 10s. Staunton king and Nyayo Fountain 6·00 8·00

69 Cooking with Wood-burning Stove and Charcoal Fire

1985. Energy Conservation. Multicoloured.
339 70c. Type **69** 20 10
340 2s. Solar energy panel on roof 65 75
341 3s.50 Production of gas from cow dung 75 1·25
342 10s. Ploughing with oxen 2·25 6·00
MS343 110 × 85 mm. 20s. Designs as Nos. 339/42, but without face values 2·50 2·50

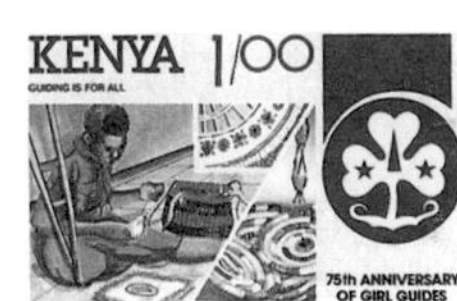

70 Crippled Girl Guide making Table-mat

1985. 75th Anniv of Girl Guide Movement. Multicoloured.
344 1s. Type **70** 75 15
345 3s. Girl Guides doing community service 1·75 1·50
346 5s. Lady Olave Baden-Powell (founder) 2·50 3·00
347 7s. Girl Guides gardening 4·00 6·50

71 Stylized Figures and Globe

1985. World Red Cross Day.
348 **71** 1s. black and red 80 15
349 – 4s. multicoloured 3·00 3·00
350 – 5s. multicoloured 3·25 3·50
351 – 7s. multicoloured 4·50 6·50
DESIGNS: 4s. First Aid Team; 5s. Hearts containing crosses ("Blood Donation"); 7s. Cornucopia ("Famine Relief").

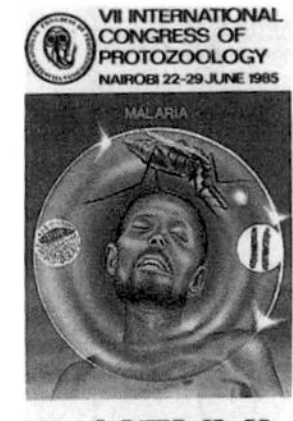

72 Man with Malaria **73** Repairing Water Pipes

1985. 7th International Congress of Protozoology, Nairobi. Multicoloured.
352 1s. Type **72** 1·75 20
353 3s. Child with Leishmaniasis 3·75 2·75
354 5s. Cow with Trypanosomiasis 4·25 4·25
355 7s. Dog with Babesiosis 7·00 7·50

1985. United Nations Women's Decade Conference. Multicoloured.
356 1s. Type **73** 20 10
357 3s. Traditional food preparation 60 70
358 5s. Basket-weaving 75 1·25
359 7s. Dressmaking 1·00 3·00

74 The Last Supper

1985. 43rd International Eucharistic Congress, Nairobi. Multicoloured.
360 1s. Type **74** 50 10
361 3s. Village family ("The Eucharist and the Christian Family") 2·25 2·00
362 5s. Congress altar, Uhuru Park 2·50 3·00
363 7s. St. Peter Claver's Church, Nairobi 3·00 5·00
MS364 117 × 80 mm. 25s. Pope John Paul II 7·00 7·00

75 Black Rhinoceros

1985. Endangered Animals. Multicoloured.
365 1s. Type **75** 2·50 40
366 3s. Cheetah 3·25 2·75
367 5s. De Brazza's monkey 3·50 4·00
368 10s. Grevy's zebra 7·00 8·00
MS369 129 × 122 mm. 25s. Endangered species (122 × 114 mm). Imperf 9·00 7·00

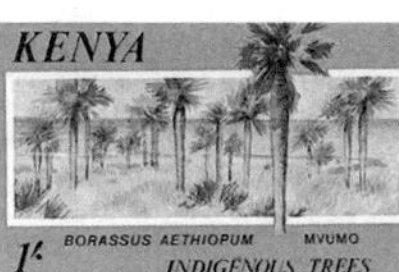

76 "Borassus aethiopum"

1986. Indigenous Trees. Multicoloured.
370 1s. Type **76** 80 15
371 3s. "Acacia xanthophloea" 3·00 2·50
372 5s. "Ficus natalensis" 4·00 4·00
373 7s. "Spathodea nilotica" 5·00 8·00
MS374 117 × 96 mm. 25s. Landscape with trees (109 × 90 mm). Imperf 3·25 4·00

77 Dove and U.N. Logo (from poster) **78** Dribbling the Ball

1986. International Peace Year. Multicoloured.
375 1s. Type **77** 30 10
376 3s. U.N. General Assembly (horiz) 1·00 75
377 7s. Nuclear explosion 2·50 3·50
378 10s. Quotation from Wall of Isaiah, U.N. Building, New York (horiz) 5·00 5·50

1986. World Cup Football Championship, Mexico. Multicoloured.
379 1s. Type **78** 1·25 20
380 3s. Scoring from a penalty 2·75 1·25
381 5s. Tackling 3·50 2·25
382 7s. Cup winners 4·25 3·75
383 10s. Heading the ball 5·50 4·75
MS384 110 × 86 mm. 30s. Harambee Stars football team (102 × 78 mm). Imperf 4·25 3·75

79 Rural Post Office and Telephone

1986. "Expo '86" World Fair, Vancouver. Mult.
385 1s. Type **79** 50 15
386 3s. Container depot, Embakasi 2·75 1·75
387 5s. Piper Twin Commanche airplane landing at game park airstrip 5·50 3·00
388 7s. Container ship 5·50 6·00
389 10s. Transporting produce to market 6·00 7·00

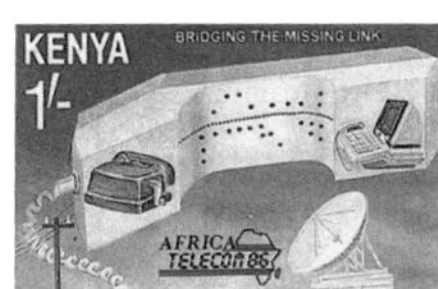

80 Telephone, Computer and Dish Aerial

1986. African Telecommunications. Multicoloured.
390 1s. Type **80** 35 10
391 3s. Telephones of 1876, 1936 and 1986 1·00 85
392 5s. Dish aerial, satellite, telephones and map of Africa 1·25 1·25
393 7s. Kenyan manufacture of telecommunications equipment 1·75 2·25

81 Mashua

1986. Dhows of Kenya. Multicoloured.
394 1s. Type **81** 80 20
395 3s. Mtepe 2·25 1·50
396 5s. Dau La Mwao 2·75 2·75
397 10s. Jahazi 4·50 6·00
MS398 118 × 80 mm. 25s. Lamu dhow and map of Indian Ocean 5·00 5·00

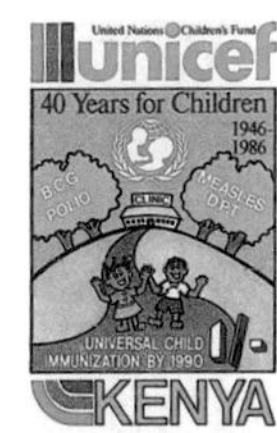

82 Nativity **83** Immunization

1986. Christmas. Multicoloured.
399 1s. Type **82** 30 10
400 3s. Shepherd and sheep 1·00 55
401 5s. Angel and slogan "LOVE PEACE UNITY" (horiz) 1·60 1·40
402 7s. The Magi riding camels (horiz) 1·90 2·75

1987. 40th Anniv of U.N.I.C.E.F. Multicoloured.
403 1s. Type **83** 45 10
404 3s. Food and nutrition 1·00 70
405 4s. Oral rehydration therapy 1·75 1·50
406 5s. Family planning 1·75 1·50
407 10s. Female literacy 2·50 4·00

84 Akamba Woodcarvers

1987. Tourism. Multicoloured.
408 1s. Type **84** 45 10
409 3s. Tourism on beach 3·00 1·75
410 5s. Tourist and guide at view point 3·75 3·75
411 7s. Pride of lions 5·50 6·50
MS412 118 × 81 mm. 30s. Geysers 9·50 11·00

1987. Ceremonial Costumes (3rd series). As T **45**. Multicoloured.
413 1s. Embu 80 10
414 3s. Kisii 2·50 70
415 5s. Samburu 3·00 1·75
416 7s. Taita 3·75 3·75
417 10s. Boran 4·00 4·25

85 Telecommunications by Satellite

1987. 10th Anniv of Kenya Posts and Telecommunications Corporation. Multicoloured.
418 1s. Type **85** 75 30
419 3s. Rural post office, Kajiado 1·75 1·75
420 4s. Awarding trophy, Welfare Sports 1·90 2·00
421 5s. Village and telephone box 2·00 2·25
422 7s. Speedpost labels and outline map of Kenya 3·00 3·75
MS423 110 × 80 mm. 25s. Corporation flag 2·50 2·75

86 Volleyball **87** "Aloe volkensii"

1987. 4th All-Africa Games, Nairobi. Mult.
424 1s. Type **86** 20 10
425 3s. Cycling 85 45
426 4s. Boxing 35 65
427 5s. Swimming 40 75
428 7s. Steeplechasing 60 1·40
MS429 117 × 80 mm. 30s. Kasarani Sports Complex (horiz) 2·50 2·75

1987. Medicinal Herbs. Multicoloured.
430 1s. Type **87** 75 10
431 3s. "Cassia didymobotrya" 1·75 1·00
432 5s. "Erythrina abyssinica" 2·50 2·25
433 7s. "Adenium obesum" 3·00 3·50
434 10s. Herbalist's clinic 3·25 3·75

Kenya 20c

88 "Epamera sidus" **89** "Papilio rex"

1988. Butterflies. Multicoloured.
434a 10c. "Cyrestis camillus" 1·50 2·25
435 20c. Type **88** 35 70
436 40c. "Cynthia cardui" 50 70
437 50c. "Colotis evippe" 50 70
438 70c. "Precis westermanni" 50 70
439 80c. "Colias electo" 50 70
440 1s. "Eronia leda" 50 30
440a 1s.50 "Papilio dardanus" 5·50 30
441 2s. Type **89** 70 40
442 2s.50 "Colotis phisadia" 75 90
443 3s. "Papilio desmondi" 80 90

444 3s.50 "Papilio demodocus" 80 60
445 4s. "Papilio phorcas" . . . 85 60
446 5s. "Charaxes druceanus" 90 70
447 7s. "Cymothoe teita" . . . 1·00 1·75
448 10s. "Charaxes zoolina" . . 1·00 1·75
449 20s. "Papilio dardanus" . . 1·25 3·00
450 40s. "Charaxes cithaeron" 2·00 5·50
The 10c. to 1s.50 are in the same format as T **88**.

90 Samburu Lodge and Crocodiles

1988. Kenyan Game Lodges. Multicoloured.
451 1s. Type **90** 70 10
452 3s. Naro Moru River Lodge and rock climbing . . . . 1·00 60
453 4s. Mara Serena Lodge and zebra with foal . . . . . . 1·25 1·25
454 5s. Voi Safari Lodge and buffalo . . . . 1·25 1·25
455 7s. Kilimanjaro Buffalo Lodge and giraffes . . . . 2·50 2·50
456 10s. Meru Mulika Lodge and rhinoceroses . . . . 2·75 3·00

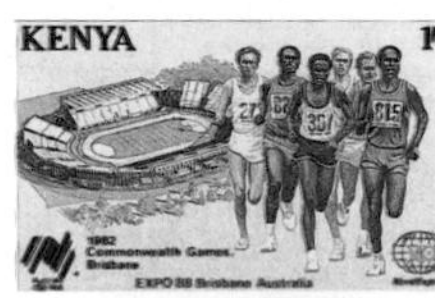

91 Athletes and Stadium, Commonwealth Games, Brisbane, 1982

1988. "Expo '88" World Fair, Brisbane, and Bicent of Australian Settlement. Multicoloured.
457 1s. Type **91** 40 10
458 3s. Flying Doctor Service De Havilland Drover 3 and Piper Twin Commanche aircraft . . . . 2·50 1·25
459 4s. H.M.S. "Sirius" (frigate), 1788 . . . . 2·75 2·25
460 5s. Ostrich and emu . . . . 3·00 2·25
461 7s. Queen Elizabeth II, Pres. Arap Moi of Kenya and Prime Minister Hawke of Australia . . . . 2·75 3·50
MS462 117 × 80 mm. 30s. Entrance to Kenya Pavilion . . . . . . 1·90 2·00

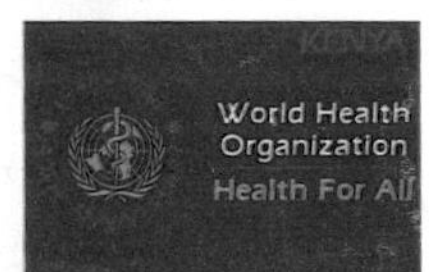

92 W.H.O. Logo and Slogan

1988. 40th Anniv of W.H.O.
463 **92** 1s. blue, gold and deep blue 25 10
464 – 3s. multicoloured 85 70
465 – 5s. multicoloured . . . . . 1·25 1·25
466 – 7s. multicoloured . . . . . 1·75 2·25
DESIGNS: 3s. Mother with young son and nutritious food; 5s. Giving oral vaccine to baby; 7s. Village women drawing clean water from pump.

93 Handball

94 Calabashes

1988. Olympic Games, Seoul. Multicoloured.
467 1s. Type **93** 40 10
468 3s. Judo 65 55
469 5s. Weightlifting 85 90
470 7s. Javelin . . . . 1·00 1·40
471 10s. Relay racing . . . . . . 1·40 2·00
MS472 110 × 78 mm. 30s. Tennis 2·25 2·50

1988. Kenyan Material Culture (1st issue). Mult.
473 1s. Type **94** 30 10
474 3s. Milk gourds 75 55
475 5s. Cooking pots (horiz) . . 85 85
476 7s. Winnowing trays (horiz) 1·25 1·60
477 10s. Reed baskets (horiz) . . 1·60 2·25
MS478 118 × 80 mm. 25s. Gourds, calabash and horn (horiz) . . . 1·50 1·60
See also Nos. 646/50.

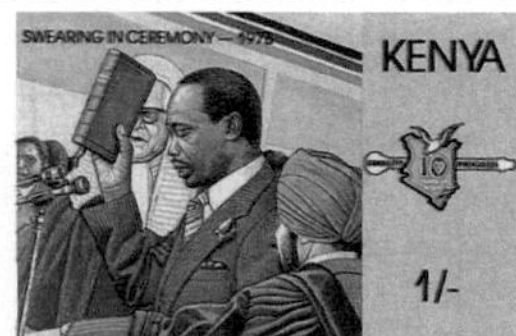

95 Pres. Arap Moi taking Oath, 1978

1988. 10th Anniv of "Nyayo" Era. Mult.
479 1s. Type **95** 30 10
480 3s. Building soil conservation barrier . . . . 1·00 70
481 3s.50 Passengers boarding bus . . . . 2·75 1·40
482 4s. Metalwork shop . . . . 1·25 1·50
483 5s. Moi University, Eldoret 1·25 1·50
484 7s. Aerial view of hospital . . 3·00 3·50
485 10s. Pres. Arap Moi and Mrs. Thatcher at Kapsabet Telephone Exchange . . . 7·50 6·00

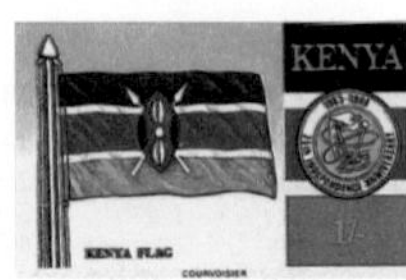

96 Kenya Flag

1988. 25th Anniv of Independence. Mult.
486 1s. Type **96** 60 10
487 3s. Coffee picking 70 50
488 5s. Proposed Kenya Posts and Telecommunications Headquarters building . . 1·00 1·10
489 7s. Kenya Airways Airbus Industrie A310-300 "Harambee Star" . . . . 5·00 2·75
490 10s. New diesel locomotive No. 9401 . . . . 7·00 4·50

97 Gedi Ruins, Malindi

1989. Historic Monuments. Multicoloured.
491 1s.20 Type **97** 50 10
492 3s.40 Vasco Da Gama Pillar, Malindi (vert) . . . . . . 1·25 1·10
493 4s.40 Ishiakani Monument, Kiunga . . . . 1·40 1·50
494 5s.50 Fort Jesus, Mombasa 1·60 1·75
495 7s.50 She Burnan Omwe, Lamu (vert) . . . . 2·50 3·25

98 125th Anniversary and Kenya Red Cross Logos

1989. 125th Anniv of International Red Cross. Multicoloured.
496 1s.20 Type **98** 50 10
497 3s.40 Red Cross workers with car crash victim . . . . . 1·25 90
498 4s.40 Disaster relief team distributing blankets . . . 1·40 1·40
499 5s.50 Henri Dunant (founder) 1·50 2·00
500 7s.70 Blood donor . . . . . 1·75 3·25

99 Female Giraffe and Calf

100 "Lentinus sajor-caju"

1989. Reticulated Giraffe. Multicoloured.
501 1s.20 Type **99** . . . . 1·75 30
502 3s.40 Giraffe drinking . . . 3·25 3·00
503 4s.40 Two giraffes . . . . . 3·75 4·00
504 5s.50 Giraffe feeding . . . . 4·50 5·50
MS505 80 × 110 mm. 30s. Designs as Nos. 501/4, but without face values . . . . 5·50 7·00
Designs from No. **MS**505 are without the Worldwide Fund for Nature logo.

1989. Mushrooms. Multicoloured.
506 1s.20 Type **100** . . . . . . 1·50 30
507 3s.40 "Agaricus bisporus" . . 2·50 2·00
508 4s.40 "Agaricus bisporus" (different) . . . . 2·75 2·50
509 5s.50 "Termitomyces schimperi" . . . . 3·50 3·50
510 7s.70 "Lentinus edodes" . . 4·25 5·50

101 Independence Monuments

1989. Birth Centenary of Jawaharlal Nehru (Indian statesman). Multicoloured.
511 1s.20 Type **101** . . . . . . 1·25 30
512 3s.40 Nehru with graduates and open book . . . . . 3·25 1·75
513 5s.50 Jawaharlal Nehru . . . 4·25 4·00
514 7s.70 Industrial complex and cogwheels . . . . 4·50 6·50

1989. Ceremonial Costumes (4th series). As T **45**. Multicoloured.
515 1s.20 Kipsigis . . . . 1·50 20
516 3s.40 Rabai . . . . 2·50 1·60
517 5s.50 Duruma . . . . 3·00 2·75
518 7s.70 Kuria . . . . 4·00 4·25
519 10s. Bajuni . . . . 4·25 6·00

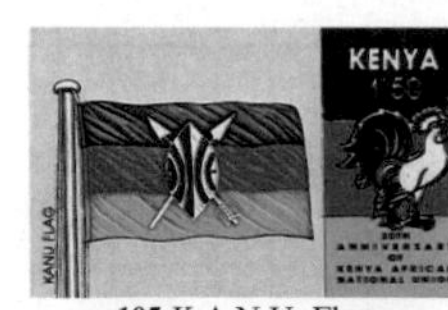

102 EMS Speedpost Letters and Parcel

1990. 10th Anniv of Pan African Postal Union. Multicoloured.
520 1s.20 Type **102** 15 10
521 3s.40 Mail runner 35 35
522 5s.50 Mandera Post Office . . 55 70
523 7s.70 EMS Speedpost letters and globe (vert) . . . . . 80 1·60
524 10s. P.A.P.U. logo (vert) . . 90 1·60

103 "Stamp King" with Tweezers and Magnifying Glass

104 Moi Golden Cup

1990. "Stamp World London '90" International Stamp Exhibition.
525 **103** 1s.50 multicoloured . . . 35 10
526 – 4s.50 multicoloured . . . 1·25 1·25
527 – 6s.50 black, red and blue 1·40 1·60
528 – 9s. multicoloured . . . . 1·75 2·75
MS529 113 × 77 mm. Nos. 525/8 4·50 6·50
DESIGNS: 4s.50, Penny Black and Kenya Stamp Bureau postmark; 6s.50, Early British cancel-lations; 9s. Ronald Ngala Street Post Office, Nairobi.

1990. World Cup Football Championship, Italy. Trophies. Multicoloured.
530 1s.50 Type **104** 85 10
531 4s.50 East and Central Africa Challenge Cup . . . . . . 2·50 1·75
532 6s.50 East and Central Africa Club Championship Cup 3·50 3·50
533 9s. World Cup . . . . 3·75 6·00

105 K.A.N.U. Flag

1990. 30th Anniv of Kenya African National Union. Multicoloured.
534 1s.50 Type **105** 15 10
535 2s.50 Nyayo Monument . . . 15 15
536 4s.50 Party Headquarters . . 35 35
537 5s. Jomo Kenyatta (Party founder) 40 40
538 6s.50 President Arap Moi . . 50 85
539 9s. President Moi addressing rally . . . . 70 1·60
540 10s. Queue of voters . . . . 80 1·60

106 Desktop Computer

1990. 125th Anniv of I.T.U. Multicoloured.
541 1s.50 Type **106** 15 10
542 4s.50 Telephone switchboard assembly, Gilgil 35 50
543 6s.50 "125 YEARS" . . . . 45 1·00
544 9s. Urban and rural telecommunications . . . . 70 2·25

107 Queen Mother at British Museum, 1988

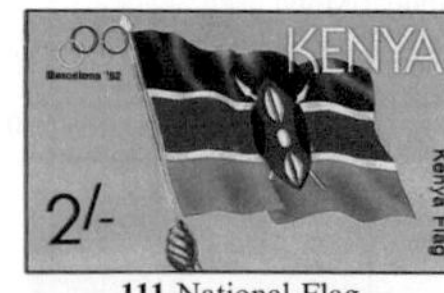

108 Queen Elizabeth at Hospital Garden Party, 1947

1990. 90th Birthday of Queen Elizabeth the Queen Mother.
545 **107** 10s. multicoloured . . . . 1·50 1·75
546 **108** 40s. black and green . . . 3·25 5·00

109 Kenya 1988 2s. Definitive

110 Adult Literacy Class

1990. Cent of Postage Stamps in Kenya. Mult.
547 1s.50 Type **109** . . . . . . 1·25 10
548 4s.50 East Africa and Uganda 1903 1a. . . . . . 2·50 90
549 6s.50 British East Africa Co 1890 ½a. optd on G.B. 1d. 3·00 2·00
550 9s. Kenya and Uganda 1922 20c. . . . . 3·50 3·25
551 20s. Kenya, Uganda, Tanzania 1971 2s.50 railway commemorative . . 6·25 8·50

1990. International Literacy Year. Multicoloured.
552 1s.50 Type **110** 30 10
553 4s.50 Teaching by radio . . . 1·00 1·10
554 6s.50 Technical training . . . 1·25 1·75
555 9s. International Literacy Year logo . . . . 2·00 3·50

111 National Flag

1991. Olympic Games, Barcelona (1992) (1st issue). Multicoloured.
556 2s. Type **111** 85 10
557 6s. Basketball . . . . 2·50 1·25
558 7s. Hockey . . . . 2·50 2·00
559 8s.50 Table tennis . . . . . 2·25 3·25
560 11s. Boxing . . . . 2·25 3·75
See also Nos. 580/4.

112 Symbolic Man and Pointing Finger

114 Leopard

113 Queen and Prince Philip with Pres. Moi

1992. AIDS Day. Multicoloured.
561 2s. Type **112** . . . . 1·00 15
562 6s. Victim and drugs . . . . 2·50 1·25
563 8s.50 Male and female symbols . . . . 3·00 3·25
564 11s. Symbolic figure and hypodermic syringe . . . . 4·50 4·75

1992. 40th Anniv of Queen Elizabeth II's Accession.
565 3s. Type **113** 50 10
566 8s. Marabou storks in tree 2·00 85
567 11s. Treetops Hotel . . . . . 1·25 1·00
568 14s. Three portraits of Queen Elizabeth . . . . 1·25 1·25
569 40s. Queen Elizabeth II . . . 2·50 4·50

1992. Kenya Wildlife. Multicoloured.
570 3s. Type **114** . . . . 1·75 30
571 8s. Lion . . . . 2·50 1·50
572 10s. Elephant . . . . 4·25 3·50
573 11s. Buffalo . . . . 2·50 3·50
574 14s. Black rhinoceros . . . . 5·50 6·50

115 International Harvester Safari Truck, 1926

1992. Vintage Cars. Multicoloured.
575 3s. Type **115** . . . . 1·50 20
576 8s. Fiat "509", 1924 . . . . 2·75 1·50
577 10s. Hupmobile, 1923 . . . . 3·00 2·50
578 11s. Chevrolet "Box Body", 1928 . . . . 3·00 2·75
579 14s. Bentley/Parkward, 1934 3·50 4·00

116 Kenyan Athlete winning Race

1992. Olympic Games, Barcelona (2nd issue). Mult.
580 3s. Type **116** . . . . 1·00 10
581 8s. Men's judo . . . . 2·00 1·25
582 10s. Kenyan women's volleyball players . . . . . 2·50 2·25
583 11s. Kenyan men's 4 × 100 m relay runners . . 2·50 2·50
584 14s. Men's 10,000 m . . . . 2·75 4·00

117 Holy Child, Joseph and Animals

118 Asembo Bay Lighthouse, Lake Victoria

1992. Christmas. Multicoloured.
585 3s. Type **117** 30 10
586 8s. Mary with Holy Child . . 75 50
587 11s. Christmas tree . . . . . 1·00 80
588 14s. Adoration of the Magi 1·25 2·00

1993. Lighthouses. Multicoloured.
589 3s. Type **118** . . . . 1·75 40
590 8s. Old Ras Serani lighthouse, Mombasa . . . 2·75 1·50
591 11s. New Ras Serani lighthouse, Mombasa . . . 3·00 2·50
592 14s. Gingira, Lake Victoria 3·75 4·25

119 Superb Starling

120 Yellow-billed Hornbill

1993. Birds. Multicoloured. (a) As T **119**.
593 50c. Type **119** 15 60
594 1s. Red and yellow barbet 25 50
594a 1s.50 Lady Ross's turaco . . 50 60
595 3s. Black-throated honeyguide ("Greater honeyguide") 50 10
595a 5s. African fish eagle . . . 60 60
595b 6s. Vulturine guineafowl . . 2·50 75
596 7s. Malachite kingfisher . . 70 30
597 8s. Speckled pigeon 70 20
598 10s. Cinnamon-chested bee eater 70 20
599 11s. Scarlet-chested sunbird 70 25
600 14s. Bagalafecht weaver ("Reichenow's weaver") 75 30

(b) As T **120**.
601 50s. Type **120** . . . . 1·25 1·75
602 80s. Lesser flamingo . . . . 1·60 2·50
603 100s. Hadada ibis . . . . . 1·90 2·75

121 Nurse bandaging Boy's Legs

123 "Ansellia africana"

122 Maendeleo House, Nairobi

1993. 17th World Congress of Rehabilitation International.
611 **121** 3s. multicoloured 70 10
612 – 8s. multicoloured . . . . 1·10 70
613 – 10s. multicoloured . . . . 1·25 1·40
614 – 11s. multicoloured . . . . 1·25 1·60
615 – 14s. black, blue and orange . . . . 1·50 2·25
DESIGNS—HORIZ: 8s. Singing group on crutches; 10s. Vocational training; 11s. Wheelchair race. VERT: 14s. Congress emblem.

1994. 40th Anniv of Maendeleo Ya Wanawake Organization. Multicoloured.
616 3s.50 Type **122** 75 20
617 9s. Planting saplings . . . . 1·00 60
618 11s. Rural family planning clinic (vert) . . . . 1·25 1·25
619 12s.50 Women carrying water 1·50 2·00
620 15s.50 Improved wood-burning cooking stove (vert) . . . . 1·75 2·50

1994. Orchids. Multicoloured.
621 3s.50 Type **123** . . . . . . 1·75 30
622 9s. "Aerangis luteoalba var rhodosticta" . . . . 2·25 85
623 12s.50 "Polystachya bella" 2·50 2·00
624 15s.50 "Brachycorythis kalbreyeri" . . . . 2·75 2·75
625 20s. "Eulophia guineensis" 3·25 3·50

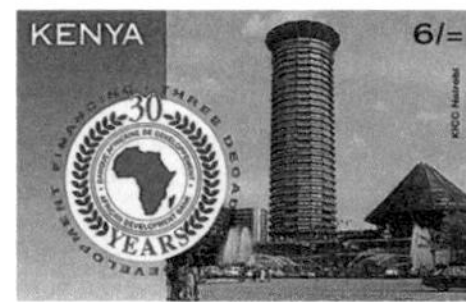

124 Emblem and K.I.C.C. Building, Nairobi

1994. 30th Anniv of African Development Bank. Multicoloured.
626 6s. Type **124** 75 25
627 25s. Isinya-Kajiado project 3·00 3·75

125 Kenyan Family

126 Paul Harris (founder of Rotary)

1994. International Year of the Family. Mult.
628 6s. Type **125** 65 10
629 14s.50 Nurse with mother and baby . . . . 2·50 1·40
630 20s. Schoolchildren and teacher (horiz) . . . . . 2·75 3·00
631 25s. Emblem (horiz) . . . . 3·00 3·50

1994. 50th Anniv of Rotary Club of Mombasa. Multicoloured.
632 6s. Type **126** 25 10
633 14s.50 Anniversary logo . . . 70 70
634 17s.50 Administering polio vaccine . . . . 1·00 1·60
635 20s. Women at stand pipe . . 1·00 1·75
636 25s. Rotary emblem . . . . 1·10 1·90

127 Donkey

128 Male Golfer in Bunker

1995. Kenya Society for Prevention of Cruelty to Animals. Multicoloured.
637 6s. Type **127** 30 10
638 14s.50 Cow 45 45
639 17s.50 Sheep 55 75
640 20s. Dog . . . . 1·50 2·00
641 25s. Cat . . . . 1·50 2·00

1995. Golf. Multicoloured.
642 6s. Type **128** 85 15
643 17s.50 Female golfer on fairway . . . . 2·00 1·75
644 20s. Male golfer teeing-off . . 2·00 2·50
645 25s. Head of golf club . . . 2·25 2·75

129 Perfume Containers

1995. Kenyan Material Culture (2nd issue). Mult.
646 6s. Type **129** 30 10
647 14s.50 Basketry 75 75
648 17s.50 Preserving pots . . . 85 1·25
649 20s. Gourds . . . . 1·10 1·60
650 25s. Wooden containers . . . 1·25 1·90

130 Tsetse Fly

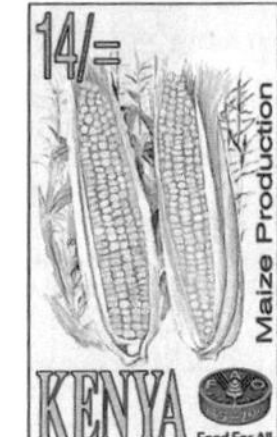

131 Maize

1995. 25th Anniv of I.C.I.P.E. Insect Pests. Multicoloured.
651 14s. Type **130** 50 30
652 26s. Tick 80 80
653 32s. Wild silkmoth . . . . . 95 1·10
654 33s. Maize borer . . . . . . 1·00 1·75
655 40s. Locust . . . . 1·60 2·50

1995. 50th Anniv of F.A.O. Multicoloured.
656 14s. Type **131** 70 30
657 28s. Cattle . . . . 1·10 80
658 32s. Chickens . . . . 1·60 1·60
659 33s. Fisherman with catch . . 1·90 2·50
660 40s. Fruit . . . . 2·25 3·00

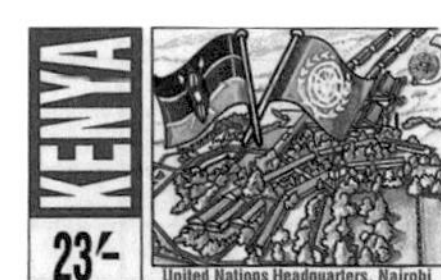

132 Kenyan and United Nations Flags over Headquarters, Nairobi

1995. 50th Anniv of United Nations.
661 **132** 23s. multicoloured 70 70
662 – 26s. multicoloured 80 90
663 – 32s. multicoloured . . . . 95 1·10
664 – 40s. blue, red and black 1·40 2·00
DESIGNS: 26s. Multi-racial group with emblem; 32s. United Nations helmet; 40s. 50th anniversary emblem.

133 Swimming

1996. Olympic Games, Atlanta (1st issue). Events and Gold Medal Winners. Multicoloured.
665 14s. Type **133** . . . . 1·00 1·10
666 20s. Archery . . . . 1·00 1·10
667 20s. Weightlifting . . . . . 1·00 1·10
668 20s. Pole vault (vert) . . . . 1·00 1·10
669 20s. Equestrian (vert) . . . . 1·00 1·10
670 20s. Diving (vert) . . . . . 1·00 1·10
671 20s. Sprinting (vert) . . . . 1·00 1·10
672 20s. Athlete carrying Olympic Torch (vert) . . . . 1·00 1·10
673 20s. Hurdling (vert) . . . . 1·00 1·10
674 20s. Kayak (vert) . . . . . 1·00 1·10
675 20s. Boxing (vert) . . . . . 1·00 1·10
676 20s. Gymnastics (vert) . . . 1·00 1·10
677 25s. Greg Louganis (U.S.A.) (diving, 1984 and 1988) (vert) . . . . 1·00 1·10
678 25s. Cassius Clay (U.S.A.) (boxing, 1960) (vert) . . . 1·00 1·10
679 25s. Nadia Comaneci (Rumania) (gymnastics, 1980) (vert) . . . . 1·00 1·10
680 25s. Daley Thompson (Great Britain) (decathlon, 1980 and 1984) (vert) . . . . . 1·00 1·10
681 25s. Kipchoge Keino (Kenya) (running, 1968) (vert) . . . 1·00 1·10
682 25s. Kornelia Enders (Germany) (swimming, 1976) (vert) . . . . 1·00 1·10
683 25s. Jackie Joyner-Kersee (U.S.A.) (long jump, 1988) (vert) . . . . 1·00 1·10
684 25s. Michael Jordan (U.S.A.) (basketball, 1984) (vert) . . 1·00 1·10
685 25s. Shun Fujimoto (Japan) (gymnastics, 1972) (vert) 1·00 1·10
686 32s. Javelin . . . . 1·00 1·10
687 40s. Fencing . . . . 1·10 1·25
688 50s. Discus . . . . 1·40 1·60
MS689 Two sheets, each 79 × 109 mm. (a) 100s. Athlete with medal (vert). (b) 100s. Athlete carrying Olympic Torch (different) (vert) Set of 2 sheets . . . . . 7·00 9·00
Nos. 665/7 with 686/8, 668/76 and 677/85 respectively were printed together, se-tenant, forming composite designs.
See also Nos. 702/6.

134 Lions

135 Water Buck

1996. Tourism. Multicoloured. (a) Designs as T **134**.
690 6s. Type **134** 30 10
691 14s. Mt. Kenya 35 30
692 20s. Sail boards 55 70
693 25s. Hippopotami . . . . . 1·25 1·40
694 40s. Couple in traditional dress . . . . 1·25 2·25
MS695 100 × 80 mm. 50s. Female giraffe and calf (vert) . . . . . 2·50 3·00

(b) Horiz designs as T **135**.
696 20s. Type **135** . . . . 1·25 1·50
697 20s. Pair of rhinoceroses . . 1·25 1·50
698 20s. Cheetah . . . . 1·25 1·50
699 20s. Group of oryx . . . . . 1·25 1·50
700 20s. Pair of giraffes . . . . . 1·25 1·50
701 20s. Monkey and bongo . . 1·25 1·50

136 Women's 10,000 Metres

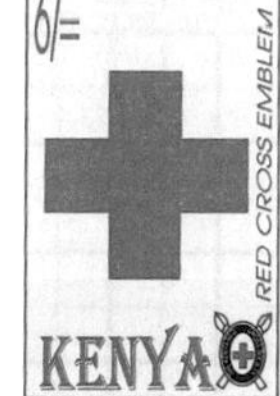

137 Red Cross Emblem

1996. Olympic Games, Atlanta (2nd issue). Multicoloured.
702 6s. Type **136** 25 10
703 14s. Steeple-chasing 45 30
704 20s. Victorious athletes with flag 70 80
705 25s. Boxing . . . . 70 1·00
706 40s. Men's 1500 m . . . . . 1·25 2·00

1996. Kenya Red Cross Society.
707 **137** 6s. red and black 25 10
708 – 14s. multicoloured 45 35
709 – 20s. multicoloured 70 80
710 – 25s. multicoloured 80 95
711 – 40s. multicoloured . . . . 1·40 2·00
DESIGNS: 14s. Giving blood; 20s. Immunization; 25s. Refugee child with food; 40s. Cleaning the environment.

138 Impala

139 Kenya Lions Club Logo

1996. East African Wildlife Society. Multicoloured.

712	6s. Type **138**	20	10
713	20s. Colobus monkey	60	60
714	25s. African elephant	1·60	1·40
715	40s. Black rhinoceros	2·25	3·00

1996. Work of Lions Club International in Kenya. Multicoloured.

716	6s. Type **139**	15	10
717	14s. Eye operation	55	45
718	20s. Two disabled children in wheelchair	70	1·25
719	25s. Modern ambulance	1·00	1·50

140 C.O.M.E.S.A. Logo

1997. Inauguration of Common Market for Eastern and Southern Africa. Multicoloured.

720	6s. Type **140**	15	15
721	20s. Kenyan flag and logo	85	1·10

141 "Haplochromis cinctus"

1997. Endangered Species. Lake Victoria Cichlid Fishes. Multicoloured.

722	25s. Type **141**	75	1·00
723	25s. "Haplochromis" "Orange Rock Hunter"	75	1·00
724	25s. "Haplochromis chilotes"	75	1·00
725	25s. "Haplochromis nigricans"	75	1·00

142 Class 94 Diesel-electric Locomotive No. 9401, 1981

1997. Kenya Railway Locomotives. Multicoloured.

726	6s. Type **142**	60	15
727	14s. Class 87 diesel-electric No. 8721, 1964	90	40
728	20s. Class 59 Garratt steam No. 5905, 1955	1·25	65
729	25s. Class 57 Garratt steam No. 5701, 1939	1·25	1·00
730	30s. Class 23 steam No. 2305, 1923	1·40	1·60
731	40s. Class 10 steam No. 1001, 1914	1·60	2·25

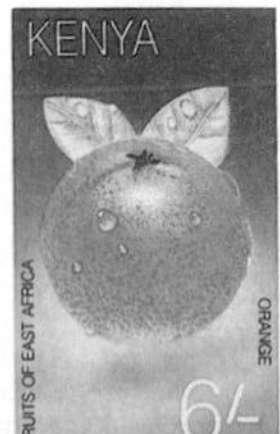

143 Orange

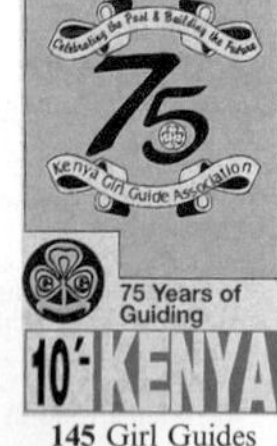

145 Girl Guides Anniversary Logo

144 Crocodile

1997. Fruits of East Africa. Multicoloured.

732	6s. Type **143**	50	15
733	14s. Pineapple	1·00	45
734	20s. Mango	1·60	1·60
735	25s. Pawpaw	1·90	2·25

1997. Local Tourist Attractions. Multicoloured.

736	10s. Type **144**	1·00	25
737	27s. Lake Bogoria hot springs	1·60	1·25
738	30s. Warthogs	1·60	1·60
739	33s. Windsurfing	1·60	1·90
740	42s. Traditional huts	1·75	2·75

1997. 75th Anniv of Kenyan Girl Guides Anniversary. Multicoloured.

741	10s. Type **145**	40	70
742	10s. Lord Baden-Powell	40	70
743	27s. Girl guides hiking	75	1·10
744	27s. Rangers in camp	75	1·10
745	33s. Girl guides planting seedlings	85	1·25
746	33s. Boy scouts giving first aid	85	1·25
747	42s. Boy scouts in camp	90	1·25
748	42s. Brownies entertaining the elderly	90	1·25

146 Portuguese Ships arriving at Malindi

1998. 500th Anniv of Vasco da Gama's Arrival at Malindi. Multicoloured.

749	10s. Type **146**	45	25
750	24s. Portuguese ships	90	70
751	33s. Map of Africa	1·10	1·50
752	42s. Vasco da Gama Pillar and harbour	1·25	1·90

147 Lion

1998. 18th Anniv of Pan African Postal Union. Wildlife. Multicoloured.

753	10s. Type **147**	85	25
754	24s. Buffalo	1·25	70
755	33s. Grant's gazelle	1·50	2·00
756	42s. Cheetah	2·75	3·25
MS757	94×76 mm. 50s. Hirola gazelle	2·00	2·50

148 Pres. Arap Moi taking Oath, 1998

1998. Daniel Arap Moi's 5th Presidential Term.

758 **148**	14s. multicoloured	1·00	70

149 Leatherback Turtle

2000. Turtles. Multicoloured.

759	17s. Type **149**	80	35
760	20s. Green sea turtle	90	40
761	30s. Hawksbill turtle	1·25	1·00
762	47s. Olive Ridley turtle	1·75	1·90
763	59s. Loggerhead turtle	2·25	2·50

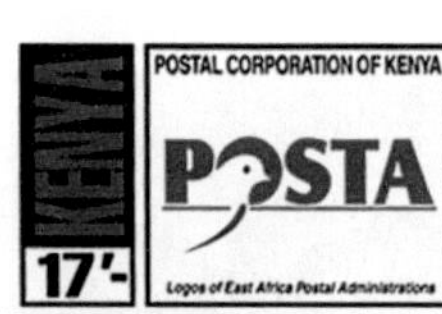

150 Kenya Postal Corporation Logo

2000. East Africa Postal Administrations' Co-operation. Multicoloured (except 17s.).

764	17s. Type **150** (red, blue and black)	55	35
765	35s. Uganda Post Ltd logo	1·00	90
766	50s. Tanzania Posts Corporation logo	1·40	2·00
MS767	100×80 mm. 70s. As 50s.	2·00	2·50

151 Cotton

152 Tea

2001. Crops. Multicoloured. (a) Vert designs as T **151**.

768	2s. Type **151**	10	10
769	4s. Bananas	10	10
770	5s. Avocado	10	10
771	6s. Cassava	10	10
772	8s. Arrowroot	10	15
773	10s. Pawpaw	15	20
774	19s. Orange	25	30
775	20s. Pyrethrum	30	35
776	30s. Groundnuts	40	45
777	35s. Coconut	50	55
778	40s. Sisal	55	60
779	50s. Cashew nuts	70	75

(b) Vert designs as T **152**.

780	60s. Type **152**	85	95
781	80s. Maize	1·10	1·20
782	100s. Coffee	1·40	1·50
783	200s. Finger millet	2·75	3·00
784	400s. Sorghum	5·50	5·75
785	500s. Sugar cane	7·00	7·25

153 Source of the Nile, Jinja, Uganda

2002. Historical Sites of East Africa. Multicoloured.

786	19s. Type **153**	50	35
787	35s. Kamu Fort, Kenya (35×35 mm)	90	75
788	40s. Olduvai Gorge, Tanzania	1·40	1·25
789	50s. Thimlich Ohinga (ancient settlement), Kenya (35×35 mm)	1·60	1·75

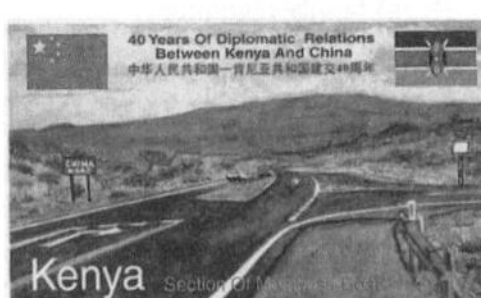

154 Section of Mombasa Road

2003. 40th Anniv of Kenya—China Diplomatic Relations. Multicoloured.

790	21s. Type **154**	30	35
791	66s. Kasarani Stadium	90	95

OFFICIAL STAMPS

Intended for use on official correspondence of the Kenya Government only, but there is no evidence that they were so used.

1964. Stamps of 1963 optd **OFFICIAL**.

O21	**46**	5c. multicoloured	10
O22	–	10c. brown	10
O23	–	15c. mauve	1·25
O24	–	20c. black and green	20
O25	–	30c. black and yellow	30
O26	–	50c. red, black and green	2·75

POSTAGE DUE STAMPS

D 3

1967.

D13	D **3**	5c. red	15	2·75
D41		10c. green	40	1·50
D42		20c. blue	40	1·50
D44		30c. brown	15	75
D45		40c. purple	15	75
D49		50c. green	10	10
D46		80c. red	20	90
D50		1s. orange	10	10
D51		2s. violet	10	10
D52		3s. blue	10	10
D53		5s. red	10	10

KENYA, UGANDA AND TANGANYIKA (TANZANIA) Pt. 1

From 1903 joint issues were made for British East Africa (later Kenya) and Uganda. In 1933 the postal administrations of Kenya, Uganda and Tanganyika were combined.

On independence of the constituent territories in the 1960s the postal administration became the East African Posts and Telecommunications Corporation. As well as separate issues for each state (q.v.), joint commemorative issues (which however were not valid in Zanzibar) were made until the dissolution of the Corporation in 1977.

1903. 16 annas = 100 cents = 1 rupee.
1922. 100 cents = 1 shilling.

1

2

1903.

17a	**1**	½a. green	7·50	3·25
2		1a. grey and red	1·75	1·00
19a		2a. purple	2·75	2·75
21		2½a. blue	7·50	17·00
22a		3a. purple and green	3·75	32·00
23		4a. green and black	7·50	18·00
24		5a. grey and brown	8·00	15·00
25		8a. grey and blue	7·00	8·50
9	**2**	1r. green	16·00	55·00
27		2r. purple	38·00	55·00
28		3r. green and black	55·00	£100
29		4r. grey and green	75·00	£140
30		5r. grey and red	85·00	£110
31		10r. grey and blue	£160	£190
15		20r. grey and stone	£550	£1100
16		50r. grey and brown	£1400	£2500

1907.

34	**1**	1c. brown	2·50	15
35		3c. green	12·00	70
36		6c. red	2·75	10
37		10c. lilac and olive	9·00	8·50
38		12c. purple	10·00	2·75
39		15c. blue	20·00	8·50
40		25c. green and black	8·50	7·00
41		50c. green and brown	12·00	12·00
42		75c. grey and blue	4·50	32·00

1912. As T **1/2** but portraits of King George V.

44	1c. black	30	1·75
45	3c. green	2·00	60
46	6c. red	70	60
47	10c. orange	2·00	50
48	12c. grey	2·75	50
49	15c. blue	2·75	80
50	25c. black and red on yellow	50	1·25
51	50c. black and lilac	1·50	1·25
52b	75c. black and green	6·00	7·50
53	1r. black and green	1·75	4·25
54	2r. red and black on blue	20·00	38·00
55	3r. violet and green	20·00	85·00
56	4r. red and green on yellow	45·00	£100
57	5r. blue and purple	48·00	£140
58	10r. red and green on green	£110	£180
59	20r. black and purple on red	£300	£300
60	20r. purple and blue on blue	£350	£400
61	50r. red and green	£550	£600
62	100r. purple and black on red	£4250	£2250
63	500r. green and red on green	£16000	

1919. No. 46 surch **4 cents**.

64	4c. on 6c. red	1·25	15

6

7

1922.

76	**6**	1c. brown	1·00	3·00
77		5c. violet	3·50	75
78		5c. green	2·00	50
79		10c. green	1·50	30
80		10c. black	4·00	20
81a		12c. black	4·25	26·00
82		15c. red	1·25	10
83		20c. orange	3·25	10
84		30c. blue	2·00	50
85		50c. grey	2·50	10
86		75c. olive	4·50	9·00
87	**7**	1s. green	4·00	2·50
88		2s. purple	8·00	9·00
89		2s.50 brown	18·00	75·00
90		3s. grey	17·00	6·50
91		4s. grey	21·00	80·00
92		5s. red	22·00	22·00
93		7s.50 orange	70·00	£150
94		10s. blue	48·00	48·00
95		£1 black and orange	£150	£225
96		£2 green and purple	£650	£1000
97		£3 purple and yellow	£850	
98		£4 black and mauve	£1700	
99		£5 black and blue	£1800	
100		£10 black and green	£8000	
101		£20 red and green	£16000	
102		£25 black and red	£1900	
103		£50 black and brown	£26000	
104		£75 purple and grey	£65000	
105		£100 red and black	£65000	

8 South African Crowned Cranes

9 Dhow on Lake Victoria

1935. King George V.
110 **8** 1c. black and brown . . . . 1·00 1·50
111 **9** 5c. black and green . . . . 1·75 60
112 – 10c. black and yellow . . . 3·50 60
113 – 15c. black and red . . . . 2·00 10
114 **8** 20c. black and orange . . . 3·00 20
115 – 30c. black and blue . . . . 2·00 1·00
116 **9** 50c. purple and black . . . 1·75 10
117 – 65c. black and brown . . . 2·75 2·00
118 – 1s. black and green . . . . 1·50 75
119 – 2s. red and purple . . . . . 4·75 4·00
120 – 3s. blue and black . . . . . 6·50 15·00
121 – 5s. black and red . . . . . 17·00 27·00
122 **8** 10s. purple and blue . . . . 65·00 85·00
123 – £1 black and red £150 £180
DESIGNS—VERT: 10c., £1 Lion; 30c., 5s. Nile Railway Bridge, Ripon Falls. HORIZ: 15c., 2s. Kilimanjaro; 65c. Mt. Kenya; 1s., 3s. Lake Naivasha.

14a Windsor Castle

1935. Silver Jubilee.
124 **14a** 20c. blue and olive . . . 60 10
125 30c. brown and blue . . . 2·50 3·50
126 65c. green and blue . . . 1·75 2·75
127 1s. grey and purple . . . 2·00 2·50

14b King George VI and Queen Elizabeth

1937. Coronation.
128 **14b** 5c. green 20 10
129 20c. orange 40 30
130 30c. blue . . . . 60 1·50

15 Dhow on Lake Victoria

1938. As 1935 (except 10c.) but with portrait of King George VI as in T **15**.
131a **8** 1c. black and brown . . 30 50
132 **15** 5c. black and green . . . 4·00 50
133 5c. brown and orange . . 50 3·00
134 – 10c. brown and orange 2·00 10
135 – 10c. black and green . . 30 85
136 – 10c. brown and grey . . 1·00 55
137a – 15c. black and red . . . 4·75 3·75
138 – 15c. black and green . . 2·00 4·00
139b **8** 20c. black and orange . . 6·50 10
140 **15** 25c. black and red . . . 1·25 2·25
141b – 30c. black and blue . . . 2·75 10
142 – 30c. purple and brown 1·50 40
143 **8** 40c. black and blue . . . 1·75 3·25
144e **15** 50c. purple and black . . 7·00 55
145a – 1s. black and brown . . 11·00 30
146b – 2s. red and purple . . . 19·00 30
147ac – 3s. blue and black . . . 25·00 3·00
148b – 5s. black and red . . . . 25·00 1·25
149b **8** 10s. purple and blue . . 40·00 3·75
150a – £1 black and red . . . . 23·00 15·00
DESIGN—HORIZ: 10c. Lake Naivasha.

1941. Stamps of South Africa surch **KENYA TANGANYIKA UGANDA** and value. Alternate stamps inscr in English or Afrikaans.
151 **7** 5c. on 1d. black and red 1·00 15
152 **22a** 10c. on 3d. blue . . . . . 2·50 30
153 **8** 20c. on 6d. green and red 2·50 20
154 – 70c. on 1s. brown and blue (No. 120) . . . . 15·00 45
Prices for Nos. 151/4 are for unused pairs and used singles.

1946. Victory. As T **4a** of Pitcairn Islands.
155 20c. orange 30 10
156 30c. blue 30 65

1948. Silver Wedding. As T **4b/c** of Pitcairn Islands.
157 20c. orange 15 10
158 £1 red . . . . 35·00 50·00

1949. U.P.U. As T **4d/g** of Pitcairn Islands.
159 20c. orange 15 10
160 30c. blue . . . . 1·75 1·50
161 50c. grey 45 20
162 1s. brown 50 40

1952. Visit of Queen Elizabeth II (as Princess) and Duke of Edinburgh. As Nos. 135 and 145ba but inscr "ROYAL VISIT 1952".
163 10c. black and green . . . . 10 1·50
164 1s. black and brown . . . . 20 2·00

1953. Coronation. As T **4h** of Pitcairn Islands.
165 20c. black and orange . . . 15 10

1954. Royal Visit. As No. 171 but inscr "ROYAL VISIT 1954".
166 **18** 30c. black and blue 40 15

18 Owen Falls Dam

21 Queen Elizabeth II

20 Royal Lodge, Sagana

1954.
167 **18** 5c. black and brown . . . 60 50
168 – 10c. red 75 10
169a – 15c. black and blue . . . 55 1·25
170 – 20c. black and orange . . 1·00 10
171 **18** 30c. black and blue . . . 80 10
172 – 40c. brown . . . . 1·25 75
173 – 50c. purple . . . . 1·75 10
174 – 65c. green and purple . . 2·75 1·50
175 – 1s. black and purple . . . 1·50 10
176 – 1s.30 lilac and orange . . 9·50 10
177 – 2s. black and green . . . 7·00 80
178 – 5s. black and orange . . . 18·00 2·00
179 **20** 10s. black and blue . . . 24·00 2·75
180 **21** £1 red and black . . . . 16·00 12·00
DESIGNS—VERT (Size as Type **18**): 10, 50c. Giraffe; 20, 40c., 1s. Lion. HORIZ: 15c., 1s.30, 5s. Elephants; 65c., 2s. Mt. Kilimanjaro.

25 Map of E. Africa showing Lakes

1958. Centenary of Discovery of Lakes Tanganyika and Victoria by Burton and Speke.
181 **25** 40c. blue and green 30 40
182 1s.30 green and purple . . 30 1·40

26 Sisal

29 Queen Elizabeth II

28 Mt. Kenya and Giant Plants

1960.
183 **26** 5c. blue 10 15
184 – 10c. green 10 10
185 – 15c. purple 30 10
186 – 20c. mauve 20 10
187 – 25c. green . . . . 3·25 1·25
188 – 30c. red 15 10
189 – 40c. blue 15 20
190 – 50c. violet 15 10
191 – 65c. olive . . . . 30 1·25
192 **28** 1s. violet and purple . . . 80 10
193 – 1s.30 brown and red . . . 2·75 15
194 – 2s. indigo and blue . . . . 3·00 40
195 – 2s.50 olive and turquoise 4·50 2·75
196 – 5s. red and purple . . . . 3·75 60
197 – 10s. myrtle and green . . . 8·00 6·50
198 **29** 20s. blue and lake . . . . 16·00 21·00
DESIGNS—As Type **26**: 10c. Cotton; 15c. Coffee; 20c. Blue wildebeest; 25c. Ostrich; 30c. Thomson's gazelle; 40c. Manta; 50c. Common zebra; 65c. Cheetah. As Type **28**: 1s.30, Murchison Falls and hippopotamus; 2s. Mt. Kilimanjaro and giraffe; 2s.50, Candelabra tree and black rhinoceros; 5s. Crater Lake and Mountains of the Moon; 10s. Ngorongoro Crater and African buffalo.

30 Land Tillage

1963. Freedom from Hunger.
199 **30** 15c. blue and olive 10 10
200 – 30c. brown and yellow . . 20 10
201 **30** 50c. blue and orange . . . 30 10
202 – 1s.30 brown and blue . . . 55 1·75
DESIGN: 30c., 1s.30, African with corncob.

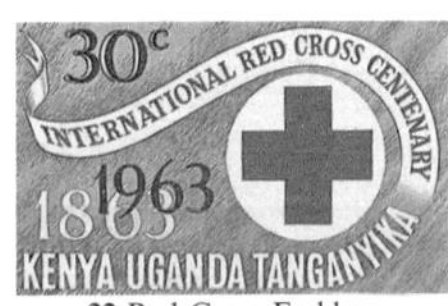

31 Scholars and Open Book

1963. Founding of East African University.
203 **31** 30c. multicoloured 10 10
204 1s.30 multicoloured 20 20

32 Red Cross Emblem

1963. Centenary of Red Cross.
205 **32** 30c. red and blue . . . . 1·00 10
206 50c. red and brown . . . . 1·25 55

35 East African "Flags"

1964. Olympic Games, Tokyo.
207 – 30c. yellow and purple . . 10 10
208 – 50c. purple and yellow . . 15 10
209 **35** 1s.30 yellow, green and blue 40 10
210 2s.50 mauve, violet & blue 45 1·40
DESIGN—VERT: 30, 50c. Chrysanthemum emblem.

36 Rally Badge

1965. 13th East African Safari Rally.
211 **36** 30c. black, yellow & turq 10 10
212 50c. black, yellow & brown 10 10
213 – 1s.30 green, ochre and blue 25 10
214 – 2s.50 green, red and blue 40 1·50
DESIGN: 1s.30, 2s.50, Cars en route.

38 I.T.U. Emblem and Symbols

1965. Centenary of I.T.U. "I.T.U." and symbols in gold.
215 **38** 30c. brown and mauve . . 15 10
216 50c. brown and grey . . . 15 10
217 1s.30 brown and blue . . . 40 10
218 2s.50 brown and turquoise 75 2·25

39 I.C.Y. Emblem

1965. International Co-operation Year.
219 **39** 30c. green and gold 10 10
220 50c. black and gold 15 10
221 1s.30 blue and gold 30 10
222 2s.50 red and gold . . . . 75 2·50

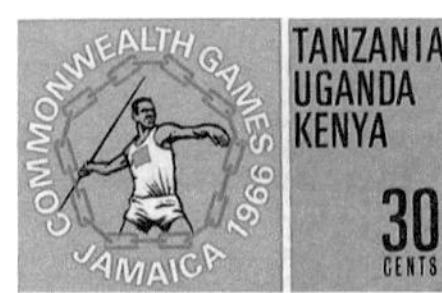

40 Game Park Lodge, Tanzania

1966. Tourism. Multicoloured.
223 30c. Type **40** 15 10
224 50c. Murchison Falls, Uganda 50 10
225 1s.30 Lesser flamingoes, Lake Nakuru, Kenya . . . . . 2·75 30
226 2s.50 Deep sea fishing, Tanzania . . . . 2·00 2·25

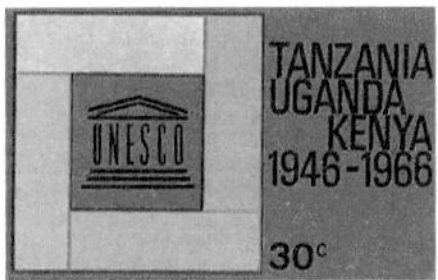

41 Games Emblem

1966. 8th British Empire and Commonwealth Games, Jamaica.
227 **41** 30c. multicoloured 10 10
228 50c. multicoloured 15 10
229 1s.30 multicoloured 20 10
230 2s.50 multicoloured . . . . 35 1·50

42 U.N.E.S.C.O. Emblem

1966. 20th Anniv of U.N.E.S.C.O.
231 **42** 30c. black, green and red 30 10
232 50c. black, green and brown 35 10
233 1s.30 black, green and grey 1·00 15
234 2s.50 black, green & yellow 1·75 3·75

43 De Havilland Dragon Rapide

1967. 21st Anniv of East African Airways.
235 **43** 30c. violet, blue and green 30 10
236 – 50c. multicoloured 40 10
237 – 1s.30 multicoloured 85 30
238 – 2s.50 multicoloured . . . . 1·25 2·50
DESIGNS: 50c. Vickers Super VC-10; 1s.30, Hawker Siddeley Comet 4B; 2s.50, Fokker Friendship.

44 Pillar Tomb

1967. Archaeological Relics.
239 **44** 30c. ochre, black and purple 15 10
240 – 50c. red, black and brown 65 10
241 – 1s.30 black, yellow & green 85 15
242 – 2s.50 black, ochre and red 1·40 2·50
DESIGNS: 50c. Rock painting; 1s.30, Clay head; 2s.50, Proconsul skull.

48 Unified Symbols of Kenya, Tanzania and Uganda

1967. Foundation of East African Community.
243 **48** 5s. gold, black and grey . . 40 1·25

49 Mountaineering

1968. Mountains of East Africa. Multicoloured.
244 30c. Type **49** 15 10
245 50c. Mt. Kenya 30 10
246 1s.30 Mt. Kilimanjaro . . . 60 10
247 2s.50 Ruwenzori Mountains 90 2·25

50 Family and Rural Hospital

1968. World Health Organization.
248 **50** 30c. green, lilac and brown 10 10
249 – 50c. slate, lilac and black 15 10
250 – 1s.30 brown, lilac & lt brown 20 15
251 – 2s.50 grey, black and lilac 30 1·90
DESIGNS: 50c. Family and nurse; 1s.30, Family and microscope; 2s.50, Family and hypodermic syringe.

51 Olympic Stadium, Mexico City

1968. Olympic Games, Mexico.
252 **51** 30c. green and black . . . 10 10
253 – 50c. green and black . . . 15 10
254 – 1s.30 red, black and grey 25 15
255 – 2s.50 sepia and brown . . 35 1·50
DESIGNS—HORIZ: 50c. High-diving boards; 1s.30, Running tracks. VERT: 2s.50, Boxing ring.

52 "Umoja" (railway ferry)

1969. Water Transport.
256 **52** 30c. blue and grey 30 10
257 – 50c. multicoloured 35 10
258 – 1s.30 green and blue . . . 60 20
259 – 2s.50 orange and blue . . . 1·10 3·25
DESIGNS: 50c. S.S. "Harambee"; 1s.30, M.V. "Victoria"; 2s.50, "St. Michael".

53 I.L.O. Emblem and Agriculture

1969. 50th Anniv of Int Labour Organization.
260 **53** 30c. black, green and yellow 10 10
261 – 50c. multicoloured 10 10
262 – 1s.30 black, brown and orange 10 10
263 – 2s.50 black, blue & turq . . 20 90
DESIGNS—I.L.O. emblem and: 50c. Building-work; 1s.30, Factory-workers; 2s.50, Shipping.

54 Pope Paul VI and Ruwenzori Mountains **55** Euphorbia Tree shaped as Africa, and Emblem

1969. Visit of Pope Paul VI to Uganda.
264 **54** 30c. black, gold and blue 15 10
265 70c. black, gold and red . . 20 10
266 1s.50 black, gold and blue 25 20
267 2s.50 black, gold and violet 30 1·40

1969. 5th Anniv of African Development Bank.
268 **55** 30c. green and gold 10 10
269 70c. green, gold and violet 15 10
270 1s.50 green, gold and blue 30 10
271 2s.50 green, gold & brown 35 1·00

56 Marimba

1970. Musical Instruments.
272 **56** 30c. buff and brown . . . 15 10
273 – 70c. green, brown & yellow 25 10
274 – 1s.50 brown and yellow . . 50 10
275 – 2s.50 orange, yellow and brown . . . . 75 2·50
DESIGNS: 70c. Amadinda; 1s.50, Nzomari; 2s.50, Adeudeu.

57 Satellite Earth Station

1970. Inauguration of Satellite Earth Station.
276 **57** 30c. multicoloured 10 10
277 – 70c. multicoloured 15 10
278 – 1s.50 black, violet & orge 25 10
279 – 2s.50 multicoloured . . . . 55 2·25
DESIGNS: 70c. Transmitter—daytime; 1s.50, Transmitter—night; 2s. 50, Earth and satellite.

58 Athlete

1970. 9th Commonwealth Games.
280 **58** 30c. brown and black . . . 10 10
281 70c. green, brown and black 10 10
282 1s.50 lilac, brown and black 15 10
283 2s.50 blue, brown and black . . . . 20 1·25

59 "25" and U.N. Emblem

1970. 25th Anniv of United Nations.
284 **59** 30c. multicoloured 10 10
285 70c. multicoloured 10 10
286 1s.50 multicoloured 20 10
287 2s.50 multicoloured . . . . 45 2·00

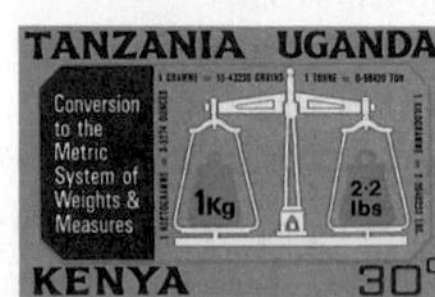

60 Balance and Weight Equivalents

1970. Conversion to Metric System. Multicoloured.
288 30c. Type **60** 10 10
289 70c. Fahrenheit and Centigrade thermometers 10 10
290 1s.50 Petrol pump and liquid capacities 15 10
291 2s.50 Surveyors and land measures . . . . 35 2·00

61 Class 11 Tank Locomotive

1971. Railway Transport. Multicoloured.
292 30c. Type **61** 30 10
293 70c. Class 90 diesel-electric locomotive 35 10
294 1s.50 Class 59 steam locomotive 50 20
295 2s.50 Class 30 steam locomotive . . . . 75 2·25
MS296 120 × 88 mm. Nos. 292/5 5·50 10·00

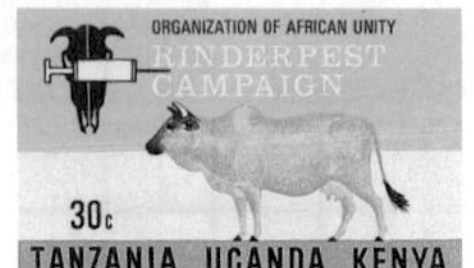

62 Syringe and Cow

1971. O.A.U. Rinderpest Campaign.
297 **62** 30c. black, brown and green 10 10
298 – 70c. black, blue and brown 10 10
299 **62** 1s.50 black, purple & brn 15 10
300 – 2s.50 black, red and brown 25 70
DESIGN: 70c., 2s.50, as Type **62** but with bull facing right.

63 Livingstone meets Stanley

1971. Centenary of Livingstone and Stanley meeting at Ujiji.
301 **63** 5s. multicoloured 30 75

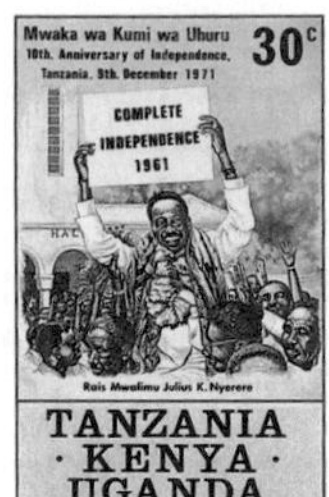

64 Pres. Nyerere and Supporters

1971. 10th Anniv of Tanzanian Independence. Multicoloured.
302 30c. Type **64** 10 10
303 70c. Ujamaa village 15 10
304 1s.50 Dar-es-Salaam University 30 25
305 2s.50 Kilimanjaro International Airport . . . 1·00 3·25

65 Flags and Trade Fair Emblem

1972. All-Africa Trade Fair.
306 **65** 30c. multicoloured 10 10
307 70c. multicoloured 10 10
308 1s.50 multicoloured 10 10
309 2s.50 multicoloured 25 80

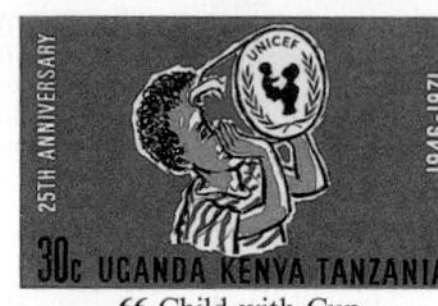

66 Child with Cup

1972. 25th Anniv of U.N.I.C.E.F. Multicoloured.
310 30c. Type **66** 10 10
311 70c. Children with ball . . . 10 10
312 1s.50 Child at blackboard . . 10 10
313 2s.50 Child and tractor . . . 25 80

67 Hurdling

1972. Olympic Games, Munich. Multicoloured.
314 40c. Type **67** 10 10
315 70c. Running 10 10
316 1s.50 Boxing 20 15
317 2s.50 Hockey . . . . 30 1·75
MS318 131 × 98 mm. Nos. 314/17 4·50 7·00

68 Ugandan Kobs

1972. 10th Anniv of Ugandan Independence. Multicoloured.
319 40c. Type **68** 20 10
320 70c. Conference Centre . . . 20 10
321 1s.50 Makerere University . . 45 30
322 2s.50 Coat of arms . . . . . 70 3·50
MS323 132 × 120 mm. Nos. 319/22 4·00 3·50

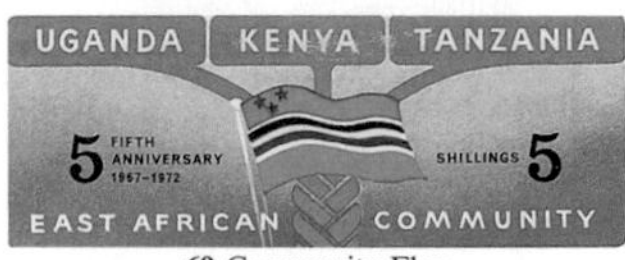

69 Community Flag

1972. 5th Anniv of East African Community.
324 **69** 5s. multicoloured . . . . . 55 1·90

70 Run-of-the-wind Anemometer

1972. Centenary of IMO/WMO. Multicoloured.
325 40c. Type **70** 10 10
326 70c. Weather balloon (vert) 20 10
327 1s.50 Meteorological rocket 30 15
328 2s.50 Satellite receiving aerial 55 2·25

71 "Learning by Serving" **73** Police Dog-handler

72 Kenyatta Conference Centre

1973. 24th World Scouting Conference, Nairobi.
329 **71** 40c. multicoloured 15 10
330 – 70c. red, violet and black 20 10
331 – 1s.50 blue, violet and black 45 30
332 – 2s.50 multicoloured . . . . 1·00 2·25
DESIGNS: 70c. Baden-Powell's grave, Nyeri; 1s.50, World Scout emblem; 2s.50, Lord Baden-Powell.

1973. I.M.F./World Bank Conference.
333 **72** 40c. green, grey and black 10 10
334 – 70c. brown, grey and black 10 10
335 – 1s.50 multicoloured 25 35
336 – 2s.50 orange, grey & black 35 1·75
MS337 166 × 141 mm. Nos. 333/6. Imperf . . . . 1·40 3·75
DESIGNS: Nos. 334/6 show different arrangements of Bank emblems and the Conference Centre, the 1s.50 being vertical.

1973. 50th Anniv of Interpol.
338 **73** 40c. yellow, blue and black 55 15
339 – 70c. green, yellow and black 90 15
340 – 1s.50 violet, yellow & black 1·50 90

341 – 2s.50 green, orange & black . . . . 3·75 6·00
342 – 2s.50 green, orange & black . . . . 3·75 6·00
DESIGNS: 70c. East African policemen; 1s.50, Interpol emblem; 2s.50 (2), Interpol H.Q.
No. 341 is inscribed "St. Clans" and 342 "St. Cloud".

74 Tea Factory

1973. 10th Anniv of Kenya's Independence. Mult.
343 40c. Type **74** 10 10
344 70c. Kenyatta Hospital . . . 15 10
345 1s.50 Nairobi Airport 50 20
346 2s.50 Kindaruma hydro-electric scheme . . . . . . 65 1·75

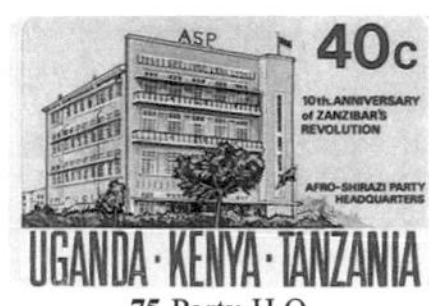

75 Party H.Q.

1973. 10th Anniv of Zanzibar's Revolution. Mult.
347 40c. Type **75** 10 10
348 70c. Housing scheme 15 10
349 1s.50 Colour T.V. 35 30
350 2s.50 Amaan Stadium . . . 70 3·00

76 "Symbol of Union"

1974. 10th Anniv of Tanganyika–Zanzibar Union. Multicoloured.
351 40c. Type **76** 10 10
352 70c. Handclasp and map . . 15 10
353 1s.50 "Communications" . . 35 30
354 2s.50 Flags of Tanu, Tanzania and Afro-Shirazi Party . . . . 70 3·00

77 East African Family ("Stability of the Home")

1974. 17th Social Welfare Conference, Nairobi.
355 **77** 40c. yellow, brown & black 10 10
356 – 70c. multicoloured 10 10
357 – 1s.50 yellow, green & black 20 30
358 – 2s.50 red, violet and black 1·00 2·00
DESIGNS: 70c. Dawn and drummer (U.N. Second Development Plan); 1s.50, Agricultural scene (Rural Development Plan); 2s.50, Transport and telephone ("Communications").

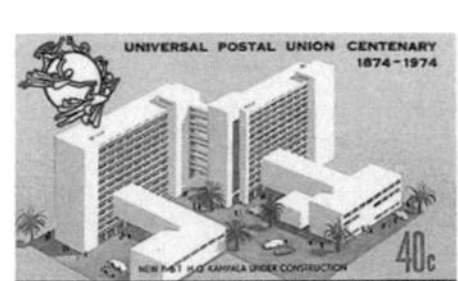

78 New Postal H.Q., Kampala

1974. Centenary of U.P.U. Multicoloured.
359 40c. Type **78** 10 10
360 70c. Mail-train and post-van 20 10
361 1s.50 U.P.U. Building, Berne 15 20
362 2s.50 Loading mail into Vickers Super VC-10 . . . 55 1·50

79 Family-planning Clinic

1974. World Population Year.
363 **79** 40c. multicoloured 10 10
364 – 70c. mauve and red 10 10
365 – 1s.50 multicoloured 15 20
366 – 2s.50 blue, emerald and green . . . . 30 1·90
DESIGNS: 70c. "Tug of War"; 1s.50, "Population scales"; 2s.50, W.P.Y. emblem.

80 Seronera Wildlife Lodge, Tanzania

1975. East African Game Lodges. Multicoloured.
367 40c. Type **80** 15 10
368 70c. Mweya Safari Lodge, Uganda 20 10
369 1s.50 "Ark"—Aberdare Forest Lodge, Kenya . . . 25 30
370 2s.50 Paraa Safari Lodge, Uganda . . . . 60 2·50

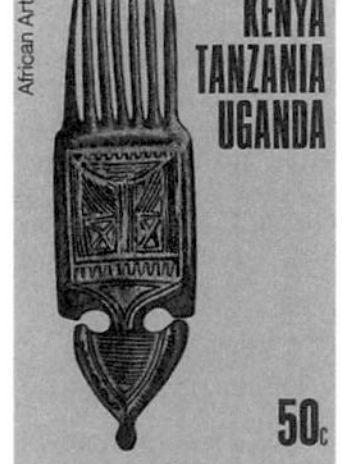

81 Kitana (wooden comb), Bajun of Kenya

83 Ahmed ("Presidential" Elephant)

82 International Airport, Entebbe

1975. African Arts. Multicoloured.
371 50c. Type **81** 10 10
372 1s. Earring, Chaga of Tanzania 15 10
373 2s. Okoco (armlet), Acholi of Uganda 35 70
374 3s. Kitete, Kamba gourd, Kenya . . . . 65 1·40

1975. O.A.U. Summit Conf, Kampala. Mult.
375 50c. Type **82** 30 10
376 1s. Map of Africa and flag (vert) 30 10
377 2s. Nile Hotel, Kampala . . 30 85
378 3s. Martyrs' Shrine, Namugongo (vert) . . . . 40 1·60

1975. Rare Animals. Multicoloured.
379 50c. Type **83** 50 10
380 1s. Albino buffalo 50 10
381 2s. Ahmed in grounds of National Museum . . . . 1·10 1·50
382 3s. Abbott's duiker . . . . . 1·25 3·00

84 Maasai Manyatta (village), Kenya

1975. 2nd World Black and African Festival of Arts and Culture, Nigeria (1977). Multicoloured.
383 50c. Type **84** 15 10
384 1s. "Heartbeat of Africa" (Ugandan Dancers) 15 10
385 2s. Makonde sculpture, Tanzania 50 85
386 3s. "Early Man and Technology" (skinning animal) . . . . 75 1·40

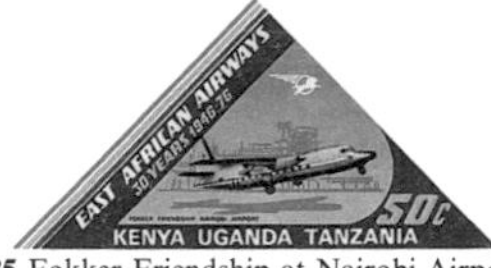

85 Fokker Friendship at Nairobi Airport

1975. 30th Anniv of East African Airways. Multicoloured.
387 50c. Type **85** . . . . 1·00 40
388 1s. Douglas DC-9 at Kilimanjaro Airport . . . 1·10 40
389 2s. Vickers Super VC-10 at Entebbe Airport . . . . 3·50 3·25
390 3s. East African Airways crest . . . . 3·75 3·75

Further commemorative sets were released during 1976–78 using common designs, but each inscribed for one republic only. See Kenya, Tanzania and Uganda.
Co-operation between the postal services of the three member countries virtually ceased after 30 June 1977. The postal services of Kenya, Tanzania and Uganda then operated independently.

OFFICIAL STAMPS

For use on official correspondence of the Tanganyika Government only.

1959. Stamps of 1954 optd **OFFICIAL**.
O 1 **18** 5c. black and brown . . . 10 1·00
O 2 – 10c. red . . . . 15 1·00
O 3 – 15c. black and blue . . . 30 1·10
O 4 – 20c. black and orange . . 20 20
O 5 **18** 30c. black and blue . . . 15 75
O 6 – 50c. purple 20 20
O 7 – 1s. black and red 20 65
O 8 – 1s.30 orange and lilac . . 2·75 1·75
O 9 – 2s. black and green . . . 1·25 1·00
O10 – 5s. black and orange . . . 3·25 2·50
O11 **20** 10s. black and blue . . . 2·00 3·00
O12 **21** £1 red and black . . . . 6·50 14·00

1960. Stamps of 1960 optd **OFFICIAL**.
O13 **26** 5c. blue . . . . 10 1·00
O14 – 10c. green . . . . 10 1·00
O15 – 15c. purple . . . . 10 1·00
O16 – 20c. mauve 10 20
O17 – 30c. red 10 10
O18 – 50c. violet 30 70
O19 **28** 1s. violet and purple . . . 30 10
O20 – 5s. red and purple . . . . 12·00 65

POSTAGE DUE STAMPS

D 1

D 2

1923.
D1 **D 1** 5c. violet . . . . 2·50 50
D2 10c. red . . . . 2·50 15
D3 20c. green . . . . 2·50 3·00
D4 30c. brown . . . . 17·00 14·00
D5 40c. blue . . . . 6·50 14·00
D6 1s. green . . . . 65·00 £130

1935.
D 7 **D 2** 5c. violet . . . . 2·75 1·75
D 8 10c. red 30 50
D 9 20c. green 40 50
D10 30c. brown . . . . . . 1·25 50
D11 40c. blue . . . . 1·50 3·00
D12 1s. grey . . . . 19·00 19·00

KHMER REPUBLIC Pt. 21

Cambodia was renamed Khmer Republic on 9 October 1970.
Following the fall of the Khmer Republic, the People's Republic of Kampuchea was proclaimed on 10 January 1979.

100 cents = 1 riel.

78 "Attack"

1971. Defence of Khmer Territory.
285 **78** 1r. multicoloured 15 10
286 3r. multicoloured 15 15
287 10r. multicoloured 50 25

79 "World Races" and U.N. Emblem

1971. Racial Equality Year.
288 **79** 3r. multicoloured 25 15
289 7r. multicoloured 40 25
290 8r. multicoloured 60 40

80 General Post Office, Phnom Penh

1971.
291 **80** 3r. multicoloured 15 10
292 9r. multicoloured 50 35
293 10r. multicoloured 60 40

81 Global Emblem

1971. World Telecommunications Day.
294 **81** 3r. multicoloured 25 15
295 4r. multicoloured 35 15
296 – 7r. multicoloured 40 25
297 – 8r. red, black and orange 50 25
DESIGN: 7, 8r. I.T.U. emblem.

82 Indian Coral Bean

1971. Wild Flowers. Multicoloured.
298 2r. Type **82** 40 15
299 3r. Orchid tree 50 40
300 6r. Flame-of-the-forest . . . 1·00 40
301 10r. Malayan crape myrtle (vert) . . . . 1·20 65

83 Arms of the Republic

84 Monument and Flag

1971. 1st Anniv of Republic.
302 **83** 3r. bistre and green 25 10
303 **84** 3r. multicoloured 25 10
304 4r. multicoloured 35 15
305 **83** 8r. bistre and orange . . . 40 15
306 10r. bistre and brown . . . 60 25
307 **84** 10r. multicoloured 50 35

85 U.N.I.C.E.F. Emblem

86 Book Year Emblem

1971. 25th Anniv of U.N.I.C.E.F.
309 **85** 3r. purple 25 15
310 5r. blue 35 25
311 9r. red and violet 65 40

1972. International Book Year.
312 **86** 3r. green, purple and blue 25 15
313 8r. blue, green and purple 40 25
314 9r. bistre, blue and green 60 40

87 Lion of St. Mark's

1972. U.N.E.S.C.O. "Save Venice" Campaign.
316 **87** 3r. brown, buff and purple 35 15
317 – 5r. brown, buff and green 60 25
318 – 10r. brown, blue and green 75 40
DESIGNS—HORIZ: 5r. St. Mark's Basilica. VERT: 10r. Bridge of Sighs.

88 U.N. Emblem

89 Dancing Apsaras (relief), Angkor

1972. 25th Anniv of Economic Commission for Asia and the Far East (C.E.A.E.O.).

320	**88**	3r. red	25	15
321		6r. blue	40	25
322		9r. red	60	40

1972.

324	**89**	1r. brown	25	15
325		3r. violet	25	15
326		7r. purple	40	25
327		8r. brown	40	25
328		9r. green	50	25
329		10r. blue	65	25
330		12r. purple	90	35
331		14r. blue	1·20	40

90 "UIT" on T.V. Screen

91 Conference Emblem

1972. World Telecommunications Day.

332	**90**	3r. black, blue and yellow	25	15
333		9r. black, blue and mauve	50	25
334		14r. black, blue and brown	75	40

1972. United Nations Environmental Conservation Conference, Stockholm.

335	**91**	3r. green, brown and violet	25	15
336		12r. violet and green	40	25
337		15r. green and violet	60	40

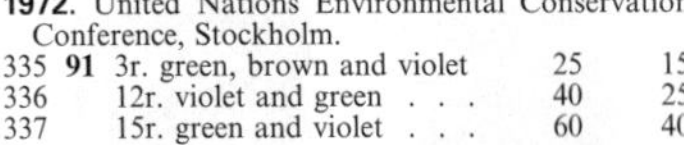

92 Javan Rhinoceros

94 Hoisting Flag

1972. Wild Animals.

339	**92**	3r. black, red and violet	40	15
340	–	4r. violet, bistre and purple	50	15
341	–	6r. brown, green and blue	90	35
342	–	7r. ochre, green and brown	1·30	35
343	–	8r. black, green and blue	1·50	40
344	–	10r. black, blue and green	2·00	60

DESIGNS: 4r. Mainland serow; 6r. Thamin; 7r. Banteng; 8r. Water buffalo; 10r. Gaur.

1972. Olympic Games, Munich. Nos. 164 of Cambodia and 302, 306 and 336/7 of Khmer Republic optd **XXe JEUX OLYMPIQUES MUNICH 1972**, Olympic rings and emblem.

345	**83**	3r. bistre and green	35	35
346		10r. bistre and brown	1·20	65
347	–	12r. green and brown	1·40	85
348	**91**	12r. violet and green	1·40	85
349		15r. green and violet	1·70	1·10

1972. 2nd Anniv of Republic.

350	**94**	3r. multicoloured	15	10
351		5r. multicoloured	25	15
352		9r. multicoloured	60	40

1972. Red Cross Aid for War Victims. No. 164 of Cambodia and 302, 306 and 336/7 of Khmer Republic surch **SECOURS AUX VICTIMES DE GUERRE**, red cross and value.

353	**83**	3r.+2r. bistre and green	25	25
354		10r.+6r. bistre and brown	65	65
355	–	12r.+7r. green and brown	75	65
356	**91**	12r.+7r. violet and green	75	75
357		15r.+8r. green and violet	1·30	1·30

96 Garuda

97 Crest and Temple

1973. Air.

358	**96**	3r. red	25	15
359		30r. blue	1·80	1·00
360		50r. lilac	3·25	1·80
361		100r. green	4·50	2·75

1973. New Constitution.

362	**97**	3r. multicoloured	15	10
363		12r. multicoloured	25	15
364		14r. multicoloured	40	35

98 Apsara

99 Interpol Emblem

1973. Angkor Sculptures.

366	**98**	3r. black	25	15
367	–	8r. blue	40	25
368	–	10r. brown	50	40

DESIGNS: 8r. Devata (12th century); 10f. Devata (10th century).

1973. 50th Anniv of International Criminal Police Organization (Interpol).

370	**99**	3r. green and turquoise	25	15
371		7r. green and red	35	25
372		10r. green and brown	40	40

100 Marshal Lon Nol

1973. Honouring Marshal Lon Nol, 1st President of Republic.

374	**100**	3r. black, brown and green	15	15
375		8r. black, brown and green	25	25
376		14r. black, brown and agate	40	25

102 Copernicus and Space Rocket

1974. 500th Birth Anniv of Nicolas Copernicus (astronomer). Multicoloured.

382	1r. Type **102** (postage)	20	20
383	5r. Copernicus and "Mariner II"	20	20
384	10r. Copernicus and "Apollo"	50	25
385	25r. Copernicus and "Telstar"	1·10	55
386	50r. Copernicus and space-walker	2·00	1·00
387	100r. Copernicus and spaceship landing on Moon	4·75	2·50
388	150r. Copernicus and Moon-landing craft leaving "Apollo"	7·00	4·00
389	200r. Copernicus and "Skylab III" (air)	8·50	4·00
390	250r. Copernicus and Concorde	14·00	7·50

1974. 4th Anniv of Republic. Various stamps optd **4E ANNIVERSAIRE DE LA REPUBLIQUE**.

391	**78**	10r. multicoloured	90	85
392	**77**	50r. on 3r. multicoloured	3·00	2·10
393	**94**	100r. on 5r. multicoloured	5·75	5·50

No. 392 is additionally optd **REPUBLIQUE KHMERE** in French and Cambodian.

104 Xylophone

1975. Unissued stamps of Cambodia showing musical instruments, surch **REPUBLIQUE KHMERE** in French and Cambodian and new value. Multicoloured.

394	5r. on 8r. Type **104**	
395	20r. on 1r. So (two-stringed violin)	
396	160r. on 7r. Khoung vong (bronze gongs)	
397	180r. on 14r. Two drums	
398	235r. on 12r. Barrel-shaped drum	
399	500r. on 9r. Xylophone (different)	
400	1000r. on 10r. Boat-shaped xylophone	
401	2000r. on 3r. Twenty-stringed guitar on legs	
	Set of 8	£250

POSTAGE DUE STAMPS

D 101 Frieze, Angkor Vat

1974.

D378	**D 101**	2r. brown	25	25
D379		6r. green	35	35
D380		8r. red	50	50
D381		10r. blue	65	75

APPENDIX

The following stamps have either been issued in excess of postal needs or have not been available to the public in reasonable quantities at face value. Such stamps may later be given full listing if there is evidence of regular postal use.

1972.

Moon Landing of "Apollo 16". Embossed on gold foil. Air 900r. × 2.

Visit of Pres. Nixon to China. Embossed on gold foil. Air 900r. × 2.

Olympic Games, Munich. Embossed on gold foil. Air 900r. × 2.

1973.

Gold Medal Winners, Munich Olympics. Embossed on gold foil. Air 900r. × 2.

World Cup Football Championship, West Germany (1974). Embossed on gold foil. Air 900r. × 4.

1974.

Pres. Kennedy and "Apollo 11". Embossed on gold foil. Air 1100r. × 2.

500th Birth Anniv of Nicolas Copernicus (astronomer). Embossed on gold foil. Air 1200r.

Centenary of U.P.U. (1st issue). Postage 10, 60r.; Air 700; 1200r. embossed on gold foil.

1975.

Olympic Games, Montreal (1976). Postage 5, 10, 15, 25r.; Air 50, 100, 150, 200, 250r.; 1200r. embossed on gold foil.

World Cup Football Championship, West Germany (1974). Postage 1, 5, 10, 25r.; Air 50, 100, 150, 200, 250, 1200r. embossed on gold foil.

Centenary of U.P.U. (2nd issue). Postage 15, 20, 70, 160, 180, 235r.; Air 500, 1000, 2000, 2000r. embossed on gold foil.

KHOR FAKKAN Pt. 19

From 1965 various issues were produced for this dependency, some being overprinted on, or in the same designs as, issues for Sharjah.

APPENDIX

The following stamps have either been issued in excess of postal needs or have not been available to the public in reasonable quantities at face value. Such stamps may later be given full listing if there is evidence of regular postal use.

1965.

Views. Nos. 75/80 of Sharjah optd. Air 10, 20, 30, 40, 75, 100n.p.

Boy and Girl Scouts. Nos. 74 and 89 of Sharjah optd. 2, 2r.

Birds. Nos. 101/6 of Sharjah optd. Air 30, 40, 75, 150n.p., 2, 3r.

Olympic Games, Tokyo 1964. Nos. 95/7 of Sharjah optd. 40, 50n.p., 2r.

New York World's Fair. Nos. 81/3 of Sharjah optd. Air 20, 40n.p., 1r.

Pres. Kennedy Commem. Nos. 98/100 of Sharjah optd. Air 40, 60, 100n.p.

Centenary of I.T.U. Postage 1, 2, 3, 4, 5, 50n.p., 1r., 120n.p.

Pan-Arab Games, Cairo. 50p. × 5.

1966.

International Co-operation Year. 50n.p. × 8.

Churchill Commemoration. 2, 3, 4, 5r.

Roses. 20, 35, 60, 80n.p., 1r., 125n.p.

Fish. 1, 2, 3, 4, 5, 15, 20, 30, 40, 50, 75n.p., 1, 2, 3, 4, 5, 10r.

Int Stamp Exhibition, Washington D.C. (SIPEX). 80, 120n.p., 2r.

New Currency Surcharges in Rials and Piastres.

(a) 1965 I.T.U. Centenary issue. 10p. on 50n.p., 16p. on 120n.p., 1r. on 1r.

(b) Churchill issue. 1r. on 2r., 2r. on 3r., 3r. on 4r., 4r. on 5r.

(c) Roses issue. 1p. on 20n.p., 2p. on 35n.p., 4p. on 60n.p., 6p. on 80n.p., 10p. on 125n.p., 12p. on 1r.

New Currency Surcharges in Dirhams and Riyals.

(a) 1965 Pan-Arab Games issue. 20d. on 50p. × 5.

(b) Fish issue. 1d. on 1n.p., 2d. on 2n.p., 3d. on 3n.p., 4d. on 4n.p., 5d. on 5n.p., 15d. on 15n.p., 20d. on 20n.p., 30d. on 30n.p., 40d. on 40n.p., 50d. on 50n.p., 75d. on 75n.p., 1r. on 1r., 2r. on 2r., 3r. on 3r., 4r. on 4r., 5r. on 5r., 10r. on 10r.

3rd Death Anniv of Pres. J. Kennedy. Optd on Int Stamp Exhibition, Washington issue. 80d. on 80n.p., 120d. on 120n.p., 2r. on 2r.

World Football Cup Championship, England. ½r. × 7.

1967.

4th Death Anniv of Pres. J. Kennedy. Optd on 1966 Int Stamp Exhibition issue. 80d. on 80n.p., 120d. on 120n.p., 2r. on 2r.

1968.

Famous Paintings. Optd on Sharjah. Postage 1, 2, 3, 4, 5, 30, 40, 60, 75d.; Air 1, 2, 3, 4, 5r.

Winter Olympic Games, Grenoble. Optd on Sharjah. Postage 1, 2, 3, 4, 5d.; Air 1, 2, 3r.

Previous Olympic Games. Optd on Sharjah. Air 25, 50, 75d., 1r.50, 3, 4r.

Olympic Games, Mexico. Optd on Sharjah. 10, 20, 30d., 2, 2r.40, 5r.

1969.

12th World Jamboree. Optd on 1968 issue of Sharjah. Postage 1, 2, 3, 4, 5, 10d.; Air 30, 50, 60d., 1r.50.

Martyrs of Liberty. Optd on 1968 issue of Sharjah. Air 35d. × 4, 60d. × 4, 1r. × 4

Sportsmen and Women. Optd on 1968 issue of Sharjah. Postage 20, 30, 40, 60d., 1r.50, 2r.50; Air 35, 50d., 1, 2, 3r.25, 4, 4r.

A number of issues on gold or silver foil also exist, but it is understood that these were mainly for presentation purposes, although valid for postage.

In common with the other states of the United Arab Emirates the Khor Fakkan stamp contract was terminated on 1 August 1972, and any further new issues released after that date were unauthorised.

KIAUTSCHOU (KIAOCHOW) Pt. 7

A port in Shantung, China, leased by Germany from China in 1898. It was occupied by Japan in 1914, but reverted to China in 1922.

1900. 100 pfennige = 1 mark.
1905. 100 cents = 1 dollar (Chinese).

1900. No. 9 of German Post Offices in China surch **5 Pfg.**
3 5pf. on 10pf. red . . . . 40·00 45·00

1901. "Yacht" key-types inscr "KIAUTSCHOU".
11 N 3pf. brown . . . . 2·00 2·40
12 5pf. green 80 60
13 10pf. red . . . . 2·75 1·40
14 20pf. blue . . . . 7·50 8·00
15 25pf. black & red on yellow 15·00 15·00
16 30pf. black & orge on buff 15·00 15·00
17 40pf. black and red . . . . 15·00 15·00
18 50pf. black & purple on buff 15·00 19·00
19 80pf. black and red on pink 29·00 40·00
20 O 1m. red . . . . 55·00 65·00
21 2m. blue . . . . 75·00 80·00
22 3m. black . . . . 80·00 £150
23 5m. red and black £200 £600

1905. Chinese currency. "Yacht" key-types inscr "KIAUTSCHOU".
34 N 1c. brown 50 80
35 2c. green . . . . 1·25 50
36 4c. red 80 60
37 10c. blue . . . . 1·10 2·40
38 20c. black and red . . . . . 1·90 12·00
39 40c. black and red on pink 3·75 42·00
40 O ½d. red . . . . 6·75 48·00
41 1d. blue . . . . 5·75 48·00
42 1½d. black . . . . 7·00 £120
43 2½d. red and black . . . . . 16·00 £350

KING EDWARD VII LAND Pt. 1

Stamp issued in connection with the Shackleton Antarctic Expedition in 1908. The expedition landed at Cape Royds in Victoria Land, instead of King Edward VII Land, the intended destination.

1908. Stamp of New Zealand optd **KING EDWARD VII LAND.**
A1 **42** 1d. red . . . . £400 35·00

KIONGA Pt. 9

Part of German E. Africa, occupied by the Portuguese during the 1914/18 war, and now incorporated in Mozambique.

1916. "King Carlos" key-type of Lourenco Marques optd **REPUBLICA** and surch **KIONGA** and new value.
1 S ¼c. on 100r. blue on blue . . . 9·75 7·75
2 1c. on 100r. blue on blue . . . 9·75 7·75
3 2½c. on 100r. blue on blue . . . 9·75 7·75
4 5c. on 100r. blue on blue . . . 9·75 7·75

KIRIBATI Pt. 1

This group of islands in the Pacific, formerly known as the Gilbert Islands, achieved independence on 12 July 1979 and was renamed Kiribati.

100 cents = 1 dollar.

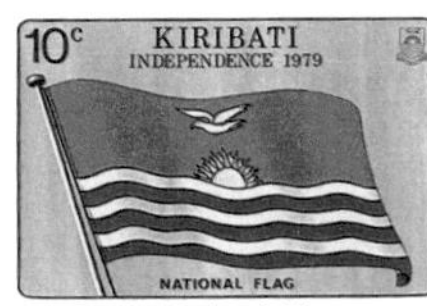

15 National Flag

1979. Independence. Multicoloured.
84 10c. Type **15** 10 35
85 45c. Houses of Parliament and Maneaba ni Maungatabu (House of Assembly) . . . 20 65

16 "Teraaka" (training ship)

1979. Multicoloured.
86 1c. Type **16** 10 90
122 3c. "Tautunu" (inter-island freighter) 15 30
123 5c. Hibiscus 10 15
124 7c. Catholic Cathedral, Tarawa 10 15
125 10c. Maneaba, Bikenibeu . . 10 15
91 12c. Betio Harbour 15 20
92 15c. Reef heron 35 25
93 20c. Flamboyant tree 20 25
129 25c. Moorish idol (fish) . . . 30 30
95 30c. Frangipani 25 30
96 35c. G.I.P.C. Chapel, Tangintebu 25 30
97 50c. "Hypolimnas bolina" (butterfly) 75 55
133 $1 "Tabakea" (Tarawa Lagoon ferry) 50 75
134 $2 Evening scene 50 75
135 $5 National flag . . . . . . 1·00 2·00

17 Gilbert and Ellice Islands 1911 ½d. Stamp

18 Boy with Giant Clam Shell

1979. Death Cent of Sir Rowland Hill. Mult.
100 10c. Type **17** 10 10
101 20c. Gilbert & Ellice Islands 1956 2s.6d. definitive . . . 15 20
102 25c. G.B. Edward VII 2s.6d. 15 20
103 45c. Gilbert and Ellice Islands 1924 10s. 25 35
MS104 113 × 110 mm. Nos. 100/3 70 1·00

1979. International Year of the Child. Mult.
105 10c. Type **18** 10 10
106 20c. Child climbing coconut palm (horiz) 10 10
107 45c. Girl reading 15 20
108 $1 Child in traditional costume 30 50

19 Downrange Station, Christmas Island

1980. Satellite Tracking. Multicoloured.
109 25c. Type **19** 10 10
110 45c. Map showing satellite trajectory 15 15
111 $1 Rocket launch, Tanegashima, Japan (vert) 30 35

20 T.S. "Teraaka"

1980. "London 1980" Int Stamp Exhibition. Mult.
112 12c. Type **20** 15 10
113 25c. Loading Air Tungaru Britten Norman Islander, Bonriki Airport 15 10
114 30c. Radio operator 15 10
115 $1 Bairiki Post Office 20 35
MS116 139 × 116 mm. Nos. 112/15 60 85

21 "Achaea janata"

1980. Moths. Multicoloured.
117 12c. Type **21** 10 10
118 25c. "Ethmia nigroapicella" 15 15
119 30c. "Utetheisa pulchelloides" 15 15
120 50c. "Anua coronata" . . . 25 25

22 Captain Cook Hotel

1980. Development. Multicoloured.
136 10c. Type **22** 10 10
137 20c. Sports stadium 10 10
138 25c. International Airport, Bonriki 15 10
139 35c. National Library and Archives, Bairiki 15 10
140 $1 Otintai Hotel, Bikenibeu 20 40

23 "Acalypha godseffiana"

1981. Flowers. Multicoloured.
141 12c. Type **23** 10 10
142 30c. "Hibiscus schizopetalus" 15 15
143 35c. "Calotropis gigantea" 15 15
144 50c. "Euphorbia pulcherrima" 20 20

25 Maps of Abaiang and Marakei, and String Figures

1981. Islands (1st series). Multicoloured.
145 12c. Type **25** 15 10
146 30c. Maps of Little Makin and Butaritari, and village house 20 10
147 35c. Map of Maiana and coral road 25 15
148 $1 Map of Christmas Island, and Captain Cook's H.M.S. "Resolution" . . . 70 75

See also Nos. 201/4, 215/18, 237/40, 256/60 and 270/3.

26 "Katherine"

27 Prince Charles and Lady Diana Spencer (½-size illustration)

1981. Royal Wedding. Royal Yachts. Multicoloured.
149 12c. Type **26** 10 15
150 12c. Type **27** 20 30
151 50c. "Osborne" 25 40
152 50c. Type **27** 50 75
153 $2 "Britannia" 35 80
154 $2 Type **27** . . . . 1·50 2·50
MS155 120 × 109 mm. $1.20 Type **27** 75 1·00

28 Tuna Bait Breeding Centre, Bonriki Fish Farm

1981. Tuna Fishing Industry. Multicoloured.
158 12c. Type **28** 15 10
159 30c. Tuna fishing 20 20
160 35c. Cold storage, Betio . . . 20 25
161 50c. Government Tuna Fishing Vessel "Nei Manganibuka" 30 50
MS162 134 × 99 mm. Nos. 158/61 1·00 1·40

29 Pomarine Skua

1982. Birds. Multicoloured.
163 1c. Type **29** 15 15
164 2c. Mallard 15 15
165 4c. Collared petrel 20 20
166 5c. Blue-faced booby . . . 20 20
167 7c. Friendly quail dove . . 20 20
168 8c. Common shoveler ("Shoveler") 20 20
169 12c. Polynesian reed warbler 20 20
170 15c. Pacific golden plover ("Pacific Plover") 25 25
171 20c. Reef heron 30 30
171a 25c. Common noddy ("Brown Noddy") . . . . 2·25 1·50
172 30c. Brown booby 30 30
173 35c. Audubon's shearwater 60 35
174 40c. White-throated storm petrel (vert) 35 40
175 50c. Bristle-thighed curlew (vert) 40 45
175a 55c. White tern ("Fairy Tern") (vert) . . . . . . 11·00 16·00
176 $1 Kuhl's lory ("Scarlet-breasted Lorikeet") (vert) 1·25 40
177 $2 Long-tailed koel ("Long-tailed Cuckoo") (vert) . . 1·25 55
178 $5 Great frigate bird (vert) 1·75 1·25

30 Riley Turbo Skyliner

1982. Air. Inaug of Tungaru Airline. Mult.
179 12c. Type **30** 15 10
180 30c. Britten Norman "short nose" Trislander 20 20
181 35c. Casa-212 Aviocar 20 25
182 50c. Boeing 727-200 . . . . 30 35

No. 179 is inscr "De Havilland DH114 Heron" in error.

31 Mary of Teck, Princess of Wales, 1893

1982. 21st Birthday of Princess of Wales. Mult.
183 12c. Type **31** 10 10
184 50c. Coat of arms of Mary of Teck 20 35
185 $1 Diana, Princess of Wales 30 70

1982. Birth of Prince William of Wales. Nos. 183/5 optd **ROYAL BABY.**
186 12c. Type **31** 10 15
187 50c. Coat of arms of Mary of Teck 25 50
188 $1 Diana, Princess of Wales 40 70

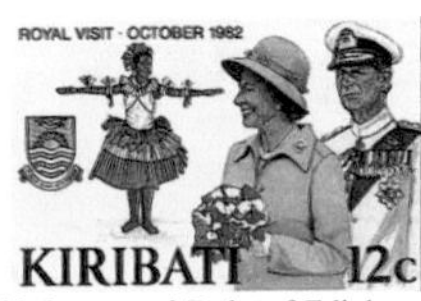

32 First Aid Practice

1982. 75th Anniv of Boy Scout Movement. Mult.
189 12c. Type **32** 20 15
190 25c. Boat repairs 20 30
191 30c. On parade 25 35
192 40c. Gilbert Islands 1977 8c. Scouting stamp and "75" 25 60

33 Queen and Duke of Edinburgh with Local Dancer

1982. Royal Visit. Multicoloured.
193 12c. Type **33** 15 15
194 25c. Queen, Duke of Edinburgh and outrigger canoe 20 20
195 35c. New Philatelic Bureau building 30 30
MS196 88 × 76 mm. 50c. Queen Elizabeth II 60 60

On No. **MS**196 the captions on the map for the islands of Teraina and Tabuaeran have been transposed.

34 "Obaia, The Feathered" (Kiribati legend)

1983. Commonwealth Day. Multicoloured.
197 12c. Type **34** 10 10
198 30c. Robert Louis Stevenson Hotel, Abemama 15 10
199 50c. Container ship off Betio 15 25
200 $1 Map of Kiribati 20 50

1983. Island Maps (2nd series). As T **25**. Mult.
201 12c. Beru, Nikunau and canoe 20 15
202 25c. Abemama, Aranuka, Kuria and fish 20 20
203 35c. Nonouti and reef fishing (vert) 25 35
204 50c. Tarawa and House of Assembly (vert) 30 50

35 Collecting Coconuts

1983. Copra Industry. Multicoloured.
205 12c. Type **35** 20 15
206 25c. Selecting coconuts for copra 35 25
207 30c. Removing husks 35 30
208 35c. Drying copra 35 35
209 50c. Loading copra at Betio 40 45

36 War Memorials

1983. 40th Anniv of Battle of Tarawa. Multicoloured.
210 12c. Type **36** 15 15
211 30c. Maps of Tarawa and Pacific Ocean 20 30
212 35c. Gun emplacement 20 35
213 50c. Modern and war-time landscapes 25 55
214 $1 Aircraft carrier U.S.S. "Tarawa" 40 75

1983. Island Maps (3rd series). As T **25**. Mult.
215 12c. Teraina and Captain Fanning's ship "Betsey", 1798 25 15
216 30c. Nikumaroro and hawksbill turtle 30 35
217 35c. Kanton and local postmark 35 40
218 50c. Banaba and flying fish 40 55

37 Tug "Riki"

1984. Kiribati Shipping Corporation. Mult.
219 12c. Type **37** 50 15
220 35c. Ferry "Nei Nimanoa" 90 35
221 50c. Ferry "Nei Tebaa" 1·25 60
222 $1 Cargo ship "Nei Momi" 1·50 1·10
MS223 115 × 98 mm. Nos. 219/22 3·25 5·50

38 Water and Sewage Schemes

1984. "Ausipex" International Stamp Exhibition, Melbourne. Multicoloured.
224 12c. Type **38** 15 15
225 30c. "Nouamake" (game fishing boat) 20 30
226 35c. Overseas training schemes 20 40
227 50c. International communications link 25 55

39 "Tabakea supporting Banaba"

1984. Kiribati Legends (1st series). Multicoloured.
228 12c. Type **39** 15 20
229 30c. "Nakaa, Judge of the Dead" 15 35
230 35c. "Naareau and Dragonfly" 15 45
231 50c. "Whistling Ghosts" 20 55
See also Nos. 245/8.

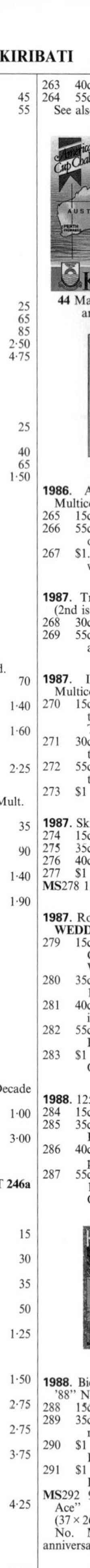

40 Sail-finned Tang

1985. Reef Fishes. Multicoloured.
232 12c. Type **40** 60 25
233 25c. Picasso triggerfish 1·00 65
234 35c. Clown surgeonfish 1·25 85
235 80c. Red squirrelfish 2·00 2·50
MS236 140 × 107 mm. Nos. 232/5 6·00 4·75

1985. Island Maps (4th series). As T **25**. Mult.
237 12c. Tabuaeran and great frigate bird ("Frigate Bird") 1·75 25
238 35c. Rawaki and germinating coconuts 2·25 40
239 50c. Arorae and xanthid crab 2·50 65
240 $1 Tamana and fish hook 3·00 1·50

41 Youths playing Football on Beach

1985. International Youth Year. Multicoloured.
241 15c. Type **41** 70 70
242 35c. Logos of I.Y.Y. and Kiribati Youth Year 1·10 1·40
243 40c. Girl preparing food (vert) 1·25 1·60
244 55c. Map illustrating Kiribati's youth exchange links 1·40 2·25

1985. Kiribati Legends (2nd series). As T **39**. Mult.
245 15c. "Nang Kineia and the Tickling Ghosts" 50 35
246 35c. "Auriaria and Tituabine" 85 90
247 40c. "The first coming of Babai at Arorae" 1·00 1·40
248 55c. "Riiki and the Milky Way" 1·25 1·90

42 Map showing Telecommunications Satellite Link

1985. Transport and Telecommunications Decade (1st issue). Multicoloured.
249 15c. Type **42** 1·50 1·00
250 40c. M. V. "Moanaraoi" (Tarawa–Suva service) 2·75 3·00
See also Nos. 268/9, 293/4 and 314/15.

1986. 60th Birthday of Queen Elizabeth II. As T **246a** of Papua New Guinea. Multicoloured.
251 15c. Princess Elizabeth in Girl Guide uniform, Windsor Castle, 1938 15 15
252 35c. At Trooping the Colour, 1980 20 30
253 40c. With Duke of Edinburgh in Kiribati, 1982 20 35
254 55c. At banquet, Austrian Embassy, London, 1966 25 50
255 $1 At Crown Agents Head Office, London, 1983 45 1·25

1986. Island Maps (5th series). As T **25**. Mult.
256 15c. Manra and coconut crab 2·75 1·50
257 30c. Birnie and McKean Islands and cowrie shells 3·50 2·75
258 35c. Orona and red-footed booby 4·25 2·75
259 40c. Malden Island and whaling ship, 1844 4·25 3·75
260 55c. Vostok, Flint and Caroline Islands and Bellingshausen's "Vostok", 1820 4·25 4·25

43 "Lepidodactylus lugubris"

1986. Geckos. Multicoloured.
261 15c. Type **43** 1·50 70
262 35c. "Gehyra mutilata" 1·75 1·50
263 40c. "Hemidactylus frenatus" 1·90 1·75
264 55c. "Gehyra oceanica" 2·25 2·50
See also Nos. 274/7.

44 Maps of Australia and Kiribati

46 Henri Dunant (founder)

45 Freighter "Moamoa"

1986. America's Cup Yachting Championship. Multicoloured.
265 15c. Type **44** 20 65
266 55c. America's Cup and map of course 50 1·25
267 $1.50 "Australia II" (1983 winner) 1·00 1·50

1987. Transport and Telecommunications Decade (2nd issue). Multicoloured.
268 30c. Type **45** 2·75 2·50
269 55c. Telephone switchboard and automatic exchange 3·75 3·50

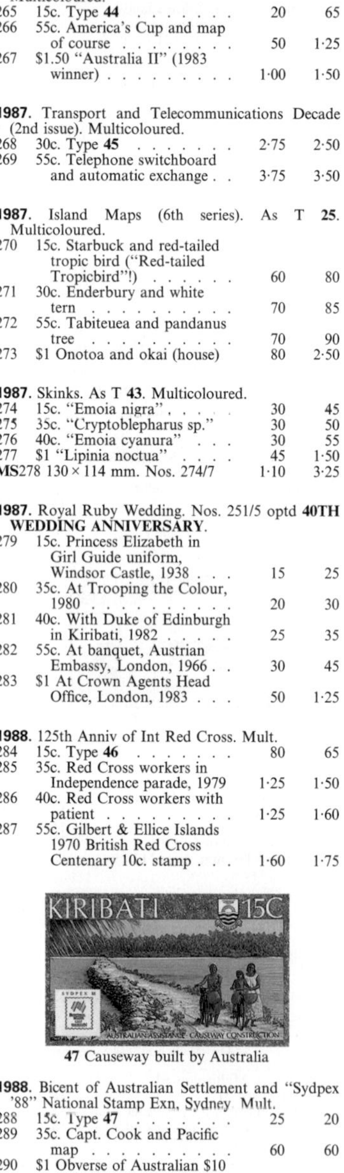

1987. Island Maps (6th series). As T **25**. Multicoloured.
270 15c. Starbuck and red-tailed tropic bird ("Red-tailed Tropicbird"!) 60 80
271 30c. Enderbury and white tern 70 85
272 55c. Tabiteuea and pandanus tree 70 90
273 $1 Onotoa and okai (house) 80 2·50

1987. Skinks. As T **43**. Multicoloured.
274 15c. "Emoia nigra" 30 45
275 35c. "Cryptoblepharus sp." 30 50
276 40c. "Emoia cyanura" 30 55
277 $1 "Lipinia noctua" 45 1·50
MS278 130 × 114 mm. Nos. 274/7 1·10 3·25

1987. Royal Ruby Wedding. Nos. 251/5 optd **40TH WEDDING ANNIVERSARY**.
279 15c. Princess Elizabeth in Girl Guide uniform, Windsor Castle, 1938 15 25
280 35c. At Trooping the Colour, 1980 20 30
281 40c. With Duke of Edinburgh in Kiribati, 1982 25 35
282 55c. At banquet, Austrian Embassy, London, 1966 30 45
283 $1 At Crown Agents Head Office, London, 1983 50 1·25

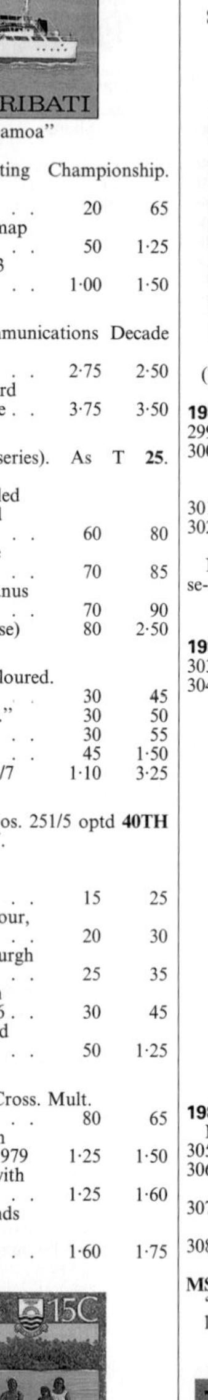

1988. 125th Anniv of Int Red Cross. Mult.
284 15c. Type **46** 80 65
285 35c. Red Cross workers in Independence parade, 1979 1·25 1·50
286 40c. Red Cross workers with patient 1·25 1·60
287 55c. Gilbert & Ellice Islands 1970 British Red Cross Centenary 10c. stamp 1·60 1·75

47 Causeway built by Australia

1988. Bicent of Australian Settlement and "Sydpex '88" National Stamp Exn, Sydney. Mult.
288 15c. Type **47** 25 20
289 35c. Capt. Cook and Pacific map 60 60
290 $1 Obverse of Australian $10 Bicentenary banknote 1·25 1·75
291 $1 Reverse of $10 Bicentenary banknote 1·25 1·75
MS292 95 × 76 mm. $2 "Logistic Ace" (container ship) (37 × 26 mm) 4·25 4·75
No. **MS**292 also commemorates the 150th anniversary of the first screw-driven steamship.

48 Manual Telephone Exchange and Map of Kiritimati

1988. Transport and Telecommunications Decade (3rd issue). Multicoloured.
293 35c. Type **48** 75 75
294 45c. Betio-Bairiki Causeway 1·00 1·00

49 "Hound" (brigantine), 1835

1989. Nautical History (1st series). Multicoloured.
295 15c. Type **49** 90 55
296 30c. "Phantom" (brig), 1854 1·50 1·10
297 40c. H.M.S. "Alacrity" (schooner), 1873 1·60 1·60
298 $1 "Charles W. Morgan" (whaling ship), 1851 3·00 3·75
See also Nos. 343/7 and 523/6.

50 Reef Heron ("Eastern Reef Heron")

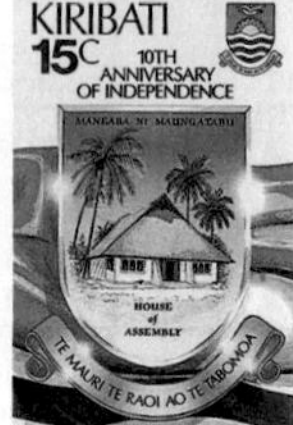

51 House of Assembly

1989. Birds with Young. Multicoloured.
299 15c. Type **50** 1·25 1·50
300 15c. Reef heron ("Eastern Reef Heron") chicks in nest 1·25 1·50
301 $1 White-tailed tropic bird 2·50 3·25
302 $1 Young white-tailed tropic bird 2·50 3·25
Nos. 299/300 and 301/2 were each printed together, se-tenant, each pair forming a composite design.

1989. 10th Anniv of Independence. Mult.
303 15c. Type **51** 25 25
304 $1 Constitution 1·25 1·75

51a "Apollo 10" on Launch Gantry

1989. 20th Anniv of First Manned Landing on Moon. Multicoloured.
305 20c. Type **51a** 30 30
306 50c. Crew of "Apollo 10" (30 × 30 mm) 70 90
307 60c. "Apollo 10" emblem (30 × 30 mm) 80 1·00
308 75c. "Apollo 10" splashdown, Hawaii 95 1·25
MS309 82 × 100 mm. $2.50 "Apollo 11" command module in lunar orbit 6·50 7·50

51b Gilbert and Ellice Islands, 1949 75th Anniv of U.P.U. 3d. Stamp

51c Examining Fragment of Statue

1989. "Philexfrance 89" International Stamp Exhibition, Paris, and "World Stamp Expo '89", Washington (1st issue). Sheet 104 × 86 mm.
MS310 **51b** $2 multicoloured 3·50 5·00

1989. "Philexfrance 89" International Stamp Exhibition, Paris, and "World Stamp Expo '89", Washington (2nd issue). Designs showing Statue of Liberty. Multicoloured.
311 35c. Type **51c** 1·10 1·40
312 35c. Workman drilling Statue 1·10 1·40
313 35c. Surveyor with drawing 1·10 1·40

52 Telecommunications Centre

1989. Transport and Telecommunications Decade (4th issue). Multicoloured.
314 30c. Type **52** . . . . 1·50 1·25
315 75c. "Mataburo" (inter-island freighter) . . . . 3·50 4·00

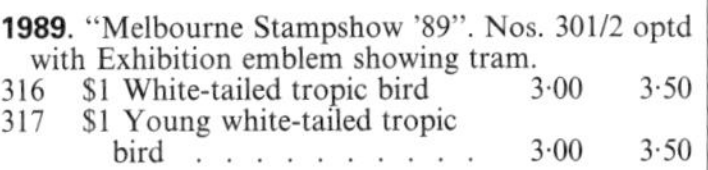

1989. "Melbourne Stampshow '89". Nos. 301/2 optd with Exhibition emblem showing tram.
316 $1 White-tailed tropic bird 3·00 3·50
317 $1 Young white-tailed tropic bird . . . . 3·00 3·50

54 Virgin and Child (detail, "The Adoration of the Holy Child" (Denys Calvert))

1989. Christmas. Paintings. Multicoloured.
318 10c. Type **54** . . . . 1·00 55
319 15c. "The Adoration of the Holy Child" (Denys Calvert) . . . . 1·25 70
320 55c. "The Holy Family and St. Elizabeth" (Rubens) . . 3·00 1·25
321 $1 "Madonna with Child and Maria Magdalena" (School of Correggio) . . . . . . 4·50 7·00

55 Gilbert and Ellice Islands 1912 1d. and G.B. Twopence Blue Stamps

1990. 150th Anniv of the Penny Black and "Stamp World London 90" International Stamp Exhibition. Multicoloured.
322 15c. Type **55** . . . . 1·00 1·00
323 50c. Gilbert and Ellice Islands 1911 ½d. and G.B. Penny Black . . . . 2·50 2·75
324 60c. Kiribati 1982 1c. bird and G.B. 1870 ½d. . . . . 2·50 2·75
325 $1 Gilbert Islands 1976 1c. ship and G.B. 1841 1d. brown . . . . 2·75 3·50

56 Blue-barred Orange Parrotfish

1990. Fishes. Multicoloured.
326 1c. Type **56** 30 75
327 5c. Honeycomb grouper 45 75
328 10c. Blue-finned trevally . . . 55 85
329 15c. Hump-backed snapper 70 50
330 20c. Variegated emperor . . 75 70
356 23c. Bennett's pufferfish . . . 1·25 1·50
331 25c. Rainbow runner 80 65
332 30c. Black-saddled coral grouper 90 65
333 35c. Great barracuda . . . . 1·00 75
334 40c. Convict tang . . . . . 1·00 80
335 50c. Violet squirrelfish . . . 1·25 90
336 60c. Stocky hawkfish . . . . 1·75 1·40
337 75c. Pennant coralfish . . . 1·90 1·60
338 $1 Common blue-striped snapper ("Yellow and blue sea perch") . . . . 2·25 1·90
339 $2 Sailfish . . . . 3·25 4·75
340 $5 White-tipped reef shark 6·50 9·50

1990. 90th Birthday of Queen Elizabeth the Queen Mother. As T **107** (75c.) or **108** ($2) of Kenya.
341 75c. multicoloured . . . . . 1·25 1·50
342 $2 black and green . . . . . 2·75 3·50
DESIGNS—21 × 36 mm: 75c. Queen Elizabeth the Queen Mother. 29 × 37 mm: $2 King George VI and Queen Elizabeth with air raid victim, London, 1940.

1990. Nautical History (2nd series). As T **49**. Multicoloured.
343 15c. "Herald" (whaling ship), 1851 . . . . 75 55
344 50c. "Belle" (barque), 1849 1·50 1·50
345 60c. "Supply" (schooner), 1851 . . . . 1·75 2·25
346 75c. "Triton" (whaling ship), 1848 . . . . 1·75 2·25
MS347 95 × 75 mm. $2 "Charlotte" (convict transport), 1789 . . . 7·50 8·50

57 Manta

1991. Endangered Species. Fishes. Multicoloured.
348 15c. Type **57** . . . . 1·10 55
349 20c. Manta (different) . . . . 1·25 90
350 30c. Whale shark . . . . . . 1·75 2·00
351 35c. Whale shark (different) 2·00 2·25

58 Queen Elizabeth II

1991. 65th Birthday of Queen Elizabeth II and 70th Birthday of Prince Philip. Multicoloured.
366 65c. Type **58** . . . . 1·25 1·50
367 70c. Prince Philip in R.A.F. uniform . . . . 1·25 1·50

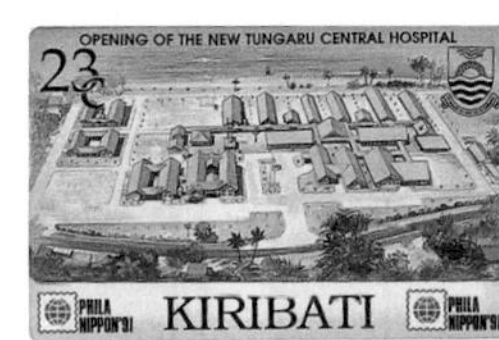

59 Aerial View of Hospital

1991. "Phila Nippon '91" International Stamp Exhibition, Tokyo, and Opening of Tungaru Central Hospital. Multicoloured.
368 23c. Type **59** 40 30
369 50c. Traditional dancers . . . 75 85
370 60c. Hospital entrance . . . 85 1·10
371 75c. Foundation stone and plaques . . . . 1·25 1·60
MS372 125 × 83 mm. $5 Casualty on trolley and ambulance . . . . 7·00 8·00

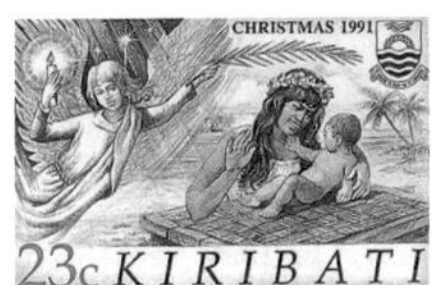

60 Mother and Child

1991. Christmas. Multicoloured.
373 23c. Type **60** 60 40
374 50c. The Holy Family in Pacific setting . . . . . . 1·10 90
375 60c. The Holy Family in traditional setting . . . . 1·25 1·50
376 75c. Adoration of the Shepherds . . . . 1·50 2·00

1992. 40th Anniv of Queen Elizabeth II's Accession. As T **214** of Lesotho. Multicoloured.
377 23c. Kiribati village 30 30
378 30c. Lagoon at sunset 40 45
379 50c. Tarawa waterfront . . . 60 70
380 60c. Three portraits of Queen Elizabeth 70 90
381 75c. Queen Elizabeth II . . . 90 1·10

1992. "EXPO '92" World's Fair, Seville. Nos. 356, 336/7 and 339 optd **EXPO'92 SEVILLA**.
382 23c. Bennett's pufferfish . . . 55 40
383 60c. Stocky hawkfish . . . . 1·25 1·50
384 75c. Pennant coralfish . . . 1·40 1·60
385 $2 Sailfish . . . . 3·00 4·00

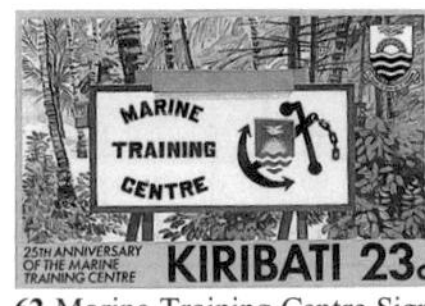

62 Marine Training Centre Sign

1992. 25th Anniv of Marine Training Centre. Multicoloured.
386 23c. Type **62** 45 40
387 50c. Cadets on parade . . . 80 1·00
388 60c. Fire school . . . . . . 80 1·00
389 75c. Lifeboat training . . . . 1·10 1·40

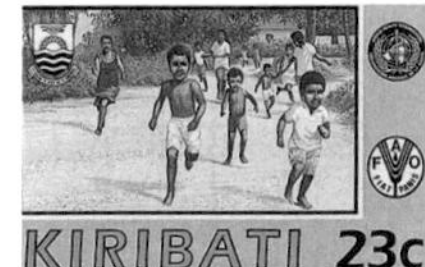

63 Healthy Children

1992. United Nations World Health and Food and Agriculture Organizations. Multicoloured.
390 23c. Type **63** 55 50
391 50c. Fishing at night . . . . 1·00 1·00
392 60c. Fruit . . . . 1·25 1·50
393 75c. "Papuan Chief" (container ship) . . . . . 2·50 2·50

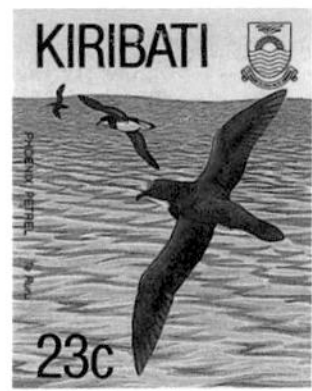

64 Phoenix Petrel **65** "Chilocorus nigritus"

1993. Birds. Multicoloured.
394 23c. Type **64** 40 70
395 23c. Cook's petrel 40 70
396 60c. Pintail ("Northern Pintail") . . . . 90 1·25
397 60c. European wigeon ("Eurasian Wigeon") . . . 90 1·25
398 75c. Spectacled tern . . . . 1·00 1·25
399 75c. Black-naped tern . . . . 1·00 1·25
400 $1 Australian stilt ("Stilt Wader") . . . . 1·25 1·40
401 $1 Wandering tattler . . . . 1·25 1·40

1993. Insects. Multicoloured.
402 23c. Type **65** . . . . 1·25 55
403 60c. "Rodolia pumila" (ladybird) . . . . 2·25 2·25
404 75c. "Rodolia cardinalis" (ladybird) . . . . 2·50 2·75
405 $1 "Cryptolaemus montrouzieri" . . . . . . 2·75 3·25

66 U.S. Air Reconnaissance Consolidated B-24 Liberator

1993. 50th Anniv of Battle of Tarawa. Multicoloured.
406 23c. Type **66** 75 75
407 23c. U.S.S. "Nautilus" (submarine) 75 75
408 23c. U.S.S. "Indianapolis" (cruiser) 75 75
409 23c. U.S.S. "Pursuit" (destroyer) 75 75
410 23c. Vought Sikorsky Kingfisher spotter seaplane 75 75
411 23c. U.S.S. "Ringgold" and "Dashiell" (destroyers) . . 75 75
412 23c. Sherman tank on seabed 75 75
413 23c. Grumman Hellcat fighter aircraft in lagoon 75 75
414 23c. Naval wreck on seabed 75 75
415 23c. First U.S. aircraft to land on Betio 75 75
416 75c. Landing craft leaving transports . . . . 1·25 1·25
417 75c. Marines landing on Betio . . . . 1·25 1·25
418 75c. Landing craft approaching beach . . . . 1·25 1·25
419 75c. Marines pinned down in surf . . . . 1·25 1·25
420 75c. U.S.S. "Maryland" (battleship) . . . . 1·25 1·25
421 75c. Aerial view of Betio Island . . . . 1·25 1·25
422 75c. U.S. Navy memorial . . 1·25 1·25
423 75c. Memorial to expatriates 1·25 1·25
424 75c. Japanese memorial . . . 1·25 1·25
425 75c. Plan of Betio Island . . 1·25 1·25

67 Shepherds and Angels

1993. Christmas. Pacific Nativity Scenes. Mult.
426 23c. Type **67** 40 30
427 40c. Three Kings 65 70
428 60c. Holy Family . . . . . . 85 1·25
429 75c. Virgin and Child . . . . 1·10 1·50
MS430 100 × 81 mm. $3 Virgin and Child (different) . . . . 3·75 5·50

68 Group of Dogs

1994. "Hong Kong '94" International Stamp Exhibition. Chinese New Year ("Year of the Dog"). Sheet 120 × 90 mm.
MS431 **68** $3 multicoloured . . . 4·00 5·50

69 Bryde's Whale and Calf

1994. Whales. Multicoloured.
432 23c. Type **69** . . . . 1·00 1·25
433 23c. Bryde's whale with two calves . . . . 1·00 1·25
434 40c. Blue whale and calf (face value at left) . . . . . . 1·25 1·40
435 40c. Blue whales and calf (face value at right) . . . . 1·25 1·40
436 60c. Humpback whale and calf (face value at left) . . 1·90 2·25
437 60c. Humpback whale and calf (face value at right) . . 1·90 2·25
438 75c. Killer whale and calf . . 1·90 2·25
439 75c. Killer whale and two calves . . . . 1·90 2·25

70 Family silhouetted on Beach

1994. 15th Anniv of Independence. Protecting the Environment. Multicoloured.
440 40c. Type **70** 60 60
441 60c. Fish and coral . . . . . 1·00 1·25
442 75c. Great frigate birds in flight . . . . 1·25 1·50

71 "Diaphania indica" **72** "Nerium oleander"

1994. Butterflies and Moths. Multicoloured.
443 1c. Type **71** 10 15
444 5c. "Herpetogramma licarsisalis" 15 20
445 10c. "Parotis suralis" 25 20
446 12c. "Sufetula sunidesalis" . . 25 20
447 20c. "Aedia sericea" 35 25
448 23c. "Anomis vitiensis" . . . 35 25
449 30c. "Anticarsia irrorata" . . 45 30
450 35c. "Spodoptera litura" . . 55 40
451 40c. "Mocis frugalis" 65 50
452 45c. "Agrius convolvuli" . . 70 50
453 50c. "Cephonodes picus" . . 75 55
454 55c. "Gnathothlibus erotus" 80 60
455 60c. "Macroglossum hirundo" 80 60
456 75c. "Badamia exclamationis" 1·00 75
457 $1 "Precis villida" . . . . . 1·40 1·40
458 $2 "Danaus plexippus" . . . 2·25 2·50
459 $3 "Hypolimnas bolina" (male) . . . . 2·75 3·25
460 $5 "Hypolimnas bolina" (female) . . . . 3·75 4·50
See also No. **MS**527.

1994. Seasonal Flowers. Multicoloured.
461 23c. Type **72** 30 30
462 60c. "Catharanthus roseus" 80 1·25
463 75c. "Ipomea pes-caprae" . . 1·00 1·40
464 $1 "Calophyllum inophyllum" . . . . 1·40 2·00

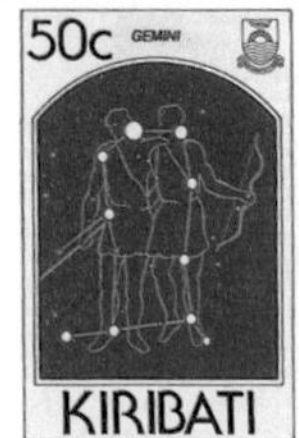

73 Gemini (The Twins)

74 Church and Traditional Meeting Hut

1995. Night Sky over Kiribati. Multicoloured.
465 50c. Type **73** 75 75
466 60c. Cancer (The Crab) . . . 85 1·00
467 75c. Cassiopeia (The Queen of Ethiopia) . . . . 1·00 1·40
468 $1 Southern Cross . . . . . 1·25 1·75

1995. Tourism. Multicoloured.
469 30c. Type **74** 85 95
470 30c. Fishermen and outrigger canoes 85 95
471 30c. Gun emplacement and map 85 95
472 30c. Children with marine creatures 85 95
473 30c. Sports 85 95
474 40c. Local girls in traditional costume 85 95
475 40c. Windsurfing 85 95
476 40c. Fishermen and wood carver 85 95
477 40c. Underwater sport . . . 85 95
478 40c. Women weaving 85 95

75 Grumman TBF Avenger

1995. 50th Anniv of End of Second World War. American Aircraft. Multicoloured.
489 23c. Type **75** 60 45
490 40c. Curtiss SOC.3-1 Seagull seaplane 80 70
491 50c. Consolidated B-24 Liberator bomber 90 90
492 60c. Grumman G-21 Goose amphibian . . . . 1·10 1·10
493 75c. Martin B-26 Marauder bomber . . . . 1·40 1·50
494 $1 Northrop P-61 Black Widow bomber . . . . . 1·60 1·75
MS495 75 × 85 mm. $2 Reverse of 1939–45 War Medal (vert) . . 2·50 3·00

76 Eclectus Parrots, Great Frigate Bird and Coconut Crabs

1995. Protecting the Environment. Multicoloured.
496 60c. Type **76** . . . . 85 1·10
497 60c. Red-tailed tropic birds, common dolphin and pantropical spotted dolphin 85 1·10
498 60c. Blue-striped snapper ("Yellow and blue sea perch"), blue-barred orange parrotfish and green turtle 85 1·10
499 60c. Red-breasted wrasse, pennant coralfish and violet squirrelfish . . . . 85 1·10

1995. "Jakarta '95" Stamp Exhibition, Indonesia. Nos. 496/9 optd **JAKARTA 95** within emblem.
500 60c. Type **76** . . . . 1·75 2·00
501 60c. Red-tailed tropic birds, common dolphin and pantropical spotted dolphin 1·75 2·00
502 60c. Blue-striped snapper, blue-barred orange parrotfish and green turtle 1·75 2·00
503 60c. Red-breasted wrasse, pennant coralfish and violet squirrelfish . . . . 1·75 2·00

78 Sow feeding Piglets

1995. "Singapore '95" International Stamp Exhibition and Beijing International Coin and Stamp Expo '95. Two sheets, each 113 × 85 mm, containing T **78**.
MS504 $2 multicoloured ("Singapore '95") . . . . . . 2·50 3·25
MS505 $2 multicoloured ("Beijing '95") . . . . 3·00 3·75

Nos. **MS**504/5 show the exhibition logos on the sheet margins.

79 "Teanoai" (police patrol boat)

1995. Police Maritime Unit. Multicoloured.
506 75c. Type **79** . . . . 1·40 1·75
507 75c. "Teanoai" at sea . . . . 1·40 1·75

80 Pantropical Spotted Dolphins

1996. Dolphins. Multicoloured.
508 23c. Type **80** . . . . 1·00 55
509 60c. Spinner dolphins . . . . 1·75 1·25
510 75c. Fraser's dolphins . . . . 1·90 1·75
511 $1 Rough-toothed dolphins 2·00 2·25

81 Tap and Top Left Segment of U.N.I.C.E.F. Emblem

1996. 50th Anniv of U.N.I.C.E.F. Multicoloured.
512 30c. Type **81** 50 70
513 30c. Documents and top right segment 50 70
514 30c. Syringe and bottom left segment 50 70
515 30c. Open book and bottom right segment 50 70

Nos. 512/15 were printed together, se-tenant, with each block of 4 showing the complete emblem.

82 Chinese Dragon

1996. "CHINA '96" 9th Asian International Stamp Exhibition, Peking. Sheet 110 × 86 mm.
MS516 **82** 50c. multicoloured . . 1·00 1·50

83 L.M.S. No. 5609 "Gilbert and Ellice Islands" Locomotive

1996. "CAPEX '96" International Stamp Exhibition, Toronto. Sheet 111 × 80 mm.
MS517 **83** $2 multicoloured . . . 2·40 3·00

84 Rathbun Red Crab

1996. Sea Crabs. Multicoloured.
518 23c. Type **84** 50 40
519 60c. Red and white painted crab 90 80
520 75c. Red-spotted crab . . . 1·10 1·10
521 $1 Red-spotted white crab . . 1·60 2·50

85 Kiribati Canoe

1996. "Taipei '96" International Stamp Exhibition, Taiwan. Sheet 110 × 86 mm.
MS522 **85** $1.50 multicoloured 3·00 3·50

1996. Nautical History (3rd series). As T **49**. Multicoloured.
523 23c. "Potomac" (whaling ship), 1843 . . . . 60 40
524 50c. "Southern Cross IV" (missionary ship), 1891 . . 90 90
525 60c. "John Williams III" (missionary sailing ship), 1890 . . . . 1·10 1·10
526 $1 H.M.S. "Dolphin" (frigate), 1765 . . . . . . 1·60 2·00

1997. "HONG KONG '97" International Stamp Exhibition. Sheet 130 × 90 mm, containing No. 457. Multicoloured.
MS527 $1 "Precis villida" . . . 1·10 1·60

1997. "Pacific '97" International Stamp Exhibition, San Francisco. Nos. 489/94 optd **PACIFIC 97 World Philatelic Exhibition San Francisco, California 29 May - 8 June**.
528 23c. Type **75** 40 35
529 40c. Curtiss SOC.3-1 Seagull seaplane 60 55
530 50c. Consolidated B-24 Liberator bomber 70 70
531 60c. Grumman G-21 Goose amphibian 80 90
532 75c. Martin B-26 Marauder bomber . . . . 90 1·10
533 $1 Northrop P-61 Black Widow bomber . . . . . 1·10 1·40
MS534 75 × 85 mm. $2 Reverse of 1939–45 War Medal (vert) . . 2·10 2·75

87 Queen Elizabeth II in 1996

88 Young Rock Dove

1997. Golden Wedding of Queen Elizabeth and Prince Philip. Multicoloured.
535 50c. Type **87** . . . . 1·25 1·50
536 50c. Prince Philip carriage-driving at Windsor Horse Show . . . . 1·25 1·50
537 60c. Queen in phaeton at Trooping the Colour . . . 1·25 1·50
538 60c. Prince Philip on Montserrat, 1993 . . . . . 1·25 1·50
539 75c. Queen Elizabeth and Prince Philip, 1989 . . . . 1·25 1·50
540 75c. Prince Edward on horseback . . . . 1·25 1·50
MS541 110 × 70 mm. $2 Queen Elizabeth and Prince Philip in Landau (horiz) . . . . . . 4·00 4·50

Nos. 535/6, 537/8 and 539/40 respectively were printed together, se-tenant, with the backgrounds forming composite designs.

1997. Birds. Multicoloured.
542 50c. Type **88** . . . . 1·00 1·25
543 50c. Adult rock dove . . . . 1·00 1·25
544 60c. Adult Pacific pigeon . . 1·00 1·25
545 60c. Young Pacific pigeon . . 1·00 1·25
546 75c. Adult Micronesian pigeon . . . . 1·00 1·25
547 75c. Young Micronesian pigeon . . . . 1·00 1·25

1997. "ASIA '97" Stamp Exhibition, Bangkok. Nos. 542/3 and 546/7 optd **ASIA '97 KIRIBATI 5 - 14 OCTOBER** and elephant.
548 50c. Type **88** . . . . 85 1·25
549 50c. Adult rock dove . . . . 85 1·25
550 75c. Adult Micronesian pigeon . . . . 1·00 1·40
551 75c. Young Micronesian pigeon . . . . 1·00 1·40

90 Spiny Lobster

1998. Endangered Species. Spiny Lobster. Multicoloured.
552 25c. Type **90** 40 60
553 25c. Facing right 40 60
554 25c. With coral in foreground 40 60
555 25c. On sponge 40 60
MS556 69 × 49 mm. $1.50 Spiny Lobster . . . . 1·90 2·50

No. **MS**556 does not show the W.W.F. panda emblem.

91 Diana, Princess of Wales, 1992

1998. Diana, Princess of Wales Commemoration.
557 **91** 25c. multicoloured 50 60
MS558 145 × 70 mm. 25c. Type **91**; 50c. Wearing black evening dress, 1981; 60c. With scarf over head, 1992; 75c. Wearing brown jacket, 1993 (sold at $2.10 + 50c. charity premium) . . . . 2·50 3·00

92 Children and Smiling Sun

1998. "Towards the Millennium" (1st issue). Sheet 102 × 69 mm.
MS559 **92** $1 multicoloured . . . 1·25 2·00

See also Nos. 580/4 and 594/8.

93 Indo-Pacific Humpbacked Dolphin

1998. Whales and Dolphins. Multicoloured.
560 25c. Type **93** 55 65
561 25c. Bottlenose dolphin . . . 55 65
562 60c. Short-snouted spinner dolphin . . . . 80 1·00
563 60c. Risso's dolphin . . . . 80 1·00
564 75c. Striped dolphin . . . . 1·00 1·10
565 75c. Sei whale . . . . 1·00 1·10
566 $1 Fin whale . . . . 1·25 1·40
567 $1 Minke whale . . . . . . 1·25 1·40

94 Reuben K. Uatioa Stadium, Kiribati

1998. "Italia '98" International Stamp Exhibition, Milan. Sheet 110 × 85 mm.
MS568 **94** $2 multicoloured . . . 2·00 2·75

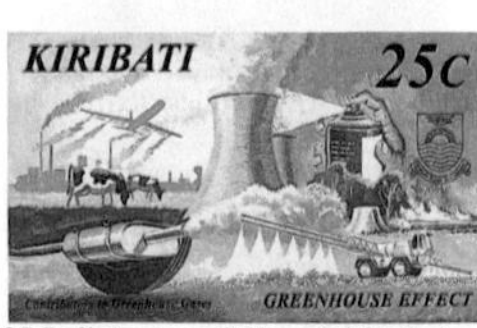

95 Pollutants and Harmful Emissions

1998. The Greenhouse Effect. Multicoloured.
569 25c. Type **95** 30 30
570 50c. Diagram of greenhouse effect 50 50
571 60c. Diagram of rising sea levels on Tarawa 60 65
572 75c. Diagram of rising sea levels on Kiritimati 70 85
MS573 103 × 69 mm. $1.50 Outrigger canoe . . . . 3·25 3·25

96 H.M.S. "Resolution" (Cook) at Christmas Island, 1777

1999. "Australia '99" World Stamp Exhibition, Melbourne. Sheet 136 × 56 mm.
MS574 **96** $2 multicoloured . . . 2·25 2·75

97 Northern Shoveler (male)

1999. "iBRA '99" International Stamp Exhibition, Nuremberg. Ducks. Multicoloured.
575 25c. Type **97** 60 50
576 50c. Northern Shoveler (female) and ducklings . . 75 65
577 60c. Green-winged teal (male) 80 80
578 75c. Green-winged teal (female) and ducklings . . 90 1·00
MS579 100 × 70 mm. $3 Green-winged teal (male) and duckling 3·00 3·75

98 Map of Millennium Island

1999. "Towards the Millennium" (2nd issue). 20th Anniv of Independence. Multicoloured.
580 25c. Type **98** 80 80
581 60c. Map of Kiribati . . . . 1·25 1·25
582 75c. Map of Nikumaroro . . 1·25 1·25
583 $1 Amelia Earhart (aviator) 1·75 1·75
MS584 100 × 80 mm. Nos. 582/3 2·75 3·25
No. 581 shows Tarawa as "TAROWA" in error.
See also Nos. 594/8.

98a Buzz Aldrin (astronaut)

1999. 30th Anniv of First Manned Landing on Moon. Multicoloured.
585 25c. Type **98a** 35 35
586 60c. Service module docking with lunar module 65 75
587 75c. "Apollo 11" on Moon's surface 75 85
588 $1 Command module separating from service section . . . . 95 1·10
MS589 90 × 80 mm. $2 Kiribati as seen from Moon (circular, 40 mm diam) . . . . 1·90 2·50

99 Santa Claus in Sailing Canoe

1999. Christmas and 125th Anniv of Universal Postal Union. Multicoloured.
590 25c. Type **99** 35 25
591 60c. Santa and unloading freighter 65 65
592 75c. Santa in sleigh passing aircraft 80 85
593 $1 Santa using computer . . 1·00 1·40

100 Open Hands around Globe ("FAITH")

2000. "Towards the Millennium" (3rd issue). "A Region of Peace". Multicoloured.
594 25c. Type **100** 30 35
595 40c. Solar eclipse ("HARMONY") 45 55
596 60c. Stars and Sun over Earth ("HOPE") 60 75
597 75c. Sun over Earth ("ENLIGHTENMENT") 75 90
598 $1 Dove over Earth ("PEACE") . . . . 90 1·10

101 Bert feeding Pigeons

2000. "Sesame Street" (children's T.V. programme). Multicoloured.
599 20c. Type **101** 20 30
600 20c. Little Bear flying kite . . 20 30
601 20c. Grover calling 20 30
602 20c. Elmo and Cookie Monster 20 30
603 20c. Telly leaning out of window 20 30
604 20c. Zoe painting house . . . 20 30
605 20c. Ernie with bird 20 30
606 20c. Big Bird and Rosita reading 20 30
607 20c. Oscar the Grouch and Slimey in dustbin 20 30
MS608 139 × 86 mm. $1.50 Grover as postman . . . . 1·40 1·75
Nos. 599/607 were printed together, se-tenant, with the backgrounds forming a composite design.

102 Queen Elizabeth II in Kiribati, 1982

2000. "The Stamp Show 2000" International Stamp Exhibition, London. Sheet 80 × 70 mm.
MS609 **102** $5 multicoloured . . 4·25 5·00

2000. "EXPO 2000" World's Fair, Hanover. Nos. 444/5, 447, 457 and 459 optd **KIRIBATI AT EXPO 2000 1.06-31.10.2000**.
610 5c. *Herpetogramma licarsisalis* 15 25
611 10c. *Parotis suralis* 15 25
612 20c. *Aedia sericea* 25 30
613 $1 *Precis villida* . . . . . . 1·00 1·25
614 $3 *Hypolimnas bolina* (male) 2·75 3·25

104 Prince William as a Baby with Prince Charles

2000. 18th Birthday of Prince William. Each showing Prince William with Prince Charles. Multicoloured.
615 25c. Type **104** 40 35
616 60c. In Italy, 1985 . . . . . 75 75
617 75c. At Sandringham, Christmas, 1992 . . . . . 85 85
618 $1 At Balmoral, 1997 . . . . 1·10 1·40

105 Wandering Whistling Duck

2001. Ducks. Multicoloured.
619 25c. Type **105** 45 45
620 25c. Green-winged teal . . . 45 45
621 25c. Mallard 45 45
622 25c. Northern shoveler . . . 45 45
623 25c. Pacific black duck . . . 45 45
624 25c. Mountain duck ("Blue Duck") 45 45
MS625 85 × 75 mm. $1 Grey teal 2·00 2·25

106 Man with Tap (Tiare Hongkai)

2001. Water Conservation. Children's Drawings. Multicoloured.
626 25c. Type **106** 35 30
627 50c. Cooking pot on fire and house in rain (Gilbert Tluanga) 50 45
628 60c. Map in raindrop and cup (Mantokataake Tebaiuea) (vert) 55 50
629 75c. Hand holding drop (Tokaman Karanebo) (vert) 70 70
630 $2 Water management system (Taom Simon) . . . . . . 1·60 2·25

107 Betio Port

2001. "Philanippon '01" International Stamp Exhibition, Tokyo. Development Projects. Multicoloured.
631 75c. Type **107** 75 65
632 $2 New Parliament House complex . . . . 1·75 2·25

108 Norwegian Cruise Liner and Map of Route

2001. Tourism. Fanning Island. Multicoloured.
633 75c. Type **108** 75 60
634 $3 *Betsey* (full-rigged sealer) and map of Fanning Island 2·75 3·25

109 *Paracanthrus hepatus*

2002. Tropical Fish. Multicoloured.
635 5c. Type **109** 10 10
636 10c. *Centropyge flavissimus* 10 10
637 15c. *Anthias squamipinnis* . . 15 20
638 20c. *Centropyge loriculus* . . 15 20
639 25c. *Acanthurus lineatus* . . . 20 25
640 30c. *Oxycirrhites typus* . . . 25 30
641 40c. *Dascyllus trimaculatus* 35 40
642 50c. *Acanthurus achilles* . . . 40 45
643 60c. *Pomacentrus caeruleus* 50 55
644 75c. *Acanthurus glaucopareius* 65 70
645 80c. *Thalassoma lunare* . . . 65 70
646 90c. *Arothron meleagris* . . . 75 80
647 $1 *Odonus niger* 85 90
648 $2 *Cephalopholis miniatus* . . 1·70 1·80
649 $5 *Pomacanthus imperator* . . 4·25 4·50
650 $10 *Balistoides conspicillum* 8·50 8·75
The 60c. is inscribed "coeruleus" in error.

110 Admiral Bellinghausen and *Vostok*, 1820

2002. Pacific Explorers. Multicoloured.
651 25c. Type **110** 40 35
652 40c. Captain Wilkes and the U.S.S. *Vincennes* (sail frigate), 1838–42 . . . . . 60 45
653 60c. Captain Fanning and *Betsey* (full-rigged sealer), 1798 . . . . 70 65
654 75c. Captain Coffin and *Transit* (full-rigged ship), 1823 . . . . 75 70
655 $1 Commodore Byron and H.M.S. *Dolphin* (frigate), 1765 . . . . 90 1·00
656 $3 Captain Broughton and H.M.S. *Providence* (sloop), 1795 . . . . 2·50 3·00
MS657 92 × 63 mm. $5 Captain Cook (vert) . . . . 5·00 5·50

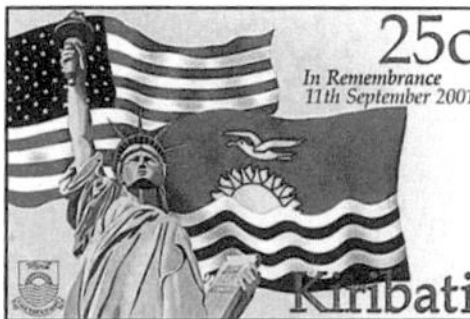

111 Statue of Liberty with U.S. and Kiribati Flags

2002. In Remembrance. Victims of Terrorist Attacks on U.S.A. (11 September 2001).
658 **111** 25c. multicoloured 50 30
659 $2 multicoloured . . . . 2·00 2·50

112 Queen Elizabeth in 1953 **113** Woven "Parcel"

2002. Golden Jubilee. Featuring photographs by Dorothy Wilding. Multicoloured.
660 25c. Type **112** 60 60
MS661 135 × 110 mm. $2 Queen Elizabeth wearing Garter sash; $2 Queen Elizabeth in evening dress 4·50 5·00

2002. Christmas.
662 **113** 25c. multicoloured 35 25
663 – 60c. multicoloured 55 50
664 – 75c. multicoloured 70 60
665 – $1 multicoloured 80 80
666 – $2.50 multicoloured . . . 2·25 2·50
DESIGNS: 60c. to $2.50 show different weave patterns.

114 *Cypraea mappa*

2003. Cowrie Shells of Kiribati. Multicoloured.
667 25c. Type **114** 20 25
668 50c. *Cypraea eglantine* . . . 40 45
669 60c. *Cypraea mauritiana* . . . 50 55
670 75c. *Cypraea cribraria* . . . 65 70
671 $1 *Cypraea talpa* 85 90
672 $2.50 *Cypraea depressa* . . . 2·10 2·20
MS673 130 × 95 mm. Nos. 667/72 4·75 5·00

115 Queen Elizabeth II and Duke of Edinburgh waving from Palace Balcony

2003. 50th Anniv of Coronation. Multicoloured.
674 25c. Type **114** 20 25
675 $3 Newly crowned Queen in Coronation ceremony . . . 2·50 2·75
MS676 95 × 115 mm. $2 As Type **115**; $5 As $3 . . . . . 4·25 4·50

116 Sopwith Camel

2003. Centenary of Powered Flight. Multicoloured.
674 25c. Type **116** 20 25
675 50c. Northrop Alpha 40 45
676 60c. De Havilland D.H.106 Comet 50 55
677 75c. Boeing 727 . . . . . . 65 70
678 $1 English Electric Canberra 85 90
679 $2.50 Lockheed Martin F22 2·10 2·25
MS680 115 × 65 mm. 40c. Mitsubishi A6M-5 Zero; 60c. Grumman F6F Hellcat 85 90
No. **MS**680 also commemorates the 60th anniversary of the Battle of Tarawa.

117 Teareba Teomeka, Tabwakea

2003. Christmas. Churches of Christmas Island. Multicoloured.

681 25c. Type **117**	20	25
682 40c. Seventh-Day Adventist Church, London (Port Camp)	35	40
683 50c. St. Teresa Catholic Church, Tabakea Village	40	45
684 60c. Betaera Fou, London	50	55
685 75c. Children standing by church bells, London	75	80
686 $1.50 Emanuira Church, London	1·30	1·40
687 $2.50 Church of Christ (Ana Ekaretia Kristo) (58 × 22 mm)	2·10	2·20
MS688 144 × 82 mm. Nos. 681/7	5·50	6·00

OFFICIAL STAMPS

1981. Nos. 86/135 optd **O.K.G.S.**

O11 1c. Type **16**	10	50
O12 3c. M.V. "Tautunu" (inter-island freighter)	10	30
O13 5c. Hibiscus	10	20
O14 7c. Catholic Cathedral, Tarawa	10	20
O15 10c. Maneaba, Bikenibeu	10	20
O16 12c. Betio Harbour	30	30
O17 15c. Reef heron	1·75	30
O18 20c. Flamboyant tree	20	30
O19 25c. Moorish idol (fish)	30	30
O20 30c. Frangipani	30	35
O21 35c. G.I.P.C. Chapel, Tangintebu	35	40
O22 50c. "Hypolimnas bolina" (butterfly)	1·00	55
O23 $1 "Tabakea" (Tarawa Lagoon ferry)	65	50
O24 $2 Evening scene	70	70
O25 $5 National flag	1·25	1·75

1983. Nos. 169, 172/3, 175 and 177 optd **O.K.G.S.**

O36 12c. Polynesian reed warbler	40	30
O37 30c. Brown booby	70	50
O38 35c. Audubon's shearwater	80	60
O39 50c. Bristle-thighed curlew	1·00	80
O40 $2 Long-tailed koel	3·00	2·75

POSTAGE DUE STAMPS

D 1 Kiribati Coat of Arms

1981.

D1 **D 1** 1c. black and mauve	10	10
D2 2c. black and blue	10	10
D3 5c. black and green	10	10
D4 10c. black and brown	10	15
D5 20c. black and blue	15	25
D6 30c. black and brown	15	35
D7 40c. black and purple	20	45
D8 50c. black and green	20	50
D9 $1 black and red	30	75

KISHANGARH Pt. 1

A state of Rajasthan, India. Now uses Indian stamps.

12 pies = 1 anna; 16 annas = 1 rupee.

1

1899. Imperf or perf.

1 **1** 1a. green	22·00	55·00
3 1a. blue	£400	

2 (¼a.)

5 (2a.) Maharaja Sardul Singh

1899. Various arms designs. Perf or imperf.

21 **2** ¼a. green	£200	£375
22a ¼a. red	25	40
25 ½a. green	13·00	16·00
8 ½a. red	£2000	£1100
26a ½a. blue	85	50
7 ½a. lilac	£130	£225
27 1a. grey	4·75	3·25
29 1a. mauve	75	1·00
12b 1a. pink	60·00	£170
15 **5** 2a. orange	4·50	4·50
31 **2** 4a. brown	2·00	5·50
32 1r. green	10·00	15·00
17 1r. lilac	20·00	25·00
33 1r. yellow	£700	
34 2r. red	32·00	48·00
35 5r. mauve	32·00	48·00

11 (½a.)

12 Maharaja Sardul Singh

1903. Imperf or perf.

39 **11** ½a. pink	10·00	3·00
40 **12** 2a. orange	3·00	6·00
41 **2** 8a. grey	5·00	7·50

13 Maharaja Madan Singh

14 Maharaja Madan Singh

1904.

42 **13** ¼a. red	45	65
43a ½a. brown	75	30
44a 1a. blue	1·75	1·75
45 2a. orange	15·00	7·00
46a 4a. brown	14·00	16·00
47 8a. violet	8·00	20·00
48 1r. green	24·00	35·00
49 2r. yellow	25·00	£140
50 5r. brown	23·00	£170

1912.

63 **14** ¼a. blue	20	45
64 ½a. green	20	1·00
65 1a. red	1·00	2·50
54 2a. purple	2·50	5·00
67 4a. blue	6·00	8·00
68 8a. brown	7·00	38·00
69 1r. mauve	16·00	£110
70 2r. green	90·00	£275
71 5r. brown	40·00	£375

15

16 Maharaja Yagyanarayan Singh

1913.

59 **15** ¼a. blue	30	90
60 2a. purple	7·00	18·00

1928.

72 **16** ¼a. blue	80	2·00
73 ½a. green	2·75	1·75
74 – 1a. red	75	1·50
75 – 2a. purple	3·00	8·50
76 **16** 4a. brown	1·50	1·75
77 8a. violet	3·50	26·00
78 1r. green	15·00	55·00
79 2r. yellow	28·00	£180
80 5r. red	35·00	£200

Nos. 74/5 are larger.

OFFICIAL STAMPS

1918. Optd **ON K S D**.

O 5 **2** ¼a. green	—	£120
O 6 ¼a. pink	2·25	60
O 7 ½a. blue	£150	38·00
O 9 1a. mauve	40·00	1·50
O10 **5** 2a. orange	—	£130
O11 **2** 4a. brown	50·00	16·00
O16 8a. grey	75·00	22·00
O12 1r. green	£150	£100
O13 2r. brown	—	£800
O14 5r. mauve	—	£1600

1918. Optd **ON K S D**.

O15 **12** 2a. orange	70·00	5·00

1918. Optd **ON K S D**.

O17 **13** ¼a. red	—	£275
O18 ½a. brown	75	35
O19 1a. blue	7·50	4·00
O20 2a. orange	—	£850
O21 4a. brown	55·00	18·00
O22 8a. violet	£325	£190
O23 1r. green	£650	£600
O24 5r. brown		

1918. Optd **ON K S D**.

O28 **14** ¼a. blue	60	50
O29 ½a. green	90	75
O30a 1a. red	1·00	1·00
O31 2a. purple	6·00	4·00
O32 4a. blue	21·00	15·00
O33 8a. brown	£110	40·00
O34 1r. mauve	£325	£325
O35 2r. green		
O36 5r. brown	£1500	

1918. Optd **ON K S D**.

O25 **15** ¼a. blue	6·00	
O27 2a. purple	£450	£475

For later issues see **RAJASTHAN**.

KOREA Pt. 18

A peninsula to the S. of Manchuria in E. Asia. Formerly an empire under Chinese suzerainty, it was annexed by Japan in 1910 and used Japanese stamps. After the defeat of Japan in 1945, Russian and United States Military administrations were set up in Korea to the north and south of the 38th Parallel respectively; in 1948 South Korea and North Korea became independent republics.

KOREAN EMPIRE

1884. 100 mon = 1 tempo.
1895. 5 poon = 1 cheun.
1900. 10 re (or rin) = 1 cheun; 100 cheun = 1 weun.

1

3 Korean Flag

(4)

1894.

1 **1** 5m. pink	34·00	£4000
2 – 10m. blue	7·50	£2500

DESIGN: 10m. Central motif as in Type **1** but different frame and inscribed "CORGAN POST POST".

1895.

7 **3** 5p. green	14·00	12·00
8 10p. blue	18·00	10·00
9 25p. red	14·00	16·00
10a 50p. lilac	12·00	6·50

1897. Optd with T **4**.

12 **3** 5p. green	20·00	15·00
13 10p. blue	24·00	20·00
14 25p. red	30·00	24·00
16 50p. lilac	30·00	20·00

1899. Surch in Korean characters.

17 **3** 1(p.) on 5p. green (No. 7)	£1200	£750
20 1(p.) on 5p. green (No. 12)	£250	£200
18 1(p.) on 25p. red (No. 9)	£150	75·00
21 1(p.) on 25p. red (No. 14)	50·00	32·00

6

7 National Emblems

8

1900. T **6**, **7** (2ch.), **8** (2ch.) and similar designs.

22a 2r. grey	75	1·50
23 1ch. green	5·50	4·00
24 2ch. blue (T **7**)	35·00	38·00
25 2ch. blue (T **8**)	8·00	7·00
26 3ch. orange	7·50	7·50
27 4ch. red	10·00	9·00
28 5ch. pink	10·00	10·00
29 6ch. blue	12·00	11·00
30 10ch. purple	18·00	16·00
31a 15ch. purple	30·00	25·00
32 20ch. red	50·00	38·00
33 50ch. green and pink	£200	£140
34 1wn. multicoloured	£300	£200
35 2wn. green and purple	£500	£250

9 Imperial Crown

17 Falcon, Sceptre and Orb

1902. 40th Anniv of Emperor's Accession as King.

36 **9** 3ch. orange	32·00	25·00

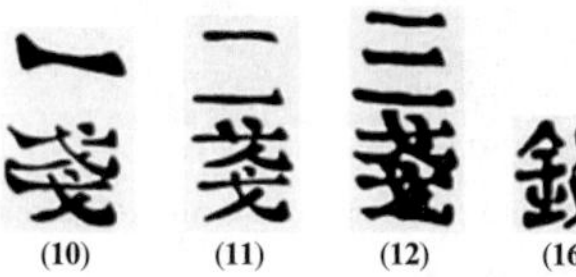

(10) **(11)** **(12)** **(16)**

Types **10** to **12** are in two parts, the horizontal strokes (one, two or three) representing the value figures and the bottom part being the character for "cheun".

Some variation can be found in these woodblock overprints.

1902. (a) Surch as Types **10** to **12**.

37 **3** 1ch. on 25p. red (No. 9)	8·50	6·50
38 1ch. on 25p. red (No. 14)	45·00	45·00
39 2ch. on 25p. red (No. 9)	8·50	7·00
40 2ch. on 25p. red (No. 14)	42·00	40·00
42 2ch. on 50p. lilac (No 10a)	–	£350
43 3ch. on 25p. red (No. 9)	42·00	90·00
44 3ch. on 25p. red (No. 14)		
46 3ch. on 50p. lilac (No. 10a)	8·00	10·00
47 3ch. on 50p. lilac (No. 16)	12·00	12·00

(b) Surch as T **16** (Japanese "sen" character) and strokes.

49 **3** 3ch. on 50p. lilac	£650	£500

1903.

50 **17** 2r. grey	50	75
51 1ch. purple	4·50	4·50
52 2ch. green	4·50	4·50
53 3ch. orange	5·50	5·50
54 4ch. pink	6·50	6·00
55 5ch. brown	9·00	8·00
56 6ch. lilac	9·00	8·50
57 10ch. blue	12·00	10·00
58 15ch. red on yellow	22·00	22·00
59 20ch. purple on yellow	30·00	32·00
60 50ch. red on green	90·00	95·00
61 1wn. lilac on lilac	£150	£160
62 2wn. purple on orange	£250	£250

SOUTH KOREA

1946. 100 cheun = 1 weun.
1953. 100 weun = 1 hwan.
1962. 100 chon = 1 won.

A. UNITED STATES MILITARY GOVERNMENT

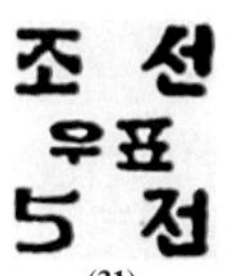

(31)

33 National Emblem

1946. Stamps of Japan surch as T **31**.

69 5ch. on 5s. purple (No. 396)	7·00	7·00
70 5ch. on 14s. red & brn (No. 324)	1·50	1·75
71 10ch. on 40s. purple (No. 407)	1·50	1·50
72 20ch. on 6s. blue (No. 397)	1·50	1·25
73 30ch. on 27s. red (No. 404)	1·50	1·25
74 5w. on 17s. violet (No. 402)	6·50	5·50

1946. Liberation from Japanese Rule.

75 – 3ch. orange	75	65
76 – 5ch. green	75	55
77 – 10ch. red	75	45
78 – 20ch. blue	75	45
79 **33** 50ch. purple	1·10	80
80 1w. brown	1·40	70

DESIGN : 3ch. to 20ch. Family and flag.

34 Dove of Peace and Map of Korea

1946. 1st Anniv of Liberation.

81 **34** 50ch. violet	5·00	2·75

35 U.S. and Korean Flags

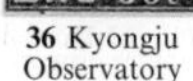

36 Kyongju Observatory

39 Golden Crown of Silla **40** Admiral Li Sun Sin

1946. Resumption of Postal Service between Korea and U.S.A.

82 **35** 10w. red . . . . 6·00 4·00

1946.

83 **36** 50ch. blue 75 45
84 – 1w. brown . . . . 1·25 60
85 – 2w. blue . . . . 1·50 40
86 **39** 5w. mauve . . . . 14·00 6·00
87 **40** 10w. green . . . . 14·00 7·00

DESIGNS—As Type **36**: 1w. Hibiscus; 2w. Map of Korea.

41 Korean Alphabet **42** Li Jun, patriot

44 16th-century "Turtle" Ship **45** Letters Surrounding Globe

1946. 500th Anniv of Creation of Korean Alphabet.

88 **41** 50ch. blue . . . . 3·50 2·00

1947.

89 **42** 5w. green . . . . 8·50 3·00
90 – 10w. blue . . . . 8·50 3·00
91 – 20w. red . . . . 3·00 65
92 **44** 50w. brown . . . . 40·00 10·00

DESIGNS: 10w. Admiral Li Sun Sin; 20w. Independence Arch, Seoul.

1947. Resumption of Int Postal Service.

93 **45** 10w. blue . . . . 12·00 5·00

46 Douglas DC-4 Airliner

1947. Air. Inauguration of Air Mail Service.

94 **46** 50w. red . . . . 6·00 2·50
126 150w. blue . . . . 1·00 90
127 150w. green . . . . 8·50 4·00

47 Hand and Ballot Slip **48** Casting Votes

1948. South Korea Election.

95 **47** 2w. orange . . . . 10·00 7·00
96 5w. mauve . . . . 10·00 6·00
97 10w. violet . . . . 20·00 8·00
98 **48** 20w. red . . . . 30·00 16·00
99 50w. blue . . . . 28·00 17·00

49 Korean Flag and Laurel Wreath

1948. Olympic Games.

100 **49** 5w. green . . . . 65·00 35·00
101 – 10w. violet . . . . 25·00 14·00

DESIGN—VERT: 10w. Runner with torch.

50 Capitol and Ears of Rice

1948. Meeting of First National Assembly.

102 **50** 4w. brown . . . . 16·00 8·00

51 Korean Family

1948. Promulgation of Constitution.

103 **51** 4w. green . . . . 45·00 16·00
104 – 10w. brown . . . . 32·00 10·00

DESIGN—HORIZ: 10w. Flag of Korea.

52 Dr. Syngman Rhee (First President) **53** Hibiscus

1948. Election of First President.

105 **52** 5w. blue . . . . 60·00 25·00

B. REPUBLIC OF KOREA

1948. Proclamation of Republic.

106 – 4w. blue . . . . 30·00 18·00
107 **53** 5w. mauve . . . . 26·00 16·00

DESIGN: 4w. Dove and olive branch.

54 Li Jun **55** Kyongju Observatory

1948.

108 **54** 4w. red 40 20
109 **55** 14w. blue 40 25

56 Doves and U.N. Emblem **57** Citizen and Date

1949. Arrival of U.N. Commission.

110 **56** 10w. blue . . . . 30·00 14·00

1949. National Census.

111 **57** 15w. violet . . . . 30·00 14·00

58 Children and Plant

1949. 20th Anniv of Children's Day.

112 **58** 15w. violet . . . . 15·00 7·00

59 Hibiscus **61** Dove and Globe

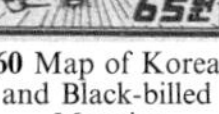

60 Map of Korea and Black-billed Magpies **62** Admiral Li Sun Sin

1949.

113 – 1w. red . . . . 3·00 1·50
114 – 2w. grey . . . . 1·50 60
115 – 5w. green . . . . 7·50 2·25
116 – 10w. green . . . . 2·75 1·40
117 **59** 15w. red 45 20
118 – 20w. brown 45 20
119 – 30w. green 50 20
120 – 50w. blue 45 20
121 **60** 65w. blue . . . . 2·10 1·40
122 – 100w. green 50 20
123 **61** 200w. green 60 35
124 – 400w. brown 60 40
125 **62** 500w. blue 60 45

DESIGNS—As Type **59**: 1w. Postman; 2w. Worker and factory; 5w. Harvesting rice; 10w. Manchurian cranes; 20w. Diamond Mountains; 30w. Ginseng plant; 50w. South Gate, Seoul; 100w. Tabo Pogoda, Kyongju. As Type **61**: 400w. Diamond Mountains.

63 Symbol and Phoenix **65** Korean Flag

64 Steam Train

1949. 1st Anniv of Independence.

128 **63** 15w. blue . . . . 18·00 7·50

1949. 50th Anniv of Korean Railways.

129 **64** 15w. blue . . . . 65·00 35·00

1949. 75th Anniv of U.P.U.

130 **65** 15w. multicoloured . . . . 12·00 8·00

66 Post-horse Warrant **67** Douglas DC-2 Airplane and Globe

1950. 50th Anniv of Membership of U.P.U.

131 **66** 15w. green . . . . 15·00 6·00
132 65w. brown . . . . 10·00 3·50

1950. Air. Opening of Internal Air Mail Service.

133 **67** 60w. blue . . . . 10·00 3·50

68 Demonstrators **69** Capitol, Seoul

1950. 31st Anniv of Abortive Proclamation of Independence.

134 **68** 15w. green . . . . 14·00 6·00
135 65w. violet . . . . 6·00 2·50

1950. 2nd South Korean Election.

136 **69** 30w. multicoloured . . . . 8·00 3·00

70 Dr. Syngman Rhee **71** Flag and Mountains

1950. Unification of Korea.

137 **70** 100w. blue . . . . 2·50 1·00
138 **71** 100w. green . . . . 3·50 1·00
139 – 200w. green . . . . 2·00 75

DESIGN—35 × 24 mm: 200w. Map of Korea and flags of U.N. and Korea.

73 Manchurian Crane **76** Post-horse Warrant

77 Fairy (8th cent painting)

1951. Perf or roul.

140 **73** 5w. brown . . . . 2·40 1·40
181 – 20w. violet . . . . 1·00 30
187 – 50w. green . . . . 2·00 30
183 **76** 100w. blue . . . . 1·25 25
193 **77** 1000w. green . . . . . . 2·25 40

DESIGNS—HORIZ: 20w. Astrological Tiger (ancient painting); 50w. Dove and Korean flag.

1951. Surch with new value.

145 **54** 100w. on 4w. red . . . . . 2·75 75
146 **59** 200w. on 15w. red . . . . 4·50 2·00
147 **54** 300w. on 4w. red . . . . . 1·50 1·00
156 – 300w. on 10w. green (116) 13·00 4·00
149 **55** 300w. on 14w. blue . . . . 2·25 75
150 **59** 300w. on 15w. red . . . . 1·75 75
151 – 300w. on 20w. brown (118) 2·50 85
152 – 300w. on 30w. green (119) 2·00 75
153 – 300w. on 50w. blue (120) 2·00 80
154 **60** 300w. on 65w. blue . . . . 5·75 3·50
155 – 300w. on 100w. green (122) 2·25 75

80 Statue of Liberty and Flags

1951. Participation in Korean War. Flags in national colours. A. As Type **80** in green. B. As Type **80** but showing U.N. Emblem and doves in blue.

158A 500w. Australia . . . . . 6·00 6·00
159A 500w. Belgium . . . . . . 6·00 6·00
160A 500w. Britain . . . . . . 6·00 6·00
161A 500w. Canada . . . . . . 6·00 6·00
162A 500w. Colombia . . . . . 6·00 6·00
163A 500w. Denmark . . . . . 12·00 12·00
164A 500w. Ethiopia . . . . . . 6·00 6·00
165A 500w. France . . . . . . 6·00 6·00
166A 500w. Greece . . . . . . 6·00 6·00
167A 500w. India . . . . 10·00 10·00
168A 500w. Italy (with crown) . . 15·00 15·00
169A 500w. Italy (without crown) 7·00 7·00
170A 500w. Luxembourg . . . . 10·00 10·00
171A 500w. Netherlands . . . . 6·00 6·00
172A 500w. New Zealand . . . . 6·00 6·00
173A 500w. Norway . . . . . . 10·00 10·00
174A 500w. Philippines . . . . . 6·00 6·00
175A 500w. Sweden . . . . . . 6·00 6·00
176A 500w. Thailand . . . . . . 6·00 6·00
177A 500w. Turkey . . . . . . 6·00 6·00
178A 500w. Union of South Africa . . . . 6·00 6·00
179A 500w. U.S.A. . . . . . . 5·00 5·00
158B 500w. Australia . . . . . 6·00 6·00
159B 500w. Belgium . . . . . . 6·00 6·00
160B 500w. Britain . . . . . . 6·00 6·00
161B 500w. Canada . . . . . . 6·00 6·00
162B 500w. Colombia . . . . . 6·00 6·00
163B 500w. Denmark . . . . . 15·00 15·00
164B 500w. Ethiopia . . . . . . 6·00 6·00
165B 500w. France . . . . . . 6·00 6·00
166B 500w. Greece . . . . . . 6·00 6·00
167B 500w. India . . . . 10·00 10·00
168B 500w. Italy (with crown) . . 15·00 15·00
169B 500w. Italy (without crown) 7·00 7·00
170B 500w. Luxembourg . . . . 10·00 10·00
171B 500w. Netherlands . . . . 6·00 6·00
172B 500w. New Zealand . . . . 6·00 6·00
173B 500w. Norway . . . . . . 10·00 10·00
174B 500w. Philippines . . . . . 6·00 6·00
175B 500w. Sweden . . . . . . 6·00 6·00
176B 500w. Thailand . . . . . . 6·00 6·00
177B 500w. Turkey . . . . . . 6·00 6·00

178B 500w. Union of South Africa . . . . 6·00 6·00
179B 500w. U.S.A. . . . . 5·00 5·00

1951. Air. No. **126** surch **500 WON**.
180 **46** 500w. on 150w. blue . . . 2·50 75

82 Buddha of Sokkuram
83 Pulguksa Temple, Kyongju

84 Monument to King Muryol, Kyongju
85 Shrine of Admiral Li Sun Sin, Tongyong

1952. Inscr "KOREA".
184 **82** 200w. red . . . . 1·00 25
185 **83** 300w. green 80 25
191 **84** 500w. red . . . . 2·00 40
192 500w. blue . . . . 10·00 50·00
194 **85** 2000w. blue . . . . 1·50 40
See also Nos. 200/1 and 205.

86 President Syngman Rhee

1952. President's Election to 2nd Term of Office.
195 **86** 1000w. green . . . . . . 2·00 70

87 Douglas DC-3 over Freighter

1952. Air.
196 **87** 1200w. brown . . . . . . 1·10 40
197 1800w. blue . . . . 1·25 40
198 4200w. violet . . . . . . 1·50 50
For stamps in new currency, see Nos. 210/12.

88 Tree-planting
89 Monument to King Muryol, Kyongju

91 Pagoda Park, Seoul
92 Sika Deer
93 Sika Deer

1953. New currency. With character "hwan" after figure of value.
244 **88** 1h. blue 25 10
200 **84** 2h. blue 50 10
201 5h. green 60 10
202 **89** 5h. green 50 10
203 **88** 10h. green . . . . 1·00 10
204 – 10h. brown . . . . 2·50 10
205 **85** 20h. brown . . . . 3·25 10
206 **91** 30h. blue . . . . 1·00 10
242 **92** 100h. brown . . . . 7·50 30
243 **91** 200h. violet . . . . 3·50 25
208 **93** 500h. orange . . . . . . 28·00 1·60
209 1000h. brown . . . . . . 60·00 3·00
DESIGN: No. 204, "Metopta rectifasciata" (moth) and Korean flag.
For designs without character after figure of value, see 1955 issue (No. 273 etc).

1953. Air. Colours changed and new Currency.
210 **87** 12h. blue . . . . 1·25 35
211 18h. violet . . . . 1·50 40
212 42h. green . . . . 2·00 70

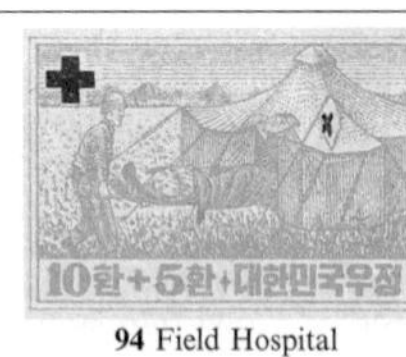

94 Field Hospital

1953. Red Cross Fund. Crosses in red.
213 **94** 10h.+5h. green . . . . . . 5·00 1·50
214 – 10h.+5h. blue . . . . . . 5·00 1·50
DESIGN—VERT: No. 214, Nurses supporting wounded soldier.

95 Y.M.C.A. Badge and Map

96 Douglas DC-6 over East Gate, Seoul

1953. 50th Anniv of Korean Young Men's Christian Association.
215 **95** 10h. red and black . . . . 2·00 70

1954. Air.
216 **96** 25h. brown . . . . 2·00 80
217 35h. purple . . . . 2·75 1·00
218 38h. green . . . . 2·75 1·10
219 58h. blue . . . . 2·50 1·25
258 70h. green . . . . 4·75 2·00
220 71h. blue . . . . 6·50 1·50
259 110h. brown . . . . 4·75 2·00
260 205h. mauve . . . . 7·00 2·00

98 Tokto Island

99 Erosion Control

1954.
221 – 2h. purple . . . . 1·00 15
222 – 5h. blue 80 15
223 **98** 10h. green . . . . 1·25 15
DESIGN: 2, 5h. Rocks off Tokto Island.

1954. 4th World Forestry Congress, Dehru Dun.
224 **99** 10h. light green and green 1·00 15
225 19h. light green and green 1·00 15

100 Presidents Syngman Rhee and Eisenhower

101 "Rebirth of Industry"

1954. Korea–United States Mutual Defence Treaty.
226 **100** 10h. blue . . . . 1·75 40
227 19h. brown . . . . 1·25 40
228 71h. green . . . . 2·50 85

1955. Reconstruction.
229 **101** 10h. brown . . . . 2·50 15
230 15h. violet . . . . 2·25 15
231 20h. blue . . . . 2·25 15
232 50h. mauve . . . . 3·00 25
269 50h. red . . . . 5·00 15

102 Rotary Emblem

103 Pres. Syngman Rhee

1955. 50th Anniv of Rotary International.
236 **102** 20h. violet . . . . 2·50 85
237 25h. green . . . . 1·25 45
238 71h. purple . . . . 1·50 50

1955. 80th Birthday of President.
239 **103** 20h. blue . . . . 3·25 1·00

104 Independence Arch, Seoul

1955. 10th Anniv of Liberation.
240 **104** 40h. green . . . . 2·00 70
241 100h. brown . . . . . . 2·00 1·00

105 Hibiscus

106 King Sejong

107 Kyongju Observatory

1955. Without character after figure of value.
273 **88** 2h. blue 25 10
309 **89** 4h. blue 60 10
310 5h. green 60 10
247 **105** 10h. mauve . . . . 1·00 10
277 – 10h. green 75 10
248 **106** 20h. purple . . . . 2·50 10
279 **105** 20h. mauve 60 15
280 – 30h. violet 75 15
281 **106** 40h. purple 85 15
249 **107** 50h. violet . . . . 2·75 10
315 – 55h. purple . . . . 2·00 10
250 **92** 100h. purple . . . . . . 12·00 10
284 **107** 100h. violet . . . . . . 2·75 15
285 **92** 200h. purple . . . . . . 3·25 15
286 **91** 400h. violet . . . . . . 32·00 35
251 **93** 500h. brown . . . . . . 28·00 40
288 1000h. brown . . . . . . 50·00 2·25
DESIGNS—HORIZ: No. 277, South Gate, Seoul; 280, Tiger. VERT: No. 315, Haegumgang (cliff face).

108 Runners and Torch

109 U.N. Emblem

1955. 36th National Athletic Meeting.
252 **108** 20h. purple . . . . 3·00 1·00
253 55h. green . . . . 3·00 1·00

1955. 10th Anniv of U.N.
254 **109** 20h. green . . . . 2·25 60
255 55h. blue . . . . 2·25 60

110 Admiral Li Sun Sin and 16th-century "Turtle" Ship

1955. 10th Anniv of Korean Navy.
256 **110** 20h. blue . . . . 3·00 1·50

111 Admiration Pagoda

112 Pres. Syngman Rhee

1956. 81st Birthday of President.
257 **111** 20h. green . . . . 3·00 1·00

1956. President's Election to Third Term of Office.
261 **112** 20h. brown . . . . 16·00 5·00
262 55h. blue . . . . 7·50 3·00

113 Torch and Olympic Rings

114 Central P.O., Seoul

1956. Olympic Games.
263 **113** 20h. brown . . . . 3·00 80
264 55h. green . . . . 3·00 80

1956. Stamp Day. Inscr "4289.12.4".
265 **114** 20h. turquoise . . . . . 3·00 55
266 – 50h. red . . . . 3·75 1·00
267 – 55h. green . . . . 1·50 55
DESIGNS—VERT: 50h. Stamp of 1884. HORIZ: 55h. Man leading post-pony.

119 I.T.U. Emblem and Radio Mast

1957. 5th Anniv of Korea's Admission to I.T.U.
290 **119** 40h. blue . . . . 1·50 60
291 55h. green . . . . 1·50 60

120 Korean Scout and Badge

1957. 50th Anniv of Boy Scout Movement.
293 **120** 40h. purple . . . . 1·75 60
294 55h. purple . . . . 1·75 60

1957. Flood Relief Fund. As No. 281 but Korean inscr and premium added and colour changed.
299 40h.+10h. green . . . . . . 2·50 50

123 Mercury, Flags and Freighters

124 Star of Bethlehem and Pine Cone

1957. Korean–American Friendship Treaty.
301 **123** 40h. orange . . . . . . 1·25 60
302 205h. green . . . . 1·60 80

1957. Christmas and New Year Issue.
304 **124** 15h. brown, green & orange . . . . 2·50 50
305 – 25h. green, red and yellow 2·50 30
306 – 30h. blue, green and yellow . . . . 4·25 1·25
DESIGNS: 25h. Christmas tree and tassels; 30h. Christmas tree and dog by window.

125 Winged Letter

126 Korean Children regarding future

1958. Postal Week.
321 **125** 40h. blue and red 80 25

1958. 10th Anniv of Republic of Korea.
323 **126** 20h. grey 80 25
324 – 40h. red . . . . 1·25 25
DESIGN—HORIZ: 40h. Hibiscus flowers forming figure "10".

127 U.N.E.S.C.O. Headquarters, Paris
128 Children flying Kites

1958. Inaug of U.N.E.S.C.O. Building, Paris.
326 **127** 40h. orange and green . . 1·00 25

1958. Christmas and New Year.
330 **128** 15h. green . . . . 1·00 30
331 – 25h. red, yellow and blue 1·00 30
332 – 30h. red, blue and yellow 2·00 50
DESIGNS—VERT: 25h. Christmas tree, tassels and wicker basket (cooking sieve); 30h. Children in traditional festive costume.

129 Rejoicing Crowds in Pagoda Park, Flag and Torch

1959. 40th Anniv of Abortive Proclamation of Independence.
334 **129** 40h. purple and brown . . 1·00 25

130 Marines going Ashore from Landing-craft

1959. 10th Anniv of Korean Marine Corps.
336 **130** 40h. green . . . . 1·00 25

131

1959. 10th Anniv of Korea's Admission to W.H.O.
339 **131** 40h. purple and pink . . 1·00 25

132 Diesel Train

1959. 60th Anniv of Korean Railways.
341 **132** 40h. sepia and brown . . 1·90 1·00

133 Runners in Relay Race

1959. 40th Korean National Games.
343 **133** 40h. brown and blue . . . 1·00 25

134 Red Cross and Korea

1959. Red Cross. Inscr "1959 4292".
345 **134** 40h. red and green . . . 1·00 25
346 – 55h. red and mauve . . . 1·00 25
DESIGN: 55h. Red Cross on Globe.

135 Korean Postal Flags Old and New

136 Mice in Korean Costume and New Year Emblem

1959. 75th Anniv of Korean Postal Service.
348 **135** 40h. red and blue . . . . 1·00 25

1959. Christmas and New Year.
350 **136** 15h. pink, blue and grey 1·00 15
351 – 25h. red, green and blue 80 15
352 – 30h. red, black and mauve 1·40 15
DESIGNS: 25h. Carol singers; 30h. Crane.

137 U.P.U. Monument

138 Honey Bee and Clover

1960. 60th Anniv of Admission of Korea to U.P.U.
354 **137** 40h. brown and blue . . . 1·60 75

1960. Children's Savings Campaign.
356 **138** 10h. yellow, brown and green 75 10
357 – 20h. brown, blue and pink 1·25 10
DESIGN: 20h. Snail and Korean money-bag.
For these stamps in new currency, see Nos. 452 etc.

139 "Uprooted Tree"

140 Pres. Eisenhower

1960. World Refugee Year.
358 **139** 40h. red, blue and green 80 10

1960. Visit of President Eisenhower of United States.
360 **140** 40h. blue, red and green 3·00 80

141 Schoolchildren

1960. 75th Anniv of Educational System.
362 **141** 40h. purple, brown & green . . . . 1·00 25

142 Assembly

143 "Liberation"

1960. Inauguration of House of Councillors.
364 **142** 40h. blue . . . . 1·00 25

1960. 15th Anniv of Liberation.
366 **143** 40h. red, blue and brown 1·00 25

144 Weightlifting

145 Barn Swallow and Insulators

1960. Olympic Games.
368 **144** 20h. brown, flesh & turq 1·00 35
369 – 40h. brown, blue & turq 1·00 35
DESIGN: 40h. South Gate, Seoul.

1960. 75th Anniv of Korean Telegraph Service.
371 **145** 40h. violet, grey and blue 1·50 65

146 "Rebirth of Republic"

147 "Torch of Culture"

1960. Establishment of New Government.
373 **146** 40h. green, blue and orange . . . . 1·00 25

1960. Cultural Month.
376 **147** 40h. yellow, lt blue & blue 1·00 25

148 U.N. Flag

149 U.N. Emblem and Gravestones

1960. 15th Anniv of U.N.
378 **148** 40h. blue, green and mauve . . . . 1·00 25

1960. Establishment of U.N. Memorial Cemetery.
380 **149** 40h. brown and orange 1·00 25

150 "National Stocktaking"

151 Festival Stocking

1960. Census of Population and Resources.
382 **150** 40h. red, drab and blue 1·00 25

1960. Christmas and New Year Issue.
384 – 15h. brown, yellow & grey 50 15
385 **151** 25h. red, green and blue 40 10
386 – 30h. red, yellow and blue 75 15
DESIGNS: 15h. Ox's head; 30h. Girl bowing in New Year's greeting.

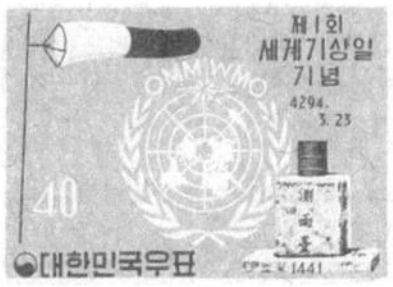

152 Wind-sock and Ancient Rain-gauge

1961. World Meteorological Day.
388 **152** 40h. ultramarine and blue 1·00 25

153 Family, Sun and Globe

1961. World Health Day.
390 **153** 40h. brown and orange 1·00 25

154 Students' Demonstration

1961. 1st Anniv of April Revolution (Overthrow of Pres. Syngman Rhee).
392 **154** 40h. green, red and blue 1·00 30

155 Workers and Conference Emblem

157 Soldier's Grave

156 Girl Guide, Camp and Badge

1961. Int Community Development Conf, Seoul.
394 **155** 40h. green 80 25

1961. 15th Anniv of Korean Girl Guide Movement.
396 **156** 40h. green . . . . 1·00 25

1961. Memorial Day.
398 **157** 40h. black and drab . . . 1·00 30

158 Soldier with Torch

159 "Three Liberations"

1961. Revolution of 16 May (Seizure of Power by Gen. Pak Chung Hi).
400 **158** 40h. brown and yellow . . 1·00 30

1961. Liberation Day.
402 **159** 40h. multicoloured . . . 1·00 30

160 Korean Forces, Flag and Destroyer

1961. Armed Forces Day.
404 **160** 40h. multicoloured . . . 1·25 30

161 "Korean Art" (Kyongbok Palace Art Gallery)

1961. 10th Korean Art Exhibition.
406 **161** 40h. chocolate and brown 1·00 25

162 Birthday Candle

1961. 15th Anniv of U.N.E.S.C.O.
408 **162** 40h. blue and green . . . 25 25

163 Mobile X-Ray Unit

1961. Tuberculosis Vaccination Week.
410 **163** 40h. brown, black & lt brn 75 25

164 Ginseng

165 King Sejong

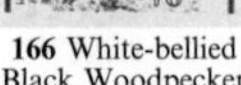

166 White-bellied Black Woodpecker

167 Rice Harvester

168 Korean Drum

169 Douglas DC-8 Jetliner over Pagoda

1961.
412 **164** 20h. red 80 10
413 **165** 30h. purple 80 10
414 **166** 40h. blue and red . . . . 4·00 65
415 **167** 40h. green . . . . 1·10 10
416 **168** 100h. brown . . . . . . 1·75 10
See also 1962 issue (No. 537 etc), and for stamps inscribed "REPUBLIC OF KOREA", see Nos. 641 etc and 785/95.

1961. Air.
417 **169** 50h. violet and blue . . . 10·00 3·50
418 – 100h. brown and blue . . 15·00 12·00
419 – 200h. brown and blue . . 20·00 6·00
420 – 400h. green and blue . . 20·00 6·50
DESIGNS—Plane over: 100h. West Gate, Suwon; 200h. Gateway and wall of Toksu Palace, Seoul; 400h. Pavilion, Kyongbok Palace, Seoul.
See also Nos. 454 etc.

170 I.T.U. Emblem as Satellite

1962. 10th Anniv of Admission to I.T.U.
421 **170** 40h. red and blue . . . . 1·25 40

171 Triga Mark II Reactor

1962. 1st Korean Atomic Reactor.
423 **171** 40h. green, drab and blue 1·00 25

172 Mosquito and Emblem

1962. Malaria Eradication.
424 **172** 40h. red and green . . . 50 25

173 Girl and Y.W.C.A. Emblem

1962. 40th Anniv of Korean Young Women's Christian Association.
426 **173** 40h. blue and orange . . 1·00 30

174 Emblem of Asian Film Producers' Federation

175 Soldiers crossing Han River Bridge

1962. 9th Asian Film Festival, Seoul.
427 **174** 40h. violet, red & turquoise . . . . 1·25 25

1962. 1st Anniv of 16th May Revolution.
428 – 30h. green and brown . . 1·50 50
429 **175** 40h. brown, green & turq 1·50 50
430 – 200h. yellow, red and blue 11·00 3·00
DESIGNS—HORIZ: 30h. "Industrial Progress" (men moving cogwheel up slope); 200h. "Egg" containing Korean badge and industrial skyline.

176 20-oared "Turtle" Ship

1962. 370th Anniv of Hansan Naval Victory over Japanese.
433 **176** 2w. blue and light blue . . 1·50 70
434 – 4w. black, violet & turq 2·75 1·00
DESIGN: 4w. 16-oared "turtle" ship.

177 Chindo Dog

178 "Hanabusaya asiatica"

179 Statue of Goddess Mikuk Besal

213 Longhorn Beetle

180 Farmers' Dance

181 12th-century Wine-jug

214 Factory, Fishes and Corn

182 Mison

183 13th-century Printing-block and Impression used for "Tripitaka Koreana"

191 Sika Deer

192 Bell of King Kyongdok

215 Boddhisatva, Sokkuram Shrine

216 Tile, Silla Dynasty

217 "Azure Dragon", Koguryo period

1962. New Currency.
537 **177** 20ch. brown 25 10
436 **178** 40ch. blue 30 10
785 – 40ch. green 40 10
539 **179** 50ch. brown 30 10
540 **213** 60ch. brown 40 10
541 **180** 1w. blue . . . . 1·00 10
542 **179** 1w.50 grey 30 10
543 **164** 2w. red . . . . 1·25 10
472 **165** 3w. purple . . . . 2·25 10
545 **167** 4w. green 30 10
442 **181** 5w. blue . . . . 4·25 10
547 **214** 7w. mauve . . . . 1·10 10
548 **168** 10w. brown . . . . 2·00 10
549 **182** 20w. mauve . . . . . . 3·00 10
550 **183** 40w. purple . . . . . . 4·50 10
551 **191** 50w. brown . . . . . . 6·00 15
552 **192** 100w. green . . . . . . 15·00 20
553 **215** 200w. deep green and green . . . . 5·00 10
554 **216** 300w. green and brown 10·00 10
555 **217** 500w. blue and light blue 7·00 10
DESIGN—18 × 72 mm: No. 785, motif as Type **178** but inscriptions differently arranged.
See also Nos. 607, 609 and 641/9.

184 Scout Badge and Korean Flag

185 Chub Mackerel, Trawler and Nets

1962. 40th Anniv of Korean Scout Movement.
446 **184** 4w. brown, red and blue 80 25
447 4w. green, red and blue 80 25

1962. 10th Indo-Pacific Fishery Council Meeting, Seoul.
449 **185** 4w. ultramarine and blue 1·40 30

186 I.C.A.O. Emblem

1962. 10th Anniv of Korea's Entry into I.C.A.O.
450 **186** 4w. blue and brown . . . 1·25 25

1962. Children's Savings Campaign. As Nos. 356/7 but new currency.
452 1w. yellow, brown and green 3·25 10
453 2w. brown, blue and pink . . 8·25 65

1962. Air. New Currency.
454 **169** 5w. blue and violet . . . 12·50 2·40
512 – 10w. brown and green (As No. 418) . . . . 2·75 30
513 – 20w. brown and green (As No. 419) . . . . 3·50 35
563 **169** 39w. drab and blue . . . 4·75 35
514 – 40w. green and blue (As No. 420) . . . . 4·00 50
564 – 64w. green and blue (As No. 418) . . . . 2·10 25
565 – 78w. blue and green (As No. 419) . . . . 3·00 30
566 – 112w. green and blue (As No. 420) . . . . 3·00 30

187 Electric Power Plant

1962. Inauguration of 1st Korean Economic Five Year Plan.
458 **187** 4w. violet and orange . . 1·25 40
459 – 4w. ultramarine and blue 1·25 40
DESIGN: No. 459, Irrigation Dam.
See also Nos. 482/3, 528/9, 593/4 and 634/5.

188 Campaign Emblem

1963. Freedom from Hunger.
460 **188** 4w. green, buff and blue 75 25

189 Globe and Letters

1963. 1st Anniv of Asian-Oceanic Postal Union.
462 **189** 4w. purple, green and blue 90 25

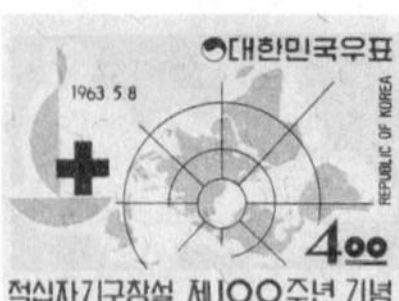

190 Centenary Emblem and Map

1963. Centenary of Red Cross.
464 **190** 4w. red, grey and blue . . 90 25
465 4w. red, grey and orange 90 25

1963. Flood Relief. As No. 545, but new colour and inscr with premium.
479 4w.+1w. blue . . . . 1·50 45

193 "15" and Hibiscus

1963. 15th Anniv of Republic.
480 **193** 4w. red, violet and blue 1·40 30

194 Nurse and Emblem

1963. 15th Anniv of Korean Army Nursing Corps.
481 **194** 4w. black, turquoise & grn . . . . 1·00 25

1963. Five Year Plan. Dated "1963". As T **187**.
482 4w. violet and blue 90 25
483 4w. chocolate and brown . . 4·25 85
DESIGNS: No. 482, Cement Factory, Mun'gyong, and bag of cement; 483, Miner and coal train, Samch'ok region.

195/6 Rock Temples of Abu Simbel

1963. Nubian Monuments Preservation.
484 **195** 3w. green and drab . . . 2·25 40
485 **196** 4w. green and drab . . . 2·25 40
Nos. 484/5 were issued together, se-tenant, forming the composite design illustrated.

197 Rugby Football and Athlete

1963. 44th National Games.
487 **197** 4w. green, brown and blue . . . . 1·00 25

198 Nurse and Motor Clinic

1963. 10th Anniv of Korean Tuberculosis Prevention Society.

488 **198** 4w. blue and red . . . . 1·00 25

199 Eleanor Roosevelt **200** U.N. Headquarters

1963. 15th Anniv of Declaration of Human Rights.

489 **199** 3w. brown and blue . . . 80 25

490 – 4w. blue, green and buff 80 25

DESIGN: 4w. Freedom torch and globe.

1963. 15th Anniv of U.N. Recognition of Korea.

492 **200** 4w. green, blue and black 1·00 25

201 Pres. Pak Chong Hi and Capitol

1963. Inaug of President Pak Chong Hi.

494 **201** 4w. blue, turquoise & black . . . . 11·00 3·50

202 "Tai-Keum" (Bamboo Flute) **204** "U.N.E.S.C.O."

203 Symbols of Metric System

1963. Musical Instruments and Players. As T **202**.

495 4w. green, brown and drab 2·25 60

496 4w. black, blue and light blue 2·25 60

497 4w. green, mauve and pink 2·25 60

498 4w. brown, violet and grey 2·25 60

499 4w. blue, brown and pink . . 2·25 60

500 4w. turquoise, black and blue 2·25 60

501 4w. violet, bistre and yellow 2·25 60

502 4w. blue, brown and mauve 2·25 60

503 4w. black, blue and purple 2·25 60

504 4w. black, brown and pink 2·25 60

MUSICAL INSTRUMENTS (and players)—VERT: No. 495, Type **202**; 496, "Wul-keum" (banjo); 497, "Tang-piri" (flageolet); 498, "Na-bal" (trumpet); 499, "Hyang-pipa" (lute); 500, "Pyenkyeng" jade chimes; 501, "Taipyeng-so" (clarinet); 502, "Chang-ko" (double-ended drum). HORIZ: No. 503, "Wa-kong-hu" (harp); 504, "Kaya-ko" (zither).

1964. Introduction of Metric System in Korea.

505 **203** 4w. multicoloured 90 25

1964. 10th Anniv of Korean U.N.E.S.C.O. Committee.

506 **204** 4w. ultramarine, red & blue 90 25

205 Symbols of Industry and Census

1964. National Industrial Census (1963).

507 **205** 4w. brown, black and grey . . . . 1·25 60

206 Y.M.C.A. Emblem and Profile of Young Man

1964. 50th Anniv of Korean Young Men's Christian Association.

508 **206** 4w. red, blue and green 75 25

207 Fair Emblem, Ginseng Root and Freighter

1964. New York World's Fair.

509 **207** 40w. brown, green & yellow . . . . 2·00 40

510 – 100w. ultramarine, brown and blue . . . . 9·00 1·50

DESIGN: 100w. Korean pavilion at Fair.

208 Secret Garden

1964. Background in light blue.

517 **208** 1w. green 60 20

518 – 2w. green . . . . 1·00 25

519 – 3w. green . . . . 1·00 25

520 – 4w. green . . . . 1·50 30

521 – 5w. violet . . . . 2·00 30

522 – 6w. blue . . . . 2·00 40

523 – 7w. brown . . . . 2·40 40

524 – 8w. brown . . . . 2·50 40

525 – 9w. violet . . . . 2·50 40

526 – 10w. green . . . . 2·75 45

DESIGNS: 2w. Whahong Gate; 3w. Uisang Pavilion; 4w. Mt. Songni; 5w. Paekma River; 6w. Anab Pond; 7w. Choksok Pavilion; 8w. Kwanghan Pavilion; 9w. Whaom Temple; 10w. Chonjeyon Falls.

1964. Five Year Plan. Dated "1964". As T **187**.

528 4w. black and blue . . . . . 1·50 30

529 4w. blue and yellow . . . . 1·00 30

DESIGNS: No. 528, Trawlers and fish; 529, Oil refinery and barrels.

209 Wheel and Globe

1964. Colombo Plan Day.

530 **209** 4w. lt brown, brown & grn 70 25

210 "Helping Hand"

1964. 15th Anniv of Korea's Admission to W.H.O.

532 **210** 4w. black, green and light green 50 25

211 Running

1964. 45th National Games, Inchon.

534 **211** 4w. pink, green and purple . . . . 1·00 25

212 U.P.U. Monument, Berne, and Ribbons

1964. 90th Anniv of U.P.U.

535 **212** 4w. brown, blue and pink 75 25

218 Federation Emblem **219** Olympic "V" Emblem

1964. 5th Meeting of Int Federation of Asian and Western Pacific Contractors' Assns.

556 **218** 4w. green, light green and brown 75 25

1964. Olympic Games, Tokyo.

557 **219** 4w. blue, turquoise & brn 1·50 60

558 – 4w. mauve, blue and green . . . . 1·50 60

559 – 4w. brown, ultram & blue 1·50 60

560 – 4w. red, brown and blue 1·50 60

561 – 4w. brown, purple and blue . . . . 1·50 60

DESIGNS—HORIZ: No. 558, Running; 559, Rowing; 560, Horse-jumping; 561, Gymnastics.

220 Unissued 1884 100m. Stamp **221** Pine Cone

1964. 80th Anniv of Korean Postal Services.

567 **220** 3w. blue, violet and mauve . . . . 1·00 40

568 – 4w. black, violet and green . . . . 1·60 60

DESIGN: 4w. Hong Yong Sik, 1st Korean Postmaster-general.

1965. Korean Plants. Plants multicoloured, background colours given.

571 **221** 4w. green . . . . 1·25 40

572 – 4w. brown (Plum blossom) . . . . 1·25 40

573 – 4w. blue (Forsythia) . . . 1·25 40

574 – 4w. green (Azalea) . . . 1·25 40

575 – 4w. pink (Lilac) . . . . . 1·25 40

576 – 4w. grey (Wild rose) . . . 1·25 40

577 – 4w. green (Balsam) . . . 1·25 40

578 – 4w. grey (Hibiscus) . . . 1·25 40

579 – 4w. flesh (Crepe myrtle) 1·25 40

580 – 4w. blue (Ullung chrysanthemum) . . . 1·25 40

581 – 4w. buff (Paulownia, tree) 1·25 40

582 – 4w. blue (Bamboo) . . . 1·25 40

222 Folk Dancing

1965. Pacific Area Travel Assn Conf, Seoul.

584 **222** 4w. violet, brown & green 1·00 25

223 Flag and Doves

1965. Military Aid for Vietnam.

586 **223** 4w. brown, blue and yellow 60 50

224 "Food Production"

1965. Agricultural Seven Year Plan.

588 **224** 4w. brown, green and black 50 25

225 "Family Scales"

1965. Family Planning Month.

589 **225** 4w. green, drab & lt green 65 25

226 I.T.U. Emblem and Symbols

1965. Centenary of I.T.U.

591 **226** 4w. black, red and blue 65 20

1965. Five Year Plan. Dated "1965". As T **187**.

593 4w. blue and pink . . . . . 1·00 25

594 4w. sepia and brown 80 25

DESIGNS: No. 593, "Korea" (freighter) at quayside and crates; 594, Fertilizer plant and wheat.

227 Flags of Australia, Belgium, Great Britain, Canada and Colombia

1965. 15th Anniv of Outbreak of Korean War.

595 **227** 4w. multicoloured . . . . 1·00 40

596 – 4w. multicoloured . . . . 1·00 40

597 – 4w. multicoloured . . . . 1·00 40

598 – 4w. multicoloured . . . . 1·00 40

599 – 10w. multicoloured . . . 2·50 60

DESIGNS—U.N. Emblem and flags of: No. 596, Denmark, Ethiopia, France, Greece and India; 597, Italy, Luxembourg, Netherlands, New Zealand and Norway; 598, Philippines, Sweden, Thailand, Turkey and South Africa; 599, General MacArthur and flags of Korea, U.N. and U.S.A.

228 Flag and Sky-writing ("20") **229** Ants and Leaf

1965. 20th Anniv of Liberation.

601 **228** 4w. red, violet and blue 65 25

602 – 10w. red, blue and violet 1·10 40

DESIGN: 10w. South Gate and fireworks.

1965. Savings Campaign.

603 **229** 4w. brown, ochre and green 50 25

230 Hoisting Flag **231** Radio Aerial

1965. 15th Anniv of Recapture of Seoul.
604 **230** 3w. green, blue and orange . . . . 1·10 35

1965. 80th Anniv of Korean Telecommunications.
605 **231** 3w. green, black and blue 60 25
606 – 10w. black, blue and yellow . . . . 1·00 35
DESIGN: 10w. Telegraphist of 1885.

1965. Flood Relief. As No. 545 (1962 issue), but colour changed and inscr with premium.
607 4w.+2w. blue . . . . 1·00 30

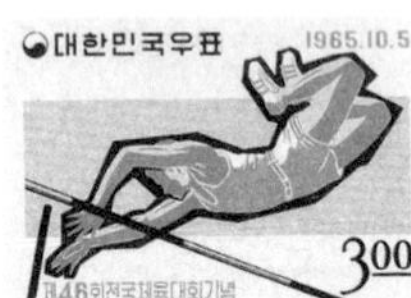

232 Pole Vaulting

1965. National Athletic Meeting, Kwangju.
608 **232** 3w. multicoloured . . . . 1·00 40

1965. Aid for Children. As No. 545 (1962 issue), but colour changed and inscr with premium.
609 4w.+2w. purple . . . . . . 1·10 30

233 I.C.Y. Emblem

1965. International Co-operation Year and 20th Anniv of United Nations.
610 **233** 3w. red, green & dp green 50 25
611 – 10w. ultramarine, grn & bl . . . . 1·10 25
DESIGN—VERT: 10w. U.N. flag and headquarters, New York.

234 Child posting Letter **235** Children with Toboggan

1965. 10th Communications Day.
613 **234** 3w. multicoloured . . . . 1·00 25
614 – 10w. red, blue and green 1·60 30
DESIGN: 10w. Airmail envelope and telephone receiver.

1965. Christmas and New Year.
615 **235** 3w. blue, red and green 60 25
616 – 4w. blue, red and green 75 25
DESIGN: 4w. Boy and girl in traditional costume.

236 Freedom House

1966. Opening of Freedom House, Panmunjom.
618 **236** 7w. black, emerald & grn 1·00 40
619 39w. black, lilac and green . . . . 4·25 60

237 Mandarins

1966. Korean Birds. Multicoloured.
621 3w. Type **237** . . . . 2·40 1·25
622 5w. Manchurian crane . . . 2·50 1·25
623 7w. Common pheasant . . . 3·75 1·25

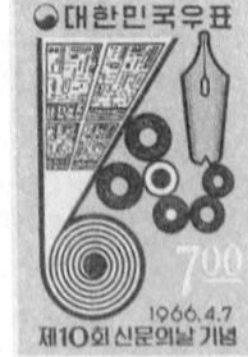

238 Pine Forest **239** Printing Press and Pen

1966. Reafforestation Campaign.
625 **238** 7w. brown, green and light green 70 15

1966. 10th Newspaper Day.
626 **239** 7w. purple, yellow & green 60 15

240 Curfew Bell and Young Koreans **241** W.H.O. Building

1966. Youth Guidance Month.
627 **240** 7w. orange, green and blue 60 15

1966. Inauguration of W.H.O. Headquarters, Geneva.
628 **241** 7w. black, blue and yellow . . . . 1·00 40
629 39w. red, grey and yellow 4·00 1·00

242 Pres. Pak, Handclasp and Flags

1966. Pres. Pak Chung Hi's State Tour of South-East Asia.
631 **242** 7w. multicoloured . . . . 3·00 1·00

243 Girl Scout and Flag

1966. 20th Anniv of Korean Girl Scouts.
632 **243** 7w. black, green and yellow . . . . 1·00 20

244 Student and Ehwa Women's University

1966. 80th Anniv of Korean Women's Education.
633 **244** 7w. multicoloured 65 20

1966. 5-Year Plan. Dated "1966". As T **187**.
634 7w. ultramarine and blue . . 1·75 60
635 7w. black and yellow . . . . 1·00 30
DESIGNS: No. 634, Map and transport; 635, Radar aerials and telephone.

246 Wall-eyed Pollack

1966. Korean Fishes. Multicoloured.
637 3w. Type **246** . . . . 1·00 45
638 5w. Lenok . . . . 1·60 45
639 7w. Manchurian croaker . . 1·75 45

247 Incense-burner **249** Buddha, Kwanchok Temple

1966. As previous issues (some redrawn) and new designs, all inscr "REPUBLIC OF KOREA".
641 **213** 60ch. green 20 10
642 **180** 1w. green . . . . 1·10 10
643 **164** 2w. green 15 10
644 **165** 3w. brown 15 10
645 **181** 5w. blue . . . . 2·00 10
646 **214** 7w. blue . . . . 1·75 10
789 **168** 10w. blue (22 × 18 mm) 3·50 10
647 **247** 13w. blue . . . . 1·90 10
709 **182** 20w. green and light green 6·00 10
710 **183** 40w. green and olive . . . 7·00 10
793 40w. blue and pink (18 × 22 mm) . . . . . 6·50 10
711 **191** 50w. brown and bistre . . 5·75 10
648 – 60w. green . . . . 2·25 10
649 **249** 80w. green . . . . 2·25 10
DESIGN—As Type **247**: 60w. 12th-century porcelain vessel.

250 Children and Hemispheres

1966. 15th Assembly of World Conf of Teaching Profession (WCOTP), Seoul.
650 **250** 7w. violet, brown and blue 45 15

251 Factory within Pouch

1966. Savings Campaign.
652 **251** 7w. multicoloured 45 15

252 People on Map of Korea

1966. National Census.
653 **252** 7w. multicoloured 45 15

253 "Lucida lateralis"

1966. Insects. Multicoloured.
654 3w. Type **253** 90 50
655 5w. "Hexacentrus japonicus" (grasshopper) 90 50
656 7w. "Sericinus montela" (butterfly) . . . . 1·00 50

254 C.I.S.M. Emblem and "Round Table" Meeting

1966. 21st General Assembly of International Military Sports Council (C.I.S.M.), Seoul.
658 **254** 7w. multicoloured 50 15

255 Soldiers and Flags

1966. 1st Anniv of Korean Troops in Vietnam.
660 **255** 7w. multicoloured . . . . 3·00 90

256 Wrestling

1966. 47th Athletic Meeting, Seoul.
661 **256** 7w. multicoloured . . . . 2·00 45

257 Lions Emblem and Map

1966. 5th Orient and South-East Asian Lions Convention, Seoul.
662 **257** 7w. multicoloured 50 15

258 University Emblem, "20" and Shields

1966. 20th Anniv of Seoul University.
664 **258** 7w. multicoloured 40 15

259 A.P.A.C.L. Emblem

1966. 12th Conference of Asian People's Anti-Communist League (A.P.A.C.L.), Seoul.
665 **259** 7w. multicoloured 50 25

260 Presidents Pak and Johnson **261** U.N.E.S.C.O. Symbols and Emblem

1966. President Johnson's Visit to Korea.
667 **260** 7w. multicoloured . . . . 1·00 25
668 83w. multicoloured . . . 5·00 70

1966. 20th Anniv of U.N.E.S.C.O.
670 **261** 7w. multicoloured 55 20

1966. Hurricane Relief. As No. 646 but colour changed and premium added.
672 **214** 7w.+2w. red . . . . . . 1·10 15

262 "Lucky Bag" **263** Eurasian Badger

1966. Christmas and New Year. Multicoloured.
673 5w. Type **262** 45 15
674 7w. Sheep (vert) 45 15

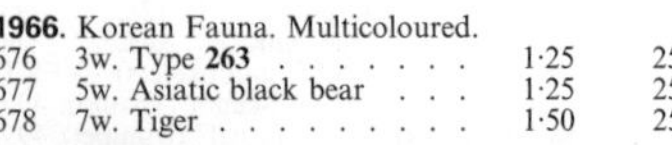

1966. Korean Fauna. Multicoloured.
676 3w. Type **263** . . . . 1·25 25
677 5w. Asiatic black bear . . . 1·25 25
678 7w. Tiger . . . . 1·50 25

264 "Syncom" Satellite **265** Presidents Pak and Lubke

1967. 15th Anniv of Korea's Admission to I.T.U.
680 **264** 7w. multicoloured 70 30

1967. Visit of Pres. Lubke of West Germany to Korea.
682 **265** 7w. multicoloured . . . . 2·00 80

266 Coin, Factories and Houses

267 Okwangdae Mask

1967. 1st Anniv of Korean Revenue Office.
684 **266** 7w. sepia and green . . . 50 25

1967. Folklore. Multicoloured.
685 4w. Type **267** . . . . 1·00 25
686 5w. Sandi mask (horiz) . . . 1·00 25
687 7w. Mafoe mask . . . . . . 1·00 25

268 J.C.I. Emblem and Pavilion

269 Map Emblem

1967. International Junior Chamber of Commerce Conference, Seoul.
689 **268** 7w. multicoloured 50 25

1967. 5th Asian Pacific Dental Congress, Seoul.
691 **269** 7w. multicoloured 55 25

270 Korean Pavilion

271 Worker and Soldier

1967. World Fair, Montreal.
693 **270** 7w. black, red and yellow 1·00 35
694 83w. black, red and blue 6·50 70

1967. Veterans' Day.
696 **271** 7w. multicoloured 50 25

272 Railway Wheel and Rail

1967. 2nd Five Year Plan. Dated "1967".
697 **272** 7w. black, yellow & brown . . . . 2·40 1·10
698 – 7w. orange, brown & black . . . . 1·00 30
DESIGN: No. 698, Nut and bolt.
See also Nos. 773/4, 833/4, 895/6 and 981/2.

273 Sword Dance

1967. Folklore. Multicoloured.
699 4w. Type **273** 85 25
700 5w. Peace dance (vert) . . . 85 25
701 7w. Buddhist dance (vert) . . 1·10 25

274 Soldier and Family

275 President Pak and Phoenix

1967. Fund for Korean Troops Serving in Vietnam.
703 **274** 7w.+3w. black & purple 1·00 15

1967. Inaug of President Pak for 2nd Term.
704 **275** 7w. multicoloured . . . . 4·00 1·00

276 Scout, Badge and Camp

1967. 3rd Korean Scout Jamboree. Multicoloured.
706 7w. Type **276** . . . . 1·00 30
707 20w. Scout badge, bridge and tent . . . . 2·50 50

280 Girls on Swing

1967. Folklore. Multicoloured.
712 4w. Type **280** . . . . 1·00 25
713 5w. Girls on seesaw (vert) . . 1·00 25
714 7w. Girls dancing (vert) . . . 1·40 25

281 Freedom Centre

282 Boxing

1967. 1st World Anti-Communist League Conference, Taipei. Multicoloured.
716 5w. Type **281** 50 25
717 7w. Hand grasping chain (vert) 50 25

1967. National Athletic Meeting, Seoul. Mult.
719 5w. Type **282** . . . . 1·10 25
720 7w. Basketball . . . . 1·10 25

283 Students' Memorial, Kwangjoo

284 Decade Emblem

1967. Students' Day.
721 **283** 7w. multicoloured 50 25

1967. International Hydrological Decade.
722 **284** 7w. multicoloured 50 25

285 Children spinning Top

286 Playing Shuttlecock

1967. Christmas and New Year.
723 **285** 5w. blue, red and pink . . 50 15
724 – 7w. brown, blue and bistre 50 15
DESIGN: 7w. Monkey and Signs of the Zodiac.

1967. Folklore. Multicoloured.
726 4w. Type **286** 90 25
727 5w. "Dalmaji" (horiz) . . . 90 25
728 7w. Archery . . . . 1·25 25

287 Microwave Transmitter

1967. Inaug of Microwave Telecommunications Service.
730 **287** 7w. black, green and blue 50 25

288 Carving, King Songdok's Bell

289 5th–6th century Earrings

290 Korean Flag

1968.
732 **288** 1w. brown and yellow . . 25 10
733 **289** 5w. yellow and green . . 1·25 10
734 **290** 7w. red and blue 70 10
787 7w. blue 45 10
788 7w. blue* 30 10
790 10w. blue* 60 10
*Nos. 788 and 790 have their face values shown as "7" or "10" only, omitting the noughts shown on Nos. 734 and 787.
For designs similar to Type **290** see Nos. 771, 780 and 827.

291 W.H.O. Emblem

292 E.A.T.A. Emblem and Korean Motif

1968. 20th Anniv of W.H.O.
735 **291** 7w. multicoloured 55 25

1968. 2nd East Asia Travel Association Conference, Seoul.
737 **292** 7w. multicoloured 50 25

293 C.A.C.C.I. Emblem, Korean Doorknocker and Factories

1968. 2nd Conference of Confederation of Asian Chambers of Commerce and Industry (C.A.C.C.I.), Seoul.
739 **293** 7w. multicoloured 50 25

294 Pres. Pak and Emperor Haile Selassie

1968. Visit of Emperor of Ethiopia.
741 **294** 7w. multicoloured . . . . 2·00 75

295 Post-bag

1968. Postman's Day. Multicoloured.
743 5w. Type **295** . . . . 1·25 50
744 7w. Postman 50 25

296 Atomic and Development Symbols

1968. Promotion of Science and Technology.
745 **296** 7w. blue, green and red 50 25

297 Kyung Hi University and Conference Emblem

1968. 2nd Conf of Int Assn of University Presidents.
746 **297** 7w. multicoloured 50 25

298 "Liberation"

299 Reservist

1968. Liberation of Suppressed Peoples' Campaign.
748 **298** 7w. multicoloured 50 25

1968. Army Reservists' Fund.
749 **299** 7w.+3w. black & green 1·50 30

300 Stylized Peacock

301 Fair Entrance

1968. 20th Anniv of Republic.
750 **300** 7w. multicoloured 60 25

1968. 1st Korean Trade Fair, Seoul.
751 **301** 7w. multicoloured 50 25

302 Assembly Emblem

303 Scout Badge

1968. 3rd General Assembly of Asian Pharmaceutical Association Federation.
752 **302** 7w. multicoloured 50 25

1968. 6th Far East Scout Conference, Seoul.
753 **303** 7w. multicoloured . . . . 1·25 25

304 Soldier and Battle Scene

305 Colombo Plan Emblem and Globe

1968. 20th Anniv of Korean Armed Forces.
754 **304** 7w. orange and green . . 2·00 40
755 – 7w. blue and light blue . . 2·00 40
756 – 7w. blue and orange . . . 2·00 40
757 – 7w. light blue and blue . . 2·00 40
758 – 7w. green and orange . . 2·00 40
DESIGNS: No. 755, Sailor and naval guns; 756, Servicemen and flags; 757, Airman and jet fighters; 758, Marine and landings.

1968. 19th Meeting of Colombo Plan Consultative Committee, Seoul.
759 **305** 7w. multicoloured 50 15

306 (I) Olympic Emblems

307 (II) Olympic Emblems

1968. Olympic Games, Mexico. Multicoloured.
760 7w. Type **306** . . . . 2·00 60
761 7w. Type **307** . . . . 2·00 60
762 7w. Cycling (I) . . . . . . 2·00 60
763 7w. Cycling (II) . . . . . . 2·00 60
764 7w. Boxing (I) . . . . 2·00 60
765 7w. Boxing (II) . . . . . . 2·00 60
766 7w. Wrestling (I) . . . . . 2·00 60
767 7w. Wrestling (II) . . . . . 2·00 60
The two types of each design may be identified by the position of the country name at the foot of the design—ranged right in types I, and left in types II. On three of the designs (excluding "Cycling") the figures of value are on left and right respectively. Types I and II of each design were issued together horizontally se-tenant within the sheets of 50 stamps.

308 Statue of Woman **309** Coin and Symbols

1968. 60th Anniv of Women's Secondary Education.
769 **308** 7w. multicoloured 50 20

1968. National Wealth Survey.
770 **309** 7w. multicoloured 50 20

1968. Disaster Relief Fund. As No. 734, but with additional inscr and premium added.
771 **290** 7w.+3w. red and blue . . 5·00 50
The face value on No. 771 is expressed as "7 00+3 00", see also Nos. 780 and 827.

310 Shin Eui Ju Memorial **311** Demonstrators

1968. Anniv of Student Uprising, Shin Eui Ju (1945).
772 **310** 7w. multicoloured 50 20

1968. 2nd Five Year Plan. As T **272**. Dated "1968". Multicoloured.
773 7w. Express motorway . . . 60 25
774 7w. "Clover-leaf" road junction 60 25

1968. Human Rights Year.
775 **311** 7w. multicoloured 50 20

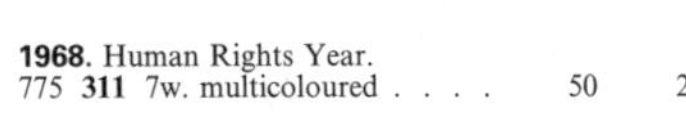

312 Christmas Lanterns **314** Korean House and U.N. Emblems

1968. Christmas and New Year. Multicoloured.
776 5w. Type **312** 75 10
777 7w. Cockerel 75 10

1968. 20th Anniv of South Korea's Admission to U.N.
779 **314** 7w. multicoloured 50 20

1969. Military Helicopter Fund. As No. 734 but colours changed and inscr with premium added.
780 **290** 7w.+3w. red, blue & grn 1·25 40

315 Torch and Monument, Pagoda Park, Seoul **316** Hyun Choong Sa and "Turtle" Ships

1969. 50th Anniv of Samil (Independence) Movement.
781 **315** 7w. multicoloured 60 25

1969. Dedication of Rebuilt Hyun Choong Sa (Shrine of Admiral Li Sun Sin).
782 **316** 7w. multicoloured 80 25

317 President Pak and Yang di-Pertuan Agong **318** Stone Temple Lamp

1969. Visit of Yang di-Pertuan Agong (Malaysian Head-of-State).
783 **317** 7w. multicoloured . . . . 2·00 75

1969.
786 **318** 5w. purple 50 10
791 – 20w. green . . . . 1·50 10
792 – 30w. green . . . . 2·25 10
794 – 40w. mauve and blue . . 1·75 10
795 – 100w. brown and purple 28·00 10
DESIGNS—As Type **318**. VERT: 20w. Wine jug; 40w. Porcelain Jar, Yi Dynasty; 100w. Seated Buddha (bronze). HORIZ: 30w. "Duck" vase.

323 "Red Cross" between Faces **324** "Building the Nation's Economy"

1969. 50th Anniv of League of Red Cross Societies.
796 **323** 7w. multicoloured 85 20

1969. "Second Economy Drive".
798 **324** 7w. multicoloured 40 15

325 Presidents Pak and Nguyen van Thieu

1969. Visit of President Nguyen van Thieu of South Vietnam.
799 **325** 7w. multicoloured . . . . 2·00 65

326 Reafforestation and Flooded Fields **327** Ignition of Second-stage Rocket

1969. Flood and Drought Damage Prevention Campaign. Multicoloured.
801 7w. Type **326** 60 25
802 7w. Withered and flourishing plants 60 25

1969. First Man on the Moon.
803 **327** 10w. blue, black and red 1·50 50
804 – 10w. blue, black and red 1·50 50
805 – 20w. multicoloured . . . 1·50 50
806 – 20w. multicoloured . . . 1·50 50
807 – 40w. blue, red and black 1·50 50
DESIGNS: No. 804, Separation of modules from rocket; 805, Diagram of lunar orbit; 806, Astronauts on Moon; 807, Splashdown of "Apollo 11".

328 Stepmother admonishing Kongji **332** Steam Locomotive of 1899

1969. Korean Fairy Tales (1st series). "Kongji and Patji". Multicoloured.
809 5w. Type **328** 65 25
810 7w. Kongji and sparrows . . 75 25
811 10w. Kongji and ox . . . . 1·10 40
812 20w. Kongji in sedan-chair 1·25 40
See also Nos. 828/31, 839/42, 844/7 and 853/6.

1969. 70th Anniv of Korean Railways. Multicoloured.
814 7w. Type **332** . . . . 1·50 50
815 7w. Early steam and modern diesel locomotives . . . . 1·50 50

333 Northrop F-5A Freedom Jet Fighters

1969. 20th Anniv of Korean Air Force. Multicoloured.
816 10w. Type **333** . . . . . . 1·25 25
817 10w. McDonnell-Douglas F-4D Phantom II jet fighter . . . . 1·25 25

334 Game of Cha-jun

1969. 10th Korean Traditional Arts Contest, Taegu.
818 **334** 7w. multicoloured 60 15

335 Molecule and Institute Building

1969. Completion of Korean Institute of Science and Technology.
819 **335** 7w. multicoloured 60 15

336 Presidents Pak and Hamani

1969. Visit of President Hamani of Niger Republic.
820 **336** 7w. multicoloured . . . . 1·25 40

337 Football **342** Students ringing "Education"

1969. 50th Anniv of National Athletic Meeting. Multicoloured.
822 10w. Type **337** . . . . 1·10 40
823 10w. Volleyball . . . . . . 1·10 40
824 10w. Korean wrestling (horiz) 1·10 40
825 10w. Fencing (horiz) . . . . 1·10 40
826 10w. Taekwondo (karate) (horiz) . . . . 1·10 40

1969. Searchlight Fund. As T **290** but with additional inscr and premium. Face value expressed as "7+3".
827 7w.+3w. red and blue 80 25

1969. Korean Fairy Tales (2nd series). "The Hare's Liver". As T **328**. Multicoloured.
828 5w. Princess and Doctors . . 65 30
829 7w. Hare arriving at Palace 70 30
830 10w. Preparing to remove the Hare's liver . . . . . . 1·10 40
831 20w. Escape of the Hare . . 1·25 40

1969. 2nd Five-year Plan. As T **272**. Dated "1969". Multicoloured.
833 7w. "Agriculture and Fisheries" 75 40
834 7w. Industrial emblems . . . 50 15

1969. 1st Anniv of National Education Charter.
835 **342** 7w. multicoloured 50 15

343 Toy Dogs **344** Woman with Letter and U.P.U. Monument, Berne

1969. Lunar New Year ("Year of the Dog"). Multicoloured.
836 5w. Type **343** 60 25
837 7w. Candle and lattice doorway 60 25

1970. 70th Anniv of Korea's Admission to U.P.U.
838 **344** 10w. multicoloured . . . 3·00 70

1970. Korean Fairy Tales (3rd series). "The Sun and the Moon". As T **328**. Multicoloured.
839 5w. Mother meets the tiger 65 25
840 7w. Tiger in disguise 70 25
841 10w. Children chased up a tree . . . . 1·10 40
842 20w. Children escape to Heaven . . . . 1·25 40

1970. Korean Fairy Tales (4th series). "The Woodcutter and the Fairy". As T **328**. Mult.
844 10w. Woodcutter hiding Fairy's dress . . . . 1·10 40
845 10w. Fairy as Woodcutter's Wife . . . . 1·10 40
846 10w. Fairy and children fly to Heaven . . . . 1·10 40
847 10w. Happy reunion . . . . 1·10 40

353 I.E.Y. Emblem on Open Book **354** Seated Buddha and Korean Pavilion

1970. International Education Year.
849 **353** 10w. multicoloured . . . 3·00 70

1970. "EXPO 70" World Fair, Osaka, Japan.
850 **354** 10w. multicoloured . . . 2·25 60

355 "4-11" Club Emblem **356** Bank Emblem and Cash

1970. 15th "4-11" Club (young farmers' organization) Central Contest, Suwon.
851 **355** 10w. multicoloured . . . 80 30

1970. 3rd General Meeting of Asian Development Bank, Seoul.
852 **356** 10w. multicoloured . . . 80 30

1970. Korean Fairy Tales (5th series). "Heungbu and Nolbu". As T **328**. Multicoloured.
853 10w. Heungbu tending swallow . . . . 1·00 25
854 10w. Heungbu finds treasure in pumpkin . . . . 1·00 25
855 10w. Nolbu with pumpkin . . 1·00 25
856 10w. Nolbu chased by devil 1·00 25

361 Royal Palanquin (Yi dynasty) **362** New Headquarters Building

1970. Early Korean Transport.
858 **361** 10w. multicoloured . . . 1·00 25
859 – 10w. multicoloured . . . 2·25 85
860 – 10w. multicoloured . . . 1·00 25
861 – 10w. black, stone and blue . . . . 1·25 25
DESIGNS—HORIZ: No. 859, Tramcar, 1899; 860, Emperor Sunjong's cadillac, 1903; 861, An Chang Nam's Nieuport 28 biplane, 1922.

1970. Opening of New U.P.U. Headquarters Building, Berne.
862 **362** 10w. multicoloured . . . 70 30

363 Dish Aerial and Hemispheres

1970. Inauguration of Satellite Communications Station, Kum San.
863 **363** 10w. multicoloured . . . 1·10 30

364 "PEN" and Quill Pen

366 Postal Code Symbol

365 Section of Motorway

1970. 37th International P.E.N. (literary organization) Congress, Seoul.
864 **364** 10w. multicoloured . . . 70 25

1970. Opening of Seoul–Pusan Motorway.
865 **365** 10w. multicoloured . . . 1·25 30

1970. Introduction of Postal Codes.
866 **366** 10w. multicoloured . . . 60 25

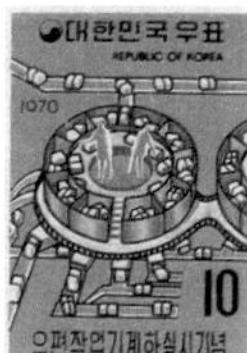
367 Parcel Sorting Area

368 Children's Hall and Boy

1970. Inauguration of Postal Mechanization.
867 **367** 10w. multicoloured . . . 60 25

1970. Opening of Children's Hall, Seoul.
869 **368** 10w. multicoloured . . . 60 30

369 "Mountain and River" (Yi In Moon)

1970. Korean Paintings of Yi Dynasty (1st series). Multicoloured.
870 10w. Type **369** . . . . . . 1·25 30
871 10w. "Jongyangsa Temple" (Chong Son) . . . . . . 1·25 30
872 10w. "Mountain and River by Moonlight" (Kim Doo Ryang) (vert) . . . . . . 1·25 30
See also Nos. 887/89, 897/899, 947/52, 956/8 and 961/5.

370 P.T.T.I. Emblem

371 WAC and Corps Badge

1970. Councillors' Meeting, Asian Chapter of Postal, Telegraph and Telephone International (Post Office Trade Union Federation).
874 **370** 10w. multicoloured . . . 55 25

1970. 20th Anniv of Korean Women's Army Corps.
875 **371** 10w. multicoloured . . . 60 25

372 Pres. Pak and Flag

1970.
876 **372** 10w. multicoloured . . . 3·75 55
877 – 10w. black, green and blue . . . . 2·75 50
DESIGN—VERT: No. 877, Pres. Pak and industrial complex.

373 Presidents Pak and Sanchez Hernandez

1970. Visit of Pres. Sanchez Hernandez of El Salvador.
878 **373** 10w. multicoloured . . . 2·00 60

374 "People and Houses"

1970. National Census.
880 **374** 10w. multicoloured . . . 90 25

375 Diving

1970. 51st National Athletic Games, Seoul.
881 10w. Type **375** . . . . . . 1·40 50
882 10w. Hockey . . . . 1·40 50
883 10w. Baseball . . . . 1·40 50

376 Police Badge and Activities

377 Bell and Globe

1970. National Police Day.
885 **376** 10w. multicoloured . . . 1·00 30

1970. 25th Anniv of United Nations.
886 **377** 10w. multicoloured . . . 75 30

1970. Korean Paintings of the Yi Dynasty (2nd series). Vert designs at T **369**, showing animals. Multicoloured.
887 30w. "Fierce Tiger" (Shim Sa Yung) . . . . 2·50 75
888 30w. "Cats and Sparrows" (Pyun Sang Byuk) . . . . 2·50 75
889 30w. "Dog with Puppies" (Yi Am) . . . . 2·50 75

378 Kite and Reel

380 Fields ("Food Production")

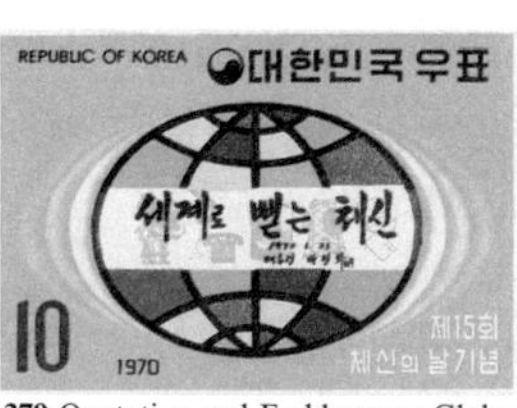
379 Quotation and Emblems on Globe

1970. Lunar New Year ("Year of the Pig"). Multicoloured.
891 10w. Type **378** 65 20
892 10w. Toy pig 65 20

1970. 15th Communications Day.
894 **379** 10w. multicoloured . . . 65 30

1970. 2nd Five Year Plan. At T **272**. Dated "1970". Multicoloured.
895 10w. "Port Development" . . 50 20
896 10w. "House Construction" 50 20

1970. Korean Paintings of the Yi Dynasty (3rd series). Vert designs as T **369**. Multicoloured.
897 10w. "Chokpyokdo" (river cliff) (Kim Hong Do) . . . 1·75 30
898 10w. "Hen and Chicks" (Pyn Sang Byuk) . . . . 1·75 30
899 10w. "The Flute-player" (Shin Yun Bok) . . . . . 1·75 30

1971. Economic Development (1st series). Mult.
901 10w. Type **380** 65 30
902 10w. Dam ("Electric Power") (horiz) 65 30
903 10w. Map on crate ("Exports") (horiz) 65 30
See also Nos. 905/7 and 910/12.

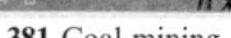
381 Coal-mining

382 Globe, Torch and Spider

1971. Economic Development (2nd series). Mult.
905 10w. Type **381** . . . . . . 1·10 40
906 10w. Cement works (vert) . . 60 20
907 10w. Fertilizer plant 60 20

1971. Anti-espionage Month.
909 **382** 10w. multicoloured . . . 70 20

383 Motorway Junction

384 Reservist and Badge

1971. Economic Develepment (3rd series). Mult.
910 10w. Type **383** 60 20
911 10w. Scales ("Gross National Income") (horiz) 60 20
912 10w. Bee and coins ("Increased Savings") (horiz) 60 20

1971. 3rd Home Reserve Forces Day.
914 **384** 10w. multicoloured . . . 1·00 30

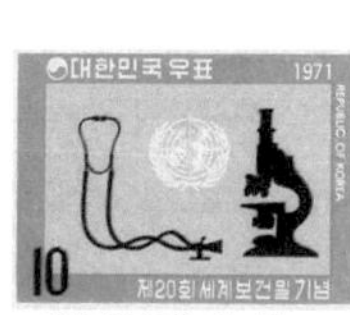
385 W.H.O. Emblem, Stethoscope and Microscope

386 Underground Train

1971. 20th World Health Day.
915 **385** 10w. multicoloured . . . 50 30

1971. Construction of Seoul Underground Railway System.
916 **386** 10w. multicoloured . . . 1·10 20

387 Footballer

388 Veteran and Association Flag

1971. 1st Asian Soccer Games, Seoul.
917 **387** 10w. multicoloured . . . 1·40 40

1971. 20th Korean Veterans' Day.
918 **388** 10w. multicoloured . . . 50 20

389 Girl Scouts

390 Torch and Economic Symbols

1971. 25th Anniv of Korean Girl Scouts Federation.
919 **389** 10w. multicoloured . . . 55 20

1971. 10th Anniv of May 16th Revolution.
920 **390** 10w. multicoloured . . . 50 20

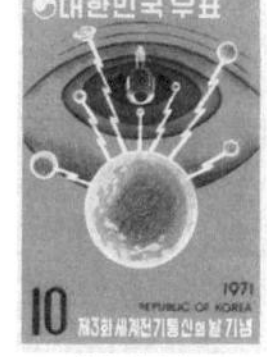
391 "Telecommunications"

392 F.A.O. Emblem

1971. 3rd World Telecommunications Day.
921 **391** 10w. multicoloured . . . 50 20

1971. "The Work of the United Nations Organization".
922 – 10w. mauve, black & green . . . . 1·50 50
923 **392** 10w. blue, black and mauve . . . . 1·50 50
924 – 10w. multicoloured . . . 1·50 50
925 – 10w. blue, black and mauve . . . . 1·50 50
926 – 10w. mauve, black & green . . . . 1·50 50
927 – 10w. blue, black and mauve . . . . 1·50 50
928 – 10w. mauve, black and blue . . . . 1·50 50
929 – 10w. black, green & mauve . . . . 1·50 50
930 – 10w. mauve, black and blue . . . . 1·50 50
931 – 10w. blue, black and mauve . . . . 1·50 50
932 – 10w. mauve, black and blue . . . . 1·50 50
933 – 10w. black, mauve & green . . . . 1·50 50
934 – 10w. mauve, blue and black . . . . 1·50 50
935 – 10w. black, mauve & green . . . . 1·50 50
936 – 10w. mauve, black and blue . . . . 1·50 50
937 – 10w. blue, black and mauve . . . . 1·50 50
938 – 10w. mauve, black and blue . . . . 1·50 50
939 – 10w. black, mauve & green . . . . 1·50 50
940 – 10w. mauve, black and blue . . . . 1·50 50
941 – 10w. blue, black and mauve . . . . 1·50 50
942 – 10w. mauve, black & green . . . . 1·50 50
943 – 10w. black, blue and mauve . . . . 1·50 50
944 – 10w. multicoloured . . . 1·50 50
945 – 10w. black, blue and mauve . . . . 1·50 50
946 – 10w. black, mauve & green . . . . 1·50 50
EMBLEMS: No. 992, I.L.O.; 924, General Assembly and New York Headquarters; 925, U.N.E.S.C.O.; 926, W.H.O.; 927, World Bank; 928, International Development Association; 929, Security Council; 930, International Finance Corporation; 931, International Monetary Fund; 932, International Civil Aviation Organization; 933, Economic and Social Council; 934, South Korean flag; 935, Trusteeship Council; 936, U.P.U.; 937, I.T.U.; 938, World Meteorological Organization; 939, Int Court of Justice; 940, I.M.C.O.; 941, U.N.I.C.E.F.; 942, International Atomic Energy Agency; 943, United Nations Industrial Development Organization; 944, United Nations Commission for the Unification and Rehabilitation of Korea; 945, United Nations Development Programme; 946, United Nations Conference on Trade and Development.

393 "Boating" (Shin Yun Bok)

1971. Korean Paintings of the Yi Dynasty (4th series). Multicoloured.
947 10w. Type **393** . . . . . . 2·75 75
948 10w. "Greeting Travellers" 2·75 75
949 10w. "Tea Ceremony" . . . 2·75 75

950 10w. "Lady and Servants on Country Road" . . . . . 2·75 75
951 10w. "Couple Walking" . . . 2·75 75
952 10w. "Fairy and Boy beneath Pine Tree" (Li Chae Kwan) (vert) . . . . 2·75 75
Nos. 947/51 show "Folk Customs" paintings by Shin Yun Bok.

394 Pres. Pak, Emblem and Motorway
395 Campfire and Badge

1971. Re-election of Pres. Pak for 3rd Term.
954 **394** 10w. multicoloured . . . 2·00 1·00

1971. Korean Paintings of the Yi Dynasty (5th series). As T **393**. Multicoloured.
956 10w. "Chasing the Cat" (Kim Deuk Shin) . . . . 2·00 50
957 10w. "Valley Family" (Li Chae Kwan) (vert) . . . . 2·00 50
958 10w. "Man Reading" (Li Chae Kwan) (vert) . . . . 2·00 50

1971. 13th World Scout Jamboree, Asagiri, Japan.
960 **395** 10w. multicoloured . . . 55 20

1971. Korean Paintings of the Yi Dynasty (6th series). As T **393** but vert. Multicoloured.
961 10w. "Classroom" . . . . . 2·50 85
962 10w. "Wrestling Match" . . 2·50 85
963 10w. "Dancer with Musicians" . . . . 2·50 85
964 10w. "Weavers" . . . . . . 2·50 85
965 10w. "Drawing Water at the Well" . . . . 2·50 85
Nos. 961/5 depict genre paintings by Kim Hong Do.

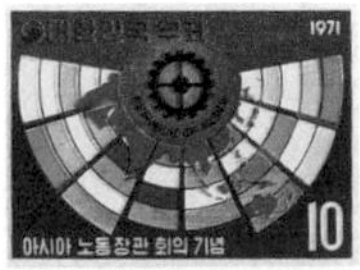

396 Cogwheel and Asian Map

1971. 3rd Asian Labour Minister's Conference, Seoul.
967 **396** 10w. multicoloured . . . 50 20

397 Judo

1971. 52nd National Athletic Meeting, Seoul. Multicoloured.
969 10w. Type **397** . . . . 1·25 40
970 10w. Archery . . . . 1·25 40

398 Korean Symbol on Palette

1971. 20th National Fine Art Exhibition.
972 **398** 10w. multicoloured . . . 50 20

399 Doctor and Globe
400 Emblems and "Vocational Skills"

1971. 7th Congress of Medical Associations from Asia and Oceania.
973 **399** 10w. multicoloured . . . 55 20

1971. 2nd National Vocational Skill Contest for High School Students.
974 **400** 10w. multicoloured . . . 50 20

401 Callipers and "K" Emblem

1971. 10th Anniv of Industrial Standardisation.
976 **401** 10w. multicoloured . . . 50 20

402 Fairy Tale Rats
403 Emblem and Hangul Alphabet

1971. Lunar New Year ("Year of the Rat"). Multicoloured.
977 10w. Type **402** . . . . 1·00 50
978 10w. Flying crane . . . . . 1·00 50

1971. 50th Anniv of Hangul Hakhoe (Korean Language Research Society).
980 **403** 10w. multicoloured . . . 50 20

1971. 2nd Five Year Plan. As T **272**. Dated "1971". Multicoloured.
981 10w. Atomic power plant . . 60 20
982 10w. Hydro-electric power project 65 20

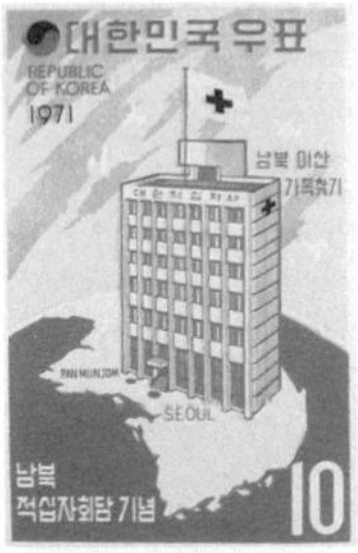

404 Korean Red Cross Building on Map
405 Globe and Open Book

1971. South–North Korean Red Cross Conference, Panmunjom.
983 **404** 10w. multicoloured . . . 1·00 30

1971. International Book Year.
985 **405** 10w. multicoloured . . . 60 20

406 "Intelsat 4" and Korean Earth Station
407 Speed Skating

1971. 20th Anniv of Korea's Membership of I.T.U.
987 **406** 10w. multicoloured . . . 50 20

1972. Winter Olympic Games, Sapporo, Japan. Multicoloured.
988 10w. Type **407** . . . . 1·00 30
989 10w. Figure-skating . . . . 1·00 30

408 Forestry Map
410 E.C.A.F.E. Emblem and Industrial Symbols

409 Scarab Beetles and Emblem

1972. "Trees for Unity" Campaign.
991 **408** 10w. multicoloured . . . 50 20

1972. 20th Anniv of Korean Junior Chamber of Commerce.
992 **409** 10w. multicoloured . . . 70 20

1972. 25th Anniv of U.N. Economic Commission for Asia and the Far East.
993 **410** 10w. multicoloured . . . 55 20

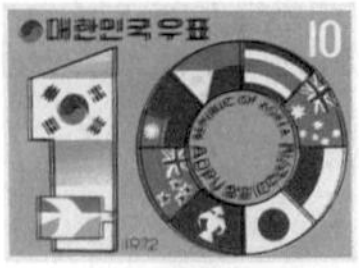

411 Flags of Member Countries
412 Reserve Forces' Flag

1972. 10th Anniv of Asian and Oceanic Postal Union.
994 **411** 10w. multicoloured . . . 50 20

1972. Home Reserve Forces Day.
995 **412** 10w. multicoloured . . . 1·00 30

413 Emblem and "Terias harina"
414 Rural Activities

1972. 50th Anniv of Korean Young Women's Christian Association.
996 **413** 10w. multicoloured . . . 1·75 50

1972. "New Community" (rural development) Movement.
997 **414** 10w. multicoloured . . . 50 20

415 "Anti-Espionage" and Korean Flag
416 Children with Balloons

1972. Anti-Espionage Month.
998 **415** 10w. multicoloured . . . 50 20

1972. 50th Children's Day.
999 **416** 10w. multicoloured . . . 50 20

417 Leaf Ornament from Gold Crown
418 Lake Paengnokdam, Mt. Halla Park

419 Kalkot, Koje Island, Hanryo Straits Park

1972. Treasures from King Munyong's Tomb. Multicoloured.
1000 10w. Type **417** 60 20
1001 10w. Gold earrings (horiz) 65 20

1972. National Parks (1st series).
1002 **418** 10w. multicoloured . . . 75 40
1003 **419** 10w. multicoloured . . . 75 40
See also Nos. 1018/19 and 1026/7.

420 Marguerite and Conference Emblem
421 Gwanghwa Gate and National Flags

1972. U.N. Environmental Conservation Conference, Stockholm.
1004 **420** 10w. multicoloured . . . 45 20

1972. 7th Asian and Pacific Council (ASPAC) Ministerial Meeting, Seoul.
1006 **421** 10w. multicoloured . . . 60 25

422 Pasture ("Development of Rural Economy")
423 "Love Pin"

1972. 3rd Five Year Plan. Dated "1972". Multicoloured.
1007 10w. Type **422** 60 25
1008 10w. Foundry ladle ("Heavy Industries") 60 25
1009 10w. Crate and Globe ("Increased Exports") . . 60 25

1972. Disaster Relief Fund.
1010 **423** 10w.+5w. red and blue 75 20

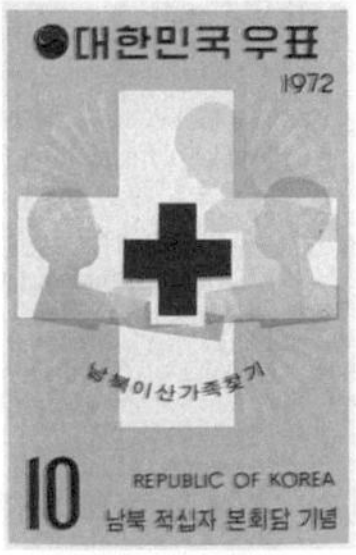

424 Judo
425 Family Reunion through Red Cross

1972. Olympic Games, Munich. Multicoloured.
1011 20w. Type **424** 75 20
1012 20w. Weightlifting 75 20
1013 20w. Wrestling 75 20
1014 20w. Boxing 75 20

1972. 1st Plenary Meeting of South–North Korean Red Cross Conference, Pyongyang.
1016 **425** 10w. multicoloured . . . 1·25 35

426 Bulkuk Temple, Kyongju Park
428 Conference Emblem within "5"

427 Statue and Bopju Temple, Mt. Sokri Park

1972. National Parks (2nd series).
1018 **426** 10w. multicoloured . . . 75 40
1019 **427** 10w. multicoloured . . . 75 40

1972. 5th Asian Judicial Conference, Seoul.
1020 **428** 10w. multicoloured . . . 55 20

429 Lions Badge between Korean Emblems

1972. 11th Orient and South-East Asian Lions Convention, Seoul.
1021 **429** 10w. multicoloured . . . 50 20

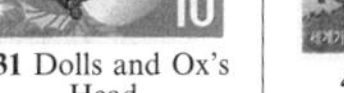

430 Scout taking Oath **431** Dolls and Ox's Head

1972. 50th Anniv of Korean Boy Scouts Movement.
1022 **430** 10w. multicoloured . . . 1·00 25

1972. Lunar New Year ("Year of the Ox"). Multicoloured.
1023 10w. Type **431** 60 20
1024 10w. Revellers in balloon . . 60 20

432 Temple, Mt. Naejang Park **433** Madeungryong Pass, Mt. Sorak Park

1972. National Parks (3rd series).
1026 **432** 10w. multicoloured . . . 75 40
1027 **433** 10w. multicoloured . . . 75 40

434 President Pak, Flag and "Development"

1972. Re-election of President Pak.
1028 **434** 10w. multicoloured . . . 2·00 65

435 National Central Museum, Kyongbok Palace **437** Korean Family

436 Temple, Mt. Sorak

1973. Korean Tourist Attractions (1st series).
1030 **435** 10w. multicoloured . . . 75 15
1031 **436** 10w. multicoloured . . . 75 15
See also Nos. 1042/3, 1048/9, 1057/8 and 1075/6.

1973. Korean Unification Campaign.
1032 **437** 10w. multicoloured . . . 50 15

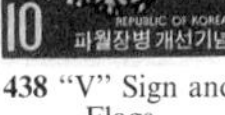

438 "V" Sign and Flags **439** Construction Workers and Cogwheel

1973. Return of Korean Forces from South Vietnam.
1033 **438** 10w. multicoloured . . . 60 20

1973. 10th Workers' Day.
1034 **439** 10w. multicoloured . . . 50 15

440 W.M.O. Emblem and Satellite **442** Wonsam Costume (woman's ceremonial)

1973. Centenary of World Meteorological Organization.
1035 **440** 10w. multicoloured . . . 50 15

1973. Korean Court Costumes of the Yi Dynasty (1st series). Multicoloured. Background colours given.
1037 – 10w. orange . . . . . . 1·10 30
1038 **442** 10w. orange . . . . . . 1·10 30
DESIGN: No. 1037, Kujangbok (king's ceremonial costume).
See also Nos. 1045/6, 1053/4, 1060/1 and 1078/9.

443 Nurse with Lamp **444** Reservists and Flag

1973. 50th Anniv of Korean Nurses' Association.
1040 **443** 10w. multicoloured . . . 65 15

1973. Home Reserve Forces Day.
1041 **444** 10w. multicoloured . . . 75 30

445 Palmi Island **446** Sain-am Rock, Mt. Dokjol

1973. Korean Tourist Attractions (2nd series).
1042 **445** 10w. multicoloured . . . 75 25
1043 **446** 10w. multicoloured . . . 75 25

447 Table Tennis Player

1973. Victory of South Korean Women's Team in World Table Tennis Championships, Sarajevo.
1044 **447** 10w. multicoloured . . . 1·25 30

1973. Korean Court Costumes of the Yi Dynasty (2nd series). As T **442**. Mult. Background colours given.
1045 10w. purple 80 15
1046 10w. green 80 15
DESIGNS: No. 1045, Konryongpo (king's costume); 1046, Jokui (queen's ceremonial costume).

450 Admiral Li Sun Sin's Shrine, Asan **451** Limestone Cavern, Kusan-ni

1973. Korean Tourist Attractions (3rd series).
1048 **450** 10w. multicoloured . . . 80 25
1049 **451** 10w. multicoloured . . . 80 25

452 Children's Choir

1973. 20th Anniv of World Vision Int.
1050 **452** 10w. multicoloured . . . 75 25

453 Love Pin and "Disasters"

1973. Disaster Relief Fund.
1051 **453** 10w.+5w. mult 45 15

454 Steel Converter **457** Table Tennis Bat and Ball

1973. Inauguration of Pohang Steel Works.
1052 **454** 10w. multicoloured . . . 50 15

1973. Korean Court Costumes of the Yi Dynasty (3rd series). As T **442**. Mult. Background colours given.
1053 10w. blue . . . . 1·25 15
1054 10w. pink . . . . 1·25 15
DESIGNS: No. 1053, Kangsapo (crown prince's) costume; 1054, Tangui (princess's) costume.

1973. Table Tennis Gymnasium Construction Fund.
1056 **457** 10w.+5w. mauve & grn 75 20

458 Namhae Suspension Bridge

459 Hongdo Island

1973. Korean Tourist Attractions (4th series).
1057 **458** 10w. multicoloured . . . 55 10
1058 **459** 10w. multicoloured . . . 55 10

460 Interpol and Korean Police Emblems

1973. 50th Anniv of International Criminal Police Organization (Interpol).
1059 **460** 10w. multicoloured . . . 65 10

1973. Korean Court Costumes of the Yi Dynasty (4th series). As T **442**. Mult. Background colours given.
1060 10w. yellow 75 10
1061 10w. blue 75 10
DESIGNS: No. 1060, Kumkwanchobok (court official's) costume; 1061, Hwalot (queen's wedding) costume.

465 Manchurian Cranes **466** Sommal Lily **467** Motorway and Farm

1973.
1063 – 1w. brown 40 10
1063a – 3w. black and blue . . 25 10
1064 – 5w. brown 10 10
1064a – 6w. turquoise and green 30 10
1065 **465** 10w. ultramarine & blue 80 10
1066 **466** 10w. red, black & green 75 10
1067 **467** 10w. green and red . . 50 10
1068 – 30w. brown and yellow 65 10
1068a – 50w. green and brown 50 10
1068b – 60w. brown and yellow 50 10
1068c – 80w. black and brown 75 10
1069 – 100w. yellow and brown . . . . 15·00 40
1069a – 100w. red . . . . . . 1·00 15
1069b – 200w. brown and pink 1·40 20
1069c – 300w. red and lilac . . 2·00 25
1069d – 500w. multicoloured . . 10·00 30
1069e – 500w. purple and brown . . . . 4·00 25
1069f – 1000w. green . . . . . 5·00 60
DESIGNS—VERT: 1w. Mask of old man; 5w. Siberian chipmunk; 6w. Lily; 30w. Honey bee; 50w. Pot with lid; 60w. Jar; 100w. (No. 1069) Gold Crown, Silla dynasty; 100w. (No. 1069a) Admiral Yi Soon Shin; 300w. Pobjusa Temple; 500w. (No. 1069d) Gold Crown; 500w. (No. 1069e) Carved dragon (tile Backje Dynasty). LARGER 24 × 33 mm: 100w. Flying deities (relief from bronze bell, Sangweon Temple). HORIZ: 3w. Black-billed magpie; 80w. Ceramic horseman; 200w. Muryangsujeon Hall, Busok Temple.
For designs similar to Type **465** but with frame, see Type **703**.

470 Tennis

1973. 54th National Athletic Meeting, Pusan. Multicoloured.
1070 10w. Type **470** 65 15
1071 10w. Hurdling 65 15

471 Children with Stamp Albums

1973. Philatelic Week.
1072 **471** 10w. multicoloured . . . 40 10

472 Soyang River Dam

1973. Inauguration of Soyang River Dam.
1074 **472** 10w. multicoloured . . . 40 10

473 Mt. Mai, Chinan

474 Tangerine Grove, Cheju Island

1973. Korean Tourist Attractions (5th series).
1075 **473** 10w. multicoloured . . . 50 10
1076 **474** 10w. multicoloured . . . 50 10

475 Match, Cigarette and Flames **478** Tiger and Candles

1973. 10th Fire Prevention Day.
1077 **475** 10w. multicoloured . . . 40 10

1973. Korean Court Costumes of the Yi Dynasty (5th series). As T **442**. Mult. Background colours given.
1078 10w. orange 75 10
1079 10w. pink 75 10

DESIGNS: No. 1078, Pyongsangbok (official's wife) costume; 1079, Kokunbok (military officer's) costume.

1973. Lunar New Year ("Year of the Tiger"). Multicoloured.
1081 10w. Type **478** 75 10
1082 10w. Decorated top 75 10

479 Korean Girl and Flame Emblem

1973. 25th Anniv of Declaration of Human Rights.
1084 **479** 10w. multicoloured . . . 40 10

480 Boeing 747-200 Jetliner and Polar Zone

1973. Air.
1085 **480** 110w. blue and pink . . 3·00 30
1086 – 135w. red and green . . 3·00 30
1087 – 145w. red and blue . . . 3·00 30
1088 – 180w. yellow and lilac 3·00 30
DESIGNS—Boeing 747-200 jetliner and postal zones on map: 135w. South-east Asia; 145w. India, Australasia and North America; 180w. Europe, Africa and South America.

481 "Komunko" (zither)

1974. Traditional Musical Instruments (1st series). Multicoloured. Background colours given.
1089 **481** 10w. blue . . . . 1·00 10
1090 – 30w. orange . . . . . . 1·00 40
DESIGN: 30w. "Nagak" (trumpet triton).
See also Nos. 1098/9, 1108/9, 1117/18 and 1132/3.

483 Apricots

485 Reservist and Factory

1974. Fruits (1st series). Multicoloured.
1092 10w. Type **483** 30 10
1093 30w. Strawberries 60 15
See also Nos. 1104/5, 1111/2, 1120/1 and 1143/4.

1974. Home Reserve Forces Day.
1095 **485** 10w. multicoloured . . . 30 10

486 W.P.Y. Emblem

489 Diesel Mail Train and Communications Emblem

1974. World Population Year.
1096 **486** 10w. multicoloured . . . 25 10

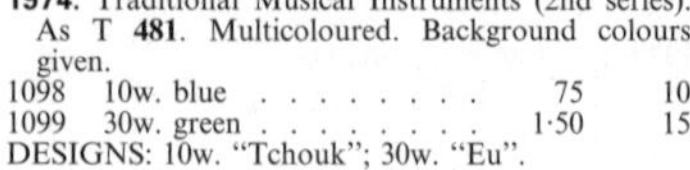

1974. Traditional Musical Instruments (2nd series). As T **481**. Multicoloured. Background colours given.
1098 10w. blue 75 10
1099 30w. green . . . . 1·50 15
DESIGNS: 10w. "Tchouk"; 30w. "Eu".

1974. Communications Day.
1101 **489** 10w. multicoloured . . . 75 15

490 C.A.F.E.A.-I.C.C. Emblem on Globe

491 Port Installations

1974. 22nd Session of International Chamber of Commerce's Commission on Asian and Far Eastern Affairs, Seoul.
1102 **490** 10w. multicoloured . . . 30 10

1974. Inaug of New Port Facilities, Inchon.
1103 **491** 10w. multicoloured . . . 40 10

1974. Fruits (2nd series). As T **483**. Mult.
1104 10w. Peaches 40 10
1105 30w. Grapes 60 15

494 U.N.E.S.C.O. Emblem and Extended Fan

499 Cross and Emblems

1974. 20th Anniv of South Korean U.N.E.S.C.O. Commission.
1107 **494** 10w. multicoloured . . . 30 10

1974. Traditional Musical Instruments (3rd series). As T **481**. Multicoloured. Background colours given.
1108 10w. orange 65 10
1109 30w. pink . . . . 1·25 15
DESIGNS: 10w. "A-chaing" (stringed instrument); 30w. "Kyobang-ko" (drum).

1974. Fruits (3rd series). As T **483**. Multicoloured.
1111 10w. Pears 40 10
1112 30w. Apples 60 15

1974. "Explo 74" 2nd International Training Congress on Evangelism. Multicoloured.
1114 10w. Type **499** 30 10
1115 10w. Emblem and Korean map on Globe 30 10

501 Underground Train

1974. Opening of Seoul Underground Railway.
1116 **501** 10w. multicoloured . . . 85 10

1974. Traditional Musical Instruments (4th series). As T **481**. Multicoloured. Background colours given.
1117 10w. blue 65 10
1118 30w. pink . . . . 1·10 15
DESIGNS: No. 1117, So ("Pan pipes"); 1118, Haikem (Two-stringed fiddle).

1974. Fruits (4th series). As T **483**. Multicoloured.
1120 10w. Cherries 40 10
1121 30w. Persimmons 60 10

506 Rifle Shooting

1974. 55th National Athletic Meeting, Seoul. Multicoloured.
1123 10w. Type **506** 30 10
1124 30w. Rowing 80 10

508 U.P.U. Emblem

509 Symbols of Member Countries

1974. Centenary of U.P.U.
1125 **508** 10w. multicoloured (postage) 30 10
1126 110w. multicoloured (air) 1·25 50

1974. 1st World Conference of People-to-People International.
1128 **509** 10w. multicoloured . . . 30 10

510 Korean Stamps of 1884

1974. Philatelic Week and 90th Anniv of First Korean Stamps.
1129 **510** 10w. multicoloured . . . 50 10

511 Taekwondo Contestants

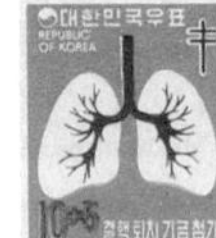

514 Lungs

1974. 1st Asian Taekwondo Championships, Seoul.
1131 **511** 10w. multicoloured . . . 50 10

1974. Traditional Musical Instruments (5th series). As T **481**. Multicoloured. Background colours given.
1132 10w. pink 50 10
1133 30w. ochre 75 15
DESIGNS: 10w. Pak (clappers); 30w. Pyenchong (chimes).

1974. Tuberculosis Control Fund.
1135 **514** 10w.+5w. red & green 40 10

515 Presidents Pak and Ford

516 Yook Young Soo (wife of Pres. Pak)

1974. State Visit of President Ford of United States.
1136 **515** 10w. multicoloured . . . 55 20

1974. Yook Young Soo Memorial Issue.
1138 **516** 10w. green 50 15
1139 10w. orange 50 15
1140 10w. violet 50 15
1141 10w. blue 50 15

1974. Fruits (5th series). As T **483**. Multicoloured.
1143 10w. Tangerines 40 10
1144 30w. Chestnuts 50 15

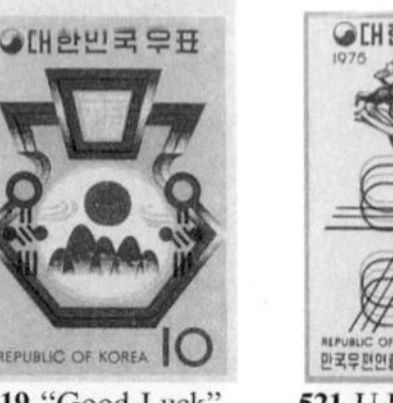

519 "Good Luck" Purse

521 U.P.U. Emblem and "75"

1974. Lunar New Year ("Year of the Rabbit"). Multicoloured.
1146 10w. Type **519** 40 10
1147 10w. Toy rabbits 40 10

1975. 75th Anniv of Korea's Membership of U.P.U. Multicoloured.
1149 10w. Type **521** 30 10
1150 10w. U.P.U. emblem and paper dart 30 10

523 Dove with "Good Luck" Card

1975. Inauguration of National Welfare Insurance System.
1151 **523** 10w. multicoloured . . . 20 10

524 Dr. Schweitzer, Map and Syringe

525 Salpuli Dancer

1975. Birth Centenary of Dr. Albert Schweitzer.
1152 **524** 10w. bistre 50 15
1153 10w. mauve 50 15
1154 10w. orange 50 15
1155 10w. green 50 15

1975. Korean Folk Dances (1st series). Multicoloured. Background colour given.
1156 **525** 10w. green 40 10
1157 – 10w. blue 40 10
DESIGN: No. 1157, Exorcism in dance.
See also Nos. 1168/9, 1175/6, 1193/4 and 1208/9.

527 Globe and Rotary Emblem

1975. 70th Anniv of Rotary International.
1159 **527** 10w. multicoloured . . . 25 10

528 Women and I.W.Y. Emblem

1975. International Women's Year.
1160 **528** 10w. multicoloured . . . 25 10

529 Violets

531 Saemaeul Township

1975. Flowers (1st series). Multicoloured.
1161 10w. Type **529** 40 10
1162 10w. Anemones 40 10
See also Nos. 1171/2, 1184/5, 1199/1200 and 1213/4.

1975. National Afforestation Campaign. Mult.
1163 10w. Type **531** 50 10
1164 10w. Lake and trees 50 10
1165 10w. "Green" forest 50 10
1166 10w. Felling timber 50 10
Nos. 1163/6 were issued together, se-tenant, forming a composite design.

535 H.R.F. Emblem on Map of Korea

536 Butterfly Dance

1975. Homeland Reserve Forces Day.
1167 **535** 10w. multicoloured . . . 40 10

1975. Folk Dances (2nd series). Multicoloured. Background colour given.
1168 **536** 10w. green 45 10
1169 – 10w. yellow 45 10
DESIGN: No. 1169, Victory dance.

538 Rhododendron **540** Metric Symbols

1975. Flowers (2nd series). Multicoloured.
1171 10w. Type **538** 40 10
1172 10w. Clematis 40 10

1975. Centenary of Metric Convention.
1173 **540** 10w. multicoloured . . . 25 10

541 Soldier and Incense Pot **542** Mokjoong Dance

1975. 20th Memorial Day.
1174 **541** 10w. multicoloured . . . 25 10

1975. Folk Dances (3rd series). Multicoloured.
1175 **542** 10w. blue 45 10
1176 – 10w. pink 45 10
DESIGN: No. 1176, Malttungi dancer.

544 Flags of South Korea, U.N. and U.S.

1975. 25th Anniv of Korean War. Multicoloured.
1178 10w. Type **544** 45 10
1179 10w. Flags of Ethiopia, France, Greece, Canada and South Africa 45 10
1180 10w. Flags of Luxembourg, Australia, U.K., Colombia and Turkey 45 10
1181 10w. Flags of Netherlands, Belgium, Philippines, New Zealand and Thailand . . 45 10

548 Presidents Pak and Bongo **549** Iris

1975. State Visit of President Bongo of Gabon.
1182 **548** 10w. multicoloured . . . 40 10

1975. Flowers (3rd series). Multicoloured.
1184 10w. Type **549** 40 10
1185 10w. Thistle 40 10

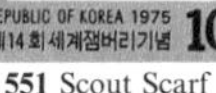

551 Scout Scarf **552** Freedom Flame

1975. "Nordjamb 75" World Scout Jamboree, Norway. Multicoloured.
1186 10w. Type **551** 40 10
1187 10w. Scout oath 40 10
1188 10w. Scout camp 40 10
1189 10w. Axe and rope 40 10
1190 10w. Camp fire 40 10

1975. 30th Anniv of Liberation. Multicoloured.
1191 20w. Type **552** 45 10
1192 20w. Balloon emblems . . . 45 10

554 Drum Dance **556** Taekwondo Contestant

1975. Folk Dances (4th series). Multicoloured. Background colour given.
1193 **554** 20w. yellow 60 10
1194 – 20w. orange 60 10
DESIGN: No. 1194, Bara dance.

1975. 2nd World Taekwondo Championships, Seoul.
1196 **556** 20w. multicoloured . . . 30 10

557 Assembly Hall

1975. Completion of National Assembly Hall.
1197 **557** 20w. multicoloured . . . 30 10

558 Dumper Truck and Emblem **559** Broad-bell Flower

1975. Contractors' Association Convention, Seoul.
1198 **558** 20w. multicoloured . . . 40 10

1975. Flowers (4th series). Multicoloured.
1199 20w. Type **559** 45 10
1200 20w. Bush clover 45 10

561 Morse Key and Dish Aerial

1975. 90th Anniv of Korean Telecommunications.
1201 **561** 20w. black, orange & pur 35 10

562 Yeongweol Caves **564** Flag and Missiles

1975. International Tourism Day. Multicoloured.
1202 20w. Type **562** 30 10
1203 20w. Mount Sorak 30 10

1975. Korean Armed Forces Day.
1204 **564** 20w. multicoloured . . . 30 10

565 "Gymnastics" **567** "Kangaroo" Collector

1975. 56th National Athletic Meeting. Multicoloured.
1205 20w. Type **565** 25 10
1206 20w. "Handball" 25 10

1975. Philatelic Week.
1207 **567** 20w. multicoloured . . . 30 10

568 Sogo Dance **570** U.N. Emblem and Handclasps

1975. Folk Dances (5th series). Multicoloured. Background colour given.
1208 **568** 20w. blue 45 10
1209 – 20w. yellow 55 10
DESIGN: No. 1209, Bupo Nori dance.

1975. 30th Anniv of United Nations.
1211 **570** 20w. multicoloured . . . 25 10

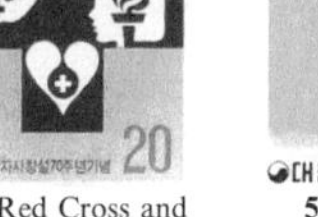

571 Red Cross and Emblems **572** Camellia

1975. 70th Anniv of Korean Red Cross.
1212 **571** 20w. multicoloured . . . 35 10

1975. Flowers (5th series). Multicoloured.
1213 20w. Type **572** 50 10
1214 20w. Gentian 50 10

574 Union Emblem **575** Children Playing

1975. 10th Anniv of Asian Parliamentary Union.
1215 **574** 20w. multicoloured . . . 30 10

1975. Lunar New Year. Multicoloured.
1216 20w. Type **575** 30 10
1217 20w. Dragon ("Year of the Dragon") 30 10

577 Electric Train

1975. Opening of Cross-country Electric Railway.
1219 **577** 20w. multicoloured . . . 50 10

578 "Dilipa fenestra"

1976. Butterflies (1st series). Multicoloured, background colour given.
1220 **578** 20w. red . . . . 1·00 10
1221 – 20w. blue . . . . 1·00 10
DESIGN: No. 1221, "Luehdorfia puziloi".
See also Nos. 1226/7, 1246/7, 1254/5 and 1264/5.

580 Institute Emblem and Science Emblems **581** Japanese White-naped Crane

1976. 10th Anniv of Korean Institute of Science and Technology.
1222 **580** 20w. multicoloured . . . 25 10

1976. Birds (1st series). Multicoloured.
1223 20w. Type **581** . . . . . . 1·00 30
1224 20w. Great bustard . . . . 1·00 30
See also Nos. 1243/4, 1251/2, 1257/8 and 1266/7.

583 Globe and Telephones

1976. Telephone Centenary.
1225 **583** 20w. multicoloured . . . 20 10

584 "Papilio xuthus"

1976. Butterflies (2nd series). Multicoloured, background colour given.
1226 **584** 20w. yellow . . . . . . 1·00 10
1227 – 20w. green . . . . . . 1·00 10
DESIGN: No. 1227, "Parnassius bremeri".

586 "National Development" **587** Eye and People

1976. Homeland Reserve Forces Day.
1228 **586** 20w. multicoloured . . . 30 10

1976. World Health Day. Prevention of Blindness.
1229 **587** 20w. multicoloured . . . 30 10

588 Pres. Pak and Flag **589** Ruins of Moenjodaro

1976. 6th Anniv of Saemaul Movement (community self-help programme). Multicoloured.
1230 20w. Type **588** 45 15
1231 20w. People ("Intellectual edification") 45 15
1232 20w. Village ("Welfare") . . 45 15
1233 20w. Produce and fields ("Production") 45 15
1234 20w. Produce and factory ("Increase of Income") . . 45 15

1976. Moenjodaro (Pakistan) Preservation Campaign.
1235 **589** 20w. multicoloured . . . 40 10

590 U.S. Flags of 1776 and 1976 **591** Camp Scene on Emblem

1976. Bicentenary of American Revolution. Each black, blue and red.
1236 100w. Type **590** . . . . . 1·60 45
1237 100w. Statue of Liberty . . 1·60 45
1238 100w. Map of United States 1·60 45
1239 100w. Liberty Bell . . . . . 1·60 45
1240 100w. American astronaut 1·60 45

1976. 30th Anniv of Korean Girl Scouts Federation.
1242 **591** 20w. multicoloured . . . 60 10

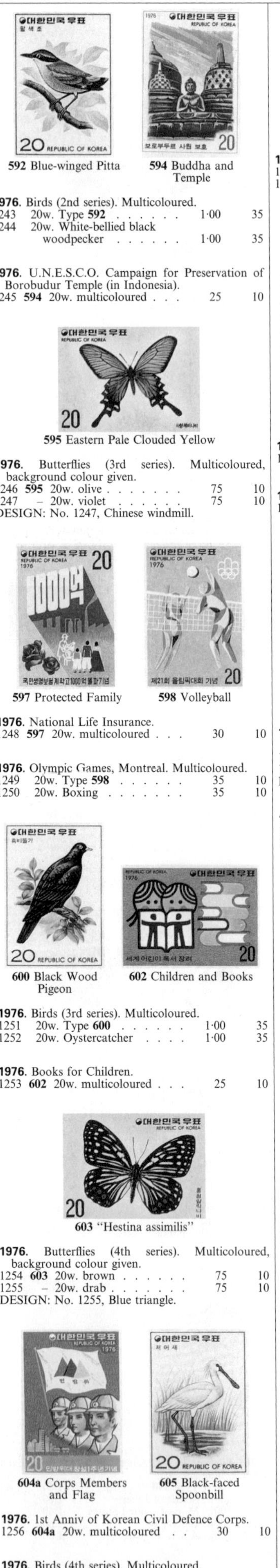

592 Blue-winged Pitta

594 Buddha and Temple

1976. Birds (2nd series). Multicoloured.
1243 20w. Type **592** . . . . . . 1·00 35
1244 20w. White-bellied black woodpecker . . . . . . 1·00 35

1976. U.N.E.S.C.O. Campaign for Preservation of Borobudur Temple (in Indonesia).
1245 **594** 20w. multicoloured . . . 25 10

595 Eastern Pale Clouded Yellow

1976. Butterflies (3rd series). Multicoloured, background colour given.
1246 **595** 20w. olive 75 10
1247 – 20w. violet 75 10
DESIGN: No. 1247, Chinese windmill.

597 Protected Family

598 Volleyball

1976. National Life Insurance.
1248 **597** 20w. multicoloured . . . 30 10

1976. Olympic Games, Montreal. Multicoloured.
1249 20w. Type **598** 35 10
1250 20w. Boxing 35 10

600 Black Wood Pigeon

602 Children and Books

1976. Birds (3rd series). Multicoloured.
1251 20w. Type **600** . . . . . . 1·00 35
1252 20w. Oystercatcher . . . . 1·00 35

1976. Books for Children.
1253 **602** 20w. multicoloured . . . 25 10

603 "Hestina assimilis"

1976. Butterflies (4th series). Multicoloured, background colour given.
1254 **603** 20w. brown 75 10
1255 – 20w. drab 75 10
DESIGN: No. 1255, Blue triangle.

604a Corps Members and Flag

605 Black-faced Spoonbill

1976. 1st Anniv of Korean Civil Defence Corps.
1256 **604a** 20w. multicoloured . . 30 10

1976. Birds (4th series). Multicoloured.
1257 20w. Type **605** . . . . . . 1·00 35
1258 20w. Black stork . . . . . 1·00 35

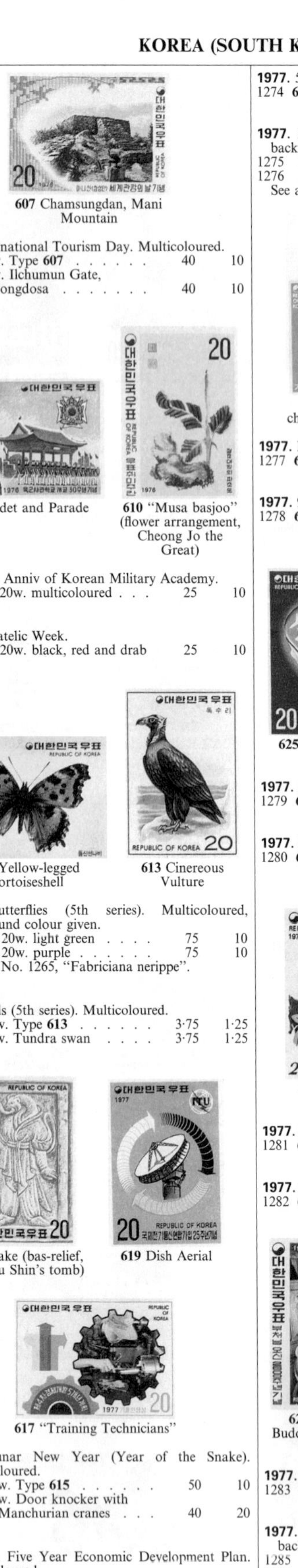

607 Chamsungdan, Mani Mountain

1976. International Tourism Day. Multicoloured.
1259 20w. Type **607** 40 10
1260 20w. Ilchumun Gate, Tongdosa 40 10

609 Cadet and Parade

610 "Musa basjoo" (flower arrangement, Cheong Jo the Great)

1976. 30th Anniv of Korean Military Academy.
1261 **609** 20w. multicoloured . . . 25 10

1976. Philatelic Week.
1262 **610** 20w. black, red and drab 25 10

611 Yellow-legged Tortoiseshell

613 Cinereous Vulture

1976. Butterflies (5th series). Multicoloured, background colour given.
1264 **611** 20w. light green 75 10
1265 – 20w. purple 75 10
DESIGN: No. 1265, "Fabriciana nerippe".

1976. Birds (5th series). Multicoloured.
1266 20w. Type **613** . . . . . . 3·75 1·25
1267 20w. Tundra swan . . . . 3·75 1·25

615 Snake (bas-relief, Kim Yu Shin's tomb)

619 Dish Aerial

617 "Training Technicians"

1976. Lunar New Year (Year of the Snake). Multicoloured.
1268 20w. Type **615** 50 10
1269 20w. Door knocker with Manchurian cranes . . . 40 20

1977. 4th Five Year Economic Development Plan. Multicoloured.
1271 20w. Type **617** 40 10
1272 20w. Tanker ("Heavy Industries") 50 10

1977. 25th Anniv of Korea's I.T.U. Membership.
1273 **619** 20w. multicoloured . . . 30 10

620 Korean Broadcasting Centre

621 Jar with Grape Design

1977. 50th Anniv of Broadcasting in Korea.
1274 **620** 20w. multicoloured . . . 35 10

1977. Korean Ceramics (1st series). Multicoloured, background colours given.
1275 20w. Type **621** (brown) . . 75 10
1276 20w. Celadon vase (grey) . . 75 10
See also Nos. 1285/6, 1287/8, 1290/1 and 1300/1.

623 "Two-children" Family

624 Reserve Soldier

1977. Family Planning.
1277 **623** 20w. green, turq & orge 30 10

1977. 9th Homeland Reserve Forces Day.
1278 **624** 20w. multicoloured . . . 35 10

625 Diagram of Brain

626 Medical Book and Equipment

1977. 10th Anniv of Science Day.
1279 **625** 20w. multicoloured . . . 25 10

1977. 35th International Military Medicine Meeting.
1280 **626** 20w. multicoloured . . . 45 10

627 Child with Flowers

628 Veterans' Flag and Emblem

1977. 20th Anniv of Children's Charter.
1281 **627** 20w. multicoloured . . . 25 10

1977. 25th Anniv of Korean Veterans' Day.
1282 **628** 20w. multicoloured . . . 40 10

629 Statue of Buddha, Sokkulam Grotto

630 Celadon Jar

1977. 2600th Birth Anniv of Buddha.
1283 **629** 20w. green and brown 40 10

1977. Korean Ceramics (2nd series). Multicoloured, background colours given.
1285 20w. Type **630** (pink) . . . 45 10
1286 20w. Porcelain vase (blue) (vert) 45 10

632 "Buddha" Celadon Wine Jar

1977. Korean Ceramics (3rd series). Multicoloured, background colours given.
1287 20w. Type **632** (mauve) . . 45 10
1288 20w. Celadon vase (pale blue) 45 10

수해구제
+10
(**634**)

635 Celadon Vase, Black Koryo Ware

1977. Flood Relief. No. 791 surch with T **634**.
1289 20w.+10w. green . . . . . 1·25 40

1977. Korean Ceramics (4th series). Multicoloured, background colours given.
1290 20w. Type **635** (stone) . . . 45 10
1291 20w. White porcelain bowl (green) (horiz) 45 10

637 Ulleung-do Island

639 Servicemen

1977. World Tourism Day. Multicoloured.
1292 20w. Type **637** 30 10
1293 20w. Haeundae Beach . . . 30 10

1977. Armed Forces Day.
1294 **639** 20w. multicoloured . . . 20 10

640/1 "Mount Inwang Clearing-up after the Rain" (detail from drawing by Chung Seon)

1977. Philatelic Week.
1295 **640** 20w. multicoloured . . . 40 10
1296 **641** 20w. multicoloured . . . 40 10
Nos. 1294/5 were issued together, se-tenant, forming the composite design illustrated.

642 Rotary Emblem and Koryo Dynasty Bronze Bell

643 South Korean Flag over Everest

1977. 50th Anniv of Korean Rotary Club.
1298 **642** 20w. multicoloured . . . 50 10

1977. South Korean Conquest of Mount Everest.
1299 **643** 20w. multicoloured . . . 50 10

644 Punch'ong Bottle

646 Hands preserving Nature

1977. Korean Ceramics (5th series). Multicoloured, background colours given.
1300 20w. Type **644** (brown) . . 50 10
1301 20w. Celadon cylindrical bottle (pale brown) . . . 50 10

1977. Nature Conservation.
1302 **646** 20w. blue, green & brown 30 10

647 Children with Kites

649 Clay Pigeon Shooting

1977. Lunar New Year ("Year of the Horse"). Multicoloured.
1303 20w. Type **647** 30 10
1304 20w. Horse (bas-relief, Kim Yu Shin's tomb) 30 10

1977. 42nd World Shooting Championships, Seoul. Multicoloured.
1306 20w. Type **649** 35 10
1307 20w. Air pistol shooting . . 35 10
1308 20w. Air rifle shooting . . . 35 10

652 Korean Airlines Boeing 747-200

1977. 25th Anniv of Korean Membership of I.C.A.O.
1310 **652** 20w. multicoloured . . . 45 10

653 "Exports"

1977. Korean Exports.
1311 **653** 20w. multicoloured . . . 35 10

654 Ships and World Map

1978. National Maritime Day.
1312 **654** 20w. multicoloured . . . 30 10

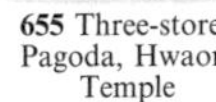
655 Three-storey Pagoda, Hwaom Temple

656 Seven-storey Pagoda, T'app'yong-ri

1978. Stone Pagodas (1st series).
1313 **655** 20w. multicoloured . . . 35 10
1314 **656** 20w. multicoloured . . . 35 10
See also Nos. 1319/20, 1322/5 and 1340/1.

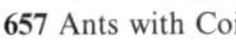
657 Ants with Coins

658 Seoul Sejong Cultural Centre, Hahoe Mask and Violin

1978. Savings Encouragement.
1315 **657** 20w. multicoloured . . . 30 10

1978. Opening of Seoul Sejong Cultural Centre.
1316 **658** 20w. multicoloured . . . 60 10

659 Standard Bearer

660 Pigeon and Young

1978. 10th Homeland Reserve Forces Day.
1317 **659** 20w. multicoloured . . . 25 10

1978. Family Planning.
1318 **660** 20w. black and green . . 35 10

661 Pagoda, Punhwang Temple

662 Pagoda, Miruk Temple

1978. Stone Pagodas (2nd series).
1319 **661** 20w. multicoloured . . . 35 10
1320 **662** 20w. multicoloured . . . 35 10

663 National Assembly

1978. 30th Anniv of National Assembly.
1321 **663** 20w. multicoloured . . . 25 10

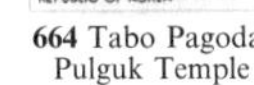
664 Tabo Pagoda, Pulguk Temple

665 Three-storey Pagoda, Pulguk Temple

1978. Stone Pagodas (3rd series).
1322 **664** 20w. multicoloured . . . 35 10
1323 **665** 20w. multicoloured . . . 35 10

666 Ten-storey Pagoda, Kyongch'on Temple

667 Nine-storey Octagonal Pagoda, Wolchong Temple

1978. Stone Pagodas (4th series).
1324 **666** 20w. multicoloured . . . 45 10
1325 **667** 20w. multicoloured . . . 45 10

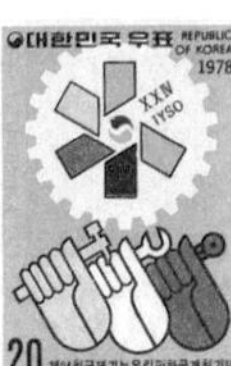
668 Emblem and Hands with Tools

669 Crater Lake, Mt. Baeguda and Bell of Joy

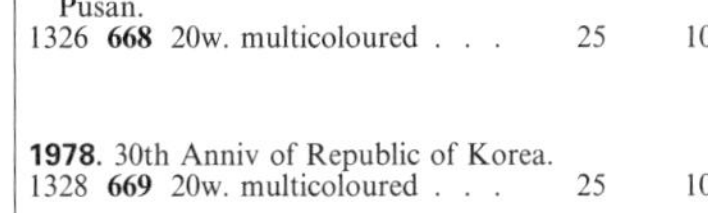
1978. 24th International Youth Skill Olympics, Pusan.
1326 **668** 20w. multicoloured . . . 25 10

1978. 30th Anniv of Republic of Korea.
1328 **669** 20w. multicoloured . . . 25 10

670 Army Nursing Officer

671 Sobaeksan Observatory and Telescope

1978. 30th Anniv of Army Nursing Corps.
1329 **670** 20w. multicoloured . . . 25 10

1978. Opening of Sobaeksan Observatory.
1330 **671** 20w. multicoloured . . . 40 10

672 Kyonghoeru Pavilion, Kyonbok Palace

673 Baeg-do Island

1978. World Tourism Day.
1331 **672** 20w. multicoloured . . . 30 10
1332 **673** 20w. multicoloured . . . 30 10

674 Customs Officers and Flag

1978. Centenary of Custom House.
1333 **674** 20w. multicoloured . . . 25 10

675 Armed Forces

676 Earthenware Figures, Silla Dynasty

1978. 30th Anniv of Korean Armed Forces.
1334 **675** 20w. multicoloured . . . 40 10

1978. Culture Month.
1335 **676** 20w. black and green . . 25 10

677 Painting of a Lady (Shin Yoon-bok)

678 Young Men and Y.M.C.A. Emblem

1978. Philatelic Week.
1336 **677** 20w. multicoloured . . . 35 10

1978. 75th Anniv of Korean Y.M.C.A.
1338 **678** 20w. multicoloured . . . 25 10

679 Hand smothering Fire

1978. Fire Prevention Campaign.
1339 **679** 20w. multicoloured . . . 25 10

680 Thirteen-storey Pagoda, Jeonghye Temple

681 Three-storey Pagoda, Jinjeon Temple

1978. Stone Pagodas (5th series).
1340 **680** 20w. multicoloured . . . 30 10
1341 **681** 20w. multicoloured . . . 30 10

682 Snow Scene

684 People within Hibiscus

1978. Lunar New Year ("Year of the Sheep"). Multicoloured.
1342 20w. Type **682** 30 10
1343 20w. Sheep (bas-relief, Kim Yu Shin's tomb) 30 10

1978. 10th Anniv of National Education Charter.
1345 **684** 20w. multicoloured . . . 25 10

685 President Pak

1978. Re-election of President Pak.
1346 **685** 20w. multicoloured . . . 40 10

686 Golden Mandarinfish

687 Lace Bark Pine

1979. Nature Conservation.
1348 **686** 20w. multicoloured . . . 35 10
1349 **687** 20w. multicoloured . . . 35 10

688 Samil Monument

689 Worker and Bulldozer

1979. 60th Anniv of Samil Independence Movement.
1350 **688** 20w. multicoloured . . . 25 10

1979. Labour Day.
1351 **689** 20w. multicoloured . . . 25 10

690 Tabo Pagoda, Pulgak Temple

695 Hand holding Symbols of Security

1979. Korean Art. Multicoloured.

1352	20w. Type **690**	25	10
1353	20w. Gilt-bronze Maitreya	25	10
1354	20w. Gold crown of Silla	25	10
1355	20w. Celadon vase	25	10
1356	60w. "Tano Day Activities" (silk screen) (50 × 33 mm)	45	10

1979. Strengthening National Security.

1358 **695** 20w. multicoloured . . . 25 10

696 Pulguk Temple and P.A.T.A. Emblem

1979. 28th Pacific Area Travel Association Conference, Seoul.

1359 **696** 20w. multicoloured . . . 25 10

697 Presidents Pak and Senghor

1979. Visit of President Senghor of Senegal.

1360 **697** 20w. multicoloured . . . 25 10

698 Basketball

699 Children playing

1979. 8th World Women's Basketball Championships, Seoul.

1362 **698** 20w. multicoloured . . . 40 10

1979. International Year of the Child.

1363 **699** 20w. multicoloured . . . 30 10

700 Children on Swing

1979. Family Planning.

1364 **700** 20w. multicoloured . . . 30 10

701 Mandarins

702 "Neofinettia falcata" (orchid)

1979. Nature Conservation.

1365	**701**	20w. multicoloured	1·00	20
1366	**702**	20w. multicoloured	40	10

703 Manchurian Cranes

1979.

1367	**703**	10w. black and green	65	15
1368	–	15w. deep green & green	15	10
1369	–	20w. bistre, black & blue	20	10
1370	–	30w. multicoloured	25	10
1371	–	40w. multicoloured	30	10
1372	–	50w. brown, red & orge	20	10
1373	–	60w. grey, purple & mve	30	10
1374	–	70w. multicoloured	50	10
1375	–	80w. yellow, black & red	60	10
1376	–	90w. buff, green and orange	75	10
1377	–	100w. purple and mauve	45	10
1377a	–	100w. black	45	10
1378	–	150w. black, bistre and blue	50	10
1379	–	200w. brown and green	1·10	10
1380	–	300w. blue	2·00	20
1381	–	400w. green, brown and deep green	2·25	20
1381a	–	400w. blue, ochre, brown and grey	3·00	30
1382	–	450w. brown	1·60	40
1383	–	500w. dp green & green	2·00	40
1383a	–	550w. black	2·00	50
1384	–	600w. multicoloured	2·25	1·00
1385	–	700w. multicoloured	3·25	40
1386	–	800w. multicoloured	2·40	50
1387	–	1000w. lt brown & brn	3·25	40
1388	–	1000w. lt brown & brn	3·25	40
1389	–	5000w. multicoloured	18·00	4·00

DESIGNS—As T **703**: HORIZ: 15w. Mt. Sorak; 50w. Earthenware model of wagon; 90w. Paikryung Island; 1000w. Duck earthenware vessels (1387 facing right; 1388 facing left). VERT: 20w. Tolharubang (stone grandfather); 30w. National flag; 40w. "Hibiscus syriacus"; 60w. Porcelain jar, Yi Dynasty; 70w. Kyongju Observatory; 80w. Mounted warrior (pottery vessel); 100w. (1377) Ryu Kwan Soon; 100w. (1377a) Chung Yak Yong (writer); 150w. Porcelain jar, Chosun Dynasty; 200w. Ahn Joong Geun; 300w. Ahn Chang Ho; 400w. Koryo celadon incense burner; 450, 550w. Kim Ku (organizer of Korean Independence Party); 500w. Brick with mountain landscape; 600w. Hong Yung Sik (postal reformer); 700w. Duck (lid of incense burner). 29 × 41 mm: 800w. Dragon's head flagpole finial; 5000w. Tiger.

See also No. 1065.

725 People suffering from Traffic Pollution

1979. Environmental Protection.

1390 **725** 20w. brown and green 30 10

726 Common Goral

727 "Convallaria leiskei" Miquel

1979. Nature Conservation.

1391	**726**	20w. multicoloured	40	10
1392	**727**	20w. multicoloured	40	10

728 Presidents Pak and Carter

1979. Visit of President Carter of United States.

1393 **728** 20w. multicoloured . . . 20 10

729 Exhibition Building and Emblem

1979. Opening of Korea Exhibition Centre.

1395 **729** 20w. multicoloured . . . 20 10

730 Boeing 747-200 Jetliner and Globe

1979. 10th Anniv of Korean Air Lines.

1396 **730** 20w. multicoloured . . . 30 10

731 "The Courtesans' Sword Dance" (Shin Yun-bok)

1979. United States "5000 Years of Korean Art" Exhibition (1st issue).

1397 **731** 60w. multicoloured . . . 75 15

See also Nos. 1402/3, 1406/7, 1420/1, 1426/7, 1433/4, 1441/2 and 1457/8.

732 Mount Mai, North Cholla Province

733 Dragon's Head Rock, Cheju Island

1979. World Tourism Day.

1399	**732**	20w. multicoloured	25	10
1400	**733**	20w. multicoloured	25	10

734 Heart, Donors and Blood Drop

1979. Blood Donors.

1401 **734** 20w. red and green . . . 50 10

735 White Porcelain Jar with Grape Design

736 Mounted Warrior (pottery vessel)

1979. "5000 Years of Korean Art" Exhibition (2nd issue).

1402	**735**	20w. multicoloured	40	10
1403	**736**	20w. multicoloured	40	10

737 "Moon Travel" (Park Chung Jae)

1979. Philatelic Week.

1404 **737** 20w. multicoloured . . . 20 10

738 Hahoe Mask

739 Golden Amitabha with Halo

1979. "5000 Years of Korean Art" Exhibition (3rd issue).

1406	**738**	20w. multicoloured	40	10
1407	**739**	20w. multicoloured	40	10

740 Rain Frog

741 Asian Polypody

1979. Nature Conservation.

1408	**740**	20w. multicoloured	45	10
1409	**741**	20w. multicoloured	45	10

742 Monkey (bas-relief, Kim Yun Shin's tomb)

743 Children playing Yut

1979. Lunar New Year ("Year of the Monkey").

1410	**742**	20w. multicoloured	20	10
1411	**743**	20w. multicoloured	20	10

744 President Choi Kyu Hah

1979. Presidential Inauguration.

1413 **744** 20w. multicoloured . . . 30 10

745 Firefly

746 Meesun Tree

1980. Nature Conservation (5th series).

1415	**745**	30w. multicoloured	45	10
1416	**746**	30w. multicoloured	45	10

747 President Pak

748 Earthenware Kettle

749 "Landscape" (Kim Hong Do)

1980. President Pak Commemoration.

1417	**747**	30w. red	25	10
1418		30w. purple	25	10

1980. "5000 Years of Korean Art" Exhibition (4th issue).

1420	**748**	30w. multicoloured	40	10
1421	**749**	60w. multicoloured	55	10

750 "Lotus" 751 "Magpie and Tiger"

1980. Folk Paintings (1st series).
1423 **750** 30w. multicoloured . . . 50 20
1424 **751** 60w. multicoloured . . . 1·25 40
See also Nos. 1429/31, 1437/40 and 1453/6.

752 Merchant Ships

1980. Korean Merchant Navy.
1425 **752** 30w. multicoloured . . . 30 10

753 "Heavenly Horse" (tomb painting) 754 Banner Staff with Dragonhead Finial

1980. "5000 Years of Korean Art" Exhibition (5th series).
1426 **753** 30w. multicoloured . . . 40 10
1427 **754** 30w. multicoloured . . . 40 10

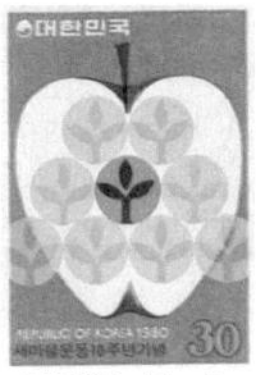

755 "Fruition"

1980. 10th Anniv of Saemaul Movement (community self-help programme).
1428 **755** 30w. multicoloured . . . 25 10

756 "Red Phoenix"

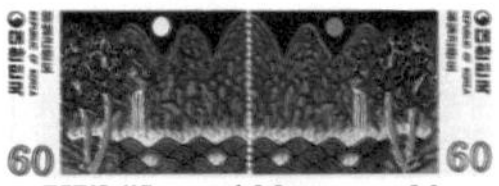

757/8 "Sun and Moon over Mt. Konryun" (½-size illustration)

1980. Folk Paintings (2nd series).
1429 **756** 30w. multicoloured . . . 30 10
1430 **757** 60w. multicoloured . . . 50 40
1431 **758** 60w. multicoloured . . . 50 40
Nos. 1430/1 were issued together, se-tenant, forming a composite design.

759 "Man on a Horse" (mural, Koguryo period) 760 "Tiger" (granite sculpture)

1980. "5000 Years of Korean Art" Exhibition (6th issue).
1433 **759** 30w. multicoloured . . . 40 10
1434 **760** 30w. multicoloured . . . 40 10

761 U.N. Flag and Rifle 762 "Venus de Milo" and Contestants

1980. 30th Anniv of Intervention of U.N. Forces in Korean War.
1435 **761** 30w. multicoloured . . . 30 10

1980. "Miss Universe" Beauty Contest, Seoul.
1436 **762** 30w. multicoloured . . . 30 10

763 "Rabbits pounding Grain in a Mortar" 764 "Dragon in Cloud"

1980. Folk Paintings (3rd series).
1437 **763** 30w. multicoloured . . . 40 10
1438 **764** 30w. multicoloured . . . 40 10

765 "Pine Tree" 766 "Flowers and Manchurian Cranes" (detail, folding screen)

1980. Folk Paintings (4th series).
1439 **765** 30w. multicoloured . . . 40 10
1440 **766** 30w. multicoloured . . . 75 20

767 Human faced Roof Tile 768 "White Tiger" (mural)

1980. "5000 Years of Korean Art" Exhibition (7th issue).
1441 **767** 30w. multicoloured . . . 30 10
1442 **768** 30w. multicoloured . . . 30 10

769 Football 770 President Chun Doo Hwan

1980. 10th President's Cup Football Tournament.
1443 **769** 30w. multicoloured . . . 30 10

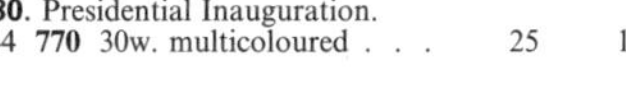

1980. Presidential Inauguration.
1444 **770** 30w. multicoloured . . . 25 10

771 Woman Soldier and Emblem

1980. 30th Anniv of Women's Army Corps.
1446 **771** 30w. multicoloured . . . 25 10

772 River Baegma

773 Three Peaks of Dodam

1980. World Tourism Day.
1447 **772** 30w. pink and purple . . 30 10
1448 **773** 30w. yellow, green & blue 30 10

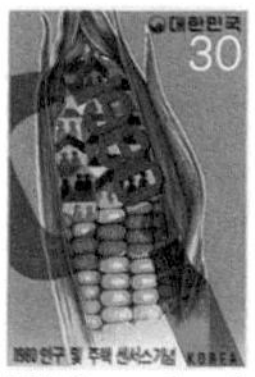

774 Corn-cob and Micrometer 775 Tree

1980. Population and Housing Census.
1449 **774** 30w. multicoloured . . . 30 10

1980. 75th Anniv of Korean Red Cross.
1450 **775** 30w. multicoloured . . . 35 10

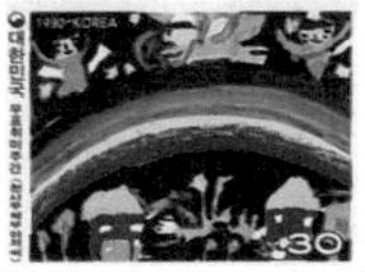

776 "Angels delivering Mail" (Kim Ki Chul)

1980. Philatelic Week.
1451 **776** 30w. multicoloured . . . 25 10

777 "Ten Long-life Symbols" 781 Deva King (sculpture)

1980. Folk Paintings (5th series). Multicoloured.
1453 30w. Type **777** . . . . . . 1·40 25
1454 30w. "Herb of eternal youth" and deer 30 10
1455 30w. Pine and deer eating herb 30 10
1456 30w. Pine, water and rock 30 10
Nos. 1453/6 were issued together, se-tenant, forming a composite design.

1980. "5000 Years of Korean Art" Exhibition (8th series).
1457 **781** 30w. black 40 10
1458 30w. red 40 10

782 "Cable Enterprise" (cable ship) and Cross-section of Cable

1980. Inauguration of Korea–Japan Submarine Cable.
1459 **782** 30w. multicoloured . . . 35 10

783 Cock (bas-relief, Kim Yu Shin's tomb) 784 Cranes

1980. Lunar New Year ("Year of the Cock").
1460 **783** 30w. multicoloured . . . 30 10
1461 **784** 30w. multicoloured . . . 30 10

785 President Chun Doo Hwan and Factory within "Hibiscus syriacus"

1981. Presidential Inauguration.
1463 **785** 30w. multicoloured . . . 25 10

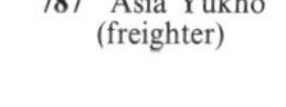

786 "Korea Sun" (tanker) 787 "Asia Yukho" (freighter)

1981. Ships (1st series).
1465 **786** 30w. multicoloured . . . 55 15
1466 **787** 90w. multicoloured . . . 85 25
See also Nos. 1470/1, 1482/5 and 1501/2.

788 National Assembly Building

1981. Inaugural Session of 11th National Assembly.
1467 **788** 30w. brown and gold . . 30 10

789 Symbols of Disability and I.Y.D.P. Emblem 790 Disabled Person in Wheelchair at Foot of Steps

1981. International Year of Disabled Persons.
1468 **789** 30w. multicoloured . . . 30 10
1469 **790** 90w. multicoloured . . . 60 35

791 "Saturn" (bulk-carrier)

792 "Hanjin Seoul" (container ship)

1981. Ships (2nd series).
1470 **791** 30w. deep purple, purple and blue 55 15
1471 **792** 90w. grey, blue and red 85 25

793 Council Emblem on Ribbon

1981. Advisory Council on Peaceful Unification Policy.
1472 **793** 40w. multicoloured . . . 30 10

794 "Clean Rivers and Air"

795 White Storks visiting Breeding Grounds

1981. World Environment Day.
1473 **794** 30w. multicoloured . . . 30 10
1474 **795** 90w. multicoloured . . . 65 20

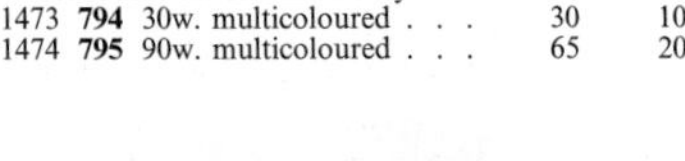

796 Presidents Chun and Suharto of Indonesia

1981. Presidential Visit to A.S.E.A.N. Countries. Multicoloured.
1475 40w. Type **796** 50 10
1476 40w. Pres. Chun and Sultan of Malaysia 50 10
1477 40w. Handshake and flags of South Korea and Singapore 50 10
1478 40w. Pres. Chun and King of Thailand 50 10
1479 40w. Presidents Chun and Marcos of Philippines . . 50 10
1480 40w. Pres. Chun and flags of Korea, Singapore, Malaysia and Philippines (39 × 43 mm) 50 10

802 "Chung Ryong No. 3" (tug)

803 "Soo Gong No. 71" (trawler)

1981. Ships (3rd series).
1482 **802** 40w. multicoloured . . . 65 15
1483 **803** 100w. multicoloured . . 95 25

804 "Aldebaran" (log carrier)

805 "Hyundai No. 1" (car carrier)

1981. Ships (4th series).
1484 **804** 40w. multicoloured . . . 65 15
1485 **805** 100w. multicoloured . . 95 25

806 Korean with Flag and Dates on Graph

812 W.H.O. Emblem and Citizens

807 Glider

1981. 36th Anniv of Liberation.
1486 **806** 40w. multicoloured . . . 30 10

1981. 3rd Model Aeronautic Competition. Mult.
1487 10w. Type **807** 40 10
1488 20w. Elastic-powered airplane 40 10
1489 40w. Line-controlled airplane 40 15
1490 50w. Radio-controlled airplane 60 20
1491 80w. Radio-controlled helicopter 75 30

1981. 32nd Session of W.H.O. Regional Committee for the Western Pacific, Seoul.
1492 **812** 40w. multicoloured . . . 30 10

813 Seoul Communications Tower

814 Ulreung Island

1981. World Tourism Day.
1493 **813** 40w. multicoloured . . . 30 10
1494 **814** 40w. multicoloured . . . 30 10

815 Cycling

816 Swimming

1981. 62nd National Sports Meeting, Seoul.
1495 **815** 40w. multicoloured . . . 35 10
1496 **816** 40w. multicoloured . . . 35 10

817 Presidents Chun and Carazo Odio

818 Hand holding Plate with F.A.O. Emblem

1981. Visit of President Carazo Odio of Costa Rica.
1497 **817** 40w. multicoloured . . . 30 10

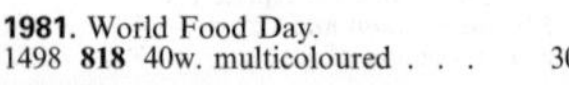

1981. World Food Day.
1498 **818** 40w. multicoloured . . . 30 10

819 Airliner and Clouds

820 South Gate of Seoul and Olympic Rings

1981. National Aviation Day.
1499 **819** 40w. orange, brown and silver 40 10

1981. Choice of Seoul as 1988 Olympic Host City.
1500 **820** 40w. multicoloured . . . 30 10

821 "Stolt Hawk" (chemical carrier)

822 Passenger Ferry

1981. Ships (5th series).
1501 **821** 40w. black 65 15
1502 **822** 100w. blue 95 25

823 "Hang-gliding" (Kim Kyung Jun)

1981. Philatelic Week.
1503 **823** 40w. multicoloured . . . 30 10

824 Camellia and Dog

825 Children flying Kite

1981. Lunar New Year ("Year of the Dog").
1505 **824** 40w. multicoloured . . . 30 10
1506 **825** 40w. multicoloured . . . 30 10

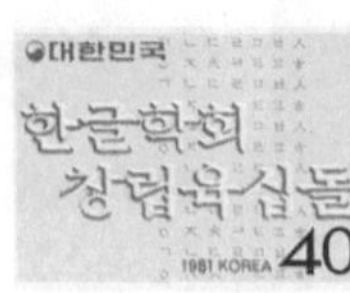

826 "Hangul Hakhoe"

1981. 60th Anniv of Hangul Hakhoe (Korean Language Society).
1508 **826** 40w. multicoloured . . . 35 10

827 Telephone and Dish Aerial

828 Scout Emblem and Logs forming "75"

1982. Inauguration of Korea Telecommunication Authority.
1509 **827** 60w. multicoloured . . . 40 10

1982. 75th Anniv of Boy Scout Movement.
1510 **828** 60w. multicoloured . . . 60 10

829 Young Woman

830 Dividers and World Map

1982. 60th Anniv of Korean Young Women's Christian Association.
1511 **829** 60w. multicoloured . . . 35 10

1982. Centenary of International Polar Year.
1512 **830** 60w. multicoloured . . . 50 10

831 Music and "Hibiscus syriacus"

1982. Children's Day.
1513 **831** 60w. multicoloured . . . 40 10

832 President Chun and Samuel Doe

1982. Visit of Samuel Doe (Liberian Head of State).
1514 **832** 60w. multicoloured . . . 35 10

833 Centenary Emblem

1982. Centenary of Korea–United States Friendship Treaty.
1516 **833** 60w. multicoloured . . . 30 10
1517 – 60w. multicoloured . . . 30 10
DESIGN: No. 1517, Statue of Liberty and Seoul South Gate.

835 Presidents Chun and Mobutu

1982. Visit of President Mobutu of Zaire.
1519 **835** 60w. multicoloured . . . 30 10

836 "Territorial Expansion by Kwanggaeto the Great" (Lee Chong Sang)

837 "General Euljimunduck's Great Victory at Salsoo" (Park Kak Soon)

1982. Documentary Paintings (1st series).
1521 **836** 60w. multicoloured . . . 40 10
1522 **837** 60w. multicoloured . . . 40 10
See also Nos. 1523/4, 1537/8 and 1548/9.

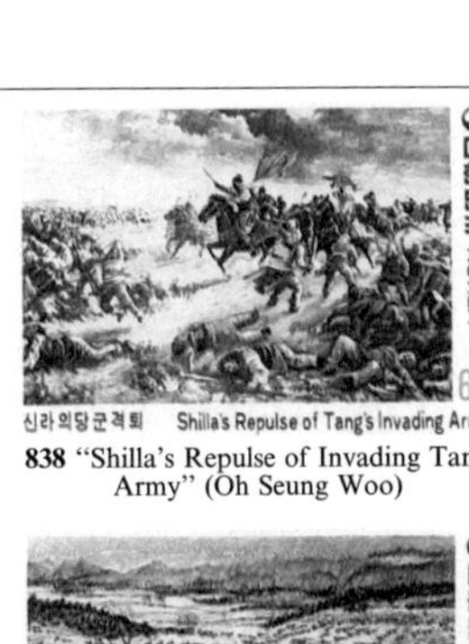

838 "Shilla's Repulse of Invading Tang Army" (Oh Seung Woo)

839 "General Kang Kam Chan's Great Victory at Kyiju" (Lee Yong Hwan)

1982. Documentary Paintings (2nd series).
1523 **838** 60w. multicoloured . . . 40 10
1524 **839** 60w. multicoloured . . . 40 10

840 Convention Emblem and Globe

841 Presidents Chun and Moi of Kenya

1982. 55th International Y's Men's Club Convention, Seoul.
1525 **840** 60w. multicoloured . . . 20 10

1982. Presidential Visits to Africa and Canada. Multicoloured.
1526 60w. Type **841** 35 10
1527 60w. Presidents Chun and Shagari of Nigeria 35 10
1528 60w. Presidents Chun and Bongo of Gabon 35 10
1529 60w. Presidents Chun and Diouf of Senegal 35 10
1530 60w. Flags of South Korea and Canada 35 10

846 National Flag

1982. Centenary of National Flag.
1532 **846** 60w. multicoloured . . . 40 10

847 Emblem and Player

1982. 2nd Seoul Table Tennis Championships.
1534 **847** 60w. multicoloured . . . 40 10

848 Baseball Player

1982. 27th World Baseball Championship Series, Seoul.
1535 **848** 60w. brown 40 10

849 Exhibition Centre

1982. Seoul International Trade Fair.
1536 **849** 60w. multicoloured . . . 30 10

850 "Admiral Yi Sun Sin's Great Victory at Hansan" (Kim Hyung Ku)

851 "General Kim Chwa Jin's Chungsanri Battle" (Sohn Soo Kwang)

1982. Documentary Paintings (3rd series).
1537 **850** 60w. multicoloured . . . 60 15
1538 **851** 60w. multicoloured . . . 35 10

852 "Miners reading Consolatory Letters" (Um Soon Keun)

1982. Philatelic Week.
1539 **852** 60w. multicoloured . . . 45 10

853 Presidents Chung and Suharto

1982. Visit of President Suharto of Indonesia.
1541 **853** 60w. multicoloured . . . 30 10

854 J.C.I. Emblem over World Map

855 "Intelsat 5" and "4-A" orbiting Globe

1982. 37th Junior Chamber International World Congress, Seoul.
1543 **854** 60w. multicoloured . . . 30 10

1982. Second U.N. Conference on the Exploration and Peaceful Uses of Outer Space, Vienna.
1544 **855** 60w. multicoloured . . . 30 10

856 Pig (bas-relief, Kim Yu Shin's tomb)

1982. Lunar New Year ("Year of the Pig").
1545 60w. Type **856** 35 10
1546 60w. Black-billed magpies and Korean moneybag . . 40 10

858 "General Kwon Yul's Great Victory at Haengju" (Oh Seung Woo)

859 "Kim Chong Suh's Exploitation of Yukin" (Kim Tae)

1982. Documentary Paintings (4th series).
1548 **858** 60w. multicoloured . . . 40 10
1549 **859** 60w. multicoloured . . . 40 10

860 Flags of South Korea and Turkey

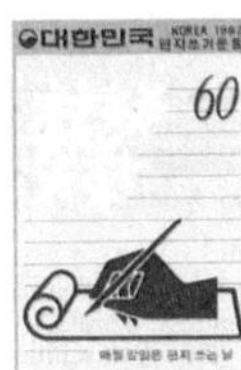

861 Hand writing Letter

1982. Visit of President Evran of Turkey.
1550 **860** 60w. multicoloured . . . 35 10

1982. Letter Writing Campaign.
1552 **861** 60w. multicoloured . . . 30 10

862 Emblem, Airliner, Container Ship and Cranes

1983. International Customs Day.
1553 **862** 60w. multicoloured . . . 50 15

863 Hyundai "Pony 2"

1983. Korean-made Vehicles (1st series). Multicoloured.
1554 60w. Type **863** 50 10
1555 60w. Keohwa Jeep 50 10
See also Nos. 1558/9, 1564/5, 1572/3 and 1576/7.

865 President Chun and Sultan of Malaysia

1983. Visit of King of Malaysia.
1556 **865** 60w. multicoloured . . . 30 10

866 Daewoo "Maepsy"

867 Kia "Bongo" Minibus

1983. Korean-made Vehicles (2nd series).
1558 **866** 60w. multicoloured . . . 50 10
1559 **867** 60w. multicoloured . . . 50 10

868 Former General Bureau of Postal Administration

869 Central Post Office, Seoul

1983. "Philakorea 84" International Stamp Exhibition, Seoul. Centenary of Korean Postal Service (1st series).
1560 **868** 60w. multicoloured . . . 30 10
1561 **869** 60w. multicoloured . . . 30 10
See also Nos. 1566/7, 1574/5 and 1603/6.

870 Old Village Schoolroom

1983. Teachers' Day.
1562 **870** 60w. multicoloured . . . 35 10

871 Asia Motor Co. Bus

872 Kia "Super Titan" Truck

1983. Korean-made Vehicles (3rd series).
1564 **871** 60w. multicoloured . . . 45 10
1565 **872** 60w. multicoloured . . . 45 10

873 Early Postman

1983. "Philakorea 84" International Stamp Exhibition, Seoul. Centenary of Korean Postal Service (2nd series).
1566 **873** 70w. multicoloured . . . 40 10
1567 – 70w. multicoloured . . . 40 10
DESIGN: No. 1567, Modern postman on motor-cycle.

875 "Communications in Outer Space" (Chun Ja Eun)

1983. World Communications Year.
1568 **875** 70w. multicoloured . . . 35 10

876 Whooper Swans at Sunrise

1983. Inaug of Communications Insurance.
1570 **876** 70w. multicoloured . . . 50 15

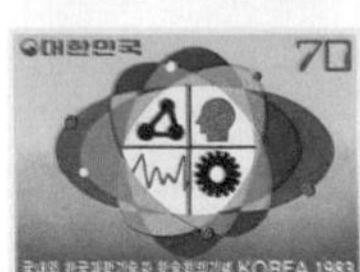

877 Emblems of Science and Engineering

1983. Korean Symposium on Science and Technology, Seoul.
1571 **877** 70w. multicoloured . . . 35 10

878 Daewoo Dump Truck

879 Hyundai Cargo Lorry

1983. Korean-made Vehicles (4th series).
1572 **878** 70w. multicoloured . . . 45 10
1573 **879** 70w. multicoloured . . . 45 10

880 Mail carried by Horse

1983. "Philakorea 84" International Stamp Exhibition, Seoul. Centenary of Korean Postal Service (3rd series). Multicoloured.
1574 70w. Type **880** 35 10
1575 70w. Mail truck and Douglas DC-8-60 Super Sixty jetliner 40 10

882 Dong-A Concrete Mixer Truck

883 Dong-A Tanker

1983. Korean-made Vehicles (5th series).
1576 **882** 70w. multicoloured . . . 50 10
1577 **883** 70w. multicoloured . . . 50 10

884 President Chun and King Hussein

1983. Visit of King Hussein of Jordan.
1578 **884** 70w. multicoloured . . . 35 10

885 Woman with Fan

886 I.P.U. Emblem and Flags

1983. 53rd American Society of Travel Agents World Congress, Seoul.
1580 **885** 70w. multicoloured . . . 35 10

1983. 70th Inter-Parliamentary Union Conference, Seoul.
1581 **886** 70w. multicoloured . . . 35 10

887 Gymnastics

888 Football

1983. 64th National Sports Meeting, Inchon.
1583 **887** 70w multicoloured . . . 40 10
1584 **888** 70w. multicoloured . . . 40 10

889 Presidents Chun and U San Yu of Burma

894 Rain Drops containing Symbols of Industry, Light and Food

1983. Presidential Visits. Multicoloured.
1585 70w. Type **889** 60 50
1586 70w. Presidents Chun and Giani Zail Singh of India 60 50
1587 70w. Presidents Chun and Jayewardene of Sri Lanka 60 50
1588 70w. Flags of South Korea and Australia 60 50
1589 70w. Flags of South Korea and New Zealand 60 50

1983. Development of Water Resources and 10th Anniv of Soyang-gang Dam.
1591 **894** 70w. multicoloured . . . 35 10

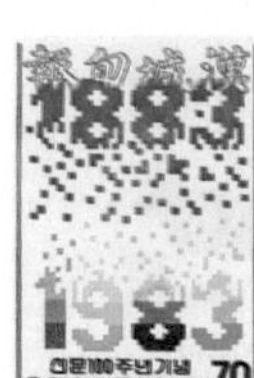

895 Centenary Dates

896 Tree with Lungs and Cross of Lorraine

1983. Centenary of 1st Korean Newspaper "Hansong Sunbo".
1592 **895** 70w. multicoloured . . . 35 10

1983. 30th Anniv of Korean National Tuberculosis Association.
1593 **896** 70w. multicoloured . . . 35 10

897 Presidents Chun and Reagan

898 Child collecting Stamps

1983. Visit of President Reagan of United States of America.
1594 **897** 70w. multicoloured . . . 35 10

1983. Philatelic Week.
1596 **898** 70w. multicoloured . . . 35 10

899 Rat (bas-relief, Kim Yu Shin's tomb)

1983. Lunar New Year ("Year of the Rat"). Multicoloured.
1598 70w. Type **899** 35 10
1599 70w. Manchurian cranes and pine 40 10

901 Bicentenary Emblem

902 5m. and 10m. Stamps, 1884

1984. Bicentenary of Catholic Church in Korea.
1601 **901** 70w. red, violet and silver 35 10

1984. "Philakorea 84" International Stamp Exhibition, Seoul. Centenary of Korean Postal Service (4th series). Multicoloured.
1603 70w. Type **902** 40 10
1604 70w. 5000w. stamp, 1983 . . 40 10

904 Old Postal Emblem and Post Box

1984. "Philakorea 84" International Stamp Exhibition, Seoul. Centenary of Korean Postal Service (5th series). Multicoloured.
1605 70w. Type **904** 40 10
1606 70w. Modern postal emblem and post box 40 10

906 President Chun and Sultan

1984. Visit of Sultan of Brunei.
1607 **906** 70w. multicoloured . . . 40 10

907 President Chun and Sheikh Khalifa

1984. Visit of Sheikh Khalifa of Qatar.
1609 **907** 70w. multicoloured . . . 35 10

908 Child posting Letter

1984. Centenary of Korean Postal Administration. Multicoloured.
1611 70w. Type **908** 35 10
1612 70w. Postman in city . . . 35 10

910 Pope John Paul II

911 Cogwheel, Worker's Tools and Flowers

1984. Visit of Pope John Paul II.
1614 **910** 70w. black 35 10
1615 70w. multicoloured . . . 35 10

1984. Labour Festival.
1617 **911** 70w. multicoloured . . . 30 10

912 Globe, Jetliner, Container Ship and Emblem

913 Map and Flags of S. Korea and Sri Lanka

1984. 63rd/64th Sessions of Customs Co-operation Council, Seoul.
1618 **912** 70w. multicoloured . . . 65 15

1984. Visit of President Jayewardene of Sri Lanka.
1619 **913** 70w. multicoloured . . . 35 10

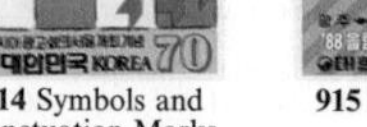

914 Symbols and Punctuation Marks

915 Expressway

1984. 14th Asian Advertising Congress, Seoul.
1621 **914** 70w. multicoloured . . . 35 10

1984. Opening of 88 Olympic Expressway.
1622 **915** 70w. multicoloured . . . 35 10

916 Laurel, "Victory" and Olympic Rings

917 A.B.U. Emblem and Microphone

1984. 90th Anniv of International Olympic Committee.
1623 **916** 70w. multicoloured . . . 35 10

1984. 20th Anniv of Asia-Pacific Broadcasting Union.
1624 **917** 70w. multicoloured . . . 35 10

918 Flags of S. Korea and Senegal

1984. Visit of President Abdou Diouf of Senegal.
1625 **918** 70w. multicoloured . . . 35 10

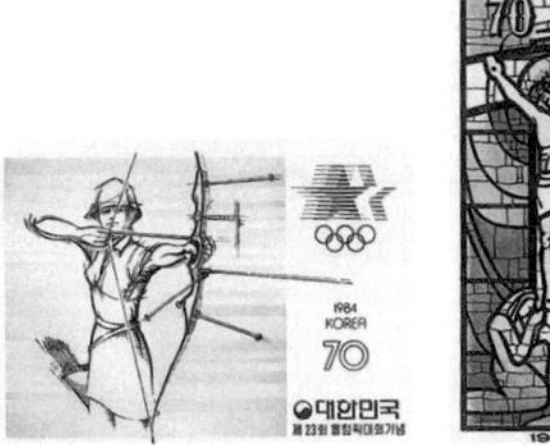

919 Archery **921** Crucifixion

1984. Olympic Games, Los Angeles. Multicoloured.
1627 70w. Type **919** 40 10
1628 440w. Fencing . . . . . . 1·60 35

1984. Centenary of Korean Protestant Church. Multicoloured.
1629 70w. Type **921** 40 10
1630 70w. Cross, vine and dove 40 10

923 Man carrying Silk-covered Lantern

1984. Folk Customs (1st series). "Wedding" (Kim Kyo Man). Multicoloured.
1632 70w. Type **923** 40 10
1633 70w. Bridegroom on horse 40 10
1634 70w. Man playing clarinet 40 10
1635 70w. Bride in sedan chair (51 × 35 mm) 40 10
See also Nos. 1657/8, 1683/4, 1734/8, 1808/11, 1840/3, 1858/61 and 1915/18.

927 Pres. Chun and Mt. Fuji

1984. Pres. Chun's Visit to Japan.
1637 **927** 70w. multicoloured . . . 40 10

928 Flags of S. Korea and Gambia

1984. Visit of President Sir Dawada Kairaba Jawara of Gambia.
1639 **928** 70w. multicoloured . . . 40 10

929 Symbols of International Trade **930** Namsan Tower and National Flags

1984. "Sitra '84" International Trade Fair, Seoul.
1641 **929** 70w. multicoloured . . . 40 10

1984. Visit of President El Hadj Omar Bongo of Gabon.
1642 **930** 70w. multicoloured . . . 40 10

931 Badminton **932** Magnifying Glass and Exhibition Emblem

1984. 65th National Sports Meeting, Taegu. Multicoloured.
1644 70w. Type **931** 40 10
1645 70w. Wrestling 40 10

1984. "Philakorea 1984" International Stamp Exhibition, Seoul. Multicoloured.
1646 70w. Type **932** 40 10
1647 70w. South Gate, Seoul, and stamps (horiz) 40 10

934 Presidents Chun and Gayoom

1984. Visit of President Maumoon Abdul Gayoom of the Maldives.
1650 **934** 70w. multicoloured . . . 40 10

935 "100" and Industrial Symbols

1984. Centenary of Korean Chamber of Commerce and Industry.
1652 **935** 70w. multicoloured . . . 40 10

936 Children playing Jaegi-chagi **937** Ox (bas-relief, Kim Yu Shin's tomb)

1984. Lunar New Year ("Year of the Ox").
1653 **936** 70w. multicoloured . . . 40 10
1654 **937** 70w. multicoloured . . . 40 10

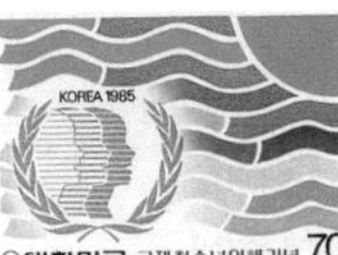

938 I.Y.Y. Emblem

1985. International Youth Year.
1656 **938** 70w. multicoloured . . . 40 10

939 Pounding Rice for New Year Rice Cake **940** Welcoming Year's First Full Moon

1985. Folk Customs (2nd series).
1657 **939** 70w. multicoloured . . . 40 10
1658 **940** 70w. multicoloured . . . 40 10

941 Seoul Olympic Emblem

1985. Olympic Games, Seoul (1988) (1st issue). Multicoloured.
1659 70w.+30w. Type **941** . . . 45 20
1660 70w.+30w. Hodori (mascot) 45 20
See also Nos. 1673/4, 1678/8, 1694/5, 1703/10, 1747/50, 1752/5, 1784/7, 1814/17, 1826/7, 1835/6 and 1844/7.

943 "Still Life with Doll" (Lee Chong Woo)

944 "Rocky Mountain in Early Spring Morning" (Ahn Jung Shik)

1985. Modern Art (1st series).
1662 **943** 70w. multicoloured . . . 40 10
1663 **944** 70w. multicoloured . . . 40 10
See also Nos. 1680/1, 1757/60, 1791/4 and 1875/8.

945 Flags, Statue of Liberty and President Chun **946** Flags, Seoul South Gate and National Flower

1985. Presidential Visit to United States.
1664 **945** 70w. multicoloured . . . 40 10

1985. Visit of President Mohammed Zia-ul-Haq of Pakistan.
1666 **946** 70w. multicoloured . . . 40 10

947 Underwood Hall

1985. Centenary of Yonsei University.
1668 **947** 70w. black, buff and green 40 10

948 Flags and Map

1985. Visit of President Luis Alberto Monge of Costa Rica.
1669 **948** 70w. multicoloured . . . 40 10

949 Rasbora

950 Sailfish

1985. Fishes (1st series).
1671 **949** 70w. multicoloured . . . 75 15
1672 **950** 70w. multicoloured . . . 75 15
See also Nos. 1730/3, 1797/1800, 1881/4, 1903/6 and 1951/4.

951 Rowing **952** National Flags

1985. Olympic Games, Seoul (1988) (2nd issue). Multicoloured.
1673 70w.+30w. Type **951** . . . 45 30
1674 70w.+30w. Hurdling 45 30

1985. Visit of President Hussain Muhammed Ershad of Bangladesh.
1676 **952** 70w. multicoloured . . . 40 10

953 National Flags

1985. Visit of President Joao Bernardo Vieira of Guinea-Bissau.
1678 **953** 70w. multicoloured . . . 40 10

954 "Spring Day on the Farm" (Huh Paik Ryun)

955 "The Exorcist" (Kim Chung Hyun)

1985. Modern Art (2nd issue).
1680 **954** 70w. multicoloured . . . 40 10
1681 **955** 70w. multicoloured . . . 40 10

956 Heavenly Lake, Paekdu and National Flower

1985. 40th Anniv of Liberation.
1682 **956** 70w. multicoloured . . . 40 10

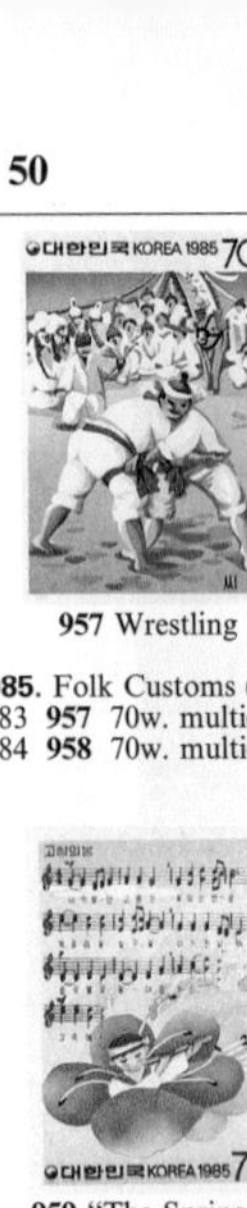

957 Wrestling 958 Janggi

1985. Folk Customs (3rd series).
1683 **957** 70w. multicoloured . . . 40 10
1684 **958** 70w. multicoloured . . . 40 10

959 "The Spring of My Home" (Lee Won Su and Hong Nan Pa) 960 "A Leaf Boat" (Park Hong Keun and Yun Yong Ha)

1985. Korean Music (1st series).
1685 **959** 70w. multicoloured . . . 45 10
1686 **960** 70w. multicoloured . . . 45 10
See also Nos. 1728/9, 1776/7, 1854/5, 1862/3, 1893/4, 1935/6, 1996/7 and 2064/5.

1985. Olympic Games, Seoul (1988) (3rd issue). As T **951**. Multicoloured.
1687 70w.+30w. Basketball . . . 45 20
1688 70w.+30w. Boxing 45 20

961 Satellite, "100" and Dish Aerial 962 Meetings Emblem

1985. Centenary of First Korean Telegraph Service.
1690 **961** 70w. multicoloured . . . 40 10

1985. World Bank and International Monetary Fund Meetings, Seoul.
1691 **962** 70w. multicoloured . . . 40 10

963 U.N. Emblem and Doves

1985. 40th Anniv of U.N.O.
1692 **963** 70w. multicoloured . . . 40 10

964 Red Cross and Hands (detail "Creation of Adam", Michelangelo)

1985. 80th Anniv of Korea Red Cross.
1693 **964** 70w. black, red and blue 45 10

1985. Olympic Games, Seoul (1988) (4th issue). As T **951**. Multicoloured.
1694 70w.+30w. Cycling 40 20
1695 70w.+30w. Canoeing . . . 40 20

965 Cancelled Stamp on Envelope 966 Tiger (bas-relief, Kim Yu Shin's tomb)

1985. Philatelic Week.
1697 **965** 70w. multicoloured . . . 40 10

1985. Lunar New Year ("Year of the Tiger").
1698 **966** 70w. multicoloured . . . 40 10

967 Mount Fuji and Boeing 747 Jetliner

1985. 20th Anniv of Korea–Japan Treaty on Basic Relations.
1699 **967** 70w. mult (postage) . . 45 10
1700 370w. multicoloured (air) 1·50 50

968 Doves and Globe 970 Pres. Chun, Big Ben and Korean and British Flags

1986. International Peace Year.
1701 **968** 70w. multicoloured . . . 35 10
1702 400w. multicoloured . . 1·75 40

1986. Olympic Games, Seoul (1988) (5th series). As T **951**. Multicoloured.
1703 70w.+30w. Show jumping (postage) 40 20
1704 70w.+30w. Fencing 40 20
1705 70w.+30w. Football 40 20
1706 70w.+30w. Gymnastics . . . 40 20
1707 370w.+100w. As No. 1703 (air) . . . . 1·60 70
1708 400w.+100w. As No. 1704 1·75 70
1709 440w.+100w. As No. 1705 1·90 70
1710 470w.+100w. As No. 1706 2·00 70

1986. Presidential Visit to Europe. Multicoloured.
1711 70w. Type **970** 40 10
1712 70w. Pres. Chun, Eiffel Tower and Korean and French flags 40 10
1713 70w. Pres. Chun, Belgian Parliament and Korean and Belgian flags 40 10
1714 70w. Pres. Chun, Cologne Cathedral and Korean and West German flags 40 10

974/5 Kyongju and Kwanchon Observatories

1986. Science (1st series). Appearance of Halley's Comet.
1716 **974** 70w. multicoloured . . . 30 10
1717 **975** 70w. multicoloured . . . 30 10
See also Nos. 1781/2, 1833/4, 1864/5 and 1898/9.

976 General Assembly Emblem 977 Swallowtail and Flowers

1986. 5th Association of National Olympic Committees General Assembly, Seoul.
1718 **976** 70w. multicoloured . . . 45 10

1986. "Ameripex '86" International Stamp Exhibition, Chicago. Multicoloured.
1719 70w. Type **977** . . . . . . 2·00 75
1720 370w. "Papilio bianor" . . 2·00 75
1721 400w. Swallowtails . . . . 2·00 75
1722 440w. Swallowtail and frog 2·00 75
1723 450w. Swallowtail . . . . . 2·00 75
1724 470w. "Papilio bianor" . . 2·00 75
Nos. 1719/24 were printed together, se-tenant, forming a composite design.

983 Male and Female Symbols in Balance

1986. Centenary of Korean Women's Education.
1725 **983** 70w. multicoloured . . . 35 10

984 National Flags

1986. Visit of President Andre Kolingba of Central African Republic.
1726 **984** 70w. multicoloured . . . 35 10

985 "Half Moon" (Yun Keuk Young) 986 "Let's Go and Pick the Moon" (Yun Seok Jung and Park Tae Hyun)

1986. Korean Music (2nd series).
1728 **985** 70w. multicoloured . . . 35 10
1729 **986** 70w. multicoloured . . . 35 10

987 Cyprinid Fish

988 Ayu

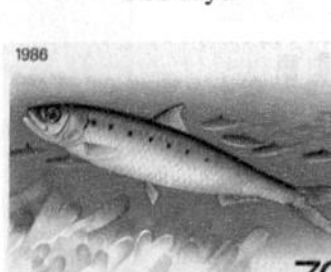

989 Black-spotted Sardine

990 Hammerheads

1986. Fishes (2nd series).
1730 **987** 70w. multicoloured . . . 85 20
1731 **988** 70w. multicoloured . . . 85 20
1732 **989** 70w. multicoloured . . . 85 20
1733 **990** 70w. multicoloured . . . 85 20

991 Flag Carrier and Gong Player 996 Child

1986. Folk Customs (4th series). Farm Music. Multicoloured.
1734 70w. Type **991** 30 10
1735 70w. Drummer and piper 30 10
1736 70w. Drummer and gong player 30 10
1737 70w. Men with ribbons . . 30 10
1738 70w. Man and woman with child 30 10
Nos. 1734/8 were printed together, se-tenant, forming a composite design.

1986. Family Planning.
1739 **996** 80w. multicoloured . . . 40 10

997 Bridge and "63" Building, Seoul

1986. Completion of Han River Development. Multicoloured.
1740 30w. Type **997** 85 25
1741 60w. Buildings and excursion boat 60 25
1742 80w. Rowing boat and Seoul Tower 40 10
Nos. 1740/2 were printed together, se-tenant, forming a composite design.

1000 Emblem 1004 Boy fishing for Stamp

1002 "5", Delegates and Juan Antonio Samaranch (President of International Olympic Committee)

1986. 10th Asian Games, Seoul. Multicoloured.
1743 80w. Type **1000** 40 10
1744 80w. Firework display . . . 40 10

1986. 5th Anniv of Choice of Seoul as 1988 Olympic Games Host City.
1746 **1002** 80w. multicoloured . . 45 10

1986. Olympic Games, Seoul (1988) (6th issue). As T **951**. Multicoloured.
1747 80w.+50w. Weightlifting (postage) . . . . 1·25 60
1748 80w.+50w. Handball . . . . 1·25 60
1749 370w.+100w. As No. 1747 (air) . . . . 1·75 75
1750 400w.+100w. As No. 1748 1·90 75

1986. Olympic Games, Seoul (1988) (7th issue). As T **951**. Multicoloured.
1752 80w.+50w. Judo (postage) 1·10 60
1753 80w.+50w. Hockey . . . . 1·10 60
1754 440w.+100w. As No. 1752 (air) . . . . 1·75 70
1755 470w.+100w. As No. 1753 1·90 70

1986. Philatelic Week.
1756 **1004** 80w. multicoloured . . 40 10

1005 "Chunhyang-do" (Kim Un Ho) 1006 "Flowers" (Lee Sang Bum)

1007 "Portrait of a Friend" (Ku Bon Wung)

1008 "Woman in a Ski Suit" (Son Ung Seng)

1986. Modern Art (3rd series).
1757 **1005** 80w. multicoloured . . 40 10
1758 **1006** 80w. multicoloured . . 40 10
1759 **1007** 80w. multicoloured . . 40 10
1760 **1008** 80w. multicoloured . . 40 10

1009 Rabbit **1010** Eastern Broad-billed Roller ("Roller")

1986. Lunar New Year ("Year of the Rabbit").
1761 **1009** 80w. multicoloured . . 35 10

1986. Birds. Multicoloured.
1762 80w. Type **1010** . . . . . 1·00 10
1763 80w. Japanese waxwing ("Waxwing") . . . . . . 1·00 10
1764 80w. Black-naped oriole ("Oriole") . . . . 1·00 10
1765 80w. Black-capped kingfisher ("Kingfisher") 1·00 10
1766 80w. Hoopoe . . . . 1·00 10

1011 Siberian Tiger **1012** Bleeding Heart ("Dicentra spectabilis")

1987. Endangered Animals. Multicoloured.
1767 80w. Type **1011** . . . . . 1·00 30
1768 80w. Leopard cat . . . . . 1·00 30
1769 80w. Red fox . . . . 1·00 30
1770 80w. Wild boar . . . . . . 1·00 30

1987. Flowers. Multicoloured.
1771 550w. Type **1012** . . . . . 1·50 25
1772 550w. Diamond bluebell ("Hanabusaya asiatica") 1·50 25
1773 550w. "Erythronium japonicum" . . . . . . 1·50 25
1774 550w. Pinks ("Dianthus chinensis") . . . . 1·50 25
1775 550w. "Chrysanthemum zawadskii" . . . . 1·50 25

1013 "Barley Field" (Park Wha Mok and Yun Yong Ha) **1014** "Magnolia" (Cho Young Shik and Kim Dong Jin)

1987. Korean Music (3rd series).
1776 **1013** 80w. multicoloured . . 40 10
1777 **1014** 80w. multicoloured . . 40 10

1015 National Flags and Korean National Flower

1987. Visit of President Ahmed Abdallah Abderemane of Comoros.
1778 **1015** 80w. multicoloured . . 35 10

1016 "100", Light Bulb and Hyang Woen Jeong

1987. Centenary of Electric Light in Korea.
1780 **1016** 80w. multicoloured . . 35 10

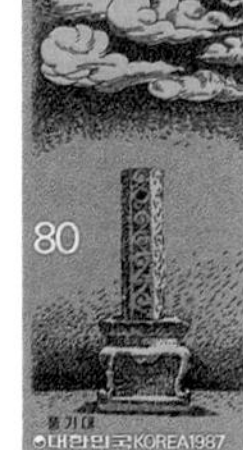

1017 Punggi Wind Observatory **1019** Globes, Crane and Ship

1987. Science (2nd series).
1781 **1017** 80w. dp brown & brown 40 10
1782 – 80w. brown & dp brown 40 10
DESIGN: No. 1782, Rain gauge.

1987. 15th International Association of Ports and Harbours General Session, Seoul.
1783 **1019** 80w. multicoloured . . 40 10

1987. Olympic Games, Seoul (1988) (8th issue). As T **951**. Multicoloured.
1784 80w.+50w. Wrestling . . . 80 25
1785 80w.+50w. Tennis 80 25
1786 80w.+50w. Diving 80 25
1787 80w.+50w. Show jumping 80 25

1020 Flags and Doves

1987. Visit of President U San Yu of Burma.
1789 **1020** 80w. multicoloured . . 40 10

1021 "Valley of Peach Blossoms" (Pyen Kwan Sik)

1022 "Rural Landscape" (Lee Yong Wu)

1023 "Man" (Lee Ma Dong)

1024 "Woman with Water Jar on Head" (sculpture, Yun Hyo Chung)

1987. Modern Art (4th series).
1791 **1021** 80w. multicoloured . . 35 10
1792 **1022** 80w. multicoloured . . 35 10
1793 **1023** 80w. multicoloured . . 35 10
1794 **1024** 80w. multicoloured . . 35 10

1025 Map and Digital Key Pad

1987. Completion of Automatic Telephone Network (1795) and Communications for Information Year (1796).
1795 80w. Type **1025** 35 10
1796 80w. Emblem 35 10

1027 Cyprinid Fishes

1028 Russell's Oarfish

1029 Cyprinid Fish

1030 Spine-tailed Mobula

1987. Fishes (3rd series).
1797 **1027** 80w. multicoloured . . 85 20
1798 **1028** 80w. multicoloured . . 85 20
1799 **1029** 80w. multicoloured . . 85 20
1800 **1030** 80w. multicoloured . . 85 20

1031 Statue of Indomitable Koreans (detail) and Flags **1033** Map and Pen within Profile

1987. Opening of Independence Hall. Mult.
1801 80w. Type **1031** 35 10
1802 80w. Monument of the Nation and aerial view of Hall 35 10

1987. 16th Pacific Science Congress, Seoul.
1804 **1033** 80w. multicoloured . . 35 10

1034 Flags and Seoul South Gate

1987. Visit of President Virgilio Barco of Colombia.
1806 **1034** 80w. multicoloured . . 40 10

1035/1038 Festivities (½-size illustration)

1987. Folk Customs (5th series). Harvest Moon Day.
1808 **1035** 80w. multicoloured . . 35 10
1809 **1036** 80w. multicoloured . . 35 10
1810 **1037** 80w. multicoloured . . 35 10
1811 **1038** 80w. multicoloured . . 35 10
Nos. 1808/11 were issued together, se-tenant, forming a composite design.

1039 Telephone Dials forming Number **1040** Service Flags and Servicemen

1987. Installation of over 10,000,000 Telephone Lines.
1812 **1039** 80w. multicoloured . . 40 10

1987. Armed Forces Day.
1813 **1040** 80w. multicoloured . . 40 10

1987. Olympic Games, Seoul (1988) (9th issue). As T **951**. Multicoloured.
1814 80w.+50w. Table tennis . . 70 20
1815 80w.+50w. Shooting 70 20
1816 80w.+50w. Archery 70 20
1817 80w.+50w. Volleyball . . . 70 20

1041 Stamps around Child playing Trumpet **1042** Korean Scientist and Map

1987. Philatelic Week.
1819 **1041** 80w. multicoloured . . 35 10

1987. 1st Anniv of South Korea's Signing of Antarctic Treaty.
1820 **1042** 80w. multicoloured . . 80 30

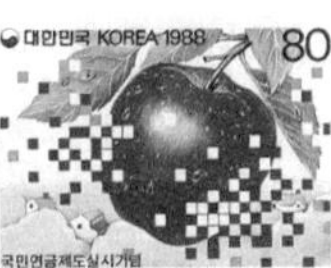

1043 Dragon **1044** Scattered Sections of Apple

1987. Lunar New Year ("Year of the Dragon").
1821 **1043** 80w. multicoloured . . 35 10

1988. Compulsory Pension Programme.
1822 **1044** 80w. multicoloured . . 30 10

1045 Base and Gentoo Penguins **1046** Flag, Olympic Stadium and President Roh Tae Woo

1988. Completion of Antarctic Base.
1823 **1045** 80w. multicoloured . . 70 25

1988. Presidential Inauguration.
1824 **1046** 80w. multicoloured . . 30 10

1047 Dinghy Racing **1049** Crane

1988. Olympic Games, Seoul (1988) (10th issue). Multicoloured.
1826 80w.+20w. Type **1047** . . . 35 20
1827 80w.+20w. Taekwondo . . 35 20

1988. Japanese White-naped Crane. Mult.
1829 80w. Type **1049** . . . . . 1·25 60
1830 80w. Crane taking off . . . 1·25 60
1831 80w. Crane with wings spread . . . . 1·25 60
1832 80w. Two cranes in flight . . 1·25 60

1053 Water Clock **1055** Torch Carrier

1988. Science (3rd series). Multicoloured.
1833 80w. Type **1053** 30 10
1834 80w. Sundial 30 10
Nos. 1833/4 were issued together, se-tenant, forming a composite design.

1988. Olympic Games, Seoul (1988) (11th issue). Multicoloured.
1835 80w.+20w. Type **1055** . . . 35 20
1836 80w.+20w. Stadium 35 20

1057 Globe and Red Cross as Candle **1058** Computer Terminal

1988. 125th Anniv of International Red Cross.
1838 **1057** 80w. multicoloured . . 30 10

1988. 1st Anniv of National Use of Telepress.
1839 **1058** 80w. multicoloured . . 30 10

1059 Woman sitting by Pool and Woman on Swing **1063** Olympic Flag and Pierre de Coubertin (founder of modern Games)

1988. Folk Customs (6th series). Tano Day. Multicoloured.
1840 80w. Type **1059** 65 35
1841 80w. Women dressing their hair 65 35
1842 80w. Woman on swing and boy smelling flowers . . . 65 35
1843 80w. Boys wrestling 65 35

Nos. 1840/3 were issued together, se-tenant, forming a composite design.

1988. Olympic Games, Seoul (1988) (12th issue). Multicoloured.
1844 80w. Type **1063** 30 10
1845 80w. Olympic monument . . 30 10
1846 80w. View of Seoul (vert) 30 10
1847 80w. Women in Korean costume (vert) 30 10

1067 Stamps forming Torch Flame **1068** Pouring Molten Metal from Crucible

1988. "Olymphilex '88" Olympic Stamps Exhibition, Seoul.
1849 **1067** 80w. multicoloured . . 30 10

1988. 22nd International Iron and Steel Institute Conference, Seoul.
1851 **1068** 80w. multicoloured . . 30 10

1069 Gomdoori (mascot)

1988. Paralympic Games, Seoul.
1852 80w. Type **1069** . . . . . 1·00 50
1853 80w. Archery 50 10

1071 "Homesick" (Lee Eun Sang and Kim Dong Jin) **1072** "The Pioneer" (Yoon Hae Young and Cho Doo Nam)

1988. Korean Music (4th series).
1854 **1071** 80w. multicoloured . . 35 10
1855 **1072** 80w. multicoloured . . 35 10

1073 Girls on See-saw **1075** Dancers

1988. Lunar New Year ("Year of the Snake").
1856 **1073** 80w. multicoloured . . 25 10

1989. Folk Customs (7th series). Mask Dance. Multicoloured.
1858 80w. Type **1075** 25 10
1859 80w. Dancer with fans . . 25 10
1860 80w. Dancer holding branch 25 10
1861 80w. Dancer with "Lion" 25 10
Nos. 1858/61 were issued together, se-tenant, forming a composite design.

1079 "Arirang" **1080** "Doraji-taryong"

1989. Korean Music (5th series).
1862 **1079** 80w. multicoloured . . 25 10
1863 **1080** 80w. multicoloured . . 25 10

1081/2 Wooden and metal Type Printing

1989. Science (4th series).
1864 **1081** 80w. brown, bis & stone 25 10
1865 **1082** 80w. brown, bis & stone 25 10
Nos. 1864/5 were issued together, se-tenant, forming a composite design.

1083 Teeth, Globe, Pencil and Book **1084** Hand with Stick in Heart

1989. 14th Asian–Pacific Dental Congress.
1866 **1083** 80w. multicoloured . . 25 10

1989. Respect for the Elderly.
1867 **1084** 80w. multicoloured . . 25 10

1085 Emblem **1086** Profiles within Heart

1989. Rotary Int Convention, Seoul.
1868 **1085** 80w. multicoloured . . 25 10

1989. 19th International Council of Nurses Congress, Seoul.
1869 **1086** 80w. multicoloured . . 25 10

1087 "Communication" **1088** "Longevity"

1989. National Information Technology Month.
1870 **1087** 80w. multicoloured . . 25 10

1989. World Environment Day.
1871 **1088** 80w. multicoloured . . 30 10

1089 Satellite, Globe and Dish Aerial **1090** "Liberty guiding the People" (detail, Eugene Delacroix)

1989. 10th Anniv of Asia–Pacific Telecommunity.
1872 **1089** 80w. multicoloured . . 25 10

1989. Bicentenary of French Revolution.
1873 **1090** 80w. multicoloured . . 25 10

1091 Apple and Flask

1989. 5th Asian and Oceanic Biochemists Federation Congress, Seoul.
1874 **1091** 80w. multicoloured . . 25 10

1092 "White Ox" (Lee Joong Sub)

1093 "Street Stall" (Park Lae Hyun)

1094 "Little Girl" (Lee Bong Sang)

1095 "Autumn Scene" (Oh Ji Ho)

1989. Modern Art (5th series).
1875 **1092** 80w. multicoloured . . 30 10
1876 **1093** 80w. multicoloured . . 30 10
1877 **1094** 80w. multicoloured . . 30 10
1878 **1095** 80w. multicoloured . . 30 10

1096 Hunting Scene **1097** Goddess of Law and Ancient Law Code

1989. Seoul Olympics Commemorative Festival and World Sports Festival for Ethnic Koreans.
1879 **1096** 80w. multicoloured . . 25 10

1989. 1st Anniv of Constitutional Court.
1880 **1097** 80w. multicoloured . . 25 10

1098 Banded Knifejaw

1099 Banded Loach

1100 Torrent Catfish

1101 Japanese Pinecone Fish

1989. Fishes (4th series).
1881 **1098** 80w. multicoloured . . 85 20
1882 **1099** 80w. multicoloured . . 85 20
1883 **1100** 80w. multicoloured . . 85 20
1884 **1101** 80w. multicoloured . . 85 20

1102 Emblem

1989. 44th International Eucharistic Congress, Seoul.
1885 **1102** 80w. multicoloured . . 25 10

1103 Control Tower and Boeing 747 Jetliner

1989. 29th International Civil Airports Association World Congress, Seoul.
1886 **1103** 80w. multicoloured . . 35 10

1104 Scissors cutting Burning Banner

1105 Lantern

1989. Fire Precautions Month.
1887 **1104** 80w. multicoloured . . 25 10

1989. Philatelic Week.
1888 **1105** 80w. multicoloured . . 25 10

1106 Cranes

1107 New Year Custom

1989. Lunar New Year ("Year of the Horse").
1890 **1106** 80w. multicoloured . . 25 10
1891 **1107** 80w. multicoloured . . 25 10

1108 "Pakyon Fall"

1109 "Chonan Samgori"

1990. Korean Music (6th series).
1893 **1108** 80w. multicoloured . . 25 10
1894 **1109** 80w. multicoloured . . 25 10

1110 Clouds, Umbrella and Satellite

1111 Child with Rose

1990. World Meteorological Day.
1895 **1110** 80w. multicoloured . . 40 10

1990. 40th Anniv of U.N.I.C.E.F. Work in Korea.
1896 **1111** 80w. multicoloured . . 25 10

1112 Cable, Fish and Route Map

1990. Completion of Cheju Island–Kohung Optical Submarine Cable.
1897 **1112** 80w. multicoloured . . 40 10

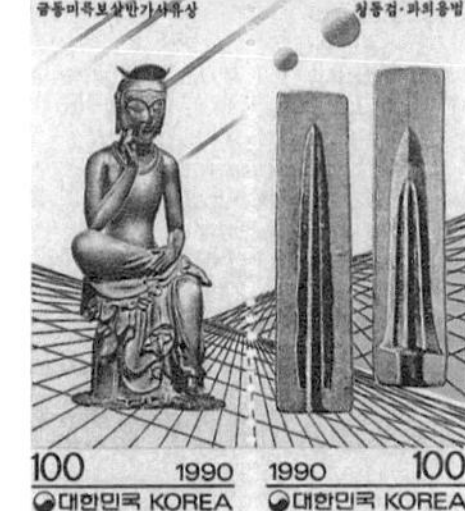
1113/4 Gilt-bronze Maitreya, Spear and Dagger Moulds

1990. Science (5th series). Metallurgy.
1898 **1113** 100w. multicoloured . . 30 15
1899 **1114** 100w. multicoloured . . 30 15
Nos. 1898/9 were issued together, se-tenant, forming the composite design illustrated.

1115 Housing and "20"

1990. 20th Anniv of Saemaul Movement (community self-help programme).
1900 **1115** 100w. multicoloured . . 30 15

1116 Youths

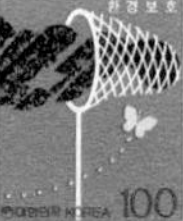
1117 Butterfly Net catching Pollution

1990. Youth Month.
1901 **1116** 100w. multicoloured . . 30 15

1990. World Environmental Day.
1902 **1117** 100w. multicoloured . . 30 15

1118 Belted Bearded Grunt

1119 Kusa Pufferfish

1120 Cherry Salmon

1121 Rosy Bitterling

1990. Fishes (5th series).
1903 **1118** 100w. multicoloured . . 75 20
1904 **1119** 100w. multicoloured . . 75 20
1905 **1120** 100w. multicoloured . . 75 20
1906 **1121** 100w. multicoloured . . 75 20

1122 Automatic Sorting Machines

1123 Bandaged Teddy Bear in Hospital Bed

1990. Opening of Seoul Mail Centre.
1907 **1122** 100w. multicoloured . . 30 15

1990. Road Safety Campaign.
1909 **1123** 100w. multicoloured . . 75 30

1124 Campfire

1125 Lily

1990. 8th Korean Boy Scouts Jamboree, Kosong.
1910 **1124** 100w. multicoloured . . 30 15

1990. Wild Flowers (1st series). Multicoloured.
1911 370w. Type **1125** . . . . . 1·25 60
1912 400w. Asters . . . . 1·40 60
1913 440w. Pheasant's eye . . . 1·25 60
1914 470w. Scabious . . . . . . 1·90 60
See also Nos. 1956/9, 1992/5, 2082/5, 2133/6, 2162/5, 2191/4 and 2244/7.

1129 Washing Wool

1133 Church

1990. Folk Customs (8th series). Hand Weaving.
1915 **1129** 100w. red, yellow & blk 30 15
1916 – 100w. multicoloured . . 30 15
1917 – 100w. multicoloured . . 30 15
1918 – 100w. multicoloured . . 30 15
DESIGNS: No. 1916, Spinning; 1917, Dyeing spun yarn; 1918, Weaving.

1990. Centenary of Anglican Church in Korea.
1919 **1133** 100w. multicoloured . . 30 15

1134 Top of Tower

1135 Peas in Pod

1990. 10th Anniv of Seoul Communications Tower.
1920 **1134** 100w. black, blue & red 30 15

1990. Census.
1921 **1135** 100w. multicoloured . . 30 15

1136 "40" and U.N. Emblem

1137 Inlaid Case with Mirror

1990. 40th Anniv of U.N. Development Programme.
1922 **1136** 100w. multicoloured . . 30 15

1990. Philatelic Week.
1923 **1137** 100w. multicoloured . . 30 15

1138 Children feeding Ram

1140 Mascot

1990. Lunar New Year ("Year of the Sheep"). Multicoloured.
1925 100w. Type **1138** 30 15
1926 100w. Crane flying above mountains 30 15

1990. "Expo '93" World's Fair, Taejon (1st issue). Multicoloured.
1928 100w. Type **1140** 30 20
1929 440w. Yin and Yang (exhibition emblem) . . . 1·25 60
See also Nos. 1932/3, 2000/1 and 2058/61.

1142 Books and Emblem

1143 Earth

1991. 30th Anniv of Saemaul Minilibrary.
1931 **1142** 100w. multicoloured . . 30 15

1991. "Expo '93" World's Fair, Taejon (2nd issue). Multicoloured.
1932 100w. Type **1143** 30 15
1933 100w. Expo Tower 30 15

1145 "In a Flower Garden" (Uh Hyo Sun and Kwon Kil Sang)

1146 "Way to the Orchard" (Park Hwa Mok and Kim Kong Sun)

1991. Korean Music (7th series).
1935 **1145** 100w. multicoloured . . 30 15
1936 **1146** 100w. multicoloured . . 30 15

1147 Moth

1148 Beetle

1149 Butterfly

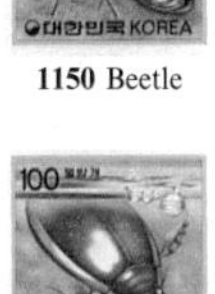
1150 Beetle

1151 Cicada

1152 Water Beetle

1153 Hornet

1154 Ladybirds

1155 Dragonfly **1156** Grasshopper

1991. Insects.

1937 **1147** 100w. multicoloured . . 40 15
1938 **1148** 100w. multicoloured . . 40 15
1939 **1149** 100w. multicoloured . . 40 15
1940 **1150** 100w. multicoloured . . 40 15
1941 **1151** 100w. multicoloured . . 40 15
1942 **1152** 100w. multicoloured . . 40 15
1943 **1153** 100w. multicoloured . . 40 15
1944 **1154** 100w. multicoloured . . 40 15
1945 **1155** 100w. multicoloured . . 40 15
1946 **1156** 100w. multicoloured . . 40 15

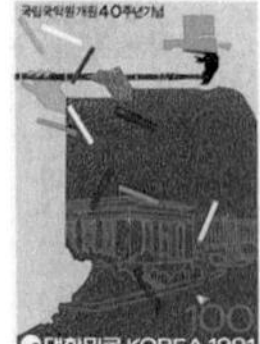

1157 Flautist and Centre **1158** Flag and Provisional Government Building

1991. 40th Anniv of Korean Traditional Performing Arts Centre.

1947 **1157** 100w. multicoloured . . 30 15

1991. 72nd Anniv of Establishment of Korean Provisional Government in Shanghai.

1948 **1158** 100w. multicoloured . . 30 15

1159 Urban Landscape and Emblem

1991. Employment for Disabled People.

1949 **1159** 100w. multicoloured . . 30 15

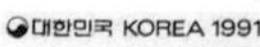

1160 Bouquet

1991. Teachers' Day.

1950 **1160** 100w. multicoloured . . 30 15

1161 Asian Minnow

1162 Majime Minnows

1163 Blotched Grunter

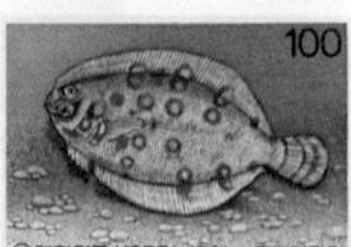

1164 Ijima's Left-eyed Flounder

1991. Fishes (6th series).

1951 **1161** 100w. multicoloured . . 65 25
1952 **1162** 100w. multicoloured . . 65 25
1953 **1163** 100w. multicoloured . . 65 25
1954 **1164** 100w. multicoloured . . 65 25

1165 Animals waiting to Board Bus **1166** "Aerides japonicum"

1991. "Waiting One's Turn" Campaign.

1955 **1165** 100w. multicoloured . . 30 15

1991. Wild Flowers (2nd series). Mult.

1956 100w. Type **1166** 35 15
1957 100w. "Heloniopsis orientalis" 35 15
1958 370w. "Aquilegia buergeriana" 90 40
1959 440w. "Gentiana zollingeri" 1·25 40

1167 Scout with Semaphore Flags **1168** "Y.M.C.A."

1991. 17th World Scout Jamboree.

1960 **1167** 100w. multicoloured . . 30 10

1991. Young Men's Christian Association World Assembly, Seoul.

1962 **1168** 100w. multicoloured . . 25 10

1169 Derelict Steam Locomotive and Family Members Reunited **1170** Globe, Rainbow, Dove and U.N. Emblem

1991. "North–South Reunification".

1963 **1169** 100w. multicoloured . . 90 20

1991. Admission of South Korea to United Nations Organization.

1964 **1170** 100w. multicoloured . . 25 10

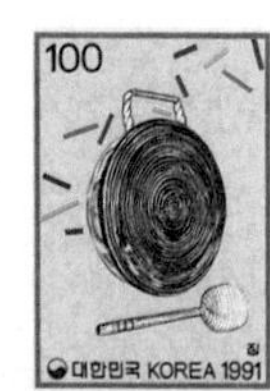

1171 Unra **1172** Jing

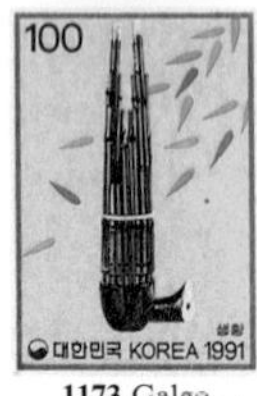

1173 Galgo **1174** Saeng-hwang

1991. Traditional Musical Instruments (1st series).

1965 **1171** 100w. multicoloured . . 40 20
1966 **1172** 100w. multicoloured . . 40 20
1967 **1173** 100w. multicoloured . . 40 20
1968 **1174** 100w. multicoloured . . 40 20

See also Nos. 1981/4.

1175 Film and Theatrical Masks **1176** Globe and Satellite

1991. Culture Month.

1969 **1175** 100w. multicoloured . . 25 10

1991. "Telecom 91" Int Telecommunications Exhibition, Geneva.

1970 **1176** 100w. multicoloured . . 25 10

1177 Hexagonals **1178** Bamboo

1179 Geometric **1180** Tree

1991. Korean Beauty (1st series). Kottams (patterns on walls) from Jakyung Hall, Kyungbok Palace.

1971 **1177** 100w. multicoloured . . 55 25
1972 **1178** 100w. multicoloured . . 55 25
1973 **1179** 100w. multicoloured . . 55 25
1974 **1180** 100w. multicoloured . . 55 25

See also Nos. 2006/9, 2068/71, 2103/6, 2157/60, 2219/22, 2257/60, 2308/15, 2350/6 and 2437/40.

1181 Light Bulb turning off Switch **1182** "Longevity"

1991. Energy Saving Campaign.

1975 **1181** 100w. multicoloured . . 25 10

1991. Lunar New Year ("Year of the Monkey"). Multicoloured.

1976 100w. Type **1182** 40 10
1977 100w. Flying kites 55 10

1184 Stamps

1991. Philatelic Week.

1979 **1184** 100w. multicoloured . . 25 10

1185 Yonggo **1186** Chwago

1187 Kkwaenggwari **1188** T'ukchong

1992. Traditional Musical Instruments (2nd series).

1981 **1185** 100w. multicoloured . . 40 15
1982 **1186** 100w. multicoloured . . 40 15
1983 **1187** 100w. multicoloured . . 40 15
1984 **1188** 100w. multicoloured . . 40 15

1189 White Hibiscus **1191** Satellite

1992. "Hibiscus syriacus" (national flower). Multicoloured.

1985 100w. Type **1189** 45 25
1986 100w. Pink hibiscus 45 25

1992. Science Day.

1987 **1191** 100w. multicoloured . . 25 10

1192 Yoon Pong Gil **1193** Children and Heart

1992. 60th Death Anniv of Yoon Pong Gil (independence fighter).

1988 **1192** 100w. multicoloured . . 25 10

1992. Child Protection.

1989 **1193** 100w. multicoloured . . 30 10

1194 Japanese Warship attacking Korean Settlement **1195** Farmer

1992. 400th Anniv of Start of Im-Jin War.

1990 **1194** 100w. multicoloured . . 35 10

1992. 60th International Fertilizer Industry Association Conference, Seoul.

1991 **1195** 100w. multicoloured . . 25 10

1992. Wild Flowers (3rd series). As T **1166**. Multicoloured.

1992 100w. "Lychnis wilfordii" 30 10
1993 100w. "Lycoris radiata" . . 30 10
1994 370w. "Commelina communis" . . . . 1·00 45
1995 440w. "Calanthe striata" . . 1·00 45

1196 "Longing for Mt. Keumkang" (Han Sang Ok and Choi Young Shurp) **1197** "The Swing" (Kim Mal Bong and Geum Su Hyeon)

1992. Korean Music (8th series).

1996 **1196** 100w. multicoloured . . 30 10
1997 **1197** 100w. multicoloured . . 30 10

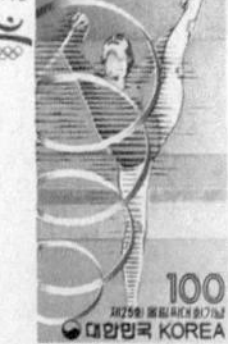

1198 Gymnastics **1199** Stylized View of Exhibition

1992. Olympic Games, Barcelona. Multicoloured.

1998 100w. Type **1198** 30 10
1999 100w. Pole vaulting 30 10

1992. "Expo '93" World's Fair, Taejon (3rd issue). Multicoloured.

2000 100w. Type **1199** 25 10
2001 100w. "Expo 93" 25 10

1201 Korea Exhibition Centre and South Gate, Seoul

1992. 21st Universal Postal Union Congress, Seoul (1st issue). Multicoloured.
2003 100w. Type **1201** 25 10
2004 100w. Tolharubang (stone grandfather), Cheju . . . 25 10
See also Nos. 2075/6, 2088 and 2112/15.

1203 Woven Pattern **1204** Fruit and Flower Decorations

1205 Carved Decorations **1206** Coral, Butterfly and Pine Resin Decorations

1992. Korean Beauty (2nd series). Maedeups (tassels).
2006 **1203** 100w. multicoloured . . 40 15
2007 **1204** 100w. multicoloured . . 40 15
2008 **1205** 100w. multicoloured . . 40 15
2009 **1206** 100w. multicoloured . . 40 15

1207 Lee Pong Chang **1208** Hwang Young Jo (Barcelona, 1992)

1992. 60th Death Anniv of Lee Pong Chang (independence fighter).
2010 **1207** 100w. brown and orange 30 10

1992. Korean Winners of Olympic Marathon. Multicoloured.
2011 100w. Type **1208** 60 15
2012 100w. Shon Kee Chung (Berlin, 1936) 60 15

1209 Sails on Map of Americas **1210** Heads and Speech Balloon

1992. 500th Anniv of Discovery of America by Columbus.
2014 **1209** 100w. multicoloured . . 70 10

1992. Campaign for Purification of Language.
2015 **1210** 100w. multicoloured . . 70 10

1211 Flowers and Stamps **1212** Cockerels in Snow-covered Yard

1992. Philatelic Week.
2016 **1211** 100w. multicoloured . . 70 10

1992. Lunar New Year ("Year of the Cock"). Mult.
2018 100w. Type **1212** 60 10
2019 100w. Flying kites 60 10

1214 Emblem, Globe and Woman holding Bowl

1992. International Nutrition Conference, Rome.
2021 **1214** 100w. multicoloured . . 85 10

1215 View of Centre and Logo

1993. Inauguration of Seoul Arts Centre's Opera House.
2022 **1215** 110w. multicoloured . . 85 15

1216 Pres. Kim Young Sam, Flag and Mt. Paekdu Lake **1217** National Flag

1993. Inauguration of 14th President.
2023 **1216** 110w. multicoloured . . 85 15

1993. No. 2036a orange, black and pink, others multicoloured.
2025 10w. Type **1217** 10 10
2026 20w. White stork 40 10
2026a 20w. Black-crowned night heron 10 10
2027 30w. White magnolia . . . 10 10
2028 40w. Korean white pine . . 10 10
2028a 40w. "Purpuricenus lituralus" (beetle) . . . 10 10
2028b 50w. Water cock 10 10
2029 60w. Squirrel 10 10
2030 70w. Chinese lanterns (plant) 10 10
2030a 80w. Japanese white eye on japonica branch 10 10
2031 90w. Oriental scops owl . . 15 10
2031a 100w. Dishcloth gourd . . 35 10
2032 110w. "Hibiscus syriacus" (plant) 25 10
2033 120w. As 110w. 15 10
2034 130w. Narcissi 20 10
2034c 140w. As 130w. 15 10
2035 150w. Painted porcelain jar 25 10
2036 160w. Pine tree (horiz) . . 30 10
2036a 170w. Crayfish 20 10
2036c 170w. Far eastern curlew 20 10
2037 180w. Little tern (horiz) . . 50 15
2037a 190w. As 110w. 20 10
2038 200w. Turtle (horiz) . . . 30 10
2038a 200w. Snow crab (horiz) 30 10
2038b 210w. As 180w. 35 10
2038c 260w. As 180w. 25 10
2039 300w. Eurasian skylark (horiz) 45 15
2040 370w. Drum and drum dance (horiz) 65 15
2041 400w. Celadon cockerel water dropper (horiz) . . 65 15
2042 420w. As 370w. 65 15
2043 440w. Haho'i mask and Ssirum wrestlers (horiz) 80 15
2044 480w. As 440w. 75 15
2045 500w. Celadon pomegranate water dropper 80 15
2045a 600w. Hong Yong-sik (first Postmaster General) . . 90 15
2046 700w. Gilt-bronze Bongnae-san incense burner (23 × 34 mm) . . 1·10 25
2046a 700w. Cloud and crane jade ornament, Koryo Dynasty . . . . 1·10 25
2046b 710w. King Sejong and alphabet . . . . 1·25 25
2046c 800w. Cheju ponies . . . . 1·25 20
2047 900w. Gilt-bronze buddha triad (23 × 34 mm) . . . 1·60 30
2048 910w. As 710w. . . . . . 1·60 30
2049 930w. Celadon pitcher (blue background) (23 × 31 mm) . . . . . 1·50 25
2049a 930w. As No. 2049 (brown background) . . . . . . 1·60 25
2049b 1000w. Stone guardian animal (from tomb of King Muryong) (32 × 21 mm) . . . . . 1·60 35
2050 1050w. As 930w. . . . . . 1·60 40
2050a 1170w. Bronze incense burner . . . . 2·25 25
2050b 1190w. As 930w. . . . . . 2·75 30
2050c 2000w. Crown from tomb of Shinch'on-ni . . . . 3·00 35

1243 Student and Computer **1244** Emblem and Map

1993. Korean Student Inventions Exhibition.
2051 **1243** 110w. mauve and silver 85 10

1993. International Human Rights Conference, Vienna, Austria.
2052 **1244** 110w. multicoloured . . 85 10

1245 Hand scooping Globe from Water **1246** Matsu-take Mushroom ("Tricholoma matsutake")

1993. "Water is Life".
2053 **1245** 110w. multicoloured . . 85 10

1993. Fungi (1st series). Multicoloured.
2054 110w. Type **1246** 60 10
2055 110w. "Ganoderma lucidum" 60 10
2056 110w. "Lentinula edodes" 60 10
2057 110w. Oyster fungus ("Pleurotus ostreatus") . . 60 10
See also Nos. 2095/8, 2146/9, 2207/10, 2249/52 and 2293/6.

1247 Government Pavilion

1248 International Pavilion and Mascot

1249 Recycling Art Pavilion

1250 Telecom Pavilion

1993. "Expo '93" World's Fair, Taejon (4th issue).
2058 **1247** 110w. multicoloured . . 50 10
2059 **1248** 110w. multicoloured . . 50 10
2060 **1249** 110w. multicoloured . . 50 10
2061 **1250** 110w. multicoloured . . 50 10

1251 Emblems

1993. 19th Congress of International Society of Orthopaedic and Trauma Surgery.
2063 **1251** 110w. multicoloured . . 85 10

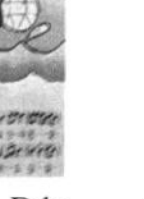

1252 "O Dol Ddo Gi" (Cheju Island folk song) **1253** "Ong He Ya" (barley threshing song)

1993. Korean Music (9th series).
2064 **1252** 110w. multicoloured . . 60 10
2065 **1253** 110w. multicoloured . . 60 10

1254 Janggu Drum Dance **1255** Emblem

1993. "Visit Korea" Year (1994) (1st issue).
2066 **1254** 110w. multicoloured . . 50 10
2067 **1255** 110w. multicoloured . . 50 10
See also Nos. 2086/7.

1256 "Twin Tigers" (military officials, 1st to 3rd rank) **1260** Campaign Emblem

1993. Korean Beauty (3rd series). Hyoongbae (embroidered insignia of the Chosun dynasty). Multicoloured.
2068 110w. Type **1256** 50 10
2069 110w. "Single Crane" (civil officials, 4th to 9th rank) 50 10
2070 110w. "Twin Cranes" (civil officials, 1st to 3rd rank) 50 10
2071 110w. "Dragon" (King) . . 50 10

1993. Anti-litter Campaign.
2072 **1260** 110w. multicoloured . . 50 10

1261 "Eggplant and Oriental Long-nosed Locust" (Shin Saim Dang) **1262** "Weaving"

1993. Philatelic Week.
2073 **1261** 110w. multicoloured . . 50 10

1993. 21st U.P.U. Congress, Seoul (2nd issue). Paintings by Kim Hong Do. Multicoloured.
2075 110w. Type **1262** 50 10
2076 110w. "Musicians and a Dancer" (vert) 50 10

1263 Ribbon and Globe as "30", Freighter and Ilyushin Il-86 Airliner

1993. 30th Trade Day.
2078 **1263** 110w. multicoloured . . 60 10

1264 Sapsaree and Kite

1993. Lunar New Year ("Year of the Dog"). Multicoloured.

2079 110w. Type **1264** 50 10

2080 110w. Puppy with New Year's Greetings bow . . 50 10

1993. Wild Flowers (4th series). As T **1166**.

2082 110w. "Weigela hortensis" 75 10

2083 110w. "Iris ruthenica" . . . 75 10

2084 110w. "Aceriphyllum rosii" 75 10

2085 110w. Marsh marigold ("Caltha palustris") . . . 75 10

1266 Flautist on Cloud **1267** T'alch'um Mask Dance

1994. "Visit Korea" Year (2nd issue).

2086 **1266** 110w. multicoloured . . 50 10

2087 **1267** 110w. multicoloured . . 50 10

1268 Map'ae, Horse, Envelope and Emblem **1269** Monument

1994. 21st U.P.U. Congress, Seoul (3rd issue).

2088 **1268** 300w. multicoloured . . 1·25 15

The map'ae was a token which gave authority to impress post horses.

1994. 75th Anniv of Samil (Independence) Movement.

2090 **1269** 110w. multicoloured . . 65 10

1270 Great Purple ("Sasakia charonda")

1994. Protection of Wildlife and Plants (1st series). Multicoloured.

2091 110w. Type **1270** (butterfly) 60 10

2092 110w. "Allomyrina dichotoma" (beetle) . . . 60 10

See also Nos. 2143/4, 2186/7, 2241/2, 2275/8, 2326/9, 2383/6 and 2481/4.

1271 Family of Mandarins

1994. International Year of the Family.

2094 **1271** 110w. multicoloured . . 65 10

1994. Fungi (2nd series). As T **1246**. Multicoloured.

2095 110w. Common morel ("Morchella esculenta") 50 10

2096 110w. "Gomphus floccosus" 50 10

2097 110w. "Cortinarius purpurascens" 50 10

2098 110w. "Oudemansiella platyphylla" 50 10

1272 Museum

1994. Inauguration of War Memorial Museum, Yongsan (Seoul).

2100 **1272** 110w. multicoloured . . 65 10

1273 Text and Dove

1994. "Philakorea 1994" International Stamp Exhibition, Seoul (1st issue).

2101 **1273** 910w. multicoloured . . 2·00 40

See also Nos. 2107/9.

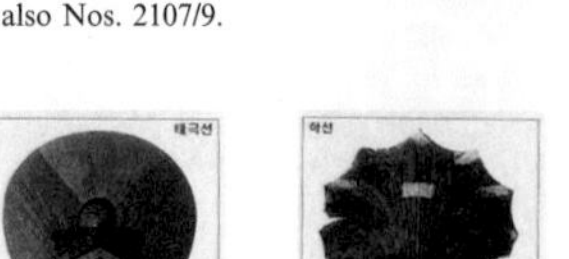

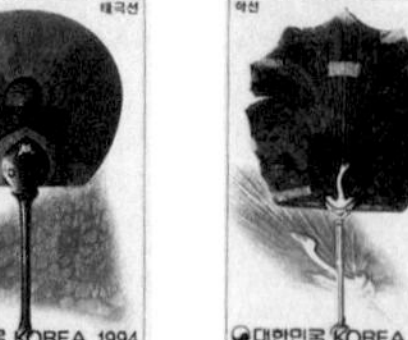

1274 Taeguk (Yin-Yang) Fan **1275** Crane Fan

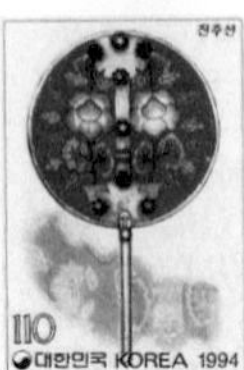

1276 Pearl Fan **1277** Wheel Fan

1994. Korean Beauty (4th series). Fans.

2103 **1274** 110w. multicoloured . . 50 10

2104 **1275** 110w. multicoloured . . 50 10

2105 **1276** 110w. multicoloured . . 50 10

2106 **1277** 110w. multicoloured . . 50 10

1278 "Wintry Days" (Kim Chong Hui) **1282** "Sword Dance" (Sin Yun Bok)

1994. "Philakorea 1994" International Stamp Exhibition, Seoul (2nd issue). Multicoloured.

2107 130w. Type **1278** 50 10

2108 130w. "Grape" (Choe Sok Hwan) 50 10

2109 130w. "Riverside Scene" (Kim Duk Sin) 50 10

1994. 21st U.P.U. Congress, Seoul (4th issue). Multicoloured.

2112 130w. Type **1282** 50 10

2113 130w. "Book Shelves" (detail of folk painting showing stamps) 50 10

2114 130w. Congress emblem . . 50 10

2115 130w. Hong Yung Sik (postal reformer) and Heinrich von Stephan (founder of U.P.U.) (horiz) 75 10

1283 Old Map **1284** Mail Van

1994. 600th Anniv of Adoption of Seoul as Capital of Korea (1st issue).

2118 **1283** 130w. multicoloured . . 60 10

See also No. 2139.

1994. Transport. Multicoloured.

2121 300w. Type **1284** 60 15

2122 330w. Airplane 80 15

2122a 340w. Airplane facing left 70 10

2122b 380w. As 340w. 60 10

2123 390w. Airplane (different) 1·10 15

2124 400w. As 330w. . . . . . 1·25 15

2126 540w. Streamlined diesel train . . . . 2·10 15

2127 560w. As 330w. . . . . . 2·25 15

2130 1190w. River cruiser . . . 3·75 25

2131 1300w. As 330w. . . . . . 4·00 40

2132 1340w. As 340w. . . . . . 4·25 35

2132a 1380w. As 340w. . . . . . 4·50 35

1994. Wild Flowers (5th series). As T **1166**. Multicoloured.

2133 130w. "Gentiana jamesii" 45 10

2134 130w. "Geranium eriostemon var. megalanthum" 45 10

2135 130w. "Leontopodium japonicum" 45 10

2136 130w. "Lycoris aurea" . . . 45 10

1285 "Water Melon and Field Mice" (detail of folding screen, Shin Saimdang) **1286** "600"

1994. Philatelic Week.

2137 **1285** 130w. multicoloured . . 65 10

1994. 600th Anniv of Seoul as Capital (2nd issue).

2139 **1286** 130w. multicoloured . . 65 10

1287 Pigs travelling in Snow

1994. Lunar New Year ("Year of the Pig"). Multicoloured.

2140 130w. Type **1287** 60 10

2141 130w. Family in forest . . . 60 10

1995. Protection of Wildlife and Plants (2nd series). Multicoloured.

2143 130w. Plancy's green pond frog ("Rana plancyi") . . 60 10

2144 130w. Common toad ("Bufo bufo") 60 10

1995. Fungi (3rd series). As T **1246**. Multicoloured.

2146 130w. Shaggy ink caps ("Coprinus comatus") . . 45 10

2147 130w. Chicken mushroom ("Laetiporus sulphureus") 45 10

2148 130w. "Lentinus lepideus" 45 10

2149 130w. Cracked green russula ("Russula virescens") . . 45 10

1290 Spheres around Reactor **1291** Scales of Justice

1995. Completion of Hanaro Research Reactor.

2151 **1290** 130w. multicoloured . . 65 10

1995. Centenary of Judicial System.

2152 **1291** 130w. multicoloured . . 65 10

1292 Tiger

1995. Centenary of Law Education.

2153 **1292** 130w. multicoloured . . 65 10

1293 Dooly the Little Dinosaur (Kim Soo Jeung)

1294 Kochuboo (Kim Yong Hwan)

1995. Cartoons (1st series). Multicoloured.

2154 **1293** 130w. multicoloured . . 70 10

2155 **1294** 440w. multicoloured . . 1·25 15

See also Nos. 2196/7, 2234/5, 2280/1, 2322/4 and 2498/500.

1295 Gate of Eternal Youth, Changdokkung Palace **1296** Fish Water Gate, Chuhamru Pavilion, Changdokkung Palace

1297 Pomosa Temple Gate, Pusan City **1298** Yangban Residence Gate, Hahoe Village

1995. Korean Beauty (5th series). Gates.

2157 **1295** 130w. multicoloured . . 50 10

2158 **1296** 130w. multicoloured . . 50 10

2159 **1297** 130w. multicoloured . . 50 10

2160 **1298** 130w. multicoloured . . 50 10

1299 Lion and Emblem

1995. 78th Convention of Lions Clubs International.

2161 **1299** 130w. multicoloured . . 65 10

1995. Wild Flowers (6th series). As T **1166**. Multicoloured.

2162 130w. "Halenia corniculata" 50 10

2163 130w. "Erythronium japonicum" 50 10

2164 130w. "Iris odaesanensis" 50 10

2165 130w. "Leontice microrrhyncha" 50 10

1300 National Flag **1301** Telescope

1995. 50th Anniv of Liberation. Multicoloured.

2166 130w. Type **1300** 60 10

2167 440w. Anniversary emblem (96 × 19 mm) . . . . . . 1·40 15

1995. Inauguration of Mt. Bohyun Optical Astronomy Observatory.

2169 **1301** 130w. multicoloured . . 65 10

1302 Turtle's Back Song **1303** Song from "Standards of Musical Science"

1995. Literature (1st series).

2170 **1302** 130w. multicoloured . . 60 10

2171 **1303** 130w. multicoloured . . 60 10

See also Nos. 2212/13, 2269/70, 2301/2 and 2344/7.

1304 "50 Th" incorporating Man with Wheat

1995. 50th Anniv of F.A.O.

2172 **1304** 150w. black and violet 70 10

1305 Open Bible **1306** Families in Houses

1995. Centenary of Korean Bible Society.
2174 **1305** 150w. multicoloured . . 70 10

1995. Population and Housing Census.
2175 **1306** 150w. multicoloured . . 70 10

1307 Dove of Flags

1995. 50th Anniv of United Nations Organization.
2176 **1307** 150w. multicoloured . . 70 10

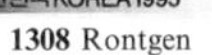

1308 Rontgen **1309** "Water Pepper and Mantis" (detail of folding screen, Shin Saim Dang)

1995. Centenary of Discovery of X-Rays by Wilhelm Rontgen.
2177 **1308** 150w. multicoloured . . 70 10

1995. Philatelic Week.
2178 **1309** 150w. multicoloured . . 70 10

1310 Rat and Snowman **1312** Miroku Bosatsu, Koryu Temple, Kyoto

1995. Lunar New Year ("Year of the Rat"). Multicoloured.
2180 150w. Type **1310** 60 10
2181 150w. Cranes and pine trees (horiz) 60 10

1995. 30th Anniv of Resumption of Korea–Japan Diplomatic Relations.
2183 **1312** 420w. multicoloured . . 1·40 15

1313 Cable Route **1314** "30" and Molecule

1996. Inauguration of Korea–China Submarine Cable.
2184 **1313** 420w. multicoloured . . 70 15

1996. 30th Anniv of Korea Institute of Science and Technology.
2185 **1314** 150w. multicoloured . . 70 10

1996. Protection of Wildlife and Plants (3rd series). As T **1270**. Multicoloured.
2186 150w. Black pond turtle ("Geoclemys reevesii") . . 60 10
2187 150w. Ground skink ("Scincella laterale") . . . 60 10

1315 Satellite and Launching Pad

1996. Launch of "Mugunghwa 2" Telecommunications Satellite.
2189 **1315** 150w. multicoloured . . 70 10

1316 So Chae P'il (founder) and Leader from First Issue

1996. Centenary of "Tongnip Shinmun" (first independent newspaper).
2190 **1316** 150w. multicoloured . . 70 10

1996. Wild Flowers (7th series). As T **1166**. Multicoloured.
2191 150w. "Cypripedium macranthum" 55 10
2192 150w. "Trilium tschonoskii" 55 10
2193 150w. "Viola variegata" . . 55 10
2194 150w. "Hypericum ascyron" 55 10

1317 Anniversary Emblem and Cadets

1996. 50th Anniv of Korean Military Academy.
2195 **1317** 150w. multicoloured . . 70 10

1318 Gobau (Kim Song Hwan)

1319 Battle between Kkach'i and Caesarius (Lee Hyun Se) (from film "Armageddon")

1996. Cartoons (2nd series).
2196 **1318** 150w. multicoloured . . 60 10
2197 **1319** 150w. multicoloured . . 60 10

1320 Anniversary Emblem **1321** Globe and Congress Emblem

1996. 50th Anniv of Korean Girl Scouts.
2199 **1320** 150w. multicoloured . . 70 10

1996. 35th World Congress of International Advertising Association, Seoul.
2200 **1321** 150w. multicoloured . . 70 10

1322 Syringes and Drugs

1996. International Anti-drug Day.
2201 **1322** 150w. multicoloured . . 70 10

1323 Skater **1324** Torch Bearer

1996. World University Students' Games, Muju and Chonju (1st issue). Multicoloured.
2202 150w. Type **1323** 90 10
2203 150w. Games emblem (vert) 90 10
See also Nos. 2228/9.

1996. Olympic Games, Atlanta. Multicoloured.
2204 150w. Type **1324** 65 10
2205 150w. Games emblem . . . 65 10

1996. Fungi (4th series). As T **1246**. Multicoloured.
2207 150w. "Amanita inaurata" 70 10
2208 150w. "Paxillus atrotomentosus" 70 10
2209 150w. "Rhodophyllus crassipes" 70 10
2210 150w. "Sarcodon imbricatum" 70 10

1327 Requiem for a Deceased Sister

1328 Ode to Knight Kip'a

1996. Literature (2nd series).
2212 **1327** 150w. multicoloured . . 75 10
2213 **1328** 150w. multicoloured . . 75 10

1329 Alphabet **1330** Castle

1996. 550th Anniv of Han-Gul (Korean alphabet created by King Sejong).
2215 **1329** 150w. black and grey 70 10

1996. Bicentenary of Suwon Castle.
2217 **1330** 400w. multicoloured . . 1·90 15

1331 Front Gate, University Flag and Emblem

1996. 50th Anniv of Seoul National University.
2218 **1331** 150w. multicoloured . . 70 10

1332 Five-direction Pouch **1333** Chinese Phoenix Pouch (Queen's Court Pouch)

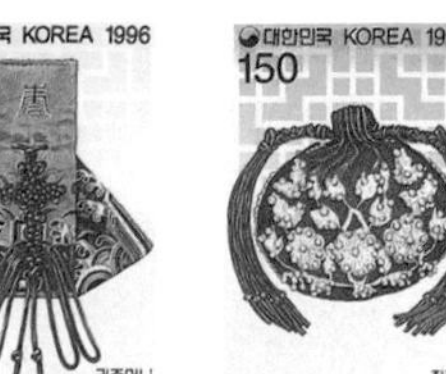

1334 Princess Pokon's Wedding Pouch **1335** Queen Yunbi's Pearl Pouch

1996. Korean Beauty (6th series). Pouches.
2219 **1332** 150w. multicoloured . . 70 10
2220 **1333** 150w. multicoloured . . 70 10
2221 **1334** 150w. multicoloured . . 70 10
2222 **1335** 150w. multicoloured . . 70 10

1336 "Poppy and Lizard" (detail of folding screen, Shin Saimdang) **1337** Children riding Ox

1996. Philatelic Week.
2223 **1336** 150w. multicoloured . . 70 10

1996. Lunar New Year ("Year of the Ox"). Multicoloured.
2225 150w. Type **1337** 95 10
2226 150w. Boy piper and resting ox 95 10

1339 Figure Skating **1340** Coins forming "100"

1997. World University Students' Games, Muju and Chonju (2nd issue). Multicoloured.
2228 150w. Type **1339** 95 10
2229 150w. Skiing 95 10

1997. Centenary of Foundation of Hansong Bank (first commercial bank in Korea).
2231 **1340** 150w. multicoloured . . 70 10

1341 "Auspicious Turtles" (painting) **1342** Globe, Pen and open Book (Jeon Chong Kwan)

1997. Interparliamentary Union Conference, Seoul.
2232 **1341** 150w. multicoloured . . 70 10

1997. World Book and Copyright Day.
2233 **1342** 150w. multicoloured . . 70 10

1343 A Long, Long Journey in Search of Mummy (Kim Chong Nae)

1344 Run, Run, Hannie (Lee Chin Ju)

1997. Cartoons (3rd series).
2234 **1343** 150w. multicoloured . . 70 10
2235 **1344** 150w. multicoloured . . 70 10

1345 Torch Bearer

1997. 2nd East Asian Games, Pusan.
2237 **1345** 150w. multicoloured . . 70 10

1346 Jules Rimet (founder)
1347 "Chukkuk" (Lee Chul Joo)

1997. World Cup Football Championship (2002), South Korea and Japan (1st issue).
2238 **1346** 150w. multicoloured . . 60 10
2239 **1347** 150w. multicoloured . . 60 10
See also Nos. 2284/7.

1997. Protection of Wildlife and Plants (4th series). As T **1270**. Multicoloured.
2241 150w. Chinese nine-spined sticklebacks ("Pungitius sinensis") 70 10
2242 150w. Spot-eared brook perch ("Coreoperca kawamebari") 70 10

1997. Wild Flowers (8th series). As T **1166**. Multicoloured.
2244 150w. "Belamcanda chinensis" 75 10
2245 150w. "Belamcanda chinensis" 75 10
2246 150w. "Campanula takesimana" 75 10
2247 150w. "Magnolia sieboldii" 75 10

1348 Emblem and "97" forming Face
1349 Seoul South Gate and Emblem

1997. 2nd Art Biennale, Kwangju.
2248 **1348** 150w. multicoloured . . 70 10

1997. Fungi (5th series). As T **1246**. Multicoloured.
2249 150w. "Inocybe fastigiata" 75 10
2250 150w. "Panaeolus papilionaceus" 75 10
2251 150w. "Ramaria flava" . . 75 10
2252 150w. Fly agaric ("Amanita muscaria") 75 10

1997. 85th World Dental Congress, Seoul.
2254 **1349** 170w. multicoloured . . 20 10

1350 Harbour and Score

1997. Centenary of Mokpo Port.
2255 **1350** 170w. multicoloured . . 70 10

1351 Main Building, Pyongyang

1997. Centenary of Founding of Soongsil Academy in Pyongyang (now situated in Seoul).
2256 **1351** 170w. multicoloured . . 70 10

1352 Concentric Squares
1353 Green Silk

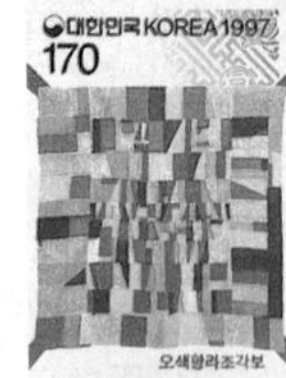

1354 Pattern of Squares
1355 Pattern of Squares and Triangles

1997. Korean Beauty (7th series). Patchwork Pojagi (wrapping cloths).
2257 **1352** 170w. multicoloured . . 65 10
2258 **1353** 170w. multicoloured . . 65 10
2259 **1354** 170w. multicoloured . . 65 10
2260 **1355** 170w. multicoloured . . 65 10

1356 "Hollyhock and Frog" (detail of folding screen, Shin Saimdang)
1357 Tiger's Head

1997. Philatelic Week.
2261 **1356** 170w. multicoloured . . 70 10

1997. Lunar New Year ("Year of the Tiger"). Multicoloured.
2263 170w. Type **1357** 70 10
2264 170w. "Magpie and Tiger" (folk painting) 70 10

1359 Buddha, Sokkuram Shrine

1360 Pulguk Temple

1997. World Heritage Sites (1st series).
2266 **1359** 170w. multicoloured . . 20 10
2267 **1360** 380w. multicoloured . . 40 10
See also Nos. 2317/18, 2365/6 and 2457/8.

1361 "Poem to Sui General Yu Zhong Wen" (Ulchi Mundok)
1362 "Record of Travel to Five Indian Kingdoms" (Hye Ch'o)

1997. Literature (3rd series).
2269 **1361** 170w. multicoloured . . 70 10
2270 **1362** 170w. multicoloured . . 70 10

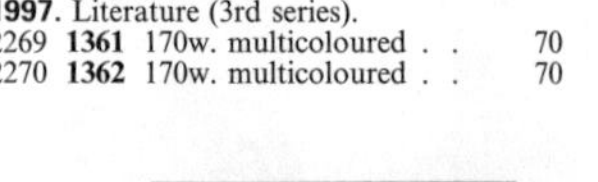

1363 Neon Lights on Globe and Nuclear Power Plant

1998. Centenary of Introduction of Electricity to Korea.
2272 **1363** 170w. multicoloured . . 70 10

1364 Pres. Kim Dae Jung and Flag

1998. Inauguration of 15th President of South Korea.
2273 **1364** 170w. multicoloured . . 60 10

1998. Protection of Wildlife and Plants (5th series). Vert designs as T **1270**. Multicoloured.
2275 340w. Korean leopard ("Panthera pardus orientalis") . . . . 1·25 75
2276 340w. Asiatic black bears ("Selenarctos thibetanus") 1·25 75
2277 340w. European otters ("Lutra lutra") . . . . . 1·25 75
2278 340w. Siberian musk deers ("Moschus moschiferus") 1·25 75

1365 Aktong-i (Lee Hi Jae)

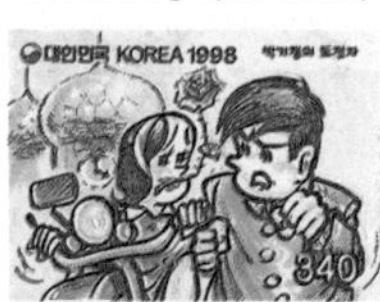

1366 Challenger (Park Ki Jong)

1998. Cartoons (4th series).
2280 **1365** 170w. multicoloured . . 40 10
2281 **1366** 340w. multicoloured . . 70 10

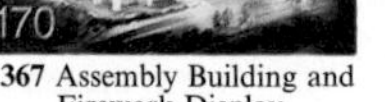

1367 Assembly Building and Firework Display
1368 Player with Ball

1998. 50th Anniv of National Assembly.
2283 **1367** 170w. multicoloured . . 60 10

1998. World Cup Football Championship (2002), Korea and Japan (2nd issue). Multicoloured.
2284 170w. Type **1368** 50 10
2285 170w. Two players chasing ball 50 10
2286 170w. Players heading ball 50 10
2287 170w. Player kicking ball over head 50 10

1369 Writing on Stone Tablets

1998. Information Technology. Multicoloured.
2289 170w. Type **1369** 50 10
2290 170w. Pony Express 50 10
2291 170w. Man using telephone and post box 50 10
2292 170w. Old and modern forms of communication (68 × 22 mm) 50 10

1998. Fungi (6th series). As T **1246**. Multicoloured.
2293 170w. "Pseudocolus schellenbergiae" 50 10
2294 170w. "Cyptotrama asprata" 50 10
2295 170w. "Laccaria vinaceoavellanea" 50 10
2296 170w. "Phallus rugulosus" 50 10

1373 Flag and Runners
1374 "Grapes" (Lady Shin Saimdang)

1998. 50th Anniv of Proclamation of Republic.
2298 **1373** 170w. multicoloured . . 60 10

1998. Philatelic Week.
2299 **1374** 170w. multicoloured . . 60 10

1375 Thinking of Mother
1376 Would You Leave Me Now?

1998. Literature (4th series). Sogyo Songs.
2301 **1375** 170w. multicoloured . . 60 10
2302 **1376** 170w. multicoloured . . 60 10

1377 Film Strips and Masks

1998. 3rd Pusan International Film Festival.
2304 **1377** 170w. multicoloured . . 20 10

1378 Myungnyundang Hall

1998. 600th Anniv of Sungkyunkwan University.
2305 **1378** 170w. multicoloured . . 20 10

1379 National Constabulary, Badge and Lake Ch'onji
1380 Hot-air Balloon

1998. 50th Anniv of Korean Armed Forces.
2306 **1379** 170w. multicoloured . . 20 10

1998. World Stamp Day.
2307 **1380** 170w. multicoloured . . 20 10

1381 Peach
1382 Double Crane

1383 Carp
1384 Peach

1385 Toad

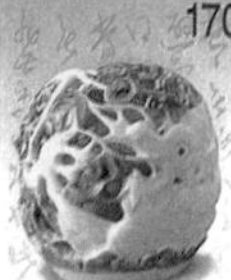
1386 Dragon and Cloud

1387 Monkey

1388 House

1998. Korean Beauty (8th series). Porcelain Water Droppers.

2308 **1381** 170w. multicoloured . . 20 10
2309 **1382** 170w. multicoloured . . 20 10
2310 **1383** 170w. multicoloured . . 20 10
2311 **1384** 170w. multicoloured . . 20 10
2312 **1385** 170w. multicoloured . . 20 10
2313 **1386** 170w. multicoloured . . 20 10
2314 **1387** 170w. multicoloured . . 20 10
2315 **1388** 170w. multicoloured . . 20 10

1389 Rabbits

1390 Tripitaka Koreana (scriptures engraved on wooden blocks)

1391 Changgyong P'anjon (woodblock repository)

1998. Lunar New Year ("Year of the Rabbit").

2316 **1389** 170w. multicoloured . . 20 10

1998. World Heritage Sites (2nd series). Haein Temple.

2317 **1390** 170w. multicoloured . . 20 10
2318 **1391** 380w. multicoloured . . 40 10

1392 Maize, Compass and Ship's Wheel

1999. Centenary of Kunsan Port.

2320 **1392** 170w. multicoloured . . 20 10

1393 Masan and Score of "I Want to Go" by Lee Eun Sang

1999. Centenary of Masan Port.

2321 **1393** 170w. multicoloured . . 20 10

1394 Rai-Fi (Kim San Ho)

1395 Tokgo T'ak (Lee Sang Mu)

1396 Im Kkuk Jung (Lee Du Ho)

1999. Cartoons (5th series).

2322 **1394** 170w. multicoloured . . 20 10
2323 **1395** 170w. multicoloured . . 20 10
2324 **1396** 170w. multicoloured . . 20 10

1999. Protection of Wildlife and Plants (6th series). Vert designs as T **1270**.

2326 170w. Peregrine falcon ("Falco peregrinus") . . . 20 10
2327 170w. Grey frog hawk ("Accipiter soloensis") . . 20 10
2328 340w. Steller's sea eagle ("Haliaeetus pelagicus") 35 10
2329 340w. Northern eagle owl ("Bubo bubo") 35 10

1397 Five clasped Hands

1398 Goethe (after Joseph Stieler)

1999. 109th International Olympic Committee Congress, Seoul.

2331 **1397** 170w. multicoloured . . 20 10

1999. 250th Birth Anniv of Johann Wolfgang von Goethe (poet and playwright).

2332 **1398** 170w. multicoloured . . 20 10

1399 "Kumgang Mountain" (Kyomjae Chong Son)

1999. Philatelic Week.

2334 **1399** 170w. multicoloured . . 20 10

1400 Mogul Tank Locomotive No. 101 (first locomotive in Korea)

1999. Centenary of Railway in Korea.

2336 **1400** 170w. multicoloured . . 20 10

1401 Flint Tools and Paleolithic Ruins, Chungok-ri, Yonch'on

1999. New Millennium (1st series). Multicoloured.

2337 170w. Type **1401** 20 10
2338 170w. Comb-patterned pottery, burnt-out and reconstructed Neolithic dwellings, Amsa-dong, Seoul 20 10
2339 170w. Shell bracelets, bone spear heads and Neolithic shell mounds, Tongsam-dong, Pusan 20 10
2340 170w. Dolmen, Pukon-ri, Kanghwa-do Island . . . 20 10
2341 170w. Bronze and stone daggers and Bronze-age earthenware, Son-gguk-ri, Puyo 20 10
2342 170w. Rock carvings, Pan'gudae 20 10

See also Nos. 2357/62, 2374/8, 2388/92, 2397/2401, 2406/10, 2420/5, 2431/6, 2460/5, 2487/91 and 2511/15.

1402 Bird carrying Letter

1999. 125th Anniv of Universal Postal Union.

2343 **1402** 170w. multicoloured . . 20 10

1403 Little Odes on the Kwandong Area (Chong Ch'ol)

1404 Alas! How foolish I am! (Hwang Jin-i)

1405 Story of Hong Kil-dong (Ho Kyun)

1406 Story of Ch'unhyang

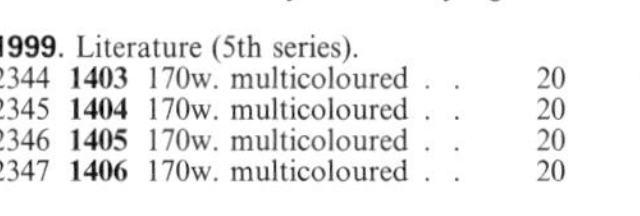

1999. Literature (5th series).

2344 **1403** 170w. multicoloured . . 20 10
2345 **1404** 170w. multicoloured . . 20 10
2346 **1405** 170w. multicoloured . . 20 10
2347 **1406** 170w. multicoloured . . 20 10

1407 Chrysanthemum, Bird and Duck

1408 Birds in Tree and Snake on Korean Character

1409 Pot Plant with Butterfly on Korean Character

1410 Fish on Korean Character

1411 Plant behind Tub of Fishes

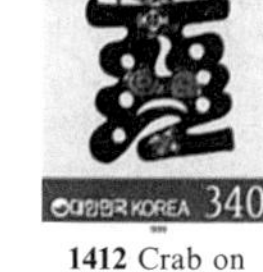
1412 Crab on Korean Character

1413 Bird on Korean Character

1414 Chest and Plant behind Deer

1999. Korean Beauty (9th series).

2349 **1407** 340w. multicoloured . . 40 10
2350 **1408** 340w. multicoloured . . 40 10
2351 **1409** 340w. multicoloured . . 40 10
2352 **1410** 340w. multicoloured . . 40 10
2353 **1411** 340w. multicoloured . . 40 10
2354 **1412** 340w. multicoloured . . 40 10
2355 **1413** 340w. multicoloured . . 40 10
2356 **1414** 340w. multicoloured . . 40 10

1415 Ornament and Bird-shaped Vase

1416 Crown and Bowl

1417 Man on Horseback and Cave Paintings

1418 Gold Ornament and Jade Jewellery

1419 Stone Crafts

1420 Carved Stone Face

1999. New Millennium (2nd series).
2357 **1415** 170w. multicoloured . . 20 10
2358 **1416** 170w. multicoloured . . 20 10
2359 **1417** 170w. multicoloured . . 20 10
2360 **1418** 170w. multicoloured . . 20 10
2361 **1419** 170w. multicoloured . . 20 10
2362 **1420** 170w. multicoloured . . 20 10

1421 Dragon

1999. Lunar New Year "Year of the Dragon".
2363 **1421** 170w. multicoloured . . 20 10

1422 Building

1423 Man and Musicians

1999. World Heritage Sites (3rd series).
2365 **1422** 170w. multicoloured . . 20 10
2366 **1423** 340w. multicoloured . . 40 10

1424 Player

1426 Sunset, Altar and Tablet

1425 Emblem

1999. World Cup Football Championship, Japan and Korea (2002). Multicoloured.
2368 170w. Type **1424** 20 10
2369 170w. Players tackling . . . 20 10
2370 170w. Player receiving ball 20 10
2371 170w. Goalkeeper catching ball 20 10
Nos. 2368/71 were issued together, se-tenant, forming a composite design.

2000. Centenary of South Korea's Membership of Universal Postal Union.
2373 **1425** 170w. multicoloured . . 20 10

2000. New Millennium (3rd series). Multicoloured.
2374 170w. Type **1426** 20 10
2375 170w. Cave painting of wrestlers 20 10
2376 170w. Inscribed bronze disc and warrior 20 10
2377 170w. Silhouettes of archers and inscribed standing stone 20 10
2378 170w. Junk and warrior . . 20 10

1427 Pashi Steam Locomotive

1428 Teho Steam Locomotive

1429 Mika Steam Locomotive

1430 Hyouki Steam Locomotive

2000. Railways (1st series).
2379 **1427** 170w. black, violet and mauve 20 10
2380 **1428** 170w. black, violet and mauve 20 10
2381 **1429** 170w. black, violet and grey 20 10
2382 **1430** 170w. black, violet and bistre 20 10
See also Nos. 2477/80.

2000. Protection of Wildlife and Plants (7th series). As T **1270**. Multicoloured.
2383 170w. *Lilium cernum* 20 10
2384 170w. *Sedirea japonica* . . . 20 10
2385 170w. *Hibiscus hamabo* . . . 20 10
2386 170w. *Cypripedium japonicum* 20 10
Nos. 2383/6 are impregnated with the scent of flowers.

1431 State Civil Service Examination and Text

2000. New Millennium (4th series). Multicoloured.
2388 170w. Type **1431** 20 10
2389 170w. Man carving wood blocks 20 10
2390 170w. Pieces of metal type 20 10
2391 170w. An-Hyang (scholar) and Korean script 20 10
2392 170w. Mun Ik-jom (scholar), spinning wheel and cotton plant 20 10

1432 Children playing and House (Kim Chin Sook)

1433 Globe and Satellite

2000. World Water Day. Winning Design in Children's Painting Competition.
2393 **1432** 170w. multicoloured . . 20 10

2000. 50th Anniv of World Meteorological Organization.
2394 **1433** 170w. multicoloured . . 20 10

1434 Hand holding Rose

2000. "Share Love" (good neighbour campaign).
2395 **1434** 170w. multicoloured . . 20 10
No. 2395 is impregnated with the scent of roses.

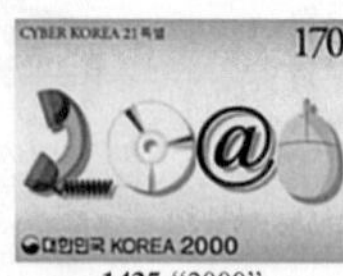
1435 "2000"

2000. "CYBER KOREA 21".
2396 **1435** 170w. multicoloured . . 20 10

1436 King Sejong and Korean Script

2000. New Millennium (5th series). Multicoloured.
2397 170w. Type **1436** 20 10
2398 170w. Lady Shin Saimdang (caligrapher poet and painter) and detail of "Ch'ochung-do" (painting) 20 10
2399 170w. Yi Hwang and Yi I (founders of Confucian Academy) 20 10
2400 170w. Admiral Yi Sun-shin and model of "turle" ship 20 10
2401 170w. Sandae-nori (mask-dance drama) 20 10

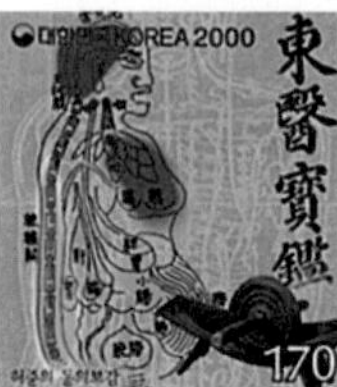
1437 Park Soo Dong

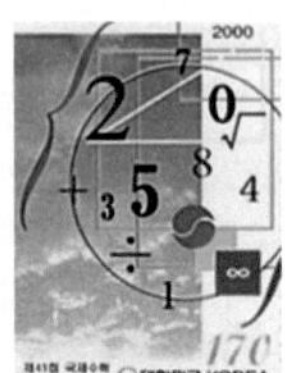
1438 Bae Gum Taek

2000. Cartoons (6th series).
2402 **1437** 170w. multicoloured . . 20 10
2403 **1438** 170w. multicoloured . . 20 10

1439 Seedling on Map of Korean Peninsula

2000. Pyongyang, Korean Summit.
2405 **1439** 170w. multicoloured . . 20 10

1440 Anatomical Diagram from *Tonui Pogam* (medical treatise by Huh Joan)

1441 Numbers and Mathematical Symbols

2000. Millennium (6th series). Multicoloured.
2406 170w. Type **1440** 20 10
2407 170w. "Dancer with Musicians" (illustration by Kim Hong Do) 20 10
2408 170w. "Plum Blossoms and Bird" (painting, Chong Yak Yong) and house in Kangjin where he served his exile 20 10
2409 170w. Map of Korea by Kim Chong Ho and wheel chart 20 10
2410 170w. Chon Bong Joan (revolutionary) and Tonghak Peasant Uprising monument . . . 20 10

2000. International Mathematical Olympiad (high school mathematics competition).
2411 **1441** 170w. multicoloured . . 20 10

1442 *Yolha Diary* (Park Ji Won)

1443 *Fisherman's Calender*

1444 *The Nine-Cloud Dream*

1445 *Tears of Blood*

1446 *From the Sea to a Child*

2000. Literature (6th series).
2412 **1442** 170w. multicoloured . . 20 10
2413 **1443** 170w. multicoloured . . 20 10
2414 **1444** 170w. multicoloured . . 20 10
2415 **1445** 170w. multicoloured . . 20 10
2416 **1446** 170w. multicoloured . . 20 10

1447 Mountain

2000. Philately Week.
2418 **1447** 340w. multicoloured . . 40 10

1448 Porcelain

2000. Millennium (7th series). Multicoloured.
2420 170w. Type **1448** 20 10
2421 170w. "Bongjongsa" Temple (Paradise Pavilion) . . . 20 10
2422 170w. Hahoe Tal masks . . 20 10
2423 170w. Royal Palace 20 10
2424 170w. Landscape painting 20 10
2425 170w. Water clock 20 10

1454 Taekwondo

2000. Olympic Games, Sydney.
2426 **1454** 170w. multicoloured . . 20 10

1455 Former Kyunngi High School Building, Hwadong

2000. Centenary of Public Secondary Schools.
2427 **1455** 170w. multicoloured . . 10 10

1456 "Returning to the Retirement House" (illustration from "Album of the Gathering of Old Statesmen")

2000. 3rd Asia-Europe Meeting, Seoul.
2428 **1456** 170w. multicoloured . . 10 10

1457 Emblem

2000. Icograde Millennium Congress, Seoul.
2429 **1457** 170w. black and yellow 10 10

1458 Mr. Gobau

2000. 50th Anniv of Mr. Gobau (cartoon character).
2430 **1458** 170w. multicoloured . . 10 10

1459 18th-Century Painting (Sin Yun Bok)

2000. Millennium (8th series). Multicoloured.
2431 170w. Type **1459** 10 10
2432 170w. Calligraphy by Kim Jeong Hui 10 10
2433 170w. Bongdon-Chiseong Hwaseong Fortress, Suwon 10 10
2434 170w. Myeongdong Cathedral 10 10
2435 170w. Wongaska theatre actors 10 10
2436 170w. The KITSat-satellite 10 10

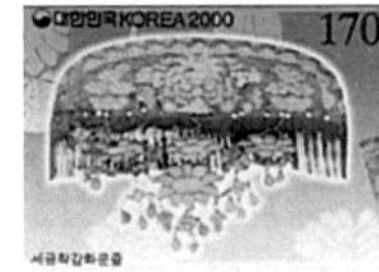
1460 Decorated Comb

2000. Korean Beauty (10th series). Multicoloured.
2437 170w. Type **1460** 10 10
2438 170w. Woman's ceremonial headdress 10 10
2439 170w. Butterfly-shaped hairpin 10 10
2440 170w. Hairpin with dragon decoration and jade hairpin with Chinese phoenix decoration . . . 10 10

1461 Seoul World Cup Stadium

1462 Busan Sports Complex Main Stadium

1463 Daegu Sports Complex Stadium

1464 Incheon Munhak Stadium

1465 Gwangu World Cup Stadium

1466 Daejeon World Cup Stadium

1467 Ulsan Munsu Football Stadium

1468 Suwon World Cup Stadium

1469 Jeonju World Cup Stadium

1470 Jeju World Cup Stadium

2000. World Cup Football Championship (2002), South Korea and Japan.
2441 **1461** 170w. multicoloured . . 10 10
2442 **1462** 170w. multicoloured . . 10 10
2443 **1463** 170w. multicoloured . . 10 10
2444 **1464** 170w. multicoloured . . 10 10
2445 **1465** 170w. multicoloured . . 10 10
2446 **1466** 170w. multicoloured . . 10 10
2447 **1467** 170w. multicoloured . . 10 10
2448 **1468** 170w. multicoloured . . 10 10
2449 **1469** 170w. multicoloured . . 10 10
2450 **1470** 170w. multicoloured . . 10 10

1471 Snake

2000. Lunar New Year "Year of the Snake". Ordinary or self-adhesive gum.
2452 **1471** 170w. multicoloured . . 10 10

1472 President Kim Dae Jung and Children

2000. Award of Nobel Peace Prize to President Kim Dae Jung.
2455 **1472** 170w. multicoloured . . 10 10

1473 Repository, Jeongjok Mountain and Taejo Sillok (script)

2000. World Heritage Sites (4th series). Multicoloured.
2457 340w. Type **1473** 35 10
2458 340w. King Sejong and script 35 10

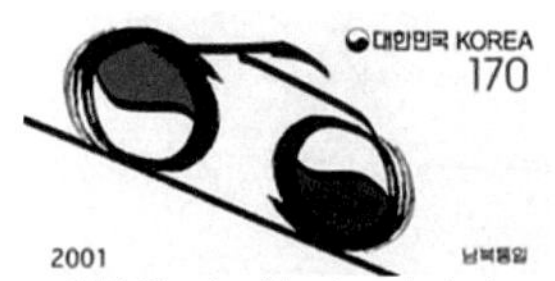
1474 Bicycle with coloured wheels (reunification of Korea)

2001. Millennium (9th series). Multicoloured.
2460 170w. Type **1474** 10 10
2461 170w. Rainbow (environmental protection) 10 10
2462 170w. Human D.N.A. and figure (eradication of incurable diseases) 10 10
2463 170w. Satellite and mobile telephone (communications technology) 10 10
2464 170w. Space (space travel) 10 10
2465 170w. Solar panels, solar-powered car and windmills (alternative energy sources) 10 10

1475 "Oksunn Peaks" (Kim Hong Do)

2001. Visit Korea Year 2001.
2466 **1475** 170w. multicoloured . . 10 10

1476 Plough

2001. Agricultural Implements. Multicoloured.
2467 170w. Type **1476** 10 10
2468 170w. Harrow 10 10
2469 170w. Sowing basket and namtae 10 10
2470 170w. Short-handled hoes 10 10
2471 170w. Manure barrel and fertilizer ash container . . 10 10
2472 170w. Water dipper 10 10
2473 170w. Winnower and thresher 10 10
2474 170w. Square straw drying mat and wicker tray . . . 10 10
2475 170w. Pestle, mortar and grinding stones 10 10
2476 170w. Rice basket and carrier 10 10

1486 2000 Series Diesel-electric Locomotive

1487 7000 Series Diesel-electric Locomotive

1488 Diesel Urban Commuter Train

1489 Diesel Saemaul Train

2001. Railways (2nd series).
2477 **1486** 170w. multicoloured . . 10 10
2478 **1487** 170w. multicoloured . . 10 10
2479 **1488** 170w. multicoloured . . 10 10
2480 **1489** 170w. multicoloured . . 10 10

2001. Protection of Wildlife and Plants (8th series). Vert designs as T **1270**. Multicoloured.
2481 170w. *Jeffersonia dubia* . . . 10 10
2482 170w. *Diapensia lapponica* 10 10
2483 170w. *Rhododendron aureum* 10 10
2484 170w. *Sedum orbiculatum* . . 10 10
Nos. 2481/4 are impregnated with the scent of the Ume tree.

1490 Incheon Airport and Emblem

2001. Inauguration of Incheon Airport.
2486 **1490** 170w. multicoloured . . 10 10

1491 Kim Ku (leader of Independence Movement)

2001. Millennium (10th series). Multicoloured.
2487 170w. Type **1491** 10 10
2488 170w. Statue commemorating the March 1st Independence Movement 10 10
2489 170w. Interim Korean Government Headquarters, Shanghai and Members 10 10
2490 170w. Ahn Ik Tae (composer) and music score 10 10
2491 170w. Yun Dong Ju (poet) and *Seosi* (poem) 10 10

1492 Emblem

2001. International Olympic Fair, Seoul.
2492 **1492** 170w. multicoloured . . 10 10
MS2493 105 × 70 mm. No. 2492 × 2 15 15

1493 Bears hugging

2001. Greetings Stamps. Multicoloured.
2494 170w. Type **1493** 10 10
2495 170w. Flower 10 10
2496 170w. Trumpets (Congratulations) 10 10
2497 170w. Cake 10 10

1494 Iljimae (Ko Woo Young)

1495 Kkeobeongi (Kil Chang Duk)

2001. Cartoons (7th series).
2498 **1494** 170w. multicoloured . . 10 10
2499 **1495** 170w. multicoloured . . 10 10
MS2500 Two sheets, each 90 × 60 mm. (a) No. 2498. (b) No. 2499 Price for 2 sheets . . 15 15

1496 Players and Mountains (Switzerland, 1954)

2001. World Cup Football Championship, Japan and South Korea. Multicoloured.
2501 170w. Type **1496** 10 10
2502 170w. Players and Ancient settlement (Mexico, 1986) 10 10
2503 170w. Players and Coliseum (Italy, 1990) 10 10
2504 170w. Players and buildings (United States of America, 1994) 10 10
2505 170w. Players and Eiffel Tower (France, 1998) . . 10 10
MS2506 Five sheets, each 60 × 90 mm. (a) No. 2501 × 2. (b) No. 2502 × 2. (c) No. 2503 × 2. (d) No. 2504 × 2. (e) No. 2505 × 2 Set for 5 sheets 90 90

1497 Baechu Kimchi (Chinese Cabbage)

1498 Bossam Kimchi

1499 Dongchimi

1500 Klakdugi

2001. Korean Foods (1st series).
2507 **1497** 170w. multicoloured . . 10 10
2508 **1498** 170w. multicoloured . . 10 10
2509 **1499** 170w. multicoloured . . 10 10
2510 **1500** 170w. multicoloured . . 10 10

1501 Raising Flag (Liberation, 1945)

2001. Millennium (11th series). Multicoloured.
2511 170w. Type **1501** 10 10
2512 170w. Soldiers embracing (statue) (Korean War) . . 10 10
2513 170w. Seoul–Busan Expressway 10 10
2514 170w. Working in fields (Saemaul Undong movement) 10 10
2515 170w. Athletes forming emblem (Olympic Games, Seoul, 1988) 10 10

1502 Red Queen

1503 Pink Lady

2001. "Philakorea 2002" International Stamp Exhibition, Seoul. Roses.
2516 **1502** 170w. multicoloured . . 10 10
2517 **1503** 170w. multicoloured . . 10 10
MS2518 Two sheets, each 115 × 73 mm. (a) No. 2516 × 2. (b) No. 2517 × 2 Set for 2 sheets 35 35

C. NORTH KOREAN OCCUPATION.

(**1** "Democratic People's Republic of Korea")

1950. Nos. 116 and 118/19 optd with Type **1**.
1 10w. green . . . . 45·00
2 20w. brown . . . . 12·50
3 30w. green . . . . 15·00

NORTH KOREA

100 cheun = 1 won.

GUM. All stamps of North Korea up to No. N1506 are without gum, except where otherwise stated.

A. RUSSIAN OCCUPATION

1 Hibiscus

2 Diamond Mountains

1946. Perf, roul or imperf.
N1 **1** 20ch. red . . . . 55·00 38·00
N2 **2** 50ch. green . . . . 17·00 15·00
N4b 50ch. red . . . . 10·00 10·00
N5b 50ch. violet . . . . 10·00 12·00

4 Gen. Kim Il Sung and Flag

5 Peasants

1946. 1st Anniv of Liberation from Japan.
N6 **4** 50ch. brown £190 £190

1947. Perf, roul or imperf.
N 7 **5** 1wn. green . . . . 5·00 4·00
N 8 1wn. violet . . . . 15·00 10·00
N 9 1wn. blue on buff . . . . 5·50 4·50
N10 1wn. blue . . . . 3·25 2·50

6

7

1948. 2nd Anniv of Labour Law.
N11 **6** 50ch. blue £225 £180

1948. 3rd Anniv of Liberation from Japan.
N12 **7** 50ch. red . . . . — £325

8

1948. Promulgation of Constitution.
N13 **8** 50ch. blue and red . . . . £160 40·00

B. KOREAN PEOPLE'S DEMOCRATIC REPUBLIC

9 North Korean Flag

10

1948. Establishment of People's Republic. Roul.
N16 **9** 25ch. violet . . . . 3·50 3·50
N17 50ch. blue . . . . 6·00 6·00

1949. Roul or perf.
N18 **10** 6wn. red and blue . . . . 2·00 2·00

11 Kim Il Sung University, Pyongyang

12 North Korean Flags

11a Kim Il Sung University, Pyongyang

1949. Roul.
N19 **11** 1wn. violet . . . . . . 45·00 20·00
N20 **11a** 1wn. blue . . . . 45·00 20·00

1949. 4th Anniv of Liberation from Japan. Roul or perf.
N22 **12** 1wn. red, green and blue 35·00 14·00

13 Order of the National Flag

14 Liberation Monument, Pyongyang

15 Soldier and Flags

16 Peasant and Worker

17 Tractor

18 Capitol, Seoul

1950. Perf, roul or imperf. Various sizes.
N24 **13** 1wn. green (A) . . . . . 4·00 1·00
N25 1wn. orange (A) . . . . . — 25·00
N26 1wn. orange (B) . . . . . 17·00 12·00
N27 1wn. green (C) . . . . . 4·00 1·25
N28 1wn. olive (D) . . . . . 7·00 4·50
SIZES: (A) 23½ × 37½ mm. (B) 20 × 32½ mm. (C) 22 × 35½ mm. (D) 22½ × 36½ mm.

1950. 5th Anniv of Liberation from Japan. Roul, perf or imperf. Various sizes.
N29 **14** 1wn. red, indigo and blue 1·25 90
N30 1wn. orange . . . . . . 7·00 5·00
N31 **15** 2wn. black, blue and red 1·25 90
N32 **16** 6wn. green (A) . . . . . 1·75 1·25
N36 6wn. red (B) . . . . . . 12·50 11·00
N33 **17** 10wn. brown (C) . . . . 2·50 2·00
N37 10wn. brown (D) . . . . 18·00 13·50
SIZES: (A) 20 × 30 mm. (B) 22 × 33 mm. (C) 20 × 28 mm. (D) 22 × 30 mm.

1950. Capture of Seoul by North Korean Forces. Roul.
N38 **18** 1wn. red, blue and green 40·00 32·00

19

20 Kim Gi Ok and Aeroplane

1951. Order of Admiral Li Sun Sin. Imperf or perf.
N39 **19** 6wn. orange . . . . . . 6·50 5·00

1951. Air Force Hero Kim Gi Ok. Imperf.
N40 **20** 1wn. blue . . . . 8·00 3·00

21 Russian and North Korean Flags **22** Kim Ki U (hero) **23** N. Korean and Chinese Soldiers

1951. 6th Anniv of Liberation from Japan. Roul or perf.
N41 **21** 1wn. blue . . . . 3·50 2·50
N42 1wn. red . . . . 3·50 2·50
N43 **22** 1wn. blue . . . . 3·50 2·50
N44 1wn. red . . . . 3·75 2·50
N45 **23** 2wn. blue . . . . 6·50 5·00
N46 2wn. red . . . . 10·00 7·50
All values exist on buff and on white paper.

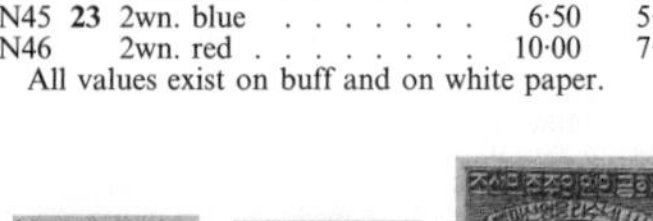

24 Order of Soldier's Honour **25** **26** Woman Partisan, Li Su Dok

1951. Imperf or perf.
N47 **24** 40wn. red . . . . 9·00 4·50

1951. Co-operation of Chinese People's Volunteers. Imperf or perf.
N49 **25** 10wn. blue . . . . 5·00 3·25

1952. Partisan Heroes. Imperf or perf.
N50 **26** 70wn. brown . . . . . . 4·00 1·00

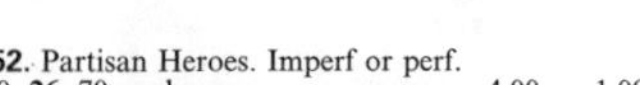

27

28 Gen. P'eng Teh-huai

29 Munition Worker

1952. Peace Propaganda. Imperf or perf.
N51 **27** 20wn. blue, green and red 6·00 2·00

1952. Honouring Commander of Chinese People's Volunteers. Imperf.
N52 **28** 10wn. purple . . . . . . 8·00 4·00

1952. Labour Day. Imperf or perf.
N53 **29** 10wn. red . . . . 17·00 17·00

30

31

32

1952. 6th Anniv of Labour Law. Imperf or perf.
N54a **30** 10wn. blue . . . . . . 11·00 11·00

1952. Anti-U.S. Imperialism Day. Imperf or perf.
N55 **31** 10wn. red . . . . 13·00 13·00

1952. North Korean and Chinese Friendship. Imperf or perf.
N56b **32** 20wn. deep blue . . . . 9·00 9·00

33

34

1952. 7th Anniv of Liberation from Japan. Imperf or perf.
N57 **33** 10wn. red . . . . 10·00 10·00
N58 **34** 10wn. red . . . . 12·00 12·00

35

1952. Int Youth Day. With gum. Imperf or perf.
N59 **35** 10wn. green . . . . . . 8·00 8·00

36

37

1953. 5th Anniv of People's Army. Imperf or perf.
N60 **36** 10wn. red . . . . 12·50 12·50
N61 **37** 40wn. purple . . . . . . 12·50 12·50

38

39

1953. Int Women's Day. With gum. Imperf or perf.
N62 **38** 10wn. red . . . . 10·00 8·00
N63 **39** 40wn. green . . . . . . 10·00 8·00

40

41

1953. Labour Day. Imperf or perf.
N64 **40** 10wn. green . . . . . . 7·50 7·50
N65 **41** 40wn. orange . . . . . . 7·50 7·50

42

43

1953. Anti-U.S. Imperialism Day. With gum. Imperf or perf.
N66 **42** 10wn. turquoise . . . . . 15·00 13·00
N67 **43** 40wn. red . . . . 15·00 13·00

44

45

1953. 4th World Youth Festival, Bucharest. With gum. Imperf or perf.
N68 **44** 10wn. blue and green . . 4·00 3·25
N69 **45** 20wn. green and pink . . 4·00 3·25

46

47

1953. Armistice and Victory Issue. With gum. Imperf or perf.
N70a **46** 10wn. brown and yellow 38·00 32·00

1953. 8th Anniv of Liberation from Japan. Imperf.
N71 **47** 10wn. red . . . . £120 90·00

48

49 Liberation Monument, Pyongyang

1953. 5th Anniv of People's Republic. Imperf or perf.
N72 **48** 10wn. blue and red . . . 11·00 11·00

1953. With gum. Imperf or perf.
N73 **49** 10wn. slate . . . . 3·75 3·50

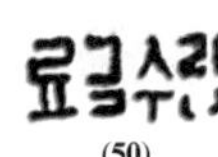
(50)

(51)

1954. No. N18 optd "Fee Collected" in Korean characters, T **50**.
N74 **10** 6wn. red and blue £150 £150

1954. Nos. N18 and N39 surch with T **51**.
N75 **10** 5wn. on 6wn. red and blue 12·00 12·00
N76 **19** 5wn. on 6wn. orange . . . 55·00 45·00

52

53

1954. Post-war Economic Reconstruction. With gum. Imperf or perf.
N77 **52** 10wn. blue . . . . 15·00 9·00

1954. 6th Anniv of People's Army. With gum. Imperf or perf.
N78 **53** 10wn. red . . . . 13·00 10·00

54

55

1954. Int Women's Day. With gum. Imperf or perf.
N79 **54** 10wn. red . . . . 5·50 5·50

1954. Labour Day. With gum. Imperf or perf.
N80 **55** 10wn. red . . . . 6·00 6·00

56

57 Taedong Gate, Pyongyang

1954. Anti-U.S. Imperialism Day. With gum. Imperf or perf.
N81 **56** 10wn. red . . . . 17·00 15·00

1954. Imperf or perf.
N82 **57** 5wn. lake . . . . 2·00 75
N83 5wn. brown . . . . 2·00 75

58

59 Soldier

1954. National Young Activists' Conference With gum. Imperf or perf.
N84 **58** 10wn. red, blue and slate 3·00 3·00

1954. 9th Anniv of Liberation from Japan. With gum. Imperf or perf.
N85 **59** 10wn. red . . . . 6·00 6·00

60 North Korean Flag

61 Hwanghae Iron Works

62 Hwanghae Iron Works and Workers

1954. 6th Anniv of People's Republic. With gum. Imperf or perf.
N86 **60** 10wn. blue and red . . . 5·00 5·00

1954. Economic Reconstruction. Imperf or perf.
N87 **61** 10wn. blue . . . . 4·50 50
N88 **62** 10wn. brown . . . . . . 4·50 50

63

64

1955. 7th Anniv of People's Army. With gum. Imperf or perf.
N89 **63** 10wn. red . . . . 4·50 3·50

1955. Int Women's Day. With gum. Imperf or perf.
N90 **64** 10wn. deep blue . . . . . 5·00 3·50

65

66

1955. Labour Day. With gum. Imperf or perf.
N91 **65** 10wn. green . . . . . . 3·25 3·25
N92 **66** 10wn. red . . . . 3·25 3·25

67 Admiral Li Sun Sin

68

1955. Imperf or perf.
N93 **67** 1wn. blue on green . . . 1·25 20
N94 2wn. red on buff . . . . 1·75 25
N95 2wn. red . . . . 3·00 50

1955. 9th Anniv of Labour Law. With gum. Imperf or perf.
N96 **68** 10wn. red . . . . 3·50 2·50

69 Liberation Monument and Flags

1955. 10th Anniv of Liberation from Japan. Imperf or perf.
N97 **69** 10wn. green . . . . . . 2·00 1·50
N98 10wn. red, blue and brown ($29\frac{1}{2} \times 42\frac{1}{2}$ mm) . . . . 1·25 1·00

70

71

1955. Soviet Union Friendship Month. Imperf or perf.
N 99 **70** 10wn. red . . . . . . 1·50 1·00
N100 10wn. red and blue . . . 2·25 1·50
N101 **71** 20wn. red and slate . . . 3·25 2·50
N102 20wn. red and blue . . . 1·50 1·25
SIZES: No. N99, $22 \times 32\frac{1}{2}$ mm; N100, $29\frac{1}{2} \times 43$ mm; N101, $18\frac{1}{2} \times 32$ mm; N102, 25×43 mm.

72 Son Rock

73

1956. Haegumgang Maritime Park. Imperf or perf.
N103 **72** 10wn. blue on blue . . . 3·00 1·75

1956. 8th Anniv of People's Army. Imperf or perf.
N104 **73** 10wn. red on green . . . 5·50 5·50

74

1956. Labour Day. Imperf or perf.
N105 **74** 10wn. blue . . . . . . 4·50 2·75

75 Machinist

76 Taedong Gate, Pyongyang

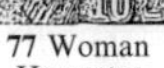

77 Woman Harvester **78** Moranbong Theatre, Pyongyang

1956. Imperf or perf.
N106 **75** 1wn. brown 1·25 60
N107 **76** 2wn. blue 90 60
N108 **77** 10wn. red 90 60
N109 **78** 40wn. green 8·00 3·50

79 Miner **80** Boy Bugler and Girl Drummer

1956. 10th Anniv of Labour Law. Imperf or perf.
N110 **79** 10wn. brown 2·50 1·00

1956. 10th Anniv of Children's Union. Imperf or perf.
N111 **80** 10wn. brown 4·00 2·75

81 Workers **82** Industrial Plant

1956. 10th Anniv of Sex Equality Law. Imperf or perf.
N112 **81** 10wn. brown 2·00 1·40

1956. 10th Anniv of Nationalization of Industry. Imperf or perf.
N113 **82** 10wn. brown 45·00 16·00

83 Liberation Tower **84** Kim Il Sung University

1956. 11th Anniv of Liberation from Japan. Imperf or perf.
N114 **83** 10wn. red 3·00 1·25

1956. 10th Anniv of Kim Il Sung University. Imperf or perf.
N115 **84** 10wn. brown 2·50 1·75

85 Boy and Girl **86** Pak Ji Won

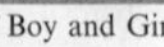

1956. 4th Democratic Youth League Congress. Imperf or perf.
N116 **85** 10wn. brown 2·50 1·50

1957. 220th Birth Anniv of Pak Ji Won "Yonam", (statesman). Imperf or perf.
N117 **86** 10wn. blue 1·50 90

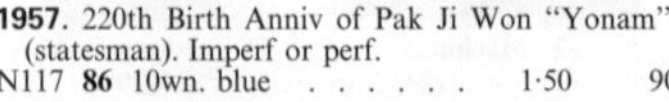

87 Tabo Pagoda, Pulguksa **88** Ulmil Pavilion, Pyongyang **89** Furnaceman

1957. Imperf, perf or roul.
N118 **87** 5wn. blue 1·00 75
N119 **88** 40wn. green 2·00 1·25

1957. Production and Economy Campaign. With or without gum. Imperf or perf.
N121 **89** 10wn. blue 2·50 1·25

90 Furnaceman **91** Voters and Polling Booth

1957. 2nd General Election. Imperf or perf.
N122 **90** 1wn. orange 75 30
N123 2wn. brown 75 30
N124 **91** 10wn. red 3·75 1·25

92 Ryongwangjong, Pyongyang **93** Lenin and Flags

94 Kim Il Sung at Pochonbo **95** Lenin **96** Pouring Steel

1957. 1530th Anniv of Pyongyang. Imperf or perf.
N125 **92** 10wn. green 1·00 25

1957. 40th Anniv of Russian Revolution. Imperf or perf.
N126 **93** 10wn. green 75 40
N127 **94** 10wn. red 75 40
N128 **95** 10wn. blue 75 40
N129 **96** 10wn. orange 2·00 40
No. N126 exists with gum.

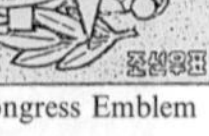

97 Congress Emblem **98** Liberation Monument, Spassky Tower and Flags

1957. 4th World Trade Unions Federation Congress. Leipzig. Imperf (with or without gum) or perf.
N130 **97** 10wn. blue and green 1·25 50

1957. Russian Friendship Month. Imperf or perf.
N131 **98** 10wn. green 1·75 50

99 Weighing a Baby **100** Bandaging a Hand

1957. Red Cross. Imperf, perf or roul.
N132 **99** 1wn. red 6·00 1·00
N133 2wn. red 6·00 1·00
N134 **100** 10wn. red 15·00 2·75
No. N133 exists with or without gum.

101 Koryo Celadon Jug (12th century) **102** Koryo Incense-burner (12th century)

1958. Korean Antiquities. Imperf (with or without gum) or perf.
N135 **101** 10wn. blue 4·50 75
N136 **102** 10wn. green 4·50 75

103 Woljong Temple Pagoda **104** Soldier

1958. With gum (5wn.), without gum (10wn.). Imperf or perf.
N137 **103** 5wn. green 1·00 50
N138 10wn. blue 1·50 75

1958. 10th Anniv of People's Army. No gum (No. N139) with or without gum (No. N140). Imperf or perf.
N139 **104** 10wn. blue 1·75 50
N140 – 10wn. red 4·50 65
DESIGN—HORIZ ($37\frac{1}{2} \times 26$ mm): No. N140, Soldier, flag and Hwanghae Iron Works.

106 Lisunov Li-2 Airliner over Pyongyang

1958. Air. Imperf or perf.
N141 **106** 20wn. blue 5·50 1·00

107 Sputniks **108** Sputnik encircling Globe

1958. I.G.Y. Inscr "1957–1958". Imperf or perf.
N142 **107** 10wn. slate 45 10
N143 **108** 20wn. slate 45 10
N144 – 40wn. slate 1·75 30
N145 **107** 70wn. slate 50 20
DESIGN—HORIZ: 40wn. Sputnik over Pyongyang Observatory.
Nos. N142/4 exist with or without gum.

109 Furnaceman **110** Hwanghae Iron Works

1958. Young Socialist Constructors' Congress, Pyongyang. Imperf or perf.
N146 **109** 10wn. blue 2·75 50

1958. Opening of Hwanghae Iron Works. Imperf or perf.
N147 **110** 10wn. blue 4·25 65

111 Commemorative Badge **112** Federation Emblem

1958. Farewell to Chinese People's Volunteers (1st issue). Imperf or perf.
N148 **111** 10wn. purple and blue 1·50 40
See also No. N158.

1958. 4th International Women's Federation Democratic Congress. Imperf or perf.
N149 **112** 10wn. blue 1·00 35

113 Conference Emblem

1958. 1st World Young Workers' Trade Union Federation Conference, Prague. Imperf or perf.
N150 **113** 10wn. brown and green 1·75 35

114 Flats, East Ward, Pyongyang **115** Workers' Flats, Pyongyang

1958. Rehousing Progress. Imperf or perf.
N151 **114** 10wn. blue 2·00 50
N152 **115** 10wn. green 2·00 50

117 Pyongyang Railway Station **119** Textile Worker

1958. 10th Anniv of Korean People's Republic. Imperf or perf.
N153 – 10wn. green 3·00 50
N154 **117** 10wn. green 11·00 1·50
N155 – 10wn. brown and buff 1·50 50
N156 **119** 10wn. brown 7·50 1·75
N157 – 10wn. brown 6·50 1·00
DESIGNS—HORIZ: No. N153, Hungnam Fertiliser Plant; N157, Yongp'ung Dam, Pyongyang. VERT: No. N155, Arms of People's Republic.

121 Volunteer and Steam Troop Train **122** Transplanting Rice

1958. Farewell to Chinese People's Volunteers (2nd issue). Imperf or perf.
N158 **121** 10wn. sepia 24·00 8·00

1958. Imperf or perf.
N159 **122** 10wn. sepia 75 15

123 Winged Horse of Chollima **124** N. Korean and Chinese Flags

1958. National Production Executives' Meeting, Pyongyang. With or without gum. Imperf or perf.
N160 **123** 10wn. red 1·60 30

1958. North Korean–Chinese Friendship Month. With or without gum. Imperf or perf.
N161 **124** 10wn. red, blue green 1·25 30

125 Farm Workers **126** Gen. Ulji Mun Dok

1959. National Co-operative Farming Congress, Pyongyang. With or without gum. Imperf or perf.
N162 **125** 10wn. blue 90 25

1959. With gum. Imperf or perf.
N163 **126** 10wn. red and yellow 2·00 50
See also Nos. N165/7 and N216/19.

127 Women with Banner

128 Rocket and Moon

1959. National Conference of Women Socialist Constructors, Pyongyang. With or without gum.
N164 **127** 10ch. brown and red . . 75 30

1959. Revalued currency. Portraits as T **126**. Imperf (with or without gum) or perf (with gum).
N165 – 2ch. blue on green . . . 60 10
N166 – 5ch. purple on buff . . 70 10
N167 **126** 10ch. red on cream . . 85 10
PORTRAITS: 2ch. General Kang Gam Chan; 5ch. General Chon Bong Jun.

1959. Launch of Soviet Moon Rocket. With or without gum. Imperf or perf.
N168 **128** 2ch. purple on buff . . 1·25 25
N169 10ch. blue on green . . 1·50 35

129 "Irrigation"

130 Inscribed Tree at Partisan H.Q., Chongbong

131 Kim Il Sung Statue

132 Mt. Paekdu

1959. Land Irrigation Project. Imperf or perf.
N170 **129** 10ch. multicoloured . . 3·75 65

1959. Partisan Successes against Japanese, 1937–39. With gum (No. N172) or no gum (others). Perf (N172) or imperf or perf (others).
N171 **130** 5ch. multicoloured . . . 2·75 45
N172 **131** 10ch. blue and turquoise 1·00 10
N173 **132** 10ch. violet . . . . . . 2·25 40

133 "Flying Horse" Tractor

1959. "Great Perspectives" (1st issue: Development of Industrial Mechanization). With or without gum. Perf, roul or imperf.
N174 **133** 1ch. red, olive and green 65 10
N175 – 2ch. multicoloured . . . 3·25 75
N176 – 2ch. red, pink and violet 60 10
N177 – 5ch. orange, brown and ochre 60 15
N178 – 10ch. blue, green & brn 70 15
N179 – 10ch. grn, lt grn & brn 1·50 25
DESIGNS: No. N175, Electric mine locomotive; N176, "Red Star 58" bulldozer; N177, "Flying Horse" excavator; N178, "SU-50" universal lathe; N179, "Victory 58" lorry.
See also Nos. N189a/200 and N275/79.

134 Armistice Building, Panmunjom

135 Protest Meeting

136 "Hoisting link between N. and S. Korea"

1959. Campaign for Withdrawal of U.S. Forces from S. Korea. With gum. Perf (20ch.) or imperf or perf (others).
N180 **134** 10ch. blue & ultramarine 55 20
N181 **135** 20ch. deep blue and blue 75 30
N182 **136** 70ch. brown, cream and purple . . . . 13·00 6·00

137 Emigration "Pickets"

1959. Campaign Against Emigration of South Koreans. With gum.
N183 **137** 20ch. brown and sepia 3·50 1·00

138 Korean Type of "1234"

139 Books breaking Chains

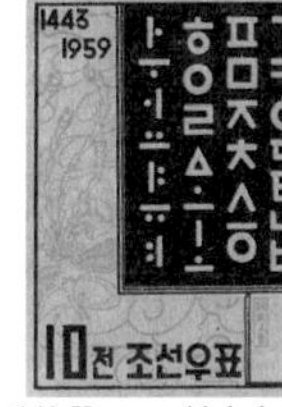
141 Korean Alphabet of 1443

140 Emblems of Peace, Labour and Letters

1959. International Book Exibition, Leipzig. With gum (No. N184, N186) or no gum (others).
N184 **138** 5ch. sepia . . . . . . 15·00 5·00
N185 **139** 5ch. red and green . . . 4·50 1·50
N186 **140** 10ch. blue . . . . . . 4·50 1·50
N187 **141** 10ch. violet and blue . . 7·00 2·50

142 Pig Farm

1959. Animal Husbandry. With gum (5ch.) or no gum (2ch.).
N188 – 2ch. brown, green & buff 75 15
N189 **142** 5ch. cream, blue & brn 1·00 20
DESIGN—HORIZ: 2ch. Cow-girl with Cattle.

143 Rotary Cement Kiln

1959. "Great Perspectives" (2nd issue: Production Targets). With gum (Nos. N190 and N192) or no gum (others). Perf (N197/8 and N200), perf or imperf (others)
N189a **143** 1ch. cinnamon, brn & bl 40 10
N190 – 2ch. multicoloured . . 60 10
N191 – 5ch. multicoloured . . 1·00 25
N192 – 10ch. multicoloured . . 1·25 35
N193 – 10ch. purple, yell & bl 60 10
N194 – 10ch. yellow, grn & red 90 10
N195 – 10ch. multicoloured . . 60 10
N196 – 10ch. blue, light blue and green 75 10
N197 – 10ch. multicoloured . . 60 10
N198 – 10ch. green, buff and brown 90 10
N199 – 10ch. brown and orange 60 10
N200 – 10ch. multicoloured . . 1·10 15
DESIGNS—VERT: No. N190, Electric power lines and dam; N191, Loading fertilizers into goods wagon. HORIZ: No. N192, Factory, electric power lines and dam; N163, Harvesting; N194, Sugar-beet, factory and pieces of sugar; N195, Steel furnace; N196, Trawlers; N197, Pig-iron workers; N198, Coal miners; N199, Girl picking apples; N200, Textile worker.

144 Sika Deer

145 Congress Emblem

1959. Game Preservation. No gum (5ch.), with gum (10ch.).
N201 – 5ch. multicoloured . . . 1·75 20
N202 – 5ch. yellow, brown & bl 1·75 10
N203 – 5ch. sepia, green & brn 1·75 10
N204 – 5ch. brown, black & blue . . . . 1·75 10
N205 **144** 10ch. multicoloured . . 1·75 25
N206 – 10ch. red, brown and green on cream . . . 12·00 1·75
DESIGNS—HORIZ: No. N201, Chinese water deer; N202, Siberian weasel; N203, Steppe polecat; N204, European otter; N206, Common pheasant.

1960. 3rd Korean Trade Unions Federation Congress. With gum.
N207 **145** 5ch. multicoloured . . . 45 20

146 "Chungnyon-ho" (freighter)

1959. Transport. With gum.
N208 – 5ch. purple . . . . . . 6·75 75
N209 **146** 10ch. green . . . . . . 2·50 60
DESIGN: 5ch. Electric train.

147 Soldier, Tractor and Plough

148 Knife Dance

1960. 12th Anniv of Korean People's Army. With gum.
N210 **147** 5ch. violet and blue . . 35·00 28·00

1960. Korean National Dances. Multicoloured.
N211 5ch. Type **148** . . . . . . 3·50 20
N212 5ch. Drum dance . . . . . 3·50 20
N213 10ch. Farmers' dance . . . 3·50 25

149 Women of Three Races

150 Kim Jong Ho (geographer)

1960. 50th Anniv of Int Women's Day. With gum.
N214 **149** 5ch. mauve and blue . . 90 15
N215 – 10ch. green and orange 90 25
DESIGN—VERT: 10ch. Woman operating lathe.

1960. Korean Celebrities. With gum.
N216 **150** 1ch. grey and green . . 75 10
N217 – 2ch. blue and yellow . . 90 10
N218 – 5ch. blue and yellow . . 3·00 20
N219 – 10ch. brown and ochre 85 10
PORTRAITS: 2ch. Kim Hong Do (painter); 5ch. Pak Yon (musician); 10ch. Chong Da San (scholar).

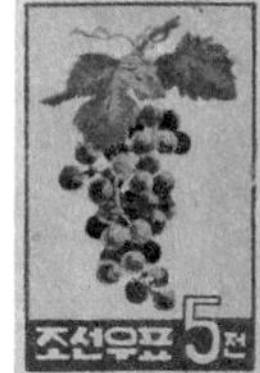
151 Grapes

152 Lenin

1960. Wild Fruits. Fruits in natural colours. With or without gum (N221/2), with gum (others).
N220 5ch. olive and turquoise . . 80 15
N221 5ch. drab and blue 80 15
N222 5ch. olive and blue 80 15
N223 10ch. olive and orange . . 1·25 20
N224 10ch. green and pink . . . 1·25 20
FRUITS: No. N220, T **151**; N221, Fruit of "Actinidia arguta planch"; N222, Pine-cone; N223, Hawthorn berries; N224, Horse-chestnut.

1960. 90th Birth Anniv of Lenin. With gum.
N225 **152** 10ch. purple 55 15

153 Koreans and American Soldier (caricature)

154 Arch of Triumph Square, Pyongyang

1960. Campaign Day for Withdrawal of U.S. Forces from South Korea. With gum.
N226 **153** 10ch. blue . . . . . . 3·25 40

1960. Views of Pyongyang.
N227 **154** 10ch. green 75 20
N228 – 20ch. slate . . . . . . 1·00 30
N229 – 40ch. green . . . . . . 2·25 50
N230 – 70ch. green . . . . . . 3·00 60
N231 – 1wn. blue . . . . . . 4·50 90
VIEWS OF PYONGYANG: 20ch. River Taedong promenade; 40ch. Youth Street; 70ch. People's Army Street; 1wn. Sungri Street.

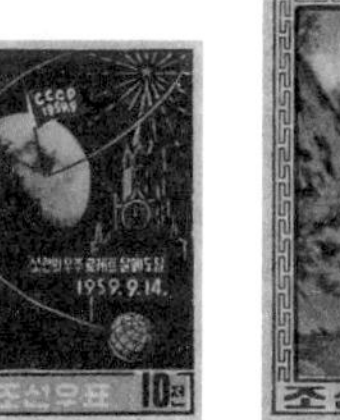
155 Russian Flag on Moon (14.9.59)

156 "Mirror Rock"

1960. Russian Cosmic Rocket Flights. With gum (5ch.) or no gum (10ch.).
N232 – 5ch. turquoise . . . . . 2·00 1·10
N233 **155** 10ch. multicoloured . . 2·00 75
DESIGN: 5ch. "Lunik 3" approaching Moon (4.10.59).

1960. Diamond Mountains Scenery (1st issue). Multicoloured.
N234 5ch. Type **156** . . . . . . 1·00 10
N235 5ch. Devil-faced Rock . . . 1·00 10
N236 10ch. Dancing Dragon Bridge (horiz) . . . . . 3·00 25
N237 10ch. Nine Dragon Falls 3·50 25
N238 10ch. Mt. Diamond on the Sea (horiz.) 90 10
See also Nos. N569/72, N599/601 and N1180/4.

157 Lily

158 Guerrillas in the Snow

1960. Flowers. Multicoloured. With gum (N242), with or without gum (others).
N239 5ch. Type **157** 90 15
N240 5ch. Rhododendron 90 15

N241 10ch. Hibiscus . . . . . . 1·75 20
N242 10ch. Blue campanula . . . 1·75 20
N243 10ch. Mauve campanula . . 1·75 20

1960. Revolutionary Leadership of Kim Il Sung.
N244 **158** 5ch. red 45 10
N245 – 10ch. blue 70 10
N246 – 10ch. red 70 10
N247 – 10ch. blue 70 10
N248 – 10ch. red 70 10
DESIGNS: No. N245, Kim Il Sung talks to guerrillas; N246, Kim Il Sung at Pochonbo; N247, Kim Il Sung on bank of Amnok River; N248, Kim Il Sung returns to Pyongyang.

159 Korean and Soviet Flags

160 "North Korean–Soviet Friendship"

1960. 15th Anniv of Liberation from Japan.
N249 **159** 10ch. red, blue & brown 60 15

1960. North Korean–Soviet Friendship Month.
N250 **160** 10ch. lake on cream . . 35 15

161 Okryu Bridge, Pyongyang

1960. Pyongyang Buildings.
N251 **161** 10ch. blue . . . . . . 2·25 20
N252 – 10ch. violet . . . . . . 1·50 15
N253 – 10ch. green 75 10
DESIGNS: No. N252, Grand Theatre, Pyongyang; N253, Okryu Restaurant.

162 Tokro River Dam

1960. Inauguration of Tokro River Hydro-electric Power Station. With gum.
N254 **162** 5ch. blue 70 10

163

164 Quayside Welcome

1960. 15th Anniv of World Federation of Trade Unions.
N255 **163** 10ch. lt blue, ultram & bl 25 10

1960. Repatriation of Korean Nationals from Japan.
N256 **164** 10ch. purple . . . . . 2·50 35

165 Lenin and Workers

166 Football

1960. Korea–Soviet Friendship. With gum.
N257 **165** 10ch. brown and flesh 35 15

1960. Liberation Day Sports Meeting, Pyongyang. Multicoloured.
N258 5ch. Running (vert) 60 10
N259 5ch. Weightlifting (vert) . . 60 10
N260 5ch. Cycling (vert) . . . . 2·25 15
N261 5ch. Gymnastics (vert) . . 60 10
N262 5ch. Type **166** . . . . . . 1·10 15
N263 10ch. Swimming 60 10
N264 10ch. Moranbong Stadium, Pyongyang 60 10

167 Friendship Monument, Pyongyang

168 Federation Emblem

1960. 10th Anniv of Entry of Chinese Volunteers into Korean War. With gum.
N265 – 5ch. mauve 30 10
N266 **167** 10ch. blue 30 10
DESIGN—HORIZ: 5ch. Chinese and Korean soldiers celebrating.

1960. 15th Anniv of World Democratic Youth Federation.
N267 **168** 10ch. multicoloured . . 30 10

169 White-backed Woodpecker

170 Korean Wrestling

1960. Birds.
N268 **169** 2ch. multicoloured . . 9·00 15
N268a – 5ch. multicoloured . . 12·50 35
N269 – 5ch. brown, yellow & bl . . . . 17·00 70
N270 – 10ch. yellow, brn & grn . . . . 11·00 55
DESIGNS—HORIZ: 5ch. (N268a), Mandarins; 10ch. Black-naped oriole. VERT: 5ch. (N269), Oriental scops owl.

1960. Sports and Games. Multicoloured.
N271 5ch. Type **170** 60 10
N272 5ch. Riding on swing (vert) 60 10
N273 5ch. Archery . . . . 2·25 30
N274 10ch. Jumping on see-saw (vert) 60 10

171 Cogwheel and Textiles

172 Wild Ginseng (perennial herb)

1961. "Great Perspectives" (3rd issue: Targets of Seven-Year Plan, 1961–67. Inscr "1961"). Mult.
N275 5ch. Type **171** 60 10
N276 5ch. Cogwheel and Corn ("Mechanization of Rural Economy") . . . . . . 1·10 10
N277 10ch. Hammer, sickle and torch on flag (vert) . . . 30 10
N278 10ch. Cogwheels around power station 60 10
N279 10ch. Cogwheel and molten steel 45 10

1961. Multicoloured.
N280 5ch. Type **172** . . . . . . 1·50 10
N281 10ch. Cultivated ginseng . . 1·50 10

173 Aldehyde Shop

1961. Construction of Vinalon Factory. With gum.
N282 **173** 5ch. red and yellow . . 60 10
N283 – 10ch. green and yellow 1·10 10
N284 – 10ch. blue and yellow 1·10 10
N285 – 20ch. purple and yellow 1·25 15
DESIGNS: No. N283, Glacial acetic acid shop; N284, Polymerization and saponification shop; N285, Spinning shop.
See also Nos. N338/41.

174 Construction Work

175 Museum Building

1961. Construction of Children's Palace, Pyongyang. With gum.
N286 **174** 2ch. red on yellow . . . 35 15

1961. Completion of Museum of Revolution, Pyongyang. With gum.
N287 **175** 10ch. red 25 10

176 Cosmic Rocket

177 Wheat Harvester

1961. Launching of Soviet Venus Rocket.
N288 **176** 10ch. red, yellow & blue 60 15

1961. Agricultural Mechanization. With gum.
N289 – 5ch. violet 50 10
N290 – 5ch. green 50 10
N291 **177** 5ch. green 50 10
N292 – 10ch. blue 60 10
N293 – 10ch. purple 60 10
DESIGNS: No. N289, Tractor-plough; N290, Disc-harrow; N292, Maize-harvester; N293, Tractors.

178

179 Agriculture

1961. Opening of Training Institute.
N294 **178** 10ch. brown on buff . . 25 10

1961. 15th Anniv of Land Reform Law. With gum.
N295 **179** 10ch. green on yellow 45 15

180

182 Tractor-crane

181 Chub Mackerel

1961. 15th Anniv of National Programme. With gum.
N296 **180** 10ch. purple and yellow 20 10

1961. Marine Life.
N297 **181** 5ch. multicoloured . . . 1·25 10
N298 – 5ch. black and blue . . 2·00 25
N299 – 10ch. blue, black & lt bl 2·50 25
N300 – 10ch. multicoloured . . 1·25 10
N301 – 10ch. brown, yell & grn 1·25 10
DESIGNS: No. N298, Common dolphin; N299, Whale sp; N300, Yellow-finned tuna; N301, Pacific cod.

1961. With gum.
N302 **182** 1ch. brown 65 10
N303 – 2ch. brown 65 10
N304 – 5ch. green 90 10
N305 – 10ch. violet 90 20
DESIGNS—HORIZ: 2ch. Heavy-duty lorry; 5ch. Eight-metres turning lathe. VERT: 10ch. 3000-ton press.
See also Nos. N378/9c.

183 Tree-planting

184 "Peaceful Unification" Banner

1961. Re-afforestation Campaign. With gum.
N306 **183** 10ch. green . . . . . . 1·00 25

1961. Propaganda for Peaceful Reunification of Korea.
N307 **184** 10ch. multicoloured . . 6·50 1·50

185 Pioneers visiting Battlefield

1961. 15th Anniv of Children's Union. Mult.
N308 5ch. Pioneers bathing . . . 40 10
N309 10ch. Pioneer bugler . . . 1·25 20
N310 10ch. Type **185** 40 10

186 "Labour Law"

1961. 15th Anniv of Labour Law. With gum.
N311 **186** 10ch. blue on yellow . . 45 20

187 Apples

1961. Fruit. Multicoloured.
N312 5ch. Peaches 75 10
N313 5ch. Plums 75 10
N314 5ch. Type **187** 75 10
N315 10ch. Persimmons 75 10
N316 10ch. Pears 75 10

188 Yuri Gagarin and "Vostok 1"

1961. World's First Manned Space Flight.
N317 **188** 10ch. ultramarine & blue 35 10
N318 10ch. violet and blue . . 35 10

189 Power Station

1961. 15th Anniv of Nationalization of Industries Law. With gum.
N319 **189** 10ch. brown . . . . . 4·50 60

190 Women at Work

191 Children planting Tree

1961. 15th Anniv of Sex Equality Law. With gum.
N320 **190** 10ch. red 35 10

1961. Children. Multicoloured.
N321 5ch. Type **191** 60 10
N322 5ch. Reading book 30 10
N323 10ch. Playing with ball . . 30 10
N324 10ch. Building a house . . 30 10
N325 10ch. Waving flag 30 10

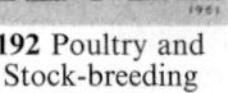

192 Poultry and Stock-breeding

193 Soldiers on March (statue)

1961. Improvement in Living Standards. Mult.
N326 5ch. Type **192** 60 10
N327 10ch. Fabrics and textile factory 1·10 10
N328 10ch. Trawler and fish (horiz) 1·50 20
N329 10ch. Grain-harvesting (horiz) 50 10

1961. 25th Anniv of Fatherland Restoration Association. With gum.
N330 – 10ch. violet 40 10
N331 – 10ch. violet 25 10
N332 **193** 10ch. blue and buff 25 10
DESIGNS—Marshal Kim Il Sung: No. N330, Seated under tree; N331, Working at desk.

194 Party Emblem and Members **195** Miner

1961. 4th Korean Workers' Party Congress, Pyongyang. With gum.
N333 **194** 10ch. green 20 10
N334 – 10ch. purple 20 10
N335 – 10ch. red 20 10
DESIGNS—VERT: No. N334, "Chollima" statue, Pyongyang. HORIZ: No. N335, Marshal Kim Il Sung.

1961. Miners' Day. With gum.
N336 **195** 10ch. brown 1·75 60

196 Pak in Ro **197** Aldehyde Shop

1961. 400th Birth Anniv of Pak in Ro (poet).
N337 **196** 10ch. indigo on blue 45 15

1961. Completion of Vinalon Factory. With gum.
N338 **197** 5ch. red and yellow 60 10
N339 – 10ch. brown and yellow 90 10
N340 – 10ch. blue and yellow 90 10
N341 – 20ch. purple and yellow 1·40 20
DESIGNS: No. N339, Glacial-acetic shop; N340, Polymerization and saponification shop; N341, Spinning shop.

198 Korean and Chinese Flags **199** Basketball

1961. North Korean Friendship Treaties with China and the U.S.S.R.
N342 – 10ch. multicoloured 40 10
N343 **198** 10ch. red, blue & yellow 40 10
DESIGN: No. N342, Korean and Soviet flags.

1961. Physical Culture Day. With gum.
N344 – 2ch. grey 75 10
N345 – 5ch. blue 90 10
N346 **199** 10ch. blue 90 10
N347 – 10ch. blue 90 10
N348 – 10ch. purple 90 10
N349 – 20ch. purple 75 10
DESIGNS: 2ch. Table tennis; 5ch. Flying model glider; 10ch. (N347) Rowing; 10ch. (N348) High jumping; 20ch. Sports emblem.

5ch 100

(200)

1961. Centenary of Publication of Map "Taidong Yu Jido" by Kim Jung Ho. No. N216 surch with T **200**.
N350 **150** 5ch. on 1ch. grey & grn 38·00 24·00

201 General Rock **202** "Agriculture and Industry"

1961. Mt. Chilbo Scenery. With gum.
N351 **201** 5ch. blue 75 10
N352 – 5ch. brown 75 10
N353 – 10ch. violet 1·40 20
N354 – 10ch. blue 1·40 20
N355 – 10ch. blue 1·40 20
DESIGNS—HORIZ: No. N352, Chonbul Peak; N354, Tiled House Rock; N355, Rainbow Rock. VERT: No. N353, Mansa Peak.

1961. With gum.
N356 **202** 10ch. green 35 10

203 Winged Horse and Congress Emblem

1961. 5th World Federation of Trade Unions Congress, Moscow. With gum.
N357 **203** 10ch. blue, purple & vio 25 10

204 Class "Red Banner" Electric Locomotive

1961. Railway Electrification. With gum.
N358 **204** 10ch. violet and yellow 4·00 1·60

205 Ice Hockey

1961. Winter Sports. With gum.
N359 – 10ch. brown and green 75 10
N360 – 10ch. brown and green 75 10
N361 **205** 10ch. brown and blue 75 10
N362 – 10ch. brown and blue 75 10
DESIGNS: No. N359, Figure skating; N360, Speed skating; N362, Skiing.

206 Grain Harvest **207** Tiger

1962. "Six Heights" of Production Targets (1st series). Inscr "1962". With gum.
N363 – 5ch. red, violet and grey 30 10
N364 – 5ch. brown and grey 1·75 30
N365 **206** 10ch. yellow, black & bl 30 10
N366 – 10ch. red, yellow & blue 90 10
N367 – 10ch. black and blue 1·10 15
N368 – 10ch. yellow, brown & bl 30 10
DESIGNS: No. N363, Ladle and molten steel; N364, Electric mine train; N366, Fabrics and mill; N367, Trawler and catch; N368, Construction of flats.
See also Nos. N440/5.

1962. Animals.
N369 **207** 2ch. multicoloured 2·00 15
N370 – 2ch. brown and green 1·50 10
N371 – 5ch. yellow and green 1·50 10
N372 – 10ch. brown and green 1·75 15
ANIMALS—HORIZ: 2ch. (N370), Racoon-dog; 5ch. Chinese ferret-badger; 10ch. Asiatic black bear.

208 Kayagum Player **209** "Leuhdorfia puziloi"

1962. Musical Instruments and Players (1st series). Multicoloured.
N373 10ch. Type **208** 1·75 20
N374 10ch. Man playing haegum (two-stringed bowed instrument) 1·75 20
N375 10ch. Woman playing wolgum (banjo) 1·75 20
N376 10ch. Man playing chotdae (flute) 1·75 20
N377 10ch. Woman playing wagonghu (harp) 1·75 20
See also Nos. N473/7.

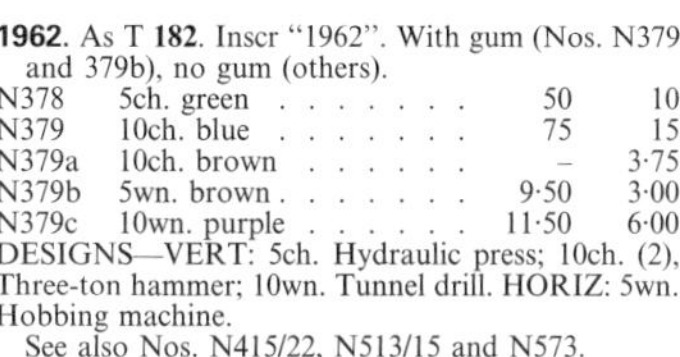

1962. As T **182**. Inscr "1962". With gum (Nos. N379 and 379b), no gum (others).
N378 5ch. green 50 10
N379 10ch. blue 75 15
N379a 10ch. brown – 3·75
N379b 5wn. brown 9·50 3·00
N379c 10wn. purple 11·50 6·00
DESIGNS—VERT: 5ch. Hydraulic press; 10ch. (2), Three-ton hammer; 10wn. Tunnel drill. HORIZ: 5wn. Hobbing machine.
See also Nos. N415/22, N513/15 and N573.

1962. Butterflies. Multicoloured.
N380 5ch. Type **209** 2·50 15
N381 10ch. "Sericinus telamon" (purple background) 2·50 15
N382 10ch. Keeled apollo (lilac background) 2·50 15
N383 10ch. Peacock (green background) 2·50 15

210 G. S. Titov and "Vostok 2"

1962. 2nd Soviet Manned Space Flight.
N384 **210** 10ch. multicoloured 45 15

211 Marshal Kim Il Sung and (inset) addressing Workers

1962. Marshal Kim Il Sung's 50th Birthday. With gum.
N385 **211** 10ch. red 45 15
N386 – 10ch. green 45 15
N387 – 10ch. blue 45 10
DESIGN: No. 387, Kim Il Sung in fur hat and (inset) inspecting battle-front.

212 Kim Chaek **214** Black-faced Spoonbill

213 Mother with Children

1962. Korean Revolutionaries (1st series). With gum.
N388 **212** 10ch. sepia 35 10
N389 – 10ch. blue 35 10
N390 – 10ch. red 35 10
N391 – 10ch. purple 35 10
N392 – 10ch. green 35 10
N393 – 10ch. blue 35 10
N394 – 10ch. brown 35 10
PORTRAITS: No. N389, Kang Gon; N390, An Gil; N391, Ryu Gyong Su; N392/3, Kim Jong Suk; N394, Choe Chun Guk.
See also Nos. N478/82 and N733/5.

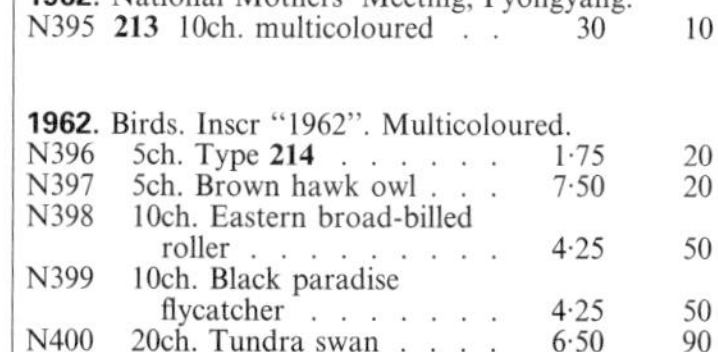

1962. National Mothers' Meeting, Pyongyang.
N395 **213** 10ch. multicoloured 30 10

1962. Birds. Inscr "1962". Multicoloured.
N396 5ch. Type **214** 1·75 20
N397 5ch. Brown hawk owl 7·50 20
N398 10ch. Eastern broad-billed roller 4·25 50
N399 10ch. Black paradise flycatcher 4·25 50
N400 20ch. Tundra swan 6·50 90

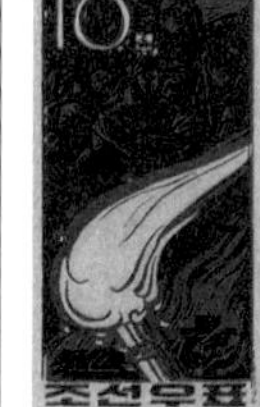

215 Victory Flame **216** Japanese Croaker

1962. 25th Anniv of Battle of Pochonbo.
N401 **215** 10ch. multicoloured 55 10

1962. Fishes. Multicoloured.
N402 5ch. Type **216** 1·50 10
N403 5ch. Hairtail 1·50 10
N404 10ch. Dotted gizzard shad (head pointing to right) 1·75 20
N405 10ch. Japanese spotted seabass (blue background) 1·75 20
N406 10ch. Japanese croaker (green background) 1·75 20

217 Waterdropper **218** Radial Drill

1962. Antiques. With gum.
N407 – 4ch. black and blue 1·00 10
N408 **217** 5ch. black and ochre 1·00 10
N409 A 10ch. black and green 1·25 10
N410 B 10ch. black and orange 1·25 10
N411 C 10ch. black and purple 1·25 10
N412 D 10ch. black and brown 1·25 10
N413 E 10ch. black and yellow 1·25 10
N414 – 40ch. black and grey 3·50 35
DESIGNS—VERT: 4ch. Brush pot; 40ch. Porcelain decanter. HORIZ: A, Inkstand; B, Brushstand; C, Turtle paperweight; D, Inkstone; E, Document case.

1962. Double frame-line. With gum.
N415 – 2ch. green 40 10
N415a – 2ch. brown — 4·00
N416 – 4ch. blue 1·75 10
N417 **218** 5ch. blue 40 10
N418 – 5ch. purple 40 10
N419 – 10ch. purple 50 10
N420 – 40ch. blue 3·75 20
N421 – 90ch. blue 1·60 30
N422 – 1wn. brown 4·75 50
DESIGNS—VERT: 2ch. Vertical milling machine; 5ch. (N418), Hydraulic hammer; 1wn. Spindle drill. HORIZ: 4ch. "Victory April 15" motor-car; 10ch. All-purpose excavator; 40ch. Trolley-bus; 90ch. Planing machine.
See also Nos. N513/15 and N573.

219 Chong Da San **220** Voter

1962. Birth Bicentenary of Chong Da San (philosopher).
N423 **219** 10ch. purple 35 10

1962. Election of Deputies to National Assembly. Multicoloured.
N424 10ch. Type **220** 80 10
N425 10ch. Family going to poll 80 10

221 Pyongyang

1962. 1535th Anniv of Pyongyang. With gum.
N426 **221** 10ch. black and blue . . 65 10

222 Globe and "Vostok 3" and "4"

223 Spiraea

1962. 1st "Team" Manned Space Flight.
N427 **222** 10ch. indigo, blue & red 60 20

1962. Korean Plants. Plants in natural colours; frame and inscr colours given.
N428 **223** 5ch. light green & green 1·25 10
N429 – 10ch. green and red . . 1·25 10
N430 – 10ch. blue and purple 1·25 10
N431 – 10ch. green and olive 1·25 10
PLANTS: No. N429, Ginseng; N430, Campanula; N431, "Rheumcoreanum makai (Polyonaceae)".

224 "Uibang Ryuchui"

225 Science Academy

1962. 485th Anniv of Publication of "Uibang Ryuchui" (medical encyclopaedia).
N432 **224** 10ch. multicoloured . . 3·50 30

1962. 10th Anniv of Korean Science Academy.
N433 **225** 10ch. blue and turquoise 1·00 10

226 Fisherwomen

227 European Mink

1962.
N434 **226** 10ch. blue . . . . . . 1·00 10

1962. Animals.
N435 **227** 4ch. brown and green 70 10
N436 – 5ch. blue, drab and green 70 10
N437 – 10ch. blue and yellow 90 10
N438 – 10ch. sepia and turquoise 90 10
N439 – 20ch. brown and blue 1·50 15
ANIMALS—HORIZ: No. N436, Chinese hare. VERT: No. N437, Eurasian red squirrel; N438, Common goral; N439, Siberian chipmunk.

228 Harvesting

1963. "Six Heights" of Production Targets (2nd issue). Inscr "1963". Multicoloured.
N440 5ch. Miner . . . . 1·00 20
N441 10ch. Type **228** 40 10
N442 10ch. Furnaceman 30 10
N443 10ch. Construction worker 30 10
N444 10ch. Textiles loom operator 65 10
N445 40ch. Fisherman and trawler . . . . 2·25 40

229 Soldier

230 Peony

1963. 15th Anniv of Korean People's Army. With gum.
N446 – 5ch. brown 50 10
N447 **229** 10ch. red 60 10
N448 – 10ch. blue 85 10
DESIGNS: 5ch. Airman; 10ch. Sailor.

1963. Korean Flowers. Multicoloured.
N449 5ch. Type **230** 60 10
N450 10ch. Rugosa rose 90 10
N451 10ch. Azalea 90 10
N452 20ch. Campion 90 10
N453 40ch. Orchid . . . . 2·50 35

231 "Sadang-ch'um" (Korean folk dance)

1963. International Music and Dancing Contest, Pyongyang. Multicoloured.
N454 10ch. Type **231** . . . . . 1·75 15
N455 10ch. Dancer with fan . . . 1·75 15

232 Revolutionaries

1963. 3rd Anniv of South Korean Rising of April, 1960.
N456 **232** 10ch. multicoloured . . 40 15

233 Karl Marx

234 Children in Chemistry Class

1963. 145th Birth Anniv of Karl Marx. With gum.
N457 **233** 10ch. blue 30 10

1963. Child Care and Amenities. Multicoloured.
N458 2ch. Type **234** 80 20
N459 5ch. Children running . . . 70 15
N460 10ch. Boy conducting choir 1·75 20
N461 10ch. Girl chasing butterfly 3·50 25

235 Armed Koreans and American Soldier (caricature)

1963. Campaign Month for Withdrawal of U.S. Forces from South Korea.
N462 **235** 10ch. multicoloured . . 45 10

236 "Cyrtoclytus capra"

237 Soldier with Flag

1963. Korean Beetles. Multicoloured designs. Colours of beetles given.
N463 5ch. Type **236** 75 10
N464 10ch. multicoloured . . . . 1·10 10
N465 10ch. red and blue . . . . 1·10 10
N466 10ch. indigo, blue and purple . . . . 1·10 10
BEETLES: No. N464, "Cicindela chinensis" (tiger beetle); N465, "Purpuricenus lituratus"; N466, "Agapanthia pilicornis".

1963. 10th Anniv of Victory in Korean War.
N467 **237** 10ch. multicoloured . . 50 10

238 North Korean Flag

239 Namdae Gate, Kaesong

1963. 15th Anniv of People's Republic. Mult.
N468 10ch. Type **238** 30 10
N469 10ch. North Korean Badge 30 10

1963. Ancient Korean Buildings (1st series). With gum.
N470 **239** 5ch. black 20 10
N471 – 10ch. blue 40 10
N472 – 10ch. brown 40 10
BUILDINGS: No. N471, Taedong Gate, Pyongyang; N472, Potong Gate, Pyongyang.
See also Nos. N537/8.

240 Ajaeng (bowed zither)

241 Nurse with Children

1963. Musical Instruments and Players (2nd series). Multicoloured. Nos. N473 and N476 with gum.
N473 3ch. Type **240** . . . . . . 1·25 15
N474 5ch. Pyongyon (jade chimes) . . . . 1·25 15
N475 10ch. Saenap (brass bowl) 1·50 15
N476 10ch. Rogo (drums in frame) . . . . 1·50 15
N477 10ch. Piri ("wooden pipe") 1·50 15

1963. Korean Revolutionaries (2nd issue). As T **212**. With gum.
N478 5ch. brown 40 10
N479 5ch. purple 40 10
N480 10ch. rose 50 10
N481 10ch. slate 50 10
N482 10ch. dull purple 50 10
PORTRAITS: No. N478, Kwon Yong Byok; N479, Ma Dong Hui; N480, Li Je Sun; N481, Pak Dal; N482, Kim Yong Bom.

1963. Child Welfare. Multicoloured.
N483 10ch. Type **241** 50 10
N484 10ch. Children in playground 50 10

242 Hwajang Hall

243 Furnaceman

1963. Mount Myohyang Resort. Multicoloured.
N485 5ch. Type **242** 35 10
N486 10c. Mountain stream and chalet 75 10
N487 10ch. Kwanum Pavilion and stone pagoda (horiz) 65 10
N488 10ch. Rope bridge across river (horiz) . . . . . . 1·75 15

1963. Seven Year Plan. With gum.
N489 **243** 5ch. red 20 10
N490 – 10ch. grey . . . . . . 1·50 20
N491 – 10ch. red . . . . 1·50 20
N492 – 10ch. lilac 85 10
DESIGNS—VERT: No. N490, Construction workers. HORIZ: No. N491, Power technicians; N492, Miners.

244 Children hoeing

1963. "Hung Bo" (fairytale). Multicoloured.
N493 5ch. Type **244** 30 10
N494 10ch. Tying up broken leg of swallow 90 10
N495 10ch. Barn swallow dropping gourd seed . . 90 15
N496 10ch. Sawing through giant gourd 50 10
N497 10ch. Treasure inside gourd 50 10

245 Marksman

1963. Marksmanship. Multicoloured.
N498 5ch. Type **245** 30 10
N499 10ch. Marksman with small-bore rifle 55 10
N500 10ch. Marksman with standard rifle 55 10

246 Sinuiju Chemical Fibre Factory

1964. Chemical Fibres Factories. With gum.
N501 **246** 10ch. slate 75 10
N502 – 10ch. purple 75 10
DESIGN: No. N502, Chongjin Chemical Fibre Factory.

247 Strikers

1964. 35th Anniv of Wonsan General Strike. With gum.
N503 **247** 10ch. brown 60 10

248 Korean Alphabet

1964. 520th Anniv of Korean Alphabet.
N504 **248** 10ch. green, buff & brn 60 20

249 Lenin

250 Whale-catcher

1964. 40th Death Anniv of Lenin. With gum.
N505 **249** 10ch. red 30 10

1964. Fishing Industry. Multicoloured.
N506 5ch. Type **250** 50 10
N507 5ch. Trawler No. 051 . . . 50 10
N508 10ch. Trawler No. 397 . . 1·00 20
N509 10ch. Trawler No. 738 . . 1·00 20

251 Insurgents

1964. 45th Anniv of Rising of 1st March. With gum.
N510 **251** 10ch. purple 30 10

252 Warring Peasants

1964. 70th Anniv of Kabo Peasants' War. With gum.
N511 **252** 10ch. purple 30 10

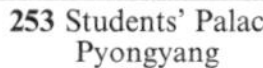

253 Students' Palace, Pyongyang

254 "Changbaek" Excavator

1964. With gum.
N512 **253** 10ch. green 30 10

1964. Single frame-line. Dated "1964" or "1965" (No. N573). With gum.
N513 – 5ch. violet 60 10
N514 **254** 10ch. green 90 10
N515 – 10ch. blue 90 10
N573 – 10ch. violet 75 20
DESIGNS—VERT: 5ch. 200 metre drill; 10ch. (N573) "Horning 500" machine. HORIZ: 10ch. (N515) 400 h.p. Diesel engine.

255 "On the March"

1964. 5th Korean Democratic Youth League Congress, Pyongyang.
N516 **255** 10ch. multicoloured . . 30 10

256 Electric Train

1964. Inauguration of Pyongyang–Sinuiju Electric Railway.
N517 **256** 10ch. multicoloured . . 2·50 20

257 Rejoicing in Chongsan-ri Village

1964. Popular Movement at Chongsan-ri. With gum.
N517a **257** 5ch. brown . . . . .

258 Drum Dance

259 "For the Sake of the Fatherland"

1964. Korean Dances.
N518 **258** 2ch. mauve, buff & black . . . . 1·50 15
N519 – 5ch. red, black & yellow 1·75 15
N520 – 10ch. multicoloured . . 2·00 15
DESIGNS: 5ch. "Ecstasy" (solo); 10ch. Tabor.

1964. Li Su Bok Commemorative. With gum.
N521 **259** 5ch. red 20 10

260 Nampo Smelting Works

1964. With gum.
N522 **260** 5ch. green . . . . . . 2·50 10
N523 – 10ch. slate . . . . . . 2·75 20
DESIGN: 10ch. Hwanghae iron works.

261 Torch, Chollima Statue and Cogwheel

1964. Asian Economic Seminar, Pyongyang. Multicoloured.
N524 5ch. Type **261** 25 10
N525 10ch. Flags, statue and cogwheel 30 10

262 Korean People and Statue of Kang Ho Yong (war hero)

1964. Struggle for Reunification of Korea.
N526 **262** 10ch. multicoloured . . 45 10

263 Hawk Fowl

1964. Domestic Poultry. Multicoloured.
N527 2ch. Type **263** 35 10
N528 4ch. White fowl 35 10
N529 5ch. Ryongyon fowl . . . 55 10
N530 5ch. Black fowl 55 10
N531 40ch. Helmet guineafowl . . 4·00 1·40

264 Skiing

1964. Winter Olympic Games, Innsbruck.
N532 **264** 5ch. red, blue and buff 50 10
N533 – 10ch. blue, green & buff 75 10
N534 – 10ch. blue, red and buff 75 10
DESIGNS: No. N533, Ice skating; N534, Skiing (slalom).

265 "Tobolsk" (passenger ship) and Flags

266 Tonggun Pavilion Uiju

1964. 5th Anniv of Agreement for Repatriation of Koreans in Japan.
N535 **265** 10ch. red, blue & lt blue 1·40 30
N536 – 30ch. multicoloured . . 1·10 15
DESIGN: 30ch. Return of repatriates.

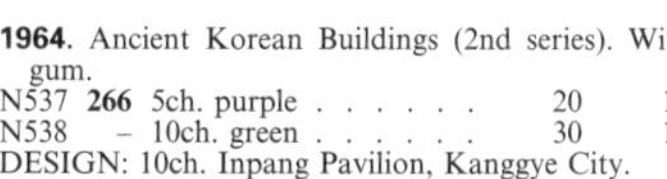

1964. Ancient Korean Buildings (2nd series). With gum.
N537 **266** 5ch. purple 20 10
N538 – 10ch. green 30 10
DESIGN: 10ch. Inpang Pavilion, Kanggye City.

267 Cycling

268 Burning of the "General Sherman"

1964. Olympic Games, Tokyo.
N539 – 2ch. brown and blue . . 25 10
N540 **267** 5ch. brown and green 75 10
N541 – 10ch. orange and blue 35 10
N542 – 10ch. orange and green 35 10
N543 – 40ch. brown and blue 60 35
DESIGNS—HORIZ: 2ch. Rifle-shooting; 10ch. blue, Running. VERT: 10ch. green, Wrestling; 40ch. Volleyball.

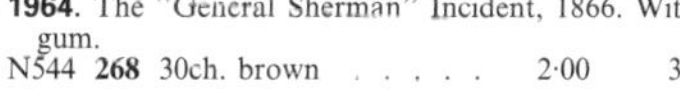

1964. The "General Sherman" Incident, 1866. With gum.
N544 **268** 30ch. brown . . . . . 2·00 30

269 Organizing Guerrillas

1964. Guerrilla Operations in the 1930s against the Japanese. With gum.
N545 **269** 2ch. violet 25 10
N546 – 5ch. blue 35 10
N547 – 10ch. black 45 10
DESIGNS: 5ch. Kim Il Sung addressing guerillas; 10ch. Battle scene at Xiaowangqing.

270 Students attacking

271 Weightlifting

1964. Kwangju Students Rising, 1929. With gum.
N548 **270** 10ch. violet . . . . . . 1·60 15

1964. "GANEFO" Athletic Games, Djakarta, Indonesia (1963). Multicoloured.
N549 2ch. Type **271** 40 10
N550 5ch. Athlete breasting tape 40 10
N551 5ch. Boxing (horiz) 40 10
N552 10ch. Football (horiz) . . . 1·00 15
N553 10ch. Globe emblem (horiz) 40 15

272 Lynx

1964. Animals. With gum.
N554 2ch. sepia (Type **272**) . . . 75 10
N555 5ch. sepia (Leopard cat) . . 1·75 10
N556 10ch. brown (Leopard) . . 2·25 10
N557 10ch. sepia (Yellow-throated marten) . . . . 2·25 10

273 Vietnamese Attack

1964. Support for People of Vietnam.
N558 **273** 10ch. multicoloured . . 30 10

274 Prof. Kim Bong Han and Emblems

1964. Kyongrak Biological Systems.
N559 **274** 2ch. purple and olive . . 65 10
N560 – 5ch. green, orange & bl 90 10
N561 – 10ch. red, yellow & blue 1·25 10
DESIGNS—33 × 23½ mm: 5ch. "Bonghan" duct; 10ch. "Bonghan" corpuscle. Each include emblems as in Type **274**.

275 Farmers, Tractor and Lorry

1964. Agrarian Programme. Multicoloured.
N562 5ch. Type **275** 20 10
N563 10ch. Peasants with scroll and book 30 10
N564 10ch. Peasants, one writing in book 30 10

276 Chung Jin gets a Pistol

1964. The Struggle to capture Japanese Arms. With gum.
N565 **276** 4ch. brown 25 10

277 Girl with Korean Products

278 Three Fairies Rock

1964. Economic 7 Year Plan. Multicoloured. With gum (5ch.) or no gum (others).
N566 5ch. Type **277** 40 10
N567 10ch. Farm girl 40 10
N568 10ch. Couple on winged horse (23½ × 23½ mm) . . 25 10

1964. Diamond Mountains Scenery (2nd issue). Inscr "1964". Multicoloured. Without gum (2, 4ch.) or with gum (others).
N569 2ch. Type **278** 75 10
N570 4ch. Ryonju Falls . . . . 2·75 10
N571 10ch. The Ten Thousand Rocks, Manmulsang . . 75 10
N572 10ch. Chinju Falls . . . . 2·75 10

280 Soldiers Advancing, Fusong

1965. Guerrilla Operations against the Japanese, 1934–40. With gum.
N574 **280** 10ch. violet 50 10
N575 – 10ch. violet 50 10
N576 – 10ch. green 50 10
DESIGNS: No. N575, Soldiers descending hill, Hongqihe; N576, Soldiers attacking hill post, Luozigou.

281 Tuman River

1965. Korean Rivers. Multicoloured.
N577 2ch. Type **281** 60 10
N578 5ch. Taedong (vert) . . . . 1·75 15
N579 10ch. Amnok 75 10

282 Union Badge

1965. 1st Congress of Landworkers' Union, Pyongyang. With gum.
N580 **282** 10ch. multicoloured . . 30 10

283 Furnacemen and Workers

1965. 10 Major Tasks of 7 Year Plan. With gum.
N581 **283** 10ch. multicoloured . . 30 10

284 Miners' Strike, Sinhung Colliery

1965. 35th Anniv of Strikes and Peasants' Revolt. With gum.
N582 **284** 10ch. olive . . . . . 1·25 15
N583 – 10ch. brown . . . . . 1·50 15
N584 – 40ch. purple . . . . . 1·00 15
DESIGNS: 10ch. Strikers at Pyongyang Rubber Factory; 40ch. Revolt of Tanchon peasants.

285 Embankment Construction

1965. Sunhwa River Works. With gum.
N585 **285** 10ch. multicoloured . . 30 10

286 Hand holding Torch

1965. 5th Anniv of South Korean Rising of April 19th. Multicoloured. With gum.
N586 10ch. Type **286** 20 10
N587 40ch. Student-hero, Kim Chio 45 20

287 Power Station under Construction

1965. Construction of Thermal Power Station, Pyongyang. With gum.
N588 **287** 5ch. brown and blue . . 25 10

288 African and Asian

1965. 10th Anniv of 1st Afro-Asian Conference, Bandung. With gum.
N589 **288** 10ch. multicoloured . . 30 10

289 Rejoicing of Koreans

1965. 10th Anniv of General Assn of Koreans in Japan. With gum.
N590 **289** 10ch. blue and red . . . 25 10
N591 – 40ch. indigo, blue & red 45 15
DESIGN: 40ch. Patriot and flag.

290 Workers in Battle

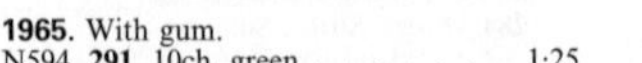

291 "Victory 64" 10-ton Lorry

1965. 2nd Afro-Asian Conf, Algiers. With gum.
N592 **290** 10ch. black, yellow red 75 10
N593 – 40ch. black, yellow red 1·25 25
DESIGN: 40ch. Korean and African soldiers.
The Algiers Conference did not take place.

1965. With gum.
N594 **291** 10ch. green . . . . . . 1·25 20

292 Kim Chang Gol

1965. War Heroes (1st series). With gum.
N595 **292** 10ch. green 30 10
N596 – 10ch. brown 30 10
N597 – 40ch. purple 75 20
PORTRAITS: No. N596, Cho Gun Sil and machine-gun; N597, An Hak Ryong and machine-gun.
See also Nos. N781/3 and N842/3.

293 Marx and Lenin

1965. Postal Ministers' Congress, Peking. With gum.
N598 **293** 10ch. black, yellow red 1·50 15

294 Lake Samil

1965. Diamond Mountains Scenery (3rd issue). Multicoloured. With gum.
N599 2ch. Type **294** 60 10
N600 5ch. Chipson Peak . . . . 1·00 10
N601 10ch. Kwanum Falls . . . 2·75 25

295 Amnok River, Kusimuldong

1965. Scenes of Japanese War. With gum.
N602 **295** 5ch. green and blue . . 35 10
N603 – 10ch. turquoise and blue 60 10
DESIGN: 10ch. Lake Samji.

296 Footballer and Games' Emblem **297** Workers and Map

1965. "GANEFO" Football Games, Pyongyang. Multicoloured. With gum.
N604 10ch. Type **296** . . . . . 1·25 10
N605 10ch. Games emblem and Moranbong Stadium . . 1·25 10

1965. 20th Anniv of Liberation from Japan. With gum.
N606 **297** 10ch. multicoloured . . 30 10

298 Engels **299** Pole Vaulting

1965. 145th Birth Anniv of Engels. With gum.
N607 **298** 10ch. brown 30 10

1965. Sports. Multicoloured. With gum.
N608 2ch. Type **299** 50 10
N609 4ch. Throwing the javelin 1·75 20
N610 10ch. Throwing the discus 50 10
N611 10ch. High jumping (horiz) 50 10
N612 10ch. Putting the shot (horiz) 50 10

301 Korean Fighters

1965. 20th Anniv of Korean Workers' Party. Each black, yellow and red. With gum.
N613 10ch. Type **301** 45 10
N614 10ch. Party emblem 45 10
N615 10ch. Lenin and Marx . . 45 10
N616 10ch. Workers marching . . 45 10
N617 10ch. Fighters 45 10
N618 40ch. Workers 45 10
Nos. N613/8 each have a red banner in the background and were issued together in blocks of 6 (3 × 2), forming a composite design, within the sheet.

302 Kim Chaek Iron Works **303** Grass Carp

1965. With gum.
N620 **302** 10ch. purple . . . . . 3·50 10
N621 – 10ch. brown . . . . . 3·50 10
DESIGN: No. 621, Chongjin Steel Works.

1965. Freshwater Fish. Multicoloured. With gum.
N622 2ch. Rainbow trout 70 10
N623 4ch. Dolly Varden charr . . 90 10
N624 10ch. Brown trout (surfacing water) . . . . 2·25 15
N625 10ch. Common carp diving (date at left) . . . . . . 2·25 15
N626 10ch. Type **303** . . . . . 2·25 15
N627 40ch. Crucian carp . . . . 3·25 55

304 Building House **305** Children in Workshop

1965. Kim Hong Do's Drawings. With gum.
N628 2ch. green (Type **304**) . . . 45 10
N629 4ch. purple (Weaving) . . . 90 10
N630 10ch. brown (Wrestling) . . . 80 10
N631 10ch. blue (School class) . . 80 10
N632 10ch. red (Dancing) . . . . 1·25 10
N633 10ch. violet (Blacksmiths) 1·10 10

1965. Life at Pyongyang Children's and Students' Palace. Multicoloured. With gum.
N634 2ch. Type **305** 20 10
N635 4ch. Boxing 20 10
N636 10ch. Chemistry 75 10
N637 10ch. Playing violin and accordion 75 10

306 Whale-catcher

1965. Korean Fishing Boats. With gum.
N638 **306** 10ch. blue . . . . . . 1·40 25
N639 – 10ch. green . . . . . . 1·40 25
DESIGN: No. N639, Fishing fleet service vessel.

307 Great Tit **308** Silkworm Moth ("Bombyx mori") and Cocoon

1965. Korean Birds. Inscr "1965". Multicoloured. With gum.
N640 4ch. Black-capped kingfisher (vert) . . . . 2·40 50
N641 10ch. Type **307** . . . . . 3·50 1·25
N642 10ch. Pied wagtail (facing left) . . . . 3·50 1·25
N643 10ch. Azure-winged magpie (facing right) . . . . . . 3·50 1·25
N644 40ch. Black-tailed hawfinch 8·00 4·50

1965. Korean Sericulture. With gum.
N645 **308** 2ch. green . . . . . . 5·00 20
N646 – 10ch. brown . . . . . 5·00 30
N647 – 10ch. purple . . . . . 5·00 30
MOTHS AND COCOONS: No. N646, Ailathus silk moth ("Samia cynthia"); N647, Chinese oak silk moth ("Antheraea pernyi").

309 Hooded Crane **310** Japanese Common Squid

1965. Wading Birds. With gum.
N648 **309** 2ch. brown . . . . . . 4·25 15
N649 – 10ch. blue . . . . . . 4·50 45
N650 – 10ch. purple . . . . . 4·50 45
N651 – 40ch. green . . . . . . 8·75 90
BIRDS: No. N649, Japanese white-naped crane; N650, Manchurian crane; N651, Grey heron.

1965. Korean Molluscs. Multicoloured. With gum.
N652 5ch. Type **310** . . . . . . 1·25 10
N653 10ch. Giant Pacific octopus 1·75 10

311 Spotbill Duck

1965. Korean Ducks. Multicoloured. With gum.
N654 2ch. Type **311** . . . . . . 2·75 15
N655 4ch. Ruddy shelduck . . . 2·75 25
N656 10ch. Mallard . . . . . . 4·25 55
N657 40ch. Baikal teal . . . . . 6·25 1·25

312 Circus Theatre, Pyongyang **313** "Marvel of Peru" ("Mirabilis jalapa")

1965. Korean Circus. With gum except No. N661.
N658 **312** 2ch. blue, black & brown 75 10
N659 – 10ch. blue, red and black . . . . 1·50 10
N660 – 10ch. red, black & green 1·50 10
N661 – 10ch. orange, sepia & grn . . . . 1·50 10
N662 – 10ch. red, yellow & turq 1·50 10
DESIGNS—VERT: No. N659, Trapeze artistes; N660, Performer with hoops on seesaw; N661, Tightrope dancers; N662, Performer with revolving cap on stick.

1965. Korean Flowers. Multicoloured. With gum except No. N663.
N663 4ch. Type **313** . . . . . . 1·10 10
N664 10ch. Peony . . . . 1·50 10
N665 10ch. Moss rose . . . . . 1·50 10
N666 10ch. Magnolia . . . . . 1·50 10

314 "Finn" Class Dinghy **315** Cuban, Korean and African

1965. Yachts. Multicoloured. With gum.
N667 2ch. Type **314** 70 20
N668 10ch. "5.5m" class yacht 1·00 30
N669 10ch. "Dragon" class yacht 1·00 30
N670 40ch. "Star" class yacht . . 2·00 60

1966. African-Asian and Latin American Friendship Conference, Havana. With gum.
N671 **315** 10ch. multicoloured . . 30 10

316 Hosta

1966. Wild Flowers. Mult. With gum. (a) 1st series.

N672 2ch. Type **316** 50 10
N673 4ch. Dandelion 50 10
N674 10ch. Pink convolvulus . . 75 10
N675 10ch. Lily-of-the-valley . . 75 10
N676 40ch. Catalpa blossom . . 2·00 20

(b) 2nd series.

N677 2ch. Polyanthus 50 10
N678 4ch. Lychnis 50 10
N679 10ch. Adonis 75 10
N680 10ch. Orange lily 75 10
N681 90ch. Rhododendron . . . 3·00 30

Nos. N672/6 exist imperf and without gum.

317 Farmer and Wife

1966. 20th Anniv of Land Reform Law. With gum.

N682 **317** 10ch. multicoloured . . 20 10

318 Troops advancing, Dashahe **319** Silla Bowl

1966. Paintings of Guerrilla Battles, 1937–39. With gum, except No. N684.

N683 **318** 10ch. red 30 10
N684 – 10ch. turquoise 30 10
N685 – 10ch. purple 30 10

DESIGNS AND BATTLES: No. N684, Troops firing from trees, Taehongdan; N685, Troops on hillside, Jiansanfeng.

1966. Art Treasures of Silla Dynasty. With gum.

N686 **319** 2ch. ochre . . . . . . 1·25 10
N687 – 5ch. black . . . . . . 1·25 10
N688 – 10ch. violet . . . . . . 1·25 10

DESIGNS: 5ch. Earthenware jug. 10ch. Censer.

320 Hands holding Torch, Rifle and Hammer **321** Torch and Patriots

1966. 80th Anniv of Labour Day. With gum.

N689 **320** 10ch. multicoloured . . 30 10

1966. 30th Anniv of Association for Restoration of Fatherland.

N690 **321** 10ch. red and yellow . . 30 10

322 Harvester

1966. Aid for Agriculture. Multicoloured.

N691 5ch. Type **322** 25 10
N692 10ch. Labourer 35 10

323 Young Pioneers

1966. 20th Anniv of Korean Children's Union. Without gum.

N693 **323** 10ch. multicoloured . . 50 10

324 Kangson Steel Works

1966. Korean Industries. With gum.

N694 **324** 10ch. grey . . . . . . 3·50 15
N695 – 10ch. red (Pongung Chemical Works) . . 3·50 15

325 Pacific Saury

1966. Korean Fishes. With gum, except Nos. N699/700.

N696 **325** 2ch. blue, green & purple 80 10
N697 – 5ch. purple, green & brn 1·00 10
N698 – 10ch. blue, buff & green 1·50 15
N699 – 10ch. purple and & green . . . . 1·50 15
N700 – 40ch. green, buff & blue 3·50 60

FISHES: 5ch. Pacific cod; 10ch. (N698), Chum salmon, (N699), Yellowfish; 40ch. Pink salmon.

326 Professor Kim Bong Han

1966. Kyungrak Biological System. With gum.

N701 **326** 2ch. blue, green & yellow 60 10
N702 – 4ch. multicoloured . . . 60 10
N703 – 5ch. multicoloured . . . 60 10
N704 – 10ch. multicoloured . . 60 10
N705 – 10ch. multicoloured . . 60 10
N706 – 10ch. multicoloured . . 60 10
N707 – 15ch. multicoloured . . 60 10
N708 – 40ch. multicoloured . . 60 10

DESIGNS: No. N704, Kyongrak Institute; N708, Figure of Man; N702/3, 705/7, Diagram of system.

Nos. N701/8 were issued together, se-tenant, forming a composite design.

327 Leonov in Space ("Voskhod 2")

1966. Cosmonauts Day. Multicoloured.

N710 5ch. Type **327** 20 10
N711 10ch. "Luna 9" 55 10
N712 40ch. "Luna 10" . . . . . 1·10 20

328 Footballers

1966. World Cup Football Championship. Mult.

N713 10ch. Type **328** . . . . . 1·25 25
N714 10ch. Jules Rimet Cup, football and boots . . . 1·25 25
N715 10ch. Goalkeeper saving goal (vert) . . . . 1·25 25

329 Defence of Seoul

1966. Korean War of 1950–53. With gum.

N716 **329** 10ch. green 35 10
N717 – 10ch. purple 35 10
N718 – 10ch. purple 35 10

DESIGNS: No. N717, Battle on Mt. Napal; N718, Battle for Height 1211.

330 Women in Industry

1966. 20th Anniv of Sex Equality Law.

N719 **330** 10ch. multicoloured . . 30 10

331 Industrial Workers **332** Water-jar Dance

1966. 20th Anniv of Industrial Nationalization.

N720 **331** 10ch. multicoloured . . 90 10

1966. Korean Dances. Multicoloured. 5, 40ch. with or without gum; others without.

N721 5ch. Type **332** . . . . . . 1·00 10
N722 10ch. Bell dance . . . . . 1·75 15
N723 10ch. "Dancer in a Mural Painting" . . . . 1·75 15
N724 15ch. Sword dance . . . . 1·75 20
N725 40ch. Gold Cymbal dance 3·25 30

333 Korean attacking U.S. Soldier **334** Yakovlev Yak-12M Crop-spraying

1966. Korean Reunification Campaign. With gum.

N726 **333** 10ch. green 60 10
N727 – 10ch. purple 60 10
N728 – 10ch. lilac . . . . . . 3·75 45

DESIGNS: No. N727, Korean with young child; N728, Korean with shovel, industrial scene and electric train.

1966. Industrial Uses of Aircraft. With gum except 2 and 5ch.

N729 **334** 2ch. green and purple 50 10
N730 – 5ch. brown and green 6·00 20
N731 – 10ch. brown and blue 1·50 10
N732 – 40ch. brown and blue 1·50 10

DESIGNS: 5ch. Yakovlev Yak-18U (forest-fire observation); 10ch. Lisunov Li-2 (geological survey); 40ch. Lisunov Li-2 (detection of fish shoals).

1966. Korean Revolutionaries (3rd issue). As T **212**. With gum.

N733 10ch. violet (O Jung Hub)
N734 10ch. green (Kim Gyong Sok) . . . .
N735 10ch. blue (Li Dong Gol)

335 Kim Il Sung University

1966. 20th Anniv of Kim Il Sung University. With gum.

N736 **335** 10ch. violet 50 10

336 Judo

1966. Ganefo Games, Phnom Penh.

N737 **336** 5ch. black, green & blue 60 10
N738 – 10ch. blk, grn & dp grn 60 10
N739 – 10ch. black and red . . 60 10

DESIGNS: No. N738, Basketball; N739, Table tennis.

337 Hoopoe

1966. Korean Birds. Multicoloured. Inscr "1966".

N740 2ch. Common rosefinch (horiz) . . . . 2·00 15
N741 5ch. Type **337** . . . . . . 2·40 20
N742 10ch. Black-breasted thrush (blue background) (horiz) 2·75 35
N743 10ch. Crested lark (green background) (horiz) . . . 2·75 35
N744 40ch. White-bellied black woodpecker . . . . . . 6·00 90

338 Building Construction

1966. "Increased Production with Economy". Multicoloured. Without gum (40ch.) or with gum (others).

N745 5ch. Type **338** 25 10
N746 10ch. Furnaceman and graph 45 10
N747 10ch. Machine-tool production 45 10
N748 40ch. Miners and pit-head 1·40 15

339 Parachuting

1966. National Defence Sports. With gum.

N749 **339** 2ch. brown 75 10
N750 – 5ch. red 55 10
N751 – 10ch. blue . . . . . . 2·75 30
N752 – 40ch. green . . . . . 1·60 20

DESIGNS: 5ch. Show jumping; 10ch. Motor cycle racing; 40ch. Radio receiving and transmitting competition.

340 "Samil Wolgan" (Association Magazine)

1966. 30th Anniv of "Samil Wolgan" Magazine.

N753 **340** 10ch. multicoloured . . 90 15

341 Red Deer **342** Blueberries

1966. Korean Deer. Multicoloured.

N754 2ch. Type **341** 30 10
N755 5ch. Sika deer 50 10
N756 10ch. Indian muntjac (erect) 90 10
N757 10ch. Reindeer (grazing) . . 90 10
N758 70ch. Fallow deer . . . . 2·25 25

1966. Wild Fruit. Multicoloured.

N759 2ch. Type **342** 50 10
N760 5ch. Wild pears 70 10
N761 10ch. Wild raspberries . . . 90 10
N762 10ch. Schizandra 90 10
N763 10ch. Wild plums 90 10
N764 40ch. Jujube . . . . 2·25 15

343 Onpo Rest Home

1966. Korean Rest Homes. With gum.

N765 **343** 2ch. violet 25 10
N766 – 5ch. turquoise 35 10
N767 – 10ch. green 50 10
N768 – 40ch. black 80 20

REST HOMES: 5ch. Mt. Myohyang; 10ch. Songdowon; 40ch. Hongwon

344 Soldier

1967. 19th Anniv of Army Day. Without gum.

N769 **344** 10ch. green, yellow & red 25 10

345 Sow

1967. Domestic Animals. Multicoloured. Without gum. 40ch. also with gum.

N770 5ch. Type **345** 40 10
N771 10ch. Goat 50 10
N772 40ch. Ox . . . . 1·00 25

346 Battle Scene

1967. 30th Anniv of Battle of Pochonbo. With gum.

N773 **346** 10ch. orange, red & grn 50 10

347 Students

1967. Compulsory Technical Education for Nine Years.

N774 **347** 10ch. multicoloured . . 25 10

348 Table Tennis Player

1967. 29th Int Table Tennis Championships, Pyongyang. Designs showing players in action. 5ch. with or without gum.

N775 **348** 5ch. multicoloured . . . 40 10
N776 – 10ch. multicoloured . . 70 10
N777 – 40ch. multicoloured . . 1·10 15

349 Anti-aircraft Defences

1967. Paintings of Guerrilla War against the Japanese. With gum.

N778 **349** 10ch. blue 35 10
N779 – 10ch. purple . . . . . 3·00 25
N780 – 10ch. violet 35 10

PAINTINGS: No. N779, Blowing-up railway bridge; N780, People helping guerrillas in Wangyugou.

1967. War Heroes (2nd series). As T **292**. Designs showing portraits and combat scenes. With gum.

N781 10ch. slate 40 10
N782 10ch. violet 40 10
N783 10ch. blue 75 10

PORTRAITS: No. N781, Li Dae Hun and grenade-throwing; N782, Choe Jong Un and soldiers charging; N783, Kim Hwa Ryong and air dog-fighter aircraft.

350 Workers

1967. Labour Day.

N784 **350** 10ch. multicoloured . . 25 10

351 Card Game

1967. Korean Children. Multicoloured.

N785 5ch. Type **351** . . . . . . 1·00 10
N786 10ch. Children modelling tractor 60 10
N787 40ch. Children playing with ball . . . . 1·10 20

352 Victory Monument

1967. Unveiling of Battle of Ponchonbo Monument.

N788 **352** 10ch. multicoloured . . 30 10

353 Attacking Tank

354 "Polygonatum japonicum"

1967. Monuments to War of 1950–53. 2ch. with or without gum.

N789 **353** 2ch. green and turquoise 20 10
N790 – 5ch. sepia and green . . 85 10
N791 – 10ch. brown and buff 30 10
N792 – 40ch. brown and blue 60 15

MONUMENTS: 5ch. Soldier-musicians; 10ch. Soldier; 40ch. Soldier with children.

1967. Medicinal Plants. Mult; background colour of 10ch. values given to aid identification. Nos. 793/5 and 797 with or without gum.

N793 2ch. Type **354** . . . . . . 1·00 10
N794 5ch. "Hibiscus manihot" 1·00 10
N795 10ch. "Scutellaria baicalensis" (turquoise) 1·25 10
N796 10ch. "Pulsatilla koreana" (blue) . . . . 1·25 10
N797 10ch. "Rehmannian glutinosa" (yellow) . . . 1·25 10
N798 40ch. "Tanacetum boreale" 3·25 35

355 Servicemen

1967. People's Army. Multicoloured. 5ch. with or without gum.

N799 5ch. Type **355** 20 10
N800 10ch. Soldier and farmer 25 10
N801 10ch. Officer decorating soldier 25 10

356 Freighter "Chollima"

1967. With gum.

N802 **356** 10ch. green . . . . . . 1·10 10

357 "Reclamation of Tideland"

1967. "Heroic Struggle of the Chollima Riders". Paintings. Without gum (5ch.) or with gum (others).

N803 – 5ch. brown 40 10
N804 **357** 10ch. grey 55 10
N805 – 10ch. green 85 10

DESIGNS—VERT: 5ch. "Drilling Rock Precipice"; 10ch. (N805), "Felling Trees".

358 "Erimaculus isenbeckii"

1967. Crabs. Multicoloured.

N806 2ch. Type **358** 90 15
N807 5ch. "Neptunus trituberculatus" . . . . 1·10 15
N808 10ch. "Paralithodes camtschatica" . . . . . 1·60 15
N809 40ch. "Chionoecetes opilio" 2·50 40

359 Electric Train and Hand switching Points

1967. Propaganda for Reunification of Korea.

N810 **359** 10ch. multicoloured . . 2·25 40

360 Tongrim Waterfall

361 Chollima Flying Horse and Banners

1967. Korean Waterfalls. 2ch. with or without gum. Multicoloured.

N811 2ch. Type **360** . . . . . . 2·75 15
N812 10ch. Sanju waterfall, Mt. Myohyang . . . . 3·25 20
N813 40ch. Sambang waterfall, Mt. Chonak . . . . . . 5·00 45

1967. "The Revolutionary Surge Upwards". Various designs incorporating the Chollima Flying Horse.

N814 – 5ch. blue . . . . 1·40 20
N815 – 10ch. red 25 10
N816 – 10ch. green 25 10
N817 – 10ch. lilac 25 10
N817 **361** 10ch. red 20 10

DESIGNS—HORIZ: 5ch. Ship, electric train and lorry (Transport); N815, Bulldozers (Building construction); N816, Tractors (Rural development); N817, Heavy presses (Machine-building industry).

362 Lenin

1967. 50th Anniv of Russian October Revolution.

N819 **362** 10ch. brown, yell & red 25 10

363 Voters and Banner

1967. Korean Elections. Multicoloured.

N820 10ch. Type **363** 35 10
N821 10ch. Woman casting vote (vert) 35 10

364 Cinereous Black Vulture

1967. Birds of Prey. Multicoloured. With gum.

N822 2ch. Type **364** . . . . . . 3·00 45
N823 10ch. Booted eagle (horiz) 5·75 75
N824 40ch. White-bellied sea eagle . . . . 7·25 1·10

365 Chongjin

1967. North Korean Cities. With gum.

N825 **365** 5ch. green 70 10
N826 – 10ch. lilac 70 10
N827 – 10ch. violet 70 10

DESIGNS: No. N826, Humhung; N827, Sinuiju.

366 Soldier brandishing Red Book

1967. "Let us carry out the Decisions of the Workers' Party Conference!". Multicoloured.

N828 10ch. Type **366** 25 10
N829 10ch. Militiaman holding bayonet 25 10
N830 10ch. Foundryman and bayonet 25 10

367 Whaler firing Harpoon

1967. With gum.

N831 **367** 10ch. blue . . . . . . 2·00 25

368 Airman, Soldier and Sailor

1968. 20th Anniv of People's Army. Mult. With gum.

N832 10ch. Type **368** 30 10
N833 10ch. Soldier below attack in snow 30 10
N834 10ch. Soldier below massed ranks 30 10
N835 10ch. Soldier holding flag 30 10
N836 10ch. Soldier holding book 30 10
N837 10ch. Soldiers and armed workers with flag 30 10
N838 10ch. Furnaceman and soldier 30 10
N839 10ch. Soldier saluting . . . 30 10

N840 10ch. Charging soldiers . . 30 10
N841 10ch. Soldier, sailor and airman below flag . . . 30 10

1968. War Heroes (3rd series). As T **292**. With gum.
N842 10ch. violet 25 10
N843 10ch. purple 25 10
PORTRAITS: No. N842, Han Gye Ryol firing Bren gun; N843, Li Su Bok charging up hill.

369 Dredger "September 2"

370 Ten-storey Flats, East Pyongyang

371 Palace of Students and Children, Kaesong

1968. With gum.
N844 **369** 5ch. green 75 10
N845 **370** 10ch. blue 30 10
N846 **371** 10ch. blue 30 10

372 Marshal Kim Il Sung

1968. Marshal Kim Il Sung's 56th Birthday. With gum.
N847 **372** 40ch. multicoloured . . 65 40

373 Kim Il Sung with Mother

1968. Childhood of Kim Il Sung. Multicoloured.
N848 10ch. Type **373** 35 10
N849 10ch. Kim Il Sung with his father 35 10
N850 10ch. Setting out from home, aged 13 . . . . . 35 10
N851 10ch. Birthplace at Mangyongdae 35 10
N852 10ch. Mangyong Hill . . . 35 10

374 Matsu-take Mushroom

1968. Mushrooms. With gum.
N853 **374** 5ch. brown and green 4·25 50
N854 – 10ch. ochre, brn & grn 6·00 75
N855 – 10ch. brown and green 6·00 75
DESIGNS: No. N854, Black mushroom; N855, Cultivated mushroom.

375 Leaping Horseman

1968. 20th Anniv of Korean People's Democratic Republic. Multicoloured. With gum.
N856 10ch. Type **375** . . . . . 1·25 10
N857 10ch. Four servicemen . . 1·25 10
N858 10ch. Soldier with bayonet 1·25 10
N859 10ch. Advancing with banners . . . . 1·25 10
N860 10ch. Statue . . . . 1·25 10
N861 10ch. Korean flag . . . . 1·25 10
N862 10ch. Soldier and peasant with flag . . . . 1·25 10
N863 10ch. Machine-gunner with flag . . . . 1·25 10

376 Domestic Products

377 Proclaiming the Ten Points

1968. Development of Light Industries. Multicoloured. With gum.
N864 2ch. Type **376** 25 10
N865 5ch. Textiles . . . . 1·00 10
N866 10ch. Tinned produce . . . 40 10

1968. Kim Il Sung's Ten Point Political Programme. Multicoloured.
N867 2ch. Type **377** 15 10
N868 5ch. Soldier and artisan (horiz) 20 10

378 Livestock

1968. Development of Agriculture. Mult. With gum.
N869 5ch. Type **378** 25 10
N870 10ch. Fruit-growing 25 10
N871 10ch. Wheat-harvesting . . 25 10

379 Yesso Scallop

1968. Shellfish. Multicoloured. With gum.
N872 5ch. Type **379** . . . . . . 1·10 10
N873 5ch. Meretrix chione (venus clam) . . . . 1·10 10
N874 10ch. "Modiolus hanleyi" (mussel) . . . . 1·75 20

380 Kim Il Sung at Head of Columns

1968. Battle of Pochonbo Monument. Detail of Monument. Multicoloured.
N875 10ch. Type **380** 25 10
N876 10ch. Head of right-hand column 25 10
N877 10ch. Tail of right-hand column 25 10
N878 10ch. Head of left-hand column 25 10
N879 10ch. Tail of left-hand column 25 10
N880 10ch. Centre of right-hand column 25 10
N881 10ch. Centre of left-hand column 25 10
SIZES—HORIZ: Nos. N876/8, 43 × 28 mm. 880/1, 56 × 28 mm.
The centrepiece of the Monument is flanked by two columns of soldiers, headed by Kim Il Sung.

381 Museum of the Revolution, Pochonbo

382 Grand Theatre, Pyongyang

1968.
N883 **381** 2ch. green 20 10
N884 **382** 10ch. brown 65 10

383 Irrigation

1969. Rural Development. Multicoloured.
N885 3ch. Type **383** 20 10
N886 5ch. Agricultural mechanization 20 10
N887 10ch. Electrification 40 10
N888 40ch. Applying fertilizers and spraying trees . . . 60 10

384 Grey Rabbits

1969. Rabbits. Mult. With or without gum.
N889 2ch. Type **384** 45 10
N890 10ch. Black rabbits 45 10
N891 10ch. Brown rabbits . . . 45 10
N892 10ch. White rabbits 45 10
N893 40ch. Doe and young . . . 1·40 15

385 "Age and Youth"

1969. Public Health Service.
N894 **385** 2ch. brown and blue . . 35 10
N895 – 10ch. blue and red . . . 75 10
N896 – 40ch. green and yellow 1·50 20
DESIGNS: 10ch. Nurse with syringe; 40ch. Auscultation by woman doctor.

386 Sowing Rice Seed

1969. Agricultural Mechanization.
N897 **386** 10ch. green 75 10
N898 – 10ch. orange 75 10
N899 – 10ch. black 75 10
N900 – 10ch. brown 75 10
DESIGNS: No. N898, Rice harvester; N899, Weed-spraying machine; N900, Threshing machine.

387 Ponghwa

1969. Revolutionary Historical Sites. Multicoloured.
N901 10ch. Type **387** 25 10
N902 10ch. Mangyongdae, birthplace of Kim Il Sung 25 10

388 Kim crosses into Manchuria, 1926, aged 13

1969. Kim Il Sung in Manchuria. Multicoloured. No. N907 with gum.
N903 10ch. Type **388** 40 10
N904 10ch. Leading strike of Yuwen Middle School boys, 1927 . . . . 40 10
N905 10ch. Leading anti-Japanese demonstration in Kirin, 1928 . . . . 40 10
N906 10ch. Presiding at meeting of Young Communist League, 1930 . . . . . 40 10
N907 10ch. Meeting of young revolutionaries 40 10

389 Birthplace at Chilgol

1969. Commemoration of Mrs. Kang Ban Sok, mother of Kim Il Sung. Multicoloured.
N908 10ch. Type **389** 30 10
N909 10ch. With members of Women's Association . . 30 10
N910 10ch. Resisting Japanese police . . . . 2·50 40

390 Pegaebong Bivouac

1969. Bivouac Sites in the Guerrilla War against the Japanese. Multicoloured.
N911 5ch. Type **390** 20 10
N912 10ch. Mupo site (horiz) . . 30 10
N913 10ch. Chongbong site . . . 30 10
N914 40ch. Konchang site (horiz) 1·00 20

391 Chollima Statue

392 Museum of the Revolution, Pyongyang

1969.
N915 **391** 10ch. blue 25 10
N916 **392** 10ch. green 25 10

393 Mangyong Chickens

395 Statue of Marshal Kim Il Sung

394 Marshal Kim Il Sung and Children

1969. Korean Poultry.
N917 **393** 10ch. blue 45 10
N918 – 10ch. violet . . . . . . 1·25 15
DESIGN: No. N918, Kwangpo ducks.

1969. Kim Il Sung's Educational System. Mult.
N919 2ch. Type **394** 25 10
N920 10ch. Worker with books 25 10
N921 40ch. Students with books 50 20

1969. Memorials on Pochonbo Battlefield. Inscr "1937.6.4". Multicoloured.
N922 5ch. Machine-gun post . . 25 10
N923 10ch. Type **395** 25 10
N924 10ch. "Aspen-tree" monument 25 10
N925 10ch. Glade Konjang Hill 25 10

396 Teaching at Myongsin School

1969. Commemoration of Kim Hyong Jik, father of Kim Il Sung. Multicoloured.
N926 10ch. Type **396** 30 10
N927 10ch. Secret meeting with Korean National Association members . . 30 10

397 Relay Runner

1969. 20th Anniv of Sports Day.
N928 **397** 10ch. multicoloured . . 35 10

398 President Nixon attacked by Pens

1969. Anti-U.S. Imperialism Journalists' Conference, Pyongyang.
N929 **398** 10ch. multicoloured . . 35 10

399 Fighters and Battle

1969. Implementation of Ten-Point Programme of Kim Il Sung. Multicoloured.
N930 5ch. Type **399** (Reunification of Korea) 30 10
N931 10ch. Workers upholding slogan (vert) 30 10

400 Bayonet Attack over U.S. Flag

1969. Anti-American Campaign.
N932 **400** 10ch. multicoloured . . 35 10

401 Armed Workers

1969. Struggle for the Reunification of Korea. Multicoloured.
N933 10ch. Workers stabbing U.S. soldier (vert) . . . 20 10
N934 10ch. Kim Il Sung and crowd with flags (vert) 20 10
N935 50ch. Type **401** 50 20

402 Buri

1969. Korean Fishes. Multicoloured.
N936 5ch. Type **402** . . . . . . 1·00 10
N937 10ch. Eastern dace . . . . 1·75 10
N938 40ch. Flat-headed grey mullet . . . . 3·00 40

403 Freighter "Taesungsan"

1969.
N939 **403** 10ch. purple 75 10

405 Dahwangwai (1935)

407 Vietnamese Soldier and Furnaceman

406 Lake Chon

1970. Guerrilla Conference Places.
N940 **405** 2ch. blue and green . . 25 10
N941 – 5ch. brown and green 25 10
N942 – 10ch. lt green & green 25 10
DESIGNS: 5ch. Yaoyinggou (barn) (1935); 10ch. Xiaohaerbaling (tent) (1940).

1970. Mt. Paekdu, Home of Revolution (1st issue). Inscr "1970".
N943 **406** 10ch. black, brown & grn 60 10
N944 – 10ch. black, green & yell 60 10
N945 – 10ch. purple, blue & yell 60 10
N946 – 10ch. black, blue and pink 60 10
DESIGNS: No. N944, Piryu Peak; N945, Pyongsa (Soldier) Peak; N946, Changgun (General) Peak.
See also Nos. N979/81.

1970. Help for the Vietnamese People.
N947 **407** 10ch. green, brown & red 20 10

408 Receiving his Father's Revolvers from his Mother

1970. Revolutionary Career of Kim Il Sung. Multicoloured.
N948 10ch. Type **408** 65 20
N949 10ch. Receiving smuggled weapons from his mother 65 20
N950 10ch. Talking to farm workers 65 20
N951 10ch. At Kalun meeting, 1930 . . . . 65 20

409 Lenin

410 March of Koreans

1970. Birth Centenary of Lenin.
N952 **409** 10ch. brown & cinnamon 30 10
N953 – 10ch. brown and green 30 10
DESIGN: No. N953, Lenin making a speech.

1970. 15th Anniv of Association of Koreans in Japan.
N954 **410** 10ch. red 20 10
N955 10ch. purple 20 10

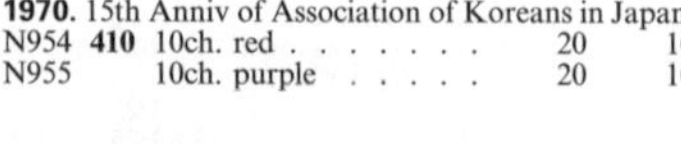

411 Uniformed Factory Worker

413 "Electricity Flows"

412 Students and Newspapers

1970. Workers' Militia.
N956 **411** 10ch. green, brn & mve 20 10
N957 – 10ch. green, brown & bl 20 10
DESIGN—HORIZ: No. N957, Militiaman saluting.

1970. Peasant Education. Multicoloured.
N958 2ch. Type **412** 35 10
N959 5ch. Peasant with book . . 20 10
N960 10ch. Students in class . . 20 10

1970. Commemoration of Army Electrical Engineers.
N961 **413** 10ch. brown 40 10

414 Soldier with Rifle

1970. Campaign Month for Withdrawal of U.S. Troops from South Korea.
N962 **414** 5ch. violet 15 10
N963 – 10ch. purple 30 10
DESIGN: 10ch. Soldier and partisan.

415 Rebel wielding Weapons

1970. Struggle in South Korea against U.S. Imperialism.
N964 **415** 10ch. violet 20 10

416 Labourer ("Fertilizers")

1970. Encouragement of Increased Productivity.
N965 **416** 10ch. green, pink & brn 40 10
N966 – 10ch. green, red & brn 70 10
N967 – 10ch. blue, green & brn 40 10
N968 – 10ch. bistre, brn & grn 40 10
N969 – 10ch. violet, green & brn 50 10
DESIGNS: No. N966, Furnaceman ("Steel"); N967, Operative ("Machines"); N968, Labourer ("Building Construction"); N969, Miner ("Mining").

417 Railway Guard

1970. "Speed the Transport System".
N970 **417** 10ch. blue, orange & grn . . . . 1·25 15

418 Agriculture

421 Emblem of League

419 Chollima Statue and Workers' Party Banner

1970. Executive Decisions of the Workers' Party Congress. Designs embodying book.
N971 **418** 5ch. red 20 10
N972 – 10ch. green . . . . . . 1·10 15
N973 – 40ch. green . . . . . . 1·10 15
DESIGNS: 10ch. Industry; 40ch. The Armed Forces.

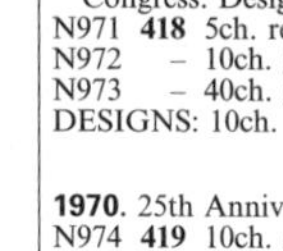

1970. 25th Anniv of Korean Workers' Party.
N974 **419** 10ch. red, brown & buff 20 10

1971. 25th Anniv of League of Socialist Working Youth.
N976 **421** 10ch. red, brown & blue 20 10

422 Log Cabin, Nanhutou

1971. 35th Anniv of Nanhutou Guerrilla Conference.
N977 **422** 10ch. multicoloured . . 20 10

423 Tractor Driver

1971. 25th Anniv of Land Reform Law.
N978 **423** 2ch. red, green and black 20 10

1971. Mt. Paekdu, Home of Revolution (2nd issue). As T **406** but inscr "1971".
N979 2ch. black, olive and green 35 10
N980 5ch. pink, black and slate 2·25 15
N981 10ch. black, red and grey 60 10
DESIGNS—HORIZ: 2ch. General view; 10ch. Western peak. VERT: 5ch. Waterfall.

424 Popyong Museum

1971. Museum of the Revolution.
N982 **424** 10ch. brown and yellow 20 10
N983 – 10ch. blue and orange 20 10
N984 – 10ch. green and orange 20 10
DESIGNS: No. N983, Mangyongdae Museum; N984, Chunggang Museum.

425 Miner

1971. Six Year Plan for Coal Industry.
N985 **425** 10ch. multicoloured . . 40 10

426 Kim Il Sung

1971. Founding of Anti-Japanese Guerrilla Army. Multicoloured.
N986 10ch. Type **426** 35 10
N987 10ch. Kim Il Sung founding Anti-Japanese Guerrilla Army (horiz) 35 10
N988 10ch. Kim Il Sung addressing the people (horiz) 35 10
N989 10ch. Kim Il Sung and members of Children's Corps (horiz) 35 10

428 Hands holding Hammer and Rifle

1971. 85th Anniv of Labour Day.
N990 **428** 1wn. red, brown and buff . . . . 2·25 40

429 Soldiers and Map **430** Monument

1971. 35th Anniv of Association for Restoration of Fatherland.
N991 **429** 10ch. red, buff and black 35 10

1971. Battlefields in Musan Area, May 1939. Multicoloured.
N992 5ch. Type **430** 15 10
N993 10ch. Machine guns in perspex cases (horiz) . . 20 10
N994 40ch. Huts among birch trees (horiz) 55 15

431 Koreans Marching **432** Flame Emblem

1971. Solidarity of Koreans in Japan.
N995 **431** 10ch. brown 20 10

1971. 25th Anniv of Korean Childrens' Union.
N996 **432** 10ch. red, yellow and blue 20 10

433 Marchers and Banners **434** Foundryman

1971. 6th Congress of League of Socialist Working Youth.
N997 **433** 5ch. red, buff and black 10 10
N998 – 10ch. red, green & black 20 10
DESIGN: 10c. Marchers and banner under globe.

1971. 25th Anniv of Labour Law.
N999 **434** 5ch. black, purple & buff 20 10

435 Young Women

1971. 25th Anniv of Sex Equality Law.
N1000 **435** 5ch. multicoloured . . 20 10

436 Schoolchildren

1971. 15th Anniv of Compulsory Primary Education.
N1001 **436** 10ch. multicoloured . . 50 10

437 Choe Yong Do and Combat Scene

1971. Heroes of the Revolutionary Struggle in South Korea.
N1002 **437** 5ch. black and green 25 10
N1003 – 10ch. red and brown 25 10
N1004 – 10ch. black and red . . 25 10
DESIGNS: No. N1003, Revolutionary with book; N1004, Kim Jong Tae and scene of triumph.

438 Two Foundrymen

1971. 25th Anniv of Nationalization of Industry Law.
N1005 **438** 5ch. black, green & brn . . . . 1·50 10

439 Struggle in Korea

1971. The Anti-Imperialist and Anti-U.S. Imperialist Struggles.
N1006 **439** 10ch. red, black and brown 25 10
N1007 – 10ch. brown, black and blue 35 10
N1008 – 10ch. red, black and pink 50 10
N1009 – 10ch. black, olive and green 25 10
N1010 – 10ch. orange, black and red 50 10
N1011 – 40ch. green, black and pink 50 15
DESIGNS: No. N1007, Struggle in Vietnam; N1008, Soldier with rifle and airplane marked "EC"; N1009, Struggle in Africa; N1010, Cuban soldier and Central America; N1011, Bayoneting U.S. soldier.

440 Kim Il Sung University

1971. 25th Anniv of Kim Il Sung University.
N1012 **440** 10ch. grey, red & yellow 20 10

441 Iron-ore Ladle (Mining)

1971. Tasks of Six Year Plan. Multicoloured.
N1013 10ch. Type **441** . . . . . 2·75 15
N1014 10ch. Workers and text . . 30 10
N1015 10ch. Electric train and track (Transport) . . . 2·75 15
N1016 10ch. Hand and wrench (Industry) 30 10
N1017 10ch. Mechanical scoop (Construction) . . . . 2·75 15
N1018 10ch. Manufactured goods (Trade) 30 10
N1019 10ch. Crate on hoists (Exports) 25 10
N1020 10ch. Lathe (Heavy Industries) . . . . . . 2·75 15
N1021 10ch. Freighter (Shipping) 60 10
N1022 10ch. Household equipment (Light Industries) 25 10
N1023 10ch. Corncob and wheat (Agriculture) 40 10

442 Technicians

1971. Cultural Revolution. Multicoloured.
N1024 2ch. Type **442** 20 10
N1025 5ch. Mechanic 25 10
N1026 10ch. Schoolchildren . . . 30 10
N1027 10ch. Chemist 50 10
N1028 10ch. Composer at piano 85 15

443 Workers with Red Books

1971. Ideological Revolution. Multicoloured.
N1029 10ch. Type **443** 20 10
N1030 10ch. Workers reading book 20 10
N1031 10ch. Workers' lecture . . 20 10
N1032 10ch. Worker and pneumatic drill 20 10

444 Korean Family

1971. Improvement in Living Standards.
N1033 **444** 10ch. multicoloured . . 15 10

445 Furnaceman

1971. Implementation of Decisions of Fifth Workers' Party Conference.
N1034 **445** 10ch. multicoloured . . 1·00 10

446 **447** 6000-ton Press

1971. Solidarity with South Korean Revolutionaries.
N1036 **446** 10ch. brown, bl & blk 30 10
N1037 – 10ch. brn, flesh & red 30 10
N1038 – 10ch. multicoloured . . 30 10
N1039 – 10ch. multicoloured . . 30 10
DESIGNS—VERT: No. N1037, U.S. soldier attacked by poster boards; N1038, Hands holding rifles aloft. HORIZ: No. N1039, Men advancing with rifles.

1971.
N1040 **447** 2ch. brown 70 10
N1041 – 5ch. blue 90 15
N1042 – 10ch. green . . . . . 1·10 10
N1043 – 10ch. green . . . . . 1·10 10
DESIGNS: No. N1041, Refrigerated freighter "Ponghwasan"; N1042, 300 h.p. bulldozer; N1043, "Sungrisan" lorry.

448 Title-page and Militants

1971. 35th Anniv of "Samil Wolgan" Magazine.
N1044 **448** 10ch. red, green & black 45 10

452 Poultry Chicks

1972. Poultry Breeding.
N1051 **452** 5ch. yellow, black and brown 25 10
N1052 – 10ch. orange, bistre and brown 35 10
N1053 – 40ch. blue, orange and deep blue 55 15
DESIGNS: 10ch. Chickens and battery egg house; 40ch. Eggs and fowls suspended from hooks.

453 Scene from "Village Shrine"

1972. Films of Guerrilla War.
N1054 **453** 10ch. grey and green 60 10
N1055 – 10ch. blue, pur & orge 60 10
N1056 – 10ch. purple, blue & yell 60 10
DESIGNS: No. N1055, Patriot with pistol ("A Sea of Blood"); N1056, Guerrilla using bayonet ("The Lot of a Self-Defence Corps Member").

454 Kim Il Sung acknowledging Greetings

1972. Kim Il Sung's 60th Birthday. Scenes in the life of Kim Il Sung, dated "1912–1972". Mult.
N1057 5ch. Type **454** 20 10
N1058 5ch. In campaign H.Q. . . 20 10
N1059 5ch. Military conference (horiz) 20 10
N1060 10ch. In wheatfield (horiz) 30 10
N1061 10ch. Directing construction (horiz) . . 2·00 40
N1062 10ch. Talking to foundry workers (horiz) 20 10
N1063 10ch. Aboard whaler (horiz) 55 10
N1064 10ch. Visiting a hospital (horiz) 75 10
N1065 10ch. Viewing orchard (horiz) 20 10
N1066 10ch. With survey party on Haeju–Hasong railway line (horiz) . . . 2·00 40
N1067 10ch. Meeting female workers at silk factory (horiz) . . . . 1·00 15
N1068 10ch. Village conference (horiz) 20 10
N1069 10ch. Touring chicken factory (horiz) 35 10
N1070 40ch. Relaxing with children 45 20
N1071 1wn. Giant portrait and marchers 70 40

455 Bugler sounding "Charge"

1972. 40th Anniv of Guerrilla Army.

N1073	**455**	10ch. multicoloured . .	45	10

456 Pavilion of Ryongpo

1972. Historic Sites of the 1950–53 War. Mult.

N1074	2ch. Type **456**	15	10
N1075	5ch. Houses at Onjong . .	15	10
N1076	10ch. Headquarters, Kosanjin	15	10
N1077	40ch. Victory Museum, Chonsung-dong	30	10

457 Volleyball

1972. Olympic Games, Munich. Multicoloured.

N1078	2ch. Type **457**	35	10
N1079	5ch. Boxing (horiz) . . .	50	10
N1080	10ch. Judo	50	10
N1081	10ch. Wrestling (horiz) . .	50	10
N1082	40ch. Rifle-shooting . . .	1·10	20

458 Chollima Street, Pyongyang

1971. Chollima Street, Pyongyang.

N1083	–	5ch. orange and black	1·60	15
N1084	**458**	10ch. yellow and black	60	15
N1085	–	10ch. green and black	60	15

DESIGNS: No. N1083, Bridge and skyscraper blocks; N1085, Another view looking up street.

459 Dredger

1972. Development of Natural Resources. Multicoloured.

N1086	5ch. Type **459**	35	10
N1087	10ch. Forestry	50	10
N1088	40ch. Reclaiming land from the sea	60	15

460 Ferrous Industry

1972. Tasks of the Six-Year Plan. The Metallurgical Industry. Inscr "1971–1976". Multicoloured.

N1089	10ch. Type **460**	1·40	10
N1090	10ch. Non-ferrous Industry	40	10

461 Iron Ore Industry

1972. Tasks of the Six-Year Plan. The Mining Industry. Inscr "1971–1976". Multicoloured.

N1091	10ch. Type **461**	40	10
N1092	10ch. Coal mining industry	1·50	15

462 Electronic and Automation Industry

1972. Tasks of the Six-Year Plan. The Engineering Industry. Inscr "1971–1976". Multicoloured.

N1093	10ch. Type **462**	60	10
N1094	10ch. Single-purpose machines	40	10
N1095	10ch. Machine tools . . .	40	10

463 Clearing Virgin Soil

1972. Tasks of the Six-Year Plan. Rural Economy. Multicoloured.

N1096	10ch. Type **463**	45	10
N1097	10ch. Irrigation	45	10
N1098	10ch. Harvesting	45	10

464 Automation

1972. Tasks of the Six-Year Plan. Inscr "1971–1976". Multicoloured.

N1099	10ch. Type **464**	1·60	10
N1100	10ch. Agricultural mechanization	50	10
N1101	10ch. Lightening of household chores . . .	50	10

465 Chemical Fibres and Materials

1972. Tasks of the Six-Year Plan. The Chemical Industry. Inscr "1971–1976". Multicoloured.

N1102	10ch. Type **465**	60	10
N1103	10ch. Fertilizers, insecticides and weed killers	60	10

466 Textiles

1972. Tasks of the Six-Year Plan. Consumer Goods. Inscr "1971–1976". Multicoloured.

N1104	10ch. Type **466**	65	10
N1105	10ch. Kitchen ware and overalls	45	10
N1106	10ch. Household goods . .	45	10

467 Fish, Fruit and Vegetables

1972. Tasks of the Six-Year Plan. The Food Industry. Multicoloured.

N1107	10ch. Type **467**	90	10
N1108	10ch. Tinned foods . . .	65	10
N1109	10ch. Food packaging . .	65	10

468 Electrifying Railway Lines

1972. Tasks of the Six-Year Plan. Transport. Inscr "1971–1976". Multicoloured.

N1110	10ch. Type **468**	45	10
N1111	10ch. Laying new railway track	45	10
N1112	10ch. Freighters	55	10

469 Soldier with Shell

1972. North Korean Armed Forces. Multicoloured.

N1113	10ch. Type **469**	35	10
N1114	10ch. Marine	35	10
N1115	10ch. Air Force pilot . . .	35	10

470 "Revolution of 19 April 1960"

1972. The Struggle for Reunification of Korea. Multicoloured.

N1116	10ch. Type **470**	15	10
N1117	10ch. Marchers with banner	15	10
N1118	10ch. Insurgents with red banner	15	10
N1119	10ch. Attacking U.S. and South Korean soldiers	15	10
N1120	10ch. Workers with posters	15	10
N1121	10ch. Workers acclaiming revolution	3·50	40
N1122	10ch. Workers and manifesto	15	10

471 Single-spindle Automatic Lathe

1972. Machine Tools.

N1123	**471**	5ch. green and purple	25	10
N1124	–	10ch. blue and green	35	10
N1125	–	40ch. green and brown	80	15

DESIGNS—HORIZ: 10ch. "Kusong-3" lathe; VERT: 40ch. 2,000 ton crank press.

472 Casting Vote

1972. National Elections. Multicoloured.

N1126	10ch. Type **472**	25	10
N1127	10ch. Election campaigner	25	10

475 Soldier

1973. 25th Anniv of Founding of Korean People's Army. Multicoloured.

N1130	5ch. Type **475**	20	10
N1131	10ch. Sailor	30	10
N1132	40ch. Airman	70	25

476 Wrestling Site

1973. Scenes of Kim Il Sung's Childhood, Mangyongdae. Multicoloured.

N1133	2ch. Type **476**	15	10
N1134	5ch. Warship rock	15	10
N1135	10ch. Swinging site (vert)	20	10
N1136	10ch. Sliding rock	20	10
N1137	40ch. Fishing site	60	15

477 Monument to Socialist Revolution and Construction, Mansu Hill

1973. Museum of the Korean Revolution.

N1138	**477**	10ch. multicoloured . .	25	10
N1139	–	10ch. multicoloured . .	25	10
N1140	–	40ch. multicoloured . .	50	15
N1141	–	3wn. green and yellow	2·50	60

DESIGNS—As Type **477**: 10ch. (N1139) Similar monument but men in military clothes; 40ch. Statue of Kim Il Sung. HORIZ—60 × 29 mm: 3wn. Museum building.

478 Karajibong Camp

1973. Secret Camps by Tuman-Gang in Guerrilla War, 1932. Multicoloured.

N1142	10ch. Type **478**	15	10
N1143	10ch. Soksaegol Camp . .	15	10

479

1973. Menace of Japanese Influence in South Korea.

N1144	**479**	10ch. multicoloured . .	20	10

480 Wrecked U.S. Tanks

1973. Five-point Programme for Reunification of Korea. Multicoloured.

N1145	2ch. Type **480**	40	10
N1146	5ch. Electric train and crane lifting tractor . .	2·50	20
N1147	10ch. Leaflets falling on crowd	20	10
N1148	10ch. Hand holding leaflet and map of Korea . . .	40	10
N1149	40ch. Banner and globe	60	20

481 Lorries

482 Volleyball

1973. Lorries and Tractors. Multicoloured.
N1150 10ch. Type **481** 50 10
N1151 10ch. Tractors and earth-moving machine 50 10

1973. Socialist Countries' Junior Women's Volleyball Games, Pyongyang.
N1152 **482** 10ch. multicoloured . . 50 10

483 Battlefield

1973. 20th Anniv of Victory in Korean War.
N1153 **483** 10ch. green, pur & blk 20 10
N1154 – 10ch. brown, bl & blk 20 10
DESIGN: 10ch. Urban fighting.

484 "The Snow Falls"

1973. Mansudae Art Troupe. Dances. Multicoloured.
N1155 10ch. Type **484** 60 10
N1156 25ch. "A Bumper Harvest of Apples" . . . . . . 1·50 25
N1157 40ch. "Azalea of the Fatherland" . . . . . 1·75 30

485 Schoolchildren

1973. Ten Years Compulsory Secondary Education.
N1158 **485** 10ch. multicoloured . . 25 10

486 "Fervour in the Revolution"

1973. The Works of Kim Il Sung (1st series).
N1159 **486** 10ch. brown, red and yellow 15 10
N1160 – 10ch. brown, green and yellow 15 10
N1161 – 10ch. lake, brown and yellow 15 10
DESIGNS: No. N1160, Selected works; N1161, "Strengthen the Socialist System".
See also Nos. N1217/18.

487 Celebrating Republic

1973. 25th Anniv of People's Republic. Multicoloured.
N1162 5ch. Type **487** 10 10
N1163 10ch. Fighting in Korean War 10 10
N1164 40ch. Peace and reconstruction . . . . . 1·60 40

488 Pobwang Peak

1973. Mt. Myohyang. Multicoloured.
N1165 2ch. Type **488** 25 10
N1166 5ch. Inhodae Pavilion . . 35 10
N1167 10ch. Taeha Falls (vert) 1·75 30
N1168 40ch. Rongyon Falls (vert) 2·50 30

489 Party Memorial Building

1973. Party Memorial Building.
N1169 **489** 1wn. brn, grey & buff 1·25 30

490 Football and Handball

1973. National People's Sports Meeting. Mult.
N1170 2ch. Type **490** 60 10
N1171 5ch. High jumper and woman sprinter 40 10
N1172 10ch. Skaters and skiers 50 10
N1173 10ch. Wrestling and swinging 40 10
N1174 40ch. Parachutist and motor cyclists . . . . . 3·00 25

491 Weightlifting

492 Chongryu Cliff

1973. Junior Weightlifting Championships of Socialist Countries.
N1175 **491** 10ch. blue, brn & grn 50 10

1973. Scenery of Moran Hill, Pyongyang. Multicoloured.
N1176 2ch. Type **492** 70 15
N1177 5ch. Moran Waterfall . . 2·75 40
N1178 10ch. Pubyok Pavilion . . 75 10
N1179 40ch. Ulmil Pavilion . . . 90 15

493 Rainbow Bridge

494 Magnolia Flower

1973. Diamond Mountains Scenery (4th issue). Multicoloured.
N1180 2ch. Type **493** . . . . . 1·50 15
N1181 5ch. Suspension footbridge, Okryudong (horiz) . . . . 1·50 15
N1182 10ch. Chonnyo Peak . . . 75 10
N1183 10ch. Chilchung Rock and Sonji Peak (horiz) . . . 75 10
N1184 40ch. Sujong and Pari Peaks (horiz) 85 15

1973.
N1185 **494** 10ch. multicoloured . . 60 10

495 S. Korean Revolutionaries

1973. South Korean Revolution. Multicoloured
N1186 10ch. Type **495** 30 10
N1187 10ch. Marching revolutionaries 30 10

496 Cock sees Butterflies

1973. Scenes from "Cock Chasing Butterflies". Fairy Tale. Multicoloured.
N1188 2ch. Type **496** . . . . . 1·50 10
N1189 5ch. Butterflies discuss how to repel cock . . . 1·50 10
N1190 10ch. Cock chasing butterflies with basket 2·00 15
N1191 10ch. Cock chasing butterfly up cliff . . . . 2·00 20
N1192 40ch. Cock chasing butterflies over cliff . . 2·25 25
N1193 90ch. Cock falls into sea and butterflies escape 2·75 30

497 Yonpung

1973. Historical Sites of War and Revolution (40ch.). Multicoloured.
N1196 2ch. Type **497** 10 10
N1197 5ch. Hyangha 10 10
N1198 10ch. Changgol 15 10
N1199 40ch. Paeksong 55 10

498 Science Library, Kim Il Sung University

1973. New Buildings in Pyongyang.
N1200 **498** 2ch. violet 50 10
N1201 – 5ch. green 15 10
N1202 – 10ch. brown 25 10
N1203 – 40ch. brown and buff 55 15
N1204 – 90ch. buff 95 30
DESIGNS—HORIZ: 10ch. Victory Museum; 40ch. People's Palace of Culture; 90ch. Indoor stadium. VERT: 5ch. Building No. 2, Kim Il Sung University.

499 Red Book

1973. Socialist Constitution of North Korea. Multicoloured.
N1205 10ch. Type **499** 15 10
N1206 10ch. Marchers with red book and banners . . . 15 10
N1207 10ch. Marchers with red book and emblem . . . 15 10

500 Oriental Great Reed Warbler

1973. Korean Songbirds. Multicoloured.
N1208 5ch. Type **500** . . . . . 2·40 40
N1209 10ch. Grey starling (facing right) . . . . 3·50 70
N1210 10ch. Daurian starling (facing left) . . . . . . 3·50 70

503 Chollima Statue

1974. The Works of Kim Il Sung (2nd series). Multicoloured.
N1217 10ch. Type **503** 65 10
N1218 10ch. Bayonets threatening U.S. soldier 15 10

504 Train in Station

1974. Opening of Pyongyang Metro. Multicoloured.
N1219 10ch. Type **504** 45 10
N1220 10ch. Escalators 45 10
N1221 10ch. Station hall 45 10

505 Capital Construction Front

1974. Five Fronts of Socialist Construction. Multicoloured.
N1222 10ch. Type **505** 15 10
N1223 10ch. Agricultural front 25 10
N1224 10ch. Transport front . . 1·25 15
N1225 10ch. Fisheries front . . . 90 15
N1226 10ch. Industrial front (vert) 25 10

506 Marchers with Banners

1974. 10th Anniv of Publication of "Theses on the Socialist Rural Question in Our Country". Multicoloured.
N1227 10ch. Type **506** 15 10
N1228 10ch. Book and rejoicing crowd 15 10
N1229 10ch. Tractor and banners 15 10
Nos. N1227/9 were issued together, se-tenant, forming a composite design.

507 Manure Spreader

1974. Farm Machinery.
N1230 **507** 2ch. green, black & red 60 10
N1231 – 5ch. red, black and blue 60 10
N1232 – 10ch. red, black and green 60 10
DESIGNS: 5ch. "Progress" tractor; 10ch. "Mount Taedoksan" tractor.

508 Archery (Grenoble)

1974. North Korean Victories at International Sports Meetings. Multicoloured.

N1233 2ch. Type **508** . . . . . 1·00 15
N1234 5ch. Gymnastics (Varna) 25 10
N1235 10ch. Boxing (Bucharest) 40 10
N1236 20ch. Volleyball (Pyongyang) 25 10
N1237 30ch. Rifle shooting (Sofia) 60 10
N1238 40ch. Judo (Tbilisi) . . . 80 15
N1239 60ch. Model aircraft flying (Vienna) (horiz) . . . . 1·25 20
N1240 1wn. 50 Table tennis (Peking) (horiz) . . . . 2·25 30

509 Book and Rejoicing Crowd

1974. The First Country with No Taxes.

N1241 **509** 10ch. multicoloured . . 20 10

510 Drawing up Programme in Woods

1974. Kim Il Sung during the Anti-Japanese Struggle. Multicoloured.

N1242 10ch. Type **510** 25 10
N1243 10ch. Giving directions to Pak Dal 25 10
N1244 10ch. Presiding over Nanhutou Conference 25 10
N1245 10ch. Supervising creation of strongpoint 25 10

511 Sun Hui loses her Sight

1974. Scenes from "The Flower Girl" (revolutionary opera). Multicoloured.

N1246 2ch. Type **511** 65 10
N1247 5ch. Death of Ggot Bun's mother 65 10
N1248 10ch. Ggot Bun throws boiling water at landlord . . . . 1·40 10
N1249 40ch. Ggot Bun joins revolutionaries . . . . 1·75 15

512 Leopard Cat

1974. 15th Anniv of Pyongyang Zoo. Multicoloured.

N1251 2ch. Type **512** 60 10
N1252 5ch. Lynx 60 10
N1253 10ch. Red fox 60 10
N1254 10ch. Wild boar 60 10
N1255 20ch. Dhole 60 15
N1256 40ch. Brown bear 75 25
N1257 60ch. Leopard . . . . . 1·25 25
N1258 70ch. Tiger . . . . 1·75 30
N1259 90ch. Lion . . . . 2·00 35

513 "Rosa acucularis lindly"

1974. Roses. Multicoloured.

N1261 2ch. Type **513** 40 10
N1262 5ch. Yellow sweet briar . . 45 10
N1263 10ch. Pink aromatic rose 55 10
N1264 10ch. Aronia sweet briar (yellow centres) 55 10
N1265 40ch. Multi-petal sweet briar . . . . 1·40 10

515 Weigela

1974. Flowering Plants of Mt. Paekdu. Mult.

N1267 2ch. Type **515** 50 10
N1268 5ch. Amaryllis 50 10
N1269 10ch. Red lily 50 10
N1270 20ch. Orange lily 65 10
N1271 40ch. Azalea 90 10
N1272 60ch. Yellow lily . . . . 1·50 10

516 Postwoman and Construction Site

1974. Centenary of U.P.U. and Admission of North Korea to Union. Multicoloured.

N1273 10ch. Type **516** . . . . 1·50 15
N1274 25ch. Chollima monument 25 10
N1275 40ch. Globe and Antonov An-12 transport planes 1·00 15

517 Common Pond Frog

1974. Amphibians. Multicoloured.

N1276 2ch. Type **517** . . . . . 1·00 10
N1277 5ch. Oriental fire-bellied toad . . . . 1·25 10
N1278 10ch. Bullfrog . . . . . . 1·50 15
N1279 40ch. Common toad . . . 2·00 25

518 "Women of Namgang Village"

1974. Korean Paintings. Multicoloured.

N1281 2ch. Type **518** 60 10
N1282 5ch. "An Old Man on the Rakdong River" (60 × 49 mm) 75 10
N1283 10ch. "Morning in the Nae-kumgang" (bridge) 1·50 10
N1284 20ch. "Mt. Kumgang" (60 × 49 mm) . . . . . 1·25 15

519 "Elektron 1" and "Elektron 2", 1964

1974. Cosmonauts Day. Multicoloured.

N1286 10ch. Type **519** 15 10
N1287 20ch. "Proton 1", 1965 . . 25 10
N1288 30ch. "Venera 3", 1966 . . 40 10
N1289 40ch. "Venera 5" and "Venera 6", 1969 . . . 50 10

521 Antonov An-2 Biplane

1974. Civil Aviation. Multicoloured

N1292 2ch. Type **521** 65 10
N1293 5ch. Lisunov Li-2 . . . . 65 10
N1294 10ch. Ilyushin Il-14P . . . 90 10
N1295 40ch. Antonov An-24 . . 1·25 35
N1296 60ch. Ilyushin Il-18 . . . 2·00 50

522 "Rhododendron redowskianum"

1974. Plants of Mt. Paekdu. Multicoloured.

N1298 2ch. Type **522** 45 10
N1299 5ch. "Dryas octopetala" 45 10
N1300 10ch. "Potentilla fruticosa" 50 10
N1301 20ch. "Papaver somniferum" 65 10
N1302 40ch. "Phyllodoce caerulea" 90 20
N1303 60ch. "Oxytropis anertii" 1·50 40

523 "Sobaek River in the Morning"

1974. Modern Korean Paintings (1st series). Multicoloured.

N1304 10ch. Type **523** 60 10
N1305 20ch. "Combatants of Mt. Laohei" (60 × 40 mm) 65 10
N1306 30ch. "Spring in the Fields" 75 15
N1307 40ch. "Tideland Night" 5·25 60
N1308 60ch. "Daughter" (60 × 54 mm) . . . . . 1·10 40

See also Nos. N1361/5, N1386/96 and N1485/9.

525 Log Cabin, Unha Village

1974. Historic Sites of the Revolution. Multicoloured.

N1310 5ch. Munmyong 25 10
N1311 10ch. Type **525** 25 10

526 Sesame

1974. Oil-producing Plants. Multicoloured.

N1312 2ch. Type **526** 75 10
N1313 5ch. "Perilla frutescens" 80 10
N1314 10ch. Sunflower 90 10
N1315 40ch. Castor bean . . . . 1·25 40

527 Kim Il Sung as Guerrilla Leader

1974. Kim Il Sung. Multicoloured.

N1316 10ch. Type **527** 20 10
N1317 10ch. Commander of the People's Army (52 × 35 mm) 20 10
N1318 10ch. "The commander is also a son of the people" (52 × 35 mm) 20 10
N1319 10ch. Negotiating with the Chinese anti-Japanese unit (52 × 35 mm) . . . 20 10

528

1974. Grand Monument on Mansu Hill. Mult.

N1320 10ch. Type **528** 15 10
N1321 10ch. As T **528** but men in civilian clothes 15 10
N1322 10ch. As T **528** but men facing left 15 10
N1323 10ch. As No. N1322 but men in civilian clothes 15 10

529 Factory Ship "Chilbosan"

1974. Deep-sea Fishing. Multicoloured.

N1324 2ch. Type **529** 70 25
N1325 5ch. Trawler support ship "Paekdusan" 70 25
N1326 10ch. Freighter "Moranbong" 70 25
N1327 20ch. Whale-catcher . . . 70 25
N1328 30ch. Trawler 70 25
N1329 40ch. Stern trawler 70 25

539 Kim Il Sung crossing River Agrok

1975. 50th Anniv of Kim Il Sung's crossing of River Agrok.

N1349 **539** 10ch. multicoloured . . 25 10

540 Pak Yong Sun "World Table Tennis Queen"

1975. Pak Yong Sun, Winner of 33rd World Table Tennis Championships, Calcutta.

N1350 **540** 10ch. multicoloured . . 1·00 10

541 Common Zebra

1975. Pyongyang Zoo. Multicoloured.

N1352 10ch. Type **541** 30 10
N1353 10ch. African buffalo . . 30 10
N1354 20ch. Giant panda (horiz) 80 10
N1355 25ch. Bactrian camel . . . 70 15
N1356 30ch. Indian elephant . . 1·25 20

542 "Blue Dragon"

1975. 7th-century Mural Paintings from Koguryo Tombs, Kangso.

N1357 10ch. Type **542** 75 10
N1358 15ch. "White Tiger" . . . 1·00 10
N1359 25ch. "Red Phoenix" (vert) . . . . 1·25 10
N1360 40ch. "Snake-turtle" . . . 1·75 25

543 "Spring in the Guerrilla Base" (1968)

1975. Modern Korean Paintings (2nd series). Anti-Japanese struggle. Multicoloured.

N1361 10ch. Type **543** 35 10
N1362 10ch. "Revolutionary Army landing at Unggi" (1969) 35 10
N1363 15ch. "Sewing Team Members" (1961) . . . 55 10
N1364 20ch. "Girl Watering Horse" (1969) . . . . . 1·00 15
N1365 30ch. "Kim Jong Suk giving Guidance to Children's Corps" (1970) 80 20

544 Cosmonaut

1975. Cosmonauts' Day. Multicoloured.

N1366 10ch. Type **544** 15 10
N1367 30ch. "Lunokhod" moon vehicle (horiz) 40 10
N1368 40ch. "Soyuz" spacecraft and "Salyut" space laboratory (horiz) . . . 55 15

546 The Beacon lit at Pochonbo, 1937

1975. Kim Il Sung during the Guerrilla War against the Japanese. Multicoloured.

N1370 10ch. Type **546** 25 10
N1371 10ch. "A Bowl of Parched-rice Powder", 1938 . . . . 25 10
N1372 10ch. Guiding the Nanpaizi meeting, November, 1938 . . . . 25 10
N1373 10ch. Welcoming helper 25 10
N1374 10ch. Lecturing the guerrillas 25 10
N1375 15ch. Advancing into the homeland, May 1939 . . 35 10
N1376 25ch. By Lake Samji, May 1939 . . . . 45 10
N1377 30ch. At Sinsadong, May 1939 . . . . 55 10
N1378 40ch. Xiaohaerbaling meeting, 1940 . . . . . 65 15

547 Vase of Flowers and Kim Il Sung's Birthplace

1975. Kim Il Sung's 63rd Birthday. Multicoloured.

N1379 10ch. Type **547** 10 10
N1379a 40ch. Kim Il Sung's birthplace, Mangyongdae 35 10

548 South Korean Insurgent

1975. 15th Anniv of April 19th Rising.

N1380 **548** 10ch. multicoloured . . 15 10

549 "Kingfisher at a Lotus Pond"

1975. Paintings of Li Dynasty. Multicoloured.

N1381 5ch. Type **549** . . . . . 1·50 10
N1382 10ch. "Crabs" . . . . . 1·00 10
N1383 15ch. "Rose of Sharon" 1·75 20
N1384 25ch. "Lotus and Water Cock" . . . . 2·50 45
N1385 30ch. "Tree Peony and Red Junglefowl" . . . 4·25 45

1975. Modern Korean Paintings (3rd series). Fatherland Liberation War. Dated designs as T **543**. Multicoloured.

N1386 5ch. "On the Advance Southward" (1966) (vert) 30 10
N1387 10ch. "The Assigned Post" (girl sentry) (1968) (vert) 40 10
N1388 15ch. "The Heroism of Li Su Bok" (1965) 40 10
N1389 25ch. "Retaliation" (woman machine-gunner) (1970) 65 20
N1390 30ch. "The awaited Troops" (1970) 80 20

1975. Modern Korean Paintings (4th series). Socialist Construction. As T **543**. Multicoloured.

N1391 10ch. "Pine Tree" (1966) (vert) 90 10
N1392 10ch. "The Blue Signal Lamp" (1960) (vert) . . 2·75 10
N1393 15ch. "A Night of Snowfall" (1963) . . . 90 10
N1394 20ch. "Smelters" (1968) 1·00 15
N1395 25ch. "Tideland Reclamation" (1961) . . 1·00 15
N1396 30ch. "Mount Paekgum" (1966) . . . . 1·00 20

550 Flag and Building **552** "Feet first" entry (man)

1975. 20th Anniv of "Chongryon" Association of Koreans in Japan.

N1397 **550** 10ch. multicoloured . . 15 10
N1398 3wn. multicoloured . . 2·50 55

1975. Diving. Multicoloured.

N1400 10ch. Type **552** 25 10
N1401 25ch. Piked somersault (man) 50 10
N1402 40ch. "Head first" entry (woman) . . . . 1·00 15

553

1975. Campaign against U.S. Imperialism.

N1403 **553** 10ch. multicoloured . . 30 10

554 Silver Carp

1975. Fresh-water Fish. Multicoloured.

N1404 10ch. Type **554** 70 10
N1405 10ch. Elongate ilisha (swimming to right) . . 70 10
N1406 15ch. Banded minnow . . 1·00 15
N1407 25ch. Bare-headed bagrid 1·60 20
N1408 30ch. Amur catfish (swimming to right) . . 2·00 30
N1409 30ch. Chevron snakehead (swimming to left) . . . 2·00 30

555

1975. 10th Socialist Countries' Football Tournament, Pyongyang.

N1410 **555** 5ch. multicoloured . . 35 10
N1411 – 10ch. multicoloured . . 35 10
N1412 – 15ch. multicoloured . . 40 10
N1413 – 20ch. multicoloured . . 50 15
N1414 – 50ch. multicoloured . . 90 35

DESIGNS: 10ch. to 50ch. Various footballers.

556 Blue and Yellow Macaw **557** Flats

1975. Birds. Multicoloured.

N1416 10ch. Type **556** . . . . . 1·50 20
N1417 15ch. Sulphur-crested cockatoo . . . . 1·75 25
N1418 20ch. Blyth's parakeet . . 2·25 40
N1419 25ch. Rainbow lory . . . 2·75 45
N1420 30ch. Budgerigar . . . . 3·25 60

1975. New Buildings in Pyongyang. Multicoloured.

N1421 90ch. Saesallim (formerly Sarguson) Street . . . . 1·50 40
N1422 1wn. Type **557** . . . . . 1·75 45
N1423 2wn. Potonggang Hotel 2·75 60

558 White Peach Blossom **559** Sejongbong

1975. Blossoms of Flowering Trees. Multicoloured.

N1424 10ch. Type **558** 40 10
N1425 15ch. Red peach blossom 40 10
N1426 20ch. Red plum blossom 60 15
N1427 25ch. Apricot blossom . . 75 15
N1428 30ch. Cherry blossom . . 1·00 20

1975. Landscapes in the Diamond Mountains. Multicoloured.

N1429 5ch. Type **559** 40 10
N1430 10ch. Chonsondae 65 10
N1431 15ch. Pisamun 85 10
N1432 25ch. Manmulsang . . . . 1·10 20
N1433 30ch. Chaehabong . . . . 1·25 20

560 Azalea

1975. Flowers of the Azalea Family. Multicoloured.

N1434 5ch. Type **560** 50 10
N1435 10ch. White azalea 50 10
N1436 15ch. Wild rhododendron 60 10
N1437 20ch. White rhododendron 60 15
N1438 25ch. Rhododendron . . . 80 15
N1439 30ch. Yellow rhododendron . . . . . 1·10 20

561 Gliders

1975. Training for National Defence. Mult.

N1440 5ch. Type **561** 60 10
N1441 5ch. Radio-controlled model airplane 60 10
N1442 10ch. "Free fall parachutist" (vert) . . . 75 10
N1443 10ch. Parachutist landing on target (vert) 75 10
N1444 20ch. Parachutist with bouquet of flowers (vert) 1·10 15

562 Wild Apple

1975. Fruit Tree Blossom. Multicoloured.

N1446	10ch. Type **562**	40	10
N1447	15ch. Wild pear	40	10
N1448	20ch. Hawthorn	50	15
N1449	25ch. Chinese quince	70	20
N1450	30ch. Flowering quince	80	20

563 Torch of Juche

1975. 30th Anniv of Korean Workers' Party. Multicoloured.

N1451	2ch. "Victory" and American graves	10	10
N1452	2ch. Sunrise over Mt. Paekdu-san	10	10
N1453	5ch. Type **563**	10	10
N1454	5ch. Chollima Statue and sunset over Pyongyang	10	10
N1455	10ch. Korean with Red Book	10	10
N1456	10ch. Chollima Statue	10	10
N1457	25ch. Crowds and burning building	35	10
N1458	70ch. Flowers and map of Korea	95	15

564 Welcoming Crowd

1975. 30th Anniv of Kim Il Sung's Return to Pyongyang.

N1460	**564** 20ch. multicoloured	25	15

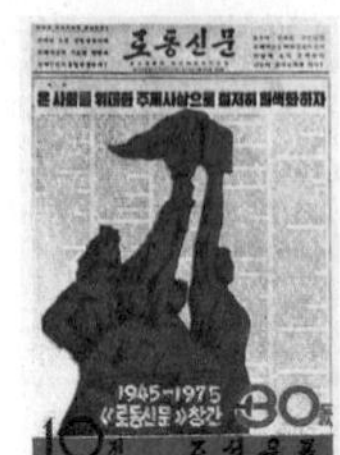
565 Workers holding "Juche" Torch

1975. 30th Anniv of "Rodong Simmun" (Journal of the Central Committee of the Worker's Party.)

N1461	**565** 10ch. multicoloured	50	10

566 Hyonmu Gate

1975. Ancient Wall-Gates of Pyongyang. Mult.

N1463	10ch. Type **566**	10	10
N1464	10ch. Taedong Gate	10	10
N1465	15ch. Potong Gate	20	10
N1466	20ch. Chongum Gate	35	15
N1467	30ch. Chilsong Gate (vert)	45	25

567

1975. Views of Mt. Chilbo.

N1468	**567** 10ch. multicoloured	40	10
N1469	– 10ch. multicoloured	40	10
N1470	– 15ch. multicoloured	65	10
N1471	– 20ch. multicoloured	75	15
N1472	– 30ch. multicoloured	85	20

DESIGNS: Nos. N1468/72, Various views.

568 Right-hand Section of Monument

1975. Historic Site of Revolution in Wangjaesan. Multicoloured.

N1473	10ch. Type **568**	10	10
N1474	15ch. Left-hand section of monument	20	10
N1475	25ch. Centre section of monument (38 × 60mm)	30	15
N1476	30ch. Centre section, close up (60 × 38mm)	40	20

569 Marchers with Flags

1976. 30th Anniv of Korean League of Socialist Working Youth. Multicoloured.

N1477	2ch. Flags and Emblem	15	10
N1478	70ch. Type **569**	90	40

570 Geese

1976. Ducks and Geese. Multicoloured.

N1479	10ch. Type **570**	40	10
N1480	20ch. "Perennial" duck	90	10
N1481	40ch. Kwangpo duck	1·60	20

571 "Oath"

1976. Korean Peoples Army (sculptural works). Multicoloured.

N1482	5ch. Type **571**	10	10
N1483	10ch. "Union of Officers with Men" (horiz)	15	10
N1484	10ch. "This Flag to the Height"	15	10

572 "Rural Road at Evening"

1976. Modern Korean Paintings (5th series). Social Welfare. Multicoloured.

N1485	10ch. Type **572**	60	10
N1486	15ch. "Passing on Technique" (1970)	70	10
N1487	25ch. "Mother (and Child)" (1965)	85	15
N1488	30ch. "Medical Examination at School" (1970) (horiz)	1·50	15
N1489	40ch. "Lady Doctor of Village" (1970) (horiz)	1·75	20

573 Worker holding Text of Law

1976. 30th Anniv of Agrarian Reform Law.

N1490	**573** 10ch. multicoloured	20	10

574 Telephones and Satellite

1976. Centenary of First Telephone Call. Multicoloured. With or without gum.

N1491	2ch. Type **574**	40	10
N1492	5ch. Satellite and antenna	40	10
N1493	10ch. Satellite and telecommunications systems	40	10
N1494	15ch. Telephone and linesman	1·10	10
N1495	25ch. Satellite and map of receiving stations	1·50	15
N1496	40ch. Satellite and cable-laying barge	1·75	20

575 Cosmos

1976. Flowers. Multicoloured.

N1498	5ch. Type **575**	25	10
N1499	10ch. Dahlia	25	10
N1500	20ch. Zinnia	45	15
N1501	40ch. China aster	70	25

576 Fruit and Products

1976. Pukchong Meeting of Korean Workers' Party Presidium. Multicoloured.

N1502	5ch. Type **576**	75	10
N1503	10ch. Fruit and orchard scene	75	10

577 "Pulgungi" Electric Locomotive

1976. Railway Locomotives. Multicoloured.

N1504	5ch. Type **577**	40	10
N1505	10ch. "Chaju" underground train	75	10
N1506	15ch. "Saebyol" diesel locomotive	95	15

GUM. All the following stamps were issued with gum, except where otherwise stated.

578 Satellite

1976. Space Flight. With or without gum.

N1507	**578** 2ch. multicoloured	15	10
N1508	– 5ch. multicoloured	15	10
N1509	– 10ch. multicoloured	20	10
N1510	– 15ch. multicoloured	30	10
N1511	– 25ch. multicoloured	45	15
N1512	– 40ch. multicoloured	70	20

DESIGNS: 5ch. to 40ch. Various satellites and space craft.

579 Kim Il Sung beside Car

1976. Kim Il Sung's 64th Birthday.

N1514	**579** 10ch. multicoloured	40	10

580 Bat and Ribbon

1976. 3rd Asian Table Tennis Championships. Multicoloured. Without gum.

N1516	5ch. Type **580**	40	10
N1517	10ch. Three women players with flowers	40	10
N1518	20ch. Player defending	65	10
N1519	25ch. Player making attacking shot	1·00	15

581 Kim Il Sung announcing Establishment of Association

1976. 40th Anniv of Association for the Restoration of the Fatherland. Without gum.

N1521	**581** 10ch. multicoloured	10	10

582 Golden Pheasant

1976. Pheasants. Multicoloured. With or without gum.

N1522	2ch. Type **582**	1·00	15
N1523	5ch. Lady Amherst's pheasant	1·10	15
N1524	10ch. Silver pheasant	1·40	25
N1525	15ch. Reeves's pheasant	1·50	35
N1526	25ch. Temminck's tragopan	2·00	60
N1527	40ch. Common pheasant (albino)	2·40	1·00

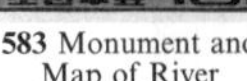

583 Monument and Map of River

585 Bronze Medal (Hockey, Pakistan)

584 Running

1976. Potong River Monument. Without gum.

N1529	**583** 10ch. brown and green	20	10

1976. Olympic Games, Montreal. Multicoloured.

N1530	2ch. Type **584**	30	10
N1531	5ch. Diving	30	10
N1532	10ch. Judo	30	10
N1533	15ch. Gymnastics	40	10
N1534	25ch. Gymnastics	80	15
N1535	40ch. Fencing	3·00	20

1976. Olympic Medal Winners (1st issue). Multicoloured.

N1537	2ch. Type **585**	75	10
N1538	5ch. Bronze medal (shooting, Rudolf Dollinger)	25	10
N1539	10ch. Silver medal (boxing, Li Byong Uk)	25	15
N1540	15ch. Silver medal (cycling, Daniel Morelon)	2·00	15
N1541	25ch. Gold medal (marathon, Waldemar Cierpinski)	90	20
N1542	40ch. Gold medal (boxing, Ku Yong Jo)	1·10	25

586 Boxing (Ku Yong Jo)

1976. Olympic Medal Winners (2nd issue). Multicoloured.

N1544	2ch. Type **586**	25	10
N1545	5ch. Gymnastics (Nadia Comaneci)	25	10
N1546	10ch. Pole vaulting (Tadeusz Slusarki)	25	10
N1547	15ch. Hurdling (Guy Drut)	30	10
N1548	20ch. Cycling (Bernt Johansson)	2·50	15
N1549	40ch. Football (East Germany)	1·50	20

587 U.P.U. Headquarters, Berne

1976. International Festivities. Multicoloured.

N1551	2ch. Type **587**	40	10
N1552	5ch. Footballers (World Cup)	40	10
N1553	10ch. Olympic Stadium	40	10
N1554	15ch. Olympic Village	40	10
N1555	25ch. Junk and satellite	70	20
N1556	40ch. Satellites	75	20

588 Azure-winged Magpies

1976. Embroidery. Multicoloured. With or without gum.

N1558	2ch. Type **588**	1·75	20
N1559	5ch. White magpie	90	15
N1560	10ch. Roe deer	30	10
N1561	15ch. Black-naped oriole and magnolias	2·10	20
N1562	25ch. Fairy with flute (horiz)	70	15
N1563	40ch. Tiger	1·60	40

589 Roman "5" and Flame

1976. 5th Non-aligned States' Summit Conference, Colombo. Without gum.

N1565	**589** 10ch. multicoloured	10	10

590 Trophy and Certificate

1976. World Model Plane Championships (1975). Multicoloured. Without gum.

N1566	5ch. Type **590**	20	10
N1567	10ch. Trophy and medals	30	10
N1568	20ch. Model airplane and emblem	45	10
N1569	40ch. Model glider and medals	75	15

591 "Pulgungi" Diesel Shunting Locomotive

1976. Locomotives. Multicoloured.

N1570	2ch. Type **591**	40	10
N1571	5ch. "Saebyol" diesel locomotive	55	10
N1572	10ch. "Saebyol" diesel shunting locomotive	65	10
N1573	15ch. Electric locomotive	75	10
N1574	25ch. "Kumsong" diesel locomotive	95	15
N1575	40ch. "Pulgungi" electric locomotive	1·10	20

592 House of Culture

1976. House of Culture. Without gum.

N1577	**592** 10ch. brown and black	15	10

593 Kim Il Sung visiting Tosongrang

1976. Revolutionary Activities of Kim Il Sung. Multicoloured.

N1578	2ch. Type **593**	20	10
N1579	5ch. Kim Il Sung visits pheasants	20	10
N1580	10ch. Kim Il Sung on hilltop	25	10
N1581	15ch. Kim Il Sung giving house to farmhand	30	10
N1582	25ch. Kim Il Sung near front line	70	10
N1583	40ch. Kim Il Sung walking in rain	70	15

594 Kim Il Sung with Union Members

1976. 50th Anniv of Down-with-Imperialism Union. Without gum.

N1585	**594** 20ch. multicoloured	35	15

604 Searchlights and Kim Il Sung's Birthplace

605 Spring Costume

1977. New Year. Without gum.

N1589	**604** 10ch. multicoloured	10	10

1977. National Costumes of Li Dynasty. Mult.

N1590	10ch. Type **605** (postage)	45	10
N1591	15ch. Summer costume	60	10
N1592	20ch. Autumn costume	70	15
N1593	40ch. Winter costume (air)	1·10	20

606 Two Deva Kings (Koguryo Dynasty)

1977. Korean Cultural Relics. Multicoloured.

N1594	2ch. Type **606** (postage)	40	10
N1595	5ch. Gold-copper decoration, Koguryo Dynasty	40	10
N1596	10ch. Copper Buddha, Koryo Dynasty	60	10
N1597	15ch. Gold-copper Buddha, Paekje Dynasty	70	10
N1598	25ch. Gold crown, Koguryo Dynasty	85	15
N1599	40ch. Gold-copper sun decoration, Koguryo Dynasty (horiz)	1·00	20
N1600	50ch. Gold crown, Silla Dynasty (air)	1·10	35

607 Worker with Five-point Programme

1977. Five-point Programme for Remaking Nature. Without gum.

N1601	**607** 10ch. multicoloured	20	10

608 Pine Branch and Map of Korea

1977. 60th Anniv of Korean National Association. Without gum.

N1602	**608** 10ch. multicoloured	35	10

609 Championship Emblem and Trophy

1977. 34th World Table Tennis Championships. Multicoloured. Without gum.

N1603	10ch. Type **609** (postage)	30	10
N1604	15ch. Pak Yong Sun	40	10
N1605	20ch. Pak Yong Sun with trophy	70	15
N1606	40ch. Pak Yong Ok and Yang Ying (air)	1·10	20

610 Kim Il Sung founds Guerrilla Army at Mingyuegou

1977. Kim Il Sung's 65th Birthday. Multicoloured.

N1607	2ch. Type **610**	10	10
N1608	5ch. In command of army	10	10
N1609	10ch. Visiting steel workers in Kangson	25	10
N1610	15ch. Before battle	20	10
N1611	25ch. In schoolroom	25	10
N1612	40ch. Viewing bumper harvest	35	10

611 "Chollima 72" Trolleybus

1977. Trolleybuses. Without gum.

N1614	**611** 5ch. blue, lilac and black	1·00	10
N1615	– 10ch. red, green & black	1·00	10

DESIGN: 10ch. "Chollima 74" trolleybus.

612 Red Flag and Hand holding Rifle

1977. 45th Anniv of Korean People's Revolutionary Army. Without gum.
N1616 **612** 40ch. red, yellow & blk . . . 50 20

613 Proclamation and Watchtower

1977. 40th Anniv of Pochonbo Battle. Without gum.
N1617 **613** 10ch. multicoloured . . . 10 10

614 Koryo White Ware Teapot

1977. Korean Porcelain. Multicoloured.
N1618 10ch. Type **614** (postage) . . . 70 10
N1619 15ch. White vase, Li Dynasty 85 10
N1620 20ch. Celadon vase, Koryo Dynasty . . . . 1·00 10
N1621 40ch. Celadon vase with lotus decoration, Koryo Dynasty (air) . . . . . 1·50 15

615 Postal Transport

1977. Postal Services. Multicoloured. Without gum.
N1623 2ch. Type **615** . . . . . 1·00 15
N1624 10ch. Postwoman delivering letter 40 10
N1625 30ch. Mil Mi-8 helicopter 1·00 30
N1626 40ch. Ilyushin Il-18 airliner and world map 1·10 30

616 "Rapala arata"

1977. Butterflies and Dragonflies. Multicoloured.
N1627 2ch. Type **616** (postage) 60 10
N1628 5ch. "Colias aurora" . . . 80 10
N1629 10ch. Poplar admiral . . . 1·00 10
N1630 15ch. "Anax partherope" (dragonfly) . . . . . . 1·50 10
N1631 25ch. "Sympetrum pedemontanum" (dragonfly) . . . . . . 1·75 10
N1632 50ch. "Papilio maackii" (air) . . . . 2·25 20

617 Grey Cat **618**

1977. Cats. Multicoloured.
N1634 2ch. Type **617** . . . . . 1·25 10
N1635 10ch. Black and white cat 1·60 15
N1636 25ch. Ginger cat . . . . . 2·75 20

1977. Dogs. Multicoloured.
N1638 5ch. Type **618** (postage) 1·00 10
N1639 15ch. Chow . . . . 1·25 10
N1640 50ch. Pungsang dog (air) 1·75 15

619 Kim Il Sung and President Tito

1977. Visit of President Tito.
N1642 **619** 10ch. multicoloured . . 10 10
N1643 15ch. multicoloured . . 15 10
N1644 20ch. multicoloured . . 20 10
N1645 40vh. multicoloured . . 25 10

620 Girl and Symbols of Education

1977. 5th Anniv of 11-year Compulsory Education. Without gum.
N1646 **620** 10ch. multicoloured . . 10 10

621 Chinese Mactra and Cobia **622** Students and "Theses"

1977. Shellfish and Fish. Multicoloured.
N1647 2ch. Type **621** (postage) 45 10
N1648 5ch. Bladder moon . . . 65 10
N1649 10ch. "Arca inflata" and pomfret 95 15
N1650 25ch. Thomas's rapa whelk and grouper . . . 1·40 40
N1651 50ch. Thomas's rapa whelk and globefish (air) 2·10 75

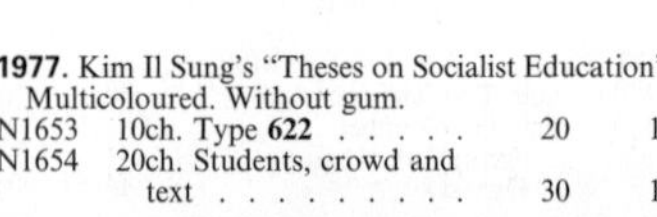

1977. Kim Il Sung's "Theses on Socialist Education". Multicoloured. Without gum.
N1653 10ch. Type **622** 20 10
N1654 20ch. Students, crowd and text 30 10

623 "Juche" Torch **624** Jubilant Crowd

1977. Seminar on the Juche Idea. Multicoloured. Without gum.
N1655 2ch. Type **623** 10 10
N1656 5ch. Crowd and red book 10 10
N1657 10ch. Chollima Statue and flags 10 10
N1658 15ch. Handclasp and red flag on world map . . . 10 10
N1659 25ch. Map of Korea and anti-U.S. slogans . . . 15 10
N1660 40ch. Crowd and Mt. Paekdu-san 20 10

1977. Election of Deputies to Supreme People's Assembly. Without gum.
N1662 **624** 10ch. multicoloured . . 10 10

625 Footballers

1977. World Cup Football Championship, Argentina. Without gum.
N1663 **625** 10ch. multicoloured . . 90 15
N1664 – 15ch. multicoloured . . 1·25 20
N1665 – 40ch. multicoloured . . 2·00 25
DESIGNS: 15, 40ch. Different football scenes.

626 Kim Il Sung with Rejoicing Crowds

1977. Re-election of Kim Il Sung. Without gum.
N1667 **626** 10ch. multicoloured . . 20 10

627 Chollima Statue and Symbols of Communication

1977. 20th Anniv of Socialist Countries' Communication Organization. Without gum.
N1668 **627** 10ch. multicoloured . . 20 10

638 Chollima Statue and City Skyline

1978. New Year. Without gum.
N1687 **638** 10ch. multicoloured . . 20 10

639 Skater in 19th-century Costume

1978. Winter Olympic Games, Sapporo and Innsbruck. Multicoloured.
N1688 2ch. Type **639** (postage) 50 10
N1699 5ch. Skier 50 10
N1690 10ch. Woman skater . . . 50 10
N1691 15ch. Hunter on skis . . . 60 10
N1692 20ch. Woman (in 19th-century costume) on skis 60 10
N1693 25ch. Viking with longbow 2·75 15
N1694 40ch. Skier (air) . . . . . 1·50 15

640 Post-rider and "Horse-ticket"

1978. Postal Progress. Multicoloured.
N1696 2ch. Type **640** (postage) 40 10
N1697 5ch. Postman on motor cycle . . . . 1·75 10
N1698 10ch. Electric train and post-van . . . . 1·75 15
N1699 15ch. Mail steamer and Mil Mi-8 helicopter . . 1·00 15
N1700 25ch. Tupolev Tu-154 jetliner and satellite . . 90 15
N1701 40ch. Dove and U.P.U. headquarters (air) . . . 60 15

641 Self-portrait

1978. 400th Birth Anniv of Rubens.
N1703 **641** 2ch. multicoloured . . 25 10
N1704 5ch. multicoloured . . 25 10
N1705 40ch. multicoloured . . 1·50 20

642 "Chungsong" Tractor

1978. Farm Machines. Without gum.
N1707 **642** 10ch. red and black . . 45 10
N1708 – 10ch. brown and black 45 10
DESIGN: No. N1708, Sprayer.

643 Show Jumping

1978. Olympic Games, Moscow (1980). Equestrian Events. Multicoloured.
N1709 2ch. Type **643** 25 10
N1710 5ch. Jumping bar 35 10
N1711 10ch. Cross-country . . . 45 10
N1712 15ch. Dressage 50 10
N1713 25ch. Water splash . . . 75 15
N1714 40ch. Dressage (different) 1·25 15

644 Soldier

1978. Korean People's Army Day. Multicoloured. Without gum.
N1716 5ch. Type **644** 10 10
N1717 10ch. Servicemen saluting 10 10

645 "Mangyongbong" (Freighter)

1978. Korean Ships. Multicoloured.
N1718 2ch. Type **645** (postage) 1·75 45
N1719 5ch. "Hyoksin" (freighter) 35 15
N1720 10ch. "Chongchongang" (gas carrier) 35 15
N1721 30ch. "Sonbong" (tanker) 60 20
N1722 50ch. "Taedonggang" (freighter) (air) . . . . 1·10 40

646 Uruguayan Footballer

1978. World Cup Football Championship Winners. Multicoloured.
N1724 5ch. Type **646** (postage) 50 10
N1725 10ch. Italian player . . . 50 10
N1726 15ch. West German player 50 10
N1727 25ch. Brazilian player . . 50 10
N1728 40ch. English player . . . 1·00 10
N1729 50ch. Hands holding World Cup (vert) (air) 1·50 15

647 Footballers (1930 Winners, Uruguay)

1978. History of World Cup Football Championship. Multicoloured.
N1731 20ch. Type **647** (postage) 85 15
N1732 20ch. Italy, 1934 . . . . 85 15
N1733 20ch. France, 1938 . . . . 85 15
N1734 20ch. Brazil, 1950 . . . . 85 15
N1735 20ch. Switzerland, 1954 . . 85 15
N1736 20ch. Sweden, 1958 . . . 85 15
N1737 20ch. Chile, 1962 . . . . 85 15
N1738 20ch. England, 1966 . . . 85 15
N1739 20ch. Mexico, 1970 . . . 85 15
N1740 20ch. West Germany, 1974 85 15
N1741 20ch. Argentina, 1978 . . 85 15
N1742 50ch. Footballers and emblem (air) 85 15

648 "Sea of Blood" (opera)

1978. Art from the Period of Anti-Japanese Struggle. Multicoloured.
N1744 10ch. Type **648** 40 10
N1745 15ch. Floral kerchief embroidered with map of Korea 50 10
N1746 20ch. "Tansimjul" (maypole dance) 75 15

649 Red Flag and "7", Electricity and Coal

1978. Second 7 Year Plan. Multicoloured. Without gum.
N1748 5ch. Type **649** 25 10
N1749 10ch. Steel and non-ferrous metal 30 10
N1750 15ch. Engineering and chemical fertilizer . . . 35 10
N1751 30ch. Cement and fishing 70 10
N1752 50ch. Grain and tideland reclamation 75 10

650 Gymnastics (Alfred Flatow)

1978. Olympic Games History and Medal-winners. Multicoloured.
N1753 20ch. Type **650** 75 15
N1754 20ch. Runners (Michel Theato) 75 15
N1755 20ch. Runners (Wyndham Halswelle) 75 15
N1756 20ch. Rowing (William Kinnear) 75 15
N1757 20ch. Fencing (Paul Anspach) . . . . 1·50 25
N1758 20ch. Runners (Ugo Frigerio) 75 15
N1759 20ch. Runners (Ahmed El Quafi) 75 15
N1760 20ch. Cycling (Robert Charpentier) . . . . . 1·75 35
N1761 20ch. Gymnastics (Josep Stalder) 75 15
N1762 20ch. Boxing (Lazio Papp) 1·00 20
N1763 20ch. Runners (Ronald Delany) 75 15
N1764 20ch. High jump (Jolanda Balas) 75 15
N1765 20ch. High jump (Valery Brumel) 75 15
N1766 20ch. Gymnastics (Vera Caslavska) 75 15
N1767 20ch. Rifle shooting (Li Ho Jun) 75 15

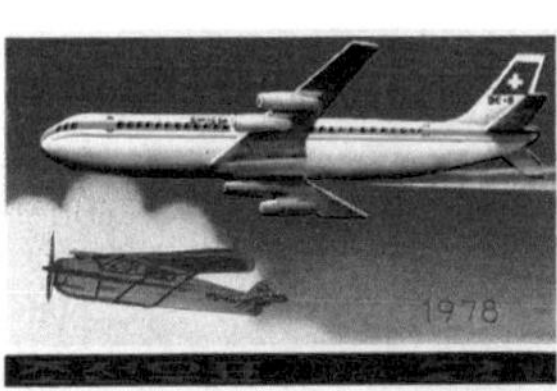

651 Douglas DC-8-63 and Comte Gentleman

1978. Airplanes. Multicoloured.
N1769 2ch. Type **651** 70 10
N1770 10ch. Ilyushin Il-62M and Avia BH-25 . . . . . 80 10
N1771 15ch. Douglas DC-8-63 and Savoia Marchetti S-71 . . . . 90 10
N1772 20ch. Tupolev Tu-144 and Kalinin K-5 . . . . . 1·10 10
N1773 25ch. Tupolev Tu-154 and Antonov An-2 biplane 1·10 10
N1774 30ch. Ilyushin Il-18 . . . 1·10 10
N1775 40ch. Concorde and Wibault 283 trimotor 2·25 40

652 White-bellied Black Woodpecker and Map

1978. White-bellied Black Woodpecker Preservation. Multicoloured.
N1777 5ch. Type **652** . . . . . 1·50 15
N1778 10ch. Woodpecker and eggs . . . . 1·75 20
N1779 15ch. Woodpecker feeding young . . . . 2·25 30
N1780 25ch. Woodpecker feeding young (different) . . . 2·75 60
N1781 50ch. Adult woodpecker on tree trunk . . . . . 5·00 1·25

653 Demonstrators and Korean Map

1978. 30th Anniv of Democratic People's Republic of Korea. Multicoloured. Without gum.
N1783 10ch. Type **653** 10 10
N1784 10ch. Flag and soldiers . . 10 10
N1785 10ch. Flag and "Juche" 10 10
N1786 10ch. Red Flag 10 10
N1787 10ch. Chollima Statue and city skyline 10 10
N1788 10ch. "Juche" torch and men of three races . . . 10 10

654 Cat and Pup

668 Red Flag and Pine Branch

655 Footballers

1978. Animal Paintings by Li Am. Multicoloured.
N1789 10ch. Type **654** . . . . . 2·50 30
N1790 15ch. Cat up a tree . . . 2·50 30
N1791 40ch. Wild geese . . . . 2·50 30

1978. Argentina's Victory in World Cup Football Championship. Without gum.
N1792 **655** 10ch. multicoloured . . 75 10
N1793 – 15ch. multicoloured . . 85 15
N1794 – 25ch. multicoloured . . 1·10 20
DESIGNS: 15, 25ch. Different football scenes.

1979. New Year. Without gum.
N1812 **668** 10ch. multicoloured . . 15 10

669 Kim Il Sung with Children's Corps Members, Maanshan

1979. International Year of the Child (1st issue). Multicoloured. (a) Paintings of Kim Il Sung and children.
N1813 5ch. Type **669** 15 10
N1814 10ch. Kim Il Sung and Children's Corps members in classroom 25 10
N1815 15ch. New Year gathering 30 10
N1816 20ch. Kim Il Sung and children in snow 45 10
N1817 30ch. Kim Il Sung examines children's schoolbooks (vert) . . . 50 10

(b) Designs showing children
N1818 10ch. Tug-of-war 15 10
N1819 15ch. Dance "Growing up Fast" 40 15
N1820 20ch. Children of many races and globe 40 10
N1821 25ch. Children singing . . 65 15
N1822 30ch. Children in toy spaceships 40 10
See also Nos. N1907/17.

670 Rose

1979. Roses. Multicoloured.
N1824 1wn. Red rose . . . . .
N1825 3wn. White rose . . . . .
N1826 5wn. Type **670** . . . . .
N1827 10wn. Deep pink rose . .
See also Nos. N1837/42.

671 Warriors on Horseback

1979. "The Story of Two Generals". Multicoloured. Without gum.
N1828 5ch. Type **671** 20 10
N1829 10ch. Farm labourer blowing feather 30 10
N1830 10ch. Generals fighting on foot 30 10
N1831 10ch. Generals on horseback 30 10

672 Red Guard and Industrial Skyline

1979. 20th Anniv of Worker-Peasant Red Guards. Without gum.
N1832 **672** 10ch. multicoloured . . 15 10

673 Clement-Bayard Airship "Fleurus"

1979. Airships. Multicoloured. Without gum.

N1833	10ch. Type **673**	1·25	15
N1834	20ch. N.1 "Norge"	1·25	15

674 Crowd of Demonstrators

1979. 60th Anniv of 1st March Popular Uprising. Without gum.

N1836 **674**	10ch. blue and red	15	10

1979. Roses. As Nos. N1824/7. Multicoloured.

N1837	5ch. Type **670** (postage)	40	10
N1838	10ch. As No. N1827	45	10
N1839	15ch. As No. N1824	50	10
N1840	20ch. Yellow rose	60	10
N1841	30ch. As No. 1825	70	10
N1842	50ch. Deep pink rose (different) (air)	90	15

675 Table Tennis Trophy

1979. 35th World Table Tennis Championship, Pyongyang. Multicoloured. With or without gum.

N1843	5ch. Type **675**	20	10
N1844	10ch. Women's doubles	20	10
N1845	15ch. Women's singles	40	10
N1846	20ch. Men's doubles	60	10
N1847	30ch. Men's singles	80	10

676 Marchers with Red Flag

1979. Socialist Construction under Banner of Juche Idea. Multicoloured. Without gum.

N1849	5ch. Type **676**	10	10
N1850	10ch. Map of Korea	10	10
N1851	10ch. Juche torch	10	10

677 Badge **678** Emblem, Satellite orbiting Globe and Aerials

1979. Order of Honour of the Three Revolutions. Without gum.

N1852 **677**	10ch. blue	10	10

1979. World Telecommunications Day. Without gum.

N1853 **678**	10ch. multicoloured	25	10

679 Advancing Soldiers and Monument

1979. 40th Anniv of Battle in Musan Area. Without gum.

N1854 **679**	10ch. mauve, light blue and blue	20	10

680 Exhibition Entrance

1979. Int Friendship Exhibition. Without gum.

N1855 **680**	10ch. multicoloured	10	10

681 "Peonies"

1979. 450th Death Anniv (1978) of Albrecht Durer (artist) (1st issue). Multicoloured.

N1856	15ch. Type **681**	75	20
N1857	20ch. "Columbines"	1·25	20
N1858	25ch. "A Great Tuft of Grass"	1·25	20
N1859	30ch. "Wing of a Bird"	2·10	55

See also No. N2012.

682 Fencing

1979. Olympic Games, Moscow (2nd issue). Multicoloured. With gum (10, 40ch. only).

N1861	5ch. Type **682**	1·50	10
N1862	10ch. Gymnastics	40	10
N1863	20ch. Yachting	75	15
N1864	30ch. Athletics	60	15
N1865	40ch. Weightlifting	60	15

683 Hunting

1979. Horse-riding (people of Koguryo Dynasty). Multicoloured.

N1867	5ch. Type **683**	65	10
N1868	10ch. Archery contest	65	10
N1869	15ch. Man beating drum on horseback	25	10
N1870	20ch. Man blowing horn	25	10
N1871	30ch. Man and horse, armoured with chainmail	25	10
N1872	50ch. Hawking (air)	2·00	15

684 Judo **685** Warrior's Costume

1979. Olympic Games, Moscow (3rd issue). Multicoloured. With gum (5, 15, 20, 30ch. only).

N1873	5ch. Type **684**	40	10
N1874	10ch. Volleyball	40	10
N1875	15ch. Cycling	1·50	25
N1876	20ch. Basketball	60	15
N1877	25ch. Canoeing	60	15
N1878	30ch. Boxing	90	25
N1879	40ch. Shooting	85	20

1979. Warrior Costumes of Li Dynasty.

N1881 **685**	5ch. multicoloured	20	10
N1882 –	10ch. multicoloured	20	10
N1883 –	15ch. multicoloured	30	10
N1884 –	20ch. multicoloured	45	10
N1885 –	30ch. multicoloured	60	10
N1886 –	50ch. multicoloured (air)	90	15

DESIGNS: 10ch. to 50ch. Different costumes.

686 Wrestling **687** Monument

1979. Olympic Games, Moscow (4th issue). Multicoloured.

N1887	10ch. Type **686**	25	10
N1888	15ch. Handball	30	10
N1889	20ch. Archery	1·60	25
N1890	25ch. Hockey	1·60	45
N1891	30ch. Rowing	75	15
N1892	40ch. Football	1·50	25

1979. Chongbong Monument. Without gum.

N1894 **687**	10ch. multicoloured	20	10

688 Bottle-feeding Fawn

1979. Sika Deer. Multicoloured.

N1895	5ch. Type **688** (postage)	20	10
N1896	10ch. Doe and fawn	20	10
N1897	15ch. Stag drinking from stream	20	15
N1898	20ch. Stag	25	15
N1899	30ch. Stag and doe	35	25
N1900	50ch. Antlers and deer (air)	50	35

689 Moscovy Ducks

1979. Central Zoo, Pyongyang. Multicoloured.

N1901	5ch. Type **689** (postage)	40	10
N1902	10ch. Ostrich	85	10
N1903	15ch. Common turkey	1·10	10
N1904	20ch. Dalmatian pelican	1·25	10
N1905	30ch. Vulturine guineafowl	1·75	15
N1906	50ch. Mandarins (air)	2·75	20

690 Girl with Model Viking Ship

1979. International Year of the Child (2nd issue). Multicoloured.

N1907	20ch. Type **690**	1·00	20
N1908	20ch. Boys with model steam railway locomotive	2·50	85
N1909	20ch. Boy with model biplane	1·25	20
N1910	20ch. Boy with model spaceman	80	20
N1911	30ch. Boy with model speedboat	1·50	30
N1912	30ch. Boy sitting astride toy electric train	2·50	85
N1913	30ch. Boy and model airplane	1·60	30
N1914	30ch. Boy and flying spaceman	1·00	30

691 Footballers

1979. International Year of the Child (3rd issue). Multicoloured.

N1916	20ch. Type **691**	1·25	20
N1917	30ch. Footballers (different)	1·75	30

692 Japanese Stonefish

1979. Marine Life. Multicoloured.

N1919	20ch. Type **692**	1·25	10
N1920	30ch. Schlegel's redfish	1·40	20
N1921	50ch. Northern sealion	1·75	30

693 Cross-country Skiing (Sergei Saveliev)

1979. Winter Olympic Games, Lake Placid. Mult.

N1922	10ch. Figure skating (Irina Rodnina and Aleksandr Zaitsev) (horiz)	40	15
N1923	20ch. Ice hockey (Russian team) (horiz)	65	20
N1924	30ch. Women's 5 km relay (horiz)	1·10	25
N1925	40ch. Type **693**	1·25	30
N1926	50ch. Women's speed skating (Tatiana Averina)	1·50	35

694 The Honey Bee collecting Nectar

1979. The Honey Bee. Multicoloured.

N1928	20ch. Type **694**	1·40	10
N1929	30ch. Bee and flowers	1·75	15
N1930	50ch. Bee hovering over flower	2·00	25

695 Kim Jong Suk's Birthplace, Heoryong

1979. Historic Revolutionary Sites.

N1931 **695**	10ch. multicoloured	15	10
N1932 –	10ch. brown, blue & blk	15	10

DESIGN: No. N1932, Sinpa Revolutionary Museum.

696 Mt. Paekdu

1980. New Year.

N1933 **696**	10ch. multicoloured	55	10

697 Student and Books

1980. Studying.

N1934 **697**	10ch. multicoloured	25	10

698 Conveyor Belt

1980. Unryul Mine Conveyor Belt.

N1935 **698**	10ch. multicoloured	55	10

699 Children of Three Races

1980. International Day of the Child. Multicoloured.

N1936	10ch. Type **699**	30	10
N1937	10ch. Girl dancing to accordion	50	10
N1938	10ch. Children in fairground airplane	40	10
N1939	10ch. Children as astronauts	30	10
N1940	10ch. Children on tricycles	1·25	30
N1941	10ch. Children with toy diesel train	1·75	45
N1942	10ch. "His loving care for the children, future of the fatherland" (59½ × 38 mm)	30	10

700 Monument

1980. Chongsan-ri Historic Site. Multicoloured.

N1944	5ch. Type **700**	10	10
N1945	10ch. Meeting place of the General Membership	15	10

701 Monument

1980. Monument marking Kim Jong Suk's Return.

N1946 **701**	10ch. multicoloured	15	10

702 Vasco Nunez de Balboa

1980. Conquerors of the Earth. Multicoloured.

N1947	10ch. Type **702**	50	10
N1948	20ch. Francisco de Orellana	75	20
N1949	30ch. Haroun Tazieff	1·00	35
N1950	40ch. Edmund Hillary and Sherpa Tenzing	1·50	45

703 Museum

1980. Ryongpo Revolutionary Museum.

N1952 **703**	10ch. blue and black	20	10

704 Rowland Hill and Stamps

1980. Death Centenary (1979) of Sir Rowland Hill. Multicoloured.

N1953	30ch. Type **704**	3·50	75
N1954	50ch. Rowland Hill and stamps (different)	3·50	75

705 North Korean Red Cross Flag

1980. World Red Cross Day. Multicoloured.

N1955	10ch. Type **705**	70	20
N1956	10ch. Henri Dunant (founder)	70	20
N1957	10ch. Nurse and child	70	20
N1958	10ch. Polikarpov Po-2 biplane and ship	1·00	25
N1959	10ch. Mil Mi-4 helicopter	1·00	25
N1960	10ch. Children playing at nurses	70	20
N1961	10ch. Red Cross map over Korea and forms of transport	3·50	60

706 Fernando Magellan

1980. Conquerors of the Sea. Multicoloured.

N1963	10ch. Type **706**	1·75	25
N1964	20ch. Fridtjof Nansen	1·75	25
N1965	30ch. Auguste and Jacques Piccard	2·25	25
N1966	40ch. Jacques-Yves Cousteau	3·00	55

707 Korean Stamps and Penny Black

1980. "London 1980" International Stamp Exhibition. Multicoloured.

N1968	10ch. Type **707** (postage)	2·00	40
N1969	20ch. Korean cover and British Guiana 1c. black and red	3·00	40
N1970	30ch. Early Korean stamp and modern cover	2·00	40
N1971	50ch. Korean stamps	2·50	35
N1972	40ch. Korean stamp and miniature sheet (air)	1·60	35

708 Wright Brothers

1980. Conquerors of Sky and Space. Multicoloured.

N1974	10ch. Type **708**	75	15
N1975	20ch. Louis Bleriot	1·00	25
N1976	30ch. Anthony Fokker	1·50	40
N1977	40ch. Secondo Campini and Sir Frank Whittle	2·00	45

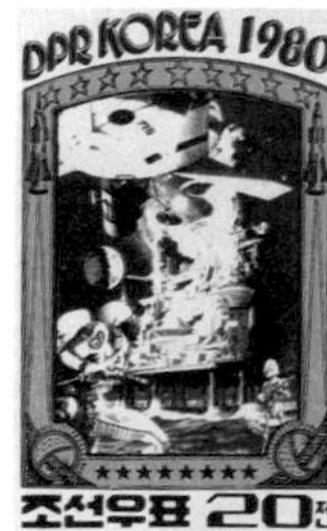

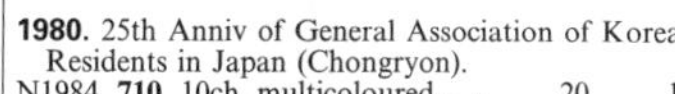
709 Space Station on Planet **710** Flag and Banners

1980. Conquerors of the Universe. Multicoloured.

N1979	10ch. Orbiting space station	20	10
N1980	20ch. Type **709**	25	20
N1981	30ch. Prehistoric animals and spaceships	90	35
N1982	40ch. Prehistoric animals and birds and spaceship	1·10	45

1980. 25th Anniv of General Association of Korean Residents in Japan (Chongryon).

N1984 **710**	10ch. multicoloured	20	10

711 Hospital

1980. Pyongyang Maternity Hospital.

N1985 **711**	10ch. blue, purple & blk	45	15

712 Health Centre

1980. Changgangwon Health Centre, Pyongyang.

N1986 **712**	2ch. black and blue	25	10

713 Hand holding Rifle **714** Workers' Hostel, Samjiyon

1980. 50th Anniv of Revolutionary Army.

N1987 **713**	10ch. multicoloured	25	10

1980.

N1988 **714**	10ch. brown, blue & blk	30	10
N1989 –	10ch. black and green	50	20
N1990 –	10ch. black and red	50	20
N1991 –	10ch. black and yellow	50	20
N1992 –	10ch. multicoloured	30	10
N1993 –	10ch. multicoloured	30	10
N1994 –	10ch. multicoloured	1·00	35
N1995 –	10ch. green and black	75	25
N1996 –	10ch. grey, blue & black	3·50	60
N1997 –	10ch. multicoloured	6·00	85

DESIGNS: No. N1989, "Taedonggang" rice transplanter; N1990, "Chongsan-ri" rice harvester; N1991, Maize harvester; N1992, Revolutionary building, Songmun-ri; N1993, Revolutionary building, Samhwa; N1994, Sundial of 1438; N1995, 16th-century "turtle" ship; N1996, Pungsan dog; N1997, Japanese quail.

715 Party Emblem

1980. 6th Korean Workers' Party Congress. Multicoloured.

N1998	10ch. Type **715**	15	10
N1999	10ch. Students and Laurel leaf on globe	15	10
N2000	10ch. Group with accordion	45	15
N2001	10ch. Group with banner, microscope, book and trophy	25	10
N2002	10ch. Worker with book and flag	75	25
N2003	10ch. Worker with spanner and flag	75	25
N2004	10ch. Marchers with torch and flags	15	10
N2005	10ch. Emblem, marchers and map	20	10

716 Dribbling Ball

1980. World Cup Football Championship, 1978–82. Multicoloured.

N2007	20ch. Type **716**	2·50	60
N2008	30ch. Tackle	3·00	80

717 Irina Rodnina and Aleksandr Zaitsev

1980. Winter Olympic Gold Medal Winners.

N2010 **717**	20ch. multicoloured	4·00	1·75

718 "Soldier with Horse"

719 Kepler, Astrolabe and Satellites

1980. 450th Death Anniv (1978) of Albrecht Durer (artist) (2nd issue).
N2012 **718** 20ch. multicoloured . . 5·00 1·50

1980. 350th Death Anniv of Johannes Kepler (astronomer).
N2014 **719** 20ch. multicoloured . . 2·50 90

720 German 1m. and Russian 30k. Zeppelin Stamps

1980. 3rd International Stamp Fair, Essen. Mult.
N2016 10ch. Type **720** 85 25
N2017 20ch. German 2m. and Russian 35k. Zeppelin stamps . . . . 1·75 45
N2018 30ch. German 4m. and Russian 1r. Zeppelin stamps . . . . 2·50 65

721 Shooting (Aleksandr Melentev)

1980. Olympic Medal Winners. Multicoloured.
N2020 10ch. Type **721** 30 15
N2021 20ch. Cycling (Robert Dill-Bundi) . . . . . . 3·25 75
N2022 25ch. Gymnastics (Stoyan Deltchev) 50 25
N2023 30ch. Wrestling (Chang Se Hong and Li Ho Pyong) 50 25
N2024 35ch. Weightlifting (Ho Bong Chol) 50 25
N2025 40ch. Running (Marita Koch) 50 30
N2026 50ch. Modern Pentathlon (Anatoli Starostin) . . . 70 35

722 Tito

1980. President Tito of Yugoslavia Commemoration.
N2028 **722** 20ch. multicoloured . . 30 10

723 Convair CV 340 Airliner

1980. 25th Anniv of First Post-War Flight of Lufthansa.
N2029 **723** 20ch. multicoloured . . 4·75 1·75

724 Early Steam Locomotive

1980. 150th Anniv of Liverpool–Manchester Railway.
N2031 **724** 20ch. multicoloured . . 5·00 1·75

725 Steam and Electric Locomotives

1980. Centenary of First Electric Train.
N2033 **725** 20ch. multicoloured . . 5·00 1·75

726 Hammarskjold

1980. 75th Birth Anniv of Dag Hammarskjold (Former Secretary General of United Nations).
N2035 **726** 20ch. multicoloured . . 2·50 1·25

727 Bobby Fischer and Boris Spassky

1980. World Chess Championship, Merano.
N2037 **727** 20ch. multicoloured . . 5·50 1·75

728 Stolz

1980. Birth Centenary of Robert Stolz (composer).
N2039 **728** 20ch. multicoloured . . 2·50 75

729 Chollima Statue

730 Russian Fairy Tale

1981. New Year. Without gum.
N2041 **729** 10ch. multicoloured . . 25 10

1981. International Year of the Child (1979) (4th issue). Fairy Tales. Multicoloured.
N2042 10ch. Type **730** . . . . . 1·10 30
N2043 10ch. Icelandic tale . . . 1·10 30
N2044 10ch. Swedish tale . . . . 1·10 30
N2045 10ch. Irish tale . . . . . 1·40 30
N2046 10ch. Italian tale . . . . 1·10 30
N2047 10ch. Japanese tale . . . 1·10 30
N2048 10ch. German tale . . . . 1·10 30

731 Changgwang Street

1981. Changgwang Street, Pyongyang.
N2050 **731** 10ch. multicoloured . . 35 10

732 Footballers

1981. World Cup Football Championship, Spain (1982) (1st issue). Multicoloured.
N2051 10ch. Type **732** . . . . . 2·25 45
N2052 20ch. Hitting ball past defender . . . . 2·25 45
N2053 30ch. Disputing possession of ball . . . . 2·25 45
See also Nos. N2055/9 and N2201/6.

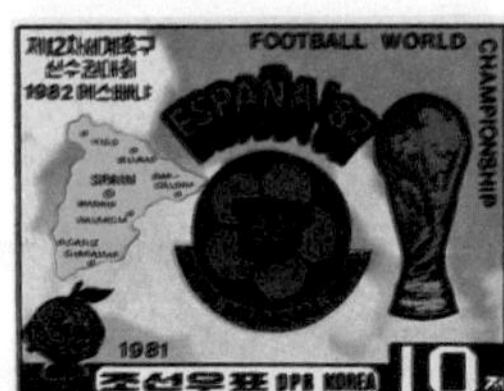
733 Map, Emblem and World Cup

1981. World Cup Football Championship, Spain (1982) (2nd issue). Multicoloured.
N2055 10ch. Type **733** . . . . . 1·50 30
N2056 15ch. Footballers . . . . 1·50 30
N2057 20ch. Heading ball . . . . 1·50 30
N2058 25ch. Footballers (different) . . . . . . 1·50 30
N2059 30ch. Footballers (different) . . . . . . 1·50 30

734 Workers with Book and Marchers with Banner

1981. Implementation of Decision of the 6th Koreans' Party Congress. Multicoloured.
N2061 2ch. Type **734** 10 10
N2062 10ch. Worker with book 10 10
N2063 10ch. Workers and industrial plant 25 10
N2064 10ch. Electricity and coal (horiz) . . . . 1·25 25
N2065 10ch. Steel and non-ferrous metals (horiz) 25 10
N2066 10ch. Cement and fertilizers (horiz) 25 10
N2067 30ch. Fishing and fabrics (horiz) 35 10
N2068 40ch. Grain and harbour (horiz) 25 10
N2069 70ch. Clasped hands . . . 20 10
N2070 1wn. Hand holding torch 30 15

735 Footballers

1981. Gold Cup Football Championship, Uruguay.
N2071 **735** 20ch. multicoloured . . 2·50 75

736 Dornier Do-X Flying Boat

1981. "Naposta '81" International Stamp Exhibition, Stuttgart. Multicoloured.
N2073 10ch. Type **736** . . . . . 2·75 50
N2074 20ch. Airship LZ-120 "Bodensee" . . . . . . 2·75 50
N2075 30ch. "Gotz von Berlichingen" . . . . . 1·50 40

737 Telecommunications Equipment

1981. World Telecommunications Day.
N2077 **737** 10ch. multicoloured . . 1·75 20

738 "Iris pseudacorus"

1981. Flowers. Multicoloured.
N2078 10ch. Type **738** . . . . . 1·00 15
N2079 20ch. "Iris pallasii" . . . 1·25 20
N2080 30ch. "Gladiolus gandavensis" . . . . . 1·60 30

739 Austrian "WIPA 1981" and Rudolf Kirchschlager Stamps

1981. "WIPA 1981" International Stamp Exhibition, Vienna. Multicoloured.
N2081 20ch. Type **739** . . . . . 1·90 60
N2082 30ch. Austrian Maria Theresa and Franz Joseph stamps . . . . 2·50 80

740 Rings Exercise

741 Armed Workers

1981. Centenary of International Gymnastic Federation. Multicoloured.

N2084	10ch. Type **740**	50	20
N2085	15ch. Horse exercise	60	20
N2086	20ch. Backwards somersault	80	20
N2087	25ch. Floor exercise	90	25
N2088	30ch. Exercise with hoop	1·10	25

1981. 50th Anniv of Mingyuehgou Meeting.

N2090 **741** 10ch. multicoloured . . 20 10

742 Farm Building, Sukchon

1981. 20th Anniv of Agricultural Guidance System and Taean Work System.

N2091	**742** 10ch. green, black and gold	20	10
N2092	– 10ch. blue, black and gold	20	10

DESIGN: No. N2092, Taean Revolutionary Museum.

743 Woman and Banner

1981. 55th Anniv of Formation of Women's Anti-Japanese Association.

N2093 **743** 5wn. multicoloured . . 2·75 75

743a Scene from Opera

1981. 10th Anniv of "Sea of Blood" (opera).

N2094 **743a** 10wn. multicoloured

744 Joan of Arc

1981. 550th Death Anniv of Joan of Arc. Multicoloured.

N2095	10ch. Type **744**	2·00	50
N2096	10ch. Archangel Michael	2·25	50
N2097	70ch. Joan of Arc in armour	2·25	50

745 Torch, Mountains and Flag

1981. 55th Anniv of Down with Imperialism Union.

N2099 **745** 1wn.50 multicoloured 40 20

746 "Young Girl by the Window"

1981. 375th Birth Anniv of Rembrandt (artist). Multicoloured.

N2100	10ch. Type **746**	70	25
N2101	20ch. "Rembrandt's Mother"	1·50	45
N2102	30ch. "Saskia van Uylenburgh"	2·00	70
N2103	40ch. "Pallas Athene"	2·50	90

747 Emblem and Banners over Pyongyang

1981. Symposium of Non-Aligned Countries on Food Self-Sufficiency, Pyongyang. Multicoloured.

N2105	10ch. Type **747**	20	10
N2106	50ch. Harvesting	50	10
N2107	90ch. Factories, tractors and marchers with banner	70	15

748 St. Paul's Cathedral

1981. Wedding of Prince of Wales (1st issue). Multicoloured.

N2108	10ch. Type **748**	1·40	35
N2109	20ch. Great Britain Prince of Wales Investiture stamp	1·40	35
N2110	30ch. Lady Diana Spencer	1·40	35
N2111	40ch. Prince Charles in military uniform	1·40	35

See also Nos. N2120/3.

749 "Four Philosophers" (detail)

1981. Paintings by Rubens. Multicoloured.

N2113	10ch. Type **749**	40	20
N2114	15ch. "Portrait of Helena Fourment"	60	25
N2115	20ch. "Portrait of Isabella Brandt"	90	25
N2116	25ch. "Education of Maria de Medici"	1·10	30
N2117	30ch. "Helena Fourment and her Child"	1·40	35
N2118	40ch. "Helena Fourment in her Wedding Dress"	1·75	40

750 Royal Couple

1981. Wedding of Prince of Wales (2nd issue). Multicoloured.

N2120	10ch. Type **750**	1·75	45
N2121	20ch. Couple on balcony after wedding	1·75	45
N2122	30ch. Couple outside St. Paul's Cathedral	1·75	45
N2123	70ch. Full-length wedding portrait of couple	1·75	45

751 Rowland Hill and Stamps

1981. "Philatokyo '81" International Stamp Exhibition. Multicoloured.

N2125	10ch. Korean 2ch. Seminar on Juche Idea stamp (41 × 29 mm)	75	20
N2126	10ch. Korean and 70ch. stamps (41 × 29 mm)	2·00	75
N2127	10ch. Type **751**	2·00	75
N2128	20ch. Korean Fairy Tale stamps	1·75	40
N 2129	30ch. Japanese stamps	3·00	90

752 League Members and Flag

1981. Seventh League of Socialist Working Youth Congress, Pyongyang.

N2131	**752** 10ch. multicoloured	20	10
N2132	80ch. multicoloured	60	10

753 Government Palace, Sofia, Bulgarian Arms and Khan Asparuch

1981. 1300th Anniv of Bulgarian State.

N2133 **753** 10ch. multicoloured . . 25 10

754 Dimitrov

1981. Birth Centenary of Georgi Dimitrov (Bulgarian statesman).

N2134 **754** 10ch. multicoloured . . 25 10

755 Emblem, Boeing 747-200, City Hall and Mercedes "500"

1981. "Philatelia '81" International Stamp Fair, Frankfurt-am-Main.

N2135 **755** 20ch. multicoloured . . 2·50 35

756 Concorde, Airship "Graf Zeppelin" and Count Ferdinand von Zeppelin

1981. "Philexfrance 82" International Stamp Exhibition, Paris. Multicoloured. (a) As T **756**.

N2136	10ch. Type **756**	2·75	40
N2137	20ch. Concorde, Breguet Provence airliner and Santos-Dumont's biplane "14 bis"	3·25	75
N2138	30ch. "Mona Lisa" (Leonardo da Vinci) and stamps	1·75	30

(b) Size 32 × 53 mm.

N2140	10ch. Hotel des Invalides, Paris	1·00	45
N2141	20ch. President Mitterrand of France	1·00	45
N2142	30ch. International Friendship Exhibition building	1·00	45
N2143	70ch. Kim Il Sung	1·00	45

757 Rising Sun **758** Emblem and Flags

1982. New Year.

N2144 **757** 10ch. multicoloured . . 30 10

1982. "Prospering Korea". Multicoloured.

N2145	2ch. Type **758**	15	10
N2146	10ch. Industry	25	10
N2147	10ch. Agriculture	25	10
N2148	10ch. Mining	45	10
N2149	10ch. Arts	25	10
N2150	10ch. Al Islet lighthouse, Uam-ri	2·50	40
N2151	40ch. Buildings	50	15

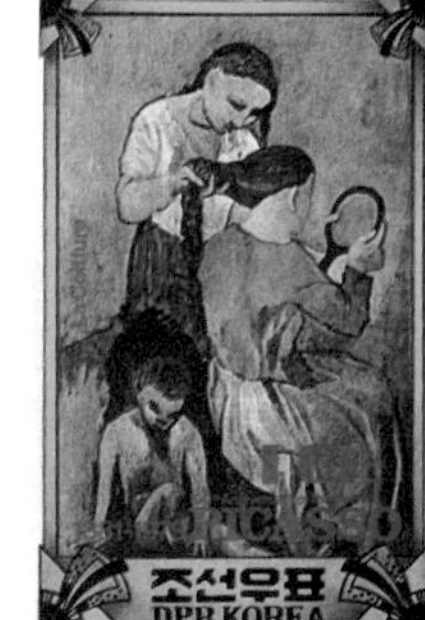

759 "The Hair-do"

1982. Birth Centenary of Pablo Picasso (artist). Multicoloured.

N2152	10ch. Type **759**	75	20
N2153	10ch. "Paulo on a donkey"	1·75	35
N2154	20ch. "Woman leaning on Arm"	90	25
N2155	20ch. "Harlequin"	1·75	35
N2156	25ch. "Child with Pigeon"	1·90	50
N2157	25ch. "Reading a Letter"	1·75	35
N2158	35ch. "Portrait of Gertrude Stein"	1·50	30

N2159 35ch. "Harlequin" (different) . . . . . . 1·75 35
N2160 80ch. "Minotaur" . . . . 1·75 35
N2161 90ch. "Mother with Child" . . . . 1·75 35

760 Fireworks over Pyongyang

1982. Kim Il Sung's 70th Birthday. Multicoloured.
N2163 10ch. Kim Il Sung's birthplace, Mangyongdae 20 10
N2164 10ch. Type **760** 20 10
N2165 10ch. "The Day will dawn on downtrodden Korea" (horiz) 20 10
N2166 10ch. Signalling start of Pochonbo Battle (horiz) 20 10
N2167 10ch. Kim Il Sung starting Potong River project (horiz) 20 10
N2168 10ch. Embracing bereaved children (horiz) 20 10
N2169 10ch. Kim Il Sung as Supreme Commander (horiz) 20 10
N2170 10ch. "On the Road of Advance" (horiz) . . . 20 10
N2171 10ch. Kim Il Sung kindling flame of Chollima Movement, Kansong Steel Plant (horiz) 75 25
N2172 10ch. Kim Il Sung talking to peasants (horiz) . . . 20 10
N2173 10ch. Kim Il Sung fixing site of reservoir (horiz) 30 10
N2174 20ch. Kim Il Sung visiting Komdok Valley (horiz) 75 25
N2175 20ch. Kim Il Sung visiting Red Flag Company (horiz) 20 10
N2176 20ch. Kim Il Sung teaching Juche farming methods (horiz) 20 10
N2177 20ch. Kim Il Sung visiting iron works (horiz) . . . 35 10
N2178 20ch. Kim Il Sung talking with smelters (horiz) . . 35 10
N2179 20ch. Kim Il Sung at chemical plant (horiz) 45 10
N2180 20ch. Kim Il Sung with fishermen (horiz) . . . 40 10

761 Soldier saluting

1982. 50th Anniv of People's Army.
N2182 **761** 10ch. multicoloured . . 25 10

762 "The Bagpiper" (Durer) 763 Surveyors

1982. 4th Essen International Stamp Fair.
N2183 **762** 30ch. multicoloured . . 3·75 40

1982. Implementation of Four Nature-remaking Tasks.
N2184 **763** 10ch. multicoloured . . 45 10

764 Princess as Baby 765 Tower of the Juche Idea, Pyongyang

1982. 21st Birthday of Princess of Wales.
N2185 **764** 10ch. multicoloured . . 30 20
N2186 – 20ch. multicoloured . . 65 35
N2187 – 30ch. multicoloured . . 75 45
N2188 – 50ch. multicoloured . . 1·00 40
N2189 – 60ch. multicoloured . . 1·00 40
N2190 – 70ch. multicoloured . . 1·00 40
N2191 – 80ch. multicoloured . . 1·00 40
DESIGNS: 20 to 80ch. Princess at various ages.

1982.
2193 **765** 2wn. multicoloured . . . 1·25 30
2194 – 3wn. orange and black 1·75 40
DESIGN (26 × 38 mm): 3wn. Arch of Triumph.

766 Tiger

1982. Tigers.
N2195 **766** 20ch. multicoloured . . 1·25 35
N2196 – 30ch. multicoloured . . 1·90 35
N2197 – 30ch. mult (horiz) . . 2·75 45
N2198 – 40ch. mult (horiz) . . 2·75 45
N2199 – 80ch. mult (horiz) . . 2·75 45
DESIGNS: 30 to 80ch. Tigers.

767 Group 1 Countries

1982. World Cup Football Championship, Spain (3rd issue). Multicoloured.
N2201 10ch. Type **767** 45 20
N2202 20ch. Group 2 countries 1·00 25
N2203 30ch. Group 3 countries 1·40 30
N2204 40ch. Group 4 countries 1·75 40
N2205 50ch. Group 5 countries 2·00 50
N2206 60ch. Group 6 countries 2·25 50

768 Rocket Launch 769 Charlotte von Stein

1982. The Universe. Multicoloured.
N2208 10ch. Type **768** . . . . . 1·25 40
N2209 20ch. Spaceship over globe 1·25 40
N2210 80ch. Spaceship between globe and moon . . . . 1·50 40

1982. 150th Death Anniv of Johann von Goethe (writer). Multicoloured.
N2212 10ch. Type **769** 50 25
N2213 10ch. Goethe's mother . . 1·50 45
N2214 20ch. Goethe's sister . . . 75 30
N2215 20ch. Angelika Kauffmann 1·50 45
N2216 25ch. Charlotte Buff . . . 90 35
N2217 25ch. Anna Amalia . . . 1·50 45
N2218 35ch. Lili Schonemann . . 1·25 40
N2219 35ch. Charlotte von Lengefeld . . . . 1·50 45
N2220 80ch. Goethe . . . . 1·60 45

770 Player holding aloft World Cup

1982. World Cup Football Championship Results. Multicoloured.
N2222 20ch. Type **770** . . . . . 1·25 30
N2223 30ch. Group of players with World Cup . . . . 1·75 50
N2224 30ch. Type **770** . . . . . 2·50 65
N2225 40ch. As No. N2203 . . . 2·50 65
N2226 80ch. King Juan Carlos of Spain and two players with World Cup . . . . 2·50 65

771 Princess and Prince William of Wales

1982. 1st Wedding Anniv of Prince and Princess of Wales.
N2228 **771** 30ch. multicoloured . . 2·75 90

772 Royal Couple with Prince William

1982. Birth of Prince William of Wales. Mult.
N2230 10ch. Couple with Prince William (different) . . . 75 25
N2231 10ch. Princess of Wales holding bouquet . . . . 1·50 75
N2232 20ch. Couple with Prince William (different) . . . 90 30
N2233 20ch. Prince Charles carrying baby, and Princess of Wales . . . 1·50 75
N2234 30ch. Type **772** . . . . . 1·00 40
N2235 30ch. Prince Charles carrying baby, and Princess of Wales (different) . . . . . . 1·50 75
N2236 40ch. Princess with baby 1·40 45
N2237 40ch. Prince and Princess of Wales (horiz) . . . . 2·40 95
N2238 50ch. Princess with baby (different) . . . . . . 1·75 50
N2239 50ch. Prince and Princess of Wales in evening dress (horiz) . . . . . 2·40 95
N2240 80ch. Couple with Prince William (different) . . . 1·50 75
N2241 80ch. Prince Charles holding baby, and Princess of Wales (horiz) . . . . 2·40 95

773 Airship "Nulli Secundus II", 1908

1982. Bicentenary of Manned Flight (1st issue). Multicoloured.
N2243 10ch. Type **773** . . . . . 1·25 40
N2244 10ch. Pauley and Durs Egg's dirigible balloon "The Dolphin", 1818 2·50 60
N2245 20ch. Tissandier Brothers' airship, 1883 . . . . . 1·50 50
N2246 20ch. Guyton de Morveau's balloon with oars, 1784 . . . . 2·50 60
N2247 30ch. Parseval airship PL-VII, 1912 . . . . 2·00 60
N2248 30ch. Sir George Cayley's airship design, 1837 . . 2·50 60
N2249 40ch. Count de Lennox's balloon "Eagle", 1834 2·25 60
N2250 40ch. Camille Vert's balloon "Poisson Volant", 1859 . . . . . 2·50 60
N2251 80ch. Dupuy de Lome's airship, 1872 . . . . . 2·50 60

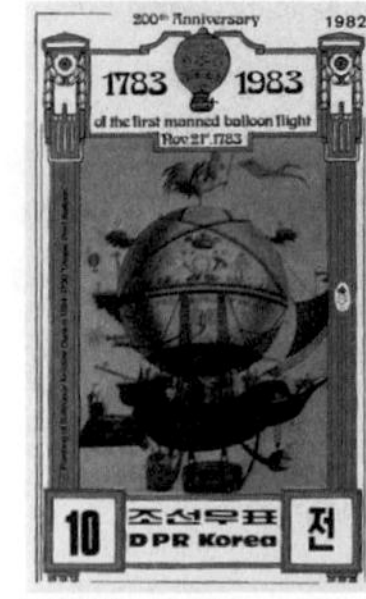

774 "Utopic Balloon Post" (Balthasar Antoine Dunker)

1982. Bicentenary of Manned Flight (2nd issue). Multicoloured.
N2253 10ch. Type **774** . . . . . 1·50 40
N2254 10ch. Montgolfier balloon at Versailles, 1783 . . . 3·00 60
N2255 20ch. "... and they fly into heaven and have no wings ..." . . . . 2·00 50
N2256 20ch. Montgolfier Brothers' balloon, 1783 3·00 60
N2257 30ch. Pierre Testu-Brissy's balloon ascent on horseback, 1798 . . . . 2·50 60
N2258 30ch. Charles's hydrogen balloon landing at Nesle, 1783 . . . . . . 3·00 60
N2259 40ch. Gaston Tissandier's test flight of "Zenith", 1875 . . . . 3·00 60
N2260 40ch. Blanchard and Jeffries' balloon flight over English Channel, 1785 . . . . 3·00 60
N2261 80ch. Henri Giffard's balloon "Le Grand Ballon Captif" at World Fair, 1878 . . . . . . 3·00 60

775 Turtle with Scroll

1982. Tale of the Hare. Multicoloured.
N2263 10ch. Type **775** . . . . . 1·00 15
N2264 20ch. Hare riding on turtle 1·50 20
N2265 30ch. Hare and turtle before Dragon King . . 1·75 30
N2266 40ch. Hare back on land 2·25 40

776 Flag, Red Book and City 777 Tower of Juche Idea

1982. 10th Anniv of Socialist Constitution.
N2267 **776** 10ch. multicoloured . . 25 10

1983. New Year.
N2268 **777** 10ch. multicoloured . . 15 10

778 Children reading "Saenal"

1983. 55th Anniv of "Saenal" Newspaper.
N2269 **778** 10ch. multicoloured . . 50 10

779 "Man in Oriental Costume"

1983. Paintings by Rembrandt. Multicoloured.
N2270 10ch. Type **779** 60 20
N2271 10ch. "Child with dead Peacocks" (detail) . . . 2·00 40
N2272 20ch. "The Noble Slav" 1·25 30
N2273 20ch. "Old Man in Fur Hat" . . . . 2·00 40
N2274 30ch. "Dr. Tulp's Anatomy Lesson" (detail) . . . . 3·25 50
N2275 30ch. "Portrait of a fashionable Couple" . . 2·00 40
N2276 40ch. "Two Scholars disputing" . . . . . . 1·50 35
N2277 40ch. "Woman with Child" . . . . 2·00 40
N2278 80ch. "Woman holding an Ostrich Feather Fan" 2·00 40

780 Airships "Gross Basenach II" and "Graf Zepplin" over Cologne

1983. "Luposta" International Air Mail Exhibition, Cologne. Multicoloured.
N2280 30ch. Type **780** . . . . . 3·00 90
N2281 40ch. Parsevel airship PL-II over Cologne . . . . 3·00 90

781 Banner and Monument

1983. 50th Anniv of Wangjaesan Meeting.
N2283 **781** 10ch. multicoloured . . 20 10

782 Karl Marx

1983. Death Centenary of Karl Marx.
N2284 **782** 10ch. multicoloured . . 50 25

783 Scholar, Marchers and Map of Journey

1983. 60th Anniv of Thousand-ri Journey for Learning.
N2285 **783** 10ch. multicoloured . . 1·00 10

784 "Madonna of the Goldfinch"

1983. 500th Birth Anniv of Raphael. Multicoloured.
N2286 10ch. Type **784** . . . . . 1·75 50
N2287 20ch. "The School of Athens" (detail) . . . . 1·50 40
N2288 30ch. "Madonna of the Grand Duke" . . . . . 1·75 45
N2289 50ch. "Madonna of the Chair" . . . . 1·90 45
N2290 50ch. "Madonna of the Lamb" . . . . 1·50 50
N2291 80ch. "The Beautiful Gardener" . . . . . . 1·50 50

785 Department Store No. 1

1983. Pyongyang Buildings. Multicoloured.
N2293 2ch. Chongryu Restaurant 20 10
N2294 10ch. Part of Munsu Street 30 10
N2295 10ch. Ice Rink 40 10
N2296 40ch. Type **785** 60 15
N2297 70ch. Grand People's Study House 75 25

786 Emblem and Crowd **788** Satellite, Masts and Dish Aerial

787 Judo

1983. 5th Anniv of International Institute of Juche Idea.
N2298 **786** 10ch. multicoloured . . 15 10

1983. Olympic Games, Los Angeles (1st issue). Multicoloured.
N2299 20ch. Type **787** 65 40
N2300 20ch. Wrestling . . . . . 1·25 40
N2301 30ch. Judo (different) (value in gold) 65 40
N2302 30ch. Judo (different) (value in black) . . . . 1·25 40
N2303 40ch. Boxing 65 40
N2304 40ch. Li Ho Jun (1972 shooting gold medalist) 1·25 40
N2305 50ch. Weightlifting 65 40
N2306 50ch. Wrestling (different) 1·25 40
N2307 80ch. Boxing (different) 1·25 40
See also Nos. N2359/64.

1983. World Communications Year (1st issue).
N2309 **788** 10ch. multicoloured . . 1·50 20
See also Nos. N2349/53.

789 Emblem, Giant Panda and Stamp

1983. "Tembal 83" International Thematic Stamp Exhibition, Basel. Multicoloured.
N2310 20ch. Type **789** . . . . . 1·75 35
N2311 30ch. Emblem, flag and Basel Town Post stamp 1·90 35

790 "Colourful Cow" (kogge), 1402

1983. Old Ships. Multicoloured.
N2312 20ch. Type **790** . . . . . 1·10 45
N2313 20ch. "Kwi-Sun" ("turtle" ship), 1592 . . . . . . 2·50 75
N2314 35ch. "Great Harry" (warship), 1555 . . . . 1·50 55
N2315 35ch. Admiral Li Sun Sin and "turtle" ship . . . 2·50 75
N2316 50ch. "Eagle of Lubeck" (galleon), 1567 . . . . 2·10 70
N2317 50ch. "Merkur" (full-rigged sailing ship), 1847 . . . . 2·50 75
N2318 80ch. "Herzogin Elisabeth" (cadet ship) 2·50 75

791 "Locomotion", 1825, Great Britain

1983. Railway Locomotives. Multicoloured.
N2320 20ch. Type **791** . . . . . 1·50 60
N2321 20ch. "Drache", 1848, Germany . . . . . . 4·75 1·00
N2322 35ch. "Adler", 1835, Germany . . . . . . 2·00 80
N2323 35ch. Korean steam locomotive . . . . . 4·50 1·00
N2324 50ch. "Austria", 1837, Austria . . . . . . 3·25 80
N2325 50ch. Bristol and Exeter Railway steam locomotive, 1853 . . . 4·75 1·00
N2326 80ch. Caledonian Railway locomotive, 1859 . . . 4·75 1·00

792 Map, Hand and Weapons

1983. 10th Anniv of Publication of Five-point Policy for Korea's Reunification.
N2328 **792** 10ch. multicoloured . . 25 10

793 Emblem, Tower of Juche Idea and Fireworks

1983. World Conference on Journalists against Imperialism and for Friendship and Peace, Pyongyang. Multicoloured.
N2329 10ch. Type **793** 20 10
N2330 40ch. Emblem and rainbow and clasped hands 40 15
N2331 70ch. Emblem, map and hand with raised forefinger 50 20

794 Worker and Banners

1983. "Let's Create the Speed of the 80s".
N2332 **794** 10ch. multicoloured . . 25 10

795 Soldier and Rejoicing Crowd

1983. 30th Anniv of Victory in Liberation War.
N2333 **795** 10ch. multicoloured . . 25 10

796 "Gorch Fock" (cadet barque) and Korean 1978 2ch. Stamp

1983. "Bangkok 1983" International Stamp Exhibition.
N2334 **796** 40ch. multicoloured . . 3·00 1·25

797 Skiing

1983. Winter Olympic Games, Sarajevo (1984). Multicoloured.
N2336 10ch. Type **797** 55 25
N2337 20ch. Figure skating (vert) 2·00 45
N2338 30ch. Skating (pair) . . . 1·60 55
N2339 50ch. Ski jumping . . . . 1·60 55
N2340 50ch. Ice hockey (vert) . . 2·00 45
N2341 80ch. Speed skating (vert) 2·00 45

798 Workers and Soldier with Books

1983. 35th Anniv of Korean People's Democratic Republic.
N2343 **798** 10ch. multicoloured . . 35 10

799 Archery **800** Girls holding Hands

1983. Folk Games. Multicoloured.
N2344 10ch. Type **799** . . . . . 2·50 40
N2345 10ch. Flying kites 65 20
N2346 40ch. See-sawing 65 20
N2347 40ch. Swinging 65 20

1983. Korean–Chinese Friendship.
N2348 **800** 10ch. multicoloured . . 50 10

801 Envelopes and Forms of Transport

1983. World Communications Year (2nd issue). Multicoloured.

N2349	30ch. Mail van, motorcyclist and hand holding magazines	4·75	90
N2350	30ch. Satellite, globe and dish aerial	1·25	40
N2351	40ch. Type **801**	4·75	1·10
N2352	40ch. Television cameraman	1·25	40
N2353	80ch. Telephone and aerial	1·25	40

802 Portrait

1983. Paintings by Rubens. Multicoloured.

N2355	40ch. Type **802**	1·40	60
N2356	40ch. Portrait (different) (horiz)	1·75	75
N2357	80ch. "The Sentencing of Midas" (horiz)	1·75	75

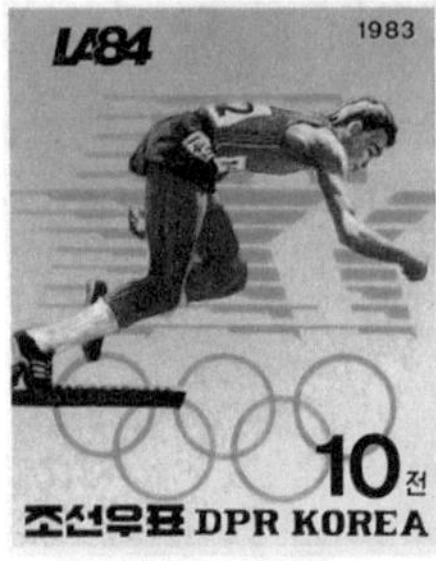

803 Sprinting

1983. Olympic Games, Los Angeles (2nd issue). Multicoloured.

N2359	10ch. Type **803**	75	20
N2360	20ch. Show jumping	1·75	45
N2361	30ch. Cycling	3·00	55
N2362	50ch. Handball	2·00	60
N2363	50ch. Fencing	1·75	45
N2364	80ch. Gymnastics	1·75	45

804 "St. Catherine" **805** Kimilsungflower

804a Cat

1983. 450th Death Anniv (1984) of Antonio Correggio (artist). Multicoloured.

N2366	20ch. Type **804**	1·75	60
N2367	20ch. "Morning" (detail)	2·50	75
N2368	35ch. "Madonna"	1·75	60
N2369	35ch. "Morning" (different)	2·50	75
N2370	50ch. "Madonna with St. John"	1·75	60
N2371	50ch. "St. Catherine" (different)	2·50	75
N2372	80ch. "Madonna and Child"	2·50	75

1983. Cats. Multicoloured, frame colour given.

N2373a	**804a**	10ch. green	1·25	10
N2373b	–	10ch. gold	1·25	10
N2373c	–	10ch. blue	1·25	10
N2373d	–	10ch. red	1·25	10
N2373e	–	10ch. silver	1·25	10

DESIGNS: Different cats' heads.

1983. New Year.

N2374 **805** 10ch. multicoloured . . 85 10

806 Worker and Workers' Party Flag

1984. "Under the Leadership of the Workers' Party". Multicoloured.

N2375	10ch. Type **806**	25	10
N2376	10ch. Ore-dressing plant No. 3, Komdok General Mining Enterprise, and Party Flag	40	10

807 Farm Worker, Rice and Maize

1984. 20th Anniv of Publication of "Theses of the Socialist Rural Question in Our Country".

N2377 **807** 10ch. multicoloured . . 25 10

808 Changdok School, Chilgol

1984. Kim Il Sung's 72nd Birthday.

N2378	**808**	5ch. green, black & blue	25	10
N2379	–	10ch. multicoloured	25	10

DESIGN: 10ch. Birthplace, Mangyongdae, and rejoicing crowd.

809 "Spanish Riding School" (Julius von Blaas)

1984. "Espana 84" International Stamp Exhibition, Madrid. Multicoloured.

N2380	10ch. Type **809**	1·75	50
N2381	20ch. "Ferdinand of Austria" (Rubens)	1·75	50

810 "La Donna Velata" **812** Construction Site

811 Map and Second Stage Pumping Station

1984. 500th Birth Anniv (1983) of Raphael (artist). Multicoloured.

N2383	10ch. "Portrait of Agnolo Doni"	1·50	50
N2384	20ch. Type **810**	1·50	50
N2385	30ch. "Portrait of Jeanne d'Aragon"	1·50	50

1984. 25th Anniv of Kiyang Irrigation System.

N2387 **811** 10ch. multicoloured . . 50 10

1984. Construction on Five District Fronts.

N2388 **812** 10ch. red, black & yell 50 10

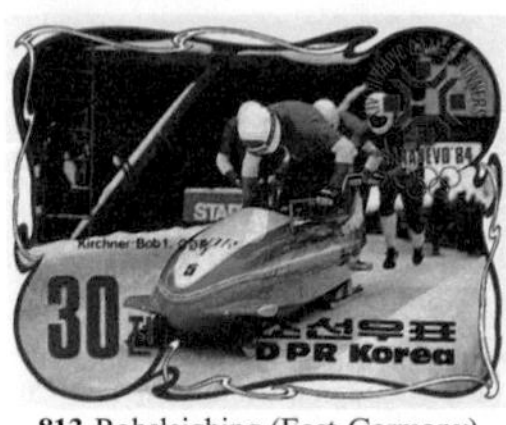

813 Bobsleighing (East Germany)

1984. Winter Olympic Games Medal Winners. Multicoloured.

N2389	10ch. Ski jumping (Matti Nykaenen)	1·75	50
N2390	20ch. Speed skating (Karin Enke)	1·50	40
N2391	20ch. Slalom (Max Julen)	1·75	50
N2392	30ch. Type **813**	1·50	40
N2393	30ch. Downhill skiing (Maria Walliser)	1·75	50
N2394	40ch. Cross-country skiing (Thomas Wassberg)	2·75	60
N2395	80ch. Cross-country skiing (Marja-Liisa Hamalainen)	2·75	60

814 Steam Locomotive, 1919

1984. Essen International Stamp Fair. Mult.

N2397	20ch. Streamlined steam locomotive, 1939	4·00	65
N2398	30ch. Type **814**	4·00	65

815 "Mlle. Fiocre in the Ballet 'La Source' "

1984. 150th Birth Anniv of Edgar Degas (artist). Multicoloured.

N2400	10ch. Type **815**	1·50	25
N2401	20ch. "The Dance Foyer at the Rue le Peletier Opera"	2·50	25
N2402	30ch. "Race Meeting"	3·75	40

816 Map of Pyongnam Irrigation System and Reservoir

1984. Irrigation Experts Meeting, Pyongyang.

N2404 **816** 2ch. multicoloured . . 40 10

817 Korean Stamp and Building **818** Crowd and Banners

1984. U.P.U. Congress Stamp Exn, Hamburg.

N2405 **817** 20ch. multicoloured . . 3·00 40

1984. Proposal for Tripartite Talks.

N2407 **818** 10ch. multicoloured . . 40 10

819 Nobel experimenting

1984. 150th Birth Anniv (1983) of Alfred Bernhard Nobel (inventor). Multicoloured.

N2408	20ch. Type **819**	3·00	45
N2409	30ch. Portrait of Nobel	3·00	45

820 Drinks, Tinned Food, Clothes and Flats

1984. Improvements of Living Standards.

N2411 **820** 10ch. multicoloured . . 55 10

821 Sunhwa School, Mangyongdae

1984. School of Kim Hyong Jik (Kim Il Sung's Father).

N2412 **821** 10ch. multicoloured . . 40 10

822 Armed Crowd with Banners

1984. 65th Anniv of Kuandian Conference.

N2413 **822** 10ch. multicoloured . . 40 10

823 "Thunia bracteata"

1984. Flowers. Multicoloured.

N2414	10ch. "Cattleya loddigesii"	1·00	10
N2415	20ch. Type **823**	1·25	25
N2416	30ch. "Phalaenopsis amabilis"	1·75	40

824 Swordfish and Trawler

1984. Fishing Industry. Multicoloured.
N2418 5ch. Type **824** 1·25 15
N2419 10ch. Blue marlin and trawler 1·75 25
N2420 40ch. Sailfish and game fishing launch 4·50 1·25

825 Revolutionary Museum, Chilgol

1984.
N2421 **825** 10ch. multicoloured 40 10

826 Kim Hyok, Cha Gwang Su and Youth

828 Clock Face

827 Inauguration of a French Railway Line, 1860

1984. "Let's All become the Kim Hyoks and Cha Gwang Sus of the '80s".
N2422 **826** 10ch. multicoloured 60 10

1984. Centenary (1983) of "Orient Express". Multicoloured.
N2423 10ch. Type **827** 1·40 25
N2424 20ch. Opening of a British railway line, "1821" 2·50 50
N2425 30ch. Inauguration of Paris–Rouen line, 1843 3·00 90

1984. Centenary of Greenwich Meridian.
N2427 **828** 10ch. multicoloured 2·50 1·00

829 Grand Theatre, Hamburg

830 Turning on Machinery

1984.
N2429 **829** 10ch. blue 40 10

1984. Automation of Industry.
N2430 **830** 40ch. multicoloured 60 30

831 "Dragon Angler"

1984. Paintings. Multicoloured.
N2431 10ch. Type **831** 1·00 10
N2432 20ch. "Ox Driver" (Kim Du Ryang) (47 × 35 mm) 1·25 25
N2433 30ch. "Bamboo" (Kim Jin U) (47 × 35 mm) 1·75 40

832 Tsiolkovsky

1984. K. E. Tsiolkovsky (space scientist). Mult.
N2435 20ch. Type **832** 90 25
N2436 30ch. "Sputnik" orbiting Earth 1·25 40

833 "Pongdaesan"

1984. Container Ships. Multicoloured.
N2438 10ch. Type **833** 95 10
N2439 20ch. "Ryongnamsan" 1·10 35
N2440 30ch. "Rungrado" 1·50 55

834 Caracal

1984. Animals. Multicoloured.
N2442 10ch. Spotted hyenas 60 10
N2443 20ch. Type **834** 90 25
N2444 30ch. Black-backed jackals 1·25 40
N2445 40ch. Foxes 1·60 60

835 Marie Curie

836 Chestnut-eared Aracari ("Toucan")

1984. 50th Anniv of Marie Curie (physicist).
N2447 **835** 10ch. multicoloured 2·00 25

1984. Birds. Multicoloured.
N2449 10ch. Hoopoe 1·40 20
N2450 20ch. South African crowned cranes ("Crowned Crane") 1·75 50
N2451 30ch. Saddle-bill stork ("Stork") 2·50 70
N2452 40ch. Type **836** 3·50 90

837 Cosmonaut

1984. Space Exploration. Multicoloured.
N2454 10ch. Type **837** 50 10
N2455 20ch. Cosmonaut on space-walk 75 25
N2456 30ch. Cosmonaut (different) 1·00 40

838 "Arktika"

1984. Russian Ice-breakers. Multicoloured.
N2458 20ch. Type **838** 1·25 35
N2459 30ch. "Ermak" 1·75 50

839 Mendeleev

1984. 150th Birth Anniv of Dmitri Mendeleev (chemist).
N2461 **839** 10ch. multicoloured 95 10

840 Kim Il Sung in U.S.S.R.

1984. Kim Il Sung's Visits to Eastern Europe. Multicoloured.
N2463 10ch. Type **840** 60 10
N2464 10ch. In Poland 60 10
N2465 10ch. In German Democratic Republic 60 10
N2466 10ch. In Czechoslovakia 60 10
N2467 10ch. In Hungary 60 10
N2468 10ch. In Bulgaria 60 10
N2469 10ch. In Rumania 60 10

841 Freesia

1985. New Year.
N2471 **841** 10ch. multicoloured 75 10

842 Journey Route, Steam Locomotive and Memorials

1985. 60th Anniv of 1000 ri Journey by Kim Il Sung. Multicoloured.
N2472 5ch. Type **842** 1·25 10
N2473 10ch. Boy trumpeter and schoolchildren following route 50 10
Nos. N2472/3 were issued together, se-tenant, forming a composite design.

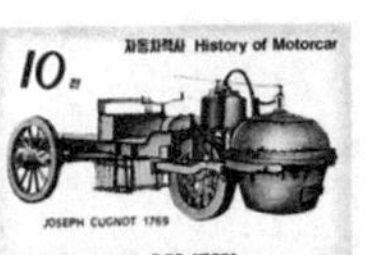

843 Cugnot's Steam Car, 1769

844 Camp, Mt. Paekdu

1985. History of the Motor Car (1st series). Multicoloured.
N2474 10ch. Type **843** 1·40 10
N2475 15ch. Goldsworthy Gurney steam omnibus, 1825 1·40 15
N2476 20ch. Gottlieb Daimler diesel car, 1885 1·40 25
N2477 25ch. Benz three-wheeled diesel car, 1886 1·60 35
N2478 30ch. Peugeot diesel car, 1891 2·00 40
See also Nos. N2562/6.

1985. Korean Revolution Headquarters.
N2480 **844** 10ch. multicoloured 40 20

845 Taechodo Lighthouse

846 Hedgehog challenges Tiger

1985. Lighthouses. Multicoloured.
N2481 10ch. Type **845** 1·75 10
N2482 20ch. Sodo 1·90 30
N2483 30ch. Pido 2·25 45
N2484 40ch. Suundo 2·75 70

1985. "The Hedgehog defeats the Tiger" (fable). Multicoloured.
N2485 10ch. Type **846** 60 10
N2486 20ch. Tiger goes to stamp on rolled-up hedgehog 90 25
N2487 30ch. Hedgehog clings to tiger's nose 1·25 40
N2488 35ch. Tiger flees 1·40 50
N2489 40ch. Tiger crawls before hedgehog 1·60 60

847 "Pleurotus cornucopiae"

848 West Germany v. Hungary, 1954

1985. Fungi. Multicoloured.
N2490 10ch. Type **847** 1·10 10
N2491 20ch. Oyster fungus 1·40 25
N2492 30ch. "Catathelasma ventricosum" 1·90 40

1985. World Cup Football Championship Finals.
N2493 **848** 10ch. black, buff & brn 60 10
N2494 – 10ch. multicoloured 60 10
N2495 – 20ch. black, buff & brn 90 25
N2496 – 20ch. multicoloured 90 25
N2497 – 30ch. black, buff & brn 1·25 40
N2498 – 30ch. multicoloured 1·25 40
N2499 – 40ch. black, buff & brn 1·60 60
N2500 – 40ch. multicoloured 1·60 60
DESIGNS—VERT: No. N2496 West Germany v. Netherlands, 1974; N2499, England v. West Germany, 1966. HORIZ: No. N2494, Brazil v. Italy, 1970; N2495, Brazil v. Sweden, 1958; N2497, Brazil v. Czechoslovakia, 1962; N2498, Argentina v. Netherlands, 1968; N2500, Italy v. West Germany, 1982.

849 Date and Kim Il Sung's Birthplace

850 Horn Player

1985. 73rd Birthday of Kim Il Sung.
N2502 **849** 10ch. multicoloured . . 40 10

1985. 4th-century Musical Instruments. Mult.
N2503 10ch. Type **850** . . . . . 1·40 10
N2504 20ch. So (pipes) player . . 1·40 25

851 Chongryon Hall, Tokyo **852** Common Marmoset

1985. 30th Anniv of Chongryon (General Association of Korean Residents in Japan).
N2505 **851** 10ch. brown 40 10

1985. Mammals. Multicoloured.
N2506 5ch. Type **852** 85 10
N2507 10ch. Ring-tailed lemur . . 85 10

854 Buenos Aires and Argentina 1982 Stamp **855** Dancer and Gymnast

1985. "Argentina '85" International Stamp Exhibition, Buenos Aires. Multicoloured.
N2509 10ch. Type **854** 75 10
N2510 20ch. Iguacu Falls and Argentina 1984 and North Korea 1978 stamps (horiz) . . . . . 2·50 25

1985. 12th World Youth and Students' Festival, Moscow. Multicoloured.
N2512 10ch. Type **855** 60 10
N2513 20ch. Spassky Tower, Moscow, and Festival emblem 90 25
N2514 40ch. Youths of different races . . . . 1·60 60

856 Peace Pavilion, Youth Park **857** Liberation Celebrations

1985. Pyongyang Buildings.
N2515 **856** 2ch. black and green 20 10
N2516 – 40ch. brown & lt brn 45 20
DESIGN: 40ch. Multi-storey flats, Chollima Street.

1985. 40th Anniv of Liberation.
N2517 – 5ch. red, black and blue 20 10
N2518 – 10ch. multicoloured . . 40 10
N2519 – 10ch. brown, blk & grn 40 10
N2520 – 10ch. multicoloured . . 40 10
N2521 **857** 10ch. yellow, blk & red 40 10
N2522 – 10ch. red, orange & blk 40 10
N2523 – 40ch. multicoloured . . 60 20
DESIGNS—HORIZ: No. N2517, Soldiers with rifles and flag; N2518, Crowd with banners and Flame of Juche; N2519, Korean and Soviet soldiers raising arms; N2520, Japanese soldiers laying down weapons; N2523, Students bearing banners. VERT: No. N2522, Liberation Tower, Moran Hill, Pyongyang.

858 Halley and Comet

1985. Appearance of Halley's Comet. Multicoloured.
N2525 10ch. Type **858** 90 10
N2526 20ch. Diagram of comet's flight and space probe 1·25 25

859 "Camellia japonica" **861** Party Founding Museum

860 "Hunting"

1985. Flowers. Multicoloured.
N2528 10ch. "Hippeastrum hybridum" 90 10
N2529 20ch. Type **859** . . . . . 1·25 25
N2530 30ch. "Cyclamen persicum" . . . . . . 1·75 40

1985. Koguryo Culture.
N2531 10ch. "Hero" (vert) . . . 60 10
N2532 15ch. "Heroine" (vert) . . 75 15
N2533 20ch. "Flying Fairy" . . . 90 25
N2534 25ch. Type **860** . . . . . 1·10 35

1985. 40th Anniv of Korean Workers' Party. Multicoloured.
N2536 5ch. Type **861** 20 10
N2537 10ch. Soldier with gun and workers 40 10
N2538 10ch. Soldiers and flag . . 40 10
N2539 40ch. Statue of worker, peasant and intellectual holding aloft party emblem 60 20

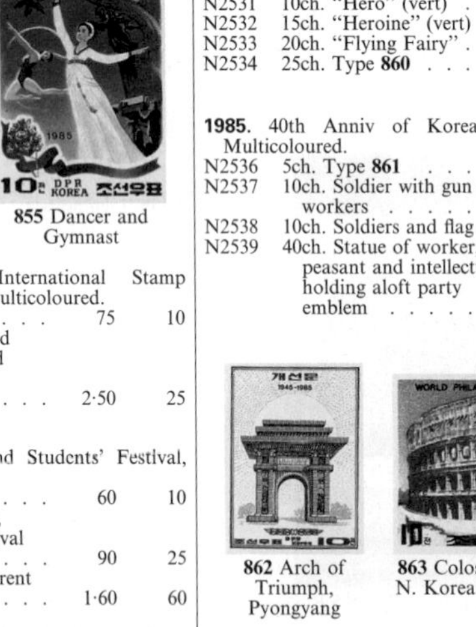

862 Arch of Triumph, Pyongyang **863** Colosseum, Rome, and N. Korea 1975 10ch. Stamp

1985. 40th Anniv of Kim Il Sung's Return.
N2541 **862** 10ch. brown and green 40 10

1985. "Italia '85" International Stamp Exhibition, Rome. Multicoloured.
N2542 10ch. Type **863** 60 10
N2543 20ch. "The Holy Family" (Raphael) (vert) 90 25
N2544 30ch. Head of "David" (statue, Michelangelo) (vert) . . . . 1·25 40

864 Mercedes Benz Type "300"

1985. South-West German Stamp Fair, Sindelfingen. Multicoloured.
N2546 10ch. Type **864** . . . . . 1·00 10
N2547 15ch. Mercedes Benz Type "770" . . . . . . 1·40 15
N2548 20ch. Mercedes Benz "W 150" . . . . 1·75 25
N2549 30ch. Mercedes Type "600" . . . . . . 2·00 40

865 Tackle

1985. World Cup Football Championship, Mexico (1st issue). Multicoloured.
N2551 20ch. Type **865** . . . . . 1·10 25
N2552 30ch. Three players . . . 1·40 40
See also Nos. N2558/9 and N2577/82.

866 Dancers

1985. International Youth Year. Multicoloured.
N2554 10ch. Type **866** 60 10
N2555 20ch. Sports activities . . 90 25
N2556 30ch. Technology . . . . 1·25 40

867 Players

1985. World Cup Football Championship, Mexico (2nd issue). Multicoloured.
N2558 20ch. Type **867** . . . . . 1·25 25
N2559 30ch. Goalkeeper and players . . . . 1·60 40

868 Juche Torch **869** Amedee Bollee and Limousine, 1901

1986. New Year.
N2561 **868** 10ch. multicoloured . . 40 10

1986. History of the Motor Car (2nd series). Multicoloured.
N2562 10ch. Type **869** 75 10
N2563 20ch. Stewart Rolls, Henry Royce and "Silver Ghost", 1906 . . . . . 1·25 25
N2564 25ch. Giovanni Agnelli and Fiat car, 1912 . . . 1·40 35
N2565 30ch. Ettore Bugatti and "Royal" coupe, 1928 . . 1·60 40
N2566 40ch. Louis Renault and fiacre, 1906 . . . . . . 2·25 60

870 Gary Kasparov **872** Tongdu Rock, Songgan

871 Cemetery Gate

1986. World Chess Championship, Moscow.
N2568 **870** 20ch. multicoloured . . 2·25 25

1986. Revolutionary Martyrs' Cemetery, Pyongyang. Multicoloured.
N2570 5ch. Type **871** 20 10
N2571 10ch. Bronze sculpture (detail) 55 10

1986. 37th Anniv of Pres. Kim Il Sung's Visit to Songgan Revolutionary Site.
N2572 **872** 10ch. multicoloured . . 40 10

873 Buddhist Scriptures Museum

1986. Mt. Myohyang Buildings.
N2573 **873** 10ch. brown and green 40 10
N2574 – 20ch. violet and red . . 50 10
DESIGN: 20ch. Taeung Hall.

874 Tomato Anemonefish

1986. Fishes. Multicoloured.
N2575 10ch. Pennant coralfish . . 1·50 20
N2576 20ch. Type **874** . . . . . 2·25 45

875 Footballers and Flags of Italy, Bulgaria and Argentina

1986. World Cup Football Championship, Mexico (3rd issue). Designs showing footballers and flags of participating countries. Multicoloured.
N2577 10ch. Type **875** 60 10
N2578 20ch. Mexico, Belgium, Paraguay and Iraq . . . 90 25
N2579 25ch. France, Canada, U.S.S.R. and Hungary 1·10 35
N2580 30ch. Brazil, Spain, Algeria and Northern Ireland . . . . 1·25 40
N2581 35ch. West Germany, Uruguay, Scotland and Denmark . . . . 1·40 50
N2582 40ch. Poland, Portugal, Morocco and England 1·60 60

876 Singer, Pianist and Emblem

1986. 4th Spring Friendship Art Festival, Pyongyang.
N2584 **876** 1wn. multicoloured . . 1·25 55

877 Daimler "Motorwagen", 1886 **878** Mangyong Hill

1986. 60th Anniv of Mercedes-Benz (car manufacturers). Multicoloured.
N2585 10ch. Type **877** 75 10
N2586 10ch. Benz "velo", 1894 75 10
N2587 20ch. Mercedes car, 1901 1·00 25
N2588 20ch. Benz limousine, 1909 1·00 25
N2589 30ch. Mercedes "tourenwagen", 1914 . . 1·40 40
N2590 30ch. Mercedes-Benz "170" 6-cylinder, 1931 1·40 40
N2591 40ch. Mercedes-Benz "380", 1933 . . . . . 1·75 60
N2592 40ch. Mercedes-Benz "540 K", 1936 . . . . 1·75 60

1986. 74th Birthday of Kim Il Sung.
N2594 **878** 10ch. multicoloured . . 30 10

879 Crowd

1968. 50th Anniv of Association for the Restoration of the Fatherland.
N2595 **879** 10ch. multicoloured . . 30 10

880 Dove carrying Letter

1986. International Peace Year. Multicoloured.
N2596 10ch. Type **880** 50 10
N2597 20ch. U.N. Headquarters, New York 80 25
N2598 30ch. Dove, globe and broken missiles . . . . 1·10 40

881 "Mona Lisa" (Leonardo da Vinci)

1986.
N2600 **881** 20ch. multicoloured . . 90 25

882 Pink Iris **883** Kim Un Suk

1986. Irises. Multicoloured.
N2601 20ch. Type **882** . . . . . 1·25 25
N2602 30ch. Violet iris . . . . . 1·75 40

1986. Tennis Players. Multicoloured.
N2604 10ch. Type **883** (postage) 2·00 35
N2605 20ch. Ivan Lendl . . . . 2·00 35
N2606 30ch. Steffi Graf . . . . . 2·00 35
N2607 50ch. Boris Becker (air) 2·00 35

884 Sulphur-crested Cockatoo ("Cockatoo")

1986. "Stampex '86" Stamp Exhibition, Adelaide, Australia.
N2608 **884** 10ch. multicoloured . . 1·60 20

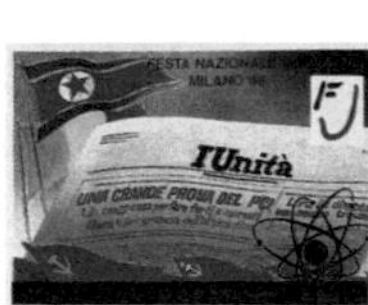

885 First Issue of "L'Unita" **886** "Express II" (icebreaker) and Sweden 1872 20 ore Stamp

1986. National "L'Unita" (Italian Communist Party newspaper) Festival, Milan. Multicoloured.
N2610 10ch. Type **885** 60 10
N2611 20ch. Milan Cathedral . . 90 25
N2612 30ch. "Pieta" (Michelangelo) (vert) . . 1·25 40

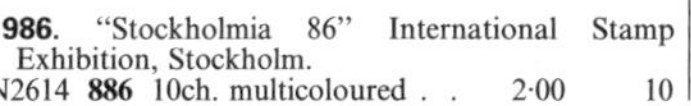
1986. "Stockholmia 86" International Stamp Exhibition, Stockholm.
N2614 **886** 10ch. multicoloured . . 2·00 10

887 Reprint of First Stamp

1986. 40th Anniv of First North Korean Stamps (1st issue). Multicoloured.
N2616 10ch. Type **887** (postage) 75 10
N2617 15ch. Imperforate reprint of first stamp 50 35
N2618 50ch. 1946 50ch. violet stamp (air) . . . . . . 2·00 75
See also Nos. N2619/21.

888 Postal Emblems and 1962 and 1985 Stamps

1986. 40th Anniv of First North Korean Stamps (2nd issue). Multicoloured.
N2619 10ch. Type **888** (postage) 2·00 25
N2620 15ch. General Post Office and 1976 and 1978 stamps . . . . 2·00 35
N2621 50ch. Kim Il Sung, first stamp and reprint (vert) (air) . . . . 1·60 45

1986. World Cup Football Championship Results. Nos. N2577/82 optd **1st: ARG 2nd: FRG 3rd: FRA 4th: BEL**.
N2622 10ch. multicoloured . . . 80 10
N2623 20ch. multicoloured . . . 1·10 25
N2624 25ch. multicoloured . . . 1·40 35
N2625 30ch. multicoloured . . . 1·50 40
N2626 35ch. multicoloured . . . 1·60 50
N2627 40ch. multicoloured . . . 1·90 60

890 Flag and Man with raised Fist **892** Schoolchildren

891 Gift Animals House

1986. 60th Anniv of Down-with-Imperialism Union.
N2629 **890** 10ch. multicoloured . . 30 10

1986. 1st Anniv of Gift Animals House, Central Zoo, Pyongyang.
N2630 **891** 2wn. multicoloured . . 3·00 1·10

1986. 40th Anniv of U.N.E.S.C.O. Multicoloured.
N2631 10ch. Type **892** 60 10
N2632 50ch. Anniversary emblem, Grand People's Study House and telecommunications (horiz) . . . . 1·50 75

893 Communications Satellite

1986. 15th Anniv of Intersputnik.
N2633 **893** 5wn. multicoloured . . 7·00 3·00

894 Oil tanker leaving Lock

1986. West Sea Barrage.
N2634 **894** 10ch. multicoloured . . 50 10
N2635 – 40ch. grn, blk & gold 1·25 20
N2636 – 1wn. 20 multicoloured 2·75 60
DESIGNS: 20ch. Aerial view of dam; 1wn.20, Aerial view of lock.

895 Common Morel

1986. Minerals and Fungi. Multicoloured.
N2637 10ch. Lengenbachite (postage) . . . . . . 2·00 25
N2638 10ch. Common funnel cap 2·00 25
N2639 15ch. Rhodochrosite . . . 2·00 25
N2640 15ch. Type **895** . . . . . 2·00 25
N2641 50ch. Annabergite (air) . . 2·00 25
N2642 50ch. Blue russula . . . . 2·00 25

896 Machu Picchu, Peru, and N. Korea Taedong Gate Stamp

1986. North Korean Three-dimensional Photographs and Stamps Exhibition, Lima, Peru.
N2643 **896** 10ch. multicoloured . . 1·25 20

897 Pine Tree **898** "Pholiota adiposa"

1987. New Year. Multicoloured.
N2645 10ch. Type **897** 75 15
N2646 40ch. Hare 90 25

1987. Fungi. Multicoloured.
N2647 10ch. Type **898** . . . . . 1·50 20
N2648 20ch. Chanterelle . . . . 1·75 20
N2649 30ch. "Boletus impolitus" 2·00 30

899 Kim Ok Song (composer) **901** East Pyongyang Grand Theatre

1987. Musicians' Death Anniversaries. Mult.
N2651 10ch. Maurice Ravel (composer, 50th anniv) 1·50 20
N2652 10ch. Type **899** (22nd anniv) . . . . 1·50 20
N2653 20ch. Giovanni Lully (composer, 300th anniv) 1·50 20
N2654 30ch. Franz Liszt (composer, centenary (1986)) . . . . 1·50 20
N2655 40ch. Violins (250th anniv of Antonio Stradivari (violin maker)) . . . . 1·50 20
N2656 40ch. Christoph Gluck (composer, bicent) . . . 1·50 20

1987. Buildings.
N2658 **901** 5ch. green 35 10
N2659 – 10ch. brown 45 10
N2660 – 3wn. blue . . . . . . 3·00 90
DESIGNS—VERT: 10ch. Pyongyang Koryo Hotel. HORIZ: 3wn. Rungnado Stadium.

902 "Gorch Fock" (German cadet barque)

1987. Sailing Ships. Multicoloured.
N2661 20ch. Type **902** (postage) 70 20
N2662 30ch. "Tovarishch" (Russian cadet barque) (vert) . . . . 1·00 30
N2663 50ch. "Belle Poule" (cadet schooner) (vert) (air) . . 1·50 50
N2664 50ch. "Sagres II" (Portuguese cadet barque) (vert) . . . . . 1·50 50
N2665 1wn. Koryo period merchantman . . . . . 3·00 1·00
N2666 1wn. "Dar Mlodziezy" (Polish cadet full-rigged ship) (vert) . . . . . . 3·00 1·00

903 Road Signs

1987. Road Safety.
N2667 **903** 10ch. blue, red and black (postage) . . . 1·00 10
N2668 – 10ch. red and black . . 1·00 10
N2669 – 20ch. blue, red & black 1·25 20
N2670 – 50ch. red and black (air) . . . . 1·50 50
DESIGNS: Nos. N2668/70, Different road signs.

904 Fire Engine

1987. Fire Engines.
N2671 **904** 10ch. mult (postage) 1·75 25
N2672 – 20ch. multicoloured . . 1·90 25
N2673 – 30ch. multicoloured . . 2·50 30
N2674 – 50ch. multicoloured (air) . . . . 3·25 50
DESIGNS: N2672/4, 20ch. to 50ch. Different machines.

905 "Apatura ilia" and Spiraea

1987. Butterflies and Flowers. Multicoloured.
N2675 10ch. Type **905** 70 10
N2676 10ch. "Ypthima argus" and fuchsia 70 10
N2677 20ch. "Neptis philyra" and aquilegia . . . . . 1·00 20
N2678 20ch. "Papilio protenor" and chrysanthemum . . 1·00 20
N2679 40ch. "Parantica sita" and celosia . . . . 1·60 40
N2680 40ch. "Vanessa indica" and hibiscus . . . . . 1·60 40

906 Association Monument, Pyongyang **907** Doves, Emblem and Tree

1987. 70th Anniv of Korean National Association (independence movement).
N2681 **906** 10ch. red, silver & black 25 10

1987. 5th Spring Friendship Art Festival, Pyongyang.
N2682 **907** 10ch. multicoloured . . 25 10

908 Mangyong Hill **909** Bay

1987. 75th Birthday of Kim Il Sung. Mult.
N2683 10ch. Type **908** 25 10
N2684 10ch. Kim Il Sung's birthplace, Mangyongdae (horiz) 25 10
N2685 10ch. "A Bumper Crop of Pumpkins" (62 × 41 mm) 25 10
N2686 10ch. "Profound Affection for the Working Class" 25 10

1987. Horses. Multicoloured.
N2687 10ch. Type **909** 40 10
N2688 10ch. Bay (different) . . . 40 10
N2689 40ch. Grey rearing . . . . 1·25 40
N2690 40ch. Grey on beach . . . 1·25 40

910 "Sputnik 1" (first artificial satellite)

1987. Transport. Multicoloured.
N2691 10ch. "Juche" high speed train (horiz) 40 10
N2692 10ch. Electric locomotive "Mangyongdae" (horiz) 40 10
N2693 10ch. Type **910** (30th anniv of flight) 40 10
N2694 20ch. Laika (30th anniv of first animal in space) . . 70 20
N2695 20ch. Tupolev Tu-144 supersonic airliner (horiz) 70 20
N2696 20ch. Concorde (11th anniv of first commercial flight) (horiz) 70 20
N2697 30ch. Count Ferdinand von Zeppelin (70th death anniv) and airship LZ-4 (horiz) . . . . . 1·00 30
N2698 80ch. Zeppelin and diagrams and drawings of airships (horiz) . . . 3·00 1·00

911 Musk Ox

1987. "Capex '87" International Stamp Exhibition, Toronto. Multicoloured.
N2699 10ch. Type **911** 65 10
N2700 40ch. Jacques Cartier, his ship "Grande Hermine" and "Terry Fox" (ice-breaker) (horiz) . . . . 1·75 40
N2701 60ch. Ice hockey (Winter Olympics, Calgary, 1988) (horiz) . . . . . 1·75 60

912 Trapeze Artistes

1987. International Circus Festival, Monaco. Multicoloured.
N2702 10ch. Type **912** 40 10
N2703 10ch. "Brave Sailors" (North Korean acrobatic act) (vert) . . 40 10
N2704 20ch. Clown and elephant (vert) 70 20
N2705 20ch. North Korean artiste receiving "Golden Clown" award 70 20
N2706 40ch. Performing horses and cat act . . . . . . 2·10 40
N2707 50ch. Prince Rainier and his children applauding 1·50 50

913 Attack on Watch Tower

1987. 50th Anniv of Battle of Pochonbo.
N2708 **913** 10ch. brown, black and ochre 25 10

914 Sports

1987. Angol Sports Village.
N2709 **914** 5ch. brown and gold 15 10
N2710 – 10ch. blue and gold . . 25 10
N2711 – 40ch. brown and gold 75 25
N2712 – 70ch. blue and gold . . 1·25 40
N2713 – 1wn. red and gold . . 1·90 60
N2714 – 1wn.20 violet . . . . 2·25 70
DESIGNS: Exteriors of—10ch. Indoor swimming pool; 40ch. Weightlifting gymnasium; 70ch. Table tennis gymnasium; 1wn. Football stadium; 1wn.20, Handball gymnasium.

915 Mandarins

1987. Mandarins. Multicoloured.
N2715 20ch. Type **915** . . . . . 1·50 40
N2716 20ch. Mandarins on shore 1·50 40
N2717 20ch. Mandarins on branch . . . . 1·50 40
N2718 40ch. Mandarins in water 2·25 60

916 Exhibition Site and 1987 3wn. Stamp

1987. "Olymphilex '87" Olympic Stamps Exhibition, Rome.
N2719 **916** 10ch. multicoloured . . 90 10

917 Underground Station and Guard

1987. Railway Uniforms. Multicoloured.
N2721 10ch. Type **917** 40 10
N2722 10ch. Underground train and station supervisor 40 10
N2723 20ch. Guard and electric train 60 15
N2724 30ch. Guard with flag and electric train 85 20
N2725 40ch. "Orient Express" guard and steam locomotive . . . . . . 1·10 25
N2726 40ch. German ticket controller and diesel train . . . . 1·10 25

918 White Stork **920** Victory Column

919 Ice Skating

1987. "Hafnia 87" International Stamp Exhibition, Copenhagen. Multicoloured.
N2727 40ch. Type **918** . . . . . 2·40 50
N2728 60ch. "Danmark" (cadet full-rigged ship) and "Little Mermaid", Copenhagen . . . . . 1·75 40

1987. Winter Olympic Games, Calgary (1988). Multicoloured.
N2729 40ch. Type **919** . . . . . 1·00 30
N2730 40ch. Ski jumping . . . . 1·00 30
N2731 40ch. Skiing (value on left) (horiz) . . . . 1·00 30
N2732 40ch. Skiing (value on right) (horiz) . . . . . 1·00 30

1987. 750th Anniv of Berlin and "Philatelia '87" International Stamp Exhibition, Cologne. Mult.
N2734 10ch. Type **920** 40 10
N2735 20ch. Reichstag (horiz) . . 70 20
N2736 30ch. Pfaueninsel Castle 1·00 30
N2737 40ch. Charlottenburg Castle (horiz) . . . . . 1·25 40

921 Garros and Bleriot XI

1987. Birth Centenary of Roland Garros (aviator) and Tennis as an Olympic Sport. Multicoloured.
N2739 20ch. Type **921** . . . . . 1·50 20
N2740 20ch. Ivan Lendl (tennis player) . . . . 2·25 20
N2741 40ch. Steffi Graf (tennis player) . . . . 3·00 40

923 Pyongyang Buildings

1988. New Year. Multicoloured.
N2744 10ch. Type **923** 20 10
N2745 40ch. Dragon 75 25

924 Banner and Newspaper **925** Birthplace, Mt. Paekdu

1988. 60th Anniv of "Saenal" Newspaper.
N2746 **924** 10ch. multicoloured . . 45 10

1988. Kim Jong Il's Birthday.
N2747 **925** 10ch. multicoloured . . 20 10

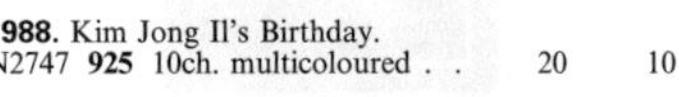

926 Henry Dunant (founder)

1988. 125th Anniv of International Red Cross. Multicoloured.
N2749 10ch. Type **926** 75 10
N2750 20ch. North Korean Red Cross emblem and map 1·00 15
N2751 20ch. International Committee headquarters, Geneva 1·10 15
N2752 40ch. Pyongyang Maternity Hospital, doctor and baby . . . . 1·25 25

927 "Santa Maria"

1988. 500th Anniv (1992) of Discovery of America by Christopher Columbus. Multicoloured.
N2754 10ch. Type **927** . . . . . 1·25 10
N2755 20ch. "Pinta" . . . . . . 1·25 20
N2756 30ch. "Nina" . . . . . . 1·25 30
Nos. N2754/6 were issued together, se-tenant, forming a composite design of Columbus's ships leaving Palos.

928 Montgolfier Balloon and Modern Hot-air Balloons **929** Dancers

1988. "Juvalux '88" International Youth Stamp Exhibition, Luxembourg. Multicoloured.
N2758 40ch. Type **928** 90 25
N2759 60ch. Steam locomotive and railway map of Luxembourg, 1900 . . . 1·60 35

1988. 6th Spring Friendship Art Festival, Pyongyang. Multicoloured.
N2760 10ch. Singer (poster) . . . 20 10
N2761 1wn.20 Type **929** . . . . 1·90 75

930 Inaugural Congress Emblem
931 Birthplace, Mangyongdae

1988. 10th Anniv of International Institute of the Juche Idea.

N2762 **930** 10ch. multicoloured . . 20 10

1988. 76th Birthday of Kim Il Sung.

N2763 **931** 10ch. multicoloured . . 20 10

932 "Urho" (ice-breaker)

1988. "Finlandia 88" International Stamp Exhibition, Helsinki. Multicoloured.

N2765 40ch. Type **932** 1·40 25

N2766 60ch. Matti Nykaenen (Olympic Games ski-jumping medallist) 1·10 35

933 Postcard for 1934 Championship
934 Emblem

1988. World Cup Football Championship, Italy (1st issue). Multicoloured.

N2767 10ch. Football match 50 10

N2768 20ch. Type **933** 85 15

N2769 30ch. Player tackling (horiz) 1·25 20

See also Nos. N2924/7.

1988. 13th World Youth and Students' Festival, Pyongyang (1st issue). Multicoloured.

N2771 5ch. Type **934** 10 10

N2772 10ch. Dancer 40 10

N2773 10ch. Gymnast and gymnasium, Angol Sports Village 20 10

N2774 10ch. Map of Korea, globe and doves 30 10

N2775 10ch. Finger pointing at shattered nuclear rockets 75 10

N2776 1wn.20 Three differently coloured hands and dove 2·10 75

See also Nos. N2860/3 and N2879/80.

935 Fairy
936 Mallards

1988. "Eight Fairies of Mt. Kumgang" (tale). Multicoloured.

N2777 10ch. Type **935** 20 10

N2778 15ch. Fairy at pool and fairies on rainbow 30 10

N2779 20ch. Fairy and woodman husband 40 15

N2780 25ch. Couple with baby 70 20

N2781 30ch. Couple with son and daughter 55 20

N2782 35ch. Family on rainbow 1·00 35

1988. "Praga '88" International Stamp Exhibition, Prague. Multicoloured.

N2783 20ch. Type **936** 1·90 25

N2784 40ch. Vladimir Remek (Czechoslovak cosmonaut) 75 25

937 Red Crossbill

1988. Birds. Multicoloured.

N2785 10ch. Type **937** 70 20

N2786 15ch. Common stonechat 1·00 30

N2787 20ch. Eurasian nuthatch 1·40 35

N2788 25ch. Great spotted woodpecker 1·60 45

N2789 30ch. River kingfisher 2·00 50

N2790 35ch. Bohemian waxwing 2·10 65

938 Fair Emblem

1988. 40th International Stamp Fair, Riccione.

N2791 **938** 20ch. multicoloured 40 15

939 Emu

1988. Bicentenary of Australian Settlement. Mult.

N2793 10ch. Type **939** 60 15

N2794 15ch. Satin bowerbirds 85 20

N2795 25ch. Laughing kookaburra (vert) 1·40 35

940 Floating Crane "5-28"

1988. Ships. Multicoloured.

N2797 10ch. Type **940** 40 15

N2798 20ch. Freighter "Hwanggumsan" 60 20

N2799 30ch. Freighter "Changjasan Chongnyon-ho" 75 25

N2800 40ch. Liner "Samjiyon" 1·00 30

941 "Hansa"

1988. 150th Birth Anniv of Count Ferdinand von Zeppelin (airship pioneer). Multicoloured.

N2801 10ch. Type **941** 40 10

N2802 20ch. "Schwaben" 75 15

N2803 30ch. "Viktoria Luise" 90 20

N2804 40ch. LZ-3 1·25 25

942 Kim Il Sung and Jambyn Batmunkh

1988. Kim Il Sung's Visit to Mongolia.

N2806 **942** 10ch. multicoloured 20 10

943 Hero and Labour Hero of the D.P.R.K. Medals

1988. National Heroes Congress.

N2807 **943** 10ch. multicoloured 20 10

944 Tower of Juche Idea

1988. 40th Anniv of Democratic Republic. Multicoloured.

N2808 5ch. Type **944** 10 10

N2809 10ch. Smelter and industrial buildings 20 10

N2810 10ch. Soldier and Mt. Paekdu 20 10

N2811 10ch. Map of Korea and globe 20 10

N2812 10ch. Hand holding banner, globe and doves 20 10

945 "Sunflowers" (Vincent van Gogh)
946 Emblem 

1988. "Filacept 88" Stamp Exhibition, The Hague. Multicoloured.

N2814 40ch. Type **945** 1·50 25

N2815 60ch. "The Chess Game" (Lucas van Leyden) (horiz) 2·50 35

1988. 16th Session of Socialist Countries' Post and Telecommunications Conference, Pyongyang.

N2816 **946** 10ch. multicoloured 20 10

947 Chaju "82" 10-ton Truck
948 "Owl"

1988. Tipper Trucks. Multicoloured.

N2817 20ch. Type **947** 40 15

N2818 40ch. Kumsusan-ho 40-ton truck 75 25

1988. Paintings by O Un Byol. Multicoloured.

N2819 10ch. Type **948** 2·25 25

N2820 15ch. "Dawn" (red junglefowl) 1·00 25

N2821 20ch. "Beautiful Rose received by Kim Il Sung" 60 15

N2822 25ch. "Sun and Bamboo" 75 15

N2823 30ch. "Autumn" (fruit tree) 1·10 35

949 "Chunggi" Steam Locomotive No. 35

1988. Railway Locomotives. Multicoloured.

N2824 10ch. Type **949** 70 10

N2825 20ch. "Chunggi" steam locomotive No. 22 95 15

N2826 30ch. "Chongiha" electric locomotive No. 3 1·10 20

N2827 40ch. "Chunggi" steam locomotive No. 307 1·40 25

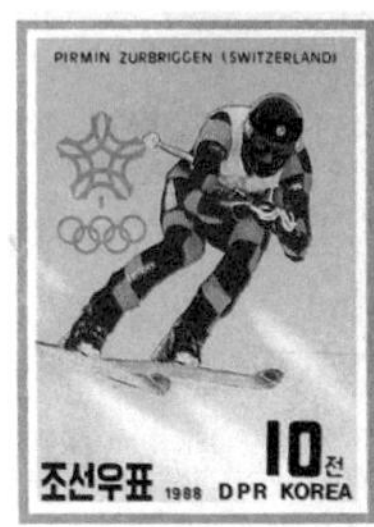

950 Pirmen Zurbriggen (downhill skiing)

1988. Winter Olympic Games, Calgary, Medal Winners. Multicoloured.

N2828 10ch. Type **950** 20 10

N2829 20ch. Yvonne van Gennip (speed skating) 40 15

N2830 30ch. Marjo Matikainen (cross-country skiing) 55 20

N2831 40ch. U.S.S.R. (ice hockey) (horiz) 75 25

951 Yuri Gagarin

1988. 1st Man and Woman in Space. Mult.

N2833 20ch. Type **951** 40 15

N2834 40ch. Valentina Tereshkova 75 25

952 Nehru
953 Chollima Statue

1988. Birth Centenary of Jawaharlal Nehru (Indian statesman) and "India 89" International Stamp Exhibition, New Delhi.

N2835 **952** 20ch. purple, black and gold 60 15

1989. New Year. Multicoloured.

N2837 10ch. Type **953** 20 10

N2838 20ch. "The Dragon Angler" (17th-century painting) 60 15

N2839 40ch. "Tortoise and Serpent" (Kangso tomb painting) (horiz) 90 25

954 Archery

1989. National Defence Training. Multicoloured.

N2840	10ch. Type **954**	90	10
N2841	15ch. Rifle shooting	30	10
N2842	20ch. Pistol shooting	40	15
N2843	25ch. Parachuting	50	15
N2844	30ch. Launching model glider	55	20

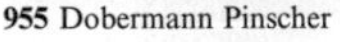
955 Dobermann Pinscher   **957** Agriculture

1989. Animals presented to Kim Il Sung. Mult.

N2845	10ch. Type **955**	50	10
N2846	20ch. Labrador	70	15
N2847	25ch. German shepherd	1·00	15
N2848	30ch. Rough collies (horiz)	1·00	20
N2849	35ch. Serval (horiz)	1·25	20

1989. 25th Anniv of Publication of "Theses on the Socialist Rural Question in our Country" by Kim Il Sung.

N2852	**957** 10ch. multicoloured	40	10

958 The Gypsy and Grapes   **959** Korean Girl

1989. Fungi and Fruits. Multicoloured.

N2853	10ch. Type **958**	50	10
N2854	20ch. Caesar's mushroom and magnolia vine	80	15
N2855	25ch. "Lactarius hygrophoides" and "Eleagnus crispa"	1·10	15
N2856	30ch. "Agaricus placomyces" and Chinese gooseberries	1·25	20
N2857	35ch. Horse mushroom and "Lycium chinense"	1·50	20
N2858	40ch. Elegant boletus and "Juglans cordiformis"	1·75	25

1989. 13th World Youth and Students' Festival, Pyongyang (2nd issue). Multicoloured.

N2860	10ch. Type **959**	20	10
N2861	20ch. Children of different races	40	15
N2862	30ch. Fairy and rainbow	55	20
N2863	40ch. Young peoples and Tower of Juche Idea	45	25

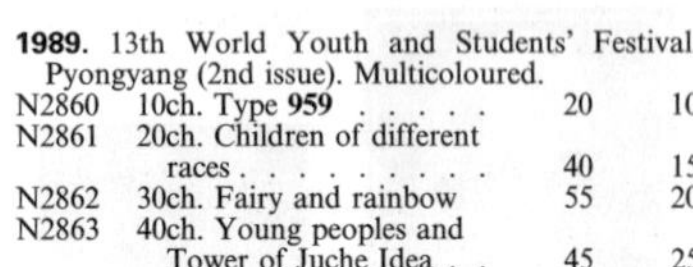

960 "Parnassius eversmanni"

1969. Insects. Multicoloured.

N2864	10ch. Type **960**	50	15
N2865	15ch. "Colias heos"	60	15
N2866	20ch. "Dilipa fenestra"	70	15
N2867	25ch. "Buthus martensis"	80	15
N2868	30ch. "Trichogramma ostriniae"	95	15
N2869	40ch. "Damaster constricticollis"	1·00	15

961 Dancers (poster)   **962** Birthplace, Mangyongdae

1989. Spring Friendship Art Festival, Pyongyang.

N2871	**961** 10ch. multicoloured	45	10

1989. 77th Birthday of Kim Il Sung.

N2872	**962** 10ch. multicoloured	20	10

963 Battle Plan and Monument to the Victory

1989. 50th Anniv of Battle of the Musan Area.

N2873	**963** 10ch. blue, flesh and red	60	10

964 Modern Dance

1989. Chamo System of Dance Notation. Multicoloured.

N2874	10ch. Type **964**	55	10
N2875	20ch. Ballet	70	15
N2876	25ch. Modern dance (different)	85	15
N2877	30ch. Traditional dance	1·00	20

965 Hands supporting Torch   **966** Victorious Badger

1989. 13th World Youth and Students' Festival, Pyongyang (3rd issue).

N2879	**965** 5ch. blue	10	10
N2880	– 10ch. brown	20	10

DESIGN: 10ch. Youth making speech.

1989. "Badger measures the Height" (cartoon film). Multicoloured.

N2881	10ch. Cat, bear and badger race to flag pole	80	10
N2882	40ch. Cat and bear climb pole while badger measures shadow	1·25	25
N2883	50ch. Type **966**	1·50	30

967 Kyongju Observatory and Star Chart   **969** Pele (footballer) and 1978 25ch. Stamp

1989. Astronomy.

N2884	**967** 20ch. multicoloured	1·00	15

1989. "Brasiliana 89" International Stamp Exhibition, Rio de Janeiro.

N2887	**969** 40ch. multicoloured	1·25	25

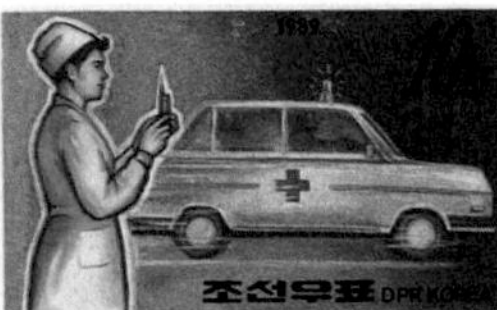
970 Nurse and Ambulance

1989. Emergency Services. Multicoloured.

N2888	10ch. Type **970**	20	10
N2889	20ch. Surgeon and ambulance	30	15
N2890	30ch. Fireman and fire engine	2·25	20
N2891	40ch. Fireman and engine (different)	2·25	25

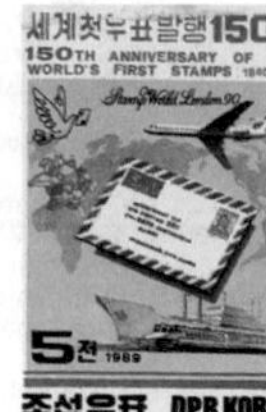
971 Kaffir Lily   **972** Air Mail Letter and Postal Transport

1989. Plants presented to Kim Il Sung. Mult.

N2892	10ch. Type **971**	40	10
N2893	15ch. Tulips	50	10
N2894	20ch. Flamingo lily	75	15
N2895	25ch. "Rhododendron obtusum"	90	15
N2896	30ch. Daffodils	1·00	20

1989. 150th Anniv of the Penny Black and "Stamp World London 90" International Stamp Exhibition (1st issue). Multicoloured.

N2898	5ch. Type **972**	40	10
N2899	10ch. Post box and letters	55	10
N2900	20ch. Stamps, tweezers and magnifying glass	60	15
N2901	30ch. First North Korean stamps	75	20
N2902	40ch. Universal Postal Union emblem and headquarters, Berne	1·00	25
N2903	50ch. Sir Rowland Hill and Penny Black	1·25	30

See also No. N2956.

973 "Bistorta incana"

1989. Alpine Flowers. Multicoloured.

N2904	10ch. "Iris setosa"	50	10
N2905	15ch. "Aquilegia japonica"	60	10
N2906	20ch. Type **973**	75	15
N2907	25ch. "Rodiola elongata"	90	15
N2908	30ch. "Sanguisorba sitchensis"	95	20

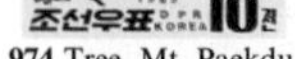
974 Tree, Mt. Paekdu   **975** Skipping

1989. Slogan-bearing Trees (1st series). Mult.

N2910	10ch. Type **974**	20	10
N2911	3wn. Tree, Oun-dong, Pyongyang	5·50	1·75
N2912	5wn. Tree, Mt. Kanbaek	9·50	3·25

See also No. N2931.

1989. Children's Games. Multicoloured.

N2913	10ch. Type **975**	20	10
N2914	20ch. Windmill	1·25	15
N2915	30ch. Kite	55	20
N2916	40ch. Whip and top	75	25

977 Diesel Train and Sinpa Youth Station

1989. Railway Locomotives. Multicoloured.

N2918	10ch. Type **977**	40	10
N2919	20ch. "Pulgungi" electric locomotive	60	15
N2920	25ch. Diesel goods train	70	15
N2921	30ch. Diesel train	85	20
N2922	40ch. Steam locomotive	1·00	25
N2923	50ch. Steam locomotive (different)	1·10	30

978 Players and Map of Italy

1989. World Cup Football Championship, Italy (2nd issue). Multicoloured.

N2924	10ch. Type **978**	1·00	10
N2925	20ch. Free kick	50	15
N2926	30ch. Goal mouth scrimmage	75	20
N2927	40ch. Goalkeeper diving for ball	95	25

979 Magellan (navigator) and his Ship "Vitoria"

1989. "Descobrex '89" International Stamp Exhibition, Portugal.

N2928	**979** 30ch. multicoloured	1·25	20

980 Mangyong Hill and Pine Branches   **981** Ryukwoli

1990. New Year. Multicoloured.

N2929	10ch. Type **980**	20	10
N2930	20ch. Koguryo mounted archers	90	15

1990. Slogan-bearing Trees (2nd series). As T **974**. Multicoloured.

N2931	5ch. Tree, Mt. Paekdu	25	10

1990. Dogs. Multicoloured.

N2932	20ch. Type **981**	1·25	20
N2933	30ch. Palryuki	1·25	20
N2934	40ch. Komdungi	1·25	20
N2935	50ch. Oulruki	1·25	20

982 Birthplace, Mt. Paekdu   **983** Stone Instruments and Primitive Man

1990. Birthday of Kim Jong Il.

N2936	**982** 10ch. brown	20	10

1990. Evolution of Man. Multicoloured.

N2937	10ch. Type **983**	45	10
N2938	40ch. Palaeolithic and Neolithic man	90	25

984 Rungna Bridge, Pyongyang

1990. Bridges. Multicoloured.

N2939	10ch. Type **984**	45	10
N2940	20ch. Potong bridge, Pyongyang	60	15
N2941	30ch. Sinuiji-Ryucho Island Bridge	85	20
N2942	40ch. Chungsongui Bridge, Pyongyang	1·10	25

985 Infantryman

987 Dancers

986 "Atergatis subdentatus"

1990. Warriors' Costumes. Multicoloured.
N2943 20ch. Type **985** 40 15
N2944 30ch. Archer 55 20
N2945 50ch. Military commander in armour 95 30
N2946 70ch. Officer's costume, 10th–14th centuries . . 1·25 40
Nos. N2943/5 depict costumes from the 3rd century B.C. to the 7th century A.D.

1990. Crabs. Multicoloured.
N2947 20ch. Type **986** 60 15
N2948 30ch. "Platylambrus validus" 75 20
N2949 50ch. "Uca arcuata" . . . 1·10 30

1990. Spring Friendship Art Festival, Pyongyang.
N2950 **987** 10ch. multicoloured . . 30 10

988 Monument at Road Folk, Mangyongdae

989 "Gymnocalycium sp."

1990. 78th Birthday of Kim Il Sung.
N2951 **988** 10ch. green and gold 20 10

1990. Cacti. Multicoloured.
N2953 10ch. Type **989** 50 10
N2954 30ch. "Pyllocactus hybridus" 90 20
N2955 50ch. "Epiphyllum truncatum" . . . . . . 1·50 30

990 Exhibition Emblem

991 Congo Peafowl

1990. "Stamp World London 90" International Stamp Exhibition (2nd issue).
N2956 **990** 20ch. red and black . . 40 15

1990. Peafowl. Multicoloured.
N2958 10ch. Type **991** 75 25
N2959 20ch. Common peafowl 2·00 60

992 Dolphin and Submarine

1990. Bio-engineering. Multicoloured.
N2961 10ch. Type **992** . . . . . 1·10 25
N2962 20ch. Bat and dish aerial 1·10 25
N2963 30ch. Owl and Tupolev Tu-154 jetliner . . . . 1·25 35
N2964 40ch. Squid, "Soyuz" rocket and Concorde supersonic jetliner . . . 1·10 25

993 "Self-portrait" (Rembrandt)

994 K. H. Rummenigge (footballer)

1990. "Belgica 90" International Stamp Exhibition, Brussels. Multicoloured.
N2965 10ch. Type **993** 30 10
N2966 20ch. "Self-portrait" (Raphael) 60 15
N2967 30ch. "Self-portrait" (Rubens) 75 20

1990. "Dusseldorf '90" International Youth Stamp Exhibition. Multicoloured.
N2968 20ch. Steffi Graf (tennis player) 85 15
N2969 30ch. Exhibition emblem 55 20
N2970 70ch. Type **994** . . . . . 1·25 40

995 Workers' Stadium, Peking, and Games Mascot

1990. 11th Asian Games, Peking (Nos. N2971/2) and 3rd Asian Winter Games, Samjiyon (N2973). Multicoloured.
N2971 10ch. Type **995** 30 10
N2972 30ch. Chollima Statue and sportsmen 75 20
N2973 40ch. Sportsmen and Games emblem . . . . 1·00 25

996 Ball

1990. West Germany, Winners of World Cup Football Championship. Multicoloured.
N2974 15ch. Emblem of F.I.F.A. (International Federation of Football Associations) 40 10
N2975 20ch. Jules Rimet 50 15
N2976 25ch. Type **996** 60 15
N2977 30ch. Olympic Stadium, Rome (venue of final) 65 20
N2978 35ch. Goalkeeper 75 20
N2979 40ch. Emblem of West German Football Association 90 25

997 Kakapo and Map of New Zealand

1990. "New Zealand 1990" International Stamp Exhibition, Auckland.
N2981 **997** 30ch. multicoloured . . 1·60 50

999 Head of Procession

1990. Koguryo Wedding Procession. Mult.
N2983 10ch. Type **999** . . . . . 1·00 20
N2984 30ch. Bridegroom . . . . 1·00 20
N2985 50ch. Bride in carriage . . 1·00 20
N2986 1wn. Drummer on horse 1·00 20
Nos. N2983/6 were issued together, se-tenant, forming a composite design.

1000 Marchers descending Mt. Paekdu

1990. Rally for Peace and Reunification of Korea.
N2987 **1000** 10ch. multicoloured 20 10

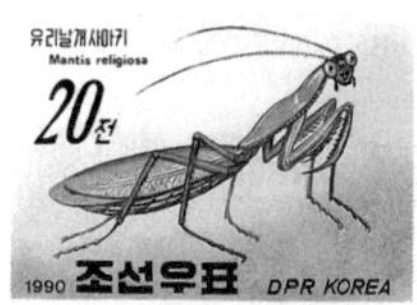

1001 Praying Mantis

1990. Insects. Multicoloured.
N2989 20ch. Type **1001** 40 15
N2990 30ch. Ladybird 55 20
N2991 40ch. "Pheropsophus jessoensis" 75 25
N2992 70ch. "Phyllium siccifolium" . . . . . . 1·25 40

1002 Footballers

1990. North–South Reunification Football Match, Pyongyang. Multicoloured.
N2993 10ch. Type **1002** 75 10
N2994 20ch. Footballers (different) 75 15

1003 Concert Emblem

1004 Ox

1990. National Reunification Concert.
N2996 **1003** 10ch. multicoloured 20 10

1990. Farm Animals.
N2997 **1004** 10ch. brown and green 20 10
N2998 – 20ch. lilac and yellow 40 15
N2999 – 30ch. grey and red . . 55 20
N3000 – 40ch. green and yellow 75 25
N3001 – 50ch. brown and blue 95 30
DESIGNS: 20ch. Pig; 30ch. Goat; 40ch. Sheep; 50ch. Horse.

1005 Chinese and North Korean Soldiers

1990. 40th Anniv of Participation of Chinese Volunteers in Korean War. Multicoloured.
N3002 10ch. Type **1005** 20 10
N3003 20ch. Populace welcoming volunteers (horiz) . . . 40 15
N3004 30ch. Rejoicing soldiers and battle scene (horiz) 50 20
N3005 40ch. Post-war reconstruction (horiz) 60 25

1006 Anniversary Emblem

1990. 40th Anniv of United Nations Development Programme.
N3007 **1006** 1wn. blue, silver & blk . . . . 1·90 65

1007 Mikado Sturgeon

1008 Sheep

1990. Fishes.
N3008 **1007** 10ch. brown and green 25 10
N3009 – 20ch. green and blue 55 15
N3010 – 30ch. blue and purple 75 25
N3011 – 40ch. brown and blue 1·00 30
N3012 – 50ch. violet and green 1·25 35
DESIGNS: 20ch. Large-headed sea bream; 30ch. Agoo flyingfish; 40ch. Fat greenling; 50ch. Tobij-ei eagle ray.

1990. New Year.
N3013 **1008** 40ch. multicoloured 75 25

1009 Moorhen

1010 Giant Panda

1990. Birds.
N3014 **1009** 10ch. blue, green & blk 55 15
N3015 – 20ch. brown, bistre and black 90 30
N3016 – 30ch. green, grey and black . . . . . . 1·10 50
N3017 – 40ch. brown, orange and black . . . . 1·75 60
N3018 – 50ch. ochre, brown and black . . . . 2·25 70
DESIGNS: 20ch. Jay; 30ch. Three-toed woodpecker; 40ch. Whimbrel; 50ch. Water rail.

1991. "Phila Nippon '91" International Stamp Exhibition, Tokyo. Multicoloured.
N3019 10ch. Type **1010** 30 10
N3020 20ch. Two giant pandas feeding 50 15
N3021 30ch. Giant panda clambering onto branch 70 20
N3022 40ch. Giant panda on rock 90 25
N3023 50ch. Two giant pandas 1·10 30
N3024 60ch. Giant panda in tree fork . . . . 1·25 35

1011 Changsan

1991. Revolutionary Sites.
N3026 5ch. Type **1011** 10 10
N3027 10ch. Oun 20 10

1012 Black-faced Spoonbills

1014 Hedgehog Fungus

1013 "Clossiana angarensis"

1991. Endangered Birds. Multicoloured.

N3028	10ch. Type **1012**	30	10
N3029	20ch. Grey herons	60	15
N3030	30ch. Great egrets	85	25
N3031	40ch. Manchurian cranes	1·10	30
N3032	50ch. Japanese white-naped cranes	1·75	35
N3033	70ch. White storks	2·25	50

1991. Alpine Butterflies. Multicoloured.

N3034	10ch. Type **1013**	25	10
N3035	20ch. "Erebia embla"	40	15
N3036	30ch. Camberwell beauty	60	20
N3037	40ch. Comma	75	30
N3038	50ch. Eastern pale clouded yellow	90	35
N3039	60ch. "Theela betulae"	1·10	45

1991. Fungi. Multicoloured.

N3040	10ch Type **1014**	25	10
N3041	20ch. "Phylloporus rhodoxanthus"	45	15
N3042	30ch. "Calvatia craniiformis"	60	20
N3043	40ch. Cauliflower clavaria	80	30
N3044	50ch. "Russula integra"	1·00	35

1015 Kumchon

1991. Revolutionary Sites. Multicoloured.

N3045	10ch. Type **1015**	15	10
N3046	40ch. Samdung	60	30

1016 Dr. Kye Ung Sang (researcher)

1017 Emblem and Venue

1991. Silkworm Research. Multicoloured.

N3047	10ch. Type **1016**	15	10
N3048	20ch. Chinese oak silk moth	30	15
N3049	30ch. "Attacus ricini"	45	20
N3050	40ch. "Antheraea yamamai"	60	30
N3051	50ch. Silkworm moth	75	35
N3052	60ch. "Aetias artemis"	90	45

1991. 9th Spring Friendship Art Festival, Pyongyang.

N3053	**1017** 10ch. multicoloured	10	10

1018 Emperor Penguins

1020 Map and Kim Jong Ho

1019 People's Palace of Culture (venue)

1991. Antarctic Exploration. Multicoloured.

N3054	10ch. Type **1018**	35	20
N3055	20ch. Research station	40	15
N3056	30ch. Elephant seals	75	20
N3057	40ch. Research ship	90	40
N3058	50ch. Southern black-backed gulls	1·60	40

1991. 85th Interparliamentary Union Conference, Pyongyang.

N3060	**1019** 10ch. dp green, grn & sil	15	10
N3061	– 1wn.50 multicoloured	2·25	1·10

DESIGN: 1wn.50, Conference emblem and azalea.

1991. 130th Anniv of Publication of Kim Jong Ho's Map "Taidong Yu Jido".

N3062	**1020** 90ch. black, brn & sil	1·40	70

1021 Cynognathus

1991. Dinosaurs. Multicoloured.

N3063	10ch. Type **1021**	25	10
N3064	20ch. Brontosaurus	40	15
N3065	30ch. Stegosaurus and allosaurus	55	20
N3066	40ch. Pterosauria	70	30
N3067	50ch. Ichthyosaurus	85	35

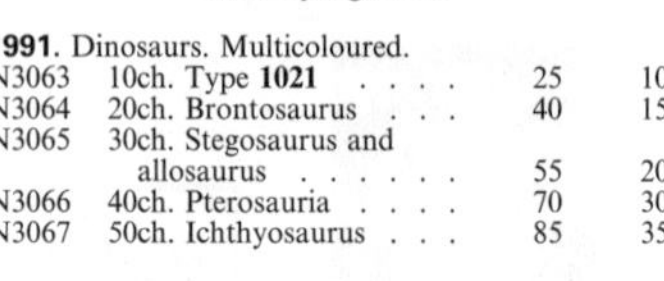

1022 Sprinting

1991. Olympic Games, Barcelona (1992 (1st issue). Multicoloured.

N3068	10ch. Type **1022**	15	10
N3069	10ch. Hurdling	15	10
N3070	20ch. Long jumping	30	15
N3071	20ch. Throwing the discus	30	15
N3072	30ch. Putting the shot	45	20
N3073	30ch. Pole vaulting	45	20
N3074	40ch. High jumping	60	30
N3075	40ch. Throwing the javelin	60	30

See also Nos. N3142/7.

1023 Cats and Eurasian Tree Sparrows

1991. Cats. Multicoloured.

N3077	10ch. Type **1023**	50	35
N3078	20ch. Cat and rat	40	15
N3079	30ch. Cat and butterfly	55	20
N3080	40ch. Cats with ball	75	30
N3081	50ch. Cat and frog	90	35

1025 Wild Horse

1991. Horses. Multicoloured.

N3083	10ch. Type **1025**	25	10
N3084	20ch. Hybrid of wild ass and wild horse	40	15
N3085	30ch. Przewalski's horse	60	20
N3086	40ch. Wild ass	75	30
N3087	50ch. Wild horse (different)	90	35

1026 Pennant Coralfish

1991. Fishes. Multicoloured.

N3088	10ch. Type **1026** (postage)	40	10
N3089	20ch. Clown triggerfish	75	25
N3090	30ch. Tomato anemonefish	1·00	30
N3091	40ch. Palette surgeonfish	1·40	45
N3092	50ch. Freshwater angelfish (air)	1·60	55

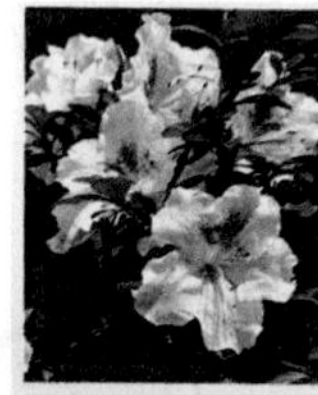

1027 Rhododendrons

1991. Flowers. Multicoloured.

N3094	10ch. Begonia	25	10
N3095	20ch. Gerbera	40	15
N3096	30ch. Type **1027**	55	20
N3097	40ch. Phalaenopsis	70	30
N3098	50ch. "Impatiens sultanii"	85	35
N3099	60ch. Streptocarpus	1·00	45

Nos. N3097/9 commemorate "CANADA '92" international youth stamp exhibition, Montreal.

1028 Panmunjom

1991.

N3100	**1028** 10ch. multicoloured	15	10

1029 Magnolia

1030 Players

1991. National Flower.

N3101	**1029** 10ch. multicoloured	40	10

1991. Women's World Football Championship, China. Multicoloured.

N3102	10ch. Type **1030**	25	10
N3103	20ch. Dribbling the ball	40	15
N3104	30ch. Heading the ball	55	20
N3105	40ch. Overhead kick	70	30
N3106	50ch. Tackling	85	35
N3107	60ch. Goalkeeper	1·10	45

1031 Squirrel Monkeys

1992. Monkeys. Multicoloured.

N3108	10ch. Type **1031**	25	10
N3109	20ch. Pygmy marmosets	40	15
N3110	30ch. Red-handed tamarins	60	20

1032 Eagle Owl

1992. Birds of Prey. Multicoloured.

N3112	10ch. Type **1032**	25	20
N3113	20ch. Common buzzard	55	30
N3114	30ch. African fish eagle	2·00	60
N3115	40ch. Steller's sea eagle	1·25	65
N3116	50ch. Golden eagle	1·40	75

1033 Birthplace, Mt. Paekdu

1992. Birthday of Kim Jong Il. Mt. Paekdu. Multicoloured.

N3118	10ch. Type **1033**	15	10
N3119	20ch. Mountain summit	30	15
N3120	30ch. Lake Chon (crater lake)	45	20
N3121	40ch. Lake Sarryi	60	30

1034 Service Bus

1992. Transport.

N3123	**1034** 10ch. multicoloured	25	10
N3124	– 20ch. multicoloured	40	15
N3125	– 30ch. multicoloured	60	20
N3126	– 40ch. multicoloured	75	30
N3127	– 50ch. multicoloured	90	35
N3128	– 60ch. multicoloured	1·10	45

DESIGNS: 20ch. to 60ch. Different buses and electric trams.

1035 Dancers and Emblem

1992. Spring Friendship Art Festival, Pyongyang.

N3129	**1035** 10ch. multicoloured	30	10

1036 Birthplace, Mangyongdae

1992. 80th Birthday of Kim Il Sung. Revolutionary Sites. Multicoloured.

N3130	10ch. Type **1036** (postage)	15	10
N3131	10ch. Party emblem and Turubong monument	15	10
N3132	10ch. Map and Ssuksom	15	10
N3133	10ch. Statue of soldier and Tongchang	15	10
N3134	40ch. Cogwheels and Taean	60	30
N3135	40ch. Chollima Statue and Kangson	60	30

N3136 1wn.20 Monument and West Sea Barrage (air) 1·75 85

1038 Soldiers on Parade

1992. 60th Anniv of People's Army. Multicoloured.

N3139 10ch. Type **1038** 15 10
N3140 10ch. Couple greeting soldier 15 10
N3141 10ch. Army, air force and navy personnel 15 10

1039 Hurdling

1992. Olympic Games, Barcelona (2nd issue). Multicoloured.

N3142 10ch. Type **1039** 25 10
N3143 20ch. High jumping . . . 40 15
N3144 30ch. Putting the shot . . 60 20
N3145 40ch. Sprinting 75 30
N3146 50ch. Long jumping . . . 90 35
N3147 60ch. Throwing the javelin 1·10 45

1040 Planting Crops

1992. Evolution of Man. Designs showing life in the New Stone Age (10, 20ch.) and the Bronze Age (others). Multicoloured.

N3149 10ch. Type **1040** (postage) 15 10
N3150 20ch. Family around cooking pot 30 15
N3151 30ch. Ploughing fields . . 45 20
N3152 40ch. Performing domestic chores 60 30
N3153 50ch. Building a dolmen (air) 75 35

1041 White-bellied Black Woodpecker

1042 Map and Hands holding Text

1992. Birds. Multicoloured.

N3154 10ch. Type **1041** 20 15
N3155 20ch. Common pheasant 40 25
N3156 30ch. White stork 60 35
N3157 40ch. Blue-winged pitta . . 85 55
N3158 50ch. Pallas's sandgrouse 1·10 60
N3159 60ch. Black grouse . . . . 1·25 80

1992. 20th Anniv of Publication of North–South Korea Joint Agreement.

N3161 **1042** 1wn.50 multicoloured 90 30

1043 "Bougainvillea spectabilis"

1044 Venus, Earth, Mars and Satellite

1992. Flowers. Multicoloured.

N3163 10ch. Type **1043** 25 10
N3164 20ch. "Ixora chinensis" . . 40 15
N3165 30ch. "Dendrobium taysuwie" 60 20
N3166 40ch. "Columnea gloriosa" 75 30
N3167 50ch. "Crinum" 90 35
N3168 60ch. "Ranunculus asiaticus" . . . . 1·10 45

1992. The Solar System. Multicoloured.

N3169 50ch. Type **1044** 90 35
N3170 50ch. Jupiter 90 35
N3171 50ch. Saturn 90 35
N3172 50ch. Uranus 90 35
N3173 50ch. Neptune and Pluto 90 35

Nos. N3169/73 were issued together, se-tenant, forming a composite design.

1045 "470" Dinghy

1046 Moreno Mannini (defender)

1992. "Riccione '92" Stamp Fair. Multicoloured.

N3175 10ch. Type **1045** 15 10
N3176 20ch. Sailboard 30 15
N3177 30ch. Sailing dinghy . . . 45 20
N3178 40ch. "Finn" dinghy . . . 60 30
N3179 50ch. "420" dinghy . . . 75 35
N3180 60ch. Fair emblem 90 45

1992. Sampdoria, Italian Football Champion, 1991. Multicoloured.

N3181 20ch. Type **1046** 30 15
N3182 30ch. Gianluca Vialli (forward) 45 30
N3183 40ch. Pietro Vierchowod (defender) 60 30
N3184 50ch. Fausto Pari (defender) 75 35
N3185 60ch. Roberto Mancini (forward) 90 45
N3186 1wn. Paolo Mantovani (club president) . . . . 1·50 75

1047 Black-belts warming up

1992. 8th World Taekwondo Championship, Pyongyang. Multicoloured.

N3188 10ch. Type **1047** 15 10
N3189 30ch. "Roundhouse" kick 45 30
N3190 50ch. High kick 75 35
N3191 70ch. Flying kick . . . . 1·00 50
N3192 90ch. Black-belt breaking tiles with fist . . . . . 1·40 70

1048 Common Toad ("Bufo bufo")

1992. Frogs and Toads. Multicoloured.

N3194 40ch. Type **1048** (postage) 75 30
N3195 40ch. Moor frog ("Rana arvalis") 75 30
N3196 40ch. "Rana chosenica" 75 30
N3197 70ch. Common pond frog ("Rana nigromaculata") 1·25 50
N3198 70ch. Japanese tree toad ("Hyla japonica") . . . 1·25 50
N3199 70ch. "Rana coreana" (air) . . . . 1·25 50

1049 "Rhododendron mucronulatum"

1992. World Environment Day. Multicoloured.

N3200 10ch. Type **1049** (postage) 15 10
N3201 30ch. Barn swallow . . . 55 35
N3202 40ch. "Stewartia koreana" (flower) 60 30
N3203 50ch. "Dictyoptera aurora" (beetle) 75 35
N3204 70ch. "Metasequoia glyptostroboides" (tree) 1·00 50
N3205 90ch. Chinese salamander 1·40 70
N3206 1wn. 20 "Ginkgo biloba" (tree) (air) . . . . . . 1·75 85
N3207 1wn. 40 Alpine bullhead 3·00 1·25

1050 Fin Whale ("Balaenoptera physalus")

1992. Whales and Dolphins. Multicoloured.

N3208 50ch. Type **1050** (postage) 1·00 35
N3209 50ch. Common dolphin ("Delphinus delphis") 1·00 35
N3210 50ch. Killer Whale ("Orcinus orca") . . . 1·00 35
N3211 50ch. Hump-backed whale ("Megaptera nodosa") 1·00 35
N3212 50ch. Bottle-nosed whale ("Berardius bairdii") . . 1·00 35
N3213 50ch. Sperm whale ("Physeter catadon") (air) . . . . 1·00 35

1051 Mother and Chicks

1992. New Year. Roosters in various costumes. Multicoloured.

N3214 10ch. Type **1051** 15 10
N3215 20ch. Lady 30 15
N3216 30ch. Warrior 45 20
N3217 40ch. Courtier 60 30
N3218 50ch. Queen 75 35
N3219 60ch. King 90 45

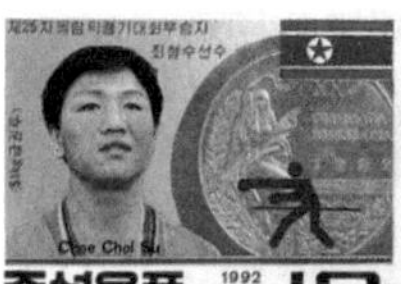

1052 Choe Chol Su (boxing)

1992. Gold Medal Winners at Barcelona Olympics. Multicoloured.

N3221 10ch. Type **1052** 15 10
N3222 20ch. Pae Kil Su (gymnastics) 30 15
N3223 50ch. Ri Hak Son (freestyle wrestling) . . 75 35
N3224 60ch. Kim Il (freestyle wrestling) 90 45

1053 Golden Mushroom

1055 League Members and Flag

1054 "Keumkangsania asiatica"

1993. Fungi. Multicoloured.

N3227 10ch. Type **1053** 15 10
N3228 20ch. Shaggy caps 30 15
N3229 30ch. "Ganoderma lucidum" 45 20
N3230 40ch. Brown mushroom 60 30
N3231 50ch. "Volvaria bombycina" 75 35
N3232 60ch. "Sarcodon aspratus" 90 45

1993. Plants. Multicoloured.

N3234 10ch. Type **1054** 25 10
N3235 20ch. "Echinosophora koreensis" 80 15
N3236 30ch. "Abies koreana" . . 55 20
N3237 40ch. "Benzoin angustifolium" 75 30
N3238 50ch. "Abeliophyllum distichum" 85 35
N3239 60ch. "Abelia mosanensis" 1·00 45

1993. 8th League of Socialist Working Youth Congress. Multicoloured.

N3241 10ch. Type **1055** 15 10
N3242 40ch. Flame, League emblem and text 60 30

1056 Phophyong Revolutionary Site Tower and March Corps Emblem

1057 Tower of Juche Idea and Grand Monument, Mt. Wangjae

1993. 70th Anniv of 1000-ri Journey for Learning.

N3243 **1056** 10ch. multicoloured 15 10

1993. 60th Anniv of Wangjaesan Meeting.

N3244 **1057** 5ch. multicoloured . . 10 10

1058 "Kimjomgil" (begonia)

1993. 51st Birthday of Kim Jong Il.

N3245 **1058** 10ch. multicoloured 40 10

1059 Pilot Fish

1993. Fishes. Multicoloured.

N3247 10ch. Type **1059** 25 10
N3248 20ch. Japanese stingray . . 55 20
N3249 30ch. Opah 80 30
N3250 40ch. Coelacanth . . . . 1·10 45
N3251 50ch. Moara grouper . . 1·25 50

1060/1064 "Spring on the Hill" (¼-size illustration)

1993. 18th-century Korean Painting.

N3253 **1060** 40ch. multicoloured 60 30
N3254 **1061** 40ch. multicoloured 60 30
N3255 **1062** 40ch. multicoloured 60 30
N3256 **1063** 40ch. multicoloured 60 30
N3257 **1064** 40ch. multicoloured 60 30

Nos. N3253/7 were issued together, se-tenant, forming the composite design illustrated.

1065 Violinist, Dancers and Emblem

1993. Spring Friendship Art Festival, Pyongyang.

N3258 **1065** 10ch. multicoloured 15 10

1066 Books

1993. 81st Birthday of Kim Il Sung and Publication of his Reminiscences "With the Century".

N3259 **1066** 10ch. multicoloured 15 10

1067 Kwangbok Street

1993. Pyongyang. Multicoloured.
N3261 10ch. Type **1067** 15 10
N3262 20ch. Chollima Street . . 30 15
N3263 30ch. Munsu Street . . . 45 20
N3264 40ch. Moranbong Street 60 30
N3265 50ch. Thongil Street . . . 75 35

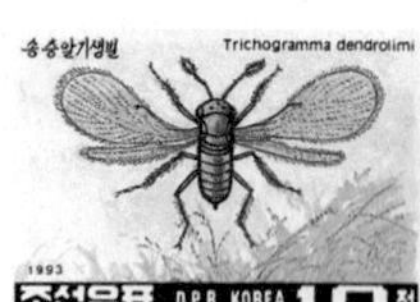

1068 "Trichogramma dendrolimi" (fly)

1993. Insects. Multicoloured.
N3267 10ch. Type **1068** 15 10
N3268 20ch. "Brachymeria obscurata" (fly) 30 15
N3269 30ch. "Metrioptera brachyptera" (cricket) 45 20
N3270 50ch. European field cricket 75 35
N3271 70ch. "Geocoris pallidipennis" (beetle) 1·00 50
N3272 90ch. "Cyphonony x dorsalis" (wasp) fighting spider . . . . 1·40 70

1069 Ri In Mo

1071 Grey-headed Woodpecker

1070 Footballers

1993. Return from Imprisonment of Ri In Mo (war correspondent).
N3273 **1069** 10ch. multicoloured 15 10

1993. World Cup Football Championship, U.S.A.
N3275 **1070** 10ch. multicoloured 25 10
N3276 – 20ch. multicoloured 40 15
N3277 – 30ch. multicoloured 60 20
N3278 – 50ch. multicoloured 90 35
N3279 – 70ch. multicoloured 1·25 50
N3280 – 90ch. multicoloured 1·75 70
DESIGNS: 20ch. to 90ch. Various footballing scenes.

1993. Birds. Multicoloured.
N3281 10ch. Type **1071** 20 15
N3282 20ch. King bird of paradise 40 20
N3283 30ch. Lesser bird of paradise 45 35
N3284 40ch. Paradise whydah . . 80 55
N3285 50ch. Magnificent bird of paradise . . . . 1·00 60
N3286 60ch. Greater bird of paradise . . . . 1·25 80
Nos. N3283/4 also commemorate "Indopex '93" international stamp exhibition, Surabaya.

1072 Korean Peninsula and Flag (½-size illustration)

1993. Self-adhesive. Roul.
N3287 **1072** 1wn.50 multicoloured 2·00 30
No. N3287 is for any one of the six stamps which together make up the design illustrated. They are peeled from a card backing.

1073 Kim Myong Nam (weightlifting, 1990)

1993. World Champions. Multicoloured.
N3293 10ch. Type **1073** 15 10
N3294 20ch. Kim Kwang Suk (gymnastics, 1991) . . . 30 15
N3295 30ch. Pak Yong Sun (table tennis, 1975, 1977) . . . 45 20
N3296 50ch. Kim Yong Ok (radio direction-finding, 1990) 75 35
N3297 70ch. Han Yun Ok (taekwondo, 1987, 1988, 1990) . . . . 1·00 50
N3298 90ch. Kim Yong Sik (free-style wrestling, 1986, 1989) . . . . 1·40 70

1074 Cabbage and Chilli Peppers

1075 State Arms

1993. Fruits and Vegetables. Multicoloured.
N3299 10ch. Type **1074** 15 10
N3300 20ch. Squirrels and horse chestnuts 30 15
N3301 30ch. Grapes and peach 45 20
N3302 40ch. Birds and persimmon 60 30
N3303 50ch. Tomatoes, aubergine and cherries 75 35
N3304 60ch. Radish, onion and garlic 90 45

1993.
N3305 **1075** 10ch. red 15 10

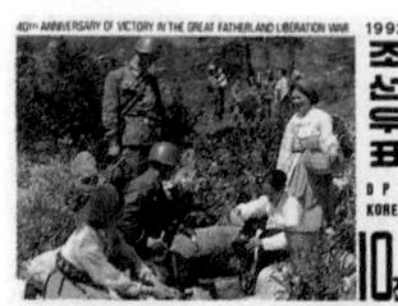

1076 Soldiers and Civilians

1993. 40th Anniv of Victory in Liberation War. Multicoloured.
N3306 10ch. Type **1076** 15 10
N3307 10ch. Officer and soldier 15 10
N3308 10ch. Guided missiles on low-loaders on parade 15 10
N3309 10ch. Anti-aircraft missiles on lorries on parade . . 15 10
N3310 10ch. Self-propelled missile launchers (tracked vehicles) on parade . . 15 10
N3311 10ch. Machine gun emplacement (30 × 48 mm) 15 10
N3312 10ch. Soldier holding flag (bronze statue) (30 × 48 mm) 15 10
N3314 10ch. Kim Il Sung at strategic policy meeting 15 10
N3315 10ch. Kim Il Sung directing battle for Height 1211 . . . . . 15 10
N3316 10ch. Kim Il Sung at munitions factory . . . 15 10
N3317 10ch. Kim Il Sung with tank commanders . . . 15 10
N3318 10ch. Kim Il Sung with triumphant soldiers . . 15 10
N3319 20ch. Kim Il Sung with artillery unit 30 15
N3320 20ch. Kim Il Sung encouraging machine gun crew 30 15
N3321 20ch. Kim Il Sung studying map of Second Front 30 15
N3322 20ch. Kim Il Sung with airmen 30 15
N3323 20ch. Musicians ("Alive is art of Korea") 30 15
N3313 40ch. Soldiers and flags ("Let us become Kim Jims and Ri Su Boks of the 90s") (30 × 48 mm) 60 30

1077 Choe Yong Do

1078 "Robinia sp."

1993. National Reunification Prize Winners. Multicoloured.
N3325 10ch. Type **1077** 15 10
N3326 20ch. Kim Ku 30 15
N3327 30ch. Hong Myong Hui 45 20
N3328 40ch. Ryo Un Hyong . . 60 30
N3329 50ch. Kim Jong Thae . . 75 35
N3330 60ch. Kim Chaek 90 45

1993. "Taipei '93" International Stamp Exhibition, Taipeh. Multicoloured.
N3331 20ch. Type **1078** 40 15
N3332 30ch. "Hippeastrum" . . 60 20

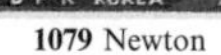

1079 Newton

1080 King Tongmyong shooting Bow

1993. 350th Birth Anniv (1992) of Sir Isaac Newton (mathematician and scientist). Multicoloured.
N3334 10ch. Type **1079** 25 10
N3335 20ch. Apple tree and formula of law of gravitation 40 15
N3336 30ch. Satellite, reflecting telescope, dish aerial, globe and rocket . . . 60 20
N3337 50ch. Formula of binomial theorem 90 35
N3338 70ch. Newton's works and statue . . . . 1·10 50

1993. Restoration of King Tongmyong of Koguryo's Tomb. Multicoloured.
N3339 10ch. Type **1080** 15 10
N3340 20ch. King Tongmyong saluting crowd 30 15
N3341 30ch. Restoration monument 45 20
N3342 40ch. Temple of the Tomb of King Tongmyong (horiz) 60 30
N3343 50ch. Tomb (horiz) . . . 75 35

1082 "Cyrtopodium andresoni"

1084 Mao Tse-tung at Yanan, 1944

1993. Orchids. Multicoloured.
N3346 10ch. Type **1082** 25 10
N3347 20ch. "Cattleya" 40 15
N3348 30ch. "Cattleya intermedia" "Oculata" 60 20
N3349 40ch. Potinaria "Maysedo godensia" 75 30
N3350 50ch. Kim Il Sung flower 1·00 35

1993. Birth Centenary of Mao Tse-tung. Multicoloured.
N3352 10ch. Type **1084** 15 10
N3353 20ch. Seated portrait (Peking, 1960) 30 15
N3354 30ch. Casting a vote, 1953 45 20
N3355 40ch. With pupils at Shaoshan Secondary School, 1959 . . . . . . 60 30

1085 Phungsan

1086 Purple Hyosong Flower

1994. New Year. Dogs. Multicoloured.
N3358 10ch. Type **1085** 15 10
N3359 20ch. Yorkshire terriers 30 15
N3360 30ch. Gordon setter . . . 45 20
N3361 40ch. Pomeranian 60 30
N3362 50ch. Spaniel with pups 75 35

1994. 52nd Birthday of Kim Jong Il. Multicoloured.
N3364 10ch. Type **1086** 25 10
N3365 40ch. Yellow hyosong flower 80 30

1087 Red and Black Dragon-eyed

1994. Goldfishes. Multicoloured.
N3367 10ch. Type **1087** 20 10
N3368 30ch. Red and white bubble-eyed 70 30
N3369 50ch. Red and white veil-tailed wenyu . . . . . 1·10 50
N3370 70ch. Red and white fringe-tailed . . . . . . 1·60 75

1088 Crowd with Banners

1089 Wheat, Banner and Woman writing

1994. 20th Anniv of Publication of "Programme for Modelling the Whole Society on the Juche Idea" by Kim Jong Il.
N3371 **1088** 20ch. multicoloured 30 15

1994. 30th Anniv of Publication of "Theses on the Socialist Rural Question in Our Country" by Kim Il Sung. Multicoloured.
N3373 10ch. Type **1089** 15 10
N3374 10ch. Electricity generating systems and pylon . . . 15 10
N3375 10ch. Lush fields, grain and tractor 15 10
N3376 40ch. Modern housing, books, food crops and laboratory technician . . 60 30
N3377 40ch. Revellers 60 30

1090 "Mangyongbong-92" (ferry)

1091 National Flag

1994. Ships. Multicoloured.
N3379 20ch. Type **1090** 30 15
N3380 30ch. "Osandok" (freighter) 45 20
N3381 40ch. "Ryongaksan" (stern trawler) 60 30
N3382 50ch. Stern trawler 75 35

1994.
N3384 **1091** 10ch. red and blue . . 15 10

1092 Birthplace and Magnolia (national flower)

1093 "Chrysosplenium sphaerospermum"

1994. 82nd Birthday of Kim Il Sung. Multicoloured.
N3385 10ch. Type **1092** 15 10
N3386 40ch. Birthplace, Manyongdae, and Kim Il Sung flower 60 30

1994. Alpine Plants on Mt. Paekdu. Multicoloured.
N3388 10ch. Type **1093** 25 10
N3389 20ch. "Campanula cephalotes" 40 15
N3390 40ch. "Trollius macropetalus" 75 30
N3391 40ch. "Gentiana algida" 75 30
N3392 50ch. "Sedum kamtschaticum" 90 35

1094 National Olympic Committee Emblem

1095 Red Cross Launch ("Relief on the Sea")

1994. Centenary of International Olympic Committee. Multicoloured.

N3394	10ch. Type **1094**	15	10
N3395	20ch. Pierre de Coubertin (founder)	30	15
N3396	30ch. Olympic flag and flame	45	20
N3397	50ch. Emblem of Centennial Olympic Congress, Paris	75	35

1994. 75th Anniv of International Red Cross and Red Crescent Federation. Multicoloured.

N3399	10ch. Electric tram, pedestrians on footbridge and traffic lights ("Prevention of Traffic Accident")	45	10
N3400	20ch. Type **1095**	30	15
N3401	30ch. Planting tree ("Protection of Environment")	45	20
N3402	40ch. Dam ("Prevention of Drought Damage")	60	30

1994. No. N3287 surch **160** in circle.

N3403	**1072** 1wn.60 on 1wn.50 multicoloured	2·10	1·00

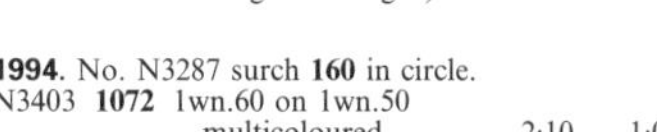

1097 Northern Fur Seal

1994. Marine Mammals. Multicoloured.

N3404	10ch. Type **1097**	25	10
N3405	40ch. Southern elephant seal	75	30
N3406	60ch. Southern sealion	1·10	45

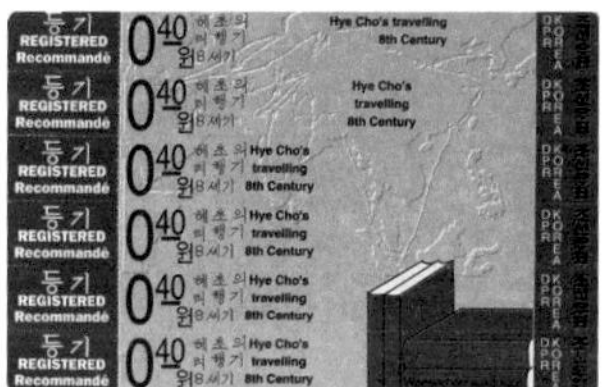
1098 Map of Asia and Books (½-size illustration)

1994. 8th-century Travels of Hye Cho. Self-adhesive. Roul.

N3408	**1098** 40ch. multicoloured	55	25

No. N3408 is for any one of the six stamps which together make up the design illustrated. They are peeled from a card backing.

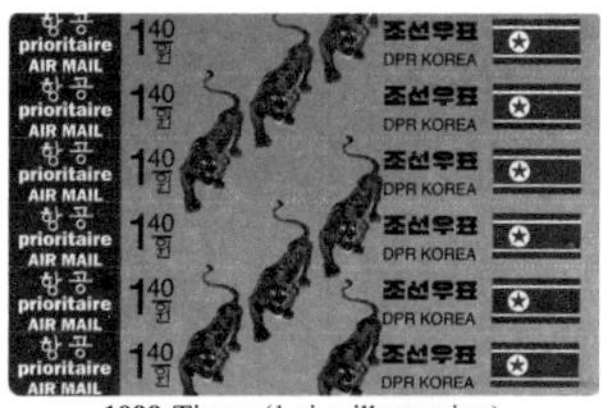
1099 Tigers (½-size illustration)

1994. Self-adhesive. Roul.

N3409	**1099** 1wn.40 multicoloured	1·90	95

No. N3409 is for any one of the six stamps which together make up the design illustrated. They are peeled from a card backing.

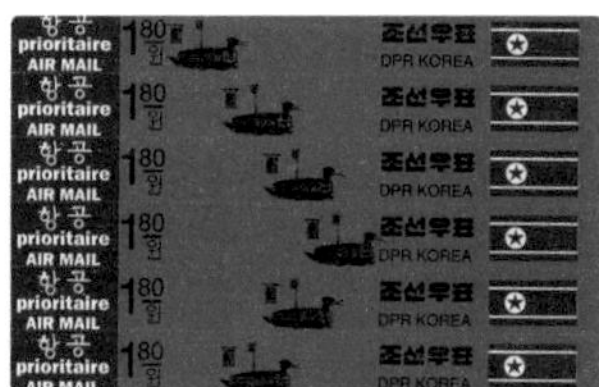
1101 "Turtle" Ships (½-size illustration)

1994. Self-adhesive. Roul.

N3411	**1101** 1wn.80 multicoloured	2·40	1·10

No. N3411 is for any one of the six stamps which together make up the design illustrated. They are peeled from a card backing.

1102 Striped Bonnet

1994. Molluscs. Multicoloured.

N3412	30ch. Type **1102**	60	20
N3413	40ch. Equilateral venus	1·00	30

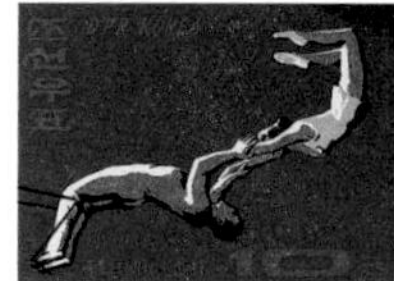
1103 Trapeze

1994. Circus Acrobatics. Multicoloured.

N3416	10ch. Type **1103**	15	10
N3417	20ch. Reino (Swedish acrobat) performing rope dance	30	15
N3418	30ch. Seesaw performer	45	20
N3419	40ch. Unicycle juggler	60	30

1104 Korean Script and "100"

1994. Birth Centenary of Kim Hyong Jik (father of Kim Il Sung). Multicoloured.

N3420	**1104** 10ch. multicoloured	10	10

1105 Jon Pong Jun and Battle Scene

1994. Centenary of Kabo Peasant War.

N3422	**1105** 10ch. multicoloured	15	10

1107 Workers and Banner

1109 "Acorus calamus"

1108 Onsong Fish

1994. Revolutionary Economic Strategy.

N3424	**1107** 10ch. multicoloured	15	10

1994. Fossils. Multicoloured.

N3425	40ch. Type **1108**	90	30
N3426	40ch. Metasequoia	75	30
N3427	40ch. Mammoth teeth	75	30
N3428	80ch. Archaeopteryx	1·60	2·50

1994. Medicinal Plants. Multicoloured.

N3429	20ch. Type **1109**	30	15
N3430	30ch. "Arctium lappa"	45	20

1110 Ribbon Exercise

1111 Chou En-lai at Tianjun, 1919

1994. Callisthenics. Multicoloured.

N3432	10ch. Type **1110**	15	10
N3433	20ch. Ball exercise	30	15
N3434	30ch. Hoop exercise	45	20
N3435	40ch. Ribbon exercise (different)	60	30
N3436	50ch. Club exercise	75	35

1994. 96th Birth Anniv of Chou En-lai (Chinese statesman). Multicoloured.

N3437	10ch. Type **1111**	15	10
N3438	20ch. Arrival in Northern Shanxi from Long March	30	15
N3439	30ch. At Conference of Asian and African Countries, Bandung, Indonesia, 1955	45	20
N3440	40ch. Surrounded by children in Wulumuqi, Xinjiang Province	60	30

1113 Kim Il Sung as Youth, 1927

1994. Kim Il Sung Commemoration (1st issue). (a) As T **1113**. Each red, gold and black.

N3444	40ch. Type **1113**	60	30
N3445	40ch. Kim Il Sung and Kim Jong Suk	60	30
N3446	40ch. Kim Il Sung as young man	60	30

(b) Horiz designs as T **1115**. Each purple, gold and black.

N3447	40ch. Kim Il Sung making speech, Pyongyang, 1945	60	30
N3448	40ch. Kim Il Sung sitting at desk	60	30
N3449	40ch. Kim Il Sung at microphone	60	30

See also Nos. N3459/63.

1114 Player No. 4

1994. World Cup Football Championship, U.S.A. Multicoloured.

N3451	10ch. Type **1114**	15	10
N3452	20ch. Player No. 5	30	15
N3453	30ch. Player No. 6	45	20
N3454	40ch. Player No. 7	60	30
N3455	1wn. Player No. 8	1·50	75
N3456	1wn.50 Player No. 9	2·25	1·10

1115 Kim Il Sung making Radio Broadcast, 1950

1994. Kim Il Sung Commemoration (2nd issue). (a) Each green, gold and black.

N3458	40ch. Type **1115**	60	30
N3459	40ch. Kim Il Sung with four soldiers, 1951	60	30
N3460	40ch. Kim Il Sung and crowd of soldiers, 1953	60	30

(b) Multicoloured (N3463) or lilac, gold and black (others).

N3461	40ch. Kim Il Sung with workers at Chongjin Steel Plant, 1959	60	30
N3462	40ch. Kim Il Sung on Onchon Plain	60	30
N3463	40ch. Kim Il Sung at desk using telephone	60	30

1116 National Flags and Flowers

1117 Ri Myon Sang and Score of "Snow Falls"

1994. Korean–Chinese Friendship.

N3465	**1116** 40ch. multicoloured	60	30

1994. Composers. Multicoloured.

N3467	50ch. Type **1117**	1·00	35
N3468	50ch. Pak Han Kyu and score of "Nobody Knows"	1·00	35
N3469	50ch. Ludwig van Beethoven and score of piano sonata No. 14	1·00	35
N3470	50ch. Wolfgang Amadeus Mozart and score of symphony No. 39	1·00	35

1118 National Emblem

1994.

N3471	**1118** 1wn. green	1·50	75
N3472	3wn. brown	4·00	2·00

1119 P. Wiberg (Alpine combined skiing)

1994. Winter Olympic Games, Lillehammer, Gold Medal Winners. Multicoloured.

N3473	10ch. Type **1119**	15	10
N3474	20ch. D. Compagnoni (slalom)	30	15
N3475	30ch. O. Baiul (figure skating)	45	20
N3476	40ch. D. Jansen (speed skating)	60	30
N3477	1wn. L. Yegorova (cross-country sking)	1·50	75
N3478	1wn.50 B. Blair (speed skating)	2·25	1·10

1120 Pig Couple

1121 Pison Waterfalls, Mt. Myohyang

1995. New Year. Year of the Pig. Multicoloured.

N3480	20ch. Type **1120**	45	15
N3481	40ch. Pigs carrying bucket and spade	80	30

1995. 20th Anniv of World Tourism Organization. Multicoloured.

N3483	30ch. Tower of Juche Idea, Pyongyang	45	20
N3484	30ch. Type **1121**	45	20
N3485	30ch. Myogilsang (cliff-face carving of Buddha), Mt. Kumgang	45	20

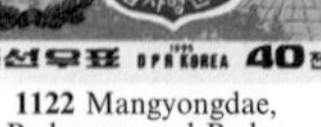

1122 Mangyongdae, Badaogou and Badge

1123 Monument bearing 50th Birthday Ode, Mt. Paekdu

1995. 70th Anniv of 1000-ri (250 mile) Journey by Kim Il Sung to Restore Fatherland.

N3486	**1122** 40ch. multicoloured	60	30

1995. 53rd Birthday of Kim Jong Il.

N3487	**1123** 10ch. multicoloured	15	10

1124 Reconstruction Monument

1125 Jamaedo Lighthouse

1995. Completion of Reconstruction of King Tangun's Tomb. Multicoloured.

N3489	10ch. Type **1124**	15	10
N3490	30ch. Bronze dagger on plinth	45	20
N3491	50ch. Monument inscribed with exploits of King Tangun	75	15
N3492	70ch. Gateway (horiz)	1·00	50

1995. Lighthouses. Multicoloured.

N3494	20ch. Type **1125**	30	15
N3495	1wn. Phido Lighthouse, West Sea Barrage	1·75	85

1126 Cracked Green Russula

1127 Couple planting Tree

1995. Fungi. Multicoloured.

N3496	20ch. Type **1126**	50	15
N3497	30ch. "Russula atropurpurea"	75	20

1995. Tree Planting Day.

N3499	**1127** 10ch. multicoloured	30	10

1128 Birthplace, Mangyongdae

1995. 83rd Birth Anniv of Kim Il Sung. Multicoloured.

N3500	10ch. Type **1128**	15	10
N3501	40ch. Tower of Juche Idea and Kim Il Sung flower (vert)	60	30

1129 Deng Xiaoping waving

1995. 20th Anniv of Kim Il Sung's Visit to China. Multicoloured.

N3503	10ch. Type **1129**	15	10
N3504	20ch. Deng Xiaoping of China sitting in armchair (vert)	30	15

1130 Venue

1995. 40th Anniv of Asian–African Conference, Bandung.

N3506	**1130** 10ch. black, buff and red	15	10
N3507	– 50ch. brown, gold and black	75	35

DESIGN: 50ch. Kim Il Sung receiving honorary Doctorate at Indonesia University.

1131 Emblem

1132 Amethyst

1995. International Sports and Cultural Festival for Peace, Pyongyang. Multicoloured.

N3509	20ch. Type **1131**	30	15
N3510	40ch. Dancer	60	30
N3511	40ch. Inoki Kanji (leader of Sports Peace Party of Japan)	60	30

1995. Minerals.

N3513	**1132** 20ch. multicoloured	50	15

1133 Eurasian Tree Sparrow

1134 Ostrea

1995. White Animals. Multicoloured.

N3514	40ch. Type **1133**	60	30
N3515	40ch. "Stichopus japonicus" (sea slug)	60	30

1995. Fossils. Multicoloured.

N3516	50ch. Type **1134**	1·00	35
N3517	1wn. Cladophlebis (fern)	1·50	75

1135 Chess

1136 National Flag and Korean Hall, Tokyo

1995. Traditional Games. Multicoloured.

N3518	30ch. Type **1135**	50	20
N3519	60ch. Taekwondo	1·00	45
N3520	70ch. Yut	1·25	50

1995. 40th Anniv of Association of Koreans in Japan.

N3521	**1136** 1wn. multicoloured	1·50	75

1137 Weightlifting

1138 "Russula citrina"

1995. Olympic Games, Atlanta (1996). Multicoloured.

N3522	50ch. Type **1137**	90	35
N3523	50ch. Boxing	90	35

1995. Fungi. Multicoloured.

N3525	40ch. Type **1138**	75	30
N3526	60ch. Black trumpets	1·00	45
N3527	80ch. Shaggy caps	1·40	60

1140 Mt. Paekdu and Revolutionaries

1141 Markswoman

1995. 50th Anniv of Liberation. Multicoloured.

N3529	10ch. Type **1140**	15	10
N3530	30ch. Map of Korea and family	45	20
N3531	60ch. Medal	90	45

1995. 1st Military World Games, Rome.

N3534	**1141** 40ch. multicoloured	60	30

1143 Emblem and Banner

1144 Arch of Triumph, Pyongyang

1995. 50th Anniv of Korean Workers' Party. Multicoloured.

N3536	10ch. Type **1143**	15	10
N3537	20ch. Statue of worker, peasant and intellectual	30	15
N3538	30ch. Party monument	45	20

1995. 50th Anniv of Kim Il Sung's Return to Homeland.

N3540	**1144** 10ch. multicoloured	15	10

1145 Tuna

1147 Guinea Pig

1995. Designs as T **1145**. Each brown and black.

(a) Fishes.

N3541	40ch. Type **1145**	70	30
N3542	50ch. Pennant coralfish (with two bands)	90	35
N3543	50ch. Needlefish	90	35
N3544	60ch. Seascorpion	1·00	45
N3545	5wn. Emperor angelfish	6·50	3·25

(b) Buildings on Kwangbok Street, Pyongyang.

N3546	60ch. Circus	90	45
N3547	70ch. Flats	1·00	50
N3548	80ch. Ryanggang Hotel	1·25	60
N3549	90ch. Tower apartment block (vert)	1·40	70
N3550	1wn. Sosan Hotel (vert)	1·50	75

(c) Machines.

N3551	10ch. Kamsusan tipper truck	15	10
N3552	20ch. Bulldozer	30	15
N3553	30ch. Excavator	45	20
N3554	40ch. Earth mover (vert)	60	30
N3555	10wn. "Chollima 80" tractor (vert)	13·00	6·50

(d) Animals.

N3556	30ch. Giraffe (vert)	45	20
N3557	40ch. Ostrich (vert)	60	30
N3558	60ch. Bluebuck (vert)	90	45
N3559	70ch. Bactrian camel	1·00	50
N3560	3wn. Indian rhinoceros	4·25	2·00

(e) Sculptures of Children.

N3561	30ch. Boy holding bird (vert)	45	20
N3562	40ch. Boy with goose (vert)	60	30
N3563	60ch. Girl with geese (vert)	90	45
N3564	70ch. Boy and girl with football (vert)	1·00	50
N3565	2wn. Boy and girl arguing over football (vert)	3·00	1·50

1996. Rodents. Multicoloured.

N3567	20ch. Type **1147**	50	15
N3568	20ch. Squirrel	50	15
N3569	30ch. White mouse	70	20

1148 Emblem, Badge and Flag

1149 Restoration Mounument

1996. 50th Anniv of League of Socialist Working Youth.

N3570	**1148** 10ch. multicoloured	15	10

1996. Reconstruction of Tomb of King Wanggon. Multicoloured.

N3571	30ch. Type **1149**	60	20
N3572	40ch. Entrance gate	75	30
N3573	50ch. Tomb	90	35

1152 Jong Il Peak and Kim Jong Il Flower

1153 Pairs Skating

1996. 54th Birthday of Kim Jong Il.

N3576	**1152** 10ch. multicoloured	40	10

1996. 5th Paektusan Prize Figure Skating Championships. Multicoloured.

N3578	10ch. Type **1153**	25	10
N3579	20ch. Pairs skating (different)	40	15
N3580	30ch. Pairs skating (different)	60	20
N3581	50ch. Women's individual skating	90	35

1155 Farm Worker

1156 1946 20ch. Stamp and Tower of Juche Idea

1996. 50th Anniv of Agrarian Reform Law.

N3584	**1155** 10ch. multicoloured	15	10

1996. 50th Anniv of First North Korean Stamps.

N3585	**1156** 1wn. multicoloured	1·40	70

1158 Birthplace, Mangyongdae

1996. 84th Birth Anniv of Kim Il Sung.

N3587	**1158** 10ch. multicoloured	15	10

1159 Gateway

1996. "China '96" Asian International Stamp Exhibition, Peking. Landmarks in Zhejiang. Multicoloured.

N3589	10ch. Type **1159**	25	10
N3590	10ch. Haiyin Pool	25	10

1160 Hopscotch

1161 Association Pamphlets

1996. Children's Games. Multicoloured.
N3592 20ch. Type **1160** 40 15
N3593 40ch. Shuttlecock 75 30
N3594 50ch. Sledging 90 35

1996. 60th Anniv of Association for Restoration of the Fatherland.
N3595 **1161** 10ch. multicoloured 15 10

1163 Arctic Fox **1164** Boy Saluting

1996. Polar Animals. Multicoloured.
N3597 50ch. Type **1163** 75 35
N3598 50ch. Polar bear 75 35
N3599 50ch. Emperor penguins 75 35
N3600 50ch. Leopard seals . . . 75 35

1996. 50th Anniv of Korean Children's Union.
N3601 **1164** 10ch. multicoloured 40 10

1165 Steam Locomotive **1167** Open Book and Characters

1996. Railway Locomotives. Multicoloured.
N3603 50ch. Type **1165** 75 35
N3604 50ch. Electric locomotive (green livery) 75 35
N3605 50ch. Steam locomotive (facing right) 75 35
N3606 50ch. Diesel locomotive (red and yellow livery) 75 35

1996. 760th Anniv of Publication of "Complete Collection of Buddhist Scriptures printed from 80,000 Wooden Blocks".
N3608 **1167** 40ch. multicoloured 60 30

1168 Worker using Microphone

1996. 50th Anniv of Labour Law.
N3609 **1168** 50ch. multicoloured 75 35

1171 Kumsusan Memorial Palace

1996. 2nd Death Anniv of Kim Il Sung.
N3612 **1171** 10ch. multicoloured 15 10

1172 Kim Il Sung meeting Jiang Zemin of China, 1991 **1173** Football and Ancient Greek Athletes

1996. 35th Anniv of Korean–Chinese Treaty for Friendship, Co-operation and Mutual Assistance.
N3614 **1172** 10ch. brown, gold and black 15 10
N3615 – 10ch. green, gold and black 15 10

DESIGN: 10ch. Kim Il Sung meeting Pres. Mao Tse-tung of China, 1954.

1996. Centenary of Modern Olympic Games and Olympic Games, Atlanta. Multicoloured.
N3617 50ch. Type **1173** 85 35
N3618 50ch. Tennis, Olympic Anthem and 1896 5l. Greek stamp 85 35
N3619 50ch. Throwing the hammer and advertisement poster for first modern olympics 85 35
N3620 50ch. Baseball and Olympic stadium, Atlanta 85 35

1174 Couple **1175** State Arms and Symbols of Industry and Communications

1996. 50th Anniv of Sex Equality Law.
N3621 **1174** 50ch. multicoloured 70 35

1996. 50th Anniv of Nationalization of Industries.
N3623 **1175** 50ch. bistre and brown 65 30

1176 Boy with Ball **1178** University Buildings, Pyongyang

1996. 50th Anniv of U.N.I.C.E.F. Multicoloured.
N3624 10ch. Type **1176** 25 10
N3625 20ch. Boy with building blocks 35 15
N3626 50ch. Boy eating melon . . 75 30
N3627 60ch. Girl playing accordion 90 40

1996. 50th Anniv of Kim Il Sung University.
N3629 **1178** 10ch. multicoloured 15 10

1179 Tiger **1180** Red Flag and Tower of Juche Idea

1996. World Conservation Union Congress, Montreal, Canada. Multicoloured.
N3630 50ch. Type **1179** 75 30
N3631 50ch. Royal spoonbill . . 75 30

1996. 70th Anniv of Down-with-Imperialism Union.
N3633 **1180** 10ch. multicoloured 30 10

1183 Japanese Eel

1996. Freshwater Fishes. Multicoloured.
N3636 20ch. Type **1183** 70 15
N3637 20ch. Menada grey mullet ("Liza haematocheila") 70 15

1184 Soldiers and Supreme Commander's Flag

1996. 5th Anniv of Appointment of Kim Jong Il as Supreme Commander of the People's Army.
N3639 **1184** 20ch. multicoloured 50 15

1185 "Ox Driver" (Kim Tu Ryang)

1997. New Year. Year of the Ox. Multicoloured.
N3640 70ch. Type **1185** . . . . 2·25 45
N3641 70ch. Bronze ritual plate of two bulls and a tiger 2·25 45
N3642 70ch. Boy with bull (ceramic) . . . . 2·25 45
N3643 70ch. Boy flautist sitting on bull (sculpture) . . . 2·25 45

1186 Left-hand Detail **1187** Kitten with Dogs in Basket

1997. "Flowers and Butterflies" by Nam Kye U. Multicoloured.
N3645 50ch. Type **1186** . . . . 1·25 30
N3646 50ch. Centre detail . . . . 1·25 30
N3647 50ch. Right-hand detail . . 1·25 30
Nos. N3645/7 were issued together, se-tenant, forming a composite design of the painting.

1997. Paintings of Cats and Dogs. Multicoloured.
N3648 50ch. Type **1187** . . . . 1·25 30
N3649 50ch. Pup in vine-wreathed basket, kitten and pumpkin . . . . . 1·50 30

1189 Birthplace, Mt. Paekdu

1997. 55th Birthday of Kim Jong Il.
N3652 **1189** 10ch. multicoloured 40 10

1190 Pair

1997. 6th Paektusan Prize International Figure Skating Championships, Pyongyang. Multicoloured.
N3654 50ch. Type **1190** . . . . 1·50 30
N3655 50ch. Pair (mauve) . . . . 1·50 30
N3656 50ch. Pair (green) . . . . 1·50 30

1193 "Prunus ansu" **1194** Foundation Monument

1997. Apricots. Multicoloured.
N3659 50ch. Type **1193** . . . . 1·40 30
N3660 50ch. "Prunus mandshurica" . . . . . 1·40 30
N3661 50ch. Hoeryong white apricot ("Prunus armeniaca") . . . . . 1·40 30
N3662 50ch. Puksan apricot ("Prunus sibirica") . . . 1·40 30

1997. 80th Anniv of Foundation of Korean National Association.
N3663 **1194** 10ch. brown and green 50 10

1195 Sapling **1196** Birthplace, Mangyongdae

1997. 50th Anniv of Reforestation Day.
N3664 **1195** 10ch. multicoloured

1997. 85th Birth Anniv of Kim Il Sung. Multicoloured.
N3666 10ch. Type **1196** 50 10
N3667 20ch. Sliding Rock (horiz) 1·00 10
N3668 40ch. Warship Rock (horiz) . . . . 1·25 25

1197 Cap Badge and Modern Weapons

1997. 65th Anniv of People's Army.
N3670 **1197** 10ch. multicoloured 10 10

1198 Map of Korea **1199** Tower of Juche Idea, People and Flag

1997. 25th Anniv of Publication of North–South Korea Joint Agreement.
N3672 **1198** 10ch. multicoloured 10 10

1997. Posters reflecting Joint New Year Newspaper Editorials. Multicoloured.
N3674 10ch. Type **1199** 10 10
N3675 10ch. Man with flag . . . 10 10
N3676 10ch. Soldier, miner, farmer, intellectual and bugler 10 10

1201 Memorial Post and Blazing Fortress **1204** "Redlichia chinensis"

1997. 60th Anniv of Battle of Pochonbo.
N3678 **1201** 40ch. multicoloured 35 15

1997. Fossils. Multicoloured.
N3681 50ch. Type **1204** 45 20
N3682 1wn. "Ptychoparia coreanica" 90 45

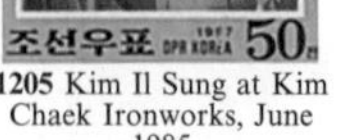
1205 Kim Il Sung at Kim Chaek Ironworks, June 1985

1207 Spring

1206 Blindman's Buff

1997. 3rd Death Anniv of Kim Il Sung. Multicoloured.
N3683 50ch. Kim Il Sung at microphones (party conference, October 1985) 45 20
N3684 50ch. Type **1205** 45 20
N3685 50ch. Kim Il Sung and farmers holding wheat (Songsin Co-operative Farm, Sadong District, 1993) 45 20
N3686 50ch. Performing artists applauding Kim Il Sung, 1986 . . . . . . 45 20
N3687 50ch. Kim Il Sung at Jonchon Factory, Jagang Province, 1991 45 20
N3688 50ch. Kim Il Sung receiving flowers at People's Army Conference, 1989 . . . 45 20

1997. Children's Games. Multicoloured.
N3689 30ch. Type **1206** 30 15
N3690 60ch. Five stones 55 25
N3691 70ch. Arm wrestling . . . 65 30

1997. Women's National Costumes. Multicoloured.
N3692 10ch. Type **1207** 10 10
N3693 40ch. Summer 35 15
N3694 50ch. Autumn 45 20
N3695 60ch. Winter 55 25

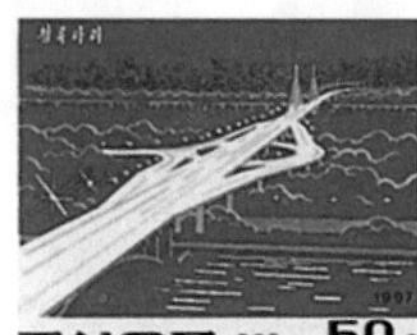
1208 Aerial View

1997. Chongryu Bridge, Pyongyang. Multicoloured.
N3696 50ch. Type **1208** 45 20
N3697 50ch. Chongryu Bridge and birds 45 20

1209 Sun, Magnolias and Balloons

1997. 85th Anniv of Juche Era and Sun Day.
N3698 **1209** 10ch. multicoloured 10 10

1210 Korean Text and Kim Il Sung University

1997. 20th Anniv of Publication of Theses on Socialist Education.
N3700 **1210** 10ch. multicoloured 10 10

1212 Chonbul Peak

1997. 10th Anniv of Korean Membership of World Tourism Organization. Mt Chilbo. Multicoloured.
N3702 50ch. Type **1212** 45 20
N3703 50ch. Sea-Chilbo (coast) 45 20
N3704 50ch. Rojok Peak 45 20

1213 Podok Hermitage

1997. Kumgang Mountains. Multicoloured.
N3705 50ch. Type **1213** 45 20
N3706 50ch. Kumgang Gate . . 45 20

1214 School, Pupil and Mt. Paekdu

1997. 50th Anniv of Mangyongdae Revolutionary School.
N3707 **1214** 40ch. multicoloured 35 15

1215 Lion

1217 Ten-pin Bowling

1997. Animals presented as Gifts to Kim Il Sung. Multicoloured.
N3708 20ch. Type **1215** (Ethiopia, 1987) 15 10
N3709 30ch. Jaguar (Japan, 1992) 30 15
N3710 50ch. Barbary sheep (Czechoslovakia, 1992) 45 20
N3711 80ch. Scarlet macaw (Austria, 1979) 70 35

1997. Sports. Multicoloured.
N3713 50ch. Type **1217** 45 20
N3714 50ch. Golf 45 20
N3715 50ch. Fencing 45 20

1218 Snails

1220 "Juche 87" and Temple

1997. Snails. Multicoloured.
N3716 50ch. Type **1218** 45 20
N3717 50ch. Two snails on leaf 45 20
N3718 50ch. Snail laying eggs . . 45 20

1997. New Year. Year of the Tiger. Multicoloured.
N3720 10ch. Type **1220** 10 10
N3721 50ch. Tiger in rocket (24 × 34 mm) 45 20
N3722 50ch. Tiger steering ship (24 × 34 mm) 45 20

1221 Birthplace, Hoeryong

1997. 80th Birth Anniv of Kim Jong Suk (revolutionary).
N3724 **1221** 10ch. multicoloured 10 10

1222 Skiing

1223 Birthdate and Celebration Ribbon

1998. Winter Olympic Ganes, Nagano, Japan. Multicoloured.
N3726 20ch. Type **1222** 15 10
N3727 40ch. Speed skating . . . 35 15

1998. 56th Birth Anniv of Kim Jong Il.
N3728 **1223** 10ch. multicoloured 10 10

1224 Korean Tigers

1998. Wildlife Paintings. Multicoloured.
N3730 50ch. Type **1224** 45 20
N3731 50ch. Manchurian cranes 45 20

1225 Route Map, Birthplace at Mangyongdae and Trail Followers

1998. 75th Anniv of 1000-ri (250 mile) Journey by Kim Il Sung.
N3733 **1225** 10ch. multicoloured 10 10

1226 Soldiers and Balloons

1998. 5th Anniv of Appointment of Kim Jong Il as Chairman of National Defence Commission.
N3734 **1226** 10ch. multicoloured 10 10

1227 Flags and Birthplace, Mangyongdae

1229 United Front Tower and Moranbong Theatre

1998. 86th Birth Anniv of Kim Il Sung.
N3735 **1227** 10ch. multicoloured 10 10

1998. 50th Anniv of North–South Conference, Pyongyang.
N3737 **1229** 10ch. brown, blue and black 10 10

1230 Players and Championship Emblem

1231 Cabbages

1998. World Cup Football Championship, France. Multicoloured.
N3738 30ch. Type **1230** 30 15
N3739 50ch. Player winning ball and emblem 45 20

1998. Vegetables. Multicoloured.
N3741 10ch. Type **1231** 10 10
N3742 40ch. Radishes 35 15
N3743 50ch. Spring onions . . . 45 20

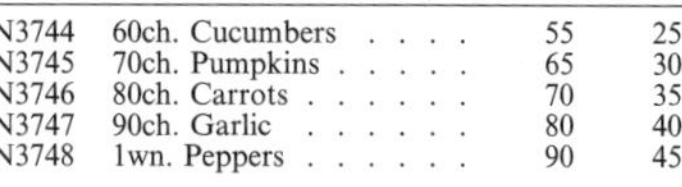
N3744 60ch. Cucumbers 55 25
N3745 70ch. Pumpkins 65 30
N3746 80ch. Carrots 70 35
N3747 90ch. Garlic 80 40
N3748 1wn. Peppers 90 45

1232 "Countryside in May" (Jong Jong Yo)

1998. Paintings. Multicoloured.
N3749 60ch. Type **1232** 55 25
N3750 1wn.40 "Dance" (Kim Yong Jun) . . . . . . 1·25 65

1233 Model of Automatic Space Station (from U.S.S.R.)

1998. International Friendship Exhibition, Myohyang Mountains (2nd series). Multicoloured.
N3752 1wn. Type **1233** 90 45
N3753 1wn. Ceramic flower vase (from Egypt) 90 45
N3754 1wn. "Crane" (statuette, from Billy Graham (evangelist)) 90 45

1234 Research Ship, Buoy and Dolphins in Globe and Hydro-meteorological Headquarters

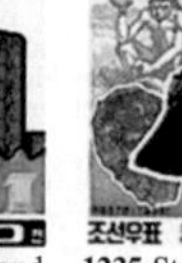
1235 Stone Age Implement

1998. International Year of the Ocean. Multicoloured.
N3756 10ch. Type **1234** 10 10
N3757 80ch. Sailing dinghies and mother with child . . . 70 35

1998. Korean Central History Museum, Pyongyang. Multicoloured.
N3759 10ch. Type **1235** 10 10
N3760 2wn.50 Fossil skull of monkey . . . . 2·25 1·10

1236 Commander of Hedgehog Unit and Squirrel

1998. "Squirrels and Hedgehogs" (cartoon film). Multicoloured.
N3762 20ch. Type **1236** 15 10
N3763 30ch. Commander of hedgehog unit receiving invitation to banquet . . 30 15
N3764 60ch. Weasel ordering mouse to poison bear 55 25
N3765 1wn.20 Squirrel with poisoned bear . . . . . 1·10 55
N3766 2wn. Weasel and mice invade Flower Village 1·75 90
N3767 2wn.50 Hedgehog scout rescues squirrel . . . . 2·25 1·10

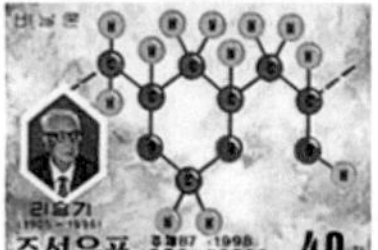
1237 Ri Sung Gi and Molecular Model

1998. 2nd Death Anniv of Ri Sung Gi (inventor of vinalon material).
N3768 **1237** 40ch. multicoloured 35 20

1238 Tiger Cub

1239 "Victory" (Liberation War Monument, Pyongyang) and Medal

1998. Young Mammals. Multicoloured.
N3770 10ch. Type **1238** 10 10
N3771 50ch. Donkey foal 45 20
N3772 1wn.60 Elephant . . . . 1·50 75
N3773 2wn. Two lion cubs . . . 1·75 90

1998. 45th Anniv of Victory in Liberation War.
N3774 **1239** 45ch. brown and pink 40 20

1240 "White Herons in Forest"

1241 Pouch

1998. Embroidery. Multicoloured.
N3776 10ch. Type **1240** 10 10
N3777 40ch. "Carp" 35 20
N3778 1wn.20 "Hollyhock" . . . 1·10 55
N3779 1wn.50 "Cockscomb" . . 1·40 70

1998. Traditional Costume Adornments. Multicoloured.
N3781 10ch. Type **1241** 10 10
N3782 50ch. Tassels 45 25
N3783 1wn.50 Hairpin . . . . . 1·40 70
N3784 1wn.90 Silver knife . . . 1·75 90

1242 Rocket and State Flag

1243 Kim Jong Il Flower

1998. Launch of First Korean Artificial Satellite "Kwangmyongsong 1".
N3785 **1242** 40ch. multicoloured 35 20

1998. Re-election of Kim Jong Il as Chairman of National Defence Commission.
N3787 **1243** 10ch. multicoloured 10 10

1244 Tower of Juche Idea, State Arms and Flag

1998. 50th Anniv of Democratic Republic (1st issue). Multicoloured.
N3789 10ch. Type **1244** 10 10
N3790 1wn. Painting "The Founding of the Democratic People's Republic of Korea, Our Glorious Fatherland" (Kim Il Sung waving from balcony) (48 × 30 mm) 90 45
N3791 1wn. Painting "Square of Victory" (Kim Il Sung and crowd with banners) (48 × 30 mm) 90 45
N3792 1wn. Poster "The Sacred Marks of the Great Leader Kim Il Sung will shine on this Land of Socialism" (Kim Il Sung with produce against panoramic background of Korea) (48 × 30 mm) 90 45

1245 "Let Us Push Ahead with the Forced March for Final Victory"

1247 Cycling

1998.
N3793 **1245** 10ch. multicoloured 10 10

1998. Olympic Games, Sydney, Australia (2000). Multicoloured.
N3795 20ch. Type **1247** 15 10
N3796 50ch. Football 45 25
N3797 80ch. Show jumping . . . 70 35
N3798 1wn.50 Throwing the javelin . . . . 1·40 70

1248 "Cyclamen persicum"

1249 Oral Vaccination

1998. Plants presented as Gifts to Kim Jong Il. Multicoloured.
N3800 20ch. Type **1248** (France, 1994) 15 10
N3801 2wn. "Dianthus chinensis" var. "laciniatus" (Japan, 1994) . . . . 1·75 90

1998. National Vaccination Day.
N3802 **1249** 40ch. multicoloured 35 20

1250 Leopard

1998. The Leopard. Multicoloured.
N3803 1wn. Type **1250** 90 45
N3804 1wn. Leopard in snow . . 90 45
N3805 1wn. Leopard looking to left 90 45
N3806 1wn. Leopard's face . . . 90 45

1251 Canal

1998. Land and Environment Conservation Day. Multicoloured.
N3807 10ch. Type **1251** 10 10
N3808 40ch. Motorway, tower blocks and lorry 35 20

1254 Liu Shaoqi

1255 Victory in Yonsong Monument, Yonan Fortress and Banners

1998. Birth Centenary of Liu Shaoqi (Chairman of Chinese People's Republic, 1959–68). Multicoloured.
N3812 10ch. Type **1254** 10 10
N3813 20ch. Liu Shaoqi and Mao Tse-tung 15 10
N3814 30ch. Liu Shaoqi and his daughter, Xiao Xiao . . 30 15
N3815 40ch. Liu Shaoqi and his wife, Wang Guangmei 35 15

1998. 400th Anniv of Victory in Korean–Japanese War. Multicoloured.
N3817 10ch. Type **1255** 10 10
N3818 30ch. Naval Victory in Myongryang Monument, General Ri Sun Sin and "turtle" ship 30 15
N3819 1wn.60 Monument to Hyujong in Kwangwon province, Hyujong (Buddhist priest), sword and helmet 90 45

1256 Dish Aerial, Artificial Satellite, Globe and Relay Tower

1257 Goat

1998. 15th Anniv of North Korean Membership of Intersputnik.
N3821 **1256** 1wn. dp grn & grn . . 90 45

1998.
N3822 **1257** 10ch. black and green 10 10
N3823 1wn. black and red 90 45

1258 "A Floral Carriage of Happiness" (sculpture) and Palace

1259 Emblem

1998. Mangyongdae Schoolchildren's Palace.
N3824 **1258** 40ch. multicoloured 35 15

1998. 50th Anniv of Universal Declaration of Human Rights.
N3826 **1259** 20ch. multicoloured 15 10

1260 Reeves's Turtle

1261 Thajong Rock

1998. Reptiles and Amphibians. Multicoloured.
N3827 10ch. Type **1260** 10 10
N3828 40ch. Skink 35 15
N3829 60ch. Loggerhead turtle 55 25
N3830 1wn.20 Leatherback turtle 1·10 55
Nos. N3827/30 were issued together, se-tenant, forming a composite design.

1998. Mt. Chilbo. Multicoloured.
N3831 30ch. Type **1261** 30 15
N3832 50ch. Peasant Rock . . . 45 20
N3833 1wn.70 Couple Rock . . . 1·50 75

1262 Ri Mong Ryong marrying Song Chun Hyang

1263 Chollima Statue

1998. Tale of Chun Hyang. Multicoloured.
N3834 40ch. Type **1262** 35 15
N3835 1wn.60 Pyon Hak Do watching Chun Hyang 1·50 75
N3836 2wn.50 Ri Mong Ryong and Chun Hyang . . . 2·40 1·10

1998. Pyongyang Monuments.
N3838 **1263** 10ch. red 10 10
N3839 A 10ch. red 10 10
N3840 B 10ch. red 10 10
N3841 A 20ch. orange 15 10
N3842 **1263** 30ch. orange 30 15
N3843 A 40ch. yellow 35 15
N3844 B 40ch. yellow 35 15
N3845 **1263** 70ch. green 65 30
N3846 B 70ch. green 65 30
N3847 1wn.20 green . . . . 1·00 50
N3848 **1263** 1wn.50 green . . . . 1·40 70
N3849 A 2wn. blue . . . . . 1·75 85
N3850 B 3wn. blue . . . . . 2·75 1·40
N3851 **1263** 5wn. blue . . . . . 4·50 2·25
N3852 A 10wn. violet . . . . 9·00 4·50
DESIGNS: A, Arch of Triumph; B, Tower of Juche Idea.

1264 Rabbit meeting Lion

1265 Automatic Rifle and Star

1999. New Year. Year of the Rabbit. Multicoloured.
N3853 10ch. Type **1264** 10 10
N3854 1wn. Rabbit with mirror and lion . . . . 1·40 70
N3855 1wn.50 Lion in trap . . . 2·00 1·00
N3856 2wn.50 Rabbit . . . . . 3·50 1·75

1999. 40th Anniv of Worker-Peasant Red Guards.
N3858 **1265** 10ch. multicoloured 10 10

1266 Log Cabin (birthplace, Mt. Paekdu)

1267 Cranes, Rice Sheaf and "35"

1999. 57th Birth Anniv of Kim Jong Il.
N3859 **1266** 40ch. multicoloured 30 15

1999. 35th Anniv of Publication of *Theses on the Socialist Rural Question in Our Country* by Kim Il Sung.
N3860 **1267** 10ch. multicoloured 10 10

1268 Korean Script and Crowd

1270 Birthplace, Mangyondae

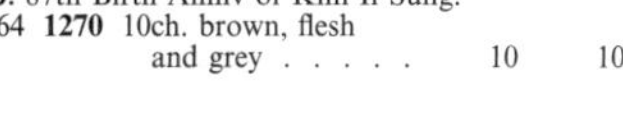
1269 16th-century "Turtle" Ship

1999. 80th Anniv of 1 March Uprising.
N3861 **1268** 10ch. black and brown 10 10

1999. "Australia '99" International Stamp Exhibition, Melbourne.
N3862 **1269** 2wn. multicoloured 1·40 70

1999. 87th Birth Anniv of Kim Il Sung.
N3864 **1270** 10ch. brown, flesh and grey 10 10

1271 Player

1999. 45th Table Tennis Championship, Belgrade, Yugoslavia.
N3866 **1271** 1wn.50 multicoloured 1·10 55

1272 Korean Sports Stamps and Emblem

1999. "iBRA'99" International Stamp Exhibition, Nuremberg, Germany.
N3867 **1272** 1wn. multicoloured 80 40

1273 *Benzoin obtus*

1274 Chimpanzee and Rhinoceros

1999. 40th Anniv of Central Botanical Garden, Mt. Taesong, Pyongyang. Multicoloured.
N3868 10ch. Type **1273** 10 10
N3869 30ch. *Styrax obassia* . . . 20 10
N3870 70ch. *Petunia hybrida* . . 45 20
N3871 90ch. *Impatiens hybrida* 60 30

1999. 40th Anniv of Central Zoo, Mt. Taesong, Pyongyang. Multicoloured.
N3873 50ch. Type **1274** 35 15
N3874 60ch. Manchurian crane and deer 45 20
N3875 70ch. Common zebra and kangaroo 50 25

1275 Light Industry Hall

1999. Three Revolutions Museum, Ryonmotdong, Pyongyang. Multicoloured.
N3877 60ch. Type **1275** 45 20
N3878 80ch. Heavy Industry Hall 60 30

1276 Methods of Communication, Satellite and Globe

1999. 20th Anniv of Asia–Pacific Telecommunications Union.
N3876 **1276** 1wn. multicoloured 75 35

1277 Monument

1999. 60th Anniv of Victory in Battle of Musan.
N3880 **1277** 10ch. multicoloured 10 10

1278 Seagulls

1279 "Princess Margarita in a White Dress"

1999. 190th Birth Anniv of Charles Darwin (naturalist). Multicoloured.
N3881 30ch. Type **1278** 15 10
N3882 50ch. Bats 35 15
N3883 1wn. Dolphins 75 35
N3884 1wn.20 Man on horseback 1·00 50
N3885 1wn.50 Dancer . . . . . 1·10 55

1999. 400th Birth Anniv of Diego Velazquez (artist). Multicoloured.
N3887 50ch. Type **1279** 35 15
N3888 50ch. "Men drawing Water from a Well" . . 35 15
N3889 3wn.50 "Self-portrait" . . 3·75 2·00

1280 Rimyongsu Power Station

1999. Hydro-electric Power Stations. Multicoloured.
N3891 50ch. Type **1280** 35 15
N3892 1wn. Jangjasan Power Station 75 35

1281 Players tackling

1999. 3rd Women's World Football Championship, U.S.A. Multicoloured.
N3893 1wn. Type **1281** 75 35
N3894 1wn.50 Player No. 3 and player wearing blue and white strip tackling . . 1·10 55
N3895 1wn.50 Player and goalkeeper . . . . . . 1·10 55
N3896 2wn. Player No. 7 and player wearing blue strip 1·50 75

1283 Man with Candlesticks

1999. *The Nation and Destiny* (Korean film). Scenes from the film. Multicoloured.
N3898 1wn. Type **1283** 80 40
N3899 1wn. Woman holding gun and man in white suit 80 40
N3900 1wn. Man behind bars . . 80 40
N3901 1wn. Man with protective goggles on head 80 40

1284 Samil Lagoon

1999. Mt. Kumgang. Multicoloured.
N3902 20ch. Type **1284** 15 10
N3903 40ch. Samson Rocks (vert) 30 15
N3904 60ch. Rock, Kumgang Sea 45 20
N3905 80ch. Kuryong Waterfall (vert) 60 30
N3906 1wn. Kwimyon Rock (vert) . . . . 1·10 55

1287 Mercedes Motor Car

1999. 5th Death Anniv of Kim Il Sung. Multicoloured.
N3909 1wn. Type **1287** 70 35
N3910 1wn. Railway carriage . . 70 35

1288 Chinese Characters and Mangyong Hill

1999. 105th Birth Anniv of Kim Hyong Jik (revolutionary).
N3911 **1288** 10ch. multicoloured 10 10

1289 Patterned Vessel

1999. Ceramics. Multicoloured.
N3912 70ch. Type **1289** 50 25
N3913 80ch. Wit and Beauty jar 60 50
N3914 1wn. Patterned vase . . . 80 40
N3915 1wn.50 Celadon kettle . . 1·10 55
N3916 2wn.50 White china vase 1·75 85

1290 Silver Carp

1999. Fish Breeding. Multicoloured.
N3917 50ch. Type **1290** 35 15
N3918 1wn. Common carp . . . 80 40
N3919 1wn.50 Spotted silver carp 1·10 55

1291 Map and Crowd

1999. Year of National Independence and Solidarity.
N3920 **1291** 40ch. multicoloured 35 15

1292 Samjiyon with Maps of Japan and Korea

1999. 40th Anniv of Repatriation of Korean Nationals in Japan.
N3921 **1292** 1wn.50 multicoloured 1·10 55

1293 Symbols of Prosperity

1999.
N3922 **1293** 40ch. multicoloured 55 25

1294 100 m Race

1295 *Acalypha hispida*

1999. World Athletics Championships, Seville, Spain. Multicoloured.
N3923 30ch. Type **1294** 40 20
N3924 40ch. Hurdles 55 25
N3925 80ch. Discus . . . . . . 1·10 55

1999. Plants presented to Kim Il Sung. Multicoloured.
N3926 40ch. Type **1295** 55 25
N3927 40ch. *Allamanda neriifolia* 55 25
N3928 40ch. *Begonia x hiemalis* 55 25
N3929 40ch. *Fatsia japonica* . . 55 25
N3930 40ch. *Streptocarpus hybrida* 55 25
N3931 40ch. *Streptocarpus rexii* 55 25
Nos. N3926/31 were issued together, se-tenant, forming a composite design.

1297 *Grifola frondosa*

1999. Mushrooms. Multicoloured.
N3933 40ch. Type **1297** 55 25
N3934 60ch. *Lactarius volemus* 80 40
N3935 1wn. *Coriolus versicolor* 1·40 70

1298 *Aporocactus flagelliformis*

1300 Shrimp

1999. Cacti. Multicoloured.
N3936 40ch. Type **1298** 55 25
N3937 50ch. *Astrophytum ornatum* 70 35
N3938 60ch. *Gymnocalycium michano vichii* 80 40

1999. Crustacea. Multicoloured.
N3943 50ch. Type **1300** 70 35
N3944 70ch. Shrimp 95 45
N3945 80ch. Lobster . . . . . . 1·10 55

1301 Jong Song Ok (marathon runner)

1999. Victory of Jong Song Ok at World Athletics Championship, Seville.
N3946 **1301** 40ch. multicoloured 55 25

1302 Mt. Kumgang, North Korea

1999. 50th Anniv of North Korean–China Diplomatic Relations. Multicoloured.
N3948 40ch. Type **1302** 30 15
N3949 60ch. Mt. Lushan, China 40 20

1304 Steel Worker holding Torch

1305 Yellow Dragon

2000. New Year. 40th Anniv of 19 April Rising.
N3952 **1304** 10ch. multicoloured 10 10

2000. Koguryo Era Tomb Murals, Jian.
N3953 **1035** 70ch. multicoloured 50 25

1306 Weeding

2000. "Rural Life" (anon). Showing details from the painting. Multicoloured.
N3955 40ch. Type **1306** 30 10
N3956 40ch. Hemp cloth weaving 30 10
N3957 40ch. Threshing 30 10
N3958 40ch. Riverside market . . 30 10

1307 Views across Lake Chou

2000. Mt. Paektu. Multicoloured.
N3959 20ch. Type **1307** 15 10
N3960 20ch. Eagle-shaped rock formation 15 10
N3961 20ch. Owl-shaped rock formation 15 10

1308 Chuibari Mask Dance

1309 Cat

2000. Pongsan Mask Dance. Depicting masks and characters from component dances. Multicoloured.
N3962 50ch. Type **1308** 35 15
N3963 80ch. Ryangban Mask Dance 55 25
N3964 1wn. Malttugi Mask Dance 70 35

2000. Cats. Multicoloured.
N3965 50ch. Type **1309** 35 15
N3966 50ch. Three kittens . . . 35 15
N3967 50ch. Mother and kittens 35 15

1310 Singapura Cat

1312 Styracosaurus

1311 Log Cabin (birthplace, Mt. Paekdu)

2000. Fauna. Multicoloured.
N3968 2wn. Type **1310** . . . . . 1·10 25
N3969 2wn. Blue Abyssinian cat 1·10 25
N3970 2wn. Oriental cat . . . . 1·10 25
N3971 2wn. Scottish fold tabby cat . . . . 1·10 25
N3972 2wn. Shiba inu . . . . . 1·10 25
N3973 2wn. Yorkshire terrier . . 1·10 25
N3974 2wn. Japanese chin . . . 1·10 25
N3975 2wn. Afghan hound . . . 1·10 25
N3976 2wn. Przewalski's horse 1·10 25
N3977 2wn. Grey cob . . . . 1·10 25
N3978 2wn. White horse rearing 1·10 25
N3979 2wn. Donkeys . . . . . . 1·10 25
N3980 2wn. Panda in tree . . . . 1·10 25
N3981 2wn. Panda eating . . . . 1·10 25
N3982 2wn. Panda scratching against tree . . . . . . 1·10 25
N3983 2wn. Mother and cub . . 1·10 25
N3984 2wn. Two polar bears (*Ursus maritimus*) . . . 1·10 25
N3985 2wn. Mother and cub . . 1·10 25
N3986 2wn. Standing bear . . . 1·10 25
N3987 2wn. Bear lying down . . 1·10 25
N3988 2wn. Mexican lance-headed rattlesnake (*Crotalus polystictus*) . . 1·10 25
N3989 2wn. Scarlet king snake (*Lampropeltis triangulum elapsoides*) . . . . . . 1·10 25
N3990 2wn. Green tree python (*Chondropython viridis*) 1·10 25
N3991 2wn. Blood python (*Python curtus*) . . . . 1·10 25
N3992 2wn. Corythosaurus . . . 1·10 25
N3993 2wn. Psittacosaurus . . . 1·10 25
N3994 2wn. Megalosaurus . . . 1·10 25
N3995 2wn. Muttaburrasaurus . . 1·10 25
N3996 2wn. Burmeister's porpoise (*Phocoena spinipinnis*) 1·10 25
N3997 2wn. Finless porpoise (*Neophocaena phocaenoides*) . . . . . 1·10 25
N3998 2wn. Bottle-nosed dolphin (*Tursiops truncatus*) . . 1·10 25
N3999 2wn. Curvier's beaked whale (*Ziphius cavirostris*) . . . . . . 1·10 25
N4000 2wn. Port Jackson shark (*Heterodontus portusjacksoni*) . . . . 1·10 25
N4001 2wn. Great hammerhead shark (*Sphyrna mokarran*) (inscr "mokkarran") . . . . . 1·10 25
N4002 2wn. Zebra shark (*Stegostoma fasciatum*) 1·10 25
N4003 2wn. Ornate wobbegong (*Orectolobus ornatus*) . . 1·10 25
N4004 2wn. Ruddy shelduck (*Tadorna ferruginea*) . . 1·10 25
N4005 2wn. European widgeon (*Anas penelope*) . . . . 1·10 25
N4006 2wn. Mandarin drake (*Aix galericulata*) . . . . . 1·10 25
N4007 2wn. Hottentot teal (*Anas hottentota*) . . . . . . 1·10 25
N4008 2wn. Little owl (*Athene noctua*) . . . . 1·10 25
N4009 2wn. Ural owl (*Strix uralensis*) . . . . 1·10 25
N4010 2wn. Great horned owl (*Bubo virginianus*) . . . 1·10 25
N4011 2wn. Snowy owl (*Nyctea scandiaca*) . . . . . . 1·10 25
N4012 2wn. Slaty-headed parakeet (*Psittacula himalayana*) . . . . . . 1·10 25
N4013 2wn. Male eclectus parrot (*Eclectus roratus*) . . . 1·10 25
N4014 2wn. Major Mitchell's cockatoo (*Cacatua leadbeateri*) . . . . . . 1·10 25
N4015 2wn. Female eclectus parrot (*Eclectus roratus*) 1·10 25
N4016 2wn. Indian leaf butterfly (*Kallima paralekta*) . . 1·10 25
N4017 2wn. Spanish festoon (*Zerynthia rumina*) . . . 1·10 25
N4018 2wn. Male and female emerald swallowtails (*Papilio palinurus*) . . . 1·10 25
N4019 2wn. *Bhutanitis lidderdalii* 1·10 25
N4020 2wn. Bumble bee . . . . 1·10 25
N4021 2wn. Bumble bee on flower . . . . 1·10 25
N4022 2wn. Honey bee (*Apis mellifera*) . . . . 1·10 25
N4023 2wn. Honey bee attacking spider . . . . 1·10 25
N4024 2wn. *Micrommata virescens* (spider) . . . 1·10 25
N4025 2wn. *Araneus quadratus* (spider) . . . . 1·10 25
N4026 2wn. *Dolomedes fimbriatus* (spider) . . . . 1·10 25
N4027 2wn. *Aculepeira ceropegia* (spider) . . . . 1·10 25
Nos. N3980/3 are wrongly inscr "Aculepeira ceropegia".

2000. 58th Birth Anniv of Kim Jong II.
N4028 **1311** 40ch. multicoloured 20 10

2000. Dinosaurs. Sheet 120 × 80 mm, containing T **1312** and similar multicoloured designs.
MSN4029 1wn. Type **1312**; 1wn. Saltasaurus (29 × 41 mm); 1wn. Tyrannosaurus . . . 1·75 40

1313 Peacock (*Inachis io*)

2000. Butterflies. Multicoloured.
N4030 40ch. Type **1313** 20 10
N4031 60ch. Swallowtail (*Papilio machaon*) 35 10
N4032 80ch. Mimic (*Hypolimnas misippus*) 45 10
N4034 1wn.20 *Papilio bianor Cramer* 70 15

1314 Patas Monkey (*Erythrocebus patas*)

1315 Red Flag, Top of Chollima Statue and Emblem

2000. Primates. Multicoloured.
N4035 50ch. Type **1314** 30 10
N4036 50ch. Western tarsier (*Tarsius spectrm*) . . . 30 10
MSN4037 Sheet 75 × 65 mm. 2wn. Mona monkey (*Cercopithecus mona*) . . . . 1·10 25

2000. 55th Anniv of Korean Worker's Party (1st issue).
N4038 **1315** 10ch. multicoloured 10 10
See also Nos. N4083/**MS**N4084.

1316 Demonstrators

2000. 40th Anniv of 19 April Uprising, South Korea.
N4039 **1316** 40ch. multicoloured 20 10

1317 Kim Il Sun Flower

2000. 88th Birth Anniv of Kim II Sung.
N4040 **1317** 40ch. multicoloured 20 10

1318 Mun Ik Hwan

1319 Symbols of Technology, Globe, Flag and Chollima Statue

2000. 6th Death Anniv of Mun Ik Hwan (National Reunification Prize winner).
N4041 **1318** 50ch. multicoloured 30 10

2000. New Millennium. 55th Anniv of Korean Worker's Party. Multicoloured.
N4042 40ch. Type **1319** 20 10
N4043 1wn.20 Dove with envelope, globe and satellites 70 15

1320 *Cattleya intermedia*

2000. Orchids. Multicoloured.
N4044 20ch. Type **1320** 10 10
N4045 50ch. *Dendrobium moschatum* 30 10
N4046 70ch. *Brassolaeliocattleya* 40 10
MSN4047 85 × 60 mm. 2wn. *Laeliocattleya* . . . . 1·10 25

1321 Okryu Bridge (River Taedong)

2000. Bridges.
N4048 20ch. Type **1321** 10 10
N4049 30ch. Ansan Bridge (River Pothong) 15 10
N4050 1wn. Rungna Bridge (River Taedong) 60 15

1322 Okryugum and Jaengggang Dancers

1323 Half Moon (Yun Kuk Yong)

2000. Air. "WIPA 2000" International Stamp Exhibition, Vienna. Traditional Instruments and Folk Dances. Sheet 150 × 84 mm, containing T **1322** and similar vert designs. Multicoloured.
MSN4051 Type **1322**; 1wn.50 Oungum and Full Moon Viewing; 1wn.50 Janggo (drum) and Trio 1·75 40
The 1wn. stamp does not carry an airmail inscription.

2000. Children's Songs. Multicoloured.
N4052 40ch. Type **1323** 20 10
N4053 60ch. Kangnam Nostalgia (Kim Sok Song and An Ki Yong) 35 10
MSN4054 95 × 80 mm. 2wn. Spring in Home Village (Ri Won Su and Hong Ran Pha) . . . . 1·10 25

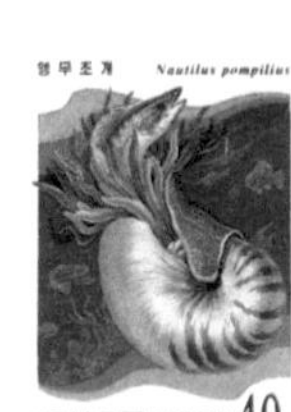

1324 Pearly Nautilus (*Nautilus pompilius*)

1325 Drake and Duck

2000. Cephalopods. Multicoloured.
N4055 40ch. Type **1324** 20 10
N4056 60ch. Common octopus (*Octopus vulgaris*) . . . 35 10
N4057 1w.50 Squid (*Ommastrephes sloanei pacificus*) 85 20
MSN4058 60 × 70 mm. 1wn.50 No. N4057 . . . . 85 20

2000. Mandarin Ducks. Multicoloured.
N4059 50ch. Type **1325** 30 10
N4060 50ch. Drake with duck and couple on bridge 30 10
MSN4061 92 × 75 mm. 1wn. Duck, drake and ducklings 60 15

1326 Table Tennis

2000. "World Expo 2000" International Stamp Exhibition, Anaheim, California. Sport. Multicoloured.
N4062 80ch. Type **1326** 45 10
N4063 1wn. Basketball 60 15
N4064 1wn.20 Baseball 70 15

1327 Sungri-61 NA

2000. Trucks. Multicoloured.
N4065 40ch. Type **1327** 20 10
N4066 70ch. Tipper truck 40 10
N4067 1wn.50 Konsol 25 ton dump truck 85 20

1328 Ri Tae Hun (artillery company commander) and 76 mm Field Gun

2000. Weaponry. Multicoloured.
N4068 60ch. Type **1328** 35 10
N4069 80ch. Ko Hyon Bin (tank commander) and T-34 tank 45 10
N4070 1wn. Squadron leader Paek Ki Rak and Yakovlev Yak-9P pursuit plane 60 15

1329 Fluorite

2000. Minerals. Multicoloured.

N4071 30ch. Type **1329** 15 10
N4072 60ch. Graphite 35 10
N4073 1w.60 Magnesite 90 20
MSN4074 74 × 74 mm. 1w.60 No. N4073 . . . . 90 20

2000. "Indonesia 2000" International Stamp Exhibition, Jakarta. Nos. N4059/**MS**N4061 optd **WORLD PHILATELIC EXHIBITION JAKARTA 15-21 AUGUST 2000** and emblem, No. **MS**N4061 optd in the margin.

N4075 50ch. multicoloured . . . 30 10
N4076 50ch. multicoloured . . . 30 10
MSN4077 multicoloured 60 15

1331 Swimming

2000. Olympic Games, Sydney. Triathlon. Sheet 78 × 110 mm, containing T **1331** and similar horiz designs. Multicoloured.

MSN4078 Type **1331**; 1w.20 Cycling; 2w. Running . . . . 2·00 50

1332 Sanju Falls

2000. Myohyang Mountain. Multicoloured.

N4079 40ch. Type **1332** 20 10
N4080 40ch. Inho rock 20 10
N4081 1w.20 Sangwon valley . . 70 15

2000. "Espana 2000" International Stamp Exhibition, Madrid. No. **MS**N4029 optd **Exposioion Mundial de Filatolia 2000. 0.6 - 14.** in the margin.

MSN4082 120 × 80 mm. 1w. Type **1312**; 1w. Saltasaurus; 1w. Tyrannosaurus . . . . 1·10 25

1334 Anniversary Emblem and Party Museum

2000. 55th Anniv of Korean Worker's Party (2nd issue). Multicoloured.

N4083 40ch. Type **1334** 20 10
MSN4084 120 × 85 mm. 50ch. Kim Il Sung (35 × 56 mm); 50ch. Kim Jong Il (35 × 56 mm); 50ch. Kim Jong Suk (35 × 56 mm) 80 20

1335 Flag, Bulldozer and Fields

2000. Land Re-organization.

N4085 **1335** 10ch. multicoloured 10 10

1336 Potatoes, Pigs, Fields and Scientist

2000. Taehongdan (potato production centre). Multicoloured.

N4086 40ch. Type **1336** 20 10
MSN4087 110 × 92 mm. 2w. Kim Il Sung with farmers in potato field (42 × 34 mm) . . . . 1·10 25

1337 Kim Jong Il and Pres. Jiang Zemin

2000. Visit of Kim Jong Il to People's Republic of China. Sheet 110 × 80 mm.

MSN4088 multicoloured 70 15

1338 Kim Jong Il and Pres. Kim Dae Jung

2000. North Korea–South Korea Summit Meeting, Pyongyang. Sheet 85 × 110 mm.

MSN4089 multicoloured . . . . 1·10 25

1339 Kim Jong Il and Pres. Putin

2000. Visit of Pres. Vladimir Putin of Russian Federation. Sheet 94 × 108 mm.

MSN4090 multicoloured 85 20

1340 Soldiers crossing River Amnok

2000. 50th Anniv of Chinese People's Volunteers Participation in Korean War (1st issue). Sheet 139 × 164 mm, containing T **1340** and similar horiz designs. Multicoloured.

MSN4091 Type **1340**; 10ch. Battle; 50ch. Chinese and Korean soldiers; 50ch. Mao Tse-tung and Chinese leaders; 80ch. Soldiers and gun emplacement . . . . . . 1·10 25

1341 Chinese and Korean Soldiers

1342 *Aquilegia oxysepala*

2000. 50th Anniv of Chinese People's Volunteers Participation in Korean War (2nd issue).

N4092 **1341** 30ch. multicoloured 15 10

2000. Alpine Flowers. Multicoloured.

N4093 30ch. Type **1342** 15 10
N4094 50ch. Brilliant campion (*Lychnis fulgens*) 25 10
N4095 70ch. Self-heal (*Prunela vulgaris*) 40 10

1343 Women presenting Prisoners with Flowers (½-size illustration)

2000. Repatriation of Long-term Prisoners of War. Sheets containing horiz designs as T **1343**. Multicoloured.

MSN4096 Two sheets. (a) 139 × 87 mm. 80ch. Type **1343**. (b) 165 × 120 mm. 1w.20 Prisoners and crowd Price for 2 sheets 1·10 25

1344 Flag, Factories and Trees

2001. New Year (1st issue).

N4097 **1344** 10ch. multicoloured 10 10

1345 White Snake meeting Xu Xian

2001. New Year (2nd issue). Tale of the White Snake. Multicoloured.

N4098 10ch. Type **1345** 10 10
N4099 40ch. Stealing the Immortal Grass 20 10
N4100 50ch. White and Green snakes and Xu Xian . . 25 10
N4101 80ch. Flooding of Jinshan Hill 45 10
MSN4102 105 × 80 mm. 1wn 20 White snake and Green snake (32 × 52 mm) 70 15

1346 E. Lasker and J-R. Capablanca

2001. World Chess Champions. 165th Birth Anniv of Wilhelm Steinitz (19th-century champion) (**MS**N4109). Multicoloured.

N4103 10ch. Type **1346** 10 10
N4104 20ch. A. Alekhine and M. Euwe 10 10
N4105 30ch. M. Botvinnik and V. Smylov 15 10
N4106 40ch. T. Petrosian and M. Tal 20 10
N4107 50ch. B. Spassky and R. Fischer 25 10
N4108 1wn. A. Karpov and G. Kasparov 50 10
MSN4109 105 × 80 mm. 2wn.50 Wilhelm Steinitz (32 × 52 mm) 1·40 30

1347 White Suit and Black Hat

2001. Ri-Dynasty Men's Costumes. Multicoloured.

N4110 10ch. Type **1347** 10 10
N4111 40ch. White suit with blue waistcoat 20 10
N4112 50ch. White trousers, brown jacket and pagoda-shaped hat . . . 25 10
N4113 70ch. Knee-length pale blue coat, black hat and stick 40 10
MSN4114 110 × 80 mm. 1wn.50 Blue knee-length coat with ornamental cummerbund and black boots 85 20

1348 Small Appliance (fire)

2001. Fire Engines. Designs showing engines and fire hazards. Multicoloured.

N4115 20ch. Type **1348** 10 10
N4116 30ch. Large engine with hydraulic ladder (oil can) 15 10
N4117 40ch. Small engine with two-door cab and closed back (match) 20 10
N4118 60ch. Small engine with ladder, spotlight and external hose reel (gas canister) 30 10
N4119 2wn. Older-style engine (cigarette) 80 20
MSN4120 95 × 90 mm. 2wn. As No. N4119 (32 × 52 mm) . . . . . 1·10 25

1349 Black-naped Oriole (*Oriolus chinensis*)

2001. "HONG KONG 2001" International Stamp Exhibition. Sheet 72 × 80 mm.

MSN4121 **1349** 1wn.40 mult . . 80 20

1350 Jjong Il Peak and Flower

2001. 59th Birth Anniv of Kim Jong Il.

N4122 **1350** 10ch. multicoloured 10 10

1351 Flag and Symbols of Industry and Agriculture

2001. New Millennium. Rodong Sinmun, Josoninmingun and Chongnyonjonwi Newspapers Joint Editorial.

N4123 **1351** 10ch. multicoloured 10 10

1352 Log Cabin (revolutionary headquarters, Mt. Paekdu)

2001.

N4124 **1352** 40ch. multicoloured 20 10

APPENDIX

The following stamps have either been issued in excess of postal needs or have not been available to the public in reasonable quantities at face value. Such stamps may later be given full listing if there is evidence of regular postal use.

1976.

Olympic Games, Montreal. Three-dimensional stamps showing Olympic events. 5, 10, 15, 20, 25, 40ch.

1977.

Olympic Games, Montreal. Three-dimensional stamps showing medals. 5, 10, 15, 20, 25, 40ch.

Olympic Games, Montreal. 1976 Olympic Games issue optd with winners' names. 5, 10, 15, 20, 25, 40ch.

1979.

XIII Winter Olympic Games, 1980. Nos. N1688/94 optd. 2, 5, 10, 15, 20, 25, 40ch.

1981.

Nobel Prizes for Medicine. Nos. N1955/61 optd. 7 × 10ch.

World Cup Football Championship, Spain (1982). Nos. N1731/41 optd. 12 × 20ch.

World Cup Football Championship, Spain (1982). Three-dimensional stamps. Air 20, 30ch.

1982.

21st Birthday of Princess of Wales. Nos. N2108/11 and N2120/3 optd. 10, 20, 30, 40ch.; 10, 20, 30, 70ch.

Birth of Prince William of Wales. Nos. N2185/91 optd. 10, 20, 30, 50, 60, 70, 80ch.

World Cup Football Championship, Spain, Results. Nos. N2201/6 optd. 10, 20, 30, 40, 50, 60ch.

Birth of Prince William of Wales. Three-dimensional stamps. 3 × 30ch.

1983.

XXIII Olympic Games, Los Angeles, 1984. Nos. N2084/8 optd. 10, 15, 20, 25, 30ch.

1984.

European Royal History. 81 × 10ch.

KOUANG TCHEOU (KWANGCHOW) Pt. 17

An area and port of S. China, leased by France from China in April 1898. It was returned to China in February 1943.

1906. 100 centimes = 1 franc.
1919. 100 cents = 1 piastre.

Unless otherwise stated the following are optd or surch on stamps of Indo-China.

1906. Surch **Kouang Tcheou-Wan** and value in Chinese.
1 8 1c. green . . . 4·25 4·25
2 2c. red on yellow . . . 4·00 4·00
3 4c. mauve on blue . . . 4·00 4·25
4 5c. green . . . 4·50 5·00
5 10c. red . . . 4·50 4·50
6 15c. brown on blue . . . 10·50 10·50
7 20c. red on green . . . 5·00 4·75
8 25c. blue . . . 4·50 4·75
9 30c. brown on cream . . . 5·75 6·25
10 35c. black on yellow . . . 8·25 8·25
11 40c. black on grey . . . 5·75 5·50
12 50c. brown on cream . . . 25·00 25·00
13 D 75c. brown on orange . . . 32·00 32·00
14 8 1f. green . . . 32·00 35·00
15 2f. brown on yellow . . . 32·00 35·00
16 D 5f. mauve on lilac . . . £160 £160
17 8 10f. red on green . . . £180 £200

1908. Native types surch **KOUANG-TCHEOU** and value in Chinese.
18 10 1c. black and brown . . . 85 65
19 2c. black and brown . . . 45 1·60
20 4c. black and blue . . . 1·25 1·75
21 5c. black and green . . . 1·75 1·25
22 10c. black and red . . . 1·75 1·90
23 15c. black and violet . . . 3·00 3·50
24 11 20c. black and violet . . . 3·75 5·00
25 25c. black and blue . . . 6·00 6·25
26 30c. black and brown . . . 8·25 11·00
27 35c. black and green . . . 14·00 15·00
28 40c. black and brown . . . 12·50 15·00
29 50c. black and red . . . 16·00 16·00
30 12 75c. black and orange . . . 16·00 16·00
31 – 1f. black and red . . . 19·00 19·00
32 – 2f. black and green . . . 35·00 38·00
33 – 5f. black and blue . . . 65·00 70·00
34 – 10f. black and violet . . . 65·00 £110

1919. Nos. 18/34 surch in figures and words.
35 10 ⅖ on 1c. black and brown . . 60 2·50
36 ⅘c. on 2c. black and brown 35 2·75
37 1⅕c. on 4c. black and blue 1·10 2·25
38 2c. on 5c. black and green 3·00 3·25
39 4c. on 10c. black and red 4·00 2·50
40 6c. on 15c. black and violet 2·75 3·00
41 11 8c. on 20c. black and violet 5·00 4·75
42 10c. on 25c. black and blue 13·50 12·50
43 12c. on 30c. black & brown 3·75 3·75
44 14c. on 35c. black and green 4·00 3·50
45 16c. on 40c. black & brown 3·25 3·25
46 20c. on 50c. black and red 3·50 3·25
47 12 30c. on 75c. black & orange 7·75 8·75
48 – 40c. on 1f. black and red . . 11·00 9·50
49 – 80c. on 2f. black and green 11·50 10·00
50 – 2p. on 5f. black and blue . . £130 £120
51 – 4p. on 10f. black and violet 21·00 25·00

1923. Native types optd **KOUANG-TCHEOU** only. (Value in cents and piastres).
52 10 1/10c. red and grey . . . 15 2·75
53 ⅕c. black and blue . . . 15 3·00
54 ⅖c. black and brown . . . 15 2·50
55 ⅘c. black and red . . . 15 3·00
56 1c. black and brown . . . 30 2·75
57 2c. black and green . . . 55 3·25
58 3c. black and violet . . . 45 3·25
59 4c. black and orange . . . 55 3·00
60 5c. black and red . . . 1·25 2·50
61 11 6c. black and red . . . 55 3·50
62 7c. black and green . . . 40 3·00
63 8c. black on lilac . . . 1·75 3·25
64 9c. black and yellow on green . . . 2·50 3·25
65 10c. black and blue . . . 1·75 3·25
66 11c. black and violet . . . 2·75 3·25
67 12c. black and brown . . . 3·00 3·25
68 15c. black and orange . . . 3·50 4·00
69 20c. black and blue on buff 3·00 3·75
70 40c. black and red . . . 4·25 4·75
71 1p. black and green on green . . . 9·25 13·00
72 2p. black and purple on pink . . . 15·00 20·00

1927. Pictorial types optd **KOUANG-TCHEOU**.
73 22 1/10c. green . . . 15 2·75
74 ⅕c. yellow . . . 20 2·50
75 ⅖c. blue . . . 25 3·00
76 ½c. brown . . . 20 2·25
77 1c. orange . . . 85 3·00
78 2c. green . . . 35 3·00
79 3c. blue . . . 95 3·25
80 4c. pink . . . 55 3·00
81 5c. violet . . . 80 3·25
82 23 6c. red . . . 55 2·25
83 7c. brown . . . 1·10 3·25
84 8c. green . . . 1·60 3·00
85 9c. purple . . . 1·50 3·00
86 10c. blue . . . 1·90 3·00
87 11c. orange . . . 3·00 3·50
88 12c. grey . . . 1·75 3·00
89 24 15c. brown and red . . . 3·50 4·00
90 20c. grey and violet . . . 3·75 4·00
91 – 25c. mauve and brown . . 3·50 4·00
92 – 30c. olive and blue . . . 3·50 3·50
93 – 40c. blue and red . . . 3·25 3·25
94 – 50c. grey and green . . . 3·50 3·50
95 – 1p. black, yellow and blue 4·75 6·25
96 – 2p. blue, orange and red 6·25 7·00

1937. 1931 issue optd **KOUANG-TCHEOU**.
98 33 1/10c. blue . . . 15 2·75
99 ⅕c. lake . . . 15 3·00
100 ⅖c. red . . . 15 3·00
101 ½c. brown . . . 15 2·75
102 ⅘c. violet . . . 30 2·75
103 33 1c. brown . . . 15 2·75
104 2c. green . . . 15 2·50
126 – 3c. brown . . . 50 30
105 – 3c. green . . . 75 3·00
106 – 4c. blue . . . 2·50 3·25
127 – 4c. green . . . 50 30
128 – 4c. yellow . . . 1·75 1·00
107 – 5c. purple . . . 2·50 3·00
129 – 5c. green . . . 50 35
108 – 6c. red . . . 20 3·00
130 – 7c. black . . . 50 45
131 – 8c. lake . . . 50 45
132 – 9c. black on yellow . . . 50 45
109 – 10c. blue . . . 2·50 3·00
133 – 10c. blue on pink . . . 75 55
110 – 15c. blue . . . 70 3·00
134 – 18c. blue . . . 30 30
111 – 20c. red . . . 20 3·00
112 – 21c. green . . . 20 3·00
135 – 22c. green . . . 50 35
113 – 25c. purple . . . 2·00 1·60
136 – 25c. blue . . . 70 45
114 – 30c. brown . . . 3·50 4·75
115 36 50c. brown . . . 1·40 3·00
116 60c. purple . . . 35 3·25
137 70c. blue . . . 40 3·25
117 1p. green . . . 2·00 3·25
118 2p. red . . . 2·75 3·75

1939. New York World's Fair. As T **28** of Mauritania.
119 13c. red . . . 75 3·25
120 23c. deep blue and blue . . . 1·40 3·25

1939. 150th Anniv of French Revolution. As T **29** of Mauritania.
121 6c.+2c. green . . . 6·00 9·25
122 7c.+3c. brown . . . 6·00 9·25
123 9c.+4c. orange . . . 7·25 9·25
124 13c.+10c. red . . . 5·50 9·25
125 23c.+20c. blue . . . 6·75 9·25

KUWAIT Pt. 1, Pt. 19

An independent Arab Shaikhdom on the N.W. coast of the Persian Gulf with Indian and later British postal administration. On 1 February 1959 the Kuwait Government assumed responsibility for running its own postal service. In special treaty relations with Great Britain until 19 June 1961 when Kuwait became completely independent.

1923. 12 pies = 1 anna; 16 annas = 1 rupee.
1957. 100 naye paise = 1 rupee.
1961. 1000 fils = 1 dinar.

Stamps of India optd **KUWAIT**.

1923. King George V.
16 56 ½a. green . . . 3·25 1·40
16b 79 ½a. green . . . 4·50 1·40
2 57 1a. brown . . . 2·75 3·25
17b 81 1a. brown . . . 5·50 1·25
3 58 1½a. brown (No. 163) . . 2·25 4·25
4 59 2a. lilac . . . 3·75 4·00
19c 2a. red . . . 4·50 2·50
18 70 2a. lilac . . . 3·25 1·25
19 2a. red . . . 20·00 85·00
5 61 2a.6p. blue . . . 2·75 8·00
6 62 3a. orange . . . 4·25 20·00
20 3a. blue . . . 2·75 1·75
21 3a. red . . . 5·50 4·25
22 71 4a. green . . . 25·00 80·00
22a 63 4a. green . . . 6·50 14·00
9 64 6a. bistre . . . 8·50 13·00
23 65 8a. mauve . . . 19·00 13·00
11 66 12a. red . . . 14·00 42·00
12 67 1r. brown and green . . . 21·00 32·00
26 2r. red and orange . . . 10·00 65·00
27 5r. blue and violet . . . 80·00 £200
28 10r. green and red . . . £170 £375
29 15r. blue and olive . . . £500 £750

1933. Air.
31 72 2a. green . . . 14·00 27·00
32 3a. blue . . . 3·00 2·50
33 4a. olive . . . 85·00 £170
34 6a. bistre . . . 3·50 4·50

1939. King George VI.
36 91 ½a. brown . . . 7·00 1·75
38 1a. red . . . 7·00 1·50
39 92 2a. red . . . 7·00 2·50
41 – 3a. green . . . 7·00 2·00
43 – 4a. brown . . . 38·00 18·00
44 – 6a. green . . . 25·00 8·50
45 – 8a. violet . . . 28·00 32·00
46 – 12a. red . . . 20·00 60·00
47 93 1r. slate and brown . . . 12·00 3·25
48 2r. purple and brown . . . 3·75 16·00
49 5r. green and blue . . . 13·00 19·00
50 10r. purple and red . . . 60·00 75·00
51 15r. brown and green . . . £150 £200

1942. King George VI stamps of 1940.
52 100a 3p. slate . . . 2·25 3·50
53 ½a. purple . . . 1·75 3·00
54 9p. green . . . 3·75 9·00
55 1a. red . . . 1·50 2·25
56 101 1½a. violet . . . 4·25 8·50
57 2a. red . . . 4·25 3·25
58 3a. violet . . . 5·50 5·50
59 3½a. blue . . . 4·25 8·50
60 102 4a. brown . . . 5·50 3·00
60a 6a. green . . . 14·00 9·00
61 8a. violet . . . 7·00 4·25
62 12a. purple . . . 8·00 4·25
63 – 14a. purple (No. 277) . . 15·00 18·00

From 1948 onwards, for stamps with similar surcharges, but without name of country, see British Postal Agencies in Eastern Arabia.

Stamps of Great Britain surch **KUWAIT** and new values in Indian currency.

1948. King George VI.
64 128 ½a. on ½d. green . . . 1·50 1·75
84 ½a. on ½d. orange . . . 2·50 1·50
65 1a. on 1d. red . . . 1·50 1·75
85 1a. on 1d. blue . . . 2·00 1·60
66 1½a. on 1½d. brown . . . 2·00 1·50
86 1½a. on 1½d. green . . . 2·00 2·25
67 2a. on 2d. orange . . . 1·50 1·50
87 2a. on 2d. brown . . . 2·00 1·50
68 2½a. on 2½d. blue . . . 2·00 1·00
88 2½a. on 2½d. red . . . 2·00 2·75
69 3a. on 3d. violet . . . 1·50 70
89 129 4a. on 4d. blue . . . 1·75 1·50
70 6a. on 6d. purple . . . 1·50 75
71 130 1r. on 1s. brown . . . 3·50 1·75
72 131 2r. on 2s.6d. green . . . 3·75 4·50
73 5r. on 5s. red . . . 5·50 4·50
73a – 10r. on 10s. blue (No. 478a) . . . 38·00 6·00

1948. Silver Wedding.
74 137 2½a. on 2½d. blue . . . 2·00 2·00
75 138 15r. on £1 blue . . . 30·00 30·00

1948. Olympic Games.
76 139 2½a. on 2½d. blue . . . 1·00 2·25
77 140 3a. on 3d. violet . . . 1·00 2·25
78 – 6a. on 6d. purple . . . 1·25 2·25
79 – 1r. on 1s. brown . . . 1·25 2·25

1949. U.P.U.
80 143 2½a. on 2½d. blue . . . 1·00 2·25
81 144 3a. on 3d. violet . . . 1·00 3·00
82 – 6a. on 6d. purple . . . 1·00 3·00
83 – 1r. on 1s. brown . . . 1·00 1·25

1951. Pictorial high values.
90 147 2r. on 2s.6d. green . . . 15·00 4·75
91 – 5r. on 5s. red (No. 510) . . 22·00 5·00
92 – 10r. on 10s. blue (No. 511) 30·00 8·00

1952. Queen Elizabeth II.
93 154 ½a. on ½d. orange . . . 20 1·50
94 1a. on 1d. blue . . . 20 10
95 1½a. on 1½d. green . . . 15 1·00
96 2a. on 2d. brown . . . 35 10
97 155 2½a. on 2½d. red . . . 15 1·00
98 3a. on 3d. lilac . . . 40 10
99 4a. on 4d. blue . . . 1·25 75
100 157 6a. on 6d. purple . . . 1·25 10
101 160 12a. on 1s.3d. green . . . 5·00 2·50
102 1r. on 1s.6d. blue . . . 4·50 10

1953. Coronation.
103 161 2½a. on 2½d. red . . . 3·50 3·25
104 – 4a. on 4d. blue . . . 3·50 3·25
105 163 12a. on 1s.3d. green . . . 5·00 5·50
106 – 1r. on 1s.6d. blue . . . 4·00 1·25

1955. Pictorials.
107 166 2r. on 2s.6d. brown . . . 8·00 2·25
108 – 5r. on 5s. red . . . 8·50 6·50
109 – 10r. on 10s. blue . . . 8·50 4·75

1957. Queen Elizabeth II.
120 157 1n.p. on 5d. brown . . . 10 70
121 154 3n.p. on ½d. orange . . . 60 3·25
122 6n.p. on 1d. blue . . . 60 1·25
123 9n.p. on 1½d. green . . . 60 2·25
124 12n.p. on 2d. brown . . . 60 3·25
125 155 15n.p. on 2½d. red . . . 60 2·75
126 20n.p. on 3d. lilac . . . 60 30
127 25n.p. on 4d. blue . . . 2·25 3·25
128 157 40n.p. on 6d. purple . . . 1·00 30
129 158 50n.p. on 9d. olive . . . 5·50 4·00
130 160 75n.p. on 1s.3d. green . . . 5·50 4·50

20 Shaikh Abdullah 21 Dhow

1958.
131 20 5n.p. green . . . 50 10
132a 10n.p. red . . . 20 10
133 15n.p. brown . . . 20 15
134 20n.p. violet . . . 20 10
135 25n.p. orange . . . 35 10
136 40n.p. purple . . . 1·50 55
137 21 40n.p. blue . . . 45 20
138 – 50n.p. red . . . 40 20
139 – 75n.p. green . . . 45 30
140 – 1r. purple . . . 50 35
141 – 2r. blue and brown . . . 2·50 70
142 – 5r. green . . . 4·00 1·50
143 – 10r. lilac . . . 13·00 4·50

DESIGNS—HORIZ: As Type **21**: 50n.p. Oil pipelines; 75n.p. Shuwaikh Power Station. 36 × 20 mm: 1r. Oil rig; 2r. Single-masted dhow; 5r. Kuwait Mosque; 10r. Main Square, Kuwait Town.

22 Shaikh Abdullah and Flag

1960. 10th Anniv of Shaikh's Accession.
144 22 40n.p. red and green . . . 35 10
145 60n.p. red and blue . . . 45 20

1961. As 1958 issue but currency changed and new designs.
146 20 1f. green . . . 15 10
147 2f. red . . . 15 10
148 4f. brown . . . 15 10
149 5f. violet . . . 15 10
150 8f. red . . . 20 10
151 15f. purple . . . 25 10
152 – 20f. green (as No. 142) . . 50 10
153 – 25f. blue . . . 1·50 10
154 – 30f. blue and brown (as No. 141) . . . 1·75 10
155 – 35f. black and red . . . 75 40
156 21 40f. blue (32 × 22 mm) . . 1·50 15
157 – 45f. brown . . . 50 10
158 – 75f. brown & grn (as No. 141) . . . 3·00 60
159 – 90f. brown and blue . . . 1·75 35
160 – 100f. red . . . 3·75 10
161 21 250f. green (32 × 22 mm) 8·50 1·50
162 – 1d. orange . . . 10·00 1·50
163 – 3d. red (as No. 142) . . 25·00 18·00

NEW DESIGNS—37 × 20 mm: 25, 100f. Vickers Viscount 700 airliner over South Pier, Mina al Ahmadi; 35, 90f. Shuwaikh Secondary School; 45f., 1d. Wara Hill.

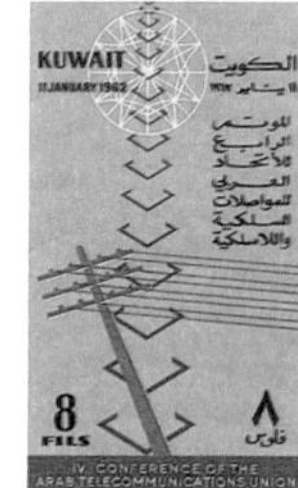

23 Telegraph Pole

1962. 4th Arab Telecommunications Union Conference.
164 23 8f. blue and black . . . 15 10
165 20f. red and black . . . 35 20

1962. Arab League Week. As T **76** of Libya.
166 20f. purple . . . 20 10
167 45f. brown . . . 50 20

25 Mubarakiya School, Shaikh Abdullah and Shaikh Mubarak

1962. Golden Jubilee of Mubarakiya School.
168 25 8f. multicoloured . . . 20 10
169 20f. multicoloured . . . 50 20

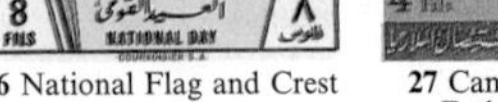
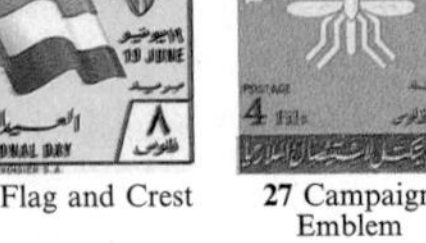

26 National Flag and Crest

27 Campaign Emblem

1962. National Day.
170 **26** 8f. multicoloured 10 10
171 20f. multicoloured 35 20
172 45f. multicoloured 80 30
173 90f. multicoloured . . . . 1·25 1·25

1962. Malaria Eradication.
174 **27** 4f. green and turquoise . . 15 10
175 25f. grey and green 55 25

28 "Industry and Progress"

1962. Bicentenary of Sabah Dynasty.
176 **28** 8f. multicoloured 10 10
177 20f. multicoloured 35 15
178 45f. multicoloured 75 15
179 75f. multicoloured . . . . 1·25 50

29 Mother and Child

31 "Education from Oil"

30 Campaign Emblem, Palm and Domestic Animals

1963. Mothers' Day. Centres black and green; value black; country name red.
180 **29** 8f. yellow 10 10
181 20f. blue 20 15
182 45f. olive 50 25
183 75f. grey 80 40

1963. Freedom from Hunger. Design in brown and green. Background colours given.
184 **30** 4f. blue 10 10
185 8f. yellow 25 15
186 20f. lilac 50 25
187 45f. pink . . . . 1·10 70

1963. Education Day.
188 **31** 4f. brown, blue and yellow 10 10
189 20f. green, blue and yellow 50 15
190 45f. purple, blue and yellow 90 35

32 Shaikh Abdullah and Flags

1963. 2nd Anniv of National Day. Flags in green, black and red; values in black.
191 **32** 4f. blue 40 30
192 5f. ochre 60 55
193 20f. violet . . . . 3·25 2·25
194 50f. brown . . . . 6·50 3·75

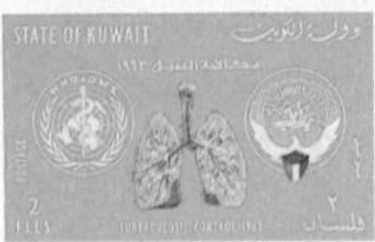

33 Human Lungs, and Emblems of W.H.O. and Kuwait

1963. W.H.O. "Tuberculosis Control" Campaign. Emblem yellow; arms black, green and red.
195 **33** 2f. black and stone 10 10
196 4f. black and green 20 10
197 8f. black and blue 25 10
198 20f. black and red . . . . 1·00 35

34 Municipal Hall and Scroll

1963. New Constitution. Centres dull purple; Amir red.
199 **34** 4f. red 15 10
200 8f. green 20 10
201 20f. purple 35 10
202 45f. brown 60 15
203 75f. violet . . . . 1·25 50
204 90f. blue . . . . 1·40 75

35 Football

36 Scales of Justice and Globe

1963. Arab Schools Games. Multicoloured.
205 1f. Type **35** 10 10
206 4f. Basketball 10 10
207 5f. Swimming (horiz) 10 10
208 8f. Running 15 10
209 15f. Throwing the javelin (horiz) 30 15
210 20f. Pole vaulting (horiz) . . 40 20
211 35f. Gymnastics (horiz) . . . 90 35
212 45f. Gymnastics . . . . . . 1·25 75

1963. 15th Anniv of Declaration of Human Rights.
213 **36** 8f. black, green and violet 10 10
214 20f. black, yellow and grey 40 20
215 25f. black, brown and blue 60 30

37 Shaikh Abdullah

38 Rameses II in War Chariot

1964. Multicoloured, frame colours given.
216 **37** 1f. grey 10 10
217 2f. blue 10 10
218 4f. brown 15 10
219 5f. brown 15 10
220 8f. brown 25 10
221 10f. green 25 10
222 15f. green 35 35
223 20f. blue 35 10
224 25f. green 40 10
225 30f. green 50 10
226 40f. violet 70 15
227 45f. violet 85 15
228 50f. yellow 90 20
229 70f. purple . . . . 1·10 25
230 75f. red . . . . 1·25 35
231 90f. blue . . . . 1·60 35
232 100f. lilac . . . . 1·75 40
233 250f. brown (25 × 30 mm) 5·00 90
234 1d. purple (25 × 30 mm) . . 14·00 3·75

1964. Nubian Monuments Preservation.
235 **38** 8f. purple, blue and buff 15 10
236 20f. violet, blue & light blue 40 20
237 30f. violet, blue & turquoise 55 35

39 Mother and Child

1964. Mother's Day.
238 **39** 8f. blue, green and grey . . 10 10
239 20f. blue, green and red . . 25 10
240 30f. blue, green and bistre 40 20
241 45f. indigo, green and blue 65 30

40 Nurse giving B.C.G. Vaccine to Patient, and Bones of Chest

41 Dhow and Microscope

1964. World Health Day.
242 **40** 8f. green and brown . . . 30 10
243 20f. red and green 85 25

1964. Education Day.
244 **41** 8f. multicoloured 15 10
245 15f. multicoloured 30 10
246 20f. multicoloured 35 15
247 30f. multicoloured 60 25

42 Dhow and Doves

1964. 3rd Anniv of National Day. Badge in blue, brown, black, red and green.
248 **42** 8f. black and brown . . . 25 15
249 20f. black and green . . . 40 25
250 30f. black and grey 60 35
251 45f. black and blue 85 55

43 A.P.U. Emblem

44 Hawker Siddeley Comet 4C and Douglas DC-3 Airliners

1964. 10th Anniv of Arab Postal Union's Permanent Office, Cairo.
252 **43** 8f. brown and blue 25 10
253 20f. blue and yellow . . . 45 20
254 45f. brown and green . . . 85 50

1964. Air. 10th Anniv of Kuwait Airways. Sky in blue; aircraft blue, red and black.
255 **44** 20f. black and bistre . . . 45 25
256 25f. black and brown . . . 60 30
257 30f. black and green . . . 70 30
258 45f. black and brown . . . 1·00 40

45 Conference Emblem

46 Dhow, Doves and Oil-drilling Rig

1965. 1st Arab Journalists' Conference, Kuwait.
259 **45** 8f. multicoloured 30 10
260 20f. multicoloured 55 20

1965. 4th Anniv of National Day.
261 **46** 10f. multicoloured 15 10
262 15f. multicoloured 35 15
263 20f. multicoloured 75 20

47 I.C.Y. Emblem

48 Mother and Children

1965. International Co-operation Year.
264 **47** 8f. black and red 25 10
265 20f. black and blue 55 25
266 30f. black and green . . . 1·00 40
The stamps are inscribed "CO-OPERATIVE".

1965. Mothers' Day.
267 **48** 8f. multicoloured 20 10
268 15f. multicoloured 40 20
269 20f. multicoloured 65 25

49 Weather Kite

1965. World Meteorological Day.
270 **49** 4f. blue and yellow 25 10
271 5f. blue and orange 25 10
272 20f. blue and green . . . . 1·10 25

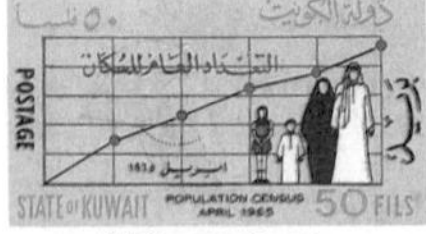

50 Census Graph

1965. Population Census.
273 **50** 8f. black, brown and blue 20 10
274 20f. black, pink and green 60 25
275 50f. black, green and red 1·40 60

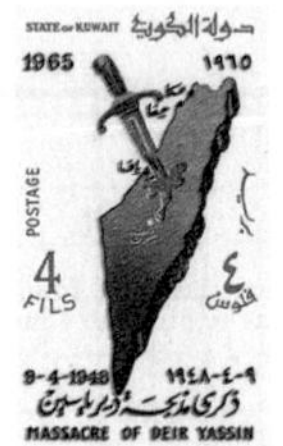

50a Dagger on Deir Yassin, Palestine

51 Atomic Symbol and Tower of Shuwaikh Secondary School

1965. Deir Yassin Massacre.
276 **50a** 4f. red and blue 40 20
277 45f. red and green . . . . 1·90 65

1965. Education Day.
278 **51** 4f. multicoloured 15 10
279 20f. multicoloured 45 15
280 45f. multicoloured 80 30

52 I.T.U. Emblem and Symbols

53 Saker Falcon

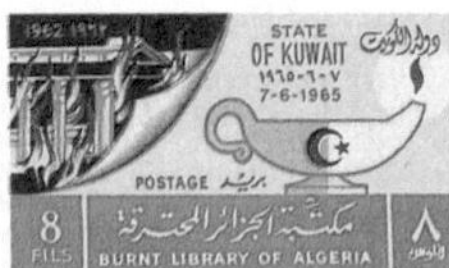

52a Lamp and Burning Library

1965. I.T.U. Centenary.
281 **52** 8f. red and blue 40 25
282 20f. red and green 80 40
283 45f. blue and red . . . . . 1·50 70

1965. Reconstitution of Burnt Algiers Library.
284 **52a** 8f. green, red and black 40 15
285 15f. red, green and black 1·00 20

1965. Centre in brown.
286 **53** 8f. purple . . . . 1·60 25
287 15f. green . . . . 1·40 25
288 20f. blue . . . . 2·25 40
289 25f. red . . . . 2·50 60
290 30f. green . . . . 3·00 70
291 45f. blue . . . . 5·25 1·00
292 50f. purple . . . . 6·50 1·25
293 90f. red . . . . 10·50 2·40

54 Open Book

55 Shaikh Sabah

1966. Education Day.
294 **54** 8f. multicoloured 20 10
295 20f. multicoloured 45 10
296 30f. multicoloured 85 25

1966.
297 **55** 4f. multicoloured 15 10
298 5f. multicoloured 15 10
299 20f. multicoloured 40 15
300 30f. multicoloured 55 25
301 40f. multicoloured 70 35
302 45f. multicoloured 75 40
303 70f. multicoloured . . . . 1·75 60
304 90f. multicoloured . . . . 2·00 80

56 Pomfrets and Ears of Wheat

1966. Freedom from Hunger.
305 **56** 20f. multicoloured . . . . 1·00 50
306 45f. multicoloured . . . . 2·25 95

57 Eagle and Scales of Justice

1966. 5th Anniv of National Day.
307 **57** 20f. multicoloured 80 30
308 25f. multicoloured 90 30
309 45f. multicoloured . . . . 1·60 60

58 Cogwheel and Map of Arab States

1966. Arab Countries Industrial Development Conference, Kuwait.
310 **58** 20f. green black and blue 50 15
311 50f. green, black and brown . . . . 1·00 45

59 Mother and Children

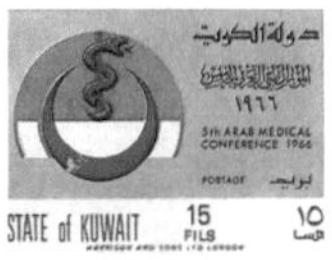

60 Red Crescent and Emblem of Medicine

1966. Mothers' Day.
312 **59** 20f. multicoloured 50 15
313 45f. multicoloured . . . . 1·00 30

1966. 5th Arab Medical Conference, Kuwait.
314 **60** 15f. red and blue 35 15
315 30f. red, blue and pink . . 80 40

61 "Man and his Cities"

62 W.H.O. Building

1966. World Health Day.
316 **61** 8f. multicoloured 50 15
317 10f. multicoloured 75 20

1966. Inaug of W.H.O. Headquarters, Geneva.
318 **62** 5f. green, blue and red . . 50 10
319 10f. green, blue & turquoise 90 15

62a Traffic Signals

63 Symbol of Blood Donation

1966. Traffic Day.
320 **62a** 10f. red, emerald and green 50 10
321 20f. emerald, red and green 75 25

1966. Blood Bank Day.
322 **63** 4f. multicoloured 40 10
323 8f. multicoloured 85 25

64 Shaikh Ahmad and "British Fusilier" (tanker)

1966. 20th Anniv of 1st Crude Oil Shipment.
324 **64** 20f. multicoloured 60 25
325 45f. multicoloured . . . . 1·40 55

65 Ministry Building

1966. Inauguration of Ministry of Guidance and Information Building.
326 **65** 4f. red and brown 20 10
327 5f. brown and green . . . 20 10
328 8f. green and violet . . . 30 10
329 20f. orange and blue . . . 65 20

66 Dhow, Lobster, Fish and Crab

67 U.N. Flag

1966. F.A.O. Near East Countries Fisheries Conference, Kuwait.
330 **66** 4f. multicoloured 85 25
331 20f. multicoloured . . . . 1·10 50

1966. U.N. Day.
332 **67** 20f. multicoloured 75 25
333 45f. multicoloured . . . . 1·10 50

68 UNESCO Emblem

1966. 20th Anniv of UNESCO.
334 **68** 20f. multicoloured 75 60
335 45f. multicoloured . . . . 1·50 1·25

69 Ruler and University Shield

1966. Opening of Kuwait University.
336 **69** 8f. multicoloured 25 10
337 10f. multicoloured 25 15
338 20f. multicoloured 75 25
339 45f. multicoloured . . . . 1·50 75

70 Ruler and Heir-Apparent

1966. Appointment of Heir-Apparent.
340 **70** 8f. multicoloured 25 10
341 20f. multicoloured 60 30
342 45f. multicoloured . . . . 1·25 70

71 Scout Badge

72 Symbols of Learning

1966. 30th Anniv of Kuwait Scouts.
343 **71** 4f. brown and green . . . 50 15
344 20f. green and brown . . . 1·75 50

1967. Education Day.
345 **72** 10f. multicoloured 30 15
346 45f. multicoloured 80 35

73 Fertiliser Plant

1967. Inauguration of Chemical Fertiliser Plant.
347 **73** 8f. multicoloured 40 15
348 20f. multicoloured . . . . 1·00 30

74 Ruler, Dove and Olive-branch

76 Arab Family

75 Map and Municipality Building

1967. 6th Anniv of National Day.
349 **74** 8f. multicoloured 30 10
350 20f. multicoloured 80 30

1967. 1st Arab Cities Organization Conf, Kuwait.
351 **75** 20f. multicoloured . . . . 1·00 25
352 30f. multicoloured . . . . 1·40 60

1967. Family's Day.
353 **76** 20f. multicoloured 80 25
354 45f. multicoloured . . . . 1·60 60

77 Arab League Emblem

78 Sabah Hospital

1967. Arab Cause Week.
355 **77** 8f. blue and grey 30 10
356 10f. green and yellow . . . 60 15

1967. World Health Day.
357 **78** 8f. multicoloured 85 15
358 20f. multicoloured . . . . 1·00 40

79 Nubian Statues

1967. Arab Week for Nubian Monuments Preservation.
359 **79** 15f. green, brown and yellow 60 20
360 20f. green, purple and blue 90 25

80 Traffic Policeman

1967. Traffic Day.
361 **80** 8f. multicoloured 80 25
362 20f. multicoloured . . . . 1·75 65

81 I.T.Y. Emblem

1967. International Tourist Year.
363 **81** 20f. black, blue & turquoise 65 40
364 45f. black, blue and mauve 1·25 85

82 "Reaching for Knowledge"

83 Map of Palestine

1967. "Eliminate Illiteracy" Campaign.
365 **82** 8f. multicoloured 75 10
366 20f. multicoloured . . . . 1·50 35

1967. U.N. Day.
367 **83** 20f. red and blue 50 20
368 45f. red and orange . . . 1·10 50

84 Factory and Cogwheels

1967. 3rd Arab Labour Ministers' Conference.
369 **84** 20f. yellow and red 60 20
370 45f. yellow and grey . . . 1·40 50

85 Open Book and Kuwaiti Flag

86 Oil Rig and Map

1968. Education Day.
371 **85** 20f. multicoloured 50 30
372 45f. multicoloured . . . . 1·25 60

1968. 30th Anniv of Oil Discovery in Greater Burgan Field.
373 **86** 10f. multicoloured 75 40
374 20f. multicoloured . . . . 1·25 70

87 Ruler and Sun's Rays
88 Book, Eagle and Sun

1968. 7th Anniv of National Day.
375 **87** 8f. multicoloured 25 10
376 10f. multicoloured 25 20
377 15f. multicoloured 45 25
378 20f. multicoloured 60 35

1968. Teachers' Day.
379 **88** 8f. multicoloured 30 10
380 20f. multicoloured 40 15
381 45f. multicoloured 75 40

89 Family Picnicking

1968. Family Day.
382 **89** 8f. multicoloured 20 10
383 10f. multicoloured 20 10
384 15f. multicoloured 30 10
385 20f. multicoloured 45 20

90 Ruler, W.H.O. and State Emblems

1968. World Health Day and 20th Anniv of W.H.O.
386 **90** 20f. multicoloured 60 50
387 45f. multicoloured . . . . 1·50 1·10

91 Dagger on Deir Yassin, and Scroll

1968. 20th Anniv of Deir Yassin Massacre.
388 **91** 20f. red and blue 80 25
389 45f. red and violet . . . . 2·75 50

92 Pedestrians on Road Crossing
93 Torch and Map

1968. Traffic Day.
390 **92** 10f. multicoloured 75 60
391 15f. multicoloured . . . . 1·25 85
392 20f. multicoloured . . . . 1·75 1·00

1968. Palestine Day.
393 **93** 10f. multicoloured 70 10
394 20f. multicoloured . . . . 1·25 25
395 45f. multicoloured . . . . 2·50 50

94 Palestine Refugees

1968. Human Rights Year.
396 **94** 20f. multicoloured 25 15
397 30f. multicoloured 35 15
398 45f. multicoloured 65 15
399 90f. multicoloured . . . . 1·25 45

95 National Museum
96 Man reading Book

1968.
400 **95** 1f. green and brown . . . 10 10
401 2f. green and purple . . . 10 10
402 5f. red and black 15 10
403 8f. green and brown . . . 20 10
404 10f. purple and blue . . . 20 10
405 20f. blue and brown . . . 45 10
406 25f. orange and blue . . . 55 10
407 30f. green and blue 70 20
408 45f. deep purple and purple 1·10 20
409 50f. red and green . . . . 1·60 45

1968. International Literacy Day.
410 **96** 15f. multicoloured 30 10
411 20f. multicoloured 70 15

97 Refugee Children and U.N. Headquarters

1968. United Nations Day.
412 **97** 20f. multicoloured 30 10
413 30f. multicoloured 40 20
414 45f. multicoloured 70 25

98 Chamber of Commerce Building

1968. Inauguration of Kuwait Chamber of Commerce and Industry Building.
415 **98** 10f. purple and orange . . 25 10
416 15f. blue and mauve . . . 30 15
417 20f. green and brown . . . 45 15

99 Conference Emblem

1968. 14th Arab Chambers of Commerce, Industry and Agriculture Conference.
418 **99** 10f. multicoloured 25 10
419 15f. multicoloured 30 10
420 20f. multicoloured 40 15
421 30f. multicoloured 70 30

100 Refinery Plant
101 Holy Koran, Scales and People

1968. Inauguration of Shuaiba Refinery.
422 **100** 10f. multicoloured 30 15
423 20f. multicoloured 60 20
424 30f. multicoloured 95 35
425 45f. multicoloured . . . . 1·75 45

1968. 1,400th Anniv of the Holy Koran.
426 **101** 8f. multicoloured 30 15
427 20f. multicoloured 75 40
428 30f. multicoloured . . . . 1·25 60
429 45f. multicoloured . . . . 1·60 85

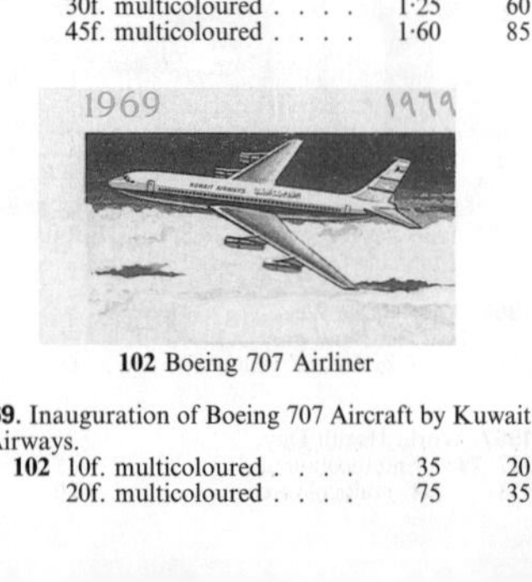

102 Boeing 707 Airliner

1969. Inauguration of Boeing 707 Aircraft by Kuwait Airways.
430 **102** 10f. multicoloured 35 20
431 20f. multicoloured 75 35
432 25f. multicoloured . . . . 1·10 45
433 45f. multicoloured . . . . 2·00 65

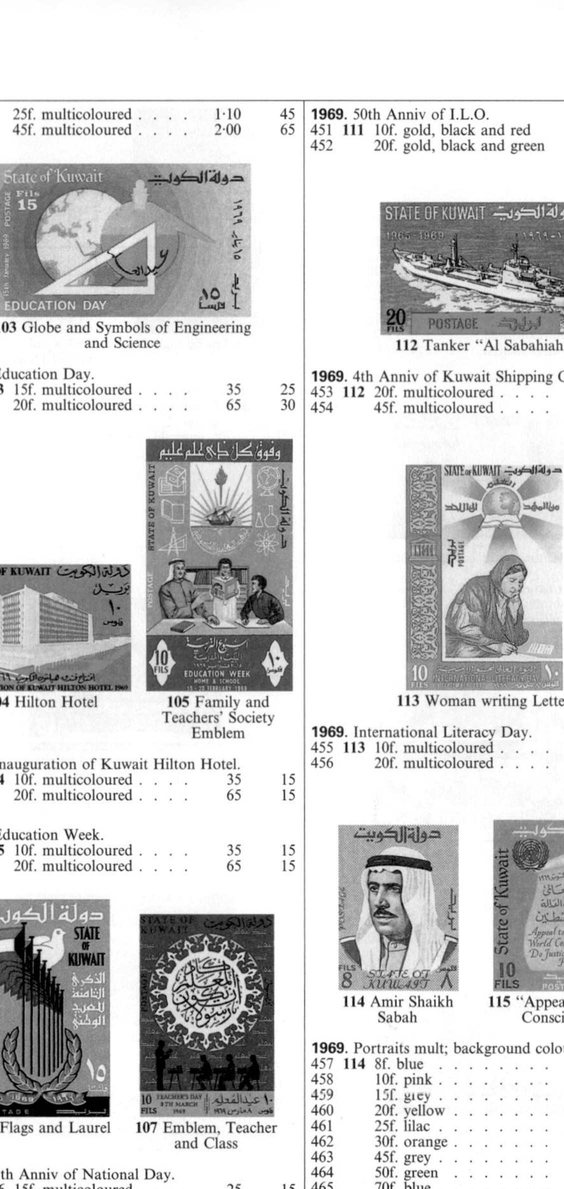
103 Globe and Symbols of Engineering and Science

1969. Education Day.
434 **103** 15f. multicoloured 35 25
435 20f. multicoloured 65 30

104 Hilton Hotel
105 Family and Teachers' Society Emblem

1969. Inauguration of Kuwait Hilton Hotel.
436 **104** 10f. multicoloured 35 15
437 20f. multicoloured 65 15

1969. Education Week.
438 **105** 10f. multicoloured 35 15
439 20f. multicoloured 65 15

106 Flags and Laurel
107 Emblem, Teacher and Class

1969. 8th Anniv of National Day.
440 **106** 15f. multicoloured 25 15
441 20f. multicoloured 40 20
442 30f. multicoloured 60 40

1969. Teachers' Day.
443 **107** 10f. multicoloured 30 15
444 20f. multicoloured 55 15

108 Kuwaiti Family

1969. Family Day.
445 **108** 10f. multicoloured 30 15
446 20f. multicoloured 55 20

109 Ibn Sina, Nurse with Patient and W.H.O. Emblem
110 Motor-cycle Police

1969. World Health Day.
447 **109** 15f. multicoloured 70 15
448 20f. multicoloured 80 20

1969. Traffic Day.
449 **110** 10f. multicoloured 75 15
450 20f. multicoloured . . . . 2·00 25

111 I.L.O. Emblem

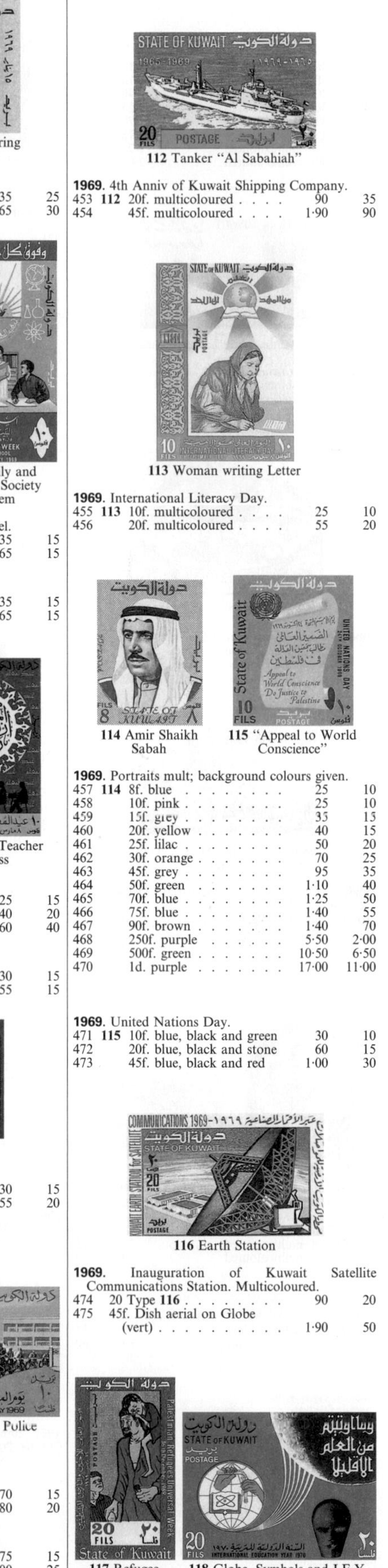

1969. 50th Anniv of I.L.O.
451 **111** 10f. gold, black and red 30 10
452 20f. gold, black and green 50 15

112 Tanker "Al Sabahiah"

1969. 4th Anniv of Kuwait Shipping Company.
453 **112** 20f. multicoloured 90 35
454 45f. multicoloured . . . . 1·90 90

113 Woman writing Letter

1969. International Literacy Day.
455 **113** 10f. multicoloured 25 10
456 20f. multicoloured 55 20

114 Amir Shaikh Sabah
115 "Appeal to World Conscience"

1969. Portraits mult; background colours given.
457 **114** 8f. blue 25 10
458 10f. pink 25 10
459 15f. grey 35 15
460 20f. yellow 40 15
461 25f. lilac 50 20
462 30f. orange 70 25
463 45f. grey 95 35
464 50f. green . . . . 1·10 40
465 70f. blue . . . . 1·25 50
466 75f. blue . . . . 1·40 55
467 90f. brown . . . . 1·40 70
468 250f. purple . . . . . . 5·50 2·00
469 500f. green . . . . 10·50 6·50
470 1d. purple . . . . 17·00 11·00

1969. United Nations Day.
471 **115** 10f. blue, black and green 30 10
472 20f. blue, black and stone 60 15
473 45f. blue, black and red 1·00 30

116 Earth Station

1969. Inauguration of Kuwait Satellite Communications Station. Multicoloured.
474 20 Type **116** 90 20
475 45f. Dish aerial on Globe (vert) . . . . 1·90 50

117 Refugee Family
118 Globe, Symbols and I.E.Y. Emblem

1969. Palestinian Refugee Week.
476 **117** 20f. multicoloured . . . . 1·40 40
477 45f. multicoloured . . . . 3·00 1·25

1970. International Education Year.
478 **118** 20f. multicoloured 40 25
479 45f. multicoloured . . . . 1·00 60

119 Shoue

1970. Kuwait Sailing Dhows. Multicoloured.
480 8f. Type **119** 40 10
481 10f. Sambuk 40 10
482 15f. Baggala 60 20
483 20f. Battela 75 15
484 25f. Bum 90 25
485 45f. Baggala . . . . 1·75 55
486 50f. Dhow-building . . . . . 2·00 55

120 Kuwaiti Flag

1970. 9th Anniv of National Day.
487 **120** 15f. multicoloured 65 15
488 20f. multicoloured 75 15

121 Young Commando and Dome of the Rock, Jerusalem

1970. Support for Palestinian Commandos. Multicoloured.
489 10f. Type **121** 50 20
490 20f. Commando in battle-dress . . . . 1·00 40
491 45f. Woman commando . . . 2·50 90

122 Parents with "Children"

1970. Family Day.
492 **122** 20f. multicoloured 40 15
493 30f. multicoloured 60 25

123 Arab League Flag, Emblem and Map

1970. 25th Anniv of Arab League.
494 **123** 20f. brown, green and blue 50 10
495 45f. violet, green and orange 75 30

124 Census Emblem and Graph

1970. Population Census.
496 **124** 15f. multicoloured 20 10
497 20f. multicoloured 50 10
498 30f. multicoloured 70 20

125 Cancer the Crab in "Pincers" 126 Traffic Lights and Road Signs

1970. World Health Day.
499 **125** 20f. multicoloured 45 10
500 30f. multicoloured 65 20

1970. Traffic Day.
501 **126** 20f. multicoloured . . . . 1·00 45
502 30f. multicoloured . . . . 1·50 70

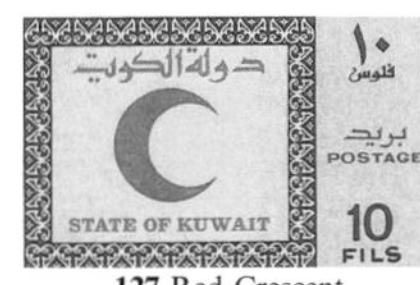

127 Red Crescent

1970. International Red Cross and Crescent Day.
503 **127** 10f. multicoloured 40 15
504 15f. multicoloured 60 20
505 30f. multicoloured . . . . 1·50 50

128 New Headquarters Building

1970. Opening of New U.P.U. Headquarters Building, Berne.
506 **128** 20f. multicoloured 60 20
507 30f. multicoloured 90 35

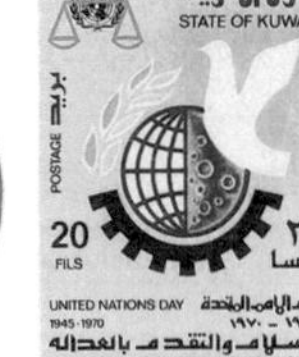

129 Amir Shaikh Sabah 130 U.N. Symbols

1970.
508 **129** 20f. multicoloured 65 20
509 45f. multicoloured . . . . 1·60 75

1970. 25th Anniv of United Nations.
511 **130** 20f. multicoloured 40 15
512 45f. multicoloured 70 30

131 "Medora" (tanker) at Sea Island Jetty

1970. Oil Shipment Facilities, Kuwait.
513 **131** 20f. multicoloured 90 30
514 45f. multicoloured . . . . 2·10 65

132 Kuwaiti and U.N. Emblems and Hand writing

1970. International Literacy Day.
515 **132** 10f. multicoloured 70 15
516 15f. multicoloured 90 15

133 Guards and Badge

1970. First Graduation of National Guards.
517 **133** 10f. multicoloured 55 15
518 20f. multicoloured . . . . 1·10 20

134 Symbols and Flag 136 Map of Palestine on Globe

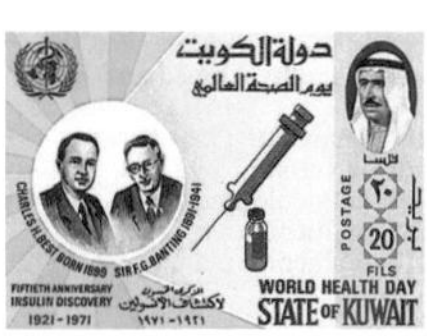

135 Dr. C. Best and Sir F. Banting (discoverers of insulin) and Syringe

1971. 10th Anniv of National Day.
519 **134** 20f. multicoloured 70 30
520 30f. multicoloured 95 45

1971. World Health Day, and 50th Anniv of Discovery of Insulin.
521 **135** 20f. multicoloured 50 15
522 45f. multicoloured . . . . 1·10 40

1971. Palestine Week.
523 **136** 20f. multicoloured . . . . 1·00 75
524 45f. multicoloured . . . . 2·25 1·50

137 I.T.U. Emblem

1971. World Telecommunications Day.
525 **137** 20f. black, brown and silver 70 20
526 45f. black, brown and gold . . . . 1·60 60

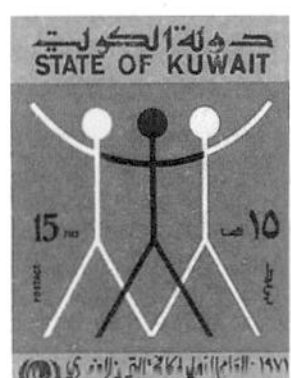

138 "Three Races"

1971. Racial Equality Year.
527 **138** 15f. multicoloured 35 20
528 30f. multicoloured 65 50

139 A.P.U. Emblem

1971. 25th Anniv of Founding of Arab Postal Union at Sofar Conference.
529 **139** 20f. multicoloured 50 25
530 45f. multicoloured . . . . 1·00 40

140 Book, Pupils, Globes and Pen

1971. International Literacy Day.
531 **140** 25f. multicoloured 60 20
532 60f. multicoloured . . . . 1·50 60

141 Footballers

1971. Regional Sports Tournament, Kuwait. Multicoloured.
533 20f. Type **141** 95 35
534 30f. Footballer blocking attack . . . . 1·40 50

142 Emblems of UNICEF and Kuwait

1971. 25th Anniv of UNICEF.
535 **142** 25f. multicoloured 40 25
536 60f. multicoloured 90 50

143 Book Year Emblem

1972. International Book Year.
537 **143** 20f. black and brown . . 50 30
538 45f. black and green . . . 1·10 60

144 Crest and Laurel

1972. 11th Anniv of National Day.
539 **144** 20f. multicoloured 85 50
540 45f. multicoloured . . . . 1·40 85

145 Telecommunications Centre

1972. Inauguration of Telecommunications Centre, Kuwait.
541 **145** 20f. multicoloured . . . . 1·00 40
542 45f. multicoloured . . . . 2·50 1·00

146 Human Heart 147 Nurse and Child

1972. World Health Day and World Heart Month.
543 **146** 20f. multicoloured . . . . 1·25 25
544 45f. multicoloured . . . . 2·75 50

1972. International Red Cross and Crescent Day.
545 **147** 8f. multicoloured 75 10
546 40f. multicoloured . . . . 2·40 75

148 Football

1972. Olympic Games, Munich. Multicoloured.
547 2f. Type **148** 10 10
548 4f. Running 15 10
549 5f. Swimming 20 10
550 8f. Gymnastics 30 10
551 10f. Throwing the discus . . 35 10
552 15f. Show jumping 45 15
553 20f. Basketball 50 20
554 25f. Volleyball 65 30

149 Produce and Fishing Boat

151 Ancient Capitals

150 Bank Emblem

1972. 11th F.A.O. Near East Regional Conference, Kuwait.
555 **149** 5f. multicoloured 40 30
556 10f. multicoloured . . . . 1·25 75
557 20f. multicoloured . . . . 2·50 1·40

1972. 20th Anniv of National Bank of Kuwait.
558 **150** 10f. multicoloured 30 15
559 35f. multicoloured . . . . 1·00 70

1972. Archaeological Excavations on Failaka Island. Multicoloured.
560 2f. Type **151** 10 15
561 5f. View of excavations . . . 25 10
562 10f. "Leaf" capital 45 10
563 15f. Excavated building . . . 95 20

152 Floral Emblem

153 Interpol Emblem

1973. 12th Anniv of National Day.
564 **152** 10f. multicoloured 30 15
565 20f. multicoloured 65 45
566 30f. multicoloured 95 65

1973. 50th Anniv of International Criminal Police Organization (Interpol).
567 **153** 10f. multicoloured 50 45
568 15f. multicoloured . . . . 1·00 65
569 20f. multicoloured . . . . 1·50 95

154 C.I.S.M. Badge and Flags

155 Airways Building

1973. 25th Anniv of International Military Sports Council (C.I.S.M.).
570 **154** 30f. multicoloured 65 40
571 40f. multicoloured . . . . 1·00 50

1973. Opening of Kuwait Airways H.Q. Building.
572 **155** 10f. multicoloured 35 15
573 15f. multicoloured 55 25
574 20f. multicoloured 70 30

156 Weather Map of Middle East

1973. Centenary of World Meteorological Organization.
575 **156** 5f. multicoloured 30 10
576 10f. multicoloured 50 15
577 15f. multicoloured 85 25

157 Shaikhs Ahmed and Sabah

1973. 50th Anniv of 1st Kuwait Stamp Issue (overprints on India of 1923).
578 **157** 10f. multicoloured 40 15
579 20f. multicoloured 75 25
580 70f. multicoloured . . . . 2·50 1·10

158 Mourning Dove

1973. Birds and Hunting Equipment. Multicoloured.
(a) Size 32 × 32 mm.
581 5f. Type **158** 65 15
582 5f. Hoopoe ("Upupa epops") 65 15
583 5f. Feral rock pigeon ("Columba livia") 65 15
584 5f. Stone-curlew ("Burhinus oedicnemus") 65 15
585 8f. Great grey shrike ("Lanius excubitor") . . . 85 15
586 8f. Red-backed shrike ("Lanius collurio") 85 15
587 8f. Black-headed shrike ("Lanius schach") 85 15
588 8f. Golden oriole ("Orielus chinensis") 85 15
589 10f. Willow warbler ("Phylloscopus trochilus") 85 15
590 10f. Great reed warbler ("Acrocephalus arundinaceus") 85 15
591 10f. Blackcap ("Sylvia atricapilla") 85 15
592 10f. Barn swallow ("Hirundo rustica") 85 15
593 15f. Rock thrush ("Monticola solitarius") . . . . 1·25 35
594 15f. Common redstart ("Phoenicurus phoenicurus") . . . . . . 1·25 35
595 15f. Northern wheatear ("Oenanthe oenanthe") . . 1·25 35
596 15f. Bluethroat ("Luscinia svecica") . . . . 1·25 35
597 20f. Houbara bustard ("Chlamydotis undulata") 1·75 35
598 20f. Pin-tailed sandgrouse ("Pterocles alchata") . . . 1·75 35
599 20f. Greater wood rail ("Aramides ypecaha") . . 1·75 35
600 20f. Spotted crake ("Porzana porzana") . . . . 1·75 35
(b) Size 38 × 38 mm.
601 25f. American kestrel ("Falco sparverius") . . . . 2·50 50
602 25f. Great black-backed gull ("Larus marinus") . . . . 2·50 50
603 25f. Purple heron ("Ardea purpurea") . . . . 2·50 50
604 25f. Wryneck ("Jynx torquilla") . . . . 2·50 50
605 30f. European bee eater ("Merops apiaster") . . . 2·75 65
606 30f. Saker falcon ("Accipiter") . . . . 2·75 65
607 30f. Grey wagtail ("Motacilla cinerea") . . . . 2·75 65
608 30f. Pied wagtail ("Motacilla alba") . . . . 2·75 65
609 45f. Bird traps . . . . 4·00 1·25
610 45f. Driving great grey shrikes into net . . . . . 4·00 1·25
611 45f. Stalking Feral rock pigeon with hand net . . . 4·00 1·25
612 45f. Great grey shrike and disguised lure . . . . . . 4·00 1·25

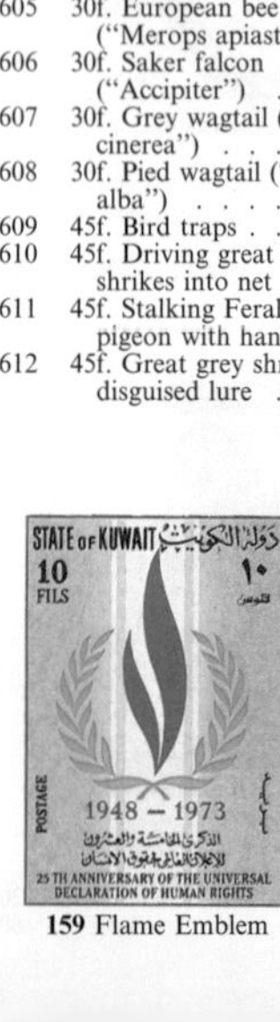
159 Flame Emblem

160 Congress Emblem

1973. 25th Anniv of Declaration of Human Rights.
613 **159** 10f. multicoloured 40 10
614 40f. multicoloured . . . . 1·10 35
615 75f. multicoloured . . . . 1·75 60

1974. 4th Congress of Arab Veterinary Union, Kuwait.
616 **160** 30f. multicoloured 60 20
617 40f. multicoloured 85 35

161 Flag and Wheat Ear Symbol

163 Tournament Emblem

162 A.M.U. Emblem

1974. 13th Anniv of National Day.
618 **161** 20f. multicoloured 30 10
619 30f. multicoloured 50 25
620 70f. multicoloured . . . . 1·40 1·00

1974. 12th Conference of Arab Medical Union and 1st Conference of Kuwait Medical Society.
621 **162** 30f. multicoloured . . . . 1·25 30
622 40f. multicoloured . . . . 1·75 80

1974. 3rd Arabian Gulf Trophy Football Tournament, Kuwait.
623 **163** 25f. multicoloured 80 15
624 45f. multicoloured . . . . 1·75 70

164 Institute Buildings

1974. Inauguration of Kuwait Institute for Scientific Research.
625 **164** 15f. multicoloured 70 25
626 20f. multicoloured . . . . 1·40 30

165 Emblems of Kuwait, Arab Postal Union and U.P.U.

1974. Centenary of U.P.U.
627 **165** 20f. multicoloured 25 15
628 30f. multicoloured 30 30
629 60f. multicoloured 50 45

166 Symbolic Telephone Dial

167 Council Emblem and Flags of Member States

1974. World Telecommunications Day.
630 **166** 10f. multicoloured 60 20
631 30f. multicoloured . . . . 1·90 75
632 40f. multicoloured . . . . 3·00 1·00

1974. 17th Anniv of Signing Arab Economic Unity Agreement.
633 **167** 20f. green, black and red 60 25
634 30f. red, black and green 70 40

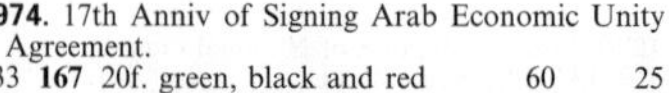

168 "Population Growth"

1974. World Population Year.
635 **168** 30f. multicoloured 75 30
636 70f. multicoloured . . . . 1·75 70

169 Fund Building

1974. Kuwait Fund for Arab Economic Development.
637 **169** 10f. multicoloured 45 10
638 20f. multicoloured 75 25

170 Shuaiba Emblem

1974. 10th Anniv of Shuaiba Industrial Area.
639 **170** 10f. multicoloured 40 15
640 20f. multicoloured . . . . 1·00 30
641 30f. multicoloured . . . . 1·40 55

171 Arms of Kuwait and "14"

1975. 14th Anniv of National Day.
642 **171** 20f. multicoloured 40 20
643 70f. multicoloured . . . . 1·25 60
644 75f. multicoloured . . . . 1·60 70

172 Census Symbols

1975. Population Census.
645 **172** 8f. multicoloured 15 10
646 20f. multicoloured 35 10
647 30f. multicoloured 50 25
648 70f. multicoloured . . . . 1·40 75
649 100f. multicoloured . . . 1·75 1·10

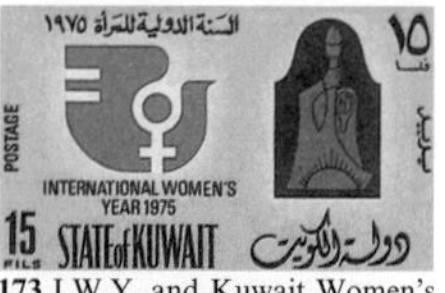
173 I.W.Y. and Kuwait Women's Union Emblems

1975. International Women's Year.
650 **173** 15f. multicoloured 50 15
651 20f. multicoloured 60 30
652 30f. multicoloured 85 45

174 Classroom within Open Book

1975. International Literacy Day.
653 **174** 20f. multicoloured 50 15
654 30f. multicoloured 85 45

175 I.S.O. Emblem

176 U.N. Flag, Rifle and Olive-branch

1975. World Standards Day.

655 **175** 10f. multicoloured 30 15
656 20f. multicoloured 55 25

1975. 30th Anniv of U.N.O.

657 **176** 20f. multicoloured 50 15
658 45f. multicoloured . . . . 1·10 50

177 Shaikh Sabah

1975.

659 **177** 8f. multicoloured 35 15
660 20f. multicoloured 60 20
661 30f. multicoloured 70 30
662 50f. multicoloured . . . . 1·25 50
663 90f. multicoloured . . . . 2·40 85
664 100f. multicoloured . . . 3·00 1·10

178 Kuwait "Skyline"

1976. 15th Anniv of National Day.

665 **178** 10f. multicoloured 50 15
666 20f. multicoloured 90 15

178a Emblem, Microscope and Operation

179 Early and Modern Telephones

1976. 2nd Annual Conference of Kuwait Medical Association.

667 **178a** 5f. multicoloured 30 15
668 10f. multicoloured . . . 60 20
669 30f. multicoloured . . . 1·90 55

1976. Telephone Centenary.

670 **179** 5f. black and orange . . . 20 15
671 15f. black and blue . . . 65 15

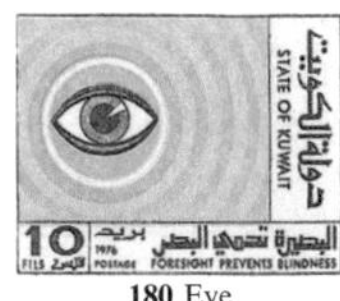

180 Eye

1976. World Health Day.

672 **180** 10f. multicoloured 40 15
673 20f. multicoloured 75 15
674 30f. multicoloured . . . . 1·25 35

181 Red Crescent Emblem

1976. 10th Anniv of Kuwait Red Crescent Society.

675 **181** 20f. multicoloured 40 15
676 30f. multicoloured 70 30
677 45f. multicoloured . . . . 1·25 55
678 75f. multicoloured . . . . 2·00 1·40

182 Suburb of Manama

183 Basketball

1976. U.N. Human Settlements Conference.

679 **182** 10f. multicoloured 35 15
680 20f. multicoloured 65 15

1976. Olympic Games, Montreal. Multicoloured.

681 4f. Type **183** 10 10
682 8f. Running 15 10
683 10f. Judo 20 10
684 15f. Handball 30 10
685 20f. Figure-skating 35 10
686 30f. Volleyball 55 25
687 45f. Football 70 35
688 70f. Swimming . . . . 1·10 85

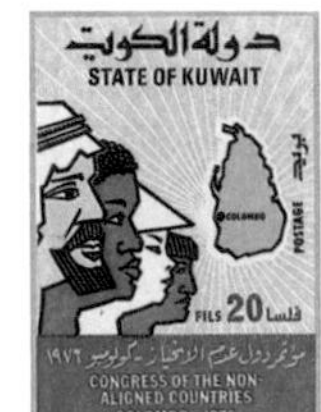

184 Ethnic Heads and Map of Sri Lanka

1976. Non-Aligned Countries' Congress, Colombo.

689 **184** 20f. multicoloured 35 10
690 30f. multicoloured 50 30
691 45f. multicoloured 85 45

185 Torch, UNESCO Emblem and Kuwaiti Arms

1976. 30th Anniv of UNESCO.

692 **185** 20f. multicoloured 45 10
693 45f. multicoloured . . . . 1·00 50

186 Pot-throwing

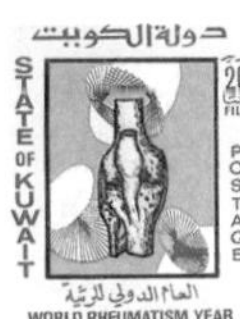

187 Diseased Knee

1977. Popular Games. Multicoloured.

694 5f. Type **186** 20 10
695 5f. Kite-flying 20 10
696 5f. Balancing sticks 20 10
697 5f. Spinning tops 20 10
698 10f. Blind-man's-buff (horiz) 25 15
699 10f. Rowing (horiz) 25 15
700 10f. Rolling hoops (horiz) . . 25 15
701 10f. Rope game (horiz) . . . 25 15
702 15f. Skipping 50 25
703 15f. Marbles 50 25
704 15f. Carting 50 25
705 15f. Teetotum (tops) 50 25
706 20f. Halma (horiz) 80 40
707 20f. Model boating (horiz) . . 80 40
708 20f. Pot and candle (horiz) 80 40
709 20f. Hide-and-seek (horiz) . . 80 40
710 30f. Knucklebones 90 50
711 30f. Hiding the stone 90 50
712 30f. Hopscotch 90 50
713 30f. Catch-as-catch-can . . . 90 50
714 40f. Bowls (horiz) . . . . . 1·60 70
715 40f. Hockey (horiz) . . . . . 1·60 70
716 40f. Guessing which hand (horiz) . . . . 1·60 70
717 40f. Jacks (horiz) . . . . . . 1·60 70
718 60f. Hiding the cake (horiz) 2·00 1·25
719 60f. Chess (horiz) . . . . . 2·00 1·25
720 60f. Story-telling (horiz) . . . 2·00 1·25
721 60f. Treasure hunt (horiz) . . 2·00 1·25
722 70f. Hobby horses (horiz) . . 2·25 1·40
723 70f. Hide-and-seek (horiz) . . 2·25 1·40
724 70f. Catch shadow (horiz) . . 2·25 1·40
725 70f. Throwing game (horiz) 2·25 1·40

1977. World Rheumatism Year.

726 **187** 20f. multicoloured 40 15
727 30f. multicoloured 60 30
728 45f. multicoloured 90 45
729 75f. multicoloured . . . . 1·25 85

188 Shaikh Sabah

1977. 16th National Day.

730 **188** 10f. multicoloured 15 10
731 15f. multicoloured 30 15
732 30f. multicoloured 65 20
733 80f. multicoloured . . . . 1·40 55

189 Kuwait Tower

190 A.P.U. Emblem and Flags

1977. Inauguration of Kuwait Tower.

734 **189** 30f. multicoloured 75 15
735 80f. multicoloured . . . . 2·00 55

1977. 25th Anniv of Arab Postal Union.

736 **190** 5f. multicoloured 20 10
737 15f. multicoloured 20 10
738 30f. multicoloured 40 20
739 80f. multicoloured . . . . 1·10 60

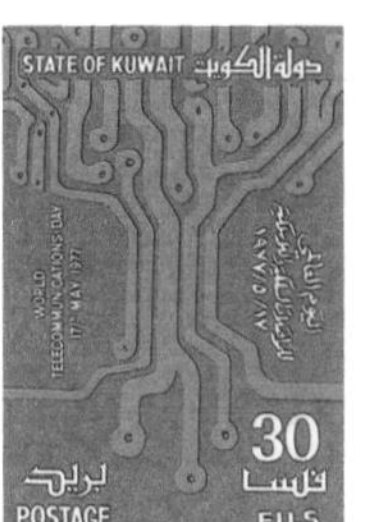

191 Printed Circuit

192 Shaikh Sabah

1977. World Telecommunications Day.

740 **191** 30f. orange and brown . . 60 30
741 80f. orange and green . . 1·50 70

1977.

742 **192** 15f. brown, black and blue 80 35
743 25f. brown, black & yellow . . . . 1·40 35
744 30f. brown, black and red 1·75 50
745 80f. brown, black and lilac . . . . 4·00 1·25
746 100f. brown, black & orge 5·00 1·40
747 150f. brown, black & blue 9·00 2·25
748 200f. brown, black & green . . . . 10·00 3·25

192a Aerogramme stamp

193 Championship Emblem

1977. Aerogramme stamp. Imperf.

748a **192a** 55f. red and blue . . .

No. 748a was applied before sale to aerogrammes to uprate the imprinted 25f. stamp. It was not available separately.

1977. 4th Asian Youth Basketball Championships.

749 **193** 30f. multicoloured 50 50
750 80f. multicoloured . . . . 1·50 1·00

194 "Popular Dancing" (O. Al-Nakeeb)

1977. Children's Paintings. Multicoloured.

751 15f. Type **194** 35 20
752 15f. "Al Deirah" (A. M. al-Onizi) 35 20
753 30f. "Fishing" (M. al-Jasem) 60 45
754 30f. "Dugg al-Harees" (B. al-Sa'adooni) (vert) 60 45
755 80f. "Fraisa Dancing" (M. al-Mojaibel) (vert) . . . . . 1·50 1·25
756 80f. "Kuwaiti Girl" (K. Ghazi) (vert) . . . . . 1·50 1·25

195 Dome of the Rock and Palestinian Freedom Fighters

1978. Palestinian Freedom Fighters.

757 **195** 30f. multicoloured . . . . 1·25 70
758 80f. multicoloured . . . . 2·40 1·50

196 Dentist treating Patient

1978. 10th Arab Dental Union Congress.

759 **196** 30f. multicoloured 70 55
760 80f. multicoloured . . . . 1·75 1·10

197 Carrying Water from Dhows

1978. Water Resources. Multicoloured.

761 5f. Type **197** 25 10
762 5f. Camel 25 10
763 5f. Water carrier 25 10
764 5f. Pushing water in cart . . 25 10
765 10f. Irrigation with donkey 35 10
766 10f. Water troughs in desert 35 10
767 10f. Pool by a town 35 10
768 10f. Watering crops 35 10
769 15f. Bedouin watering sheep 50 10
770 15f. Bedouin women by pool 50 10
771 15f. Camels watered by pipeline 50 10
772 15f. Water skins in Bedouin tent 50 10
773 20f. Oasis with wells 55 10
774 20f. Washing and drinking at home 55 10
775 20f. Water urn 55 10
776 20f. Filling vessels from taps 55 10
777 25f. Desalination plant 65 15
778 25f. Water tanker 65 15
779 25f. Filling water tankers . . 65 15
780 25f. Modern water tanks . . 65 15
781 30f. Catching water during storm (vert) 85 15
782 30f. Water tank (vert) 85 15
783 30f. Sheet to catch rain (vert) 85 15
784 30f. Trees by water tanks (vert) 85 15
785 80f. Carrying water on donkey (vert) . . . . . . 2·00 60
786 80f. Woman carrying water-can (vert) . . . . 2·00 60
787 80f. Woman with water-skins (vert) . . . . 2·00 60
788 80f. Tanker delivering water to house (vert) . . . . . . 2·00 60
789 100f. Tanker delivering to courtyard tank (vert) . . . 2·75 90
790 100f. Household cistern (vert) 2·75 90
791 100f. Filling cistern (vert) . . 2·75 90
792 100f. Drawing water from well (vert) . . . . 2·75 90

198 Symbols of Development

1978. 17th National Day.

793 **198** 30f. multicoloured 35 25
794 80f. multicoloured . . . . 1·00 70

199 Face of Smallpox Victim

1978. Global Eradication of Smallpox.

No.	Type	Description	Unused	Used
795	**199**	30f. multicoloured	40	30
796		80f. multicoloured	1·10	70

200 Microwave Antenna

201 Shaikh Jabir

1978. 10th World Telecommunications Day.

No.	Type	Description	Unused	Used
797	**200**	30f. multicoloured	35	25
798		80f. multicoloured	1·10	70

1978. Portrait in brown; background colour given.

No.	Type	Description	Unused	Used
799	**201**	15f. green	40	15
800		30f. orange	80	35
801		80f. purple	1·75	85
802		100f. green	2·00	1·00
803		130f. brown	3·25	1·40
804		180f. violet	4·75	2·00
805		1d. red (24 × 29 mm)	15·00	9·00
806		4d. blue (24 × 29 mm)	50·00	22·00

202 Mount Arafat, Pilgrims and Kaaba

1978. Pilgrimage to Mecca.

No.	Type	Description	Unused	Used
807	**202**	30f. multicoloured	50	40
808		80f. multicoloured	1·40	1·00

203 U.N. and Anti-Apartheid Emblems

1978. International Anti-Apartheid Year.

No.	Type	Description	Unused	Used
809	**203**	30f. multicoloured	40	25
810		80f. multicoloured	1·00	70
811		180f. multicoloured	2·10	1·50

204 Refugees

1978. 30th Anniv of Declaration of Human Rights.

No.	Type	Description	Unused	Used
812	**204**	30f. multicoloured	40	30
813		80f. multicoloured	1·25	75
814		100f. multicoloured	1·75	1·00

205 Information Centre

1978. Kuwait Information Centre.

No.	Type	Description	Unused	Used
815	**205**	5f. multicoloured	10	10
816		15f. multicoloured	20	10
817		30f. multicoloured	35	20
818		80f. multicoloured	90	60

206 Kindergarten

207 Kuwaiti Flag and Doves

1979. International Year of the Child.

No.	Type	Description	Unused	Used
819	**206**	30f. multicoloured	40	35
820		80f. multicoloured	1·00	85

1979. 18th National Day.

No.	Type	Description	Unused	Used
821	**207**	30f. multicoloured	40	30
822		80f. multicoloured	95	75

208 Crops and Greenhouse

1979. 4th Arab Agriculture Ministers' Congress.

No.	Type	Description	Unused	Used
823	**208**	30f. multicoloured	40	25
824		80f. multicoloured	95	75

209 World Map, Koran and Symbols of Arab Achievements

1979. The Arabs.

No.	Type	Description	Unused	Used
825	**209**	30f. multicoloured	40	30
826		80f. multicoloured	95	75

210 Children flying Kites

1979. Children's Paintings. Multicoloured.

No.	Description	Unused	Used
827	30f. Type **210**	40	35
828	30f. Girl and doves	40	35
829	30f. Crowd and balloons	40	35
830	80f. Boys smiling (horiz)	1·00	90
831	80f. Children in landscape (horiz)	1·00	90
832	80f. Tug-of-war (horiz)	1·00	90

211 Wave Pattern and Television Screen

212 International Military Sports Council Emblem

1979. World Telecommunications Day.

No.	Type	Description	Unused	Used
833	**211**	30f. multicoloured	35	30
834		80f. multicoloured	95	85

1979. 29th International Military Football Championship.

No.	Type	Description	Unused	Used
835	**212**	30f. multicoloured	45	25
836		80f. multicoloured	1·25	85

213 Child and Industrial Landscape

1979. World Environment Day.

No.	Type	Description	Unused	Used
837	**213**	30f. multicoloured	50	40
838		80f. multicoloured	1·40	1·10

214 Children supporting Globe

215 Children with Television

1979. 50th Anniv of Int Bureau of Education.

No.	Type	Description	Unused	Used
839	**214**	30f. multicoloured	35	25
840		80f. multicoloured	85	75
841		130f. multicoloured	1·40	1·25

1979. 25th Anniv of Kuwaiti Kindergartens. Children's Drawings. Multicoloured.

No.	Description	Unused	Used
842	30f. Type **215**	40	25
843	80f. Children with flags	1·00	75

216 The Kaaba, Mecca

1979. Pilgrimage to Mecca.

No.	Type	Description	Unused	Used
844	**216**	30f. multicoloured	40	30
845		80f. multicoloured	1·50	85

217 Figure, with Dove and Torch, clothed in Palestinian Flag

1979. Int Day of Solidarity with Palestinians.

No.	Type	Description	Unused	Used
846	**217**	30f. multicoloured	1·50	65
847		80f. multicoloured	3·00	1·25

218 Boeing 747 and Douglas DC-3 Airliners

1979. 25th Anniv of Kuwait Airways.

No.	Type	Description	Unused	Used
848	**218**	30f. multicoloured	55	40
849		80f. multicoloured	1·50	1·25

219 "Pinctada" Shell bearing Map of Kuwait

1980. 19th National Day.

No.	Type	Description	Unused	Used
850	**219**	30f. multicoloured	40	30
851		80f. multicoloured	1·10	75

220 Graph with Human Figures

1980. Population Census.

No.	Type	Description	Unused	Used
852	**220**	30f. black, silver and blue	50	25
853		80f. black, gold and orange	1·10	60

221 Campaign Emblem

1980. World Health Day. Anti-smoking Campaign.

No.	Type	Description	Unused	Used
854	**221**	30f. multicoloured	60	35
855		80f. multicoloured	1·75	1·10

222 Municipality Building

1980. 50th Anniv of Kuwait Municipality.

No.	Type	Description	Unused	Used
856	**222**	15f. multicoloured	20	10
857		30f. multicoloured	40	30
858		80f. multicoloured	1·25	75

223 "The Future"

1980. Children's Imagination of Future Kuwait. Multicoloured.

No.	Description	Unused	Used
859	30f. Type **223**	50	30
860	80f. Motorways	1·50	95

224 Hand blotting out Factory

1980. World Environment Day.

No.	Type	Description	Unused	Used
861	**224**	30f. multicoloured	55	30
862		80f. multicoloured	1·50	60

225 Volleyball

226 O.P.E.C. Emblem and Globe

1980. Olympic Games, Moscow. Multicoloured.

No.	Description	Unused	Used
863	15f. Type **225**	20	20
864	15f. Tennis	20	20
865	30f. Swimming	35	25
866	30f. Weightlifting	35	25
867	30f. Basketball	35	25
868	30f. Judo	35	25
869	80f. Gymnastics	95	60
870	80f. Badminton	95	60
871	80f. Fencing	95	60
872	80f. Football	95	60

1980. 20th Anniv of Organization of Petroleum Exporting Countries.

No.	Type	Description	Unused	Used
873	**226**	30f. multicoloured	50	35
874		80f. multicoloured	1·50	55

227 Mosque and Kaaba, Mecca

1980. 1400th Anniv of Hegira.

No.	Type	Description	Unused	Used
875	**227**	15f. multicoloured	25	15
876		30f. multicoloured	50	30
877		80f. multicoloured	1·40	85

228 Dome of the Rock

1980. International Day of Solidarity with Palestinian People.

No.	Type	Description	Unused	Used
878	**228**	30f. multicoloured	1·00	40
879		80f. multicoloured	2·50	1·25

229 Ibn Sina (Avicenna)

1980. Birth Millenary of Ibn Sina (philosopher and physician).
880 **229** 30f. multicoloured 60 25
881 80f. multicoloured . . . . 1·25 85

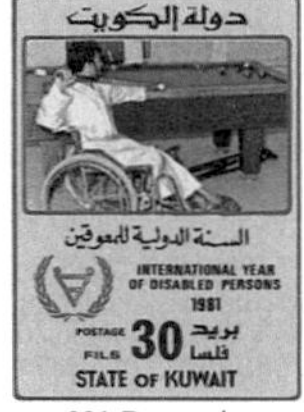

230 Islamic Symbols
231 Person in Wheelchair playing Snooker

1981. 1st Islamic Medicine Conference, Kuwait.
882 **230** 30f. multicoloured 50 30
883 80f. multicoloured . . . . 1·50 85

1981. International Year of Disabled Persons. Multicoloured.
884 30f. Type **231** 50 30
885 80f. Girl in wheelchair . . . 1·50 85

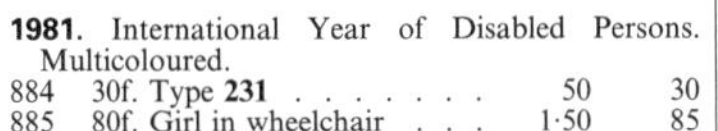

232 Symbols of Development and Progress

1981. 20th National Day.
886 **232** 30f. multicoloured 50 30
887 80f. multicoloured . . . . 1·50 85

233 Emblem of Kuwait Dental Association
234 "Lamp"

1981. 1st Kuwait Dental Association Conference.
888 **233** 30f. multicoloured . . . . 1·00 55
889 80f. multicoloured . . . . 2·50 1·50

1981. World Red Cross and Red Crescent Day.
890 **234** 30f. multicoloured 90 55
891 80f. multicoloured . . . . 2·50 1·50

235 Emblems of I.T.U. and W.H.O. and Ribbons forming Caduceus
236 Tanker polluting Sea and Car polluting Atmosphere

1981. World Telecommunications Day.
892 **235** 30f. multicoloured 70 50
893 80f. multicoloured . . . . 2·25 1·40

1981. World Environment Day.
894 **236** 30f. multicoloured 75 50
895 80f. multicoloured . . . . 2·40 1·25

237 Sief Palace

1981.
896 **237** 5f. multicoloured 10 10
897 10f. multicoloured 10 10
898 15f. multicoloured 10 10
899 25f. multicoloured 15 15
900 30f. multicoloured 20 15
901 40f. multicoloured 25 15
902 60f. multicoloured 40 20
903 80f. multicoloured 50 30
904 100f. multicoloured . . . 65 45
905 115f. multicoloured . . . 70 50
906 130f. multicoloured . . . 80 70
907 150f. multicoloured . . . 1·10 70
908 180f. multicoloured . . . 1·25 75
909 250f. multicoloured . . . 1·50 80
910 500f. multicoloured . . . 3·25 1·10
911 1d. multicoloured . . . . 6·25 1·50
912 2d. multicoloured . . . . 12·00 2·25
913 3d. multicoloured . . . . 16·00 6·75
914 4d. multicoloured . . . . 25·00 8·50
Nos. 911/14 are larger, 33 × 28 mm and have a different border.

238 Pilgrims

1981. Pilgrimage to Mecca.
915 **238** 30f. multicoloured 60 50
916 80f. multicoloured . . . . 2·25 1·25

239 Palm Trees, Sheep, Camel, Goat and F.A.O. Emblem

1981. World Food Day.
917 **239** 30f. multicoloured 65 45
918 80f. multicoloured . . . . 2·00 1·25

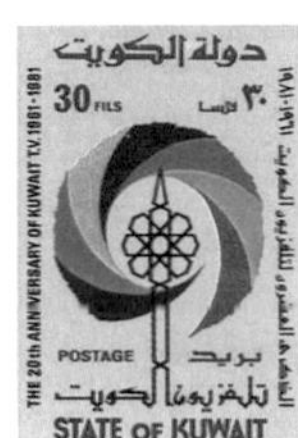

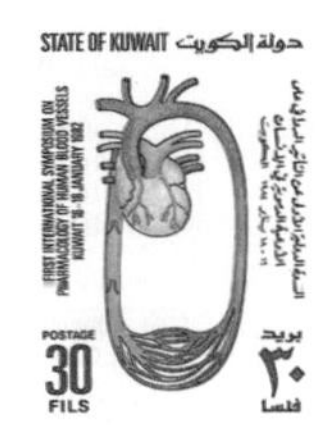

240 Television Emblem
241 Blood Circulation Diagram

1981. 20th Anniv of Kuwait Television.
919 **240** 30f. multicoloured 70 45
920 80f. multicoloured . . . . 2·00 1·25

1982. 1st International Symposium on Pharmacology of Human Blood Vessels.
921 **241** 30f. multicoloured . . . . 1·00 80
922 80f. multicoloured . . . . 2·25 1·10

242 Symbols of Development, Progress and Peace

1982. 21st National Day.
923 **242** 30f. multicoloured 50 30
924 80f. multicoloured . . . . 1·40 85

243 Emblem of Kuwait Boy Scouts Association on Globe

1982. 75th Anniv of Boy Scout Movement.
925 **243** 30f. multicoloured 60 40
926 80f. multicoloured . . . . 1·75 1·00

244 Emblem of Arab Pharmacists Union

1982. Arab Pharmacists Day.
927 **244** 30f. multicoloured 85 60
928 80f. multicoloured . . . . 2·75 1·75

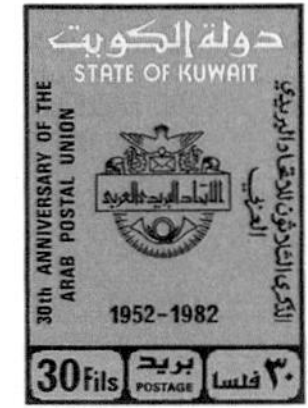

245 Red Crescent, Arab and W.H.O. Emblem
246 A.P.U. Emblem

1982. World Health Day.
929 **245** 30f. multicoloured . . . . 1·00 65
930 80f. multicoloured . . . . 3·00 1·75

1982. 30th Anniv of Arab Postal Union.
931 **246** 30f. black, orange and green 85 60
932 80f. black, green and orange . . . . 2·75 1·50

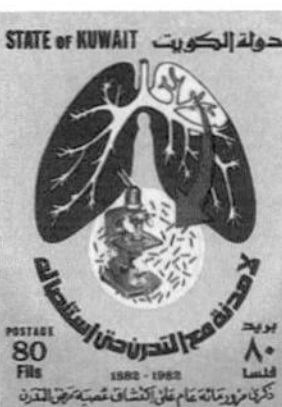

247 Lungs and Microscope
249 Museum Exhibits

248 Crest and Emblems of Kuwait Football Association and Olympic Committee

1982. Centenary of Discovery of Tubercle Bacillus.
933 **247** 30f. multicoloured . . . . 1·00 60
934 80f. multicoloured . . . . 2·75 1·60

1982. World Cup Football Championship, Spain.
935 **248** 30f. multicoloured 75 40
936 80f. multicoloured . . . . 2·00 1·25

1982. 10th Anniv of Science and Natural History Museum.
937 **249** 30f. multicoloured . . . . 1·50 1·00
938 80f. multicoloured . . . . 4·50 3·00

250 "Al-Wattyah" (container ship)

1982. 6th Anniv of United Arab Shipping Company. Multicoloured.
939 30f. Type **250** 75 35
940 80f. "Al-Salimiah" (freighter) 1·75 90

251 Palm Trees
253 Desert Flower

252 Pilgrims

1982. Arab Palm Tree Day.
941 **251** 30f. multicoloured 50 30
942 80f. multicoloured . . . . 1·50 90

1982. Pilgrimage to Mecca.
943 **252** 15f. multicoloured 30 20
944 30f. multicoloured 70 45
945 80f. multicoloured . . . . 1·90 1·25

1983. Desert Plants. As T **253**. Multicoloured; background colours given. (a) Vert designs.
946 10f. green 10 10
947 10f. violet 10 10
948 10f. salmon 10 10
949 10f. pink (blue flowers) . . . 10 10
950 10f. bistre 10 10
951 10f. green 10 10
952 10f. light orange 10 10
953 10f. red (poppy) 10 10
954 10f. brown 10 10
955 10f. blue 10 10
956 15f. green 15 15
957 15f. purple 15 15
958 15f. blue 15 15
959 15f. blue (iris) 15 15
960 15f. olive 15 15
961 15f. red 15 15
962 15f. brown 15 15
963 15f. blue (bellflowers) 15 15
964 15f. mauve 15 15
965 15f. pink 15 15
966 30f. brown 40 25
967 30f. mauve 40 25
968 30f. blue 40 25
969 30f. green 40 25
970 30f. pink 40 25
971 30f. blue 40 25
972 30f. green 40 25
973 30f. mauve 40 25
974 30f. bistre 40 25
975 30f. yellow 40 25

(b) Horiz designs.
976 40f. red (fungi) 75 35
977 40f. green (fungi) 75 35
978 40f. violet 50 35
979 40f. blue 50 35
980 40f. grey 50 35
981 40f. green 50 35
982 40f. mauve 50 35
983 40f. brown 50 35
984 40f. blue 50 35
985 40f. green (daisies) 50 35
986 80f. violet 90 70
987 80f. green 90 70
988 80f. yellow (yellow flowers) . 90 70
989 80f. brown (green leaves) . . 90 70
990 80f. blue 90 70
991 80f. yellow 90 70
992 80f. green 90 70
993 80f. violet (red berries) . . . 90 70
994 80f. brown (yellow flowers) 90 70
995 80f. yellow (red and blue flowers) 90 70
DESIGNS: Various plants.

254 Peace Dove on Map of Kuwait

1983. 22nd National Day.
996 **254** 30f. multicoloured 60 35
997 80f. multicoloured . . . . 1·50 95

255 I.M.O. Emblem

1983. 25th Anniv of International Maritime Organization.
998 **255** 30f. multicoloured 35 20
999 80f. multicoloured . . . . 1·00 60

256 Virus and Map of Africa

1983. 3rd International Conference on Impact of Viral Diseases on Development of Middle East and African Countries.
1000 **256** 15f. multicoloured . . . 30 15
1001 30f. multicoloured . . . 60 35
1002 80f. multicoloured . . . 1·50 95

257 Stylized Figures exercising

1983. World Health Day.
1003 **257** 15f. multicoloured . . . 30 20
1004 30f. multicoloured . . . 65 45
1005 80f. multicoloured . . . 1·90 1·25

258 U.P.U., W.C.Y. and I.T.U. Emblems

1983. World Communications Year.
1006 **258** 15f. multicoloured . . . 35 20
1007 30f. multicoloured . . . 65 45
1008 80f. multicoloured . . . 1·60 1·25

259 Map of Kuwait and Dhow

1983. World Environment Day.
1009 **259** 15f. multicoloured . . . 45 20
1010 30f. multicoloured . . . 85 45
1011 80f. multicoloured . . . 2·00 1·25

260 Walls of Jerusalem

1983. World Heritage Convention.
1012 **260** 15f. multicoloured . . . 35 20
1013 30f. multicoloured . . . 65 45
1014 80f. multicoloured . . . 1·60 1·25

261 Pilgrims in Mozdalipha

1983. Pilgrimage to Mecca.
1015 **261** 15f. multicoloured . . . 35 20
1016 30f. multicoloured . . . 65 45
1017 80f. multicoloured . . . 1·60 1·25

262 Arab within Dove

1983. International Day of Solidarity with Palestinian People.
1018 **262** 15f. multicoloured . . . 35 20
1019 30f. multicoloured . . . 65 45
1020 80f. multicoloured . . . 1·60 1·25

263 Kuwait Medical Association and Congress Emblems

1984. 21st Pan-Arab Medical Congress.
1021 **263** 15f. multicoloured . . . 35 20
1022 30f. multicoloured . . . 65 45
1023 80f. multicoloured . . . 1·60 1·25

264 State Arms within Key

1984. Inauguration of New Health Establishments.
1024 **264** 15f. multicoloured . . . 35 20
1025 30f. multicoloured . . . 65 45
1026 80f. multicoloured . . . 1·60 1·25

265 Dove and Globe
266 Symbols of Medicine within Head 

1984. 23rd National Day.
1027 **265** 15f. multicoloured . . . 35 20
1028 30f. multicoloured . . . 65 45
1029 80f. multicoloured . . . 1·60 1·25

1984. 2nd International Medical Science Conference.
1030 **266** 15f. multicoloured . . . 35 20
1031 30f. multicoloured . . . 65 45
1032 80f. multicoloured . . . 1·60 1·25

267 Douglas DC-3 Airliner

1984. 30th Anniv of Kuwait Airways Corporation.
1033 **267** 30f. blue, dp blue & yell 75 60
1034 80f. blue, dp blue & mve 2·00 1·10

268 Magazine Covers
269 Family and Emblems 

1984. 25th Anniv of "Al-Arabi" (magazine).
1035 **268** 15f. multicoloured . . . 30 20
1036 30f. multicoloured . . . 60 35
1037 80f. multicoloured . . . 1·50 1·00

1984. World Health Day.
1038 **269** 15f. multicoloured . . . 30 20
1039 30f. multicoloured . . . 70 40
1040 80f. multicoloured . . . 1·90 1·10

270 Sudanese Orphan and Village

1984. Hanan Kuwaiti Village, Sudan.
1041 **270** 15f. multicoloured . . . 35 20
1042 30f. multicoloured . . . 75 40
1043 80f. multicoloured . . . 1·90 1·10

271 I.C.A.O., Kuwait Airport and Kuwait Airways Emblems

1984. 40th Anniv of I.C.A.O.
1044 **271** 15f. multicoloured . . . 35 20
1045 30f. multicoloured . . . 75 40
1046 80f. multicoloured . . . 1·90 1·10

272 Map of Arab Countries and Youths

1984. Arab Youth Day.
1047 **272** 30f. multicoloured . . . 70 40
1048 80f. multicoloured . . . 1·90 1·10

273 Swimming

1984. Olympic Games, Los Angeles. Multicoloured.
1049 30f. Type **273** 40 25
1050 30f. Hurdling 40 25
1051 80f. Judo 75 60
1052 80f. Equestrian 75 60

274 Anniversary Emblem, Camera, Airplane, Al-Aujairy Observatory and Wind Tower

1984. 10th Anniv of Science Club.
1053 **274** 15f. multicoloured . . . 35 15
1054 30f. multicoloured . . . 85 40
1055 80f. multicoloured . . . 2·10 1·10

275 Stoning the Devil

1984. Pilgrimage to Mecca.
1056 **275** 30f. multicoloured . . . 80 40
1057 80f. multicoloured . . . 1·75 1·10

276 Anniversary Emblem

1984. 20th Anniv of International Telecommunications Satellite Consortium (Intelsat).
1058 **276** 30f. multicoloured . . . 80 40
1059 80f. multicoloured . . . 1·75 1·10

277 Council Emblem
278 Hands breaking Star 

1984. 5th Supreme Council Session of Gulf Co-operation Council.
1060 **277** 30f. multicoloured . . . 70 40
1061 80f. multicoloured . . . 1·75 1·10

1984. International Day of Solidarity with Palestinian People.
1062 **278** 30f. multicoloured . . . 70 40
1063 80f. multicoloured . . . 1·75 1·10

279 Company Emblem as Satellite
280 I.Y.Y. Emblem 

1984. 50th Anniv of Kuwait Oil Company.
1064 **279** 30f. multicoloured . . . 70 40
1065 80f. multicoloured . . . 1·75 1·10

1985. International Youth Year.
1066 **280** 30f. multicoloured . . . 40 20
1067 80f. multicoloured . . . 1·25 75

281 "24", Hand holding Flame and Dove
282 Programme Emblem 

1985. 24th National Day.
1068 **281** 30f. multicoloured . . . 60 30
1069 80f. multicoloured . . . 1·75 1·10

1985. International Programme for Communications Development.
1070 **282** 30f. multicoloured . . . 70 40
1071 80f. multicoloured . . . 1·75 1·10

283 Emblem
284 Molar 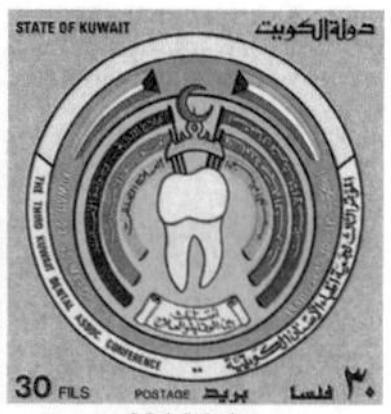

1985. 1st Arab Gulf Social Work Week.
1072 **283** 30f. multicoloured . . . 70 40
1073 80f. multicoloured . . . 1·75 1·10

1985. 3rd Kuwait Dental Association Conference.
1074 **284** 30f. multicoloured . . . 70 40
1075 80f. multicoloured . . . 1·75 1·10

285 Emblem
286 Globe and Figures 

1985. Population Census.
1076 **285** 30f. multicoloured . . . 85 40
1077 80f. multicoloured . . . 1·75 1·10

1985. World Health Day.
1078 **286** 30f. multicoloured . . . 85 40
1079 80f. multicoloured . . . 1·75 1·10

287 Arabic Script

No. 1080

No. 1081

No. 1082

No. 1083

No. 1084

No. 1085

No. 1086

No. 1087

1985. 50th Anniv of Central Library. Designs showing titles of books and names of authors in Arabic script (first line of text illustrated above).

1080 30f. gold . . . . 1·00 45
1081 30f. gold . . . . 1·00 45
1082 30f. gold . . . . 1·00 45
1083 30f. gold . . . . 1·00 45
1084 80f. black and gold . . . . 2·50 1·00
1085 80f. black and gold . . . . 2·50 1·00
1086 80f. black and gold . . . . 2·50 1·00
1087 80f. black and gold . . . . 2·50 1·00

288 Seascape

1985. World Environment Day.

1088 **288** 30f. multicoloured . . . 1·50 40
1089 80f. multicoloured . . . 3·00 1·10

289 Anniversary Emblem

1985. 25th Anniv of Organization of Petroleum Exporting Countries.

1090 **289** 30f. ultramarine, bl & mve 85 40
1091 80f. ultramarine, bl & brn . . . . 1·90 1·10

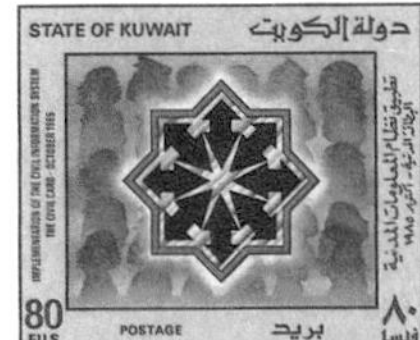

290 Emblem and Heads

1985. Introduction of Civilian Identity Cards.

1092 **290** 30f. multicoloured . . . 85 40
1093 80f. multicoloured . . . 1·90 1·10

291 Flag on Globe within Symbolic Design

1985. International Day of Solidarity with Palestinian People.

1094 **291** 15f. multicoloured . . . 75 30
1095 30f. multicoloured . . . 1·40 60
1096 80f. multicoloured . . . 2·50 1·50

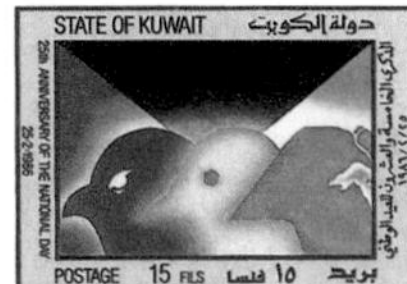

292 Birds

1986. 25th National Day.

1097 **292** 15f. multicoloured . . . 20 15
1098 30f. multicoloured . . . 75 35
1099 80f. multicoloured . . . 2·00 90

293 Emblem

294 W.H.O. Emblem as Flower

1986. 20th Anniv of Kuwait Red Crescent.

1100 **293** 20f. multicoloured . . . 60 45
1101 25f. multicoloured . . . 85 70
1102 70f. multicoloured . . . 2·50 1·90

1986. World Health Day.

1103 **294** 20f. multicoloured . . . 60 45
1104 25f. multicoloured . . . 85 70
1105 70f. multicoloured . . . 2·50 1·90

295 I.P.Y. Emblem

1986. International Peace Year.

1106 **295** 20f. green, blue and black 50 45
1107 25f. blue, yellow and black 75 50
1108 70f. blue, mauve and black . . . . 2·25 1·40

296 "Al Mirqab"

1986. 10th Anniv of United Arab Shipping Company. Container Ships. Multicoloured.

1109 20f. Type **296** . . . . 1·00 45
1110 70f. "Al Mubarakiah" . . . 3·50 1·90

297 Bank Emblem on Map

1986. 25th Anniv of Gulf Bank.

1111 **297** 20f. multicoloured . . . 50 30
1112 25f. multicoloured . . . 75 40
1113 70f. multicoloured . . . 2·25 1·50

298 Zig-zags and Diamonds

1986. Sadu Art. Multicoloured.

1114 20f. Type **298** 50 25
1115 70f. Triangles and symbols 1·60 95
1116 200f. Stripes and triangles 3·75 2·75

299 Dove on Manacled Hand pointing to Map

1986. International Day of Solidarity with Palestinian People.

1117 **299** 20f. multicoloured . . . 75 50
1118 25f. multicoloured . . . 1·00 70
1119 70f. multicoloured . . . 3·00 2·00

300 Conference Emblem

1987. 5th Islamic Summit Conference.

1120 **300** 25f. multicoloured . . . 60 30
1121 50f. multicoloured . . . 1·25 70
1122 150f. multicoloured . . . 3·25 2·00

301 Map in National Colours and Symbols of Development

1987. 26th National Day.

1123 **301** 50f. multicoloured . . . 1·25 50
1124 150f. multicoloured . . . 3·00 1·50

302 Health Science Centre

1987. 3rd Kuwait International Medical Sciences Conference: Infectious Diseases in Developing Countries.

1125 **302** 25f. multicoloured . . . 75 25
1126 150f. multicoloured . . . 3·00 1·50

303 Campaign Emblem

1987. World Health Day. Child Immunization Campaign.

1127 **303** 25f. multicoloured . . . 60 25
1128 50f. multicoloured . . . 1·00 50
1129 150f. multicoloured . . . 2·40 1·50

304 Jerusalem

1987. "Jerusalem is an Arab City".

1130 **304** 25f. multicoloured . . . 60 15
1131 50f. multicoloured . . . 1·00 40
1132 150f. multicoloured . . . 2·40 1·25

305 Pilgrims in Miqat Wadi Mihrim

1987. Pilgrimage to Mecca.

1133 **305** 25f. multicoloured . . . 50 15
1134 50f. multicoloured . . . 75 40
1135 150f. multicoloured . . . 2·25 1·00

306 Emblem

308 Project Monument and Site Plan

307 Buoy and Container Ship

1987. Arab Telecommunications Day.

1136 **306** 25f. multicoloured . . . 50 15
1137 50f. multicoloured . . . 75 40
1138 150f. multicoloured . . . 2·25 1·00

1987. World Maritime Day.

1139 **307** 25f. multicoloured . . . 50 20
1140 50f. multicoloured . . . 75 40
1141 150f. multicoloured . . . 2·25 1·00

1987. Al-Qurain Housing Project.

1142 **308** 25f. multicoloured . . . 50 15
1143 50f. multicoloured . . . 75 40
1144 150f. multicoloured . . . 2·25 1·00

309 Unloading Container Ship

1987. 10th Anniv of Ports Public Authority.

1145 **309** 25f. multicoloured . . . 20 10
1146 50f. multicoloured . . . 55 25
1147 150f. multicoloured . . . 2·00 85

310 Symbolic Design

311 Emblem

1987. International Day of Solidarity with Palestinian People.

1148 **310** 25f. multicoloured . . . 20 10
1149 50f. multicoloured . . . 60 25
1150 150f. multicoloured . . . 2·00 85

1988. 25th Anniv of Women's Cultural and Social Society.

1151 **311** 25f. multicoloured . . . 20 10
1152 50f. multicoloured . . . 60 25
1153 150f. multicoloured . . . 2·00 85

312 Emblem

313 Hands holding W.H.O. Emblem

1988. 27th National Day.

1154 **312** 25f. multicoloured . . . 20 10
1155 50f. multicoloured . . . 60 25
1156 150f. multicoloured . . . 2·00 85

1988. World Health Day. 40th Anniv of W.H.O.

1157 **313** 25f. multicoloured . . . 20 10
1158 50f. multicoloured . . . 60 25
1159 150f. multicoloured . . . 2·00 85

314 Regional Maritime Protection Organization Symbol

315 Society Emblem

1988. 10th Anniv of Kuwait Regional Convention for Protection of Marine Environment.

1160	**314**	35f. ultram, blue & brn	25	15
1161		50f. ultram, blue & grn	60	25
1162		150f. ultram, blue & pur	2·00	85

1988. 25th Anniv of Kuwait Teachers' Society.

1163	**315**	25f. multicoloured	20	10
1164		50f. multicoloured	60	25
1165		150f. multicoloured	2·00	75

316 Pilgrims at al-Sail al-Kabir Miqat

1988. Pilgrimage to Mecca.

1166	**316**	25f. multicoloured	20	10
1167		50f. multicoloured	60	25
1168		150f. multicoloured	2·00	75

317 Gang of Youths lying in wait for Soldiers

318 Ring of Dwellings around Key

1988. Palestinian "Intifida" Movement.

1169	**317**	50f. multicoloured	75	40
1170		150f. multicoloured	3·00	1·50

1988. Arab Housing Day.

1171	**318**	50f. multicoloured	50	30
1172		100f. multicoloured	1·00	60
1173		150f. multicoloured	2·00	75

319 Map of Palestine highlighted on Globe

320 Volunteers embracing Globe

1988. International Day of Solidarity with Palestinian People.

1174	**319**	50f. multicoloured	40	25
1175		100f. multicoloured	1·00	60
1176		150f. multicoloured	2·00	75

1988. International Volunteer Day.

1177	**320**	50f. multicoloured	50	30
1178		100f. multicoloured	1·00	60
1179		150f. multicoloured	2·00	75

321 Conference, Kuwait Society of Engineers and Arab Engineers Union Emblems

1989. 18th Arab Engineering Conference.

1180	**321**	50f. multicoloured	50	30
1181		100f. multicoloured	1·00	60
1182		150f. multicoloured	2·00	75

322 Flags as Figures supporting Map

323 Conference Emblem

1989. 28th National Day.

1183	**322**	50f. multicoloured	50	30
1184		100f. multicoloured	1·00	60
1185		150f. multicoloured	2·00	75

1989. 5th Kuwait Dental Association Conference.

1186	**323**	50f. multicoloured	50	30
1187		150f. multicoloured	1·00	70
1188		250f. multicoloured	1·75	1·10

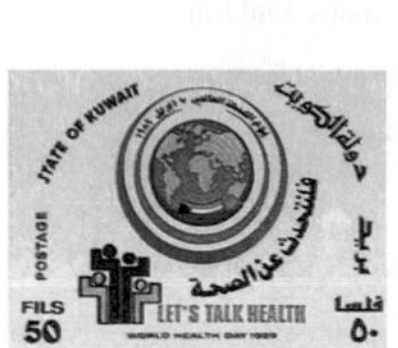

324 Emblems

325 Anniversary Emblem

1989. World Health Day.

1189	**324**	50f. multicoloured	50	30
1190		150f. multicoloured	1·00	70
1191		250f. multicoloured	1·75	1·10

1989. 10th Anniv of Arab Board for Medical Specializations.

1192	**325**	50f. multicoloured	50	20
1193		150f. multicoloured	1·00	55
1194		250f. multicoloured	1·75	85

326 Torch, Pen and Flag

1989. 25th Anniv of Kuwait Journalists' Association.

1195	**326**	50f. multicoloured	40	35
1196		200f. multicoloured	1·50	1·00
1197		250f. multicoloured	2·00	1·40

327 Attan'eem Miqat, Mecca

1989. Pilgrimage to Mecca.

1198	**327**	50f. multicoloured	85	55
1199		150f. multicoloured	2·75	1·75
1200		200f. multicoloured	3·50	2·25

328 Al-Qurain Housing Project

329 Tree

1989. Arab Housing Day.

1201	**328**	25f. multicoloured	45	30
1202		50f. multicoloured	85	55
1203		150f. multicoloured	2·75	1·75

1989. Greenery Week.

1204	**329**	25f. multicoloured	45	30
1205		50f. multicoloured	85	55
1206		150f. multicoloured	2·75	1·75

330 Dhow

331 Emblem and Map

1989. Coil Stamps.

1207	**330**	50f. gold and green	1·25	85
1208		100f. gold and blue	2·50	1·75
1209		200f. gold and red	5·00	3·50

1989. 5th Anniv of Gulf Investment Corporation.

1210	**331**	25f. multicoloured	45	30
1211		50f. multicoloured	85	55
1212		150f. multicoloured	2·75	1·75

332 Emblem

333 Zakat House

1989. 1st Anniv of "Declaration of Palestine State".

1213	**332**	50f. multicoloured	85	55
1214		150f. multicoloured	2·75	1·75
1215		200f. multicoloured	3·50	2·25

1989. Orphanage Sponsorship Project.

1216	**333**	25f. multicoloured	45	30
1217		50f. multicoloured	85	55
1218		150f. multicoloured	2·75	1·75

334 Shaikh Sabah al-Salem as-Sabah (former Chief) and Officers

335 Globe and Dove

1989. 50th Anniv (1988) of Kuwait Police.

1219	**334**	25f. multicoloured	45	30
1220		50f. multicoloured	85	55
1221		150f. multicoloured	2·75	1·75

1990. 29th National Day.

1222	**335**	25f. multicoloured	45	30
1223		50f. multicoloured	85	55
1224		150f. multicoloured	2·75	1·75

336 Earth, Clouds and Weather Balloon

1990. World Meteorological Day.

1225	**336**	50f. multicoloured	85	55
1226		100f. multicoloured	1·75	1·10
1227		150f. multicoloured	2·75	1·75

337 Map bordered by National Flag

338 Lanner Falcon

1990. World Health Day.

1228	**337**	50f. multicoloured	85	55
1229		100f. multicoloured	1·75	1·10
1230		150f. multicoloured	2·75	1·75

1990.

1231	**338**	50f. gold and blue	5·50	5·50
1232		100f. gold and red	10·50	10·50
1233		150f. gold and green	17·00	17·00

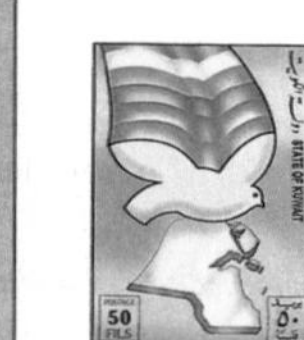

339 Soldiers carrying Kuwait Flag

340 Dove and Map

1991. Liberation (1st issue).

1234	**339**	25f. multicoloured	40	25
1235		50f. multicoloured	80	50
1236		150f. multicoloured	2·40	1·60

See also Nos. 1243/84.

1991. Peace.

1237	**340**	50f. multicoloured	80	50
1238		100f. multicoloured	1·60	1·00
1239		150f. multicoloured	2·40	1·60

341 Flag, Map, Kuwait Towers and Globe

1991. Reconstruction.

1240	**341**	50f. multicoloured	80	50
1241		150f. multicoloured	2·40	1·60
1242		200f. multicoloured	3·00	1·90

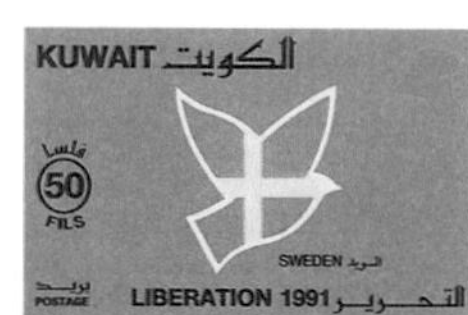

342 Sweden

1991. Liberation (2nd issue). Each showing a dove coloured with the flag of one of the assisting nations. Multicoloured.

1243	50f. Type **342**	45	30
1244	50f. Soviet Union	45	30
1245	50f. United States of America	45	30
1246	50f. Kuwait	45	30
1247	50f. Saudi Arabia	45	30
1248	50f. United Nations	45	30
1249	50f. Singapore	45	30
1250	50f. France	45	30
1251	50f. Italy	45	30
1252	50f. Egypt	45	30
1253	50f. Morocco	45	30
1254	50f. United Kingdom	45	30
1255	50f. Philippines	45	30
1256	50f. United Arab Emirates	45	30
1257	50f. Syria	45	30
1258	50f. Poland	45	30
1259	50f. Australia	45	30
1260	50f. Japan	45	30
1261	50f. Hungary	45	30
1262	50f. Netherlands	45	30
1263	50f. Denmark	45	30
1264	50f. New Zealand	45	30
1265	50f. Czechoslovakia	45	30
1266	50f. Bahrain	45	30
1267	50f. Honduras	45	30
1268	50f. Turkey	45	30
1269	50f. Greece	45	30
1270	50f. Oman	45	30
1271	50f. Qatar	45	30
1272	50f. Belgium	45	30
1273	50f. Sierra Leone	45	30
1274	50f. Argentina	45	30
1275	50f. Norway	45	30
1276	50f. Canada	45	30
1277	50f. Germany	45	30
1278	50f. South Korea	45	30
1279	50f. Bangladesh	45	30
1280	50f. Bulgaria	45	30
1281	50f. Senegal	45	30
1282	50f. Spain	45	30
1283	50f. Niger	45	30
1284	50f. Pakistan	45	30

343 "Human Terror"

344 Emblem

1991. 1st Anniv of Iraqi Invasion. Multicoloured.
1286 50f. Type **343** 80 50
1287 100f. "Invasion of Kuwait" 1·60 1·00
1288 150f. "Environmental Terrorism" (horiz) . . . . 2·40 1·60

1991. 30th Anniv (1990) of Organization of Petroleum Exporting Countries.
1290 **344** 25f. multicoloured . . . 45 30
1291 50f. multicoloured . . . 80 50
1292 150f. multicoloured . . . 2·40 1·60

345 National Flag, Arabic Script and Broken Chains

1991. Campaign to Free Kuwaiti Prisoners of War. Each black and yellow.
1293 50f. Type **345** 70 45
1294 150f. Prison bars, "Don't Forget Our P.O.W.'s" and broken chains . . . . . 2·00 1·25

346 Names of Member Countries forming Tree

1991. 12th Gulf Co-operation Council Summit Conference, Kuwait. Multicoloured.
1296 25f. Type **346** 35 25
1297 150f. National flags as leaves of plant . . . . . 2·00 1·25

347 I.L.Y. Emblem

1992. International Literacy Year (1990).
1299 **347** 50f. blue and brown . . 70 45
1300 100f. blue and yellow . . 1·40 90
1301 150f. blue and mauve . . 2·00 1·25

348 Doves and National Flag

1992. 31st National Day (1302) and 1st Anniv of Liberation (1303).
1302 **348** 50f. black, green and red 40 25
1303 – 150f. multicoloured . . . 1·25 80
DESIGN: 150f. Assisting nations' flags.

349 Dromedaries

1992.
1305 **349** 25f. multicoloured . . . 15 10
1306 50f. multicoloured . . . 30 20
1307 150f. multicoloured . . . 95 60
1308 200f. multicoloured . . . 1·25 80
1309 350f. multicoloured . . . 2·10 1·25

350 Paddle, La Giralda Tower and Kuwaiti Pavilion

1992. "Expo '92" World's Fair, Seville. Multicoloured.
1310 50f. Type **350** 30 20
1311 50f. Dhows 30 20
1312 50f. Dhow 30 20
1313 50f. Kuwaiti Pavilion and dhow 30 20
1314 150f. Kuwaiti Pavilion on Spanish flag 90 60
1315 150f. Paddle and La Giralda Tower on hoist of Kuwaiti flag 90 60
1316 150f. Paddle, La Giralda Tower and dhow on Spanish flag 90 60
1317 150f. Kuwaiti Pavilion and dhow on fly of Kuwaiti flag 90 60

351 Snake around Top of Palm Tree

1992. 2nd U.N. Conference on Environment and Development, Rio de Janeiro, Brazil. Mult.
1319 150f. Type **351** . . . . . . 1·25 80
1320 150f. Snakes, Kuwait colours on map and palm tree . . . . 1·25 80
1321 150f. Skull, snake around tree trunk and dead fish 1·25 80
1322 150f. Snake around camel's neck and bird . . . . . 1·25 80
Nos. 1319/22 were issued together, se-tenant, forming a composite design of the painting "Environmental Terrorism".

352 Palace of Justice

1992.
1324 **352** 25f. multicoloured . . . 20 10
1325 50f. multicoloured . . . 40 25
1326 100f. multicoloured . . . 80 50
1327 150f. multicoloured . . . 1·25 80
1328 250f. multicoloured . . . 2·00 1·25

353 Running and Handball

1992. Olympic Games, Barcelona. Multicoloured.
1329 50f. Swimming and football 65 40
1330 100f. Type **353** . . . . . . 1·25 80
1331 150f. Judo and show jumping . . . . 1·90 1·25
Each value also portrays the Olympic flag and Prince Fahed al-Ahmad al-Sabah, President of several sports organizations, who was killed in the Iraqi invasion.

354 Tanks, Demonstrators with Placards and Executed Civilians

1992. 2nd Anniv of Iraqi Invasion. Children's Drawings. Multicoloured.
1332 50f. Type **354** 30 20
1333 50f. Soldiers rounding up civilians 30 20
1334 50f. Military vehicles and Kuwait Towers 30 20
1335 50f. Battle scene 30 20
1336 150f. Tanks, bleeding eye and soldiers 95 60
1337 150f. Battle scene around fortifications 95 60
1338 150f. Liberation 95 60
1339 150f. Soldiers and military vehicles 95 60

355 Burning Well

1992. 1st Anniv of Extinguishing of Oil Well Fires. Multicoloured.
1341 25f. Type **355** 15 10
1342 50f. Spraying dampener on fire 30 20
1343 150f. Close-up of spraying 95 60
1344 250f. Extinguished well (horiz) . . . . 1·60 1·00

356 Kuwait Towers

357 Laying Bricks to form "32"

1993.
1345 **356** 25f. multicoloured . . . 15 10
1346 100f. multicoloured . . . 70 45
1347 150f. multicoloured . . . 95 60

1993. 32nd National Day.
1348 **357** 25f. multicoloured . . . 15 10
1349 50f. multicoloured . . . 30 20
1350 150f. multicoloured . . . 95 60

358 Symbols of Oppression and Freedom

359 Hands Signing

1993. 2nd Anniv of Liberation.
1351 **358** 25f. multicoloured . . . 15 10
1352 50f. multicoloured . . . 30 20
1353 150f. multicoloured . . . 95 60

1993. Deaf Child Week.
1354 **359** 25f. multicoloured . . . 15 10
1355 50f. multicoloured . . . 30 20
1356 150f. multicoloured . . . 95 60
1357 350f. multicoloured . . . 2·10 1·40

360 Chained Prisoner

361 Hand scratching Map

1993. Campaign to Free Kuwaiti Prisoners of War. Multicoloured.
1358 50f. Type **360** 35 20
1359 150f. Chained hand, hoopoe and barred window (horiz) . . . . 1·10 70
1360 200f. Screaming face on wall of empty cell . . . . . . 1·50 1·00

1993. 3rd Anniv of Iraqi Invasion.
1361 **361** 50f. multicoloured . . . 30 20
1362 150f. multicoloured . . . 85 55

362 Emblem

1993. 40th Anniv of Kuwait Air Force.
1363 **362** 50f. multicoloured . . . 40 25
1364 150f. multicoloured . . . 1·10 70

363 Flower and Dove

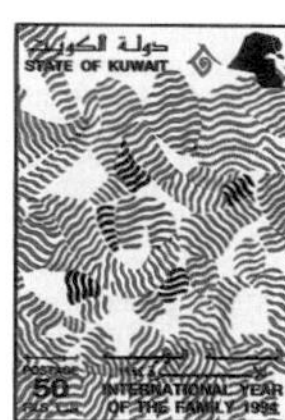

364 Anniversary Emblem

1994. 33rd National Day.
1365 **363** 25f. multicoloured . . . 15 10
1366 50f. multicoloured . . . 30 20
1367 150f. multicoloured . . . 90 60

1994. 3rd Anniv of Liberation.
1368 **364** 25f. multicoloured . . . 15 10
1369 50f. multicoloured . . . 30 20
1370 150f. multicoloured . . . 90 60

365 Anniversary Emblem

366 Stylized Emblems

1994. 25th Anniv of Central Bank of Kuwait.
1371 **365** 25f. multicoloured . . . 15 10
1372 50f. multicoloured . . . 30 20
1373 150f. multicoloured . . . 90 60

1994. Int Year of the Family. Mult.
1374 50f. Type **366** 30 20
1375 150f. Three I.Y.F. emblems 90 60
1376 200f. Globe, emblem and spheres (horiz) . . . . . 1·00 65

367 Emblem on Sky

368 Fingerprint in Water

1994. 20th Anniv of Industrial Bank of Kuwait.
1377 **367** 50f. multicoloured . . . 25 10
1378 100f. gold, blue and black 55 35
1379 150f. multicoloured . . . 80 50

1994. Martyrs' Day. Multicoloured.
1380 50f. Type **368** 30 10
1381 100f. Fingerprint in sand . . 60 40
1382 150f. Fingerprint in national colours 90 60
1383 250f. Fingerprint in clouds over Kuwait Towers . . . 1·50 1·00

369 Anniversary Emblem

370 Free and Imprisoned Doves

1994. 75th Anniv of I.L.O.
1385 **369** 50f. multicoloured . . . 25 10
1386 150f. multicoloured . . . 80 50
1387 350f. gold, blue and black . . . . 1·75 1·10

1994. 4th Anniv of Iraqi Invasion.
1388 **370** 50f. multicoloured . . . 25 10
1389 150f. multicoloured . . . 80 50
1390 350f. multicoloured . . . 1·75 1·10

371 Emblem

372 Anniversary Emblem

1994. Kuwait Ports Authority.
1391 **371** 50f. multicoloured . . . 25 10
1392 150f. multicoloured . . . 80 50
1393 350f. multicoloured . . . 1·75 1·10

1994. 20th Anniv of Kuwait Science Club.
1394 **372** 50f. multicoloured . . . 25 10
1395 100f. multicoloured . . . 55 35
1396 150f. multicoloured . . . 75 50

373 Map and Building

374 I.C.A.O. and Kuwait International Airport Emblems

1994. Inauguration of Arab Towns Organization Permanent Headquarters. Multicoloured.
1397 50f. Type **373** 25 10
1398 100f. Close-up of arched facade 55 35
1399 150f. Door 75 50

1994. 50th Anniv of I.C.A.O. Mult.
1400 100f. Type **374** 55 35
1401 150f. Emblems and control tower 85 55
1402 350f. Airplane and "50 years" . . . . 1·90 1·25

375 Anniversary Emblem

376 Family

1994. 40th Anniv of Kuwait Airways.
1403 **375** 50f. multicoloured . . . 20 10
1404 100f. multicoloured . . . 50 35
1405 150f. multicoloured . . . 75 50

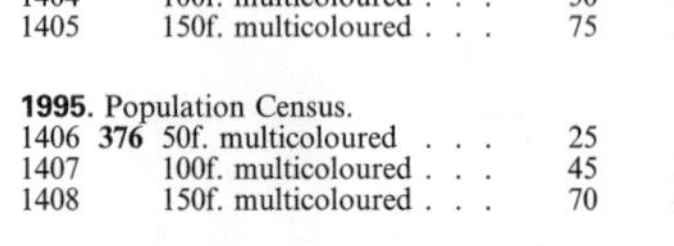

1995. Population Census.
1406 **376** 50f. multicoloured . . . 25 10
1407 100f. multicoloured . . . 45 30
1408 150f. multicoloured . . . 70 45

377 Children waving Flags

378 Falcon dragging Kuwaiti Flag from Snake's Grip

1995. 34th National Day.
1409 **377** 25f. multicoloured . . . 10 10
1410 50f. multicoloured . . . 25 10
1411 150f. multicoloured . . . 70 45

1995. 4th Anniv of Liberation.
1412 **378** 25f. multicoloured . . . 10 10
1413 50f. multicoloured . . . 25 10
1414 150f. multicoloured . . . 70 45

379 Conference Venue

1995. International Medical Conference. Mult.
1415 50f. Type **379** 25 10
1416 100f. Lecture 45 30
1417 150f. Emblem on map of Kuwait in national colours 70 45

380 Anniversary Emblem and Flags

381 Emblem

1995. 50th Anniv of Arab League. Multicoloured.
1418 50f. Type **380** 25 10
1419 100f. Kuwaiti and League flags and League emblem (horiz) 45 30
1420 150f. Handshake and League emblem 70 45

1995. World Health Day. "A World without Polio".
1421 **381** 50f. multicoloured . . . 30 20
1422 150f. multicoloured . . . 1·00 90
1423 200f. multicoloured . . . 1·40 1·40

382 "100"

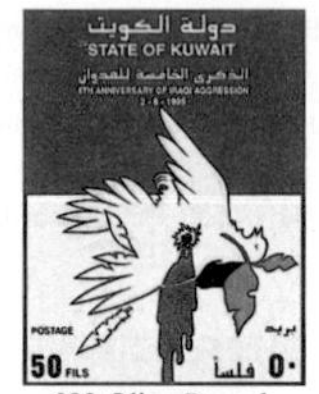

383 Olive Branch falling from Wounded Dove's Beak

1995. Centenary of Volleyball.
1424 **382** 50f. multicoloured . . . 25 10
1425 100f. multicoloured . . . 45 30
1426 150f. multicoloured . . . 70 45

1995. 5th Anniv of Iraqi Invasion.
1427 **383** 50f. multicoloured . . . 20 10
1428 100f. multicoloured . . . 40 25
1429 150f. multicoloured . . . 60 40

384 Doves and Anniversary Emblem

385 Farmer with Animals

1995. 50th Anniv of U.N.O.
1430 **384** 25f. multicoloured . . . 10 10
1431 50f. multicoloured . . . 20 10
1432 150f. multicoloured . . . 60 40

1995. 50th Anniv of F.A.O. Multicoloured.
1433 50f. Type **385** 20 10
1434 100f. Fish market 40 25
1435 150f. Agriculture 60 40

386 Emblems within Ruler

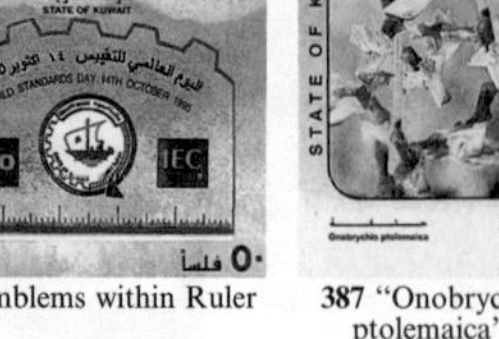

387 "Onobrychis ptolemaica"

1995. World Standards Day. Multicoloured.
1437 50f. Type **386** 20 10
1438 100f. Emblems and aspects of industry (48 × 27 mm) 40 25
1439 150f. As No. 1438 . . . . . 60 40

1995. Flowers. Multicoloured.
1440 5f. Type **387** 10 10
1441 15f. "Convolvulus oxyphyllus" 10 10
1442 25f. Corn poppy 10 10
1443 50f. "Moltkiopsis ciliata" . . 20 10
1444 150f. "Senecio desfontainei" 60 40

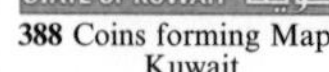

388 Coins forming Map of Kuwait

389 Boy Scout in Watchtower

1996. Money Show.
1445 **388** 25f. multicoloured . . . 10 10
1446 100f. multicoloured . . . 40 25
1447 150f. multicoloured . . . 60 40

1996. 60th Anniv of Scout Movement in Kuwait. Multicoloured.
1448 50f. Type **389** 20 10
1449 100f. Scout drawing water from well 40 25
1450 150f. Scouts planting sapling 60 40

390 Hands supporting Ear of Wheat

391 Saker Falcon trailing National Colours, Falcon and City

1996.
1451 **390** 50f. multicoloured . . . 20 10
1452 100f. multicoloured . . . 40 25
1453 150f. multicoloured . . . 60 40

1996. 35th National Day.
1454 **391** 25f. multicoloured . . . 10 10
1455 50f. multicoloured . . . 20 10
1456 150f. multicoloured . . . 60 40

392 Horses

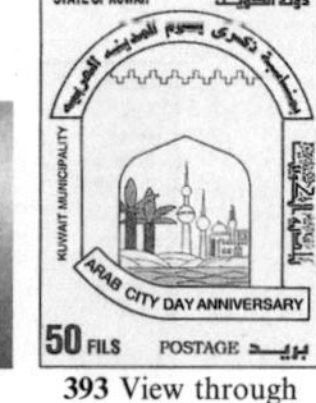

393 View through Gateway

1996. 5th Anniv of Liberation.
1457 **392** 25f. multicoloured . . . 10 10
1458 50f. multicoloured . . . 20 10
1459 150f. multicoloured . . . 60 40

1996. Arab City Day.
1460 **393** 50f. multicoloured . . . 20 10
1461 100f. multicoloured . . . 40 25
1462 150f. multicoloured . . . 60 40

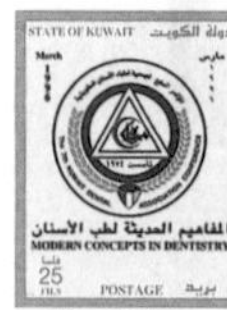

394 Emblem

395 Figures holding Open Book within Bird

1996. 7th Kuwait Dental Association Conference.
1463 **394** 25f. multicoloured . . . 10 10
1464 50f. multicoloured . . . 20 10
1465 150f. multicoloured . . . 60 40

1996. 50th Anniv of UNESCO.
1466 **395** 25f. multicoloured . . . 10 10
1467 100f. multicoloured . . . 40 25
1468 150f. multicoloured . . . 60 40

396 Flags, Anniversary Emblem and Tanker

397 Shaikh Mubarak al-Sabah

1996. 50th Anniv of First Oil Shipment from Kuwait.
1469 **396** 25f. multicoloured . . . 10 10
1470 100f. multicoloured . . . 40 25
1471 150f. multicoloured . . . 60 40

1996. Centenary of Accession as Emir of Shaikh Mubarak al-Sabah. Multicoloured.
1472 25f. Type **397** 10 10
1473 50f. Shaikh Mubarak al-Sabah and ribbons . . . 20 10
1474 150f. Type **397** 60 40

398 Rifle Shooting

399 Festival Emblem

1996. Olympic Games, Atlanta. Multicoloured.
1475 25f. Type **398** 10 10
1476 50f. Running 20 10
1477 100f. Weightlifting 40 25
1478 150f. Fencing 60 40

1996. National Council for Culture, Art and Letters. First Children's Cultural Festival.
1479 **399** 25f. multicoloured . . . 10 10
1480 100f. multicoloured . . . 40 25
1481 150f. multicoloured . . . 60 40

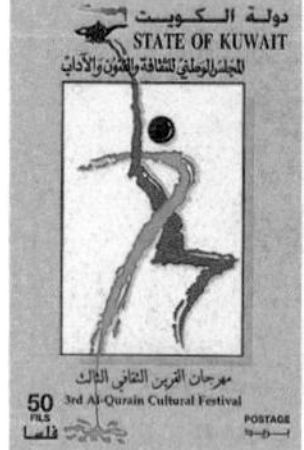

400 Emblem

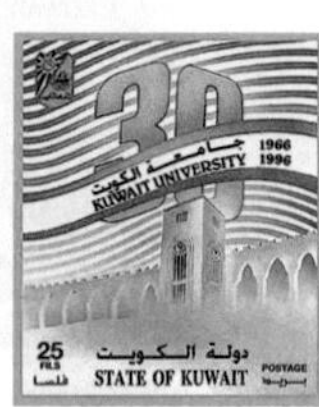

401 University

1996. 3rd Al-Qurain Cultural Festival
1482 **400** 50f. multicoloured . . . 20 10
1483 100f. multicoloured . . . 40 25
1484 150f. multicoloured . . . 60 40

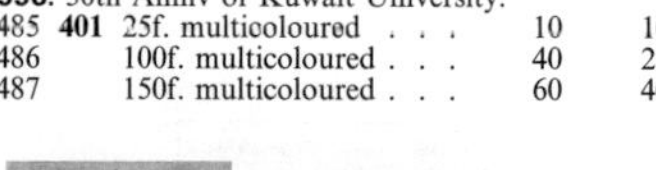

1996. 30th Anniv of Kuwait University.
1485 **401** 25f. multicoloured . . . 10 10
1486 100f. multicoloured . . . 40 25
1487 150f. multicoloured . . . 60 40

402 Liberation Tower

403 Sehel's Grey Mullet

1996.
1488 **402** 5f. multicoloured 10 10
1489 10f. multicoloured . . . 10 10
1490 15f. multicoloured . . . 10 10
1491 25f. multicoloured . . . 10 10
1492 50f. multicoloured . . . 20 10
1493 100f. multicoloured . . . 40 25
1494 150f. multicoloured . . . 60 40
1495 200f. multicoloured . . . 80 50
1496 250f. multicoloured . . . 1·00 65
1497 350f. multicoloured . . . 1·40 90

1997. Marine Life. Multicoloured. (a) Fishes.
1498 25f. Type **403** 10 10
1499 50f. Yellow-finned seabream 20 10
1500 100f. Greasy grouper . . . 40 25
1501 150f. Silver-backed seabream 60 40
1502 200f. Silver grunt 80 50
1503 350f. Silver pomfret . . . . 1·40 90

(b) Shrimps.
1504 25f. Tail and body segments of shrimps 10 10
1505 25f. Head and body segments of shrimps . . . 10 10
1506 25f. Underside of fish and body and legs of shrimp 10 10
1507 25f. Head of shrimp, fish and body and legs of shrimp 10 10
1508 50f. Tail and body segments of two shrimps 20 10
1509 50f. Legs and body segments of shrimp 20 10
1510 50f. Body segments of shrimp and fish 20 10
1511 50f. Head of shrimp, seaweed and body and legs of shrimp 20 10
1512 100f. Tail and body segments of two shrimps 40 25
1513 100f. Head, legs and body segments of shrimps . . . 40 25
1514 100f. Body of shrimp . . . 40 25
1515 100f. Part of head, legs, tail and body of three shrimps 40 25
1516 150f. Body segments of two shrimps and upper half of fish 60 40

1517 150f. Front part of bodies of two shrimps and tail of fish 60 40
1518 150f. Heads of two shrimps, complete shrimp and fish 60 40
1519 150f. Body segments of two shrimps and front part of shrimps head 60 40

Nos. 1504/19 were issued together, se-tenant, forming a composite design of shrimps in a marine environment.

404 Flag, Cupped Hands and Sunflower

1997. 36th National Day.
1520 **404** 25f. multicoloured . . . 10 10
1521 50f. multicoloured . . . 20 10
1522 150f. multicoloured . . . 60 40

405 Flag, rejoicing Crowd and Shaikh Jabir

1997. 6th Anniv of Liberation.
1523 **405** 25f. multicoloured . . . 10 10
1524 50f. multicoloured . . . 20 10
1525 150f. multicoloured . . . 60 40

406 Emblem **407** Emblem

1997. 10th Anniv of Montreal Protocol (on reduction of use of chlorofluorocarbons).
1526 **406** 25f. multicoloured . . . 10 10
1527 50f. multicoloured . . . 20 10
1528 150f. multicoloured . . . 60 40

1997. Kuwait Industries Exhibition.
1529 **407** 25f. multicoloured . . . 10 10
1530 50f. multicoloured . . . 20 10
1531 150f. multicoloured . . . 60 40

408 Signs of Zodiac and Whale

1997. 25th Anniv of Educational Science Museum.
1532 25f. Type **408** 10 10
1533 50f. Space shuttle orbiting Earth, whale, astronaut and dinosaur (horiz) . . . 20 10
1534 150f. Symbols of past, present and future around whale 60 40

409 National Council for Culture, Arts and Letters Emblem

1997. 22nd Kuwait Arabic Book Exhbition.
1536 **409** 25f. multicoloured . . . 10 10
1537 50f. multicoloured . . . 20 10
1538 150f. multicoloured . . . 60 40

410 Ink-well and Book (first book fair, 1975)

1997. Kuwait Cultural History.
1539 25f. Type **410** 10 10
1540 25f. Front page of "Kuwait Magazine" (1928) 10 10
1541 25f. Front page "A'lam al-Fikr" (periodical) (1970) 10 10
1542 25f. Pyramids and dhow ("Al'Bitha" magazine, 1946) 10 10
1543 25f. Rising sun over open book and quill ("Al'am al Ma'rifa" (periodical), 1978) 10 10
1544 25f. Book with dhow on front cover ("Dalil Almohtar Fi Alaam Al-Bihar", 1923) 10 10
1545 25f. Arabic script and "brick" design ("Al-Arabi" magazine, 1958) 10 10
1546 25f. Open book (inauguration of first public library, 1923) . . . 10 10
1547 25f. Two covers showing Arabic script in boxes and cosmic explosion ("Al Thaqafa Al-Alamiya" (periodical), 1981) 10 10
1548 25f. Actors and curtain ("The World Theatre" (periodical), 1969) 10 10
1549 50f. Entrance to Qibliya Girls' School (1937) . . . 20 10
1550 50f. Scissors cutting ribbon (first Fine Arts Exhibition, 1959) 20 10
1551 50f. Mubarakiya School (1912) 20 10
1552 50f. Family entering Kuwait National Museum (1958) 20 10
1553 50f. Shuwaikh Secondary School (1953) 20 10
1554 50f. Door and three windows (Al-Marsam Al-Hor, 1959) 20 10
1555 50f. Decorated screen (Alma'had Aldini, 1947) 20 10
1556 50f. Courtyard of Folklore Centre (1956) 20 10
1557 50f. Three columns of Arabic script (Al Ma'arif printing press, 1947) . . . 20 10
1558 50f. Class photograph (Literary Club, 1924) . . 20 10
1559 150f. Heads and curtains (Folk Theatre Group, 1956) 60 40
1560 150f. Musical instruments and notes (Academy of Music, 1972) 60 40
1561 150f. Film frames, audience and camera (opening of Al-Sharqiya cinema, 1955) 60 40
1562 150f. Curtains around couple at oasis (Theatrical Academy, 1967) 60 40
1563 150f. Marine views in film frame ("Bas Ya Bahar" (first Kuwaiti feature film), 1970) 60 40

411 Doves flying over Members' Flags

1997. 18th Gulf Co-operation Council Summit, Kuwait. Multicoloured.
1564 25f. Type **411** 10 10
1565 50f. Members' flags forming doves wheeling over map (horiz) 20 10
1566 150f. Doves perched atop wall of members' flags . . 60 40

412 State Flag

1998. 37th National Day.
1567 **412** 25f. multicoloured . . . 10 10
1568 50f. multicoloured . . . 20 10
1569 150f. multicoloured . . . 60 40

413 Flag, Map and Dove

1998. 7th Anniv of Liberation.
1570 **413** 25f. multicoloured . . . 10 10
1571 50f. multicoloured . . . 20 10
1572 150f. multicoloured . . . 60 40

414 Emblem **415** Text on Open Page with Flowers

1998. Anti-drugs Campaign.
1573 **414** 25f. multicoloured . . . 10 10
1574 50f. multicoloured . . . 20 10
1575 150f. multicoloured . . . 60 40

1998. Martyrs' Day. Multicoloured.
1576 25f. Type **415** 10 10
1577 50f. Tree 20 10
1578 150f. Calligraphy 60 40

416 Woman selling Cooked Vegetables **417** Child's Face

1998. Life in Pre-Oil Kuwait (1st series). Mult.
1580 25f. Type **416** 10 10
1581 50f. Ship-building 20 10
1582 100f. Sailor strapping his box 40 25
1583 150f. Pearl divers wading out to boat 60 40
1584 250f. Delivering fresh water 1·00 65
1585 350f. Pigeon trainer . . . . 1·40 90
See also Nos. 1599/604.

1998. 12th Anniv of Chernobyl Nuclear Disaster.
1586 **417** 25f. multicoloured . . . 10 10
1587 50f. multicoloured . . . 20 10
1588 150f. multicoloured . . . 60 40

418 World Map and Emblem

1998. International Year of the Ocean. Multicoloured.
1589 25f. Type **418** 10 10
1590 50f. Motifs as in Type **418** but differently arranged in rectangle (27 × 37 mm) . . 20 10
1591 150f. Type **418** 60 40

419 Emblem

1998. 25th Anniv of Union of Consumer Co-operative Societies. Multicoloured.
1592 **419** 25f. multicoloured . . . 10 10
1593 50f. multicoloured . . . 20 10
1594 150f. multicoloured . . . 60 40

420 Men on Crutches

1998. Anti-landmine Campaign. Details from painting by Jafar Islah. Multicoloured.
1595 25f. Type **420** 10 10
1596 50f. Man on crutch 20 10
1597 150f. Man on crutches and woman helping child . . 60 40

1998. Life in Pre-Oil Kuwait (2nd series). As T **416**. Multicoloured.
1599 25f. Hairdresser 10 10
1600 50f. Hand-grinding 20 10
1601 100f. Tailor 40 25
1602 150f. Artist 60 40
1603 250f. Potter . . . . 1·00 65
1604 350f. Hand-spinning . . . . 1·40 90

421 New Postal Emblem

1998.
1605 **421** 25f. multicoloured . . . 10 10
1606 50f. multicoloured . . . 20 10
1607 100f. multicoloured . . . 40 25
1608 150f. multicoloured . . . 60 40
1609 250f. multicoloured . . . 1·00 65

422 Child's Painting

1998. Children's Cultural House.
1610 **422** 25f. multicoloured . . . 10 10
1611 50f. multicoloured . . . 20 10
1612 150f. multicoloured . . . 60 40

423 Collage **424** Falcon

1998. 50th Anniv of Universal Declaration of Human Rights.
1613 **423** 25f. multicoloured . . . 10 10
1614 50f. multicoloured . . . 20 15
1615 150f. multicoloured . . . 60 40

1998.
1616 25f. Type **424** 10 10
1617 50f. Young camels 20 10
1618 150f. Dhow 65 40

425 Emblem

1998. 25th Anniv of Public Authority for Applied Education and Training.
1619 **425** 25f. multicoloured . . . 10 10
1620 50f. multicoloured . . . 20 10
1621 150f. multicoloured . . . 65 40

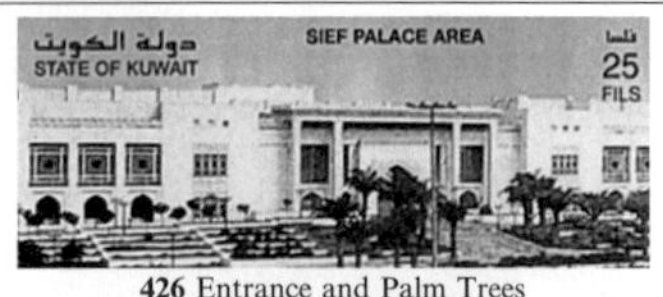

426 Entrance and Palm Trees

1999. Seif Palace. Different views of the Palace. Mult.
1622 25f. Type **426** 10 10
1623 50f. Palace buildings 20 10
1624 100f. Tower 45 30
1625 150f. Type **426** 65 40
1626 250f. As No. 1623 . . . . . 1·10 70
1627 350f. As No. 1624 . . . . . 1·60 1·00

427 "38"

1999. 38th National Day.
1628 **427** 50f. multicoloured . . . 20 10
1629 150f. multicoloured . . . 65 40

428 Building, Dove and "8"

1999. 8th Anniv of Liberation.
1630 **428** 50f. multicoloured . . . 20 10
1631 150f. multicoloured . . . 65 40

429 Liver and Kuwait Flag

1999. 20th Anniv of Organ Transplantation in Kuwait. Multicoloured.
1632 50f. Type **429** 20 10
1633 150f. Heart and Kuwait flag 65 40

430 Emblem and Kuwait Flag

432 "2000" and Emblem

431 Emblem

1999. 40th Anniv of *Al-Arabi* (magazine).
1634 **430** 50f. multicoloured . . . 20 10
1635 150f. multicoloured . . . 65 40

2000. International Civil Aviation Day.
1636 **431** 50f. multicoloured . . . 20 10
1637 150f. multicoloured . . . 65 40
1638 250f. multicoloured . . . 1·10 70

2000. Kuwait International Airport.
1639 **432** 50f. multicoloured . . . 20 10
1640 150f. multicoloured . . . 65 40
1641 250f. multicoloured . . . 1·10 70

433 Children, Globe and Jigsaw Pieces

2000. International Conference on Autism and Communication Deficiencies, Kuwait. Children's paintings. Multicoloured.
1642 25f. Type **433** 10 10
1643 50f. Globe and children . . 20 10
1644 150f. Children holding hands 65 40

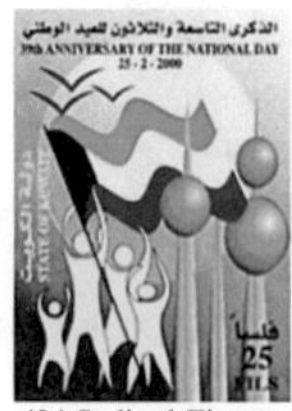

434 Stylized Figures and Flag

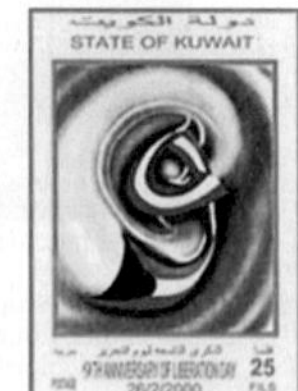

435 State Flag

2000. 39th National Day.
1645 **434** 25f. multicoloured . . . 10 10
1646 50f. multicoloured . . . 20 10
1647 150f. multicoloured . . . 65 40

2000. 9th Anniv of Liberation.
1648 **435** 25f. multicoloured . . . 10 10
1649 50f. multicoloured . . . 20 10
1650 150f. multicoloured . . . 65 40

436 Emblem

2000. 25th Anniv (1999) of Kuwait Science Club.
1651 **436** 50f. multicoloured . . . 20 10
1652 150f. multicoloured . . . 65 40
1653 350f. multicoloured . . . 1·60 1·00

437 Emblem

2000. International Investment Forum, Kuwait.
1654 **437** 25f. multicoloured . . . 10 10
1655 50f. multicoloured . . . 25 15
1656 150f. multicoloured . . . 70 30

438 View over City

439 Emblem and Hand holding Scroll

2000. Kuwait City.
1657 **438** 50f. multicoloured . . . 25 15
1658 150f. multicoloured . . . 70 30
1659 350f. multicoloured . . . 1·60 1·00

2000. 3rd Private Education Week.
1660 **439** 50f. multicoloured . . . 25 15
1661 150f. multicoloured . . . 70 30
1662 350f. multicoloured . . . 1·60 1·00

440 Emblem and Stamps Encircling Globe

2000. 125th Anniv of Universal Postal Union.
1663 **440** 50f. multicoloured . . . 25 15
1664 150f. multicoloured . . . 70 30
1665 350f. multicoloured . . . 1·60 1·00

441 Hands and Emblem

2000. World Environment Day.
1667 **441** 50f. multicoloured . . . 25 15
1668 150f. multicoloured . . . 70 30
1669 350f. multicoloured . . . 1·60 1·00

442 Galleon and Emblem

2000. Cent of General Customs' Administration.
1670 **442** 50f. multicoloured . . . 25 15
1671 150f. multicoloured . . . 70 30
1672 350f. multicoloured . . . 1·60 1·50

443 Emblem

2000. 10th Anniv of Committee for Missing and Prisoners of War Affairs. Multicoloured.
1674 25f. Type **443** 10 10
1675 50f. Emblem and chains . . 20 10
1676 150f. Emblem forming "10" 60 35

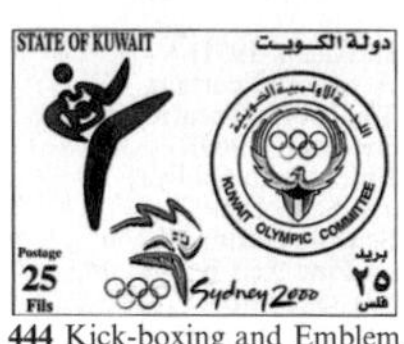

444 Kick-boxing and Emblem

2000. Olympic Games, Sydney. Multicoloured.
1677 25f. Type **444** 10 10
1678 50f. Shooting 20 10
1679 150f. Swimming 60 35
1680 200f. Weight-lifting 80 45
1681 250f. Running . . . . . . 1·00 60
1682 350f. Football . . . . . . 1·40 80

A 1d. imperforate miniature sheet, the design consisting of the emblem and pictograms as depicted on the stamps, exists in a cover inscribed "With the Compliments of Ministry of Communications - Post Sector".

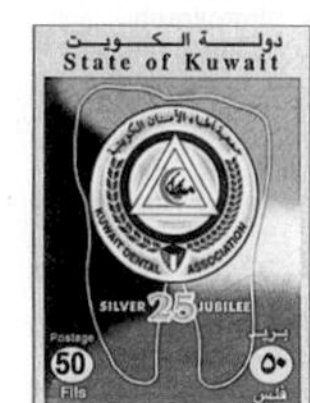

445 Emblem and Outline of Tooth

2000. 25th Anniv of Kuwait Dental Association.
1683 **445** 50f. multicoloured . . . 20 10
1684 150f. multicoloured . . . 60 35
1685 350f. multicoloured . . . 1·40 80

446 Emblem

2000. 6th Gulf Cooperation Council (G.C.C.) Joint Stamp Exhibition, Kuwait.
1686 **446** 25f. multicoloured . . . 10 10
1687 50f. multicoloured . . . 20 10
1688 150f. multicoloured . . . 60 35
MS1689 146 × 111 mm. 1d. Emblems of current and previous exhibitions. Imperf 40 20

447 Building and "15" in Laurel Wreath

2000. 15th Anniv of Gulf Investment Corporation and Inauguration of New Headquarters Building. Multicoloured.
1690 25f. Type **447** 10 10
1691 50f. Building in centre with "15" at left 20 10
1692 150f. Building at right with "15" in centre 60 35

448 Letters and Book

2000. National Council for Culture, Arts and Letters.
1693 **448** 25f. multicoloured . . . 10 10
1694 50f. multicoloured . . . 20 10
1695 150f. multicoloured . . . 60 35
MS1695a 448 500f. multicoloured (85 × 95 mm) . . . . 2·40 1·90

449 Map and Emblems

2001. Arab Cultural Capital.
1696 **449** 25f. multicoloured . . . 10 10
1697 50f. multicoloured . . . 20 10
1698 150f. multicoloured . . . 60 35

450 Emblem

451 Anniversary Emblem

2001. "Long Live February".
1699 **450** 25f. multicoloured . . . 10 10
1700 50f. multicoloured . . . 20 10
1701 150f. multicoloured . . . 60 30

2001. 40th Anniv of National Day.
1702 **451** 25f. multicoloured . . . 10 10
1703 50f. multicoloured . . . 20 10
1704 150f. multicoloured . . . 60 35

452 Doves

453 Buildings

2001. 10th Anniv of Liberation Day.
1705 **452** 25f. multicoloured . . . 10 10
1706 50f. multicoloured . . . 20 10
1707 150f. multicoloured . . . 60 35

2001. 40th Anniv of Kuwait Fund For Arab Economic Development.
1708 **453** 25f. multicoloured . . . 10 10
1709 50f. multicoloured . . . 20 10

454 Anniversary Emblem

2001. 50th Anniv of United Nations Commissioner for Refugees. Multicoloured.
1710 25f. Type **454** 10 10
1711 50f. Anniversary emblem (vertical blue band) . . . 20 10
1712 150f. Anniversary emblem (different) 60 35

455 Pierced Flag

2001. Prisoners.
1713 **455** 25f. multicoloured . . . 10 10
1714 50f. multicoloured . . . 20 10
1715 150f. multicoloured . . . 60 35

456 Anniversary Emblem

2001. 50th Anniv of Radio Kuwait.
1716 **456** 25f. multicoloured . . . 10 10
1717 50f. multicoloured (vert) 20 10
1718 150f. multicoloured (vert) 60 35

457 Mosque and Colours

2001. Al Aqsa Uprising. Multicoloured.
1719 25f. Type **457** 10 10
1720 50f. Mosque dome and uprising 20 10
1721 150f. Mosque dome and uprising (different) . . . 60 35

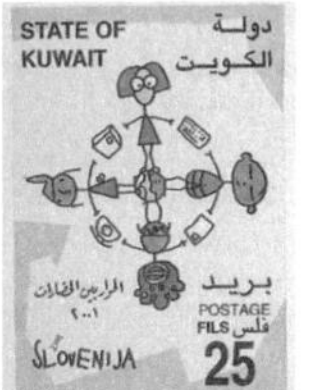

458 Children encircling Globe

459 Script

2001. United Nations Year of Dialogue among Civilizations.
1722 **458** 25f. multicoloured . . . 10 10
1723 50f. multicoloured . . . 20 10
1724 150f. multicoloured . . . 60 35

2001. Heritage Management Foundation. Multicoloured.
1725 25f. Type **459** 10 10
1726 50f. Sheikh Abdulla 20 10
1727 150f. Sheikh Jabir 60 35

460 Stylised Tree with Nine Leaves

461 Face covered by Hands

2001. 25th Anniv of Tourism Enterprise. Multicoloured.
1728 25f. Type **460** 10 10
1729 50f. Twig with six long leaves 20 10
1730 100f. Many-branched tree with falling leaves 40 25
1731 150f. Tree with two branches 60 35
MS1732 60 × 80 mm. 250f. As Nos. 1728/31. Imperf . . . . . 1·30 1·30

2001. Human Rights. Multicoloured.
1733 25f. Type **461** 20 10
1734 50f. Faces and barbed wire (horiz) 20 10
1735 150f. Chains, globe and child's face (horiz) 60 35

462 Metal Artefact

2001. 10th Anniv of Scientific Diving Team. Multicoloured.
1736 25f. Type **462** 10 10
1737 50f. Divers 20 10
1738 150f. Turtle (vert) 60 35

463 Original Building Facade

2002. 50th Anniv of National Bank. Multicoloured.
1739 50f. Type **463** 20 10
1740 100f. Modern building . . . 40 25
1741 150f. Anniversary emblem and camels 60 35

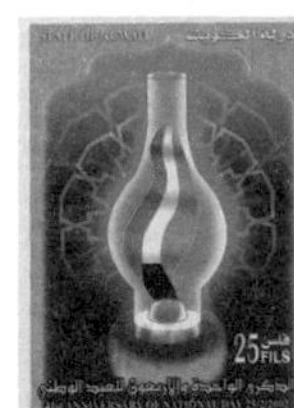
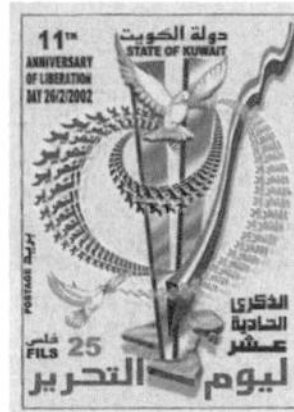
464 Flag enclosed Lamp

465 Monument, Doves, Flag and Map

2002. 1st Anniv of National Day. Multicoloured.
1742 **464** 25f. multicoloured . . . 10 10
1743 50f. multicoloured . . . 20 10
1744 150f. multicoloured . . . 60 35

2002. 11th Anniv of Liberation Day. Multicoloured.
1745 **465** 25f. multicoloured . . . 10 10
1746 50f. multicoloured . . . 20 10
1747 150f. multicoloured . . . 60 35

466 Camel Caravan

467 Emblem and Gas Tower

2002. Arab Nomads. Multicoloured.
1748 **466** 25f. multicoloured . . . 10 10
1749 50f. multicoloured . . . 20 10
1750 150f. multicoloured . . . 60 35

2002. Rehabilitation of Al-Qurain Landfill Site. Multicoloured.
1751 **467** 25f. multicoloured . . . 10 10
1752 50f. multicoloured . . . 20 10
1753 150f. multicoloured . . . 60 35

468 Northern Lapwing

469 Adult and Child's Hands

2002. Kuwait Scientific Centre. Multicoloured.
1754 25f. Type **468** 10 10
1755 25f. Spur-winged plover . . 10 10
1756 25f. Otter 10 10
1757 25f. Crocodile 10 10
1758 25f. Fennec fox 10 10
1759 25f. Caracal 10 10
1760 25f. Protoreaster 10 10
1761 25f. Sepia 10 10
1762 25f. Nurse shark 10 10
1763 25f. Lionfish 10 10
1764 25f. Kestrel 10 10
1765 25f. Fruit bat 10 10
1766 50f. Centre building (45 × 27 mm) 20 10
MS1767 80 × 60 mm. 250f. Dock and building. Imperf . . . . 1·00 60

2002. 10th Anniv of Social Development Office. Multicoloured.
1768 **469** 25f. multicoloured . . . 10 10
1769 50f. multicoloured . . . 20 10

470 Engineering Symbols

2002. 40th Anniv of Society of Engineers. Multicoloured.
1770 **470** 25f. multicoloured . . . 10 10
1771 50f. multicoloured . . . 20 10
1772 150f. multicoloured . . . 60 35

471 Anniversary Emblems

2002. 25th Anniv of Science Foundation. Multicoloured.
1773 25f. Type **471** 10 10
1774 50f. Building 20 10
1775 150f. Map of Kuwait (vert) 60 35

472 Organization Emblem

473 Engineering Workers

2002. International Year of Volunteers. KNPVC (welfare organization).
1776 **472** 25f. multicoloured . . . 10 10
1777 50f. multicoloured . . . 20 10
1778 150f. multicoloured . . . 60 35

2002. 20th Anniv of Professional Education Programme. Multicoloured.
1779 25f. Type **473** 10 10
1780 50f. Theatre nurse 20 10
1781 100f. Man checking dials . . 40 25
1782 150f. Flag and "20" 60 35
1783 250f. Emblem . . . . 1·00 60

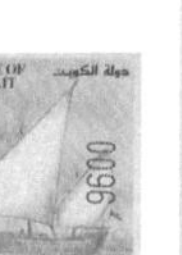

474 Traditional Boat

475 Greek Ruins, Failaka Island

2003.
1784 **474** 100f. multicoloured . . .

2003. 42nd Anniv of National Day. Multicoloured.
1785 **475** 25f. multicoloured . . . 10 10
1786 50f. multicoloured . . . 20 10
1787 150f. multicoloured . . . 60 35

OFFICIAL STAMPS

1923. Stamps of India (King George V) optd **KUWAIT SERVICE.**
O 1 **56** ¼a. green . . . . 2·25 26·00
O 2 **57** 1a. brown . . . . 3·00 15·00
O 3 **58** 1½a. brown (No. 163) . . 3·50 38·00
O 4 **59** 2a. lilac . . . . 5·50 27·00
O17 **70** 2a. lilac . . . . 55·00 £170
O 5 **61** 2a.6p. blue . . . . . . 4·50 65·00
O 6 **62** 3a. orange . . . . 3·50 65·00
O19 3a. blue . . . . 4·50 40·00
O 8 **63** 4a. green . . . . 3·50 60·00
O20 **71** 4a. green . . . . 4·25 70·00
O 9 **65** 8a. mauve . . . . 6·00 90·00
O22 **66** 12a. red . . . . 26·00 £170
O10 **67** 1r. brown and green . . 18·00 £150
O11 2r. red and orange . . . . 18·00 £200
O12 5r. blue and violet . . . . 75·00 £400
O13 10r. green and red £120 £350
O14 15r. blue £180 £475

POSTAGE DUE STAMPS

D 34 D 51

1963.
D199 **D 34** 1f. brown and black 10 20
D200 2f. lilac and black . . 15 25
D201 5f. blue and black . . 25 20
D202 8f. green and black . . 50 35
D203 10f. yellow and black 70 65
D204 25f. red and black . . 1·60 2·00
The above stamps were not sold to the public unused until 1 July 1964.

1965.
D276 **D 51** 4f. pink and yellow . . 15 20
D277 15f. red and blue . . 50 35
D278 40f. blue and green . . 1·00 75
D279 50f. green and mauve 1·40 1·00
D280 100f. blue and yellow 2·50 2·00

KYRGYZSTAN Pt. 10

Formerly Kirghizia, a constituent republic of the Soviet Union, Kyrgyzstan became independent in 1991. Its capital Frunze reverted to its previous name of Bishkek.

1992. 100 kopeks = 1 rouble.
1993. 100 tyin = 1 som.

1 Sary-C'helek Nature Reserve

2 Golden Eagle

1992.
1 **1** 15k. multicoloured 15 15

1992.
2 **2** 50k. multicoloured 25 20

3 "Cattle at Issyk-Kule" (G. A. Aitiev)

1992.
3 **3** 1r. multicoloured 25 15

4 Carpet and Samovar

1992.
4 **4** 1r.50 multicoloured 25 15

5 Cave Paintings

1993. National Monuments. Multicoloured.
5 10k. Type **5** 10 10
6 50k. 11th-century tower, Burana (vert) 10 10
7 1r.+25k. Mausoleum of Manas, Talas (vert) 10 10
8 2r.+50k. Mausoleum, Uzgen 15 10
9 3r. Yurt 20 15
10 5r.+50k. Statue of Manas, Bishkek 35 25
11 9r. Cultural complex, Bishkek 55 35
MS12 61 × 91 mm. 10r. Cockle jewellery . . . . 1·25 1·00
The premium on Nos. 7/8 and 10 were used for the financing of a Manas museum.

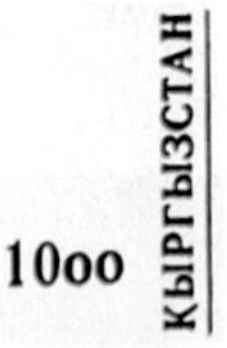

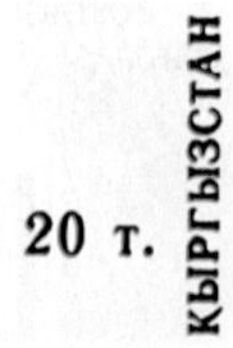

(6) (7)

1993. Nos. 5940, 6073 and 4671 of Russia surch as T **6**.
13 10k. on 1k. brown 15 10
14 20k. on 2k. brown 40 20
15 30k. on 3k. red 60 40

1993. Nos. 4672/3 of Russia surch as T **7**.
16 20t. on 4k. red 20 10
17 30t. on 6k. blue 40 30

8 Map

1993. 2nd Anniv of Independence (18) and 1st Anniv of Admission to United Nations (19). Multicoloured.
18 50t. Type **8** 35 25
19 60t. U.N. emblem, national flag and Government Palace, Bishkek (vert) 45 30
See also No. **MS**35.

9 Komuz

1993. Music.
20 **9** 30t. multicoloured 25 15

10 Dog 12 Mauve Flowers

11 Adult and Cub

1994. New Year. Year of the Dog.
22 **10** 60t. multicoloured 20 15
MS21 84 × 67 mm. 14t. Similar design to Type **9** but with motifs reversed (51 × 39 mm) 4·00 3·00

1994. The Snow Leopard. Multicoloured.
23 10t. Type **11** 15 10
24 20t. Lying curled-up 35 20
25 30t. Sitting 45 30
26 40t. Head 60 40

1994. Flowers. Multicoloured.
27 1t. Type **12** 10 10
28 3t. Daisies (horiz) 10 10
29 10t. Tulip 10 10
30 16t. Narcissi 10 10
31 20t. Deep pink flower 15 10
32 30t. White flower 20 15
33 40t. Yellow flower 30 25
MS34 70 × 90 mm. 50t. *Trollius altaicum* 35 35

1994. 3rd Anniv of Independence and Second Anniv of Admission to United Nations. Sheet containing stamps as Nos. 18/19 but with face values changed. Multicoloured.
MS35 110 × 80 mm. 120t. Type **8**; 130t. As No. 19 1·75 1·75

13 Fluorite 15 Woman with Rug

14 Turkestan Catfish

1994. Minerals. Multicoloured.
36 80t. Type **13** 20 15
37 90t. Calcite 20 15
38 100t. Getchellite 20 15
39 110t. Barite 25 20
40 120t. Auripigment 25 20
41 140t. Antimonite 30 20
MS42 135 × 95 mm. 200t. Cinnabar 75 75

1994. Fishes. Multicoloured.
43 110t. Type **14** 30 20
44 120t. Schmidt's dace 40 30
45 130t. Scaleless osman 50 40
46 140t. Spotted stone loach 60 45
MS47 82 × 57 mm. 200t. Common carp (*Cyprinus carpio*) 75 75

1995. Traditional Costumes. Multicoloured.
48 50t. Type **15** 10 10
49 50t. Musician 10 10
50 100t. Falconer 25 15
51 100t. Woman with long plaits 25 15

16 Butterfly, Traffic Lights and Emblem 17 Brown Bear

1995. Road Safety Week.
52 **16** 200t. multicoloured 30 20

1995. Animals. Multicoloured.
53 110t. Type **17** 10 10
54 120t. Snow leopard (horiz) 15 10
55 130t. Golden eagle 30 15
56 140t. Menzbier's marmot (horiz) 25 15
57 150t. Short-toed eagle (horiz) 35 15
58 160t. Golden eagle (different) 40 20
59 190t. Red fox (horiz) 35 20
MS60 90 × 70 mm. 130t. Golden eagle (*different*); 170t. Argali 60 60

18 Memorial Flame, Bishkek

1995. 50th Anniv of End of Second World War. Sheet 90 × 70 mm.
MS61 **18** 150t. multicoloured 40 40

19 Aitschurek (wife of Manas) 20 Osprey

1995. Millenary of "Manas" (epic poem). Each blue and gold.
62 10t.+5t. Type **19** 10 10
63 20t.+10t. Hoopoe on youth's wrist 10 10
64 30t.+10t. Birth of Semetey, son of Manas 10 10
65 30t.+10t. Woman carrying spear and leading horse 10 10
66 40t.+15t. Warrior astride dead dragon 15 10
67 50t.+15t. Jakyp, father of Manas 20 15
68 50t.+15t. Manas on horseback 20 15
69 50t.+15t. Seytek, grandson of Manas 20 15
MS70 Two sheets. (a) 166 × 107 mm. 2s. + 50t. Saryakbai (Manas singer) cradling injured warrier (37 × 51 mm). (b) 148 × 131 mm. 2s.+50t. Sagymbai (Manas singer) (37 × 51 mm) 90 90

1995. Birds. Multicoloured.
71 10t. Type **20** 10 10
72 50t. Tawny eagle 10 10
73 100t. Lammergeier 20 15
74 140t. Saker falcon 25 15
75 150t. Short-toed eagle 25 15
76 200t. Lammergeier 35 25
77 300t. Golden eagle 50 30
MS78 90 × 70 mm. 600t. White-tailed sea eagle (*Haliaeetus albicilla*) (29 × 40 mm) 1·00 1·00

21 Envelopes on Map and U.P.U. Emblem 22 State Arms

1995. Postage Stamp Week.
79 **21** 200t. multicoloured 30 20

1995.
80 **22** 20t. violet 10 10
81 50t. blue 10 10
82 100t. brown 15 10
83 500t. green 65 50

23 Mare and Foal Galloping

1995. Horses. Multicoloured.
89 10t. Type **23** 10 10
90 50t. Palamino mare and foal (vert) 10 10
91 100t. Brown mare and foal (vert) 20 15
92 140t. Chestnut mare and foal (vert) 25 15
93 150t. Chestnut mare and foal 25 15
94 200t. Grey mare and foal 35 25
95 300t. Pair of foals 50 30
MS96 91 × 71 mm. 600t. brown and cream (Mongolian wild horses) (*Equus caballus*) (vert) 90 90

24 Headquaters, New York

1995. 50th Anniv of United Nations Organization. Sheet 71 × 91 mm containing T b24b and similar horiz design. Multicoloured.
MS97 100t. Type **24**; 100t. Rainbow and mountains 35 35

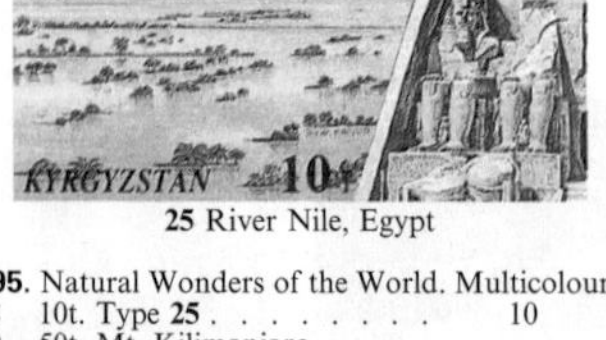

25 River Nile, Egypt

1995. Natural Wonders of the World. Multicoloured.
98 10t. Type **25** 10 10
99 50t. Mt. Kilimanjaro, Tanzania 10 10
100 100t. Sahara Desert, Algeria 15 10
101 140t. Amazon River, Brazil (vert) 20 15
102 150t. Grand Canyon, U.S.A. (vert) 20 15
103 200t. Victoria Falls, Zimbabwe (vert) 25 20
104 350t. Mt. Everest, Nepal 50 35
105 400t. Niagara Falls, Canada 55 40
MS106 Two sheets, each 90 × 70 mm. (a) Gull over Issyk-Kule lake, Kyrgyzstan; (b) Eagle over Issyk-Kule lake 1·90 1·90
No. 98 is wrongly inscribed "Egipt".

26 Steppe Ribbon Snake

1996. Reptiles. Multicoloured.
107 20t. Type **26** 10 10
108 50t. Fat-tailed panther gecko 10 10
109 50t. Tessellated water snake 10 10
110 100t. Central Asian viper 15 10
111 150t. Arguta 25 20
112 200t. Dione snake 35 25
113 250t. "Asyblepharus sp." (wrongly inscr "Asymblepharus") 40 30
MS114 91 × 71 mm. 500t. Sand lizard (*Lacerta agilis*) 75 75

27 Kaufmann's Shovelnose (*Pseudoscphirhyncus kafmanni*)

1996. "Save the Aral Sea". Sheet 128 × 108 mm containing T **27** and similar horiz designs. Multicoloured.
MS115 100t. Caracal (*Felis caracal*); 100t. Aral trout (*Salmo trutta aralensis*); 100t. Striped hyena (*Hyaena hyaena*); 100t. Type **27**; 100t. Pike asp (*Aspiolucius esocinus*) 1·10 1·10

28 Show Jumping and Traditional Horse Race

1996. Olympic Games, Atlanta, U.S.A. Multicoloured.
116 100t.+20t. Type **28** 25 15
117 140t.+30t. Boxing and traditional wrestling match 35 25
118 150t.+30t. Archer and mounted archer shooting at eagle 50 40
119 300t.+50t. Judo competitor, ballooning, yachting and water-skiing 85 65

29 Golden Eagle

1997. Animals.
120 600t. Type **29** 85 60
121 600t. Markhor ("Capra falconeri") 85 60
122 600t. Argali ("Ovis ammon") 85 60
123 600t. Himalayan griffon ("Gyps himalayensis") 85 60
124 600t. Asiatic wild ass ("Equus hemionus") 85 60
125 600t. Wolf ("Canis lupus") 85 60
126 600t. Brown bear ("Ursus arctos") (wrongly inscr "arctor") 85 60
127 600t. Saiga ("Saiga tatarica") 85 60

30 Tiger

1998. New Year. Year of the Tiger.
128 **30** 600t. multicoloured 65 45

31 "Parnassius actius"

1998. Butterflies. Multicoloured.
129 600t. Type **31** (wrongly inscr "Parnasius") 65 45
130 600t. "Colias christophi" . . 65 45
131 600t. Swallowtail ("Papilio machaon") 65 45
132 600t. "Colias thisoa" 65 45
133 600t. "Parnassius delphius" 65 45
134 600t. "Parnassius tianschanicus" 65 45

32 Roe Deer

1998. Animals. Multicoloured.
135 600t. Type **32** 60 45
136 600t. Osprey ("Pandion haliaetus") 60 45
137 600t. Hoopoe ("Upupa epops") 60 45
138 600t. White stork ("Ciconia ciconia") 60 45
139 1000t. Golden oriole ("Oriolus oriolus") 60 45
140 1000t. Snow leopard 60 45
141 1000t. River kingfisher ("Alcedo althis") 60 45
142 1000t. Common kestrel ("Falco tinnunculus") . . . 60 45

33 Andrei Dimitriyevich Sakharov (physicist)

1998. 50th Anniv of Universal Declaration of Human Rights. Multicoloured.
143 10s. Type **33** 80 45
144 10s. Crowd cheering 80 45
145 10s. Martin Luther King (civil rights leader) 80 45
146 10s. Mahatma Ghandi (Indian leader) 80 45
147 10s. Eleanor Roosevelt (humanitarian) 80 45

34 Tyrannosaurus

1998. Prehistoric Animals. Multicoloured.
148 10s. Type **34** 80 45
149 10s. Saurolophus 80 45
150 10s. Gallimimus (horiz) . . . 80 45
151 10s. Euoplocephalus (horiz) 80 45
152 10s. Protoceratops (horiz) . . 80 45
153 10s. Velociraptor (horiz) . . 80 45

35 Fish

1998. Fauna. Multicoloured.
154 600t. Type **35** 50 30
155 600t. Fish (with orange tail and fins) 50 30
156 1000t. Bar-headed goose . . . 80 45
157 1000t. Chukar partridge . . . 80 45
158 1000t. Goosander by water 80 45
159 1000t. Common shelduck swimming 80 45
160 1000t. Rodent 80 45
161 1000t. Himalayan snowcock standing on one leg 80 45

36 Map of Kyrgyzstan

1998. 5th Anniv of Constitution.
162 **36** 1000t. multicoloured . . . 80 45

37 Fox

1999. "iBRA" International Stamp Exhibition, Nuremberg, Germany. The Corsac Fox (*Vulpes corsac*). Multicoloured.
163 10s. Type **37** 85 50
164 10s. Fox sleeping 85 50
165 30s. Two foxes standing . . . 2·50 1·50
166 50s. Mother and cubs . . . . 4·25 2·50

38 Fox

1999. The Corsac Fox (*Vulpes corsac*). Multicoloured.
167 10s. Type **38** 85 50
168 10s. Fox sleeping 85 50
169 30s. Two foxes standing . . . 2·50 1·50
170 50s. Mother and cubs . . . . 4·25 2·50

39 "The Fisherman and the Golden Fish" (poem)

40 State Arms

1999. Birth Bicentenary of Alexander Sergeevich Pushkin. Multicoloured.
171 36t. "Ruslan and Lyudmila" (poem) 10 10
172 6s. Type **39** 50 30
173 10s. "Tsar Saltan" (poem) . . 85 50
174 10s. "The Golden Cockerel" (fairy tale) 85 50
MS175 74 × 99 mm. 20s. Pushkin 1·70 1·70

1999.
176 **40** 20t. blue 10 10

41 Giant Panda (*Ailuropoda melanoleuca*)

1999. "China '99" International Stamp Exhibition, Beijing, China. Sheet 90 × 90 mm containing T **41** and similar horiz design. Multicoloured.
MS180 10s. Type **41**; 15s. Brown wood owl (*Strix leptogrammica*) 2·20 2·20

42 State Flag and Emblem

1999. World Kick Boxing Championships, Bishkek. Multicoloured.
181 3s. Type **42** 20 15
182 3s. Emblem on blue background with Cyrillic championship title in red 20 15
183 3s. "WORLD" in green across globe and emblem 20 15
MS184 121 × 62 mm 6s. "WORLD" in blue across globe and emblem (different); 6s. "KICKBOXING" and emblem on yellow rectangle 1·00 1·00

43 Envelopes and Emblem

1999. 125th Anniv of Universal Postal Union. Multicoloured.
185 3s. Type **43** 25 15
186 6s. Airplane, envelopes, horseman and emblem . . 50 30

44 Anniversary Emblem

2000. 3000th Anniv of Osh. Sheet 139 × 109 mm containing Multicoloured.
MS187 6s.+25t. Type **44**; 6s.+25t. Ravat Abdullakhan Mosque; 6s.+25t. Tahti Suleiman Mosque; 6s.+25t. Asaf ibn Burhia tower 2·20 2·20

45 Taigan

2000. Asian Dogs. Multicoloured.
188 3s. Type **45** 25 15
189 6s. Tasy 50 30
190 6s. Afghan hound 50 30
191 10s. Saluki 85 50
192 15s. Mid-Asian shepherd . . 1·25 75
193 15s. Akbash . . . . 1·25 75
194 20s. Chow Chow . . . . . . 1·70 1·00
195 25s. Akita-inu . . . . 2·00 1·30

46 Minjilkiev

2000. 60th Birth Anniv of Bulat Minzhilkiev (opera singer).
196 **46** 5s. multicoloured 40 25
No. 196 is wrongly inscribed "1940–1998" instead of "1940–1997".

47 Private Cholponbai Tuleberdiev and Medal

2000. 55th Anniv of End of Second World War. Showing recipients of Gold Star of Hero of Soviet Union Medal. Multicoloured.
197 6s. Type **47** 50 30
198 6s. Major-General Ivan Vasilievich Panfilov (vert) 50 30
199 6s. Private Duishenkul Shopokov 50 30

2000. No. 27 surch **36t.**
200 36t. on 1t. multicoloured . . 10 10

49 Wrestling

2000. Olympic Games, Sydney. Multicoloured.
201 1s. Type **49** 20 20
202 3s. Hurdling (vert) 30 30
203 6s. Boxing 60 60
204 10s. Weightlifting (vert) . . . 75 75

50 Atai Ogonbaev

2000. Birth Centenary of Atai Ogonbaev (musician).
205 **50** 6s. multicoloured 60 60

51 Dark Green Fritillary (*Argynnis aglaja*)

2000. Butterflies. Multicoloured.
206 3s. Type **51** 30 30
207 3s. Swallowtail (*Papilio machaon*) 30 30
208 3s. Peacock (*Inachis io*) . . . 30 30
209 3s. Apollo (*Parnassius Apollo*) 30 30
210 3s. Small tortoiseshell (*Aglais urticae*) 30 30
211 3s. *Colias thisoa* 30 30

52 Khan-Tegri

2000. International Year of Mountains (1st series). Multicoloured.
212 10s. Type **52** 75 75
213 10s. Lenin Peak 75 75
214 10s. Victory Peak 75 75
See also Nos. 228/**MS**231.

53 Dank Medal (bravery)

2001. Orders and Medals. Multicoloured.
215 36t. Type **53** 10 10
216 48t. Baatyrene (women's medal) 10 10
217 1s. Manas 3rd class order . . 10 10
218 2s. Manas 2nd class order . . 20 20
219 3s. Manas 1st class order . . 30 30
220 6s. Danaker order (bravery) 60 60
221 10s. Ak Shumkar (Hero of Kyrgyz Republic) 75 75

54 Crying Child and Military Aircraft

2001. 50th Anniv of United Nations High Commissioner for Refugees.
222 **54** 10s. multicoloured 75 75

55 Snake

2001. New Year. Year of the Snake.
223 **55** 6s. multicoloured 60 60

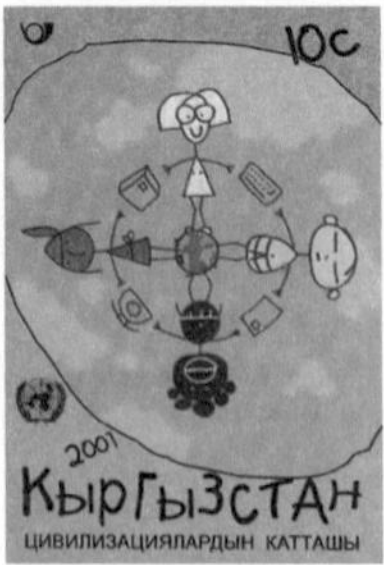

56 Children encircling Globe

2001. United Nations Year of Dialogue among Civilizations.
224 **56** 10s. multicoloured 75 75

57 Communication House

2001. Bishkek.
225 **57** 48t. green 10 10
226 – 1s. green 10 10
227 – 3s. brown 30 30
DESIGNS: 1s. Government House; 3s. National Opera House.

58 Yaks in Pasture

2001. International Year of Mountains (2nd series). Multicoloured.
228 10s. Type **58** 75 75
229 10s. Horses crossing river . . 75 75
230 10s. Forested slopes 75 75
MS231 10 × 83 mm. Designs as Nos. 228/30 . . . . 2·25 2·25

59 Yacht on Lake Issyk-Kul

2001. International Year of Eco-tourism. Multicoloured.
232 10s. Type **59** 75 75
233 10s. Lake Sary-Chelek . . . 75 75
234 10s. Suusamyr Valley 75 75
MS235 119 × 89 mm. 10s. Mosque, Naryn (vert) 75 75

60 Ak-Shumkar (legendary bird) and Khan-Tengri Mountain

2001. 10th Anniv of Independence. Multicoloured.
236 1s.50 Type **60** 10 10
237 7s. Pres. Askar Akaev and national flag 60 60
MS238 126 × 90 mm. 11s.50 Government House, Bishkek 85 85

61 Kurmanbek (statue), Djalal-Abad

2001. 500th Birth Anniv of Kurmanbek Khan (military leader).
239 **61** 1s.50 multicoloured 10 10

2001. 40th Anniv of Worldwide Fund for Nature. Nos. 163/6 overprinted **40th Anniversary 1961–2001** or surcharged.
240 25s. on 10s. Fox . . . . . .
241 25s. on 10s. Fox sleeping . . . 85 85
242 30s. Two foxes standing . . . 1·75 1·75
243 50s. Mother and cubs . . . . 1·75 1·75
Nos. 240/1 with both change of face value and celebratory inscription, and Nos. 242/3 with only celebratory inscription.

63 Kurmandjan Datka

2001. 190th Birth Anniv of Kurmandjan Dakta (aka Alai Queen, female tribal leader).
244 **63** 10s.+70t. black 75 75

64 RCC and Kyrgyzstan Post
65 Union Emblem Office Emblems

2001. 10th Anniv of Regional Communications Community.
245 **64** 7s. multicoloured 60 60

2001. 10th Anniv of Union of Independent States.
246 **65** 6s. blue and yellow 60 60

LA AGUERA Pt. 9

An administrative district of Spanish Sahara, whose stamps it later used.

1920. Rio de Oro stamps optd **LA AGUERA**.
1 **15** 1c. green . . . . 1·90 1·90
2 2c. brown . . . . 1·90 1·90
3 5c. green . . . . 1·90 1·90
4 10c. red . . . . 1·90 1·90
5 15c. yellow . . . . 1·90 1·90
6 20c. violet . . . . 1·90 1·90
7 25c. blue . . . . 1·90 1·90
8 30c. brown . . . . 1·90 1·90
9 40c. pink . . . . 1·90 1·90
10 50c. blue . . . . 6·25 6·25
11 1p. red . . . . 11·50 11·50
12 4p. purple . . . . 36·00 36·00
13 10p. orange . . . . 70·00 70·00

2

1923.
14 **2** 1c. blue 85 85
15 2c. green 85 85
16 5c. green 85 85
17 10c. red 85 85
18 15c. brown 85 85
19 20c. yellow 85 85
20 25c. blue 85 85
21 30c. brown 85 85
22 40c. red . . . . 1·10 1·10
23 50c. purple . . . . 3·50 3·50
24 1p. mauve . . . . 7·25 7·25
25 4p. violet . . . . 19·00 19·00
26 10p. orange . . . . 30·00 30·00

LABUAN Pt. 1

An Island off the N. coast of Borneo, ceded to Great Britain in 1846, and a Crown Colony from 1902. Incorporated with Straits Settlements in 1906, it used Straits stamps till it became part of N. Borneo in 1946.

100 cents = 1 dollar.

1 18

1879.
17 **1** 2c. green . . . . 18·00 27·00
39 2c. red . . . . 4·25 3·50
6 6c. orange £100 £110
40 6c. green . . . . 8·00 4·50
7 8c. red £100 £100
41 8c. violet . . . . 4·00 9·00
43 10c. brown . . . . 11·00 8·00
9 12c. red £250 £325
45 12c. blue . . . . 5·50 6·50
4 16c. blue . . . . 60·00 £120
46 16c. grey . . . . 6·00 9·50
47 40c. orange . . . . 20·00 32·00

1880. (a) Surch **8**.
11 **1** 8 on 12c. red £1200 £750

(b) Surch **6 6** or **8 8**.
12 **1** 6 on 16c. blue £2000 £850
13 8 on 12c. red £1400 £950

1881. Surch **EIGHT CENTS**.
14 **1** 8c. on 12c. red £325 £375

1881. Surch **Eight Cents**.
15 **1** 8c. on 12c. red £110 £120

1883. Manuscript surch **one Dollar A.S.H.**
22 **1** $1 on 16c. blue £3250

1885. Surch **2 CENTS** horiz.
23 **1** 2c. on 8c. red £200 £400
24 2c. on 16c. blue £950 £850

1885. Surch **2 Cents** horiz.
25 **1** 2c. on 16c. blue £110 £160

1885. Surch with large **2 Cents** diag.
26 **1** 2c. on 8c. red . . . . 65·00 £100

1891. Surch **6 Cents**.
35 **1** 6c. on 8c. violet . . . . . . 9·00 8·00
37 6c. on 16c. blue £2000 £1800
38 6c. on 40c. orange £8000 £4250

1892. Surch as **Two CENTS** or **Six CENTS**.
49 **1** 2c. on 40c. orange . . . . . £160 90·00
50 6c. on 16c. grey £350 £150

Most issues from 1894 exist cancelled-to-order with black bars. Our prices are for stamps postally used, cancelled-to-order examples being worth considerably less.

1894. Types of North Borneo (different colours) optd **LABUAN**.
62 **24** 1c. black and mauve . . . 1·50 8·50
63 **25** 2c. black and blue . . . . 2·50 8·00
64a **26** 3c. black and yellow . . . 8·50 9·00
65a **27** 5c. black and green . . . . 38·00 14·00
67 **28** 6c. black and red . . . . 2·50 15·00
69 **29** 8c. black and pink . . . . 7·00 23·00
70 **30** 12c. black and orange . . 23·00 48·00
71 **31** 18c. black and brown . . . 22·00 55·00
74a **32** 24c. blue and mauve . . . 13·00 45·00
80 **10** 25c. green . . . . 24·00 28·00
81 – 50c. purple (as No. 82) . . 24·00 28·00
82 – $1 blue (as No. 83) . . . . 60·00 55·00

1895. No. 83 of North Borneo surch **LABUAN** and value in cents.
75 4c. on $1 red . . . . 1·25 2·00
76 10c. on $1 red . . . . 4·00 1·40
77 20c. on $1 red . . . . 28·00 10·00
78 30c. on $1 red . . . . 32·00 40·00
79 40c. on $1 red . . . . 28·00 30·00

1896. Jubilee of Cession of Labuan to Gt. Britain. Nos. 62/8 optd **1846 JUBILEE 1896**.
83 **24** 1c. black and mauve . . . 18·00 21·00
84d **25** 2c. black and blue . . . . 38·00 15·00
85 **26** 3c. black and yellow . . . 35·00 22·00
86 **27** 5c. black and green . . . . 55·00 16·00
87 **28** 6c. black and red . . . . 27·00 21·00
88b **29** 8c. black and pink . . . . 40·00 11·00

1897. Stamps of North Borneo, Nos. 92 to 106 (different colours), optd **LABUAN**. Opt at top of stamp.
89 1c. black and purple . . . . 4·00 4·75
90 2c. black and blue . . . . . 14·00 4·25
91b 3c. black and yellow . . . . 8·50 6·50
92a 5c. black and green . . . . . 48·00 55·00
93b 6c. black and red . . . . . 6·50 21·00
94a 8c. black and pink . . . . . 18·00 12·00
95a 12c. black and orange . . . 42·00 50·00

Overprint at foot of stamp.
98a – 12c. black and orange (as No. 106) . . . . 42·00 50·00

Opt at foot. Inscr "POSTAL REVENUE".
96b – 18c. black and bistre (as No. 108) . . . . 16·00 45·00

Opt at foot. Inscr "POSTAGE AND REVENUE".
99a – 18c. black and bistre (as No. 110) . . . . 80·00 60·00

Opt at top Inscr "POSTAGE AND REVENUE".
101b – 18c. black and bistre (as No. 110) . . . . 38·00 55·00

Opt at top. "POSTAGE AND REVENUE" omitted.
97a – 24c. blue and lilac (as No. 109) . . . . 14·00 50·00

Opt at top. Inscr "POSTAGE AND REVENUE".
100 – 24c. blue and mauve (No. 111) . . . . 29·00 55·00

1899. Stamps of Labuan surch 4 **CENTS**.
102 4c. on 5c. black & grn (92a) 35·00 26·00
103 4c. on 6c. black & red (93b) 23·00 19·00
104a 4c. on 8c. black and pink (94a) . . . . 32·00 32·00
105 4c. on 12c. black and orange (98a) . . . . 38·00 35·00
106 4c. on 18c. black and olive (101b) . . . . 26·00 18·00
107a 4c. on 24c. blue and mauve (100) . . . . 20·00 25·00
108 4c. on 25c. green (80) . . . 6·00 7·50
109 4c. on 50c. purple (81) . . . 6·50 7·50
110 4c. on $1 blue (82) . . . . 6·50 7·50

1900. Stamps of North Borneo, as Nos. 95 to 107, optd **LABUAN**.
111 2c. black and green . . . . 3·75 2·50
112 4c. black and brown . . . . 8·50 42·00
113a 4c. black and red . . . . . 6·50 9·50
114 5c. black and blue . . . . . 29·00 18·00
115 10c. brown and grey . . . . 50·00 80·00
116 16c. green and brown . . . 50·00 £110

1902.
117 **18** 1c. black and purple . . . 4·00 7·00
118 2c. black and green . . . . 3·75 4·75
119 3c. black and brown . . . . 3·25 12·00
120 4c. black and red . . . . . 3·25 3·50
121 8c. black and orange . . . 9·00 9·00
122 10c. brown and blue . . . . 3·25 12·00
123 12c. black and yellow . . . 6·00 14·00
124 16c. green and brown . . . 4·75 15·00
125 18c. black and brown . . . 3·25 22·00
126 25c. green and blue . . . . 7·50 18·00
127 50c. purple and lilac . . . 10·00 42·00
128 $1 red and orange . . . . 8·50 50·00

1904. Surch **4 cents**.
129 – 4c. on 5c. black and green (92a) . . . . 40·00 40·00
130 – 4c. on 6c. black and red (93b) . . . . 12·00 38·00
131 – 4c. on 8c. black and pink (94a) . . . . 25·00 42·00
132 – 4c. on 12c. black and orange (98a) . . . . 19·00 42·00
133 – 4c. on 18c. black and olive (101b) . . . . 23·00 45·00
134a – 4c. on 24c. blue and mauve (100) . . . . 27·00 38·00
135 **10** 4c. on 25c. green (80) . . 8·50 24·00
136 4c. on 50c. purple (81) . . 8·50 24·00
137 4c. on $1 blue (82) . . . 8·50 24·00

POSTAGE DUE STAMPS

1901. Optd **POSTAGE DUE**.
D1 2c. black and green (111) . . 15·00 23·00
D2 3c. black and yellow (91) . . 18·00 75·00
D3b 4c. black and red (113) . . . 32·00 75·00
D4 5c. black and blue (114) . . 50·00 95·00
D5 6c. black and red (93b) . . . 26·00 90·00
D6 8c. black and pink (94a) . . 55·00 85·00
D7b 12c. black and orange (98a) 80·00 £100
D8 18c. black and olive (101b) 21·00 95·00
D9c 24c. blue and mauve (100) 45·00 80·00

LAGOS Pt. 1

A British colony on the southern coast of Nigeria. United with Southern Nigeria in 1906 to form the Colony and Protectorate of Southern Nigeria.

12 pence = 1 shilling;
20 shillings = 1 pound.

1 3

1874.
21 **1** ½d. green . . . . 2·00 80
17 1d. mauve . . . . 19·00 10·00
22 1d. red . . . . 2·00 80
11 2d. blue . . . . 42·00 13·00
23 2d. grey . . . . 60·00 5·50
19 3d. brown . . . . 15·00 5·00
5 4d. red . . . . 85·00 40·00
24 4d. lilac . . . . £100 8·50
25 6d. green . . . . 8·00 40·00
26 1s. orange . . . . 7·00 20·00
27 2s.6d. black £275 £250
28 5s. blue £500 £425
29 10s. brown £1300 £950

1887.
30 **1** 2d. mauve and blue . . . . 3·00 2·00
31 2½d. blue . . . . 3·50 1·75
32 3d. mauve and brown . . . 2·50 3·25
33 4d. mauve and black . . . 2·25 1·75
34 5d. mauve and green . . . 2·00 11·00
35 6d. mauve . . . . 4·75 3·00
35a 6d. mauve and red . . . . 5·00 12·00
36 7½d. mauve and red . . . . 2·25 29·00
37 10d. mauve and yellow . . . 3·25 13·00
38 1s. green and black . . . . 5·50 24·00
39 2s.6d. green and red . . . . 23·00 80·00
40 5s. green and blue . . . . . 40·00 £150
41 10s. green and brown . . . 75·00 £200

1893. Surch **HALF PENNY** and bars.
42 **1** ½d. on 4d. mauve and black 4·00 2·50

1904.
44 **3** ½d. green . . . . 1·50 5·50
45 1d. purple and black on red 1·00 15
56 2d. purple and blue . . . . 2·25 2·00
47 2½d. purple and blue on blue . . . . 1·00 1·50
48 3d. purple and brown . . . 2·25 1·75
59a 6d. purple and mauve . . . 4·25 1·50
60a 1s. green and black . . . . 23·00 2·25
61 2s.6d. green and red . . . . 16·00 55·00
62 5s. green and blue . . . . . 22·00 95·00
63 10s. green and brown . . . 60·00 £200

LAOS Pt. 21

Previously part of French Indo-China, the Kingdom of Laos was proclaimed in 1947. In 1949 it became an Associated State within the French Union and in 1953 it became fully independent within the Union.

Laos left the French Union in 1956. In 1976 it became a Republic.

1951. 100 cents = 1 piastre.
1955. 100 cents = 1 kip.

1 River Mekong

2 King Sisavang Vong

1951.

1 1 10c. green and turquoise . . 35 35
2 20c. red and purple 35 35
3 30c. blue and indigo . . . . 1·50 1·10
4 – 50c. brown and deep brown 35 35
5 – 60c. orange and red 35 35
6 – 70c. turquoise and blue . . . 35 35
7 – 1p. violet and deep violet . . 75 75
8 2 1p.50 purple and brown . . . 1·10 1·10
9 – 2p. green and turquoise . . . 15·00 5·50
10 – 3p. red and purple . . . . . 1·10 90
11 – 5p. blue and indigo . . . . . 1·50 1·10
12 – 10p. purple and brown . . . 2·20 1·50

DESIGNS—As Type **1**: 50c. to 70c. Luang Prabang; 1p. and 2p. to 10p. Vientiane.

3 Laotian Woman

4 Laotian Woman Weaving

1952.

13 3 30c. violet and blue (postage) 75 35
14 80c. turquoise and green . . 75 35
15 1p.10 red and crimson . . . 75 75
16 1p.90 blue and indigo . . . . 1·10 1·10
17 3p. deep brown and brown 1·10 1·10

18 – 3p.30 violet and deep violet (air) . . . . 1·10 75
19 4 10p. green and blue . . . . 1·80 1·10
20 20p. red and crimson . . . . 3·75 2·50
21 30p. brown and black . . . . 5·50 5·50

DESIGN—As Type **4**: 3p.30, Vat Pra Keo shrine.

5 King Sisavang Vong and U.P.U. Monument

1952. 1st Anniv of Admission to U.P.U.

22 5 80c. violet, bl & ind (postage) 1·10 1·10
23 1p. brown, red and lake . . . 1·10 1·10
24 1p.20 blue and violet . . . . 1·10 1·10
25 1p.50 brown, emerald & grn 1·10 1·10
26 1p.90 turquoise and sepia . . 1·10 1·10

27 25p. indigo and blue (air) . . 4·50 4·50
28 50p. sepia, purple and brown 4·50 4·50

6 Girl carrying her Brother **7** Court of Love

1953. Red Cross Fund. Cross in red.

29 6 1p.50+1p. purple and blue . . 2·50 2·50
30 3p.+1p.50 red and green . . 2·50 2·50
31 3p.90+2p.50 purple & brn . . 3·00 3·00

1953.

32 7 4p.50 turquoise and blue . . 95 75
33 6p. brown and slate 95 75

8 Buddha

1953. Air. Statues of Buddha.

34 – 4p. green 95 75
35 – 6p.50 green . . . . 1·30 95
36 – 9p. green . . . . 1·90 1·30
37 8 11p.50 orange, brown and red . . . . 3·00 2·50
38 – 40p. purple . . . . 7·00 2·50
39 – 100p. green . . . . 13·50 9·50

DESIGNS—HORIZ: 4p. Reclining. VERT: 6p.50, Seated; 9p. Standing (full-face); 40p. Standing (facing right); 100p. Buddha and temple dancer.

9 Vientiane

1954. Golden Jubilee of King Sisavang Vong.

40 9 2p. violet and blue (postage) 48·00 31·00
41 3p. red and brown . . . . . 48·00 34·00

42 50p. turquoise and blue (air) £150 £150

10 Ravana

1955. Air. "Ramayana" (dramatic poem).

43 10 2k. blue, emerald and green 95 75
44 – 4k. red and brown . . . . 1·30 1·10
45 – 5k. green, brown and red . . 2·50 1·50
46 – 10k. black, orange and brown . . . . 4·50 3·00
47 – 20k. olive, green and violet 5·50 3·75
48 – 30k. black, brown and blue 7·50 5·25

DESIGNS—HORIZ: 4k. Hanuman, the white monkey; 5k. Ninh Laphath, the black monkey. VERT: 10k. Sita and Rama; 20k. Luci and Ravana's friend; 30k. Rama.

11 Buddha and Worshippers

1956. 2500th Anniv of Buddhist Era.

49 11 2k. brown (postage) . . . . 3·00 2·50
50 3k. black . . . . 3·75 2·50
51 5k. sepia . . . . 5·50 3·00

52 20k. carmine and red (air) 34·00 27·00
53 30k. green and bistre . . . 35·00 32·00

Nos. 49/53 were wrongly inscribed as commemorating the birth anniversary of Buddha.

12 U.N. Emblem **13** U.N. Emblem

1956. 1st Anniv of Admission to U.N.

54 12 1k. black (postage) 75 60
55 2k. blue 95 90
56 4k. red . . . . 1·30 95
57 6k. violet . . . . 1·60 1·30

58 13 15k. blue (air) . . . . . . 6·25 6·25
59 30k. red . . . . 8·75 8·75

14 Flute Player

1957. Native Musicians.

60 14 2k. multicoloured (postage) 1·80 1·30
61 – 4k. multicoloured . . . . . 1·80 1·30
62 – 8k. blue, brown and orange 3·25 1·50

63 – 12k. multicoloured (air) . . 2·50 2·50
64 – 14k. multicoloured . . . . 3·00 3·00
65 – 20k. multicoloured . . . . 3·75 3·75

DESIGNS—VERT: 4k. Piper; 14k. Violinist; 20k. Drummer. HORIZ: 8k. Xylophonist; 12k. Bells player.

15 Harvesting Rice

1957. Rice Cultivation.

66 15 3k. multicoloured . . . . . 1·10 60
67 – 5k. brown, red and green . . 1·10 75
68 – 16k. violet, olive and blue 2·20 1·30
69 – 26k. chocolate, brown & grn 3·00 2·20

DESIGNS—VERT: 5k. Drying rice; 16k. Winnowing rice. HORIZ: 26k. Polishing rice.

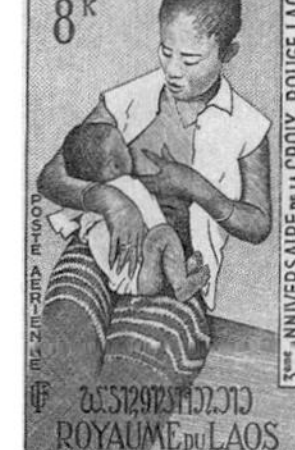

16 "The Offertory" **18** Mother and Child

17 Carrier Elephants

1957. Air. Buddhism.

70 16 10k. multicoloured 90 90
71 – 15k. brown, yellow & choc 1·30 1·30
72 – 18k. yellow and green . . . 1·60 1·60
73 – 24k. red, black and yellow 3·75 3·75

DESIGNS—As T **16**: HORIZ: 15k. "Meditation" (children on river craft). 48 × 36½ mm: 24k. "The Great Renunciation" (dancers with horse). VERT: 18k. "Serenity" (head of Buddhist).

1958. Laotian Elephants. Multicoloured.

74 10c. Type **17** 50 35
75 20c. Elephant's head with head-dress 50 35
76 30c. Elephant with howdah (vert) 50 35
77 2k. Elephant hauling log . . . 1·00 35
78 5k. Elephant walking with calf (vert) . . . . 2·40 1·10
79 10k. Caparisoned elephant (vert) . . . . 3·00 1·10
80 13k. Elephant bearing throne (vert) . . . . 4·00 2·20

1958. Air. 3rd Anniv of Laotian Red Cross. Cross in red.

81 18 8k. black and grey . . . . 1·10 1·10
82 12k. olive and brown . . . 1·10 1·10
83 15k. turquoise and green . . 1·30 1·30
84 20k. violet and bistre . . . 1·50 1·50

19

1958. Inauguration of UNESCO Headquarters Building, Paris.

85 19 50c. blue, orange and red 35 20
86 – 60c. violet, brown and green 35 20
87 – 70c. blue, brown and red . . 35 20
88 – 1k. red, blue and bistre . . 75 45

DESIGNS—VERT: 60c. Woman, children and part of exterior of UNESCO building; 70c. Woman and children hailing UNESCO building superimposed on globe. HORIZ: 1k. General view of UNESCO building and Eiffel Tower.

20 King Sisavang Vong

1959.

89 20 4k. lake 50 50
90 6k.50 red 50 50
91 9k. mauve 50 50
92 13k. green 75 75

21 Stage Performance **22** Portal of Vat Phou Temple, Pakse

1959. Education and Fine Arts.

93 21 1k. multicoloured 35 20
94 – 2k. lake, violet and black . . 35 20
95 – 3k. black, green and purple 75 20
96 – 5k. green, yellow and violet 75 45

DESIGNS—VERT: 2k. Student and "Lamp of Learning"; 5k. Stage performers and Buddhist temple. HORIZ: 3k. Teacher and children with "Key to Education".

1959. Laotian Monuments. Multicoloured.

97 50c. Type **22** 20 15
98 1k.50 That Ing Hang, Savannakhet (horiz) . . . 35 20
99 2k.50 Vat Phou Temple, Pakse (horiz) 45 35
100 7k. That Luang, Vientiane . . 75 45
101 11k. As 7k., but different view (horiz) 80 65
102 12k.50 Phou-Si Temple, Luang Prabang . . . . . 1·10 80

1960. World Refugee Year. Nos. 89 and 79 surch **ANNEE MONDIALE DU REFUGIE 1959–1960** and premium.

103 4k.+1k. red . . . . 3·75 3·75
104 10k.+1k. multicoloured . . . 5·50 5·50

24 Plain of Jars, Xieng Khouang **25** Funeral Urn

1960. Air. Tourism.

105 24 9k.50 red, bistre and blue 75 75
106 – 12k. brown, violet and green 95 95
107 – 15k. red, green and brown 1·20 1·20
108 – 19k. brown, orange and green . . . . 1·40 1·40

DESIGNS—HORIZ: 12k. Phapheng Falls, Champassak; 15k. Pair of bullocks with cart. VERT: 19k. Buddhist monk and village.

1961. Funeral of King Sisavang Vong.

109 25 4k. bistre, black and red 1·10 1·10
110 – 6k.50 brown and black . . 1·10 1·10
111 – 9k. brown and black . . . 1·10 1·10
112 – 25k. black . . . . 3·00 3·00

DESIGNS: 6k.50, Urn under canopy; 9k. Catafalque on dragon carriage; 25k. King Sisavang Vong.

26 Temples and Statues ("Pou Gneu Nha Gneu")

27 King Savang Vatthana

1962. Air. Festival of Makha Bousa.
113 **26** 11k. brown, red and green . . . 75 75
114 – 14k. blue and orange . . . 90 90
115 – 20k. green, yellow and mauve . . . . 1·30 1·30
116 – 25k. red, blue and green 1·60 1·60
DESIGNS—As T **26**: 14k. Bird ("Garuda"); 20k. Flying deities ("Hanuman"). 36×48 mm: 25k. Warriors ("Nang Teng One").

1962.
117 **27** 1k. brown, red and blue . . 20 20
118 2k. brown, red and mauve 45 20
119 5k. brown, red and blue . . 45 35
120 10k. brown, red and bistre 80 45

28 Laotian Boy

29 Royal Courier

1962. Malaria Eradication.
121 **28** 4k. olive, black and green 35 15
122 – 9k. brown, black & turq 45 35
123 – 10k. red, yellow and green 80 45
DESIGNS: 9k. Laotian girl; 10k. Campaign emblem.

1962. Philatelic Exhibition, Vientiane, and Stamp Day.
124 – 50c. multicoloured 50 50
125 – 70c. multicoloured 50 50
126 – 1k. black, green and red 1·10 1·10
127 **29** 1k.50 multicoloured . . . 90 90
DESIGNS—HORIZ: 50c. Modern mail transport; 70c. Dancer and globe. VERT: 1k. Royal courtier on elephant.

30 Fisherman

1963. Freedom from Hunger.
128 **30** 1k. bistre, violet and green 35 20
129 – 4k. blue, brown and green 50 35
130 – 5k. blue, bistre and green 50 45
131 – 9k. blue, green and brown 90 50
DESIGNS—VERT: 4k. Threshing rice; 9k. Harvesting rice. HORIZ: 5k. Ploughing paddy field.

31 Queen of Laos

1963. Red Cross Centenary.
132 **31** 4k. red, blue and brown . . 50 50
133 6k. multicoloured 60 60
134 10k. red, blue and brown 95 95

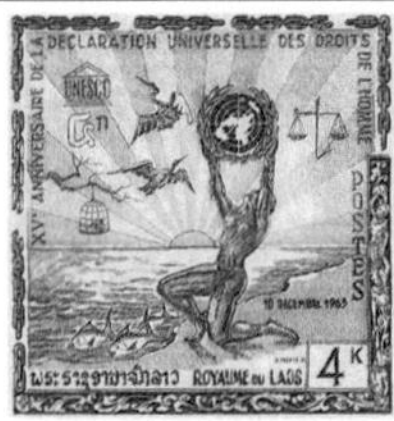

32 Laotian supporting U.N. Emblem

1963. 15th Anniv of Declaration of Human Rights.
135 **32** 4k. purple, blue and red . . 1·30 90

33 Temple, Map and Rameses II

1964. Nubian Monuments Preservation.
136 **33** 4k. multicoloured 35 35
137 6k. multicoloured 50 50
138 10k. multicoloured 75 75

34 Offertory Vase and Horn

1964. "Constitutional Monarchy". Multicoloured.
139 10k. Type **34** 45 20
140 15k. Seated Buddha of Vat Pra Keo 50 30
141 20k. Laotians walking across map 60 45
142 40k. Royal Palace, Luang Prabang . . . . 1·10 60

35 Phra Vet and Wife 36 Meo Warrior

1964. Folklore. Phra Vet Legend. Multicoloured.
143 10k. Type **35** 45 45
144 32k. "Benediction" 65 65
145 45k. Phame and wife 95 95
146 55k. Arrest of Phame . . . . 1·30 1·30

1964. "People of Laos".
147 – 25k. black, brown and green (postage) 75 75
148 **36** 5k. multicoloured (air) . . 30 15
149 – 10k. pink, grey and purple 45 20
150 – 50k. brown, drab and lilac 1·60 90
DESIGNS: 10k. Kha hunter; 25k. Girls of three races; 50k. Thai woman.

37 Red Lacewing

1965. Butterflies and Moths.
151 **37** 10k. chestnut, brown and green (postage) 95 50
152 – 25k. blue, black and yellow 1·90 75
153 – 40k. yellow, brown & green 4·00 1·50
154 – 20k. red and yellow (air) 2·20 1·10
BUTTERFLIES—As Type **37**: 25k. Yellow pansy. 48×27 mm: 20k. Atlas moth; 40k. "Dysphania militaris" (moth).

38 Wattay Airport ("French Aid")

1965. Foreign Aid.
155 **38** 25k. mauve, brown & turq 35 20
156 – 45k. brown and green . . . 50 45
157 – 55k. brown and blue . . . 75 60
158 – 75k. multicoloured . . . . 1·10 80
DESIGNS—VERT: 45k. Mother bathing child (water resources: "Japanese Aid"); 75k. School and plants (education and cultivation: "American Aid"). HORIZ: 55k. Studio of radio station ("British Aid").

39 Hophabang

1965.
159 **39** 10k. multicoloured 30 20

40 Teleprinter Operator, Globe and Map

1965. I.T.U. Centenary.
160 **40** 5k. brown, violet and purple 35 20
161 – 30k. brown, blue and green 50 45
162 – 50k. multicoloured 95 80
DESIGNS: 30k. Globe, map, telephonist and radio operator; 50k. Globe, radio receiver and mast.

1965. Nos. 89/90 surch.
163 **20** 1k. on 4k. lake 15 10
164 5k. on 6k.50 brown . . . 20 15

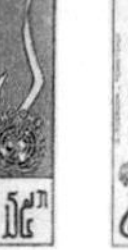

42 Mother and Baby 43 Leopard Cat

1965. 6th Anniv of U.N. "Protection of Mother and Child".
165 **42** 35k. blue and red 90 75

1965. Air. Laotian Fauna.
166 **43** 25k. yellow, brown & green 45 35
167 – 55k. brown, sepia and blue 75 65
168 – 75k. brown and green . . . 90 80
169 – 100k. brown, black & yell 1·60 1·10
170 – 200k. black and red . . . 3·75 2·50
DESIGNS: 55k. Phayre's flying squirrel; 75k. Javan mongoose; 100k. Chinese porcupine; 200k. Binturong.

44 U.N. Emblem on Map

45 Bulls in Combat

1965. 20th Anniv of U.N.
171 **44** 5k. blue, grey and green . . 20 20
172 25k. blue, grey and mauve 45 35
173 40k. blue, grey and turquoise 65 65

1965. Laotian Pastimes.
174 **45** 10k. brown, black and orange 35 20
175 – 20k. blue, red and green 35 30
176 – 25k. red, blue and green 50 35
177 – 50k. multicoloured 75 60
DESIGNS: 20k. Tikhy (form of hockey); 25k. Pirogue race; 50k. Rocket festival.

46 Slaty-headed Parakeet

1966. Birds.
178 **46** 5k. green, brown and red 50 45
179 – 15k. brown, black & turq 75 50
180 – 20k. sepia, ochre and blue 1·30 90
181 – 45k. blue, sepia and violet 3·00 2·20
BIRDS: 15k. White-crested laughing thrush; 20k. Osprey; 45k. Indian roller (or "blue jay").

47 W.H.O. Building

1966. Inaug of W.H.O. Headquarters, Geneva.
182 **47** 10k. blue and turquoise . . 35 20
183 25k. green and red 35 30
184 50k. black and blue . . . 75 60

48 Ordination of Priests

1966. Laotian Ceremonies. Multicoloured.
186 10k. Type **48** 35 20
187 25k. Sand-hills ceremony . . 45 35
188 30k. "Wax pagoda" procession (vert) 65 45
189 40k. "Sou-Khouan" ceremony (vert) 80 50

49 UNESCO Emblem

1966. 20th Anniv of UNESCO.
190 **49** 20k. orange and black . . 20 20
191 30k. blue and black . . . 45 35
192 40k. green and black . . . 50 45
193 60k. red and black 75 65

50 Letter, Carrier Pigeon and Emblem

1966. International Correspondence Week.
195 **50** 5k. blue, brown and red . . 20 15
196 20k. purple, black and green 45 30
197 40k. brown, red and blue 50 35
198 45k. black, green and purple 75 60

51 Flooded Village

52 Carving, Siprapouthbat Pagoda

1967. Mekong Delta Flood Relief. Multicoloured.
200 20k.+5k. Type **51** 50 50
201 40k.+10k. Flooded market-place 80 80
202 60k.+15k. Flooded airport . . 1·30 1·30

1967. Buddhist Art.
204 **52** 5k. green and brown . . . 20 20
205 – 20k. blue and sepia 45 20
206 – 50k. purple and sepia . . . 95 60
207 – 70k. grey and brown . . . 1·30 90

DESIGNS (carvings in temple pagodas, Luang Prabang): 30k. Visoun; 50k. Xiengthong; 70k. Visoun (different).

53 General Post Office

1967. Opening of New G.P.O. Building, Vientiane.
208 **53** 25k. brown, green & purple 30 15
209 50k. blue, green and slate 45 35
210 70k. red, green and brown 75 60

54 Giant Snakehead **55** "Cassia fistula"

1967. Fishes.
211 **54** 20k. black, bistre and blue 50 35
212 – 35k. slate, bistre and blue 60 45
213 – 45k. sepia, ochre and green 1·10 65
214 – 60k. black, bistre and green 1·50 75
DESIGNS: 35k. Giant catfish; 45k. Tire-track spiny eel; 60k. Bronze knifefish.

1967. Flowers.
215 **55** 30k. yellow, green and mauve 50 35
216 – 55k. red, green and orange 75 45
217 – 75k. red, green and blue 1·10 80
218 – 80k. yellow, mauve and green 1·50 90
DESIGNS: 55k. "Cucuma singulario"; 75k. "Poinciana regia"; 80k. "Plumeria acutifolia".

56 Harvesting

1967. 10th Anniv of Laotian Red Cross.
219 **56** 20k.+5k. multicoloured 35 35
220 50k.+10k. multicoloured 75 75
221 60k.+15k. multicoloured 1·20 1·20

57 Banded Krait

1967. Reptiles.
223 **57** 5k. blue, yellow and green 35 35
224 – 40k. brown, bistre and green 75 60
225 – 100k. chocolate, brown and green 2·75 1·60
226 – 200k. black, brown and green 5·25 3·00
DESIGNS: 40k. Marsh crocodile; 100k. Pit viper; 200k. Water monitor.

58 Human Rights Emblem

1968. Human Rights Year. Emblem in red and green.
227 **58** 20k. green 35 20
228 30k. brown 35 20
229 50k. blue 75 50

59 Military Parade

1968. Army Day. Multicoloured.
231 15k. Type **59** (postage) 35 20
232 20k. Soldiers and tank in battle 35 30
233 60k. Soldiers and Laotian flag 65 50
234 200k. Parade of colours before National Assembly building (air) 1·30 90
235 300k. As No. 234 2·10 1·30

60 W.H.O. Emblem

1968. 20th Anniv of W.H.O.
237 **60** 15k. brown, red and purple 20 20
238 30k. brown, green and blue 35 30
239 70k. brown, purple and red 60 35
240 110k. light brown, purple and brown 95 75
241 250k. brown, blue and green 2·20 1·60

61 "Chrysochroa mnizechi" **62** "Mangifera indica"

1968. Beetles.
243 **61** 30k. blue, yellow and green (postage) 60 35
244 – 50k. black, orange & purple 95 45
245 – 90k. blue, orange and ochre 1·60 80
246 – 120k. black and orange (air) 1·30 50
247 – 160k. multicoloured 1·90 80
INSECTS—VERT: 50k. "Aristobia approximator"; 90k. "Eutaenia corbetti". HORIZ: 120k. "Dorysthenes walkeri"; 160k. "Megaloxantha bicolor".

1968. Laotian Fruits.
248 **62** 20k. green, blue and black 35 20
249 – 50k. green, red and blue 50 30
250 – 180k. green, brown & orge 1·80 1·10
251 – 250k. green, brown & yell 2·50 1·60
DESIGNS—VERT: 50k. "Tamarindus indica". HORIZ: 180k. "Artocarpus intregrifolia"; 250k. "Citrullus vulgaris".

63 Hurdling

1968. Olympic Games, Mexico.
252 **63** 15k. green, blue & brown 20 20
253 – 80k. brown, turquoise & blue 60 45
254 – 100k. blue, brown and green 75 50
255 – 110k. brown, red and blue 80 60
DESIGNS: 80k. Tennis; 100k. Football; 110k. High jumping.

64 Oriental Door, Wat Ongtu (detail)

1969. Wat Ongtu Temple.
256 **64** 150k. gold, black and red 1·80 1·10
257 – 200k. gold, black and red 2·40 1·60
DESIGN: 200k. Central door, Wat Ongtu.

65 "Pharak praying to the Gods"

1969. Laotian "Ballet Royal". Designs showing dance characters. Multicoloured.
258 10k. Type **65** (postage) 35 20
259 15k. "Soukhib ordered to attack" 50 35
260 20k. "Thotsakan reviewing troops" 60 50
261 30k. "Nang Sida awaiting punishment" 95 60
262 40k. "Pharam inspecting his troops" 1·30 75
263 60k. "Hanuman about to rescue Nang Sida" 1·90 1·30
264 110k. "Soudagnou battling with Thotsakan" (air) 2·75 2·20
265 300k. "Pharam dancing with Thotsakkan" 6·25 4·00

66 Handicrafts Workshop, Vientiane

1969. 10th Anniv of I.L.O.
267 **66** 30k. violet & purple (postage) 35 35
268 60k. brown and green 75 65
269 – 300k. black & brown (air) 4·00 2·75
DESIGN: 300k. Elephants moving logs.

67 Chinese Pangolin

1969. "Wild Animals" (1st series). Multicoloured.
270 15k. Type **67** (postage) 35 15
271 30k. Type **67** 75 35
272 70k. Sun bear (air) 95 60
273 120k. Common gibbon (vert) 1·80 1·10
274 150k. Tiger 2·40 1·30
See also Nos. 300/3 and 331/5.

68 Royal Mausoleum, Luang Prabang

1969. 10th Death Anniv of King Sisavang Vong.
275 **68** 50k. ochre, blue and green 75 50
276 – 70k. ochre and lake 75 50
DESIGN: 70k. King Sisavang Vong (medallion).

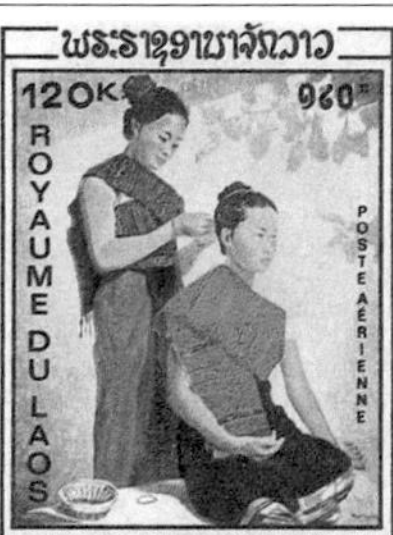

69 "Lao Woman being Groomed" (Leguay)

1969. Air. Paintings by Marc Leguay (1st series). Multicoloured.
277 10k. Type **69** 1·50 75
278 150k. "Village Market" (horiz) 2·20 1·10
See also Nos. 285, 307/9 and 357/61.

70 Carved Capital, Wat Xiengthong

1970. Laotian Pagodas. Multicoloured.
279 70k. Type **70** (postage) 1·10 75
280 100k. Library, Wat Sisaket (air) 90 35
281 120k. Wat Xiengthong (horiz) 1·30 75

71 "Noon" Drum

1970. Laotian Drums.
282 **71** 30k. mult (postage) 75 60
283 – 55k. black, green and brown 1·10 90
284 – 125k. brown, yellow and flesh (air) 2·20 1·50
DESIGNS—HORIZ: 55k. Bronze drum. VERT: 125k. Wooden drum.

1970. Air. Paintings by Marc Leguay (2nd series). As T **69**. Multicoloured.
285 150k. "Banks of the Mekong" (horiz) 1·80 1·30

72 Franklin D. Roosevelt

1970. Air. 25th Death Anniv of Franklin D. Roosevelt (American statesman).
286 **72** 120k. slate and green 1·80 1·10

73 "Lenin explaining Electrification Plan" (L. Shmatko)

1970. Birth Centenary of Lenin.
287 **73** 30k. multicoloured . . . . 1·30 45
288 70k. multicoloured 80 60

1970. "Support for War Victims". Nos. 258/65 ("Ballet Royal") surch **Soutien aux Victimes de la Guerre** and premium.
289 10k.+5k. mult (postage) . . . 45 45
290 15k.+5k. multicoloured . . . 45 45
291 20k.+5k. multicoloured . . . 45 45
292 30k.+5k. multicoloured . . . 45 45
293 40k.+5k. multicoloured . . . 90 90
294 60k.+5k. multicoloured . . . 1·00 1·00
295 110k.+5k. mult (air) . . . . 2·20 2·20
296 300k.+5k. multicoloured . . 3·25 3·25

75 Weaving Silk

1970. "EXPO 70" World Fair, Osaka, Japan. Laotian Silk Industry.
297 **75** 30k. bl, brn & red (postage) 45 30
298 – 70k. multicoloured 90 60
299 – 125k. multicoloured (air) 1·30 90
DESIGNS: 70k. Silk-spinning; 125k. Winding skeins.

76 Wild Boar

77 Buddha, U.N. Emblem and New York H.Q.

1970. Wild Animals (2nd series).
300 **76** 20k. brown & grn (postage) 45 20
301 – 60k. brown and olive . . . 90 45
302 – 210k. brown, red and yellow (air) . . . . . . 2·20 1·60
303 – 500k. green, brown & orge 4·50 3·00
ANIMALS: 210k. Leopard; 500k. Gaur.

1970. 25th Anniv of U.N.O.
304 **77** 30k. brown, mauve and blue (postage) 60 35
305 70k. brown, blue and green 90 50
306 – 125k. multicoloured (air) 1·90 1·10
DESIGN—26 × 36 mm: 125k. Nang Thorani ("Goddess of the Earth") and New York Headquarters.

1970. Air. Paintings by Marc Leguay (3rd series). As T **69**. Multicoloured.
307 100k. "Village Track" . . . 1·10 50
308 120k. "Paddy-field in the Rainy Season" (horiz) . . 1·50 60
309 150k. "Village Elder" . . . . 1·60 80

78 "Nakhanet"

1971. Laotian Mythology (1st series). Frescoes from Triumphal Arch, Vientiane. Multicoloured.
310 **78** 70k. orange, brown and red (postage) 60 45
311 – 85k. green, yellow and blue 75 50
312 – 125k. multicoloured (air) 1·50 80
DESIGNS: As T **78**: 85k. "Rahu". 49 × 36 mm: 125k. "Underwater duel between Nang Matsa and Hanuman".
See also Nos. 352/4 and 385/7.

79 Silversmiths

1971. Laotian Traditional Crafts. Multicoloured.
313 30k. Type **79** 20 20
314 50k. Potters 35 20
315 70k. Pirogue-builder (49 × 36 mm) 65 35

80 Laotian and African Children

1971. Racial Equality Year.
316 **80** 30k. blue, red and green 30 20
317 – 60k. violet, red and yellow 50 30
DESIGN: 60k. Laotian dancers and musicians.

81 Buddhist Monk at That Luang

1971. 50th Anniv of Vientiane Rotary Club.
318 **81** 30k. violet, brown and blue 35 20
319 – 70k. grey, red and blue . . 1·10 50
DESIGN—VERT: 70k. Laotian girl on "Dragon" staircase.

82 "Dendrobium agregatum"

83 Dancers from France and Laos

1971. Laotian Orchids. Multicoloured.
320 30k. Type **82** (postage) . . . 75 35
321 40k. "Rynchostylis giganterum" 75 50
322 50k. "Ascocentrum miniatur" (horiz) . . . . 1·10 45
323 60k. "Paphiopedilum exul" 1·30 75
324 70k. "Trichoglottis fasciata" (horiz) . . . . 1·50 80
325 80k. Cattleya (horiz) . . . . 1·60 80
326 125k. Brazilian cattleya (horiz) (air) . . . . . . 3·25 1·10
327 150k. "Vanda teres" (horiz) 3·75 1·30
Nos. 321, 323 and 325 are smaller, 22 × 36 or 36 × 22 mm. Nos. 326/7 are larger, 48 × 27 mm.

1971. Air. "Twin Cities" of St. Astier (France) and Keng-Kok (Laos).
328 **83** 30k. brown and light brown 20 15
329 70k. purple and plum . . . 35 15
330 100k. green and deep green 50 20

84 Common Palm Civet

1971. Wild Animals (3rd series).
331 **84** 25k. black, violet and blue (postage) 50 30
332 40k. black, green and olive 75 45
333 – 50k. orange and green . . 1·10 60
334 – 85k. brown, green & emerald . . . . 1·80 95
335 – 300k. brown and green (air) . . . . 4·00 2·40
DESIGNS: 50k. Lesser Malay chevrotain; 85k. Sambar; 300k. Javan rhinoceros.

85 Laotian Woman (design from 1952 issue)

1971. 20th Anniv of Laotian Stamps.
336 **85** 30k. chocolate, brown and violet (postage) 20 15
337 – 40k. multicoloured 45 20
338 – 50k. black, flesh and blue 60 35
339 – 125k. violet, brn & grn (air) . . . . 1·40 90
DESIGNS—36 × 48 mm: 40k. Violinist (As No. 64); 50k. Rama (As No. 48); 125k. "The Offertory" (As Type **16**).

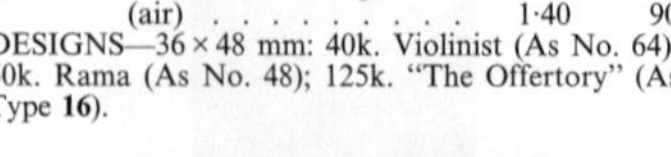

86 "Sunset on the Mekong"

1971. Air. Paintings by Chamnane Prisayane. Mult.
341 125k. Type **86** . . . . . . 1·20 90
342 150k. "Quiet Morning at Ban Tane Pieo" . . . . 1·60 1·10

87 Children reading Book

1972. International Book Year.
343 **87** 30k. green (postage) . . . 20 15
344 – 70k. brown 50 35
345 – 125k. violet (air) . . . . 1·10 80
DESIGNS—36 × 22 mm: 70k. Laotian illustrating manuscript. 48 × 27 mm: 125k. Father showing manuscripts to children.

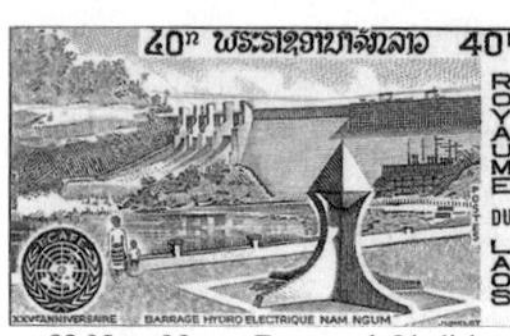

88 Nam Ngum Dam and Obelisk

1972. 25th Anniv of U.N. Economic Commission for Asia and the Far East (E.C.A.F.E.). Multicoloured.
346 40k. Type **88** (postage) . . . 30 20
347 80k. Type **88** 60 35
348 145k. Lake and spill-way, Nam Ngum Dam (air) . . 1·10 75

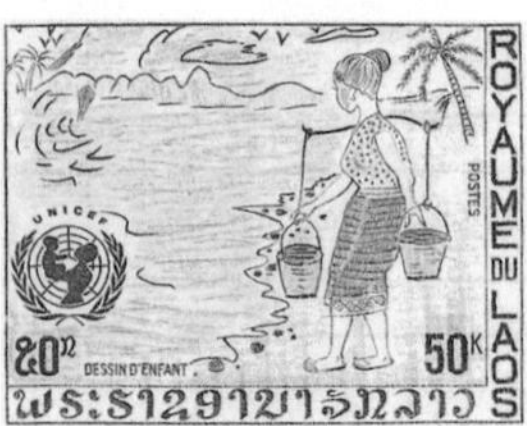

89 "The Water-carrier"

1972. 25th Anniv of UNICEF Drawings by Lao Schoolchildren. Multicoloured.
349 50k. Type **89** (postage) . . . 60 35
350 80k. "Teaching Bamboo-weaving" 75 45
351 120k. "Riding a Water-buffalo" (air) . . . . . . 1·10 80

90 "Nakharath"

1972. Air. Laotian Mythology (2nd series).
352 **90** 100k. turquoise 75 60
353 – 120k. lilac 95 75
354 – 150k. brown . . . . 1·30 90
DESIGNS: 120k. "Nang Kinnali"; 150k. "Norasing".

91 Festival Offerings

1972. Air. That Luang Religious Festival.
355 **91** 110k. brown 75 50
356 – 125k. purple . . . . 1·10 75
DESIGN: 125k. Festival procession.

1972. Air. Paintings by Marc Leguay (4th series). As T **69**. Multicoloured.
357 50k. "In the Paddy Field" (detail) 45 35
358 50k. "In the Paddy Field" (different detail) 45 35
359 70k. "Village in the Rainy Season" (detail) 65 45
360 70k. "Village in the Rainy Season" (different detail) 65 45
361 120k. "Laotian Mother" . . 1·50 90
Nos. 357/8 and 359/60 when placed together form the complete painting in each case.

92 Attopeu Religious Costume

93 "Lion" Guardian, That Luang

1973. Regional Costumes.
362 **92** 40k. yellow, mauve & brown (postage) 45 20
363 – 90k. black, red and brown 95 45
364 – 120k. brown, sepia and mauve (air) 90 60
365 – 150k. ochre, red and brown 1·10 80
DESIGNS: 90k. Phongsaly festival costume; 120k. Luang Prabang wedding costume; 150k. Vientiane evening dress.

1973. 55th Anniv of Lions International.
366 **93** 40k. red, pur & bl (postage) 45 20
367 80k. red, yellow and blue 75 45
368 – 150k. multicoloured (air) 1·20 90
DESIGN—48 × 27 mm: 150k. Lions emblems and statue of King Saysetthathirath, Vientiane.

94 Satellite passing Rahu

1973. Traditional and Modern Aspects of Space. Multicoloured.
369 80k. Type **94** 50 35
370 150k. Landing module and Laotian festival rocket . . 95 50

95 Dr. Gerhard Hansen and Map of Laos

1973. Centenary of Identification of Leprosy Bacillus by Hansen.
371 **95** 40k. purple, dp pur & orge 50 35
372 80k. purple, brown & yell 95 45

96 "Benediction" 97 "Nang Mekhala". (Goddess of the Sea)

1973. 25th Anniv of Laotian Boy Scouts Association.
373 **96** 70k. yellow & brn (postage) 65 35
374 – 110k. violet and orange (air) 65 35
375 – 150k. blue, drab and brown 90 50
DESIGNS—48 × 27 mm: 110k. Campfire entertainment; 150k. Scouts helping flood victims, Vientiane, 1966.

1973. Air. Centenary of World Meteorological Organization.
376 **97** 90k. lilac, red and brown 65 35
377 – 150k. brown, red & lt brn 1·20 50
DESIGN—HORIZ: 150k. "Chariot of the Sun".

99 Interpol H.Q., Paris

1973. 50th Anniv of Int Criminal Police Organization (Interpol).
382 **99** 40k. blue (postage) 30 20
383 80k. brown and light brown 45 30
384 – 150k. violet, red and green (air) 90 50
DESIGN—48 × 27 mm: 150k. Woman in opium poppy field.

100 "Phra Sratsvady"

1974. Air. Laotian Mythology (3rd series).
385 **100** 100k. red, brown and lilac 75 45
386 – 110k. brown, lilac and red 95 50
387 – 150k. violet, brown and light brown . . . . . 1·50 80
DESIGNS: 110k. "Phra Indra"; 150k. "Phra Phrom".

101 Boy and Postbox 102 "Eranthemum nervosum"

1974. Centenary of U.P.U.
388 **101** 70k. brown, green and blue (postage) 50 35
389 80k. brown, blue and green 60 50
390 – 200k. brown and red (air) 2·20 1·50
DESIGN—48 × 36 mm: 200k. Laotian girls with letters, and U.P.U. Monument, Berne (Type **105**).

1974. Laotian Flora.
391 **102** 30k. violet & grn (postage) 50 35
392 – 50k. multicoloured . . . 75 45
393 – 80k. red, green and brown 1·10 75
394 – 500k. green & brown (air) 4·00 2·50
DESIGNS—As T **102**: HORIZ: 50k. Water lily; 80k. Red silk-cotton. 36 × 36 mm: 500k. Pitcher plant.

103 Mekong Ferry carrying Bus

1974. Laotian Transport.
395 **103** 25k. brown & orge (postage) 35 20
396 – 90k. brown and bistre . . 1·80 90
397 – 250k. brown & green (air) 1·90 1·10
DESIGNS—VERT: 90k. Bicycle rickshaw. HORIZ: 250k. Mekong house boat.

104 Marconi, and Laotians with Transistor Radio

1974. Birth Centenary of Guglielmo Marconi (radio pioneer).
398 **104** 60k. grey, green and brown (postage) 35 20
399 90k. grey, brown and green . . . . 1·80 90
400 – 200k. blue and brown (air) . . . . 1·90 1·10
DESIGN: 200k. Communications methods.

105 U.P.U. Monument and Laotian Girls

1974. Air. Centenary of U.P.U.
401 **105** 500k. lilac and red . . . 4·50 2·75

106 "Diastocera wallichi"

1974. Beetles.
403 **106** 50k. brown, black and green (postage) 75 45
404 – 90k. black, turquoise & grn . . . . 1·10 60
405 – 100k. black, orange & brn 1·50 90
406 – 110k. violet, red & grn (air) . . . . 1·30 50
DESIGNS: 90k. "Macrochenus isabellunus"; 100k. "Purpuricenus malaccensis"; 110k. "Sternocera multipunctata".

107 Pagoda and Sapphire

1974. "Mineral Riches".
407 **107** 100k. brown, green & blue 75 50
408 – 110k. brown, blue & yellow 90 50
DESIGN: 110k. Gold-panning and necklace.

108 King Savang Vatthana, Prince Souvanna Phouma and Prince Souvanouvong

1975. 1st Anniv (1974) of Laotian Peace Treaty.
409 **108** 80k. brown, ochre & green 75 35
410 300k. brown, ochre & pur 1·30 1·10
411 420k. brown, ochre and turquoise . . . . 1·50 1·10

109 Fortune-teller's Chart

1975. Chinese New Year ("Year of the Rabbit").
413 **109** 40k. brown and green . . 50 20
414 – 200k. black, brown and green . . . . 1·30 50
415 – 350k. brown, green and blue . . . . 2·40 1·30
DESIGNS—HORIZ: 200k. Fortune-teller. VERT: 350k. Woman riding hare.

110 U.N. Emblem and Frieze 112

1975. International Women's Year.
416 **110** 100k. blue and turquoise 35 30
417 – 200k. orange and green 75 35
DESIGN: 200k. I.W.Y. Emblem.

1975. "Pravet Sandone" Religious Festival.
420 **112** 80k. multicoloured . . . 50 30
421 – 110k. multicoloured . . . 50 35
422 – 120k. multicoloured . . . 65 45
423 – 130k. multicoloured . . . 1·10 60
DESIGNS: 110k. to 130k. Various legends.

113 Buddha and Stupas

1975. UNESCO Campaign for Preservation of Borobudur Temple (in Indonesia).
424 **113** 100k. green, blue & brown 65 35
425 – 200k. ochre, green & brown . . . . 1·30 80
DESIGN: 200k. Temple sculptures.

114 Laotian Arms 115 Thathiang, Vien-Tran

1976. Multicoloured, background colour given.
427 **114** 1k. blue 15 15
428 2k. mauve 15 15
429 5k. green 20 15
430 10k. violet 45 35
431 200k. orange . . . . . . 3·00 2·20

1976. Pagodas. Multicoloured.
433 1k. Type **115** 15 15
434 2k. Phonsi, Luang Prabang 20 15
435 30k. Type **115** 75 50
436 80k. As 2k. . . . . 1·50 1·10
437 100k. As 2k. . . . . 2·20 1·50
438 300k. Type **115** . . . . . . 3·75 2·75

116 Silversmith

1977. Laotian Crafts. Multicoloured.
440 1k. Type **116** 10 10
441 2k. Weaver 15 10
442 20k. Potter 75 20
443 50k. Basket-weaver (vert) . . 1·30 45

117 Gubarev, Grechko and "Salyut" Space Station

1977. 60th Anniv of Russian Revolution. Mult.
445 5k. Type **117** 10 10
446 20k. Lenin 20 15
447 50k. As 20k. 50 30
448 60k. Type **117** 60 45
449 100k. Government Palace, Vientiane, and Kremlin, Moscow (horiz) . . . . . 1·00 75
450 250k. As 100k. . . . . 2·40 1·90

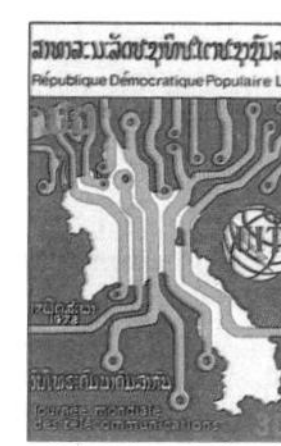

118 Laotian Arms 119 Soldiers with Flag

1978.
452 **118** 5k. yellow and black . . . 15 15
453 10k. sepia and black . . . 15 15
454 50k. purple and black . . 50 15
455 100k. green and black . . 95 50
456 250k. violet and black . . 1·90 1·10

1978. Army Day. Multicoloured.
457 20k. Type **119** 15 15
458 40k. Soldiers attacking village (horiz) 20 15
459 300k. Anti-aircraft guns . . . 1·80 1·10

120 Marchers with Banner 121 Printed Circuit and Map of Laos

1978. National Day. Multicoloured.
460 20k. Type **120** 35 15
461 50k. Women with flag . . . 35 15
462 400k. Dancer . . . . 2·20 1·50

1979. World Telecommunications Day.
464 **121** 30k. orange, brown & sil 15 10
465 – 250k. multicoloured . . . 1·50 80
DESIGN: 250k. Printed circuit, map of Laos and transmitter tower.

122 Woman posting Letter

1979. 15th Anniv of Asian-Oceanic Postal Union. Multicoloured.
466 5k. Type **122** 10 10
467 10k. Post Office counter . . . 10 10
468 80k. As 10k. 80 35
469 100k. Type **122** 95 50

123 Children playing Ball

1979. International Year of the Child (1st issue). Multicoloured. Without gum.

470	20k. Type **123**	20	15
471	50k. Children at school (horiz)	45	15
472	200k. Mother feeding child	2·20	80
473	500k. Nurse immunising child	6·25	1·80

124 Elephant, Buffalo and Pirogues

1979. Transport. Multicoloured.

475	5k. Type **124**	15	15
476	10k. Buffalo carts	15	15
477	70k. As No. 476	75	20
478	500k. Type **124**	2·75	1·50

125 Dancing Child

1979. International Year of the Child (2nd issue). Multicoloured. Without gum.

479	100k. Children playing musical instruments (horiz)	50	35
480	200k. Child releasing dove	95	75
481	600k. Type **125**	3·25	1·80

126 Forest and Paddy Field

1980. 5th Anniv of Republic (1st issue) and 25th Anniv of People's Front. Mult. Without gum.

483	30c. Type **126**	15	15
484	50c. Classroom and doctor examining baby (horiz)	35	15
485	1k. Three women	50	35
486	2k. Dam and electricity pylons (horiz)	1·30	1·10

127 Lenin Reading

1980. 110th Birth Anniv of Lenin. Multicoloured.

488	1k. Type **127**	20	15
489	2k. Lenin writing	45	20
490	3k. Lenin and Red Flag (vert)	60	35
491	4k. Lenin making speech (vert)	1·10	50

128 Workers in Field

1980. 5th Anniv of Republic (2nd issue). Multicoloured. Without gum.

493	50c. Type **128**	15	10
494	1k.60 Loading logs on lorry and elephant hauling logs	35	15
495	4k.60 Veterinary workers tending animals	75	30
496	5k.40 Workers in paddy field	1·10	45

129 Emblems of Industry, Technology, Transport, Sport and Art

1981. 26th P.C.U.S. (Communist Party) Congress. Multicoloured.

498	60c. Type **129**	15	10
499	4k.60 Communist star breaking manacles and globe	1·50	45
500	5k. Laurel branch and broken bomb	2·10	50

131 Player heading Ball

132 Disabled Person on Telephone

1981. World Cup Football Championship, Spain (1982) (1st issue). Multicoloured.

503	1k. Type **131**	15	10
504	2k. Receiving ball	35	15
505	3k. Passing ball	50	15
506	4k. Goalkeeper diving for ball (horiz)	80	15
507	5k. Dribbling	1·10	35
508	6k. Kicking ball	1·60	45

See also Nos. 545/50.

1981. International Year of Disabled Persons. Multicoloured.

509	3k. Type **132**	1·10	35
510	5k. Disabled teacher	1·30	75
511	12k. Person in wheelchair mending net	3·25	1·10

133 Wild Cat

1981. Wild Cats. Multicoloured.

512	10c. Type **133**	15	15
513	20c. Fishing cat	15	15
514	30c. Caracal	15	15
515	40c. Clouded leopard	15	15
516	50c. Flat-headed cat	15	15
517	9k. Jungle cat	3·25	65

134 Dish Aerial and Flag

1981. 6th National Day Festival. Multicoloured.

518	3k. Type **134**	45	30
519	4k. Soldier and flag	65	35
520	5k. Girls presenting flowers to soldier, flag and map of Laos	95	45

135 Indian Elephant

1982. Indian Elephant. Multicoloured.

521	1k. Type **135**	20	15
522	2k. Elephant carrying log	50	15
523	3k. Elephant with passengers	65	20
524	4k. Elephant in trap	90	30
525	5k. Elephant and young	1·20	35
526	5k.50 Herd of elephants	1·50	50

136 Laotian Wrestling

1982. Wrestling.

527	**136**	50c. multicoloured	15	15
528	–	1k.20 multicoloured	15	15
529	–	2k. multicoloured	35	15
530	–	2k.50 multicoloured	60	20
531	–	4k. multicoloured	95	35
532	–	5k. multicoloured	1·50	50

DESIGNS: 1k.20 to 5k. Various wrestling scenes.

137 "Nymphaea zanzibariensis"

1982. Water Lilies. Multicoloured.

533	30c. Type **137**	15	15
534	40c. "Nelumbo nucifera" "Gaertn Rose"	15	15
535	60c. "Nymphaea rosea"	15	15
536	3k. "Nymphaea nouchali"	65	35
537	4k. "Nymphaea" White	95	35
538	7k. "Nelumbo nucifera" "Gaertn White"	1·90	45

138 Barn Swallow

1982. Birds. Multicoloured.

539	50c. Type **138**	15	15
540	1k. Hoopoe	15	15
541	2k. River kingfisher	50	15
542	3k. Black-naped blue monarch	75	20
543	4k. Grey wagtail (horiz)	1·00	20
544	10k. Long-tailed tailor bird (horiz)	2·50	75

139 Football

1982. World Cup Football Championship, Spain (2nd issue).

545	**139**	1k. multicoloured	20	15
546	–	2k. multicoloured	35	15
547	–	3k. multicoloured	50	15
548	–	4k. multicoloured	75	20
549	**139**	5k. multicoloured	95	30
550	–	6k. multicoloured	1·30	45

DESIGNS: 2, 3, 4, 6k. Various football scenes.

140 "Herona marathus"

1982. Butterflies. Multicoloured.

552	1k. Type **140**	20	15
553	2k. "Neptis paraka"	45	15
554	3k. "Euripus halitherses"	65	20
555	4k. "Lebadea martha"	95	20
556	5k. "Iton semamora" (42 × 26 mm)	1·50	35
557	6k. Common palm fly (59 × 41 mm)	1·80	45

142 River Raft

1982. River Craft. Multicoloured.

559	50c. Type **142**	15	15
560	60c. River sampan	15	15
561	1k. River house boat	20	15
562	2k. River passenger steamer	50	15
563	3k. River ferry	65	20
564	8k. Self-propelled barge	1·60	50

143 Vat Chanh

1982. Pagodas. Multicoloured.

565	50c. Type **143**	15	15
566	60c. Vat Inpeng	15	15
567	1k. Vat Dong Mieng	20	15
568	2k. Ho Tay	50	15
569	3k. Vat Ho Pha Keo	65	20
570	8k. Vat Sisaket	1·60	50

1982. Various stamps optd **1982**.

571	**114**	1k. multicoloured
572	**116**	1k. multicoloured
573	–	2k. multicoloured (441)
574	**117**	5k. multicoloured
575	**118**	5k. yellow and black
576	**122**	5k. multicoloured
577	**124**	5k. multicoloured
578	–	10k. multicoloured (467)
579	–	10k. multicoloured (476)
580	–	20k. multicoloured (446)
581	**119**	20k. multicoloured
582	**121**	30k. orange, brown & sil
583	–	40k. multicoloured (458)
584	–	50k. multicoloured (443)
585	–	70k. multicoloured (477)
586	–	80k. multicoloured (468)
587	**122**	100k. multicoloured
588	**114**	200k. multicoloured
589	**121**	250k. multicoloured

145 Poodle

1982. Dogs. Multicoloured.

591	50c. Type **145**	15	15
592	60c. Samoyed	15	15
593	1k. Boston terrier	20	15
594	2k. Cairn terrier	65	15
595	3k. Chihuahua	90	35
596	8k. Bulldog	2·40	60

146 Woman watering Crops

1982. World Food Day. Multicoloured.

597	7k. Type **146**	1·30	45
598	8k. Woman transplanting rice	1·50	50

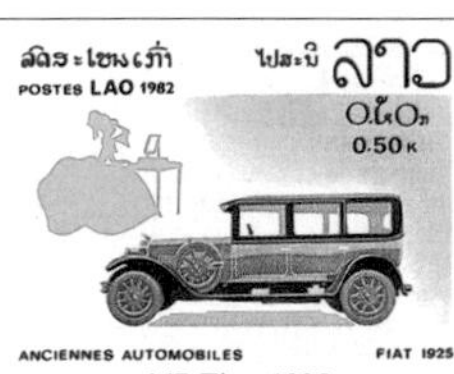

147 Fiat, 1925

1982. Cars. Multicoloured.

599	50c. Type **147**	15	15
600	60c. Peugeot, 1925	15	15
601	1k. Berliet, 1925	30	15
602	2k. Ballot, 1925	60	15
603	3k. Renault, 1926	90	35
604	8k. Ford, 1925	1·80	60

148 President Souphanouvong

1982. 7th Anniv of Republic. Multicoloured.

605	50c. Type **148**	15	15
606	1k. Tractors (horiz)	20	15
607	2k. Cow (horiz)	30	15
608	3k. Lorry passing dish aerial (horiz)	50	20
609	4k. Nurse examining child	75	35
610	5k. Classroom (horiz)	1·00	35
611	6k. Dancer	1·50	45

149 Dimitrov, Flag and Arms of Bulgaria

1982. Birth Centenary of Georgi Dimitrov (Bulgarian statesman).

612 **149**	10k. multicoloured	1·60	90

150 Kremlin and Arms of U.S.S.R.

151 Hurdling

1982. 60th Anniv of U.S.S.R. Multicoloured.

613	3k. Type **150**	50	35
614	4k. Doves and maps of U.S.S.R. and Laos	95	50

1983. Olympic Games, Los Angeles (1984) (1st issue). Multicoloured.

616	50c. Type **151**	15	15
617	1k. Javelin	20	15
618	2k. Basketball	30	15
619	3k. Diving	50	15
620	4k. Gymnastics	75	35
621	10k. Weightlifting	2·20	75

See also Nos. 708/14.

152 Bucking Horse

1983. Horses. Multicoloured.

623	50c. Type **152**	15	15
624	1k. Rearing black horse	20	15
625	2k. Trotting brown horse	35	15
626	3k. Dappled grey horse	65	20
627	4k. Wild horse crossing snow	80	30
628	10k. Horse in paddock	2·50	75

153 "St. Catherine of Alexandria"

1983. 500th Birth Anniv of Raphael (artist). Multicoloured.

629	50c. Type **153**	15	15
630	1k. "Adoration of the Kings"	20	15
631	2k. "Madonna of the Grand Duke"	35	15
632	3k. "St. George and the Dragon"	65	20
633	4k. "The Vision of Ezekiel"	80	30
634	10k. "Adoration of the Kings" (different)	2·50	75

154 A. Gubarev (Soviet) and V. Remek (Czechoslovak)

1983. Cosmonauts. Multicoloured.

636	50c. Type **154**	15	15
637	50c. P. Klimuk (Soviet) and Miroslaw Hermaszewski (Polish)	15	15
638	1k. V. Bykovsky (Soviet) and Sigmund Jahn (East German)	20	15
639	1k. Nikolai Rukavishnikov (Soviet) and Georgi Ivanov (Bulgarian)	20	15
640	2k. V. Kubasov (Soviet) and Bertalan Farkas (Hungarian)	35	15
641	3k. V. Dzhanibekov (Soviet) and Gurragchaa (Mongolian)	60	20
642	4k. L. Popov (Soviet) and D. Prunariu (Rumanian)	75	20
643	6k. Soviet cosmonaut and Arnaldo Tamayo (Cuban)	1·10	35
644	10k. Soviet and French cosmonauts	2·20	75

155 Jacques Charles's Hydrogen Balloon, 1783

1983. Bicentenary of Manned Flight. Mult.

646	50c. Type **155**	15	15
647	1k. Blanchard and Jeffries' balloon, 1785	20	15
648	2k. Vincenzo Lunardi's balloon (London–Ware flight), 1784	35	15
649	3k. Modern hot-air balloon over city	75	20
650	4k. Massed balloon ascent, 1890	90	35
651	10k. Auguste Piccard's stratosphere balloon "F.N.R.S.", 1931	2·50	75

157 "Dendrobium sp."

1983. Flowers. Multicoloured.

654	1k. Type **157**	20	15
655	2k. "Aerides odoratum"	35	15
656	3k. "Dendrobium aggregatum"	60	20
657	4k. "Dendrobium"	75	20
658	5k. "Moschatum"	1·00	30
659	6k. "Dendrobium sp." (different)	1·50	45

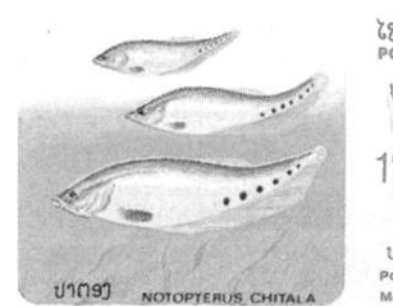

158 Downhill Skiing

1983. Winter Olympic Games, Sarajevo (1984) (1st issue). Multicoloured.

660	50c. Type **158**	15	15
661	1k. Slalom	20	15
662	2k. Ice hockey	35	15
663	3k. Speed skating	65	20
664	4k. Ski jumping	80	30
665	10k. Luge	2·20	75

See also Nos. 696/702.

160 Clown Knifefish

1983. Fishes of Mekong River. Multicoloured.

668	1k. Type **160**	20	15
669	2k. Common carp	35	15
670	3k. Lesser Mekong catfish	65	20
671	4k. Giant barb	75	20
672	5k. Black shark	1·20	30
673	6k. Nile mouthbrooder	1·60	45

161 Magellan and "Vitoria"

1983. Explorers and their Ships. Multicoloured.

674	1k. Type **161**	20	15
675	2k. Jacques Cartier and "Grande Hermine"	35	15
676	3k. Columbus and "Santa Maria"	75	20
677	4k. Pedro Alvares Cabral and "El Ray"	90	20
678	5k. Cook and H.M.S. "Resolution"	1·10	30
679	6k. Charcot and "Pourquoi-pas?"	1·60	45

No. 679 is wrongly inscribed "Cabot".

162 Tabby Cat

1983. Domestic Cats. Multicoloured.

680	1k. Type **162**	20	15
681	2k. Long-haired Persian	75	15
682	3k. Siamese	65	20
683	4k. Burmese	80	20
684	5k. Persian	1·20	30
685	6k. Tortoiseshell	1·60	45

1983. Nos. 430 and 466 optd **1983**.

685a **122**	5k. multicoloured		
685b **114**	10k. multicoloured		

163 Marx, Book, Sun and Signature

1983. Death Centenary of Karl Marx. Mult.

686	1k. Marx, dove, globe and flags	30	15
687	4k. Type **163**	1·00	15
688	6k. Marx and flags	1·80	50

164 Elephant dragging Log

1983. 8th Anniv of Republic. Multicoloured.

689	1k. Type **164**	30	15
690	4k. Cattle and pig (horiz)	1·00	15
691	6k. Crops	1·80	50

165 Carrier Pigeon and Telex Machine

1983. World Communications Year. Multicoloured.

692	50c. Type **165**	15	15
693	1k. Early telephone, handset and receiver	20	15
694	4k. Television tube and aerial	90	30
695	6k. Satellite and dish aerial	1·50	50

166 Ice Skating

167 Tiger

1984. Winter Olympic Games, Sarajevo (2nd issue). Multicoloured.

696	50c. Type **166**	15	15
697	1k. Speed skating	20	15
698	2k. Biathlon	35	15
699	3k. Luge (horiz)	90	30
700	4k. Downhill skiing (horiz)	95	30
701	5k. Ski jumping	1·30	45
702	6k. Slalom	1·60	50

1984. Endangered Animals. The Tiger. Mult.

704	25c. Type **167**	35	15
705	25c. Tigers (horiz)	35	15
706	3k. Tiger and cubs (horiz)	4·00	50
707	4k. Tiger cubs	6·25	1·00

168 Diving

1984. Olympic Games, Los Angeles (2nd issue). Multicoloured.

708	50c. Type **168**	15	15
709	1k. Volleyball	30	15
710	2k. Running	60	15
711	4k. Basketball	1·20	15
712	5k. Judo	1·30	30
713	6k. Football	1·80	35
714	7k. Gymnastics	2·10	45

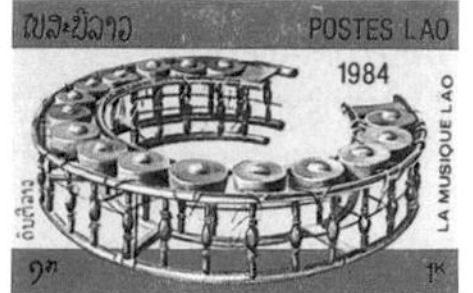

169 Tuned Drums

1984. Musical Instruments. Multicoloured.

716	1k. Type **169**	20	15
717	2k. Xylophone	45	15
718	3k. Pair of drums	80	20
719	4k. Hand drum	1·00	30

720 5k. Barrel drum 1·30 30
721 6k. Pipes and string instrument 2·10 45

170 National Flag

171 Chess Game

1984. National Day. Multicoloured.
722 60c. Type **170** 20 15
723 1k. National arms 45 15
724 2k. As No. 723 60 20

1984. 60th Anniv of World Chess Federation. Multicoloured.
725 50c. Type **171** 15 15
726 1k. Renaissance game from "The Three Ages of Man" (miniature attr. to Estienne Porchier) 20 15
727 2k. Woman teaching girls 50 15
728 2k. Margrave Otto IV of Brandenburg playing chess with his wife 50 15
729 3k. Four men at chessboard 90 30
730 4k. Two women playing 1·30 30
731 8k. Two men playing 2·75 45
Nos. 725, 727 and 729/31 show illustrations from King Alfonso X's "Book of Chess, Dice and Tablings".

172 "Cardinal Nino de Guevara" (El Greco)

173 "Adonis aestivalis"

1984. "Espana 84" International Stamp Exhibition, Madrid. Multicoloured.
733 50c. Type **172** 15 15
734 1k. "Gaspar de Guzman, Duke of Olivares, on Horseback" (Velazquez) 30 15
735 2k. "The Annunciation" (Murillo) 45 15
736 2k. "Portrait of a Lady" (Zurbaran) 45 15
737 3k. "The Family of Charles IV" (Goya) 65 30
738 4k. "Two Harlequins" (Picasso) 95 30
739 8k. "Abstract" (Miro) 1·90 45

1984. Woodland Flowers. Multicoloured.
741 50c. Type **173** 15 15
742 1k. "Alpinia speciosa" 20 15
743 2k. "Cassia lechenaultiana" 45 15
744 2k. "Aeschynanthus speciosus" 45 15
745 3k. "Datura meteloides" 75 30
746 4k. "Quamoclit pennata" 95 30
747 8k. "Commelina benghalensis" 1·90 45

174 Nazzaro

1984. 19th Universal Postal Union Congress Philatelic Salon, Hamburg. Cars. Multicoloured.
748 50c. Type **174** 15 15
749 1k. Daimler 20 15
750 2k. Delage 45 15
751 2k. Fiat "S 57/14B" 45 15
752 3k. Bugatti 90 30
753 4k. Itala 1·30 30
754 8k. Blitzen Benz 2·40 45

175 "Madonna and Child"

1984. 450th Death Anniv of Correggio (artist). Multicoloured.
756 50c. Type **175** 15 15
757 1k. Detail showing horsemen resting 30 15
758 2k. "Madonna and Child" (different) 50 15
759 2k. "Mystical Marriage of St. Catherine" 50 15
760 3k. "Four Saints" 75 30
761 4k. "Noli me Tangere" 1·10 30
762 8k. "Christ bids Farewell to the Virgin Mary" 2·20 45

176 "Luna 1"

1984. Space Exploration. Multicoloured.
764 50c. Type **176** 15 15
765 1k. "Luna 2" 20 15
766 2k. "Luna 3" 45 15
767 2k. Kepler and "Sputnik 2" 45 15
768 3k. Newton and Lunokhod 2 95 20
769 4k. Jules Verne and "Luna 13" 1·30 35
770 8k. Copernicus and space station 2·40 60

177 Malaclemys Terrapin

1984. Reptiles. Multicoloured.
771 50c. Type **177** 15 15
772 1k. Banded krait 20 15
773 2k. Indian python (vert) 45 15
774 2k. Reticulated python 45 15
775 3k. Tokay gecko 95 20
776 4k. "Natrix subminiata" (snake) 1·30 35
777 8k. Dappled ground gecko 2·50 60

178 Greater Glider

1984. "Ausipex 84" International Stamp Exhibition, Melbourne. Marsupials. Mult.
778 50c. Type **178** 15 15
779 1k. Platypus 30 15
780 2k. Southern hairy-nosed wombat ("Lasiorhinus latifrons") 45 15
781 2k. Tasmanian devil ("Sarcophilus harrisii") 45 15
782 3k. Thylacine 95 20
783 4k. Tiger cat 1·20 35
784 8k. Wallaby 2·10 60

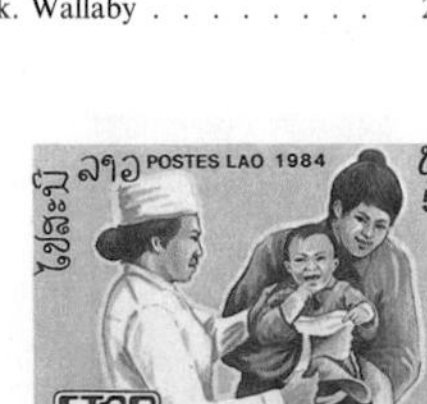
179 Nurse with Mother and Child

1984. Anti-poliomyelitis Campaign. Multicoloured.
786 5k. Type **179** 1·10 50
787 6k. Doctor inoculating child 1·30 50

180 Dragon Stair-rail

1984. Laotian Art. Multicoloured.
788 50c. Type **180** 15 15
789 1k. Capital of column 20 15
790 2k. Decorative panel depicting god 35 15
791 2k. Decorative panel depicting leaves 35 15
792 3k. Stylized leaves (horiz) 75 20
793 4k. Triangular flower decoration (horiz) 1·30 35
794 8k. Circular lotus flower decoration 2·40 60

181 River House Boats

1984. 9th Anniv of Republic. Multicoloured.
795 1k. Type **181** 45 15
796 2k. Passengers boarding Fokker Friendship airliner 65 20
797 4k. Building a bridge 1·30 60
798 10k. Building a road 2·75 1·20

182 Players with Ball

1985. World Cup Football Championship, Mexico (1986) (1st issue). Multicoloured.
799 50c. Type **182** 15 15
800 1k. Heading the ball 20 15
801 2k. Defending the ball 60 15
802 3k. Running with ball 90 15
803 4k. Taking possession of ball 1·30 30
804 5k. Heading the ball (different) 1·60 35
805 6k. Saving a goal 1·90 60
See also Nos. 868/74.

183 Motor Cycle

1985. Centenary of Motor Cycle. Multicoloured.
807 50c. Type **183** 15 15
808 1k. Gnome Rhone, 1920 20 15
809 2k. F.N. "M67C", 1928 50 15
810 3k. Indian "Chief", 1930 75 15
811 4k. Rudge Multi, 1914 1·10 30
812 5k. Honda "Benly J", 1953 1·30 35
813 6k. CZ, 1938 1·60 60

1985. Various stamps optd **1985**.
813a – 40k. multicoloured (458)
813b – 50k. multicoloured (443)
813c – 50k. multicoloured (447)
813d – 70k. multicoloured (477)
813e – 80k. multicoloured (468)
813f – 100k. multicoloured (449)
813g **122** 100k. multicoloured
813h **114** 200k. multicoloured
813i – 250k. multicoloured (450)
813j **118** 250k. violet and black
813k **121** 250k. multicoloured
813m – 300k. multicoloured (459)

184 Fly Agaric

1985. Fungi. Multicoloured.
814 50c. Type **184** 15 15
815 1k. Cep 20 15
816 2k. Shaggy ink cap ("Coprinus comatus") 50 15
817 2k. The blusher ("Amanita rubescens") 50 15
818 3k. Downy boletus 1·00 30
819 4k. Parasol mushroom 1·60 35
820 8k. Brown roll-rim 2·75 65

184a Battle Plan, Kursk, and Tanks

1985. 40th Anniv of End of Second World War. Multicoloured.
820a 1k. Type **184a** 35 15
820b 2k. Monument and military parade, Red Square, Moscow 65 15
820c 4k. Street battle and battle plan, Stalingrad 1·30 35
820d 5k. Battle plan and Reichstag, Berlin 1·60 45
820e 6k. Soviet Memorial, Berlin-Treptow, and military parade at Brandenburg Gate 1·90 50

185 Lenin reading "Pravda"

1985. 115th Birth Anniv of Lenin. Multicoloured.
821 1k. Type **185** 35 15
822 2k. Lenin (vert) 60 15
823 10k. Lenin addressing meeting (vert) 2·50 75

186 "Cattleya percivaliana"

1985. "Argentina '85" International Stamp Exhibition, Buenos Aires. Orchids. Multicoloured.
824 50c. Type **186** 15 15
825 1k. "Odontoglossum luteo-purpureum" 20 15
826 2k. "Cattleya lueddemanniana" 45 15
827 2k. "Maxillaria sanderiana" 45 15
828 3k. "Miltonia vexillaria" 75 20
829 4k. "Oncidium varicosum" 1·00 30
830 8k. "Cattleya dowiana" 2·20 60

187 Rhesus Macaque

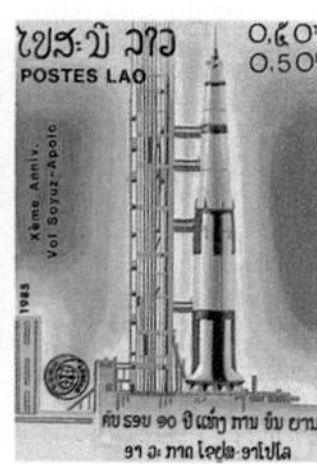
188 "Saturn" Rocket on Launch Pad

1985. Mammals. Multicoloured.
832 2k. Type **187** 30 15
833 3k. Kouprey 60 15
834 4k. Porcupine (horiz) 90 30
835 5k. Asiatic black bear (horiz) 1·10 30
836 10k. Chinese pangolin 2·40 60

1985. 10th Anniv of "Apollo"–"Soyuz" Space Link. Multicoloured.
837 50c. Type **188** 15 15
838 1k. Soviet rocket on launch pad 30 15
839 2k. "Apollo" approaching "Soyuz 19" (horiz) 45 15
840 2k. "Soyuz 19" approaching "Apollo" (horiz) 45 15
841 3k. "Apollo" and crew T. Stafford, V. Brand and D. Stayton (horiz) 75 20
842 4k. "Soyuz 19" and crew A. Leonov and V. Kubasov (horiz) 1·00 30
843 8k. "Apollo" and "Soyuz 19" docked (horiz) 2·10 60

189 Fiat Biplane

1985. "Italia '85" International Stamp Exhibition, Rome. Multicoloured. (a) Aircraft. As T **189**.
844 50c. Type **189** 15 15
845 1k. Cant Z.501 Gabbiano flying boat 20 15
846 2k. Marina Fiat MF.5 flying boat 45 15
847 3k. Macchi Castoldi MC-100 flying boat 65 20
848 4k. Anzani biplane 90 30
849 5k. Ambrosini biplane . . . 95 30
850 6k. Piaggio P-148 . . . . . 1·30 45

(b) Columbus and his Ships. Size 40 × 29 mm.
852 1k. "Pinta" 20 15
853 2k. "Nina" 45 15
854 3k. "Santa Maria" 65 20
855 4k. Christopher Columbus . . 90 30
856 5k. Map of Columbus's first voyage . . . . 1·10 35

190 U.N. and National Flags on Globe
191 Woman feeding Child

1985. 40th Anniv of U.N.O. Multicoloured.
857 2k. Type **190** 65 20
858 3k. U.N. emblem and Laotian arms on globe . . 95 30
859 10k. Map on globe . . . . . 2·75 95

1985. Lao Health Services. Multicoloured.
860 1k. Type **191** 20 15
861 3k. Red Cross nurse injecting child (horiz) 80 15
862 4k. Red Cross nurse tending patient (horiz) . . . . . . 1·00 30
863 10k. Mother breast-feeding baby . . . . 2·20 75

192 Soldier, Workers and Symbols of Industry and Agriculture

1985. 10th Anniv of Republic. Multicoloured.
864 3k. Type **192** 65 20
865 10k. Soldier, workers and symbols of transport and communications . . . . . 2·50 90

193 Soldier with Flag and Workers

1985. 30th Anniv of Lao People's Revolutionary Party. Multicoloured.
866 2k. Type **193** 90 15
867 8k. Soldier with flag and workers (different) . . . . 2·75 60

194 Footballers

1986. World Cup Football Championship, Mexico (2nd issue).
868 **194** 50c. multicoloured 15 15
869 – 1k. multicoloured 20 15
870 – 2k. multicoloured 45 15
871 – 3k. multicoloured 65 20
872 – 4k. multicoloured 75 20
873 – 5k. multicoloured 95 30
874 – 6k. multicoloured . . . . 1·30 35
DESIGNS: 1k. to 6k. Various football scenes.

194a Cosmonaut, "Mir" Space Complex and Earth

1986. 17th Soviet Communist Party Congress. Multicoloured.
875a 4k. Type **194a** . . . . . . 1·00 30
875b 20k. Lenin and Red Flag 4·00 95

195 "Pelargonium grandiflorum"
196 "Aporia hippia"

1986. Flowers. Multicoloured.
876 50c. Type **195** 15 15
877 1k. Columbine 20 15
878 2k. "Fuchsia globosa" . . . 45 15
879 3k. "Crocus aureus" 65 20
880 4k. Hollyhock 75 20
881 5k. "Gladiolus purpureo" . . 95 30
882 6k. "Hyacinthus orientalis" 1·30 35

1986. Butterflies. Multicoloured.
883 50c. Type **196** 15 15
884 1k. "Euthalia irrubescens" . . 20 15
885 2k. "Japonica lutea" 45 15
886 3k. "Pratapa ctesia" 65 20
887 4k. Leaf butterfly 75 20
888 5k. Yellow orange-tip 95 30
889 6k. Chestnut tiger . . . . . 1·30 35

197 Rocket launch at Baikanur Space Centre

1986. 25th Anniv of First Man in Space. Mult.
890 50c. Type **197** 15 15
891 1k. "Molniya" communications satellite 30 15
892 2k. "Salyut" space station (horiz) 45 15
893 3k. Yuri Gagarin, "Sputnik 1" and rocket debris (horiz) 80 15
894 4k. "Luna 3" and Moon . . 1·10 20
895 5k. Vladimir Komarov on first space walk . . . . . 1·60 35
896 6k. "Luna 16" lifting off from Moon . . . . 1·80 45

198 Giraffe

1986. Animals. Multicoloured.
898 50c. Type **198** 15 15
899 1k. Lion 20 15
900 2k. African elephant 45 15
901 3k. Red kangaroo 65 20
902 4k. Koala 90 20
903 5k. Greater flamingo . . . . 1·00 30
904 6k. Giant panda . . . . . . 1·80 50

199 Boeing 747-100

1986. Air. Aircraft. Multicoloured.
906 20k. Type **199** . . . . . . 3·75 30
907 50k. Ilyushin Il-86 . . . . . 8·75 80

200 Great Argus Pheasant (½-size illustration)

1986. Pheasants. Multicoloured.
908 50c. Type **200** 15 15
909 1k. Silver pheasant 20 15
910 2k. Common pheasant . . . 45 15
911 3k. Lady Amherst's pheasant 65 20
912 4k. Reeves's pheasant 75 20
913 5k. Golden pheasant 95 30
914 6k. Copper pheasant . . . . 1·30 35

201 Scarlet King Snake

1986. Snakes. Multicoloured.
915 50c. Corn snake 15 15
916 1k. Type **201** 20 15
917 1k. Richard's blind snake (vert) 45 15
918 2k. Western ring-necked snake 65 20
919 4k. Mangrove snake 75 20
920 5k. Indian python 95 30
921 6k. Common cobra (vert) . . 1·30 35

202 Bayeux Tapestry (detail) and Comet Head

1986. Appearance of Halley's Comet. Multicoloured.
922 50c. Comet over Athens (65 × 21 mm) 15 15
923 1k. Type **202** 20 15
924 2k. Edmond Halley (astronomer) and comet tail (20 × 21 mm) . . . 45 15
925 3k. "Vega" space probe and comet head 65 20
926 4k. Galileo and comet tail (20 × 21 mm) 75 20
927 5k. Comet head (20 × 21 mm) 95 30
928 6k. "Giotto" space probe and comet tail . . . . 1·30 35
Nos. 923/4, 925/6 and 927/8 resepctively were issued together, se-tenant, each pair forming a composite design.

203 Keeshond
204 "Mammillaria matudae"

1986. "Stockholmia 86" International Stamp Exhibition. Dogs. Multicoloured.
930 50c. Type **203** 15 15
931 1k. Elkhound (horiz) 20 15
932 2k. Bernese (horiz) 50 15
933 3k. Pointing griffon (horiz) 80 20
934 4k. Collie (horiz) 80 20
935 5k. Irish water spaniel (horiz) 1·00 30
936 6k. Briard (horiz) . . . . . 1·60 50

1986. Cacti. Multicoloured.
938 50c. Type **204** 15 15
939 1k. "Mammillaria theresae" 20 15
940 2k. "Ariocarpus trigonus" . . 45 15
941 3k. "Notocactus crassigibbus" 65 20
942 4k. "Astrophytum asterias" hybrid 75 20
943 5k. "Melocactus manzanus" 95 30
944 6k. "Astrophytum ornatum" hybrid . . . . 1·30 35

205 Arms and Dove on Globe
206 Vat Phu Champasak

1986. International Peace Year.
945 **205** 3k. multicoloured 80 20
946 – 5k. black, blue and red 1·30 35
947 – 10k. multicoloured . . . 2·50 90
DESIGNS: 5k. Dove on smashed bomb; 10k. People supporting I.P.Y. emblem.

1987. 40th Anniv of UNESCO. Multicoloured.
948 3k. Type **206** 65 20
949 4k. Dish aerial and map of Laos on globe 90 30
950 9k. People reading books (horiz) . . . . 1·80 60

207 Speed Skating

1987. Winter Olympic Games, Calgary (1988) (1st issue). Multicoloured.
951 50c. Type **207** 15 15
952 1k. Biathlon 20 15
953 2k. Figure skating (pairs) . . 45 15
954 3k. Luge (horiz) 65 20
955 4k. Four-man bobsleigh (horiz) 75 20
956 5k. Ice hockey (horiz) 95 30
957 6k. Ski jumping (horiz) . . . 1·30 35
See also Nos. 1046/51.

208 Gymnast and Urn

1987. Olympic Games, Seoul (1988) (1st issue). Sports and Greek Pottery. Multicoloured.
959 50c. Type **208** 15 15
960 1k. Throwing the discus and vase (horiz) 20 15
961 2k. Running and urn 45 15
962 3k. Show jumping and bowl (horiz) 65 20
963 4k. Throwing the javelin and plate 75 20
964 5k. High jumping and bowl with handles (horiz) . . . 95 30
965 6k. Wrestling and urn . . . 1·30 35
See also Nos. 1053/9.

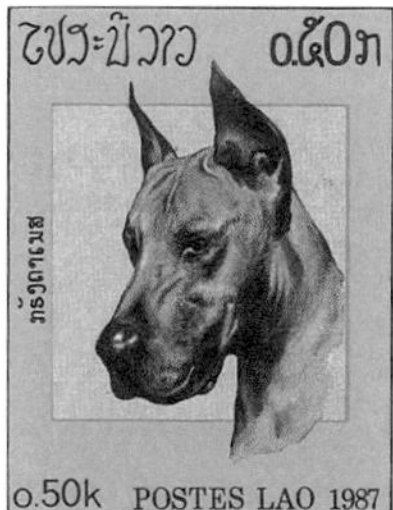

209 Great Dane

1987. Dogs. Multicoloured.
967 50c. Type **209** 15 15
968 1k. Black labrador 20 15
969 2k. St. Bernard 45 15
970 3k. Tervuren shepherd dog 75 20
971 4k. German shepherd 80 20
972 5k. Beagle . . . . 1·30 30
973 6k. Golden retriever . . . . 1·50 50

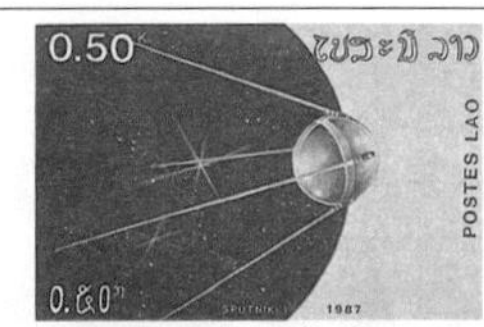

210 "Sputnik 1"

1987. 30th Anniv of Launch of First Artificial Satellite. Multicoloured.

974 50c. Type **210** 15 15
975 1k. "Sputnik 2" 20 15
976 2k. "Cosmos 97" 45 15
977 3k. "Cosmos" 65 20
978 4k. "Mars" 75 20
979 5k. "Luna 1" 95 30
980 9k. "Luna 3" (vert) . . . . . 1·50 45

211 "MONTREAL" Handstamp on Letter to Quebec and Schooner

1987. "Capex 87" International Stamp Exhibition, Toronto. Ships and Covers. Multicoloured.

981 50c. Type **211** 15 15
982 1k. "PAID MONTREAL" on letter and schooner . . 20 15
983 2k. Letter from Montreal to London and "William D. Lawrence" (full-rigged ship) 45 15
984 3k. 1840 letter to Williamsburgh and "Neptune" (steamer) . . . 65 20
985 4k. 1844 letter to London and "Athabasca" (screw-steamer) 75 20
986 5k. 1848 letter and "Chicora" (paddle-steamer) 95 30
987 6k. 1861 letter and "Passport" (river paddle-steamer) . . . . 1·30 35

212 Horse

1987. Horses. Multicoloured.

989 50c. Type **212** 15 15
990 1k. Chestnut (vert) 20 15
991 2k. Black horse with sheepskin noseband (vert) 45 15
992 3k. Dark chestnut (vert) . . . 65 20
993 4k. Black horse (vert) 75 20
994 5k. Chestnut with plaited mane (vert) 95 30
995 6k. Grey (vert) . . . . 1·30 35

213 Volvo "480"

1987. Motor Cars. Multicoloured.

996 50c. Type **213** 15 15
997 1k. Alfa Romeo "33" . . . 20 15
998 2k. Ford "Fiesta" 45 15
999 3k. Ford "Fiesta" (different) 75 20
1000 4k. Ford "Granada" . . . 80 20
1001 5k. Citroen "AX" . . . . . 1·30 30
1002 6k. Renault "21" . . . . . 1·50 50

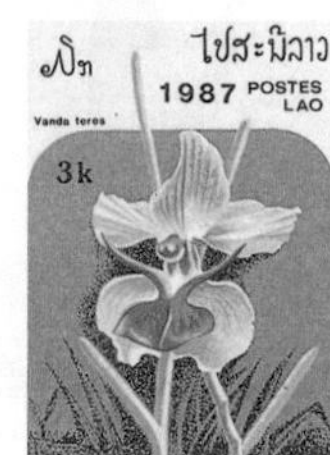

214 "Vanda teres"

1987. Orchids. Multicoloured.

1004 3k. Type **214** 15 15
1005 7k. "Laeliocattleya" sp. . . 15 15
1006 10k. "Paphiopedilum" hybrid 20 15
1007 39k. "Sobralia" sp. 80 20
1008 44k. "Paphiopedilum" hybrid (different) 90 30
1009 47k. "Paphiopedilum" hybrid (different) . . . . 1·00 35
1010 50k. "Cattleya trianaei" . . 1·20 35

215 Elephants

1987. "Hafnia 87" International Stamp Exhibition, Copenhagen. Elephants. Multicoloured.

1012 50c. Type **215** 15 15
1013 1k. Three elephants 20 15
1014 2k. Elephant feeding 45 15
1015 3k. Elephant grazing on grass 65 20
1016 4k. Adult with calf 75 20
1017 5k. Elephant walking . . . 95 30
1018 6k. Elephant (vert) . . . . 1·30 35

216 Building Bamboo House

1987. International Year of Shelter for the Homeless. Multicoloured.

1020 1k. Type **216** 15 15
1021 27k. Building wooden house 60 20
1022 46k. House on stilts . . . . 1·20 30
1023 70k. Street of houses on stilts . . . . 1·80 60

217 Clown Loach

1987. Fishes. Multicoloured.

1024 3k. Type **217** 15 15
1025 7k. Harlequin filefish . . . 15 15
1026 10k. Silver-spotted squirrelfish 20 15
1027 39k. Mandarin fish 80 20
1028 44k. Coral hind 90 30
1029 47k. Zebra lionfish . . . . 1·00 35
1030 50k. Semicircle angelfish . . 1·20 35

218 Watering Seedlings

1987. World Food Day. Multicoloured.

1031 1k. Type **218** 15 15
1032 3k. Harvesting maize (vert) 15 15
1033 5k. Harvesting rice 15 15
1034 63k. Children with fish (vert) 1·30 45
1035 142k. Tending pigs and poultry . . . . 3·00 90

219 Wounded Soldiers on Battlefield

1987. 70th Anniv of Russian Revolution. Multicoloured.

1036 1k. Type **219** 20 15
1037 2k. Mother and baby . . . 45 20
1038 4k. Storming the Winter Palace 80 20
1039 8k. Lenin amongst soldiers and sailors . . . . . . 1·60 45
1040 10k. Lenin labouring in Red Square . . . . 2·20 60

220 Hoeing

1987. Rice Culture in Mountain Regions. Mult.

1041 64k. Type **220** . . . . . . 1·40 30
1042 100k. Working in paddy fields . . . . 2·40 75

221 Laotheung Costume

1987. Ethnic Costumes. Multicoloured.

1043 7k. Type **221** 15 15
1044 38k. Laoloum costume . . . 80 20
1045 144k. Laosoun costume . . 3·00 1·00

222 Two-man Bobsleigh

1988. Winter Olympic Games, Calgary (2nd issue). Multicoloured.

1046 1k. Type **222** 15 15
1047 4k. Biathlon (shooting) . . . 15 15
1048 20k. Cross-country skiing 45 15
1049 42k. Ice hockey 90 30
1050 63k. Speed skating . . . . 1·30 45
1051 70k. Slalom . . . . 1·50 50

223 Throwing the Javelin

1988. Olympic Games, Seoul (2nd issue). Mult.

1053 2k. Type **223** 15 15
1054 5k. Triple jumping 15 15
1055 10k. Men's gymnastics . . . 20 15
1056 12k. Pirogue racing 35 15
1057 38k. Women's gymnastics 1·00 20
1058 46k. Fencing . . . . 1·30 30
1059 100k. Wrestling . . . . . . 2·75 65

224 Tyrannosaurus

1988. "Juvalux 88" Youth Philately Exhibition, Luxembourg. Prehistoric Animals. Multicoloured.

1061 3k. Type **224** (wrongly inscr "Trachodon") 15 15
1062 7k. "Ceratosaurus nasicornis" (vert) 20 15
1063 39k. "Iguanodon bernissartensis" (vert) . . 1·10 20
1064 44k. Scolosaurus (vert) . . . 1·10 35
1065 47k. "Phororhacus" sp. (vert) . . . . 1·10 35
1066 50k. Anatosaurus (wrongly inscr "Tyrannosaurus") 1·50 35

225 Adults in Hygiene Class

1988. 40th Anniv of W.H.O. Multicoloured.

1068 5k. Type **225** 15 15
1069 27k. Fumigating houses . . 50 15
1070 164k. Woman pumping fresh water (vert) . . . . 3·50 1·20

226 "Sans Pareil", 1829 **227** Red Frangipani

1988. "Essen 88" International Stamp Fair. Early Railway Locomotives. Multicoloured.

1071 6k. Type **226** 15 15
1072 15k. "Rocket", 1829 . . . . 35 15
1073 20k. "Royal George", 1827 (horiz) 45 15
1074 25k. Trevithick's locomotive, 1803 (horiz) 60 20
1075 30k. "Novelty", 1829 (horiz) 90 20
1076 100k. "Tom Thumb", 1829 (horiz) . . . . 2·40 75

1988. "Finlandia 88" International Stamp Exhibition, Helsinki. Flowers. Multicoloured.

1078 8k. Type **227** 15 15
1079 9k. Hollyhock 20 15
1080 15k. Flame-of-the forest . . 30 15
1081 33k. Golden shower 65 20
1082 64k. "Dahlia coccinea" (red) 1·30 45
1083 69k. "Dahlia coccinea" (yellow) . . . . 1·50 50

228 Sash Pattern

1988. Decorative Stencil Patterns.

1085 **228** 1k. multicoloured . . . 15 15
1086 – 2k. yellow, red and black 15 15
1087 – 3k. multicoloured . . . 20 15
1088 – 25k. multicoloured . . . 65 20
1089 – 163k. multicoloured . . 3·25 1·40

DESIGNS (stencils for)—VERT: 2k. Pagoda doors; 3k. Pagoda walls. HORIZ: 25k. Pagoda pillars; 163k. Skirts.

229 Dove and Figures **230** Stork-billed Kingfisher

1988. 125th Anniv of Red Cross Movement. Multicoloured.

1090 4k. Type **229** 15 15
1091 52k. Red Cross workers with handicapped people 1·20 50
1092 144k. Red Cross worker vaccinating baby (horiz) 4·00 1·60

1988. Birds. Multicoloured.

1093 6k. Type **230** 15 15
1094 10k. Japanese quail 20 15
1095 13k. Blossom-headed parakeet 30 15
1096 44k. Orange-breasted green pigeon 65 20
1097 63k. Black-crested bulbul . . 1·30 45
1098 64k. Mountain imperial pigeon . . . . 1·50 50

231 Red Cross Workers loading Supplies into Pirogue

1988. Completion of 1st Five Year Plan. Multicoloured.

1099 20k. Type **231** 50 20
1100 40k. Library 90 35
1101 50k. Irrigating fields . . . . 1·30 50
1102 100k. Improvement in communications . . . . . 2·20 1·00

232 Ruy Lopez Segura

1988. Chess Masters. Multicoloured.
1103 1k. Type **232** 15 15
1104 2k. Karl Anderssen 15 15
1105 3k. Paul Morphy (wrongly inscr "Murphy") 15 15
1106 6k. Wilhelm Steinitz 20 15
1107 7k. Emanuel Lasker 30 15
1108 12k. Jose Raul Capablanca 45 20
1109 172k. Aleksandr Alekhine 4·00 1·00

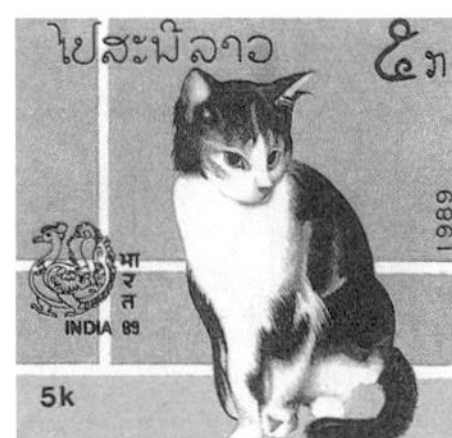

233 Tortoiseshell and White

1989. "India 89" International Stamp Exhibition, New Delhi. Cats. Multicoloured.
1110 5k. Type **233** 15 15
1111 6k. Brown tabby 15 15
1112 10k. Black and white . . . 35 15
1113 20k. Red tabby 60 15
1114 50k. Black . . . . 1·20 35
1115 172k. Silver tabby and white 4·00 90

234 Gunboat, Tank, Soldiers and Flags

1989. 40th Anniv of People's Army. Multicoloured.
1117 1k. Type **234** 15 15
1118 2k. Soldier teaching mathematics (vert) 15 15
1119 3k. Army medics vaccinating civilians 15 15
1120 250k. Peasant, revolutionary, worker and soldiers . . . . 6·75 95

235 Footballers

1989. World Cup Football Championship, Italy (1990) (1st issue). Multicoloured.
1121 10k. Type **235** 20 15
1122 15k. Footballer looking to pass ball 30 15
1123 20k. Ball hitting player on chest 45 15
1124 25k. Tackle 60 20
1125 45k. Dribbling ball 90 30
1126 105k. Kicking ball . . . . . 2·40 75
See also Nos. 1168/73.

236 Couple planting Sapling

1989. Preserve Forests Campaign. Multicoloured.
1128 4k. Type **236** 15 15
1129 10k. Burning and fallen trees 20 15
1130 12k. Man felling tree (vert) 20 20
1131 200k. Trees on map (vert) 4·50 90

237 Camilo Cienfuegos, Fidel Castro and Flag

238 Skaters

1989. 30th Anniv of Cuban Revolution. Multicoloured.
1132 45k. Type **237** . . . . . . 1·10 35
1133 50d. Cuban and Laotian flags . . . . 1·10 35

1989. Winter Olympic Games, Albertville (1992) (1st issue). Figure Skating. Multicoloured.
1134 9k. Type **238** 20 15
1135 10k. Pair (horiz) 30 15
1136 15k. Ice dancing 45 15
1137 24k. Female skater 50 20
1138 29k. Pair 65 20
1139 114k. Male skater . . . . . 2·75 90
See also Nos. 1196/1201, 1237/41 and 1276/80.

239 High Jumping

241 Sapodillas

240 "Poor on Seashore"

1989. Olympic Games, Barcelona (1992) (1st issue). Multicoloured.
1141 5k. Type **239** 15 15
1142 15k. Gymnastics 30 15
1143 20k. Cycling (horiz) 45 20
1144 25k. Boxing (horiz) 50 30
1145 70k. Archery . . . . 1·30 50
1146 120k. Swimming . . . . . 2·75 60
See also Nos. 1179/84, 1231/5 and 1282/6.

1989. "Philexfrance '89" International Stamp Exhibition, Paris. Paintings by Picasso. Mult.
1148 5k. Type **240** 15 15
1149 7k. "Motherhood" 20 15
1150 8k. "Portrait of Jaime S. le Bock" 20 15
1151 9k. "Harlequins" 45 20
1152 105k. "Boy with Dog" . . . 2·75 60
1153 114k. "Girl on Ball" . . . . 2·75 75

1989. Fruits. Multicoloured.
1155 5k. Type **241** 15 15
1156 20k. Sugar-apples 50 20
1157 20k. Guavas 50 20
1158 30k. Durians 75 30
1159 50k. Pomegranates . . . . 1·30 45
1160 172k. "Moridica charautia" 4·50 90

242 Sikhotabong Temple, Khammouane

243 Nehru and Woman

1989. Temples. Multicoloured.
1161 5k. Type **242** 15 15
1162 15k. Dam Temple, Vientiane 30 20
1163 61k. Ing Hang Temple, Savannakhet . . . . . . 1·20 50
1164 161k. Ho Vay Phra Luang Temple, Vientiane . . . . 3·75 1·00

1989. Birth Centenary of Jawaharlal Nehru (Indian statesman). Multicoloured.
1165 1k. Type **243** 15 15
1166 60k. Nehru and group of children (horiz) . . . . . 1·30 45
1167 200k. Boy garlanding Nehru 4·50 1·00

244 Footballer

1990. World Cup Football Championship, Italy (2nd issue).
1168 **244** 10k. multicoloured . . . 20 15
1169 – 15k. multicoloured . . . 30 15
1170 – 20k. multicoloured . . . 45 15
1171 – 25k. multicoloured . . . 50 20
1172 – 45k. multicoloured . . . 95 30
1173 – 105k. multicoloured . . 2·40 75
DESIGNS: 15 to 105k. Different footballing scenes.

245 Teacher and Adult Class

1990. International Literacy Year. Multicoloured.
1175 10k. Type **245** 20 15
1176 50k. Woman teaching child (vert) . . . . 1·20 65
1177 60k. Monk teaching adults 1·30 45
1178 150k. Group reading and writing under tree . . . . 3·25 1·00

246 Basketball

1990. Olympic Games, Barcelona (1992) (2nd issue). Multicoloured.
1179 10k. Type **246** 20 15
1180 30k. Hurdling 60 15
1181 45k. High jumping 95 20
1182 50k. Cycling . . . . 1·20 30
1183 60k. Throwing the javelin 1·30 45
1184 90k. Tennis . . . . 2·20 75

247 Great Britain 1840 Penny Black and Mail Coach

1990. "Stamp World London 90" International Stamp Exhibition. Multicoloured.
1186 15k. Type **247** 30 15
1187 20k. U.S 1847 5c. stamp and early steam locomotive 45 20
1188 40k. France 1849 20c. stamp and mail balloons, Paris, 1870 . . . . 90 20
1189 50k. Sardinia 1851 5c. stamp and post rider . . . . . 1·00 30
1190 60k. Indo-China 1892 1c. stamp and elephant . . . 1·30 45
1191 100k. Spain 1850 6c. stamp and Spanish galleon . . . 1·90 65

248 Ho Chi Minh addressing Crowd

1990. Birth Centenary of Ho Chi Minh. Mult.
1193 40k. Type **248** . . . . . . 1·00 45
1194 60k. Ho Chi Minh and Laotian President . . . . 1·60 60
1195 160k. Ho Chi Minh and Vietnamese flag (vert) . . 4·50 1·60

249 Speed Skating

1990. Winter Olympic Games, Albertville (1992) (2nd issue). Multicoloured.
1196 10k. Type **249** 20 15
1197 25k. Cross-country skiing (vert) 50 15
1198 30k. Downhill skiing . . . 60 20
1199 35k. Tobogganing 90 20
1200 80k. Figure skating (pairs) (vert) . . . . 1·60 50
1201 90k. Biathlon . . . . 2·10 60

250 That Luang, 1990

1990. 430th Anniv of That Luang. Multicoloured.
1203 60k. That Luang, 1867 (horiz) . . . . 1·60 45
1204 70k. That Luang, 1930 (horiz) . . . . 2·20 60
1205 130k. Type **250** . . . . . 3·75 1·00

251 Parson Bird

1990. "New Zealand 1990" International Stamp Exhibition, Auckland. Multicoloured.
1206 10k. Type **251** 20 15
1207 15k. Eurasian sky lark . . . 30 15
1208 20k. Oystercatcher 45 20
1209 50k. Variable cormorant . . 1·30 30
1210 60k. Great Reef heron . . . 1·50 45
1211 100k. Brown kiwi . . . . . 2·75 75

252 Brown-antlered Deer

1990. Mammals. Multicoloured.
1213 10k. Type **252** 20 15
1214 20k. Gaur 45 15
1215 40k. Wild water buffalo . . 95 20
1216 45k. Kouprey . . . . 1·10 30
1217 120k. Javan rhinoceros . . . 2·75 90

253 Surgeons Operating

1990. 40th Anniv of United Nations Development Programme. Multicoloured.
1218 30k. Type **253** 90 30
1219 45k. Fishermen inspecting catch . . . . 1·50 30
1220 80k. Air-traffic controller (vert) . . . . 2·20 90
1221 90k. Electricity plant workers . . . . 2·50 1·20

254 Rice Ceremony

1990. New Year. Multicoloured.
1222 5k. Type **254** 20 15
1223 10k. Elephant in carnival parade 30 15
1224 50k. Making offerings at temple . . . . 1·10 30
1225 150k. Family ceremony . . 3·25 1·10

255 Memorial, Wreath and Eternal Flame

1990. 15th National Day Festival. Multicoloured.
1226 15k. Type **255** 45 20
1227 20k. Celebration parade . . 65 45
1228 80k. Hospital visit . . . . . 2·20 90
1229 120k. Girls parading with banner . . . . 3·25 1·20

257 Two-man Kayak

1991. Olympic Games, Barcelona (1992) (3rd issue). Multicoloured.
1231 22k. Type **257** 15 15
1232 32k. Canoeing 15 15
1233 285k. Diving (vert) 90 20
1234 330k. Racing dinghies (vert) 1·10 30
1235 1000k. Swimming . . . . . 2·75 90

258 Bobsleighing

1991. Winter Olympic Games, Albertville (1992) (3rd issue). Multicoloured.
1237 32k. Type **258** 15 15
1238 135k. Cross-country skiing (horiz) 45 15
1239 250k. Ski jumping (horiz) 75 20
1240 275k. Biathlon (horiz) . . . 90 30
1241 900k. Speed skating (horiz) 2·75 90

259 Pha Pheng Falls, Champassak

1991. Tourism. Multicoloured.
1243 155k. Type **259** 50 20
1244 220k. Pha Tang mountains, Vangvieng 75 30
1245 235k. Tat Set waterfall, Saravane (vert) 90 50
1246 1000k. Plain of Jars, Xieng Khouang (vert) . . . . . 3·50 1·10

260 Match Scene

1991. World Cup Football Championship, U.S.A. (1994) (1st issue). Multicoloured.
1247 32k. Type **260** 15 15
1248 330k. Goalkeeper catching ball 95 20
1249 340k. Player controlling ball (vert) . . . . 1·20 20
1250 400k. Player dribbling ball 1·50 30
1251 500k. Tackle . . . . 1·80 75
See also Nos. 1292/6, 1370/4 and 1386/90.

261 Planting Saplings

1991. National Tree Planting Day. Multicoloured.
1253 350k. Type **261** 75 30
1254 700k. Planting saplings (different) . . . . 2·20 75
1255 800k. Removing saplings from store . . . . 2·50 1·10

262 "Mallard", 1938, Great Britain

1991. "Espamer '91" Spain–Latin America Stamp Exhibition, Buenos Aires. Railway Locomotives. Multicoloured.
1256 25k. Type **262** 15 15
1257 32k. Class 4500 steam locomotive, France (inscr "Pacific 231") 20 15
1258 285k. Streamlined steam locomotive, U.S.A. . . . 95 30
1259 650k. Canadian Pacific Class T1b steam locomotive, 1938 . . . . 1·90 65
1260 750k. East African Railways Class 59 steam locomotive, 1955 . . . . 2·75 95

263 Spindle Festival

1991. Traditional Music. Multicoloured.
1262 20k. Type **263** 15 15
1263 220k. Mong player (vert) . . 65 20
1264 275k. Siphandone singer (vert) 75 30
1265 545k. Khap ngum singer . . 1·80 65
1266 690k. Phouthaydam dance 2·20 90

264 Great Purple

1991. "Phila Nippon '91" International Stamp Exhibition, Tokyo. Butterflies. Multicoloured.
1267 55k. Type **264** 20 15
1268 90k. "Luehdorfia puziloi" (wrongly inscr "Luendorfia") 30 15
1269 255k. "Papilio bianor" . . . 90 20
1270 285k. Swallowtail . . . . . 1·00 30
1271 900k. Mikado swallowtail 3·00 90

265 Emblem and Pattern **266** Bobsleighing

1991. International Decade for Cultural Development (1988–97). Multicoloured.
1273 285k. Type **265** 75 30
1274 330k. Emblem and drum . . 90 30
1275 1000k. Emblem and pipes 2·75 1·10

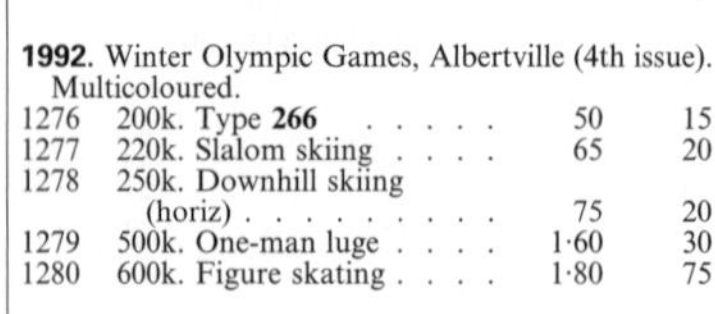

1992. Winter Olympic Games, Albertville (4th issue). Multicoloured.
1276 200k. Type **266** 50 15
1277 220k. Slalom skiing 65 20
1278 250k. Downhill skiing (horiz) 75 20
1279 500k. One-man luge . . . . 1·60 30
1280 600k. Figure skating . . . . 1·80 75

267 Running **269** Argentinian and Italian Players and Flags

268 Pest Control

1992. Olympic Games, Barcelona (4th issue). Multicoloured.
1282 32k. Type **267** 15 15
1283 245k. Baseball 65 20
1284 275k. Tennis 90 20
1285 285k. Basketball 90 30
1286 900k. Boxing (horiz) . . . . 3·00 75

1992. World Health Day. Multicoloured.
1288 200k. Type **268** 60 20
1289 255k. Anti-smoking campaign 65 30
1290 330k. Donating blood . . . 95 60
1291 1000k. Vaccinating child (vert) . . . . 3·00 1·20

1992. World Cup Football Championship, U.S.A. (1994) (2nd issue). Multicoloured.
1292 260k. Type **269** 60 15
1293 305k. German and English players and flags 80 20
1294 310k. United States flag, ball and trophy 90 30
1295 350k. Italian and English players and flags . . . . 1·30 45
1296 800k. German and Argentinian players and flags . . . . 2·75 90

270 Common Cobra

1992. Snakes. Multicoloured.
1298 280k. Type **270** 80 20
1299 295k. Common cobra . . . 80 20
1300 420k. Wagler's pit viper . . 1·30 30
1301 700k. King cobra (vert) . . 2·75 90

271 Doorway and Ruins

1992. Restoration of Wat Phou. Multicoloured.
1302 185k. Type **271** 60 35
1303 220k. Doorway (different) 65 35
1304 1200k. Doorway with collapsed porch (horiz) . . 4·00 1·60

272 "Pinta" and Juan Martinez's Map

1992. "Genova '92" International Thematic Stamp Exhibition. Multicoloured.
1305 100k. Type **272** 20 15
1306 300k. Piri Reis's letter and caravelle (vert) 90 20
1307 350k. Magellan's ship and Paolo del Pozo Toscanelli's world map . . 1·20 20
1308 400k. Gabriel de Vallesca's map and Vasco da Gama's flagship "Sao Gabriel" . . . . 1·30 45
1309 455k. Juan Martinez's map and Portuguese four-masted caravel . . . . . 1·60 65

273 Woman in Traditional Costume **274** Boy Drumming

1992. Traditional Costumes of Laotian Mountain Villages.
1311 **273** 25k. multicoloured . . . 15 15
1312 – 55k. multicoloured . . . 20 15
1313 – 400k. multicoloured . . 1·30 45
1314 – 1200k. multicoloured . . 4·00 1·20
DESIGNS: 55 to 1200k. Different costumes.

1992. International Children's Day. Children at Play. Multicoloured.
1315 220k. Type **274** 60 20
1316 285k. Girls skipping (horiz) 80 20
1317 330k. Boys racing on stilts 1·20 30
1318 400k. Girls playing "escape" game (horiz) . . . . . . 1·50 60

275 Praying before Buddha

276 Crested Gibbon

1992. National Customs. Multicoloured.
1319 100k. Type **275** 30 15
1320 140k. Wedding (horiz) . . . 45 20
1321 160k. Religious procession (horiz) 75 20
1322 1500k. Monks receiving alms (horiz) . . . . . . 4·75 2·20

1992. Climbing Mammals. Multicoloured.
1323 10k. Type **276** 20 15
1324 100k. Variegated langur . . 30 20
1325 250k. Pileated gibbon . . . 80 30
1326 430k. Francois's monkey . . 1·50 45
1327 800k. Lesser slow loris . . . 3·00 80

277 New York

1993. 130th Anniv of Underground Railway Systems. Multicoloured.
1328 15k. Type **277** 15 15
1329 50k. West Berlin 20 15
1330 100k. Paris 30 20
1331 200k. London 80 30
1332 900k. Moscow 3·00 1·20

278 Malayan Bullfrog

1993. Amphibians. Multicoloured.
1334 55k. Type **278** 20 15
1335 90k. Muller's clawed frog 30 15
1336 100k. Glass frog (vert) 45 20
1337 185k. Giant toad 65 30
1338 1200k. Common tree frog (vert) 4·00 1·20

279 Common Tree-shrew **280** Noble Scallop

1993. Mammals. Multicoloured.
1339 45k. Type **279** 20 15
1340 60k. Philippine flying lemur 20 15
1341 120k. Loris 45 20
1342 500k. Eastern tarsier 1·60 65
1343 600k. Giant gibbon 1·90 1·20

1993. Molluscs. Multicoloured.
1344 20k. Type **280** 15 15
1345 30k. Precious wentletrap 15 15
1346 70k. Spider conch 30 20
1347 500k. Aulicus cone 1·60 65
1348 1000k. Milleped spider conch 3·00 1·20

281 Drugs and Skull smoking

1993. Anti-drugs Campaign. Multicoloured.
1349 200k. Type **281** 65 30
1350 430k. Burning seized drugs 1·40 60
1351 900k. Instructing on dangers of drugs 3·00 1·20

282 House **283** Greater Spotted Eagle

1993. Traditional Houses. Multicoloured.
1352 32k. Type **282** 15 15
1353 200k. Thatched house with gable end (horiz) 75 20
1354 650k. Thatched house (horiz) 1·90 60
1355 750k. House with tiled roof (horiz) 2·40 1·20

1993. Birds of Prey. Multicoloured.
1356 10k. Type **283** 15 15
1357 100k. Spotted little owl 45 20
1358 330k. Pied harrier (horiz) 1·60 45
1359 1000k. Short-toed eagle 4·00 1·30

284 Fighting Forest Fire

1993. Environmental Protection. Multicoloured.
1360 32k. Type **284** 15 15
1361 40k. Wildlife on banks of River Mekong 15 15
1362 260k. Paddy fields 90 30
1363 1100k. Oxen in river 4·00 1·20

285 "Narathura atosia"

1993. "Bangkok 1993" International Stamp Exhibition. Butterflies. Multicoloured.
1364 35k. Type **285** 15 15
1365 80k. "Parides philoxenus" 20 15
1366 150k. "Euploea harrisi" 45 20
1367 220k. Yellow orange-tip 65 30
1368 500k. Female common palm fly 1·90 80

286 Footballer

1993. World Cup Football Championship, U.S.A. (3rd issue). Multicoloured.
1370 10k. Type **286** 15 15
1371 20k. Brazil player 15 15
1372 285k. Uruguay player 80 20
1373 400k. Germany player 1·40 45
1374 800k. Forward challenging goalkeeper 2·75 1·20

287 Hesperornis

1994. Prehistoric Birds. Multicoloured.
1376 10k. Type **287** 15 15
1377 20k. Mauritius dodo 15 15
1378 150k. Archaeopteryx 60 20
1379 600k. Phororhachos 1·80 45
1380 700k. Giant moa 2·50 90

288 Olympic Flag and Flame **289** Bridge and National Flags

1994. Centenary of International Olympic Committee. Multicoloured.
1382 100k. Type **288** 30 15
1383 250k. Ancient Greek athletes (horiz) 80 20
1384 1000k. Pierre de Coubertin (founder) and modern athlete 3·50 1·40

1994. Opening of Friendship Bridge between Laos and Thailand.
1385 **289** 500k. multicoloured 1·90 1·20

290 World Map and Players

1994. World Cup Football Championship, U.S.A. (4th issue).
1386 **290** 40k. multicoloured 15 15
1387 – 50k. multicoloured 20 15
1388 – 60k. multicoloured 20 15
1389 – 320k. multicoloured 1·20 45
1390 – 900k. multicoloured 3·50 1·20
DESIGNS: 50 to 900k. Different players on world map.

291 Pagoda

1994. Pagodas.
1392 **291** 30k. multicoloured 15 15
1393 – 150k. multicoloured 45 20
1394 – 380k. multicoloured 1·20 30
1395 – 1100k. multicoloured 3·50 1·20
DESIGNS: 150 to 1100k. Different gabled roofs.

292 Bear eating

1994. The Malay Bear. Multicoloured.
1396 50k. Type **292** 35 15
1397 90k. Bear's head 80 20
1398 200k. Adult and cub 1·80 30
1399 220k. Bear 1·90 45

293 Grass Snake

1994. Amphibians and Reptiles. Multicoloured.
1400 70k. Type **293** 20 15
1401 80k. Tessellated snake 20 15
1402 90k. Fire salamander 30 15
1403 600k. Alpine newt 1·90 60
1404 800k. Green lizard (vert) 2·50 1·20

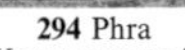
294 Phra Xayavoraman 7 **295** Family supporting Healthy Globe

1994. Buddhas. Multicoloured.
1406 15k. Type **294** 15 15
1407 280k. Phra Thong Souk 90 30
1408 390k. Phra Manolom 1·30 45
1409 800k. Phra Ongtu 2·50 1·20

1994. International Year of the Family. Multicoloured.
1410 200k. Type **295** 65 30
1411 500k. Mother taking child to school (horiz) 1·60 80
1412 700k. Mother and children 2·40 1·20

296 Kong Hang

1994. Traditional Laotian Drums. Multicoloured.
1414 370k. Type **296** 1·30 35
1415 440k. Kong Leng (portable drum) 1·50 45
1416 450k. Kong Toum (drum on stand) 1·50 45
1417 600k. Kong Phene (hanging drum) 2·10 65

297 Elephant in Procession

1994. Ceremonial Elephants. Multicoloured.
1418 140k. Type **297** 45 20
1419 400k. Elephant in pavilion 1·30 80
1420 890k. Elephant in street procession (vert) 2·75 1·30

298 Theropodes

1994. Prehistoric Animals. Multicoloured.
1421 50k. Type **298** 20 15
1422 380k. Iguanodontides 1·80 60
1423 420k. Sauropodes 2·10 65

299 Playing Musical Instruments

1995. 20th Anniv of World Tourism Organization. Multicoloured.
1424 60k. Type **299** 20 15
1425 250k. Women dancing 80 20
1426 400k. Giving alms to monks 1·30 45
1427 650k. Waterfall (vert) 1·80 80

300 Trachodon **302** Children and Emblem

301 Indian Jungle Mynah

1995. Prehistoric Animals. Multicoloured.
1429 50k. Type **300** 15 15
1430 70k. Protoceratops 15 15
1431 300k. Brontosaurus 80 30
1432 400k. Stegosaurus 1·10 45
1433 600k. Tyrannosaurus 1·80 65

1995. Birds. Multicoloured.
1434 50k. Type **301** 15 15
1435 150k. Jerdon's starling 45 15
1436 300k. Common mynah 90 35
1437 700k. Southern grackle 1·90 80

1995. 25th Anniv of Francophonie. Multicoloured.
1438 50k. Type **302** 15 15
1439 380k. Golden roof decorations 1·20 60
1440 420k. Map 1·30 65

303 Pole Vaulting **304** Chalice

1995. Olympic Games, Atlanta, U.S.A. (1st issue). Multicoloured.

1441 60k. Type **303** 15 15
1442 80k. Throwing the javelin 20 15
1443 200k. Throwing the hammer 60 20
1444 350k. Long jumping 1·00 35
1445 700k. High jumping 2·10 80

See also Nos. 1484/9.

1995. Antique Vessels. Multicoloured.

1447 70k. Type **304** 15 15
1448 200k. Resin and silver bowl (horiz) 50 20
1449 450k. Geometrically decorated bowl (horiz) 1·30 50
1450 600k. Religious chalice (horiz) 1·80 65

305 Procession

1995. Rocket Festival. Multicoloured.

1451 80k. Launching rocket (vert) 20 15
1452 160k. Type **305** 45 15
1453 500k. Musicians in procession 1·40 50
1454 700k. Crowds and rockets 2·10 80

306 Red Tabby Longhair

1995. Cats. Multicoloured.

1455 40k. Type **306** 15 15
1456 50k. Siamese sealpoint 20 15
1457 250k. Red tabby longhair (different) 80 20
1458 400k. Tortoiseshell shorthair 1·30 30
1459 650k. Head of tortoiseshell shorthair (vert) 1·60 65

307 "Nepenthes villosa"

1995. Insectivorous Plants. Multicoloured.

1461 90k. Type **307** 20 15
1462 100k. "Dionaea muscipula" 30 15
1463 350k. "Sarracenia flava" 1·00 30
1464 450k. "Sarracenia purpurea" 1·30 30
1465 500k. "Nepenthes ampullaria" 1·50 60

308 Stag Beetle

1995. Insects. Multicoloured.

1467 40k. Type **308** 15 15
1468 50k. May beetle 20 15
1469 500k. Blue carpenter beetle 1·40 45
1470 800k. Great green grasshopper 2·40 80

309 Cattle grazing

1995. 50th Anniv of F.A.O. Multicoloured.

1471 80k. Type **309** 20 15
1472 300k. Working paddy-field 90 45
1473 1000k. Agriculture 3·00 1·20

310 At Meeting

1995. 50th Anniv of U.N.O. Peoples of Different Races. Multicoloured.

1474 290k. Type **310** 80 35
1475 310k. Playing draughts 90 45
1476 440k. Children playing 1·40 65

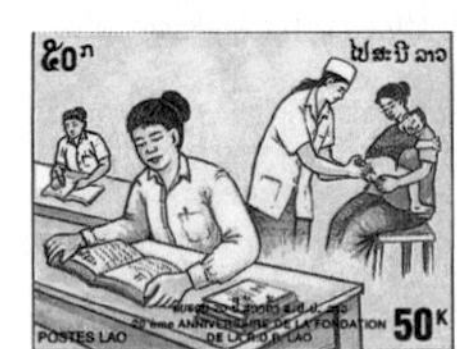

311 Students and Nurse vaccinating Child

1995. 20th Anniv of Republic. Multicoloured.

1477 50k. Type **311** 15 15
1478 280k. Agricultural land 80 45
1479 600k. Bridge 1·80 90

312 Mong

1996. Traditional New Year Customs. Multicoloured.

1480 50k. Type **312** 15 15
1481 280k. Phouthai 90 30
1482 380k. Ten Xe 1·20 45
1483 420k. Lao Loum 1·30 45

313 Cycling

1996. Olympic Games, Atlanta, U.S.A. (2nd issue). Multicoloured.

1484 30k. Type **313** 15 15
1485 150k. Football 30 15
1486 200k. Basketball (vert) 45 20
1487 300k. Running (vert) 65 30
1488 500k. Shooting 1·20 60

314 Sun Bear

1996. Animals. Multicoloured.

1490 40k. Type **314** 15 15
1491 60k. Grey pelican 15 15
1492 200k. Leopard 45 20
1493 250k. Swallowtail 60 30
1494 700k. Indian python 1·50 80

315 Weaving

1996. International Women's Year. Multicoloured.

1495 20k. Type **315** 15 15
1496 290k. Physical training instructress 65 30
1497 1000k. Woman feeding child (vert) 2·20 1·10

316 Rat **317** Players

1996. New Year. Year of the Rat.

1498 **316** 50k. multicoloured 15 15
1499 – 340k. multicoloured 1·20 60
1500 – 350k. multicoloured 1·30 60
1501 – 370k. multicoloured 1·30 65

DESIGNS: 340k. to 370k. Different rats.

1996. World Cup Football Championship, France (1998) (1st issue).

1502 **317** 20k. multicoloured 15 15
1503 – 50k. multicoloured 15 15
1504 – 300k. multicoloured 65 30
1505 – 400k. multicoloured 90 45
1506 – 500k. multicoloured 1·10 50

DESIGNS: 50k. to 500k. Different footballing scenes.

See also Nos. 1589/94.

318 Village Women grinding Rice

1996. Children's Drawings. Multicoloured.

1508 180k. Type **318** 65 30
1509 230k. Women picking fruit 80 35
1510 310k. Village women preparing food 1·10 50
1511 370k. Women tending vegetable crops 1·30 65

319 Morane Monoplane

1996. "Capex'96" International Stamp Exhibition, Toronto, Canada. Aircraft. Multicoloured.

1512 25k. Type **319** 15 15
1513 60k. Sopwith Camel biplane 15 15
1514 150k. De Havilland D.H.4 biplane 30 15
1515 250k. Albatros biplane 50 30
1516 800k. Caudron biplane 1·80 90

320 Front View

1996. Ox-carts. Multicoloured.

1517 50k. Type **320** 15 10
1518 100k. Side view 20 15
1519 440k. Oxen pulling cart 1·00 50

321 "Dendrobium secundum" **322** White Horse

1996. Orchids. Multicoloured.

1520 50k. Type **321** 15 15
1521 200k. "Ascocentrum miniatum" 45 20
1522 500k. "Aerides multiflorum" 1·10 60
1523 520k. "Dendrobium aggregatum" 1·30 60

1996. Saddle Horses. Multicoloured.

1524 50k. Type **322** 15 15
1525 80k. Horse with red and black bridle 15 15
1526 200k. Bay horse with white bridle and reins 45 20
1527 400k. Horse with red and yellow cords braided into mane 90 45
1528 600k. Chestnut horse with white blaze 1·30 65

323 Pupils displaying Slates to Teacher

1996. 50th Anniv of UNICEF. Multicoloured.

1530 200k. Type **323** 65 30
1531 500k. Mother breastfeeding (vert) 1·80 80
1532 600k. Woman drawing water at public well 2·10 1·10

324 Leatherback Turtle

1996. 25th Anniv of Greenpeace (environmental organization). Turtles. Multicoloured.

1533 150k. Type **324** 50 20
1534 250k. Leatherback turtle at water's edge 90 45
1535 400k. Hawksbill turtle 1·50 75
1536 450k. "Chelonia agassizi" 1·60 80

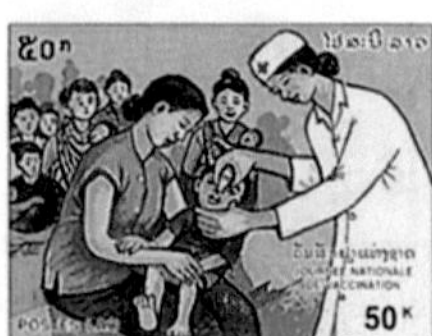

325 Oral Vaccination

1997. National Vaccination Day. Multicoloured.

1537 50k. Type **325** 15 15
1538 340k. Nurse injecting child's leg 1·20 60
1539 370k. Nurse pushing child in wheelchair 1·30 65

326 George Stephenson and "Pioneer", 1836

1997. Steam Railway Locomotives. Multicoloured.

1540 100k. "Kinnaird", 1846 (44 × 27 mm) 20 15
1541 200k. Type **326** 45 20
1542 300k. Robert Stephenson and long-boiler express locomotive, 1848 65 30
1543 400k. Stephenson locomotive "Adler", 1835, Germany 90 45
1544 500k. "Lord of the Isles", 1851–84 1·20 60
1545 600k. "The Columbine", 1845 1·40 65

The 200 and 300k. are wrongly inscr "Stepheson".

327 Pseudoryx lying down

1997. Pseudoryx (Saola). Multicoloured.

1547	350k. Type **327**	1·30	1·30
1548	380k. Grazing (vert)	1·40	1·40
1549	420k. Scratching with hind leg	1·50	1·50

328 Masked Lovebirds ("Agapornis personata") **330** Steaming Rice

329 Signs of the Chinese Zodiac

1997. Lovebirds. Multicoloured.

1550	50k. Type **328**	15	15
1551	150k. Grey-headed lovebird ("Agapornis cana")	30	15
1552	200k. Nyasa lovebirds ("Agapornis lilianae")	45	20
1553	400k. Fischer's lovebirds ("Agapornis fischeri")	90	45
1554	500k. Black-cheeked lovebirds ("Agapornis nigregenis")	1·10	60
1555	800k. Peach-faced lovebird ("Agapornis roseicollis")	1·90	90

1997. New Year. Year of the Ox. Multicoloured.

1557	50k. Type **329**	15	15
1558	300k. Woman riding ox (vert)	1·20	1·20
1559	440k. Ox on float in procession	1·60	1·60

1997. Food Preparation. Multicoloured.

1560	50k. Type **330**	15	15
1561	340k. Water containers (horiz)	75	35
1562	370k. Table laid with meal (horiz)	80	35

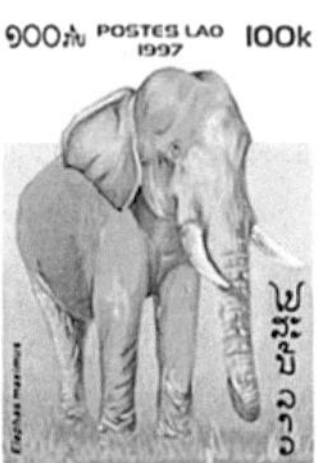
331 "Vanda roeblingiana" **332** Indian Elephant ("Elephas maximus")

1997. Orchids. Multicoloured.

1563	50k. Type **331**	15	15
1564	100k. "Dendrobium findleyanum"	20	15
1565	150k. "Dendrobium crepidatum"	30	15
1566	250k. "Sarcanthus birmanicus"	50	30
1567	400k. "Cymbidium lowianum"	90	45
1568	1000k. "Dendrobium gratiosissimum"	2·40	1·10

1997. Elephants. Multicoloured.

1570	100k. Type **332**	20	15
1571	250k. Indian elephant carrying log (horiz)	50	30
1572	300k. Indian elephant with young (horiz)	65	30
1573	350k. African elephant ("Loxodonta africana") (horiz)	80	35
1574	450k. African elephant in water (horiz)	1·00	50
1575	550k. African elephant with ears flapping	1·30	60

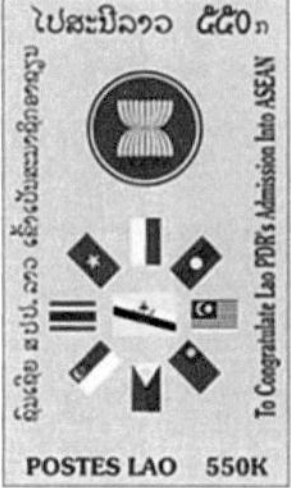

333 Emblem and Brunei Flag **336** Players

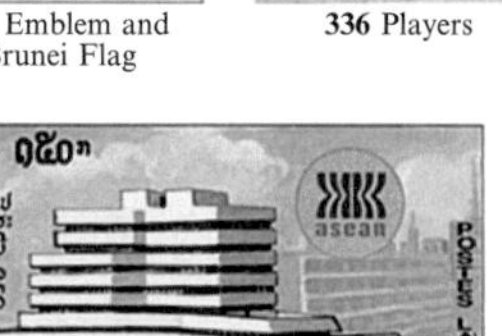
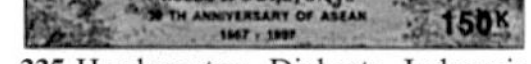
335 Headquarters, Djakarta, Indonesia

1997. Admission of Laos into Association of South East Asian Nations. Members' flags, centre flag given.

1577	550k. Type **333**	80	80
1578	550k. Indonesia (red and white bands)	80	80
1579	550k. Laos (red, blue with white circle, red bands)	80	80
1580	550k. Malaysia (crescent and star on blue quarter, red and white stripes)	80	80
1581	550k. Myanmar (flower and stars on blue quarter, red)	80	80
1582	550k. Philippines (sun and stars on white triangle, blue and red bands)	80	80
1583	550k. Singapore (crescent and five stars on red band, white band)	80	80
1584	550k. Thailand (red, white, blue, red bands)	80	80
1585	550k. Vietnam (yellow star on red)	80	80

1997. 30th Anniv of Association of South East Asian Nations. Multicoloured.

1587	150k. Type **335**	60	60
1588	600k. Map of Laos and state flag	2·50	2·50

1997. World Cup Football Championship, France (1998) (2nd issue).

1589 **336**	100k. multicoloured	20	15
1590 –	200k. multicoloured	45	20
1591 –	250k. multicoloured	50	30
1592 –	300k. multicoloured	65	30
1593 –	350k. multicoloured	80	35
1594 –	700k. multicoloured	1·50	75

DESIGNS: 200k. to 700k. Various football scenes.

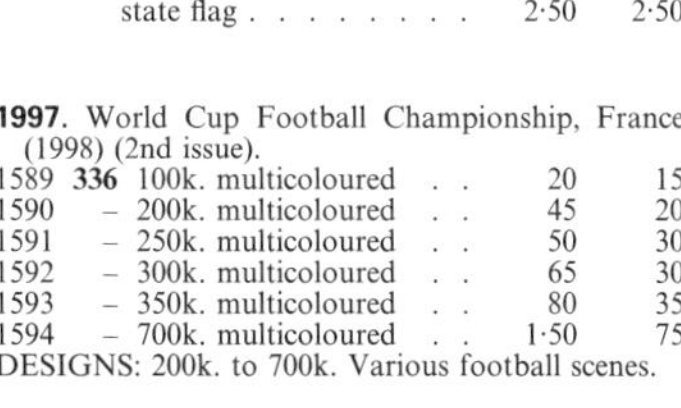

337 Phoenician Nef

1997. Sailing Ships. Multicoloured.

1596	50k. Type **337**	15	15
1597	100k. 13th-century nef	20	15
1598	150k. 15th-century nef	30	15
1599	200k. 16th-century Portuguese caravel	45	20
1600	400k. 17th-century Dutch ship	90	45
1601	900k. H.M.S. "Victory" (Nelson's flagship)	2·10	1·00

338 Headdress

1997. Headdresses and Masks. Multicoloured.

1603	50k. Type **338**	15	15
1604	100k. Headdress with flower at left	20	15
1605	150k. Mask with curved tusks (horiz)	30	15
1606	200k. Mask tipped with headdress decorated with two faces	50	20
1607	350k. Mask with green face	75	35

339 Two Pirogues

1997. Pirogue Race. Multicoloured.

1608	50k. Type **339**	15	15
1609	100k. Crowd cheering competitors from land	20	15
1610	300k. Side view of two competing pirogues	65	30
1611	500k. People cheering on spectator boat	1·10	50

340 Sunken Net

1998. Traditional Fishing Methods. Multicoloured.

1612	50k. Type **340**	15	15
1613	100k. Fisherman throwing net (horiz)	30	30
1614	450k. Funnel net	1·40	1·40
1615	650k. Lobster pots (horiz)	1·90	1·90

341 Man riding Tiger

1998. New Year. Year of the Tiger.

1616 **341**	150k. multicoloured	60	60
1617	350k. multicoloured	1·40	1·40
1618	400k. multicoloured	1·80	1·80

342 Wat Sisaket Shrine **344** Buddha, Luang Phabang Temple

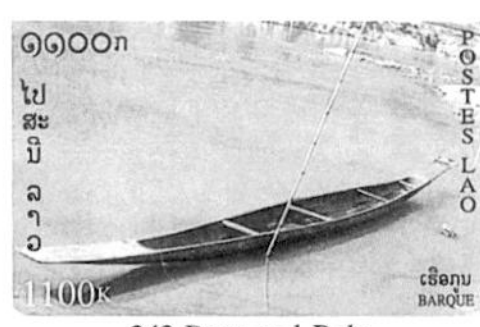
343 Boat and Pole

1998. Temples. Multicoloured.

1619	10000k. Type **342**	7·50	7·50
1620	25000k. Wat Phou temple, Pakse (horiz)	15·00	15·00
1621	45000k. That Luang (royal mausoleum) (horiz)	22·00	22·00

1998. Water Transport. Multicoloured.

1622	1100k. Type **343**	1·10	1·10
1623	1200k. Covered canoe	1·20	1·20
1624	2500k. Motorized canoe	2·50	2·50

1998.

1625 **344**	3000k. multicoloured	2·10	2·10

345 *Paphiopedilum callosum*

1998. Orchids. Multicoloured.

1626	900k. Type **345**	1·40	1·40
1627	950k. *Paphiopedilum concolor*	1·50	1·50
1628	1000k. *Dendrobium thyrsiflorum* (vert)	1·60	1·60
1629	1050k. *Dendrobium lindleyi* (vert)	1·60	1·60

346 Children in Classroom

1998. 50th Anniv of Universal Declaration of Human Rights. Multicoloured.

1630	300k. Type **346**	35	35
1631	1700k. Woman posting vote into ballot box	2·20	2·20

347 Gaeng

1998. Wind Instruments. Multicoloured.

1632	900k. Type **347**	1·30	1·30
1633	1200k. Khuoy (flute)	1·80	1·80
1634	1500k. Khaen (bamboo pipes of various lengths)	2·20	2·20

348 Military Personnel and Flag

1999. 50th Anniv of People's Army. Multicoloured.

1635	1300k. Type **348**	1·10	1·10
1636	1500k. Soldier with upraised arm and jungle fighters (vert)	1·30	1·30

349 Inscribed Monument (world heritage)

1999. UNESCO World Heritage Site. Luang Prabang. Multicoloured.

1637	400k. Type **349**	35	35
1638	1150k. House with veranda and dovecote (horiz)	95	95
1639	1250k. Wat Xiengthong (horiz)	1·00	1·00

350 Yao Children celebrating New Year, Muong Sing

1999. Tourism Year (1st issue). Multicoloured.

1640	200k. Type **350**	15	15
1641	500k. Phadeang, Vangvieng district	35	35
1642	1050k. Wat That Makmo, Luang Prabang	80	80
1643	1300k. Patuxay (victory monument), Vientiane (vert)	1·00	1·00

See also No. **MS**1653 and 1714/17.

351 Rabbit and Chinese Zodiac Animals

353 Collared Owlet (*Glaucidium brodiei*)

352 Iron Plough

1999. New Year. Year of the Rabbit. Multicoloured.
1644 1500k. Type **351** 75 75
1645 1600k. White rabbit (horiz) 1·60 1·60

1999. Traditional Farming Implements. Multicoloured.
1646 1500k. Type **352** . . . . . 1·10 1·10
1647 2000k. Harrow . . . . . . 1·50 1·50
1648 3200k. Wooden plough . . 2·40 2·40

1999. Owls and Bat. Multicoloured.
1649 900k. Type **353** 75 75
1650 1600k. Collared scops owl (*Otus lempiji*) . . . . . . 1·50 1·50
1651 2100k. Barn owl (*Tyto alba*) 2·20 2·20
1652 2800k. Black capped fruit bat (*Chironax melanocephalus*) . . . . . 3·00 3·00

354 Patuxay (victory monument), Vientiane

1999. Tourism (2nd issue). Sheet 135 × 100 mm containing T **354** and similar horiz designs.
MS1653 2500k. Type **354**; 4000k. Ho Phra Keo, Vientiane; 5500k. Wat Xieng Thong, Luang Prabang; 8000k. Pha That Luang, Vientiane 10·50 10·50

355 Envelope and Globe

1999. 125th Anniv of Universal Postal Union. Multicoloured.
1654 2600k. Type **355** . . . . . 1·80 1·80
1655 3400k. Postman delivering letter . . . . 2·50 2·50

356 Carved Tree Stump

1999. International Horticultural Exposition, Kunming, China. Exposition buildings. Multicoloured.
1656 300k. Type **356** 20 20
1657 900k. China Hall 45 45
1658 2300k. Science and Technology Hall . . . . 1·20 1·20
1659 2500k. Traditional Laotian house . . . . 1·40 1·40

357 Javan Rhino (*Rhinoceros sondaicus*)

1999. Animals. Multicoloured.
1660 700k. Type **357** 50 50
1661 900k. Water buffalo (*Bubalus bubalis*) (vert) . . 65 65
1662 1700k. Spotted linsang (*Prionodon pardicolor*) . . 1·30 1·30
1663 1800k. Sambar deer (*Cervus unicolor*) . . . . 1·30 1·30
1664 1900k. Lion (*Panthera leo*) (vert) . . . . 1·40 1·40

358 Airport and Hospital

2000. Millennium (1st issue). Multicoloured.
1665 2000k. Type **358** 75 75
1666 2000k. Temple 75 75
1667 2000k. Building with portico 75 75
1668 2000k. River and traditional buildings 75 75
MS1669 124 × 181 mm. Nos. 1665/8 3·00 3·00
Nos. 1665/8 were issued together, se-tenant, forming a composite design.
See also Nos. 1718/19.

359 Kor Loma

360 *Dendrobium draconis*

2000. Women's Regional Costumes. Multicoloured.
1670 100k. Type **359** 10 10
1671 200k. Kor Pchor 10 10
1672 500k. Nhuan Krom 15 15
1673 900k. Taidam 30 30
1674 2300k. Yao 65 65
1675 2500k. Meuy 75 75
1676 2600k. Sila 80 80
1677 2700k. Hmong 80 80
1678 2800k. Yao (different) . . . 80 80
1679 3100k. Kor Nukkuy 90 90
1680 3200k. Kor Pouxang 95 95
1681 3300k. Yao Lanten . . . . 1·00 1·00
1682 3400k. Khir . . . . 1·10 1·10
1683 3500k. Kor . . . . 1·00 1·00
1684 3900k. Hmong (different) . . 1·20 1·20

2000. Orchids. Bangkok 2000 International Stamp Exhibition (**MS**1689). Multicoloured.
1685 500k. Type **360** 15 15
1686 900k. *Paphiopedilum hirsutissimum* 30 30
1687 3000k. *Dendrobium sulcatum* 95 95
1688 3400k. *Rhynchostylis gigantean* . . . . 1·10 1·10
MS1689 111 × 145 mm. Nos. 1686/90 3·00 3·00

361 Dragon and Chinese Zodiac

2000. Year of the Dragon. Multicoloured.
1690 1800k. Type **361** 50 50
1691 2300k. Dragon swimming 75 75

362 River, Deer and Trees

2000. Children's Paintings. Multicoloured.
1692 300k. Type **362** 15 15
1693 400k. Animals running from fire 15 15
1694 2300k. Animals and birds 95 95
1695 3200k. Animals and birds (vert) . . . . 1·30 1·30

363 Peacock

2000. The Peacock. Multicoloured.
1696 700k. Type **363** 20 20
1697 1000k. With tail displayed 35 35
1698 1800k. Peahen (horiz) . . . 60 60
1699 3500k. Pair (horiz) . . . . 1·20 1·20
MS1700 146 × 110 mm. 10000k. Front showing tail displayed 3·50 3·50

364 Bridge

2000. Pakse Bridge over Mekong River. Multicoloured.
1701 900k. Type **364** 30 30
1702 2700k. Overview of bridge 95 95
1703 3200k. Bridge from right . . 1·10 1·10
MS1704 180 × 122 mm. 4000k. No. 1701; 7500k. No. 1702; 8500k. No. 1703r . . . . 6·75 6·75

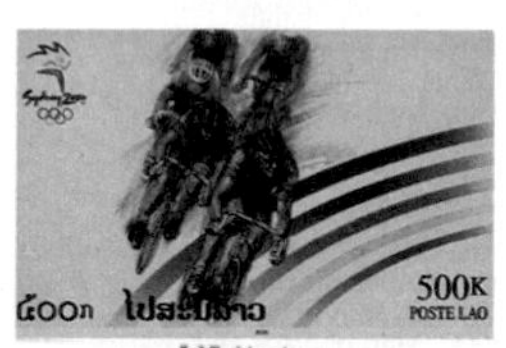

365 Cycling

2000. Olympic Games, Sydney. Multicoloured.
1705 500k. Type **365** 15 15
1706 900k. Boxing 30 30
1707 2600k. Kick boxing 90 90
1708 3600k. Canoeing . . . . . 1·30 1·30
MS1709 124 × 180 mm. Nos. 1705/8 3·25 3·25

366 Lao Theung

367 Phousy Stupa, Luang Prabang

2000. Regional Wedding Costumes. Multicoloured.
1710 800k. Type **366** 30 30
1711 2300k. Lao Lum 75 75
1712 3400k. Lao Sung . . . . . 1·20 1·20

2000. Tourism (3rd issue). Multicoloured.
1713 300k. Type **367** 15 15
1714 600k. Tham Chang cave . . 20 20
1715 2800k. Inhang Stupa . . . 1·20 1·20
1716 3300k. Buddha, Phiawal temple, Xiengkhuang . . 1·40 1·40

368 Building Facade

2000. 25th Anniv of Republic of Laos.
1717 **368** 4000k. multicoloured . . 1·30 1·30

369 Satellites and Child writing

371 Yao mane Huaphanh

370 Roadway

2001. Millennium (2nd issue). Multicoloured.
1718 3200k. Type **369** . . . . . 1·00 1·00
1719 4000k. Electricity pylons and dam . . . . 1·30 1·30

2001. Route 13 Highway Improvement Project. Sheet 120 × 190 mm containing T **370** and similar horiz designs. Multicoloured.
MS1720 4000k. Type **370**; 4000k. Bridge and mountains; 4000k. Bridge (different) . . . . . . 4·00 4·00

2001. Men's Regional Costumes. Multicoloured.
1721 100k. Type **371** 10 10
1722 200k. Gnaheun Champasak 10 10
1723 500k. Katou Sarvane . . . 15 15
1724 2300k. Hmong Dam Oudomxay 80 80
1725 2500k. Harlak Xekong . . . 90 90
1726 2600k. Kui Luangnamtha 90 90
1727 2700k. Krieng Xekong . . . 95 95
1728 3100k. Khmu Nhuan Luangnamtha . . . . . 1·10 1·10
1729 3200k. Ta Oy Saravane . . 1·10 1·10
1730 3300k. TaiTheng Bolihamxay . . . . . . 1·20 1·20
1731 3400k. Hmong Khao Huaphanh . . . . 1·20 1·20
1732 3500k. Gnor Khammouane 1·30 1·30
1733 3600k. Phouthai Na Gnom ZVK . . . . 1·30 1·30
1734 4000k. Yao Ventiane . . . 1·40 1·40
1735 5000k. Hmong LPQ . . . . 1·80 1·80

372 Cocks

2001. Fighting Cocks. Multicoloured.
1736 500k. Type **372** 20 20
1737 900k. Pair with wings outstretched 35 35
1738 3200k. Pair, one in flight . . 1·30 1·30
1739 3500k. Pair resting . . . . 1·40 1·40
MS1740 140 × 111 mm. 10000k. Cock crowing (36 × 51 mm) . . 4·00 4·00

373 Pou Nyer and Nya Nyer

2001. Luang Prabang New Year Celebrations. Multicoloured.
1741 300k. Type **373** 10 10
1742 600k. Hae Nang Sangkhan 20 20
1743 1000k. Sand Stupa (horiz) 35 35
1744 2300k. Hae Prabang 80 80
1745 4000k. Takbat . . . . . . 1·50 1·50

374 Snake

2001. Year of the Snake. Multicoloured.
1746 900k. Type **374** 30 30
1747 3500k. Snake and Chinese zodiac symbols . . . . . 1·20 1·20

375 That Luang, Ventiane and Forbidden City, Beijing (½-size illustration)

2001. 40th Anniv of Laos–China Diplomatic Relations.
1748 **375** 1000k. multicoloured . . 35 35

376 Nurse, Mother and Children

2001. Polio Eradication Campaign. Sheet 135 × 101 mm containing T **376** and similar horiz design.
MS1749 900k. Type **376**; 2500k. Family and map . . . . 1·10 1·10

377 Mekong River

2001. Mekong River at Twilight. Multicoloured.
1750 900k. Type **377** 30 30
1751 2700k. River with boats in foreground 90 90
1752 3400k. River (different) . . 1·10 1·10

378 Poppy Field

2001. Anti-Drug Campaign. Multicoloured.
1753 100k. Type **378** 35 35
1754 4000k. Burning seized drugs 1·10 1·10

379 Intermediate Egret (*Egretta intermedia*)

2001. Birds. Philanippon '01 International Stamp Exhibition. Multicoloured.
1755 700k. Type **379** 20 20
1756 800k. Bulbucus ibis (33 × 49 mm) 20 20
1757 3100k. Grey heron (*Ardea cinera*) (33 × 49 mm) . . . 95 95
1758 3400k. Great egret (*Egretta alba*) . . . . 1·00 1·00
MS1759 200 × 146 mm. Nos. 1755/8 3·00 3·00

380 Temple Door

382 Women using Pestles and Mortar

381 White Frangipani

2001. Buddhist Temple Doors.
1760 **380** 600k. multicoloured . . 20 20
1761 – 2300k. multicoloured . . 80 80
1762 – 2500k. multicoloured . . 90 90
1763 – 2600k. multicoloured . . 90 90
DESIGNS: 2300k. to 2600k. Different temple doors.

2001. The Frangipani. Multicoloured.
1764 1000k. Type **381** 35 35
1765 2500k. Pink frangipani (vert) 90 90
1766 3500k. Red frangipani . . . 1·20 1·20
MS1767 145 × 111 mm. Nos. 1764/6 2·40 2·40

2001. Traditional Mortars. Multicoloured.
1768 900k. Type **382** 30 30
1769 2600k. Wheel driven pestle and mortar (horiz) . . . 80 80
1770 3500k. Fulcrum and lever pestle and mortar . . . . 1·10 1·10

383 Himavanta

2001. Vessantara (Buddhist story illustrating charity). Multicoloured.
1771 200k. Type **383** 10 10
1772 900k. Vanapavesa 35 35
1773 3200k. Kumarakanda . . . 1·30 1·30
1774 3600k. Sakkapabba . . . . 1·50 1·50
MS1775 120 × 151 mm. Nos. 1772/4 3·25 3·25

384 People and Emblem

2001. International Year of Volunteers.
1776 **384** 1000k. multicoloured . . 35 35

POSTAGE DUE STAMPS

D 5 Vat Sisaket Shrine

D 6 Sampans

D 98 Serpent

1952.
D22 D **5** 10c. brown 15 15
D23 20c. violet 15 15
D24 50c. red 15 15
D25 1p. green 20 20
D26 2p. blue 20 20
D27 5p. purple 75 75
D28 D **6** 10p. blue . . . . . . 1·10 1·10

1973.
D378 D **98** 10k. black, brn & yell 15 15
D379 15k. black, yell & grn 15 15
D380 20k. black, green & bl 15 15
D381 50k. black, blue & red 35 35

APPENDIX

The following stamps have either been issued in excess of postal needs or have not been available to the public in reasonable quantities at face value. Such stamps may later be given full listing if there is evidence of regular postal use.

1975.

Centenary of U.P.U. Postage 10, 15, 30, 40k.; Air 1000, 1500k. On gold foil 2500, 3000k.

"Apollo–Soyuz" Space Link. Postage 125, 150, 200, 300k.; Air 450, 700k.

Bicentenary of American Revolution. Postage 10, 15, 40, 50, 100, 125, 150, 200k.; Air 1000, 1500k.

LAS BELA Pt. 1

A state of Baluchistan. Now part of Pakistan.

12 pies = 1 anna; 16 annas = 1 rupee.

1

1897.
1 **1** ½a. black on white . . . . . 22·00 15·00
11 ½a. black on blue . . . . . 12·00 7·00
3 ½a. black on grey . . . . . 13·00 7·50
12 ½a. black on green . . . . . 12·00 7·00
8 – 1a. black on orange . . . . 17·00 19·00
The 1a. has the English inscription in a circle with the native inscription across the centre.

LATAKIA Pt. 19

The former state of the Alaouites which changed its name to Latakia in 1930.
Latakia was merged with Syria in 1936.

100 centimes = 1 piastre.

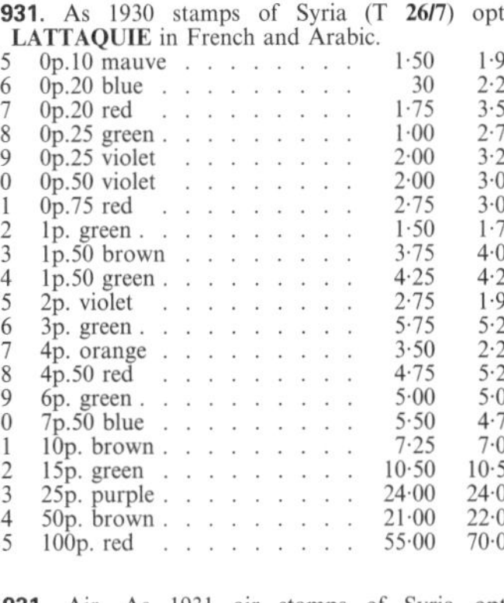

1931. As 1930 stamps of Syria (T **26/7**) optd **LATTAQUIE** in French and Arabic.
65 0p.10 mauve . . . . 1·50 1·90
66 0p.20 blue . . . . 30 2·25
67 0p.20 red . . . . 1·75 3·50
68 0p.25 green . . . . 1·00 2·75
69 0p.25 violet . . . . 2·00 3·25
70 0p.50 violet . . . . 2·00 3·00
71 0p.75 red . . . . 2·75 3·00
72 1p. green . . . . 1·50 1·75
73 1p.50 brown . . . . 3·75 4·00
74 1p.50 green . . . . 4·25 4·25
75 2p. violet . . . . 2·75 1·90
76 3p. green . . . . 5·75 5·25
77 4p. orange . . . . 3·50 2·25
78 4p.50 red . . . . 4·75 5·25
79 6p. green . . . . 5·00 5·00
80 7p.50 blue . . . . 5·50 4·75
81 10p. brown . . . . 7·25 7·00
82 15p. green . . . . 10·50 10·50
83 25p. purple . . . . 24·00 24·00
84 50p. brown . . . . 21·00 22·00
85 100p. red . . . . 55·00 70·00

1931. Air. As 1931 air stamps of Syria optd **LATTAQUIE** in French and Arabic.
86 0p.50 yellow . . . . 1·40 2·25
87 0p.50 brown . . . . 1·50 2·75
88 1p. brown . . . . 2·50 3·25
89 2p. blue . . . . 3·50 3·25
90 3p. green . . . . 3·25 3·25
91 5p. purple . . . . 7·25 7·25
92 10p. blue . . . . 9·00 9·00
93 15p. red . . . . 10·50 10·50
94 25p. orange . . . . 24·00 24·00
95 50p. black . . . . 30·00 35·00
96 100p. mauve . . . . 29·00 34·00

POSTAGE DUE STAMPS

1931. Nos. D197/8 of Syria optd **LATTAQUIE** in French and Arabic.
D86 8p. black on blue . . . . . 22·00 24·00
D87 15p. black on pink . . . . . 11·50 17·00

LATVIA Pt. 10

A country on the Baltic Sea. Previously part of the Russian Empire, Latvia was independent from 1918 to 1940 when it became part of the U.S.S.R.
Following the dissolution of the U.S.S.R. in 1991, Latvia once again became an independent republic.

1918. 100 kapeikas = 1 rublis.
1923. 100 santimu = 1 lats.
1991. 100 kopeks = 1 (Russian) rouble.
1992. 100 kopeks = 1 Latvian rouble.
1993. 100 santimu = 1 lats.

1

4

5 Rising Sun

1918. Printed on back of German war maps. Imperf or perf.
15 **1** 3k. lilac 10 10
16 5k. red 10 10
17 10k. blue 10 10
18 15k. green 10 10
41 20k. orange 10 10
20 25k. grey 50 35
21 35k. brown 20 20
42 40k. purple 30 10
22 50k. violet 20 20
44 75k. green 25 15
29 3r. red and blue . . . . . . 1·25 75
30 5r. red and brown . . . . . 1·25 60

1919. Liberation of Riga. Imperf.
24 **4** 5k. red 20 20
25 15k. green 20 20
26 35k. brown 35 45
For stamps of Types **1** and **4** optd with a cross, with or without Russian letters "Z A", see under North-West Russia Nos. 21/42.

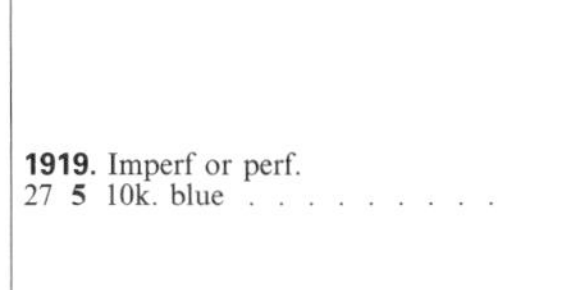

1919. Imperf or perf.
27 **5** 10k. blue 50 35

6

7

1919. 1st Anniv of Independence. (a) Size 33 × 45 mm.
32 **6** 10k. red and brown 35 35
(b) Size 28 × 38 mm.
33 **6** 10k. red and brown 20 20
34 35k. green and blue 20 20
35 1r. red and green 75 75

1919. Liberation of Courland.
36 **7** 10k. red and brown 10 10
37 25k. green and blue 20 20
38 35k. blue and black 30 30
39 1r. brown and green 55 55

8

1920. Red Cross stamps. (a) On backs of blue Bolshevist notes. Perf.
46 **8** 20-30k. red and brown . . . 50 1·50
47 40-55k. red and blue . . . . 50 1·50
48 50-70k. red and green . . . . 50 1·75
49 1r.-1r.30 red and grey . . . . 75 2·00
(b) On backs of green Western Army notes. Perf.
50 **8** 20-30k. red and brown . . . 40 90
51 40-55k. red and blue 40 90
52 50-70k. red and green 60 90
53 1r.-1r.30 red and grey . . . . 75 1·75
(c) On backs of red, green and brown Bolshevist notes. Imperf.
54 **8** 20-30k. red and brown . . . 1·00 2·75
55 40-55k. red and blue . . . . 1·00 2·75
56 50-70k. red and green . . . . 1·00 2·75
57 1r.-1r.30 red and grey . . . . 2·00 4·00

CHARITY PREMIUMS. In the above and later issues where two values are expressed, the lower value represents the franking value and the higher the price charged, the difference being the charity premium.

9

10

1920. Liberation of Latgale.
58 **9** 50k. pink and green 20 30
59 1r. brown and green 30 40

1920. 1st Constituent Assembly.
60 **10** 50k. red 50 20
61 1r. blue 50 15

62		3r. green and brown	90	70
63		5r. purple and grey	1·00	80

1920. Surch in white figures on black oval.

64	6	10r. on 1r. red and green	2·00	1·10
65		20r. on 1r. red and green	3·50	2·50
66		30r. on 1r. red and green	4·50	4·00

1920. Surch **2 DIWI RUBLI**. Perf.

67	1	2r. on 10k. blue	2·00	1·25
68	4	2r. on 35k. brown	50	30

1920. (a) Surch **WEENS** or **DIVI**, value and **RUBLI**.

69	7	1 (WEENS) r. on 35k. blue and black	30	30
70		2 (DIVI) r. on 10k. red and brown	45	40
71		2 (DIVI) r. on 25k. green and blue	70	30

(b) Surch **DIWI RUBLI 2.**

72	6	2r. on 35k. green and blue	90	70

(c) Surch **DIVI 2 RUB. 2.**

73	10	2r. on 50k. red	25	40

(d) Surch **Desmit rubli.**

74	6	10r. on 10r. on 1r. red and green (No. 64)	1·00	65

1921. Red Cross. Nos. 51/3 surch **RUB 2 RUB.**

75	8	2r. on 20-30k. red and brown	2·50	4·50
76		2r. on 40-55k. red and blue	2·50	4·50
77		2r. on 50-70k. red and green	2·50	4·50
78		2r. on 1r.-1r.30k. red and grey	2·50	4·50

1921. Surch in figures and words over thick bar of crossed lines.

79	9	10r. on 50k. pink and green	90	70
80		20r. on 50k. pink and green	4·25	3·25
81		30r. on 50k. pink and green	4·00	3·00
82		50r. on 50k. pink and green	7·00	6·50
83		100r. on 50k. pink and green	18·00	15·00

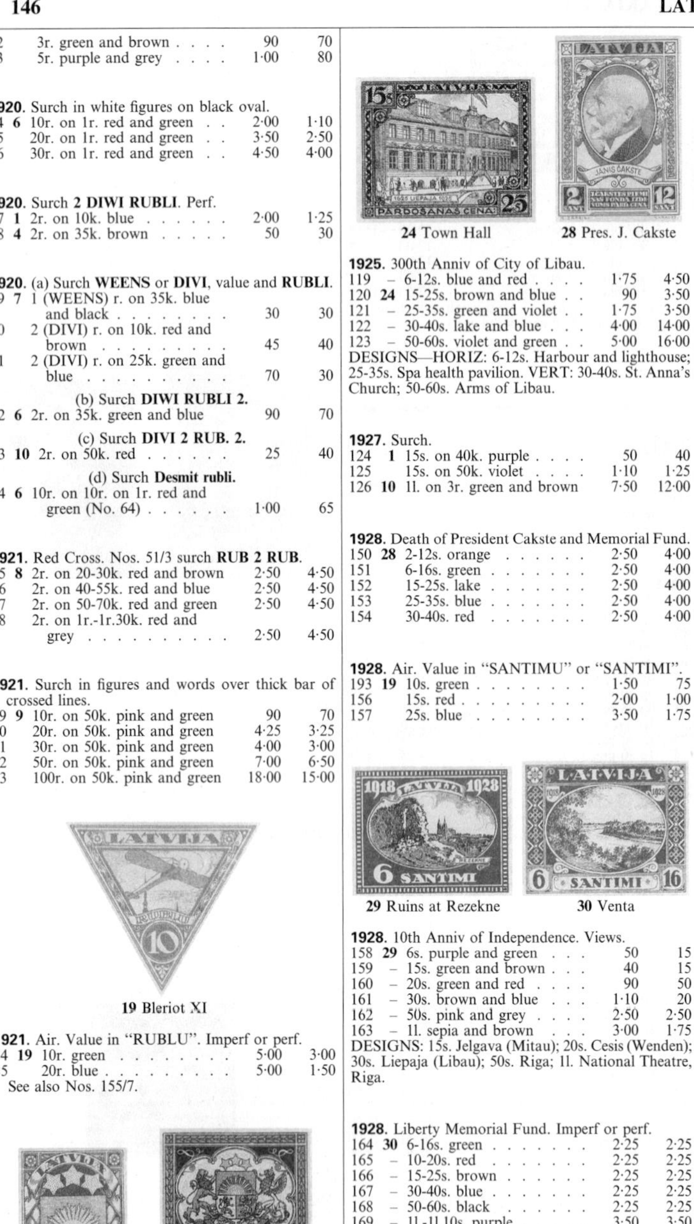

19 Bleriot XI

1921. Air. Value in "RUBLU". Imperf or perf.

84	19	10r. green	5·00	3·00
85		20r. blue	5·00	1·50

See also Nos. 155/7.

21 Latvian Coat of Arms   22 Great Seal of Latvia

1921. Value in "Kopeks" or "Roubles".

86	21	50k. violet	25	10
87b		1r. yellow	25	25
88		2r. green	20	10
89		3r. green	30	25
90		5r. red	80	10
91		6r. red	1·25	75
92		9r. orange	90	25
93		10r. blue	1·10	10
94		15r. blue	4·50	1·00
95c		20r. lilac	11·00	1·50
96	22	50r. brown	20·00	5·00
97		100r. blue	24·00	4·25

1923. Value in "Santimi" or "Lats".

127	21	1s. mauve	15	10
129		2s. yellow	15	10
130		3s. red	15	10
100		4s. green	45	10
132		5s. green	30	10
133		6s. green and yellow	10	10
134		7s. green	30	15
103		10s. red	85	10
136d		10s. green and yellow	7·00	10
104		12s. mauve	25	20
105c		15s. purple and orange	2·75	10
107		20s. blue	1·50	10
139		20s. pink	3·00	20
108		25s. blue	20	10
109		30s. pink	4·00	15
140		30s. blue	1·25	10
141		35s. blue	1·50	10
110		40s. purple	1·50	15
143		50s. grey	3·00	15
144	22	1l. brown and bistre	6·00	15
116		2l. blue and light blue	14·00	90
117		5l. green and light green	48·00	3·75
118		10l. red and light red	6·00	15·00

1923. Charity. War Invalids. Surch **KARA INVALIDIEM S.10S.** and cross.

112	21	1s.+10s. mauve	50	1·00
113		2s.+10s. yellow	50	1·00
114		4s.+10s. green	50	1·00

24 Town Hall   28 Pres. J. Cakste

1925. 300th Anniv of City of Libau.

119	–	6-12s. blue and red	1·75	4·50
120	24	15-25s. brown and blue	90	3·50
121	–	25-35s. green and violet	1·75	3·50
122	–	30-40s. lake and blue	4·00	14·00
123	–	50-60s. violet and green	5·00	16·00

DESIGNS—HORIZ: 6-12s. Harbour and lighthouse; 25-35s. Spa health pavilion. VERT: 30-40s. St. Anna's Church; 50-60s. Arms of Libau.

1927. Surch.

124	1	15s. on 40k. purple	50	40
125		15s. on 50k. violet	1·10	1·25
126	10	1l. on 3r. green and brown	7·50	12·00

1928. Death of President Cakste and Memorial Fund.

150	28	2-12s. orange	2·50	4·00
151		6-16s. green	2·50	4·00
152		15-25s. lake	2·50	4·00
153		25-35s. blue	2·50	4·00
154		30-40s. red	2·50	4·00

1928. Air. Value in "SANTIMU" or "SANTIMI".

193	19	10s. green	1·50	75
156		15s. red	2·00	1·00
157		25s. blue	3·50	1·75

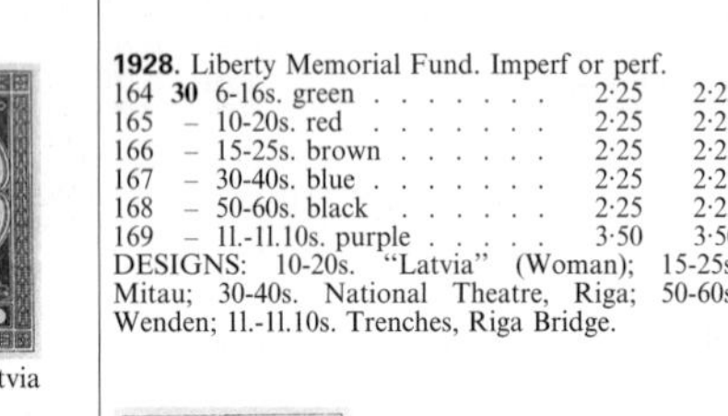

29 Ruins at Rezekne   30 Venta

1928. 10th Anniv of Independence. Views.

158	29	6s. purple and green	50	15
159	–	15s. green and brown	40	15
160	–	20s. green and red	90	50
161	–	30s. brown and blue	1·10	20
162	–	50s. pink and grey	2·50	2·50
163	–	1l. sepia and brown	3·00	1·75

DESIGNS: 15s. Jelgava (Mitau); 20s. Cesis (Wenden); 30s. Liepaja (Libau); 50s. Riga; 1l. National Theatre, Riga.

1928. Liberty Memorial Fund. Imperf or perf.

164	30	6-16s. green	2·25	2·25
165	–	10-20s. red	2·25	2·25
166	–	15-25s. brown	2·25	2·25
167	–	30-40s. blue	2·25	2·25
168	–	50-60s. black	2·25	2·25
169	–	1l.-1l.10s. purple	3·50	3·50

DESIGNS: 10-20s. "Latvia" (Woman); 15-25s. Mitau; 30-40s. National Theatre, Riga; 50-60s. Wenden; 1l.-1l.10s. Trenches, Riga Bridge.

32 Z. A. Meierovics

33 J. Rainis

1929. 3rd Death Anniv of Meierovics (Foreign Minister). Imperf or perf.

170	32	2-4s. yellow	3·00	3·00
171		6-12s. green	3·00	3·00
172		15-25s. purple	3·00	3·00
173		25-35s. blue	3·00	3·00
174		30-40s. blue	3·00	3·00

1930. Memorial Fund for J. Rainis (writer and politician). Imperf or perf.

175	33	1-2s. purple	75	1·75
176		2-4s. orange	75	1·75
177		4-8s. green	75	1·75
178		6-12s. brown and green	75	1·75
179		10-20s. red	15·00	32·00
180		15-30s. green and brown	15·00	32·00

34 Klemm KI-20 over Durbe Castle

1930. Air. J. Rainis Memorial Fund. Imperf or perf.

181	34	10-20s. green and red	10·00	11·50
182		15-30s. red and green	10·00	11·50

35

36

1930. Anti-T.B. Fund.

183	–	1-2s. red and purple	50	50
184	–	2-4s. red and orange	50	50
185	35	4-8s. red and green	65	80
186	–	5-10s. brown and green	75	1·10
187	–	6-12s. yellow and green	75	1·10
188	–	10-20s. black and red	1·00	1·60
189	–	15-30s. green and brown	1·50	1·50
190	–	20-40s. blue and red	1·50	1·75
191	–	25-50s. lilac, blue and red	2·00	2·50
192	36	30-60s. lilac, green and blue	2·75	3·00

DESIGNS—VERT: As Type **35**: 1-2s., 2-4s. The Crusaders' Cross; 5-10s. G. Zemgalis; 6-12s. Tower; 10-20s. J. Cakste; 15-30s. Floral design; 20-40s. A. Kviesis. HORIZ: As Type **36**: 25-50s. Sanatorium.

1931. Nos. 183/92 surch.

196		9 on 6-12s. yellow and green	65	1·00
197		16 on 1-2s. red and purple	10·00	20·00
198		17s. on 2-4s. red and orange	1·25	2·25
199		19 on 4-8s. red and green	3·00	7·00
200		20 on 5-10s. brown and green	2·00	8·00
201		23 on 15-30s. green and brown	75	1·00
202		25 on 10-20s. black and red	2·00	3·75
203		35 on 20-40s. blue and red	3·75	4·50
204		45 on 25-50s. lilac, blue and red	12·00	16·00
205		55 on 30-60s. lilac, green & bl	13·00	17·00

1931. Air. Charity. Nos. 155/7 surch **LATVIJAS AIZSARGI** and value. Imperf or perf.

206	19	50 on 10s. green	13·00	18·00
207		1l. on 15s. red	13·00	18·00
208		1l.50 on 2s. blue	13·00	18·00

38 Foreign Invasion

1932. Militia Maintenance Fund. Imperf or perf.

209	–	1-11s. blue and purple	1·90	2·10
210	38	2-17s. orange and olive	1·90	2·10
211	–	3-23s. red and brown	1·90	2·10
212	–	4-34s. green	1·90	2·10
213	–	5-45s. green	1·90	2·10

DESIGNS: 1-11s. The Holy Oak and Kriva telling stories; 3-23s. Lacplesis, the deliverer; 4-34s. The Black Knight (enemy) slaughtered; 5-45s. Laimdota, the spirit of Latvia, freed.

39 Infantry Manoeuvres

1932. Militia Maintenance Fund. Imperf or perf.

214	–	6-25s. purple and brown	4·00	4·50
215	39	7-35s. blue and green	4·00	4·50
216	–	10-45s. sepia and green	4·00	4·50
217	–	12-55s. green and red	4·00	4·50
218	–	15-75s. violet and red	4·00	4·50

DESIGNS—HORIZ: 6-25s. Troops on march. VERT: 10-45s. First aid to soldier; 12-55s. Army kitchen; 15-75s. Gen. J. Balodis.

41

1932. Air. Charity. Imperf or perf.

219	41	10-20s. black and green	12·00	18·00
220		15-30s. red and grey	12·00	18·00
221		25-50s. blue and grey	12·00	18·00

1932. Riga Exn of Lettish Products. Optd **Latvijas razojumu izstade Riga. 1932.g.10.-18.IX.**

222	21	3s. red	50	40
223		10s. green on yellow	1·50	80
224		20s. pink	1·50	70
225		35s. blue	2·40	1·60

43 Leonardo da Vinci

44 "Mourning Mother" Memorial, Riga

1932. Air. Charity. Pioneers of Aviation. Imperf or perf.

226	–	5-25s. green and brown	10·00	15·00
227	43	10-50s. green and brown	10·00	15·00
228	–	15-75s. green and red	13·50	17·00
229	–	20-100s. mauve and green	13·50	17·00
230	–	25-125s. blue and brown	13·50	17·00

DESIGNS—VERT: 5s. Icarus; 15s. Jacques Charles's hydrogen balloon, 1783 (inscr "Charliers"). HORIZ: 20s. Wright Type A biplane; 25s. Bleriot XI monoplane.

1933. Air. Wounded Latvian Airmen Fund. Imperf or perf.

231	–	2-52s. brown and black	6·00	14·00
232	44	3-53s. red and black	6·00	14·00
233	–	10-60s. green and black	6·00	14·00
234	–	20-70s. red and black	6·00	14·00

DESIGNS: 2s. Fall of Icarus; 10s., 20s. Proposed tombs for airmen.

1933. Air. Charity. Riga–Bathurst Flight. Nos. 155/7 optd **LATVIJA-AFRIKA 1933** or surch also.

235		10s. green	15·00	50·00
236		15s. red	15·00	50·00
237		25s. blue	18·00	50·00
238		50s. on 15s. red	£120	£325
239		100s. on 25s. blue	£120	£325

In the event the aircraft crashed at Neustettin, Germany, and the mail was forwarded by ordinary post.

46 Biplane under Fire at Riga

1933. Air. Charity. Wounded Latvian Airmen Fund. Imperf or perf.

240	–	3-53s. blue and orange	20·00	24·00
241	46	7-57s. brown and blue	20·00	24·00
242	–	35-135s. black and blue	20·00	24·00

DESIGNS: 3s. Monoplane taking off; 35s. Map and aircraft.

47 Glanville Brothers' Gee Bee Super Sportster

1933. Air. Charity. Wounded Latvian Airmen Fund. Imperf or perf.

243	47	8-68s. grey and brown	30·00	50·00
244	–	12-112s. green and purple	30·00	50·00
245	–	30-130s. grey and blue	30·00	50·00
246	–	40-190s. blue and purple	30·00	50·00

DESIGNS: 12s. Supermarine S6B seaplane; 30s. Airship "Graf Zeppelin" over Riga; 40s. Dornier Do-X flying boat.

48 President's Palace

50 A. Kronvalds

51

1934. 15th Anniv of New Constitution.

247	48	3s. red	10	15
248	–	5s. green	15	10
249	–	10s. green	1·75	10
250	–	20s. red	1·75	10
251	–	35s. blue	10	15
252	48	40s. brown	20	15

DESIGNS: 5, 10s. Arms and shield; 20s. Allegory of Latvia; 35s. Government Building.

1936. Lettish Intellectuals.

253	50	3s. red	1·10	4·00
254	–	10s. green	1·10	4·00
255	–	20s. mauve	1·10	5·00
256	–	35s. blue	1·10	5·00

PORTRAITS: 10s. A. Pumpurs; 20s. J. Maters; 35s. Auseklis.

1936. White Cross Fund. Designs incorporating Cross and Stars device as in T **51**.

257	51	3s. red	1·50	4·00
258	–	10s. green	1·50	4·00

259 – 20s. mauve 1·50 5·00
260 – 35s. blue 1·50 5·00
DESIGNS: 10s. Oak leaves; 20s. Doctors and patient; 35s. Woman holding shield.

53 Independence Monument, Rauna (Ronneburg)

54 President Ulmanis

1937. Monuments.
261 **53** 3s. red 35 1·40
262 – 5s. green 35 60
263 – 10s. green 35 35
264 – 20s. red 85 1·00
265 – 30s. blue 90 1·25
266 – 35s. blue 1·40 1·50
267 – 40s. brown 2·25 2·50
DESIGNS—VERT: 10s. Independence Monument, Jelgava (Mitau); 20s. War Memorial, Valka (Walk); 30s. Independence Monument, Iecava (Eckau); 35s. Independence Monument, Riga; 40s. Col. Kalpak's Grave, Visagalas Cemetery. HORIZ: 5s. Cemetery Gate, Riga.

1937. President Ulmanis's 60th Birthday.
268 **54** 3s. red and orange 15 10
269 5s. light green and green 15 15
270 10s. deep green and green 25 35
271 20s. purple and red 55 35
272 25s. grey and blue 85 70
273 30s. deep blue and blue 85 60
274 35s. indigo and blue 75 50
275 40s. light brown and brown 85 75
276 50s. green and black 90 80

55 Palace of Justice

1938. National Building Fund. Sheet 140×100 mm comprising 35 (s.) blue (T **55**) and 40 (s.) brown (Power Station, Kegums).
MS277 Sold at 2l. 11·00 3·00

56 Gaizinkalns, Livonia

57 General J. Balodis

1938. 20th Anniv of Independence.
278 **56** 3s. red 10 10
279 – 5s. green 10 10
280 **57** 10s. green 30 10
281 – 20s. mauve 20 10
282 – 30s. blue 60 20
283 – 35s. slate 90 10
284 – 40s. mauve 80 15
DESIGNS: As Type **56**: 5s. Latgale landscape; 30s. City of Riga; 35s. Rumba waterfall, Courland; 40s. Zemgale landscape. As Type **57**: 20s. President Ulmanis.

58 Elementary School, Riga

1939. 5th Anniv of Authoritarian Government.
285 **58** 3s. brown 30 60
286 – 5s. green 30 60
287 – 10s. green 95 60
288 – 20s. red 95 65
289 – 30s. blue 1·40 1·00
290 – 35s. blue 1·40 1·50
291 – 40s. purple 1·75 1·00
292 – 50s. black 2·00 1·25
DESIGNS: 5s. Jelgava Castle; 10s. Riga Castle; 20s. Independence Memorial; 30s. Eagle and National Flag; 35s. Town Hall, Daugavpils; 40s. War Museum and Powder-magazine, Riga; 50s. Pres. Ulmanis.

1939. 5th Year of Office of Pres. Ulmanis. Sheet as **MS**277 optd "1934 1939 14/V".
MS293 Sold at 2l. 14·00 40·00

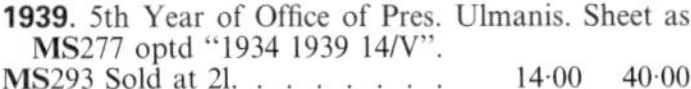

59 Reaping

60 Arms of Courland, Livonia and Latgale

61 Arms of Latvian Soviet Socialist Republic

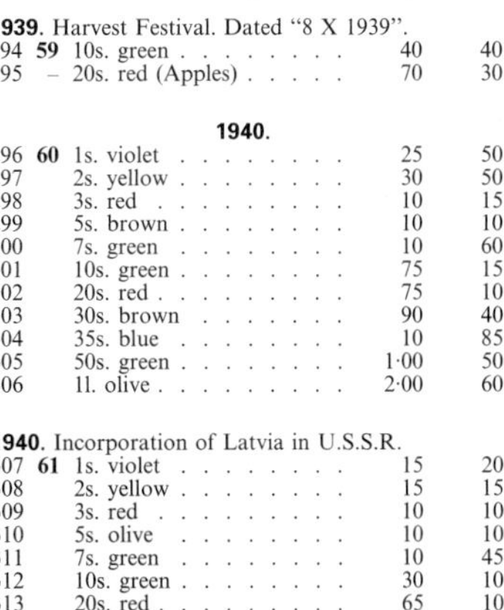

1939. Harvest Festival. Dated "8 X 1939".
294 **59** 10s. green 40 40
295 – 20s. red (Apples) 70 30

1940.
296 **60** 1s. violet 25 50
297 2s. yellow 30 50
298 3s. red 10 15
299 5s. brown 10 10
300 7s. green 10 60
301 10s. green 75 15
302 20s. red 75 10
303 30s. brown 90 40
304 35s. blue 10 85
305 50s. green 1·00 50
306 1l. olive 2·00 60

1940. Incorporation of Latvia in U.S.S.R.
307 **61** 1s. violet 15 20
308 2s. yellow 15 15
309 3s. red 10 10
310 5s. olive 10 10
311 7s. green 10 45
312 10s. green 30 10
313 20s. red 65 10
314 30s. blue 80 30
315 35s. blue 10 55
316 40s. brown 60 20
317 50s. grey 90 25
318 1l. brown 2·00 35
319 5l. green 11·00 5·50

64 Latvian Arms

65 Latvian Arms

1991.
320 **64** 5k. silver, brown & lt brn 35 20
321 10k. silver, brown & drab 15 10
322 15k. silver, sepia & brown 15 10
323 20k. silver, blue & lt blue 60 20
324 40k. silver, green and light green 1·25 40
325 50k. silver, brown and lilac 1·40 45
326 **65** 100k. multicoloured 2·75 80
327 200k. multicoloured 5·00 1·40

1991. Nos. 6073 and 6077a of Russia surch **LATVIJA** and new value.
332 100k. on 7k. blue 10 10
333 300k. on 2k. brown 35 25
334 500k. on 2k. brown 60 40
335 1000k. on 2k. brown 1·25 70

67 Main Statue, Liberty Monument, Riga

68 Olympic Committee Symbol

1991.
336 **67** 10k. multicoloured 10 10
337 15k. multicoloured 10 10
338 20k. multicoloured 15 10
339 30k. multicoloured 25 15
340 50k. multicoloured 40 20
341 100k. multicoloured 80 45

1992. Recognition of Latvian Olympic Committee.
342 **68** 50k.+25k. red, silver and drab 40 20
343 – 50k.+25k. red, silver and grey 40 20
344 **68** 100k.+50k. red, gold and bistre 80 45
DESIGN: No. 343, as T **68** but symbols smaller and inscribed "BERLIN 18.09.91." at left.

69 Vaidelotis

72 Children in Fancy Dress around Christmas Tree

1992. Statues from the base of the Liberty Monument, Riga.
345 – 10k. black and brown 10 10
346 **69** 20k. brown and grey 15 10
347 – 30k. deep lilac and lilac 25 15
348 **69** 30k. deep brown and brown 25 15
349 – 40k. blue and grey 35 20
350 **69** 50k. green and grey 40 25
351 – 50k. black and grey 40 25
352 – 100k. purple and mauve 85 45
353 – 200k. deep blue and blue 1·60 80
DESIGNS: Nos. 345, 347, 353, Kurzeme (warrior with shield); 349, 351/2, Lachplesis (two figures).

1992. Nos. 4672, 6073 and 6077a of Russia surch **LATVIJA** and new value.
354a 1r. on 7k. blue 10 10
355 3r. on 2k. brown 10 10
356 5r. on 2k. brown 20 10
357 10r. on 2k. brown 40 20
358 25r. on 4k. red 95 45

1992. Birds of the Baltic. As Nos. 506/9 of Lithuania.
359 5r. black and red 50 45
360 5r. brown, black and red 50 45
361 5r. sepia, brown and red 50 45
362 5r. brown, black and red 50 45
DESIGNS: Nos 359, Osprey ("Pandion haliaetus"); 360, Black-tailed godwit ("Limosa limosa"); 361, Goosander ("Mergus merganser"); 362, Common shelducks ("Tadorna tadorna").

1992. Christmas. Multicoloured.
363 2r. Type **72** 20 10
364 3r. Angel choir 30 15
365 10r. Type **72** 50 20
366 15r. Adoration of the Kings 65 30

1993. Nos. 4855, 5296 and 5295 of Russia surch **LATVIJA** and new value.
367 50r. on 6k. multicoloured 75 35
368 100r. on 6k. multicoloured 1·50 75
369 300r. on 6k. multicoloured 3·25 1·60

74 Kuldiga Couple

75 Emblem

1993. Traditional Costumes. Multicoloured.
370 5s. Type **74** 15 10
371 10s. Alsunga 30 20
372 20s. Lielvarde 55 35
373 50s. Rucava 1·40 1·00
374 100s. Zemgale 3·00 2·00
375 500s. Ziemellatgale 13·50 9·00
MS376 103×88 mm. Nos. 370/5 18·00 8·00
See also Nos. 428/**MS**429, 442/**MS**443, 467/**MS**468 and 491/**MS**492.

1993. National Song Festival.
377 **75** 3s. black, gold and brown 15 10
378 5s. black, gold and lilac 30 15
379 – 15s. multicoloured 1·00 50
DESIGN: 15s. Abstract.

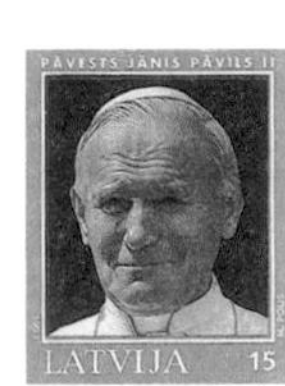

76 Pope John Paul II

77 Flags

1993. Papal Visit.
380 **76** 15s. multicoloured 50 35

1993. 75th Anniv of First Republic.
381 **77** 5s. multicoloured 15 10
382 15s. multicoloured 45 35

78 Valters

79 Biathlon

1994. 100th Birthday of Evalds Valters (actor).
383 **78** 15s. brown, light brown and gold 50 35

1994. Winter Olympic Games, Lillehammer, Norway. Multicoloured.
384 5s. Type **79** 15 10
385 10s. Two-man bobsleigh 25 15
386 15s. One-man luge 50 35
387 100s. Figure skating 2·75 1·50
MS388 55×80 mm. 200s. As No. 385 4·75 4·75

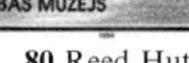
80 Reed Hut

1994. 70th Anniv of Latvian Ethnological Open-air Museum, Bergi.
389 **80** 5s. multicoloured 25 10

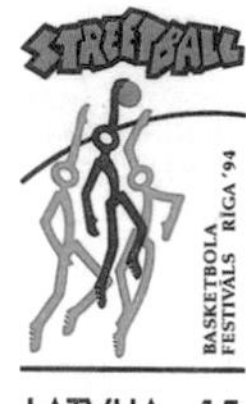

81 Streetball

82 Kurzeme

1994. Basketball Festival, Riga.
390 **81** 15s. black, grey and orange 50 35

1994. Arms (1st series). (a) Size 18×21 mm.
391 **82** 1s. red, black and silver 10 10
392 – 2s. multicoloured 10 10
393 – 3s. silver, black and blue 10 10
394 – 5s. silver, black and red 10 10
395 – 8s. silver, black and blue 20 10
396 – 10s. silver, black and blue 25 10
396a – 10s. multicoloured 20 10
397 – 13s. black, gold and silver 30 15
397a – 16s. multicoloured 35 15
398 – 20s. silver, black and grey 50 25
398a – 20s. multicoloured 45 20
399 – 24s. green, black and silver 55 25
399a – 28s. multicoloured 60 30
400 – 30s. multicoloured 65 30
401 – 36s. silver, black and red 75 35
402 – 50s. multicoloured 1·10 55

(b) Size 29×23½ mm.
403 – 100s. multicoloured 2·10 1·00
404 – 200s. multicoloured 4·25 1·10
DESIGNS: 2s. Auce; 3s. Zemgale; 5s. Vidzeme; 8s. Livani; 10s. (396) Latgale; 10s. (396a) Valmiera; 13s. Preila; 16s. Ainazi; 20s. (398) Grobina; 20s. (398a) Rezekne; 24s. Tukums; 28s. Madona; 30, 100s. Riga; 36s. Priekule; 50, 200s. State arms.
See also Nos. 501/6.

83 Emblem

84 Coins in Scales

1994. 75th Anniv of Latvia University.
405 **83** 5s. gold, blue and green 10 10

1994. Europa. Multicoloured.
406 10s. Type **84** 25 20
407 50s. Money chest and notes in scales 1·25 60

85 Eating Cherries

86 Angel

1994. The Fat Dormouse. Multicoloured.
408 5s. Type **85** 15 10
409 10s. Eating strawberries 30 15
410 10s. On leafy branch 30 15
411 15s. On branch of apple tree 60 30

1994. Christmas. Multicoloured.
412 3s. Type **86** 10 10
413 8s. Angels playing violin and flute 30 15
414 13s. Angels singing 50 25
415 100s. Wreath of candles 2·75 1·40

87 Gnome with Candle

88 Emblem

1994. 80th Birthday of Margarita Staraste (children's writer and illustrator). Multicoloured.
416 5s. Type **87** 15 10
417 10s. Bear 30 15
418 10s. Child on sledge 30 15

1994. Road Safety Year.
419 **88** 10s. multicoloured 35 10

89 Emblem

90 Bauska Castle (Latvia)

1995. 50th Anniv of U.N.O.
420 **89** 15s. blue, red and silver . . 50 25

1995. Via Baltica Motorway Project. Multicoloured.
421 8s. Type **90** 30 15
MS422 100×110 mm. 18s. Beach Hotel, Parnu (Estonia); 18s. Type **90**; 18s. Kaunas (Lithuania) 1·60 1·60

91 White-backed Woodpecker

92 Vaivods

1995. European Nature Conservation Year. Birds. Multicoloured.
423 8s. Type **91** 30 15
424 20s. Corncrake 75 40
425 24s. White-winged black tern 95 50

1995. Birth Centenary of Cardinal Julijans Vaivods.
426 **92** 8s. multicoloured 20 10

93 Sun and Open Book

1995. 60th Anniv of Karlis Ulmaris Schools Appeal.
427 **93** 8s. multicoloured 20 10

1995. Traditional Costumes. As T **74**. Multicoloured.
428 8s. Nica 30 15
MS429 100s. As No. 428 . . . . 2·25 2·25

94 National Opera House

95 Lacplesis, the Bear Slayer

1995. 800th Anniv of Riga (1st issue). Multicoloured.
430 8s. Type **94** 25 10
431 16s. National Theatre 45 20
432 24s. Art School (44×26 mm) 70 35
433 36s. Art Museum (44×26 mm) 95 45

See also Nos. 456/9, 479/82, 493/6, 522/5, 540/3 and 560/3.

1995. European Peace and Freedom. Multicoloured.
434 16s. Type **95** 50 25
435 50s. Spidola . . . . 1·60 80

96 Christmas Tree at Night

97 Stradins

1995. Christmas. Multicoloured.
436 6s. Type **96** 20 10
437 6s. Elf flying with candle . . 20 10
438 15s. Cottage at night 40 20
439 24s. Elf with dog and cat . . 75 35

1996. Birth Centenary of Pauls Stradins (surgeon).
440 **97** 8s. multicoloured 20 10

98 Zenta Maurina (writer)

99 Children with Toys

1996. Europa. Famous Women.
441 **98** 36s. multicoloured . . . . 1·10 50

1996. Traditional Costumes. As T **74**. Multicoloured.
442 8s. Barta 25 15
MS443 100×70 mm. 100s. As No. 422 . . . . 2·75 2·75

100 Cycling

101 Swallowtail

1996. Sheet 96×97 mm.
MS444 **99** 48s. multicoloured . . 1·50 1·50

1996. Olympic Games, Atlanta. Multicoloured.
445 8s. Type **100** 20 10
446 16s. Basketball 40 20
447 24s. Walking 65 30
448 36s. Canoeing (horiz) . . . . 1·00 50
MS449 85×60 mm. 100s. Throwing the javelin (horiz) . . . . . . 2·75 2·75

1996. Butterflies. Multicoloured.
450 8s. Type **101** 25 10
451 24s. Clifden's nonpareil . . . 75 40
452 80s. Large tiger moth . . . . 2·00 1·00

102 1912 Russo-Balt Fire Engine

103 Apartment Block (E. Laube)

1996. Latvian Car Production. Multicoloured.
453 8s. Type **102** 25 10
454 24s. 1899 Leutner-Russia carriage 70 35
455 36s. 1939 Ford-Vairogs motor car . . . . 1·00 50

1996. 800th Anniv of Riga (2nd issue). Multicoloured.
456 8s. Type **103** 25 10
457 16s. Stained glass window (F. Sefels) (30×26 mm) . . 45 20
458 24s. Turreted buildings (E. Laube) (38×26 mm) 75 35
459 30s. Couple welcoming charioteer (mural, J. Rozentals) (38×26 mm) 1·00 50

104 Elves and Presents

1996. Christmas. Multicoloured.
460 6s. Type **104** 15 10
461 14s. Children with dog and Father Christmas on skis 35 20
462 20s. Child at tree and Father Christmas in armchair . . 50 25

105 European Nightjar

106 Symbols of Independence

1997. 75th Anniv of Birdlife International (conservation organization). Multicoloured.
463 10s. Type **105** 30 15
464 20s. Greater spotted eagle . . 75 35
465 30s. Aquatic warbler . . . . 1·10 55

1997. 6th Anniv of Independence.
466 **106** 10s. multicoloured 30 15

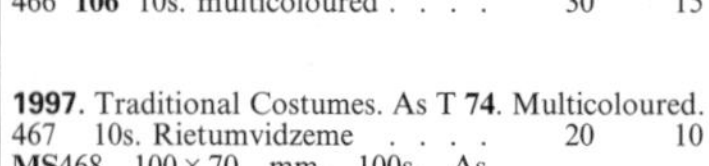

1997. Traditional Costumes. As T **74**. Multicoloured.
467 10s. Rietumvidzeme 20 10
MS468 100×70 mm. 100s. As No. 467 . . . . 1·75 1·75

107 Turaidas Roze

108 "Wappen der Herzogin von Kurland" (galleon)

1997. Europa. Tales and Legends.
469 **107** 32s. multicoloured 90 45

1997. Baltic Sailing Ships. Multicoloured.
470 10s. Type **108** 30 15
MS471 110×70 mm. 20s. As No. 470 but with different frame; 20s. Kurshes ship (Lithuania); 20s. Maasilinn ship (Estonia) . . . 2·75 2·75

109 Hermes and Neptune

1997. Centenary of Ventspils International Commercial Port.
472 **109** 20s. blue, silver and yellow 60 30

110 Stamp Collecting

1997. Children's Leisure Pursuits. Multicoloured.
473 10s. Type **110** 25 10
474 12s. Motor cycle trials (vert) 40 20
475 20s. Ice hockey and skiing (vert) 60 30
476 30s. Tennis, football and basketball . . . . 1·00 50

111 Moricsala

1997. Nature Reserves. Multicoloured.
477 10s. Type **111** 25 10
478 30s. Slitere 75 35

112 Woman, Wooden Building and Jewellery (12th century)

1997. 800th Anniv of Riga (3rd issue). 12th–16th Centuries. Multicoloured.
479 10s. Type **112** 25 10
480 20s. 13th-century Cathedral cloister, statue (K. Bernevics) and seal of Bishop Albert, rosary beads and writing implement 55 25
481 30s. Livonian Order's castle, statue of V. von Plettenberg (Order Master) and weapons 80 40
482 32s. "Three Brothers" terrace, statue of St. John and seal (27×27 mm) 90 45

113 Man and Bear

1997. Christmas. Mummers. Multicoloured.
483 8s. Type **113** 20 10
484 18s. Witches 50 25
485 28s. Horse 70 35

114 Flames

115 Sculpture of Character

1998. Winter Olympic Games, Nagano, Japan.
486 **114** 20s. multicoloured 55 25

1998. Spridisi Memorial (to Anna Brigadere (writer)) Museum, Tervete.
487 **115** 10s. multicoloured 25 10

116 Song Festival

1998. Europa. National Festivals.
488 **116** 30s. multicoloured 65 30

117 Grini

1998. Nature Reserves. Multicoloured.
489 10s. Type **117** 20 10
490 30s. Teici 65 30

1998. Traditional Costumes. As T **74**. Multicoloured.
491 10s. Krustpils 20 10
MS492 100×69 mm. 100s. As No. 491 but man with Midsummer Festival headdress . . . . . . 2·10 2·10

118 Dannenstern House, Wooden Sculpture and Polish and Swedish Coins

1998. 800th Anniv of Riga (4th issue). 16th–20th Centuries. Multicoloured.
493 10s. Type **118** 20 10
494 20s. Library, medallion and monument to G. Herder (poet and philosopher) . . 45 20
495 30s. Arsenal, Victory column, octant and compass . . . 65 30
496 40s. Entrance gate to Warrior's Cemetery, "Mother Latvia" (statue) and 5l. coin 85 40

1998. Arms (2nd series). As T **82**.
497 5s. multicoloured 10 10
497a 5s. multicoloured 10 10
499 10s. multicoloured 20 10
499a 10s. multicoloured 20 10
499b 10s. black, red and silver . . 20 10
500 15s. multicoloured 30 15
501 15s. black, blue and silver 30 15
502 15s. multicoloured 30 15

503 15s. multicoloured 30 15
504 15s. black, silver and red . . 30 15
504a 15s. multicoloured 30 15
504b 15s. silver and black 30 15
504c 20s. multicoloured 35 15
505 30s. multicoloured 65 30
506 40s. multicoloured 75 35

DESIGNS: No. 497, Smiltene; 497a Ludza; 499, Valmiera; 499a, Dobeje; 499b Balvi; 500, Bauska; 501, Ogre; 502, Daugavpils; 503, Jurmala; 504 Kuldiga; 504a, Sigulda; 504b, Gulbene; 504c, Ventspils; 505, Liepaja; 506, Jelgava.

119 1918 5k. Stamp

120 Dome Church, Riga

1998. 70th Anniv of First Latvian Stamp.
510 **119** 30s. red, cream and grey 65 30

1998. Churches.
511 **120** 10s. multicoloured 20 10

121 Janis Cakste (1922–27)

122 State Flag

1998. Presidents.
512 **121** 10s. multicoloured 20 10

1998. 80th Anniv of Declaration of Independence. Multicoloured.
513 10s. Type **122** 20 10
514 30s. State arms and flags . . 65 30

123 Elves building Snowman

1998. Christmas. Multicoloured.
515 10s. Type **123** 20 10
516 20s. Elves decorating tree . . 40 20
517 30s. Elves sledging 65 30

124 Krustkalnu Nature Reserve

125 Playing Cards and Edgars (from novel "Purva Bridejs")

1999. Europa. Parks and Gardens.
518 30s. Type **124** 65 30
519 60s. Gauja National Nature Park . . . . 1·25 60

1999. Latvian Literature. Rudolfs Blaumanis.
520 **125** 110s. multicoloured . . . 2·25 1·10

126 Council Emblem

1999. 50th Anniv of Council of Europe.
521 **126** 30s. multicoloured 65 30

127 "Widwud" (schooner)

1999. 800th Anniv of Riga (5th issue). Transport. Multicoloured.
522 10s. Electric tramcar No. 258 (30 × 26½ mm) 20 10
523 30s. Type **127** 65 30
524 40s. Biplane 75 35
525 70s. Steam locomotive No. Tk-236 . . . . 1·50 75

128 Aglona Basilica

129 Family and State Flag

1999. Churches.
526 **128** 15s. multicoloured 30 15

1999. 10th Anniv of Baltic Chain (human chain uniting capitals of Latvia, Lithuania and Estonia).
527 **129** 15s. multicoloured 30 15
MS528 110 × 72 mm. 30s. Type **129**; 30s. Family and Lithuanian flag; 30s. Family and Estonian flag 1·90 1·90

130 Rundale Palace

1999. Palaces.
529 **130** 20s. multicoloured 40 20

131 "Perse"

1999. 90th Death Anniv of Julijs Feders (painter).
530 **131** 15s. multicoloured 30 15

132 Gustavs Zemgals (1927–30)

133 Harbour, Letters and Emblem

1999. Presidents.
531 **132** 15s. multicoloured 35 15

1999. 125th Anniv of Universal Postal Union.
532 **133** 40s. multicoloured 90 45

134 Father Christmas and Candle

135 "Artist's Model" (J. Rosentals)

1999. Christmas. Multicoloured.
533 12s. Type **134** 25 10
534 15s. Children watching television 35 15
535 40s. Father Christmas placing toys under tree 90 45

2000.
536 **135** 40s. multicoloured 90 45

136 Scene from *The Wagon Driver* (poem)

137 "Building Europe"

2000. 50th Death Anniv of Aleksandrs Caks (poet).
537 **136** 40s. multicoloured 90 45

2000. Europa.
538 **137** 60s. multicoloured . . . . 1·40 70

138 Ice Hockey Players

2000. Ice Hockey.
539 **138** 70s. multicoloured . . . . 1·50 75

140 Central Market

2000. 800th Anniv of Riga (6th issue). Tourist Sights. Multicoloured.
540 20s. Type **140** 45 20
541 40s. Dome Church organ (25 × 30 mm) 90 45
542 40s. Zoo (44 × 26 mm) . . . 90 45
543 70s. The Powder Tower (25 × 30 mm) . . . . . . 1·50 75

141 Jelgava Palace

2000. Palaces.
544 **141** 40s. multicoloured 45 20

142 Globe and Olympic Rings

2000. Olympic Games, Sydney.
545 **142** 40s. multicoloured 45 20
546 70s. multicoloured . . . . 1·60 80

143 Main Statue, Liberty Monument, Riga (Karlis Zale)

144 Alberts Kviesis (1930–36)

2000. New Millennium. Multicoloured.
547 15s. Type **143** 30 15
548 50s. Brotherhood of Blackheads meeting house, Riga . . . . 1·10 55

2000. Presidents.
549 **144** 15s. multicoloured 30 15

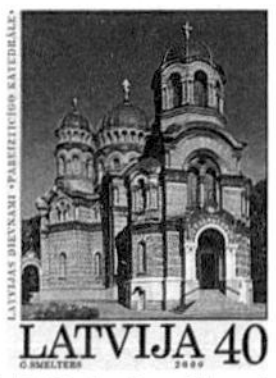

145 Orthodox Church, Riga

146 Nurses tending to Elderly Lady

2000. Churches.
550 **145** 40s. multicoloured 45 20

2000. Latvian Red Cross.
551 **146** 15s. multicoloured 30 15

147 Elf and Sleigh

148 People around Bonfire

2000. Christmas. Multicoloured.
552 12s. Type **147** 25 10
553 15s. Cherubs 30 15
554 15s. Mary and baby Jesus . . 30 15

2001. Sovereignty.
555 **148** 40s. multicoloured 45 20

149 "When Silava's Forest Wakes" (V. Purvitis)

2001.
556 **149** 40s. multicoloured 45 20

150 Karlis Ulmanis (1936–40)

152 Ventas Rumba (waterfall), Kuldiga

151 ML Series Steam Locomotive

2001. Presidents.
557 **150** 15s. multicoloured 30 15

2001. Narrow-gauge Railway.
558 **151** 40s. multicoloured 45 20

2001. Europa. Water Resources.
559 **152** 60s. multicoloured . . . . 1·40 70

153 Modern View of Riga

2001. 800th Anniv of Riga (7th issue). Multicoloured.
560 15s. Type **153** 30 15
561 15s. Modern View of Riga with three spires 30 15
562 60s. 16th-century view of Riga . . . . 1·40 70
563 70s. 17th-century view of Riga . . . . 1·50 75

Nos. 560/1 were issued together, se-tenant, forming a composite design.

154 Cat with Pipe ("Pussy's Water Mill" (fairytale))

2001. Literature. Karlis Skalbe (writer) Commemoration.
564 **154** 40s. multicoloured 45 20

155 Tals

2001. 10th Death Anniv of Mikhail Nekhemevich Tal (World Chess Champion, 1960–1961). Sheet 98 × 68 mm.
MS565 **155** 100s. multicoloured . . . 2·25 2·25

156 Beach, Vidzeme, Latvia

2001. Baltic Sea Coast. Multicoloured.
566 15s. Type **156** 30 15
MS567 125 × 60 mm. 30s. As Type **156**; 30 s. Sand dunes, Palanga, Lithuania; 30s. Rocky coastline, Lahemaa, Estonia . . 2·00 2·00
Stamps in similar designs were issued by Estonia and Lithuania.

157 Cesvaines Palace

2001. Palaces.
568 **157** 40s. multicoloured 45 20

158 Synagogue, Riga **160** White Rabbits

159 Krisjanis Valdemars (½-size illustration)

2001.
569 **158** 70s. multicoloured . . . . 1·50 75

2001. Ship Building, Trade and Discovery. Multicoloured.
570 15s. Type **159** (founder of Naval College and ship builder) 30 15
571 70s. Hercogs Jekabs, Duke of Courland (ship builder) . . 1·50 75

2001. Christmas. Multicoloured.
572 12s. Type **160** 25 10
573 15s. Dog and rabbit 30 15
574 15s. Sheep 30 15

161 Cross-country Skiers

2002. Winter Olympic Games, Salt Lake City.
575 **161** 40s. multicoloured 80 40

162 Downhill Skier **163** "Refugees" (Jekabs Kazaks)

2002. Winter Paralympic Games, Salt Lake City.
576 **162** 15s. multicoloured 30 15

2002. Art.
577 **163** 40s. multicoloured 80 40

164 Clowns

2002. Europa. Circus.
578 **164** 60s. multicoloured . . . . 1·20 60

165 Lady's Slipper Orchid **166** Soldier and Flag (*Cypripedium calceolus*)

2002. Plants. Multicoloured.
579 15s. Type **165** 50 15
580 40s. Water chestnut (*Trapa natans*) 80 40

2002. Armed Forces.
581 **166** 40s. multicoloured 80 40

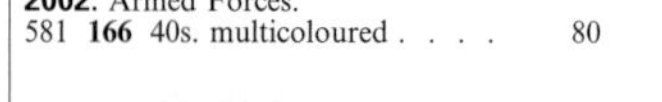

167 Jancis standing in Brook ("The White Book") **169** Atlantic Cod (*Gadus morhua*)

168 Kristians Johan Dals

2002. Literature. 40th Death Anniv of Janis Jaunsudrabins (writer).
582 **167** 40s. multicoloured 80 40

2002. Kristians Johan Dals (sailor and founder of maritime school) Commemoration.
584 **168** 70s. multicoloured . . . . 1·40 70

2002. Fish. Multicoloured.
585 15s. Type **169** 30 15
586 40s. Wels (*Silurus glanis*) . . 80 40

170 Bridge over River Venta

2002. Sheet 100 × 70 mm.
MS587 **170** 100s. multicoloured 2·00 1·00

171 Jaunmoku Palace **172** Grebenschikov Old Believers Praying House, Riga

2002. Palaces.
588 **171** 40s. multicoloured 80 40

2002. Churches.
589 **172** 70s. multicoloured . . . . 1·40 70

173 Mittens and Couple wearing Traditional Winter Clothes.

2002. Mittens.
590 **173** 15s. multicoloured 30 15

174 Christmas Tree and Elf Musician **175** Man enters Room (Niklavs Srtunke)

2002. Christmas. Multicoloured.
591 12s. Type **174** 25 10
592 15s. Elf musicians on present 30 15
593 15s. Angel 30 15

2003. Art.
594 **175** 40s. multicoloured 80 40

176 Fly Orphide (*Ophrys insectifera*) **177** Scene from "Straumei" (poem)

2003. Plants. Multicoloured.
595 15s. Type **176** 30 15
596 40s. Yew (*Taxus baccata*) . . 80 40

2003. Literature. 40th Death Anniv of Edvarts Virza (writer)
597 **177** 40s. multicoloured 80 40

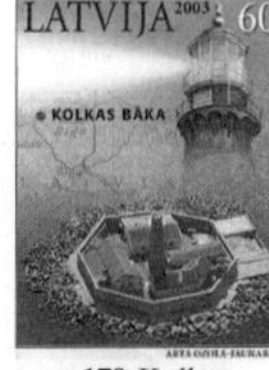
178 "Riga's Towers" (Valda Batraks) **179** Kolka Lighthouse

2003. Europa. Poster Art.
598 **178** 60s. multicoloured . . . . 1·20 60

2003.
599 **179** 60s. multicoloured . . . . 1·20 60

180 Baptist Church, Riga

2003. Churches.
600 **180** 70s. multicoloured . . . . 1·40 70

181 Bridge over River Gauja, Sigulda.

2003. Sheet 100 × 70 mm.
MS601 **181** 100s. multicoloured 2·00 1·00

LEBANON Pt. 19

A territory north of the Holy Land, formerly part of the Turkish Empire, Greater Lebanon was given a separate status under French Mandate in 1920. Until September 1923, the French occupation stamps of Syria were used and these were followed by the joint issue of 1923, Nos. 97 etc, of Syria. Independence was proclaimed in 1941, but the country was not evacuated by French troops until 1946.

100 centimes = 1 piastre;
100 piastres = 1 Lebanese pound.

1924. Stamps of France surch **GRAND LIBAN** and value. (a) Definitive stamps.
1 **11** 10c. on 2c. purple . . . . . 55 1·75
2 **18** 25c. on 5c. orange 95 90
3 50c. on 10c. green . . . . . 1·50 1·00
4 **15** 75c. on 15c. green . . . . . 1·40 3·00
5 **18** 1p. on 20c. brown . . . . . 2·25 1·10
6 1,25p. on 25c. blue . . . . 2·75 2·50
7 1,50p. on 30c. orange . . . 2·00 3·25
8 1,50p. on 30c. red . . . . . 1·75 3·25
9 **15** 2,50p. on 50c. blue . . . . 1·75 95
10 **13** 2p. on 40c. red and blue . . 1·25 1·40
11 3p. on 60c. violet and blue 5·75 5·50
12 5p. on 1f. red and yellow . . 7·50 8·00
13 10p. on 2f. orange and green . . . . 13·00 9·25
14 25p. on 5f. blue and buff . . 20·00 28·00

(b) Pasteur issue.
15 **30** 50c. on 10c. green . . . . . 95 2·50
16 1,50p. on 30c. red . . . . . 2·50 3·75
17 2,50p. on 50c. blue . . . . 85 3·00

(c) Olympic Games issue.
18 **31** 50c. on 10c. green and light green . . . . 28·00 65·00
19 – 1,25p. on 25c. deep red and red . . . . 16·00 65·00
20 – 1,50p. on 30c. red and black 19·00 48·00
21 – 2,50p. on 50c. blue . . . . 15·00 48·00

1924. Air. Stamps of France surch **Poste par Avion GRAND LIBAN** and value.
22 **13** 2p. on 40c. red and blue . . 13·50 15·00
23 3p. on 60c. violet and blue 11·00 16·00
24 5p. on 1f. red and yellow . . 11·00 11·00
25 10p. on 2f. orange and green . . . . 10·00 13·50

1924. Stamps of France surch **Grand Liban** (T **13**) or **Gd Liban** (others) and value in French and Arabic. (a) Definitive stamps.
26 **11** 0p.10 on 2c. purple 30 95
27 **18** 0p.25 on 5c. orange . . . . 75 1·00
28 0p.50 on 10c. green . . . . 2·25 2·25
29 **15** 0p.75 on 15c. green . . . . 1·10 3·00
30 **18** 1p. on 20c. brown . . . . . 1·00 3·00
31 1p.25 on 25c. blue . . . . . 2·25 2·50
32 1p.50 on 30c. red . . . . . 1·90 2·25
33 1p.50 on 30c. orange . . . 48·00 48·00
34 2p. on 35c. violet . . . . . 2·00 3·50
35 **13** 2p. on 40c. red and blue . . 1·75 50
36 2p. on 45c. green and blue 16·00 18·00
37 3p. on 60c. violet and blue 2·25 2·25
38 **15** 3p. on 60c. violet . . . . . 3·00 4·00
39 4p. on 85c. red . . . . . . 75 2·50
40 **13** 5p. on 1f. red and yellow . . 2·25 2·50
41 10p. on 2f. orange and green . . . . 6·00 13·00
42 25p. on 5f. blue and buff . . 8·50 14·50

(b) Pasteur issue.
43 **30** 0p.50 on 10c. green 65 25
44 0p.75 on 15c. green . . . . 2·75 3·25
45 1p.50 on 30c. red . . . . . 2·25 80
46 2p. on 45c. red . . . . . . 3·25 4·00
47 2p.50 on 50c. blue 75 40
48 4p. on 75c. blue . . . . . . 1·50 2·75

(c) Olympic Games issue.
49 **31** 0p.50 on 10c. green and light green . . . . 16·00 42·00
50 – 1p.25 on 25c. deep red and red . . . . 19·00 42·00
51 – 1p.50 on 30c. red and black 13·50 40·00
52 – 2p.50 on 50c. ultramarine and blue . . . . 21·00 40·00

(d) Ronsard issue.
53 **35** 4p. on 75c. blue on bluish 65 4·25

1924. Air. Stamps of France surch **Gd Liban Avion** and value in French and Arabic.
54 **13** 2p. on 40c. red and blue . . 7·25 13·50
55 3p. on 60c. violet and blue 5·50 13·50
56 5p. on 1f. red and yellow . . 5·25 13·50
57 10p. on 2f. orange and green . . . . 6·50 14·50

5 Cedar of Lebanon **7** Tripoli

6 Beirut

1925. Views.
58 5 0p.10c. violet . . . . 25 1·25
59 6 0p.25c. black . . . . 40 1·25
60 – 0p.50c. green (Tripoli) . . . 90 1·25
61 – 0p.75c. red (Beit ed-Din) . . 95 2·50
62 – 1p. purple (Baalbek ruins) . . 1·25 55
63 – 1p.25 green (Mouktara) . . . 1·90 2·25
64 – 1p.50 pink (Tyre) . . . . . 1·00 50
65 – 2p. brown (Zahle) . . . . . 1·75 35
66 – 2p.50 blue (Baalbek) 45 50
67 – 3p. brown (Deir el-Kamar) . . 1·00 1·00
68 – 5p. violet (Sidon) . . . . . . 6·75 6·75
69 7 10p. purple . . . . 6·50 6·00
70 – 25p. blue (Beirut) . . . . . 12·00 29·00

1925. Air. Nos. 65 and 67/9 optd **AVION** in French and Arabic.
71 – 2p. brown . . . . 4·00 6·00
72 – 3p. brown . . . . 4·25 5·75
73 – 5p. violet . . . . 4·00 5·75
74 7 10p. purple . . . . 4·00 5·75

1926. Air. Nos. 65 and 67/9 optd with Bleriot XI airplane.
75 – 2p. brown . . . . 3·00 5·75
76 – 3p. brown . . . . 3·00 5·75
77 – 5p. violet . . . . 3·25 6·00
78 7 10p. purple . . . . 2·50 6·00

1926. War Refugee Charity. Various stamps surch **Secours aux Refugies Afft** and premium in French and Arabic. (a) Postage. Stamps of 1925.
79 6 0p.25+0p.25 black . . . . . 2·00 3·75
80 – 0p.50+0p.25 green . . . . . 2·50 5·25
81 – 0p.75+0p.25 red . . . . . . 1·50 4·75
82 – 1p.+0p.50 purple . . . . . . 2·25 4·75
83 – 1p.25+0p.50 green . . . . . 2·00 6·50
84 – 1p.50+0p.50 pink . . . . . . 4·00 5·50
85 – 2p.+0p.75 brown . . . . . . 3·50 5·00
86 – 2p.50+0p.75 blue . . . . . . 2·50 7·50
87 – 3p.+1p. brown . . . . 3·00 7·25
88 – 5p.+1p. violet . . . . 5·50 8·50
89 7 10p.+2p. purple . . . . . . 6·50 11·00
90 – 25p.+5p. blue . . . . 6·50 13·00

(b) Air. Nos. 75/78 surch.
91 – 2p.+1p. brown . . . . 4·75 13·00
92 – 3p.+2p. brown . . . . 4·75 13·00
93 – 5p.+3p. violet . . . . 4·75 13·00
94 7 10p.+5p. purple . . . . . . 4·75 13·50

1926. Stamps of 1925 surch in English and Arabic.
95 – 3p.50 on 0p.75 red . . . . 3·00 3·00
96 6 4p. on 0p.25 black . . . . 3·50 3·50
98 – 4p.50 on 0p.75 red . . . . 3·25 3·25
99 – 6p. on 2p.50 blue . . . . . 3·50 3·50
100 – 7p.50 on 2p.50 blue . . . . 3·25 1·25
101 – 12p. on 1p.25 green . . . . 2·50 3·75
102 – 15p. on 25p. blue . . . . . 4·50 2·25
103 – 20p. on 1p.25 green . . . . 7·25 7·25

1927. Stamps of 1925 and provisional stamps of Lebanon optd **Republique Libanaise**.
104 5 0p.10 violet . . . . 65 1·60
105 – 0p.50 green . . . . 75 1·00
106 – 1p. purple 35 15
107 – 1p.50 pink . . . . 1·60 2·00
108 – 2p. brown . . . . 2·00 1·75
109 – 3p. brown . . . . 1·25 75
110 6 4p. on 0p.25 black (No. 96) 1·10 85
111 – 4p.50 on 0p.75 red (No. 98) 1·00 40
112 – 5p. violet . . . . 3·25 3·75
113 – 7p.50 on 2p.50 bl (No. 100) 2·00 1·10
114 7 10p. purple . . . . 4·00 5·00
115 – 15p. on 25p. blue (No. 102) 11·00 9·00
117 – 25p. blue . . . . 12·00 24·00

1927. Air. Nos. 75/78 optd **Republique Libanaise**.
118 – 2p. brown . . . . 4·25 6·00
119 – 3p. brown . . . . 3·25 5·75
120 – 5p. violet . . . . 4·50 5·75
121 7 10p. purple . . . . 4·00 5·75

الجمهورية اللبنانية

(10)

1928. Nos. 104/117 optd with T **10** or surch also.
145 5 05 on 0p.10 violet . . . . 15 1·00
124 0p.10 violet 65 25
125 – 0p.50 green . . . . 2·50 2·50
146 – 0p.50 on 0p.75 red 35 40
126 – 1p. purple 95 50
127 – 1p.50 pink . . . . 2·75 3·50
128 – 2p. brown . . . . 4·25 4·50
147 – 2p. on 1p.25 green . . . . 1·40 35
129 – 3p. brown . . . . 2·25 1·00
148 6 4p. on 0p.25 black . . . . 2·50 15
131 – 4p.50 on 0p.75 red . . . . 2·50 2·25
132a – 5p. violet . . . . 2·00 3·75
149 – 7p.50 on 2p.50 blue . . . 1·00 45
134 7 10p. purple . . . . 8·50 9·00
123 – 15p. on 25p. blue . . . . 10·00 15·00
136 – 25p. blue . . . . 10·00 18·00

1928. Air. Optd or surch with airplane, **Republique Libanaise** and line of Arabic as T **10**.
151 – 0p.50 green . . . . 95 3·00
152 – 0p.50 on 0p.75 red (No. 146) . . . . 1·25 2·25
153 – 1p. purple . . . . 1·90 3·50
141 – 2p. brown . . . . 3·50 4·75
154 – 2p. on 1p.25 grn (No. 147) 2·25 3·00
142 – 3p. brown . . . . 2·50 3·25
143 – 5p. violet . . . . 3·50 4·50
144 7 10p. purple . . . . 3·75 4·25
155 – 15p. on 25p. blue (No. 123) £180 £200
156 – 25p. blue £120 £120

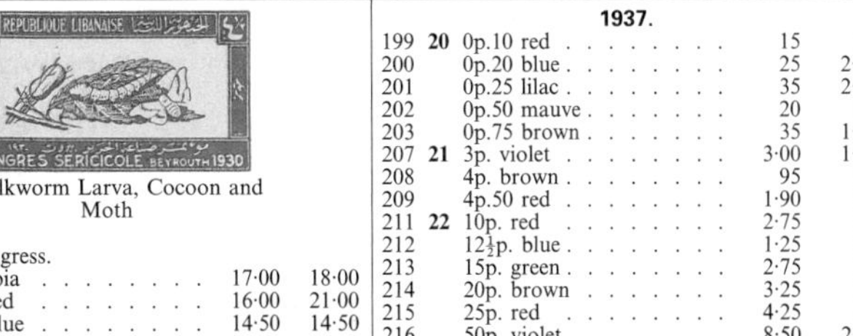

14 Silkworm Larva, Cocoon and Moth

1930. Silk Congress.
157 14 4p. sepia . . . . 17·00 18·00
158 4½p. red . . . . 16·00 21·00
159 7½p. blue . . . . 14·50 14·50
160 10p. violet . . . . 17·00 21·00
161 15p. green . . . . 19·00 14·50
162 25p. purple . . . . 16·00 17·00

15 Cedars of Lebanon

16a Baalbek

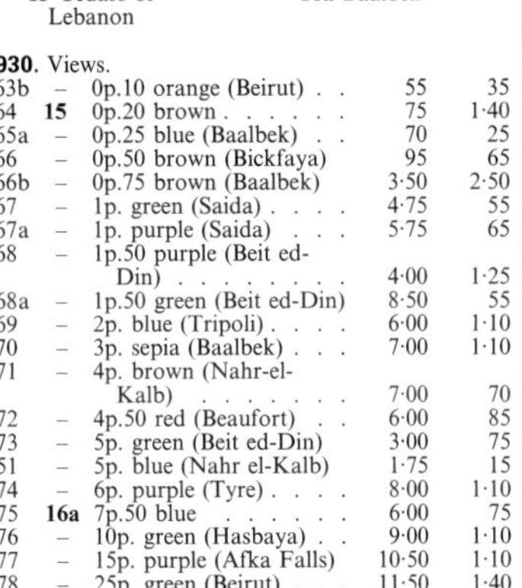

1930. Views.
163b – 0p.10 orange (Beirut) . . 55 35
164 15 0p.20 brown . . . . . . 75 1·40
165a – 0p.25 blue (Baalbek) . . 70 25
166 – 0p.50 brown (Bickfaya) 95 65
166b – 0p.75 brown (Baalbek) 3·50 2·50
167 – 1p. green (Saida) . . . . 4·75 55
167a – 1p. purple (Saida) . . . 5·75 65
168 – 1p.50 purple (Beit ed-Din) . . . . 4·00 1·25
168a – 1p.50 green (Beit ed-Din) 8·50 55
169 – 2p. blue (Tripoli) . . . . 6·00 1·10
170 – 3p. sepia (Baalbek) . . . 7·00 1·10
171 – 4p. brown (Nahr-el-Kalb) . . . . 7·00 70
172 – 4p.50 red (Beaufort) . . 6·00 85
173 – 5p. green (Beit ed-Din) 3·00 75
251 – 5p. blue (Nahr el-Kalb) 1·75 15
174 – 6p. purple (Tyre) . . . . 8·00 1·10
175 16a 7p.50 blue . . . . 6·00 75
176 – 10p. green (Hasbaya) . . 9·00 1·10
177 – 15p. purple (Afka Falls) 10·50 1·10
178 – 25p. green (Beirut) . . . 11·50 1·40
179 – 50p. green (Deir el-Kamar) . . . . 60·00 15·00
180 – 100p. black (Baalbek) . . 60·00 20·00

17 Jebeil (Byblos)

1930. Air. Potez 29-4 biplane and views as T **17**.
181 0p.50 purple (Rachaya) . . . 1·25 2·00
182 1p. green (Broumana) 30 90
183 2p. orange (Baalbek) . . . . 1·10 75
184 3p. red (Hasroun) . . . . . 1·75 1·75
185 5p. green (Byblos) . . . . . 1·75 1·60
186 10p. red (Kadisha) . . . . . 2·00 1·75
187 15p. brown (Beirut) . . . . 1·75 1·40
188 25p. violet (Tripoli) . . . . 2·25 1·75
189 50p. lake (Kabelais) . . . . 6·00 4·75
190 100p. brown (Zahle) . . . . 7·25 9·00

18 Skiing

1936. Air. Tourist Propaganda.
191 18 0p.50 green . . . . 2·75 2·50
192 – 1p. orange . . . . 3·25 3·25
193 18 2p. violet . . . . 1·75 2·75
194 – 3p. green . . . . 2·50 2·75
195 18 5p. red . . . . 4·00 4·00
196 – 10p. brown . . . . 3·75 4·25
197 – 15p. red . . . . 38·00 35·00
198 18 25p. green £100 £100
DESIGN: 1, 3, 10, 15p. Jounieh Bay.

20 Cedar of Lebanon

21 President Edde

22 Lebanese Landscape

1937.
199 20 0p.10 red 15 15
200 0p.20 blue . . . . 25 2·40
201 0p.25 lilac . . . . 35 2·40
202 0p.50 mauve 20 20
203 0p.75 brown . . . . 35 1·25
207 21 3p. violet . . . . 3·00 1·40
208 4p. brown 95 25
209 4p.50 red . . . . 1·90 20
211 22 10p. red . . . . 2·75 25
212 12½p. blue . . . . 1·25 20
213 15p. green . . . . 2·75 25
214 20p. brown . . . . 3·25 25
215 25p. red . . . . 4·25 50
216 50p. violet . . . . 8·50 2·00
217 100p. sepia . . . . 9·00 2·75

23 Exhibition Pavilion, Paris

1937. Air. Paris International Exhibition.
218 23 0p.50 black . . . . 1·25 1·75
219 1p. green . . . . 80 3·00
220 2p. brown . . . . 1·50 3·00
221 3p. green . . . . 1·10 3·00
222 5p. green . . . . 1·25 3·25
223 10p. red . . . . 9·75 13·50
224 15p. purple . . . . 6·00 13·50
225 25p. brown . . . . 17·00 20·00

25 Ruins of Baalbek

1937. Air.
226 – 0p.50 blue 10 35
227 – 1p. red . . . . 1·00 1·60
228 – 2p. sepia . . . . 1·75 1·75
229 – 3p. red . . . . 3·25 2·50
230 – 5p. green . . . . 1·50 40
231 25 10p. violet 70 40
232 – 15p. blue . . . . 1·50 2·25
233 – 25p. violet . . . . 4·25 2·75
234 – 50p. green . . . . 8·75 2·25
235 – 100p. brown . . . . 4·25 3·50
DESIGN: 0p.50 to 5p. Beit ed-Din.

1938. Nos. 207/8 surch in English and Arabic figures.
236 21 2p. on 3p. violet 75 20
237 2½p. on 4p. brown . . . . 1·10 25

27 Medical College, Beirut

32 Emir Bechir Chehab

28 Maurice Nogues and Liore et Olivier LeO H.24-3 Flying Boat over Beirut

1938. Air. Medical Congress.
238 27 2p. green . . . . 2·75 3·50
239 3p. orange . . . . 3·00 4·00
240 5p. violet . . . . 3·75 5·50
241 10p. red . . . . 9·50 14·50

1938. Air. 10th Anniv of 1st Air Service between France and Lebanon.
242 28 10p. purple . . . . 4·25 6·00

1938. Surch.
243 16a 6p. on 7p.50 blue . . . . 2·50 95
244 – 7p.50 on 50p. grn (No. 179) . . . . . . 2·75 1·75
245 – 7p.50 on 100p. blk (No. 180) . . . . . . 1·90 2·50
246 22 12p.50 on 7p.50 blue . . 3·00 2·00
247 12½p. on 7p.50 blue . . . 1·00 30

1939. As T **16a**, but with differing figures and Arabic inscriptions in side panels, and imprint at foot "IMP. CATHOLIQUE-BEYROUTH-LIBAN" instead of "HELIO VAUGIRARD".
248 1p. green . . . . 1·10 75
249 1p.50 purple . . . . 1·50 45
250 7p.50 red . . . . 3·00 40
DESIGN: 1p. to 7p.50, Beit ed-Din.

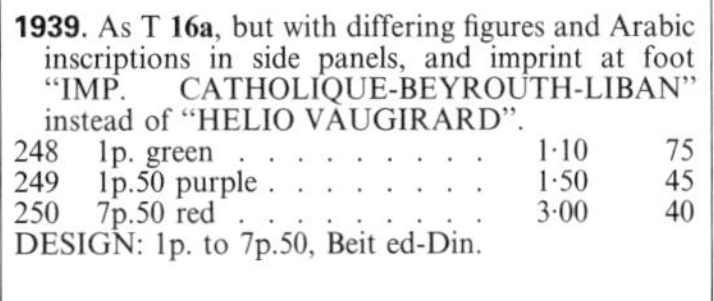

1942. 1st Anniv of Proclamation of Independence.
252 32 0p.50 green (postage) . . . 2·00 2·00
253 1p.50 purple . . . . 2·00 2·00
254 6p. red . . . . 2·00 2·00
255 15p. blue . . . . 2·00 2·00
256 – 10p. purple (air) . . . . . 3·75 3·75
257 – 50p. green . . . . 3·75 3·75
DESIGN: 10, 50p. Airplane over mountains.

1943. Surch in English and Arabic and with old values cancelled with ornaments.
258 21 2p. on 4p. brown . . . . 4·25 3·75
261 – 2p. on 5p. blue (No. 251) 55 40
262 – 3p. on 5p. blue (No. 251) 55 40
259 – 6p. on 7p.50 red (No. 250) 85 55
263 22 6p. on 12½p. blue 75 55
264 7½p. on 12½p. blue . . . . 1·25 1·25
260 10p. on 12½p. blue 95 65

37 Parliament House

38 Bechamoun

1944. 2nd Anniv of Proclamation of Independence.
265 37 25p. red (postage) . . . . 7·50 7·50
266 – 50p. blue . . . . 7·50 7·50
267 37 150p. blue . . . . 7·50 7·50
268 – 200p. purple . . . . 7·50 7·50
DESIGN: 50p., 200p. Government House.

269 38 25p. green (air) . . . . . 2·25 2·00
270 50p. orange . . . . 3·25 2·50
271 – 100p. brown . . . . 3·50 2·25
272 – 200p. violet . . . . 4·75 3·75
273 – 300p. green . . . . 15·00 12·00
274 – 500p. brown . . . . 35·00 25·00
DESIGNS: 100p., 200p. Rachaya Citadel; 300p., 500p. Beirut.

38a Beirut Isolation Hospital

المؤتمر الطبي العربي الثامن
١٩٤٤

(39)

1944. 6th Medical Congress. Optd with T **39**.
275 38a 10p. red (postage) . . . . 5·00 5·00
276 20p. blue . . . . 5·00 5·00

277 – 20p. orange (air) . . . . 2·25 2·25
278 – 50p. blue . . . . 2·25 2·25
279 – 100p. purple . . . . . . 3·75 3·75
DESIGN: Nos. 277/9, Bhannes Sanatorium.

(**40** Trans "Nov. 23, 1943")

1944. 1st Anniv of President's Return to Office. Nos. 265/74 optd with T **40**.
280 37 25p. red (postage) . . . . 10·00 10·00
281 – 50p. blue . . . . 10·00 10·00
282 37 150p. blue . . . . 10·00 10·00
283 – 200p. purple . . . . 10·00 10·00

284 38 25p. green (air) . . . . . 3·75 3·75
285 – 50p. orange . . . . 6·75 6·75
286 – 100p. brown . . . . 8·75 8·75
287 – 200p. violet . . . . 16·00 16·00
288 – 300p. green . . . . 21·00 21·00
289 – 500p. brown . . . . 40·00 40·00

41 Crusader Castle, Byblos

42 Falls of R. Litani

1945.
397 41 7p.50 red (postage) . . . . 2·40 20
398 10p. purple . . . . 3·75 25
399 12p.50 blue . . . . 8·75 30
290 15p. brown . . . . 2·50 2·25
291 20p. green . . . . 2·50 2·25
292 – 25p. blue . . . . 2·50 2·25
400 41 25p. violet . . . . 16·00 65
293 – 50p. red . . . . 4·75 2·50
401 41 50p. green . . . . 38·00 4·25

294 42 25p. brown (air) . . . . . 1·90 1·25
295 50p. purple . . . . 2·50 1·90
296 – 200p. violet . . . . 8·75 3·25
297 – 300p. black . . . . 18·00 6·25
DESIGNS—HORIZ: Nos. 292/3, Crusader Castle, Tripoli; 296/7, Cedar of Lebanon and skier.

43 V(ictory) and National Flag

44 V(ictory) and Lebanese Soldiers at Bir-Hakeim

1946. Victory. "V" in design. (a) Postage.
298 **43** 7p.50 brown, red and pink . . 70 10
299 10p. purple, pink and red . . 1·00 10
300 12p.50 purple, blue and red 1·25 15
301 15p. green, emerald and red . . . . 1·25 25
302 20p. myrtle, green and red 2·00 25
303 25p. blue, light blue and red . . . . 3·00 45
304 50p. blue, violet and red 5·75 1·50
305 100p. black, blue and red 9·50 3·50

(b) Air.
306 **44** 15p. blue, yellow and red 50 20
307 20p. red and blue 50 35
308 25p. blue, yellow and red 60 35
309 50p. black, violet and red 1·00 40
310 100p. violet and red . . . 3·25 90
311 150p. brown and red . . . 4·00 1·75

1946. As T **43** but without "V" sign.
312 7p.50 lake, red and mauve . . 70 10
313 10p. violet, mauve and red 1·00 10
314 12p.50 brown, green and red 1·25 20
315 15p. brown, pink and red . . 2·25 25
316 20p. blue, orange and red . . 1·90 25
317 25p. myrtle, green and red . . 3·25 40
318 50p. blue, light blue and red 7·00 1·50
319 100p. black, blue and red . . 11·50 3·50

45 Grey Herons

1946.
320 **45** 12p.50 red (postage) . . . 18·00 70

321 10p. orange (air) . . . . . 4·50 95
322 25p. blue . . . . 6·50 45
323 50p. green . . . . 15·50 1·40
324 100p. purple . . . . 27·00 6·50

46 Cedar of Lebanon

47

1946.
325 **46** 0p.50 brown 25 20
326 1p. purple 35 20
327 2p.50 violet . . . . 1·25 20
328 5p. red . . . . 1·90 20
329 6p. grey . . . . 2·50 20

1946. Air. Arab Postal Congress.
330 **47** 25p. blue 75 50
331 50p. green . . . . 1·10 75
332 75p. red . . . . 1·90 1·25
333 150p. violet . . . . 4·50 2·25

48 Cedar of Lebanon

49 President, Bridge and Tablet

1947.
333a **48** 0p.50 brown . . . . . . 1·00 10
333b 2p.50 green . . . . . . 1·50 10
333c 5p. red . . . . 2·50 20

1947. Air. Evacuation of Foreign Troops from Lebanon.
334 **49** 25p. blue 75 65
335 50p. red . . . . 1·10 95
336 75p. black . . . . 2·50 1·25
337 150p. green . . . . 4·50 2·50

50 Crusader Castle, Tripoli

51 Jounieh Bay

1947.
338 **50** 12p.50 red (postage) . . . 6·25 30
339 25p. blue . . . . 7·75 40
340 50p. green . . . . 25·00 75
341 100p. violet . . . . . . 32·00 5·50

342 **51** 5p. green (air) 30 10
343 10p. mauve 40 10
344 15p. red 60 10
403 15p. green . . . . 7·50 1·00
345 20p. orange 95 10
345a 20p. red . . . . 1·25 20
346 25p. blue . . . . 1·25 10
347 50p. red . . . . 3·00 25
348 100p. purple . . . . . . 6·25 25
349 – 150p. purple . . . . . . 12·50 1·10
350 – 200p. slate . . . . 19·00 5·00
351 – 300p. black . . . . 30·00 11·50
DESIGN: 150p. to 300p. Grand Serail Palace.

54 Phoenician Galley

1947. Air. 12th Congress of U.P.U., Paris.
352 – 10p. blue 75 35
353 – 15p. red . . . . 1·10 50
354 – 25p. blue . . . . 1·50 85
355 **54** 50p. green . . . . 3·50 1·00
356 – 75p. violet . . . . 4·50 1·40
357 – 100p. brown . . . . 6·25 3·00
DESIGN—VERT: 10p. to 25p. Posthorn.

55 Faraya Bridge and Statue

1947. Air. Red Cross Fund. Cross in red.
358 **55** 12p.50+25p. green . . . . 6·25 5·00
359 25p.+50p. blue . . . . . 7·00 5·75
360 50p.+100p. brown . . . . 9·50 7·00
361 – 75p.+150p. violet . . . . . 20·00 14·00
362 – 100p.+200p. grey . . . . . 35·00 25·00
DESIGN: 50p. to 100p. Djounie Bay and statue.

56 Cedar of Lebanon

58 Lebanese Landscape

1948.
363 **56** 0p.50 blue (postage) . . . 15 10
364 1p. brown 65 10
395 1p. orange 30 10
365 2p.50 mauve 60 10
366 3p. green . . . . 1·40 10
367 5p. red . . . . 2·00 10
368 – 7p.50 red . . . . 5·00 20
369 – 10p. purple . . . . 3·25 20
370 – 12p.50 blue . . . . 8·25 25
371 – 25p. blue . . . . 11·00 65
372 – 50p. green . . . . 25·00 5·00

373 **58** 5p. red (air) 50 10
374 10p. mauve . . . . 1·10 10
375 15p. brown . . . . 2·75 10
376 20p. slate . . . . 4·50 20
377 25p. blue . . . . 8·25 90
378 50p. black . . . . 14·50 1·75
DESIGN—As T **58**: Nos. 368/72, Zebaide Aqueduct.

59 Europa on Bull

61 Apollo on Sun Chariot

1948. 3rd Meeting of UNESCO, Beirut.
379 **59** 10p. orange and red (postage) . . . . 1·90 1·25
380 12p.50 mauve and violet 2·50 1·90
381 25p. green and light green 3·00 1·90
382 – 30p. buff and brown . . . 3·75 2·25
383 – 40p. green and turquoise 5·75 2·25
DESIGN—VERT: 30, 40p. Avicenna (philosopher and scientist).

384 **61** 7p.50 blue & lt blue (air) 1·60 1·25
385 15p. black and grey . . . 1·90 1·25
386 20p. brown and pink . . . 3·25 1·90

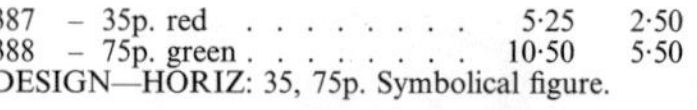
387 – 35p. red . . . . 5·25 2·50
388 – 75p. green . . . . 10·50 5·50
DESIGN—HORIZ: 35, 75p. Symbolical figure.

63 Camel

64 Sikorsky S-51 Helicopter

1949. 75th Anniv of U.P.U.
389 **63** 5p. violet (postage) . . . . 1·00 75
390 7p.50 red . . . . 1·50 1·25
391 12p.50 blue . . . . 2·25 1·60

392 **64** 25p. blue (air) . . . . . . 5·00 2·50
393 50p. green . . . . 7·50 3·75

65 Cedar of Lebanon

66 Nahr el-Kalb Bridge

1950.
407 **65** 0p.50 red 25 10
408 1p. red 65 10
409 2p.50 violet . . . . 1·00 10
410 5p. purple . . . . 1·90 10
411 **66** 7p.50 red . . . . 2·25 10
412 10p. lilac . . . . 2·75 10
413 12p.50 blue . . . . 4·50 20
414 25p. blue . . . . 8·75 95
415 50p. green . . . . 25·00 5·00

67 Congressional Flags

1950. Lebanese Emigrants' Congress. Inscr "MOIS DES EMIGRES–ETE 1950".
416 **67** 7p.50 green (postage) . . . 65 20
417 12p. mauve 65 20

418 – 5p. blue (air) . . . . . . 2·25 60
419 – 15p. violet . . . . 3·00 85
420 – 25p. brown . . . . 1·25 75
421 – 35p. green . . . . 2·50 1·25
DESIGNS: 5, 15p. House martins; 25, 35p. Pres. Bishara al-Khoury and building.

70 Crusader Castle, Sidon

1950. Air.
422 **70** 10p. brown 50 20
423 15p. green . . . . 1·00 15
424 20p. red . . . . 2·25 30
425 25p. blue . . . . 5·00 1·25
426 50p. grey . . . . 7·50 2·50

1950. Surch with figures and bars.
427 **56** 1p. on 3p. green 50 20
428 **46** 2p.50 on 6p. grey 75 20

73 Cedar of Lebanon

74 Nahr el-Kalb Bridge

75 Crusader Castle, Sidon

1951.
429 **73** 0p.50 red (postage) 25 10
430 1p. brown 50 10
431 2p.50 grey . . . . 2·50 10
432 5p. purple . . . . 2·75 10
433 **74** 7p.50 red . . . . 3·00 30
434 10p. purple . . . . 3·75 20
435 12p.50 turquoise . . . . . 7·50 35
436 25p. blue . . . . 11·50 1·25
437 50p. green . . . . 25·00 6·75

438 **75** 10p. turquoise (air) 80 10
439 15p. brown . . . . 1·75 10
440 20p. red . . . . 1·75 20
441 25p. blue . . . . 2·00 20
442 35p. mauve . . . . 5·00 2·50
443 50p. blue . . . . 9·00 2·00
Type **74** is similar to Type **66** but left value tablets differ.
For design as Type **74** but inscr "LIBAN", see Nos. 561/3.

76 Cedar of Lebanon

77 Baalbek

1952.
444 **76** 0p.50 green (postage) . . . 60 10
445 1p. brown 60 10
446 2p.50 blue 90 20
447 5p. red . . . . 1·60 25
448 **77** 7p.50 red . . . . 1·90 45
449 10p. violet . . . . 4·50 50
450 12p.50 blue . . . . 4·50 50
451 25p. blue . . . . 5·75 1·25
452 – 50p. green . . . . 17·00 2·25
453 – 100p. brown . . . . 35·00 7·00

454 – 5p. red (air) 30 10
455 – 10p. grey 45 10
456 – 15p. mauve 80 10
457 – 20p. orange . . . . 1·25 30
458 – 25p. blue . . . . 1·25 40
459 – 35p. blue . . . . 2·10 45
460 – 50p. green . . . . 7·00 50
461 – 100p. blue . . . . 48·00 2·10
462 – 200p. green . . . . 28·00 4·00
463 – 300p. sepia . . . . 38·00 8·75
DESIGNS—As Type **77**: Nos. 452/3, Beaufort Castle; 454/9, Beirut Airport; 460/3, Amphitheatre, Byblos.

78 Cedar of Lebanon

79 General Post Office

80 Douglas DC-4

1953.
559 **78** 0p.50 blue (postage) . . . 20 10
465 1p. red 70 10
466 2p.50 violet 90 20
560 2p.50 purple 60 10
467 5p. green . . . . 1·60 25
468 **79** 7p.50 red . . . . 2·50 35
469 10p. green . . . . 3·00 50
470 12p.50 turquoise . . . . . 4·25 55
471 25p. blue . . . . 6·25 1·10
472 50p. brown . . . . 11·50 2·50

473 **80** 5p. green (air) 30 10
474 10p. red 55 10
475 15p. red 80 10
476 20p. turquoise . . . . . . 1·25 10
477 25p. blue . . . . 3·25 10
478 35p. brown . . . . 4·50 20
479 50p. blue . . . . 6·50 45
480 100p. sepia . . . . 12·00 4·25
For 20p. green as Type **79** see No. 636.

81 Cedar of Lebanon

82 Beit ed-Din Palace

83 Baalbek

1954.
481 **81** 0p.50 blue (postage) . . . 20 10
482 1p. orange 35 10
483 2p.50 violet 60 20
484 5p. green . . . . 1·10 20
485 **82** 7p.50 red . . . . 1·90 45
486 10p. green . . . . 2·75 45
487 12p.50 blue . . . . 4·50 60
488 25p. deep blue . . . . . . 6·25 2·25
489 50p. turquoise . . . . . . 11·00 3·75
490 100p. sepia . . . . 25·00 7·50

491 **83** 5p. green (air) 40 10
492 10p. lilac 70 10
493 15p. red 80 10
494 20p. brown . . . . 1·10 10
495 25p. blue . . . . 1·25 20
496 35p. sepia . . . . 1·75 25
497 – 50p. green . . . . 5·50 40
498 – 100p. red . . . . 9·00 60
499 – 200p. sepia . . . . 20·00 1·90
500 – 300p. blue . . . . 32·00 3·75

DESIGN—As T **83**: 50p. to 300p. Litani Irrigation Canal.

For other values as Nos. 497/500, see Nos. 564/7.

84 Khalde Airport, Beirut

1954. Air. Opening of Beirut International Airport.

501	**84**	10p. red and pink	45	25
502		25p. blue and ultramarine	1·25	40
503		35p. brown and sepia	1·75	65
504		65p. green and turquoise	4·25	2·50

84a

1955. Arab Postal Union.

505	**84a**	12p.50 green (postage)	50	35
506		25p. violet	75	35
507		2p.50 brown (air)	40	30

85 Rotary Emblem **86** Cedar of Lebanon

87 Jeita Grotto **88** Skiers

1955. Air. 50th Anniv of Rotary International.

508	**85**	35p. green	90	65
509		65p. blue	1·60	95

1955.

510	**86**	0p.50 blue (postage)	20	10
511		1p. red	25	10
512		2p.50 violet	45	10
552		2p.50 blue	6·25	25
513		5p. green	70	10
514	**87**	7p.50 orange	95	10
515		10p. green	1·60	10
516		12p.50 blue	1·60	10
517		25p. blue	4·00	25
518		50p. green	5·75	75
519	**88**	5p. turquoise (air)	50	35
520		15p. red	85	20
521		20p. violet	1·50	20
522		25p. blue	2·75	30
523		35p. brown	4·50	50
524		50p. brown	7·50	70
525		65p. blue	14·00	2·25

The face value on No. 510 reads "0.50 PIASTRE"; on No. 512 the "2" and "50" are different sizes and the 1 and 5p. have no dash under "P".

For other colours and new values as Type **88** see Nos. 568/70 and for redrawn Type **86** see Nos. 582/5, 686 and 695/7.

89 Visitor from Abroad **90** Cedar of Lebanon **91** Globe and Columns

92 Oranges

1955. Air. Tourist Propaganda.

526	**89**	2p.50 slate and purple	10	10
527		12p.50 blue & ultramarine	30	20
528		25p. blue and indigo	80	35
529		35p. blue and green	1·25	50

1955.

530	**90**	0.50p. blue (postage)	20	10
531		1p. orange	20	10
532		2p.50 violet	25	10
533		5p. green	50	10
534	**91**	7p.50 red and orange	65	10
535		10p. green and brown	75	10
536		12p.50 blue and green	95	10
537		25p. blue and mauve	1·90	20
538		50p. green and blue	2·75	35
539		100p. brown and orange	4·50	1·10
540	**92**	5p. yellow and green (air)	25	10
541		10p. orange and green	60	10
542		15p. orange and green	60	10
543		20p. orange and brown	1·00	10
544	–	25p. violet and blue	1·25	10
545	–	35p. purple and green	2·50	25
546	–	50p. yellow and black	2·50	25
547	–	65p. yellow and green	5·00	35
548	–	100p. orange and green	8·25	1·00
549	–	200p. red and green	15·00	4·50

DESIGNS—VERT: 25p. to 50p. Grapes. HORIZ: 4p. to 200p. Quinces.

93 U.N. Emblem

1956. Air. 10th Anniv of U.N.

550	**93**	35p. blue	4·00	3·25
551		65p. green	5·25	3·75

94 Masks, Columns and Gargoyle

1956. Air. Baalbek International Drama Festival. Inscr "FESTIVAL INTERNATIONAL DE BAALBECK".

553	**94**	2p.50 sepia	30	15
554		10p. green	45	25
555	–	12p.50 blue	45	35
556	–	25p. violet	1·00	45
557	–	35p. purple	1·90	65
558	–	65p. slate	3·00	1·90

DESIGNS—HORIZ: 12p.50, 25p. Temple ruins at Baalbek. VERT: 35p., 65p. Double bass, masks and columns.

1957. As earlier designs but redrawn. (a) Postage. As T **74** but inscr "LIBAN".

561		7p.50 red	1·10	10
562		10p. brown	1·60	10
563		12p.50 blue	1·90	10

(b) Air. Arabic inscription changed. New values and colours.

564	–	10p. violet	25	10
565	–	15p. orange	40	10
566	–	20p. green	50	10
567	–	25p. blue	60	10
568	**88**	35p. green	2·10	20
569		65p. purple	3·75	55
570		100p. brown	6·25	1·25

DESIGN: 10p. to 25p. As Nos. 497/500.

95 Pres. Chamoun and King Faisal II of Iraq

1957. Air. Arab Leaders' Conference, Beirut.

571	**95**	15p. orange	65	40
572	–	15p. blue	65	40
573	–	15p. maroon	65	40
574	–	15p. purple	65	40
575	–	15p. green	65	40
576	–	25p. turquoise	65	40
577	–	100p. brown	4·50	2·25

DESIGNS—As T **95**: 15p. values show Pres. Chamoun and: King Hussein of Jordan (No. 572), Abdallah Khalil of Sudan (No. 573), Pres. Shukri Bey al-Quwatli of Syria (No. 574) and King Saud of Saudi Arabia (No. 575); 25p. Map and Pres. Chamoun. 44 × 44 mm (Diamond shape): 100p. The six Arab Leaders.

97 Runners **98** Miners

1957. 2nd Pan-Arabian Games, Beirut.

578	**97**	2p.50 sepia (postage)	65	40
579	–	12p.50 blue	95	50
580	–	35p. purple (air)	2·50	1·00
581	–	50p. green	3·00	1·50

DESIGNS—VERT: 12p.50, Footballers. HORIZ: 35p. Fencers; 50p. Stadium.

1957.

582	**86**	0p.50 blue (16½ × 20½ mm) (postage)	15	10
582a		0p.50 violet (17 × 21½ mm)	25	10
583		1p. brown (16½ × 20½ mm)	20	10
583a		1p. purple (17 × 21½ mm)	25	10
584		2p.50 violet (16½ × 20½ mm)	35	10
584a		2p.50 blue (17 × 21¼ mm)	40	10
585		5p. green (16½ × 20½ mm)	50	10
586	**98**	7½p. pink	75	10
587		10p. brown	1·00	10
588		12½p. blue	1·40	10
589	–	25p. blue	1·40	10
590	–	50p. green	2·50	30
591	–	100p. brown	4·50	90
592	–	5p. green (air)	20	10
593	–	10p. orange	25	10
594	–	15p. brown	25	10
595	–	20p. purple	40	10
596	–	25p. blue	50	15
597	–	35p. purple	80	30
598	–	50p. green	1·50	45
599	–	65p. brown	2·50	45
600	–	100p. grey	3·25	1·25

DESIGNS: POSTAGE—As Type **86**: 50c. inscr "0 P.50", 2p.50, Figures in uniform size; 1p., 5p. Short dash under "P". As Type **98**: VERT: 25p. to 100p. Potter. AIR—As Type **98**: HORIZ: 5p. to 25p. Cedar of Lebanon with signs of the Zodiac, bird and ship; 35 to 100p. Chamoun Electric Power Station.

99 Cedar of Lebanon **100** Soldier and Flag

101 Douglas DC-6B at Khalde Airport

1959.

601	**99**	0p.50 blue (postage)	15	10
602		1p. orange	25	10
603		2p.50 violet	35	10
604		5p. green	50	10
605	**100**	12p.50 blue	1·00	10
606		25p. blue	1·10	10
607		50p. brown	1·90	25
608		100p. sepia	3·50	45
609	**101**	5p. green (air)	55	10
610		10p. purple	55	10
611		15p. violet	80	10
612		20p. red	1·10	15
613		25p. violet	1·50	25
614	–	35p. myrtle	1·10	25
615	–	50p. turquoise	1·40	25
616	–	65p. sepia	2·75	45
617	–	100p. blue	3·25	75

DESIGN—HORIZ: Nos. 614/17, Factory, cogwheel and telegraph pylons.

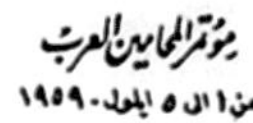

(**102**)

1959. Lawyers' Conference. Nos. 538 and 546 surch as T **102**.

618		30p. on 50p. myrtle and blue (postage)	1·10	65
619		40p. on 50p. yellow & blk (air)	1·00	65

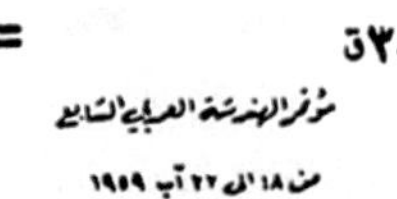

(**103**)

1959. Air. Engineers' Conference. Nos. 614 and 616 surch as T **103**.

620		30p. on 35p. myrtle	65	50
621		40p. on 65p. sepia	1·25	75

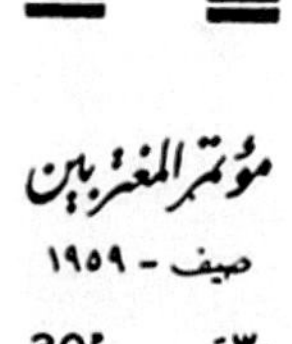

(**104**) **105** Discus Thrower

1959. Emigrants' Conference. No. 590 surch as T **104**.

622		30p. on 50p. green	75	30
623		40p. on 50p. green	1·10	60

1959. Air. 3rd Mediterranean Games, Beirut.

624	**105**	15p. green	50	25
625	–	30p. brown	75	40
626	–	40p. blue	1·60	65

DESIGNS—VERT: 30p. Weightlifting. HORIZ: 40p. Games emblem.

106 Soldiers with Standard **108** Planting Tree

1959. Air. 16th Anniv of Independence.

627	**106**	40p. red and black	95	65
628		60p. red and green	1·25	90

1959. Surch.

629	**100**	7p.50 on 12p.50 blue	50	10
630		10p. on 12p.50 blue	65	10
631		15p. on 25p. blue	75	10
632	–	40p. on 50p. green (No. 590)	1·25	90
633	**88**	40p. on 65p. purple (No. 569) (air)	2·50	60

1960. Air. 25th Anniv of Friends of the Tree Society.

634	**108**	20p. purple and green	75	50
635		40p. sepia and green	1·10	75

1960. Air. As T **79** but colours of name and value tablets reversed.

636		20p. green	70	45

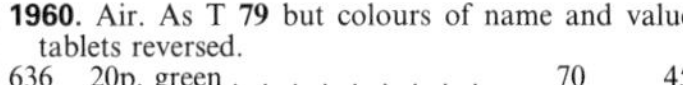

109 Pres. Chehab **111** "Uprooted Tree"

110 Arab League Centre

1960. Air.

637	**109**	5p. green	10	10
638		10p. blue	10	10
639		15p. brown	10	10
640		20p. sepia	15	10
641		30p. olive	20	10
642		40p. red	45	15
643		50p. blue	60	20

644 70p. purple . . . . 1·10 25
645 100p. green . . . . 2·25 65

1960. Inaug of Arab League Centre, Cairo.
646 **110** 15p. turquoise 50 40

1960. Air. World Refugee Year. (a) Size 20½ × 36½ mm.
647 **111** 25p. brown 75 50
648 40p. green . . . . 1·10 75
(b) Size 19½ × 35½ mm.
648b **111** 25p. brown . . . . . . 1·00 1·00
648c 40p. green . . . . . . 1·25 1·25

112 Martyrs' Monument

1960. Air. Martyrs' Commemoration.
649 **112** 20p. purple and green . . 50 30
650 40p. blue and green . . . 75 50
651 – 70p. olive and black . . . 1·60 75
DESIGN—VERT: 70p. Detail of statues on monument.

113 Pres. Chehab and King Mohammed V
114 Pres. Chehab

1960. Air. Visit of King Mohammed V of Morocco.
652 **113** 30p. chocolate and brown 75 50
653 70p. brown and black . . 1·50 75

1960.
654 **114** 50c. green 10 10
655 2p.50 olive 10 10
656 5p. green 15 10
657 7p.50 red 30 10
658 15p. blue 50 25
659 50p. purple . . . . . . 1·25 30
660 100p. brown . . . . . . 2·50 50

115 Child
116 Dove, Map and Flags

1960. Air. Mother and Child Days.
661 **115** 20p. red and yellow . . . 50 25
662 20p.+10p. red and yellow 75 40
663 – 60p. blue and light blue 1·25 85
664 – 60p.+15p. blue & lt bl . . 1·90 1·00
DESIGN: Nos. 663/4, Mother and child.

1960. Air. World Lebanese Union Meeting, Beirut. Multicoloured.
665 20p. Type **116** 25 20
666 40p. Cedar of Lebanon and homing pigeons 75 40
667 70p. Globes and Cedar of Lebanon (horiz) 90 50

(**117**)

1960. Arabian Oil Congress, Beirut. Optd with T **117**.
668 **86** 5p. green (No. 585) . . . 30 10
669 **110** 15p. turquoise 65 40

1960. Air. World Refugee Year. Nos. 648b/c surch in English and Arabic.
669a **111** 20p.+10p. on 40p. grn 7·00 7·00
669b 30p.+15p. on 25p. brn 10·00 10·00

119 Boxing

1961. Olympic Games.
670 **119** 2p.50+2p.50 brown and blue (postage) 20 20
671 – 5p.+5p. brown & orge . . 30 25
672 – 7p.50+7p.50 brn & vio . . 50 40
673 – 15p.+15p. brown & red (air) . . . . 2·50 2·25
674 – 25p.+25p. brown & grn 2·50 2·25
675 – 35p.+35p. brown & bl . . 2·50 2·25
DESIGNS: 5p. Wrestling; 7p.50, Putting the shot; 15p. Fencing; 25p. Cycling; 35p. Swimming.

120 Pres. Chehab
121 Pres. Chehab and Map of Lebanon
122 U.N. Emblem and Map

1961.
676 **120** 2p.50 ultramarine and blue (postage) 20 10
677 7p.50 violet and mauve 25 10
678 10p. brown and yellow . . 50 10
679 **121** 5p. green & lt green (air) 15 10
680 10p. brown and ochre . . 45 10
681 70p. violet and mauve . . 1·90 60
682 – 200p. blue and bistre . . 4·25 2·50
DESIGN—HORIZ: 200p. Casino, Maameltein.

1961. Air. 15th Anniv of U.N.O.
683 **122** 20p. purple and blue . . . 50 25
684 – 30p. green and brown . . 75 40
685 – 50p. blue and ultramarine 1·25 60
DESIGNS—VERT: 30p. U.N. emblem and Baalbek ruins. HORIZ: 50p. View of U.N. Headquarters and Manhattan.

123 Cedar of Lebanon
124 Bay of Maameltein

1961. Redrawn version of T **86** (different arrangement at foot). Shaded background.
686 **123** 2p.50 myrtle 50 10
See also Nos. 695/7.

1961. Air.
687 **124** 15p. lake 40 20
688 30p. blue 65 30
689 40p. sepia 90 45

125 Weaving

1961. Air. Labour Day.
690 – 30p. red . . . . 1·25 60
691 **125** 70p. blue . . . . 2·50 1·25
DESIGN: 30p. Pottery.

126 Water-skiers

1961. Air. Tourist Month.
692 – 15p. violet and blue . . . 60 35
693 **126** 40p. blue and flesh . . . 1·25 50
694 – 70p. olive and flesh . . . 1·90 1·00
DESIGNS—VERT: 15p. Firework display. HORIZ: 70p. Tourists in punt.

1961. As T **123** but plain background.
695 2p.50 yellow 30 10
696 5p. lake 40 15
697 10p. black 65 25

127 G.P.O., Beirut

1961.
698 **127** 2p.50 mauve (postage) . . 30 10
699 5p. green 50 20
700 15p. blue . . . . 1·00 35
701 – 35p. green (air) 60 45
702 – 50p. brown 90 55
703 – 100p. black . . . . 1·25 90
DESIGN: 35p. to 100p. Motor highway, Dora.

128 Cedars of Lebanon
129 Tyre Waterfront

1961.
704 **128** 0p.50 green (postage) . . 10 10
705 1p. brown 10 10
706 2p.50 blue 10 10
707 5p. red 25 10
708 7p.50 violet 35 10
709 – 10p. purple 80 10
710 – 15p. blue . . . . 1·10 20
711 – 50p. green . . . . 1·25 75
712 – 100p. black . . . . 3·00 1·10
713 **129** 5p. red (air) 20 10
714 10p. violet 25 10
715 15p. blue 45 10
716 20p. orange 45 10
717 30p. green 50 15
718 – 40p. purple 75 25
719 – 50p. blue 90 40
720 – 70p. green . . . . 1·25 60
721 – 100p. sepia . . . . 2·25 95
DESIGNS—HORIZ: Nos. 709/12, Zahle. VERT: Nos. 718/21, Afka Falls.
See also Nos. 729/34.

130 UNESCO Building, Beirut

1961. Air. 15th Anniv of UNESCO. Mult.
722 20p. Type **130** 35 25
723 30p. UNESCO emblem and cedar (vert) 65 40
724 50p. UNESCO Building, Paris . . . . 1·00 60

131 Tomb of Unknown Soldier
132 Scout Bugler

1961. Independence and Evacuation of Foreign Troops Commemoration. Multicoloured.
725 10p. Type **131** (postage) . . . 35 10
726 15p. Soldier and flag 50 10
727 25p. Cedar emblem (horiz) (air) 45 25
728 50p. Emirs Bashir and Fakhreddine (horiz) . . . 65 50

1962. As Nos. 704/21 but with larger figures of value.
729 **128** 50c. green (postage) . . . 20 10
730 1p. brown 20 10
731 2p.50 blue 25 10
732 – 15p. blue . . . . 3·00 25
733 **129** 5p. red (air) 35 10
734 – 40p. purple . . . . 5·50 75

1962. Lebanese Scout Movement Commemorative.
735 ½p. black, yell & grn (postage) 10 10
736 1p. multicoloured 10 10
737 2½p. green, black and red . . 10 10
738 6p. multicoloured 35 10
739 10p. yellow, black and blue 65 10
740 15p. multicoloured (air) . . . 65 25
741 20p. yellow, black and violet 75 35
742 25p. multicoloured . . . . . 1·25 65
DESIGNS—VERT: ½p. Type **132**; 6p. Lord Baden-Powell; 20p. Saluting hand. HORIZ: 1p. Scout with flag, cedar and badge; 2½p. Stretcher party, badge and laurel; 10p. Scouts at campfire; 15p. Cedar and Guide badge; 25p. Cedar and Scout badge.

133 Arab League Centre, Cairo, and Emblem
134 Blacksmith

1962. Air. Arab League Week.
743 **133** 20p. ultramarine and blue 40 25
744 30p. lake and pink . . . 45 40
745 50p. green and turquoise 75 65
See also Nos. 792/5.

1962. Air. Labour Day.
746 **134** 5p. green and blue . . . 20 10
747 10p. blue and pink . . . 30 10
748 – 25p. violet and pink . . . 50 20
749 – 35p. mauve and blue . . 65 40
DESIGN—HORIZ: 25, 35p. Tractor.

1962. European Shooting Championships. Nos. 670/5 optd **CHAMPIONNAT D'EUROPE DE TIR 2 JUIN 1962** in French and Arabic.
750 **119** 2p.50+2p.50 (postage) . . 40 25
751 – 5p.+5p. 65 50
752 – 7p.50+7p.50 . . . . . . 95 60
753 – 15p.+15p. (air) 95 95
754 – 25p.+25p. . . . . 2·25 2·25
755 – 35p.+35p. . . . . 2·50 2·50

136 Hand grasping Emblem
137 Rock Temples of Abu Simbel

1962. Air. Malaria Eradication.
756 **136** 30p. brown & light brown 75 50
757 – 70p. violet and lilac . . . 1·25 75
DESIGN: 70p. Campaign emblem.

1962. Nubian Monuments.
758 **137** 5p. bl & ultram (postage) 50 20
759 15p. lake and brown . . . 75 25
760 – 30p. yellow and green (air) . . . . 1·25 60
761 – 50p. olive and grey . . . 2·50 1·25
DESIGNS: 30, 50p. Bas-relief.

138 Playing-card Symbols
139 Schoolboy

1962. Air. European Bridge Championships.
762 **138** 25p. multicoloured . . . 3·00 1·90
763 40p. multicoloured . . . 3·25 1·90

1962. Schoolchildren's Day.
764 **139** 30p. mult (postage) . . . 50 25
765 – 45p. multicoloured (air) 75 40
DESIGN: 45p. Teacher.

140
141 Cherries

1962. Air. 19th Anniv of Independence.
766 **140** 25p. green, red & turq . . 75 35
767 25p. violet, red & turq . . 75 35
768 25p. blue, red & turquoise 75 35

1962. Fruits. Multicoloured.
769 0p.50 Type **141** (postage) . . 25 10
770 1p. Figs 25 10
771 2p.50 Type **141** 40 10
772 5p. Figs 50 10
773 7p.50 Type **141** 25 10
774 10p. Grapes 35 10
775 17p.50 Grapes 75 10
776 30p. Grapes . . . . 1·25 25
777 50p. Oranges . . . . 2·25 65
778 100p. Pomegranates . . . . 5·00 1·40
779 5p. Apricots (air) 20 10
780 10p. Plums 25 10
781 20p. Apples 55 10
782 30p. Plums 75 25
783 40p. Apples 90 25
784 50p. Pears . . . . 1·10 40
785 70p. Medlars . . . . 1·90 50
786 100p. Lemons . . . . 3·25 1·10

142 Reaping
143 Nurse tending Baby 

1963. Air. Freedom from Hunger.
787 **142** 2p.50 yellow and blue . . 15 10
788 5p. yellow and green . . . 15 10
789 7p.50 yellow and purple 20 10
790 – 15p. green and red . . . 50 25
791 – 20p. green and red . . . 65 40
DESIGN—HORIZ: 15, 20p. Three ears of wheat within hand.

1963. Air. Arab League Week. As T **133** but inscr "1963".
792 5p. violet and blue 10 10
793 10p. green and blue 20 20
794 15p. brown and blue 30 25
795 20p. grey and blue 65 45

1963. Air. Red Cross Centenary.
796 – 5p. green and red 10 10
797 – 20p. blue and red 30 10
798 **143** 35p. red and black . . . 55 25
799 40p. violet and red . . . 90 45
DESIGN—HORIZ: 5, 20p. Blood transfusion.

144 Allegory of Music
145 Flag and rising Sun 

1963. Air. Baalbek Festival.
800 **144** 35p. orange and blue . . 95 50

1963. Air. 20th Anniv of Independence. Flag and sun in red and yellow.
801 **145** 5p. turquoise 15 10
802 10p. green 25 25
803 25p. blue 50 40
804 40p. drab 75 65

146 Cycling
147 Hyacinth 

1964. 4th Mediterranean Games, Naples (1963).
805 **146** 2p.50 brown and purple (postage) 20 10
806 – 5p. orange and blue . . . 25 10
807 – 10p. brown and violet . . 40 10
808 – 15p. orange and green (air) 40 25
809 – 17p.50 brown and blue . . 50 30
810 – 30p. brown and turquoise 75 50
DESIGNS—VERT: 5p. Basketball; 10p. Running; 15p. Tennis. HORIZ: 17p.50, Swimming; 30p. Skiing.

1964. Flowers. Multicoloured.
811 0p.50 Type **147** (postage) . . 10 10
812 1p. Type **147** 10 10
813 2p.50 Type **147** 10 10
814 5p. Cyclamen 10 10
815 7p.50 Cyclamen 15 10
816 10p. Poinsettia (vert) 25 10
817 17p.50 Anemone (vert) . . . 50 10
818 30p. Iris (vert) . . . . 1·10 40
819 50p. Poppy (vert) . . . . . 2·50 65
820 5p. Lily (vert) (air) 25 20
821 10p. Ranunculus (vert) . . . 45 20
822 20p. Anemone (vert) 60 20
823 40p. Tuberose (vert) . . . . 1·00 40
824 45p. Rhododendron (vert) . . 1·10 40
825 50p. Jasmine (vert) . . . . . 1·25 40
826 70p. Yellow broom (vert) . . 1·90 65
Nos. 816/26 are size 26½ × 37 mm.

148 Cedar of Lebanon
149 Cedar of Lebanon 

1964.
827 **148** 0p.50 green 25 10
828 **149** 0p.50 green 15 10
829 2p.50 blue 15 10
830 5p. mauve 20 10
831 7p.50 orange 40 10
832 17p.50 purple 70 10

150 Child on Rocking-horse
152 "Flame of Freedom" 

151 League Session

1964. Air. Children's Day.
833 – 5p. red, orange and green 15 10
834 – 10p. red, orange and brown 25 15
835 **150** 20p. orange, blue and ultramarine 50 35
836 40p. yellow, blue and purple 90 65
DESIGN—HORIZ: 5, 10p. Girls skipping.

1964. Air. Arab League Meeting.
837 **151** 5p. buff, brown and black 25 20
838 10p. black 35 25
839 15p. turquoise 65 40
840 20p. mauve, brn & sepia 1·00 45

1964. Air. 15th Anniv of Declaration of Human Rights.
841 **152** 20p. red, pink and brown 25 25
842 – 40p. orange, blue and light blue 50 35
DESIGN: 40p. Flame on pedestal bearing U.N. emblem.

153 Sick Child
154 Clasped Wrists 

1964. Air. "Bal des Petits Lits Blancs" (Ball for children's charity).
843 **153** 2p.50 multicoloured . . . 15 10
844 5p. multicoloured 15 10
845 15p. multicoloured . . . 25 10
846 – 17p.50 multicoloured . . 40 25
847 – 20p. multicoloured . . . 50 25
848 – 40p. multicoloured . . . 80 40
DESIGN—55 × 25½ mm: 17p.50 to 40p. Children in front of palace (venue of ball).

1964. Air. World Lebanese Union Congress, Beirut.
849 **154** 20p. black, yellow & green 50 25
850 40p. black, yellow & pur 90 50

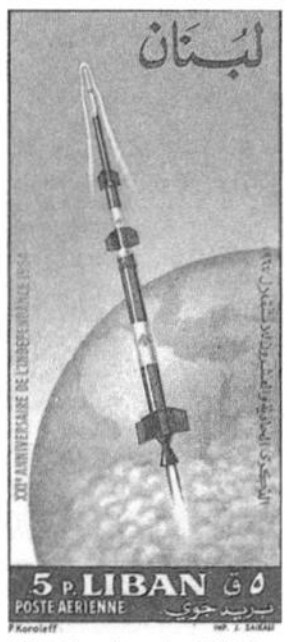

155 Rocket in Flight

1964. Air. 21st Anniv of Independence.
851 **155** 5p. multicoloured 25 20
852 10p. multicoloured . . . 25 20
853 – 40p. blue and black . . . 95 45
854 – 70p. purple and black . . 1·40 1·10
DESIGNS—HORIZ: 40p. to 70p. "Struggle for Independence" (battle scene).

156 Temple Columns

1965. Baalbek Festival.
855 **156** 2p.50 black and orange (postage) 25 20
856 – 7p.50 black and blue . . 50 35
857 – 10p. multicoloured (air) 10 10
858 – 15p. multicoloured . . . 25 10
859 – 25p. multicoloured . . . 50 40
860 – 40p. multicoloured . . . 1·00 50
DESIGNS—28 × 55 mm: 10, 15p. Man in costume; 25, 40p. Woman in costume.

157 Swimming

1965. Olympic Games, Tokyo.
861 **157** 2p.50 black, blue and mauve (postage) . . . 20 10
862 – 7p.50 purple, green & brn 75 50
863 – 10p. grey, brown & green 95 60
864 – 15p. black and green (air) 25 10
865 – 25p. green and purple 50 25
866 – 40p. brown and blue . . . 80 40
DESIGNS—HORIZ: 7p.50, Fencing; 15p. Horse-jumping; 40p. Gymnastics. VERT: 10p. Basketball; 25p. Rifle-shooting.

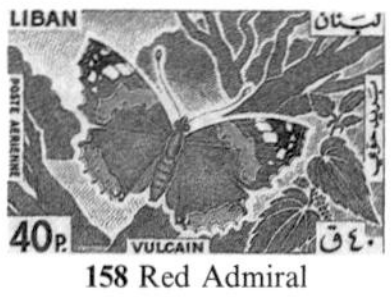

158 Red Admiral

1965. (a) Postage. Birds.
867 – 5p. multicoloured 45 10
868 – 10p. multicoloured 60 10
869 – 15p. chocolate, orange & brn . . . . 1·10 15
870 – 17p.50 purple, red and blue 1·60 20
871 – 20p. black, yellow and green 1·75 20
872 – 32p.50 yellow, brown & grn 4·50 75

(b) Air. Butterflies.
873 – 30p. yellow, brown and red 75 10
874 – 35p. blue, red and bistre 1·10 20
875 **158** 40p. brown, red and green 1·40 20
876 – 45p. brown, yellow & blue 1·75 40
877 – 70p. multicoloured . . . 2·75 50
878 – 85p. black, orange & green . . . . 3·00 65
879 – 100p. blue and plum . . . 4·50 75
880 – 200p. brown, blue & pur 8·00 90
881 – 300p. sepia, yellow & green . . . . 12·00 2·50
882 – 500p. brown, blue and light blue . . . . . . 20·00 5·00
DESIGNS—As T **158**. BIRDS: 5p. Northern bullfinch; 10p. Eurasian goldfinch; 15p. Hoopoe; 17p.50, Red-legged partridge; 20p. Golden oriole; 32p.50, European bee eater. BUTTERFLIES: 30p. Large tiger moth; 35p. Small postman; 45p. Common grayling; 70p. Swallowtail; 85p. Orange-tip; 100p. Blue morpho; 200p. "Erasmia sanguiflua"; 300p. "Papilio crassus". 35½ × 25 mm: 500p. Amelia's charakes.

159 Pope Paul and Pres. Helou

1965. Air. Pope Paul's Visit to Lebanon.
883 **159** 45p. violet and gold . . . 3·25 1·90

160 Sheep

1965.
884 – 50c. multicoloured 50 10
885 – 1p. grey, black and mauve 65 10
886 **160** 2p.50 yellow, sepia & grn 75 10
DESIGNS: 50c. Cow and calf; 1p. Rabbit.

161 "Cedars of Friendship"
162 "Silk Manufacture" 

1965. Air.
887 **161** 40p. multicoloured . . . 1·25 25

1965. Air. World Silk Congress, Beirut. Mult.
888 2p.50 Type **162** 20 10
889 5p. Type **162** 20 10
890 7p.50 Type **162** 25 10
891 15p. Weaver and loom . . . 25 10
892 30p. As 15p. 65 25
893 40p. As 15p. . . . . 1·00 40
894 50p. As 15p. . . . . 1·25 50

163 Parliament Building

1965. Air. Centenary of Lebanese Parliament.
895 **163** 35p. brown, ochre and red 40 25
896 40p. brown, ochre & green 65 40

164 U.N. Emblem and Headquarters
165 Playing-card "King" 

1965. Air. 20th Anniv of U.N.O.
897 **164** 2p.50 blue 10 10
898 10p. red 10 10
899 17p.50 violet 10 10
900 30p. green 40 25
901 40p. brown 50 40

1965. Air. World Bridge Championships, Beirut.
902 **165** 2p.50 multicoloured . . . 20 10
903 15p. multicoloured . . . 45 10
904 17p.50 multicoloured . . 65 25
905 40p. multicoloured . . . 1·25 50

166 Dagger on Deir Yassin, Palestine
167 I.T.U. Emblem and Symbols

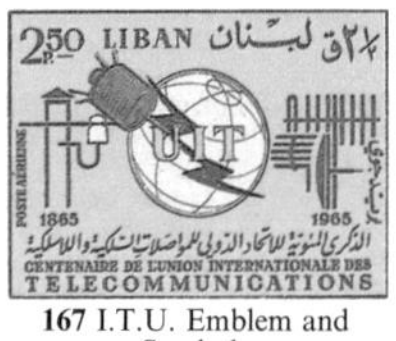

1965. Air. Deir Yassin Massacre.
906 **166** 50p. multicoloured . . . 2·25 50

1966. Air. Centenary (1965) of I.T.U.
907 **167** 2p.50 multicoloured . . . 20 10
908 15p. multicoloured . . . 20 10
909 17p.50 multicoloured . . 45 15
910 25p. multicoloured . . . 75 30
911 40p. multicoloured . . . 1·00 40

168 Stage Performance

1966. Air. Baalbek Festival. Multicoloured.
912 2p.50 Type **168** 20 10
913 5p. Type **168** 20 10
914 7p.50 Ballet performance (vert) 20 10
915 15p. Ballet performance (vert) 30 10
916 30p. Concert 65 25
917 40p. Concert . . . . 1·00 40

169 Tabarja

1966. Tourism. Multicoloured.
918 50c. Hippodrome, Beirut (postage) 10 10
919 1p. Pigeon Grotto, Beirut . . 10 10
920 2p.50 Type **169** 10 10
921 5p. Ruins, Beit-Mery 10 10
922 7p.50 Ruins, Anjar 10 10
923 10p. Djezzine Falls (air) . . . 10 10
924 15p. Sidon Castle 15 10
925 20p. Amphitheatre, Byblos 25 10
926 30p. Sun Temple, Baalbek . . 40 10
927 50p. Palace, Beit ed-Din . . . 65 10
928 60p. Nahr-el Kalb . . . . . 1·50 45
929 70p. Tripoli . . . . 1·25 40

170 W.H.O. Building

1966. Air. Inauguration of W.H.O. Headquarters, Geneva.
930 **170** 7p.50 green 25 10
931 17p.50 red 35 25
932 25p. blue 65 35

171 Skiing

1966. Air. International Cedars Festival.
933 **171** 2p.50 brown, red & green 25 10
934 – 5p. multicoloured 25 10
935 – 17p.50 multicoloured . . 35 20
936 – 25p. red, brown and green 1·00 40
DESIGNS: 5p. Tobogganing; 17p.50, Cedar in snow; 25p. Ski-lift.

172 Inscribed Sarcophagus

1966. Air. Phoenician Invention of the Alphabet.
937 **172** 10p. brown, black & green 10 10
938 – 15p. brown, ochre & mve 25 10
939 – 20p. sepia, blue and ochre 40 25
940 – 30p. brown, orange & yell 65 40
DESIGNS: 15p. Phoenician sailing ship; 20p. Mediterranean route map showing spread of Phoenician alphabet; 30p. Kadmus with alphabet tablet.

173 Child in Bath

174 Decade Emblem

1966. Air. Int Children's Day. Multicoloured.
941 2p. Type **173** 10 10
942 5p. Boy and doll in rowing boat 15 10
943 7p.50 Girl skiing 25 10
944 15p. Girl giving food to bird 40 25
945 20p. Boy doing homework 65 40

1966. Air. International Hydrological Decade.
947 **174** 5p. ultramarine, bl & orge 20 10
948 10p. red, blue and orange 20 10
949 – 15p. sepia, green & orange 25 15
950 – 20p. blue, green & orange 40 25
DESIGN: 15p., 20p. Similar "wave" pattern.

175 Rev. Daniel Bliss (founder)

176 I.T.Y. Emblem

177 Beit ed-Din Palace

1966. Air. Centenary of American University, Beirut.
951 **175** 20p. brown, yellow & grn 35 15
952 – 30p. green, brown and blue 45 30
DESIGN: 30p. University Chapel.

1967. International Tourist Year (1st issue). (a) Postage.
954 **176** 50c. multicoloured 10 10
955 1p. multicoloured 10 10
956 2p.50 multicoloured . . . 10 10
957 5p. multicoloured 15 10
958 7p.50 multicoloured . . . 25 10

(b) Air. Multicoloured.
959 10p. Tabarja 20 10
960 15p. Pigeon Rock, Beirut . . 25 10
961 17p.50 Type **177** 30 10
962 20p. Sidon 30 10
963 25p. Tripoli 35 10
964 30p. Byblos 45 10
965 35p. Ruins, Tyre 55 10
966 40p. Temple, Baalbek 75 10
See also Nos. 977/80.

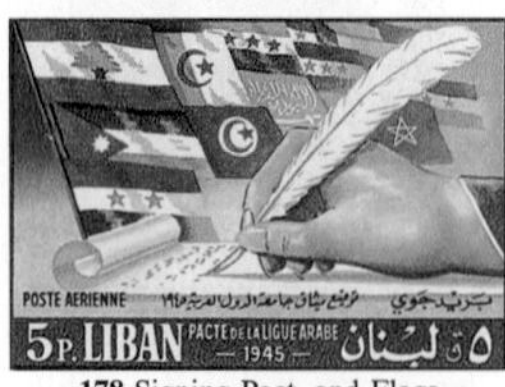

178 Signing Pact, and Flags

1967. Air. 22nd Anniv of Arab League Pact.
967 **178** 5p. multicoloured 10 10
968 10p. multicoloured . . . 15 10
969 15p. multicoloured . . . 25 20
970 20p. multicoloured . . . 35 30

179 Veterans War Memorial Building, San Francisco

1967. Air. San Francisco Pact of 1945. Mult.
971 2p.50 Type **179** . . . . . . 1·00 30
972 5p. Type **179** . . . . 1·00 30
973 7p.50 Type **179** . . . . . . 1·00 30
974 10p. Scroll and flags of U.N. and Lebanon 20 20
975 20p. As 10p. 25 20
976 30p. As 10p. 50 20

180 Temple Ruins, Baalbek

1967. Air. International Tourist Year (2nd issue). Multicoloured.
977 5p. Type **180** 10 10
978 10p. Ruins, Anjar 15 10
979 15p. Ancient bridge, Nahr-Ibrahim 25 10
980 20p. Grotto, Jeita 40 15

181

1967. Air. India Day.
981 **181** 2p.50 red 10 10
982 5p. purple 10 10
983 7p.50 brown 10 10
984 10p. blue 20 10
985 15p. green 45 15

182

1967. Air. 22nd Anniv of Lebanon's Admission to U.N.O.
986 **182** 2p.50 red 10 10
987 5p. blue 10 10
988 7p.50 green 10 10
989 – 10p. red 10 10
990 – 20p. blue 25 10
991 – 30p. green 45 25
DESIGN: 10, 20, 30p. U.N. Emblem.

183 Goat and Kid

1967. Animals and Fishes. Multicoloured.
992 50c. Type **183** (postage) . . 20 10
993 1p. Cattle 20 10
994 2p.50 Sheep 20 10
995 5p. Dromedaries 20 10
996 10p. Donkey 25 10
997 15p. Horses 55 10
998 20p. Basking shark (air) . . 80 10
999 30p. Garfish 80 10
1000 40p. Pollack . . . . 1·25 10
1001 50p. Cuckoo wrasse . . . . 1·40 20
1002 70p. Striped red mullet . . . 3·00 25
1003 100p. Rainbow trout . . . 4·50 25

184 Ski Jumping

1968. Air. International Ski Congress, Beirut.
1004 **184** 2p.50 multicoloured . . 10 10
1005 – 5p. multicoloured . . . 20 10
1006 – 7p.50 multicoloured . . 20 10
1007 – 10p. multicoloured . . . 25 20
1008 – 25p. multicoloured . . . 50 25
DESIGNS: 5p. to 10p. Skiing (all different); 25p. Congress emblem of Cedar and skis.

185 Princess Khaskiah

1968. Air. Emir Fakhreddine II Commem. Mult.
1009 2p.50 Type **185** 10 10
1010 5p. Emir Fakhreddine II . . 10 10
1011 10p. Sidon Citadel (horiz) 10 10
1012 15p. Chekif Citadel (horiz) 25 10
1013 17p.50 Beirut Citadel (horiz) 40 15

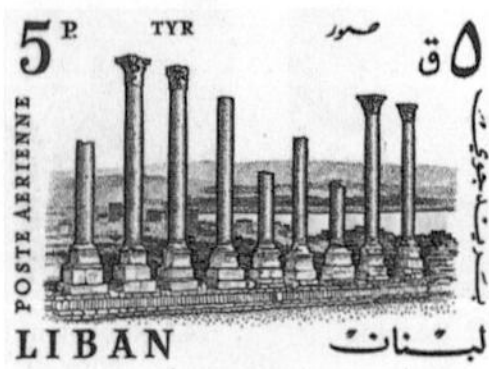

186 Colonnade

1968. Air. Tyre Antiquities.
1014 – 2p.50 brn, cream & pink 20 10
1015 **186** 5p. brown, blue & yellow 20 10
1016 – 7p.50 brown, buff & grn 25 20
1017 – 10p. brown, blue & orange 25 20
DESIGNS—VERT: 2p.50, Roman bust; 10p. Bas-relief. HORIZ: 7p.50, Arch.

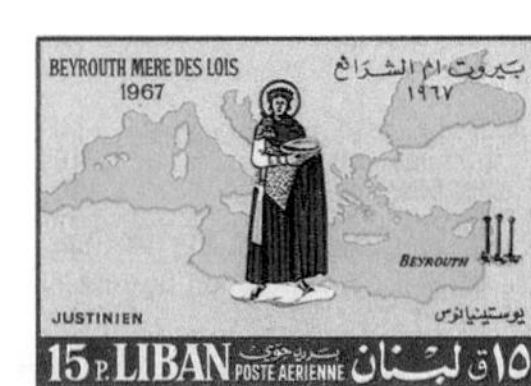

187 Justinian and Mediterranean Map

1968. Air. 1st Anniv of Faculty of Law, Beirut.
1019 5p. Justinian (vert) 10 10
1020 10p. Justinian (vert) 10 10
1021 15p. Type **187** 20 10
1022 20p. Type **187** 25 15

188 Arab League Emblem

1968. Air. Arab Appeal Week.
1023 **188** 5p. multicoloured . . . 10 10
1024 10p. multicoloured . . . 10 10
1025 15p. multicoloured . . . 25 15
1026 20p. multicoloured . . . 40 15

189 Cedar on Globe

1968. Air. 3rd World Lebanese Union Congress, Beirut.
1027 **189** 2p.50 multicoloured . . 10 10
1028 5p. multicoloured . . . 10 10
1029 7p.50 multicoloured . . 20 10
1030 10p. multicoloured . . . 20 15

190 Jupiter's Temple Ruins, Baalbek

1968. Air. Baalbek Festival. Multicoloured.
1031 5p. Type **190** 10 10
1032 10p. Bacchus's Temple . . . 10 10
1033 15p. Corniche, Jupiter's Temple 25 15
1034 20p. Portal, Bacchus's Temple 40 20
1035 25p. Columns, Bacchus's Temple 50 30

191 Long Jumping and Atlantes

1968. Air. Olympic Games, Mexico.
1036 **191** 5p. black, yellow and blue 10 10
1037 – 10p. black, blue & purple 10 10
1038 – 15p. multicoloured . . . 25 10
1039 – 20p. multicoloured . . . 40 20
1040 – 25p. brown 65 40
DESIGNS (each incorporating Aztec relic): 10p. High jumping; 15p. Fencing; 20p. Weightlifting; 25p. "Sailing boat" with oars.

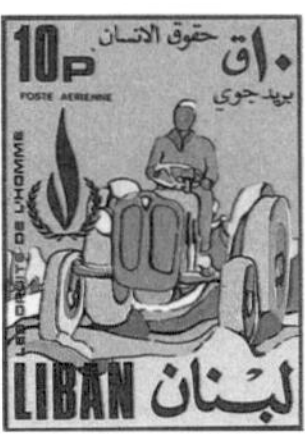

192 Lebanese driving Tractor ("Work protection") **193** Minshiya Stairs

1968. Air. Human Rights Year. Multicoloured.
1041 10p. Type **192** 10 10
1042 15p. Citizens ("Social Security") 20 10
1043 25p. Young men of three races ("Unity") 25 20

1968. Air. Centenary of 1st Municipal Council (Deir el-Kamar). Multicoloured.
1044 10p. Type **193** 10 10
1045 15p. Serai kiosk 20 10
1046 25p. Ancient highway . . . 25 20

194 Nurse and Child

1969. Air. UNICEF. Multicoloured.
1047 **194** 5p. black, brown and blue 10 10
1048 – 10p. black, green & yell 10 10
1049 – 15p. black, red and purple 10 10
1050 – 20p. black, blue & yellow 25 20
1051 – 25p. black, ochre & mve 40 20
DESIGNS: 10p. Produce; 15p. Mother and child; 20p. Child with book; 25p. Children with flowers.

195 Ancient Coin

1969. Air. 20th Anniv of International Museums Council (I.C.O.M.). Exhibits in National Museum, Beirut. Multicoloured.
1052 2p.50 Type **195** 10 10
1053 5p. Gold dagger, Byblos . . 20 10
1054 7p.50 Detail of Ahiram's Sarcophagus 20 10
1055 30p. Jewelled pectoral . . . 40 25
1056 40p. Khalde "bird" vase . . 50 40

196 Water-skiing

1969. Air. Water Sports. Multicoloured.
1057 2p.50 Type **196** 10 10
1058 5p. Water-skiing (group) . . 10 10
1059 7p.50 Paraskiing (vert) . . . 35 10
1060 30p. Racing dinghies (vert) 50 35
1061 40p. Racing dinghies . . . 75 60

197 Frontier Guard

1969. Air. 25th Anniv of Independence. The Lebanese Army.
1062 2p. Type **197** 10 10
1063 5p. Unknown Soldier's Tomb 10 10
1064 7p.50 Army Foresters . . . 20 10
1065 15p. Road-making 20 15
1066 30p. Military ambulance and Sud Aviation Alouette III helicopter 40 35
1067 40p. Skiing patrol 60 50

198 Concentric Red Crosses

1971. Air. 25th Anniv of Lebanese Red Cross.
1068 **198** 15p. red and black . . . 40 25
1069 – 85p. red and black . . . 1·50 1·00
DESIGN: 85p. Red Cross in shape of cedar of Lebanon.

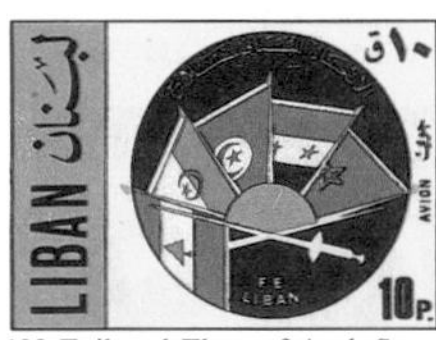

199 Foil and Flags of Arab States

1971. Air. 10th International Fencing Championships. Multicoloured.
1070 10p. Type **199** 10 10
1071 15p. Foil and flags of foreign nations 10 10
1072 35p. Contest with foils . . . 50 40
1073 40p. Epee contest 65 40
1074 50p. Contest with sabres . . 80 50

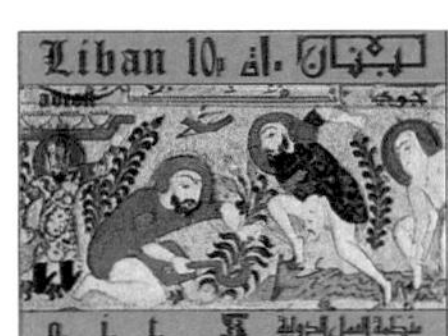

200 "Farmers at Work" (12th-century Arab painting)

1971. Air. 50th Anniv (1969) of I.L.O.
1075 **200** 10p. multicoloured . . . 20 10
1076 40p. multicoloured . . . 65 40

201 U.P.U. Monument and New H.Q. Building, Berne

1971. Air. New U.P.U. Headquarters Building, Berne.
1077 **201** 15p. red, black and yellow 20 10
1078 35p. yellow, black and orange 65 40

202 "Ravens setting fire to Owls" (14th-century painting)

1971. Air. Children's Day. Multicoloured.
1079 15p. Type **202** 35 20
1080 85p. "The Lion and the Jackal" (13th-century painting) (39 × 29 mm) . . 1·60 75

203 Arab League Flag and Map

1971. Air. 25th Anniv of Arab League.
1081 **203** 30p. multicoloured . . . 40 15
1082 70p. multicoloured . . . 75 50

204 Jamhour Electricity Sub-station

1971. Air. Multicoloured.
1083 5p. Type **204** 10 10
1084 10p. Maameltein Bridge . . 10 10
1085 15p. Hoteliers' School . . . 10 10
1086 20p. Litani Dam 20 10
1087 25p. Interior of T.V. set . . 25 10
1088 35p. Bziza Temple 40 10
1089 40p. Jounieh Harbour . . . 40 15
1090 45p. Radar scanner, Beirut Airport 55 20
1091 50p. Hibiscus 75 20
1092 70p. School of Sciences Building . . . . 1·00 25
1093 85p. Oranges . . . . 1·25 40
1094 100p. Satellite Communications Station, Arbanieh . . . . 1·50 65

205 Insignia of Imam al Ouzai (theologian)

1971. Air. Lebanese Celebrities.
1095 **205** 25p. brown, gold & green 35 20
1096 – 25p. brown, gold & yell 35 20
1097 – 25p. brown, gold & yell 35 20
1098 – 25p. brown, gold & green 35 20
PORTRAITS: No. 1096, Bechara el Khoury (poet and writer); 1097, Hassan Kamel el Sabbah (scientist); 1098, Gibran Khalil Gibran (writer).

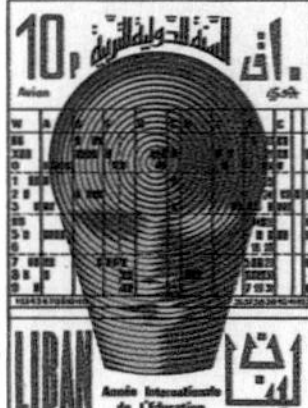

206 I.E.Y. Emblem and Computer Card

1971. Air. International Education Year.
1099 **206** 10p. black, blue and violet 10 10
1100 40p. black, yellow and red 40 25

207 Dahr-el-Basheq Sanatorium **208** "Solar Wheel" Emblem

1971. Air. Tuberculosis Relief Campaign.
1101 **207** 50p. multicoloured . . . 75 40
1102 – 100p. multicoloured . . 1·10 65
DESIGN: 100p. Different view of Sanatorium.

1971. Air. 16th Baalbek Festival.
1103 **208** 15p. orange and blue . . 20 10
1104 – 85p. black, blue & orange 80 55
DESIGN: 85p. Corinthian capital.

209 Field-gun

1971. Air. Army Day. Multicoloured.
1105 15p. Type **209** 25 20
1106 25p. Dassault Mirage IIICJ jet fighters 80 30
1107 40p. Army Command H.Q. 75 50
1108 70p. "Tarablous" (naval patrol boat) . . . . . . 1·50 90

210 Interior Decoration **212** U.N. Emblem

211 Lenin

1971. Air. 2nd Anniv of Burning of Al-Aqsa Mosque, Jerusalem.
1109 **210** 15p. brown and deep brown 50 20
1110 35p. brown and deep brown . . . . 1·00 65

1971. Air. Birth Centenary of Lenin. Mult.
1111 30p. Type **211** 50 25
1112 70p. Lenin in profile . . . . 1·10 65

1971. Air. 25th Anniv of United Nations.
1113 **212** 15p. multicoloured . . . 20 10
1114 85p. multicoloured . . . 95 50

213 "Europa" Mosaic, Byblos

1971. Air. World Lebanese Union.
1115 **213** 10p. multicoloured . . . 25 10
1116 40p. multicoloured . . . 1·00 40

1972. Various stamps surch.
1117 5p. on 7p.50 (No. 922) (postage) 10 10
1118 5p. on 7p.50 (No. 958) . . . 10 10
1119 25p. on 32p.50 (No. 872) . . 90 10
1120 5p. on 7p.50 (No. 1016) (air) 10 10
1121 100p. on 300p. (No. 881) . . 3·25 90
1122 100p. on 500p. (No. 882) . . 3·25 90
1123 200p. on 300p. (No. 881) . . 4·50 1·75

217 Morning Glory 218 Ornate Arches

1973. Air. Multicoloured.
1124 2p.50 Type **217** 10 10
1125 5p. Roses 20 10
1126 15p. Tulips 25 10
1127 25p. Lilies 40 10
1128 40p. Carnations 50 20
1129 50p. Iris 75 10
1130 70p. Apples . . . . 1·25 20
1131 75p. Grapes . . . . 1·25 20
1132 100p. Peaches . . . . . . 2·00 60
1133 200p. Pears . . . . 3·25 45
1134 300p. Cherries . . . . . . 4·50 85
1135 500p. Oranges . . . . . . 6·25 1·50

1973. Air. Lebanese Domestic Architecture.
1136 – 35p. multicoloured . . . 50 25
1137 **218** 50p. multicoloured . . . 75 35
1138 – 85p. multicoloured . . . 1·25 45
1139 – 100p. multicoloured . . 1·40 60
DESIGNS: Nos. 1136 and 1138/39, Various Lebanese dwellings.

219 Girl with Lute

1973. Air. Ancient Costumes. Multicoloured.
1140 5p. Woman with rose . . . 15 10
1141 10p. Shepherd 25 10
1142 20p. Horseman 25 20
1143 25p. Type **219** 40 20

220 Swimming

1973. Air. 5th Pan-Arab Schools' Games, Beirut. Multicoloured.
1144 5p. Type **220** 10 10
1145 10p. Running 15 10
1146 15p. Gymnastics 25 10
1147 20p. Volleyball 40 10
1148 25p. Basketball 40 20
1149 50p. Table-tennis 75 35
1150 75p. Handball . . . . . . 1·00 45
1151 100p. Football . . . . . . 2·00 1·10

221 Brasilia

1973. Air. 150th Anniv of Brazil's Independence. Multicoloured.
1153 5p. Type **221** 10 10
1154 20p. Salvador (Bahia) in 1823 . . . . 25 10
1155 25p. Map and Phoenician galley 40 20
1156 50p. Emperor Pedro I and Emir Fakhreddine II . . 85 40

222 Marquetry 223 Cedar of Lebanon

1973. Air. Lebanese Handicrafts. Multicoloured.
1157 10p. Type **222** 15 10
1158 20p. Weaving 25 10
1159 35p. Glass-blowing 40 15
1160 40p. Pottery 65 20
1161 50p. Metal-working 75 20
1162 70p. Cutlery-making . . . . 1·00 25
1163 85p. Lace-making . . . . . 1·40 40
1164 100p. Handicrafts Museum 1·75 50

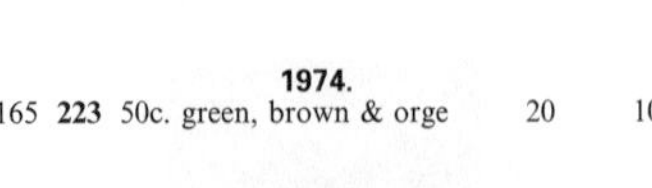

1974.
1165 **223** 50c. green, brown & orge 20 10

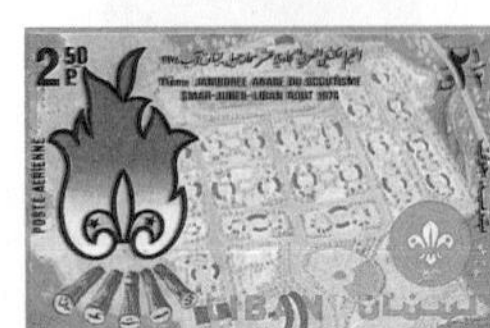
224 Camp Site and Emblems

1974. Air. 11th Arab Scout Jamboree, Smar-Jubeil, Lebanon. Multicoloured.
1166 2p.50 Type **224** 10 10
1167 5p. Scout badge and map 10 10
1168 7p.50 Map of Arab countries 20 10
1169 10p. Lord Baden-Powell and Baalbek 20 10
1170 15p. Guide and camp . . . 20 10
1171 20p. Lebanese Guide and Scout badge 30 10
1172 25p. Scouts around campfire 45 10
1173 30p. Globe and Scout badge 50 20
1174 35p. Flags of participating countries 70 20
1175 50p. Scout chopping wood for old man . . . . . . 1·00 35

225 Mail Train

1974. Centenary of U.P.U. Multicoloured.
1176 5p.50 Type **225** 75 45
1177 20p. Container ship 45 10
1178 25p. Congress building, Lausanne, and U.P.U. H.Q., Berne 45 10
1179 50p. Mail plane 75 45

226 Congress Building, Sofar 227 "Mountain Road" (O. Onsi)

1974. Air. 25th Anniv of Arab Postal Union. Multicoloured.
1180 5p. Type **226** 10 10
1181 20p. View of Sofar 20 10
1182 25p. A.P.U. H.Q., Cairo . . 25 10
1183 50p. Ministry of Posts, Beirut . . . . 1·00 55

1974. Air. Lebanese Paintings. Multicoloured.
1184 50p. Type **227** 65 30
1185 50p. "Clouds" (M. Farroukh) 65 30
1186 50p. "Woman" (G. K. Gebran) 65 30
1187 50p. "Embrace" (C. Gemayel) 65 30
1188 50p. "Self-portrait" (H. Serour) 65 30
1189 50p. "Portrait" (D. Corm) 65 30

228 Hunter killing Lion

1974. Air. Hermel Excavations. Multicoloured.
1190 5p. Type **228** 10 10
1191 10p. Astarte 15 10
1192 25p. Dogs hunting boar . . 40 20
1193 35p. Greco-Roman tomb . . 65 40

229 Book Year Emblem

1974. Air. International Book Year (1972).
1194 **229** 5p. multicoloured . . . 10 10
1195 10p. multicoloured . . . 15 10
1196 25p. multicoloured . . . 40 15
1197 35p. multicoloured . . . 50 60

230 Magnifying Glass 231 Georgina Rizk in Lebanese Costume

1974. Air. Stamp Day. Multicoloured.
1198 5p. Type **230** 10 10
1199 10p. Linked posthorns . . . 10 10
1200 15p. Stamp-printing 20 10
1201 20p. "Stamp" in mount . . 35 20

1974. Air. Miss Universe 1971 (Georgina Rizk). Multicoloured.
1202 5p. Type **231** 10 10
1203 20p. Head-and-shoulders portrait 15 10
1204 25p. Type **231** 25 15
1205 50p. As 20p. 65 40

232 Winds 234 Discus-throwing

233 UNICEF Emblem and Sikorsky S-55 Helicopter

1974. Air. U.N. Conference on Human Environment, Stockholm, 1972. Multicoloured.
1207 5p. Type **232** 10 10
1208 25p. Mountains and plain 40 10
1209 30p. Trees and flowers . . . 40 20
1210 40p. Sea 50 40

1974. Air. 25th Anniv of UNICEF. Multicoloured.
1212 20p. Type **233** 45 10
1213 25p. Emblem and child welfare clinic 25 10
1214 35p. Emblem and kindergarten class 45 20
1215 70p. Emblem and schoolgirls in laboratory 85 25

1974. Air. Olympic Games, Munich (1972). Mult.
1217 5p. Type **234** 10 10
1218 10p. Putting the shot . . . 10 10
1219 15p. Weight-lifting 15 10
1220 35p. Running 50 25
1221 50p. Wrestling 65 25
1222 85p. Javelin-throwing . . . 1·25 40

235 Symbols of Archaeology

1975. Air. Beirut—"University City". Mult.
1224 20p. Type **235** 25 10
1225 25p. Science and medicine 25 10
1226 35p. Justice and commerce 45 35
1227 70p. Industry and commerce 90 50

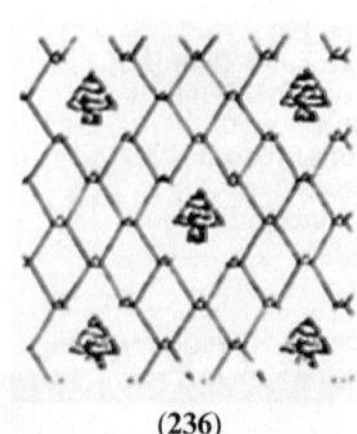
(236)

1978. Air. Various stamps optd with different patterns as T **236**. (a) Tourist Views. Nos. 1090, 1092/3.
1228 45p. Radar scanner, Beirut Airport 45 20
1229 70p. School of Sciences Building 90 25
1230 85p. Oranges . . . . 1·00 35

(b) Flowers and Fruits. Nos. 1124/35.
1231 2p.50 Type **217** 10 10
1232 5p. Roses 10 10
1233 15p. Tulips 25 10
1234 25p. Lilies 45 10
1235 40p. Carnations 45 15
1236 50p. Iris 65 15
1237 70p. Apples 90 25
1238 75p. Grapes . . . . 1·25 25
1239 100p. Peaches . . . . . . 1·25 40
1240 200p. Pears . . . . 2·50 1·40
1241 300p. Cherries . . . . . . 3·75 2·50
1242 500p. Oranges . . . . . . 6·25 3·75

(c) Lebanese Domestic Architecture. Nos. 1136/9.
1243 – 35p. multicoloured . . . 55 10
1244 **218** 50p. multicoloured . . . 65 15
1245 – 85p. multicoloured . . . 1·00 35
1246 – 100p. multicoloured . . 1·25 40

(d) Ancient Costumes. Nos. 1140/3.
1247 5p. Woman with rose . . . 10 10
1248 10p. Shepherd 15 10
1249 20p. Horseman 30 10
1250 25p. Type **219** 45 10

(e) Lebanese Handicrafts. Nos. 1157/8, 1160/4.
1251 10p. Type **222** 15 10
1252 20p. Weaving 30 10
1253 40p. Pottery 45 15
1254 50p. Metal-working 75 15
1255 70p. Cutlery-making 90 25
1256 85p. Lace-making . . . . . 1·00 35
1257 100p. Handicraft Museum 1·25 40

237 Mikhail Naimy (poet) and View of al-Chakroub Baskinta

1978. Air. Mikhail Naimy Festival Week. Mult.
1258 25p. Mikhail Naimy and Sannine mountains . . . 25 10
1259 50p. Type **237** 50 25
1260 75p. Mikhail Naimy (vert) 80 40

238 Heart and Arrow 239 Army Badge

1978. Air. World Health Day. "Down with Blood Pressure".
1261 **238** 50p. blue, red and black 75 40

1980. Army Day. Multicoloured.
1262 25p. Type **239** (postage) . . 40 20
1263 50p. Statue of Emir Fakhr el Dine on horseback (air) 65 25
1264 75p. Soldiers with flag (horiz) 95 25

240 13th-century European King

1980. Air. 50th Anniv (1974) of International Chess Federation. Multicoloured.

1265 50p. Rook, knight and Jubilee emblem (horiz) . . 75 25
1266 75p. Type **240** . . . . . . 1·25 40
1267 100p. Rook and Lebanon Chess Federation emblem 1·90 65
1268 150p. 18th-century French rook, king and knight . . 2·50 1·00
1269 200p. Painted faience rook, queen and bishop . . . . 3·25 1·50

241 Congress, U.P.U. and Lebanon Post Emblems

1981. Air. 18th U.P.U. Congress, Rio de Janeiro (1979).

1270 **241** 25p. blue, brown and black 40 15
1271 50p. pink, brown & black 65 25
1272 75p. green, brown and black . . . . 1·00 40

242 Children on Raft

1981. Air. International Year of the Child (1979).

1273 **242** 100p. multicoloured . . 1·25 65

243 President Sarkis

1981. 5th Anniv of Election of President Sarkis.

1274 **243** 125p. multicoloured . . 95 50
1275 300p. multicoloured . . 2·75 1·10
1276 500p. multicoloured . . 4·50 1·60

244 Society Emblem and Children

1981. Air. Centenary (1978) of Al-Makassed Islamic Welfare Society. Multicoloured.

1277 50p. Type **244** 50 15
1278 75p. Institute building . . . 75 20
1279 100p. Al-Makassed (founder) 95 35

245 Stork carrying Food

1982. World Food Day (1981). Multicoloured.

1280 50p. Type **245** 50 25
1281 75p. Ear of wheat and globe 75 40
1282 100p. Fruit, fish and grain 1·50 65

246 W.C.Y. Emblem

247 Phoenician Galley flying Scout Flag

1983. World Communications Year.

1283 **246** 300p. multicoloured . . 2·50 1·25

1983. 75th Anniv of Boy Scout Movement. Multicoloured.

1284 200p. Type **247** . . . . . 1·90 95
1285 300p. Scouts lowering flag and signalling by semaphore . . . . 2·50 1·25
1286 500p. Camp . . . . 4·50 1·90

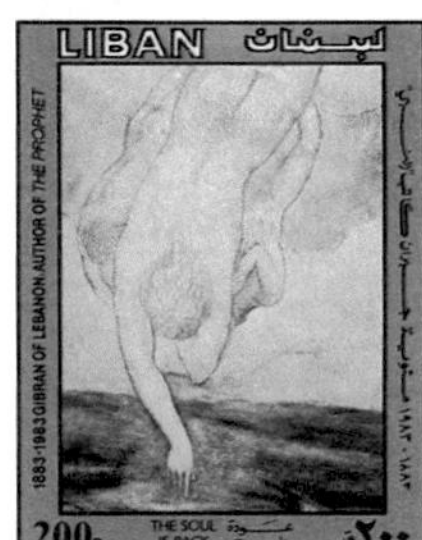

248 "The Soul is Back"

1983. Birth Centenary of Gibran (poet and painter). Multicoloured.

1287 200p. Type **248** . . . . . 1·90 95
1288 300p. "The Family" . . . . 2·50 1·25
1289 500p. "Gibran" . . . . . . 4·50 1·90
1290 1000p. "The Prophet" . . . 8·75 4·75

249 Cedar of Lebanon

250 Iris

1984.

1292 **249** 5p. multicoloured . . . 20 10

1984. Flowers. Multicoloured.

1293 10p. Type **250** 25 10
1294 25p. Periwinkle 40 25
1295 50p. Barberry 95 40

251 Dove with Laurel over Buildings

1984. Lebanese Army. Multicoloured.

1296 75p. Type **251** 70 40
1297 150p. Cedar and soldier holding rifle . . . . . . 1·50 90
1298 300p. Broken chain, hand holding laurel wreath and cedar . . . . 3·25 1·90

252 Temple Ruins, Fakra

1984. Multicoloured.

1299 100p. Type **252** 95 40
1300 200p. Temple ruins, Bziza 1·90 90
1301 500p. Roman arches and relief, Tyre . . . . 4·75 1·90

253 President taking Oath

1988. Installation of President Amin Gemayel.

1302 **253** L£25 multicoloured . . . 60 40

254 Map of South America and Cedar of Lebanon

1988. 1st World Festival of Lebanese Youth in Uruguay.

1303 **254** L£5 multicoloured . . . 20 10

255 Satellite, Flags and Earth

256 Children

1988. "Arabsat" Telecommunications Satellite.

1304 **255** L£10 multicoloured . . . 40 25

1988. UNICEF Child Survival Campaign.

1305 **256** L£15 multicoloured . . . 65 40

257 Arabic "75" and Scout Emblems

258 President, Map and Dove

1988. 75th Anniv (1987) of Arab Scouts Movement.

1306 **257** L£20 multicoloured . . . 65 40

1988. International Peace Year (1986).

1307 **258** L£50 multicoloured . . . 1·25 65

259 Red Cross and Figures

260 Cedar of Lebanon

1988. Red Cross.

1308 **259** L£10+L£1 red, silver and black 40 25
1309 – L£20+L£2 multicoloured 65 40
1310 – L£30+L£3 silver, green and red . . . . 1·00 60

DESIGNS: L£20, Helmeted heads; L£30, Globe, flame, and dove holding map of Lebanon.

1989.

1311 **260** L£50 green and mauve 25 15
1312 L£70 green and brown 40 20
1313 L£100 green and yellow 65 30
1314 L£200 green and blue . . 1·25 65
1315 L£500 deep green & green . . . . 3·25 1·60

261 Dining in the Open at Zahle, 1883

1993. 50th Anniv of Independence. Multicoloured.

1316 L£200 Type **261** 40 25
1317 L£300 Castle ruins, Saida (vert) 55 40
1318 L£500 Presidential Palace, Baabda 95 65
1319 L£1000 Sword ceremony (vert) . . . . 1·90 1·25
1320 L£3000 Model for the rebuilding of central Beirut . . . . 5·50 3·00
1321 L£5000 President Elias Hrawi and state flag (vert) 10·00 6·75

262 Protection of Plants

263 Martyrs' Monument, Beirut

1994. Environmental Protection. Multicoloured.

1323 L£100 Type **262** 15 10
1324 L£200 Protection against forest fires 30 20
1325 L£500 Reforesting with cedars 75 50
1326 L£1000 Creation of urban green zones . . . . 1·50 1·00
1327 L£2000 Trees . . . . 2·50 1·60
1328 L£5000 Green tree in town 8·00 5·25

1995. Martyrs' Day.

1329 **263** L£1500 multicoloured . . 1·75 1·10

264 Arabic Script under Magnifying Glass and Headquarters

1996. Anniversaries and Events. Multicoloured.

1330 L£100 Type **264** (inauguration of Postal Museum, Arab League Headquarters, Cairo) . . 10 10
1331 L£500 Anniversary emblem (50th anniv of UNICEF) (horiz) 40 25
1332 L£500 Ears of wheat and anniversary emblem (50th anniv (1995) of F.A.O.) 40 25
1333 L£1000 U.N. Building (New York) and anniversary emblem (50th anniv (1995) of U.N.O.) 80 55
1334 L£1000 Emblem (International Year of the Family (1994)) (horiz) . . 80 55
1335 L£2000 Anniversary emblem (75th anniv (1994) of I.L.O.) (horiz) . . . . . 1·60 1·10
1336 L£2000 Emblem (50th anniv of Arab League) . . . . 1·60 1·10
1337 L£3000 Emblem (75th anniv (1994) of Lebanese Law Society) . . . . 2·40 1·60
1338 L£3000 Rene Moawad (former President, 70th birth anniv (1995)) . . . 2·40 1·60

265 Commemorative Medallion

1997. 1st Anniv of Shelling of Cana Refugee Camp.

1339 **265** L£1100 multicoloured . . 90 60

266 Pope John Paul II and President Hrawi

1998. Papal Visit.
1340 **266** L£10000 multicoloured 8·00 5·25

1999. Various stamps optd with a Fleuon values unchanged. Original numbers given.
1341 L£100 multicoloured (No. 1330) 10 10
1342 L£200 multicoloured (No. 1316) 15 10
1343 L£500 multicoloured (No. 1318) 40 25
1344 L£500 multicoloured (No. 1319) 40 25
1346 L£500 multicoloured (No. 1331) 40 25
1347 L£500 multicoloured (No. 1332) 40 25
1348 L£1000 multicoloured (No. 1326) 80 50
1349 L£1000 multicoloured (No. 1333) 80 50
1350 L£1100 multicoloured (No. 1339) 90 55
1351 L£1500 multicoloured (No. 1329) 1·20 70
1352 L£2000 multicoloured (No. 1335) 1·60 95
1353 L£3000 multicoloured (No. 1337) 2·40 1·40
1354 L£5000 multicoloured (No. 1328) 4·00 2·40
1355 L£10000 multicoloured (No. 1340) 8·00 4·75

268 Cedar of Lebanon

1999.
1356 **268** L£100 red 10 10
1359 L£300 turquoise 25 10
1357 L£500 grey 40 25
1358 L£1000 blue 80 50
1360 L£1100 brown 90 55
1361 L£1500 violet 1·20 70

100L.L. ·ل.ل١٠٠

(269) (270)

1999. Nos. 1295/6 surch as T **269**. No. 1092 surch as T **270**.
1368 L£100 on L£50 multicoloured 10 10
1369 L£300 on L£75 multicoloured 25 10
1370 L£1100 on L£70 multicoloured 90 55

271 Emir Chehab's Palace, Hasbaya

272 Flag and Soldiers

1999. Buildings. Multicoloured.
1371 L£100 Type **271** 10 10
1372 L£300 UN Economic and Social Commission for Western Asia, Beirut 35 15
1373 L£500 Emir Fakhreddine's Palace, Deir-el-Kamar (horiz) 40 25
1374 L£1100 Grand Serail, Beirut (horiz) 90 55

1999. Nos. 1335 and 1338 optd with a Fleuron, values unchanged.
1375 L£2000 multicoloured 1·60 95
1376 L£3000 multicoloured 2·40 1·40

2001. Return of South Lebanon (1st series).
1377 **272** L£1100 multicoloured 90 55
See also No. **MS**1991.

273 Ibrahim Abd el Al

2001. 93rd Birth Anniv of Ibrahim Abd el Al (engineer).
1378 **273** L£1000 multicoloured 80 50

274 Hand and Bars

2001. Prisoners.
1379 **274** L£500 multicoloured 40 25

275 Emblem

2001. SOS Children's Villages.
1380 **275** L£300 multicoloured 25 15

276 Hand holding "50"

2001. 50th Anniversaries.
1381 **276** L£500 olive (Geneva Convention) 40 25
1382 – L£1100 lilac (Geneva Convention) 90 55
1383 – L£1500 multicoloured (Red Cross and Red Crescent) 1·20 70
DESIGNS: L£500 Type **276**; L£1100 Fist around bars and "50"; L£1500 Hand holding stylized people.

277 Ahas Abu Chabke

2001. 97th Birth Anniv of Ahas Abu Chabke (writer).
1384 **277** L£1500 multicoloured 1·20 70

278 Father Monnot and Emblem

2001. 125th Anniv of Saint Joseph University, Beirut.
1385 **278** L£5000 multicoloured 4·00 2·40

279 Abdallah Zakher

2001. 319th Birth Anniv of Abdallah Zakher (first Arab printer).
1386 **279** L£1000 multicoloured 80 50

280 UN Emblem

2001. 25th. Anniv of UN Economic and Social Commission for Western Asia.
1387 **280** L£10000 ultramarine, blue and mauve 8·00 4·75

281 Arabic Script

2002. Day of the Arab Woman.
1388 **281** L£1000 multicoloured 80 50

282 Emblem

2002. Arab Summit Conference, Beirut. Multicoloured.
1389 L£2000 Type **282** 1·60 95
1390 L£3000 Cedar tree and Pres. Emile Lahoud 2·40 1·40

283 Pres. Emile Lahoud

2002. Return of Southern Lebanon (2nd series). Sheet 160 × 108 mm containing T **283** and similar vert designs. Multicoloured.
MS1391 L£1100 × 4 Type **283**; Pres. Lahoud with raised arm; Pres. Lahoud and map; Sword ceremony 1·60 1·60

284 Judges, Scales and Cedar Tree

2002. Martyrs. Sheet 120 × 90 mm.
MS1392 multicoloured 2·40 2·40

285 UPU Emblem and Cedar Tree

2002. 125th Anniv of Universal Postal Union.
1393 **285** L£2000 multicoloured 1·60 95

286 Men seated at Table, Zouk Mikael

2002. Souks. Multicoloured.
1394 L£100 Type **286** 10 10
1395 L£300 Vendor with wheeled stall, Saida Souk 25 15
1396 L£500 Byblos (UNESCO world heritage site) 40 25
1397 L£1000 Carpet mender, Tripoli 80 50

287 Emblem and National Colours

2002. 9th Francophile States Summit, Beirut. Multicoloured.
1398 L£1500 Type **287** 1·20 70
1399 L£1500 Pres. Lahoud 1·20 70

288 Emblem

2002. Beirut, Arab Culture Capital, 2002.
1400 **288** L£2000 multicoloured 1·60 95

289 Roman Temple, Bziza

2002. Ruins. Multicoloured.
1401 L£1100 Type **289** 90 55
1402 L£1500 Arqa 1·20 70
1403 L£2000 Niha 1·60 95
1404 L£3000 Castle, Mousailaha 2·40 1·40

290 Lebanese Amber

2002. Fossils. Multicoloured.
1405 L£5000 Type **290** 4·00 2·40
1406 L£10000 *Nematonotus longispinus* 8·00 4·75

POSTAGE DUE STAMPS

1924. Postage Due stamps of France surch **GRAND LIBAN** and value in "CENTIEMES" or "PIASTRES".
D26 **D 11** 50c. on 10c. brown 1·90 3·25
D27 1p. on 20c. green 3·50 7·00
D28 2p. on 30c. red 1·90 5·25
D29 3p. on 50c. purple 2·25 5·25
D30 5p. on 1f. purple on yellow 1·75 3·75

1924. Postage Due stamps of France surch **Gd Liban** and value in French and Arabic.
D58 **D 11** 0p.50 on 10c. brown 1·00 3·75
D59 1p. on 20c. green 1·25 3·75
D60 2p. on 30c. red 1·25 3·00
D61 3p. on 50c. purple 1·25 3·75
D62 5p. on 1f. purple on yell 75 4·00

D 7 Nahr el-Kalb

1925.
D75 **D 7** 0p.50 brown on yellow 95 1·75
D76 – 1p. red on pink 75 3·00
D77 – 2p. black on blue 1·75 3·25
D78 – 3p. brown on orange 1·90 4·50
D79 – 5p. black on green 1·75 5·00
DESIGNS—HORIZ: 1p. Pine Forest, Beirut; 2p. Pigeon Grotto, Beirut; 3p. Beaufort Castle; 5p. Baalbeck.

1927. Optd **Republique Libanaise**.
D122 **D 7** 0p.50 brown on yellow 40 2·00
D123 – 1p. red on pink 70 3·00
D124 – 2p. black on blue 1·90 3·75

D125	–	3p. brown on orange	2·00	3·00
D126	–	5p. black on green . .	3·25	6·75

1928. Nos. D122/6 optd with T **10**.

D145	D **7**	0p.50 brown on yellow	1·50	3·75
D146	–	1p. red on pink	1·60	3·25
D147	–	2p. black on blue . . .	1·75	3·50
D148	–	3p. brown on orange	2·25	6·00
D149	–	5p. black on green . .	2·75	8·25

D **18**

D **19** Bas-relief from Sarcophagus of King Ahiram at Byblos

D **32**

1931.

D191	D **18**	0p.50 black on pink	80	1·60
D192	–	1p. black on blue . .	1·50	1·00
D193	–	2p. black on yellow . .	2·25	1·75
D194	–	3p. black on green . .	3·25	2·25
D195	D **32**	5p. black on orange	8·25	9·75
D196	D **19**	8p. black on pink . .	4·75	5·25
D252	D **32**	10p. green	8·25	7·25
D197	–	15p. black	3·50	3·50

DESIGNS: 1p. Bas-relief of Phoenician galley; 2p. Arabesque; 3p. Garland; 15p. Statuettes.

D **43** National Museum

1945.

D298	D **43**	2p. black on lemon . .	2·75	2·75
D299		5p. blue on pink . . .	3·25	3·25
D300		25p. blue on green . .	4·75	4·75
D301		50p. purple on blue . .	5·00	5·00

D **53**

1947.

D352	D **53**	5p. black on green . .	3·75	1·25
D353		25p. black on yellow	38·00	3·25
D354		50p. black on blue . .	22·00	8·25

D **59** Monument at Hermel

1948.

D379	D **59**	2p. black on yellow . .	2·50	65
D380		3p. black on pink . .	5·75	2·50
D381		10p. black on blue . .	14·00	5·00

D **67**

1950.

D416	D **67**	1p. red	95	20
D417		5p. blue	2·75	75
D418		10p. green	5·00	1·60

D **78**

1952.

D464	D **78**	1p. mauve	20	10
D465		2p. violet	30	20
D466		3p. green	45	20
D467		5p. blue	65	25
D468		10p. brown	1·25	50
D469		25p. black	9·75	1·25

D **81** D **93**

1953.

D481	D **81**	1p. red	15	10
D482		2p. green	15	10
D483		3p. orange	15	10
D484		5p. purple	25	20
D485		10p. brown	65	20
D486		15p. blue	1·25	65

1955.

D550	D **93**	1p. brown	10	10
D551		2p. green	10	10
D552		3p. turquoise	10	10
D553		5p. purple	10	10
D554		10p. green	30	20
D555		15p. blue	30	20
D556		25p. purple	75	50

D **178** D **184** Emir Fakhreddine II

1967.

D967	D **178**	1p. green	10	10
D968		5p. mauve	10	10
D969		15p. blue	30	30

1968.

D1004	D **184**	1p. slate and grey	10	10
D1005		2p. turquoise & green	10	10
D1006		3p. orange & yellow	10	10
D1007		5p. purple and red	10	10
D1008		10p. olive and yellow	10	10
D1009		15p. blue and violet	35	35
D1010		25p. blue & lt blue	60	60

POSTAL TAX STAMPS

These were issued between 1945 and 1962 for compulsory use on inland mail (and sometimes on mail to Arab countries) to provide funds for various purposes.

T **41** (T **42**)

1945. Lebanese Army. Fiscal stamp as Typeno-wrap T /no-wrap**41** surch with Typeno-wrap T /no-wrap**42**.

T289	T **41**	5p. on 30c. brown . .	£425	1·75

(T **50**) (T **51**)

(T **52**) (T **56** "Palestine stamp")

1947. Aid to War in Palestine. Surch as Typeno-wrap T /no-wrap**42**. (a) With top line Typeno-wrap T / no-wrap**50**.

T338	T **41**	5p. on 25c. green . . .	13·00	1·40
T339		5p. on 30c. brown . .	18·00	2·75
T340		5p. on 60c. blue . . .	27·00	2·00
T341		5p. on 3p. pink	13·50	2·50
T342		5p. on 15p. blue . . .	13·50	1·00

(b) With top line Typeno-wrap T /no-wrap**51**.

T343	T **41**	5p. on 10p. red	60·00	3·00

(c) With top line Typeno-wrap T /no-wrap**52**.

T344	T **41**	5p. on 3p. pink	13·50	1·75

(d) As No. T344 but with figure "5" at left instead of "0" and without inscr between figures.

T345	T **41**	5p. on 3p. pink	£300	22·00

1948. Palestine Aid. No. T289 optd with Typeno-wrap T /no-wrap**56**.

T363	T **41**	5p. on 30c. brown . .	18·00	2·40

T **95** Family and Ruined House

1956. Earthquake Victims.

T559	T **95**	2p.50 brown	2·00	20

T **99** Rebuilding T **100** Rebuilding

1957. Earthquake Victims.

T601	T **99**	2p.50 brown	2·00	20
T602		2p.50 green	1·25	20
T603	T **100**	2p.50 brown	1·25	10

T **132** Rebuilding T **133** Rebuilding

1961. Earthquake Victims.

T729	T **132**	2p.50 brown	1·25	10
T730	T **133**	2p.50 blue	1·00	10

LEEWARD ISLANDS Pt.1

A group of islands in the Br. W. Indies, including Antigua, Barbuda, British Virgin Islands, Dominica (till end of 1939), Montserrat, Nevis and St. Christopher (St. Kitts). Stamps of Leeward Islands were used concurrent with the respective islands until they were withdrawn on the 1 July 1956.

1890. 12 pence = 1 shilling;
20 shillings = 1 pound.
1951. 100 cents = 1 West Indian dollar.

1

(3)

1890.

No.	Type	Description	Unused	Used
1	1	½d. mauve and green	3·50	1·25
2		1d. mauve and red	3·75	20
3		2½d. mauve and blue	4·75	20
4		4d. mauve and orange	4·50	7·50
5		6d. mauve and brown	11·00	12·00
6		7d. mauve and grey	4·50	11·00
7		1s. green and red	19·00	50·00
8		5s. green and blue	£120	£250

1897. Diamond Jubilee. Optd with T **3**.

No.	Type	Description	Unused	Used
9	1	½d. mauve and green	4·00	13·00
10		1d. mauve and red	4·50	13·00
11		2½d. mauve and blue	4·75	13·00
12		4d. mauve and orange	35·00	70·00
13		6d. mauve and brown	48·00	90·00
14		7d. mauve and grey	48·00	90·00
15		1s. green and red	£120	£190
16		5s. green and blue	£450	£750

1902. Surch **One Penny**.

No.	Type	Description	Unused	Used
17	1	1d. on 4d. mauve and orange	3·00	5·00
18		1d. on 6d. mauve and brown	4·00	11·00
19		1d. on 7d. mauve and grey	3·50	7·00

1902. As T **1**, but portrait of King Edward VII.

No.	Type	Description	Unused	Used
29		½d. purple and green	3·50	2·00
21		1d. purple and red	7·00	20
22		2d. purple and brown	2·75	4·25
23		2½d. purple and blue	5·50	2·25
24		3d. purple and black	4·50	7·50
25		6d. purple and brown	2·50	8·00
26		1s. green and red	3·50	19·00
27		2s.6d. green and black	27·00	70·00
28		5s. green and blue	48·00	75·00

1907. As last, but colours changed.

No.	Type	Description	Unused	Used
36		¼d. brown	2·75	1·75
37		½d. green	3·50	1·25
38		1d. red	10·00	80
39		2d. grey	3·50	7·50
40		2½d. blue	7·00	4·25
41		3d. purple and yellow	3·50	7·50
42		6d. purple	8·50	7·00
43		1s. black on green	5·50	21·00
44		2s.6d. black and red on blue	40·00	48·00
45		5s. green and red on yellow	42·00	65·00

10 King George V

14 King George VI

1912.

No.	Type	Description	Unused	Used
46	10	¼d. brown	1·75	1·00
59		½d. green	1·00	75
60		1d. red	2·25	55
61		1d. violet	2·25	1·00
63		1½d. red	3·25	2·00
64		1½d. brown	1·25	10
65		2d. grey	2·00	80
67		2½d. blue	3·50	1·25
66		2½d. yellow	6·50	50·00
69		3d. purple on yellow	1·50	6·50
68		3d. blue	4·75	26·00
70		4d. black and red on yellow	3·00	21·00
71		5d. purple and green	2·50	4·25
53		6d. purple	3·00	8·00
54		1s. black on green	3·00	8·00
74a		2s. purple and blue on blue	7·50	48·00
75		2s.6d. black and red on blue	6·50	23·00
76		3s. green and violet	12·00	25·00
77		4s. black and red	12·00	42·00
57b		5s. green and red on yellow	26·00	70·00

Larger type, as T **15** of Malta.

No.	Type	Description	Unused	Used
79	13	10s. green and red on green	55·00	85·00
80		£1 purple and black on red	£225	£250

1935. Silver Jubilee. As T **14a** of Kenya, Uganda and Tanganyika.

No.	Type	Description	Unused	Used
88		1d. blue and red	1·60	1·50
89		1½d. blue and grey	2·25	70
90		2½d. brown and blue	2·25	3·50
91		1s. grey and purple	9·00	18·00

1937. Coronation. As T **14b** of Kenya, Uganda and Tanganyika.

No.	Type	Description	Unused	Used
92		1d. red	70	20
93		1½d. brown	70	40
94		2½d. blue	80	1·00

1938.

No.	Type	Description	Unused	Used
95a	14	¼d. brown	30	1·75
96		½d. green	70	70
97		½d. grey	75	1·50
99		1d. red	2·25	1·75
100		1d. green	55	15
101		1½d. brown	1·00	50
102		1½d. orange and black	85	40
103		2d. grey	3·00	1·25
104		2d. red	1·40	1·25
105a		2½d. blue	80	1·25
106		2½d. black and purple	55	15
107a		3d. orange	50	85
108		3d. blue	65	15
109a		6d. purple	6·50	2·25
110b		1s. black on green	4·25	1·00
111a		2s. purple and blue on blue	10·00	2·00
112b		5s. green and red on yellow	32·00	15·00
113c	–	10s. green and red on green	£120	75·00
114b	–	£1 purple and black on red	35·00	24·00

The 10s. and £1 are as Type **15** of Bermuda but with portrait of King George VI.

1946. Victory. As T **4a** of Pitcairn Islands.

No.	Type	Description	Unused	Used
115		1½d. brown	15	50
116		3d. orange	15	50

1949. Silver Wedding. As T **4b/c** of Pitcairn Islands.

No.	Type	Description	Unused	Used
117		2½d. blue	10	10
118		5s. green	4·25	3·25

1949. U.P.U. As T **4d/g** of Pitcairn Islands.

No.	Type	Description	Unused	Used
119		2½d. black	15	1·75
120		3d. blue	2·00	1·75
121		6d. mauve	15	1·75
122		1s. turquoise	15	1·75

15a Arms of University

15b Princess Alice

1951. Inauguration of B.W.I. University College.

No.	Type	Description	Unused	Used
123	15a	3c. orange and black	30	1·00
124	15b	12c. red and violet	70	1·00

1953. Coronation. As T **4h** of Pitcairn Islands.

No.	Type	Description	Unused	Used
125		3c. black and green	50	2·25

1954. As T **14** but portrait of Queen Elizabeth II facing left.

No.	Type	Description	Unused	Used
126		½c. brown	10	60
127		1c. grey	1·00	1·00
128		2c. green	1·50	10
129		3c. yellow and black	2·25	1·00
130		4c. red	1·50	10
131		5c. black and purple	2·00	1·00
132		6c. yellow	2·25	60
133		8c. blue	2·50	10
134		12c. purple	1·75	10
135		24c. black and green	1·75	20
136		48c. purple and blue	6·00	2·75
137		60c. brown and green	6·00	2·25
138		$1.20 green and red	5·00	3·25

Larger type as T **15** of Malta, but portrait of Queen Elizabeth II facing left.

No.	Type	Description	Unused	Used
139		$2.40 green and red	6·50	5·50
140		$4.80 purple and black	6·50	7·00

LESOTHO Pt. 1

Formerly Basutoland, attained independence on 4 October 1966 and changed its name to Lesotho.

1966. 100 cents = 1 rand.
1979. 100 lisente = 1 (ma)loti.

33 Moshoeshoe I and Moshoeshoe II

1966. Independence.

No.	Type	Description	Unused	Used
106	33	2½c. brown, black and red	10	10
107		5c. brown, black and blue	10	10
108		10c. brown, black and green	15	10
109		20c. brown, black and purple	20	15

1966. Nos. 69 etc. of Basutoland optd **LESOTHO**.

No.	Type	Description	Unused	Used
110A	8	½c. black and sepia	10	10
111A	–	1c. black and green	10	10
112A	–	2c. blue and orange	60	10
113B	26	2½c. sage and red	50	10
114A	–	3½c. indigo and blue	30	10
115A	–	5c. brown and green	10	10
116A	–	10c. bronze and purple	10	10
117B	–	12½c. brown and turquoise	30	20
118A	–	25c. blue and red	30	20
119B	–	50c. black and red	60	50
120B	9	1r. black and purple	65	75

35 "Education, Culture and Science"

36 Maize

1966. 20th Anniv of UNESCO.

No.	Type	Description	Unused	Used
121	35	2½c. yellow and green	10	10
122		5c. green and olive	15	10
123		12½c. blue and red	35	15
124		25c. orange and blue	60	75

1967.

No.	Type	Description	Unused	Used
125	36	½c. green and violet	10	10
126	–	1c. sepia and red	10	10
149	–	2c. yellow and green	10	10
128	–	2½c. black and ochre	10	10
151	–	3c. chocolate, green & brn	15	15
152	–	3½c. blue and yellow	15	10
130	–	5c. bistre and blue	20	10
131	–	10c. brown and grey	10	10
132	–	12½c. black and orange	20	10
133	–	25c. black and blue	55	20
134	–	50c. black, blue & turquoise	4·50	1·25
135	–	1r. multicoloured	65	75
136	–	2r. black, gold and purple	1·00	1·75

DESIGNS—HORIZ: 1c. Cattle; 2c. Aloes; 2½c. Basotho hat; 3c. Sorghum; 3½c. Merino sheep ("Wool"); 5c. Basotho pony; 10c. Wheat; 12½c. Angora goat ("Mohair"); 25c. Maletsunyane Falls; 50c. Diamonds; 1r. Arms of Lesotho. VERT: 2r. Moshoeshoe II.

See also Nos. 191/203.

46 Students and University

1967. 1st Conferment of University Degrees.

No.	Type	Description	Unused	Used
137	46	1c. sepia, blue and orange	10	10
138		2½c. sepia, ultramarine & bl	10	10
139		12½c. sepia, blue and red	10	10
140		25c. sepia, blue and violet	15	15

47 Statue of Moshoeshoe I

1967. 1st Anniv of Independence.

No.	Type	Description	Unused	Used
141	47	2½c. black and green	10	10
142	–	12½c. multicoloured	25	15
143	–	25c. black, green and ochre	35	25

DESIGNS: 12½c. National flag; 25c. Crocodile (national emblem).

50 Lord Baden-Powell and Scout Saluting

1967. 60th Anniv of Scout Movement.

No.	Type	Description	Unused	Used
144	50	15c. multicoloured	20	10

51 W.H.O. Emblem and World Map

1968. 20th Anniv of World Health Organization.

No.	Type	Description	Unused	Used
145	51	2½c. blue, gold and red	15	10
146	–	25c. multicoloured	45	60

DESIGN: 25c. Nurse and child.

55 Running Hunters

1968. Rock Paintings.

No.	Type	Description	Unused	Used
160	55	3c. brown, turquoise & grn	25	10
161	–	3½c. yellow, olive and sepia	30	10
162	–	5c. red, ochre and brown	35	10
163	–	10c. yellow, red and purple	45	10
164	–	15c. buff, yellow and brown	75	30
165	–	20c. green, yellow & brown	90	55
166	–	25c. yellow, brown & black	1·00	75

DESIGNS—HORIZ: 3½c. Baboons; 10c. Archers; 20c. Eland; 25c. Hunting scene. VERT: 5c. Javelin thrower; 15c. Blue cranes.

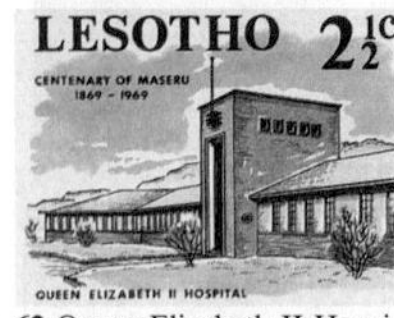

62 Queen Elizabeth II Hospital

1969. Centenary of Maseru (capital). Mult.

No.	Type	Description	Unused	Used
167		2½c. Type **62**	10	10
168		10c. Lesotho Radio Station	10	10
169		12½c. Leabua Jonathan Airport	35	10
170		25c. Royal Palace	25	15

66 Rally Car passing Basuto Tribesman

1969. "Roof of Africa" Car Rally.

No.	Type	Description	Unused	Used
171	66	2½c. yellow, mauve & plum	15	10
172	–	12½c. blue, yellow and grey	20	10
173	–	15c. blue, black and mauve	20	10
174	–	20c. black, red and yellow	20	10

DESIGNS: 12½c. Rally car on mountain road; 15c. Chequered flags and "Roof of Africa" Plateau; 20c. Map of rally route and Independence Trophy.

71 Gryponyx and Footprints

1970. Prehistoric Footprints (1st series).

No.	Type	Description	Unused	Used
175	–	3c. brown and sepia	90	70
176	71	5c. purple, pink and sepia	1·10	30
177	–	10c. yellow, black and sepia	1·40	35
178	–	15c. yellow, black and sepia	2·00	2·25
179	–	25c. blue and black	2·75	2·25

DESIGNS: 3c. Dinosaur footprints at Moyeni; 10c. Plateosauravus and footprints; 15c. Tritylodon and footprints; 25c. Massospondylus and footprints.

No. 175 is larger, 60 × 23 mm.

See also Nos. 596/8.

75 Moshoeshoe I as a Young Man

1970. Death Centenary of Chief Moshoeshoe I.

No.	Type	Description	Unused	Used
180	75	2½c. green and mauve	10	10
181	–	25c. blue and brown	20	20

DESIGN: 25c. Moshoeshoe I as an old man.

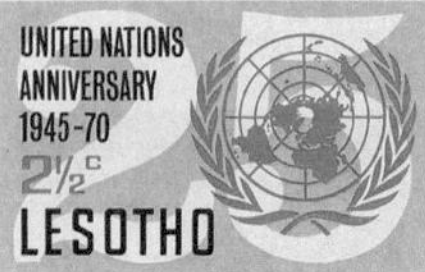

77 U.N. Emblem and "25"

1970. 25th Anniv of United Nations.

No.	Type	Description	Unused	Used
182	77	2½c. pink, blue and purple	10	10
183	–	10c. multicoloured	10	10
184	–	12½c. red, blue and drab	10	25
185	–	25c. multicoloured	15	65

DESIGNS: 10c. U.N. Building; 12½c. "People of the World"; 25c. Symbolic dove.

78 Gift Shop, Maseru

1970. Tourism. Multicoloured.
186 2½c. Type **78** 10 10
187 5c. Trout fishing 20 10
188 10c. Pony trekking 25 10
189 12½c. Skiing, Maluti Mountains 50 10
190 20c. Holiday Inn, Maseru 40 50

79 Maize **80** Lammergeier

1971. As Nos. 147/58 but in new format omitting portrait, as in T **79**. New designs for 4c., 2r.
191 **79** ½c. green and violet 10 10
192 – 1c. brown and red 10 10
193 – 2c. yellow and green 10 10
194 – 2½c. black, green & yellow 10 10
195 – 3c. brown, green & yellow 10 10
196 – 3½c. blue and yellow 10 10
196a – 4c. multicoloured 20 10
197 – 5c. brown and blue 15 10
198 – 10c. brown and grey 15 10
199 – 12½c. brown and orange 25 30
200 – 25c. slate and blue 60 40
201 – 50c. black, blue and green 6·00 4·50
202 – 1r. multicoloured 1·25 1·75
401 – 2r. brown and blue 70 2·25
DESIGNS—HORIZ: 4c. National flag. VERT: 2r. Statue of Moshoeshoe I.

1971. Birds. Multicoloured.
204 2½c. Type **80** 2·50 20
205 5c. Bald ibis 3·50 2·50
206 10c. Orange-breasted rockjumper 3·50 2·00
207 12½c. Blue bustard ("Blue korhaan") 3·75 3·50
208 15c. Painted-snipe 4·25 4·50
209 20c. Golden-breasted bunting 4·25 4·50
210 25c. Ground woodpecker 4·75 4·50

81 Lionel Collett Dam

1971. Soil Conservation. Multicoloured.
211 4c. Type **81** 10 10
212 10c. Contour ridges 10 10
213 15c. Earth dams 25 10
214 25c. Beaver dams 35 35

82 Diamond Mining

1971. Development. Multicoloured.
215 4c. Type **82** 75 40
216 10c. Pottery 30 10
217 15c. Weaving 45 60
218 20c. Construction 55 1·50

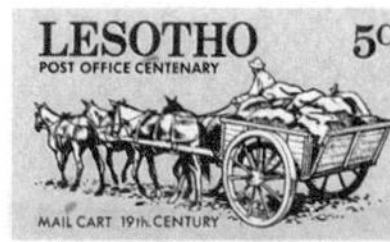

83 Mail Cart

1972. Centenary of Post Office.
219 **83** 5c. brown and pink 15 20
220 – 10c. multicoloured 15 10
221 – 15c. blue, black and brown 20 15
222 – 20c. multicoloured 30 90
DESIGNS—HORIZ: 10c. Postal bus; 20c. Maseru Post Office. VERT: 15c. 4d. Cape of Good Hope stamp of 1876.

84 Sprinting

1972. Olympic Games, Munich. Multicoloured.
223 4c. Type **84** 15 10
224 10c. Shot putting 20 10
225 15c. Hurdling 30 10
226 25c. Long-jumping 35 55

85 "Adoration of the Shepherds" (Matthias Stomer)

1972. Christmas.
227 **85** 4c. multicoloured 10 10
228 10c. multicoloured 10 10
229 25c. multicoloured 15 20

86 W.H.O. Emblem

1973. 25th Anniv of W.H.O.
230 **86** 20c. yellow and blue 30 30

1973. O.A.U. 10th Anniv. Nos. 194 and 196a/8 optd **O.A.U. 10th Anniversary Freedom in Unity**.
231 2½c. black, green and brown 10 10
232 4c. multicoloured 10 10
233 5c. brown and blue 10 10
234 10c. brown and blue 15 15

88 Basotho Hat and W.F.P. Emblem

1973. 10th Anniv of World Food Programme. Multicoloured.
235 4c. Type **88** 10 10
236 15c. School feeding 20 15
237 20c. Infant feeding 20 20
238 25c. "Food for work" 25 25

89 "Aeropetes tulbaghia"

1973. Butterflies. Multicoloured.
239 4c. Type **89** 75 10
240 5c. "Papilio demodocus" 85 50
241 10c. "Cynthia cardui" 1·25 50
242 15c. "Precis hierta" 2·25 1·75
243 20c. "Precis oenone" 2·25 1·75
244 25c. "Danaus chrysippus" 2·50 2·75
245 30c. "Colotis evenina" 2·50 3·75

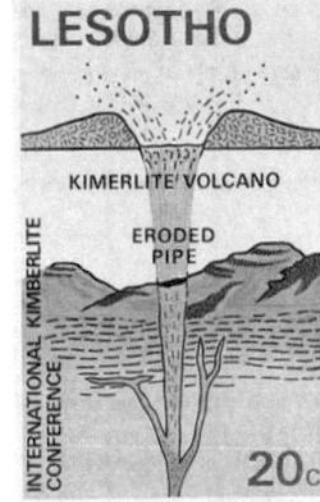

90 Kimberlite Volcano **92** Open Book and Wreath

91 "Health"

1973. International Kimberlite Conference. Mult.
246 10c. Map of diamond mines (horiz) 2·00 50
247 15c. Kimberlite-diamond rock (horiz) 2·25 2·25
248 20c. Type **90** 2·25 2·50
249 30c. Diamond prospecting 3·75 7·00

1974. Youth and Development. Multicoloured.
250 4c. Type **91** 10 10
251 10c. "Education" 15 10
252 20c. "Agriculture" 20 10
253 25c. "Industry" 30 20
254 30c. "Service" 30 25

1974. 10th Anniv of U.B.L.S. Multicoloured.
255 10c. Type **92** 15 10
256 15c. Flags, mortar-board and scroll 20 20
257 20c. Map of Africa 25 25
258 25c. King Moshoeshoe II capping a graduate 25 65

93 Senqunyane River Bridge, Marakabei

1974. Rivers and Bridges. Multicoloured.
259 4c. Type **93** 10 10
260 5c. Tsoelike River and bridge 10 10
261 10c. Makhaleng River Bridge 20 10
262 15c. Seaka Bridge, Orange/ Senqu River 35 35
263 20c. Masianokeng Bridge, Phuthiatsana River 40 40
264 25c. Mahobong Bridge, Hlotse River 45 45

94 U.P.U. Emblem

1974. Centenary of U.P.U.
265 **94** 4c. green and black 10 10
266 – 10c. orange, yellow & black 15 10
267 – 15c. multicoloured 20 60
268 – 20c. multicoloured 45 85
DESIGNS: 10c. Map of airmail routes; 15c. Post Office H.Q., Maseru; 20c. Horseman taking rural mail.

95 Siege of Thaba-Bosiu

1974. 150th Anniv of Siege of Thaba-Bosiu. Multicoloured.
269 4c. Type **95** 10 10
270 5c. The wreath-laying 10 10
271 10c. Moshoeshoe I (vert) 25 10
272 20c. Makoanyane, the warrior (vert) 90 55

96 Mamokhorong

1974. Basotho Musical Instruments. Multicoloured.
273 4c. Type **96** 10 10
274 10c. Lesiba 10 10
275 15c. Setolotolo 15 20
276 20c. Meropa 15 20
MS277 108 × 92 mm. Nos. 273/6 1·00 2·00

97 Horseman in Rock Archway

1975. Sehlabathebe National Park. Mult.
278 4c. Type **97** 30 10
279 5c. Mountain view through arch 30 10
280 15c. Antelope by stream 50 45
281 20c. Mountains and lake 50 50
282 25c. Tourists by frozen waterfall 65 75

98 Morena Moshoeshoe I **99** Mokhibo Dance

1975. Leaders of Lesotho.
283 **98** 3c. black and blue 10 10
284 – 4c. black and mauve 10 10
285 – 5c. black and pink 10 10
286 – 6c. black and brown 10 10
287 – 10c. black and red 10 10
288 – 15c. black and red 20 20
289 – 20c. black and green 25 30
290 – 25c. black and blue 25 40
DESIGNS: 4c. King Moshoeshoe II; 5c. Morena Letsie I; 6c. Morena Lerotholi; 10c. Morena Letsie II; 15c. Morena Griffith; 20c. Morena Seeiso Griffith Lerotholi; 25c. Mofumahali Mantsebo Seeiso, O.B.E.
The 25c. also commemorates International Women's Year.

1975. Traditional Dances. Multicoloured.
291 4c. Type **99** 15 10
292 10c. Ndlamo 20 10
293 15c. Baleseli 35 75
294 20c. Mohobelo 40 1·25
MS295 111 × 100 mm. Nos. 291/4 3·75 3·50

100 Enrolment

1976. 25th Anniv of Lesotho Red Cross. Mult.
296 4c. Type **100** 50 10
297 10c. Medical aid 70 10
298 15c. Rural service 1·00 1·25
299 25c. Relief supplies 1·40 2·50

101 Tapestry

1976. Multicoloured.
300 2c. Type **101** 10 35
301 3c. Mosotho horseman 20 30
302 4c. Map of Lesotho 1·50 10
303 5c. Lesotho Brown diamond 75 1·00
304 10c. Lesotho Bank 30 10
305 15c. Lesotho and O.A.U. flags 2·00 1·00
306 25c. Sehlabathebe National Park 60 35
307 40c. Pottery 60 1·00
308 50c. Prehistoric rock art 2·75 2·00
309 1r. King Moshoeshoe II (vert) 60 1·75

102 Football **103** "Rising Sun"

1976. Olympic Games, Montreal. Mult.
310 4c. Type **102** 15 10
311 10c. Weightlifting 15 10

312 15c. Boxing 35 35
313 25c. Throwing the discus 50 80

1976. 10th Anniv of Independence. Multicoloured.
314 4c. Type **103** 10 10
315 10c. Open gates 10 10
316 15c. Broken chains 40 20
317 25c. Britten Norman Islander aircraft over hotel 50 35

104 Telephones, 1876 and 1976

1976. Centenary of Telephone. Multicoloured.
318 4c. Type **104** 10 10
319 10c. Early handset and telephone-user, 1976 15 10
320 15c. Wall telephone and telephone exchange 25 20
321 25c. Stick telephone and Alexander Graham Bell 45 50

105 "Aloe striatula" **106** Large-toothed Rock Hyrax

1977. Aloes and Succulents. Multicoloured.
322 3c. Type **105** 25 10
323 4c. "Aloe aristata" 25 10
324 5c. "Kniphofia caulescens" 25 10
325 10c. "Euphorbia pulvinata" 35 10
326 15c. "Aloe saponaria" 1·00 30
327 20c. "Caralluma lutea" 1·00 50
328 25c. "Aloe polyphylla" 1·25 70
See also Nos. 347/54.

1977. Animals. Multicoloured.
329 4c. Type **106** 3·50 30
330 5c. Cape porcupine 3·50 75
331 10c. Zorilla (polecat) 3·50 30
332 15c. Klipspringer 11·00 2·50
333 25c. Chacma baboon 12·00 3·75

107 "Rheumatic Man" **110** Black and White Heads

108 Small-mouthed Yellowfish

1977. World Rheumatism Year.
334 **107** 4c. yellow and red 10 10
335 – 10c. blue and deep blue 15 10
336 – 15c. yellow and blue 30 10
337 – 25c. red and black 40 45
DESIGNS—Each show the "Rheumatic Man" as Type **107**: 10c. Surrounded by "pain"; 15c. Surrounded by "chain"; 25c. Supporting globe.

1977. Fish. Multicoloured.
338 4c. Type **108** 30 10
339 10c. Mudfish 45 10
340 15c. Rainbow trout 1·00 35
341 25c. Barnard's mudfish 1·10 60

1977. No. 198 surch **3**.
342 3c. on 10c. brown and blue 1·00 1·00

1977. Decade for Action to Combat Racism.
343 **110** 4c. black and mauve 10 10
344 – 10c. black and blue 10 10
345 – 15c. black and orange 15 15
346 – 25c. black and green 25 25
DESIGNS: 10c. Jigsaw pieces; 15c. Cogwheels; 25c. Handshake.

1978. Flowers. As T **105**. Multicoloured.
347 2c. "Papaver aculeatum" 10 50
348 3c. "Diascia integerrima" 10 50
349 4c. "Helichrysum trilineatum" 10 10
350 5c. "Zaluzianskya maritima" 10 10
351 10c. "Gladiolus natalensis" 15 10
352 15c. "Chironia krebsii" 20 40
353 25c. "Wahlenbergia undulata" 35 1·00
354 40c. "Brunsvigia radulosa" 65 2·00

111 Edward Jenner vaccinating Child **112** Tsoloane Falls

1978. Global Eradication of Smallpox. Mult.
355 5c. Type **111** 25 35
356 25c. Head of child and W.H.O. emblem 75 90

1978. Waterfalls. Multicoloured.
357 4c. Type **112** 15 10
358 10c. Qiloane Falls 25 10
359 15c. Tsoelikana Falls 35 60
360 25c. Maletsunyane Falls 55 1·75

113 Wright Flyer III, 1903

1978. 75th Anniv of First Powered Flight. Mult.
361 5c. Type **113** 15 30
362 25c. Wilbur and Orville Wright 40 60

114 "Orthetrum farinosum" **115** Oudehout Branch in Flower

1978. Insects. Multicoloured.
363 4c. Type **114** 10 10
364 10c. "Phymateus viridipes" 20 10
365 15c. "Belonogaster lateritis" 30 50
366 25c. "Sphodromantis gastrica" 50 90

1979. Trees. Multicoloured.
367 4c. Type **115** 15 10
368 10c. Wild olive 20 10
369 15c. Blinkblaar 35 80
370 25c. Cape holly 70 1·50

116 Mampharoane

1979. Reptiles. Multicoloured.
371A 4s. Type **116** 10 10
372A 10s. Qoaane 20 10
373A 15s. Leupa 30 70
374A 25s. Masumu 60 1·40

117 Basutoland 1933 1d. Stamp **118** Detail of painting "Children's Games" by Brueghel

1979. Death Centenary of Sir Rowland Hill.
375 **117** 4s. multicoloured 10 10
376 – 15s. multicoloured 30 20
377 – 25s. black, orange & bistre 40 30
MS378 118 × 95 mm. 50s. multicoloured 60 80

DESIGNS: 15s. Basutoland 1962 ½c. new currency definitive; 25s. Penny Black; 50s. 1972 15c. Post Office Centenary commemorative.

1979. International Year of the Child.
379 **118** 4s. multicoloured 10 10
380 – 10s. multicoloured 10 10
381 – 15s. multicoloured 15 15
MS382 113 × 88 mm. 25s. multicoloured (horiz) 55 45
DESIGNS: 10, 15s, 25s. Different details taken from Brueghel's "Children's Games".

119 Beer Strainer, Broom and Mat

1980. Grasswork. Multicoloured.
383 4s. Type **119** 10 10
384 10s. Winnowing basket 10 10
385 15s. Basotho hat 20 25
386 25s. Grain storage 35 40

120 Praise Poet

1980. Centenary of Gun War. Multicoloured.
387 4s. Type **120** 15 10
388 5s. Lerotholi, Commander of Basotho Army 15 10
389 10s. Ambush at Qalabane 20 10
390 15s. Snider and Martini-Henry rifles 60 45
391 25s. Map showing main areas of action 70 55

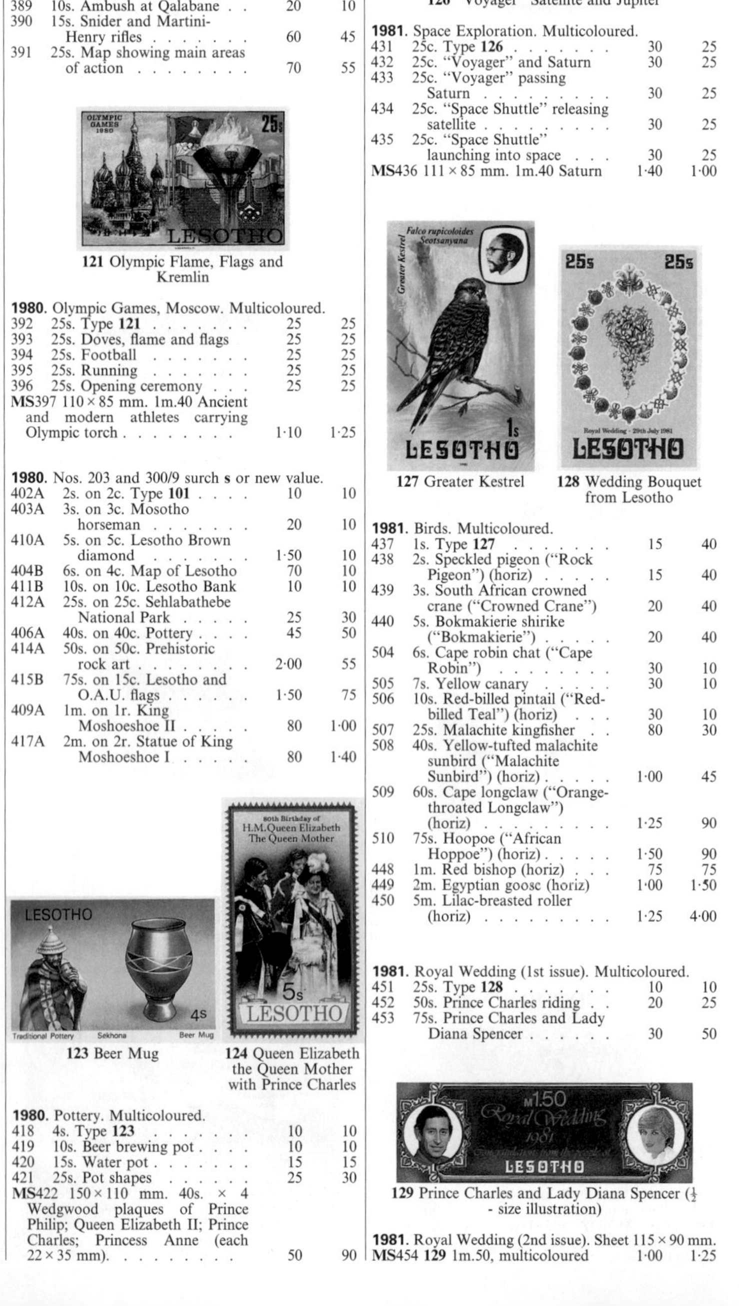

121 Olympic Flame, Flags and Kremlin

1980. Olympic Games, Moscow. Multicoloured.
392 25s. Type **121** 25 25
393 25s. Doves, flame and flags 25 25
394 25s. Football 25 25
395 25s. Running 25 25
396 25s. Opening ceremony 25 25
MS397 110 × 85 mm. 1m.40 Ancient and modern athletes carrying Olympic torch 1·10 1·25

1980. Nos. 203 and 300/9 surch **s** or new value.
402A 2s. on 2c. Type **101** 10 10
403A 3s. on 3c. Mosotho horseman 20 10
410A 5s. on 5c. Lesotho Brown diamond 1·50 10
404B 6s. on 4c. Map of Lesotho 70 10
411B 10s. on 10c. Lesotho Bank 10 10
412A 25s. on 25c. Sehlabathebe National Park 25 30
406A 40s. on 40c. Pottery 45 50
414A 50s. on 50c. Prehistoric rock art 2·00 55
415B 75s. on 15c. Lesotho and O.A.U. flags 1·50 75
409A 1m. on 1r. King Moshoeshoe II 80 1·00
417A 2m. on 2r. Statue of King Moshoeshoe I 80 1·40

123 Beer Mug **124** Queen Elizabeth the Queen Mother with Prince Charles

1980. Pottery. Multicoloured.
418 4s. Type **123** 10 10
419 10s. Beer brewing pot 10 10
420 15s. Water pot 15 15
421 25s. Pot shapes 25 30
MS422 150 × 110 mm. 40s. × 4 Wedgwood plaques of Prince Philip; Queen Elizabeth II; Prince Charles; Princess Anne (each 22 × 35 mm) 50 90

No. **MS**422 was issued to commemorate the 250th birth anniversary of Josiah Wedgwood.

1980. 80th Birthday of The Queen Mother. Mult.
423 5s. Type **124** 25 25
424 10s. The Queen Mother 25 25
425 1m. 1947 Basutoland Royal Visit 2d. stamp (54 × 43 mm) 90 90

125 Lesotho Evangelical Church, Morija

1980. Christmas. Multicoloured.
426 4s. Type **125** 10 10
427 15s. St. Agnes' Anglican Church, Teyateyaneng 10 10
428 25s. Cathedral of Our Lady of Victories, Maseru 15 10
429 75s. University Chapel, Roma 45 50
MS430 110 × 85 mm. 1m.50 Nativity scene (43 × 29 mm) 50 80

126 "Voyager" Satellite and Jupiter

1981. Space Exploration. Multicoloured.
431 25c. Type **126** 30 25
432 25c. "Voyager" and Saturn 30 25
433 25c. "Voyager" passing Saturn 30 25
434 25c. "Space Shuttle" releasing satellite 30 25
435 25c. "Space Shuttle" launching into space 30 25
MS436 111 × 85 mm. 1m.40 Saturn 1·40 1·00

127 Greater Kestrel **128** Wedding Bouquet from Lesotho

1981. Birds. Multicoloured.
437 1s. Type **127** 15 40
438 2s. Speckled pigeon ("Rock Pigeon") (horiz) 15 40
439 3s. South African crowned crane ("Crowned Crane") 20 40
440 5s. Bokmakierie shrike ("Bokmakierie") 20 40
504 6s. Cape robin chat ("Cape Robin") 30 10
505 7s. Yellow canary 30 10
506 10s. Red-billed pintail ("Red-billed Teal") (horiz) 30 10
507 25s. Malachite kingfisher 80 30
508 40s. Yellow-tufted malachite sunbird ("Malachite Sunbird") (horiz) 1·00 45
509 60s. Cape longclaw ("Orange-throated Longclaw") (horiz) 1·25 90
510 75s. Hoopoe ("African Hoppoe") (horiz) 1·50 90
448 1m. Red bishop (horiz) 75 75
449 2m. Egyptian goosc (horiz) 1·00 1·50
450 5m. Lilac-breasted roller (horiz) 1·25 4·00

1981. Royal Wedding (1st issue). Multicoloured.
451 25s. Type **128** 10 10
452 50s. Prince Charles riding 20 25
453 75s. Prince Charles and Lady Diana Spencer 30 50

129 Prince Charles and Lady Diana Spencer (½ - size illustration)

1981. Royal Wedding (2nd issue). Sheet 115 × 90 mm.
MS454 **129** 1m.50, multicoloured 1·00 1·25

130 "Santa planning his Annual Visit"

1981. Christmas. Paintings by Norman Rockwell. Multicoloured.

455	6s. Type **130**	15	10
456	10s. "Santa reading his Mail"	25	10
457	15s. "The Little Spooners"	30	20
458	20s. "Raleigh Rockwell Travels"	30	25
459	25s. "Ride 'em Cowboy"	30	30
460	60s. "The Discovery"	50	1·00
MS461	111 × 85 mm. 1m.25 "Mystic Nativity" (48 × 31 mm)	1·10	1·10

131 Duke of Edinburgh, Award Scheme Emblem and Flags

1981. 25th Anniv of Duke of Edinburgh Award Scheme. Multicoloured.

462	6s. Type **131**	10	10
463	7s. Tree planting	10	10
464	25s. Gardening	25	20
465	40s. Mountain climbing	40	40
466	75s. Award Scheme emblem	70	75
MS467	111 × 85 mm. 1m.40 Duke of Edinburgh (45 × 30 mm)	1·25	1·25

132 Wild Cat

1981. Wildlife. Multicoloured.

468	6s. Type **132**	1·25	30
469	20s. Chacma baboon (44 × 31 mm)	2·00	70
470	25s. Cape eland	2·50	75
471	40s. Porcupine	3·25	1·75
472	50s. Oribi (44 × 31 mm)	3·25	1·75
MS473	111 × 85 mm. 1m.50 Black-backed Jackal (47 × 31 mm)	2·75	1·90

133 Scout Bugler

1982. 75th Anniv of Boy Scout Movement. Multicoloured.

474	6s. Type **133**	30	25
475	30s. Scouts hiking	35	50
476	40s. Scout sketching	40	60
477	50s. Scout with flag	40	65
478	75s. Scouts saluting	45	80
MS479	117 × 92 mm. 1m.50 Lord Baden-Powell	1·00	2·00

134 Jules Rimet Trophy with Footballers and Flags of 1930 Finalists (Argentina and Uruguay)

1982. World Cup Football Championship, Spain. Each showing Trophy with Players and Flags from Past Finals. Multicoloured.

480	15s. Type **134**	25	25
481	15s. Czechoslovakia and Italy, 1934	25	25
482	15s. Hungary and Italy, 1938	25	25
483	15s. Brazil and Uruguay, 1950	25	25
484	15s. Hungary and W. Germany, 1954	25	25
485	15s. Sweden and Brazil, 1958	25	25
486	15s. Czechoslovakia and Brazil, 1962	25	25
487	15s. W. Germany and England, 1966	25	25
488	15s. Italy and Brazil, 1970	25	25
489	15s. Holland and W. Germany, 1974	25	25
490	15s. Holland and Argentina, 1978	25	25
491	15s. Map of World on footballs	25	25
MS492	118 × 93 mm. 1m.25 Bernabeu Stadium, Madrid (47 × 35 mm)	1·10	1·25

Nos. 480/8 show the Jules Rimet Trophy and Nos. 489/91 the World Cup Trophy.

135 Portrait of George Washington

1982. 250th Birth Anniv of George Washington. Multicoloured.

493	6s. Type **135**	10	10
494	7s. Washington with step-children and dog	10	10
495	10s. Washington with Indian chief	15	10
496	25s. Washington with troops	30	30
497	40s. Washington arriving in New York	40	40
498	1m. Washington on parade	1·00	1·10
MS499	117 × 92 mm. 1m.25 Washington crossing the Delaware	1·00	1·00

136 Lady Diana Spencer in Tetbury, May 1981 **137** Mosotho reading Sesotho Bible

1982. 21st Birthday of Princess of Wales. Mult.

514a	30s. Lesotho coat of arms	40	40
515	50s. Type **136**	60	60
516	75s. Wedding picture at Buckingham Palace	80	1·00
517	1m. Formal portrait	1·25	1·40

1982. Centenary of Sesotho Bible. Multicoloured.

518	6s. Type **137**	15	20
519	15s. Sesotho bible and Virgin Mary holding infant Jesus	20	25
520	1m. Sesotho bible and Cathedral (62 × 42 mm)	50	75

138 Birthday Greetings

1982. Birth of Prince William of Wales. Mult.

521	6s. Type **138**	2·25	2·75
522	60s. Princess Diana and Prince William	1·00	1·00

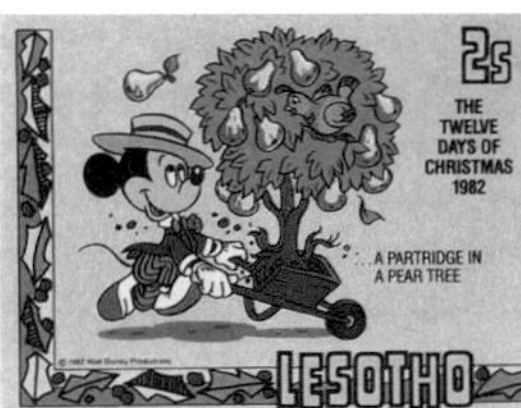

139 "A Partridge in a Pear Tree"

1982. Christmas. "The Twelve Days of Christmas". Walt Disney cartoon characters. Multicoloured.

523	2s. Type **139**	10	10
524	2s. "Two turtle doves"	10	10
525	3s. "Three French hens"	10	10
526	3s. "Four calling birds"	10	10
527	4s. "Five golden rings"	10	10
528	4s. "Six geese a-laying"	10	10
529	75s. "Seven swans a-swimming"	1·40	1·75
530	75s. "Eight maids a-milking"	1·40	1·75
MS531	126 × 101 mm. 1m.50, "Nine ladies dancing, ten lords a-leaping, eleven pipers piping, twelve drummers drumming"	2·40	2·75

140 "Lepista caffrorum"

1983. Fungi. Multicoloured.

532	10s. Type **140**	15	10
533	30s. "Broomeia congregata"	30	40
534	50s. "Afroboletus luteolus"	60	90
535	75s. "Lentinus tuber-regium"	90	1·40

141 Ba-Leseli Dance

1983. Commonwealth Day. Multicoloured.

536	5s. Type **141**	10	10
537	30s. Tapestry weaving	20	30
538	60s. Queen Elizabeth II (vert)	35	65
539	75s. King Moshoeshoe II (vert)	40	80

142 "Dancers in a Trance" (rock painting from Ntloana Tsoana)

1983. Rock Paintings. Multicoloured.

540	6s. Type **142**	20	10
541	25s. "Baboons", Sehonghong	55	35
542	60s. "Hunters attacking Mountain Reedbuck", Makhetha	60	1·10
543	75s. "Eland", Lehaha la Likhomo	65	1·60
MS544	166 × 84 mm. Nos. 540/3 and 10s. "Cattle herding", Sehonghong (52 × 52 mm)	1·25	3·50

143 Montgolfier Balloon, 1783

1983. Bicentenary of Manned Flight. Mult.

545	7s. Type **143**	15	10
546	30s. Wright brothers and Flyer I	30	40
547	60s. First airmail flight	50	1·25
548	1m. Concorde	2·25	2·50
MS549	180 × 92 mm. Nos. 545/8 and 6s. Dornier Do-28D Skyservant of Lesotho Airways (60 × 60 mm)	2·75	2·75

144 Rev. Eugene Casalis

1983. 150th Anniv of Arrival of the French Missionaries. Multicoloured.

550	6s. Type **144**	10	10
551	25s. The founding of Morija	10	10
552	40s. Baptism of Libe	10	15
553	75s. Map of Lesotho	20	25

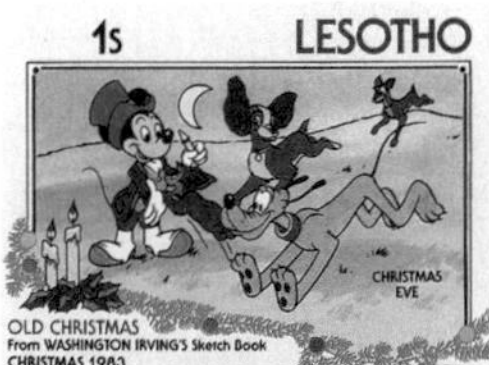

145 Mickey Mouse and Pluto greeted by Friends

1983. Christmas. Walt Disney Characters in scenes from "Old Christmas" (Washington Irving's sketchbook). Multicoloured.

554	1s. Type **145**	10	10
555	2s. Donald Duck and Pluto	10	10
556	3s. Donald Duck with Huey, Dewey and Louie	10	10
557	4s. Goofy, Donald Duck and Mickey Mouse	10	10
558	5s. Goofy holding turkey, Donald Duck and Mickey Mouse	10	10
559	6s. Goofy and Mickey Mouse	10	10
560	75s. Donald and Daisy Duck	2·00	2·40
561	1m. Goofy and Clarabell	2·50	2·75
MS562	132 × 113 mm. 1m.75 Scrooge McDuck, Pluto and Donald Duck	3·25	4·50

146 "Danaus chrysippus"

1984. Butterflies. Multicoloured.

563	1s. Type **146**	30	40
564	2s. "Aeropetes tulbaghia"	30	40
565	3s. "Colotis evenina"	35	40
566	4s. "Precis oenone"	35	40
567	5s. "Precis hierta"	35	40
568	6s. "Catopsilia florella"	35	10
569	7s. "Phalanta phalantha"	35	10
570	10s. "Acraea stenobea"	40	10
571	15s. "Cynthia cardui"	75	10
572	20s. "Colotis subfasciatus"	75	10
573	30s. "Charaxes jasius"	75	30
574	50s. "Terias brigitta"	75	40
575	60s. "Pontia helice"	75	50
576	75s. "Colotis regina"	75	50
577	1m. "Hypolimnas misippus"	75	1·50
578	5m. "Papilio demodocus"	1·50	7·50

147 "Thou shalt not have Strange Gods before Me"

1984. Easter. The Ten Commandments. Mult.

579	20s. Type **147**	30	30
580	20s. "Thou shalt not take the name of the Lord thy God in vain"	30	30
581	20s. "Remember thou keep holy the Lord's Day"	30	30
582	20s. "Honour thy father and mother"	30	30
583	20s. "Thou shalt not kill"	30	30
584	20s. "Thou shalt not commit adultery"	30	30
585	20s. "Thou shalt not steal"	30	30
586	20s. "Thou shalt not bear false witness against thy neighbour"	30	30
587	20s. "Thou shalt not covet thy neighbour's wife"	30	30
588	20s. "Thou shalt not covet thy neighbour's goods"	30	30
MS589	102 × 73 mm. 1m.50 Moses with Tablets (45 × 28 mm)	1·00	2·25

148 Torch Bearer

1984. Olympic Games, Los Angeles. Multicoloured.

590	10s. Type **148**	10	10
591	30s. Horse-riding	10	10
592	50s. Swimming	15	20

593 75s. Basketball 20 25
594 1m. Running 25 30
MS595 101 × 72mm. 1m.50 Olympic Flame and flags . . . . 1·25 2·50

149 Sauropodomorph Footprints

1984. Prehistoric Footprints (2nd series). Mult.
596 10s. Type **149** 50 30
597 30s. Lesothosaurus footprints 60 1·25
598 50s. Footprint of carnivorous dinosaur . . . . 70 2·00

150 Wells Fargo Coach, 1852

1984. "Ausipex" Int Stamp Exhibition, Melbourne. Bicent of First Mail Coach Run. Mult.
599 6s. Type **150** 10 10
600 7s. Basotho mail cart, circa 1900 . . . . 10 10
601 10s. Bath mail coach, 1784 10 10
602 30s. Cobb coach, 1853 . . . 15 15
603 50s. Exhibition logo and Royal Exhibition Buildings, Melbourne (82 × 25 mm) 50 80
MS604 147 × 98 mm. 1m.75 G.B. Penny Black, Basutoland 1934 "OFFICIAL" optd 6d. and Western Australia 1854 4d. with frame inverted (82 × 25 mm) . . 2·25 3·75

151 "The Orient Express" (1900)

1984. Railways of the World. Multicoloured.
605 6s. Type **151** 30 15
606 15s. Class 05 streamlined steam locomotive No. 001, Germany (1935) 30 30
607 30s. Caledonian Railway steam locomotive "Cardean" (1906) 35 60
608 60s. Atchison, Topeka & Santa Fe "Super Chief" express (1940) . . . . . . 40 1·75
609 1m. L.N.E.R. "Flying Scotsman" (1934) . . . . 40 2·00
MS610 108 × 82mm. 2m. South African Railways "The Blue Train" (1972) . . . . 1·00 2·50

152 Eland Calf

1984. Baby Animals. Multicoloured.
611 15s. Type **152** 35 20
612 20s. Young chacma baboons 35 25
613 30s. Oribi calf 35 40
614 75s. Young Natal red hares 50 1·60
615 1m. Black-backed jackal pups (46 × 27 mm) . . . . . . 50 2·00

153 Crown of Lesotho

154 Christ condemned to Death

1985. Silver Jubilee of King Moshoeshoe II. Mult.
616 6s. Type **153** 10 10
617 30s. King Moshoeshoe in 1960 . . . . 20 30
618 75s. King Moshoeshoe in traditional dress, 1985 . . 50 75
619 1m. King Moshoeshoe in uniform, 1985 . . . . . . 70 1·10

1985. Easter. The Stations of the Cross. Mult.
620 20s. Type **154** 25 35
621 20s. Christ carrying the Cross 25 35
622 20s. Falling for the first time 25 35
623 20s. Christ meets Mary . . . 25 35
624 20s. Simon of Cyrene helping to carry the Cross 25 35
625 20s. Veronica wiping the face of Christ 25 35
626 20s. Christ falling a second time 25 35
627 20s. Consoling the women of Jerusalem 25 35
628 20s. Falling for the third time 25 35
629 20s. Christ being stripped . . 25 35
630 20s. Christ nailed to the Cross 25 35
631 20s. Dying on the Cross . . . 25 35
632 20s. Christ taken down from the Cross 25 35
633 20s. Christ being laid in the sepulchre 25 35
MS634 138 × 98 mm. 2m. "The Crucifixion" (Mathias Grunewald) 1·50 3·50

155 Duchess of York with Princess Elizabeth, 1931

1985. Life and Times of Queen Elizabeth the Queen Mother. Multicoloured.
635 10s. Type **155** 35 10
636 30s. The Queen Mother in 1975 . . . . 70 50
637 60s. Queen Mother with Queen Elizabeth and Princess Margaret, 1980 . . 80 90
638 2m. Four generations of Royal Family at Prince Harry's christening, 1984 1·25 2·50
MS639 139 × 98 mm. 2m. Queen Elizabeth with the Princess of Wales and her children at Prince Harry's christening (37 × 50 mm) 2·25 2·75

156 B.M.W. "732i"

1985. Century of Motoring. Multicoloured.
640 6s. Type **156** 25 15
641 10s. Ford "Crown Victoria" 35 15
642 30s. Mercedes-Benz "500SE" 75 50
643 90s. Cadillac "Eldorado Biarritz" . . . . 1·50 2·50
644 2m. Rolls-Royce "Silver Spirit" . . . . 2·00 4·00
MS645 139 × 98 mm. 2m. Rolls-Royce "Silver Ghost Tourer", 1907 (37 × 50 mm) . . . . . . 4·00 6·00

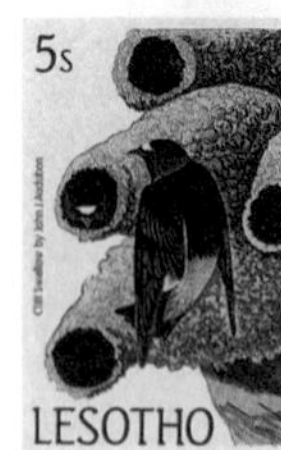

157 American Cliff Swallow

158 Two Youths Rock-climbing

1985. Birth Bicentenary of John J. Audubon (ornithologist). Designs showing original paintings. Multicoloured.
646 5s. Type **157** 40 30
647 6s. Great crested grebe (horiz) 40 30
648 10s. Vesper sparrow ("Vester Sparrow") (horiz) . . . 55 30
649 30s. Common greenshank ("Greenshank") (horiz) . . 1·25 75
650 60s. Stilt sandpiper (horiz) . . 1·75 2·75
651 2m. Glossy ibis (horiz) . . . 2·50 6·00

1985. International Youth Year and 75th Anniv of Girl Guide Movement. Multicoloured.
652 10s. Type **158** 20 10
653 30s. Young technician in hospital laboratory 50 40
654 75s. Three guides on parade 1·00 1·25
655 2m. Guide saluting . . . . . 1·75 3·00
MS656 138 × 98 mm. 2m. "Olave, Lady Baden-Powell" (Grace Wheatley) (37 × 50 mm) . . . 2·40 2·75

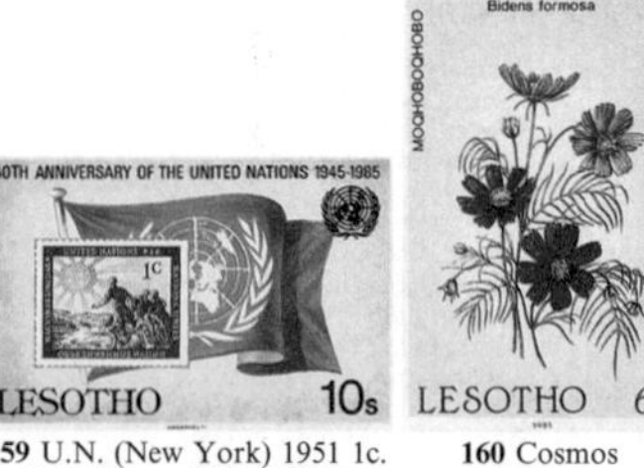

159 U.N. (New York) 1951 1c. Definitive and U.N. Flag

160 Cosmos

1985. 40th Anniversary of U.N.O.
657 **159** 10s. multicoloured 25 10
658 – 30s. multicoloured 60 35
659 – 50s. multicoloured 95 85
660 – 2m. black and green . . . 5·00 6·50
DESIGNS—VERT: 30s. Ha Sofonia Earth Satellite Station; 2m. Maimonides (physician, philosopher and scholar). HORIZ: 50s. Lesotho Airways Fokker F.27 Friendship at Maseru Airport.

1985. Wild Flowers. Multicoloured.
661 6s. Type **160** 40 15
662 10s. Small agapanthus . . . 55 15
663 30s. Pink witchweed . . . . 1·10 70
664 60s. Small iris . . . . 1·50 2·00
665 90s. Wild geranium or cranesbill . . . . 1·75 3·00
666 1m. Large spotted orchid . . 3·00 5·00

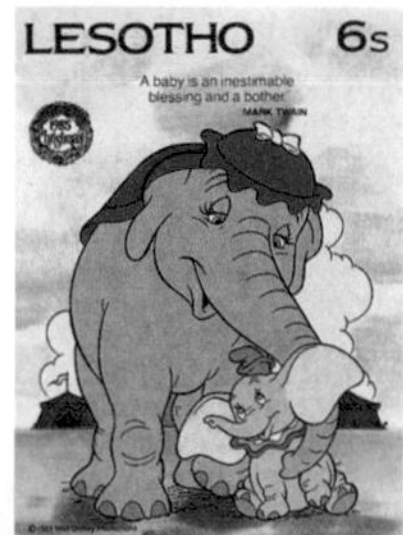

160a Mrs Jumbo and Baby Dumbo

1985. 150th Birth Anniv of Mark Twain. Walt Disney cartoon characters illustrating various Mark Twain quotations. Multicoloured.
667 6s. Type **160a** 40 15
668 50s. Uncle Scrooge and Goofy reading newspaper 1·25 1·00
669 90s. Winnie the Pooh, Tigger, Piglet and Owl . . . . . . 1·75 2·00
670 1m.50 Goofy at ship's wheel 2·75 3·00
MS671 127 × 102 mm. 1m.25 Mickey Mouse as astronaut . . . . . 4·75 3·75

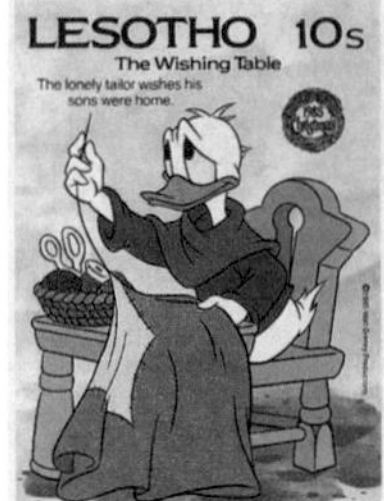

160b Donald Duck as the Tailor

1985. Birth Bicentenaries of Grimm Brothers (folklorists). Walt Disney cartoon characters in scenes from "The Wishing Table". Mult.
672 10s. Type **160b** 50 20
673 60s. The second son (Dewey) with magic donkey and gold coins . . . . 1·50 1·50
674 75s. The eldest son (Huey) with wishing table laden with food . . . . 1·75 1·75
675 1m. The innkeeper stealing the third son's (Louie) magic cudgel . . . . . . 2·00 2·75
MS676 127 × 102 mm. 1m.50 The tailor and eldest son with wishing table . . . . 4·75 5·50

161 Male Lammergeier on Watch

162 Two Players chasing Ball

1986. Flora and Fauna of Lesotho. Multicoloured.
677 7s. Type **161** . . . . 1·75 65
678 9s. Prickly pear 70 20
679 12s. Stapelia 70 20
680 15s. Pair of lammergeiers . . 2·50 60
681 35s. Pig's ears . . . . 1·10 60

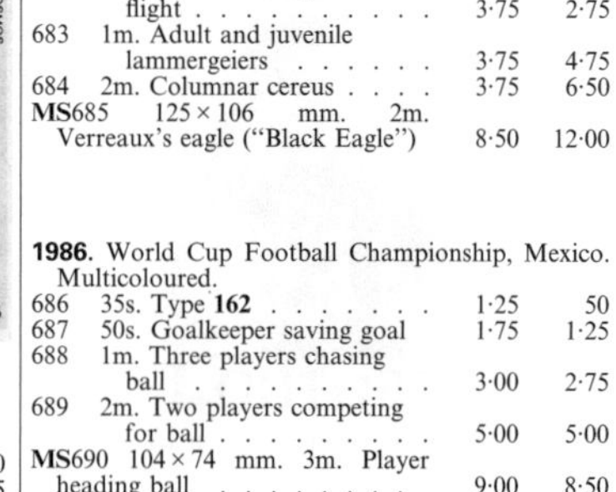

682 50s. Male lammergeier in flight . . . . 3·75 2·75
683 1m. Adult and juvenile lammergeiers . . . . . . 3·75 4·75
684 2m. Columnar cereus . . . . 3·75 6·50
MS685 125 × 106 mm. 2m. Verreaux's eagle ("Black Eagle") 8·50 12·00

1986. World Cup Football Championship, Mexico. Multicoloured.
686 35s. Type **162** . . . . 1·25 50
687 50s. Goalkeeper saving goal 1·75 1·25
688 1m. Three players chasing ball . . . . 3·00 2·75
689 2m. Two players competing for ball . . . . 5·00 5·00
MS690 104 × 74 mm. 3m. Player heading ball . . . . 9·00 8·50

162a Galileo and 200 inch Hale Telescope at Mount Palomar Observatory, California

1986. Appearance of Halley's Comet. Multicoloured.
691 9s. Type **162a** 50 15
692 15s. Halley's Comet and "Pioneer Venus 2" spacecraft 75 20
693 70s. Halley's Comet of 684 A.D. (from "Nuremberg Chronicle", 1493) . . . . 1·60 1·40
694 3m. Comet and landing of William the Conqueror, 1066 . . . . 4·00 5·50
MS695 101 × 70 mm. 4m. Halley's Comet over Lesotho . . . . . 6·50 7·00

163 International Year of the Child Gold Coin

1986. 1st Anniv of New Currency (1980). Mult.
696 30s. Type **163** . . . . 4·00 6·50
697 30s. Five maloti banknote . . 4·00 6·50
698 30s. Fifty lisente coin . . . . 4·00 6·50
699 30s. Ten maloti banknote . . 4·00 6·50
700 30s. One sente coin . . . . . 4·00 6·50
These stamps were prepared in 1980, but were not issued at that time.

163a Princess Elizabeth in Pantomime

1986. 60th Birthday of Queen Elizabeth II.
701 **163a** 90s. black and yellow . . 50 60
702 – 1m. multicoloured . . . 55 65
703 – 2m. multicoloured . . . 90 1·40
MS704 119 × 85 mm. 4m. black and grey-brown . . . . 1·75 3·25
DESIGNS: 1m. Queen at Windsor Horse Show, 1971; 2m. At Royal Festival Hall, 1971; 4m. Princess Elizabeth in 1934.

163b Statue of Liberty and Bela Bartok (composer)

1986. Centenary of Statue of Liberty. Immigrants to the U.S.A. Multicoloured.
705 15s. Type **163b** 85 30
706 35s. Felix Adler (philosopher) 85 30
707 1m. Victor Herbert (composer) . . . . 3·00 2·00
708 3m. David Niven (actor) . . 4·25 4·25
MS709 103 × 74 mm. 3m. Statue of Liberty (vert) . . . . 3·50 5·00

163c Mickey Mouse and Goofy as Japanese Mail Runners

1986. "Ameripex" International Stamp Exhibition, Chicago. Walt Disney cartoon characters delivering mail. Multicoloured.

710 15s. Type **163c** 80 20
711 35s. Mickey Mouse and Pluto with mail sledge 1·10 30
712 1m. Goofy as postman riding Harley-Davidson motorcycle 2·25 2·75
713 2m. Donald Duck operating railway mailbag apparatus 2·50 4·00
MS714 127 × 101 mm. 4m. Goofy driving mail to aircraft 6·50 7·00

1986. Various stamps surch. (a) On Nos. 437 etc (Birds)

729 9s. on 5s. Bokmakierie shrike 75 20
715 9s. on 10s. Red-billed pintail (horiz) 3·50 1·25
716 15s. on 1s. Type **127** 7·00 3·00
717 15s. on 2s. Speckled pigeon (horiz) 4·00 4·50
718 15s. on 5s. Bokmakierie shrike 2·25 35
719 15s. on 60s. Cape longclaw (horiz) 20 10
730 16s. on 25s. Malachite kingfisher 2·75 1·00
731 35s. on 25s. Malachite kingfisher 1·50 60
721 35s. on 75s. Hoopoe 16·00 15·00

(b) On Nos. 563 etc (Butterflies).

722 9s. on 30s. "Charaxes jasius" 15 10
723 9s. on 60s. "Pontia helice" 3·25 4·00
724 15s. on 1s. Type **146** 2·00 2·25
725 15s. on 2s. "Aeropetes tulbaghia" 20 20
726 15s. on 3s. "Colotis evenina" 20 20
727 15s. on 5s. "Precis hierta" 20 20
732 20s. on 4s. "Precis oenone" 10 10
728 35s. on 75s. "Colotis regina" 35 35
733 40s. on 7s. "Phalanta phalantha" 15 20

(c) No. 722 further surch.

734 3s. on 9s. on 30s. "Charaxes jasius" 1·00 1·00
735 7s. on 9s. on 30s. "Charaxes jasius" 1·25 1·00

170a Prince Andrew and Miss Sarah Ferguson

1986. Royal Wedding. Multicoloured.

736 50s. Type **170a** 40 40
737 1m. Prince Andrew 70 80
738 3m. Prince Andrew piloting helicopter 2·75 2·25
MS739 88 × 88 mm. 4m. Prince Andrew and Miss Sarah Ferguson (different) 3·50 4·50

171 Basotho Pony and Rider

1986. 20th Anniv of Independence. Multicoloured.

740 9s. Type **171** 40 10
741 15s. Basotho woman spinning mohair 40 15
742 35s. Crossing river by rowing boat 50 30
743 3m. Thaba Tseka Post Office 1·00 3·00
MS744 109 × 78 mm. 4m. King Moshoeshoe I 4·75 8·00

171a Chip'n' Dale pulling Christmas Cracker

1986. Christmas. Walt Disney cartoon characters. Multicoloured.

745 15s. Type **171a** 80 20
746 35s. Mickey and Minnie Mouse 1·10 30
747 1m. Pluto pulling Christmas taffy 1·90 2·75
748 2m. Aunt Matilda baking 2·25 4·00
MS749 126 × 102 mm. 5m. Huey and Dewey with gingerbread house 5·50 7·00

172 Rally Car **173** Lawn Tennis

1987. Roof of Africa Motor Rally. Multicoloured.

750 9s. Type **172** 30 10
751 15s. Motorcyclist 35 15
752 35s. Motorcyclist (different) 55 35
753 4m. Rally car (different) 3·00 5·00

1987. Olympic Games, Seoul (1988) (1st issue). Multicoloured.

754 9s. Type **173** 70 10
755 15s. Judo 70 15
756 20s. Athletics 75 20
757 35s. Boxing 85 30
758 1m. Diving 1·10 1·75
759 3m. Ten-pin bowling 2·75 5·50
MS760 Two sheets, each 75 × 105 mm. (a) 2m. Lawn tennis (different). (b) 4m. Football. Set of 2 sheets 6·00 5·00

See also Nos. 838/41.

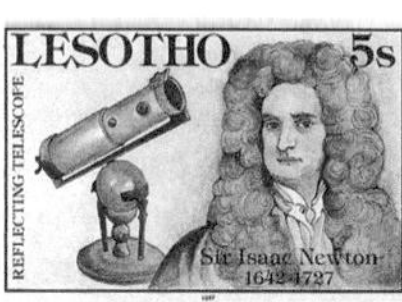

174 Isaac Newton and Reflecting Telescope

1987. Great Scientific Discoveries. Multicoloured.

761 5s. Type **174** 30 10
762 9s. Alexander Graham Bell and first telephone 30 15
763 75s. Robert Goddard and liquid fuel rocket 80 75
764 4m. Chuck Yeager and Bell XS-1 rocket plane 2·75 4·50
MS765 98 × 68 mm. 4m. "Mariner 10" spacecraft 2·75 3·00

175 Grey Rhebuck

1987. Flora and Fauna. Multicoloured.

766 5s. Type **175** 40 15
767 9s. Cape clawless otter 40 15
768 15s. Cape grey mongoose 55 20
769 20s. Free State daisy (vert) 60 20
770 35s. River bells (vert) 75 30
771 1m. Turkey flower (vert) 1·75 2·50
772 2m. Sweet briar (vert) 2·25 3·75
773 3m. Mountain reedbuck 2·75 5·00
MS774 Two sheets, each 114 × 98 mm. (a) 2m. Pig-Lily (vert). (b) 4m. Cape Wildebeest. Set of 2 sheets 5·50 9·00

176 Scouts hiking **178** "Madonna and Child" (detail)

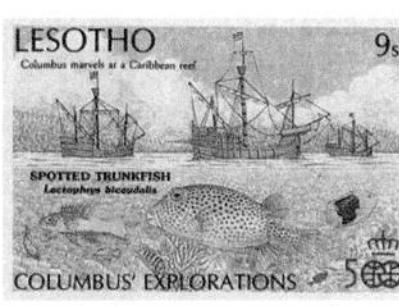

177 Spotted Trunkfish and Columbus's Fleet

1987. World Scout Jamboree, Australia. Mult.

775 9s. Type **176** 60 20
776 15s. Scouts playing football 65 20
777 35s. Kangaroos 80 50
778 75s. Scout saluting 1·75 1·25
779 4m. Australian scout windsurfing 3·75 6·50
MS780 96 × 66 mm. 4m. Outline map and flag of Australia 3·25 4·00

1987. 500th Anniv (1992) of Discovery of America by Columbus. Multicoloured.

781 9s. Type **177** 65 20
782 15s. Green turtle and ships 80 20
783 35s. Columbus watching common dolphins from ship 1·00 40
784 5m. White-tailed tropic bird and fleet at sea 6·00 7·50
MS785 105 × 76 mm. 4m. "Santa Maria" and Cuban Amazon in flight 5·00 4·00

No. 782 is inscribed "Carribbean" in error.

1987. Christmas. Paintings by Raphael. Mult.

786 9s. Type **178** 30 10
787 15s. "Marriage of the Virgin" 45 15
788 35s. "Coronation of the Virgin" (detail) 90 40
789 90s. "Madonna of the Chair" 2·00 3·50
MS790 75 × 100 mm. 3m. "Madonna and Child enthroned with Five Saints" (detail) 3·00 3·00

179 Lesser Pied Kingfisher

1988. Birds. Multicoloured.

791 2s. Type **179** 20 30
792 3s. Three-banded plover 20 30
793 5s. Spur-winged goose 20 30
794 10s. Clapper lark 20 20
795 12s. Red-eyed bulbul 30 10
796 16s. Cape weaver 30 10
797 20s. Paradise sparrow ("Red-headed Finch") 30 10
798 30s. Mountain wheater ("Mountain Chat") 35 20
799 40s. Common stonechat ("Stone Chate") 40 20
800 55s. Pied barbet 50 25
801 60s. Red-shouldered glossy starling 55 50
802 75s. Cape sparrow 60 60
803 1m. Cattle egret 60 80
804 3m. Giant kingfisher 90 2·50
805 10m. Helmeted guineafowl 1·90 7·00

1988. Royal Ruby Wedding. Nos. 701/3 optd **40TH WEDDING ANNIVERSARY H.M. QUEEN ELIZABETH II H.R.H. THE DUKE OF EDINBURGH**.

806 90s. black and yellow 80 65
807 1m. multicoloured 90 80
808 2m. multicoloured 1·60 1·40
MS809 119 × 85 mm. 4m. black and grey-brown 3·00 2·75

181 Mickey Mouse and Goofy outside Presidential Palace, Helsinki

1988. "Finlandia '88" International Stamp Exhibition, Helsinki. Designs showing Walt Disney cartoon characters in Finland. Mult.

810 1s. Type **181** 10 10
811 2s. Goofy and Mickey Mouse in sauna 10 10
812 3s. Goofy and Mickey Mouse fishing in lake 10 10
813 4s. Mickey and Minnie Mouse and Finlandia Hall, Helsinki 10 10
814 5s. Mickey Mouse photographing Goofy at Sibelius Monument, Helsinki 10 10
815 10s. Mickey Mouse and Goofy pony trekking 10 10
816 3m. Goofy, Mickey and Minnie Mouse at Helsinki Olympic Stadium 4·00 3·00
817 5m. Mickey Mouse and Goofy meeting Santa at Arctic Circle 5·00 4·00
MS818 Two sheets, each 127 × 102 mm. (a) 4m. Mickey Mouse and nephew as Lapps. (b) 4m. Daisy Duck, Goofy, Mickey and Minnie Mouse by fountain, Helsinki. Set of 2 sheets 5·50 7·00

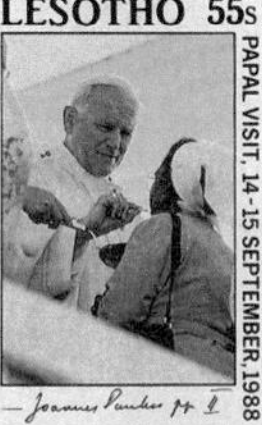

182 Pope John Paul II giving Communion **183** Large-toothed Rock Hyrax

1988. Visit of Pope John Paul II. Mult.

819 55s. Type **182** 40 25
820 2m. Pope leading procession 1·25 1·50
821 3m. Pope at airport 1·75 2·00
822 4m. Pope John Paul II 2·25 2·75
MS823 98 × 79 mm. 5m. Archbishop Morapeli (horiz) 5·00 4·50

1988. Small Mammals of Lesotho. Mult.

824 16s. Type **183** 55 15
825 40s. Ratel and black-throated honey guide (bird) 1·75 55
826 75s. Small-spotted genet 1·50 85
827 3m. Yellow mongoose 3·25 5·50
MS828 110 × 78 mm. 4m. Meerkat 3·25 4·00

184 "Birth of Venus" (detail) (Botticelli)

1988. Famous Paintings. Multicoloured.

829 15s. Type **184** 30 15
830 25s. "View of Toledo" (El Greco) 35 20
831 40s. "Maids of Honour" (detail) (Velasquez) 45 25
832 50s. "The Fifer" (Manet) 55 30
833 55s. "Starry Night" (detail) (Van Gogh) 55 30
834 75s. "Prima Ballerina" (Degas) 70 70
835 2m. "Bridge over Water Lilies" (Monet) 1·75 2·25
836 3m. "Guernica" (detail) (Picasso) 1·75 2·75
MS837 Two sheets, each 110 × 95 mm. (a) 4m. "The Presentation of the Virgin in the Temple" (Titian). (b) 4m. "The Miracle of the Newborn Infant" (Titian). Set of 2 sheets 4·00 4·50

185 Wrestling

1988. Olympic Games, Seoul (2nd series). Mult.

838 12s. Type **185** 10 10
839 16s. Show jumping (vert) 10 10
840 55s. Shooting 20 30
841 3m.50 As 16s. (vert) 1·40 2·00
MS842 108 × 77 mm. 4m. Olympic flame (vert) 2·75 3·50

186 Yannick Noah and Eiffel Tower, Paris

1988. 75th Anniv of Int Tennis Federation. Mult.

843 12s. Type **186** 60 25

844 20s. Rod Laver and Sydney Harbour Bridge and Opera House . . . . 1·00 30

845 30s. Ivan Lendl and Prague 65 25

846 65s. Jimmy Connors and Tokyo (vert) 80 40

847 1m. Arthur Ashe and Barcelona (vert) . . . . . 1·25 60

848 1m.55 Althea Gibson and New York (vert) . . . . . 1·25 90

849 2m. Chris Evert and Vienna (vert) . . . . 1·50 1·25

850 2m.40 Boris Becker and Houses of Parliament, London (vert) . . . . . . 1·75 1·75

851 3m. Martina Navratilova and Golden Gate Bridge, San Francisco . . . . 2·00 2·00

MS852 98 × 72 mm. 4m. Steffi Graf and Berlin . . . . 3·00 3·75

No. 844 is inscribed "SIDNEY" in error.

186a "The Averoldi Polyptych" (detail)

1988. Christmas. 500th Birth Anniv of Titian (artist). Multicoloured.

853 12s. Type **186a** 20 10

854 20s. "Christ and the Adulteress" (detail) 20 10

855 35s. "Christ and the Adulteress" (different detail) 30 20

856 45s. "Angel of the Annunciation" 40 30

857 65s. "Saint Dominic" 55 50

858 1m. "The Vendramin Family" (detail) 75 80

859 2m. "Mary Magdalen" . . . 1·25 1·75

860 3m. "The Tribute Money" 1·75 2·50

MS861 (a) 94 × 110 mm. 5m. "Mater Dolorosa". (b) 110 × 94 mm. 5m. "Christ and the Woman taken in Adultery" (horiz). Set of 2 sheets 6·00 8·00

187 Pilatus PC-6 Turbo Porter

1989. 125th Anniv of International Red Cross. Aircraft. Multicoloured.

862 12s. Type **187** 50 10

863 20s. Unloading medical supplies from Cessna Caravan I 60 20

864 55s. De Havilland D.H.C.6 Twin Otter 200/300 . . . . 90 50

865 3m. Douglas DC-3 . . . . . 2·75 3·50

MS866 109 × 80 mm. 4m. Red Cross logo and Douglas DC-3 (vert) 6·50 3·75

187a "Dawn Mist at Mishima"

1989. Japanese Art. Paintings by Hiroshige. Mult.

867 12s. Type **187a** 30 10

868 16s. "Night Snow at Kambara" 35 10

869 20s. "Wayside Inn at Mariko Station" 35 10

870 35s. "Shower at Shono" . . 55 10

871 55s. "Snowfall on the Kisokaido near Oi" . . . 65 40

872 1m. "Autumn Moon at Seba" 85 85

873 3m.20 "Evening Moon at Ryogoku Bridge" . . . . 2·25 3·00

874 5m. "Cherry Blossoms at Arashiyama" . . . . . . 2·75 3·75

MS875 Two sheets, each 102 × 76 mm. (a) 4m. "Listening to the Singing Insects at Dokanyama". (b) 4m. "Moonlight, Nagakubo". Set of 2 sheets . . . . 6·00 7·00

188 Mickey Mouse as General

189 "Paxillus involutus"

1989. "Philexfrance 89" International Stamp Exhibition, Paris. Designs showing Walt Disney cartoon characters in French military uniforms of the Revolutionary period. Multicoloured.

876 1s. Type **188** 10 10

877 2s. Ludwig von Drake as infantryman 10 10

878 3s. Goofy as grenadier . . . 10 10

879 4s. Horace Horsecollar as cavalryman 10 10

880 5s. Pete as hussar 10 10

881 10s. Donald Duck as marine 10 10

882 3m. Gyro Gearloose as National Guard . . . . . 3·25 3·25

883 5m. Scrooge McDuck as admiral . . . . 4·00 4·25

MS884 Two sheets, each 127 × 102 mm. (a) 4m. Mickey and Minnie Mouse as King Louis XVI and Marie Antoinette with Goofy as a National Guard (horiz). (b) 4m. Mickey Mouse as drummer. Set of 2 sheets . . . . 7·50 9·00

No. 879 is inscribed "CALVARYMAN" in error.

1989. Fungi. Multicoloured.

900 12s. Type **189** 20 10

901 16s. "Ganoderma applanatum" 20 15

902 55s. "Suillus granulatus" . . 45 35

903 5m. "Stereum hirsutum" . . 3·25 4·50

MS904 96 × 69 mm. 4m. "Scleroderma cepa" ("flavidum") 5·00 5·50

190 Sesotho Huts

192 Launch of "Apollo 11"

191 Marsh Sandpiper

1989. Maloti Mountains. Multicoloured.

905 1m. Type **190** . . . . 70 1·00

906 1m. American aloe and mountains . . . . 70 1·00

907 1m. River valley with waterfall . . . . 70 1·00

908 1m. Sesotho tribesman on ledge . . . . 70 1·00

MS909 86 × 117 mm. 4m. Spiral Aloe . . . . 3·00 4·00

Nos. 905/8 were printed together, se-tenant, forming a composite design.

1989. Migrant Birds. Multicoloured.

910 12s. Type **191** 80 30

911 65s. Little stint . . . . 1·50 70

912 1m. Ringed plover . . . . . 2·00 1·50

913 4m. Curlew sandpiper . . . 3·50 5·50

MS914 97 × 69 mm. 5m. Ruff (vert) 8·50 9·00

1989. 20th Anniv of First Manned Landing on Moon. Multicoloured.

915 12s. Type **192** 25 10

916 16s. Lunar module "Eagle" landing on Moon (horiz) 25 15

917 40s. Neil Armstrong leaving "Eagle" 45 25

918 55s. Edwin Aldrin on Moon (horiz) 50 30

919 1m. Aldrin performing scientific experiment (horiz) 85 85

920 2m. "Eagle" leaving Moon (horiz) . . . . 1·50 1·75

921 3m. Command module "Columbia" in Moon orbit (horiz) . . . . 2·00 2·25

922 4m. Command module on parachutes . . . . 2·50 2·75

MS923 81 × 111 mm. 5m. Astronaut on Moon . . . . 5·00 6·00

193 English Penny Post Paid Mark, 1680

1989. "World Stamp Expo '89" International Stamp Exhibition, Washington (1st issue). Stamps and Postmarks.

924 **193** 75s. red, black and stone 70 75

925 – 75s. black, grey and red 70 75

926 – 75s. violet, black & brown 70 75

927 – 75s. brown, black & lt brn 70 75

928 – 75s. black and yellow . . 70 75

929 – 75s. multicoloured 70 75

930 – 75s. black and lilac . . . 70 75

931 – 75s. black, red and brown 70 75

932 – 75s. red, black and yellow 70 75

DESIGNS: No. 925, German postal seal and feather, 1807; 926, British Post Office in Crete 1898 20pa. stamp; 927, Bermuda 1848 Perot 1d. provisional; 928, U.S.A. Pony Express cancellation, 1860; 929, Finland 1856 5k. stamp; 930, Fiji 1870 "Fiji Times" 1d. stamp, 1870; 931, Sweden newspaper wrapper handstamp, 1823; 932, Bhor 1879 ½a. stamp.

193a Cathedral Church of St. Peter and St. Paul, Washington

1989. "World Stamp Expo '89" International Stamp Exhibition, Washington (2nd issue). Sheet 78 × 61 mm.

MS933 **193a** 4m. multicoloured 2·50 3·00

193b "The Immaculate Conception"

1989. Christmas. Paintings by Velazquez. Mult.

934 12s. Type **193b** 10 10

935 20s. "St. Anthony Abbot and St. Paul the Hermit" . . . 15 10

936 35s. "St. Thomas the Apostle" 25 25

937 55s. "Christ in the House of Martha and Mary" 35 35

938 1m. "St. John writing The Apocalypse on Patmos" . . 60 75

939 3m. "The Virgin presenting the Chasuble to St. Ildephonsus" . . . . . 1·60 2·25

940 4m. "The Adoration of the Magi" . . . . 2·00 2·75

MS941 71 × 96 mm. 5m. "The Coronation of the Virgin" . . 6·50 7·50

194 Scene from 1966 World Cup Final, England

1989. World Cup Football Championship, Italy. Scenes from past finals. Multicoloured.

942 12s. Type **194** 50 10

943 16s. 1970 final, Mexico . . . 50 15

944 55s. 1974 final, West Germany . . . . 1·00 40

945 5m. 1982 final, Spain . . . . 3·75 5·50

MS946 106 × 85 mm. 4m. Player's legs and symbolic football . . 6·00 7·00

1990. No. 889 and 798/9 surch **16 s.**

948 16s. on 12s. Red-eyed bulbul 1·50 20

948e 16s. on 30s. Common wheater 60 15

948f 16s. on 40s. Common stonechat 60 15

197 "Byblia anvatara"

198a Lady Elizabeth Bowes-Lyon and Brother in Fancy Dress

198 "Satyrium princeps"

1990. Butterflies. Multicoloured.

949 12s. Type **197** 70 15

950 16s. "Cynthia cardui" . . . 80 15

951 55s. "Precis oenone" . . . . 1·25 40

952 65s. "Pseudacraea boisduvali" 1·25 65

953 1m. "Precis orithya" . . . . 2·00 1·25

954 2m. "Precis sophia" . . . . 3·00 2·50

955 3m. "Danaus chrysippus" . . 4·00 4·25

956 4m. "Druryia antimachus" 5·00 6·50

MS957 105 × 70 mm. 5m. "Papilio demodocus" . . . . 7·50 9·00

1990. "EXPO 90" International Garden and Greenery Exhibition, Osaka. Local Orchids. Multicoloured.

958 12s. Type **198** 55 15

959 16s. "Huttonaea pulchra" . . 60 15

960 55s. "Herschelia graminifolia" . . . . . . 1·25 30

961 1m. "Ansellia gigantea" . . . 1·75 75

962 1m.55 "Polystachya pubescens" . . . . 2·00 1·75

963 2m.40 "Penthea filicornis" . . 2·00 2·25

964 3m. "Disperis capensis" . . . 2·25 3·25

965 4m. "Disa uniflora" . . . . 3·00 4·00

MS966 95 × 68 mm. 5m. "Stenoglottis longifolia" . . . 7·50 9·00

1990. 90th Birthday of Queen Elizabeth the Queen Mother.

967 **198a** 1m.50 black and mauve 1·25 1·25

968 – 1m.50 black and mauve 1·25 1·25

969 – 1m.50 black and mauve 1·25 1·25

MS970 90 × 75 mm. 5m. brown, black and mauve . . . . . . 4·00 4·00

DESIGNS: No. 968, Lady Elizabeth Bowes-Lyon in evening dress; 969, Lady Elizabeth Bowes-Lyon wearing hat; **MS**970, Lady Elizabeth Bowes-Lyon as a child.

199 King Moshoeshoe II and Prince Mohato wearing Seana-Marena Blankets

200 Filling Truck at No. 1 Quarry

1990. Traditional Blankets. Multicoloured.

971 12s. Type **199** 10 10

972 16s. Prince Mohato wearing Seana-Marena blanket . . 10 10

973 1m. Pope John Paul II wearing Seana-Marena blanket . . . . 1·75 1·10

974 3m. Basotho horsemen wearing Matlama blankets 2·00 3·00

MS975 85 × 104 mm. 5m. Pope John Paul II wearing hat and Seana-Marena blanket (horiz) . . . . 4·50 4·75

1990. Lesotho Highlands Water Project. Mult.

976 16s. Type **200** 75 10

977 20s. Tanker lorry on Pitseng–Malibamatso road 80 10

978 55s. Piers for Malibamatso Bridge 90 30

979 2m. Excavating Mphosong section of Pitseng–Malibamatso road . . . . 3·00 3·75

MS980 104 × 85 mm. 5m. Sinking blasting boreholes on Pitseng–Malibamatso road . . . . . . 6·50 7·50

201 Mother breastfeeding Baby

202 Men's Triple Jump

1990. UNICEF Child Survival Campaign. Multicoloured.

981 12s. Type **201** 60 10
982 55s. Baby receiving oral rehydration therapy . . . 1·10 45
983 1m. Weight monitoring . . . 1·75 2·75

1990. Olympic Games, Barcelona (1992). Mult.

984 16s. Type **202** 65 10
985 55s. Men's 200 m race . . . 85 25
986 1m. Men's 5000 m race . . . 1·40 1·25
987 4m. Show jumping . . . . . 4·00 6·00
MS988 100 × 70 mm. 5m. Olympic flame (horiz) . . . . 6·50 7·50

203 "Virgin and Child" (detail, Rubens)

1990. Christmas. Paintings by Rubens. Mult.

989 12s. Type **203** 20 10
990 16s. "Adoration of the Magi" (detail) 20 10
991 55s. "Head of One of the Three Kings" 45 25
992 80s. "Adoration of the Magi" (different detail) 60 60
993 1m. "Virgin and Child" (different detail) 70 70
994 2m. "Adoration of the Magi" (different detail) . . . . . 1·25 1·75
995 3m. "Virgin and Child" (different detail) . . . . . 2·00 2·50
996 4m. "Adoration of the Magi" (different detail) . . . . . 2·25 3·25
MS997 71 × 100 mm. 5m. "Assumption of the Virgin" (detail) . . . . 4·00 5·50

204 Mickey Mouse at Nagasaki Peace Park

1991. "Phila Nippon '91" International Stamp Exhibition, Tokyo. Walt Disney cartoon characters in Japan. Multicoloured.

998 20s. Type **204** 70 15
999 30s. Mickey Mouse on Kamakura Beach 75 20
1000 40s. Mickey and Donald Duck with Bunraku puppet 85 25
1001 50s. Mickey and Donald eating soba 95 35
1002 75s. Mickey and Minnie Mouse at tea house . . . 1·25 70
1003 1m. Mickey running after "Hikari" express train . . 1·25 1·00
1004 3m. Mickey Mouse with deer at Todaiji Temple, Nara . . . . 3·00 3·50
1005 4m. Mickey and Minnie outside Imperial Palace 3·00 4·00
MS1006 Two sheets, each 127 × 112 mm. (a) 5m. Mickey Mouse skiing. (b) 5m. Mickey and Minnie having a picnic. Set of 2 sheets . . . . 7·00 8·00

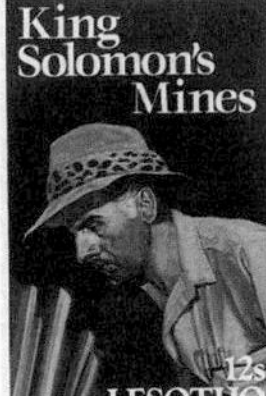

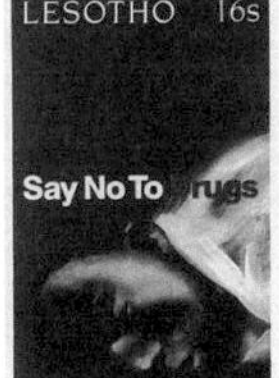

205 Stewart Granger ("King Solomon's Mines")

207 Victim of Drug Abuse

206 "Satyrus aello"

1991. Famous Films with African Themes. Mult.

1007 12s. Type **205** 35 20
1008 16s. Johnny Weissmuller ("Tarzan the Ape Man") 35 20
1009 30s. Clark Gable and Grace Kelly ("Mogambo") . . . 50 35
1010 55s. Sigourney Weaver and gorilla ("Gorillas in the Mist") 75 55
1011 70s. Humphrey Bogart and Katharine Hepburn ("The African Queen") 90 80
1012 1m. John Wayne and capture of rhinoceros ("Hatari!") . . . . 1·25 1·00
1013 2m. Meryl Streep and De Havilland Gipsy Moth light aircraft ("Out of Africa") . . . . 2·00 2·25
1014 4m. Arsenio Hall and Eddie Murphy ("Coming to America") . . . . 2·75 3·50
MS1015 108 × 77 mm. 5m. Elsa the Lioness ("Born Free") . . . . 3·75 4·50

1991. Butterflies. Multicoloured.

1016B 2s. Type **206** 10 30
1017B 3s. "Erebia medusa" . . 10 30
1018A 5s. "Melanargia galathea" 10 30
1019B 10s. "Erebia aethiops" . . 15 30
1020A 20s. "Coenonympha pamphilus" 20 10
1021B 25s. "Pyrameis atalanta" 20 10
1022B 30s. "Charaxes jasius" . . 25 10
1023B 40s. "Colias palaeno" . . 25 10
1024B 50s. "Colias cliopatra" 30 10
1025B 60s. "Colias philodice" 30 10
1026B 70s. "Rhumni gonepterix" 30 10
1027B 1m. "Colias caesonia" . . 50 25
1028B 2m. "Pyrameis cardui" 90 75
1029cA 3m. "Danaus chrysippus" 1·40 1·75
1030B 10m. "Apatura iris" . . . 4·00 4·50

1991. "Say No To Drugs" Campaign.

1031 **207** 16s. multicoloured . . . 1·50 60

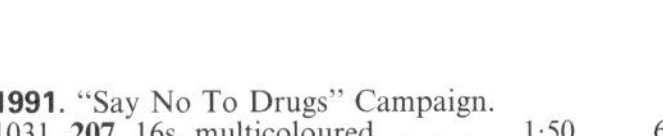

208 Wattled Cranes

1991. Southern Africa Development Co-ordination Conference Tourism Promotion. Multicoloured.

1032 12s. Type **208** . . . . . . 1·25 1·00
1033 16s. Butterfly on flowers . . 1·25 1·00
1034 25s. Zebra and tourist bus at Mukorob (rock formation), Namibia . . . 1·50 60
MS1035 75 × 117 mm. 3m. Basotho women in ceremonial dress . . 3·75 4·50

209 De Gaulle in 1939

211 "St. Anne with Mary and the Child Jesus"

210 Prince and Princess of Wales

1991. Birth Centenary of Charles de Gaulle (French statesman).

1036 **209** 20s. black and brown . . 80 15
1037 – 40s. black and purple . . 1·00 25
1038 – 50s. black and green . . 1·00 40
1039 – 60s. black and blue . . . 1·00 70
1040 – 4m. black and red . . . 3·50 5·50

DESIGNS: 40s. General De Gaulle as Free French leader; 50s. De Gaulle as provisional President of France, 1944–46; 60s. Charles de Gaulle in 1958; 4m. Pres. De Gaulle.

1991. 10th Wedding Anniv of Prince and Princess of Wales. Multicoloured.

1041 50s. Type **210** . . . . . . 1·50 25
1042 70s. Prince Charles at polo and Princess Diana holding Prince Harry . . 1·50 45
1043 1m. Prince Charles with Prince Harry and Princess Diana in evening dress . . 1·60 70
1044 3m. Prince William and Prince Harry in school uniform . . . . 2·25 3·00
MS1045 68 × 91 mm. 4m. Portraits of Prince with Princess and sons 5·50 4·25

1991. Christmas. Drawings by Albrecht Durer.

1046 **211** 20s. black and mauve . . 60 10
1047 – 30s. black and blue . . . 75 20
1048 – 50s. black and green . . 90 25
1049 – 60s. black and red . . . 95 30
1050 – 70s. black and yellow . . 1·00 60
1051 – 1m. black and orange . . 1·25 1·10
1052 – 2m. black and purple . . 2·50 2·75
1053 – 4m. black and blue . . . 3·50 6·00
MS1054 Two sheets, each 102 × 127 mm. (a) 5m. black and red. (b) 5m. black and blue. Set of 2 sheets . . . . . . 6·00 7·50

DESIGNS: 30s. "Mary on Grass Bench"; 50s. "Mary with Crown of Stars"; 60s. "Mary with Child beside Tree"; 70s. "Mary with Child beside Wall"; 1m. "Mary in Halo on Crescent Moon"; 2m. "Mary breastfeeding Child"; 4m. "Mary with Infant in Swaddling Clothes".

212 Mickey Mouse and Pluto pinning the Tail on the Donkey

1991. Children's Games. Walt Disney cartoon characters. Multicoloured.

1055 20s. Type **212** 65 15
1056 30s. Mickey playing mancala 70 20
1057 40s. Mickey rolling hoop . . 80 20
1058 50s. Minnie Mouse hula-hooping 90 25
1059 70s. Mickey and Pluto throwing a frisbee . . . . 1·25 75
1060 1m. Donald Duck with a diabolo . . . . 1·60 1·40
1061 2m. Donald's nephews playing marbles . . . . . 2·50 3·00
1062 3m. Donald with Rubik's cube . . . . 3·00 4·00
MS1063 Two sheets, each 127 × 112 mm. (a) 5m. Donald's and Mickey's nephews playing tug-of-war. (b) 5m. Mickey and Donald mock fighting. Set of 2 sheets . . . . 8·00 9·00

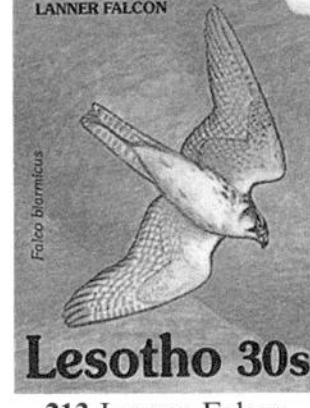

213 Lanner Falcon

1992. Birds. Multicoloured.

1064 30s. Type **213** 65 60
1065 30s. Bateleur 65 60
1066 30s. Paradise sparrow (inscr "Red-headed Finch") . . 65 60
1067 30s. Lesser striped swallow 65 60
1068 30s. Alpine swift 65 60
1069 30s. Didric cuckoo ("Diederik Cuckoo") . . 65 60
1070 30s. Yellow-tufted malachite sunbird ("Malachite Sunbird") 65 60
1071 30s. Burchell's gonolek ("Crimson-breasted Shrike") 65 60
1072 30s. Pin-tailed whydah . . . 65 60
1073 30s. Lilac-breasted roller . . 65 60
1074 30s. Black bustard ("Korhaan") 65 60
1075 30s. Black-collared barbet 65 60
1076 30s. Secretary bird 65 60
1077 30s. Red-billed quelea . . . 65 60
1078 30s. Red bishop 65 60
1079 30s. Ring-necked dove . . . 65 60
1080 30s. Yellow canary 65 60
1081 30s. Cape longclaw ("Orange-throated Longclaw") 65 60
1082 30s. Cordon-bleu (inscr "Blue Waxbill") 65 60
1083 30s. Golden bishop 65 60

Nos. 1064/83 were printed together, se-tenant, forming a composite design.

214 Queen Elizabeth and Cooking at a Mountain Homestead

1992. 40th Anniv of Queen Elizabeth II's Accession. Multicoloured.

1084 20s. Type **214** 35 15
1085 30s. View from mountains 35 20
1086 1m. Cacti and mountain . . 1·00 65
1087 4m. Thaba-Bosiu . . . . . 3·00 3·50
MS1088 75 × 97 mm. 5m. Mountains at sunset . . . . 4·25 4·50

215 Minnie Mouse as Spanish Lady, 1540–1660

1992. International Stamp Exhibitions. Walt Disney cartoon characters. Multicoloured. (a) "Granada '92", Spain. Traditional Spanish Costumes.

1089 20s. Type **215** 80 20
1090 50s. Mickey Mouse as Don Juan at Lepanto, 1571 . . 95 40
1091 70s. Donald in Galician costume, 1880 . . . . . 1·25 70
1092 2m. Daisy Duck in Aragonese costume, 1880 2·50 3·25
MS1093 127 × 112 mm. 5m. Goofy the bullfighter . . . . 4·50 5·00

(b) "World Columbian Stamp Expo '92". Red Indian Life.

1094 30s. Donald Duck making arrowheads 70 30
1095 40s. Goofy playing lacrosse 75 40
1096 1m. Mickey Mouse and Donald Duck planting corn . . . . 1·25 1·10
1097 3m. Minnie Mouse doing bead work . . . . 2·75 3·25
MS1098 127 × 112 mm. 5m. Mickey paddling canoe . . . . 4·50 5·00

216 Stegosaurus

1992. Prehistoric Animals. Multicoloured.

1099 20s. Type **216** 90 30
1100 30s. Ceratosaurus . . . . . 1·00 35
1101 40s. Procompsognathus . . 1·25 45
1102 50s. Lesothosaurus . . . . 1·50 55
1103 70s. Plateosaurus . . . . . 1·50 70
1104 1m. Gasosaurus . . . . . . 1·75 1·25
1105 2m. Massospondylus . . . 2·25 2·75
1106 3m. Archaeopteryx . . . . 2·50 3·50
MS1107 Two sheets, each 105 × 77 mm. (a) 5m. As 50s. (b) 5m. As 3m. Set of 2 sheets . . 11·00 9·50

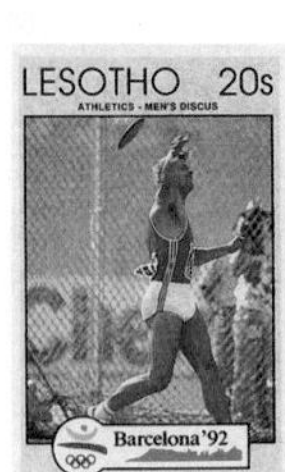

217 Men's Discus **218** "Virgin and Child" (Sassetta)

1992. Olympic Games, Albertville and Barcelona. Multicoloured.

No.	Description	Mint	Used
1108	20s. Type **217**	20	15
1109	30s. Men's long jump	25	15
1110	40s. Women's 4 × 100 m relay	30	25
1111	70s. Women's 100 m	50	50
1112	1m. Men's parallel bars	70	70
1113	2m. Men's double luge (horiz)	1·40	1·75
1114	3m. Women's 30k cross-country skiing (horiz)	1·75	2·50
1115	4m. Men's biathlon	2·00	2·75
MS1116	Two sheets, each 100 × 70 mm. (a) 5m. Women's figure skating. (b) 5m. Ice hockey (horiz). Set of 2 sheets	6·75	7·50

1992. Christmas. Religious Paintings. Mult.

No.	Description	Mint	Used
1117	20s. Type **218**	45	15
1118	30s. "Coronation of the Virgin" (Master of Bonastre)	55	20
1119	40s. "Virgin and Child" (Master of SS. Cosmas and Damian)	65	25
1120	70s. "The Virgin of Great Panagia" (detail) (12th-century Russian school)	1·00	55
1121	1m. "Madonna and Child" (Vincenzo Foppa)	1·60	1·10
1122	2m. "Madonna and Child" (School of Lippo Memmi)	2·25	2·50
1123	3m. "Virgin and Child" (Barnaba da Modena)	2·75	3·25
1124	4m. "Virgin and Child with Saints" (triptych) (Simone dei Crocifissi)	3·00	3·50
MS1125	Two sheets, each 76 × 102 mm. (a) 5m. "Virgin and Child with Saints" (different detail) (Simone dei Crocifissi). (b) 5m. "Virgin and Child enthroned and surrounded by Angels" (Cimabue). Set of 2 sheets	8·00	10·00

219 World Trade Centre, New York

1992. Postage Stamp Mega Event, New York. Sheet 100 × 70 mm.

No.	Description	Mint	Used
MS1126	5m. multicoloured	5·50	6·50

220 Baby Harp Seal (Earth Summit '92, Rio)

1993. Anniversaries and Events. Multicoloured.

No.	Description	Mint	Used
1127	20s. Type **220**	85	40
1128	30s. Giant panda (Earth Summit '92, Rio)	1·10	40
1129	40s. Airship "Graf Zeppelin" over globe (75th death anniv of Count Ferdinand von Zeppelin)	1·10	40
1130	70s. Woman grinding maize (International Conference on Nutrition, Rome)	60	45
1131	4m. Lt. Robinson's Royal Aircraft Factory B.E.2C shooting down Schutte Lanz SL-11 airship (75th death anniv of Count Ferdinand von Zeppelin)	3·50	4·25
1132	5m. Valentina Tereshkova and "Vostok 6" (30th anniv of first woman in space)	3·50	4·25
MS1133	Two sheets, each 100 × 70 mm. (a) 5m. Dr. Ronald McNair ("Challenger" astronaut) (International Space Year). (b) 5m. South African crowned crane (Earth Summit '92, Rio). Set of 2 sheets	9·00	9·00

221 "Orpheus and Eurydice" (detail)

1993. Bicentenary of the Louvre, Paris. Paintings by Poussin. Multicoloured.

No.	Description	Mint	Used
1134	70s. Type **221**	80	80
1135	70s. "Rape of the Sabine Women" (left detail)	80	80
1136	70s. "Rape of the Sabine Women" (right detail)	80	80
1137	70s. "The Death of Sapphira" (left detail)	80	80
1138	70s. "The Death of Sapphira" (right detail)	80	80
1139	70s. "Echo and Narcissus" (left detail)	80	80
1140	70s. "Echo and Narcissus" (right detail)	80	80
1141	70s. "Self-portrait"	80	80
MS1142	70 × 100 mm. 5m. "The Money Lender and his Wife" (57 × 89 mm) (Metsys)	4·75	5·00

222 Aloe

1993. Flowers. Multicoloured.

No.	Description	Mint	Used
1143	20s. Type **222**	40	10
1144	30s. Calla lily	45	15
1145	40s. Bird of paradise plant	45	15
1146	70s. Amaryllis	75	40
1147	1m. Agapanthus	90	60
1148	2m. Crinum	2·75	2·25
1149	4m. Watsonia	2·50	3·25
1150	5m. Gazania	2·50	3·50
MS1151	Two sheets, each 98 × 67 mm. (a) 7m. Plumbago. (b) 7m. Desert Rose. Set of 2 sheets	7·50	8·50

223 "Precis westermanni"

1993. Butterflies. Multicoloured.

No.	Description	Mint	Used
1152	20s. Type **223**	40	15
1153	40s. "Precis sophia"	50	20
1154	70s. "Precis terea"	65	45
1155	1m. "Byblia acheloia"	75	75
1156	2m. "Papilio antimachus"	1·25	1·50
1157	5m. "Pseudacraea boisduvali"	1·75	3·00
MS1158	Two sheets, each 96 × 62 mm. (a) 7m. "Precis oenone". (b) 7m. "Precis octavia". Set of 2 sheets	7·00	7·00

No. 1157 is inscribed "Pesudacraea boisduvali" in error.

224 Queen Elizabeth II at Coronation (photograph by Cecil Beaton)

1993. 40th Anniv of Coronation.

No.	Description	Mint	Used
1159	**224** 20s. multicoloured	80	85
1160	– 40s. multicoloured	1·00	1·10
1161	– 1m. black and green	1·40	1·50
1162	– 5m. multicoloured	3·25	3·50
MS1163	70 × 100 mm. 7m. multicoloured ($42\frac{1}{2} \times 28\frac{1}{2}$ mm)	6·00	6·50

DESIGNS—VERT: 40s. St. Edward's Crown and Sceptre; 1m. Queen Elizabeth the Queen Mother; 5m. Queen Elizabeth II and family. HORIZ: 7m. "Conversation Piece at Royal Lodge, Windsor" (detail) (Sir James Gunn).

225 East African Railways Vulcan Steam Locomotive, 1929

1993. African Railways. Multicoloured.

No.	Description	Mint	Used
1164	20s. Type **225**	75	25
1165	30s. Beyer-Garratt Class 15A steam locomotive, Zimbabwe Railways, 1952	85	30
1166	40s. Class 25 steam locomotive, South African Railways, 1953	90	30
1167	70s. Class A 58 steam locomotive, East African Railways	1·25	60
1168	1m. Class 9E electric locomotives, South African Railways	1·40	85
1169	2m. Class 87 diesel-electric locomotive, East African Railways, 1971	1·75	1·60
1170	3m. Class 92 diesel locomotive, East African Railways, 1971	2·00	2·25
1171	5m. Class 26 steam locomotive No. 3450, South African Railways, 1982	2·50	3·50
MS1172	Two sheets, each 104 × 82 mm. (a) 7m. Class 6E electric locomotive, South African Railways, 1969. (b) 7m. Class 231-132BT steam locomotive, Algerian Railways, 1937. Set of 2 sheets	10·00	10·00

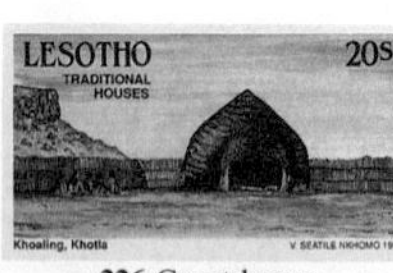

226 Court-house

1993. Traditional Houses. Multicoloured.

No.	Description	Mint	Used
1173	20s. Type **226**	50	10
1174	30s. House with reed fence	55	15
1175	70s. Unmarried girls' house	1·00	40
1176	4m. Hut made from branches	3·50	5·00
MS1177	81 × 69 mm. 4m. Decorated houses	3·00	4·00

227 Black and White Shorthair

1993. Domestic Cats. Multicoloured.

No.	Description	Mint	Used
1178	20s. Type **227**	60	25
1179	30s. Shorthair tabby lying down	60	25
1180	70s. Head of shorthair tabby	80	40
1181	5m. Black and white shorthair with shorthair tabby	2·75	4·00
MS1182	113 × 89mm. 5m. Shorthair Tabby with rat (vert)	3·75	4·00

228 Pluto in Chung Cheng Park, Keelung

1993. "Taipei '93" Asian International Stamp Exhibition, Taiwan. Walt Disney cartoon characters in Taiwan. Multicoloured.

No.	Description	Mint	Used
1183	20s. Type **228**	65	10
1184	30s. Donald Duck at Chiao-Tienkung Temple Festival	75	15
1185	40s. Goofy with lantern figures	85	20
1186	70s. Minnie Mouse shopping at temple festival	1·25	40
1187	1m. Daisy Duck at Queen's Head Rock, Yehliu (vert)	1·50	70
1188	1m.20 Mickey and Minnie at National Concert Hall (vert)	1·60	1·60
1189	2m. Donald at Chiang Kai-shek Memorial Hall (vert)	1·75	2·00
1190	2m.50 Donald and Daisy at the Grand Hotel, Taipei	2·00	2·75
MS1191	Two sheets, each 128 × 102 mm. (a) 5m. Goofy over National Palace Museum, Taipei. (b) 6m. Mickey and Minnie at Presidential Palace Museum, Taipei (vert). Set of 2 sheets	8·50	8·50

229 Tseliso "Frisco" Khomari (Lesotho) **230** King Letsie III signing Oath of Office

1994. World Cup Football Championship, U.S.A. Multicoloured.

No.	Description	Mint	Used
1192	20s. Type **229**	50	10
1193	30s. Thato "American Spoon" Mohale (Lesotho)	55	15
1194	40s. Jozic Davor (Yugoslavia) and Freddy Rincorn (Colombia)	65	20
1195	50s. Lefika "Mzee" Lekhotla (Lesotho)	70	25
1196	70s. Litsiso "House-on-fire" Khali (Lesotho)	85	55
1197	1m. Roger Milla (Cameroun)	1·00	85
1198	1m.20 David Platt (England)	1·50	2·00
1199	2m. Karl Heinz Rummenigge (Germany) and Soren Lerby (Denmark)	1·75	2·50
MS1200	Two sheets, each 100 × 70 mm. (a) 6m. Klaus Lindenberger (Czechoslovakia). (b) 6m. Franco Baresi (Italy) and Ivan Hasek (Czechoslovakia) (horiz). Set of 2 sheets	8·50	8·50

1994. 1st Anniv of Restoration of Democracy. Multicoloured.

No.	Description	Mint	Used
1201	20s. Type **230**	20	15
1202	30s. Parliament building (horiz)	25	15
1203	50s. Swearing-in of Dr. Ntsu Mokhehle as Prime Minister (horiz)	40	20
1204	70s. Maj-Gen P. Ramaema handing Instruments of Government to Dr. Ntsu Mokhehle (horiz)	70	40

231 Aquatic River Frog

1994. "Philakorea '94" International Stamp Exhibition, Seoul. Frogs and Toads. Mult.

No.	Description	Mint	Used
1205	35s. Type **231**	25	10
1206	50s. Bubbling kassina	35	15
1207	1m. Guttural toad	60	60
1208	1m.50 Common river frog	80	1·25
MS1209	Two sheets, each 102 × 72 mm. (a) 5m. Jade frog (sculpture). (b) 5m. Black Spotted frog and oriental white-eye (bird) (vert). Set of 2 sheets	8·50	8·50

232 De Havilland D.H.C.6 Twin Otter and Emblem

1994. 50th Anniv of I.C.A.O. Multicoloured.
1210 35s. Type **232** 40 15
1211 50s. Fokker F.27 Friendship on runway 55 20
1212 1m. Fokker F.27 Friendship over Moshoeshoe I International Airport . . 90 70
1213 1m.50 Cessna light aircraft over mountains . . . . . 1·25 1·50

1995. No. 1022 surch **20s**.
1214a 20s. on 30s. "Charaxes jasius" . . . . 1·00 65

234 "Tagetes minuta"
235 Pius XII College, 1962

1995. Medicinal Plants. Multicoloured.
1215 35s. Type **234** 20 10
1216 50s. "Plantago lanceolata" 25 15
1217 1m. "Amaranthus spinosus" 45 45
1218 1m.50 "Taraxacum officinale" . . . . 80 1·10
MS1219 120 × 91 mm. 5m. "Dativa stramonium" . . . . 2·00 2·25

1995. 50th Anniv of University Studies in Lesotho. Multicoloured.
1220 35s. Type **235** 15 10
1221 50s. Campus, University of Basutoland, Bechuanaland and Swaziland, 1966 . . . 20 15
1222 70s. Campus, University of Botswana, Lesotho and Swaziland, 1970 . . . . . 30 15
1223 1m. Administration Block, University of Botswana, Lesotho and Swaziland, 1975 . . . . 45 40
1224 1m.50 Administration Block, National University of Lesotho, 1988 . . . . . 65 85
1225 2m. Procession of Vice-Chancellors, National University of Lesotho, 1995 . . . . 80 1·40

236 Qiloane Pinnacle, Thaba-Bosiu
237 "Peace"

1995. 20th Anniv of World Tourism Organization. Multicoloured.
1226 35s. Type **236** 25 10
1227 50s. Ha Mohalenyane rock formation 30 15
1228 1m. Botsoela Falls (vert) . . 55 45
1229 1m.50 Backpackers in Makhaleng River Gorge 80 1·25
MS1230 143 × 88 mm. 4m. Red Hot Pokers (38 × 57 mm) . . . . . 2·00 2·25
No. **MS**1230 is inscribed "RED HOT PORKERS" in error.

1995. 50th Anniv of United Nations. Multicoloured.
1231 35s. Type **237** 30 10
1232 50s. "Justice" (scales) . . . 40 20
1233 1m.50 "Reconciliation" (clasped hands) (horiz) . . 1·00 1·40

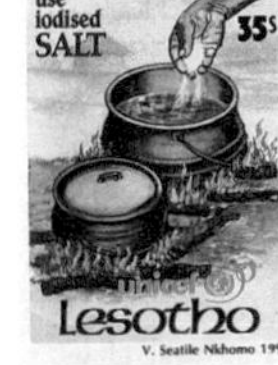

238 "Sutter's Gold Rose"
240 Adding Iodized Salt to Cooking Pot

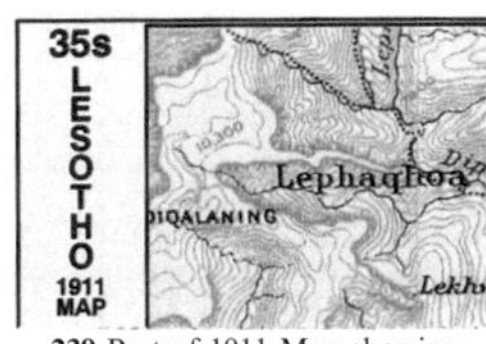

239 Part of 1911 Map showing Lephaqhoa

1995. Christmas. Roses. Multicoloured.
1234 5s. Type **238** 10 30
1235 50s. "Michele Meilland" . . 35 10
1236 1m. "J. Otto Thilow" . . . 60 40
1237 2m. "Papa Meilland" . . . 95 1·40

1996. Completion of New Standard Map of Lesotho (1994). Map Sections of Malibamatso Valley. Multicoloured. (a) 1911 Map.
1238 35s. Type **239** 30 30
1239 35s. Boritsa Tsuene 30 30
1240 35s. Molapo 30 30
1241 35s. Nkeu 30 30
1242 35s. Three rivers flowing east 30 30
1243 35s. Tibedi and Rafanyane 30 30
1244 35s. Two rivers flowing east 30 30
1245 35s. Madibatmatso River . . 30 30
1246 35s. Bokung River 30 30
1247 35s. Semena River 30 30

(b) 1978 Map.
1248 35s. Mountains and river valley 30 30
1249 35s. Pelaneng and Lepaqoa 30 30
1250 35s. Mamohau 30 30
1251 35s. Ha Lejone 30 30
1252 35s. Ha Thoora 30 30
1253 35s. Ha Mikia 30 30
1254 35s. Ha Kosetabole 30 30
1255 35s. Ha Seshote 30 30
1256 35s. Ha Rapooane 30 30
1257 35s. Bokong Ha Kennan . . 30 30

(c) 1994 Map.
1258 35s. Mafika-Lisiu Pass . . . 30 30
1259 35s. Ha Lesaoana 30 30
1260 35s. Ha Masaballa 30 30
1261 35s. Ha Nkisi 30 30
1262 35s. Ha Rafanyane 30 30
1263 35s. Laitsoka Pass 30 30
1264 35s. "Katse Reservoir" . . . 30 30
1265 35s. Seshote 30 30
1266 35s. Sephareng 30 30
1267 35s. Katse Dam 30 30
Nos. 1238/47, 1248/57 and 1258/67 respectively were printed together, se-tenant, forming composite designs.

1996. 50th Anniv of UNICEF. Multicoloured.
1268 35s. Type **240** 25 10
1269 50s. Herdboys with livestock (horiz) 35 20
1270 70s. Children in class (horiz) 45 20
1271 1m.50 Boys performing traditional dance (horiz) 90 1·25

241 U.S.A. Basketball Team, 1936

1996. Olympic Games, Atlanta. Previous Gold Medal Winners. Multicoloured.
1272 1m. Type **241** 50 20
1273 1m.50 Brandenburg Gate and stadium, Berlin, 1936 50 30
1274 1m.50 Glen Morris (U.S.A.) (decathlon, 1936) (vert) 50 50
1275 1m.50 Saidi Aouita (Morocco) (5000 m running, 1984) (vert) 50 50
1276 1m.50 Arnie Robinson (U.S.A.) (long jump, 1976) (vert) 50 50
1277 1m.50 Hans Woellke (Germany) (shot put, 1936) (vert) 50 50
1278 1m.50 Renate Stecher (Germany) (100 m running, 1972) (vert) 50 50
1279 1m.50 Evelyn Ashford (U.S.A.) (100 m running, 1984) (vert) 50 50
1280 1m.50 Willie Davenport (U.S.A.) (110 m hurdles, 1968) (vert) 50 50
1281 1m.50 Bob Beamon (U.S.A.) (long jump, 1968) (vert) 50 50
1282 1m.50 Heidi Rosendhal (Germany) (long jump, 1972) (vert) 50 50
1283 2m. Jesse Owens (U.S.A.) (track and field, 1936) (vert) 65 70
1284 3m. Speed boat racing . . . 85 1·00
MS1285 Two sheets, each 110 × 80 mm. (a) 8m. Michael Gross (Germany) (swimming, 1984) (vert). (b) 8m. Kornelia Ender (Germany) (swimming, 1976) (vert). Set of 2 sheets . . 6·50 7·00
No. 1273 is inscribed "BRANDEBOURG GATE" in error. No. 1274 incorrectly identifies Glen Morris as the gold medal winner in the 1936 long jump.
Nos. 1274/82 were printed together, se-tenant, with the backgrounds forming a composite design.

242 Class WP Steam Locomotive (India)

1996. Trains of the World. Multicoloured.
1286 1m.50 Type **242** 75 75
1287 1m.50 Canadian Pacific steam locomotive No. 2471 (Canada) . . . 75 75
1288 1m.50 The "Caledonian" (Great Britain) 75 75
1289 1m.50 Steam locomotive "William Mason" (U.S.A.) 75 75
1290 1m.50 "Trans-Siberian Express" (Russia) 75 75
1291 1m.50 Steam train (Switzerland) 75 75
1292 1m.50 ETR 450 high speed train (Italy) 75 75
1293 1m.50 TGV express train (France) 75 75
1294 1m.50 XPT high speed train (Australia) 75 75
1295 1m.50 "Blue Train" (South Africa) 75 75
1296 1m.50 Intercity 225 express train (Great Britain) . . . 75 75
1297 1m.50 "Hikari" express train (Japan) 75 75
MS1298 Two sheets, each 98 × 68 mm. (a) 8m. Class 52 steam locomotive (Germany) (57 × 43 mm). (b) 8m. ICE high speed train (Germany) (57 × 43 mm). Set of 2 sheets 7·50 8·00

243 Mothers' Union Member, Methodist Church

1996. Christmas. Mothers' Unions. Multicoloured.
1299 35s. Type **243** 25 10
1300 50s. Roman Catholic Church 30 10
1301 1m. Lesotho Evangelical Church 55 35
1302 1m.50 Anglican Church . . 80 1·25
No. 1302 is inscribed "Anglian" in error.

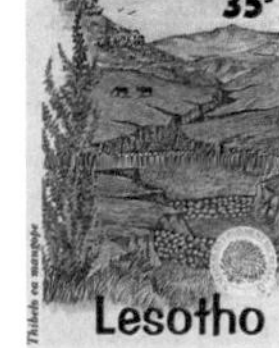

244 Hand Clasp (Co-operation for Development)
245 Land Reclamation

1997. 10th Anniv of Lesotho Highland Water Project (1996). Multicoloured.
1303 35s. Type **244** 25 10
1304 50s. Lammergeier and rock painting (Nature and Heritage) 50 20
1305 1m. Malibamatso Bridge (Engineering) 60 40
1306 1m.50 Katse Valley in 1986 and 1996 (75 × 28 mm) . . 90 1·25
No. 1305 is inscribed "Developement" in error.

1997. Environment Protection. Multicoloured.
1307 35s. Type **245** 25 10
1308 50s. Throwing rubbish into bin 30 15
1309 1m. Hands holding globe and tree 55 30
1310 1m.20 Recycling symbol and rubbish 65 65
1311 1m.50 Collecting rain water 75 85

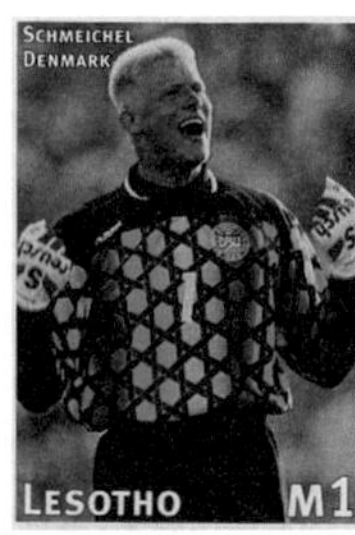

246 Schmeichel, Denmark

1997. World Cup Football Championship, France (1998). Multicoloured.
1312 1m. Type **246** 40 20
1313 1m.50 Bergkamp, Netherlands 55 55
1314 1m.50 Argentine players celebrating 55 55
1315 1m.50 Argentine and Dutch players competing for ball 55 55
1316 1m.50 Players heading ball 55 55
1317 1m.50 Goalkeeper deflecting ball 55 55
1318 1m.50 Goal-mouth melee . . 55 55
1319 1m.50 Argentine player kicking ball 55 55
1320 2m. Southgate, England . . 70 70
1321 2m.50 Asprilla, Colombia 80 85
1322 3m. Gascoigne, England . . 90 95
1323 4m. Giggs, Wales . . . . . 1·10 1·25
MS1324 Two sheets, each 127 × 102 mm. (a) 8m. Littbarski, West Germany (horiz). (b) 8m. Shearer, England. Set of 2 sheets 6·50 7·00

247 "Spialia spio"

1997. Butterflies. Multicoloured.
1325 1m.50 Type **247** 60 60
1326 1m.50 "Leptotes pirithous" 60 60
1327 1m.50 "Acratea satis" . . . 60 60
1328 1m.50 "Belenois aurota aurota" 60 60
1329 1m.50 "Spindasis natalensis" 60 60
1330 1m.50 "Torynesis orangica" 60 60
1331 1m.50 "Lepidochysops variabilis" 60 60
1332 1m.50 "Pinacopteryx eriphia" 60 60
1333 1m.50 "Anthene butleri livida" 60 60
MS1334 Two sheets, each 106 × 76 mm. (a) 8m. "Bematistes aganice". (b) 8m. "Papilio demodocus". Set of 2 sheets . . 6·50 6·50
Nos. 1325/33 were printed together, se-tenant, with the backgrounds forming a composite design.
No. 1326 is inscribed "Cyclyrius pirithous", No. 1332 "Pinacopteryx eriphea" and No. **MS**1334(b) "Papalio demodocus", all in error.

248 Rock Paintings and Boy
249 Diana, Princess of Wales

1998. 40th Anniv of Morija Museum and Archives. Multicoloured.
1335 35s. Type **248** 10 10
1336 45s. Hippopotamus and lower jaw bone (horiz) . . 10 10
1337 50s. Woman and cowhide skirt 10 10
1338 1m. Drum and "thomo" (musical bow) 15 20
1339 1m.50 Warrior with "khau" (gorget awarded for valour) 25 30
1340 2m. Herders with ox (horiz) 35 40

1998. Diana, Princess of Wales Commemoration. Multicoloured.
1341 3m. Type **249** . . . . 1·10 1·25
1342 3m. Wearing grey jacket . . 1·10 1·25
1343 3m. Wearing white polo-necked jumper . . . . . 1·10 1·25
1344 3m. Wearing pearl necklace 1·10 1·25
1345 3m. Wearing white evening dress . . . . 1·10 1·25
1346 3m. Wearing pale blue jacket . . . . 1·10 1·25
MS1347 70 × 100 mm. 9m. Accepting bouquet . . . . . . 6·50 6·50

250 Atitlan Grebe

1998. Fauna of the World. Multicoloured. (a) Vert designs as T **250**.
1348 1m. Type **250** 15 20
1349 1m. Cabot's tragopan . . . 15 20
1350 1m. Spider monkey 15 20
1351 1m. Dibatag 15 20
1352 1m. Right whale 15 20

1353 1m. Imperial amazon ("Imperial Parrot") . . . 15 20
1354 1m. Cheetah 15 20
1355 1m. Brown-eared pheasant 15 20
1356 1m. Leatherback turtle . . . 15 20
1357 1m. Imperial woodpecker 15 20
1358 1m. Andean condor 15 20
1359 1m. Barbary deer 15 20
1360 1m. Grey gentle lemur . . . 15 20
1361 1m. Cuban amazon ("Cuban Parrot") 15 20
1362 1m. Numbat 15 20
1363 1m. Short-tailed albatross 15 20
1364 1m. Green turtle 15 20
1365 1m. White rhinoceros . . . 15 20
1366 1m. Diademed sifaka . . . 15 20
1367 1m. Galapagos penguin . . 15 20

(b) Horiz designs, each 48 × 31 mm.

1368 1m.50 Impala 25 30
1369 1m.50 Black bear 25 30
1370 1m.50 American buffalo . . 25 30
1371 1m.50 African elephant . . 25 30
1372 1m.50 Kangaroo 25 30
1373 1m.50 Lion 25 30
1374 1m.50 Giant panda 25 30
1375 1m.50 Tiger 25 30
1376 1m.50 Zebra 25 30
MS1377 Four sheets, each 98 × 68 mm. (a) 8m. White-bellied sunbird. (b) 8m. Golden-shouldered parrot. (c) 8m. Snail darter. (d) 8m. Monkey (47 × 31 mm). Set of 4 sheets 5·25 5·50

251 Cape Vulture

1998. Endangered Species. Cape Vulture. Mult.
1378 1m. Type **251** 15 20
1379 1m. Looking towards ground 15 20
1380 1m. Looking over shoulder 15 20
1381 1m. Facing right 15 20

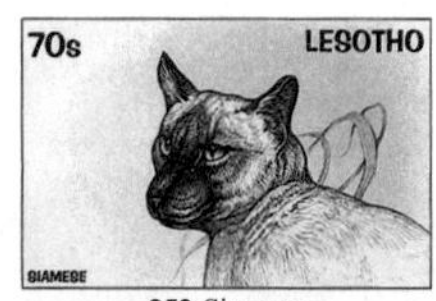

252 Siamese

1998. Cats of the World. Multicoloured.
1382 70s. Type **252** 10 10
1383 1m. Chartreux 15 20
1384 2m. Korat 35 40
1385 2m. Japanese bobtail . . . 35 40
1386 2m. British white 35 40
1387 2m. Bengal 35 40
1388 2m. Abyssinian 35 40
1389 2m. Snowshoe 35 40
1390 2m. Scottish fold 35 40
1391 2m. Maine coon 35 40
1392 2m. Balinese 35 40
1393 2m. Persian 35 40
1394 2m. Javanese 35 40
1395 2m. Turkish angora 35 40
1396 2m. Tiffany 35 40
1397 3m. Egyptian mau 50 55
1398 4m. Bombay 65 70
1399 5m. Burmese 85 90
MS1400 Two sheets, each 98 × 69 mm. (a) 8m. Tonkinese. (b) 8m. Singapura. Set of 2 sheets 2·75 3·00
Nos. 1385/90 and 1391/6 respectively were printed together, se-tenant, with the backgrounds forming composite designs.

253 "Laccaria laccata"

1998. Fungi of the World. Multicoloured.
1401 70s. Type **253** 10 15
1402 1m. "Mutinus caninus" . . 15 20
1403 1m. "Hygrophorus psittacinus" 15 20
1404 1m. "Cortinarius obtusus" 15 20
1405 1m. "Volvariella bombycina" 15 20
1406 1m. "Cortinarius caerylescens" 15 20
1407 1m. "Laccaria amethystina" 15 20
1408 1m. "Tricholoma aurantium" 15 20
1409 1m. "Amanita excelsa (spissa)" 15 20
1410 1m. "Clavaria helvola" . . 15 20
1411 1m. Unidentified species (inscr "Cortinarius caerylescens") 15 20
1412 1m. "Russula queletii" . . . 15 20
1413 1m. "Amanita phalloides" 15 20
1414 1m. "Lactarius deliciosus" 15 20
1415 1m.50 "Tricholoma lascivum" 25 30
1416 2m. "Clitocybe geotropa" 35 40
1417 3m. "Amanita excelsa" . . 50 55
1418 4m. Red-capped bolete . . . 65 70
MS1419 Two sheets, each 98 × 68 mm. (a) 8m. "Amanita pantherina". (b) 8m. "Boletus satanas". Set of 2 sheets . . . 2·75 3·00
Nos. 1406, 1407, 1414, 1416 and **MS**1419b are inscribed "Continarius caerylescens", "Laccaria amethystea", "Lactarius delicious", "Clitocybe geotrapa" and "Boletys satanus", all in error.

254 "Simba"

1998. World Cinema. Multicoloured. (a) Films about Africa.
1420 2m. Type **254** 35 40
1421 2m. "Call to Freedom" . . 35 40
1422 2m. "Cry the Beloved Country" 35 40
1423 2m. "King Solomon's Mines" 35 40
1424 2m. "Flame and the Fire" 35 40
1425 2m. "Cry Freedom" 35 40
1426 2m. "Bopha!" 35 40
1427 2m. "Zulu" 35 40

(b) Japanese Film Stars.

1428 2m. Takamine Hideko . . . 35 40
1429 2m. James Shigeta 35 40
1430 2m. Miyoshi Umeki 35 40
1431 2m. May Ishimara 35 40
1432 2m. Sessue Hayakawa . . . 35 40
1433 2m. Miiko Taka 35 40
1434 2m. Mori Masayuki 35 40
1435 2m. Hara Setsuko 35 40
1436 2m. Kyo Machiko 35 40
MS1437 Two sheets. (a) 68 × 98 mm. 10m. Lion cubs from "Born Free" (horiz). (b) 70 × 100 mm. 10m. Toshiro Mifune. Set of 2 sheets 3·25 3·50
Nos. 1420/7 and 1428/36 respectively were printed together, se-tenant, with the backgrounds forming composite designs.
No. 1423 is inscribed "KING SOLOMAN'S MINES" in error.

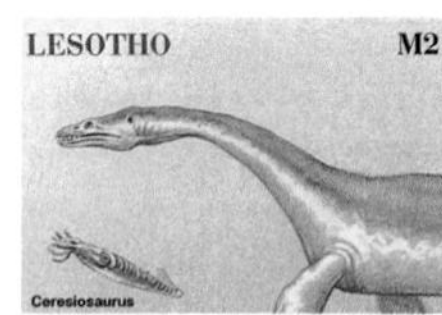

255 Ceresiosaurus

1998. Prehistoric Animals. Multicoloured.
1438 2m. Type **255** 35 40
1439 2m. Rhomaleosaurus . . . 35 40
1440 2m. Anomalocaris 35 40
1441 2m. Mixosaurus 35 40
1442 2m. Stethacanthus 35 40
1443 2m. Dunklosteus 35 40
1444 2m. Tommotia 35 40
1445 2m. Sanctacaris 35 40
1446 2m. Ammonites 35 40
1447 2m. Rhamphorhynchus . . 35 40
1448 2m. Brachiosaurus 35 40
1449 2m. Mamenchisaurus hochuanensis 35 40
1450 2m. Ceratosaurus nasicornis 35 40
1451 2m. Archaeopteryx 35 40
1452 2m. Leaellynasaura amicagraphica 35 40
1453 2m. Chasmosaurus belli . . 35 40
1454 2m. Deinonychus and Pachyrhinosaurus 35 40
1455 2m. Deinonychus 35 40
1456 2m. Nyctosaurus 35 40
1457 2m. Volcanoes 35 40
1458 2m. Eudimorphodon . . . 35 40
1459 2m. Apatosaurus 35 40
1460 2m. Peteinosaurus 35 40
1461 2m. Tropeognathus 35 40
1462 2m. Pteranodon ingens . . . 35 40
1463 2m. Ornithodesmus 35 40
1464 2m. Wuerhosaurus 35 40
MS1465 Three sheets, each 100 × 70 mm. (a) 10m. Coelophysis (vert). (b) 10m. Tyrannosaurus (vert). (c) 10m. Woolly Rhinoceros. Set of 3 sheets . . 5·00 5·25
Nos. 1438/46, 1447/55 and 1456/64 respectively were printed together, se-tenant, with the backgrounds forming composite designs.

256 Treefish

1998. Year of the Ocean. Fishes. Multicoloured.
1466 1m. Type **256** 15 20
1467 1m. Tigerbarb 15 20
1468 1m. Bandtail puffer 15 20
1469 1m. Cod 15 20
1470 1m.50 Clown loach 25 30
1471 1m.50 Christy's lyretail . . . 25 30
1472 1m.50 Filefish 25 30
1473 1m.50 Sicklefin killie 25 30
1474 2m. Brook trout 35 40
1475 2m. Emerald betta 35 40
1476 2m. Pacific electric ray . . . 35 40
1477 2m. Bighead searobin . . . 35 40
1478 2m. Weakfish 35 40
1479 2m. Red drum 35 40
1480 2m. Blue marlin 35 40
1481 2m. Yellowfin tuna 35 40
1482 2m. Barracuda 35 40
1483 2m. Striped bass 35 40
1484 2m. White shark 35 40
1485 2m. Permit 35 40
1486 2m. Purple firefish 35 40
1487 2m. Harlequin sweetlips . . 35 40
1488 2m. Clown wrasse 35 40
1489 2m. Bicolour angelfish . . . 35 40
1490 2m. False cleanerfish . . . 35 40
1491 2m. Mandarinfish 35 40
1492 2m. Regal tang 35 40
1493 2m. Clownfish 35 40
1494 2m. Bluegill 35 40
1495 2m. Grayling 35 40
1496 2m. Walleye 35 40
1497 2m. Brown trout 35 40
1498 2m. Atlantic salmon 35 40
1499 2m. Northern pike 35 40
1500 2m. Large-mouth bass . . . 35 40
1501 2m. Rainbow trout 35 40
1502 2m. Platy variatus 35 40
1503 2m. Archerfish 35 40
1504 2m. Clown knifefish 35 40
1505 2m. Angelicus 35 40
1506 2m. Black arowana 35 40
1507 2m. Spotted scat 35 40
1508 2m. Kribensis 35 40
1509 2m. Golden pheasant . . . 35 40
1510 3m. Harlequin tuskfish . . . 50 55
1511 4m. Half-moon angelfish . . 65 70
1512 5m. Spotted trunkfish . . . 85 90
1513 6m. Wolf eel . . . . 1·00 1·10
1514 7m. Cherubfish . . . . . . 1·20 1·30
MS1515 Four sheets, each 98 × 73 mm. (a) 12m. Common Carp. (b) 12m. Sockeye Salmon. (c) 12m. Winter Flounder. (d) 12m. Horn Shark. Set of 4 sheets 8·00 8·25
Nos. 1470/3 show the face value as "M1.5".

257 Crowning of King Letsie III

1998. 1st Anniv of Coronation of King Letsie III. Multicoloured.
1516 1m. Type **257** 15 20
1517 1m. King saluting Basotho nation 15 20
1518 1m. King Letsie in profile 15 20

258 "Pelargonium sidoides"

1998. Flowers. Multicoloured.
1519 10s. Type **258** 10 10
1520 15s. "Aponogeton ranunculiflorus" 10 10
1521 20s. "Sebaea leiostyla" . . . 10 10
1522 40s. "Sebaea grandis" . . . 10 10
1523 50s. "Satyrium neglectum" 10 10
1524 60s. "Massonia jasminiflora" 10 10
1525 70s. "Ajuga ophrydis" . . . 10 15
1526 80s. "Nemesia fruticans" . . 10 15
1527 1m. "Aloe broomii" 15 20
1528 2m. "Wahlenbergia androsacea" 35 40
1529 2m.50 "Phygelius capensis" 40 45
1530 3m. "Dianthus basuticus" 50 55
1531 4m.50 "Rhodohypoxis baurii" 75 80
1532 5m. "Turbina oblongata" 85 90
1533 6m. "Hibiscus microcarpus" 1·00 1·10
1534 10m. "Lobelia erinus" ("Moraea stricta") . . . 1·70 1·80

259 Japanese Akita

1999. Dogs. Multicoloured.
1535 70s. Type **259** 10 15
1536 1m. Canaan dog 15 20
1537 2m. Husky ("ESKIMO DOG") 35 40
1538 2m. Cirneco dell'Etna . . . 35 40
1539 2m. Afghan hound 35 40
1540 2m. Finnish spitz 35 40
1541 2m. Dalmatian 35 40
1542 2m. Basset hound 35 40
1543 2m. Shar-pei 35 40
1544 2m. Boxer 35 40
1545 2m. Catalan sheepdog . . . 35 40
1546 2m. English toy spaniel . . 35 40
1547 2m. Greyhound 35 40
1548 2m. Keeshond 35 40
1549 2m. Bearded collie 35 40
1550 4m.50 Norwegian elkhound 75 80
MS1551 Two sheets, each 98 × 69 mm. (a) 8m. Rough Collie. (b) 8m. Borzoi. Set of 2 sheets 2·75 3·00
Nos. 1538/43 and 1544/9 were printed together, se-tenant, with the backgrounds forming composite designs.

260 Belted Kingfisher

1999. Birds. Multicoloured.
1552 70s. Type **260** 10 15
1553 1m.50 Palm cockatoo (vert) 25 30
1554 2m. Red-tailed hawk 35 40
1555 2m. Evening grosbeak . . . 35 40
1556 2m. Blue-winged pitta ("Lesser Blue-winged Pitta") 35 40
1557 2m. Lichtenstein's oriole ("Atlamira Oriole") . . . 35 40
1558 2m. Rose-breasted grosbeak 35 40
1559 2m. Yellow warbler 35 40
1560 2m. Akiapolaau 35 40
1561 2m. American goldfinch . . 35 40
1562 2m. Common flicker ("Northern Flicker") . . 35 40
1563 2m. Western tanager 35 40
1564 2m. Blue jay (vert) 35 40
1565 2m. Common cardinal ("Northern Cardinal") (vert) 35 40
1566 2m. Yellow-headed blackbird (vert) 35 40
1567 2m. Red crossbill (vert) . . 35 40
1568 2m. Cedar waxwing (vert) 35 40
1569 2m. Vermilion flycatcher (vert) 35 40
1570 2m. Pileated woodpecker (vert) 35 40
1571 2m. Western meadowlark (vert) 35 40
1572 2m. Belted kingfisher ("Kingfisher") (vert) . . . 35 40
1573 3m. Tufted puffin 50 55
1574 4m. Reddish egret 65 70
1575 5m. Hoatzin (vert) 85 90
MS1576 Two sheets. (a) 76 × 106 mm. 8m. Great egret. (b) 106 × 76 mm. 8m. Chestnut-flanked white-eye "Zosterops erythropleura". Set of 2 sheets 2·75 3·00
No. 1553 shows the face value as "M1.5".
Nos. 1555/63 and 1564/72 were printed together, se-tenant, with the backgrounds forming composite designs.

261 "Cattleya dowiana"

1999. Orchids of the World. Multicoloured.
1577 1m.50 Type **261** 25 30
1578 2m. "Cochleanthes discolor" 35 40
1579 2m. "Cischweinfia dasyandra" 35 40
1580 2m. "Ceratostylis retisquama" 35 40
1581 2m. "Comparettia speciosa" 35 40
1582 2m. "Cryptostylis subulata" 35 40
1583 2m. "Cycnoches ventricosum" 35 40
1584 2m. "Dactylorhiza maculata" 35 40
1585 2m. "Cypripedium calceolus" 35 40
1586 2m. "Cymbidium finlaysonianum" 35 40
1587 2m. "Apasia epidendroides" 35 40
1588 2m. "Barkaria lindleyana" 35 40
1589 2m. "Bifrenaria tetragona" 35 40
1590 2m. "Bulbophyllum graveolens" 35 40
1591 2m. "Brassavola flagellaris" 35 40
1592 2m. "Bollea lawrenceana" 35 40
1593 2m. "Caladenia carnea" . . 35 40
1594 2m. "Catasetum macrocarpum" 35 40
1595 2m. "Cattleya aurantiaca" 35 40
1596 2m. "Dendrobium bellatulum" 35 40
1597 2m. "Dendrobium trigonopus" 35 40

1598 2m. "Dimerandra emarginata" 35 40
1599 2m. "Dressleria eburnea" . . 35 40
1600 2m. "Dracula tubeana" . . 35 40
1601 2m. "Disa kirstenbosch" . . 35 40
1602 2m. "Encyclia alata" . . . 35 40
1603 2m. "Epidendrum pseudepidendrum" . . . 35 40
1604 2m. "Eriopsis biloba" . . . 35 40
1605 3m. "Diurus behrii" 50 55
1606 4m. "Ancistrochilus rothchildianus" 65 70
1607 5m. "Aerangis curnowiana" 85 90
1608 7m. "Arachnis flos-aeris" . . 1·20 1·30
1609 8m. "Aspasia principissa" 1·30 1·40
MS1610 Four sheets, each 110 × 82 mm. (a) 10m. "Paphiopedilum tonsum". (b) 10m. "Ansellia africana". (c) 10m. "Laelia rubescens". (d) 10m. "Ophrys apifera". Set of 4 sheets 6·75 7·00

No. 1583 was inscribed "Cycnoches ventricsum" in error.

262 "Austerity" Type Series 52 Steam Locomotive, Frankfurt, 1939

1999. "iBRA '99" International Stamp Exhibition, Nuremburg. Railway Locomotives. Multicoloured.
1611 7m. Type **262** . . . . 1·20 1·30
1612 8m. "Adler" and Brandenburg Gate, Berlin, 1835 . . . . 1·30 1·40

263 "View of Sumida River in Snow"

1999. 150th Death Anniv of Katsushika Hokusai (Japanese artist). Multicoloured.
1613 3m. Type **263** 50 55
1614 3m. "Two Carp" 50 55
1615 3m. "The Blind" (woman with eyes closed) 50 55
1616 3m. "The Blind" (woman with one eye open) . . . 50 55
1617 3m. "Fishing by Torchlight" 50 55
1618 3m. "Whaling off the Goto Islands" 50 55
1619 3m. "Makamaro watching the Moon from a Hill" 50 55
1620 3m. "Peonies and Butterfly" 50 55
1621 3m. "The Blind" (old man with open eyes) 50 55
1622 3m. "The Blind" (old man with one eye open) . . . 50 55
1623 3m. "People crossing an Arched Bridge" (four people on bridge) 50 55
1624 3m. "People crossing an Arched Bridge" (two people on bridge) 50 55
MS1625 Two sheets, each 102 × 72 mm. (a) 10m. "Bell-flower and Dragonfly" (vert). (b) 10m. "Moon above Yodo River and Osaka Castle" (vert). Set of 2 sheets . . . . 3·25 3·50

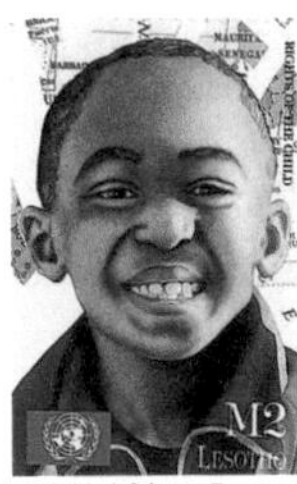

264 African Boy

1999. 10th Anniv of United Nations Rights of the Child Convention. Multicoloured.
1626 2m. Type **264** 35 40
1627 2m. Asian girl 35 40
1628 2m. European boy 35 40

Nos. 1626/8 were printed together, se-tenant, the backgrounds forming a composite design.

265 Mephistopheles appearing as Dog in Faust's Study

1999. 250th Birth Anniv of Johann von Goethe (German writer).
1629 **265** 6m. multicoloured . . . 1·00 1·10
1630 – 6m. blue, lilac and black 1·00 1·10
1631 – 6m. multicoloured . . . 1·00 1·10
MS1632 76 × 106 mm. 12m. red, violet and black . . . . 2·00 2·10

DESIGNS—HORIZ: No. 1630, Goethe and Schiller; 1631, Mephistopheles disguised as a dog scorching the Earth. VERT: No. **MS**1632, Mephistopheles.

No. 1629, in addition to the normal country name, shows "GUYANA" twice in violet across the centre of the design.

266 "Water Lily at Night" (Pan Tianshou)

267 Queen Elizabeth, 1938

1999. "China '99" International Stamp Exhibition, Beijing. Paintings of Pan Tianshou (Chinese artist). Multicoloured.
1633 1m.50 Type **266** 25 30
1634 1m.50 "Hen and Chicks" . . 25 30
1635 1m.50 "Plum Blossom and Orchid" 25 30
1636 1m.50 "Plum Blossom and Banana Tree" 25 30
1637 1m.50 "Crane and Pine" . . 25 30
1638 1m.50 "Swallows" 25 30
1639 1m.50 "Eagle on the Pine" (bird looking up) 25 30
1640 1m.50 "Palm Tree" 25 30
1641 1m.50 "Eagle on the Pine" (bird looking down) . . . 25 30
1642 1m.50 "Orchids" 25 30
MS1643 138 × 105 mm. 6m. "Sponge Gourd" (51 × 39 mm); 6m. "Dragonfly" (51 × 39 mm) . . 2·00 2·10

1999. "Queen Elizabeth the Queen Mother's Century".
1644 **267** 5m. black and gold . . . 85 90
1645 – 5m. multicoloured . . . 85 90
1646 – 5m. black and gold . . . 85 90
1647 – 5m. multicoloured . . . 85 90
MS1648 153 × 152 mm. 15m. multicoloured . . . . 2·50 2·75

DESIGNS: No. 1645, King George VI and Queen Elizabeth, 1948; 1646, Queen Mother wearing tiara, 1963; 1647, Queen Mother wearing blue hat, Canada, 1989. 37 × 50 mm.—No. **MS**1648, Queen Mother outside Clarence House.

No. **MS**1648 also shows the Royal Arms embossed in gold.

268 Chinese Soldier firing Rocket, 1150

270 King Letsie III and Miss Karabo Anne Motsoeneng

269 U.S.S. "New Jersey" (battleship)

1999. New Millennium. People and Events of Twelfth Century (1150–99). Multicoloured.
1649 1m.50 Type **268** 25 30
1650 1m.50 Burmese temple guardian, 1150 . . . . . 25 30
1651 1m.50 Troubadour serenading Lady, 1150 . . 25 30
1652 1m.50 Abbot Suger (advisor to French Kings), 1150 25 30
1653 1m.50 Pope Adrian IV, 1154 25 30
1654 1m.50 Henry II of England, 1154 . . . . 25 30
1655 1m.50 Bust of Frederick Barbarossa, King of Germany, and Holy Roman Emperor, 1155 . . 25 30
1656 1m.50 Shogun Yoritomo of Japan, 1156 . . . . . . 25 30
1657 1m.50 Count and Countess of Vaudemont (Crusader monument), 1165 . . . . 25 30
1658 1m.50 Ibn Rushd (Arab translator), 1169 . . . . 25 30
1659 1m.50 Archbishop Thomas a Becket, 1170 . . . . . 25 30
1660 1m.50 Leaning Tower of Pisa, 1174 . . . . 25 30
1661 1m.50 Pivot windmill, 1180 25 30
1662 1m.50 Saladin (Saracen general), 1187 . . . . . 25 30
1663 1m.50 King Richard the Lionheart of England, 1189 . . . . 25 30
1664 1m.50 Moai (statues), Easter Island, 1150 (59 × 39 mm) 25 30
1665 1m.50 Crusader, 1189 . . . 25 30

1999. Maritime Developments 1700–2000. Mult.
1666 4m. Type **269** 65 70
1667 4m. "Aquila" (Italian aircraft carrier) 65 70
1668 4m. "De Zeven Provincien" (Dutch cruiser) 65 70
1669 4m. H.M.S. "Formidable" (aircraft carrier) 65 70
1670 4m. "Vittorio Veneto" (Italian cruiser) 65 70
1671 4m. H.M.S. "Hampshire" (destroyer) 65 70
1672 4m. "France" (French liner) 65 70
1673 4m. "Queen Elizabeth 2" (liner) 65 70
1674 4m. "United States" (American liner) 65 70
1675 4m. "Queen Elizabeth" (liner) 65 70
1676 4m. "Michelangelo" (Italian liner) 65 70
1677 4m. "Mauretania" (British liner) 65 70
1678 4m. "Shearwater" (British hydrofoil ferry) 65 70
1679 4m. British Class M submarine 65 70
1680 4m. SRN 130 hovercraft . . 65 70
1681 4m. Italian Second World War submarine 65 70
1682 4m. SRN 3 hovercraft . . . 65 70
1683 4m. "Soucoupe Plongeante" (oceanographic submersible) 65 70
1684 4m. "James Watt" (early steamship) 65 70
1685 4m. "Savannah" (steam/sail ship), 1819 . . . . 65 70
1686 4m. "Amistad" (slave schooner) 65 70
1687 4m. American Navy brig . . 65 70
1688 4m. "Great Britain" (liner) 65 70
1689 4m. "Sirius" (paddle steamer) 65 70
MS1690 Four sheets, each 106 × 76 mm. (a) 15m. U.S.S. "Enterprise" (aircraft carrier) (vert). (b) 15m. "Titanic" (liner). (c) 15m. German U-boat. (d) 15m. "E. W. Morrison" (Great Lakes schooner) (vert). Set of 4 sheets 10·00 10·50

Nos. 1686 and 1687 both have their names wrongly inscribed as "ARMISTAD" and "BRICK" on the sheet margin.

2000. Wedding of King Letsie III. Multicoloured.
1691 1m. Type **270** 15 20
1692 1m. Miss Karabo Anne Motsoeneng 15 20
1693 1m. King Letsie III 15 20
1694 1m. King Letsie III and Miss Karabo Motsoeneng in traditional dress . . . 15 20

271 "Apollo 18" and "Soyuz 19" docked in Orbit

2000. 25th Anniv of "Apollo–Soyuz" Joint Project. Multicoloured.
1695 8m. Type **271** . . . . 1·30 1·40
1696 8m. "Apollo 18" and docking module . . . . . 1·30 1·40
1697 8m. "Soyuz 19" . . . . . . 1·30 1·40
MS1698 106 × 76mm. 15m. Docking module and "Soyuz 19" . . . 2·50 2·75

272 Gena Rowlands (actress), 1978

274 Johann Sebastian Bach

273 George Stephenson

2000. 50th Anniv of Berlin Film Festival. Showing actors, directors and film scenes with awards. Multicoloured.
1699 6m. Type **272** . . . . 1·00 1·10
1700 6m. Vlastimil Brodsky (actor), 1975 . . . . . . 1·00 1·10
1701 6m. Carlos Saura (director), 1966 . . . . 1·00 1·10
1702 6m. Scene from *La Collectionneuse*, 1967 . . 1·00 1·10
1703 6m. Scene from *Le Depart*, 1967 . . . . 1·00 1·10
1704 6m. Scene from *Le Diable Probablement*, 1977 . . . 1·00 1·10
MS1705 97 × 103 mm. 15m. Scene from *Stammeheim*, 1986 . . . 2·50 2·75

No. 1704 is inscribed "LE DIIABLE PROBABLEMENT" in error.

2000. 175th Anniv of Stockton and Darlington Line (first public railway). Multicoloured.
1706 8m. Type **273** . . . . 1·30 1·40
1707 8m. Stephenson's Patent locomotive . . . . 1·30 1·40
1708 8m. Robert Stephenson's Britannia Tubular Bridge, Menai Straits . . . . . . 1·30 1·40

2000. 250th Death Anniv of Johann Sebastian Bach (German composer). Sheet 105 × 101 mm.
MS1709 **274** 15m. multicoloured 2·50 2·75

275 Albert Einstein

2000. Election of Albert Einstein (mathematical physicist) as *Time Magazine* "Man of the Century". Sheet 117 × 91 mm.
MS1710 **275** 15m. multicoloured 2·50 2·75

276 Ferdinand Zeppelin and LZ-127 *Graf Zeppelin*, 1928

2000. Centenary of First Zeppelin Flight. Mult.
1711 8m. Type **276** . . . . 1·30 1·40
1712 8m. LZ-130 *Graf Zeppelin II*, 1938 . . . . 1·30 1·40
1713 8m. LZ-10 *Schwaben*, 1911 1·30 1·40
MS1714 83 × 119 mm. 15m. LZ-130 *Graf Zeppelin II*, 1938 (50 × 37 mm) . . . . 2·50 2·75

277 Nedo Nadi (Italian fencer), 1920

2000. Olympic Games, Sydney. Multicoloured.
1715 6m. Type **277** . . . . 1·00 1·10
1716 6m. Swimming (butterfly stroke) . . . . 1·00 1·10
1717 6m. Aztec Stadium, Mexico City, 1968 . . . . 1·00 1·10
1718 6m. Ancient Greek boxing 1·00 1·10

278 Prince William in Evening Dress
279 Spotted-leaved Arum

2000. 18th Birthday of Prince William. Multicoloured.

1719 4m. Type **278** 65 70
1720 4m. Wearing coat and scarf 65 70
1721 4m. Wearing striped shirt and tie 65 70
1722 4m. Getting out of car . . . 65 70
MS1723 100 × 80 mm. 15m. Prince William (37 × 50 mm) . . . . 2·50 2·75

2000. African Flowers. Multicoloured.

1724 3m. Type **279** 50 55
1725 3m. Christmas bells 50 55
1726 3m. Lady Monson 50 55
1727 3m. Wild pomegranate . . . 50 55
1728 3m. Blushing bride 50 55
1729 3m. Bot River protea . . . 50 55
1730 3m. Drooping agapanthus 50 55
1731 3m. Yellow marsh Afrikander 50 55
1732 3m. Weak-stemmed painted lady 50 55
1733 3m. Impala lily 50 55
1734 3m. Beatrice Watsonia . . . 50 55
1735 3m. Pink arum 50 55
1736 3m. Starry gardenia 50 55
1737 3m. Pink hibiscus 50 55
1738 3m. Dwarf poker 50 55
1739 3m. Coast kaffirboom . . . 50 55
1740 3m. Rose cockade 50 55
1741 3m. Pride of Table Mountain 50 55
1742 4m. Moore's crinum 65 70
1743 5m. Flame lily 85 90
1744 6m. Cape clivia . . . . . . 1·00 1·10
1745 8m. True sugarbush . . . . 1·30 1·40
MS1746 Two sheets, each 107 × 77 mm. (a) 15m. Red Hairy Erika (horiz). (b) 15m. Green Arum. Set of 2 sheets . . . . 5·00 5·25

Nos. 1724/9, 1730/5 and 1736/41 were each printed together, se-tenant, with the backgrounds forming composite designs.

No. 1733 is inscribed "LIly", No. 1736 "Gardenia thunbengii" and No. 1741 "Disa unoflora", all in error.

280 Black Rhinoceros

2000. "The Stamp Show 2000", International Stamp Exhibition, London. Endangered Wildlife. Multicoloured.

1747 4m. Type **280** 65 70
1748 4m. Leopard 65 70
1749 4m. Roseate tern 65 70
1750 4m. Mountain gorilla . . . 65 70
1751 4m. Mountain zebra 65 70
1752 4m. Zanzibar red colobus monkey 65 70
1753 4m. Cholo alethe 65 70
1754 4m. Temminck's pangolin 65 70
1755 4m. Cheetah 65 70
1756 4m. African elephant . . . 65 70
1757 4m. Chimpanzee 65 70
1758 4m. Northern white rhinoceros 65 70
1759 5m. Blue wildebeest 85 90
1760 5m. Tree hyrax 85 90
1761 5m. Red lechwe 85 90
1762 5m. Eland 85 90
MS1763 Two sheets, each 65 × 118 mm. (a) 15m. Dugong (vert). (b) 15m. West African Manatee (vert). Set of 2 sheets 5·00 5·25

Nos. 1747/52, 1753/8 and 1759/62 were each printed together, se-tenant, with the backgrounds forming composite designs.

281 Cadillac Eldorado Seville (1960)

2000. Classic Cars. Multicoloured.

1764 3m. Type **281** 50 55
1765 3m. Citroen DS (1955–75) 50 55
1766 3m. Ford Zephyr Zodiac MK II (1961) 50 55
1767 3m. MG TF (1945–55) . . . 50 55
1768 3m. Porsche 356 (1949–65) 50 55
1769 3m. Ford Thunderbird (1955) 50 55
1770 3m. Cisitalia 202 Coupe (1948–52) 50 55
1771 3m. Dodge Viper (1990s) . . 50 55
1772 3m. TVR Vixen SI (1968–69) 50 55
1773 3m. Lotus 7 (1957–70) . . . 50 55
1774 3m. Ferrari 275 GTB/4 (1964–68) 50 55
1775 3m. Pegasus - Touring Spider (1951–58) 50 55
1776 4m. Fiat Type O (1913) . . 65 70
1777 4m. Stutz Bearcat (1914) . . 65 70
1778 4m. French Leyat (1924) . . 65 70
1779 4m. Benz gasoline-driven Motorwagon (1886) . . . 65 70
1780 4m. Isotta Fraschini Type 8A (1925) 65 70
1781 4m. Markus Motor Carriage (1887) 65 70
1782 4m. Morris Minor (1951) . . 65 70
1783 4m. Hispano-Suiza Type 68 (1935) 65 70
1784 4m. MG TC (1949) 65 70
1785 4m. Morgan 4/4 (1955) . . 65 70
1786 4m. Jaguar XK120 (1950) 65 70
1787 4m. Triumph 1800/2000 Roadster (1946–49) . . . 65 70
MS1788 Four sheets. (a) 110 × 85 mm. 15m. AC ACE (1953–63). (b) 110 × 85 mm. 15m. Morris Minor 1000 (1948–71). (c) 85 × 110 mm. 15m. Ferrari F 40 (vert). (d) 110 × 85 mm. 15m. Bersey Electric Cab (1896). Set of 4 sheets . . . . 10·00 10·50

282 Basotho Warrior fighting "AIDS"

2001. Fight Against Aids. Multicoloured.

1789 70c. Type **282** 10 15
1790 1m. "Speed Kills So Does Aids" 15 20
1791 1m.50 "People with Aids need friends not rejection" 25 30
1792 2m.10 "Even when you're off duty protect the nation" 35 40

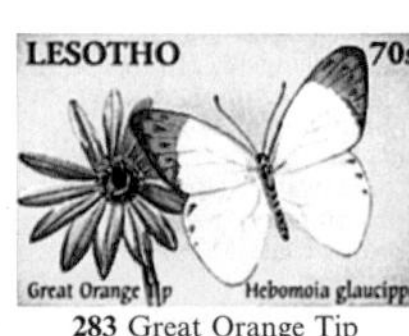

283 Great Orange Tip

2001. Butterflies. Multicoloured.

1793 70s. Type **283** 10 15
1794 1m. Red-banded pereute . . 15 20
1795 1m.50 Sword grass brown 25 30
1796 2m. Striped blue crow . . . 35 40
1797 2m. Orange-banded sulphur 35 40
1798 2m. Large wood nymph . . 35 40
1799 2m. The postman 35 40
1800 2m. Palmfly 35 40
1801 2m. Gulf fritillary 35 40
1802 2m. Cairns birdwing 35 40
1803 2m. Common morpho 35 40
1804 2m. Common dotted border 35 40
1805 2m. African migrant 35 40
1806 2m. Large oak blue 35 40
1807 2m. The wanderer 35 40
1808 2m. Tiger swallowtail . . . 35 40
1809 2m. Union jack 35 40
1810 2m. Saturn 35 40
1811 2m. Broad-bordered grass yellow 35 40
1812 2m. Hewitson's uraneis . . 35 40
1813 3m. Bertoni's antwren bird 50 55
1814 3m. Clorinde 50 55
1815 3m. Iolas blue 50 55
1816 3m. Mocker swallowtail . . 50 55
1817 3m. Common Indian crow 50 55
1818 3m. Grecian shoemaker . . 50 55
1819 3m. Small flambeau 50 55
1820 3m. Orchid swallowtail . . . 50 55
1821 3m. Alfalfa butterfly 50 55
1822 4m. Doris butterfly 65 70
MS1823 Two sheets, each 70 × 100 mm. (a) 15m. Forest Queen. (b) 15m. Crimson Tip. Set of 2 sheets . . . . . . 5·00 5·25

Nos. 1797/1804, 1805/12 and 1813/20 were each printed together, se-tenant, with the backgrounds forming composite designs.

284 Roman General and Soldiers from "Battle of Lepanto and Map of the World" (anon)

2001. "Philanippon 01" International Stamp Exhibition, Tokyo. Paintings from Momoyama Era. Multicoloured.

1824 1m.50 Type **284** 25 30
1825 2m. Pikemen and musketeers from "Battle of Lepanto and Map of the World" 35 40
1826 3m. Manchurian crane from "Birds and Flowers of the Four Seasons" (Kano Eitoku) 50 55
1827 4m. Travellers in the mountains from "Birds and Flowers of the Four Seasons" 65 70
1828 5m. "Portrait of a Lady" (24½ × 81¼ mm) 85 90
1829 5m. "Honda Tadakatsu" (24½ × 81¼ mm) 85 90
1830 5m. "Wife of Goto Tokujo" (24½ × 81¼ mm) 85 90
1831 5m. "Emperor Go-Yozei" (Kano Takanobu) (24½ × 81¼ mm) 85 90
1832 5m. "Tenzuiin Hideyoshi's Mother, Hoshuku Sochin" (24½ × 81¼ mm) 85 90
1833 6m. "Hosokawa Yusai" (Ishin Suden) (24½ × 81¼ mm) . . . . . 1·00 1·10
1834 6m. "Sen No Rikyu" (attr Hasegawa Tohaku) (24½ × 81¼ mm) . . . . . 1·00 1·10
1835 6m. "Oichi No Kata" (24½ × 81¼ mm) . . . . . 1·00 1·10
1836 6m. "Inaba Ittetsu" (attr Hasegawa Tohaku) (24½ × 81¼ mm) . . . . . 1·00 1·10
1837 6m. "Oda Nobunaga" (Kokei Sochin) (24½ × 81¼ mm) . . . . . 1·00 1·10
1838 7m. "Viewing the Maples at Mount Takao" . . . . . 1·20 1·30
1839 8m. "The Four Accomplishments" (Kaiho Yusho) . . . . 1·30 1·40
MS1840 Two sheets. (a) 98 × 131 mm. 15m. "Tokugawa Ieyasu". (b) 114 × 134 mm. 15m. "Toyotomi Hideyoshi". Set of 2 sheets . . . . 5·00 5·25

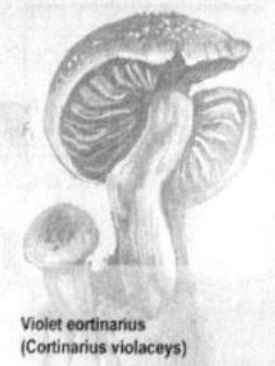

285 *Cortinarius violaceus*
287 Black Kite

286 "Woman with Baby in Sunset" (Leila Hall)

2001. "Belgica 2001" International Stamp Exhibition, Brussels. African Fungi. Multicoloured.

1841 3m. Type **285** 50 55
1842 3m. *Pleurocybella porrigens* 50 55
1843 3m. *Collybia velutibes* . . . 50 55
1844 3m. *Lentinellus cochleatus* 50 55
1845 3m. *Anthurua aseroiformis* 50 55
1846 3m. Caesar's mushroom . . 50 55
1847 4m. *Cortinarius traganus* . . 65 70
1848 4m. *Peziza sarcosphaera* . . 65 70
1849 4m. *Russula emetica* 65 70
1850 4m. *Stropharia ambigua* . . 65 70
1851 4m. *Phlogiotis helvelloides* 65 70
1852 4m. *Clitocybe odora* 65 70
1853 5m. Golden false pholiota 85 90
1854 5m. *Coprinus micaceus* . . . 85 90
1855 5m. *Hygrophorus camarophyllus* 85 90
1856 5m. *Panaeolus campanulatus* 85 90
MS1857 Two sheets, each 75 × 55 mm. (a) 15m. *Boletus parasiticus* (horiz). (b) 15m. *Hygrophorus hygrocybe conicus* (horiz). Set of 2 sheets . . . . 5·00 5·25

No. 1841 is inscribed "violaceys", 1842 "Pleyrocybella", 1844 "Cochleathus", 1852 "Clitoeybe" and 1856 "Panaelus companulatus", all in error.

2001. Winners of United Nations Children's Art Competition. Multicoloured.

1858 70s. Type **286** 10 15
1859 1m. "Herdboy with Lamb" (Chambeli Ramathe) . . . 15 20
1860 1m.50 "Girl with A.I.D.S. Ribbon" (Chambeli Ramathe) (vert) 25 30
1861 2m.10 "Satellite Dish and Map seen through Keyhole" (Mika Sejake) (vert) 35 40

2001. Birds of Prey. Multicoloured.

1862 70s. Type **287** 10 15
1863 1m. Martial eagle 15 20
1864 1m.50 Bateleur 25 30
1865 2m.10 African goshawk . . 35 40
1866 2m.50 Lammergeier ("Bearded Vulture") . . . 40 45
1867 3m. Jackal buzzard 50 55

No. 1865 is inscribed "GASHAWK" in error.

288 Grass Owl

2001. Wildlife of Southern Africa. Multicoloured.

1868 1m. Type **288** 15 20
1869 2m.10 Klipspringer 35 40
1870 3m. Saddle-backed jackal . . 50 55
1871 4m. Aardvark 65 70
1872 4m. Common kestrel ("Rock Kestrel") 65 70
1873 4m. Black-footed cat 65 70
1874 4m. Springhare 65 70
1875 4m. Aardwolf 65 70
1876 4m. Rock hyrax 65 70
1877 4m. Damara zebra 65 70
1878 4m. Bontebok 65 70
1879 4m. Eland 65 70
1880 4m. Lion 65 70
1881 4m. Saddle-backed jackal . . 65 70
1882 4m. Black kite ("Yellow-billed Kite") 65 70
1883 5m. Black wildebeest . . . 85 90
MS1884 Two sheets, each 90 × 64 mm. (a) 15m. Black-shouldered kite. (b) 15m. Caracal (vert). Set of 2 sheets . . . . . 5·00 5·25

Nos. 1871/6 and 1877/82 were each printed together, se-tenant, with the backgrounds forming composite designs.

289 Queen Elizabeth wearing Purple Coat

2002. Golden Jubilee. Multicoloured.

1885 8m. Type **289** . . . . . . 1·30 1·40
1886 8m. Queen Elizabeth with Duke of Edinburgh on launch . . . . 1·30 1·40
1887 8m. Queen Elizabeth with mayor . . . . 1·30 1·40
1888 8m. Duke of Edinburgh wearing sunglasses . . . 1·30 1·40
MS1889 76 × 108 mm. 20m. Queen Elizabeth inspecting R.A.F. guard of honour . . . . 3·25 3·50

290 Homer Wood (Rotary pioneer)

2002. 25th Anniv of Rotary International in Lesotho. Multicoloured.

1890 8m. Type **290** . . . . . . 1·30 1·40
1891 10m. Paul Harris (founder of Rotary International) 1·70 1·80
MS1892 Two sheets. (a) 60 × 75 mm. 25m. Coloured globe and Rotary logo. (b) 75 × 60 mm. 25m. Golden Gate Bridge, San Francisco, and Rotary logo (horiz) . . . . . 8·25 8·50

No. 1890 is inscribed "HORNER" in error.

291 Machache

2002. International Year of Mountains. Showing Lesotho mountains (except No. **MS**1897). Multicoloured.
1893 8m. Type **291** 1·30 1·40
1894 8m. Thabana-li-Mele 1·30 1·40
1895 8m. Qiloane 1·30 1·40
1896 8m. Thaba-Bosiu 1·30 1·40
MS1897 64 × 83 mm. 25m. The Matterhorn, Switzerland (vert) 4·25 4·50
No. MS1897 is inscribed "Mount Rainer" in error.

292 Boys with Calf, Lithabaneng

2002. S.O.S. Children's Villages (Kinderdorf International).
1898 **292** 10m. multicoloured 1·70 1·80

293 Spiral Aloe

2002. U.N. Year of Eco Tourism. Multicoloured.
1899 6m. Type **293** 1·00 1·10
1900 6m. Athrixia gerradii (flower) 1·00 1·10
1901 6m. Horseman and packhorse 1·00 1·10
1902 6m. Lion 1·00 1·10
1903 6m. Frog 1·00 1·10
1904 6m. Thatched building 1·00 1·10
MS1905 77 × 83 mm. 20m. European bee eater (vert) 3·25 3·50

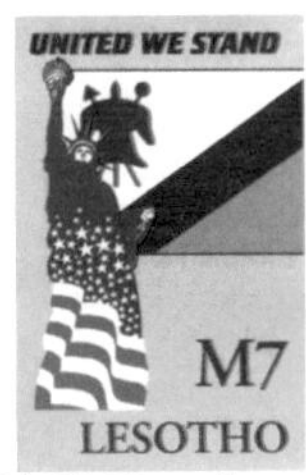

294 U.S. Flag as Statue of Liberty with Lesotho Flag

2002. "United We Stand". Support for Victims of 11 September 2001 Terrorist Attacks.
1906 **294** 7m. multicoloured 1·20 1·30

295 Sheet Bend Knot

2002. 20th World Scout Jamboree, Thailand. Multicoloured.
1907 9m. Type **295** 1·50 1·60
1908 9m. Pup and forester tents 1·50 1·60
1909 9m. Scouts in canoe 1·50 1·60
1910 9m. Life-saving 1·50 1·60
MS1911 75 × 59 mm. 25m. Scouts asleep in tent 4·25 4·50

296 Angel's Fishing Rod (*Dierama pulcherrimum*)

2002. Flowers, Orchids and Insects. Multicoloured.
MS1912 100 × 180 mm. 6m. Type **296**; 6m. Marigold (*Calendula officinalis*); 6m. Dianthus "Joan's Blood"; 6m. Mule pink (*Dianthus plumarius*); 6m. Tiger lily (*Lilium lancifolium*); 6m. Clematis viticella "Comtesse de Bouchaud" 4·25 4·50
MS1913 180 × 100 mm. 6m. Leaf grasshopper (*Brochopeplu exalatus*); 6m. Golden-ringed dragonfly (*Cordulegaster boltoni*); 6m. Weevil-hunting wasp (*Cerceris arenaria*); 6m. European grasshopper (*Oedipoda miniata*); 6m. Mantid (*Mantis acontista*) (all horiz) 4·25 4·50
MS1914 95 × 103 mm. 6m. *Phragmipedium besseae*; 6m.*Cypripedium calceolus*; 6m. Cattleya "Louise Georgiana"; 6m.*Brassocattleya binosa*; 6m. *Laelia gouldiana*; 6m. *Paphiopedilum maudiae* "Alba" 4·25 4·50
MS1915 Three sheets. (a) 63 × 75 mm. 20m. Bleeding heart(*Dicentra spectabilis*. (b) 75 × 63 mm. 20m. Orb web spider (*Argiope bruennichi*). (c) 75 × 63 mm. 20m. *Brassavola tuberculata* Set of 3 10·00 10·00

POSTAGE DUE STAMPS

1966. Nos. D9/10 of Basutoland optd **LESOTHO**.
D11 D **2** 1c. red 30 75
D12 5c. violet 30 90

D 1

D 2

1967.
D13 D **1** 1c. blue 15 3·00
D14 2c. red 15 3·50
D15 5c. green 20 3·50

1986.
D19 D **2** 2s. green 20 1·25
D20 5s. blue 20 1·25
D21 35s. violet 60 1·50

APPENDIX

The following stamps have either been issued in excess of postal needs, or have not been available to the public in reasonable quantities at face value.

1981.

15th Anniv of Independence. Classic Stamps of the World. 10m. × 40, each embossed on gold foil.

LIBERIA Pt. 13

A republic on the W. coast of Africa, founded as a home for freed slaves.

100 cents = 1 dollar.

1

2

1860.
7 **1** 6c. red 23·00 32·00
8 12c. blue 20·00 32·00
9 24c. green 23·00 32·00

1880.
13 **1** 1c. blue 3·25 4·75
14 2c. red 2·25 3·25
15 6c. mauve 4·25 5·50
16 12c. yellow 4·25 6·00
17 24c. red 5·00 6·75

1881.
18 **2** 3c. black 4·25 4·00

3

4

5 "Alligator" (first settlers' ship)

1882.
47 **3** 8c. blue 3·25 3·25
20 16c. red 4·25 3·25

1886.
49 **3** 1c. red 95 95
50 2c. green 95 1·00
23 3c. mauve 1·00 1·00
52 4c. brown 1·10 1·00
27 6c. grey 1·50 1·50
54 **4** 8c. grey 2·75 2·75
55 16c. yellow 4·25 4·25
29 **5** 32c. blue 17·00 17·00

7 Liberian Star

8 African Elephant

9 Oil Palm

10 Pres. H. R. W. Johnson

11 Vai Woman

12 Seal

13 Star

15 Hippopotamus

17 President Johnson

1892.
75 **7** 1c. red 30 30
76 2c. blue 30 30
77 **8** 4c. black and green 2·10 1·60
78 **9** 6c. green 85 75
79 **10** 8c. black and brown 60 75
80 **11** 12c. red 60 85
81 **12** 16c. lilac 2·10 1·60
82 **13** 24c. green on yellow 1·50 1·25
83 **12** 32c. blue 3·00 2·50
84 **15** $1 black and blue 10·00 5·75
85 **13** $2 brown on buff 4·25 3·75
86 **17** $5 black and red 5·50 5·50

1893. Surch **5 5 Five Cents.**
103 **9** 5c. on 6c. green 1·50 1·50

24

1894. Imperf or roul.
117 **24** 5c. black and red 6·25 6·25

35

36

1897.
144 **9** 1c. purple 70 35
145 1c. green 85 50
146 **15** 2c. black and bistre 1·50 1·10
147 2c. black and red 1·60 1·40
148 **8** 5c. black and lake 1·60 1·10
149 5c. black and blue 3·00 2·00
150 **10** 10c. blue and yellow 60 50
151 **11** 15c. black 60 65
152 **12** 20c. red 1·90 1·25
153 **13** 25c. green 1·25 85
154 **12** 30c. blue 4·25 3·00
155 **35** 50c. black and brown 2·10 2·75

1897.
156 **36** 3c. red and green 25 40

1901. Official stamps of 1892–98 optd **ORDINARY.**
175 **9** 1c. purple (No. O157) 50·00 35·00
176 1c. green (O158) 28·00 32·00
177 **7** 2c. blue (O120) 75·00 80·00
178 **15** 2c. black and brown (O159) £100 45·00
179 2c. black and red (O160) 28·00 32·00
180 **24** 5c. green and lilac (O130) £225 £225
181 **8** 5c. black and red (O161) £150 £150
182 5c. black and blue (O162) 22·00 28·00
183 **10** 8c. black and brown (O122) 75·00
184 10c. blue and yellow (O163) 28·00 32·00
169 **11** 12c. red (O92) £100 £100
185 15c. black (O164) 28·00 32·00
170 **12** 16c. lilac (O93)
186 16c. lilac (O124) £325 £325
187 20c. red (O165) 32·00 38·00
171 **13** 24c. green and yellow (O94) £300 £300
188 24c. green on yellow (O125) 32·00 38·00
189 25c. green (O166) 32·00 38·00
190 **12** 30c. blue (O167) 28·00 32·00
191 **13** 32c. blue (O126) £150 £150
192 **35** 50c. black & brown (O168) 38·00 42·00
172 **15** $1 black and blue (O96) £1300 £1300
193 $1 black and blue (O127) £225 £250
194 **13** $2 brown on buff (O128) £1300 £1300
174 **17** $5 black and red (O98) £3000 £3000
196 $5 black and red (O129) £1400 £1400

1902. Surch **75c.** and bar.
206 **15** 75c. on $1 black and blue 8·25 7·75

40 Liberty

1903.
209 **40** 3c. black 25 15

1903. Surch in words.
216 **12** 10c. on 16c. lilac 2·50 4·50
217 **13** 15c. on 24c. green on yell 3·00 5·00
218 **12** 20c. on 32c. blue 4·25 5·25

1904. Surch.
219 **9** 1c. on 5c. on 6c. green (No. 103) 60 80
220 **8** 2c. on 4c. black and green (No. O89) 2·50 3·25
221 **12** 2c. on 30c. blue (No. 154) 6·25 9·25

50 African Elephant

51 Head of Mercury

52 Mandingo Tribesmen

53 Pres. Barclay and Executive Mansion

1906.
224 **50** 1c. black and green 1·00 50
225 **51** 2c. black and red 15 15
226 – 5c. black and blue 2·00 75
227 – 10c. black and red 3·00 90
228 – 15c. green and violet 7·00 2·75
229 – 20c. black and orange 7·25 2·50
230 – 25c. grey and blue 75 20
231 – 30c. violet 70 15
232 – 50c. black and green 75 20
233 – 75c. black and brown 7·00 2·10
234 – $1 black and pink 1·90 25
235 **52** $2 black and green 3·00 35
236 **53** $5 grey and red 5·75 50

DESIGNS—As Type **50**: 5c. Chimpanzee; 15c. Agama lizard; 75c. Pygmy hippopotamus. As Type **51**: 10c. Great blue turaco; 20c. Great egret; 25c. Head of Liberty on coin; 30c. Figures "30"; 50c. Liberian flag. As Type **53**: $1 Head of Liberty.

55 Coffee Plantation

56 Gunboat "Lark"

57 Commerce

1909†. The 10c. is perf or roul.
250 **55** 1c. black and green 25 15
251 – 2c. black and red 25 15
252 **56** 5c. black and blue 1·75 35
254 **57** 10c. black and purple 25 20
255 – 15c. black and blue 1·25 35
256 – 20c. green and red 2·50 50
257 – 25c. black and brown 1·75 35
258 – 30c. brown 1·75 35
259 – 50c. black and green 2·75 60
260 – 75c. black and brown 2·25 45
DESIGNS—As Type **55**: 2c. Pres. Barclay; 15c. Vai woman spinning cotton; 20c. Pepper plant; 25c. Village hut; 30c. Pres. Barclay (in picture frame). As Type **56**: 50c. Canoeing; 75c. Village (design shaped like a book).

1909. No. 227 surch **Inland 3 Cents.**
261 3c. on 10c. black and red 4·75 5·25

1910†. Surcharged **3 CENTS INLAND POSTAGE.** Perf or rouletted.
274 **57** 3c. on 10c. black and purple 35 25

1913. Various types surch with new value and bars or ornaments.
322 – 1c. on 2c. black and red (No. 251) 2·25 3·00
290 **57** + 2c. on 3c. on 10c. black and purple 60 2·00
323 **56** 2c. on 5c. black and blue 2·25 3·00
292 – 2c. on 15c. black and blue (No. 255) 1·25 1·25
279 – 2c. on 25c. grey & blue (A) (No. 230) 7·50 3·75
281 – 2c. on 25c. black and brown (A) (No. 257) 7·50 3·75
295 – 2c. on 25c. black and brown (B) (No. 257) 6·25 6·25
296 – 5c. on 20c. green and red (No. 256) 85 4·50
280 – 5c. on 30c. violet (C) (No. 231) 7·50 3·75
282 – 5c. on 30c. brown (C) (No. 258) 7·50 3·75
297 – 5c. on 30c. brown (D) (No. 258) 3·75 3·75
278 **36** 8c. on 3c. red and green 60 30
283 – 10c. on 50c. black and green (E) (No. 259) 9·25 5·75
299 – 10c. on 50c. black and green (F) (No. 259) 6·75 6·75
303 – 20c. on 75c. black and brown (No. 260) 3·25 6·25
304 **53** 25c. on $1 black and pink 32·00 32·00
305 – 50c. on $2 black and green (No. 235) 9·25 9·25
308 – $1 on $5 grey and red (No. 236) 42·00 42·00
Descriptions of surcharges. (A) **1914 2 CENTS**. (B) **2** over ornaments. (C) **1914 5 CENTS**. (D) **5** over ornaments. (E) **1914 10 CENTS**. (F) **10** and ornaments.

64 House on Providence Is

65 Monrovia Harbour, Providence Is

1915.
288 **64** 2c. red 20 10
289 **65** 3c. violet 20 10

1916. Liberian Frontier Force. Surch **LFF 1 C.**
332 **9** 1c. on 1c. green £120 £120
333 **50** 1c. on 1c. black and green £375 £375
334 **55** 1c. on 1c. black and green 2·75 4·25
335 – 1c. on 2c. black and red (No. 251) 2·75 4·25

1916. Surch **1916** over new value.
339 **1** 3c. on 6c. mauve 32·00 32·00
340 5c. on 12c. yellow 4·00 4·00
341 10c. on 24c. red 3·25 3·75

1917. Surch **1917** and value in words.
342 **13** 4c. on 25c. green 8·25 9·25
343 **52** 5c. on 30c. violet (No. 231) 60·00 65·00

1918. Surch **3 CENTS.**
345 **57** 3c. on 10c. black & purple 2·40 3·75

91 Bongo

93

92 African Palm Civet

94 Traveller's Tree

1918.
349 **91** 1c. black and green 65 25
350 **92** 2c. black and red 65 25
351 – 5c. black and blue 15 10
352 **93** 10c. green 20 10
353 – 15c. green and black 2·50 20
354 – 20c. black and red 50 15
355 **94** 25c. green 3·25 25
356 – 30c. black and mauve 11·00 95
357 – 50c. black and blue 13·00 1·10
358 – 75c. black and olive 1·00 25
359 – $1 blue and brown 4·25 25
360 – $2 black and violet 6·00 30
361 – $5 brown 6·00 40
DESIGNS—As Type **91**: 5c. Coat of Arms; 15c. Oil palm; 20c. Statue of Mercury; 75c. Heads of Mandingos; $5 "Liberia" seated. As Type **92**: 50c. West African mudskipper; $1 Coast view; $2 Liberia College. As Type **93**: 30c. Palm-nut Vulture.

1918. Geneva Red Cross Fund. Surch **TWO CENTS** and red cross.
375 **91** 1c.+2c. black and green 75 75
376 **92** 2c.+2c. black and red 75 75
377 – 5c.+2c. black and blue 25 1·00
378 **93** 10c.+2c. green 50 1·00
379 – 15c.+2c. green and black 2·40 1·75
380 – 20c.+2c. black and red 1·50 3·00
381 **94** 25c.+2c. green 3·25 3·25
382 – 30c.+2c. black and mauve 10·50 5·75
383 – 50c.+2c. black and blue 7·00 5·75
384 – 75c.+2c. black and olive 2·10 5·25
385 – $1+2c. blue and brown 4·25 7·00
386 – $2+2c. black and violet 5·75 11·50
387 – $5+2c. brown 14·00 23·00

1920. Surch **1920** and value and two bars.
393 **91** 3c. on 1c. black & green 1·50 2·75
394 **92** 4c. on 2c. black and red 1·50 3·00
395 R **42** 5c. on 10c. black & blue 3·75 4·25
396 5c. on 10c. black and red 3·75 4·25
397 5c. on 10c. black & grn 3·75 4·25
398 5c. on 10c. black & vio 3·75 4·25
399 5c. on 10c. black and red 3·75 4·25

100 Cape Mesurado

101 Pres. D. E. Howard

1921.
402 **100** 1c. green 20 10
403 **101** 5c. black and blue 25 10
404 – 10c. blue and red 80 10
405 – 15c. green and purple 3·00 50
406 – 20c. green and red 1·50 25
407 – 25c. black and yellow 2·75 50
408 – 30c. purple and green 1·00 15
409 – 50c. blue and yellow 1·00 25
410 – 75c. sepia and red 1·00 40
411 – $1 black and red 17·00 1·00
412 – $2 violet and yellow 24·00 1·40
413 – $5 red and purple 22·00 1·50
DESIGNS—VERT: 10c. Arms. HORIZ: 15c. Crocodile; 20c. Pepper plant; 25c. Leopard; 30c. Village; 50c. "Kru" boatman; 75c. St. Paul's River; $1 Bongo (antelope); $2 Great Indian hornbill; $5 African elephant.

1921. Optd **1921.**
414 **100** 1c. green 9·25 50
415 **64** 2c. red 9·25 50
416 **65** 3c. violet 12·50 50
417 **101** 5c. black and blue 2·75 50
418 – 10c. blue and red 20·00 50
419 – 15c. green and purple 11·50 1·00
420 – 20c. green and red 5·25 60
421 – 25c. black and yellow 11·50 1·00
422 – 30c. purple and green 3·00 50
423 – 50c. blue and yellow 3·00 70
424 – 75c. sepia and red 3·75 50
425 – $1 black and red 30·00 1·50
426 – $2 violet and yellow 28·00 1·60
427 – $5 red and purple 32·00 5·25

107 Arrival of First Settlers in "Alligator"

1923. Centennial issue.
466 **107** 1c. black and blue 14·00 70
467 2c. brown and red 17·00 70
468 5c. blue and olive 17·00 70
469 10c. mauve and green 4·75 70
470 $1 brown and red 7·00 70

108 J. J. Roberts Memorial

109 House of Representatives, Monrovia

110 Rubber Plantation

1923.
471 **108** 1c. green 3·75 10
472 **109** 2c. brown and red 3·75 10
473 – 3c. black and lilac 25 10
474 – 5c. black and blue 42·00 15
475 – 10c. brown and grey 25 10
476 – 15c. blue and bistre 18·00 50
477 – 20c. mauve and green 2·00 50
478 – 25c. brown and red 65·00 50
479 – 30c. mauve and brown 50 20
480 – 50c. orange and purple 1·00 40
481 – 75c. blue and grey 1·50 65
482 **110** $1 violet and red 3·75 1·00
483 – $2 blue and orange 4·00 65
484 – $5 brown and green 10·00 65
DESIGNS—As Type **108**: 3c. Star; 5, 10c. Pres. King; 50c. Pineapple. As Type **109**: 15c. Hippopotamus; 20c. Kob (antelope); 25c. African buffalo; 30c. Natives making palm oil; 75c. Carrying elephant tusk. As Type **110**: $2 Stockton lagoon; $5 Styles of huts.

1926. Surch **Two Cents** and thick bar or wavy lines or ornamental scroll.
504 **91** 2c. on 1c. black and green 3·00 3·25

116 Palm Trees

117 Map of Africa **118** President King

1928.
511 **116** 1c. green 40 15
512 2c. violet 20 20
513 3c. brown 35 20
514 **117** 5c. blue 55 35
515 **118** 10c. grey 70 35
516 **117** 15c. purple 3·75 1·40
517 $1 brown 42·00 15·00

1936. Nos. O518 and 512/13 surch **AIR MAIL SIX CENTS.**
525 **116** 6c. on 1c. green £170 90·00
526 6c. on 2c. violet £170 90·00
527 6c. on 3c. brown £170 90·00

122 Ford "Tin Goose"

1936. Air. 1st Air Mail Service of 28th February.
530 **122** 1c. black and green 25 10
531 2c. black and red 25 10
532 3c. black and violet 40 10
533 4c. black and orange 40 15
534 5c. black and blue 45 15
535 6c. black and green 45 20

1936. Nos. 350/61 surch **1936** and new values in figures.
536 1c. on 2c. black and red 30 50
537 3c. on 5c. black and blue 30 45
538 4c. on 10c. green 25 40
539 6c. on 15c. green and black 30 55
540 8c. on 20c. black and red 20 60
541 12c. on 30c. black and mauve 1·25 1·40
542 14c. on 50c. black and blue 1·50 1·75
543 16c. on 75c. black and olive 50 60
544 18c. on $1 blue and brown 60 80
545 22c. on $2 black and violet 60 95
546 24c. on $5 brown 75 1·25

1936. Nos. O363/74 optd with star and **1936** or surch also in figures and words.
547 1c. on 2c. black and red 30 50
548 3c. on 5c. black and blue 25 50
549 4c. on 10c. green 20 45
550 6c. on 15c. green and brown 25 60
551 8c. on 20c. black and lilac 30 60
552 12c. on 30c. black and violet 95 1·25
553 14c. on 50c. black and brown 1·00 1·50
554 16c. on 75c. black and brown 45 60
555 18c. on $1 blue and olive 50 65
556 22c. on $2 black and olive 60 90
557 24c. on $5 green 75 95
558 25c. green and brown 75 1·25

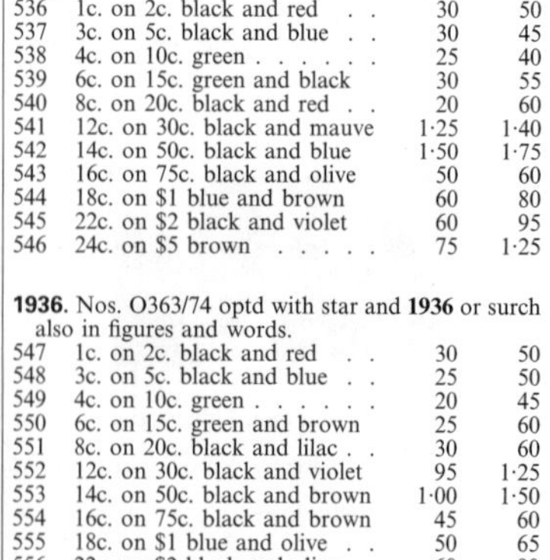

126 Hippopotamus

1937.
559 – 1c. black and green 1·25 60
560 – 2c. black and red 1·00 30
561 – 3c. black and purple 1·00 35
562 **126** 4c. black and orange 1·50 60
563 – 5c. black and blue 1·75 85
564 – 6c. black and green 45 20
DESIGNS: 1c. Black and white casqued hornbill; 2c. Bushbuck; 3c. African buffalo; 5c. Western reef heron; 6c. Pres. Barclay.

127 Tawny Eagle in Flight

128 Three-engine Flying Boat

129 Little Egrets

1938. Air.
565 **127** 1c. green 25 20
566 **128** 2c. red 15 10
567 – 3c. olive 35 20
568 **129** 4c. orange 50 10
569 – 5c. green 65 20
570 **128** 10c. violet 25 10
571 – 20c. mauve 30 15
572 – 30c. grey 1·25 20
573 **127** 50c. brown 1·75 20
574 – $1 blue 1·40 25
DESIGNS—VERT: 20c., $1 Sikorsky S-43 amphibian. HORIZ: 3, 30c. Lesser black-backed gull in flight.

130 Immigrant Ships nearing Liberian Coast

1940. Centenary of Founding of Liberian Commonwealth.
575 **130** 3c. blue 50 15
576 – 5c. brown 20 10
577 – 10c. green 25 15

DESIGNS: 5c. Seal of Liberia and Flags of original Settlements; 10c. Thos. Buchanan's house and portrait.

1941. Centenary of First Postage Stamps. Nos. 575/7 optd **POSTAGE STAMP CENTENNIAL 1840–1940** and portrait of Rowland Hill.
578 **130** 3c. blue (postage) . . . . 1·75 1·75
579 – 5c. brown . . . . 1·75 1·75
580 – 10c. green . . . . 1·75 1·75

581 **130** 3c. blue (air) . . . . . . 1·40 1·40
582 – 5c. brown . . . . 1·40 1·40
583 – 10c. green . . . . 1·40 1·40
Nos. 581/3 are additionally optd with airplane and **AIR MAIL**.

1941. Red Cross Fund. Nos. 575/7 surch **RED CROSS** plus Red Cross and **TWO CENTS**.
584 **130** + 2c. on 3c. bl (postage) 1·40 1·40
585 – + 2c. on 5c. brown . . . 1·40 1·40
586 – + 2c. on 10c. green . . . 1·40 1·40

587 **130** + 2c. on 3c. blue (air) . . 1·40 1·40
588 – + 2c. on 5c. brown . . . 1·40 1·40
589 – + 2c. on 10c. green . . . 1·40 1·40
Nos. 587/9 are additionally optd with airplane and **AIR MAIL**.

1941. Air. 1st Flight to U.S.A. Nos. 565/74 surch **First Flight LIBERIA - U.S. 1941 50c** and bar.
594 **127** 50c. on 1c. £2500 £225
595 **128** 50c. on 2c. . . . . . . £150 75·00
596 – 50c. on 3c. . . . . . . £180 90·00
597 **129** 50c. on 4c. . . . . . . 60·00 38·00
598 50c. on 5c. . . . . . . 60·00 38·00
599 **128** 50c. on 10c. . . . . . . 45·00 38·00
600 – 50c. on 20c. £1500 £150
601 – 50c. on 30c. . . . . . . 60·00 24·00
602 **127** 50c. brown . . . . 60·00 24·00
603 – $1 blue . . . . 45·00 30·00
The first flight was cancelled and covers were sent by ordinary mail. The flight took place in 1942 and the stamps were reissued but with the date obliterated.

1942. As Nos. 594/601 but with date "1941" obliterated by two bars.
604 **127** 50c. on 1c. green . . . . 7·00 7·00
605 **128** 50c. on 2c. red . . . . . 6·00 6·75
606 – 50c. on 3c. green . . . . 5·50 4·75
607 **129** 50c. on 4c. orange . . . . 4·00 6·25
608 50c. on 5c. green . . . . 2·40 2·40
609 **128** 50c. on 10c. violet . . . . 5·25 6·25
610 – 50c. on 20c. mauve . . . . 5·25 6·25
611 – 50c. on 30c. grey . . . . 4·00 4·00
612 **127** 50c. brown . . . . 4·00 4·00
613 – $1 blue . . . . 6·25 7·50

138 Miami–Monrovia Air Route

1942. Air.
614 **138** 10c. red 20 10
615 – 12c. blue 30 10
616 – 24c. green 35 10
617 **138** 30c. green 35 10
618 35c. lilac 40 15
619 50c. purple 50 15
620 70c. olive 55 30
621 $1.40 red 75 50
DESIGN: 12, 24c. Boeing 247 airliner over Liberian Agricultural and Industrial Fair.

139 Bushbuck

1942.
622 – 1c. brown and violet . . . 80 20
623 – 2c. brown and blue . . . 80 20
624 – 3c. brown and green . . . 1·25 45
625 **139** 4c. red and black . . . . 2·00 70
626 – 5c. brown and olive . . . 1·75 70
627 – 10c. black and red . . . . 3·75 1·10
DESIGNS—HORIZ: 1c. Royal antelope; 2c. Water chevrotain; 3c. Jentink's duiker; 5c. Banded duiker. VERT: 10c. Diana monkey.

1944. Stamps of 1928 and 1937 surch.
628 **116** 1c. on 2c. violet . . . . . 7·50 7·50
634 **126** 1c. on 4c. black & orange 48·00 40·00
629 **118** 1c. on 10c. grey . . . . . 10·00 6·25
635 – 2c. on 3c. black and purple (No. 561) . . . 50·00 40·00
630 **117** 2c. on 5c. blue . . . . . 3·25 3·25
632 **116** 3c. on 2c. violet . . . . . 27·00 30·00
636 – 4c. on 5c. black and blue (No. 563) . . . . . . 18·00 18·00
633 **118** 4c. on 10c. grey . . . . . 3·25 3·25
637 – 5c. on 1c. black and green (No. 559) . . . . . . 85·00 45·00
638 – 6c. on 2c. black and red (No. 560) . . . . . . 12·50 12·50
639 – 10c. on 6c. black and green (No. 564) . . . . 14·00 12·50

1944. Air stamps of 1936 and 1938 surch.
643 **128** 10c. on 2c. red . . . . . 27·00 30·00
644 **129** 10c. on 5c. green . . . . 9·50 9·50
640 **122** 30c. on 1c. black & green 80·00 50·00
645 30c. on 3c. olive (No. 567) £120 55·00
646 **129** 30c. on 4c. orange . . . . 9·50 9·50
641 **122** 50c. on 3c. black & violet 20·00 23·00
642 70c. on 2c. black and red 50·00 50·00
647 – $1 on 3c. olive (No. 567) 25·00 25·00
648 **127** $1 on 50c. brown . . . . 35·00 25·00

150 Pres. Roosevelt reviewing Troops

1945. Pres. Roosevelt Memorial.
650 **150** 3c. black & pur (postage) 15 15
651 5c. black and blue 30 25

652 70c. black and brown (air) 1·00 1·00

151 Opening Monrovia Harbour Project

1946. Opening of Monrovia Harbour Project by Pres. Tubman.
653 **151** 5c. blue (postage) 25 15

654 24c. green (air) . . . . . 1·90 2·10

1947. As T **151**, but without inscr at top.
655 5c. violet (postage) 15 15

656 25c. red (air) . . . . 1·00 1·10

152 1st Postage Stamps of United States and Liberia

1947. U.S. Postage Stamps Centenary and 87th Anniv of Liberian Postal Issues.
657 **152** 5c. red (postage) 30 15

658 12c. green (air) 40 15
659 22c. violet 50 20
660 50c. blue 60 25

153 Matilda Newport Firing Canon

1947. 125th Anniv of Defence of Monrovia.
662 **153** 1c. black & green (postage) 15 10
663 3c. black and violet . . . 20 10
664 5c. black and blue 20 15
665 10c. black and yellow . . 1·50 45

666 25c. black and red (air) . . 1·40 35

154 Liberty

156 Douglas DC-3

1947. Centenary of National Independence.
667 – 1c. green (postage) . . . 20 10
668 **154** 2c. purple 20 10
669 – 3c. purple 30 15
670 – 5c. blue 40 15

671 – 12c. orange (air) 60 20
672 – 25c. red 75 35
673 – 50c. brown 90 70
DESIGNS—VERT: 1c. Liberian star; 3c. Arms of Liberia; 4c. Map of Liberia; 12c. J. J. Roberts Monument; 25c. Liberian Flag; 50c. ($26\frac{1}{2} \times 33$ mm) Centenary Monument.

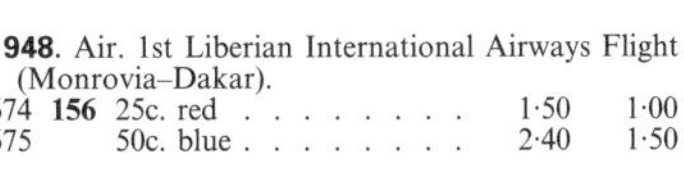
1948. Air. 1st Liberian International Airways Flight (Monrovia–Dakar).
674 **156** 25c. red . . . . 1·50 1·00
675 50c. blue . . . . 2·40 1·50

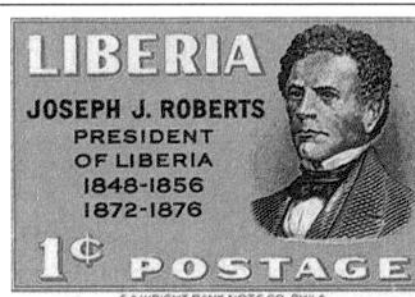

157 Joseph J. Roberts

1949. Liberian Presidents. Portrait and name in black. (a) Postage.
676 – 1c. green (Roberts) . . . 1·60 3·25
677 **157** 1c. green 15 10
678 – 1c. pink (Roberts) 25 15
679 – 2c. pink (Benson) 35 35
680 – 2c. yellow (Benson) . . . 35 15
681 – 3c. mauve (Warner) . . . 35 35
682 – 4c. olive (Payne) 35 55
683 – 5c. blue (Mansion) . . . 45 55
684 – 6c. orange (Roye) 55 95
685 – 7c. green (Gardner and Russell) . . . . 70 1·25
686 – 8c. red (Johnson) . . . . 70 1·40
687 – 9c. purple (Cheeseman) 1·10 1·10
688 – 10c. yellow (Coleman) . . 75 35
689 – 10c. grey (Coleman) . . . 40 20
690 – 15c. orange (Gibson) . . 85 40
691 – 15c. blue (Gibson) 25 15
692 – 20c. grey (A. Barclay) . . 1·25 70
693 – 20c. red (A. Barclay) . . 50 45
694 – 25c. red (Howard) . . . . 1·60 1·10
695 – 25c. blue (Howard) . . . 50 45
696 – 50c. turquoise (King) . . 3·25 95
697 – 50c. purple (King) 70 60
698 – $1 mauve (E. Barclay) . . 5·75 70
699 – $1 brown (E. Barclay) . . 4·00 55

(b) Air.
700 – 25c. blue (Tubman) . . . . 1·00 55
701 – 25c. green (Tubman) 75 35
Nos. 676 and 678 have a different portrait of Roberts wearing a moustache.

158 Colonists and Map

1949. Multicoloured.
702 1c. Settlers approaching village (postage) 50 75
703 2c. Rubber tapping and planting 50 75
704 3c. Landing of first colonists in 1822 . . . . 1·00 1·50
705 5c. Jehudi Ashmun and Matilda Newport defending stockade 50 75

706 25c. Type **158** (air) . . . . . 1·25 1·50
707 50c. Africans and coat of arms . . . . 2·75 3·25

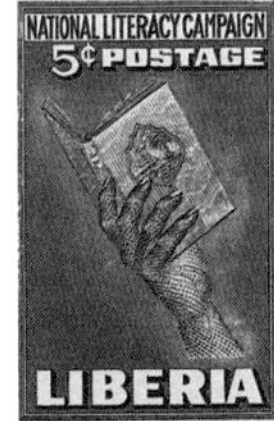

159 Hand holding Book

1950. National Literacy Campaign.
708 **159** 5c. blue (postage) 20 15

709 – 25c. red (air) 70 70
DESIGN—VERT: 25c. Open book and rising sun.

160 U.P.U. Monument, Berne

1950. 75th Anniv of U.P.U.
711 **160** 5c. black and green (post) 20 15
712 – 10c. black and mauve . . 30 30

713 – 25c. purple & orange (air) 3·25 3·25
DESIGNS—HORIZ: 10c. Standehaus, Berne. VERT: 25c. U.P.U. Monument, Berne.

161 Carey, Ashmun and Careysburg

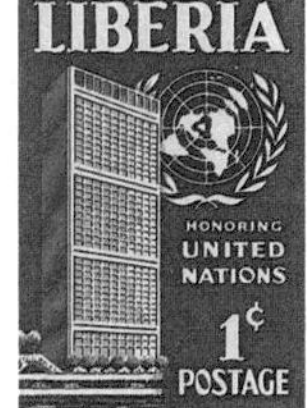

162 U.N. Headquarters

163 Flags and U.N. Emblem

1952. Designs all show portrait of Ashmun.
715 – 1c. green (postage) . . . 10 10
716 **161** 2c. blue and red 10 10
717 – 3c. green and purple . . . 10 10
718 – 4c. green and brown . . . 15 10
719 – 5c. red and blue 20 15
720 – 10c. blue and red 25 20

721 – 25c. black and purple (air) 35 35
722 – 50c. red and blue . . . . 1·00 45
DESIGNS—VERT: 1c. Seal of Liberia; 3c. Harper and Harper City; 5c. Buchanan and Upper Buchanan. HORIZ: 4c. Marshall and Marshall City; 10c. Roberts and Robertsport; 25c. Monroe and Monrovia; 50c. Tubman and map.

1952. U.N. Commemoration.
724 **162** 1c. blue (postage) 10 10
725 – 4c. blue and pink 15 10
726 – 10c. brown and yellow . . 25 20

727 **163** 25c. red and blue (air) . . 55 45
DESIGNS—HORIZ: 4c. Liberian and U.N. flags and scroll; 10c. Liberian and U.N. emblems.

164 Modern Road-building

1953. Air. Transport.
729 **164** 12c. brown 15 15
730 – 25c. purple 75 30
731 – 35c. violet . . . . 1·60 30
732 – 50c. orange 65 25
733 – 70c. green . . . . 1·25 40
734 – $1 blue . . . . 1·40 55
DESIGNS: 25c. "African Glen" (freighter) in Monrovia Harbour; 35c. Diesel locomotive; 50c. Free Port of Monrovia; 70c. Roberts Field Airport; $1 Tubman Bridge.

165 Garden Bulbul ("Pepper Bird")

166 Blue-throated Roller ("Roller")

1953. Imperf or perf.
735 **165** 1c. red and blue . . . . 1·00 20
736 **166** 3c. blue and salmon . . . 1·00 25
737 – 4c. brown and yellow . . 1·50 30
738 – 5c. turquoise and mauve 1·75 35
739 – 10c. mauve and green . . 1·75 35
740 – 12c. orange and brown . . 2·75 50
BIRDS: As Type **165**: 4c. Yellow-casqued hornbill ("Hornbill"); 5c. Giant kingfisher ("Kingfisher"). As Type **166**: 10c. African jacana ("Jacana"); 12c. Broad-tailed paradise whydah ("Weaver").

167 Hospital

1954. Liberian Govt. Hospital Fund.
741 – 5c.+5c. black and purple (postage) 20 15
742 – 10c.+5c. black and red (air) 15 20
743 **167** 20c.+5c. black & green . . 25 25
744 – 25c.+5c. black, red and blue 30 20
DESIGNS—As Type **167**: 5c. Medical research workers; 10c. Nurses. 46×35 mm: 25c. Doctor examining patient.

168 Children of the World

1954. Air. UNICEF.
745 **168** $5 ultramarine, red and blue . . . . 27·00 23·00

169 U.N. Organizations

1954. Air. U.N. Technical Assistance.
746 **169** 12c. black and blue . . . 25 15
747 – 15c. brown and yellow . . 25 15
748 – 20c. black and green . . . 30 20
749 – 25c. blue and red 35 25
DESIGNS: 15c. Printers; 20c. Mechanic; 25c. Teacher and students.

1954. Air. Visit of President Tubman to U.S.A. As Nos. 729/34 but colours changed and inscr "COMMEMORATING PRESIDENTIAL VISIT U.S.A.—1954".
750 12c. orange 20 20
751 25c. blue 80 25
752 35c. red . . . . 4·00 1·50
753 50c. mauve 80 30
754 70c. brown . . . . 1·10 50
755 $1 green . . . . 1·60 3·25

170 Football

171 "Callichilia stenosepala"

1955. Sports.
756 – 3c. red and green (postage) 15 10
757 **170** 5c. black and orange . . 15 10
758 – 25c. violet and yellow . . 25 20
759 – 10c. blue and mauve (air) 20 15
760 – 12c. brown and blue . . . 15 15
761 – 25c. red and green 20 20
DESIGNS—VERT: 3c. Tennis; 25c. Boxing (No. 758). HORIZ: 10c. Baseball; 12c. Swimming; 25c. Running (No. 761).

1955. Flowers.
763 **171** 6c. yellow, salmon and green (postage) 15 10
764 – 7c. red, yellow and green 15 10
765 – 8c. buff, blue and green 20 10
766 – 9c. green and orange . . 25 15
767 – 20c. yellow, green and violet (air) 15 15
768 – 25c. yellow, green and red 20 20
FLOWERS—VERT: 7c. "Gomphia subcordata"; 8c. "Listrostachys chudata"; 9c. "Mussaenda isertiana". HORIZ: 20s. "Costus"; 25c. "Barteria nigritiana".

172 U.N. General Assembly

173 Tapping Rubber and Rotary Emblem

1955. Air. 10th Anniv of U.N.
769 – 10c. blue and red 20 10
770 **172** 15c. black and violet . . . 25 15
771 – 25c. brown and green . . 35 15
772 – 50c. green and red . . . . 1·00 20
DESIGNS—VERT: 10c. U.N. emblem; 25c. Liberian Secretary of State signing U.N. Charter. HORIZ: 50c. Page from U.N. Charter.

1955. 50th Anniv of Rotary International.
773 **173** 5c. green & yell (postage) 25 15
774 – 10c. blue and red (air) . . 15 50
775 – 15c. brown, yellow and red 20 65
DESIGNS: 10c. Rotary International H.Q., Evanston; 15c. View of Monrovia.

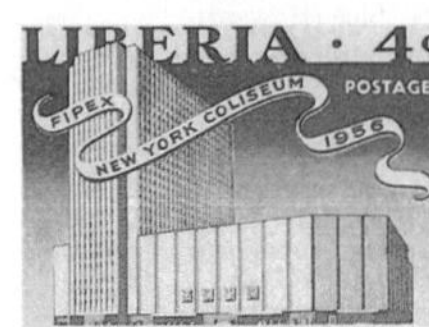

174 Coliseum, New York

1956. 5th Int Philatelic Exhibition, New York.
777 – 3c. brown and green (postage) 15 10
778 **174** 4c. brown and green 10 25
779 – 6c. purple and black . . . 20 10
780 **174** 10c. blue and red (air) . . 25 15
781 – 12c. violet and orange . . 20 15
782 – 15c. purple and turquoise 25 20
DESIGNS—VERT: 3c., 15c. Statue of Liberty. HORIZ: 6c., 12c. The Globe.

175 Chariot Race

1956. Olympic Games.
784 – 4c. brown & olive (postage) 10 10
785 – 6c. black and green . . . 15 10
786 – 8c. brown and blue . . . 20 10
787 **175** 10c. black and red 25 10
788 – 12c. purple and green (air) 20 15
789 – 20c. multicoloured 30 20
DESIGNS—HORIZ: 4c. Olympic rings, eastern grey kangaroo and emu; 8c. Goddess of Victory; 12c., 20c. Olympic torch superimposed on map of Austrialia. VERT: 6c. Discus thrower.

176 Douglas DC-6B "John Alden" at Idlewild Airport

1957. 1st Anniv of Inauguration of Liberia–U.S. Direct Air Service.
791 **176** 3c. blue & orange (postage) 15 15
792 – 5c. black and mauve . . . 20 20
793 **176** 12c. blue and green (air) 30 25
794 – 15c. black and brown . . 30 25
795 **176** 25c. blue and red 45 25
796 – 50c. black and blue . . . 85 30
DESIGN: 5, 15, 50c. President Tubman and "John Alden" at Roberts Field, Liberia.

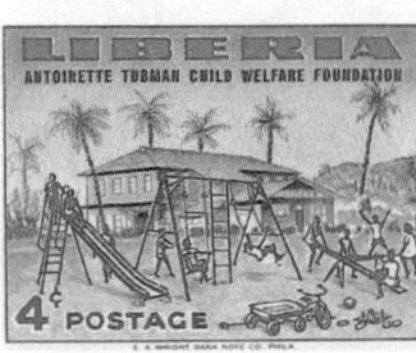

177 Children's Playground

1957. Inauguration of Antoinette Tubman Child Welfare Foundation. Inscr as in T **177**.
797 **177** 4c. green and red (postage) 10 10
798 – 5c. brown and turquoise 15 10
799 – 6c. violet and bistre . . . 15 10
800 – 10c. blue and red 20 15
801 – 15c. brown and blue (air) 20 15
802 – 35c. purple and grey . . . 35 25
DESIGNS: 5c. Teacher with pupil; 6c. National anthem with choristers; 10c. Children viewing welfare home; 15c. Nurse inoculating youth; 35c. Kamara triplets.

178 German Flag and Brandenburg Gate

1958. Pres. Tubman's European Tour. Flags in national colours.
804 **178** 5c. blue (postage) 15 10
805 – 5c. brown 15 10
806 – 5c. red 15 10
807 – 10c. black (air) 25 15
808 – 15c. green 25 20
809 – 15c. blue 25 20
810 – 15c. violet 25 20
DESIGNS: Flags of: Netherlands and windmill (No. 805); Sweden and Royal Palace, Stockholm (No. 806); Italy and Colosseum (No. 807); France and Arc de Triomphe (No. 808); Switzerland and Alpine chalet (No. 809); Vatican City and St. Peter's Basilica (No. 810).

179 Map of the World

180 Africans and Map

1958. 10th Anniv of Declaration of Human Rights.
811 **179** 3c. blue and black 25 15
812 – 5c. brown and blue . . . 20 20
813 – 10c. orange and black . . 30 75
814 – 12c. black and red 40 35
DESIGNS: 5c. U.N. Emblem and H.Q. building; 10c. U.N. Emblem; 12c. U.N. Emblem and initials of U.N. agencies.

1959. Africa Freedom Day.
816 **180** 20c. orge & brn (postage) 30 30
817 – 25c. brown and blue (air) 35 20
DESIGN: 25c. Two Africans looking at Pres. Tubman's declaration of Africa Freedom Day.

181

182 Abraham Lincoln

1959. Inaug of UNESCO Building, Paris.
818 **181** 25c. purple & grn (postage) 35 40
819 – 25c. red and blue (air) . . 35 30
DESIGN—HORIZ: No. 819 UNESCO Headquarters, Paris.

1959. 150th Birth Anniv of Abraham Lincoln.
821 **182** 10c. black & blue (postage) 25 30
822 15c. black and orange . . 30 30
823 25c. black and green (air) 55 50

183 Presidents Toure, Tubman and Nkrumah at Conference Table

184 "Care of Refugees"

1960. "Big Three" Conf, Saniquellie, Liberia.
825 **183** 25c. black & red (postage) 35 25
826 – 25c. black, bl & buff (air) 35 25
DESIGN: No. 826, Medallion portraits of Presidents Toure (Guinea), Tubman (Liberia) and Nkrumah (Ghana).

1960. World Refugee Year.
827 **184** 25c. green & blk (postage) 35 30
828 25c. blue and black (air) 55 40

185

186 Weightlifting

1960. 10th Anniv of African Technical Co-operation Commission (C.C.T.A.).
830 **185** 25c. green & blk (postage) 35 50
831 – 25c. brown and blue (air) 45 35
DESIGN: No. 831, Map of Africa with symbols showing fields of assistance.

1960. Olympic Games, Rome.
832 **186** 5c. brown & grn (postage) 20 15
833 – 10c. brown and purple . . 40 75
834 – 15c. brown and orange . . 35 30
835 – 25c. brown and blue (air) 70 80
DESIGNS—HORIZ: 10c. Rowing; 25c. ,Javelin-throwing. VERT: 15c. Walking.

187 Stamps of 1860 and Map

188 "Guardians of Peace"

1960. Liberian Stamp Centenary. Stamps, etc., in green, red and blue. Colours of map and inscriptions given.
837 **187** 5c. black (postage) . . . 25 15
838 20c. brown 40 40
839 25c. blue (air) 50 40

1961. Membership of U.N. Security Council.
841 **188** 25c. blue and red (postage) 45 35
842 – 25c. blue and red (air) . . 45 25
DESIGN—HORIZ: No. 842, Dove of Peace, Globe and U.N. Emblem.

189 Anatomy Class, University of Liberia

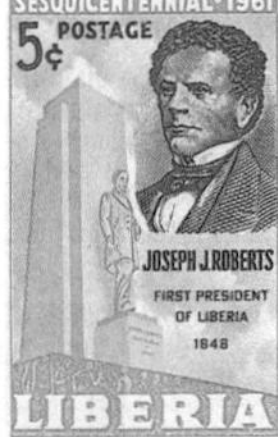

190 President Roberts

1961. 15th Anniv of UNESCO.
845 **189** 25c. brown & grn (postage) 35 35
846 – 25c. brown and violet (air) 35 25
DESIGN: No. 846, Science class, University of Liberia.

1961. 150th Birth Anniv of Joseph J. Roberts (first President of Liberia).
848 **190** 5c. sepia & orge (postage) 20 15
849 – 10c. sepia and blue . . . 35 15
850 – 25c. sepia and green (air) 45 35
DESIGNS—HORIZ: 10c. Pres. Roberts and old and new presidential mansions; 25c. Pres. Roberts and Providence Is.

191 Scout and Sports

1961. Liberian Boy Scout Movement.
852 **191** 5c. sepia & violet (postage) 25 20
853 – 10c. ochre and blue . . . 30 20
854 – 25c. sepia and green (air) 40 30
DESIGNS—HORIZ: 10c. Scout badge and scouts in camp. VERT: 25c. Scout and badge.

192 Hammarskjold and U.N. Emblem
193 Campaign Emblem

1962. Dag Hammarskjold Commem.
856 **192** 20c. black & blue (postage) 30 20
857 25c. black and purple (air) 35 25

1962. Malaria Eradication.
859 **193** 25c. green & red (postage) 35 25
860 – 25c. orange and violet (air) 35 25
DESIGN—HORIZ: No. 860, Campaign emblem and slogan.

194 Pres. Tubman and New York Skyline

1962. Air. President's Visit to U.S.A.
862 **194** 12c. multicoloured 25 15
863 25c. multicoloured 35 30
864 50c. multicoloured 70 55

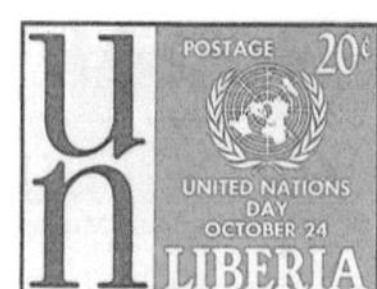

195 U.N. Emblem

1962. U.N. Day.
865 **195** 20c. bistre & grn (postage) 35 30
866 – 25c. blue & deep blue (air) 45 30
DESIGN: 25c. U.N. emblem and flags.

196 Treasury Building
197 F.A.O. Emblem, Bowl and Spoon

1962. Liberian Government Buildings.
868 – 1c. orange & blue (postage) 10 15
869 **196** 5c. violet and blue 15 10
870 – 10c. brown and buff . . . 20 15
871 – 15c. blue and salmon . . 25 20
872 – 80c. yellow and brown . . 1·60 1·00
873 – 12c. red and green (air) 25 15
874 – 50c. blue and orange . . 1·00 90
875 – 70c. blue and mauve . . . 1·40 1·00
876 **196** $1 black and orange . . . 2·00 1·10
BUILDINGS: 1, 80c. Executive; 10, 50c. Information; 12, 15, 70c. Capitol.

1963. Freedom from Hunger.
877 **197** 5c. purple & turq (postage) 15 10
878 – 25c. yellow and green (air) 35 20
DESIGN: 25c. F.A.O. emblem and Globe.

198 Rocket

1963. Space Exploration.
880 **198** 10c. yellow & bl (postage) 20 15
881 – 15c. brown and blue . . . 35 40
882 – 25c. green and orange (air) 45 30
DESIGNS—HORIZ: 15c. Space capsule. VERT: 25c. "Telstar" TV satellite.

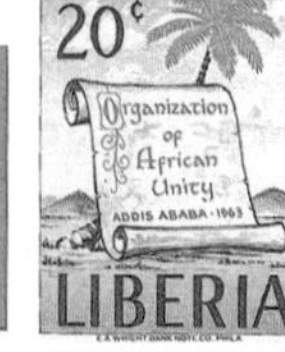

199 Red Cross
200 "Unity" Scroll

1963. Red Cross Centenary.
884 **199** 5c. green and red (postage) 15 15
885 – 10c. grey and red 20 20
886 – 25c. violet and red (air) 35 30
887 – 50c. blue and red . . . . 1·00 85
DESIGNS—VERT: 10c. Emblem and torch. HORIZ: 25c. Red Cross and Globe; 50c. Emblem and Globe.

1963. Conference of African Heads of State, Addis Ababa.
888 **200** 20c. brn & grn (postage) 40 35
889 – 25c. red and green (air) 45 30
DESIGN: 25c. Map of Africa (inscr "AFRICAN SUMMIT CONFERENCE").

201 Ski-jumping
202 President Kennedy

1963. Winter Olympic Games, Innsbruck. (1964).
890 **201** 5c. blue and red (postage) 20 20
891 – 10c. red and blue (air) . . 25 25
892 – 25c. orange and green . . 35 35
DESIGNS—VERT: 10c. Olympic flame. HORIZ: 25c. Olympic rings. All have mountain scenery as backgrounds.

1964. President Kennedy Memorial Issue.
894 **202** 20c. black & blue (postage) 35 20
895 – 25c. black and purple (air) 45 25
DESIGN—VERT: 25c. Pres. Kennedy, full face portrait.

203 "Relay I" Satellite
204 Mt. Fuji

1964. Space Communications.
897 – 10c. orange and green . . 20 15
898 **203** 15c. blue and mauve . . . 25 20
899 – 25c. yellow, black and blue 45 25
SATELLITES—HORIZ: 10c. "Syncom"; 25c. "Mariner II".

1964. Olympic Games, Tokyo.
901 **204** 10c. green and yellow . . 15 10
902 – 15c. purple and red . . . 20 15
903 – 25c. red and buff 45 20
DESIGNS: 15c. Japanese arch and Olympic Flame; 25c. Cherry blossom and stadium.

205 Scout Bugle
206 "The Great Emancipator" (statue)

1965. Liberian Boy Scouts.
905 – 5c. brown and blue (postage) 25 15
906 **205** 10c. ochre and green . . . 40 25
907 – 25c. blue and red (air) . . 50 35
DESIGNS—VERT: 5c. Scout badge and saluting hand; 25c. Liberian flag within scout badge.

1965. Death Centenary of Abraham Lincoln.
909 **206** 5c. brown and sepia . . . 20 25
910 – 20c. green and light brown 35 30
911 – 25c. blue and purple . . . 40 40
DESIGNS—HORIZ: 20c. Bust of Lincoln, and Pres. Kennedy. VERT: 25c. Lincoln statue, Chicago (after St. Gaudens).

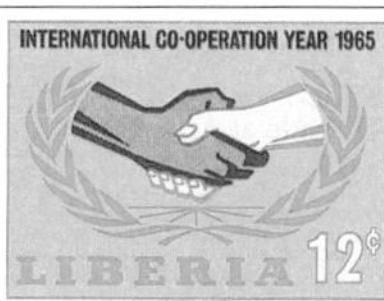

207 I.C.Y. Emblem

1965. International Co-operation Year.
913 **207** 12c. brown and orange . . 70 25
914 25c. brown and blue . . . 40 25
915 50c. brown and green . . 80 70

208 I.T.U. Emblem and Symbols

1965. Centenary of I.T.U.
917 **208** 25c. brn & grn (postage) 40 50
918 35c. mauve and black . . 60 50
919 50c. blue and red (air) . . 80 45

209 Pres. Tubman and Flag
210 Sir Winston Churchill

1965. Pres. Tubman's 70th Birthday. Multicoloured.
921 25c. Type **209** (postage) . . . 35 30
922 25c. President and Liberian arms (air) 35 25

1966. Churchill Commemoration.
924 **210** 15c. black & orge (postage) 30 30
925 – 20c. black and green . . . 35 25
926 – 25c. black and blue (air) 40 30
DESIGNS—HORIZ: 20c. Churchill in uniform of Trinity House Elder Brother; 25c. Churchill and Houses of Parliament.

211 Pres. Roberts
212 Footballers and Hemispheres

1966. Liberian Presidents.
928 **211** 1c. black & pink (postage) 10 10
929 – 2c. black and yellow . . . 10 10
930 – 3c. black and violet . . . 10 10
931 – 4c. black and yellow . . . 75 50
932 – 5c. black and orange . . . 10 10
933 – 10c. black and green . . . 15 10
934 – 25c. black and blue . . . 35 20
935 – 50c. black and mauve . . . 70 65
936 – 80c. black and red . . . . 1·25 95
937 – $1 black and brown . . . 1·40 15
938 – $2 black and purple . . . 3·25 2·75
939 – 25c. black and green (air) 35 25
PRESIDENTS: 2c. Benson; 3c. Warner; 4c. Payne; 5c. Roye; 10c. Coleman; 25c. (postage) Howard; 25c. (air) Tubman; 50c. King; 80c. Johnson; $1 Barclay; $2 Cheesman.

1966. World Cup Football Championships.
940 **212** 10c. brown and turquoise 15 15
941 – 25c. brown and mauve . . 35 30
942 – 35c. brown and orange . . 50 45
DESIGNS—VERT: 25c. Presentation cup, football and boots; 35c. Footballer.

213 Pres. Kennedy taking Oath

1966. 3rd Death Anniv of Pres. Kennedy.
944 **213** 15c. black & red (postage) 25 15
945 – 20c. purple and blue . . . 35 20
946 – 25c. blue, black and ochre (air) 45 30
947 – 35c. blue and pink . . . 85 45
DESIGNS: 20c. Kennedy stamps of 1964; 25c. U.N. General Assembly and Pres. Kennedy; 35c. Pres. Kennedy and rocket on launching pad.

214 Children on See-saw

1966. 20th Anniv of UNICEF.
949 **214** 5c. blue and red 20 20
950 – 80c. brown and green . . 1·50 1·50
DESIGN: 80c. Child playing "Doctors".

215 Giraffe
216 Scout Emblem and Various Sports

1966. Wild Animals. Multicoloured.
951 2c. Type **215** 10 10
952 3c. Lion 20 15
953 5c. Crocodile (horiz) 15 10
954 10c. Chimpanzees 40 20
955 15c. Leopard (horiz) 50 25
956 20c. Black rhinoceros (horiz) 60 40
957 25c. African elephant 70 50

1967. World Scout Jamboree, Idaho.
958 – 10c. purple and green . . 20 15
959 **216** 25c. red and blue 35 50
960 – 40c. brown and green . . 85 60
DESIGNS—VERT: 10c. Jamboree emblem. HORIZ: 40c. Scout by campfire, and Moon landing.

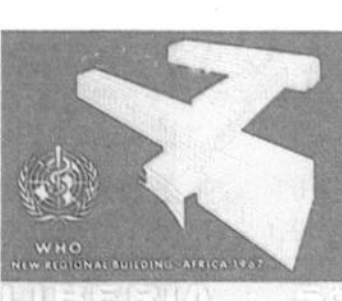

217 Pre-Hispanic Sculpture
218 W.H.O. Building, Brazzaville

1967. Publicity for Olympic Games, Mexico (1968).
962 **217** 10c. violet and orange . . 75 85
963 – 25c. orange, black and blue 35 40
964 – 40c. red and green 60 65
DESIGNS—VERT: 25c. Aztec calendar. HORIZ: 40c. Mexican sombrero, guitar and ceramics.

1967. Inauguration of W.H.O.'s Regional Office, Brazzaville.
966 **218** 5c. yellow and blue . . . 20 20
967 – 80c. green and yellow . . 1·25 1·25
DESIGN—VERT: 80c. As Type **218** but in vertical format.

219 Boy with Rattle
220 Ice-hockey

1967. Musicians and Instruments. Multicoloured.
968 2c. Type **219** 15 15
969 3c. Tomtom and soko violin (horiz) 20 20
970 5c. Mang harp (horiz) . . . 25 25
971 10c. Alimilim 30 30
972 15c. Xylophone drums . . . 35 35
973 25c. Tomtoms 50 40
974 35c. Oral harp 75 60

1967. Publicity for Winter Olympic Games, Grenoble (1968).
975 **220** 10c. blue and green . . . 15 20
976 – 25c. violet and blue . . . 35 30
977 – 40c. brown and orange . . 85 50
DESIGNS: 25c. Ski-jumping; 40c. Tobogganing.

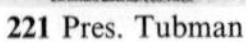

221 Pres. Tubman **222** Human Rights Emblem

1967. Re-election of Pres. Tubman for 6th Term.
979 **221** 25c. brown and blue . . . 35 25

1968. Human Rights Year.
981 **222** 3c. blue and red 10 10
982 80c. green and brown . . 1·60 1·60

223 Dr. King and Hearse **224** Throwing the Javelin and Statue of Diana

1968. Martin Luther King Commemoration.
984 **223** 15c. brown and blue . . . 25 20
985 – 25c. brown and blue . . . 40 30
986 – 35c. black and olive . . . 60 65
DESIGNS—VERT: 25c. Dr. Martin Luther King. HORIZ: Dr. King and Lincoln Monument.

1968. Olympic Games, Mexico.
988 **224** 15c. violet and brown . . 25 15
989 – 25c. blue and red 35 15
990 – 35c. brown and green . . 50 30
DESIGNS: 25c. Throwing the discus and Quetzalcoatl sculpture; 35c. High-diving and Xochilcalco bas-relief.

225 President Tubman

1968. 25th Anniv of Pres. Tubman's Administration.
992 **225** 25c. black, brown & silver 1·10 50

226 I.L.O. Symbol

1969. 50th Anniv of I.L.O.
994 **226** 25c. blue & gold (postage) 35 35
995 – 80c. green and gold (air) 1·50 1·40
DESIGN: 80c. As Type **226** but vert.

227 "Prince Balthasar Carlos" (Velasquez) **228** Bank Emblem on "Tree"

1969. Paintings (1st series). Multicoloured.
996 3c. Type **227** 10 10
997 5c. "Red Roofs" (Pissarro) (horiz) 20 10
998 10c. "David and Goliath" (Caravaggio) (horiz) . . . 30 15
999 12c. "Still Life" (Chardin) (horiz) 30 15
1000 15c. "The Last Supper" (Leonardo da Vinci) (horiz) 35 15
1001 20c. "Regatta at Argenteuil" (Monet) (horiz) 50 20
1002 25c. "Judgement of Solomon" (Giorgione) . . 45 25
1003 35c. "The Sistine Madonna" (Raphael) 85 30
See also Nos. 1010/1017.

1969. 5th Anniv of African Development Bank.
1004 **228** 25c. brown and blue . . 45 40
1005 80c. red and green . . . 1·50 1·10

229 Memorial Plaque

1969. 1st Man on the Moon.
1006 **229** 15c. blue and ochre . . . 25 15
1007 – 25c. blue and orange . . 70 20
1008 – 35c. red and slate . . . 1·00 25
DESIGNS—VERT: 25c. Moon landing and Liberian; 35c. "Kennedy" stamp of 1966; 35c. Module lifting off from Moon.

1969. Paintings (2nd series). As T **227**. Multicoloured.
1010 3c. "The Gleaners" (Millet) (horiz) 15 10
1011 5c. "View of Toledo" (El Greco) 20 15
1012 10c. "Heads of Negroes" (Rubens) (horiz) 30 15
1013 12c. "The Last Supper" (El Greco) (horiz) 30 20
1014 15c. "Peasants Dancing" (Brueghel) (horiz) 35 20
1015 20c. "Hunters in the Snow" (Brueghel) (horiz) 40 25
1016 25c. "Descent from the Cross" (detail, Weyden) 45 30
1017 35c. "The Conception" (Murillo) 60 40

230 Peace Dove and Emblems

1970. 25th Anniv of United Nations.
1018 **230** 5c. green & sil (postage) 15 25
1019 – $1 blue and silver (air) 1·25 1·00
DESIGN: $1, U.N. emblem and olive branch.

231 World Cup "Football" Emblem

1970. World Cup Football Championship, Mexico.
1020 **231** 5c. brown and blue . . . 20 15
1021 – 10c. brown and green . . 25 20
1022 – 25c. gold and purple . . 45 30
1023 – 35c. red and blue . . . 60 45
DESIGN—VERT: 10c. Tialoc, Mexican Rain God; 25c. Jules Rimet Cup. HORIZ: 35c. Football in sombrero.

232 Japanese Singer and Festival Plaza

1970. Expo 70. Multicoloured.
1025 2c. Type **232** 10 10
1026 3c. Japanese singer and Expo hall 15 10
1027 5c. Aerial view of "EXPO 70" 30 10
1028 7c. "Tanabata" Festival . . 30 10
1029 8c. "Awa" Dance Festival 30 15
1030 25c. "Sado-Okesa" Dance Festival . . . . 1·10 25

233 New H.Q. Building

1970. Inauguration of New U.P.U. Headquarters Building, Berne.
1032 **233** 25c. brown and blue . . 35 35
1033 – 80c. brown and chestnut 1·50 1·50
DESIGN—VERT: 80c. Similar to Type **233** but with larger U.P.U. monument.

234 "The First Consul" (Vien)

1970. Birth Bicentenary of Napoleon Bonaparte. Multicoloured.
1034 3c. Type **234** 20 10
1035 5c. "Napoleon visiting school" (unknown artist) 30 15
1036 10c. "Napoleon Bonaparte" (detail, Isabey) 35 15
1037 12c. "The French Campaign" (Meissonier) 40 20
1038 20c. "The Abdication" (Bouchot) 80 30
1039 25c. "Meeting of Napoleon and Pope Pius VII" (Demarne) . . . . 1·50 35
Design of 10c. is incorrectly attributed to Gerard on the stamp.

235 Pres. Tubman

1970. Pres. Tubman's 75th Birthday.
1041 **235** 25c. multicoloured . . . 75 25

236 "Adoration of the Magi" (Van der Weyden)

1970. Christmas. "The Adoration of the Magi" by artists as below. Multicoloured.
1043 3c. Type **236** 10 10
1044 5c. H. Memling 15 10
1045 10c. S. Lochner 25 15
1046 12c. A. Altdorfer (vert) . . 30 15
1047 20c. H. van der Goes . . . 35 15
1048 25c. H. Bosch (vert) 40 30

237 Bapende Mask **239** Pres. Tubman and Women at Ballot Box

238 Astronauts on Moon

1971. African Ceremonial Masks. Masks from different tribes. Multicoloured.
1050 2c. Type **237** 10 10
1051 3c. Dogon 15 10
1052 5c. Baoule 15 15
1053 6c. Dedougou 20 15
1054 9c. Dan 25 15
1055 15c. Bamileke 30 20
1056 20c. Bapende (different) . . 40 30
1057 25c. Bamileke costume . . . 60 30

1971. "Apollo 14" Moon Mission. Multicoloured.
1058 3c. Type **238** 15 10
1059 5c. Astronaut and Moon vehicle 15 10
1060 10c. Erecting U.S. flag on Moon 20 10
1061 12c. Splashdown 40 15
1062 20c. Astronauts leaving capsule 45 15
1063 25c. "Apollo 14" crew . . . 60 20

1971. 25th Anniv of Liberian Women's Suffrage.
1065 **239** 3c. blue and brown 15 30
1066 – 80c. brown and green . . 1·50 1·50
DESIGN—HORIZ: 80c. Pres. Tubman, women and map.

240 Hall of Honour, Munich

1971. Olympic Games, Munich (1972) (1st issue). Views of Munich. Multicoloured.
1067 3c. Type **240** 15 10
1068 5c. View of central Munich 15 10
1069 10c. National Museum . . . 20 10
1070 12c. Max Joseph's Square 25 10
1071 20c. Propylaen, King's Square 40 15
1072 25c. Liesel-Karistadt Fountain 60 20

241 American Scout **242** Pres. William Tubman

1971. World Scout Jamboree, Asagiri, Japan. Scouts in national uniforms. Multicoloured.
1074 3c. Type **241** 15 10
1075 5c. West Germany 15 10
1076 10c. Australia 20 15
1077 12c. Great Britain 25 15
1078 20c. Japan 40 20
1079 25c. Liberia 60 30

1971. Pres. Tubman Memorial Issue.
1081 **242** 3c. brown, blue and black 10 10
1082 25c. brown, purple & blk 35 35

243 Common Zebra and Foal

1971. 25th Anniv of UNICEF. Animals with young. Multicoloured.
1083 5c. Type **243** 20 10
1084 7c. Koalas 30 15
1085 8c. Guanaco 35 15
1086 10c. Red fox and cubs . . . 45 15
1087 20c. Savanna monkeys . . . 65 25
1088 25c. Brown bears 90 35

244 Cross-country Skiing and Sika Deer

1971. Winter Olympic Games, Sapporo, Japan. Sports and Hokkaido Animals. Multicoloured.

1090	2c. Type **244**	10	10
1091	3c. Tobogganing and black woodpecker	70	20
1092	5c. Ski-jumping and brown bear	15	10
1093	10c. Bobsleighing and common guillemots	1·00	20
1094	15c. Figure-skating and northern pika	30	20
1095	25c. Slalom skiing and Manchurian cranes	2·00	50

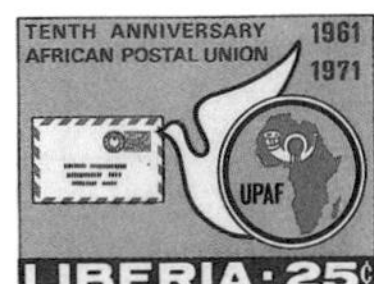

245 A.P.U. Emblem, Dove and Letter

1971. 10th Anniv of African Postal Union.

1097 **245**	25c. orange and blue	35	50
1098	80c. brown and grey	1·10	1·00

246 "Elizabeth" (emigrant ship) at Providence Island

1972. 150th Anniv of Liberia.

1099 **246**	3c. green and blue	70	50
1100 –	20c. blue and orange	35	20
1101 **246**	25c. purple and orange	2·00	55
1102 –	35c. purple and green	1·10	75

DESIGNS—VERT: 20, 35c. Arms and Founding Fathers Monument, Monrovia.

247 Pres. Tolbert and Map

1972. Inaug of Pres. Wm. R. Tolbert Jnr.

1104 **247**	25c. brown and green	35	25
1105 –	80c. brown and blue	1·60	80

DESIGN—VERT: 80c. Pres. Tolbert standing by desk.

248 Football

1972. Olympic Games, Munich (2nd issue). Multicoloured.

1106	3c. Type **248**	10	10
1107	5c. Swimming	15	10
1108	10c. Show-jumping	25	10
1109	12c. Cycling	30	15
1110	20c. Long-jumping	45	20
1111	25c. Running	60	25

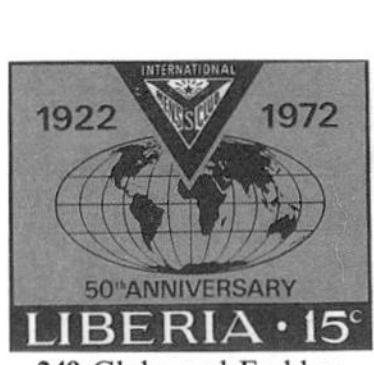

249 Globe and Emblem

251 Emperor Haile Selassie

250 Astronaut and Moon Rover

1972. 50th Anniv of Int Y's Men's Clubs.

1113 **249**	15c. violet and gold	40	15
1114 –	90c. green and blue	1·75	1·75

DESIGN: 90c. Club emblem on World Map.

1972. Moon Mission of "Apollo 16". Mult.

1115	3c. Type **250**	10	10
1116	5c. Reflection on visor	10	10
1117	10c. Astronauts with cameras	15	10
1118	12c. Setting up equipment	50	15
1119	20c. "Apollo 16" emblem	65	20
1120	25c. Astronauts in Moon Rover	90	50

1972. Emperor Haile Selassie of Ethiopia's 80th Birthday.

1122 **251**	20c. green and yellow	40	30
1123	25c. purple and yellow	45	40
1124	35c. brown and yellow	85	85

252 H.M.S. "Ajax" (ship of the line), 1809

1972. Famous Ships of the British Royal Navy. Multicoloured.

1125	3c. Type **252**	35	25
1126	5c. HMS "Hogue" (screw ship of the line), 1848	65	25
1127	7c. HMS "Ariadne" (frigate), 1816	85	30
1128	15c. HMS "Royal Adelaide" (ship of the line), 1828	1·00	55
1129	20c. HMS "Rinaldo" (screw sloop), 1860	1·40	70
1130	25c. HMS "Nymphe" (screw sloop), 1888	1·90	1·00

253 Pres. Tolbert taking Oath

1972. 1st Year of President Tolbert Presidency.

1132 **253**	15c. multicoloured	65	55
1133	25c. multicoloured	95	95

254 Klaus Dibiasi and Italian Flag

1973. Olympic Games, Munich. Gold-medal Winners. Multicoloured.

1135	5c. Type **254**	10	10
1136	8c. Borzov and Soviet flag	15	10
1137	10c. Yanagida and Japanese flag	15	10
1138	12c. Spitz and U.S. flag	20	15
1139	15c. Keino and Kenyan flag	25	15
1140	25c. Meade and Union Jack	35	25

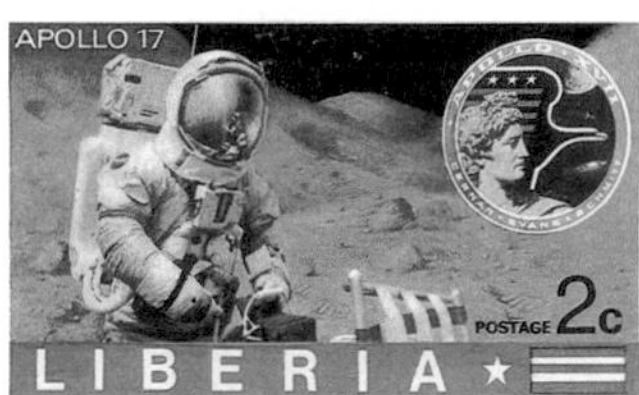

255 Astronaut on Moon

1973. Moon Flight of "Apollo 17". Multicoloured.

1142	2c. Type **255**	10	10
1143	3c. Testing lunar rover at Cape Kennedy	10	10
1144	10c. Collecting Moon rocks	15	10
1145	15c. Lunar rover on Moon	20	15
1146	20c. "Apollo 17" crew at Cape Kennedy	30	20
1147	25c. Astronauts on Moon	35	25

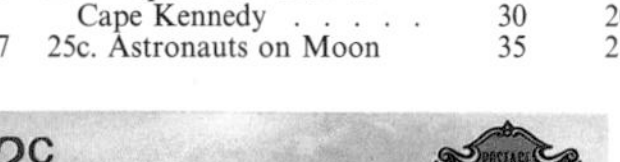

256 Steam Locomotive, Great Britain

1973. Historical Railways. Steam locomotives of 1895–1905 Multicoloured.

1149	2c. Type **256**	25	10
1150	3c. Netherlands	35	10
1151	10c. France	65	15
1152	15c. No. 1800, U.S.A.	95	20
1153	20c. Class 150 No. 1, Japan	2·00	25
1154	25c. Germany	3·00	30

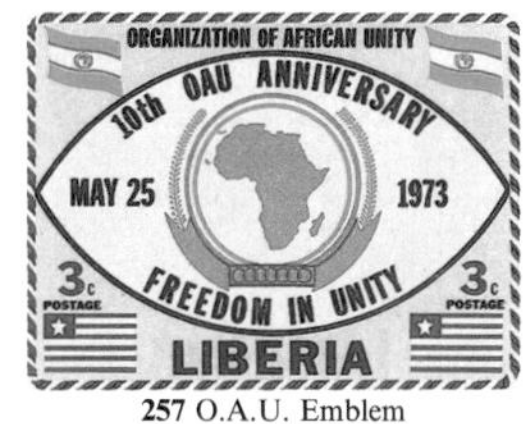

257 O.A.U. Emblem

1973. 10th Anniv of Organization of African Unity.

1156 **257**	3c. multicoloured	10	10
1157	5c. multicoloured	10	10
1158	10c. multicoloured	15	10
1159	15c. multicoloured	20	15
1160	25c. multicoloured	35	25
1161	50c. multicoloured	1·00	1·00

258 Edward Jenner and Roses

1973. 25th Anniv of W.H.O. Multicoloured.

1162	1c. Type **258**	15	10
1163	4c. Sigmund Freud and violets	15	10
1164	10c. Jonas Salk and chrysanthemums	25	10
1165	15c. Louis Pasteur and scabious	40	15
1166	20c. Emil von Behring and mallow	45	20
1167	25c. Sir Alexander Fleming and rhododendrons	85	25

259 Stanley Steamer, 1910

1973. Vintage Cars. Multicoloured.

1169	2c. Type **259**	10	10
1170	3c. Cadillac Model A, 1903	10	10
1171	10c. Clement-Baynard, 1904	15	10
1172	15c. Rolls-Royce Silver Ghost tourer, 1907	25	15
1173	20c. Maxwell gentleman's speedster, 1905	35	20
1174	25c. Chadwick, 1907	50	25

260 Copernicus, Armillary Sphere and Satellite Communications System

1973. 500th Birth Anniv of Copernicus. Mult.

1176	1c. Type **260**	10	10
1177	4c. Eudoxus solar system	10	10
1178	10c. Aristotle, Ptolemy and Copernicus	15	10
1179	15c. "Saturn" and "Apollo" spacecraft	25	15
1180	20c. Astronomical observatory satellite	35	20
1181	25c. Satellite tracking-station	50	25

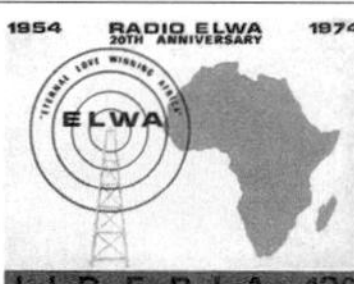

261 Radio Mast and Map of Africa

1974. 20th Anniv of "Eternal Love Winning Africa". Radio Station. Multicoloured.

1183	13c. Type **261**	25	25
1184	15c. Radio mast and map of Liberia	35	25
1185	17c. Type **261**	35	50
1186	25c. As 15c.	50	40

262 "Thomas Coutts" (full-rigged sailing ship) and "Aureol" (liner)

1974. Cent of U.P.U. Multicoloured.

1187	2c. Type **262**	20	10
1188	3c. Boeing 707 airliner and "Brasil" (liner), satellite and Monrovia Post Office	30	10
1189	10c. U.S. and Soviet Telecommunications satellites	15	10
1190	15c. Postal runner and Boeing 707 airliner	25	20
1191	20c. British Advanced Passenger Train (APT) and Liberian mail-van	1·50	25
1192	25c. American Pony Express rider	50	35

263 Fox Terrier

1974. Dogs. Multicoloured.

1194	5c. Type **263**	15	10
1195	10c. Boxer	20	10
1196	16c. Chihuahua	30	15
1197	19c. Beagle	35	20
1198	25c. Golden retriever	40	25
1199	50c. Collie	1·10	50

264 West Germany v. Chile Match

1974. World Cup Football Championship, West Germany. Scenes from semi-final matches. Multicoloured.

1201	1c. Type **264**	10	10
1202	2c. Australia v. East Germany	10	10
1203	5c. Brazil v. Yugoslavia	15	10
1204	10c. Zaire v. Scotland	20	10
1205	12c. Netherlands v. Uruguay	25	15
1206	15c. Sweden v. Bulgaria	30	15
1207	20c. Italy v. Haiti	40	20
1208	25c. Poland v. Argentina	60	25

265 "Chrysiridia madagascariensis"

1974. Tropical Butterflies. Multicoloured.

1210	1c. Type **265**	10	10
1211	2c. "Catagramma sorana"	10	10
1212	5c. "Erasmia pulchella"	20	10
1213	17c. "Morpho cypris"	50	25
1214	25c. "Agrias amydon"	70	35
1215	40c. "Vanessa cardui"	1·40	45

266 Pres. Tolbert and Gold Medallion

1974. "Family of Man" Award to President Tolbert. Multicoloured.

No.	Description	Mint	Used
1217	3c. Type **266**	10	25
1218	$1 Pres. Tolbert, medallion and flag	1·40	1·40

267 Churchill with Troops

1975. Birth Centenary of Sir Winston Churchill. Multicoloured.

No.	Description	Mint	Used
1219	3c. Type **267**	10	10
1220	10c. Churchill and aerial combat	30	10
1221	15c. Churchill aboard "Liberty" ship in Channel	55	15
1222	17c. Churchill reviewing troops in desert	30	15
1223	20c. Churchill crossing Rhine	40	20
1224	25c. Churchill with Roosevelt	50	25

268 Marie Curie

1975. International Women's Year. Multicoloured.

No.	Description	Mint	Used
1226	2c. Type **268**	10	10
1227	3c. Mahalia Jackson	10	10
1228	5c. Joan of Arc	10	10
1229	10c. Eleanor Roosevelt . . .	15	10
1230	25c. Matilda Newport . . .	50	25
1231	50c. Valentina Tereshkova	70	55

269 Old State House, Boston, and U.S. 2c. "Liberty Bell" Stamp of 1926

1975. Bicentenary of American Independence.

No.	Description	Mint	Used
1233	5c. Type **269**	15	10
1234	10c. George Washington and 1928 "Valley Forge" stamp	30	10
1235	15c. Philadelphia and 1937 "Constitution" stamp . .	45	15
1236	20c. Benjamin Franklin and 1938 "Ratification" stamp	50	15
1237	25c. Paul Revere's Ride and 1925 "Lexington-Concord" stamp	70	20
1238	50c. "Santa Maria" and 1893 "Columbus' Landing" stamp	2·25	55

270 Dr. Schweitzer, Yellow Baboon and Lambarene Hospital

1975. Birth Centenary of Dr Albert Schweitzer. Multicoloured.

No.	Description	Mint	Used
1240	1c. Type **270**	10	10
1241	3c. Schweitzer, African elephant and canoe . . .	15	10
1242	5c. Schweitzer, African buffalo and canoe	25	20
1243	6c. Schweitzer, kob and dancer	30	10
1244	25c. Schweitzer, lioness and village woman	75	25
1245	50c. Schweitzer, common zebras and clinic scene . .	1·40	65

271 "Apollo" Spacecraft

1975. "Apollo–Soyuz" Space Link. Multicoloured.

No.	Description	Mint	Used
1247	5c. Type **271**	10	10
1248	10c. "Soyuz" spacecraft . .	15	10
1249	15c. American–Russian handclasp	20	15
1250	20c. Flags and maps of America and Russia . . .	25	15
1251	25c. Leonov and Kubasov	35	20
1252	50c. Slayton, Brand and Stafford	95	50

272 Presidents Tolbert and Stevens, and Signing Ceremony

1975. Liberia–Sierra Leone Mano River Union Agreement.

No.	Description	Mint	Used
1254	**272** 2c. multicoloured	10	10
1255	3c. multicoloured	10	10
1256	5c. multicoloured	10	10
1257	10c. multicoloured . . .	15	10
1258	25c. multicoloured . . .	35	25
1259	50c. multicoloured . . .	70	70

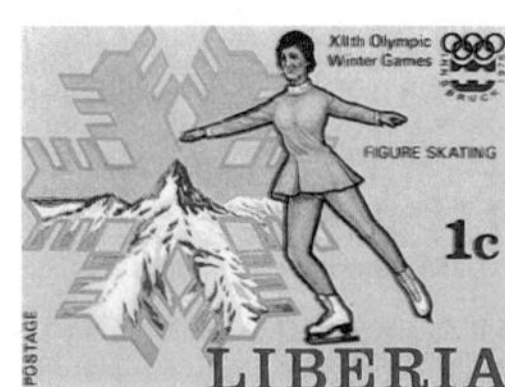

273 Figure Skating

1976. Winter Olympic Games, Innsbruck. Multicoloured.

No.	Description	Mint	Used
1260	1c. Type **273**	10	10
1261	4c. Ski jumping	20	20
1262	10c. Skiing (slalom)	30	20
1263	25c. Ice hockey	60	30
1264	35c. Speed skating	90	40
1265	50c. Two-man bobsledding	1·25	65

274 Pres. Tolbert taking Oath

1976. Inauguration of President William R. Tolbert, Jr. Multicoloured.

No.	Description	Mint	Used
1267	3c. Type **274**	10	10
1268	25c. Pres. Tolbert in Presidential Chair (vert)	35	25
1269	$1 Liberian crest, flag and commemorative gold coin	1·90	1·40

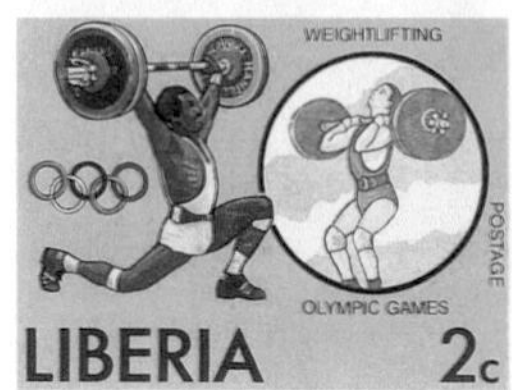

275 Weightlifting

1976. Olympic Games, Montreal. Multicoloured.

No.	Description	Mint	Used
1270	2c. Type **275**	10	10
1271	3c. Pole-vaulting	10	10
1272	10c. Hammer and shot-put	30	15
1273	25c. "Tempest" dinghies . .	65	35
1274	35c. Gymnastics	90	60
1275	50c. Hurdling	1·25	65

276 Bell's Telephone and Receiver

1976. Telephone Centenary. Multicoloured.

No.	Description	Mint	Used
1277	1c. Type **276**	10	10
1278	4c. Mail-coach	10	10
1279	5c. "Intelsat 4" satellite . .	15	10
1280	25c. Cable-ship "Dominia", 1926	1·25	30
1281	40c. British Advanced Passenger Train (APT) . .	1·60	50
1282	50c. Wright Flyer I, airship "Graf Zeppelin" and Concorde	1·75	60

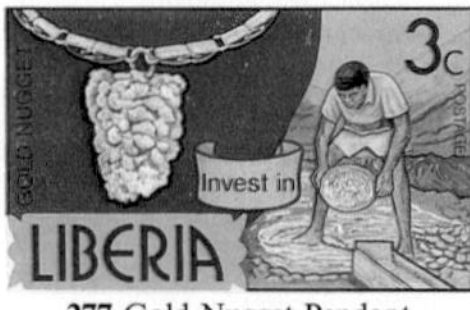

277 Gold Nugget Pendant

1976. Liberian Products (1st series). Multicoloured.

No.	Description	Mint	Used
1284	1c. Mano River Bridge . .	10	10
1285	3c. Type **277**	10	10
1286	5c. "V" ring	10	10
1286a	7c. As No. 1286	15	25
1287	10c. Rubber tree and tyre	15	10
1287a	15c. Combine harvester . .	20	10
1287b	17c. As No. 1289	45	10
1287c	20c. Hydro-electric plant	60	45
1288	25c. Mesurado shrimp . .	75	25
1288a	27c. Dress and woman tie-dying cloth	80	60
1289	55c. Great barracuda . . .	1·40	35
1289a	$1 Train carrying iron ore	4·50	60

For designs as T **277** but in a smaller size, see Nos. 1505/8.

278 Black Rhinoceros

1976. Animals. Multicoloured.

No.	Description	Mint	Used
1290	2c. Type **278**	10	10
1291	3c. Bongo	10	10
1292	5c. Chimpanzee (vert) . . .	15	10
1293	15c. Pygmy hippopotamus	40	15
1294	25c. Leopard	80	40
1295	$1 Gorilla	3·00	90

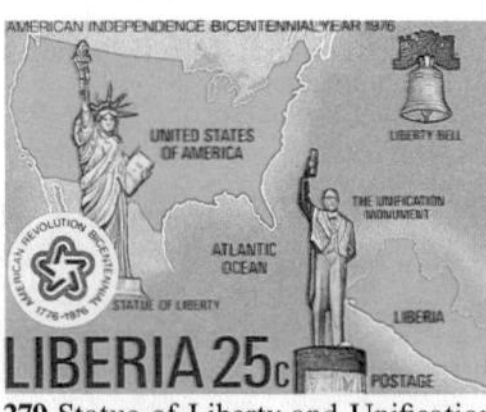

279 Statue of Liberty and Unification Monument on Maps of U.S.A. and Liberia

1976. Bicentenary of American Revolution. Multicoloured.

No.	Description	Mint	Used
1297	25c. Type **279**	35	25
1298	$1 Presidents Washington and Ford (U.S.A.), Roberts and Tolbert (Liberia)	1·75	65

280 Baluba Masks

1977. Second World Black and African Festival of Arts and Culture, Lagos (Nigeria). Tribal Masks. Multicoloured.

No.	Description	Mint	Used
1300	5c. Type **280**	10	10
1301	10c. Bateke	15	10
1302	15c. Basshilele	20	15
1303	20c. Igungun	30	15
1304	25c. Maisi	60	20
1305	50c. Kifwebe	1·10	45

281 Latham's Francolin

1977. Liberian Wild Birds. Multicoloured.

No.	Description	Mint	Used
1307	5c. Type **281**	50	10
1308	10c. Narina's trogon ("Narina Trogon") . . .	80	15
1309	15c. Rufous-crowned roller	80	20
1310	20c. Brown-cheeked hornbill	85	25
1311	25c. Garden bulbul ("Pepper Bird")	1·00	35
1312	50c. African fish eagle ("Fish Eagle")	1·10	85

282 Alwin Schockemohle (individual jumping)

1977. Olympic Games, Montreal. Equestrian Gold-medal Winners. Multicoloured.

No.	Description	Mint	Used
1314	5c. Edmund Coffin (military dressage) (postage) . . .	15	10
1315	15c. Type **282**	40	20
1316	20c. Christine Stuckelberger (dressage)	50	30
1317	25c. "Nations Prize" (French team)	70	35
1318	55c. Military dressage (U.S.A. team) (air) . . .	1·25	70

283 Queen Elizabeth II

1977. Silver Jubilee of Queen Elizabeth II. Multicoloured.

No.	Description	Mint	Used
1320	15c. Type **283**	35	15
1321	25c. Queen Elizabeth and Prince Philip with President and Mrs. Tubman of Liberia . . .	55	25
1322	80c. Queen Elizabeth, Prince Philip and Royal Arms	2·40	70

284 "Blessing the Children"

1977. Christmas. Multicoloured.

No.	Description	Mint	Used
1324	20c. Type **284**	50	25
1325	25c. "The Good Shepherd"	70	35
1326	$1 "Jesus and the Woman of Samaria at the Well"	2·00	1·00

285 Dornier Do-X Flying Boat

1978. "Progress in Aviation". Multicoloured.
1327 2c. Type **285** 10 10
1328 3c. Space shuttle "Enterprise" on Boeing 747 . . . . 10 10
1329 5c. Edward Rickenbacker and Douglas DC-3 . . . 10 10
1330 25c. Charles Lindbergh and "Spirit of St. Louis" . . . 45 20
1331 35c. Louis Bleriot and Bleriot XI monoplane . . 65 35
1332 50c. Wright Brothers and Flyer I 90 55

286 Santos-Dumont's Airship "Ballon No. 9 La Badaleuse", 1903

1978. 75th Anniv of First Zeppelin Flight. Multicoloured.
1334 2c. Type **286** 10 10
1335 3c. Thomas Baldwin's airship "U.S. Military No. 1", 1908 . . . . . . 10 10
1336 5c. Tissandier brothers' airship, 1883 . . . . . . 10 10
1337 25c. Parseval airship PL-VII, 1912 . . . . 40 20
1338 40c. Airship "Nulli Secundus II", 1908 . . . 75 35
1339 50c. Beardmore airship R-34, 1919 . . . . 85 55

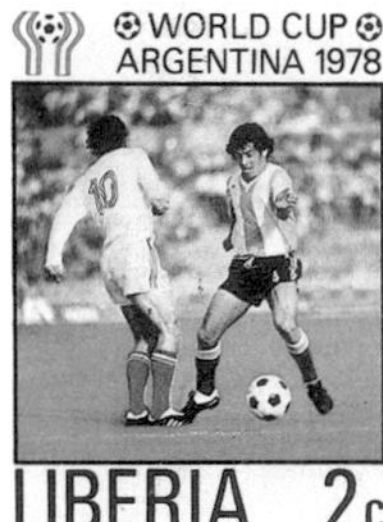

287 Tackling

1978. World Cup Football Championship, Argentina.
1341 **287** 2c. multicoloured 10 10
1342 – 3c. multicoloured (horiz) 10 10
1343 – 10c. multicoloured (horiz) 15 10
1344 – 25c. multicoloured (horiz) 60 20
1345 – 35c. multicoloured . . . 80 25
1346 – 50c. multicoloured (horiz) . . . . 1·25 50
DESIGNS: Nos. 1342/6, Different match scenes.

288 Coronation Chair

1978. 25th Anniv of Coronation. Multicoloured.
1348 5c. Type **288** 10 25
1349 25c. Imperial State Crown 35 25
1350 $1 Buckingham Palace (horiz) . . . . 1·75 1·00

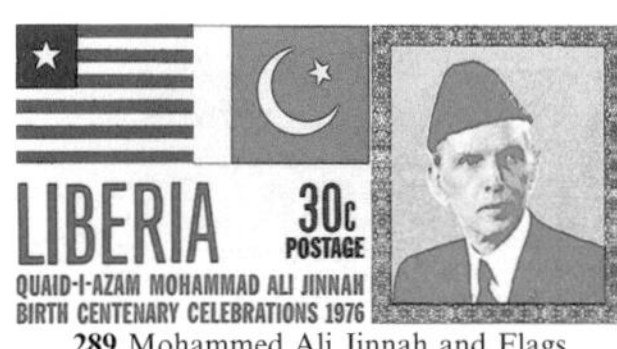

289 Mohammed Ali Jinnah and Flags

1978. Birth Centenary of Mohammed Ali Jinnah (first Governor-General of Pakistan).
1352 **289** 30c. multicoloured . . . 1·50 1·50

290 Carter and Tolbert Families

1978. Visit of President Carter of U.S.A. Mult.
1353 5c. Type **290** 10 10
1354 25c. Presidents Carter and Tolbert with Mrs. Carter at microphones 50 45
1355 $1 Presidents Carter and Tolbert in open car . . . 2·00 2·00

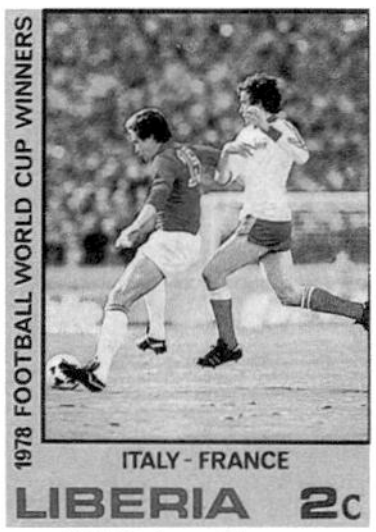

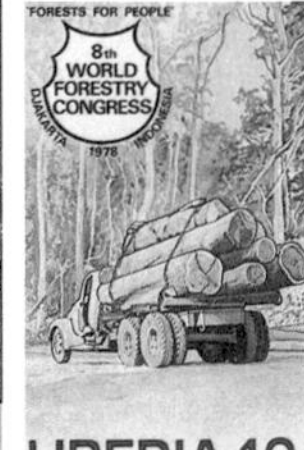

291 Italy v. France **292** Timber Truck

1978. Argentina's Victory in World Cup Football Championship. Multicoloured.
1356 1c. Brazil v. Spain (horiz) 10 10
1357 2c. Type **291** 10 10
1358 10c. Poland v. West Germany (horiz) 15 10
1359 27c. Peru v. Scotland . . . 65 25
1360 35c. Austria v. West Germany 80 55
1361 50c. Argentinian players with Cup . . . . 1·25 80

1978. 8th World Forestry Congress, Djakarta. Multicoloured.
1363 5c. Chopping up log (horiz) 10 10
1364 10c. Type **292** 15 10
1365 25c. Felling trees (horiz) . . 60 20
1366 50c. Loggers (horiz) . . . . 1·10 70

293 Presidents Gardner and Tolbert with Monrovia Post Office

1979. Centenary of U.P.U. Membership. Mult.
1367 5c. Type **293** 10 10
1368 35c. Presidents Gardner and Tolbert with U.P.U. emblem 90 90

294 "25" and Radio Waves

1979. 25th Anniv of Radio ELWA. Multicoloured.
1369 35c. Type **294** 75 75
1370 $1 Radio tower . . . . . . 2·10 2·10

295 I.Y.C., Decade of the African Child and S.O.S. Villages Emblems

1979. International Year of the Child. Multicoloured.
1371 5c. Type **295** 10 10
1372 25c. As Type **295** but with UNICEF instead of S.O.S. Villages emblem 25 20
1373 35c. Type **295** 50 25
1374 $1 As No. 1372 . . . . . . 1·40 1·40

296 Clasped Arms and Torches

1979. Organization for African Unity Summit Conference, Monrovia. Multicoloured.
1375 5c. Type **296** 10 10
1376 27c. Masks 40 25
1377 35c. African animals 50 50
1378 50c. Thatched huts and garden bulbuls . . . . . 1·50 65

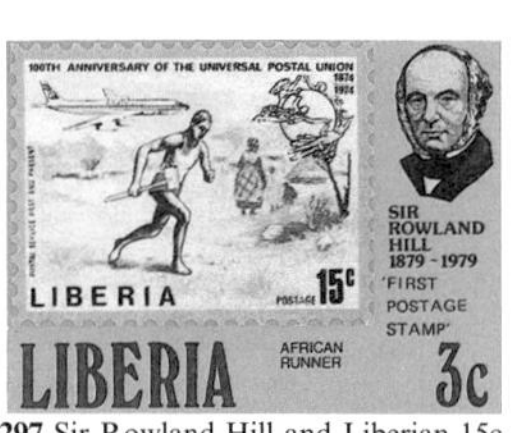

297 Sir Rowland Hill and Liberian 15c. Stamp, 1974

1979. Death Centenary of Sir Rowland Hill. Multicoloured.
1379 3c. Type **297** 10 10
1380 10c. Pony Express rider . . 15 10
1381 15c. British mail coach . . . 20 35
1382 25c. "John Penn" (paddle-steamer) 75 55
1383 27c. Class "Coronation" streamlined steam locomotive No. 6235, Great Britain . . . . . . 1·10 25
1384 50c. Concorde . . . . . . 1·50 90

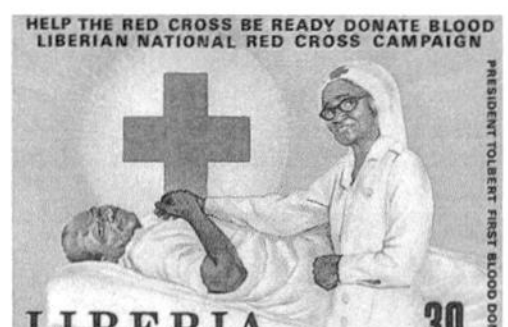

298 President Tolbert giving Blood

1979. National Red Cross Blood Donation Campaign. Multicoloured.
1386 30c. Type **298** 45 25
1387 50c. President Tolbert and Red Cross . . . . 1·00 1·00

299 "World Peace" (tanker)

1979. 2nd World Maritime Day and 30th Anniv of Liberia Maritime Programme. Multicoloured.
1388 5c. Type **299** 30 15
1389 $1 "World Peace" (different) 2·25 2·00

300 "A Good Turn"

1979. Scout Paintings by Norman Rockwell. Multicoloured.
1390 5c. Scout giving first aid to pup ("A Good Scout") 20 15
1391 5c. Type **300** 20 15
1392 5c. "Good Friends" 20 15
1393 5c. "Spirit of America" . . 20 15
1394 5c. "Scout Memories" . . . 20 15
1395 5c. "The Adventure Trail" 20 15
1396 5c. "On My Honour" . . . 20 15
1397 5c. "A Scout is Reverent" 20 15
1398 5c. "The Right Way" . . . 20 15
1399 5c. "The Scoutmaster" . . . 20 15
1400 10c. "A Scout is Loyal" . . 40 25
1401 10c. "An Army of Friendship" 35 20
1402 10c. "Carry on" 35 20
1403 10c. "A Good Scout" . . . 35 20
1404 10c. "The Campfire Story" 35 20
1405 10c. "High Adventure" . . 35 20
1406 10c. "Mighty Proud" . . . 35 20
1407 10c. "Tomorrow's Leader" 35 20
1408 10c. "Ever Onward" 35 20
1409 10c. "Homecoming" 35 20
1410 15c. "Scouts of Many Trails" 40 25
1411 15c. "America builds for Tomorrow" 40 25
1412 15c. "The Scouting Trail" 40 25
1413 15c. "A Scout is Reverent" 40 25
1414 15c. "A Scout is Helpful" 40 25
1415 15c. "Pointing the Way" . . 40 25
1416 15c. "A Good Sign All Over the World" 40 25
1417 15c. "To Keep Myself Physically Strong" . . . 40 25
1418 15c. "A Great Moment" . . 40 25
1419 15c. "Growth of a Leader" 40 25
1420 25c. "A Scout is Loyal" . . 60 35
1421 25c. "A Scout is Friendly" 60 35
1422 25c. "We Too, Have a Job to Do" 60 35
1423 25c. "I Will do my Best" . . 60 35
1424 25c. "A Guiding Hand" . . 60 35
1425 25c. "Breakthrough for Freedom" . . . . 1·25 40
1426 25c. "Scouting is Outing" . 60 35
1427 25c. "Beyond the Easel" . . 60 35
1428 25c. "Come and Get It" . . 60 35
1429 25c. "America's Manpower begins with Boypower" 60 35
1430 35c. "All Together" 80 45
1431 35c. "Men of Tomorrow" 80 45
1432 35c. "Friend in Need" . . . 80 45
1433 35c. "Our Heritage" 80 45
1434 35c. "Forward America" . . 80 45
1435 35c. "Can't Wait" 80 45
1436 35c. "From Concord to Tranquility" 80 45
1437 35c. "We Thank Thee" . . 80 45
1438 35c. "So Much Concern" 80 45
1439 35c. "Spirit of '76" 80 45

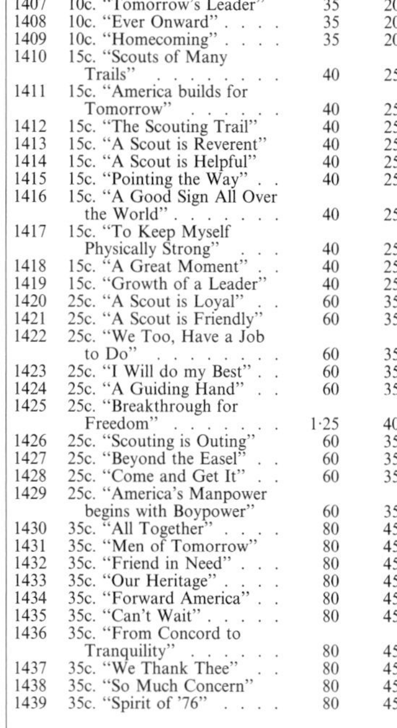
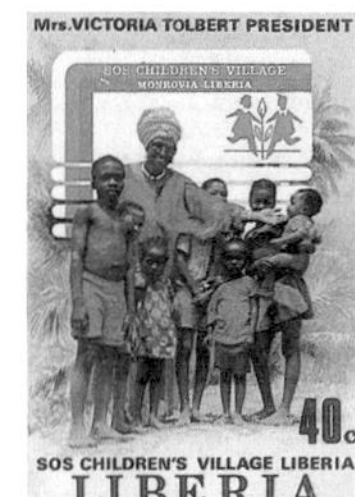

301 Mrs. Tolbert and Children

1979. S.O.S. Children's Village, Monrovia. Multicoloured.
1440 25c. Mrs. Tolbert and children (different) (horiz) 35 50
1441 40c. Type **301** 90 90

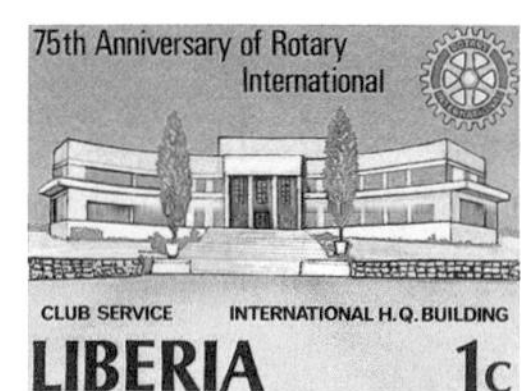

302 International Headquarters, Evanston, Illinois

1979. 75th Anniv of Rotary International. Multicoloured.
1442 1c. Type **302** 10 10
1443 5c. Vocational services . . . 10 10
1444 17c. Wheelchair patient and nurse (community service) (vert) 20 35
1445 27c. Flags (international service) 40 50
1446 35c. Different races holding hands around globe (health, hunger and humanity) 50 50
1447 50c. President Tolbert and map of Africa (17th anniv of Monrovia Rotary Club) (vert) . . . . . . 1·00 1·00

303 Ski Jumping

1980. Winter Olympic Games, Lake Placid. Multicoloured.
1449 1c. Type **303** 10 10
1450 5c. Pairs figure skating . . . 10 10
1451 17c. Bobsleigh 20 35
1452 27c. Cross-country skiing . . 75 75
1453 35c. Speed skating 75 75
1454 50c. Ice hockey . . . . . . 1·00 1·00

304 Presidents Tolbert of Liberia and Stevens of Sierra Leone and View of Mano River

1980. 5th Anniv of Mano River Union and 1st Anniv (1979) of Postal Union.

1456 **304** 8c. multicoloured 15 10
1457 27c. multicoloured . . . 45 50
1458 35c. multicoloured . . . 80 75
1459 80c. multicoloured . . . 1·75 1·75

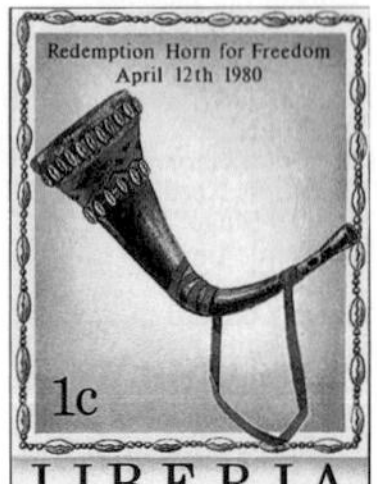

305 Redemption Horn

1981. People's Redemption Council (1st series). Multicoloured.

1460 1c. Type **305** 10 10
1461 10c. M/Sgt. Doe and allegory of redemption (horiz) 10 10
1462 14c. Map, soldier and citizens (horiz) 15 15
1463 $2 M/Sgt. Samuel Doe (chairman of Council) . . 3·75 3·75

See also Nos. 1475/8.

306 Players and Flags of Argentine, Uruguay, Italy and Czechoslovakia

1981. World Cup Football Championship, Spain (1982). Multicoloured.

1464 3c. Type **306** 10 10
1465 5c. Players and flags of Hungary, Italy, Germany, Brazil and Sweden . . . 10 10
1466 20c. Players and flags of Italy, Germany, Brazil and Sweden 20 20
1467 27c. Players and flags of Czechoslovakia, Brazil, Great Britain and Germany 25 25
1468 40c. Players and flags of Italy, Brazil, Germany and Netherlands 60 60
1469 55c. Players and flags of Netherlands and Uruguay 1·10 1·10

307 M/Sgt. Doe and Crowd

1981. 1st Anniv of People's Redemption Council. Multicoloured.

1471 22c. Type **307** 20 20
1472 27c. M/Sgt. Doe and national flag 25 25
1473 30c. Hands clasping arms, sunrise and map 45 45
1474 $1 M/Sgt. Doe, "Justice" and soldiers . . . . . . 1·75 1·75

1981. People's Redemption Council (2nd series).

1475 6c. Type **305** 10 10
1476 23c. As No. 1461 . . . . . 20 20
1477 31c. As No. 1462 . . . . . 45 45
1478 41c. As No. 1463 . . . . . 60 60

308 John Adams

1981. Presidents of the United States (1st series). Multicoloured.

1479 4c. Type **308** 10 10
1480 5c. William Henry Harrison 10 10
1481 10c. Martin Van Buren . . 15 15
1482 17c. James Monroe 20 20
1483 20c. John Quincy Adams . . 25 25
1484 22c. James Madison 25 25
1485 27c. Thomas Jefferson . . . 35 30
1486 30c. Andrew Jackson . . . 55 50
1487 40c. John Tyler 80 70
1488 80c. George Washington . . 1·50 1·50

See also Nos. 1494/1503, 1519/27 and 1533/42.

309 Prince Charles and Lady Diana Spencer

1981. British Royal Wedding. Multicoloured.

1490 31c. Type **309** 30 30
1491 41c. Intertwined initials . . 40 40
1492 62c. St. Paul's Cathedral . . 1·10 1·10

1981. Presidents of the United States (2nd series). As T **308**. Multicoloured.

1494 6c. Rutherford B. Hayes . . 10 10
1495 12c. Ulysses S. Grant . . . 15 15
1496 14c. Millard Fillmore . . . 20 15
1497 15c. Zachary Taylor 20 15
1498 20c. Abraham Lincoln . . . 25 20
1499 27c. Andrew Johnson . . . 30 25
1500 31c. James Buchanan . . . 50 45
1501 41c. James A. Garfield . . . 70 60
1502 50c. James K. Polk 80 70
1503 55c. Franklin Pierce . . . . 1·00 85

1981. Liberian Products (2nd series). As T **277**, but smaller, 33 × 20 mm. Multicoloured.

1504a 1c. Mano River Bridge . . 10 10
1505 3c. Type **277** 10 10
1506 6c. Rubber tree and tyre . . 10 10
1506a 15c. Combine harvester . . 20 15
1507 25c. Mesurado shrimp . . 35 35
1508 31c. Hydro-electric plant . . 70 70
1509 41c. Dress and woman tie-dying cloth 60 55
1509a 80c. Great barracuda . . . 2·50 1·50
1510 $1 Diesel train carrying iron ore . . . . 5·75 1·60

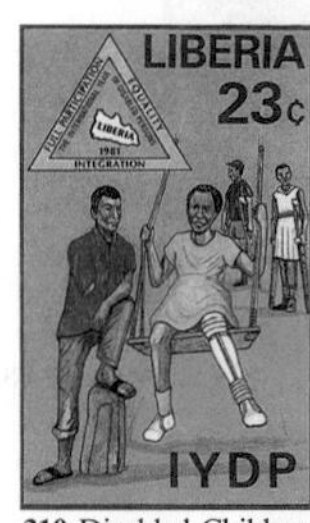

310 Disabled Children

312 Lady Diana Spencer

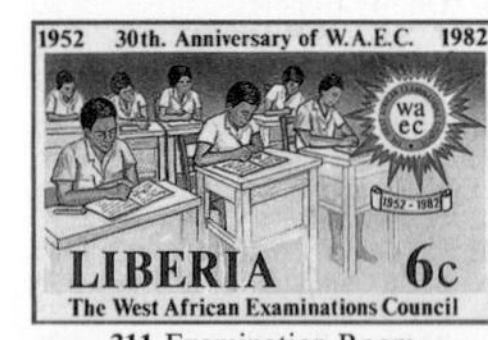

311 Examination Room

1982. International Year of Disabled People (1981). Multicoloured.

1515 23c. Type **310** 35 35
1516 62c. Child leading blind woman . . . . 1·25 95

1982. 30th Anniv of West African Examination Council.

1517 **311** 6c. multicoloured 10 10
1518 31c. multicoloured . . . 45 45

1982. Presidents of the United States (3rd series). As T **308**. Multicoloured.

1519 4c. William Taft 10 25
1520 5c. Calvin Coolidge 10 10
1521 6c. Benjamin Harrison . . . 15 15
1522 10c. Warren Harding . . . 20 25
1523 22c. Grover Cleveland . . . 45 45
1524 27c. Chester Arthur 50 70
1525 31c. Woodrow Wilson . . . 60 60
1526 41c. William McKinley . . 70 80
1527 80c. Theodore Roosevelt . . 1·50 1·60

1982. Princess of Wales. 21st Birthday. Mult.

1529 31c. Type **312** 70 70
1530 41c. Lady Diana Spencer (different) 85 85
1531 62c. Lady Diana accepting flower . . . . 1·25 1·25

1982. Presidents of the United States (4th series). As T **308**. Multicoloured.

1533 4c. Jimmy Carter 10 10
1534 6c. Gerald Ford 15 15
1535 14c. Harry Truman 25 25
1536 17c. Franklin D. Roosevelt 30 30
1537 23c. Lyndon B. Johnson . . 40 40
1538 27c. Richard Nixon 45 50
1539 31c. John F. Kennedy . . . 50 60
1540 35c. Ronald Reagan 60 80
1541 50c. Herbert Hoover 80 90
1542 55c. Dwight D. Eisenhower 1·00 1·00

1982. Birth of Prince William of Wales. Nos. 1529/31 optd **ROYAL BABY 21-6-82 PRINCE WILLIAM**.

1544 31c. Type **312** 45 45
1545 41c. Lady Diana Spencer (different) 60 60
1546 62c. Lady Diana accepting flower 95 95

314 Lt. Col. Fallah nGaida Varney

1983. 3rd Anniv of National Redemption Day. Multicoloured.

1548 3c. Type **314** 10 10
1549 6c. Commander-in-Chief Samuel Doe 10 10
1550 10c. Major-General Jlatoh Nicholas Podier 15 15
1551 15c. Brigadier-General Jeffery Sei Gbatu 20 15
1552 31c. Brigadier-General Thomas Gunkama Quiwonkpa 50 45
1553 41c. Colonel Abraham Doward Kollie 60 80

315 National Archives Centre

1983. Opening of National Archives Centre. Multicoloured.

1555 6c. Type **315** 10 10
1556 31c. National Archives Centre 50 45

316 "Circumcision of Christ"

1983. Christmas. 500th Birth Anniv of Raphael. Multicoloured.

1557 6c. Type **316** 10 10
1558 15c. "Adoration of the Magi" (detail) 20 15
1559 25c. "The Annunciation" (detail) 40 35
1560 31c. "Madonna of the Baldachino" 50 45
1561 41c. "Holy Family" (detail) 60 55
1562 62c. "Madonna and Child with Five Saints" (detail) 90 85

317 Graduates of M.U.R. Training Programmes

1984. 10th Anniv (1983) of Mano River Union. Multicoloured.

1564 6c. Type **317** 10 10
1565 25c. Map of Africa 40 35
1566 31c. Presidents and map of member states 50 45
1567 41c. President of Guinea signing Accession Agreement 70 85

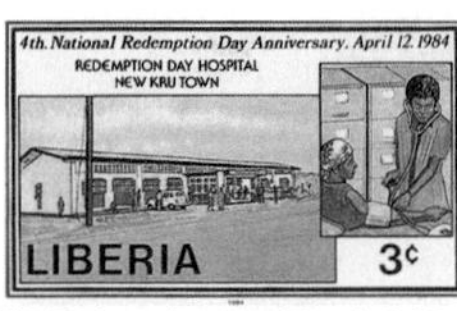

318 Redemption Day Hospital, New Kru Town

1984. 4th Anniv of National Redemption Day. Multicoloured.

1569 3c. Type **318** 10 10
1570 10c. Ganta–Harpa Highway project 15 15
1571 20c. Opening of Constitution Assembly . . 35 30
1572 31c. Commander-in-Chief Doe launching Ganta–Harper Highway project 50 45
1573 41c. Presentation of Draft Constitution 70 85

319 "Adoration of the Magi"

1984. Rubens Paintings (1st series). Multicoloured.

1574 6c. Type **319** 10 10
1575 15c. "Coronation of Catherine" 25 20
1576 25c. "Adoration of the Magi" 70 70
1577 31c. "Madonna and Child with Halo" 85 85
1578 41c. "Adoration of the Shepherds" . . . . 1·10 1·10
1579 62c. "Madonna and Child with Saints" . . . . . . 1·75 1·75

See also Nos. 1612/17.

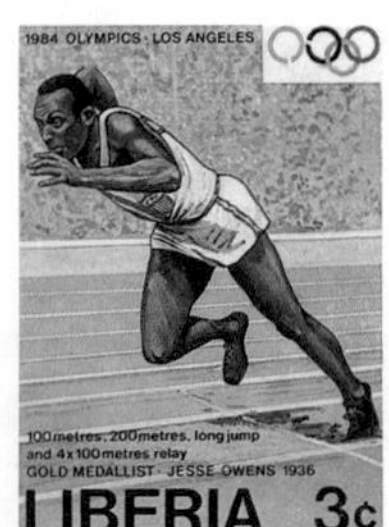

320 Jesse Owens

1984. Olympic Games, Los Angeles. Multicoloured.

1581 3c. Type **320** 10 10
1582 4c. Rafer Johnson 10 10
1583 25c. Miruts Yifter 65 65
1584 41c. Kipchoge Keino . . . 1·10 1·10
1585 62c. Muhammad Ali . . . . 1·75 1·75

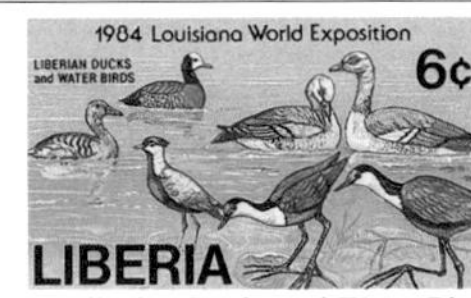

321 Liberian Ducks and Water Birds

1984. Louisiana World Exposition. Multicoloured.
1587 6c. Type **321** 20 20
1588 31c. Bulk carrier loading ore at Buchanan Harbour . . 1·60 75
1589 41c. Peters' mormyrid, electric catfish, Nile perch, krib and jewel cichlid . . 1·50 1·10
1590 62c. Diesel train carrying iron ore . . . . 1·75 90

322 Mother and Calf

1984. Pygmy Hippopotami. Multicoloured.
1591 6c. Type **322** 20 10
1592 10c. Pair of hippopotami . . 80 80
1593 20c. Close-up of hippopotamus . . . . . 1·40 1·40
1594 31c. Hippopotamus and map . . . . 2·10 2·10

323 Mrs. Doe and Children

1984. Indigent Children's Home, Bensonville. Multicoloured.
1595 6c. Type **323** 10 10
1596 31c. Mrs. Doe and children (different) 50 50

324 New Soldiers' Barracks

1985. 5th Anniv of National Redemption Day. Multicoloured.
1597 6c. Type **324** 10 10
1598 31c. Pan-African Plaza . . . 50 50

325 Bohemian Waxwing

1985. Birth Bicentenary of John J. Audubon (ornithologist). Multicoloured.
1599 1c. Type **325** 15 10
1600 3c. Bay-breasted warbler . . 30 10
1601 6c. White-winged crossbill 35 15
1602 31c. Grey phalarope ("Red Phalarope") . . . . . . 2·00 1·00
1603 41c. Eastern bluebird . . . 2·50 1·50
1604 62c. Common cardinal ("Northern Cardinal") . . 3·50 2·40

326 Germany v. Morocco, 1970

1985. World Cup Football Championship, Mexico (1986). Multicoloured.
1605 6c. Type **326** 10 10
1606 15c. Zaire v. Brazil, 1974 . . 20 15
1607 25c. Tunisia v. Germany, 1978 . . . . 60 60
1608 31c. Cameroun v. Peru, 1982 (vert) 75 75
1609 41c. Algeria v. Germany, 1982 . . . . 95 95
1610 62c. Senegal team . . . . . 1·40 1·40

327 "Mirror of Venus" (detail)
328 Women transplanting Rice

1985. Rubens Paintings (2nd series). Mult.
1612 6c. Type **327** 10 10
1613 15c. "Adam and Eve in Paradise" (detail) 20 15
1614 25c. "Andromeda" (detail) 60 60
1615 31c. "The Three Graces" (detail) 75 75
1616 41c. "Venus and Adonis" (detail) 95 95
1617 62c. "The Daughters of Leucippus" (detail) . . . 1·40 1·40

1985. World Food Day.
1619 **328** 25c. multicoloured . . . 1·25 85
1620 31c. multicoloured . . . 1·50 1·10

329 Queen Mother in Garter Robes
330 Alamo, San Antonio, Texas

1985. 85th Birthday of Queen Elizabeth the Queen Mother. Multicoloured.
1621 31c. Type **329** 35 30
1622 41c. At the races 80 75
1623 62c. Waving to the crowds 1·10 1·10

1986. "Ameripex '86" International Stamp Exhibition, Chicago. Multicoloured.
1625 25c. Type **330** 60 60
1626 31c. Liberty Bell, Philadelphia 75 75
1627 80c. Magnifying glass, emblem and Liberian stamps . . . . 3·00 2·25

331 Unveiling Ceremony, 1886 (after E. Moran)
333 Royal Theatre, Gendarmenmarkt

332 Max Julen (Men's Giant Slalom)

1986. Centenary of Statue of Liberty. Multicoloured.
1628 20c. Type **331** 30 50
1629 31c. Frederic-Auguste Bartholdi (sculptor) and statue 75 75
1630 $1 Head of statue . . . . . 2·40 2·40

1987. Winter Olympic Games, Calgary (1988). 1984 Games Gold Medallists. Multicoloured.
1631 3c. Type **332** 10 10
1632 6c. Debbi Armstrong (women's giant slalom) . . 10 10
1633 31c. Peter Angerer (biathlon) 35 55
1634 60c. Bill Johnson (men's downhill) . . . . 1·10 1·10
1635 80c. East German team (four-man bobsleigh) . . 1·40 1·40

1987. Liberian–German Friendship. 750th Anniv of Berlin. Multicoloured.
1637 6c. Type **333** 10 10
1638 31c. Kaiser Friedrich Museum, River Spree . . 35 55
1639 60c. Charlottenburg Palace 1·10 1·10
1640 80c. Kaiser Wilhelm Memorial Church . . . . 1·40 1·40

334 Othello and Desdemona ("Othello")

1987. William Shakespeare. Multicoloured.
1642 3c. Type **334** 10 10
1643 6c. Romeo and Juliet ("Romeo and Juliet") . . 10 10
1644 10c. Falstaff ("The Merry Wives of Windsor") . . . 15 10
1645 15c. Falstaff, Doll Tearsheet and Prince Hal ("Henry IV", Part 2) 20 15
1646 31c. Hamlet holding Yorick's skull ("Hamlet") 60 50
1647 60c. Macbeth and the three witches ("Macbeth") . . . 1·25 1·25
1648 80c. Lear and companions in the storm ("King Lear") . . . . 1·75 1·75
1649 $2 William Shakespeare and Globe Theatre, Southwark 4·00 4·00

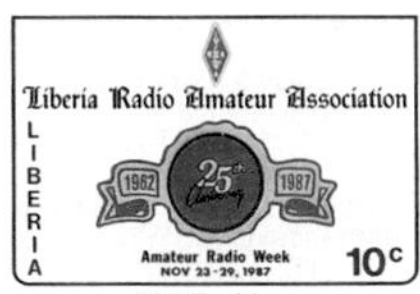

335 Emblem

1987. Amateur Radio Week. 25th Anniv of Liberia Radio Amateur Association. Multicoloured.
1650 10c. Type **335** 15 10
1651 10c. Amateur radio enthusiasts 15 10
1652 35c. Certificate awarded to participants in anniversary "On the Air" activity . . 80 70
1653 35c. Globe, flags and banner 80 70

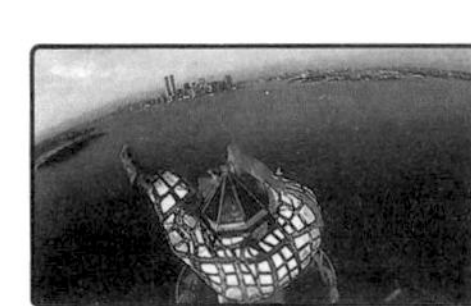

336 Illuminated Torch Flame

1987. Centenary of Statue of Liberty. Multicoloured.
1654 6c. Type **336** 10 10
1655 6c. Scaffolding around statue's head 10 10
1656 6c. Men working on head 10 10
1657 6c. Men working on crown 10 10
1658 6c. Statue's toes 10 10
1659 15c. Statue behind "Sir Winston Churchill" (cadet schooner) 45 20
1660 15c. "Bay Queen" (harbour ferry) 45 20
1661 15c. Posters on buildings and crowd 20 15
1662 15c. Tug and schooner in bay 45 20
1663 15c. Decorated statues around building 20 15
1664 31c. Fireworks display around statue 60 50
1665 31c. Statue floodlit 60 50
1666 31c. Statue's head 60 50
1667 31c. Fireworks display around statue (different) 60 50
1668 31c. Statue (half-length) . . 60 50
1669 60c. Wall poster on building (vert) . . . . 1·10 1·00
1670 60c. Yachts and cabin cruisers on river (vert) . . 1·50 1·00
1671 60c. Measuring statue's nose (vert) . . . . 1·10 1·00
1672 60c. Plastering nose (vert) 1·10 1·00
1673 60c. Finishing off repaired nose (vert) . . . . 1·10 1·00

337 Dr. Doe (President), Dr. Moniba (Vice-President), Flags and Hands

1988. 2nd Anniv of Second Republic.
1674 **337** 10c. multicoloured . . . 15 10
1675 35c. multicoloured . . . 65 55

338 Breast-feeding

1988. UNICEF Child Survival and Development Campaign. Multicoloured.
1676 3c. Type **338** 10 10
1677 6c. Oral rehydration therapy (vert) 10 10
1678 31c. Immunization 60 50
1679 $1 Growth monitoring (vert) 2·00 2·00

339 Chief Justice Emmanuel N. Gbalazeh swearing-in Dr. Samuel Kanyon Doe

1988. Inauguration of Second Republic.
1680 **339** 6c. multicoloured 10 10

340 Footballer and Stadium

1988. 2nd Anniv of Opening of Samuel Kanyon Doe Sports Complex.
1681 **340** 31c. multicoloured . . . 60 50

341 Child and Volunteer reading

1988. 25th Anniv of U.S. Peace Corps in Liberia.
1682 **341** 10c. multicoloured . . . 10 10
1683 35c. multicoloured . . . 70 60

342 Pres. Doe, Farm Workers and Produce

1988. Green Revolution.
1684 **342** 10c. multicoloured . . . 25 10
1685 35c. multicoloured . . . 85 35

344 Emblem
345 Type GP10 Diesel Locomotive, Nimba

1988. 25th Anniv of Organization of African Unity.
1687 **344** 10c. multicoloured 10 10
1688 35c. multicoloured 70 60
1689 $1 multicoloured 2·00 2·00

1988. Locomotives. Multicoloured.
1690 10c. Type **345** 25 15
1691 35c. Triple-headed diesel iron ore train 85 50

346 Helping Boy to Walk

347 Baseball

1988. 25th Anniv of St. Joseph's Catholic Hospital. Multicoloured.
1693 10c. Type **346** 10 10
1694 10c. Medical staff and hospital 10 10
1695 35c. Monk, child, candle and hospital 65 65
1696 $1 Map behind doctor with nurse holding baby 1·90 1·90

1988. Olympic Games, Seoul. Multicoloured.
1697 10c. Type **347** 10 10
1698 35c. Hurdling 65 65
1699 45c. Fencing 80 80
1700 80c. Synchronized swimming 1·40 1·40
1701 $1 Yachting 1·75 1·75

348 Monkey Bridge

349 Tending Crops

1988.
1703 10c. Type **348** 10 10
1704 35c. Sasa players (horiz) 40 60
1705 45c. Snake dancers 70 75

1988. 10th Anniv of International Fund for Agricultural Development. Multicoloured.
1706 10c. Type **349** 10 10
1707 35c. Farmers tending livestock and spraying crops 70 60

350 Destruction of Royal Exchange, 1838

1988. 300th Anniv of Lloyd's of London. Multicoloured.
1708 10c. Type **350** 10 10
1709 35c. Britten Norman Islander airplane (horiz) 60 60
1710 45c. "Chevron Antwerp" (tanker) (horiz) 70 75
1711 $1 "Lakonia" (liner) ablaze, 1963 2·00 2·00

351 Honouring Head of Operational Smile Team

1989. 3rd Anniv of Second Republic.
1712 **351** 10c. black and blue 10 10
1713 35c. black and red 80 85
1714 – 50c. black and mauve 1·25 1·25
DESIGN: 50c. Pres. Samuel Doe at John F. Kennedy Memorial Hospital.

1989. Presidents of United States (5th series). As T **308**. Multicoloured.
1715 $1 George Bush 2·50 2·50

352 "Harmony"

353 Union Glass Factory, Gardersville, Monrovia

1989. Liberia–Japan Friendship. 50th Anniv of Rissho Kosei-Kai (lay Buddhist association). Multicoloured.
1716 10c. Type **352** 10 10
1717 10c. Nikkyo Niwano (founder and president of association) 10 10
1718 10c. Rissho Kosei-Kai headquarters, Tokyo 10 10
1719 50c. Eternal Buddha, Great Sacred Hall 1·40 1·40

1989. 15th Anniv of Mano River Union. Mult.
1721 10c. Type **353** 15 10
1722 35c. Presidents of Guinea, Sierra Leone and Liberia 70 60
1723 45c. Monrovia–Freetown highway 85 80
1724 50c. Flags, map and mail van 85 85
1725 $1 Presidents at 1988 Summit 2·00 1·90

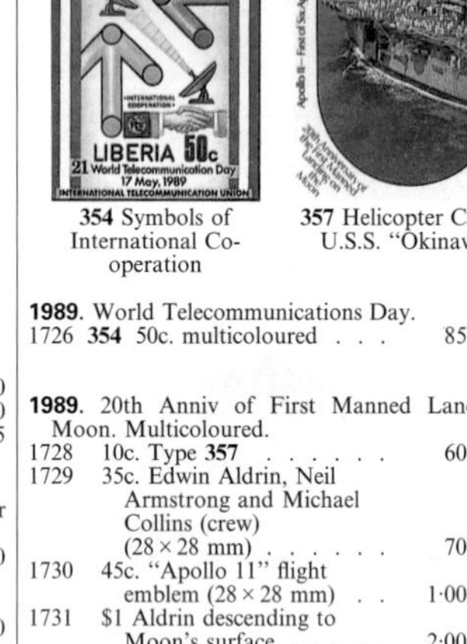

354 Symbols of International Co-operation

357 Helicopter Carrier U.S.S. "Okinawa"

1989. World Telecommunications Day.
1726 **354** 50c. multicoloured 85 85

1989. 20th Anniv of First Manned Landing on Moon. Multicoloured.
1728 10c. Type **357** 60 15
1729 35c. Edwin Aldrin, Neil Armstrong and Michael Collins (crew) (28 × 28 mm) 70 60
1730 45c. "Apollo 11" flight emblem (28 × 28 mm) 1·00 1·00
1731 $1 Aldrin descending to Moon's surface 2·00 2·00

358 Renovation of Statue of Liberty

360 Nehru and Flag

1989. "Philexfrance '89" International Stamp Exhibition, Paris, and "World Stamp Expo '89" International Stamp Exhibition, Washington D.C. Multicoloured.
1733 25c. Type **358** 55 45
1734 25c. French contingent at statue centenary celebrations 55 45
1735 25c. Statue, officials and commemorative plaque 55 45

1989. Birth Centenary of Jawaharlal Nehru (Indian statesman). Multicoloured.
1737 45c. Type **360** 85 70
1738 50c. Nehru 95 80

361 Close View of Station

1990. New Standard A Earth Satellite Station. Multicoloured.
1739 10c. Type **361** 15 10
1740 35c. Distant view of station 85 85

362 Emblem

1990. 25th Anniv of United States Educational and Cultural Foundation in Liberia. Multicoloured.
1741 10c. Type **362** 15 10
1742 45c. Similar to Type **362** but differently arranged 85 70

363 Flags, Arms, Map and Union Emblem

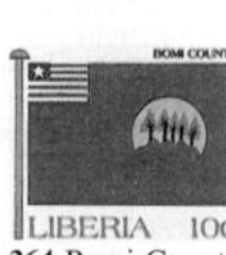

364 Bomi County

1990. 10th Anniv of Pan-African Postal Union.
1743 **363** 35c. multicoloured 70 55

1990. County Flags. Multicoloured.
1744 10c. Type **364** 10 10
1745 10c. Bong 10 10
1746 10c. Grand Bassa 10 10
1747 10c. Grand Cape Mount 10 10
1748 10c. Grand Gedeh 10 10
1749 10c. Grand Kru 10 10
1750 10c. Lofa 10 10
1751 10c. Margibi 10 10
1752 10c. Maryland 10 10
1753 10c. Montserrado 10 10
1754 10c. Nimba 10 10
1755 10c. Rivercess 10 10
1756 10c. Sinoe 10 10
1757 35c. Type **364** 65 55
1758 35c. Bong 65 55
1759 35c. Grand Bassa 65 55
1760 35c. Grand Cape Mount 65 55
1761 35c. Grand Gedeh 65 55
1762 35c. Grand Kru 65 55
1763 35c. Lofa 65 55
1764 35c. Margibi 65 55
1765 35c. Maryland 65 55
1766 35c. Montserrado 65 55
1767 35c. Nimba 65 55
1768 35c. Rivercess 65 55
1769 35c. Sinoe 65 55
1770 45c. Type **364** 85 70
1771 45c. Bong 85 70
1772 45c. Grand Bassa 85 70
1773 45c. Grand Cape Mount 85 70
1774 45c. Grand Gedeh 85 70
1775 45c. Grand Kru 85 70
1776 45c. Lofa 85 70
1777 45c. Margibi 85 70
1778 45c. Maryland 85 70
1779 45c. Montserrado 85 70
1780 45c. Nimba 85 70
1781 45c. Rivercess 85 70
1782 45c. Sinoe 85 70
1783 50c. Type **364** 1·10 1·10
1784 50c. Bong 1·10 1·10
1785 50c. Grand Bassa 1·10 1·10
1786 50c. Grand Cape Mount 1·10 1·10
1787 50c. Grand Gedeh 1·10 1·10
1788 50c. Grand Kru 1·10 1·10
1789 50c. Lofa 1·10 1·10
1790 50c. Margibi 1·10 1·10
1791 50c. Maryland 1·10 1·10
1792 50c. Montserrado 1·10 1·10
1793 50c. Nimba 1·10 1·10
1794 50c. Rivercess 1·10 1·10
1795 50c. Sinoe 1·10 1·10
1796 $1 Type **364** 2·00 2·00
1797 $1 Bong 2·00 2·00
1798 $1 Grand Bassa 2·00 2·00
1799 $1 Grand Cape Mount 2·00 2·00
1800 $1 Grand Gedeh 2·00 2·00
1801 $1 Grand Kru 2·00 2·00
1802 $1 Lofa 2·00 2·00
1803 $1 Margibi 2·00 2·00
1804 $1 Maryland 2·00 2·00
1805 $1 Montserrado 2·00 2·00
1806 $1 Nimba 2·00 2·00
1807 $1 Rivercess 2·00 2·00
1808 $1 Sinoe 2·00 2·00

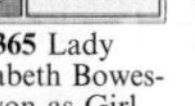

365 Lady Elizabeth Bowes-Lyon as Girl

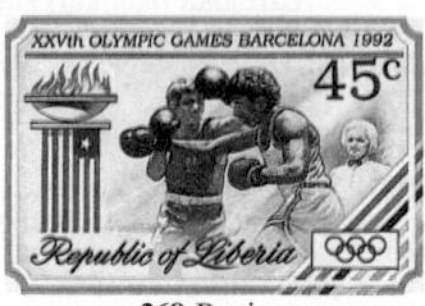

368 Boxing

367 Clasped Hands and Map

1991. 90th Birthday (1990) of Queen Elizabeth the Queen Mother. Multicoloured.
1809 10c. Type **365** 15 10
1810 $2 As Duchess of York (29 × 36½ mm) 4·00 4·00

1991. National Unity. Multicoloured.
1812 35c. Type **367** 65 50
1813 45c. National flag and map of Africa (ECOMOG (West African States Economic Community peace-keeping forces)) 85 65
1814 50c. Brewer, Konneh and Michael Francis (co-chairmen) and national flag (All-Liberia Conference) 95 75

1992. Olympic Games, Barcelona. Multicoloured.
1815 45c. Type **368** 85 65
1816 50c. Football 95 75
1817 $1 Weightlifting 1·90 1·75
1818 $2 Water polo 3·75 3·50

369 "Disarm Today"

1993. Peace and Redevelopment. Multicoloured.
1820 50c. Type **369** 95 70
1821 $1 "Join your Parents and build Liberia" 1·90 1·40
1822 $2 "Peace must prevail in Liberia" 3·75 2·75

OFFICIAL STAMPS

1892. Stamps of 1892 optd **OFFICIAL**.
O 87 **7** 1c. red 30 40
O 88 2c. blue 30 50
O 89 **8** 4c. black and green 50 50
O104 **9** 5c. on 6c. green (No. 89) 80 80
O 90 6c. green 60 50
O 91 **10** 8c. black and brown 45 45
O 92 **11** 12c. red 1·10 1·10
O 93 **12** 16c. lilac 1·10 1·10
O 94 **13** 24c. green on yellow 1·10 1·10
O 95 **12** 32c. blue 1·10 1·10
O 96 **15** $1 black and blue 22·00 8·75
O 97 **13** $2 brown on buff 9·00 6·25
O 98 **17** $5 black and red 13·50 5·75

1894. Stamps of 1892 optd **O S**.
O119 **7** 1c. red 30 20
O120 2c. blue 60 25
O121 **8** 4c. black and green 95 35
O122 **10** 8c. black and brown 80 35
O123 **11** 12c. red 1·10 40
O124 **12** 16c. lilac 1·10 40
O125 **13** 24c. green on yellow 1·10 45
O126 **12** 32c. blue 1·60 55
O127 $1 black and blue 13·50 13·50
O128 $2 brown on buff 13·50 13·50
O129 $5 black and red 80·00 55·00

1894. Stamp of 1894 in different colours optd **O S**. Imperf or roul.
O130 **24** 5c. green and lilac 1·75 2·00

1898. Stamps of 1897 optd **O S**.
O157 **9** 1c. purple 35 35
O158 1c. green 35 35
O159 **15** 2c. black and bistre 1·00 30
O160 2c. black and red 1·50 70
O161 **8** 5c. black and lake 1·50 70
O162 5c. black and blue 1·90 70
O163 **10** 10c. blue and yellow 85 80
O164 **11** 15c. black 85 80
O165 **12** 20c. red 1·40 95
O166 **13** 25c. green 85 80
O167 **12** 30c. blue 2·40 1·40
O168 **35** 50c. black and brown 2·10 1·40

1903†. Stamp of 1903, but different colour, optd **O S**.
O210 **40** 3c. green 20 15

1904. Nos. O104 and 167 surch **ONE O.S.** and bars or **OS 2** and bars.
O222 **9** 1c. on 5c. on 6c. green 1·10 1·10
O223 **12** 2c. on 30c. blue 7·75 7·50

1906†. Stamps of 1906, but different colours, optd **OS**.
O237 **50** 1c. black and green 50 50
O238 **51** 2c. black and red 15 15
O239 – 5c. black and blue 55 35
O240 – 10c. black and violet 2·50 60
O241 – 15c. black and brown 2·00 40
O242 – 20c. black and green 2·50 50
O243 – 25c. grey and purple 30 15
O244 – 30c. brown 50 15

O245 – 50c. green and brown 50 20
O246 – 75c. black and blue 1·10 75
O247 – $1 black and green 55 25
O248 **52** $2 black and purple 1·50 25
O249 **53** $5 black and orange 3·75 30

1909†. Stamps of 1909, but different colours, optd **OS**. 10c. perf or roul.
O262 **55** 1c. black and green 15 10
O263 – 2c. brown and red 15 10
O264 **56** 5c. black and blue 1·00 15
O266 **57** 10c. blue and black 50 25
O267 – 15c. black and purple 50 25
O268 – 20c. green and bistre 75 45
O269 – 25c. green and blue 70 50
O270 – 30c. blue 60 40
O271 – 50c. green and brown 2·25 40
O272 – 75c. black and violet 1·10 40

1910. No. O266 surch **3 CENTS INLAND POSTAGE**. Perf or roul.
O276 **57** 3c. on 10c. blue and black 55 45

1914. Official stamps surch: (A) **1914 2 CENTS**. (B) **+2c**. (C) **5**. (D) **CENTS 20 OFFICIAL**.
O291 **57** +2c. on 3c. on 10c. blue and black (B) (No. O275) 60 1·60
O284 – 2c. on 25c. grey and purple (A) (No. O243) 15·00 6·25
O285 – 5c. on 30c. blue (C) (No. O270) 5·25 3·00
O286 – 20c. on 75c. black and violet (D) (No. O272) 7·00 3·00

1914. No. 233 surch **CENTS 20 OFFICIAL**.
O287 20c. on 75c. black and brown 5·25 3·00

1915. Official stamps of 1906 and 1909 surch in different ways.
O325 – 1c. on 2c. brown and red (No. O263) 2·25 2·50
O326 **56** 2c. on 5c. black and blue (No. O264) 2·50 3·00
O310 – 2c. on 15c. black and purple (No. O267) 65 45
O311 – 2c. on 25c. green and blue (No. O269) 3·75 3·75
O312 – 5c. on 20c. green and bistre (No. O268) 65 50
O313 – 5c. on 30c. green and brown (No. O270) 5·75 5·75
O314 – 10c. on 50c. green and brown (No. O271) 6·50 7·50
O316 – 20c. on 75c. black and violet (No. O272) 2·00 2·00
O317 – 25c. on $1 black and green (No. O247) 13·50 13·50
O318 **52** 50c. on $2 black and purple (No. O248) 15·00 15·00
O320 **53** $1 on $5 black and orange (No. O249) 15·00 15·00

1915. No. O168 surch **10 10** and ornaments and bars.
O321 **35** 10c. on 50c. black & brn 9·75 9·75

1915. Military Field Post. Official stamps surch **L E F 1 c.**
O336 **50** 1c. on 1c. black and green (No. O237) £325 £325
O337 **55** 1c. on 1c. black and green (No. O262) 3·00 3·50
O338 – 1c. on 2c. brown and red (No. O263) 2·40 2·50

1917. No. O244 surch **FIVE CENTS 1917** and bars.
O344 5c. on 30c. brown 15·00 15·00

1918. No. O266 surch **3 CENTS**.
O348 **57** 3c. on 10c. blue and black 1·40 1·50

1918†. Stamps of 1918, but in different colours, optd **O S**.
O362 **91** 1c. brown and green 50 15
O363 **92** 2c. black and red 50 15
O364 – 5c. black and blue 75 10
O365 **93** 10c. blue 35 10
O366 – 15c. green and brown 1·75 40
O367 – 20c. black and lilac 55 10
O368 **94** 25c. green and brown 3·25 45
O369 – 30c. black and violet 4·75 50
O370 – 50c. black and brown 5·00 50
O371 – 75c. black and brown 2·00 15
O372 – $1 blue and olive 3·75 30
O373 – $2 black and olive 6·25 20
O374 – $5 green 8·25 20

1920. Nos. O362/3 surch **1920** and value and two bars.
O400 **91** 3c. on 1c. brown & green 95 50
O401 **92** 4c. on 2c. black and red 60 50

1921†. Stamps of 1915 and 1921, in different colours, optd **O S** or **OFFICIAL**.
O428 **100** 1c. green 70 10
O429 **64** 2c. red 4·50 10
O430 **65** 3c. brown 70 10
O431 **101** 5c. brown and blue 70 10
O432 – 10c. black and purple 35 15
O433 – 15c. green and black 2·75 50
O434 – 20c. blue and brown 1·10 25
O435 – 25c. green and orange 3·75 50
O436 – 30c. red and brown 75 15
O437 – 50c. green and black 75 25
O438 – 75c. purple and blue 1·90 25
O439 – $1 black and blue 12·50 55
O440 – $2 green and orange 16·00 1·00
O441 – $5 blue and green 17·00 1·75

1921†. Nos. O400/41 optd **1921**.
O442 **100** 1c. green 4·00 20
O443 **64** 2c. red 4·00 20
O444 **65** 3c. brown 4·00 25
O445 **101** 5c. brown and blue 2·40 25
O446 – 10c. black and purple 4·00 25
O447 – 15c. green and black 4·25 15
O448 – 20c. blue and brown 4·25 35
O449 – 25c. green and orange 5·00 40
O450 – 30c. red and brown 4·00 30
O451 – 50c. green and black 4·75 15
O452 – 75c. purple and blue 2·75 15
O453 – $1 black and blue 8·75 1·10
O454 – $2 green and orange 15·00 1·75
O455 – $5 blue and green 16·00 3·00

1923†. Stamps of 1923, but different colours, optd **O S**.
O485 **108** 1c. black and green 5·25 10
O486 **109** 2c. brown and red 5·25 10
O487 – 3c. black and blue 5·25 10
O488 – 5c. green and orange 5·25 10
O489 – 10c. purple and olive 5·25 10
O490 – 15c. blue and green 75 40
O491 – 20c. blue and lilac 75 40
O492 – 25c. brown 16·00 40
O493 – 30c. brown and blue 70 20
O494 – 50c. brown and bistre 70 30
O495 – 75c. green and grey 70 25
O496 **110** $1 green and red 1·50 40
O497 – $2 red and purple 2·00 50
O498 – $5 brown and blue 3·75 50

1926. No. O362 surch **Two Cents** and either thick bar, wavy lines, ornamental scroll or two bars.
O506 **91** 2c. on 1c. brown & green 90 80

1928. Stamps of 1928 optd **OFFICIAL SERVICE**.
O518 **116** 1c. green 70 35
O519 2c. violet 1·40 50
O520 3c. brown 1·40 15
O521 **117** 5c. blue 80 15
O522 **118** 10c. grey 2·40 1·00
O523 **117** 15c. lilac 1·40 60
O524 $1 brown 40·00 16·00

1944. No. O522 surch.
O649 **118** 4c. on 10c. grey 8·00 8·00

POSTAGE DUE STAMPS

1892. Stamps of 1886 surch **POSTAGE DUE** and value in frame.
D 99 **4** 3c. on 3c. mauve 1·25 1·25
D100 6c. on 6c. grey 6·25 6·25

D 23

1894.
D110 **D 23** 2c. black and orange on yellow 95 55
D111 4c. black & red on rose 95 55
D112 6c. black & brn on buff 95 75
D113 8c. black & blue on bl 1·00 75
D114 10c. black and green on mauve 1·25 95
D115 20c. black and violet on grey 1·25 95
D116 40c. black and brown on green 2·50 1·75

REGISTRATION STAMPS

R 22

1893.
R105 **R 22** (10c.) black (Buchanan) £275 £350
R106 (10c.) blk ("Grenville") £1000 £1250
R107 (10c.) black (Harper) £1000 £1250
R108 (10c.) black (Monrovia) 40·00 £175
R109 (10c.) blk (Robertsport) £500 £575

1894. Surch **10 CENTS 10** twice.
R140 **R 22** 10c. blue on pink (Buchanan) 3·75 3·75
R141 10c. green on buff (Harper) 3·75 3·75
R142 10c. red on yellow (Monrovia) 3·75 3·75
R143 10c. red on blue (Robertsport) 3·75 3·75

R 42 Pres. Gibson

1904†.
R211 **R 42** 10c. black and blue (Buchanan) 1·50 25
R212 10c. black and red ("Grenville") 1·50 25
R213 10c. black and green (Harper) 1·50 25
R214 10c. black and violet (Monrovia) 1·50 25
R215 10c. black and purple (Robertsport) 1·50 25

R 96 Patrol Boat "Quail"

1919. Roul or perf.
R388 **R 96** 10c. blue and black (Buchanan) 90 5·75
R389 10c. black and brown ("Grenville") 90 7·50
R390 10c. black and green (Harper) 90 5·25
R391 10c. blue and violet (Monrovia) 90 5·75
R392 10c. black and red (Robertsport) 90 7·50

R 106 Gabon Viper

1921†.
R456 **R 106** 10c. black and red (Buchanan) 23·00 2·50
R457 10c. black and red (Greenville) 14·00 2·50
R458 10c. black and blue (Harper) 18·00 2·50
R459 10c. black and orange (Monrovia) 14·00 2·50
R460 10c. black and green (Robertsport) 14·00 2·50

1921†. Optd **1921**.
R461 **R 106** 10c. black and lake 20·00 4·25
R462 10c. black and red 20·00 4·25
R463 10c. black and blue 20·00 4·25
R464 10c. black and orange 20·00 4·25
R465 10c. black and green 20·00 4·25

R 111 Sailing Skiff (Buchanan)

1923†. Various sea views.
R499 **R 111** 10c. red and black 8·50 55
R500 – 10c. green and black 8·50 55
R501 – 10c. orange and black 8·50 55
R502 – 10c. blue and black 8·50 55
R503 – 10c. violet and black 8·50 55
DESIGNS: No. R500, Lighter (Greenville); R501, Full-rigged sailing ship (Harper); R502, "George Washington" (liner) (Monrovia); R503, Canoe (Robertsport).

1941. No. 576 surch **REGISTERED 10 CENTS 10**.
R592 10c. on 5c. brown (postage) 1·40 1·40
R593 10c. on 5c. brown (air) 1·40 1·40
No. R593 is additionally optd with airplane and **AIR MAIL**.

SPECIAL DELIVERY STAMPS

1941. No. 576 surch with postman and **SPECIAL DELIVERY 10 CENTS 10**.
S590 10c. on 5c. brown (postage) 1·40 1·40
S591 10c. on 5c. brown (air) 1·40 1·40
No. S591 is additionally optd with airplane and **AIR MAIL**.

LIBYA Pt. 8; Pt. 13

A former Italian colony in N. Africa, comprising the governorates of Cyrenaica and Tripolitania. From the end of 1951 an independent kingdom including the Fezzan also. Following a revolution in 1969 the country became the Libyan Arab Republic.

1912. 100 centesimi = 1 lira.
1952. 1000 milliemes = 1 Libyan pound.
1972. 1000 dirhams = 1 dinar.

A. ITALIAN COLONY

1912. Stamps of Italy optd **LIBIA** (No. 5) or **Libia** (others).
1 **30** 1c. brown 85 85
2 **31** 2c. brown 85 50
3 **37** 5c. green 85 35
4 10c. red 85 35
5 **41** 15c. grey £100 1·70
6 **37** 15c. grey 3·50 3·50
7 **33** 20c. orange 2·40 35
8 **41** 20c. orange 2·75 3·50
9 **39** 25c. blue 2·75 35
10 40c. brown 5·25 1·00
11 **33** 45c. green 22·00 17·00
12 **39** 50c. violet 17·00 1·40
13 60c. red 12·00 13·50
14 **34** 1l. brown and green 50·00 1·70
15 5l. blue and red £275 £200
16 10l. green and pink 24·00 80·00

1915. Red Cross stamps of Italy optd **LIBIA**.
17 **53** 10c.+5c. red 2·10 8·50
18 **54** 15c.+5c. grey 11·00 19·00
19 20c. on 15c.+5c. grey 11·00 19·00
20 20c.+5c. orange 3·50 19·00

1916. No. 100 of Italy optd **LIBIA**.
21 **41** 20c. on 15c. grey 27·00 5·25

4 Roman Legionary

5 Goddess of Plenty

6 Roman Galley leaving Tripoli

7 Victory

1921.
22A **4** 1c. brown and black 35 2·50
23A 2c. brown and black 35 2·50
24A 5c. green and black 50 45
50 7½c. brown and black 35 4·00
51 **5** 10c. pink and black 35 25
52 15c. orange and brown 4·25 1·00
27A 25c. blue and deep blue 50 15
54 **6** 30c. brown and black 25 50
55 50c. green and black 25 50
30A 55c. violet and black 3·50 7·50
57 **7** 75c. red and purple 1·90 10
58 1l. brown 6·00 35
59 **6** 1l.25 blue and indigo 25 10
32A **7** 5l. blue and black 21·00 13·50
33A 10l. green and blue £150 75·00

1922. Victory stamps of Italy optd **LIBIA**.
34 **62** 5c. green 1·20 5·25
35 10c. red 1·20 5·25
36 15c. grey 1·20 6·75
37 25c. blue 1·20 6·75

1922. Nos. 9 and 12 of Libya surch.
38 **39** 40c. on 50c. mauve 2·20 1·70
39 80c. on 25c. blue 2·20 5·25

9 "Libyan Sibyl" by Michelangelo

10 Bedouin Woman

1924.
41 **9** 20c. green 70 10
42 40c. brown 1·70 50
43 60c. blue 70 10
44 1l.75 orange 25 10

45 2l. red 2·10 85
46 2l.55 violet 4·00 5·75

1928. Air. Air stamps of Italy optd **Libia**.
63 **88** 50c. pink 6·75 8·50
64 80c. brown and purple 21·00 33·00

1928. Types of Italy optd **LIBIA** (No. 67) or Libia (others).
65 **92** 7½c. brown 5·25 26·00
66 **34** 1l.25 blue 38·00 13·50
67 **91** 1l.75 brown 43·00 1·70

1936. 10th Tripoli Trade Fair.
68 **10** 50c. violet 1·20 2·40
69 1l.25 blue 1·40 6·25

1936. Air. Nos. 96 and 99 of Cyrenaica optd **LIBIA**.
70 – 50c. violet 1·70 35
71 **17** 1l. black 3·50 17·00

1937. Air. Stamps of Tripolitania optd **LIBIA**.
72 **18** 50c. red 10 10
73 60c. red 60
74 75c. blue 60 17·00
75 80c. purple 60 31·00
76 **19** 1l. blue 1·50 85
77 1l.20 brown 60 38·00
78 1l.50 orange 60
79 5l. green 60

11 Triumphal Arch
12 Roman Theatre, Sabrata

1937. Inauguration of Coastal Highway.
80 **11** 50c. red (postage) 2·20 3·50
81 1l.25 blue 2·20 7·75
82 **12** 50c. purple (air) 2·20 4·25
83 1l. black 2·20 4·25

1937. 11th Tripoli Trade Fair. Optd **XI FIERA DI TRIPOLI.**
84 **11** 50c. red (postage) 10·50 24·00
85 1l.25 blue 10·50 24·00
86 **12** 50c. purple (air) 10·50 24·00
87 1l. black 10·50 24·00

14 Benghazi Waterfront

1938. 12th Tripoli Trade Fair.
88 **14** 5c. brown (postage) 10 1·00
89 – 10c. brown 10 70
90 **14** 25c. green 45 1·20
91 – 50c. violet 50 50
92 **14** 75c. red 85 1·70
93 – 1l.25 blue 95 3·50
DESIGN: 10c., 50c., 1l.25, Fair Buildings.
94 50c. brown (air) 1·00 1·90
95 1l. blue 1·00 4·00
DESIGN—VERT: View of Tripoli.

16 Statue of Augustus
17 Eagle and Serpent

1938. Birth Bimillenary of Augustus the Great.
96 **16** 5c. green (postage) 10 1·00
97 – 10c. red 10 1·00
98 **16** 25c. green 50 60
99 – 50c. mauve 50 45
100 **16** 75c. red 1·50 3·25
101 – 1l.25 blue 1·50 2·20
102 **17** 50c. brown (air) 35 1·40
103 1l. mauve 50 3·00
DESIGN: 10, 50c., 1l.25, Statue of Goddess of Plenty.

18 Agricultural Landscape

1939. 13th Tripoli Trade Fair. Inscr "XIII FIERA CAMPIONARIA DE TRIPOLI" etc.
104 **18** 5c. green (postage) 25 85
105 – 20c. red 50 85
106 **18** 50c. mauve 55 85
107 – 75c. red 55 1·70
108 **18** 1l.25 blue 55 2·50
DESIGN: 20, 75c. View of Ghadames.
109 – 25c. green (air) 25 1·30
110 – 50c. green 35 1·30
111 – 1l. mauve 45 1·70
DESIGNS—Fiat G18V airplane over: 25c., 1l. Arab and camel in desert; 50c. Fair entrance.

19 Buildings

1940. Naples Exhibition.
112 **19** 5c. brown (postage) 1·50 1·00
113 – 10c. orange 1·00 70
114 – 25c. green 60 1·00
115 **19** 50c. violet 60 70
116 – 75c. red 70 2·20
117 – 1l.25 blue 85 3·75
118 – 2l.+75c. red 85 13·00
DESIGNS—HORIZ: 10, 75c., 2l. Oxen and plough. VERT: 25c., 1l.25, Mosque.
119 – 50c. black (air) 50 85
120 – 1l. brown 50 1·70
121 – 2l.+75c. blue 85 5·25
122 – 5l.+2l.50 brown 85 7·75
DESIGNS—HORIZ: 50c., 2l. Savoia Marchetti S.M.75 airplane over city; 1, 5l. Savoia Marchetti S-73 airplane over oasis.

19a Hitler and Mussolini

1941. Rome–Berlin Axis Commemoration.
123 **19a** 5c. orange (postage) 10 2·75
124 10c. brown 10 2·75
125 20c. purple 85 2·75
126 25c. green 85 2·75
127 50c. violet 85 2·75
128 75c. red 85 8·50
129 1l.25 blue 85 8·50
130 50c. green (air) 85 12·00

B. INDEPENDENT

LIBYA (20)
4 MAL. LIBYA (21)
8 FRANCS LIBYA (22)

1951. Stamps of Cyrenaica optd. (a) For use in Cyrenaica, optd as T **20**.
131 **24** 1m. brown 15 15
132 2m. red 20 20
133 3m. yellow 25 25
134 4m. green 28·00 19·00
135 5m. brown 35 35
136 8m. orange 40 40
137 10m. violet 60 60
138 12m. red 1·10 1·10
139 20m. blue 1·50 1·50
140 **25** 50m. blue and brown 8·75 8·75
141 100m. red and black 14·50 14·50
142 200m. violet and blue 45·00 40·00
143 500m. yellow and green £150 £130

(b) For use in Tripolitania. Surch as T **21** in Military Authority lire.
151 **24** 1mal. on 2m. red 25 25
152 2mal. on 4m. green 25 25
153 4mal. on 8m. orange 25 25
154 5mal. on 10m. violet 35 35
155 6mal. on 12m. red 35 35
156 10mal. on 20m. blue 65 65
157 **25** 24 mal. on 50m. blue and brown 3·00 3·00
158 48mal. on 100m. red 11·00 11·00
159 96mal. on 200m. violet and blue 27·00 27·00
160 240mal. on 500m. yellow and green 70·00 70·00

(c) For use in Fezzan. Surch as T **22**.
166 **24** 2f. on 2m. red 20 20
167 4f. on 4m. green 30 30
168 8f. on 8m. orange 35 40
169 10f. on 10m. violet 50 50
170 12f. on 12m. red 75 75
171 20f. on 20m. blue 2·00 2·00
172 **25** 48f. on 50m. blue & brown 38·00 35·00
173 96f. on 100m. red and black 40·00 35·00
174 192f. on 200m. violet and blue £110 80·00
175 480f. on 500m. yellow and green £190 £190

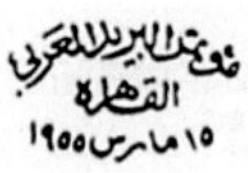

23 King Idris
(28)
30

1952.
176 **23** 2m. brown 10 10
177 4m. grey 10 10
178 5m. green 12·50 35
179 8m. red 40 25
180 10m. violet 12·50 15
181 12m. red 75 15
182 20m. blue 13·50 45
183 25m. brown 13·50 45
184 – 50m. blue and brown 1·75 65
185 – 100m. red and black 3·75 1·90
186 – 200m. violet and blue 6·00 3·50
187 – 500m. orange and green 25·00 17·00
Nos. 184/7 are larger.

1955. Arab Postal Union. As T **84a** of Lebanon but inscr "LIBYE" at top.
200 5m. brown 1·25 60
201 10m. green 1·90 90
202 30m. violet 4·25 2·00

1955. 2nd Arab Postal Congress, Cairo. Nos. 200/2 optd with T **28**.
203 5m. brown 40 30
204 10m. green 95 50
205 30m. violet 2·25 1·25

1955. No. 177 surch.
206 **23** 5m. on 4m. grey 1·25 45

1955.
207 **30** 1m. black on yellow 10 10
208 2m. bistre 1·40 50
209 2m. brown 10 10
210 3m. blue 10 10
211 4m. black 1·50 50
212 4m. lake 20 15
213 5m. green 40 20
214 10m. lilac 65 25
215 18m. red 15 10
216 20m. orange 25 15
217 30m. blue 50 20
218 35m. brown 65 25
219 40m. lake 1·10 40
220 50m. olive 85 25
221 – 100m. purple and slate 1·75 50
222 – 200m. lake and blue 9·25 1·40
223 – 500m. orange and green 15·00 7·25
224 – £L1 green, brown and sepia on yellow 21·00 11·50
Nos. 221/4 are larger, 27 × 32 mm.
See also Nos. 242/57.

33 Immam's Tomb at Djaghboub

1956. Death Centenary of Imam Essayed Mohamed Aly el Senussi.
225 **33** 5m. green 20 20
226 10m. lilac 35 20
227 15m. red 95 75
228 30m. blue 1·60 1·25

34 Map of Libya
35

1956. 1st Anniv of Admission to U.N.
229 **34** 15m. buff and blue 30 15
230 35m. buff, purple and blue 1·00 30

1957. Arab Postal Congress, Tripoli.
231 **35** 15m. blue 1·75 90
232 500m. brown 12·50 6·50

36
39

37 F.A.O. Emblem and Date Palms

1958. 10th Anniv of Declaration of Human Rights.
233 **36** 10m. violet 20 15
234 15m. green 25 20
235 30m. blue 95 50

1959. 1st Int Dates Conf, Tripoli.
236 **37** 10m. black and violet 20 15
237 15m. black and green 50 20
238 45m. black and blue 1·00 50

1960. Inauguration of Arab League Centre, Cairo. As T **110** of Lebanon, but with Arms of Libya and inscr "LIBYA".
239 10m. black and green 50 20

1960. World Refugee Year.
240 **39** 10m. black and violet 25 15
241 45m. black and blue 1·25 75

1960. As Nos. 207 etc. On coloured paper.
242 **30** 1m. black on grey 10 10
243 2m. brown on buff 10 10
244 3m. indigo on blue 10 10
245 4m. lake on red 10 10
246 5m. green on green 10 10
247 10m. lilac on violet 10 10
248 15m. sepia on buff 10 10
249 20m. orange on orange 20 10
250 30m. red on pink 20 15
251 40m. lake on red 30 20
252 45m. blue on blue 35 20
253 50m. olive on bistre 35 20
254 – 100m. purple & slate on blue 1·25 35
255 – 200m. lake and blue on blue 3·25 1·40
256 – 500m. orange and green on green 23·00 5·50
257 – £L1 green, brown and sepia 23·00 11·00

40 Palm Tree and Radio Mast
41 Military Watchtower (medallion)

1960. 3rd Arab Telecommunications Conf, Tripoli.
258 **40** 10m. violet 15 10
259 15m. turquoise 20 10
260 45m. lake 1·40 65

1961. Army Day.
261 **41** 5m. brown and green 20 10
262 15m. brown and blue 60 15

42 Zelten Field and Marsa Brega Port

1961. Inaug of First Libyan Petrol Pipeline.
263 **42** 15m. green and buff 25 10
264 50m. brown and lavender 75 40
265 100m. blue and light blue 2·25 90

43 Broken Chain and Agricultural Scenes

1961. 10th Anniv of Independence.
266 **43** 15m. sepia, turquoise and green 15 10
267 – 50m. sepia, brown and buff 45 25
268 – 100m. sepia, blue & salmon 2·10 80
DESIGNS—(embodying broken chain): 50m. Modern highway and buildings; 100m. Industrial machinery.

44 Tuareg Camel Riders

1962. International Fair, Tripoli.
269 **44** 10m. chestnut and brown . . . 60 10
270 – 15m. green and purple . . 75 25
271 – 50m. blue and green . . . 2·00 1·60
DESIGNS: 15m. Well; 50m. Oil derrick.

45 Campaign Emblem **46** Ahmed Rafik

1962. Malaria Eradication.
273 **45** 15m. multicoloured 25 20
274 50m. multicoloured . . . . 1·10 90

1962. 1st Death Anniv of Ahmed Rafik el Mehdawi (poet).
276 **46** 15m. green 15 10
277 20m. brown 55 20

47 Scout Badge and Handclasp **48** City within Oildrop

1962. 3rd Boy Scouts' Meeting, Tripoli.
278 **47** 5m. sepia, red and yellow 10 10
279 – 10m. sepia, yellow and blue 20 10
280 – 15m. sepia, yellow and grey 25 20
DESIGNS: 10m. Scouts and badge; 15m. Badge and camp.

1962. Inauguration of Essider Terminal, Sidrah Oil Pipeline.
282 **48** 15m. purple and green . . 45 15
283 50m. olive and brown . . . 1·10 45

49 Red Crescent encircling Globe

1963. International Red Cross Centenary.
284 **49** 10m. multicoloured 20 15
285 15m. multicoloured 25 20
286 20m. multicoloured 90 60

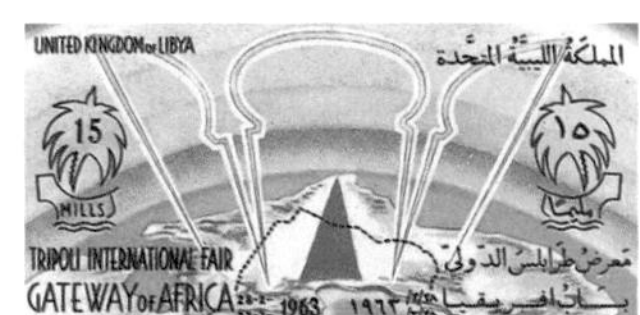

50 Rainbow over Map of Tripoli

1963. International Trade Fair, Tripoli.
287 **50** 15m. multicoloured 25 20
288 30m. multicoloured 70 20
289 50m. multicoloured . . . . 1·40 60

51 Palm and Well

1963. Freedom from Hunger.
290 **51** 10m. green, brown and blue 20 10
291 – 15m. ochre, purple & green 25 20
292 – 45m. sepia, blue and salmon . . . . 1·10 75
DESIGNS: 15m. Camel and sheep; 45m. Farmer sowing and tractor.

52 "Emancipation"

1963. 15th Anniv of Declaration of Human Rights.
293 **52** 5m. brown and blue . . . 10 10
294 15m. purple and blue . . . 20 10
295 50m. green and blue . . . 45 30

54 Map and Fair Entrance **55** Child playing in Sun

1964. International Fair, Tripoli.
300 **54** 10m. green, brown and red 75 15
301 15m. green, brown & purple . . . . 1·00 50
302 30m. green, brown and blue . . . . 1·40 75

1964. Children's Day. Sun gold.
303 **55** 5m. violet, red and pink . . 10 10
304 – 15m. brown, bistre and buff 20 15
305 **55** 45m. violet, blue & lt blue 1·25 65
DESIGN: 15m. Child in bird's nest.

56 Lungs and Stethoscope

1964. Anti-tuberculosis Campaign.
307 **56** 20m. violet 90 25

57 Crown and Map **58** Libyan Woman, Silk Moth and Cocoon

1964. 1st Anniv of Libyan Union.
308 **57** 5m. orange and green . . . 15 10
309 50m. yellow and blue . . . 1·00 50

1964. Emancipation of Libyan Women.
310 **58** 10m. blue and green . . . 15 10
311 20m. blue and yellow . . . 55 35
312 35m. blue and pink 85 80

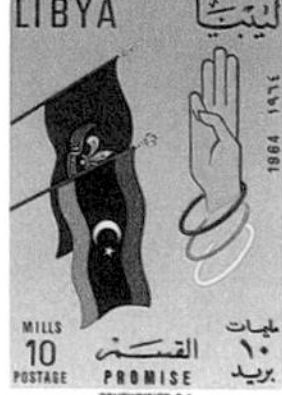

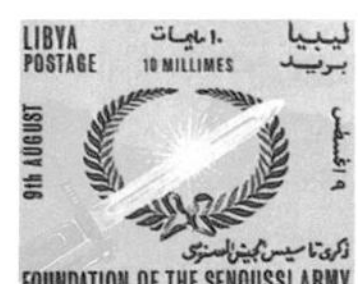

59 Flags and Scout Salute **60** Bayonet

1964. Libyan Scouts. Multicoloured.
314 10m. Type **59** 65 20
315 20m. Scout badge and saluting hands . . . . . . 1·25 60

1964. Foundation of the Senussi Army.
317 **60** 10m. brown and green . . 15 10
318 20m. black and orange . . 65 40

61 Ahmed Bahloul (poet) **62** Football

1964. Ahmed Bahloul El-Sharef Commem.
319 **61** 15m. purple 20 10
320 20m. blue 65 20

1964. Olympic Games, Tokyo. Rings in Gold.
321 5m. black and blue (Type **62**) 25 20
322 10m. black & purple (Cycling) 25 20
323 20m. black and red (Boxing) 50 20
324 30m. black and buff (Runner) 65 50
325 35m. black and olive (High-diving) 65 50
326 50m. black & green (Hurdling) 65 50
Nos. 321/6 were arranged together se-tenant in the sheets, each block of six being superimposed with the Olympic "rings" symbol.

63 A.P.U. Emblem **64** I.C.Y. Emblem

1964. 10th Anniv of Arab Postal Union.
328 **63** 10m. blue and yellow . . . 10 10
329 15m. brown and lilac . . . 20 10
330 30m. brown and green . . 95 65

1965. International Co-operation Year.
331 **64** 5m. gold and blue (postage) 25 10
332 15m. gold and red 90 25
333 50m. gold and violet (air) 1·50 35

65 European Bee Eater

1965. Birds. Multicoloured.
335 5m. Long-legged buzzard (vert) . . . . 1·10 30
336 10m. Type **65** . . . . 1·50 30
337 15m. Black-bellied sandgrouse . . . . 2·25 30
338 20m. Houbara bustard . . . 2·75 55
339 30m. Spotted sandgrouse . . 3·50 90
340 40m. Barbary partridge (vert) 4·25 1·25

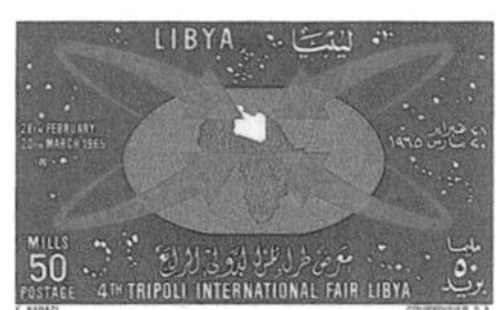

66 Fair Emblem

1965. International Trade Fair, Tripoli.
341 **66** 50m. multicoloured 75 50

67 Compass, Rocket and Balloons

1965. World Meteorological Day.
342 **67** 10m. multicoloured 10 10
343 15m. multicoloured 20 15
344 50m. multicoloured . . . . 1·00 70

68 I.T.U. Emblem and Symbols

1965. Centenary of I.T.U.
345 **68** 10m. brown 10 10
346 20m. purple 15 10
347 50m. mauve 90 65

69 Lamp and Burning Library **70** Rose

1965. Reconstitution of Burnt Algiers Library.
348 **69** 15m. multicoloured 20 10
349 50m. multicoloured 90 25

1965. Flowers. Multicoloured.
351 1m. Type **70** 10 10
352 2m. Iris 10 10
353 3m. Cactus flower 10 10
354 4m. Sunflower 50 10

71 Sud Aviation Super Caravelle over Globe **72** Forum, Cyrene

1965. Inaug of Kingdom of Libya Airlines.
355 **71** 5m. multicoloured 10 10
356 10m. multicoloured 20 10
357 15m. multicoloured 70 10

1965.
358 **72** 50m. olive and blue . . . 70 25
359 – 100m. brown and blue . . 1·25 45
360 – 200m. blue and purple . . 3·00 95
361 – 500m. green and red . . . 6·50 2·75
362 – £L1 brown and green . . . 14·00 6·50
DESIGNS—VERT: 100m. Trajan's Arch, Leptis Magna; 200m. Apollo's Temple, Cyrene. HORIZ: 500m. Antonine Temple, Sabratha; £L1 Theatre, Sabratha.

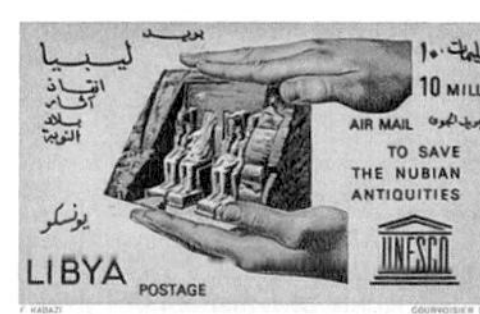

73 "Helping Hands"

1966. Air. Nubian Monuments Preservation.
363 **73** 10m. brown and bistre . . 20 10
364 15m. brown and green . . 25 10
365 40m. brown and chestnut 1·10 50

74 Germa Mausoleum

1966.
367 **74** 70m. violet and brown . . 1·40 75
See also No. E368.

75 Globe and Satellites

1966. International Trade Fair, Tripoli.
369 **75** 15m. black, gold and green 20 10
370 45m. black, gold and blue 70 20
371 55m. black, gold and purple 95 60

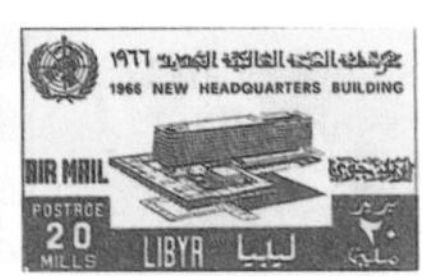

76 League Centre, Cairo, and Emblem

77 W.H.O. Building

1966. Arab League Week.
372 **76** 20m. red, green and black . . . 10 10
373 55m. blue, red and black . . . 65 50

1966. Air. Inaug of W.H.O. Headquarters, Geneva.
374 **77** 20m. black, yellow and blue 20 10
375 50m. black, green and red . . 65 25
376 65m. black, salmon and lake 95 70

78 Tuareg with Camel

80 Leaping Deer

1966. Tuaregs.
378 **78** 10m. red 95 65
379 – 20m. blue . . . . 2·25 1·25
380 – 50m. multicoloured . . . . 4·50 3·25
DESIGNS—VERT: 20m. As Type **78** but positions of Tuareg and camel reversed. 62 × 39 mm: 50m. Tuareg with camel (different).

1966. 1st Arab Girl Scouts Camp (5m.) and 7th Arab Boy Scouts Camp (25 and 65m.). Multicoloured.
382 5m. Type **80** 10 10
383 25m. Boy scouts Camp emblem (vert) 20 10
384 65m. As 25m. . . . . 1·00 50

81 Airline Emblem

1966. Air. 1st Anniv of Kingdom of Libya Airlines.
385 **81** 25m. multicoloured 20 15
386 60m. multicoloured . . . . 1·00 75
387 85m. multicoloured . . . . 1·40 1·00

82 UNESCO Emblem

83 Castle of Columns, Tolemaide

1967. 20th Anniv of UNESCO.
388 **82** 15m. multicoloured 20 10
389 25m. multicoloured 90 20

1967. Tourism.
390 **83** 25m. black, brown & violet 20 10
391 – 55m. brown, violet & black 90 50
DESIGN—HORIZ: 55m. Sebba Fort.

84 "British Confidence" (tanker) at Oil Terminal

1967. Inaug of Marsa al Hariga Oil Terminal.
392 **84** 60m. multicoloured . . . . 1·75 65

85 Fair Emblem

86 I.T.Y. Emblem

1967. International Fair, Tripoli.
393 **85** 15m. multicoloured 50 10
394 55m. multicoloured 75 50

1967. International Tourist Year.
395 **86** 5m. black and blue 10 10
396 10m. blue and black . . . 10 10
397 45m. black, blue and pink 60 15

87 Running

88 Open Book and Arab League Emblem

1967. Mediterranean Games, Tunisia. Designs showing action "close-ups".
398 **87** 5m. black, orange and blue 10 10
399 – 10m. black, brown and blue 10 10
400 – 15m. black, violet and blue 10 10
401 – 45m. black, red and blue 30 25
402 – 75m. black, green and blue 75 30
DESIGNS: 10m. Throwing the javelin; 15m. Cycling; 45m. Football; 75m. Boxing.

1967. Literacy Campaign.
403 **88** 5m. orange and violet . . . 10 10
404 10m. green and violet . . . 10 10
405 15m. purple and violet . . 15 10
406 25m. blue and violet . . . 20 15

89 Human Rights Emblem

90 Cameleers, Fokker Friendship, Oil Rig and Map

1968. Human Rights Year.
407 **89** 15m. red and green 15 10
408 60m. blue and orange . . . 65 25

1968. International Fair, Tripoli.
409 **90** 55m. multicoloured 95 30

91 Arab League Emblem

1968. Arab League Week.
410 **91** 10m. red and blue 10 10
411 45m. green and orange . . 65 50

92 Children "Wrestling" (statue)

93 W.H.O. Emblem and Reaching Hands

1968. Children's Day. Multicoloured.
412 25m. Type **92** 45 15
413 55m. Libyan mother and children 80 55

1968. 20th Anniv of W.H.O.
414 **93** 25m. blue and purple . . . 25 15
415 55m. brown and blue . . . 40 25

94 Oil Pipeline Map

1968. Inauguration of Zueitina Oil Terminal.
416 **94** 10m. multicoloured 20 10
417 60m. multicoloured . . . . 1·10 65

95 "Teaching the People"

1968. "Eliminate Illiteracy".
418 **95** 5m. mauve 10 10
419 10m. orange 10 10
420 15m. blue 10 10
421 20m. green 20 20

96 Conference Emblem

1968. 4th Session of Arab Labour Ministries Conference, Tripoli.
422 **96** 10m. multicoloured 10 10
423 15m. multicoloured 20 10

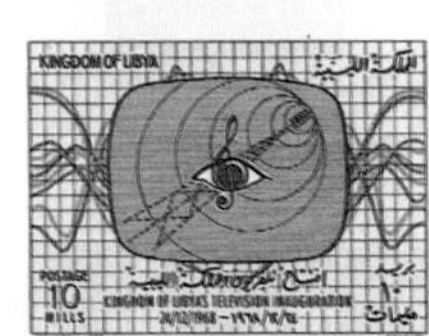

97 Treble Clef, Eye and T.V. Screen

1968. Inauguration of Libyan Television Service.
424 **97** 10m. multicoloured 10 10
425 30m. multicoloured 65 20

98 Bridge, Callipers and Road Sign

1968. Opening of Wadi El Kuf Bridge.
426 **98** 25m. multicoloured 15 15
427 60m. multicoloured 70 25

99 Melons

100 Fair Emblem

1969. Fruits. Multicoloured.
428 5m. Type **99** 10 10
429 10m. Dates 10 10
430 15m. Lemons 10 10
431 20m. Oranges 15 10
432 25m. Peaches 50 15
433 35m. Pears 90 50

1969. 8th International Trade Fair, Tripoli.
434 **100** 25m. multicoloured . . . 15 10
435 35m. multicoloured . . . 25 15
436 40m. multicoloured . . . 60 20

101 Hoisting Weather Balloon

1969. World Meteorological Day.
437 **101** 60m. multicoloured . . . 1·10 65

102 Family on Staircase within Cogwheel

103 I.L.O. Emblem

1969. 10th Anniv of Libyan Social Insurance.
438 **102** 15m. multicoloured . . . 15 10
439 55m. multicoloured . . . 30 25

1969. 50th Anniv of I.L.O.
440 **103** 10m. green, black & turq 10 10
441 60m. green, black and red 70 50

104 Emblem and Desert Scene

1969. African Tourist Year.
442 **104** 15m. multicoloured . . . 15 10
443 30m. multicoloured . . . 65 50

105 Members of the Armed Forces and Olive Branch

106 Dish Aerial and Flags

1969. Revolution of 1st September.
444 **105** 5m. multicoloured 25 10
445 10m. multicoloured . . . 35 20
446 15m. multicoloured . . . 55 25
447 25m. multicoloured . . . 85 40
448 45m. multicoloured . . . 1·00 60
449 60m. multicoloured . . . 2·10 1·00
On Nos. 444/9 the value is in white and the designer's name appears at the foot of design.

1970. 5th Anniv of Arab Satellite Communications Co-operation Agreement.
450 **106** 15m. multicoloured . . . 50 15
451 20m. multicoloured . . . 75 20
452 25m. multicoloured . . . 1·00 25
453 40m. multicoloured . . . 1·50 75

107 Arab League Flag, Arms and Map

1970. Silver Jubilee of Arab League.
454 **107** 10m. sepia, green and blue 10 10
455 15m. brown, green & orge 15 15
456 20m. purple, green & olive 50 25

1970. Revolution of 1 September. Designs as T **105**, but without imprint "M. A. Siala" at foot, and figures of value differently inscr.
457 **87** 5m. multicoloured 25 10
458 10m. multicoloured 35 20
459 15m. multicoloured 55 25
460 25m. multicoloured 85 40
461 45m. multicoloured . . . . 1·00 60
462 60m. multicoloured . . . . 2·10 1·00

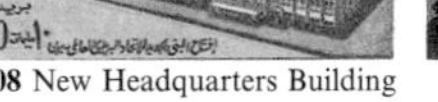
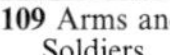

108 New Headquarters Building **109** Arms and Soldiers

1970. New U.P.U. Headquarters Building, Berne.
463 **108** 10m. multicoloured . . . 15 10
464 25m. multicoloured . . . 20 20
465 60m. multicoloured . . . 95 60

1970. Nos. 358 and 360/2 with "KINGDOM OF LIBYA" inscriptions obliterated.
465a **72** 50m. olive and blue . . .
466 – 200m. blue and purple . .
467 – 500m. green and pink . .
468 – £L1 brown and green . .
These stamps were sold only for use on parcel post items. Other values may exist so overprinted, but were unauthorized.
See also Nos. 518/23.

1970. Evacuation of Foreign Military Bases in Libya.
469 **109** 15m. black and red . . . 15 15
470 25m. yellow, blue and red 45 20
471 45m. yellow, red and green . . . . 1·25 30

110 Soldiers and Libyan Flag **111** U.N. Emblem, Dove and Scales

1970. 1st Anniv of Libyan Arab Republic.
472 **110** 20m. multicoloured . . . 55 15
473 25m. multicoloured . . . 70 15
474 30m. multicoloured . . . 1·25 75

1970. 25th Anniv of United Nations.
475 **111** 5m. brown, red and green 25 10
476 10m. green, red & emerald 65 15
477 60m. green, red and blue 1·75 75

112 Map and Flags **113** Dove, U.N. Emblem and Globe

1970. Signing of Tripoli Charter of Co-operation.
478 **112** 15m. green, black and red 5·00 1·50

1971. 10th Anniv of U.N. De-colonisation Declaration.
479 **113** 15m. multicoloured . . . 50 15
480 20m. multicoloured . . . 75 20
481 60m. multicoloured . . . 1·90 75

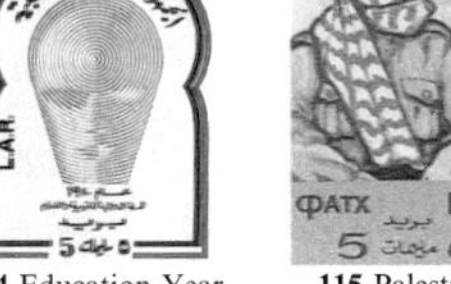

114 Education Year Emblem **115** Palestinian Guerrilla

1971. International Education Year.
482 **114** 5m. brown, red and black 15 10
483 10m. green, red and black 50 10
484 20m. blue, red and black 1·10 15

1971. "Al-Fatah" Movement for the Liberation of Palestine.
485 **115** 5m. multicoloured 15 10
486 10m. multicoloured . . . 50 15
487 100m. multicoloured . . . 1·75 1·00

116 Fair Emblem **117** O.P.E.C. Emblem

1971. 9th International Trade Fair, Tripoli.
488 **116** 15m. multicoloured . . . 15 10
489 30m. multicoloured . . . 65 20

1971. Organization of Petroleum Exporting Countries (O.P.E.C.).
490 **117** 10m. brown and yellow 15 10
491 70m. violet and pink . . . 1·25 65

118 Global Symbol

1971. World Telecommunications Day (Nos. 494/5) and Pan-African Telecommunications Network.
492 – 5m. multicoloured 10 10
493 – 15m. multicoloured . . . 10 10
494 **118** 25m. multicoloured . . . 20 15
495 35m. multicoloured . . . 50 25
DESIGN: 5m., 15m. Telecommunications map of Africa.

119 Soldier, Torch and Flag **120** Ramadan Suehli

1971. 1st Anniv of Evacuation of Foreign Troops.
496 **119** 5m. multicoloured 10 10
497 10m. multicoloured . . . 15 10
498 15m. multicoloured . . . 20 15

1971. Ramadan Suehli (patriot). Commem.
499 **120** 15m. multicoloured . . . 15 10
500 55m. multicoloured . . . 75 35
For similar portraits see Nos. 503/4, 507/8, 526/7 and 553/4.

121 Palm and Dates **122** Pres. Gamal Nasser

1971. 2nd Anniv of 1 September Revolution.
501 **121** 5m. multicoloured 20 10
502 15m. multicoloured . . . 1·00 15

1971. 40th Death Anniv of Omar el Mukhtar (patriot). As T **120**.
503 5m. multicoloured 10 10
504 100m. multicoloured . . . . 1·75 90

1971. 1st Death Anniv of Pres. Nasser of Egypt.
505 **122** 5m. black, green & purple 10 10
506 15m. black, purple & green 95 10

1971. 21st Death Anniv of Ibrahim Usta Omar (poet). As T **120**.
507 25m. multicoloured 25 15
508 30m. multicoloured 80 20

123 Racial Equality Year Emblem **124** A.P.U. Emblem

1971. Racial Equality Year.
509 **123** 25m. multicoloured . . . 25 15
510 35m. multicoloured . . . 70 15

1971. 25th Anniv of Founding of Arab Postal Union at Sofar Conference.
511 **124** 5m. multicoloured 10 10
512 10m. multicoloured . . . 20 10
513 15m. multicoloured . . . 15 10

125 Arab Postal Union Emblem and Envelopes **126** Book Year Emblem

1971. 10th Anniv of African Postal Union. Mult.
514 10m. Type **125** 10 10
515 15m. Type **125** 15 10
516 25m. A.P.U. Emblem and dove with letter 25 15
517 55m. As 25m. 95 35

1971. Nos. 423/33 with "KINGDOM OF LIBYA" inscriptions obliterated.
518 5m. Type **99** . . . .
519 10m. Dates . . . .
520 15m. Lemons . . . .
521 20m. Oranges . . . .
522 25m. Peaches . . . .
523 35m. Pears . . . .

1972. International Book Year.
524 **126** 15m. multicoloured . . . 15 10
525 20m. multicoloured . . . 25 20

1972. Ahmed Gnaba (poet) Commem. As T **120**.
526 20m. multicoloured 25 10
527 35m. multicoloured 65 20

127 Libyan Arms **128** Tombs, Ghirza

1972. Values in Milliemes.
528 **127** 5m. multicoloured 10 10
529 10m. multicoloured . . . 10 10
530 25m. multicoloured . . . 15 10
531 30m. multicoloured . . . 20 10
532 35m. multicoloured . . . 25 10
533 40m. multicoloured . . . 50 15
534 45m. multicoloured . . . 60 15
535 55m. multicoloured . . . 85 20
536 60m. multicoloured . . . 1·00 35
537 90m. multicoloured . . . 1·60 90
For values in dirhams and dinars see Nos. 555/62.

1972. Libyan Antiquities. Multicoloured.
538 5m. Type **128** 10 10
539 10m. Cufic inscription, Ajdabiya 10 10
540 15m. Marcus Aurelius' Arch, Tripoli (horiz) 15 10
541 25m. Exchanging Weapons (cave painting, Wadi Zigza) 65 15
542 55m. Garamantian chariot (wall drawing, Wadi Zigza) 1·40 65
543 70m. "Libya crowning Cyrene" (Roman relief, Cyrene) . . . . 2·50 90

129 Fair Emblem **130** Heart and Skeletal Arm

1972. 10th International Trade Fair, Tripoli.
544 **129** 25m. multicoloured . . . 20 15
545 35m. multicoloured . . . 25 20
546 50m. multicoloured . . . 95 25
547 70m. multicoloured . . . 1·40 35

1972. World Health Day.
548 **130** 15m. multicoloured . . . 1·10 25
549 25m. multicoloured . . . 2·25 75

131 "Unity" Symbol on Map **132**

1972. 1st Anniv of Libyan–Egyptian Federation Agreement.
550 **131** 15m. yellow, blue and black 10 10
551 20m. yellow, green & emer 20 10
552 25m. yellow, red and black 80 20

1972. Birth Centenary (1970) of Suleiman el Baruni (writer). As T **120**.
553 10m. multicoloured 95 15
554 70m. multicoloured . . . . . 1·25 75

1972. New Currency (Dirhams and Dinars). As T **127**. (a) Size 19 × 24 mm.
555 **127** 15dh. multicoloured . . . 10 10
556 65dh. multicoloured . . . 75 50
557 70dh. multicoloured . . . 90 65
558 80dh. multicoloured . . . 1·25 65

(b) Size 27 × 32 mm.
559 **127** 100dh. multicoloured . . 1·75 2·00
560 200dh. multicoloured . . 3·25 1·60
561 500dh. multicoloured . . 7·50 5·00
562 1D. multicoloured . . . . 13·50 10·00

1972.
563 **132** 5m. multicoloured . . . . 1·90 50
564 20m. multicoloured . . . 7·50 1·40
565 50m. multicoloured . . . 18·00 3·75
Nos. 563/5 were also issued with the Arabic face values expressed in the new currency.
See also Nos. 657/9.

133 Environmental Emblem **134** Olympic Emblems

1972. U.N. Environmental Conservation Conference, Stockholm.
566 **133** 15dh. multicoloured . . . 50 10
567 55dh. multicoloured . . . 1·10 35

1972. Olympic Games, Munich.
568 **134** 25dh. multicoloured . . . 1·50 35
569 35dh. multicoloured . . . 2·25 90

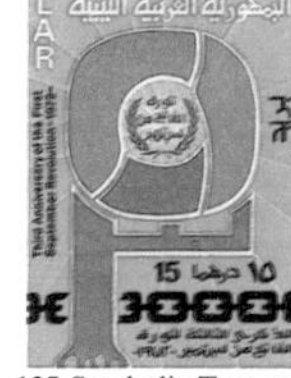
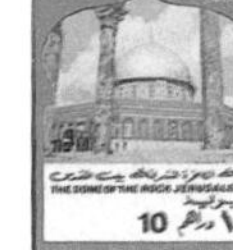

135 Symbolic Tree and "Fruit" **136** Dome of the Rock

1972. 3rd Anniv of 1 September Revolution.
570 **135** 15dh. multicoloured . . . 15 10
571 25dh. multicoloured . . . 70 15

1973. Dome of the Rock, Jerusalem.
572 **136** 10dh. multicoloured . . . 10 10
573 25dh. multicoloured . . . 50 15

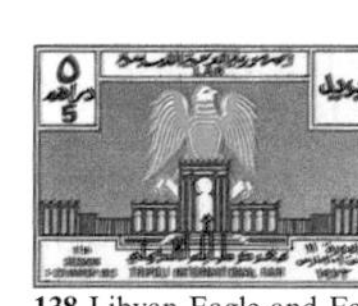

137 Nicolas Copernicus **138** Libyan Eagle and Fair

1973. 500th Birth Anniv of Copernicus. Mult.
574 15dh. Type **137** 15 10
575 25dh. "Copernicus in his Observatory" (horiz) . . . 50 15

1973. 11th International Trade Fair, Tripoli.
576 **138** 5dh. multicoloured . . . 15 10
577 10dh. multicoloured . . . 50 10
578 15dh. multicoloured . . . 90 15

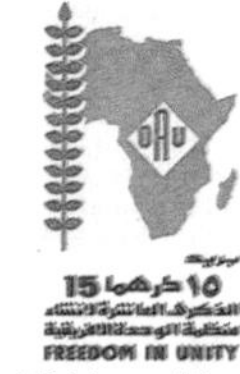

139 Blind Persons and Occupations **140** Map and Laurel

1973. Role of the Blind in Society.
579 **139** 20dh. multicoloured . . . 5·50 1·25
580 25dh. multicoloured . . . 10·00 2·50

1973. 10th Anniv of Organization of African Unity.
584 **140** 15dh. multicoloured . . . 20 10
585 25dh. multicoloured . . . 65 45

141 Interpol H.Q., Paris

1973. 50th Anniv of International Criminal Police Organization (Interpol).
586 **141** 10dh. multicoloured . . . 10 10
587 15dh. multicoloured . . . 15 10
588 25dh. multicoloured . . . 60 20

142 Map and Emblems

143 W.M.O. Emblem

1973. Census.
589 **142** 10dh. blue, black and red 3·00 65
590 25dh. green, black and blue . . . . 4·25 1·25
591 35dh. orange, black and grn . . . . 8·00 2·50

1973. W.M.O. Centenary.
592 **143** 5dh. blue, black and red 10 10
593 10dh. blue, black and green 15 10

144 Footballers

1973. 2nd Palestine Cup Football Championship.
594 **144** 5dh. brown and green . . 45 20
595 25dh. brown and red . . 80 15

145 Revolutionary Torch

146 "Writing Ability"

1973. 4th Anniv of 1 September Revolution.
596 **145** 15dh. multicoloured . . . 20 10
597 25dh. multicoloured . . . 85 10

1973. Literacy Campaign.
598 **146** 25dh. multicoloured . . . 50 15

147 Doorway of Old City Hall

148 Militiamen and Flag

1973. Cent of Tripoli Municipality. Mult.
599 10dh. Type **147** 20 10
600 25dh. Khondok fountain . . 50 10
601 35dh. Clock tower 75 40

1973. Libyan Militia.
602 **148** 15dh. multicoloured . . . 15 10
603 25dh. multicoloured . . . 55 10

149 Arabic Quotation from Speech of 15 April 1973

1973. Declaration of Cultural Revolution by Col. Gaddafi. Multicoloured.
604 25dh. Type **149** 20 10
605 70dh. As Type **149** but text in English 60 30

150 Ploughing with Camel

151 Human Rights Emblem

1973. 10th Anniv of World Food Programme.
606 **150** 10dh. multicoloured . . . 10 10
607 25dh. multicoloured . . . 20 10
608 35dh. multicoloured . . . 55 15

1973. 25th Anniv of Declaration of Human Rights.
609 **151** 25dh. red, purple and blue 20 10
610 70dh. red, green and blue 1·10 30

152 Flat-headed Grey Mullet

154 Emblem formed with National Flags

153 Lookout Post and Scout Salute

1973. Fishes. Multicoloured.
611 5dh. Type **152** 15 10
612 10dh. Zebra seabream . . . 70 10
613 15dh. Grouper . . . . 1·00 15
614 20dh. Painted comber . . . . 1·50 20
615 25dh. Yellow-finned tunny . . 2·75 30

1974. 20th Anniv of Scouting in Libya.
616 **153** 5dh. multicoloured . . . 95 10
617 20dh. multicoloured . . . 2·50 50
618 25dh. multicoloured . . . 4·00 1·25

1974. 12th International Trade Fair, Tripoli.
619 **154** 10dh. multicoloured . . . 50 10
620 25dh. multicoloured . . . 75 15
621 35dh. multicoloured . . . 1·25 35

155 Family within Protective Hands

156 Minaret within Star

1974. World Health Day.
622 **155** 5dh. multicoloured . . . 15 10
623 25dh. multicoloured . . . 50 20

1974. Inauguration of Benghazi University.
624 **156** 10dh. multicoloured . . . 20 10
625 25dh. multicoloured . . . 75 15
626 35dh. multicoloured . . . 1·10 25

157 U.P.U. Emblem within Star

158 Traffic Lights and Signs

1974. Centenary of U.P.U.
627 **157** 25dh. multicoloured . . . 5·50 75
628 70dh. multicoloured . . . 10·00 1·50

1974. Motoring and Touring Club of Libya.
629 **158** 5dh. multicoloured . . . 10 10
630 10dh. multicoloured . . . 15 10
631 25dh. multicoloured . . . 15 10

159 Tank, Refinery and Pipeline

160 W.P.Y. Emblem and People

1974. 5th Anniv of 1 September Revolution.
632 **159** 5dh. multicoloured . . . 10 10
633 20dh. multicoloured . . . 15 10
634 25dh. multicoloured . . . 15 10
635 35dh. multicoloured . . . 20 15

1974. World Population Year.
637 **160** 25dh. multicoloured . . . 20 10
638 35dh. multicoloured . . . 50 20

161

162 Congress Emblem

1975. 13th International Trade Fair, Tripoli. Libyan Costumes.
639 **161** 5dh. multicoloured . . . 10 10
640 – 10dh. multicoloured . . . 10 10
641 – 15dh. multicoloured . . . 10 10
642 – 20dh. multicoloured . . . 20 10
643 – 25dh. multicoloured . . . 75 10
644 – 50dh. multicoloured . . . 1·10 20
DESIGNS: 10dh. to 50dh. Various costumes.

1975. Arab Workers' Congress.
645 **162** 10dh. multicoloured . . . 10 10
646 25dh. multicoloured . . . 15 15
647 35dh. multicoloured . . . 50 15

163 Teacher at Blackboard

1975. Teachers' Day.
648 **163** 10dh. multicoloured . . . 10 10
649 25dh. multicoloured . . . 20 10

164 Human Figures, Text and Globe

1975. World Health Day.
650 **164** 20dh. multicoloured . . . 15 10
651 25dh. multicoloured . . . 20 10

165 Readers and Bookshelves

166 Festival Emblem

1975. Arab Book Exhibition.
652 **165** 10dh. multicoloured . . . 10 10
653 20dh. multicoloured . . . 20 10
654 25dh. multicoloured . . . 50 15

1975. 2nd Arab Youth Festival.
655 **166** 20dh. multicoloured . . . 15 10
656 25dh. multicoloured . . . 20 15

1975. As Nos. 563/5 but without "L.A.R.".
657 **132** 5dh. black, orange & blue 35 10
658 20dh. black, yellow & blue 75 10
659 50dh. black, green and blue . . . . 1·40 15

167 Games Emblem

168 Dove of Peace

1975. 7th Mediterranean Games, Algiers.
660 **167** 10dh. multicoloured . . . 10 10
661 25dh. multicoloured . . . 45 10
662 50dh. multicoloured . . . 85 20

1975. 6th Anniv of 1 September Revolution. Multicoloured.
663 25dh. Type **168** 20 10
664 70dh. Peace dove with different background . . . 95 25

169 Khalil Basha Mosque

170 Arms and Crowds

1975. Mosques. Multicoloured.
666 5dh. Type **169** 10 10
667 10dh. Sidi Abdulla El Shaab 10 10
668 15dh. Sidi Ali El Fergani . . 10 10
669 20dh. Al Kharruba (vert) . . 15 10
670 25dh. Katiktha (vert) 20 10
671 30dh. Murad Agha (vert) . . 45 15
672 35dh. Maulai Mohamed (vert) 55 15

1976. National People's Congress.
673 **170** 35dh. multicoloured . . . 20 10
674 40dh. multicoloured . . . 25 10

171 Dialogue Emblem

172 Woman blowing Bugle

1976. Islamic–Christian Dialogue Seminar.
675 **171** 40dh. multicoloured . . . 50 15
676 115dh. multicoloured . . 1·40 60

1976. International Trade Fair, Tripoli. Mult.
677 10dh. Type **172** 10 10
678 20dh. Lancer 15 10
679 30dh. Drummer 65 10
680 40dh. Bagpiper 75 20
681 100dh. Woman with jug on head . . . . 1·90 35

173 Early and Modern Telephones

1976. Telephone Centenary. Multicoloured.
682 40dh. Type **173** 1·60 15
683 70dh. Alexander Graham Bell 2·75 50

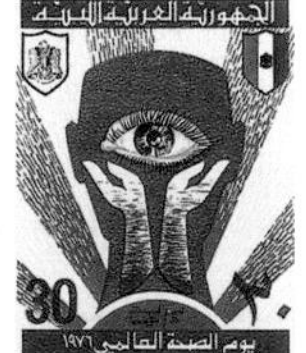
174 Mother and Child **175** Hands supporting Eye

1976. International Children's Day.
685 **174** 85dh. multicoloured 75 30
686 110dh. multicoloured 1·10 40

1976. World Health Day.
687 **175** 30dh. multicoloured 20 10
688 35dh. multicoloured 20 10
689 40dh. multicoloured 50 15

176 Great Grey Shrike

1976. Libyan Birds. Multicoloured.
690 5dh. Little bittern 75 25
691 10dh. Type **176** 1·40 40
692 15dh. Fulvous babbler 2·00 50
693 20dh. European bee eater (vert) 2·75 70
694 25dh. Hoopoe 3·00 95

177 Barabekh Plant **178** Cycling

1976. Natural History Museum. Multicoloured.
695 10dh. Type **177** 10 10
696 15dh. Fin whale (horiz) 15 10
697 30dh. Lizard (horiz) 20 10
698 40dh. Elephant's skull (horiz) 70 15
699 70dh. Bonnelli's eagle 4·50 55
700 115dh. Barbary sheep 2·00 40

1976. Olympic Games, Montreal. Multicoloured.
701 15dh. Type **178** 10 10
702 25dh. Boxing 20 10
703 70dh. Football 95 20

179 Global "Tree" **180** Agricultural and Industrial Symbols

1976. Non-Aligned Countries' Colombo Conference.
705 **179** 115dh. multicoloured 95 35

1976. 7th Anniv of Revolution.
706 **180** 30dh. multicoloured 15 10
707 40dh. multicoloured 45 15
708 100dh. multicoloured 90 55

181 Various Sports **182** Chessboard and Pieces

1976. 5th Arab Games, Damascus.
710 **181** 15dh. multicoloured 10 10
711 30dh. multicoloured 15 10
712 100dh. multicoloured 1·00 55

1976. Arab Chess Olympiad, Tripoli.
714 **182** 15dh. multicoloured 95 15
715 30dh. multicoloured 1·60 60
716 100dh. multicoloured 5·00 95

183 Ratima **186** Kaaba, Mecca

184 Emblem and Text

1976. Libyan Flora. Multicoloured.
717 15dh. Type **183** 15 10
718 20dh. "Sword of Crow" 15 10
719 35dh. "Lasef" 50 10
720 40dh. "Yadid" 80 15
721 70dh. Esparto grass 1·90 25

1976. International Archives Council.
722 **184** 15dh. multicoloured 10 10
723 35dh. multicoloured 15 10
724 70dh. multicoloured 55 20

1976. Pilgrimage to Mecca.
729 **186** 15dh. multicoloured 10 10
730 30dh. multicoloured 15 10
731 70dh. multicoloured 30 20
732 100dh. multicoloured 75 30

187 **188** Basket

1977. Coil Stamps.
733 **187** 5dh. multicoloured 10 10
734 20dh. multicoloured 10 10
735 50dh. multicoloured 55 40

1977. 15th International Trade Fair, Tripoli. Mult.
736 10dh. Type **188** 10 10
737 20dh. Leather bag 10 10
738 30dh. Vase 15 10
739 40dh. Slippers 45 15
740 50dh. Saddle 60 15

189 Girl with Flowers

1977. Children's Day. Multicoloured.
742 10dh. Type **189** 10 10
743 30dh. Clothes shop 15 10
744 40dh. Orchard 20 15

190 Fighters and Machine-gun **191** Protected Child

1977. 9th Anniv of Battle of Al-Karamah.
745 **190** 15dh. multicoloured 10 10
746 25dh. multicoloured 15 10
747 70dh. multicoloured 80 25

1977. World Health Day.
748 **191** 15dh. multicoloured 10 10
749 30dh. multicoloured 15 10

192 A.P.U. Emblem

1977. 25th Anniv of Arab Postal Union.
750 **192** 15dh. multicoloured 10 10
751 20dh. multicoloured 15 10
752 40dh. multicoloured 20 15

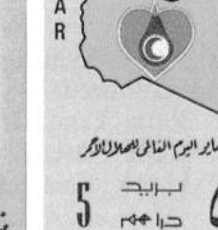
193 Maps of Libya and Africa **194** Heart on Map of Libya

1977. Organization of African Unity Conference, Tripoli.
753 **193** 40dh. multicoloured 1·00 20
754 70dh. multicoloured 1·50 30

1977. Red Crescent Commemoration.
755 **194** 5dh. multicoloured 10 10
756 10dh. multicoloured 15 10
757 30dh. multicoloured 65 15

195 Messenger and Jet Fighter

1977. Communications Progress. Multicoloured.
758 20dh. Type **195** 15 10
759 25dh. Arab rider and Concorde 30 15
760 60dh. Satellite and aerial 55 20
761 115dh. Television relay via satellite 1·10 65
762 150dh. Camel rider and Boeing 727 airliner loading 1·75 90
763 200dh. "Apollo–Soyuz" link 2·25 1·10

196 Mosque **197** Archbishop Capucci

1977. Libyan Mosques.
765 **196** 40dh. multicoloured 20 15
766 – 50dh. multicoloured (vert) 50 15
767 – 70dh. multicoloured 70 20
768 – 90dh. multicoloured 85 30
769 – 100dh. multicoloured (vert) 1·00 35
770 – 115dh. multicoloured 1·25 75
DESIGNS: 50dh. to 115dh. Various mosques.

1977. 3rd Anniv of Archbishop Capucci's Imprisonment.
771 **197** 30dh. multicoloured 15 10
772 40dh. multicoloured 20 15
773 115dh. multicoloured 1·25 60

198 Clasped Hands and Emblems **199** Swimming

1977. 8th Anniv of Revolution.
774 **198** 15dh. multicoloured 10 10
775 30dh. multicoloured 15 10
776 85dh. multicoloured 80 25

1977. Arab School Sports. Multicoloured.
778 5dh. Type **199** 10 10
779 10dh. Handball (horiz) 10 10
780 15dh. Football 15 10
781 25dh. Table tennis (horiz) 50 20
782 40dh. Basketball 1·10 65

200 Championship Emblem **201** Dome of the Rock

1977. 1st International Turf Championships, Tripoli. Multicoloured.
783 5dh. Horse jumping fence (facing left) 10 10
784 10dh. Arab horseman 10 10
785 15dh. Type **200** 15 10
786 45dh. Horse jumping fence (facing right) 55 15
787 115dh. Arab horseman racing 1·40 80

1977. Palestine Welfare.
789 **201** 5dh. multicoloured 10 10
790 10dh. multicoloured 10 10

202 Fort, and Hands writing Arabic Script in Book **203** Emblem

1977. "The Green Book". Multicoloured.
791 35dh. Type **202** 15 10
792 40dh. Type **202** (text in English) 20 15
793 115dh. Dove with "Green Book" and map 1·25 70

1977. World Standards Day.
794 **203** 5dh. multicoloured 10 10
795 15dh. multicoloured 10 10
796 30dh. multicoloured 15 10

204 Giraffe

1978. Rock Drawings from Wadi Mathendous. Multicoloured.
797 10dh. Crocodiles (horiz) 10 10
798 15dh. Elephant hunt (horiz) 10 10
799 20dh. Type **204** 15 10
800 30dh. Antelope (horiz) 45 15
801 40dh. Elephant (horiz) 65 20

205 Silver Pendant **206** Compass and Lightning Flash

1978. 16th Tripoli International Fair.
802 **205** 5dh. silver, black and red . . . 10 10
803 – 10dh. silver, black & violet 10 10
804 – 20dh. silver, black & green 10 10
805 – 25dh. silver, black and blue 15 10
806 – 115dh. silver, black & blue . . . . 1·10 70
DESIGNS: 10dh. Silver ornamental plate; 20dh. Necklace with three pendants; 25dh. Crescent-shaped silver brooch; 115dh. Silver armband.

1978. Arab Cultural Education Organization.
807 **206** 30dh. multicoloured . . . 20 15
808 115dh. multicoloured . . 1·40 65

207 Dancing a Round

1978. Children's Day. Children's Paintings. Multicoloured.
809 40dh. Type **207** 20 15
810 40dh. Children with placards 20 15
811 40dh. Shopping street 20 15
812 40dh. Playground 20 15
813 40dh. Wedding ceremony . . 20 15

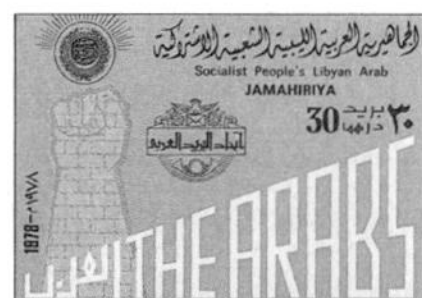

208 Brickwork Clenched Fist

1978. The Arabs.
814 **208** 30dh. multicoloured . . . 20 15
815 115dh. multicoloured . . 1·10 35

209 Blood Pressure Meter **211** Games Emblem

210 Microwave Antenna

1978. World Hypertension Month.
816 **209** 30dh. multicoloured . . . 15 15
817 115dh. multicoloured . . 1·25 35

1978. World Telecommunications Day.
818 **210** 30dh. multicoloured . . . 15 15
819 115dh. multicoloured . . 1·00 35

1978. 3rd African Games, Algiers.
820 **211** 15dh. copper, violet & blk 10 10
821 30dh. silver, lilac and black 15 10
822 115dh. gold, purple & blk 1·10 35

212 Aerial View of Airport

1978. Inauguration of Tripoli International Airport. Multicoloured.
823 40dh. Type **212** 30 10
824 115dh. Terminal building . . 1·25 65

213 Ankara

1978. Turkish–Libyan Friendship.
825 **213** 30dh. multicoloured . . . 15 10
826 35dh. multicoloured . . . 15 10
827 115dh. multicoloured . . 1·10 35

214 "Armed Forces" **215** Crater

1978. 9th Anniv of 1 September Revolution. Multicoloured.
828 30dh. Type **214** 60 15
829 35dh. Tower, Green Book and symbols of progress 15 10
830 115dh. "Industry" 95 70

1978. 2nd Symposium on Geology of Libya. Multicoloured.
832 30dh. Type **215** 15 10
833 40dh. Oasis 20 15
834 115dh. Crater (different) . . 1·10 60

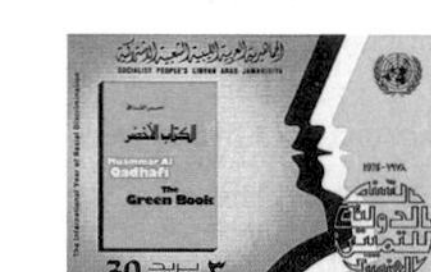

216 "Green Book" and Different Races

1978. International Anti-Apartheid Year.
835 **216** 30dh. multicoloured . . . 15 10
836 40dh. multicoloured . . . 20 15
837 115dh. multicoloured . . 85 35

217 Pilgrims, Minarets and Kaaba **218** Clasped Hands and Globe

1978. Pilgrimage to Mecca.
838 **217** 5dh. multicoloured . . . 10 10
839 10dh. multicoloured . . . 10 10
840 15dh. multicoloured . . . 10 10
841 20dh. multicoloured . . . 15 10

1978. U.N. Conference for Technical Co-operation between Developing Countries.
842 **218** 30dh. multicoloured . . . 15 10
843 40dh. multicoloured . . . 20 15
844 115dh. multicoloured . . 85 35

219 Workers, Rifles, Torch and Flag **220** Human Figure and Scales

1978. Arab Countries Summit Conference. Multicoloured.
845 30dh. Type **219** 15 10
846 40dh. Map of Middle East, eagle and crowd (horiz) . . 20 15
847 115dh. As 40
848 145dh. Type **219** . . . . . . 1·00 45

1978. 30th Anniv of Declaration of Human Rights.
849 **220** 15dh. multicoloured . . . 10 10
850 30dh. multicoloured . . . 20 15
851 115dh. multicoloured . . 50 35

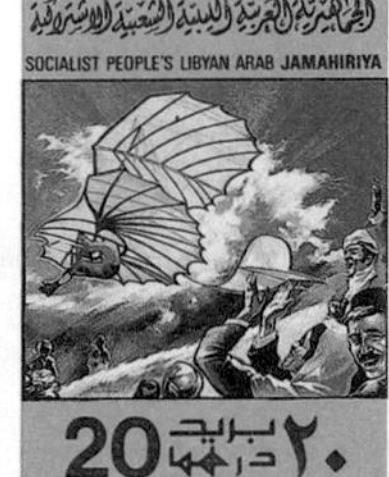

221 Horse Racing and Fort **222** Lilienthal's Biplane Glider

1978. Libyan Study Centre.
852 **221** 20dh. multicoloured . . . 15 10
853 40dh. multicoloured . . . 20 15
854 115dh. multicoloured . . 95 60

1978. 75th Anniv of First Powered Flight. Mult.
855 20dh. Type **222** 10 10
856 25dh. Lindbergh's "Spirit of St. Louis" 10 10
857 30dh. Admiral Richard Byrd's Trimotor "Floyd Bennett" 80 25
858 50dh. Bleriot 5190 Santos Dumont flying boat and airship "Graf Zeppelin" . . 95 35
859 115dh. Wright brothers and Wright Type A . . . . . 1·10 75

223 Libyans, Torch and Laurel Wreath **224** Mounted Dorcas Gazelle Head

1979.
861 **223** 5dh. multicoloured . . . 10 10
862 10dh. multicoloured . . 10 10
863 15dh. multicoloured . . 10 10
864 30dh. multicoloured . . 20 10
865 50dh. multicoloured . . 20 10
866 60dh. multicoloured . . 25 15
867 70dh. multicoloured . . 30 15
868 100dh. multicoloured . . 75 25
869 115dh. multicoloured . . 85 30
870 200dh. multicoloured . . 1·10 45
871 250dh. multicoloured . . 1·90 65
871 500dh. multicoloured . . 3·50 65
872 1000dh. multicoloured 6·75 3·50
872a 1500dh. multicoloured 12·50 4·25
872b 2500dh. multicoloured 23·00 7·50
Nos. 861/9 measure 18 × 23 mm and Nos. 870/2b 26 × 32 mm.

1979. Coil Stamps.
873 **224** 5dh. multicoloured . . . 15 10
874 20dh. multicoloured . . . 25 10
875 50dh. multicoloured . . . 80 25

225 Tortoise

1979. Libyan Animals. Multicoloured.
876 5dh. Type **225** 10 10
877 10dh. Addax (vert) 10 10
878 15dh. Algerian hedgehog . . 20 10
879 20dh. North African crested porcupine 20 10
880 30dh. Dromedaries 30 15
881 35dh. Wild cat (vert) 40 15
882 45dh. Dorcas gazelle (vert) 95 25
883 115dh. Cheetah . . . . . . 1·90 75

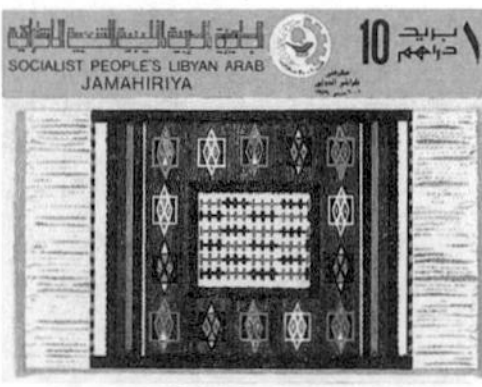

226 Carpet

1979. 17th Tripoli International Trade Fair.
884 **226** 10dh. multicoloured . . . 10 10
885 – 15dh. multicoloured . . . 10 10
886 – 30dh. multicoloured . . . 15 10
887 – 45dh. multicoloured . . . 15 10
888 – 115dh. multicoloured . . 85 35
DESIGNS: 15dh. to 115dh. Different carpets

227 Aircraft and People

1979. International Year of the Child. Children's Paintings (1st series). Multicoloured.
889 20dh. Type **227** 10 10
890 20dh. Shepherd with flock . . 10 10
891 20dh. Open air cafe 10 10
892 20dh. Boat in storm 10 10
893 20dh. Policeman on traffic duty 10 10
See also Nos. 975/9.

228 World Map, Koran and Symbols of Arab Achievements **229** Radar Tower and Map

1979. The Arabs.
894 **228** 45dh. multicoloured . . . 20 15
895 70dh. multicoloured . . . 55 20

1979. World Meteorological Day.
896 **229** 15dh. multicoloured . . . 10 10
897 30dh. multicoloured . . . 15 10
898 50dh. multicoloured . . . 20 15

230 Medical Care

1979. World Health Day.
899 **230** 40dh. multicoloured . . . 20 15

231 "Carpobrotus acinaciformis"

1979. Libyan Flowers. Multicoloured.
900 10dh. Type **231** 10 10
901 15dh. "Caralluma europaea" 10 10
902 20dh. "Arum cirenaicum" . . 10 10
903 35dh. "Lavatera arborea" . . 50 15
904 40dh. "Capparis spinosa" . . 50 15
905 50dh. "Ranunculus asiaticus" 60 15

232 Farmer and Sheep

1979. 10th Anniv of Revolution. Mult.
906 15dh. Type **232** 10 10
907 15dh. Crowd with Green Book 10 10
908 15dh. Oil field 10 10
909 15dh. Refinery 10 10
910 30dh. Dish aerial 15 10
911 30dh. Hospital 15 10
912 30dh. Doctor examining patient 15 10
913 30dh. Surgeon 15 10
914 40dh. Street, Tripoli 20 15
915 40dh. Steel mill 20 15
916 40dh. Tanks 20 15

917 40dh. Tuareg horsemen . . . 20 15
918 70dh. Revolutionaries and Green Book 70 20
919 70dh. Crowd within map of Libya 70 20
920 70dh. Mullah 70 20
921 70dh. Student 70 20

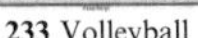

233 Volleyball **234** Emblem

1979. "Universiada '79" World University Games, Mexico City. Multicoloured.
923 45dh. Type **233** 20 15
924 115dh. Football . . . . . . 1·10 30

1979. 3rd World Telecommunications Exhibition, Geneva.
925 **234** 45dh. multicoloured . . . 20 15
926 115dh. multicoloured . . 1·25 30

235 Seminar Emblem and Crowd

1979. International Seminar on the "Green Book". Multicoloured.
927 10dh. Type **235** 10 10
928 35dh. Seminar in progress (horiz) (70 × 43 mm) . . . 45 15
929 100dh. Colonel Gaddafi with "Green Book" . . . . . . 1·00 30

236 Horsemen in Town

1979. Evacuation of Foreign Forces. Multicoloured.
931 30dh. Type **236** 15 10
932 40dh. Tuareg horsemen . . . 20 15

237 Football Match

1979. Mediterranean Games, Split.
934 **237** 15dh. multicoloured . . . 10 10
935 30dh. multicoloured . . . 50 10
936 70dh. multicoloured . . . 1·25 20

238 Cyclist and Emblem

1979. Junior Cycling Championships, Tripoli. Multicoloured.
937 15dh. Type **238** 10 10
938 30dh. Cyclists and emblem 15 10

239 Horse-jumping

1979. Pre-Olympics. Multicoloured.
939 45dh. Type **239** 20 15
940 60dh. Javelin 55 15
941 115dh. Hurdles . . . . . . 1·10 55
942 160dh. Football . . . . . . 1·40 65

Nos. 939/42 exist from sheets on which an overall Moscow Olympics emblem in silver was superimposed on the stamps.

240 Figure clothed in Palestinian Flag

1979. Solidarity with Palestinian People.
944 **240** 30dh. multicoloured . . . 15 10
945 115dh. multicoloured . . 1·10 30

241 Ploughing

1980. World Olive Oil Year.
946 **241** 15dh. multicoloured . . . 10 10
947 30dh. multicoloured . . . 15 10
948 45dh. multicoloured . . . 20 15

242 Hockey (left) **243** Pipes

1980. National Sports. Multicoloured.
949 10dh. Type **242** 10 10
950 10dh. Hockey (right) 10 10
951 10dh. Leap-frog (left) 10 10
952 10dh. Leap-frog (right) . . . 10 10
953 15dh. Long jump (left) . . . 10 10
954 15dh. Long jump (right) . . 10 10
955 15dh. Ball catching (left) . . 10 10
956 15dh. Ball catching (right) . . 10 10
957 20dh. Wrestling (left) 10 10
958 20dh. Wrestling (right) . . . 10 10
959 20dh. Stone throwing (left) 10 10
960 20dh. Stone throwing (right) 10 10
961 30dh. Tug-of-war (left) . . . 15 10
962 30dh. Tug-of-war (right) . . 15 10
963 30dh. Jumping (left) 15 10
964 30dh. Jumping (right) 15 10
965 45dh. Horsemen (left) 45 15
966 45dh. Horsemen (right) . . . 45 15
967 45dh. Horsemen with whips (left) 45 15
968 45dh. Horsemen with whips (right) 45 15

Nos. 949/68 were issued together, divided into se-tenant blocks of four within the sheet, each horizontal pair forming a composite design.

1980. 18th Tripoli International Fair. Multicoloured.
969 5dh. Drum (horiz) 10 10
970 10dh. Drum (different) (horiz) 10 10
971 15dh. Type **243** 10 10
972 20dh. Bagpipes (horiz) . . . 10 10
973 25dh. Stringed instrument and bow (horiz) 15 10

1980. International Year of the Child (1979) (2nd issue). As T **227**. Multicoloured.
975 20dh. "Horse Riding" . . . 10 10
976 20dh. "Beach scene" 10 10
977 20dh. "Fish" 10 10
978 20dh. "Birthday party" . . . 10 10
979 20dh. "Sheep Festival" . . . 10 10

244 Mosque and Kaaba

1980. 400th Anniv of Hejira.
980 **244** 50dh. multicoloured . . . 25 15
981 115dh. multicoloured . . 1·10 55

245 Surgical Operation and Hospital

1980. World Health Day.
982 **245** 20dh. multicoloured . . . 10 10
983 50dh. multicoloured . . . 50 15

246 Battle of Shoghab "Shahat", 1913

1980. Battles (1st series). Multicoloured.
984 20dh. Gardabia, 1915 . . . . 20 15
986 20dh. Type **246** 10 10
988 20dh. Fundugh al-Shibani "Garian" 10 10
990 20dh. Yefren 10 10
992 20dh. Ghira "Brak" 20 15
994 20dh. El Hani (Shiat) 35 15
996 20dh. Sebah 20 15
998 20dh. Sirt 10 10
985 35dh. Gardabia 10 10
987 35dh. Shoghab "Shahat" . . 20 15
989 35dh. Fundagh al-Shibani "Garian" 20 15
991 35dh. Yefren 20 15
993 35dh. Ghira "Brak" 20 15
995 35dh. El Hani (Shiat) 60 25
997 35dh. Sebah 20 15
999 35dh. Sirt 10 10

The two values commemorating each battle were issued in se-tenant pairs, each pair forming a composite design.

See also Nos. 1027/50, 1140/63 and 1257/80.

247 Flame **248** Ghadames

1980. Sheikh Zarruq Festival.
1000 **247** 40dh. multicoloured . . 20 15
1001 115dh. multicoloured . . 1·00 65

1980. Arabian Towns Organization. Mult.
1003 15dh. Type **248** 10 10
1004 30dh. Derna 15 10
1005 50dh. Ahmad Pasha Mosque, Tripoli 50 15

249 Guides on Hike

1980. 14th Pan-Arab Scout Jamboree. Multicoloured.
1006 15dh. Type **249** 10 10
1007 30dh. Guides cooking . . . 15 10
1008 50dh. Cub Scouts cooking 25 15
1009 115dh. Scouts map-reading 1·10 60

250 Oil Refinery

1980. 11th Anniv of Revolution. Multicoloured.
1011 5dh. Type **250** 10 10
1012 10dh. Recreation and youth 10 10
1013 15dh. Agriculture 10 10
1014 25dh. Boeing 727-200 airplane and liner 60 15
1015 40dh. Education 20 15
1016 115dh. Housing 95 30

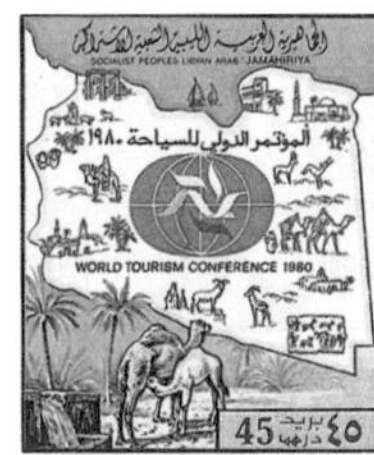

251 Camels, Map of Libya and Conference Emblem

1980. World Tourism Conference, Manila. Mult.
1018 45dh. Type **251** 20 15
1019 115dh. Emblem, map and camel riders 95 30

252 Figures supporting O.P.E.C. Emblem

1980. 20th Anniv of Organization of Petroleum Exporting Countries. Multicoloured.
1020 45dh. O.P.E.C. emblem and globe 20 15
1021 115dh. Type **252** 95 30

253 Death of Omar el Mukhtar

1980. 49th Death Anniv of Omar el Mukhtar (patriot).
1022 **253** 20dh. multicoloured . . 10 10
1023 35dh. multicoloured . . 20 15

253a Map of Libya and Science Symbols

1980. Birth Millenary of Avicenna (philosopher) and School Scientific Exhibition. Multicoloured.
1025 45dh. Type **253a** 20 15
1026 115d. Avicenna and Exhibition Emblem . . . 1·10 30

1981. Battles (2nd series). As T **246**. Mult.
1027 20dh. Zuara 10 10
1029 20dh. Tawargha 10 10
1031 20dh. Dernah 10 10
1033 20dh. Bir Tagreft 10 10
1035 20dh. Funduk El Jamel "Misurata" 10 10
1037 20dh. Sidi El Khemri "Gusbat" 10 10
1039 20dh. El Khoms 10 10
1041 20dh. Roghdalin "Menshia" 10 10
1043 20dh. Ain Zara "Tripoli" 10 10
1045 20dh. Rughbat el Naga "Benina" 10 10

1047 20dh. Tobruk 10 10
1049 20dh. Ikshadia "Werfella" 10 10
1028 35dh. Zuara 15 15
1030 35dh. Tawargha 15 15
1032 35dh. Dernah 15 15
1034 35dh. Bir Tagreft 15 15
1036 35dh. Funduk El Jamel "Misurata" 15 15
1038 35dh. Sidi El Khemri "Gusbat" 15 15
1040 35dh. El Khoms 15 15
1042 35dh. Roghdalin "Menshia" 15 15
1044 35dh. Ain Zara "Tripoli" 15 15
1046 35dh. Rughbat el Naga "Benina" 15 15
1048 35dh. Tobruk 15 15
1050 35dh. Ikshadia "Werfella" 15 15

The two values commemorating each battle were issued in se-tenant pairs, each pair forming a composite design.

254 Tent, Trees and Sun

1981. Children's Day. Children's Paintings. Multicoloured.
1051 20dh. Type **254** 10 10
1052 20dh. Women 10 10
1053 20dh. Picnic 10 10
1054 20dh. Aeroplane and playing children 10 10
1055 20dh. Mosque and man with camel 10 10

255 Central Bank

257 Crowd and "Green Book" Stamp of 1977

256 Pots

1981. 25th Anniv of Central Bank of Libya.
1056 **255** 45dh. multicoloured . . 15 15
1057 115dh. multicoloured . . 95 35

1981. Tripoli International Fair. Multicoloured.
1059 5dh. Type **256** 10 10
1060 10dh. Silver coffee pot (vert) 10 10
1061 15dh. Long-necked vase (vert) 10 10
1062 45dh. Round-bellied vase . . 45 15
1063 115dh. Jug . . . . 1·10 35

1981. People's Authority Declaration.
1064 **257** 50dh. multicoloured . . 15 15
1065 115dh. multicoloured . . 95 35

258 Tajoura Hospital, Medical Complex, Patients receiving Treatment and W.H.O. Emblem

1981. World Health Day.
1066 **258** 45dh. multicoloured . . 15 15
1067 115dh. multicoloured . . 95 35

259 Eye and Man on Crutches

1981. International Year of Disabled People.
1068 **259** 20dh. green, blue & black 10 10
1069 – 45dh. green, black & blue 15 15
1070 – 115dh. blue and green 1·00 35

DESIGNS: 45dh. Globe and I.Y.D.P. emblem; 115dh. Hands holding shield with I.Y.D.P. emblem, eye and man on crutch.

260 Horse

1981. Libyan Mosaics. Multicoloured.
1071 10dh. Type **260** 10 10
1072 20dh. Ship 10 10
1073 30dh. Birds, fish and flowers 10 10
1074 40dh. Leopard 40 15
1075 50dh. Man playing musical instrument 50 15
1076 115dh. Fishes . . . . 1·10 35

261 Racial Discrimination Emblem

262 Jet Fighters and Sud Aviation Alouette III Helicopter (left-hand stamp)

1981. Int Year Against Racial Discrimination.
1077 **261** 45dh. multicoloured . . 25 25
1078 50dh. multicoloured . . 55 30

1981. 12th Anniv of Revolution.
1079 **262** 5dh. blue and light blue 15 10
1080 – 5dh. blue and light blue 15 10
1081 – 5dh. blue and light blue 10 10
1082 – 5dh. blue and light blue 10 10
1083 – 10dh. black and blue . . 10 10
1084 – 10dh. black and blue . . 10 10
1085 – 10dh. black and blue . . 10 10
1086 – 10dh. black and blue . . 10 10
1087 – 15dh. brown & lt brown 10 10
1088 – 15dh. brown & lt brown 10 10
1089 – 15dh. brown & lt brown 10 10
1090 – 15dh. brown & lt brown 10 10
1091 – 20dh. blue and green . . 15 15
1092 – 20dh. blue and green . . 15 15
1093 – 20dh. blue and green . . 15 15
1094 – 20dh. blue and green . . 15 15
1095 – 25dh. brown and yellow 15 15
1096 – 25dh. brown and yellow 15 15
1097 – 25dh. brown and yellow 15 15
1098 – 25dh. brown and yellow 15 15

DESIGNS—VERT: No. 1080, Jet fighter (right-hand stamp); 1081/2, Parachutists; 1083/4, Tank parade; 1085/6, Marching frogmen; 1087/8, Anti-aircraft rocket trucks; 1089/90, Missile trucks. HORIZ: 1091/2, Marching sailors; 1093/4, Jeeps and anti-aircraft rocket trucks; 1095/6, Armoured vehicles and landrovers; 1097/8, Tank parade.

Each pair forms a horizontal composite design, the first number being the left-hand stamp in each instance.

263 Wheat and Plough

1981. World Food Day.
1100 **263** 45dh. multicoloured . . 25 25
1101 200dh. multicoloured . . 1·75 95

264 "Pseudotergumia fidia"

1981. Butterflies. Multicoloured.
1102 5dh. Type **264** 15 10
1103 5dh. "Chazara prieuri" (sun in background) 15 10
1104 5dh. "Polygonia c-album" (trees in background) . . 15 10
1105 5dh. "Colias crocea" (mosque in background) 15 10
1106 10dh. "Anthocharis bellia" (face value bottom right) 15 10
1107 10dh. "Pandoriana pandora" (face value bottom left) 15 10
1108 10dh. "Melanargia ines" (face value top right) . . 15 10
1109 10dh. "Charaxes jasius" (face value top left) . . . 15 10
1110 15dh. "Nymphales antiopa" (face value bottom right) 30 30
1111 15dh. "Eurodryas desfontainii" (face value bottom left) 30 30
1112 15dh. "Iphiclides podalirius" (face value top right) . . 30 30
1113 15dh. "Glaucopsyche melanops" (face value top left) 30 30
1114 25dh. "Spialia sertorius" (face value bottom right) 50 45
1115 25dh. "Pieris brassicae" (face value bottom left) 50 45
1116 25dh. "Lysandra albicans" (face value top right) . . 50 45
1117 25dh. "Celastrina argiolus" (face value top left) . . 50 45

The four designs of each value were issued together in small sheets of four, showing composite background designs.

265 Grapes

266 I.Y.D.P. Emblem and Globe

1981. Fruit. Multicoloured.
1119 5dh. Type **265** 10 10
1120 10dh. Dates 10 10
1121 15dh. Lemons 10 10
1122 20dh. Oranges 15 15
1123 35dh. Barbary figs 20 20
1124 55dh. Pomegranate 65 30

1981. International Year of Disabled Persons.
1125 **266** 45dh. multicoloured . . 25 25
1126 115dh. multicoloured . . 90 55

267 Animals (looking right)

1982. Libyan Mosaics. Multicoloured.
1127 45dh. Type **267** 50 25
1128 45dh. Orpheus 50 25
1129 45dh. Animals (looking left) 50 25
1130 45dh. Fishes 50 25
1131 45dh. Fishermen 50 25
1132 45dh. Fishes and ducks . . 50 25
1133 45dh. Farm 50 25
1134 45dh. Birds and fruit . . . 50 25
1135 45dh. Milking 50 25

268 Koran Texts leading to Ka'aba

269 Grinding Flour

1982. 3rd Koran Reading Contest. Multicoloured.
1136 10dh. Type **268** 10 10
1137 35dh. Koran and formation of the World 20 20
1138 115dh. Reading the Koran 95 55

1982. Battles (3rd series). As T **246**. Multicoloured.
1140 20dh. Hun "Gioffra" . . . 15 15
1142 20dh. Gedabia 15 15
1144 20dh. El Asaba "Gianduba" 15 15
1146 20dh. El Habela 15 15
1148 20dh. Suk El Ahad "Tarhuna" 15 15
1150 20dh. El Tangi 15 15
1152 20dh. Sokna 15 15
1154 20dh. Wadi Smalus "Jabel El Akdar" 15 15
1156 20dh. Sidi Abuagela "Agelat" 15 15
1158 20dh. Sidi Surur "Zeliten" 15 15
1160 20dh. Kuefia 15 15
1162 20dh. Abunjeim 15 15
1141 35dh. Hun "Gioffra" . . . 20 20
1143 35dh. Gedabia 20 20
1145 35dh. El Asaba "Gianduba" 20 20
1147 35dh. El Habela 20 20
1149 35dh. Suk El Ahad "Tarhuna" 20 20
1151 35dh. El Tangi 20 20
1153 35dh. Sokna 20 20
1155 35dh. Wadi Smalus "Jabel El Akdar" 20 20
1157 35dh. Sidi Abuagela "Agelat" 20 20
1159 35dh. Sidi Surur "Zeliten" 20 20
1161 35dh. Kuefia 20 20
1163 35dh. Abunjeim 20 20

The two values commemorating each battle were issued in se-tenant pairs, each pair forming a composite design.

1982. Tripoli International Fair. Multicoloured.
1164 5dh. Type **269** 10 10
1165 10dh. Ploughing 10 10
1166 25dh. Stacking hay 15 15
1167 35dh. Weaving 20 20
1168 45dh. Cooking 50 25
1169 100dh. Harvesting 95 50

270 "ALFATAH" forming Farm Vehicle

1982. People's Authority Declaration. Multicoloured.
1170 100dh. Type **270** 75 50
1171 200dh. Colonel Gaddafi, old man, "Green Book" and guns . . . . 1·75 95
1172 300dh. Rejoicing crowd . . 2·50 1·40

271 Scout flying Model Airship

272 Map of Africa and A.F.C. Emblem

1982. 75th Anniv of Boy Scout Movement. Mult.
1173 100dh. Type **271** 75 50
1174 200dh. Scouts helping injured dog . . . . 1·75 95
1175 300dh. Scout reading to old man . . . . 1·75 1·40
1176 400dh. Scout with model rocket . . . . 3·75 2·25

1982. African Football Cup Competition.
1178 **272** 100dh. multicoloured . . 95 50
1179 200dh. multicoloured . . 1·90 95

273 Footballer

1982. World Cup Football Championship, Spain. Multicoloured.
1180 45dh. Type **273** 25 25
1181 100dh. Footballer (different) 75 50
1182 200dh. As No. 1173 . . . . 1·60 95
1183 300dh. Footballer and goalkeeper . . . . 2·25 1·40

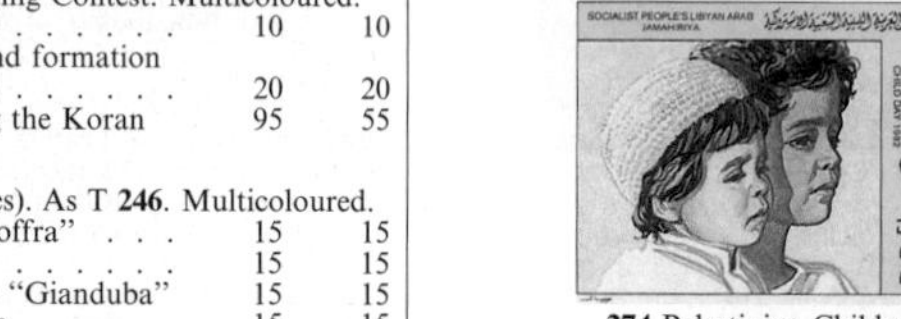

274 Palestinian Children

1982. Palestinian Children's Day. Multicoloured.

1185	20dh. Type **274**	15	15
1186	20dh. Girl with dish	15	15
1187	20dh. Child with turban	15	15
1188	20dh. Young child	15	15
1189	20dh. Young boy	15	15

275 Lanner Falcon

277 Map of Libya and A.P.U. Emblem

276 Nurses' Class, Operating Theatre and Doctor examining Child

1982. Birds. Multicoloured.

1190	15dh. Type **275**	35	25
1191	15dh. Eurasian swift	35	25
1192	15dh. Peregrine falcon	35	25
1193	15dh. Greater flamingo	35	25
1194	25dh. Whitethroat	60	35
1195	25dh. Turtle dove	60	35
1196	25dh. Black-bellied sandgrouse	60	35
1197	25dh. Egyptian vulture	60	35
1198	45dh. Golden oriole	1·00	60
1199	45dh. European bee eater	1·00	60
1200	45dh. River kingfisher	1·00	60
1201	45dh. European roller	1·00	60
1202	95dh. Barbary partridge	2·00	1·25
1203	95dh. Barn owl	2·00	1·25
1204	95dh. Cream-coloured courser	2·00	1·25
1205	95dh. Hoopoe	2·00	1·25

The four designs of each value were printed together in se-tenant blocks of four, forming a composite design.

1982. Teaching Hospitals.

1207	**276** 95dh. multicoloured	85	50
1208	100dh. multicoloured	85	50
1209	205dh. multicoloured	2·00	1·10

1982. 30th Anniv of Arab Postal Union.

1210	**277** 100dh. multicoloured	95	50
1211	200dh. multicoloured	1·90	95

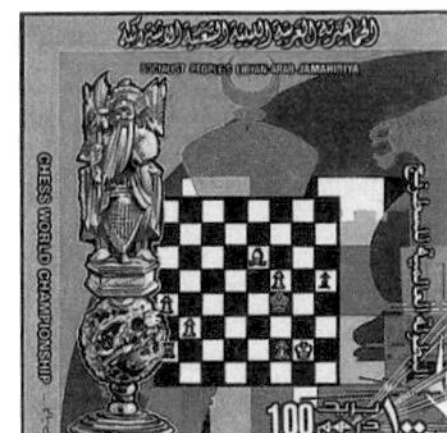

278 19th-century Chinese King and Diagram of Fischer v Spassky, 1972

1982. World Chess Championship, Moscow. Mult.

1212	100dh. Type **278**	1·25	50
1213	100dh. African king and diagram of Karpov v Korchnoi, 1978	1·25	50
1214	100dh. Modern bishop and diagram of Smyslov v Karpov, 1971	1·25	50
1215	100dh. 19th-century European rook and diagram of Tal v Vadasz, 1977	1·25	50

Nos. 1212/15 were printed together, se-tenant, forming a composite design.

279 Hexagonal Pattern

1982. World Telecommunications Day.

1217	**279** 100dh. multicoloured	75	50
1218	200dh. multicoloured	1·50	95

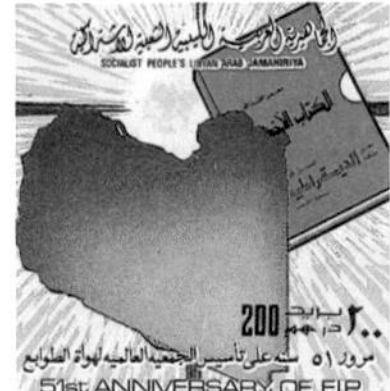

280 Map of Libya and "Green Book"

1982. 51st Anniv of International Philatelic Federation (F.I.P.).

1219	**280** 200dh. multicoloured	1·75	95

281 Family and Flag

283 Palm Tree and Red Crescent

282 Pres. Gaddafi and Jet Aircraft

1982. Organization of African Unity Summit. Multicoloured.

1221	50dh. Type **281**	30	30
1222	100dh. Map, dove and symbols of industry and agriculture	75	50
1223	200dh. Pres. Gaddafi and crowd with "Green Book" (65 × 36 mm.)	1·90	95

1982. 13th Anniv of Revolution. Multicoloured.

1225	15dh. Type **282**	15	10
1226	20dh. Gaddafi, soldiers and rockets	15	10
1227	30dh. Gaddafi, sailors and naval vessels	50	25
1228	45dh. Gaddafi, soldiers and tanks	25	25
1229	70dh. Gaddafi, and armed forces	60	35
1230	100dh. Gaddafi and women soldiers	90	50

1982. 25th Anniv of Libyan Red Crescent. Multicoloured.

1232	100dh. Type **283**	95	50
1233	200dh. "25" within crescents	1·90	95

284 Globe, Dove and Rifle

286 Philadelphus

285 Gaddafi, Crowd, "Green Book" and Emblems

1982. Solidarity with Palestinian People.

1234	**284** 100dh. black, mauve and green	95	40
1235	200dh. black, blue and green	1·90	80

1982. Al Fateh University Symposium on the "Green Book". Multicoloured.

1236	100dh. Type **285**	95	45
1237	200dh. Gaddafi, "Green Book", map and emblems	1·90	95

1983. Flowers. Multicoloured.

1238	25dh. Type **286**	15	10
1239	25dh. Hypericum	15	10
1240	25dh. Antirrhinum	15	10
1241	25dh. Lily	15	10
1242	25dh. Capparis	15	10
1243	25dh. Tropaeolum	15	10
1244	25dh. Roses	15	10
1245	25dh. Chrysanthemum	15	10
1246	25dh. "Nigella damascena"	15	10
1247	25dh. "Guilladia lanceolata"	15	10
1248	25dh. Dahlia	15	10
1249	25dh. "Dianthus caryophyllus"	15	10
1250	25dh. "Notobasis syriaca"	15	10
1251	25dh. "Nerium oleander"	15	10
1252	25dh. "Iris histroides"	15	10
1253	25dh. "Scolymus hispanicus"	15	10

287 Customs Council Building, Brussels, and Warrior on Horseback

288 Camel

1983. 30th Anniv of Customs Co-operation Council. Multicoloured.

1254	25dh. Type **287**	15	10
1255	50dh. Customs building	25	20
1256	100dh. Customs building and warrior with sword	50	45

1983. Battles (4th series). As T **246**. (a) Battle of Ghaser Ahmed.

1257	50dh. multicoloured	25	20
1258	50dh. multicoloured	25	20
	(b) Battle of Sidi Abuarghub.		
1259	50dh. multicoloured	25	20
1260	50dh. multicoloured	25	20
	(c) Battle of Ghar Yunes.		
1261	50dh. multicoloured	25	20
1262	50dh. multicoloured	25	20
	(d) Battle of Bir Otman.		
1263	50dh. multicoloured	25	20
1264	50dh. multicoloured	25	20
	(e) Battle of Sidi Sajeh.		
1265	50dh. multicoloured	25	20
1266	50dh. multicoloured	25	20
	(f) Battle of Ras el-Hamam.		
1267	50dh. multicoloured	25	20
1268	50dh. multicoloured	25	20
	(g) Battle of Zawiet Ishghefa.		
1269	50dh. multicoloured	25	20
1270	50dh. multicoloured	25	20
	(h) Battle of Wadi Essania.		
1271	50dh. multicoloured	25	20
1272	50dh. multicoloured	25	20
	(i) Battle of El-Meshiashta.		
1273	50dh. multicoloured	25	20
1274	50dh. multicoloured	25	20
	(j) Battle of Gharara.		
1275	50dh. multicoloured	25	20
1276	50dh. multicoloured	25	20
	(k) Battle of Abughelan.		
1277	50dh. multicoloured	20	20
1278	50dh. multicoloured	20	20
	(l) Battle of Mahruka.		
1279	50dh. multicoloured	20	20
1280	50dh. multicoloured	20	20

The two values for each battle were printed together in se-tenant pairs, forming composite designs.

1983. Farm Animals. Multicoloured.

1281	25dh. Type **288**	15	10
1282	25dh. Cow	15	10
1283	25dh. Horse	15	10
1284	25dh. Bull	15	10
1285	25dh. Goat	15	10
1286	25dh. Sheep dog	15	10
1287	25dh. Ewe	15	10
1288	25dh. Ram	15	10
1289	25dh. Greylag goose	35	25
1290	25dh. Helmeted guineafowl	35	25
1291	25dh. Rabbit	15	10
1292	25dh. Wood pigeon	35	25
1293	25dh. Common turkey	35	25
1294	25dh. Cockerel	15	10
1295	25dh. Hen	15	10
1296	25dh. Goose	15	10

289 Musician with Twin-horned Pipe

1983. Tripoli International Fair. Multicoloured.

1297	40dh. Type **289**	20	15
1298	45dh. Bagpipes (horiz)	25	20
1299	50dh. Horn	25	20
1300	55dh. Flute (horiz)	30	25
1301	75dh. Pipe	65	35
1302	100dh. Man and woman at well	90	45

290 Phoenician Galley

1983. 25th Anniv of International Maritime Organization. Multicoloured.

1303	100dh. Type **290**	1·25	55
1304	100dh. Ancient Greek galley	1·25	55
1305	100dh. Ancient Egyptian ship	1·25	55
1306	100dh. Roman sailing ship	1·25	55
1307	100dh. Viking longship	1·25	55
1308	100dh. Libyan xebec	1·25	55

291 Motorist

1983. Children's Day. Multicoloured.

1309	20dh. Type **291**	10	10
1310	20dh. Tractor and trailer	10	10
1311	20dh. Child with dove and globe	10	10
1312	20dh. Scout camp	10	10
1313	20dh. Dinosaur	10	10

292 Pres. Gaddafi with Children

1983. World Health Day. Multicoloured.

1314	25dh. Type **292**	15	10
1315	50dh. Gaddafi and old man in wheelchair	25	20
1316	100dh. Gaddafi visiting sick girl (horiz)	80	45

293 Gaddafi, Map and "Green Book"

294 Economic Emblems on Map of Africa

1983. 1st World "Green Book" Symposium. Mult.

1317	50dh. Type **293**	25	20
1318	70dh. Syposium in session and emblem (56 × 37 mm)	60	30
1319	80dh. Gaddafi, "Green Book", emblem and "Jamahiriya"	65	35

1983. 25th Anniv of African Economic Committee.

1321	**294** 50dh. multicoloured	25	20
1322	100dh. multicoloured	90	45
1323	250dh. multicoloured	1·90	1·10

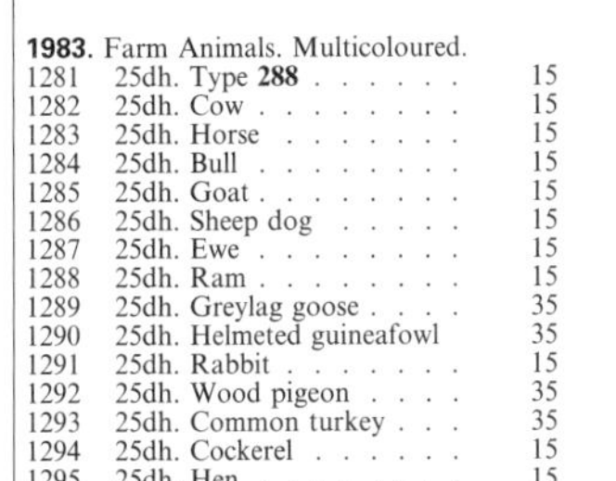

296 Cuckoo Wrasse ("Labrus bimaculatus")

1983. Fishes. Multicoloured.

No.	Description	Unused	Used
1325	25dh. Type **296**	30	15
1326	25dh. Streaked gurnard ("Trigoporus lastoviza")	30	15
1327	25dh. Peacock wrasse ("Thalassoma pavo")	30	15
1328	25dh. Mediterranean cardinal-fish ("Apogon imberbis")	30	15
1329	25dh. Atlantic mackerel ("Scomber scombrus")	30	15
1330	25dh. Black seabream ("Spondyliosoma cantharus")	30	15
1331	25dh. Greater weaver ("Trachinus draco")	30	15
1332	25dh. Peacock blenny ("Blennius pavo")	30	15
1333	25dh. Lesser red scorpionfish ("Scorpaena notata")	30	15
1334	25dh. Painted comber ("Serranus scriba")	30	15
1335	25dh. Angler ("Lophius piscatorius")	30	15
1336	25dh. Stargazer ("Uranoscopus scaber")	30	15
1337	25dh. Frigate mackerel ("Auxis thazard")	30	15
1338	25dh. John dory ("Zeus faber")	30	15
1339	25dh. Flying gurnard ("Dactylopterus volitans")	30	15
1340	25dh. Corb ("Umbrina cirrosa")	30	15

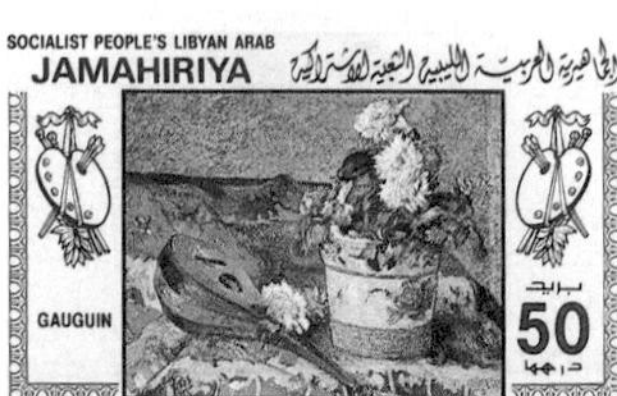

297 "Still-life" (Gauguin)

1983. Paintings. Multicoloured.

No.	Description	Unused	Used
1341	50dh. Type **297**	25	20
1342	50dh. Abstract	25	20
1343	50dh. "The Conquest of Tunis by Charles V" (Rubens)	25	20
1344	50dh. "Arab Band in Horse-drawn Carriage"	25	20
1345	50dh. "Apotheosis of Gaddafi" (vert)	25	20
1346	50dh. Horses (detail of Raphael's "The Triumph of David over the Assyrians") (vert)	25	20
1347	50dh. "Workers" (vert)	25	20
1348	50dh. "Sunflowers" (Van Gogh) (vert)	25	20

298 Basketball

1983. Olympic Games, Los Angeles. Mult.

No.	Description	Unused	Used
1349	10dh. Type **298**	10	10
1350	15dh. High jumping	10	10
1351	25dh. Running	15	10
1352	50dh. Gymnastics	25	20
1353	100dh. Windsurfing	80	45
1354	200dh. Shot-putting	1·50	95

299 I.T.U. Building, Antenna and W.C.Y. Emblem

1983. World Communications Year.

No.	Description	Unused	Used
1356 **299**	10dh. multicoloured	10	10
1357	50dh. multicoloured	25	20
1358	100dh. multicoloured	75	45

300 "The House is to be served by its Residents"

1983. Extracts from the Green Book. Mult.

No.	Description	Unused	Used
1359	10dh. Type **300**	10	10
1360	15dh. "Power, wealth and arms are in the hands of the people"	10	10
1361	20dh. "Masters in their own castles" (vert)	10	10
1362	35dh. "No democracy without popular congresses"	20	15
1363	100dh. "The authority of the people" (vert)	50	45
1364	140dh. "The Green Book is the guide of humanity for final release"	1·10	70

301 Handball

1983. 2nd African Youth Festival. Multicoloured.

No.	Description	Unused	Used
1366	100dh. Type **301**	85	45
1367	100dh. Basketball	85	45
1368	100dh. High jumping	85	45
1369	100dh. Running	85	45
1370	100dh. Football	85	45

302 Marching Soldiers

1983. 14th Anniv of September Revolution. Mult.

No.	Description	Unused	Used
1371	65dh. Type **302**	35	30
1372	75dh. Weapons and communications training	40	35
1373	90dh. Women with machine-guns and bazookas	70	40
1374	100dh. Machine-gun training	75	45
1375	150dh. Bazooka training	1·10	70
1376	250dh. Rifle training	2·00	1·10

303 Saluting Scouts

1983. Scout Jamborees. Multicoloured.

No.	Description	Unused	Used
1378	50dh. Type **303**	25	20
1379	100dh. Scouts around camp fire	90	45

EVENTS. 50dh. Second Islamic Scout Jamboree; 100dh. 15th Pan Arab Scout Jamboree.

304 Traffic Cadets **305** Saadun

1983. Traffic Day. Multicoloured.

No.	Description	Unused	Used
1381	30dh. Type **304**	40	15
1382	70dh. Traffic policeman	70	30
1383	200dh. Police motorcyclists	1·90	1·25

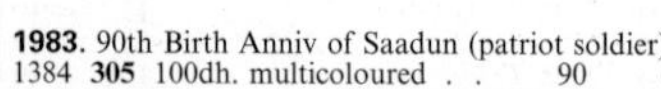

1983. 90th Birth Anniv of Saadun (patriot soldier).

No.	Description	Unused	Used
1384 **305**	100dh. multicoloured	90	45

306 Walter Wellman's airship "America", 1910

1983. Bicentenary of Manned Flight. Mult.

No.	Description	Unused	Used
1385	100dh. Type **306**	1·00	55
1386	100dh. Airship "Nulli Secundus", 1907	1·00	55
1387	100dh. Jean-Baptiste Meusnier's balloon design, 1784	1·00	55
1388	100dh. Blanchard and Jeffries' Channel crossing, 1785 (vert)	1·00	55
1389	100dh. Pilatre de Rozier's hydrogen/hot-air balloon flight, 1784 (vert)	1·00	55
1390	100dh. First Montgolfier balloon, 1783 (vert)	1·00	55

307 Globe and Dove

1983. Solidarity with Palestinian People.

No.	Description	Unused	Used
1393 **307**	200dh. green, blue & blk	1·60	95

308 Gladiators fighting

1983. Mosaics. Multicoloured.

No.	Description	Unused	Used
1394	50dh. Type **308**	50	20
1395	50dh. Gladiators fighting (different)	50	20
1396	50dh. Gladiators and slave	50	20
1397	50dh. Two musicians	50	20
1398	50dh. Three musicians	50	20
1399	50dh. Two gladiators	50	20
1400	50dh. Two Romans and bound victim	50	20
1401	50dh. Leopard and man hunting deer	50	20
1402	50dh. Deer and man with boar	50	20

309 Traditional Architecture

1983. Achievements of the Revolution. Mult.

No.	Description	Unused	Used
1403	10dh. Type **309**	10	10
1404	15dh. Camels drinking and mechanization of farming	10	10
1405	20dh. Computer operator and industrial scene	10	10
1406	35dh. Modern architecture	15	10
1407	100dh. Surgeons and nurses treating patients and hospital	90	40
1408	140dh. Airport and airplane	1·25	75

310 Flooding a River Bed **311** Mahmud Burkis

1983. Colonel Gaddafi—River Builder. Multicoloured.

No.	Description	Unused	Used
1410	50dh. Type **310**	20	15
1411	50dh. Irrigation pipe and agricultural produce	20	15
1412	100dh. Colonel Gaddafi, irrigation pipe and farmland (62 × 44 mm)	1·00	40
1413	100dh. Colonel Gaddafi and map (68 × 32 mm)	1·00	40
1414	150dh. Colonel Gaddafi explaining irrigation project (35 × 32 mm)	1·40	65

Nos. 1410/12 were printed together in se-tenant strips of three forming a composite design.

1984. Personalities. Multicoloured.

No.	Description	Unused	Used
1416	100dh. Type **311**	1·00	40
1417	100dh. Ahmed el-Bakbak	1·00	40
1418	100dh. Mohamed el-Misurati	1·00	40
1419	100dh. Mahmud Ben Musa	1·00	40
1420	100dh. Abdulhamid el-Sherif	1·00	40
1421	100dh. Mehdi el-Sherif	1·00	40
1422	100dh. Mahmud Mustafa Dreza	1·00	40
1423	100dh. Hosni Fauzi el-Amir	1·00	40
1424	100dh. Ali Haidar el-Saati	1·00	40
1425	200dh. Ahmed el-Feghi Hasan	1·50	80
1426	200dh. Bashir el-Jawab	1·50	80
1427	200dh. Ali el-Gariani	1·50	80
1428	200dh. Muktar Shakshuki	1·50	80
1429	200dh. Abdurrahman el-Busayri	1·50	80
1430	200dh. Ibbrahim Bakir	1·50	80
1431	200dh. Mahmud el-Janzuri	1·50	80

312 Windsurfing **313** Col. Gaddafi with Schoolchildren

1984. Water Sports. Multicoloured.

No.	Description	Unused	Used
1432	25dh. Type **312**	30	10
1433	25dh. Dinghy sailing (orange and red sails)	30	10
1434	25dh. Dinghy sailing (mauve sails)	30	10
1435	25dh. Hang-gliding on water skis	20	10
1436	25dh. Water-skiing	20	10
1437	25dh. Angling from boat	30	10
1438	25dh. Men in speed boat	30	10
1439	25dh. Water-skiing (different)	20	10
1440	25dh. Fishing	30	10
1441	25dh. Canoeing	20	10
1442	25dh. Surfing	20	10
1443	25dh. Water-skiing (different)	20	10
1444	25dh. Scuba diving	30	10
1445	25dh. Diving	30	10
1446	25dh. Swimming in snorkel and flippers	30	10
1447	25dh. Scuba diving for fish	30	10

1984. African Children's Day. Multicoloured.

No.	Description	Unused	Used
1448	50dh. Type **313**	50	15
1449	50dh. Colonel Gaddafi and children in national dress	50	15
1450	100dh. Colonel Gaddafi on map and children at various activities (62 × 43 mm)	1·90	60

314 Women in National, Casual and Military Dress

1984. Libyan Women's Emancipation. Multicoloured.

No.	Description	Unused	Used
1451	55dh. Type **314**	50	20
1452	70dh. Women in traditional, casual and military dress (vert)	75	25
1453	100dh. Colonel Gaddafi and women in military dress	95	40

315 Theatre, Sabratha

1984. Roman Ruins of Cyrenaica. Multicoloured.

No.	Description	Unused	Used
1454	50dh. Type **315**	20	15
1455	60dh. Temple, Cyrene	50	20
1456	70dh. Monument, Sabratha (vert)	60	25
1457	100dh. Amphitheatre, Leptis Magna	90	40

1458 150dh. Temple, Cyrene (different) . . . . 1·40 65
1459 200dh. Basilica, Leptis Magna . . . . 1·90 80

316 Silver Dirham, 115h. **318** Muktar Shiaker Murabet

317 Men at Tea Ceremony

1984. Arabic Islamic Coins (1st series).

1460 **316** 200dh. silver, yellow and black . . . . 1·90 85
1461 – 200dh. silver, mauve and black . . . . 1·90 85
1462 – 200dh. silver, green and black . . . . 1·90 85
1463 – 200dh. silver, orange and black . . . . 1·90 85
1464 – 200dh. silver, blue and black . . . . 1·90 85

DESIGNS: No. 1461, Silver dirham, 93h; 1462, Silver dirham, 121h; 1463, Silver dirham, 49h; 1464, Silver dirham, 135h.

See also Nos. 1643/5.

1984. International Trade Fair, Tripoli. Mult.

1465 25dh. Type **317** 15 10
1466 35dh. Woman making tea 15 15
1467 45dh. Men taking tea . . . 20 15
1468 55dh. Family taking tea . . 50 20
1469 75dh. Veiled women pouring tea 70 30
1470 100dh. Robed men taking tea . . . . 1·00 40

1984. Musicians. Multicoloured.

1471 100dh. Type **318** . . . . . 1·25 65
1472 100dh. El-Aref el-Jamal . . 1·25 65
1473 100dh. Ali Shiaalia . . . . 1·25 65
1474 100dh. Bashir Fehmi . . . 1·25 65

319 Playing among Trees

1984. Children's Day. Designs showing children's paintings. Multicoloured.

1475 20dh. Type **319** 10 10
1476 20dh. A rainy day 10 10
1477 20dh. Weapons of war . . . 10 10
1478 20dh. Playing on the swing 10 10
1479 20dh. Playing in the park 10 10

320 Crest and "39"

1984. 39th Anniv of Arab League.

1480 **320** 30dh. multicoloured . . 15 15
1481 40dh. multicoloured . . 20 15
1482 50dh. multicoloured . . 55 20

321 Red Four-seater Car

1984. Motor Cars and Steam Locomotives. Mult.

1483 100dh. Type **321** . . . . . 1·25 65
1484 100dh. Red three-seater car 1·25 65
1485 100dh. Yellow two-seater car with three lamps . . . 1·25 65
1486 100dh. Covered red four-seater car . . . . 1·25 65
1487 100dh. Yellow two-seater car with two lamps . . . 1·25 65
1488 100dh. Cream car with spare wheel at side . . . . . . 1·25 65
1489 100dh. Green car with spare wheel at side . . . . . . 1·25 65
1490 100dh. Cream four-seater car with spare wheel at back . . . . 1·25 65
1491 100dh. Locomotive pulling wagon and coach . . . . 1·40 45
1492 100dh. Purple and blue locomotive . . . . 1·40 45
1493 100dh. Cream locomotive 1·40 45
1494 100dh. Lilac and brown locomotive . . . . 1·40 45
1495 100dh. Lilac and black locomotive with red wheels . . . . 1·40 45
1496 100dh. Cream and red locomotive . . . . 1·40 45
1497 100dh. Purple and black locomotive with red wheels . . . . 1·40 45
1498 100dh. Green and orange locomotive . . . . 1·40 45

322 Stylized People and Campaign Emblem

1984. World Health Day. Anti-Polio Campaign. Multicoloured.

1499 20dh. Type **322** 10 10
1500 30dh. Stylized people and 1981 20dh. stamp 15 15
1501 40dh. Stylized people and Arabic emblem 50 15

323 Man making Slippers

1984. Handicrafts. Multicoloured.

1502 150dh. Type **323** . . . . . 1·60 65
1503 150dh. Man making decorative harness . . . . 1·60 65
1504 150dh. Women forming cotton into skeins . . . . 1·60 65
1505 150dh. Woman spinning by hand . . . . 1·60 65
1506 150dh. Man weaving . . . 1·60 65
1507 150dh. Women weaving . . 1·60 65

324 Telephones, Dial and Mail

1984. Postal and Telecommunications Union Congress. Multicoloured.

1508 50dh. Type **324** 50 20
1509 50dh. Woman working at computer console, dial and man working on computer 50 20
1510 100dh. Satellite, map, laurel branches and telephone handset . . . . 1·00 40

325 Armed Soldiers and Civilians **326** Children behind Barbed Wire

1984. Abrogation of 17 May Treaty. Multicoloured.

1511 50dh. Type **325** 65 20
1512 50dh. Map, dove and burning banner 65 20
1513 50dh. Soldiers shaking hands and crowd with banners (30 × 40 mm) . . 65 20
1514 100dh. Hands tearing treaty, Gaddafi and crowd (62 × 40 mm) . . . . . . 1·25 40
1515 100dh. Gaddafi addressing crowd . . . . 1·25 40

Nos. 1512/14 were printed together in se-tenant strips of three, forming a composite design.

1984. Child Victims of Invasion Day. Multicoloured.

1516 70dh. Torn flags on barbed wire 70 25
1517 100dh. Type **326** . . . . . 1·00 40

327 "The Party System Aborts Democracy" **328** Man in Brown Robes

1984. Quotations from "The Green Book". Multicoloured.

1518 100dh. Type **327** 95 40
1519 100dh. Colonel Gaddafi . . 95 40
1520 100dh. "Partners not wage-workers" 95 40
1521 100dh. "No representation in lieu of the people. Representation is falsification" 95 40
1522 100dh. The Green Book . . 95 40
1523 100dh. "Committees everywhere" 95 40
1524 100dh. "Forming parties splits societies" 95 40
1525 100dh. Skyscraper and earthmover 95 40
1526 100dh. "No democracy without popular congresses" 95 40

1984. Costumes. Multicoloured.

1527 100dh. Type **328** . . . . . 1·25 65
1528 100dh. Woman in green dress and red shawl . . . 1·25 65
1529 100dh. Man in ornate costume and turban . . . 1·25 65
1530 100dh. Man in short trousers and plain shirt 1·25 65
1531 100dh. Woman in shift and trousers with white shawl 1·25 65
1532 100dh. Man in long white robe and red shawl . . . 1·25 65

329 Footballer tackling

1984. World Cup Football Championship. Mult.

1533 70dh. Type **329** 70 25
1534 70dh. Footballers in magenta and green shirts 70 25
1535 70dh. Footballers in orange and lemon shirts 70 25
1536 70dh. Goalkeeper failing to save ball 70 25
1537 70dh. Footballers in yellow and brown shirts 70 25
1538 70dh. Top of Trophy and footballer in green striped shirt 70 25
1539 70dh. Top of Trophy and footballers in blue and pink shirts 70 25
1540 70dh. Footballers in black and white striped and green and red striped shirts 70 25
1541 70dh. Footballers in green and red striped shirts . . 70 25
1542 70dh. Foot of trophy and footballers in orange striped and blue shirts . . 70 25
1543 70dh. Foot of trophy and goalkeeper 70 25
1544 70dh. Goalkeeper saving headed ball 70 25
1545 70dh. Referee and footballers 70 25
1546 70dh. Footballers in white with red striped sleeves and orange shirts 70 25
1547 70dh. Footballers in white and green striped and orange shirts 70 25
1548 70dh. Footballer in pink shirt 70 25

Nos. 1533/48 were printed in sheetlets of 16 stamps, the backgrounds to the stamps forming an overall design of a stadium.

330 Football **331** Palm Trees

1984. Olympic Games, Los Angeles. Mult.

1549 100dh. Type **330** . . . . . 1·25 65
1550 100dh. Swimming . . . . . 1·25 65
1551 100dh. Throwing the discus 1·25 65
1552 100dh. Windsurfing . . . . 1·25 65
1553 100dh. Basketball . . . . . 1·25 65
1554 100dh. Running . . . . . . 1·25 65

1984. 9th World Forestry Congress. Mult.

1556 100dh. Four types of forest 1·10 40
1557 200dh. Type **331** . . . . . 2·10 1·10

332 Modern Building

1984. 15th Anniv of Revolution. Multicoloured.

1558 25dh. Type **332** 15 10
1559 25dh. Front of building . . . 15 10
1560 25dh. Building by pool . . . 15 10
1561 25dh. Col. Gaddafi (three-quarter portrait) 15 10
1562 25dh. High-rise block . . . 15 10
1563 25dh. Crane and mosque . . 15 10
1564 25dh. Motorway interchange 15 10
1565 25dh. House and garden . . 15 10
1566 25dh. Shepherd and flock 15 10
1567 25dh. Combine harvester . . 15 10
1568 25dh. Tractors 15 10
1569 25dh. Scientific equipment 15 10
1570 25dh. Col. Gaddafi (full face) 15 10
1571 25dh. Water pipeline . . . 15 10
1572 25dh. Lighthouse 15 10
1573 25dh. Liner at quay 45 10

333 Armed Man

334 Soldier flogging Civilian

1984. Evacuation of Foreign Forces. Mult.

(a) As T **333**.

1574 50dh. Type **333** 50 20
1575 50dh. Armed man (different) 50 20
1576 100dh. Men on horseback charging (62 × 40 mm) . . 1·00 40

(b) As T **334**.

1577 100dh. Type **334** . . . . . 1·00 40
1578 100dh. Girl on horse charging soldiers . . . . 1·00 40
1579 100dh. Mounted soldiers and wounded being tended by women . . . . 1·00 40

335 Woman riding Skewbald Showjumper

1984. Equestrian Events. Multicoloured.
1580 25dh. Type **335** 15 10
1581 25dh. Man riding black showjumper (stands in background) 15 10
1582 25dh. Jockey riding chestnut horse (stands in background) 15 10
1583 25dh. Man on chestnut horse jumping in cross-country event 15 10
1584 25dh. Man riding bay horse in showjumping competition 15 10
1585 25dh. Woman on black horse in dressage competition 15 10
1586 25dh. Man on black horse in dressage competition 15 10
1587 25dh. Woman riding chestnut horse in cross-country event 15 10
1588 25dh. Jockey riding bay horse 15 10
1589 25dh. Woman on bay horse in dressage competition 15 10
1590 25dh. Man on grey horse in dressage competition . . . 15 10
1591 25dh. Jockey riding grey steeplechaser 15 10
1592 25dh. Woman riding grey showjumper 15 10
1593 25dh. Woman riding through water in cross-country competition . . . 15 10
1594 25dh. Woman on chestnut horse in cross-country competition 15 10
1595 25dh. Man riding dun showjumper 15 10
Nos. 1580/95 were printed together in sheetlets of 16 stamps, the backgrounds of the stamps forming an overall design of an equestrian ring.

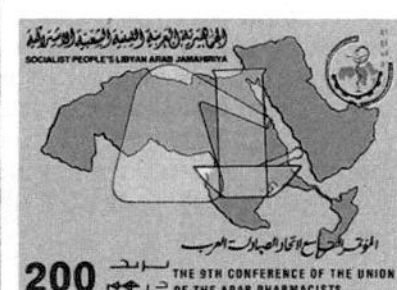

336 Man cleaning Corn **337** Map and Pharmaceutical Equipment

1984. Traditional Agriculture. Multicoloured.
1596 100dh. Type **336** . . . . . 1·25 65
1597 100dh. Man using oxen to draw water from well . . 1·25 65
1598 100dh. Man making straw goods . . . . 1·25 65
1599 100dh. Shepherd with sheep 1·25 65
1600 100dh. Man treating animal skin . . . . 1·25 65
1601 100dh. Man climbing coconut tree . . . . . . 1·25 65

1984. 9th Conference of Arab Pharmacists Union.
1602 **337** 100dh. multicoloured . . 1·25 40
1603 200dh. multicoloured . . 2·50 1·10

338 Crowd with Banner showing Map of North Africa

1984. Arab–African Unity. Multicoloured.
1604 100dh. Type **338** . . . . . 1·25 65
1605 100dh. Crowd and men holding flags . . . . . . 1·25 65

339 1982 and 1983 Solidarity Stamps and Map of Palestine

1984. Solidarity with Palestinian People.
1606 **339** 100dh. multicoloured . . 1·25 40
1607 150dh. multicoloured . . 1·90 1·00

340 Boeing 747SP, 1975

1984. 40th Anniv of International Civil Aviation Organization. Multicoloured.
1608 70dh. Type **340** 95 30
1609 70dh. Concorde, 1969 . . . 95 30
1610 70dh. Lockheed TriStar 500, 1978 . . . . 95 30
1611 70dh. Airbus Industrie A310, 1982 . . . . 95 30
1612 70dh. Tupolev Tu-134A, 1962 . . . . 95 30
1613 70dh. Shorts 360, 1981 . . . 95 30
1614 70dh. Boeing 727-100, 1963 95 30
1615 70dh. Sud Aviation Caravelle 10R, 1965 . . . 95 30
1616 70dh. Fokker Friendship, 1955 . . . . 95 30
1617 70dh. Lockheed Constellation, 1946 . . . 95 30
1618 70dh. Martin M-130 flying boat, 1955 . . . . 95 30
1619 70dh. Douglas DC-3, 1936 95 50
1620 70dh. Junkers Ju-52/3m, 1932 . . . . 95 30
1621 70dh. Lindbergh's "Spirit of St. Louis", 1927 . . . . 95 30
1622 70dh. De Havilland Moth, 1925 . . . . 95 30
1623 70dh. Wright Flyer I, 1903 95 30
Nos. 1608/23 were printed together in sheetlets of 16 stamps, the backgrounds of the stamps forming an overall design of a runway.

341 Coin **342** Mother and Son

1984. 20th Anniv of African Development Bank. Multicoloured.
1624 50dh. Type **341** 55 20
1625 70dh. Map of Africa and "20" . . . . 1·00 25
1626 100dh. "20" and symbols of industry and agriculture 1·25 65

1985. UNICEF Child Survival Campaign. Multicoloured.
1627 70dh. Type **342** . . . . . . 1·00 50
1628 70dh. Couple and children 1·00 50
1629 70dh. Col. Gaddafi and children . . . . 1·00 50
1630 70dh. Boys in uniform . . . 1·00 50

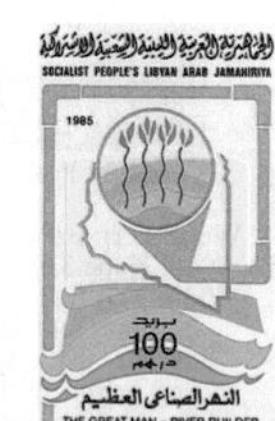

343 Mohamed Hamdi **344** Pipeline, River, Plants and Map

1985. Musicians and Instruments. Multicoloured.
1631 100dh. Kamel el-Ghadi . . 1·25 65
1632 100dh. Fiddle rebab . . . . 1·25 65
1633 100dh. Ahmed el-Khogia . . 1·25 65
1634 100dh. Violin . . . . 1·25 65
1635 100dh. Mustafa el-Fallah . . 1·25 65
1636 100dh. Zither . . . . 1·25 65
1637 100dh. Type **343** . . . . . 1·25 65
1638 100dh. Mask . . . . 1·25 65

1985. Col. Gaddafi—River Builder. Multicoloured.
1639 100dh. Type **344** . . . . . 1·25 65
1640 100dh. Water droplet, river and flowers . . . . 1·25 65
1641 100dh. Dead tree with branch thriving in water droplet . . . . 1·25 65

345 Gold Dinar, 105h.

1985. Arabic Islamic Coins (2nd series). Mult.
1643 200dh. Type **345** . . . . . 2·50 1·25
1644 200dh. Gold dinar, 91h. . . 2·50 1·25
1645 200dh. Gold dinar, 77h. . . 2·50 1·25

346 Fish **347** Gaddafi in Robes and Hat

1985. Fossils. Multicoloured.
1647 150dh. Type **346** . . . . . 3·00 90
1648 150dh. Frog . . . . 1·90 55
1649 150dh. Mammal . . . . . 1·90 55

1985. People's Authority Declaration. Mult.
1650 100dh. Type **347** . . . . . 1·25 65
1651 100dh. Gaddafi in black robe holding book . . . 1·25 65
1652 100dh. Gaddafi in dress uniform without cap . . . 1·25 65
1653 100dh. Gaddafi in black dress uniform with cap . . 1·25 65
1654 100dh. Gaddafi in white dress uniform . . . . . . 1·25 65

348 Cymbal Player

1985. International Trade Fair, Tripoli. Mult.
1655 100dh. Type **348** . . . . . 1·25 65
1656 100dh. Piper and drummer 1·25 65
1657 100dh. Drummer and bagpipes player . . . . . 1·25 65
1658 100dh. Drummer . . . . . 1·25 65
1659 100dh. Tambour player . . 1·25 65

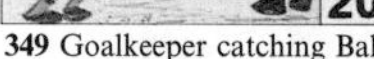

349 Goalkeeper catching Ball **350** Emblem, Radio Transmitter and Satellite

1985. Children's Day. Multicoloured.
1660 20dh. Type **349** 10 10
1661 20dh. Child on touchline with ball 10 10
1662 20dh. Letters of alphabet as players 10 10
1663 20dh. Goalkeeper saving ball 10 10
1664 20dh. Player heading ball 10 10

1985. International Communications Development Programme.
1665 **350** 30dh. multicoloured . . 15 10
1666 70dh. multicoloured . . 75 25
1667 100dh. multicoloured . . 1·10 65

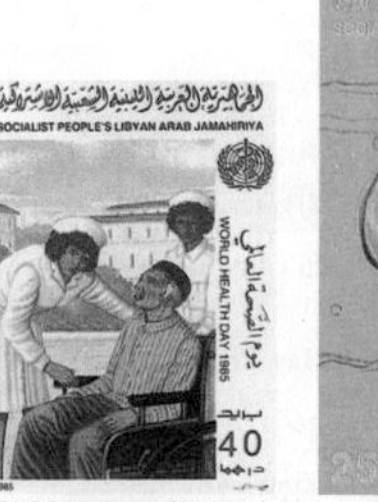

351 Nurses and Man in Wheelchair **352** "Mytilidae"

1985. World Health Day. Multicoloured.
1668 40dh. Type **351** 50 10
1669 60dh. Nurses and doctors 75 15
1670 100dh. Nurse and child . . 1·25 65

1985. Sea Shells. Multicoloured.
1671 25dh. Type **352** 40 15
1672 25dh. Purple dye murex ("Muricidae") 40 15
1673 25dh. Tuberculate cockle ("Cardiidae") 40 15
1674 25dh. "Corallophilidae" . . 40 15
1675 25dh. Trunculus murex ("Muricidae") 40 15
1676 25dh. "Muricacea" 40 15
1677 25dh. "Turridae" 40 15
1678 25dh. Nodose paper nautilus ("Argonautidae") 40 15
1679 25dh. Giant tun ("Tonnidae") 40 15
1680 25dh. Common pelican's-foot ("Aporrhaidae") . . 40 15
1681 25dh. "Trochidae" 40 15
1682 25dh. "Cancellariidae" . . . 40 15
1683 25dh. "Epitoniidae" 40 15
1684 25dh. "Turbinidae" 40 15
1685 25dh. Zoned mitre ("Mitridae") 40 15
1686 25dh. Cat's-paw scallop ("Pectinidae") 40 15
Nos. 1671/86 were printed se-tenant, the backgrounds forming an overall design of the sea bed.

353 Books and Emblem **354** Girls Skipping

1985. International Book Fair, Tripoli.
1687 **353** 100dh. multicoloured . . 1·25 60
1688 200dh. multicoloured . . 2·25 1·25

1985. International Youth Year. Multicoloured.
1689 20dh. Type **354** 10 10
1690 20dh. Boys playing with stones 10 10
1691 20dh. Girls playing hopscotch 10 10
1692 20dh. Boys playing with sticks 10 10
1693 20dh. Boys playing with spinning top 10 10

355 Abdussalam Lasmar Mosque **356** Jamila Zemerli

1985. Minarets. Multicoloured.
1695 50dh. Type **355** 50 15
1696 50dh. Zaoviat Kadria Mosque 50 15
1697 50dh. Zaoviat Amura Mosque 50 15
1698 50dh. Gurgi Mosque . . . 50 15
1699 50dh. Mizran Mosque . . . 50 15
1700 50dh. Salem Mosque . . . 50 15
1701 50dh. Ghat Mosque 50 15
1702 50dh. Ahmed Karamanli Mosque 50 15
1703 50dh. Atya Mosque 50 15
1704 50dh. El Kettani Mosque 50 15
1705 50dh. Benghazi Mosque . . 50 15
1706 50dh. Derna Mosque . . . 50 15
1707 50dh. El Derug Mosque . . 50 15
1708 50dh. Ben Moussa Mosque 50 15
1709 50dh. Ghadames Mosque 50 15
1710 50dh. Abdulwahab Mosque 50 15

1985. Teachers' Day. Multicoloured.
1711 100dh. Type **356** . . . . . 1·25 65
1712 100dh. Hamida El-Anezi . . 1·25 65

357 "Philadelphia" exploding

358 Gaddafi and Followers

1985. Battle of the "Philadelphia". Multicoloured.

1713 50dh. Type **357** 60 20
1714 50dh. Men with swords . . 60 20
1715 100dh. Men fighting and ship's rigging (59 × 45 mm) . . . . . . 1·25 45

Nos. 1713/15 were printed together, se-tenant, forming a composite design.

1986. Colonel Gaddafi's Islamic Pilgrimage. Multicoloured.

1716 200dh. Gaddafi writing . . 2·50 1·25
1717 200dh. Gaddafi praying . . 2·50 1·25
1718 200dh. Gaddafi, crowds and Kaaba . . . . 2·50 1·25
1719 200dh. Gaddafi and mirror 2·50 1·25
1720 200dh. Type **358** . . . . . 2·50 1·25

359 "Leucopaxillus lepistoides"

1985. Mushrooms. Multicoloured.

1722 50dh. Type **359** . . . . . . 1·10 25
1723 50dh. "Amanita caesarea" 1·10 25
1724 50dh. "Coriolus hirsutus" 1·10 25
1725 50dh. "Cortinarius subfulgens" . . . . . . 1·10 25
1726 50dh. "Dermocybe pratensis" . . . . 1·10 25
1727 50dh. "Macrolepiota excoriata" . . . . 1·10 25
1728 50dh. "Amanita curtipes" 1·10 25
1729 50dh. "Trametes ljubarskyi" 1·10 25
1730 50dh. "Pholiota aurivella" 1·10 25
1731 50dh. "Boletus edulis" . . . 1·10 25
1732 50dh. "Geastrum sessile" . . 1·10 25
1733 50dh. "Russula sanguinea" 1·10 25
1734 50dh. "Cortinarius herculeus" . . . . 1·10 25
1735 50dh. "Pholiota lenta" . . . 1·10 25
1736 50dh. "Amanita rubescens" 1·10 25
1737 50dh. "Seleroderma polyrhizum" . . . . . . 1·10 25

Nos. 1722/37 were printed together, se-tenant, the backgrounds of the stamps forming an overall design of map of Mediterranean.

360 Woman in Purple Striped Dress

361 "In Need Freedom is Latent"

1985. Traditional Women's Costumes. Multicoloured.

1738 100dh. Type **360** . . . . . 1·25 65
1739 100dh. Woman in robes covering her face . . . . 1·25 65
1740 100dh. Woman in colourful robes with heavy jewellery 1·25 65
1741 100dh. Woman in long blue striped dress . . . . . . 1·25 65
1742 100dh. Woman in red dress and trousers . . . . . . 1·25 65

1985. Quotations from "The Green Book".

1743 **361** 100dh. lt green, grn & blk 45 35
1744 – 100dh. multicoloured . . 45 35
1745 – 100dh. lt green, grn & blk 45 35
1746 – 100dh. lt green, grn & blk 45 35
1747 – 100dh. multicoloured . . 45 35
1748 – 100dh. lt green, grn & blk 45 35
1749 – 100dh. lt green, grn & blk 45 35
1750 – 100dh. multicoloured . . 45 35
1751 – 100dh. lt green, grn & blk 45 35

DESIGNS: No. 1744, Gaddafi in uniform reading; 1745, "To make a party you split society"; 1746, "Public sport is for all the masses"; 1747, "Green Books" and doves; 1748, "Wage-workers are a type of slave, however improved their wages may be"; 1749, "People are only harmonious with their own arts and heritages"; 1750, Gaddafi addressing crowd; 1751, "Democracy means popular rule not popular expression".

362 Tree and Citrus Fruits

1985. 16th Anniv of Revolution. Multicoloured.

1752 100dh. Type **362** . . . . . 1·25 65
1753 100dh. Oil pipeline and tanks . . . . 1·25 65
1754 100dh. Capital and olive branch . . . . 1·25 65
1755 100dh. Mosque and modern buildings . . . . 1·25 65
1756 100dh. Flag and mountains 1·25 65
1757 100dh. Telecommunications 1·25 65

363 Zauiet Amoura, Janzour

364 Players in Red No. 5 and Green Shirts

1985. Mosque Gateways. Multicoloured.

1759 100dh. Type **363** . . . . . 1·25 65
1760 100dh. Shiaieb El-Ain, Tripoli . . . . 1·25 65
1761 100dh. Zauiet Abdussalam El-Asmar, Zliten . . . . 1·25 65
1762 100dh. Karamanli, Tripoli 1·25 65
1763 100dh. Gurgi, Tripoli . . . 1·25 65

1985. Basketball. Multicoloured.

1764 25dh. Type **364** 15 10
1765 25dh. Players in green number 7 and red shirts 15 10
1766 25dh. Players in green number 8 and red shirts 15 10
1767 25dh. Players in red number 6 and green shirts 15 10
1768 25dh. Players in red number 4 and green number 7 shirts 15 10
1769 25dh. Players in green numbers 6 and 5 and red number 9 shirts 15 10
1770 25dh. Basket and one player in red and two in green shirts 15 10
1771 25dh. Players in red number 8 and green number 7 shirts 15 10
1772 25dh. Two players in green shirts and two in red shirts, one number 4 . . . 15 10
1773 25dh. Players in red numbers 4 and 7 and green shirts 15 10
1774 25dh. Players in red numbers 4 and 9 and green numbers 7 and 4 shirts 15 10
1775 25dh. Players in red number 6 and green shirts 15 10
1776 25dh. Players in red number 9 and green number 8 shirts 15 10
1777 25dh. Players in red number 8 and green number 5 shirts 15 10
1778 25dh. Players in red number 4 and green shirts 15 10
1779 25dh. Players in red number 5 and green number 10 shirts 15 10

Nos. 1764/79 were printed together se-tenant, the backgrounds of the stamps forming an overall design of basketball court and basket.

365 People in Light Ray

1985. Evacuation of Foreign Forces. Multicoloured.

1780 100dh. Man on crutches in web and light shining on tree . . . . 1·25 65
1781 100dh. Hands pulling web away from man . . . . . 1·25 65
1782 100dh. Type **365** . . . . . 1·25 65

366 Stockbook, Magnifying Glass and Stamps

367 Players

1985. Stamp Day. "Italia '85" International Stamp Exhibition, Rome. Multicoloured.

1783 50dh. Man and desk on flying stamp above globe 65 15
1784 50dh. Type **366** 65 15
1785 50dh. Stamps escaping from wallet 65 15

1986. World Cup Football Championship, Mexico (1st issue). Multicoloured.

1786 100dh. Type **367** . . . . . 1·25 65
1787 100dh. Players in red and white number 10 and yellow shirts . . . . . . 1·25 65
1788 100dh. Goalkeeper and player defending goal against attack . . . . . 1·25 65
1789 100dh. Goalkeeper diving to make save . . . . 1·25 65
1790 100dh. Goalkeeper jumping to make save . . . . . . 1·25 65
1791 100dh. Player in red and white shirt tackling player in lime shirt . . . . . . 1·25 65

See also Nos. 1824/9.

368 Hands releasing Dove

1985. Solidarity with Palestinian People.

1793 **368** 100dh. multicoloured . . 95 35
1794 150dh. multicoloured . . 1·60 75

370 Headquarters and Dish Aerial

371 Paper and Quill in Hand

1986. 1st Anniv of General Posts and Telecommunications Corporation.

1807 **370** 100dh. multicoloured . . 1·00 30
1808 150dh. multicoloured . . 1·50 75

1986. Peoples' Authority Declaration. Multicoloured.

1809 50dh. Type **371** 65 40
1810 50dh. Paper and globe in hand 65 40
1811 100dh. "Green Books" and dove (53 × 37 mm) . . . 1·25 65

372 Flute

1986. International Trade Fair, Tripoli. Mult.

1812 100dh. Type **372** . . . . . 1·25 65
1813 100dh. Drums . . . . . . 1·25 65
1814 100dh. Double pipes . . . . 1·25 65
1815 100dh. Tambourines . . . . 1·25 65
1816 100dh. Drum hung from shoulder . . . . 1·25 65

373 Boy Scout with Fish on Hook

1986. Children's Day. Multicoloured.

1817 50dh. Type **373** . . . . . . 1·10 25
1818 50dh. Boy on camel 65 15
1819 50dh. Boy catching butterflies 65 15
1820 50dh. Boy playing drum . . 65 15
1821 50dh. Boy and giant goalkeeper on football pitch 65 15

374 Emblem, Man and Skull in Blood Droplet

1986. World Health Day. Multicoloured, background colours given.

1822 **374** 250dh. silver . . . . . . 2·50 1·25
1823 250dh. gold . . . . . . 2·50 1·25

375 Footballers

1986. World Cup Football Championship, Mexico (2nd issue). Multicoloured.

1824 50dh. Type **375** 65 15
1825 50dh. Player jumping over player on ground 65 15
1826 50dh. Referee and players 65 15
1827 50dh. Goalkeeper trying to save ball 65 15
1828 50dh. Player about to tackle 65 15
1829 50dh. Player jumping over ball 65 15

376 Peas

377 Health Programmes

1986. Vegetables. Multicoloured.

1831 50dh. Type **376** 45 15
1832 50dh. Marrow 45 15
1833 50dh. Beans 45 15
1834 50dh. Aubergine 45 15
1835 50dh. Corn on the cob . . . 45 15
1836 50dh. Tomato 45 15
1837 50dh. Red pepper 45 15
1838 50dh. Zucchini 45 15
1839 50dh. Garlic 45 15
1840 50dh. Cabbage 45 15
1841 50dh. Cauliflower 45 15
1842 50dh. Celery 45 15
1843 50dh. Onions 45 15
1844 50dh. Carrots 45 15
1845 50dh. Potato 45 15
1846 50dh. Radishes 45 15

Nos. 1831/46 were printed together in sheetlets of 16 stamps, the backgrounds of the stamps forming an overall design of a garden.

1986. Jamahiriya Thought. Multicoloured.

1847 50dh. Type **377** 50 15
1848 50dh. Education programmes 50 15
1849 100dh. "Green Book", agricultural scenes and produce (agriculture programmes) (62 × 41 mm) . . . . . . 1·75 45

378 Gaddafi studying Plan

1986. Colonel Gaddafi, "Great man-made River Builder". Multicoloured.
1850 100dh. Type **378** 95 30
1851 100dh. Gaddafi showing planned route on map 95 30
1852 100dh. Gaddafi and old well 95 30
1853 100dh. Gaddafi in desert 95 30
1854 100dh. Gaddafi and pipe 95 30
1855 100dh. Gaddafi at pumping station 95 30
1856 100dh. Gaddafi and storage tank 95 30
1857 100dh. Workers' hut 95 30
1858 100dh. Water in cupped hands and irrigation equipment 95 30
1859 100dh. Gaddafi turning wheel at opening ceremony 95 30
1860 100dh. Laying pipes 95 30
1861 100dh. Pipe sections on lorries 95 30
1862 100dh. Gaddafi in robes holding "Green Book" 95 30
1863 100dh. Boy giving Gaddafi bowl of fruit 95 30
1864 100dh. Boy drinking from tap 95 30
1865 100dh. Gaddafi praying 95 30

379 Gaddafi with Children

1986. Colonel Gaddafi, "Man of Peace". Mult.
1866 100dh. Type **379** 1·10 30
1867 100dh. Reading book in tent 1·10 30
1868 100dh. With his mother 1·10 30
1869 100dh. Praying in tent with his sons 1·10 30
1870 100dh. Talking to hospital patient 1·10 30
1871 100dh. Driving tractor 1·10 30

380 General Dynamics F-111 Exploding above Man with injured Child

381 Gaddafi, Ruined buildings and Stretcher-bearers

1986. Battle of the U.S.S. "Philadelphia" and American Attack on Libya. Multicoloured.

(a) As T **380**.
1872 50dh. Type **380** 40 25
1873 50dh. American aircraft carrier and escaping family 60 25
1874 100dh. "Philadelphia" exploding (59 × 38 mm) 1·25 50

(b) As T **381**.
1875 70dh. Type **381** 80 20
1876 70dh. Burning wreckage of car and man and boy in rubble 80 20
1877 70dh. Woman and child by burning ruin 80 20
1878 70dh. Men running from bomb strike 80 20
1879 70dh. Covered body and rescue workers searching ruins 80 20
1880 70dh. Libyans and General Dynamics F-111 airplane tail and wing 80 25
1881 70dh. Libyans waving fists 80 20
1882 70dh. Rescue workers lifting child from rubble 80 20
1883 70dh. Weeping women and soldier carrying baby 80 20
1884 70dh. Libyans and glare of explosion 80 20
1885 70dh. Libyans and General Dynamics F-111 airplane wing and nose 80 25
1886 70dh. Man carrying girl 80 20
1887 70dh. Coffins held aloft by crowd 80 20
1888 70dh. Crowd carrying pictures of Gaddafi 80 20
1889 70dh. Wounded being tended 80 20
1890 70dh. Hands tending wounded baby 80 20

(c) Size 89 × 32 mm.
1891 100dh. General Dynamics F-111 bombers, Gaddafi and anti-aircraft rockets 1·25 35

Nos. 1872/4 were printed together in se-tenant strips of three within the sheet, each strip forming a composite design.

382 "The House must be served by its own Tenant"

1986. Quotations from the "Green Book".
1892 **382** 100dh. lt green, grn & blk 1·00 30
1893 – 100dh. multicoloured 1·00 30
1894 – 100dh. lt green, grn & blk 1·00 30
1895 – 100dh. lt green, grn & blk 1·00 30
1896 – 100dh. multicoloured 1·00 30
1897 – 100dh. lt green, grn & blk 1·00 30
1898 – 100dh. lt green, grn & blk 1·00 30
1899 – 100dh. multicoloured 1·00 30
1900 – 100dh. lt green, grn & blk 1·00 30

DESIGNS: No. 1893, Gaddafi; 1894, "The Child is raised by his mother"; 1895, "Democracy is the Supervision of the People by the People"; 1896, "Green Books"; 1897, "Representation is a Falsification of Democracy"; 1898, "The Recognition of Profit is an Acknowledgement of Exploitation"; 1899, Vase of roses, iris, lilies and jasmine; 1900, "Knowledge is a Natural Right of every Human Being which Nobody has the Right to deprive him of under any Pretext".

383 Map, Chrysanthemum and Health Services

1986. 17th Anniv of Revolution. Multicoloured.
1901 200dh. Type **383** 2·50 95
1902 200dh. Map, sunflower and agriculture programme 2·50 95
1903 200dh. "Sunflowers" (Van Gogh) 2·50 95
1904 200dh. Map, rose and defence programme 2·50 95
1905 200dh. Map, campanula and oil exploration programme 2·50 95

384 Moroccan and Libyan Women

1986. Arab–African Union. Multicoloured.
1906 250dh. Type **384** 2·50 80
1907 250dh. Libyan and Moroccan horsemen 2·50 80

385 Libyan Horseman

1986. Evacuation of Foreign Forces. Multicoloured.
1908 50dh. Type **385** 50 15
1909 100dh. Libyan horsemen trampling Italian soldiers 1·10 30
1910 150dh. Italian soldiers charging 1·50 50

386 Globe and Rose

1986. International Peace Year. Multicoloured, background colours given.
1911 **386** 200dh. green 1·90 70
1912 200dh. blue 1·90 70

387 Brick "Fists" and Maps within Laurel Wreath

1986. Solidarity with Palestinian People. Multicoloured, background colours given.
1913 **387** 250dh. blue 2·50 80
1914 250dh. red 2·50 80

388 Drummer

1986. Folk Music. Multicoloured.
1915 70dh. Type **388** 95 20
1916 70dh. Masked stick dancer 95 20
1917 70dh. Woman dancer with pot headdress 95 20
1918 70dh. Bagpipe player 95 20
1919 70dh. Tambour player 95 20

389 Gazelles

1987. Endangered Animals. Sand Gazelle. Multicoloured.
1920 100dh. Type **389** 1·25 30
1921 100dh. Mother and calf 1·25 30
1922 100dh. Gazelle drinking 1·25 30
1923 100dh. Gazelle lying down 1·25 30

390 Oil Derricks and Crowd

391 Sheep and Shepherd

1987. People's Authority Declaration. Multicoloured.
1924 500dh. Type **390** 4·00 1·75
1925 500dh. Buildings and crowd 4·00 1·75
1926 1000dh. Gaddafi addressing crowd and globe (40 × 38 mm) 8·00 3·25

1987. 18th Anniv of Revolution. Multicoloured.
1927 150dh. Type **391** 1·50 50
1928 150dh. Col. Gaddafi in robes 1·50 50
1929 150dh. Mosque 1·50 50
1930 150dh. Water flowing from irrigation pipe 1·50 50
1931 150dh. Combine harvester 1·50 50
1932 150dh. Col. Gaddafi in army uniform with microphone 1·50 50
1933 150dh. Harvesting crop 1·50 50
1934 150dh. Irrigation 1·50 50
1935 150dh. Soldier with rifle 1·50 50
1936 150dh. Buildings behind Libyan with rifle 1·50 50
1937 150dh. Fountain 1·50 50
1938 150dh. Buildings and beach 1·50 50
1939 150dh. Fort and girls 1·50 50
1940 150dh. Children and hand on rifle butt 1·50 50
1941 150dh. Theatre 1·50 50
1942 150dh. Couple 1·50 50

392 Omar Abed Anabi al Mansusri

1988. Personalities. Multicoloured.
1943 100dh. Type **392** 75 30
1944 200dh. Ahmed Ali al Emrayd 1·50 70
1945 300dh. Khalifa Said Ben Asker 2·50 1·00
1946 400dh. Mohamed Ben Farhat Azawi 3·00 1·10
1947 500dh. Mohamed Souf al Lafi al Marmori 3·75 1·50

393 Gaddafi and Crowd with Raised Fists around Earthmover Bucket

1988. Freedom Festival Day.
1948 **393** 100dh. multicoloured 95 30
1949 150dh. multicoloured 1·60 75
1950 250dh. multicoloured 2·50 1·25

394 Woman and Children running

1988. 2nd Anniv of American Attack on Libya. Multicoloured.
1951 150dh. Type **394** 1·40 50
1952 150dh. Gaddafi playing chess with boy 1·40 50
1953 150dh. Gaddafi and children 1·40 50
1954 150dh. Gaddafi in robes 1·40 50
1955 150dh. Gaddafi and boys praying 1·40 50
1956 150dh. Gaddafi and injured girl 1·40 50
1957 150dh. Gaddafi in robes with children (horiz.) 1·40 50
1958 150dh. Gaddafi making speech (horiz.) 1·40 50
1959 150dh. Gaddafi and family (horiz.) 1·40 50

395 Roses

1988. 19th Anniv of Revolution.
1961 **395** 100dh. multicoloured 75 30
1962 250dh. multicoloured 2·00 80
1963 300dh. multicoloured 2·25 1·00
1964 500dh. multicoloured 4·25 1·50

396 Relay

397 Dates

1988. Olympic Games, Seoul. Multicoloured.
1965 150dh. Type **396** 1·25 50
1966 150dh. Cycling 1·25 50
1967 150dh. Football 1·25 50

1968 150dh. Tennis . . . . . . 1·25 50
1969 150dh. Running . . . . . . 1·25 50
1970 150dh. Showjumping . . . 1·25 50

1988. The Palm Tree. Multicoloured.
1972 500dh. Type **397** . . . . . 4·25 1·50
1973 1000dh. Tree . . . . 8·00 3·75

398 Petrol Bomb, Sling and Map

399 Globe, Declaration and Dove

1988. Palestinian "Intifada" Movement. Mult.
1974 100dh. Type **398** 95 30
1975 200dh. Boy holding stones (45 × 38 mm) . . . . . . 1·60 70
1976 300dh. Map and flag . . . 2·50 1·00

1989. People's Authority Declaration.
1977 **399** 260dh. multicoloured . . 1·10 65
1978 500dh. multicoloured . . 2·00 1·25

400 Crowd and Green Books (½-size illustration)

1989. 20th Anniv of Revolution. Multicoloured.
1979 150dh. Type **400** . . . . . 1·25 40
1980 150dh. Soldiers, Colonel Gaddafi and water pipeline . . . . 1·25 40
1981 150dh. Military hardware, Gaddafi in uniform, education, communications and medicine . . . . 1·25 40
1982 150dh. Armed horsemen . . 1·25 40
1983 150dh. U.S.S. "Philadelphia" exploding 1·25 55

401 Execution Victims, Soldiers and Colonel Gaddafi

1989. 78th Anniv of Deportation of Libyans to Italy. Multicoloured.
1985 100dh. Type **401** 40 25
1986 100dh. Colonel Gaddafi and Libyans 40 25
1987 100dh. Soliders, deportees and Gaddafi 40 25
1988 100dh. Deportees on jetty and in boats 55 25
1989 100dh. Gaddafi and corpses 40 25

402 Demoliton of Wall

403 Emblem of Committee for supporting "Intifida"

1989. "Demolition of Borders".
1991 **402** 150dh. multicoloured . . 1·60 1·60
1992 200dh. multicoloured . . 2·10 2·10

1989. Palestinian "Intifada" Movement. Mult.
1993 100dh. Type **403** . . . . . 1·10 1·10
1994 300dh. Crowd of youths . . 3·00 3·00
1995 500dh. Emblem (1st anniv of declaration of state of Palestine) . . . . 4·75 4·75

404 Circulation Diagram and Annafis

1989. Ibn Annafis (physician) Commemoration.
1996 **404** 100dh. multicoloured . . 1·25 1·25
1997 150dh. multicoloured . . 1·90 1·90

405 Green Books and Fort

406 Libyan People and Soldier

1990. People's Authority Declaration.
1998 **405** 300dh. multicoloured . . 2·75 2·75
1999 500dh. multicoloured . . 5·00 5·00

1990. 20th Anniv of American Forces Evacuation.
2000 **406** 100dh. multicoloured . . 1·00 1·00
2001 400dh. multicoloured . . 4·00 4·00

407 Eagle

408 Anniversary Emblem

1990. 21st Anniv of Revolution.
2002 **407** 100dh. multicoloured . . 1·00 1·00
2003 400dh. multicoloured . . 4·00 4·00
2004 1000dh. multicoloured 10·50 10·50

1990. 30th Anniv of Organization of Petroleum Exporting Countries.
2006 **408** 100dh. multicoloured . . 1·00 1·00
2007 400dh. multicoloured . . 4·00 4·00

409 I.L.Y. Emblem and Figures

410 Player, Globe and Ball

1990. International Literacy Year.
2008 **409** 100dh. multicoloured . . 1·10 1·10
2009 300dh. multicoloured . . 3·00 3·00

1990. World Cup Football Championship, Italy.
2010 **410** 100dh. multicoloured . . 1·00 1·00
2011 400dh. multicoloured . . 4·00 4·00
2012 500dh. multicoloured . . 5·00 5·00

411 Hand holding Ears of Wheat

412 Members' Flags

1990. World Food Day. Multicoloured.
2014 500dh. Type **411** . . . . . 5·00 5·00
2015 2000dh. Ploughing . . . . 20·00 20·00

1991. 2nd Anniv of Union of Arab Maghreb.
2016 **412** 100dh. multicoloured . . 1·10 1·10
2017 300dh. multicoloured . . 3·00 3·00

413 Flame, Scroll and Koran

1991. People's Authority Declaration.
2018 **413** 300dh. multicoloured . . 2·75 2·75
2019 400dh. multicoloured . . 3·75 3·75

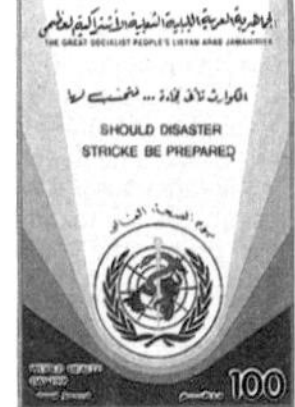

414 Girl and International Year of the Child Emblem

415 World Health Organization Emblem

1991. Children's Day. Multicoloured.
2020 100dh. Type **414** 95 95
2021 400dh. Boy and Day of the African Child emblem . . 3·75 3·75

1991. World Health Day. Multicoloured.
2022 100dh. Type **415** 95 95
2023 200dh. As Type **415** but with emblem additionally inscr "WHO OMS" . . . 1·90 1·90

416 Wadi el Hayat

1991. Scenes from Libya. Multicoloured.
2024 100dh. Type **416** 95 95
2025 250dh. Mourzuk (horiz) . . 2·50 2·50
2026 500dh. Ghadames (horiz) . . 5·00 5·00

417 Digging Riverbed and laying Pipes

1991. Great Man-made River. Multicoloured.
2027 50dh. Type **417** 25 15
2028 50dh. Col. Gaddafi, agricultural projects and livestock (59 × 37 mm) . . 25 15
2029 50dh. Produce 25 15
Nos. 2027/9 were printed together, se-tenant, forming a composite design.

418 "22", Roses and Broken Chain

1991. 22nd Anniv of Revolution. Multicoloured.
2030 300dh. Type **418** . . . . . 2·75 2·75
2031 400dh. "22" within wheat/ cogwheel wreath and broken chain . . . . . . 3·75 3·75

419 Emblem and Globe

1991. "Telecom 91" International Telecommunications Exhibition, Geneva. Multicoloured.
2033 100dh. Type **419** 95 95
2034 500dh. Buldings and dish aerial (horiz) . . . . . . 4·50 4·50

420 Monument and Soldier

1991. 80th Anniv of Deportation of Libyans to Italy. Multicoloured.
2035 100dh. Type **420** 95 95
2036 400dh. Naval transport, Libyans and soldiers . . . 3·75 3·75

421 Map

1991. Arab Unity.
2038 **421** 50dh. multicoloured . . 20 10
2039 100dh. multicoloured . . 40 20

422 Lorry

424 State Arms

423 Gaddafi and Camels

1991. Paris–Dakar Trans-Sahara Rally. Mult.
2040 50dh. Type **422** 20 10
2041 50dh. Blue lorry 20 10
2042 50dh. African Product lorry 20 10
2043 50dh. Tomel lorry 20 10
2044 50dh. All-terrain vehicle No. 173 . . . . 20 10
2045 50dh. Mitsusuki all-terrain vehicle 20 10
2046 50dh. Michedop all-terrain vehicle 20 10
2047 50dh. All-terrain vehicle No. 401 . . . . 20 10
2048 50dh. Motor cycle No. 100 20 10
2049 50dh. Rider pushing red motor cycle 20 10
2050 50dh. Rider pushing white motor cycle 20 10
2051 50dh. Motor cycle No. 98 20 10
2052 50dh. Motor cycle No. 101 20 10
2053 50dh. Motor cycle No. 80 20 10
2054 50dh. Motor cycle No. 12 20 10
2055 50dh. Motor cycle No. 45 20 10

1992. "Gaddafi, Man of Peace 1992". Multicoloured, colour of frame given.
2056 **423** 100dh. green 40 20
2057 100dh. grey 40 20
2058 100dh. red 40 20
2059 100dh. ochre 40 20

1992.
2061 **424** 100dh. green, brn & yell 40 20
2062 150dh. green, brn & grey 60 30
2063 200dh. green, brown & bl 85 45
2064 250dh. green, brn & orge 1·10 55
2065 300dh. green, brn & vio 1·25 65
2066 400dh. green, brn & mve 1·75 90
2067 450dh. emerald, brn & grn . . . . 1·90 95

425 1991 100dh. Stamp, Tweezers, Magnifying Glass and Stamps

1992. 3rd Anniv of Union of Arab Maghreb.
2068 **425** 75dh. multicoloured 30 15
2069 80dh. multicoloured 35 20

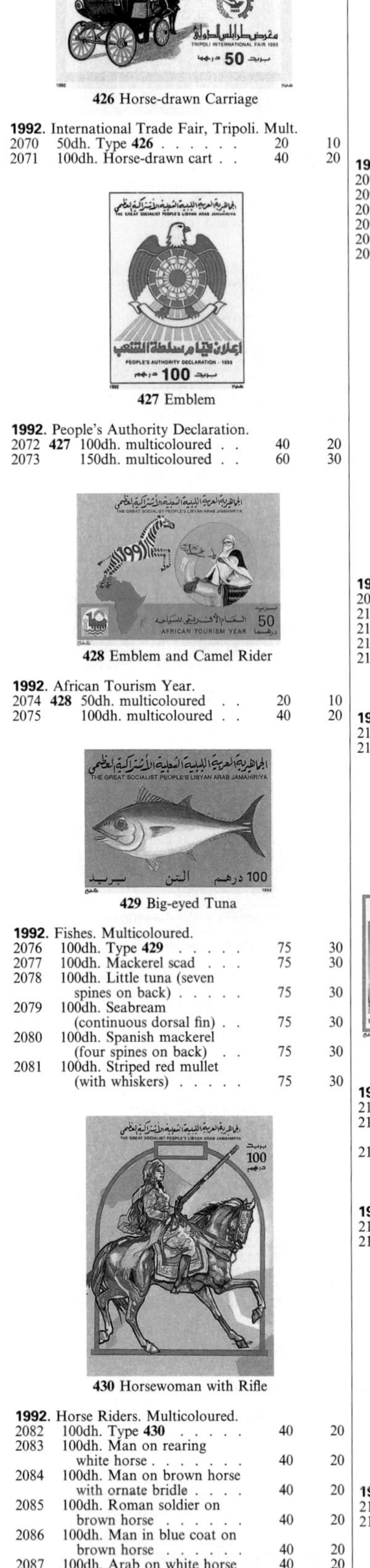
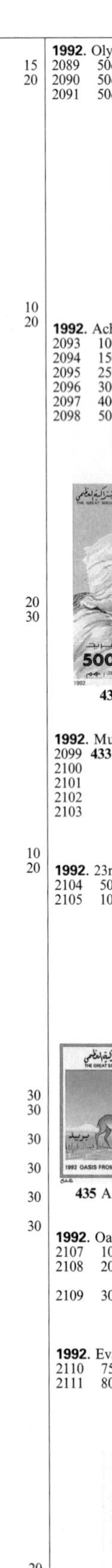
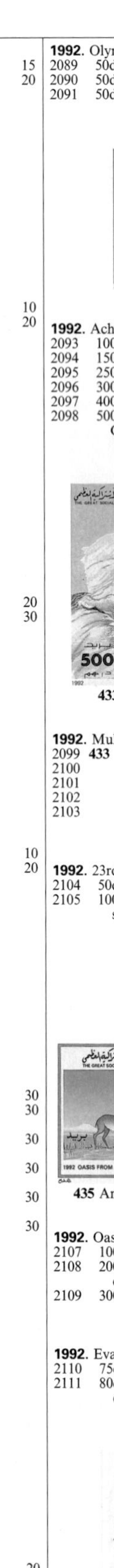

426 Horse-drawn Carriage

1992. International Trade Fair, Tripoli. Mult.
2070 50dh. Type **426** 20 10
2071 100dh. Horse-drawn cart 40 20

427 Emblem

1992. People's Authority Declaration.
2072 **427** 100dh. multicoloured 40 20
2073 150dh. multicoloured 60 30

428 Emblem and Camel Rider

1992. African Tourism Year.
2074 **428** 50dh. multicoloured 20 10
2075 100dh. multicoloured 40 20

429 Big-eyed Tuna

1992. Fishes. Multicoloured.
2076 100dh. Type **429** 75 30
2077 100dh. Mackerel scad 75 30
2078 100dh. Little tuna (seven spines on back) 75 30
2079 100dh. Seabream (continuous dorsal fin) 75 30
2080 100dh. Spanish mackerel (four spines on back) 75 30
2081 100dh. Striped red mullet (with whiskers) 75 30

430 Horsewoman with Rifle

1992. Horse Riders. Multicoloured.
2082 100dh. Type **430** 40 20
2083 100dh. Man on rearing white horse 40 20
2084 100dh. Man on brown horse with ornate bridle 40 20
2085 100dh. Roman soldier on brown horse 40 20
2086 100dh. Man in blue coat on brown horse 40 20
2087 100dh. Arab on white horse 40 20

431 Long Jumping

1992. Olympic Games, Barcelona. Multicoloured.
2089 50dh. Type **431** 20 10
2090 50dh. Throwing the discus 20 10
2091 50dh. Tennis 20 10

432 Palm Trees

1992. Achievements of the Revolution. Mult.
2093 100dh. Type **432** 40 20
2094 150dh. Ingots and foundry 60 30
2095 250dh. Container ship 1·10 55
2096 300dh. Airplane 1·25 65
2097 400dh. Assembly hall 1·75 90
2098 500dh. Water pipes and Gaddafi 2·10 1·10

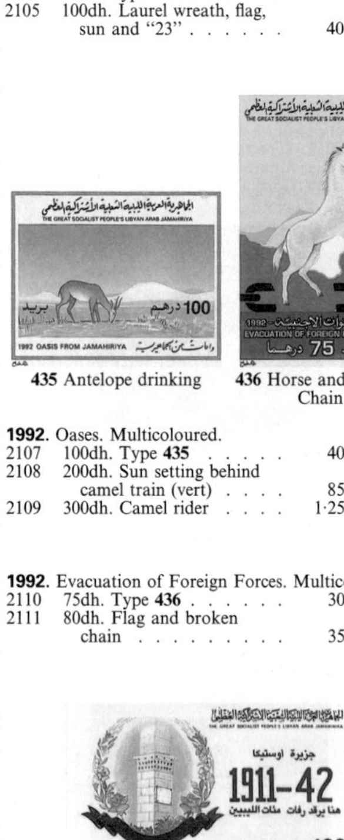

433 Gaddafi

434 Laurel Wreath, Torch and "23"

1992. Multicoloured, background colours given.
2099 **433** 500dh. green 2·50 1·10
2100 1000dh. pink 5·00 2·50
2101 2000dh. blue 10·00 5·00
2102 5000dh. violet 25·00 12·50
2103 6000dh. orange 32·00 16·00

1992. 23rd Anniv of Revolution. Multicoloured.
2104 50dh. Type **434** 20 10
2105 100dh. Laurel wreath, flag, sun and "23" 40 20

435 Antelope drinking

436 Horse and Broken Chain

1992. Oases. Multicoloured.
2107 100dh. Type **435** 40 20
2108 200dh. Sun setting behind camel train (vert) 85 45
2109 300dh. Camel rider 1·25 65

1992. Evacuation of Foreign Forces. Multicoloured.
2110 75dh. Type **436** 30 15
2111 80dh. Flag and broken chain 35 20

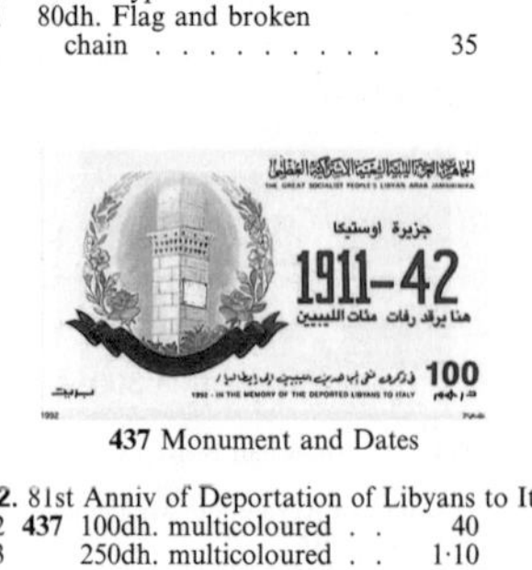

437 Monument and Dates

1992. 81st Anniv of Deportation of Libyans to Italy.
2112 **437** 100dh. multicoloured 40 20
2113 250dh. multicoloured 1·10 55

438 Dome of the Rock and Palestinian

1992. Palestinian "Intifada" Movement. Mult.
2114 100dh. Type **438** 40 20
2115 300dh. Map, Dome of the Rock, flag and fist (vert) 1·25 65

439 Red and White Striped Costume

440 Mohamed Ali Imsek

1992. Women's Costumes. Multicoloured.
2116 50dh. Type **439** 20 10
2117 50dh. Large red hat with silver decorations, white tunic and red wrap 20 10
2118 50dh. Brown and orange striped costume with small gold necklace and horseshoe brooch 20 10
2119 50dh. Purple and white costume 20 10
2120 50dh. Orange striped costume 20 10

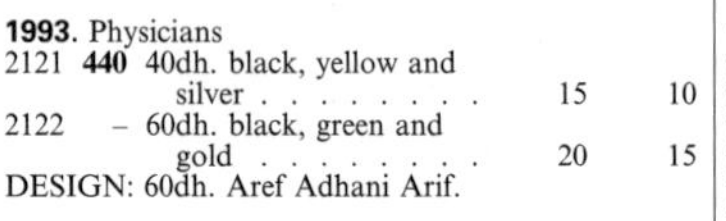

1993. Physicians
2121 **440** 40dh. black, yellow and silver 15 10
2122 – 60dh. black, green and gold 20 15
DESIGN: 60dh. Aref Adhani Arif.

441 Globe, Crops and Spoon-feeding Man

1993. International Nutrition Conference, Rome.
2123 **441** 70dh. multicoloured 35 25
2124 80dh. multicoloured 40 30

442 Gaddafi, Eagle and Oil Refinery

1993. People's Authority Declaration.
2125 **442** 60dh. multicoloured 20 15
2126 65dh. multicoloured 25 15
2127 75dh. multicoloured 25 15

443 Crowd with Tambours

445 Girl

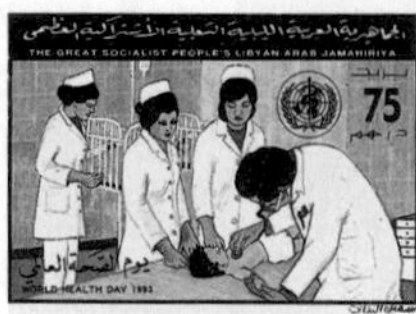

444 Examining Baby

1993. International Trade Fair, Tripoli. Mult.
2128 60dh. Type **443** 20 15
2129 60dh. Crowd with camel 20 15
2130 60dh. Dance of veiled men (horiz) 20 15
2131 60dh. Women preparing food (horiz) 20 15

1993. World Health Day. Multicoloured.
2133 75dh. Type **444** 25 15
2134 85dh. Medical staff attending patient 30 20

1993. Children's Day. Multicoloured.
2135 75dh. Type **445** 25 15
2136 75dh. Girl wearing blue and white veil and gold cuff 25 15
2137 75dh. Girl with white fluted collar and silver veil 25 15
2138 75dh. Girl with hands clasped 25 15
2139 75dh. Girl wearing blue scallop-edged veil 25 15

446 Phoenician Ship

1993. Ships. Multicoloured
2140 50dh. Type **446** 20 15
2141 50dh. Arab galley 20 15
2142 50dh. Pharaonic ship 20 15
2143 50dh. Roman bireme 20 15
2144 50dh. Carvel 20 15
2145 50dh. Yacht (globe showing Italy) 20 15
2146 50dh. Yacht (globe showing Greece) 20 15
2147 50dh. Galeasse 20 15
2148 50dh. Nau 20 15
2149 50dh. Yacht (globe showing left half of Libya) 20 15
2150 50dh. Yacht (globe showing right half of Libya) 20 15
2151 50dh. "Santa Maria" 20 15
2152 50dh. "France" (liner) 20 15
2153 50dh. Schooner 20 15
2154 50dh. Sail/steam warship 20 15
2155 50dh. Modern liner 20 15

Nos. 2140/55 were issued together, se-tenant, the centre four stamps forming a composite design.

447 Combine Harvesters

448 Woman tending Youth

1993. 24th Anniv of Revolution. Multicoloured.
2156 50dh. Type **447** 20 15
2157 50dh. Col. Gaddafi 20 15
2158 50dh. Cattle behind men filling sack with grain 20 15
2159 50dh. Chickens behind shepherd with flock 20 15
2160 50dh. Oil rig 20 15
2161 50dh. Eagle and camel 20 15
2162 50dh. Industrial plant 20 15
2163 50dh. Water pipeline 20 15
2164 50dh. Man harvesting dates 20 15
2165 50dh. Man in field and boxes of produce 20 15
2166 50dh. Pile of produce 20 15
2167 50dh. Man picking courgettes 20 15
2168 50dh. Children reading 20 15
2169 50dh. Typist and laboratory worker 20 15
2170 50dh. Hand-picking crop and ploughing with tractor 20 15
2171 50dh. Tractor towing circular harrow 20 15

Nos. 2156/71 were issued together, se-tenant, forming several composite designs.

1993. 82nd Anniv of Deportation of Libyans to Italy. Multicoloured.
2172 50dh. Type **448** 20 15
2173 50dh. Soldiers and Libyan family 20 15
2174 50dh. Col. Gaddafi (in turban) 20 15
2175 50dh. Libyans in food queue 20 15
2176 50dh. Man being flogged 20 15
2177 50dh. Horseman charging between soldiers and Libyans 20 15
2178 50dh. Soldier with manacled Libyan before court 20 15
2179 50dh. Libyans gazing at hanged man 20 15
2180 50dh. Crowd of Libyans and two soldiers 20 15
2181 50dh. Soldiers guarding procession of Libyans 20 15

2182 50dh. Soldiers and manacled Libyans on quayside . . . 20 15
2183 50dh. Deportees in boat . . 20 15
2184 50dh. Col. Gaddafi (bare-headed) 20 15
2185 50dh. Two Libyan families and branch of palm tree 20 15
2186 50dh. Soldiers in disarray (ruins in background) . . 20 15
2187 50dh. Libyan horsemen . . 20 15

Nos. 2172/87 were issued together, se-tenant, forming several composite designs.

449 Brooch　**451** Player and Trophy

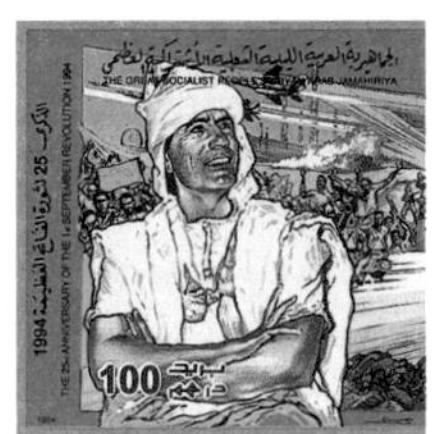

450 Gaddafi, Soldiers and Jet Fighters

1994. Silver Jewellery. Multicoloured.

2188 55dh. Type **449** 20 15
2189 55dh. Armlet 20 15
2190 55dh. Pendant 20 15
2191 55dh. Pendants hanging from oblong 20 15
2192 55dh. Necklace 20 15
2193 55dh. Slippers 20 15

1994. 25th Anniv of Revolution. Multicoloured.

2194 100dh. Type **450** 35 25
2195 100dh. Libyan tribesmen and Gaddafi in uniform (59 × 38 mm) 35 25
2196 100dh. Peaceful pursuits and elderly couple 35 25

Nos. 2194/6 were issued together, se-tenant, forming a composite design.

1994. World Cup Football Championship, U.S.A. Multicoloured.

2198 100dh. Type **451** . . . . .
2199 100dh. Kicking ball with inside of foot 35 25
2200 100dh. Kicking ball in air 35 25
2201 100dh. Goalkeeper 35 25
2202 100dh. Running with ball 35 25
2203 100dh. Player taking ball on chest 35 25

452 Gaddafi

1994. 83rd Anniv of Deportation of Libyans to Italy. Multicoloured.

2205 95dh. Type **452** 35 25
2206 95dh. Light plane over rifleman 35 25
2207 95dh. Couple running from biplane 35 25
2208 95dh. Biplane flying over men and boy 35 25
2209 95dh. Man trapped beneath fallen horse 35 25
2210 95dh. Soldiers and Libyans fighting (camel's head and neck in foreground) . . . 35 25
2211 95dh. Soldiers surrounding fallen Libyan 35 25
2212 95dh. Man carrying boy . . 35 25
2213 95dh. Soldier with whip raised 35 25
2214 95dh. Robed man shouting 35 25
2215 95dh. Tank and battle scene 35 25
2216 95dh. Women fleeing mounted soliers 35 25
2217 95dh. Man being flogged and woman cradling head of fallen Libyan 35 25
2218 95dh. Soldiers and Libyans fighting (camels in background) 35 25
2219 95dh. Women and soldiers on quayside 35 25
2220 95dh. Deportees in two boats 35 25

Nos. 2205/20 were issued together, se-tenant, forming several composite designs.

453 Darghut　**454** Armed Forces

1994. Mosques. Multicoloured.

2221 70dh. Type **453** 25 15
2222 70dh. Benghazi 25 15
2223 70dh. Kabao 25 15
2224 70dh. Gouzgu 25 15
2225 70dh. Siala 25 15
2226 70dh. El Kettani 25 15

1994. People's Authority Declaration. Multicoloured.

2227 80dh. Type **454** 30 20
2228 80dh. Truck, hand holding Green Book and ears of wheat 30 20
2229 80dh. Pipes on trailers, water pipeline and family 30 20
2230 80dh. Crowd with Green Books 30 20
2231 80dh. Col. Gaddafi 30 20
2232 80dh. Youths and produce 30 20

Nos. 2227/32 were issued together, se-tenant, forming a composite design.

455 Sun over Cemetery, National Flag, Dove and Footprints　**457** Declaration and Flowers

456 Men with Weapons and Troops in Background

1994. Evacuation of Foreign Forces.

2233 **455** 65dh. multicoloured . . 25 15
2234 95dh. multicoloured . . 35 20

1994. Gaddafi Prize for Human Rights. Multicoloured.

2235 95dh. Type **456** 35 20
2236 95dh. Men with weapons . . 35 20
2237 95dh. President Nelson Mandela of South Africa 35 20
2238 95dh. President Gaddafi . . 35 20
2239 95dh. Amerindian meditating 35 20
2240 95dh. Warriors on horseback 35 20
2241 95dh. Amerindian chief . . 35 20
2242 95dh. Amerindian 35 20
2243 95dh. Riflemen and aircraft 35 20
2244 95dh. Bomber, women, fire and left page of book . . 35 20
2245 95dh. Right page of book and surgeon operating . . 35 20
2246 95dh. Surgeons operating 35 20
2247 95dh. Masked revolutionaries with flag 35 20
2248 95dh. Revolutionaries raising arms with flag . . 35 20
2249 95dh. Young boys with stones 35 20
2250 95dh. Revolutionaries, fire and troops 35 20

Nos. 2235/50 were issued together, se-tenant, forming a composite design.

1995. People's Authority Declaration. Multicoloured, colour of background given.

2251 **457** 100dh. yellow 35 20
2252 100dh. blue 35 20
2253 100dh. green 35 20

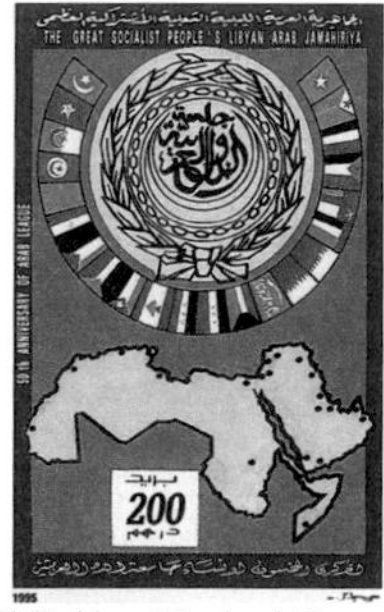

458 Emblem, Members' Flags and Map showing Member Countries

1995. 50th Anniv of Arab League. Multicoloured, frame colour given.

2254 **458** 200f. blue 70 45
2255 200f. green 70 45

459 Messaud Zentuti

1995. 60th Anniv of National Football Team. Designs showing players. Multicoloured.

2257 100dh. Type **459** 35 20
2258 100dh. Salem Shermit . . . 35 20
2259 100dh. Ottoman Marfua . . 35 20
2260 100dh. Ghaleb Siala 35 20
2261 100dh. Team, 1935 . . . . 35 20
2262 100dh. Senussi Mresila . . . 35 20

Nos. 2257/62 were issued together, se-tenant, forming a composite design.

460 Dromedary　**461** Grapefruit

1995. Libyan Zoo. Multicoloured.

2263 100dh. Type **460** 35 20
2264 100dh. Secretary bird . . . 35 20
2265 100dh. African wild dog . . 35 20
2266 100dh. Oryx 35 20
2267 100dh. Baboon 35 20
2268 100dh. Golden jackal . . . 35 20
2269 100dh. Crowned eagle . . . 35 20
2270 100dh. Desert eagle owl ("Eagle Owl") 35 20
2271 100dh. Desert hedgehog . . 35 20
2272 100dh. Sand gerbil 35 20
2273 100dh. Addax 35 20
2274 100dh. Fennec fox 35 20
2275 100dh. Lanner falcon . . . 35 20
2276 100dh. Desert wheatear . . 35 20
2277 100dh. Pin-tailed sandgrouse 35 20
2278 100dh. Jerboa 35 20

Nos. 2263/78 were issued together, se-tenant, the backgrounds forming a composite design.

1995. Fruit. Multicoloured.

2279 100dh. Type **461** 35 20
2280 100dh. Wild cherry 35 20
2281 100dh. Mulberry 35 20
2282 100dh. Strawberry 35 20
2283 100dh. Plum 35 20
2284 100dh. Pear 35 20
2285 100dh. Apricot 35 20
2286 100dh. Almond 35 20
2287 100dh. Prickly pear 35 20
2288 100dh. Lemon 35 20
2289 100dh. Peach 35 20
2290 100dh. Dates 35 20
2291 100dh. Olive 35 20
2292 100dh. Orange 35 20
2293 100dh. Fig 35 20
2294 100dh. Grape 35 20

Nos. 2279/94 were issued together, se-tenant, the backgrounds forming a composite design.

462 Students

1995. 26th Anniv of Revolution. Multicoloured.

2295 100dh. Type **462** 35 20
2296 100dh. Mosque, teacher and students 35 20
2297 100dh. President Gaddafi . . 35 20
2298 100dh. Laboratory workers 35 20
2299 100dh. Hospital patient, doctor examining child, and nurse 35 20
2300 100dh. Surgeons operating 35 20
2301 100dh. Cobblers and keyboard operator . . . 35 20
2302 100dh. Sound engineers and musician 35 20
2303 100dh. Crane and apartment block 35 20
2304 100dh. Silos 35 20
2305 100dh. Oil rig platform . . 35 20
2306 100dh. Airplane and ships 35 20
2307 100dh. Animals grazing and farmer 35 20
2308 100dh. Pipeline 35 20
2309 100dh. Camels at trough and crops 35 20
2310 100dh. Crops and farm vehicle 35 20

Nos. 2295/2310 were issued together, se-tenant, forming a composite design.

463 Scout Badge and Wildlife

1995. Scouting. Multicoloured.

2311 250dh. Type **463** 85 55
2312 250dh. Badge, butterflies and scouts with animals (59 × 39 mm) 85 55
2313 250dh. Badge and scouts . . 85 55

Nos. 2311/13 were issued together, se-tenant, forming a composite design.

464 Warships and Rocket

1995. 9th Anniv of American Attack on Libya. Multicoloured.

2314 100dh. Type **464** 35 20
2315 100dh. Bombers, helicopters, warships and Libyans (59 × 49 mm) 35 20
2316 100dh. Bomber and woman holding baby 35 20

Nos. 2314/16 were issued together, se-tenant, forming a composite design.

465 Gaddafi on Horseback　**466** Dromedary and Woman with Water Jars

1995. International Trade Fair, Tripoli. Multicoloured.

2317 100dh. Type **465** 35 20
2318 100dh. Horseman 35 20

2319 100dh. Horseman (horse galloping to right) 35 20
2320 100dh. Horsemen with whips (horiz) 35 20
2321 100dh. Horseman holding rifle (horiz) 35 20
2322 100dh. Horsewoman brandishing rifle in air (horiz) 35 20

1995. City of Ghadames. Multicoloured.
2324 100dh. Type **466** 35 20
2325 100dh. Making cheeses . . . 35 20
2326 100dh. Woman holding jar 35 20
2327 100dh. Feeding chickens . . 35 20
2328 100dh. Spinning wool . . . 35 20
2329 100dh. Woman in traditional costume . . . 35 20
2330 100dh. Drying grain 35 20
2331 100dh. Milking goat 35 20
2332 100dh. Making shoes . . . 35 20
2333 100dh. Weaving 35 20
2334 100dh. Engraving brass tabletops 35 20
2335 100dh. Harvesting dates . . 35 20
2336 100dh. Reading scriptures 35 20
2337 100dh. Potter 35 20
2338 100dh. Washing clothes in well 35 20
2339 100dh. Picking fruit 35 20

467 Family with Torch and National Flag

1995. Evacuation of Foreign Forces.
2340 **467** 50dh. multicoloured . . 20 10
2341 100dh. multicoloured . . 35 20
2342 200dh. multicoloured . . 70 45

468 Honeycomb and Bees on Flowers

1995. Arab Beekeepers' Association. Multicoloured, colour of border given.
2343 **468** 100dh. mauve 35 20
2344 100dh. lilac 35 20
2345 100dh. green 35 20

469 Stubbing out Cigarette and holding Rose

470 Dr. Mohamed Feituri

1995. World Health Day. Multicoloured, colour of central band given.
2346 **469** 100dh. yellow 35 20
2347 100dh. orange 35 20

1995.
2348 **470** 200dh. multicoloured . . 70 45

471 Gaddafi and Horsemen

1995. 84th Anniv of Deportation of Libyans to Italy. Multicoloured.
2349 100dh. Type **471** 35 20
2350 100dh. Horsemen 35 20
2351 100dh. Battle scene 35 20
2352 100dh. Bomber over battle scene 35 20
2353 100dh. Libyans with rifles 35 20
2354 100dh. Soldiers fighting with Libyans 35 20
2355 100dh. Soldiers with weapons and man on ground 35 20
2356 100dh. Soldiers with rifles and building in background 35 20
2357 100dh. Libyans 35 20
2358 100dh. Soldiers charging men on ground 35 20
2359 100dh. Soldiers shooting at horseman 35 20
2360 100dh. Soldiers pushing Libyan to ground 35 20
2361 100dh. Horsemen charging 35 20
2362 100dh. Horses falling to ground 35 20
2363 100dh. Children 35 20
2364 100dh. Deportees in boats 35 20
Nos. 2349/64 were issued together, se-tenant, forming a composite design.

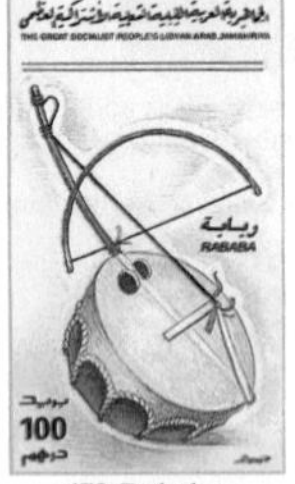

472 Rababa

473 Blue Door

1995. Musical Instruments. Multicoloured.
2365 100dh. Type **472** 35 20
2366 100dh. Nouba 35 20
2367 100dh. Clarinet 35 20
2368 100dh. Drums 35 20
2369 100dh. Magruna 35 20
2370 100dh. Zukra 35 20
2371 100dh. Zil 35 20
2372 100dh. Kaman 35 20
2373 100dh. Guitar 35 20
2374 100dh. Trumpet 35 20
2375 100dh. Tapla 35 20
2376 100dh. Gonga 35 20
2377 100dh. Saxophone 35 20
2378 100dh. Piano 35 20
2379 100dh. Ganoon 35 20
2380 100dh. Ood 35 20

1995. Doors from Mizda. Multicoloured.
2381 100dh. Type **473** 35 20
2382 100dh. Door with arch detail 35 20
2383 100dh. Door made of logs 35 20
2384 100dh. Arched door 35 20
2385 100dh. Wide door with bolts 35 20

474 Sports within Olympic Rings

1995. Centenary of International Olympic Committee. Multicoloured, colour of face value given.
2386 **474** 100dh. black 35 20
2387 100dh. red 35 20

475 Baryonyx

1995. Prehistoric Animals. Multicoloured.
2388 100dh. Type **475** 35 20
2389 100dh. Oviraptor 35 20
2390 100dh. Stenonychosaurus . . 35 20
2391 100dh. Tenontosaurus . . . 35 20
2392 100dh. Yangchuanosaurus 35 20
2393 100dh. Stegotetrabelodon (facing right) 35 20
2394 100dh. Stegotetrabelodon (facing left) 35 20
2395 100dh. Psittacosaurus . . . 35 20
2396 100dh. Heterodontosaurus 35 20
2397 100dh. "Loxodonta atlantica" 35 20
2398 100dh. "Mammuthus africanavus" 35 20
2399 100dh. Erlikosaurus 35 20
2400 100dh. Cynognathus 35 20
2401 100dh. Plateosaurus 35 20
2402 100dh. Staurikosaurus . . . 35 20
2403 100dh. Lystrosaurus 35 20
Nos. 2388/2403 were issued together, se-tenant, the backgrounds forming a composite design.

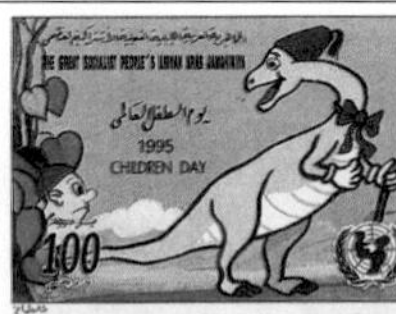

476 Child and Dinosaur walking with Stick

1995. Children's Day. Multicoloured.
2405 100dh. Type **476** 35 20
2406 100dh. Child on mammoth's back 35 20
2407 100dh. Child on way to school and tortoise under mushroom 35 20
2408 100dh. Dinosaur playing football 35 20
2409 100dh. Child pointing rifle at pteranodon 35 20

477 Helicopter, Soldier and Stone-thrower

1995. Palestinian "Intifada" Movement. Mult.
2410 100dh. Type **477** 35 20
2411 100dh. Dome of the Rock and Palestinian with flag 35 20
2412 100dh. Women with flag . . 35 20
Nos. 2410/12 were issued together, se-tenant, forming a composite design.

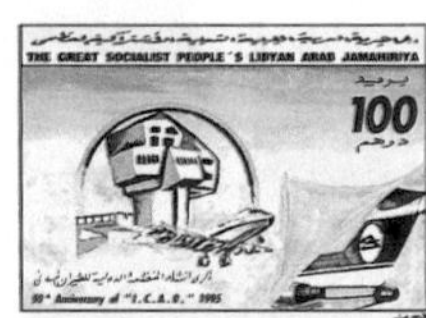

478 Airplane, Control Tower and Tailfin

1995. 50th Anniv of I.C.A.O. Multicoloured, colour of face value given.
2413 **478** 100dh. blue 35 20
2414 100dh. black 35 20

479 Headquarters, New York

480 "Iris germanica"

1995. 50th Anniv of U.N.O. Multicoloured, colour of background given.
2415 **479** 100dh. pink 35 20
2416 100dh. lilac 35 20

1995. Flowers. Multicoloured.
2417 200dh. Type **480** 35 20
2418 200dh. "Canna edulis" . . . 35 20
2419 200dh. "Nerium oleander" 35 20
2420 200dh. Corn poppy ("Papaver rhoeas") . . . 35 20
2421 200dh. Bird of Paradise flower ("Strelitzia reginae") 35 20
2422 200dh. "Amygdalus communis" 35 20

481 Open Hand

483 Man holding Fruit

482 Football

1996. People's Authority Declaration. Multicoloured.
2423 **481** 100dh. multicoloured . . 35 20
2424 150dh. multicoloured . . 50 30
2425 200dh. multicoloured . . 65 40

1996. Olympic Games, Atlanta, U.S.A. Multicoloured.
2426 100dh. Type **482** 35 20
2427 100dh. Long jumping . . . 35 20
2428 100dh. Tennis 35 20
2429 100dh. Cycling 35 20
2430 100dh. Boxing 35 20
2431 100dh. Equestrian show jumping 35 20
Nos. 2426/31 were issued together, se-tenant, the background forming a composite design of the Games emblem.

1996. 27th Anniv of Revolution. Multicoloured.
2433 100dh. Type **483** 35 20
2434 100dh. Water flowing along chute and out of pipe . . 35 20
2435 100dh. Tractor, water and women with flowers . . . 35 20
2436 100dh. Man working on pipe by water 35 20
2437 100dh. Man sewing 35 20
2438 100dh. Woman textile worker 35 20
2439 100dh. President Gaddafi in white shirt and red cape 35 20
2440 100dh. Women laboratory workers 35 20
2441 100dh. Anatomy instruction and man using microscope 35 20
2442 100dh. Child holding hand to face 35 20
2443 100dh. Woman praying before open Koran . . . 35 20
2444 100dh. Man weaving . . . 35 20
2445 100dh. Two aircraft 35 20
2446 100dh. Man on camel, liner and dish aerial 35 20
2447 100dh. Stern of liner and television camera 35 20
2448 100dh. Woman using microphone and woman being filmed 35 20
Nos. 2433/48 were issued together, se-tenant, forming a composite design.

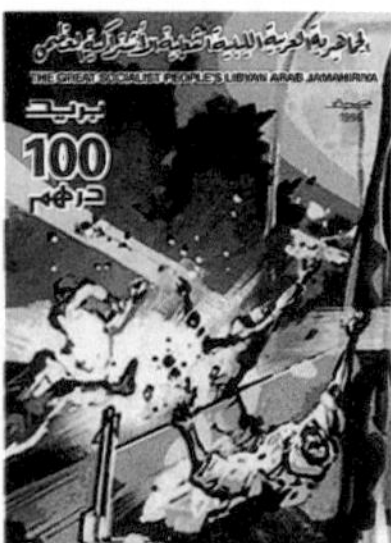

484 Bomb Exploding

1996. 10th Anniv of American Attack on Libya. Multicoloured.
2449 100dh. Type **484** 35 20
2450 100dh. Man with raised arms 35 20
2451 100dh. Woman carrying child 35 20
2452 100dh. Injured man on ground and fighter plane 35 20
2453 100dh. Fireman hosing down burning car 35 20
2454 100dh. Exploding plane . . 35 20
2455 100dh. Head of President Gaddafi 35 20
2456 100dh. Airplane bombing tented camp 35 20
2457 100dh. Rescuers helping two women 35 20
2458 100dh. Man with bandaged head and hand 35 20
2459 100dh. Woman with hankerchief to mouth . . 35 20
2460 100dh. Stretcher bearers . . 35 20
2461 100dh. Explosion and man being carried away . . . 35 20
2462 100dh. Explosion and man with injured hand 35 20
2463 100dh. Rescuers helping injured mother with baby 35 20
2464 100dh. Burning car and helpers tending injured boy 35 20
Nos. 2449/64 were issued together, se-tenant, forming a composite design.

485 "Necora puber" (crab)

1996. Crustaceans. Multicoloured.
2465 100dh. Type **485** 35 20
2466 100dh. "Lissa chiragra" (crab) 35 20
2467 100dh. Rock lobster ("Palinurus elephas") . . 35 20
2468 100dh. "Scyllarus arctus" 35 20
2469 100dh. Green crab ("Carcinus maenas") . . 35 20
2470 100dh. Helmet crab ("Calappa granulata") . . 35 20
2471 100dh. "Parapenaeus longirostris" (prawn) . . 35 20
2472 100dh. Norway lobster ("Nephrops norvegicus") 35 20
2473 100dh. "Eriphia verrucosa" (crab) 35 20
2474 100dh. Edible crab ("Cancer pagurus") 35 20
2475 100dh. "Penaeus kerathurus" (prawn) . . . 35 20
2476 100dh. Mantis shrimp ("Squilla mantis") 35 20
2477 100dh. Spider crab ("Maja squinado") 35 20
2478 100dh. "Pilumnus hirtellus" (crab) 35 20
2479 100dh. "Pagurus alatus" (crab) 35 20
2480 100dh. "Macropodia tenuirostris" 35 20
Nos. 2465/80 were issued together, se-tenant, the backgrounds forming a composite design.

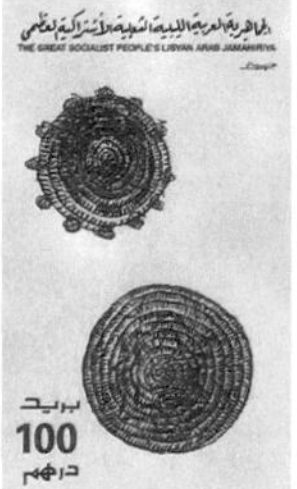

486 Mats

487 Woman kneeling over Boy

1996. Maghreb Handicrafts Day. Basketwork. Multicoloured.
2481 100dh. Type **486** 35 20
2482 100dh. Lidded storage vessel 35 20
2483 100dh. Bowl 35 20
2484 100dh. Mug and teapot . . 35 20
2485 100dh. Box with open lid . . 35 20
2486 100dh. Bird's-eye view of dish 35 20
2487 100dh. Pot with wide base and mouth and narrower neck 35 20
2488 100dh. Lidded pot with carrying handle 35 20
2489 100dh. Bulbous bottle-shaped carrier 35 20
2490 100dh. Large dish 35 20
2491 100dh. Oval dish with well in centre 35 20
2492 100dh. Straight-sided bottle-shaped carrier 35 20
2493 100dh. Vessel with double carrying handles and open lid 35 20
2494 100dh. Dish on stand . . . 35 20
2495 100dh. Pot with wide base and narrow mouth . . . 35 20
2496 100dh. Bag with lid 35 20

1996. 85th Anniv of Deportation of Libyans to Italy. Multicoloured.
2497 100dh. Type **487** 35 20
2498 100dh. Horseman leading prisoner 35 20
2499 100dh. President Gaddafi wearing turban 35 20
2500 100dh. Old man holding stick in camp 35 20
2501 100dh. Man being flogged 35 20
2502 100dh. Horseman, soldiers and crowd wearing fezzes 35 20
2503 100dh. Prisoner, advocate and man in tricolour sash 35 20
2504 100dh. Family and soldier 35 20
2505 100dh. Soldiers guarding prisoners (boy at front) 35 20
2506 100dh. Soldiers escorting woman on camel and man on donkey 35 20
2507 100dh. Prisoners being escorted through street . . 35 20
2508 100dh. Prisoners in boat . . 35 20
2509 100dh. President Gaddafi in white embroided shirt with open hand 35 20
2510 100dh. Group of prisoners including man with raised arm 35 20
2511 100dh. Horsemen charging and soldiers 35 20
2512 100dh. Horseman with rifle 35 20
Nos. 2497/2512 were issued together, se-tenant, forming several composite designs.

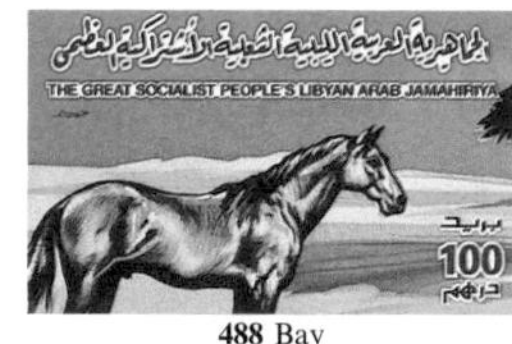

488 Bay

1996. Horses. Multicoloured.
2513 100dh. Type **488** 35 20
2514 100dh. Light brown horse under tree (branches at right of stamp) 35 20
2515 100dh. Light brown horse by lake under tree (branch at left) 35 20
2516 100dh. Dark brown horse (edge of lake at left) . . . 35 20
2517 100dh. Black horse with hoof raised 35 20
2518 100dh. Chestnut horse . . . 35 20
2519 100dh. Grey horse running 35 20
2520 100dh. Piebald 35 20
2521 100dh. Head of grey and tail of black horses 35 20
2522 100dh. Head of black and tail of chestnut horses . . 35 20
2523 100dh. Head and rump of chestnut horses 35 20
2524 100dh. Head of chestnut horse with white mane . . 35 20
2525 100dh. Head of black horse and parts of three other horses 35 20
2526 100dh. Head of chestnut horse with blond mane and parts of three other horses 35 20
2527 100dh. Head of dark brown horse and parts of three other horses 35 20
2528 100dh. Head of dark brown and part of chestnut horses 35 20
Nos. 2513/28 were issued together, se-tenant, forming a composite design.

489 Camel

490 Photographer, Newspapers and Computer

1996. Camels. Multicoloured.
2529 200dh. Type **489** 65 40
2530 200dh. Head of camel . . . 65 40
2531 200dh. Dark brown dromedary 65 40
2532 200dh. Long-haired Bactrian camel 65 40
2533 200dh. Light brown Bactrian camel 65 40
2534 200dh. Brown Bactrian camel with white stripe and tail 65 40
Nos. 2529/34 were issued together, se-tenant, forming a composite design.

1996. The Press and Information. Multicoloured.
2535 100dh. Type **490** 35 20
2536 200dh. Television, control desk, musicians, computer and dish aerial 65 40

491 "Mene rhombea"

492 Palestinian Flag and Hands holding up Stones

1996. Fossils. Multicoloured.
2537 200dh. Type **491** 65 40
2538 200dh. "Mesodon macrocephalus" 65 40
2539 200dh. "Eyron arctiformis" 65 40
2540 200dh. Stegosaurus 65 40
2541 200dh. Pteranodon 65 40
2542 200dh. Allosaurus 65 40

1996. Palestinian "Intifada" Movement.
2543 **492** 100dh. multicoloured . . 35 20
2544 150dh. multicoloured . . 50 30
2545 200dh. multicoloured . . 65 40

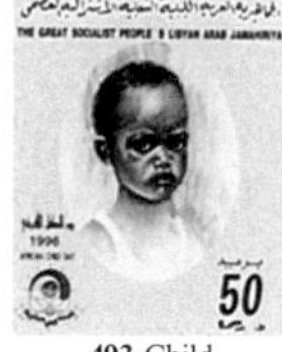

493 Child **494** Cat

1996. African Child Day. Multicoloured.
2546 50dh. Type **493** 10 10
2547 150dh. Type **493** 40 25
2548 200dh. Mother and child . . 50 35

1996. Children's Day. Cats. Multicoloured.
2549 100dh. Type **494** 25 15
2550 100dh. Tabby (back view with head turned) 25 15
2551 100dh. Colourpoint (black and white) 25 15
2552 100dh. Tabby adult and kitten 25 15
2553 100dh. Tortoiseshell white (sitting) 25 15

495 Family and Tower Block

1996. World Family Day. Multicoloured.
2554 150dh. Type **495** 40 25
2555 150dh. Family and car parked by palm trees . . 40 25
2556 200dh. Family, symbolic globe and flowers (45 × 26 mm) 50 35
Nos. 2554/6 were issued together, se-tenant, forming a composite design.

496 Mohamed Kamel el-Hammali

1996. Libyan Teachers. Multicoloured.
2557 100dh. Type **496** 25 15
2558 100dh. Mustafa Abdalla ben-Amer 25 15
2559 100dh. Mohamed Messaud Fesheka 25 15
2560 100dh. Kairi Mustafa Serraj 25 15
2561 100dh. Muftah el-Majri . . 25 15
2562 100dh. Mohamed Hadi Arafa 25 15

497 Mohamed Salim

1996. Libyan Singers. Multicoloured.
2563 100dh. Type **497** 25 15
2564 100dh. Mohamed M. Sayed Bumedyen 25 15
2565 100dh. Otman Najim . . . 25 15
2566 100dh. Mahmud Sherif . . 25 15
2567 100dh. Mohamed Ferjani Marghani 25 15
2568 100dh. Mohamed Kabazi 25 15

498 Snake

1996. Reptiles. Multicoloured.
2569 100dh. Type **498** 25 15
2570 100dh. Diamond-back snake beside river 25 15
2571 100dh. Turtle on water (segmented shell and large flippers) 25 15
2572 100dh. Snake wrapped around tree branch . . . 25 15
2573 100dh. Brown lizard on tree trunk 25 15
2574 100dh. Coiled snake with head raised and mouth open 25 15
2575 100dh. Snake with head raised beside water . . . 25 15
2576 100dh. Turtle on water (flat shell, pointed snout and small flippers) 25 15
2577 100dh. Green lizard on tree trunk 25 15
2578 100dh. Snake with wavy pattern on ground 25 15
2579 100dh. Snake with horns . . 25 15
2580 100dh. Chameleon 25 15
2581 100dh. Tortoise on ground (facing right) 25 15
2582 100dh. Snake on rock with head raised 25 15
2583 100dh. Tortoise on ground (facing left) 25 15
2584 100dh. Grey lizard on rock 25 15
Nos. 2569/84 were issued together, se-tenant, forming a composite design.

499 Mirror and Clothes Brush

1996. International Trade Fair, Tripoli. Each silver, pink and black.
2585 100dh. Type **499** 25 15
2586 100dh. Decanter on tray . . 25 15
2587 100dh. Two round-bottomed flasks 25 15
2588 100dh. Two long-necked flasks 25 15
2589 100dh. Covered bowl . . . 25 15
2590 100dh. Backs of hairbrush and mirror 25 15

500 Gaddafi and Symbolic Scenes **501** Scouts and Stamp Album

1997. People's Authority Declaration.
2591 **500** 100dh. multicoloured . . 25 15
2592 200dh. multicoloured . . 25 15
2593 300dh. multicoloured . . 25 15

1997. Postal Savings Bank. Multicoloured.
2594 50dh. Type **501** 10 10
2595 50dh. Two Girl Guides and albums 10 10
2596 100dh. Bank books and butterflies 25 15
Nos. 2594/6 were issued together, se-tenant, forming a composite design.

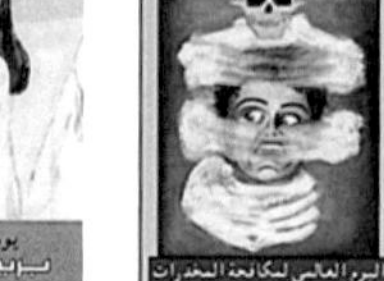

502 Scientist with Test Tubes **503** Death enveloping Man's Head

1997. World Health Day. Multicoloured.
2597 50dh. Type **502** 10 10
2598 50dh. Scientist at microscope 10 10
2599 100dh. Doctor and nurse examining baby 25 15

Nos. 2597/9 were issued together, se-tenant, forming a composite design.

1997. Anti-drugs Campaign.
2600 **503** 100dh. multicoloured . . 25 15
2601 150dh. multicoloured . . 40 25
2602 200dh. multicoloured . . 50 35

504 Library

1997. Arab National Central Library.
2603 **504** 100dh. multicoloured . . 25 15
2604 200dh. multicoloured . . 50 35

505 Dancer and Local Crafts

1997. Arab Tourism Year.
2606 **505** 100dh. multicoloured . . 25 15
2607 200dh. multicoloured . . 50 25
2608 250dh. multicoloured . . 65 45

CONCESSIONAL LETTER POST

1929. No. CL227 of Italy optd **LIBIA**.
CL68 CL **93** 10c. blue . . . . . . 22·00 17·00

1941. No. CL267 of Italy optd **LIBIA**.
CL123 CL **109** 10c. brown . . . . 8·50 8·50

EXPRESS LETTER STAMPS
A. ITALIAN ISSUES

1915. Express Letter stamps of Italy optd **Libia**.
E17 E **35** 25c. pink . . . . 19·00 8·50
E18 E **41** 30c. blue and pink . . . 5·25 22·00

E 8

1921.
E34 E **8** 30c. red and blue . . . . 1·70 5·25
E35 50c. brown and red . . . 2·50 6·75
E42 60c. brown and red . . . 5·25 10·50
E43 2l. red and blue . . . . 8·50 21·00
Nos. E34 and E43 are inscribed "EXPRES".

1922. Nos. E17/18 surch.
E40 E **35** 60c. on 25c. pink . . . 9·50 11·00
E41 E **41** 1l.60 on 30c. blue and pink . . . . 11·00 23·00

1926. Nos. E42/3 surch.
E62 E **8** 70 on 60c. brown and red 5·25 10·50
E64 1l.25 on 60c. brown and red . . . . 4·25 1·50
E63 2.50 on 2l. red and blue 8·50 21·00

B. INDEPENDENT ISSUES

1966. Design similar to T **74** inscr "EXPRES".
E368 90m. red and green . . . 2·30 1·30
DESIGN—HORIZ: 90m. Saracen Castle, Zuela.

OFFICIAL STAMPS

1952. Optd **Official** in English and Arabic.
O192 **23** 2m. brown 40 35
O193 4m. grey 65 50
O194 5m. green . . . . 4·50 1·60
O195 8m. red . . . . 2·50 75
O196 10m. violet . . . . . 3·75 1·25
O197 12m. red . . . . 6·75 2·50
O198 20m. blue . . . . . . 13·50 5·25
O199 25m. brown . . . . . . 17·00 6·75

PARCEL POST STAMPS
Unused prices are for complete pairs, used prices for a half.

1915. Parcel Post stamps of Italy optd **LIBIA** on each half of the stamp.
P17 P **53** 5c. brown . . . . 85 3·50
P18 10c. blue . . . . 85 3·50
P19 20c. black . . . . . . 1·00 3·50
P20 25c. red . . . . 1·00 3·50
P21 50c. orange . . . . . . 1·90 3·50
P22 1l. violet . . . . 1·90 5·25
P23 2l. green . . . . 2·75 5·25
P24 3l. yellow . . . . 3·50 5·25
P25 4l. grey . . . . 3·50 5·25
P26 10l. purple . . . . . . 43·00 39·00
P27 12l. brown . . . . . . 85·00 £110
P28 15l. green . . . . . . 85·00 £140
P29 20l. purple £110 £150

1927. Parcel Post stamps of Italy optd **LIBIA** on each half of the stamp.
P62 P **92** 5c. brown £9000
P63 10c. blue . . . . 2·10 3·50
P64 25c. red . . . . 2·10 3·50
P65 30c. blue . . . . 35 1·70
P66 50c. orange . . . . . . 48·00 £100
P67 60c. red . . . . 35 1·70
P68 1l. violet . . . . 19·00 50·00
P69 2l. green . . . . 22·00 50·00
P70 3l. bistre . . . . 1·00 4·25
P71 4l. black . . . . 1·00 7·75
P72 10l. mauve £180 £200
P73 20l. purple £180 £250

POSTAGE DUE STAMPS
A. ITALIAN ISSUES

1915. Postage Due stamps of Italy optd **Libia**.
D17 D **12** 5c. mauve and orange 1·40 4·25
D18 10c. mauve and orange 1·50 2·50
D19 20c. mauve and orange 2·10 3·50
D20 30c. mauve and orange 2·50 4·25
D21 40c. mauve and orange 3·75 6·00
D22 50c. mauve and orange 2·50 3·50
D23 60c. mauve and orange 4·00 7·75
D24 60c. brown and orange 60·00 85·00
D25 1l. mauve and blue . . 2·50 7·75
D26 2l. mauve and blue . . 38·00 50·00
D27 5l. mauve and blue . . 50·00 75·00

1934. Postage Due stamps of Italy optd **LIBIA**.
D68 D **141** 5c. brown . . . . . . 10 2·10
D69 10c. blue . . . . . . 10 2·10
D70 20c. red . . . . 1·00 1·20
D71 25c. green . . . . . . 1·00 1·20
D72 30c. red . . . . 1·00 4·25
D73 40c. brown . . . . . . 1·00 3·00
D74 50c. violet . . . . . . 1·20 35
D75 60c. blue . . . . . . 1·50 10·50
D76 D **142** 1l. orange . . . . . . 1·40 35
D77 2l. green . . . . . . 38·00 10·50
D78 5l. violet . . . . . . 60·00 21·00
D79 10l. blue . . . . . . 10·50 31·00
D80 20l. red . . . . 10·50 41·00

B. INDEPENDENT ISSUES

1951. Postage Due stamps of Cyrenaica optd. (a) For use in Cyrenaica. Optd as T **20**.
D144 D **26** 2m. brown . . . . . . 5·00 5·00
D145 4m. green . . . . . . 5·00 5·00
D146 8m. red . . . . 6·75 6·25
D147 10m. orange . . . . . 7·50 6·25
D148 20m. yellow . . . . . 11·00 10·00
D149 40m. blue . . . . . . 30·00 20·00
D150 100m. black . . . . . 40·00 23·00
(b) For use in Tripolitania. Surch as T **21**.
D161 D **26** 1mal. on 2m. brown 5·50 5·00
D162 2mal. on 4m. green . . 7·50 5·50
D163 4mal. on 8m. red . . . 12·50 10·00
D164 10mal. on 20m. yellow 27·00 20·00
D165 20mal. on 40m. blue 45·00 35·00

D 25

D 53 Government Building, Tripoli 1952.

1951.
D188 D **25** 2m. brown 65 25
D189 5m. green 95 50
D190 10m. red . . . . . . 2·25 95
D191 50m. blue . . . . . . 7·50 2·25

1964.
D296 D **53** 2m. brown 10 10
D297 6m. green 20 10
D298 10m. red 70 45
D299 50m. blue . . . . . . 1·25 85

D 185 Men in Boat

1976. Ancient Mosaics. Multicoloured.
D725 5dh. Type D **185** 10 10
D726 10dh. Head of Medusa . . 10 10
D727 20dh. Peacock 10 10
D728 50dh. Fish 80 25

LIECHTENSTEIN Pt. 8

A small independent principality lying between Austria and Switzerland.

1912. 100 heller = 1 krone.
1921. 100 rappen = 1 franc (Swiss).

1 Prince John II

1912.
4 **1** 5h. green . . . . 8·75 6·00
2 10h. red . . . . 40·00 6·00
3 25h. blue . . . . 40·00 20·00

2

3

1917.
7 **2** 3h. violet 75 55
8 5h. green 75 55
9 **3** 10h. purple 95 85
10 15h. brown 95 75
11 20h. green 95 85
12 25h. blue 95 75

1918. 60th Anniv of Prince John's Accession. As T **3** but dated "1858–1918" in upper corners.
13 **3** 20h. green . . . . 60 1·00

1920. Optd with a scroll pattern.
14 **2** 5h. green . . . . 1·60 4·50
15 **3** 10h. purple . . . . 1·60 4·50
16 25h. blue . . . . 1·60 4·50

1920. Surch.
17 **2** 40h. on 3h. violet . . . . . 1·60 4·50
18 **3** 1k. on 15h. brown . . . . . 1·60 4·50
19 2½k. on 20h. green . . . . . 1·60 4·50

7

8 Castle of Vaduz

1920. Imperf.
20 **7** 5h. bistre . . . . 15 2·40
21 10h. orange . . . . 15 2·40
22 15h. blue . . . . 15 2·40
23 20h. brown . . . . 15 2·40
24 25h. green . . . . 15 2·40
25 30h. grey . . . . 15 2·40
26 40h. red . . . . 15 2·40
27 **8** 1k. blue . . . . 15 2·40

9 Prince John I

10 Arms

1920. Perf.
28 **7** 5h. bistre 10 35
29 10h. orange 10 35
30 15h. blue 10 35
31 20h. brown 10 35
32 – 25h. green 10 35
33 **7** 30h. grey 10 35
34 – 40h. purple 10 35
35 – 50h. green 10 35
36 – 60h. brown 10 35
37 – 80h. pink 10 35
38 **8** 1k. lilac 20 55
39 – 2k. blue 25 60
40 **9** 5k. black 40 70
41 – 7½k. grey 55 90
42 **10** 10k. brown . . . . 60 1·00
DESIGNS—As Type **8**: 25h. St. Mamertus Chapel; 40h. Gutenberg Castle; 50h. Courtyard, Vaduz Castle; 60h. Red House, Vaduz; 80h. Church Tower, Schaan; 2k. Bendern. As Type **9**: 7½k. Prince John II.

11 Madonna

14 Arms

15 St. Mamertus Chapel

16 Vaduz

1920. Prince John's 80th Birthday. Imperf or perf.
43 **11** 50h. green . . . . 50 1·80
44 80h. red . . . . 50 1·80
45 2k. blue . . . . 50 1·80

1921. Surch **2 Rp.** and bars.
47 **7** 2r. on 10h. orange (No. 21) 40 13·50

1921.
47a **14** 2r. yellow . . . . 65 6·00
48 2½r. brown . . . . 55 6·00
49 3r. orange . . . . 65 5·00
50 5r. green . . . . 6·50 85
51 7½r. blue . . . . 7·25 20·00
65 10r. green . . . . 14·00 3·00
53 13r. brown . . . . 5·00 43·00
54 15r. violet . . . . 10·50 11·50
55 **15** 20r. black and violet . . . 30·00 85
56 – 25r. black and red . . . . 1·90 3·00
57 – 30r. black and green . . . 38·00 5·75
66 – 30r. black and blue . . . . 9·75 90
58 – 35r. black and brown . . . 2·75 6·25
59 – 40r. black and blue . . . . 4·75 2·50
60 – 50r. black and green . . . 5·75 3·25
61 – 80r. black and grey . . . 16·00 38·00
62 **16** 1f. black and red . . . . . 31·00 23·00
DESIGNS—As Type **15**: 25r. Vaduz Castle; 30r. Bendern; 35r. Prince John II; 40r. Church Tower at Schaan; 50r. Gutenberg Castle; 80r. Red House, Vaduz.

1924. Surch.
63 **14** 5 on 7½r. blue . . . . . . 75 1·10
64 10 on 13r. brown . . . . . 55 1·60

19 Vine-dresser

21 Government Bldg. and Church, Vaduz

1924.
67 **19** 2½r. mauve and green . . . 85 3·50
68 5r. blue and brown . . . . 1·20 55
69 7½r. brown and green . . . 90 4·00
70 – 10r. green . . . . 8·50 50
71 **19** 15r. green and purple . . . 4·75 17·00
72 – 20r. red . . . . 20·00 60
73 **21** 1½f. blue . . . . 60·00 50·00
DESIGN—As Type **19**: 10, 20r. Castle of Vaduz.

22 Prince John II

23

1925. 85th Birthday of Prince John.
74 **22** 10+5r. green . . . . 21·00 9·25
75 20+5r. red . . . . 15·00 9·25
76 30+5r. blue . . . . 4·75 2·00

1927. 87th Birthday of Prince. Arms multicoloured.
77 **23** 10+5r. green . . . . 5·75 13·50
78 20+5r. purple . . . . 5·75 13·50
79 30+5r. blue . . . . 5·50 12·50

24 Salvage Work by Austrian soldiers

1928. Flood Relief.
80 – 5r.+5r. brown and purple 13·50 18·00
81 – 10r.+10r. brown and green 13·00 16·00
82 **24** 20r.+10r. brown and red . . 13·00 16·00
83 – 30r.+10r. brown and blue 8·75 16·00
DESIGNS: 5r. Railway bridge between Buchs and Schaan; 10r. Village of Ruggell; 30r. Salvage work by Swiss soldiers.

26 Prince John II, 1858–1928

1928. 70th Anniv of Accession of Prince John II.

No.	Type	Description	Unused	Used
84	–	10r. green and brown	2·10	2·30
85	–	20r. green and red	4·75	5·75
86	–	30r. green and blue	11·00	13·00
87	–	60r. green and mauve	35·00	65·00
88	**26**	1f.20 blue	36·00	65·00
89		1f.50 brown	65·00	£160
90		2f. red	65·00	£160
91		5f. green	65·00	£200

DESIGN—VERT: 10r. to 60r. Prince John II.

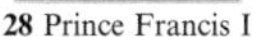

28 Prince Francis I **31** Girl Vintager

32 Prince Francis I and Princess Elsa **34** Monoplane over Vaduz Castle and Rhine Valley

1929. Accession of Prince Francis I.

No.	Type	Description	Unused	Used
92	–	10r. green	50	1·60
93	**28**	20r. red	75	2·10
94	–	30r. blue	1·10	12·00
95	–	70r. brown	10·50	60·00

PORTRAITS: 10r. Prince Francis I as a boy; 30r. Princess Elsa; 70r. Prince Francis and Princess Elsa.

1930.

No.	Type	Description	Unused	Used
96	**31**	3r. red	45	65
97	–	5r. green	1·00	75
98	–	10r. lilac	1·00	50
99	–	20r. red	21·00	80
100	–	25r. green	5·00	18·00
101	–	30r. blue	5·00	1·10
102	–	35r. green	6·25	10·50
103	–	40r. brown	6·25	3·50
104	–	50r. black	60·00	9·50
105	–	60r. green	60·00	18·00
106	–	90r. purple	60·00	£100
107	–	1f.20 brown	80·00	£160
108	–	1f.50 blue	34·00	42·00
109	**32**	2f. brown and green	48·00	75·00

DESIGNS—VERT: 5r. Mt. Three Sisters–Edelweiss; 10r. Alpine cattle-alpine roses; 20r. Courtyard of Vaduz Castle; 25r. Mt. Naafkopf; 30r. Valley of Samina; 35r. Rofenberg Chapel; 40r. St. Mamertus' Chapel; 50r. Kurhaus at Malbun; 60r. Gutenberg Castle; 90r. Schellenberg Monastery; 1f.20, Vaduz Castle; 1f.50, Pfaelzer club hut.

1930. Air.

No.	Type	Description	Unused	Used
110	–	15r. brown	4·50	6·00
111	–	20r. green	11·50	12·00
112	–	25r. brown	5·75	19·00
113	–	35r. blue	9·00	13·00
114	**34**	45r. green	25·00	44·00
115		1f. purple	40·00	30·00

DESIGNS—VERT: 15, 20r. Biplane over snowy mountain peak. HORIZ: 25, 35r. Biplane over Vaduz Castle.

35 Airship "Graf Zeppelin" over Alps

1931. Air.

No.	Type	Description	Unused	Used
116	**35**	1f. green	28·00	24·00
117	–	2f. blue	80·00	£225

DESIGN: 2f. Airship "Graf Zeppelin" (different).

37 Princess Elsa **38** Mt. Naafkopf **39** Prince Francis I

1932. Youth Charities.

No.	Type	Description	Unused	Used
118	–	10r.+5r. green	14·50	22·00
119	**37**	20r.+5r. red	15·00	23·00
120	–	30r.+10r. blue	17·00	27·00

DESIGNS—22 × 29 mm: 10r. Arms of Liechtenstein. As Type **37**: 30r. Prince Francis.

1933.

No.	Type	Description	Unused	Used
121	**38**	25r. orange	£190	60·00
122	–	90r. green	6·50	48·00
123	–	1f.20 brown	48·00	£180

DESIGNS: 90r. Gutenberg Castle; 1f.20, Vaduz Castle.

1933. Prince Francis's 80th Birthday.

No.	Type	Description	Unused	Used
124	**39**	10r. violet	13·00	33·00
125		20r. red	13·00	33·00
126		30r. blue	13·00	33·00

40 **41** "Three Sisters"

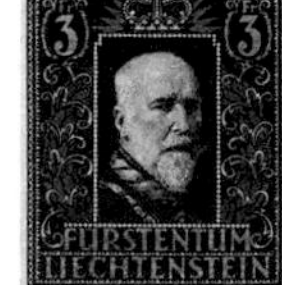

42 Vaduz Castle **44** Prince Francis I

45 Arms of Liechtenstein **46** Golden Eagle

1933.

No.	Type	Description	Unused	Used
127	**40**	3r. red	20	45
128	**41**	5r. green	2·50	45
129	–	10r. violet	65	35
130	–	15r. orange	25	85
131	–	20r. red	60	45
132	–	25r. brown	15·00	40·00
133	–	30r. blue	3·25	85
134	–	35r. green	85	3·50
135	–	40r. brown	95	2·40
136	**42**	50r. brown	17·00	11·00
137	–	60r. purple	1·70	4·00
138	–	90r. green	5·25	13·50
139	–	1f.20 blue	1·90	12·50
140	–	1f.50 brown	2·30	16·00
141	–	2f. brown	42·00	£130
142	**44**	3f. blue	55·00	£130
143	**45**	5f. purple	£300	£650

DESIGNS—As Type **41**: 10r. Schaan Church; 15r. Bendern am Rhein; 20r. Town Hall, Vaduz; 25r. Saminatal. As Type **44**: 2f. Princess Elsa. As Type **42**: 30r. Saminatal (different); 35r. Schellenberg ruins; 40r. Government Building, Vaduz; 60r. Vaduz Castle (different); 90r. Gutenberg Castle; 1f.20, Pfalzer Hut, Bettlerjoch; 1f.50, Valuna.

See also Nos. **MS**144, **MS**153, 174, 225/6 and 258.

1934. Vaduz First Liechtenstein Philatelic Exhibition. Sheet 105 × 125 mm.

No.	Type	Description	Unused	Used
MS144	**45**	5f. chocolate	£1100	£1700

1934. Air.

No.	Type	Description	Unused	Used
145	**46**	10r. violet	5·25	13·50
146	–	15r. orange	13·00	30·00
147	–	20r. red	14·00	30·00
148	–	30r. blue	14·00	30·00
149	–	50r. green	20·00	25·00

DESIGNS: 10r. to 20r. Golden eagles in flight; 30r. Ospreys in nest; 50r. Golden eagle on rock.

1935. Air. No. 115 surch **60 Rp**.

No.	Type	Description	Unused	Used
150	**34**	60r. on 1f. purple	21·00	32·00

49 "Hindenburg" and Schaan Church

1936. Air.

No.	Type	Description	Unused	Used
151	**49**	1f. red	26·00	55·00
152	–	2f. violet	22·00	55·00

DESIGN: 2f. "Graf Zeppelin" over Schaan Airport.

1936. 2nd Liechtenstein Philatelic Exhibition and Opening of Postal Museum, Vaduz. Sheet 165 × 119 mm containing two each of Nos. 131 and 133.

No.	Type	Description	Unused	Used
MS153		Sold at 2fr.	35·00	35·00

51 Masescha am Triesenberg **52** Schellenberg Castle

1937.

No.	Type	Description	Unused	Used
154	–	3r. brown	20	13·50
155	**51**	5r. green and buff	15	20
156	–	10r. violet and buff	15	15
157	–	15r. black and buff	40	50
158	–	20r. red and buff	25	30
159	–	25r. brown and buff	60	2·20
160	–	30r. blue and buff	1·40	55
161	**52**	40r. green and buff	1·40	1·20
162	–	50c. brown and buff	95	1·80
163	–	60r. purple and buff	1·40	1·70
164	–	90r. violet and buff	7·50	8·75
165	–	1f. purple and buff	1·30	8·25
166	–	1f.20 brown and buff	6·00	11·50
167	–	1f.50 grey and buff	3·00	12·00

DESIGNS—As Type **51**: 3r. Schalun ruins; 10r. Knight and Vaduz Castle; 15r. Upper Saminatal; 20r. Church and Bridge at Bendern; 25r. Steg Chapel and girl. As Type **52**: 30r. Farmer and orchard, Triesenberg; 50r. Knight and Gutenberg Castle; 60r. Baron von Brandis and Vaduz Castle; 90r. "Three Sisters" mountain; 1f. Boundary-stone on Luziensteig; 1f.20, Minstrel and Gutenberg Castle; 1f.50, Lawena (Schwarzhorn).

53 Roadmakers at Triesenberg

1937. Workers' Issue.

No.	Type	Description	Unused	Used
168	–	10r. mauve	80	45
169	**53**	20r. red	1·10	75
170	–	30r. blue	1·50	1·60
171	–	50r. brown	95	2·10

DESIGNS: 10r. Bridge at Malbun; 30r. Binnen Canal Junction; 50r. Francis Bridge, near Planken.

1938. 3rd Liechtenstein Philatelic Exhibition, Vaduz. Sheet 100 × 135 mm containing stamps as No. 175 in different colour in a block of four.

No.	Type	Description	Unused	Used
MS173	**54**	50r. blue	35·00	21·00

1938. Death of Prince Francis I.

No.	Type	Description	Unused	Used
174	**44**	3f. black on yellow	6·25	49·00

54 Josef Rheinberger **55** Black-headed Gulls

1939. Birth Centenary of Rheinberger (composer).

No.	Type	Description	Unused	Used
175	**54**	50r. grey	55	2·75

1939. Air.

No.	Type	Description	Unused	Used
176	–	10r. violet (Barn swallows)	25	50
177	**55**	15r. orange	40	1·40
178	–	20r. red (Herring gull)	80	45
179	–	30r. blue (Common buzzard)	80	1·10
180	–	50r. green (Northern goshawk)	2·75	1·70
181	–	1f. red (Lammergeier)	2·20	11·00
182	–	2f. violet Lammergeier	1·90	11·50

56 Offering Homage to First Prince

1939. Homage to Francis Joseph II.

No.	Type	Description	Unused	Used
183	**56**	20r. red	75	1·20
184		30r. blue	75	1·20
185		50r. green	75	1·30

57 Francis Joseph II

1939.

No.	Type	Description	Unused	Used
186	–	2f. green on cream	5·00	25·00
187	–	3f. violet on cream	4·50	25·00
188	**57**	5f. brown on cream	10·50	21·00

DESIGNS: 2f. Cantonal Arms; 3f. Arms of Principality.

58 Prince John when a Child

1940. Birth Centenary of Prince John II.

No.	Type	Description	Unused	Used
189	**58**	20r. red	50	1·40
190	–	30r. blue	70	2·20
191	–	50r. green	1·10	5·75
192	–	1f. violet	6·50	43·00
193	–	1f.50 black	5·25	42·00
194	–	3f. brown	3·50	12·00

DESIGNS—As Type **58**: Portraits of Prince John in early manhood (30r.), in middle age (50r.) and in later life (1f.), and Memorial tablet (1f.50). As Type **44**: 3f. Framed portrait of Prince John II.

60 Wine Press

1941. Agricultural Propaganda.

No.	Type	Description	Unused	Used
195	–	10r. brown	45	40
196	**60**	20r. purple	65	75
197	–	30r. blue	75	1·40
198	–	50r. green	2·30	10·50
199	–	90r. violet	2·30	11·50

DESIGNS: 10r. Harvesting maize; 30r. Sharpen-ing scythe; 50r. Milkmaid and cow; 90r. Girl wearing traditional headdress.

61 Madonna and Child **62** Prince Hans Adam

1941.

No.	Type	Description	Unused	Used
200	**61**	10f. purple on stone	33·00	70·00

1941. Princes (1st issue).

No.	Type	Description	Unused	Used
201	**62**	20r. red	35	1·20
202	–	30r. blue (Wenzel)	65	1·90
203	–	1f. grey (Anton Florian)	1·90	11·00
204	–	1f.50 green (Joseph)	1·90	11·50

See also Nos. 210/13 and 217/20.

63 St. Lucius preaching

1942. 600th Anniv of Separation from Estate of Montfort.

No.	Type	Description	Unused	Used
205	**63**	20r. red on pink	75	65
206	–	30r. blue on pink	70	1·40
207	–	50r. green on pink	1·60	5·00
208	–	1f. brown on pink	2·00	9·75
209	–	2f. violet on pink	2·30	9·75

DESIGNS: 30r. Count of Montfort replanning Vaduz; 50r. Counts of Montfort-Werdenberg and Sargans signing treaty; 1f. Battle of Gutenberg; 2f. Homage to Prince of Liechtenstein.

64 Prince John Charles **65** Princess Georgina

1942. Princes (2nd issue).

No.	Type	Description	Unused	Used
210	**64**	20r. pink	25	75
211	–	30r. blue (Francis Joseph I)	45	1·40
212	–	1f. purple (Alois I)	1·40	9·50
213	–	1f.50 brown (John I)	1·40	9·50

1943. Marriage of Prince Francis Joseph II and Countess Georgina von Wildczek.

No.	Type	Description	Unused	Used
214	–	10r. purple	50	70
215	**65**	20r. red	50	1·10
216	–	30r. blue	50	1·10

PORTRAITS—VERT: 10r. Prince Francis Joseph II. HORIZ (44 × 25 mm): 30r. Prince and Princess.

66 Alois II 67 Marsh Land

1943. Princes (3rd issue).
217 **66** 20r. brown 50 50
218 – 30r. blue 80 95
219 – 1f. brown . . . . 1·30 5·50
220 – 1f.50 green . . . . 1·30 5·50
PORTRAITS: 30r. John II; 1f. Francis I; 1f.50, Francis Joseph II.

1943. Completion of Irrigation Canal.
221 **67** 10r. violet 20 35
222 – 30r. blue . . . . 35 1·70
223 – 50r. green . . . . 65 6·25
224 – 2f. brown . . . . 1·60 9·75
DESIGNS: 30r. Draining the canal; 50r. Ploughing reclaimed land; 2f. Harvesting crops.

1943. Castles. As T **41**.
225 10r. grey (Vaduz) 40 55
226 20r. brown (Gutenberg) . . . 35 70

69 Planken 70 Prince Francis Joseph II

1944. Various designs. Buff backgrounds.
227 **69** 3r. brown 20 20
228 – 5r. green (Bendern) . . . 20 15
228a – 5r. brown (Bendern) . . . 10·00 45
229 – 10r. grey (Triesen) . . . . 12·00 45
230 – 15r. grey (Ruggell) . . . 40 55
231 – 20r. red (Vaduz) 40 35
232 – 25r. brown (Triesenberg) 45 55
233 – 30r. blue (Schaan) 50 40
234 – 40r. brown (Balzers) . . . 65 1·10
235 – 50r. blue (Mauren) . . . 1·50 1·70
236 – 60r. green (Schellenberg) 4·25 3·25
237 – 90r. green (Eschen) . . . 4·25 3·50
238 – 1f. purple (Vaduz Castle) 3·00 3·75
239 – 1f.20 brown (Valunatal) 3·25 4·00
240 – 1f.50 blue (Lawena) . . . 3·25 3·75

1944.
241 **70** 2f. brown and buff . . . . 4·00 10·00
242 – 3f. green and buff . . . . 3·50 8·00
DESIGN: 3f. Princess Georgina.
See also Nos. 302/3.

72 73

1945. Birth of Crown Prince Johann Adam Pius (known as Prince Hans Adam).
243 **72** 20r. red, yellow and gold 65 40
244 30r. blue, yellow and gold 80 1·00
245 100r. grey, yellow and gold 2·10 4·00

1945.
246 **73** 5f. blue on buff . . . . . 16·00 18·00
247 5f. brown on buff . . . . 17·00 27·00

74 First Aid 75 St. Lucius

1945. Red Cross. Cross in red.
248 – 10r.+10r. purple and buff 1·40 1·40
249 **74** 20r.+20r. purple and buff 1·40 2·00
250 – 1f.+1f.40 blue and buff . . 6·25 18·00
DESIGNS: 10r. Mother and children; 1f. Nurse and invalid.

1946.
251 **75** 10f. grey on buff . . . . . 24·00 22·00

1946. 4th Liechtenstein Philatelic Exhibition, Vaduz and 25th Anniv of Postal Agreement with Switzerland. Sheet 84 × 60 mm.
MS251a 10r. (× 2) Old Postal Coach (*horiz*), violet, brown and buff (sold at 3f.) . . . . 28·00 38·00

76 Red Deer Stag 79 Wilbur Wright

1946. Wild Life.
252 **76** 20r. red . . . . 1·20 1·30
255 – 20r. red (Chamois) . . . . 2·00 2·10
283 – 20r. red (Roebuck) . . . . 7·75 2·30
253 – 30r. blue (Arctic hare) . . 1·60 2·10
256 – 30r. blue (Alpine marmot) 3·00 2·75
284 – 30r. green (Black grouse) 13·50 7·75
285 – 80r. brown (Eurasian badger) . . . . 27·00 30·00
254 – 1f.50 green (Western capercaillie) . . . . . 5·75 8·50
257 – 1f.50 brown (Golden eagle) 6·75 12·00

1947. Death of Princess Elsa. As No. 141.
258 – 2f. black on yellow . . . . 2·20 9·25

1948. Air. Pioneers of Flight.
259 – 10r. green 65 20
260 – 15r. violet . . . . 65 1·00
261 – 20r. brown 80 25
262 – 25r. red . . . . 1·10 1·25
263 – 40r. blue . . . . 1·30 1·60
264 – 50r. blue . . . . 1·70 1·60
265 – 1f. purple . . . . 3·50 2·40
266 – 2f. purple . . . . 4·00 3·75
267 **79** 5f. green . . . . 5·25 4·75
268 – 10f. black . . . . 28·00 14·00
PORTRAITS: 10r. Leoardo da Vinci; 15r. Joseph Montgolfier; 20r. Jakob Degen; 25r. Wilhelm Kress; 40r. Étienne Robertson; 50r. William Henson; 1f. Otto Lilienthal; 2f. Salomon Andree; 10f. Icarus

80 "Ginevra de Benci" (Da Vinci)

1949. Paintings.
269 **80** 10r. green 45 25
270 – 20r. red 95 50
271 – 30r. brown . . . . 2·50 1·20
272 – 40r. blue . . . . 5·25 60
273 – 50r. violet . . . . 4·50 5·25
274 – 60r. grey . . . . 9·25 4·75
275 – 80r. brown . . . . 2·30 3·25
276 – 90r. green . . . . 9·25 4·00
277 – 120r. mauve . . . . 2·30 4·00
DESIGNS: 20r. "Portrait of a Young Girl" (Rubens); 30r. Self-portrait of Rembrandt in plumed hat; 40r. "Stephan Gardiner, Bishop of Winchester" (Quentin Massys); 50r. "Madonna and Child" (Hans Memling); 60r. "Franz Meister in 1456" (Jehan Fouquet); 80r. "Lute Player" (Orazio Gentileschi); 90r. "Portrait of a Man" (Bernhardin Strigel); 120r. "Portrait of a Man (Duke of Urbino)" (Raphael).

1949. No. 227 surch **5 Rp.** and bars.
278 **69** 5r. on 3r. brown and buff 50 35

82 Posthorn and Map of World

1949. 75th Anniv of U.P.U.
279 **82** 40r. blue . . . . 2·75 3·25

1949. 5th Liechtenstein Philatelic Exhibition, Vaduz. Sheet 122 × 70 mm containing paintings as 1949 issue in new colours.
MS279a 10r. green (as 10r.); 20r. mauve (as 80r.); 40r. blue (as 120r.). Sold at 3f. . . . . . . 90·00 £110

83 Rossauer Castle 86 Boy cutting Loaf

1949. 250th Anniv of Acquisition of Domain of Schellenberg.
280 **83** 20r. purple . . . . 1·50 1·40
281 – 40r. blue . . . . 5·25 6·00
282 – 1f.50 red . . . . 8·00 7·50

DESIGN—HORIZ: 40r. Bendern Church. VERT: 1f.50, Prince Johann Adam I.

1950. Surch **100 100**.
286 **82** 100r. on 40r. blue . . . . 19·00 31·00

1951. Agricultural scenes.
287 **86** 5r. mauve 25 10
288 – 10r. green 50 10
289 – 15r. brown . . . . 4·25 4·75
290 – 20r. brown 95 20
291 – 25r. purple . . . . 4·25 4·75
292 – 30r. green . . . . 2·50 50
293 – 40r. blue . . . . 7·50 4·25
294 – 50r. purple . . . . 6·50 3·00
295 – 60r. brown . . . . 6·25 3·00
296 – 80r. brown . . . . 6·25 6·75
297 – 90r. green . . . . 13·00 4·50
298 – 1f. blue . . . . 42·00 5·50
DESIGNS: 10r. Man whetting scythe; 15r. Mowing; 20r. Girl and sweet corn; 25r. Haywain; 30r. Gathering grapes; 40r. Man with scythe; 50r. Herdsman with cows; 60r. Ploughing; 80r. Girl carrying basket of fruit; 90r. Woman gleaning; 1f. Tractor hauling corn.

87 "Lock on the Canal" (Aelbert Cuyp) 88 "Willem von Heythuysen, Burgomaster of Haarlem" (Frans Hals)

1951. Paintings.
299 **87** 10r.+10r. green . . . . . 7·50 5·25
300 **88** 20r.+10r. brown . . . . . 8·00 10·50
301 – 40r.+10r. blue . . . . . . 6·75 7·00
DESIGN—As Type **87**: 40r. "Landscape" (Jacob van Ruysdael).

90 Vaduz Castle 96 Lord Baden-Powell

1951.
302 **70** 2f. blue . . . . 12·50 22·00
303 – 3f. brown . . . . £110 75·00
304 **90** 5f. green £130 £110
DESIGN: 3f. Princess Georgina.

1952. No. 281 surch **1.20**
308 1f.20 on 40r. blue . . . . . 17·00 37·00

1952. Paintings from Prince's Collection. (a) As T **80** but size 25 × 30 mm.
309 10r. green . . . . 1·00 65
305 20r. purple . . . . 25·00 2·20
307 40r. blue . . . . 9·00 3·75
312 40r. blue . . . . 24·00 34·00
PAINTINGS: No. 309, "Portrait of a Young Man" (A. G.); 305, "Portrait" (Giovanni Salvoldo); 307, "St. John" (Andrea del Sarto); 312, "Leonhard, Count of Hag" (Hans von Kulmbach).

(b) As T **88** (22½ × 24 mm).
310 20r. brown . . . . 11·00 1·70
306 30r. green . . . . 17·00 5·75
311 30r. brown . . . . 22·00 5·25
PAINTINGS: No. 310, "St. Nicholas" (Bartholomaus Zeitblom); 306, "Madonna and Child" (Sandro Botticelli); 311, "St. Christopher" (Lucas Cranach the elder).

1953. 14th International Scout Conference.
313 **96** 10r. green . . . . 1·40 90
314 20r. brown . . . . 9·50 1·50
315 25r. red . . . . 9·00 15·00
316 40r. blue . . . . 8·75 3·25

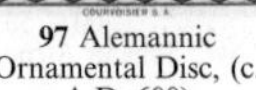

97 Alemannic Ornamental Disc, (c. A.D. 600) 98 Prehistoric Walled Settlement, Borscht

1953. Opening of National Museum, Vaduz.
317 **97** 10r. brown . . . . 7·00 8·25
318 **98** 20r. green . . . . 7·00 8·00
319 – 1f.20 blue . . . . 36·00 24·00
DESIGN—VERT: 1f.20, Rossen jug (3000 B.C.).

99 Footballers 100 Madonna and Child

1954. Football.
320 **99** 10r. brown and red . . . . 1·60 75
321 – 20r. deep green and green 5·75 2·00
322 – 25r. deep brown and brown . . . . 13·00 21·00
323 – 40r. violet and grey . . . . 11·50 7·25
DESIGNS: 20r. Footballer kicking ball; 25r. Goalkeeper; 40r. Two footballers.
For stamps in similar designs see Nos. 332/5, 340/3, 351/4 and 363/6.

1954. Nos. 299/301 surch in figures.
324 **87** 35r. on 10r.+10r. green . . 3·00 1·60
325 **88** 60r. on 20r.+10r. brown 11·00 8·25
326 – 65r. on 40r.+10r. blue . . 6·50 5·75

1954. Termination of Marian Year.
327 **100** 20r. brown . . . . 2·50 2·75
328 40r. black . . . . 13·00 14·00
329 1f. brown . . . . 14·00 13·50

101 Princess Georgina 102 Crown Prince John Adam Pius

1955.
330 – 2f. brown . . . . 55·00 31·00
331 **101** 3f. green . . . . 55·00 31·00
PORTRAIT: 2f. Prince Francis Joseph II.

1955. Mountain Sports. As T **99**.
332 10r. purple and blue . . . . 1·70 75
333 20r. green and bistre . . . . 4·00 75
334 25r. brown and blue . . . . 13·00 12·50
335 40r. green and red . . . . . 11·50 3·50
DESIGNS: 10r. Slalom racer; 20r. Mountaineer hammering in piton; 25r. Skier; 40r. Mountaineer resting on summit.

1955. 10th Anniv of Liechtenstein Red Cross. Cross in red.
336 **102** 10r. violet . . . . 1·30 40
337 – 20r. green . . . . 3·00 1·20
338 – 40r. brown . . . . 5·00 5·25
339 – 60r. red . . . . 5·00 3·50
PORTRAITS: 20r. Prince Philip; 40r. Prince Nicholas; 60r. Princess Nora.
See also No. 350.

1956. Athletics. As T **99**.
340 10r. green and brown 90 50
341 20r. purple and green . . . . 2·50 75
342 40r. brown and blue . . . . 3·75 4·25
343 1f. brown and red . . . . . 7·50 8·75
DESIGNS: 10r. Throwing the javelin; 20r. Hurdling; 40r. Pole vaulting; 1f. Running.

103 104 Prince Francis Joseph II

1956. 150th Anniv of Sovereignty of Liechtenstein.
344 **103** 10r. purple and gold . . . 2·00 60
345 1f.20 blue and gold . . . 8·50 3·25

1956. 50th Birthday of Prince Francis Joseph II.
346 **104** 10r. green . . . . 1·30 35
347 15r. blue . . . . 2·10 2·10
348 25r. purple . . . . 2·10 2·10
349 60r. brown . . . . 6·00 2·10

1956. 6th Philatelic Exhibition, Vaduz. As T **102** but inscr "6. BRIEFMARKEN-AUSSTELLUNG".
350 20r. green . . . . 2·30 40

1956. Gymnastics. As T **99**.
351 10r. green and pink . . . . 2·00 70
352 15r. purple and green . . . . 4·25 4·75
353 25r. green and drab . . . . 5·00 6·25
354 1f.50 brown and yellow . . . 13·00 11·00
DESIGNS: 10r. Somersaulting; 15r. Vaulting; 25r. Exercising with rings; 1f.50, Somersaulting on parallel bars.

105 Norway Spruce

106 Lord Baden-Powell

1957. Liechtenstein Trees and Bushes.
355 **105** 10r. purple . . . . 2·75 1·40
356 – 20r. red . . . . 3·00 50
357 – 1f. green . . . . 5·00 5·00
DESIGNS: 20r. Wild rose bush; 1f. Silver birch.
See also Nos. 369/71, 375/7 and 401/3.

1957. 50th Anniv of Boy Scout Movement and Birth Centenary of Lord Baden-Powell (founder).
358 – 10r. blue . . . . 1·00 1·00
359 **106** 20r. brown . . . . 1·00 1·00
DESIGN: 10r. Torchlight procession.

107 St. Mamertus Chapel

108 Relief Map of Liechtenstein

1957. Christmas.
360 **107** 10r. brown 70 20
361 – 40r. blue . . . . 2·20 5·00
362 – 1f.50 purple . . . . . . 7·75 8·00
DESIGNS—(from St. Mamertus Chapel): 40r. Altar shrine; 1f.50, "Pieta" (sculpture).
See also Nos. 372/4 and 392/4.

1958. Sports. As T **99**.
363 15r. violet and blue . . . . . 90 1·00
364 30r. green and purple . . . . 3·00 5·25
365 40r. green and orange . . . . 5·00 5·50
366 90r. brown and green . . . . 2·75 3·50
DESIGNS: 15r. Swimmer; 30r. Fencers; 40r. Tennis player; 90r. Racing cyclists.

1958. Brussels International Exhibition.
367 **108** 25r. violet, stone and red 50 50
368 40r. purple, blue and red 65 55

1958. Liechtenstein Trees and Bushes. As T **105**.
369 20r. brown (Sycamore) . . . 2·30 50
370 50r. green (Holly) . . . . . 9·00 3·75
371 90r. violet (Yew) . . . . . . 2·30 2·50

1958. Christmas. As T **107**.
372 20r. green . . . . 2·20 1·90
373 35r. violet . . . . 2·20 2·50
374 80r. brown . . . . 2·50 2·10
DESIGNS: 20r. "St. Maurice and St. Agatha"; 35r. "St. Peter"; 80r. St. Peter's Chapel, Mals-Balzers.

1959. Liechtenstein Trees and Bushes. As T **105**.
375 20r. lilac (Red-berried larch) 3·75 1·90
376 50r. red (Red-berried elder) 3·50 2·10
377 90r. green (Linden) . . . . . 3·00 2·50

109

111 Harvester

110 Flags of Vaduz Castle and Rhine Valley

1959. Pope Pius XII Mourning.
378 **109** 30r. purple and gold . . . 60 60

1959. Views.
379 – 5r. brown 10 10
380 **110** 10r. purple 10 10
381 – 20r. mauve 25 10
382 – 30r. red 35 25
383 – 40r. green 70 40
384 – 50r. blue 50 40
385 – 60r. blue 65 50
386 **111** 75r. brown . . . . . . 95 1·10
387 – 80r. green 85 65
388 – 90r. purple . . . . . . 1·00 95
389 – 1f. brown . . . . 1·00 80
390 – 1f.20 red . . . . 1·30 1·20
390a – 1f.30 green . . . . . . 1·30 1·40
391 – 1f.50 blue . . . . 1·50 1·50
DESIGNS—HORIZ: 5r. Bendern Church; 20r. Rhine Dam; 30r. Gutenberg Castle; 40r. View from Schellenberg; 50r. Vaduz Castle; 60r. Naafkopf-Falknis Mountains (view from the Bettlerjoch); 1f.20, Harvesting apples; 1f.30, Farmer and wife; 1f.50, Saying grace at table. VERT: 80r. Alpine haymaker; 90r. Girl in vineyard; 1f. Mother in kitchen.

1959. Christmas. As T **107**.
392 5r. green 50 20
393 60r. brown . . . . 5·00 3·75
394 1f. purple . . . . 3·00 2·00
DESIGNS: 5r. Bendern Church belfry; 60r. Relief on bell of St. Theodul's Church; 1f. Sculpture on tower of St. Lucius's Church.

112 Bell 47J Ranger Helicopter

1960. Air. 30th Anniv of 1st Liechtenstein Air Stamps.
395 **112** 30r. red . . . . 1·80 1·90
396 – 40r. blue . . . . 4·00 1·90
397 – 50r. purple . . . . 6·00 3·75
398 – 75r. green . . . . 2·00 2·00
DESIGNS: 40r. Boeing 707 jetliner; 50r. Convair Coronado jetliner; 75r. Douglas DC-8 jetliner.

1960. World Refugee Year. Nos. 367/8 surch **WELTFLUCHTLINGSJAHR 1960**, uprooted tree and new value.
399 **108** 30+10r. on 40r. purple, blue and red 80 80
400 50+10r. on 25r. violet, stone and red . . . . . 1·20 1·20

1960. Liechtenstein Trees and Bushes. As T **105**.
401 20r. brown (Beech) . . . . . 5·50 5·25
402 30r. purple (Juniper) . . . . 6·25 8·00
403 50r. turquoise (Mountain pines) . . . . 18·00 10·00

114 Europa "Honeycomb"

115 Princess Gina

1960. Europa.
404 **114** 50r. multicoloured . . . . 65·00 44·00

1960.
404a – 1f.70 violet . . . . . . 1·40 1·00
405 **115** 2f. blue . . . . 1·90 1·60
406 – 3f. brown . . . . 2·40 1·60
PORTRAITS: 1f.70, Crown Prince Hans Adam; 3f. Prince Francis Joseph II.

116 Heinrich von Frauenberg

117 "Power Transmission"

1961. Minnesingers (1st issue). Multicoloured. Reproduction from the Manessian Manuscript of Songs.
407 15r. Type **116** 30 30
408 25r. Ulrich von Liechtenstein 50 45
409 35r. Ulrich von Gutenberg 70 60
410 1f. Konrad von Altstatten . . 1·10 1·00
411 1f.50 Walther von der Vogelweide . . . . 4·75 7·25
See also Nos. 415/18 and 428/31.

1961. Europa.
412 **117** 50r. multicoloured 30 30

117a Prince John II

1962. 50th Anniv of First Liechtenstein Postage Stamps. Sheet 133 × 118 mm. T **117a** and similar horiz design.
MS412a 5r. green; 10r. red; 25r. blue. Sold at 2f.60 . . . . 8·25 4·50
DESIGNS: 0r. Prince Francis I; 25r. Prince Francis Joseph I.

118 Clasped Hands

119 Campaign Emblem

1962. Europa.
413 **118** 50r. red and blue 40 40

1962. Malaria Eradication.
414 **119** 50r. blue 35 35

1962. Minnesingers (2nd issue). As T **116**. Mult.
415 20r. King Konradin 25 25
416 30r. Kraft von Toggenburg 65 70
417 40r. Heinrich von Veldig . . 65 70
418 2f. Tannhauser . . . . . . 1·90 2·00

120 Pieta

121 Prince Francis Joseph II

1962. Christmas.
419 **120** 30r. mauve 40 45
420 – 50r. red 55 55
421 – 1f.20 blue . . . . 1·20 1·20
DESIGNS: 50r. Fresco with angel; 1f.20, View of Mauren.
See also Nos. 438/40.

1963. 25th Anniv of Reign of Prince Francis Joseph II.
422 **121** 5f. green . . . . 3·50 2·50

122 Milk and Bread

1963. Freedom from Hunger.
423 **122** 50r. brown, purple and red 35 40

123 "Angel of Annunciation"

124 "Europa"

1963. Red Cross Cent. Cross in red; background grey.
424 **123** 20r. yellow and green . . 25 25
425 – 80r. violet and mauve . . 40 55
426 – 1f. blue and ultramarine 95 75
DESIGNS: 80r. "The Epiphany"; 1f. "Family".

1963. Europa.
427 **124** 50r. multicoloured 60 50

1963. Minnesingers (3rd issue). As T **116**. Mult.
428 25r. Heinrich von Sax . . . 20 20
429 30r. Kristan von Hamle . . 35 35
430 75r. Werner von Teufen . . 60 60
431 1f.70 Hartmann von Aue . . 1·40 1·40

125 Olympic Rings and Flags

126 Arms of Counts of Werdenberg, Vaduz

1964. Olympic Games, Tokyo.
432 **125** 50r. red, black and blue 35 40

1964. Arms (1st issue). Multicoloured.
433 20f. Type **126** 20 20
434 30f. Barons of Brandis . . . 25 25
435 80r. Counts of Sulz 70 70
436 1f.50 Counts of Hohenems 90 95
See also Nos. 443/6.

127 Roman Castle, Schaan

128 P. Kaiser

1964. Europa.
437 **127** 50f. multicoloured 65 45

1964. Christmas. As T **120**.
438 10r. purple 10 10
439 40r. blue 20 20
440 1f.30 purple 85 85
DESIGNS: 10r. Masescha Chapel; 40r. "Mary Magdalene" (altar painting); 1f.30, "St. Sebastian, Madonna and Child, and St. Rochus" (altar painting).

1964. Death Centenary of Peter Kaiser (historian).
441 **128** 1f. green on cream . . . 55 45

129 "Madonna" (wood sculpture, c. 1700)

130 Europa "Links" (ancient belt-buckle)

1965.
442 **129** 10f. red . . . . 7·25 3·00

1965. Arms (2nd issue). As T **126**. Multicoloured.
443 20r. Von Schellenberg . . . 20 20
444 30r. Von Gutenberg 30 20
445 80r. Von Frauenberg 80 70
446 1f. Von Ramschwag 80 70

1965. Europa.
447 **130** 50r. brown, grey and blue 45 35

131 "Jesus in the Temple"

1965. Birth Centenary of Ferdinand Nigg (painter).
448 – 10r. deep green and green 15 15
449 – 30r. brown and orange . . 20 20
450 **131** 1f.20 green and blue . . . 85 85
DESIGNS—VERT: 10r. "The Annunciation"; 30r. "The Magi".

132 Princess Gina and Prince Franz (after painting by Pedro Leitao)

133 Telecommunications Symbols

1965. Special Issue.
451 **132** 75r. multicoloured 45 45
See also No. 457.

1965. Centenary of I.T.U.
452 **133** 25r. multicoloured 20 25

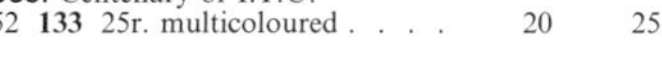

134 Tree ("Wholesome Earth")

1966. Nature Protection.
453 **134** 10r. green and yellow . . 10 10
454 – 20r. blue and light blue 10 10
455 – 30r. blue and green . . . 10 10
456 – 1f.50 red and yellow . . 55 55
DESIGNS: 20r. Bird ("Pure Air"); 30r. Fish ("Clean Water"); 1f.50, Sun ("Protection of Nature").

1966. Prince Franz Joseph II's 60th Birthday. As T **132**, but with portrait of Prince Franz and inscr "1906–1966".
457 1f. multicoloured 45 45

135 Arms of Herren von Richenstein **136** Europa "Ship"

1966. Arms of Triesen Families. Multicoloured.
458 20r. Type **135** 10 10
459 30r. Jinker Vaistli 15 15
460 60r. Edle von Trisun 40 40
461 1f.20 Die von Schiel 55 55

1966. Europa.
462 **136** 50r. multicoloured 35 35

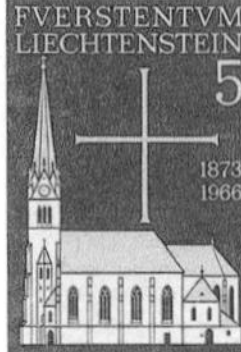

137 Vaduz Parish Church **138** Cogwheels

1966. Restoration of Vaduz Parish Church.
463 **137** 5r. green and red 10 10
464 – 20r. purple and bistre 10 10
465 – 30r. blue and red 10 15
466 – 1f.70 brown and green 65 70
DESIGNS: 20r. St. Florin; 30r. Madonna; 1f.70, God the Father.

1967. Europa.
467 **138** 50r. multicoloured 35 35

139 "The Man from Malanser" **140** Crown Prince Hans Adam

1967. Liechtenstein Sagas (1st series). Multicoloured.
468 20r. Type **139** 10 15
469 30r. "The Treasure of Gutenberg" 25 25
470 1f.20 "The Giant of Guflina" 70 60
See also Nos. 492/4 and 516/18.

1967. Royal Wedding. Sheet 86×95 mm comprising T **140** and similar vert design.
MS471 1f.50 indigo and blue (T **140**); 1f.50 brown and light brown (Princess Marie) 2·50 2·20

141 "Alpha and Omega"

1967. Christian Symbols. Multicoloured.
472 20r. Type **141** 10 10
473 30r. "Tropaion" (Cross as victory symbol) 10 10
474 70r. Christ's monogram 75 55

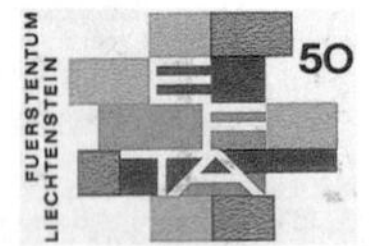

142 Father J. B. Buchel (educator, historian and poet) **143** "E.F.T.A."

1967. Buchel Commemoration.
475 **142** 1f. red and green 60 50

1967. European Free Trade Association.
476 **143** 50r. multicoloured 35 30

144 "Peter and Paul", Mauren **145** Campaign Emblem

1967. "Patrons of the Church". Multicoloured.
477 5r. "St. Joseph", Planken 10 10
478 10r. "St. Lawrence", Schaan 10 10
479 20r. Type **144** 20 10
480 30r. "St. Nicholas", Balzers 25 15
480a 40r. "St. Sebastian", Nendeln 50 25
481 50r. "St. George", Schellenberg 60 30
482 60r. "St. Martin", Eschen 60 35
483 70r. "St. Fridolin", Ruggell 60 45
484 80r. "St. Gallus", Triesen 75 55
485 1f. "St. Theodolus", Triesenberg 85 55
486 1f.20 "St. Anna", Vaduz Castle 1·20 80
487 1f.50 "St. Marie", Bendern-Camprin 1·70 1·10
488 2f. "St. Lucius", (patron saint of Liechtenstein) 1·90 1·30

1967. "Technical Assistance".
489 **145** 50r.+20r. multicoloured 50 35

146 Europa "Key"

1968. Europa.
490 **146** 50r. multicoloured 35 35

147 Arms of Liechtenstein and Wilczek **148** Sir Rowland Hill

1968. Silver Wedding Anniv of Prince Francis Joseph II and Princess Gina.
491 **147** 75r. multicoloured 50 55

1968. Liechtenstein Sagas (2nd series). As T **139**. Multicoloured.
492 30r. "The Treasure of St. Mamerten" 10 10
493 50r. "The Hobgoblin in the Bergerwald" 25 25
494 80r. "The Three Sisters" 70 60

1968. "Pioneers of Philately" (1st series).
495 **148** 20r. green 10 10
496 – 30r. brown 10 10
497 – 1f. black 85 70
PORTRAITS: 30r. Philippe de Ferrary; 1f. Maurice Burrus.
See also Nos. 504/5 and 554/6.

150 Arms of Liechtenstein **151** Colonnade

1969.
498 **150** 3f.50 brown 2·50 1·20

1969. Europa.
499 **151** 50r. multicoloured 60 40

152 "Biology"

1969. 250th Anniv of Liechtenstein. Multicoloured.
500 10r. Type **152** 10 10
501 30r. "Physics" 10 15
502 50r. "Astronomy" 35 30
503 80r. "Art" 60 60

1969. "Pioneers of Philately" (2nd series). As T **148**.
504 80r. brown 50 50
505 1f.20 blue 1·10 85
PORTRAITS: 80r. Carl Lindenberg; 1f.20, Theodore Champion.

153 Arms of St. Luzi Monastery **154** Symbolic "T"

1969. Arms of Church Patrons. Multicoloured.
506 20r. St. Johann's Abbey 20 25
507 30r. Type **153** 30 25
508 30r. Ladies' Priory, Schanis 25 20
509 30r. Knights Hospitallers, Feldkirch 35 25
510 50r. Pfafers Abbey 30 40
511 50r. Weingarten Abbey 40 45
512 75r. St. Gallen Abbey 55 65
513 1f.20 Ottobeuren Abbey 1·40 1·00
514 1f.50 Chur Episcopate 1·30 1·20

1969. Centenary of Liechtenstein Telegraph System.
515 **154** 30r. multicoloured 25 25

1969. Liechtenstein Sagas (3rd series). As T **139**. Multicoloured.
516 20r. "The Cheated Devil" 10 10
517 50r. "The Fiery Red Goat" 40 35
518 60r. "The Grafenberg Treasure" 60 50

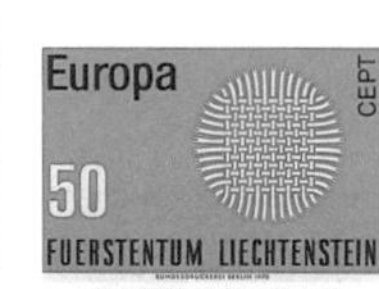

155 Orange Lily **156** "Flaming Sun"

1970. Nature Conservation Year. Multicoloured.
519 20r. Type **155** 20 10
520 30r. Wild orchid 25 20
521 50r. Ranunculus 40 35
522 1f.20 Bog bean 85 85
See also Nos. 532/5 and 548/51.

1970. Europa.
523 **156** 50r. yellow, blue and green 45 35

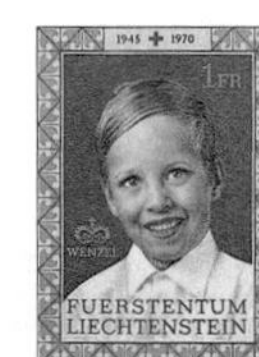

157 Prince Wenzel **158** Prince Francis Joseph II

1970. 25th Anniv of Liechtenstein Red Cross.
524 **157** 1f. multicoloured 85 70

1970. 800th Anniv of Wolfram von Eschenbach. Sheet 73×96 mm containing vert designs similar to T **116** from the "Codex Manaesse". Multicoloured.
MS525 30r. Wolfram von Eschenbach; 50r. Reinmar the Fiddler; 80r. Hartmann von Starkenberg; 1f.20 Friedrich von Hausen. Sold for 3f. 2·50 2·50

1970.
526 – 1f.70 green 2·00 1·50
526a – 2f.50 blue 2·10 1·70
527 **158** 3f. black 2·50 1·80
DESIGNS: 1f.70, Prince Hans Adam; 2f.50, Princess Gina.

159 "Mother and Child" (R. Schadler) **160** Bronze Boar (La Tene period)

1970. Christmas.
528 **159** 30r. multicoloured 30 20

1971. National Museum Inauguration.
529 **160** 25r. black, blue & ultram 20 20
530 – 30r. green and brown 25 20
531 – 75r. multicoloured 55 50
DESIGNS: 30r. Ornamental peacock (Roman, 2nd-century); 75r. Engraved bowl (13th-century).

1971. Liechtenstein Flowers (2nd series). As T **155**. Multicoloured.
532 10r. Cyclamen 20 10
533 20r. Moonwort 20 20
534 50r. Superb pink 40 35
535 1f.50 Alpine columbine 1·30 1·00

161 Europa Chain

1971. Europa.
536 **161** 50r. yellow, blue & black 40 40

162 Part of Text **163** Cross-country Skiing

1971. 50th Anniv of 1921 Constitution. Mult.
537 70r. Type **162** 65 55
538 80r. Princely crown 70 60

1971. Winter Olympic Games, Sapporo, Japan (1972). Multicoloured.
539 15r. Type **163** 20 10
540 40r. Ice hockey 35 30
541 65r. Downhill skiing 60 35
542 1f.50 Figure skating 1·60 1·10

164 "Madonna and Child" (sculpture, Andrea della Robbia) **165** Gymnastics

1971. Christmas.
543 **164** 30r. multicoloured 30 20

1972. Olympic Games, Munich. Multicoloured.
544 10r. Type **165** 10 10
545 20r. High jumping 15 10
546 40r. Running 30 25
547 60r. Throwing the discus 45 35

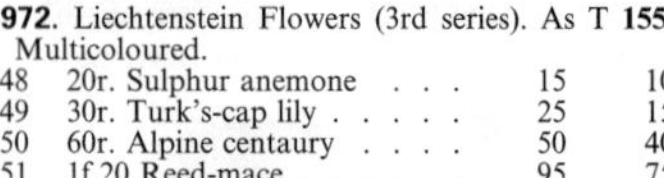
1972. Liechtenstein Flowers (3rd series). As T **155**. Multicoloured.
548 20r. Sulphur anemone 15 10
549 30r. Turk's-cap lily 25 15
550 60r. Alpine centaury 50 40
551 1f.20 Reed-mace 95 75

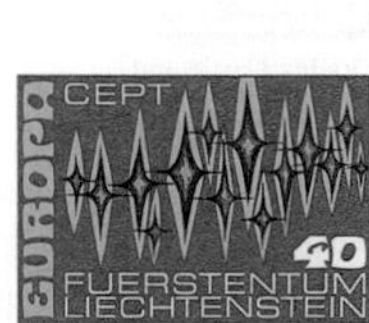

166 "Communications" **168** "Faun"

167 Bendern

1972. Europa.
552 **166** 40r. multicoloured 30 30

1972. "Liba '72" Stamp Exhibition, Vaduz. Sheet 101 × 65 mm containing T **167** and similar horiz design.
MS553 1f. violet; 2f. red . . . . 2·50 2·50
DESIGN: 2f. Vaduz castle.

1972. "Pioneers of Philately" (3rd series). As T **148**.
554 30r. green 25 25
555 40r. purple 30 30
556 1f.30 blue . . . . 1·10 85
PORTRAITS: 30r. Emilio Diena; 40r. Andre de Cock; 1f.30, Theodore E. Steinway.

1972. "Natural Art". Motifs fashioned from roots and branches. Multicoloured.
557 20r. Type **168** 10 10
558 30r. "Dancer" 20 20
559 1f.10 "Owl" 85 80

169 "Madonna with Angels" (F. Nigg)   **170** Lawena Springs

1972. Christmas.
560 **169** 30r. multicoloured 30 20

1972. Landscapes.
561 – 5r. purple and yellow . . 15 10
562 **170** 10r. green and light green 10 10
563 – 15r. brown and green . . 10 10
564 – 25r. purple and blue . . . 30 20
565 – 30r. purple and brown . . 35 30
566 – 40r. purple and brown . . 45 30
567 – 50r. blue and lilac 40 35
568 – 60r. green and yellow . . 60 50
569 – 70r. blue and cobalt . . . 70 60
570 – 80r. green and light green 80 60
571 – 1f. brown and green . . . 1·00 75
572 – 1f.30 blue and green . . . 1·10 1·00
573 – 1f.50 brown and blue . . 1·40 1·20
574 – 1f.80 brown & lt brown 1·70 1·50
575 – 2f. brown and blue . . . 2·20 1·50
DESIGNS: 5r. Silum; 15r. Ruggeller Reed; 25r. Steg Kirchlispitz; 30r. Feld Schellenberg; 40r. Rennhof Mauren; 50r. Tidrufe; 60r. Eschner Riet; 70r. Mittagspitz; 80r. Schaan Forest; 1f. St. Peter's Chapel, Mals; 1f.30, Frommenhaus; 1f.50, Ochsenkopf; 1f.80, Hehlawangspitz; 2f. Saminaschlucht.

171 Europa "Posthorn"

1973. Europa.
576 **171** 30r. multicoloured 35 20
577 40r. multicoloured 40 30

172 Chambered Nautilus Goblet   **173** Arms of Liechtenstein

1973. Treasures from Prince's Collection (1st issue). Drinking Vessels. Multicoloured.
578 30r. Type **172** 25 20
579 70r. Ivory tankard 60 45
580 1f.10 Silver cup 85 70
See also Nos. 589/92.

1973.
581 **173** 5f. multicoloured . . . . 4·75 3·00

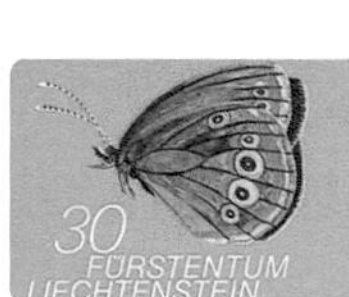

174 False Ringlet

175 "Madonna" (Bartolomeo di Tommaso da Foligno)

1973. Small Fauna of Liechtenstein (1st series). Multicoloured.
582 30r. Type **174** 20 20
583 40r. Curlew 90 35
584 60r. Edible frog 35 40
585 80r. Grass snake 70 55
See also Nos. 596/9.

1973. Christmas.
586 **175** 30r. multicoloured 30 25

176 "Shouting Horseman" (sculpture, Andrea Riccio)   **177** Footballers

1974. Europa. Multicoloured.
587 30r. Type **176** 30 20
588 40r. "Squatting Aphrodite" (sculpture, Antonio Susini) 45 35

1974. Treasures from Prince's Collection (2nd issue). Porcelain. As T **172**. Multicoloured.
589 30r. Vase, 19th century . . . 20 20
590 50r. Vase, 1740 . . . . . . 40 25
591 60r. Vase, 1830 . . . . . . 45 35
592 1f. Vase, c. 1700 . . . . . . 75 65

1974. World Cup Football Championship, West Germany.
593 **177** 80f. multicoloured 75 50

178 Posthorn and U.P.U. Emblem   **179** Bishop Marxer

1974. Centenary of Universal Postal Union.
594 **178** 40r. black, green and gold 35 25
595 60r. black, red and gold 45 35

1974. Small Fauna of Liechtenstein (2nd series). As T **174**. Multicoloured.
596 15r. Mountain newt 10 10
597 25r. Adder 10 10
598 70r. Cynthia's fritillary (butterfly) 80 55
599 1f.10 Three-toed woodpecker 1·20 80

1974. Death Centenary of Bishop Franz Marxer.
600 **179** 1f. multicoloured 75 50

180 Prince Francis Joseph II and Princess Gina

1974.
601 **180** 10f. brown and gold . . . 9·25 6·25

181 "St. Florian"   **182** Prince Constantin

1974. Christmas. Glass Paintings. Multicoloured.
602 30r. Type **181** 25 15
603 50r. "St. Wendelin" 50 30
604 60r. "St. Mary, Anna and Joachim" 65 35
605 70r. "Jesus in Manger" . . . 85 55

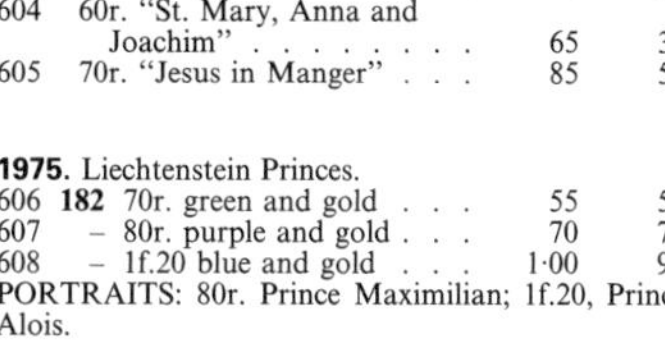

1975. Liechtenstein Princes.
606 **182** 70r. green and gold . . . 55 50
607 – 80r. purple and gold . . . 70 70
608 – 1f.20 blue and gold . . . 1·00 90
PORTRAITS: 80r. Prince Maximilian; 1f.20, Prince Alois.

183 "Cold Sun" (M. Frommelt)   **184** Imperial Cross

1975. Europa. Paintings. Multicoloured.
609 30r. Type **183** 25 20
610 60r. "Village" (L. Jager) . . 70 55

1975. Imperial Insignia (1st series). Multicoloured.
611 30r. Type **184** 30 20
612 60r. Imperial sword 45 35
613 1f. Imperial orb 90 65
614 1f.30 Imperial robe (50 × 32 mm) . . . . . . 6·25 4·75
615 2f. Imperial crown . . . . . 2·75 1·90
See also Nos. 670/3.

185 "Red Cross Activities"   **186** St. Mamerten, Triesen

1975. 30th Anniv of Liechtenstein Red Cross.
616 **185** 60r. multicoloured 75 45

1975. European Architectural Heritage Year. Multicoloured.
617 40r. Type **186** 30 25
618 50r. Red House, Vaduz . . . 35 30
619 70r. Prebendary buildings, Eschen 60 55
620 1f. Gutenberg Castle, Balzers 90 80

187 Speed Skating   **188** "Daniel in the Lions' Den"

1975. Winter Olympic Games, Innsbruck (1976). Multicoloured.
621 20r. Type **187** 20 10
622 25r. Ice hockey 25 20
623 70r. Downhill skiing 65 55
624 1f.20 Slalom . . . . 1·10 90

1975. Christmas and Holy Year. Capitals in Chur Cathedral.
625 **188** 30r. violet and gold . . . 25 20
626 – 60r. green and gold . . . 50 35
627 – 90r. red and gold 70 85
DESIGNS: 60r. "Madonna"; 90r. "St. Peter".

189 Mouflon   **190** Crayfish

1976. Europa. Ceramics by Prince Hans von Liechtenstein. Multicoloured.
628 40r. Type **189** 50 30
629 80r. "Ring-necked Pheasant and Brood" 75 70

1976. World Wildlife Fund. Multicoloured.
630 25r. Type **190** 30 30
631 40r. Turtle 60 30
632 70r. European otter 85 70
633 80r. Northern lapwing . . . 1·70 90

191 Roman Fibula   **193** Judo

192 Obverse of 50f. Coin depicting portrait of Prince

1976. 75th Anniv of National Historical Society.
634 **191** 90r. multicoloured 85 60

1976. 70th Birthday of Prince Francis Joseph II. Sheet 102 × 65 mm containing T **192** and similar horiz design. Multicoloured.
MS635 1f. Type **192**; 1f. Reverse of 50f. coin depicting Arms of Liechtenstein . . . . 1·70 2·00

1976. Olympic Games, Montreal. Multicoloured.
636 35r. Type **193** 30 25
637 50r. Volleyball 35 40
638 80r. Relay 60 50
639 1f.10 Long jumping 85 75

194 "Singing Angels"   **195** "Pisces"

1976. 400th Birth Anniv (1977) of Peter Paul Rubens (painter). Multicoloured.
640 50r. Type **194** 60 65
641 70r. "Sons of the Artist" . . 90 85
642 1f. "Daughters of Cecrops" (49 × 39 mm) . . . . . . 3·50 3·50

1976. Signs of the Zodiac (1st series). Multicoloured.
643 20r. Type **195** 20 20
644 40r. "Aries" 30 25
645 80r. "Taurus" 60 55
646 90r. "Gemini" 85 70
See also Nos. 666/9 and 710/13.

196 "Child Jesus of Prague"   **197** Sarcophagus Statue, Chur Cathedral

1976. Christmas. Monastic Wax Sculptures. Mult.
647 20r. Type **196** 20 10
648 50r. "The Flight into Egypt" (vert) 60 35
649 80r. "Holy Trinity" (vert) . . 90 55
650 1f.50 "Holy Family" . . . . 1·40 1·00

1976. Bishop Ortlieb von Brandis of Chur Commemoration.
651 **197** 1f.10 brown and gold . . 1·00 70

199 Map of Liechtenstein, 1721 (J. Heber)   **200** Coin of Emperor Constantine II

1977. Europa. Multicoloured.
664 40r. Type **199** 25 25
665 80r. "View of Vaduz, 1815" (F. Bachmann) 60 60

1977. Signs of the Zodiac (2nd series). As T **195**. Multicoloured.
666 40r. "Cancer" 30 25
667 70r. "Leo" 60 55

668 80r. "Virgo" 75 70
669 1f.10 "Libra" 85 90

1977. Imperial Insignia (2nd series). As T **184**. Multicoloured.
670 40r. Holy Lance and Reliquary with Particle of the Cross 30 25
671 50r. "St. Matthew" (Imperial Book of Gospels) 35 50
672 80r. St. Stephen's Purse . . . 50 50
673 90r. Tabard of Imperial Herald 70 75

1977. Coins (1st series). Multicoloured.
674 35r. Type **200** 30 30
675 70r. Lindau Brakteat 55 55
676 80r. Coin of Ortlieb von Brandis 65 55
See also Nos. 707/9.

201 Frauenthal Castle, Styria **202** Children in Costume

1977. Castles.
677 **201** 20r. green and gold . . . 25 20
678 – 50r. red and gold 50 40
679 – 80r. lilac and gold 75 60
680 – 90r. blue and gold 80 70
DESIGNS: 50r. Gross-Ullersdorf, Moravia; 80r. Liechtenstein Castle, near Modling, Austria; 90r. Palais Liechtenstein, Alserbachstrasse, Vienna.

1977. National Costumes. Multicoloured.
681 40r. Type **202** 30 25
682 70r. Two girls in traditional costume 45 45
683 1f. Woman in festive costume 65 65

203 Princess Tatjana

1977. Princess Tatjana.
684 **203** 1f.10 lt brn, brn & gold 95 95

204 "Angel"

205 Palais Liechtenstein, Bankgasse, Vienna

1977. Christmas. Sculptures by Erasmus Kern. Multicoloured.
685 20r. Type **204** 15 15
686 50r. "St. Rochus" 40 35
687 80r. "Madonna" 65 60
688 1f.50 "God the Father" . . . 1·00 1·00

1978. Europa.
689 **205** 40r. blue and gold 35 30
690 – 80r. red and gold 80 60
DESIGN: 80r. Feldsberg Castle.

206 Farmhouse, Triesen

207 Vaduz Castle

1978. Buildings. Multicoloured.
691 10r. Type **206** 10 10
692 20r. Upper village of Triesen 15 15
693 35r. Barns at Balzers 30 30
694 40r. Monastery building, Bendern 30 25
695 50r. Rectory tower, Balzers-Mals 40 40
696 70r. Rectory, Mauren 55 55
697 80r. Farmhouse, Schellenberg 65 65
698 90r. Rectory, Balzers 75 85
699 1f. Rheinberger House, Vaduz 80 80
700 1f.10 Vaduz Mitteldorf . . . 85 90
701 1f.50 Town Hall, Triesenberg 1·20 1·20
702 2f. National Museum and Administrator's residence, Vaduz . . . . 1·70 1·60

1978. 40th Anniv of Prince Francis Joseph II's Accession. Royal Residence. Multicoloured.
703 40r. Type **207** 35 35
704 50r. Courtyard 35 35
705 70r. Hall 65 55
706 80r. High Altar, Castle Chapel 70 60

208 Coin of Prince Charles

209 "Portrait of a Piebald" (J. G. von Hamilton and A. Faistenberger)

1978. Coins (2nd series). Multicoloured.
707 40r. Type **208** 30 30
708 50r. Coin of Prince John Adam 40 35
709 80r. Coin of Prince Joseph Wenzel 65 60

1978. Signs of the Zodiac (3rd series). As T **195**. Multicoloured.
710 40r. "Scorpio" 30 25
711 50r. "Sagittarius" 40 35
712 80r. "Capricorn" 65 55
713 1f.50 "Aquarius" . . . . . . 1·10 1·00

1978. Paintings. Multicoloured.
714 70r. Type **209** 60 60
715 80r. "Portrait of a Blackish-brown Stallion" (J. G. von Hamilton) 80 80
716 1f.10 "Golden Carriage of Prince Joseph Wenzel" (Martin von Meytens) (48½ × 38 mm) . . . . . . 1·00 1·00

210 "Adoration of the Shepherds"

211 Comte AC-8 Mail Plane "St. Gallen" over Schaan

1978. Christmas. Church Windows, Triesenberg. Multicoloured.
717 20r. Type **210** 15 15
718 50r. "Enthroned Madonna with St. Joseph" 40 40
719 80r. "Adoration of the Magi" 70 75

1979. Europa. Multicoloured.
720 40r. Type **211** 55 50
721 80r. Airship "Graf Zeppelin" over Vaduz Castle 95 75

212 Child Drinking

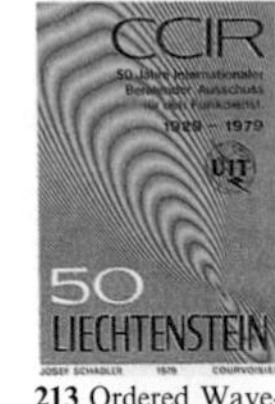

213 Ordered Wave-field

1979. International Year of the Child. Multicoloured.
722 80r. Type **212** 50 60
723 90r. Child eating 55 70
724 1f.10 Child reading . . . . . 1·00 85

1979. 50th Anniv of International Radio Consultative Committee (CCIR).
725 **213** 50r. blue and black . . . 40 35

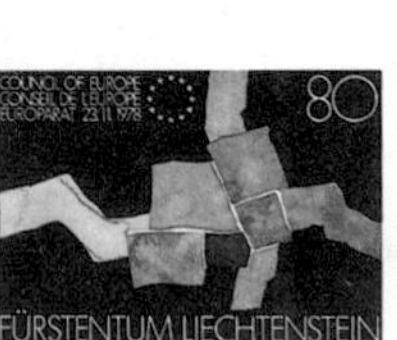

214 Abstract Composition

215 Sun rising over Continents

1979. Liechtenstein's Entry into Council of Europe.
726 **214** 80r. multicoloured 70 60

1979. Development Aid.
727 **215** 1f. multicoloured 85 75

216 Arms of Carl Ludwig von Sulz

1979. Heraldic Windows in the Liechtenstein National Museum. Multicoloured.
728 40r. Type **216** 35 30
729 70r. Arms of Barbara von Sulz 70 60
730 1f.10 Arms of Ulrich von Ramschwag and Barbara von Hallwil 90 80

217 Sts. Lucius and Florian (fresco, Waltensberg-Vuorz Church)

1979. Patron Saints.
731 **217** 20f. multicoloured . . . . 16·00 11·00

218 Base of Ski Slope, Valuna

1979. Winter Olympic Games, Lake Placid (1980). Multicoloured.
732 40r. Type **218** 30 25
733 70r. Malbun and Ochsenkopf 65 60
734 1f.50 Ski-lift, Sareis . . . . . 1·20 1·00

219 "The Annunciation"

1979. Christmas. Embroideries by Ferdinand Nigg. Multicoloured.
735 20r. Type **219** 20 40
736 50r. "Christmas" 40 35
737 80r. "Blessed are the Peacemakers" 60 75

220 Maria Leopoldine von Esterhazy (bust by Canova)

221 Arms of Andreas Buchel, 1690

1980. Europa.
738 **220** 40r. green, turq & gold 50 50
739 – 80r. brown, red and gold 80 75
DESIGN: 80r. Maria Theresia von Liechtenstein (after Martin von Meytens).

1980. Arms of Bailiffs (1st series). Multicoloured.
740 40r. Type **221** 30 25
741 70r. Georg Marxer, 1745 . . 60 55
742 80r. Luzius Frick, 1503 . . . 70 85
743 1f.10 Adam Oehri, 1634 . . . 85 75
See also Nos. 763/6, and 788/91.

222 3r. Stamp of 1930

223 Milking Pail

1980. 50th Anniv of Postal Museum.
744 **222** 80r. red, green and grey 70 65

1980. Alpine Dairy Farming Implements. Mult.
745 20r. Type **223** 20 10
746 50r. Wooden heart dairy herd descent marker 40 35
747 80r. Butter churn 65 60

224 Crossbow

1980. Hunting Weapons.
748 **224** 80r. brown and lilac . . . 65 60
749 – 90r. black and green . . . 75 65
750 – 1f.10 black and stone . . 90 80
DESIGNS: 90r. Spear and knife; 1f.10, Rifle and powder-horn.

225 Triesenberg Costumes

1980. Costumes. Multicoloured.
751 40r. Type **225** 30 30
752 70r. Dancers, Schellenberg . . 65 60
753 80r. Brass band, Mauren . . 75 70

226 Beech Trees, Matrula (spring)

227 Angel bringing Shepherds Good Tidings

1980. The Forest in the Four Seasons. Multicoloured.
754 40r. Type **226** 30 30
755 50r. Firs in the Valorsch (summer) 40 35
756 80r. Beech tree, Schaan (autumn) 65 55
757 1f.50 Edge of forest at Oberplanken (winter) . . . 1·10 1·20

1980. Christmas. Multicoloured.
758 20r. Type **227** 20 45
759 50r. Crib 40 35
760 80r. Epiphany 60 60

228 National Day Procession

229 Prince Alois and Princess Elisabeth with Francis Joseph

1981. Europa. Multicoloured.
761 40r. Fireworks at Vaduz Castle 35 25
762 80r. Type **228** 80 70

1981. Arms of Bailiffs (2nd series). As T **221**. Multicoloured.
763 40r. Anton Meier, 1748 . . . 25 25
764 70r. Kaspar Kindle, 1534 . . 55 45
765 80r. Hans Adam Negele, 1600 . . . . 65 55
766 1f.10 Peter Matt, 1693 . . 80 75

1981. 75th Birthday of Prince Francis Joseph II. Sheet 120 × 87 mm containing T **229** and similar vert designs. Multicoloured.
MS767 70r. Type **229**; 80r. Princes Alois and Francis Joseph; 150r. Prince Francis Joseph II . . . 3·00 3·00

230 Scout Emblems

1981. 50th Anniv of Liechtenstein Boy Scout and Girl Guide Movements.
768 **230** 20r. multicoloured 45 35

231 Symbols of Disability

232 St. Theodul (sculpture)

1981. International Year of Disabled Persons.
769 **231** 40r. multicoloured 35 35

1981. 1600th Birth Anniv of St. Theodul.
770 **232** 80r. multicoloured 65 60

233 "Xanthoria parietina"

1981. Mosses and Lichens. Multicoloured.
771 40r. Type **233** 25 25
772 50r. "Parmelia physodes" . . 50 40
773 70r. "Sphagnum palustre" . . 65 60
774 80r. "Amblystegium serpens" 75 70

234 Gutenberg Castle

1981. Gutenberg Castle. Multicoloured.
775 20r. Type **234** 20 20
776 40r. Courtyard 25 30
777 50r. Parlour 45 35
778 1f.10 Great Hall . . . . . . 1·00 90

235 Cardinal Karl Borromaus von Mailand

236 St. Nicholas blessing Children

1981. Famous Visitors to Liechtenstein (1st series). Multicoloured.
779 40r. Type **235** 30 30
780 70r. Johann Wolfgang von Goethe (writer) 70 75
781 89r. Alexander Dumas the younger (writer) 75 65
782 1f. Hermann Hesse (writer) 85 75
See also Nos. 804/7 and 832/5.

1981. Christmas. Multicoloured.
783 20r. Type **236** 20 20
784 50r. Adoration of the Kings 40 40
785 80r. Holy Family 75 65

237 Peasant Revolt, 1525

1982. Europa. Multicoloured.
786 40r. Type **237** 35 35
787 80r. King Wenceslaus with Counts (Imperial direct rule, 1396) 75 70

1982. Arms of Bailiffs (3rd series). As T **221**. Multicoloured.
788 40r. Johann Kaiser, 1664 . . 35 25
789 70r. Joseph Anton Kaufmann, 1748 . . . . . 65 50
790 80r. Christoph Walser, 1690 75 60
791 1f.10 Stephan Banzer, 1658 1·00 95

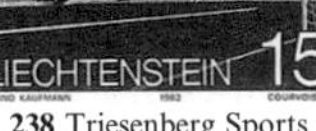

238 Triesenberg Sports Ground

239 Crown Prince Hans Adam

1982. World Cup Football Championship, Spain. Multicoloured.
792 15r. Type **238** 15 60
793 25r. Eschen/Mauren playing fields 25 25
794 1f.80 Rheinau playing fields, Balzers . . . . 1·50 1·40

1982. "Liba 82" Stamp Exhibition. Multicoloured.
795 1f. Type **239** 85 85
796 1f. Princess Marie Aglae . . 85 85

240 Tractor (agriculture)

1982. Rural Industries. Multicoloured.
797 30r. Type **240** 25 20
798 50r. Cutting flowers (horticulture) 45 35
799 70r. Workers with logs (forestry) 60 55
800 150r. Worker and milk (dairy farming) . . . . 1·30 1·20

241 "Neu Schellenberg"

1982. 150th Birth Anniv of Mortiz Menzinger (artist). Multicoloured.
801 40r. Type **241** 30 30
802 50r. "Vaduz" 60 45
803 100r. "Bendern" 95 90

242 Angelika Kauffmann (artist, self-portrait)

243 Angel playing Lute

1982. Famous Visitors to Liechtenstein (2nd series). Multicoloured.
804 40r. Emperor Maximilian I (after Benhard Strigel) . . 25 25
805 70f. Georg Jenatsch (liberator of Grisons) 55 50
806 80r. Type **242** 65 55
807 1f. St. Fidelis of Sigmaringen 85 80

1982. Christmas. Details from High Altar by Jakob Russ, Chur Cathedral. Multicoloured.
808 20r. Type **243** 15 15
809 50r. Madonna and child . . 45 35
810 80r. Angel playing organ . . 70 65

244 Notker Balbulus of St. Gall

245 Shrove Thursday

1983. Europa. Multicoloured.
811 40r. Type **244** 30 25
812 80r. Hildegard of Bingen . . 80 55

1983. Shrovetide and Lent Customs. Mult.
813 40r. Type **245** 30 25
814 70r. Shrovetide carnival . . 70 50
815 1f.80 Lent Sunday bonfire . . 1·70 1·40

246 River Bank

247 "Schaan"

1983. Anniversaries and Events. Multicoloured.
816 20r. Type **246** 35 20
817 40r. Montgolfier Brothers' balloon 50 35
818 50r. Airmail envelope 55 45
819 80r. Plant and hands holding spade 75 65
EVENTS: 20r. Council of Europe river and coasts protection campaign; 40r. Bicentenary of manned flight; 50r. World Communications Year; 80r. Overseas aid.

1983. Landscape Paintings by Anton Ender. Mult.
820 40r. Type **247** 35 25
821 50r. "Gutenberg Castle" . . 60 45
822 200r. "Steg Reservoir" . . . 2·50 1·90

248 Princess Gina

249 Pope John Paul II

1983. Multicoloured.
823 2f.50 Type **248** . . . . . . 2·75 2·50
824 3f. Prince Francis Joseph II 3·25 3·00

1983. Holy Year.
825 **249** 80r. multicoloured . . . . 1·20 80

250 Snowflakes and Stripes

251 Seeking Shelter

1983. Winter Olympic Games, Sarajevo. Mult.
826 40r. Type **250** 30 25
827 80r. Snowflake 85 75
828 1f.80 Snowflake and rays . . 1·70 1·70

1983. Christmas. Multicoloured.
829 20r. Type **251** 15 20
830 50r. Infant Jesus 55 35
831 80r. Three Kings 80 70

252 Aleksandr Vassilievich Suvorov (Russian general)

253 Bridge

1984. Famous Visitors to Liechtenstein (3rd series). Multicoloured.
832 40r. Type **252** 40 30
833 70r. Karl Rudolf von Buol-Schauenstein, Bishop of Chur 70 60
834 80r. Carl Zuckmayer (dramatist) 80 65
835 1f. Curt Goetz (actor) 95 90

1984. Europa. 25th Anniv of E.P.T. Conf.
836 **253** 50r. blue and deep blue 55 40
837 80r. pink and brown . . . 80 80

254 The Warning Messenger

255 Pole Vaulting

1984. Liechtenstein Legends. The Destruction of Trisona. Each brown, grey and blue.
838 35r. Type **254** 25 25
839 50r. The buried town 55 40
840 80r. The spared family . . . 80 70

1984. Olympic Games, Los Angeles. Mult.
841 70r. Type **255** 65 65
842 80r. Throwing the discus . . 80 80
843 1f. Putting the shot . . . . . 1·00 1·00

256 Currency (trade and banking)

1984. Occupations. Multicoloured.
844 5r. Type **256** 10 10
845 10r. Plumber adjusting pipe (building trade) 10 10
846 20r. Operating machinery (industry—production) . . 25 25
847 35r. Draughtswoman (building trade—planning) 35 35
848 45r. Office worker and world map (industry—sales) . . . 50 50
849 50r. Cook (tourism) 50 25
850 60r. Carpenter (building trade—interior decoration) 60 50
851 70r. Doctor injecting patient (medical services) 70 70
852 80r. Scientist (industrial research) 80 75
853 100r. Bricklayer (building trade) . . . . 1·00 85
854 120r. Flow chart (industry—administration) . . . . . . 1·20 1·40
855 150r. Handstamping covers (post and communications) 1·90 1·40

257 Princess Marie

258 Annunciation

1984. Multicoloured.
856 1f.70 Type **257** . . . . . . 1·40 1·40
857 2f. Crown Prince Hans Adam 1·40 1·70

1984. Christmas. Multicoloured.
858 35r. Type **258** 40 30
859 50r. Holy Family 35 40
860 80r. The Three Kings 65 70

259 Apollo and the Muses playing Music (detail from 18th-century harpsichord lid)

1985. Europa. Music Year. Multicoloured.
861 50r. Type **259** 60 50
862 80r. Apollo and the Muses playing music (different) 85 75

260 St. Elisabeth Convent, Schaan

1985. Monasteries. Multicoloured.
863 50r. Type **260** 60 45
864 1f. Schellenberg Convent . . 1·10 1·00
865 1f.70 Gutenberg Mission, Balzers . . . . 1·50 1·50

261 Princess Gina and handing out of Rations

1985. 40th Anniv of Liechtenstein Red Cross. Multicoloured.
866 20r. Type **261** 30 25
867 50r. Princess Gina and Red Cross ambulance 55 60
868 120r. Princess Gina with refugee children . . . . . 95 1·20

262 Justice **263** Papal Arms

1985. Cardinal Virtues. Multicoloured.
869 35r. Type **262** 35 30
870 50r. Temperance 55 50
871 70r. Prudence 70 65
872 1f. Fortitude 75 85

1985. Papal Visit. Sheet 100 × 67 mm containing T **263** and similar vert designs. Multicoloured.
MS873 50r. Type **263**; 80r. St. Maria zum Trost Chapel; 170r. Our Lady of Liechtenstein (statue) (29 × 43 mm) . . . . 3·25 3·25

264 "Portrait of a Canon" (Quentin Massys)

1985. Paintings in Metropolitan Museum, New York. Multicoloured.
874 50r. Type **264** 70 60
875 1f. "Clara Serena Rubens" (Rubens) . . . . 1·10 1·10
876 1f.20 "Duke of Urbino" (Raphael) . . . . 70 1·20

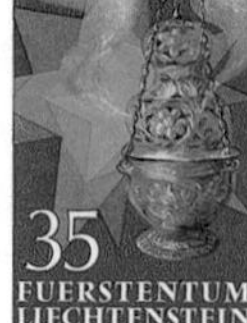

265 Halberd used by Charles I's Bodyguard

1985. Guards' Weapons and Armour. Mult.
877 35r. Type **265** 45 35
878 50r. Morion used by Charles I's bodyguard 55 50
879 80r. Halberd used by Carl Eusebius's bodyguard . . . 75 70

266 Frankincense **267** Puppets performing Tragedy

1985. Christmas. Multicoloured.
880 35r. Type **266** 40 30
881 50r. Gold 65 60
882 80r. Myrrh 65 75

1985. Theatre. Multicoloured.
883 50r. Type **267** 65 65
884 80r. Puppets performing comedy 85 80
885 1f.50 Opera . . . . 1·30 1·20

268 Courtyard **269** Barn Swallows

1986. Vaduz Castle. Multicoloured.
886 20r. Type **268** 25 20
887 25r. Keep 40 35
888 50r. Castle 60 55
889 90r. Inner gate 90 75
890 1f.10 Castle from gardens . . 1·20 1·00
891 1f.40 Courtyard (different) . . 1·50 1·30

1986. Europa. Birds. Multicoloured.
892 50r. Type **269** 60 55
893 90r. European robin 95 85

270 "Offerings" **271** Palm Sunday

1986. Lenten Fast.
894 **270** 1f.40 multicoloured . . . 1·40 1·40

1986. Religious Festivals. Multicoloured.
895 35r. Type **271** 45 30
896 50r. Wedding 55 35
897 70r. Rogation Day procession 80 55

272 Karl Freiherr Haus von Hausen **273** Francis Joseph II

1986. 125th Anniv of Liechtenstein Land Bank.
898 **272** 50r. brown, ochre and buff 55 55

1986. 80th Birthday of Prince Francis Joseph II.
899 **273** 3f.50 multicoloured . . . 3·25 3·00

274 Roebuck in Ruggeller Riet **275** Cabbage and Beetroot

1986. Hunting. Multicoloured.
900 35r. Type **274** 45 45
901 50r. Chamois at Rappenstein 70 70
902 1f.70 Stag in Lawena . . . . 1·50 1·50

1986. Field Crops. Multicoloured.
903 50r. Type **275** 50 50
904 80r. Red cabbages 85 85
905 90r. Potatoes, onions and garlic 95 95

276 Archangel Michael **277** Silver Fir

1986. Christmas. Multicoloured.
906 35r. Type **276** 30 30
907 50r. Archangel Gabriel . . . 65 65
908 90r. Archangel Raphael . . . 90 90

1986. Tree Bark. Multicoloured.
909 35r. Type **277** 30 30
910 90r. Norway spruce 95 95
911 1f.40 Pedunculate oak . . . 1·50 1·50

278 Gamprin Primary School **280** Niklaus von Flue

1987. Europa. Multicoloured.
912 50r. Type **278** 60 55
913 90r. Schellenberg parish church 95 90

1987. 500th Death Anniv of Niklaus von Flue (martyr).
914 **280** 1f.10 multicoloured . . . 1·20 1·20

281 Bullhead **282** Prince Alois (frame as in first stamps)

1987. Fishes (1st series). Multicoloured.
915 50r. Type **281** 55 55
916 90r. Brown trout 85 85
917 1f.10 European grayling . . . 1·40 1·40
See also Nos. 959/61.

1987. 75th Anniv of First Liechtenstein Stamps.
918 **282** 2f. multicoloured . . . . 2·20 2·20

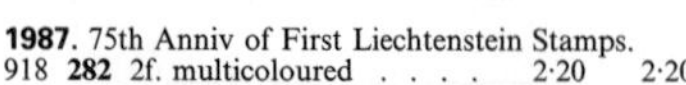

283 Staircase **284** Arms

1987. Liechtenstein City Palace, Vienna. Multicoloured.
919 35r. Type **283** 35 35
920 50r. Minoritenplatz doorway 75 70
921 90r. Staircase (different) . . . 1·00 1·00

1987. 275th Anniv of Transfer of County of Vaduz to House of Liechtenstein.
922 **284** 1f.40 multicoloured . . . 1·50 1·50

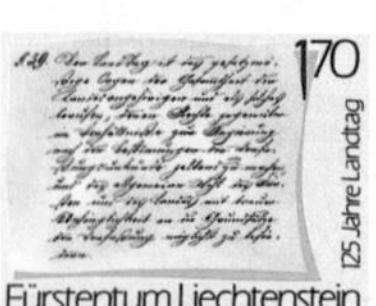

285 Constitution Charter, 1862 **286** St. Matthew

1987. 125th Anniv of Liechtenstein Parliament.
923 **285** 1f.70 multicoloured . . . 1·80 1·80

1987. Christmas. Illuminations from Golden Book of Pfafers Abbey. Multicoloured.
924 35r. Type **286** 40 35
925 50r. St. Mark 60 60
926 60r. St. Luke 65 65
927 90r. St. John . . . . 1·20 1·20

287 "The Toil of the Cross-country Skier" **288** Dish Aerial

1987. Winter Olympic Games, Calgary (1988). Multicoloured.
928 25r. Type **287** 35 35
929 90r. "The Courageous Pioneers of Skiing" . . . . 1·00 1·00
930 1f.10 "As our Grandfathers used to ride on a Bobsled" 1·40 1·40

1988. Europa. Transport and Communications. Mult.
931 50r. Type **288** 40 40
932 90r. Maglev monorail . . . . 1·10 1·00

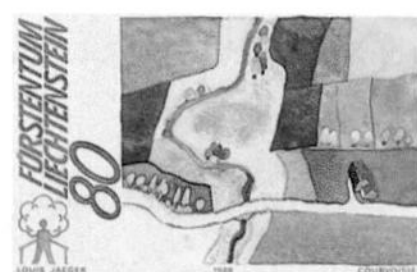

289 Agriculture

1988. European Campaign for Rural Areas. Multicoloured.
933 80r. Type **289** 80 80
934 90r. Village centre . . . . . 1·20 1·20
935 1f.70 Road . . . . 1·90 1·90

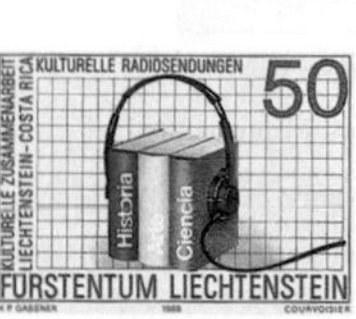

290 Headphones on Books (Radio Broadcasts) **291** Crown Prince Hans Adam

1988. Costa Rica–Liechtenstein Cultural Co-operation.
936 **290** 50r. multicoloured 60 60
937 – 1f.40 red, brown and green . . . . 1·50 1·50
DESIGN: 1f.40, Man with pen and radio (Adult education).

1988. 50th Anniv of Accesion of Prince Francis Joseph II. Sheet 100 × 68 mm containing T **291** and similar vert designs. Multicoloured.
MS938 50r. Type **291**; 50r. Prince Alois; 2f. Prince Francis Joseph II 4·50 4·25

292 St. Barbara's Shrine, Balzers

1988. Wayside Shrines. Multicoloured.
939 25r. Type **292** 35 35
940 35r. Shrine containing statues of Christ, St. Peter and St. Paul at Oberdorf, Vaduz 40 40
941 50r. St. Anthony of Egypt's shrine, Fallagass, Ruggel 50 50

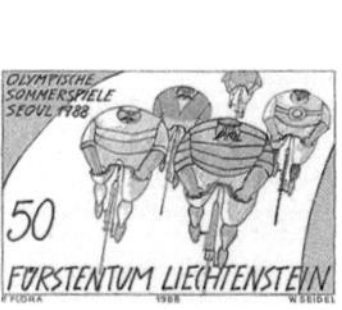

293 Cycling **294** Joseph and Mary

1988. Olympic Games, Seoul. Multicoloured.
942 50r. Type **293** 45 45
943 80r. Gymnastics 80 85
944 90r. Running . . . . 1·00 1·10
945 1f.40 Equestrian event . . . 1·80 1·90

1988. Christmas. Multicoloured.
946 35r. Type **294** 35 30
947 50r. Baby Jesus 65 70
948 90r. Wise Men presenting gifts to Jesus . . . . . . 1·10 1·10

295 Letter beside Footstool (detail) **296** "Cat and Mouse"

1988. "The Letter" (portrait of Marie-Theresa, Princesse de Lamballe by Anton Hickel). Multicoloured.
949 50r. Type **295** 65 75
950 90r. Desk and writing materials (detail) . . . . . 1·00 1·10
951 2f. "The Letter" (complete painting) . . . . 2·10 2·40

1989. Europa. Children's Games. Multicoloured.
952 50r. Type **296** 65 65
953 90r. "Hide and Seek" . . . . 1·20 1·20

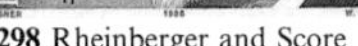

298 Rheinberger and Score **299** Little Ringed Plover

1989. 150th Birth Anniv of Josef Gabriel Rheinberger (composer).
954 **298** 2f.90 black, blue & purple 3·50 3·75

1989. Endangered Animals. Multicoloured.
955 25r. Type **299** 65 30
956 35r. Green tree frog 45 45
957 50r. "Libelloides coccajus" (lace-wing) 65 60
958 90r. Polecat . . . . 1·30 1·20

300 Northern Pike

1989. Fishes (2nd series). Multicoloured.
959 50r. Type **300** 50 55
960 1f.10 Brown trout . . . . . 1·20 1·30
961 1f.40 Stone loach . . . . . . 1·70 1·90

301 Return of Cattle from Alpine Pastures **302** Falknis

1989. Autumn Customs. Multicoloured.
962 35r. Type **301** 40 45
963 50r. Peeling corn cobs . . . 70 75
964 80r. Cattle market 80 80

1989. Mountains. Watercolours by Josef Schadler.
965 – 5r. multicoloured 10 10
966 – 10r. multicoloured 10 10
967 – 35r. multicoloured 30 35
968 – 40r. multicoloured 40 50
969 – 45r. multicoloured 45 55
970 **302** 50r. multicoloured 45 55
971 – 60r. multicoloured 55 60
972 – 70r. multicoloured 65 75
973 – 75r. multicoloured 70 80
974 – 80r. violet, brown & black 75 85
975 – 1f. multicoloured . . . . 90 1·10
976 – 1f.20 multicoloured . . . 1·10 1·20
977 – 1f.50 multicoloured . . . 1·50 1·40
978 – 1f.60 multicoloured . . . 1·90 1·70
979 – 2f. multicoloured . . . . 1·60 1·75
DESIGNS: 5r. Augstenberg; 10r. Hahenespiel; 35r. Nospitz; 40r. Ochsenkopf; 45r. Three Sisters; 60r. Kuhgrat; 70r. Galinakopf; 75r. Plassteikopf; 80pf. Naafkopf; 1f. Schonberg; 1f.20, Bleikaturm; 1f.50, Garselliturm; 1f.60, Schwarzhorn; 2f. Scheienkopf.

303 "Melchior and Balthasar" **304** Mace Quartz

1989. Christmas. Details of triptych by Hugo van der Goes. Multicoloured.
981 35r. Type **303** 55 45
982 50r. "Kaspar and Holy Family" (27 × 34 mm) . . 55 65
983 90r. "St. Stephen" 90 90

1989. Minerals. Multicoloured.
984 50r. Type **304** 60 60
985 1f.10 Globe pyrite . . . . . 1·50 1·50
986 1f.50 Calcite . . . . 1·90 1·90

305 Nendeln Forwarding Agency, 1864 **306** Penny Black

1990. Europa. Post Office Buildings. Mult.
987 50r. Type **305** 65 65
988 90r. Vaduz post office, 1976 1·00 1·00

1990. 150th Anniv of the Penny Black.
989 **306** 1f.50 multicoloured . . . 1·90 1·80

307 Footballers **308** Tureen, Oranges and Grapes

1990. World Cup Football Championship, Italy.
990 **307** 2f. multicoloured . . . . 2·30 2·20

1990. 9th Death Anniv of Benjamin Steck (painter). Multicoloured.
991 50r. Type **308** 75 75
992 80r. Apples and pewter bowl 1·00 1·00
993 1f.50 Basket, apples, cherries and pewter jug . . . . . . 1·50 1·50

309 Princess Gina **310** Common Pheasant

1990. Prince Francis Joseph II and Princess Gina Commemoration. Multicoloured.
994 2f. Type **309** . . . . 2·10 2·10
995 3f. Prince Francis Joseph II 3·25 3·25

1990. Game Birds. Multicoloured.
996 25r. Type **310** 35 35
997 50r. Black grouse 65 65
998 2f. Mallard . . . . 2·40 2·40

311 Annunciation **312** St. Nicholas

1990. Christmas. Paintings. Multicoloured.
999 35r. Type **311** 45 45
1000 50r. Nativity 55 60
1001 90r. Adoration of the Magi 1·00 1·00

1990. Winter Customs. Multicoloured.
1002 35r. Type **312** 45 45
1003 50r. Awakening on New Year's Eve 55 55
1004 1f.50 Giving New Year greetings . . . . 1·60 1·60

313 Mounted Courier **314** "Olympus 1" Satellite

1990. 500th Anniv of Regular European Postal Services.
1005 **313** 90r. multicoloured . . . 1·00 1·00

1991. Europa. Europe in Space. Multicoloured.
1006 50r. Type **314** 60 60
1007 90r. "Meteosat" satellite . . 1·00 1·00

315 St. Ignatius de Loyola (founder of Society of Jesus) **316** U.N. Emblem and Dove

1991. Anniversaries. Multicoloured.
1008 80r. Type **315** (500th birth anniv) 95 90
1009 90r. Wolfgang Amadeus Mozart (composer, death bicentenary) . . . . . . 1·00 1·00

1991. Admission to U.N. Membership (1990).
1010 **316** 2f.50 multicoloured . . . 2·75 2·75

317 Non-Commissioned Officer and Private **318** "Near Maloja" (Giovanni Giacometti)

1991. 125th Anniv of Last Mobilization of Liechtenstein's Military Contingent (to the Tyrol). Multicoloured.
1011 50r. Type **317** 55 60
1012 70r. Tunic, chest and portrait 75 70
1013 1f. Officer and private . . . 1·20 1·20

1991. 700th Anniv of Swiss Confederation. Paintings by Swiss artists. Multicoloured.
1014 50r. Type **318** 55 55
1015 80r. "Rhine Valley" (Ferdinand Gehr) 90 85
1016 90r. "Bergell" (Augusto Giacometti) 95 95
1017 1f.10 "Hoher Kasten" (Hedwig Scherrer) . . . . 1·20 1·20

319 Stampless and Modern Covers **320** Princess Marie

1991. "Liba 92" National Stamp Exhibition, Vaduz.
1018 **319** 90r. multicoloured . . . 1·00 1·00

1991. Multicoloured.
1019 3f. Type **320** . . . . 3·25 3·25
1020 3f.40 Prince Hans Adam II 3·50 3·50

321 Virgin of the Annunciation (exterior of left wing) **322** Cross-country Skiers and Testing for Drug Abuse

1991. Christmas. Details of the altar from St. Mamertus Chapel, Triesen. Multicoloured.
1021 50r. Type **321** 55 55
1022 80r. Madonna and Child (wood-carving attr. Jorg Syrlin, inner shrine) . . . 85 85
1023 90r. Angel Gabriel (exterior of right wing) 95 90

1991. Winter Olympic Games, Albertville. Mult.
1024 70r. Type **322** 80 80
1025 80r. Ice hockey player tackling opponent and helping him after fall . . 85 85
1026 1f.60 Downhill skier and fallen skier caught in safety net . . . . 1·90 1·80

323 Relay Race, Drugs and Shattered Medal **324** Aztecs

1992. Olympic Games, Barcelona. Multicoloured.
1027 50r. Type **323** 50 55
1028 70r. Cycling road race . . . 95 90
1029 2f.50 Judo . . . . 2·75 2·75

1992. Europa. 500th Anniv of Discovery of America by Columbus. Multicoloured.
1030 80r. Type **324** 80 80
1031 90r. Statue of Liberty and New York skyline 95 90

325 Clown in Envelope ("Good Luck") **327** "Blechnum spicant"

326 Arms of Liechtenstein—Kinsky Alliance

1992. Greetings Stamps. Multicoloured.

1032	50r. Type **325**	50	50
1033	50r. Wedding rings in envelope and harlequin violinist	50	50
1034	50r. Postman blowing horn (31 × 21 mm)	50	50
1035	50r. Flying postman carrying letter sealed with heart (31 × 21 mm)	50	50

1992. "Liba '92" National Stamp Exhibition. Silver Wedding Anniv of Prince Hans Adam and Princess Marie. Sheet 100 × 67 mm containing T **326** and similar vert design. Multicoloured.

MS1036	2f. Type **326**; 2f.50 Royal couple (photo by Anthony Buckley)	5·50	5·25

1992. Ferns. Multicoloured.

1037	40r. Type **327**	40	40
1038	50r. Maidenhair spleenwort	55	50
1039	70r. Hart's-tongue	75	70
1040	2f.50 "Asplenium ruta-muraria"	2·40	2·50

328 Reading Edict

329 Chapel of St. Mamertus, Triesen

1992. 650th Anniv of County of Vaduz.

1041	**328** 1f.60 multicoloured	1·70	1·70

1992. Christmas. Multicoloured.

1042	50r. Type **329**	55	50
1043	90r. Crib, St. Gallus's Church, Triesen	95	95
1044	1f.60 St. Mary's Chapel, Triesen	1·70	1·70

330 Crown Prince Alois

331 "Nafkopf and Huts, Steg"

1992.

1045	**330** 2f.50 multicoloured	2·50	2·40

1993. 1400th Birth Anniv of Hans Gantner (painter). Multicoloured.

1046	50r. Type **331**	40	40
1047	60r. "Hunting Lodge, Sass"	70	70
1048	1f.80 "Red House, Vaduz"	2·20	2·20

332 "910805" (Bruno Kaufmann)

333 "Tale of the Ferryman" (painting)

1993. Europa. Contemporary Art. Multicoloured.

1049	80r. Type **332**	1·00	1·00
1050	1f. "The Little Blue" (Evi Kliemand)	1·20	1·20

1993. Tibetan Collection in the National Museum. Multicoloured.

1051	60r. Type **333**	75	70
1052	80r. Religious dance mask	75	90
1053	1f. "Tale of the Fish" (painting)	1·10	1·40

334 "Tree of Life"

335 "The Black Hatter"

1993. Missionary Work.

1054	**334** 1f.80 multicoloured	2·20	2·00

1993. Homage to Liechtenstein.

1055	**335** 2f.80 multicoloured	3·75	3·75

336 Crown Prince Alois and Duchess Sophie of Bavaria

1993. Royal Wedding. Sheet 100 × 67 mm.

MS1056	**336** 4f. multicoloured	5·00	5·00

337 Origanum

338 Eurasian Badger

1993. Flowers. Illustrations from "Hortus Botanicus Liechtensteinsis". Multicoloured.

1057	50r. Type **337**	75	65
1058	60r. Meadow sage	85	70
1059	1f. "Seseli annuum"	1·40	1·10
1060	2f.50 Large self-heal	2·20	2·75

1993. Animals. Multicoloured.

1061	60r. Type **338**	70	75
1062	80r. Beech marten	1·00	1·00
1063	1f. Red fox	1·30	1·30

339 "Now that the Quiet Days are Coming ..." (Rainer Maria Rilke)

340 Ski Jump

1993. Christmas. Multicoloured.

1064	60r. Type **339**	70	70
1065	80r. "Can You See the Light ..." (Th. Friedrich)	1·00	1·00
1066	1f. "Christmas, Christmas ..." (R. A. Schroder)	1·10	1·10

1993. Winter Olympic Games, Lillehammer, Norway (1994). Multicoloured.

1067	60r. Type **340**	90	90
1068	80r. Slalom	1·10	1·10
1069	2f.40 Bobsleighing	2·50	2·50

341 Seal and Title Page

342 Andean Condor

1994. Anniversaries. Multicoloured.

1070	60r. Type **341** (275th anniv of Principality)	75	75
1071	1f.80 State, Prince's and Olympic flags (centenary of International Olympic Committee)	2·10	2·10

1994. Europa. Discoveries of Alexander von Humboldt. Multicoloured.

1072	80r. Type **342**	95	95
1073	1f. "Rhexia cardinalis" (plant)	1·20	1·20

343 Football Pitch and Hopi Indians playing Kickball

344 Elephant with Letter

1994. World Cup Football Championship, U.S.A.

1074	**343** 2f.80 multicoloured	3·25	3·25

1994. Greetings Stamps. Multicoloured.

1075	60r. Type **344**	75	75
1076	60r. Cherub with flower and hearts	75	75
1077	60r. Pig with four-leaf clover	75	75
1078	60r. Dog holding bunch of tulips	75	75

345 "Eulogy of Madness" (mobile, Jean Tinguely)

1994. Homage to Liechtenstein.

1079	**345** 4f. black, pink and violet	5·00	5·00

346 Spring

1994. Seasons of the Vine. Multicoloured.

1080	60r. Type **346**	75	75
1081	60r. Vine leaves (Summer)	75	75
1082	60r. Trunk in snowy landscape (Winter)	75	75
1083	60r. Grapes (Autumn)	75	75

Nos. 1080/3 were issued together, se-tenant, forming a composite design.

347 Strontium

1994. Minerals. Multicoloured.

1084	60r. Type **347**	85	90
1085	80r. Quartz	1·10	1·10
1086	3f.50 Iron dolomite	4·00	3·75

348 "The True Light"

349 Earth

1994. Christmas. Multicoloured.

1087	60r. Type **348**	70	70
1088	80r. "Peace on Earth"	95	95
1089	1f. "Behold, the House of God"	1·20	1·20

1994. The Four Elements. Multicoloured.

1090	60r. Type **349**	75	75
1091	80r. Water	95	95
1092	1f. Fire	1·20	1·20
1093	2f.50 Air	2·75	2·75

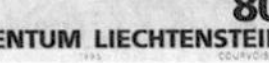

350 "The Theme of all our Affairs must be Peace"

351 U.N. Flag and Bouquet of Flowers

1995. Europa. Peace and Freedom. Quotations of Franz Josef II. Multicoloured.

1094	80r. Type **350**	95	95
1095	1f. "Through Unity comes Strength and the Bearing of Sorrows"	1·30	1·30

1995. Anniversaries and Event. Multicoloured.

1096	60r. Princess Marie with children (50th anniv of Liechtenstein Red Cross) (horiz)	75	75
1097	1f.80 Type **351** (50th anniv of U.N.O.)	2·20	2·20
1098	3f.50 Alps (European Nature Conservation Year)	4·25	4·25

352 "Falknis Mountains"

353 "One Heart and One Soul"

1995. Birth Centenary of Anton Frommelt (painter). Multicoloured.

1099	60r. Type **352**	75	75
1100	80r. "Three Oaks"	1·00	1·00
1101	4f.10 "The Rhine"	4·75	4·75

1995. Greetings Stamps. Multicoloured.

1102	60r. Type **353**	75	75
1103	60r. Bandage round sunflower ("Get Well")	75	75
1104	60r. Baby arriving over rainbow ("Here I am")	75	75
1105	60r. Delivering letter by hot-air balloon ("Write again")	75	75

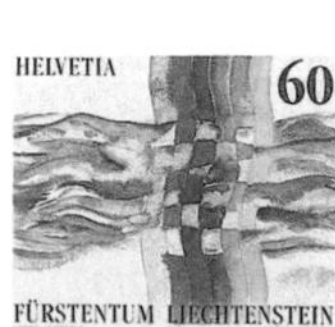

354 Coloured Ribbons woven through River

355 Arnica

1995. Liechtenstein–Switzerland Co-operation.

1106	**354** 60r. multicoloured	75	75

No. 1106 was valid for use in both Liechtenstein and Switzerland (see No. 1308 of Switzerland).

1995. Medicinal Plants. Multicoloured.

1107	60r. Type **355**	70	75
1108	80r. Giant nettle	95	75
1109	1f.80 Common valerian	2·20	2·20
1110	3f.50 Fig-wort	3·50	3·75

356 Angel (detail of painting)

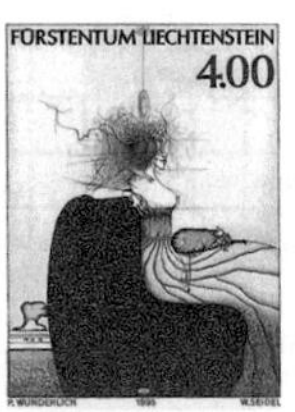

357 "Lady with Lap-dog" (Paul Wunderlich)

1995. Christmas. Painting by Lorenzo Monaco. Multicoloured.

1111	60r. Type **356**	70	70
1112	80r. "Virgin Mary with Infant and Two Angels"	95	95
1113	1f. Angel facing left (detail of painting)	1·20	1·20

1995. Homage to Liechtenstein.

1114	**357** 4f. multicoloured	4·75	4·75

358 Eschen

359 Crucible

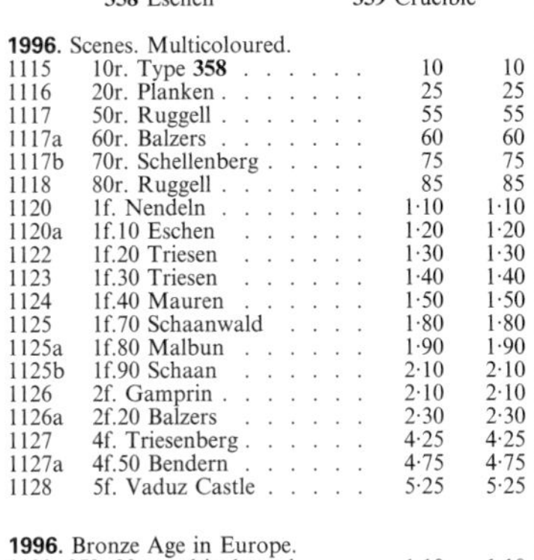

1996. Scenes. Multicoloured.
1115 10r. Type **358** 10 10
1116 20r. Planken 25 25
1117 50r. Ruggell 55 55
1117a 60r. Balzers 60 60
1117b 70r. Schellenberg 75 75
1118 80r. Ruggell 85 85
1120 1f. Nendeln 1·10 1·10
1120a 1f.10 Eschen 1·20 1·20
1122 1f.20 Triesen 1·30 1·30
1123 1f.30 Triesen 1·40 1·40
1124 1f.40 Mauren 1·50 1·50
1125 1f.70 Schaanwald 1·80 1·80
1125a 1f.80 Malbun 1·90 1·90
1125b 1f.90 Schaan 2·10 2·10
1126 2f. Gamprin 2·10 2·10
1126a 2f.20 Balzers 2·30 2·30
1127 4f. Triesenberg 4·25 4·25
1127a 4f.50 Bendern 4·75 4·75
1128 5f. Vaduz Castle 5·25 5·25

1996. Bronze Age in Europe.
1130 **359** 90r. multicoloured 1·10 1·10

360 Kinsky and Diary Extract, 7 March 1917

1996. Europa. Famous Women. Nora, Countess Kinsky (mother of Princess Gina of Liechtenstein)
1131 **360** 90r. grey, purple and blue 1·00 1·00
1132 – 1f.10 grey, blue and purple 1·20 1·20
DESIGN: 1f.10, Kinsky and diary extract for 28 February 1917.

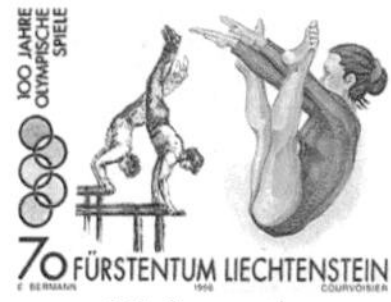

361 Gymnastics

1996. Centenary of Modern Olympic Games. Multicoloured.
1133 70r. Type **361** 75 75
1134 90r. Hurdling 95 95
1135 1f.10 Cycling 1·30 1·30

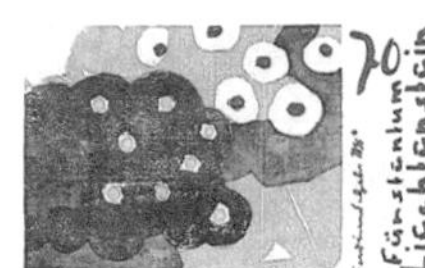

362 "Primroses"

1996. Birth Centenary of Ferdinand Gehr (painter). Multicoloured.
1136 70r. Type **362** 80 80
1137 90r. "Daisies" 1·00 1·00
1138 1f.10 "Poppy" 1·20 1·20
1139 1f.80 "Buttercups" (33 × 23 mm) 2·00 2·00

363 State Arms

1996.
1140 **363** 10f. multicoloured 10·50 10·50

364 Veldkirch, 1550

1996. Millenary of Austria.
1141 **364** 90r. multicoloured 1·10 1·10

365 "Poltava"

366 St. Matthew

1996. 43rd Death Anniv of Eugen Zotow (painter). Multicoloured.
1142 70r. Type **365** 75 75
1143 1f.10 "Three Bathers in a Berlin Park" 75 75
1144 1f.40 "Vaduz" 1·00 1·00

1996. Christmas. Illustrations from Illuminated Manuscript "Liber Viventium Fabariensis". Multicoloured.
1145 70r. Type **366** 80 75
1146 90r. Emblems of St. Mark 1·00 95
1147 1f.10 Emblems of St. Luke 1·20 1·20
1148 1f.80 Emblems of St. John 2·00 2·00

367 Schubert

368 The Wild Gnomes

1997. Birth Bicent of Franz Schubert (composer).
1149 **367** 70r. multicoloured 85 85

1997. Europa. Tales and Legends. Multicoloured.
1150 90r. Type **368** 90 90
1151 1f.10 Man, pumpkin and rabbit (The Foal of Planken) 1·20 1·20

369 "Madonna and Child with St. Lucius and St. Florinus" (Gabriel Dreher)

1997. National Patron Saints.
1152 **369** 20f. multicoloured 17·00 17·00

370 "Phaeolepiota aurea"

1997. Fungi (1st series). Multicoloured.
1153 70r. Type **370** 70 70
1154 90r. "Helvella silvicola" 90 90
1155 1f.10 Orange peel fungus 1·20 1·20
See also Nos. 1238/40.

371 Steam Train, Schaanwald Halt

372 "Girl with Flower" (Enrico Baj)

1997. 125th Anniv of Liechtenstein Railways. Mult.
1156 70r. Type **371** 75 75
1157 90r. Diesel-electric train, Nendeln station 95 95
1158 1f.80 Electric train, Schaan-Vaduz station 1·90 1·90

1997. Homage to Liechtenstein.
1159 **372** 70r. multicoloured 75 75

373 Basket of Roses

374 Cross-country skiing

1997. Christmas. Glass Tree Decorations. Multicoloured.
1160 70r. Type **373** 70 70
1161 90r. Bell 90 90
1162 1f.10 Bauble 1·10 1·10

1997. Winter Olympic Games, Nagano, Japan (1998). Skiing. Multicoloured.
1163 70r. Type **374** 70 70
1164 90r. Slalom 95 95
1165 1f.80 Downhill 1·90 1·90

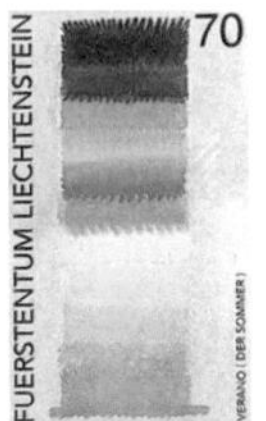

375 "Verano (The Summer)"

1998. Homage to Liechtenstein. Paintings by Heinz Mack. Multicoloured.
1166 70r. Type **375** 70 70
1167 70r. "Homage to Liechtenstein" 70 70
1168 70r. "Between Day and Dream" 70 70
1169 70r. "Salute Cirico!" 70 70

376 Prince's Festival Procession, Vaduz

1998. Europa. National Festivals. Multicoloured.
1170 90r. Type **376** 95 95
1171 1f.10 Music Societies Festival, Gutenberg Castle, Balzers 1·20 1·20

377 National Flags on Bridge

1998. 75th Anniv of Liechtenstein–Switzerland Customs Treaty.
1172 **377** 1f.70 multicoloured 1·80 1·80

378 Goalkeeper

1998. World Cup Football Championship, France.
1173 **378** 1f.80 multicoloured 1·90 1·90

379 Clown with Queen of Hearts

380 Wooden Milk Vat

1998. Greeting Stamps. Clowns. Multicoloured.
1174 70r. Type **379** 70 70
1175 70r. Clown holding four-leaf clovers 70 70
1176 70r. Clown raising hat 70 70
1177 70r. Clown holding heart 70 70

1998. Traditional Crafts (1st series). Multicoloured.
1178 90r. Type **380** 90 90
1179 2f.20 Clog 2·20 2·20
1180 3f.50 Wheel 3·50 3·50
See also Nos. 1257/9.

381 Expelling Johann Langer from Liechtenstein

1998. 150th Anniv of 1848 Revolutions in Europe.
1181 **381** 1f.80 multicoloured 1·90 1·90

382 Virgin Mary

1998. Christmas. Multicoloured.
1182 70r. Type **382** 75 75
1183 90r. "The Nativity" (35 × 26 mm) 90 90
1184 1f.10 Joseph 1·20 1·20
Nos. 1182 and 1184 show details of the complete relief depicted on No. 1183.

383 Zum Lowen Guest House

384 Automatic and Manual Switchboards

1998. Preservation of Historical Environment. Hinterschellenberg. Multicoloured.
1185 90r. Type **383** 90 95
1186 1f.70 St. George's Chapel (vert) 1·90 1·90
1187 1f.80 Houses 1·90 1·90

1998. Centenary of Telephone in Liechtenstein.
1188 **384** 2f.80 multicoloured 3·00 3·00

385 Eschen

1999. 300th Anniv of Purchase of Unterland by Prince Johann Adam. Sheet 107 × 68 mm containing T **385** and similar horiz design. Multicoloured.
MS1189 90r. × 5 plus label, Composite design of the Unterland showing the villages of Eschen, Gamprin, Mauren, Ruggell and Schellenberg 4·50 4·50

386 Smooth Snake and Schwabbrunnen-Aescher Nature Park

387 Council Anniversary Emblem and Silhouettes

1999. Europa. Parks and Gardens. Multicoloured.
1190 90r. Type **386** 1·00 1·00
1191 1f.10 Corn crake and Ruggell marsh 1·10 1·10

1999. Anniversaries and Event. Multicoloured.
1192 70r. Type **387** (50th anniv of Council of Europe and European Convention on Human Rights) 75 75
1193 70r. Bird with envelope in beak (125th anniv of U.P.U.) 75 75
1194 70r. Heart in hand (75th anniv of Caritas Liechtenstein (welfare organization)) 75 75

388 Judo

1999. 8th European Small States Games, Liechtenstein. Multicoloured.
1195 70r. Type **388** 70 70
1196 70r. Swimming 70 70
1197 70r. Throwing the javelin . . 70 70
1198 90r. Cycling 95 95
1199 90r. Shooting 95 95
1200 90r. Tennis 95 95
1201 90r. Squash 95 95
1202 90r. Table tennis 95 95
1203 90r. Volleyball 95 95

389 "Herrengasse"

1999. Paintings by Eugen Verling. Multicoloured.
1204 70r. Type **389** 85 85
1205 2f. "Old Vaduz with Castle" 1·20 1·20
1206 4f. "House in Furst-Franz-Josef Street, Vaduz" . . . 5·00 5·00

390 Scene from "Faust", Act I

1999. 250th Birth Anniv of Johann Wolfgang Goethe (poet and playwright). Multicoloured.
1207 1f.40 Type **390** . . . . . . 1·50 1·50
1208 1f.70 Faust and the Devil sealing wager . . . . . . 1·80 1·80

391 "The Annunciation" **392** Identification Mark on Door, Ubersaxen

1999. Christmas. Paintings by Joseph Walser from Chapel of Our Lady of Comfort, Dux. Mult.
1209 70r. Type **391** 75 75
1210 90r. "Nativity" 95 95
1211 1f.10 "Adoration" . . . . . 1·20 1·20

1999. Walser Identification Marks. Multicoloured.
1212 70r. Type **392** 75 75
1213 90r. Mark on mural 95 95
1214 1f.80 Mark on axe . . . . 1·90 1·90

393 Gutenberg **395** Emblem

394 "The Adoration of the Shepheards" (Matthia Stomer)

1999. 600th Birth Anniv of Johannes Gutenberg (inventor of printing press).
1215 **393** 3f.60 multicoloured . . . 2·75 2·75

2000. 2000 Years of Christianity. Sheet 108 × 68 mm containing T **394** and similar square design. Multicoloured.
MS1216 70r. Type **394**; 1f.10 "Three Kings" (Ferdinand Gehr) . . . 1·75 1·75

2000. Provision of Postal Services by Liechtenstein Post in Partnership with Swiss Post.
1217 **395** 90r. multicoloured . . . 95 95

396 "Mars and Rhea Silvia" (Peter Paul Rubens)

2000. Paintings. Multicoloured.
1218 70r. Type **396** 75 75
1219 1f.80 "Cupid with Soap-Bubble" (Rembrandt) . . 1·90 1·90

397 "Fragrance of Humus" **398** "Building Europe"

2000. "EXPO 2000" World's Fair, Hanover, Germany. Paintings by Friedensreich Hundertwasser. Multicoloured.
1220 70r. Type **397** 75 75
1221 90r. "Do Not Wait Houses-Move" . . . . 1·00 1·00
1222 1f.10 "The Car: a Drive Towards Nature and Creation" . . . . . . 1·20 1·20

2000. Europa.
1223 **398** 1f.10 multicoloured . . . 1·10 1·10

399 "Dove of Peace" (Antonio Martini)

2000. "Peace 2000". Paintings by members of Association of Mouth and Foot Painting Artists. Mult.
1224 1f.40 Type **399** . . . . . . 1·50 1·50
1225 1f.70 "World Peace" (Alberto Alvarez) . . . . 1·80 1·80
1226 2f.20 "Rainbow" (Eiichi Minami) . . . . 2·30 2·30

400 Koalas on Rings (Gymnastics)

2000. Olympic Games, Sydney. Multicoloured.
1227 80r. Type **400** 80 80
1228 1f. Joey leaping over crossbar (High jump) . . 95 95
1229 1f.30 Emus approaching finish line (Athletics) . . . 1·40 1·40
1230 1f.80 Duckbill platypuses in swimming race . . . . . 1·90 1·90

401 "The Dreaming Bee" (Joan Miro)

2000. Inauguration of Art Museum. Multicoloured.
1231 80r. Type **401** 85 85
1232 1f.20 "Cube" (Sol LeWitt) 1·30 1·30
1233 2f. "Bouquet of Flowers" (Raelant Savery) (31 × 46 mm) . . . . . . 2·00 2·00

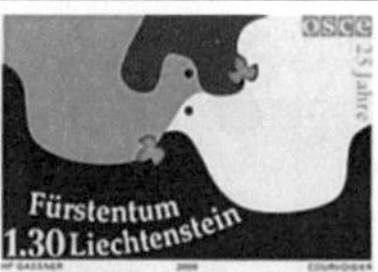

402 "Peace Doves"

2000. 25th Anniv of Organization for Security and Co-operation in Europe.
1234 **402** 1f.30 multicoloured . . . 1·40 1·40

403 Root Crib

2000. Christmas. Cribs. Multicoloured.
1235 80r. Type **403** 80 80
1236 1f.30 Oriental crib . . . . . 1·40 1·40
1237 1f.80 Crib with cloth figures 1·90 1·90

2000. Fungi (2nd series). As T **370**. Multicoloured.
1238 90r. Mycena adonis 90 90
1239 1f.10 Chalciporus amarellus 1·20 1·20
1240 2f. Pink waxcap . . . . . . 2·10 2·10

404 Postman delivering Parcel

2001. Greetings Stamps. Multicoloured.
1241 70r. Type **404** 75 75
1242 70r. Postman delivering flowers 75 75

Nos. 1241/2 are for the stamps with the parcel (1241) and flowers (1242) intact. The parcel and flowers can be scratched away to reveal a greetings message.

405 Silver Easter Egg **406** Mountain Spring

2001. Decorated Easter Eggs. Multicoloured.
1243 1f.20 Type **405** . . . . . . 1·30 1·30
1244 1f.80 Cloissonne egg . . . . 2·00 2·00
1245 2f. Porcelain egg . . . . . 2·00 2·00

2001. Europa. Water Resources.
1246 **406** 1f.30 multicoloured . . . 1·40 1·40

407 Emblem

2001. Liechtenstein Presidency of Council of Europe.
1247 **407** 1f.80 multicoloured . . . 1·90 1·90

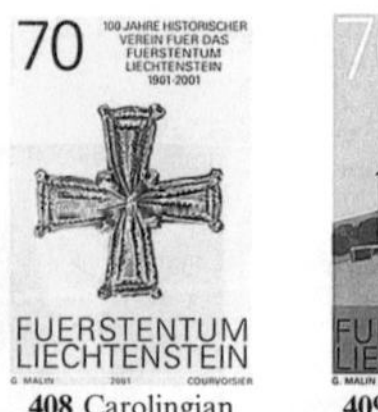

408 Carolingian Cruciform Fibula **409** St. Theresa's Chapel, Schaanwald

2001. Centenary of Historical Association. Multicoloured.
1248 70r. Type **408** 75 75
1249 70r. "Mars of Gutenberg" (statue) 75 75

2001. Preservation of Historical Environment (2nd series). Multicoloured.
1250 70r. Type **409** 75 75
1251 90r. St. Johann's Torkel (wine press), Mauren . . 1·00 1·00
1252 1f.10 Pirsch Transformer Station, Schaanwald . . . 1·10 1·10

See also Nos. 1274/5 and 1292/3.

410 Mary and kneeling Votant (Chapel of Our Lady, Dux, Schann)

2001. Votive Paintings. Multicoloured.
1253 70r. Type **410** 70 70
1254 1f.20 Mary and Jesus, St. George among other Saints, and text of vow (St. George's Chapel, Schellenberg) . . . . . . 1·20 1·20
1255 1f.30 Mary, St. Joseph of Arimathea, St. Christopher, Johann Christoph Walser (votant) and text of vow (Chapel of Our Lady, Dux, Schann) . . . . 1·50 1·50

411 Rheinberger and Scene from *Zauberwort* (song cycle) **412** "Annunciation"

2001. Death Centenary of Josef Gabriel Rheinberger (composer).
1256 **411** 3f.50 multicoloured . . . 3·75 3·75

2001. Traditional Crafts (2nd series). As T **380**. Multicoloured.
1257 70r. Agricultural implements and horseshoe 75 75
1258 90r. Rake . . . . 1·00 1·00
1259 1f.20 Harness . . . . 1·30 1·30

2001. Christmas. Medallions from The Joyful, Sorrowful and Glorious Rosary Cycle. Multicoloured.
1260 70r. Type **412** 70 70
1261 90r. Nativity 90 90
1262 1f.30 Presentation of Jesus at the Temple . . . . . . 1·50 1·50

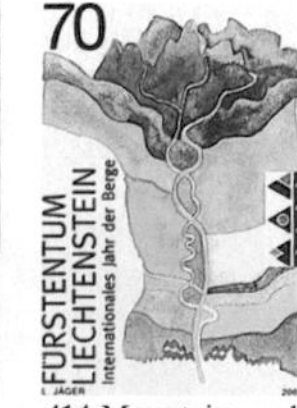

413 Square **414** Mountains and River

2001. Paintings by Gottfried Honeggar. Mult.
1263 1f.80 Type **413** . . . . . . 2·00 2·00
1264 2f.20 Circle . . . . 2·20 2·20

2002. International Year of Mountains and 50th Anniv of the International Commission of Alpine Protection. Multicoloured.
1265 70r. Type **414** 65 65
1266 1f.20 Stylized mountains . . 1·10 1·10

415 "Schellenberg"

2002. 30th Death Anniv of Friedrich Kaufmann (artist). Multicoloured.
1267 70r. Type **415** 65 65
1268 1f.30 "Schaan" . . . . . . 1·20 1·20
1269 1f.80 "Steg" . . . . 3·50 3·50

416 Space Shuttle and Bee

2002. Liechtenstein's participation in N.A.S.A. Space Technology and Research Students Project.
1270 **416** 90r. multicoloured . . . 85 85

The project submitted by the Liechtenstein Gymnasium concerned the study of the effects of space on carpenter bees.

417 Man on Tightrope

2002. Europa. Circus. Multicoloured.
1271 90r. Type **417** 85 85
1272 1f.30 Juggler . . . . 1·20 1·20

418 Emblem

2002. "Liba '02" National Stamp Exhibition, Vaduz (1st issue).
1273 **418** 1f.20 multicoloured . . . 1·10 1·10
See also Nos. 1282/3 and 1318/20.

419 Houses, Popers

2002. Preservation of Historical Environment (2nd series). Multicoloured.
1274 70r. Type **419** 65 65
1275 1f.20 House, Weiherring . . 1·10 1·10

420 Footballers

2002. World Cup Football Championship, Japan and South Korea.
1276 **420** 1f.80 multicoloured . . . 1·70 1·70

421 Princess Marie

2002. The Royal Couple. Multicoloured.
1277 3f. Type **421** . . . . 2·75 2·75
1278 3f.50 Prince Hans-Adam II 3·25 3·25

422 Ghost Orchid (*Epipogium aphyllum*) **423** Stamps and Emblem

2002. Orchids. Multicoloured.
1279 70r. Type **422** 65 65
1280 1f.20 Fly orchid (*Ophrys insectifera*) . . . . 1·10 1·10
1281 1f.30 Black vanilla orchid (*Nigritella nigra*) . . . . 1·20 1·20

2002. "Liba 02" National Stamp Exhibition, Vaduz (2nd issue). 90th Anniv of First Liechtenstein Stamps. Multicoloured.
1282 90r. Type **423** 85 85
1283 1f.30 Stamps showing royal family . . . . 1·20 1·20

424 Princess Sophie

2002. Prince Alois and Princess Sophie. Multicoloured.
1284 2f. Type **424** . . . . 1·90 1·90
1285 2f.50 Prince Alois . . . . . 2·30 2·30

425 Mary and Joseph

2002. Christmas. Batik. Multicoloured.
1286 70r. Type **425** 65 65
1287 1f.20 Nativity . . . . . . 1·10 1·10
1288 1f.80 Flight into Egypt . . . 1·70 1·70

426 The Eagle, Vaduz

2002. Inn Signs. Multicoloured.
1289 1f.20 Type **426** . . . . . . 1·10 1·10
1290 1f.80 The Angel, Balzers . . 1·70 1·70
1291 3f. The Eagle, Bendern . . . 2·75 2·75

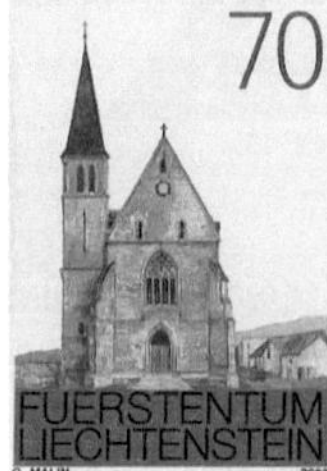

427 St. Fridolin Parish Church **429** Pruning Vines

428 Postal Emblem

2003. Preservation of Historical Environment (3rd series). Multicoloured.
1292 70r. Type **427** 60 60
1293 2f. 50 House, Spidach (horiz) . . . . 2·10 2·10

2003. Europa. Poster Art.
1294 **428** 1f. 20 multicoloured . . 1·10 1·10

2003. Viticulture (1st issue). Multicoloured.
1295 1f. 30 Type **429** . . . . . . 1·10 1·10
1296 1f. 80 Tying up vines . . . 1·60 1·60
1297 2f. 20 Hoeing . . . . 2·00 2·00
See also Nos. 1301/3, 1304/6 and 1312/14.

430 Bridge

2003. 50th Anniv of Liechtenstein Association for the Disabled.
1298 **430** 70r. multicoloured . . . 60 60

431 Renovated Buildings and Ammonite

2003. Renovation of National Museum. Multicoloured.
1299 1f. 20 Type **431** . . . . . . 1·10 1·10
1300 1f. 30 Verweserhaus building and bailiff's shield . . . . 1·10 1·10

2003. Viticulture (2nd issue). As T **429**. Multicoloured.
1301 1f. 20 Looping the tendrils 1·10 1·10
1302 1f. 80 Removing leaves from around grapes . . . . . 1·60 1·60
1303 3f. 50 Reducing top growth 3·00 3·50

2003. Viticulture (3rd issue). As T **429**. Multicoloured.
1304 70r. Thinning out 60 60
1305 90r. Harvesting 80 80
1306 1f. 10 Pressing the grapes 1·00 1·00

432 St. George **433** Parents and Young on Nest

2003. Saints (1st series). Multicoloured.
1307 1f. 20 Type **432** . . . . . . 1·10 1·10
1308 1f. 20 St. Blaise . . . . . . 1·10 1·10
1309 1f. 30 St. Vitus . . . . . . 1·10 1·10
1310 1f. 30 St. Erasmus . . . . . 1·10 1·10
See also Nos. 1323/8.

2003. Conservation of White Storks in Rhine Valley.
1311 **433** 2f. 20 multicoloured . . 2·00 2·00

2003. Viticulture (4th issue). As T **429**. Multicoloured
1312 70r. Tasting 60 60
1313 90r. Harvesting ice-wine grapes 80 80
1314 1f. 20 Bottling . . . . . . 1·10 1·10

434 Archangel Gabriel appearing to Mary

2003. Christmas. Multicoloured.
1315 70r. Type **434** 60 60
1316 90r. Nativity 80 80
1317 1f. 30 Three Kings . . . . 1·10 1·10

435 Cow (Laura Beck)

2003. "Liba 02" National Stamp Exhibition, Vaduz (3rd issue). Children's Drawing Competition Winners. Multicoloured.
1318 70r. Type **435** 60 60
1319 1f. 80 Bee (Laura Lingg) . . 1·60 1·60
1320 1f. 80 Apple tree (Patrick Marxer) (vert) . . . . . 1·60 1·60

436 Hands enclosing Leaves

2004. 50th Anniv of AHV (retirement insurance).
1321 **436** 85r. multicoloured . . . 75 75

437 Hot Air Balloon

2004. Europa. Holidays.
1322 **437** 1f. 30 multicoloured . . 1·10 1·10

2004. Saints (2nd series). As T **432**. Multicoloured.
1323 1f. St. Achatius 90 90
1324 1f. St. Margaret 90 90
1325 1f.20 St. Christopher . . . 1·10 1·10
1326 1f.20 St. Pantaleon . . . . 1·10 1·10
1327 2f.50 St. Cyriacus . . . . . 2·00 2·00
1328 2f.50 St. Aegidius . . . . . 2·00 2·00

OFFICIAL STAMPS

1932. Stamps of 1930 optd **REGIERUNGS DIENSTSACHE** under crown.
O118 5r. green . . . . 8·00 6·25
O119 10r. lilac . . . . 40·00 6·25
O120 20r. red . . . . 40·00 6·25
O121 30r. blue . . . . 8·75 8·00
O122 35r. green . . . . 6·25 16·00
O123 50r. black . . . . 36·00 10·00
O124 60r. green . . . . 7·50 21·00
O125 1f.20 brown . . . . 90·00 £225

1933. Nos. 121 and 123 optd **REGIERUNGS DIENSTSACHE** in circle round crown.
O126 **38** 25r. orange . . . . . . 25·00 25·00
O127 – 1f.20 brown . . . . . . 55·00 £170

1934. Nos. 128 etc. optd **REGIERUNGS DIENSTSACHE** in circle round crown.
O150 **41** 5r. green . . . . 1·00 1·20
O151 – 10r. violet . . . . . . 2·50 95
O152 – 15r. orange . . . . . . 30 1·50
O153 – 20r. red 35 95
O155 – 25r. brown . . . . . . 1·90 9·25
O156 – 30r. blue . . . . 2·50 5·00
O157 **42** 50r. brown . . . . . . 1·00 1·90
O158 – 90r. green . . . . . . 5·50 25·00
O159 – 1f.50 brown . . . . . . 32·00 £110

1937. Stamps of 1937 optd **REGIERUNGS DIENSTSACHE** in circle round crown.
O174 **51** 5r. green and buff . . . 20 20
O175 – 10r. violet and buff . . . 35 60
O176 – 20r. red and buff . . . . 95 1·10
O177 – 25r. brown and buff . . 55 1·40
O178 – 30r. blue and buff . . . 1·10 1·40
O179 – 50r. brown and buff . . 60 1·10
O180 – 1f. purple and buff . . . 75 5·50
O181 – 1f.50 grey and buff . . . 2·20 8·00

1947. Stamps of 1944 optd **DIENSTMARKE** and crown.
O255 5r. green . . . . 1·10 75
O256 10r. violet . . . . 1·10 95
O257 20r. red . . . . 1·60 1·00
O258 30r. blue . . . . 1·70 1·40
O259 50r. grey . . . . 1·70 2·75
O260 1f. red . . . . 7·50 9·25
O261 1f.50 blue . . . . 7·50 9·25

O 86 **O 198** Government Building, Vaduz

1950. Buff paper.
O287 **O 86** 5r. purple and grey . . 10 10
O288 10r. green and mauve 10 10
O289 20r. brown and blue 25 25
O290 30r. purple and red . . 35 35
O291 40r. blue and brown 50 50
O292 55r. green and red . . 85 1·00
O293 60r. grey and mauve 1·40 1·10
O294 80r. orange and grey 95 95
O295 90r. brown and blue 1·00 1·00
O296 1f.20 turquoise and orange . . . . . . 1·40 1·40

1968. White paper.
O495 **O 86** 5r. brown and orange 10 10
O496 10r. violet and red . . 10 10
O497 20r. red and green . . 25 25
O498 30r. green and red . . 35 35
O499 50r. blue and red . . . 60 60
O500 60r. orange and blue 60 60
O501 70r. purple and green 75 75
O502 80r. green and red . . 75 75
O503 95r. green and red . . 1·20 1·20
O504 1f. purple & turquoise 1·00 1·00
O505 1f.20 brown & turq . . 1·20 1·20
O506 2f. brown and orange 2·50 2·50

1976.
O652 **O 198** 10r. brown and violet 10 10
O653 20r. red and blue . . 10 25
O654 35r. blue and red . . 20 60
O655 40r. violet and green 30 30
O656 50r. green and mauve 35 30
O657 70r. purple and green 45 50
O658 80r. green and purple 50 60
O659 90r. violet and blue 55 60
O660 1f. grey and purple 60 50
O661 1f.10 brown and blue 75 1·20
O662 1f.50 green and red 95 75
O663 2f. orange and blue 1·20 60
O664 5f. purple and orange 8·75 7·50

POSTAGE DUE STAMPS

D 11 D 25 D 58

1920.
D43 D 11 5h. red 20 35
D44 10h. red 20 35
D45 15h. red 20 35
D46 20h. red 20 35
D47 25h. red 20 35
D48 30h. red 20 35
D49 40h. red 20 35
D50 50h. red 20 35
D51 80h. red 20 35
D52 1k. blue 20 35
D53 2k. blue 20 35
D54 5k. blue 20 35

1928.
D84 D 25 5r. red and violet . . . 60 1·90
D85 10r. red and violet . . . 1·20 1·70
D86 15r. red and violet . . . 2·50 10·00
D87 20r. red and violet . . . 2·10 1·90
D88 25r. red and violet . . . 2·10 7·50
D89 30r. red and violet . . . 5·00 9·25
D90 40r. red and violet . . . 6·75 10·50
D91 50r. red and violet . . . 6·75 15·00

1940.
D189 D 58 5r. red and blue . . . 1·20 2·50
D190 10r. red and blue . . . 50 1·00
D191 15r. red and blue . . . 60 5·00
D192 20r. red and blue . . . 75 1·20
D193 25r. red and blue . . . 1·40 2·75
D194 30r. red and blue . . . 2·75 5·00
D195 40r. red and blue . . . 2·75 4·25
D196 50r. red and blue . . . 3·00 5·00

LITHUANIA Pt. 10

A country on the Baltic Sea, under Russian rule until occupied by the Germans in the first World War (see German Eastern Command). It was an independent republic from 1918 to 1940, when it was incorporated into the U.S.S.R.

Lithuania declared its independence in 1990, and the U.S.S.R. formally recognized the republic in 1991.

1918. 100 skatiku = 1 auksinas.
1922. 100 centu = 1 litas.
1990. 100 kopeks = 1 rouble.
1992. Talons.
1993. 100 centu = 1 litas.

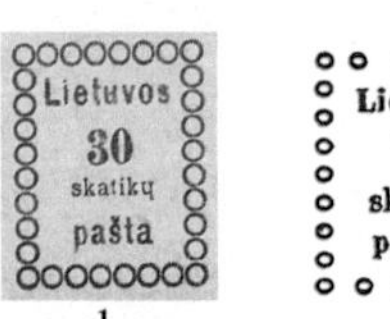

1 2

1918.
3 1 10s. black on buff . . . . . . 40·00 22·00
4 15s. black on buff . . . . . . 35·00 22·00
5 20s. black on buff . . . . . . 4·50 3·25
6 30s. black on buff . . . . . . 4·50 3·25
7 40s. black on buff . . . . . . 12·00 6·00
8 50s. black on buff . . . . . . 4·50 3·25

1919.
9 2 10s. black on buff . . . . . 5·50 1·90
10 15s. black on buff . . . . . 5·50 1·90
11 20s. black on buff . . . . . 5·50 1·90
12 30s. black on buff . . . . . 5·50 1·90

3 4

1919.
13 3 10s. black on buff . . . . . 1·60 1·00
14 15s. black on buff . . . . . 1·60 1·00
15 20s. black on buff . . . . . 1·60 1·00
16 30s. black on buff . . . . . 1·60 1·00
17 40s. black on buff . . . . . 1·60 1·00
18 50s. black on buff . . . . . 1·60 1·00
19 60s. black on buff . . . . . 1·60 1·40

1919.
20 4 10s. black on buff . . . . . 2·00 1·00
21 15s. black on buff . . . . . 2·00 1·00
22 20s. black on buff . . . . . 2·00 1·00
23 30s. black on buff . . . . . 2·00 1·00
24 40s. black on buff . . . . . 2·00 1·50
25 50s. black on buff . . . . . 2·00 1·50
26 60s. black on buff . . . . . 2·00 2·00

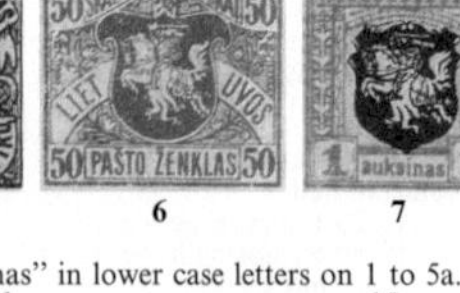

5 Arms 6 7

1919. "auksinas" in lower case letters on 1 to 5a.
40 5 10s. pink 15 15
50 10s. orange 15 10
51 15s. violet 15 10
52 20s. blue 15 10
43 30s. orange 15 15
53 30s. bistre 15 10
54 40s. brown 15 10
55 6 50s. green 15 10
56 60s. red and violet 15 10
57 75s. red and yellow 15 10
37 7 1a. red and grey 35 20
38 3a. red and brown 35 20
39 5a. red and green 40 30

1921. As T 7, but "AUKSINAS" or "AUKSINAI" in capital letters.
58 7 1a. red and grey 15 10
59 3a. red and brown 25 15
60 5a. red and green 40 25

11 Lithuania receiving Independence 12 Lithuania arises

1920. 2nd Anniv of Independence.
65 11 10s. lake . . . . 1·50 2·00
66 15s. lilac . . . . 1·50 2·00
67 20s. blue . . . . 1·50 2·00
68 12 30s. brown . . . . 1·50 2·00
69 – 40s. green and brown . . . 1·50 2·00
70 12 50s. red . . . . 1·50 2·00
71 60s. lilac . . . . 1·50 2·00
72 – 80s. red and violet . . . . . 1·50 2·00
73 – 1a. red and green . . . . . 1·50 2·00
74 – 3a. red and brown . . . . . 1·60 2·00
75 – 5a. red and green . . . . . 1·60 2·00
DESIGNS—VERT: 40s., 80s., 1a. Lithuania with chains broken; 3, 5a. (25 × 25 mm) Arms.

16 Arms 17 Vytautas

1920. National Assembly.
76 16 10s. red 40 30
77 15s. violet 50 40
78 17 20s. green 50 40
79 16 30s. brown 60 50
80 – 40s. violet and green 60 50
81 17 50s. brown and orange . . . 60 50
82 60s. red and orange 60 50
83 – 80s. red, grey and black . . 60 60
84 – 1a. yellow and black 60 60
85 – 3a. green and black 75 70
86 – 5a. violet and black . . . . 2·00 1·75
DESIGNS—As Type 17: 40s., 80s. Gediminas. As Type 16: 1a. to 5a. Sacred Oak and Altar.

20 Sower 21 Kestutis 22 Reaper

23 28 Allegory of Flight

24 Flying Posthorn 25 Junkers F-13 over River Niemen

1921.
87 20 10s. red . . . . 30 1·75
88 15s. mauve . . . . 15 1·00
89 20s. blue 10 10
90 22 30s. brown . . . . 50 4·25
91 21 40s. red 15 10
92 22 50s. olive 10 10
93 60s. mauve and green . . 40 5·00
94 21 80s. red and orange . . . 20 15
95 1a. green and brown . . . 15 10
96 2a. red and blue 15 10
97 23 3a. blue and brown . . . 50 2·00
124 20 4a. blue and yellow . . . 30 75
98 23 5a. red and grey . . . . . 60 3·25
125 20 8a black and green . . . 35 1·00
99 23 10a. mauve and red . . . 75 35
100 25a. green and brown . . 1·40 1·25
101 100a. grey and red . . . 6·00 6·00

1921. Air. Inauguration of Kaunas–Konigsberg Air Service.
102 24 20s. blue 65 55
103 40s. orange 65 55
104 60s. green 75 65
105 80s. red 75 65
106 25 1a. green and red . . . . 2·00 1·25
107 – 2a. brown and blue . . . . 2·00 1·50
108 – 5a. grey and yellow . . . . 2·75 2·75
DESIGNS—As Type 25: 2a. Three Junkers F-13 monoplanes; 5a. Junkers F-13 over Gediminas Castle.

1921. Air. Inauguration of Air Mail Service.
109 28 20s. lilac and orange . . . 90 1·50
110 40s. red and blue . . . . . 90 1·50
111 60s. olive and blue . . . . 1·00 1·60
112 80s. green and yellow . . . 1·00 1·60
113 1a. blue and green . . . . 90 1·60
114 2a. red and grey . . . . . 1·50 1·75
115 5a. green and purple . . . 1·50 1·75

1922. Surch **4 AUKSINAI** with or without frame.
116 6 4a. on 75s. red and yellow 40 40

30 Junkers F-13

1922. Air.
118 30 1a. red and brown . . . . 1·40 2·00
119 3a. green and violet . . . 1·40 2·00
120 5a. yellow and blue . . . . 1·90 2·75

31 Junkers F-13 over Gediminas Castle 33 Pte. Luksis

1922. Air.
121 31 2a. red and blue . . . . . 1·25 1·00
122 4a. red and brown . . . . 1·25 1·00
123 10a. blue and black . . . . 2·00 1·50

1922. "De jure" Recognition of Lithuania by League of Nations. Inscr "LIETUVA DE JURE".
126 33 20s. red and black 50 50
127 – 40s. violet and green . . . 40 40
128 – 50s. blue and purple . . . 40 40
129 – 60s. orange and violet . . 40 40
130 – 1a. blue and red 40 40
131 – 2a. brown and blue 50 50
132 – 3a. blue and brown 50 50
133 – 4a. purple and green . . . 50 50
134 – 5a. red and brown 50 50
135 – 6a. blue 60 50
136 – 8a. yellow and blue 60 50
137 – 10a. green and violet . . . 90 75
DESIGNS—VERT: 40s. Lt. Juozapavicius; 50s. Dr. Basanavicius; 60s. Mrs. Petkevicaite; 1a. Prof. Voldemaras; 2a. Dovidaitis; 3a. Dr. Slezevicius; 4a. Dr. Galvanauskas; 5a. Dr. Grinius; 6a. Dr. Stulginskis; 8a. Pres. Smetona. HORIZ: (39 × 27 mm): 10a. Stauguitis, Pres. Smetona and Silingas.

1922. Surch.
138 5 1c. on 10s. orange (postage) . . . . . . 50 5·00
139 1c. on 15s. violet . . . . 50 5·00
143 1c. on 20s. blue . . . . . 50 4·00
144 1c. on 30s. orange . . . . 40·00 £100
145 1c. on 30s. bistre 20 40
146 1c. on 40s. brown . . . . 50 4·00
148 22 1c. on 50s. olive 10 15
149 6 2c. on 50s. green . . . . . 75 4·00
150 2c. on 60s. red and violet 10 10
151 2c. on 75s. red and yellow 50 5·00
152 20 3c. on 10s. red . . . . . . 1·10 6·00
153 3c. on 15s. mauve 15 15
154 3c. on 20s. blue . . . . . 20 3·00
155 22 3c. on 30s. brown . . . . 90 8·50
156 21 3c. on 40s. red 15 15
157 7 3c. on 1a. (No. 37) . . . 75·00 £120
158 3c. on 1a. (No. 58) . . . 25 1·25
159 3c. on 3a. (No. 38) . . . 60·00 £100
160 3c. on 3a. (No. 59) . . . 10 65
161 3c. on 5a. (No. 39) . . . 32·00 55·00
162 3c. on 5a. (No. 60) . . . 20 80
163 22 5c. on 50s. olive 10 10
164 5c. on 60s. mauve & green 2·75 16·00
165 21 5c. on 80s. red and orange 20 40
166 6 5c. on 4a. on 75s. red and yellow . . . . 50 11·00
168 21 10c. on 1a. green & brown 25 10
169 10c. on 2a. red and blue 10 10
170 20 15c. on 4a. blue and yellow 20 10
171 23 25c. on 3a. blue and green 5·00 24·00
172 25c. on 5a. red and grey 3·00 8·50
173 25c. on 10a. mauve and red . . . . 75 1·60
174 20 30c. on 8a. black and green 25 25
175 23 50c. on 25a. green & brown . . . . 1·10 3·00
176 1l. on 100 a grey and red 2·00 3·25
177 24 10c. on 20s. blue (air) . . . 1·00 3·50
178 10c. on 40s. orange . . . . 1·25 5·00
179 10c. on 60s. green . . . . 1·00 5·00
180 10c. on 80s. red . . . . . 1·25 5·00
181 25 20c. on 1a. green and red 4·75 12·50
182 – 20c. on 2a. (No. 107) . . . 8·00 18·00
183 31 25c. on 2a. red and blue 1·00 85
184 30c. on 4a. red and brown 1·00 80
185 – 50c. on 5a. (No. 108) . . . 1·40 1·25
186 31 50c. on 10a. blue and black 65 1·25
187 30 1l. on 5a. yellow and blue 12·50 27·00

38 Wayside Cross 39 Ruins of Kaunas Castle 40 Seminary Church

1923.
201 38 2c. brown 60 30
202 3c. bistre 85 25
203 5c. green 85 10
204 10c. violet . . . . 1·50 10
189 15c. red . . . . 1·00 10
190 20c. green . . . . 1·00 15
191 25c. blue . . . . 1·00 10
206 36c. brown . . . . 7·50 65
192 39 50c. green . . . . 1·00 10
193 60c. red . . . . 1·10 15
194 40 1l. orange and green . . . 5·50 10
195 3l. red and grey . . . . . 5·50 55
196 5l. brown and blue . . . . 7·00 90

43 Arms of Memel 44 Ruins of Trakai

1923. Union of Memel with Lithuania.
210 43 1c. red and green . . . . 80 1·25
211 – 2c. mauve . . . . 80 1·25
212 – 3c. yellow . . . . 80 1·25
213 43 5c. buff and blue . . . . . 80 1·25
214 – 10c. red . . . . 1·50 1·50
215 – 15c. green . . . . 1·50 1·50
216 44 25c. violet . . . . 2·00 1·75
217 – 30c. red . . . . 2·00 2·50
218 – 60c. green . . . . 4·50 4·75
219 – 1l. green . . . . 3·00 3·00
220 – 2l. red . . . . 5·00 6·00
221 44 3l. blue . . . . 5·50 7·00
222 – 5l. blue . . . . 13·50 14·50
DESIGNS—As Type 43: 3c., 2l. Chapel of Biruta; 10c., 15c. War Memorial Kaunas; As Type 44: 2, 30c. Arms of Lithuania; 60c., 5l. Memel Lighthouse; 1l. Memel Harbour.

45 Biplane

46 Biplane

1924. Air.
223 45 20c. yellow . . . . 1·40 70
224 40c. green . . . . 1·40 70
225 60c. red . . . . 1·50 75
226 46 1l. brown . . . . 3·25 65

1924. Charity. War Orphans Fund. Surch **KARO NASLAICIAMS** and premium.
227 38 2c.+2c. bistre (postage) . . 1·00 1·50
228 3c.+3c. bistre . . . . . . 1·00 1·50
229 5c.+5c. green . . . . . . 1·00 1·50
231 10c.+10c. violet . . . . . 1·00 2·50
232 15c.+15c. red . . . . . . 1·00 2·50
233 20c.+20c. olive . . . . . 2·00 3·00
235 25c.+25c. blue . . . . . . 4·00 7·00
236 36c.+34c. brown . . . . . 6·00 9·00
237 39 50c.+50c. green . . . . . 6·00 9·00
238 60c.+60c. red . . . . . . 7·50 12·00
239 40 1l.+1l. orange and green 7·50 12·00
240 3l.+2l. red and grey . . . 12·00 16·00
241 5l.+3l. brown and blue . . 18·00 25·00

242 **45** 20c.+20c. yellow (air) . . . 8·00 10·00
243 40c.+40c. green . . . . . 8·00 10·00
244 60c.+60c. red . . . . . . 8·00 10·00
245 **46** 1l.+1l. brown . . . . . . 12·00 14·00

49 Barn Swallow carrying Letter **56** **57**

1926. Air.
246 **49** 20c. red . . . . 1·25 55
247 40c. orange and mauve . . 1·25 55
248 60c. black and blue . . . . 2·75 65

1926. Charity. War Invalids. Nos. 227/39 surch with new values and small ornaments.
249 **38** 1c.+1c. on 2c.+2c. . . . . 1·00 1·25
250 2c.+2c. on 3c.+3c. . . . . 1·00 1·25
251 2c.+2c. on 5c.+5c. . . . . 1·00 1·25
253 5c.+5c. on 10c.+10c. . . . 1·75 2·00
254 5c.+5c. on 15c.+15c. . . . 1·75 2·00
255 10c.+10c. on 20c.+20c. . . 1·75 2·00
257 10c.+10c. on 25c.+25c. . . 4·00 5·00
258 14c.+14c. on 36c.+34c. . . 6·00 7·00
259 **39** 20c.+20c. on 50c.+50c. . . 4·00 5·00
260 25c.+25c. on 60c.+60c. . . 6·00 9·00
261 **40** 30c.+30c. on 1l.+1l. . . . 10·00 15·00

1926. Charity. War Orphans. Nos. 227/39 surch **V.P.** and new values in circular ornament.
262 **38** 1c.+1c. on 2c.+2c. . . . . 1·00 1·25
263 2c.+2c. on 3c.+3c. . . . . 1·00 1·25
264 2c.+2c. on 5c.+5c. . . . . 1·00 1·25
266 5c.+5c. on 10c.+10c. . . . 2·00 2·50
267 10c.+10c. on 15c.+15c. . . 2·00 2·50
268 15c.+15c. on 20c.+20c. . . 2·50 2·50
270 15c.+15c. on 25c.+25c. . . 5·00 5·00
271 19c.+19c. on 36c.+34c. . . 5·00 6·00
272 **39** 25c.+25c. on 50c.+50c. . . 6·00 7·50
273 30c.+30c. on 60c.+60c. . . 9·00 12·00
274 **40** 50c.+50c. on 1l.+1l. . . . 12·00 18·00

1927.
275 **56** 2c. orange 75 10
276 3c. brown 75 10
277 5c. green . . . . 1·00 10
278 10c. violet . . . . 2·00 10
279 15c. red . . . . 1·75 10
280 25c. blue . . . . 1·75 10
283 30c. blue . . . . 12·00 1·00

1927. Dr. Basanavicius Mourning Issue.
285 **57** 15c. red . . . . 90 1·00
286 25c. blue . . . . 90 1·00
287 50c. green . . . . 1·10 1·00
288 60c. violet . . . . 2·00 2·75

58 "Vytis" of the Lithuanian Arms

1927.
289 **58** 1l. green and grey . . . . 1·25 50
290 3l. violet and green . . . . 3·25 50
291 5l. brown and grey . . . . 5·00 1·25

59 President Antanas Smetona **60** Lithuania liberated

1928. 10th Anniv of Independence.
292 **59** 5c. green and brown . . . 25 10
293 10c. black and violet . . . 25 10
294 15c. brown and orange . . 30 10
295 25c. slate and blue 65 10
296 **60** 50c. purple and blue . . . 85 20
297 60c. black and red . . . . 1·10 45
298 – 1l. brown . . . . 1·75 90
DESIGN—HORIZ: 1l. Lithuania's resurrection (angel and soldiers). Dated "1918-1928".

62

63

64 J. Tubelis **66** Railway Station, Kaunas

1930. 500th Death Anniv of Grand Duke Vytautas.
299 **62** 2c. brown (postage) . . . 25 10
300 3c. violet and brown . . . 25 10
301 5c. red and green 25 10
302 10c. green and violet . . . 25 10
303 15c. violet and red 25 10
304 30c. purple and blue . . . 25 10
305 36c. olive and purple . . . 35 15
306 50c. blue and green 35 20
307 60c. red and blue 60 10
308 **63** 1l. purple, grey and green 1·50 40
309 3l. violet, pink and mauve 3·25 1·25
310 5l. red, grey and brown . . 4·00 1·75
311 10l. black and blue . . . . 13·00 18·00
312 25l. green and brown . . . 35·00 48·00
313 **64** 5c. brown, yellow and black (air) 35 35
314 10c. black, drab and blue 40 40
315 15c. blue, grey and purple 40 40
316 – 20c. red, orange and brown 1·00 55
317 – 40c. violet, light blue & blue . . . . 1·40 80
318 – 60c. black, lilac and green 1·60 1·40
319 – 1l. black, lilac and red . . 3·00 1·50
DESIGNS—HORIZ: 20c., 40c. Vytautas and Kaunas; 60c., 1l. Vytautas and Smetona.

1932. Orphans' Fund. Imperf or perf.
320 **66** 5c. blue and brown . . . . 1·00 1·00
321 10c. purple and brown . . 1·00 1·00
322 – 15c. brown and green . . . 30 30
323 – 25c. blue and green 45 50
324 – 50c. grey and olive . . . . 70 1·25
325 – 60c. grey and mauve . . . 1·00 4·25
326 – 1l. blue and grey . . . . . 2·50 3·25
327 – 3l. purple and green . . . 4·50 5·00
DESIGNS—As Type **66**: 15, 25c. "The Two Pines" (painting); 50c. G.P.O. VERT: 60c., 1, 3l. Vilnius Cathedral.

68 Map of Lithuania, Memel and Vilna

1932. Air. Orphans' Fund. Imperf or perf.
328 **68** 5c. red and green 25 25
329 10c. purple and brown . . 25 25
330 – 15c. blue and buff 40 40
331 – 20c. black and brown . . . 2·40 2·00
332 – 40c. purple and yellow . . 2·00 2·50
333 – 60c. blue and buff . . . . 3·00 5·50
334 – 1l. purple and green . . . 3·50 5·50
335 – 2l. blue and green . . . . 3·75 5·50
DESIGNS: 15, 20c. Airplane over R. Niemen; 40, 60c. Town Hall, Kaunas; 1, 2l. Vytautas Church, Kaunas.

69 Vytautas escapes from Prison

71 Coronation of Mindaugas

1932. 15th Anniv of Independence. Imperf or perf.
336 **69** 5c. purple and red (postage) 50 50
337 10c. brown and grey . . . 50 50
338 – 15c. green and red 50 50
339 – 25c. brown and purple . . 75 1·25
340 – 50c. brown and green . . . 1·00 1·25
341 – 60c. red and green . . . . 2·50 5·00
342 – 1l. black and blue . . . . 3·25 3·25
343 – 3l. green and purple . . . 3·50 5·50
344 – 5c. lilac and green (air) . . 15 20
345 – 10c. red and green 15 25
346 **71** 15c. brown and violet . . . 20 30
347 – 20c. black and red 45 45
348 – 40c. black and purple . . . 65 1·25
349 – 60c. black and orange . . 1·90 6·00
350 – 1l. green and violet . . . . 3·00 3·50
351 – 2l. brown and blue . . . . 3·25 4·00
DESIGNS—POSTAGE. As Type **69**: 15, 25c. Vytautas and Jagello preaching the gospel; 50, 60c. Battle of Grunewald; 1, 3l. Proclamation of Independence. AIR. As Type **71**: 5, 10c. Battle of Saules; 40c. Gediminas in Council; 60c. Founding of Vilnius; 1l. Russians surrendering to Gediminas; 2l. Algirdas before Moscow.

72 A. Visteliauskas

1933. 50th Anniv of Publication of "Ausra".
352 **72** 5c. red and green 20 25
353 10c. red and blue 20 25
354 – 15c. red and orange . . . 20 25
355 – 25c. brown and blue . . . 55 75
356 – 50c. blue and green . . . . 65 1·00
357 – 60c. deep brown & lt brown . . . . 2·00 5·00
358 – 1l. purple and red . . . . 2·50 3·75
359 – 3l. purple and blue . . . . 3·50 6·00
PORTRAITS: 15, 25c. P. Vileisis; 50, 60c. J. Sliupas; 1, 3l. J. Basanavicius.

73 Trakai Castle

1933. Air. 550th Death Anniv of Grand Duke Kestutis.
360 **73** 5c. blue and green 20 35
361 10c. brown and violet . . . 20 35
362 – 15c. violet and blue 20 35
363 – 20c. purple and brown . . 55 80
364 – 40c. purple and blue . . . 90 1·60
365 – 60c. blue and red . . . . 2·25 7·00
366 – 1l. blue and green . . . . 3·00 4·50
367 – 2l. green and violet . . . . 3·75 9·00
DESIGNS: 15, 20c. Kestutis encounters Birute; 40, 60c. Birute; 1, 2l. Kestutis and Algirdas.

74 Mother and Child

75 J. Tumas Vaizgantas

1933. Child Welfare. (a) Postage.
373 **74** 5c. brown and green . . . 15 20
374 10c. blue and red 15 20
375 – 15c. purple and green . . . 20 25
376 – 25c. black and orange . . 40 75
377 – 50c. red and green . . . . 55 1·00
378 – 60c. orange and black . . 1·90 4·50
379 – 1l. blue and brown . . . . 2·50 3·50
380 – 3l. green and purple . . . 3·50 6·00
DESIGNS—VERT: 15, 25c. Boy reading a book; 50, 60c. Boy with building bricks; 1, 3l. Mother and child weaving.

(b) Air. Various medallion portraits in triangular frames.
381 – 5c. blue and red 15 15
382 – 10c. green and violet . . . 15 15
383 **75** 15c. brown and green . . . 15 15
384 20c. blue and red 25 35
385 – 40c. green and lake . . . . 85 1·25
386 – 60c. brown and blue . . . 1·75 3·25
387 – 1l. blue and yellow . . . . 1·90 2·75
388 – 2l. lake and green . . . . 3·25 4·00
DESIGNS: 5, 10c. Maironis; 40, 60c. Vincas Kudirka; 1, 2l. Zemaite.

76 Captains S. Darius and S. Girenas

78 "Flight" mourning over Wreckage

81 President A. Smetona

1934. Air. Death of Darius and Girenas (trans-Atlantic airmen).
389 **76** 20c. red and black 10 10
390 – 40c. blue and red 10 10
391 **76** 60c. violet and black . . . 10 10
392 **78** 1l. black and red 35 15
393 – 3l. orange and green . . . 1·00 2·00
394 – 5l. blue and brown . . . . 4·00 4·25
DESIGNS—HORIZ: 40c. Bellanca monoplane "Lituanica" over Atlantic. VERT: 3l. "Lituanica" and globe; 5l. "Lituanica" and Vytis.

1934. President's 60th Birthday.
395 **81** 15c. red . . . . 3·00 10
396 30c. green . . . . 5·00 15
397 60c. blue . . . . 10·00 30

82

83

84 Gleaner

85

1934.
398 **82** 2c. red and orange 25 10
399 5c. green 30 10
400 **83** 10c. brown 75 10
401 **84** 25c. brown and green . . . 2·00 10
402 **83** 35c. red . . . . 2·00 10
403 **84** 50c. blue . . . . 3·50 10
404 **85** 1l. purple and red . . . . 18·00 10
405 3l. green 20 10
406 – 5l. purple and blue 20 20
407 – 10l. brown and yellow . . 1·25 1·25
DESIGNS—HORIZ: as Type **85**: 5l., 10l. Knight.
For design as Type **82** but smaller, see Nos. 411/12.

1935. Air. Honouring Atlantic Flyer Vaitkus. No. 390 optd **F. VAITKUS nugalejo Atlanta 21-22-IX-1935**.
407a 40c. blue and red £190 £300

87 Vaitkus and Air Route

88 President Smetona

1936. Air. Felix Vaitkus's New York–Ireland Flight.
408 **87** 15c. purple . . . . 1·40 45
409 30c. green . . . . 1·60 1·10
410 60c. blue . . . . 2·50 1·10

1936. As T **82** but smaller (18 × 23 mm).
411 **82** 2c. orange 10 10
412 5c. green 10 10

1936.
413 **88** 15c. red . . . . 4·00 10
414 30c. green . . . . 9·00 10
415 60c. blue . . . . 7·50 10

89

90 Archer

1937.
416 **89** 10c. green . . . . 1·10 10
417 25c. mauve 10 10
418 35c. red 60 10
419 50c. brown 30 10
419a 1l. blue 15 30

1938. 1st National Olympiad Fund.
420 **90** 5c.+5c. green . . . . . . 7·00 9·00
421 – 15c.+5c. red . . . . 9·00 10·00

422 – 30c.+10c. blue . . . . . . 12·00 14·00
423 – 60c.+15c. brown . . . . . 18·00 20·00
DESIGNS: 15c. Throwing the javelin; 30c. Diving; 60c. Relay runner breasting tape.

1938. Scouts' and Guides' National Camp Fund. Nos. 420/3 optd **TAUTINE SKAUCIU** (or **SKAUTU**) **STOVYKLA** and badge.
424 **90** 5c.+5c. green . . . . . . 7·00 8·50
425 – 15c.+5c. red . . . . 9·00 9·50
426 – 30c.+10c. blue . . . . . . 12·00 14·00
427 – 60c.+15c. brown . . . . . 17·00 19·00

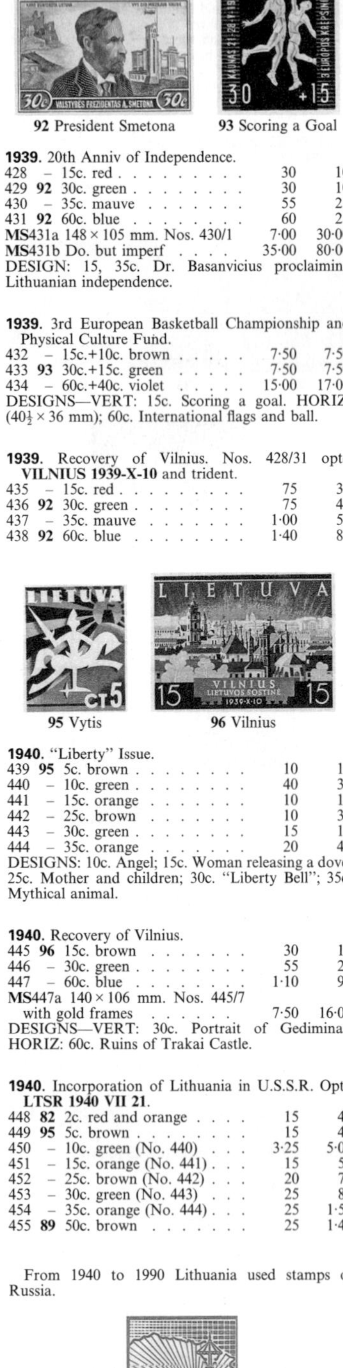

92 President Smetona **93** Scoring a Goal

1939. 20th Anniv of Independence.
428 – 15c. red 30 10
429 **92** 30c. green 30 10
430 – 35c. mauve 55 25
431 **92** 60c. blue 60 25
MS431a 148 × 105 mm. Nos. 430/1 7·00 30·00
MS431b Do. but imperf . . . . 35·00 80·00
DESIGN: 15, 35c. Dr. Basanvicius proclaiming Lithuanian independence.

1939. 3rd European Basketball Championship and Physical Culture Fund.
432 – 15c.+10c. brown . . . . . 7·50 7·50
433 **93** 30c.+15c. green . . . . . 7·50 7·50
434 – 60c.+40c. violet . . . . . 15·00 17·00
DESIGNS—VERT: 15c. Scoring a goal. HORIZ: (40½ × 36 mm); 60c. International flags and ball.

1939. Recovery of Vilnius. Nos. 428/31 optd **VILNIUS 1939-X-10** and trident.
435 – 15c. red 75 30
436 **92** 30c. green 75 40
437 – 35c. mauve . . . . 1·00 55
438 **92** 60c. blue . . . . 1·40 85

95 Vytis **96** Vilnius

1940. "Liberty" Issue.
439 **95** 5c. brown 10 10
440 – 10c. green 40 30
441 – 15c. orange 10 10
442 – 25c. brown 10 30
443 – 30c. green 15 10
444 – 35c. orange 20 45
DESIGNS: 10c. Angel; 15c. Woman releasing a dove; 25c. Mother and children; 30c. "Liberty Bell"; 35c. Mythical animal.

1940. Recovery of Vilnius.
445 **96** 15c. brown 30 15
446 – 30c. green 55 25
447 – 60c. blue . . . . 1·10 90
MS447a 140 × 106 mm. Nos. 445/7 with gold frames . . . . . . 7·50 16·00
DESIGNS—VERT: 30c. Portrait of Gediminas. HORIZ: 60c. Ruins of Trakai Castle.

1940. Incorporation of Lithuania in U.S.S.R. Optd **LTSR 1940 VII 21**.
448 **82** 2c. red and orange 15 40
449 **95** 5c. brown 15 40
450 – 10c. green (No. 440) . . . 3·25 5·00
451 – 15c. orange (No. 441) . . . 15 50
452 – 25c. brown (No. 442) . . . 20 75
453 – 30c. green (No. 443) . . . 25 80
454 – 35c. orange (No. 444) . . . 25 1·50
455 **89** 50c. brown . . . . 25 1·40

From 1940 to 1990 Lithuania used stamps of Russia.

99 Angel and Map

1990. No gum. Imperf.
456 **99** 5k. green 10 10
457 10k. lilac 10 10
458 20k. blue 20 10
459 50k. red 75 40

1990. No gum. Imperf (simulated perfs).
460 **99** 5k. green and brown . . . 10 10
461 10k. purple and brown . . . 10 10
462 20k. blue and brown . . . 30 20
463 50k. red and brown . . . 90 45

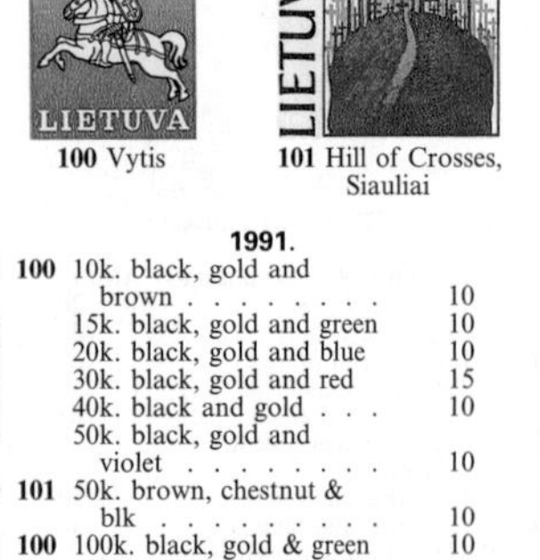

100 Vytis **101** Hill of Crosses, Siauliai

1991.
464 **100** 10k. black, gold and brown 10 10
465 15k. black, gold and green 10 10
466 20k. black, gold and blue 10 10
467 30k. black, gold and red 15 10
468 40k. black and gold . . . 10 10
469 50k. black, gold and violet 10 10
470 **101** 50k. brown, chestnut & blk 10 10
471 **100** 100k. black, gold & green 10 10
472 – 200k. brown, chest & blk 80 40
473 **100** 500k. black, gold and blue 40 20
DESIGN: As T **101**—200k. Lithuanian Liberty Bell.
See also Nos. 482 and 488/9.

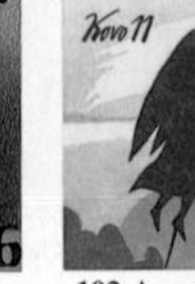

102 Liberty Statue, Kaunas **103** Angel with Trumpet

1991. National Day.
480 **102** 20k. mauve, silver & black 15 10

1991. 1st Anniv of Declaration of Independence from U.S.S.R.
481 **103** 20k. deep green and green 15 10

1991. No gum. Imperf (simulated perfs).
482 **100** 15k. green and black . . 10 10

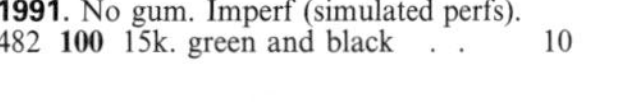

104 Wayside Crosses

1991.
483 **104** 40k. green and silver . . . 15 10
484 – 70k. brown, buff and gold 30 15
485 – 100k. brown, yellow & sil 45 20
DESIGNS: 70k. "Madonna" (icon from Pointed Gate Chapel, Vilnius); 100k. Towers of St. Anne's Church, Vilnius.

105 Candle

1991. 50th Anniv of Resistance to Soviet and German Occupations.
486 **105** 20k. yellow, black & bistre 10 10
487 – 50k. rose, black and red 25 10
488 – 70k. multicoloured . . . 35 15
DESIGNS: 50k. Shield pierced by swords; 70k. Sword and wreath.

1991. No gum. Imperf.
489 **100** 25k. black and brown . . 10 10
490 30k. black and purple . . 15 10

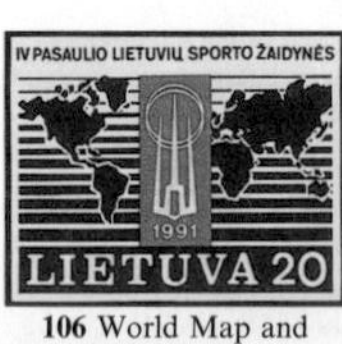

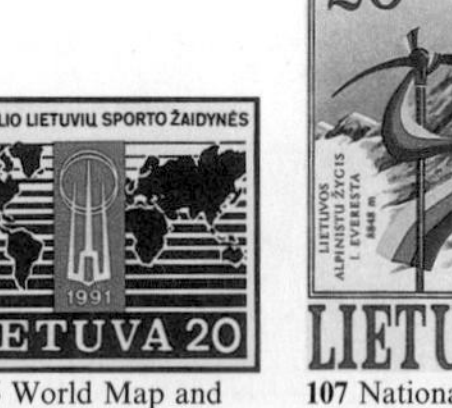

106 World Map and Games Emblem **107** National Flag in Ice-axe and Mt. Everest

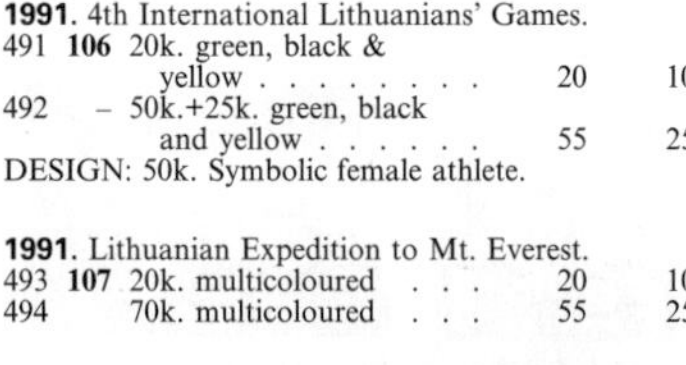

1991. 4th International Lithuanians' Games.
491 **106** 20k. green, black & yellow 20 10
492 – 50k.+25k. green, black and yellow 55 25
DESIGN: 50k. Symbolic female athlete.

1991. Lithuanian Expedition to Mt. Everest.
493 **107** 20k. multicoloured . . . 20 10
494 70k. multicoloured . . . 55 25

108 Trakai Castle **109** Black Storks

1991. 650th Death Anniv of Grand Duke Gediminas. Each brown, ochre and green.
495 30k. Type **108** 15 10
496 50k. Gediminas 25 15
497 70k. Vilnius in 14th century 40 20

1991. Birds in the Red Book. Multicoloured.
498 30k.+15k. Type **109** . . . . 1·10 75
499 50k. Common cranes . . . . 1·40 90

110 U.N. and National Emblems and National Flag **111** National Team Emblem and Colours

1992. Admission to U.N.O.
500 **110** 100k. multicoloured . . . 15 10

1992. Winter Olympic Games, Albertville, and Summer Games, Barcelona. Multicoloured.
501 50k.+25k. Type **111** 15 10
502 130k. Winter Games emblem 30 15
503 280k. Summer Games emblem 55 25

112 Slipper Orchid **113** Goosander ("Mergus merganser")

1992. Plants in the Red Book. Multicoloured.
504 200k. Type **112** 30 15
505 300k. Sea holly 50 25

1992. Birds of the Baltic. No value expressed.
506 **113** B (15t.) black and green 70 45
507 – B (15t.) brown, blk & grn 70 45
508 – B (15t.) sepia, brown & grn 70 45
509 – B (15t.) brown, blk & grn 70 45
DESIGNS: No. 506, Osprey ("Pandion haliaetus"); 507, Black-tailed godwit ("Limosa limosa"); 509, Common shelduck ("Tadorna tadorna").

114 Kedainiai **115** Couple

1992. Arms. Multicoloured.
510 2t. Type **114** 10 10
511 3t. Vilnius 10 10
512 10t. State arms 30 15
See also Nos. 531/3, 569/71, 594/5, 628/30, 663/5, 682/4, 712/14, 742/4, 769/71 and 781/3.

1992. Costumes of Suvalkija.
513 **115** 2t. multicoloured 15 10
514 – 5t. multicoloured 30 15
515 – 7t. multicoloured 45 20
DESIGNS: 5, 7t. Different costumes.

116 Zapyskis Church

1993. Churches.
516 **116** 3t. black and stone . . . 10 10
517 – 10t. black and blue . . . 25 10
518 – 15t. black and grey . . . 40 20
DESIGNS: 10t. Church of St. Peter and St. Paul, Vilnius; 15t. Church of the Resurrection, Kaunas.

1993. Nos. 467, 490 and 468 surch.
519 **100** 1t. on 30k. blk, gold & red 10 10
520 1t. on 30k. black & purple 10 10
521 3t. on 40k. black and gold 15 10

118 Jonas Basanavicius (statesman)

1993. National Day. No value expressed.
522 **118** A (3t.) red, cinn & brn . . 10 10
523 – B (15t.) grn, stone & brn 55 25
DESIGN: No. 523, Jonas Vileisis (politician).

119 Vytautas **120** Simonas Daukantas (historian)

1993. 600th Anniv (1987) of Accession of Grand Duke Vytautas.
524 – 5t. gold, red and black . . 10 10
525 **119** 10t. green, black and red 25 10
526 – 15t. black, yellow and red 40 20
MS527 80 × 120 mm. 50t. olive, black and red . . . . 1·10 70
DESIGNS: 5t. Seal; 15t. "Battle of Grunwald" (Jan Matejka) 50t. Type **119**.

1993. Birth Anniversaries. Each brown and yellow.
528 10t. Type **120** (bicent) 15 10
529 20t. Vydunas (125th anniv) 35 20
530 45t. Vincas Mykolaitis-Putinas (philosopher, centenary) 80 40

1993. Town Arms. As T **114**. Multicoloured.
531 5c. Skuodas 10 10
532 30c. Telsiai 20 10
533 50c. Klaipeda 35 15

121 "Watchtower" (M. K. Ciurlionis) **122** State Arms

1993. World Unity Day (5c.) and Transatlantic Flight (80c.). Multicoloured.
534 5c. Type **121** 10 10
535 80c. Steponas Dariaus and Stasys Gireno 50 25

1993. No value expressed.
536 **122** A, green, brown and red 10 10
537 B, red, green and bistre 35 20

123 Pope John Paul II and View of Siluva **124** Couple

1993. Papal Visit. Multicoloured.
538 60c. Type **123** 35 20
539 60c. Pope and Hill of Crosses 35 20

540 80c. Pope and Kaunas . . . 50 25
541 80c. Pope and Ausra Gates, Vilnius 50 25

1993. Costumes of Dzukai.
542 **124** 60c. multicoloured 25 10
543 – 80c. multicoloured 40 20
544 – 1l. multicoloured 55 25
DESIGNS: 80c. to 1l. Different costumes.

125 Klaipeda Post Office

1993. 75th Anniv of First Lithuanian Postage Stamps.
545 **125** 60c. multicoloured 35 15
546 – 60c. multicoloured 30 15
547 – 80c. multicoloured 50 25
548 – 1l. black, brown and green 60 30
DESIGNS: No. 546, Kaunas post office; 547, Ministry for Post and Information, Vilnius; 548, First Lithuanian stamp.

126 "The Ladle Carver" (A. Gudaitis) **127** European Pond Turtle

1993. Europa. Contemporary Art.
549 **126** 80c. multicoloured 45 25

1993. Pond Life. Multicoloured.
550 80c. Type **127** 40 20
551 1l. Running toad 45 25

128 Games Emblem and Team Colours **130** Kristijonas Donelaitis

129 Antanas Smetona (President 1919–22 and 1926–40)

1994. Winter Olympic Games, Lillehammer, Norway.
552 **128** 1l.10 multicoloured . . . 45 20

1994. National Day.
553 **129** 1l. red and black 30 15
554 – 1l. brown and black . . . 30 15
DESIGN: No. 554, Aleksandras Stulginskis (President 1922–26).

1994. Writers. Each cream, brown and orange.
555 60c. Type **130** 25 10
556 80c. Vincas Kudirka 35 15
557 1l. Jonas Maciulis Maironis 45 20

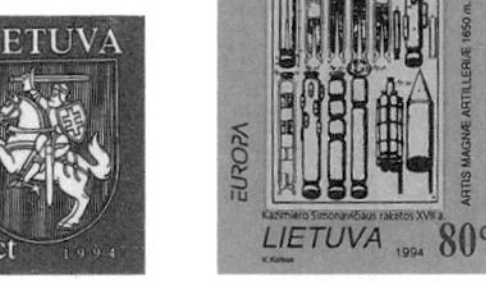

131 State Arms **132** Rockets by Kazimieras Simonavicius (illus from "Artis Magnae Artilleriae")

1994.
558 **131** 5c. brown 10 10
559 10c. lilac 10 10
560 20c. green 10 10
612 40c. purple 15 10
613 50c. blue 20 10

1994. Europa. Inventions and Discoveries.
561 **132** 80c. multicoloured 45 20

1994. 100th Postage Stamp. Sheet 80 × 62 mm.
MS562 **99** 10l. green and red (sold at 12l.) . . . . 4·75 4·75

133 Couple **134** Music Note, Globe and Flag

1994. 19th-century Costumes of Zemaiciai (Lowlands).
563 **133** 5c. multicoloured 10 10
564 – 80c. multicoloured 35 15
565 – 1l. multicoloured 45 20
DESIGNS: 80c., 1l., Different costumes from Zemaiciai.

1994. Lithuanians of the World Song Festival.
566 **134** 10c. multicoloured 10 10

135 State Arms **136** Common Bat

1994.
567 **135** 2l. multicoloured 80 40
568 3l. multicoloured . . . . 1·25 60
See also **MS**580.

1994. Town Arms. As T **114** but size 25 × 32 mm. Multicoloured.
569 10c. Punia 10 10
570 60c. Alytus 25 10
571 80c. Perloja 35 15

1994. Mammals. Multicoloured.
572 20c. Type **136** 15 10
573 20c. Fat dormouse 15 10

137 Kaunas Town Hall

1994. Town Halls.
574 **137** 10c. black and mauve . . 10 10
575 – 60c. black and blue . . . 25 10
576 – 80c. black and green . . . 35 15
DESIGNS: 60c. Kedainiai; 80c. Vilnius.

138 Madonna and Child

1994. Christmas.
577 **138** 20c. multicoloured 15 10

139 Steponas Kairys

1995. National Day. Signatories to 1918 Declaration of Independence.
578 **139** 20c. lilac, grey and black 10 10
579 – 20c. blue, grey and black 10 10
DESIGN: No. 579, Pranas Dovydaitis (Head of Government, March–April 1919).

1995. 5th Anniv of Independence. Sheet 75 × 105 mm.
MS580 **135** 4 × 1l. multicoloured 1·90 1·90

140 Kaunas (Lithuania) **141** "Lithuanian School, 1864–1904" (P. Rimsa)

1995. Via Baltica Motorway Project. Multicoloured.
581 20c. Type **140** 10 10
MS582 100 × 110 mm. 1l. Beach Hotel, Parnu (Estonia); 1l. Bauska Castle (Latvia); 1l. Type **140** 1·50 1·50

1995. Europa. Peace and Freedom.
583 **141** 1l. multicoloured 40 20

142 Couple **143** Motiejus Valancius (120th death)

1995. Costumes of the Highlands.
584 – 20c. multicoloured 10 10
585 – 70c. multicoloured 25 15
586 **142** 1l. multicoloured 40 20
DESIGNS: 70c. to 1l. Different 19th-century costumes.

1995. Anniversaries.
587 **143** 30c. cream, pur & yell . . 10 10
588 – 40c. cream, grn & orge . . 20 10
589 – 70c. cream, dp bl & pink 30 15
DESIGNS: 40c. Zemaite (150th birth); 70c. Kipras Petrauskas (110th birth).

144 Pieta **145** Torch-bearer

1995. Day of Mourning and Hope.
590 **144** 20c. multicoloured 10 10

1995. 5th World Lithuanians Games.
591 **145** 30c. multicoloured 15 10

146 "Baptria tibiale" **147** "Valerija Mesalina"

1995. Butterflies and Moths in "The Red Book". Multicoloured.
592 30c. Type **146** 20 10
593 30c. Cream-spot tiger moth ("Arctia villica") 20 10

1995. Town Arms. As T **114**. Multicoloured.
594 40c. Virbalis 20 10
595 1l. Kudirkos Naumiestis (horiz) 40 20

1995. 250th Birth Anniv of Pranciskus Smuglevicius (painter).
596 **147** 40c. multicoloured 20 10

148 Trakai Island Castle

1995. Castles.
597 – 40c. multicoloured 15 10
598 **148** 70c. blue, dp blue & black 30 15
599 – 1l. multicoloured 35 20
DESIGNS: 40c. Vilnius Upper Castle; 1l. Birzai Castle.

149 Star over Winter Scene **150** Bison

1995. Christmas. Multicoloured.
600 40c. Type **149** 20 10
601 1l. Churchgoers with lanterns 40 20

1996. The European Bison. Multicoloured.
602 30c. Type **150** 10 10
603 40c. Pair of bison 15 10
604 70c. Adult and calf 25 10
605 1l. Parents and calf 30 15

151 Kazys Grinius (130th)

1996. Birth Anniversaries.
606 **151** 40c. cream, brown & blue 15 10
607 – 1l. cream, bistre & yellow 40 20
608 – 1l. cream, blue and red 40 20
DESIGNS: No. 607, Antanas Zmuidzinavicius (120th); 608, Balys Sruoga (centenary).

152 Vladas Mironas

1996. National Day. Signatories to 1918 Declaration of Independence.
609 **152** 40c. cream, grey and black 15 10
610 – 40c. bistre, brown and black 15 10
DESIGN: No. 610, Jurgis Saulys.

153 Barbora Radvilaite **154** Couple

1996. Europa. Famous Women
611 **153** 1l. multicoloured 30 15

1996. Costumes of Klaipeda. 19th-century costumes. Multicoloured.
618 40c. Type **154** 15 10
619 1l. Woman in red skirt and man in frock-coat 45 20
620 1l. Woman in black skirt and man in blue waistcoat . . 45 20

155 Angel **156** "The Discus Thrower"

1996. Day of Mourning and Hope.
621 **155** 40c. blue, red and black 20 10
622 – 40c. green, red and black 20 10
DESIGN: No. 622, Head of crucifix.

1996. Olympic Games, Atlanta. Multicoloured.
623 1l. Type **156** 35 15
624 1l. Basketball 35 15

157 “Sacrifice”  **158** Players

1996. 85th Death Anniv of Mikolajus Ciurlionis (artist). Multicoloured.
625 40c. Type **157** 15 10
626 40c. “Cemetery” 15 10
MS627 80 × 102 mm. 3l. “Sonata of the Andante” (25 × 36 mm); 3l. “Sonata of the Stars—Allegro” (25 × 36 mm)

1996. Town Arms. As T **114** but size 25 × 32 mm.
628 50c. multicoloured 20 10
629 90c. red, black and yellow 40 20
630 1l.20 multicoloured 50 25
DESIGN: 50c. Seduva; 90c. Panevezys; 1l.20, Zarasai.

1996. Lithuanian Basketball Team, Bronze Medallist, Olympic Games, Atlanta. Sheet 50 × 72 mm.
MS631 **158** 4l.20 multicoloured 1·40 1·40

159 Angels heralding

1996. Christmas. Multicoloured.
632 50c. Type **159** 20 10
633 1l.20 Elf riding on “Pegasus” 40 20

160 Ieva Simonaityte (writer, birth centenary) 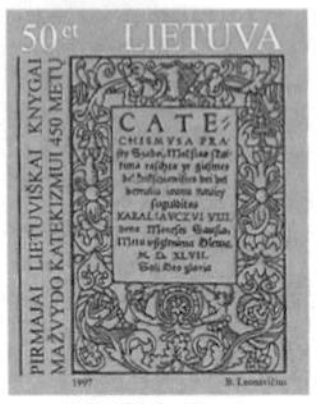 **161** Title Page

1997. Anniversaries.
634 **160** 50c. stone, brown and green 15 10
635 – 90c. stone, grey and yellow 35 20
636 – 1l.20 stone, grn & orge 40 20
MS638 94 × 56 mm. **161** 4l.80 brown and grey (26 × 36 mm) 1·90 1·25
DESIGNS: 90c. Jonas Sliupas (physician, 53rd death); 1l.20, Vladas Jurgutis (financier, 31st death).

1997. 450th Anniv of Publication of “Catechism of Mazvydas” (first Lithuanian book).
637 **161** 50c. brown and grey 20 10

162 Mykolas Birziska

1997. National Day. Signatories to 1918 Declaration of Independence.
639 **162** 50c. green, lt grn & blk 20 10
640 – 50c. purple, stone and black 20 10
DESIGN: No. 640, Kazimieras Saulys.

163 Flag on Mountain Peak

1997. Completion of Ascent of World's Highest Mountains by Vladas Vitauskas. Sheet 80 × 60 mm.
MS641 **163** 4l.80 multicoloured 1·90 1·25

164 “Little Witch” (Jovita Jankeviciute)  **165** Lecture

1997. Europa. Tales and Legends. Multicoloured.
642 1l.20 Type **164** 45 20
643 1l.20 “Rainbow” (Ieva Staseviciute) (horiz) 45 20

1997. 600th Anniv of First Lithuanian School.
644 **165** 50c. multicoloured 20 10

166 Kurshes Ship

1997. Baltic Sailing Ships. Multicoloured.
645 50c. Type **166** 20 10
MS646 110 × 70 mm. 1l.20 Kushes ship (as in T **166** but with frame etc); 1l.20 Maasilinn ship (Estonia); 1l.20 *Wappen der Herzogin von Kurland* (galleon) (Estonia) 1·50 1·50

167 Park

1997. Centenary of Palanga Botanical Park.
647 **167** 50c. yellow, black and brown 20 10

168 Ship of Flags 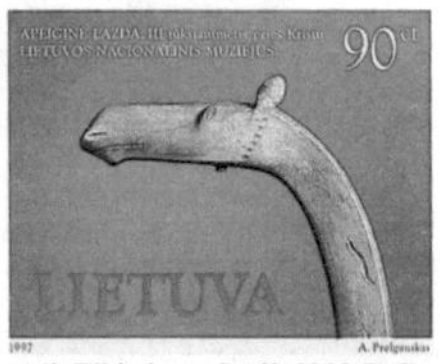 **169** Elk's-horn Staff, 3000 B.C.

1997. 2nd Baltic Sea Games, Lithuania.
648 **168** 90c. multicoloured 35 15

1997. Museum Exhibits. Multicoloured.
649 90c. Type **169** 35 15
650 1l.20 Silver coins of Grand Duke Kazimierz IV, 15th century A.D. 45 20

170 Vytis's Cross  **171** Black Morel

1997.
651 **170** 5c. yellow & light yellow 10 10
652 10c. yellow and cream 10 10
653 20c. green and brown 10 10
654 35c. purple and lilac 10 10
655 50c. brown and cinnamon 15 10
656 70c. yellow and cream 20 10

1997. Fungi in the Red Book. Multicoloured.
660 1l.20 Type **171** 50 25
661 1l.20 Bronze boletus 50 25

172 Letter and Seal  **173** Cherub holding Lantern above Town

1997. 674th Anniv of Letters of Invitation for Migrants sent by Grand Duke Gediminas to European Cities.
662 **172** 50c. multicoloured 20 10

1997. Town Arms. As T **114** but size 25 × 33 mm.
663 50c. Neringa 15 10
664 90c. Vilkaviskis 30 15
665 1l.20 Pasvalys 40 20

1997. Christmas. Multicoloured.
666 50c. Type **173** 15 10
667 1l.20 Snow-covered trees 40 20

174 Figure Skaters

1998. Winter Olympic Games, Nagano, Japan.
668 **174** 1l.20 ultramarine and blue 35 15

175 Alfonsas Petrulis (priest)

1998. National Day. Signatories to 1918 Declaration of Independence.
669 **175** 50c. green, grey and black 15 10
670 – 90c. brown, lt brn & blk 30 15
DESIGN: No. 670, Jokubas Sernas (lawyer and politician).

176 Text of Declaration and State Emblem  **177** Lyrics and Kudirka's Memorial

1998. 80th Anniv of Declaration of Independence. Sheet 123 × 50 mm.
MS671 **176** 6l.60 multicoloured 2·00 2·00

1998. Centenary of *Tautiskai giesmei* (national anthem) by Vincas Kudirka (lyricist). Sheet 90 × 64 mm.
MS672 **177** 5l.20 multicoloured 1·60 1·60

178 Gustaitis and ANBO-41 (reconnaissance plane)

1998. Birth Centenary of Antanas Gustaitis (pilot and aircraft constructor). Multicoloured.
673 2l. Type **178** 60 30
674 3l. ANBO-VIII (light bomber) and diagrams 90 45

179 National Song Festival  **180** Tadas Ivanauskas (zoologist, 27th death anniv)

1998. Europa. National Festivals.
675 **179** 1l.20 multicoloured 35 15

1998. Anniversaries.
676 **180** 50c. green, lt yell & yell 15 10
677 – 90c. red, yellow & orge 30 15
678 – 90c. green, yellow & orge 30 15
DESIGNS—45 × 25 mm: No. 677, Stasys Lozoraitis (diplomat, birth centenary) and Stasys Lozoraitis (diplomat, 10th death anniv); No. 678, Jurgis Baltrusaitis (writer and diplomat, 125th birth anniv) and Jurgis Baltrusaitis (art historian, 4th death anniv).

181 Long Jumping

1998. 6th World Lithuanian Games and Second National Games.
679 **181** 1l.35 multicoloured 40 20

182 Atlantic Salmon

1998. Fishes in the Red Book. Multicoloured.
680 1l.40 Type **182** 45 20
681 1l.40 Whitefish (“Coregonus lavaretus”) 45 20

1998. Town Arms. As T **114** but size 25 × 33 mm. Multicoloured.
682 70c. Kernave 20 10
683 70c. Trakai 20 10
684 1l.35 Kaunas 40 20

183 Vilnius–Cracow Postal Service, 1562

1998. Postal History. Multicoloured.
685 70c. Type **183** 20 10
MS686 55 × 86 mm. 13l. Hologram of posthorn and map of Europe, Africa and Asia (80th anniv of first Lithuanian stamps) (39 × 29 mm) 4·00 4·00

184 “All Night Long” (Antanas Zmuidzinavicius)

1998. Paintings. Multicoloured.
687 70c. Type **184** 20 10
688 1l.35 “Vilnius: Bernardines' Garden” (Juozapas Marsevskis) 40 20

185 Girl holding Church

1998. Christmas. Multicoloured.
689 70c. Type **185** 20 10
690 1l.35 Couple going into tree house 40 20

186 Mickiewicz (statue, G. Jokuonis)

187 Angwels holding Title Page

1998. Birth Bicentenary of Adam Mickiewicz (poet).
691 **186** 70c. multicoloured 20 10

1999. 400th Anniv of Publication of Translation into Lithuanian by Mikalojus Dauksa of *Postilla Catholicka* by Jacob Wujek. Sheet 60 × 67 mm.
MS692 **187** 5l.90 brown and silver 1·90 1·90

188 Petras Klimas (historian and diplomat)

1999. National Day. Signatories to 1918 Declaration of Independence.
693 **188** 70c. red and black 20 10
694 – 70c. blue and black . . . 20 10
DESIGN: No. 694, Donatas Malinauskas (diplomat).

189 Augustinas Gricius (dramatist)

190 Emblem and State Flag

1999. Birth Centenaries.
695 **189** 70c. black, cream & orge 20 10
696 – 70c. brown, cream & pink 20 10
697 – 1l.35 green, cream and orange 40 20
DESIGNS: No. 696, Juozas Matulis (chemist); 697, Pranas Skardzius (philologian).

1999. 50th Anniv of North Atlantic Treaty Organization.
698 **190** 70c. multicoloured 20 10

191 Aukstaitija National Park

1999. Europa. Parks and Gardens. Multicoloured.
699 1l.35 Type **191** 40 20
700 1l.35 Curonian Spit National Park 40 20

192 Council Flag

193 Boarded Clay Windmill, Melniai

1999. 50th Anniv of Council of Europe.
701 **192** 70c. multicoloured 20 10

1999. Windmills. Multicoloured.
702 70c. Type **193** 20 10
703 70c. Red-brick windmill, Pumpenai 20 10

194 "Dasypoda argentata"

195 Sculpture of U.P.U. Emblem, Berne

1999. Bumble Bees. Multicoloured.
704 70c. Type **194** 20 10
705 2l. "Bombus pomorum" . . 60 30

1999. 125th Anniv of Universal Postal Union.
706 **195** 70c. multicoloured 20 10

196 1918 and 1990 Stamps and Society Emblems

1999. 75th Anniv of Lithuanian Philatelic Society.
707 **196** 1l. multicoloured 30 15

197 Cast and Producers

1999. Centenary of First Public Performance of Lithuanian Drama (*America in the Bath* by Keturakis). Sheet 99 × 59 mm containing T **197** and similar vert design. Multicoloured.
MS708 4l. Type **197**; 4l. Playbill 2·50 2·50

198 Family and State Flag

199 Emblem

1999. 10th Anniv of the Baltic Chain (human chain uniting the capitals of Lithuania, Estonia and Latvia). Multicoloured.
709 1l. Type **198** 30 15
MS710 110 × 72 mm. 2l. Type **198**; 2l. Family and Estonian flag; 2l. Family and Latvian flag . . . 1·75 85

1999. 50th Anniv of Establishment of Lithuanian Freedom Fight Movement.
711 **199** 70c. multicoloured 20 10

1999. Town Arms. Designs as T **114** but size 25 × 33 mm. Multicoloured.
712 70c. Marijampole 20 10
713 1l. Siauliai 30 15
714 1l.40 Rokiskis 40 20

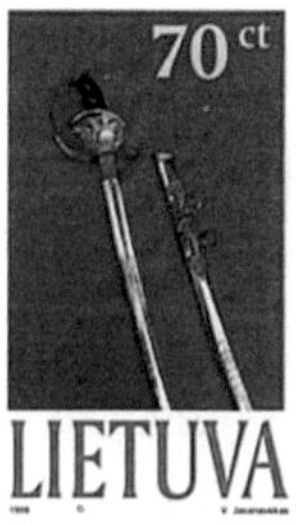

200 Sword of General S. Zukauskas, 1927

201 "Horse and Bear" (fable)

1999. Exhibits in Vytautas Magnus War Museum. Multicoloured.
715 70c. Type **200** 20 10
716 3l. 17th-century Hussar's armour 90 45

1999. Birth Bicentenary of Simonas Stanevicius (writer).
717 **201** 70c. multicoloured 20 10

202 "Winter Symphony"

203 Top of Monument

1999. Christmas. Multicoloured.
718 70c. Type **202** 20 10
719 1l.35 Cathedral, candles and bell 40 20

2000. Ironwork.
720 **203** 10c. blue and brown . . . 10 10
721 – 20c. blue and stone . . . 10 10
722 – 1l. blue and pink 30 15
723 – 1l.30 blue and green . . . 40 20
724 – 1l.70 blue and light blue 50 25
DESIGNS: 20c. to 1l.70, Different examples of ornamental ironwork.

204 Jonas Vailokaitis

2000. National Day. Signatories to 1918 Declaration of Independence.
725 **204** 1l.30 orange, stone & blk 40 25
726 – 1l.70 brown, stone & blk 50 25
DESIGN: 1l.70, Jonas Smilgevicius.

205 Declaration

2000. 10th Anniv of Restoration of Independence. Sheet 86 × 71 mm.
MS727 **205** 7l.40 multicoloured 2·25 2·25

206 Vincas Pietaris (writer, 150th anniv)

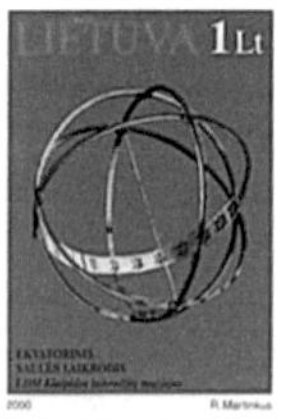

207 Equatorial Sundial

2000. Birth Anniversaries.
728 **206** 1l. green, black and purple 30 15
729 – 1l.30 blue, black & brown 40 20
730 – 1l.70 brown, black & bl 50 25
DESIGNS: 1l.30, Kanutas Ruseckas (painter, bicentenary); 1l.70, Povilas Visinskis (literary critic, 125th anniv).
See also Nos. 753/5.

2000. Exhibits in Klaipeda Clock Museum. Mult.
731 1l. Type **207** 35 15
732 2l. Renaissance-style clock case 70 35

208 "Building Europe"

209 Osprey

2000. Europa.
733 **208** 1l.70 multicoloured . . . 60 30

2000. Birds of Prey. Multicoloured.
734 1l. Type **209** 35 15
735 2l. Black kite 70 35

210 Grey Seal

2000. Lithuanian Marine Museum, Kopgalis. Mult.
736 1l. Type **210** 35 15
737 1l. Magellanic penguin (*Spheniscus magellanicus*) 35 15

211 Cycling

2000. Olympic Games, Sydney. Multicoloured.
738 1l. Type **211** 35 15
739 3l. Swimming . . . . 1·00 50

212 "Fairy Tail Castle" (Ciurlionis)

2000. 125th Birth Anniv of Mikalojus Konstantinas Ciurlionis (artist and composer). Sheet 59 × 56 mm.
MS740 **212** 4l. multicoloured . . 1·25 1·25

213 Tree and Emblem

2000. 10th Anniv of Lithuanian Postal Service.
741 **213** 1l. multicoloured 35 15

2000. Town Arms. As T **114** but size 25 × 33 mm. Multicoloured.
742 1l. Raseiniai 35 15
743 1l. Taurage 35 15
744 1l.30 Utena 45 20

214 Snow-covered Village

215 The Nativity

2000. Christmas. Multicoloured.
745 1l. Type **214** 35 15
746 1l.70 Snow-covered church 60 30

2000. Holy Year (2000). Sheet 69 × 87 mm containing T **215** and similar vert designs. Multicoloured.
MS747 2l. Type **215**; 2l. Jesus with James and John; 2l. Crucifixion; 2l. Jesus entering Heaven . . . 2·50 2·50

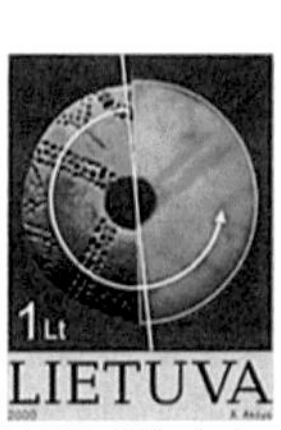

216 Neolithic Amber Artefact

2000. New Millennium.
748 **216** 1l. multicoloured 35 15

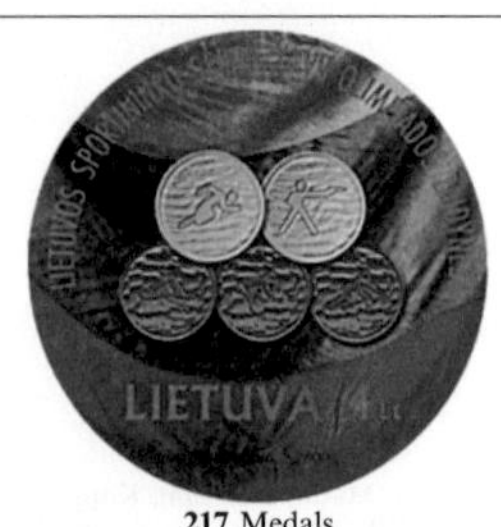

217 Medals

2000. Lithuanian Victories in Olympic Games, Sydney. Sheet 65 × 102 mm.
MS749 **217** 4l. multicoloured . . 1·25 1·25

218 Vilnius Television Tower and Flag

220 Lake Galve

219 Saliamonas Banaitis

2001. 10th Anniv of Soviet Action in Vilnius.
750 **218** 1l. multicoloured 35 15

2001. National Day. Signatories to 1918 Declaration of Independence.
751 **219** 1l. brown, grey and black 35 15
752 – 2l. lilac, grey and black 70 35
DESIGN: 2l. Justinas Staugaitis.

2001. Anniversaries. As T **206**.
753 1l. blue, red and black . . . 35 15
754 1l. green, red and black . . . 35 15
755 1l.70 brown, violet and black 60 30
DESIGNS: No. 753, Juozas MikEnas (artist, birth centenary); 754, Pranas Vaicaitis (poet, death centenary); 755, Petras Vileisis (civil engineer, 150th birth anniv).

2001. Europa. Water Resources. Multicoloured.
756 1l.70 Type **220** 60 30
757 1l.70 River Nemunas 60 30

221 Floating Bogbean (*Nymphoides peltata*)

2001. Plants in the Red Book. Multicoloured.
758 2l. Type **221** 70 35
759 3l. Crossleaf heather (*Erica tetralix*) . . . . 1·10 55

222 Paplauja Bridge, Vilnius

2001. Bridges. Multicoloured.
760 1l. Type **222** 35 15
761 1l.30 Pakruojis, Kruoja . . . 50 25

223 National Flag

2001. Millenary of Lithunania. Sheet 125 × 100 mm containing T **223** and similar horiz designs. Multicoloured.
MS762 2l. Type **223**; 2l. State emblem; 2l. Map of Lithuania; 2l. Map of Europe . . . . 1·90 1·90

224 Sand Dunes, Palanga, Lithuania

2001. Baltic Sea Coast. Multicoloured.
763 1l. Type **224** 35 15
MS764 125 × 60 mm. 2l. As Type **224** but with Palanga at left; 2l. Rocky coastline, Lahemaa, Estonia; 2l. Beach, Vidzeme, Latvia . . . . 1·90 1·90

225 19th-century Cottage, Kirdeikiai, Utena District

2001. 35th Anniv of Open Air Museum, Rumsiskes. Multicoloured.
765 1l. Type **225** 35 15
766 2l. Farmer's house, Darlenai, Kretinga district 70 35

226 "Sadness" (sculpture)

2001. 120th Birth Anniv of Juozas Zikaras (artist).
767 **226** 3l. multicoloured . . . . 1·10 55

227 Charter and King Stephan I Batory of Poland

2001. 418th Anniv of Introduction of Postal Rates based on Weight.
768 **227** 1l. multicoloured 35 15

2001. Town Arms. As T **114** but size 25 × 33 mm. Multicoloured.
769 1l. Lazdijai 35 15
770 1l.30 Birzai 50 25
771 1l.70 Veliuona 60 30

228 Birds on Straw and Pine Pyramid ("Winter troubles")

2001. Christmas and New Year. Multicoloured.
772 1l. Type **228** 40 20
773 1l.70 Birds and crib ("Jesus' cradle") 70 35

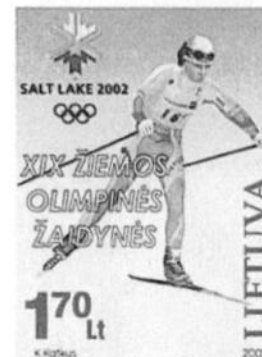

229 Basanavicius

230 Skier

2001. 150th Birth Anniv of Jonas Basanavicius (politician and signatory to 1918 Declaration of Independence). Sheet 82 × 60 mm.
MS774 **229** 5l. multicoloured . . 2·10 2·10

2002. Winter Olympic Games, Salt Lake City, U.S.A.
775 **230** 1l. 70 multicoloured . . . 70 35

231 Kazys Bizauskas

2002. National Day. Signatories to 1918 Declaration of Independence.
776 **231** 1l. sepia, brown and black 40 20
777 — 1l. violet, brown and black 40 20
DESIGN: No. 777 Stanislovas Narutavicius (politician).

232 Antanas Salys

2002. Birth Anniversaries. Multicoloured.
778 1l. Type **232** (linguist, centenary) 40 20
779 1l. 30 Satrijos Ragana (writer, 125th anniv) . . . 55 25
780 1l. 70 Oskaras Milasius (poet, 125th anniv) 70 35

2002. Town Arms. As T **114** but size 25 × 33 mm. Multicoloured.
781 1l. Birstonas 40 20
782 1l. Anyksciai 40 20
783 1l. 70 Prienai 70 35

233 Book, Archives and Seal

2002. 150th Anniv of State Archives.
784 **233** 1l. multicoloured 40 20

234 Stoat (*Mustela erminea*)

2002. Endangered Species. Multicoloured.
785 1l. Type **234** 40 20
786 3l. Lynx (*Lynx (Felis) lynx*) 1·10 55

235 Strongman

2002. Europa. Circus.
787 **235** 1l. 70 multicoloured . . . 65 30

236 Ford 350 Fire Engine

2002. Bicentenary of Vilnius Fire and Rescue Service.
788 **236** 1l. multicoloured 40 20

237 Diesel Locomotive TU 2

2002. Narrow-gauge Railway. Multicoloured.
789 1l. 30 Type **237** 50 25
790 2l. Steam locomotive PT 4 75 35

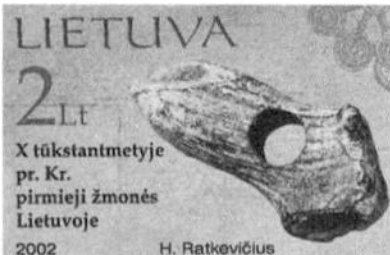

238 Flint Tool

2002. Millenary of Lithuania (2009). Sheet 126 × 100 mm containing T **238** and similar horiz designs. Multicoloured.
MS791 2l. Type **238**; 2l. Publius Cornelius Tacitus (chronicler); 2l. Viking ship; 2l. Annals of Quedlinburg (manuscript containing first reference to Lithuania) . . . . 3·00 1·50

239 Rooftops

240 Script and Exhibits

2002. 750th Anniv of Klaipeda. Sheet 88 × 59 mm.
MS792 **239** 5l. multicoloured . . 2·00 1·00

2002. Maironis Literature Museum, Kaunas. Multicoloured.
793 1l. Type **240** 40 20
794 3l. Museum buildings . . . . 1·10 55

241 King Zigmantas Vaza (founder of postal system)

2002. Postal History.
795 **241** 1l. multicoloured 40 20

242 Star and Clock-face

243 Mother and Child (Danielius Peciulis)

2002. Christmas and New Year. Multicoloured.
796 1l. Type **242** 40 20
797 1l. 70 Christmas tree 65 30

2002. European Children's Day.
798 **243** 1l. multicoloured 40 20

244 Laurynas Stuoka-Gucevicius (architect)

2003. Personalities. Multicoloured.
799 1l. Type **244** 40 20
800 1l. Juozas Eretas (writer) . . 40 20

245 Gargzdai

246 Pervalka Lighthouse

2003. Town Arms. Multicoloured.
801 1l. Type **245** 40 20
802 1l. Kretinga 40 20
803 1l. Palanga 40 20
804 1l. Papile 40 20
805 1l. Rietavas 40 20
See also Nos. 827/9.

2003. Lighthouses. Multicoloured.
806 1l. Type **246** 40 20
807 3l. Uostadvaris . . . . 1·10 55

247 Face and Pencils

2003. Europa. Poster Art.
808 **247** 1l.70 multicoloured . . . 65 30

248 Royal Palace, Vilnius

2003. Royal Palace Restoration.
809 **248** 1l. multicoloured 40 20

249 Observatory Building **250** *Cerambyx cerdo*

2003. 250th Anniv of Astronomical Observatory, Vilnius University.
810 **249** 1l. multicoloured 40 20

2002. Endangered Species. Beetles. Multicoloured.
811 3l. Type **250** . . . . 1·10 55
812 3l. Stag beetle (*Lucanus cervus*) . . . . 1·10 55

251 Fortifications, 1183

2003. Lithuania Millenary. Sheet 125 × 100 mm containing T **251** and similar horiz designs. Multicoloured.
MS813 2l. Type **251**; 2l. The Battle of Shiauliai, 1236; 2l. The Coronation of King Mindaugas, 1253; 2l. Vilnius, 1323 . . . . 3·00 1·50

252 King Mindaugas

2003. 750th Anniv of Coronation of King Mindaugas. Sheet 87 × 58 mm.
MS814 **252** 5l. multicoloured . . 2·00 2·00

253 Hot Air Balloons

2003. 13th European Hot Air Balloon Championships, Vilnius.
815 **253** 1l. 30 multicoloured . . . 50 25

254 Cardinal Sladkevicius **255** City Arms

2003. 3rd Death Anniv of Cardinal Vincentas Sladkevicius.
816 **254** 1l. multicoloured 40 20

2003. 500th Anniv of Panevezys City.
817 **255** 1l. multicoloured 40 20

256 Post Office, Map and Postal Seal

2003. Postal History.
818 **256** 1l. multicoloured 40 20

257 Christmas Tree, Church and Houses **258** Trophy and Basketball

2003. Christmas. Multicoloured.
819 1l. Type **257** 40 20
820 1l.70 Street lamps through houses 40 20

2003. Lithuania, European Men's Basketball Champions, 2003. Sheet 62 × 75 mm.
MS821 **258** 5l. multicoloured . . 2·00 2·00

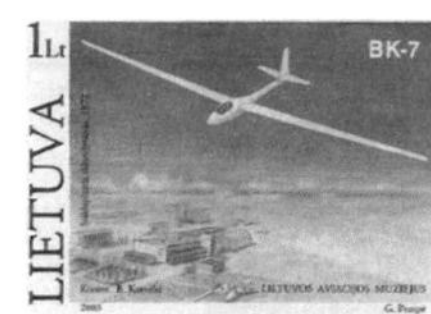

259 Plastic Glider BK-7

2003. Aviation Museum, Kaunas.
822 1l. Type **259** 40 20
823 1l. Training glider BRO-12 40 20

260 Jonas Aistis

2004. Anniversaries. Multicoloured.
824 1l. Type **260** (writer) (birth centenary) 40 20
825 1l. Kazimieras Buga (philologist) (80th death anniv) 40 20
826 1l. Adolfas Jucys (scientist) (birth centenary) 40 20

2004. Town Arms. As T **245**. Multicoloured.
827 1l. Mazeikiai 40 20
828 1l.30 Radviliskis 40 20
829 1l.40 Ukmerge Palanga . . . 40 20

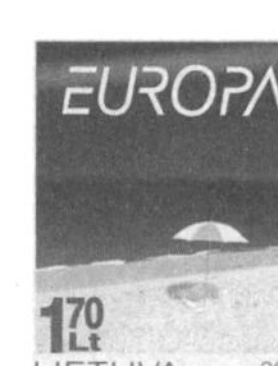

261 King Steponas Batoras, Petras Skarga **262** Parasol on Beach and University Building

2004. 425th Anniv of Vilnius University.
830 **261** 1l. multicoloured 40 20

2004. Europa. Holidays. Multicoloured.
831 1l.70 Type **262** 65 30
832 1l.70 Yacht at sea 65 30

263 Frontispieces

2004. Centenary of the Re-establishment of printing using Latin Characters.
833 **263** 1l.30 multicoloured . . . 50 55

264 Lithuania Flag, Map of Europe, Stars and Shield

2004. Lithuania's Accession to the European Union. Multicoloured.
834 1l.70 Type **264** 65 30
835 1l.70 Flags of new members 65 30

265 Football

2004. Centenary of FIFA (Federation Internationale de Football Association).
836 **265** 3l. multicoloured . . . . 1·10 55

LOMBARDY AND VENETIA Pt. 2

Formerly known as Austrian Italy. Although these provinces used a different currency the following issues were valid throughout Austria. Lombardy was annexed by Sardinia in 1859 and Venetia by Italy in 1866.

1850. 100 centesimi = 1 lira.
1858. 100 soldi = 1 florin.
100 kreuzer = 1 gulden.

1 Arms of Austria

1850. Imperf.
1c **1** 5c. orange . . . . £1000 75·00
2c 10c. black . . . . £1900 70·00
7 15c. red . . . . £475 2·75
4a 30c. brown . . . . £1700 5·50
5e 45c. blue . . . . £4500 13·50

1859. As T **4** and **5** of Austria (Emperor Francis Joseph I) but value in soldi. Perf.
16 **5** 2s. yellow . . . . £350 70·00
17 **4** 3s. black £1600 £190
18 3s. green . . . . £225 50·00
19 **5** 5s. red . . . . £150 3·00
20 10s. brown . . . . £250 38·00
21 15s. blue . . . . £1100 13·50

3 Emperor Francis Joseph I **4** Arms of Austria

1861.
25 **3** 5s. red . . . . £1000 1·70
26 10s. brown . . . . £1600 17·00

1863.
27 **4** 2s. yellow . . . . 65·00 £120
33 3s. green . . . . 6·25 12·50
34 5s. red . . . . 2·10 1·00
35 10s. blue . . . . 12·50 3·75
36 15s. brown . . . . 45·00 37·00

JOURNAL STAMPS

J **5**

1858. Imperf.
J22 **J 5** 1k. black £1100 £3000
J23 2k. red . . . . £170 60·00
J24 4k. red £2750

LOURENCO MARQUES Pt. 9

A Portuguese colony in E. Africa, now part of Mozambique, whose stamps it uses.

1895. 1000 reis = 1 milreis.
1913. 100 centavos = 1 escudo.

1895. "Figures" key-type inscr "LOURENCO MARQUES".

1 R	5r. yellow	20	15
2	10r. mauve	25	15
3	15r. brown	40	35
4	20r. lilac	40	35
10	25r. green	30	15
12	50r. blue	35	15
18	75r. pink	80	40
14	80r. green	1·10	75
7	100r. brown on yellow	85	50
16	150r. red on pink	90	75
8	200r. blue on blue	1·50	90
9	300r. blue on brown	1·50	90

1895. 700th Death Anniv of St. Anthony. Optd **L. MARQUES CENTENARIO DE S. ANTONIO MDCCCXCV** on (a) "Embossed" key-type inscr "PROVINCIA DE MOCAMBIQUE".

19 Q	5r. black	4·50	4·00
20	10r. green	7·00	4·50
21	20r. red	8·00	5·50
22	25r. purple	10·00	7·25
23	40r. brown	8·00	6·75
27a	50r. blue	5·50	4·50
25	100r. brown	15·00	11·00
26	200r. violet	12·00	11·00
27	300r. orange	18·00	16·00

(b) "Figures" key-type inscr "MOCAMBIQUE"

28 R	5r. orange	5·25	3·75
29	10r. mauve	8·50	7·50
30	50r. blue	13·00	7·50
35	75r. pink	14·00	9·50
32	80r. green	23·00	17·00
33	100r. brown on yellow	25·00	23·00
35a	150r. red on pink	16·00	13·00

1897. No. 9 surch **50 reis**.

36 R	50r. on 300r. blue on brown	70·00	50·00

1898. "King Carlos" key-type inscr "LOURENCO MARQUES". Name and value in black.

37 S	2½r. grey	15	15
38	5r. orange	15	15
39	10r. green	15	15
40	15r. brown	50	45
83	15r. green	20	15
41	20r. lilac	30	15
42	25r. green	35	15
84	25r. red	20	15
43	50r. blue	50	25
85	50r. brown	45	35
86	65r. blue	2·25	2·00
44	75r. pink	1·00	80
87	75r. purple	65	60
45	80r. mauve	95	65
46	100r. blue on blue	50	25
88	115r. brown on pink	2·50	2·00
89	130r. brown on yellow	2·50	2·00
47	150r. brown on yellow	85	75
48	200r. purple on pink	1·50	75
49	300r. blue on pink	1·00	80
90	400r. blue on yellow	2·50	2·00
50	500r. black on blue	2·10	1·25
51	700r. mauve on yellow	3·75	2·75

1899. Green and brown fiscal stamps of Mozambique, as T 9 of Macao, bisected and each half surch **Correio de Lourenco Marques** and value. Imperf.

55 –	5r. on half of 10r.	60	30
56 –	25r. on half of 10r.	60	30
57 –	50r. on half of 30r.	60	30
58 –	50r. on half of 800r.	90	50

1899. No. 44 surch **50 Reis**.

59 S	50r. on 75r. pink	1·50	1·10

1902. "Figures" and "Newspaper" key-types surch.

60 V	65r. on 2½r. brown	1·25	1·10
62 R	65r. on 5r. yellow	1·25	1·10
63	65r. on 15r. brown	1·25	1·10
64	65r. on 20r. lilac	1·25	1·10
66	115r. on 10r. mauve	1·25	1·10
67	115r. on 200r. blue on blue	1·25	1·10
68	115r. on 300r. blue on brn	1·25	1·10
70	130r. on 25r. green	1·25	1·10
72	130r. on 80r. green	1·25	1·10
73	130r. on 150r. red on pink	1·25	1·10
74	400r. on 50r. blue	4·25	1·90
76	400r. on 75r. pink	3·25	2·10
78	400r. on 100r. brown on yellow	2·10	1·40

1902. "King Carlos" key type inscr "LOURENCO MARQUES" optd **PROVISORIO**.

79 S	15r. brown	75	50
80	25r. green	65	40
81	50r. blue	80	60
82	75r. pink	1·25	75

1905. No. 86 surch **50 REIS**.

91 S	50r. on 65r. blue	1·00	95

1911. "King Carlos" key-type inscr "LOURENCO MARQUES" optd **REPUBLICA**.

92 S	2½r. grey	10	10
93	5r. orange	10	10
94	10r. green	15	15
95	15r. green	15	15
96	20r. lilac	30	20
97	25r. red	20	15
98	50r. brown	35	25
99	75r. purple	35	25
100	100r. blue on blue	35	25
178	115r. brown on pink	35	35
102	130r. brown on yellow	30	25
103	200r. purple on pink	30	25
104	400r. blue on yellow	50	35
105	500r. black on blue	60	50
106	700r. mauve on yellow	80	50

1913. Surch **REPUBLICA LOURENCO MARQUES** and value on "Vasco da Gama" issues of (a) Portuguese Colonies.

107	¼c. on 2½r. green	50	45
108	½c. on 5r. red	50	45
109	1c. on 10r. purple	50	45
110	2½c. on 25r. green	50	45
111	5c. on 50r. blue	50	45
112	7½c. on 75r. brown	1·25	85
113	10c. on 100r. brown	65	45
114	15c. on 150r. brown	65	45

(b) Macao.

115	¼c. on ½a. green	60	45
116	½c. on 1a. red	60	45
117	1c. on 2a. purple	60	45
118	2½c. on 4a. green	60	45
119	5c. on 8a. blue	60	45
120	7½c. on 12a. brown	1·00	85
121	10c. on 16a. brown	75	45
122	15c. on 24a. brown	75	45

(c) Timor.

123	¼c. on ½a. green	60	45
124	½c. on 1a. red	60	45
125	1c. on 2a. purple	60	45
126	2½c. on 4a. green	60	45
127	5c. on 8a. blue	60	45
128	7½c. on 12a. brown	1·00	90
129	10c. on 16a. brown	80	45
130	15c. on 24a. brown	80	45

1914. "Ceres" key-type inscr "LOURENCO MARQUES".

147 U	¼c. green	10	10
148	½c. black	10	10
149	1c. green	10	10
150	1½c. brown	15	15
151	2c. red	15	15
152	2½c. violet	15	15
153	5c. blue	15	15
154	7½c. brown	15	15
155	8c. grey	15	15
140	10c. red	80	40
157	15c. purple	35	35
142	20c. green	45	35
143	30c. brown on green	70	50
144	40c. brown on pink	2·50	2·00
145	50c. orange on orange	1·00	90
146	1e. green on blue	1·10	90

1914. Provisionals of 1902 overprinted **REPUBLICA**.

166 R	115r. on 10r. mauve	30	30
167	115r. on 200r. blue on blue	35	30
168	115r. on 300r. blue on brn	30	30
161	130r. on 25r. green	50	40
164	130r. on 80r. green	50	40
169	130r. on 150r. red on pink	30	30
184	400r. on 50r. blue	80	45
185	400r. on 75r. pink	80	25

1915. Nos. 93 and 148 perf diagonally and each half surch ½.

170 S	½ on half of 5r. orange	1·40	1·10
171 U	½ on half of ½c. black	1·40	1·10

Prices for Nos. 170/1 are for whole stamps.

1915. Surch **Dois centavos**.

172 S	2c. on 15r. (No. 83)	45	35
173	2c. on 15c. (No. 95)	45	35

1918. Red Cross Fund. "Ceres" key-type inscr "LOURENCO MARQUES", optd **9-3-18** and Red Cross or surch with value in figures and bars also.

188 U	½c. green	85	85
189	½c. black	85	85
190	1c. green	85	85
191	2½c. violet	85	85
192a	5c. blue	85	85
193	10c. red	1·75	85
194	20c. on 1½c. brown	1·75	85
195	30c. brown on green	1·75	1·50
196	40c. on 2c. red	1·75	1·50
197	50c. on 7½c. brown	1·75	1·50
198	70c. on 8c. grey	1·75	1·50
199	1e. on 15c. purple	1·75	1·50

1920. No. 166 surch **Um quarto de centavo**.

200 R	¼c. on 115r. on	10	

1920. No. 152 surch in figures or words.

201 U	1c. on 2½c. violet	20	15
202	1½c. on 2½c. violet	20	15
203	4c. on 2½c. violet	20	15

For other surcharges on "Ceres" key-type of Lourenco Marques, see Mozambique Nos. 309/10 and Nos. D44 and 46.

NEWSPAPER STAMPS

1893. "Newspaper" key-type inscr "LOURENCO MARQUES".

N1 V	2½r. brown	15	15

1895. 700th Death Anniv of St. Anthony. "Newspaper" key-type inscr "MOCAMBIQUE" optd **L. MARQUES CENTENARIO DE S. ANTONIO MDCCCXCV**.

N36 V	2½r. brown	2·25	1·90

LUBECK Pt. 7

Formerly one of the free cities of the Hanseatic League. In 1868 joined the North German Confederation.

16 schilling = 1 mark.

1 3

1859. Imperf.

9 1	½s. lilac	12·50	£1400
10	1s. orange	24·00	£1400
3	2s. brown	18·00	£225
4	2½s. red	36·00	£700
6	4s. green	18·00	£550

1863. Rouletted.

11 3	½s. green	36·00	60·00
13	1s. orange	£120	£140
14	2s. red	22·00	55·00
16	2½s. blue	90·00	£350
17	4s. bistre	38·00	95·00

4 5

1864. Imperf.

19 4	1¼s. brown	22·00	60·00

1865. Roul.

21 5	1½s. mauve	22·00	75·00

LUXEMBOURG Pt. 4

An independent Grand Duchy lying between Belgium and the Saar District. Under German Occupation from 1940 to 1944.

1852. 12½ centimes = 1 silver groschen.
100 centimes = 1 franc.
1940. 100 pfennig = 1 reichsmark.
1944. 100 centimes = 1 franc (Belgian).
2002. 100 cents = 1 euro.

1 Grand Duke William III 3 4

1852. Imperf.

2 1	10c. black	£1900	32·00
3a	1s. red	£1200	£100

1859. Imperf or roul.

23 3	1c. brown	30·00	7·25
21	1c. orange	25·00	5·75
17	2c. black	14·00	10·50
8	4c. yellow	£160	£150
20	4c. green	30·00	21·00
10 4	10c. blue	£160	13·50
24	10c. purple	£100	1·60
25	10c. lilac	£110	2·50
28	12½c. red	£140	4·50
30	20c. brown	£120	10·50
12	25c. brown	£325	£225
32	25c. blue	£1000	9·00
13	30c. purple	£220	£190
14	37½c. green	£275	£140
35	37½c. bistre	£650	£225
39	40c. orange	42·00	75·00

1872. Surch **UN FRANC**. Roul.

37 4	1f. on 37½c. bistre	£900	55·00

1874. Perf.

57a 3	1c. brown	6·50	6·00
58a	2c. black	6·00	1·25
42	4c. green	1·00	9·00
43	5c. yellow	£150	12·00
60a 4	10c. lilac	£150	75
61	12½c. red	£160	£160
62a	20c. brown	14·00	13·50
63a	25c. blue	£225	3·75
64	30c. red	2·75	15·00
55	40c. orange	85	5·00

1879. Surch **Un Franc**. Perf.

56 4	1f. on 37½c. bistre	6·25	42·00

7 Agriculture and Trade 8 Grand Duke Adolf 9

1882.

81a 7	1c. grey	20	50
82c	2c. brown	10	25
83c	4c. bistre	30	1·50
84c	5c. green	55	25
85a	10c. red	4·50	75
86a	12½c. blue	1·00	21·00
87c	20c. orange	2·00	1·75
88a	25c. blue	£130	1·50
89a	30c. green	13·00	11·00
90c	50c. brown	1·00	6·25
91a	1f. lilac	60	23·00
92a	5f. orange	28·00	£150

1891.

125a 8	10c. red	15	25
126b	12½c. green	45	50
128	20c. orange	11·00	65
129c	25c. blue	85	40
130b	30c. green	1·00	85
131b	37½c. green	2·40	2·75
132b	50c. brown	6·00	3·25
133a	1f. purple	11·00	11·50
134	2½f. black	1·50	19·00
135	5f. lake	32·00	60·00

1895.

152 9	1c. grey	1·40	30
153	2c. brown	15	15
154	4c. bistre	20	70
155	5c. green	1·40	15
156	10c. red	6·50	15

10 11 Grand Duke William IV 13 Grand Duchess Adelaide

1906.

157 10	1c. grey	10	15
158	2c. brown	10	15
159	4c. bistre	15	20
160	5c. green	25	15
231	5c. mauve	10	15
161	6c. lilac	20	30
161a	7½c. orange	15	2·10
162 11	10c. red	1·50	10
163	12½ slate	1·50	30
164	15c. brown	1·50	50
165	20c. orange	3·00	45
166	25c. blue	45·00	30
166a	30c. olive	70	50
167	37½c. green	75	55
168	50c. brown	4·25	70
169	87½c. blue	1·75	6·25
170	1f. purple	4·75	1·25
171	2½f. red	50·00	60·00
172	5f. purple	7·00	42·00

1912. Surch **62½ cts.**

173 11	62½c. on 87½c. blue	1·25	1·75
173a	62½c. on 2½f. red	1·40	3·00
173b	62½c. on 5f. purple	55	1·90

1914.

174 13	10c. purple	10	10
175	12½c. green	10	10
176	15c. brown	10	10
176a	17½c. brown	10	30
177	25c. blue	10	10
178	30c. brown	10	40
179	35c. blue	10	30
180	37½c. brown	10	30
181	40c. red	15	30
182	50c. grey	25	40
183	62½c. green	35	1·90
183a	87½c. orange	35	1·90
184	1f. brown	2·00	60
185	2½f. red	45	1·90
186	5f. violet	7·00	32·00

1916. Surch in figures and bars.

187 10	2½ on 5c. green	10	10
188	3 on 2c. brown	10	10
212	5 on 1c. grey	10	15
213	5 on 4c. bistre	10	20
214	5 on 7½c. orange	10	15
215	6 on 2c. brown	25	25
189 13	7½ on 10c. red	10	10
190	17½ on 30c. brown	10	35
191	20 on 17½c. brown	10	20
216	25 on 37½c. sepia	10	20
217	75 on 62½c. green	10	20
218	80 on 87½c. orange	10	20
192	87½ on 1f. brown	55	6·25

17 Grand Duchess Charlotte 18 Vianden Castle

1921. Perf.
194 **17** 2c. brown 10 15
195 3c. green 10 15
196 6c. purple 10 15
197 10c. green 10 15
193a 15c. red* 10 15
198 15c. green 10 15
234 15c. orange 10 30
199 20c. orange 15 30
235 20c. green 10 30
200 25c. green 15 15
201 30c. red 15 15
202 40c. orange 15 15
203 50c. blue 15 35
236 50c. red 10 75
204 75c. red . . . . 15 1·25
237 75c. blue 10 25
205 80c. black 15 65
206a **18** 1f. red 20 35
238 1f. blue 25 40
207 – 2f. blue 40 55
239 – 2f. brown . . . . 2·40 1·40
208 – 5f. violet . . . . 12·00 6·00
DESIGNS—As Type **18**: 2f. Factories at Esch; 5f. Railway viaduct over River Alzette.
*No. 193a was originally issued on the occasion of the birth of Crown Prince Jean.
See also Nos. 219/20.

21 Monastery at Clervaux

1921. War Monument Fund.
209 **21** 10c.+5c. green . . . . . 30 2·40
210 – 15c.+10c. orange . . . . . 30 4·25
211 – 25c.+10c. green . . . . . 30 2·40
DESIGNS—HORIZ: 15c. Pfaffenthal; 25c. as Type **26**.

1922. Philatelic Exhibition. Imperf.
219 **17** 25c. green . . . . 1·75 4·50
220 30c. red . . . . 1·75 4·50

26 Luxembourg **28** Echternach

1923. Birth of Princess Elisabeth. Sheet 78 × 59 mm to 79 × 61 mm.
MS221 **26** 10f. green £1000 £1700

1923.
222a **26** 10f. black . . . . 4·00 8·75

1923. Unveiling of War Memorial by Prince Leopold of Belgium. Nos. 209/11 surch **27 mai 1923** and additional values.
223 **21** 10+5+25c. green . . . . . 1·40 14·00
224 – 15+10+25c. orange . . . . 1·40 19·00
225 – 25+10+25c. green . . . . 1·40 14·00

1923.
226a **28** 3f. blue 75 55

1924. Charity. Death of Grand Duchess Marie Adelaide. Surch **CARITAS** and new value.
227 **13** 12½c.+7½c. green . . . . . . 15 1·75
228 35c.+10c. blue . . . . . . 15 1·75
229 2½f.+1f. red . . . . 75 19·00
230 5f.+2f. violet . . . . . . 60 13·50

1925. Surch 5.
240 **17** 5 on 10c. green 10 15

31 **32** Grand Duchess Charlotte

1925. Anti-T.B. Fund.
241 **31** 5c.+5c. violet 25 50
242 30c.+5c. orange . . . . . 25 2·25
243 50c.+5c. brown . . . . . 25 4·25
244 1f.+10c. blue . . . . . . 65 10·50

1926.
245 **32** 5c. mauve 10 15
246 10c. olive 10 20
246a 15c. black 10 20
247 20c. orange 25 25
248 25c. green 25 30
248a 25c. brown 20 25
248b 30c. green 20 25
248c 30c. violet 20 20
248d 35c. violet . . . . 1·75 20
248e 35c. green 10 15
249 40c. brown 10 20
250 50c. brown 10 20
250a 60c. green . . . . 1·75 20
251 65c. brown . . . . 20 1·40
251a 70c. violet 10 10
252 75c. red 15 45
252a 75c. brown 10 20
253 80c. brown . . . . 20 1·10
253a 90c. red 50 10
254 1f. black 55 30
254a 1f. red 35 30
255 1¼f. blue 10 35
255a 1¼f. yellow . . . . 6·00 95
255b 1¼f. green 35 25
255c 1¼f. red . . . . 9·00 1·60
255d 1½f. blue . . . . 1·10 1·25
255e 1¾f. blue 75 30

33 Prince Jean **34** Grand Duchess and Prince Felix

1926. Child Welfare.
256 **33** 5c.+5c. black and mauve 15 35
257 40c.+10c. black & green . . 15 75
258 50c.+15c. black & yellow 15 75
259 75c.+20c. black and red . . 30 8·00
260 1f.50+30c. black & bl . . . 3·00 8·50

1927. International Philatelic Exhibition.
261 **34** 25c. purple . . . . 1·25 11·00
262 50c. green . . . . 1·75 15·00
263 75c. red . . . . 1·25 11·00
264 1f. black . . . . 1·25 11·00
265 1½f. blue . . . . 1·25 11·00

35 Princess Elisabeth **37** Clervaux

1927. Child Welfare.
266 **35** 10c.+5c. black and blue . . 15 40
267 50c.+10 black and brown 15 75
268 75c.+20c. black & orange 15 1·10
269 1f.+30c. black and red . . 30 8·00
270 1½f.+50c. black and blue 30 8·00

1927. Stamps of 1921 and 1926 surch.
270a **32** 10 on 30c. green 35 30
271 **17** 15 on 20c. green 10 20
272 **32** 15 on 25c. green 15 50
273 **17** 35 on 40c. orange . . . 15 15
274 **32** 60 on 65c. brown 15 35
275 **17** 60 on 75c. blue 15 25
276 **32** 60 on 75c. red 15 35
277 **17** 60 on 80c. black 15 35
278 **32** 60 on 80c. brown 15 45
278a 70 on 75c. brown . . . . 4·50 30
278b 75 on 90c. red . . . . . 1·40 55
278c 1¾ on 1½f. blue . . . . . 3·25 1·25

1928. Perf.
279a **37** 2f. black 85 60
See also No. 339.

38 Princess Marie Adelaide **39** Princess Marie Gabrielle

1928. Child Welfare.
280 **38** 10c.+5c. purple & green . . 20 85
281 60c.+10c. olive & brown 30 2·25
282 75c.+15c. green and red . . 50 5·00
283 1f.+25c. brown & green . . 1·25 16·00
284 1½f.+50c. blue & yellow . . 1·25 16·00

1928. Child Welfare.
285 **39** 10c.+10c. green & brown 20 55
286 35c.+15c. brown & green 85 4·75
287 75c.+30c. black and red . . 85 6·50
288 1¼f.+50c. green and red . . 2·00 17·00
289 1¾f.+75c. black and blue 2·50 22·00

40 Prince Charles **41** Arms of Luxembourg

1930. Child Welfare.
290 **40** 10c.+5c. brown & green . . 20 90
291 75c.+10c. green & brown 1·40 4·75
292 1f.+25c. violet and red . . 3·00 17·00
293 1¼f.+75c. black & yellow 4·25 24·00
294 1¾f.+1f.50 brown & blue 5·00 24·00

1930.
295 **41** 5c. red 35 35
296 10c. green 45 20

42 Biplane over River Alzette **43** Luxembourg, Lower Town

1931. Air.
296a **42** 50c. green . . . . 60 1·10
297 75c. brown . . . . 60 1·25
298 1f. red . . . . 60 1·40
299 1¼f. purple . . . . 60 1·40
300 1¾f. blue . . . . 60 1·40
300a 3f. black . . . . 90 5·00

1931.
301 **43** 20f. green . . . . 3·25 19·00

44 Princess Alix **45** Countess Ermesinde **46** Emperor Henry VII

1931. Child Welfare.
302 **44** 10c.+5c. grey and brown 20 85
303 75c.+10c. green and red . . 3·50 11·00
304 1f.+25c. grey and green . . 6·00 23·00
305 1¼f.+75c. green and violet 6·00 23·00
306 1¾f.+1f.50 grey and blue 10·50 45·00

1932. Child Welfare.
307 **45** 10c.+5c. brown 35 90
308 75c.+10c. violet . . . . . 2·10 13·50
309 1f.+25c. red . . . . . . 9·25 38·00
310 1¼f.+75c. lake . . . . . . 9·25 38·00
311 1¾f.+1f.50 blue . . . . . 9·25 38·00

1933. Child Welfare.
312 **46** 10c.+5c. brown 35 80
313 75c.+10c. purple . . . . . 4·25 13·00
314 1f.+25c. red . . . . . . 12·00 32·00
315 1¼f.+75c. brown . . . . . 14·50 40·00
316 1¾f.+1f.50 blue . . . . . 14·50 60·00

47 Gateway of the Three Towers **48** Arms of John the Blind

1934.
317 **47** 5f. green . . . . 1·00 7·25

1934. Child Welfare.
318 **48** 10c.+5c. violet 10 85
319 35c.+10c. green . . . . . 2·75 9·25
320 75c.+15c. red . . . . . . 2·75 9·25
321 1f.+25c. red . . . . 14·50 40·00
322 1¼f.+75c. orange . . . . . 16·00 50·00
323 1¾f.+1½f. blue . . . . . . 15·00 50·00

50 Surgeon

1935. International Relief Fund for Intellectuals.
324 – 5c. violet . . . . 20 1·00
325 – 10c. red . . . . 40 1·00
326 – 15c. olive . . . . 35 1·75
327 – 20c. orange . . . . 55 3·00
328 – 35c. green . . . . 80 4·00
329 – 50c. black . . . . 95 5·50
330 – 70c. green . . . . 2·00 6·00
331 **50** 1f. red . . . . 2·00 6·00
332 – 1f.25 turquoise . . . . . . 8·00 50·00
333 – 1f.75 blue . . . . 10·00 50·00
334 – 2f. brown . . . . 30·00 £110
335 – 3f. brown . . . . 42·00 £150
336 – 5f. blue . . . . 70·00 £275
337 – 10f. purple £180 £476
338 **50** 20f. green £200 £575
DESIGNS—HORIZ: 5c., 10f. Schoolteacher; 15c., 3f. Journalist; 20c., 1f.75, Engineer; 35c., 1f.25, Chemist. VERT: 10c., 2f. "The Arts"; 50c., 5f. Barrister; 70c. University.
This set was sold at the P.O. at double face value.

1935. Esch Philatelic Exhibition. Imperf.
339 **37** 2f.(+50c.) black . . . . . 6·00 16·00

52 Vianden

1935.
340 **52** 10f. green . . . . 1·40 9·00

53 Charles I **54** Town Hall

1935. Child Welfare.
341 **53** 10c.+5c. violet 10 40
342 35c.+10c. green 35 60
343 70c.+20c. brown . . . . . 85 1·50
344 1f.+25c. red . . . . 12·50 38·00
345 1f.25+75c. brown . . . . . 12·50 38·00
346 1f.75+1f.50 blue . . . . . 12·50 48·00

1936. 11th Int Philatelic Federation Congress.
347 **54** 10c. brown 35 40
348 35c. green 45 75
349 70c. orange . . . . 55 1·10
350 1f. red . . . . 1·60 6·50
351 1f.25 violet . . . . 2·75 8·50
352 1f.75 blue . . . . 1·60 7·25

55 Wenceslas I **56** Wenceslas II

1936. Child Welfare.
353 **55** 10c.+5c. brown 10 25
354 35c.+10c. green 15 45
355 70c.+20c. slate 35 60
356 1f.+25c. red . . . . 2·10 10·00
357 1f.25+75c. violet . . . . . 4·00 23·00
358 1f.75+1f.50 blue . . . . . 4·00 14·50

1937. Dudelange Philatelic Exhibition. Sheet 125 × 85 mm. As No. 207 (pair) in new colour.
MS359 2f. (+3f.) brown . . . . 1·40 9·50

1937. Child Welfare.
360 **56** 10c.+5c. black and red . . 10 20
361 35c.+10c. green & purple 25 35
362 70c.+20c. red and blue . . 25 35
363 1f.+25c. red and green . . 1·25 11·00
364 1f.25+75c. purple & brn . . 1·60 11·50
365 1f.75+1f.50 blue & blk . . 1·75 13·00

57 St. Willibrord **61** Sigismond of Luxembourg

1938. Echternach Abbey Restoration Fund (1st issue). 1200th Death Anniv of St. Willibrord.
366 **57** 35c.+10c. green 35 45
367 – 70c.+10c. black 85 55
368 – 1f.25+25c. red . . . . . . 1·40 2·25
369 – 1f.75+50c. blue . . . . . 2·40 2·40
370 – 3f.+2f. red . . . . 6·25 7·50
371 – 5f.+5f. violet . . . . . . 7·00 7·25
DESIGNS—As Type **57**: 70c. Town Hall, Echternach; 1f.25, Pavilion, Echternach Municipal Park. 31 × 51 mm: 1f.75, St. Willibrord (from miniature). 42 × 38 mm: 3f. Echternach Basilica; 5f. Whitsuntide dancing procession.
See also Nos. 492/7 and 569/70.

1938. Child Welfare.
372 **61** 10c.+5c. black & mauve . . 10 35
373 35c.+10c. black & green . . 25 40
374 70c.+20c. black & brown 35 40
375 1f.+25c. black and red . . 2·00 11·50

376 1f.25+75c. black & grey . . 2·00 11·50
377 1f.75+1f.50 black & bl . . 2·75 17·00

62 Arms of Luxembourg
63 William I

1939. Centenary of Independence.
378 **62** 35c. green 15 20
379 **63** 50c. orange 20 20
380 – 70c. green 10 20
381 – 75c. olive 45 75
382 – 1f. red 1·00 1·50
383 – 1f.25 violet 15 30
384 – 1f.75 blue 15 30
385 – 3f. brown 30 45
386 – 5f. black 30 3·00
387 – 10f. red 85 7·00
PORTRAITS—As Type **63**: 70c. William II; 75c. William III; 1f. Prince Henry; 1f.25 Grand Duke Adolphe; 1f.75 William IV; 3f. Marie-Anne, wife of William IV; 5f. Grand Duchess Marie Adelaide; 10f. Grand Duchess Charlotte.

1939. Surch in figures.
388 **32** 30c. on 60c. green 15 1·60

65 Allegory of Medicinal Spring
66 Prince Jean

1939. Mondorf-les-Bains Propaganda.
389 **65** 2f. red 40 2·50

1939. 20th Anniv of Reign and of Royal Wedding.
390 **66** 10c.+5c. brn on cream . . 10 40
391 – 35c.+10c. green on cream 25 1·25
392 – 70c.+20c. black on cream 95 1·60
393 **66** 1f.+25c. red on cream . . 4·00 35·00
394 – 1f.25+75c. violet on cream 5·00 48·00
395 – 1f.75+1f.50 blue on cream 6·00 65·00
PORTRAITS: 35c., 1f.25, Prince Felix; 70c., 1f.75, Grand Duchess Charlotte.

1939. Twentieth Year of Reign of Grand Duchess Charlotte. Sheet 144 × 163 mm with designs as T **66** but without "CARITAS".
MS395a 2f. red (T **66**); 3f. green (Prince Felix); 5f. blue (Grand Duchess Charlotte) 35·00 75·00

1940. Anti-T.B. Fund. Surch with Cross of Lorraine and premium.
396 **65** 2f.+50c. grey 1·25 13·00

1940–44. GERMAN OCCUPATION.

1940. T **94** of Germany optd **Luxemburg**.
397 **94** 3pf. brown 10 35
398 4pf. blue 10 40
399 5pf. green 10 40
400 6pf. green 10 35
401 8pf. red 10 35
402 10pf. brown 10 40
403 12pf. red 10 30
404 15pf. purple 20 65
405 20pf. blue 20 1·10
406 25pf. blue 45 1·25
407 30pf. green 45 1·00
408 40pf. mauve 45 1·25
409 50pf. black and green . . 45 1·60
410 60pf. black and purple . . 1·75 3·25
411 80pf. black and blue . . 2·40 12·00
412 100pf. black and yellow . . 90 4·25

1940. Types of Luxembourg surch.
413 **32** 3 Rpf. on 15c. black . . 10 50
414 4 Rpf. on 20c. orange . . 10 50
415 5 Rpf. on 35c. green . . 10 50
416 6 Rpf. on 10c. green . . 10 50
417 8 Rpf. on 25c. brown . . 10 50
418 10 Rpf. on 40c. brown . . 10 50
419 12 Rpf. on 60c. green . . 10 50
420 15 Rpf. on 1f. red . . 10 3·50
421 20 Rpf. on 50c. brown . . 10 85
422 25 Rpf. on 5c. mauve . . 30 2·75
423 30 Rpf. on 70c. violet . . 10 85
424 40 Rpf. on 75c. brown . . 10 1·10
425 50 Rpf. on 1¼f. green . . 10 85
426 **65** 60 Rpf. on 2f. red . . 1·25 18·00
427 **47** 80 Rpf. on 5f. green . . 20 3·25
428 **52** 100 Rpf. on 10f. green . . 20 3·25

1941. Nos. 739/47 of Germany optd **Luxemburg**.
429 3pf.+2pf. brown 20 75
430 4pf.+3pf. blue 20 75
431 5pf.+3pf. green 20 75
432 6pf.+4pf. green 20 75
433 8pf.+4pf. orange 20 75
434 12pf.+6pf. red 20 75
435 15pf.+10pf. purple 1·40 5·50
436 25pf.+15pf. blue 1·40 6·00
437 40pf.+35pf. purple 1·40 6·00

1944. INDEPENDENCE REGAINED.

70 Grand Duchess Charlotte
71 "Britannia"

1944.
438 **70** 5c. brown 10 15
439 10c. slate 10 15
440 20c. orange 30 15
441 25c. brown 10 15
442 30c. red 40 35
443 35c. green 15 30
444 40c. blue 40 35
445 50c. violet 15 15
445a 60c. orange 2·25 15
446 70c. red 15 20
447 70c. green 75 1·10
448 75c. brown 40 20
449 1f. olive 10 15
450 1¼f. orange 20 55
451 1½f. orange 40 20
452 1¾f. blue 10 45
453 2f. red 3·50 30
454 2½f. mauve 8·00 5·50
455 3f. green 75 60
456 3½f. blue 90 75
457 5f. green 10 40
458 10f. red 15 1·10
459 20f. blue 50 19·00

1945. Liberation.
460 – 60c.+1f.40 green 20 25
461 – 1f.20+1f.80 red 20 25
462 **71** 2f.50+3f.50 blue 20 25
463 – 4f.20+4f.80 violet 20 25
DESIGNS: 60c. Ship symbol of Paris between Cross of Lorraine and Arms of Luxembourg; 1f.20, Man killing snake between Arms of Russia and Luxembourg; 4f.20, Eagle between Arms of U.S.A. and Luxembourg.

72 Statue of the Madonna in Procession

74 Lion of Luxembourg

73 Altar and Shrine of the Madonna

1945. Our Lady of Luxembourg.
464 **72** 60c.+40c. green 30 1·00
465 – 1f.20+80c. red 30 1·00
466 – 2f.50+2f.50 blue 40 5·50
467 – 5f.50+6f.50 violet 1·25 65·00
468 **73** 20f.+20f. brown 1·25 65·00
MS468a 83 × 96 mm. 50f+50f. grey (as 1f.20) 2·00 38·00
DESIGNS: As Type **72**: 1f.20, The Madonna; 2f.50, The Madonna and Luxembourg; 5f.50, Portal of Notre Dame Cathedral.

1945.
469 **74** 20c. black 20 20
470 30c. green 20 20
470a 60c. violet 20 25
471 75c. brown 20 20
472 1f.20 red 20 20
473 1f.50 violet 20 15
474 2f.50 blue 30 30

75 Members of the Maquis

76

1945. National War Victims Fund.
475 **75** 20c.+30c. green and buff 20 1·00
476 – 1f.50+1f. red and buff . . 20 1·00
477 – 3f.50+3f.50 blue & buff . . 40 9·25
478 – 5f.+10f. brown and buff . . 35 9·25
MS478a 100 × 110 mm. Designs and colours as Nos. 475/8 but values changed; 2f.50+2f.50, 3f.50+6f.50, 5f.+15f., 20f.+20f. 20·00 £275
DESIGNS: 1f.50, Mother and children; 3f.50, Political prisoner; 5f. Executed civilian.

1946. Air.
479 – 1f. green and blue 35 20
480 **76** 2f. brown and yellow 20 35
481 – 3f. brown and yellow 35 20
482 – 4f. violet and grey 50 30
483 **76** 5f. purple and yellow 45 30
484 – 6f. purple and blue 50 35
485 – 10f. brown and yellow 1·75 50
486 **76** 20f. blue and grey 2·10 1·25
487 – 50f. green and light green 4·00 1·50
DESIGNS: 1, 4, 10f. Airplane wheel; 3, 6, 50f. Airplane engine and castle.

76a Old Rolling Mill, Dudelange

1946. National Stamp Exhibition, Dudelange. Sheet 100 × 80 mm.
MS487a **76a** 50f. (+5f.) blue on buff 14·00 35·00

77 John the Blind, King of Bohemia
78 Exterior Ruins of St. Willibrord Basilica

79 St. Willibrord

1946. 600th Death Anniv of John the Blind.
488 **77** 60c.+40c. green and grey 30 1·60
489 1f.50+50c. red and buff . . 35 2·10
490 3f.50+3f.50 blue & grey . . 1·75 23·00
491 5f.+10f. brown and grey 1·00 19·00

1947. Echternach Abbey Restoration (2nd issue). Inscr "ECHTERNACH".
492 **78** 20c.+10c. black 35 30
493 – 60c.+10c. green 55 60
494 – 75c.+25c. red 85 75
495 – 1f.50c.+50c. brown 1·00 70
496 – 3f.50c.+ 2f.50 blue 5·00 4·50
497 **79** 25f.+25f. purple 27·00 21·00
DESIGNS—As Type **78**: 60c. Statue of Abbot Bertels; 75c. Echternach Abbey emblem; 1f.50, Ruined interior of Basilica; 3f.50, St. Irmine and Pepin II carrying model of Abbey.

80 U.S. Military Cemetery, Hamm
82 Michel Lentz (national poet)

1947. Honouring Gen. George S. Patton.
498 **80** 1f.50 red and buff 40 20
499 – 3f.50 blue and buff 2·25 2·25
500 **80** 5f. green and grey 2·25 2·25
501 – 10f. purple and grey 9·25 35·00
PORTRAIT: 3f.50, 10f. Gen. G. S. Patton.

1947. National Welfare Fund.
502 **82** 60c.+40c. brown & buff . . 65 75
503 1f.50+50c. pur & buff . . 75 75
504 3f.50+3f.50 blue & grey . . 6·00 17·00
505 10f.+5f. green and grey . . 6·50 17·00

83 L'Oesling

85 "Dicks" (Edmund de la Fontaine)

1948. Tourist Propaganda.
505a – 2f.50 brown and chocolate 1·75 35
505b – 3f. violet 5·00 95
505c – 4f. blue 3·75 95
506 **83** 7f. brown 15·00 65
507 – 10f. green 1·90 20
508 – 15f. red 1·90 35
509 – 20f. blue 1·90 35
DESIGNS—HORIZ: 2f.50, Television transmitter, Dudelange; 3f. Radio Luxembourg; 4f. Victor Hugo's house, Vianden; 10f. River Moselle; 15f. Mining district. VERT: 20f. Luxembourg.

1948. National Welfare Fund.
510 **85** 60c.+40c. brown & bistre 45 75
511 1f.50+50c. red and pink . . 70 85
512 3f.50+3f.50 blue & grey . . 9·25 18·00
513 10f.+5f. green and grey . . 11·50 18·00

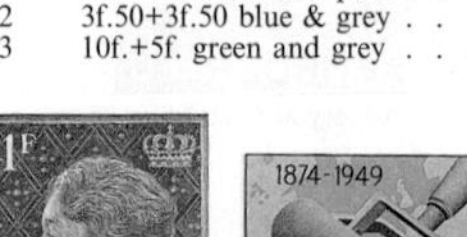

86 Grand Duchess Charlotte

87 Date-stamp and Map

1948.
513a **86** 5c. orange 10 20
513b 10c. blue 10 25
514 15c. olive 10 20
514a 20c. purple 20 20
515 25c. grey 10 20
515a 30c. olive 20 20
515b 40c. red 40 40
515c 50c. orange 40 20
516 60c. bistre 30 25
517 80c. green 30 20
518 1f. red 85 20
518a 1f.20 black 85 30
518b 1f.25 brown 85 35
519 1f.50 turquoise 85 15
520 1f.60 grey 1·25 1·25
521 2f. purple 85 15
521a 2f.50 red 1·40 30
521b 3f. blue 10·00 40
521c 3f.50 red 3·25 45
522 4f. blue 3·25 45
522a 5f. violet 8·00 40
523 6f. purple 6·00 55
524 8f. green 4·50 1·00

1949. 30th Year of Reign of Grand Duchess Charlotte. Sheet 110 × 75 mm.
MS524a **86** 8f.+3f. blue; 12f. + 5f. green; 15f.+7f. brown 75·00 35·00

1949. 75th Anniv of U.P.U.
525 **87** 80c. green, lt green & black 60 55
526 2f.50 red, pink and black 2·75 1·60
527 4f. ultramarine, blue & black 5·00 5·25
528 8f. brown, buff and black 16·00 26·00

88 Michel Rodange

89 Young Girl

1949. National Welfare Fund.
529 **88** 60c.+40c. green and grey 55 45
530 2f.+1f. purple and claret 5·50 4·50
531 4f.+2f. blue and grey 9·00 9·00
532 10f.+5f. brown and buff . . 9·00 17·00

1950. War Orphans Relief Fund.
533 – 60c.+15c. turquoise 1·75 75
534 **89** 1f.+20c. red 4·50 1·10
535 – 2f.+30c. brown 2·10 1·10
536 **89** 4f.+75c. blue 12·00 14·00
537 – 8f.+3f. black 32·00 38·00
538 **89** 10f.+5f. purple 32·00 38·00
DESIGN: 60c., 2f., 8f. Mother and boy.

90 J. A. Zinnen (composer)

91 Ploughman and Factories

1950. National Welfare Week.
539 **90** 60c.+10c. violet and grey 55 25
540 2f.+15c. red and buff 70 35
541 4f.+15c. blue and grey 5·50 6·00
542 8f.+5f. brown and buff 19·00 23·00

1951. To Promote United Europe.
543 **91** 80c. green and light green 10·05 8·25
544 – 1f. violet and light violet 4·50 50
545 – 2f. brown and grey 21·00 50
546 **91** 2f.50 red and orange 21·00 17·00
547 – 3f. brown and yellow 35·00 26·00
548 – 4f. blue and light blue 50·00 35·00
DESIGNS: 1, 3f. Map, people and "Rights of Man" Charter; 2, 4f. Scales balancing "United Europe" and "Peace".

92 L. Menager (composer)

1951. National Welfare Fund.
549 **92** 60c.+10c. black and grey 40 35
550 2f.+15c. green and grey 40 35
551 4f.+15c. blue and grey 4·50 3·00
552 8f.+5f. purple and grey 24·00 27·00

92a T **1** and **86**

92b T **1**

1952. National Philatelic Exhibition ("CENTILUX") and Stamp Centenary.
552a **92a** 80c. black, pur & grn (air) 50 55
552b 2f.50 black, purple & red 1·25 1·40
552c 4f. black, purple and blue 3·25 3·25
552d 8f. black, purple and red 40·00 50·00
552e 10f. black, purple & brn 35·00 42·00
552f **92b** 2f. blk & grn (postage) 26·00 35·00
552g 4f. red and green 26·00 35·00

93 Hurdling

1952. 15th Olympic Games, Helsinki.
553 **93** 1f. black and green 55 40
554 – 2f. blk & lt brn (Football) 2·25 40
555 – 2f.50 blk & pink (Boxing) 3·50 1·25
556 – 3f. blk & drab (Water polo) 4·50 1·40
557 – 4f. black and blue (Cycling) 21·00 6·75
558 – 8f. black and lilac (Fencing) 13·50 4·00

94 J. B. Fresez (painter) **95** Prince Jean and Princess Josephine Charlotte

1952. National Welfare Fund.
559 **94** 60c.+15c. green and blue 40 40
560 2f.+25c. brown & orange 40 40
561 4f.+25c. violet and grey 3·50 3·50
562 8f.+4f.75 purple & lt pur 25·00 32·00

1953. Royal Wedding.
563 **95** 80c. violet and deep mauve 45 35
564 1f.20 deep brown & brown 45 35
565 2f. deep green and green 1·40 35
566 3f. deep purple and purple 1·40 55
567 4f. deep blue and blue 6·00 1·00
568 9f. brown and red 6·00 1·00

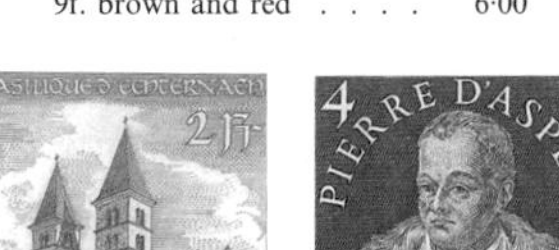

96 Echternach Basilica **97** Pierre D'Aspelt

1953. Echternach Abbey Restoration (3rd issue).
569 **96** 2f. red 3·50 35
570 – 2f.50 olive 5·00 5·25
DESIGN: 2f.50, Interior of Basilica.

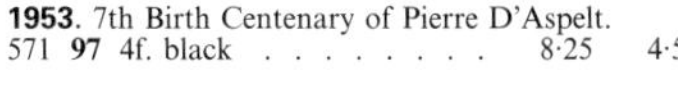

1953. 7th Birth Centenary of Pierre D'Aspelt.
571 **97** 4f. black 8·25 4·50

98 "Candlemas Singing" **99** Foils, Mask and Gauntlet

1953. National Welfare Fund.
572 **98** 25c.+15c. carmine and red 40 40
573 – 80c.+20c. blue and brown 40 40
574 – 1f.20+30c. green & turq 95 75
575 **98** 2f.+25c. brown and red 50 40
576 – 4f.+50c. blue & turquoise 6·75 6·50
577 – 7f.+3f.35 lilac and violet 19·00 18·00
DESIGNS: 80c., 4f. "The Rattles"; 1f.20, 7f. "The Easter-eggs".

1954. World Fencing Championships.
578 **99** 2f. deep brown and brown on cream 4·25 60

100 Fair Emblem **101** Earthenware Whistle

1954. Luxembourg International Fair.
579 **100** 4f. multicoloured 10·00 4·00

1954. National Welfare Fund.
580 **101** 25c.+5c. red and orange 50 45
581 – 80c.+20c. grey & black 50 45
582 – 1f.20+30c. green and cream 1·75 1·40
583 **101** 2f.+25c. brown and buff 70 55
584 – 4f.+50c. dp blue & blue 6·50 6·25
585 – 7f.+3f.45 violet & mve 26·00 22·00
DESIGNS: 80c., 4f. Sheep and drum; 1f.20, 7f. Merry-go-round horses.

102 Tulips **103**

1955. Mondorf-les-Bains Flower Show.
586 **102** 80c. red, green and brown 25 25
587 – 2f. yellow, green and red 35 25
588 – 3f. purple, green & emer 2·75 4·50
589 – 4f. orange, green and blue 4·50 4·50
FLOWERS: 2f. Daffodils; 3f. Hyacinths; 4f. Parrot tulips.

1955. 1st National Crafts Exhibition.
590 **103** 2f. black and grey 1·50 35

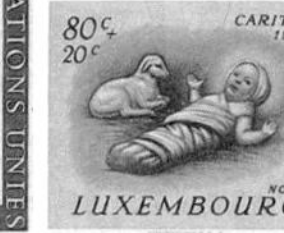

104 "Charter" **105** "Christmas Day"

1955. 10th Anniv of U.N.
591 **104** 80c. blue and black 65 55
592 – 2f. brown and red 5·00 30
593 – 4f. red and blue 3·75 3·00
594 – 9f. green and brown 1·60 85
SYMBOLIC DESIGNS: 2f. "Security"; 4f. "Justice"; 9f. "Assistance".

1955. National Welfare Fund.
595 – 25c.+5c. red and pink 35 30
596 **105** 80c.+20c. black and grey 35 30
597 – 1f.20+30c. deep green and green 60 80
598 – 2f.+25c. deep brown and brown 70 30
599 **105** 4f.+50c. blue & lt blue 6·50 9·50
600 – 7f.+3f.45 purple & mve 13·00 13·50
ALLEGORICAL DESIGNS: 25c., 2f. "St. Nicholas's Day"; 1f.20, 7f. "Twelfth Night".

1956. Mondorf-les-Bains Flower Show. As T **102** but inscription at top in one line. Multicoloured.
601 2f. Anemones 75 25
602 3f. Crocuses 3·00 1·60

1956. Roses. As T **102** but inscr at top "LUXEMBOURG-VILLE DES ROSES". Multicoloured.
603 2f.50 Yellow roses 5·00 4·00
604 4f. Red roses 2·50 2·25

108 Steel Plant and Girder **109** Blast Furnaces and Map

1956. 50th Anniv of Esch-sur-Alzette.
605 **108** 2f. red, black & turquoise 2·75 45

1956. European Coal and Steel Community. Inscr as in T **109**.
606 **109** 2f. red 26·00 50
607 – 3f. blue 26·00 20·00
608 – 4f. green 5·00 4·25
DESIGNS—VERT: 3f. Girder supporting City of Luxembourg. HORIZ: 4f. Chain and miner's lamp.

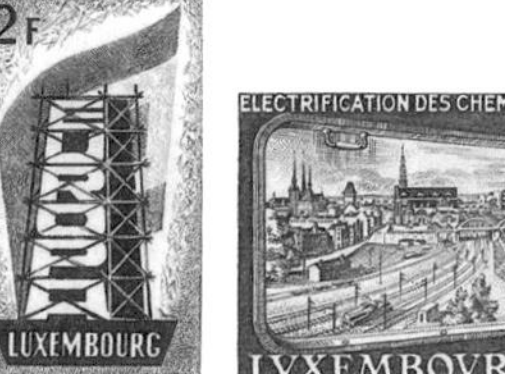

110 **111** Luxembourg Central Station

1956. Europa.
609 **110** 2f. black and brown £250 35
610 3f. red and orange 42·00 35·00
611 4f. deep blue and blue 2·50 2·50

1956. Electrification of Luxembourg Railways.
612 **111** 2f. sepia and black 2·00 45

112 I. de la Fontaine **113** Arms of Echternach

1956. Council of State Centenary. Inscr as in T **112**.
613 **112** 2f. sepia 1·40 35
614 – 7f. purple 2·75 75
DESIGN: 7f. Grand Duchess Charlotte.

1956. National Welfare Fund. Inscr "CARITAS 1956". Arms. Multicoloured.
615 25c.+5c. Type **113** 30 35
616 80c.+20c. Esch-sur-Alzette 30 35
617 1f.20+30c. Grevenmacher 45 70
618 2f.+25c. Type **113** 35 35
619 4f.+50c. Esch-sur-Alzette 3·50 4·00
620 7f.+3f.45 Grevenmacher 7·50 11·50

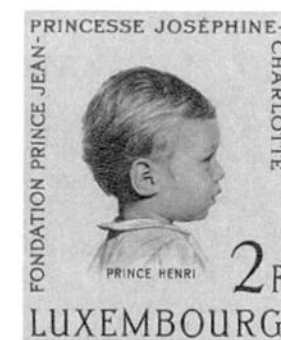

114 Lord Baden-Powell and Scout Emblems **115** Prince Henri

1957. Birth Centenary of Lord Baden-Powell, and 50th Anniv of Scouting Movement.
621 **114** 2f. brown and green 1·00 25
622 – 2f.50 red and violet 2·50 2·40
DESIGN: 2f.50, as Type **114** but showing Girl Guide emblems.

1957. "Prince Jean and Princess Josephine-Charlotte Foundation" Child Welfare Clinic.
623 **115** 2f. deep brown and brown 1·00 25
624 – 3f. deep green and green 3·50 3·00
625 – 4f. deep blue and blue 2·50 2·50
DESIGNS—HORIZ: 3f. Children's Clinic Project. VERT: 4f. Princess Marie-Astrid.

116 "Peace" **117** Fair Entrance and Flags

1957. Europa.
626 **116** 2f. brown 2·40 25
627 3f. red 38·00 15·00
628 4f. purple 32·00 15·00

1957. National Welfare Fund. Arms as T **113** inscr "CARITAS 1957". Multicoloured.
629 25c.+5c. Luxembourg 35 40
630 80c.+20c. Mersch 35 40
631 1f.20+30c. Vianden 45 60
632 2f.+25c. Luxembourg 30 35
633 4f.+50c. Mersch 3·50 4·50
634 7f.+3f.45 Vianden 5·50 7·00

1958. 10th Anniv of Luxembourg Int Fair.
635 **117** 2f. multicoloured 30 25

118 Luxembourg Pavilion **119** St. Willibrord holding Child (after Puseel)

1958. Brussels Exhibition.
636 **118** 2f.50 blue and red 30 25

1958. 1300th Birth Anniv of St. Willibrord.
637 – 1f. red 30 30
638 **119** 2f.50 sepia 35 20
639 – 5f. blue 90 85
DESIGNS: 1f. St. Willibrord and St. Irmina holding inscribed plaque; 5f. St. Willibrord and suppliant. (Miracle of the wine-cask).

119a Europa **120** Open-air Theatre at Wiltz

1958. Europa.
640 **119a** 2f.50 blue and red 15 15
641 3f.50 brown and green 2·50 25
642 5f. red and blue 65 65

1958. Wiltz Open-air Theatre Commemoration.
643 **120** 2f.50 sepia and grey 55 15

121 Vineyard   **122** Grand Duchess Charlotte

1958. Bimillenary of Moselle Wine Industry.
644 **121** 2f.50 brown and green . . 55 15

1958. National Welfare Fund. Arms as T **113** inscr "CARITAS 1958". Multicoloured.
645 30c.+10c. Capellen 35 30
646 1f.+25c. Diekirch 35 30
647 1f.50+25c. Redange 55 45
648 2f.50+50c. Capellen 35 30
649 5f.+50c. Diekirch . . . . . . 3·25 4·00
650 8f.50+4f.60 Redange . . . . 5·00 6·75

1959. 40th Anniv of Accession of Grand Duchess Charlotte.
651 **122** 1f.50 deep green & green 70 35
652 2f.50 brown & lt brown 70 35
653 5f. lt blue and ultramarine 1·40 1·10

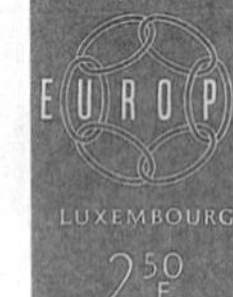

123 N.A.T.O. Emblem   **123a** Europa

1959. 10th Anniv of N.A.T.O.
654 **123** 2f.50 blue and olive . . . 20 15
655 8f.50 blue and brown . . 55 40

1959. Mondorf-les-Bains Flower Show. As T **102** but inscr "1959".
656 1f. violet, yellow and turquoise 30 30
657 2f.50 red, green and blue . . 40 25
658 3f. blue, green and purple . . 65 60
FLOWERS: 1f. Iris; 2f.50, Peony; 3f. Hortensia.

1959. Europa.
659 **123a** 2f.50 green 45 20
660 5f. blue 75 85

124 Steam Locomotive and First Bars of Hymn "De Feierwon"

1959. Railways Centenary.
661 **124** 2f.50 blue and red . . . . 1·90 40

1959. National Welfare Fund. Arms as T **113** inscr "CARITAS 1959". Multicoloured.
662 30c.+10c. Clervaux 35 30
663 1f.+25c. Remich 35 30
664 1f.50+25c. Wiltz 60 45
665 2f.50+50c. Clervaux 35 30
666 5f.+50c. Remich . . . . . . 1·50 1·90
667 8f.50+4f.60 Wiltz . . . . . . 6·50 9·50

125 Refugees seeking Shelter   **126** Steel Worker

1960. World Refugee Year.
668 **125** 2f.50 blue and salmon . . 20 15
669 – 5f. blue and violet 35 40
DESIGN—HORIZ: 5f. "The Flight into Egypt" (Biblical scene).

1960. 10th Anniv of Schuman Plan.
670 **126** 2f.50 lake 30 25

127 European School, Luxembourg   **128** Grand Duchess Charlotte

1960. European School Commemoration.
671 **127** 5f. black and blue 95 95

1960.
672 **128** 10c. red 10 25
673 20c. red 10 25
673a 25c. orange 20 25
674 30c. drab 10 15
675 50c. green 50 15
676 1f. violet 50 15
677 1f.50 mauve 50 15
678 2f. turquoise 55 25
679 2f.50 purple 85 25
680 3f. dull purple . . . . 2·40 15
680a 3f.50 turquoise . . . . . 2·50 1·75
681 5f. brown . . . . 1·25 25
681a 6f. turquoise . . . . . . 2·40 25

129 Heraldic Lion, and Tools

1960. 2nd National Crafts Exhibition.
682 **129** 2f.50 multicoloured . . . 1·40 35

129a Conference Emblem   **130** Princess Marie-Astrid

1960. Europa.
683 **129a** 2f.50 green and black . . 40 15
684 5f. black and red 65 35

1960. National Welfare Fund. Inscr "CARITAS 1960". Centres and inscr in sepia.
685 **130** 30c.+10c. blue 20 25
686 – 1f.+25c. pink 20 25
687 – 1f.50+25c. turquoise . . . 50 60
688 **130** 2f.50+50c. yellow 40 35
689 – 5f.+50c. lilac . . . . . . 85 2·40
690 – 8f.50+4f.60 sage . . . . 3·25 12·00
DESIGNS: Princess Marie-Astrid standing (1, 5f.), sitting with book on lap (1f.50, 8f.50).

131 Great Spotted Woodpecker   **132** Patton Monument, Ettelbruck

1961. Animal Protection Campaign. Inscr "PROTECTION DES ANIMAUX".
691 **131** 1f. multicoloured 20 25
692 – 1f.50 buff, blue and black 25 25
693 – 3f. brown, buff and violet 40 40
694 – 8f.50 multicoloured . . . 60 70
DESIGNS—VERT: 8f.50, Dachshund. HORIZ: 1f.50, Cat; 3f. Horse.

1961. Tourist Publicity.
695 **132** 2f.50 blue and black . . . 50 25
696 – 2f.50 green 50 25
DESIGN—VERT: No. 696, Clervaux.

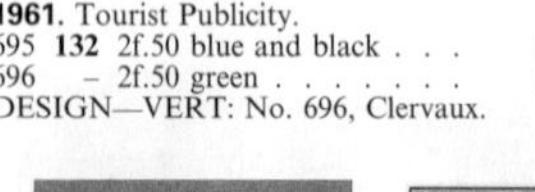

133 Doves   **134** Prince Henri

1961. Europa.
697 **133** 2f.50 red 15 15
698 5f. blue 25 25

1961. National Welfare Fund. Inscr "CARITAS 1961". Centres and inscr in sepia.
699 **134** 30c.+10c. mauve 35 35
700 – 1f.+25c. lavender 35 35
701 – 1f.50+25c. salmon 45 50
702 **134** 2f.50+50c. green 45 35
703 – 5f.+50c. yellow . . . . . 2·40 2·40
704 – 8f.50+4f.60 grey . . . . 4·00 6·50

DESIGNS: Prince Henri when young boy (1, 5f.); youth in formal dress (1f.50, 8f.50).

135 Cyclist carrying Cycle   **136** Europa "Tree"

1962. World Cross-country Cycling Championships, Esch-sur-Alzette.
705 **135** 2f.50 multicoloured . . . 30 25
706 – 5f. multicoloured (Emblem) 30 40

1962. Europa.
707 **136** 2f.50 multicoloured . . . 25 15
708 5f. brown, green & purple 35 30

137 St. Laurent's Church, Diekirch   **138** Prince Jean and Princess Margaretha as Babies

1962.
709 **137** 2f.50 black and brown . . 45 25

1962. National Welfare Fund. inscr "CARITAS 1962". Centres and inscr in sepia.
710 **138** 30c.+10c. buff 30 25
711 – 1f.+25c. blue 30 25
712 – 1f.50+25c. olive 35 40
713 – 2f.50+50c. pink 35 25
714 – 5f.+50c. green . . . . . 1·40 2·40
715 – 8f.50+4f.60 violet . . . . 3·25 4·50
PORTRAITS—VERT: 1f., 2f.50, Prince Jean and: 2f.50, 5f. Princess Margaretha, at various stages of childhood. HORIZ: 8f.50, The Royal Children.

139 Blackboard   **140** Benedictine Abbey, Munster

1963. 10th Anniv of European Schools.
716 **139** 2f.50 green, red and grey 20 15

1963. Millenary of City of Luxembourg and International Philatelic Exhibition. (a) Horiz views.
717 – 1f. blue 20 25
718 **140** 1f.50 red 20 25
719 – 2f.50 green 20 25
720 – 3f. brown 20 25
721 – 5f. violet 45 60
722 – 11f. blue . . . . 1·40 1·75
VIEWS: 1f. Bock Rock; 2f.50, Rham Towers; 3f. Grand Ducal Palace; 5f. Castle Bridge; 11f. Millenary Buildings.

(b) Vert multicoloured designs.
723 1f. "Three Towers" Gate 20 25
724 1f.50 Great Seal 20 30
725 2f.50 "The Black Virgin" (statue), St. John's Church 20 30
726 3f. Citadel 35 30
727 5f. Town Hall 20 45

141 Colpach Castle

1963. Red Cross Centenary.
728 **141** 2f.50 red and slate 30 25

142 "Human Rights"

1963. 10th Anniv of European "Human Rights" Convention.
729 **142** 2f.50 blue on gold 20 25

143 "Co-operation"   **144** Brown trout snapping Bait

1963. Europa.
730 **143** 3f. green, orange & turq 20 15
731 6f. orange, red and brown 35 35

1963. World Fishing Championships, Wormeldange.
732 **144** 3f. slate 25 15

145 Telephone Dial   **146** St. Roch (patron saint of bakers)

1963. Inauguration of Automatic Telephone System.
733 **145** 3f. green, black and blue 25 15

1963. National Welfare Fund. Patron Saints of Crafts and Guilds. Inscr "CARITAS 1963". Multicoloured.
734 50c.+10c. Type **146** 20 25
735 1f.+25c. St. Anne (tailors) . . 20 25
736 2f.+25c. St. Eloi (smiths) . . 20 35
737 3f.+50c. St. Michel (haberdashers) 20 25
738 6f.+50c. St. Barthelemy (butchers) . . . . 1·00 1·90
739 10f.+5f.90 St. Thibaut (seven crafts) . . . . 1·75 3·25

147 Power House   **148** Barge entering Canal

1964. Inauguration of Vianden Reservoir.
740 **147** 2f. blue, brown and red 20 15
741 – 3f. blue, turq & red . . . 20 15
742 – 6f. brown, blue and green 30 30
DESIGNS—HORIZ: 3f. Upper reservoir. VERT: 6f. Lohmuhle Dam.

1964. Inauguration of Moselle Canal.
743 **148** 3f. indigo and blue . . . 30 15

149 Europa "Flower"   **150** Students thronging "New Athenaeum"

1964. Europa.
744 **149** 3f. blue, brown and cream 20 15
745 6f. sepia, green and yellow 30 25

1964. Opening of "New Athenaeum" (education centre).
746 **150** 3f. black and green . . . 20 25

150a King Baudouin, Queen Juliana and Grand Duchess Charlotte

1964. 20th Anniv of "BENELUX".
747 **150a** 3f. brown, yellow & blue . . . 20 25

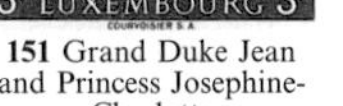

151 Grand Duke Jean and Princess Josephine-Charlotte
152 Three Towers

1964. Accession of Grand Duke Jean.
748 **151** 3f. deep blue and light blue 30 15
749 6f. sepia and light brown . . . 35 30

1964. National Welfare Fund. Inscr "CARITAS 1964". Multicoloured.
750 50c.+10c. Type **152** 20 25
751 1f.+25c. Grand Duke Adolphe Bridge 20 25
752 2f.+25c. Lower Town 20 25
753 3f.+50c. Type **152** 20 25
754 6f.+50c. Grand Duke Adolphe Bridge . . . . . 85 1·75
755 10f.+5f.90 Lower Town . . . 1·40 2·50

153 Rotary Emblem and Cogwheels
154 Grand Duke Jean

1965. 60th Anniv of Rotary International.
756 **153** 3f. multicoloured 20 15

1965.

757	**154**	25c. brown	20	10
758		50c. red	20	10
759		1f. blue	20	10
760		1f.50 purple	10	10
761a		2f. red	35	10
762		2f.50 orange	35	30
763a		3f. green	45	10
763b		3f.50 brown	45	45
764a		4f. purple	50	10
764ba		5f. green	45	10
765a		6f. lilac	55	10
765b		7f. orange	50	20
765c		8f. blue	70	25
766		9f. green	70	25
766a		10f. black	50	10
767		12f. red	1·00	25
767a		14f. blue	70	40
767b		16f. green	1·00	30
767c		18f. green	35	45
767d		20f. blue	85	25
767e		22f. brown	1·25	85

155 I.T.U. Emblem and Symbols

1965. Centenary of I.T.U.
768 **155** 3f. blue, lake and violet . . . 30 25

156 Europa "Sprig"
157 "The Roman Lady of the Titelberg"

1965. Europa.
769 **156** 3f. turquoise, red and black 20 25
770 6f. brown, blue and green . . . 30 30

1965. National Welfare Fund. Fairy Tales. Inscr "CARITAS 1965". Multicoloured.
771 50c.+10c. Type **157** 15 25
772 1f.+25c. "Schappchen, the Huntsman" 15 25
773 2f.+25c. "The Witch of Koerich" 20 25
774 3f.+50c. "The Goblins of Schoendels" 20 25
775 6f.+50c. "Tollchen, Watchman of Hesperange" . . 35 1·10
776 10f.+5f.90 "The Old Spinster of Heispelt" . . . . 1·10 3·00

158 "Flag" and Torch
159 W.H.O. Building

1966. 50th Anniv of Luxembourg Workers' Union.
777 **158** 3f. red and grey 20 15

1966. Inaug of W.H.O. Headquarters, Geneva.
778 **159** 3f. green 20 15

160 Golden Key
161 Europa "Ship"

1966. Tercentenary of Solemn Promise to Our Lady of Luxembourg.
779 **160** 1f.50 green 10 15
780 – 2f. red 10 15
781 – 3f. blue 15 15
782 – 6f. brown 30 30
DESIGNS: 2f. Interior of Luxembourg Cathedral (after painting by J. Martin); 3f. Our Lady of Luxembourg (after engraving by R. Collin); 6f. Gallery pillar, Luxembourg Cathedral (after sculpture by D. Muller).

1966. Europa.
783 **161** 3f. blue and grey 20 25
784 6f. green and brown 35 30

162 Class 1800 Diesel-electric Locomotive

1966. Luxembourg Railwaymen's Philatelic Exhibition. Multicoloured.
785 1f.50 Type **162** 50 25
786 3f. Class 3600 electric locomotive 50 30

163 Grand Duchess Charlotte Bridge
164 Kirchberg Building and Railway Viaduct

1966. Tourism.
787 **163** 3f. lake 20 15
See also Nos. 807/8, 828 and 844/5.

1966. "Luxembourg-European Centre".
788 **164** 1f.50 green 20 25
789 – 13f. blue (Robert Schuman monument) . . . 50 35

165 "Mary, Veiled Matron of Wormeldange"
166 City of Luxembourg, 1850 (after engraving by N. Liez)

1966. National Welfare Fund. Luxembourg Fairy Tales. Multicoloured.
790 50c.+10c. Type **165** 15 25
791 1f.50+25c. "Jekel Warden of the Wark" 15 25
792 2f.+25c. "The Black Gentleman of Vianden" . . 15 30
793 3f.+50c. "The Gracious Fairy of Rosport" 20 25
794 6f.+1f. "The Friendly Shepherd of Donkolz" . . 45 85
795 13f.+6f.90 "The Little Sisters of Trois-Vierges" . . . . . 60 2·50

1967. Centenary of Treaty of London.
796 **166** 3f. brown, blue and green . . 20 25
797 – 6f. red, brown and blue . . 30 30
DESIGN—VERT: 6f. Plan of Luxembourg fortress c. 1850 (after T. de Cederstolpe).

167 Cogwheels
168 Lion on Globe

1967. Europa.
798 **167** 3f. purple, grey and buff . . 35 25
799 6f. sepia, purple and blue . . 40 35

1967. 50th Anniv of Lions International.
800 **168** 3f. yellow, purple & black . . 20 25

169 European Institutions Building, Luxembourg
170 Hikers and Hostel

1967. N.A.T.O. Council Meeting, Luxembourg.
801 **169** 3f. turquoise and green . . 20 25
802 6f. red and pink 35 40

1967. Luxembourg Youth Hostels.
803 **170** 1f.50 multicoloured . . . 15 25

171 Shaving-dish (after Degrotte)
172 "Gardener"

1967. "200 Years of Luxembourg Pottery".
804 **171** 1f.50 multicoloured . . . 20 25
805 – 3f. multicoloured 20 25
DESIGN—VERT: 3f. Vase, c. 1820.

1967. "Family Gardens" Congress, Luxembourg.
806 **172** 1f.50 orange and green . . 15 25

1967. Tourism. As T **163**.
807 3f. indigo and blue 30 25
808 3f. purple, green and blue . . 45 25
DESIGNS—HORIZ: No. 807, Moselle River and quayside, Mertert. VERT: No. 808, Moselle, Church and vines, Wormeldange.

173 Prince Guillaume
174 Football

1967. National Welfare Fund. Royal Children and Residence.
809 **173** 50c.+10c. brown & buff . . 20 25
810 – 1f.50+25c. brown & bl . . 20 25
811 – 2f.+25c. brown and red . . 20 25
812 – 3f.+50c. brown & yell . . 65 25
813 – 6f.+1f. brown & lav . . . 45 1·00
814 – 13f.+6f.90 brn, grn & bl . . 60 3·25
DESIGNS: 1f.50, Princess Margaretha; 2f. Prince Jean; 3f. Prince Henri; 6f. Princess Marie-Astrid; 13f. Berg Castle.

1968. Olympic Games, Mexico.
815 – 50c. light blue and blue . . 20 15
816 **174** 1f.50 green and emerald . . 20 15
817 – 2f. yellow and green . . . 25 15
818 – 3f. light orange and orange 20 15
819 – 6f. green and blue 25 25
820 – 13f. red and crimson . . . 45 35
DESIGNS: 50c. Diving; 2f. Cycling; 3f. Running; 6f. Walking; 13f. Fencing.

175 Europa "Key"

1968. Europa.
821 **175** 3f. brown, black and green 35 15
822 6f. green, black and orange 40 35

176 Thermal Bath Pavilion, Mondorf-les-Bains

1968. Mondorf-les-Bains Thermal Baths.
823 **176** 3f. multicoloured 25 15

177 Fair Emblem

1968. 20th Anniv of Luxembourg Int Fair.
824 **177** 3f. multicoloured 25 25

178 Village Project
179 "Blood Transfusion"

1968. Luxembourg SOS Children's Village.
825 **178** 3f. purple and green . . . 30 15
826 – 6f. black, blue and purple . 35 30
DESIGN—VERT: 6f. Orphan with foster-mother.

1968. Blood Donors of Luxembourg Red Cross.
827 **179** 3f. red and blue 40 25

180 Fokker Friendship over Luxembourg
181 Cap Institute

1968. Tourism.
828 **180** 50f. dp blue, brown & blue . . . . 2·50 25

1968. National Welfare Fund. Luxembourg Handicapped Children.
829 **181** 50c.+10c. brown and blue . 20 25
830 – 1f.50+25c. brn & grn . . 20 25
831 – 2f.+25c. brown & yell . . 30 35
832 – 3f.+50c. brown and blue . 30 25
833 – 6f.+1f. brown and buff . . 50 90
834 – 13f.+6f.90 brown and pink . . . . 1·25 3·00
DESIGNS: 1f.50, Deaf and dumb child; 2f. Blind child; 3f. Nurse supporting handicapped child; 6f. and 13f. Mentally handicapped children (different).

182
183 Colonnade

1969. "Juventus 1969" Junior International Philatelic Exhibition. Sheet 111 × 70 mm containing T **182** and similar vert designs. Multicoloured.
MS835 3f. Type **182**; 6f. "Sport"; 13f. Sun, open book and ball . . 2·50 3·25

1969. Europa.
836 **183** 3f. multicoloured 35 15
837 6f. multicoloured 40 35

184 "The Wooden Horse" (Kutter)

1969. 75th Birth Anniv of Joseph Kutter (painter). Multicoloured.
838 3f. Type **184** 50 25
839 6f. "Luxembourg" (Kutter) 50 40

185 ILO Emblem **186** National Colours

1969. 50th Anniv of Int Labour Organization.
840 **185** 3f. gold, violet and green 30 15

1969. 25th Anniv of "BENELUX" Customs Union.
841 **186** 3f. multicoloured 30 15

187 N.A.T.O. Emblem **188** Ear of Wheat and Agrocentre, Mersch

1969. 20th Anniv of N.A.T.O.
842 **187** 3f. orange and brown . . 35 15

1969. "Modern Agriculture".
843 **188** 3f. grey and green 20 15

189 Echternach **190** Vianden Castle

1969. Tourism.
844 **189** 3f. indigo and blue . . . 30 25
845 – 3f. blue and green 30 25
DESIGN: No. 845, Wiltz.

1969. National Welfare Fund. Castles (1st series). Multicoloured.
846 50c.+10c. Type **190** 15 25
847 1f.50+25c. Lucilinburhuc . . 15 25
848 2f.+25c. Bourglinster 20 25
849 3f.+50c. Hollenfels 20 25
850 6f.+1f. Ansembourg . . . . 50 1·40
851 13f.+6f.90 Beaufort . . . . . 85 3·25
See also Nos. 862/7.

191 Pasque Flower **192** Firecrest

1970. Nature Conservation Year. Multicoloured.
852 3f. Type **191** 20 25
853 6f. West European hedgehogs 35 40

1970. 50 Years of Bird Protection.
854 **192** 1f.50 green, black & orge 20 20

193 "Flaming Sun"

1970. Europa.
855 **193** 3f. multicoloured 35 15
856 6f. multicoloured 40 40

194 Road Safety Assoc. Emblem and Traffic

1970. Road Safety.
857 **194** 3f. black, red and lake . . 20 15

195 "Empress Kunegonde and Emperor Henry II" (stained-glass windows, Luxembourg Cathedral)

1970. Centenary of Luxembourg Diocese.
858 **195** 3f. multicoloured 20 25

196 Population Pictograph

1970. Population Census.
859 **196** 3f. red, blue and green . . 20 15

197 Facade of Town Hall, Luxembourg

1970. 50th Anniv of Union of Four Suburbs with Luxembourg City.
860 **197** 3f. brown, ochre and blue 20 15

198 U.N. Emblem **199** Monks in the Scriptorium

1970. 25th Anniv of United Nations.
861 **198** 1f.50 violet and blue . . . 10 15

1970. National Welfare Fund. Castles (2nd series). Designs as T **190**.
862 50c.+10c. Clervaux 15 25
863 1f.50+25c. Septfontaines . . 15 25
864 2f.+25c. Bourschied 20 25
865 3f.+50c. Esch-sur-Sure . . . 20 25
866 6f.+1f. Larochette . . . . . 50 1·40
867 13f.+6f.90 Brandenbourg . . 80 3·25

1971. Medieval Miniatures produced at Echternach. Multicoloured.
868 1f.50 Type **199** 20 25
869 3f. Vine-growers going to work 20 15
870 6f. Vine-growers at work and returning home 20 25
871 13f. Workers with spades and hoe 50 55

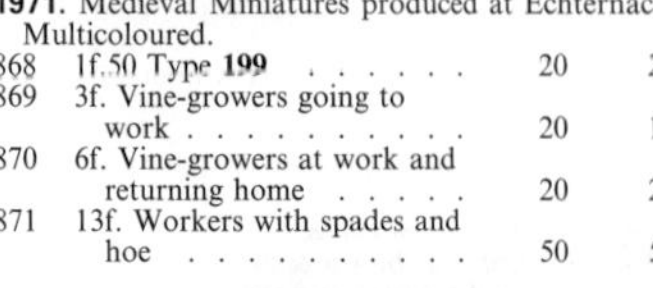

200 Europa Chain

1971.
872 **200** 3f. black, brown and red 35 15
873 6f. black, brown and green 50 55

201 Olympic Rings and Arms of Luxembourg **202** "50" and Emblem

1971. Int Olympic Committee Meeting, Luxembourg.
874 **201** 3f. red, gold and blue . . 20 25

1971. 50th Anniv of Luxembourg's Christian Workers' Union (L.C.G.B.).
875 **202** 3f. purple, orange & yell 20 15

203 Artificial Lake, Upper Sure Valley **204** Child with Coin

1971. Man-made Landscapes.
876 **203** 3f. blue, grey and brown 35 15
877 – 3f. brown, green and blue 35 25
878 – 15f. black, blue and brown 65 15
DESIGNS: No. 877, Water-processing plant, Esch-sur-Sure; No. 878, ARBED (United Steelworks) Headquarters Building, Luxembourg.

1971. Schoolchildren's Saving Campaign.
879 **204** 3f. multicoloured 25 25

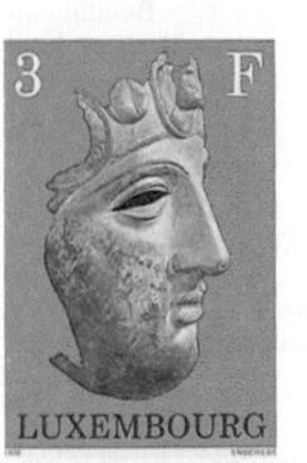

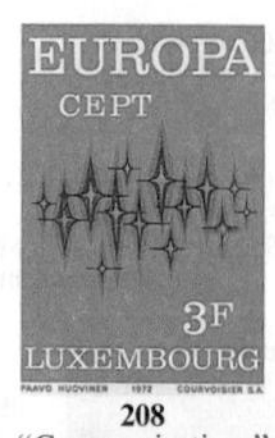

205 "Bethlehem Children" **206** Coins of Belgium and Luxembourg

1971. National Welfare Fund. "The Nativity"–wood-carvings in Beaufort Church. Multicoloured.
880 1f.+25c. Type **205** 30 25
881 1f.50+25c. "Shepherds" . . . 30 25
882 3f.+50c. "Virgin, Child Jesus and St. Joseph" 30 25
883 8f.+1f. "Herdsmen" . . . . 85 2·40
884 18f.+6f.50 "One of the Magi" 1·60 5·25

1972. 50th Anniv of Belgium–Luxembourg Economic Union.
885 **206** 1f.50 silver, black & green 20 25

207 Bronze Mask (1st cent) **208** "Communications"

1972. Gallo-Roman Exhibits from Luxembourg State Museum. Multicoloured.
886 1f. Samian bowl (2nd century) (horiz) 20 15
887 3f. Type **207** 35 15
888 8f. Limestone head (2nd/3rd century) 65 75
889 15f. Glass "head" flagon (4th century) 60 65

1972. Europa.
890 **208** 3f. multicoloured 35 15
891 8f. multicoloured 85 85

209 Archer **210** R. Schuman (after bronze by R. Zilli)

1972. 3rd European Archery Championships, Luxembourg.
892 **209** 3f. multicoloured 35 15

1972. 20th Anniv of Establishment of European Coal and Steel Community in Luxembourg.
893 **210** 3f. green and grey 45 15

211 National Monument **212** "Renert"

1972. Monuments and Buildings.
894 **211** 3f. brown, green and violet 35 25
895 – 3f. brown, green and blue 55 25
DESIGN: No. 895, European Communities' Court of Justice.

1972. Cent of Publication of Michel Rodange's "Renert" (satirical poem).
896 **212** 3f. multicoloured 30 25

213 "Angel" **214** "Epona on Horseback"

1972. National Welfare Fund. Stained Glass Windows in Luxembourg Cathedral. Multicoloured.
897 1f.+25c. Type **213** 20 25
898 1f.50+25c. "St. Joseph" . . . 20 25
899 3f.+50c. "Holy Virgin with Child Jesus" 20 25
900 8f.+1f. "People of Bethlehem" . . . . 85 2·40
901 18f.+6f.50 "Angel" (facing left) . . . . 2·50 6·00

1973. Archaeological Relics. Multicoloured.
902 1f. Type **214** 20 15
903 4f. "Panther attacking swan" (horiz) 30 25
904 8f. Celtic gold coin 85 85
905 15f. Bronze boar (horiz) . . . 70 60

215 Europa "Posthorn" **216** Bee on Honeycomb

1973. Europa.
906 **215** 4f. orange, blue and violet 35 25
907 8f. green, yellow & purple 1·00 90

1973. Bee-keeping.
908 **216** 4f. multicoloured 45 15

217 Nurse and Child **218** Capital, Vianden Castle

1973. Day Nurseries in Luxembourg.
909 **217** 4f. multicoloured 35 15

1973. Romanesque Architecture in Luxembourg.
910 **218** 4f. purple and green . . . 30 15
911 – 8f. blue and brown . . . 70 75
DESIGN: 8f. Detail of altar, St. Irmina's Chapel, Rosport.

219 Labour Emblem
220 J. de Busleyden

1973. 50th Anniv of Luxembourg Board of Labour.
912 **219** 3f. multicoloured 25 15

1973. 500th Anniv of Great Council of Malines.
913 **220** 4f. purple and brown . . 30 15

221 Monument, Wiltz
222 Joachim and St. Anne

1973. National Strike Monument.
914 **221** 4f. green, brown and grey 35 15

1973. National Welfare Fund. "The Nativity". Details from 16th-century reredos, Hachiville Hermitage. Multicoloured.
915 1f.+25c. Type **222** 20 25
916 3f.+25c. "Mary meets Elizabeth" 20 25
917 4f.+50c. "Magus presenting gift" 25 25
918 8f.+1f. "Shepherds at the manger" . . . . 85 2·25
919 15f.+7f. "St. Joseph with Candle" . . . . 2·50 6·75

223 Princess Marie-Astrid, Association President
224 Flame Emblem

1974. Luxembourg Red Cross Youth Association.
920 **223** 4f. multicoloured . . . . 1·40 30

1974. 50th Anniv of Luxembourg Mutual Insurance Federation.
921 **224** 4f. multicoloured 45 30

225 Seal of Henry VII, King of the Romans
226 "Hind" (A. Tremont)

1974. Seals in Luxembourg State Archives.
922 **225** 1f. brown, yellow & purple 20 15
923 – 3f. brown, yellow & green 30 30
924 – 4f. dk brown, yellow & brn 35 25
925 – 19f. brown, yellow & blue 85 75
DESIGNS: 3f. Equestrian seal of John the Blind, King of Bohemia; 4f. Municipal seal of Diekirch; 19f. Seal of Marienthal Convent.

1974. Europa. Sculptures. Multicoloured.
926 4f. Type **226** 80 25
927 8f. "Abstract" (L. Wercollier) 1·90 1·50

227 Churchill Memorial, Luxembourg
228 Diagram of Fair

1974. Birth Centenary of Sir Winston Churchill.
928 **227** 4f. multicoloured 35 15

1974. New International Fair, Luxembourg-Kirchberg.
929 **228** 4f. multicoloured 35 15

229 "Theis the Blind" (artist unknown)
230 "Crowning of St. Cecily and St. Valerien" (Hollenfels Church)

1974. 150th Death Anniv of "Theis the Blind" (Mathias Schou, folk singer).
930 **229** 3f. multicoloured 35 40

1974. Gothic Architecture.
931 **230** 4f. brown, green and violet 30 15
932 – 4f. black, brown and blue 30 15
DESIGN: No. 932, Interior of Septfontaines Church.

231 U.P.U. Emblem on "100"

1974. Centenary of Universal Postal Union.
933 **231** 4f. multicoloured 25 25
934 8f. multicoloured 35 75

232 "Benelux"

1974. 30th Anniv of Benelux (Customs Union).
935 **232** 4f. turquoise, green & blue 85 25

233 Differdange

1974. Tourism.
936 **233** 4f. purple 85 15

234 "Annunciation"
235 "Crucifixion"

1974. National Welfare Fund. Illustrations from "Codex Aureus Epternacensis". Multicoloured.
937 1f.+25c. Type **234** 20 25
938 3f.+25c. "Visitation" 20 25
939 4f.+50c. "Nativity" 25 25
940 8f.+1f. "Adoration of the Magi" . . . . 1·00 2·40
941 15f.+7f. "Presentation at the Temple" . . . . 1·90 5·25

1974. 50th Anniv of Christmas Charity Stamps. Detail of cover from "Codex Aureus Epternacensis". Sheet 80 × 90 mm.
MS942 **235** 20f.+10f. multicoloured 3·50 8·25

236 The Fish Market, Luxembourg

1975. European Architectural Heritage Year.
943 **236** 1f. green 35 25
944 – 3f. brown 85 35
945 – 4f. lilac . . . . 1·00 25
946 – 19f. red . . . . 1·00 90
DESIGNS—HORIZ: 3f. Bourglinster Castle; 4f. Market Square, Echternach. VERT: 19f. St. Michael's Square, Mersch.

237 "Joseph Kutter" (self-portrait)
238 Dr. Albert Schweitzer

1975. Luxembourg Culture, and Europa. Paintings. Multicoloured.
947 1f. Type **237** 30 25
948 4f. "Remich Bridge" (N. Klopp) (horiz) . . . . 1·00 30
949 8f. "Still Life" (J. Kutter) (horiz) . . . . 2·00 1·75
950 20f. "The Dam" (D. Lang) 1·25 50

1975. Birth Centenary of Dr. Albert Schweitzer (medical missionary).
951 **238** 4f. blue 55 25

239 Robert Schuman, G. Martino and P.-H. Spaak
240 Civil Defence Emblem

1975. 25th Anniv of Robert Schuman Declaration for European Unity.
952 **239** 4f. black, gold and green 55 25

1975. 15th Anniv of Civil Defence Reorganization.
953 **240** 4f. multicoloured 50 25

241 Ice Skating
242 Fly Orchid

1975. Sports. Multicoloured.
954 **241** 3f. purple, blue and green 35 30
955 – 4f. brown, green & dp brn 50 15
956 – 15f. blue, brown and green . . . . 1·00 70
DESIGNS—HORIZ: 4f. Water-skiing. VERT: 15f. Rock-climbing.

1975. National Welfare Fund. Protected Plants (1st series). Multicoloured.
957 1f.+25c. Type **242** 20 25
958 3f.+25c. Pyramid orchid . . . 40 30
959 4f.+50c. Marsh helleborine 50 15
960 8f.+1f. Pasque flower . . . . 1·10 1·75
961 15f.+7f. Bee orchid . . . . . 2·50 5·00
See also Nos. 976/80 and 997/1001.

243 Grand Duchess Charlotte (80th)
244 7th-century Disc-shaped Brooch

1976. Royal Birthdays. Multicoloured.
962 6f. Type **243** . . . . 1·25 35
963 6f. Prince Henri (21st) . . . 1·25 35

1976. Luxembourg Culture. Ancient Treasures from Merovingian Tombs. Multicoloured.
964 2f. Type **244** 20 15
965 5f. 5th-6th century glass beaker (horiz) 30 30
966 6f. Ancient pot (horiz) . . . 30 25
967 12f. 7th century gold coin . . 90 90

245 Soup Tureen

1976. Europa. 19th-century Pottery. Multicoloured.
968 6f. Type **245** 65 25
969 12f. Bowl . . . . 1·50 1·40

246 Independence Hall, Philadelphia
247 Symbol representing "Strength and Impetus"

1976. Bicentenary of American Revolution.
970 **246** 6f. multicoloured 35 30

1976. Olympic Games, Montreal.
971 **247** 6f. gold, magenta and mauve 35 30

248 Association Emblem and "Sound Vibrations"
249 "Virgin and Child"

1976. 30th Anniv of "Jeunesses Musicales" (Youth Music Association).
972 **248** 6f. multicoloured 35 30

1976. Renaissance Art. Multicoloured.
973 6f. Type **249** 35 25
974 12f. Bernard de Velbruck, Lord of Beaufort (funeral monument) 85 85

250 Alexander Graham Bell

1976. Telephone Centenary.
975 **250** 6f. green 35 25

1976. National Welfare Fund. Protected Plants (2nd series). As T **242**. Multicoloured.
976 2f.+25c. Gentian 20 25
977 5f.+25c. Wild daffodil . . . 20 25
978 6f.+50c. Red helleborine (orchid) 30 25
979 12f.+1f. Late spider orchid 85 2·00
980 20f.+8f. Twin leaved squill 2·50 5·00

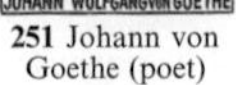

251 Johann von Goethe (poet) **252** Fish Market, Luxembourg

1977. Luxembourg Culture. Famous Visitors to Luxembourg.
981 **251** 2f. purple 20 15
982 – 5f. violet 30 30
983 – 6f. black 50 25
984 – 12f. violet 65 70
DESIGNS: 5f. Joseph Mallard William Turner (painter); 6f. Victor Hugo (writer); 12f. Franz Liszt (musician).

1977. Europa. Multicoloured.
985 6f. Type **252** 45 30
986 12f. Grand Duke Adolphe railway bridge and European Investment Bank 1·40 1·25

253 Esch-sur-Sure **254** Marguerite de Busbach (founder)

1977. Tourism.
987 **253** 5f. blue 45 25
988 – 6f. brown 35 25
DESIGNS 6f. Ehnen.

1977. Anniversaries. Multicoloured.
989 6f. Type **254** 40 25
990 6f. Louis Braille (after Filippi) 40 25
ANNIVERSARIES: No. 989, 350th anniv of foundation of Notre Dame Congregation; No. 990, 125th death anniv.

LUXEMBOURG 40F

255 10c. and 1sgr. Stamps of 1852

1977. 125th Anniv of Luxembourg Stamps. Sheet 90 × 60 mm.
MS991 **255** 40f. black, chestnut and grey . . . . 4·00 5·25

256 St. Gregory the Great **257** Head of Medusa

1977. Baroque Art. Sculpture from Feulen Parish Church pulpit attributed to J.-G. Scholtus.
992 **256** 6f. purple 40 25
993 – 12f. grey 70 80
DESIGN: 12f. St. Augustine.

1977. Roman Mosaic at Diekirch.
994 **257** 6f. multicoloured 70 25

258 Scene from "Orpheus and Eurydice" (Gluck)

1977. 25th Wiltz International Festival.
995 **258** 6f. multicoloured 65 25

259 Map of E.E.C. and "Europa" (R. Zilli)

1977. 20th Anniv of Rome Treaties.
996 **259** 6f. multicoloured 55 25

1977. National Welfare Fund. Protected Plants (3rd series). As T **242**. Multicoloured.
997 2f.+25c. Lily of the valley 20 25
998 5f.+25c. Columbine 30 30
999 6f.+50c. Mezereon 50 30
1000 12f.+1f. Early spider orchid 1·40 2·40
1001 20f.+8f. Spotted orchid . . 2·40 5·00

260 Grand Duke Jean and Duchess Josephine-Charlotte **261** Fountain and Youth

1978. Royal Silver Wedding. Sheet 116 × 67 mm.
MS1002 **260** 6f., 12f. multicoloured 1·25 1·50

1978. "Juphilux 78" Junior International Philatelic Exhibition. Sheet 103 × 72 mm containing T **261** and similar vert designs. Multicoloured.
MS1003 5f. Type **261**; 6f. Streamer; 20f. Dancing youths . . . . . 3·00 4·50
MS1003 was on sale at 60f., including entrance fee of 29f., at the Exhibition, by postal application and at post offices.

262 Charles IV **263** Head of Our Lady of Luxembourg

1978. Europa.
1004 **262** 6f. lilac 35 25
1005 – 12f. red . . . . 1·00 1·10
DESIGN: 12f. Pierre d'Aspelt (funeral monument, Mainz Cathedral).

1978. Anniversaries. Multicoloured.
1006 6f. Type **263** (300th anniv of election as patron saint) 35 30
1007 6f. Trumpeters (135th anniv of Grand Ducal Military Band) 35 30

264 Emile Mayrisch (after T. van Rysselberghe) **265** Child with Ear of Millet

1978. 50th Death Anniv of Emile Mayrisch (iron and steel magnate).
1008 **264** 6f. multicoloured 85 25

1978. "Solidarity 1978". Multicoloured.
1009 2f. Type **265** (Terre des Hommes) 20 15
1010 5f. Flower and lungs (70th anniv of Luxembourg Anti-tuberculosis League) 20 25
1011 6f. Open cell (Amnesty International and 30th anniv of Declaration of Human Rights) 30 25

266 Perfect Ashlar **267** "St. Matthew"

1978. 175th Anniv of Luxembourg Grand Lodge.
1012 **266** 6f. blue 35 30

1978. National Welfare Fund. Glass Paintings (1st series). Multicoloured.
1013 2f.+25c. Type **267** 15 25
1014 5f.+25c. "St. Mark" 30 30
1015 6f.+50c. "Nativity" 40 30
1016 12f.+1f. "St. Luke" . . . . 1·40 65
1017 20f.+8f. "St. John" . . . . 1·75 4·50
See also Nos. 1035/9 and 1055/8.

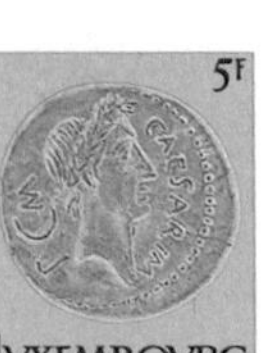

268 Denarius of Gaius Julius Caesar **269** Mondorf-les-Bains

1979. Luxembourg Culture. Roman Coins in the State Museum. Multicoloured.
1018 5f. Type **268** 30 25
1019 6f. Sestertius of Faustina I 50 25
1020 9f. Follis of Helena 70 45
1021 26f. Solidus of Valens . . . 1·40 1·25
See also Nos. 1040/3 and 1060/3.

1979. Tourism.
1022 **269** 5f. green, brown and blue 50 15
1023 – 6f. red 85 15
DESIGN: 6f. Luxembourg Central Station.

270 Stage Coach **271** Antoine Meyer (poet)

1979. Europa. Multicoloured.
1024 6f. Type **270** . . . . 2·40 25
1025 12f. Old wall telephone (vert) . . . . 2·40 1·50

1979. Anniversaries.
1026 – 2f. purple 45 25
1027 **271** 5f. red 35 25
1028 – 6f. turquoise 35 25
1029 – 9f. grey-black 35 35
DESIGNS—36 × 36 mm: 2f. Michel Pintz on trial (after L. Piedboeuf) and monument to rebels (180th anniv of peasant uprising against French). 22 × 36 mm: 5f. Type **271** (150th anniv of first publication in Luxembourg dialect); 6f. S. G. Thomas (cent of purchase of Thomas patent for steel production); 9f. "Abundance crowning Work and Saving" (ceiling painting by August Vinet) (50th anniv of Stock Exchange).

272 "European Assembly" **273** Blindfolded Cherub with Chalice

1979. First Direct Elections to European Assembly.
1030 **272** 6f. multicoloured . . . . 1·10 60

1979. Rococo Art. Details from altar of St. Michael's Church by Barthelemy Namur. Multicoloured.
1031 6f. Type **273** 35 30
1032 12f. Cherub with anchor . . 50 75

274 Child with Traffic Symbol Balloons jumping over Traffic

1979. International Year of the Child.
1033 **274** 2f. blue, brown and red 20 15

275 Radio Waves, "RTL" and Dates

1979. 50th Anniv of Broadcasting in Luxembourg.
1034 **275** 6f. blue and red 45 25

1979. National Welfare Fund. Glass Paintings (2nd series). As T **267**. Multicoloured.
1035 2f.+25c. "Spring" 15 20
1036 5f.+25c. "Summer" 30 30
1037 6f.+50c. "Charity" 40 30
1038 12f.+1f. "Autumn" 70 15
1039 20f.+8f. "Winter" . . . . . 1·25 4·50

1980. Luxembourg Culture. Medieval Coins in the State Museum. As T **268**. Multicoloured.
1040 2f. Grosso of Emperor Henry VII 15 15
1041 5f. Grosso of John the Blind of Bohemia 20 25
1042 6f. "Mouton d'or" of Wenceslas I and Jeanne, Duke and Duchess of Brabant 65 25
1043 20f. Grosso of Wenceslas II, Duke of Luxembourg . . 1·60 75

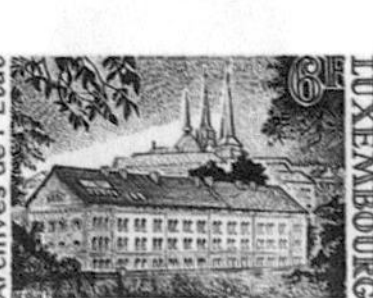

276 State Archives Building **277** Jean Monnet (statesman)

1980. Tourism.
1044 **276** 6f. purple, ultram & bl 50 15
1045 – 6f. red and brown . . . 60 15
DESIGN—VERT: No. 1045, Ettelbruck Town Hall.

1980. Europa.
1046 **277** 6f. black 50 25
1047 – 12f. olive . . . . 1·00 90
DESIGN: 12f. St. Benedict of Nursia (founder of Benedictine Order) (statue in Echternach Abbey).

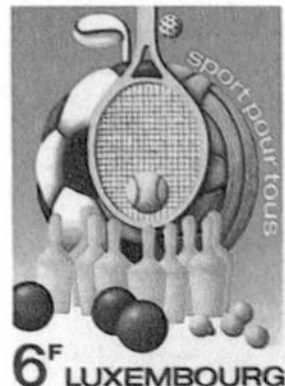

278 Sports Equipment **279** Gloved Hand protecting Worker from Machinery

1980. "Sports for All".
1048 **278** 6f. black, orange & green 1·40 30

1980. 9th World Congress on the Prevention of Accidents at Work and Occupational Diseases, Amsterdam.
1049 – 2f. multicoloured 20 15
1050 **279** 6f. brown, grey and red 40 25
DESIGN—VERT: 2f. Worker pouring molten iron.

280 "Mercury" (Jean Mich) **281** Postcoded Letter

1980. Art Nouveau Sculpture. Statues beside entrance to State Savings Bank.
1051 **280** 8f. lilac 45 30
1052 – 12f. blue 65 60
DESIGN: 12f. "Ceres" (Jean Mich).

1980. Postcode Publicity.
1053 **281** 4f. brown, ochre and red 50 15

282 Policemen and Patrol Car

1980. 50th Anniv of National Police Force.
1054 **282** 8f. multicoloured 55 25

1980. National Welfare Fund. Glass Paintings (3rd series). As T **267**. Multicoloured.
1055 4f.+50c. "St. Martin" . . . 30 25
1056 6f.+50c. "St. Nicholas" . . 30 25
1057 8f.+1f. "Virgin and child" 40 1·00
1058 30f.+10f. "St. George" . . . 2·25 4·50

283 Grand Duke Jean

1981. Grand Duke Jean's 60th Birthday. Sheet 115×73 mm containing T **283** and similar vert design.
MS1059 8f. Type **283**; 12f. Grand Duke Jean's coat of arms; 30f. Type **283** . . . . 1·75 2·10

1981. Luxembourg Culture. Coins in the State Museum. As T **268**.
1060 4f. Patagon of Philip IV of Spain, 1635 . . . . . . 20 25
1061 6f. 12 sols coin of Maria Theresa, 1775 . . . . . . 30 30
1062 8f. 12 sols coin of Emperor Joseph II, 1789 . . . . . 30 30
1063 30f. Siege crown of Emperor Francis II, 1795 . . . . . 1·00 1·00

284 European Parliament Building, Luxembourg

285 Cock-shaped Whistle sold at Easter Monday Market

1981. Tourism.
1064 **284** 8f. brown and blue . . . 35 25
1065 – 8f. red and blue 35 25
DESIGN: No. 1065, National Library.

1981. Europa. Multicoloured.
1066 8f. Procession of beribboned sheep and town band to local fair 45 25
1067 12f. Type **285** 70 65

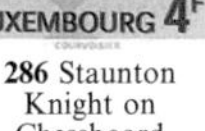

286 Staunton Knight on Chessboard

287 Prince Henri and Princess Maria Teresa

1981. Anniversaries.
1068 **286** 4f. multicoloured 30 25
1069 – 8f. ochre, brown & silver 40 30
1070 – 8f. multicoloured 40 30
DESIGNS—VERT: 4f. Type **286** (50th anniv of Luxembourg Chess Federation); 8f. (1070), Pass-book and State Savings Bank (125th anniv of State Savings Bank). HORIZ: 8f. (1069), First Luxembourg banknote (125th anniv of International Bank of Luxembourg's issuing rights).

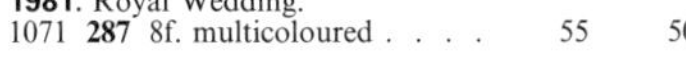

1981. Royal Wedding.
1071 **287** 8f. multicoloured 55 50

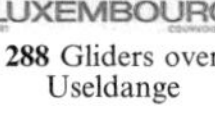

288 Gliders over Useldange

289 Flame

1981. Aviation. Multicoloured.
1072 8f. Type **288** 45 30
1073 16f. Cessna 172F Skyhawk and 182H Skylane sports planes 70 65
1074 35f. Boeing 747-200F 182H over Luxembourg-Findel airport terminal . . . . . 1·40 90

1981. Energy Conservation.
1075 **289** 8f. multicoloured 50 20

290 Arms of Petange

291 "Apple Trees in Blossom" (Frantz Seimetz)

1981. National Welfare Fund. Arms of Local Authorities (1st series). Multicoloured.
1076 4f.+50c. Type **290** 20 25
1077 6f.+50c. Larochette 25 25
1078 8f.+1f. "Adoration of the Magi" (School of Rubens) 40 35
1079 16f.+2f. Stadtbredimus . . . 70 1·75
1080 35f.+12f. Weiswampach . . 2·50 4·50
See also Nos. 1097/1101 and 1119/23.

1982. Luxembourg Culture. Landscapes through the Four Seasons. Multicoloured.
1081 4f. Type **291** 30 30
1082 6f. "Landscape" (Pierre Blanc) 40 40
1083 8f. "The Larger Hallerbach" (Guido Oppenheim) . . . 45 30
1084 16f. "Winter Evening" (Eugene Mousset) 85 80

292 Cross of Hinzert and Statue "Political Prisoner" (Lucien Wercollier)

293 Treaty of London, 1867, and Luxembourg Fortress

1982. National Monument of the Resistance and Deportation, Notre-Dame Cemetery.
1085 **292** 8f. multicoloured 40 20

1982. Europa. Multicoloured.
1086 8f. Type **293** 50 30
1087 16f. Treaty of Paris, 1951, and European Coal and Steel Community Building, Luxembourg . . 85 80

294 St. Theresa of Avila (wood statue, Carmel Monastery)

295 State Museum

1982. Anniversaries. Multicoloured.
1088 4f. Type **294** (400th death anniv) 20 15
1089 8f. Raoul Follereau (social worker for lepers, 5th death anniv) 35 25

1982. Tourism.
1090 **295** 8f. brown, blue and black 40 20
1091 – 8f. buff, black and blue 40 20
DESIGN: No. 1091, Luxembourg Synagogue.

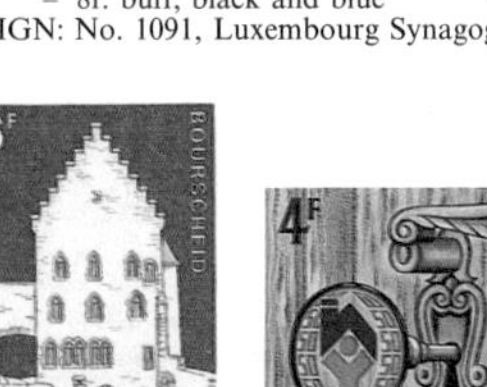

296 Bourscheid Castle

297 Key in Lock

1982. Classified Monuments (1st series).
1092 **296** 6f. blue 30 20
1093 – 8f. red 45 20
DESIGN—HORIZ: 8f. Vianden Castle.
See also Nos. 1142/3 and 1165/6.

1982. Anniversaries. Multicoloured.
1094 4f. Type **297** (50th anniv of International Youth Hostel Federation) . . . 45 30
1095 8f. Scouts holding hands around globe (75th anniv of Scouting Movement) (vert) 70 30

298 Monument to Civilian and Military Deportation

1982. Civilian and Military Deportation Monument, Hollerich Station.
1096 **298** 8f. multicoloured 40 30

1982. National Welfare Fund. Arms of Local Authorities (2nd series) and Stained Glass Window (8f.). As T **290**. Multicoloured.
1097 4f.+50c. Bettembourg . . . 25 25
1098 6f.+50c. Frisange 30 25
1099 8f.+1f. "Adoration of the Shepherds" (Gustav Zanter, Hoscheid parish church) 45 80
1100 16f.+2f. Mamer . . . . . . 85 1·75
1101 35f.+12f. Heinerscheid . . . 2·40 4·75

299 Modern Fire Engine

300 "Mercury" (Auguste Tremont)

1983. Centenary of National Federation of Fire Brigades. Multicoloured.
1102 8f. Type **299** 45 30
1103 16f. Hand fire-pump (18th century) 70 75

1983. Anniversaries and Events.
1104 **300** 4f. multicoloured 30 30
1105 – 6f. multicoloured 30 30
1106 – 8f. brown, black and blue 40 30
1107 – 8f. deep blue and blue 40 30
DESIGNS: No. 1104, Type **300** (25th Congress of International Association of Foreign Exchange Dealers); 1105, N.A.T.O. emblem surrounded by flags of member countries (25th anniv of N.A.T.O.); 1106, Echternach Cross of Justice (30th Congress of International Union of Barristers); 1107, Globe and customs emblem (30th anniv of Customs Co-operation Council).

301 Robbers attacking Traveller

1983. Europa. Miniatures from "Codex Aureus Escorialensis", illustrating Parable of the Good Samaritan. Multicoloured.
1108 8f. Type **301** . . . . 1·25 40
1109 16f. Good Samaritan helping traveller . . . . . 2·75 1·25

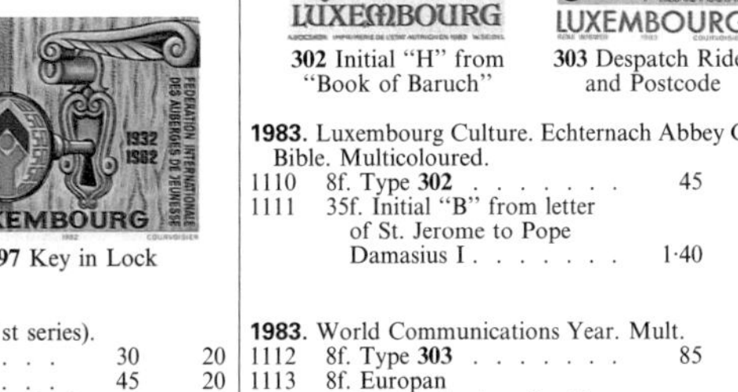

302 Initial "H" from "Book of Baruch"

303 Despatch Rider and Postcode

1983. Luxembourg Culture. Echternach Abbey Giant Bible. Multicoloured.
1110 8f. Type **302** 45 35
1111 35f. Initial "B" from letter of St. Jerome to Pope Damasius I . . . . 1·40 1·10

1983. World Communications Year. Mult.
1112 8f. Type **303** 85 20
1113 8f. European Communications Satellite (horiz) . . . . 1·75 30

304 St. Lawrence's Church, Diekirch

305 Basketball

1983. Tourism.
1114 **304** 7f. orange, brown and blue 35 20
1115 – 10f. orange, brown & bl 55 20
DESIGN—HORIZ: 10f. Dudelange Town Hall.

1983. Anniversaries and Events. Multicoloured.
1116 7f. Type **305** (50th anniv of Luxembourg basketball Federation) 45 35
1117 10f. Sheepdog (European Working Dog Championships) 65 35
1118 10f. City of Luxembourg ("The Green Heart of Europe") . . . . 1·10 35

1983. National Welfare Fund. Arms of Local Authorities (3rd series) and Painting. As T **290**. Multicoloured.
1119 4f.+1f. Winseler 30 30
1120 7f.+1f. Beckerich 40 35
1121 10f.+1f. "Adoration of the Shepherds" (Lucas Bosch) 45 50
1122 16f.+2f. Feulen . . . . . . 85 1·75
1123 40f.+13f. Mertert . . . . . 2·40 4·25

306 Lion and First Luxembourg Stamp

307 Pedestrian Precinct

1984. Anniversaries. Each black, red and blue.
1124 10f. Type **306** 70 35
1125 10f. Lion and ministry buildings 70 35
1126 10f. Lion and postman's bag 70 35
1127 10f. Lion and diesel locomotive 70 35
ANNIVERSARIES: No. 1124, 50th anniv of Federation of Luxembourg Philatelic Societies; 1125, 75th anniv of Civil Service Trade Union Movement; 1126, 75th anniv of Luxembourg Postmen's Trade Union; 1127, 125th anniv of Luxembourg Railways.

1984. Environmental Protection. Multicoloured.
1128 7f. Type **307** 45 35
1129 10f. City of Luxembourg sewage treatment plant . . 45 35

308 Hands supporting European Parliament Emblem

309 Bridge

1984. 2nd Direct Elections to European Parliament.
1130 **308** 10f. multicoloured . . . 70 40

1984. Europa. 25th Anniv of European Post and Telecommunications Conference.
1131 **309** 10f. green, dp green & blk . . . . 1·60 35
1132 16f. orange, brown & blk 3·25 1·40

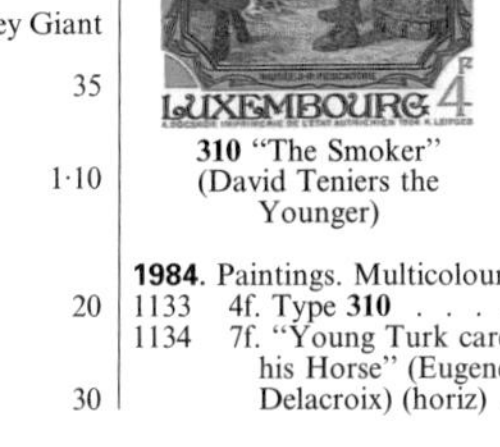

310 "The Smoker" (David Teniers the Younger)

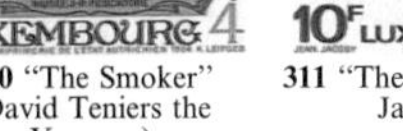

311 "The Race" (Jean Jacoby)

1984. Paintings. Multicoloured.
1133 4f. Type **310** 50 30
1134 7f. "Young Turk caressing his Horse" (Eugene Delacroix) (horiz) 65 35

1135 10f. "Ephiphany" (Jan Steen) (horiz) 85 35
1136 50f. "The Lacemaker" (Pieter van Slingelandt) 3·50 2·50

1984. Olympic Games, Los Angeles.
1137 **311** 10f. orange, black & blue 65 30

312 "Pecten sp."

313 "American Soldier" (statue by Michel Heitz at Clervaux)

1984. Luxembourg Culture. Fossils in the Natural History Museum. Multicoloured.
1138 4f. Type **312** 45 20
1139 7f. Devil's toe-nail 50 35
1140 10f. "Coeloceras raquinianum" (ammonite) 85 35
1141 16f. Dapedium (fish) . . . . 1·00 85

1984. Classified Monuments (2nd series). As T **296**.
1142 7f. turquoise 35 35
1143 10f. brown 45 30
DESIGNS: 7f. Hollenfels Castle; 10f. Larochette Castle.

1984. 40th Anniv of Liberation.
1144 **313** 10f. black, red and blue 1·40 30

314 Infant astounded by Surroundings

315 Jean Bertels (abbot of Echternach Abbey)

1984. National Welfare Fund. The Child. Mult.
1145 4f.+1f. Type **314** 35 35
1146 7f.+1f. Child dreaming . . . 50 50
1147 10f.+1f. "Nativity (crib, Steinsel church) 85 55
1148 16f.+2f. Child sulking . . . 2·40 2·50
1149 40f.+13f. Girl admiring flower . . . . 6·00 6·75

1985. Luxembourg Culture. Portrait Medals in State Museum (1st series). Multicoloured.
1150 4f. Type **315** (steatite medal, 1595) 25 30
1151 7f. Emperor Charles V (bronze medal, 1537) . . 35 35
1152 10f. King Philip II of Spain (silver medal, 1555) . . . 45 35
1153 30f. Maurice of Orange-Nassau (silver medal, 1615) . . . . 1·40 1·00
See also Nos. 1173/6.

316 Fencing

317 Papal Arms

1985. Anniversaries. Multicoloured.
1154 10f. Type **316** (50th anniv of Luxembourg Fencing Federation) 60 30
1155 10f. Benz "Velo" (centenary of automobile) 60 30
1156 10f. Telephone within concentric circles (centenary of Luxembourg telephone service) 60 30

1985. Visit of Pope John Paul II.
1157 **317** 10f. multicoloured . . . 45 30

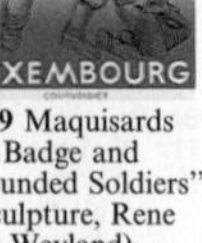

318 Treble Clef within Map of National Anthem

319 Maquisards Badge and "Wounded Soldiers" (sculpture, Rene Weyland)

1965. Europa. Music Year. Multicoloured.
1158 10f. Type **318** (Grand Duke Adolphe Union of choral, instrumental and folklore societies) . . . . 1·50 35
1159 16f. Neck of violin, music school and score of Beethoven's Violin Concerto opus 61 . . . . 3·00 1·60

1985. 40th Anniv of V.E. (Victory in Europe) Day. Sheet 120×72 mm containing T **319** and similar vert designs.
MS1160 10f. multicoloured (Type **319**); 10f. brown, black and blue (War medal); 10f. multicoloured (Union of Resistance Movements badge); 10f. black, red and blue (dove and barbed wire hands) (liberation of prison camps) . . . . 2·40 2·75

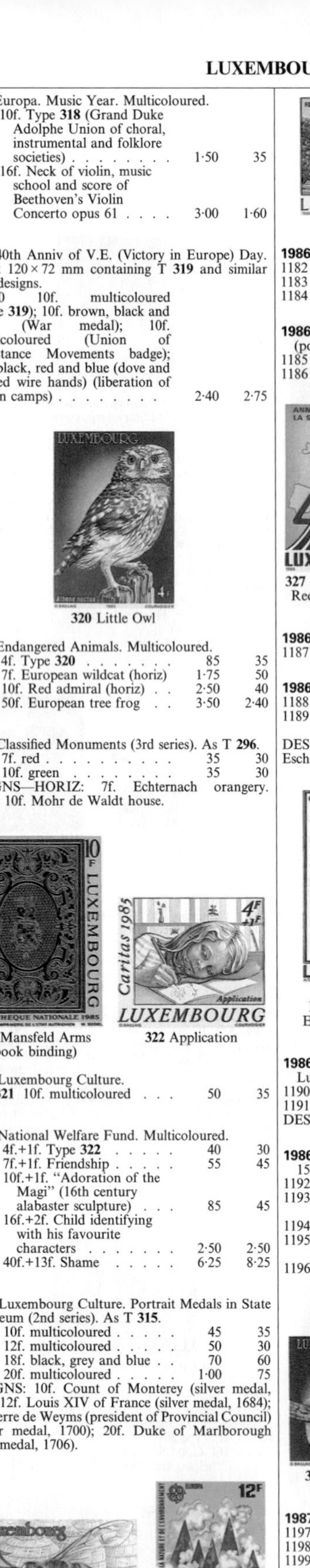

320 Little Owl

1985. Endangered Animals. Multicoloured.
1161 4f. Type **320** 85 35
1162 7f. European wildcat (horiz) 1·75 50
1163 10f. Red admiral (horiz) . . 2·50 40
1164 50f. European tree frog . . 3·50 2·40

1985. Classified Monuments (3rd series). As T **296**.
1165 7f. red 35 30
1166 10f. green 35 30
DESIGNS—HORIZ: 7f. Echternach orangery. VERT: 10f. Mohr de Waldt house.

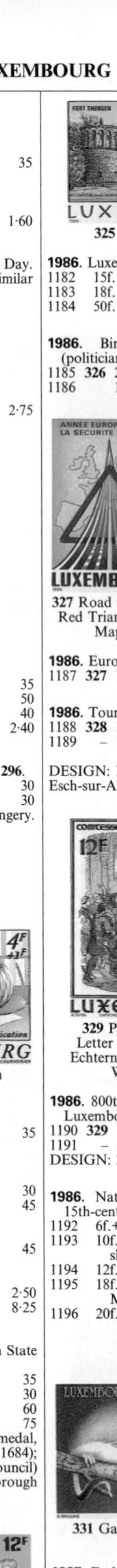

321 Mansfeld Arms (book binding)

322 Application

1985. Luxembourg Culture.
1167 **321** 10f. multicoloured . . . 50 35

1985. National Welfare Fund. Multicoloured.
1168 4f.+1f. Type **322** 40 30
1169 7f.+1f. Friendship 55 45
1170 10f.+1f. "Adoration of the Magi" (16th century alabaster sculpture) . . . 85 45
1171 16f.+2f. Child identifying with his favourite characters . . . . 2·50 2·50
1172 40f.+13f. Shame . . . . . 6·25 8·25

1986. Luxembourg Culture. Portrait Medals in State Museum (2nd series). As T **315**.
1173 10f. multicoloured 45 35
1174 12f. multicoloured 50 30
1175 18f. black, grey and blue . . 70 60
1176 20f. multicoloured . . . . . 1·00 75
DESIGNS: 10f. Count of Monterey (silver medal, 1675); 12f. Louis XIV of France (silver medal, 1684); 18f. Pierre de Weyms (president of Provincial Council) (pewter medal, 1700); 20f. Duke of Marlborough (silver medal, 1706).

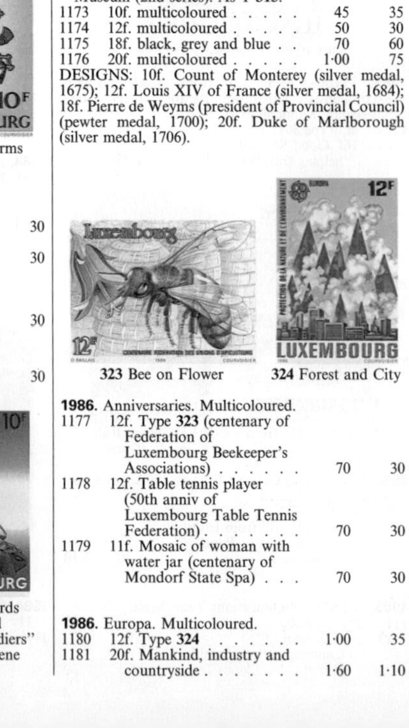

323 Bee on Flower

324 Forest and City

1986. Anniversaries. Multicoloured.
1177 12f. Type **323** (centenary of Federation of Luxembourg Beekeeper's Associations) 70 30
1178 12f. Table tennis player (50th anniv of Luxembourg Table Tennis Federation) 70 30
1179 11f. Mosaic of woman with water jar (centenary of Mondorf State Spa) . . . 70 30

1986. Europa. Multicoloured.
1180 12f. Type **324** . . . . . . 1·00 35
1181 20f. Mankind, industry and countryside . . . . 1·60 1·10

325 Fort Thungen

326 Schuman

1986. Luxembourg Town Fortifications. Mult.
1182 15f. Type **325** . . . . . . 1·25 50
1183 18f. Invalids' Gate (vert) . . 1·25 50
1184 50f. Malakoff Tower (vert) 2·00 65

1986. Birth Centenary of Robert Schuman (politician).
1185 **326** 2f. black and red 15 15
1186 10f. black and blue . . . 40 35

327 Road through Red Triangle on Map

328 Ascent to Chapel of the Cross, Grevenmacher

1986. European Road Safety Year.
1187 **327** 10f. multicoloured . . . 50 30

1986. Tourism.
1188 **328** 12f. multicoloured . . . 65 30
1189 – 12f. brown, stone and red 65 30
DESIGN: No. 1189, Relief from Town Hall facade, Esch-sur-Alzette.

329 Presentation of Letter of Freedom to Echternach (after P. H. Witkamp)

330 Annunciation

1986. 800th Birth Anniv of Countess Ermesinde of Luxembourg.
1190 **329** 12f. brown and stone . . 55 35
1191 – 30f. buff, black and grey 1·60 1·00
DESIGN: 30f. Seal, 1238.

1986. National Welfare Fund. Illustrations from 15th-century "Book of Hours". Multicoloured.
1192 6f.+1f. Type **330** 85 35
1193 10f.+1f. Angel appearing to shepherds 45 35
1194 12f.+2f. Nativity 85 45
1195 18f.+2f. Adoration of the Magi . . . . 2·50 3·00
1196 20f.+8f. Flight into Egypt 4·25 5·50

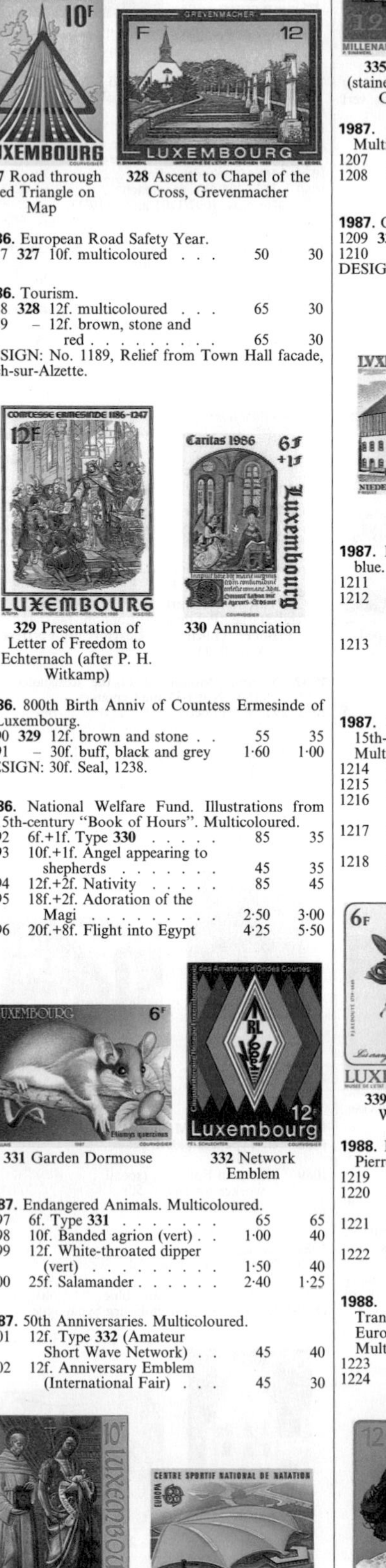

331 Garden Dormouse

332 Network Emblem

1987. Endangered Animals. Multicoloured.
1197 6f. Type **331** 65 65
1198 10f. Banded agrion (vert) . . 1·00 40
1199 12f. White-throated dipper (vert) . . . . 1·50 40
1200 25f. Salamander . . . . . . 2·40 1·25

1987. 50th Anniversaries. Multicoloured.
1201 12f. Type **332** (Amateur Short Wave Network) . . 45 40
1202 12f. Anniversary Emblem (International Fair) . . . 45 30

333 "St. Bernard of Siena and St. John the Baptist"

334 National Swimming Centre (Roger Taillibert)

1987. Paintings by Giovanni Ambrogio Bevilacqua in State Museum. Multicoloured.
1203 10f. Type **333** 45 40
1204 18f. "St. Jerome and St. Francis of Assisi" . . 70 80

1987. Europa. Architecture. Multicoloured.
1205 12f. Type **334** . . . . . . 1·00 40
1206 20f. European Communities' Court of Justice . . . . . 2·40 1·25

335 "Consecration" (stained glass window by Gustav Zanter)

336 Charles Metz (first President) (after Jean-Baptiste Fresez)

1987. Millenary of St. Michael's Church. Multicoloured.
1207 12f. Type **335** 45 30
1208 20f. Baroque organ-chest . . 85 80

1987. Chamber of Deputies.
1209 **336** 6f. brown 30 30
1210 – 12f. blue 55 50
DESIGN: 12f. Chamber of Deputies building.

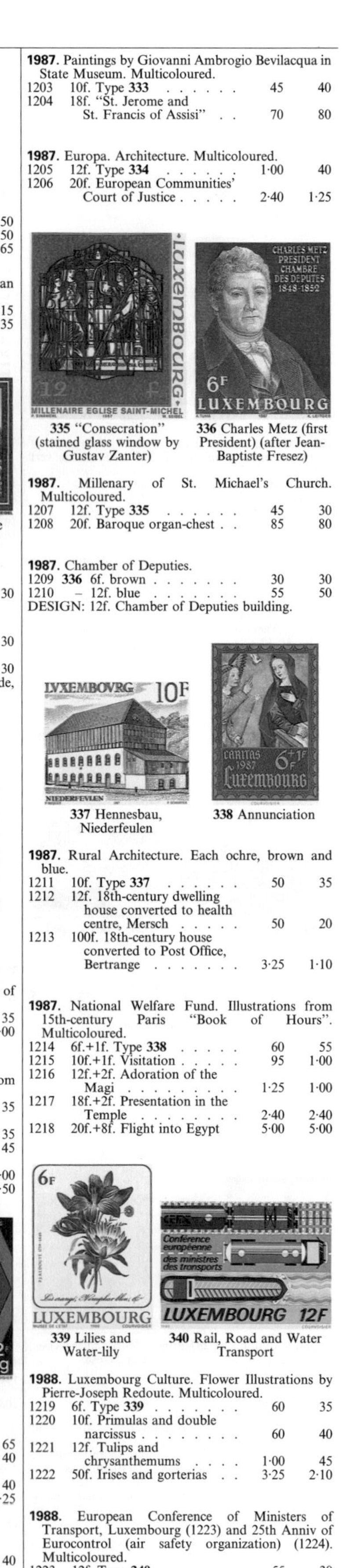

337 Hennesbau, Niederfeulen

338 Annunciation

1987. Rural Architecture. Each ochre, brown and blue.
1211 10f. Type **337** 50 35
1212 12f. 18th-century dwelling house converted to health centre, Mersch 50 20
1213 100f. 18th-century house converted to Post Office, Bertrange . . . . 3·25 1·10

1987. National Welfare Fund. Illustrations from 15th-century Paris "Book of Hours". Multicoloured.
1214 6f.+1f. Type **338** 60 55
1215 10f.+1f. Visitation . . . . . 95 1·00
1216 12f.+2f. Adoration of the Magi . . . . 1·25 1·00
1217 18f.+2f. Presentation in the Temple . . . . 2·40 2·40
1218 20f.+8f. Flight into Egypt 5·00 5·00

339 Lilies and Water-lily

340 Rail, Road and Water Transport

1988. Luxembourg Culture. Flower Illustrations by Pierre-Joseph Redoute. Multicoloured.
1219 6f. Type **339** 60 35
1220 10f. Primulas and double narcissus 60 40
1221 12f. Tulips and chrysanthemums . . . . 1·00 45
1222 50f. Irises and gorterias . . 3·25 2·10

1988. European Conference of Ministers of Transport, Luxembourg (1223) and 25th Anniv of Eurocontrol (air safety organization) (1224). Multicoloured.
1223 12f. Type **340** 55 30
1224 20f. Boeing 747 airplane . . 1·00 85

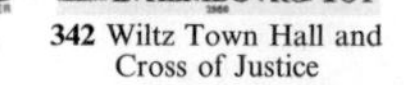

341 Princess Maria Teresa

342 Wiltz Town Hall and Cross of Justice

1988. "Juvalux 88" Ninth Youth Philately Exhibition, Luxembourg. Sheet 11 × 72 mm containing T **341** and similar vert designs. Multicoloured.
MS1225 12f. Type **341**; 18f. Princes Guillaume, Felix and Louis; 50f. Crown Prince Henri . . . . . 5·00 5·75

1988. Tourism. Multicoloured.
1226 10f. Type **342** 60 40
1227 12f. Differdange Castle (vert) 60 40
See also Nos. 1254/5 and 1275/6.

343 Athletes

1988. 50th Anniv of League of Luxembourg Student Sports Associations.
1228 **343** 12f. multicoloured . . . 70 45

344 Automated Mail Sorting

1988. Europa. Transport and Communications. Multicoloured.
1229 12f. Type **344** . . . . . . 2·40 35
1230 20f. Electronic communications . . . . . 2·50 1·75

345 Jean Monnet (statesman, birth centenary)
346 Emblem and Flame

1988. European Anniversaries.
1231 **345** 12f. pink, brn & lt brn 50 35
1232 – 12f. brown and green . . 85 35
DESIGN: No. 1232, European Investment Bank headquarters, Kirchberg (30th anniv).

1988. Olympic Games, Seoul.
1233 **346** 12f. multicoloured . . . 50 35

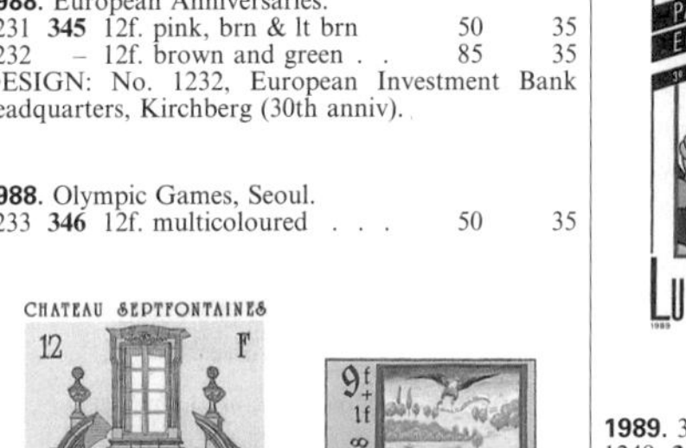

347 Septfontaines Castle
348 Annunciation to Shepherds

1988. Doorways.
1234 **347** 12f. black and brown . . 60 30
1235 – 25f. black and green . . 1·25 90
1236 – 50f. black and brown . . 2·25 1·40
DESIGNS: 25f. National Library; 50f. Holy Trinity Church.

1988. National Welfare Fund. Illustrations from 16th-century "Book of Hours". Multicoloured.
1237 9f.+1f. Type **348** 45 45
1238 12f.+2f. Adoration of the Magi 50 50
1239 18f.+2f. Madonna and Child 2·40 2·40
1240 20f.+8f. Pentecost . . . . . 1·50 2·50

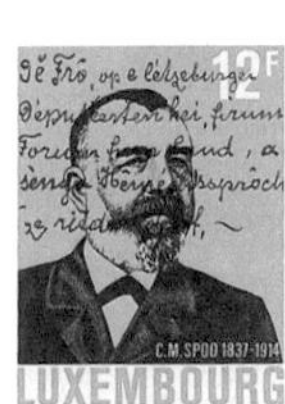

349 C. M. Spoo (promoter of Luxembourgish)
350 Grand Ducal Family Vault Bronze (Auguste Tremont)

1989. Anniversaries.
1241 **349** 12f. black, red and brown 50 45
1242 – 18f. multicoloured . . . 85 60·00
1243 – 20f. red, black and grey 1·25 1·00
DESIGNS: 12f. Type **349** (75th death anniv); 18f. Stylized inking pad (125th anniv of Book Workers' Federation); 20f. Henri Dunant (founder of International Red Cross) (75th anniv of Luxembourg Red Cross).

1989. 150th Anniv of Independence.
1244 **350** 12f. multicoloured . . . 65 30

351 "Astra" Satellite and Map on T.V. Screens
352 Cyclist

1989. Launch of 16-channel T.V. Satellite.
1245 **351** 12f. multicoloured . . . 60 40

1989. Start in Luxembourg of Tour de France Cycling Race.
1246 **352** 9f. multicoloured 65 40

353 Assembly and Flag
354 Emblem

1989. 40th Anniv of Council of Europe.
1247 **353** 12f. multicoloured . . . 65 30

1989. Centenary of Interparliamentary Union.
1248 **354** 12f. yellow, blue & indigo 70 30

355 Hands
356 "Three Children in a Park" (anon)

1989. 3rd Direct Elections to European Parliament.
1249 **355** 12f. multicoloured . . . 65 30

1989. Europa. Children's Games and Toys. Multicoloured.
1250 12f. Type **356** 65 35
1251 20f. "Child with Drum" (anon) . . . . 1·40 1·00

357 Grand Duke Jean
358 Charles IV

1989. 25th Anniv of Accession of Grand Duke Jean.
1252 **357** 3f. black and orange . . 1·00 75
1253 9f. black and green . . . 1·00 95

1989. Tourism. As T **342**. Multicoloured.
1254 12f. Clervaux Castle 50 30
1255 18f. 1st-century bronze wild boar, Titelberg 85 70

1989. Luxembourg History. Stained Glass Windows by Joseph Oterberger, Luxembourg Cathedral. Multicoloured.
1256 12f. Type **358** 60 40
1257 20f. John the Blind 85 90
1258 25f. Wenceslas II . . . . . 1·00 1·10

359 St. Lambert and St. Blase, Fennange
360 Funfair (650th anniv of Schueberfouer)

1989. National Welfare Fund. Restored Chapels (1st series). Multicoloured.
1259 9f.+1f. Type **359** 50 50
1260 12f.+2f. St. Quirinus, Luxembourg (horiz) . . . 60 65
1261 18f.+3f. St. Anthony the Hermit, Reisdorf (horiz) 2·00 2·00
1262 25f.+8f. The Hermitage, Hachiville . . . . . . 3·00 3·00
See also Nos. 1280/3 and 1304/7.

1990. Anniversaries.
1263 **360** 9f. multicoloured 65 35
1264 – 12f. brown, pink & black 50 35
1265 – 18f. multicoloured . . . 80 75
DESIGNS: 12f. Batty Weber (writer, 50th death anniv); 18f. Dish aerial (125th anniv of International Telecommunications Union).

361 Troops at Fortress

1990. Luxembourg Culture. Etchings of the Fortress by Christoph Wilhelm Selig. Multicoloured.
1266 9f. Type **361** 45 40
1267 12f. Soldiers by weir 50 40
1268 20f. Distant view of fortress 1·25 90
1269 25f. Walls . . . . 1·60 1·10

362 Paul Eyschen (75th anniv)
363 "Psallus pseudoplatini" (male and female) on Maple

1990. Statesmen's Death Anniversaries.
1270 **362** 9f. brown and blue . . . 45 40
1271 – 12f. blue and brown . . 55 35
DESIGN: 12f. Emmanuel Servais (centenary).

1990. Centenary of Luxembourg Naturalists' Society.
1272 **363** 12f. multicoloured . . . 60 35

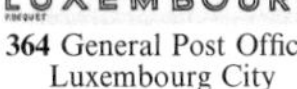

364 General Post Office, Luxembourg City
365 Hammelsmarsch Fountain (Will Lofy)

1990. Europa. Post Office Buildings.
1273 **364** 12f. black and brown . . 1·50 35
1274 – 20f. black and blue . . . 2·10 1·25
DESIGN—VERT: 20f. Esch-sur-Alzette Post Office.

1990. Tourism. As T **342**. Multicoloured.
1275 12f. Mondercange administrative offices . . 60 30
1276 12f. Schifflange town hall and church 60 30

1990. Fountains. Multicoloured.
1277 12f. Type **365** 50 35
1278 25f. Doves Fountain . . . . 1·00 90
1279 50f. Maus Ketty Fountain, Mondorf-les-Bains (Will Lofy) . . . . 2·00 2·40

366 Congregation of the Blessed Virgin Mary, Vianden
367 Grand Duke Adolf

1990. National Welfare Fund. Restored Chapels (2nd series). Multicoloured.
1280 9f.+1f. Type **366** 60 60
1281 12f.+2f. Notre Dame, Echternach (horiz) 85 70
1282 18f.+3f. Consoler of the Afflicted, Grentzingen (horiz) . . . . 1·75 1·75
1283 25f.+8f. St. Pirmin, Kaundorf . . . . 3·00 2·75

1990. Centenary of Nassau-Weilbourg Dynasty. Sheet 115 × 160 mm containing T **367** and similar vert designs. Multicoloured.
MS1284 12f. Type **367**; 12f. Grand Duchess Marie Adelaide; 18f. Grand Ducal arms; 18f. Grand Duchess Charlotte; 20f. Grand Duke William IV; 20f. Grand Duke Jean . . . . 6·00 6·75

368 "Geastrum varians"
370 Dicks (after Jean Goedert)

369 "View from the Trier Road"

1991. Fungi. Illustrations by Pierre-Joseph Redoute. Multicoloured.
1285 14f. Type **368** 65 40
1286 14f. "Agaricus (Gymnopus) thiebautii" 65 50
1287 18f. "Agaricus (Lepiota) lepidocephalus" 85 95
1288 25f. "Morchella favosa" . . 1·40 1·25

1991. Luxembourg Culture. 50th Death Anniv of Sosthene Weis (painter). Multicoloured.
1289 14f. Type **369** 60 40
1290 18f. "Vauban Street and the Viaduct" 70 75
1291 25f. "St. Ulric Street" (vert) 1·25 1·10

1991. Death Centenary of Edmond de la Fontaine (pen-name Dicks) (poet).
1292 **370** 14f. multicoloured . . . 70 45

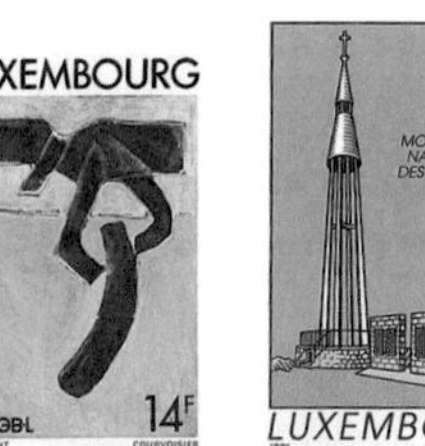

371 Claw grasping Piece of Metal (after Emile Kirscht)
372 National Miners' Monument, Kayl

1991. 75th Anniv of Trade Union Movement in Luxembourg.
1293 **371** 14f. multicoloured . . . 70 45

1991. Tourism. Multicoloured.
1294 14f. Type **372** 70 40
1295 14f. Magistrates' Court, Redange-sur-Attert (horiz) 70 40

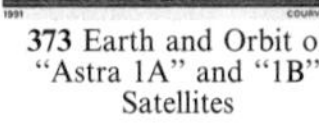

373 Earth and Orbit of "Astra 1A" and "1B" Satellites
374 Telephone

1991. Europa. Europe in Space. Multicoloured.
1296 14f. Type **373** . . . . . . 1·10 45
1297 18f. Betzdorf Earth Station 1·75 1·00

1991. Posts and Telecommunications.
1298 **374** 4f. brown . . . . 2·00 1·40
1299 – 14f. blue 55 55
DESIGN: 14f. Postbox.

375 1936 International Philatelic Federation Congress Stamp

376 Girl's Head

1991. 50th Stamp Day.
1300 **375** 14f. multicoloured . . . 70 40
The stamp illustrated on No. 1300 incorrectly shows a face value of 10f.

1991. Mascarons (stone faces on buildings) (1st series).
1301 **376** 14f. black, buff & brown 60 40
1302 – 25f. black, buff and pink 1·10 90
1303 – 50f. black, buff and blue 1·90 1·75
DESIGNS: 25f. Woman's head; 50f. Man's head.
See also Nos. 1320/22.

377 Chapel of St. Donatus, Arsdorf

378 Jean-Pierre Pescatore Foundation

1991. National Welfare Fund. Restored Chapels (3rd series). Multicoloured.
1304 14f.+2f. Type **377** 85 70
1305 14f.+2f. Chapel of Our Lady of Sorrows, Brandenbourg (horiz) 85 90
1306 18f.+3f. Chapel of Our Lady, Luxembourg (horiz) 1·75 1·25
1307 22f.+7f. Chapel of the Hermitage, Wolwelange 2·50 2·75

1992. Buildings. Multicoloured.
1308 14f. Type **378** 70 50
1309 14f. Higher Technology Institute, Kirchberg . . . 70 50
1310 14f. New Fairs and Congress Centre, Kirchberg 70 50

379 Inner Courtyard, Bettembourg Castle

1992. Tourism. Multicoloured.
1311 18f. Type **379** 70 65
1312 25f. Walferdange railway station . . . . 1·00 95

380 Athlete (detail of mural, Armand Strainchamps)

1992. Olympic Games, Barcelona.
1313 **380** 14f. multicoloured . . . 1·25 35

381 Luxembourg Pavilion

382 Lions Emblem

1992. "Expo '92" World's Fair, Seville.
1314 **381** 14f. multicoloured . . . 65 40

1992. 75th Anniv of Lions International.
1315 **382** 14f. multicoloured . . . 60 40

383 Memorial Tablet (Lucien Wercollier)

384 Nicholas Gonner (editor)

1992. 50th anniv of General Strike.
1316 **383** 18f. brown, grey and red 70 70

1992. Europa. 500th anniv of Discovery of America by Columbus. Luxembourg Emigrants to America.
1317 **384** 14f. brown, black & green 85 45
1318 – 22f. blue, black & orange 1·40 1·25
DESIGN: 22f. Nicolas Becker (writer).

385 Star and European Community Emblem

386 Posthorn and Letters

1992. Single European Market.
1319 **385** 14f. multicoloured . . . 65 40

1992. Mascarons (2nd series). As T **376**.
1320 14f. black, buff and green 55 40
1321 22f. black, buff and blue . . 1·10 1·00
1322 50f. black, buff and purple 1·75 1·60
DESIGNS: 14f. Ram's head; 22f. Lion's head; 50f. Goat's head.

1992. 150th Anniv of Post and Telecommunications Office. Designs showing stained glass windows by Auguste Tremont. Mult.
1323 14f. Type **386** 50 45
1324 22f. Post rider . . . . . . 1·40 1·25
1325 50f. Telecommunications . . 1·60 1·60

387 Hazel Grouse

388 Grand Duke Jean

1992. National Welfare Fund. Birds (1st series). Multicoloured.
1326 14f.+2f. Type **387** 85 95
1327 14f.+2f. Golden oriole (vert) 85 95
1328 18f.+3f. Black stork . . . . 2·40 2·10
1329 22f.+7f. Red kite (vert) . . . 3·00 3·00
See also Nos. 1364/7 and 1383/6.

1993.
1330 **388** 1f. black and yellow . . 10 10
1331 2f. black and green . . . 10 10
1332 5f. black and yellow . . 20 20
1333 7f. black and brown . . 30 20
1334 8f. black and green . . . 30 25
1335 9f. black and mauve . . 35 35
1336 10f. black and blue . . . 45 30
1337 14f. black and purple . . 1·40 30
1338 15f. black and green . . 50 45
1339 16f. black and orange . . 50 45
1340 18f. black and yellow . . 70 40
1341 20f. black and red . . . 70 55
1342 22f. black and green . . 90 55
1343 25f. black and blue . . . 85 70
1344 100f. black and brown 3·00 2·00

389 Old Ironworks Cultural Centre, Steinfort

1993. Tourism. Multicoloured.
1350 14f. Type **389** 65 35
1351 14f. "Children with Grapes" Fountain, Schwebsingen 65 35

390 Collage by Maurice Esteve

1993. New Surgical Techniques.
1352 **390** 14f. multicoloured . . . 60 40

391 Hotel de Bourgogne (Prime Minister's offices)

1993. Historic Houses. Multicoloured.
1353 14f. Type **391** 55 40
1354 20f. Simons House (now Ministry of Agriculture) 85 70
1355 50f. Cassal House . . . . . 2·40 1·75

392 "Rezlop" (Fernand Roda)

1993. Europa. Contemporary Art. Multicoloured.
1356 14f. Type **392** 70 45
1357 22f. "So Close" (Sonja Roef) . . . . 1·40 1·00

393 Monument (detail, D. Donzelli), Tetange Cemetery

394 Emblem

1993. 75th Death Anniv of Jean Schortgen (first worker elected to parliament).
1358 **393** 14f. multicoloured . . . 60 40

1993. Centenary of Artistic Circle of Luxembourg.
1359 **394** 14f. mauve and violet . . 60 40

395 European Community Ecological Label

396 Tram No. 1 (Transport Museum, Luxembourg)

1993. Protection of Environment.
1360 **395** 14f. blue, green & emerald 60 40

1993. Museum Exhibits (1st series). Multicoloured.
1361 14f. Type **396** 70 40
1362 22f. Iron ore tipper wagon (National Mining Museum, Rumelange) . . 1·00 1·00
1363 60f. Horse-drawn carriage (Arts and Ancient Crafts Museum, Wiltz) . . . . 2·40 4·75
See also Nos. 1404/6 and 1483/4.

1993. National Welfare Fund. Birds (2nd series). As T **387**. Multicoloured.
1364 14f.+2f. Common snipe ("Becassine") 70 70
1365 14f.+2f. River kingfisher ("Martin-Pecheur") (vert) 70 70
1366 18f.+3f. Little ringed plover ("Petit Gravelot") . . . . 1·40 1·40
1367 22f.+7f. Sand martin ("Hirondelle de Rivage") (vert) . . . . 2·50 2·50

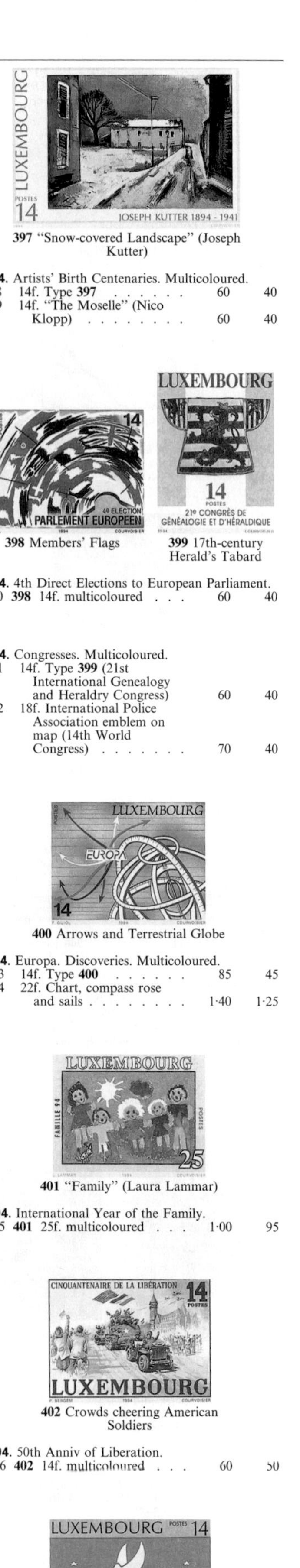

397 "Snow-covered Landscape" (Joseph Kutter)

1994. Artists' Birth Centenaries. Multicoloured.
1368 14f. Type **397** 60 40
1369 14f. "The Moselle" (Nico Klopp) 60 40

398 Members' Flags

399 17th-century Herald's Tabard

1994. 4th Direct Elections to European Parliament.
1370 **398** 14f. multicoloured . . . 60 40

1994. Congresses. Multicoloured.
1371 14f. Type **399** (21st International Genealogy and Heraldry Congress) 60 40
1372 18f. International Police Association emblem on map (14th World Congress) 70 40

400 Arrows and Terrestrial Globe

1994. Europa. Discoveries. Multicoloured.
1373 14f. Type **400** 85 45
1374 22f. Chart, compass rose and sails . . . . 1·40 1·25

401 "Family" (Laura Lammar)

1994. International Year of the Family.
1375 **401** 25f. multicoloured . . . 1·00 95

402 Crowds cheering American Soldiers

1994. 50th Anniv of Liberation.
1376 **402** 14f. multicoloured . . . 60 50

403 Western European Union Emblem (40th anniv)

1994. Anniversaries and Campaign.
1377 **403** 14f. blue, lilac and ultramarine 70 50
1378 – 14f. multicoloured . . . 70 45
1379 – 14f. multicoloured . . . 2·40 70
DESIGNS—No. 1378, Emblem (25th anniv in Luxembourg of European Communities' Office for Official Publications); 1379, 10th-century B.C. ceramic bowl from cremation tomb, Bigelbach (European Bronze Age Campaign).

404 Munster Abbey (General Finance Inspectorate)

1994. Former Refuges now housing Government Offices. Multicoloured.
1380 15f. Type **404** 70 65
1381 25f. Holy Spirit Convent (Ministry of Finance) . . 85 1·00
1382 60f. St. Maximine Abbey of Trier (Ministry of Foreign Affairs) . . . . 2·00 2·75

1994. National Welfare Fund. Birds (3rd series). As T **387**. Multicoloured.
1383 14f.+2f. Common stonechat ("Traquet Patre") (vert) 70 85
1384 14f.+2f. Grey partridge ("Perdix Grise") 70 85
1385 18f.+3f. Yellow wagtail ("Bergeronnette Printaniere") . . . . . . 1·40 1·40
1386 22f.+7f. Great grey shrike ("Pie-Grieche Grise") (vert) . . . . 2·50 2·50

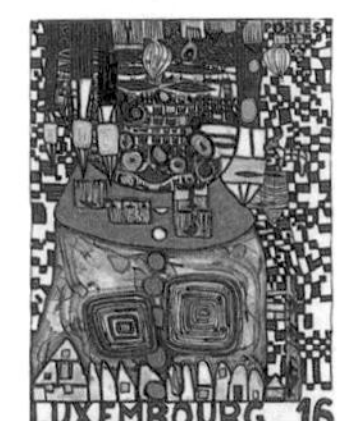

405 "King of the Antipodes"

406/409 Panoramic View of City (½-size illustration)

1995. Luxembourg, European City of Culture.
1387 **405** 16f. multicoloured . . . 1·00 65
1388 – 16f. multicoloured . . . 1·00 65
1389 – 16f. multicoloured . . . 1·00 65
1390 **406** 16f. multicoloured . . . 70 60
1391 **407** 16f. multicoloured . . . 70 60
1392 **408** 16f. multicoloured . . . 70 60
1393 **409** 16f. multicoloured . . . 70 60
1394 – 16f. multicoloured . . . 70 60
DESIGNS—As T **405**: No. 1388, "House with Arcades and Yellow Tower"; 1389, "Small Path" (maze). 35 × 26 mm: No. 1394, Emblem.
Nos. 1390/3 were issued together, se-tenant, forming the composite design illustrated.

410 Landscape and Slogan

411 Colour Spectrum and Barbed Wire

1995. European Nature Conservation Year.
1395 **410** 16f. multicoloured . . . 70 40

1995. Europa. Peace and Freedom. 50th Anniv of Liberation of Concentration Camps. Mult.
1396 16f. Type **411** 70 65
1397 25f. Wire barbs breaking through symbolic sky and earth . . . . 1·10 1·10

412 Emblem

1995. Anniversaries and Event. Multicoloured.
1398 16f. Type **412** (6th Small European States Games, Luxembourg) 60 60
1399 32f. Diagram of section through Earth (27th anniv of underground Geodynamics Laboratory, Walferdange) (33 × 34 mm) . . . . . . 1·25 1·25
1400 80f. Anniversary emblem (50th anniv of U.N.O.) 2·75 2·75

413 Boeing 757

1995. 40th Anniv of Luxembourg–Iceland Air Link.
1401 **413** 16f. multicoloured . . . 60 60

414 Erpeldange Castle

415 Stained Glass Window from Alzingen Church

1995. Tourism. Multicoloured.
1402 16f. Type **414** 60 65
1403 16f. Schengen Castle 60 65

1995. Museum Exhibits (2nd series). Vert designs as T **396**. Multicoloured.
1404 16f. Churn (Country Art Museum, Vianden) . . . 70 70
1405 32f. Wine-press (Wine Museum, Ehnen) . . . . 1·25 1·50
1406 80f. Sculpture of potter (Leon Nosbusch) (Pottery Museum, Nospelt) . . . . 3·25 3·00

1995. Christmas.
1407 **415** 16f.+2f. multicoloured 1·00 1·25

416 Broad-leaved Linden ("Tilia platyphyllos")

417 Mayrisch (after Theo van Rysselberghe)

1995. National Welfare Fund. Trees (1st series). Multicoloured.
1408 16f.+2f. Type **416** 70 95
1409 16f.+2f. Horse chestnut ("Aesculus hippocastanum") (horiz) 70 95
1410 20f.+3f. Pedunculate oak (horiz) . . . . 1·25 1·40
1411 32f.+7f. Silver birch . . . . 2·25 2·40
See also Nos. 1432/5 and 1458/61.

1996. 68th Death Anniv of Emile Mayrisch (engineer).
1412 **417** A (16f.) multicoloured 70 65

418 Mounument, Place Clairefontaine (Jean Cardot)

420 "Marie Munchen"

419 Electric Railcar

1996. Birth Centenary of Grand Duchess Charlotte.
1413 **418** 16f. multicoloured . . . 85 60

1996. 50th Anniv of Luxembourg National Railway Company. Multicoloured.
1414 16f. Type **419** 70 70
1415 16f. Linked cars 70 70
1416 16f. Train (right-hand detail) 70 70

Nos. 1414/16 were issued together, se-tenant, forming a composite design of a Series 2000 electric railcar set.

1996. 96th Death Anniv of Mihaly Munkacsy (painter). Multicoloured.
1417 16f. Type **420** 70 80
1418 16f. Munkacsy (after Edouard Charlemont) (horiz) 70 80

421 Workers and Emblem

422 Marie de Bourgogne

1996. Anniversaries.
1419 **421** 16f. green, orge & blk 60 65
1420 – 20f. multicoloured . . . 70 90
1421 – 25f. multicoloured . . . 1·00 1·25
1422 – 32f. multicoloured . . . 1·25 1·40
DESIGNS—HORIZ: 16f. Type **421** (75th anniv of Luxembourg Confederation of Christian Trade Unions); 32f. Film negative (centenary of motion pictures). VERT: 20f. Transmitter and radio waves (centenary of Guglielmo Marconi's patented wireless telegraph); 25f. Olympic flame and rings (centenary of modern Olympic Games).

1996. Europa. Famous Women. Duchesses of Luxembourg. Multicoloured.
1423 16f. Type **422** 60 65
1424 25f. Maria-Theresa of Austria . . . . 1·00 1·25

423 Handstamp

1996. Bicentenary (1995) of Registration and Property Administration.
1425 **423** 16f. multicoloured . . . 60 65

424 Children of different Cultures (Michele Dockendorf)

1996. "Let us Live Together". Multicoloured.
1426 16f. Type **424** 65 65
1427 16f. "L'Abbraccio" (statue, Marie-Josee Kerschen) (vert) 65 65

425 Eurasian Badger

1996. Mammals. Multicoloured.
1428 16f. Type **425** 65 65
1429 20f. Polecat 65 70
1430 80f. European otter . . . . 3·00 3·25

426 "The Birth of Christ" (icon, Eva Mathes)

427 John the Blind

1996. Christmas.
1431 **426** 16f.+2f. multicoloured 1·40 1·40

1996. National Welfare Fund. Trees (2nd series). As T **416**. Multicoloured.
1432 16f.+2f. Willow ("Salix sp.") (horiz) 65 85
1433 16f.+2f. Ash ("Fraxinus excelsior") 65 85
1434 20f.+3f. Mountain ash (horiz) . . . . 1·25 1·60
1435 32f.+7f. Common beech . . 2·40 2·75

1996. 700th Birth Anniv of John the Blind (King of Bohemia and Count of Luxembourg).
1436 **427** 32f. multicoloured . . . 1·25 1·40

428 Koerich Church

1997. Tourism. Multicoloured.
1437 16f. Type **428** 70 50
1438 16f. Servais House, Mersch (horiz) 70 50

429 Birthplace of Robert Schuman (politician), Luxembourg-Clausen

1997. Anniversaries. Multicoloured.
1439 16f. Type **429** (40th anniv of Treaties of Rome establishing European Economic Community and European Atomic Energy Community) . . . 70 50
1440 20f. National colours forming wing of Mercury (75th anniv of Belgium–Luxembourg Economic Union) 85 75

430 "Grand Duchess Charlotte"

1997. 11th World Federation of Rose Societies Congress, Belgium, Mondorf (Luxembourg) and the Netherlands. Roses. Multicoloured.
1441 16f. Type **430** 70 70
1442 20f. "The Beautiful Sultana" (33 × 26 mm) 70 80
1443 80f. "In Memory of Jean Soupert" (33 × 26 mm) . . 2·75 2·50

431 Badge, Luxembourg Fortress, Shako and Sword

432 The Beautiful Melusina

1997. Anniversaries.
1444 **431** 16f. multicoloured . . . 60 60
1445 – 16f. black, blue and red 60 60
1446 – 16f. brown, green and pink 60 60
DESIGNS—As T **431**: No. 1444, Type **431** (bicentenary of Grand Ducal Gendarmerie Corps); 1445, Cock and rabbit (75th anniv of Luxembourg Union of Small Domestic Animals Farming Societies). 33 × 33 mm: No. 1446, Bather and attendant, early 1900s (150th anniv of Mondorf spa).

1997. Europa. Tales and Legends. Multicoloured.
1447 16f. Type **432** 70 65
1448 25f. The Hunter of Hollenfels . . . . 1·00 1·25

433 Face on Globe

1997. "Juvalux 98" Youth Stamp Exhibition (1st issue). Multicoloured.
1449 16f. Type **433** 70 65
1450 80f. Postmen (painting, Michel Engels) . . . . . 2·75 2·75
See also Nos. 1475/8.

434 Emblem

1997. Sar–Lor–Lux (Saarland–Lorraine–Luxembourg) European Region.
1451 **434** 16f. multicoloured . . . 70 65
Stamps in similar designs were issued by France and Germany.

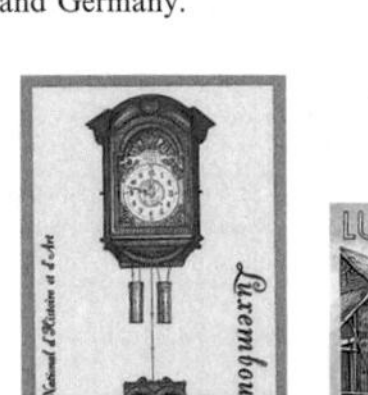

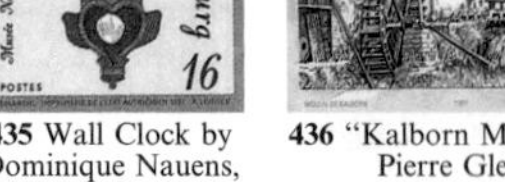

435 Wall Clock by Dominique Nauens, 1816 436 "Kalborn Mill"(Jean-Pierre Gleis)

1997. Clocks. Multicoloured.
1452 16f. Type **435** 70 65
1453 32f. Astronomical clock by J. Lebrun, 1850 (26 × 44 mm) . . . . . . 1·10 1·40
1454 80f. Wall clock by Mathias Hebeler, 1815 . . . . . . 2·75 2·50

1997. Water Mills. Multicoloured.
1455 16f. Type **436** 70 65
1456 50f. Interior of Ramelli mill, 1588 (from book "The Water Wheel" by Wilhelm Wolfel) (vert) . . . . . . 1·75 2·10

437 Holy Family 438 Count Henri V

1997. Christmas.
1457 **437** 16f.+2f. multicoloured 1·25 1·25

1997. National Welfare Fund. Trees (3rd series). As T **416**. Multicoloured.
1458 16f.+2f. Wych elm ("Ulmus glabra") 70 85
1459 16f.+2f. Norway maple ("Acer platanoides") . . . 70 85
1460 20f.+3f. Wild cherry . . . . 1·00 1·00
1461 32f.+7f. Walnut (horiz) . . 1·75 1·75

1997. 750th Anniv of Accession of Henri V, Count of Luxembourg.
1462 **438** 32f. multicoloured . . . 1·25 1·00

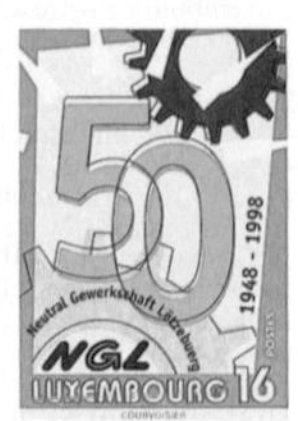

439 Rodange Church 440 Cog and "50"

1998. Tourism. Multicoloured.
1463 16f. Type **439** 70 65
1464 16f. Back of local authority building, Hesperange (horiz) 70 65

1998. Anniversaries.
1465 **440** 16f. multicoloured . . . 70 65
1466 – 16f. multicoloured . . . 70 65
1467 – 20f. multicoloured . . . 70 90
1468 – 50f. black, red and stone 1·75 2·10
DESIGNS: No. 1465, Type **440** (50th anniv of Independent Luxembourg Trade Union); 1466, Festival poster (Rene Wismer) (50th anniv of Broom Festival, Wiltz); 1467, Memorial (death centenary of Jean Antoine Zinnen (composer of national anthem)); 1468, Typewriter keys and page from first issue of "Luxemburger Wort" (150th anniv of abolition of censorship).

441 Brown Trout

1998. Freshwater Fishes. Multicoloured.
1469 16f. Type **441** 70 65
1470 25f. Bullhead . . . . 1·00 1·25
1471 50f. Riffle minnow . . . . 2·00 2·10

442 Henri VII and Flags outside Fair Venue, Kirchberg

1998. 700th Anniv of Granting to Count Henri VII of Right to Hold a Fair. Value indicated by letter.
1472 **442** A (16f.) multicoloured 70 70

443 Fireworks over Adolphe Bridge (National Day) 444 Town Postman, 1880

1998. Europa. National Festivals. Multicoloured.
1473 16f. Type **443** 85 70
1474 25f. Stained-glass window and flame (National Remembrance Day) . . . 1·00 1·25

1998. "Juvalux '98" Youth Stamp Exhibition (2nd issue). Multicoloured.
1475 16f. Type **444** 70 65
1476 25f. Letter, 1590 (horiz) . . 80 1·25
1477 50f. Rural postman, 1880 1·75 2·10
MS1478 125 × 76 mm 16f., 80f. Railway viaduct and city (composite design) . . . . . . 4·50 5·00

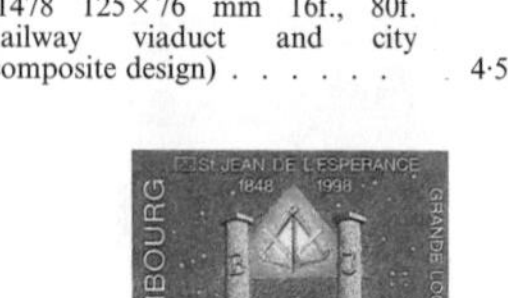

445 Masonic Symbols (Paul Moutschen)

1998. 150th Anniv of St. John of Hope Freemason Lodge.
1479 **445** 16f. multicoloured . . . 60 65

446 Echternach

1998. 1300th Anniv of Echternach Abbey. Multicoloured.
1480 16f. Type **446** 60 65
1481 48f. Buildings in Echternach 2·40 2·10
1482 60f. Echternach Abbey . . . 2·00 2·25

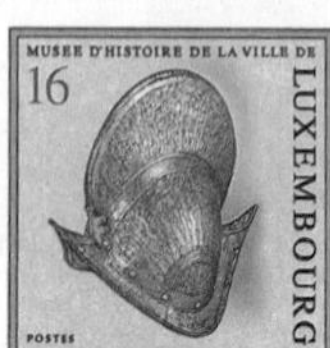

447 Spanish Morion (late 16th century)

1998. Museum Exhibits (3rd series). City of Luxembourg History Museum. Multicoloured.
1483 16f. Type **447** 70 65
1484 80f. Wayside Cross from Hollerich (1718) . . . . . 2·75 3·00

448 "Nativity" (altarpiece by Georges Saget, St. Mauritius Abbey, Clervaux)

1998. Christmas.
1485 **448** 16f.+2f. multicoloured 1·40 1·10

449 "Bech"

1998. National Welfare Fund (1st series). Villages. 16th-century drawings by Jean Bertels. Multicoloured.
1486 16f.+2f. Type **449** 70 85
1487 16f.+2f. "Ermes Turf" (now Ermsdorf) 70 85
1488 20f.+3f. "Itsich" (now Itzig) 1·00 1·25
1489 32f.+7f. "Stein Hem" (now Steinheim) . . . . 1·75 1·90
See also Nos. 1510/13 and 1550/3.

450 Globe and Jigsaw

1998. 40th Anniv of North Atlantic Maintenance and Supply Agency.
1490 **450** 36f. multicoloured . . . 1·40 1·50

451 Council Building and Emblem

1999. 50th Anniv of Council of Europe.
1491 **451** 16f. multicoloured . . . 70 70

452 Euro Coin and Map

1999. Introduction of the Euro (European currency). Value expressed by letter.
1492 **452** A (16f.) multicoloured 1·00 65

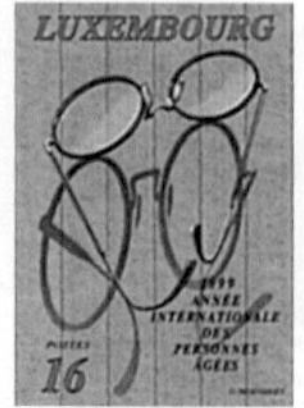

453 Tawny Owl 455 Spectacles

454 Globe and Emblem

1999. Owls. Multicoloured.
1493 A (16f.) Type **453** 70 65
1494 32f. Eagle owl (horiz) . . . 1·25 1·25
1495 60f. Barn owl (horiz) . . . 2·50 3·00

1999. 50th Anniv of N.A.T.O.
1496 **454** 80f. multicoloured . . . 3·00 3·50

1999. International Year of the Elderly.
1497 **455** 16f. multicoloured . . . 70 65

456 Emblem and Envelopes

1999. 125th Anniv of Universal Postal Union.
1498 **456** 16f. multicoloured . . . 70 65

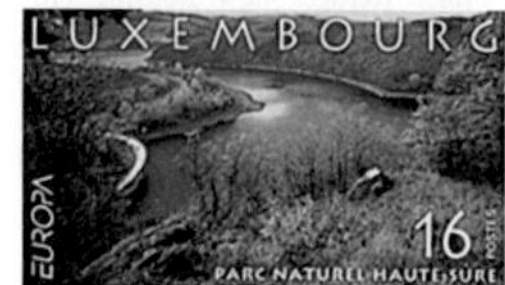

457 Haute-Sure National Park

1999. Europa. Parks and Gardens. Multicoloured.
1499 16f. Type **457** 70 70
1500 25f. Ardennes-Eifel National Park . . . . 1·00 1·25

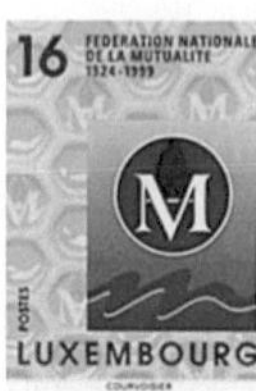

458 Emblem

1999. Anniversaries. Multicoloured.
1501 16f. Type **458** (75th anniv of National Federation of Mutual Socieites) 70 65
1502 32f. Camera and roll of film (50th anniv of Luxembourg Federation of Amateur Photographers) . . . . . 1·40 1·40
1503 80f. Gymnasts (centenary of Luxembourg Gymnastics Federation) . . . . 3·50 3·50

459 Prince Guillaume 461 A. Mayrisch de Saint-Hubert

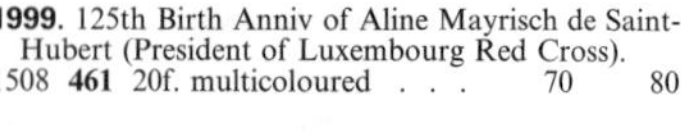

460 Cars on Motorway

1999. 18th Birthday of Prince Guillaume.
1504 **459** 16f. multicoloured . . . 70 70

1999. Communications of the Future. Mult.
1505 16f. Type **460** 60 70
1506 20f. Earth and satellite . . . 70 85
1507 80f. Planets and spacecraft 3·00 3·00

1999. 125th Birth Anniv of Aline Mayrisch de Saint-Hubert (President of Luxembourg Red Cross).
1508 **461** 20f. multicoloured . . . 70 80

462 Decorated Church Tower

1999. Christmas
1509 **462** 16f.+2f. multicoloured 1·00 90

1999. National Welfare Fund. Villages (2nd series). As T **449**, showing 6th-century drawings by Jean Bertels. Multicoloured.
1510 16f.+2f. "Oswiler" (now Osweiler) 70 80
1511 16f.+2f. "Bettem Burch" (now Bettembourg) . . . 70 80

1512 20f.+3f. "Cruchte auf der Alset" (now Cruchten) . . 80 1·00
1513 32f.+7f. "Berchem" . . . . 2·00 2·10

463 "Gateway" (sketch by Goethe)

1999. 250th Birth Anniv of Johann Wolfgang von Goethe (poet and playwright).
1514 **463** 20f. chestnut, cream & brn 70 80

464 "2000"

2000. New Millennium. Value expressed by letter. Multicoloured. Self-adhesive.
1515 A (16f.) Type **464** (blue streaks emanating from bottom right) 70 65
1516 A (16f.) Blue streaks emanating from bottom left 70 65
1517 A (16f.) Blue streaks emanating from top right 70 65
1518 A (16f.) Blue streaks emanating from top left 70 65

465 Charles V

2000. 500th Birth Anniv of Emperor Charles V. Value expressed by letter.
1519 **465** A (16f.) multicoloured 70 60

466 Walferdange Castle

2000. Tourism. Value expressed by letter. Multicoloured.
1520 A (16f.) Type **466** 70 60
1521 A (16f.) Local government offices, Wasserbillig (vert) 70 60

467 "2000" and Formulae 468 French Horn

2000. World Mathematics Year.
1522 **467** 80f. multicoloured . . . 2·75 3·00

2000. Musical Instruments.
1523 **468** 3f. black and violet . . . 20 10
1524 – 9f. black and green . . . 40 35
1525 – 12f. black and yellow . . 45 40
1526 – 21f. black and pink . . 75 75
1527 – 24f. black and blue . . . 80 55
1528 – 30f. black and pink . . . 85 65
DESIGNS: 9f. Electric guitar; 12f. Saxophone; 21f. Violin; 24f. Accordion; 30f. Grand piano.

469 Production and Storage Facilities, 1930s (Harry Rabinger)

2000. Centenary (1999) of Esch-sur-Alzette Gas Works.
1535 **469** 18f. multicoloured . . . 70 75

470 Mallard 471 "Building Europe"

2000. Ducks. Multicoloured.
1536 18f. Type **470** 70 75
1537 24f. Common pochard (vert) 80 80
1538 30f. Tufted duck (vert) . . . 1·00 85

2000. Europa.
1539 **471** 21f. multicoloured . . . 85 70

472 Jean Monnet and Robert Schuman

2000. 50th Anniv of Schuman Plan (proposal for European Coal and Steel Community).
1540 **472** 21f. black, blue & yellow 85 70

473 Blast Furnace

2000. 20th Anniv of Blast Furnace "B", Esch-Belval.
1541 **473** A (18f.) multicoloured 55 35

474 Castle Walls and Tower (Wenzel Walk)

2000. Circular City Walks. Multicoloured.
1542 18f. Type **474** 55 35
1543 42f. Bridge and tower (Vauban walk) . . . . . 1·25 75

475 Will Kesseler

2000. Modern Art (1st series). Showing paintings by artist named. Multicoloured.
1544 21f. Type **475** 55 35
1545 24f. Joseph Probst (vert) . . 85 85
1546 36f. Mett Hoffmann 65 40
See also Nos. 1612/14.

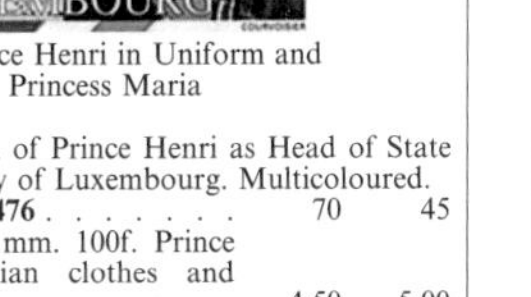

476 Prince Henri in Uniform and Princess Maria

2000. Swearing in of Prince Henri as Head of State of Grand Duchy of Luxembourg. Multicoloured.
1547 18f. Type **476** 70 45
MS1548 125 × 90 mm. 100f. Prince Henri in civilian clothes and Princess Maria . . . . 4·50 5·00

477 Child before Christmas Tree

2000. Christmas.
1549 **477** 18f.+2f. multicoloured 85 85

2000. National Welfare Fund. Villages (3rd series). As T **449** showing 16th-century drawings by Jean Bertels. Multicoloured.
1550 18f.+2f. "Lorentzwiller" (now dorentzweiler) . . . 70 70
1551 21f.+3f. "Coosturf" (now Consdorf) 95 95
1552 24f.+3f. "Elfingen" (now Elvange) 95 95
1553 36f.+7f. "Sprenckigen" (now Sprinkange) . . . . . . 1·75 1·75

478 Bestgensmillen Mill, Schifflange

2001. Tourism. Multicoloured.
1554 18f. Type **478** 70 50
1555 18f. Vineyard, Wormeldange (vert) 70 50

479 Nik Welter

2001. Writers' Death Anniversaries. Multicoloured.
1556 18f. Type **479** (50th anniv) 70 50
1557 24f. Andre Gide (50th anniv) . . . . 1·00 65
1558 30f. Michel Rodange (125th anniv) . . . . 1·40 1·00

480 Signatures and Seal

2001. 50th Anniv of Treaty of Paris.
1559 **480** 21f. multicoloured . . . 85 65

481 Citroen 2CV Mini-Van 482 Stream, Mullerthal

2001. Postal Vehicles. Mult. Self-adhesive.
1560 3f. Type **481** 20 15
1561 18f. Volkswagen Beetle . . . 65 50

2001. Europa. Water Resources. Multicoloured. Value expressed by letter (No. 1562) or with face value (No. 1563).
1562 A (18f.) Type **482** 70 70
1563 21f. Pond and Kaltreis water tower (vert) . . . . 1·00 70

483 "Mother and Child" (Ger Maas)

484 Helicopter and Rescuer

2001. Humanitarian Projects. Multicoloured.
1564 18f. Type **483** (humanitarian aid) 65 50
1565 24f. International Organization for Migration emblem 85 65

2001. Rescue Services. Multicoloured.
1566 18f. Type **484** 65 50
1567 30f. Divers and rubber dinghy . . . . 1·00 85
1568 45f. Fire engine and fireman wearing protective clothing . . . . 1·75 1·40

DENOMINATION. From No. 1569 Luxembourg stamps are denominated in euros only.

485 Five Cent Coin 486 Grand Duke Henri

2001. Euro Currency. Coins. Multicoloured.
1569 5c. Type **485** 20 20
1570 10c. Ten cent coin 20 20
1571 20c. Twenty cent coin . . . 35 35
1572 50c. Fifty cent coin 65 65
1573 €1 One euro coin . . . . 1·40 1·40
1574 €2 Two euro coin . . . . 2·75 2·75

2001. Grand Duke Henri.
1575 1c. indigo, blue and ultramarine 10 10
1576 3c. olive, green and ultramarine 10 10
1580 **486** 7c. dp blue, blue & red 10 10
1583 22c. sepia, brown & red 35 30
1584 25c. lilac and ultramarine 35 30
1585 30c. dp green, grn & red 40 35
1588 45c. dp violet, vio & red 60 40
1589 50c. black and ultramarine 60 45
1590 52c. brown, buff and red 65 40
1591 59c. deep blue, blue and red 75 45
1592 60c. black, green and blue 75 45
1593 74c. brown, stone and red 95 55
1594 80c. agate, green and blue 95 55
1595 89c. mauve, brown and red . . . . 1·10 80

487 Emblem

2001. European Year of Languages. Value expressed by letter.
1596 **487** A (45c.) multicoloured 60 50

488 Sun, Wind-powered Generators and Houses (renewable energy)

2001. Environment and Medicine of the Future. Multicoloured.
1597 45c. Type **488** 65 55
1598 59c. Tyre, tins, bottle and carton (recycling) 85 65
1599 74c. Microscope and test-tubes (biological research) 1·00 1·00

489 St. Nicholas

2001. Christmas.
1600 **489** 45c.+5c. multicoloured 60 45

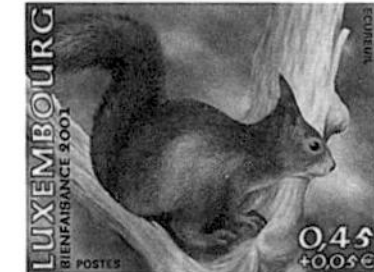

490 Squirrel

2001. National Welfare Fund. Animals (1st issue). Multicoloured.
1601 45c.+5c. Type **490** 60 45
1602 52c.+8c. Wild boar 75 55
1603 59c.+11c. Hare (vert) . . . 90 65
1604 89c.+21c. Wood pigeon (vert) . . . . 1·40 1·40
See also Nos. 1632/5 and 1660/3.

491 Emblem

2001. Kiwanis International (community organization).
1605 **491** 52c. dp blue, bl & gold 65 40

New Currency. 100 cents = 1 euro.

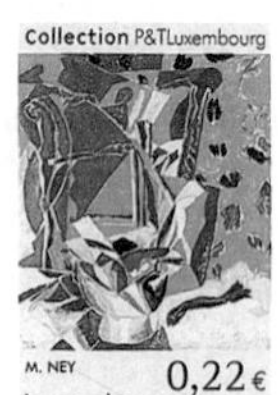

492 Snowboarding 493 Mortiz Ney

2002. Sports. Self-adhesive. Multicoloured.
1606 7c. Type **492** 10 10
1607 7c. Skateboarding 10 10
1608 7c. Inline skating 10 10
1609 45c. BMX biking 55 35
1610 45c. Beach volleyball . . . 55 35
1611 45c. Street basketball . . . 55 35

2002. Modern Art (2nd series). Showing works by artist named. Multicoloured.
1612 22c. Type **493** 30 20
1613 45c. Dany Prum (horiz) . . . 55 35
1614 59c. Christiane Schmit . . . 75 45

494 Map of Europe and "1977"

2002. Anniversaries. Multicoloured.
1615 45c. Type **494** (25th anniv of European Court of Auditors) 55 35
1616 52c. Scales of Justice and map of Europe (50th anniv of European Communities Court of Justice) 65 40

495 Tightrope Walker

2002. Europa. The Circus. Multicoloured.
1617 45c. Type **495** 55 35
1618 52c. Clown juggling 65 40

496 Emblem

2002. 2002 Tour de France (starting in Luxembourg). Multicoloured.
1619 45c. Type **496** 55 35
1620 52c. Francois Faber (winner of 1909 Tour de France) (vert) 65 40
1621 €2.45 "The Champion" (Joseph Kutter) (vert) . . 3·00 1·90

497 Orchestra on Stage (50th Anniv of Festival of Wiltz)

2002. Cultural Anniversaries. Value expressed by letter (No. 1622) or face value (No. 1623). Multicoloured.
1622 A (45c.) Type **497** 55 35
1623 €1.12 Victor Hugo and signature (birth bicentenary) . . . . . . 1·40 85

498 Grand Duke William III of Netherlands

2002. 150th Anniv of First Luxembourg Stamp (1st issue). Sheet 121 × 164 mm, containing T **498** and similar horiz designs. Multicoloured.
MS1624 45c. Type **498**; 45c. Grand Duke Adolphe; 45c. Grand Duchess Charlotte; 45c. Grand Duke Henri . . . . 2·25 2·25
See also Nos. 1630/1.

499 Water Droplet on Spruce

2002. Natural History Museum. Multicoloured. Value expressed by letter. Self-adhesive.
1625 A (45c.) Type **499** 55 35
1626 A (45c.) Mocker swallowtail 55 35
1627 A (45c.) Houseleek 55 35
1628 A (45c.) Blackthorn berries 55 35

500 Emblem 501 Postmen in Flying Vehicles (Clare Nothumb)

2002. 750th Anniv of Grevenmacher City Charter.
1629 **500** 74c. multicoloured . . . 90 55

2002. 150th Anniv of First Luxembourg Stamp (2nd issue). Winning Entries in Stamp Design Competition. (a) With face value.
1630 22c. Type **501** 30 15

(b) Value expressed by letter.
1631 A (45c.) Symbols of communications and flying saucer orbiting planet (Christine Hengen) (horiz) 55 35

502 Fox

2002. National Welfare Fund. Animals (2nd series). Multicoloured.
1632 45c. + 5c. Type **502** 60 45
1633 52c. + 8c. Hedgehog (vert) 75 60
1634 59c. + 11c. Pheasant 90 65
1635 89c. + 21c. Deer (vert) . . . 1·40 1·40

503 Place d'Armes

2002. Christmas.
1636 **503** 45c. + 5c. multicoloured 60 45
No. 1636 was issued in se-tenant sheetlets of 12 stamps, the margins of which were impregnated with the scent of cinnamon.

504 Grand Duke Jean and Grand Duchess Josephine-Charlotte

2003. Golden Wedding Anniversary of Grand Duke Jean and Grand Duchess Josephine-Charlotte.
1637 **504** 45c. multicoloured . . . 65 40

505 Catherine Schleimer-Kill

2003. 30th Death Anniversaries. Multicoloured.
1638 45c. Type **505** (political pioneer) 65 40
1639 45c. Lou Koster (composer) 65 40

506 Citeaux Abbey, Differdange

2003. Tourism. Multicoloured.
1640 50c. Type **506** 70 40
1641 €1 Mamer Castle . . . . . 1·40 85
1642 €2.50 St. Joseph Church, Esch-sur-Alzette (vert) . . 3·50 2·10

507 Pamphlets and Compact Discs

2003. 50th Anniv of Official Journal of European Communities (daily publication of official reports).
1643 **507** 52c. multicoloured . . . 75 45

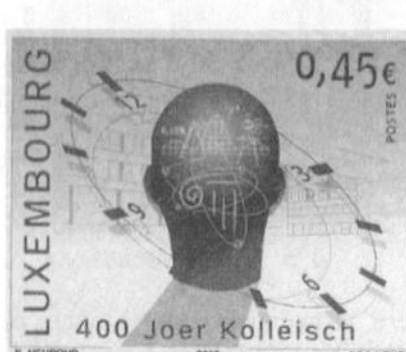

508 Head and Symbols

2003. 400th Anniv of the Athenee (secondary school), Luxembourg.
1644 **508** 45c. multicoloured . . . 60 35

509 1952 National Lottery Poster (Roger Gerson)

2003. Europa. Poster Art. Multicoloured.
1645 45c. Type **509** 60 35
1646 52c. Tiger (1924 Commercial Fair poster) (Auguste Tremont) 70 40

510 Adolphe Bridge

2003. Bridges and Viaducts. Multicoloured.
1647 45c. Type **510** (centenary) 60 35
1648 59c. Stierchen bridge (14th-century) (38 × 28 mm) 80 60
1649 89c. Victor Bodson bridge (Hesperange viaduct) (38 × 28 mm) . . . . . . 1·20 90

511 Woman Hoeing

2003. 75th Anniv of Gaart an Heem (gardening association). Multicoloured.
1650 25c. Type **511** 35 20
1651 A (45c.) Woman holding rake 60 35
1652 €2 Children . . . . 2·75 2·00

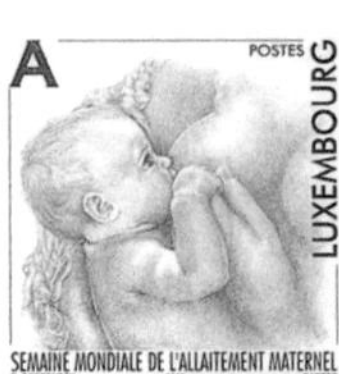

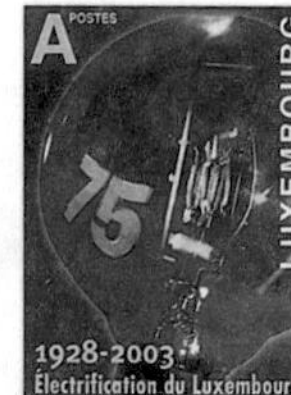

512 Baby at Breast 513 Light Bulb

2003. Breastfeeding Campaign.
1653 **512** A (45c.) brown, chestnut and black 60 35

2003. 75th Anniv of Electricity.
1654 **513** A (45c.) multicoloured 60 35

514 Engineering Steel Sheet Piles

2003. Made in Luxembourg. Multicoloured.
1655 60c. Type **514** 80 60
1656 70c. Medical valve 90 55
1657 80c. Technician and polyester film . . . . . . 1·10 65

515 Church and Cloud containing Buildings

2003. Christmas. Multicoloured.
1658 50c. + 5c. Type **515** 85 85
1659 50c. + 5c. Child, church and Christmas tree 85 85

516 Roe-deer

2003. Fauna (3rd series). Multicoloured.
1660 50c. + 5c. Type **516** 85 85
1661 60c. + 10c. Raccoon (horiz) 90 90
1662 70c. + 10c. Weasel . . . . 1·10 1·10
1663 €1 +25c. Goshawk (horiz) 1·60 1·60

517 *Cantharellus tubaeformis*

2004. Fungi. Multicoloured. Self-adhesive.
1664 10c. Type **517** 15 10
1665 10c. *Ramaria flava* 15 10
1666 10c. *Stropharia cynea* 15 10
1667 50c. *Helvella lacunose* 65 40
1668 50c. *Anthurus archeri* 65 40
1669 50c. *Clitopilus prunulus* 65 40

518 Annual Street Market, Luxembourg-Ville

2004. Anniversaries. Multicoloured.
1670 50c. Type **518** (75th anniv) 65 40
1671 50c. Haberdashery (centenary of Esch-sur-Alzette Commercial Union) 65 40

519 Edward Steichen

2004. Birth Anniversaries. Multicoloured.
1672 **519** 50c. lilac, brown and black 65 40
1673 – 70c. blue, buff and black 95 60
DESIGNS: 50c. Type **519** (photographer) (125th); 70c. Hugo Gernsback (science fiction writer) (120th and centenary of his emigration to USA).

520 Stylized Figures

2004. European Elections.
1674 **520** 50c. multicoloured 65 40

521 Hikers on Bridge, Mullerthal

2004. Europa. Holidays. Multicoloured.
1675 50c. Type **521** 65 40
1676 60c. Camp site, Bourscheid-Beach 80 60

522 Runners carrying Olympic Flame (A. Bilska)

2004. Sport. Winning Entries in Children's Drawing Competition. Multicoloured.
1677 50c. Type **522** (Olympic Games, Athens, 2004) 60 40
1678 60c. Basketball (L. Eyschen) (European Year of Education through Sport) 80 60

523 Building and Anniversary Emblem

2004. 50th Anniv of European School, Luxembourg.
1679 **523** 70c. multicoloured 95 55

OFFICIAL STAMPS

1875. Stamps of 1859–72 optd **OFFICIEL**. Roul.
O79 **3** 1c. brown 26·00 35·00
O80 2c. black 26·00 35·00
O81 **4** 10c. lilac £1900 £1900
O82 12½c. red £425 £450
O83 20c. brown 35·00 55·00
O84 25c. blue £225 £150
O85 30c. purple 29·00 70·00
O88b 40c. orange £250 £250
O87 1f. on 37½c. bistre (No. 37) £100 23·00

1875. Stamps of 1874–79 optd **OFFICIEL**. Perf.
O 89 **3** 1c. brown 8·00 32·00
O 90 2c. black 10·00 32·00
O 91 4c. green 85·00 £130
O 92 5c. yellow 48·00 70·00
O 93a **4** 10c. lilac 75·00 80·00
O111 12½c. red 60·00 £100
O 99a 25c. blue 3·00 2·50
O 96 1f. on 37½c. bistre (No. 56) 29·00 40·00

1881. Stamp of 1859 optd **S. P.** Roul.
O116 **3** 40c. orange 32·00 60·00

1881. Stamps of 1874–79 optd **S. P.** Perf.
O121 **3** 1c. brown 23·00 50·00
O122 2c. black 23·00 50·00
O118 4c. green £140 £170
O123 5c. yellow 70·00 85·00
O124 **4** 10c. lilac 95·00 £140
O125 12½c. red £110 £140
O126 20c. brown 60·00 £100
O127 25c. blue 60·00 £100
O128 30c. red 70·00 £100
O120 1f. on 37½c. bistre (No. 56) 30·00 42·00

1882. Stamps of 1882 optd **S. P.**
O141 **7** 1c. grey 30 40
O142 2c. brown 30 40
O143 4c. olive 35 50
O144 5c. green 35 55
O145 10c. red 16·00 15·00
O146 12½c. blue 2·50 4·00
O147 20c. orange 2·50 4·00
O148 25c. blue 17·00 23·00
O149 30c. olive 5·25 8·50
O150 50c. brown 1·00 2·25
O151 1f. lilac 1·00 2·75
O152 5f. orange 16·00 30·00

1891. Stamps of 1891 optd **S. P.**
O188 **8** 10c. red 30 45
O189 12½c. green 6·00 6·00
O190 20c. orange 9·50 7·00
O191a 25c. blue 30 40
O192 30c. green 6·50 6·75
O193a 37½c. green 6·00 7·50
O194 50c. brown 5·00 8·25
O195a 1f. purple 5·00 10·00
O196 2½f. black 38·00 60·00
O197 5f. lake 29·00 55·00

1898. Stamps of 1895 optd **S. P.**
O213 **9** 1c. grey 1·90 1·75
O214 2c. brown 1·40 1·50
O215 4c. bistre 1·40 1·50
O216 5c. green 3·25 4·00
O217 10c. red 40·00 32·00

1908. Stamps of 1906 optd **Officiel**.
O218 **10** 1c. grey 10 30
O219 2c. brown 10 30
O220 4c. bistre 10 30
O221 5c. green 10 30
O271 5c. mauve 10 30
O222 6c. lilac 10 30
O223 7½c. yellow 25 30
O224 10c. red 30 45
O225 12½c. slate 30 50
O226 15c. brown 40 65
O227 20c. orange 40 65
O228 25c. blue 40 60
O229 30c. olive 4·50 4·50
O230 37½c. green 70 75
O231 50c. brown 1·10 1·40
O232 87½c. blue 1·75 3·25
O233 1f. purple 2·50 3·50
O234 2½f. red 70·00 65·00
O235 5f. purple 65·00 40·00

1915. Stamps of 1914 optd **Officiel**.
O236 **13** 10c. purple 20 60
O237 12½c. green 20 60
O238 15c. brown 20 60
O239 17½c. brown 20 60
O240 25c. blue 20 60
O241 30c. brown 1·40 3·75
O242 35c. blue 25 25
O243 37½c. brown 25 1·00
O244 40c. red 35 95
O245 50c. grey 35 85
O246 62½c. green 35 1·25
O247 87½c. orange 35 1·40
O248 1f. brown 35 1·25
O249 2½f. red 40 2·50
O250 5f. violet 40 3·25

1922. Stamps of 1921 optd **Officiel**.
O251 **17** 2c. brown 15 20
O252 3c. green 15 15
O253 6c. purple 15 30
O272 10c. green 10 30
O273 15c. green 10 30
O274 15c. orange 10 30
O256 20c. orange 25 40
O275 20c. green 10 30
O257 25c. green 25 40
O258 30c. red 25 40
O259 40c. orange 25 40
O260 50c. blue 30 55
O276 50c. red 15 35
O261 75c. red 30 55
O277 75c. blue 20 45
O266 80c. black 25 50
O263 **18** 1f. red 50 1·50
O278 1f. blue 40 1·25
O267 – 2f. blue 40 1·75
O279 – 2f. brown 1·50 4·75
O269 – 5f. violet 5·00 8·50

1922. Stamps of 1923 optd **Officiel**.
O268b **28** 3f. blue 40 1·40
O270 **26** 10f. black 9·50 25·00

1926. Stamps of 1926 optd **Officiel**.
O280 **32** 5c. mauve 10 20
O281 10c. green 10 20
O298 15c. black 30 95
O282 20c. orange 10 20
O283 25c. green 10 20
O300 25c. brown 35 70
O301 30c. green 30 1·25
O302 30c. violet 40 1·00
O303 35c. violet 40 35
O304 35c. green 40 95
O286 40c. brown 15 25
O287 50c. brown 15 25
O307 60c. green 40 75
O288 65c. brown 15 40
O308 70c. violet 1·90 6·00
O289 75c. red 15 40
O309 75c. brown 40 75
O291 80c. brown 25 45
O292 90c. red 35 65
O293 1f. black 30 50
O312 1f. red 45 1·50
O294 1¼f. blue 15 15
O313 1¼f. yellow 1·40 4·00
O314 1¼f. green 2·50 4·75
O315 1½f. blue 40 1·25
O316 1¾f. blue 45 1·25

1928. Stamp of 1928 optd **Officiel**.
O317 **37** 2f. black 55 1·40

1931. Stamp of 1931 optd **Officiel**.
O318 **43** 20f. green 2·40 6·50

1934. Stamp of 1934 optd **Officiel**.
O319 **47** 5f. green 1·75 5·00

1935. No. 340 optd **Officiel**.
O341 **52** 10f. green 1·60 6·75

POSTAGE DUE STAMPS

D **12** Arms of Luxembourg

D **77**

1907.
D173 D **12** 5c. black and green 10 20
D174 10c. black and green 85 20
D175 12½c. black and green 30 85
D176 20c. black and green 55 60
D177 25c. black and green 17·00 1·10
D178 50c. black and green 45 3·00
D179 1f. black and green 30 3·25

1920. Surch.
D193 D **12** 15 on 12½c. blk & grn 2·00 5·25
D194 30 on 25c. black & grn 2·50 7·50

1922.
D221 D **12** 5c. red and green 10 30
D222 10c. red and green 10 30
D223 20c. red and green 25 30
D224 25c. red and green 30 45
D225 30c. red and green 30 50
D226 35c. red and green 40 65
D227 50c. red and green 40 65
D228 60c. red and green 40 60
D229 70c. red and green 4·50 4·50
D230 75c. red and green 70 75
D231 1f. red and green 1·10 1·40
D232 2f. red and green 1·75 3·25
D233 3f. red and green 2·50 3·50

1946.
D488 D **77** 5c. green 35 65
D489 10c. green 35 45
D490 20c. green 35 45
D491 30c. green 35 45
D492 50c. green 35 35
D493 70c. green 45 70
D494 75c. green 1·40 30
D495 1f. red 35 30
D496 1f.50 red 35 30
D497 2f. red 45 30
D498 3f. red 70 30
D499 5f. red 1·00 35
D500 10f. red 1·75 3·50
D501 20f. red 3·50 20·00

MACAO Pt. 9; Pt. 17

A former Portuguese territory in China at the mouth of the Canton River.

1884. 1000 reis = 1 milreis.
1894. 78 avos = 1 rupee.
1913. 100 avos = 1 pataca.

1884. "Crown" key-type inscr "MACAU".
10 P 5r. black 7·75 5·75
2 10r. orange 11·50 10·50
21 10r. green 11·00 9·00
12 20r. bistre 19·00 14·50
27 20r. red 19·00 17·00
13 25r. red 11·50 5·50
22 25r. lilac 11·00 9·25
14 40r. blue 35·00 32·00
23 40r. buff 21·00 14·50
15 50r. green 42·00 34·00
24 50r. blue 11·50 11·50
31 80r. grey 37·00 29·00
16 100r. lilac 19·00 17·00
17 200r. orange 21·00 17·00
9 300r. brown 22·00 18·00

1885. "Crown" key type of Macao surch **80 reis** in circle. No gum.
19 P 80r. on 100r. lilac 50·00 32·00

1885. "Crown" key type of Macao surch in Reis. With gum (43, 44, 45), no gum (others).
32 P 5r. on 25r. pink 12·50 8·25
43 5r. on 80r. grey 8·25 7·00
46 5r. on 100r. lilac 45·00 37·00
33 10r. on 25r. pink 21·00 13·50
38 10r. on 50r. green 70·00 70·00
44 10r. on 80r. grey 24·00 26·00
47 10r. on 200r. orange 44·00 37·00
35 20r. on 50r. green 16·00 10·00
45 20r. on 80r. grey 30·00 21·00
40 40r. on 50r. green 60·00 45·00

1885. "Crown" key-type of Macao surch with figure of value only and bar. No gum.
41 P 5 on 25r. red 30·00 18·00
42a 10 on 50r. green 22·00 16·00

9

1887. Fiscal stamps as T **9** surch **CORREIO** and new value. No gum.
50 5r. on 10r. green and brown 90·00 80·00
51 5r. on 20r. green and brown 90·00 80·00
52 5r. on 60r. green and brown 90·00 80·00
53 10r. on 10r. green and brown £110 90·00
54 10r. on 60r. green and brown £110 90·00
55 40r. on 20r. green and brown £180 £130

1888. "Embossed" key-type inscr "PROVINCIA DE MACAU".
56 Q 5r. black 8·50 4·00
57 10r. green 8·50 6·75
58 20r. red 14·50 6·75
59 25r. mauve 14·50 6·75
60 40r. brown 14·50 6·75
61 50r. blue 14·50 6·75
62 80r. grey 17·00 11·50
63 100r. brown 19·00 12·50
71 200r. lilac 30·00 17·00
72 300r. orange 29·00 17·00

1892. No. 71 surch **30 30**.
73 Q 30 on 200r. lilac 30·00 23·00

1894. "Embossed" key-type of Macao surch **PROVISORIO**, value and Chinese characters. No gum.
75b Q 1a. on 5r. black 7·25 3·75
76 3a. on 20r. red 10·00 4·25
77 4a. on 25r. violet 12·00 7·00
89 5a. on 30 on 200r. lilac (No. 73) 60·00 55·00
78 6a. on 40r. brown 10·00 7·00
79 8a. on 50r. blue 27·00 11·50
80 13a. on 80r. grey 13·00 10·00
81 16a. on 100r. brown 18·00 8·25
82 31a. on 200r. lilac 55·00 32·00
83 47a. on 300r. orange 60·00 17·00

1894. "Figures" key-type inscr "MACAU".
91 R 5r. yellow 5·00 2·50
92 10r. mauve 5·00 2·50
93 15r. brown 6·00 4·00
94 20r. lilac 10·00 4·00
95 25r. green 15·00 9·25
96 50r. blue 22·00 9·25
97 75r. pink 40·00 28·00
98 80r. green 27·00 18·00
99 100r. brown on buff 28·00 14·50
100 150r. red on pink 32·00 14·50

101 200r. blue on blue . . . . 45·00 19·00
102 300r. blue on brown . . . 55·00 19·00

1898. As Vasco da Gama types of Portugal but inscr "MACAU".
104 ½a. green 3·25 2·50
105 1a. red 3·25 2·50
106 2a. purple 3·25 2·50
107 4a. green 4·00 2·50
108 8a. blue 7·00 3·75
109 12a. brown 8·00 4·25
110 16a. brown 8·00 3·75
111 24a. brown 11·00 7·25

1898. "King Carlos" key-type inscr "MACAU". Name and value in black.
112 S ½a. grey 1·40 75
113 1a. yellow 1·40 75
114 2a. green 1·60 55
115 2½a. brown 2·50 1·40
116 3a. lilac 2·50 1·40
174 3a. grey 3·25 1·60
117 4a. green 4·25 2·50
175 4a. red 3·00 1·60
176 5a. brown 4·00 2·50
177 6a. brown 4·25 3·00
119 8a. blue 4·75 2·50
178 8a. brown 5·00 2·50
120 10a. blue 5·00 3·25
121 12a. pink 7·00 5·75
179 12a. purple 17·00 11·00
122 13a. mauve 8·50 6·00
180 13a. lilac 8·75 5·50
123 15a. green 17·00 11·50
124 16a. blue on blue 8·00 5·75
181 18a. brown on pink 16·00 13·00
125 20a. brown on cream 9·50 8·25
126 24a. brown on yellow 12·50 6·75
127 31a. purple 15·00 6·75
182 31a. purple on pink 15·00 13·50
128 47a. blue on pink 24·00 11·00
183 47a. blue on yellow 25·00 22·00
129 78a. black on blue 29·00 14·00

1900. "King Carlos" key-type of Macao surch **PROVISORIO** and new value.
132 S 5 on 13a. mauve 4·50 3·75
133 10 on 16a. blue on blue 6·00 4·00
134 15 on 24a. brown on yellow 14·00 4·00
135 20 on 31a. purple 18·00 4·00

1902. Various types of Macao surch.
138 Q 6a. on 5r. black 3·75 2·50
142 R 6a. on 5r. yellow 3·50 2·50
136 P 6a. on 10r. yellow 12·00 7·00
137 6a. on 10r. green 8·00 5·50
139 Q 6a. on 10r. green 3·75 2·50
143 R 6a. on 10r. mauve 8·00 5·00
144 6a. on 15r. brown 8·00 9·25
145 6a. on 25r. green 4·75 3·25
140 Q 6a. on 40r. brown 3·75 2·50
146 R 6a. on 80r. green 4·75 3·00
148 6a. on 100r. brown on buff 11·00 3·50
149 6a. on 200r. blue on blue 3·50 2·50
151 V 18a. on 2½r. brown 4·75 4·00
153 Q 18a. on 20r. red 12·00 4·25
162 R 18a. on 20r. lilac 12·00 4·75
154 Q 18a. on 25r. mauve 60·00 28·00
163 R 18a. on 50r. blue 12·00 4·75
165 18a. on 75r. pink 12·00 4·75
155 Q 18a. on 80r. grey 80·00 44·00
156 18a. on 100r. brown 9·25 8·25
166 R 18a. on 150r. red on pink 8·75 4·75
158 Q 18a. on 200r. lilac 70·00 45·00
160 18a. on 300r. orange 15·00 7·00
167 R 18a. on 300r. blue on brn 12·00 6·00

1902. "King Carlos" type of Macao optd **PROVISORIO**.
168 S 2a. green 8·25 4·75
169 4a. green 8·25 4·75
170 8a. blue 8·25 4·75
171 10a. blue 8·75 5·50
172 12a. pink 14·50 8·25

1905. No. 179 surch **10 AVOS** and bar.
184 S 10a. on 12a. purple 15·00 9·75

1910. "Due" key-type of Macao, but with words "PORTEADO" and "RECEBER" cancelled.
185 W ½a. green 7·50 5·25
186 1a. green 7·50 5·25
187 2a. grey 7·50 5·25

1911. "King Carlos" key-type of Macao optd **REPUBLICA**.
188 S ½a. grey 70 60
189 1a. orange 70 60
190 2a. green 70 60
191 3a. grey 70 60
192 4a. red 2·50 2·30
193 5a. brown 2·50 1·90
194 6a. brown 2·50 1·90
195 8a. brown 2·50 1·90
196 10a. blue 2·50 1·90
197 13a. lilac 3·75 2·00
198 16a. blue on blue 3·75 2·00
199 18a. brown on pink 8·50 5·75
200 20a. brown on cream 8·50 5·75
201 31a. purple on pink 8·50 5·75
202 47a. blue on yellow 12·00 9·00
203 78a. black on blue 20·00 13·00

30

32

1911. Fiscal stamp surch **POSTAL 1 AVO** and bar.
204 **30** 1a. on 5r. brown, yellow and black 7·50 3·75

1911. Stamps bisected and surch.
205 S 2a. on half of 4a. red (No. 175) 20·00 10·00
206 5a. on half of 10a. blue (No. 120) £160 £160
207 5a. on half of 10a. blue (No. 171) 65·00 60·00

1911.
210 **32** 1a. black £325 £325
211 2a. black £350 £350

1913. Provisionals of 1902 surch in addition with new value and bars over old value and optd **REPUBLICA**.
212 R 2a. on 18a. on 20r. lilac (No. 162) 6·00 2·50
213 2a. on 18a. on 50r. blue (No. 163) 6·00 2·50
215 2a. on 18a. on 75r. pink (No. 165) 7·00 2·50
216 2a. on 18a. on 150r. red on pink (No. 166) 7·00 2·50

1913. Provisionals of 1902 and 1905 optd **REPUBLICA**.
218 Q 6a. on 5r. (No. 138) 4·25 3·75
284 R 6a. on 5r. (No. 142) 2·50 2·10
217 P 6a. on 10r. (No. 137) 13·00 8·75
285 Q 6a. on 10r. (No. 139) 9·25 8·75
286 R 6a. on 10r. (No. 143) 4·75 4·75
287 6a. on 15r. (No. 144) 4·25 3·25
288 6a. on 25r. (No. 145) 4·50 4·00
220 Q 6a. on 40r. (No. 140) 4·50 3·25
289 R 6a. on 80r. (No. 146) 4·50 3·25
291 6a. on 100r. (No. 148) 11·00 8·25
292 6a. on 200r. (No. 149) 3·00 1·70
281 S 8a. (No. 170) 2·10 1·80
282 10a. (No. 171) 2·10 1·80
283 10a. on 12a. (No. 184) 4·50 4·50
293 V 18a. on 2½r. (No. 151) 1·90 1·70
229 Q 18a. on 20r. (No. 153) 7·25 5·25
295 R 18a. on 20r. (No. 162) 4·25 3·25
296 18a. on 50r. (No. 163) 4·75 3·75
298 18a. on 75r. (No. 165) 4·75 3·75
230 Q 18a. on 100r. (No. 156) 35·00 27·00
299 R 18a. on 150r. (No. 166) 4·75 3·75
233 Q 18a. on 300r. (No. 160) 17·00 10·50
300 R 18a. on 300r. (No. 167) 9·75 5·50

1913. Stamps of 1911 issue surch.
252 S ½a. on 5a. brown 3·75 2·50
255 1a. on 13a. lilac 4·75 3·75
253 4a. on 8a. brown 4·75 3·75

1913. Vasco da Gama stamps of Macao optd **REPUBLICA**, and the 12a. surch **10 A.**
256 ½a. green 2·50 1·50
257 1a. red 4·25 1·60
258 2a. purple 4·25 1·60
259 4a. green 3·75 1·60
260 8a. blue 4·25 2·00
261 10a. on 12a. brown 12·00 4·00
262 16a. brown 6·00 2·50
263 24a. brown 8·00 3·25

1913. "Ceres" key-type inscr "MACAU".
264 U ½a. green 1·40 70
310 1a. black 1·40 70
311 1½a. green 1·10 60
280 2a. green 1·40 70
313 3a. orange 3·25 2·30
267 4a. red 2·50 1·50
315 4a. yellow 2·75 2·50
268 5a. brown 3·00 2·00
269 6a. violet 3·00 2·00
270 8a. brown 3·00 2·00
271 10a. blue 3·00 2·00
272 12a. brown 3·00 2·00
320 14a. mauve 8·25 8·50
321 16a. grey 5·50 4·25
274 20a. red 7·75 5·25
322 24a. green 8·25 7·00
323 32a. brown 11·50 9·75
275 40a. purple 8·00 5·25
324 56a. pink 18·00 15·00
276 58a. brown on green 14·50 11·00
325 72a. brown 32·00 11·50
277 76a. brown on pink 15·00 12·50
278 1p. orange on orange 19·00 15·00
326 1p. orange 40·00 23·00
279 3p. green on blue 65·00 47·00
327 3p. turquoise £100 80·00
328 5p. red £160 £120

1919. Surch.
301 U ½a. on 5a. brown (No. 268) 32·00 25·00
330 1a. on 24a. grn (No. 322) 2·75 2·30
302 R 2 on 6a. on 25r. green (No. 288) £150 80·00
303 2 on 6a. on 80r. green (No. 289) 46·00 36·00
304 S 2a. on 6a. (No. 177) 28·00 25·00
331 U 2a. on 32a. (No. 323) 2·75 2·30
332 4a. on 12a. (No. 272) 2·75 2·30
329 5a. on 6a. violet (No. 269) 3·75 3·50
334 7a. on 8a. brn (No. 270) 16·00 10·00
335 12a. on 14a. (No. 320) 3·75 3·25
336 15a. on 16a. (No. 321) 3·75 3·75
337 20a. on 56a. pink (No. 324) 32·00 23·00

50 "Portugal" and Galeasse

1934.
338 **50** ½a. brown 35 35
339 1a. brown 35 35
340 2a. green 60 55
341 3a. mauve 60 55
342 4a. black 70 65
343 5a. grey 70 65
344 6a. brown 70 65
345 7a. red 95 85
346 8a. blue 95 85
347 10a. red 1·50 90
348 12a. blue 1·50 90
349 14a. green 1·50 90
350 15a. purple 1·50 90
351 20a. orange 1·50 90
352 30a. green 4·00 2·75
353 40a. violet 4·00 2·50
354 50a. brown 7·50 4·75
355 1p. blue 18·00 10·00
356 2p. brown 25·00 15·00
357 3p. green 40·00 22·00
358 5p. mauve 85·00 29·00

1936. Air. Stamps of 1934 optd **Aviao** and with Greek characters or surch also.
359 **40** 2a. green 3·00 1·80
360 3a. mauve 3·00 1·80
361 5a. on 6a. brown 3·00 1·80
362 7a. red 3·00 1·80
363 8a. blue 5·75 4·25
364 15a. purple 17·00 9·50

54 Vasco da Gama

56 Airplane over Globe

1938. Name and value in black.
365 **54** 1a. green (postage) 60 50
366 2a. brown 60 50
367 3a. violet 60 50
368 4a. green 60 50
369 – 5a. red 60 50
370 – 6a. grey 1·50 95
371 – 8a. purple 1·50 95
372 – 10a. mauve 2·00 1·10
373 – 12a. red 2·00 1·10
374 – 15a. orange 2·00 1·10
375 – 20a. blue 3·25 1·70
376 – 40a. black 6·00 2·40
377 – 50a. brown 6·00 2·40
378 – 1p. red 18·00 7·25
379 – 2p. green 32·00 11·00
380 – 3p. blue 50·00 18·00
381 – 5p. brown 85·00 22·00
382 **56** 1a. red (air) 45 40
383 2a. violet 55 40
384 3a. orange 55 40
385 5a. blue 1·30 75
386 10a. red 2·20 1·20
387 20a. green 3·50 2·00
388 50a. brown 6·00 2·75
389 70a. red 11·50 5·00
390 1p. mauve 22·00 7·25

DESIGNS: Nos. 369/71, Mousinho de Albuquerque; 372/4, Henry the Navigator; 375/7, Dam; 378/81, Afonso de Albuquerque.

1940. Surch.
391 **50** 1a. on 6a. brown (No. 344) 5·25 4·25
394 2a. on 6a. brown (No. 344) 2·30 2·20
395 3a. on 6a. brown (No. 344) 2·30 2·10
401 – 3a. on 6a. grey (No. 370) 50·00 41·00
396 **50** 5a. on 7a. red (No. 345) 2·30 2·20
397 5a. on 8a. blue (No. 346) 2·30 2·20
398 8a. on 30a. (No. 352) 5·00 3·00
399 8a. on 40a. (No. 353) 5·00 3·00
400 8a. on 50a. (No. 354) 5·50 4·75

61 Mountain Fort

62 Our Lady of Fatima

1948.
410 – 1a. brown and orange 1·40 25
427 – 1a. violet and pink 2·10 85
411 **61** 2a. purple 85 25
428 2a. brown and yellow 2·10 85
412 – 3a. purple 2·50 70
429 – 3a. orange 3·25 85
413 – 8a. red 3·00 1·00
430 – 8a. grey 2·00 85
414 – 10a. purple 3·50 85
431 – 10a. brown and orange 4·75 1·10
415 – 20a. blue 6·00 1·60
416 – 30a. grey 6·50 1·20
432 – 30a. blue 10·00 2·50
417 – 50a. brown and buff 8·00 1·80
433 – 50a. olive and green 22·00 2·50
418 – 1p. green 80·00 11·50
419 – 1p. blue 85·00
434 – 1p. brown 43·00 7·75
420 – 2p. red 55·00 14·50
421 – 3p. green 80·00 40·00
422 – 5p. violet 90·00 17·00

DESIGNS—HORIZ: 1a. Macao house; 3a. Port of Macao; 8a. Praia Grande Bay; 10a. Leal Senado Sq; 20a. Sao Jerome Hill; 30a. Street scene, Macao; 50a. Relief of goddess of Ma (allegory); 5p. Forest road. VERT: 1p. Cerco Gateway; 2p. Barra Pagoda, Ma-Cok-Miu; 3p. Post Office.

1948. Honouring the Statue of Our Lady of Fatima.
423 **62** 8a. red 15·00 4·25

64 Globe and Letter

65 Bells and Dove

1949. 75th Anniv of U.P.U.
424 **64** 32a. purple 80·00 19·00

1950. Holy Year.
425 **65** 32a. black 10·00 3·75
426 – 50a. red 13·00 5·00

DESIGN: 50a. Angel holding candelabra.

66 Arms and Dragon

1950.
435 **66** 1a. yellow on cream 1·40 90
436 2a. green on green 1·40 90
437 10a. purple on green 1·40 90
438 10a. mauve on green 1·40 90

67 F. Mendes Pinto

68 Junk

1951.
439 **67** 1a. indigo and blue 40 20
440 – 2a. brown and green 70 20
441 – 3a. green and light green 1·40 25
442 – 6a. violet and blue 2·75 30
443 – 10a. brown and orange 4·00 95
444 **67** 20a. purple and light purple 12·00 2·30
445 – 30a. brown and green 16·00 2·40
446 – 50a. red and orange 32·00 10·50

DESIGNS: 2, 10a. St. Francis Xavier; 3, 50a. J. Alvaras; 6, 30a. L. de Camoens.

1951.
447 – 1p. ultramarine and blue 26·00 2·50
448 – 3p. black and blue 85·00 6·75
449 **68** 5p. brown and orange £100 22·00

DESIGNS—HORIZ: 1p. Sampan. VERT: 3p. Junk.

69 Our Lady of Fatima

71 St. Raphael Hospital

1951. Termination of Holy Year.
450 **69** 60a. mauve and pink 20·00 6·00

1952. 1st Tropical Medicine Congress, Lisbon.
451 **71** 6a. lilac and black 5·75 3·50

72 St. Francis Xavier Statue **73** The Virgin

1952. 400th Death Anniv of St. Francis Xavier.
452 **72** 3a. black on cream . . . . 1·20 50
453 – 16a. brown on buff . . . . 4·00 1·50
454 – 40a. black on blue . . . . 8·25 3·25
DESIGNS: 16a. Miraculous Arm of St. Francis; 40a. Tomb of St. Francis.

1953. Missionary Art Exhibition.
455 **73** 8a. brown and drab . . . 1·90 45
456 10a. blue and brown . . . 5·00 1·80
457 50a. green and drab . . . 14·00 3·00

74 Honeysuckle **75** Portuguese Stamp of 1853 and Arms of Portuguese Overseas Provinces

1953. Indigenous Flowers.
458 **74** 1a. yellow, green and red 40 40
459 – 3a. purple, green and yellow 40 40
460 – 5a. red, green and brown 70 75
461 – 10a. multicoloured 70 80
462 – 16a. yellow, green & brown 70 80
463 – 30a. pink, brown and green 2·30 2·75
464 – 39a. multicoloured . . . . 2·40 2·75
465 – 1p. yellow, green and purple . . . . 5·50 3·00
466 – 3p. red, brown and grey 14·00 5·25
467 – 5p. yellow, green and red 25·00 7·75
FLOWERS: 3a. Myosotis; 5a. Dragon claw; 10a. Nunflower; 16a. Narcissus; 30a. Peach blossom; 39a. Lotus blossom; 1p. Chrysanthemum; 3p. Plum blossom; 5p. Tangerine blossom.

1954. Portuguese Stamp Centenary.
468 **75** 10a. multicoloured . . . . 8·00 2·00

76 Father M. de Nobrega and View of Sao Paulo **77** Map of Macao

1954. 4th Centenary of Sao Paulo.
469 **76** 39a. multicoloured . . . . 6·00 5·50

1956. Map multicoloured. Values in red, inscr in brown. Colours given are of the backgrounds.
470 **77** 1a. drab 45 30
471 3a. slate 45 30
472 5a. brown 45 30
473 10a. buff . . . . 1·90 75
474 30a. blue . . . . 2·40 75
475 40a. green . . . . 3·25 1·50
476 90a. grey . . . . 8·50 2·75
477 1p.50 pink . . . . 14·00 3·00

78 Exhibition Emblem and Atomic Emblems **79** "Cinnamomum camphora"

1958. Brussels International Exhibition.
478 **78** 70a. multicoloured . . . . 5·00 1·90

1958. 6th International Congress of Tropical Medicine.
479 **79** 20a. multicoloured . . . . 5·25 3·50

80 Globe girdled by Signs of the Zodiac **81** Boeing 707 over Ermida da Penha

1960. 500th Death Anniv of Prince Henry the Navigator.
480 **80** 2p. multicoloured . . . . 9·50 2·75

1960. Air. Multicoloured.
481 50a. Praia Grande Bay . . . 2·25 55
482 76a. Type **81** . . . . 4·00 55
483 3p. Macao . . . . 10·00 1·50
484 5p. Mong Ha . . . . 16·00 1·40
485 10p. Shore of Praia Grande Bay . . . . 23·00 2·20

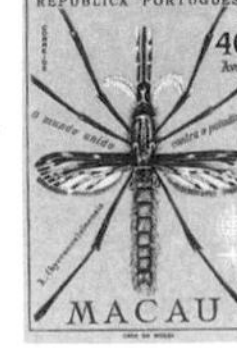

82 Hockey **83** "Anopheles hycranus sinensis"

1962. Sports. Multicoloured.
486 10a. Type **82** 30 25
487 16a. Wrestling . . . . 2·75 1·80
488 20a. Table tennis . . . . . . 2·00 1·60
489 50a. Motor cycle racing . . . 3·50 2·30
490 1p.20 Relay racing . . . . . 9·00 4·00
491 2p.50 Badminton . . . . . . 20·00 7·25

1962. Malaria Eradication.
492 **83** 40a. multicoloured . . . . 5·50 2·75

84 Bank Building **85** I.T.U. Emblem and St. Gabriel

1964. Centenary of National Overseas Bank.
493 **84** 20a. multicoloured . . . . 8·50 3·00

1965. Centenary of I.T.U.
494 **85** 10a. multicoloured . . . . 4·25 1·00

86 Infante Dom Henrique Academy and Visconde de Sao Januario Hospital **87** Drummer, 1548

1966. 40th Anniv of Portuguese National Revolution.
495 **86** 10a. multicoloured . . . . 6·00 1·80

1966. Portuguese Military Uniforms. Mult.
496 10a. Type **87** . . . . 1·00 35
497 15a. Soldier, 1548 . . . . . 2·00 35
498 20a. Arquebusier, 1649 . . . 2·00 35
499 40a. Infantry officer, 1783 . . 3·50 1·00
500 50a. Infantryman, 1783 . . . 3·75 1·40
501 60a. Infantryman, 1902 . . . 5·00 1·40
502 1p. Infantryman, 1903 . . . 7·50 2·00
503 3p. Infantryman, 1904 . . . 17·00 8·00

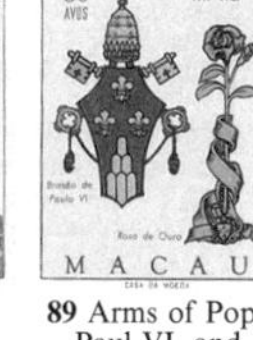

88 O. E. Carmo and Patrol Boat "Vega" **89** Arms of Pope Paul VI, and "Golden Rose"

1967. Centenary of Military Naval Assn. Mult.
504 10a. Type **88** . . . . 1·30 85
505 20a. Silva Junior and sail frigate "Don Fernando" 5·50 2·20

1967. 50th Anniv of Fatima Apparitions.
506 **89** 50a. multicoloured . . . . 5·00 1·50

90 Cabral Monument, Lisbon **91** Adm. Gago Coutinho with Sextant

1968. 500th Birth Anniv of Pedro Cabral (explorer). Multicoloured.
507 20a. Type **90** . . . . 3·50 1·00
508 70a. Cabral's statue, Belmonte . . . . 5·00 2·20

1969. Birth Centenary of Admiral Gago Coutinho.
509 **91** 20a. multicoloured . . . . 3·25 1·40

92 Church and Convent of Our Lady of the Reliquary, Vidigueira **93** L. A. Rebello da Silva

1969. 500th Birth Anniv of Vasco da Gama (explorer).
510 **92** 1p. multicoloured . . . . 8·00 1·20

1969. Centenary of Overseas Administrative Reforms.
511 **93** 90a. multicoloured . . . . 3·25 2·20

94 Bishop D. Belchoir Carneiro **95** Facade of Mother Church, Golega

1969. 400th Anniv of Misericordia Monastery, Macao.
512 **94** 50a. multicoloured . . . . 3·25 95

1969. 500th Birth Anniv of King Manoel I.
513 **95** 30a. multicoloured . . . . 5·50 95

96 Marshal Carmona **97** Dragon Mask

1970. Birth Centenary of Marshal Carmona.
514 **96** 5a. multicoloured . . . . 2·00 95

1971. Chinese Carnival Masks. Multicoloured.
515 5a. Type **97** . . . . 1·10 40
516 10a. Lion mask . . . . . . 2·00 40

98 Portuguese Traders at the Chinese Imperial Court

1972. 400th Anniv of Camoens' "The Lusiads" (epic poem).
517 **98** 20a. multicoloured . . . . 8·00 4·50

99 Hockey

1972. Olympic Games, Munich.
518 **99** 50a. multicoloured . . . . 2·50 95

100 Fairey IIID Seaplane "Santa Cruz" arriving at Rio de Janeiro

1972. 50th Anniv of First Flight from Lisbon to Rio de Janeiro.
519 **100** 5p. multicoloured . . . . 14·00 7·00

101 Lyre Emblem and Theatre Facade **102** W.M.O. Emblem

1972. Centenary of Pedro V Theatre, Macao.
520 **101** 2p. multicoloured . . . . 9·00 2·40

1973. Centenary of W.M.O.
521 **102** 20a. multicoloured . . . 2·75 1·70

103 Visconde de Sao Januario **104** Chinnery (self-portrait)

1974. Centenary of Visconde de Sao Januario Hospital. Multicoloured.
522 15a. Type **103** 95 35
523 60a. Hospital buildings of 1874 and 1974 . . . . . . 3·50 95

1974. Birth Bicent of George Chinnery (painter).
524 **104** 30a. multicoloured . . . 3·00 1·20

105 Macao–Taipa Bridge

1975. Inauguration of Macao–Taipa Bridge. Multicoloured.
525 20a. Type **105** . . . . 1·40 45
526 2p.20 View of Bridge from below . . . . 8·00 2·00

106 Man waving Banner

1975. 1st Anniv of Portuguese Revolution.
527 **106** 10a. multicoloured . . . 2·30 2·75
528 1p. multicoloured . . . . 10·00 6·25

107 Pou Chai Pagoda

1976. Pagodas. Multicoloured.
529 10p. Type **107** . . . . . . 12·50 5·75
530 20p. Tin Hau Pagoda . . . . 21·00 8·25

108 Symbolic Figure

1977. Legislative Assembly.
531 **108** 5a. blue, dp blue & black . . . 7·00 2·50
532 2p. brown and black . . . 37·00 10·00
533 5p. yellow, green and black . . . . 26·00 9·75

1979. Nos. 462, 464, 469, 482, 523 and 526 surch.
536 – 10a. on 16a. yellow, green and brown . . . . . . 8·25 4·75
537 – 30a. on 39a. multicoloured 9·50 4·75
538 **76** 30a. on 39a. multicoloured 37·00 25·00
539 – 30a. on 60a. multicoloured 6·75 5·25
540 **81** 70a. on 76a. multicoloured 34·00 8·75
541 – 2p. on 2p.20 multicoloured 8·25 7·25

111 Camoes and Macao Harbour **113** Buddha and Macao Cathedral

1981. 400th Death Anniv (1980) of Camoes (Portuguese poet).
542 **111** 10a. multicoloured . . . 35 35
543 30a. multicoloured . . . 55 35
544 1p. multicoloured . . . . 1·60 1·40
545 3p. multicoloured . . . . 3·75 2·10

1981. Transcultural Psychiatry Symposium.
547 **113** 15a. multicoloured . . . 65 30
548 40a. multicoloured . . . 65 40
549 50a. multicoloured . . . 1·10 65
550 60a. multicoloured . . . 1·10 65
551 1p. multicoloured . . . . 1·90 90
552 2p.20 multicoloured . . . 4·50 1·80

115 Health Services Buildings

1982. Buildings.
554 – 10a. grey, blue and yellow 15 15
555 – 20a. black, green & lt grn 15 15
556 **115** 30a. green, grey and stone 20 20
557 – 40a. yellow, lt green & grn 25 20
558 – 60a. orange, chocolate and brown 45 15
559 – 80a. pink, green & brown 45 15
560 – 90a. purple, blue and red 75 30
561 – 1p. multicoloured 60 55
562 – 1p.50 yellow, brn & grey 1·10 45
563 – 2p. purple, ultramarine and blue . . . . 1·60 95
564 – 2p.50 ultramarine, pink and blue . . . . 1·90 1·20
565 – 3p. yellow, green and olive . . . . 1·90 95
566 – 7p.50 lilac, blue and red 5·50 2·00
567 – 10p. grey, lilac and mauve 6·50 3·25
568 – 15p. yellow, brown and red . . . . 9·50 4·25

DESIGNS: 10a. Social Welfare Institute; 20a. Holy House of Mercy; 40a. Guia lighthouse; 60a. St. Lawrence's Church; 80a. St. Joseph's Seminary; 90a. Pedro V Theatre; 1p. Cerco city gate; 1p.50, St. Domenico's Church; 2p. Luis de Camoes Museum; 2p.50, Ruins of St. Paul's Church; 3p. Palace of St. Sancha (Governor's residence); 7p.50, Senate House; 10p. Schools Welfare Service building; 15p. Barracks of the Moors (headquarters of Port Captaincy and Maritime Police).

116 Heng Ho (Moon goddess)

1982. Autumn Festival. Multicoloured.
569 40a. Type **116** 25 15
570 1p. Decorated gourds 95 40
571 2p. Paper lantern . . . . . . 1·30 1·10
572 5p. Warrior riding lion . . . 3·25 2·30

117 Aerial View of Macao, Taipa and Coloane Islands **118** "Switchboard Operators" (Lou Sok Man)

1982. Macao's Geographical Situation. Mult.
573 50a. Type **117** 55 35
574 3p. Map of South China . . 1·80 1·90

1983. World Communications Year. Children's Drawings. Multicoloured.
575 60a. Type **118** 35 25
576 3p. Postman and pillar box (Lai Sok Pek) . . . . . . 2·00 1·60
577 6p. Globe with methods of communication (Loi Chak Keong) . . . . 4·00 2·75

119 "Asclepias curassavica" **120** Galleon and Map of Macao (left)

1983. Medicinal Plants. Multicoloured.
578 20a. Type **119** 55 50
579 40a. "Acanthus ilicifolius" . . 95 50
580 60a. "Melastoma sanguineum" . . . . . . 1·20 1·00
581 70a. Indian lotus ("Nelumbo nucifera") . . . . 1·80 1·20
582 1p.50 "Bombax malabaricum" . . . . . . 3·50 2·10
583 2p.50 "Hibiscus mutabilis" 6·50 4·00
MS584 143 × 90 mm. Nos. 578/83 (sold at 6p.50) . . . .

1983. 16th Century Portuguese Discoveries. Multicoloured.
585 4p. Type **120** . . . . 2·75 1·70
586 4p. Galleon, astrolabe and map of Macao (right) . . . 2·75 1·70
Nos. 585/6 were printed together, se-tenant, forming a composite design.

121 Rat **122** Detail of First Macao Stamp, 1884

1984. New Year. "Year of the Rat".
587 **121** 60a. multicoloured . . . 4·75 4·25

1984. Centenary of Macao Stamps.
588 **122** 40a. black and red . . . 45 25
589 3p. black and red . . . . 2·00 1·30
590 5p. black and brown . . . 3·50 2·10
MS591 116 × 139 mm. Nos. 588/90 13·00 11·00

123 Jay

1984. "Ausipex 84" International Stamp Exhibition, Melbourne. Birds. Multicoloured.
592 30a. White-throated and river kingfishers 60 25
593 40a. Type **123** 75 30
594 50a. Japanese white-eye . . . 1·00 35
595 70a. Hoopoe . . . . 1·30 55
596 2p.50 Pekin robin . . . . . 4·00 1·80
597 6p. Mallard . . . . 9·00 2·75

124 Hok Lou T'eng

1984. "Philakorea 84" International Stamp Exhibition, Seoul. Fishing Boats. Multicoloured.
598 20a. Type **124** 15 15
599 60a. Tai Tong 40 30
600 2p. Tai Mei Chai . . . . . 1·50 1·00
601 5p. Ch'at Pong T'o . . . . . 3·50 2·75

125 Ox and Moon **126** Open Hand with Stylized Doves

1985. New Year. Year of the Ox.
602 **125** 1p. multicoloured . . . . 3·75 3·75

1985. International Youth Year. Multicoloured.
603 2p.50 Type **126** . . . . . . 1·40 95
604 3p. Open hands and plants 2·10 1·30

127 Pres. Eanes

1985. Visit of President Ramalho Eanes of Portugal.
605 **127** 1p.50 multicoloured . . . 1·30 60

128 Riverside Scene **129** "Euploea midamus"

1985. 25th Anniv of Luis de Camoes Museum. Paintings by Cheng Chi Yun. Multicoloured.
606 2p.50 Type **128** . . . . . 3·50 1·00
607 2p.50 Man on seat and boy filling jar from river . . . 3·50 1·00
608 2p.50 Playing harp in summerhouse . . . . . . 3·50 1·00
609 2p.50 Three men by river . . 3·50 1·00

1985. World Tourism Day. Butterflies. Mult.
610 30a. Type **129** 35 15
611 50a. Great orange-tip 35 20
612 70a. "Lethe confusa" 55 25
613 2p. Purple sapphire . . . . . 1·30 90
614 4p. "Euthalia phemius seitzi" 2·50 1·40
615 7p.50 Common birdwing . . 4·75 2·40
MS616 95 × 120 mm. Nos. 610/15 22·00 14·00

130 Tou (sailing barge) **131** Tiger and Moon

1985. "Italia '85" International Stamp Exhibition, Rome. Cargo Boats. Multicoloured.
617 50a. Type **130** 35 20
618 70a. "Veng Seng Lei" (motor junk) 45 30
619 1p. "Tong Heng Long No. 2" (motor junk) . . . 60 45
620 6p. "Fong Vong San" (container ship) . . . . . 3·50 1·70

1986. New Year. Year of the Tiger.
621 **131** 1p.50 multicoloured . . . 1·80 1·00

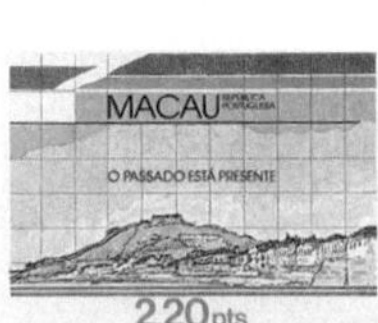

132 View of Macao **133** Suo-na

1986. Macao, "the Past is still Present".
622 **132** 2p.20 multicoloured . . . 1·40 90

1986. "Ameripex '86" International Stamp Exn, Chicago. Musical Instruments. Multicoloured.
623 20a. Type **133** 15 15
624 50a. Sheng (pipes) 35 25
625 60a. Er-hu (bowed instrument) 35 25
626 70a. Ruan (string instrument) 50 45
627 5p. Cheng (harp) . . . . . . 5·50 2·20
628 8p. Pi-pa (lute) . . . . 9·00 5·00
MS629 119 × 111 mm. Nos. 623/8

134 "Flying Albatros" (hydrofoil)

1986. "Stockholmia 86" International Stamp Exhibition. Passenger Ferries. Multicoloured.
630 10a. Type **134** 15 25
631 40a. "Tejo" (hovercraft) . . . 25 35
632 3p. "Tercera" (jetfoil) . . . . 1·70 1·50
633 7p.50 "Cheung Kong" (high speed ferry) . . . . 4·50 3·50

135 Taipa Fortress **136** Sun Yat-sen

1986. 10th Anniv of Security Forces. Fortresses. Multicoloured.
634 2p. Type **135** . . . . 1·70 1·10
635 2p. St. Paul on the Mount . . 1·70 1·10
636 2p. St. Francis . . . . 1·70 1·10
637 2p. Guia . . . . 1·70 1·10
Nos. 634/7 were printed together, se-tenant, forming a composite design.

1986. 120th Birth Anniv of Dr. Sun Yat-sen. Multicoloured.
638 70a. Type **136** . . . . 3·50 3·00
MS639 95 × 70 mm. 1p.30 Dr. Sun Yat-sen (*different*) . . . . . . 15·00 10·00

137 Hare and Moon **138** Wa To (physician)

1987. New Year. Year of the Hare.
640 **137** 1p.50 multicoloured . . . 2·75 85

1987. Shek Wan Ceramics. Multicoloured.
641 2p.20 Type **138** . . . . . . 1·80 85
642 2p.20 Choi San, God of Fortune . . . . 1·80 85
643 2p.20 Yi, Sun God . . . . . 1·80 85
644 2p.20 Cung Kuei, Keeper of Demons . . . . 1·80 85

139 Boats

1987. Dragon Boat Festival. Multicoloured.
645 50a. Type **139** 55 30
646 5p. Dragon boat prow . . . 3·25 2·00

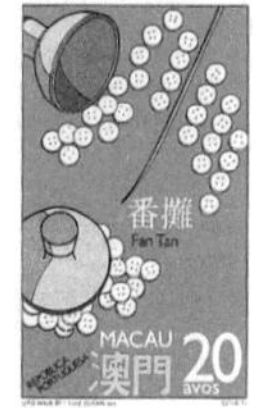

140 Circular Fan **141** Fantan

1987. Fans. Multicoloured.

647 30a. Type **140** 50 30
648 70a. Folding fan with tree design . . . . 1·00 40
649 1p. Square-shaped fan with peacock design . . . . . . 3·00 1·00
650 6p. Heart-shaped fan with painting of woman and tree . . . . 7·50 2·40
MS651 113 × 139 mm. Nos. 647/50 48·00 38·00

1987. Casino Games. Multicoloured.

652 20a. Type **141** 35 20
653 40a. Cussec 55 25
654 4p. Baccarat . . . . 2·50 1·30
655 7p. Roulette . . . . 7·00 3·00

142 Goods Hand-cart **143** Dragon and Moon

1987. Traditional Vehicles. Multicoloured.

656 10a. Type **142** 30 20
657 70a. Open sedan chair . . . 1·00 45
658 90a. Rickshaw . . . . 1·40 60
659 10p. Cycle rickshaw . . . . 7·00 4·00
MS660 90 × 65 mm. 7p.50 Covered sedan chair . . . .

1988. New Year. Year of the Dragon.

661 **143** 2p.50 multicoloured . . . 2·30 1·50

144 West European Hedgehog

1988. Protected Mammals. Multicoloured.

662 3p. Type **144** . . . . 2·30 1·00
663 3p. Eurasian badger . . . . 2·30 1·00
664 3p. European otter . . . . . 2·30 1·00
665 3p. Chinese pangolin . . . . 2·30 1·00

145 Breastfeeding

1988. 40th Anniv of W.H.O. Multicoloured.

666 60a. Type **145** 45 20
667 80a. Vaccinating child . . . 80 30
668 2p.40 Donating blood . . . 1·60 1·10

146 Bicycles

1988. Transport. Multicoloured.

669 20a. Type **146** 20 20
670 50a. Lambretta and Vespa . . 45 45
671 3p.30 Open-sided motor car 1·60 1·20
672 5p. Renault delivery truck, 1912 . . . . 2·75 2·75
MS673 68 × 57 mm. 7p.50 Rover (1907) . . . . 12·00 10·50

147 Hurdling **148** Intelpost (electronic mail)

1988. Olympic Games, Seoul. Multicoloured.

674 40a. Type **147** 45 45
675 60a. Basketball 60 50
676 1p. Football . . . . 1·50 60
677 8p. Table tennis . . . . . . 4·75 2·50
MS678 112 × 140 mm. Nos. 673/6; 5p. Taekwondo . . . . 9·25 9·25

1988. New Postal Services. Multicoloured.

679 13p.40 Type **148** . . . . . 6·25 5·75
680 40p. Express Mail Service (EMS) . . . . 20·00 8·50

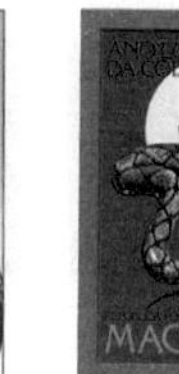

149 B.M.W. Saloon Car **150** Snake and Moon

1988. 35th Macao Grand Prix. Multicoloured.

681 80a. Type **149** 45 35
682 2p.80 Motor cycle . . . . . 1·10 1·10
683 7p. Formula 3 car . . . . . 3·75 2·10
MS684 115 × 139 mm. Nos. 681/3

1989. New Year. Year of the Snake.

685 **150** 3p. multicoloured . . . . 2·40 2·10

151 Water Carrier **152** White Building

1989. Traditional Occupations (1st series). Multicoloured.

686 50a. Type **151** 30 30
687 1p. Tan-kya (boat) woman 80 45
688 4p. Tin-tin man (pedlar) . . 1·80 1·40
689 5p. Tao-fu-fa (soya bean cheese) vendor . . . . . . 2·30 2·00
See also Nos. 714/17 and 743/6.

1989. Paintings by George Vitalievich Smirnoff in Luis Camoes Museum. Multicoloured.

690 2p. Type **152** . . . . 1·40 95
691 2p. Building with railings . . 1·40 95
692 2p. Street scene . . . . . . 1·40 95
693 2p. White thatched cottage 1·40 95

153 Common Cobra **154** Talu

1989. "Philexfrance 89" International Stamp Exhibition, Paris. Snakes of Macao. Mult.

694 2p.50 Type **153** . . . . . . 1·60 1·00
695 2p.50 Banded krait ("Bungarus fasciatus") . . 1·60 1·00
696 2p.50 Bamboo pit viper ("Trimeresurus albolabris") 1·60 1·00
697 2p.50 Rat snake ("Elaphe radiata") . . . . 1·60 1·00

1989. Traditional Games. Multicoloured.

698 10a. Type **154** 15 15
699 60a. Triol (marbles) 35 30
700 3p.30 Chiquia (shuttlecock) 1·90 1·00
701 5p. Chinese chequers . . . . 2·50 1·80

155 Piaggio P-136L Flying Boat **156** Malacca

1989. Aircraft. Multicoloured.

702 50a. Type **155** 25 15
703 70a. Martin M-130 flying boat 55 25
704 2p.80 Fairey 111D seaplane 1·40 90
705 4p. Hawker Osprey seaplane 2·20 1·70
MS706 105 × 82 mm. 7p.50 De Havilland D.H.80A Puss Moth

1989. "World Stamp Expo '89" International Stamp Exhibition, Washington D.C. Portuguese Presence in Far East. Multicoloured.

707 40a. Type **156** 30 15
708 70a. Thailand 55 25
709 90a. India 55 30
710 2p.50 Japan . . . . 1·50 85
711 7p.50 China . . . . 3·25 1·80
MS712 14 × 130 mm. Nos. 707/11; 3p.Macao . . . . 8·50 8·00

157 Horse and Moon **159** Long-finned Grouper ("Epinephelus megachir")

158 Penny Black and Sir Rowland Hill (postal reformer)

1990. New Year. Year of the Horse.

713 **157** 4p. multicoloured . . . . 1·60 1·20

1990. Traditional Occupations (2nd series). As T **151**. Multicoloured.

714 30a. Long-chau singer . . . 25 15
715 70a. Cobbler 60 25
716 1p.50 Travelling penman . . 90 60
717 7p.50 Fisherman with wide nets . . . . 3·25 1·80

1990. 150th Anniv of the Penny Black. Sheet 91 × 130 mm.

MS718 **158** 10p. multicoloured 7·75 6·00

1990. Fishes. Multicoloured.

719 2p.40 Type **159** . . . . . . 1·00 60
720 2p.40 Malabar snapper ("Lutianus malabaricus") 1·00 60
721 2p.40 Spotted snakehead ("Ophiocepalus maculatus") . . . . 1·00 60
722 2p.40 Paradise fish ("Macropodus opercularis") . . . . . . 1·00 60

160 Porcelain

1990. "New Zealand 1990" International Stamp Exhibition, Auckland. Industrial Diversification. Multicoloured.

723 3p. Type **160** . . . . 1·20 85
724 3p. Furniture . . . . 1·20 85
725 3p. Toys . . . . 1·20 85
726 3p. Artificial flowers . . . . 1·20 85
MS727 131 × 95 mm. Nos. 723/6 10·00 9·00

161 Cycling **162** Rose by Lazaro Luis

1990. 11th Asian Games, Peking. Multicoloured.

728 80a. Type **161** 45 30
729 1p. Swimming 55 45
730 3p. Judo . . . . 1·20 90
731 4p.20 Shooting . . . . . . 2·20 1·70
MS732 95 × 140 mm. Nos. 728/31; 6p. Athlete with bamboo pole 5·00 4·25

1990. Compass Roses. Designs showing roses from ancient charts by cartographer named. Mult.

733 50a. Type **162** 30 20
734 1p. Diogo Homem 55 25
735 3p.50 Diogo Homem (different) . . . . 1·30 75
736 6p.50 Fernao Vaz Dourado 3·00 1·70
MS737 107 × 100 mm. 5p. Luiz Teixeira (29 × 39 mm) . . . . 23·00 19·00

163 Cricket Fight **164** Goat and Moon

1990. Betting on Animals. Multicoloured.

738 20a. Type **163** 15 15
739 80a. Melodious laughing thrush fight 35 20
740 1p. Greyhound racing . . . 60 30
741 10p. Horse racing . . . . . 3·75 2·50

1991. New Year. Year of the Goat.

742 **164** 4p.50 multicoloured . . . 1·70 1·40

1991. Traditional Occupations (3rd series). As T **151**. Multicoloured.

743 80a. Knife-grinder 30 15
744 1p.70 Flour-puppets vendor 70 30
745 3p.50 Street barber . . . . . 1·20 65
746 4p.20 Fortune-teller . . . . 1·70 1·00

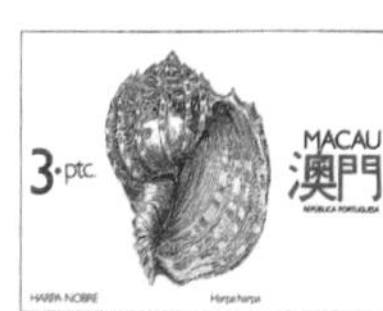

165 True Harp ("Harpa harpa")

1991. Sea Shells. Multicoloured.

747 3p. Type **165** . . . . 1·20 70
748 3p. Oil-lamp tun ("Tonna zonata") . . . . 1·20 70
749 3p. Bramble murex ("Murex pecten") . . . . 1·20 70
750 3p. Rose-branch murex ("Chicoreus rosarius") . . 1·20 70
The Latin names on Nos. 749/50 are incorrect.

166 Character and Backcloth

1991. Chinese Opera. Multicoloured.

751 **166** 60a. multicoloured . . . 20 10
752 – 80a. multicoloured . . . 35 15
753 – 1p. multicoloured 50 25
754 – 10p. multicoloured . . . 3·75 2·00
DESIGNS: Nos. 752/4, Different backcloths and costumes.

167 "Delonix regia" and Lou Lim Ioc Garden

1991. Flowers and Gardens (1st series). Mult.
755 1p.70 Type **167** 55 25
756 3p. "Ipomoea cairica" and Sao Francisco Garden . . 1·00 55
757 3p.50 "Jasminum mesyi" and Sun Yat Sen Park . . . . 1·10 70
758 4p.20 "Bauhinia variegata" and Seac Pai Van Park . . 1·40 75
MS759 95 × 137 mm. Nos. 755/8 8·00 6·00
See also Nos. 815/**MS**19.

168 Portuguese Traders unloading Boats **169** Firework Display

1991. Cultural Exchange. Nambam Paintings attr. Kano Domi. Multicoloured.
760 4p.20 Type **168** . . . . . . 1·40 70
761 4p.20 Portuguese traders displaying goods to buyers 1·40 70
MS762 107 × 74 mm. Nos. 760/1 5·25 4·50

1991. Christmas. Multicoloured.
763 1p.70 Type **169** 45 25
764 3p. Father Christmas 95 45
765 3p.50 Man dancing . . . . . 1·10 60
766 4p.20 January 1st celebrations 1·50 80

170 Concertina Door

1992. Doors and Windows. Multicoloured.
767 1p.70 Type **170** 55 20
768 3p. Window with four shutters 95 45
769 3p.50 Window with two shutters . . . . 1·10 65
770 4p.20 Louvred door . . . . 1·40 95

171 Monkey and Moon **172** T'it Kuai Lei

1992. New Year. Year of the Monkey.
771 **171** 4p.50 multicoloured . . . 1·60 1·30

1992. Gods of Chinese Mythology (1st series). Multicoloured.
772 3p.50 (1) Type **172** . . . . 1·60 95
773 3p.50 (2) Chong Lei Kun . . 1·60 95
774 3p.50 (3) Cheong Kuo Lou on donkey . . . . 1·60 95
775 3p.50 (4) Loi Tong Pan . . . 1·60 95
See also Nos. 796/9.

173 Lion Dance

1992. "World Columbian Stamp Expo '92", Chicago. Chinese Dances. Multicoloured.
776 1p. Type **173** 30 15
777 2p.70 Lion dance (different) 85 40
778 6p. Dragon dance . . . . . 1·90 95

174 High Jumping

1992. Olympic Games, Barcelona. Multicoloured.
779 80a. Type **174** 20 15
780 4p.20 Badminton . . . . . . 1·20 55
781 4p.70 Roller hockey . . . . 1·50 1·00
782 5p. Yachting . . . . 2·75 1·00
MS783 137 × 95 mm. Nos. 779/82 17·00 14·00

175 Na Cha Temple

1992. Temples (1st series). Multicoloured.
784 1p. Type **175** 30 15
785 1p.50 Kun Iam 45 20
786 1p.70 Hong Kon 65 35
787 6p.50 A Ma . . . . 2·10 1·10
See also Nos. 792/5 and 894/8.

176 Tung Sin Tong Services

1992. Centenary of Tung Sin Tong (medical and educational charity).
788 **176** 1p. multicoloured 35 15

177 Rooster and Dragon

1992. Portuguese–Chinese Friendship.
789 **177** 10p. multicoloured . . . 3·00 1·50
MS790 109 × 74 mm. **177** 10p. multicoloured . . . .

178 Red Junglefowl **179** Children carrying Banners

1992. New Year. Year of the Cock.
791 **178** 5p. multicoloured . . . . 1·80 1·10
See also No. **MS**917.

1993. Temples (2nd series). As T **175**. Mult.
792 50a. T'am Kong 15 10
793 2p. T'in Hau 70 30
794 3p.50 Lin Fong . . . . . . 1·20 60
795 8p. Pau Kong . . . . 2·40 1·20

1993. Gods of Chinese Mythology (2nd series). As T **172**. Multicoloured.
796 3p.50 (1) Lam Ch'oi Wo flying on crane . . . . . . 1·50 95
797 3p.50 (2) Ho Sin Ku (goddess) on peach blossom . . . . 1·50 95
798 3p.50 (3) Hon Seong Chi crossing sea on basket of flowers . . . . 1·50 95
799 3p.50 (4) Ch'ou Kuok K'ao crossing river on plank . . 1·50 95

1993. Chinese Wedding. Multicoloured.
800 3p. Type **179** 95 50
801 3p. Bride 95 50
802 3p. Bridegroom 95 50
803 3p. Wedding guests 95 50
MS804 124 × 106 mm. 8p. Bride and groom (50 × 40 mm) . . . . . .

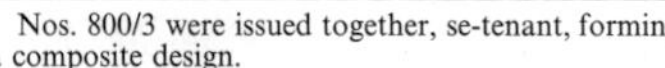
Nos. 800/3 were issued together, se-tenant, forming a composite design.

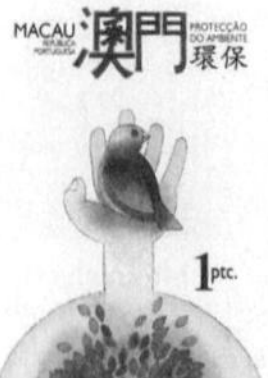

180 Bird perched on Hand **181** Eurasian Scops Owl

1993. Environmental Protection.
805 **180** 1p. multicoloured 55 20

1993. Birds of Prey. Multicoloured.
806 3p. Type **181** 95 60
807 3p. Barn owl ("Tyto alba") 95 60
808 3p. Peregrine falcon ("Falco peregrinus") 95 60
809 3p. Golden eagle ("Aquila obrysaetos") 95 60
MS810 107 × 128 mm. Nos. 806/9

182 Town Hall

1993. Union of Portuguese-speaking Capital Cities.
811 **182** 1p.50 green, blue and red 40 20

183 Portuguese Missionaries

1993. 450th Anniv of First Portuguese Visit to Japan. Multicoloured.
812 50a. Japanese man with musket 15 10
813 3p. Type **183** 90 45
814 3p.50 Traders carrying goods 1·00 55

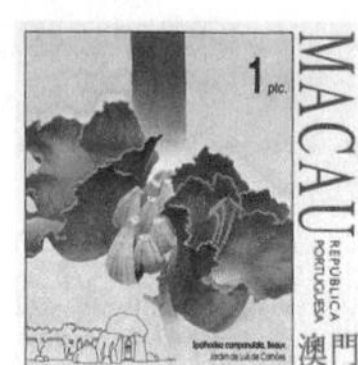

184 "Spathodea campanulata" and Luis de Camoes Garden

1993. Flowers and Gardens (2nd series). Multicoloured.
815 1p. Type **184** 30 15
816 2p. "Tithonia diversifolia" and Montanha Russa Garden 60 25
817 3p. "Rhodomyrtus tomentosa" and Cais Garden 90 40
818 8p. "Passiflora foetida" and Flora Garden . . . . . . 2·20 1·20
MS819 90 × 120 mm. Nos. 815/18 4·75 3·50

185 Caravel

1993. 16th-century Sailing Ships. Multicoloured.
820 1p. Type **185** 30 15
821 2p. Caravel (different) . . . 60 25
822 3p.50 Nau 95 60
823 4p.50 Galleon . . . . 1·20 60
MS824 160 × 105 mm. Nos. 820/3 3·75 3·00

186 Saloon Car

1993. 40th Anniv of Macao Grand Prix. Multicoloured.
825 1p.50 Type **186** 40 15
826 2p. Motor cycle 60 25
827 4p.50 Racing car . . . . . . 1·30 70

187 Chow-chow and Moon

1994. New Year. Year of the Dog.
828 **187** 5p. multicoloured . . . . 1·40 70
See also No. **MS**917.

188 Map and Prince Henry (½-size illustration)

1994. 600th Birth Anniv of Prince Henry the Navigator.
829 **188** 3p. multicoloured 85 40

189 Lakeside Hut

1994. Birth Bicentenary of George Chinnery (artist). Multicoloured.
830 3p.50 Type **189** . . . . . . 1·00 50
831 3p.50 Fisherman on sea wall 1·00 50
832 3p.50 Harbour . . . . 1·00 50
833 3p.50 Sao Tiago Fortress . . 1·00 50
MS834 138 × 87 mm. Nos. 830/3

190 Lai Sis Exchange

1994. Spring Festival of Lunar New Year. Multicoloured.
835 1p. Type **190** 30 15
836 2p. Flower and tangerine tree decorations 55 25
837 3p.50 Preparing family meal 1·00 50
838 4p.50 Paper decorations bearing good wishes . . . 1·40 70

191 "Longevity" **192** Footballer

1994. Legends and Myths (1st series). Chinese Gods. Multicoloured.
839 3p. Type **191** 85 40
840 3p. "Prosperity" 85 40
841 3p. "Happiness" 85 40
MS842 138 × 90 mm. Nos. 839/41
See also Nos. 884/**MS**888, 930/**MS**933 and 994/**MS**998.

1994. World Cup Football Championship, U.S.A. Multicoloured.
843 2p. Type **192** 60 25
844 3p. Tackling 85 40
845 3p.50 Heading ball . . . . . 1·00 55
846 4p.50 Goalkeeper saving goal 1·30 75
MS847 138 × 90 mm. Nos. 843/6

193 Rice Shop **194** Astrolabe

1994. Traditional Chinese Shops. Multicoloured.
848 1p. Type **193** 25 10
849 1p.50 Medicinal tea shop . . 35 15
850 2p. Salt-fish shop 55 20
851 3p.50 Pharmacy . . . . . . 1·00 60

1994. Nautical Instruments. Multicoloured.
852 3p. Type **194** 75 35
853 3p.50 Quadrant 95 50
854 4p.50 Sextant . . . . 1·20 65

195 Fencing

1994. 12th Asian Games, Hiroshima, Japan. Multicoloured.
855 1p. Type **195** 25 10
856 2p. Gymnastics 50 20
857 3p. Water-polo 75 35
858 3p.50 Pole vaulting . . . . . 1·00 60

196 Nobre de Carvalho Bridge

1994. Bridges. Multicoloured.
859 1p. Type **196** 30 15
860 8p. Friendship Bridge . . . . 2·10 1·10

197 Carp **199** Pig and Moon

198 Angel's Head (stained glass window, Macao Cathedral)

1994. Good Luck Signs. Multicoloured.
861 3p. Type **197** 75 35
862 3p.50 Peaches 95 50
863 4p.50 Water lily . . . . . . 1·20 65

1994. Religious Art. Multicoloured.
864 50a. Type **198** 10 10
865 1p. Holy Ghost (stained glass window, Macao Cathedral) 25 10
866 1p.50 Silver sacrarium . . . 40 15
867 2p. Silver salver 55 25
868 3p. "Escape into Egypt" (ivory statuette) 75 50
869 3p.50 Gold and silver cup . . 1·00 70

1995. New Year. Year of the Pig.
870 **199** 5p.50 multicoloured . . . 1·60 80

200 "Lou Lim Iok Garden"

1995. Paintings of Macao by Lio Man Cheong. Multicoloured.
871 50a. Type **200** 10 10
872 1p. "Guia Fortress and Lighthouse" 20 10
873 1p.50 "Barra Temple" . . . 35 15
874 2p. "Avenida da Praia, Taipa" 55 25
875 2p.50 "Kun Iam Temple" . . 65 30
876 3p. "St. Paul's Seminary" . . 80 40
877 3p.50 "Penha Hill" 95 55
878 4p. "Gates of Understanding Monument" . . . . 1·20 80

201 Magnifying Glass over Goods

1995. World Consumer Day.
879 **201** 1p. multicoloured 25 15

202 Pangolin **203** Kun Sai Iam

1995. Protection of Chinese ("Asian") Pangolin. Multicoloured.
880 1p.50 In fork of tree 35 30
881 1p.50 Hanging from tree by tail 35 30
882 1p.50 On leafy branch . . . 35 30
883 1p.50 Type **202** 35 30

1995. Legends and Myths (2nd series). Kun Sai Iam (Buddhist god). Multicoloured.
884 3p. Type **203** 80 40
885 3p. Holding baby 80 40
886 3p. Sitting behind water lily 80 40
887 3p. With water lily and dragonfish 80 40
MS888 138 × 90 mm. 8p. Kun Sai Iam (*different*) . . . .

204/7 Senado Square (½-size illustration)

1995. Senado Square.
889 **204** 2p. multicoloured 50 25
890 **205** 2p. multicoloured 50 25
891 **206** 2p. multicoloured 50 25
892 **207** 2p. multicoloured 50 25
MS893 138 × 90 mm. 8p. multicoloured (Leal Senado building and Post Office Clock tower) (*horiz*) . . . .
Nos. 889/92 were issued together, se-tenant, forming the composite design illustrated.

1995. Temples (3rd series). As T **175**. Multicoloured.
894 50a. Kuan Tai 10 10
895 1p. Pak Tai 25 10
896 1p.50 Lin K'ai 35 15
897 3p. Se Kam Tong 75 40
898 3p.50 Fok Tak 95 55

208 Pekin Robin ("Leiothrix lutea")

1995. "Singapore'95" International Stamp Exhibition. Birds. Multicoloured.
899 2p.50 Type **208** 65 35
900 2p.50 Japanese white-eye ("Zosterops japonica") . . 65 35
901 2p.50 Island canary ("Serinus canarius canarius") 65 35
902 2p.50 Melodious laughing thrush ("Gurrulax canorus") 65 35
MS903 137 × 90 mm. 10p. Magpie robin (*Copyschus saularis*) . . . 2·10 2·00

209 Pipa

1995. International Music Festival. Musical Instruments. Multicoloured.
904 1p. Type **209** 25 10
905 1p. Erhu (string instrument) 25 10
906 1p. Gong (hand-held drum) 25 10
907 1p. Sheng (string instrument) 25 10
908 1p. Xiao (flute) 25 10
909 1p. Tambor (drum) 25 10
MS910 137 × 90 mm. 8p. Two players with instruments (40 × 29 mm) . . . .

210 Anniversary Emblem, World Map and U.N. Headquarters, New York

1995. 50th Anniv of United Nations Organization.
911 **210** 4p.50 multicoloured . . . 1·10 60

211 Terminal Building

1995. Inauguration of Macao International Airport. Multicoloured.
912 1p. Type **211** 25 10
913 1p.50 Terminal (different) . . 35 20
914 2p. Loading airplane and cargo building 55 25
915 3p. Control tower 80 45
MS916 137 × 90 mm. 8p. Airplane taking off . . . . 2·10 1·00

1995. Lunar Cycle. Sheet 180 × 216 mm containing previous New Year designs.
MS917 12 × 1p.50, As Nos. 791, 828, 870, 587, 771, 602, 742, 621, 713, 685, 661 and 640 . . . . . . 4·75 3·75

212 Rat

1996. New Year. Year of the Rat.
918 **212** 5p. multicoloured . . . . 1·30 65
MS919 137 × 90 mm. **212** 10p. multicoloured . . . . 2·75 2·50

213 Cage

1996. Traditional Chinese Cages.
920 **213** 1p. multicoloured 20 10
921 – 1p.50 multicoloured . . . 35 15
922 – 3p. multicoloured 75 40
923 – 4p.50 multicoloured . . . 1·20 60
MS924 137 × 90 mm. 10p. multicoloured . . . . 2·75 2·50
DESIGNS: 1p.50 to 10p., Different cages.

214 Street **215** Tou Tei (God of Earth)

1996. Paintings of Macao by Herculano Estorninho. Multicoloured.
925 50a. Fishing boats (horiz) . . 10 10
926 1p.50 Town square 35 15
927 3p. Type **214** 75 35
928 5p. Townscape (horiz) . . . 1·30 70
MS929 137 × 90 mm. 10p. Colonnaded entrance . . . . . 2·75 2·50

1996. Legends and Myths (3rd series). Multicoloured.
930 3p.50 Type **215** 90 50
931 3p.50 Choi San (God of Fortune) 90 50
932 3p.50 Chou Kuan (God of the Kitchen) 90 50
MS933 137 × 89 mm. Nos. 930/2 2·75 2·30

216 Customers

1996. Traditional Chinese Tea Houses. Mult.
934 2p. Type **216** 50 25
935 2p. Waiter with tray of steamed stuffed bread . . . 50 25
936 2p. Newspaper vendor . . . 50 25
937 2p. Waiter pouring tea at table 50 25
MS938 138 × 90 mm. 8p. Jar and food snacks . . . . 2·10 3·75
Nos. 934/7 were issued together, se-tenant, forming a composite design.

217 Get Well Soon

1996. Greetings stamps. Multicoloured.
939 50a. Type **217** 10 10
940 1p.50 Congratulations on new baby 35 15
941 3p. Happy birthday 75 35
942 4p. Wedding congratulations 1·10 55

218 Swimming

1996. Olympic Games, Atlanta, U.S.A. Mult.
943 2p. Type **218** 45 20
944 3p. Football 75 35
945 3p.50 Gymnastics 95 40
946 4p.50 Sailboarding . . . . . 1·20 70
MS947 137 × 90 mm. 10p. Boxing 2·75 2·50

219 Crane (civil, 1st rank)

1996. Civil and Military Insignia of the Mandarins (1st series). Multicoloured.
948 2p.50 Type **219** 60 30
949 2p.50 Lion (military, 2nd rank) 60 30
950 2p.50 Golden pheasant (civil, 2nd rank) 60 30
951 2p.50 Leopard (military, 3rd rank) 60 30
See also Nos. 1061/4.

220 Trawler with Multiple Nets

1996. Nautical Sciences: Fishing Nets. Mult.
952 3p. Type **220** 75 35
953 3p. Modern trawler with net from stern 75 35
954 3p. Two sailing junks with common net 75 35
955 3p. Junk with two square nets at sides 75 35
Nos. 952/5 were issued together, se-tenant, forming a composite design.

221 National Flag and Statue (½-size illustration)

1996. 20th Anniv of Legislative Assembly.
956 **221** 2p.80 multicoloured . . . 70 35
MS957 138 × 90 mm. **221** 8p. multicoloured . . . . 2·00 2·00

222 Dragonfly

1996. Paper Kites. Multicoloured.
958 3p.50 Type **222** 85 50
959 3p.50 Butterfly 85 50
960 3p.50 Owl 85 50
961 3p.50 Swallow 85 50
MS962 138 × 90 mm. 8p.Chinese dragon (50 × 37 mm) . . . . . 2·00 2·00

223 Doll

1996. Traditional Chinese Toys. Multicoloured.
963 50a. Type **223** 10 10
964 1p. Fish 25 10
965 3p. Painted doll 75 35
966 4p.50 Dragon . . . . 1·10 60

224 Ox

1997. New Year. Year of the Ox.
967 **224** 5p.50 multicoloured . . . 1·30 75
MS968 137 × 89 mm. **224** 10p. multicoloured. . . . . 2·50 2·50

225 Colourful and Gold Twos

1997. Lucky Numbers. Multicoloured.
969 2p. Type **225** 45 20
970 2p.80 Eights 75 35
971 3p. Threes 75 35
972 3p.90 Nines . . . . 1·00 55
MS973 137 × 90 mm. 9p. Numbers around doorway of café . . . 2·30 2·20
No. **MS**973 also commemorates "Hong Kong '97" International Stamp Exhibition.

226 "Sail Boats" **227** Elderly Woman

1997. Paintings of Macao by Kwok Se. Multicoloured.
974 2p. Type **226** 45 20
975 3p. "Fortress on the Hill" . . 70 35
976 3p.50 "Asilum" 85 55
977 4p.50 "Portas do Cerco" . . 1·20 65
MS978 138 × 90 mm. 8p. "Rua de Sao Paulo" (detail) (horiz) . . 2·00 2·00

1997. Tan-Ka (boat) People. Multicoloured.
979 1p. Type **227** 20 50
980 1p.50 Elderly woman holding tiller 35 50
981 2p.50 Woman with child on back 65 50
982 5p.50 Man mending fishing nets . . . . 1·40 50

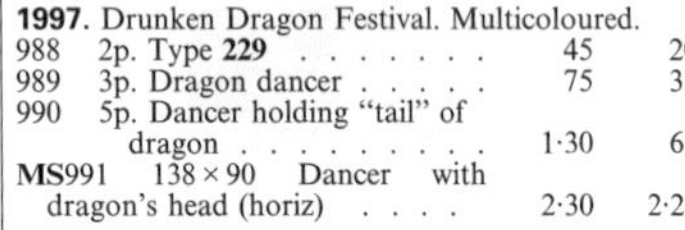

228 Entrance to Temple **229** Dragon Dancers

1997. A-Ma Temple. Multicoloured.
983 3p.50 Type **228** 75 50
984 3p.50 Wall and terraces of Temple 75 50
985 3p.50 View of incense smoke through gateway 75 50
986 3p.50 Incense smoke emanating from pagoda . . 75 50
MS987 138 × 90 mm. Ship (representative of land reclamation in front of temple) . . . . . . 2·00 2·00

1997. Drunken Dragon Festival. Multicoloured.
988 2p. Type **229** 45 20
989 3p. Dragon dancer 75 35
990 5p. Dancer holding "tail" of dragon . . . . 1·30 65
MS991 138 × 90 Dancer with dragon's head (horiz) . . . . 2·30 2·20

230 Frois with Japanese Man

1997. 400th Death Anniv of Father Luis Frois (author of "The History of Japan"). Multicoloured.
992 2p.50 Type **230** 60 35
993 2p.50 Father Frois and church (vert) 60 35

231 Wat Lot

1997. Legends and Myths (4th series). Door Gods. Multicoloured.
994 2p.50 Type **231** 60 35
995 2p.50 San Su 60 35
996 2p.50 Chon Keng 60 35
997 2p.50 Wat Chi Kong 60 35
MS998 138 × 90 mm. 10p. Chon Keng and Wat Chi Kong on doors (39 × 39 mm) . . . . 2·50 2·50

232 Globe and First Aid and Family Health School

1997. 77th Anniv of Macao Red Cross.
999 **232** 1p.50 multicoloured . . . 35 25

233 Balconies

1997. Balconies.
1000 **233** 50a. multicoloured . . . 10 10
1001 – 1p. multicoloured . . . 20 10
1002 – 1p.50 multicoloured . . 35 15
1003 – 2p. multicoloured . . . 45 20
1004 – 2p.50 multicoloured . . 60 30
1005 – 3p. multicoloured . . . 80 40
MS1006 137 × 90 mm. 8p. multicoloured (29 × 39 mm) . . 2·00 1·90
DESIGNS: 1p. to 8p. Various balcony styles.

234 Plant Leaf Fan

1997. Fans. Multicoloured.
1007 50a. Type **234** 10 10
1008 1p. Paper fan 20 10
1009 3p.50 Silk fan 80 40
1010 4p. Feather fan . . . . . . 1·00 55
MS1011 138 × 90 mm. 9p. Woman holding sandalwood fan . . . 2·20 2·20

235 Wood **236** Kung Fu

1997. Feng Shui. The Five Elements. Mult.
1012 50a. Type **235** 10 10
1013 1p. Fire 20 10
1014 1p.50 Earth 35 15
1015 2p. Metal 35 20
1016 2p.50 Water 70 40
MS1017 138 × 90 mm. 10p. Centre of geomancer's chart . . . . . . 2·50 2·40

1997. Martial Arts. Multicoloured.
1018 1p.50 Type **236** 35 15
1019 3p.50 Judo 80 40
1020 4p. Karate . . . . 1·00 50

237 Tiger

1998. New Year. Year of the Tiger.
1021 **237** 5p.50 multicoloured . . 1·30 65
MS1022 138 × 90 mm. **237** 10p. multicoloured . . . .

238 Soup Stall

1998. Street Traders. Multicoloured.
1023 1p. Type **238** 20 10
1024 1p.50 Snack stall 35 15
1025 2p. Clothes stall 45 20
1026 2p.50 Balloon stall 60 30
1027 3p. Flower stall 70 35
1028 3p.50 Fruit stall 90 50
MS1029 138 × 90 mm. 6p. Fruit stall (different) . . . . 1·50 1·40

239 Beco da Se

1998. Gateways. Multicoloured.
1030 50a. Type **239** 10 10
1031 1p. Patio da Ilusao 20 10
1032 3p.50 Travessa das galinhas 80 40
1033 4p. Beco das Felicidades . . 1·00 55
MS1034 138 × 90 mm. 9p. St. Joseph's Seminary . . . . 2·30 2·20

240 Woman and Child

1998. Legends and Myths (5th series). Gods of Ma Chou. Multicoloured.
1035 4p. Type **240** 95 50
1036 4p. Woman and man's face in smoke 95 50
1037 4p. Woman with children playing instruments . . . 95 50
1038 4p. Goddess and sailing barges 95 50
MS1039 138 × 90 mm. 10p. Head of goddess . . . . 2·50 2·40

241 "Sao Gabriel" (flagship)

1998. 500th Anniv of Vasco da Gama's Voyage to India via Cape of Good Hope. Multicoloured.
(a) Wrongly dated "1598 1998".
1040 1p. Type **241** 20 10
1041 1p.50 Vasco da Gama . . . 35 15
1042 2p. "Sao Gabriel" and map of India 50 30
MS1043 138 × 90 mm. 8p. Compass rose . . . . 2·20 2·20

(b) Correctly dated "1498 1998".
1044 1p. Type **241** 20 10
1045 1p.50 As No. 1041 . . . . 35 15
1046 2p. As No. 1042 . . . . . 50 30
MS1047 138 × 90 mm. 8p. As No **MS**1043 . . . . 2·00 1·90

242 Mermaid and Caravel

1998. International Year of the Ocean. Mult.
1048 2p.50 Type **242** 60 30
1049 3p. Whale and oil-rig . . . 70 35
MS1050 138 × 90 mm. Caravel and whale . . . . 2·00 1·90

243 Players

1998. World Cup Football Championship, France. Multicoloured.
1051 3p. Type **243** 70 35
1052 3p.50 Players competing for ball 80 40
1053 4p. Player kicking ball clear while being tackled . . . 95 50
1054 4p.50 Player beating another to ball . . . . 1·10 65
MS1055 138 × 90 mm. 9p. Players and ball . . . . 2·20 2·20

244 Lio Seak Chong Mask

1998. Chinese Opera Masks. Multicoloured.
1056 1p.50 Type **244** 35 15
1057 2p. Wat Chi Kong 45 20
1058 3p. Kam Chin Pao 70 35
1059 5p. Lei Kwai . . . . 1·20 65
MS1060 138 × 90 mm. Opera mask 2·00 1·90

1998. Civil and Military Insignia of the Mandarins (2nd series). As T **219**. Multicoloured.
1061 50a. Lion (military, 2nd rank) 10 10
1062 1p. Bear (military, 5th rank) 20 10
1063 1p.50 Golden pheasant (civil, 2nd rank) 35 15
1064 2p. Silver pheasant (civil, 5th rank) 55 30
MS1065 138 × 90 mm. 9p. Crane (civil, 1st rank) . . . . 2·20 2·20

245 Smiling Buddha

1998. Kun Iam Temple. Multicoloured.
1066 3p.50 Type **245** 80 40
1067 3p.50 Pavilion and temple gardens 80 40
1068 3p.50 Temple gateway . . . 80 40
1069 3p.50 Pagoda, stream and gardens 80 40
MS1070 138 × 90 mm. 10p. Temple 2·40 2·30
Nos. 1066/9 were issued together, se-tenant, forming a composite design.

246 Carriage in Street

1998. Paintings of Macao by Didier Rafael Bayle. Multicoloured.
1071 2p. Type **246** 45 20
1072 3p. Street (horiz) 65 35
1073 3p.50 Building (horiz) . . . 80 40
1074 4p.50 Kiosk in square . . . 1·10 60
MS1075 138 × 90 mm. 8p. Balcony (horiz) . . . . 1·90 1·90

247 Dragon

1998. Tiles by Eduardo Nery (from panel at Departure Lounge of Macao Airport). Multicoloured.
1076 1p. Type **247** 20 10
1077 1p.50 Galleon 35 15
1078 2p.50 Junk 60 30
1079 5p.50 Phoenix . . . . . . 1·30 65
MS1080 138 × 90 mm. 10p. Guia Lighthouse . . . . 2·40 2·30

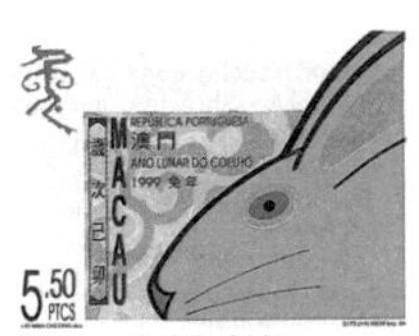
248 Rabbit

1999. New Year. Year of the Rabbit.
1081 **248** 5p.50 multicoloured . . 1·30 65
MS1082 138 × 90 mm. **248** 10p. multicoloured . . . . 1·30 65

249 Jia Bao Yu

1999. Literature. Characters from "A Dream of Red Mansions" by Cao Xue Qin. Multicoloured.
1083 2p. Type **249** 45 25
1084 2p. Lin Dai Yu holding pole and cherry blossom . . . 45 25
1085 2p. Bao Chai holding fan 45 25
1086 2p. Wang Xi Feng sitting in chair 45 25
1087 2p. You San Jie holding sword 45 25
1088 2p. Qing Wen sewing "peacock" cloak 45 25
MS1089 138 × 90 mm. 8p. Jia Bao Yu and Lin Dai Yu . . . . . 1·90 1·90

250 Sailing Ships

1999. "Australia'99" International Stamp Exhibition, Melbourne. Oceans and Maritime Heritage. Multicoloured.
1090 1p.50 Type **250** 35 15
1091 2p.50 Marine life 60 30
MS1092 138 × 90 mm. 6p. Head of wale (vert) . . . . 1·40 1·40

251 De Havilland D.H.9 Biplane

1999. 75th Anniv of Sarmento de Beires and Brito Pais's Portugal–Macao Flight. Multicoloured.
1093 3p. Breguet 16 Bn2 Patria 70 35
1094 3p. Type **251** 70 35
MS1095 137 × 104 mm. Nos. 1093/4 1·40 1·40

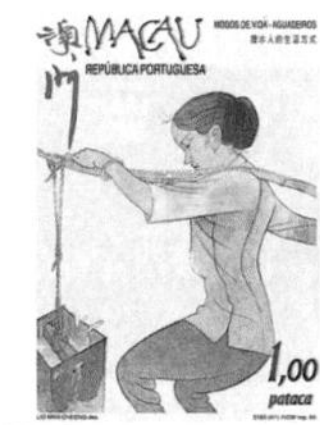
252 Carrying Containers on Yoke

1999. The Water Carrier. Multicoloured.
1096 1p. Type **252** 20 10
1097 1p.50 Filling containers from pump 35 15
1098 2p. Lowering bucket down well 45 20
1099 2p.50 Filling containers from tap 60 35
MS1100 138 × 90 mm. 7p. Woman with containers on yoke climbing steps . . . . 1·70 1·60

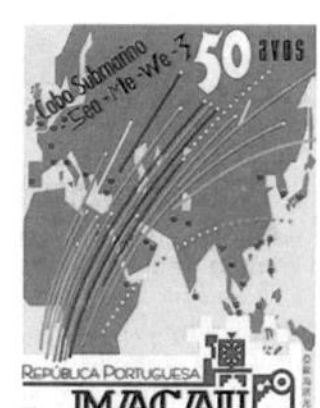
253 "Sea-Me-We-3" Undersea Fibre Optic Cable

1999. Telecommunications Services. Multicoloured.
1101 50a. Type **253** 10 10
1102 1p. Dish aerial at Satellite Earth Station 25 10
1103 3p.50 Analogue mobile phone 80 40
1104 4p. Televisions 90 45
1105 4p.50 Internet and e-mail . . 1·10 60
MS1106 138 × 90 mm. 8p. Emblem and computer mouse (horiz) 1·90 1·90

254 Macao Cultural Centre

1999. Modern Buildings. Multicoloured.
1107 1p. Type **254** 25 10
1108 1p.50 Museum of Macao . . 35 15
1109 2p. Macao Maritime Museum 45 25
1110 2p.50 Ferry Terminal . . . 55 30
1111 3p. Macao University . . . 75 35
1112 3p.50 Public Administration building (vert) 80 45
1113 4p.50 Macao World Trade Centre (vert) . . . . . . 1·00 55
1114 5p. Coloane kart-racing track (vert) . . . . . . 1·20 60
1115 8p. Bank of China (vert) . . 1·80 95
1116 12p. National Overseas Bank (vert) . . . . 2·75 1·40

255 Health Department

1999. Classified Buildings in Tap Seac District. Multicoloured.
1117 1p.50 Type **255** 35 20
1118 1p.50 Central Library (face value in salmon) 35 20
1119 1p.50 Centre of Modern Art of the Orient Foundation (face value in yellow) . . 35 20
1120 1p.50 Portuguese Institute of the Orient (face value in light blue) 35 20
MS1121 138 × 90 mm. 10p. I.P.O.R. building . . . . 2·40 2·30
Nos. 1117/20 were issued together, se-tenant, forming a composite design.

256 Teapot and Plate of Food

258 Chinese and Portuguese Ships, Christ's Cross and Yin Yang

257 "Portuguese Sailor and Chinese Woman" (Lagoa Henriques), Company of Jesus Square

1999. Dim Sum. Multicoloured.
1122 2p.50 Type **256** 55 30
1123 2p.50 Plates of food, chopsticks and left half of bowls 55 30
1124 2p.50 Plates of food, glass, cups and right half of bowls 55 30
1125 2p.50 Plates of food and large teapot 55 30
MS1126 138 × 90 mm. 9p. Plates of food . . . . 2·40 2·30
Nos. 1122/5 were issued together, se-tenant, forming a composite design.

1999. Contemporary Sculptures (1st series). Multicoloured.
1127 1p. Type **257** 25 10
1128 1p.50 "The Gate of Understanding" (Charters de Almeida), Praia Grande Bay (vert) 35 20
1129 2p.50 "Statue of the Goddess Kun Iam" (Cristina Leiria), Macao Cultural Centre (vert) . . 55 20
1130 3p.50 " Taipa Viewing Point" (Dorita Castel-Branco), Nobre de Carvalho Bridge, Taipa 80 35
MS1131 138 × 90 mm. 10p. "The Pearl" (Jose Rodrigues), Amizade rounderbout . . . . 2·40 2·30
See also Nos. 1186/**MS**1190.

1999. Portuguese–Chinese Cultural Mix. Mult.
1132 1p. Type **258** 20 10
1133 1p.50 Ah Mah Temple and Portuguese and Macanese architecture 35 20
1134 2p. Bridge, steps and Chinese architecture . . . 45 20
1135 3p. Macanese architecture and Portuguese terrace . . 65 35
MS1136 138 × 90 mm. Enlargement of right-hand part of design in No. 1135 . . . . 2·40 2·30
Nos. 1132/5 were issued together, se-tenant, forming a composite design.

259 Globe

1999. Macao Retrospective. Multicoloured.
1137 1p. Type **259** 25 10
1138 1p.50 Roof terrace 35 20
1139 2p. Portuguese and Chinese people 55 30
1140 3p.50 Modern Macao . . . 80 45
MS1141 138 × 90 mm. 9p. City coat of arms . . . . 2·20 2·10

260 Gateway

1999. Establishment of Macao as Special Administrative Region of People's Republic of China. Multicoloured.
1142 1p. Type **260** 20 10
1143 1p.50 Bridge and boat race 25 20
1144 2p. Wall of ruined church 35 25
1145 2p.50 Lighthouse and racing cars 40 30
1146 3p. Building facade 55 45
1147 3p.50 Stadium and orchestra 60 50
MS1148 138 × 90 mm. 8p. Pink flower . . . . 1·90 1·90

261 Sight-seeing Tower

2000. A New Era. Sheet 138 × 90 mm.
MS1149 **261** 8p. multicoloured 1·90 1·90

262 Dragon

2000. New Year. Year of the Dragon.
1150 **262** 5p.50 multicoloured . . 95 75

263 Buildings

2000. Classified Buildings in Almeida Ribeiro Avenue, Macao City. Multicoloured.
1152 1p. Type **263** 20 15
1153 1p.50 Yellow and pink buildings 25 20
1154 2p. Yellow building 35 25
1155 3p. Purple, green and pink buildings 55 45
MS1156 138 × 90 mm. 9p. Beige building . . . .

SERIAL NUMBERS. In sets containing several stamps of the same denomination, the serial number is quoted in brackets to assist identification. This is the last figure in the bottom right corner of the stamp.

264 Zhong (Leong Pai Wan)

2000. Arts in Macao. Chinese Calligraphy. Showing Chinese characters by named calligraphy masters. Each black and red.
1157 3p. (1) Type **264** 55 45
1158 3p. (2) Guo (Lin Ka Sang) 55 45
1159 3p. (3) Shu (Lok Hong) . . 55 45
1160 3p. (4) Fa (Sou Su Fai) . . 55 45
MS1161 138 × 90 mm. 8p. Zhong, guo, shu and fa . . . . 1·90 1·90

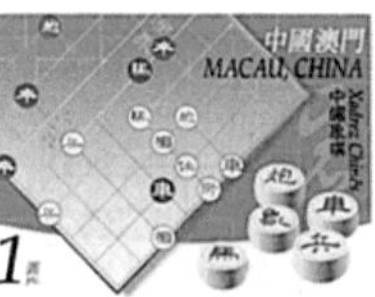
265 Chinese Chess

2000. Board Games. Multicoloured.
1162 1p. Type **265** 20 15
1163 1p.50 Chess 25 20
1164 2p. Go 35 25
1165 2p.50 Flying chess 40 30
MS1166 138 × 90 mm. 9p. Chinese checkers . . . . 2·20 2·10

266 Group of Friends

2000. Tea. Multicoloured.
1167 2p. Type **266** 35 25
1168 3p. Family drinking tea 55 45
1169 3p.50 Women drinking tea 60 50
1170 4p.50 Men drinking tea 80 65
MS1171 138 × 90 mm. 8p. Woman making tes 1·90 1·90

267 Tricycle Driver and Foreign Tourists

2000. Tricycle Drivers. Multicoloured.
1172 2p. (1) Type **267** 35 25
1173 2p. (2) With couple in carriage 35 25
1174 2p. (3) With empty carriage 35 25
1175 2p. (4) With feet resting on saddle 35 25
1176 2p. (5) Sitting in carriage 35 25
1177 2p. (6) Mending tyre 35 25
MS1178 138 × 90 mm. 8p. Standing beside tricycle (vert) 1·90 1·90

268 Monkey King standing on Tiger Skin

2000. Classical Literature. *Journey to the West* (Ming dynasty novel). Multicoloured.
1179 1p. Type **268** 20 15
1180 1p.50 Monkey King tasting the heavenly peaches 25 20
1181 2p. Monkey King, Prince Na Zha and flaming wheels 35 25
1182 2p.50 Erlang Deity with spear 40 30
1183 3p. Heavenly Father Lao Jun 55 45
1184 3p.50 Monkey King in Buddha's hand 60 55
MS1185 138 × 90 mm. 9p. Monkey King holding baton (horiz) 2·20 2·10

269 "Wing of Good Winds" (Augusto Cid), Pac On Roundabout, Taipa

2000. Contemporary Sculptures (2nd series). Multicoloured.
1186 1p. Type **269** 15 10
1187 2p. "The Embrace" (Irene Vilar), Luis de Camoes Garden (vert) 35 25
1188 3p. Monument (Soares Branco), Guia's Tunnel, Outer Harbour (vert) 55 40
1189 4p. "The Arch of the Orient" (Zulmiro de Carvalho), Avienda Rodrigo Rodrigues Viaduct 70 55
MS1190 90 × 138 mm. 10p. "Goddess A-Ma" (Leong Man Lin). Coloane Iland 2·40 2·30

270 Decorated Pot

2000. Ceramics. Multicoloured.
1191 2p.50 (1) Type **270** 45 35
1192 2p.50 (2) Vase, dish and teapot 45 35
1193 2p.50 (3) Blue vase 45 35
1194 2p.50 (4) Cabbage-shaped pot and leaf-shaped dish 45 35
1195 2p.50 (5) Plate and fishes 45 35
1196 2p.50 (6) Blue and white vase 45 35
MS1197 138 × 90 mm. 8p. Decorated plate (round-design) 1·90 1·90
Nos. 1191/6 were issued together, se-tenant, with the backgrounds forming a composite design.

271 Phoenix crouching, Shang Dynasty

2000. Jade Ornaments. Multicoloured.
1198 1p.50 Type **271** 25 20
1199 2p. Archer's white jade ring, Warring States period 35 25
1200 2p.50 Dragon and phoenix, Six Dynasties 45 35
1201 3p. Pendant with dragon decoration, Western Han Dynasty 55 40
MS1202 138 × 90 mm. 9p. Medallion (detail) (vert) 2·20 2·10

272 Dancers with National and Special Administrative Flags

2000. 1st Anniv of Macau as Special Administrative Region of People's Republic of China. Multicoloured.
1203 2p. Type **272** 35 25
1204 3p. Chinese dragons and lotus flower 55 40
MS1205 138 × 90 mm. 18p. Flags, statesmen and lotus flower (59 × 39 mm) 4·50 4·50
Nos. 1203/4 were issued together, se-tenant, forming a composite design.

273 Snake

2001. New Year. Year of the Snake.
1206 **273** 5p.50 multicoloured 95 75
MS1207 138 × 90 mm. **272** 10p. multicoloured 2·40 2·30

274 Man holding Bottle ("Nursing Vengeance despite Hardships")

2001. Ancient Proverbs. Multicoloured.
1208 2p. (1) Type **274** 35 25
1209 2p. (2) Man waiting for a rabbit ("Trusting to Chance and Windfalls") 35 25
1210 2p. (3) Fox and tiger ("Bullying Others by Flaunting One's Powerful Connections") 35 25
1211 2p. (4) Mother with child ("Selecting a Proper Surrounding to Bring up Children") 35 25
MS1212 138 × 90 mm. 8p. Man stealing bell ("Burying Ones' Head in the Sand") 1·90 1·90

275 Abacus

2001. Traditional Tools. Multicoloured.
1213 1p. Type **275** 15 10
1214 2p. Plane 35 25
1215 3p. Iron 55 40
1216 4p. Scales 70 55
MS1217 138 × 90 mm. 8p. Text, scales and iron 1·90 1·90

276 Buddha

2001. Religions. Multicoloured.
1218 1p. Type **276** 15 10
1219 1p.50 Worshippers 25 20
1220 2p. Man carrying Cross and religious procession 35 25
1221 2p.50 Procession 45 35
MS1222 138 × 90 mm. 8p. Religious Symbols (circular design,(59 × 59 mm) 1·90 1·90
Nos. 1218/19 and 1220/1 respectively were issued together, se-tenant, forming a composite design.

277 Fireman and Platform Car

2001. Fire Brigade. Multicoloured.
1223 1p.50 Type **277** 25 20
1224 2p.50 Fireman wearing chemical protection suit using portable flammable gases detector and Pumping Tank vehicle 45 35
1225 3p. Foam car and fireman wearing asbestos suit using foam hose 55 40
1226 4p. Fire officers in dress uniforms and ambulance 70 55
MS1227 138 × 90 mm. 8p. Fireman (59 × 39 mm) 1·90 1·90

278 Electronic Keys

2001. E-Commerce. Multicoloured.
1228 1p.50 Type **278** 25 20
1229 2p. Hands passing letter (e-mail) 35 25
1230 2p.50 Mobile phone 45 35
1231 3p. Palm hand-held computer 55 40
MS1232 138 × 90 6p. Lap-top computers (59 × 39 mm) 1·10 1·10

279 Emblem

2001. Choice of Beijing as 2008 Olympic Games Host City.
1233 **279** 1p. multicoloured 15 10

280 Praying

2001. Classical Literature. *Romance of the Three Kingdoms* (novel by Luo Guanzhong). Multicoloured.
1234 3p. (1) Type **280** 55 40
1235 3p. (2) Soldier and man fighting 55 40
1236 3p. (3) Men talking 55 40
1237 3p. (4) Man dreaming 55 40
MS1238 138 × 90 nn. 7p. Head of Soldier (horiz) 1·20 1·20

281 Baby, Doctor and Schoolchildren

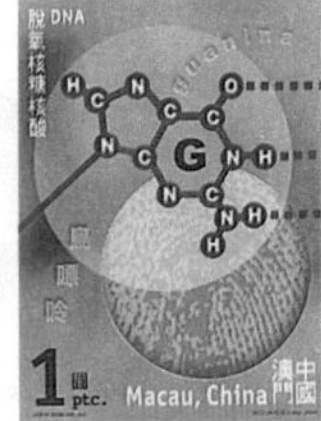
283 DNA Helix containing Guanine Base

282 Municipal Market

2001. National Census. Multicoloured.
1239 1p. Type **281** 15 10
1240 1p.50 Street scene 25 20
1241 2p.50 Suspension bridge and crowd 45 35
MS1242 137 × 90 nn. 6p. Subjects as Nos 1239/41 (86 × 37) 85 65

2001. Macau Markets. Multicoloured.
1243 1p.50 Type **282** 25 20
1244 2p.50 Building and road-side stall 45 35
1245 3p.50 Covered market 60 45
1246 4p.50 Multi-storey building 80 60
MS1242 137 × 90 nn. 6p. Subjects as Nos 1239/41 (86 × 37) 85 65

2001. Science and Technology. Composition and Structure of DNA. Showing chemical bases of DNA. Multicoloured.
1248 1p. Type **283** 15 10
1249 2p. Helix containing cytosine base 35 25
1250 3p. Helix containing adenine base 55 40
1251 4p. Helix containing thymine base 70 55
MS1252 137 × 90 mm. 8p. Helix containing adenine base (different) (44 × 29 mm) 1·90 1·90

284 Commander Ho Yin's Garden

2001. Parks and Gardens. Multicoloured.
1253 1p.50 Type **284** 25 20
1254 2p.50 Mong Há Hill municipal park 45 35
1255 3p. City of Flowers Garden 55 40
1256 4p.50 Great Taipa Natural Park 80 60
MS1257 138 × 90 mm. 8p. Garden of Art 1·90 1·90

285 Trigrams and Dragons

2001. Pa Kua (martial art) (1st series). Multicoloured.
1258 2p. (1) Type **285** 35 25
1259 2p. (4) Trigrams, couple and deer 35 25
1260 2p. (7) Trigrams, fields and buffaloes 35 25
1261 2p. (3) Trigrams and volcano 35 25
1262 2p. (6) Trigrams and three men crawling 35 25
1263 2p. (2) Trigrams, man and donkey 35 25

1264 2p. (5) Trigrams, horse and carriage 35 25
1265 2p. (8) Trigrams, men with gifts and potentate . . . 35 25
MS1266 15 × 90 mm. 8p. Yu Fu (Pa Kua master) (59 × 27 mm) . . 1·90 1·90
See also Nos. 1323/MS1331.

286 Horse's Head

2002. New Year. Year of the Horse. Multicoloured.
1267 5p. 50 Type **286** . . . . . 1·00 60
MS1268 138 × 91 mm. 10p. As No. 1267 but design enlarged 1·60 1·60

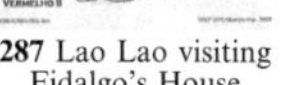

287 Lao Lao visiting Fidalgo's House

289 Facade and bas-relief of St. Paul

288 Cantao San Kong Opera Performers

2002. Classical Literature. Dream of Red Mansions. Multicoloured.
1269 2p. Type **287** 35 20
1270 2p. Jin Chuan suffering injustice 35 20
1271 2p. Proof of Dada's love for Zi Juan 35 20
1272 2p. Xiang Yun adorned with peony flowers 35 20
1273 2p. Liu Lang combing her hair 35 20
1274 2p. Miao Yu offering tea . . 35 20
MS1275 139 × 90 mm. 8p. Woman reading (The wonderful dream of love) . . . . 1·40 1·40

2002. Festivals. Tou-Tei (God of Earth) Festival. Multicoloured.
1276 1p. 50 Type **288** 25 15
1277 2p. 50 Respected elders dinner 45 25
1278 3p. 50 Burning of cult objects 60 35
1279 4p. 50 Cooking suckling pig 80 50
MS1280 139 × 90 mm. 8p. Bearded man with sword (vert) . . . . 1·40 85

2002. 400th Anniv St. Paul's Church, Macao. Multicoloured
1281 1p. Type **289** 20 10
1282 3p. 50 Corner of faÇade and ornament 60 35
MS1283 139 × 90 mm. 8p. Statue in alcove (30 × 40 mm) . . . . . 1·40 1·40

290 Goalkeeper diving for Ball

2002. World Cup Football Championships, Japan and South Korea. Multicoloured.
1284 1p. Type **290** 20 10
1285 1p. 50 Players tackling for ball 25 15

291 Underwater Animals and Oil Refinery

2002. Environmental Protection. Multicoloured.
1286 1p. Type **291** (marine conservation) 20 10
1287 1p. 50 Boy planting tree (reforestation) 25 15
1288 2p. Emblem and bins (recycling) 35 20
1289 2p. 50 Spoonbills (wetland conservation) 40 25
1290 3p. Energy plant and waste truck (energy regeneration) 50 30
1291 3p. 50 Boy sweeping leaves (clean urban environment) 60 35
1292 4p. Girl blowing bubbles (air purification) 70 35
1293 4p. 50 Nurse and elderly patient (health and hygiene) 80 50
1294 8p. Owl (improving city living) . . . . 1·40 85

292 Zheng Guanying at Home

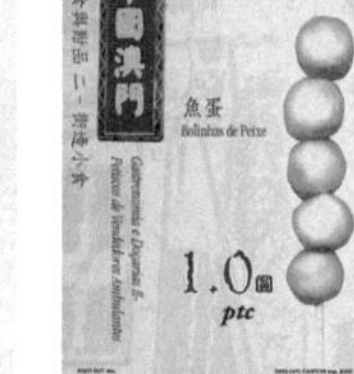

294 Fish Balls

293 Macau Tower and Skyline

2002. 160th Birth Anniv of Zheng Guanying (industrialist, reformer and philanthropist). Multicoloured.
1295 1p. Type **292** 20 10
1296 2p. As young man and docks 35 20
1297 3p. As young man and alms giving 55 35
1298 3p. 50 As older man and writing 60 35
MS1299 138 × 90 mm. 6p. Seated at table (40 × 60 mm) . . . . . . 1·00 60

2001. Honesty and Transparency. Multicoloured.
1300 1p. Type **293** 20 10
1301 3p. 50 Macau skyline from Monte Fort 55 35

2002. Street Vendor's Food. Multicoloured.
1302 1p. Type **294** 20 10
1303 1p. 50 Dried beef 25 15
1304 2p. Tongue roll 35 20
1305 2p. 50 Sat Kei Ma 45 30
MS1306 138 × 91 mm. 7p. Cookie (50 × 50 mm) . . . . 1·20 1·20

295 Shun ploughing

296 Electroweak Unification with the help of Elephant Diagram

2002. The Twenty-four Paragons of Filial Devotion (book by Guo Jujing). Multicoloured
1307 1p. Type **295** 20 10
1308 1p. 50 Huang Xiang cooling his father's bed with fan 25 15
1309 2p. Meng Zong crying over bamboo shoots for mother 35 20
1310 2p.50 Wang Xiang melting ice to get fish for stepmother 45 30
1311 4p.50 Min Ziqian pleading for cruel stepmother . . . 80 50
1312 4p.50 Jiang Shi, wife and bubbling spring 80 50
1313 4p.50 Bin Chen surrendering to be with mother 80 50
1314 4p.50 Wang Gang pleading for father's body 80 50
MS1315 95 × 139 mm. 7p. Tanzi bringing deer milk to his parents 1·20 1·20

2002. Science and Technology. Particle Physics. Multicoloured.
1316 1p. 50 Type **296** 25 15
1317 1p. 50 Scales (spontaneous symmetry breaking) . . . 25 15
1318 1p. 50 Higgs boson diagram 25 15
1319 1p. 50 Three families Z decay curve diagram . . . 25 15
1320 1p. 50 Quark groups (quantum cromodynamics) 25 15
1321 1p. 50 Graph showing interactions and predicted interactions 25 15
MS1322 138 × 90 mm. 8p. DELPHI detector . . . . 1·40 1·40

2002. Pa Kua (martial art) (2nd series). As T **285**. Multicoloured.
1323 2p. (1) Trigrams, stream and tiger 35 20
1324 2p. (4) Trigrams, man and woman 35 20
1325 2p. (7) Trigrams, couple feeding elderly person . . 35 20
1326 2p. (3) Trigrams, birds, men and path 35 20
1327 2p. (6) Trigrams and man sat in tree 35 20
1328 2p. (2) Trigrams and two men bowing 35 20
1329 2p. (5) Trigrams, yin/yang symbols and storks . . . 35 20
1330 2p. (8) Trigrams and potentate 35 20
MS1331 135 × 90mm. 8p. Woman with jug (59 × 27 mm) . . . . 1·40 1·40

CHARITY TAX STAMPS

The notes under this heading in Portugal also apply here.

43

C 48 Our Lady of Charity (altarpiece, Macao Cathedral)

1919. Fiscal stamp optd **TAXA DE GUERRA**.
C305 **43** 2a. green . . . . 5·00 3·50
C306 11a. green . . . . 7·25 6·75
The above was for use in Timor as well as Macao.

1925. As Marquis de Pombal issue of Portugal but inscr "MACAU".
C329 C **73** 2a. red . . . . 1·50 1·40
C330 – 2a. red . . . . 1·80 1·70
C331 C **75** 2a. red . . . . 1·90 1·70

1930. No gum.
C332 C **48** 5a. brown and buff . . 32·00 26·00

1945. As Type C **48** but values in Arabic and Chinese numerals left and right, at bottom of design. No gum.
C486 1a. olive and green . . . . 1·00 50
C487 2a. purple and grey . . . . 1·00 50
C415 5a. brown and yellow . . . 23·00 21·00
C416 5a. blue and light blue . . . 29·00 26·00
C417 10a. green and light green 21·00 16·00
C488 10a. blue and green . . . . 1·00 50
C418 15a. orange and light orange . . . . 20·00 15·00
C419 20a. red and orange . . . . 30·00 25·00
C489 20a. brown and yellow . . 2·10 80
C420 50a. lilac and buff . . . . 30·00 25·00
C472 50a. red and pink . . . . . 20·00 7·00

1981. No. C487 and similar higher (fiscal) values surch **20 avos** and Chinese characters.
C546 20a. on 2a. purple on grey 3·00 1·50
C534 20a. on 1p. green & lt green 3·50 2·50
C535 20a. on 3p. black and pink 3·00 1·00
C536 20a. on 5p. brown & yellow

1981. No. C418 surch **10 avos** and Chinese characters.
C553 10a. on 15a. orange and light orange . . . . . . 3·00 1·50

NEWSPAPER STAMPS

1892. "Embossed" key-type of Macao surch **JORNAES** and value. No gum.
N73 Q 2½r. on 10r. green . . . . 11·00 3·75
N74 2½r. on 40r. brown . . . . 11·00 3·75
N75 2½r. on 80r. grey . . . . . 11·00 3·75

1893. "Newspaper" key-type inscr "Macau".
N80 V 2½r. brown . . . . 3·50 2·30

1894. "Newspaper" key-type of Macao surch ½ **avo PROVISORIO** and Chinese characters.
N82 V ½a. on 2½r. brown . . . . 6·00 2·50

POSTAGE DUE STAMPS

1904. "Due" key-type inscr "MACAU". No gum (12a. to 1p.), with or without gum (others).
D184 W ½a. green . . . . 1·00 90
D185 1a. green . . . . 1·00 90
D186 2a. grey . . . . 1·00 90
D187 4a. brown . . . . 1·10 90
D188 5a. orange . . . . 1·90 1·40
D189 8a. brown . . . . 2·20 1·40
D190 12a. brown . . . . 2·75 2·10
D191 20a. blue . . . . 6·75 4·50
D192 40a. red . . . . 7·50 6·00
D193 50a. orange . . . . . . 15·00 12·00
D194 1p. lilac . . . . 32·00 23·00

1911. "Due" key-types of Macao optd **REPUBLICA**.
D204 W ½a. green 90 90
D205 1a. green 90 90
D206 2a. grey 90 90
D207 4a. brown 90 90
D208 5a. orange 90 90
D209 8a. brown 90 90
D287 12a. brown . . . . . . 2·40 1·30
D211 20a. blue . . . . 3·75 2·00
D212 40a. red . . . . 8·00 3·25
D290 50a. orange . . . . . . 13·00 5·75
D291 1p. lilac . . . . 14·50 12·00

1925. Marquis de Pombal issue, as Nos. C329/31 optd **MULTA**.
D329 C **73** 4a. red . . . . 1·50 1·50
D330 – 4a. red . . . . 1·50 1·50
D331 C **75** 4a. red . . . . 1·50 1·50

1947. As Type D **1** of Portuguese Colonies, but inscr "MACAU".
D410 D **1** 1a. black and purple . . 3·75 1·90
D411 2a. black and violet . . 3·75 1·90
D412 4a. black and blue . . . 3·75 1·90
D413 5a. black and brown . . 3·75 1·90
D414 8a. black and purple . . 3·75 1·90
D415 12a. black and brown 3·75 1·90
D416 20a. black and green . . 7·00 4·25
D417 40a. black and red . . 12·00 6·50
D418 50a. black and yellow 16·00 8·50
D419 1p. black and blue . . 18·00 11·00

1949. Postage stamps of 1934 surch **PORTEADO** and new value.
D424 **50** 1a. on 4a. black . . . . 2·50 1·40
D425 2a. on 6a. brown . . . . 2·50 1·40
D426 4a. on 8a. blue . . . . . 2·50 1·40
D427 5a. on 10a. red . . . . . 2·50 1·40
D428 8a. on 12a. blue . . . . 3·75 2·30
D429 12a. on 30a. green . . . 6·00 2·75
D430 20a. on 40a. violet . . . 7·00 3·25

1951. Optd **PORTEADO** or surch also.
D439 **66** 1a. yellow on cream . . 1·20 1·20
D440 2a. green on green . . . 1·20 1·20
D441 7a. on 10a. mauve on green . . . . 1·20 1·20

D 70

1952. Numerals in red. Name in black.
D451 D **70** 1a. blue and green . . 70 55
D452 3a. brown and salmon 80 65
D453 5a. slate and blue . . 80 65
D454 10a. red and blue . . 1·40 1·10
D455 30a. blue and brown 2·40 1·80
D456 1p. brown and grey . . 4·25 3·25

MACEDONIA Pt. 3

Part of Austro-Hungarian Empire until 1918 when it became part of Yugoslavia. Separate stamps were issued during German Occupation in the Second World War.

In 1991 Macedonia became an independent republic.

A. GERMAN OCCUPATION

100 stotinki = 1 lev.

Македония

8. IX. 1944

1 лв.

(G 1)

1944. Stamps of Bulgaria, 1940–44. (a) Surch as Type G **1**.
G1 1l. on 10st. orange . . . . . 3·50 14·00
G2 3l. on 15st. blue . . . . . . 3·50 14·00

(b) Surch similar to Type G **1** but larger.
G3 6l. on 10st. blue . . . . . . 4·00 18·00
G4 9l. on 15st. green . . . . . 4·00 18·00
G5 9l. on 15st. green . . . . . . 5·00 24·00
G6 15l. on 4l. black . . . . . . 12·00 50·00
G7 20l. on 7l. blue . . . . 12·00 50·00
G8 30l. on 14l. brown . . . . . 20·00 50·00

B. INDEPENDENT REPUBLIC

1991. 100 paras = 1 dinar.
1992. 100 deni (de.) = 1 denar (d.).

1 Trumpeters

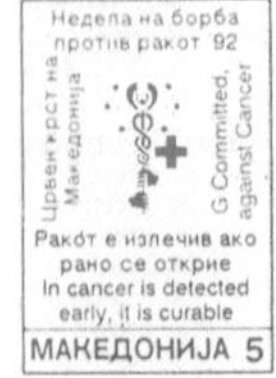

2 Emblems and Inscriptions

1991. Obligatory Tax. Independence.

1 **1** 2d.50 black and orange . . . 35 35

1992. Obligatory Tax. Anti-cancer Week. (a) T **2** showing Red Cross symbol at bottom left.

2 **2** 5d. mauve, black and blue . . 55 55
3 – 5d. multicoloured 55 55
4 – 5d. multicoloured 55 55
5 – 5d. multicoloured 55 55

DESIGNS: No. 3, Flowers, columns and scanner; 4, Scanner and couch; 5, Computer cabinet.

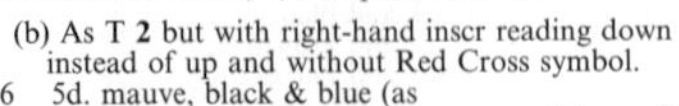

(b) As T **2** but with right-hand inscr reading down instead of up and without Red Cross symbol.

6 5d. mauve, black & blue (as No. 2) 25 25
7 5d. multicoloured (as No. 3) . . 25 25
8 5d. multicoloured (as No. 4) . . 25 25
9 5d. multicoloured (as No. 5) . . 25 25

3 Red Cross Aircraft dropping Supplies

1992. Obligatory Tax. Red Cross Week. Multicoloured.

10 10d. Red Cross slogans (dated "08–15 MAJ 1992") 15 15
11 10d. Type **3** 15 15
12 10d. Treating road accident victim 15 15
13 10d. Evacuating casualties from ruined building . . . 15 15

The three pictorial designs are taken from children's paintings.

4 "Skopje Earthquake"

6 Nurse with Baby

5 "Wood-carvers Petar and Makarie" (icon), St. Joven Bigorsk Monastery, Debar

1992. Obligatory Tax. Solidarity Week.

14 **4** 20d. black and mauve . . . 15 15
15 – 20d. multicoloured 15 15
16 – 20d. multicoloured 15 15
17 – 20d. multicoloured 15 15

DESIGNS: No. 15, Red Cross nurse with child; 16, Mothers carrying toddlers at airport; 17, Family at airport.

1992. 1st Anniv of Independence.

18 **5** 30d. multicoloured 35 35

For 40d. in same design see No. 33.

1992. Obligatory Tax. Anti-tuberculosis Week. Multicoloured.

19 20d. Anti-tuberculosis slogans (dated "14–21.IX.1992") . . 10 10
20 20d. Type **6** 10 10
21 20d. Nurse giving oxygen . . 10 10
22 20d. Baby in cot 10 10

7 "The Nativity" (fresco, Slepce Monastery)

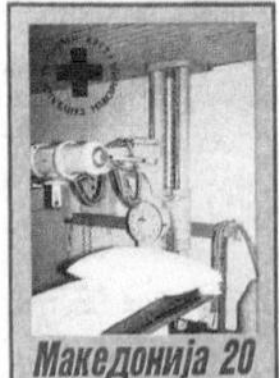

9 Radiography Equipment

8 Mixed Bouquet

1992. Christmas. Multicoloured.

23 100d. Type **7** 50 50
24 500d. "Madonna and Child" (fresco), Zrze Monastery . . 1·75 1·75

1993. Obligatory Tax. Red Cross Fund. Multicoloured.

25 20d. Red Cross slogans . . . 10 10
26 20d. Marguerites 10 10
27 20d. Carnations 10 10
28 20d. Type **8** 10 10

1993. Obligatory Tax. Anti-cancer Week. Multicoloured.

29 20d. Anti-cancer slogans (dated "1–8 MART 1993") 10 10
30 20d. Type **9** 10 10
31 20d. Overhead treatment unit 10 10
32 20d. Scanner 10 10

1993. As No. 18 but changed value.

33 **5** 40d. multicoloured 40 40

10 Macedonian Flag

1993.

34 **10** 10d. multicoloured 10 10
35 40d. multicoloured 45 45
36 50d. multicoloured 55 55

11 Macedonian Roach

1993. Fishes from Lake Ohrid. Multicoloured.

37 50d. Type **11** 15 15
38 100d. Lake Ohrid salmon . . 20 20
39 1000d. Type **11** . . . . . . 2·00 2·00
40 2000d. As No. 38 . . . . . . 3·00 3·00

12 Crucifix, St. George's Monastery

1993. Easter.

41 **12** 300d. multicoloured 70 70

13 Diagram of Telecommunications Cable and Map

1993. Opening of Trans-Balkan Telecommunications Line.

42 **13** 500d. multicoloured 70 70

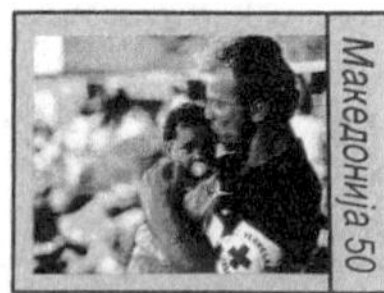

14 Red Cross Worker with Baby

1993. Obligatory Tax. Red Cross Week. Multicoloured.

43 50d. Red Cross inscriptions (dated "08–15 MAJ 1993") 10 10
44 50d. Type **14** 10 10
45 50d. Physiotherapist and child in wheelchair 10 10
46 50d. Stretcher party 10 10

See also No. 73.

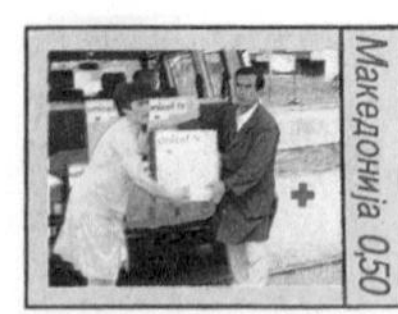

15 Unloading U.N.I.C.E.F. Supplies from Lorry

1993. Obligatory Tax. Solidarity Week.

47 – 50de. black, mauve and silver 10 10
48 **15** 50de. multicoloured 10 10
49 – 50de. multicoloured 10 10
50 – 50de. multicoloured 10 10

DESIGNS: No. 47, "Skopje Earthquake"; 49, Labelling parcels in warehouse; 50, Consignment of parcels on fork-lift truck.

See also No. 72.

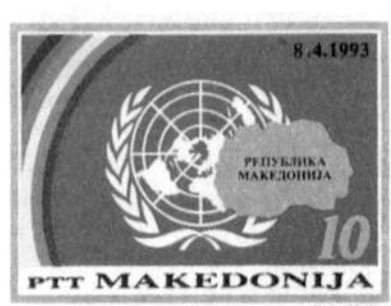

16 U.N. Emblem and Rainbow

1993. Admission to United Nations Organization.

51 **16** 10d. multicoloured . . . . 1·00 1·00

17 "Insurrection" (detail), (B. Lazeski)

19 Tapestry

18 Children in Meadow

1993. 90th Anniv of Macedonian Insurrection.

52 **17** 10d. multicoloured . . . . 1·00 1·00
MS53 116 × 73 mm. 30d. multicoloured . . . . 2·75 2·75

1993. Obligatory Tax. Anti-tuberculosis Week. Multicoloured.

54 50de. Anti-tuberculosis slogans (dated "14–21.09.1993") . . 10 10
55 50de. Type **18** 10 10
56 50de. Bee on flower 10 10
57 50de. Goat behind boulder . 10 10

See also No. 71.

1993. Centenary of Founding of Inner Macedonia Revolutionary Organization.

58 4d. Type **19** 30 30
MS59 90 × 75 mm. 40d. Two motifs as Type **19** . . . . 2·75 2·75

20 "The Nativity" (fresco from St. George's Monastery, Rajcica)

1993. Christmas. Multicoloured.

60 2d. Type **20** 25 25
61 20d. "The Three Kings" (fresco from Slepce Monastery) . . . . 1·00 1·00

21 Lily

1994. Obligatory Tax. Anti-cancer Week. Multicoloured.

62 1d. Red Cross and anti-cancer emblems 10 10
63 1d. Type **21** 10 10
64 1d. Caesar's mushroom . . . 20 20
65 1d. Mute swans on lake . . . 10 10

1994. Nos. 1, 18 and 34 surch.

66 **5** 2d. on 30d. multicoloured . . 15 15
67 **1** 8d. on 2d.50 black and orange 40 40
68 **6** 15d. on 10d. multicoloured 70 70

23 Decorated Eggs

24 Kosta Racin (writer)

1994. Easter.

69 **23** 2d. multicoloured 25 25

1994. Obligatory Tax. Red Cross Week. As previous designs but values, and date (70), changed. Multicoloured.

70 1d. Red Cross inscriptions (dated "8–15 MAJ 1994") 10 10
71 1d. Type **18** 10 10
72 1d. As No. 50 . . . . 10 10
73 1d. Type **14** 10 10

1994. Revolutionaries. Portraits by Dimitar Kondovski. Multicoloured.

74 8d. Type **24** 45 45
75 15d. Grigor Prlicev (writer) . . 1·00 1·00
76 20d. Nikola Vaptsarov (Bulgarian poet) . . . . . 1·75 1·75
77 50d. Goce Delcev (founder of Internal Macedonian–Odrin Revolutionary–Organization) . . . . 2·40 2·40

25 "Skopje Earthquake"

26 Tree and Family

1994. Obligatory Tax. Solidarity Week.

78 **25** 1d. black, red and silver . . 10 10

1994. Census.

79 **26** 2d. multicoloured 25 25

27 St. Prohor Pcinski Monastery (venue)

28 Swimmer

1994. 50th Anniv of Macedonian National Liberation Council. Multicoloured.

80 5d. Type **27** 30 30
MS81 108 × 73 mm. 50d. Aerial view of Monastery . . . . 2·75 2·75

1994. Swimming Marathon, Ohrid.

82 **28** 8d. multicoloured 45 45

29 Turkish Cancellation and 1992 30d. Stamp on Cover

1994. 150th Anniv (1993) of Postal Service in Macedonia.
83 **29** 2d. multicoloured 20 20

30 Mastheads

1994. 50th Anniversaries of "Nova Makedonija", "Mlad Borec" and "Makedonka" (newspapers).
84 **30** 2d. multicoloured 25 25

31 Open Book

1994. 50th Anniv of St. Clement of Ohrid Library. Multicoloured.
85 2d. Type **31** 15 15
86 10d. Page of manuscript (vert) 50 50

32 Globe

33 Wireless and Gramophone Record

1994. Obligatory Tax. Anti-AIDS Week.
87 – 2d. red and black 10 10
88 **32** 2d. black, red and blue . . 10 10
89 – 2d. black, yellow and red . . 10 10
90 – 2d. black and red 10 10
DESIGNS: No. 87, Inscriptions in Cyrillic (dated "01-08.12.1994"); 89, Exclamation mark in warning triangle; 90, Safe sex campaign emblem.

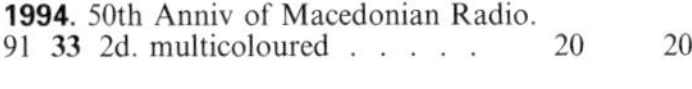

1994. 50th Anniv of Macedonian Radio.
91 **33** 2d. multicoloured 20 20

34 Macedonian Pine

1994. Flora and Fauna. Multicoloured.
92 5d. Type **34** 35 35
93 10d. Lynx 80 80

1995. Nos. 35 and 33 surch.
94 **10** 2d. on 40d. multicoloured 35 35
96 **5** 5d. on 40d. multicoloured 35 35

36 Emblems and Inscriptions

38 Voluntary Workers

37 Fresco

1995. Obligatory Tax. Anti-cancer Week. Multicoloured.
97 1d. Type **36** 10 10
98 1d. White lilies 10 10
99 1d. Red lilies 10 10
100 1d. Red roses 10 10

1995. Easter.
101 **37** 4d. multicoloured 30 30

1995. Obligatory Tax. Red Cross. Multicoloured.
102 1d. Cross and inscriptions in Cyrillic (dated "8–15 MAJ 1995") 10 10
103 1d. Type **38** 10 10
104 1d. Volunteers in T-shirts . . 10 10
105 1d. Globe, red cross and red crescent 10 10

39 Troops on Battlefield

1995. 50th Anniv of End of Second World War.
106 **39** 2d. multicoloured 25 25

40 Anniversary Emblem

1995. 50th Anniv of Macedonian Red Cross.
107 **40** 2d. multicoloured 20 20

41 Rontgen and X-Ray Lamp

1995. Centenary of Discovery of X-Rays by Wilhelm Rontgen.
108 **41** 2d. multicoloured 20 20

42 "Skopje Earthquake"

1995. Obligatory Tax. Solidarity Week.
109 **42** 1d. black, red and gold . . 10 10

43 Cernodrinski (dramatist)

1995. 50th Anniv of Vojdan Cernodrinski Theatre Festival.
110 **43** 10d. multicoloured 50 50

44 Kraljevic (fresco, Markov Monastery, Skopje)

1995. 600th Death Anniv of Marko Kraljevic (Serbian Prince).
111 **44** 20d. multicoloured . . . . 1·00 1·00

45 Puleski

1995. Death Centenary of Gorgi Puleski (linguist and revolutionary).
112 **45** 2d. multicoloured 20 20

46 Manuscript, Bridge and Emblem

1995. Writers' Festival, Struga.
113 **46** 2d. multicoloured 25 25

47 Robert Koch (discoverer of tubercule bacillus)

48 Child holding Parents' Hands

1995. Obligatory Tax. Anti-tuberculosis Week.
114 **47** 1d. brown, black and red 10 10

1995. Obligatory Tax. Childrens' Week. Self-adhesive. Imperf.
115 **48** 2d. blue 10 10

49 Maleshevija

50 Interior of Mosque

1995. Buildings. Multicoloured.
116 2d. Type **49** 15 15
117 20d. Krakornica . . . . . . 1·10 1·10

1995. Tetovo Mosque.
118 **50** 15d. multicoloured 90 90

51 Lumiere Brothers (inventors of cine-camera)

1995. Centenary of Motion Pictures. Multicoloured.
119 10d. Type **51** 55 55
120 10d. Milton and Janaki Manaki (Macedonian cinematographers) 55 55
Nos. 119/20 were issued together, se-tenant, forming a composite design.

52 Globe in Nest within Frame

1995. 50th Anniv of U.N.O. Multicoloured.
121 20d. Type **52** 80 80
122 50d. Sun within frame . . . 2·50 2·50

53 Male and Female Symbols

1995. Obligatory Tax. Anti-AIDS Week.
123 **53** 1d. multicoloured 10 10

54 Madonna and Child

1995. Christmas.
124 **54** 15d. multicoloured 75 75

55 Dalmatian Pelican

1995. Birds. Multicoloured.
125 15d. Type **55** 75 75
126 40d. Lammergeier . . . . . 2·00 2·00

56 Letters of Alphabet and Jigsaw Pieces

1995. 50th Anniv of Alphabet Reform.
127 **56** 5d. multicoloured 35 35

57 St. Clement of Ohrid (detail of fresco)

1995. 700th Anniv of Fresco, St. Bogorodica's Church, Ohrid.
128 **57** 8d. multicoloured 45 45
MS129 85 × 67 mm. **57** 50d. multicoloured. Imperf . . . . 20·00 20·00

58 Postal Headquarters, Skopje

1995. 2nd Anniv of Membership of U.P.U.
130 **58** 10d. multicoloured 60 60

59 Zip joining Flags

1995. Entry to Council of Europe and Organization for Security and Co-operation in Europe.
131 **59** 20d. multicoloured . . . . 1·10 1·10

60 Hand holding out Apple

61 Inscriptions

1996. Obligatory Tax. Anti-cancer Week.
132 **60** 1d. multicoloured 10 10

1996. Obligatory Tax. Red Cross Week. Each red, black and yellow.
133 1d. Type **61** 10 10
134 1d. Red Cross principles in Macedonian 10 10
135 1d. Red Cross principles in English 10 10
136 1d. Red Cross principles in French 10 10
137 1d. Red Cross principles in Spanish 10 10

62 Canoeing

1996. Olympic Games, Atlanta. Designs showing statue of discus thrower and sport. Multicoloured.
138 2d. Type **62** 10 10
139 8d. Basketball (vert) 40 40
140 15d. Swimming 75 75
141 20d. Wrestling 95 95
142 40d. Boxing (vert) . . . . . 1·75 1·75
143 50d. Running (vert) . . . . 2·25 2·25

63 "Skopje Earthquake"

1996. Obligatory Tax. Solidarity Week.
144 **63** 1d. gold, red and black . . 10 10

64 Scarecrow Drug Addict

65 Boy

1996. United Nations Anti-drugs Decade.
145 **64** 20d. multicoloured 75 75

1996. Children's Week. Children's Drawings. Multicoloured.
146 2d. Type **65** 10 10
147 8d. Girl 35 35

66 Fragment from Tomb and Tsar Samuel (after Dimitar Kondovski)

1996. Millenary of Crowning of Tsar Samuel (ruler of Bulgaria and Macedonia).
148 **66** 40d. multicoloured . . . . 1·50 1·50

67 Petrov

1996. 75th Death Anniv of Gorce Petrov (revolutionary).
149 **67** 20d. multicoloured 75 75

68 Ohrid Seal, 1903, and State Flag

1996. 5th Anniv of Independence.
150 **68** 10d. multicoloured 40 40

69 Lungs on Globe

70 Vera Ciriviri-Trena (freedom fighter)

1996. Obligatory Tax. Anti-tuberculosis Week.
151 **69** 1d. red, blue and black . . 10 10

1996. Europa. Famous Women. Multicoloured.
152 20d. Type **70** 65 65
153 40d. Mother Teresa (Nobel Peace Prize winner and founder of Missionaries of Charity) . . . . 1·25 1·25

71 Hand holding Syringe

1996. Obligatory Tax. Anti-AIDS Week.
154 **71** 1d. black, red and yellow 10 10

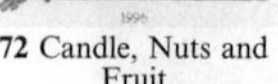

72 Candle, Nuts and Fruit

73 "Daniel in the Lions' Den"

1996. Christmas. Multicoloured.
155 10d. Type **72** 35 35
156 10d. Tree and carol singers 35 35

1996. Early Christian Terracotta Reliefs. (a) Green backgrounds.
157 4d. Type **73** 15 15
158 8d. St. Christopher and St. George 25 25
159 20d. Joshua and Caleb . . . 60 60
160 50d. Unicorn . . . . 1·40 1·40

(b) Blue backgrounds.
161 4d. Type **73** 15 15
162 8d. As No. 158 . . . . . . 25 25
163 20d. As No. 159 . . . . . . 60 60
164 50d. As No. 160 . . . . . . 1·40 1·40

74 Nistrovo

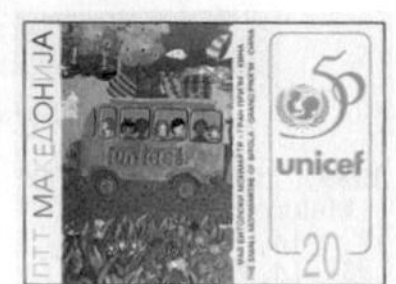

76 U.N.I.C.E.F. Coach

75 "Pseudochazara cingovskii"

1996. Traditional Houses. Multicoloured.
165 2d. Type **74** 10 10
166 8d. Brodec 30 30
167 10d. Niviste 35 35

1996. Butterflies. Multicoloured.
168 4d. Type **75** 15 15
169 40d. Danube clouded yellow 1·25 1·25

1996. 50th Anniversaries. Multicoloured.
170 20d. Type **76** (U.N.I.C.E.F.) 65 65
171 40d. Church in Mtskheta, Georgia (U.N.E.S.C.O.) . . 1·40 1·40

77 Skier

1997. 50 Years of Ski Championships at Sar Planina.
172 **77** 20d. multicoloured 70 70

78 Bell

1997. 150th Birth Anniv of Alexander Graham Bell (telephone pioneer).
173 **78** 40d. multicoloured . . . . 1·40 1·40

79 Family and Healthy Foodstuffs

81 Red Cross on Globe

80 Hound

1997. Obligatory Tax. Anti-cancer Week.
174 **79** 1d. multicoloured 10 10

1997. Roman Mosaics from Heraklia. Mult.
175 2d. Type **80** 10 10
176 8d. Steer 25 25
177 20d. Lion 70 70
178 40d. Leopard with prey . . . 1·25 1·25
MS179 85 × 60 mm. 50d. Deer and plant tub. Imperf . . . . . . 2·75 2·75

1997. Obligatory Tax. Red Cross Week.
180 **81** 1d. mult 10 10

82 Gold Plate

1997. 1100th Anniv of Cyrillic Alphabet. Mult.
181 10d. Type **82** 30 30
182 10d. Sts. Cyril and Methodius 30 30

83 School-children

84 Mountain Flowers

1997. Obligatory Tax. Solidarity Week.
183 **83** 1d. multicoloured 10 10

1997. 5th Anniv of Ecological Association.
184 **84** 15d. multicoloured 55 55

85 Itar Pejo

86 St. Naum and St. Naum's Church, Ohrid

1997. Europa. Tales and Legends. Multicoloured.
185 20d. Type **85** 70 70
186 40d. Stork-men . . . . . . 1·25 1·25

1997. 1100th Birth Anniv of St. Naum.
187 **86** 15d. multicoloured 55 55

87 Diseased Lungs

88 Stibnite

1997. Obligatory Tax. Anti-tuberculosis Week.
188 **87** 1d. multicoloured 10 10

1997. Minerals. Multicoloured.
189 27d. Type **88** 95 95
190 40d. Lorandite . . . . 1·40 1·40

89 Dove and Sun above Child in Open Hand

1997. International Children's Day.
191 **89** 27d. multicoloured 95 95

90 Chanterelle

1997. Fungi. Multicoloured.
192 2d. Type **90** 10 10
193 15d. Bronze boletus 50 50
194 27d. Caesar's mushroom . . 95 95
195 50d. "Morchella conica" . . 1·75 1·75

91 Group of Children **92** Gandhi

1998. Obligatory Tax. Anti-AIDS Week.
196 **91** 1d. multicoloured 10 10

1998. 50th Death Anniv of Mahatma Gandhi (Indian independence campaigner).
197 **92** 30d. multicoloured . . . . 1·00 1·00

93 Formula of Pythagoras's Theory

1998. 2500th Death Anniv of Pythagoras (philosopher and mathematician).
198 **93** 16d. multicoloured 55 55

94 Alpine Skiing

1998. Winter Olympic Games, Nagano, Japan. Multicoloured.

199	4d. Type **94**	15	15
200	30d. Cross-country skiing . .	1·00	1·00

95 Novo Selo

1998. Traditional Houses. Multicoloured.

201	1d. Bogomila	10	10
201a	2d. Type **95**	10	10
201b	Jachintse	10	10
202	4d. Jablanica	15	15
202a	4d. Svekani	10	10
202b	5d. Teovo	10	10
202c	6d. Zdunje	15	10
202d	6d. Mitrasinci	15	15
202e	9d. Ratevo	20	20
203	16d. Kiselica	35	35
204	20d. Konopnica	70	70
205	30d. Ambar	1·00	1·00
206	50d. Galicnik	1·75	1·75

96 "Exodus" (Kole Manev)

1998. 50th Anniv of Exodus of Children during Greek Civil War.
215 **96** 30d. multicoloured . . . . 1·00 1·00

97 "Proportions of Man" (Leonardo da Vinci)

1998. Obligatory Tax. Anti-cancer Week.
216 **97** 1d. multicoloured 10 10

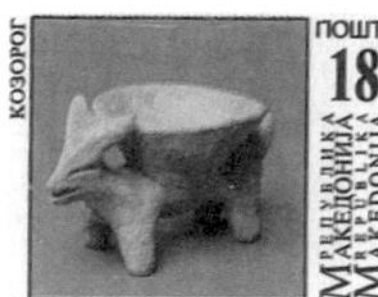

98 Bowl supported by Animal

1998. Archaeological Finds from Nedit. Mult.

217	4d. Carafes	15	15
218	18d. Type **98**	60	60
219	30d. Sacred female figurine .	1·00	1·00
220	60d. Stemmed cup	2·10	2·10

99 Football Pitch

1998. World Cup Football Championship, France. Multicoloured.

221	4d. Type **99**	15	15
222	30d. Globe and football pitch	1·00	1·00

100 Folk Dance

1998. Europa. National Festivals. Multicoloured.

223	30d. Type **100**	1·00	1·00
224	40d. Carnival	1·40	1·40

101 Profiles

1998. Obligatory Tax. Red Cross Week.
225 **101** 2d. multicoloured 10 10

102 Carnival Procession **103** Hands and Red Cross

1998. 18th Congress of Carnival Towns, Strumica.
226 **102** 30d. multicoloured . . . 1·00 1·00

1998. Obligatory Tax. Solidarity Week.
227 **103** 2d. multicoloured 10 10

104 Flower **105** Cupovski

1998. Environmental Protection. Multicoloured.

228	4d. Type **104**	15	15
229	30d. Polluting chimney uprooting tree	1·00	1·00

1998. 120th Birth Anniv of Dimitrija Cupovski.
230 **105** 16d. multicoloured . . . 55 55

106 Steam Locomotive and Station **107** Doctor and Patient

1997. 150th Anniv of Railways in Macedonia. Multicoloured.

231	30d. Type **106**	1·00	1·00
232	60d. Steam locomotive, 1873 (horiz)	2·10	2·10

1998. Obligatory Tax. Anti-tuberculosis Week.
233 **107** 2d. multicoloured 10 10

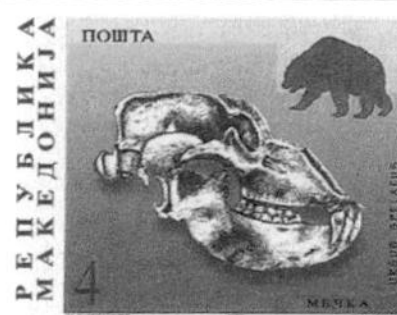

108 "Ursus spelaeus"

1998. Fossilized Skulls. Multicoloured.

234	4d. Type **108**	10	10
235	8d. "Mesopithecus pentelici"	15	15
236	18d. "Tragoceros"	40	40
237	30d. "Aceratherium incsivum"	65	65

109 Atanos Badev (composer) and Score

1998. Centenary of "Zlatoustova Liturgy".
238 **109** 25d. multicoloured . . . 50 50

110 Child with Kite

1998. Children's Day.
239 **110** 30d. multicoloured . . . 65 65

111 "Cerambyx cerdo" (longhorn beetle)

1998. Insects. Multicoloured.

240	4d. Type **111**	10	10
241	8d. Alpine longhorn beetle	15	15
242	20d. European rhinoceros beetle	40	40
243	40d. Stag beetle	85	85

112 Reindeer and Snowflakes

1998. Christmas and New Year. Multicoloured.

244	4d. Type **112**	10	10
245	30d. Bread and oak leaves . .	65	65

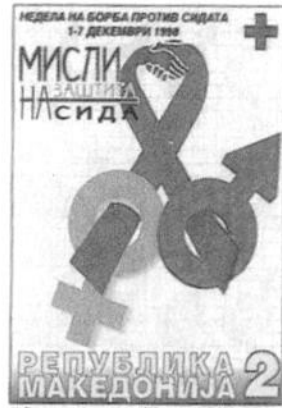

113 Ribbon and Gender Symbols

1998. Obligatory Tax. Anti-AIDS Week.
246 **113** 2d. multicoloured 10 10

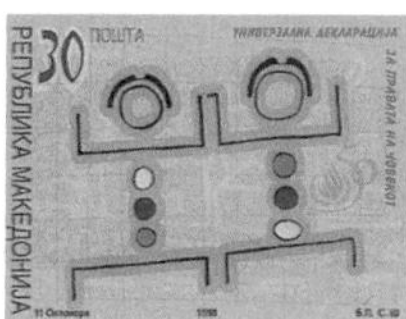

114 Stylized Couple

1998. 50th Anniv of Universal Declaration of Human Rights.
247 **114** 30d. multicoloured . . . 65 65

115 Sharplaninec

1999. Dogs.
248 **115** 15d. multicoloured . . . 30 30

116 Girl's Face **117** "The Annunciation" (Demir Hisar, Slepce Monastery)

1999. Obligatory Tax. Anti-cancer Week.
249 **116** 2d. multicoloured 10 10

1999. Icons. Multicoloured.

250	4d. Type **117**	10	10
251	8d. "Saints" (St. Nicholas's Church, Ohrid)	15	15
252	18d. "Madonna and Child" (Demir Hisar, Slepce Monastery)	40	40
253	30d. "Christ the Redeemer" (Zrze Monastery, Prilep)	65	65
MS254	53 × 74 mm. 50d. "Christ and Archangels" (Archangel Michael Church, Lesnovo Monastery, Probiotip)	2·75	2·75

118 Pandilov and "Hay Harvest"

1999. Birth Centenary of Dimitar Pandilov (painter).
255 **118** 4d. multicoloured 10 10

119 Telegraph Apparatus

1999. Centenary of the Telegraph in Macedonia.
256 **119** 4d. multicoloured 10 10

120 University and Sts. Cyril and Methodius

1999. 50th Anniv of Sts. Cyril and Methodius University.
257 **120** 8d. multicoloured 15 15

121 Anniversary Emblem and Map of Europe

1999. 50th Anniv of Council of Europe.
258 **121** 30d. multicoloured . . . 65 65

122 Pelister National Park

1999. Europa. Parks and Gardens. Multicoloured.
259 30d. Type **122** 65 65
260 40d. Mavrovo National Park 85 85

123 Figures linking Raised Arms

1999. Obligatory Tax. Red Cross Week.
261 **123** 2d. multicoloured 10 10

124 People running round Globe

125 Tree

1999. Obligatory Tax. Solidarity Week.
262 **124** 2d. multicoloured 10 10

1999. Environmental Protection.
263 **125** 30d. multicoloured . . . 65 65

126 Tsar Petur Delyan

1999. Medieval Rulers of Macedonia. Mult.
264 4d. Type **126** 10 10
265 8d. Prince Gjorgji Vojteh . . 15 15
266 18d. Prince Dobromir Hrs . . 40 40
267 30d. Prince Strez 65 65
Nos. 264/7 were issued together, se-tenant, forming a composite design.

127 Kuzman Shaikarev (author)

1999. 125th Anniv of First Macedonian Language Primer.
268 **127** 4d. multicoloured 10 10

128 Faces in Outline of Lungs

129 "Crocus scardicus"

1999. Obligatory Tax. Anti-tuberculosis Week.
269 **128** 2d. multicoloured 10 10

1999. Flowers. Multicoloured.
270 4d. Type **129** 10 10
271 8d. "Astragalus mayeri" . . 15 15
272 18d. "Campanula formanekiana" 40 40
273 30d. "Viola kosaninii" . . . 65 65

130 Child

1999. Children's Week.
274 **130** 30d. multicoloured . . . 60 60

131 Emblem

1999. 125th Anniv of Universal Postal Union. Mult.
275 5d. Type **131** 10 10
276 30d. Emblem (different) . . . 60 60

132 Men on Horseback

133 Misirkov

1999. 1400th Anniv of Slavs in Macedonia.
277 **132** 5d. multicoloured 10 10

1999. 125th Birth Anniv (2000) of Krste Petkov Misirkov (writer).
278 **133** 5d. multicoloured 10 10

134 Pine Needles

1999. Christmas. Multicoloured.
279 5d. Type **134** 10 10
280 30d. Traditional pastry (vert) 60 60

135 Stylized Figures supporting Globe

1999. Obligatory Tax. Anti-AIDS Week.
281 **135** 2d.50 multicoloured . . . 10 10

136 Altar Cross (19th-century), St. Nikita Monastery

2000. Bimillenary of Christianity. Multicoloured.
282 5d. Type **136** 10 10
283 10d. "Akathist of the Holy Mother of God" (14th-century fresco), Marko's Monastery (horiz) 20 20
284 15d. "St. Clement" (14th-century icon), Ohrid . . . 30 30
285 30d. "Paul the Apostle" (14th-century fresco), St. Andrew's Monastery . . 60 60
MS286 70 × 50 mm. 50d. Cathedral Church of St. Sophia (11th-century), Ohrid (29 × 31 mm) . . . . 2·75 2·75

137 "2000"

2000. New Year. Multicoloured.
287 5d. Type **137** 30 30
288 30d. Religious symbols . . . 60 60

138 Globe Unravelling and Medical Symbols

139 Jewelled Brooch with Icon, Ohrid

2000. Obligatory Tax. Anti-cancer Week.
289 **138** 2d.50 multicoloured . . . 10 10

2000. Jewellery. Multicoloured.
290 5d. Type **139** 10 10
291 10d. Bracelet, Bitola 20 20
292 20d. Earrings, Ohrid 40 40
293 30d. Butterfly brooch, Bitola 60 60

140 Magnifying Glass and Perforation Gauge

2000. 50th Anniv of Philately in Macedonia.
294 **140** 5d. multicoloured 10 10

141 Globe and Emblem

2000. 50th Anniv of World Meteorological Organization.
295 **141** 30d. multicoloured . . . 60 60

142 Men with Easter Eggs

144 "Building Europe"

143 Stylized Figures

2000. Easter.
296 **142** 5d. multicoloured 10 10

2000. Obligatory Tax. Red Cross Week.
297 **143** 2d.50 multicoloured . . . 10 10

2000. Europa.
298 **144** 30d. multicoloured . . . 60 60

145 Running

2000. Olympic Games, Sydney. Multicoloured.
299 5d. Type **145** 10 10
300 30d. Wrestling 60 60

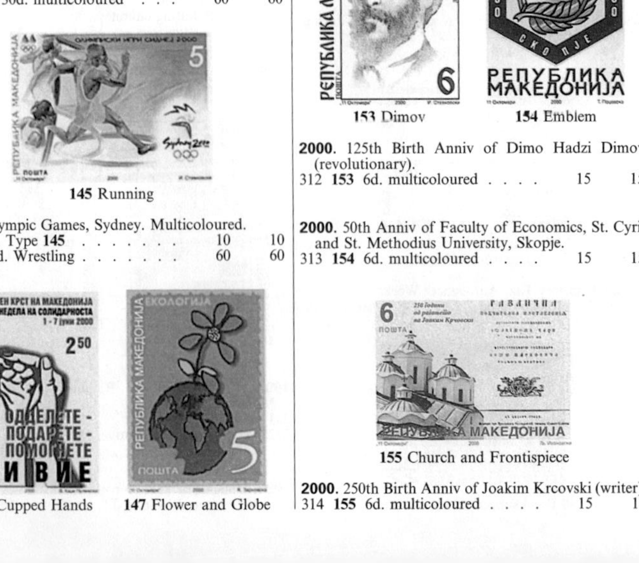

146 Cupped Hands

147 Flower and Globe

2000. Obligatory Tax. Solidarity Week.
301 **146** 2d.50 multicoloured . . . 10 10

2000. International Environmental Protection Day.
302 **147** 5d. multicoloured 10 10

148 Teodosija Sinaitski (printing pioneer)

150 Faces and Hands

149 Mother Teresa

2000. Printing. Multicoloured.
303 6d. Type **148** 10 10
304 30d. Johannes Gutenberg (inventor of printing press) 60 60

2000. 3rd Death Anniv of Mother Teresa (Order of Missionaries of Charity).
305 **149** 6d. multicoloured 10 10

2000. Obligatory Tax. Red Cross Week.
306 **150** 3d. multicoloured 10 10

151 Little Egret

2000. Birds. Multicoloured.
307 6d. Type **151** 10 10
308 10d. Grey heron 20 20
309 20d. Purple heron 40 40
310 30d. Glossy ibis 60 60

152 Children and Tree

2000. Children's Week.
311 **152** 6d. multicoloured 15 15

153 Dimov

154 Emblem

2000. 125th Birth Anniv of Dimo Hadzi Dimov (revolutionary).
312 **153** 6d. multicoloured 15 15

2000. 50th Anniv of Faculty of Economics, St. Cyril and St. Methodius University, Skopje.
313 **154** 6d. multicoloured 15 15

155 Church and Frontispiece

2000. 250th Birth Anniv of Joakim Krcovski (writer).
314 **155** 6d. multicoloured 15 15

156 Nativity

2000. Christmas.

315 **156** 30d. multicoloured . . . 70 70

157 Hand holding Condom

2000. Obligatory Tax. Anti-AIDS. Week.

316 **157** 3d. multicoloured 10 10

158 Handprints and Emblem

2001. 50th Anniv of United Nations Commissioner for Human Rights. Multicoloured.

317 6d. Type **158** 15 15

318 30d. Hands forming Globe (vert) 70 70

159 Imperial Eagle on Branch

2001. Endangered Species. The Imperial Eagle (*Aquila heliaca*). Multicoloured.

319 6d. Type **159** 15 15

320 8d. With chick 20 20

321 10d. Flying 25 25

322 30d. Head 70 70

160 Zografski

2001. 125th Death Anniv of Partenja Zografski (historian).

323 **160** 6d. multicoloured 15 15

161 Emblem 162 Woman in Costume

2001. Obligatory Tax. Anti-Cancer Week.

324 **161** 3d. multicoloured 10 10

2001. Regional Costumes. Multicoloured.

325 6d. Type **162** 15 15

326 12d. Couple in costume . . . 30 30

327 18d. Woman in costume . . 45 45

328 30d. Couple in costume . . . 70 70

MS329 76 × 64 mm. 50d. Women working (30 × 30 mm). Imperf 1·25 1·25

163 Landscape

2001. Birth Centenary of Lazar Licenoski (artist).

330 **163** 6d. multicoloured 15 15

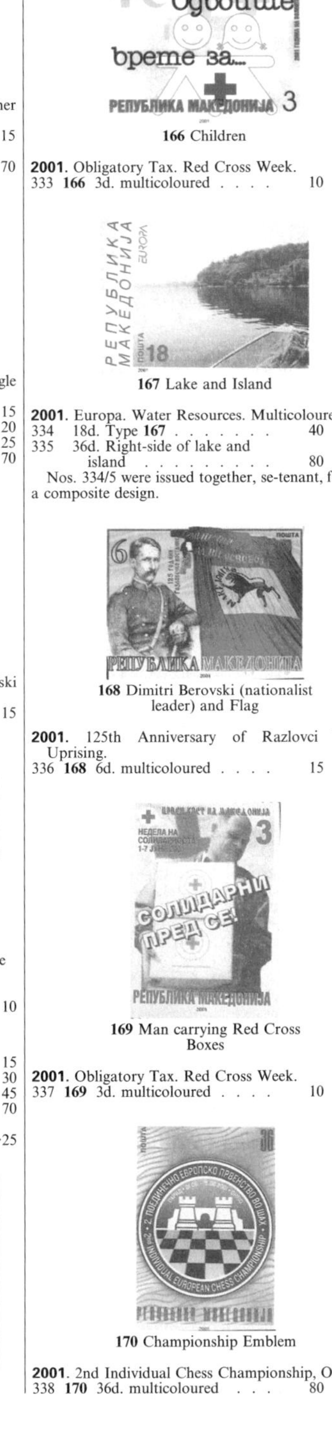

164 Text

2001. 50th Anniv of State Archives.

331 **164** 6d. multicoloured 15 15

165 Jesus and Sick Man

2001. Easter.

332 **165** 6d. multicoloured 15 15

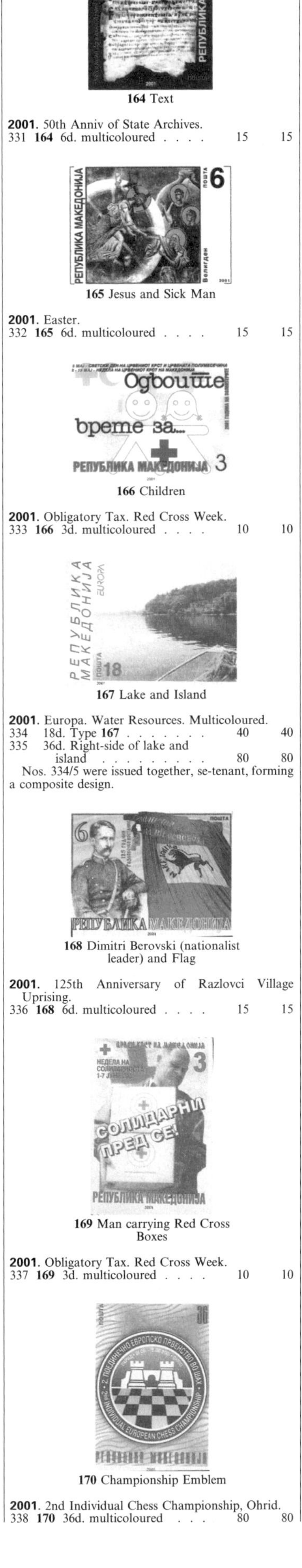

166 Children

2001. Obligatory Tax. Red Cross Week.

333 **166** 3d. multicoloured 10 10

167 Lake and Island

2001. Europa. Water Resources. Multicoloured.

334 18d. Type **167** 40 40

335 36d. Right-side of lake and island 80 80

Nos. 334/5 were issued together, se-tenant, forming a composite design.

168 Dimitri Berovski (nationalist leader) and Flag

2001. 125th Anniversary of Razlovci Village Uprising.

336 **168** 6d. multicoloured 15 15

169 Man carrying Red Cross Boxes

2001. Obligatory Tax. Red Cross Week.

337 **169** 3d. multicoloured 10 10

170 Championship Emblem

2001. 2nd Individual Chess Championship, Ohrid.

338 **170** 36d. multicoloured . . . 80 80

171 Boats on Lake

2001. Environment Protection. Lake Dojran.

339 **171** 6d. multicoloured 15 15

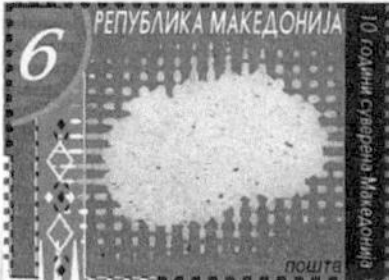

172 Emblem

2001. 10th Anniv of Independence.

340 **172** 6d. multicoloured 15 15

173 Juniper (*Juniperus exelsa*) 174 Man with raised Arms

2001. Trees. Multicoloured.

341 6d. Type **173** 15 15

342 12d. Macedonian oak (*Quercus macedonica*) . . . 25 25

343 24d. Strawberry tree (*Arbutus andrachne*) 50 50

344 36d. Kermes oak (*Quercus coccifera*) 80 80

2001. Obligatory Tax. Anti-Tuberculosis Week.

345 **174** 3d. multicoloured 10 10

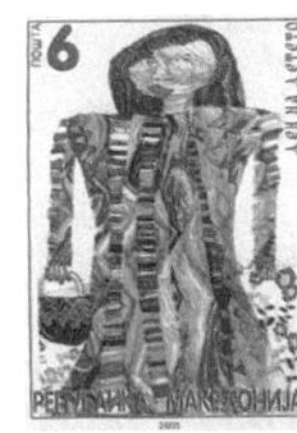

175 Stylized Woman with Basket 176 Children encircling Globe

2001. Children's Day.

346 **175** 6d. multicoloured 15 15

2001. United Nations Year of Dialogue among Civilizations.

347 **176** 36d. multicoloured . . . 80 80

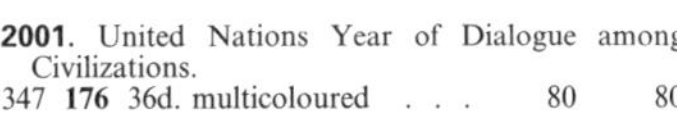

177 Fox and Cubs

2001. 75th Anniv of Zoological Museum.

348 **177** 6d. multicoloured 15 15

178 Icon 179 Faces

2001. Christmas.

349 **178** 6d. multicoloured 15 15

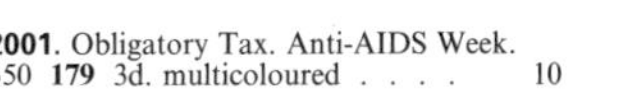

2001. Obligatory Tax. Anti-AIDS Week.

350 **179** 3d. multicoloured 10 10

180 Alfred Nobel

2001. Centenary of First Nobel Prize.

351 **180** 36d. multicoloured . . . 80 80

181 Skier

2002. Winter Olympic Games, Salt Lake City, USA. Multicoloured.

352 6d. Type **181** 15 15

353 36d. Skier (different) 80 80

182 Sunrise

2002. Obligarory Tax. Anti-Cancer Week.

354 **182** 3d. multicoloured 10 10

183 Likej (coin)

2002. Ancient Coins. Coins. Multicoloured.

355 6d. Type **183** 15 15

356 12d. Alexander III tetradrachm 25 25

357 24d. Lichnidos 50 50

358 36d. Philip II gold coin (stater) 80 80

MS359 85 × 62 mm. 50d. Coin 1·10 1·10

184 Painting and Petar Mazev

2002. Artists Birth Anniversaries. Multicoloured.

360 6d. Type **184** (75th anniv) . . 15 15

361 6d. Triptych, 1978 (Dimitar Kondovski, 75th anniv) . . 15 15

362 36d. Mona Lisa (La Gioconda) and Leonardo da Vinci (550th anniv) . . 80 80

185 "The Risen Christ"

2002. Easter.

363 **185** 6d. multicoloured 15 15

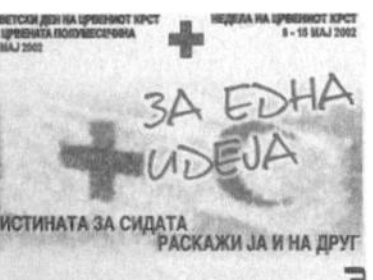

186 Red Cross and Red Crescent Flags

2002. Obligatory Tax. Red Cross Week.

364 **186** 3d. multicoloured 10 10

187 Acrobat, Bicycle, Sea Lion and Ball

2002. Europa. Circus. Multicoloured.
365 6d. Type **187** 15 15
366 36d. Circles, bicycle and ball 80 80

188 Championship Emblem, Ball and Player

2002. World Cup Football Championships, Japan and South Korea.
367 **188** 6d. multicoloured 15 15

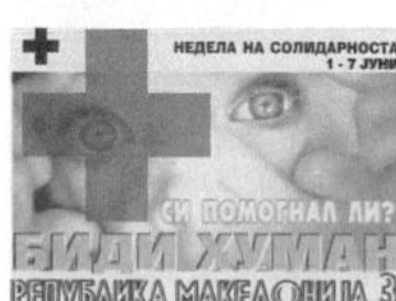

189 Red Cross and Face

2002. Obligatory Tax. Solidarity Week.
368 **189** 3d. multicoloured 10 10

190 Tree containing Shapes

2002. Environment Protection.
369 **190** 6d. multicoloured 15 15

191 1595 Korenic Neonic Coat of Arms

2002. National Arms. Multicoloured.
370 10d. Type **191** 20 20
371 36d. 1620 Coat of Arms . . 80 80

192 House, Krusevo

2002. City Architecture. Multicoloured.
372 36d. Type **192** 80 80
373 50d. House, Bitola . . . . . 1·10 1·10

193 Metodija Andonov-Cento

2002. Birth Centenary of Metodija Andonov-Cento (first Macedonian president).
374 **193** 6d. multicoloured 15 15

194 Nikola Karev

2002. 125th Birth Anniv of Nikola Karev (revolutionary leader).
375 **194** 18d. multicoloured . . . 40 40

195 Grey Partridge (*Perdix perdix*)

2002. Fauna. Multicoloured.
376 6d. Type **195** 15 15
377 12d. Wild Pig (*Sus scrofa*) . . 25 25
378 24d. Chamois (*Rupicapra rupicapra*) 50 50
379 36d. Rock Partridge (*Alectoris graeca*) 80 80

196 Face

2002. Oblgatory Tax. Anti-Tuberculosis Week.
380 **196** 3d. multicoloured 10 10

197 House and People (child's drawing)

2002. Children's Day.
381 **197** 6d. multicoloured 15 15

198 Mary and Jesus (14th-century icon)

2002. Christmas.
382 **198** 9d. multicoloured 20 20

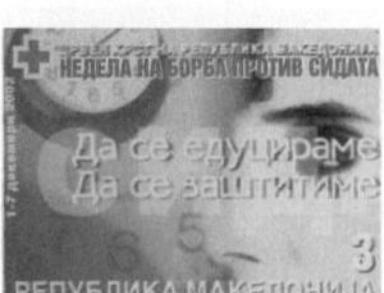

199 Clock, Numbers and Face

2002. Obligatory Tax. Anti-AIDS Week.
383 **199** 3d. multicoloured 10 10

MADAGASCAR Pt. 6

A large island in the Indian Ocean off the east coast of Africa. French Post Offices operated there from 1885.

In 1896 the island was declared a French colony, absorbing Diego-Suarez and Ste. Marie de Madagascar in 1898 and Nossi-Be in 1901.

Madagascar became autonomous as the Malagasy Republic in 1958; it reverted to the name of Madagascar in 1992.

100 centimes = 1 franc.

A. FRENCH POST OFFICES

1889. Stamps of French Colonies "Commerce" type surch with value in figures.
1 J 05 on 10c. black on lilac . . . £525 £150
2 05 on 25c. black on red . . . £525 £140
4 05 on 40c. red on yellow . . . £130 80·00
5 5 on 10c. black on lilac . . . £170 90·00
6 5 on 25c. black on red £170 £100
7 15 on 25c. black on red . . . £120 75·00
3 25 on 40c. red on yellow . . . £475 £130

5

1891. No gum. Imperf.
9 **5** 5c. black on green . . . . . £120 11·50
10 10c. black on blue . . . . . 90·00 25·00
11 15c. blue on blue . . . . . . 95·00 18·00
12 25c. brown on buff . . . . . 21·00 14·50
13 1f. black on yellow £900 £225
14 5f. black and lilac on lilac . . £1800 £900

1895. Stamps of France optd **POSTE FRANCAISE Madagascar**.
15 **10** 5c. green . . . . 6·00 6·50
16 10c. black on lilac . . . . . 45·00 32·00
17 15c. blue . . . . 50·00 12·00
18 25c. black on red . . . . . 60·00 8·25
19 40c. red on yellow . . . . . 70·00 10·00
20 50c. red . . . . £110 12·50
21 75c. brown on orange . . . £100 50·00
22 1f. olive . . . . £120 42·00
23 5f. mauve on lilac . . . . . £150 80·00

1896. Stamps of France surch with value in figures in oval.
29 **10** 5c. on 1c. black on blue . . £4250 £1600
30 15c. on 2c. brown on yellow £1700 £800
31 25c. on 3c. grey £2250 £800
32 25c. on 4c. red on grey . . £4750 £1500
33 25c. on 40c. red on yellow £1000 £600

B. FRENCH COLONY OF MADAGASCAR AND DEPENDENCIES

1896. "Tablet" key-type inscr "MADAGASCAR ET DEPENDANCES".
1 D 1c. black and red on blue 85 25
2 2c. brown and blue on buff 45 1·40
2a 2c. brown & blk on buff . . 6·75 7·00
3 4c. brown and blue on grey 95 1·25
17 5c. green and red . . . . . 3·00 15
6 10c. black and blue on lilac 11·00 1·25
18 10c. red and blue . . . . . 2·75 15
7 15c. blue and red . . . . . 9·00 1·00
19 15c. grey and red . . . . . 4·00 65
8 20c. red and blue on green 6·25 1·90
9 25c. black and red on pink 10·50 25
20 25c. blue and red . . . . . 23·00 35·00
10 30c. brown & bl on drab 8·50 2·25
21 35c. black and red on yellow . . . . 42·00 4·00
11 40c. red and blue on yellow 8·25 1·25
12 50c. red and blue on pink 15·00 1·40
22 50c. brown and red on blue 27·00 27·00
13 75c. violet & red on orge 2·75 3·25
14 1f. green and red . . . . . 17·00 2·50
15 1f. green and blue . . . . 27·00 16·00
16 5f. mauve and blue on lilac 42·00 30·00

1902. "Tablet" key-type stamps as above surch.
27 D 0,01 on 2c. brown and blue on buff . . . . 5·25 3·75
27a 0,01 on 2c. brown and black on buff . . . . . 3·75 9·00
29 0,05 on 30c. brown and blue on drab . . . . . . 3·75 5·25
23 05 on 50c. red and blue on pink . . . . 2·25 2·25
31 0,10 on 50c. red and blue on pink . . . . 3·25 5·00
24 10 on 5f. mauve and blue on lilac . . . . 18·00 13·50
32 0,15 on 75c. violet and red on orange . . . . 1·50 1·50
33 0,15 on 1f. green and red 3·50 3·75
25 15 on 1f. green and red . . 3·50 1·25

1902. Nos. 59 and 61 of Diego-Suarez surch.
34 D 0,05 on 30c. brown and blue on drab £110 £100
36 0,10 on 50c. red and blue on pink £3750 £3750

4 Zebu and Lemur

5 Transport in Madagascar

1903.
38 **4** 1c. purple 50 25
39 2c. brown 50 35
40 4c. brown . . . . 40 1·00
41 5c. green . . . . 6·75 35
42 10c. red . . . . 8·75 35
43 15c. red . . . . 9·00 30
44 20c. orange . . . . 2·75 1·50
45 25c. blue . . . . 30·00 1·40
46 30c. red . . . . 30·00 13·00
47 40c. lilac . . . . 38·00 4·00
48 50c. brown . . . . 60·00 28·00
49 75c. yellow . . . . 48·00 25·00
50 1f. green . . . . 50·00 35·00
51 2f. blue . . . . 55·00 32·00
52 5f. black . . . . 55·00 80·00

1908.
53a **5** 1c. green and violet 10 20
54 2c. green and red 10 20
55 4c. brown and green . . . 10 1·25
56 5c. olive and green . . . . 1·25 20
90 5c. red and black 30 15
57 10c. brown and pink . . . 1·60 20
91 10c. olive and green . . . 30 30
92 10c. purple and brown . . 45 30
58 15c. red and lilac 35 20
93 15c. green and olive . . . 45 2·75
94 15c. red and blue . . . . 65 3·75
59 20c. brown and orange . . 1·00 80
60 25c. black and blue . . . . 5·00 95
95 25c. black and violet . . . 25 25
61 30c. black and brown . . . 4·50 4·25
96 30c. brown and red . . . . 45 1·25
97 30c. purple and green . . . 35 20
98 30c. light green and green 2·25 3·00
62 35c. black and red . . . . 1·75 1·50
63 40c. black and brown . . . 90 70
64 45c. black and green . . . 1·50 2·75
99 45c. red and scarlet . . . . 60 2·75
100 45c. purple and lilac . . . 2·75 3·50
65 50c. black and violet . . . 1·00 1·10
101 50c. black and blue 65 30
102 50c. yellow and black . . . 20 40
103 60c. violet on pink . . . . 45 1·90
104 65c. blue and black . . . . 2·00 3·25
66 75c. black and red 90 40
105 85c. red and green . . . . 1·25 3·50
67 1f. green and brown . . . 30 40
106 1f. blue . . . . 35 1·40
107 1f. green and mauve . . . 6·75 9·25
108 1f.10 green and brown . . 1·60 3·25
68 2f. green and blue . . . . 2·75 1·40
69 5f. brown and violet . . . 16·00 8·25

1912. "Tablet" key-type surch.
70 D 05 on 15c. grey and red . . 25 75
71 05 on 20c. red and blue on green . . . . 80 1·75
72 05 on 30c. brown and blue on drab . . . . 50 3·00
73 10 on 75c. violet and red on orange . . . . 2·50 14·50
81 0.60 on 75c. violet and red on orange . . . . 9·75 11·00
82 1f. on 5f. mauve and blue on lilac . . . . 1·25 3·00

1912. Surch.
74 **4** 05 on 2c. brown . . . . . . 25 2·75
75 05 on 20c. orange . . . . . 55 1·40
76 05 on 30c. red . . . . 45 3·00
77 10 on 40c. lilac . . . . . . 1·10 3·25
78 10 on 50c. brown . . . . . 1·50 4·25
79 10 on 75c. brown . . . . . 3·50 11·50
83 1f. on 5f. black . . . . . . 90·00 90·00

1915. Surch **5c** and red cross.
80 **5** 10c.+5c. brown and pink . . 50 1·60

1921. Surch **1 cent.**
84 **5** 1c. on 15c. red and lilac . . . 20 1·60

1921. Type **5** (some colours changed) surch.
109 **5** 25c. on 15c. red and lilac . . 60 3·00
85 0,25 on 35c. black and red 6·50 7·00
86 0,25 on 40c. black and brown . . . . 4·50 5·75
87 0,25 on 45c. black and green 3·50 4·75
111 25c. on 2f. green and blue 40 1·90
112 25c. on 5f. brown and violet 40 3·00
88 0,30 on 40c. black and brown . . . . 85 2·25
113 50c. on 1f. green and brown 1·25 25
89 0,60 on 75c. black and red 2·75 3·25
114 60 on 75c. violet on pink . . 80 50
115 65c. on 75c. black and red 2·25 3·00
116 85c. on 45c. black and green 1·50 3·25
117 90c. on 75c. pink and red 80 2·25
118 1f.25 on 1f. blue . . . . . 1·00 2·50
119 1f.50 on 1f. lt blue & blue 1·75 20
120 3f. on 5f. violet and green 2·25 2·75
121 10f. on 5f. mauve and red 8·00 7·50
122 20f. on 5f. blue and mauve 12·00 9·25

14 Sakalava Chief

15 Zebus

17 Betsileo Woman

18 General Gallieni

1930.
123 **18** 1c. blue . . . . 15 2·75
124 **15** 1c. green and blue 15 15
125 **14** 2c. brown and red 10 10

177 **18** 3c. blue 15 1·50
126a **14** 4c. mauve and brown 25 25
127 **15** 5c. red and green 15 15
128 – 10c. green and red 10 10
129 **17** 15c. red 10 10
130 **15** 20c. blue and brown 10 15
131 – 25c. brown and lilac 20 10
132 **17** 30c. green 35 20
133 **14** 40c. red and green 55 30
134 **17** 45c. lilac 1·90 2·00
178 **18** 45c. green 1·25 1·75
179 50c. brown 25 10
180 60c. mauve 15 1·75
136 **15** 65c. mauve and brown 2·75 2·25
181 **18** 70c. red 1·50 2·50
137 **17** 75c. brown 2·25 20
138 **15** 90c. red 2·75 1·10
182 **18** 90c. brown 40 15
139 – 1f. blue and brown 3·25 2·50
140 – 1f. red and scarlet 1·25 1·25
140a – 1f.25 brown and blue 2·75 1·50
183 **18** 1f.40 orange 2·75 2·75
141 **14** 1f.50 ultramarine and blue 10·00 65
142 1f.50 red and brown 80 95
278 1f.50 brown and red 10 1·25
184 **18** 1f.60 violet 2·25 2·75
143 **14** 1f.75 red and brown 5·50 55
185 **18** 2f. red 40 20
186a 3f. green 60 1·50
146 **14** 5f. brown and mauve 8·75 2·75
147 **18** 10f. orange 1·90 1·40
148 **14** 20f. blue and brown 6·50 4·50
DESIGN—VERT: 10c., 25c., 1f., 1f.25, Hova girl.

1931. "Colonial Exhibition" key-types inscr "MADAGASCAR".
149 E 40c. black and green 2·50 3·00
150 F 50c. black and mauve 3·25 3·00
151 G 90c. black and red 2·75 3·00
152 H 1f.50 black and blue 3·75 3·00

19 Bloch 120 over Madagascar

20 J. Laborde and Tananarivo Palace

1935. Air.
153 **19** 50c. red and green 1·75 1·90
154 90c. red and green 30 2·75
155 1f.25 red and lake 1·50 2·25
156 1f.50 red and blue 1·50 2·25
157 1f.60 red and blue 55 2·25
158 1f.75 red and orange 9·00 5·75
159 2f. red and blue 1·60 2·00
160 3f. red and orange 70 2·25
161 3f.65 red and black 1·40 1·00
162 3f.90 red and green 40 2·50
163 4f. red and carmine 29·00 3·25
164 4f.50 red and black 16·00 60
165 5f.50 red and green 1·10 2·75
166 6f. red and mauve 85 2·50
167 6f.90 red and purple 60 2·50
168 8f. red and mauve 2·75 3·25
169 8f.50 red and green 3·00 3·25
170 9f. red and green 1·25 2·75
171 12f. red and brown 40 2·25
172 12f.50 red and violet 3·25 3·25
173 15f. red and orange 40 2·25
174 16f. red and green 3·00 4·00
175 20f. red and brown 4·00 3·75
176 50f. red and blue 5·50 7·00

1937. International Exhibition, Paris. As T **16** of Mauritania.
187 20c. violet 80 3·25
188 30c. green 1·75 3·25
189 40c. red 40 1·50
190 50c. brown and agate 35 75
191 90c. red 35 1·90
192 1f.50 blue 50 2·00

1938. 60th Death Anniv of Jean Laborde (explorer).
193 **20** 35c. green 75 40
194 55c. violet 55 65
195 65c. red 1·00 50
196 80c. purple 1·00 50
197 1f. red 65 50
198 1f.25 red 2·00 2·75
199 1f.75 blue 45 90
200 2f.15 brown 2·00 3·25
201 2f.25 blue 1·75 3·25
202 2f.50 brown 30 30
203 10f. green 40 80

1938. Int Anti-cancer Fund. As T **22** of Mauritania.
204 1f.75+50c. blue 4·50 13·50

1939. New York World's Fair. As T **28** of Mauritania.
205 1f.25 red 2·25 1·75
206 2f.25 blue 2·50 2·50

1939. 150th Anniv of French Revolution. As T **29** of Mauritania.
207 45c.+25c. green and black (postage) 5·75 13·50
208 70c.+30c. brown and black 7·25 13·50
209 90c.+35c. orange and black 5·25 13·50
210 1f.25+1f. red and black 5·75 13·50
211 2f.25+2f. blue and black 5·75 13·50
212 4f.50+4f. black and orange (air) 9·50 22·00

1942. Surch **50** and bars.
213 **15** 50 on 65c. mauve & brown 3·25 50

1942. Free French Administration. Optd **FRANCE LIBRE** or surch also.
214 **14** 2c. brown and red (postage) 2·75 3·25
215 **18** 3c. blue £120 £120
216 **15** 0,05 on 1c. green and blue 1·75 1·40
217 **20** 0,10 on 55c. violet 50 3·50
218 **17** 15c. red 15·00 14·50
219 **20** 0,30 on 65c. red 40 3·00
220 **15** 0f.50 on 0,05 on 1c. green and blue 2·25 3·25
221 50 on 65c. mauve & brown 1·25 10
222 **18** 50 on 90c. brown 2·00 10
223 **15** 65c. mauve and brown 3·25 3·25
224 **18** 70c. red 2·25 3·00
225 **20** 80c. purple 4·00 3·50
226 – 1,00 on 1f.25 brown and blue (No. 140a) 3·75 3·75
227 **20** 1,00 on 1f.25 red 9·75 8·50
228 **18** 1f.40 orange 2·75 2·75
229 **5** 1f.50 on 1f. blue 3·25 3·25
230 **14** 1f.50 ultramarine and blue 2·50 3·25
231 1f.50 red and brown 3·50 3·25
232 **18** 1,50 on 1f.60 violet 2·50 2·75
233 **14** 1,50 on 1f.75 red & brown 2·75 1·60
234 **20** 1,50 on 1f.75 blue 2·25 2·50
235 **18** 1f.60 violet 2·75 2·75
236 **20** 2,00 on 2f.15 brown 1·75 85
237 2f.25 blue 2·75 3·00
238 – 2f.25 blue (No. 206) 2·75 2·75
239 **20** 2f.50 brown 5·00 4·75
240 **5** 10f. on 5f. mauve and red 13·50 11·00
241 **20** 10f. green 5·25 5·00
242 **5** 20f. on 5f. blue and mauve 17·00 16·00
243 **14** 20f. blue and brown £700 £800
244 **19** 1,00 on 1f.25 red and lake (air) 7·00 7·00
245 1f.50 red and blue 8·25 9·25
246 1f.75 red and orange 90·00 £100
247 3,00 on 3f.65 red and black 2·75 15
248 8f. red and purple 3·25 3·25
249 8,00 on 8f.50 red and green 2·75 70
250 12f. red and brown 4·25 4·00
251 12f.50 red and violet 3·25 3·25
252 16f. red and green 7·25 7·25
253 50f. red and blue 6·00 6·00

24 Traveller's Tree

29 Gen. Gallieni

25a Legionaries by Lake Chad

1943. Free French Issue.
254 **24** 5c. brown 10 2·75
255 10c. mauve 10 10
256 25c. green 10 2·00
257 30c. orange 10 10
258 40c. blue 55 20
259 80c. purple 60 20
260 1f. blue 50 15
261 1f.50 red 60 15
262 2f. yellow 75 15
263 2f.50 blue 60 10
264 4f. blue and red 1·25 40
265 5f. green and black 60 10
266 10f. red and blue 85 15
267 20f. violet and brown 1·25 20

1943. Free French Administration. Air. As T **19a** of Oceanic Settlements, but inscr "MADAGASCAR".
268 1f. orange 30 1·50
269 1f.50 red 30 1·25
270 5f. purple 25 35
271 10f. black 1·00 1·60
272 25f. blue 90 2·50
273 50f. green 90 80
274 100f. red 1·10 35

1944. Mutual Aid and Red Cross Funds. As T **19b** of Oceanic Settlements.
275 5f.+20f. green 75 3·00

1944. Surch **1f.50.**
276 **24** 1f.50 on 5c. brown 20 60
277 1f.50 on 10c. mauve 70 3·00

1945. Eboue. As T **20a** of Oceanic Settlements.
279 2f. black 15 25
280 25f. green 70 3·50

1946. Air. Victory. As T **20b** of Oceanic Settlements.
281 8f. red 20 20

1945. Surch with new value.
282 **24** 50c. on 5c. brown 30 40
283 60c. on 5c. brown 40 2·50
284 70c. on 5c. brown 40 2·50
285 1f.20 on 5c. brown 25 2·25
286 2f.40 on 25c. green 45 60
287 3f. on 25c. green 45 30
288 4f.50 on 25c. green 1·50 2·00
289 15f. on 2f.50 blue 50 85

1946. Air. From Chad to the Rhine.
290 **25a** 5f. blue 55 3·00
291 – 10f. red 80 2·50
292 – 15f. green 1·00 3·25
293 – 20f. brown 90 3·00
294 – 25f. violet 85 3·25
295 – 50f. red 60 3·00
DESIGNS: 10f. Battle of Koufra; 15f. Tank Battle, Mareth; 20f. Normandy Landings; 25f. Liberation of Paris; 50f. Liberation of Strasbourg.

1946.
296 – 10c. green (postage) 10 60
297 – 30c. orange 10 20
298 – 40c. olive 10 40
299 – 50c. purple 10 10
300 – 60c. blue 10 1·60
301 – 80c. green 10 1·60
302 – 1f. sepia 10 10
303 – 1f.20 green 20 1·40
304 **29** 1f.50 red 10 10
305 – 2f. black 10 10
306 – 3f. purple 25 10
307 – 3f.60 red 90 2·25
308 – 4f. blue 35 10
309 – 5f. orange 40 15
310 – 6f. blue 15 10
311 – 10f. lake 45 20
312 – 15f. brown 50 10
313 – 20f. blue 30 20
314 – 25f. brown 55 25
315 – 50f. blue and red (air) 1·10 1·25
316 – 100f. brown and red 85 45
317 – 200f. brown and green 2·25 2·50
DESIGNS—As T **29**. VERT: 10 to 50c. Native with spear; 6, 10f. Gen. Duchesne; 15, 20, 25f. Lt.-Col. Joffre. HORIZ: 60, 80c. Zebus; 1f., 1f.20, Sakalava man and woman; 3f.60, 4, 5f. Betsimisaraka mother and child. 49×28 mm: 50f. Aerial view of Port of Tamatave. 28×51 mm: 100f. Allegory of flight. 51×28 mm: Douglas DC-2 airplane and map of Madagascar.

36 Gen. Gallieni and View

1946. 50th Anniv of French Protectorate.
318 **36** 10f.+5f. purple 20 3·00

1948. Air. Discovery of Adelie Land, Antarctic. No. 316 optd **TERRE ADELIE DUMONT D'URVILLE 1840.**
319 100f. brown and red 26·00 55·00

1949. Air. 75th Anniv of U.P.U. As T **38** of New Caledonia.
320 25f. multicoloured 1·40 1·75

1950. Colonial Welfare Fund. As T **39** of New Caledonia.
321 10f.+2f. purple and green 3·50 9·25

38 Cacti and Succulents

39 Long-tailed Ground Roller

40 Woman and Forest Road

1952.
322 **38** 7f.50 green & blue (postage) 35 20
323 **39** 8f. lake 90 40
324 15f. blue and green 2·40 40
325 – 50f. green and blue (air) 2·50 30
326 – 100f. black, brown and blue 6·00 1·40
327 – 200f. brown and green 20·00 8·00
328 **40** 500f. brown, sepia & green 30·00 7·50
DESIGNS—As Type **40**: 50f. Palm trees; 100f. Antsirabe Viaduct; 200f. Ring-tailed lemurs.

1952. Military Medal Centenary As T **40** of New Caledonia.
329 15f. turquoise, yellow & green 1·10 1·50

1954. Air. 10th Anniv of Liberation. As T **42** of New Caledonia.
330 15f. purple and violet 2·25 1·25

41 Marshal Lyautey

1954. Birth Centenary of Marshal Lyautey.
331 **41** 10f. indigo, blue & ultram 45 10
332 40f. lake, grey and black 55 10

42 Gallieni School

43 Cassava

1956. Economic and Social Development Fund.
333 – 3f. brown and grey 25 10
334 **42** 5f. brown and chestnut 25 10
335 – 10f. blue and grey 30 10
336 – 15f. green and turquoise 40 10
DESIGNS: 3f. Tamatave and tractor; 10f. Dredging canal; 15f. Irrigation.

1956. Coffee. As T **44** of New Caledonia.
337 20f. sepia and brown 20 10

1957. Plants.
338 **43** 2f. green, brown and blue 25 10
339 – 4f. red, brown and green 15 10
340 – 12f. green, brown and violet 70 10
DESIGNS: 4f. Cloves; 12f. Vanilla.

Issues of 1958–92. For issues between these dates, see under MALAGASY REPUBLIC.

362 Children with Mascot

363 Environmental Projects

1992. School Sports Festival (1990).
910 **362** 140f. multicoloured 35 10

1992. Air. World Environment Day.
911 **363** 140f. multicoloured 10 10

364 Post Box and Globe **365** Basenji

1992. Air. World Post Day.

912 **364** 500f. multicoloured . . . 75 25

1992. Domestic Animals. Multicoloured.

No.	Description	Unused	Used
913	140f. Type **365**	10	10
914	500f. Anglo-Arab horse	90	25
915	640f. Tortoiseshell cat and kitten	1·10	30
916	1025f. Siamese and colourpoint (cats)	1·60	50
917	1140f. Holstein horse	2·25	60
918	5000f. German shepherd dogs	6·50	75

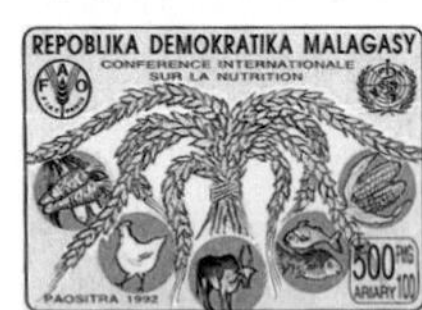

366 Foodstuffs

1992. International Nutrition Conference, Rome.

920 **366** 500f. multicoloured . . . 1·10 25

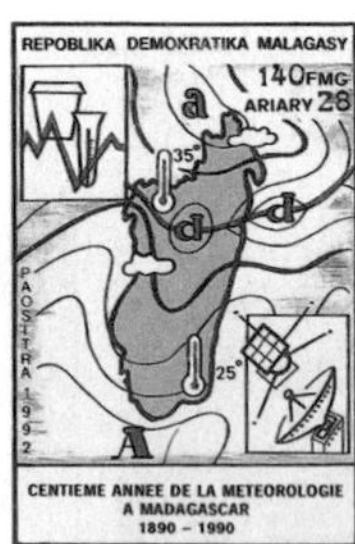

367 Weather Map

1992. Centenary of Meteorological Service.

921 **367** 140f. multicoloured . . . 35 10

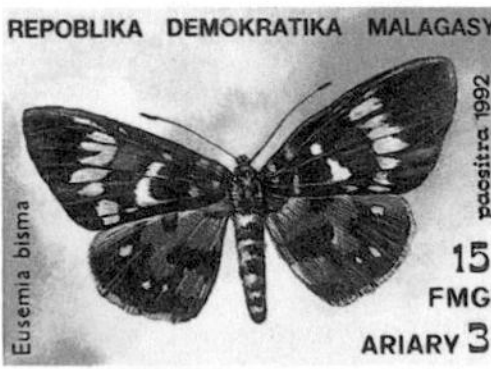

368 "Eusemia bisma"

1992. Butterflies and Moths. Multicoloured.

No.	Description	Unused	Used
922	15f. Type **368**	10	10
923	35f. Tailed comet moth (vert)	10	10
924	65f. "Alcides aurora"	10	10
925	140f. "Agarista agricola"	35	10
926	600f. "Trogonoptera croesus"	1·40	30
927	850f. "Trogonodtera priamus"	1·75	45
928	1300f. "Pereute leucodrosime"	2·25	70

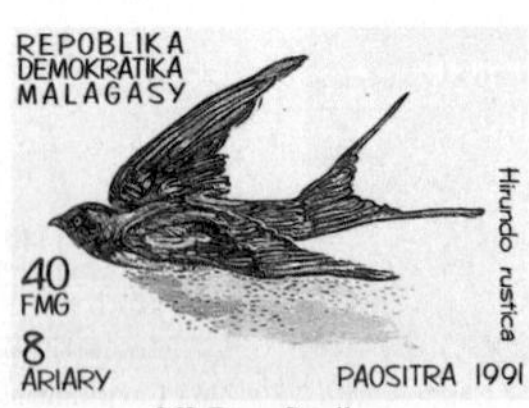

369 Barn Swallow

1992. Birds. Multicoloured.

No.	Description	Unused	Used
930	40f. Type **369**	10	10
931	55f. Pied harrier (vert)	10	10
932	60f. European cuckoo (vert)	10	10
933	140f. Sacred ibis	10	10
934	210f. Purple swamphen	45	10
935	500f. Common roller	1·10	25
936	2000f. Golden oriole	4·00	1·10

370 Gymnastics

1992. Olympic Games, Barcelona. Multicoloured.

No.	Description	Unused	Used
938	65f. Type **370**	10	10
939	70f. High jumping	10	10
940	120f. Archery	10	10
941	140f. Cycling	35	10
942	675f. Weightlifting	1·10	30
943	720f. Boxing	1·40	35
944	1200f. Two-man kayak	1·75	60

371 Pusher-tug, Pangalanes Canal

1993.

946 **371** 140f. multicoloured . . . 35 10

372 BMW **373** Hyacinth Macaw

1993. Motor Cars. Multicoloured.

No.	Description	Unused	Used
947	20f. Type **372**	10	10
948	40f. Toyota "Carina"	10	10
949	60f. Cadillac	10	10
950	65f. Volvo	10	10
951	140f. Mercedes-Benz	10	10
952	640f. Ford "Sierra"	1·00	30
953	3000f. Honda "Concerto"	4·50	90

1993. Parrot Family. Multicoloured.

No.	Description	Unused	Used
955	50f. Type **373**	10	10
956	60f. Cockatiel	10	10
957	140f. Budgerigar	10	10
958	500f. Jandaya conure	60	25
959	675f. Budgerigar (different)	1·10	35
960	800f. Red-fronted parakeet	1·40	45
961	1750f. Kea	2·75	65

375 Albert Einstein (physics, 1921) and Niels Bohr (physics, 1922)

1993. Nobel Prize Winners. Multicoloured.

No.	Description	Unused	Used
964	500f. Type **375**	60	25
965	500f. Wolfgang Pauli (physics, 1945) and Max Born (physics, 1954)	60	25
966	500f. Joseph Thomson (physics, 1906) and Johannes Stark (physics, 1919)	60	25
967	500f. Otto Hahn (physics, 1944) and Hideki Yukawa (physics, 1949)	60	25
968	500f. Owen Richardson (physics, 1928) and William Shockley (physics, 1956)	60	25
969	500f. Albert Michelson (physics, 1907) and Charles Townes (physics, 1964)	60	25
970	500f. Wilhelm Wien (physics, 1911) and Lev Landau (physics, 1962)	60	25
971	500f. Carl Braun (physics, 1909) and Sir Edward Appleton (physics, 1947)	60	25
972	500f. Percy Bridgman (physics, 1946) and Nikolai Semyonov (physics, 1956)	60	25
973	500f. Sir William Ramsay (chemistry, 1904) and Glenn Seaborg (chemistry, 1951)	60	25
974	500f. Otto Wallach (chemistry, 1910) and Hermann Staudinger (chemistry, 1953)	60	25
975	500f. Richard Synge (chemistry, 1952) and Axel Theorell (chemistry, 1955)	60	25
976	500f. Thomas Morgan (medicine, 1933) and Hermann Muller (medicine, 1946)	60	25
977	500f. Allvar Gullstrand (medicine, 1911) and Willem Einthoven (medicine, 1924)	60	25
978	500f. Sir Charles Sherrington (medicine, 1932) and Otto Loewi (medicine, 1936)	60	25
979	500f. Jules Bordet (medicine, 1936) and Sir Alexander Fleming (medicine, 1945)	60	25

376 1956 Bugatti

1993. Racing Cars and Railway Locomotives. Multicoloured.

No.	Description	Unused	Used
980	20f. Type **376**	10	10
981	20f. 1968 Ferrari	10	10
982	20f. 1948 Class C62 steam locomotive, 1948, Japan	10	10
983	20f. Electric train, 1975, Russia	10	10
984	140f. 1962 Lotus Mk 25	10	10
985	140f. 1970 Matra	10	10
986	140f. Diesel locomotive, 1954, Norway	10	10
987	140f. Class 26 steam locomotive, 1982, South Africa	10	10
988	1250f. 1963 Porsche	90	65
989	1250f. 1980 Ligier JS 11	90	65
990	1250f. Metroliner electric train, 1967, U.S.A.	90	65
991	1250f. Diesel train, 1982, Canada	90	65
992	3000f. 1967 Honda	2·10	1·50
993	3000f. 1992 Benetton B 192	2·10	1·50
994	3000f. Union Pacific Railroad diesel-electric locomotive, 1969, U.S.A.	2·10	2·10
995	3000f. TGV Atlantique express train, 1990, France	2·10	2·10

377 Pharaonic Ship

1993. Ships. Multicoloured.

No.	Description	Unused	Used
996	5f. Type **377**	10	10
997	5f. Mediterranean carrack	10	10
998	5f. "Great Western" (sail paddle-steamer), 1837	10	10
999	5f. "Mississippi" (paddle-steamer), 1850	10	10
1000	15f. Phoenician bireme	10	10
1001	15f. Viking ship	10	10
1002	15f. "Clermont" (first commercial paddle-steamer), 1806	10	10
1003	15f. "Pourquoi Pas?" (Charcot's ship), 1936	10	10
1004	140f. "Santa Maria" (Columbus's ship), 1492	10	10
1005	140f. H.M.S. "Victory" (ship of the line), 1765	10	10
1006	140f. Motor yacht	10	10
1007	140f. "Bremen" (liner), 1950	10	10
1008	10000f. "Sovereign of the Seas" (galleon), 1637	9·25	80
1009	10000f. "Cutty Sark" (clipper)	9·25	80
1010	10000f. "Savannah" (nuclear-powered freighter)	9·25	80
1011	10000f. "Condor" (hydrofoil)	9·25	80

No. 999 is wrongly inscribed "Missisipi".

378 Johannes Gutenberg and Printing Press

1993. Inventors. Multicoloured.

No.	Description	Unused	Used
1012	500f. Type **378**	60	25
1013	500f. Sir Isaac Newton and telescope	60	25
1014	500f. John Dalton and atomic theory	60	25
1015	500f. Louis Jacques Daguerre and camera	60	25
1016	500f. Michael Faraday and electric motor	60	25
1017	500f. Wright brothers and "Flyer"	60	25
1018	500f. Alexander Bell and telephone	60	25
1019	500f. Thomas Edison and telegraph	60	25
1020	500f. Karl Benz and motor vehicle	60	25
1021	500f. Sir Charles Parsons and "Turbina"	60	25
1022	500f. Rudolf Diesel and diesel locomotive	60	35
1023	500f. Guglielmo Marconi and early radio	60	25
1024	500f. Lumiere brothers and cine-camera	60	35
1025	500f. Herman Oberth and space rocket	60	25
1026	500f. John Mauchly, J. Prosper Eckert and computer	60	25
1027	500f. Arthur Shawlow, compact disc and laser	60	25

379 Leonardo da Vinci and "Virgin of the Rocks"

1993. Painters. Multicoloured.

No.	Description	Unused	Used
1028	50f. Type **379**	10	10
1029	50f. Titian and "Sacred and Profane Love"	10	10
1030	50f. Rembrandt and "Jeremiah crying"	10	10
1031	50f. J. M. W. Turner and "Ulysses"	10	10
1032	640f. Michelangelo and the Doni Tondo	70	30
1033	640f. Peter Paul Rubens and "Self-portrait"	70	30
1034	640f. Francisco Goya and "Don Manuel Osorio de Zuniga"	70	30
1035	640f. Eugene Delacroix and "Christ on Lake Gennesaret"	70	30
1036	1000f. Claude Monet and "Poppyfield"	95	50
1037	1000f. Paul Gauguin and "Two Tahitians"	95	50
1038	1000f. Henri Marie de Toulouse-Lautrec and "Woman with a Black Boa"	95	50
1039	1000f. Salvador Dali and "St. James of Compostela"	95	50
1040	2500f. Pierre Auguste Renoir and "Child carrying Flowers"	2·75	90
1041	2500f. Vincent Van Gogh and "Dr. Paul Gachet"	2·75	90
1042	2500f. Pablo Picasso and "Crying Woman"	2·75	90
1043	2500f. Andy Warhol and "Portrait of Elvis"	2·75	90

380 Sunset Moth ("Chrysiridia madagascariensis")

1993. Butterflies, Moths and Birds. Multicoloured.

No.	Description	Unused	Used
1044	45f. Type **380**	10	10
1045	45f. African monarch ("Hypolimnas misippus")	10	10
1046	45f. Southern crested Madagascar coucal ("Coua verreauxi")	10	10
1047	45f. African marsh owl ("Asio helvola")	10	10
1048	60f. "Charaxes antamboulou"	10	10
1049	60f. "Papilio antenor"	10	10
1050	60f. Crested Madagascar coucal ("Coua cristata")	10	10
1051	60f. Helmet bird ("Euryceros prevostii")	10	10
1052	140f. "Hypolimnas dexithea"	10	10
1053	140f. "Charaxes andronodorus"	10	10
1054	140f. Giant Madagascar coucal ("Couca gigas")	10	10
1055	140f. Madagascar red fody ("Foudia madagascarensis")	10	10
1056	3000f. "Euxanthe madagascarensis"	3·25	45
1057	3000f. "Papilio grosesmithi"	3·25	45
1058	3000f. Sicklebill ("Falculea palliata")	3·25	45
1059	3000f. Madagascar serpent eagle ("Eutriorchis astur")	3·25	45

Nos. 1044/59 were issued together, se-tenant, the butterfly and bird designs respectively forming composite designs.

381 Henri Dunant and Volunteers unloading Red Cross Lorry

1993. Anniversaries and Events. Multicoloured.
1060 500f. Type **381** (award of first Nobel Peace Prize, 1901) . . . 35 25
1061 640f. Charles de Gaulle and battlefield (50th anniv of Battle of Bir-Hakeim (1992)) . . . 45 30
1062 1025f. Crowd at Brandenburg Gate (bicentenary (1991) and fourth anniv of breach of Berlin Wall) . . . 1·10 55
1063 1500f. Doctors giving health instruction to women (Rotary International and Lions International) . . . 1·60 55
1064 3000f. Konrad Adenauer (German chancellor 1949–63, 24th death anniv (1991)) . . . 3·25 60
1065 3500f. "LZ-4" (airship), 1908, and Count Ferdinand von Zeppelin (75th death anniv (1992)) . . . 4·00 60

382 Guides and Anniversary Emblem
383 Player, Trophy and Ficklin Home, Macon

1993. Air. 50th Anniv of Madagascan Girl Guides.
1067 **382** 140f. multicoloured . . . 10 10

1993. World Cup Football Championship, United States (1992). Multicoloured.
1068 140f. Type **383** . . . 10 10
1069 640f. Player, trophy and Herndon Home, Atlanta . . . 65 35
1070 1025f. Player, trophy and Cultural Centre, Augusta . . . 1·40 55
1071 5000f. Player, trophy and Old Governor's Mansion, Milledgeville . . . 6·00 1·00

1993. Various stamps optd with emblem and inscription. (a) Germany, World Cup Football Champion, 1990. Nos. 778/81 optd **VAINQUEUR: ALLEMAGNE**.
1073 **328** 350f. multicoloured . . . 25 15
1074 – 1000f. multicoloured . . . 90 50
1075 – 1500f. multicoloured . . . 1·50 80
1076 – 2500f. multicoloured . . . 2·75 1·00

(b) Gold Medallists at Winter Olympic Games, Albertville (1992). Nos. 812/15 optd with Olympic rings, **"MEDAILLE D'OR"** and further inscr as below.
1077 350f. **BOB A QUATRE (AUT) INGO APPELT HARALD WINKLER GERHARD HAIDACHER THOMAS SCROLL** . . . 25 15
1078 1000f. **1000 M. - OLAF ZINKE (GER)** . . . 90 50
1079 1500f. **50 KM LIBRE BJOERN DAEHLIE (NOR)** . . . 1·50 80
1080 2500f. **SUPER G MESSIEURS KJETIL-ANDRE AAMODT (NOR)** . . . 2·75 1·25

(c) Anniversaries. Nos. 1060, 675 and 707 optd as listed below.
1082 500f. Red Cross and **130e ANNIVERSAIRE DE LA CREATION DE LA CROIX-ROUGE 1863–1993** . . . 2·25 1·10
1083 550f. Lions emblem and **75eme ANNIVERSAIRE LIONS** . . . 2·25 1·10
1084 1500f. Guitar and **THE ELVIS'S GUITAR 15TH ANNIVERSARY OF HIS DEATH 1977–1992** . . . 1·75 80
1085 1500f. Guitar and **GUITARE ELVIS 15eme ANNIVERSAIRE DE SA MORT 1977–1992** . . . 1·75 80

(d) 50th Death Anniv of Robert Baden-Powell (founder of Boy Scouts). Optd **50eme ANNIVERSAIRE DE LA MORT DE BADEN POWEL** and emblem. (i) On Nos. 870/5 with scout badge in wreath.
1086 **354** 140f. multicoloured . . . 10 10
1087 – 500f. multicoloured . . . 35 25
1088 – 640f. multicoloured . . . 45 30
1089 – 1025f. multicoloured . . . 1·10 30
1090 – 1140f. multicoloured . . . 1·10 35
1091 – 3500f. multicoloured . . . 3·25 1·10

(ii) On No. 676 with profile of Baden-Powell.
1093 1500f. multicoloured . . . 1·75 80

(e) Bicentenary of French Republic. Nos. 761/5 optd **Republique Francaise** and emblem within oval and **BICENTENAIRE DE L'AN I DE LA REPUBLIQUE FRANCAISE**.
1094 250f. multicoloured . . . 20 15
1095 350f. multicoloured . . . 25 15
1096 1000f. multicoloured . . . 1·10 50
1097 1500f. multicoloured . . . 1·75 50
1098 2500f. multicoloured . . . 2·75 90

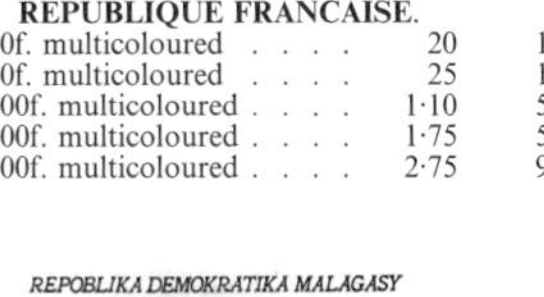

385 Great Green Turban

1993. Molluscs. Multicoloured.
1100 40f. Type **385** . . . 10 10
1101 60f. Episcopal mitre . . . 10 10
1102 65f. Common paper nautilis . . . 10 10
1103 140f. Textile cone . . . 10 10
1104 500f. European sea hare . . . 90 25
1105 675f. "Harpa amouretta" . . . 1·10 35
1106 2500f. Tiger cowrie . . . 3·50 70

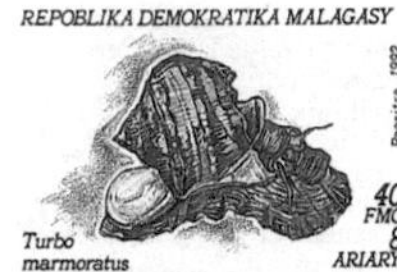

386 Tiger Shark

1993. Sharks. Multicoloured.
1108 10f. Type **386** . . . 10 10
1109 45f. Japanese sawshark . . . 10 10
1110 140f. Whale shark . . . 15 10
1111 270f. Smooth hammerhead . . . 30 20
1112 600f. Oceanic white-tipped shark . . . 65 35
1113 1200f. Zebra shark . . . 1·25 80
1114 1500f. Goblin shark . . . 1·90 1·10

387 Map of Africa and Industry

1993. Air. African Industrialization Day.
1116 **387** 500f. red, yellow and blue . . . 80 50

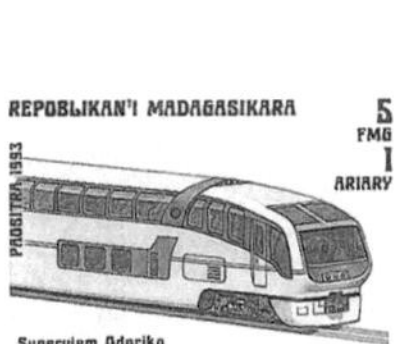

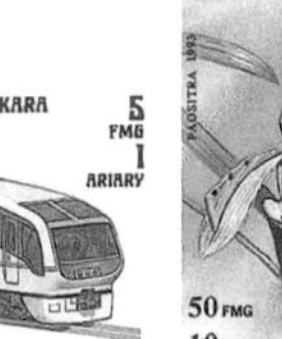

388 "Superviem Odoriko" Express Train
389 "Paphiopedilum siamense"

1993. Locomotives. Multicoloured.
1117 5f. Type **388** . . . 10 10
1118 15f. Morrison Knudsen diesel locomotive No. 801 . . . 10 10
1119 140f. ER-200 diesel train, Russia . . . 10 10
1120 265f. General Motors GP60 diesel-electric locomotive No. EKD-5, U.S.A. . . . 20 15
1121 300f. New Jersey Transit diesel locomotive, U.S.A. . . . 20 15
1122 575f. ICE high speed train, Germany . . . 40 30
1123 2500f. X2000 high speed train, Sweden . . . 1·75 1·25

1993. Orchids. Multicoloured.
1125 50f. Type **389** (wrongly inscr "Paphiopedilum") . . . 10 10
1126 65f. "Cypripedium calceolus" . . . 10 10
1127 70f. "Ophrys oestrifera" . . . 10 10
1128 140f. "Cephalanthera rubra" . . . 10 10
1129 300f. "Cypripedium macranthon" . . . 20 15
1130 640f. "Calanthe vestita" . . . 80 30
1131 2500f. "Cypripedium guttatum" . . . 3·25 90

390 "Necrophorus tomentosus"
392 Fork and Spoon, Sakalava

391 Lufthansa Airliner, Germany

1994. Beetles. Multicoloured.
1133 20f. Type **390** . . . 10 10
1134 60f. "Dynastes tityus" . . . 10 10
1135 140f. "Megaloxanta bicolor" . . . 10 10
1136 605f. Searcher . . . 40 10
1137 720f. "Chrysochroa mirabilis" . . . 50 15
1138 1000f. "Crioceris asparaqi" . . . 70 25
1139 1500f. Rose chafer . . . 1·10 35

1994. Aircraft. Multicoloured.
1141 10f. Type **391** . . . 10 10
1142 10f. British Aerospace/Aerospatiale Concorde supersonic jetliner of Air France . . . 10 10
1143 10f. Air Canada airliner . . . 10 10
1144 10f. ANA airliner, Japan . . . 10 10
1145 60f. Boeing 747 jetliner of British Airways . . . 10 10
1146 60f. Dornier Do-X flying boat, Germany . . . 10 10
1147 60f. Shinmeiwa flying boat, Japan . . . 10 10
1148 60f. Royal Jordanian airliner . . . 10 10
1149 640f. Alitalia airliner . . . 45 15
1150 640f. French-European Development Project Hydro 2000 flying boat . . . 45 15
1151 640f. Boeing 314 flying boat . . . 45 15
1152 640f. Air Madagascar airliner . . . 45 15
1153 5000f. Emirates Airlines airliner, United Arab Emirates . . . 3·50 1·10
1154 5000f. Scandinavian Airways airliner . . . 3·50 1·10
1155 5000f. KLM airliner, Netherlands . . . 3·50 1·10
1156 5000f. Air Caledonie airliner, New Caledonia . . . 3·50 1·10

Nos. 1141/56 were issued together, se-tenant, Nos. 1146/7 and 1150/1 forming a composite design.

1994. Traditional Crafts. Multicoloured.
1157 30f. Silver jewellery, Mahafaly . . . 10 10
1158 60f. Type **392** . . . 10 10
1159 140f. Silver jewellery, Antandroy . . . 10 10
1160 430f. Silver jewellery on table, Sakalava . . . 30 10
1161 580f. Frames of decorated paper, Ambalavao . . . 40 10
1162 1250f. Silver jewellery, Sakalava . . . 90 30
1163 1500f. Marquetry table, Ambositra . . . 1·10 35

393 "Chicoreus torrefactus" (shell)

1994. Marine Life. Multicoloured.
1165 15f. Type **393** . . . 10 10
1166 15f. "Fasciolaria filamentosa" (shell) . . . 10 10
1167 15f. Regal angelfish ("Pigopytes diacanthus") . . . 10 10
1168 15f. Coelacanth ("Latimeria chalumnae") . . . 10 10
1169 30f. "Stellaria solaris" (shell) . . . 10 10
1170 30f. Ventral harp ("Harpa ventricosa") . . . 10 10
1171 30f. Blue-tailed boxfish ("Ostracion cyanurus") . . . 10 10
1172 30f. Clown wrasse ("Coris gaimardi") . . . 10 10
1173 1250f. Lobster ("Panulirus sp.") . . . 90 30
1174 1250f. "Stenopus hispidus" (crustacean) . . . 90 30
1175 1250f. Undulate triggerfish ("Balistapus undulatus") . . . 90 30
1176 1250f. Forceps butterflyfish ("Forcipiger longirostris") . . . 90 30
1177 1500f. Hermit crab ("Pagure") . . . 1·10 35
1178 1500f. Hermit crab ("Bernard l'Hermite") . . . 1·10 35
1179 1500f. Diadem squirrelfish ("Adioryx diadema") . . . 1·10 35
1180 1500f. Lunulate lionfish ("Pterois lunulata") . . . 1·10 35

Nos. 1165/80 were issued together, se-tenant, the backgrounds forming a composite design.

394 Arms
395 Troops landing on Beach

1994. Air. Junior Economic Chamber Zone A (Africa, Middle East and Indian Ocean) Conference, Antananarivo. Multicoloured.
1181 140f. Type **394** . . . 10 10
1182 500f. Arms as in Type **394** but with inscriptions differently arranged (vert) . . . 70 20

1994. 50th Anniv of Allied Landings at Normandy. Multicoloured.
1183 1500f. Type **395** . . . 1·10 35
1184 3000f. German troops defending ridge and allied troops (as T **397**) . . . 2·25 75
1185 3000f. Airplanes over battle scene, trooper with U.S. flag and German officer (as T **397**) . . . 2·25 75

Nos. 1183/5 were issued together, se-tenant, forming a composite design.

396 Emperor Angelfish

1994. Aquarium Fishes. Multicoloured.
1186 10f. Type **396** . . . 10 10
1187 30f. Siamese fighting fish . . . 10 10
1188 45f. Pearl gourami . . . 10 10
1189 95f. Cuckoo-wrasse . . . 10 10
1190 140f. Blotched upsidedown catfish ("Synodontis nigreventris") . . . 10 10
1191 140f. Jack Dempsey ("Cichlasoma biocellatum") . . . 10 10
1192 3500f. Mummichog . . . 2·50 80

397 Notre Dame Cathedral, Armed Resistance Fighters and Rejoicing Crowd

1994. 50th Anniv of Liberation of Paris by Allied Forces. Multicoloured.
1194 1500f. Crowd and Arc de Triomphe (as T **395**) . . . 55 15
1195 3000f. Type **397** . . . 1·10 35
1196 3000f. Eiffel Tower and tank convoy . . . 1·10 35

Nos. 1194/6 were issued together, se-tenant, forming a composite design.

398 Emblem and "75"

1994. 75th Anniv of I.L.O.
1197 **398** 140f. multicoloured . . . 10 10

399 Biathlon

1994. Winter Olympic Games, Lillehammer, Norway. Multicoloured. (a) Without overprints.
1198 140f. Type **399** 10 10
1199 1250f. Ice hockey 45 15
1200 2000f. Figure skating . . . 75 25
1201 2500f. Skiing (downhill) . . 95 30

(b) Gold Medal Winners. Nos. 1198/1201 optd.
1203 140f. Optd **M. BEDARD CANADA** 10 10
1204 1250f. Optd **MEDAILLE D'OR SUEDE** 45 15
1205 2000f. Optd **O. BAYUL UKRAINE** 75 25
1206 2500f. Optd **M. WASMEIER ALLEMAGNE** 95 30

401 Majestic performing Dressage Exercise and Windsor Hotel, 1892

1994. Olympic Games, Atlanta, U.S.A. Mult.
1208 640f. Type **401** 25 10
1209 1000f. Covington Courthouse, 1884, and putting the shot 35 10
1210 1500f. Table tennis and Carolton Community Activities Centre 55 15
1211 3000f. Newman Commercial Court Square, 1800, and footballer . . . . 1·10 35

402 Spider on Map of Madagascar **403** "Oceonia oncidiflora"

1994. "Archaea workmani" (spider).
1213 **402** 500f. multicoloured . . . 20 15

1994. Flowers, Fruit, Fungi and Vegetables. Multicoloured.
1214 45f. Type **403** 10 10
1215 45f. Breadfruit ("Artocarpus altilis") 10 10
1216 45f. "Russula annulata" . . 10 10
1217 45f. Sweet potato 10 10
1218 60f. "Cymbidella rhodochica" 10 10
1219 60f. "Eugenia malaceensis" 10 10
1220 60f. "Lactarius claricolor" 10 10
1221 60f. Yam 10 10
1222 140f. Vanilla orchid ("Vanilla planifolia") . . 10 10
1223 140f. "Jambosa domestica" 10 10
1224 140f. "Russula tuberculosa" 10 10
1225 140f. Avocado 10 10
1226 3000f. "Phaius humblotii" 1·10 35
1227 3000f. Papaya . . . . . . 1·10 35
1228 3000f. "Russula fistulosa" 1·10 35
1229 3000f. Manioc . . . . . . 1·10 35
Nos. 1214/29 were issued together, se-tenant, the backgrounds forming a composite design.

PARCEL POST STAMPS

1919. Receipt stamp of France surch **MADAGASCAR ET DEPENDANCES 0fr.10 COLIS POSTAUX.**
P81 0f.10 on 10c. grey . . . . . 5·50 4·75

1919. Fiscal stamp of Madagascar surch **COLIS POSTAUX 0f.10.**
P82 0f.10 on 1f. pink . . . . . . 70·00 42·00

1919. Fiscal stamps surch **Madagascar et Dependances** (in capitals on No. P83) **COLIS POSTAUX 0f.10.**
P83 0f.10 pink . . . . 12·00 6·75
P84 0f.10 red and green . . . . 3·50 3·75
P85 0f.10 black and green . . . . 3·50 3·25

POSTAGE DUE STAMPS

1896. Postage Due stamps of Fr. Colonies optd **Madagascar et DEPENDANCES.**
D17 U 5c. blue . . . . 5·50 9·00
D18 10c. brown . . . . 5·50 7·00
D19 20c. yellow . . . . 4·75 8·00
D20 30c. red . . . . 8·50 7·75
D21 40c. mauve . . . . 60·00 48·00
D22 50c. violet . . . . 5·00 5·00
D23 1f. green . . . . 90·00 60·00

D 6 Governor's Palace, Tananarive **D 37**

1908.
D70 D 6 2c. red 10 10
D71 4c. violet 10 15
D72 5c. green 10 80
D73 10c. red 10 10
D74 20c. olive . . . . 10 1·90
D75 40c. brown on cream . . 15 2·50
D76 50c. brown on blue . . . 15 1·75
D77 60c. red . . . . 35 2·75
D78 1f. blue . . . . 30 1·50

1924. Surch in figures.
D123 D 6 60c. on 1f. red . . . . 55 3·75
D124 2f. on 1f. purple . . . 30 3·00
D125 3f. on 1f. blue . . . . 35 3·00

1942. Free French Administration. Optd **FRANCE LIBRE** or surch also.
D254 D 6 10c. red . . . . 1·40 3·25
D255 20c. green . . . . . . 35 3·25
D256 0,30 on 5c. green . . . 2·75 3·25
D257 40c. brown on cream 2·25 3·25
D258 50c. brown and blue . . 2·00 3·25
D259 60c. red . . . . 2·25 3·25
D260 1f. blue . . . . 30 3·00
D261 1f. on 2c. purple . . . 7·00 8·50
D262 2f. on 4c. violet . . . 3·75 4·25
D263 2f. on 1f. mauve . . . 2·00 3·25
D264 3f. on 1f. blue . . . . 2·50 3·00

1947.
D319 D 37 10c. mauve . . . . . 10 2·25
D320 30c. brown . . . . . 10 2·75
D321 50c. green . . . . . . 10 2·75
D322 1f. brown . . . . . . 10 2·00
D323 2f. red . . . . 90 1·60
D324 3f. brown . . . . . . 95 1·75
D325 4f. blue . . . . 90 2·50
D326 5f. red . . . . 1·40 2·75
D327 10f. green . . . . . . 1·10 45
D328 20f. blue . . . . . . 1·25 3·50

APPENDIX

The following stamps have either been issued in excess of postal needs or have not been available to the public in reasonable quantities at face value.

1992.

Olympic Games, Barcelona. 500f. (on gold foil).

1993.

Bicentenary of French Republic. 1989 "Philexfrance 89" issue optd. 5000f.

1994.

Elvis Presley (entertainer). 10000f. (on gold foil).

World Cup Football Championship, U.S.A. 10000f. (on gold foil).

Winter Olympic Games, Lillehammer, Norway. 10000f. (on gold foil).

Olympic Games, Atlanta, U.S.A. 5000f. (on gold foil).

MADEIRA Pt. 9

A Portuguese island in the Atlantic Ocean off the N.W. coast of Africa. From 1868 to 1929 and from 1980 separate issues were made.

1868. 1000 reis = 1 milreis.
1912. 100 centavos = 1 escudo.
2002. 100 cents = 1 euro.

Nos. 1/78b are stamps of Portugal optd **MADEIRA.**

1868. With curved value label. Imperf.
1 14 20r. bistre £140 £110
2 50r. green £140 £110
3 80r. orange £150 £110
4 100r. lilac £110 £110

1868. With curved value label. Perf.
10 14 5r. black . . . . 40·00 30·00
13 10r. yellow . . . . 65·00 55·00
14 20r. bistre . . . . £110 80·00
15 25r. red . . . . 40·00 9·00
16 50r. green £130 £120
17 80r. orange £130 £120
19 100r. mauve £130 £120
20 120r. blue . . . . 80·00 65·00
21 240r. mauve £400 £375

1871. With straight value label.
30 15 5r. black . . . . 6·50 4·50
47 10r. yellow . . . . 25·00 14·00
72a 10r. green . . . . 50·00 40·00
48 15r. brown . . . . 15·00 8·50
49 20r. bistre . . . . 23·00 16·00
34 25r. pink . . . . 8·50 5·00
51 50r. green . . . . 50·00 23·00
71 50r. blue . . . . £130 70·00
36 80r. orange . . . . 90·00 60·00
53 100r. mauve . . . . 90·00 55·00
38 120r. blue . . . . £130 90·00
55 150r. blue £180 £150
74 150r. yellow £300 £275
39 240r. lilac £750 £550
67 300r. lilac . . . . 80·00 75·00

1880. Stamps of 1880.
79 16 5r. black . . . . 28·00 22·00
78 25r. grey . . . . 30·00 11·50
78b 25r. brown . . . . 30·00 11·50
77 17 25r. grey . . . . 30·00 22·00

1898. Vasco da Gama. As Nos. 378/85 of Portugal.
134 2½r. green . . . . 2·50 1·30
135 5r. red . . . . 2·50 1·30
136 10r. purple . . . . 3·25 1·50
137 25r. green . . . . 3·00 1·40
138 50r. blue . . . . 9·25 3·50
139 75r. brown . . . . 11·50 7·75
140 100r. brown . . . . 12·00 8·00
141 150r. brown . . . . 18·00 13·00
For Nos. 134/41 with **REPUBLICA** overprint, see Nos. 455/62 of Portugal.

6 Ceres **7** 20r. Stamp, 1868

1929. Funchal Museum Fund. Value in black.
148 6 3c. violet 60 55
149 4c. yellow 60 55
150 5c. blue 60 55
151 6c. brown 85 75
152 10c. red 85 75
153 15c. green 85 75
154 16c. brown 85 75
155 25c. purple 90 85
156 32c. green 90 85
157 40c. brown 90 85
158 50c. grey 90 85
159 64c. blue 90 85
160 80c. brown 90 85
161 96c. red . . . . 3·75 3·50
162 1e. black 75 75
163 1e.20 pink 75 75
164 1e.60 blue 75 75
165 2e.40 yellow . . . . 1·10 1·10
166 3e.36 green . . . . 1·60 1·50
167 4e.50 red . . . . 1·60 1·50
168 7e. blue . . . . 3·50 3·75

1980. 112th Anniv of First Overprinted Madeira Stamps.
169 7 6e.50 black, bistre and green 20 10
170 – 19e.50 black, purple and red 90 60
MS171 140 × 115 mm. Nos. 169/70 (sold at 30e.) . . . . 4·00 4·00
DESIGN: 19e.50, 100r. stamp, 1868.

8 Ox Sledge

1980. World Tourism Conference, Manila, Philippines. Multicoloured.
172 50c. Type **8** 10 10
173 1e. Wine and grapes 10 10
174 5e. Map of Madeira 50 10
175 6e.50 Basketwork 50 15
176 8e. Orchid 90 35
177 30e. Fishing boat . . . . . . 1·70 60

9 O Bailinho (folk dance)

1981. Europa.
178 **9** 22e. multicoloured . . . . . 1·40 70
MS179 141 × 115 mm. No. 178 × 2 4·25 4·25

10 Portuguese Caravel approaching Madeira **11** "Dactylorhiza foliosa"

1981. 560th Anniv (1980) of Discovery of Madeira. Multicoloured.
180 8e.50 Type **10** 50 10
181 33e.50 Prince Henry the Navigator and map of Atlantic Ocean . . . . . . 1·80 60

1981. Regional Flowers. Multicoloured.
182 7e. Type **11** 35 15
183 8e.50 "Geranium maderense" 40 15
184 9e. "Goodyera macrophylla" 50 10
185 10e. "Armeria maderensis" 50 10
186 12e.50 "Matthiola maderensis" 20 10
187 20e. "Isoplexis sceptrum" . . 70 40
188 27e. "Viola paradoxa" . . . 1·20 55
189 30e. "Erica maderensis" . . . 85 30
190 33e.50 "Scilla maderensis" . . 1·20 75
191 37e.50 "Cirsium latifolium" 90 60
192 50e. "Echium candicans" . . 1·60 80
193 100e. "Clethra arborea" . . . 2·30 90

12 First Sugar Mill **13** Dancer holding Dolls on Staff

1982. Europa.
199 **12** 33e.50 multicoloured . . . 1·90 75
MS200 139 × 115 mm. No. 199 × 3 10·50 10·50

1982. O Brinco Dancing Dolls. Multicoloured.
201 27e. Type **13** . . . . 1·20 65
202 33e.50 Dancers . . . . . . 1·80 90

14 Los Levadas Irrigation Channels

1983. Europa.
203 **14** 37e.50 multicoloured . . . 1·50 60
MS204 114 × 140 mm. No. 203 × 3 13·00 13·00

15 Flag of Madeira **16** Rally Car

1983. Flag.
205 **15** 12e.50 multicoloured . . . 75 10

1984. Europa. As T **398** of Portugal but additionally inscr "MADEIRA".
206 51e. multicoloured . . . . . 2·00 1·10
MS207 113 × 140 mm. No. 206 × 3 10·00 10·00

1984. 25th Anniv of Madeira Rally. Multicoloured.
208 16e. Type **16** 50 10
209 51e. Rally car (different) . . 1·80 65

17 Basket Sledge **18** Braguinha Player

1984. Transport (1st series). Multicoloured.
210 16e. Type **17** 30 10
211 35e. Hammock 95 55
212 40e. Borracheiros (wine carriers) . . . . 1·40 55
213 51e. Carreira local sailing boat . . . . 1·70 75
See also Nos. 218/21.

1985. Europa.
214 **18** 60e. multicoloured . . . . 2·10 90
MS215 140 × 115 mm. No. 214 × 3 12·00 12·00

19 Black Scabbardfish

1985. Fishes (1st series). Multicoloured.
216 40e. Type **19** . . . . 1·30 50
217 60e. Opah . . . . 1·80 75
See also Nos. 222/3 and 250/3.

1985. Transport (2nd series). As T **17**. Mult.
218 20e. Ox sledge 35 10
219 40e. Mountain railway . . . 1·00 45
220 46e. Fishing boat and basket used by pesquitos (itinerant fish sellers) . . . . 1·40 90
221 60e. Coastal ferry . . . . . 1·60 75

1986. Fishes (2nd series). As T **19**. Multicoloured.
222 20e. Big-eyed tuna 60 10
223 75e. Alfonsino . . . . 3·00 80

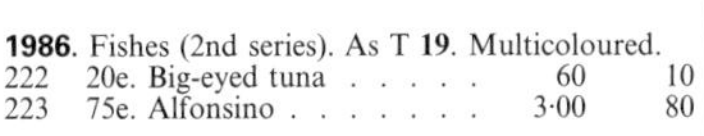

20 Cory's Shearwater and Tanker

1986. Europa.
224 **20** 68e.50 multicoloured . . . 2·40 1·00
MS225 140 × 114 mm. No. 224 × 3 12·50 12·50

21 Sao Lourenco Fort, Funchal

1986. Fortresses. Multicoloured.
226 22e.50 Type **21** 55 15
227 52e.50 Sao Joao do Pico Fort, Funchal . . . . 1·70 75
228 68e.50 Sao Tiago Fort, Funchal . . . . 2·50 1·00
229 100e. Nossa Senhora do Amparo Fort, Machico . . 3·50 85

22 Firecrest **24** Funchal Cathedral

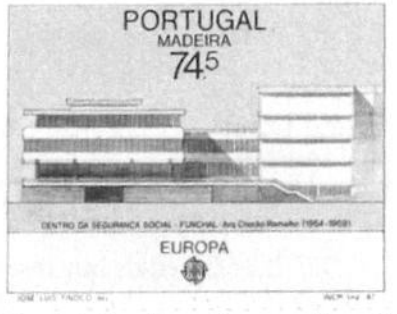

23 Social Services Centre, Funchal (Raul Chorao Ramalho)

1987. Birds (1st series). Multicoloured.
230 25e. Type **22** 55 10
231 57e. Trocaz pigeon . . . . . 1·80 90
232 74e.50 Barn owl . . . . . . 2·50 1·20
233 125e. Soft-plumaged petrel 3·25 1·40
See also Nos. 240/3.

1987. Europa. Architecture.
234 **23** 74e.50 multicoloured . . . 2·20 1·00
MS235 140 × 113 mm. No. 234 × 4 12·50 12·50

1987. Historic Buildings. Multicoloured.
236 51e. Type **24** . . . . 1·60 75
237 74e.50 Old Town Hall, Santa Cruz . . . . 1·90 75

25 "Maria Cristina" (mail boat)

1988. Europa. Transport and Communications.
238 **25** 80e. multicoloured . . . . 2·30 85
MS239 139 × 112 mm. As No. 238 × 4 but with cream background 12·50 12·50

1988. Birds (2nd series). As T **22** but horiz. Multicoloured.
240 27e. European robin 50 10
241 60e. Streaked rock sparrow 1·60 85
242 80e. Chaffinch . . . . 2·20 90
243 100e. Northern sparrowhawk 2·50 90

26 Columbus and Funchal House **27** Child flying Kite

1988. Christopher Columbus's Houses in Madeira. Multicoloured.
244 55e. Type **26** . . . . 1·70 65
245 80e. Columbus and Porto Santo house (horiz) . . . . 1·90 75

1989. Europa. Children's Games and Toys. Multicoloured.
246 80e. Type **27** . . . . 2·10 90
MS247 139 × 112 mm. 80e. × 2, Type **27**; 80E. × 2, Child flying kite (*different*) . . . . 12·50 12·50

28 Church of St. John the Evangelist **29** Spiny Hatchetfish

1989. "Brasiliana 89" Stamp Exhibition, Rio de Janeiro. Madeiran Churches. Multicoloured.
248 29e. Type **28** 50 15
249 87e. St. Clara's Church and Convent . . . . 2·10 1·00

1989. Fishes (3rd series). Multicoloured.
250 29e. Type **29** 50 10
251 60e. Dog wrasse . . . . . . 1·40 75
252 87e. Rainbow wrasse . . . . 2·10 95
253 100e. Madeiran scorpionfish 2·20 1·30

30 Zarco Post Office **31** Bananas

1990. Europa. Post Office Buildings. Multicoloured.
254 80e. Type **30** . . . .
MS255 139 × 111 mm. 80e. × 2, Type **30**; 80e. × 2, Porto da Cruz Post Office . . . .

1990. Sub-tropical Fruits. Multicoloured.
256 5e. Type **31** 15 10
257 10e. Thorn apple 15 10

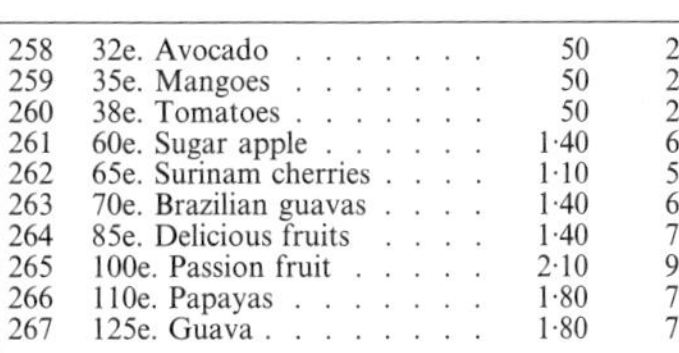
258 32e. Avocado 50 20
259 35e. Mangoes 50 20
260 38e. Tomatoes 50 20
261 60e. Sugar apple . . . . . 1·40 60
262 65e. Surinam cherries . . . . 1·10 55
263 70e. Brazilian guavas . . . . 1·40 65
264 85e. Delicious fruits . . . . 1·40 75
265 100e. Passion fruit . . . . . 2·10 95
266 110e. Papayas . . . . 1·80 70
267 125e. Guava . . . . 1·80 75

32 Tunny Boat

1990. Boats. Multicoloured.
270 32e. Type **32** 50 10
271 60e. Desert Islands boat . . . 1·10 50
272 70e. Maneiro . . . . 1·30 75
273 95e. Chavelha . . . . 2·00 1·00

33 Trocaz Pigeon

1991. The Trocaz Pigeon. Multicoloured.
274 35e. Type **33** 75 20
275 35e. Two pigeons 75 20
276 35e. Pigeon on nest 75 20
277 35e. Pigeon alighting on twig 75 20
Nos. 264/7 were issued together, se-tenant, forming a composite design.

34 European Remote Sensing ("ERS1") Satellite

1991. Europa. Europe in Space. Multicoloured.
278 80e. Type **34** 75 20
MS279 140 × 112 mm. 80e. × 2, Type **34**; 80e. × 2, "Spot" satellite 11·50 11·50

35 Columbus and Funchal House

1992. Europa. 500th Anniv of Discovery of America by Columbus.
280 **35** 85e. multicoloured . . . . 1·20 60

36 "Gaviao" (ferry)

1992. Inter-island Ships. Multicoloured.
281 38e. Type **36** 50 15
282 65e. "Independencia" (catamaran ferry) 95 50
283 85e. "Madeirense" (car ferry) 1·20 60
284 120e. "Funchalense" (freighter) . . . . 1·60 70

37 "Shadow thrown by Christa Maar" (Lourdes Castro) **39** Window of St. Francis's Convent, Funchal

38 Seals Swimming

1993. Europa. Contemporary Art. Multicoloured.
285 50e. Type **37** . . . . 1·40 60
MS286 140 × 112 mm. 90e. × 2, Type **37**; 90e. × 2, "Shadow thrown by Dahlia" . . . . . 7·50 7·50

1993. Mediterranean Monk Seal. Multicoloured.
287 42e. Type **38** 60 30
288 42e. Seal basking 60 30
289 42e. Two seals on rocks . . . 60 30
290 42e. Mother suckling young 60 30
Nos. 287/90 were issued together, se-tenant, forming a composite design.

1993. Regional Architecture. Multicoloured.
291 42e. Type **39** 50 20
292 130e. Window of Mercy, Old Hospital, Funchal . . . . 1·90 85

40 Native of Cape of Good Hope and Explorer with Model Caravel

1992. Europa. Discoveries. Multicoloured.
293 90e. Type **40** 85 60
MS294 140 × 112 mm. 100e. × 2, Type **40**; 100e. × 2, Palm tree and explorer with model caravel . . 6·25 6·25

41 Embroidery

1994. Traditional Crafts (1st series). Multicoloured.
295 45e. Type **41** 45 20
296 75e. Tapestry 90 45
297 100e. Boots . . . . 1·10 60
298 140e. Wicker chair back . . . 1·70 80
See also Nos. 301/4.

42 Funchal **43** Bread Dough Figures

1994. District Arms. Multicoloured.
299 45e. Type **42** 45 20
300 140e. Porto Santo . . . . . 1·50 75

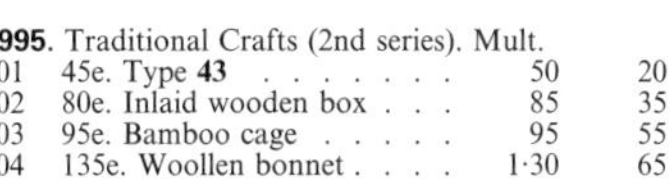
1995. Traditional Crafts (2nd series). Mult.
301 45e. Type **43** 50 20
302 80e. Inlaid wooden box . . . 85 35
303 95e. Bamboo cage 95 55
304 135e. Woollen bonnet . . . . 1·30 65

44 Guiomar Vilhena (entrepreneur)

1996. Europa. Famous Women. Multicoloured.
305 98e. Type **44** 95 50
MS306 140 × 112 mm. No. 305 × 3 3·00 3·00

45 "Adoration of the Magi"

1996. Religious Paintings by Flemish Artists. Multicoloured.
307 47e. Type **45** 45 20
308 78e. "St. Mary Magdalene" 80 45
309 98e. "The Annunciation" (horiz) 95 50
310 140e. "Saints Peter, Paul and Andrew" (horiz) . . . . . 1·20 70

46 "Eumichtis albostigmata" (moth)

1997. Butterflies and Moths. Multicoloured.
311 49e. Type **46** 45 20
312 80e. Menophra maderae (moth) 75 30
313 100e. Painted lady 90 50
314 140e. Large white . . . . . 1·30 70

47 Robert Achim and Anne of Arfet (Legend of Machico)

1997. Europa. Tales and Legends. Multicoloured.
315 100e. Type **47** . . . . 1·00 50
MS316 140 × 106 mm. No. 315 × 3 3·00 3·00

48 New Year's Eve Fireworks Display, Funchal

1998. Europa. National Festival. Multicoloured.
317 100e. Type **48** 90 45
MS318 140 × 109 mm. No. 317 × 3 2·75 2·75

49 "Gonepteryx cleopatra"

1998. Butterflies and Moths. Multicoloured.
319 50e. Type **49** 45 20
320 85e. "Xanthorhoe rupicola" 70 35
321 100e. "Noctua teixeirai" . . 90 45
322 140e. "Xenochlorodes nubigena" . . . . 1·20 65

50 Madeira Island Nature Park

1999. Europa. Parks and Gardens. Multicoloured.
323 100e. Type **50** 85 45
MS324 153 × 108 mm. No. 323 × 3 2·50 2·50

51 Medieval Floor Tile

1999. Tiles from Frederico de Freitas Collection, Funchal. Multicoloured.
325 51e. Type **51** 45 20
326 80e. English art-nouveau tile (19th–20th century) 70 35
327 95e. Persian tile (14th century) 85 45
328 100e. Spanish Moor tile (13th century) 90 45
329 140e. Dutch Delft tile (18th century) . . . . 1·20 60
330 210e. Syrian tile (13th–14th century) . . . . 1·70 90

52 "Building Europe"

2000. Europa. Multicoloured.
332 100e. Type **52** 85 45
MS333 154 × 108 mm. Nos. 332 × 3 2·50 2·50

53 Mountain Orchid

2000. Plants of Laurissilva Forest. Multicoloured.
334 52e. Type **53** 40 20
335 85e. White orchid 70 35
336 100e. Leafy plant 80 40
337 100e. Laurel 80 40
338 140e. Barbusano 90 60
339 350e. Visco . . . . 2·75 1·40

54 Marine Life

2001. Europa. Water Resources. Multicoloured.
341 105e. Type **54** 85 45
MS342 140 × 110 mm. No. 341 × 3 2·50 2·50

55 Musicians

2001. Traditions of Madeira. Multicoloured.
343 53e. Type **55** 40 20
344 85e. Couple carrying produce 65 35
345 105e. Couple selling goods 80 40
MS346 140 × 112 mm. 350e. Man carrying birds . . . . 2·75 2·75

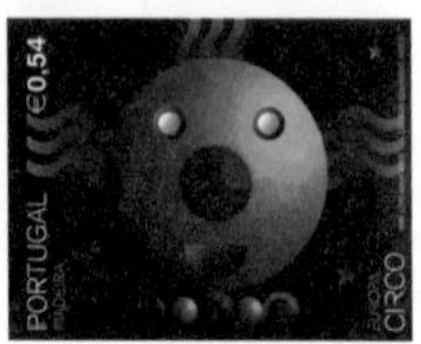

56 Clown

2002. Europa. Circus.
347 **56** 54c. multicoloured 85 40
MS348 140 × 110 mm. No. 347 × 3 2·50 2·50

57 Turtle Doves (*Streptopelia turtur*)

2002. Birds. Multicoloured.
349 28c. Type **57** 40 20
350 28c. Perching dove 40 20
351 28c. Dove with raised wings 40 20
352 28c. Dove with chicks . . . 40 20

58 1992 Theatre Festival Poster (José Brandao)

2003. Europa. Poster Art.
353 **58** 55c. multicoloured 75 35
MS354 140 × 113 mm. No. 353 × 2 1·60 1·60

CHARITY TAX STAMPS

The note under this heading in Portugal also applies here.

1925. As Marquis de Pombal stamps of Portugal but inscr "MADEIRA".
C142 C **73** 15c. grey . . . . . . 1·70 1·40
C143 – 15c. grey . . . . . . 1·70 1·40
C144 C **75** 15c. grey . . . . . . 1·70 1·40

NEWSPAPER STAMP

1876. Newspaper stamp of Portugal optd **MADEIRA**.
N69 N **17** 2½r. green . . . . . . 9·25 4·75

POSTAGE DUE STAMPS

1925. Marquis de Pombal stamps as Nos. C1/3 optd **MULTA**.
D145 C **73** 30c. grey . . . . . . 1·40 1·30
D146 – 30c. grey . . . . . . 1·40 1·30
D147 C **75** 30c. grey . . . . . . 1·40 1·30

MAFEKING Pt. 1

A town in the Cape of Good Hope. Special stamps issued by British garrison during Boer War.

12 pence = 1 shilling;
20 shillings = 1 pound.

1900. Surch **MAFEKING, BESIEGED.** and value.
(a) On Cape of Good Hope stamps.
1 **6** 1d. on ½d. green . . . . . . £180 65·00
2 **17** 1d. on ½d. green . . . . . . £225 75·00
3 3d. on 1d. red . . . . . . £200 50·00
4 **6** 6d. on 3d. mauve £26000 £250
5 1s. on 4d. olive £6000 £325

(b) On stamps of Bechuanaland Protectorate (opts on Great Britain).
6 **71** 1d. on ½d. red (No. 59) . . £180 60·00
7 **57** 3d. on 1d. lilac (No. 61) . . £850 90·00
13 **73** 6d. on 2d. green and red (No. 62) . . . . £1100 75·00
9 **75** 6d. on 3d. purple on yellow (No. 63) £4250 £275
14 **79** 1s. on 6d. purple on red (No. 65) . . . . £4250 90·00

(c) On stamps of British Bechuanaland (opts on Great Britain).
10 **3** 6d. on 3d. lilac and black (No. 12) . . . . £350 65·00
11 **76** 1s. on 4d. green and brown (No. 35) . . . . £1200 80·00
15 **79** 1s. on 6d. purple on red (No. 36) £14000 £700
16 **82** 2s. on 1s. green (No. 37) . . £7500 £375

3 Cadet Sgt.-Major Goodyear

4 General Baden-Powell

1900.
17 **3** 1d. blue on blue £800 £275
20 **4** 3d. blue on blue £1200 £350

MAHRA SULTANATE OF QISHN AND SOCOTRA Pt. 1

The National Liberation Front took control on 1 October 1967, and full independence was granted by Great Britain on 30 November 1967. Subsequently part of Southern Yemen.

1000 fils = 1 dinar.

1 Mahra Flag

1967.
1 **1** 5f. multicoloured . . . . . . 1·50 40
2 10f. multicoloured . . . . . 1·50 40
3 15f. multicoloured . . . . . 1·50 40
4 20f. multicoloured . . . . . 1·50 40
5 25f. multicoloured . . . . . 1·50 40
6 35f. multicoloured . . . . . 1·50 40
7 50f. multicoloured . . . . . 1·50 40
8 65f. multicoloured . . . . . 1·50 40
9 100f. multicoloured . . . . . 1·50 40
10 250f. multicoloured . . . . . 1·50 45
11 500f. multicoloured . . . . . 1·50 60

APPENDIX

The following stamps have either been issued in excess of postal needs or have not been available to the public in reasonable quantities at face value.

1967.

Scout Jamboree, Idaho. 15, 75, 100, 150f.

President Kennedy Commemoration. Postage 10, 15, 25, 50, 75, 100, 150f.; Air 250, 500f.

Olympic Games, Mexico (1968). Postage 10, 25, 50f.; Air 250, 500f.

For later issues see **SOUTHERN YEMEN** and **YEMEN PEOPLE'S DEMOCRATIC REPUBLIC** in Volume 4.

MALACCA Pt. 1

A British Settlement on the Malay Peninsula which became a state of the Federation of Malaya, incorporated in Malaysia in 1963.

100 cents = 1 dollar (Malayan).

1948. Silver Wedding. As T **4b/c** of Pitcairn Islands.
1 10c. violet . . . . 30 1·75
2 $5 brown . . . . 28·00 38·00

1949. As T **58** of Straits Settlements.
3 1c. black 30 70
4 2c. orange 80 45
5 3c. green . . . . 30 1·75
6 4c. brown 30 10
6a 5c. purple . . . . 60 1·50
7 6c. grey 75 85
8 8c. red . . . . 75 6·00
8a 8c. green . . . . 1·50 4·75
9 10c. mauve 30 10
9a 12c. red . . . . 1·50 6·00
10 15c. blue . . . . 2·50 60
11 20c. black and green . . . . 50 7·00
11a 20c. blue . . . . 3·50 2·50
12 25c. purple and orange . . . 50 70
12a 35c. red and purple . . . . . 1·75 3·00
13 40c. red and purple . . . . . 1·25 11·00
14 50c. black and blue . . . . . 1·00 1·25
15 $1 blue and purple . . . . . 8·50 20·00
16 $2 green and red . . . . . . 21·00 21·00
17 $5 green and brown . . . . 42·00 35·00

1949. U.P.U. As T **4d/g** of Pitcairn Islands.
18 10c. purple 30 50
19 15c. blue . . . . 2·00 1·75
20 25c. orange . . . . 85 4·75
21 50c. black . . . . 60 4·75

1953. Coronation. As T **4h** of Pitcairn Islands.
22 10c. black and purple . . . . 1·00 1·50

1 Queen Elizabeth II

1954.
23 **1** 1c. black 10 60
24 2c. orange . . . . 30 1·25
25 4c. brown 40 10
26 5c. mauve . . . . 30 2·50
27 6c. grey 10 40
28 8c. green . . . . 40 2·75
29 10c. purple . . . . 1·00 10
30 12c. red . . . . 30 3·00
31 20c. blue . . . . 20 1·25
32 25c. purple and orange . . . 20 1·50
33 30c. red and purple 20 30
34 35c. red and purple . . . . . 20 1·50
35 50c. black and blue . . . . . 75 2·50
36 $1 blue and purple . . . . . 7·00 8·00
37 $2 green and red . . . . . . 22·00 35·00
38 $5 green and brown . . . . 23·00 42·00

1957. As Nos. 92/102 of Kedah but inset portrait of Queen Elizabeth II.
39 1c. black 10 40
40 2c. red 10 40

41 4c. sepia 40 10
42 5c. lake 30 10
43 8c. green 1·25 2·50
44 10c. sepia 30 10
45 20c. blue 40 50
46 50c. black and blue 30 1·00
47 $1 blue and purple 2·75 3·00
48 $2 green and red 12·00 21·00
49 $5 brown and green 14·00 38·00

2 Copra

1960. As Nos. 39/49 but with inset picture of Melaka tree and Pelandok (mouse-deer) as in T **2**.
50 1c. black 10 30
51 2c. red 10 65
52 4c. sepia 10 10
53 5c. lake 10 10
54 8c. green 3·00 3·00
55 10c. purple 30 10
56 20c. blue 1·00 80
57 50c. black and blue 70 80
58 $1 blue and purple 2·50 2·50
59 $2 green and red 7·00 9·50
60 $5 brown and green 9·50 14·00

3 "Vanda hookeriana"

1965. As Nos. 115/21 of Kedah but with Arms of Malacca inset and inscr "MELAKA" as in T **3**.
61 **3** 1c. multicoloured 10 1·50
62 – 2c. multicoloured 10 1·50
63 – 5c. multicoloured 10 40
64 – 6c. multicoloured 30 80
65 – 10c. multicoloured 20 10
66 – 15c. multicoloured 1·75 40
67 – 20c. multicoloured 2·25 1·00
The higher values used in Malacca were Nos. 20/7 of Malaysia.

4 "Papilio demoleus"

1971. Butterflies. As Nos. 124/30 of Kedah but with Arms of Malacca as in T **4**. Inscr "melaka".
70 – 1c. multicoloured 60 2·25
71 – 2c. multicoloured 1·00 2·25
72 – 5c. multicoloured 1·50 1·00
73 **4** 6c. multicoloured 1·50 3·00
74 – 10c. multicoloured 1·50 60
75 – 15c. multicoloured 2·25 20
76 – 20c. multicoloured 2·25 2·50
The higher values in use with this issue were Nos. 64/71 of Malaysia.

5 "Durio zibethinus"

6 Rubber

1979. Flowers. As Nos. 135/41 of Kedah but with Arms of Malacca and inscr "melaka" as in T **5**.
82 1c. "Rafflesia hasseltii" 10 1·25
83 2c. "Pterocarpus indicus" 10 1·25
84 5c. "Lagerstroemia speciosa" 15 1·00
85 10c. Type **5** 20 35
86 15c. "Hibiscus rosa-sinesis" 20 10
87 20c. "Rhododendron scortechinii" 25 10
88 25c. "Etlingera elatior" (inscr "Phaeomeria speciosa") 45 80

1986. As Nos. 152/8 of Kedah but with Arms of Malacca and inscr "MELAKA" as in T **6**.
96 1c. Coffee 10 10
97 2c. Coconuts 10 10
98 5c. Cocoa 10 10
99 10c. Black pepper 10 10
100 15c. Type **6** 10 10
101 20c. Oil palm 10 10
102 30c. Rice 10 15

MALAGASY REPUBLIC Pt. 6; Pt. 13

The former areas covered by Madagascar and Dependencies were renamed the Malagasy Republic within the French Community on 14 October 1958. It became independent on 26 June 1960. In 1992 it reverted to the name of Madagascar.

1958. 100 centimes = 1 franc.
1976. 5 francs = 1 ariary.

1958. 10th Anniv of Declaration of Human Rights. As T **48** of New Caledonia.
1 10f. brown and blue 65 45

1959. Tropical Flora. As T **47** of New Caledonia.
2 6f. green, brown and yellow 25 25
3 25f. multicoloured 75 35
DESIGNS—HORIZ: 6f. "Datura"; 25f. Poinsettia.

2a Malagasy Flag and Assembly Hall

1959. Proclamation of Malagasy Republic and "French Community" Commemorative (60f.).
4 **2a** 20f. red, green and purple 35 25
5 – 25f. red, green and grey 45 25
6 – 60f. multicoloured 1·10 55
DESIGNS—VERT: 25f. Malagasy flag on map of Madagascar; 60f. Natives holding French and Malagasy flags.

3 "Chionaema pauliani" (butterfly) 3a Reafforestation

1960.
7 – 30c. multicoloured (postage) 15 10
8 – 40c. brown, chocolate & green 15 10
9 – 50c. turquoise and purple 15 10
10 **3** 1f. red, purple and black 20 10
11 – 3f. black, red and olive 20 10
12 – 5f. green, brown and red 20 20
13 – 6f. yellow and green 20 20
14 – 8f. black, green and red 20 20
15 – 10f. green, brown & turquoise 40 20
16 – 15f. green and brown 50 20
17 – 30f. multicoloured (air) 70 40
18 – 40f. brown and turquoise 1·25 30
19 – 50f. multicoloured 2·50 50
20 – 100f. multicoloured 4·00 85
21 – 200f. yellow and violet 5·50 1·50
22 – 500f. brown, blue and green 9·50 2·25
BUTTERFLIES—As Type **2**: 30c. Purple-tip; 40c. "Acraea hova"; 50c. Clouded mother-of-pearl; 3f. "Hypolimnas dexithea". 48 × 27 mm: 50f. "Charaxes antamboulou"; 100f. Sunset moth. 27 × 48 mm: 200f. Tailed comet moth.
OTHER DESIGNS—As Type **2**: 5f. Sisal; 8f. Pepper; 15f. Cotton. VERT: 6f. Ylang ylang (flower); 10f. Rice. 48½ × 27 mm: 30f. Sugar cane trucks; 40f. Tobacco plantation; 500f. Mandrare Bridge.

1960. Trees Festival.
23 **3a** 20f. brown, green and ochre 55 35

4

5 Pres. Philibert Tsiranana

1960. 10th Anniv of African Technical Co-operation Commission.
24 **4** 25f. lake and green 55 35

1960.
25 **5** 20f. brown and green 35 35

6 Young Athletes

7 Pres. Tsiranana

1960. 1st Youth Games, Tananarive.
26 **6** 25f. brown, chestnut and blue 65 35

1960.
27 **7** 20f. black, red and green 25 10

1960. Independence. Surch **+10 F FETES DE L'INDEPENDANCE**.
28 **7** 20f.+10f. black, red & grn 55 35

9 Ruffed Lemur

1961. Lemurs.
29 – 2f. purple & turq (postage) 15 15
30 **9** 4f. black, brown and myrtle 20 15
31 – 12f. brown and green 50 30
32 – 65f. brown, sepia and myrtle (air) 2·25 65
33 – 85f. black, sepia and green 2·25 1·00
34 – 250f. purple, black & turq 6·50 2·75
LEMURS—VERT: As Type **9**: 2f. Grey gentle lemur; 12f. Mongoose-lemur. 48 × 27 mm: 65f. Diadem sifaka; 85f. Indris; 250f. Verreaux's sifaka.

10 Diesel Train

1962.
35 **10** 20f. myrtle 1·50 45
36 – 25f. blue 35 15
DESIGN: 25f. President Tsiranana Bridge.

11 U.N. and Malagasy Flags, and Govt. Building, Tananarive

1962. Admission into U.N.O.
37 **11** 25f. multicoloured 35 20
38 85f. multicoloured 1·40 55

1962. Malaria Eradication. As T **43** of Mauritania.
39 25f.+5f. green 80 80

12 Ranomafana

1962. Tourist Publicity.
40 **12** 10f. purple, myrtle and blue (postage) 20 15
41 – 30f. purple, blue and myrtle 40 15
42 – 50f. blue, myrtle and purple 60 25
43 – 60f. myrtle, purple and blue 80 35
44 – 100f. brown, myrtle and blue (air) 1·75 95
DESIGNS—As Type **12**: 30f. Tritriva Lake; 50f. Foulpointe; 60f. Fort Dauphin. 27 × 47½ mm: 100f. Boeing 707 airliner over Nossi-Be.

13 G.P.O., Tamatave

1962. Stamp Day.
45 **13** 25f.+5f. brn, myrtle & bl 35 40

14 Malagasy and U.N.E.S.C.O. Emblems

1962. U.N.E.S.C.O. Conference on Higher Education in Africa, Tananarive.
46 **14** 20f. black, green and red 35 25

1962. 1st Anniv of Union of African and Malagasy States. As T **45** of Mauritania.
47 30f. green 45 35

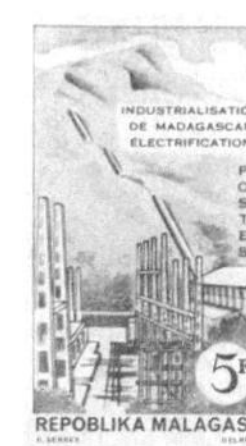

15 Hydro-electric Station

1962. Malagasy Industrialization.
48 **15** 5f. multicoloured 10 10
49 – 8f. multicoloured 15 10
50 – 10f. multicoloured 20 10
51 – 15f. brown, black and blue 35 15
52 – 20f. multicoloured 35 20
DESIGNS—HORIZ: 8f. Atomic plant; 15f. "Esso Gasikara" (tanker); 20f. Hertzian aerials at Tananarive-Fianarantsoa. VERT: 10f. Oilwell.

16 Globe and Factory

1963. International Fair, Tamatave.
53 **16** 25f. orange and black 30 20

1963. Freedom from Hunger. As T **51** of Mauritania.
54 25f.+5f. lake, brown and red 60 60

17 Douglas DC-8 Airliner

1963. Air. Malagasy Commercial Aviation.
55 **17** 500f. blue, red and green 8·50 3·25

18 Central Post Office, Tananarive

19 Madagascar Blue Pigeon

1963. Stamp Day.
56 **18** 20f.+5f. brown & turq 55 35

1963. Malagasy Birds and Orchids (8f. to 12f.). Multicoloured. (a) Postage as T **19**.
57 1f. Type **19** 70 35
58 2f. Blue Madagascar coucal 70 35
59 3f. Madagascar red fody 70 35
60 6f. Madagascar pygmy kingfisher 70 35
61 8f. "Gastrorchis humblotii" 20 15

62 10f. "Eulophiella roempleriana" 65 25
63 12f. "Angraceum sesquipedale" 65 25

(b) Air. Horiz: 49½ × 28 mm.

64 40f. Helmet bird . . . . . . 2·75 60
65 100f. Pitta-like ground roller 6·50 1·25
66 200f. Crested wood ibis . . . 8·75 2·75

20 Centenary Emblem and Map

21 U.P.U. Monument, Berne, and Map of Malagasy

1963. Red Cross Centenary.
67 **20** 30f. multicoloured 80 60

1963. Air. African and Malagasy Posts and Telecommunications Union. As T **56** of Mauritania.
68 85f. multicoloured . . . . . . 1·40 90

1963. Air. 2nd Anniv of Malagasy's Admission to U.P.U.
69 **21** 45f. blue, red and turquoise 50 25
70 85f. blue, red and violet . . 90 50

22 Arms of Fianarantsoa

23 Flame, Globe and Hands

1963. Town Arms (1st series). Multicoloured.
71 1f.50 Antsirabe 10 10
72 5f. Antalaha 15 10
73 10f. Tulear 20 10
74 15f. Majunga 30 15
75 20f. Type **22** 40 15
75a 20f. Manajary 25 10
76 25f. Tananarive 45 15
76a 30f. Nossi Be 35 15
77 50f. Diego-Suarez 85 50
77a 90f. Antsohihy . . . . 1·40 55
See also Nos. 174/7 and 208/9.

1963. 15th Anniv of Declaration of Human Rights.
78 **23** 60f. ochre, bronze and mauve 55 45

24 Meteorological Station, Tananarive

1964. Air. World Meteorological Day.
79 **24** 90f. brown, blue and grey 1·50 1·25

25 Postal Cheques and Savings Bank Building, Tananarive

26 Scouts beside Campfire

1964. Stamp Day.
80 **25** 25f.+5f. brown, bl & grn . . 50 60

1964. 40th Anniv of Malagasy Scout Movement.
81 **26** 20f. multicoloured 55 25

27 Symbolic Bird and Globe within "Egg"

28 Statuette of Woman

1964. "Europafrique".
82 **27** 45f. brown and green . . . 45 35

1964. Malagasy Art.
83 **28** 6f. brown, blue and indigo (postage) 25 15
84 – 30f. brown, bistre & green 45 20
85 – 100f. brown, red & vio (air) 1·50 95
DESIGNS: 30f. Statuette of squatting vendor. 27 × 48½ mm: 100f. Statuary of peasant family, ox and calf.

1964. French, African and Malagasy Co-operation. As T **68** of Mauritania.
86 25f. brown, chestnut and black . 40 25

29 Tree on Globe

30 Cithern

1964. University of Malagasy Republic.
87 **29** 65f. black, red and green . . 50 25

1965. Malagasy Musical Instruments.
88 – 3f. brown, blue and mauve (postage) 20 10
89 **30** 6f. sepia, purple and green 25 10
90 – 8f. brown, black and green 35 10
91 – 25f. multicoloured 90 50
92 – 200f. brown, orange and green (air) . . . . . . 4·00 2·25
DESIGNS—As Type **30**: 3f. Kabosa (lute); 8f. Hazolahy (sacred drum). LARGER—VERT: 35½ × 48 mm: 25f. "Valiha Player" (after E. Ralambo). 27 × 48 mm: 200f. Bara violin.

31 Foulpointe Post Office

1965. Stamp Day.
93 **31** 20f. brown, green and orange 20 15

32 I.T.U. Emblem

33 J.-J. Rabearivelo (poet)

1965. I.T.U. Centenary.
94 **32** 50f. green, blue and red . . 1·00 45

1965. Rabearivelo Commemorative.
95 **33** 40f. brown and orange . . . 40 25

34 Nurse weighing Baby

1965. Air. International Co-operation Year.
96 **34** 50f. black, bistre and blue 60 35
97 – 100f. purple, brown and blue . . . . 1·25 60
DESIGN: 100f. Boy and girl.

35 Pres. Tsiranana

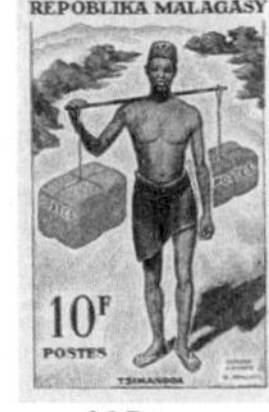

36 Bearer

1965. Pres. Tsiranana's 55th Birthday.
98 **35** 20f. multicoloured 25 15
99 25f. multicoloured 30 20

1965. Postal Transport.
102 – 3f. violet, blue and brown 30 15
103 – 4f. blue, brown and green 25 15
104 **36** 10f. multicoloured 25 15
105 – 12f. multicoloured 30 20
106 – 20f. multicoloured 90 20
107 – 25f. multicoloured 80 20
108 – 30f. red, brown and blue 2·25 1·60
109 – 65f. brown, blue and violet 1·50 50
DESIGNS—HORIZ: 3f. Early car; 4f. Filanzane (litter); 12f. Pirogue; 20f. Horse-drawn mail-cart; 25f. Bullock cart; 30f. Early railway postal carriage; 65f. Hydrofoil, "Porthos", Betsiboka.

37 Diseased Hands

1966. World Leprosy Day.
110 **37** 20f. purple, red and green 35 20

38 Planting Trees

1966. Reafforestation Campaign.
111 **38** 20f. violet, brown & turq 35 20

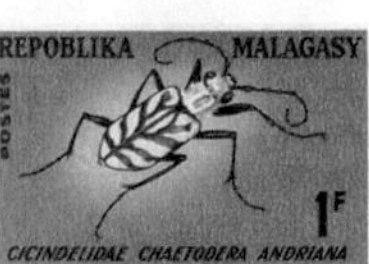

39 "Cicindelidae chaetodera andriana"

1966. Malagasy Insects. Multicoloured.
112 1f. Type **39** 10 10
113 6f. "Mantodea tisma freiji" 20 10
114 12f. "Cerambycini mastododera nodicollis" . . 45 20
115 45f. "Trachelophoru giraffa" 85 30

40 Madagascar 1c. Stamp of 1903

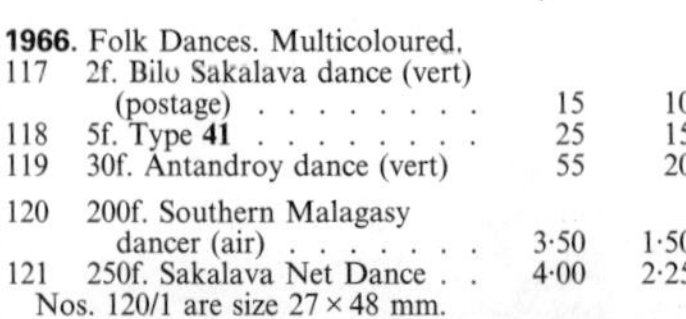

41 Betsileo Dance

1966. Stamp Day.
116 **40** 25f. bistre and red 35 25

1966. Folk Dances. Multicoloured.
117 2f. Bilo Sakalava dance (vert) (postage) 15 10
118 5f. Type **41** 25 15
119 30f. Antandroy dance (vert) 55 20
120 200f. Southern Malagasy dancer (air) . . . . . . 3·50 1·50
121 250f. Sakalava Net Dance . . 4·00 2·25
Nos. 120/1 are size 27 × 48 mm.

43 "Tree" of Emblems

1966. O.C.A.M. Conference, Tananarive.
122 **43** 25f. multicoloured 30 15
The above was issued with "Janvier 1966" obliterated by bars, and optd **JUIN 1966**.

44 Singing Anthem

45 U.N.E.S.C.O. Emblem

1966. National Anthem.
123 **44** 20f. brown, mauve & green 25 10

1966. 20th Anniv of U.N.E.S.C.O.
124 **45** 30f. blue, bistre and red . . 35 20

46 Lions Emblem

47 Harvesting Rice

1967. 50th Anniv of Lions Int.
125 **46** 30f. multicoloured 40 20

1967. International Rice Year.
126 **47** 20f. multicoloured 30 15

48 Adventist Temple, Tanambao-Tamatave

1967. Religious Buildings (1st series).
127 **48** 3f. ochre, blue and green 10 10
128 – 5f. lilac, purple and green 10 10
129 – 10f. purple, blue and green 25 10
BUILDINGS—VERT: 5f. Catholic Cathedral, Tananarive. HORIZ: 10f. Mosque, Tamatave.
See also Nos. 148/50.

49 Raharisoa at Piano

1967. 4th Death Anniv of Norbert Raharisoa (composer).
130 **49** 40f. multicoloured 55 20

50 Jean Raoult's Bleriot XI, 1911

1967. "History of Malagasy Aviation".
131 **50** 5f. brown, blue and green (postage) 35 15
132 – 45f. black, blue and brown 90 35
133 – 500f. black, blue and ochre (air) . . . . 8·75 3·75
DESIGNS: 45f. Bernard Bougault and flying boat, 1926. 48 × 27 mm: 500f. Jean Dagnaux and Breguet 19A2 biplane, 1927.

51 Ministry of Communications, Tananarive

52 Church, Torch and Map

1967. Stamp Day.
134 **51** 20f. green, blue and orange 25 15

1967. Air. 5th Anniv of U.A.M.P.T. As T **101** of Mauritania.
135 100f. mauve, bistre and red 1·25 60

1967. Centenary of Malagasy Lutheran Church.
136 **52** 20f. multicoloured 30 15

53 Map and Decade Emblem — **54** Woman's Face and Scales of Justice

1967. Int Hydrological Decade.
137 **53** 90f. brown, red and blue 85 45

1967. Women's Rights Commission.
138 **54** 50f. blue, ochre and green 50 25

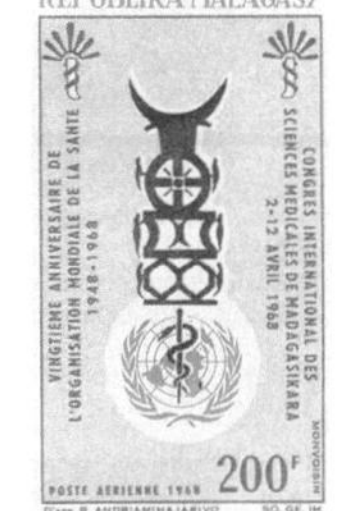

55 Human Rights Emblem — **56** Congress and W.H.O. Emblems

1968. Human Rights Year.
139 **55** 50f. red, green and black 40 25

1968. Air. 20th Anniv of W.H.O. and Int Medical Sciences Congress, Tananarive.
140 **56** 200f. red, blue and ochre 2·40 1·25

57 International Airport, Tananarive-Ivato

1968. Air. Stamp Day.
141 **57** 500f. blue, green and brown . . . . 6·75 3·25

1968. Nos. 33 and 38 surch.
142 **11** 20f. on 85f. (postage) . . . 40 30
143 – 20f. on 85f. (No. 33) (air) 50 30

59 "Industry and Construction" — **61** Isotry Protestant Church, Fitiavana, Tananarive

60 Church and Open Bible

1968. Five-year Plan (1st issue).
144 **59** 10f. plum, red and green 15 10
145 – 20f. black, red and green 20 15
146 – 40f. blue, brown & ultram 2·10 60
DESIGNS—VERT: 20f. "Agriculture". HORIZ: 40f. "Transport".
See also Nos. 156/7.

1968. 150th Anniv of Christianity in Madagascar.
147 **60** 20f. multicoloured 25 10

1968. Religious Buildings (2nd series).
148 **61** 4f. brown, green and red 10 10
149 – 12f. brown, blue and violet 20 10
150 – 50f. indigo, blue and green 45 25
DESIGNS: 12f. Catholic Cathedral, Fianarantsoa; 50f. Aga Khan Mosque, Tananarive.

62 President Tsiranana and Wife — **63** Cornucopia, Coins and Map

1968. 10th Anniv of Republic.
151 **62** 20f. brown, red and yellow 20 10
152 30f. brown, red and blue 25 15

1968. 50th Anniv of Malagasy Savings Bank.
154 **63** 20f. multicoloured 25 10

64 "Dance of the Whirlwind"

1968. Air.
155 **64** 100f. multicoloured . . . . 1·50 65

65 Malagasy Family

1968. Five-year Plan (2nd issue).
156 **65** 15f. red, yellow and blue 15 10
157 – 45f. multicoloured 40 25
DESIGN—VERT: 45f. Allegory of "Achievement".

1968. Air. "Philexafrique" Stamp Exn, Abidjan (1969) (1st issue). As T **113a** of Mauritania.
158 100f. multicoloured . . . . . 2·75 80
DESIGN: 100f. "Young Woman sealing a Letter" (J. B. Santerre).

1969. Air. "Philexafrique" Stamp Exn, Abidjan, Ivory Coast (2nd issue). As T **114a** of Mauritania.
159 50f. red, green and drab . . . 1·60 90
DESIGN: 50f. Malagasy Arms, map and Madagascar stamp of 1946.

68 "Queen Adelaide receiving Malagasy Mission, London" (1836–37)

1969.
160 **68** 250f. multicoloured . . . . 4·50 3·25

69 Hand with Spanner, Cogwheels and I.L.O. Emblem

1969. 50th Anniv of I.L.O.
161 **69** 20f. multicoloured 25 15

70 Post and Telecommunications Building, Tananarive

1969. Stamp Day.
162 **70** 30f. multicoloured 35 20

71 Map, Steering Wheel and Vehicles — **72** President Tsiranana making Speech

1969. 20th Anniv of Malagasy Motor Club.
163 **71** 65f. multicoloured 60 35

1969. 10th Anniv of President Tsiranana's Assumption of Office.
164 **72** 20f. multicoloured 20 10

73 Bananas — **74** Start of Race and Olympic Flame

1969. Fruits.
165 **73** 5f. green, brown and blue 15 10
166 – 15f. red, myrtle and green 30 10
DESIGN: 15f. Lychees.

1969. Olympic Games, Mexico (1968).
167 **74** 15f. brown, red and green 25 20

75 "Malagasy Seashore, East Coast" (A. Razafinjohany)

1969. Air. Paintings by Malagasy Artists. Multicoloured.
168 100f. Type **75** . . . . 1·25 80
169 150f. "Sunset on the High Plateaux" (H. Ratovo) . . 2·50 1·40

76 Imerino House, High Plateaux — **77** Ambalavao Arms

1969. Malagasy Traditional Dwellings (1st series).
170 – 20f. red, blue and green . . 20 10
171 – 20f. brown, red and blue 20 10
172 **76** 40f. red, blue and indigo 40 20
173 – 60f. purple, green and blue 60 25
HOUSES—HORIZ: 20f. (No. 170), Tsimihety hut, East Coast; 60f. Betsimisaraka dwellings, East Coast. VERT: 20f. (No. 171), Betsileo house, High Plateaux.
See also Nos. 205/6.

1970. Town Arms (2nd series). Multicoloured.
174 10f. Type **77** 20 10
175 25f. Morondava 35 15
176 25f. Ambatondrazaka 35 15
177 80f. Tamatave 90 35
See also Nos. 208/9.

78 Agate — **80** U.N. Emblem and Symbols

1970. Semi-precious Stones. Multicoloured.
178 5f. Type **78** . . . . 1·60 55
179 20f. Ammonite . . . . 3·25 1·10

1970. New U.P.U. Headquarters Building, Berne. As T **81** of New Caledonia.
180 20f. blue, brown and mauve 30 20

1970. 25th Anniv of United Nations.
181 **80** 50f. black, blue and orange 65 25

81 Astronaut and Module on Moon

1970. Air. 1st Anniv of "Apollo 11" Moon-landing.
182 **81** 75f. green, slate and blue 1·10 40

82 Malagasy Fruits

1970.
183 **82** 20f. multicoloured 30 15

83 Delessert's Lyria

1970. Sea Shells (1st series). Multicoloured.
184 5f. Type **83** 50 15
185 10f. Bramble murex 65 25
186 20f. Thorny oyster . . . . . 1·40 50

84 Aye-aye

1970. International Nature Conservation Conference, Tananarive.
187 **84** 20f. multicoloured 40 30

85 Boeing 737 in Flight

1970. Air.
188 **85** 200f. red, green and blue 2·40 1·25

86 Pres. Tsiranana — **87** Calcite

1970. Pres. Tsiranana's 60th Birthday.
189 **86** 30f. brown and green . . . 30 15

1971. Minerals. Multicoloured.
190 12f. Type **87** . . . . 1·60 45
191 15f. Quartz . . . . 2·25 65

88 Soap Works, Tananarive

1971. Malagasy Industries.

192	**88**	5f. multicoloured	15	10
193	–	15f. black, brown and blue	25	10
194	–	50f. multicoloured	55	15

DESIGNS: 15f. Chrome works, Comina-Andriamena; 50f. Textile complex, Sotema-Majunga.

89 Globe and Emblems

1971. Council Meeting of Common Market Countries with African and Malagasy Associated States, Tananarive.

195	**89**	5f. multicoloured	15	15

90 Rural Mobile Post Office

1971. Stamp Day.

196	**90**	25f. multicoloured	35	15

91 Gen. De Gaulle

1971. Death (1970) of Gen. Charles de Gaulle.

197	**91**	30f. black, red and blue	70	35

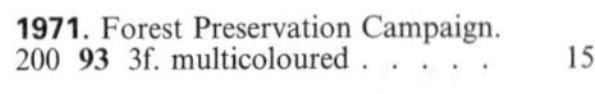

92 Palm Beach Hotel, Nossi-Be **93** Forestry Emblem

1971. Malagasy Hotels.

198	**92**	25f. multicoloured	30	20
199	–	65f. brown, blue and green	60	30

DESIGN: 65f. Hilton Hotel, Tananarive.

1971. Forest Preservation Campaign.

200	**93**	3f. multicoloured	15	10

94 Jean Ralaimongo

1971. Air. Malagasy Celebrities.

201	**94**	25f. brown, red and orange	30	15
202	–	65f. brown, myrtle & green	40	25
203	–	100f. brown, ultram & bl	90	40

CELEBRITIES: 65f. Albert Sylla; 100f. Joseph Ravoahangy Andrianavalona.

1971. Air. 10th Anniv of African and Malagasy Posts and Telecommunications Union. As T **139a** of Mauritania.

204	100f. U.A.M.P.T. H.Q., Brazzaville, and painting "Mpisikidy" (G. Rakotovao)	1·00	60

96 Vezo Dwellings, South-east Coast

1971. Malagasy Traditional Dwellings (2nd series). Multicoloured.

205	5f. Type **96**	15	10
206	10f. Antandroy hut, South coast	20	10

97 "Children and Cattle in Meadow" (G. Rasoahariјaona)

1971. 25th Anniv of U.N.I.C.E.F.

207	**97**	50f. multicoloured	65	30

1972. Town Arms (3rd series). As T **77**. Mult.

208	1f. Maintirano Arms	10	10
209	25f. Fenerive-Est	35	20

99 Cable-laying train

1972. Co-axial Cable Link, Tananarive–Tamatave.

210	**99**	45f. brown, green and red	2·75	1·25

100 Telecommunications Station

1972. Inauguration of Philibert Tsiranana Satellite Communications Station.

211	**100**	85f. multicoloured	75	45

101 Pres. Tsiranana and Voters **102** "Moped" Postman

1972. Presidential Elections.

212	**101**	25f. multicoloured	40	35

1972. Stamp Day.

213	**102**	10f. multicoloured	40	20

1972. De Gaulle Memorial. No. 197 surch **MEMORIAL +20F**.

214	**91**	30f.+20f. black, red & bl	60	60

104 Exhibition Emblem and Stamps

1972. 2nd National Stamp Exn, Antanarive.

215	**104**	25f. multicoloured	35	30
216		40f. multicoloured	60	35
217		100f. multicoloured	1·25	75

105 Road and Monument

1972. Opening of Andapa–Sambava Highway.

219	**105**	50f. multicoloured	35	25

106 Petroleum Refinery, Tamatave

1972. Malagasy Economic Development.

220	**106**	2f. blue, green and yellow	20	10
221	–	100f. multicoloured	3·00	30

DESIGN: 100f. 3600 CV diesel locomotive.

107 R. Rakotobe

1972. Air. 1st Death Anniv of Rene Rakotobe (poet).

222	**107**	40f. brown, purple & orge	40	20

108 College Buildings

1972. 150th Anniv of Razafindrahety College, Tananarive.

223	**108**	10f. purple, brown & blue	15	10

109 Volleyball

1972. African Volleyball Championships.

224	**109**	12f. black, orange & brn	40	15

110 Runners breasting Tape

1972. Air. Olympic Games, Munich. Multicoloured.

225	100f. Type **110**	1·40	60
226	200f. Judo	2·25	90

111 Hospital Complex

1972. Inauguration of Ravoahangy Andrianavalona Hospital.

227	**111**	6f. multicoloured	20	15

112 Mohair Goat

1972. Air. Malagasy Wool Production.

228	**112**	250f. multicoloured	3·75	2·25

113 Ploughing with Oxen

1972. Agricultural Expansion.

229	**113**	25f. multicoloured	25	15

114 "Virgin and Child" (15th-cent Florentine School)

1972. Air. Christmas. Religious Paintings. Mult.

230	85f. Type **114**	85	55
231	150f. "Adoration of the Magi" (A. Mantegna) (horiz)	2·00	85

115 Betsimisarka Women

1972. Traditional Costumes. Multicoloured.

232	10f. Type **115**	20	10
233	15f. Merina mother and child	30	20

116 Astronauts on Moon

1973. Air. Moon Flight of "Apollo 17".

234	**116**	300f. purple, brown & grey	3·25	1·75

117 "Natural Produce"

1973. 10th Anniv of Malagasy Freedom from Hunger Campaign Committee.

235	**117**	25f. multicoloured	30	15

118 "The Entombment" (Grunewald)

1973. Air. Easter. Multicoloured.
236 100f. Type **118** . . . . 1·00 55
237 200f. "The Resurrection" (Grunewald) (vert) . . . . 2·25 1·10

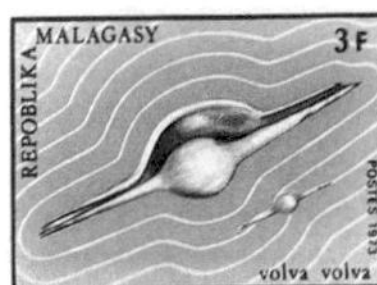

119 Shuttlecock Volva

1973. Sea Shells (2nd series). Multicoloured.
238 3f. Type **119** 15 10
239 10f. Arthritic spider conch . . 25 20
240 15f. Common harp 50 30
241 25f. Type **119** 70 45
242 40f. As 15f. . . . . 1·10 50
243 50f. As 10f. . . . . 2·25 60

120 Postal Courier, Tsimandoa **121** "Africa" within Scaffolding

1973. Stamp Day.
244 **120** 50f. blue, green and brown 45 20

1973. 10th Anniv of Organization of African Unity.
245 **121** 25f. multicoloured 30 15

122 "Cameleon campani"

1973. Malagasy Chameleons. Multicoloured.
246 1f. Type **122** 10 10
247 5f. "Cameleon nasutus" (male) 10 10
248 10f. "Cameleon nasutus" (female) 15 10
249 40f. As 5f. 55 25
250 60f. Type **122** 85 35
251 85f. As 10f. . . . . 1·25 65

123 Excursion Carriage

1973. Air. Early Malagasy Railways. Multicoloured.
252 100f. Type **123** . . . . 1·75 85
253 150f. Mallet steam locomotive No. 24, 1907 . . . . . . 2·50 1·40

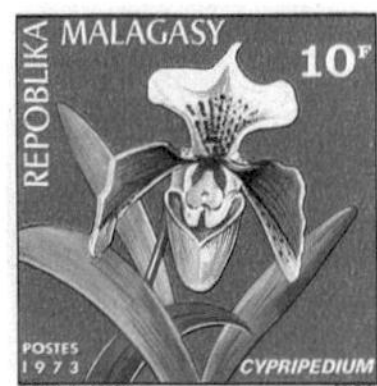

124 "Cypripedium"

1973. Orchids. Multicoloured.
254 10f. Type **124** 30 15
255 25f. "Nepenthes pervillei" . . 50 20
256 40f. As 25f. . . . . 1·00 35
257 100f. Type **124** . . . . 2·25 85

1973. Pan African Drought Relief. No. 235 surch **SECHERESSE SOLIDARITE AFRICAINE** and value.
258 **117** 100f. on 25f. multicoloured . . . . . 1·10 60

126 Dish Aerial and Meteorological Station **129** Pres. Kennedy

128 Greater Dwarf Lemur

1973. Air. W.M.O. Centenary.
259 **126** 100f. orange, blue & black 1·25 65

1973. 12th Anniv of African and Malagasy Posts and Telecommunications. As T **155a** of Mauritania.
260 100f. red, violet and green . . 90 45

1973. Malagasy Lemurs.
261 **128** 5f. brown, green and purple (postage) 55 15
262 – 25f. brown, sepia & green 1·10 65
263 – 150f. brn, grn & sepia (air) . . . . 2·75 1·25
264 **128** 200f. brown, turq & blue 4·00 1·75
DESIGN—VERT: 25f., 150f. Weasel-lemur.

1973. Air. 10th Death Anniv of Pres. John Kennedy.
265 **129** 300f. multicoloured . . . 3·25 1·75

130 Footballers

1973. Air. World Cup Football Championship. West Germany.
266 **130** 500f. mauve, brown and light brown . . . . . 5·50 2·50

CURRENCY. Issues from No. 267 to No. 389 have face values shown as "Fmg". This abbreviation denotes the Malagasy Franc which was introduced in 1966.

131 Copernicus, Satellite and Diagram

1974. Air. 500th Birth Anniv of Copernicus.
267 **131** 250f. blue, brown & green 3·25 1·50

1974. No. 76a surch.
268 25f. on 30f. multicoloured . . 25 15

133 Agricultural Training **135** Family and House

134 Male Player, and Hummingbird on Hibiscus

1974. 25th World Scouting Conference, Nairobi, Kenya.
269 **133** 4f. grey, blue and green (postage) 10 10
270 – 15f. purple, green and blue 20 15
271 – 100f. ochre, red & blue (air) 80 45
272 – 300f. brown, blue & black 3·50 1·75
DESIGNS—VERT: 15f. Building construction. HORIZ: 100f. First Aid training; 300f. Fishing.

1974. Air. Asia, Africa and Latin America Table-Tennis Championships, Peking.
273 **134** 50f. red, blue and brown 80 30
274 – 100f. red, blue and violet 1·60 70
DESIGN: 100f. Female player and stylized bird.

1974. World Population Year.
275 **135** 25f. red, orange and blue 25 10

136 Micheline Railcar

1974. Air. Malagasy Railway Locomotives.
276 **136** 50f. green, red and brown 75 25
277 – 85f. red, blue and green 1·25 30
278 – 200f. blue, lt blue & brown . . . . 3·25 80
DESIGNS: 85f. Track-inspection trolley; 200f. Garratt steam locomotive, 1926.

137 U.P.U. Emblem and Letters

1974. Air. Centenary of U.P.U.
279 **137** 250f. red, blue and violet 3·00 1·40

138 Rainibetsimisaraka

1974. Rainibetsimisaraka Commemoration.
280 **138** 25f. multicoloured 35 20

1974. Air. West Germany's Victory in World Cup Football Championship. No. 266 optd **R.F.A. 2 HOLLANDE 1**.
281 **130** 500f. mauve, brown and light brown . . . . . 5·00 2·75

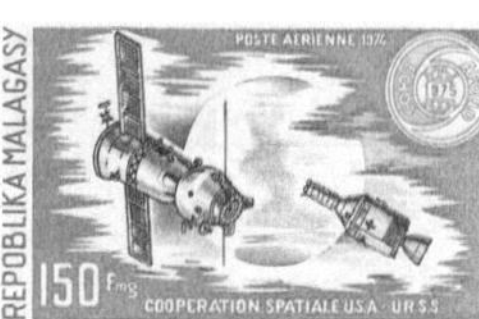

140 "Apollo" and "Soyuz" spacecraft

1974. Air. Soviet–U.S. Space Co-operation.
282 **140** 150f. orange, green & blue 1·10 60
283 – 250f. green, blue & brown 2·00 1·00
DESIGN: No. 283, As Type **140** but different view.

141 Marble Slabs

1974. Marble Industry. Multicoloured.
284 4f. Type **141** 55 15
285 25f. Quarrying . . . . 1·40 25

1974. Air. Universal Postal Union Centenary (2nd issue). No. 279 optd **100 ANS DE COLLABORATION INTERNATIONALE**.
286 **137** 250f. red, blue and violet 1·75 1·00

143 Faces and Maps

1974. Europafrique.
287 **143** 150f. brown, red & orange 1·40 70

144 "Food in Hand"

1974. "Freedom from Hunger".
288 **144** 80f. blue, brown and grey 65 35

145 "Coton" **146** Malagasy People

1974. Malagasy Dogs. Multicoloured.
289 50f. Type **145** . . . . 1·40 45
290 100f. Hunting dog . . . . . 2·25 1·10

1974. Founding of "Fokonolona" Commune.
291 **146** 5f. multicoloured 15 10
292 10f. multicoloured 15 10
293 20f. multicoloured 20 10
294 60f. multicoloured 60 30

147 "Discovering Talent"

1974. National Development Council.
295 **147** 25f. multicoloured 20 10
296 35f. multicoloured 30 15

148 "Adoration of the Magi" (David)

1974. Air. Christmas. Multicoloured.
297 200f. Type **148** . . . . 2·25 95
298 300f. "Virgin of the Cherries and Child" (Metzys) . . . 3·25 1·25

149 Malagasy Girl and Rose

1975. International Women's Year.
299 **149** 100f. brown, orange & grn 85 40

150 Colonel Richard Ratsimandrava (Head of Government)

1975.
300 **150** 15f. brown, black & yellow 15 10
301 25f. brown, black and blue 20 15
302 100f. brown, black & green 80 35

151 Sofia Bridge

1975.
303 **151** 45f. multicoloured 50 20

152 U.N. Emblem and Part of Globe

1975. Air. 30th Anniv of U.N. Charter.
304 **152** 300f. multicoloured . . . 2·75 1·25

153 De Grasse (after Mauzaisse) and "Randolph"

1975. Bicentenary of American Revolution (1st issue). Multicoloured.
305 40f. Type **153** (postage) . . . 85 25
306 50f. Lafayette, "Lexington" and H.M.S. "Edward" . . 95 30
307 100f. D'Estaing and "Languedoc" (air) . . . . 1·75 50
308 200f. Paul Jones, "Bonhomme Richard" and H.M.S. "Serapis" . . . . 2·50 1·10
309 300f. Benjamin Franklin, "Millern" and "Montgomery" . . . . . 3·50 1·60

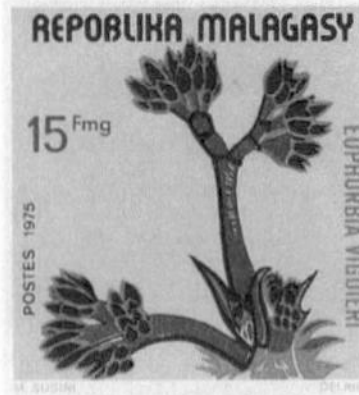

154 "Euphorbia viguieri"

1975. Malagasy Flora. Multicoloured.
311 15f. Type **154** (postage) . . . 25 15
312 25f. "Hibiscus rosesinensis" 40 20
313 30f. "Plumeria rubra acutitolia" 55 20
314 40f. "Pachypodium rosulatum" . . . . 1·00 30
315 85f. "Turraea sericea" (air) 1·75 1·00

1975. Air. "Apollo"–"Soyuz" Space Link. Nos. 282/3 optd **JONCTION 17 JUILLET 1975**.
316 **140** 150f. orange, green & blue 1·00 60
317 – 250f. green, blue & brown 2·25 1·00

156 Temple Frieze

1975. Air. "Save Borobudur Temple" (in Indonesia) Campaign.
318 **156** 50f. red, orange and blue 1·00 50

157 "Racial Unity"

1975. Namibia Day.
319 **157** 50f. multicoloured 45 20

158 Pryer's Woodpecker

1975. International Exposition, Okinawa. Fauna. Multicoloured.
320 25f. Type **158** (postage) . . . 50 25
321 40f. Ryukyu rabbit 50 20
322 50f. Toad 70 30
323 75f. Tortoise . . . . 1·40 40
324 125f. Sika deer (air) . . . . 1·50 55

159 Lily Waterfall

1975. Lily Waterfall. Multicoloured.
326 25f. Type **159** 40 15
327 40f. Lily Waterfall (distant view) 60 15

160 Hurdling

1975. Air. "Pre-Olympic Year". Olympic Games, Montreal (1976). Multicoloured.
328 75f. Type **160** 60 35
329 200f. Weightlifting (vert) . . 2·00 75

161 Bobsleigh "Fours"

1975. Winter Olympic Games, Innsbruck. Multicoloured.
330 75f. Type **161** (postage) . . . 50 25
331 100f. Ski-jumping 80 35
332 140f. Speed-skating . . . . . 1·25 50
333 200f. Cross-country skiing (air) . . . . 2·00 75
334 245f. Downhill skiing . . . . 2·25 90

162 Pirogue

1975. Malagasy Sailing-vessels. Multicoloured.
336 8f. Type **162** 55 15
337 45f. Malagasy schooner . . . 1·10 25

163 Canoeing

1976. Olympic Games, Montreal. Multicoloured.
338 40f. Type **163** (postage) . . . 25 15
339 50f. Sprinting and hurdling 35 20
340 100f. Putting the shot, and long-jumping (air) 90 35
341 200f. Gymnastics-horse and parallel bars . . . . 1·75 75
342 300f. Trampoline-jumping and high-diving . . . . . 2·40 1·00

164 "Apollo 14" Lunar Module and Flight Badge

1976. Air. 5th Anniv of "Apollo 14" Mission.
344 **164** 150f. blue, red and green 1·25 65

1976. Air. 5th Anniv of "Apollo 14" Mission. No. 344 optd **5e Anniversaire de la mission APOLLO XIV**.
345 **164** 150f. blue, red and green 1·25 75

166 "Graf Zeppelin" over Fujiyama

1976. 75th Anniv of Zeppelin. Multicoloured.
346 40f. Type **166** (postage) . . . 35 15
347 50f. "Graf Zeppelin" over Rio de Janeiro 40 15
348 75f. "Graf Zeppelin" over New York 80 25
349 100f. "Graf Zeppelin" over Sphinx and pyramids . . . 95 35
350 200f. "Graf Zeppelin" over Berlin (air) . . . . 2·25 75
351 300f. "Graf Zeppelin" over London . . . . 4·00 1·00

167 "Prevention of Blindness"

1976. World Health Day.
353 **167** 100f. multicoloured . . . 1·25 55

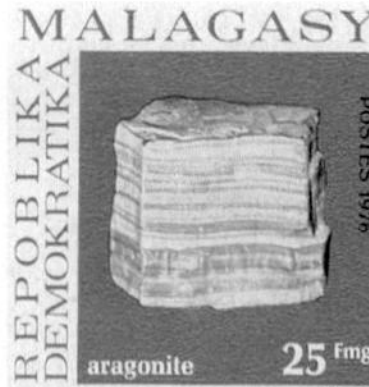

168 Aragonite

1976. Minerals and Fossils. Multicoloured.
354 25f. Type **168** 50 15
355 50f. Fossilized wood . . . . 1·10 55
356 150f. Celestyte . . . . 3·25 1·60

169 Alexander Graham Bell and Early Telephone

1976. Telephone Centenary. Multicoloured.
357 25f. Type **169** 15 10
358 50f. Cable maintenance, 1911 30 15
359 100f. Telephone operator and switchboard, 1895 . . . . 60 25
360 200f. "Emile Baudot" cable ship . . . . 2·25 90
361 300f. Man with radio-telephone . . . . 2·25 80

170 Children reading Book

1976. Children's Books Promotion. Multicoloured.
363 10f. Type **170** 15 10
364 25f. Children reading book (vert) 35 15

1976. Medal winners, Winter Olympic Games, Innsbruck. Nos. 330/4 optd **VAINQUEUR** and medal winner.
365 75f. Type **161** (postage) . . . 50 25
366 100f. Ski-jumping 80 40
367 140f. Skating . . . . 1·25 50
368 200f. Cross-country skiing (air) . . . . 1·40 75
369 245f. Downhill skiing . . . . 1·90 1·00

OPTS: 75f. **ALLEMAGNE FEDERALE**; 100f. **KARL SCHNABL, AUTRICHE**; 140f. **SHEILA YOUNG, ETATS-UNIS**; 200f. **IVAR FORMO, NORVEGE**; 245f. **ROSI MITTERMAIER, ALLEMAGNE DE L'OUEST**.

The subject depicted on No. 367 is speed-skating, an event in which the gold medal was won by J. E. Storholt, Norway.

1976. Bicentenary of American Revolution (2nd issue). Nos. 305/9 optd **4 JUILLET 1776–1976** in frame.
371 **153** 40f. multicoloured (postage) 35 25
372 – 50f. multicoloured 40 30
373 – 100f. multicoloured (air) 75 50
374 – 200f. multicoloured . . . 1·50 85
375 – 300f. multicoloured . . . 2·25 1·25

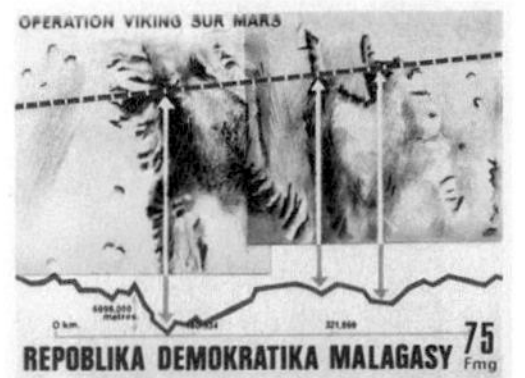

173 Descent Trajectory

1976. "Viking" Landing on Mars. Multicoloured.
377 75f. Type **173** 40 20
378 100f. "Viking" landing module separation 60 25
379 200f. "Viking" on Martian surface . . . . 1·25 55
380 300f. "Viking" orbiting Mars 2·00 80

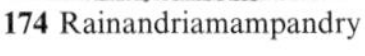

174 Rainandriamampandry **175** Doves over Globe

1976. 30th Anniv of Treaties signed by Rainandriamampandry (Foreign Minister).
382 **174** 25f. multicoloured 30 20

1976. Indian Ocean—"Zone of Peace". Multicoloured.
383 60f. Type **175** 35 20
384 160f. Doves flying across Indian Ocean (horiz) . . . 1·10 55

1976. Olympic Games Medal Winners. Nos. 338/42 optd with names of two winners on each stamp.
385 **163** 40f. multicoloured (postage) 25 15
386 – 50f. multicoloured 35 25
387 – 100f. multicoloured (air) 70 40
388 – 200f. multicoloured . . . 1·40 65
389 – 300f. multicoloured . . . 2·00 1·00
OVERPRINTS: 40f. **V. DIBA, A. ROGOV**; 50f. **H. CRAWFORD, J. SCHALLER**; 100f. **U. BEYER, A. ROBINSON**; 200f. **N. COMANECI, N. ANDRIANOV**; 300f. **K. DIBIASI, E. VAYTSEKHOVSKAIA.**

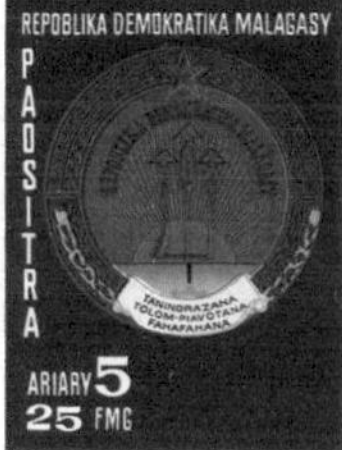

177 Malagasy Arms

1976. 1st Anniv of Malagasy Democratic Republic.
391 **177** 25f. multicoloured 20 10

178 Rabezavana (Independence Movement Leader)

1977. National Heroes. Multicoloured.
392 25f. Type **178** 20 10
393 25f. Lt. Albert Randriamaromanana . . . 20 10
394 25f. Ny Avana Ramanantoanina (politician) 20 10
395 100f. Fasam-Pirenena National Mausoleum, Tananarive (horiz) 75 40

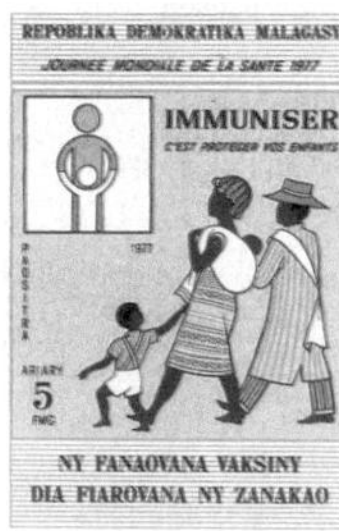

179 Family

1977. World Health Day.
396 **179** 5f. multicoloured 15 10

180 Medical School, Antananarivo

1977. 80th Anniv of Medical School, Antananarivo.
397 **180** 250f. multicoloured . . . 2·00 95

181 Rural Post Van

1977. Rural Mail.
398 **181** 35f. multicoloured 30 15

182 Morse Key and Man with Headphones

1977. 90th Anniv of Antananarivo–Tamatave Telegraph.
399 **182** 15f. multicoloured 15 10

183 Academy Emblem

1977. 75th Anniv of Malagasy Academy.
400 **183** 10f. multicoloured 15 10

184 Lenin and Russian Flag

1977. 60th Anniv of Russian Revolution.
401 **184** 25f. multicoloured . . . . 1·10 10

185 Raoul Follereau

1978. 25th Anniv of World Leprosy Day.
402 **185** 5f. multicoloured 90 10

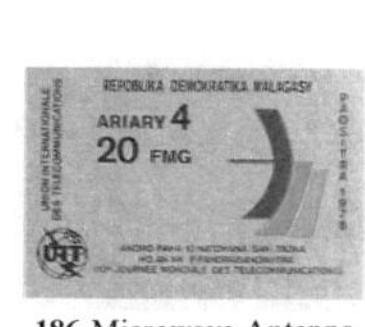

186 Microwave Antenna **187** "Co-operation"

1978. World Telecommunications Day.
403 **186** 20f. multicoloured 15 10

1978. Anti-Apartheid Year.
404 **187** 60f. red, black and yellow 40 25

188 Children with Instruments of Revolution **189** Tractor, Factory and Labourers

1978. "Youth—Pillar of the Revolution".
405 **188** 25f. multicoloured 75 45

1978. Socialist Co-operatives.
406 **189** 25f. multicoloured 15 10

190 Women at Work **191** Children with Books, Instruments and Fruit

1979. "Women, Pillar of the Revolution".
407 **190** 40f. multicoloured 25 15

1979. International Year of the Child.
408 **191** 10f. multicoloured 20 10

192 Ring-tailed Lemur **193** J. V. S. Razakandraina

1979. Animals. Multicoloured.
409 25f. Type **192** (postage) . . . 25 15
410 125f. Black lemur . . . . . 1·40 30
411 1000f. Malagasy civet . . . . 8·50 2·25
412 20f. Tortoise (air) 20 20
413 95f. Black lemur (different) 1·00 40

1979. J. V. S. Razakandraina (poet) Commem.
414 **193** 25f. multicoloured 15 10

194 "Centella asiatica"

1979. Medicinal Plant.
415 **194** 25f. multicoloured 15 10

195 Map of Malagasy and Ste. Marie Telecommunications Station

1979. Telecommunications.
416 **195** 25f. multicoloured 20 10

196 Post Office, Antsirabe

1979. Stamp Day.
417 **196** 500f. multicoloured . . . 3·25 1·10

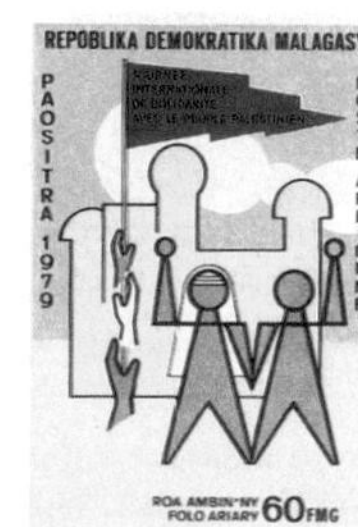

197 Palestinians with Flag

1979. Air. Palestinian Solidarity.
418 **197** 60f. multicoloured 50 20

198 Concorde and Map of Africa

1979. 20th Anniv of ASECNA (African Air Safety Organization).
419 **198** 50f. multicoloured 60 20

199 Lenin addressing Meeting

1980. 110th Birth Anniv of Lenin.
420 **199** 25f. multicoloured 45 10

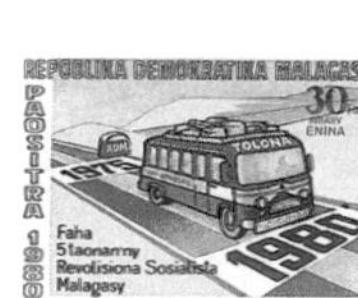

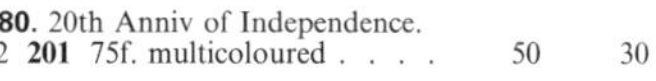

200 Taxi-bus **201** Map illuminated by Sun

1980. 5th Anniv of Socialist Revolution.
421 **200** 30f. multicoloured 20 10

1980. 20th Anniv of Independence.
422 **201** 75f. multicoloured 50 30

202 Military Parade

1980. 20th Anniv of Army.
423 **202** 50f. multicoloured 35 15

203 Joseph Raseta

1980. Dr. Joseph Raseta Commemoration.
424 **203** 30f. multicoloured 20 10

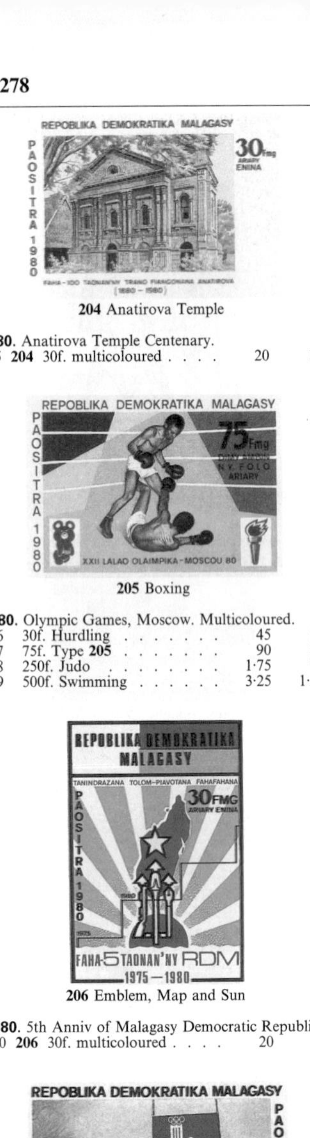

204 Anatirova Temple

1980. Anatirova Temple Centenary.
425 **204** 30f. multicoloured 20 10

205 Boxing

1980. Olympic Games, Moscow. Multicoloured.
426 30f. Hurdling 45 10
427 75f. Type **205** 90 25
428 250f. Judo . . . . 1·75 75
429 500f. Swimming . . . . . . 3·25 1·50

206 Emblem, Map and Sun

1980. 5th Anniv of Malagasy Democratic Republic.
430 **206** 30f. multicoloured 20 10

207 Skier

1981. Winter Olympic Games, Lake Placid (1980).
431 **207** 175f. multicoloured . . . 1·10 55

208 "Angraecum leonis" **209** Handicapped Student

1981. Flowers. Multicoloured.
432 5f. Type **208** 10 10
433 80f. "Angraecum famosum" 60 25
434 170f. "Angraecum sesquipedale" . . . . . . 1·25 55

1981. International Year of Disabled People. Mult.
435 25f. Type **209** 20 10
436 80f. Disabled carpenter . . . 55 25

210 Ribbons forming Caduceus, I.T.U. and W.H.O. Emblems

1981. World Telecommunications Day.
437 **210** 15f. blue, black and yellow 15 10
438 45f. multicoloured 35 15

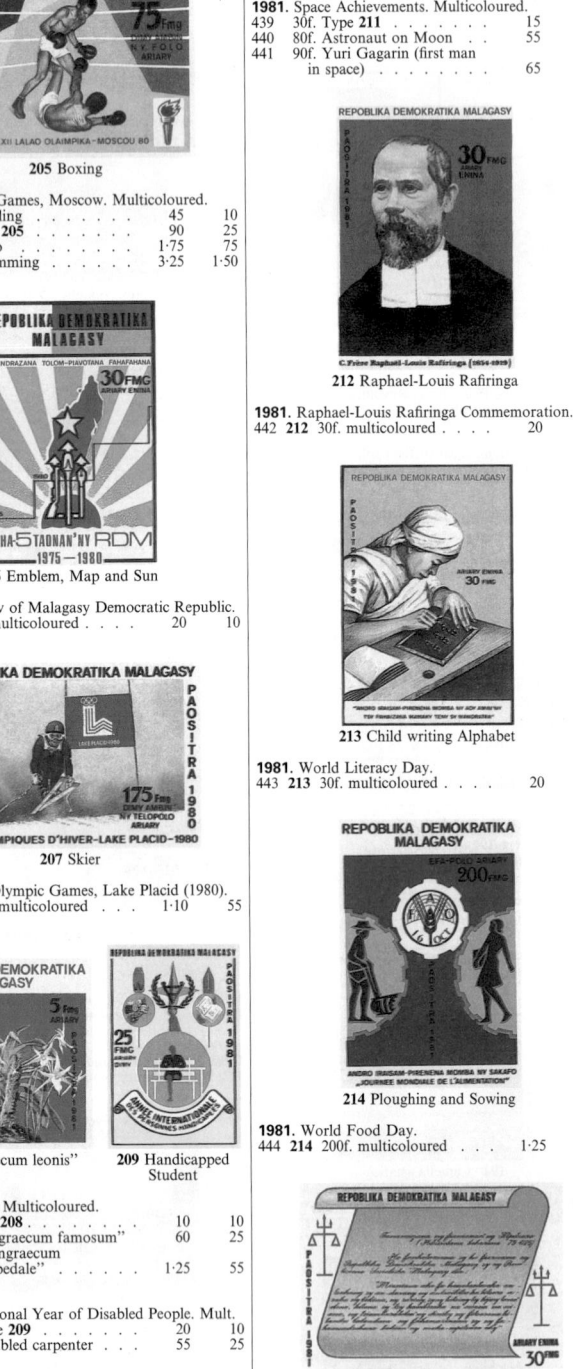

211 Valentina Tereshkova (first woman in space)

1981. Space Achievements. Multicoloured.
439 30f. Type **211** 15 10
440 80f. Astronaut on Moon . . 55 25
441 90f. Yuri Gagarin (first man in space) 65 30

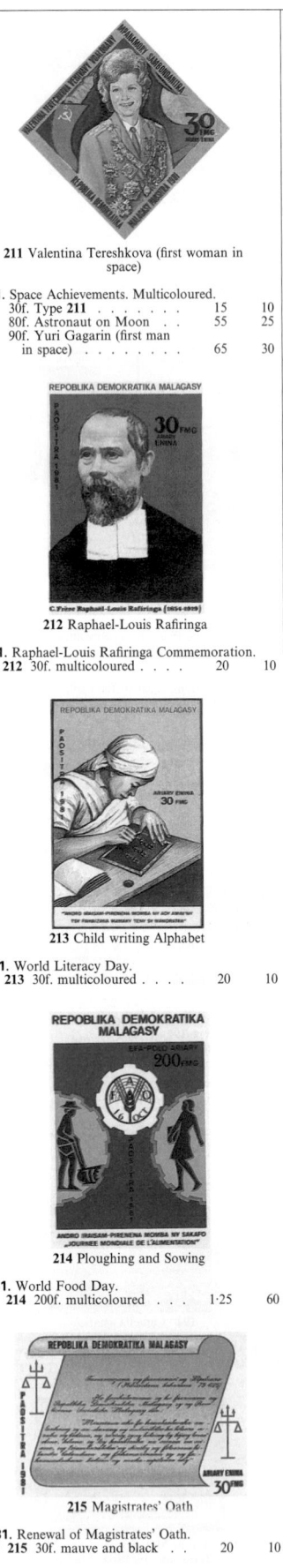

212 Raphael-Louis Rafiringa

1981. Raphael-Louis Rafiringa Commemoration.
442 **212** 30f. multicoloured 20 10

213 Child writing Alphabet

1981. World Literacy Day.
443 **213** 30f. multicoloured 20 10

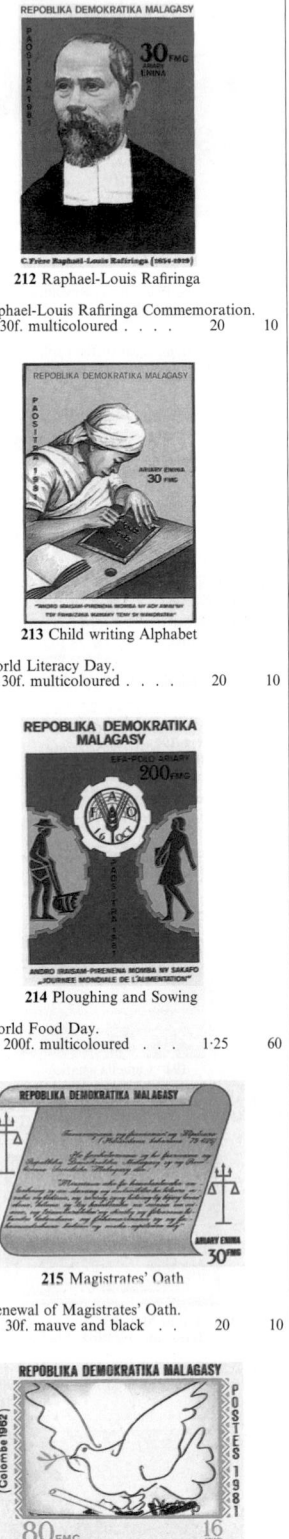

214 Ploughing and Sowing

1981. World Food Day.
444 **214** 200f. multicoloured . . . 1·25 60

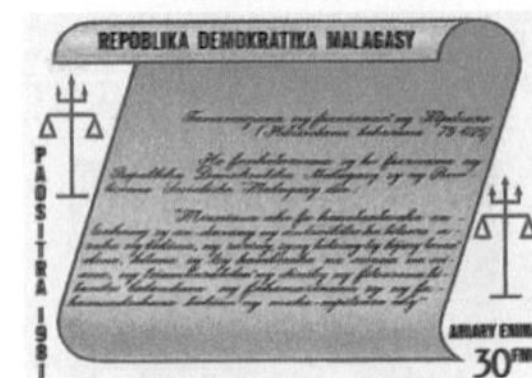

215 Magistrates' Oath

1981. Renewal of Magistrates' Oath.
445 **215** 30f. mauve and black . . 20 10

216 "Dove"

1981. Birth Centenary of Pablo Picasso.
446 **216** 80f. multicoloured 60 25

217 U.P.U. Emblem and Malagasy Stamps

1981. 20th Anniv of Admission to U.P.U.
447 **217** 5f. multicoloured 10 10
448 30f. multicoloured 20 10

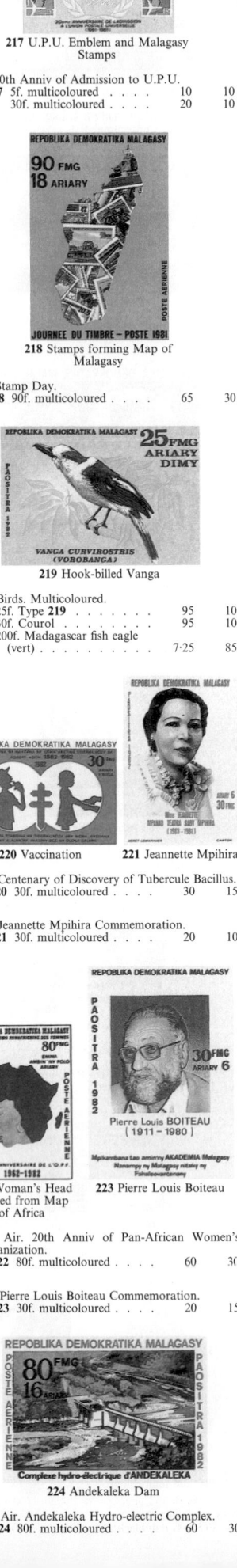

218 Stamps forming Map of Malagasy

1981. Stamp Day.
449 **218** 90f. multicoloured 65 30

219 Hook-billed Vanga

1982. Birds. Multicoloured.
450 25f. Type **219** 95 10
451 30f. Courol 95 10
452 200f. Madagascar fish eagle (vert) . . . . 7·25 85

220 Vaccination **221** Jeannette Mpihira

1982. Centenary of Discovery of Tubercule Bacillus.
453 **220** 30f. multicoloured 30 15

1982. Jeannette Mpihira Commemoration.
454 **221** 30f. multicoloured 20 10

222 Woman's Head formed from Map of Africa **223** Pierre Louis Boiteau

1982. Air. 20th Anniv of Pan-African Women's Organization.
455 **222** 80f. multicoloured 60 30

1982. Pierre Louis Boiteau Commemoration.
456 **223** 30f. multicoloured 20 15

224 Andekaleka Dam

1982. Air. Andekaleka Hydro-electric Complex.
457 **224** 80f. multicoloured 60 30

225 "Sputnik I"

1982. 25th Anniv of First Artificial Satellite. Multicoloured.
458 10f. Type **225** 10 10
459 80f. Yuri Gagarin 60 30
460 100f. "Soyuz"–"Salyut" space station 75 35

226 Heading Ball

1982. World Cup Football Championship, Spain. Multicoloured.
461 30f. Type **226** 20 10
462 40f. Running with ball . . . 30 15
463 80f. Tackle 60 30

227 Ploughing, Sowing and F.A.O. Emblem

1982. World Food Day.
465 **227** 80f. multicoloured 50 30

228 Bar Scene

1982. 150th Anniv of Edouard Manet (artist). Multicoloured.
466 5f. Type **228** 45 15
467 30f. Woman in white 65 10
468 170f. Man with pipe . . . . 2·75 65

229 Emperor Snapper

1982. Fishes. Multicoloured.
470 5f. Type **229** 20 20
471 20f. Sailfish 30 20
472 30f. Lionfish 40 20
473 50f. Yellow-finned tuna . . . 65 20
474 200f. Black-tipped grouper 3·00 85

230 Fort Mahavelona

1982. Landscapes. Multicoloured.

476	10f. Type **230** (postage)	10	10
477	30f. Ramena coast	20	10
478	400f. Jacarandas in flower (air)	2·75	1·50

231 Flags of Russia and Malagasy, Clasped Hands and Tractors

1982. 60th Anniv of U.S.S.R. Multicoloured.

479	10f. Type **231**	10	10
480	15f. Flags, clasped hands and radio antenna	10	10
481	30f. Map of Russia, Kremlin and Lenin	15	10
482	150f. Flags, clasped hands, statue and arms of Malagasy	1·00	45

232 Television, Drums, Envelope and Telephone

1983. World Communications Year. Multicoloured.

483	30f. Type **232**	15	10
484	80f. Stylized figures holding cogwheel	2·75	60

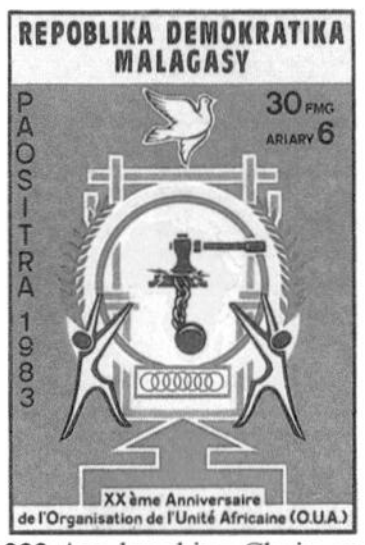

233 Axe breaking Chain on Map of Africa

234 Henri Douzon

1983. 20th Anniv of Organization of African Unity.

485	**233**	30f. multicoloured	20	10

1983. Henri Douzon (lawyer) Commemoration.

486	**234**	30f. multicoloured	20	10

237 Ruffed Lemur

1984. Lemurs. Multicoloured.

489	30f. Type **237**	35	20
490	30f. Verreaux's sifaka	35	20
491	30f. Lesser mouse-lemur (horiz)	35	20
492	30f. Aye-aye (horiz)	35	20
493	200f. Indri (horiz)	2·75	1·10

238 Ski Jumping

1984. Winter Olympic Games, Sarajevo. Mult.

495	20f. Type **238**	15	10
496	30f. Ice hockey	20	10
497	30f. Downhill skiing	20	10
498	30f. Speed skating	20	10
499	200f. Ice dancing	1·40	70

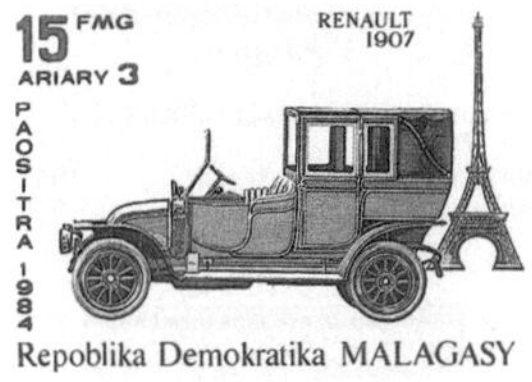

239 Renault, 1907

1984. Early Motor Cars. Multicoloured.

501	15f. Type **239**	20	10
502	30f. Benz, 1896	30	15
503	30f. Baker, 1901	30	15
504	30f. Blake, 1901	30	15
505	200f. F.I.A.L., 1908	2·00	75

240 Pastor Ravelojaona

241 "Noli me Tangere"

1984. Pastor Ravelojaona (encylopaedist) Commemoration.

507	**240**	30f. multicoloured	20	15

1984. 450th Death Anniv of Correggio. Paintings by Artist.

508	**241**	5f. multicoloured	10	10
509		20f. multicoloured	15	10
510	–	30f. multicoloured	25	15
511	–	80f. multicoloured	45	25
512	–	200f. multicoloured	1·40	65

242 Paris Landmarks and Emblem

243 Football

1984. 60th Anniv of International Chess Federation. Multicoloured.

514	5f. Type **242**	15	15
515	20f. Wilhelm Steinitz and stylized king	20	15
516	30f. Vera Menchik and stylized queen	35	15
517	30f. Anatoly Karpov and trophy	35	15
518	215f. Nona Gaprindashvili and trophy	2·75	90

1984. Olympic Games, Los Angeles.

520	**243**	100f. multicoloured	45	30

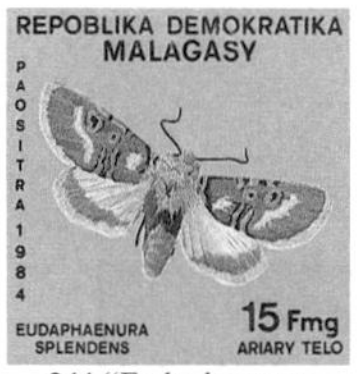

244 "Eudaphaenura splendens"

245 Ralaimongo

1984. Butterflies. Multicoloured.

521	15f. Type **244**	20	15
522	50f. "Acraea hova"	60	20
523	50f. "Othreis boesae"	60	20
524	50f. "Pharmocophagus antenor"	60	20
525	200f. "Epicausis smithii"	2·25	1·00

1984. Birth Centenary of Jean Ralaimongo (politician).

527	**245**	50f. multicoloured	30	15

246 Children in Brief-case

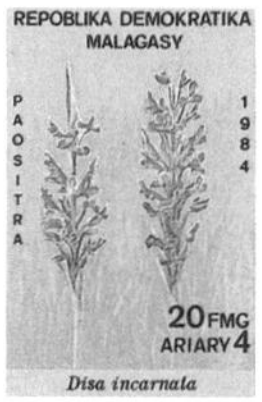

247 "Disa incarnata"

1984. 25th Anniv of Children's Rights Legislation.

528	**246**	50f. multicoloured	40	15

1984. Orchids. Multicoloured.

529	20f. Type **247** (postage)	20	10
530	235f. "Eulophiella roempleriana"	2·25	85
531	50f. "Eulophiella roempleriana" (horiz) (air)	60	25
532	50f. "Grammangis ellisii" (horiz)	60	25
533	50f. "Grammangis spectabilis"	60	25

248 U.N. Emblem and Cotton Plant

1984. 20th Anniv of United Nations Conference on Commerce and Development.

535	**248**	100f. multicoloured	60	30

249 "Sun Princess" (Sadio Diouf)

1984. 40th Anniv of International Civil Aviation Organization.

536	**249**	100f. multicoloured	65	30

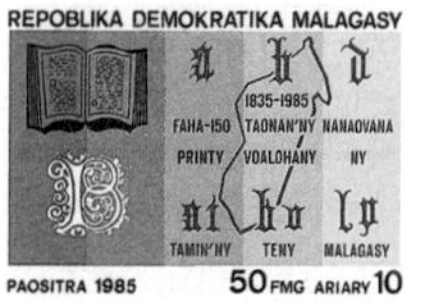

250 Bible, Map and Gothic Letters

1985. 150th Anniv of First Bible in Malagasy Language.

537	**250**	50f. brown, pink and black	30	15

251 Farming Scenes, Census-taker and Farmer

252 Lap-dog

1985. Agricultural Census.

538	**251**	50f. grey, black and mauve	30	15

1985. Cats and Dogs. Multicoloured.

539	20f. Type **252**	20	15
540	20f. Siamese cat	20	15
541	50f. Abyssinian cat (vert)	60	20
542	100f. Cocker spaniel (vert)	1·25	35
543	235f. Poodle	2·50	90

253 Russian Soldiers in Berlin

1985. 40th Anniv of Victory in Second World War.

545	20f. Type **253**	15	10
546	50f. Arms of French squadron and fighter planes	40	15
547	100f. Victory parade, Red Square, Moscow	75	30
548	100f. French troops entering Paris (vert)	1·25	30

254 Parade in Stadium

1985. 10th Anniv of Malagasy Democratic Republic.

549	**254**	50f. multicoloured	40	15

255 Medal and Independence Obelisk

256 Peace Dove and Stylized People

1985. 25th Anniv of Independence.

550	**255**	50f. multicoloured	40	15

1985. 12th World Youth and Students' Festival, Moscow.

551	**256**	50f. multicoloured	40	15

257 I.Y.Y. Emblem and Map of Madagascar

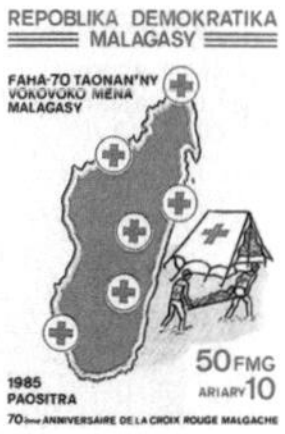

258 Red Cross Centres and First Aid Post

1985. International Youth Year.

552	**257**	100f. multicoloured	60	25

1985. 70th Anniv of Malagasy Red Cross.

553	**258**	50f. multicoloured	60	25

259 "View of Sea at Saintes-Maries" (Vincent van Gogh)

1985. Impressionist Paintings. Multicoloured.

554	20f. Type **259**	45	10
555	20f. "Rouen Cathedral in the Evening" (Claude Monet) (vert)	45	10
556	45f. "Young Girls in Black" (Pierre-Auguste Renoir) (vert)	80	20
557	50f. "Red Vineyard at Arles" (van Gogh)	80	20
558	100f. "Boulevard des Capucines, Paris" (Monet)	1·40	40

260 Indira Gandhi

1985. Indira Gandhi (Indian Prime Minister) Commemoration.

560	**260**	100f. multicoloured	80	30

261 Figures and Dove on Globe and Flag

262 "Aeranthes grandiflora"

1985. 40th Anniv of U.N.O.
561 **261** 100f. multicoloured . . . 65 25

1985. Orchids. Multicoloured.
562 20f. Type **262** 20 10
563 45f. "Angraecum magdalenae" and "Nephele oenopion" (insect) (horiz) 35 15
564 50f. "Aerangis stylosa" . . . 35 15
565 100f. "Angraecum eburneum longicalcar" and "Hippotion batschi" (insect) 80 35
566 100f. "Angraecum sesquipedale" and "Xanthopan morganipredicta" (insect) 80 35

263 Russian and Czechoslovakian Cosmonauts

1985. Russian "Interkosmos" Space Programme. Multicoloured.
568 20f. Type **263** 15 10
569 20f. Russian and American flags and "Apollo"–"Soyuz" link 15 10
570 50f. Russian and Indian cosmonauts 30 15
571 100f. Russian and Cuban cosmonauts 50 25
572 200f. Russian and French cosmonauts . . . . 1·25 60

264 Emblem in "10"

1985. 10th Anniv of Malagasy Democratic Republic.
574 **264** 50f. multicoloured 30 15

265 Headquarters

1986. 10th Anniv of ARO (State insurance system).
575 **265** 50f. yellow and brown . . 30 15

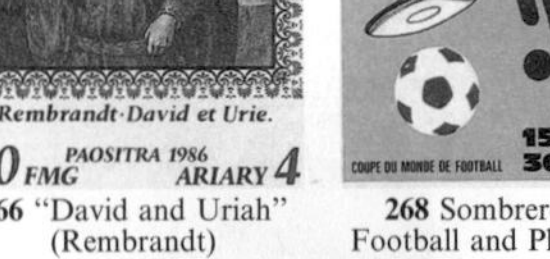

266 "David and Uriah" (Rembrandt)

268 Sombrero, Football and Player

267 Comet

1986. Foreign Paintings in Hermitage Museum, Leningrad. Multicoloured.
576 20f. Type **266** 20 10
577 50f. "Portrait of Old Man in Red" (Rembrandt) 50 30
578 50f. "Danae" (Rembrandt) (horiz) 50 30
579 50f. "Marriage of Earth and Water" (Rubens) 50 30
580 50f. "Portrait of Infanta Isabella's Maid" (Rubens) 50 30

1986. Air. Appearance of Halley's Comet.
582 **267** 150f. multicoloured . . . 1·00 50

1986. Russian Paintings in the Tretyakov Gallery, Moscow. As T **266**. Multicoloured.
583 20f. "Fruit and Flowers" (I. Khroutsky) (horiz) . . . 15 10
584 50f. "The Rooks have Returned" (A. Savrasov) 60 25
585 50f. "Unknown Woman" (I. Kramskoi) (horiz) . . . 30 20
586 50f. "Aleksandr Pushkin" (O. Kiprenski) 30 20
587 100f. "March, 1895" (I. Levitan) (horiz) 90 40

1986. World Cup Football Championship, Mexico.
589 **268** 150f. multicoloured . . . 1·10 30

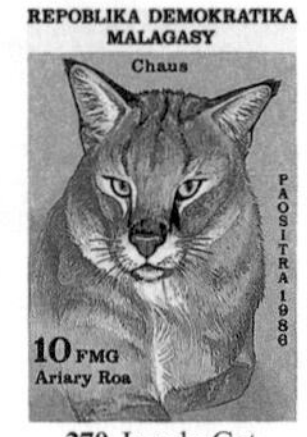

269 Child Care

270 Jungle Cat

1986. U.N.I.C.E.F. Child Survival Campaign.
590 **269** 60f. multicoloured 40 15

1986. Wild Cats. Multicoloured.
591 10f. Type **270** 20 10
592 10f. Wild cat 20 10
593 60f. Caracal 45 20
594 60f. Leopard cat 45 20
595 60f. Serval 45 20

271 Dove above Hands holding Globe

1986. International Peace Year. Multicoloured.
597 60f. Type **271** 40 15
598 150f. Doves above emblem and map . . . . 1·00 45

272 U.P.U. Emblem on Dove

273 U.P.U. Emblem on Globe

1986. World Post Day.
599 **272** 60f. multicoloured (postage) 40 15
600 150f. blue, black and red (air) . . . . 1·10 50

1986. Air. 25th Anniv of Admission to U.P.U.
601 **273** 150f. multicoloured . . . 1·10 50

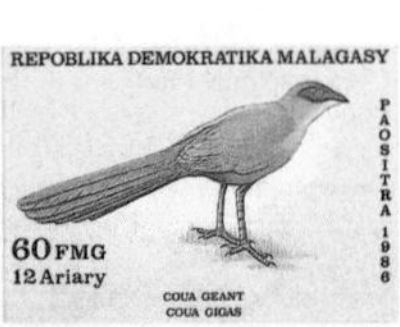

274 Giant Madagascar Coucal

1986. Birds. Multicoloured.
602 60f. Type **274** . . . . 1·10 30
603 60f. Crested Madagascar coucal . . . . 1·10 30
604 60f. Rufous vangas (vert) . . 1·10 30
605 60f. Red-tailed vangas (vert) 1·10 30
606 60f. Sicklebill . . . . 1·10 30

275 Tortoise

1987. Endangered Animals. Multicoloured.
608 60f. Type **275** 65 25
609 60f. Crocodile 65 25
610 60f. Crested wood ibis (vert) 65 25
611 60f. Vasa parrot 65 25

276 Crowd in "40"

1987. 40th Anniv of Anti-colonial Uprising.
613 **276** 60f. brown, red and yellow 35 15
614 – 60f. multicoloured 35 15
DESIGN: No. 614, Hands in broken manacles, map, rifleman and spearman.

277 Emblems, Map and Pictogram

1987. 1st Indian Ocean Towns Games.
615 **277** 60f. multicoloured 35 15
616 150f. multicoloured . . . 1·10 35

278 "Sarimanok"

1987. The "Sarimanok" (replica of early dhow). Multicoloured.
617 60f. Type **278** 50 20
618 150f. "Sarimanok" (different) 1·25 40

279 Coffee Plant

280 Rifle Shooting and Satellite

1987. 25th Anniv of African and Malagasy Coffee Producers Organization. Multicoloured.
619 60f. Type **279** 35 15
620 150f. Map showing member countries . . . . 1·10 35

1987. Winter Olympic Games, Calgary (1988). Multicoloured.
621 60f. Type **280** 25 10
622 150f. Slalom 60 20
623 250f. Luge . . . . 1·25 40
624 350f. Speed skating . . . . . 1·40 50
625 400f. Ice hockey . . . . . . 1·60 60
626 450f. Ice skating (pairs) . . . 2·00 70

281 "Giotto" Space Probe

1987. Appearance of Halley's Comet (1986). Space Probes. Multicoloured.
628 60f. Type **281** 25 10
629 150f. "Vega 1" 60 20
630 250f. "Vega 2" . . . . . . 1·25 40
631 350f. "Planet A 1" . . . . . 1·40 50
632 400f. "Planet B 1" . . . . . 1·60 60
633 450f. "I.C.E." . . . . 2·00 70

282 Piper Aztec

283 Rabearivelo

1987. Air. 25th Anniv of Air Madagascar. Mult.
635 60f. Type **282** 40 20
636 60f. De Havilland Twin Otter 40 20
637 150f. Boeing 747-200 . . . . 1·00 40

1987. 50th Death Anniv of Jean-Joseph Rabearivelo (poet).
638 **283** 60f. multicoloured 30 15

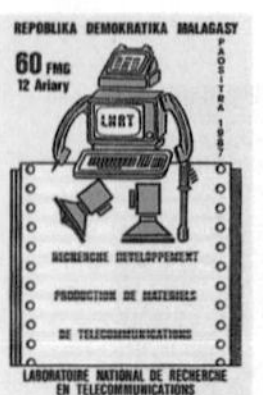

284 Communications Equipment Robot and Print-out Paper

285 Emblem

1987. National Telecommunications Research Laboratory.
639 **284** 60f. green, black and red 30 15

1987. 150th Anniv of Execution of Rafaravavy Rasalama (Christian martyr).
640 **285** 60f. black, deep blue and blue 30 15

286 Hand using Key and Telegraphist

1987. Cent of Antananarivo–Tamatave Telegraph.
641 **286** 60f. multicoloured 30 15

287 Bartholomeu Dias and Departure from Palos, 1492

1987. 500th Anniv (1992) of Discovery of America by Columbus. Multicoloured.
642 60f. Type **287** 30 20
643 150f. Route around Samana Cay and Henry the Navigator 60 25
644 250f. Columbus and crew disembarking, 1492, and A. de Marchena 75 30
645 350f. Building Fort Navidad and Paolo del Pozzo Toscanelli . . . . 1·10 40
646 400f. Columbus in Barcelona, 1493, and Queen Isabella of Spain . . . . 1·60 65
647 450f. Columbus and "Nina" 1·75 70

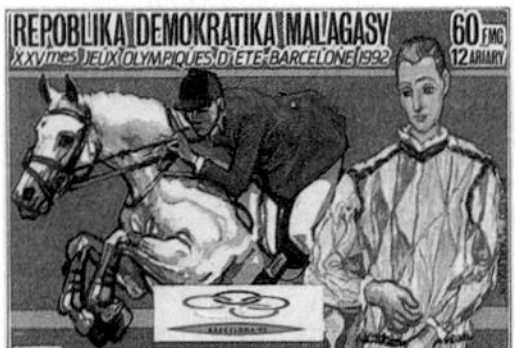

288 Showjumping and "Harlequin" (Picasso)

1987. Olympic Games, Barcelona (1992). Multicoloured.
649 60f. Type **288** (postage) . . . 15 10
650 150f. Weightlifting and Barcelona Cathedral . . . 40 20
651 250f. Hurdling and Canaletas Fountain 70 30
652 350f. High jumping and Parc d'Attractions . . . . . . 1·00 40

653 400f. Gymnast on bar and church (air) 1·40 50
654 450f. Gymnast with ribbon and Triumphal Arch 1·75 50

289 Anniversary Emblem, T.V. Tower and Interhotel "Berlin"

290 Musician and Dancers

1987. 750th Anniv of Berlin.
656 **289** 150f. multicoloured 25 15

1987. Schools Festival.
657 **290** 60f. multicoloured 15 10

291 Madagascar Pasteur Institute and Pasteur

1987. Centenary of Pasteur Institute, Paris.
658 **291** 250f. multicoloured 60 25

292 "After the Shipwreck" (Eugene Delacroix)

1987. Paintings in Pushkin Museum of Fine Arts, Moscow. Multicoloured.
659 10f. Type **292** 15 10
660 60f. "Jupiter and Callisto" (Francois Boucher) (vert) 15 10
661 60f. "Still Life with Swan" (Frans Snyders) 15 10
662 60f. "Chalet in the Mountains" (Gustave Courbet) 15 10
663 150f. "At the Market" (Joachim Bueckelaer) 40 15

293 Emblem

294 Family and House on Globe

1987. 10th Anniv of Pan-African Telecommunications Union.
665 **293** 250f. multicoloured 40 20

1988. International Year of Shelter for the Homeless (1987). Multicoloured.
666 80f. Type **294** 15 10
667 250f. Hands forming house protecting family from rain 35 20

295 Lenin addressing Crowd

1988. 70th Anniv of Russian Revolution. Mult.
668 60f. Type **295** 15 10
669 60f. Revolutionaries 15 10
670 150f. Lenin in crowd 25 15

296 Broad-nosed Gentle Lemur

1988. Endangered Species. Multicoloured.
671 60f. Type **296** 15 10
672 150f. Diadem sifaka 20 15
673 250f. Indri 35 15
674 350f. Ruffed lemur 60 25
675 550f. Purple herons (horiz) 1·60 50
676 1500f. Nossi-be chameleon (horiz) 2·40 1·25

297 Ice Skating

1988. Winter Olympic Games, Calgary. Mult.
678 20f. Type **297** 10 10
679 60f. Speed-skating 10 10
680 60f. Slalom 10 10
681 100f. Cross-country skiing 20 10
682 250f. Ice hockey 45 20

298 Dove, Axe breaking Chain and Map

1988. 25th Anniv of Organization of African Unity.
684 **298** 80f. multicoloured 15 10

299 Institute Building

1988. 20th Anniv of National Posts and Telecommunications Institute.
685 **299** 80f. multicoloured 15 10

300 College

1988. Centenary of St. Michael's College.
686 **300** 250f. multicoloured 30 20

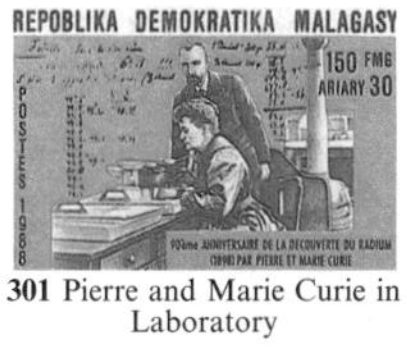

301 Pierre and Marie Curie in Laboratory

302 Emblem

1988. 90th Anniv of Discovery of Radium.
687 **301** 150f. brown and mauve 40 15

1988. 10th Anniv of Alma-Ata Declaration (on health and social care).
688 **302** 60f. multicoloured 15 10

303 Emblem

304 Ring-tailed Lemurs on Island

1988. 40th Anniv of W.H.O.
689 **303** 150f. brown, blue and black 20 15

1988. 50th Anniv of Tsimbazaza Botanical and Zoological Park. Multicoloured.
690 20f. Type **304** 15 10
691 80f. Ring-tailed lemur with young (25 × 37 mm) 20 10
692 250f. Palm tree and ring-tailed lemur within "Zoo" (47 × 32 mm) 40 20

305 Hoopoe and Blue Madagascar Coucal

306 Cattle grazing

1988. Scouts, Birds and Butterflies. Multicoloured.
694 80f. Type **305** 10 10
695 250f. "Chrysiridia croesus" (butterfly) 40 20
696 270f. Nelicourvi weaver and red forest fody 50 10
697 350f. "Papilio dardanus" (butterflies) 60 40
698 550f. Crested Madagascar coucal 1·00 25
699 1500f. "Argema mittrei" (butterfly) 2·50 2·00

1988. 10th Anniv of International Fund for Agricultural Development.
701 **306** 250f. multicoloured 30 20

307 Karl Bach and Clavier

308 Books

1988. Musicians' Anniversaries. Multicoloured.
702 80f. Type **307** (death bicentenary) 15 10
703 250f. Franz Schubert and piano (160th death) 40 15
704 270f. Georges Bizet and scene from "Carmen" (150th birth) 40 20
705 350f. Claude Debussy and scene from "Pelleas et Melisande" (70th death) 50 25
706 550f. George Gershwin at piano writing score of "Rhapsody in Blue" (90th birth) 75 45
707 1500f. Elvis Presley (10th death (1987)) 2·75 1·25

1988. "Ecole en Fete" Schools Festival.
709 **308** 80f. multicoloured 15 10

309 "Black Sea Fleet at Feodosiya" (Ivan Aivazovski)

310 "Tragocephala crassicornis"

1988. Paintings of Sailing Ships. Multicoloured.
710 20f. Type **309** 40 15
711 80f. "Lesnoie" (N. Semenov) 40 15
712 80f. "Seascape with Sailing Ships" (Simon de Vlieger) 40 15
713 100f. "Orel" (N. Golitsine) (horiz) 45 15
714 250f. "Naval Battle Exercises" (Adam Silo) 90 25

1988. Endangered Beetles. Multicoloured.
716 20f. Type **310** 15 10
717 80f. "Polybothris symptuosa-gema" 55 25
718 250f. "Euchroea auripigmenta" 1·25 60
719 350f. "Stellognata maculata" 1·60 80

311 Stretcher Bearers and Anniversary Emblem

312 Symbols of Human Rights

1988. 125th Anniv of International Red Cross. Multicoloured.
720 80f. Type **311** 15 10
721 250f. Red Cross services, emblem and Henri Dunant (founder) 35 20

1988. 40th Anniv of Declaration of Human Rights. Multicoloured.
722 80f. Type **312** 15 10
723 250f. Hands with broken manacles holding "40" 35 15

313 Mercedes-Benz "Blitzen-Benz", 1909

1989. Cars and Trains. Multicoloured.
724 80f. Type **313** 15 10
725 250f. Micheline diesel railcar "Tsikirity", 1952, Tananarive–Moramanga line 1·50 15
726 270f. Bugatti coupe binder, "41" 40 20
727 350f. Class 1020 electric locomotive, Germany 1·90 25
728 1500f. Souleze 701 diesel train, Malagasy 4·75 1·25
729 2500f. Opel racing car, 1913 3·50 2·00

314 Tyrannosaurus

1989. Prehistoric Animals. Multicoloured.
731 20f. Type **314** 15 10
732 80f. Stegosaurus 20 10
733 250f. Arsinoitherium 40 15
734 450f. Triceratops 80 30

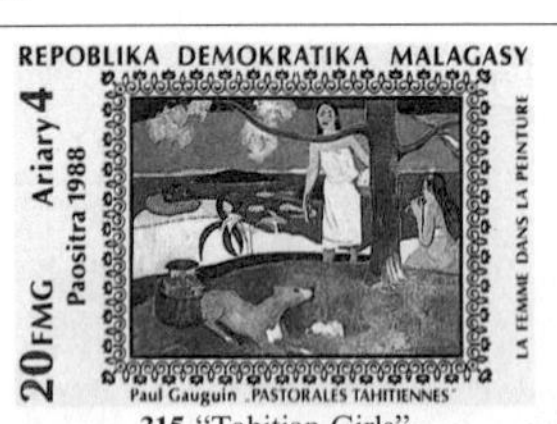
315 "Tahitian Girls"

1989. Woman in Art. Multicoloured.
736 20f. Type **315** 10 10
737 80f. "Portrait of a Girl" (Jean-Baptiste Greuze) . . 15 10
738 80f. "Portrait of a Young Woman" (Titian) 15 10
739 100f. "Woman in Black" (Auguste Renoir) 20 10
740 250f. "The Lace-maker" (Vasily Tropinine) 35 15

316 "Sobennikoffia robusta" **317** Nehru

1989. Orchids. Multicoloured.
742 5f. Type **316** 15 10
743 10f. "Grammangis fallax" (horiz) 15 10
744 80f. "Angraecum sororium" 20 10
745 80f. "Cymbidiella humblotii" 20 10
746 250f. "Oenia oncidiiflora" . . 60 20

1989. Birth Centenary of Jawaharlal Nehru (Indian statesman).
748 **317** 250f. multicoloured . . . 45 15

318 Mahamasina Sports Complex, Lake Anosy and Ampefiloha Quarter

1989. Antananarivo. Multicoloured.
749 5f. Type **318** 10 10
750 20f. Andravoahangy and Anjanahary Quarters . . . 10 10
751 80f. Zoma market and Faravohitra Quarter . . . 15 10
752 80f. Andohan' Analekely Quarter and 29 March Column 15 10
753 250f. Avenue de l'Independance and Jean Ralaimongo Column . . . 35 15
754 550f. Lake Anosy, Queen's Palace and Andohalo School 70 35

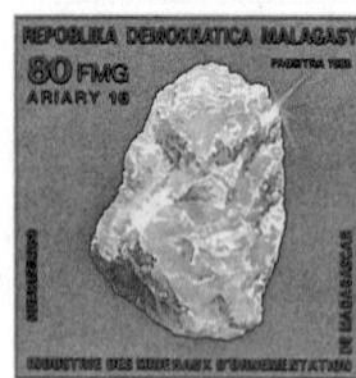
319 Rose Quartz

1989. Ornamental Minerals. Multicoloured.
755 80f. Type **319** 20 10
756 250f. Fossilized wood 60 20

320 Pope and Rasoamanarivo **321** Map and Runner with Torch

1989. Visit of Pope John Paul II and Beatification of Victoire Rasoamanarivo. Multicoloured.
757 80f. Type **320** 20 10
758 250f. Map and Pope 55 20

1989. Town Games.
759 **321** 80f.+20f. multicoloured 15 15

322 "Storming the Bastille"

1989. Bicentenary of French Revolution (1st issue).
760 **322** 250f. multicoloured . . . 35 15
See also Nos. 773/5.

323 Mirabeau and Gabriel Riqueti at Meeting of States General

1989. "Philexfrance 89" International Stamp Exhibition, Paris. Multicoloured.
761 250f. Type **323** 30 15
762 350f. Camille Desmoulins' call to arms 45 20
763 1000f. Lafayette and crowd demanding bread . . . . . 1·25 60
764 1500f. Trial of King Louis XVI . . . . 2·00 80
765 2500f. Assassination of Marat 3·25 1·25

324 "Mars 1"

1989. Space Probes. Multicoloured.
767 20f. Type **324** 10 10
768 80f. "Mars 3" 15 10
769 80f. "Zond 2" 15 10
770 250f. "Mariner 9" 35 15
771 270f. "Viking 2" 40 20

325 "Liberty guiding the People" (Eugene Delacroix)

1989. Bicentenary of French Revolution (2nd issue). Multicoloured.
773 5f. Type **325** (postage) . . . 10 10
774 80f. "La Marseillaise" (Francois Rude) 15 10
775 250f. "Oath of the Tennis Court" (Jacques Louis David) (air) 35 15

326 Rene Cassin (founder) **327** Mother and Young on Bamboo

1989. 25th Anniv of International Human Rights Institute for French Speaking Countries.
776 **326** 250f. multicoloured . . . 30 15

1989. Golden Gentle Lemur.
777 **327** 250f. multicoloured . . . 40 20

328 Footballer and Cavour Monument, Turin **330** Long Jumping

329 Pennant Coralfish

1989. World Cup Football Championship, Italy. Multicoloured.
778 350f. Type **328** 50 20
779 1000f. Footballer and Christopher Columbus monument, Genoa . . . . 1·40 50
780 1500f. Florentine footballer, 1530, and "David" (sculpture, Michelangelo) 2·00 75
781 2500f. Footballer and "Rape of Proserpina" (sculpture, Bernini), Rome . . . . . 3·25 1·40

1990. Fishes. Multicoloured.
783 5f. Type **329** 10 10
784 20f. Snub-nosed parasitic eel (vert) 20 10
785 80f. Manta ray (vert) 35 15
786 250f. Black-tipped grouper 90 30
787 320f. Smooth hammerhead 1·25 45

1990. Olympic Games, Barcelona (1992). Mult.
789 80f. Type **330** 10 10
790 250f. Pole vaulting 35 15
791 550f. Hurdling 65 25
792 1500f. Cycling . . . . 2·00 60
793 2000f. Baseball . . . . . . 2·50 80
794 2500f. Tennis . . . . 3·25 1·25

331 "Queen of the Isalo" (rock)

1990. Natural Features. Multicoloured.
796 70f. Type **331** 15 10
797 150f. Lonjy Island (as T **332**) 25 15

332 Pipe

1990. Sakalava Craft. Multicoloured.
798 70f. Type **332** 15 10
799 150f. Combs (as T **331**) . . . 25 15

333 Emblem and Projects

1990. 25th Anniv of African Development Bank.
800 **333** 80f. multicoloured 15 10

334 "Voyager II" and Neptune

1990. 20th Anniv of First Manned Landing on Moon. Multicoloured.
801 80f. Type **334** 15 10
802 250f. Hughes Hercules flying boat, Boeing 747 airliner and flying boat "of the future" 40 15
803 550f. "Noah" satellite tracking elephants 70 25
804 1500f. Venus and "Magellan" space probe . . . . 1·25 55
805 2000f. Halley's Comet and Concorde . . . . 2·25 90
806 2500f. "Apollo 11" landing capsule and crew . . . . . 3·25 1·00

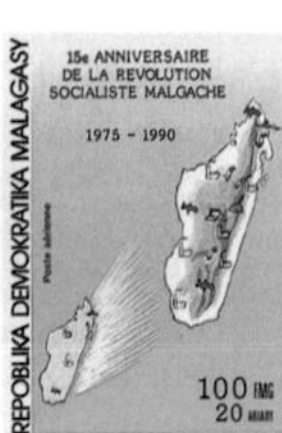
335 Liner on Globe **336** Maps showing Development between 1975 and 1990

1990. 30th Anniv of International Maritime Organization.
808 **335** 250f. ultramarine, bl & blk 55 15

1990. Air. 15th Anniv of Malagasy Socialist Revolution.
809 **336** 100f. multicoloured . . . 15 10
810 – 350f. black and grey . . . 45 25
DESIGN: 350f. Presidential Palaces, 1975 and 1990.

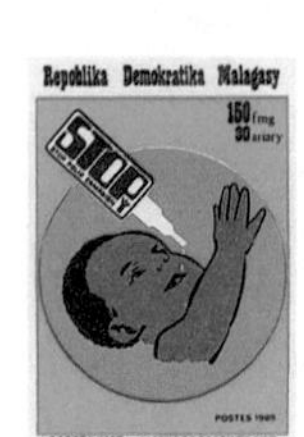
337 Oral Vaccination **338** Four-man Bobsleigh

1990. Anti-Polio Campaign.
811 **337** 150f. multicoloured . . . 30 15

1990. Winter Olympic Games, Albertville (1992) (1st issue). Multicoloured.
812 350f. Type **338** 40 20
813 1000f. Speed skating . . . . 1·25 40
814 1500f. Cross-country skiing 2·00 65
815 2500f. Super G . . . . . . 3·00 1·10
See also Nos. 862/8.

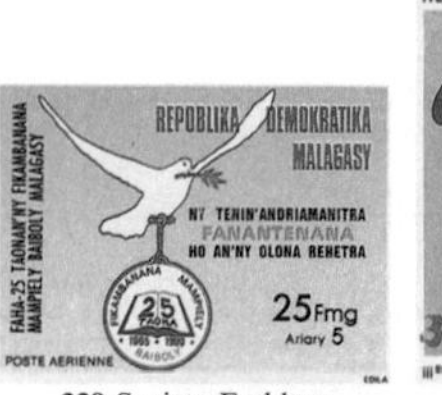

339 Society Emblem **340** Mascot

1990. Air. 25th Anniv of Malagasy Bible Society.
817 **339** 25f. multicoloured 10 10
818 – 100f. blue, black and green 15 10
DESIGN—VERT: 100f. Society emblem.

1990. 3rd Indian Ocean Island Games, Malagasy (1st issue).
819 **340** 100f.+20f. on 80f.+20f. multicoloured 15 15
820 350f.+20f. on 250f.+20f. multicoloured 75 40
The games were originally to be held in 1989 and the stamps were printed for release then. The issued stamps are handstamped with the correct date and new value.
See also Nos. 822/3.

341 Symbols of Agriculture and Industry
342 Torch

1990. 30th Anniv of Independence.
821 **341** 100f. multicoloured . . . 15 10

1990. 3rd Indian Ocean Island Games, Malagasy (2nd issue).
822 **342** 100f. multicoloured . . . 15 10
823 350f. multicoloured . . . 45 20

343 Envelopes forming Map and Mail Transportation

1990. Air. World Post Day.
824 **343** 350f. multicoloured . . . 2·00 55

344 Ho Chi Minh
345 "Avahi langer"

1990. Birth Centenary of Ho Chi Minh (President of North Vietnam, 1945–69).
825 **344** 350f. multicoloured . . . 40 20

1990. Lemurs. Multicoloured.
826 10f. Type **345** 10 10
827 20f. "Lemur fulvus albifrons" 10 10
828 20f. "Lemur fulvus sanfordi" 10 10
829 100f. "Lemur fulvus collaris" 25 15
830 100f. "Lepulemur ruficaudatus" 25 15

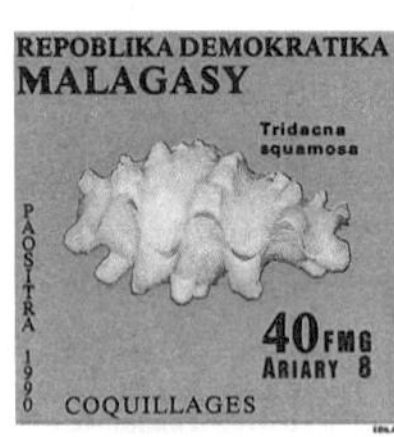

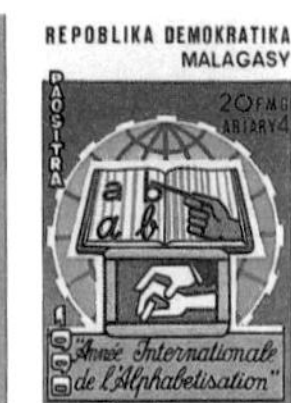

346 Fluted Giant Clam
347 Letters in Book

1990. Shells. Multicoloured.
832 40f. Type **346** 25 15
833 50f. Dimidiate and subulate augers 35 15

1990. International Literacy Year. Multicoloured.
834 20f. Type **347** 10 10
835 100f. Open book and hand holding pen (horiz) 20 15

348 Cep
349 De Gaulle, Leclerc and Parod under Arc de Triomphe, 1944

1991. Fungi. Multicoloured.
836 25f. Type **348** 10 10
837 100f. Butter mushroom . . . 35 10
838 350f. Fly agaric 55 20
839 450f. Scarlet-stemmed boletus 75 25
840 680f. Flaky-stemmed witches' mushroom . . . . 1·10 40
841 800f. Brown birch bolete . . 1·25 45
842 900f. Orange birch bolete . . 1·40 55

1991. Multicoloured.
844 100f. Type **349** 10 10
845 350f. "Galileo" space probe near Jupiter 55 10
846 800f. Crew of "Apollo 11" on Moon . . . . 1·10 25
847 900f. De Gaulle and Free French emblem, 1942 . . . 1·40 30
848 1250f. Concorde aircraft and German ICE high speed train . . . . 3·25 80
849 2500f. Gen. Charles de Gaulle (French statesman) 3·25 95

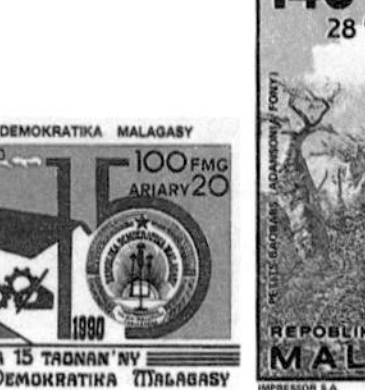

350 Industrial and Agricultural Symbols and Arms
351 Baobab Tree

1991. 15th Anniv (1990) of Republic.
851 **350** 100f. multicoloured . . . 10 10

1991. Trees. Multicoloured.
852 140f. Type **351** 55 10
853 500f. "Dideria madagascariensis" . . . . 1·10 45

352 Whippet
353 Cross-country Skiing

1991. Dogs. Multicoloured.
854 30f. Type **352** 35 10
855 50f. Japanese spaniel 45 10
856 140f. Toy terrier 90 10
857 350f. Chow-chow 65 10
858 500f. Chihuahua 90 15
859 800f. Afghan hound . . . . 1·10 25
860 1140f. Papillon . . . . 1·75 65

1991. Winter Olympic Games, Albertville (2nd issue). Multicoloured.
862 5f. Type **353** 10 10
863 15f. Biathlon 10 10
864 60f. Ice hockey 35 10
865 140f. Skiing 45 10
866 640f. Ice skating 45 30
867 1000f. Ski jumping . . . . . 1·90 50
868 1140f. Speed skating . . . . 2·75 60

354 "Helictopleurus splendidicollis"

1992. Scouts, Insects and Fungi. Multicoloured.
870 140f. Type **354** 10 10
871 500f. "Russula radicans" (mushroom) 90 25
872 640f. "Cocles contemplator" (insect) . . . . 1·10 30
873 1025f. "Russula singeri" (mushroom) . . . . 1·60 50
874 1140f. "Euchroea oberthurii" (beetle) . . . . 1·75 60
875 3500f. "Lactariopsis pandani" (mushroom) . . . . 5·50 2·00

355 Former and Present Buildings

1992. 90th Anniv (1991) of Paul Minault College.
877 **355** 140f. multicoloured . . . 45 10

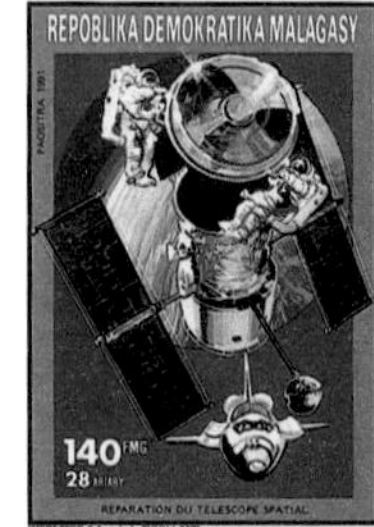

356 Repairing Space Telescope

1992. Space. Multicoloured.
878 140f. Type **356** 10 10
879 500f. "Soho" sun probe . . . 65 25
880 640f. "Topex-Poseidon" oceanic survey satellite . . 90 30
881 1025f. "Hipparcos" planetary survey satellite . . . . . . 1·25 50
882 1140f. "Voyager 2" Neptune probe . . . . 1·40 60
883 5000f. "ETS-VI" Japanese test communications satellite . . . . 6·75 1·25

357 Ryuichi Sakamoto

1992. Entertainers. Multicoloured.
885 100f. Type **357** 10 10
886 350f. John Lennon 55 15
887 800f. Bruce Lee . . . . . . 1·40 40
888 900f. Sammy Davis jun . . . 1·60 45
889 1250f. John Wayne . . . . . 1·60 60
890 2500f. James Dean . . . . . 3·25 1·25

358 Lychees

1992. Fruits. Multicoloured.
892 10f. Type **358** 10 10
893 50f. Oranges 10 10
894 60f. Apples 10 10
895 140f. Peaches 35 10
896 555f. Bananas (vert) . . . . 1·10 30
897 800f. Avocados (vert) . . . . 1·40 40
898 1400f. Mangoes (vert) . . . . 2·40 75

359 9th-century Galley
360 Couple in Heart

1992. Sailing Ships. Multicoloured.
900 15f. Type **359** 10 10
901 65f. Full-rigged sailing ship, 1878 . . . . 10 10
902 140f. "Golden Hind" (Drake's flagship) 45 10
903 500f. 18th-century dhow . . 1·00 25
904 640f. "Ostrust" (galleon), 1721 (vert) . . . . 1·10 30
905 800f. Dutch caravel, 1599 (vert) . . . . 1·40 40
906 1025f. "Santa Maria" (Columbus's flagship), 1492 1·75 50

1992. Anti-AIDS Campaign.
908 **360** 140f. black and mauve . . 35 10

361 Tending Trees

1992. Reforestation.
909 **361** 140f. dp green, black & grn 10 10

POSTAGE DUE STAMPS

D **13** Independence Obelisk

1962.
D45 D **13** 1f. green 10 10
D46 2f. brown 10 10
D47 3f. violet 10 10
D48 4f. slate 10 10
D49 5f. red 10 10
D50 10f. green 15 15
D51 20f. purple 20 20
D52 40f. blue 50 45
D53 50f. red 75 70
D54 100f. black . . . . . . 1·40 1·25

APPENDIX

The following stamps have either been issued in excess of postal needs or have not been available to the public in reasonable quantities at face value.

1987.

Winter Olympic Games, Calgary (1988). 1500f. (on gold foil).

1989.

Scout and Butterfly. 5000f. (on gold foil).

"Philexfrance 89" Int Stamp Exhibition, Paris. 5000f. (on gold foil).

World Cup Football Championship, Italy. 5000f. (on gold foil).

1990.

Winter Olympic Games, Albertville (1992). 5000f. (on gold foil).

1991.

Birth Centenary of De Gaulle. 5000f. (on gold foil).

1992.

Olympic Games, Barcelona. 500f. (on gold foil).

1993.

Bicentenary of French Republic. 1989 "Philexfrance 89" issue optd. 5000f.

1994.

Elvis Presley (entertainer). 10000f. (on gold foil).

World Cup Football Championship, U.S.A. 10000f. (on gold foil).

Winter Olympic Games, Lillehammer, Norway. 10000f. (on gold foil).

Olympic Games, Atlanta, U.S.A. 5000f. (on gold foil).

For further issues see under **MADAGASCAR**.

MALAWI Pt. 1

Formerly Nyasaland, became an independent Republic within the Commonwealth on 6 July 1966.

1964. 12 pence = 1 shilling;
20 shillings = 1 pound.
1970. 100 tambalas = 1 kwacha.

44 Dr. H. Banda (Prime Minister) and Independence Monument

1964. Independence.
211 **44** 3d. olive and sepia 10 10
212 – 6d. multicoloured 10 10
213 – 1s.3d. multicoloured . . . 35 10
214 – 2s.6d. multicoloured . . . 45 1·25
DESIGNS—each with Dr. Hastings Banda: 6d. Rising sun; 1s.3d. National flag; 2s.6d. Coat of arms.

48 Tung Tree

1964. As Nos. 199/210 of Nyasaland but inscr "MALAWI" as in T **48**. The 9d., 1s.6d. and £2 are new values and designs.

252 ½d. violet 10 10
216 1d. black and green 10 10
217 2d. brown 10 10
218 3d. brown, green and bistre 15 10
219 4d. blue and yellow 85 15
220 6d. purple, green and blue 75 10
221 9d. brown, green and yellow 30 15
258 1s. brown, blue and yellow 25 10
223 1s.3d. green and brown . . 50 60
259 1s.6d. brown and green . . 30 10
224 2s.6d. brown and blue . . . 1·10 1·00
225 5s. multicoloured (I) . . . . 65 3·00
225a 5s. multicoloured (II) . . . 7·50 90
226 10s. green, salmon and black . . . . 1·50 2·00
227 £1 brown and yellow . . . 7·00 5·50
262 £2 multicoloured . . . . . 25·00 24·00

DESIGNS (New): 1s.6d. Burley tobacco; £2 "Cyrestis camillus" (butterfly).

Two types of 5s. I, inscr "LAKE NYASA". II, inscr "LAKE MALAWI".

49 Christmas Star and Globe

1964. Christmas.

228 **49** 3d. green and gold 10 10
229 6d. mauve and gold . . . 10 10
230 1s.3d. violet and gold . . . 10 10
231 2s.6d. blue and gold . . . 20 50
MS231a 83 × 126 mm. Nos. 228/31. Imperf . . . . 1·00 1·75

50 Coins

1964. Malawi's First Coinage. Coins in black and silver.

232 **50** 3d. green 10 10
233 9d. mauve 20 10
234 1s.6d. purple 25 10
235 3s. blue 35 85
MS235a 126 × 104 mm. Nos. 232/5. Imperf . . . . 1·40 1·10

1965. Nos. 223/4 surch.

236 1s.6d. on 1s.3d. green & brown 10 10
237 3s. on 2s.6d. brown and blue 20 20

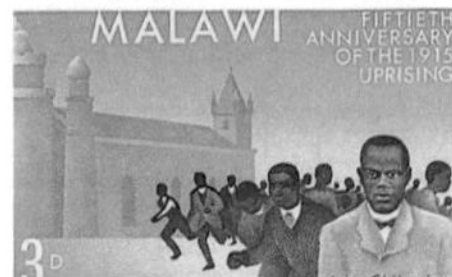

52 Chilembwe leading Rebels

1965. 50th Anniv of 1915 Rising.

238 **52** 3d. violet and green . . . 10 10
239 9d. olive and orange . . . 10 10
240 1s.6d. brown and blue . . 15 10
241 3s. turquoise and blue . . 20 25
MS241a 127 × 83 mm. Nos. 238/41 5·00 6·00

53 "Learning and Scholarship"

1965. Opening of Malawi University.

242 **53** 3d. black and green . . . 10 10
243 9d. black and mauve . . . 10 10
244 1s.6d. black and violet . . 10 10
245 3s. black and blue 15 40
MS246 127 × 84 mm. Nos. 242/5 2·50 2·50

54 "Papilio ophidicephalus"

1966. Malawi Butterflies. Multicoloured.

247 4d. Type **54** 80 10
248 9d. "Papilio desmondi" (magdae) . . . . 1·25 10
249 1s.6d. "Epamera handmani" 1·75 30
250 3s. "Amauris crawshayi" . . 2·75 6·00
MS251 130 × 100 mm. Nos. 247/50 17·00 11·00

58 British Central Africa 6d. Stamp of 1891 **59** President Banda

1966. 75th Anniv of Postal Services.

263 **58** 4d. blue and green 10 10
264 9d. blue and red 15 10
265 1s.6d. blue and lilac . . . 20 10
266 3s. grey and blue 30 70
MS267 83 × 127 mm. Nos. 263/6 5·00 3·25

1966. Republic Day.

268 **59** 4d. brown, silver and green 10 10
269 9d. brown, silver and mauve 10 10
270 1s.6d. brown, silver & violet 15 10
271 3s. brown, silver and blue 25 15
MS272 83 × 127 mm. Nos. 268/71 2·00 3·00

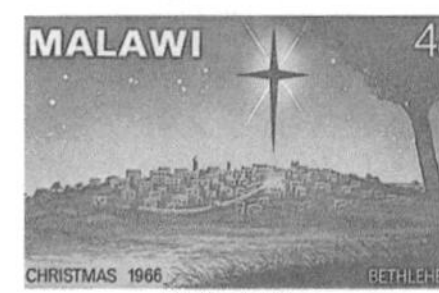

60 Bethlehem

1966. Christmas.

273 **60** 4d. green and gold 10 10
274 9d. purple and gold . . . 10 10
275 1s.6d. red and gold 15 10
276 3s. blue and gold 40 80

61 "Ilala I"

1967. Lake Malawi Steamers.

277 **61** 4d. black, yellow and green 40 10
278 – 9d. black, yellow and mauve 45 10
279 – 1s.6d. black, red and violet 65 20
280 – 3s. black, red and blue . . 1·25 1·75

DESIGNS: 9d. "Dove"; 1s.9d. "Chauncy Maples I" (wrongly inscr "Chauncey"); 3s. "Gwendolen".

62 Golden Mbuna (female)

1967. Lake Malawi Cichlids. Multicoloured.

281 4d. Type **62** 40 10
282 9d. Scraped-mouthed mbuna 55 10
283 1s.6d. Zebra mbuna 70 20
284 3s. Orange mbuna . . . . . 1·75 1·75

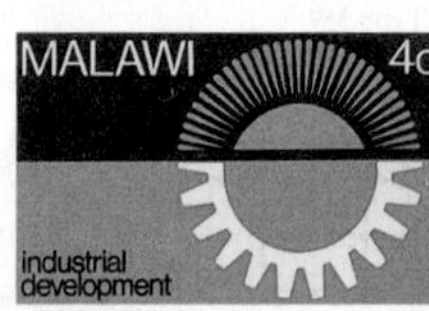

63 Rising Sun and Gearwheel

1967. Industrial Development.

285 **63** 4d. black and green . . . 10 10
286 9d. black and red 10 10
287 1s.6d. black and violet . . 10 10
288 3s. black and blue 15 30
MS289 134 × 108 mm. Nos. 285/8 75 1·40

64 Mary and Joseph beside Crib

1967. Christmas.

290 **64** 4d. blue and green 10 10
291 9d. blue and red 10 10
292 1s.6d. blue and yellow . . 10 10
293 3s. deep blue and blue . . 15 30
MS294 114 × 100 mm. Nos. 290/3 1·00 3·00

65 "Calotropis procera"

1968. Wild Flowers. Multicoloured.

295 4d. Type **65** 15 10
296 9d. "Borreria dibrachiata" . . 15 10
297 1s.6d. "Hibiscus rhodanthus" 15 10
298 3s. "Bidens pinnatipartita" 20 95
MS299 135 × 91 mm. Nos. 295/8 1·25 3·00

66 Bagnall Steam Locomotive No. 1 "Thistle"

1968. Malawi Locomotives

300 **66** 4d. green, blue and red . . 25 10
301 – 9d. red, blue and green . . 30 15
302 – 1s.6d. multicoloured . . . 40 30
303 – 3s. multicoloured . . . . . 70 3·00
MS304 120 × 88 mm. Nos. 300/3 2·00 6·00

DESIGNS: 9d. Class G steam locomotive No. 49; 1s.6d. Class "Zambesi" diesel locomotive No. 202; 3s. Diesel railcar No. DR1.

67 "The Nativity" (Piero della Francesca)

1968. Christmas. Multicoloured.

305 4d. Type **67** 10 10
306 9d. "The Adoration of the Shepherds" (Murillo) . . . 10 10
307 1s.6d. "The Adoration of the Shepherds" (Reni) 10 10
308 3s. "Nativity, with God the Father and Holy Ghost" (Pittoni) 15 15
MS309 115 × 101 mm. Nos. 305/8 35 1·60

69 Nyassa Lovebird **70** Carmine Bee Eater

1968. Birds (1st series). Multicoloured.

310 1d. Scarlet-chested sunbird (horiz) 15 10
311 2d. Violet starling (horiz) . . 20 10
312 3d. White-browed robin chat (horiz) 30 10
313 4d. Red-billed fire finch (horiz) 50 40
314 6d. Type **69** . . . . 1·25 15
315 9d. Yellow-rumped bishop . . 1·25 60
316 1s. Type **70** . . . . 1·00 15
317 1s.6d. Grey-headed bush shrike . . . . 5·00 8·00
318 2s. Paradise whydah . . . . 5·00 8·00
319 3s. African paradise flycatcher (vert) . . . . . 6·00 4·25
320 5s. Bateleur (vert) . . . . . 7·00 4·25
321 10s. Saddle-bill stork (vert) 5·50 7·50
322 £1 Purple heron (vert) . . . 10·00 18·00
323 £2 Green turaco ("Livingstone's Loerie") . . 42·00 48·00

SIZES: 1d. to 9d. as Type **69**; 1s.6d. to £2 as Type **70**.

See also Nos. 473/85.

71 I.L.O. Emblem

1969. 50th Anniv of Int Labour Organization.

324 **71** 4d. gold and green 10 10
325 9d. gold and brown . . . 10 10
326 1s.6d. gold and brown . . 10 10
327 3s. gold and blue 15 15
MS328 127 × 89 mm. Nos. 324/7 1·00 4·75

72 White-fringed Ground Orchid

1969. Orchids of Malawi. Multicoloured.

329 4d. Type **72** 15 10
330 9d. Red ground orchid . . . 20 10
331 1s.6d. Leopard tree orchid . . 30 20
332 3s. Blue ground orchid . . . 60 2·00
MS333 118 × 86 mm. Nos. 329/32 1·10 3·75

73 African Development Bank Emblem **74** Dove over Bethlehem

1969. 5th Anniv of African Development Bank.

334 **73** 4d. yellow, brown and ochre 10 10
335 9d. yellow, ochre and green 10 10
336 1s.6d. yellow, ochre & brn 10 10
337 3s. yellow, ochre and blue 15 15
MS338 102 × 137 mm. Nos. 334/7 50 90

1969. Christmas.

339 **74** 2d. black and yellow . . . 10 10
340 4d. black and turquoise . . 10 10
341 9d. black and red 10 10
342 1s.6d. black and violet . . 10 10
343 3s. black and blue 15 15
MS344 130 × 71 mm. Nos. 339/43 1·00 1·75

75 "Zonocerus elegans" (grasshopper) **77** Runner

1970. Insects of Malawi. Multicoloured.

345 4d. Type **75** 15 10
346 9d. "Mylabris dicincta" (beetle) 15 10
347 1s.6d. "Henosepilachna elaterii" (ladybird) 20 10
348 3s. "Sphodromantis speculabunda" (mantid) . . 35 65
MS349 86 × 137 mm. Nos. 345/8 1·25 2·25

1970. Rand Easter Show. No. 317 optd **Rand Easter Show 1970.**

350 1s.6d. multicoloured . . . . 50 2·25

1970. 9th Commonwealth Games, Edinburgh.

351 **77** 4d. blue and green 10 10
352 9d. blue and red 10 10
353 1s.6d. blue and yellow . . 10 10
354 3s. deep blue and blue . . 15 15
MS355 146 × 96 mm. Nos. 351/4 55 90

1970. Decimal Currency. Nos. 316 and 318 surch.

356 10t. on 1s. multicoloured . . 2·25 25
357 20t. on 2s. multicoloured . . 2·75 3·50

79 "Aegocera trimeni"

1970. Moths. Multicoloured.
358 4d. Type **79** 20 10
359 9d. "Faidherbia bauhiniae" 30 10
360 1s.6d. "Parasa karschi" . . . 50 20
361 3s. "Teracotona euprepia" . . 1·25 3·50
MS362 112 × 92 mm. Nos. 358/61 4·25 6·00

80 Mother and Child

1970. Christmas.
363 **80** 2d. black and yellow . . . 10 10
364 4d. black and green . . . 10 10
365 9d. black and red 10 10
366 1s.6d. black and purple . . 10 10
367 3s. black and blue 15 15
MS368 166 × 100 mm. Nos. 363/7 1·00 2·25

1971. No. 319 surch **30t Special United Kingdom Delivery Service**.
369 30t. on 3s. multicoloured . . 50 2·00
No. 369 was issued for use on letters carried by an emergency airmail service from Malawi to Great Britain during the British postal strike. The fee of 30t. was to cover the charge for delivery by a private service, and ordinary stamps to pay the normal airmail postage had to be affixed as well. These stamps were in use from 8 February to 8 March.

82 Decimal Coinage and Cockerel
83 Greater Kudu

1971. Decimal Coinage.
370 **82** 3t. multicoloured 15 10
371 8t. multicoloured 20 10
372 15t. multicoloured 25 20
373 30t. multicoloured . . . . 35 1·50
MS374 140 × 101 mm. Nos. 370/3 1·00 1·75

1971. Decimal Currency. Antelopes. Mult.
375 1t. Type **83** 10 10
376 2t. Nyala 15 10
377 3t. Mountain reedbuck . . . 20 50
378 5t. Puku . . . . 40 1·25
379 8t. Impala . . . . 45 1·00
380 10t. Eland 60 10
381 15t. Klipspringer . . . . . . 1·00 20
382 20t. Suni . . . . 1·50 90
383 30t. Roan antelope . . . . . 9·50 1·00
384 50t. Waterbuck . . . . . . 1·00 65
385 1k. Bushbuck . . . . 1·50 85
386 2k. Red forest duiker . . . . 2·75 1·50
387 4k. Common duiker . . . . 20·00 19·00
Nos. 380/7 are larger, size 25 × 42 mm.
No. 387 is incorrectly inscr "Gray Duiker".

85 Christ on the Cross
87 "Holarrhena febrifuga"

1971. Easter. Multicoloured.
388 **85** 3t. black and green 10 25
389 – 3t. black and green 10 25
390 **85** 8t. black and red 10 25
391 – 8t. black and red 10 25
392 **85** 15t. black and violet . . . 15 30
393 – 15t. black and violet . . . 15 30
394 **85** 30t. black and blue 20 45
395 – 30t. black and blue 20 45
MS396 Two sheets, each 95 × 145 mm. (a) Nos. 388, 390, 392 and 394. (b) Nos. 389, 391, 393 and 395 Set of 2 sheets . . 1·50 3·50
DESIGN: Nos. 389, 391, 393, 395, The Resurrection. Both designs from "The Small Passion" (Durer).

1971. Flowering Shrubs and Trees. Mult.
397 3t. Type **87** 10 10
398 8t. "Brachystegia spiciformis" 10 10
399 15t. "Securidaca longepedunculata" 15 10
400 30t. "Pterocarpus rotundifolius" . . . . . . 30 1·00
MS401 102 × 135 mm. Nos. 397/400 1·00 2·00

88 Drum Major

89 "Madonna and Child" (William Dyce)

1971. 50th Anniv of Malawi Police Force.
402 **88** 30t. multicoloured . . . . 65 1·25

1971. Christmas. Multicoloured.
403 3t. Type **89** 10 10
404 8t. "The Holy Family" (M. Schongauer) 15 10
405 15t. "The Holy Family with St. John" (Raphael) . . . 20 20
406 30t. "The Holy Family" (Bronzino) . . . . 50 1·40
MS407 101 × 139 mm. Nos. 403/6 1·10 2·50

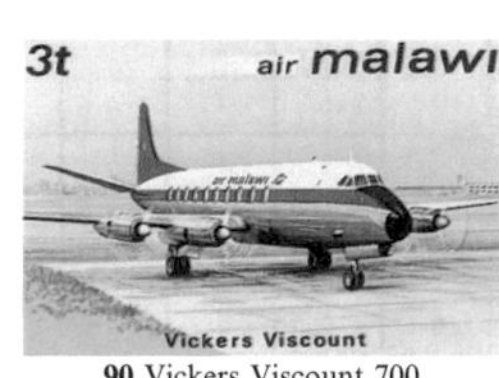

90 Vickers Viscount 700

1972. Air. Malawi Aircraft. Multicoloured.
408 3t. Type **90** 30 10
409 8t. Hawker Siddeley H.S.748 50 10
410 15t. Britten Norman Islander 75 30
411 30t. B.A.C. One Eleven . . . 1·25 2·25
MS412 143 × 94 mm. Nos. 408/11 8·00 5·50

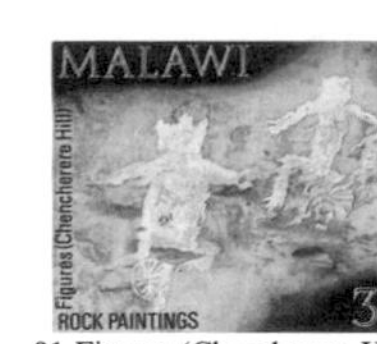

91 Figures (Chencherere Hill)

1972. Rock Paintings.
413 **91** 3t. green and black 25 10
414 – 8t. red, grey and black . . 30 10
415 – 15t. multicoloured 35 30
416 – 30t. multicoloured . . . . 45 1·00
MS417 121 × 97 mm. Nos. 413/16 2·75 2·75
DESIGNS: 8t. Lizard and cat (Chencherere Hill); 15t. Schematics (Diwa Hill); 30t. Sun through rain (Mikolongwe Hill).

92 Boxing

1972. Olympic Games, Munich.
418 **92** 3t. multicoloured 10 10
419 8t. multicoloured 15 10
420 15t. multicoloured 20 10
421 30t. multicoloured 35 45
MS422 110 × 92 mm. Nos. 418/21 1·25 1·75

93 Arms of Malawi

1972. Commonwealth Parliamentary Conf.
423 **93** 15t. multicoloured 30 35

94 "Adoration of the Kings" (Orcagna)

1972. Christmas. Multicoloured.
424 3t. Type **94** 10 10
425 8t. "Madonna and Child Enthroned" (Florentine School) 10 10
426 15t. "Virgin and Child" (Crivelli) 20 10
427 30t. "Virgin and Child with St. Anne" (Flemish School) 45 70
MS428 95 × 121 mm. Nos. 424/7 1·10 2·00

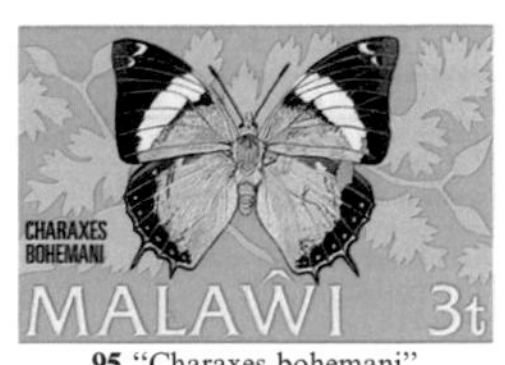

95 "Charaxes bohemani"

1973. Butterflies. Multicoloured.
429 3t. Type **95** 50 10
430 8t. "Uranothauma crawshayi" 75 10
431 15t. "Charaxes acuminatus" 1·00 30
432 30t. "Amauris ansorgei" (inscr in error "EUPHAEDRA ZADDACHI") . . . . . 4·00 8·50
433 30t. "Amauris ansorgei" (inscr corrected) . . . . . 3·75 8·50
MS434 145 × 95 mm. Nos. 429/32 7·00 11·50

96 Livingstone and Map

1973. Death Cent of David Livingstone (1st issue).
435 **96** 3t. multicoloured 10 10
436 8t. multicoloured 15 10
437 15t. multicoloured 20 10
438 30t. multicoloured 35 60
MS439 144 × 95 mm. Nos. 435/8 1·00 1·50
See also No. 450/**MS**451.

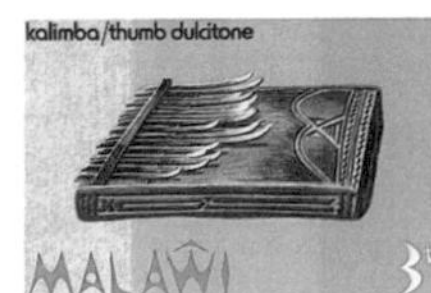

97 Thumb Dulcitone

1973. Musical Instruments. Multicoloured.
440 3t. Type **97** 10 10
441 8t. Hand zither (vert) 15 10
442 15t. Hand drum (vert) . . . 25 10
443 30t. One-stringed fiddle . . . 45 60
MS444 120 × 103 mm. Nos. 440/3 2·75 2·00

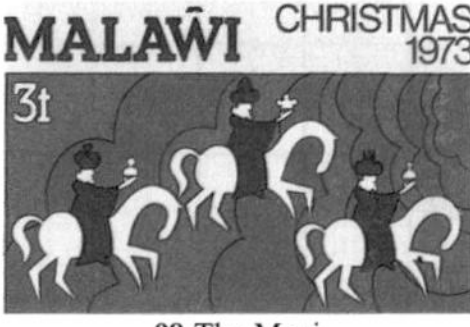

98 The Magi

1973. Christmas.
445 **98** 3t. blue, lilac & ultramarine 10 10
446 8t. red, lilac and brown . . 10 10
447 15t. mauve, blue & dp mve 15 10
448 30t. yellow, lilac and brown 30 70
MS449 165 × 114 mm. Nos. 445/8 75 1·40

99 Stained-glass Window, Livingstonia Mission

1973. Death Cent of David Livingstone (2nd issue).
450 **99** 50t. multicoloured . . . . 45 1·00
MS451 71 × 77 mm. No. 450 . . 80 1·60

100 Large-mouthed Black Bass

1974. 35th Anniv of Malawi Angling Society. Multicoloured.
452 3t. Type **100** 20 10
453 8t. Rainbow trout 25 10
454 15t. Silver alestes ("Lake salmon") 40 20
455 30t. Tigerfish . . . . 70 1·75
MS456 169 × 93 mm. Nos. 452/5 2·50 2·50

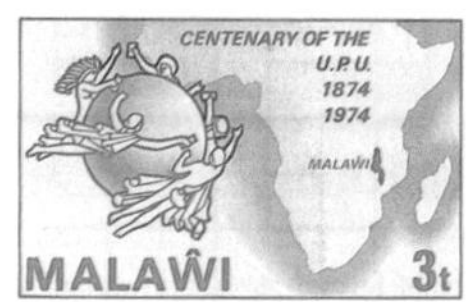

101 U.P.U. Monument and Map of Africa

1974. Centenary of U.P.U.
457 **101** 3t. green and brown . . . 10 10
458 8t. red and brown 10 10
459 15t. violet and brown . . 15 10
460 30t. blue and brown . . . 30 1·10
MS461 115 × 146 mm. Nos. 457/60 65 1·75

102 Capital Hill, Lilongwe

1974. 10th Anniv of Independence.
462 **102** 3t. multicoloured 10 10
463 8t. multicoloured 10 10
464 15t. multicoloured 10 10
465 30t. multicoloured 25 35
MS466 120 × 86 mm. Nos. 462/5 45 1·00

103 "Madonna of the Meadow" (Bellini)

1974. Christmas. Multicoloured.
467 3t. Type **103** 10 10
468 8t. "The Holy Family with Sts. John and Elizabeth" (Jordaens) 10 10
469 15t. "The Nativity" (Pieter de Grebber) 15 10
470 30t. "Adoration of the Shepherds" (Lorenzo di Credi) 30 50
MS471 163 × 107 mm. Nos. 467/70 60 1·25

104 Arms of Malawi

105 African Snipe

106 Spur-winged Goose ("Spurwing Goose")

1975.
472 **104** 1t. blue 20 40
472a 5t. red . . . . 65 2·00

1975. Birds (2nd series). Multicoloured. (a) As T **105**.
473 1t. Type **105** . . . . 1·50 2·00
474 2t. Double-banded sandgrouse (horiz) . . . . 1·50 2·00

475 3t. Indian blue quail ("Blue Quail") (horiz) 1·50 1·50
476 5t. Red-necked spurfowl ("Red-necked Francolin") 3·50 1·25
477 8t. Harlequin quail (horiz) 4·75 1·00

(b) As T **106**.
502 10t. Type **106** 2·00 1·50
503 15t. Denham's bustard ("Stanley Bustard") 2·00 2·00
480 20t. Comb duck ("Knob-billed Duck") 1·00 2·25
481 30t. Helmeted guineafowl ("Crowned Guinea Fowl") 1·25 70
482 50t. African pygmy goose ("Pigmy Goose") (horiz) 2·00 1·60
483 1k. Garganey 3·00 8·50
504 2k. White-faced whistling duck ("White Face Tree Duck") 5·00 11·00
485 4k. African green pigeon ("Green Pigeon") 13·00 16·00

107 M.V. "Mpasa"

1975. Ships of Lake Malawi. Multicoloured.
486 3t. Type **107** 30 10
487 8t. M.V. "Ilala II" 40 10
488 15t. M.V. "Chauncy Maples II" 75 30
489 30t. M.V. "Nkwazi" 1·00 3·00
MS490 105 × 142 mm. Nos. 486/9 2·25 4·25

108 "Habenaria splendens" **109** Thick-tailed Bushbaby

1975. Malawi Orchids. Multicoloured.
491 3t. Type **108** 40 10
492 10t. "Eulophia cucullata" 50 10
493 20t. "Disa welwitschii" 80 25
494 40t. "Angraecum conchiferum" 1·10 1·50
MS495 127 × 111 mm. Nos. 491/4 7·00 8·00

1976. Malawi Animals. Multicoloured.
496 3t. Type **109** 10 10
497 10t. Leopard 35 10
498 20t. Roan antelope 55 35
499 40t. Common zebra 1·00 2·75
MS500 88 × 130 mm. Nos. 496/9 2·50 3·50

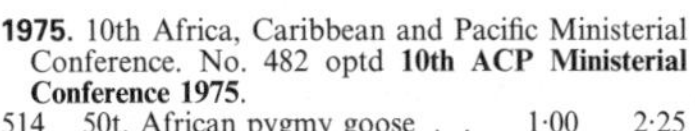

1975. 10th Africa, Caribbean and Pacific Ministerial Conference. No. 482 optd **10th ACP Ministerial Conference 1975**.
514 50t. African pygmy goose 1·00 2·25

111 "A Castle with the Adoration of the Magi"

1975. Christmas. Religious Medallions. Mult.
515 3t. Type **111** 10 10
516 10t. "The Nativity" 15 10
517 20t. "Adoration of the Magi" (different) 20 10
518 40t. "Angel appearing to Shepherds" 50 2·25
MS519 98 × 168 mm. Nos. 515/18 1·50 3·25

112 Alexander Graham Bell **113** President Banda

1976. Centenary of Telephone.
520 **112** 3t. green and black 10 10
521 10t. purple and black 10 10
522 20t. violet and black 20 10
523 40t. blue and black 50 1·40
MS524 137 × 114 mm. Nos. 520/3 1·10 1·75

1976. 10th Anniv of Republic. Multicoloured.
525 **113** 3t. green 10 10
526 10t. purple 10 10
527 20t. blue 20 10
528 40t. blue 50 1·40
MS529 102 × 112 mm. Nos. 524/8 1·00 2·50

114 Bagnall Diesel Shunter No. 100

1976. Malawi Locomotives. Multicoloured.
530 3t. Type **114** 40 15
531 10t. Class "Shire" diesel locomotive No. 503 70 15
532 20t. Nippon Sharyo diesel-hydraulic locomotive No. 301 1·40 45
533 40t. Hunslet diesel-hydraulic locomotive No. 110 2·10 6·50
MS534 130 × 118 mm. Nos. 530/3 4·25 7·00

1976. Centenary of Blantyre Mission. Nos. 479 and 481 optd **Blantyre Mission Centenary 1876–1976**.
535 15t. Denham's bustard 1·50 1·50
536 30t. Helmeted guineafowl 1·75 3·50

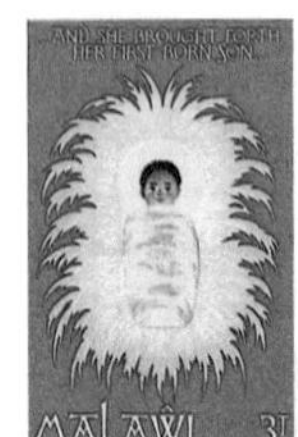

116 Child on Bed of Straw **117** Man and Woman

1976. Christmas.
537 **116** 3t. multicoloured 10 10
538 10t. multicoloured 10 10
539 20t. multicoloured 20 10
540 40t. multicoloured 40 60
MS541 135 × 95 mm. Nos. 537/40 1·40 1·75

1977. Handicrafts. Wood-carvings. Mult.
542 4t. Type **117** 10 10
543 10t. Elephant (horiz) 15 10
544 20t. Rhinoceros (horiz) 20 10
545 40t. Antelope 50 70
MS546 153 × 112 mm. Nos. 542/5 1·50 2·75

118 Chileka Airport

1977. Transport. Multicoloured.
547 4t. Type **118** 40 10
548 10t. Blantyre–Lilongwe Road 40 10
549 20t. M.V. "Ilala II" 1·00 35
550 40t. Blantyre–Nacala rail line 1·50 4·75
MS551 127 × 83 mm. Nos. 547/50 3·00 4·50

119 Blue-grey Mbuna

1977. Fish of Lake Malawi. Multicoloured.
552B 4t. Type **119** 30 10
553B 10t. Livingston mbuna 50 20
554A 20t. Zebra mbuna 1·40 30
555B 40t. Malawi scale-eater 1·50 1·25
MS556A 147 × 99 mm. Nos. 552A/5B 3·00 4·50

120 "Madonna and Child with St. Catherine and the Blessed Stefano Maconi" (Borgognone) **121** "Entry of Christ into Jerusalem" (Giotto)

1977. Christmas.
557 **120** 4t. multicoloured 10 10
558 – 10t. multicoloured 10 10
559 – 20t. multicoloured 20 10
560 – 40t. multicoloured 50 1·00
MS561 150 × 116 mm. Nos. 557/60 2·50 3·00
DESIGNS: 10t. "Madonna and Child with the Eternal Father and Angels" (Borgognone); 20t. Bottigella altarpiece (detail, Foppa); 40t. "Madonna of the Fountain" (van Eyck).

1978. Easter. Paintings by Giotto. Multicoloured.
562 4t. Type **121** 10 10
563 10t. "The Crucifixion" 15 10
564 20t. "Descent from the Cross" 30 10
565 40t. "Jesus appears before Mary" 50 55
MS566 150 × 99 mm. Nos. 562/5 1·90 2·40

122 Nyala **124** "Vanilla polylepis"

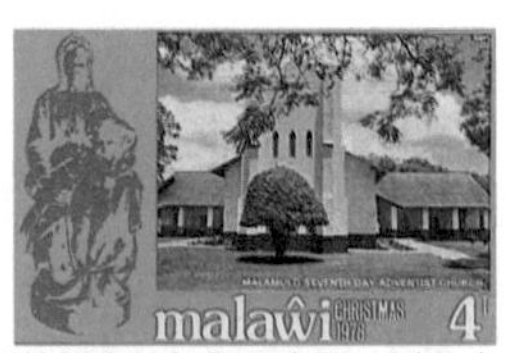

123 Malamulo Seventh Day Adventist Church

1978. Wildlife. Multicoloured.
567 4t. Type **122** 2·50 10
568 10t. Lion (horiz) 7·00 40
569 20t. Common zebra (horiz) 10·00 1·00
570 40t. Mountain reedbuck 11·00 7·50
MS571 173 × 113 mm. Nos. 567/70 30·00 11·00

1978. Christmas. Multicoloured.
572 4t. Type **123** 10 10
573 10t. Likoma Cathedral 10 10
574 20t. St. Michael's and All Angels', Blantyre 20 10
575 40t. Zomba Catholic Cathedral 40 1·50
MS576 190 × 105 mm. Nos. 572/5 70 1·50

1979. Orchids. Multicoloured.
577 1t. Type **124** 50 30
578 2t. "Cirrhopetalum umbellatum" 50 30
579 5t. "Calanthe natalensis" 50 10
580 7t. "Ansellia gigantea" 50 50
581 8t. "Tridactyle bicaudata" 50 30
582 10t. "Acampe pachyglossa" 50 10
583 15t. "Eulophia quartiniana" 50 15
584 20t. "Cyrtorchis arcuata" 50 50
585 30t. "Eulophia tricristata" 1·25 30
586 50t. "Disa hamatopetala" 85 50
587 75t. "Cynorchis glandulosa" 2·00 6·50
588 1k. "Aerangis kotschyana" 1·60 1·75
589 1k.50 "Polystachya dendrobiiflora" 1·75 6·00
590 2k. "Disa ornithantha" 1·25 2·00
591 4k. "Cyrtorchis praetermissa" 1·50 4·50

125 Tsamba

1979. National Tree Planting Day. Mult.
592 5t. Type **125** 20 10
593 10t. Mulanje cedar 25 10
594 20t. Mlombwa 40 20
595 40t. Mbawa 70 2·50
MS596 118 × 153 mm. Nos. 592/5 1·40 3·00

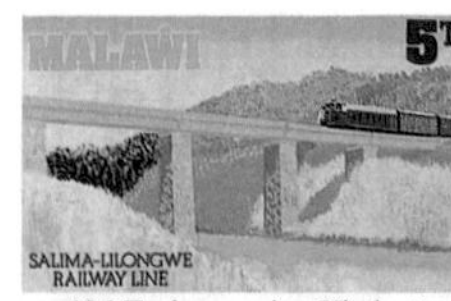

126 Train crossing Viaduct

1979. Opening of Salima–Lilongwe Railway Line. Multicoloured.
597 5t. Type **126** 25 15
598 10t. Diesel railcar at station 40 15
599 20t. Diesel train rounding bend 60 30
600 40t. Diesel train passing through cutting 85 2·00
MS601 153 × 103 mm. Nos. 597/600 4·00 4·50

127 Young Child

1979. International Year of the Child. Designs showing young children. Multicoloured; background colours given.
602 **127** 5t. green 10 10
603 – 10t. red 10 10
604 – 20t. mauve 25 10
605 – 40t. blue 45 1·40

128 1964 3d. Independence Commemorative Stamp

1979. Death Centenary of Sir Rowland Hill. Designs showing 1964 Independence Commemorative Stamps. Multicoloured.
606 5t. Type **128** 10 10
607 10t. 6d. value 10 10
608 20t. 1s.3d. value 20 10
609 40t. 2s.6d. value 35 60
MS610 163 × 108 mm. Nos. 606/9 75 1·40

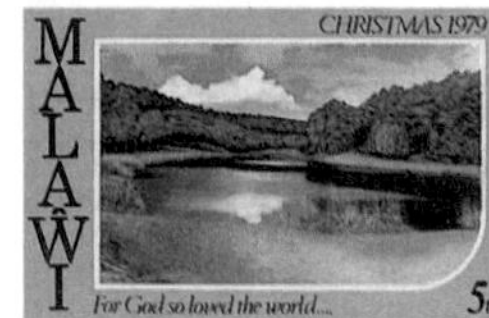

129 River Landscape

1979. Christmas. Multicoloured.
611 5t. Type **129** 10 10
612 10t. Sunset 10 10
613 20t. Forest and hill 25 15
614 40t. Plain and mountains 50 2·50

130 Limbe Rotary Club Emblem **132** Agate Nodule

131 Mangochi District Post Office

1980. 75th Anniv of Rotary International.
615 **130** 5t. multicoloured 10 10
616 – 10t. multicoloured 10 10
617 – 20t. blue, gold and red 30 15
618 – 40t. gold and blue 75 2·25
MS619 105 × 144 mm. Nos. 615/18 1·10 2·25

DESIGNS: 10t. Blantyre Rotary Club pennant; 20t. Lilongwe Rotary Club pennant; 40t. Rotary International emblem.

1980. "London 1980" International Stamp Exhibition.

620 **131** 5t. black and green . . . 10 10
621 – 10t. black and red 10 10
622 – 20t. black and violet . . . 15 10
623 – 1k. black and blue . . . 65 1·10
MS624 114 × 89 mm. Nos. 620/3 1·25 2·25

DESIGNS: 10t. New Blantyre Sorting Office; 20t. Mail transfer hut, Walala; 1k. First Nyasaland Post Office, Chiromo.

1980. Gemstones. Multicoloured.

625 5t. Type **132** 60 10
626 10t. Sunstone 80 10
627 20t. Smoky quartz . . . . . 1·40 30
628 1k. Kyanite crystal . . . . . 3·50 6·00

133 Elephants

1980. Christmas. Children's Paintings. Mult.

629 5t. Type **133** 40 10
630 10t. Flowers 30 10
631 20t. Class "Shire" diesel train 75 20
632 1k. Malachite kingfisher . . . 1·60 2·00

134 Suni

1981. Wildlife. Multicoloured.

633 7t. Type **134** 15 10
634 10t. Blue duiker 20 10
635 20t. African buffalo 30 15
636 1k. Lichtenstein's hartebeest 1·25 1·60

135 "Kanjedza II" Standard "A" Earth Station

1981. International Communications. Mult.

637 7t. Type **135** 10 10
638 10t. Blantyre International Gateway Exchange 15 10
639 20t. "Kanjedza I" standard "B" earth station 25 15
640 1k. "Satellite communications" . . . . 1·50 1·90
MS641 101 × 151 mm. Nos. 637/40 1·75 3·00

136 Maize

1981. World Food Day. Agricultural Produce. Multicoloured.

642 7t. Type **136** 15 10
643 10t. Rice 20 10
644 20t. Finger-millet 30 20
645 1k. Wheat . . . . 1·00 1·40

137 "The Adoration of the Shepherds" (Murillo)

138 Impala Herd

1981. Christmas. Paintings. Multicoloured.

646 7t. Type **137** 20 10
647 10t. "The Holy Family" (Lippi) (horiz) 25 10
648 20t. "The Adoration of the Shepherds" (Louis le Nain) (horiz) 45 15
649 1k. "The Virgin and Child, St. John the Baptist and an Angel" (Paolo Morando) 1·10 1·75

1982. National Parks. Wildlife. Multicoloured.

650 7t. Type **138** 20 10
651 10t. Lions 35 10
652 20t. Greater kudu 50 20
653 1k. Greater flamingoes . . . 1·75 5·50

139 Kamuzu Academy

1982. Kamuzu Academy.

654 **139** 7t. multicoloured 15 10
655 – 20t. multicoloured 20 10
656 – 30t. multicoloured 30 45
657 – 1k. multicoloured . . . . 1·00 3·75

DESIGNS: 20t. to 1k. Various views of the Academy.

140 Attacker challenging Goalkeeper

1982. World Cup Football Championship, Spain. Multicoloured.

658 7t. Type **140** 75 25
659 20t. FIFA World Cup trophy 1·60 1·25
660 30t. Football stadium . . . . 1·90 3·25
MS661 80 × 59 mm. 1k. Football 1·75 1·60

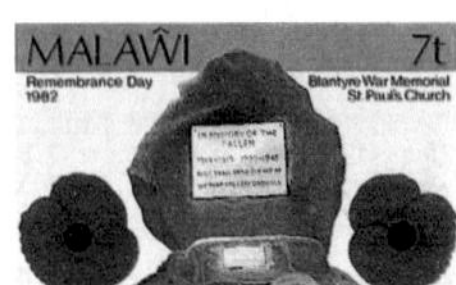

141 Blantyre War Memorial, St. Paul's Church

1982. Remembrance Day. Multicoloured.

662 7t. Type **141** 10 10
663 20t. Zomba war memorial . . 15 10
664 30t. Chichiri war memorial 20 30
665 1k. Lilongwe war memorial 65 4·25

142 Kwacha International Conference Centre

1983. Commonwealth Day. Multicoloured.

666 7t. Type **142** 10 10
667 20t. Tea-picking, Mulanje . . 20 10
668 30t. World map showing position of Malawi 25 30
669 1k. Pres. Dr. H. Kamuzu Banda . . . . 60 1·50

143 "Christ and St. Peter"

144 Pair by Lake

1983. 500th Birth Anniv of Raphael. Details from the cartoon for "The Miraculous Draught of Fishes" Tapestry. Multicoloured.

670 7t. Type **143** 35 10
671 20t. "Hauling in the Catch" 75 80
672 30t. "Fishing Village" (horiz) 90 2·50
MS673 110 × 90 mm. 1k. "Apostle" 1·60 1·60

1983. African Fish Eagle. Multicoloured.

674 30t. Type **144** . . . . 1·60 1·90
675 30t. Making gull-like call . . 1·60 1·90
676 30t. Diving on prey . . . . . 1·60 1·90
677 30t. Carrying fish . . . . . 1·60 1·90
678 30t. Feeding on catch . . . . 1·60 1·90

145 Kamuzu International Airport

1983. Bicentenary of Manned Flight. Mult.

679 7t. Type **145** 10 10
680 20t. Kamuzu International Airport (different) 25 15
681 30t. B.A.C. One Eleven . . . 40 45
682 1k. Short Empire "C" Class flying boat at Cape Maclear . . . . 1·10 2·50
MS683 100 × 121 mm. Nos. 679/82 2·00 4·00

146 "Clerodendrum myricoides"

147 Golden Mbuna

1983. Christmas. Flowers. Multicoloured.

684 7t. Type **146** 40 10
685 20t. "Gloriosa superba" . . . 90 15
686 30t. "Gladiolus laxiflorus" . . 1·00 60
687 1k. "Aframomum angustifolium" . . . . . . 2·25 7·00

1984. Fishes. Multicoloured.

688 1t. Type **147** . . . . 30 1·00
689 2t. Malawi eyebiter . . . . . 30 1·00
690 5t. Blue mbuna . . . . . . 30 1·00
691 7t. Lombardo's mbuna . . . 30 30
692 8t. Golden zebra mbuna . . 30 30
693 10t. Fairy cichlid 30 10
694 15t. Crabro mbuna 30 10
695 20t. Marbled zebra mbuna 30 10
696 30t. Sky-blue mbuna 50 20
697 40t. Venustus cichlid 60 30
698 50t. Thumbi emperor cichlid 2·25 3·25
699 75t. Purple mbuna . . . . . 2·75 5·50
700 1k. Zebra mbuna . . . . . 3·00 5·00
701 2k. Fairy cichlid (different) 4·00 7·00
702 4k. Mbenje emperor cichlid 5·00 11·00

Nos. 688 and 691/7 exist with different imprint dates at foot.

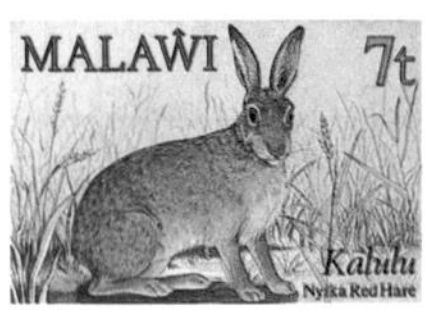

148 Smith's Red Hare

1984. Small Mammals. Multicoloured.

703 7t. Type **148** 20 10
704 20t. Gambian sun squirrel . . 35 50
705 30t. South African hedgehog 35 1·10
706 1k. Large-spotted genet . . . 50 5·50

149 Running

150 "Euphaedra neophron"

1984. Olympic Games, Los Angeles. Mult.

707 7t. Type **149** 15 10
708 20t. Boxing 35 20
709 30t. Cycling 75 70
710 1k. Long jumping . . . . . 1·00 3·75
MS711 90 × 128 mm. Nos. 707/10 2·40 5·00

1984. Butterflies.

712 **150** 7t. multicoloured 95 30
713 – 20t. yellow, brown and red . . . . 2·25 45
714 – 30t. multicoloured . . . . 2·50 1·10
715 – 1k. multicoloured . . . . 4·25 9·00

DESIGNS: 20t. "Papilio dardanus"; 30t. "Antanartia schaeneia"; 1k. "Spindasis nyassae".

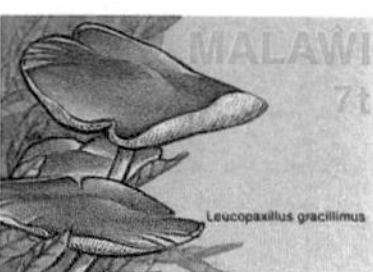

151 "Virgin and Child" (Duccio)

152 "Leucopaxillus gracillimus"

1984. Christmas. Religious Paintings. Mult.

716 7t. Type **151** 55 10
717 20t. "Madonna and Child" (Raphael) . . . . 1·40 20
718 30t. "Virgin and Child" (ascr to Lippi) . . . . 1·90 70
719 1k. "The Wilton Diptych" . . 3·50 8·00

1985. Fungi. Multicoloured.

720 7t. Type **152** . . . . 1·25 30
721 20t. "Limacella guttata" . . 2·50 45
722 30t. "Termitomyces eurrhizus" . . . . 3·00 1·25
723 1k. "Xerulina asprata" . . . 5·50 9·50

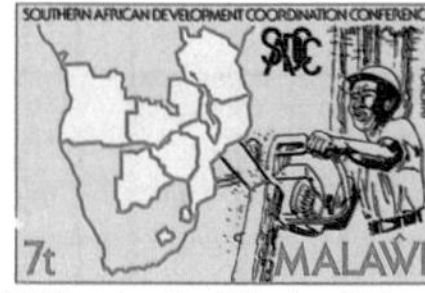

153 Map showing Member States and Lumberjack (Forestry)

1985. 5th Anniv of Southern African Development Co-ordination Conference. Designs showing map and aspects of development.

724 **153** 7t. black, green and light green 75 10
725 – 15t. black, red and pink 1·25 20
726 – 20t. black, violet and mauve . . . . 4·00 1·75
727 1k. black, blue and light blue . . . . 4·50 10·00

DESIGNS: 15t. Radio mast (Communications); 20t. Diesel locomotive (Transport); 1k. Trawler and net (Fishing).

154 M.V. "Ufulu"

1985. Ships of Lake Malawi (2nd series). Mult.

728 7t. Type **154** 90 10
729 15t. M.V. "Chauncy Maples II" . . . . 1·75 20
730 20t. M.V. "Mtendere" . . . 2·25 65
731 1k. M.V. "Ilala II" . . . . . 4·50 6·00
MS732 120 × 84 mm. Nos. 728/31 8·00 8·00

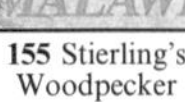

155 Stierling's Woodpecker

156 "The Virgin of Humility" (Jaime Serra)

1985. Birth Bicentenary of John J. Audubon (ornithologist). Multicoloured.

733 7t. Type **155** . . . . 1·25 30
734 15t. Lesser seedcracker . . . 2·25 30
735 20t. East coast akelat ("Gunning's Akalat") . . . 2·25 65
736 1k. Boehm's bee eater . . . 4·25 7·00
MS737 130 × 90 mm. Nos. 733/6 10·00 10·00

1985. Christmas. Nativity Paintings. Mult.

738 7t. Type **156** 30 10
739 15t. "The Adoration of the Magi" (Stefano da Zevio) 75 15
740 20t. "Madonna and Child" (Gerard van Honthorst) . . 85 25
741 1k. "Virgin of Zbraslav" (Master of Vissy Brod) . . 2·25 5·50

157 Halley's Comet and Path of "Giotto" Spacecraft

1986. Appearance of Halley's Comet. Mult.
742 8t. Type **157** 60 10
743 15t. Halley's Comet above Earth 65 15
744 20t. Comet and dish aerial, Malawi . . . . 1·00 30
745 1k. "Giotto" spacecraft . . . 2·00 6·00

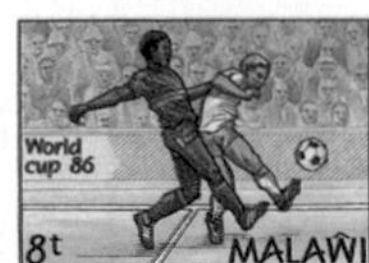

158 Two Players competing for Ball

1986. World Cup Football Championship, Mexico. Multicoloured.
746 8t. Type **158** 70 10
747 15t. Goalkeeper saving goal 95 20
748 20t. Two players competing for ball (different) . . . . 1·10 35
749 1k. Player kicking ball . . . 4·00 5·50
MS750 108 × 77 mm. Nos. 746/9 10·00 11·00

159 President Banda

160 "Virgin and Child" (Botticelli)

1986. 20th Anniv of Republic. Multicoloured.
751 8t. Type **159** . . . . 1·50 2·75
752 15t. National flag 80 15
753 20t. Malawi coat of arms . . 85 25
754 1k. Kamuzu International Airport and emblem of national airline . . . . . 3·50 6·00

1986. Christmas. Multicoloured.
755 8t. Type **160** 45 10
756 15t. "Adoration of the Shepherds" (Guido Reni) 80 15
757 20t. "Madonna of the Veil" (Carlo Dolci) . . . . . 1·25 35
758 1k. "Adoration of the Magi" (Jean Bourdichon) . . . . 3·75 9·00

161 Wattled Crane

1987. Wattled Crane. Multicoloured.
759 8t. Type **161** . . . . 1·50 40
760 15t. Two cranes . . . . . . 2·25 50
761 20t. Cranes at nest . . . . . 2·25 80
762 75t. Crane in lake . . . . . 4·50 12·00

162 Bagnall Steam Locomotive No. 2 "Shamrock"

1987. Steam Locomotives. Multicoloured.
767 10t. Type **162** . . . . 2·00 40
768 25t. Class D steam locomotive No. 8, 1914 . . 2·75 50
769 30t. Bagnall steam locomotive No. 1 "Thistle" . . . . . 3·00 85
770 1k. Kitson steam locomotive No. 6, 1903 . . . . 6·00 12·00

163 Hippopotamus grazing

164 "Stathmostelma spectabile"

1987. Hippopotamus. Multicoloured.
771 10t. Type **163** . . . . . . 1·50 40
772 25t. Hippopotami in water 2·25 50
773 30t. Female and calf in water 2·25 75
774 1k. Hippopotami and cattle egret . . . . 6·00 12·00
MS775 78 × 101 mm. Nos. 771/4 11·00 12·00

1987. Christmas. Wild Flowers. Multicoloured.
776 10t. Type **164** 65 10
777 25t. "Pentanisia schweinfurthii" . . . . . . 1·50 25
778 30t. "Chironia krebsii" . . . 1·75 55
779 1k. "Ochna macrocalyx" . . 3·00 9·00

165 African and Staunton Knights

166 High Jumping

1988. Chess. Local and Staunton chess pieces. Multicoloured.
780 15t. Type **165** . . . . 1·25 30
781 35t. Bishops . . . . 1·75 70
782 50t. Rooks . . . . 2·00 1·50
783 2k. Queens . . . . 6·00 12·00

1988. Olympic Games, Seoul. Multicoloured.
784 15t. Type **166** 30 10
785 35t. Javelin throwing 50 20
786 50t. Tennis 75 50
787 2k. Shot-putting . . . . . . 1·60 3·00
MS788 91 × 121 mm. Nos. 784/7 3·50 3·50

167 Evergreen Forest Warbler ("Eastern Forest Scrub Warbler")

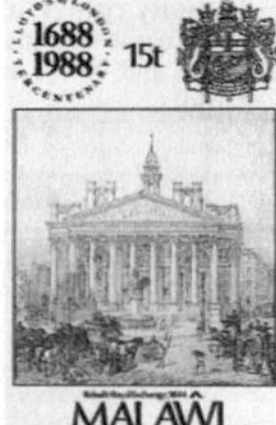

167a Rebuilt Royal Exchange, 1844

1988. Birds. Multicoloured.
789 1t. Type **167** 20 80
790 2t. Yellow-throated woodland warbler ("Yellow-throated Warbler") 30 80
791 5t. Moustached green tinkerbird 50 80
792 7t. Waller's red-winged starling ("Waller's Chestnut-wing Starling") 50 80
793 8t. Oriole-finch 50 80
794 10t. White starred robin ("Starred Robin") . . . . 2·75 80
795 15t. Bar-tailed trogon 50 10
796 20t. Green-backed twin-spot ("Green Twinspot") . . . 50 10
797 30t. African grey cuckoo shrike ("Grey Cuckoo Shrike") 50 10
798 40t. Black-fronted bush shrike 60 10
799 50t. White-tailed crested flycatcher . . . . 3·25 1·25
800 75t. Green barbet . . . . . 70 1·00
801 1k. Lemon dove ("Cinnamon Dove") . . . 70 1·00
802 2k. Silvery-cheeked hornbill 90 1·40
803 4k. Crowned eagle . . . . 1·25 2·00
804 10k. Anchieta's sunbird ("Red and Blue Sunbird") 10·00 11·00
804a 10k. As 10t. . . . . 5·00 2·25

1988. 300th Anniv of Lloyd's of London. Mult.
805 15t. Type **167a** 30 10
806 35t. Opening ceremony, Nkula Falls Hydro-electric Power Station (horiz) . . . 60 20
807 50t. Air Malawi B.A.C. One Eleven airliner (horiz) . . . 2·00 60
808 2k. "Seawise University" (formerly "Queen Elizabeth") on fire, Hong Kong, 1972 . . . . 3·75 4·00

168 "Madonna in the Church" (Jan van Eyck)

1988. Christmas. Multicoloured.
809 15t. Type **168** 60 10
810 35t. "Virgin, Infant Jesus and St. Anna" (da Vinci) . . . 90 25
811 50t. "Virgin and Angels" (Cimabue) . . . . 1·25 70
812 2k. "Virgin and Child" (Baldovinetti Apenio) . . . 3·00 6·50

169 Robust Cichlid

1989. 50th Anniv of Malawi Angling Society. Multicoloured.
813 15t. Type **169** 60 20
814 35t. Small-scaled minnow ("Mpasa") . . . . 1·10 35
815 50t. Long-scaled yellowfish 1·50 1·40
816 2k. Tigerfish . . . . 4·00 9·50

170 Independence Arch, Blantyre

1989. 25th Anniv of Independence. Multicoloured.
817 15t. Type **170** 80 20
818 35t. Grain silos . . . . . . 1·50 35
819 50t. Capital Hill, Lilongwe 2·00 1·50
820 2k. Reserve Bank Headquarters . . . . . . 5·00 9·50

171 Blantyre Digital Telex Exchange

1989. 25th Anniv of African Development Bank. Multicoloured.
821 15t. Type **171** 80 20
822 40t. Dzalanyama steer . . . 1·50 35
823 50t. Mikolongwe heifer . . . 2·00 1·50
824 2k. Zebu bull . . . . 5·00 9·50

172 Rural House with Verandah

1989. 25th Anniv of Malawi–United Nations Co-operation. Multicoloured.
825 15t. Type **172** 80 20
826 40t. Rural house . . . . . . 1·50 35
827 50t. Traditional hut and modern houses . . . . . . 2·00 1·50
828 2k. Tea plantation . . . . . 5·00 9·50

173 St. Michael and All Angels Church

1989. Christmas. Churches of Malawi. Mult.
829 15t. Type **173** 80 20
830 40t. Catholic Cathedral, Limbe . . . . 1·50 35
831 50t. C.C.A.P. Church, Nkhoma . . . . 2·00 1·50
832 2k. Cathedral, Likoma Island 5·00 9·50

174 Ford "Sedan", 1915

1990. Vintage Vehicles. Multicoloured.
833 15t. Type **174** . . . . 1·25 20
834 40t. Two-seater Ford, 1915 1·75 35
835 50t. Ford pick-up, 1915 . . . 2·00 1·50
836 1k. Chevrolet bus, 1930 . . . 5·00 9·50
MS837 120 × 85mm. Nos. 833/6 15·00 15·00

175 Player heading Ball into Net

1990. World Cup Football Championship, Italy. Multicoloured.
838 15t. Type **175** . . . . 1·00 20
839 40t. Player tackling . . . . . 1·60 35
840 50t. Player scoring goal . . . 2·00 1·50
841 2k. World Cup . . . . . . 5·50 10·00
MS842 88 × 118 mm. Nos. 838/41 9·50 11·00

176 Anniversary Emblem on Map

1990. 10th Anniv of Southern Africa Development Co-ordination Conference. Multicoloured.
843 15t. Type **176** . . . . 1·00 20
844 40t. Tilapia . . . . 1·00 40
845 50t. Cedar plantation . . . . 2·00 1·50
846 2k. Male nyala (antelope) . . 5·00 10·00
MS847 174 × 116 mm. Nos. 843/6 12·00 13·00

177 "Aerangis kotschyana"

178 "The Virgin and the Child Jesus" (Raphael)

1990. Orchids. Multicoloured.
848 15t. Type **177** . . . . 1·75 25
849 40t. "Angraecum eburneum" 2·75 80
850 50t. "Aerangis luteo-alba rhodostica" . . . . 2·75 1·60
851 2k. "Cyrtorchis arcuata whytei" . . . . 6·50 10·00
MS852 85 × 120 mm. Nos. 848/51 13·00 13·00

1990. Christmas. Paintings by Raphael. Mult.
853 15t. Type **178** . . . . 1·00 20
854 40t. "Transfiguration" (detail) 1·75 35
855 50t. "St. Catherine of Alexandrie" (detail) . . . 1·75 90
856 2k. "Transfiguration" . . . . 5·50 11·00
MS857 85 × 120 mm. Nos. 853/6 12·00 13·00

179 Buffalo

1991. Wildlife. Multicoloured.
858 20t. Type **179** . . . . 1·00 25
859 60t. Cheetah . . . . 2·25 1·00
860 75t. Greater kudu . . . . . 2·25 1·00
861 2k. Black rhinoceros . . . . 9·00 10·00
MS862 120 × 85 mm. Nos. 858/61 13·00 14·00

180 Chiromo Post Office, 1891

1991. Centenary of Postal Services. Mult.

No.	Description	Unused	Used
863	20t. Type **180**	1·25	20
864	60t. Re-constructed mail exchange hut at Walala	2·00	85
865	75t. Mangochi post office	2·00	95
866	2k. Satellite Earth station	7·50	12·00
MS867	119 × 83 mm. Nos. 863/6	11·00	12·00

181 Red Locust

182 Child in a Manger

1991. Insects. Multicoloured.

No.	Description	Unused	Used
868	20t. Type **181**	1·00	25
869	60t. Weevil	2·25	1·10
870	75t. Cotton stainer bug	2·25	1·40
871	2k. Pollen beetle	6·50	10·00

1991. Christmas. Multicoloured.

No.	Description	Unused	Used
872	20t. Type **182**	80	20
873	60t. Adoration of the Kings and Shepherds	1·75	55
874	75t. Nativity	2·00	75
875	2k. Virgin and Child	4·75	11·00

183 Red Bishop

1992. Birds. Multicoloured.

No.	Description	Unused	Used
876	75t. Type **183**	2·00	2·00
877	75t. Lesser striped swallow	2·00	2·00
878	75t. Long-crested eagle	2·00	2·00
879	75t. Lilac-breasted roller	2·00	2·00
880	75t. African paradise flycatcher	2·00	2·00
881	75t. White-fronted bee eater	2·00	2·00
882	75t. White-winged black tern	2·00	2·00
883	75t. African fire finch (“Brown-backed Fire-finch”)	2·00	2·00
884	75t. White-browed robin chat	2·00	2·00
885	75t. African fish eagle	2·00	2·00
886	75t. Malachite kingfisher	2·00	2·00
887	75t. Lesser masked weaver (“Cabani’s Masked Weaver”)	2·00	2·00
888	75t. Barn owl (“African Barn Owl”)	2·00	2·00
889	75t. Variable sunbird (“Yellow-bellied Sunbird”)	2·00	2·00
890	75t. Lesser flamingo	2·00	2·00
891	75t. South African crowned crane (“Crowned Crane!”)	2·00	2·00
892	75t. African pitta	2·00	2·00
893	75t. African darter	2·00	2·00
894	75t. White-faced whistling duck (“White-faced Tree-duck”)	2·00	2·00
895	75t. African pied wagtail	2·00	2·00

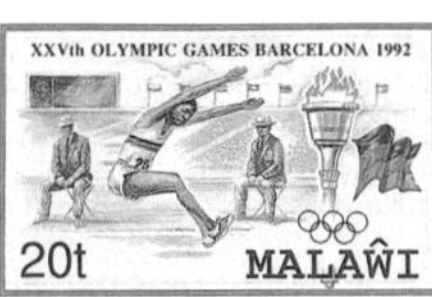

184 Long Jumping

1992. Olympic Games, Barcelona. Multicoloured.

No.	Description	Unused	Used
896	20t. Type **184**	80	20
897	60t. High jumping	1·25	60
898	75t. Javelin	1·50	90
899	2k. Running	3·50	6·50
MS900	110 × 100 mm. Nos. 896/9	6·50	8·00

185 “The Angel Gabriel” (detail, “The Annunciation”) (Philippe de Champaigne)

186 “Voyager 2” passing Saturn

1992. Christmas. Religious Paintings. Mult.

No.	Description	Unused	Used
901	20t. Type **185**	70	20
902	75t. “Virgin and Child” (Bernandino Luini)	1·50	50
903	95t. “Virgin and Child” (Sassoferrato)	1·75	90
904	2k. “Virgin Mary” (detail, “The Annunciation”) (De Champaigne)	4·50	8·50

1992. International Space Year. Multicoloured.

No.	Description	Unused	Used
905	20t. Type **186**	1·00	30
906	75t. Centre of galaxy	2·00	90
907	95t. Kanjedza II Standard A Earth Station	2·00	1·00
908	2k. Communications satellite	4·50	7·50

187 “Strychnos spinosa”

188 “Apaturopsis cleocharis”

1993. World Forestry Day. Indigenous Fruit Trees. Multicoloured.

No.	Description	Unused	Used
909	20t. Type **187**	70	20
910	75t. “Adansonia digitata”	1·50	80
911	95t. “Ximenia caffra”	1·60	1·00
912	2k. “Uapaca kirkiana”	3·25	6·50

1993. Butterflies. Multicoloured.

No.	Description	Unused	Used
913	20t. Type **188**	90	30
914	75t. “Euryphura achlys”	1·75	85
915	95t. “Cooksonia aliciae”	2·00	1·25
916	2k. “Charaxes protoclea azota”	3·00	5·50

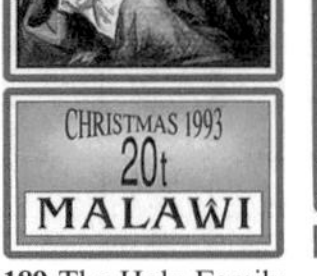

189 The Holy Family

190 Kentrosaurus

1993. Christmas. Multicoloured.

No.	Description	Unused	Used
917	20t. Type **189**	15	10
918	75t. Shepherds and star	30	20
919	95t. Three Kings	30	30
920	2k. Adoration of the Kings	75	2·50

1993. Prehistoric Animals. Multicoloured.

No.	Description	Unused	Used
921	20t. Type **190**	55	30
922	75t. Stegosaurus	90	90
923	95t. Sauropod	1·00	1·00
MS924	157 × 97 mm. 2k. Tyrannosaurus; 2k. Dilophosaurus; 2k. Brachiosaurus; 2k. Gallimimus; 2k. Triceratops; 2k. Velociraptor	11·00	12·00

191 Socolof’s Mbuna

1994. Fishes. Multicoloured.

No.	Description	Unused	Used
925	20t. Type **191**	20	10
926	75t. Golden mbuna	50	30
927	95t. Lombardo’s mbuna	55	35
928	1k. Scraper-mouthed mbuna	60	70
929	2k. Zebra mbuna	1·25	2·00
930	4k. Elongate mbuna	2·00	4·00

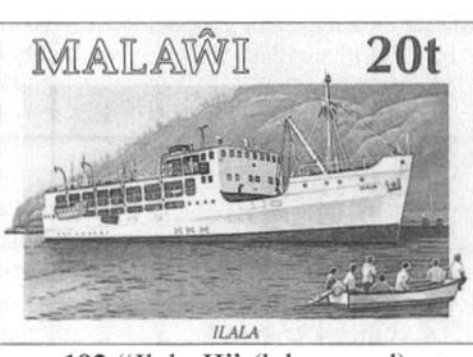

192 “Ilala II” (lake vessel)

1994. Ships of Lake Malawi. Multicoloured.

No.	Description	Unused	Used
931	20t. Type **192**	25	10
932	75t. “Ufulu” (tanker)	35	25
933	95t. “Pioneer” (steam launch)	40	30
934	2k. “Dove” (paddle-steamer)	65	2·25
MS935	85 × 51 mm. 5k. “Monteith” (lake vessel)	3·00	4·00

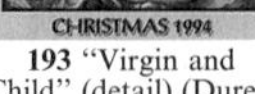

193 “Virgin and Child” (detail) (Durer)

194 Pres. Bakili Muluzi (C.O.M.E.S.A. chairman, 1994–95)

1994. Christmas. Religious Paintings. Mult.

No.	Description	Unused	Used
936	20t. Type **193**	30	10
937	75t. “Wise Men present Gifts” (Franco-Flemish Book of Hours)	60	15
938	95t. “The Nativity” (detail) (Fra Filippo Lippi) (horiz)	65	15
939	2k. “Nativity Scene with Wise Men” (Rogier van der Weyden) (horiz)	1·50	2·50

1995. Establishment of C.O.M.E.S.A. (Common Market for Eastern and Southern African States).

No.	Description	Unused	Used
940	**194** 40t. multicoloured	15	10
941	1k.40 multicoloured	30	20
942	1k.80 multicoloured	30	55
943	2k. multicoloured	40	1·00

195 Telecommunications Training

1995. 50th Anniv of the United Nations. Mult.

No.	Description	Unused	Used
944	40t. Type **195**	30	10
945	1k.40 Village women collecting water	60	25
946	1k.80 Mt. Mulanje	70	85
947	2k. Villagers in field	85	1·10
MS948	123 × 77 mm. Nos. 944/7	1·50	2·00

196 Teacher and Class

1995. Christmas. Multicoloured.

No.	Description	Unused	Used
949	40t. Type **196**	15	10
950	1k.40 Dispensing medicine	40	25
951	1k.80 Crowd at water pump	45	60
952	2k. Refugees on ferries	65	85

197 “Precis tugela”

1996. Butterflies. Multicoloured.

No.	Description	Unused	Used
953	60t. Type **197**	20	10
954	3k. “Papilio pelodorus”	45	35
955	4k. “Acrea acrita”	55	45
956	10k. “Melanitis leda”	1·00	2·25

198 Children’s Party

199 Map of Malawi

1996. Christmas. Multicoloured.

No.	Description	Unused	Used
957	10t. Type **198**	35	15
958	20t. Nativity play	55	15
959	30t. Children wearing party hats	65	20
960	60t. Mother and child	1·10	1·50

1997. 50th Death Anniv of Paul Harris (founder of Rotary International). Multicoloured.

No.	Description	Unused	Used
961	60t. Type **199**	40	10
962	3k. African fish eagle	75	70
963	4k.40 Leopard	80	1·10
964	5k. Rotary International emblem	80	1·25

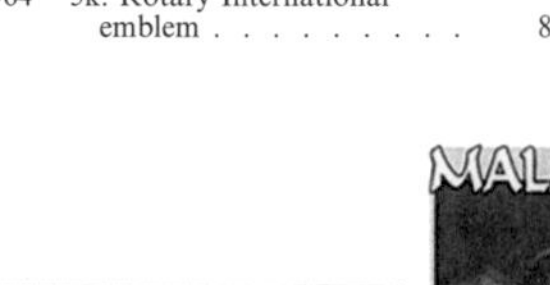

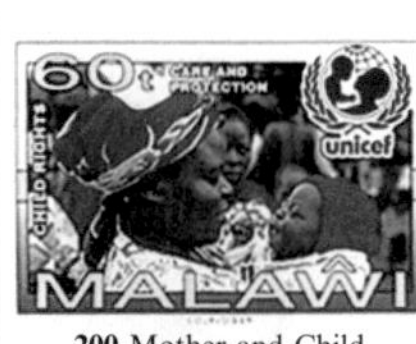

200 Mother and Child

201 The Nativity

1997. 50th Anniv of U.N.I.C.E.F. Multicoloured.

No.	Description	Unused	Used
965	60t. Type **200**	25	10
966	3k. Children in class	55	35
967	4k.40 Boy with fish	1·00	1·10
968	5k. Nurse inoculating child	1·10	1·40

1997. Christmas. Multicoloured.

No.	Description	Unused	Used
969	60t. Type **201**	15	10
970	3k. The Nativity (different)	45	20
971	4k.40 Adoration of the Magi	60	70
972	5k. The Holy Family	65	95

1998. Diana, Princess of Wales Commemoration. As T **91** of Kiribati. Multicoloured.

No.	Description	Unused	Used
973	60t. Wearing red dress	20	10
974	6k. Wearing lilac jacket	40	35
975	7k. With head scarf	50	70
976	8k. Wearing blue evening dress	55	80
MS977	145 × 70 mm. Nos. 973/6	1·25	1·75

202 Tattooed Rock, Mwalawamphini, Cape Maclear

1998. Monuments. Multicoloured.

No.	Description	Unused	Used
978	60t. Type **202**	15	10
979	6k. War Memorial Tower, Zomba	50	40
980	7k. Mtengatenga Postal Hut, Walala (horiz)	60	70
981	8k. P.I.M. Church, Chiradzulu (horiz)	75	90

No. 978 is inscribed “tatooed” and No. 979 “Memoral”, both in error.

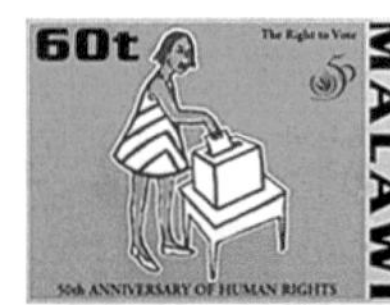

203 Woman voting

1998. 50th Anniv of Declaration of Human Rights. Multicoloured.

No.	Description	Unused	Used
982	60t. Type **203**	15	10
983	6k. Books, pens and pencils (“Education”)	50	40
984	7k. Man and woman on scales (“Justice”)	60	70
985	8k. Person hugging house and land (“Property”)	75	90

205 “Madonna and Child”

206 Ng’oma (hand drum)

1999. Christmas. Religious Paintings. Mult.

No.	Description	Unused	Used
990	60t. Type **205**	15	10
991	6k. “The Nativity”	50	20
992	7k. “Adoration of the Magi”	60	50
993	8k. “Flight into Egypt”	75	85

2000. 50th Anniv of the Commonwealth. Musical Instruments. Multicoloured.

994	60t. Type **206**	15	10
995	6k. Kaligo (single stringed fiddle)	50	40
996	7k. Kalimba (thumb dulcitone)	60	70
997	8k. Chisekese (rattle)	75	85

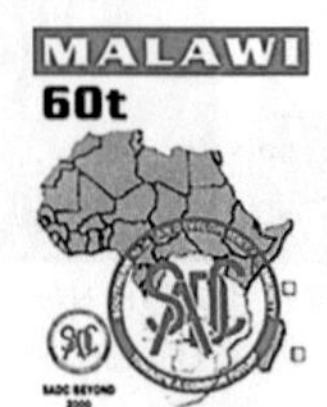

207 Map of Africa and S.A.D.C. Emblem — **208** "Madonna and Child"

2000. South African Development Community. Mult.

998	60t. Type **207**	25	10
999	6k. Bottles of Malambe fruit juice	50	40
1000	7k. *Ndunduma* (fisheries research ship) (horiz)	75	75
1001	8k. Class "Shire" diesel locomotive and goods train (horiz)	90	90

2000. Christmas. Religious Paintings. Mult.

1002	5k. Type **208**	20	10
1003	18k. "Adoration of the Shepherds"	80	90
1004	20k. "Madonna and Child"	80	90

209 *Euxanthe wakefieldi*

2002. Butterflies. Multicoloured.

1005	1k. Type **209**	10	10
1006	2k. *Pseudacraea boisdurali*	10	10
1007	4k. *Catacroptera cloanthe*	10	10
1008	5k. *Myrina silenus ficedula*	10	10
1009	10k. *Cymothoe zombana*	10	15
1010	20k. *Charaxes castor*	20	25
1011	50k. *Charaxes pythoduras ventersi*	50	55
1012	100k. *Iolaus lalos*	1·00	1·10

210 Puku

2003. Endangered Species. Puku (*Kobus vardonii*). Multicoloured.

1013	50k. Type **210**	50	55
1014	50k. Two males	50	55
1015	50k. Male and female	50	55
1016	50k. Herd	50	55
MS1017	204 × 138 mm. Nos. 1013/16, each × 2	4·00	4·25

211 Hoopoe (*Upupa epops*)

2003. Fauna and Flora of Africa. Multicoloured.

MS1018	118 × 137 mm. 50k. Type **211**; 50k. Grey parrot (*Psittacus erithacus*); 50k. Bateleur (*Terathopius ecaudatus*) 50k. Martial eagle (*Polemaetus bellicosus*); 50k. Masked lovebird (*Agapornis personatus*); 50k. Pel's pishing owl (*Scotopelia peli*)	3·00	3·25
MS1019	113 × 138 mm. 50k. *Bebearia octogramma*; 50k. *Charaxes nobilis*; 50k. *Cymothoe beckeri*; 50k. *Salamis anteva*; 50k. *Charaxes xiphares*; 50k. *Bebearia arcadius Fabricius* (all horiz)	3·00	3·25
MS1020	137 × 117 mm. 50k. *Pleurotus ostreatus*; 50k. *Macrolepiota procera*; 50k. *Amanita vaginata*; 50k.*Cantharellus tubaeformis*; 50k. *Hydnum repandum*; 50k.*Trametes versicolor* (all horiz)	3·00	3·25
MS1021	95 × 135 mm. 50k. *Angraecum eburneum*; 50k.*Ancistrochilus rothschildianus*; 50k. *Angraecum infundibulare*; 50k. *Ansellia Africana*; 50k. *Disa veitchii*; 50k.*Angraecum compactum*	3·00	3·25
MS1022	Four sheets. (a) 105 × 71 mm. 180k. Grey heron (*Arde cinerea*) (horiz). (b) 72 × 98 mm. 180k. *Carterocephalus palaemon* (horiz). (c) 68 × 94 mm. 180k. *Auricularia auricula*. (d) 93 × 66 mm. 180k. *Aerangis kotschyana* (horiz) Set of 4	7·25	7·50

POSTAGE DUE STAMPS

REPUBLIC OF MALAWI

POSTAGE DUE 1D

D 2

1967.

D 6	D **2**	1d. red	15	3·75
D 7		2d. brown	20	3·75
D 8		4d. violet	25	4·00
D 9		6d. blue	25	4·25
D10		8d. green	35	4·75
D11		1s. black	45	5·00

1971. Values in tambalas. No accent over "W" of "MALAWI".

D12	D **2**	2t. brown	30	4·50
D13		4t. mauve	50	3·00
D14		6t. blue	50	3·25
D15		8t. green	50	3·25
D16		10t. brown	60	3·25

1975. With circumflex over "W" of "MALAWI".

D27	D **2**	2t. brown	1·75	2·50
D28		4t. purple	1·75	2·50
D29		6t. blue	1·75	2·50
D21		8t. green	1·50	3·25
D31		10t. black	2·00	2·50

MALAYA (BRITISH MILITARY ADMINISTRATION) Pt.1

The following stamps were for use throughout the Malayan States and in Singapore during the period of the British Military Administration and were gradually replaced by individual issues for each state.

100 cents = 1 dollar.

1945. Straits Settlements stamps optd **B M A MALAYA**.

1a	**58**	1c. black	10	30
2a		2c. orange	20	10
4		3c. green	30	50
5		5c. brown	70	1·00
6a		6c. grey	30	20
7		8c. red	30	10
8a		10c. purple	50	10
10		12c. blue	1·75	6·00
12a		15c. blue	75	20
13a		25c. purple and red	1·40	30
14a		50c. black on green	75	10
15		$1 black and red	2·00	10
16		$2 green and red	2·75	75
17		$5 green and red on green	85·00	95·00
18		$5 purple and orange	3·75	3·00

For stamps inscribed "MALAYA" at top and with Arabic characters at foot see under Kelantan, Negri Sembilan, Pahang, Perak, Selangor or Trengganu.

MALAYA (JAPANESE OCCUPATION) Pt. 1

Japanese forces invaded Malaya on 8 December 1941 and the conquest of the Malay peninsula was completed by the capture of Singapore on 15 February.

The following stamps were used in Malaya until the defeat of Japan in 1945.

100 cents = 1 dollar.

(a) **JOHORE**

POSTAGE DUE STAMPS

馬來軍政部郵政局EP

大日本郵便

(**1**) (**2**)

1942. Nos. D1/5 of Johore optd with T **1**.

JD1a	D **1**	1c. red	20·00	70·00
JD2a		4c. green	65·00	80·00
JD3a		8c. orange	80·00	95·00
JD4a		10c. brown	16·00	50·00
JD5a		12c. purple	40·00	50·00

1943. Postage Due stamps of Johore optd with T **2**.

JD 6	D **1**	1c. red	6·50	26·00
JD 7		4c. green	6·50	28·00
JD 8		8c. orange	8·00	28·00
JD 9		10c. brown	7·50	35·00
JD10		12c. purple	9·00	50·00

(b) **KEDAH**

1942. Stamps of Kedah optd **DAI NIPPON 2602**.

J 1	**1**	1c. black	5·00	8·50
J 2		2c. green	26·00	30·00
J 3		4c. violet	4·75	4·00
J 4		5c. yellow	4·75	4·25
J 5		6c. red	4·00	12·00
J 6		8c. black	4·00	2·25
J 7	**6**	10c. blue and brown	12·00	12·00
J 8		12c. black and violet	28·00	40·00
J 9		25c. blue and purple	9·00	13·00
J10		30c. green and red	70·00	80·00
J11		40c. black and purple	35·00	50·00
J12		50c. brown and blue	35·00	50·00
J13		$1 black and green	£140	£150
J14		$2 green and brown	£170	£170
J15		$5 black and red	65·00	90·00

(c) **KELANTAN**

(**5**) Sunagawa Seal — (**6**) Handa Seal

1942. Stamps of Kelantan surch. (a) With T **5**. (i) New value in **CENTS**.

J16	**4**	1c. on 50c. green and orange	£225	£180
J17		2c. on 40c. orange and green	£650	£300
J18		4c. on 30c. violet and red	£1700	£1200
J19		5c. on 12c. blue	£225	£190
J20		6c. on 25c. red and violet	£300	£190
J21		8c. on 5c. brown	£350	£140
J22		10c. on 6c. red	75·00	£120
J23		12c. on 8c. green	50·00	£110
J24		25c. on 10c. purple	£1200	£1300
J25		30c. on 4c. red	£1800	£2000
J26		40c. on 2c. green	60·00	85·00
J27		50c. on 1c. green and yellow	£1400	£1300
J28		$1 on 4c. black and red	50·00	80·00
J29		$2 on 5c. green & red on yell	50·00	80·00
J30		$5 on 6c. red	50·00	80·00
		(ii) New Value in **Cents**.		
J32	**4**	1c. on 50c. green and orange	£160	95·00
J33		2c. on 40c. orange and green	£140	£100
J34		5c. on 12c. blue	£140	£130
J35		8c. on 5c. brown	£120	75·00
J36		10c. on 6c. red	£325	£350
		(b) With T **6** and new value.		
J41	**4**	1c. on 50c. green and orange	95·00	£140
J42		2c. on 40c. orange and green	£110	£150
J43		8c. on 5c. brown	65·00	£130
J44		10c. on 6c. red	85·00	£150
J31		12c. on 8c. green	£170	£225

(d) **PENANG**

(**11**) Okugawa Seal — (**12**) Ochiburi Seal

1942. Straits Settlements stamps optd. (a) As T **11**.

J56	**58**	1c. black	9·50	11·00
J57		2c. orange	24·00	22·00
J58		3c. green	20·00	22·00
J59		5c. brown	24·00	25·00
J60		8c. grey	26·00	32·00
J61		10c. purple	50·00	50·00
J62		12c. blue	30·00	48·00
J63		15c. blue	50·00	50·00
J64		40c. red and purple	90·00	£110
J65		50c. black on green	£200	£225
J66		$1 black and red on blue	£200	£250
J67		$2 green and red	£600	£600
J68		$5 green and red on green	£1800	£1500
		(b) With T **12**.		
J69	**58**	1c. black	£140	£110
J70		2c. orange	£140	95·00
J71		3c. green	95·00	95·00
J72		5c. brown	£1800	£1800
J73		8c. grey	80·00	90·00
J74		10c. purple	£130	£140
J75		12c. blue	90·00	£110
J76		15c. blue	£100	£110

1942. Stamps of Straits Settlements optd **DAI NIPPON 2602 PENANG**.

J77	**58**	1c. black	4·25	3·00
J78		2c. orange	4·25	4·00
J79		3c. green	4·75	3·75
J80		5c. brown	2·75	6·50
J81		8c. grey	2·25	1·40
J82		10c. purple	1·50	2·25
J83		12c. blue	3·75	14·00
J84		15c. blue	1·75	3·00
J85		40c. red and purple	4·75	14·00
J86		50c. black on green	3·75	24·00
J87		$1 black and red on blue	6·00	32·00
J88		$2 green and red	50·00	80·00
J89		$5 green and red on green	£475	£550

(e) **SELANGOR**

1942. Agri-horticultural Exhibition. Stamps of Straits Settlements optd **SELANGOR EXHIBITION DAI NIPPON 2602 MALAYA**.

J90	**58**	2c. orange	12·00	24·00
J91		8c. grey	13·00	24·00

(f) **SINGAPORE**

(**15**) "Malay Military Government Division Postal Services Bureau Seal"

1942. Stamps of Straits Settlements optd with T **15**.

J92	**58**	1c. black	13·00	17·00
J93		2c. orange	13·00	13·00
J94		3c. green	50·00	70·00
J95		8c. grey	22·00	18·00
J96		15c. blue	15·00	15·00

(g) **TRENGGANU**

1942. Stamps of Trengganu optd with T **1**.

J 97	**4**	1c. black	95·00	90·00
J 98		2c. green	£140	£140
J 99		2c. on 5c. pur & yell (No. 59)	40·00	40·00
J100		3c. brown	85·00	80·00
J101		4c. red	£160	£140
J102		5c. purple on yellow	10·00	19·00
J103		6c. orange	9·00	25·00
J104		8c. grey	9·00	13·00
J105		8c. on 10c. blue (No. 60)	13·00	48·00
J106		10c. blue	22·00	38·00
J107		12c. blue	8·00	40·00
J108		20c. purple and orange	8·50	35·00
J109		25c. green and purple	7·50	42·00
J110		30c. purple and black	8·50	35·00
J111		35c. red on yellow	25·00	48·00
J112		50c. green and red	75·00	90·00
J113		$1 purple and blue on blue	£3000	£3000
J114		$3 green and red on green	60·00	£100
J115	–	$5 green and red on yellow (No. 31)	£160	£200
J116	–	$25 purple and blue (No. 40)	£1200	
J117	–	$50 green and yellow (No. 41)	£10000	
J118	–	$100 green and red (No. 42)	£1300	

1942. Stamps of Trengganu optd **DAI NIPPON 2602 MALAYA**.

J119	**4**	1c. black	12·00	12·00
J120		2c. green	£190	£200
J121		2c. on 5c. pur on yell (No. 59)	6·00	8·00
J122		3c. brown	12·00	23·00
J123		4c. red	12·00	11·00
J124		5c. purple on yellow	5·50	13·00
J125		6c. orange	5·00	13·00
J126		8c. grey	80·00	27·00
J127		8c. on 10c. blue (No. 60)	5·50	10·00
J128		12c. blue	5·00	25·00
J129		20c. purple and orange	14·00	15·00
J130		25c. green and purple	7·00	35·00
J131		30c. purple and black	7·50	29·00
J132		$3 green and red on green	75·00	£140

1942. Stamps of Trengganu optd with T **2**.

J133	**4**	1c. black	13·00	17·00
J134		2c. green	11·00	28·00
J135		2c. on 5c. pur on yell (No. 59)	8·00	20·00
J136		5c. purple on yellow	9·50	28·00
J137		6c. orange	11·00	32·00
J138		8c. grey	60·00	£100
J139		8c. on 10c. blue (No. 60)	23·00	50·00
J140		10c. blue	90·00	£225
J141		12c. blue	15·00	45·00
J142		20c. purple and orange	20·00	45·00
J143		25c. green and purple	15·00	48·00

J144		30c. purple and black	22·00	50·00
J145		35c. red on yellow	22·00	55·00

POSTAGE DUE STAMPS

1942. Postage Due stamps of Trengganu optd with T **2**.

JD17	D **1**	1c. red	50·00	85·00
JD18a		4c. green	50·00	90·00
JD19		8c. yellow	14·00	50·00
JD20		10c. brown	14·00	50·00

(h) GENERAL ISSUES

1942. Stamps of various states optd with T **1**. (a) Straits Settlements.

J146	**58**	1c. black	3·25	3·25
J147		2c. green	£2500	£1800
J148		2c. orange	3·00	2·25
J149		3c. green	2·75	2·25
J150		5c. brown	22·00	28·00
J151		8c. grey	4·00	2·25
J152		10c. purple	45·00	45·00
J153		12c. blue	75·00	£120
J154		15c. blue	4·25	3·75
J155		30c. purple and orange	£1900	£1900
J156		40c. red and purple	90·00	95·00
J157		50c. black and green	50·00	48·00
J158		$1 black and red on blue	75·00	75·00
J159		$2 green and red	£130	£160
J160		$5 green and red on green	£170	£190

There also exists a similar overprint with double-lined frame.

(b) Negri Sembilan.

J161b	**6**	1c. black	13·00	17·00
J162		2c. orange	26·00	18·00
J163		3c. green	35·00	20·00
J164c		5c. brown	15·00	11·00
J165		6c. grey	£140	£120
J166		8c. red	£110	95·00
J167		10c. purple	£170	£170
J168		12c. blue	£1300	£1300
J169		15c. blue	21·00	8·00
J170		25c. purple and red	28·00	38·00
J171		30c. purple and orange	£190	£170
J172a		40c. red and purple	£850	£800
J173		50c. black on green	£750	£750
J174a		$1 black and red on blue	£170	£190
J175		$5 green and red on green	£500	£600

(c) Pahang.

J176	**15**	1c. black	50·00	45·00
J177a		3c. green	£250	£275
J178		5c. brown	14·00	12·00
J179		8c. grey	£750	£600
J180		8c. red	20·00	8·00
J181		10c. purple	£275	£140
J182a		12c. blue	£1200	£1200
J183		15c. blue	£130	£110
J184		25c. purple and red	21·00	29·00
J185		30c. purple and orange	12·00	28·00
J186		40c. red and purple	20·00	32·00
J187		50c. black on green	£750	£750
J188		$1 black and red on blue	£140	£150
J189		$5 green and red on green	£650	£800

(d) Perak.

J190	**51**	1c. black	55·00	35·00
J191		2c. orange	30·00	20·00
J192		3c. green	26·00	28·00
J193		5c. brown	7·00	6·00
J194		8c. grey	70·00	48·00
J195		8c. red	38·00	42·00
J196		10c. purple	26·00	24·00
J197		12c. blue	£225	£225
J198		15c. blue	24·00	32·00
J199		25c. purple and red	14·00	25·00
J200		30c. purple and orange	17·00	32·00
J201		40c. red and purple	£375	£325
J202		50c. black on green	40·00	50·00
J203		$1 black and red on blue	£425	£400
J204		$2 green and red	£2750	£2750
J205		$5 green and red on green	£475	

(e) Selangor.

J206	**46**	1c. black	12·00	24·00
J207		2c. green	£1300	£1100
J208		2c. orange	85·00	60·00
J210a		3c. green	18·00	15·00
J211		5c. brown	6·00	5·50
J212a		6c. red	£200	£250
J213		8c. grey	17·00	17·00
J214		10c. purple	13·00	21·00
J215		12c. blue	60·00	70·00
J216		15c. blue	16·00	22·00
J217a		25c. purple and red	60·00	80·00
J218		30c. purple and orange	11·00	24·00
J219		40c. red and purple	£140	£140
J220a		50c. black on green	£130	£140
J221	**48**	$1 black and red on blue	30·00	45·00
J222		$2 green and red	35·00	60·00
J223		$5 green and red on green	65·00	90·00

1942. Various stamps optd **DAI NIPPON 2602 MALAYA**. (a) Stamps of Straits Settlements.

J224	**58**	2c. orange	1·75	60
J225		3c. green	50·00	65·00
J226		8c. grey	5·00	2·50
J227		15c. blue	13·00	8·50

(b) Stamps of Negri Sembilan.

J228	**6**	1c. black	2·25	60
J229		2c. orange	6·00	50
J230		3c. green	4·50	50
J231		5c. brown	1·50	2·50
J232		6c. grey	3·50	1·75
J233		8c. red	5·00	1·25
J234		10c. purple	3·00	2·50
J235		15c. blue	15·00	2·50
J236		25c. purple and red	4·00	14·00
J237		30c. purple and orange	7·00	3·00
J238		$1 black and red on blue	80·00	95·00

(c) Stamps of Pahang.

J239	**15**	1c. black	2·50	2·75
J240		5c. brown	1·25	70
J241		8c. red	25·00	2·50
J242		10c. purple	11·00	6·50
J243		12c. blue	2·25	13·00
J244		25c. purple and red	4·50	20·00
J245		30c. purple and orange	2·50	9·00

(d) Stamps of Perak.

J246	**51**	2c. orange	2·75	2·00
J247		3c. green	1·25	1·25
J248		8c. red	70	50
J249		10c. purple	13·00	6·00
J250		15c. blue	6·00	2·00
J251		50c. black on green	2·75	4·00
J252		$1 black and red on blue	£375	£425
J253		$5 green and red on green	35·00	70·00

(e) Stamps of Selangor.

J254	**46**	3c. green	1·50	3·00
J255		12c. blue	1·10	12·00
J256		15c. blue	5·50	1·50
J257		40c. red and purple	2·00	4·00
J258	**48**	$2 green and red	10·00	40·00

1942. No. 108 of Perak surch **DAI NIPPON 2602 MALAYA 2 Cents**.

J259	**88**	2c. on 5c. brown	1·25	2·75

1942. Stamps of Perak optd **DAI NIPPON YUBIN** ("Japanese Postal Service") or surch also in figures and words.

J260	**51**	1c. black	4·50	9·00
J261		2c. on 5c. brown	2·00	6·50
J262		8c. red	4·50	2·25

1943. Various stamps optd vert or horiz with T **2** or surch in figures and words. (a) Stamps of Straits Settlements.

J263	**58**	8c. grey	1·40	50
J264		12c. blue	1·25	9·50
J265		40c. red and purple	1·75	4·25

(b) Stamps of Negri Sembilan.

J266	**6**	1c. black	30	2·00
J267		2c. on 5c. brown	80	1·00
J268		6c. on 5c. brown	40	1·50
J269		25c. purple and red	1·10	14·00

(c) Stamp of Pahang.

J270	**7**	6c. on 5c. brown	50	75

(d) Stamps of Perak.

J272	**51**	1c. black	1·00	70
J274		2c. on 5c. brown	60	50
J275		5c. brown	55	65
J276		8c. red	55	1·50
J277		10c. purple	60	50
J278		30c. purple and orange	3·50	5·50
J279		50c. black on green	3·25	18·00
J280		$5 green and red on green	55·00	95·00

(e) Stamps of Selangor.

J288	**46**	1c. black	35	50
J289		2c. on 5c. brown	40	50
J282		3c. green	40	45
J290		3c. on 5c. brown	30	4·00
J291		5c. brown	1·25	3·75
J293		6c. on 5c. brown	30	70
J283		12c. blue	45	1·60
J284		15c. blue	3·50	3·25
J285	**48**	$1 black and red on blue	3·00	19·00
J295	**46**	$1 on 10c. purple	40	1·00
J296		$1.50 on 30c. purple and orange	40	1·00
J286	**48**	$2 green and red	10·00	45·00
J287		$5 green and red on green	22·00	80·00

25 Tapping Rubber

27 Japanese Shrine, Singapore

1943.

J297	**25**	1c. green	1·00	55
J298	–	2c. green	75	20
J299	**25**	3c. grey	30	20
J300	–	4c. red	2·00	20
J301	–	8c. blue	30	20
J302	–	10c. purple	30	20
J303	**27**	15c. violet	60	3·50
J304	–	30c. olive	1·00	35
J305	–	50c. blue	3·25	5·00
J306	–	70c. blue	16·00	10·00

DESIGNS—VERT: 2c. Fruit; 4c. Tin dredger; 8c. War Memorial, Bukit Batok, Singapore; 10c. Fishing village; 30c. Sago palms; 50c. Straits of Johore. HORIZ: 70c. Malay Mosque, Kuala Lumpur.

28 Ploughman

29 Rice-planting

1943. Savings Campaign.

J307	**28**	8c. violet	9·50	2·75
J308		15c. red	6·50	2·75

1944. "Re-birth of Malaya".

J309	**29**	8c. red	14·00	3·25
J310		15c. mauve	4·00	3·25

大日本

マライ郵便

50 セント

(30)

1944. Stamps intended for use on Red Cross letters. Surch with T **30**. (a) On Straits Settlements.

J311	**58**	50c. on 50c. black on grn	10·00	24·00
J312		$1 on $1 black & red on bl	19·00	35·00
J313		$1.50 on $2 green on red	29·00	70·00

(b) On Johore.

J314	**24**	50c. on 50c. purple & red	7·00	20·00
J315		$1.50 on $2 green and red	4·00	12·00

(c) On Selangor.

J316	**48**	$1 on $2 black & red on bl	3·50	14·00
J317		$1.50 on $2 green and red	5·00	20·00

POSTAGE DUE STAMPS

1942. Postage Due stamps of Malayan Postal Union optd with T **1**.

JD21	D **1**	1c. violet	12·00	24·00
JD22		3c. green	60·00	65·00
JD23		4c. green	48·00	32·00
JD24		8c. red	85·00	70·00
JD25		10c. orange	25·00	42·00
JD26		12c. blue	25·00	50·00
JD27		50c. black	60·00	80·00

1942. Postage Due stamps of Malayan Postal Union optd **DAI NIPPON 2602 MALAYA**.

JD28	D **1**	1c. violet	2·25	8·50
JD29		3c. green	14·00	20·00
JD30		4c. green	15·00	11·00
JD31		8c. red	19·00	17·00
JD32		10c. orange	1·75	14·00
JD33		12c. blue	1·75	28·00

1943. Postage Due stamps of Malayan Postal Union optd with T **2**.

JD34	D **1**	1c. violet	1·75	4·00
JD35		3c. green	1·75	4·00
JD36		4c. green	55·00	40·00
JD37		5c. red	1·50	4·50
JD38		9c. orange	80	7·00
JD39		10c. orange	1·75	7·50
JD40		12c. blue	1·75	14·00
JD41		15c. blue	2·00	7·50

MALAYA (THAI OCCUPATION) Pt. 1

Stamps issued for use in the four Malay states of Kedah, Kelantan, Perlis and Trengganu ceded by Japan to Thailand on 19 October 1943 and restored to British rule on the defeat of the Japanese.

100 cents = 1 dollar.

TM **1** War Memorial

1943.

TM1	TM **1**	1c. yellow	30·00	32·00
TM2		2c. brown	12·00	20·00
TM3		3c. green	20·00	38·00
TM4		4c. purple	14·00	28·00
TM5		8c. red	14·00	20·00
TM6		15c. blue	38·00	60·00

MALAYAN FEDERATION Pt. 1

An independent country within the British Commonwealth, comprising all the Malay States (except Singapore) and the Settlements of Malacca and Penang. The component units retained their individual stamps. In 1963 the Federation became part of Malaysia (q.v).

100 cents (sen) = 1 Malayan dollar.

1 Tapping Rubber

1957.

1	**1**	6c. blue, red and yellow	50	10
2	–	12c. multicoloured	85	1·00
3	–	25c. multicoloured	2·75	20
4	–	30c. red and lake	1·00	20

DESIGNS—HORIZ: 12c. Federation coat of arms; 25c. Tin dredge. VERT: 30c. Map of the Federation.

5 Prime Minister Tunku Abdul Rahman and Populace greeting Independence

1957. Independence Day.

5	**5**	10c. brown	10	10

6 United Nations Emblem

8 Merdeka Stadium, Kuala Lumpur

1958. U.N. Economic Commission for Asia and Far East Conference, Kuala Lumpur.

6	**6**	12c. red	30	80
7	–	30c. purple	40	80

DESIGN: 30c. As Type **6** but vert.

1958. 1st Anniv of Independence.

8	**8**	10c. multicoloured	15	10
9	–	30c. multicoloured	40	70

DESIGN—VERT: 30c. Portrait of the Yang di-Pertuan Agong (Tuanku Abdul Rahman).

11 Malayan with "Torch of Freedom"

12 Mace and Malayan Peoples

1958. 10th Anniv of Declaration of Human Rights.

10	–	10c. multicoloured	15	10
11	**11**	30c. green	45	60

DESIGN—VERT: 10c. "Human Rights".

1959. Inauguration of Parliament.

12	**12**	4c. red	10	10
13		10c. violet	10	10
14		25c. green	75	20

14

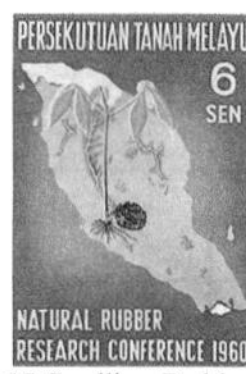

15 Seedling Rubber Tree and Map

1960. World Refugee Year.

15	–	12c. purple	10	60
16	**14**	30c. green	10	10

DESIGN: 12c. As Type **14** but horiz.

1960. Natural Rubber Research Conf and 15th Int Rubber Study Group Meeting, Kuala Lumpur.

17	**15**	6c. multicoloured	20	1·25
18		30c. multicoloured	50	75

No. 18 is inscr "INTERNATIONAL RUBBER STUDY GROUP 15th MEETING KUALA LUMPUR" at foot.

16 The Yang di-Pertuan Agong (Tuanku Syed Putra)

1961. Installation of Yang di-Pertuan Agong, Tuanku Syed Putra.

19	**16**	10c. black and blue	10	10

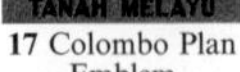

17 Colombo Plan Emblem

18 Malaria Eradication Emblem

1961. Colombo Plan Conf, Kuala Lumpur.
20 **17** 12c. black and mauve . . . 35 2·75
21 25c. black and green . . . . 80 2·25
22 30c. black and blue . . . . 70 1·00

1962. Malaria Eradication.
23 **18** 25c. brown 20 40
24 30c. lilac 20 15
25 50c. blue 40 80

19 Palmyra Palm Leaf

1962. National Language Month.
26 **19** 10c. brown and violet . . . 15 10
27 20c. brown and green . . . 50 1·25
28 50c. brown and mauve . . . 1·50 1·75

20 "Shadows of the Future"

1962. Introduction of Free Primary Education.
29 **20** 10c. purple 10 10
30 25c. ochre . . . . 50 1·25
31 30c. green . . . . 2·75 10

21 Harvester and Fisherman

1963. Freedom from Hunger.
32 **21** 25c. pink and green . . . . 2·25 3·00
33 30c. pink and lake . . . . 2·50 1·50
34 50c. pink and blue . . . . 2·50 3·00

22 Dam and Pylon

1963. Cameron Highlands Hydro-electric Scheme.
35 **22** 20c. green and violet 60 10
36 30c. turquoise and blue . . 1·00 1·50

MALAYAN POSTAL UNION Pt. 1

In 1936 postage due stamps were issued in Type D **1** for use in Negri Sembilan, Pahang, Perak, Selangor and Straits Settlements but later their use was extended to the whole of the Federation and Singapore, and from 1963 throughout Malaysia.

POSTAGE DUE STAMPS

D 1

1936.
D 7 D **1** 1c. purple . . . . 3·25 2·00
D14 1c. violet . . . . 70 1·60
D15 2c. slate . . . . 1·25 2·25
D 8 3c. green . . . . 6·00 6·00
D 2 4c. green . . . . 18·00 1·00
D17 4c. sepia . . . . 70 7·00
D 9 5c. red . . . . 6·00 4·00
D 3 8c. red . . . . 9·50 3·50
D19 8c. orange . . . . 2·25 4·50
D11 9c. orange . . . . 50·00 48·00
D 4 10c. orange . . . . . . 14·00 30
D 5 12c. blue . . . . 14·00 14·00
D20 12c. mauve . . . . . . 1·25 6·00
D12 15c. blue . . . . £150 35·00
D21 20c. blue . . . . 6·00 6·50
D 6 50c. black . . . . 28·00 6·00

1965. Surch **10 cents**.
D29 D **1** 10c. on 8c. orange . . . 60 2·75

MALAYSIA Pt. 1

Issues for use by the new Federation comprising the old Malayan Federation (Johore ("JOHOR"), Kedah, Kelantan, Malacca ("MELAKA"), Negri Sembilan ("NEGERI SEMBILAN"), Pahang, Penang ("PULAU PINANG"), Perak, Perlis, Selangor and Trengganu), Sabah (North Borneo), Sarawak and Singapore, until the latter became an independent state on 9 August 1965.

Stamps inscr "MALAYSIA" and state name are listed under the various states, as above.

100 cents (sen) = 1 Malaysian dollar.

A. NATIONAL SERIES

General issues for use throughout the Federation.

1 Federation Map

2 Bouquet of Orchids

1963. Inauguration of Federation.
1 **1** 10c. yellow and violet 40 10
2 12c. yellow and green . . . . 1·00 60
3 50c. yellow and brown . . . . 1·40 10

1963. 4th World Orchid Congress, Singapore.
4 **2** 6c. multicoloured . . . . . . 1·25 1·25
5 25c. multicoloured . . . . . . 1·25 25

4 Parliament House, Kuala Lumpur

1963. 9th Commonwealth Parliamentary Conf, Kuala Lumpur.
7 **4** 20c. mauve and gold . . . . 1·00 40
8 30c. green and gold . . . . . 1·00 15

5 "Flame of Freedom" and Emblems of Goodwill, Health and Charity

1964. Eleanor Roosevelt Commemoration.
9 **5** 25c. black, red and turquoise 20 10
10 30c. black, red and lilac . . 20 15
11 50c. black, red and yellow . . 20 10

6 Microwave Tower and I.T.U. Emblem

1965. Centenary of I.T.U.
12 **6** 2c. multicoloured . . . . . . 15 1·25
13 25c. multicoloured . . . . . 1·25 60
14 50c. multicoloured . . . . . 1·75 10

7 National Mosque

1965. Opening of National Mosque, Kuala Lumpur.
15 **7** 6c. red 10 10
16 15c. brown 20 10
17 20c. green 20 15

8 Air Terminal

1965. Opening of Int Airport, Kuala Lumpur.
18 **8** 15c. black, green and blue . . 40 10
19 30c. black, green and mauve 60 20

9 Crested Wood Partridge

17 Sepak Raga (ball game) and Football

1965. Birds. Multicoloured.
20 25c. Type **9** 50 10
21 30c. Blue-backed fairy bluebird 60 10
22 50c. Black-naped oriole . . . 1·25 10
23 75c. Rhinoceros hornbill . . . 90 10
24 $1 Zebra dove . . . . 1·50 10
25 $2 Great argus pheasant . . . 4·25 30
26 $5 Asiatic paradise flycatcher 18·00 3·00
27 $10 Blue-tailed pitta . . . . . 48·00 13·00
For the lower values see the individual sets listed under each of the states which form Malaysia.

1965. 3rd South East Asian Peninsular Games.
28 **17** 25c. black and green . . . . 40 1·25
29 – 30c. black and purple . . . 40 20
30 – 50c. black and blue 70 30
DESIGNS: 30c. Running; 50c. Diving.

20 National Monument

21 The Yang di-Pertuan Agong (Tuanku Ismail Nasiruddin Shah)

1966. National Monument, Kuala Lumpur.
31 **20** 10c. multicoloured 30 10
32 20c. multicoloured 50 40

1966. Installation of Yang di-Pertuan Agong, Tuanku Ismail Nasiruddin Shah.
33 **21** 15c. black and yellow . . . 10 10
34 50c. black and blue 20 20

22 School Building

1966. 150th Anniv of Penang Free School.
35 **22** 20c. multicoloured 70 10
36 50c. multicoloured 90 10

23 "Agriculture"

1966. 1st Malaysia Plan. Multicoloured.
37 15c. Type **23** 20 10
38 15c. "Rural Health" 20 10
39 15c. "Communications" . . . 1·90 15
40 15c. "Education" 20 10
41 15c. "Irrigation" 20 10

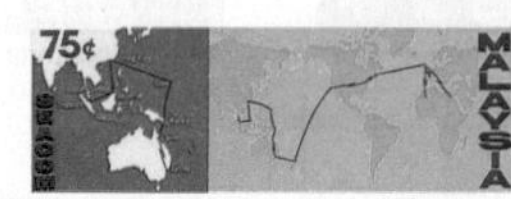

28 Cable Route Maps (½-size illustration)

1967. Completion of Malaysia–Hong Kong Link of SEACOM Telephone Cable.
42 **28** 30c. multicoloured 80 50
43 75c. multicoloured . . . . . 2·50 3·50

29 Hibiscus and Paramount Rulers

1967. 10th Anniv of Independence.
44 **29** 15c. multicoloured 20 10
45 50c. multicoloured . . . . . 1·25 80

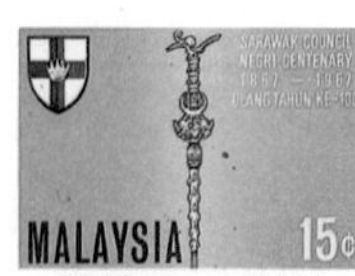

30 Mace and Shield

1967. Centenary of Sarawak Council.
46 **30** 15c. multicoloured 10 10
47 50c. multicoloured 30 60

31 Straits Settlements 1867 8c. Stamp and Malaysian 1965 25c. Stamp

1967. Stamp Centenary.
48 **31** 25c. multicoloured . . . . . 1·60 3·25
49 – 30c. multicoloured . . . . . 1·60 2·75
50 – 50c. multicoloured . . . . . 2·50 3·50
DESIGNS: 30c. Straits Settlements 1867 24c. stamp and Malaysian 1965 30c. stamp; 50c. Straits Settlements 1867 32c. stamp and Malaysian 1965 50c. stamp.

34 Tapping Rubber, and Molecular Unit

1968. Natural Rubber Conf, Kuala Lumpur. Mult.
51 25c. Type **34** 30 10
52 30c. Tapping rubber and export consignment 40 20
53 50c. Tapping rubber and aircraft tyres 40 10

37 Mexican Sombrero and Blanket with Olympic Rings

39 Tunku Abdul Rahman against background of Pandanus Weave

1968. Olympic Games, Mexico. Multicoloured.
54 30c. Type **37** 20 10
55 75c. Olympic Rings and Mexican embroidery 55 20

1969. Solidarity Week.
56 **39** 15c. multicoloured 15 10
57 – 20c. multicoloured . . . . . 45 1·75
58 – 50c. multicoloured 50 20
DESIGNS—VERT: 20c. As Type **39** (different). HORIZ: 50c. Tunku Abdul Rahman with pandanus pattern.

42 Peasant Girl with Sheaves of Paddy

1969. National Rice Year.
59 **42** 15c. multicoloured 15 10
60 75c. multicoloured . . . . . 55 1·50

43 Satellite-tracking Aerial

1970. Satellite Earth Station.
61 **43** 15c. drab, black and blue . . . 1·00 15
62 – 30c. multicoloured . . . . . 1·00 2·50
63 – 30c. multicoloured . . . . . 1·00 2·50
DESIGN—40 × 27 mm: Nos. 62/3, "Intelstat III" in Orbit.
No. 62 has inscriptions and value in white and No. 63 has them in gold.

45 "Euploea leucostictus" **46** Emblem

1970. Butterflies. Multicoloured.
64 25c. Type **45** . . . . 1·00 10
65 30c. "Zeuxidia amethystus" . . 1·50 10
66 50c. "Polyura athamas" . . . 2·00 10
67 75c. "Papilio memnon" . . . 2·00 10
68 $1 "Appias nero" . . . . . . 2·50 10
69 $2 "Trogonoptera brookiana" 3·50 10
70 $5 "Narathura centaurus" . . 5·00 3·75
71 $10 "Terinos terpander" . . . 17·00 5·00
Lower values were issued for use in the individual States.

1970. 50th Anniv of Int Labour Organization.
72 **46** 30c. grey and blue 10 20
73 75c. pink and blue 20 30

47 U.N. Emblem encircled by Doves **50** The Yang di-Pertuan Agong (Tuanku Abdul Halim Shah)

1970. 25th Anniv of United Nations.
74 **47** 25c. gold, black and brown 35 40
75 – 30c. multicoloured 35 35
76 – 50c. black and green 40 75
DESIGNS: 30c. Line of doves and U.N. emblem; 50c. Doves looping U.N. emblem.

1971. Installation of Yang di-Pertuan Agong (Paramount Ruler of Malaysia).
77 **50** 10c. black, gold and yellow 20 30
78 15c. black, gold and mauve 20 30
79 50c. black, gold and blue . . 70 1·60

51 Bank Negara Complex

1971. Opening of Bank Negara Building.
80 **51** 25c. black and silver . . . . 2·25 2·50
81 50c. black and gold . . . . 1·75 1·25

52 Aerial View of Parliament Buildings

1971. 17th Commonwealth Parliamentary Association Conference, Kuala Lumpur. Multicoloured.
82 25c. Type **52** . . . . 1·25 50
83 75c. Ground view of Parliament Buildings (horiz, 73 × 23½ mm) . . . . . . 2·75 1·75

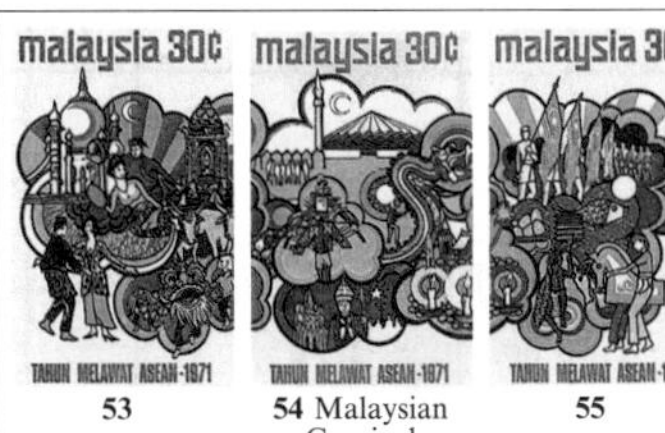

53 **54** Malaysian Carnival **55**

1971. Visit ASEAN Year.
84 **53** 30c. multicoloured . . . . . 1·60 55
85 **54** 30c. multicoloured . . . . . 1·60 55
86 **55** 30c. multicoloured . . . . . 1·60 55
ASEAN = Association of South East Asian Nations.
Nos. 84/6 form a composite design of a Malaysian Carnival, as illustrated.

56 Trees, Elephant and Tiger

1971. 25th Anniv of U.N.I.C.E.F. Multicoloured.
87 15c. Type **56** . . . . 2·50 60
88 15c. Cat and kittens . . . . . 2·50 60
89 15c. Sun, flower and bird (22 × 29 mm) . . . . 2·50 60
90 15c. Monkey, elephant and lion in jungle . . . . . . 2·50 60
91 15c. Spider and butterflies . . 2·50 60

57 Athletics

1971. 6th S.E.A.P. Games, Kuala Lumpur. Mult.
92 25c. Type **57** 45 40
93 30c. Sepak Raga players . . . 60 50
94 50c. Hockey . . . . 1·75 95
S.E.A.P. = South East Asian Peninsula.

58 **59** Map and Tourist Attractions **60**

1971. Pacific Area Tourist Association Conference.
95 **58** 30c. multicoloured . . . . . 3·00 1·50
96 **59** 30c. multicoloured . . . . . 3·00 1·50
97 **60** 30c. multicoloured . . . . . 3·00 1·50
Nos. 95/7 form a composite design of a map showing tourist attractions, as illustrated.

61 Kuala Lumpur City Hall

1972. City Status for Kuala Lumpur. Multicoloured.
98 25c. Type **61** . . . . 1·25 1·25
99 50c. City Hall in floodlights 2·00 1·25

62 SOCSO Emblem **64** Fireworks, National Flag and Flower

63 W.H.O. Emblem

1973. Social Security Organization.
100 **62** 10c. multicoloured 15 15
101 15c. multicoloured 15 10
102 50c. multicoloured . . . . 40 1·40

1973. 25th Anniv of W.H.O.
103 **63** 30c. multicoloured 50 25
104 – 75c. multicoloured . . . . 1·00 2·75
The 75c. is similar to Type **63**, but vertical.

1973. 10th Anniv of Malaysia.
105 **64** 10c. multicoloured 40 25
106 15c. multicoloured 55 15
107 50c. multicoloured . . . . 1·90 1·60

65 Emblems of Interpol and Royal Malaysian Police

1973. 50th Anniv of Interpol. Multicoloured.
108 25c. Type **65** . . . . 1·00 50
109 75c. Emblems within "50" . . 2·25 2·00

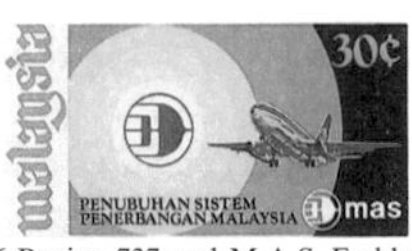

66 Boeing 737 and M.A.S. Emblem

1973. Foundation of Malaysian Airline System.
110 **66** 15c. multicoloured 35 10
111 30c. multicoloured 65 60
112 50c. multicoloured . . . . 95 1·60

67 Kuala Lumpur

1974. Establishment of Kuala Lumpur as Federal Territory.
113 **67** 25c. multicoloured 50 85
114 50c. multicoloured . . . . 1·00 1·75

68 Development Projects

1974. 7th Annual Meeting of Asian Development Bank's Board of Governors, Kuala Lumpur.
115 **68** 30c. multicoloured 25 50
116 75c. multicoloured . . . . 80 1·75

69 Scout Badge and Map

1974. Malaysian Scout Jamboree. Multicoloured.
117 10c. Type **69** . . . . 60 1·00
118 15c. Scouts saluting and flags (46 × 24 mm) 95 30
119 50c. Scout badge . . . . . . 1·75 3·00

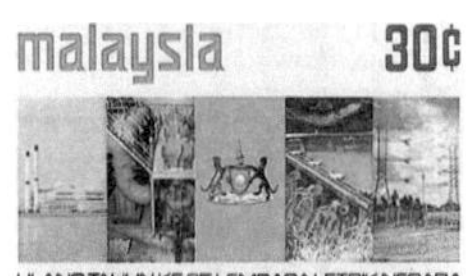

70 Coat of Arms and Power Installations

1974. 25th Anniv of National Electricity Board. Multicoloured.
120 30c. Type **70** 30 50
121 75c. National Electricity Board building (37 × 27 mm) . . . . . 1·00 2·50

71 U.P.U. and Post Office Emblems within "100"

1974. Centenary of U.P.U.
122 **71** 25c. green, yellow and red 20 35
123 30c. blue, yellow and red 25 35
124 75c. orange, yellow and red 65 1·75

72 Gravel Pump in Tin Mine

1974. 4th World Tin Conf, Kuala Lumpur. Mult.
125 15c. Type **72** . . . . 1·75 20
126 20c. Open-cast mine . . . . 2·00 2·50
127 50c. Dredger within "ingot" 3·75 5·50

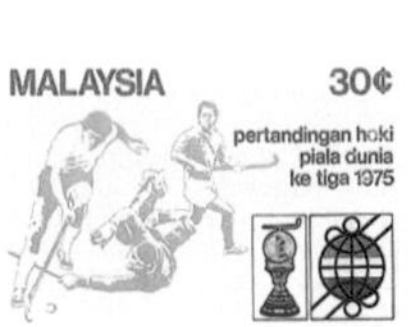

73 Hockey-players, World Cup and Federation Emblem **74** Congress Emblem

1975. 3rd World Cup Hockey Championships.
128 **73** 30c. multicoloured 90 60
129 75c. multicoloured . . . . 2·10 2·25

1975. 25th Anniv of Malaysian Trade Union Congress.
130 **74** 20c. multicoloured 15 25
131 25c. multicoloured 20 30
132 30c. multicoloured 65 60

75 Emblem of M.K.P.W. (Malayan Women's Organization) **76** Ubudiah Mosque, Kuala Kangsar

1975. International Women's Year.
133 **75** 10c. multicoloured 15 25
134 15c. multicoloured 30 25
135 50c. multicoloured . . . . 1·25 2·25

1975. Koran Reading Competition. Multicoloured.
136 15c. Type **76** . . . . 1·75 60
137 15c. Zahir Mosque, Alor Star 1·75 60
138 15c. National Mosque, Kuala Lumpur . . . . 1·75 60
139 15c. Sultan Abu Bakar Mosque, Johore Bahru . . 1·75 60
140 15c. Kuching State Mosque, Sarawak . . . . 1·75 60

77 Plantation and Emblem

1975. 50th Anniv of Malaysian Rubber Research Institute. Multicoloured.
141 10c. Type **77** 40 15
142 30c. Latex cup and emblem 1·10 70
143 75c. Natural rubber in test-tubes . . . . 2·25 2·25

77a "Hebomoia glaucippe"

1976. Multicoloured.
144 10c. Type **77a** . . . . 2·75 7·00
145 15c. "Precis orithya" . . . . 2·75 7·00

78 Scrub Typhus

79 The Yang di-Pertuan Agong (Tuanku Yahya Petra)

1976. 75th Anniv of Institute of Medical Research. Multicoloured.

146 20c. Type **78** 25 15
147 25c. Malaria diagnosis . . . 40 20
148 $1 Beri-beri . . . . 1·60 2·50

1976. Installation of Yang di-Pertuan Agong.

149 **79** 10c. black, brown & yellow 25 10
150 15c. black, brown & mauve 40 10
151 50c. black, brown and blue 2·25 2·50

80 State Council Complex

1976. Opening of State Council Complex and Administrative Building, Sarawak.

152 **80** 15c. green and yellow . . . 35 10
153 20c. green and mauve . . . 45 40
154 50c. green and blue . . . . 1·00 1·40

81 E.P.F. Building

1976. 25th Anniv of Employees' Provident Fund. Multicoloured.

155 10c. Type **81** 15 10
156 25c. E.P.F. emblems (27 × 27 mm) 35 75
157 50c. E.P.F. Building at night 60 1·40

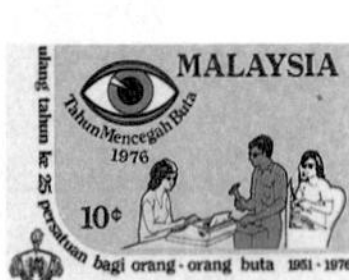

82 Blind People at Work

1976. 25th Anniv of Malayan Assn for the Blind. Multicoloured.

158 10c. Type **82** 15 15
159 75c. Blind man and shadow 1·25 2·75

83 Independence Celebrations, 1957

1977. 1st Death Anniv of Tun Abdul Razak (Prime Minister).

160 15c. Type **83** . . . . 1·50 60
161 15c. "Education" . . . . . . 1·50 60
162 15c. Tun Razak and map ("Development") . . . . . 1·50 60
163 15c. "Rukunegara" (National Philosophy) . . . . 1·50 60
164 15c. A.S.E.A.N. meeting . . 1·50 60

84 F.E.L.D.A. Village Scheme

1977. 21st Anniv of Federal Land Development Authority (F.E.L.D.A.). Multicoloured.

165 15c. Type **84** 30 10
166 30c. Oil palm settlement . . . 80 2·00

85 Figure "10"

86 Games Logos

1977. 10th Anniv of Association of South East Asian Nations (A.S.E.A.N.). Multicoloured.

167 10c. Type **85** 10 10
168 75c. Flags of members . . . 1·25 1·00

1977. 9th South East Asia Games, Kuala Lumpur. Multicoloured.

169 10c. Type **86** 15 15
170 20c. "Ball" 20 15
171 75c. Symbolic athletes . . . 75 1·75

87 Islamic Development Bank Emblem

1978. Islamic Development Bank Board of Governors' Meeting, Kuala Lumpur.

172 **87** 30c. multicoloured 25 15
173 75c. multicoloured 75 85

88 Mobile Post Office

1978. 4th Commonwealth Postal Administrations Conference, Kuala Lumpur. Multicoloured.

174 10c. Type **88** 30 10
175 25c. G.P.O., Kuala Lumpur 75 2·00
176 50c. Rural delivery by motorcycle . . . . 2·00 3·00

89 Boy Scout Emblem

1978. 4th Malaysian Scout Jamboree, Sarawak. Multicoloured.

177 15c. Type **89** 75 10
178 $1 Bees and honeycomb . . . 2·75 3·25

90 Dome of the Rock, Jerusalem

1978. Palestinian Welfare.

179 **90** 15c. multicoloured . . . . 1·00 25
180 30c. multicoloured . . . . 1·75 2·50

91 Globe and Emblems

1978. Global Eradication of Smallpox.

181 **91** 15c. black, red and blue . . 25 10
182 30c. black, red and green 40 30
183 50c. black, red and pink 70 95

92 "Seratus Tahun Getah Asli" and Tapping Knives Symbol

1978. Centenary of Rubber Industry.

184 **92** 10c. gold and green 10 10
185 – 20c. blue, brown and green 10 10
186 – 75c. gold and green . . . . 45 1·00

DESIGNS: 20c. Rubber tree seedling and part of "maxi stump"; 75c. Graphic design of rubber tree, latex cup and globe arranged to form "100".

93 Sultan of Selangor's New Palace

1978. Inauguration of Shah Alam New Town as State Capital of Selangor. Multicoloured.

187 10c. Type **93** 10 10
188 30c. Aerial view of Shah Alam 20 15
189 75c. Shah Alam . . . . . . 55 2·00

94 Tiger

1979. Animals. Multicoloured.

190 30c. Type **94** . . . . 1·75 10
191 40c. Malayan flying lemur . . 80 10
192 50c. Lesser Malay chevrotain 1·75 10
193 75c. Leathery pangolin . . . 1·00 10
194 $1 Malayan turtle . . . . . 1·50 10
195 $2 Malayan tapir . . . . . 1·50 10
196 $5 Gaur . . . . 4·50 2·00
197 $10 Orang-utang (vert) . . . 7·00 3·50

96 View of Central Bank of Malaysia

97 I.Y.C. Emblem

1979. 20th Anniv of Central Bank of Malaysia. Multicoloured.

198 10c. Type **96** 10 10
199 75c. Central Bank (vert) . . . 40 1·50

1979. International Year of the Child.

200 **97** 10c. gold, blue and salmon 35 20
201 – 15c. multicoloured 60 10
202 – $1 multicoloured . . . . . 3·00 4·00

DESIGNS: 15c. Children holding hands in front of globe; $1 Children playing.

98 Dam and Power Station

1979. Opening of Hydro-electric Power Station, Temengor.

203 **98** 15c. multicoloured 20 15
204 – 25c. multicoloured 35 70
205 – 50c. multicoloured . . . . 55 1·40

DESIGNS: 25c., 50c. Different views of dam.

99 Exhibition Emblem

100 Tuanku Haji Ahmad Shah

1979. 3rd World Telecommunications Exhibition, Geneva.

206 **99** 10c. orange, blue and silver 10 50
207 – 15c. multicoloured 15 10
208 – 50c. multicoloured . . . . 40 2·25

DESIGNS—34 × 24 mm: 15c. Telephone receiver joining the one half of World to the other. 39 × 28 mm: 50c. Communications equipment.

1980. Installation of Tuanku Haji Ahmad Shah as Yang di-Pertuan Agong.

209 **100** 10c. black, gold and yellow 10 40
210 15c. black, gold and purple 15 10
211 50c. black, gold and blue 55 2·00

101 Pahang and Sarawak Maps within Telephone Dials

1980. Kuantan–Kuching Submarine Cable Project. Multicoloured.

212 10c. Type **101** 10 40
213 15c. Kuantan and Kuching views within telephone dials 15 10
214 50c. Pahang and Sarawak maps within telephone receiver . . . . 35 1·75

102 Bangi Campus

1980. 10th Anniv of National University of Malaysia. Multicoloured.

215 10c. Type **102** 15 20
216 15c. Jalan Pantai Baru campus 20 10
217 75c. Great Hall . . . . . . 80 3·00

103 Mecca

1980. Moslem Year 1400 A.H. Commemoration.

218 **103** 15c. multicoloured 10 10
219 50c. multicoloured . . . . 30 1·50

No. 219 is inscribed in Roman lettering.

104 Disabled Child learning to Walk

105 Industrial Scene

1981. International Year for Disabled Persons. Multicoloured.

220 10c. Type **104** 30 30
221 15c. Girl sewing 55 10
222 75c. Disabled athlete . . . . 1·50 3·50

1981. Expo "81" Industrial Training Exposition, Kuala Lumpur and Seminar, Genting Highlands. Multicoloured.

223 10c. Type **105** 10 10
224 15c. Worker and bulldozer 15 10
225 30c. Workers at shipbuilding plant 25 35
226 75c. Agriculture and fishing produce, workers and machinery . . . . 65 2·25

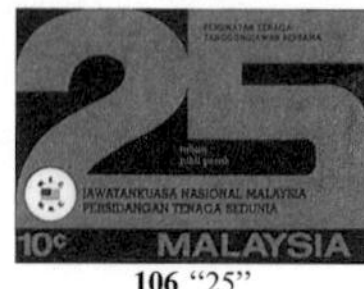

106 "25"

1981. 25th Anniv of Malaysian National Committee for World Energy Conferences. Multicoloured.

227 10c. Type **106** 20 20
228 15c. Drawings showing importance of energy sources in industry 45 10
229 75c. Symbols of various energy sources . . . . . . 2·25 3·50

107 Drawing showing development of Sabah from Village to Urbanized Area

1981. Centenary of Sabah. Multicoloured.

230 15c. Type **107** 50 15
231 80c. Drawing showing traditional and modern methods of agriculture . . 2·00 4·25

108 "Samanea saman"

1981. Trees. Multicoloured.

232 15c. Type **108** 55 10
233 50c. "Dyera costulata" (vert) 1·75 1·40
234 80c. "Dryobalanops aromatica" (vert) . . . . . 2·00 4·25

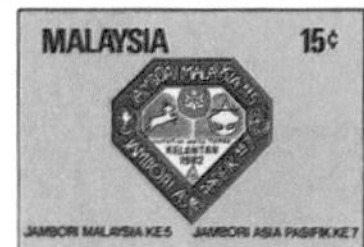

109 Jamboree Emblem

1982. 5th Malaysian/7th Asia–Pacific Boy Scout Jamboree. Multicoloured.
235 15c. Type **109** 35 10
236 50c. Malaysian flag and scout emblem 80 85
237 80c. Malaysian and Asia–Pacific scout emblem 1·25 4·25

110 A.S.E.A.N. Building and Emblem

1982. 15th Anniv of Ministerial Meeting of A.S.E.A.N. (Association of South East Asian Nations). Multicoloured.
238 15c. Type **110** 15 10
239 $1 Flags of members 1·25 3·50

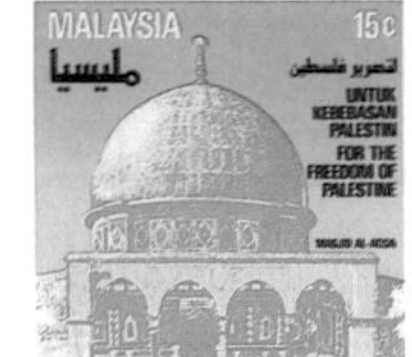

111 Dome of the Rock, Jerusalem

1982. "Freedom for Palestine".
240 **111** 15c. gold, green and black 1·00 15
241 $1 silver, green and black 3·25 4·75

112 Views of Kuala Lumpur in 1957 and 1982

1982. 25th Anniv of Independence. Multicoloured.
242 10c. Type **112** 10 10
243 15c. Malaysian industries 15 15
244 50c. Soldiers on parade 40 55
245 80c. Independence ceremony 70 3·00
MS246a 120 × 190 mm. Nos. 242/5 10·00 10·00

113 Shadow Play

1982. Traditional Games. Multicoloured.
247 10c. Type **113** 55 30
248 15c. Cross top 55 15
249 75c. Kite flying 2·25 4·75

114 Sabah Hats

1982. Malaysian Handicrafts. Multicoloured.
250 10c. Type **114** 25 30
251 15c. Gold-threaded cloth 25 20
252 75c. Sarawak pottery 1·25 3·75

115 Gas Exploitation Logo

1983. Export of Liquefied Natural Gas from Bintulu Field, Sarawak. Multicoloured.
253 15c. Type **115** 75 15
254 20c. "Tenaga Satu" (liquid gas tanker) 1·50 70
255 $1 Gas drilling equipment 3·50 6·50

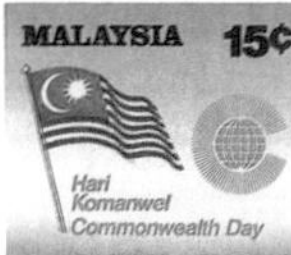

116 Flag of Malaysia

1983. Commonwealth Day. Multicoloured.
256 15c. Type **116** 20 10
257 20c. The King of Malaysia 20 20
258 40c. Oil palm tree and refinery 25 45
259 $1 Satellite view of Earth 60 2·75

117 Nile Mouthbrooder

1983. Freshwater Fishes. Multicoloured.
260 20c. Type **117** 1·25 2·00
261 20c. Common carp 1·25 2·00
262 40c. Lampan barb 1·75 2·75
263 40c. Grass carp 1·75 2·75

118 Lower Pergau River Bridge

1983. Opening of East–West Highway. Mult.
264 15c. Type **118** 80 15
265 20c. Perak river reservoir bridge 1·00 75
266 $1 Map showing East–West highway 3·75 6·50

119 Northrop Tiger II Fighter

1983. 50th Anniv of Malaysian Armed Forces. Multicoloured.
267 15c. Type **119** 1·25 15
268 20c. Missile boat 1·75 45
269 40c. Battle of Pasir Panjang 2·25 2·50
270 80c. Trooping the Colour 3·25 6·00
MS271 130 × 85 mm. Nos. 267/70 11·00 12·00

120 Helmeted Hornbill

122 Sky-scraper and Mosque, Kuala Lumpur

121 Bank Building, Ipoh

1983. Hornbills of Malaysia. Multicoloured.
280 15c. Type **120** 1·00 15
281 20c. Wrinkled hornbill 1·25 50
282 50c. Long-crested hornbill 2·00 2·00
283 $1 Rhinoceros hornbill 3·25 5·50

1984. 25th Anniv of Bank Negara. Multicoloured.
284 20c. Type **121** 40 30
285 $1 Bank building, Alor Setar 2·00 3·75

1984. 10th Anniv of Federal Territory of Kuala Lumpur. Multicoloured.
286 20c. Type **122** 80 20
287 40c. Aerial view 1·60 1·40
288 80c. Gardens and clock-tower (horiz) 2·50 6·50

123 Map showing Industries

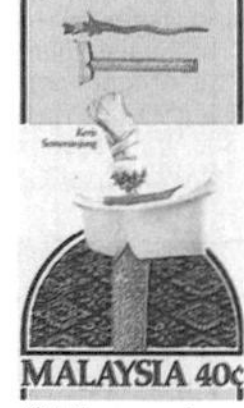

124 Semenanjung Keris

1984. Formation of Labuan Federal Territory. Multicoloured.
289 20c. Type **123** 75 25
290 $1 Flag and map of Labuan 3·75 6·00

1984. Traditional Malay Weapons. Multicoloured.
291 40c. Type **124** 1·25 2·10
292 40c. Pekakak keris 1·25 2·10
293 40c. Jawa keris 1·25 2·10
294 40c. Lada tumbuk 1·25 2·10

125 Map of World and Transmitter

1984. 20th Anniv of Asia–Pacific Broadcasting Union. Multicoloured.
295 20c. Type **125** 40 25
296 $1 Clasped hands within "20" 2·00 5·00

126 Facsimile Service

127 Yang di-Pertuan Agong (Tuanku Mahmood)

1984. Opening of New General Post Office, Kuala Lumpur. Multicoloured.
297 15c. Type **126** 35 20
298 20c. New G.P.O. building 45 45
299 $1 Mailbag conveyor 2·00 4·75

1984. Installation of Yang di-Pertuan Agong (Tuanku Mahmood).
300 **127** 15c. multicoloured 60 20
301 20c. multicoloured 65 20
302 – 40c. multicoloured 1·25 1·00
303 – 80c. multicoloured 2·50 5·00
DESIGN—HORIZ: 40c., 80c. Yang di-Pertuan Agong and federal crest.

128 White Hibiscus

129 Parliament Building

1984. Hibiscus. Multicoloured.
304 10c. Type **128** 50 30
305 20c. Red hibiscus 1·00 20
306 40c. Pink hibiscus 1·75 2·00
307 $1 Orange hibiscus 2·75 5·75

1985. 25th Anniv of Federal Parliament. Mult.
308 20c. Type **129** 30 15
309 $1 Parliament Building (different) (horiz) 1·75 3·50

130 Banded Linsang

1985. Protected Animals of Malaysia (1st series). Multicoloured.
310 10c. Type **130** 60 10
311 40c. Slow loris (vert) 2·00 1·40
312 $1 Spotted giant flying squirrel (vert) 4·00 6·50
See also Nos. 383/6.

131 Stylized Figures

1985. International Youth Year. Multicoloured.
313 20c. Type **131** 40 15
314 $1 Young workers 3·50 5·50

132 Steam Locomotive No. 1, 1885

1985. Centenary of Malayan Railways.
315 **132** 15c. black, red and orange 1·60 50
316 – 20c. multicoloured 1·75 60
317 – $1 multicoloured 4·25 7·00
MS318 119 × 59 mm. 80c. multicoloured 8·00 9·00
DESIGNS—HORIZ: 20c. Class 20 diesel-electric locomotive, 1957; $1 Hitachi Class 23 diesel-electric locomotive, 1983. 48 × 31 mm: 80c. Class 56 steam locomotive No. 564.18, "Seletar", 1938.

133 Blue Proton "Saga 1.3s" Car

1985. Production of Proton "Saga" (Malaysian national car). Multicoloured.
319 20c. Type **133** 80 15
320 40c. White Proton "Saga 1.3s" 1·40 1·00
321 $1 Red Proton "Saga 1.5s" 2·50 6·50

134 Penang Bridge

135 Offshore Oil Rig

1985. Opening of Penang Bridge. Multicoloured.
322 20c. Type **134** 90 15
323 40c. Penang Bridge and location map 1·75 90
324 $1 Symbolic bridge linking Penang to mainland (40 × 24 mm) 3·50 6·00

1985. Malaysian Petroleum Production. Mult.
325 15c. Type **135** 1·25 20
326 20c. Malaysia's first oil refinery (horiz) 1·40 50
327 $1 Map of Malaysian offshore oil and gas fields (horiz) 3·75 6·00

136 Sultan Azlan Shah and Perak Royal Crest

137 Crested Fireback Pheasant

1985. Installation of the Sultan of Perak.
328 **136** 15c. multicoloured 55 10
329 20c. multicoloured 60 25
330 $1 multicoloured 3·25 6·00

1986. Protected Birds of Malaysia (1st series). Multicoloured.
331 20c. Type **137** 2·50 3·25
332 20c. Malay peacock-pheasant 2·50 3·25
333b 40c. Bulwer's pheasant (horiz) 2·00 3·50
334b 40c. Great argus pheasant (horiz) 2·00 3·50
See also Nos. 394/7.

139 Two Kadazan Dancers, Sabah — **140** Stylized Competitors

1986. Pacific Area Travel Association Conference, Malaysia. Multicoloured.

335 20c. Type **139** . . . . 85 1·25
336 20c. Dyak dancer and longhouse, Sarawak . . . 85 1·25
337 20c. Dancers and fortress, Malacca . . . . 85 1·25
338 40c. Malay dancer and Kuala Lumpur . . . . 1·25 1·50
339 40c. Chinese opera dancer and Penang Bridge . . . . 1·25 1·50
340 40c. Indian dancer and Batu Caves . . . . 1·25 1·50

1986. Malaysia Games. Multicoloured.

341 20c. Type **140** . . . . 1·25 20
342 40c. Games emblems (vert) 2·25 2·00
343 $1 National and state flags (vert) . . . . 7·00 7·75

141 Rambutan — **142** Skull and Slogan "Drugs Can Kill"

1986. Fruits of Malaysia. Multicoloured.

344 40c. Type **141** 15 10
345 50c. Pineapple 15 10
346 80c. Durian 25 10
347 $1 Mangosteen 30 10
348 $2 Star fruit 65 10
349 $5 Banana . . . . 1·60 50
350 $10 Mango . . . . 3·25 1·25
351 $20 Papaya . . . . 6·50 3·25

1986. 10th Anniv of National Association for Prevention of Drug Addiction. Multicoloured.

352 20c. Type **142** . . . . 1·00 30
353 40c. Bird and slogan "Stay Free From Drugs" . . . . 1·40 1·10
354 $1 Addict and slogan "Drugs Can Destroy" (vert) . . . 2·25 5·00

143 MAS Logo and Map showing Routes — **144** Building Construction

1986. Inaugural Flight of Malaysian Airlines Kuala Lumpur–Los Angeles Service. Multicoloured.

355 20c. Type **143** . . . . 2·00 20
356 40c. Logo, stylized aircraft and route diagram . . . . 2·75 80
357 $1 Logo and stylized aircraft 3·75 4·25

1986. 20th Anniv of National Productivity Council and 25th Anniv of Asian Productivity Organization (40c., $1). Multicoloured.

358 20c. Type **144** 85 25
359 40c. Planning and design (horiz) . . . . 1·40 1·25
360 $1 Computer-controlled car assembly line (horiz) . . . 3·75 6·50

145 Old Seri Menanti Palace, Negri Sembilan

1986. Historic Buildings of Malaysia (1st series). Multicoloured.

361 15c. Type **145** . . . . 1·00 20
362 20c. Old Kenangan Palace, Perak . . . . 1·10 20
363 40c. Old Town Hall, Malacca 2·00 80
364 $1 Astana, Kuching, Sarawak 3·50 5·00
See also Nos. 465/8.

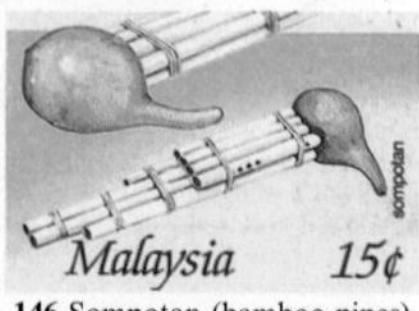

146 Sompotan (bamboo pipes)

1987. Malaysian Musical Instruments. Mult.

365 15c. Type **146** . . . . 1·00 10
366 20c. Sapih (four-stringed chordophone) . . . . . . 1·10 20
367 50c. Serunai (pipes) (vert) . . 2·25 40
368 80c. Rebab (three-stringed fiddle) (vert) . . . . 3·00 2·00

147 Modern Housing Estate

1987. International Year of Shelter for the Homeless. Multicoloured.

369 20c. Type **147** . . . . 1·00 15
370 $1 Stylized families and houses . . . . 2·50 1·50

148 Drug Addict and Family

1987. International Conference on Drug Abuse, Vienna. Multicoloured.

371 20c. Type **148** . . . . 1·75 1·40
372 20c. Hands holding drugs and damaged internal organs . . . . 1·75 1·40
373 40c. Healthy boy and broken drug capsule . . . . 2·50 1·60
374 40c. Drugs and healthy internal organs . . . . . . 2·50 1·60

Nos. 371/2 and 373/4 were printed together, se-tenant, forming composite designs.

149 Spillway and Power Station

1987. Opening of Sultan Mahmud Hydro-electric Scheme, Kenyir, Trengganu. Multicoloured.

375 20c. Type **149** 50 10
376 $1 Dam, spillway and reservoir . . . . 2·50 2·00

150 Crossed Maces and Parliament Building, Kuala Lumpur

1987. 33rd Commonwealth Parliamentary Conf. Multicoloured.

377 20c. Type **150** 25 10
378 $1 Parliament building and crossed mace emblem . . . 1·25 1·25

151 Dish Aerial, Satellite and Globe

1987. Asia/Pacific Transport and Communications Decade. Multicoloured.

379 15c. Type **151** 50 10
380 20c. Diesel train and car . . 1·50 75
381 40c. Container ships and lorry . . . . 1·75 1·40
382 $1 Malaysian Airlines Boeing 747, Kuala Lumpur Airport . . . . 3·50 6·50

152 Temminck's Golden Cat

1987. Protected Animals of Malaysia (2nd series). Multicoloured.

383 15c. Type **152** . . . . 2·25 50
384 20c. Flatheaded cat . . . . . 2·25 50
385 40c. Marbled cat . . . . . . 3·50 1·75
386 $1 Clouded leopard . . . . 6·50 7·50

153 Flags of Member Nations and "20"

1987. 20th Anniv of Association of South East Asian Nations. Multicoloured.

387 20c. Type **153** 35 10
388 $1 Flags of member nations and globe . . . . 1·25 1·50

154 Mosque and Portico

1988. Opening of Sultan Salahuddin Abdul Aziz Shah Mosque. Multicoloured.

389 15c. Type **154** 25 10
390 20c. Dome, minarets and Sultan of Selangor 25 20
391 $1 Interior and dome (vert) 1·25 2·50

155 Aerial View

1988. Sultan Ismail Hydro-electric Power Station, Paka, Trengganu. Multicoloured.

392 20c. Type **155** 30 10
393 $1 Power-station and pylons 1·10 1·25

156 Black-naped Blue Monarch — **157** Outline Map and Products of Sabah

1988. Protected Birds of Malaysia (2nd series). Multicoloured.

394 20c. Type **156** . . . . 1·75 2·25
395 20c. Scarlet-backed flowerpecker . . . . 1·75 2·25
396 50c. Yellow-backed sunbird 2·50 3·00
397 50c. Black and red broadbill 2·50 3·00

1988. 25th Anniv of Sabah and Sarawak as States of Malaysia. Multicoloured.

398 20c. Type **157** 65 80
399 20c. Outline map and products of Sarawak . . . 65 80
400 $1 Flags of Malaysia, Sabah and Sarawak (30 × 40 mm) 1·50 3·00

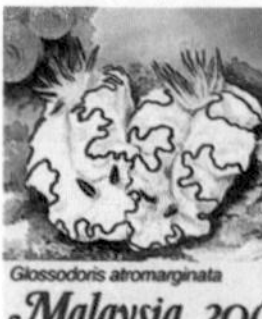

158 "Glossodoris atromarginata" — **159** Sultan's Palace, Malacca

1988. Marine Life (1st series). Multicoloured.

401 20c. Type **158** . . . . 85 1·10
402 20c. Ocellate nudibranch . . 85 1·10
403 20c. "Chromodoris annae" 85 1·10
404 20c. "Flabellina macassarana" . . . . . . 85 1·10
405 20c. Ruppell's nudibranch . . 85 1·10
MS406 100 × 75 mm. $1 Blue-ringed angelfish (50 × 40 mm) . . . . 3·00 1·75

Nos. 401/5 were printed together, se-tenant, forming a composite background design.

See also Nos. 410/13, 450/3, 492/6 and 559/62.

1989. Declaration of Malacca as Historic City. Multicoloured.

407 20c. Type **159** 25 30
408 20c. Independence Memorial Building 25 30
409 $1 Porta De Santiago Fortress (vert) . . . . . . 1·25 2·00

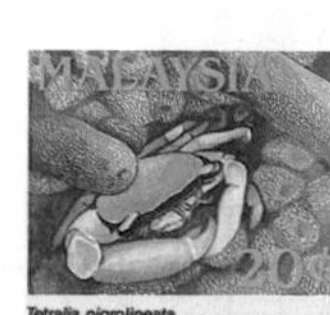
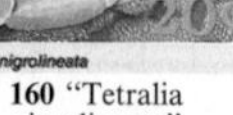

160 "Tetralia nigrolineata" — **161** Map of Malaysia and Scout Badge

1989. Marine Life (2nd series). Crustaceans. Mult.

410 20c. Type **160** 45 90
411 20c. "Neopetrolisthes maculatus" (crab) 45 90
412 40c. "Periclimenes holthuisi" (shrimp) . . . . 55 1·10
413 40c. "Synalpheus neomeris" (shrimp) . . . . 55 1·10

1989. 7th National Scout Jamboree. Multicoloured.

414 10c. Type **161** 30 10
415 20c. Saluting national flag . . 60 25
416 80c. Scouts around camp fire (horiz) . . . . 1·40 2·75

162 Cycling — **163** Sultan Azlan Shah

1989. 15th South East Asian Games, Kuala Lumpur. Multicoloured.

417 10c. Type **162** 75 40
418 20c. Athletics 40 20
419 50c. Swimming (vert) 75 85
420 $1 Torch bearer (vert) . . . 1·25 3·25

1989. Installation of Sultan Azlan Shah as Yang di-Pertuan Agong.

421 **163** 20c. multicoloured 20 15
422 40c. multicoloured 35 35
423 $1 multicoloured . . . . 1·00 2·75

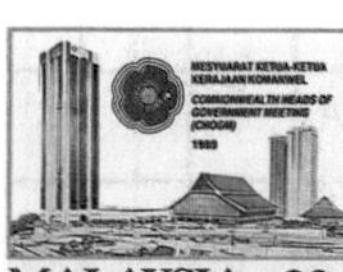

164 Putra World Trade Centre and Pan-Pacific Hotel

1989. Commonwealth Heads of Government Meeting, Kuala Lumpur. Multicoloured.

424 20c. Type **164** 20 10
425 50c. Traditional dancers (vert) 65 75
426 $1 National flag and map showing Commonwealth countries . . . . 1·25 3·00

165 Clock Tower, Kuala Lumpur City Hall and Big Ben — **166** Sloth and Map of Park

1989. Inaugural Malaysia Airlines "747" Non-stop Flight to London. Each showing Malaysia Airlines Boeing "747-400". Multicoloured.

427 20c. Type **165** . . . . 1·75 2·00
428 20c. Parliament Buildings, Kuala Lumpur, and Palace of Westminster . . . . . . 1·75 2·00
429 $1 World map showing route 4·25 4·75

1989. 50th Anniv of National Park. Multicoloured.

430 20c. Type **166** . . . . 1·00 30
431 $1 Pair of crested argus . . . 3·50 4·25

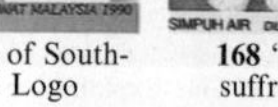

167 Outline Map of South-east Asia and Logo — **168** "Dillenia suffruticosa"

1990. "Visit Malaysia Year". Multicoloured.
432 20c. Type **167** 65 15
433 50c. Traditional drums 85 1·00
434 $1 Scuba diving, windsurfing and yachting 1·75 3·00

1990. Wildflowers (1st series). Multicoloured.
435 15c. Type **168** 25 15
436 20c. "Mimosa pudica" 30 20
437 50c. "Ipmoea carnea" 60 90
438 $1 "Nymphaea pubescens" 80 2·75
See also Nos. 505/8.

169 Monument and Rainbow

171 Alor Setar

170 Seri Negara Building

1990. Kuala Lumpur, Garden City of Lights. Multicoloured.
439 20c. Type **169** 25 20
440 40c. Mosque and skyscrapers at night (horiz) 55 55
441 $1 Kuala Lumpur skyline (horiz) 1·40 3·00

1990. 1st Summit Meeting of South–South Consultation and Co-operation Group, Kuala Lumpur. Multicoloured.
442 20c. Type **170** 40 15
443 80c. Summit logo 1·40 2·25

1990. 250th Anniv of Alor Setar. Multicoloured.
444 20c. Type **171** 40 20
445 40c. Musicians and monument (vert) 50 40
446 $1 Zahir Mosque (vert) 1·25 3·25

172 Sign Language Letters

1990. International Literacy Year. Multicoloured.
447 20c. Type **172** 50 10
448 40c. People reading 70 40
449 $1 Symbolic person reading (vert) 1·75 3·25

173 Leatherback Turtle

1990. Marine Life (3rd series). Sea Turtles. Mult.
450 15c. Type **173** 60 10
451 20c. Common green turtle 60 15
452 40c. Olive Ridley turtle 1·25 80
453 $1 Hawksbill turtle 2·25 3·75

174 Safety Helmet, Dividers and Industrial Skyline

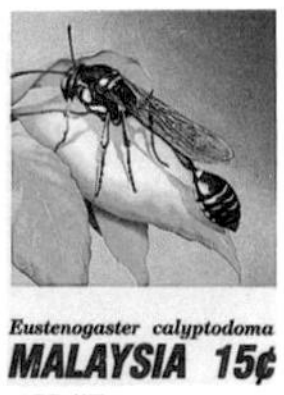

175 "Eustenogaster calyptodoma"

1991. 25th Anniv of MARA (Council of the Indigenous People). Multicoloured.
454 20c. Type **174** 15 10
455 40c. Documents and graph 30 35
456 $1 25th Anniversary logo 75 2·25

1991. Insects. Wasps. Multicoloured.
457 15c. Type **175** 25 30
458 20c. "Vespa affinis indonensis" 25 20
459 50c. "Sceliphorn javanum" 60 70
460 $1 "Ampulex compressa" 1·00 2·50
MS461 130 × 85 mm. Nos. 457/60 2·50 4·25

176 Tunku Abdul Rahman Putra and Independence Rally

1991. Former Prime Ministers of Malaysia. Multicoloured.
462 $1 Type **176** 70 1·25
463 $1 Tun Abdul Razak Hussein and jungle village 70 1·25
464 $1 Tun Hussein Onn and standard-bearers 70 1·25

177 Maziah Palace, Trengganu

1991. Historic Buildings of Malaysia (2nd series). Multicoloured.
465 15c. Type **177** 25 10
466 20c. Grand Palace, Johore 25 15
467 40c. Town Palace, Kuala Langat, Selangor 50 50
468 $1 Jahar Palace, Kelantan 1·00 2·75

178 Museum Building in 1891, Brass Lamp and Fabric

179 Rural Postman on Cycle

1991. Centenary of Sarawak Museum. Mult.
469 30c. Type **178** 20 15
470 $1 Museum building in 1991, vase and fabric 80 2·00

1992. Inauguration of Post Office Corporation. Multicoloured.
471 30c. Type **179** 60 85
472 30c. Urban postman on motorcycle 60 85
473 30c. Inner city post van 60 85
474 30c. Industrial post van 60 85
475 30c. Malaysian Airlines Boeing 747 and globe 60 85

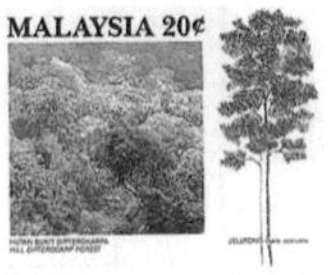

180 Hill Forest and Jelutong Tree

1992. Tropical Forests. Multicoloured.
476 20c. Type **180** 35 10
477 50c. Mangrove swamp and Bakau Minyak tree 65 50
478 $1 Lowland forest and Chengal tree 1·10 2·50

181 Tuanku Ja'afar and Coat of Arms

182 Badminton Players

1992. 25th Anniv of Installation of Tuanku Ja'afar as Yang di-Pertuan Besar of Negri Sembilan. Multicoloured.
479 30c. Type **181** 20 20
480 $1 Palace, Negri Sembilan 80 2·25

1992. Malaysian Victory in Thomas Cup Badminton Championship. Multicoloured.
481 $1 Type **182** 70 1·25
482 $1 Thomas Cup and Malaysian flag 70 1·25
MS483 105 × 80 mm. $2 Winning team (76 × 28 mm) 1·75 2·75

183 Women in National Costumes

1992. 25th Anniv of A.S.E.A.N. (Association of South East Asian Nations). Multicoloured.
484 30c. Type **183** 40 30
485 50c. Regional flowers 65 75
486 $1 Traditional architecture 1·25 2·75

184 Straits Settlements 1867 1½c. and Malaysian Federation 1957 10c. Stamps

1992. 125th Anniv of Postage Stamps and "Kuala Lumpur '92" Int Stamp Exn. Multicoloured.
487 30c. Type **184** 45 90
488 30c. Straits Settlements 1867 2c. and Malaysia 1963 Federation Inauguration 12c. 45 90
489 50c. Straits Settlements 1868 4c. and Malaysia 1990 Kuala Lumpur 40c. 70 1·10
490 50c. Straits Settlements 1867 12c. and Malaysia "Kuala Lumpur '92" $2 70 1·10
MS491 120 × 92 mm. $2 "Kuala Lumpur '92" logo on Malaysian flag 1·75 2·75

185 "Acropora"

186 Girls smiling

1992. Marine Life (4th series). Corals. Mult.
492 30c. Type **185** 80 1·10
493 30c. "Dendronephthya" 80 1·10
494 30c. "Dendrophyllia" 80 1·10
495 30c. "Sinularia" 80 1·10
496 30c. "Melithaea" 80 1·10
MS497 100 × 70 mm. $2 "Subergorgia" (38 × 28 mm) 2·50 4·00

1993. 16th Asian–Pacific Dental Congress. Mult.
498 30c. Type **186** 50 75
499 30c. Girls smiling with koala bear 50 75
500 50c. Dentists with Japanese, Malaysian and South Korean flags 1·00 1·00
501 $1 Dentists with New Zealand, Thai, Chinese and Indonesian flags 1·25 2·00

187 View of Golf Course

188 "Alpinia rafflesiana"

1993. Cent of Royal Selangor Golf Club. Mult.
502 30c. Type **187** 60 20
503 50c. Old and new club houses 90 80
504 $1 Bunker on course (horiz) 1·75 3·25

1993. Wildflowers (2nd series). Gingers. Mult.
505 20c. Type **188** 40 10
506 30c. "Achasma megalocheilos" 50 20
507 50c. "Zingiber spectabile" 90 80
508 $1 "Costus speciosus" 1·75 3·00

189 Forest under Magnifying Glass

190 White-throated Kingfisher

1993. 14th Commonwealth Forestry Conference, Kuala Lumpur. Multicoloured.
509 30c. Type **189** 40 20
510 50c. Hand holding forest 65 70
511 $1 Forest in glass dome (vert) 1·40 2·75

1993. Kingfishers. Multicoloured.
512 30c. Type **190** 1·25 1·60
513 30c. Pair of blue-eared kingfishers 1·25 1·60
514 50c. Chestnut-collared kingfisher 1·40 1·75
515 50c. Pair of three-toed kingfishers 1·40 1·75

191 SME MD3-160m Light Aircraft

1993. Langkawi International Maritime and Aerospace Exhibition '93. Multicoloured.
516 30c. Type **191** 35 20
517 50c. Eagle X-TS light aircraft 65 75
518 $1 "Kasturi" (frigate) 1·25 2·50
MS519 120 × 80 mm. $2 Map of Langkawi 1·60 2·50

192 Jeriau Waterfalls

1994. Visit Malaysia. Multicoloured.
520 20c. Type **192** 50 10
521 30c. Flowers 50 25
522 50c. Turtle and fishes 75 65
523 $1 Orang-utan and other wildlife 1·60 2·50

193 Planetarium and Planets

1994. National Planetarium, Kuala Lumpur. Mult.
524 30c. Type **193** 50 25
525 50c. Static displays 65 80
526 $1 Planetarium auditorium 1·50 2·50

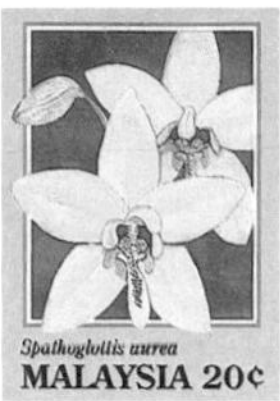

194 "Spathoglottis aurea"

195 Decorative Bowl

1994. Orchids. Multicoloured.
527 20c. Type **194** 40 15
528 30c. "Paphiopedilum barbatum" 50 25
529 50c. "Bulbophyllum lobbii" 85 90
530 $1 "Aerides odorata" 1·40 2·75
MS531 120 × 82 mm. $2 "Grammato-phyllum speciosum" (horiz) 2·50 4·00
No. **MS**531 also commemorates the "Hong Kong '94" International Stamp Exhibition.

1994. World Islamic Civilisation Festival '94, Kuala Lumpur. Multicoloured.
532 20c. Type **195** 15 10
533 30c. Celestial globe 25 20
534 50c. Dinar coins 40 65
535 $1 Decorative tile 75 2·00

196 Flock of Chickens and Vet examining Cat

197 Workers laying Electric Cable

1994. Centenary of Veterinary Services. Mult.
536 30c. Type **196** 50 25
537 50c. Vet in abattoir 70 55
538 $1 Herd of cows and veterinary equipment . . . 1·00 2·25

1994. Centenary of Electricity Supply. Mult.
539 30c. Type **197** 40 65
540 30c. Illuminated city 40 65
541 $1 City of the future . . . . 1·00 2·00

198 Expressway from the Air **199** Sultan Tuanku Ja'afar

1994. Opening of North–South Expressway. Mult.
542 30c. Type **198** 30 20
543 50c. Expressway junction . . 45 50
544 $1 Expressway bridge . . . . 90 2·00

1994. Installation of Sultan Tuanku Ja'afar as Yang di-Pertuan Agong.
545 **199** 30c. multicoloured 20 20
546 50c. multicoloured 40 50
547 $1 multicoloured . . . . 80 2·00

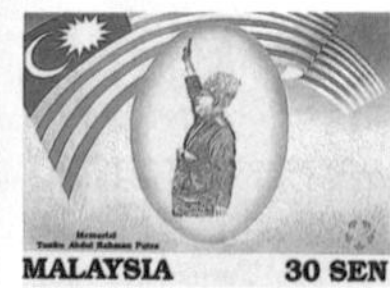

200 Map of Malaysia and Logo **201** Tunku Abdul Rahman Putra and National Flag

1994. 16th Commonwealth Games, Kuala Lumpur (1998) (1st issue). Multicoloured.
548 $1 Type **200** . . . . 90 1·50
549 $1 Wira (games mascot) holding national flag . . . 90 1·50
See also Nos. 575/6, 627/30, 668/71, **MS**678, 693/708 and **MS**715/16.

1994. 5th Death Anniv of Tunku Abdul Rahman Putra (former Prime Minister). Multicoloured.
550 30c. Type **201** 25 20
551 $1 The Residency, Kuala Lumpur . . . . 75 1·75

202 Library Building

1994. Opening of New National Library Building. Multicoloured.
552 30c. Type **202** 20 25
553 50c. Computer plan on screen 45 50
554 $1 Ancient Koran . . . . . 1·00 2·00

203 "Microporus xanthopus"

1995. Fungi. Mult.
555 20c. Type **203** 15 10
556 30c. "Cookeina tricholoma" 25 20
557 50c. "Phallus indusiatus" ("Dictyophora phalloidea") 45 55
558 $1 "Ramaria sp." . . . . . 90 2·25

204 Seafans

1995. Marine Life (5th series). Corals. Mult.
559 20c. Type **204** . . . . . . 1·00 1·25
560 20c. Feather stars . . . . . 1·00 1·25
561 30c. Cup coral . . . . 1·00 1·25
562 30c. Soft coral . . . . 1·00 1·25

205 Clouded Leopard on Branch

1995. Endangered Species. Clouded Leopard. Mult.
563 20c. Type **205** 55 25
564 30c. With cubs 60 30
565 50c. Crouched on branch . . 80 70
566 $1 Climbing tree . . . . . . 1·25 2·00

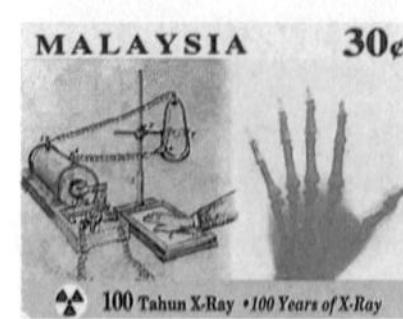

206 Early X-Ray Equipment and X-Ray of Hand

1995. Centenary of Discovery of X-Rays by Wilhelm Conrad Rontgen. Multicoloured.
567 30c. Type **206** 40 65
568 30c. Body scanner and brain scan 40 65
569 $1 Chest X-rays . . . . . . 1·00 1·75

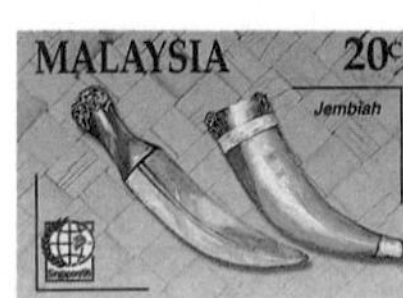

207 Jembiah (curved dagger)

1995. "Singapore '95" International Stamp Exhibition. Traditional Malay Weapons. Mult.
570 20c. Type **207** 15 10
571 30c. Keris panjang (sword) 25 20
572 50c. Kerambit (curved dagger) 40 50
573 $1 Keris sundang (sword) . . 80 2·00
MS574 100 × 70 mm. $2 Ladig terus (dagger) . . . . 2·25 3·00

208 Badminton, Cricket, Shooting, Tennis, Hurdling, Hockey and Weightlifting

1995. 16th Commonwealth Games, Kuala Lumpur (1998) (2nd issue). Multicoloured.
575 $1 Type **208** . . . . 1·75 2·00
576 $1 Cycling, bowls, boxing, basketball, rugby, gymnastics and swimming 1·75 2·00

209 Leatherback Turtle ("Dermochelys coriacea")

1995. Turtles. Multicoloured.
577 30c. Type **209** . . . . 1·25 1·25
578 30c. Green turtle ("Chelonia mydas") . . . . 1·25 1·25

210 Anniversary Emblem and Symbolic People around Globe

1995. 50th Anniv of United Nations. Multicoloured.
579 30c. Type **210** 30 20
580 $1 United Nations emblem 70 1·50

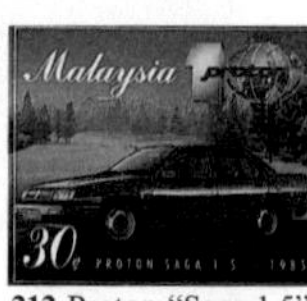

211 Boeing 747, Globe, Emblem and Malaysian Scenes **212** Proton "Saga 1.5" Saloon, 1985

1995. 50th Anniv of International Air Transport Association. Designs each showing Boeing 747 and Globe. Multicoloured.
581 30c. Type **211** 40 60
582 30c. Asian and Australasian scenes 40 60
583 50c. European and African scenes 60 80
584 50c. North and South American scenes 60 80

1995. 10th Anniv of Proton Cars. Multicoloured.
585 30c. Type **212** 70 90
586 30c. "Iswara 1.5" aeroback, 1992 . . . . 70 90
587 30c. "Iswara 1.5" saloon, 1992 . . . . 70 90
588 30c. "Wira 1.6" saloon, 1993 70 90
589 30c. "Wira 1.6" aeroback, 1993 . . . . 70 90
590 30c. Proton rally car, 1994 70 90
591 30c. "Satria 1.6" hatchback, 1994 . . . . 70 90
592 30c. "Perdana 2.0" saloon, 1995 . . . . 70 90
593 30c. "Wira 1.6" aeroback, 1995 . . . . 70 90
594 30c. "Wira 1.8" saloon, 1995 70 90

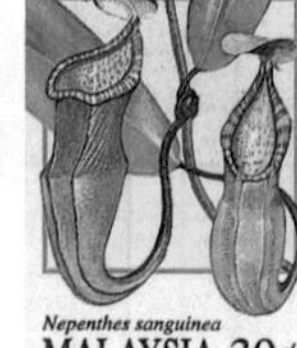

213 "Ariane 4" Launch Rocket **214** "Nepenthes sanguinea"

1996. Launch of MEASAT I (Malaysia East Asia Satellite). Multicoloured.
595 30c. Type **213** 25 20
596 50c. Satellite over Eastern Asia 40 45
597 $1 Satellite Earth station, Langkawi . . . . 90 2·00
MS598 100 × 70 mm. $5 Satellite orbiting Globe (hologram) (horiz) 5·50 6·00

1996. Pitcher Plants. Multicoloured.
599 30c. Type **214** 25 45
600 30c. "Nepenthes macfarlanei" 25 45
601 50c. "Nepenthes rajah" . . . 35 55
602 50c. "Nepenthes lowii" . . . 35 55

215 Brahminy Kite

1996. Birds of Prey. Multicoloured.
603 20c. Type **215** 25 15
604 30c. Crested serpent eagle . . 35 25
605 50c. White-bellied sea eagle 55 55
606 $1 Crested hawk eagle . . . 1·00 2·00
MS607 100 × 70 mm. $2 Blyth's Hawk Eagle (vert) . . . . . . 2·50 3·50
No. **MS**607 also includes the "CHINA '96" 9th Asian International Stamp Exhibition logo on the sheet margin.

216 Family, Globe and Burning Drugs

1996. International Day against Drug Abuse and Illicit Trafficking. Multicoloured.
608 30c. Type **216** 40 60
609 30c. Sporting activities . . . 40 60
610 $1 Family and rainbow . . . 75 1·50

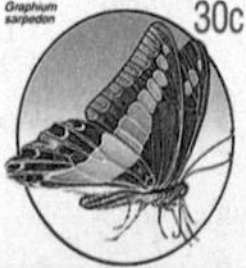

217 "Graphium sarpedon" **218** Kuala Lumpur Tower

1996. "ISTANBUL '96" International Stamp Exhibition. Butterflies. Multicoloured.
611 30c. Type **217** . . . . 1·25 1·25
612 30c. "Terinos terpander" . . 1·25 1·25
613 30c. "Melanocyma faunula" 1·25 1·25
614 30c. "Trogonoptera brookiana" . . . . 1·25 1·25
615 30c. "Delias hyparete" . . . 1·25 1·25

1996. Opening of Kuala Lumpur Telecommunications Tower. Multicoloured.
616 30c. Type **218** 20 20
617 50c. Diagram of top of tower 30 35
618 $1 Kuala Lumpur Tower at night . . . . 80 1·50
MS619 70 × 100 mm. $2 Top of Kuala Lumpur Tower (different) (vert) . . . . 1·50 2·50

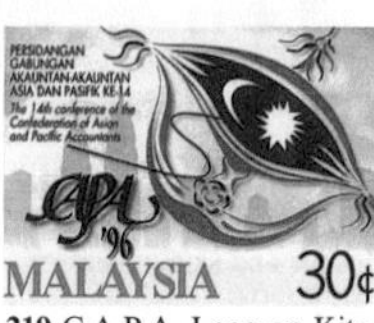

219 C.A.P.A. Logo on Kite

1996. 14th Conference of the Confederation of Asian and Pacific Accountants. Multicoloured.
620 30c. Type **219** 25 20
621 $1 Globe and C.A.P.A. logo 75 1·40

1996. "TAIPEI '96" 10th Asian International Stamp Exhibition. As No. **MS**619, but with exhibition logo added to bottom right-hand corner of sheet.
MS622 70 × 100 mm. $2 Top of Kuala Lumpur Tower (vert) . . 1·50 2·25

220 Model of D.N.A. Molecule

1996. Opening of National Science Centre, Kuala Lumpur. Multicoloured.
623 30c. Type **220** 25 20
624 50c. Planetary model and Science Centre 40 40
625 $1 National Science Centre 90 1·50

221 Slow Loris

1996. Stamp Week. Wuildlife. Sheet 165 × 75 mm, containing T **221** and similar multicoloured designs.
MS626 20c. Type **221**; 30c. Prevost's squirrel; 50c. Atlas moth; $1 Rhinoceros hornbill (60 × 30 mm); $1 White-handed gibbon (30 × 60 mm); $2 Banded palm civet (60 × 30 mm) . . . . . . 3·25 4·00

222 Running

1996. 16th Commonwealth Games, Kuala Lumpur (1998) (3rd issue). Multicoloured.
627 30c. Type **222** 35 55
628 30c. Hurdling 35 55
629 50c. High jumping 45 65
630 50c. Javelin 45 65

223 Pygmy Blue Flycatcher — **224** Transit Train leaving Station

1997. Highland Birds. Multicoloured.

631 20c. Type **223** 30 15
632 30c. Silver-eared mesia . . . 40 20
633 50c. Black-sided flower-pecker 55 55
634 $1 Scarlet sunbird . . . . . 85 1·50

1997. "HONG KONG '97" International Stamp Exhibition. As No. **MS**626, but with exhibition logo added to top sheet margin.

MS635 165 × 75 mm. 20c. Type **221**; 30c. Prevost's squirrel; 50c. Atlas moth; $1 Rhinoceros hornbill (60 × 30 mm); $1 White-handed gibbon (30 × 60 mm); $2 Banded palm civet (60 × 30 mm) . . . 4·00 5·00

1997. Opening of Kuala Lumpur Light Rail Transit System. Multicoloured.

636 30c. Type **224** . . . . 1·25 1·00
637 30c. Trains in central Kuala Lumpur . . . . 1·25 1·00

225 Bowler

1997. International Cricket Council Trophy, Kuala Lumpur. Multicoloured.

638 30c. Type **225** 35 15
639 50c. Batsman 50 45
640 $1 Wicket-keeper . . . . . . 90 1·50

226 Boeing 747-400 over World Map

1997. 50th Anniv of Aviation in Malaysia. Mult.

641 30c. Type **226** 65 15
642 50c. Boeing 747-400 over Kuala Lumpur 80 50
643 $1 Tail fins of four airliners 1·25 1·75

227 "Schima wallichii" — **228** World Youth Football Championship Mascot

1997. Highland Flowers. Multicoloured.

644 30c. Type **227** 50 70
645 30c. "Aeschynanthus longicalyx" 50 70
646 30c. "Aeschynanthus speciosa" 50 70
647 30c. "Phyllagathis tuberculata" 50 70
648 30c. "Didymocarpus quinquevulnerus" 50 70

1997. 9th World Youth Football Championship, Malaysia. Multicoloured.

649 30c. Type **228** 25 10
650 50c. Football and players . . 40 35
651 $1 Map of Malaysia and football . . . . 75 1·60

229 Members of First Conference, 1897

1997. Centenary of Rulers' Conference. Mult.

652 30c. Type **229** 15 10
653 50c. State emblem 30 35
654 $1 Seal and press . . . . . 65 1·60

230 A.S.E.A.N. Logo and Ribbons

1997. 30th Anniv of Association of South-east Asian Nations. Multicoloured.

655 30c. Type **230** 50 10
656 50c. "30" enclosing logo . . 70 45
657 $1 Chevrons and logo . . . 1·25 1·75

231 "Tubastrea sp." — **232** Women Athletes, Scientist and Politician

1997. International Year of the Coral Reefs. Multicoloured.

658 20c. Type **231** 20 10
659 30c. "Melithaea sp." 25 10
660 50c. "Aulostomus chinensis" 35 35
661 $1 "Symphillia sp." . . . . . 55 1·40
MS662 70 × 100 mm. $2 Green Turtle (horiz) . . . . 2·00 2·75

1997. 20th International Pan-Pacific and South-east Asia Women's Association Conference, Kuala Lumpur. Multicoloured.

663 30c. Type **232** 25 40
664 30c. Family and house . . . 25 40

233 1867 12c. on 4 anna with Malacca Postmark

1997. "Malpex '97" Stamp Exhibition, Kuala Lumpur. 50th Anniv of Organised Philately. Sheet 120 × 70 mm, containing T **233** and similar diamond-shaped designs. Multicoloured.

MS665 20c. Type **233**; 30c. 1997 Highland Birds set; 50c. 1996 Wildlife miniature sheet seen through magnifying glass; $1 1867 cover to Amoy . . . . 2·25 2·75

234 Group of 15 Emblem

1997. 7th Summit Conference of the Group of 15, Kuala Lumpur. Multicoloured.

666 30c. Type **234** 10 10
667 $1 Flags of member countries 90 1·25

235 Hockey

1997. 16th Commonwealth Games, Kuala Lumpur (1998) (4th issue). Multicoloured.

668 30c. Type **235** 50 55
669 30c. Netball 50 55
670 50c. Cricket 70 75
671 50c. Rugby 70 75

236 False Gharial

1997. Stamp Week '97. Endangered Wildlife. Sheet 165 × 75 mm, containing T **236** and similar multicoloured designs.

MS672 20c. Type **236**; 30c. Western tarsier (vert); 50c. Indian sambar (vert); $2 Crested wood partridge; $2 Malayan bony-tongue (fish) 2·50 3·25

1997. "INDEPEX '97" International Stamp Exhibition, New Delhi. As No. **MS**665, but with exhibition logo added to the sheet margin, in gold, at bottom right.

MS673 120 × 70 mm. 20c. Type **233**; 30c. 1997 Highlands Bird set; 50c. 1996 Wildlife miniature sheet seen through magnifying glass; $1 1867 cover to Amoy . . . . 1·25 2·00

237 Kundang

1998. Fruit. Multicoloured.

674 20c. Type **237** 15 10
675 30c. Sentul 20 10
676 50c. Pulasan 30 25
677 $1 Asam gelugur . . . . . . 70 1·60

238 Swimming Complex

1998. 16th Commonwealth Games, Kuala Lumpur (5th issue). Venues. Sheet 120 × 80 mm, containing T **238** and similar horiz designs. Multicoloured.

MS678 20c. Type **238**; 30c. Hockey Stadium; 50c. Indoor Stadium; $1 Main Stadium . . . . 1·25 2·00

239 Mas (coin) from Trengganu, 1793–1808

1998. Gold coins. Multicoloured.

679 20c. Type **239** 20 10
680 30c. Kupang from Kedah, 1661–1687 . . . . 25 10
681 50c. Kupang from Johore, 1597–1615 . . . . 45 35
682 $1 Kupang from Kelantan, 1400–1780 . . . . 60 1·50

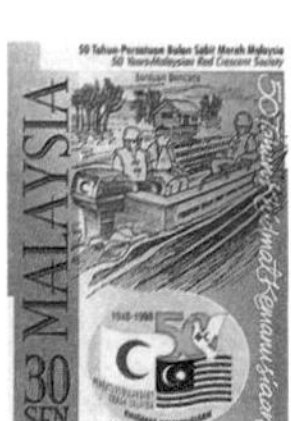

240 Red Crescent Ambulance Boat and Emblem

1998. 50th Anniv of Malaysian Red Crescent Society. Multicoloured.

683 30c. Type **240** 25 10
684 $1 Ambulance and casualty 85 1·40

241 Transit Train and Boeing 747-400 at Airport

1998. Opening of Kuala Lumpur International Airport. Designs showing control tower. Mult.

685 30c. Type **241** 30 10
686 50c. Airport Terminals . . . 45 30
687 $1 Airliner in flight . . . . 1·00 1·50
MS688 119 × 70 mm. $2 Globe and control tower (22 × 32 mm) . . 1·75 2·25

242 "Solanum torvum" — **243** Weightlifting

1998. Medicinal Plants. Multicoloured.

689 20c. Type **242** 15 10
690 30c. "Tinospora crispa" . . . 20 10
691 50c. "Jatropha podagrica" . . 35 30
692 $1 "Hibiscus rosa-sinensis" 65 1·40

1998. 16th Commonwealth Games, Kuala Lumpur, Malaysia (5th issue). Sports. Multicoloured.

693 20c. Type **243** 25 40
694 20c. Badminton 25 40
695 20c. Netball 25 40
696 20c. Shooting 25 40
697 30c. Men's hockey 35 45
698 30c. Women's hockey 35 45
699 30c. Cycling 35 45
700 30c. Bowls 35 45
701 50c. Gymnastics 35 45
702 50c. Cricket 35 45
703 50c. Rugby 35 45
704 50c. Running 35 45
705 $1 Swimming 35 55
706 $1 Squash 35 55
707 $1 Boxing 35 55
708 $1 Ten-pin bowling 35 55

244 L.R.T. "Putra" Type Train

1998. Modern Kuala Lumpur Rail Transport. Multicoloured.

709b 30c. Type **244** 50 15
710b 50c. L.R.T. "Star" type train 35 25
711 $1 K.T.M. commuter train 40 1·25

245 Globe and A.P.E.C. Logo

1998. Asia–Pacific Econmic Co-operation Conf. Multicoloured.

712b 30c. Type **245** 30 10
713 $1 Business meeting and computer office . . . . . 40 1·00

246 "Xylotrupes gideon" — **247** Nural Hudda (Women's Air Rifle Shooting)

1998. Stamp Week '98. Malaysian Insects. Sheet 165 × 75 mm, containing T **246** and similar multicoloured designs.

MS714 20c. Type **246**; 30c. "Pomponia imperatoria"; 50c. "Phyllium pulchrifolium"; $2 "Hymenopus coronatus" (43 × 27 mm); $2 "Macrolyristes corporalis" (43 × 27 mm) . . . 2·25 3·00

1998. 16th Commonwealth Games, Kuala Lumpur (7th issue). Malaysian Gold Medal Winners. Two miniature sheets, each 160 × 125 mm, containing multicoloured designs as T **247**.

MS715 $2 Malaysian badminton team celebrating (128 × 80 mm) 2·75 3·25
MS716 30c. Type **247**; 30c. Sapok Biki (48kg Boxing); 30c. G. Saravanan (50km Walk); 30c. Muhamad Hidayat Hamidon (69kg Weightlifting); 50c. Kenny Ang and Ben Heng (Tenpin Bowling Men's Doubles); 50c. Kenny Ang (Tenpin Bowling Men's Singles); 50c. Choong Tan Fook and Lee Wan Wah (Badminton Men's Doubles); 50c. Wong Choon Hann (Badminton Men's Singles); $1 Women's Rhythmic Gymnastics team (63 × 26 mm) . . . . 6·00 7·50

248 Profile of Elderly Couple, World Map and Emblem

1999. International Year of the Older Person. Multicoloured.
717 $1 Type **248** 50 90
718 $1 Four silhouettes of elderly people, world map and emblem 50 90

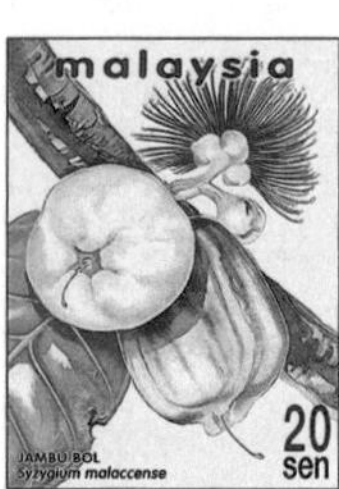

249 "Syzygium malaccense" **250** Kucing Malaysia Cat

1999. Rare Fruits of Malaysia. Multicoloured.
719 20c. Type **249** 20 15
720 30c. "Garcinia prainiana" . . 25 15
721 50c. "Mangifera caesia" . . . 30 25
722 $1 "Salacca glabrescens" . . 60 1·00

1999. Malaysian Cats. Multicoloured.
727 30c. Type **250** 30 15
728 50c. Siamese 45 35
729 $1 Abyssinian . . . . 80 1·25
MS730 Two sheets, each 81 × 90 mm. (a) $1 British shorthair; $1 Scottish fold. (B) $1 Birman; $1 Persian Set of 2 sheets 2·00 2·50

251 Sumatran Rhinoceros

1999. Protected Mammals of Malaysia (1st series). Multicoloured.
731 20c. Type **251** 50 15
732 30c. Panther 20 15
733 50c. Sun bear 25 25
734 $1 Indian elephant 65 90
739 $2 Orang-utan . . . . 1·50 2·00
MS740 119 × 80 mm. $2 No. 739 1·50 2·00
See also Nos. 923/31.

252 Hearts and AIDS Ribbons

1999. 5th International Conference on AIDS in Asia and the Pacific. Each red, blue and black.
741 30c. Type **252** 25 15
742 50c. Fragmenting and stylized AIDS ribbons 45 40
743 $1 Two AIDS ribbons . . . 75 1·25

253 P. Ramlee in Traditional Dress **254** *Monochoria hastoria* (water plant)

1999. 70th Birth Anniv of P. Ramlee (actor and film director) Commemoration. (a) Multicoloured.
744 20c. Type **253** 35 15
745 30c. Receiving an award . . 40 15
746 50c. Playing part of soldier in film 60 40
747 $1 Using film camera . . . . 90 1·25
MS748a Two sheets, each 100 × 70 mm. (a) $1 Wearing check shirt. (b) $1 In traditional dress Set of 2 sheets . . . . . 14·00 14·00

(b) Each brown, light brown and black.
749 30c. In traditional dress . . . 60 65
750 30c. With hands raised . . . 60 65
751 30c. Singing into microphone 60 65
752 30c. Wearing army uniform 60 65

1999. Freshwater Fishes of Malaysia. Mult.
753 10c. Type **254** 20 30
754 10c. *Trichopsis vittatus* . . . 20 30
755 15c. *Limnocharis flava* (water plant) 25 35
756 15c. *Betta imbellis* 25 35
757 25c. *Nymphaea pubescens* (water plant) 30 40
758 25c. *Trichogaster trichopterus* 30 40
759 50c. *Eichhornia crassipes* (water plant) 40 50
760 50c. *Sphaerichthys osphromenoides* 40 50
761 50c. *Ipomea aquatica* (water plant) 40 50
762 50c. *Helostoma temmincki* . . 40 50
No. 760 is inscribed "Sphaerichthys osphronemodies" in error.

255 *Lagerstroemia floribunda* (tree) **256** Petronas Twin Towers, Kuala Lumpur

1999. Trees of Malaysia. Multicoloured.
763 30c. Type **255** 45 50
764 30c. *Elateriospermum tapos* 45 50
765 30c. *Dryobalanops aromatica* 45 50
766 30c. *Alstonia angustiloba* . . 45 50
767 30c. *Fagraea fragrans* 45 50

1999. Completion of Petronas Twin Towers Building, Kuala Lumpur. Multicoloured (except 50c.).
768 30c. Type **256** 35 15
769 50c. Construction sketches (blue, violet and black) . . 45 35
770 $1 Twin Towers at night . . 80 1·00
MS771 100 × 75 mm. $5 Hologram of Twin Towers (30 × 50 mm) 3·50 3·75

257 Peace Hotel and Rickshaw

1999. 125th Anniv of Taiping, Perak. Mult.
772 20c. Type **257** 20 15
773 30c. Town Hall and 1930s car 20 15
774 50c. Railway Station 50 45
775 $1 Airport . . . . 1·00 1·25
MS776 120 × 69 mm. $2 Perak Museum and horse-drawn carriage 3·25 3·50

258 Power Station at Night

1999. 50th Anniv of Tenaga Nasional Berhad (electricity generating company). Multicoloured.
777 30c. Type **258** 25 15
778 50c. Control room and pylon 35 25
779 $1 Kuala Lumpur skyline at night . . . . 70 1·00
MS780 Two sheets, each 69 × 99 mm. (a) $1 Electric cart. (b) $1 Pylon Set of 2 sheets . . 1·25 1·75

259 New National Theatre and Traditional Characters

1999. Opening of New National Theatre, Kuala Lumpur. Multicoloured.
781 30c. Type **259** 25 15
782 50c. New National Theatre and horseman 40 30
783 $1 New National Theatre and traditional musician . . . 75 1·00

260 New Yang di-Pertuan Agong and Malaysian Flag

1999. Installation of Sultan Salahuddin Abdul Aziz Shah of Selangor as Yang di-Pertuan Agong. (a) Horiz designs as T **260**. Multicoloured.
784 30c. Type **260** 20 15
785 50c. Yang di-Pertuan Agong and Palace 30 25
786 $1 Yang di-Pertuan Agong and Parliament Buildings 60 90

(b) Vert designs, 24 × 29 mm, showing portrait only.
787 (30c.) multicoloured (purple frame) 45 45
788 (30c.) multicoloured (yellow frame) 45 45
789 (30c.) multicoloured (blue frame) 45 45
Nos. 787/9 are inscribed "BAYARAN POS TEMPATAN HINGGA 20GM" and were valid on local mail weighing no more than 20 gm.

261 Motorway Junction outside Kuala Lumpur

1999. 21st World Road Congress, Kuala Lumpur. Mult.
790 30c. Type **261** 20 15
791 50c. Damansara Puchong Bridge at night 30 25
792 $1 Aerial view of motorway junction, Selatan 60 90

262 Driver's Helmet and Canopy Tower, Formula 1 Circuit, Sepang

1999. Malaysian Grand Prix, Sepang. Mult. (a) Designs including driver's helmet.
793 20c. Type **262** 25 15
794 30c. Central Grandstand . . 30 15
795 50c. Formula 1 racing car . . 45 35
796 $1 Formula 1 racing car from Red Bull team 70 90

(b) Scenes from Sepang Formula 1 Circuit.
797 20c. Canopy Tower and Central Grandstand . . . 30 15
798 30c. Pit building 40 15
799 50c. Wheel-change in pits . . 55 40
800 $1 Race in progress . . . . 95 1·10

263 Sultan Haji Ahmad Shah and Flowers

1999. 25th Anniv of Installation of Sultan of Pahang. Multicoloured.
801 30c. Type **263** 35 40
802 30c. Butterfly and motorway 35 40
803 30c. Diver and beach 35 40
804 30c. Power station 35 40
805 30c. Mosque 35 40

264 World Cup

1999. World Cup Golf Championship, Mines Resort City. Multicoloured.
806 20c. Type **264** 25 10
807 30c. Emblem on golf ball . . 25 10
808 50c. Fairway 45 40
809 $1 First hole and club house 90 1·10

265 *Strelitzia augusta* **267** Fern, Pitcher Plant and Great Indian Hornbill

266 Letters and Computer Screen

1999. Stamp Week '99. Heliconias. Multicoloured.
814 30c. Type **265** 35 40
815 30c. *Heliconia rostrata* . . . 35 40
816 30c. *Heliconia psittacorum* (yellow) 35 40
817 30c. *Heliconia stricta* 35 40
818 30c. *Musa violascens* 35 40
819 30c. *Strelitzia reginae* 35 40
820 30c. *Heliconia colganta* . . . 35 40
821 30c. *Heliconia psittacorum* (white and pink) 35 40
822 30c. *Heliconia latispatha* . . . 35 40
823 30c. *Phaeomeria speciosa* . . 35 40
MS824 198 × 136 mm. Nos. 814/23 3·00 3·50

1999. 125th Anniv of Universal Postal Union. Mult.
825 20c. Type **266** 20 10
826 30c. Globe and Malaysian stamps 25 10
827 50c. World map and mail plane 50 40
828 $1 POS Malaysia emblem . . 80 1·10

1999. New Millennium (1st issue). Land and History. Multicoloured (except No. **MS**839).
829 30c. Type **267** 35 40
830 30c. Ceramic pots and Mt. Kinabalu 35 40
831 30c. Frog and tualang (tree) 35 40
832 30c. Rolling rubber and palm trees 35 40
833 30c. Angelfish and sailing barge 35 40
834 30c. Mousedeer and traditional Malay building 35 40
835 30c. Ruler on elephant and Straits of Malacca 35 40
836 30c. Malay kris (sword) and junks 35 40
837 30c. Clock Tower, Kuala Lumpur, and A Famosa ruins 35 40
838 30c. Sailing boat and palm trees 35 40
MS839 120 × 80 mm. $1 Traditional Malay sailing ship (horiz) (black and red) . . . . 1·50 1·60

2000. New Millennium (2nd issue). People and Achievements. As T **267**. Multicoloured.
840 30c. Iban playing sape and traditional costumes from East Malaysia 35 40
841 30c. Hurricane lamp, shell and couple from fishing village 35 40
842 30c. Doctor with patient and toddler with mother . . . 35 40
843 30c. Badminton player and young Malaysians 35 40
844 30c. Man with kite and traditional dancers 35 40
845 30c. Motor cycle, car and motorway 35 40
846 30c. Butterfly, Sepang motor racing circuit and airport 35 40
847 30c. High speed train and Kuala Lumpur skyline . . 35 40
848 30c. Computer operator and mosque 35 40
849 30c. Lorry and container port 35 40
MS850 120 × 80 mm. $1 Modern airliner (horiz) . . . . 1·50 1·60

268 Pottery Vase (New Stone Age)

2000. Chinese New Year ("Year of the Dragon"). Artefacts and Fish. Multicoloured.

851 30c. Type **268** 35 40
852 30c. Dragon eaves tile (Western Han Dynasty) . . 35 40
853 30c. Bronze knocker base (Tang Dynasty) 35 40
854 30c. Jade sword pommel (Western Han Dynasty) . . 35 40
855 30c. Dragon statue (Tang Dynasty) 35 40
856 30c. Arawana *(Osteoglossum bicirrhosum)* 35 40
857 30c. Spotted barramundi *(Scleropages leichardti)* . . 35 40
858 30c. Asian bonytongue (red) (Scleropages formosus) . . 35 40
859 30c. Black arawana *(Osteoglossum ferrerirai)* 35 40
860 30c. Asian bonytongue (gold) *(Scleropages formosus)* . . 35 40
MS861 Two sheets, each 120 × 65 mm. (a) $1 Dragon dance (square). (b) $1 Dragon boat (square) Set of 2 sheets . . . . 1·75 2·25

269 Table Tennis Bats and Globe

2000. World Table Tennis Championships, Bukit Jalil. Multicoloured.

862 30c. Type **269** 20 10
863 50c. Mascot and logo 35 25
864 $1 Table tennis bats and ball 60 90
MS865 100 × 70 mm. $1 Mascot and table tennis table; $1 Bats and table tennis table . . . . . . 1·00 1·50

270 Malaysian Climbers on Mt. Everest

2000. New Millennium (3rd issue). Malaysian Triumphs. Two sheets, each 120 × 80 mm, containing T **270** and similar vert designs. Multicoloured.

MS866 (a) 50c. Type **270**; 50c. Hikers; 50c. Arctic expedition and Proton car. (B) 50c. Solo yachtsman Set of 2 sheets . . . 1·75 2·25

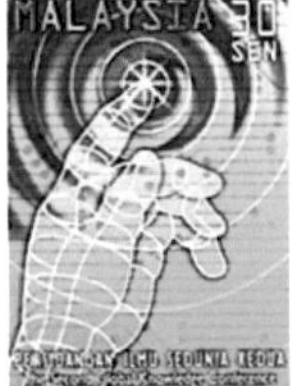

271 Outline Hand on Button

272 Internal Inverted Dome

2000. 2nd Global Knowledge Conference, Kuala Lumpur. Multicoloured.

867 30c. Type **271** 35 40
868 30c. Outline globe 35 40
869 50c. Woman's silhouette . . 45 50
870 50c. Man's silhouette 45 50

2000. Islamic Arts Museum, Kuala Lumpur. Mult.

871 20c. Type **272** 30 15
872 30c. Main dome of Museum 35 15
873 50c. Ottoman panel 50 35
874 $1 Ornate Mihrab . . . . . 90 1·25

273 Buatan Barat Prahu

274 Unit Trust Emblem and Women with Flags

2000. Traditional Malaysian Prahus (canoes). Mult.

875 30c. Type **273** 30 40
876 30c. Payang prahu (red and blue hull) 30 40
877 30c. Payang prahu (red, white and green hull) 30 40
878 30c. Burung prahu 30 40

2000. Unit Trust Week. Multicoloured.

879 30c. Type **274** 30 10
880 50c. City skyline and Malaysians in traditional costume 45 35
881 $1 Map of South East Asia and Malaysians in traditional costume . . . . 1·00 1·25

275 Badminton Player and Cup Logo

2000. Thomas Cup Badminton Championships, Bukit Jalil. Multicoloured.

882 30c. Type **275** 30 40
883 30c. Thomas Cup and flags 30 40
884 30c. Championship logo and mascot 30 40
885 30c. Uber Cup and flags . . 30 40
886 30c. Badminton player and mascot 30 40
MS887 120 × 80 mm. $1 Thomas Cup (vert) . . . . 1·25 1·40

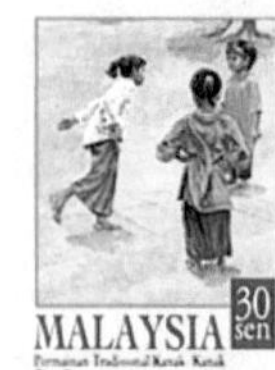

276 Children playing Ting Ting

2000. Children's Traditional Games (1st series). Multicoloured.

888 30c. Type **276** 60 60
889 30c. Tarik Upih 60 60
890 30c. Kite flying 60 60
891 30c. Marbles 60 60
892 30c. Bicycle rim racing . . . 60 60

277 Aspects of Computer Technology

2000. 27th Islamic Foreign Ministers' Conference, Kuala Lumpur. Multicoloured.

898 30c. Type **277** 30 40
899 30c. Traditonal Islamic scrollwork 30 40
900 30c. Conference logo 30 40
901 30c. Early coin 30 40
902 30c. Pens and satellite photograph 30 40

278 Malaysian Family on Map

2000. Population and Housing Census. Mult.

903 30c. Type **278** 30 40
904 30c. Symbolic house 30 40
905 30c. People on pie-chart . . . 30 40
906 30c. Diplomas and workers 30 40
907 30c. Male and female symbols 30 40

279 Rothchild's Peacock-pheasant

2000. Pheasants and Partridges. Multicoloured.

908 20c. Type **279** 30 10
909 30c. Crested argus (female) 35 10
910 50c. Great argus pheasant . . 55 40
911 $1 Crestless fireback pheasant 1·00 1·25
MS912 100 × 40 mm. $2 Crested argus (male) (31 × 26mm) . . . 1·75 2·25

280 *Hopea odorata* (fruit)

282 Otter Civet

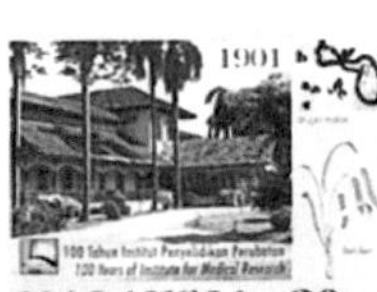

281 Institute in 1901, *Brugia malayi* and Beri-Beri

2000. International Union of Forestry Research Organisations Conference, Kuala Lumpur. Mult.

913 30c. Type **280** 50 50
914 30c. *Adenanthera pavonina* (seeds) 50 50
915 30c. *Shorea macrophylla* (seeds) 50 50
916 30c. *Dyera costulata* (fruits) 50 50
917 30c. *Alstonia angustiloba* (seeds) 50 50
MS918 Four sheets, each 92 × 71 mm. (a) Trees. 10c. *Fagraea fragrans*; 10c. *Dryobalanops aromatica*; 10c. *Terminalia catappa*; 10c. *Samanea saman*; 10c. *Dracontomelon dao*. (b) Leaves. 15c. *Heritiera javanica*; 15c. *Johannes-teijsmannia altifrons*; 15c. *Macaranga gigantea*; 15c. *Licuala grandis*; 15c. *Endospermum diadenum*. (c). Bark. 25c. *Pterocymbium javanicum*; 25c. *Dryobalanops aromatica*; 25c. *Dipterocarpus costulatus*; 25c. *Shorea leprosula*; 25c. *Ochanostachys amentacea*. (d) Forest fauna. 50c. Indian flycatcher; 50c. Slow loris; 50c. Marbled cat; 50c. Common carp; 50c. Pit viper Set of 4 sheets 5·00 5·50

No. **MS**918 contains four sheets each of five 18 × 22 mm designs, and a label showing the Conference logo.

2000. Centenary of Institute for Medical Research. Multicoloured.

919 30c. Type **281** 30 10
920 50c. Institute in 1953, bacteria and mosquito . . 45 40
921 $1 Institute in 1976, chromatogram and Eurycoma longifolia . . . 90 1·25
MS922 120 × 65 mm. $2 DNA molecule . . . . 1·75 1·75

2000. Protected Mammals of Malaysia (2nd series). Multicoloured.

923 20c. Type **282** 30 15
924 30c. Young otter civet . . . 35 40
927 30c. Hose's palm civet *(Hemigalus hosei)* 35 40
928 30c. Common palm civet *(Paradoxurus hermaphroditus)* 35 40
929 30c. Masked palm civet (Paguma larvata) 35 40
930 30c. Malay civet (Viverra tangalunga) 35 40
931 30c. Three-striped palm civet *(Arctogalidia trivirgata)* . . 35 40
925 50c. Binturong on bank . . . 50 40
926 $1 Head of binturong . . . . 90 1·00
MS932 140 × 80 mm. $1 Banded palm civet; $1 Banded linsang 1·75 1·75

283 Cogwheels

2000. 50th Anniv of RIDA-MARA (Rural and Industrial Development Authority – Council for Indigenous People). Multicoloured.

933 30c. Type **283** 30 10
934 50c. Compasses and stethoscope 45 40
935 $1 Computer disk, book and mouse . . . . 85 1·10

2000. Children's Traditional Games (2nd series). As T **276**. Multicoloured.

936 20c. Bailing tin 30 35
937 20c. Top-spinning 30 35
938 30c. Sepak Raga 40 50
939 30c. Letup-Letup 40 50

284 Cyclist and Pedestrians

285 *Rhododendron brookeanum*

2000. World Heart Day. Multicoloured.

940 30c. Type **284** 35 40
941 30c. Family at play 35 40
942 30c. Kite flying, football and no smoking sign 35 40
943 30c. Keep fit class 35 40
944 30c. Farmer, animals and food 35 40

Nos. 940/4 were printed together, se-tenant, with the backgrounds forming a composite design.

2000. Stamp Week 2000. Highland Flowers (2nd series). Multicoloured.

945 30c. Type **285** 30 35
946 30c. *Rhododendron jasminiflorum* 30 35
947 30c. *Rhododendron scortechinii* 30 35
948 30c. *Rhododendron pauciflorum* 30 35
949 30c. *Rhododendron crassifolium* 30 35
950 30c. *Rhododendron longiflorum* 30 35
951 30c. *Rhododendron javanicum* 30 35
952 30c. *Rhododendron variolosum* 30 35
953 30c. *Rhododendron acuminatum* 30 35
954 30c. *Rhododendron praetervisum* 30 35
955 30c. *Rhododendron himantodes* 30 35
956 30c. *Rhododendron maxwellii* 30 35
957 30c. *Rhododendron erocoides* 30 35
958 30c. *Rhododendron fallacinum* 30 35
MS959 55 × 90 mm. $1 *Rhododendron malayanum* 1·00 1·25

No. 955 is inscribed "Rhodadendron", No. 957 "Ericoides", both in error.

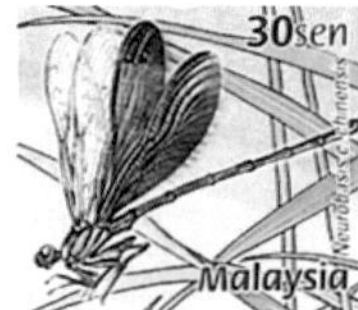

286 *Neurobasis c. chinensis*

2000. Dragonflies and Damselflies. Multicoloured.

960 30c. Type **286** 30 35
961 30c. *Aristocypha fenestrella* (blue markings on tail) . . 30 35
962 30c. *Vestalis gracilis* 30 35
963 30c. *Nannophya pymaea* . . . 30 35
964 30c. *Aristocypha fenestrella* (white markings on tail) . . 30 35
965 30c. *Rhyothemis p. phyllis* . . 30 35
966 30c. *Crocothemis s. servilia* 30 35
967 30c. *Euphaea ochracea* (male) 30 35
968 30c. *Euphaea ochracea* (female) 30 35
969 30c. *Ceriagrion cerinorubellum* 30 35
970 (30c.) *Vestalis gracilis* 30 35
971 (30c.) *Crocothemis s. servilia* (male) 30 35
972 (30c.) *Trithemis aurora* . . . 30 35
973 (30c.) *Pseudothemis jorina* . . 30 35
974 (30c.) *Diplacodes nebulosa* . . 30 35
975 (30c.) *Crocothemis s. servilia* (female) 30 35
976 (30c.) *Neurobasis c. chinensis* (male) 30 35
977 (30c.) *Burmagomphus divaricatus* 30 35
978 (30c.) *Ictinogomphus d. melaenops* 30 35
979 (30c.) *Orthetrum testaceum* 30 35
980 (30c.) *Trithemis festiva* . . . 30 35
981 (30c.) *Brachythemis contaminata* 30 35
982 (30c.) *Neurobasis c. chinensis* (female) 30 35
983 (30c.) *Neurothemis fluctuans* 30 35
984 (30c.) *Acisoma panorpoides* 30 35
985 (30c.) *Orthetrum s. sabina* . . 30 35
986 (30c.) *Rhyothemis p. phyllis* 30 35
987 (30c.) *Rhyothemis obsolescens* 30 35
988 (30c.) *Neurothemis t. tulia* . . 30 35
989 (30c.) *Lathrecista a. asiatica* 30 35
990 (30c.) *Aethriamanta gracilis* 30 35
991 (30c.) *Diplacodes trivialis* . . 30 35
992 (30c.) *Neurothemis fulvia* . . 30 35
993 (30c.) *Rhyothemis triangularis* 30 35
994 (30c.) *Orthetrum glaucum* . . 30 35

Nos. 960/9 were issued togetther, se-tenant, and show the backgrounds forming a composite design.

Nos. 970/94 are inscribed "Bayaran Pos Tempatan Hingga 20gm". They were valid at 30c. for local mail up to 20 g.

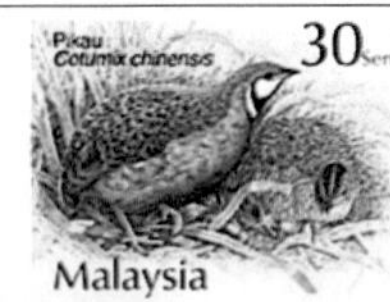

287 Indian Blue Quail

2001. Quails and Partridges. Multicoloured.
995 30c. Type **287** 35 10
996 50c. Sumatran hill partridge 50 45
997 $1 Bustard quail 90 1·25
MS998 100 × 170 mm. $2 Chestnut-breasted tree partridge; $2 Crimson-headed wood partridge 2·50 2·50

288 Federal Government Administrative Centre

2001. Formation of Putrajaya Federal Territory. Multicoloured.
999 30c. Type **288** 30 10
1000 $1 Government buildings and motorway bridge 1·10 1·25

289 Sabah and Sarawak Beadwork

2001. Sabah and Sarawak Beadwork. Mult, background colours given.
1001 **289** 30c. green 30 40
1002 – 30c. blue 30 40
1003 – 30c. buff 30 40
1004 – 30c. red 30 40
DESIGN: Nos 1001/4 Showing different styles of beadwork

290 *Cananga odorata* **291** Raja Tuanku Syed Sirajuddin

2001. Scented Flowers. Multicoloured.
1005 30c. Type **290** 30 10
1006 50c. *Mimusops elengi* 50 40
1007 $1 *Mesua ferrea* 90 1·10
MS1008 70 × 100mm. $2 *Muchelia champaca* 1·50 1·75

2001. Installation of Tuanku Syed Sirajuddin as Raja of Perlis.
1009 **291** 30c. multicoloured 30 15
1010 50c. multicoloured 50 40
1011 $1 multicoloured 90 1·25
MS1012 100 × 70 mm. $2 Raja Tuanku Syed Sirajuddin and Tengku Fauziah (horiz). Multicoloured 1·50 1·75

292 Beetlenut Leaf Arrangement

2001. Traditional Malaysian Artefacts. Mult.
1013 30c. Type **292** 35 40
1014 30c. Baby carrier 35 40
1015 50c. Quail trap 50 60
1016 50c. Ember container 50 60

293 Perodua Kancil Car, 1995

2001. Malaysia-made Motor Vehicles. Mult.
1017 30c. Type **293** 35 40
1018 30c. Proton Tiara, 1995 35 40
1019 30c. Perodua Rusa, 1995 35 40
1020 30c. Proton Putra, 1997 35 40
1021 30c. Inokom Permas, 1999 35 40
1022 30c. Perodua Kembara, 1999 35 40
1023 30c. Proton GTI, 2000 35 40
1024 30c. TD 2000, 2000 35 40
1025 30c. Perodua Kenari, 2000 35 40
1026 30c. Proton Waja, 2000 35 40

294 Serama Bantam Cock **295** Diving

2001. Malaysian Bantams. Multicoloured.
1027 30c. Type **294** 35 15
1028 50c. Kapan bantam cock 55 45
1029 $1 Serama bantam hen 1·10 1·25
MS1030 98 × 70 mm. $3 Red junglefowl hens and chicks (44 × 34 mm) 2·75 3·25

2001. 21st South East Asian Games, Kuala Lumpur. Mult.
1031 20c. Type **295** 25 10
1032 30c. Rhythmic gymnastics 30 15
1033 50c. Bowling 40 25
1034 $1 Weightlifting 75 65
1035 $2 Cycling 1·75 2·00
MS1036 110 × 90 mm. $5 Running 3·50 4·00

296 "F.D.I. 2001" Logo (½-size illustration)

2001. "F.D.I. 2001" World Dental Congress, Kuala Lumpur.
1037 **296** $1 multicoloured 1·00 1·25

297 K.W.S.P. Headquarters, Kuala Lumpur

2001. 50th Anniv of Employees' Provident Fund ("Kumpulan Wang Simpanan Pekerja"). Mult.
1038 30c. Type **297** 30 15
1039 50c. Column chart on coins and banknotes 45 40
1040 $1 Couple with K.W.S.P. logo 90 1·25

298 Satellite and Rainforest in Shape of Malaya Peninsula

2001. Centenary of Peninsular Malaysia Forestry Department. Multicoloured.
1041 30c. Type **298** 35 15
1042 50c. Cross-section through forest and soil 55 45
1043 $1 Newly-planted forest 1·00 1·25

299 *Tridacna gigas* (clam)

2001. Stamp Week. Endangered Marine Life. Multicoloured.
1044 20c. Type **299** 25 10
1045 30c. *Hippocampus sp.* (seahorse) 30 15
1046 50c. *Oreaster occidentalis* (starfish) 45 40
1047 $1 *Cassis cornu* (shell) 90 1·25
MS1048 100 × 70 mm. $3 Dugong 2·00 2·25

300 Hockey Player in Orange **301** *Couroupita guianensis*

2002. 10th Hockey World Cup, Kuala Lumpur. Multicoloured.
1049 30c. Type **300** 40 15
1050 50c. Goalkeeper 60 50
1051 $1 Hockey player in yellow 1·25 1·25
MS1052 100 × 70 mm. $3 Hockey player in blue (30 × 40 mm) 2·25 2·25

2002. Malaysia–China Joint Issue. Rare Flowers. Multicoloured.
1053 30c. Type **301** 30 10
1054 $1 *Couroupita guianensis* 80 90
1055 $1 *Camellia nitidissima* 80 90
MS1056 108 × 79 mm. $2 *Schima brevifolia* buds (horiz); $2 *Schima brevifolia* blossom 2·25 2·50

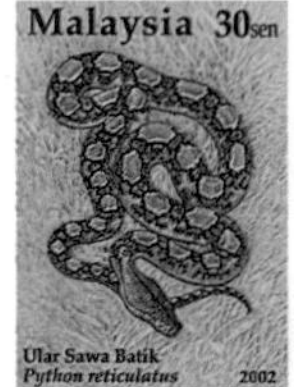

302 *Python reticulatus* **304** *Paraphalaenopsis labukensis*

303 Stesen Sentral Station, Kuala Lumpur

2002. Malaysian Snakes. Multicoloured.
1057 30c. Type **302** 30 20
1058 30c. *Gonyophis margaritatus* 30 20
1059 50c. *Bungarus candidus* 50 40
1060 $1 *Maticora bivirgata* 90 1·10
MS1061 108 × 78 mm. $2 *Ophiophagus hannah* (head of adult); $2 *Ophiophagus hannah* (juvenile) 2·75 2·75

2002. Express Rail Link from Central Kuala Lumpur to International Airport. Multicoloured.
1062 30c. Type **303** 40 20
1063 50c. Train and Central Station 60 65
1064 50c. Train and International Airport 60 65
MS1065 Two sheets, each 106 × 76 mm. (a) $1 KLIA Express and high speed train; $1 Express and local trains. (b) $2 KLIA Express Set of 2 sheets 2·75 2·75

2002. 17th World Orchid Conference. Multicoloured.
1066 30c. Type **304** 30 20
1067 30c. *Renanthera bella* 30 20
1068 50c. *Paphiopedilum sanderianum* 50 25
1069 $1 *Coelogyne pandurata* 80 90
1070 $1 *Phalaenopsis amabilis* 80 90
MS1071 76 × 105 mm. $5 *Cleisocentron merillianum* (45 × 40 mm) 3·50 4·00

305 Raja Tuanku Syed Sirajuddin of Perlis **307** White-bellied Woodpecker (*Dryocopus javensis*)

306 *Cryptocoryne purpurea*

2002. Installation of Raja Tuanku Syed Sirajuddin as Yang di-Pertuan Agong.
1072 **305** 30c. multicoloured 25 10
1073 50c. multicoloured 40 30
1074 $1 multicoloured 80 90

2002. Aquatic Plants. Multicoloured.
1075 30c. Type **306** 30 10
1076 50c. *Barclaya kunstleri* 45 25
1077 $1 *Neptunia oleracea* 80 90
1078 $1 *Monochoria hastata* 80 90
MS1079 110 × 80 mm. $1 *Eichhornia crassipes* (vert); $2 *Nymphaea pubescens* 2·75 3·00

2002. Malaysia–Singapore Joint Issue. Birds. Multicoloured.
1080 30c. Type **307** 35 25
1081 30c. Black-naped oriole (*Oriolus chinensis*) 35 25
1082 $1 Red-throated sunbird (*Anthreptes rhodolaema*) 90 1·00
1083 $1 Asian fairy bluebird (*Irena puella*) 90 1·00
MS1084 99 × 70 mm. $5 Orange-bellied flowerpecker (*Dicaeum trigonostigma*) (60 × 40 mm) 3·50 4·00
Stamps with similar designs were issued by Singapore.

308 Sibu Island, Johore

2002. Tourist Beaches (1st series). Multicoloured.
1085 30c. Type **308** 30 20
1086 30c. Perhentian Islands, Trengganu 30 20
1087 50c. Manukan Island, Sabah 45 45
1088 50c. Tioman Island, Pahang 45 45
1089 $1 Singa Besar Island, Kedah 85 95
1090 $1 Pangkor Island, Perak 85 95
MS1091 110 × 80 mm. $1 Ferringhi Bay, Penang; $1 Port Dickson, Negri Sembilan 1·50 1·75
See also Nos. 1143/**MS**1153.

309 Ethnic Musicians and Dancers

2002. Malaysian Unity. Multicoloured.
1092 30c. Type **309** 30 25
1093 30c. Children playing mancala (game) 30 25
1094 50c. Children from different races (82 × 30 mm) 50 50
MS1095 68 × 99 mm. $1 Children playing tug-of-war 1·00 1·10

310 Zainal Abidin bin Ahmad ("Za'ba") as a Student

2002. 30th Death Anniv of Zainal Abidin bin Ahmad ("Za'ba") (2003) (scholar). Multicoloured.
1096 30c. Type **310** 30 10
1097 50c. Za'ba with typewriter 45 50
1098 50c. Za'ba and traditional Malay building 45 50
MS1099 100 × 70 mm. $1 Za'ba at desk (vert) 1·00 1·10

311 Green Kebaya, Nyonya **313** Leopard Cat with Kittens

312 Suluh Budiman Building, Sultan Idris University of Education

2002. The Kebaya Nyonya (traditional Malay women's blouse). Multicoloured.
1100 30c. Type **311** 30 20
1101 30c. Red kebaya nyonya 30 20
1102 50c. Yellow kebaya nyonya 45 50
1103 50c. Pink kebaya nyonya 45 50
MS1104 70 × 100 mm. $2 Kebaya nyonya and sarong (34 × 69 mm) 1·25 1·50

2002. 80th Anniv of Sultan Idris University of Education. Multicoloured.
1105 30c. Type **312** 30 10
1106 50c. Tadahan Selatan Building 45 50
1107 50c. Chancellery Building 45 50
No. 1107 is inscribed "Chancellory" in error.

2002. Stamp Week. Wild and Domesticated Animals. Multicoloured.
1108 30c. Type **313** 30 20
1109 30c. Domestic cat and kittens 30 20
1110 $1 Lesser sulphur-crested cockatoo 80 85
1111 $1 Malay fish owl 80 85
MS1112 Two sheets, each 105 × 76 mm. (a) $1 Goldfish (horiz). $1 Porcupinefish (horiz); (b) $1 Giant squirrel; $1 Domestic rabbit with young Set of 2 sheets 2·25 2·40

314 Southern Serow

2003. Southern Serow. Multicoloured.
1113 30c. Type **314** 30 10
1114 50c. Southern serow lying down 45 50
1115 50c. Young southern serow 45 50

315 Peace Doves and Emblem

2003. 13th Conference of Heads of State or Government of the Non-Aligned Movement, Kuala Lumpur. Multicoloured.
1116 30c. Type **315** 10 15
1117 30c. Conference emblem in cupped hands 10 15
1118 50c. Emblem and outline map of Malaysia 15 20
1119 50c. "2003" with noughts containing Malaysian flag and emblem 15 20
Nos. 1116/17 and 1118/19 were each printed together, se-tenant, each pair forming a composite background design of a Malaysian flag and world map (Nos. 1116/17) or a globe (Nos. 1118/19).

316 Pale Pink Hybrid Tea Rose

2003. Roses in Malaysia. Multicoloured.
1120 30c. Type **316** 10 15
1121 30c. Red hybrid tea 10 15
1122 50c. Apricot hybrid tea 15 20
1123 50c. Pink and white striped floribunda 15 20
MS1124 70 × 100 mm. $1 Miniature floribunda (29 × 40 mm); $2 *Rosa centifolia* (29 × 81 mm) 95 1·00

317 Tunku Abdul Rahman

318 Sultan Sharafuddin Idris Shah

2003. Birth Centenary of Tunku Abdul Rahman (first Prime Minister of Federation of Malaya (1957–63) and of Malaysia (1963–70)). Multicoloured.
1125 30c. Type **317** 10 15
1126 50c. Tunku Abdul Rahman (different) 15 20
1127 $1 Tunku Abdul Rahman in ceremonial dress 30 35
1128 $1 Tunku Abdul Rahman wearing topi hat 30 35
MS1129 100 × 70 mm. $1 Tunku Abdul Rahman reading Proclamation of Independence, 1957 30 35

2003. Coronation of Sultan of Selangor. Multicoloured.
1130 30c. Type **318** 10 15
1131 50c. Sultan in uniform 15 20
1132 $1 Sultan of Selangor (wearing crown) 30 35

319 Siamese Fighting Fish

2003. Siamese Fighting Fish (*Betta splendens*). Multicoloured.
1133 30c. Type **319** 10 15
1134 50c. Siamese Fighting fish (yellow) 15 20
1135 $1 Siamese Fighting fish (blue) 30 35
1136 $1 Siamese Fighting fish (red with fringed fins) 30 35
MS1137 99 × 70 mm. 50c. *Betta imbellis* (Local Fighting Fish) (33 × 28 mm); 50c. *Betta coccina* (Red Fighting Fish) (33 × 28 mm) 30 35

320 Christ Church Clock

321 Malaysian Flag and Sultan Tower, Malacca Abdul Samad Building, Kuala Lumpur

2003. Clock Towers. Multicoloured.
1138 30c. Type **320** 10 15
1139 30c. Jubilee Clock Tower, Penang 10 15
1140 30c. Sungai Petani Clock Tower, Jalan Ibrahim 10 15
1141 30c. Teluk Intan Clock Tower 10 15
1142 30c. Sarawak State Council Monument 10 15
MS1143 99 × 70 mm. $1 Sultan Abdul Samad Building; $1 Taiping Clock Tower, Perak 65 70

2003. Islands and Beaches of Malaysia (2nd series). As T **308**. Multicoloured.
1149 30c. Aerial view of Ligitan Island 10 15
1150 30c. Outline map of Ligitan Island 10 15
1151 50c. Sipadan Island 15 20
1152 50c. Outline map of Sipadan Island 15 20
MS1153 70 × 100 mm. 50c. Aerial view of Sipadan Island (vert); 50c. Relief map of Ligitan Island (vert) 30 35

2003. 46th Independence Celebration.
1154 **321** 30c. multicoloured 10 15
1155 – $1 multicoloured 30 35
MS1156 70 × 100 mm. $1 black and grey 30 35
DESIGNS—59 × 40 mm No. 1155, Malaysian flag; No. **MS**1156, Independence delegation in motorcade, Malacca, 1956.

322 Modenas Jaguh 175

2003. Malaysian made Motorcycles and Scooters. Multicoloured.
1157 30c. Type **322** 10 15
1158 50c. Modenas Karisma 125 15 20
1159 50c. Modenas Kriss 1 15 20
1160 50c. Modenas Kriss 2 15 20
1161 50c. Modenas Kriss SG 15 20
MS1162 Four sheets, each 100 × 70 mm. (a) $1 Comel Turbulence RG125; $1 Comel Cyclone GP150. (b) $1 Demak Adventurer; $1 Demak Beetle. (c) $1 MZ 125SM; $1 MZ Perintis 120S Classic. (d) $1 Gagiva Momos 125R; $1 Nitro NE150 Windstar 2·30 2·40

323 Putrajaya Convention Centre

2003. 10th Session of Islamic Summit Conference, Putrajaya. Multicoloured.
1163 30c. Type **323** 10 15
1164 30c. Emblem 10 15
1165 50c. Putrajaya Mosque, modern Kuala Lumpur buildings and flag 15 20
1166 50c. Sultan Abdul Samad Building, Kuala Lumpur and Federal Government Administrative Centre, Putrajaya 15 20
Nos. 1165/6 were each printed together, se-tenant, forming a composite design.

2003. "Bangkok 2003" World Stamp Exhibition, Thailand. Nos. 1157/61 additionally inscr with "Bangkok" and exhibition logo.
1167 30c. Type **322** 10 15
1168 50c. Modenas Karisma 125 15 20
1169 50c. Modenas Kriss 1 15 20
1170 50c. Modenas Kriss 2 15 20
1171 50c. Modenas Kriss SG 15 20

324 Children in Circle and World Map

2003. 50th World Children's Day. Multicoloured.
1172 20c. Type **324** 10 10
1173 30c. Family outside their home 10 15
1174 30c. Girl flying kite and children with computer 10 15
1175 30c. "Sambutan 50 tahun Hari kanak-kanak Sedunia" in child's writing 10 15
1176 30c. Open book, house, Malaysian flag, rainbow, car and flower 10 15
Nos. 1173/4 were printed together, se-tenant, forming a composite design.

325 Red Leaf Monkey feeding **326** One Fathom Bank Lighthouse

2003. Stamp Week. Primates of Malaysia. Multicoloured.
1177 30c. Type **325** 10 15
1178 30c. Red leaf monkey sat on branch 10 15
1179 50c. Proboscis monkey 15 20
1180 50c. Female proboscis monkey with baby 15 20

2004. Lighthouses. Multicoloured.
1181 30c. Type **326** 10 15
1182 30c. Muka Head Lighthouse, Pulau Pinang 10 15
1183 30c. Pulau Undan Lighthouse, Melaka 10 15
1184 30c. Althingsburg Lighthouse, Selangor 10 15
MS1185 70 × 100 mm. $1 Tanjung Tuan Lighthouse 30 35

327 Fauna at Seashore and in Forest

2004. 7th Conference of Convention on Biological Diversity and First Meeting of Cartagena Protocol on Biosafety. Multicoloured.
1186 30c. Type **327** 10 15
1187 50c. Conference logo 15 20
1188 50c. DNA, leaf and test tube 15 20

328 Sultan of Kelantan

2004. Silver Jubilee of Sultan Ismail Petra Ibni Almarhum of Kelantan. Multicoloured.
1189 30c. Type **328** 10 15
1190 50c. Sultan and Istana Jahar, Museum of Royal Traditions and Customs 15 20
1191 $1 Sultan and Khota Bharu 30 35

329 Golf Ball, City Skyline and World Map

2004. 1st Commonwealth Tourism Ministers Meeting, Kuala Lumpur. Multicoloured.
1192 30c. Type **329** 10 15
1193 50c. World map and seashore 15 20
1194 $1 Logo and montage of images of Malaysia (vert) 30 35

POSTAGE DUE STAMPS

Until 15 August 1966, the postage due stamps of Malaysian Postal Union were in use throughout Malaysia.

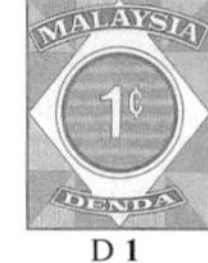

D 1

D 2

1966.

D 1	D 1	1c. red	20	4·00
D 2		2c. blue	25	2·75
D 3		4c. green	1·00	6·50
D18		8c. green	80	6·50
D19		10c. blue	80	3·00
D 6		12c. violet	60	4·50
D20		20c. brown	1·00	3·50
D21		50c. bistre	1·50	4·25

1986.

D22	D 2	5c. mauve and lilac	10	30
D23		10c. black and grey	15	30
D24		20c. red and brown	20	35
D25		50c. green and blue	30	50
D26		$1 blue and cobalt	55	90

B. FEDERAL TERRITORY ISSUES

For use in the Federal Territories of Kuala Lumpur, Labuan (from 1984) and Putrajaya (from 2001).

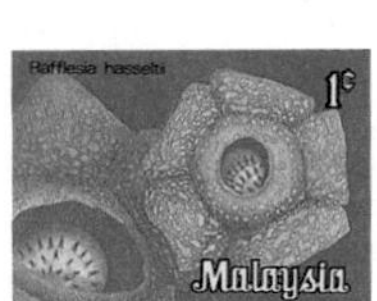

K 1 "Rafflesia hasseltii"

K 2 Coffee

1979. Flowers. Multicoloured.

K1	1c. Type **K 1**	10	40
K2	2c. "Pterocarpus indicus"	10	40
K3	5c. "Lagerstroemia speciosa"	15	40
K4	10c. "Durio zibethinus"	15	10
K5	15c. "Hibiscus rosa-sinensis"	30	10
K6	20c. "Rhododendron scortechinii"	30	10
K7	25c. "Etlingera elatior" (inscr "Phaeomeria speciosa")	70	10

1986. Agricultural Products of Malaysia. Mult.

K15	1c. Type **K 2**	10	10
K16	2c. Coconuts	10	10
K17	5c. Cocoa	10	10
K18	10c. Black pepper	10	10
K19	15c. Rubber	10	10
K20	20c. Oil palm	10	10
K21	30c. Rice	10	15

MALDIVE ISLANDS Pt. 1

A group of islands W. of Ceylon. A republic from 1 January 1953, but reverted to a sultanate in 1954. Became independent on 26 July 1965 and left the British Commonwealth, but was re-admitted as an Associate Member on 9 July 1982.

1906. 100 cents = 1 rupee.
1951. 100 larees = 1 rupee.

1906. Nos. 268, 277/9 and 283/4 of Ceylon optd **MALDIVES.**

1	**44**	2c. brown	15·00	38·00
2	**48**	3c. green	20·00	38·00
3		4c. orange and blue	35·00	75·00
4	–	5c. purple	4·00	6·50
5	**48**	15c. blue	70·00	£140
6		25c. brown	80·00	£150

2 Minaret, Juma Mosque, Male

5 Palm Tree and Dhow

1909.

7a	**2**	2c. brown	2·50	90
11A		2c. grey	2·75	2·00
8		3c. green	50	70
12A		3c. brown	70	2·75
9		5c. purple	50	35
15A		6c. red	1·50	5·50
10		10c. red	7·50	80
16A		10c. green	85	55
17A		15c. black	6·50	14·00
18A		25c. brown	6·50	14·00
19A		50c. purple	6·50	16·00
20B		1r. blue	14·00	3·25

1950.

21	**5**	2l. olive	2·25	1·25
22		3l. blue	10·00	50
23		5l. green	10·00	50
24		6l. brown	1·25	80
25		10l. red	1·25	60
26		15l. orange	1·25	60
27		25l. purple	1·25	1·00
28		50l. violet	1·25	1·75
29		1r. brown	11·00	30·00

8 Native Products

1952.

30	–	3l. blue (Fish)	2·00	60
31	**8**	5l. green	1·00	2·00

9 Male Harbour

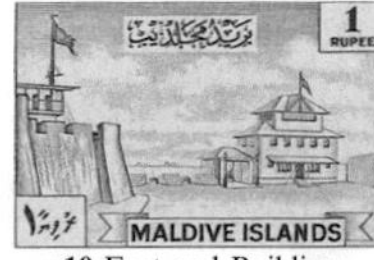

10 Fort and Building

1956.

32	**9**	2l. purple	10	10
33		3l. slate	10	10
34		5l. brown	10	10
35		6l. violet	10	10
36		10l. green	10	10
37		15l. brown	10	85
38		25l. red	10	10
39		50l. orange	10	10
40	**10**	1r. green	15	10
41		5r. blue	1·25	30
42		10r. mauve	2·75	1·25

11 Cycling

1960. Olympic Games.

43	**11**	2l. purple and green	15	25
44		3l. slate and purple	15	25
45		5l. brown and blue	15	25
46		10l. green and brown	15	25
47		15l. sepia and blue	15	25
48	–	25l. red and olive	15	25
49	–	50l. orange and violet	20	40
50	–	1r. green and purple	40	1·25

DESIGN—VERT: 25l. to 1r. Basketball.

13 Tomb of Sultan

1960.

51	**13**	2l. purple	10	10
52	–	3l. green	10	10
53	–	5l. brown	3·50	3·50
54	–	6l. blue	10	10
55	–	10l. red	10	10
56	–	15l. sepia	10	10
57	–	25l. violet	10	10
58	–	50l. grey	10	10
59	–	1r. orange	15	10
60	–	5r. blue	4·75	60
61	–	10r. green	11·00	1·25

DESIGNS: 3l. Custom House; 5l. Cowrie shells; 6l. Old Royal Palace; 10l. Road to Juma Mosque, Male; 15l. Council House; 25l. New Government Secretariat; 50l. Prime Minister's Office; 1r. Old Ruler's Tomb; 5r. Old Ruler's Tomb (distant view); 10r. Maldivian port.

Higher values were also issued, intended mainly for fiscal use.

24 "Care of Refugees"

25 Coconuts

26 Map of Male

1960. World Refugee Year.

62	**24**	2l. violet, orange and green	10	10
63		3l. brown, green and red	10	10
64		5l. green, sepia and red	10	10
65		10l. green, violet and red	10	10
66		15l. violet, green and red	10	10
67		25l. blue, brown and green	10	10
68		50l. olive, red and blue	10	10
69		1r. red, slate and violet	15	35

1961.

70	**25**	2l. brown and green	10	50
71		3l. brown and blue	10	50
72		5l. brown and mauve	10	10
73		10l. brown and orange	15	10
74		15l. brown and black	20	15
75	**26**	25l. multicoloured	45	20
76		50l. multicoloured	45	40
77		1r. multicoloured	50	70

27 5c. Stamp of 1906

1961. 55th Anniv of First Maldivian Stamp.

78	**27**	2l. purple, blue and green	10	50
79		3l. purple, blue and green	10	50
80		5l. purple, blue and green	10	15
81		6l. purple, blue and green	10	70
82	–	10l. green, red and purple	10	15
83	–	15l. green, red and purple	15	15
84	–	20l. green, red and purple	15	20
85	–	25l. red, green and black	15	20
86	–	50l. red, green and black	25	80
87	–	1r. red, green and black	40	1·75
MS87a		114 × 88 mm. No. 87 (block of four). Imperf	1·50	4·75

DESIGNS: 10l. to 20l. Posthorn and 3c. stamp of 1906; 25l. to 1r. Olive sprig and 2c. stamp of 1906.

30 Malaria Eradication Emblem

31 Children of Europe and America

1962. Malaria Eradication.

88	**30**	2l. brown	10	60
89		3l. green	10	60
90		5l. turquoise	10	15
91		10l. red	10	15
92	–	15l. sepia	15	15
93	–	25l. blue	20	20
94	–	50l. myrtle	25	55
95	–	1r. purple	55	80

Nos. 92/5 are as Type **30**, but have English inscriptions at the side.

1962. 15th Anniv of U.N.I.C.E.F.

96	**31**	2l. multicoloured	10	65
97		6l. multicoloured	10	65
98		10l. multicoloured	10	10
99		15l. multicoloured	10	10
100	–	25l. multicoloured	15	10
101	–	50l. multicoloured	20	10
102	–	1r. multicoloured	25	20
103	–	5r. multicoloured	1·00	4·00

DESIGN: Nos. 100/3, Children of Middle East and Far East.

33 Sultan Mohamed Farid Didi

39 Fishes in Net

34 Royal Angelfish

1962. 9th Anniv of Enthronement of Sultan.

104	**33**	3l. brown and green	10	65
105		5l. brown and blue	15	15
106		10l. brown and blue	20	15
107		20l. brown and olive	30	25
108		50l. brown and mauve	35	45
109		1r. brown and violet	45	65

1963. Tropical Fish. Multicoloured.

110	2l. Type **34**	10	75
111	3l. Type **34**	10	75
112	5l. Type **34**	15	35
113	10l. Moorish idol (fish)	25	35
114	25l. As 10l.	65	35
115	50l. Diadem soldierfish	90	55
116	1r. Powder-blue surgeonfish	1·25	60
117	5r. Racoon butterflyfish	6·25	10·00

1963. Freedom from Hunger.

118	**39**	2l. brown and green	30	1·25
119	–	5l. brown and red	50	90
120	**39**	7l. brown and turquoise	70	90
121	–	10l. brown and blue	85	90
122	**39**	25l. brown and red	2·50	3·50
123	–	50l. brown and violet	3·75	8·00
124	**39**	1r. brown and mauve	6·00	12·00

DESIGN—VERT: 5l., 10l., 50l. Handful of grain.

41 Centenary Emblem

42 Maldivian Scout Badge

1963. Centenary of Red Cross.

125	**41**	2l. red and purple	30	1·50
126		15l. red and green	65	80
127		50l. red and brown	1·25	1·75
128		1r. red and blue	1·75	2·00
129		4r. red and olive	4·00	21·00

1964. World Scout Jamboree, Marathon (1963).

130	**42**	2l. green and violet	10	65
131		3l. green and brown	10	65
132		25l. green and blue	15	15
133		1r. green and red	55	1·50

43 Mosque, Male

1964. "Maldives Embrace Islam".

134	**43**	2l. purple	10	60
135		3l. green	10	60
136		10l. red	10	10
137		40l. purple	30	25
138		60l. blue	50	40
139		85l. brown	60	60

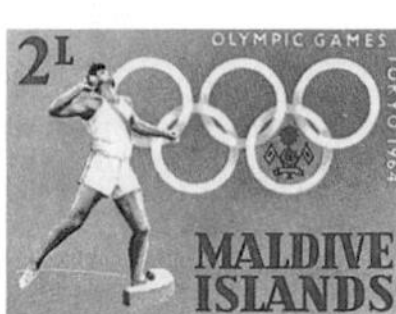

44 Putting the Shot

1964. Olympic Games, Tokyo.

140	**44**	2l. purple and blue	10	70
141		3l. red and brown	10	70
142		5l. bronze and green	15	20
143		10l. violet and purple	20	20
144	–	15l. sepia and brown	30	20
145	–	25l. indigo and blue	50	20
146	–	50l. bronze and olive	75	35
147	–	1r. purple and grey	1·25	75
MS147a		126 × 140 mm. Nos. 145/7. Imperf	2·25	3·75

DESIGN: 15l. to 1r. Running.

46 Telecommunications Satellite

1965. International Quiet Sun Years.

148	**46**	5l. blue	15	55
149		10l. brown	20	55
150		25l. green	40	55
151		1r. mauve	90	90

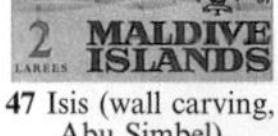

47 Isis (wall carving, Abu Simbel)

49 "XX" and U.N. Flag

48 Pres. Kennedy and Doves

1965. Nubian Monuments Preservation.

152	**47**	2l. green and purple	10	30
153	–	3l. lake and green	10	30
154	**47**	5l. green and purple	15	10
155	–	10l. blue and orange	20	10

No.	Type	Description	Unused	Used
156	**47**	15l. brown and violet	35	15
157	–	25l. purple and blue	60	15
158	**47**	50l. green and sepia	75	35
159	–	1r. ochre and green	1·10	55

DESIGN: 3, 10, 25l., 1r. Rameses II on throne (wall carving, Abu Simbel).

1965. 2nd Death Anniv of Pres. Kennedy.

No.	Type	Description	Unused	Used
160	**48**	2l. black and mauve	10	50
161		5l. brown and mauve	10	10
162		25l. blue and mauve	10	10
163	–	1r. purple, yellow and green	25	25
164	–	2r. bronze, yellow and green	40	70
MS164a		150 × 130 mm. No. 164 in block of four. Imperf	2·75	3·25

DESIGN: 1r., 2r. Pres. Kennedy and hands holding olive-branch.

1965. 20th Anniv of U.N.

No.	Type	Description	Unused	Used
165	**49**	3l. blue and brown	10	30
166		10l. blue and violet	20	10
167		1r. blue and green	1·10	35

50 I.C.Y. Emblem

1965. International Co-operation Year.

No.	Type	Description	Unused	Used
168	**50**	5l. brown and bistre	15	20
169		15l. brown and lilac	20	20
170		50l. brown and olive	45	30
171		1r. brown and red	1·25	1·50
172		2r. brown and blue	1·75	3·50
MS173		101 × 126 mm. Nos. 170/2. Imperf	6·50	6·50

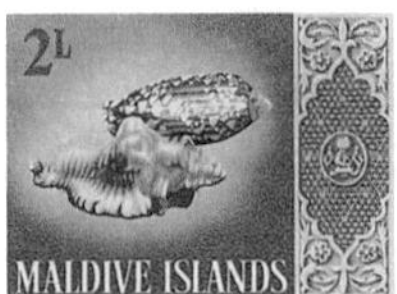

51 Princely Cone Shells

1966. Multicoloured.

No.	Type	Description	Unused	Used
174		2l. Type **51**	20	1·25
175		3l. Yellow flowers	20	1·25
176		5l. Reticulate distorsio and leopard shells	30	15
177		7l. Camellias	30	15
178		10l. Type **51**	1·00	15
179		15l. Crab plover and seagull	3·75	30
180		20l. As 3l.	80	30
181		30l. Type **51**	2·75	35
182		50l. As 15l.	6·00	55
183		1r. Type **51**	4·00	55
184		1r. As 7l.	3·50	55
185		1r.50 As 3l.	3·75	3·50
186		2r. As 7l.	5·00	4·00
187		5r. As 15l.	23·00	14·00
188		10r. As 5l.	23·00	20·00

The 3l., 7l., 20l., 1r. (No. 184), 1r.50 and 2r. are DIAMOND (43½ × 43½ mm).

52 Maldivian Flag

1966. 1st Anniv of Independence.

No.	Type	Description	Unused	Used
189	**52**	10l. green, red and turquoise	1·00	30
190		1r. multicoloured	3·25	70

53 "Luna 9" on Moon

1966. Space Rendezvous and Moon Landing.

No.	Type	Description	Unused	Used
191	**53**	10l. brown, indigo and blue	20	10
192	–	25l. green and red	30	10
193	**53**	50l. brown and green	40	15
194	–	1r. turquoise and brown	70	35
195	–	2r. green and violet	1·50	65
196	–	5r. pink and turquoise	2·25	1·60
MS197		108 × 126 mm. Nos. 194/6. Imperf	3·50	4·50

DESIGNS: 25l., 1r., 5r. "Gemini 6" and "7" rendezvous in space; 2r. "Gemini" spaceship as seen from the other spaceship.

54 U.N.E.S.C.O. Emblem and Owl on Book

1966. 20th Anniv of U.N.E.S.C.O. Multicoloured.

No.	Type	Description	Unused	Used
198		2l. Type **54**	20	1·00
199		3l. U.N.E.S.C.O. emblem and globe and microscope	20	1·00
200		5l. U.N.E.S.C.O. emblem and mask, violin and palette	50	20
201		50l. Type **54**	2·75	55
202		1r. Design as 3l.	3·75	90
203		5r. Design as 5l.	12·00	16·00

55 Sir Winston Churchill and Cortege

1966. Churchill Commem. Flag in red and blue.

No.	Type	Description	Unused	Used
204	**55**	2l. brown	15	1·10
205	–	10l. turquoise	85	10
206	**55**	15l. green	1·60	10
207	–	25l. violet	2·25	15
208	–	1r. brown	6·50	75
209	**55**	2r.50 red	13·00	11·00

DESIGN: 10l., 25l., 1r. Churchill and catafalque.

56 Footballers and Jules Rimet Cup

1967. England's Victory in World Cup Football Championship. Multicoloured.

No.	Type	Description	Unused	Used
210		2l. Type **56**	10	65
211		3l. Player in red shirt kicking ball	10	65
212		5l. Scoring goal	10	10
213		25l. As 3l.	60	10
214		50l. Making a tackle	1·00	20
215		1r. Type **56**	2·00	55
216		2r. Emblem on Union Jack	3·25	3·00
MS217		100 × 121 mm. Nos. 214/16. Imperf	9·50	6·50

57 Ornate Butterflyfish

1967. Tropical Fishes. Multicoloured.

No.	Type	Description	Unused	Used
218		2l. Type **57**	10	60
219		3l. Black-saddled pufferfish	15	60
220		5l. Blue boxfish	20	10
221		6l. Picasso triggerfish	20	20
222		50l. Semicircle angelfish	3·25	30
223		1r. As 3l.	4·50	75
224		2r. As 50l.	8·50	8·00

58 Hawker Siddeley H.S.748 over Hulule Airport Building

1967. Inauguration of Hulule Airport.

No.	Type	Description	Unused	Used
225	**58**	2l. violet and olive	20	50
226	–	5l. green and lavender	25	10
227	**58**	10l. violet and green	30	10
228	–	15l. green and ochre	50	10
229	**58**	30l. ultramarine and blue	1·00	10
230	–	50l. brown and mauve	1·75	20
231	**58**	5r. blue and orange	5·50	5·50
232	–	10r. brown and blue	7·50	9·00

DESIGN: 5, 15, 50l., 10r. Airport building and Hawker Siddeley H.S.748.

59 "Man and Music" Pavilion

1967. World Fair, Montreal. Multicoloured.

No.	Type	Description	Unused	Used
233		2l. Type **59**	10	60
234		5l. "Man and His Community" Pavilion	10	10
235		10l. Type **59**	10	10
236		50l. As 5l.	40	30
237		1r. Type **59**	75	50
238		2r. As 5l.	1·75	1·75
MS239		102 × 137 mm. Nos. 237/8. Imperf	2·25	3·00

1968. International Tourist Year (1967). Nos. 225/32 optd **International Tourist Year 1967**.

No.	Type	Description	Unused	Used
240	**58**	2l. violet and olive	10	60
241	–	5l. green and lavender	15	15
242	**58**	10l. violet and green	20	15
243	–	15l. green and ochre	20	15
244	**58**	30l. ultramarine and blue	30	20
245	–	50l. brown and mauve	45	30
246	**58**	5r. blue and orange	3·50	4·00
247	–	10r. brown and blue	5·00	6·50

61 Cub signalling and Lord Baden-Powell

63 Putting the Shot

62 French Satellite "A 1"

1968. Maldivian Scouts and Cubs.

No.	Type	Description	Unused	Used
248	**61**	2l. brown, green and yellow	10	65
249	–	3l. red, blue and light blue	10	65
250	**61**	25l. violet, lake and red	1·50	40
251	–	1r. green, brown and light green	3·50	1·60

DESIGN: 3l. and 1r. Scouts and Lord Baden-Powell.

1968. Space Martyrs.

No.	Type	Description	Unused	Used
252	**62**	2l. mauve and blue	10	40
253	–	3l. violet and brown	10	40
254	–	7l. brown and lake	15	40
255	–	10l. blue, drab and black	15	15
256	–	25l. green and violet	40	15
257	**62**	50l. blue and brown	75	30
258	–	1r. purple and green	1·10	50
259	–	2r. brown, blue and black	1·75	2·00
260	–	5r. mauve, drab and black	2·75	3·00
MS261		110 × 155 mm. Nos. 258/9. Imperf	3·75	4·00

DESIGNS: 3l., 25l. "Luna 10"; 7l., 1r. "Orbiter" and "Mariner"; 10l., 2r. Astronauts White, Grissom and Chaffee; 5r. Cosmonaut V. M. Komarov.

1968. Olympic Games, Mexico (1st Issue). Multicoloured.

No.	Type	Description	Unused	Used
262		2l. Type **63**	10	40
263		6l. Throwing the discus	10	40
264		10l. Type **63**	15	10
265		25l. As 6l.	20	10
266		1r. Type **63**	60	35
267		2r.50 As 6l.	1·50	2·00

See also Nos. 294/7.

64 "Adriatic Seascape" (Bonington)

1968. Paintings. Multicoloured.

No.	Type	Description	Unused	Used
268		50l. Type **64**	1·50	30
269		1r. "Ulysses deriding Polyphemus" (Turner)	2·00	45
270		2r. "Sailing Boat at Argenteuil" (Monet)	2·75	2·25
271		5r. "Fishing Boat at Les Saintes-Maries" (Van Gogh)	4·75	5·00

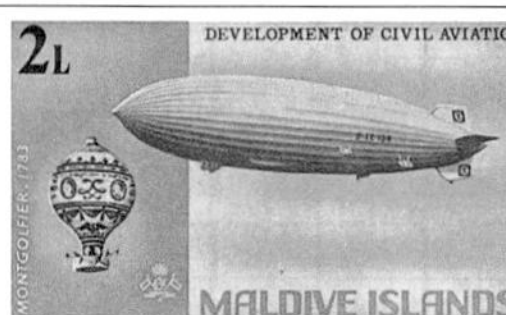

65 LZ-130 "Graf Zeppelin II" and Montgolfier's Balloon

1968. Development of Civil Aviation.

No.	Type	Description	Unused	Used
272	**65**	2l. brown, green and blue	15	50
273	–	3l. blue, violet and brown	15	50
274	–	5l. green, red and blue	15	15
275	–	7l. blue, purple and orange	90	60
276	**65**	10l. brown, blue and purple	35	15
277	–	50l. red, green and olive	1·50	20
278	–	1r. green, blue and red	2·25	50
279	–	2r. purple, bistre and blue	14·00	10·00

DESIGNS: 3l., 1r. Boeing 707-420 and Douglas DC-3; 5l., 50l. Wright Type A and Lilienthal's glider; 7l., 2r. Projected Boeing 733 and Concorde.

66 W.H.O. Building, Geneva

1968. 20th Anniv of World Health Organization.

No.	Type	Description	Unused	Used
280	**66**	10l. violet, turquoise & blue	60	10
281		25l. green, brown & yellow	1·00	15
282		1r. brown, emerald & green	3·25	90
283		2r. violet, purple and mauve	5·25	5·50

1968. 1st Anniv of Scout Jamboree, Idaho. Nos. 248/51 optd **International Boy Scout Jamboree, Farragut Park, Idaho, U.S.A. August 1–9, 1967**.

No.	Type	Description	Unused	Used
284	**61**	2l. brown, green and yellow	10	50
285	–	3l. red, blue and light blue	10	50
286	**61**	25l. violet, lake and red	1·50	40
287		1r. green, brown and light green	4·50	2·10

68 Curlew and Common Redshank

1968. Multicoloured.

No.	Type	Description	Unused	Used
288		2l. Type **68**	50	75
289		10l. Pacific grinning tun and Papal mitre shells	1·25	20
290		25l. Oriental angel wing and tapestry turban shells	1·75	25
291		50l. Type **68**	7·00	1·10
292		1r. As 10l.	4·50	1·10
293		2r. As 25l.	5·00	4·75

69 Throwing the Discus

1968. Olympic Games, Mexico (2nd issue). Mult.

No.	Type	Description	Unused	Used
294		10l. Type **69**	10	10
295		50l. Running	20	10
296		1r. Cycling	3·50	60
297		2r. Basketball	4·50	2·00

70 Fishing Dhow

1968. Republic Day.

No.	Type	Description	Unused	Used
298	**70**	10l. brown, blue and green	75	30
299	–	1r. green, red and blue	5·25	1·00

DESIGN: 1r. National flag, crest and map.

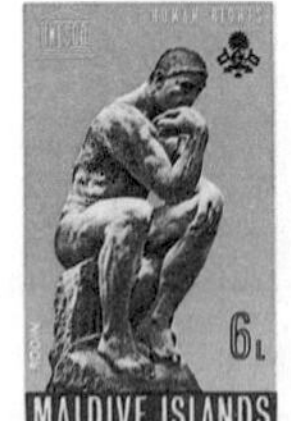

71 "The Thinker" (Rodin)

1969. U.N.E.S.C.O. "Human Rights". Designs showing sculptures by Rodin. Multicoloured.

300 6l. Type **71** 30 15
301 10l. "Hands" 30 15
302 1r.50 "Eve" . . . . 2·00 2·25
303 2r.50 "Adam" . . . . 2·50 3·00
MS304 112 × 130 mm. Nos. 302/3. Imperf . . . . 8·00 8·00

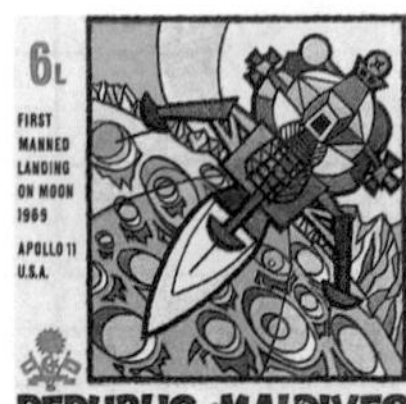

72 Module nearing Moon's Surface

1969. 1st Man on the Moon. Multicoloured.

305 6l. Type **72** 15 15
306 10l. Astronaut with hatchet . . 15 15
307 1r.50 Astronaut and module . . 2·25 1·40
308 2r.50 Astronaut using camera . . 2·50 2·00
MS309 101 × 130 mm. Nos. 305/8. Imperf . . . . 3·00 4·00

1969. Gold Medal Winner, Olympic Games, Mexico (1968). Nos. 295/6 optd **Gold Medal Winner Mohamed Gammoudi 5000m. run Tunisia REPUBLIC OF MALDIVES** or similar opt.

310 50l. multicoloured 60 60
311 1r. multicoloured . . . . . . 1·40 90

The overprint on No. 310 honours P. Trentin (cycling, France).

74 Racoon Butterflyfish

1970. Tropical Fishes. Mult.

312 2l. Type **74** 40 70
313 5l. Clown triggerfish 65 40
314 25l. Broad-barred lionfish . . 2·25 40
315 50l. Long-nosed butterflyfish . 3·00 1·00
316 1r. Emperor angelfish . . . . 4·00 1·00
317 2r. Royal angelfish . . . . . 5·50 6·50

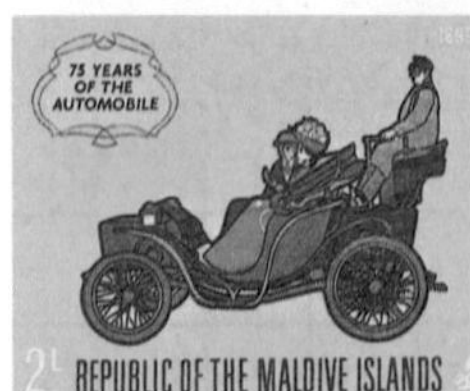

75 Columbia Dauman Victoria, 1899

1970. "75 Years of the Automobile". Mult.

318 2l. Type **75** 20 50
319 5l. Duryea phaeton, 1902 . . 25 30
320 7l. Packard S-24, 1906 . . . 30 30
321 10l. Autocar Runabout, 1907 35 30
322 25l. Type **75** . . . . 1·50 30
323 50l. As 5l. . . . . 2·75 55
324 1r. As 7l. . . . . 3·50 90
325 2r. As 10l. . . . . 4·50 5·50
MS326 95 × 143 mm. Nos. 324/5 5·00 7·50

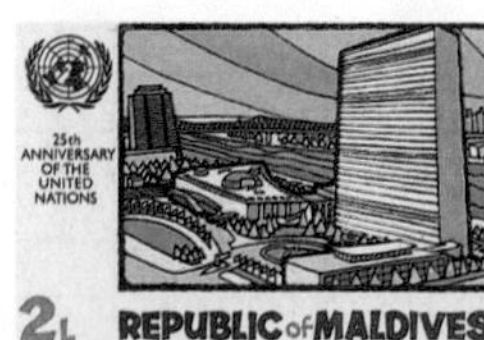

76 U.N. Headquarters, New York

1970. 25th Anniv of United Nations. Mult.

327 2l. Type **76** 10 75
328 10l. Surgical operation (W.H.O.) . . . . 1·50 25
329 25l. Student, actress and musician (U.N.E.S.C.O.) 2·50 40
330 50l. Children at work and play (U.N.I.C.E.F.) . . . . 2·00 70
331 1r. Fish, corn and farm animals (F.A.O.) . . . . . 2·00 1·00
332 2r. Miner hewing coal (I.L.O.) . . . . 6·00 6·50

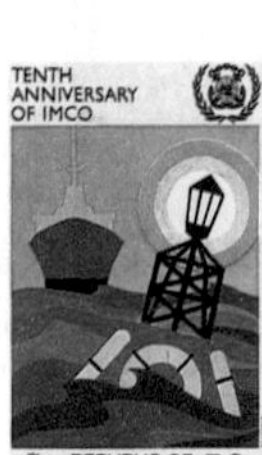

77 Ship and Light Buoy

78 "Guitar-player and Masqueraders" (A. Watteau)

1970. 10th Anniv of I.M.C.O. Multicoloured.

333 50l. Type **77** 50 40
334 1r. Ship and lighthouse . . . 4·25 85

1970. Famous Paintings showing the Guitar. Multicoloured.

335 3l. Type **78** 10 65
336 7l. "Spanish Guitarist" (Manet) 20 65
337 50l. "Costumed Player" (Watteau) 75 40
338 1r. "Mandolin-player" (Roberti) . . . . 1·25 55
339 2r.50 "Guitar-player and Lady" (Watteau) . . . . . 2·75 3·25
340 5r. "Mandolin-player" (Frans Hals) . . . . 4·75 5·50
MS341 132 × 80 mm. Nos. 339/40 7·50 8·00

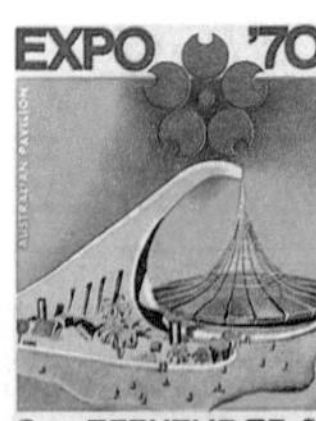

79 Australian Pavilion

82 Footballers

80 Learning the Alphabet

1970. "EXPO 70" World Fair, Osaka, Japan. Multicoloured.

342 2l. Type **79** 10 65
343 3l. West German Pavilion . . 10 65
344 10l. U.S. Pavilion 45 10
345 25l. British Pavilion . . . . 1·25 15
346 50l. Soviet Pavilion . . . . . 1·75 45
347 1r. Japanese Pavilion . . . . 2·25 65

1970. Int Education Year. Multicoloured.

348 5l. Type **80** 25 30
349 10l. Training teachers 30 15
350 25l. Geography lesson . . . 1·25 20
351 50l. School inspector . . . . 1·50 45
352 1r. Education by television 1·75 75

1970. "Philympia 1970" Stamp Exn, London. Nos. 306/8 optd **Philympia London 1970.**

353 10l. multicoloured 10 10
354 1r.50 multicoloured 65 75
355 2r.50 multicoloured . . . . . 1·00 1·50
MS356 101 × 130 mm. Nos. 305/8 optd. Imperf . . . . 6·00 7·00

1970. World Cup Football Championship, Mexico.

357 **82** 3l. multicoloured 15 40
358 – 6l. multicoloured 20 40
359 – 7l. multicoloured 20 30
360 – 25l. multicoloured 90 20
361 – 1r. multicoloured . . . . . 2·50 90

DESIGNS: 6l. to 1r. Different designs showing footballers in action.

83 Little Boy and U.N.I.C.E.F. Flag

84 Astronauts Lovell, Haise and Swigert

1970. 25th Anniv of U.N.I.C.E.F. Multicoloured.

362 5l. Type **83** 10 15
363 10l. Little girl with U.N.I.C.E.F. "balloon" . . 10 15
364 1r. Type **83** . . . . 1·75 85
365 2r. As 10l. . . . . 2·75 3·00

1971. Safe Return of "Apollo 13". Multicoloured.

366 5l. Type **84** 25 25
367 20l. Explosion in Space . . . 55 15
368 1r. Splashdown . . . . . . 1·25 50

85 "Multiracial Flower"

86 "Mme. Charpentier and her Children" (Renoir)

1971. Racial Equality Year.

369 **85** 10l. multicoloured 10 15
370 25l. multicoloured 20 15

1971. Famous Paintings showing "Mother and Child". Multicoloured.

371 5l. Type **86** 25 20
372 7l. "Susanna van Collen and her Daughter" (Rembrandt) 30 20
373 10l. "Madonna nursing the Child" (Titian) 40 20
374 20l. "Baroness Belleli and her Children" (Degas) . . . . 1·00 20
375 25l. "The Cradle" (Morisot) 1·00 20
376 1r. "Helena Fourment and her Children" (Reubens) 3·00 85
377 3r. "On the Terrace" (Renoir) . . . . 5·50 6·50

87 Alan Shepard

1971. Moon Flight of "Apollo 14". Multicoloured.

378 6l. Type **87** 40 40
379 10l. Stuart Roosa 45 30
380 1r.50 Edgar Mitchell . . . . 5·50 3·50
381 5r. Mission insignia . . . . 11·00 11·00

88 "Ballerina" (Degas)

1971. Famous Paintings showing "Dancers". Mult.

382 5l. Type **88** 20 20
383 10l. "Dancing Couple" (Renoir) 25 20
384 2r. "Spanish Dancer" (Manet) . . . . 2·75 2·50
385 5r. "Ballerinas" (Degas) . . . 5·00 5·00
386 10r. "La Goulue at the Moulin Rouge" (Toulouse-Lautrec) . . . . 7·50 8·00

1972. Visit of Queen Elizabeth II and Prince Philip. Nos. 382/6 optd **ROYAL VISIT 1972.**

387 **88** 5l. multicoloured 15 10
388 – 10l. multicoloured 20 10
389 – 2r. multicoloured . . . . . 4·50 4·00
390 – 5r. multicoloured . . . . . 8·00 8·00
391 – 10r. multicoloured . . . . 9·50 10·00

90 Book Year Emblem

1972. International Book Year.

392 **90** 25l. multicoloured 15 10
393 5r. multicoloured . . . . . 1·60 2·00

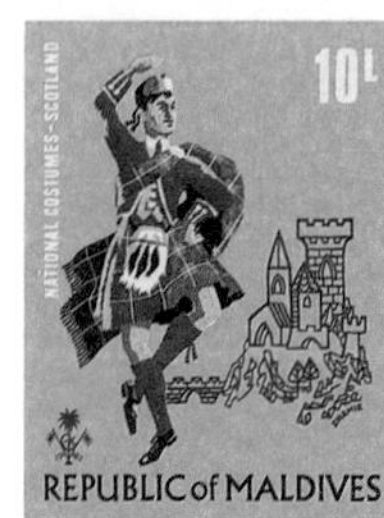

91 Scottish Costume

1972. National Costumes of the World. Mult.

394 10l. Type **91** 80 10
395 15l. Netherlands 90 15
396 25l. Norway . . . . 1·75 15
397 50l. Hungary . . . . 2·50 55
398 1r. Austria . . . . 3·00 80
399 2r. Spain . . . . 4·25 3·25

92 Stegosaurus

1972. Prehistoric Animals. Multicoloured.

400 2l. Type **92** 75 75
401 7l. Dimetrodon (inscr "Edaphosaurus") . . . . . 1·50 60
402 25l. Diplodocus . . . . . . 2·25 50
403 50l. Triceratops . . . . . . 2·50 75
404 2r. Pteranodon . . . . 5·50 5·00
405 5r. Tyrannosaurus . . . . . 9·50 9·50

93 Cross-country Skiing

1972. Winter Olympic Games, Sapporo, Japan. Multicoloured.

406 3l. Type **93** 10 50
407 6l. Bobsleighing 10 50
408 15l. Speed skating 20 20
409 50l. Ski jumping . . . . . . 1·00 45
410 1r. Figure skating (pair) . . . 1·75 70
411 2r.50 Ice hockey . . . . . . 5·50 3·25

94 Scout Saluting

95 Cycling

1972. 13th Boy Scout Jamboree, Asagiri, Japan (1971). Multicoloured.

412 10l. Type **94** 75 20
413 15l. Scout signalling 95 20
414 50l. Scout blowing bugle . . 3·25 1·25
415 1r. Scout playing drum . . . 4·50 2·25

1972. Olympic Games, Munich. Multicoloured.

416 5l. Type **95** 75 30
417 10l. Running 20 20
418 25l. Wrestling 30 20
419 50l. Hurdling 50 35
420 2r. Boxing . . . . 1·50 2·00
421 5r. Volleyball . . . . 3·00 3·75
MS422 92 × 120 mm. 3r. As 50l.; 4r. As 10l. . . . . 5·75 8·00

96 Globe and Conference Emblem

97 "Flowers" (Van Gogh)

1972. U.N. Environmental Conservation Conference, Stockholm.

423 **96** 2l. multicoloured 10 40
424 3l. multicoloured 10 40
425 15l. multicoloured 30 15
426 50l. multicoloured 75 45
427 2r.50 multicoloured . . . . 3·25 4·25

1973. Floral Paintings. Multicoloured.

428 1l. Type **97** 10 60
429 2l. "Flowers in Jug" (Renoir) 10 60
430 3l. "Chrysanthemums" (Renoir) 10 60
431 50l. "Mixed Bouquet" (Bosschaert) . . . . 1·50 30
432 1r. As 3l. . . . . 2·00 40
433 5r. As 2l. . . . . 4·25 5·50
MS434 120 × 94 mm. 2r. As 50l.; 3r. Type **97** . . . . 7·00 8·50

1973. Gold-medal Winners, Munich Olympic Games. Nos. 420/1 optd as listed below.

435 2r. multicoloured . . . . . . 3·25 2·50
436 5r multicoloured . . . . . . 4·25 2·75
MS437 92 × 120 mm. 3r. multicoloured; 4r. multicoloured 7·50 8·50

OVERPRINTS: 2r. **LEMECHEV MIDDLE-WEIGHT GOLD MEDALLIST**; 5r. **JAPAN GOLD MEDAL WINNERS**. Miniature sheet: 3r. **EHRHARDT 100 METER HURDLES GOLD MEDALLIST**; 4r. **SHORTER MARATHON GOLD MEDALLIST**.

99 Animal Care

1973. International Scouting Congress, Nairobi and Addis Ababa. Multicoloured.

438 1l. Type **99** 10 30
439 2l. Lifesaving 10 30
440 3l. Agricultural training . . . 10 30
441 4l. Carpentry 10 30
442 5l. Playing leapfrog 10 30
443 1r. As 2l. . . . . 2·75 75
444 2r. As 4l. . . . . 4·00 4·75
445 3r. Type **99** . . . . 4·50 7·00
MS446 101 × 79 mm. 5r. As 3l. 7·50 14·00

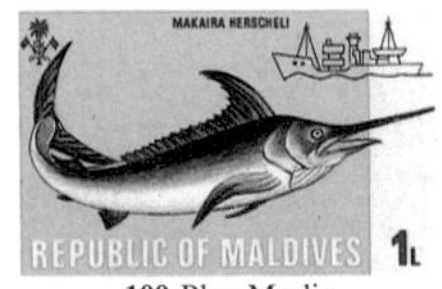

100 Blue Marlin

1973. Fishes. Multicoloured.

447 1l. Type **100** 10 40
448 2l. Skipjack tuna 10 40
449 3l. Blue-finned tuna 10 40
450 5l. Dolphin (fish) 10 40
451 60l. Humpbacked snapper . . 80 40
452 75l. As 60l. . . . . 1·00 40
453 1r.50 Yellow-edged lyretail 1·75 2·00
454 2r.50 As 5l. . . . . 2·25 3·00
455 3r. Spotted coral grouper . . 2·25 3·25
456 10r. Spanish mackerel . . . 4·75 8·00
MS457 119 × 123 mm. 4r. As 2l. 5r. Type **100** . . . . 17·00 20·00

Nos. 451/2 are smaller, size 29 × 22 mm.

101 Golden-fronted Leafbird

1973. Fauna. Multicoloured.

458 1l. Type **101** 10 50
459 2l. Indian flying fox 10 50
460 3l. Land tortoise 10 50
461 4l. Butterfly ("Kallima inachus") 30 50
462 50l. As 3l. 60 40
463 2r. Type **101** . . . . 5·00 4·50
464 3r. As 2l. . . . . 3·50 4·50
MS465 66 × 74 mm. 5r. As 4l. . . 18·00 20·00

102 "Lantana camara"

1973. Flowers of the Maldive Islands. Mult.

466 1l. Type **102** 10 30
467 2l. "Nerium oleander" . . . 10 30
468 3l. "Rosa polyantha" 10 30
469 4l. "Hibiscus manihot" . . . 10 30
470 5l. "Bougainvillea glabra" . . 10 20
471 10l. "Plumera alba" 10 20
472 50l. "Poinsettia pulcherrima" 55 30
473 5r. "Ononis natrix" . . . . 3·25 5·00
MS474 110 × 100 mm. 2r. As 3l.; 3r. As 10l. . . . . 3·25 5·25

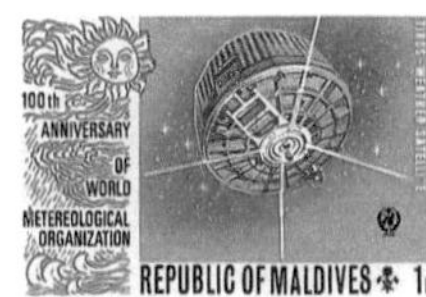

103 "Tiros" Weather Satellite

1974. Centenary of World Meteorological Organization. Multicoloured.

475 1l. Type **103** 10 20
476 2l. "Nimbus" satellite 10 20
477 3l. "Nomad" (weather ship) 10 20
478 4l. Scanner, A.P.T. Instant Weather Picture equipment 10 20
479 5l. Richard's wind-speed recorder 10 10
480 2r. Type **103** . . . . 3·25 3·50
481 3r. As 3l. . . . . 3·50 3·75
MS482 110 × 79 mm. 10r. As 2l. 8·50 14·00

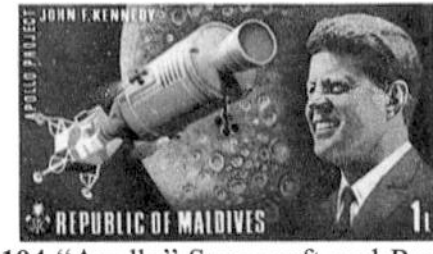

104 "Apollo" Spacecraft and Pres. Kennedy

1974. American and Russian Space Exploration Projects. Multicoloured.

483 1l. Type **104** 10 25
484 2l. "Mercury" capsule and John Glenn 10 25
485 3l. "Vostok 1" and Yuri Gagarin 10 25
486 4l. "Vostok 6" and Valentina Tereshkova 10 25
487 5l. "Soyuz 11" and "Salyut" space-station 10 20
488 2r. "Skylab" space laboratory 3·50 3·50
489 3r. As 2l. . . . . 4·00 4·00
MS490 103 × 80 mm. 10r. Type **104** 11·00 13·00

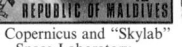

105 Copernicus and "Skylab" Space Laboratory

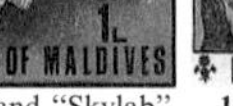

106 "Maternity" (Picasso)

1974. 500th Birth Anniv of Nicholas Copernicus (astronomer). Multicoloured.

491 1l. Type **105** 10 25
492 2l. Orbital space-station of the future 10 25
493 3l. Proposed "Space-shuttle" craft 10 25
494 4l. "Mariner 2" Venus probe 10 25
495 5l. "Mariner 4" Mars probe 10 20
496 25l. Type **105** 90 20
497 1r.50 As 2l. . . . . 2·50 3·25
498 5r. As 3l. . . . . 4·00 10·00
MS499 106 × 80 mm. 10r. "Copernicus" orbital observatory 15·00 18·00

1974. Paintings by Picasso. Multicoloured.

500 1l. Type **106** 10 30
501 2l. "Harlequin and Friend" 10 30
502 3l. "Pierrot Sitting" 10 30
503 20l. "Three Musicians" . . . 35 20
504 75l. "L'Aficionado" 80 70
505 5r. "Still Life" . . . . . . 4·50 6·00
MS506 100 × 101 mm. 2r. As 20l.; 3r. As 5r. . . . . 7·50 9·00

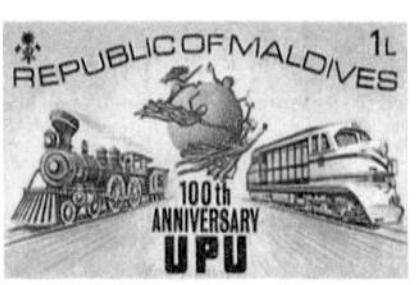

107 U.P.U. Emblem, Steam and Diesel Locomotives

1974. Cent of Universal Postal Union. Mult.

507 1l. Type **107** 10 30
508 2l. Paddle-steamer and modern mailboat 10 30
509 3l. Airship "Graf Zeppelin" and Boeing 747 airliner . . 10 30
510 1r.50 Mailcoach and motor van . . . . 1·10 1·10
511 2r.50 As 2l. . . . . 1·40 1·75
512 5r. Type **107** . . . . 2·00 3·25
MS513 126 × 105 mm. 4r. Type **107** 5·50 7·00

108 Footballers

109 "Capricorn"

1974. World Cup Football Championship, West Germany.

514 **108** 1l. multicoloured 15 20
515 – 2l. multicoloured 15 20
516 – 3l. multicoloured 15 20
517 – 4l. multicoloured 15 20
518 – 75l. multicoloured . . . . 1·25 75
519 – 4r. multicoloured . . . . 2·50 4·00
520 – 5r. multicoloured . . . . 2·50 4·00
MS521 88 × 95 mm. 10r. multicoloured . . . . 10·00 12·00

DESIGNS: Nos. 515/**MS**521 show football scenes similar to Type **108**.

1974. Signs of the Zodiac. Multicoloured.

522 1l. Type **109** 25 50
523 2l. "Aquarius" 25 50
524 3l. "Pisces" 25 50
525 4l. "Aries" 25 50
526 5l. "Taurus" 25 50
527 6l. "Gemini" 25 50
528 7l. "Cancer" 25 50
529 10l. "Leo" 40 50
530 15l. "Virgo" 40 50
531 20l. "Libra" 40 50
532 25l. "Scorpio" 40 50
533 5r. "Sagittarius" . . . . . . 6·50 12·00
MS534 119 × 99 mm. 10r. "The Sun" (49 × 37 mm) . . . . 18·00 20·00

110 Churchill and Avro Type 683 Lancaster

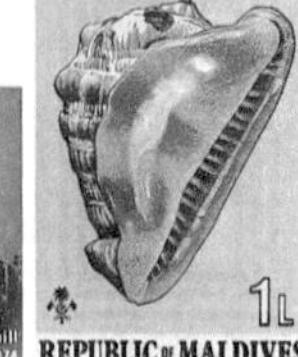

111 Bullmouth Helmet

1974. Birth Cent of Sir Winston Churchill. Mult.

535 1l. Type **110** 20 50
536 2l. Churchill as pilot 20 50
537 3l. Churchill as First Lord of the Admiralty 25 50
538 4l. Churchill and H.M.S. "Eagle" (aircraft carrier) 25 50
539 5l. Churchill and De Havilland Mosquito bombers 25 30
540 60l. Churchill and anti-aircraft battery . . . . . . 3·00 1·75
541 75l. Churchill and tank in desert . . . . 3·25 1·75
542 5r. Churchill and Short S.25 Sunderland flying boat . . 12·00 13·00
MS543 113 × 83 mm. 10r. As 4l. 17·00 20·00

1975. Sea Shells and Cowries. Multicoloured.

544 1l. Type **111** 10 30
545 2l. Venus comb murex . . . 10 30
546 3l. Common or major harp 10 30
547 4l. Chiragra spider conch . . 10 30
548 5l. Geography cone 10 30
549 60l. Dawn cowrie (22 × 30 mm) . . . . . . 3·00 2·00
550 75l. Purplish clanculus (22 × 30 mm) . . . . . . 3·50 2·00
551 5r. Ramose murex . . . . . 8·50 11·00
MS552 152 × 126 mm. 2r. As 3l.; 3r. As 2l. . . . . 12·00 15·00

112 Royal Throne

113 Guavas

1975. Historical Relics and Monuments. Mult.

553 1l. Type **112** 10 40
554 10l. Candlesticks 10 10
555 25l. Lamp-tree 15 10
556 60l. Royal umbrellas 30 30
557 75l. Eid-Miskith Mosque (horiz) 35 35
558 3r. Tomb of Al-Hafiz Abu-al Barakath-al Barubari (horiz) . . . . 1·60 2·75

1975. Exotic Fruits. Multicoloured.

559 2l. Type **113** 10 40
560 4l. Maldive mulberry 15 40
561 5l. Mountain apples 15 40
562 10l. Bananas 20 15
563 20l. Mangoes 40 25
564 50l. Papaya . . . . 1·00 60
565 1r. Pomegranates . . . . . . 1·75 70
566 5r. Coconut . . . . 5·50 11·00
MS567 136 × 102 mm. 2r. As 10l.; 3r. As 2l. . . . . 9·00 13·00

114 "Phyllangia"

1975. Marine Life. Corals, Urchins and Sea Stars. Multicoloured.

568 1l. Type **114** 10 40
569 2l. "Madrepora oculata" . . 10 40
570 3l. "Acropora gravida" . . . 10 40
571 4l. "Stylotella" 10 40
572 5l. "Acrophora cervicornis" 10 40
573 60l. "Strongylocentrotus purpuratus" 75 65
574 75l. "Pisaster ochraceus" . . 85 75
575 5r. "Marthasterias glacialis" 5·00 6·50
MS576 155 × 98 mm. 4r. As 1l. Imperf . . . . 11·00 14·00

115 Clock Tower and Customs Building within "10"

1975. 10th Anniv of Independence. Multicoloured.

577 4l. Type **115** 10 30
578 5l. Government offices . . . 10 15
579 7l. Waterfront 10 20
580 15l. Mosque and minaret . . 10 15
581 10r. Sultan Park and museum 2·25 6·00

1975. "Nordjamb 75" World Scout Jamboree, Norway. Nos. 443/5 and **MS**446 optd **14th Boy Scout Jamboree July 29–August 7, 1975**.

582 – 1r. multicoloured 85 60
583 – 2r. multicoloured . . . . . 1·25 80
584 **99** 3r. multicoloured . . . . . 1·75 1·60
MS585 101 × 79 mm. 5r. multicoloured . . . . 7·00 8·00

117 Madura Prau

1975. Ships. Multicoloured.

586 1l. Type **117** 10 20
587 2l. Ganges patela 10 20
588 3l. Indian palla (vert) 10 20
589 4l. Odhi (dhow) (vert) . . . 10 20
590 5l. Maldivian schooner . . . 10 20
591 25l. "Cutty Sark" (British tea clipper) 90 40
592 1r. Maldivian baggala (vert) 1·50 70
593 5r. "Maldive Courage" (freighter) . . . . 3·00 6·00
MS594 99 × 85 mm. 10r. As 1r. 10·00 14·00

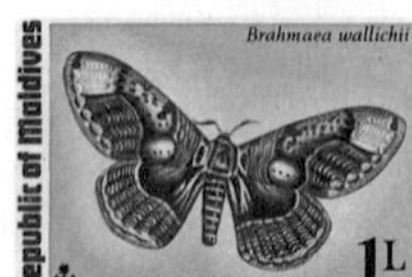

118 "Brahmophthalma wallichi" (moth)

1975. Butterflies and Moth. Multicoloured.

595 1l. Type **118** 15 30
596 2l. "Teinopalpus imperialis" 15 30
597 3l. "Cethosia biblis" 15 30
598 4l. "Idea jasonia" 15 30
599 5l. "Apatura ilia" 15 30
600 25l. "Kallima horsfieldi" . . 1·25 35
601 1r.50 "Hebomoia leucippe" 3·50 3·75
602 5r. "Papilio memnon" . . . 8·00 10·00
MS603 134 × 97 mm. 10r. As 25l. 20·00 20·00

119 "The Dying Captive"

120 Beaker and Vase

1975. 500th Birth Anniv of Michelangelo. Mult.

604 1l. Type **119** 10 20
605 2l. Detail of "The Last Judgement" 10 20
606 3l. "Apollo" 10 20
607 4l. Detail of Sistine Chapel ceiling 10 20
608 5l. "Bacchus" 10 20
609 1r. Detail of "The Last Judgement" (different) . . 1·25 30
610 2r. "David" . . . . 1·50 2·00
611 5r. "Cumaean Sibyl" . . . . 2·25 5·00
MS612 123 × 113 mm. 10r. As 2r. 5·00 11·00

1975. Maldivian Lacquerware. Multicoloured.

613 2l. Type **120** 10 50
614 4l. Boxes 10 50
615 50l. Jar with lid 30 20
616 75l. Bowls with covers . . . 40 30
617 1r. Craftsman at work . . . 50 40

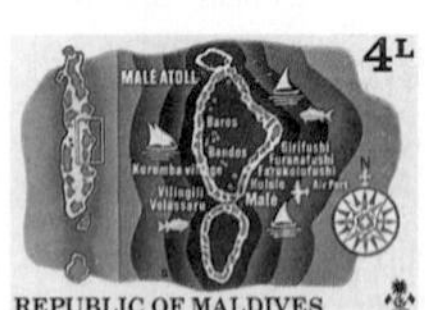

121 Map of Maldives

1975. Tourism. Multicoloured.

618 4l. Type **121** 30 40
619 5l. Motor launch and small craft 30 40
620 7l. Sailing-boats 30 40
621 15l. Underwater fishing . . . 30 30
622 3r. Hulule Airport . . . . . 4·50 3·00
623 10r. Motor cruisers . . . . . 6·50 7·50

122 Cross-country Skiing

123 "General Burgoyne" (Reynolds)

1976. Winter Olympic Games, Innsbruck. Mult.

624 1l. Type **122** 10 20
625 2l. Speed-skating (pairs) . . . 10 20
626 3l. Figure-skating (pairs) . . 10 20
627 4l. Four-man bobsleighing . . 10 20
628 5l. Ski-jumping 10 20
629 25l. Figure-skating (women's) 35 20
630 1r.15 Skiing (slalom) . . . . 90 1·25
631 4r. Ice-hockey . . . . 1·50 4·00
MS632 93 × 117 mm. 10r. Downhill Skiing . . . . 6·00 12·00

1976. Bicent of American Revolution. Mult.

633 1l. Type **123** 10 10
634 2l. "John Hancock" (Copley) 10 10
635 3l. "Death of Gen. Montgomery" (Trumbull) (horiz) 10 10
636 4l. "Paul Revere" (Copley) 10 10
637 5l. "Battle of Bunker Hill" (Trumbull) (horiz) 10 10
638 2r. "The Crossing of the Delaware" (Sully) (horiz) 2·00 2·50
639 3r. "Samuel Adams" (Copley) 2·50 3·00
640 5r. "Surrender of Cornwallis" (Trumbull) (horiz) . . . . 3·00 3·25
MS641 147 × 95 mm. 10r. "Washington at Dorchester Heights" (Stuart) . . . . . . 15·00 18·00

124 Thomas Edison

1976. Centenary of Telephone. Multicoloured.

642 1l. Type **124** 10 30
643 2l. Alexander Graham Bell 10 30
644 3l. Telephone of 1919, 1937 and 1972 . . . . 10 30
645 10l. Cable entrance into station 20 20
646 20l. Equalizer circuit assembly 30 20
647 1r. "Salernum" (cable ship) 1·75 55
648 10r. "Intelsat IV-A" and Earth Station . . . . . . 4·75 7·50
MS649 156 × 105 mm. 4r. Early telephones . . . . 7·50 9·00

1976. "Interphil 76" International Stamp Exhibition, Philadelphia. Nos. 638/**MS**641 optd **MAY 29TH–JUNE 6TH "INTERPHIL" 1976.**

650 2r. multicoloured . . . . . . 1·50 1·75
651 3r. multicoloured . . . . . . 2·00 2·25
652 5r. multicoloured . . . . . . 2·50 2·75
MS653 147 × 95 mm. 10r. multicoloured . . . . 10·00 12·00

126 Wrestling

127 "Dolichos lablab"

1976. Olympic Games, Montreal. Multicoloured.

654 1l. Type **126** 10 20
655 2l. Putting the shot 10 20
656 3l. Hurdling 10 20
657 4l. Hockey 10 20
658 5l. Running 10 20
659 6l. Javelin-throwing 10 20
660 1r.50 Discus-throwing . . . . 1·25 1·75
661 5r. Volleyball . . . . 2·75 5·25
MS662 135 × 106 mm. 10r. Throwing the hammer . . . . 8·50 12·00

1976. Vegetables. Multicoloured.

663 2l. Type **127** 10 40
664 4l. "Moringa pterygosperma" 10 40
665 10l. "Solanum melongena" 15 15
666 20l. "Moringa pterygosperma" . . . . . 2·25 2·25
667 50l. "Cucumis sativus" . . . 50 65
668 75l. "Trichosanthes anguina" 55 75
669 1r. "Momordica charantia" 65 85
670 2r. "Trichosanthes anguina" 4·00 7·50

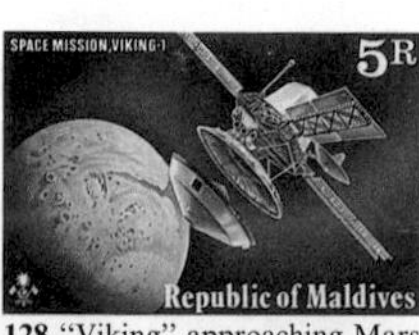

128 "Viking" approaching Mars

1977. "Viking" Space Mission. Multicoloured.

671 5r. Type **128** . . . . 2·25 2·75
MS672 121 × 89 mm. 20r. Landing module on Mars . . . . 10·00 14·00

129 Coronation Ceremony

1977. Silver Jubilee of Queen Elizabeth II. Mult.

673 1l. Type **129** 10 30
674 2l. Queen and Prince Philip 10 30
675 3l. Royal couple with Princes Andrew and Edward . . . 10 30
676 1r.15 Queen with Archbishops 55 35
677 3r. State coach in procession 90 70
678 4r. Royal couple with Prince Charles and Princess Anne 90 1·00
MS679 120 × 77 mm. 10r. Queen and Prince Charles . . . . 4·75 3·25

130 Beethoven and Organ

1977. 150th Death Anniv of Ludwig van Beethoven. Multicoloured.

680 1l. Type **130** 20 30
681 2l. Portrait and manuscript of "Moonlight Sonata" . . . 20 30
682 3l. With Goethe at Teplitz . . 20 30
683 4l. Beethoven and string instruments 20 30
684 5l. Beethoven's home, Heiligenstadt 20 20
685 25l. Hands and gold medals 1·00 20
686 2r. Portrait and "Missa solemnis" . . . . 3·50 3·50
687 5r. Composer's hearing-aids 5·50 6·50
MS688 121 × 92 mm. 4r. Death mask and room where composer died 7·00 9·00

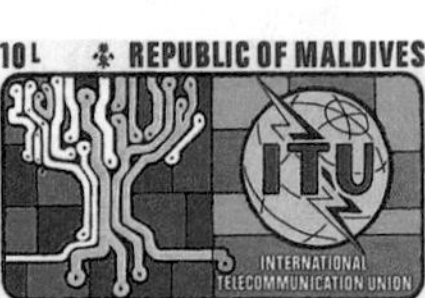

131 Printed Circuit and I.T.U. Emblem

1977. Inauguration of Satellite Earth Station. Mult.

689 10l. Type **131** 10 10
690 90l. Central Telegraph Office 45 45
691 10r. Satellite Earth Station 3·00 6·00
MS692 100 × 85 mm. 5r. "Intelsat IV-A" satellite over Maldives 4·50 5·50

132 "Miss Anne Ford" (Gainsborough)

133 Lesser Frigate Birds

1977. Artists' Birth Anniversaries. Multicoloured.

693 1l. Type **132** (250th anniv) . . 10 20
694 2l. Group painting by Rubens (400th anniv) . . . 10 20
695 3l. "Girl with Dog" (Titian) (500th Anniv) 10 20
696 4l. "Mrs. Thomas Graham" (Gainsborough) 10 20
697 5l. "Artist with Isabella Brant" (Rubens) 10 20
698 95l. Portrait by Titian . . . 1·00 30
699 1r. Portrait by Gainsborough 1·00 30
700 10r. "Isabella Brant" (Rubens) . . . . 3·75 7·00
MS701 152 × 116 mm. 5r. "Self-portrait" (Titian) . . . . . . 3·75 5·50

1977. Birds. Multicoloured.

702 1l. Type **133** 20 40
703 2l. Crab plover 20 40
704 3l. White-tailed tropic bird 20 40
705 4l. Wedge-tailed shearwater 20 40
706 5l. Grey heron 20 40
707 20l. White tern 90 30
708 95l. Cattle egret . . . . . . 2·25 1·60
709 1r.25 Black-naped tern . . . 2·50 2·50
710 5r. Pheasant coucal . . . . . 6·50 8·00
MS711 124 × 117 mm. 10r. Green-backed heron . . . . 25·00 25·00

134 Charles Lindbergh

136 Rheumatic Heart

135 Boat Building

1977. 50th Anniv of Lindbergh's Transatlantic Flight and 75th Anniv of First Navigable Airships. Multicoloured.

712 1l. Type **134** 20 30
713 2l. Lindbergh and "Spirit of St. Louis" 20 30
714 3l. Lindbergh's Miles Mohawk aircraft (horiz) . . 20 30
715 4l. Lebaudy-Juillot airship "Morning Post" (horiz) . . 20 30
716 5l. Airship "Graf Zeppelin" and portrait of Zeppelin 20 30
717 1r. Airship "Los Angeles" (horiz) . . . . 1·00 30
718 3r. Lindbergh and Henry Ford . . . . 1·75 2·00
719 10r. Vickers airship R-23 rigid airship . . . . 2·50 6·00
MS720 148 × 114 mm. 5r. Ryan NYP Special "Spirit of St. Louis", Statue of Liberty and Eiffel Tower; 7r.50, Airship L-31 over "Ostfriesland" (German battleship) . . . . 13·00 18·00

No. 715 is inscr "Lebaudy I built by H. Juillot 1902".

1977. Occupations. Multicoloured.

721 6l. Type **135** 45 30
722 15l. Fishing 75 20
723 20l. Cadjan weaving 80 20
724 90l. Mat-weaving . . . . . . 2·50 1·60
725 2r. Lace-making (vert) . . . 4·00 4·25

1977. World Rheumatism Year. Multicoloured.

726 1l. Type **136** 10 30
727 50l. Rheumatic shoulder . . 40 20
728 2r. Rheumatic hands . . . . 75 1·25
729 3r. Rheumatic knees . . . . 85 1·40

137 Lilienthal's Biplane Glider

1978. 75th Anniv of First Powered Aircraft. Multicoloured.

730 1l. Type **137** 20 40
731 2l. Chanute's glider 20 40
732 3l. Wright glider No. II, 1901 20 40
733 4l. A. V. Roe's Triplane I . . 20 40
734 5l. Wilbur Wright demonstrating Wright Type A for King Alfonso of Spain 30 40
735 10l. A. V. Roe's Avro Type D biplane 70 40
736 20l. Wright Brothers and A. G. Bell at Washington 2·00 40
737 95l. Hadley's triplane . . . . 5·00 2·25
738 5r. Royal Aircraft Factory B.E.2A biplanes at Upavon, 1914 . . . . . . 11·00 11·00
MS739 98 × 82 mm. 10r. Wright Brothers' Wright Type A . . . 14·00 16·00

No. 732 is wrongly dated "1900".

138 Newgate Prison

139 Television Set

1978. World Eradication of Smallpox. Mult.
740 15l. Foundling Hospital, London (horiz) 50 30
741 50l. Type **138** 1·25 60
742 2r. Edward Jenner (discoverer of smallpox vaccine) 2·25 4·00

1978. Inaug of Television in Maldive Islands. Mult.
743 15l. Type **139** 40 30
744 25l. Television aerials 55 30
745 1r.50 Control desk (horiz) 2·25 2·75

140 Mas Odi

1978. Ships. Multicoloured.
746 1l. Type **140** 10 25
747 2l. Battela 10 25
748 3l. Bandu odi (vert) 10 25
749 5l. "Maldive Trader" (freighter) 20 25
750 1r. "Fath-hul Baaree" (brigantine) 65 30
751 1r.25 Mas dhoni 85 1·00
752 3r. Baggala (vert) 1·10 1·75
753 4r. As 1r.25 1·10 1·75
MS754 152 × 138 mm. 1r. As No. 747; 4r. As No. 751 2·50 3·75

141 Ampulla
142 Capt. Cook

1978. 25th Anniv of Coronation. Multicoloured.
755 1l. Type **141** 10 20
756 2l. Sceptre with Dove 10 20
757 3l. Golden Orb 10 20
758 1r.15 St. Edward's Crown 25 20
759 2r. Sceptre with Cross 35 35
760 5r. Queen Elizabeth II 65 80
MS761 108 × 106 mm. 10r. Annointing spoon 1·50 2·00

1978. 250th Birth Anniv of Capt. James Cook and Bicent of Discovery of Hawaiian Islands. Mult.
762 1l. Type **142** 10 25
763 2l. Statue of Kamehameha I of Hawaii 10 25
764 3l. H.M.S. "Endeavour" 10 25
765 25l. Route of third voyage 45 45
766 75l. H.M.S. "Discovery", H.M.S. "Resolution" and map of Hawaiian Islands (horiz) 1·25 1·25
767 1r.50 Cook meeting Hawaiian islanders (horiz) 2·00 2·25
768 10r. Death of Capt. Cook (horiz) 4·00 10·00
MS769 100 × 92 mm. 5r. H.M.S. "Endeavour" (different) 15·00 20·00

143 "Schizophrys aspera"

1978. Crustaceans. Multicoloured.
770 1l. Type **143** 10 25
771 2l. "Atergatis floridus" 10 25
772 3l. "Perenon planissimum" 10 25
773 90l. "Portunus granulatus" 50 40
774 1r. "Carpilius maculatus" 50 40
775 2r. "Huenia proteus" 1·00 1·40
776 25r. "Etisus laevimanus" 5·50 13·00
MS777 147 × 146 mm. 2r. "Panulirus longipes" (vert) 2·00 2·50

144 "Four Apostles"
145 T.V. Tower and Building

1978. 450th Death Anniv of Albrecht Durer (artist).
778 **144** 10l. multicoloured 10 10
779 – 20l. multicoloured 15 10
780 – 55l. multicoloured 20 20
781 – 1r. black, brown and buff 30 30
782 – 1r.80 multicoloured 45 60
783 – 3r. multicoloured 70 1·25
MS784 141 × 122 mm. 10r. multicoloured 4·00 6·00
DESIGNS—VERT: 20l. "Self-portrait at 27"; 55l. "Madonna and Child with a Pear"; 1r.80, "Hare"; 3r. "Great Piece of Turf"; 10r. "Columbine". HORIZ: 1r. "Rhinoceros".

1978. 10th Anniv of Republic. Multicoloured.
785 1l. Fishing boat (horiz) 10 40
786 5l. Montessori School (horiz) 10 20
787 10l. Type **145** 10 10
788 25l. Islet (horiz) 20 15
789 50l. Boeing 737 aircraft (horiz) 60 25
790 95l. Beach scene (horiz) 60 30
791 1r.25 Dhow at night (horiz) 75 55
792 3r. President's residence (horiz) 80 1·25
793 5r. Masjidh Afeefuddin Mosque (horiz) 1·00 2·75
MS794 119 × 88 mm. 3r. Fisherman casting net 2·25 4·00

146 Human Rights Emblem

1978. 30th Anniv of Declaration of Human Rights.
795 **146** 30l. pink, lilac and green 15 15
796 90l. yellow, brown and green 40 60
797 1r.80 blue, deep blue and green 70 1·00

147 Great Spotted or Rare Spotted Cowrie
148 Delivery by Bellman

1979. Shells. Multicoloured.
798 1l. Type **147** 10 20
799 2l. Imperial cone 10 20
800 3l. Great green turban 10 20
801 10l. Giant spider conch 45 10
802 1r. White-toothed cowrie 2·00 40
803 1r.80 Fig cone 3·00 2·50
804 3r. Glory of the sea cone 4·50 3·75
MS805 141 × 110 mm. 5r. Common Pacific vase 11·00 10·50

1979. Death Cent of Sir Rowland Hill. Mult.
806 1l. Type **148** 10 20
807 2l. Mail coach, 1840 (horiz) 10 20
808 3l. First London letter box, 1855 10 20
809 1r.55 Penny Black 40 50
810 5r. First Maldive Islands stamp 70 1·25
MS811 132 × 107 mm. 10r. Sir Rowland Hill 1·25 3·00

149 Girl with Teddy Bear
151 Sari with Overdress

150 "White Feathers"

1979. Int Year of the Child (1st issue). Mult.
812 5l. Type **149** 10 10
813 1r.25 Boy with sailing boat 40 50
814 2r. Boy with toy rocket 45 55
815 3r. Boy with toy airship 60 75
MS816 108 × 109 mm. 5r. Boy with toy train 1·25 2·00
See also Nos. 838/**MS**847.

1979. 25th Death Anniv of Henri Matisse (artist). Multicoloured.
817 20l. Type **150** 15 15
818 25l. "Joy of Life" 15 15
819 30l. "Eggplants" 15 15
820 1r.50 "Harmony in Red" 45 65
821 5r. "Still-life" 70 2·25
MS822 135 × 95 mm. 4r. "Water Pitcher" 3·75 4·25

1979. National Costumes. Multicoloured.
823 50l. Type **151** 20 15
824 75l. Sashed apron dress 25 20
825 90l. Serape 30 25
826 95l. Ankle-length printed dress 35 30

152 "Gloriosa superba"

1979. Flowers. Multicoloured.
827 1l. Type **152** 10 10
828 3l. "Hibiscus tiliaceus" 10 10
829 50l. "Barringtonia asiatica" 20 15
830 1r. "Abutilon indicum" 40 25
831 5r. "Guettarda speciosa" 1·00 2·00
MS832 94 × 85 mm. 4r. "Pandanus odoratissimus" 1·75 2·75

153 Weaving

1979. Handicraft Exhibition. Multicoloured.
833 5l. Type **153** 10 10
834 10l. Lacquerwork 10 10
835 1r.30 Tortoiseshell jewellery 50 55
836 2r. Carved woodwork 70 90
MS837 125 × 85 mm. 5r. Gold and silver jewellery 1·25 2·25

154 Mickey Mouse attacked by Bird

1979. International Year of the Child (2nd issue). Disney Characters. Multicoloured.
838 1l. Goofy delivering parcel on motor-scooter (vert) 10 10
839 2l. Type **154** 10 10
840 3l. Goofy half-covered with letters 10 10
841 4l. Pluto licking Minnie Mouse's envelopes 10 10
842 5l. Mickey Mouse delivering letters on roller skates (vert) 10 10
843 10l. Donald Duck placing letter in mail-box 10 10
844 15l. Chip and Dale carrying letter 10 10
845 1r.50 Donald Duck on monocycle (vert) 75 95
846 5r. Donald Duck with ostrich in crate (vert) 2·25 3·25
MS847 127 × 102 mm. 4r. Pluto putting parcel in mail-box 5·50 7·00

155 Post-Ramadan Dancing

1980. National Day. Multicoloured.
848 5l. Type **155** 10 10
849 15l. Musicians and dancer, Eeduu Festival 10 10
850 95l. Sultan's ceremonial band 35 30
851 2r. Dancer and drummers Circumcision Festival 60 85
MS852 131 × 99 mm. 5r. Swordsmen 1·60 2·50

156 Leatherback Turtle

1980. Turtle Conservation Campaign. Mult.
853 1l. Type **156** 10 30
854 2l. Flatback turtle 10 30
855 5l. Hawksbill turtle 15 30
856 10l. Loggerhead turtle 20 20
857 75l. Olive Ridley turtle 80 45
858 10r. Atlantic Ridley turtle 3·00 4·25
MS859 85 × 107 mm. 4r. Green turtle 2·00 2·75

157 Paul Harris (founder)

1980. 75th Anniv of Rotary Int. Mult.
860 75l. Type **157** 35 10
861 90l. Humanity 40 20
862 1r. Hunger 40 25
863 10r. Health 2·75 4·50
MS864 109 × 85 mm. 5r. Globe 1·50 2·50

1980. "London 1980" International Stamp Exhibition. Nos. 809/**MS**811 optd **LONDON 1980**.
865 1r.55 Penny Black 2·25 1·00
866 5r. First Maldives stamp 3·75 2·75
MS867 132 × 107 mm. 10r. Sir Rowland Hill 7·00 8·00

159 Swimming

1980. Olympic Games, Moscow. Multicoloured.
868 10l. Type **159** 10 10
869 50l. Running 20 20
870 3r. Putting the shot 70 1·10
871 4r. High jumping 80 1·40
MS872 105 × 85 mm. 5r. Weightlifting 1·25 2·25

160 White-tailed Tropic Bird

1980. Birds. Multicoloured.
873 75l. Type **160** 25 15
874 95l. Sooty tern 35 30
875 1r. Common noddy 35 30
876 1r.55 Curlew 50 70
877 2r. Wilson's storm petrel ("Wilson's Petrel") 60 85
878 4r. Caspian tern 1·10 1·60
MS879 124 × 85 mm. 5r. Red-footed booby and brown booby 7·50 8·50

161 Seal of Ibrahim II

1980. Seals of the Sultans.
880 **161** 1l. brown and black 10 10
881 – 2l. brown and black 10 10
882 – 5l. brown and black 10 10
883 – 1r. brown and black 30 30
884 – 2r. brown and black 50 70
MS885 131 × 95 mm. 3r. brown and black 85 1·60
DESIGNS: 2l. Mohammed Imadudeen II; 5l. Bin Haji Ali; 1r. Kuda Mohammed Rasgefaanu; 2r. Ibrahim Iskander I; 3r. Ibrahim Iskander I (different).

162 Queen Elizabeth the Queen Mother

1980. 80th Birthday of the Queen Mother.
886 **162** 4r. multicoloured 1·00 1·25
MS887 85 × 110 mm. **162** 5r. multicoloured 1·90 2·25

163 Munnaru

1980. 1400th Anniv of Hegira. Multicoloured.
888 5l. Type **163** 15 10
889 10l. Hukuru Miskiiy mosque 20 10
890 30l. Medhuziyaaraiy (shrine of saint) 25 30
891 55l. Writing tablets with verses of Koran 35 35
892 90l. Mother teaching child Koran 55 70
MS893 124 × 101 mm. 2r. Map of Maldives and coat of arms . . 80 1·60

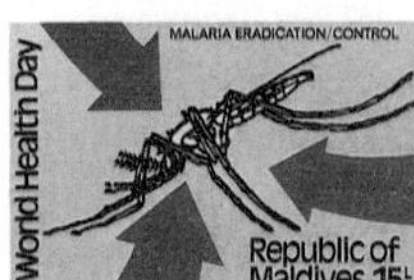

164 Malaria Eradication

1980. World Health Day.
894 **164** 15l. black, brown and red 10 10
895 – 25l. multicoloured 10 10
896 – 1r.50 brown, light brown and black . . . . . . 1·50 1·00
897 – 5r. multicoloured . . . . 2·75 2·75
MS898 68 × 85 mm. 4r. black, blue and light blue . . . . 1·25 2·50
DESIGNS: 25l. Nutrition; 1r.50, Dental health; 4, 5r. Clinics.

165 White Rabbit

1980. Walt Disney's "Alice in Wonderland". Multicoloured.
899 1l. Type **165** 10 10
900 2l. Alice falling into Wonderland 10 10
901 3l. Alice too big to go through door 10 10
902 4l. Alice with Tweedledum and Tweedledee 10 10
903 5l. Alice and caterpillar . . . 10 10
904 10l. The Cheshire cat 10 10
905 15l. Alice painting the roses 10 10
906 2r.50 Alice and the Queen of Hearts . . . . 2·00 2·25
907 4r. Alice on trial . . . . 2·25 2·50
MS908 126 × 101 mm. 5r. Alice at the Mad Hatter's tea-party . . 4·50 6·50

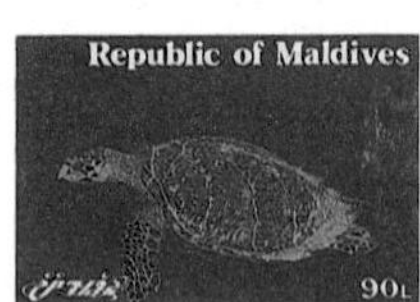

166 Indian Ocean Ridley Turtle

1980. Marine Animals. Multicoloured.
909 90l. Type **166** . . . . 2·25 60
910 1r.25 Pennant coralfish . . . 2·75 1·25
911 2r. Spiny lobster . . . . . . 3·25 1·75
MS912 140 × 94 mm. 4r. Oriental sweetlips and scarlet-finned squirrelfish . . . . 3·00 3·25

167 Pendant Lamp

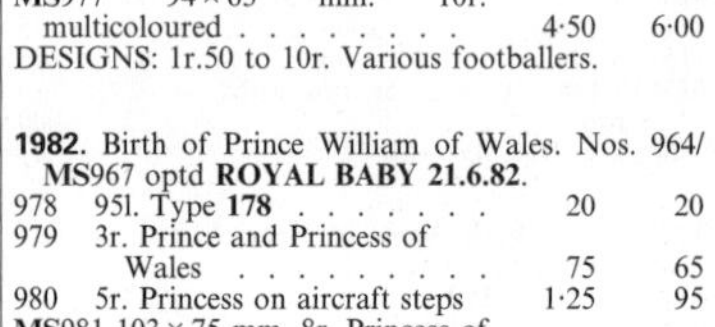

168 Prince Charles and Lady Diana Spencer

1981. National Day. Multicoloured.
913 10l. Tomb of Ghaazee Muhammad Thakurufaan (horiz) 15 10
914 20l. Type **167** 20 10
915 30l. Chair used by Muhammad Thakurufaan 25 10
916 95l. Muhammad Thakurufaan's palace (horiz) 60 30
917 10r. Cushioned divan . . . . 2·50 4·25

1981. British Royal Wedding. Multicoloured.
918 1r. Type **168** 15 15
919 2r. Buckingham Palace . . . 25 25
920 5r. Prince Charles, polo player 40 50
MS921 95 × 83 mm. 10r. State coach 75 1·10

169 First Majlis Chamber

1981. 50th Anniv of Citizens' Majlis (grievance rights). Multicoloured.
922 95l. Type **169** 30 30
923 1r. Sultan Muhammed Shamsuddin III 35 35
MS924 137 × 94 mm. 4r. First written constitution (horiz) . . 1·75 3·75

170 "Self-portrait with a Palette"

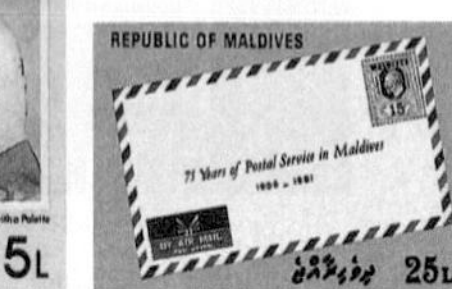

171 Airmail Envelope

1981. Birth Centenary of Pablo Picasso. Mult.
925 5l. Type **170** 15 10
926 10l. "Woman in Blue" . . . 20 10
927 25l. "Boy with Pipe" 30 10
928 30l. "Card Player" 30 10
929 90l. "Sailor" 50 40
930 3r. "Self-portrait" . . . . . 80 1·00
931 5r. "Harlequin" . . . . . . 1·00 1·25
MS932 106 × 130 mm. 10r. "Child holding a Dove". Imperf . . . 2·50 3·50

1981. 75th Anniv of Postal Service.
933 **171** 25l. multicoloured 15 10
934 75l. multicoloured 25 25
935 5r. multicoloured . . . . 70 1·25

172 Boeing 737 taking off

1981. Male International Airport. Multicoloured.
936 5l. Type **172** 20 20
937 20l. Passengers leaving Boeing 737 . . . . 40 20
938 1r.80 Refuelling . . . . . . 75 1·00
939 4r. Plan of airport . . . . . 1·00 2·00
MS940 106 × 79 mm. 5r. Aerial view of airport . . . . 2·00 2·75

173 Homer

174 Preparation of Maldive Fish

1981. International Year of Disabled People. Multicoloured.
941 2l. Type **173** 10 10
942 5l. Miguel Cervantes 10 10
943 1r. Beethoven . . . . 2·00 85
944 5r. Van Gogh . . . . 3·00 5·00
MS945 116 × 91 mm. 4r. Helen Keller and Anne Sullivan . . . 3·25 5·50

1981. Decade for Women. Multicoloured.
946 20l. Type **174** 10 10
947 90l. 16th-century Maldive women 25 25
948 1r. Farming 30 30
949 2r. Coir rope-making . . . . 55 1·10

175 Collecting Bait

1981. Fishermen's Day. Multicoloured.
950 5l. Type **175** 45 15
951 15l. Fishing boats 85 25
952 90l. Fisherman with catch . . 1·40 60
953 1r.30 Sorting fish . . . . . . 1·90 1·10
MS954 147 × 101 mm. 3r. Loading fish for export . . . . 1·50 2·50

176 Bread Fruit

1981. World Food Day. Multicoloured.
955 10l. Type **176** 40 10
956 25l. Hen with chicks 80 15
957 30l. Maize 80 20
958 75l. Skipjack tuna . . . . . 2·50 65
959 1r. Pumpkin . . . . 3·00 70
960 2r. Coconuts . . . . 3·25 3·25
MS961 110 × 85 mm. 5r. Eggplant 2·50 3·50

177 Pluto and Cat

1982. 50th Anniv of Pluto (Walt Disney Cartoon Character). Multicoloured.
962 4r. Type **177** . . . . . . 2·50 2·75
MS963 127 × 101 mm. 6r. Pluto (scene from "The Pointer") . . 3·25 4·00

178 Balmoral

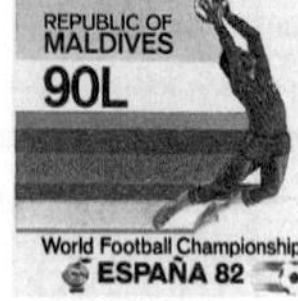

180 Footballer

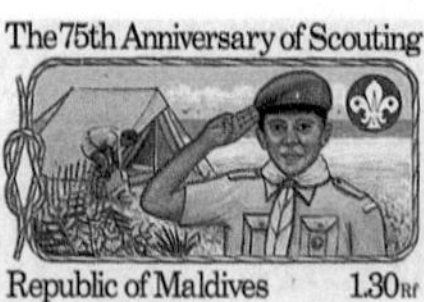

179 Scout saluting and Camp-site

1982. 21st Birthday of Princess of Wales. Mult.
964 95l. Type **178** 50 20
965 3r. Prince and Princess of Wales . . . . 1·00 65
966 5r. Princess on aircraft steps 1·75 95
MS967 103 × 75 mm. 8r. Princess of Wales . . . . 1·75 1·75

1983. 75th Anniv of Boy Scout Movement. Multicoloured.
968 1r.30 Type **179** 40 45
969 1r.80 Lighting a fire 50 60
970 4r. Life-saving . . . . 1·10 1·40
971 5r. Map-reading . . . . . . 1·40 1·75
MS972 128 × 66 mm. 10r. Scout emblem and flag of the Maldives 2·00 3·00

1982. World Cup Football Championship, Spain.
973 **180** 90l. multicoloured . . . . 1·50 60
974 – 1r.50 multicoloured . . . 2·00 1·10
975 – 3r. multicoloured . . . . 2·75 1·75
976 – 5r. multicoloured . . . . 3·25 2·50
MS977 94 × 63 mm. 10r. multicoloured . . . . 4·50 6·00
DESIGNS: 1r.50 to 10r. Various footballers.

1982. Birth of Prince William of Wales. Nos. 964/MS967 optd **ROYAL BABY 21.6.82.**
978 95l. Type **178** 20 20
979 3r. Prince and Princess of Wales 75 65
980 5r. Princess on aircraft steps 1·25 95
MS981 103 × 75 mm. 8r. Princess of Wales . . . . 3·00 2·50

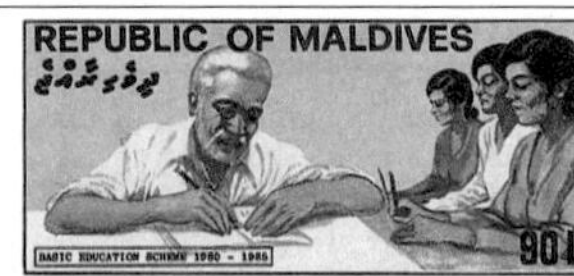

181 Basic Education Scheme

1983. National Education. Multicoloured.
982 90l. Type **181** 15 25
983 95l. Primary education . . . 15 25
984 1r.30 Teacher training . . . 20 30
985 2r.50 Printing educational material 40 60
MS986 100 × 70 mm. 6r. Thaana typewriter keyboard . . . . . 1·00 2·00

182 Koch isolates the Bacillus

183 Blohm and Voss Seaplane "Nordsee"

1983. Centenary of Robert Koch's Discovery of Tubercle Bacillus. Multicoloured.
987 5l. Type **182** 10 15
988 15l. Micro-organism and microscope 15 15
989 95l. Dr. Robert Koch in 1905 35 45
990 3r. Dr. Koch and plates from publication . . . . 85 1·50
MS991 77 × 61 mm. 5r. Koch in his laboratory (horiz) . . . . . . 1·00 2·00

1983. Bicentenary of Manned Flight. Mult.
992 90l. Type **183** . . . . 2·25 70
993 1r.45 Macchi Castoldi MC.72 seaplane . . . . 2·75 1·75
994 4r. Boeing F4B-3 biplane fighter . . . . 4·50 3·25
995 5r. Renard and Krebs airship "La France" . . . . . . 4·50 3·50
MS996 110 × 85 mm. 10r. Nadar's balloon "Le Geant" . . . . . 3·00 4·00

184 "Curved Dash" Oldsmobile, 1902

1983. Classic Motor Cars. Multicoloured.
997 5l. Type **184** 20 40
998 30l. Aston Martin "Tourer", 1932 . . . . 60 40
999 40l. Lamborghini "Muira", 1966 . . . . 60 45
1000 1r. Mercedes-Benz "300SL", 1945 . . . . 1·00 70
1001 1r.40 Stutz "Bearcat", 1913 1·25 2·00
1002 5r. Lotus "Elite", 1958 . . . 2·00 4·25
MS1003 132 × 103 mm. 10r. Grand Prix "Sunbeam", 1924 . . . . 6·00 10·00

185 Rough-toothed Dolphin

1983. Marine Mammals. Multicoloured.
1004 30l. Type **185** . . . . 1·60 60
1005 40l. Indo-Pacific hump-backed dolphin . . . . . 1·60 65
1006 4r. Finless porpoise . . . . 5·00 4·00
1007 6r. Pygmy sperm whale . . 10·00 7·00
MS1008 82 × 90 mm. 5r. Striped dolphin . . . . 6·00 5·50

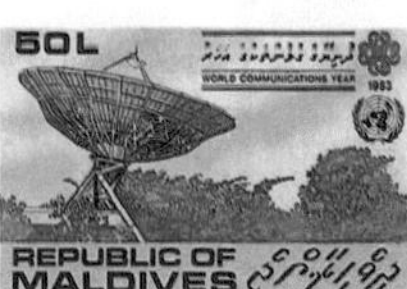

186 Dish Aerial

1983. World Communications Year. Multicoloured.
1009 50l. Type **186** 40 20
1010 1r. Land, sea and air communications . . . . . 1·25 60
1011 2r. Ship-to-shore communications . . . . . 1·75 1·50
1012 10r. Air traffic controller . . 4·00 7·00
MS1013 91 × 76 mm. 20r. Telecommunications . . . . . 3·75 4·75

187 "La Donna Gravida"

1983. 500th Birth Anniv of Raphael. Mult.
1014 90l. Type **187** 25 25
1015 3r. "Giovanna d'Aragona" (detail) . . . . 75 1·60
1016 4r. "Woman with Unicorn" 75 2·25
1017 6r. "La Muta" . . . . 1·00 2·75
MS1018 121 × 97 mm. 10r. "The Knight's Dream" (detail) . . . 3·00 5·50

188 Refugee Camp

1983. Solidarity with the Palestinian People. Multicoloured.
1019 4r. Type **188** . . . . 1·75 2·00
1020 5r. Refugee holding dead child . . . . 1·90 2·00
1021 6r. Child carrying food . . 2·00 2·50

189 Education Facilities

1983. National Development Programme. Mult.
1022 7l. Type **189** 20 10
1023 10l. Health service and education 50 10
1024 5r. Growing more food . . 1·50 1·25
1025 6r. Fisheries development 2·25 1·50
MS1026 134 × 93 mm. 10r. Air transport . . . . 2·25 2·75

190 Baseball

194 Island Resort and Common Terns

193 Hands breaking Manacles

1984. Olympic Games, Los Angeles. Multicoloured.
1027 50l. Type **190** 30 15
1028 1r.55 Backstroke swimming 65 40
1029 3r. Judo . . . . 1·40 90
1030 4r. Shot-putting . . . . . . 1·60 1·40
MS1031 85 × 105 mm. 10r. Team handball . . . . 2·40 2·75

1984. U.P.U. Congress, Hamburg. Nos. 994/**MS**996 optd **19th UPU CONGRESS HAMBURG**.
1032 4r. Boeing "F4B-3" . . . . 1·40 1·40
1033 5r. "La France" airship . . 1·60 1·60
MS1034 110 × 85 mm. 10r. Nadar's balloon "Le Geant" . . . . . . 2·75 4·50

1984. Surch **Rf.1.45**. (a) Nos. 964/**MS**967.
1035 1r.45 on 95l. Type **178** . . . 2·00 1·50
1036 1r.45 on 3r. Prince and Princess of Wales . . . . 2·00 1·50
1037 1r.45 on 5r. Princess on aircraft steps . . . . . . 2·00 1·50
MS1038 103 × 75 mm. 1r.45 on 8r. Princess of Wales . . . . . . 2·00 3·75

(b) Nos. 978/**MS**981.
1039 1r.45 on 95l. Type **178** . . . 2·00 1·50
1040 1r.45 on 3r. Prince and Princess of Wales . . . . 2·00 1·50
1041 1r.45 on 5r. Princess on aircraft steps . . . . . . 2·00 1·50
MS1042 103 × 75 mm. 1r.45 on 8r. Princess of Wales . . . . . . 2·00 3·75

1984. Namibia Day. Multicoloured.
1043 6r. Type **193** . . . . 1·00 1·25
1044 8r. Namibian family . . . . 1·00 1·75
MS1045 129 × 104 mm. 10r. Map of Namibia . . . . 1·75 2·50

1984. Tourism. Multicoloured.
1046 7l. Type **194** . . . . 1·25 60
1047 15l. Dhow 70 15
1048 20l. Snorkelling 50 15
1049 2r. Wind-surfing . . . . . 1·75 50
1050 4r. Aqualung diving . . . . 2·25 1·10
1051 6r. Night fishing . . . . . 3·00 1·75
1052 8r. Game fishing . . . . . 3·25 2·00
1053 10r. Turtle on beach . . . . 3·50 2·25

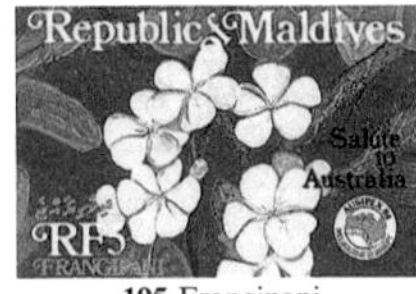

195 Frangipani

1984. "Ausipex" International Stamp Exhibition, Melbourne. Multicoloured.
1054 5r. Type **195** . . . . 2·25 1·75
1055 10r. Cooktown orchid . . . 4·75 3·75
MS1056 105 × 77 mm. 15r. Sun orchid . . . . 10·00 5·50

196 Facade of Male Mosque

1984. Opening of Islamic Centre. Multicoloured.
1057 2r. Type **196** 45 50
1058 5r. Male Mosque and minaret (vert) . . . . . . 1·10 1·25

197 Air Maldives Boeing 737

1984. 40th Anniv of I.C.A.O. Multicoloured.
1059 7l. Type **197** 60 25
1060 4r. Air Lanka Lockheed L-1011 TriStar . . . . . 2·75 1·50
1061 6r. Alitalia Douglas DC-10-30 . . . . 3·25 2·25
1062 8r. L.T.U. Lockheed L-1011 TriStar . . . . 3·50 3·00
MS1063 110 × 92 mm. 15r. Air Maldives Short S.7 Skyvan . . 3·75 4·00

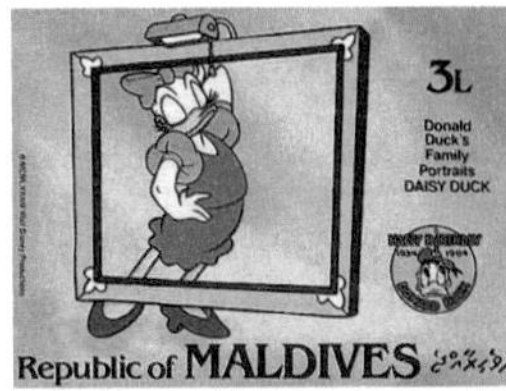

198 Daisy Duck

1984. 50th Birthday of Donald Duck. Walt Disney Cartoon Characters. Multicoloured.
1064 3l. Type **198** 10 10
1065 4l. Huey, Dewey and Louie 10 10
1066 5l. Ludwig von Drake . . . 10 10
1067 10l. Gyro Gearloose 10 10
1068 15l. Uncle Scrooge painting self-portrait 15 10
1069 25l. Donald Duck with camera 15 10
1070 5r. Donald Duck and Gus Goose . . . . 2·25 1·25
1071 8r. Gladstone Gander . . . 2·50 2·00
1072 10r. Grandma Duck . . . . 3·00 2·50
MS1073 102 × 126 mm. 15r. Uncle Scrooge and Donald Duck in front of camera . . . . 4·75 5·00
MS1074 126 × 102 mm. 15r. Uncle Scrooge . . . . 4·75 5·00

199 "The Day" (detail)

200 "Edmond Iduranty" (Degas)

1984. 450th Death Anniv of Correggio (artist). Multicoloured.
1075 5r. Type **199** . . . . 1·00 1·50
1076 10r. "The Night" (detail) . . 1·50 1·75
MS1077 60 × 80 mm. 15r. "Portrait of a Man" . . . . 3·50 3·25

1984. 150th Birth Anniv of Edgar Degas (artist). Multicoloured.
1078 75l. Type **200** 20 20
1079 2r. "James Tissot" 50 50
1080 5r. "Achille de Gas in Uniform" . . . . 1·00 1·00
1081 10r. "Lady with Chrysanthemums" . . . . 1·75 2·00
MS1082 100 × 70 mm. 15r. "Self-portrait" . . . . 3·25 3·75

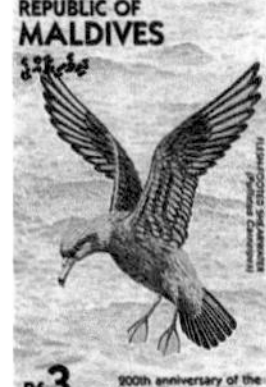

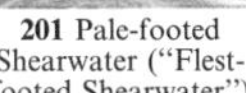
201 Pale-footed Shearwater ("Flest-footed Shearwater")

204 Queen Elizabeth the Queen Mother, 1981

202 Squad Drilling

1985. Birth Bicentenary of John J. Audubon (ornithologist) (1st issue). Designs showing original paintings. Multicoloured.
1083 3r. Type **201** . . . . . . 1·75 80
1084 3r.50 Little grebe (horiz) . . 2·00 90
1085 4r. Great cormorant . . . . 2·00 1·00
1086 4r.50 White-faced storm petrel (horiz) . . . . . . 2·00 1·10
MS1087 108 × 80 mm. 15r. Red-necked phalarope (horiz) . . . 4·25 4·25

See also Nos. 1192/200.

1985. National Security Service. Multicoloured.
1088 15l. Type **202** 50 10
1089 20l. Combat patrol 50 10
1090 1r. Fire fighting . . . . . . 2·00 40
1091 2r. Coastguard cutter . . . 2·50 1·00
1092 10r. Independence Day Parade (vert) . . . . . . 3·25 3·50
MS1093 128 × 85 mm. 10r. Cannon on saluting base and National Security Service badge . . . . 2·25 2·25

1985. Olympic Games Gold Medal Winners, Los Angeles. Nos. 1027/31 optd.
1094 50l. Type **190** (optd **JAPAN**) 30 10
1095 1r.55 Backstroke swimming (optd **GOLD MEDALIST THERESA ANDREWS USA**) 60 40
1096 3r. Judo (optd **GOLD MEDALIST FRANK WIENEKE USA**) . . . . 1·25 75
1097 4r. Shot-putting (optd **GOLD MEDALIST CLAUDIA LOCH WEST GERMANY**) . . . . . . 1·25 95
MS1098 85 × 105 mm. 10r. Team handball (optd **U.S.A.**) . . . . 1·90 2·00

1985. Life and Times of Queen Elizabeth the Queen Mother. Multicoloured.
1099 3r. Type **204** 45 60
1100 5r. Visiting the Middlesex Hospital (horiz) . . . . . 65 1·00
1101 7r. The Queen Mother . . . 85 1·25
MS1102 56 × 85 mm. 15r. With Prince Charles at Garter Ceremony . . . . 4·00 3·25

Stamps as Nos. 1099/1101 but with face values of 1r., 4r. and 10r. exist from additional sheetlets with changed background colours.

204a Lira da Braccio

1985. 300th Birth Anniversary of Johann Sebastian Bach (composer). Multicoloured (except No. **MS**1107).
1103 15l. Type **204a** 10 10
1104 2r. Tenor oboe 50 45
1105 4r. Serpent 90 85
1106 10r. Table organ . . . . . 1·90 2·25
MS1107 104 × 75 mm. 15r. Johann Sebastian Bach (black and orange) 3·00 3·50

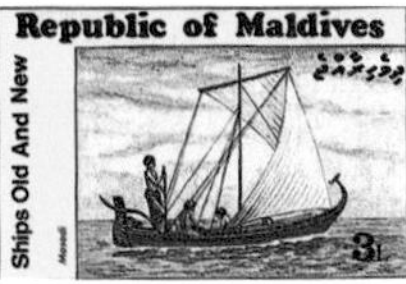

205 Mas Odi (fishing boat)

1985. Maldives Ships and Boats. Multicoloured.
1108 3l. Type **205** 10 20
1109 5l. Battela (dhow) 10 20
1110 10l. Addu odi (dhow) . . . 10 20
1111 2r.60 Modern dhoni (fishing boat) . . . . 1·50 1·60
1112 2r.70 Mas dhoni (fishing boat) . . . . 1·50 1·60
1113 3r. Baththeli dhoni . . . . 1·60 1·60
1114 5r. "Inter I" (inter-island vessel) . . . . 2·50 2·75
1115 10r. Dhoni-style yacht . . . 4·25 6·00

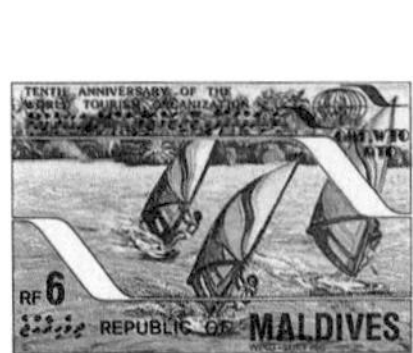

206 Windsurfing

207 United Nations Building, New York

1985. 10th Anniv of World Tourism Organization. Multicoloured.
1116 6r. Type **206** . . . . 2·50 1·75
1117 8r. Scuba diving . . . . . 2·75 2·00
MS1118 171 × 114 mm. 15r. Kuda Hithi Resort . . . . 2·75 3·00

1985. 40th Anniv of U.N.O. and International Peace Year. Multicoloured.
1119 15l. Type **207** 10 10
1120 2r. Hands releasing peace dove 40 45
1121 4r. U.N. Security Council meeting (horiz) 70 85
1122 10r. Lion and lamb . . . . 1·25 2·00
MS1123 76 × 92 mm. 15r. U.N. building and peace dove . . . 2·25 2·75

208 Maldivian Delegate voting in U.N. General Assembly

1985. 20th Anniv of United Nations Membership. Multicoloured.
1124 20l. Type **208** 10 10
1125 15r. U.N. and Maldivian flags, and U.N. Building, New York . . . . 2·00 3·00

209 Youths playing Drums

1985. International Youth Year. Multicoloured.
1126 90l. Type **209** 15 20
1127 6r. Tug-of-war . . . . . . 80 1·10
1128 10r. Community service (vert) . . . . 1·25 2·00
MS1129 85 × 84 mm. 15r. Raising the flag at youth camp (vert) 2·25 3·00

210 Quotation and Flags of Member Nations

1985. 1st Summit Meeting of South Asian Association for Regional Co-operation, Dhaka, Bangladesh.
1130 **210** 3r. multicoloured 1·50 1·25

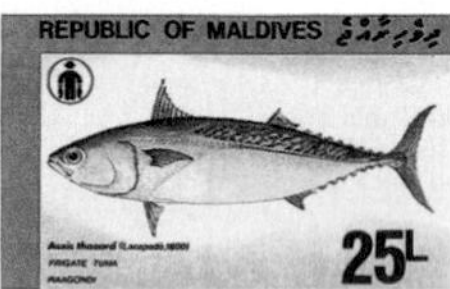

211 Mackerel Frigate

1985. Fishermen's Day. Species of Tuna. Mult.
1131 25l. Type **211** 35 10
1132 75l. Kawakawa ("Little tuna") 65 15
1133 3r. Dog-toothed tuna 2·00 75
1134 5r. Yellow-finned tuna 2·50 1·25
MS1135 130 × 90 mm. 15r. Skipjack tuna 3·50 3·50

1985. 150th Birth Anniv of Mark Twain. Designs as T **160a** of Lesotho, showing Walt Disney cartoon characters illustrating various Mark Twain quotations. Multicoloured.
1136 2l. Winnie the Pooh (vert) 10 10
1137 3l. Gepetto and Figaro the cat (vert) 10 10
1138 4l. Goofy and basket of broken eggs (vert) 10 10
1139 20l. Goofy as doctor scolding Donald Duck (vert) 25 10
1140 4r. Mowgli and King Louis (vert) 1·40 1·75
1141 13r. The wicked Queen and mirror (vert) 5·00 7·00
MS1142 126 × 101 mm. 15r. Mickey Mouse as Tom Sawyer on comet's tail 6·50 7·00

1985. Birth Bicentenaries of Grimm Brothers (folklorists). Designs as T **160b** of Lesotho, showing Walt Disney cartoon characters in scenes from "Dr. Knowall". Multicoloured.
1143 1l. Donald Duck as Crabb driving oxcart (horiz) 10 10
1144 5l. Donald Duck as Dr. Knowall (horiz) 10 10
1145 10l. Dr. Knowall in surgery (horiz) 10 10
1146 15l. Dr. Knowall with Uncle Scrooge as a lord (horiz) 10 10
1147 3r. Dr. and Mrs. Knowall in pony and trap (horiz) 1·10 1·50
1148 15r. Dr. Knowall and thief (horiz) 5·50 7·00
MS1149 126 × 101 mm. 15r. Donald and Daisy Duck as Dr. and Mrs. Knowall 6·50 7·00

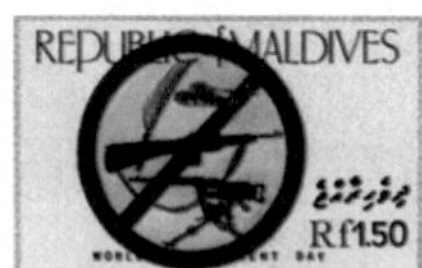

211a Weapons on Road Sign

1986. World Disarmament Day. Multicoloured.
1149a 1r.50 Type **211a**
1149b 10r. Peace dove

1986. Appearance of Halley's Comet (1st issue). As T **162a** of Lesotho. Multicoloured.
1150 20l. N.A.S.A. space telescope and Comet 50 25
1151 1r.50 E.S.A. "Giotto" spacecraft and Comet 1·25 1·50
1152 2r. Japanese "Planet A" spacecraft and Comet 1·50 1·75
1153 4r. Edmond Halley and Stonehenge 2·25 2·75
1154 5r. Russian "Vega" spacecraft and Comet 2·25 2·75
MS1155 101 × 70 mm. 15r. Halley's Comet 8·00 9·50
See also Nos. 1206/11.

1986. Centenary of Statue of Liberty. Multicoloured. As T **163b** of Lesotho, showing the Statue of Liberty and immigrants to the U.S.A.
1156 50l. Walter Gropius (architect) 40 30
1157 70l. John Lennon (musician) 2·00 1·25
1158 1r. George Balanchine (choreographer) 2·00 1·25
1159 10r. Franz Werfel (writer) 4·00 7·00
MS1160 100 × 72 mm. 15r. Statue of Liberty (vert) 7·00 8·00

1986. "Ameripex" International Stamp Exhibition, Chicago. As T **163c** of Lesotho, showing Walt Disney cartoon characters and U.S.A. stamps. Multicoloured.
1161 3l. Johnny Appleseed and 1966 Johnny Appleseed stamp 10 10
1162 4l. Paul Bunyan and 1958 Forest Conservation stamp 10 10
1163 5l. Casey and 1969 Professional Baseball Centenary stamp 10 10
1164 10l. Ichabod Crane and 1974 "Legend of Sleepy Hollow" stamp 10 10
1165 15l. John Henry and 1944 75th Anniv of completion of First Transcontinental Railroad stamp 15 15
1166 20l. Windwagon Smith and 1954 Kansas Territory Centenary stamp 15 15
1167 13r. Mike Fink and 1970 Great Northwest stamp 7·00 7·00
1168 14r. Casey Jones and 1950 Railroad Engineers stamp 8·00 8·00
MS1169 Two sheets, each 127 × 101 mm. (a) 15r. Davy Crockett and 1967 Davy Crockett stamp. (b) 15r. Daisy Duck as Pocahontas saving Captain John Smith (Donald Duck) Set of 2 sheets 12·00 15·00

1986. 60th Birthday of Queen Elizabeth II. As T **163** of Lesotho.
1170 1r. black and yellow 30 25
1171 2r. multicoloured 40 55
1172 12r. multicoloured 1·50 2·50
MS1173 120 × 85 mm. 15r. black and brown 3·75 4·25
DESIGNS: 1r. Royal Family at Girl Guides Rally, 1938; 2r. Queen in Canada; 12r. At Sandringham, 1970; 15r. Princesses Elizabeth and Margaret at Royal Lodge, Windsor, 1940.

212 Player running with Ball

1986. World Cup Football Championship, Mexico. Multicoloured.
1174 15l. Type **212** 75 30
1175 2r. Player gaining control of ball 2·50 1·75
1176 4r. Two players competing for ball 4·00 3·50
1177 10r. Player bouncing ball on knee 7·50 8·00
MS1178 95 × 114 mm. 15r. Player kicking ball 5·00 6·00

1986. Royal Wedding. As T **170a** of Lesotho. Multicoloured.
1179 10l. Prince Andrew and Miss Sarah Ferguson 15 10
1180 2r. Prince Andrew 75 70
1181 12r. Prince Andrew in naval uniform 3·25 3·75
MS1182 88 × 88 mm. 15r. Prince Andrew and Miss Sarah Ferguson (different) 4·25 4·50

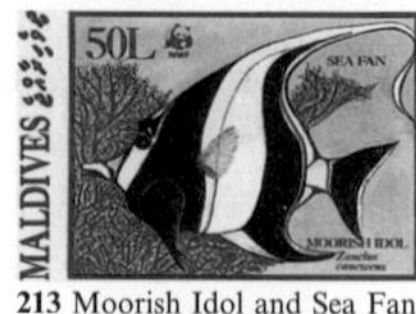

213 Moorish Idol and Sea Fan (**213b**)

1986. Marine Wildlife. Multicoloured.
1183 50l. Type **213** 1·50 40
1184 90l. Regal angelfish 2·00 55
1185 1r. Maldive anemonefish 2·00 55
1186 2r. Tiger cowrie and stinging coral 2·50 1·60
1187 3r. Emperor angelfish and staghorn coral 2·50 2·00
1188 4r. Black-naped tern 3·00 3·00
1189 5r. Fiddler crab and staghorn coral 2·50 3·00
1190 10r. Hawksbill turtle 3·00 5·00
MS1191 Two sheets, each 107 × 76 mm. (a) 15r. Long-nosed butterflyfish. (b) 15r. Oriental trumpetfish Set of 2 sheets 12·00 15·00

1986. Birth Bicentenary (1985) of John J. Audubon (ornithologist) (2nd issue). As T **201** showing original paintings. Multicoloured.
1192 3l. Little blue heron (horiz) 40 60
1193 4l. White-tailed kite 40 60
1194 5l. Greater shearwater (horiz) 40 60
1195 10l. Magnificent frigate bird 45 40
1196 15l. Black-necked grebe ("Eared Grebe") 85 40
1197 20l. Goosander ("Common Merganser") 90 40
1198 13r. Peregrine falcon ("Great Footed Hawk") (horiz) 7·00 7·50
1199 14r. Prairie chicken ("Greater Prairie Chicken") (horiz) 7·00 7·50
MS1200 Two sheets, each 74 × 104 mm. (a) 15r. Fulmar ("Northern Fulmar"). (b) 15r. White-fronted goose (horiz) Set of 2 sheets 22·00 21·00

1986. World Cup Football Championship Winners, Mexico. Nos. 1174/7 optd **WINNERS Argentina 3 W. Germany 2**.
1201 15l. Type **212** 40 30
1202 2r. Player gaining control of ball 1·25 1·10
1203 4r. Two players competing for ball 2·00 2·00
1204 10r. Player bouncing ball on knee 3·25 4·25
MS1205 95 × 114 mm. 15r. Player kicking ball 3·00 4·25

1986. Appearance of Halley's Comet (2nd issue). Nos. 1150/4 optd with T **213b**.
1206 20l. N.A.S.A. space telescope and Comet 65 40
1207 1r.50 E.S.A. "Giotto" spacecraft and Comet 1·25 1·00
1208 2r. Japanese "Planet A" spacecraft and Comet 1·50 1·50
1209 4r. Edmond Halley and Stonehenge 2·00 2·25
1210 5r. Russian "Vega" spacecraft and Comet 2·00 2·25
MS1211 101 × 70 mm. 15r. Halley's Comet 6·00 6·50

214 Servicing Aircraft **216** Ixora

215 "Hypholoma fasciculare"

1986. 40th Anniv of U.N.E.S.C.O. Multicoloured.
1212 1r. Type **214** 80 30
1213 2r. Boat building 90 1·00
1214 3r. Children in classroom 1·00 1·40
1215 5r. Student in laboratory 1·10 2·50
MS1216 77 × 100 mm. 15r. Diving bell on sea bed 2·75 4·25

1986. Fungi of the Maldives. Multicoloured.
1217 15l. Type **215** 80 25
1218 50l. "Kuehneromyces mutabilis" (vert) 1·50 45
1219 1r. "Amanita muscaria" (vert) 1·75 60
1220 2r. "Agaricus campestris" 2·50 1·50
1221 3r. "Amanita pantherina" (vert) 2·50 1·75
1222 4r. "Coprinus comatus" (vert) 2·50 2·25
1223 5r. "Gymnopilus junonius" ("Pholiota spectabilis") 2·50 2·75
1224 10r. "Pluteus cervinus" 3·75 4·50
MS1225 Two sheets, each 100 × 70 mm. (a) 15r. "Armillaria mellea". (b) 15r. "Stropharia aeruginosa" (vert) Set of 2 sheets 15·00 14·00

1987. Flowers. Multicoloured.
1226 10l. Type **216** 10 10
1227 20l. Frangipani 10 10
1228 50l. Crinum 1·75 60
1229 2r. Pink rose 40 80
1230 4r. Flamboyant flower 60 1·50
1231 10r. Ground orchid 5·00 7·50
MS1232 Two sheets, each 100 × 70 mm. (a) 15r. Gardenia. (b) 15r. Oleander Set of 2 sheets 4·75 6·50

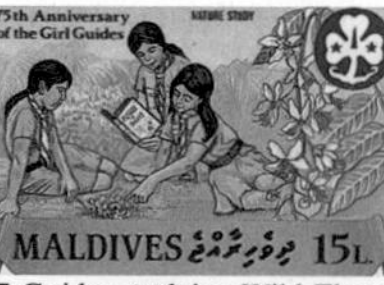

217 Guides studying Wild Flowers

1987. 75th Anniv (1985) of Girl Guide Movement. Multicoloured.
1233 15l. Type **217** 30 20
1234 2r. Guides with pet rabbits 60 80
1235 4r. Guide observing white spoonbill 2·50 2·25
1236 12r. Lady Baden-Powell and Guide flag 2·75 6·50
MS1237 104 × 78 mm. 15r. Guides in sailing dinghy 2·25 3·75

218 "Thespesia populnea" **219** "Precis octavia"

1987. Trees and Plants. Multicoloured.
1238 50l. Type **218** 15 10
1239 1r. "Cocos nucifera" 20 20
1240 2r. "Calophyllum mophyllum" 35 40
1241 3r. "Xanthosoma indica" (horiz) 55 65
1242 5r. "Ipomoea batatas" (horiz) 90 1·40
1243 7r. "Artocarpus altilis" 1·25 2·00
MS1244 75 × 109 mm. 15r. "Cocos nucifera" (different) 2·25 3·25
No. 1241 is inscr "Xyanthosomaindica" in error.

1987. America's Cup Yachting Championship. As T **218a** of Lesotho. Multicoloured.
1245 15l. "Intrepid", 1970 10 10
1246 1r. "France II", 1974 20 20
1247 2r. "Gretel", 1962 40 60
1248 12r. "Volunteer", 1887 2·00 3·00
MS1249 113 × 83 mm. 15r. Helmsman and crew on deck of "Defender", 1895 (horiz) 2·25 3·25

1987. Butterflies. Multicoloured.
1250 15l. Type **219** 45 30
1251 20l. "Atrophaneura hector" 45 30
1252 50l. "Teinopalpus imperialis" 75 40
1253 1r. "Kallima horsfieldi" 1·00 45
1254 2r. "Cethosia biblis" 1·60 1·25
1255 4r. "Idea jasonia" 2·50 2·25
1256 7r. "Papilio memnon" 3·50 4·00
1257 10r. "Aeropetes tulbaghia" 4·00 5·00
MS1258 Two sheets, each 135 × 102 mm. (a) 15r. "Acraea violae". (b) 15r. "Hebomoia leucippe" Set of 2 sheets 9·00 11·00

220 Isaac Newton experimenting with Spectrum

1988. Great Scientific Discoveries. Multicoloured.
1259 1r.50 Type **220** 1·25 1·00
1260 3r. Euclid composing "Principles of Geometry" (vert) 1·60 1·75
1261 4r. Mendel formulating theory of Genetic Evolution (vert) 1·75 2·00
1262 5r. Galileo and moons of Jupiter 3·00 3·00
MS1263 102 × 72 mm. 15r. "Apollo" lunar module (vert) 4·50 5·50

221 Donald Duck and Weather Satellite

1988. Space Exploration. Walt Disney cartoon characters. Multicoloured.
1264 3l. Type **221** 10 10
1265 4l. Minnie Mouse and navigation satellite 10 10
1266 5l. Mickey Mouse's nephews talking via communication satellite 10 10
1267 10l. Goofy in lunar rover (vert) 10 10
1268 20l. Minnie Mouse delivering pizza to flying saucer (vert) 10 10
1269 13r. Mickey Mouse directing spacecraft docking (vert) 5·00 5·00
1270 14r. Mickey Mouse and "Voyager 2" 5·00 5·00
MS1271 Two sheets, each 127 × 102 mm. (a) 15r. Mickey Mouse at first Moon landing, 1969. (b) 15r. Mickey Mouse and nephews in space station swimming pool (vert) Set of 2 sheets 12·00 12·00

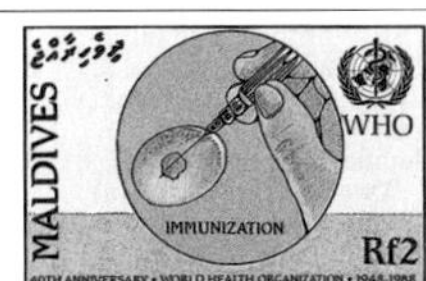

222 Syringe and Bacterium ("Immunization")

1988. 40th Anniv of W.H.O. Multicoloured.
1272 2r. Type **222** 40 40
1273 4r. Tap ("Clean Water") . . 60 85

223 Water Droplet and Atoll

1988. World Environment Day (1987). Mult.
1274 15l. Type **223** 10 10
1275 75l. Coral reef 20 40
1276 2r. Audubon's shearwaters in flight . . . . 85 1·40
MS1277 105 × 76 mm. 15r. Banyan tree (vert) . . . . 3·25 4·50

224 Globe, Carrier Pigeon and Letter
226 Discus-throwing

1988. Transport and Telecommunications Decade. Each showing central globe. Multicoloured.
1278 2r. Type **224** 60 65
1279 3r. Dish aerial and girl using telephone . . . . 1·00 1·10
1280 5r. Satellite, television, telephone and antenna tower . . . . 1·75 2·00
1281 10r. Car, ship and Lockheed TriStar airliner . . . . . 8·50 6·50

1988. Royal Ruby Wedding. Nos. 1170/3 optd **40TH WEDDING ANNIVERSARY H.M. QUEEN ELIZABETH II H.R.H. THE DUKE OF EDINBURGH.**
1282 1r. black and yellow 45 25
1283 2r. multicoloured 60 60
1284 12r. multicoloured . . . . . 2·75 3·50
MS1285 120 × 85 mm. 15r. black and brown . . . . 4·00 4·25

1988. Olympic Games, Seoul. Multicoloured.
1286 15l. Type **226** 10 10
1287 2r. 100 m race 40 40
1288 4r. Gymnastics (horiz) . . . 70 80
1289 12r. Three-day equestrian event (horiz) . . . . . . 2·25 3·25
MS1290 106 × 76 mm. 20r. Tennis (horiz) . . . . 4·00 4·75

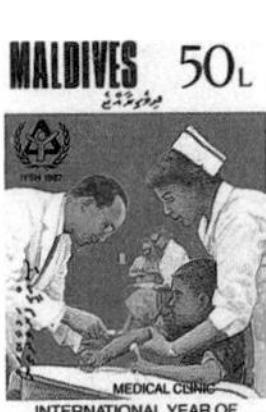

227 Immunization at Clinic
230 Pres. Kennedy and Launch of "Apollo" Spacecraft

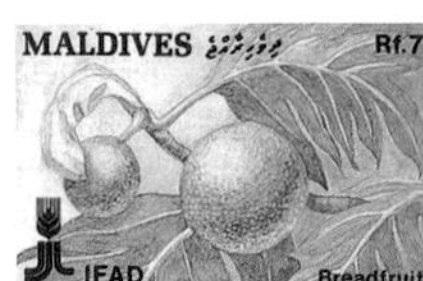

228 Breadfruit

1988. Int Year of Shelter for the Homeless. Mult.
1291 50l. Type **227** 30 30
1292 3r. Prefab housing estate . . 1·10 1·40
MS1293 63 × 105 mm. 15r. Building site . . . . 1·75 2·50

1988. 10th Anniv of International Fund for Agricultural Development. Multicoloured.
1294 7r. Type **228** . . . . 1·00 1·40
1295 10r. Mangoes (vert) . . . . 1·50 1·90
MS1296 103 × 74 mm. 15r. Coconut palm, fishing boat and yellowtail tuna . . . . 2·75 3·00

1988. World Aids Day. Nos. 1272/3 optd **WORLD AIDS DAY** and emblem.
1297 2r. Type **222** 35 45
1298 4r. "Tap" ("Clean Water") 65 80

1989. 25th Death Anniv (1988) of John F. Kennedy (American statesman). U.S. Space Achievements. Multicoloured.
1299 5r. Type **230** . . . . 1·90 2·00
1300 5r. Lunar module and astronaut on Moon . . . 1·90 2·00
1301 5r. Astronaut and buggy on Moon . . . . 1·90 2·00
1302 5r. President Kennedy and spacecraft . . . . 1·90 2·00
MS1303 108 × 77 mm. 15r. President Kennedy making speech . . . 3·50 4·25

1989. Olympic Medal Winners, Seoul. Nos. 1286/90 optd.
1304 15l. Type **226** (optd **J. SCHULT DDR**) 20 20
1305 2r. 100 m race (optd **C. LEWIS USA**) 65 65
1306 4r. Gymnastics (horiz) (optd **MEN'S ALL AROUND V. ARTEMOV USSR**) . . 1·40 1·40
1307 12r. Three-day equestrian event (horiz) (optd **TEAM SHOW JUMPING W. GERMANY**) . . . . 4·50 5·00
MS1308 106 × 76 mm. 20r. Tennis (horiz) (optd **OLYMPIC WINNERS MEN'S SINGLES GOLD M. MECIR CZECH SILVER T. MAYOTTE USA BRONZE B. GILBERT USA**) 6·00 7·00
On No. **MS**1308 the overprint appears on the sheet margin.

1989. 500th Birth Anniv of Titian (artist). As T **186a** of Lesotho, showing paintings. Multicoloured.
1309 15l. "Benedetto Varchi" . . 10 10
1310 1r. "Portrait of a Young Man" 20 15
1311 2r. "King Francis I of France" 40 40
1312 5r. "Pietro Aretino" . . . . 1·10 1·25
1313 15r. "The Bravo" . . . . . 3·50 5·00
1314 20r. "The Concert" (detail) 3·50 6·00
MS1315 Two sheets. (a) 112 × 96 mm. 20r. "An Allegory of Prudence" (detail). (b) 96 × 110 mm. 20r. "Francesco Maria della Rovere" Set of 2 sheets . . . . 7·50 8·50

1989. 10th Anniversary of Asia–Pacific Telecommunity. Nos. 1279/80 optd **ASIA–PACIFIC TELECOMMUNITY 10 YEARS** and emblem. Multicoloured.
1316 3r. Dish aerial and girl using telephone . . . . 1·25 1·50
1317 5r. Satellite, television, telephone and antenna tower . . . . 1·75 2·00

1989. Japanese Art. Paintings by Hokusai. As T **187a** of Lesotho. Multicoloured.
1318 15l. "Fuji from Hodogaya" (horiz) 10 10
1319 50l. "Fuji from Lake Kawaguchi" (horiz) . . . 15 15
1320 1r. "Fuji from Owari" (horiz) 25 15
1321 2r. "Fuji from Tsukudajima in Edo" (horiz) 50 40
1322 4r. "Fuji from a Teahouse at Yoshida" (horiz) . . . 80 90
1323 6r. "Fuji from Tagonoura" (horiz) . . . . 90 1·25
1324 10r. "Fuji from Mishima-goe" (horiz) . . . . . . 2·25 2·75
1325 12r. "Fuji from the Sumida River in Edo" (horiz) . . 2·25 2·75
MS1326 Two sheets, each 101 × 77 mm. (a) 18r. "Fuji from Inume Pass". (b) 18r. "Fuji from Fukagawa in Edo" Set of 2 sheets 8·50 9·00

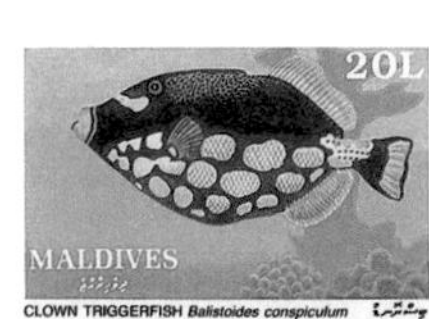

233 Clown Triggerfish

1989. Tropical Fishes. Multicoloured.
1327 20l. Type **233** 25 20
1328 50l. Blue-striped snapper . . 35 25
1329 1r. Powder-blue surgeonfish 45 30
1330 2r. Oriental sweetlips . . . 75 65
1331 3r. Six-barred wrasse . . . 1·00 85
1332 8r. Thread-finned butterflyfish . . . . . . 2·00 2·50
1333 10r. Bicoloured parrotfish 2·40 2·75
1334 12r. Scarlet-finned squirrelfish . . . . 2·40 2·75
MS1335 Two sheets, each 101 × 73 mm. (a) 15r. Butterfly perch. (b) 15r. Semicircle angelfish Set of 2 sheets . . . . 13·00 12·00

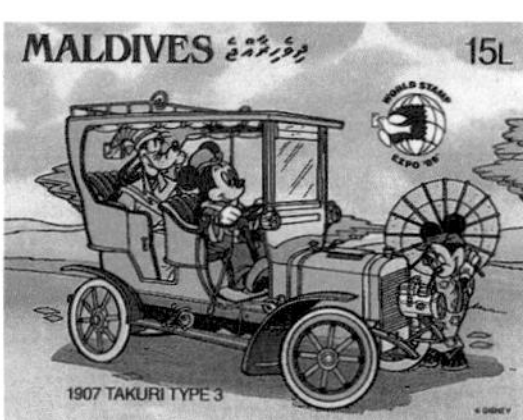

234 Goofy, Mickey and Minnie Mouse with Takuri "Type 3", 1907

1989. "World Stamp Expo '89" International Stamp Exhibition, Washington (1st issue). Designs showing Walt Disney cartoon characters with Japanese cars. Multicoloured.
1336 15l. Type **234** 20 15
1337 50l. Donald and Daisy Duck in Mitsubishi "Model A", 1917 . . . . 40 30
1338 1r. Goofy in Datsun "Roadstar", 1935 . . . . 70 50
1339 2r. Donald and Daisy Duck with Mazda, 1940 . . . . 1·00 75
1340 4r. Donald Duck with Nissan "Bluebird 310", 1959 . . . . 1·50 1·25
1341 6r. Donald and Daisy Duck with Subaru "360", 1958 1·75 1·75
1342 10r. Mickey Mouse and Pluto in Honda "5800", 1966 . . . . 3·25 3·75
1343 12r. Mickey Mouse and Goofy in Daihatsu "Fellow", 1966 . . . . . 3·75 4·25
MS1344 Two sheets, each 127 × 102 mm. (a) 20r. Daisy Duck with Chip n'Dale and Isuzu "Trooper II", 1981. (b) 20r. Mickey Mouse with tortoise and Toyota "Supra", 1985 Set of 2 sheets . . . . 11·00 13·00

1989. "World Stamp Expo '89" International Stamp Exhibition, Washington (2nd issue). Landmarks of Washington. Sheet 62 × 78 mm, containing multicoloured designs as T **193a** of Lesotho, but vert.
MS1345 8r. Marine Corps Memorial, Arlington National Cemetery . . . . 2·00 2·50

235 Lunar Module "Eagle"

1989. 20th Anniv of First Manned Landing on Moon. Multicoloured.
1346 1r. Type **235** 30 20
1347 2r. Astronaut Aldrin collecting dust samples . . 50 60
1348 6r. Aldrin setting up seismometer . . . . 1·25 1·75
1349 10r. Pres. Nixon congratulating "Apollo 11" astronauts 1·90 2·50
MS1350 107 × 75 mm. 18r. Television picture of Armstrong about to step onto Moon (34 × 47 mm) . . . . 6·50 7·00

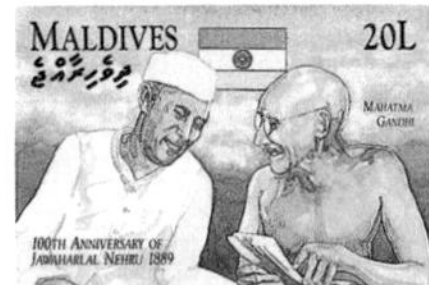

236 Jawaharlal Nehru with Mahatma Gandhi

1989. Anniversaries and Events. Multicoloured.
1351 20l. Type **236** (birth cent) 2·50 1·00
1352 50l. Opium poppies and logo (anti-drugs campaign) (vert) . . . . 1·50 45
1353 1r. William Shakespeare (425th birth anniv) . . . 1·25 45
1354 2r. Storming the Bastille (bicent of French Revolution) (vert) . . . . 1·25 1·25
1355 3r. Concorde (20th anniv of first flight) . . . . 4·50 2·25
1356 8r. George Washington (bicent of inauguration) 2·00 3·00
1357 10r. William Bligh (bicent of mutiny on the "Bounty") 7·00 5·00
1358 12r. Hamburg harbour (800th anniv) (vert) . . . 4·00 5·50
MS1359 Two sheets. (a) 115 × 85 mm. 18r. Baseball players (50th anniv of first televised game) (vert). (b) 110 × 80 mm. 18r. Franz von Taxis (500th anniv of regular European postal services) (vert) Set of 2 sheets . . . . 13·00 15·00

237 Sir William van Horne (Chairman of Canadian Pacific), Locomotive and Map, 1894
239 "Louis XVI in Coronation Robes" (Duplessis)

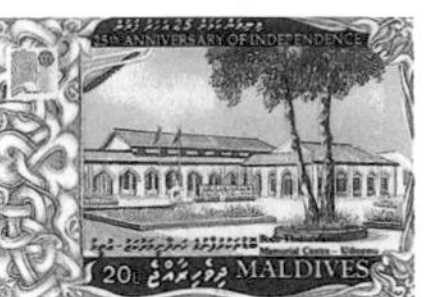

238 Bodu Thakurufaanu Memorial Centre, Utheemu

1989. Railway Pioneers. Multicoloured.
1360 10l. Type **237** 25 15
1361 25l. Matthew Murray (engineer) with Blenkinsop and Murray's rack locomotive, 1810 . . . . 35 20
1362 50l. Louis Favre (railway engineer) and steam locomotive entering tunnel 40 25
1363 2r. George Stephenson (engineer) and "Locomotion", 1825 . . . 75 55
1364 6r. Richard Trevithick and "Catch-Me-Who-Can", 1808 . . . . 1·50 1·50
1365 8r. George Nagelmackers and "Orient Express" dining car . . . . 1·75 1·75
1366 10r. William Jessop and horse-drawn wagon, Surrey Iron Railway, 1770 2·50 2·50
1367 12r. Isambard Brunel (engineer) and GWR steam locomotive, 1833 3·00 3·00
MS1368 Two sheets, each 71 × 103 mm. (a) 18r. George Pullman (inventor of sleeping cars), 1864. (b) 18r. Rudolf Diesel (engineer) and first oil engine Set of 2 sheets . . . . 8·50 9·50

1990. 25th Anniv of Independence. Multicoloured.
1369 20l. Type **238** 10 10
1370 25l. Islamic Centre, Male . . 10 10
1371 50l. National flag and logos of international organizations 10 10
1372 2r. Presidential Palace, Male 30 40
1373 5r. National Security Service 85 1·25
MS1374 128 × 90 mm. 10r. National emblem . . . . 3·50 3·75

1990. Bicentenary of French Revolution and "Philexfrance '89" International Stamp Exhibi-tion, Paris. French Paintings. Multicoloured.
1375 15l. Type **239** 15 15
1376 50l. "Monsieur Lavoisier and his Wife" (David) . . 35 25
1377 1r. "Madame Pastoret" (David) 55 35
1378 2r. "Oath of Lafayette, 14 July 1790" (anon) . . 80 70
1379 4r. "Madame Trudaine" (David) . . . . 1·40 1·50
1380 6r. "Chenard celebrating the Liberation of Savoy" (Boilly) . . . . 2·00 2·25
1381 10r. "An Officer swears Allegiance to the Constitution" (anon) . . 3·25 4·00
1382 12r. "Self Portrait" (David) 3·50 4·25
MS1383 Two sheets. (a) 104 × 79 mm. 20r. "The Oath of the Tennis Court, 20 June 1789" (David) (horiz). (b) 79 × 104 mm. 20r. "Rousseau and Symbols of the Revolution" (Jeaurat) Set of 2 sheets . . . . 11·00 12·00

239a Donald Duck, Mickey Mouse and Goofy Playing Rugby

1990. "Stamp World London '90" International Stamp Exhibition. Walt Disney cartoon characters playing British sports. Multicoloured.
1384 15l. Type **239a** 30 15
1385 50l. Donald Duck and Chip-n-Dale curling 45 25
1386 1r. Goofy playing polo . . . 65 40

1387	2r. Mickey Mouse and nephews playing soccer	90	70
1388	4r. Mickey Mouse playing cricket	1·75	1·50
1389	6r. Minnie and Mickey Mouse at Ascot races	2·25	1·90
1390	10r. Mickey Mouse and Goofy playing tennis	3·50	3·50
1391	12r. Donald Duck and Mickey Mouse playing bowls	3·50	3·50
MS1392	Two sheets, each 126 × 101 mm. (a) 20r. Minnie Mouse fox-hunting. (b) 20r. Mickey Mouse playing golf Set of 2 sheets	14·00	14·00

240 Silhouettes of Queen Elizabeth II and Queen Victoria

1990. 150th Anniv of the Penny Black.

1393	**240** 8r. black and green	2·50	2·50
1394	– 12r. black and blue	3·00	3·00
MS1395	109 × 84 mm. 18r. black and brown	4·50	5·50

DESIGN: 12r. As Type **240**, but with position of silhouettes reversed; 18r. Penny Black.

1990. 90th Birthday of Queen Elizabeth the Queen Mother. As T **198a** of Lesotho.

1396	6r. black, mauve and blue	1·10	1·40
1397	6r. black, mauve and blue	1·10	1·40
1398	6r. black, mauve and blue	1·10	1·40
MS1399	90 × 75 mm. 18r. multicoloured	3·00	3·50

DESIGNS: No. 1396, Lady Elizabeth Bowes-Lyon; 1397, Lady Elizabeth Bowes-Lyon wearing headband; 1398, Lady Elizabeth Bowes-Lyon leaving for her wedding; **MS**1399, Lady Elizabeth Bowes-Lyon wearing wedding dress.

241 Sultan's Tomb

1990. Islamic Heritage Year. Each black and blue.

1400	1r. Type **241**	25	35
1401	1r. Thakurufaan's Palace	25	35
1402	1r. Male Mosque	25	35
1403	2r. Veranda of Friday Mosque	35	45
1404	2r. Interior of Friday Mosque	35	45
1405	2r. Friday Mosque and Monument	35	45

242 Defence of Wake Island, 1941

1990. 50th Anniv of Second World War. Mult.

1406	15l. Type **242**	25	20
1407	25l. Stilwell's army in Burma, 1944	30	20
1408	50l. Normandy offensive, 1944	40	25
1409	1r. Capture of Saipan, 1944	55	40
1410	2r.50 D-Day landings, 1944	90	80
1411	3r.50 Allied landings in Norway, 1940	1·10	1·10
1412	4r. Lord Mountbatten, Head of Combined Operations, 1943	1·40	1·40
1413	6r. Japanese surrender, Tokyo Bay, 1945	1·75	2·00
1414	10r. Potsdam Conference, 1945	2·75	3·00
1415	12r. Allied invasion of Sicily, 1943	3·00	3·25
MS1416	115 × 87 mm. 18r. Atlantic convoy	5·50	6·50

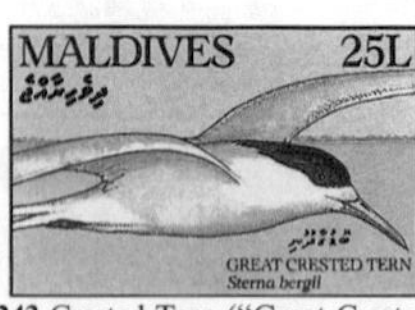

243 Crested Tern ("Great Crested Tern")

1990. Birds. Multicoloured.

1417	25l. Type **243**	15	15
1418	50l. Koel	25	25
1419	1r. White tern	35	35
1420	3r.50 Cinnamon bittern	90	1·00
1421	6r. Sooty tern	1·40	1·60
1422	8r. Audubon's shearwater	1·60	2·00
1423	12r. Common noddy ("Brown Noddy")	2·50	3·00
1424	15r. Lesser frigate bird	2·75	3·25
MS1425	Two sheets, each 100 × 69 mm. (a) 18r. Grey heron. (b) 18r. White-tailed tropic bird Set of 2 sheets	8·00	10·00

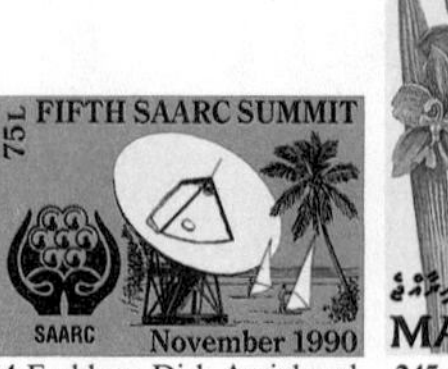

244 Emblem, Dish Aerial and Sailboards **245** "Spathoglottis plicata"

1990. 5th South Asian Association for Regional Co-operation Summit.

1426	**244** 75l. black and orange	20	25
1427	– 3r.50 multicoloured	90	1·25
MS1428	112 × 82 mm. 20r. multicoloured	4·50	5·50

DESIGN: 3r.50, Flags of member nations; 20r. Global warming diagram.

1990. "EXPO '90" International Garden and Greenery Exhibition, Osaka. Flowers. Mult.

1429	20l. Type **245**	90	30
1430	75l. "Hippeastrum puniceum"	1·40	40
1431	2r. "Tecoma stans" (horiz)	1·60	90
1432	3r.50 "Catharanthus roseus" (horiz)	1·60	1·60
1433	10r. "Ixora coccinea" (horiz)	2·75	3·00
1434	12r. "Clitorea ternatea" (horiz)	3·00	3·25
1435	15r. "Caesalpinia pulcherrima"	3·00	3·50
MS1436	Four sheets, each 111 × 79 mm. (a) 20r. "Plumeria obtusa" (horiz). (b) 20r. "Jasminum grandiflorum" (horiz). (c) 20r. "Rosa" sp (horiz). (d) 20r. "Hibiscus tiliaceous" (horiz) Set of 4 sheets	13·00	13·00

246 "The Hare and the Tortoise"

1990. International Literacy Year. Walt Disney cartoon characters illustrating fables by Aesop. Multicoloured.

1437	15l. Type **246**	30	15
1438	50l. "The Town Mouse and the Country Mouse"	50	25
1439	1r. "The Fox and the Crow"	80	35
1440	3r.50 "The Travellers and the Bear"	1·60	1·60
1441	4r. "The Fox and the Lion"	1·75	1·75
1442	6r. "The Mice Meeting"	2·25	2·25
1443	10r. "The Fox and the Goat"	2·75	3·00
1444	12r. "The Dog in the Manger"	2·75	3·25
MS1445	Two sheets, each 127 × 102 mm. (a) 20r. "The Miller, his Son and the Ass" (vert). (b) 20r. "The Miser's Gold" (vert) Set of 2 sheets	12·00	12·00

247 East African Railways Class 31 Steam Locomotive **248** Ruud Gullit of Holland

1990. Railway Steam Locomotives. Multicoloured.

1446	20l. Type **247**	75	30
1447	50l. Steam locomotive, Sudan	1·00	45
1448	1r. Class GM Garratt, South Africa	1·40	60
1449	3r. 7th Class, Rhodesia	2·25	2·00
1450	5r. Central Pacific Class No. 229, U.S.A.	2·50	2·25
1451	8r. Reading Railroad No. 415, U.S.A.	2·75	2·75
1452	10r. Porter narrow gauge, Canada	2·75	2·75
1453	12r. Great Northern Railway No. 515, U.S.A.	2·75	3·00
MS1454	Two sheets, each 90 × 65 mm. (a) 20r. 19th-century standard American locomotive No. 315. (b) 20r. East African Railways Garratt locomotive No. 5950 Set of 2 sheets	15·00	15·00

1990. World Cup Football Championship, Italy. Multicoloured.

1455	1r. Type **248**	1·50	50
1456	2r.50 Paul Gascoigne of England	2·25	1·25
1457	3r.50 Brazilian challenging Argentine player	2·25	1·60
1458	5r. Brazilian taking control of ball	2·50	2·00
1459	7r. Italian and Austrian jumping for header	3·25	3·25
1460	10r. Russian being chased by Turkish player	3·50	3·50
1461	15r. Andres Brehme of West Germany	4·00	4·25
MS1462	Four sheets, each 77 × 92 mm. (a) 18r. Head of an Austrian player (horiz). (b) 18r. Head of a South Korean player (horiz). (c) 20r. Diego Maradona of Argentina (horiz). (d) 20r. Schilacci of Italy (horiz) Set of 4 sheets	17·00	17·00

249 Winged Euonymus **251** Greek Messenger from Marathon, 490 B.C. (2480th Anniv)

250 "Summer" (Rubens)

1991. Bonsai Trees and Shrubs. Multicoloured.

1463	20l. Type **249**	40	20
1464	50l. Japanese black pine	55	35
1465	1r. Japanese five needle pine	80	55
1466	3r.50 Flowering quince	1·75	1·60
1467	5r. Chinese elm	2·25	2·25
1468	8r. Japanese persimmon	2·50	2·75
1469	10r. Japanese wisteria	2·50	2·75
1470	12r. Satsuki azalea	2·50	3·00
MS1471	Two sheets, each 89 × 88 mm. (a) 20r. Trident maple. (b) 20r. Sargent juniper Set of 2 sheets	11·00	13·00

1991. 350th Death Anniv of Rubens. Mult.

1472	20l. Type **250**	20	15
1473	50l. "Landscape with Rainbow" (detail)	35	25
1474	1r. "Wreck of Aeneas"	55	40
1475	2r.50 "Chateau de Steen" (detail)	1·00	1·00
1476	3r.50 "Landscape with Herd of Cows"	1·25	1·25
1477	7r. "Ruins on the Palantine"	2·00	2·50
1478	10r. "Landscape with Peasants and Cows"	2·25	2·50
1479	12r. "Wagon fording Stream"	2·50	3·00
MS1480	Four sheets, each 100 × 71 mm. (a) 20r. "Landscape at Sunset". (b) 20r. "Peasants with Cattle by a Stream". (c) 20r. "Shepherd with Flock". (d) 20r. "Wagon in Stream" Set of 4 sheets	15·00	16·00

1991. Anniversaries and Events (1990). Mult.

1481	50l. Type **251**	45	25
1482	1r. Anthony Fokker in Haarlem Spin monoplane (birth centenary)	80	45
1483	3r.50 "Early Bird" satellite (25th anniv)	1·50	1·50
1484	7r. Signing Reunification of Germany agreement (horiz)	1·75	2·50
1485	8r. King John signing Magna Carta (775th anniv)	2·25	2·50
1486	10r. Dwight D. Eisenhower (birth centenary)	2·25	2·50
1487	12r. Sir Winston Churchill (25th death anniv)	3·25	3·50
1488	15r. Pres. Reagan at Berlin Wall (German reunification) (horiz)	2·75	3·75
MS1489	Two sheets. (a) 180 × 81 mm. 20r. German Junkers Ju88 bomber (50th anniv of Battle of Britain) (horiz). (b) 160 × 73 mm. 20r. Brandenburg Gate (German reunification) (horiz) Set of 2 sheets	13·00	13·00

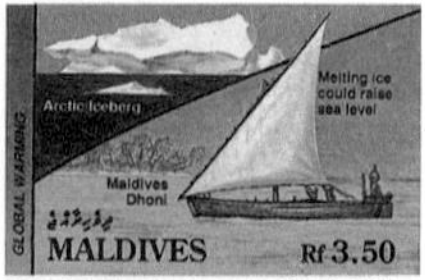

252 Arctic Iceberg and Maldives Dhoni

1991. Global Warming. Multicoloured.

1490	3r.50 Type **252**	1·25	1·25
1491	7r. Antarctic iceberg and "Maldive Trader" (freighter)	2·75	2·75

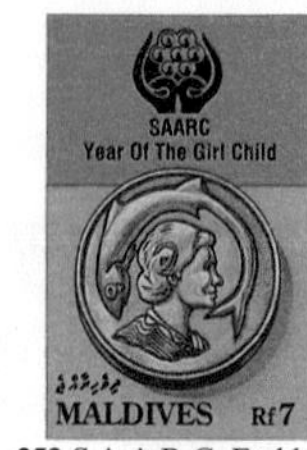

253 S.A.A.R.C. Emblem and Medal

1991. Year of the Girl Child.

1492	**253** 7r. multicoloured	1·75	1·75

254 Children on Beach

1991. Year of the Maldivian Child. Children's Paintings. Multicoloured.

1493	3r.50 Type **254**	2·25	1·40
1494	5r. Children in a park	2·75	2·25
1495	10r. Hungry child dreaming of food	3·75	4·00
1496	25r. Scuba diver	7·00	10·00

255 "Still Life: Japanese Vase with Roses and Anemones"

1991. Death Centenary (1990) of Vincent van Gogh (artist). Multicoloured.

1497	15l. Type **255**	50	25
1498	20l. "Still Life: Red Poppies and Daisies"	50	25
1499	2r. "Vincent's Bedroom in Arles" (horiz)	1·75	90
1500	3r.50 "The Mulberry Tree"	2·00	1·25
1501	7r. "Blossoming Chestnut Branches" (horiz)	3·00	3·00
1502	10r. "Peasant Couple going to Work" (horiz)	3·50	3·50
1503	12r. "Still Life: Pink Roses" (horiz)	3·75	4·00
1504	15r. "Child with Orange"	4·00	4·25
MS1505	Two sheets. (a) 77 × 101 mm. 25r. "Houses in Auvers" (70 × 94 mm). (b) 101 × 77 mm. 25r. "The Courtyard of the Hospital at Arles" (94 × 70 mm). Imperf Set of 2 sheets	12·00	13·00

1991. 65th Birthday of Queen Elizabeth II. As T **201** of Lesotho. Multicoloured.

1506	2r. Queen at Trooping the Colour, 1990	1·40	60
1507	5r. Queen with Queen Mother and Princess Margaret, 1973	2·50	1·75

1508 8r. Queen and Prince Philip in open carriage, 1986 . . 3·00 2·75
1509 12r. Queen at Royal Estates Ball . . . . 3·25 3·50
MS1510 68 × 90 mm. 25r. Separate photographs of Queen and Prince Philip . . . . 5·75 6·50

1991. 10th Wedding Anniv of Prince and Princess of Wales. As T **210** of Lesotho. Multicoloured.
1511 1r. Prince and Princess skiing, 1986 . . . . . . 80 20
1512 3r.50 Separate photographs of Prince, Princess and sons . . . . 1·75 1·10
1513 7r. Prince Henry in Christmas play and Prince William watching polo . . 2·00 2·00
1514 15r. Princess Diana at Ipswich, 1990, and Prince Charles playing polo . . . 3·50 3·75
MS1515 68 × 90 mm. 25r. Prince and Princess of Wales in Hungary, and Princes William and Harry going to school . . . . 5·75 6·50

256 Boy painting

257 Class C57 Steam Locomotive

1991. Hummel Figurines. Multicoloured.
1516 10l. Type **256** 15 15
1517 25l. Boy reading at table . . 20 20
1518 50l. Boy with school satchel 30 30
1519 2r. Girl with basket 70 70
1520 3r.50 Boy reading . . . . . 1·00 1·00
1521 8r. Girl and young child reading . . . . 2·25 2·50
1522 10r. School girls . . . . . 2·25 2·50
1523 25r. School boys . . . . . 4·75 6·50
MS1524 Two sheets, each 97 × 127 mm. (a) 5r. As No. 1519; 5r. As No. 1520; 5r. As No. 1521; 5r. As No. 1522. (b) 8r. As Type **256**; 8r. As No. 1517; 8r. As No. 1518; 8r. As No. 1523 Set of 2 sheets . . . . 9·00 11·00

1991. "Phila Nippon '91" International Stamp Exn, Tokyo. Japanese Steam Locomotives. Mult.
1525 15l. Type **257** 50 15
1526 25l. Class 6250 locomotive, 1915 (horiz) 65 25
1527 1r. Class D51 locomotive, 1936 . . . . 1·25 40
1528 3r.50 Class 8620 locomotive, 1914 (horiz) . . . . . . 2·00 1·25
1529 5r. Class 10 locomotive, 1889 (horiz) . . . . . . 2·25 1·75
1530 7r. Class C61 locomotive, 1947 . . . . 2·50 2·50
1531 10r. Class 9600 locomotive, 1913 (horiz) . . . . . . 2·50 2·75
1532 12r. Class D52 locomotive, 1943 (horiz) . . . . . . 2·75 3·50
MS1533 Two sheets, each 118 × 80 mm. (a) 20r. Class C56 locomotive, 1935 (horiz). (b) 20r. Class 1080 locomotive, 1925 (horiz) Set of 2 sheets . . . . 8·00 9·00

258 "Salamis temora" and "Vanda caerulea"

1991. Butterflies and Flowers. Multicoloured.
1534 10l. Type **258** 40 40
1535 25l. "Meneris tulbaghia" and "Incarvillea younghusbandii" 55 30
1536 50l. "Polyommatus icarus" and "Campsis grandiflora" 75 40
1537 2r. "Danaus plexippus" and "Thunbergia grandiflora" 1·25 90
1538 3r.50 "Colias interior" and "Medinilla magnifica" . . 1·75 1·75
1539 5r. "Ascalapha ordorata" and "Meconopsis horridula" . . . . 2·00 2·00
1540 8r. "Papilio memnon" and "Dillenia obovata" . . . 2·50 3·00
1541 10r. "Precis octavia" and "Thespesia populnea" . . 2·50 3·00
MS1542 Two sheets, each 100 × 70 mm. (a) 20r. "Bombax ceiba" and "Plyciodes tharos". (b) 20r. "Amauris niavius" and "Bombax insigne" Set of 2 sheets 10·00 12·00

259 "H-II" Rocket

1991. Japanese Space Programme. Multicoloured.
1543 15l. Type **259** 40 20
1544 20l. Projected "H-II" orbiting plane 40 20
1545 2r. Satellite "GMS-5" . . . 1·00 75
1546 3r.50 Satellite "MOMO-1" 1·40 1·40
1547 7r. Satellite "CS-3" . . . . 2·25 2·50
1548 10r. Satellite "BS-2a, 2b" . . 2·50 2·75
1549 12r. "H-I" Rocket (vert) . . 2·75 3·25
1550 15r. Space Flier unit and U.S. Space shuttle . . . . 2·75 3·25
MS1551 Two sheets. (a) 116 × 85 mm. 20r. Dish aerial, Katsura Tracking Station (vert). (b) 85 × 116 mm. 20r. "M-3SII" rocket (vert) Set of 2 sheets . . 11·00 11·00

260 Williams "FW-07"

1991. Formula 1 Racing Cars. Multicoloured.
1552 20l. Type **260** 30 20
1553 50l. Brabham/BMW "BT50" turbo 40 30
1554 1r. Williams/Honda "FW-11" 60 45
1555 3r.50 Ferrari "312 T3" . . . 1·25 1·25
1556 5r. Lotus/Honda "99T" . . 1·75 1·75
1557 7r. Benetton/Ford "B188" 2·00 2·25
1558 10r. Tyrrell "P34" six-wheeler . . . . 2·25 2·50
1559 21r. Renault "RE-30B" turbo . . . . 4·00 5·00
MS1560 Two sheets, each 84 × 56 mm. (a) 25r. Brabham/BMW "BT50" turbo (different). (b) 25r. Ferrari "F189" Set of 2 sheets . . . . 15·00 13·00

261 "Testa Rossa", 1957

1991. Ferrari Cars. Multicoloured.
1561 5r. Type **261** . . . . 2·00 2·00
1562 5r. "275GTB", 1966 . . . . 2·00 2·00
1563 5r. "Aspirarta", 1951 . . . 2·00 2·00
1564 5r. "Testarossa" . . . . . 2·00 2·00
1565 5r. Enzo Ferrari . . . . . 2·00 2·00
1566 5r. "Dino 246", 1958 . . . 2·00 2·00
1567 5r. "Type 375", 1952 . . . 2·00 2·00
1568 5r. Nigel Mansell's Formula 1 racing car . . . . . . 2·00 2·00
1569 5r. "312T", 1975 . . . . . 2·00 2·00

262 Franklin D. Roosevelt

1991. 50th Anniv of Japanese Attack on Pearl Harbor. American War Leaders. Multicoloured.
1570 3r.50 Type **262** . . . . . . 1·50 1·50
1571 3r.50 Douglas MacArthur and map of Philippines 1·50 1·50
1572 3r.50 Chester Nimitz and Pacific island . . . . . . 1·50 1·50
1573 3r.50 Jonathan Wainwright and barbed wire . . . . 1·50 1·50
1574 3r.50 Ernest King and U.S.S. "Hornet" (aircraft carrier) . . . . 1·50 1·50
1575 3r.50 Claire Chennault and Curtiss Tomahawk II fighters . . . . 1·50 1·50
1576 3r.50 William Halsey and U.S.S. "Enterprise" (aircraft carrier) . . . . . 1·50 1·50
1577 3r.50 Marc Mitscher and U.S.S. "Hornet" (aircraft carrier) . . . . 1·50 1·50
1578 3r.50 James Doolittle and North American B-25 Mitchell bomber . . . . 1·50 1·50
1579 3r.50 Raymond Spruance and Douglas Dauntless dive bomber . . . . . . 1·50 1·50

263 Brandenburg Gate and Postcard Commemorating Berlin Wall

1992. Anniversaries and Events. Multicoloured.
1580 20l. Type **263** 15 10
1581 50l. Schwarzenburg Palace 80 40
1582 1r. Spa at Baden . . . . . 1·10 50
1583 1r.75 Berlin Wall and man holding child 50 50
1584 2r. Royal Palace, Berlin . . 1·00 80
1585 4r. Demonstrator and border guards . . . . . 1·10 1·25
1586 5r. Viennese masonic seal 3·00 2·00
1587 6r. De Gaulle and Normandy landings, 1944 (vert) . . . . 2·50 2·25
1588 6r. Lilienthal's signature and "Flugzeug Nr. 16" . . . 2·50 2·25
1589 7r. St. Marx . . . . 3·00 2·25
1590 7r. Trans-Siberian Railway Class VL80T electric locomotive No. 1406 (vert) . . . . 3·00 2·25
1591 8r. Kurt Schwitters (artist) and Landesmuseum . . . 2·50 2·50
1592 9r. Map of Switzerland and man in Uri traditional costume . . . . 2·50 2·50
1593 10r. De Gaulle in Madagascar, 1958 . . . . 2·50 2·50
1594 10r. Scouts exploring coral reef . . . . 2·50 2·50
1595 11r. Scout salute and badge (vert) . . . . 2·50 2·50
1596 12r. Trans-Siberian Railway steam locomotive . . . . 3·25 3·25
1597 15r. Imperial German badges . . . . 2·50 3·25
1598 20r. Josepsplatz, Vienna . . 3·50 3·50
MS1599 Eight sheets. (a) 76 × 116 mm. 15r. General de Gaulle during Second World War (vert). (b) 101 × 72 mm. 18r. Ancient German helmet. (c) 101 × 72 mm. 18r. 19th-century shako. (d) 101 × 72 mm. 18r. Helmet of 1939. (e) 90 × 117 mm. 18r. Postcard of Lord Baden-Powell carried by rocket, 1937 (grey, black and mauve) (vert). (f) 75 × 104 mm. 20r. Bust of Mozart (vert). (g) 115 × 85 mm. 20r. Trans-Siberian Railway Class P36 steam locomotive stopped at signal (57 × 43 mm). (h) 117 × 90 mm. 20r. Czechoslovakia 1918 10h. "Scout Post" stamp (vert) Set of 8 sheets . . . . 32·00 35·00

ANNIVERSARIES AND EVENTS: Nos. 1580, 1583, 1585, 1597, **MS**1599b/d, Bicentenary of Brandenburg Gate, Berlin; 1581/2, 1584, 1586, 1589, 1598, **MS**1599f, Death bicentenary of Mozart (1991); 1587, 1593, **MS**1599a, Birth centenary of Charles de Gaulle (French statesman) (1990); 1588, Centenary of Otto Lilienthal's first gliding experiments; 1590, 1596, **MS**1599g, Centenary of Trans-Siberian Railway; 1591, 750th anniv of Hannover; 1592, 700th anniv of Swiss Confederation; 1594/5, **MS**1599e,h, 17th World Scout Jamboree, Korea.

264 Mickey Mouse on Flying Carpet, Arabia

1992. Mickey's World Tour. Designs showing Walt Disney cartoon characters in different countries. Multicoloured.
1600 25l. Type **264** 45 20
1601 50l. Goofy and Big Ben, Great Britain 55 25
1602 1r. Mickey wearing clogs, Netherlands 75 35
1603 2r. Pluto eating pasta, Italy 1·25 75
1604 3r. Mickey and Donald doing Mexican hat dance 1·40 1·25
1605 3r.50 Mickey, Goofy and Donald as tiki, New Zealand . . . . 1·40 1·40
1606 5r. Goofy skiing in Austrian Alps . . . . 1·50 1·50
1607 7r. Mickey and city gate, Germany . . . . 1·75 2·00
1608 10r. Donald as samurai, Japan . . . . 2·00 2·25
1609 12r. Mickey as heroic statue, Russia . . . . 2·25 2·75
1610 15r. Mickey, Donald, Goofy and Pluto as German band . . . . 2·50 3·00
MS1611 Three sheets, each 83 × 104 mm. (a) 25r. Donald chasing leprechaun, Ireland (horiz). (b) 25r. Baby kangaroo surprising Pluto, Australia. (c) 25r. Mickey and globe Set of 3 sheets 13·00 14·00

265 Whimbrel

266 Powder-blue Surgeonfish

1992. Birds. Multicoloured.
1612 10l. Type **265** 50 60
1613 25l. Great egret 50 40
1614 50l. Grey heron 60 50
1615 2r. Shag . . . . 1·40 75
1616 3r.50 Roseate tern . . . . 1·50 85
1617 5r. Greater greenshank . . 1·75 1·10
1617a 6r.50+50l. Egyptian vulture 2·25 2·25
1618 8r. Hoopoe . . . . 2·25 2·25
1619 10r. Black-shouldered kite 2·25 2·25
1620 25r. Scarlet ibis . . . . . 2·20 2·30
1620a 30r. Peregrine falcon . . . 2·75 3·00
1620b 40r. Black kite . . . . . . 3·50 3·75
1621 50r. Grey plover . . . . . 4·50 4·75
1621a 100r. Common shoveler . . 8·75 9·00
Nos. 1617a, 1620a/b and 1621a are larger, 23 × 32 mm.

1992. 40th Anniv of Queen Elizabeth II's Accession. As T **214** of Lesotho. Multicoloured.
1622 1r. Palm trees on beach . . 50 25
1623 3r.50 Path leading to jetty 1·75 1·00
1624 7r. Tropical plant . . . . . 2·50 2·75
1625 10r. Palm trees on beach (different) . . . . 2·75 3·00
MS1626 Two sheets, each 74 × 97 mm. (a) 18r. Dhow. (b) 18r. Palm trees on beach (different) Set of 2 sheets . . . 11·00 11·00

1992. Fishes. Multicoloured.
1627 7l. Type **266** 30 20
1628 20l. Catalufa 40 25
1629 50l. Yellow-finned tuna . . 55 30
1630 1r. Twin-spotted red snapper 75 35
1631 3r.50 Hawaiian squirrelfish 1·50 1·25
1632 5r. Picasso triggerfish . . . 2·00 2·00
1633 8r. Bennet's butterflyfish . . 2·25 2·50
1634 10r. Parrotfish . . . . . . 2·50 2·75
1635 12r. Coral hind . . . . . . 2·75 3·00
1636 15r. Skipjack tuna . . . . . 2·75 3·00
MS1637 Four sheets, each 116 × 76 mm. (a) 20r. Thread-finned butterflyfish. (b) 20r. Oriental sweetlips. (c) 20r. Two-banded anemonefish ("Clownfish"). (d) 20r. Clown triggerfish Set of 4 sheets . . . 13·00 15·00

1992. International Stamp Exhibitions. As T **215** of Lesotho showing Walt Disney cartoon characters. Multicoloured. (a) "Granada '92", Spain. The Alhambra.
1638 2r. Minnie Mouse in Court of the Lions 90 70
1639 5r. Goofy in Lions Fountain 1·75 1·75
1640 8r. Mickey Mouse at the Gate of Justice . . . . . 2·25 2·75
1641 12r. Donald Duck serenading Daisy at the Vermilion Towers . . . . 2·75 3·25
MS1642 127 × 102 mm. 25r. Goofy pushing Mickey in wheelbarrow 5·50 6·00

(b) "World Columbian Stamp Expo '92". Chicago Landmarks.
1643 1r. Mickey meeting Jean Baptiste du Sable (founder) . . . . 1·00 40
1644 3r.50 Donald Duck at Old Chicago Post Office . . . 2·00 1·25
1645 7r. Donald at Old Fort Dearborn . . . . 2·75 2·75
1646 15r. Goofy in Museum of Science and Industry . . 3·50 4·00
MS1647 127 × 102 mm. 25r. Mickey and Minnie Mouse at Columbian Exposition, 1893 (horiz) . . . . 5·50 6·00
On No. 1646 the design is wrongly captioned as the Science and Industry Museum.

267 Coastguard Patrol Boats

1992. Cent of National Security Service. Mult.
1648 3r.50 Type **267** . . . . . . 2·25 1·25
1649 5r. Infantry in training . . . 2·25 1·75
1650 10r. Aakoatey fort . . . . 2·50 2·75
1651 15r. Fire Service . . . . . 7·50 7·50
MS1652 100 × 68 mm. 20r. Ceremonial procession, 1892 6·00 7·00

268 Flowers of the United States of America

269 "Laetiporus sulphureus"

1992. National Flowers. Multicoloured.
1653 25l. Type **268** 50 30
1654 50l. Australia 70 30
1655 2r. England . . . . 1·40 1·10
1656 3r.50 Brazil . . . . 1·75 1·50
1657 5r. Holland . . . . 2·00 2·00
1658 8r. France . . . . 2·25 3·00
1659 10r. Japan . . . . 2·50 3·00
1660 15r. Africa . . . . 3·00 4·00
MS1661 Two sheets, each 114 × 85 mm. (a) 25r. "Plumieria rubra", "Classia fistula" and "Eugenia malaccensis" (57 × 43 mm). (b) 25r. "Bauhinia variegata", "Catharanthus roseus" and "Plumieria alba" (57 × 43 mm) Set of 2 sheets . . 9·00 10·00

1992. Fungi. Multicoloured.
1662 10l. Type **269** 30 30
1663 25l. "Coprinus atramentarius" 40 30
1664 50l. "Ganoderma lucidum" 60 40
1665 3r.50 "Russula aurata" . . 1·25 1·00
1666 5r. "Grifola umbellata" ("Polyporus umbellatus") 1·75 1·75
1667 8r. "Suillus grevillei" . . . 2·25 2·50
1668 10r. "Clavaria zollingeri" . . 2·50 2·50
1669 25r. "Boletus edulis" . . . 5·00 6·00
MS1670 Two sheets, each 100 × 70 mm. (a) 25r. "Marasmius oreades". (b) 25r. "Pycnoporus cinnabarinus" ("Trametes cinnabarina") Set of 2 sheets 12·00 13·00

1992. Olympic Games, Albertville and Barcelona (1st issue). As T **216** of Lesotho. Multicoloured.
1671 10l. Pole vault 20 10
1672 25l. Men's pommel horse (horiz) 25 15
1673 50l. Men's shot put 30 25
1674 1r. Men's horizontal bar (horiz) 35 30
1675 2r. Men's triple jump (horiz) 80 65
1676 3r.50 Table tennis . . . . . 1·10 1·10
1677 5r. Two-man bobsled . . . 1·40 1·40
1678 7r. Freestyle wrestling (horiz) . . . . 1·75 2·00
1679 8r. Freestyle ski-jump . . . 1·75 2·00
1680 9r. Baseball . . . . 2·00 2·25
1681 10r. Women's cross-country Nordic skiing . . . . . . 2·00 2·25
1682 12r. Men's 200 m backstroke (horiz) 2·00 2·25
MS1683 Three sheets. (a) 100 × 70 mm. 25r. Decathalon (horiz). (b) 100 × 70 mm. 25r. Women's slalom skiing (horiz). (c) 70 × 100 mm. 25r. Men's figure skating Set of 3 sheets . . . . 12·00 13·00
See also Nos. 1684/92.

270 Hurdling

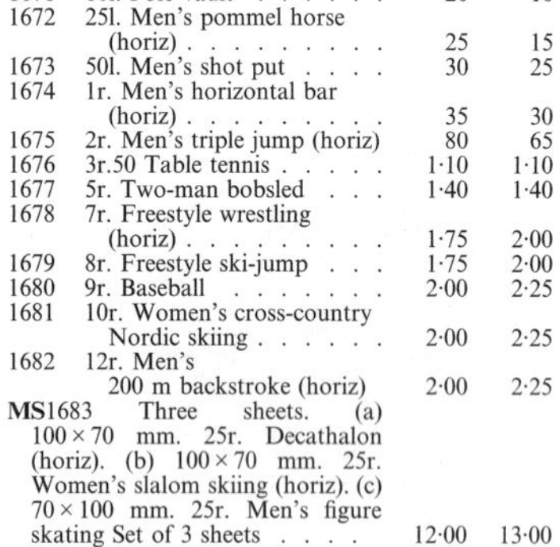

271 Deinonychus

1992. Olympic Games, Barcelona (2nd issue). Multicoloured.
1684 10l. Type **270** 10 10
1685 1r. Boxing 30 30
1686 3r.50 Women's sprinting . . 80 70
1687 5r. Discus . . . . 1·25 1·25
1688 7r. Basketball . . . . 3·00 2·50
1689 10r. Long-distance running 2·25 2·50
1690 12r. Aerobic gymnastics . . 2·50 3·00
1691 20r. Fencing . . . . 3·25 4·00
MS1692 Two sheets, each 70 × 100 mm. (a) 25r. Olympic symbol and national flags. (b) 25r. Olympic symbol and flame Set of 2 sheets . . . . 8·50 9·00

1992. "Genova '92" International Thematic Stamp Exhibition. Prehistoric Animals. Multicoloured.
1693 5l. Type **271** 40 20
1694 10l. Styracosaurus 40 20
1695 25l. Mamenchisaurus . . . 50 30
1696 50l. Stenonychosaurus . . . 60 30
1697 1r. Parasaurolophus 75 40
1698 1r.25 Scelidosaurus 85 50
1699 1r.75 Tyrannosaurus . . . . 1·10 55
1700 2r. Stegosaurus . . . . . . 1·25 60
1701 3r.50 Iguanodon . . . . . 1·50 80
1702 4r. Anatosaurus . . . . . . 1·50 1·00
1703 5r. Monoclonius . . . . . 1·60 1·10
1704 7r. Tenontosaurus . . . . . 1·90 1·90
1705 8r. Brachiosaurus . . . . . 1·90 1·90
1706 10r. Euoplocephalus . . . . 2·00 2·00
1707 25r. Triceratops . . . . . . 3·25 4·50
1708 50r. Apatosaurus . . . . . 6·00 8·00
MS1709 Four sheets, each 116 × 85 mm. (a) 25r. Hadrosaur hatchling. (b) 25r. Iguanodon fighting Allosaurus. (c) 25r. Tyrannosaurus attacking Triceratops. (d) 25r. Brachiosaurus and Iguanodons Set of 4 sheets . . . . 14·00 15·00

1992. Postage Stamp Mega Event, New York. Sheet 100 × 70 mm, containing multicoloured design as T **219** of Lesotho, but horiz.
MS1710 20r. New York Public Library . . . . 2·50 3·25

272 Destruction of LZ-129 "Hindenburg" (airship), 1937

1992. Mysteries of the Universe. T **272** and similar multicoloured designs, each in separate miniature sheet.
MS1711 Sixteen sheets, each 100 × 71 mm. (a) 25r. Type **272**. (b) 25r. Loch Ness Monster. (c) 25r. Crystal skull. (d) 25r. Space craft in Black Hole. (e) 25r. Ghosts (vert). (f) 25r. Flying saucer, 1947 (vert). (g) 25r. Bust of Plato (Atlantis). (h) 25r. U.F.O., 1973. (i) 25r. Crop circles. (j) 25r. Mil Mi-26 Russian helicopter at Chernobyl nuclear explosion. (k) 25r. Figure from Plain of Nazca. (l) 25r. Stonehenge (vert). (m) 25r. Yeti footprint (vert). (n) 25r. The Pyramid of Giza. (o) 25r. "Marie Celeste" (brigantine) (vert). (p) 25r. American Grumman TBF Avenger fighter aircraft (Bermuda Triangle) Set of 16 sheets . . . 55·00 55·00

273 Zubin Mehta (musical director)

274 Friedrich Schmiedl

1992. 150th Anniv of New York Philharmonic Orchestra. Sheet 100 × 70 mm.
MS1712 **273** 20r. multicoloured 6·00 6·00

1992. 90th Birth Anniv of Friedrich Schmiedl (rocket mail pioneer). Sheet 104 × 69 mm.
MS1713 **274** 25r. multicoloured 5·50 6·00

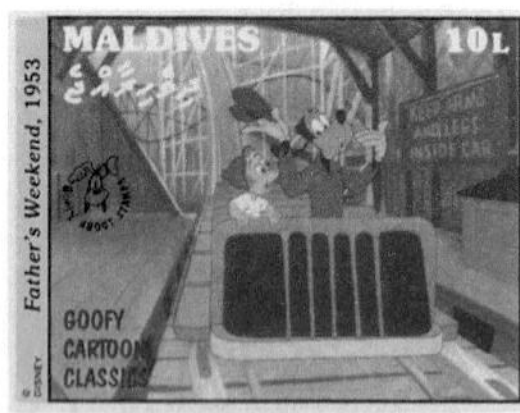

275 Goofy in "Father's Weekend", 1953

1992. 60th Anniv of Goofy (Disney cartoon character). Goofy in various cartoon films. Multicoloured.
1714 10l. Type **275** 10 10
1715 50l. "Symphony Hour", 1942 . . . . 35 20
1716 75l. "Frank Duck Brings 'Em Back Alive", 1946 . . 45 20
1717 1r. "Crazy with the Heat", 1947 . . . . 45 20
1718 2r. "The Big Wash", 1948 70 60
1719 3r.50 "How to Ride a Horse", 1950 . . . . . . 1·25 1·25
1720 5r. "Two Gun Goofy", 1952 1·50 1·50
1721 8r. "Saludos Amigos", 1943 (vert) . . . . 2·00 2·25
1722 10r. "How to be a Detective", 1952 . . . . 2·00 2·25
1723 12r. "For Whom the Bulls Toil", 1953 . . . . . . 2·25 2·50
1724 15r. "Double Dribble", 1946 (vert) . . . . 2·25 2·50
MS1725 Three sheets, each 127 × 102 mm. (a) 20r. "Double Dribble", 1946 (different) (vert). (b) 20r. "The Goofy Success Story", 1955 (vert). (c) 20r. "Mickey and the Beanstalk", 1947 Set of 3 sheets . . . . 9·00 9·50

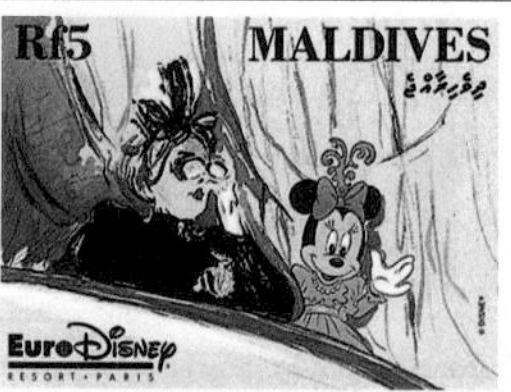

276 Minnie Mouse in "Le Missioner" (Toulouse-Lautrec)

1992. Opening of Euro-Disney Resort, France. Disney cartoon characters superimposed on Impressionist paintings. Multicoloured.
1726 5r. Type **276** . . . . . . 1·40 1·50
1727 5r. Goofy in "The Card Players" (Cezanne) . . . 1·40 1·50
1728 5r. Mickey and Minnie Mouse in "The Cafe Terrace, Place du Forum" (Van Gogh) . . . . . . 1·40 1·50
1729 5r. Mickey in "The Bridge at Langlois" (Van Gogh) 1·40 1·50
1730 5r. Goofy in "Chocolate Dancing" (Toulouse-Lautrec) . . . . 1·40 1·50
1731 5r. Mickey and Minnie in "The Seine at Asnieres" (Renoir) . . . . 1·40 1·50
1732 5r. Minnie in "Ball at the Moulin Rouge" (Toulouse-Lautrec) . . . 1·40 1·50
1733 5r. Mickey in "Wheatfield with Cypresses" (Van Gogh) . . . . 1·40 1·50
1734 5r. Minnie in "When will you Marry?" (Gauguin) 1·40 1·50
MS1735 Four sheets. (a) 128 × 100 mm. 20r. Minnie as can-can dancer. (b) 128 × 100 mm. 20r. Goofy as cyclist. (c) 100 × 128 mm. 20r. Mickey as artist. (d) 100 × 128 mm. 20r. Donald as Frenchman (vert) Set of 4 sheets 12·00 13·00

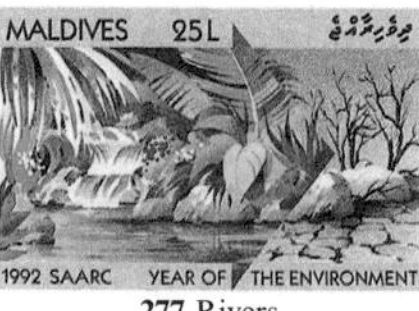

277 Rivers

1992. South Asian Association for Regional Co-operation Year of the Environment. Natural and Polluted Environments. Multicoloured.
1736 25l. Type **277** 15 10
1737 50l. Beaches 25 10
1738 5r. Oceans . . . . 80 1·00
1739 10r. Weather . . . . 1·50 2·00

278 Jurgen Klinsmann (Germany)

280 Elvis Presley

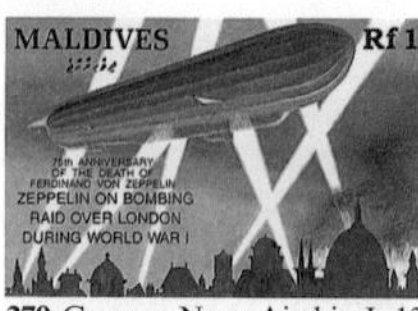

279 German Navy Airship L-13 bombing London, 1914–18

1993. World Cup Football Championship, U.S.A. (1994) (1st issue). German Players and Officials. Multicoloured.
1740 10l. Type **278** 40 20
1741 25l. Pierre Littbarski 45 20
1742 50l. Lothar Matthaus . . . 55 20
1743 1r. Rudi Voller 75 25
1744 2r. Thomas Hassler . . . . 1·25 60
1745 3r.50 Thomas Berthold . . 1·60 1·00
1746 4r. Jurgen Kohler . . . . . 1·75 1·25
1747 5r. Berti Vogts . . . . . . 1·90 1·40
1748 6r. Bodo Illgner . . . . . . 2·25 2·25
1749 7r. Klaus Augenthaler . . . 2·25 2·25
1750 8r. Franz Beckenbauer . . . 2·25 2·25
1751 10r. Andreas Brehme . . . 2·50 2·75
1752 12r. Guido Buchwald . . . 2·50 3·25
MS1753 Two sheets, each 103 × 73 mm. (a) 35r. German players celebrating (horiz). (b) 35r. Rudi Voller (horiz) Set of 2 sheets 13·00 14·00
See also Nos. 1990/7 and 2089/2100.

1993. Anniversaries and Events. Multicoloured.
1754 1r. Type **279** 80 30
1755 3r.50 Radio telescope . . . 70 80
1756 3r.50 Chancellor Adenauer and Pres. de Gaulle . . . 70 80
1757 6r. Indian rhinoceros . . . 3·25 2·00
1758 6r. Columbus and globe . . 2·50 1·75
1759 7r. Conference emblems . . 1·25 1·75
1760 8r. Green seaturtle . . . . 1·50 1·60
1761 10r. "America" (yacht), 1851 . . . . 1·75 2·00
1762 10r. Melvin Jones (founder) and emblem . . . . . . 1·75 2·00
1763 12r. Columbus landing on San Salvador . . . . . . 3·00 3·25
1764 15r. "Voyager I" approaching Saturn . . . 4·50 4·50
1765 15r. Adenauer, N.A.T.O. flag and Lockheed Starfighter aircraft . . . . 4·50 4·50
1766 20r. "Graf Zeppelin" over New York, 1929 . . . . 4·50 4·50
MS1767 Five sheets, each 111 × 80 mm. (a) 20r. Count Ferdinand von Zeppelin. (b) 20r. "Landsat" satellite. (c) 20r. Konrad Adenauer. (d) 20r. Scarlet macaw. (e) 20r. "Santa Maria" Set of 5 sheets . . . . 19·00 20·00
ANNIVERSARIES AND EVENTS: 1754, 1766, **MS**1767a, 75th death anniv of Count Ferdinand von Zeppelin; 1755, 1764, **MS**1767b, International Space Year; 1756, 1765, **MS**1767c, 25th death anniv of Konrad Adenauer; 1757, 1760, **MS**1767d, Earth Summit '92, Rio; 1758, 1763, **MS**1767e, 500th anniv of discovery of America by Columbus; 1759, International Conference on Nutrition, Rome; 1761, Americas Cup Yachting Championship; 1762, 75th anniv of International Association of Lions Clubs.

1993. 15th Death Anniv of Elvis Presley (singer). Multicoloured.
1768 3r.50 Type **280** 90 70
1769 3r.50 Elvis with guitar . . . 90 70
1770 3r.50 Elvis with microphone 90 70

1993. Bicentenary of the Louvre, Paris. As T **221a** of Lesotho. Multicoloured.
1771 8r. "The Study" (Fragonard) . . . . . . 90 1·10
1772 8r. "Denis Diderot" (Fragonard) . . . . . . 90 1·10
1773 8r. "Marie-Madelaine Guimard" (Fragonard) . . 90 1·10
1774 8r. "Inspiration" (Fragonard) . . . . . . 90 1·10
1775 8r. "Waterfalls, Tivoli" (Fragonard) . . . . . . 90 1·10
1776 8r. "The Music Lesson" (Fragonard) . . . . . . 90 1·10
1777 8r. "The Bolt" (Fragonard) 90 1·10
1778 8r. "Blind-man's Buff" (Fragonard) . . . . . . 90 1·10
1779 8r. "Self-portrait" (Corot) 90 1·10
1780 8r. "Woman in Blue" (Corot) . . . . 90 1·10
1781 8r. "Woman with a Pearl" (Corot) . . . . 90 1·10
1782 8r. "Young Girl at her Toilet" (Corot) . . . . . 90 1·10
1783 8r. "Haydee" (Corot) . . . 90 1·10
1784 8r. "Chartres Cathedral" (Corot) . . . . 90 1·10
1785 8r. "The Belfry of Douai" (Corot) . . . . 90 1·10
1786 8r. "The Bridge of Mantes" (Corot) . . . . 90 1·10
1787 8r. "Madame Seriziat" (David) . . . . 90 1·10
1788 8r. "Pierre Seriziat" (David) 90 1·10
1789 8r. "Madame De Verninac" (David) . . . . 90 1·10
1790 8r. "Madame Recamier" (David) . . . . 90 1·10
1791 8r. "Self-portrait" (David) 90 1·10
1792 8r. "General Bonaparte" (David) . . . . 90 1·10
1793 8r. "The Lictors bringing Brutus his Son's Body" (David) (left detail) . . . 90 1·10
1794 8r. "The Lictors bringing Brutus his Son's Body" (David) (right detail) . . . 90 1·10
MS1795 Two sheets, each 100 × 70 mm. (a) 20r. "Gardens of the Villa D'Este, Tivoli" (Corot) (85 × 52 mm). (b) 20r. "Tiger Cub playing with its Mother" (Delacroix) (85 × 52 mm) Set of 2 sheets . . . . 8·50 8·50

281 James Stewart and Marlene Dietrich ("Destry Rides Again")

1993. Famous Western Films. Multicoloured.
1796 5r. Type **281** . . . . 1·25 1·10
1797 5r. Gary Cooper ("The Westerner") . . . . . . 1·25 1·10
1798 5r. Henry Fonda ("My Darling Clementine") . . 1·25 1·10
1799 5r. Alan Ladd ("Shane") . . 1·25 1·10
1800 5r. Kirk Douglas and Burt Lancaster ("Gunfight at the O.K. Corral") . . . . 1·25 1·10
1801 5r. Steve McQueen ("The Magnificent Seven") . . . 1·25 1·10

1802 5r. Robert Redford and Paul Newman ("Butch Cassidy and The Sundance Kid") . . . . . 1·25 1·10
1803 5r. Jack Nicholson and Randy Quaid ("The Missouri Breaks") . . . . 1·25 1·10
MS1804 Two sheets, each 134 × 120 mm. (a) 20r. John Wayne ("The Searchers") (French poster). (b) 20r. Clint Eastwood ("Pale Rider") (French poster) Set of 2 sheets . . . . 7·00 7·00

1993. 40th Anniv of Coronation. As T **224** of Lesotho.
1805 3r.50 multicoloured . . . . 1·00 1·10
1806 5r. multicoloured . . . . . 1·25 1·40
1807 10r. blue and black . . . . 1·50 1·75
1808 10r. blue and black . . . . 1·50 1·75
DESIGNS: No. 1805, Queen Elizabeth II at Coronation (photograph by Cecil Beaton); 1806, St. Edward's Crown; 1807, Guests in the Abbey; 1808, Queen Elizabeth II and Prince Philip.

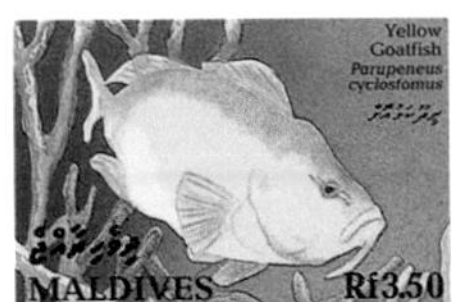

282 Blue Goatfish

1993. Fishes. Multicoloured.
1809 3r.50 Type **282** 60 70
1810 3r.50 Emperor angelfish . . 60 70
1811 3r.50 Madagascar butterflyfish 60 70
1812 3r.50 Regal angelfish . . . 60 70
1813 3r.50 Forceps fish ("Longnose butterflyfish") 60 70
1814 3r.50 Racoon butterflyfish 60 70
1815 3r.50 Harlequin filefish . . . 60 70
1816 3r.50 Rectangle triggerfish 60 70
1817 3r.50 Yellow-tailed anemonefish 60 70
1818 3r.50 Clown triggerfish . . . 60 70
1819 3r.50 Zebra lionfish 60 70
1820 3r.50 Maldive anemonefish ("Clownfish") 60 70
1821 3r.50 Black-faced butterflyfish 60 70
1822 3r.50 Bird wrasse 60 70
1823 3r.50 Checkerboard wrasse 60 70
1824 3r.50 Yellow-faced angelfish 60 70
1825 3r.50 Masked bannerfish . . 60 70
1826 3r.50 Thread-finned butterflyfish 60 70
1827 3r.50 Painted triggerfish . . 60 70
1828 3r.50 Coral hind 60 70
1829 3r.50 Pennant coralfish . . . 60 70
1830 3r.50 Black-backed butterflyfish 60 70
1831 3r.50 Red-toothed triggerfish 60 70
1832 3r.50 Melon butterflyfish . . 60 70
MS1833 Two sheets. (a) 69 × 96 mm. 25r. Klein's butterflyfish (vert). (b) 96 × 69 mm. 25r. Brown anemonefish (vert) Set of 2 sheets 8·00 8·50
Nos. 1809/20 and 1821/32 were printed together, se-tenant, with the backgrounds forming composite designs.
Nos. 1810 and 1824 are both inscribed "Angelfish" in error.

283 Gull-billed Tern

1993. Birds. Multicoloured.
1834 3r.50 Type **283** 60 70
1835 3r.50 White-tailed tropic bird ("Long-tailed Tropicbird") 60 70
1836 3r.50 Great frigate bird ("Frigate Bird") 60 70
1837 3r.50 Wilson's storm petrel ("Wilson's Petrel") . . . 60 70
1838 3r.50 White tern 60 70
1839 3r.50 Brown booby 60 70
1840 3r.50 Marsh harrier 60 70
1841 3r.50 Common noddy . . . 60 70
1842 3r.50 Green-backed heron ("Little Heron") 60 70
1843 3r.50 Ruddy turnstone ("Turnstone") 60 70
1844 3r.50 Curlew 60 70
1845 3r.50 Crab plover 60 70
1846 3r.50 Pallid harrier (vert) . . 60 70
1847 3r.50 Cattle egret (vert) . . 60 70
1848 3r.50 Koel (vert) 60 70
1849 3r.50 Tree pipit (vert) . . . 60 70
1850 3r.50 Short-eared owl (vert) 60 70
1851 3r.50 Common kestrel ("European Kestrel") (vert) 60 70
1852 3r.50 Yellow wagtail (vert) 60 70
1853 3r.50 Grey heron ("Common Heron") (vert) 60 70
1854 3r.50 Black bittern (vert) . . 60 70
1855 3r.50 Common snipe (vert) 60 70
1856 3r.50 Little egret (vert) . . . 60 70
1857 3r.50 Little stint (vert) . . . 60 70
MS1858 Two sheets, each 105 × 75 mm. (a) 25r. Caspian tern. (b) 25r. Audubon's shearwater Set of 2 sheets . . . 8·50 9·00

Nos. 1834/45 and 1846/57 were printed together, se-tenant, with the backgrounds forming composite designs.

284 Precious Wentletrap

285 Sifaka Lemur

1993. Shells. Multicoloured.
1859 7l. Type **284** 30 30
1860 15l. Common purple janthina 35 30
1861 50l. Asiatic arabian cowrie 45 30
1862 3r.50 Common or major harp . . . . 1·50 1·00
1863 4r. Amplustre or royal paper bubble . . . . . . 1·75 1·25
1864 5r. Sieve cowrie . . . . . . 1·75 1·40
1865 6r. Episcopal mitre . . . . 2·00 2·00
1866 7r. Camp pitar venus . . . 2·00 2·25
1867 8r. Spotted or eyed auger 2·25 2·50
1868 10r. Exposed cowrie . . . . 2·50 2·50
1869 12r. Geographic map cowrie 2·75 3·50
1870 20r. Bramble murex . . . . 3·50 4·50
MS1871 Three sheets, each 104 × 75 mm. (a) 25r. Black-striped triton. 25r. Scorpion conch. (c) 25r. Bull-mouth helmet Set of 3 sheets . . . . 17·00 19·00

1993. Endangered Species. Multicoloured.
1872 7l. Type **285** 50 30
1873 10l. Snow leopard 50 30
1874 15l. Numbat 50 30
1875 25l. Gorilla 90 40
1876 2r. Koala . . . . 1·00 70
1877 3r.50 Cheetah . . . . . . 1·25 1·10
1878 5r. Yellow-footed rock wallaby . . . . 1·40 1·40
1879 7r. Orang-utan . . . . . . 2·25 2·25
1880 8r. Black lemur . . . . . . 2·25 2·25
1881 10r. Black rhinoceros . . . 2·75 2·75
1882 15r. Humpback whale . . . 3·00 3·50
1883 20r. Mauritius parakeet . . 3·25 3·75
MS1884 Three sheets, each 104 × 75 mm. (a) 25r. Giant panda. (b) 25r. Tiger. (c) 25r. Indian elephant Set of 3 sheets 16·00 17·00

286 Symbolic Heads and Arrows

287 Early Astronomical Equipment

1993. Productivity Year. Multicoloured.
1885 7r. Type **286** . . . . 1·25 1·40
1886 10r. Abstract . . . . 1·60 1·75

1993. Anniversaries and Events. Multicoloured.
1887 3r.50 Type **287** . . . . . . 1·00 1·00
1888 3r.50 "Still Life with Pitcher and Apples" (Picasso) . . 1·00 1·00
1889 3r.50 "Zolte Roze" (Menasze Seidenbeurel) 1·00 1·00
1890 3r.50 Prince Naruhito and engagement photographs (horiz) . . . . 1·00 1·00
1891 5r. "Bowls and Jug" (Picasso) . . . . 1·25 1·25
1892 5r. Krysztofory Palace, Cracow . . . . 1·25 1·25
1893 8r. "Jabtka i Kotara" (Waclaw Borowski) . . . 1·75 1·90
1894 8r. Marina Kiehl (Germany) (women's downhill skiing) 1·75 1·90
1895 10r. "Bowls of Fruit and Loaves on a Table" (Picasso) . . . . 1·90 2·00
1896 10r. Masako Owada and engagement photographs (horiz) . . . . 1·90 2·00
1897 15r. American astronaut in space . . . . 2·75 3·00
1898 15r. Vegard Ulvang (Norway) (30km cross-country skiing) . . . . . 2·75 3·00
MS1899 Five sheets. (a) 105 × 75 mm. (a) 20r. Copernicus. (b) 105 × 75 mm. 20r. "Green Still Life" (detail) (Picasso) (horiz). (c) 105 × 75 mm. 25r. "Pejzaz Morski-Port z DoplywajacymStstkiem" (detail (Roman Sielski) (horiz). (d) 75 × 105 mm. 25r. Masako Owada. (e) 105 × 75 mm. 25r. Ice hockey goalkeeper Set of 5 sheets 19·00 21·00

ANNIVERSARIES AND EVENTS: Nos. 1887, 1897, **MS**1899a, 450th death anniv of Copernicus (astronomer); 1888, 1891, 1895, **MS**1899b, 20th death anniv of Picasso (artist); 1889, 1892/3, **MS**1899c, "Polska '93" International Stamp Exhibition, Poznan; 1890, 1896, **MS**1899d, Marriage of Crown Prince Naruhito of Japan; 1894, 1898, **MS**1899e, Winter Olympic Games '94, Lillehammer.

288 "Limenitis procris" and "Mussaenda"

1993. Butterflies and Flowers. Multicoloured.
1900 7l. Type **288** 30 20
1901 20l. "Danaus limniace" and "Thevetia neriifolia" . . . 45 20
1902 25l. "Amblypodia centaurus" and "Clitoria ternatea" 45 20
1903 50l. "Papilio crino" and "Crossandra infundibuliformis" 60 20
1904 5r. "Mycalesis patnia" and "Thespesia populnia" . . 1·75 1·40
1905 6r.50+50l. "Idea jasonia" and "Cassia glauca" . . . 2·00 2·25
1906 7r. "Catopsilia pomona" and "Calotropis" . . . . 2·00 2·25
1907 10r. "Precis orithyia" and "Thunbergia grandiflora" 2·25 2·50
1908 12r. "Vanessa cardui" and "Caesalpinia pulcherrima" 2·50 3·00
1909 15r. "Papilio polymnestor" and "Nerium oleander" 2·75 3·25
1910 18r. "Cirrochroa thais" and "Vinca rosea" . . . . . 3·00 3·50
1911 20r. "Pachliopta hector" and "Ixora coccinea" . . 3·00 3·50
MS1912 Three sheets, each 105 × 72 mm. (a) 25r. "Cheritra freja" and "Bauhinia purpurea" (vert). (b) 25r. "Rohana parisatis" and "Plumeria acutifolia" (vert). (c) 25r. "Hebomoia glaucippe" and "Punica granatum" (vert) Set of 3 sheets . . . . 15·00 17·00

289 Airship "Graf Zeppelin" in Searchlights

1993. Aviation Anniversaries. Multicoloured.
1913 3r.50 Type **289** . . . . . . 1·75 65
1914 5r. Homing pigeon and message from Santa Catalina mail service, 1894 . . . . 2·00 1·10
1915 10r. Eckener and airship "Graf Zeppelin" . . . . 2·50 2·50
1916 15r. Pilot's badge and loading Philadelphia–Washington mail, 1918 . . 3·50 4·00
1917 20r. U.S.S. "Macon" (airship) and mooring mast, 1933 . . . . 3·50 4·00
MS1918 Two sheets. (a) 70 × 100 mm. 25r. Santos Dumont's airship "Ballon No. 5" and Eiffel Tower, 1901. (b) 100 × 70 mm. 25r. Jean-Pierre Blanchard's balloon, 1793 (vert) Set of 2 sheets . . . . 6·50 7·50
ANNIVERSARIES: Nos. 1913, 1915, 1917, **MS**1918a, 125th birth anniv of Hugo Eckener (airship pioneer); 1914, 1916, **MS**1918b, Bicent of first airmail flight.

290 Ford Model "T"

1993. Centenaries of Henry Ford's First Petrol Engine (Nos. 1919/30) and Karl Benz's First Four-wheeled Car (others).
1919 **290** 3r.50 multicoloured . . . 90 1·00
1920 – 3r.50 multicoloured . . . 90 1·00
1921 – 3r.50 black and violet . . 90 1·00
1922 – 3r.50 multicoloured . . . 90 1·00
1923 – 3r.50 multicoloured . . . 90 1·00
1924 – 3r.50 multicoloured . . . 90 1·00
1925 – 3r.50 multicoloured . . . 90 1·00
1926 – 3r.50 multicoloured . . . 90 1·00
1927 – 3r.50 multicoloured . . . 90 1·00
1928 – 3r.50 multicoloured . . . 90 1·00
1929 – 3r.50 multicoloured . . . 90 1·00
1930 – 3r.50 black, brn & vio 90 1·00
1931 – 3r.50 multicoloured . . . 90 1·00
1932 – 3r.50 multicoloured . . . 90 1·00
1933 – 3r.50 green, blk & vio 90 1·00
1934 – 3r.50 multicoloured . . . 90 1·00
1935 – 3r.50 multicoloured . . . 90 1·00
1936 – 3r.50 multicoloured . . . 90 1·00
1937 – 3r.50 multicoloured . . . 90 1·00
1938 – 3r.50 multicoloured . . . 90 1·00
1939 – 3r.50 multicoloured . . . 90 1·00
1940 – 3r.50 multicoloured . . . 90 1·00
1941 – 3r.50 multicoloured . . . 90 1·00
1942 – 3r.50 black, brn and violet . . . . 90 1·00
MS1943 Two sheets, each 100 × 70 mm. (a) 25r. multicoloured. (b) 25r. multicoloured Set of 2 sheets 9·00 10·00
DESIGNS: No. 1920, Henry Ford; 1921, Plans of first petrol engine; 1922, Ford "Probe GT", 1993; 1923, Front of Ford "Sportsman", 1947; 1924, Back of Ford "Sportsman"; 1925, Advertisement of 1915; 1926, Ford "Thunderbird", 1955; 1927, Ford logo; 1928, Ford "Edsel Citation", 1958; 1929, Ford half-ton pickup, 1941; 1930, Silhouette of early Ford car; 1931, Daimler-Benz "Straight 8", 1937; 1932, Karl Benz; 1933, Mercedes-Benz poster; 1934, Mercedes "38-250SS", 1929; 1935, Benz "Viktoria", 1893; 1936, Benz logo; 1937, Plan of Mercedes engine; 1938, Mercedes-Benz "300SL Gullwing", 1952; 1939, Mercedes-Benz "SL", 1993; 1940, Front of Benz 4-cylinder car, 1906; 1941, Back of Benz 4-cylinder car and advertisement; 1942, Silhouette of early Benz car; **MS**1943a, Ford Model "Y", 1933; **MS**1943b, Mercedes "300S", 1955.
Nos. 1919/30 and 1931/42 were printed together, se-tenant, forming a composite design.

291 Ivan, Sonia, Sasha and Peter in the Snow

1993. "Peter and the Wolf". Scenes from Walt Disney's cartoon film. Multicoloured.
1944 7l. Type **291** 25 25
1945 15l. Grandpa and Peter . . 30 25
1946 20l. Peter on bridge 30 25
1947 25l. Yascha, Vladimir and Mischa 30 25
1948 50l. Sasha on lookout . . . 45 30
1949 1r. The wolf 60 35
1950 3r.50 Peter dreaming . . . 70 80
1951 3r.50 Peter taking gun . . . 70 80
1952 3r.50 Peter with gun in snow 70 80
1953 3r.50 Sasha and Peter . . . 70 80
1954 3r.50 Sonia and Peter . . . 70 80
1955 3r.50 Peter with Ivan and Sasha 70 80
1956 3r.50 Ivan warning Peter of the wolf 70 80
1957 3r.50 Ivan, Peter and Sasha in tree 70 80
1958 3r.50 Wolf below tree . . . 70 80
1959 3r.50 Wolf and Sonia . . . 70 80
1960 3r.50 Sasha attacking the wolf 70 80
1961 3r.50 Sasha walking into wolf's mouth 70 80
1962 3r.50 Peter firing pop gun at wolf 70 80
1963 3r.50 Wolf chasing Sonia . . 70 80
1964 3r.50 Ivan tying rope to wolf's tail 70 80
1965 3r.50 Peter and Ivan hoisting wolf 70 80
1966 3r.50 Sasha and the hunters 70 80
1967 3r.50 Ivan and Peter on wolf hanging from tree 70 80
MS1968 Two sheets. (a) 102 × 127 mm. 25r. Sonia as an angel. (b) 127 × 102 mm. 25r. Ivan looking proud Set of 2 sheets 8·00 8·50

292 "Girl with a Broom" (Rembrandt)

1994. Famous Paintings by Rembrandt and Matisse. Multicoloured.
1969 50l. Type **292** 40 25
1970 2r. "Girl with Tulips" (Matisse) 90 70
1971 3r.50 "Young Girl at half-open Door" (Rembrandt) 1·25 1·10
1972 3r.50 "Portrait of Greta Moll" (Matisse) . . . . . 1·25 1·10
1973 5r. "The Prophetess Hannah" (Rembrandt) . . 1·50 1·25
1974 6r.50 "The Idol" (Matisse) 1·75 1·75
1975 7r. "Woman with a Pink Flower" (Rembrandt) . . 1·75 1·75

1976 9r. "Mme Matisse in a Japanese Robe" (Matisse) 2·00 2·25
1977 10r. "Portrait of Mme Matisse" (Matisse) . . . 2·00 2·25
1978 12r. "Lucretia" (Rembrandt) 2·25 2·50
1979 15r. "Lady with a Ostrich Feather Fan" (Rembrandt) . . . . . . 2·25 2·75
1980 15r. "The Woman with the Hat" (Matisse) . . . . . 2·25 2·75
MS1981 Three sheets. (a) 106 × 132 mm. 25r. "The Music-makers" (detail) (Rembrandt). (b) 132 × 106 mm. 25r. "Married Couple with Three Children" (detail) (Rembrandt) (horiz). (c) 132 × 106 mm. 25r. "The Painter's Family" (detail) (Matisse) Set of 3 sheets . . . . 15·00 15·00

No. 1979 is inscribed "The Lady with an Ostich Feather Fan" in error.

293 Hong Kong 1983 Space Museum Stamp and Moon-lantern Festival

1994. "Hong Kong '94" International Stamp Exn (1st issue). Multicoloured.
1982 4r. Type **293** 65 80
1983 4r. Maldive Islands 1976 5r. "Viking" space mission stamp and Moon-lantern festival 65 80

Nos. 1982/3 were printed together, se-tenant, forming a composite design.

294 Vase

295 Windischmann (U.S.A.) and Giannini (Italy)

1994. "Hong Kong '94" International Stamp Exhibition (2nd issue). Ching Dynasty Cloisonne Enamelware. Multicoloured.
1984 2r. Type **294** 65 65
1985 2r. Flower holder 65 65
1986 2r. Elephant with vase on back 65 65
1987 2r. Tibetan style lama's teapot 65 65
1988 2r. Fo-Dog 65 65
1989 2r. Teapot with swing handle 65 65

1994. World Cup Football Championship, U.S.A. (2nd issue). Multicoloured.
1990 7l. Type **295** 30 25
1991 20l. Carnevale (Italy) and Gascoigne (England) . . . 50 25
1992 25l. England players congratulating Platt . . . 50 25
1993 3r.50 Koeman (Holland) and Klinsmann (Germany) . . . . 1·25 80
1994 5r. Quinn (Ireland) and Maldini (Italy) . . . . . 1·40 1·00
1995 7r. Lineker (England) . . . 2·00 1·50
1996 15r. Hassam (Egypt) and Moran (Ireland) . . . . 3·00 3·50
1997 18r. Canniggia (Argentina) 3·25 3·50
MS1998 Two sheets, each 103 × 73 mm. 25r. Ogris (Austria). (b) 25r. Conejo (Costa Rica) (horiz) Set of 2 sheets . . . . 13·00 12·00

296 Humpback Whale

297 Dome of the Rock, Jerusalem

1994. Centenary (1992) of Sierra Club (environmental protection society). Endangered Species. Multicoloured.
1999 6r.50 Type **296** . . . . . . 1·60 1·60
2000 6r.50 Ocelot crouched in grass . . . . 1·60 1·60
2001 6r.50 Ocelot sitting . . . . 1·60 1·60
2002 6r.50 Snow monkey . . . . 1·60 1·60
2003 6r.50 Prairie dog . . . . . 1·60 1·60
2004 6r.50 Golden lion tamarin 1·60 1·60
2005 6r.50 Prairie dog eating (horiz) . . . . 1·60 1·60
2006 6r.50 Prairie dog outside burrow (horiz) . . . . . 1·60 1·60
2007 6r.50 Herd of woodland caribou (horiz) . . . . 1·60 1·60
2008 6r.50 Woodland caribou facing left (horiz) . . . . 1·60 1·60
2009 6r.50 Woodland caribou facing right (horiz) . . . 1·60 1·60
2010 6r.50 Pair of Galapagos penguins (horiz) . . . . . 1·60 1·60
2011 6r.50 Galapagos penguin facing right . . . . 1·60 1·60
2012 6r.50 Galapagos penguin looking straight ahead . . 1·60 1·60
2013 6r.50 Bengal tiger looking straight ahead . . . . . 1·60 1·60
2014 6r.50 Bengal tiger looking right . . . . 1·60 1·60
2015 6r.50 Philippine tarsier with tree trunk at left . . . . 1·60 1·60
2016 6r.50 Philippine tarsier with tree trunk at right . . . . 1·60 1·60
2017 6r.50 Head of Philippine tarsier . . . . 1·60 1·60
2018 6r.50 Sierra Club centennial emblem (black, buff and green) . . . . 1·60 1·60
2019 6r.50 Golden lion tamarin between two branches (horiz) . . . . 1·60 1·60
2020 6r.50 Golden lion tamarin on tree trunk (horiz) . . . 1·60 1·60
2021 6r.50 Tail fin of humpback whale and coastline (horiz) . . . . 1·60 1·60
2022 6r.50 Tail fin of humpback whale at night (horiz) . . 1·60 1·60
2023 6r.50 Bengal tiger (horiz) . . 1·60 1·60
2024 5r.50 Ocelot (horiz) . . . . 1·60 1·60
2025 6r.50 Snow monkey in water climbing out of pool (horiz) . . . . 1·60 1·60
2026 6r.50 Snow monkey swimming (horiz) . . . . 1·60 1·60

1994. Solidarity with the Palestinians.
2027 **297** 8r. multicoloured . . . . 1·60 1·60

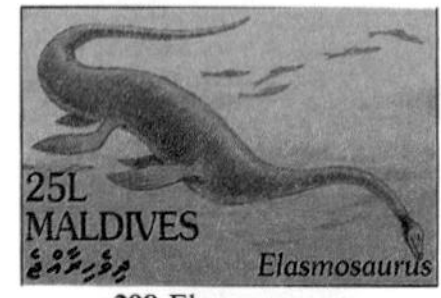

298 Elasmosaurus

1994. Prehistoric Animals. Multicoloured.
2028/59 25l., 50l., 1r., 3r. × 24, 5r., 8r., 10r., 15r., 20r. . . Set of 32 . . . . 30·00 28·00
MS2060 Two sheets, each 106 × 76 mm. (a) 25r. Gallimimus. (b) 25r. Plateosaurus (vert) Set of 2 sheets . . . . 8·00 8·50

Nos. 2031/42 and 2043/54 respectively were printed together, se-tenant, forming composite designs. The species depicted are, in addition to Type **298**, Dilophosaurus, Avimimus, Dimorphodon, Megalosaurus, Kuehneosaurus, Dryosaurus, Kentrosaurus, Baraposaurus, Tenontosaurus, Elaphrosaurus, Maiasaura, Huayangosaurus, Rutiodon, Pianitzkysaurus, Quetzalcoatlus, Daspletosaurus, Pleurocoelus, Baryonyx, Pentaceratops, Kritosaurus, Microvenator, Nodosaurus, Montanaceratops, Dromiceiomimus, Dryptosaurus, Parkosaurus, Chasmosaurus, Edmontonia, Anatosaurus, Velociraptor and Spinosaurus.

299 Mallet Steam Locomotive, Indonesia

1994. Railway Locomotives of Asia. Multicoloured.
2061 25l. Type **299** 20 20
2062 50l. Class C62 steam locomotive, Japan, 1948 25 20
2063 1r. Class D51 steam locomotive, Japan, 1936 (horiz) 30 20
2064 5r. Steam locomotive, India (horiz) 90 90
2065 6r.50+50l. Class W steam locomotive, India (horiz) 1·25 1·50
2066 6r.50+50l. Class C53 steam locomotive, Indonesia (horiz) . . . . 1·25 1·50
2067 6r.50+50l. Class C10 steam locomotive, Japan (horiz) 1·25 1·50
2068 6r.50+50l. Hanomag steam locomotive, India (horiz) 1·25 1·50
2069 6r.50+50l. "Hikari" express train, Japan (horiz) . . . 1·25 1·50
2070 6r.50+50l. Class C55 steam locomotive, Japan, 1935 (horiz) . . . . 1·25 1·50
2071 8r. Class 485 electric locomotive, Japan (horiz) 1·50 1·75
2072 10r. Class WP steam locomotive, India (horiz) 1·75 2·00
2073 15r. Class RM steam locomotive, China (horiz) 2·00 2·25
2074 20r. Class C57 steam locomotive, Japan, 1937 2·25 2·50
MS2075 Two sheets, each 110 × 80 mm. (a) 25r. Steam locomotive pulling goods train, Indonesia (horiz). (b) 25r. Class 8620 steam locomotive, Japan, 1914 (horiz) Set of 2 sheets . . 9·00 9·50

No. 2069 is inscribed "Hakari" in error.

300 Japanese Bobtail

1994. Cats. Multicoloured.
2076 7l. Type **300** 20 20
2077 20l. Siamese (vert) 35 20
2078 25l. Persian longhair 35 20
2079 50l. Somali (vert) 40 20
2080 3r.50 Oriental shorthair . . 1·00 80
2081 5r. Burmese . . . . 1·25 1·00
2082 7r. Bombay carrying kitten 1·50 1·50
2083 10r. Turkish van (vert) . . . 1·50 1·75
2084 12r. Javanese (vert) . . . . 1·75 2·00
2085 15r. Singapura . . . . . . 2·00 2·50
2086 18r. Turkish angora (vert) 2·25 2·75
2087 20r. Egyptian mau (vert) . . 2·25 2·75
MS2088 Three sheets. (a) 70 × 100 mm. 25r. Birman (vert). (b) 70 × 100 mm. 25r. Korat (vert). (c) 100 × 70 mm. 25r. Abyssinian (vert) Set of 3 sheets . . . . . 13·00 15·00

301 Franco Baresi (Italy) and Stuart McCall (Scotland)

1994. World Cup Football Championship, U.S.A. (3rd issue). Multicoloured. (a) Horiz designs.
2089 10l. Type **301** 40 40
2090 25l. Mick McCarthy (Ireland) and Gary Lineker (England) 50 50
2091 50l. J. Helt (Denmark) and R. Gordillo (Spain) . . . 50 50
2092 5r. Martin Vasquez (Spain) and Enzo Scifo (Belgium) 1·25 1·00
2093 10r. Championship emblem 1·60 1·60
2094 12r. Tomas Brolin (Sweden) and Gordon Durie (Scotland) . . . . 1·75 1·75

(b) Vert designs.
2095 6r.50 Bebeto (Brazil) . . . . 1·25 1·25
2096 6r.50 Lothar Matthaus (Germany) . . . . 1·25 1·25
2097 6r.50 Diego Maradona (Argentina) . . . . 1·25 1·25
2098 6r.50 Stephane Chapuasti (Switzerland) . . . . . . 1·25 1·25
2099 6r.50 George Hagi (Rumania) . . . . 1·25 1·25
2100 6r.50 Carlos Valderama (Colombia) . . . . 1·25 1·25
MS2101 100 × 70 mm. 10r. Egyptian players . . . . 4·25 4·25

302 Crew of "Apollo 11"

1994. 25th Anniv of First Manned Moon Landing. Multicoloured.
2102 5r. Type **302** . . . . 1·00 1·00
2103 5r. "Apollo 11" mission logo . . . . 1·00 1·00
2104 5r. Edwin Aldrin (astronaut) and "Eagle" . . . . . . 1·00 1·00
2105 5r. Crew of "Apollo 12" . . 1·00 1·00
2106 5r. "Apollo 12" mission logo . . . . 1·00 1·00
2107 5r. Alan Bean (astronaut) and equipment . . . . . 1·00 1·00
2108 5r. Crew of "Apollo 16" . . 1·00 1·00
2109 5r. "Apollo 16" mission logo . . . . 1·00 1·00
2110 5r. Astronauts with U.S. flag . . . . 1·00 1·00
2111 5r. Crew of "Apollo 17" . . 1·00 1·00
2112 5r. "Apollo 17" mission logo . . . . 1·00 1·00
2113 5r. Launch of "Apollo 17" 1·00 1·00
MS2114 100 × 76 mm. 25r. Launch of Russian rocket from Baikonur (vert) . . . . 4·00 4·75

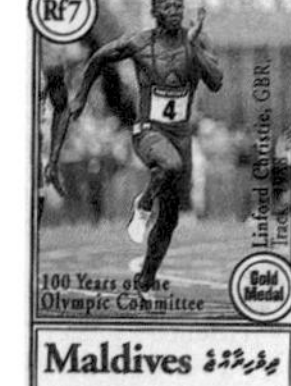

303 Linford Christie (Great Britain) (100 m), 1992

1994. Centenary of International Olympic Committee. Gold Medal Winners. Multicoloured.
2115 7r. Type **303** . . . . 1·50 1·25
2116 12r. Koji Gushiken (Japan) (gymnastics), 1984 . . . . 1·75 2·00
MS2117 106 × 71 mm. 25r. George Hackl (Germany) (single luge), 1994 . . . . 4·50 5·00

304 U.S. Amphibious DUKW

1994. 50th Anniv of D-Day. Multicoloured.
2118 2r. Type **304** 45 30
2119 4r. Tank landing craft unloading at Sword Beach 75 60
2120 18r. Infantry landing craft at Omaha Beach . . . . . 3·00 4·25
MS2121 105 × 76 mm. 25r. Landing craft with Canadian commandos 4·50 4·75

305 Duckpond, Suwan Folk Village

1994. "Philakorea '94" International Stamp Exn, Seoul. Multicoloured.
2122 50l. Type **305** 50 30
2123 3r. Pear-shaped bottle (vert) 60 70
2124 3r. Vase with dragon decoration (vert) 60 70
2125 3r. Vase with repaired lip (vert) 60 70
2126 3r. Stoneware vase with floral decoration (vert) . . 60 70
2127 3r. Celadon-glazed vase (vert) 60 70
2128 3r. Unglazed stone vase (vert) 60 70
2129 3r. Ritual water sprinkler (vert) 60 70
2130 3r. Long-necked celadon-glazed vase (vert) 60 70
2131 3r.50 Yongduson Park . . . 70 75
2132 20r. Ploughing with ox, Hahoe . . . . 3·50 4·50
MS2133 70 × 102 mm. 25r. "Hunting" (detail from eight-panel painted screen) (vert) . . 4·50 5·50

306 U.S. "Voyager 2" Satellite

1994. Space Exploration. Multicoloured.
2134 5r. Type **306** . . . . 1·25 1·25
2135 5r. Russian "Sputnik" satellite . . . . 1·25 1·25
2136 5r. "Apollo-Soyuz" mission 1·25 1·25
2137 5r. "Apollo 10" on parachutes . . . . 1·25 1·25
2138 5r. "Apollo 11" mission flag 1·25 1·25
2139 5r. Hubble space telescope 1·25 1·25
2140 5r. Edwin "Buzz" Aldrin (astronaut) . . . . 1·25 1·25
2141 5r. RCA lunar camera . . . 1·25 1·25
2142 5r. Lunar Rover (space buggy) . . . . 1·25 1·25
2143 5r. Jim Irwin (astronaut) . . 1·25 1·25
2144 5r. "Apollo 12" lunar module . . . . 1·25 1·25
2145 5r. Astronaut holding equipment . . . . 1·25 1·25
MS2146 Two sheets. (a) 70 × 100 mm. 25r. David Scott (astronaut) in open hatch of "Apollo 9". (b) 100 × 70 mm. 25r. Alan Shepherd Jr. (astronaut) (horiz) Set of 2 sheets . . . . 13·00 12·00

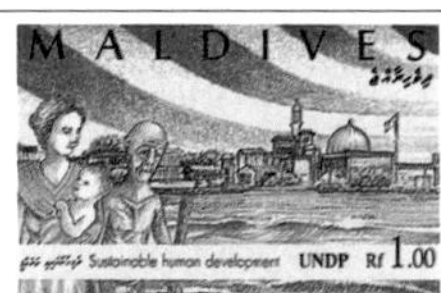

307 Mother, Child, Old Man and Town Skyline

1994. United Nations Development Programme. Multicoloured.
2147 1r. Type **307** 15 10
2148 8r. Fisherman with son and island . . . . 1·40 2·00

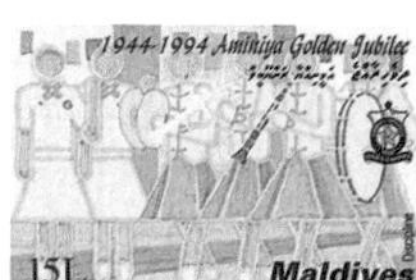

308 School Band

1994. 50th Anniv of Aminiya School. Children's Paintings. Multicoloured.
2149 15l. Type **308** 10 10
2150 50l. Classroom 20 15
2151 1r. School emblem and hand holding book (vert) . . . 30 15
2152 8r. School girls holding books (vert) . . . . . . 1·75 2·00
2153 10r. Sporting activities . . . 1·75 2·00
2154 11r. School girls holding crown (vert) . . . . . . 1·90 2·50
2155 13r. Science lesson . . . . 1·90 2·50

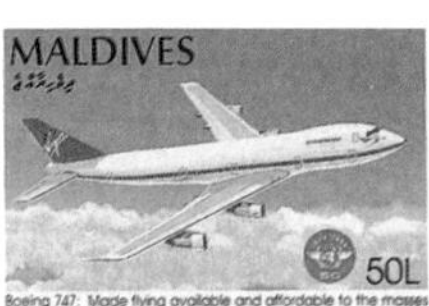

309 Boeing 747

1994. 50th Anniv of I.C.A.O. Multicoloured.
2156 50l. Type **309** 50 25
2157 1r. Hawker Siddeley ("de Havilland") Comet 4 . . 60 25
2158 2r. Male International Airport 85 55
2159 3r. Lockheed L.1649 Super Star . . . . 1·25 85
2160 8r. European Airbus . . . . 2·00 2·50
2161 10r. Dornier Do-228 . . . . 2·00 2·50
MS2162 100 × 70 mm. 25r. Concorde . . . . 4·50 5·00

310 Pintail ("Northern Pintail")

1995. Ducks. Multicoloured.
2163 5r. Type **310** . . . . . . 90 1·00
2164 5r. Comb duck . . . . . . 90 1·00
2165 5r. Ruddy shelduck . . . . 90 1·00
2166 5r. Garganey . . . . 90 1·00
2167 5r. Indian whistling duck ("Lesser Whistling Duck") 90 1·00
2168 5r. Green-winged teal . . . 90 1·00
2169 5r. Fulvous whistling duck 90 1·00
2170 5r. Common shoveler ("Northern Shoveler") . . 90 1·00
2171 5r. Cotton teal ("Cotton Pygmy Goose") . . . . . 90 1·00
2172 6r.50+50l. Common pochard ("Pochard") (vert) . . . . 90 1·00
2173 6r.50+50l. Mallard (vert) . . 90 1·00
2174 6r.50+50l. European wigeon ("Wigeon") (vert) . . . . 90 1·00
2175 6r.50+50l. Common shoveler ("Northern Shoveler") (vert) . . . . 90 1·00
2176 6r.50+50l. Pintail ("Northern Pintail") (vert) 90 1·00
2177 6r.50+50l. Garganey (vert) 90 1·00
2178 6r.50+50l. Tufted duck (vert) . . . . 90 1·00
2179 6r.50+50l. Red-crested pochard ("Ferruginous Duck") (vert) . . . . . 90 1·00
2180 6r.50+50l. Ferruginous duck ("Red-crested Pochard") (vert) . . . . 90 1·00
MS2181 Two sheets. (a) 100 × 71 mm. 25r. Spotbill duck ("Garganey"). (b) 73 × 100 mm. 25r. Cotton teal ("Cotton Pygmy Goose") (vert) Set of 2 sheets 7·50 8·50
Nos. 2163/71 and 2172/80 were printed together, se-tenant, forming composite designs.

311 Taj Mahal, India

1995. Famous Monuments of the World. Mult.
2182 7l. Type **311** 50 25
2183 10l. Washington Monument, U.S.A. 10 10
2184 15l. Mount Rushmore, U.S.A. 10 10
2185 25l. Arc de Triomphe, Paris (vert) 10 10
2186 50l. Sphinx, Egypt (vert) . . 50 20
2187 5r. El Castillo, Toltec pyramid, Yucatan 85 90
2188 8r. Toltec statue, Tula, Mexico (vert) . . . . . . 1·25 1·75
2189 12r. Victory Column, Berlin (vert) . . . . 1·60 2·25
MS2190 Two sheets, each 112 × 85 mm. (a) 25r. Easter Island statue (42 × 56 mm). (b) 25r. Stonehenge, Wiltshire (85 × 28 mm) Set of 2 sheets . . 7·50 8·50

312 Donald Duck driving Chariot

1995. History of Wheeled Transport. Scenes from Disney cartoon film "Donald and the Wheel". Multicoloured.
2191 3l. Type **312** 10 10
2192 4l. Donald with log 10 10
2193 5l. Donald driving Stephenson's "Rocket" . . 10 10
2194 10l. Donald pondering over circle (vert) 10 10
2195 20l. Donald in crashed car (vert) 10 10
2196 25l. Donald listening to early gramophone 10 10
2197 5r. Donald on mammoth . . 1·25 1·25
2198 20r. Donald pushing early car . . . . 3·75 4·75

313 Donald Duck playing Saxophone

1995. 60th Birthday of Donald Duck. Walt Disney cartoon characters. Multicoloured.
2199 5r. Type **313** 90 90
2200 5r. Moby Duck playing fiddle 90 90
2201 5r. Feathry Duck with banjo and drum 90 90
2202 5r. Daisy Duck playing harp 90 90
2203 5r. Gladstone Gander with clarinet 90 90
2204 5r. Huey, Dewey and Louie with bassoon 90 90
2205 5r. Gus Goose playing flute 90 90
2206 5r. Prof. Ludwig von Drake playing trombone 90 90
2207 5r. Daisy picking flowers . . 90 90
2208 5r. Donald with backpack 90 90
2209 5r. Grandma Duck with kitten 90 90
2210 5r. Gus Goose and pie . . . 90 90
2211 5r. Gyro Gearloose in space 90 90
2212 5r. Huey, Dewey and Louie photographing porcupine 90 90
2213 5r. Prof. Ludwig von Drake 90 90
2214 5r. Scrooge McDuck with money 90 90
MS2215 Four sheets. (a) 108 × 130 mm. 25r. Donald playing banjo. (b) 133 × 108 mm. 25r. Donald posing for photo. (c) 108 × 130 mm. 25r. Donald conducting (horiz). (d) 102 × 121 mm. 25r. Huey, Dewey and Louie (horiz) Set of 4 sheets 14·00 15·00

314 Islamic Centre, Male

1995. Eid Greetings. Multicoloured.
2216 1r. Type **314** 15 15
2217 1r. Rose 15 15
2218 8r. Orchid . . . . 1·50 1·50
2219 10r. Orchid (different) . . . 1·50 1·50

315 Killer Whale

1995. "Singapore '95" International Stamp Exhibition (1st issue). Whales, Dolphins and Porpoises. Multicoloured.
2220 1r. Type **315** 40 30
2221 2r. Bottlenose dolphins . . . 45 35
2222 3r. Right whale 60 70
2223 3r. Pair of killer whales . . 60 70
2224 3r. Humpback whale . . . 60 70
2225 3r. Pair of belugas 60 70
2226 3r. Narwhal 60 70
2227 3r. Head of blue whale . . . 60 70
2228 3r. Bowhead whale 60 70
2229 3r. Head of fin whale . . . 60 70
2230 3r. Pair of pilot whales . . . 60 70
2231 3r. Grey whale 60 70
2232 3r. Sperm whale 60 70
2233 3r. Pair of goosebeaked whales 60 70
2234 3r. Hourglass dolphin . . . 60 70
2235 3r. Bottlenose dolphin (different) 60 70
2236 3r. Dusky dolphin 60 70
2237 3r. Spectacled porpoise . . . 60 70
2238 3r. Fraser's dolphin 60 70
2239 3r. Camerson's dolphin . . 60 70
2240 3r. Pair of spinner dolphins 60 70
2241 3r. Pair of Dalls dolphins 60 70
2242 3r. Spotted dolphin 60 70
2243 3r. Indus River dolphin . . 60 70
2244 3r. Hector's dolphin 60 70
2245 3r. Amazon River dolphin 60 70
2246 8r. Humpback whale and calf . . . . 1·25 1·50
2247 10r. Common dolphin . . . 1·40 1·60
MS2248 Two sheets, each 100 × 70 mm. (a) 25r. Sperm whale (different). (b) 25r. Pair of hourglass dolphins Set of 2 sheets 9·00 9·00
See also Nos. 2302/10.

316 Scout Camp and National Flag

1995. 18th World Scout Jamboree, Netherlands. Multicoloured.
2249 10r. Type **316** . . . . . . 1·75 2·00
2250 12r. Campfire cooking . . . 1·90 2·25
2251 15r. Scouts erecting tent . . 2·00 2·40
MS2252 102 × 72 mm. 25r. Scouts around camp fire (vert) . . . . 3·50 4·00
Nos. 2249/51 were printed together, se-tenant, forming a composite design.

318 Asian Child and Dove **320** Asian Child eating Rice

317 Soviet Heavy Howitzer Battery

1995. 50th Anniv of End of Second World War in Europe. Multicoloured.
2253 5r. Type **317** 85 85
2254 5r. Ruins of Berchtesgaden 85 85
2255 5r. U.S. Boeing B-17 Flying Fortress dropping food over the Netherlands . . 85 85
2256 5r. Soviet Ilyushin Il-1 bomber 85 85
2257 5r. Liberation of Belsen . . 85 85
2258 5r. Supermarine Spitfire and V-1 flying bomb 85 85
2259 5r. U.S. tanks advancing through Cologne 85 85
2260 5r. Reichstag in ruins . . . 85 85
MS2261 107 × 76 mm. 25r. Soviet and U.S. troops celebrating . . 3·50 3·75

319 United Nations Emblem

1995. 50th Anniv of United Nations (1st issue). Multicoloured.
2262 6r.50+50l. Type **318** . . . . 90 1·25
2263 8r. Globe and dove . . . . 1·00 1·40
2264 10r. African child and dove 1·10 1·50
MS2265 72 × 102 mm. 25r. United Nations emblem and dove . . 2·75 3·75
Nos. 2262/4 were printed together, se-tenant, forming a composite design.

1995. 50th Anniv of United Nations (2nd issue).
2266 **319** 30l. black, blue & grn . . 10 10
2267 – 8r. multicoloured . . . . 1·00 1·25
2268 – 11r. multicoloured . . . 1·25 1·50
2269 – 13r. black, grey and red 1·60 1·90
DESIGNS: 8r. Symbolic women, flag and map; 11r. U.N. soldier and symbolic dove; 13r. Gun barrels, atomic explosion and bomb sight

1995. 50th Anniv of F.A.O. (1st issue). Mult
2270 6r.50+50l. Type **320** . . . . 90 1·10
2271 8r. F.A.O. emblem . . . . 1·00 1·25
2272 10r. African mother and child . . . . 1·10 1·40
MS2273 72 × 102 mm. 25r. African child and symbolic hand holding maize . . . . 2·75 3·75
See also Nos. 2311/12.

321 Queen Elizabeth the Queen Mother

1995. 95th Birthday of Queen Elizabeth the Queen Mother.
2274 **321** 5r. brown, lt brn & blk 1·00 1·10
2275 – 5r. multicoloured . . . . 1·00 1·10
2276 – 5r. multicoloured . . . . 1·00 1·10
2277 – 5r. multicoloured . . . . 1·00 1·10
MS2278 125 × 100 mm. 25r. multicoloured . . . . 5·00 5·50
DESIGNS: No. 2275, Without hat; 2276, At desk (oil painting); 2277, Queen Elizabeth the Queen Mother; MS2278, Wearing lilac hat and dress.

1995. 50th Anniv of End of Second World War in the Pacific. As T **317**. Multicoloured.
2279 6r.50+50l. Grumman F6F-3 Hellcat aircraft . . . . . 1·50 1·50
2280 6r.50+50l. F4-U1 fighter aircraft attacking beach 1·50 1·50
2281 6r.50+50l. Douglas SBD Dauntless aircraft . . . . 1·50 1·50
2282 6r.50+50l. American troops in landing craft, Guadalcanal . . . . . . 1·50 1·50
2283 6r.50+50l. U.S. marines in Alligator tanks . . . . . 1·50 1·50
2284 6r.50+50l. U.S. landing ship 1·50 1·50
MS2285 106 × 74 mm. 25r. F4-U1 fighter aircraft . . . . 4·00 4·50

322 Students using Library

1995. 50th Anniv of National Library. Mult.
2286 2r. Type **322** 25 25
2287 8r. Students using library (different) . . . . 1·00 1·50
MS2288 105 × 75 mm. 10r. Library entrance (100 × 70 mm). Imperf 1·40 1·60

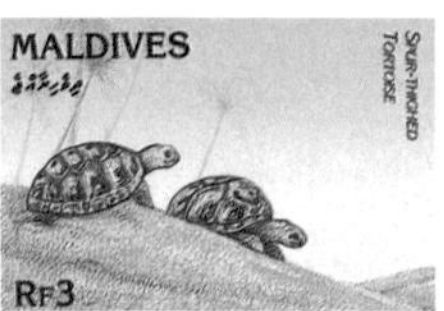

323 Spur-thighed Tortoise

1995. Turtles and Tortoises. Multicoloured.
2289 3r. Type **323** 60 70
2290 3r. Aldabra turtle 60 70
2291 3r. Loggerhead turtle . . . 60 70
2292 3r. Olive Ridley turtle . . . 60 70
2293 3r. Leatherback turtle . . . 60 70
2294 3r. Green turtle 60 70

2295 3r. Atlantic Ridley turtle . . 60 70
2296 3r. Hawksbill turtle 60 70
2297 10r. Hawksbill turtle on beach . . . . 1·40 1·60
2298 10r. Pair of hawksbill turtles 1·40 1·60
2299 10r. Hawksbill turtle climbing out of water . . 1·40 1·60
2300 10r. Hawksbill turtle swimming . . . . 1·40 1·60
MS2301 100 × 70 mm. 25r. Green turtle . . . . 3·75 4·50

Nos. 2289/96 were printed together, se-tenant, forming a composite design.

Nos. 2297/2300 include the W.W.F. Panda emblem.

324 "Russula aurata" (fungi) and "Papilio demodocus" (butterfly)

1995. "Singapore '95" International Stamp Exhibition. Butterflies and Fungi. Multicoloured.
2302 2r. Type **324** 75 75
2303 2r. "Lepista saeva" and "Kallimoides rumia" . . 75 75
2304 2r. "Lepista nuda" and "Hypolimnas salmacis" 75 75
2305 2r. "Xerocomus subtomentosus" ("Boletus subtomentosus" and "Precis octavia") 75 75
2306 5r. "Gyroporus castaneus" and "Hypolimnas salmacis" . . . . 1·10 1·10
2307 8r. "Gomphidius glutinosus" and "Papilio dardanus" 1·25 1·25
2308 10r. "Russula olivacea" and "Precis octavia" . . . . . 1·40 1·40
2309 12r. "Boletus edulis" and "Prepona praeneste" . . . 1·40 1·40
MS2310 Two sheets, each 105 × 76 mm. (a) 25r. "Amanita muscaria" and "Kallimoides rumia" (vert). (b) 25r. "Boletus rhodoxanthus" and "Hypolimnas salmacis" (vert) Set of 2 sheets 8·00 8·00

Nos. 2302/5 and 2306/9 respectively were printed together, se-tenant, forming composite designs.

No. 2304 is inscribed "Lapista" in error.

325 Planting Kaashi

1995. 50th Anniv of F.A.O. (2nd issue). Mult.
2311 7r. Type **325** . . . . 90 1·10
2312 8r. Fishing boat . . . . . . 1·10 1·25

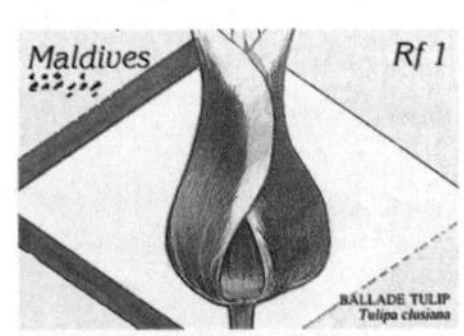

326 Ballade Tulip

1995. Flowers. Multicoloured.
2313 1r. Type **326** 20 15
2314 3r. White mallow 50 50
2315 5r. Regale trumpet lily . . . 1·00 1·00
2316 5r. "Dendrobium Waipahu Beauty" . . . . 1·00 1·00
2317 5r. "Brassocattleya Jean Murray" . . . . 1·00 1·00
2318 5r. "Cymbidium Fort George" . . . . 1·00 1·00
2319 5r. "Paphiopedilum malipoense" . . . . . . 1·00 1·00
2320 5r. "Cycnoches chlorochilon" . . . . . . 1·00 1·00
2321 5r. "Rhyncholaelia digbgana" . . . . 1·00 1·00
2322 5r. "Lycaste deppei" . . . . 1·00 1·00
2323 5r. "Masdevallia constricta" 1·00 1·00
2324 5r. "Paphiopedilum Clair de Lune" . . . . 1·00 1·00
2325 7r. "Lilactime dahlia" . . . 1·25 1·25
2326 8r. Blue ideal iris . . . . . 1·25 1·25
2327 10r. Red crown imperial . . 1·40 1·40
MS2328 Two sheets, each 106 × 76mm. (a) 25r. "Encyclia cochleata" (vert). (b) 25r. "Psychopsis kramerina" (vert) Set of 2 sheets . . . . 8·00 9·50

327 John Lennon with Microphone

329 Johannes van der Waals (1919 Physics)

328 Elvis Presley with Microphone

1995. 15th Death Anniv of John Lennon (musician). Multicoloured.
2329 5r. Type **327** . . . . 1·40 1·25
2330 5r. With glasses and moustache . . . . 1·40 1·25
2331 5r. With guitar . . . . . . 1·40 1·25
2332 5r. With guitar and wearing glasses . . . . 1·40 1·25
2333 5r. Wearing sun glasses and red jacket . . . . 1·40 1·25
2334 5r. Wearing headphones . . 1·40 1·25
MS2335 88 × 117 mm. 2, 3, 8, 10r. Different portraits of John Lennon 5·50 5·50
MS2236 102 × 72 mm. 25r. John Lennon performing . . . . . 5·50 5·50

1995. 60th Birth Anniv of Elvis Presley (entertainer). Multicoloured.
2337 5r. Type **328** 90 80
2338 5r. Wearing red jacket . . . 90 80
2339 5r. Wearing blue jacket . . 90 80
2340 5r. With microphone and wearing blue jacket . . . 90 80
2341 5r. In army uniform 90 80
2342 5r. Wearing yellow bow tie 90 80
2343 5r. In yellow shirt 90 80
2344 5r. In light blue shirt . . . 90 80
2345 5r. Wearing red and white high-collared jacket . . . 90 80
MS2346 80 × 110 mm. 25r. Elvis Presley (horiz) . . . . 4·25 4·50

1995. Cent of Nobel Prize Trust Fund. Mult.
2347/55 5r. × 9 (Type **329**; Charles Guillaume (1920 Physics); Sir James Chadwick (1935 Physics); Willem Einthoven (1924 Medicine); Henrik Dam (1943 Medicine); Sir Alexander Fleming (1945 Medicine); Hermann Muller (1946 Medicine); Rodney Porter (1972 Medicine); Werner Arber (1978 Medicine)) . . . . .
2356/64 5r. × 9 (Niels Bohr (1922 Physics); Ben Mottelson (1975 Physics); Patrick White (1973 Literature); Elias Canetti (1981 Literature); Theodor Kocher (1909 Medicine); August Krogh (1920 Medicine); William Murphy (1934 Medicine); John Northrop (1946 Chemistry); Luis Leloir (1970 Chemistry)) . . . .
2365/73 5r. × 9 (Dag Hammarskjold (1961 Peace); Alva Myrdal (1982 Peace); Archbishop Desmond Tutu (1984 Peace); Rudolf Eucken (1908 Literature); Aleksandr Solzhenitsyn (1970 Literature); Gabriel Marquez (1982 Literature); Chen Yang (1957 Physics); Karl Muller (1987 Physics); Melvin Schwartz (1988 Physics)) . . . . . .
2374/82 5r. × 9 (Robert Millikan (1923 Physics); Louis de Broglie (1929 Physics); Ernest Walton (1951 Physics); Richard Willstatter (1915 Chemistry); Lars Onsager (1968 Chemistry); Gerhard Herzberg (1971 Chemistry); William B. Yeats (1923 Literature); George Bernard Shaw (1925 Literature); Eugene O'Neill (1936 Literature)) . . . . .
2383/91 5r. × 9 (Bernardo Houssay (1947 Medicine); Paul Muller (1948 Medicine); Walter Hess (1949 Medicine); Sir MacFarlane Burnet (1960 Medicine); Baruch Blumberg (1976 Medicine); Daniel Nathans (1978 Medicine); Glenn Seaborg (1951 Chemistry); Ilya Prigogine (1977 Chemistry); Kenichi Fukui (1981 Chemistry)) . . . .
2392/2400 5r. × 9 (Carl Spitteler (1919 Literature); Henri Bergson (1927 Literature); Johannes Jensen (1944 Literature); Antoine-Henri Becquerel (1903 Physics); Sir William H. Bragg (1915 Physics); Sir William L. Bragg (1915 Physics); Frederik Bajer (1908 Peace); Leon Bourgeois (1920 Peace); Karl Benning (1921 Peace)) . . . .
Set of 54 . . . . 38·00 42·00
MS2401 Six sheets. (a) 80 × 110 mm. 25r. Konrad bloch (1964 Medicine). (b) 80 × 110 mm. 25r. Samuel Beckett (1969 Literature). (c) 80 × 110 mm. 25r. Otto Wallach (1910 Chemistry). (d) 110 × 80 mm. 25r. Hideki Yukawa (1949 Physics). (e) 110 × 80 mm. 25r. Eisaku Sato (1974 Peace). (f) 110 × 80 mm. 25r. Robert Koch (1905 Medicine) Set of 6 sheets 16·00 17·00

330 Rythmic Gymnast and Japanese Fan

1996. Olympic Games, Atlanta (1st issue). Mult.
2402 1r. Type **330** 25 10
2403 3r. Archer and Moscow Olympics logo 50 35
2404 5r. Diver and Swedish flag 80 85
2405 5r. Canadian Maple Leaf . . 80 85
2406 5r. Shot putting (decathlon) 80 85
2407 5r. Moscow Olympic medal and ribbon 80 85
2408 5r. Fencer 80 85
2409 5r. Gold medal 80 85
2410 5r. Equestrian competitor 80 85
2411 5r. Sydney Opera House . . 80 85
2412 5r. Athlete on starting blocks 80 85
2413 5r. South Korean flag . . . 80 85
2414 7r. High jumper and Tower Bridge, London . . . . . 1·00 1·10
2415 10r. Athlete on starting blocks and Brandenburg Gate, Germany . . . . . 1·40 1·60
2416 12r. Hurdler and Amsterdam Olympic logo 1·60 1·90
MS2417 Two sheets, each 113 × 80 mm. (a) 25r. Red Olympic Flame (vert). (b) 25r. Multicoloured Olympic Flame (vert) Set of 2 sheets . . . . . 8·00 9·00

See also Nos. 2469/87.

331 "Self Portrait" (Degas)

1996. 125th Anniv of Metropolitan Museum of Art, New York. Multicoloured.
2418/25 4r. × 8 ("Self-Portrait" (Degas); "Andromache and Astyanax" (Prud'hon); "Rene Grenier" (Toulouse-Lautrec); "The Banks of the Bievre near Bicetre" (Rousseau); "The Repast of the Lion" (Rousseau); "Portrait of Yves Gobillard-Morisot" (Degas); "Sunflowers" (Van Gogh); "The Singer in Green" (Degas)) . . . .
2426/33 4r. × 8 ("Still Life" (Fantin-Latour); "Portrait of a Lady in Grey" (Degas); "Apples and Grapes" (Monet); "The Englishman" (Toulouse-Lautrec); "Cypresses" (Van Gogh); "Flowers in a Chinese Vase" (Redon); "The Gardener" (Seurat); "Large Sunflowers I" (Nolde))
2434/41 4r. × 8 (All by Manet: "The Spanish Singer"; "Young Man in Costume of Majo"; "Mademoiselle Victorine"; "Boating"; "Peonies"; "Woman with a Parrot"; "George Moore"; "The Monet Family in their Garden") . . . . . .
2442/9 4r. × 8 ("Goldfish" (Matisse); "Spanish Woman: Harmony in Blue" (Matisse); "Nasturtiums and the "Dance" II" (Matisse); "The House behind Trees" (Braque); "Mada Primavesi" (Klimt); "Head of a Woman" (Picasso); "Woman in White" (Picasso); "Harlequin" (Picasso)) . . . . . .
2418/49 Set of 32 . . . . 25·00 27·00
MS2450 Four sheets, each 95 × 70 mm, containing horiz designs, 81 × 53 mm. (a) 25r. "Northeaster" (Homer). (b) 25r. "The Fortune Teller" (De La Tour). (c) 25r. "Santo (Sanzio), Ritratto de Andrea Navagero e Agostino Beazzano" (Raphael). (d) 25r. "Portrait of a Woman" (Rubens) Set of 4 sheets . . . 17·00 19·00

332 Mickey Mouse on Great Wall of China

1996. "CHINA '96" 9th Asian International Stamp Exhibition, Peking. Walt Disney cartoon characters in China. Multicoloured.
2451 2r. Type **332** 80 80
2452 2r. Pluto with temple guardian 80 80
2453 2r. Minnie Mouse with pandas 80 80
2454 2r. Mickey windsurfing near junks 80 80
2455 2r. Goofy cleaning grotto statue 80 80
2456 2r. Donald and Daisy Duck at Marble Boat 80 80
2457 2r. Mickey with terracotta warriors 80 80
2458 2r. Goofy with geese and masks 80 80
2459 2r. Donald and Goofy on traditional fishing boat . . 80 80
2460 2r. Mickey and Minnie in dragon boat 80 80
2461 2r. Donald at Peking opera 80 80
2462 2r. Mickey and Minnie in Chinese garden 80 80
2463 3r. Mickey and Minnie at the Ice Pagoda (vert) . . 1·00 1·00
2464 3r. Donald and Mickey flying Chinese kites (vert) 1·00 1·00
2465 3r. Goofy playing anyiwu (vert) . . . . 1·00 1·00
2466 3r. Paper cutouts of Mickey and Goofy (vert) . . . . 1·00 1·00
2467 3r. Donald and Mickey in dragon dance (vert) . . . 1·00 1·00
MS2468 Three sheets. (a) 108 × 133 mm. 5r. Mickey pointing. (b) 133 × 108 mm. 7r. Mickey and Minnie watching Moon. (c) 133 × 108 mm. 8r. Donald using chopsticks Set of 3 sheets . . . . 5·50 6·00

333 Stella Walsh (Poland) (100 m sprint, 1932) on Medal

1996. Olympic Games, Atlanta (2nd issue). Previous Gold Medal Winners. Multicoloured.

2469 1r. Type **333** 25 15
2470 3r. Emile Zatopek (Czechoslovakia) (10,000 m running, 1952) and Olympic torch (vert) 50 35
2471 5r. Yanko Rousseu (Bulgaria) (lightweight, 1980) (vert) 75 80
2472 5r. Peter Baczako (Hungary) (middle heavyweight, 1980) (vert) 75 80
2473 5r. Leonid Taranenko (Russia) (heavyweight, 1980) (vert) 75 80
2474 5r. Aleksandr Kurlovich (Russia) (heavyweight, 1988) (vert) 75 80
2475 5r. Assen Zlateu (Bulgaria) (middleweight, 1980) (vert) 75 80
2476 5r. Zeng Guoqiang (China) (flyweight, 1984) (vert) 75 80
2477 5r. Yurik Vardanyan (Russia) (heavyweight, 1980) (vert) 75 80
2478 5r. Sultan Rakhmanov (Russia) (super heavyweight, 1980) (vert) 75 80
2479 5r. Vassily Alexeev (Russia) (super heavyweight, 1972) (vert) 75 80
2480 5r. Ethel Catherwood (Canada) (high jump, 1928) 75 80
2481 5r. Mildred Didrikson (U.S.A.) (javelin, 1932) 75 80
2482 5r. Francina Blankers-Koen (Netherlands) (80 m hurdles, 1948) 75 80
2483 5r. Tamara Press (Russia) (shot put, 1960) 75 80
2484 5r. Lia Manoliu (Rumania) (discus, 1968) 75 80
2485 5r. Rosa Mota (Portugal) (marathon, 1988) 75 80
2486 10r. Olga Fikotova (Czechoslovakia) (discus, 1956) on medal 1·40 1·60
2487 12r. Joan Benoit (U.S.A.) (marathon, 1984) on medal 1·60 1·90
MS2488 Two sheets. (a) 76 × 106 mm. 25r. Naeem Suleymanoglu (Turkey) (weightlifting, 1988) (vert). (b) 105 × 75 mm. 25r. Irena Szewinska (Poland) (400 m running, 1976) on medal Set of 2 sheets 8·00 9·00

No. 2469 identifies the event as 10 metres in error.

334 Queen Elizabeth II

1996. 70th Birthday of Queen Elizabeth II. Mult.

2489 8r. Type **334** 1·40 1·50
2490 8r. Wearing hat 1·40 1·50
2491 8r. At desk 1·40 1·50
MS2492 125 × 103 mm. 25r. Queen Elizabeth and Queen Mother on Buckingham Palace balcony 4·50 4·50

335 African Child

1996. 50th Anniv of U.N.I.C.E.F. Multicoloured.

2493 5r. Type **335** 60 55
2494 7r. European girl 85 90
2495 7r. Maldivian boy 85 90
2496 10r. Asian girl 1·25 1·40
MS2497 114 × 74 mm. 25r. Baby with toy 3·25 3·75

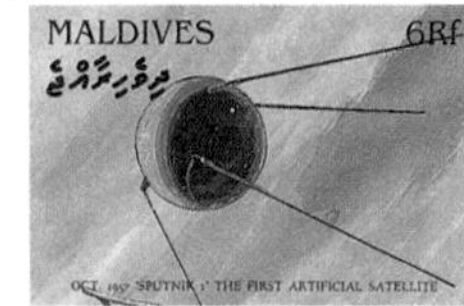

336 "Sputnik 1" Satellite

1996. Space Exploration. Multicoloured.

2498 6r. Type **336** 1·10 1·10
2499 6r. "Apollo 11" command module 1·10 1·10
2500 6r. "Skylab" 1·10 1·10
2501 6r. Astronaut Edward White walking in space 1·10 1·10
2502 6r. "Mariner 9" 1·10 1·10
2503 6r. "Apollo" and "Soyuz" docking 1·10 1·10
MS2504 104 × 74 mm. 25r. Launch of "Apollo 8" (vert) 4·00 4·25

337 "Epiphora albida"

1996. Butterflies. Multicoloured.

2505 7r. Type **337** 1·10 1·10
2506 7r. "Satyrus dryas" 1·10 1·10
2507 7r. "Satyrus lena" 1·10 1·10
2508 7r. "Papilio tynderaeus" 1·10 1·10
2509 7r. "Urota suraka" 1·10 1·10
2510 7r. "Satyrus nercis" 1·10 1·10
2511 7r. "Papilio troilus" (vert) 1·10 1·10
2512 7r. "Papilio cresphontes" (vert) 1·10 1·10
2513 7r. Lime swallowtail caterpillar (vert) 1·10 1·10
2514 7r. "Cynthia virginiensis" (vert) 1·10 1·10
2515 7r. Monarch caterpillar (vert) 1·10 1·10
2516 7r. "Danaus plexippus" (vert) 1·10 1·10
2517 7r. Monarch caterpillar and pupa (vert) 1·10 1·10
2518 7r. "Chlosyne harrisii" (vert) 1·10 1·10
2519 7r. "Cymothoe coccinata" (vert) 1·10 1·10
2520 7r. "Morpho rhetenor" (vert) 1·10 1·10
2521 7r. "Callicore lidwina" (vert) 1·10 1·10
2522 7r. "Heliconius erato reductimacula" (vert) 1·10 1·10
MS2523 Two sheets, each 106 × 76 mm. (a) 25r. "Heliconius charitonius" (vert). (b) 25r. "Heliconius cydno" (vert) Set of 2 sheets 8·50 9·00

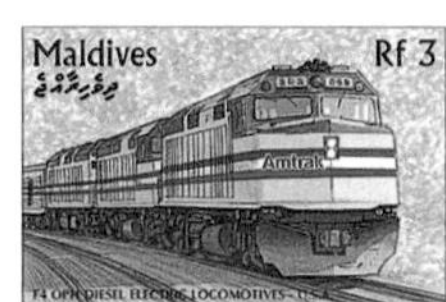

338 Amtrak F40H Diesel electric Locomotive, U.S.A.

1996. Trains of the World. Multicoloured.

2524 3r. Type **338** 70 70
2525 3r. Stephenson's "Experiment" 70 70
2526 3r. Indian-Pacific Intercontinental, Australia 70 70
2527 3r. Stephenson's Killingworth type steam locomotive, 1815 70 70
2528 3r. George Stephenson 70 70
2529 3r. Stephenson's "Rocket", 1829 70 70
2530 3r. High Speed Train 125, Great Britain 70 70
2531 3r. First rail passenger coach "Experiment", 1825 70 70
2532 3r. Union Pacific Class U25B diesel locomotive (inscr "Tofac"), U.S.A. 70 70
2533 3r. Southern Pacific's "Daylight" express, 1952, U.S.A. 70 70
2534 3r. Timothy Hackworth's "Sans Pareil", 1829 70 70
2535 3r. Chicago and North Western diesel locomotive, U.S.A. 70 70
2536 3r. Richard Trevithick's "Pen-y-Darren" locomotive, 1804 70 70
2537 3r. Isambard Kingdom Brunel 70 70
2538 3r. Great Western locomotive, 1838 70 70
2539 3r. Vistadome observation car, Canada 70 70
2540 3r. Mohawk and Hudson Railroad "Experiment", 1832 70 70
2541 3r. ICE high speed train, Germany 70 70
2542 3r. Electric container locomotive, Germany 70 70
2543 3r. John Blenkinsop's rack locomotive, 1811 70 70
2544 3r. Diesel-electric locomotive, Western Australia 70 70
2545 3r. Timothy Hackworth's "Royal George", 1827 70 70
2546 3r. Robert Stephenson 70 70
2547 3r. Trevithick's "Newcastle" 70 70
2548 3r. Deltic diesel-electric locomotive, Great Britain 70 70
2549 3r. Stockton and Darlington Railway locomotive No. 5 "Stockton", 1826 70 70
2550 3r. Channel Tunnel "Le Shuttle" train 70 70
MS2551 Three sheets, each 96 × 91 mm. (a) 25r. Peter Cooper's "Tom Thumb", 1829. (b) 25r. John Jarvis's "De Witt Clinton", 1831. (c) 25r. William Hudson's "The General", 1855 Set of 3 sheets 13·00 13·00

No. 2524 is inscribed "F4 OPH" in error.

339 Bongo

1996. Wildlife of the World. Multicoloured.

2552 5r. Type **339** 80 80
2553 5r. Bushbuck 80 80
2554 5r. Namaqua dove 80 80
2555 5r. Hoopoe 80 80
2556 5r. African fish eagle 80 80
2557 5r. Egyptian goose 80 80
2558 5r. Saddle-bill stork 80 80
2559 5r. Blue-breasted kingfisher 80 80
2560 5r. Yellow baboon 80 80
2561 5r. Banded duiker ("Zebra Duiker") 80 80
2562 5r. Yellow-backed duiker 80 80
2563 5r. Pygmy hippopotamus 80 80
2564 5r. Large-spotted genet 80 80
2565 5r. African spoonbill 80 80
2566 5r. White-faced whistling duck 80 80
2567 5r. Helmeted guineafowl 80 80
2568 7r. Cotton-headed tamarin (horiz) 1·10 1·10
2569 7r. European bison (horiz) 1·10 1·10
2570 7r. Tiger (horiz) 1·10 1·10
2571 7r. Western capercaillie (horiz) 1·10 1·10
2572 7r. Giant panda (horiz) 1·10 1·10
2573 7r. "Trogonoptera brookiana" (butterfly) (horiz) 1·10 1·10
2574 7r. American beaver (horiz) 1·10 1·10
2575 7r. "Leiopelma hamiltoni" (frog) (horiz) 1·10 1·10
2576 7r. Manatee (horiz) 1·10 1·10
MS2577 106 × 76 mm. 25r. Chimpanzee (horiz) 3·75 4·50

Nos. 2552/9, 2560/7 and 2568/76 respectively were printed together, se-tenant, with the backgrounds forming composite designs.

No. 2553 is inscribed "BUSHBACK" in error.

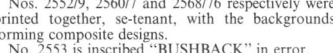

340 Giant Panda

1996. Endangered Species. Multicoloured.

2578 5r. Type **340** 85 85
2579 5r. Indian elephant 85 85
2580 5r. Arrow-poison frog 85 85
2581 5r. Mandrill 85 85
2582 5r. Snow leopard 85 85
2583 5r. California condor 85 85
2584 5r. Whale-headed stork ("Shoebill Stork") 85 85
2585 5r. Red-billed hornbill 85 85
2586 5r. Hippopotamus 85 85
2587 5r. Gorilla 85 85
2588 5r. Lion 85 85
2589 5r. South African crowned crane ("Gray Crowned Crane") 85 85
MS2590 Two sheets, each 110 × 80 mm. (a) 25r. Tiger (vert). (b) 25r. Leopard Set of 2 sheets 8·00 8·50

341 Mickey Mouse climbing out of Puddle

1996. Centenary of the Cinema. Cartoon Frames from "The Little Whirlwind" (Nos. 2591/2607) or "Pluto and the Flypaper" (Nos. 2608/24). Mult.

2591 4r. Type **341** 1·25 1·25
2592 4r. Frame 2 1·25 1·25
2593 4r. Frame 3 1·25 1·25
2594 4r. Frame 4 1·25 1·25
2595 4r. Frame 5 1·25 1·25
2596 4r. Frame 6 1·25 1·25
2597 4r. Frame 7 1·25 1·25
2598 4r. Frame 8 1·25 1·25
2599 4r. Frame 9 1·25 1·25
2600 4r. Frame 10 1·25 1·25
2601 4r. Frame 11 1·25 1·25
2602 4r. Frame 12 1·25 1·25
2603 4r. Frame 13 1·25 1·25
2604 4r. Frame 14 1·25 1·25
2605 4r. Frame 15 1·25 1·25
2606 4r. Frame 16 (Mickey holding fish above head) 1·25 1·25
2607 4r. Frame 17 (Mickey throwing fish into pool) 1·25 1·25
2608 4r. Frame 1 (Pluto) 1·25 1·25
2609 4r. Frame 2 1·25 1·25
2610 4r. Frame 3 1·25 1·25
2611 4r. Frame 4 1·25 1·25
2612 4r. Frame 5 1·25 1·25
2613 4r. Frame 6 1·25 1·25
2614 4r. Frame 7 1·25 1·25
2615 4r. Frame 8 1·25 1·25
2616 4r. Frame 9 1·25 1·25
2617 4r. Frame 10 1·25 1·25
2618 4r. Frame 11 1·25 1·25
2619 4r. Frame 12 1·25 1·25
2620 4r. Frame 13 1·25 1·25
2621 4r. Frame 14 1·25 1·25
2622 4r. Frame 15 1·25 1·25
2623 4r. Frame 16 1·25 1·25
2624 4r. Frame 17 1·25 1·25
MS2625 Two sheets, 111 × 131 mm. (a) 25r. Frame 18 ("The Little Whirlwind"). (b) 25r. Frame 18 ("Pluto and the Flypaper") Set of 2 sheets 14·00 15·00

342 Letter "O" with Chinese Character

1997. "HONG KONG '97" International Stamp Exhibition. Multicoloured.

2626 5r. Letter "H" and Chinese couple 85 85
2627 5r. Type **342** 85 85
2628 5r. Letter "N" and Chinese dragon 85 85
2629 5r. Letter "G" and carnival dragon 85 85
2630 5r. Letter "K" and modern office block 85 85
2631 5r. Letter "O" and Chinese character (different) 85 85
2632 5r. Letter "N" and Chinese fan cases 85 85
2633 5r. Letter "G" and Chinese junk 85 85
MS2634 106 × 125 mm. 25r. "HONG KONG" as on Nos. 2626/33 (76 × 38 mm) 3·75 4·50

343 California Condor

344 Ye Qiabo (China) (women's 500/1000 m speed skating, 1992)

1997. Birds of the World. Multicoloured.

2635 5r. Type **343** 85 85
2636 5r. Audouin's gull 85 85
2637 5r. Atlantic puffin 85 85
2638 5r. Resplendent quetzal 85 85
2639 5r. Puerto Rican amazon 85 85
2640 5r. Lesser bird of paradise 85 85
2641 5r. Japanese crested ibis 85 85
2642 5r. Mauritius kestrel 85 85
2643 5r. Kakapo 85 85
MS2644 76 × 106 mm. 25r. Ivory-billed woodpecker 4·25 4·50

Nos. 2635/43 were printed together, se-tenant, with the backgrounds forming a composite design.

1997. Winter Olympic Games, Nagano, Japan (1998). Multicoloured.

2645 2r. Type **344** 40 25
2646 3r. Leonhard Stock (Austria) (downhill skiing, 1980) 55 35

2647 5r. Herma von Szabo-Planck (Austria) (figure skating, 1924) 75 80
2648 5r. Katarina Witt (Germany) (figure skating, 1988) 75 80
2649 5r. Natalia Bestemianova and Andrei Bukin (Russia) (pairs ice dancing, 1988) 75 80
2650 5r. Jayne Torvill and Christopher Dean (Great Britain) (pairs ice dancing, 1984) 75 80
2651 8r. Bjorn Daehlie (Norway) (cross-country skiing, 1992) . . . . 1·25 1·40
2652 12r. Wolfgang Hoppe (Germany) (bobsleigh, 1984) . . . . 1·75 2·00
MS2653 Two sheets, each 76 × 106 mm. (a) 25r. Sonja Henie (Norway) (figure skating, 1924). (b) 25r. Andree Joly and Pierre Brunet (France) (pairs ice dancing, 1932) Set of 2 sheets . . . . . 8·00 9·00

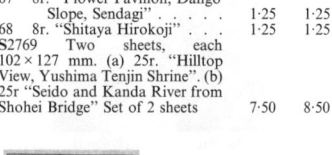

345 Crowned Solitary Eagle

1997. Eagles. Multicoloured.
2654 1r. Type **345** 35 15
2655 2r. African hawk eagle (horiz) 50 30
2656 3r. Lesser spotted eagle . . 60 40
2657 5r. Stellar's sea eagle . . . 75 80
2658 5r. Bald eagle attacking . . 75 80
2659 5r. Bald eagle on branch . . 75 80
2660 5r. Bald eagle looking left 75 80
2661 5r. Bald eagle looking right 75 80
2662 5r. Bald eagle sitting on branch with leaves . . . 75 80
2663 5r. Bald eagle soaring . . . 75 80
2664 8r. Imperial eagle ("Spanish Imperial Eagle") (horiz) 1·25 1·40
2665 10r. Harpy eagle . . . . . 1·50 1·60
2666 12r. Crested serpent eagle (horiz) . . . . 1·75 1·90
MS2667 Two sheets. (a) 73 × 104 mm. 25r. Bald eagle. (b) 104 × 73 mm. 25r. American bald eagle (horiz) Set of 2 sheets . . 8·00 8·50

346 Blitzer Benz, 1911

1997. Classic Cars. Multicoloured.
2668 5r. Type **346** 80 85
2669 5r. Datsun, 1917 . . . . . 80 85
2670 5r. Auburn 8-120, 1929 . . 80 85
2671 5r. Mercedes-Benz C280, 1996 . . . . 80 85
2672 5r. Suzuki UR-1 . . . . . 80 85
2673 5r. Chrysler Atlantic 80 85
2674 5r. Mercedes-Benz 190SL, 1961 . . . . 80 85
2675 5r. Kwaishinha D.A.T., 1916 . . . . 80 85
2676 5r. Rolls-Royce Roadster 20/25 . . . . 80 85
2677 5r. Mercedes-Benz SLK, 1997 . . . . 80 85
2678 5r. Toyota Camry, 1996 . . 80 85
2679 5r. Jaguar MK 2, 1959 . . . 80 85
MS2680 Two sheets, each 100 × 70 mm. (a) 25r. Volkswagen, 1939. (b) 25r. Mazda RX-01 Set of 2 sheets . . . . 7·50 8·50

347 "Patris II", Greece (1926)

1997. Passenger Ships. Multicoloured.
2681 1r. Type **347** 30 15
2682 2r. "Infanta Beatriz", Spain (1928) 40 25
2683 3r. "Vasilefs Constantinos", Greece (1914) 55 60
2684 3r. "Cunene", Portugal (1911) 55 60
2685 3r. "Selandia", Denmark (1912) 55 60
2686 3r. "President Harding", U.S.A. (1921) 55 60
2687 3r. "Ulster Monarch", Great Britain (1929) 55 60
2688 3r. "Matsonia", U.S.A. (1913) 55 60
2689 3r. "France", France (1911) 55 60
2690 3r. "Campania", Great Britain (1893) 55 60
2691 3r. "Klipfontein", Holland (1922) 55 60
2692 3r. "Eridan", France (1929) 55 60
2693 3r. "Mount Clinton", U.S.A. (1921) 55 60
2694 3r. "Infanta Isabel", Spain (1912) 55 60
2695 3r. "Suwa Maru", Japan (1914) 55 60
2696 3r. "Yorkshire", Great Britain (1920) 55 60
2697 3r. "Highland Chieftain", Great Britain (1929) . . . 55 60
2698 3r. "Sardinia", Norway (1920) 55 60
2699 3r. "San Guglielmo", Italy (1911) 55 60
2700 3r. "Avila", Great Britain (1927) 55 60
2701 8r. "Stavangerfjord", Norway (1918) . . . . . 1·25 1·40
2702 12r. "Baloeran", Netherlands (1929) . . . 1·75 1·90
MS2703 Four sheets. (a) 69 × 69 mm. 25r. "Mauritania", Great Britain (1907). (b) 69 × 69 mm. 25r. "United States", U.S.A. (1952). (c) 69 × 69 mm. 25r. "Queen Mary", Great Britain (1930). (d) 91 × 76 mm. 25r. Royal Yacht "Britannia" amd Chinese junk, Hong Kong (56 × 42 mm) Set of 4 sheets . . . . 15·00 15·00
No. **MS**2703d is inscribed "BRITTANIA" in error.

348 Prayer Wheels, Lhasa

1997. 50th Anniv of U.N.E.S.C.O. Multicoloured.
2704 1r. Type **348** 20 15
2705 2r. Ruins of Roman Temple of Diana, Portugal (horiz) 30 25
2706 3r. Santa Maria Cathedral, Hildesheim, Germany (horiz) 45 35
2707 5r. Vivunga National Park, Zaire 65 70
2708 5r. Valley of Mai Nature Reserve, Seychelles . . . 65 70
2709 5r. Kandy, Sri Lanka . . . 65 70
2710 5r. Taj Mahal, India 65 70
2711 5r. Istanbul, Turkey 65 70
2712 5r. Sana'a, Yemen 65 70
2713 5r. Bleinheim Palace, England 65 70
2714 5r. Grand Canyon National Park, U.S.A. 65 70
2715 5r. Tombs, Gondar, Ethiopia 65 70
2716 5r. Bwindi National Park, Uganda 65 70
2717 5r. Bemaraha National Reserve, Madagascar . . 65 70
2718 5r. Buddhist ruins at Takht-I-Bahi, Pakistan 65 70
2719 5r. Anuradhapura, Sri Lanka 65 70
2720 5r. Cairo, Egypt 65 70
2721 5r. Ruins, Petra, Jordan . . 65 70
2722 5r. Volcano, Ujung Kulon National Park, Indonesia 65 70
2723 5r. Terrace, Mount Taishan, China 65 70
2724 5r. Temple, Mount Taishan, China 65 70
2725 5r. Temple turret, Mount Taishan, China 65 70
2726 5r. Standing stones, Mount Taishan, China 65 70
2727 5r. Courtyard, Mount Taishan, China 65 70
2728 5r. Staircase, Mount Taishan, China 65 70
2729 5r. Terracotta Warriors, China 65 70
2730 5r. Head of Terracota Warrior, China 65 70
2731 7r. Doorway, Abu Simbel, Egypt 90 95
2732 8r. Mandraki, Rhodes, Greece (horiz) . . . . . 1·10 1·25
2733 8r. Agios Stefanos Monastery, Meteora, Greece (horiz) . . . . . 1·10 1·25
2734 8r. Taj Mahal, India (horiz) 1·10 1·25
2735 8r. Cistercian Abbey of Fontenay, France (horiz) 1·10 1·25
2736 8r. Yarushima, Japan (horiz) 1·10 1·25
2737 8r. Cloisters, San Gonzalo Convent, Portugal (horiz) 1·10 1·25
2738 8r. Olympic National Park, U.S.A. (horiz) . . . . . 1·10 1·25
2739 8r. Waterfall, Nahanni National Park, Canada (horiz) . . . . 1·10 1·25
2740 8r. Mountains, National Park, Argentina (horiz) 1·10 1·25
2741 8r. Bonfin Salvador Church, Brazil (horiz) . . . . . . 1·10 1·25
2742 8r. Convent of the Companions of Jesus, Morelia, Mexico (horiz) 1·10 1·25
2743 8r. Two-storey temple, Horyu Temple, Japan (horiz) . . . . 1·10 1·25
2744 8r. Summer house, Horyu Temple, Japan (horiz) . . 1·10 1·25
2745 8r. Temple and cloister, Horyu Temple, Japan (horiz) . . . . 1·10 1·25
2746 8r. Single storey temple, Horyu Temple, Japan (horiz) . . . . 1·10 1·25
2747 8r. Well, Horyu Temple, Japan (horiz) . . . . . . 1·10 1·25
2748 10r. Scandola Nature Reserve, France (horiz) 1·25 1·40
2749 12r. Temple on the Lake, China (horiz) . . . . . . 1·50 1·75
MS2750 Four sheets, each 127 × 102 mm. (a) 25r. Fatehpur Sikri Monument, India (horiz). (b) 25r. Temple, Chengde, China (horiz). (c) 25r. Serengeti National Park, Tanzania (horiz). (d) 25r. Buddha, Anuradhapura, Sri Lanka (horiz) Set of 4 sheets 13·00 14·00
No. 2717 is inscribed "MADAGASGAR" and 2737 "COVENT", both in error.

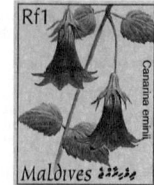

349 White Doves and S.A.A.R.C. Logo

1997. 9th South Asian Association for Regional Cooperation Summit, Male. Multicoloured.
2751 3r. Type **349** 40 35
2752 5r. Flags of member countries . . . . 1·00 75

350 Queen Elizabeth II

1997. Golden Wedding of Queen Elizabeth and Prince Philip. Multicoloured.
2753 5r. Type **350** 85 85
2754 5r. Royal coat of arms . . . 85 85
2755 5r. Queen Elizabeth and Prince Philip at opening of Parliament 85 85
2756 5r. Queen Elizabeth and Prince Philip with Prince Charles, 1948 . . . . . . 85 85
2757 5r. Buckingham Palace from the garden 85 85
2758 5r. Prince Philip 85 85
MS2759 100 × 70 mm. 25r. Queen Elizabeth II . . . . 3·50 3·50

351 Early Indian Mail Messenger

1997. "Pacific '97" International Stamp Exhibition, San Francisco. Death Centenary of Heinrich von Stephan (founder of the U.P.U.).
2760 **351** 2r. green and black . . . 50 60
2761 – 2r. brown and black . . 50 60
2762 – 2r. violet 50 60
DESIGNS: No. 2761, Von Stephan and Mercury; 2762, Autogyro, Washington.

352 "Dawn at Kanda Myojn Shrine"

1997. Birth Bicentenary of Hiroshige (Japanese painter). "One Hundred Famous Views of Edo". Multicoloured.
2763 8r. Type **352** . . . . 1·25 1·25
2764 8r. "Kiyomizu Hall and Shinobazu Pond at Ueno" 1·25 1·25
2765 8r. "Ueno Yamashita" . . . 1·25 1·25
2766 8r. "Moon Pine, Ueno" . . 1·25 1·25
2767 8r. "Flower Pavilion, Dango Slope, Sendagi" . . . . . 1·25 1·25
2768 8r. "Shitaya Hirokoji" . . . 1·25 1·25
MS2769 Two sheets, each 102 × 127 mm. (a) 25r. "Hilltop View, Yushima Tenjin Shrine". (b) 25r "Seido and Kanda River from Shohei Bridge" Set of 2 sheets 7·50 8·50

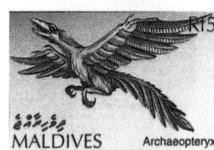

353 Common Noddy

354 "Canarina eminii"

1997. Birds. Multicoloured.
2770 30l. Type **353** 20 30
2771 1r. Spectacled owl 45 25
2772 2r. Malay fish owl 60 35
2773 3r. Peregrine falcon 70 50
2774 5r. Golden eagle 90 70
2775 7r. Ruppell's parrot . . . . 1·00 1·10
2776 7r. Blue-headed parrot . . . 1·00 1·10
2777 7r. St Vincent amazon ("St Vincent Parrot") . . . . 1·00 1·10
2778 7r. Grey parrot . . . . . . 1·00 1·10
2779 7r. Masked lovebird . . . . 1·00 1·10
2780 7r. Sun conure ("Sun Parakeet") . . . . 1·00 1·10
2781 8r. Bateleur . . . . 1·25 1·25
2782 10r. Whiskered tern with chicks . . . . 1·50 1·50
2783 10r. Common caracara . . . 1·50 1·50
2784 15r. Red-footed booby . . . 2·00 2·25
MS2785 Two sheets, each 67 × 98 mm. (a) 25r. American bald eagle. (b) 25r. Secretary bird Set of 2 sheets . . . . 8·00 8·50

1997. Flowers. Multicoloured.
2786 1r. Type **354** 25 15
2787 2r. "Delphinium macrocentron" 40 25
2788 3r. "Leucadendron discolor" 55 40
2789 5r. "Nymphaea caerulea" 75 60
2790 7r. "Rosa multiflora polyantha" (20 × 23 mm) 1·00 1·00
2791 8r. "Bulbophyllum barbigerum" . . . . . . 1·25 1·40
2792 8r. "Acacia seyal" (horiz) 1·25 1·40
2793 8r. "Gloriosa superba" (horiz) . . . . 1·25 1·40
2794 8r. "Gnidia subcordata" (horiz) . . . . 1·25 1·40
2795 8r. "Platycelyphium voense" (horiz) . . . . 1·25 1·40
2796 8r. "Aspilia mossambicensis" (horiz) 1·25 1·40
2797 8r. "Adenium obesum" (horiz) . . . . 1·25 1·40
2798 12r. "Hibiscus vitifolius" . . 2·00 2·25
MS2799 Two sheets, each 105 × 76 mm. (a) 25r. "Aerangis rhodosticta" (horiz). (b) 25r. "Dichrostachys cinerea" and two sailing boats (horiz) Set of 2 sheets 13·00 13·00
Nos. 2792/7 were printed together, se-tenant, with the backgrounds forming a composite design.

355 Archaeopteryx

1997. Prehistoric Animals. Multicoloured. (a) Horiz designs.
2800 5r. Type **355** 90 65
2801 7r. Diplodocus . . . . . . 1·00 1·00
2802 7r. Tyrannosaurus rex . . . 1·00 1·00
2803 7r. Pteranodon . . . . . . 1·00 1·00
2804 7r. Montanceratops . . . . 1·00 1·00
2805 7r. Dromaeosaurus . . . . 1·00 1·00
2806 7r. Oviraptor . . . . 1·00 1·00
2807 8r. Mosasaurus . . . . . . 1·25 1·25
2808 12r. Deinonychus . . . . . 1·60 1·75
2809 15r. Triceratops . . . . . . 1·75 2·00

(b) Square designs, 31 × 31 mm.
2810 7r. Troodon . . . . 1·00 1·00
2811 7r. Brachiosaurus . . . . . 1·00 1·00
2812 7r. Saltasaurus . . . . . . 1·00 1·00
2813 7r. Oviraptor . . . . 1·00 1·00
2814 7r. Parasaurolophus . . . . 1·00 1·00
2815 7r. Psittacosaurus . . . . . 1·00 1·00
2816 7r. Triceratops . . . . . . 1·00 1·00
2817 7r. Pachycephalosaurus . . 1·00 1·00
2818 7r. Iguanodon . . . . . . 1·00 1·00
2819 7r. Tyrannosaurus rex . . . 1·00 1·00
2820 7r. Corythosaurus . . . . . 1·00 1·00
2821 7r. Stegosaurus . . . . . . 1·00 1·00
2822 7r. Euophlocephalus . . . . 1·00 1·00
2823 7r. Compsognathus . . . . 1·00 1·00
2824 7r. Herrerasaurus . . . . . 1·00 1·00
2825 7r. Styracosaurus . . . . . 1·00 1·00
2826 7r. Baryonyx . . . . 1·00 1·00
2827 7r. Lesothosaurus . . . . . 1·00 1·00
MS2828 Two sheets. (a) 99 × 79 mm. 25r. Tyrannosaurus rex (42 × 28 mm). (b) 73 × 104 mm. 25r. Archaeopteryx (31 × 31 mm) Set of 2 sheets . . . . 17·00 17·00

Nos. 2801/6, 2810/15, 2816/21 and 2822/7 respectively were printed together, se-tenant, with the backgrounds of Nos. 2801/6 and 2810/15 forming composite designs.

1997. World Cup Football Championship, France. As T **246** of Lesotho.

2829 1r. black 30 15
2830 2r. black 45 25
2831 3r. multicoloured 55 35
2832/39 3r. × 8 (black; black; multicoloured; multicoloured; black; multicoloured; black; multicoloured) . . . . 3·75 4·00
2840/47 3r. × 8 (multicoloured; multicoloured; black; black; black; multicoloured; multicoloured; black) 3·75 4·00
2848/55 3r. × 8 (multicoloured; multicoloured; multicoloured; black; black; multicoloured; multicoloured; multicoloured) . . . . 3·75 4·00
2856 7r. black . . . . 1·10 1·10
2857 8r. black . . . . 1·40 1·40
2858 10r. multicoloured . . . 1·50 1·60
MS2859 Three sheets. (a) 103 × 128 mm. 25r. multicoloured. (b) 103 × 128 mm. 25r. multicoloured. (c) 128 × 103 mm. 25r. multicoloured Set of 3 sheets 12·00 13·00

DESIGNS—HORIZ: No. 2829, Brazilian team, 1994; 2830, German player, 1954; 2831, Maradona holding World Cup, 1986; 2832, Brazilian team, 1958; 2833, Luis Bellini, Brazil, 1958; 2834, Brazilian team, 1962; 2835, Carlos Alberto, Brazil, 1970; 2836, Mauro, Brazil, 1962; 2837, Brazilian team, 1970; 2838, Dunga, Brazil, 1994; 2839, Brazilian team, 1994; 2840, Paulo Rossi, Italy, 1982; 2841, Zoff and Gentile, Italy, 1982; 2842, Angelo Schavio, Italy; 2843, Italian team, 1934; 2844, Italian team with flag, 1934; 2845, Italian team, 1982; 2846, San Paolo Stadium, Italy; 2847, Italian team, 1938; 2848, English player with ball, 1966; 2849, Wembley Stadium, London; 2850, English player heading ball, 1966; 2851, English players celebrating, 1966; 2852, English and German players chasing ball, 1966; 2853, English player wearing No. 21 shirt, 1966; 2854, English team with Jules Rimet trophy, 1966; 2855, German player wearing No. 5 shirt, 1966; 2856, Argentine player holding trophy, 1978; 2857, English players with Jules Rimet trophy, 1966; 2858, Brazilian player with trophy, 1970; **MS**2859c, Klinsmann, Germany. VERT: No. **MS**2859a, Ronaldo, Brazil; **MS**2892b, Schmeichel, Denmark.

1998. Diana, Princess of Wales Commemoration. As T **249** of Lesotho. Multicoloured (except Nos. 2864, 2870, 2872, 2877 and **MS**2878b).

2860 7r. Laughing 60 65
2861 7r. With Prince William and Prince Harry 60 65
2862 7r. Carrying bouquets . . . 60 65
2863 7r. In white evening dress 60 65
2864 7r. Wearing bow tie (brown and black) 60 65
2865 7r. Wearing black jacket . . 60 65
2866 7r. With Indian child on lap 60 65
2867 7r. Wearing blue evening dress 60 65
2868 7r. Wearing blue jacket and poppy 60 65
2869 7r. Wearing cream jacket . . 60 65
2870 7r. Wearing blouse and jacket (brown and black) 60 65
2871 7r. Wearing red jacket . . . 60 65
2872 7r. Wearing hat (blue and black) 60 65
2873 7r. Wearing red evening dress 60 65
2874 7r. With Sir Richard Attenborough 60 65
2875 7r. Wearing jeans and white shirt 60 65
2876 7r. Wearing white jacket . . 60 65
2877 7r. Carrying bouquet (brown and black) 60 65
MS2878 Three sheets. (a) 100 × 70 mm. 25r. On ski-lift. (b) 100 × 70 mm. 25r. Wearing polkadot dress (brown and black). (c) 70 × 100 mm. 25r. Wearing garland of flowers Set of 3 sheets 6·50 6·75

356 Pres. Nelson Mandela

357 Pres. John F. Kennedy

1998. 80th Birthday of Nelson Mandela (President of South Africa).

2879 **356** 7r. multicoloured 60 65

1998. Pres. John F. Kennedy Commemoration. Multicoloured, background colours given.

2880 **357** 5r. green 45 50
2881 – 5r. green 45 50
2882 – 5r. brown (inscr at right) 45 50
2883 – 5r. yellow 45 50
2884 – 5r. violet 45 50
2885 – 5r. blue 45 50
2886 – 5r. grey 45 50
2887 – 5r. brown (inscr at left) 45 50
2888 – 5r. blue (value at bottom right) 45 50

DESIGNS: Nos. 2881/8, Various portraits.

358 Yakovlev Yak-18 (from 1947)

1998. Aircraft in Longest Continuous Production. Multicoloured.

2889 5r. Type **358** 45 50
2890 5r. Beechcraft Bonanza (from 1947) 45 50
2891 5r. Piper Cub (1937–82) . . 45 50
2892 5r. Tupolev Tu-95 (1954–90) 45 50
2893 5r. Lockheed C-130 Hercules (from 1954) . . 45 50
2894 5r. Piper PA-28 Cherokee (from 1961) 45 50
2895 5r. Mikoyan Gurevich MiG-21 (from 1959) . . . 45 50
2896 5r. Pilatus PC-6 Turbo Porter (from 1960) . . . 45 50
2897 5r. Antonov An-2 (from 1949) 45 50
MS2898 120 × 90 mm. 25r. Boeing KC-135E (from 1956) (84 × 28 mm) . . . . 2·20 2·30

359 White American Shorthair

1998. Cats. Multicoloured.

2899 5r. Type **359** 45 50
2900 7r. American curl and Maine coon (horiz) . . . 60 65
2901 7r. Maine coon (horiz) . . . 60 65
2902 7r. Siberian (horiz) 60 65
2903 7r. Somali (horiz) 60 65
2904 7r. European Burmese (horiz) 60 65
2905 7r. Nebelung (horiz) 60 65
2906 7r. Bicolour British shorthair (horiz) 60 65
2907 7r. Manx (horiz) 60 65
2908 7r. Tabby American shorthair (horiz) 60 65
2909 7r. Silver tabby Persian (horiz) 60 65
2910 7r. Oriental white (horiz) . . 60 65
2911 7r. Norwegian forest cat (horiz) 60 65
2912 8r. Sphynx cat 70 75
2913 10r. Tabby American shorthair 90 95
2914 12r. Scottish fold . . . . . 1·10 1·20
MS2915 Two sheets, each 98 × 68 mm. (a) 30r. Norwegian forest cat. (b) 30r. Snowshoe Set of 2 sheets . . . . 5·25 5·50

Nos. 2900/5 and 2906/11 respectively were printed together, se-tenant, forming composite designs.

360 Boeing 737 HS

1998. Aircraft. Multicoloured.

2916 2r. Type **360** 20 25
2917 5r. CL-215 (flying boat) . . 45 50
2918 5r. Orion 45 50
2919 5r. Yakolev Yak-54 . . . . 45 50
2920 5r. Cessna sea plane 45 50
2921 5r. CL-215 (amphibian) . . 45 50
2922 5r. CL-215 SAR (amphibian) 45 50
2923 5r. Twin Otter 45 50
2924 5r. Rockwell Quail 45 50
2925 5r. F.S.W. fighter 45 50
2926 5r. V-Jet II 45 50
2927 5r. Pilatus PC-12 . . . . . 45 50
2928 5r. Citation Exel 45 50
2929 5r. Stutz Bearcat 45 50
2930 5r. Cessna T-37 (B) 45 50
2931 5r. Peregrine Business Jet . . 45 50
2932 5r. Beech 58 Baron 45 50
2933 7r. Boeing 727 . . . . . . 60 65
2934 8r. Boeing 747-400 . . . . 70 75
2935 10r. Boeing 737 . . . . . . 90 95
MS2936 Two sheets, each 98 × 68 mm. (a) 25r. Beechcraft Model 18. (b) 25r. Falcon Jet Set of 2 sheets . . . . 4·50 4·75

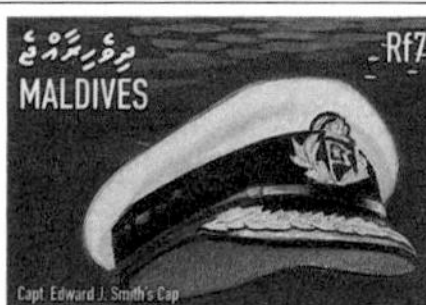

361 Captain Edward Smith's Cap

1998. "Titanic" Commemoration. Multicoloured.

2937 7r. Type **361** 60 65
2938 7r. Deck chair 60 65
2939 7r. Fifth Officer Harold Lowe's coat button . . . 60 65
2940 7r. Lifeboat 60 65
2941 7r. "Titanic's" wheel 60 65
2942 7r. Passenger's lifejacket . . 60 65
MS2943 110 × 85 mm. 25r. "Titanic" from newspaper picture . . . . 2·20 2·30

362 Guava Tree

1998. 20th Anniv of International Fund of Agriculture. Multicoloured.

2944 1r. Type **362** 10 15
2945 5r. Selection of fruit 45 50
2946 7r. Fishing boat 60 65
2947 8r. Papaya tree 70 75
2948 10r. Vegetable produce . . . 90 95

363 Thread-finned Butterflyfish

1998. Fish. Multicoloured.

2949 50l. Type **363** 10 10
2950 50l. Queen angelfish 10 10
2951 1r. Oriental sweetlips . . . 10 15
2952 3r. Mandarin fish 25 30
2953 3r. Copper-banded butterflyfish 25 30
2954 3r. Harlequin tuskfish . . . 25 30
2955 3r. Yellow-tailed demoiselle 25 30
2956 3r. Wimplefish 25 30
2957 3r. Red emperor snapper . . 25 30
2958 3r. Clown triggerfish 25 30
2959 3r. Common clown 25 30
2960 3r. Palette surgeonfish ("Regal Tang") 25 30
2961 5r. Emperor angelfish . . . 45 50
2962 5r. Common squirrelfish ("Diadem Squirrelfish") 45 50
2963 5r. Lemon-peel angelfish . . 45 50
2964 5r. Powder-blue surgeonfish 45 50
2965 5r. Moorish idol 45 50
2966 5r. Bicolor angelfish ("Bicolor Cherub") . . . 45 50
2967 5r. Duboulay's angelfish ("Scribbled Angelfish") 45 50
2968 5r. Two-banded anemonefish 45 50
2969 5r. Yellow tang 45 50
2970 7r. Red-tailed surgeonfish ("Achilles Tang") 60 65
2971 7r. Bandit angelfish 60 65
2972 8r. Hooded butterflyfish ("Red-headed Butterflyfish") 70 75
2973 50r. Blue-striped butterflyfish . . . . . . 4·50 4·75
MS2974 Two sheets, each 110 × 85 mm. (a) 25r. Long-nosed butterflyfish. (b) 25r. Porkfish Set of 2 sheets . . . . 4·50 4·75

364 Baden-Powell inspecting Scouts, Amesbury, 1909

1998. 19th World Scout Jamboree, Chile. Multicoloured.

2975 12r. Type **364** . . . . . . 1·10 1·25
2976 12r. Sir Robert and Lady Baden-Powell with children, 1927 . . . . . 1·10 1·25
2977 12r. Sir Robert Baden-Powell awarding merit badges, Chicago, 1926 . . 1·10 1·25

365 Diana, Princess of Wales

1998. 1st Death Anniv of Diana, Princess of Wales.

2978 **365** 10r. multicoloured . . . 90 95

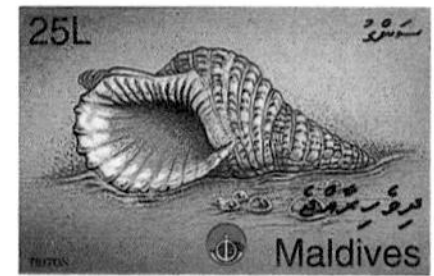

366 Triton Shell

1999. International Year of the Ocean. Marine Life. Multicoloured.

2979 25l. Type **366** 10 10
2980 50l. Napoleon wrasse . . . 10 10
2981 1r. Whale shark 10 15
2982 3r. Grey reef shark 25 30
2983 5r. Harp seal 45 50
2984 5r. Killer whale 45 50
2985 5r. Sea otter 45 50
2986 5r. Beluga 45 50
2987 5r. Narwhal 45 50
2988 5r. Walrus 45 50
2989 5r. Sea lion 45 50
2990 5r. Humpback salmon . . . 45 50
2991 5r. Emperor penguin . . . 45 50
2992 7r. Blue whale 60 65
2993 7r. Skipjack tuna 60 65
2994 8r. Ocean sunfish 70 75
2995 8r. Opalescent squid 70 75
2996 8r. Electric ray 70 75
2997 8r. Corded neptune 70 75
MS2998 Three sheets, each 110 × 85 mm. (a) 25r. Horseshoe crab. (b) 25r. Blue whale. (c) 25r. Triton shell Set of 3 sheets . . 6·50 6·75

Nos. 2983/91 were printed together, se-tenant, with the backgrounds forming a composite design.

367 Broderip's Cowrie

1999. Marine Life. Multicoloured.

2999 30l. Type **367** 10 10
3000 1r. White tern ("Fairy Tern") 10 15
3001 3r. Green-backed heron ("Darker Maldivian Green Heron") 25 30
3002 5r. Manta ray 45 50
3003 5r. Green turtle 45 50
3004 5r. Spotted dolphins 45 50
3005 5r. Moorish idols 45 50
3006 5r. Threadfin anthias . . . 45 50
3007 5r. Goldbar wrasse 45 50
3008 5r. Palette surgeonfish . . . 45 50
3009 5r. Three-spotted angelfish 45 50
3010 5r. Oriental sweetlips . . . 45 50
3011 5r. Brown booby 45 50
3012 5r. Red-tailed tropic bird . . 45 50
3013 5r. Sooty tern 45 50
3014 5r. Striped dolphin 45 50
3015 5r. Spinner dolphin 45 50
3016 5r. Crab plover 45 50
3017 5r. Hawksbill turtle 45 50
3018 5r. Indo-Pacific sergeant . . 45 50
3019 5r. Yellow-finned tuna . . . 45 50
3020 7r. Blackflag sandperch . . 60 65
3021 8r. Coral hind 70 75
3022 10r. Olive Ridley turtle . . . 90 95
MS3023 Two sheets, each 110 × 85 mm. (a) 25r. Cinnamon bittern. (b) 25r. Blue-faced angelfish Set of 2 sheets . . . 4·50 4·75

Nos. 3002/10 and 3011/19 were each printed together, se-tenant, with the backgrounds forming composite designs.

368 Mickey Mouse

1999. 70th Anniv of Mickey Mouse (Disney cartoon character). Multicoloured.
3024/9 5r. × 6 (Mickey Mouse: Type **368**; laughing; looking tired; frowning; smiling; winking) . . .
3030/5 5r. × 6 (Minnie Mouse: facing left and smiling; with eyes closed; with hand on head; looking surprised; smiling; looking cross) . . . .
3036/41 7r. × 6 (Donald Duck: facing left and smiling; laughing; looking tired; looking cross; smiling; winking) . . . .
3042/7 7r. × 6 (Daisy Duck: with half closed eyes; laughing; looking shocked; looking cross; facing forwards; with head on one side) . . .
3048/53 7r. × 6 (Goofy: facing right and smiling; with eyes closed; with half closed eyes; looking shocked; looking puzzled; looking thoughtful) . . . . . .
3054/9 7r. × 6 (Pluto: looking shocked; with eyes closed; smiling; scowling; with tongue out (orange background); with tongue out (green background) . . . . .
3024/59 Set of 30 . . . . 32·00 32·00
MS3060 Six sheets, each 127 × 102 mm. (a) 25r. Minnie Mouse wearing necklace. (b) 25r. Mickey with hand on head. (c) 25r. Mickey wearing baseball hat. (d) 25r. Mickey facing right (horiz). (e) 25r. Minnie looking left (includes label showing Mickey with bouquet). (f) 25r. Minnie drinking through straw Set of 6 sheets . . . . 22·00 22·00

369 Great Orange Tip

1999. Butterflies. Multicoloured.
3061 50l. Type **369** 10 10
3062 1r. Large green aporandria 10 15
3063 2r. Common mormon . . . 20 25
3064 3r. African migrant 25 30
3065 5r. Common pierrot 45 50
3066 7r. Crimson tip (vert) . . . 60 65
3067 7r. Tawny rajah (vert) . . . 60 65
3068 7r. Leafwing butterfly (vert) 60 65
3069 7r. Great egg-fly (vert) . . . 60 65
3070 7r. Blue admiral (vert) . . . 60 65
3071 7r. African migrant (vert) 60 65
3072 7r. Common red flash (vert) 60 65
3073 7r. Burmese lascar (vert) . . 60 65
3074 7r. Common perriot (vert) 60 65
3075 7r. Baron (vert) 60 65
3076 7r. Leaf blue (vert) 60 65
3077 7r. Great orange tip (vert) 60 65
3078 10r. Giant red-eye 90 95
MS3079 Two sheets, each 70 × 100 mm. (a) 25r. Crimson tip. (b) 25r. Large oak blue Set of 2 sheets . . . . 4·50 4·75
Nos. 3066/71 and 3072/7 were each printed together, se-tenant, with the backgrounds forming composite designs.

370 Scelidosaurus

1999. Prehistoric Animals. Multicoloured.
3080 1r. Type **370** 10 15
3081 3r. Yansudaurus 25 30
3082 5r. Ornitholestes 45 50
3083 7r. Dimorphodon (vert) . . 60 65
3084 7r. Rhamphorhynchus (vert) 60 65
3085 7r Allosaurus (vert) 60 65
3086 7r. Leaellynasaura (vert) . . 60 65
3087 7r. Troodon (vert) 60 65
3088 7r. Syntarsus (vert) 60 65
3089 7r. Anchisaurus (vert) . . . 60 65
3090 7r. Pterenodon (vert) . . . 60 65
3091 7r. Barosaurus (vert) 60 65
3092 7r. Iguanodon (vert) 60 65
3093 7r. Archaeopteryx (vert) . . 60 65
3094 7r. Ceratosaurus (vert) . . . 60 65
3095 7r. Stegosaurus 60 65
3096 7r. Corythosaurus 60 65
3097 7r. Cetiosaurus 60 65
3098 7r. Avimimus 60 65
3099 7r. Styracosaurus 60 65
3100 7r. Massospondylus 60 65
3101 8r. Astrodon 70 75
MS3102 Two sheets, each 116 × 81 mm. (a) 25r. Megalosaurus (vert). (b) 25r. Brachiosaurus (vert) Set of 2 sheets . . . . 4·50 4·75

Nos. 3083/8, 3089/94 and 3095/100 were each printed together, se-tenant, forming composite designs.

371 Express Locomotive, Egypt, 1856

1999. Trains of the World. Multicoloured.
3103 50l. Type **371** 10 10
3104 1r. Channel Tunnel Le Shuttle, France, 1994 . . 10 15
3105 2r. Gowan and Marx locomotive, U.S.A., 1839 . . 20 25
3106 3r. TGV train, France, 1981 25 30
3107 5r. "Ae 6/6" electric locomotive, Switzerland, 1954 45 50
3108 7r. Stephenson's long-boilered locomotive, Great Britain, 1846 (red livery) 60 65
3109 7r. "Cornwall", Great Britain, 1847 . . . . . 60 65
3110 7r. First locomotive, Germany, 1848 . . . . . 60 65
3111 7r. Great Western locomotive, Great Britain, 1846 . . . . 60 65
3112 7r. Standard Stephenson locomotive, France, 1837 60 65
3113 7r. "Meteor", Great Britain, 1843 . . . . 60 65
3114 7r. Class 4T diesel-electric locomotive, Great Britain, 1940–65 . . . . 60 65
3115 7r. Mainline diesel-electric locomotive No. 20101, Malaya, 1940–65 . . . . 60 65
3116 7r. Class 7000 high-speed electric locomotive, France, 1949 . . . . . . 60 65
3117 7r. Diesel hydraulic express locomotive, Thailand, 1940–65 . . . . 60 65
3118 7r. Diesel hydraulic locomotive, Burma, 1940–65 . . . . 60 65
3119 7r. "Hikari" super express train, Japan, 1940–65 . . 60 65
3120 8r. Stephenson's long-boilered locomotive, Great Britain, 1846 (orange and green livery) 70 75
3121 10r. "Philadelphia", Austria, 1838 . . . . 90 95
3122 15r. S.E. and C.R. Class E steam locomotive, Great Britain, 1940 . . . . . . 1·30 1·40
MS3123 Two sheets, each 110 × 85 mm. (a) 25r. Passenger locomotive, France, 1846. (b) 25r. Southern Railway Class "King Arthur", steam locomotive, Great Britain, 1940 Set of 2 sheets . . 4·50 4·75

1999. "Queen Elizabeth the Queen Mother's Century". As T **267** of Lesotho.
3124 7r. black and gold 60 65
3125 7r. black and gold 60 65
3126 7r. multicoloured 60 65
3127 7r. multicoloured 60 65
MS3128 153 × 157 mm. 25r. multicoloured . . . . 2·20 2·30
DESIGNS: No. 3124, King George VI and Queen Elizabeth, 1936; 3125, Queen Elizabeth, 1941; 3126, Queen Elizabeth in evening dress, 1960; 3127, Queen Mother at Ascot, 1981. 37 × 50 mm: No. **MS**3128, Queen Mother in Garter robes.

1999. "iBRA '99" International Stamp Exhibition, Nuremberg. As T **262** of Lesotho. Multicoloured.
3129 12r. "Adler" (first German railway locomotive), 1833 1·10 1·25
3130 15r. "Drache" (Henshell and Sohn's first locomotive), 1848 . . . . 1·30 1·40
The captions on Nos. 3129/30 are transposed.

1999. 150th Death Anniv of Katsushika Hokusai (Japanese artist). As T **263** of Lesotho. Multicoloured (except No. 3133).
3131 7r. "Haunted House" . . . 60 65
3132 7r. "Juniso Shrine at Yotsuya" 60 65
3133 7r. Drawing of bird (black, green and gold) 60 65
3134 7r. Drawing of two women 60 65
3135 7r. "Lover in the Snow" . . 60 65
3136 7r. "Mountain Tea House" 60 65
3137 7r. "A Coastal View" . . . 60 65
3138 7r. "Bath House by a Lake" 60 65
3139 7r. Drawing of a horse . . . 60 65
3140 7r. Drawing of two birds on branch 60 65
3141 7r. "Evening Cool at Ryogoku" 60 65
3142 7r. "Girls boating" 60 65
MS3143 Two sheets, each 100 × 70 mm. (a) 25r. "Girls gathering Spring Herbs" (vert). (b) 25r. "Scene in the Yoshiwara" (vert) Set of 2 sheets . . . . . 4·50 4·75

1999. 10th Anniv of United Nations Rights of the Child Convention. As T **264** of Lesotho. Mult.
3144 10r. Baby boy and young mother 90 95
3145 10r. Young girl laughing . . 90 95
3146 10r. Three children 90 95
MS3147 110 × 85 mm. 25r. Sir Peter Ustinov (Goodwill ambassador for U.N.I.C.E.F.) . . . . . . 2·20 2·30

372 Standard Stephenson Railway Locomotive "Versailles", 1837

1999. "PhilexFrance '99" International Stamp Exhibition, Paris. Railway Locomotives. Two sheets, each 106 × 81 mm, containing T **372** and similar horiz design. Multicoloured.
MS3148 (a) 25r. Type **372**. (b) 25r. Stephenson long-boilered locomotive, 1841 Set of 2 sheets 4·50 4·75

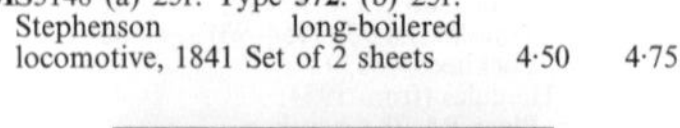

373 Phobos and Demos (Martian Moons)

2000. Future Colonization of Mars. Multicoloured.
3149 5r. Type **373** 45 50
3150 5r. Improved Hubble Telescope 45 50
3151 5r. Passenger shuttle 45 50
3152 5r. Skyscrapers on Mars . . 45 50
3153 5r. Martian taxi 45 50
3154 5r. Martian landing facilities 45 50
3155 5r. Vegetation in Martian biosphere 45 50
3156 5r. Walking on Mars and biosphere 45 50
3157 5r. Mars rover 45 50
3158 5r. Russian Phobos 25 satellite 45 50
3159 5r. Earth and Moon 45 50
3160 5r. Space shuttle leaving Earth 45 50
3161 5r. Lighthouse on Mars . . 45 50
3162 5r. Mars excursion space liner 45 50
3163 5r. Mars shuttle and skyscrapers 45 50
3164 5r. Viking Lander 45 50
3165 5r. Mars air and water purification plant 45 50
3166 5r. Family picnic on Mars 45 50
MS3167 Two sheets, each 110 × 85 mm. (a) 25r. Astronaut with jet-pack. (b) 25r. Mars Set of 2 sheets . . . . 4·50 4·75
Nos. 3149/57 and 3158/66 were each printed together, se-tenant, with the backgrounds forming composite designs.

374 Coconuts

2000. "Destination 2000 – Maldives" Campaign. Multicoloured.
3168 7r. Type **374** 60 65
3169 7r. Shoal of skipjack tuna 60 65
3170 7r. Seaplane and traditional dhow 60 65
3171 7r. "Plumeria alba" 60 65
3172 7r. Lionfish 60 65
3173 7r. Windsurfers 60 65

2000. New Millennium. People and Events of Eighteenth Century (1750–1800). As T **268** of Lesotho. Multicoloured.
3174 3r. American bald eagle and American Declaration of Independence, 1776 . . . 25 30
3175 3r. Montgolfier brothers and first manned hot- air balloon flight, 1783 . . . 25 30
3176 3r. Napoleon and mob (French Revolution, 1789) 25 30
3177 3r. James Watt and drawing of steam engine, 1769 . . 25 30
3178 3r. Wolfgang Amadeus Mozart (born 1756) . . . 25 30
3179 3r. Front cover of The Dream of the Red Chamber (Chinese novel, published 1791) 25 30
3180 3r. Napoleon and pyramid (conquest of Egypt, 1798) 25 30
3181 3r. Empress Catherine the Great of Russia and St. Petersburg, 1762 . . . 25 30
3182 3r. Joseph Priestley (discovery of oxygen, 1774) 25 30
3183 3r. Benjamin Franklin (publication of work on electricity, 1751) 25 30
3184 3r. Edward Jenner (development of smallpox vaccine, 1796) 25 30
3185 3r. Death of General Wolfe, 1759 . . . . 25 30
3186 3r. "The Swing" (Jean Honore Fragonard), 1766 25 30
3187 3r. Ludwig von Beethoven (born 1770) 25 30
3188 3r. Marriage of Louis XVI of France and Marie Antoinette, 1770 . . . . 25 30
3189 3r. Captain James Cook (exploration of Australia, 1770) (59 × 39 mm) . . . 25 30
3190 3r. Luigi Galvani and frog (experiments into the effect of electricity on nerves and muscles, 1780) 25 30
The main design on No. 3184 may depict Sir William Jenner who undertook research into typhus.
On No. 3185 the uniforms are incorrectly shown as blue instead of red.

375 Sun and Moon over Forest

2000. Solar Eclipse Showing varying stages of eclipse as seen from Earth (Nos. 3191/6) or Space (Nos. 3197/202). Mult.
3191 7r. Type **375** 60 65
3192 7r. "Second Contact" . . . 60 65
3193 7r. "Totality" 60 65
3194 7r. "Third Contact" 60 65
3195 7r. "Fourth Contact" . . . 60 65
3196 7r. Observatory 60 65
3197 7r. "First Contact" 60 65
3198 7r. "Second Contact" . . . 60 65
3199 7r. "Totality" 60 65
3200 7r. "Third Contact" 60 65
3201 7r. "Fourth Contact" . . . 60 65
3202 7r. Solar and heliospheric observatory 60 65
Nos. 3191/6 and 3197/202 were each printed together, se-tenant, with the backgrounds forming composite designs.

376 Red Lacewing

2000. Butterflies of the Maldives. Multicoloured.
3203 5r. Type **376** 45 50
3204 5r. Large oak blue 45 50
3205 5r. Yellow coster 45 50
3206 5r. Great orange-tip 45 50
3207 5r. Common pierrot 45 50
3208 5r. Cruiser 45 50
3209 5r. Hedge blue 45 50
3210 5r. Common eggfly 45 50
3211 5r. Plain tiger 45 50
3212 5r. Common wall butterfly 45 50
3213 5r. Koh-i-Noor butterfly . . 45 50
3214 5r. Painted lady ("Indian Red Admiral") 45 50
3215 5r. Tawny rajah 45 50
3216 5r. Blue triangle 45 50
3217 5r. Orange albatross 45 50
3218 5r. Common rose swallowtail 45 50
3219 5r. Jewelled nawab 45 50
3220 5r. Striped blue crow . . . 45 50
MS3221 Two sheets. (a) 85 × 110 mm. 25r. Large tree nymph. (b) 110 × 85 mm. 25r. Blue pansy Set of 2 sheets . . . . . 4·50 4·75
Nos. 3203/11 and 3212/20 were each printed together, se-tenant, with the backgrounds forming composite designs.
No. 3219 is inscribed "JEWELED NAWAB" in error.

377 "Martin Rijckaert"

2000. 400th Birth Anniv of Sir Anthony Van Dyck (Flemish painter). Multicoloured.
3222 5r. Type **377** 45 50
3223 5r. "Frans Snyders" 45 50
3224 5r. "Quentin Simons" 45 50
3225 5r. "Lucas van Uffel", 1632 45 50
3226 5r. "Nicolaes Rockox" 45 50
3227 5r. "Nicholas Lamier" 45 50
3228 5r. "Inigo Jones" 45 50
3229 5r. "Lucas van Uffel", c. 1622–25 45 50
3230 5r. Detail of "Margaretha de Vos, Wife of Frans Snyders" 45 50
3231 5r. "Peter Brueghel the Younger" 45 50
3232 5r. "Cornelis van der Geest" 45 50
3233 5r. "Francois Langlois as a Savoyard" 45 50
3234 5r. "Portrait of a Family" 45 50
3235 5r. "Earl and Countess of Denby and Their Daughter" 45 50
3236 5r. "Family Portrait" 45 50
3237 5r. "A Genoese Nobleman with his Children" 45 50
3238 5r. "Thomas Howard, Earl of Arundel, and His Grandson" 45 50
3239 5r. "La dama d'oro" 45 50
MS3240 Six sheets. (a) 102 × 127 mm. 25r. "The Painter Jan de Wael and his Wife Gertrude de Jode". (b) 102 × 127 mm. 25r. "John, Count of Nassau-Siegen, and His Family". (c) 102 × 127 mm. 25r. "The Lomellini Family". (d) 102 × 127 mm. 25r. "Lucas and Cornelis de Wael". (e) 127 × 102 mm. 25r. "Sir Kenelm and Lady Digby with their two Eldest Sons". (f) 127 × 102 mm. 25r. "Sir Philip Herbert, 4th Earl of Pembroke, and His Family" (horiz) Set of 6 sheets 13·00 13·50
No. 3230 is inscribed "Margaretha de Vos, Wife of Frans Snders" in error.

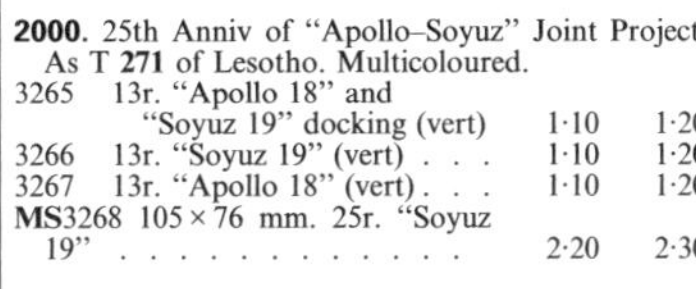
378 Japanese Railways "Shinkansen", High Speed Electric Train

2000. "The Stamp Show 2000" International Stamp Exhibition, London. Asian Railways. Mult.
3241 5r. Type **378** 45 50
3242 8r. Japanese Railways "Super Azusa", twelve-car train 70 75
3243 10r. Tobu Railway "Spacia", ten-car electric train, Japan 90 95
3244 10r. Shanghai-Nanking Railway passenger tank locomotive, China, 1909 90 95
3245 10r. Shanghai–Nanking Railway "Imperial Yellow" express mail locomotive, China, 1910 90 95
3246 10r. Manchurian Railway "Pacific" locomotive, China, 1914 90 95
3247 10r. Hankow Line mixed traffic locomotive, China, 1934 90 95
3248 10r. Chinese National Railway freight locomotive, 1949 90 95
3249 10r. Chinese National Railway mixed traffic locomotive, 1949 90 95
3250 10r. East Indian Railway passenger tank locomotive Fawn, 1856 90 95
3251 10r. East Indian Railway express locomotive, 1893 90 95
3252 10r. Bengal–Nagpur Railway Atlantic Compound loco-motive, India, 1909 90 95
3253 10r. Great Peninsular Railway passenger and mail locomotive, India, 1924 90 95
3254 10r. North Western Class XS2 Pacific locomotive, India, 1932 90 95
3255 10r. Indian National Railway Class YP Pacific locomotive, India, 1949–70 90 95
3256 15r. Japanese Railway "Nozomi", high-speed electric train 1·30 1·40
MS3257 Two sheets, each 100 × 70 mm. (a) 25r. Indian National Railways Class WP locomotive (57 × 41 mm). (b) 25r. Chinese National Railway Class JS locomotive (57 × 41 mm) Set of 2 sheets 4·50 4·75

379 Republic Monument

2000. New Millennium (2nd issue). Multicoloured.
3258 10l. Type **379** 10 10
3259 30l. Bodu Thakurufaanu Memorial Centre 10 10
3260 1r. Modern medical facilities and new hospital 10 15
3261 7r. Male International Airport 60 65
3262 7r. Hukuru Miskiiy 60 65
3263 10r. Computer room, science lab and new school 90 95
MS3264 Three sheets, each 106 × 77 mm. (a) 25r. Tourist resort and fish packing factory. (b) 25r. Islamic Centre. (c) 25r. People's Majlis (assembly) Set of 3 sheets 6·50 6·75

2000. 25th Anniv of "Apollo–Soyuz" Joint Project. As T **271** of Lesotho. Multicoloured.
3265 13r. "Apollo 18" and "Soyuz 19" docking (vert) 1·10 1·20
3266 13r. "Soyuz 19" (vert) 1·10 1·20
3267 13r. "Apollo 18" (vert) 1·10 1·20
MS3268 105 × 76 mm. 25r. "Soyuz 19" 2·20 2·30

380 George Stephenson and *Locomotion No. 1*, 1825

2000. 175th Anniv of Stockton and Darlington Line (first public railway). Multicoloured.
3269 10r. Type **380** 90 95
3270 10r. William Hedley's *Puffing Billy* locomotive 90 95

2000. Centenary of First Zeppelin Flight. As T **276** of Lesotho. Multicoloured.
3271 13r. LZ-127 *Graf Zeppelin*, 1928 1·10 1·20
3272 13r. LZ-130 *Graf Zeppelin II*, 1938 1·10 1·20
3273 13r. LZ-9 *Ersatz*, 1911 1·10 1·20
MS3274 115 × 80 mm. 25r. LZ-88 (L-40), 1917 (37 × 50 mm) 2·20 2·30
No. 3272 is inscribed "LZ-127" in error.

2000. Olympic Games, Sydney. As T **277** of Lesotho. Multicoloured.
3275 10r. Suzanne Lenglen, (French tennis player), 1920 90 95
3276 10r. Fencing 90 95
3277 10r. Olympic Stadium, Tokyo, 1964, and Japanese flag 90 95
3278 10r. Ancient Greek long jumping 90 95

381 White Tern

2000. Tropical Birds. Multicoloured.
3279 15l. Type **381** 10 10
3280 25l. Brown booby 10 10
3281 30l. White-collared kingfisher (vert) 10 10
3282 1r. Black-winged stilt (vert) 10 15
3283 10r. White-collared kingfisher (different) (vert) 90 95
3284 10r. Island thrush (vert) 90 95
3285 10r. Red-tailed tropic bird (vert) 90 95
3286 10r. Peregrine falcon (vert) 90 95
3287 10r. Black-crowned night heron ("Night Heron") (vert) 90 95
3288 10r. Great egret (vert) 90 95
3289 10r. Great frigate bird 90 95
3290 10r. Common noddy 90 95
3291 10r. Common tern 90 95
3292 10r. Red-footed booby ("Sula Sula") 90 95
3293 10r. Sooty tern 90 95
3294 10r. White-tailed tropic bird (*Phaethon lepturus*) 90 95
3295 13r. Ringed plover 1·10 1·20
3296 13r. Ruddy turnstone ("Turnstone") 1·10 1·20
3297 13r. Australian stone-curlew 1·10 1·20
3298 13r. Grey plover ("Black-bellied Plover") 1·10 1·20
3299 13r. Crab lover 1·10 1·20
3300 13r. Western curlew ("Curlew") 1·10 1·20
MS3301 Two sheets, each 77 × 103 mm. (a) 25r. Great cormorant (vert). (b) 25r. Cattle egret (vert) Set of 2 sheets 4·50 4·75
Nos. 3283/8, 3289/4 and 3295/300 were each printed together, se-tenant, with the backgrounds forming composite designs.
No. 3294 is inscribed "Leturus" in error.

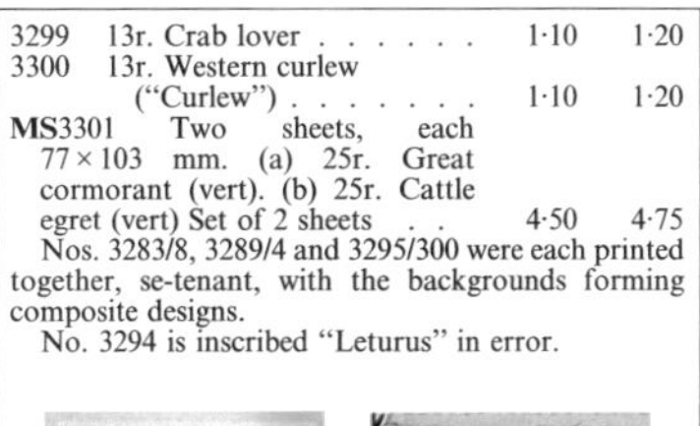

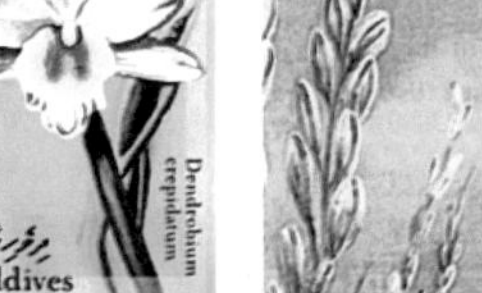
382 *Dendrobium crepidatum* **384** Corn Lily

383 Honda CB 750 Motorcycle, 1969

2000. Orchids. Multicoloured.
3302 50l. Type **382** 10 10
3303 1r. *Eulophia guineensis* 10 15
3304 2r.50 *Cymbidium finlaysonianum* 20 25
3305 3r.50 *Paphiopedilum druryi* 30 35
3306 10r. *Angraecum germinyanum* 90 95
3307 10r. *Phalaenopsis amabilis* 90 95
3308 10r. *Thrixspermum cantipeda* 90 95
3309 10r. *Phaius tankervilleae* 90 95
3310 10r. *Rhynchostylis gigantea* 90 95
3311 10r. *Papilionanthe teres* 90 95
3312 10r. Aerides odorata 90 95
3313 10r. *Dendrobium chrysotoxum* 90 95
3314 10r. *Dendrobium anosmum* 90 95
3315 10r. *Calypso bulbosa* 90 95
3316 10r. *Paphiopedilum fairrieanum* 90 95
3317 10r. *Cynorkis fastigiata* 90 95
MS3318 Two sheets, each 96 × 72 mm. (a) 25r. *Cymbidium dayanum*. (b) 25r. *Spathoglottis plicata* Set of 2 sheets 4·50 4·75
Nos. 3306/11 and 3312/17 were each printed together, se-tenant, with the backgrounds forming composite designs.

2000. A Century of Motorcycles. Multicoloured.
3319 7r. Type **383** 60 65
3320 7r. Pioneer Harley Davidson, 1913 60 65
3321 7r. Bohmerland, 1925 60 65
3322 7r. American Indian, 1910 60 65
3323 7r. Triumph Trophy 1200, 1993 60 65
3324 7r. Moto Guzzi 500S, 1928 60 65
3325 7r. Matchless, 1907 60 65
3326 7r. Manch 4 1200 TTS, 1966 60 65
3327 7r. Lambretta LD-150, 1957 60 65
3328 7r. Yamaha XJP 1200, 1990's 60 65
3329 7r. Daimler, 1885 60 65
3330 7r. John Player Norton, 1950s–60's 60 65
MS3331 Two sheets, each 62 × 46 mm. (a) 25r. Harley Davidson, 1950. (b) 25r. Electra Glide, 1960 Set of 2 sheets 4·50 4·75

2000. Flowers of the Indian Ocean. Multicoloured.
3332 5r. Type **384** 45 50
3333 5r. Clivia 45 50
3334 5r. Red hot poker 45 50
3335 5r. Crown of Thorns 45 50
3336 5r. Cape daisy 45 50
3337 5r. Geranium 45 50
3338 5r. Fringed hibiscus (horiz) 45 50
3339 5r. *Erica vestita* (horiz) 45 50
3340 5r. Bird-of-paradise flower (horiz) 45 50
3341 5r. Peacock orchid (horiz) 45 50
3342 5r. Mesembryanthemums (horiz) 45 50
3343 5r. African violets (horiz) 45 50
MS3344 Two sheets, each 112 × 80 mm. (a) 25r. Gladiolus. (b) 25r. Calla lily (horiz) Set of 2 sheets 4·50 4·75
Nos. 3332/7 and 3338/43 were each printed together, se-tenant, with the backgrounds forming composite designs.

385 Racoon Butterflyfish (*Chaetodon lunula*)

2000. Marine Life of the Indian Ocean. Multicoloured.
3345 5r. Type **385** 45 50
3346 5r. Wrasse (*Stethojulis albovittata*) 45 50
3347 5r. Green turtle 45 50
3348 5r. Jobfish 45 50
3349 5r. Damsel fish 45 50
3350 5r. Meyer's butterflyfish (*Chaetodon meyeri*) 45 50
3351 5r. Wrasse (*Cirrhilabrus exquisitus*) 45 50
3352 5r. Maldive anemonefish 45 50
3353 5r. Hind (*Cephalopholis* sp) 45 50
3354 5r. Regal angelfish (*Pygopolites diacanthus*) (red face value) 45 50
3355 5r. Forceps butterflyfish (*Forcipiger flavissimus*) 45 50
3356 5r. Goatfish 45 50
3357 5r. Trumpet fish 45 50
3358 5r. Butterfly perch (*Pseudanthias squamipinnis*) 45 50
3359 5r. Two-spined angelfish (*Centropyge bispinosus*) 45 50
3360 5r. Sweetlips 45 50
3361 5r. Twin-spotted wrasse (*Coris aygula*) 45 50
3362 5r. Snapper 45 50
3363 5r. Sea bass 45 50
3364 5r. Bennett's butterflyfish (*Chaetodon bennetti*) 45 50
3365 5r. Pelagic snapper 45 50
3366 5r. Cardinalfish 45 50
3367 5r. Six-barred wrasse (*Thalassoma hardwicke*) 45 50
3368 5r. Surgeonfish 45 50
3369 5r. Longnosed filefish 45 50
3370 5r. Hawaiian squirrelfish 45 50
3371 5r. Freckled hawkfish 45 50
3372 5r. McCosker's flasher wrasse 45 50
3373 5r. Regal angelfish (*Pygoplites diacanthus*) (white face value) 45 50
3374 5r. Angelfish (*Parseentzopyge venusta*) 45 50
MS3375 Four sheets, each 108 × 80 mm. (a) 25r. Moray eel. (b) 25r. Yellow-bellied hamlet (*Hypoplectrus aberrans*). (c) 25r. Yellow-banded angelfish (*Pomacanthus maculosus*). (d) 25r. Spiny butterflyfish (*Pygoplites diacanthus*) Set of 4 sheets 8·75 9·00
Nos. 3345/52, 3353/60, 3361/8 and 3369/74 were each printed together, se-tenant, with the backgrounds forming composite designs.

385a "Nobleman with Golden Chain" (Tintoretto)

2000. "Espana 2000" International Stamp Exhibition, Madrid. Paintings from the Prado Museum. Multicoloured.
3376 7r. Type **385a** 60 65
3377 7r. "Triumphal Arch" (Domenichino) 60 65
3378 7r. "Don Garzia de'Medici" (Bronzino) 60 65
3379 7r. Man from "Micer Marsilio and his Wife" (Lorenzo Lotto) 60 65
3380 7r. "The Infanta Maria Antonieta Fernanda" (Jacopo Amigoni) 60 65
3381 7r. Woman from "Micer Marsilio and his Wife" 60 65
3382 7r. "Self-portrait" (Albrecht Durer) 60 65
3383 7r. "Woman and her Daughter" (Adriaen van Cronenburch) 60 65
3384 7r. "Portrait of a Man" (Albrecht Durer) 60 65
3385 7r. Wife and daughters from "The Artist and his Family" (Jacob Jordaens) 60 65
3386 7r. "Artemisia" (Rembrandt) 60 65
3387 7r. Man from "The Artist and his Family" 60 65
3388 7r. "The Painter Andrea Sacchi" (Carlo Maratta) 60 65
3389 7r. Two Turks from "The Turkish Embassy to the Court of Naples" (Giuseppe Bonito) 60 65
3390 7r. "Charles Cecil Roberts" (Pompeo Girolamo Batoni) 60 65
3391 7r. "Francesco Albani" (Andrea Sacchi) 60 65
3392 7r. Three Turks from "The Turkish Embassy to the Court of Naples" 60 65
3393 7r. "Sir William Hamilton" (Pompeo Girolamo Batoni) 60 65

3394 7r. Women from "Achilles amongst the Daughters of Lycomedes" (Rubens and Van Dyck) 60 65
3395 7r. Woman in red dress from "Achilles amongst the Daughters of Lycomedes" 60 65
3396 7r. Men from "Achilles amongst the Daughters of Lycomedes" 60 65
3397 7r. "The Duke of Lerma on Horseback" (Rubens) 60 65
3398 7r. "The Death of Seneca" (workshop of Rubens) 60 65
3399 7r. "Marie de' Medici" (Rubens) 60 65
3400 7r. "The Marquesa of Villafranca" (Goya) 60 65
3401 7r. "Maria Ruthven" (Van Dyck) 60 65
3402 7r. "Cardinal-Infante Ferdinand" (Van Dyck) 60 65
3403 7r. "Prince Frederick Hendrick of Orange-Nassau" (Van Dyck) 60 65
3404 7r. Endymion Porter from "Self-portrait with Endymion Porter" (Van Dyck) 60 65
3405 7r. Van Dyck from "Self-portrait with Endymion Porter" 60 65
3406 7r. "King Philip V of Spain" (Hyacinthe Rigaud) 60 65
3407 7r. "King Louis XIV of France" (Hyacinthe Rigaud) 60 65
3408 7r. "Don Luis, Prince of Asturias" (Michel-Ange Houasse) 60 65
3409 7r. "Duke Carlo Emanuele II of Savoy with his Wife and Son" (Charles Dauphin) 60 65
3410 7r. "Kitchen Maid" (Charles-Francois Hutin) 60 65
3411 7r. "Hurdy-gurdy Player" (Georges de la Tour) 60 65
MS3412 Six sheets. (a) 110 × 90 mm. 25r. "The Devotion of Rudolf I" (Peter Paul Rubens and Jan Wildens) (horiz). (b) 110 × 90 mm. 25r. "The Artist and his Family" (Jacob Jordaens) (horiz). (c) 90 × 110 mm. 25r. "The Turkish Embassy to the Court of Naples" (Guiseppe Bonito). (d) 90 × 110 mm. 25r. "Camilla Gonzaga, Countess of San Segundo, with her Three Children" (Parmigianino). (e) 90 × 110 mm. 25r. "Elizabeth of Valois" (Sofonisba Anguisciola). (f) 110 × 90 mm. 25r. "Duke Carlo Emanuele II of Savoy with his Wife and Son" (Charles Dauphin) Set of 6 sheets 13·00 13·50

386 Steam Locomotive *Hiawatha*, 1935

2000. Milestones in Twentieth-century Transport. Multicoloured.
3413 2r. 50 Steam locomotive *Papyrus*, 1934 (vert) 20 25
3414 3r. Type **386** 25 30
3415 5r. Thrust SSC rocket car, 1997 45 50
3416 5r. Curtiss R3C-2 seaplane, 1925 45 50
3417 5r. Steam locomotive *Rocket*, 1829 45 50
3418 5r. BB-9004 electric train, 1955 45 50
3419 5r. Steam locomotive *Mallard*, 1938 45 50
3420 5r. T G V. electric train, 1980 45 50
3421 5r. Lockheed XP-80 aircraft, 1947 45 50
3422 5r. Mikoyan Mig 23 Foxbat aircraft, 1965 45 50
3423 5r. Hawker Tempest aircraft, 1943 45 50
3424 5r. *Bluebird* car, 1964 45 50
3425 5r. *Blue Flame* car, 1970 45 50
3426 5r. *Thrust 2* car, 1983 45 50
3427 12r. Supermarine S.B.G. seaplane, 1931 1·10 1·20
3428 13r. MLX01 train, 1998 1·10 1·20
MS3429 Two sheets. (a) 100 × 75 mm. 25r. Lockheed SR-71 Blackbird airplane, 1976 (vert). (b) 75 × 100 mm. 25r. Bell X-1 aircraft, 1947 Set of 2 sheets 4·50 4·75
Nos. 3415/20 and 3421/6 were each printed together, se-tenant, with the backgrounds forming composite designs.

387 Porsche 911S, 1966

2000. "The World of Porsche". Multicoloured.
3430 12r. Type **387** 1·10 1·20
3431 12r. Model 959, 1988 1·10 1·20
3432 12r. Model 993 Carrera, 1995 1·10 1·20
3433 12r. Model 356 SC, 1963 1·10 1·20
3434 12r. Model 911 Turbo, 1975 1·10 1·20
3435 12r. Contemporary model 1·10 1·20
MS3436 110 × 85 mm. 25r. Model Boxter, 2000 (56 × 42 mm) 2·20 2·30

388 Limited Edition Trans-Am, 1976

2000. "The World of the Pontiac". Multicolourd.
3437 12r. Type **388** 1·10 1·20
3438 12r. Trans-Am, 1988 1·10 1·20
3439 12r. Trans-Am Coupe, 1988 1·10 1·20
3440 12r. Yellow Trans-Am, 1970–72 1·10 1·20
3441 12r. 25th Anniv Trans-Am, 1989 1·10 1·20
3442 12r. Trans-Am GT convertible, 1994 1·10 1·20
MS3443 110 × 85 mm. 25r. Trans-Am model, 1999 (56 × 42 mm) 2·20 2·30

389 Pierce-Arrow

2000. Twentieth-century Classic Cars. Multicoloured.
3444 1r. Type **389** 10 15
3445 2r. Mercedes-Benz 540K (1938) 20 25
3446 7r. Auburn Convertible Sedan (1931) 60 65
3447 7r. Mercedes SSKL (1931) 60 65
3448 7r. Packard Roadster (1929) 60 65
3449 7r. Chevrolet (1940) 60 65
3450 7r. Mercer (1915) 60 65
3451 7r. Packard Sedan (1941) 60 65
3452 7r. Chevrolet Roadster (1932) 60 65
3453 7r. Cadillac Fleetwood Roadster (1929) 60 65
3454 7r. Bentley Speed Six (1928) 60 65
3455 7r. Cadillac Fleetwood (1930) 60 65
3456 7r. Ford Convertible (1936) 60 65
3457 7r. Hudson Phaeton (1929) 60 65
3458 8r. Duesenberg J (1934) 60 65
3459 10r. Bugatti Royale (1931) 90 95
MS3460 Two sheets, each 106 × 81 mm. (a) 25r. Rolls Royce P-1 (1931). (b) 25r. Cord Brougham (1930) Set of 2 sheets 4·50 4·75
No. 3457 is inscribed "HUDSIN" in error.

390 *Cortinarius collinitus*

2001. Fungi. Multicoloured.
3461 30l. Type **390** 10 10
3462 50l. *Russula ochroleuca* 10 10
3463 2r. *Lepiota acutesquamosa* 20 25
3464 3r. *Hebeloma radicosum* 25 30
3465 7r. *Tricholoma aurantium* 60 65
3466 7r. *Pholiota spectabilis* 60 65
3467 7r. *Russula caerulea* 60 65
3468 7r. *Amanita phalloides* 60 65
3469 7r. *Mycena strobilinoides* 60 65
3470 7r. *Boletus satanas* 60 65
3471 7r. *Amanita muscaria* 60 65
3472 7r. *Mycena lilacifolia* 60 65
3473 7r. *Coprinus comatus* 60 65
3474 7r. *Morchella crassipes* 60 65
3475 7r. *Russula nigricans* 60 65
3476 7r. *Lepiota procera* 60 65
3477 13r. *Amanita echinocephala* 1·10 1·20
3478 15r. *Collybia iocephala* 1·30 1·40
MS3479 Two sheets, each 112 × 82 mm. (a) 25r. *Tricholoma aurantium*. (b) 25r. *Lepiota procera* Set of 2 sheets 4·50 4·75

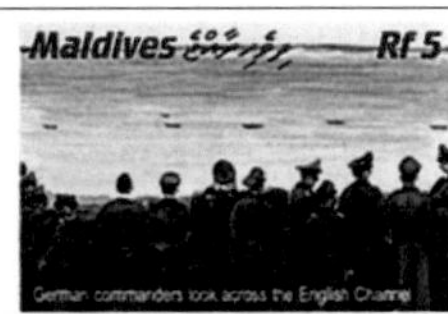

390a German Commanders looking across English Channel

2001. 60th Anniv of Battle of Britain. Multicoloured.
3480 5r. Type **390a** 45 50
3481 5r. Armourers with German bomber 45 50
3482 5r. German Stuka dive-bombers 45 50
3483 5r. Bombing the British coast 45 50
3484 5r. German bomber over Greenwich 45 50
3485 5r. St. Paul's Cathedral surrounded by fire 45 50
3486 5r. British fighter from German bomber 45 50
3487 5r. Spitfire on fire 45 50
3488 5r. Prime Minister Winston Churchill 45 50
3489 5r. British fighter pilots running to planes 45 50
3490 5r. R.A.F. planes taking off 45 50
3491 5r. British fighters in formation 45 50
3492 5r. German bomber crashing 45 50
3493 5r. British fighters attacking 45 50
3494 5r. German bomber in sea 45 50
3495 5r. Remains of German bomber in flames 45 50
MS3496 Two sheets, each 103 × 66 mm. (a) 25r. Hawker Hurricane. (b) 25r. Messerschmitt ME 109 Set of 2 sheets 4·50 4·75

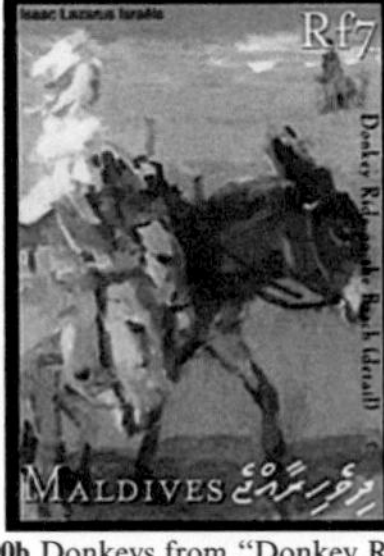

390b Donkeys from "Donkey Ride on the Beach" (Isaac Lazarus Israels)

2001. Bicentenary of Rijksmuseum, Amsterdam. Dutch Paintings. Multicoloured.
3497 7r. Type **390b** 60 65
3498 7r. "The Paternal Admonition" (Gerard ter Borch) 60 65
3499 7r. "The Sick Woman" (Jan Havicksz Steen) 60 65
3500 7r. Girls from "Donkey Ride on the Beach" 60 65
3501 7r. "Pompejus Occo" (Dick Jacobsz) 60 65
3502 7r. "The Pantry" (Pieter de Hooch) 60 65
3503 7r. Woman in doorway from "The Little Street" (Johannes Vermeer) 60 65
3504 7r. Woman with maid from "The Love Letter" (Johannes Vermeer) 60 65
3505 7r. "Woman in Blue Reading a Letter" (Johannes Vermeer) 60 65
3506 7r. Woman from "The Love Letter" 60 65
3507 7r. "The Milkmaid" (Johannes Vermeer) 60 65
3508 7r. Woman in alley from "The Little Street" 60 65
3509 7r. "Rembrandt's Mother" (Gerard Dou) 60 65
3510 7r. "Girl dressed in Blue" (Johannes Verspronck) 60 65
3511 7r. "Old Woman at Prayer" (Nicolaes Maes) 60 65
3512 7r. "Feeding the Hungry" (De Meester van Alkmaar) 60 65
3513 7r. "The Threatened Swan" (Jan Asselyn) 60 65
3514 7r. "The Daydreamer" (Nicolaes Maes) 60 65
3515 7r. "The Holy Kinship" (Geertgen Tot Sint Jans) 60 65
3516 7r. "Sir Thomas Gresham" (Anthonis Mor Vas Dashorst) 60 65
3517 7r. "Self portrait as St. Paul" (Rembrandt) 60 65
3518 7r. "Cleopatra's Banquet" (Gerard Lairesse) 60 65
3519 7r. "Flowers in a Glass" (Jan Brueghel the elder) 60 65
3520 7r. "Nicolaes Hasselaer" (Frans Hals) 60 65
MS3521 Four sheets. (a) 118 × 78 mm. 25r. "The Syndics" (Rembrandt). (b) 88 × 118 mm. 25r. "Johannes Wtenbogaert" (Rembrandt). (c) 118 × 88 mm. 25r. "The Night Watch" (Rembrandt). (d) 118 × 88 mm. 25r. "Shipwreck on a Rocky Coast" (Wijnandus Johannes Nuyen) (horiz) Set of 4 sheets 8·75 9·00

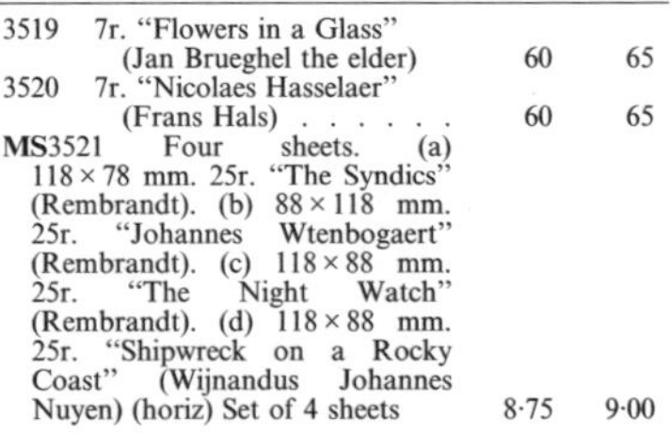

391 *Windfall* (schooner), 1962

392 Roses

2001. Maritime Disasters. Multicoloured.
3522 5r. Type **391** 45 50
3523 5r. *Kobenhavn* (barque), 1928 45 50
3524 5r. *Pearl* (schooner), 1874 45 50
3525 5r. H.M.S. *Bulwark* (battleship), 1914 45 50
3526 5r. *Patriot* (brig), 1812 45 50
3527 5r. *Lusitania* (liner), 1915 45 50
3528 5r. *Milton Iatrides* (coaster), 1970 45 50
3529 5r. *Cyclops* (freighter), 1918 45 50
3530 5r. *Marine Sulphur Queen* (tanker), 1963 45 50
3531 5r. *Rosalie* (full-rigged ship), 1840 45 50
3532 5r. *Mary Celeste* (sail merchantman), 1872 45 50
3533 5r. *Atlanta* (brig), 1880 45 50
MS3534 Two sheets, each 110 × 85 mm. (a) 25r. *L'Astrolabe* and *La Boussole* (La Perouse, 1789). (b) 25r. *Titanic* (liner), 1912 Set of 2 sheets 4·50 4·75
Nos. 3522/7 and 3528/33 were printed together, se-tenant, with the backgrounds forming composite designs.
No. 3530 is inscribed "SULPHER" and No. MS3517a "LA BAUSSOLE", both in error.

2001.
3535 **392** 10r. multicoloured 90 95

393 Interior of Dharumavantha Rasgefaanu Mosque

2001. 848th Anniv of Introduction of Islam to the Maldives. Multicoloured (except Nos. 3537/8).
3536 10r. Type **393** 90 95
3537 10r. Plaque of Hukurumiskiiy (black and green) 90 95
3538 10r. Family studying the Holy Quran (black) 90 95
3539 10r. Class at Institute of Islamic Studies 90 95
3540 10r. Centre for the Holy Quran 90 95
3541 10r. Islamic Centre, Male 90 95
MS3542 116 × 90 mm. 25r. Tomb of Sultan Abdul Barakaat 2·20 2·30

394 Emperor Angelfish

395 "Young Women in Mist"

2001. Fish. Multicoloured.
3543 10r. Type **394** 90 95
3544 10r. Indian Ocean lionfish ("*Pterois miles*") 90 95

2001. "Philanippon '01" International Stamp Exhibition, Tokyo. Japanese Art. Multicoloured.
3545 7r. Type **395** 60 65
3546 7r. "Woman with Parasol" 60 65
3547 7r. "Courtesan" 60 65
3548 7r. "Comparison of Beauties" 60 65
3549 7r. "Barber" 60 65
3550 7r. Ichikawa Danjuro V in black robes (20 × 81 mm) 60 65
3551 7r. Ichikawa Danjuro V in brown robes with sword (20 × 81 mm) 60 65

3552 7r. Ichikawa Danjuro V with arms folded (20 × 81 mm) 60 65
3553 7r. Ichikawa Danjuro V seated in brown robes (20 × 81 mm) 60 65
3554 7r. Otani Tomoeman I and Bando Mitsugaro I (53 × 81 mm) 60 65
MS3555 Two sheets, each 88 × 124 mm. (a) 25r. "Courtesan Hinazuru" (Kitagawa Utamaro). (b) 25r. "Tsutsui Jmy and the Priest Ichirai" (Torii Kiyomasu I) Set of 2 sheets . . . . 4·50 4·75

Nos. 3545/9 show paintings of women by Kitagawa Utamaro, and Nos. 3550/4 show famous actors by Katsukawa Shunsho.

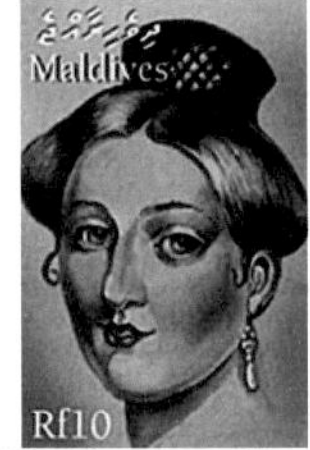

395a Victoria as a Young Girl (face value bottom left)

2001. Death Centenary of Queen Victoria. Multicoloured.
3556 10r. Type **395a** 90 95
3557 10r. Victoria in old age . . 90 95
3558 10r. Victoria as a young girl (face value top right) . . 90 95
3559 10r. Queen Victoria in mourning 90 95
MS3560 125 × 87 mm. 25r. Young Queen Victoria in evening dress 2·20 2·30

395b Mao as a teenager (brown background)

2001. 25th Death Anniv of Mao Tse-tung (Chinese leader). Multicoloured.
3561 15r. Type **395b** . . . . . . 1·30 1·40
3562 15r. Mao as leader of Communist Party in 1930s (violet background) . . . 1·30 1·40
3563 15r. Mao in 1940s (grey background) . . . . 1·30 1·40
MS3564 139 × 132 mm. 25r. Mao as leader of China in 1960s . . . 2·20 2·30

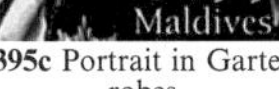

395c Portrait in Garter robes

395d Alfred Piccaver (opera singer) after Annigoni as Duke of Mantua

2001. 75th Birthday of Queen Elizabeth II. Multicoloured.
3565 7r. Type **395c** 60 65
3566 7r. Queen at Coronation . . 60 65
3567 7r. In evening gown and tiara 60 65
3568 7r. In uniform for Trooping the Colour 60 65
3569 7r. In Garter robes and hat 60 65
3570 7r. Queen wearing cloak of kiwi feathers 60 65
MS3571 112 × 138 mm. 25r. Young Queen Elizabeth . . . . 2·20 2·30

2001. Death Centenary of Giuseppe Verdi (Italian composer). Multicoloured.
3572 10r. Type **395d** 90 95
3573 10r. Heinrich's costume from Rigoletto (opera) . . 90 95
3574 10r. Cologne's costume from Rigoletto 90 95
3575 10r. Cornell MacNeil (opera singer) as Rigoletto . . . 90 95
MS3576 79 × 119 mm. 25r. Matteo Manvgerri (opera singer) as Rigoletto . . . . 2·20 2·30

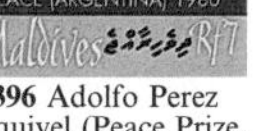

396 Adolfo Perez Esquivel (Peace Prize, 1980)

398 Eusebio and Portuguese Flag

397 Mercedes-Benz W165 Racing Car, 1939

2001. Centenary of Nobel Prizes. Prize Winners. Multicoloured.
3577 7r. Type **396** 60 65
3578 7r. Mikhail Gorbachev (Peace, 1990) 60 65
3579 7r. Betty Williams (Peace, 1976) 60 65
3580 7r. Alfonso Garcia Robles (Peace, 1982) 60 65
3581 7r. Paul d'Estournelles de Constant (Peace, 1909) . . 60 65
3582 7r. Louis Renault (Peace, 1907) 60 65
3583 7r. Ernesto Moneta (Peace, 1907) 60 65
3584 7r. Albert Luthuli (Peace, 1960) 60 65
3585 7r. Henri Dunant (Peace, 1901) 60 65
3586 7r. Albert Gobat (Peace, 1902) 60 65
3587 7r. Sean MacBride (Peace, 1974) 60 65
3588 7r. Elie Ducommun (Peace, 1902) 60 65
3589 7r. Simon Kuznets (Economics, 1971) 60 65
3590 7r. Wassily Leontief (Economics, 1973) 60 65
3591 7r. Lawrence Klein (Economics, 1980) 60 65
3592 7r. Friedrich von Hayek (Economics, 1974) 60 65
3593 7r. Leonid Kantorovich (Economics, 1975) 60 65
MS3594 Three sheets, each 108 × 127 mm. (a) 25r. Trygve Haavelmo (Economics, 1989). (b) 25r. Octavio Paz (Literature, 1990). (c) 25r. Vicente Aleixandre (Literature, 1977) Set of 3 sheets 6·50 6·75

2001. Centenary of Mercedes-Benz Cars. Multicoloured.
3595 2r.50 Type **397** 20 25
3596 5r. 460 Nurburg Sport-roadster, 1928 . . . . . 45 50
3597 7r. 680S racing car, 1927 . . 60 65
3598 7r. 150, 1934 . . . . 60 65
3599 7r. 540K Roadster, 1936 . . 60 65
3600 7r. 770 "Grosser Mercedes", 1932 . . . . 60 65
3601 7r. 220SE, 1958 . . . . . . 60 65
3602 7r. 500SL, 1990 . . . . . . 60 65
3603 7r. 290, 1933 . . . . 60 65
3604 7r. Model 680S, 1927 . . . 60 65
3605 7r. 300SL Coupe, 1953 . . . 60 65
3606 7r. Benz Victoria, 1911 . . . 60 65
3607 7r. 280SL, 1968 . . . . . . 60 65
3608 7r. W125 racing car, 1937 60 65
3609 8r. Boattail Speedster, 1938 70 75
3610 15r. "Blitzen Benz", 1909 1·30 1·40
MS3611 Two sheets, each 109 × 96 mm. (a) 25r. 370S, 1931. (b) 25r. 300SLR racing car, 1955 Set of 2 sheets . . . . 4·50 4·75

Nos. 3600 and 3606 are inscribed "GROBERMERCEDES" or "BENA", both in error.

2001. World Cup Football Championship, Japan and Korea (2002). Multicoloured.
3612 1r. Type **398** 10 15
3613 3r. Johan Cruyff and Dutch flag 25 30
3614 7r. Footballer and French flag 60 65
3615 10r. Footballer and Japanese flag 90 95
3616 12r. World Cup Stadium, Seoul, Korea (horiz) . . . 1·10 1·20
3617 15r. Poster for first World Cup Championship, Uruguay, 1930 . . . . . 1·30 1·40
MS3618 70 × 100 mm. 25r. Gerd Muller, 1974 World Cup Final (43 × 57 mm) . . . . 2·20 2·30

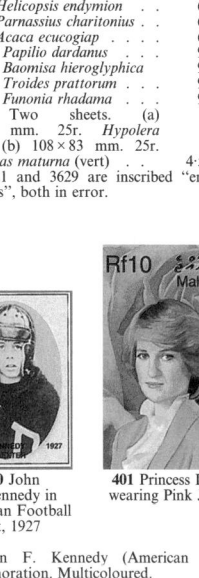

399 *Cymothoe lucasi*

2001. Moths and Butterflies. Multicoloured.
3619 7r. Type **399** 60 65
3620 7r. *Milionia grandis* 60 65
3621 7r. *Ornithoptera croesus* . . 60 65
3622 7r. *Hyantis hodeva* 60 65
3623 7r. *Ammobiota festiva* . . . 60 65
3624 7r. *Salamis temora* 60 65
3625 7r. *Zygaena occitanica* . . . 60 65
3626 7r. *Campylotes desgodinsi* . . 60 65
3627 7r. *Bhutanitis thaidina* . . . 60 65
3628 7r. *Helicopsis endymion* . . 60 65
3629 7r. *Parnassius charitonius* . . 60 65
3630 7r. *Acaca ecucogiap* 60 65
3631 10r. *Papilio dardanus* . . . 90 95
3632 10r. *Baomisa hieroglyphica* 90 95
3633 10r. *Troides prattorum* . . . 90 95
3634 10r. *Funonia rhadama* . . . 90 95
MS3635 Two sheets. (a) 83 × 108 mm. 25r. *Hypolera cassotis*. (b) 108 × 83 mm. 25r. *Euphydryas maturna* (vert) . . 4·50 4·75

Nos. 3621 and 3629 are inscribed "eroesus" or "charltonius", both in error.

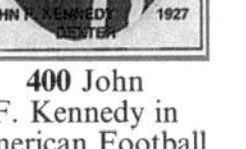

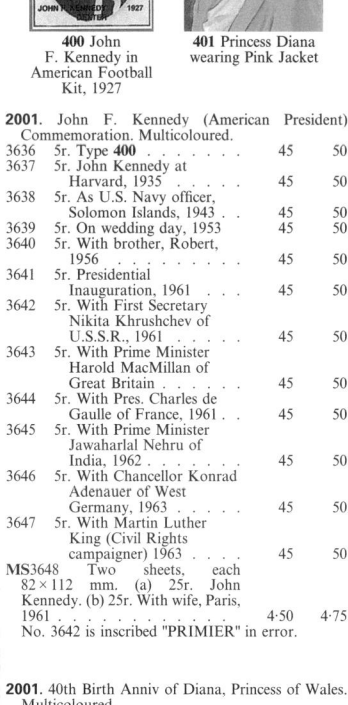

400 John F. Kennedy in American Football Kit, 1927

401 Princess Diana wearing Pink Jacket

2001. John F. Kennedy (American President) Commemoration. Multicoloured.
3636 5r. Type **400** 45 50
3637 5r. John Kennedy at Harvard, 1935 . . . . . 45 50
3638 5r. As U.S. Navy officer, Solomon Islands, 1943 . . 45 50
3639 5r. On wedding day, 1953 45 50
3640 5r. With brother, Robert, 1956 . . . . 45 50
3641 5r. Presidential Inauguration, 1961 . . . 45 50
3642 5r. With First Secretary Nikita Khrushchev of U.S.S.R., 1961 . . . . . 45 50
3643 5r. With Prime Minister Harold MacMillan of Great Britain 45 50
3644 5r. With Pres. Charles de Gaulle of France, 1961 . . 45 50
3645 5r. With Prime Minister Jawaharlal Nehru of India, 1962 . . . . 45 50
3646 5r. With Chancellor Konrad Adenauer of West Germany, 1963 . . . . . 45 50
3647 5r. With Martin Luther King (Civil Rights campaigner) 1963 . . . . 45 50
MS3648 Two sheets, each 82 × 112 mm. (a) 25r. John Kennedy. (b) 25r. With wife, Paris, 1961 . . . . 4·50 4·75

No. 3642 is inscribed "PRIMIER" in error.

2001. 40th Birth Anniv of Diana, Princess of Wales. Multicoloured.
3649 10r. Type **401** 90 95
3650 10r. In evening dress with tiara 90 95
3651 10r. Wearing matching yellow hat and coat . . . 90 95
3652 10r. In beige dress 90 95
MS3653 73 × 109 mm. 25r. Princess Diana wearing pearls . . . . . 2·20 2·30

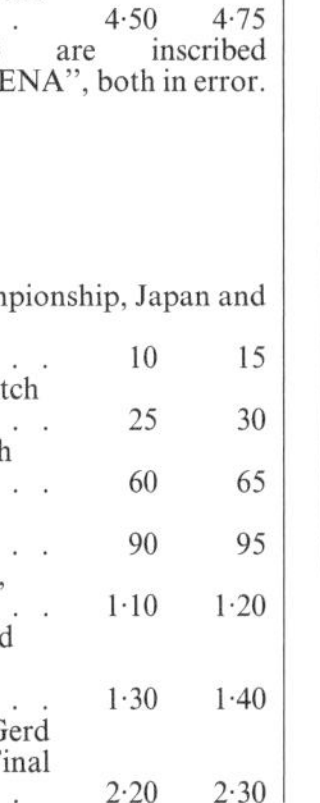

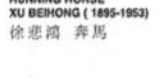

402 "Running Horse" (Xu Beihong)

404 Havana Brown

403 Swinhoe's Snipe

2001. Chinese New Year ("Year of the Horse"). Paintings by Xu Beihong. Multicoloured.
3654 5r. Type **402** 45 50
3655 5r. "Standing Horse" (from back, with head up) . . . 45 50
3656 5r. "Running Horse" (different) 45 50
3657 5r. "Standing Horse" (with head down) 45 50
3658 5r. "Horse" (with head up, from front) 45 50
MS3659 110 × 70 mm. 15r. "Six Horses running" (57 × 37 mm) 1·30 1·40

2002. Birds. Multicoloured.
3660 1r. Type **403** 10 15
3661 2r. Oriental honey buzzard 20 25
3662 3r. Asian koel 25 30
3663 5r. Red-throated pipet . . . 45 50
3664 5r. Cattle egret 45 50
3665 5r. Barn swallow 45 50
3666 5r. Osprey 45 50
3667 5r. Green-backed heron ("Little Heron") 45 50
3668 5r. Ruddy turnstone 45 50
3669 5r. Sooty tern 45 50
3670 5r. Lesser noddy 45 50
3671 5r. Roseate tern 45 50
3672 5r. Great frigate bird ("Frigate Minor") 45 50
3673 5r. Black-shafted tern ("Saunder's Tern") . . . 45 50
3674 5r. White-bellied storm petrel 45 50
3675 5r. Red-footed booby . . . 45 50
3676 7r. Rose-ringed parakeet . . 60 65
3677 7r. Common swift 60 65
3678 7r. Lesser kestrel 60 65
3679 7r. Golden oriole 60 65
3680 7r. Asian paradise flycatcher 60 65
3681 7r. Indian roller 60 65
3682 7r. Pallid harrier 60 65
3683 7r. Grey heron 60 65
3684 7r. Blue-tailed bee eater . . 60 65
3685 7r. White-breasted water hen 60 65
3686 7r. Cotton teal ("Cotton Pygmy Goose") 60 65
3687 7r. Maldivian pond heron 60 65
3688 7r. Short-eared owl 60 65
3689 10r. White spoonbill ("Eurasian Spoonbill") . . 90 95
3690 12r. Pied wheatear . . . . 1·10 1·20
3691 15r. Oriental pratincole . . 1·30 1·40
MS3692 Four sheets, each 114 × 57 mm. (a) 25r. White tern. (b) 25r. Greater flamingo. (c) 25r. Cinnamon bittern. (d) 25r. White-tailed tropicbird . . . . 8·75 9·00

Nos. 3664/9, 3670/5, 3676/81 and 3682/7 were each printed together, se-tenant, with the backgrounds forming composite designs.

2002. Cats. Multicoloured.
3693 3r. Type **404** 25 30
3694 5r. American wirehair . . . 45 50
3695 7r. Persian (horiz) 60 65
3696 7r. Exotic shorthair (horiz) 60 65
3697 7r. Ragdoll (horiz) 60 65
3698 7r. Manx (horiz) 60 65
3699 7r. Tonkinese (horiz) . . . 60 65
3700 7r. Scottish fold (horiz) . . 60 65
3701 7r. British blue 60 65
3702 7r. Red mackerel manx . . 60 65
3703 7r. Scottish fold 60 65
3704 7r. Somali 60 65
3705 7r. Balinese 60 65
3706 7r. Exotic shorthair 60 65
3707 8r. Norwegian forest cat . . 70 75
3708 10r. Seal point siamese . . . 90 95
MS3709 110 × 85 mm. 25r. Blue mackerel tabby cornish rex . . 2·20 2·30

405 Queen Elizabeth with Princess Margaret

2002. Golden Jubilee. Multicoloured.
3710 10r. Type **405** 90 95
3711 10r. Princess Elizabeth wearing white hat and coat 90 95
3712 10r. Queen Elizabeth in evening dress 90 95
3713 10r. Queen Elizabeth on visit to Canada 90 95
MS3714 76 × 108 mm. 25r. Paying homage, at Coronation, 1953 2·20 2·30

406 Sivatherium

2002. Prehistoric Animals. Multicoloured.
3715 7r. Type **406** 60 65
3716 7r. Flat-headed peccary . . 60 65
3717 7r. Shasta ground sloth . . 60 65
3718 7r. Harlan's ground sloth 60 65
3719 7r. European woolly rhinoceros 60 65
3720 7r. Dwarf pronghorn . . . 60 65
3721 7r. Macrauchenia 60 65
3722 7r. Glyptodon 60 65
3723 7r. Nesodon 60 65
3724 7r. Imperial tapir and calf 60 65
3725 7r. Short-faced bear 60 65
3726 7r. Mastodon 60 65
MS3727 Two sheets, each 94 × 67 mm. (a) 25r. Sabre-toothed cat. (b) 25r. Mammoth . . . . 4·50 4·75

Nos. 3715/20 and 3721/6 were each printed together, se-tenant, with the backgrounds forming composite designs.

Nos. 3722 and 3726 are inscribed "GIYPTODON" and "MAMMOTH", both in error.

2002. International Year of Mountains. As T **219** of Lesotho, but vert. Multicoloured.
3728 15r. Ama Dablam, Nepal 1·30 1·40
3729 15r. Mount Clements, U.S.A. . . . . 1·30 1·40
3730 15r. Mount Artesonraju, Peru . . . . 1·30 1·40
3731 15r. Mount Cholatse, Nepal 1·30 1·40
MS3732 96 × 65 mm. 25r. Mount Jefferson, U.S.A., and balloon 2·20 2·30

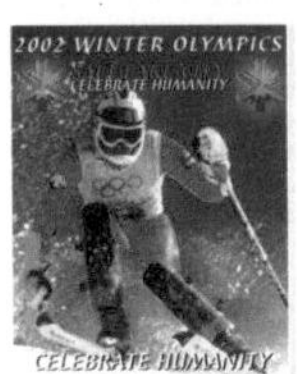

407 Downhill Skiing

2002. Winter Olympic Games, Salt Lake City. Multicoloured.
3733 12r. Type **407** . . . . . . 1·10 1·20
3734 12r. Ski jumping . . . . . 1·10 1·20
MS3735 82 × 103 mm. Nos. 3733/4 2·20 2·40

2002. 20th World Scout Jamboree, Thailand. As T **295** of Lesotho. Multicoloured.
3736 15r. Buddhist pagoda, Thailand (vert) . . . . . 1·30 1·40
3737 15r. Thai scout (vert) . . . 1·30 1·40
3738 15r. Scout badges on Thai flag (vert) . . . . 1·30 1·40
MS3739 106 × 78 mm. 25r. Mountain-climbing badge and knot diagrams . . . . 2·20 2·30

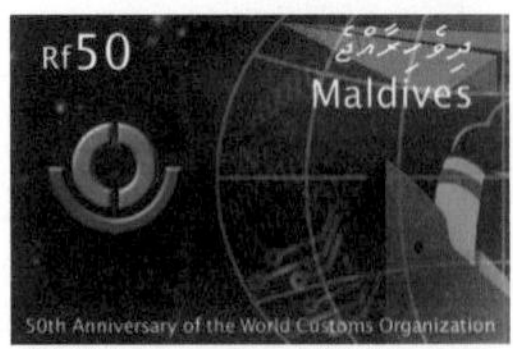

408 Ship, Aircraft and W.C.O. Logo

2002. 50th Anniv of World Customs Organization. Sheet 135 × 155 mm.
MS3740 **408** 50r. multicoloured 4·50 4·75

409 Elvis Presley

2002. 25th Death Anniv of Elvis Presley (American entertainer).
3741 **409** 5r. multicoloured 45 50

410 *Morpho menelaus*

2002. Flora and Fauna. Multicoloured.
3742 7r. Type **410** 60 65
3743 7r. *Heliconius erato* 60 65
3744 7r. *Thecla coronata* 60 65
3745 7r. *Battus philenor* 60 65
3746 7r. *Ornithoptera priamus* . . 60 65
3747 7r. *Danaus gilippus berenice* 60 65
3748 7r. *Ipomoea tricolor* Morning Glory 60 65
3749 7r. *Anemone coronaria* Wedding Bell 60 65
3750 7r. *Narcissus* Barrett Browning 60 65
3751 7r. *Nigella* Persian Jewel . . 60 65
3752 7r. *Osteospermum* Whirligig Pink 60 65
3753 7r. *Iris* Brown Lasso 60 65
3754 7r. *Laelia gouldiana* 60 65
3755 7r. *Cattleya* Louise Georgiana 60 65
3756 7r. *Laeliocattleya* Christopher Gubler . . . 60 65
3757 7r. *Miltoniopsis* Bert Field Crimson Glow 60 65
3758 7r. *Lemboglossum bictoniense* 60 65
3759 7r. *Derosara* Divine Victor 60 65
MS3760 Three sheets. (a) 72 × 50 mm. 25r. *Cymothoe lurida* (butterfly). (b) 66 × 45 mm. 25r. Perennial Aster Little Pink Beauty. (c) 50 × 72 mm. 25r. *Angraecum veitchii* (vert) . . . . 6·50 6·75

Nos. 3742/7 (butterflies), 3748/53 (flowers) and 3754/9 (orchids) were each printed together, se-tenant, with the backgrounds forming composite designs.

Nos. 3742 and 3748 are inscribed "Menelus" or "Impomoea", both in error.

411 Torsten Frings (Germany)

412 Hairdresser Bear

2002. World Cup Football Championship, Japan and Korea. Multicoloured.
3761 7r. Type **411** 60 65
3762 7r. Roberto Carlos (Brazil) 60 65
3763 7r. Torsten Frings (Germany) (different) . . 60 65
3764 7r. Ronaldo (Brazil), with one finger raised 60 65
3765 7r. Oliver Neuville (Germany) 60 65
3766 7r. Ronaldo (Brazil), heading ball 60 65
3767 7r. Eul Yong Lee (South Korea) and Alpay Ozalan (Turkey) 60 65
3768 7r. Myung Bo Hong (South Korea) and Hakan Sukur (Turkey) 60 65
3769 7r. Chong Gug Song (South Korea) and Emre Belozoglu (Turkey) . . . 60 65
3770 7r. Chong Gug Song (South Korea) and Ergun Penbe (Turkey) 60 65
3771 7r. Ki Hyeon Seol (South Korea) and Ergun Penbe (Turkey) 60 65
3772 7r. Chong Gug Song (South Korea) and Hakan Unsal (Turkey) 60 65
MS3773 Four sheets, each 82 × 82 mm. (a) 15r. Cafu (Brazil) and Oliver Neuville (Germany); 15r. World Cup Trophy. (b) 15r. Dietmar Hamann (Germany); 15r. Cafu (Brazil), holding Trophy. (c) 15r. Hakan Sukur (Turkey); 15r. Sang Chul Yoo (South Korea). (d) 15r. Ilhan Mansiz (Turkey); 15r. Young Pyo Lee (South Korea) 10·50 11·00

2002. Centenary of the Teddy Bear. Multicoloured.
3774 8r. Type **412** 70 75
3775 8r. Construction worker bear 70 75
3776 8r. Gardener bear 70 75
3777 8r. Chef bear 70 75
3778 12r. Nurse bear . . . . . . 1·10 1·20
3779 12r. Doctor bear . . . . . 1·10 1·20
3780 12r. Dentist bear . . . . . 1·10 1·20
3781 12r. Bride ("MOTHER") bear . . . . 1·10 1·20
3782 12r. Brother and sister bears 1·10 1·20
3783 12r. Groom ("FATHER") bear . . . . 1·10 1·20
MS3784 Three sheets, each 110 × 105 mm. (a) 30r. Golfer bear. (b) 30r. Footballer bear. (c) 30r. Skier bear ("SNOW BOARDER") . . . . 8·00 8·25

413 Charles Lindbergh and *Spirit of St. Louis*

414 Princess Diana

2002. 75th Anniv of First Solo Transatlantic Flight. Multicoloured.
3785 12r. Type **413** . . . . . . 1·10 1·20
3786 12r. Lindbergh in flying helmet and *Spirit of St. Louis* . . . . 1·10 1·20
3787 12r. Lindbergh holding propeller . . . . 1·10 1·20
3788 12r. Lindbergh in overalls and *Spirit of St. Louis* . . 1·10 1·20
3789 12r. Donald Hall (designer) 1·10 1·20
3790 12r. Charles Lindbergh (pilot) . . . . 1·10 1·20
3791 12r. Lindbergh under wing of *Spirit of St. Louis* . . . 1·10 1·20
3792 12r. Lindbergh, Mahoney and Hall at Ryan Airlines 1·10 1·20

2002. 5th Death Anniv of Diana, Princess of Wales. Multicoloured.
3793 12r. Type **414** . . . . . . 1·10 1·20
3794 12r. In evening dress and tiara . . . . 1·10 1·20

415 Joseph Kennedy with Sons Joseph Jr. and John, 1919

2002. Presidents John F. Kennedy and Ronald Reagan Commemoration. Multicoloured.
3795 7r. Type **415** 60 65
3796 7r. John F. Kennedy aged 11 . . . . 60 65
3797 7r. Kennedy inspecting Boston waterfront, 1951 60 65
3798 7r. Kennedy in naval ensign uniform, 1941 . . . . . 60 65
3799 7r. With sister Kathleen in London, 1939 . . . . . 60 65
3800 7r. Talking to Eleanor Roosevelt, 1951 . . . . . 60 65
3801 12r. Ronald Reagan facing right . . . . 1·10 1·20
3802 12r. Ronald Reagan (full-face portrait) . . . . . . 1·10 1·20

416 Wedding of Princess Juliana and Prince Bernhard, 1937

2002. "Amphilex '02" International Stamp Exhibition, Amsterdam. Dutch Royal Family.
3803 **416** 7r. blue and black . . . 60 65
3804 – 7r. brown and black . . 60 65
3805 – 7r. red and black 60 65
3806 – 7r. brown and black . . 60 65
3807 – 7r. violet and black . . . 60 65
3808 – 7r. green and black . . . 60 65
3809 – 7r. multicoloured 60 65
3810 – 7r. brown and black . . 60 65
3811 – 7r. multicoloured 60 65
3812 – 7r. multicoloured 60 65
3813 – 7r. multicoloured 60 65
3814 – 7r. multicoloured 60 65

DESIGNS: No. 3804, Princess Juliana and Prince Bernhard with baby Princess Beatrix, 1938; 3805, Princess Juliana with her daughters in Canada, 1940–45; 3806, Inauguration of Queen Juliana, 1948; 3807, Royal Family inspecting Zeeland floods, 1953; 3808, Queen Juliana and Prince Bernhard; 3809, "Princess Beatrix as a Baby" (Pauline Hille); 3810, "Princess Beatrix in Flying Helmet" (John Klinkenberg); 3811, "Princess Beatrix" (Beatrice Filius); 3812, "Princess Beatrix and Prince Claus" (Will Kellermann); 3813, "Queen Beatrix in Royal Robes" (Graswinkel); 3814, "Queen Beatrix" (Marjolijn Spreeuwenberg).

417 Flame Basslet

2002. Marine Life. Multicoloured.
3815 10l. Type **417** 10 10
3816 15l. Teardrop butterflyfish 10 10
3817 20l. White-tailed damselfish ("Hambug Damselfish") 10 10
3818 25l. Bridled tern (23 × 27 mm) 10 10
3819 50l. Clown surgeonfish ("Blue-lined Surgeonfish") 10 10
3820 1r. Common tern (23 × 27 mm) 10 15
3821 2r. Common noddy (23 × 27 mm) 20 25
3822 2r.50 Yellow-breasted wrasse 20 25
3823 2r.50 Blue shark (23 × 27 mm) 20 25
3824 4r. Harlequin filefish 35 40
3825 5r. Masked unicornfish ("Orangespine Unicornfish") 45 50
3826 10r. Emperor angelfish . . . 90 95
3827 12r. Catalufa ("Bullseye") 1·10 1·20
3828 20r. Scalloped hammerhead shark (23 × 27 mm) . . . 1·80 1·90

No. 3822 is inscribed "wrass" in error.

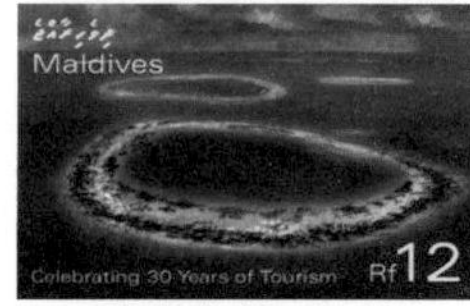

418 Atolls from the Air

2002. 30 Years of Maldives' Tourism Promotion. Multicoloured.
3829 12r. Type **418** . . . . . . 1·10 1·20
3830 12r. Island beach . . . . . 1·10 1·20
3831 12r. Surfing . . . . 1·10 1·20
3832 12r. Scuba diving . . . . . 1·10 1·20

419 Decorated Drum

2003. 50th Anniv of National Museum. Multicoloured.
3835 3r. Type **419** 30 35
3836 3r.50 Carved covered bowl 35 40
3837 6r.50 Ceremonial sunshade 65 70
3838 22r. Ceremonial headdress 2·10 2·25

420 Popeye diving

2003. "Popeye" (cartoon character). Multicoloured. Summer sports.
3839 7r. Type **420** 60 65
3840 7r. Surfing 60 65
3841 7r. Sailboarding 60 65
3842 7r. Baseball 60 65
3843 7r. Hurdling 60 65
3844 7r. Tennis 60 65
MS3845 120 × 90 mm. 25r. Volleyball (horiz) . . . . . . 2·20 2·30

Nos. 3839/45 were printed together, se-tenant, with the backgrounds forming a composite design.

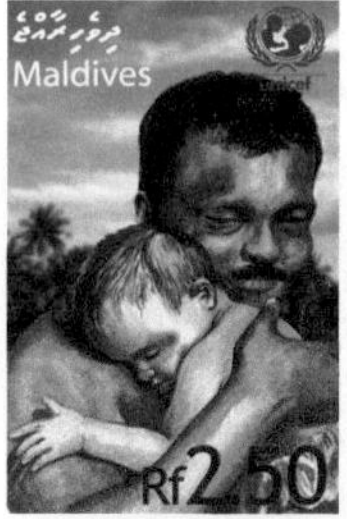

421 Father with Baby

2003. UNICEF. "First Steps" Campaign. Multicoloured.

3846	2r.50 Type **420**	25	30
3847	5r. Mother and baby . . .	50	55
3848	20r. Campaign emblem . .	1·90	2·00

422 *Cypraea caputserpentis* (Cowrie)

423 David Brown

2003. Sea Shells. Multicoloured.

3849	10r. Type **422**	90	95
3850	10r. *Trachycardium orbita* (Cardita clam)	90	95
3851	10r. *Architectonica perspective* (Sundial shell)	90	95
3852	10r. *Conus capitaneus* (Corn shell)	90	95

2003. Columbia Space Shuttle Commemoration. Sheet 184 × 145 mm, containing T **423** and similar vert designs showing crew members. Multicoloured.

MS3853 7r. Type **423**; 7r. Commander Rick Husband; 7r. Laurel Clark; 7r. Kalpana Chawla; 7r. Michael Anderson; 7r. William McCool; 7r. Ilan Ramon 4·50 4·75

424 Queen wearing Polka Dot Jacket

425 Prince William as Toddler

2003. 50th Anniv of Coronation.

MS3854 147 × 85 mm.15r. Type **424**; 15r. Queen after Coronation wearing Imperial State Crown; 15r. Queen wearing tiara (all black, deep brown and brown) 3·75 4·00

MS3855 68 × 98 mm. 25r. Queen wearing tiara and blue sash (multicoloured) . . . . 2·20 2·40

2003. 21st Birthday of Prince William. Multicoloured.

MS3856 148 × 78 mm. 15r. Type **425**; 15r. As teenager (looking forward); 15r. As teenager (looking right) . . . . 3·75 4·00

MS3857 68 × 98 mm. 25r. As young boy, wearing school cap . . . 2·20 2·30

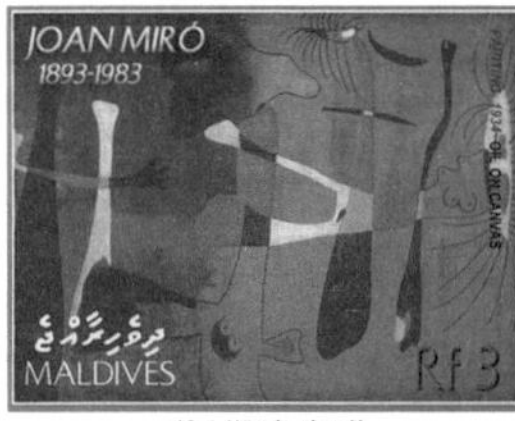

426 "Painting"

2003. 20th Death Anniv of Joan Miro (artist). Multicoloured.

3858	3r. Type **426**	25	30
3859	5r. "Hirondelle Amour" . .	45	50
3860	10r. "Two Women"	90	95
3861	15r. "Women listening to Music"	1·30	1·40

MS3862 176 × 134 mm. 12r. "Woman and Birds"; 12r. "Nocturne"; 12r. "Morning Star"; 12r. "The Escape Ladder" . . 4·50 4·75

MS3863 Two sheets, each 83 × 104 mm. (a) 25r. "Women encircled by the Flight of a Bird". (b) 25r. "Rhythmic Personages". Both imperf Set of 2 sheets . . 4·50 4·75

427 "Jabach Altarpiece" (detail of drummer and piper)

2003. 475th Death Anniv of Albrecht Dürer (artist). Multicoloured.

3864	3r. Type **427**	25	30
3865	5r. "Portrait of a Young Man"	45	50
3866	7r. "Wire-drawing Mill" (horiz)	60	65
3867	10r. "Innsbruck from the North" (horiz)	90	95

MS3868 174 × 157 mm. 12r. "Portrait of Jacob Muffel"; 12r. "Portrait of Hieronymus Holzschuher"; 12r. "Portrait of Johannes Kleburger"; 12r. "Self-portrait" . . . . 4·50 4·75

MS3869 145 × 105 mm. 25r. "The Weiden Mill" . . . . 2·20 2·30

428 "The Actor Nakamura Sojuro as Mitsukuni" (detail) (Utagawa Yoshitaki)

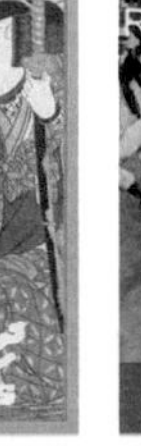

429 Maurice Garin (1903)

2003. Japanese Art. Ghosts and Demons. Multicoloured.

3870	2r. Type **428**	20	25
3871	5r. "The Actor Nakamura Sojuro as Mitsukuni" (detail of ghosts) (Utagawa Yoshitaki) . . .	45	50
3872	7r. "The Ghost of Kohada Koheiji" (Shunkoosai Hokuei)	60	65
3873	15r. "Ariwara no Narihira as Seigen" (Utagawa Kunisada)	1·30	1·40

MS3874 149 × 145 mm. 10r. "The Ghost of Shikibunojo Mitsumune" (Utagawa Kunisada); 10r. "Fuwa Bansakui" (Tsukioka Yoshitoshi); 10r. "The Lantern Ghost of Oiwa" (Shunkosai Hokuei); 10r. "The Greedy Hag" (Tsukioka Yoshitoshi) . . . . 3·50 3·75

MS3875 116 × 86 mm. 25r. "The Spirit of Sakura Sogoro haunting Hotta Kozuke" (Utagawa Kuniyoshi) . . . . 2·20 2·30

2003. Centenary of Tour de France Cycle Race. Past winners. Multicoloured.

MS3876 160 × 100 mm. 10r. Type **429**; 10r. Henri Cornet (1904); 10r. Louis Trousselier (1905); 10r. Rene Pottier (1906) 3·50 3·75

MS3877 160 × 100 mm. 10r. Lucien Petit-Breton on cycle (1907); 10r. Close up of Lucien Petit-Breton (1907); 10r. Francois Faber (1909); 10r. Octave Lapize (1910) . . . 3·50 3·75

MS3878 160 × 100 mm. 10r. Eddy Merckx (1974); 10r. Bernard Thevenet (1975); 10r. Lucien van Impe (1976); 10r. Bernard Thevenet (1977) . . . . 3·50 3·75

MS3879 Three sheets, each 100 × 70 mm. (a) 25r. Start of first Tour De France at Le Reveil Matin cafe, Montgeron. (b) 25r. Henri Desgranges (editor of L'Auto). (c) 25r. Bernard Hinault (1979) Set of 3 sheets . . . . 6·50 6·75

430 Santos-Dumont Monoplane No. 20 Demoiselle on Ground, 1909

2003. Centenary of Powered Flight. Multicoloured.

MS3880 176 × 97 mm. 10r. Type **430**; 10r. Santos-Dumont monoplane No. 20 Demoiselle taking off, 1909; 10r. Voisin-Farman No. 1 biplane, 1908; 10r. Glenn Curtiss' *Gold Bug*, 1909 . . . . 3·50 3·75

MS3881 176 × 97 mm. 10r. Santos-Dumont's *Airship No. 1*; 10r. Santos-Dumont's *Airship No. 4*; 10r. Santos Dumont's *Ballon No. 14* and *14 bis* biplane, 1906; 10r. Santos-Dumont's *Airship No. 16* . . . . 3·50 3·75

MS3882 Two sheets, each 105 × 75 mm. (a) 25r. Santos-Dumont's *Ballon No. 6* circling Eiffel Tower, Paris, 1901. (b) 25r. Santos-Dumont's *14 bis*' biplane,1906 Set of 2 sheets . . 4·50 4·75

MALI Pt. 6; Pt. 13

Federation of French Sudan and Senegal, formed in 1959 as an autonomous republic within the French Community. In August 1960 the Federation was split up and the French Sudan part became the independent Mali Republic.

100 centimes = 1 franc.

A. FEDERATION.

1 Map, Flag, Mali and Torch

1959. Establishment of Mali Federation.
1 **1** 25f. multicoloured 35 25

2

1959. Air. 300th Anniv of St. Louis, Senegal.
2 **2** 85f. multicoloured 50 40

3 West African Parrotfish

4 Violet Starling

1960. (a) Postage. Fish as T **3**.
3 **3** 5f. orange, blue and bronze . . 40 15
4 – 10f. black, brown and turquoise 40 25
5 – 15f. brown, slate and blue . . 55 25
6 – 20f. black, bistre and green . . 65 35
7 – 25f. yellow, sepia and green 80 40
8 – 30f. red, purple and blue . . . 1·00 50
9 – 85f. red, blue and green . . . 3·00 1·75

(b) Air. Birds as T **4**.
10 **4** 100f. multicoloured . . . . . 5·50 1·25
11 – 200f. multicoloured . . . . . 12·00 3·75
12 – 500f. multicoloured . . . . . 32·00 11·50
DESIGNS—HORIZ: 10f. West African triggerfish; 15f. Guinean fingerfish; 20f. Threadfish; 25f. Shining butterflyfish; 30f. Monrovian surgeonfish; 85f. Pink dentex; 200f. Bateleur. VERT: 500f. Common gonolek.

1960. 10th Anniv of African Technical Co-operation Commission. As T **4** of Malagasy Republic.
13 25f. purple and violet . . . . 1·10 65

B. REPUBLIC.

1960. Nos. 6, 7, 9 and 10/12 optd **REPUBLIQUE DU MALI** and bar or bars or surch also.
14 20f. black, bistre and green (postage) . . . . 1·50 60
15 25f. red, purple and blue . . . 2·00 60
16 85f. red, blue and green . . . 3·75 1·50

17 100f. multicoloured (air) . . . 5·50 1·50
18 200f. multicoloured . . . . . 8·50 3·50
19 300f. on 500f. multicoloured 14·00 6·00
20 500f. multicoloured . . . . . 28·00 17·00

7 Pres. Mamadou Konate

1961.
21 **7** 20f. sepia and green (postage) 25 15
22 – 25f. black and purple 35 15

23 **7** 200f. sepia and red (air) . . . 3·00 1·00
24 – 300f. black and green . . . . 4·25 1·25
DESIGN: 25, 300f. President Keita. Nos. 23/4 are larger, 27 × 38 mm.

8 U.N. Emblem, Flag and Map

1961. Air. Proclamation of Independence and Admission into U.N.
25 **8** 100f. multicoloured . . . . . 1·60 95

9 Sankore Mosque, Timbuktu

1961. Air.
26 **9** 100f. brown, blue and sepia 1·75 55
27 – 200f. brown, red and green 4·50 1·50
28 – 500f. green, brown and blue 13·00 3·25
DESIGN: 200f. View of Timbuktu; 500f. Arms and view of Bamako.

10 Africans learning Vowels

1961. 1st Anniv of Independence.
29 **10** 25f. multicoloured 60 30

11 Sheep at Pool

12 African Map and King Mohammed V of Morocco

1961.
30 **11** 50c. sepia, myrtle and red 15 15
31 A 1f. bistre, green and blue . . 15 15
32 B 2f. red, green and blue . . . 15 15
33 C 3f. brown, green and blue 15 15
34 D 4f. blue, green and bistre . . 15 15
35 **11** 5f. purple, green and blue 20 15
36 A 10f. brown, myrtle and blue 20 15
37 B 15f. brown, green and blue 20 15
38 C 20f. red, green and blue . . 30 25
39 D 25f. brown and blue 40 20
40 **11** 30f. brown, green and violet 55 30
41 A 40f. brown, green and blue 1·25 30
42 B 50f. lake, green and blue . . 50 30
43 C 60f. brown, green and blue 15 15
44 D 85f. brown, bistre and blue 1·75 35
DESIGNS: A, Oxen at pool; B, House of Arts, Mali; C, Land tillage; D, Combine-harvester in rice field.

1962. 1st Anniv of African Conf, Casablanca.
45 **12** 25f. multicoloured 25 15
46 50f. multicoloured 50 20

13 Patrice Lumumba

1962. 1st Death Anniv of Patrice Lumumba (Congo leader).
47 **13** 25f. brown and bistre . . . 20 20
48 100f. brown and green . . . 75 50

1962. Malaria Eradication. As T **43** of Mauritania.
49 25f.+5f. blue 50 60

14 Pegasus and U.P.U. Emblem

1962. 1st Anniv of Admission into U.P.U.
50 **14** 85f. multicoloured . . . . . 1·00 65

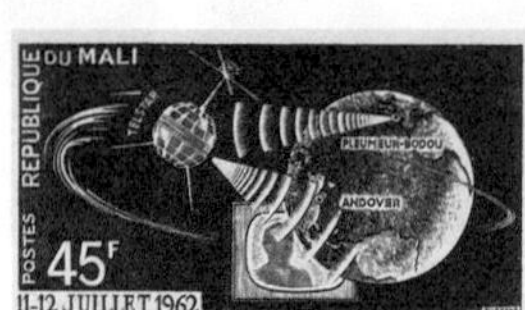

14a Posthorn on Map of Africa

15 Sansanding Dam

1962. African Postal Union Commem.
51 **14a** 25f. green and brown . . . 25 20
52 85f. orange and green . . . 75 50

1962.
53 **15** 25f. black, green and blue 40 20
54 – 45f. multicoloured . . . . . 1·25 50
DESIGN—HORIZ: 45f. Cotton plant.

16 "Telstar" Satellite, Globe and Television Receiver

1962. 1st Trans-Atlantic Telecommunications Satellite Link.
55 **16** 45f. brown, violet and lake 80 40
56 55f. violet, olive and green 95 60

17 Soldier and Family

18 Bull's Head, Laboratory Equipment and Chicks

1962. Mali–Algerian Solidarity.
57 **17** 25f.+5f. multicoloured . . . 30 30

1963. Zoological Research Centre, Sobuta.
58 **18** 25f. turq & brn (postage) . . 35 25
59 – 200f. turquoise, purple and bistre (air) . . . . . . 3·50 1·25
DESIGN: 200f. As Type **18** but horiz, 47 × 27 mm.

19 Tractor and Campaign Emblem

1963. Freedom from Hunger.
60 **19** 25f. purple, black and blue 45 20
61 45f. brown, green & turq . . 80 35

20 Balloon and W.M.O. Emblem

1963. Atmospheric Research.
62 **20** 25f. multicoloured 40 20
63 45f. multicoloured 70 35
64 60f. multicoloured 95 50

21 Race Winners

22 Centenary Emblem and Globe

1963. Youth Week. Multicoloured.
65 5f. Type **21** 15 10
66 10f. Type **21** 20 15
67 20f. Acrobatic dance (horiz) 35 20
68 85f. Football (horiz) . . . . . 1·60 55

1963. Red Cross Centenary. Inscr in black.
69 **22** 5f. multicoloured 30 15
70 10f. red, yellow and grey . . 40 20
71 85f. red, yellow and grey . . 1·25 60

23 Stretcher case entering Aero 145 Ambulance Airplane

1963. Air.
72 **23** 25f. brown, blue and green 45 20
73 – 55f. blue, ochre and brown 1·25 40
74 – 100f. blue, brown and green 2·00 75
DESIGNS: 55f. Douglas DC-3 airliner on tarmac; 100f. Illyushin Il-18 airliner taking off.

24 South African Crowned Crane standing on Giant Tortoise

26 "Kaempferia aethiopica"

25 U.N. Emblem, Doves and Banner

1963. Air. Fauna Protection.
75 **24** 25f. brown, red and orange 1·50 50
76 200f. multicoloured . . . . 5·50 2·50

1963. Air. 15th Anniv of Declaration of Human Rights.
77 **25** 50f. yellow, red and green 75 40

1963. Tropical Flora. Multicoloured.
78 30f. Type **26** 60 25
79 70f. "Bombax costatum" . . . 1·75 50
80 100f. "Adenium honghel" . . 3·00 65

27 Pharaoh and Cleopatra, Philae

28 Locust on Map of Africa

1964. Air. Nubian Monuments Preservation.
81 **27** 25f. brown and purple . . . 75 25
82 55f. olive and purple . . . . 1·60 50

1964. Anti-locust Campaign.
83 **28** 5f. brown, green and purple 20 15
84 – 10f. brown, green and olive 30 20
85 – 20f. brown, green and bistre 75 25
DESIGNS—VERT: 10f. Locust and map. HORIZ: 20f. Air-spraying, locust and village.

29 Football

1964. Olympic Games, Tokyo.
86 **29** 5f. purple, green and red . . 15 10
87 – 10f. brown, blue and sepia 30 20
88 – 15f. red and violet 40 20
89 – 85f. green, brown and violet 1·25 70
DESIGNS—VERT: 10f. Boxing; 15f. Running and Olympic Flame. HORIZ: 85f. Hurdling. Each design has a stadium in the background.

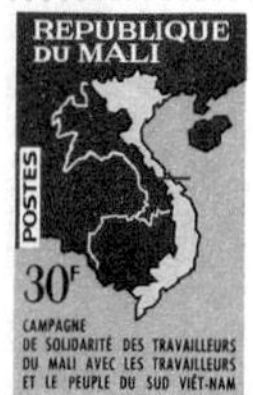

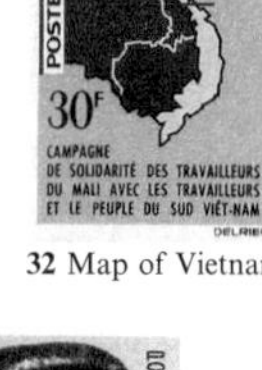

30 Solar Flares **32** Map of Vietnam

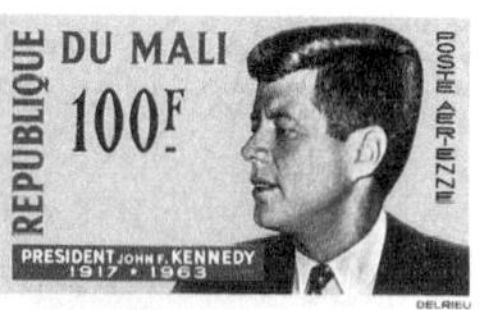

31 President Kennedy

1964. International Quiet Sun Years.
90 **30** 45f. olive, red and blue . . 1·00 35

1964. Air. 1st Death Anniv of Pres. Kennedy.
91 **31** 100f. multicoloured . . . . 1·75 1·25

1964. Mali–South Vietnam Workers' Solidarity Campaign.
92 **32** 30f. multicoloured 30 20

33 Greater Turacos ("Touraco")

1965. Air. Birds.
93 **33** 100f. green, blue and red . . 5·00 95
94 – 200f. black, red and blue . . 13·00 1·75
95 – 300f. black, ochre and green 18·00 2·50
96 – 500f. red, brown and green 29·00 4·75
BIRDS—VERT: 200f. Abyssinian ground hornbills; 300f. Egyptian vultures. HORIZ: 500f. Goliath herons.

34 I.C.Y. Emblem and U.N. Headquarters **36** Abraham Lincoln

35 African Buffalo

1965. Air. International Co-operation Year.
97 **34** 55f. ochre, purple and blue 75 40

1965. Animals.
98 – 1f. brown, blue and green 10 10
99 **35** 5f. brown, orange and green 15 10
100 – 10f. brown, mauve & green 40 25
101 – 30f. brown, green and red 75 30
102 – 90f. brown, grey and green 2·50 95
ANIMALS—VERT: 1f. Waterbuck; 10f. Scimitar oryx; 90f. Giraffe. HORIZ: 30f. Leopard.

1965. Death Centenary of Abraham Lincoln.
103 **36** 45f. multicoloured 60 40
104 55f. multicoloured 65 50

37 Hughes' Telegraph **38** "Lungs" and Mobile X-Ray Unit (Anti-T.B.)

1965. Centenary of I.T.U.
105 – 20f. black, blue and orange 30 25
106 **37** 30f. green, brown & orange 60 25
107 – 50f. green, brown & orange 90 45
DESIGNS—VERT: 20f. Denis's pneumatic tube; 50f. Lescurre's heliograph.

1965. Mali Health Service.
108 **38** 5f. violet, red and crimson 15 15
109 – 10f. green, bistre and red 25 15
110 – 25f. green and brown . . . 40 20
111 – 45f. green and brown . . . 75 40
DESIGNS: 10f. Mother and children (Maternal and Child Care); 25f. Examining patient (Marchoux Institute); 45f. Nurse (Biological Laboratory).

39 Diving

1965. 1st African Games, Brazzaville, Congo.
112 **39** 5f. red, brown and blue . . 25 10
113 – 15f. turquoise, brown and red (Judo) 75 30

40 Pope John XXIII

1965. Air. Pope John Commemoration.
114 **40** 100f. multicoloured . . . . 1·90 75

41 Sir Winston Churchill

1965. Air. Churchill Commemoration.
115 **41** 100f. blue and brown . . . 2·00 75

42 Dr. Schweitzer and Young African

1965. Air. Dr. Albert Schweitzer Commemoration.
116 **42** 100f. multicoloured . . . . 2·00 75

43 Leonov

1966. International Astronautic Conference, Athens (1965). Multicoloured.
117 100f. Type **43** . . . . 1·75 60
118 100f. White . . . . 1·75 60
119 300f. Cooper, Conrad, Leonov and Beliaiev (vert) 4·50 2·00

44 Vase, Quill and Cornet

1966. World Festival of Negro Arts, Dakar, Cameroun.
120 **44** 30f. black, red and ochre 30 20
121 – 55f. red, black and green 75 35
122 – 90f. brown, orange and blue . . . . 1·25 60
DESIGNS: 55f. Mask, brushes and palette, microphones; 90f. Dancers, mask and patterned cloth.

45 W.H.O. Building

1966. Inaug of W.H.O. Headquarters, Geneva.
123 **45** 30f. green, blue and yellow 40 20
124 45f. red, blue and yellow 60 35

46 Fisherman with Net

1966. River Fishing.
125 **46** 3f. brown and blue 15 15
126 – 4f. purple, blue and brown 20 15
127 – 20f. purple, green and blue 35 15
128 **46** 25f. purple, blue and green 75 20
129 – 60f. purple, lake and green 1·50 45
130 – 85f. plum, green and blue 1·50 50
DESIGNS: 4f., 60f. Collective shore fishing; 20f., 85f. Fishing pirogue.

47 Papal Arms, U.N. and Peace Emblems

1966. Air. Pope Paul's Visit to U.N.
131 **47** 200f. blue, green & turq . . 2·75 1·10

48 Initiation Ceremony **49** People and U.N.E.S.C.O. Emblem

1966. Mali Pioneers. Multicoloured.
132 5f. Type **48** 25 15
133 25f. Pioneers dancing 75 20

1966. Air. 20th Anniv of U.N.E.S.C.O.
134 **49** 100f. red, green and blue 1·75 70

50 Footballers, Globe, Cup and Football

1966. Air. World Cup Football Championship, England.
135 **50** 100f. multicoloured . . . . 1·75 70

51 Cancer ("The Crab") **52** U.N.I.C.E.F. Emblem and Children

1966. Air. 9th International Cancer Congress, Tokyo.
136 **51** 100f. multicoloured . . . . 1·75 55

1966. 20th Anniv of U.N.I.C.E.F.
137 **52** 45f. blue, purple and brown 60 25

53 Inoculating Cattle **55** "Diamant" Rocket and Francesco de Lana-Terzis's "Aerial Ship"

54 Desert Vehicles in Pass

1967. Campaign for Preventing Cattle Plague.
138 **53** 10f. multicoloured 25 10
139 30f. multicoloured 50 20

1967. Air. Crossing of the Hoggar (1924).
140 **54** 200f. green, brown & violet 4·75 2·25

1967. Air. French Space Rockets and Satellites.
141 **55** 50f. blue, turquoise & pur 85 30
142 – 100f. lake, purple & turq 1·60 50
143 – 200f. purple, olive and blue 2·60 1·00
DESIGNS: 100f. Satellite "A 1" and Jules Verne's "rocket"; 200f. Satellite "D 1" and Da Vinci's "bird-powered" flying machine.

56 Ancient City

1967. International Tourist Year.
144 **56** 25f. orange, blue and violet 30 20

57 Amelia Earhart and Mail Route-map

1967. Air. 30th Anniv of Amelia Earhart's Flight, via Gao.
145 **57** 500f. multicoloured . . . . 7·50 3·25

58 "The Bird Cage"

1967. Air. Picasso Commemoration. Designs showing paintings. Multicoloured.
146 50f. Type **58** . . . . 1·25 30
147 100f. "Paul as Harlequin" . . 2·00 70
148 250f. "The Pipes of Pan" . . 4·00 1·50
See also Nos. 158/9 and 164/7.

59 Scout Emblems and Rope Knots

1967. Air. World Scout Jamboree, Idaho.
149 **59** 70f. red and green . . . . 1·00 30
150 – 100f. black, lake and green 1·25 45
DESIGN: 100f. Scout with "walkie-talkie" radio.

60 "Chelorrhina polyphemus" **61** School Class

1967. Insects.
151 **60** 5f. green, brown and blue 40 20
152 – 15f. purple, brown & green 75 25
153 – 50f. red, brown and green 1·25 55
INSECTS—HORIZ: 15f. "Ugada grandicollis"; 50f. "Phymateus cinctus".

1967. International Literacy Day.
154 **61** 50f. black, red and green 60 20

62 "Europafrique"

1967. Europafrique.
155 **62** 45f. multicoloured 85 25

63 Lions Emblem and Crocodile **65** Block of Flats, Grenoble

64 "Water Resources"

1967. 50th Anniv of Lions International.
156 **63** 90f. multicoloured . . . . 1·10 55

1967. International Hydrological Decade.
157 **64** 25f. black, blue and bistre 70 20

1967. Air. Toulouse-Lautrec Commemoration. Paintings as T **58**. Multicoloured.
158 100f. "Gazelle" (horse's head) (horiz) . . . . 2·50 1·10
159 300f. "Gig drawn by Cob" (vert) . . . . 5·50 2·25

1968. Air. Winter Olympic Games, Grenoble.
160 **65** 50f. brown, green and blue 85 35
161 – 150f. brown, blue and ultramarine . . . . . . 1·75 65
DESIGN: 150f. Bobsleigh course, Huez mountain.

66 W.H.O. Emblem

1968. 20th Anniv of W.H.O.
162 **66** 90f. blue, lake and green 85 30

67 Human Figures and Entwined Hearts

1968. World "Twin Towns" Day.
163 **67** 50f. red, violet and green 40 15

1968. Air. Flower Paintings. As T **58**. Mult.
164 50f. "Roses and Anemones" (Van Gogh) 75 25
165 150f. "Vase of Flowers" (Manet) . . . . 1·75 55
166 300f. "Bouquet of Flowers" (Delacroix) . . . . 3·25 1·10
167 500f. "Marguerites" (Millet) 5·00 2·00
SIZES: 50f., 300f. 40 × 41½ mm; 150f. 36 × 47½ mm; 500f. 50 × 36 mm.

68 Dr. Martin Luther King **69** "Draisienne" Bicycle, 1809

1968. Air. Martin Luther King Commemoration.
168 **68** 100f. black, pink and purple 85 35

1968. Veteran Bicycles and Motor Cars.
169 **69** 2f. brown, mauve and green (postage) 35 15
170 – 5f. red, blue and bistre . . 75 20
171 – 10f. blue, brown and green 1·25 25
172 – 45f. black, green and brown . . . . 2·00 40
173 – 50f. red, green & brn (air) 1·00 25
174 – 100f. blue, mauve and bistre . . . . 2·00 60
DESIGNS—HORIZ: 5f. De Dion-Bouton, 1894; 45f. Panhard-Levassor, 1914; 100f. Mercedes-Benz, 1927. VERT: 10f. Michaux Bicycle, 1861; 50f. "Bicyclette, 1918".

70 Books, Graph and A.D.B.A. Emblem

1968. 10th Anniv of International African Libraries and Archives Development Association.
175 **70** 100f. red, black and brown 65 30

71 Football

1968. Air. Olympic Games, Mexico. Multicoloured.
176 100f. Type **71** . . . . 1·00 40
177 150f. Long-jumping (vert) . . 1·50 60

1968. Air. "Philexafrique" Stamp Exhibition, Abidjan, Ivory Coast, 1969 (1st issue). As T **113a** of Mauritania. Multicoloured.
178 200f. "The Editors" (F. M. Granet) . . . . 2·00 1·50

1969. Air. "Philexafrique" Stamp Exn, Abidjan, Ivory Coast (2nd issue). As T **114a** of Mauritania.
179 100f. purple, red and violet 1·50 1·25
DESIGN: 100f. Carved animal and French Sudan stamp of 1931.

1969. Air. Birth Bicentenary of Napoleon Bonaparte. Multicoloured. As T **114b** of Mauritania.
180 150f. "Napoleon Bonaparte, First Consul" (Gros) . . . 2·50 1·25
181 200f. "The Bivouac – Battle of Austerlitz" (Lejeune) (horiz) . . . . 4·25 1·75

73 Montgolfier Balloon

1969. Air. Aviation History. Multicoloured.
182 50f. Type **73** 50 20
183 150f. Ferdinand Ferber's Glider No. 5 . . . . . . 1·75 40
184 300f. Concorde . . . . . . 3·50 1·40

74 African Tourist Emblem

1969. African Tourist Year.
185 **74** 50f. red, green and blue . . 25 20

75 "O.I.T." and I.L.O. Emblem

1969. 50th Anniv of I.L.O.
186 **75** 50f. violet, blue and green 30 20
187 60f. slate, red and brown 35 20

76 Panhard of 1897 and Model "24-CT"

1969. French Motor Industry.
188 **76** 25f. lake, black and bistre (postage) 50 20
189 – 30f. green and black . . . 75 20
190 – 55f. red, black and purple (air) . . . . 1·25 35
191 – 90f. blue, black and red . . 1·75 45
DESIGNS: 30f. Citroen of 1923 and Model "DS-21"; 55f. Renault of 1898 and Model "16"; 90f. Peugeot of 1893 and Model "404".

77 Clarke (Australia), 10,000 m (1965)

1969. Air. World Athletics Records.
192 **77** 60f. brown and blue . . . 30 25
193 – 90f. brown and red 45 25
194 – 120f. brown and green . . 55 35
195 – 140f. brown and slate . . . 70 35
196 – 150f. black and red 85 50
DESIGNS: 90f. Lusis (Russia), Javelin (1968); 120f. Miyake (Japan), Weightlifting (1967); 140f. Matson (U.S.A.), Shot-putting (1968); 150f. Keino (Kenya), 3,000 m (1965).

78 Hollow Blocks

1969. International Toy Fair, Nuremberg.
197 **78** 5f. red, yellow and grey . . 15 10
198 – 10f. multicoloured 15 10
199 – 15f. green, red and pink . . 30 10
200 – 20f. orange, blue and red 35 15
DESIGNS: 10f. Toy donkey on wheels; 15f. "Ducks"; 20f. Model car and race-track.

79 "Apollo 8", Earth and Moon

1969. Air. Moon Flight of "Apollo 8".
201 **79** 2,000f. gold . . . . 14·00 14·00
This stamp is embossed on gold foil.

1969. Air. 1st Man on the Moon. Nos. 182/4 optd **L'HOMME SUR LA LUNE JUILLET 1969** and Apollo 11.
202 50f. multicoloured 95 65
203 150f. multicoloured . . . . . 2·00 1·25
204 300f. multicoloured . . . . . 3·25 2·50

81 Sheep

1969. Domestic Animals.
205 **81** 1f. olive, brown and green 10 10
206 – 2f. brown, grey and red . . 10 10
207 – 10f. olive, brown and blue 20 10
208 – 35f. slate and red 60 30
209 – 90f. brown and blue . . . 1·25 55
ANIMALS: 2f. Goat; 10f. Donkey; 35f. Horse; 90f. Dromedary.

1969. 5th Anniv of African Development Bank. As T **122a** of Mauritania.
210 50f. brown, green and purple 25 20
211 90f. orange, green and brown 45 20

83 "Mona Lisa" (Leonardo da Vinci)

1969. Air. 450th Death Anniv of Leonardo da Vinci.
212 **83** 500f. multicoloured . . . . 4·50 3·25

84 Vaccination

1969. Campaign against Smallpox and Measles.
213 **84** 50f. slate, brown and green 40 15

85 Mahatma Gandhi

1969. Air. Birth Centenary of Mahatma Gandhi.
214 **85** 150f. brown and green . . 1·75 55

1969. 10th Anniv of Aerial Navigation Security Agency for Africa and Madagascar (A.S.E.C.N.A.). As T **94a** of Niger.
215 100f. green 75 25

87 West African Map and Posthorns

1970. Air. 11th Anniv of West African Postal Union (C.A.P.T.E.A.O.).
216 **87** 100f. multicoloured 60 35

1970. Air. Religious Paintings. As T **83**. Mult.
217 100f. "Virgin and Child" (Van der Weydan School) 70 40
218 150f. "The Nativity" (The Master of Flamalle) . . . 1·10 65
219 250f. "Virgin, Child and St. John the Baptist" (Low Countries School) . . . . 2·40 1·40

89 Franklin D. Roosevelt

91 Lenin

90 Women of Mali and Japan

1970. Air. 25th Death Anniv of Franklin D. Roosevelt.
220 **89** 500f. black, red and blue 3·50 2·00

1970. "EXPO 70" World Fair, Osaka, Japan.
221 **90** 100f. orange, brown & blue 60 20
222 – 150f. red, green and yellow 80 30
DESIGN: 150f. Flags and maps of Mali and Japan.

1970. Air. Birth Centenary of Lenin.
223 **91** 300f. black, green and flesh 2·25 1·00

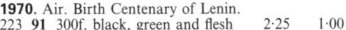

92 Verne and Moon Rockets

1970. Air. Jules Verne "Prophet of Space Travel". Multicoloured.
224 50f. Type **92** 75 25
225 150f. Moon orbit . . . . . . 1·75 50
226 300f. Splashdown . . . . . 2·50 1·10

93 I.T.U. Emblem and Map

1970. World Telecommunications Day.
227 **93** 90f. red, brown and sepia 75 25

1970. New U.P.U. Headquarters Building, Berne. As Type **81** of New Caledonia.
228 50f. brown, green and red . . 40 20
229 60f. brown, blue and mauve 60 20

1970. Air. Space Flight of "Apollo 13". Nos. 224/6 optd **APOLLO XIII EPOPEE SPATIALE 11-17 AVRIL 1970** in three lines.
230 50f. multicoloured 50 25
231 150f. multicoloured . . . . . 1·25 45
232 300f. multicoloured . . . . . 2·25 1·25

96 "Intelstat 3" Satellite

1970. Air. Space Telecommunications.
233 **96** 100f. indigo, blue & orange 75 35
234 – 200f. purple, grey and blue 1·40 50
235 – 300f. brown, orange & slate . . . . 2·50 1·10
236 – 500f. brown, blue & indigo 3·75 1·60
DESIGNS: 200f. "Molnya I" satellite; 300f. Dish aerial, Type PB 2; 500f. "Symphony Project" satellite.

97 Auguste and Louis Lumiere, Jean Harlow and Marilyn Monroe

1970. Air. Lumiere Brothers (inventors of the cine camera) Commemoration.
237 **97** 250f. multicoloured . . . . 2·50 1·25

98 Footballers

1970. Air. World Cup Football Championship, Mexico.
238 **98** 80f. green, brown and red 50 25
239 200f. red, brown and blue 1·25 55

99 Rotary Emblem, Map and Antelope

100 "Supporting United Nations"

1970. Air. Rotary International.
240 **99** 200f. multicoloured . . . . 1·75 60

1970. Air. 25th Anniv of U.N.O.
241 **100** 100f. blue, brown & violet 70 35

101 Page from 11th century Baghdad Koran

1970. Air. Ancient Muslim Art. Multicoloured.
242 50f. Type **101** 50 25
243 200f. "Tree and wild Animals" (Jordanian mosaic, c.730) . . . . . . 1·25 55
244 250f. "The Scribe" (Baghdad miniature, 1287) . . . . . 2·00 90

1970. Air. Moon Landing of "Luna 16". Nos. 234/5 surch **LUNA 16 PREMIERS PRELEVEMENTS AUTOMATIQUES SUR LA LUNE SEPTEMBRE 1970** and new values.
245 150f. on 200f. purple, grey and blue . . . . 1·25 40
246 250f. on 300f. brown, orange and grey . . . . 1·75 60

103 G.P.O., Bamako

1970. Public Buildings.
247 **103** 30f. olive, green and brown 20 20
248 – 40f. purple, brown & green 30 20
249 – 60f. grey, green and red 40 20
250 – 80f. brown, green and grey 50 25
BUILDINGS: 40f. Chamber of Commerce, Bamako; 60f. Ministry of Public Works, Bamako; 80f. Town Hall, Segou.

104 Pres. Nasser

106 Gallet Steam Locomotive, 1882

105 "The Nativity" (Antwerp School 1530)

1970. Air. Pres. Gamal Nasser of Egypt. Commemoration.
251 **104** 1000f. gold . . . . 7·50 7·50

1970. Air. Christmas. Paintings. Multicoloured.
252 100f. Type **105** 70 40
253 250f. "Adoration of the Shepherds" (Memling) . . 1·60 95
254 300f. "Adoration of the Magi" (17th-century Flemish school) . . . . . 2·25 1·25

1970. Mali Railway Locomotives from the Steam Era (1st series).
255 **106** 20f. black, red and green 1·60 1·40
256 – 40f. black, green & brown 2·40 1·75
257 – 50f. black, green & brown 2·75 2·10
258 – 80f. black, red and green 4·00 3·00
259 – 100f. black, green & brn 4·75 4·00
LOCOMOTIVES: 40f. Felou, 1882; 50f. Bechevel, 1882; 80f. Series 1100, 1930 (inscr "Type 23"); 100f. Class 40, 1927 (incr "Type 141" and "vers 1930").
See also Nos. 367/70.

107 Scouts crossing Log-bridge

108 Bambara de San Mask

1970. Scouting in Mali. Multicoloured.
260 5f. Type **107** 20 15
261 30f. Bugler and scout camp (vert) 35 15
262 100f. Scouts canoeing 90 35

1971. Mali Masks and Ideograms. Multicoloured.
263 20f. Type **108** 15 10
264 25f. Dogon de Bandiagara mask 20 10
265 50f. Kanaga ideogram . . . 45 15
266 80f. Bambara ideogram . . . 60 25

109 General De Gaulle

1971. Air. Charles De Gaulle Commem. Die-stamped on gold foil.
267 **109** 2000f. gold, red and blue 30·00 30·00

110 Alfred Nobel

111 Tennis Player (Davis Cup)

1971. Air. 75th Death Anniv of Alfred Nobel (philanthropist).
268 **110** 300f. red, brown and green . . . . 2·50 1·25

1971. Air. World Sporting Events.
269 **111** 100f. slate, purple and blue 75 25
270 – 150f. olive, brown & green . . . . 1·40 40
271 – 200f. brown, olive and blue . . . . 2·00 60
DESIGNS—HORIZ: 150f. Steeplechase (inscr "Derby at Epsom" but probably represents the Grand National). VERT: 200f. Yacht (Americas Cup).

112 Youth, Sun and Microscope

1971. 50th Anniv of 1st B.C.G. Vaccine Innoculation.
272 **112** 100f. brown, green and red 85 40

113 "The Thousand and One Nights"

1971. Air. "Tales of the Arabian Nights". Mult.
273 120f. Type **113** 70 30
274 180f. "Ali Baba and the Forty Thieves" . . . . . 1·00 40
275 200f. "Aladdin's Lamp" . . . 1·40 50

114 Scouts, Japanese Horseman and Mt. Fuji

1971. 13th World Scout Jamboree, Asagiri, Japan.
276 **114** 80f. plum, green and blue 75 20

115 Rose between Hands **116** Rural Costume

1971. 25th Anniv of U.N.I.C.E.F.
277 **115** 50f. brown, red and orange 30 20
278 – 60f. blue, green and brown 40 20
DESIGN—VERT: 60f. Nurses and children.

1971. National Costumes. Multicoloured.
279 5f. Type **116** 15 10
280 10f. Rural costume (female) 20 15
281 15f. Tuareg 20 15
282 60f. Embroidered "boubou" 45 20
283 80f. Women's ceremonial costume 60 25

117 Olympic Rings and Events

1971. Air. Olympic Games Publicity.
284 **117** 80f. blue, purple and green 40 20

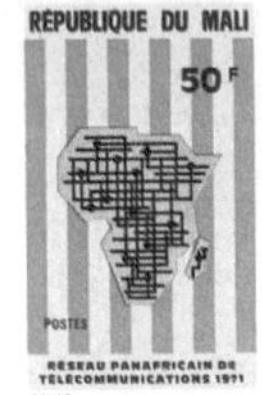

118 Telecommunications Map

1971. Pan-African Telecommunications Network Year.
285 **118** 50f. multicoloured 25 20

119 "Mariner 4" and Mars

1971. Air. Exploration of Outer Space.
286 **119** 200f. green, blue & brown 1·25 50
287 – 300f. blue, plum & purple 1·75 60
DESIGN: 300f. "Venera 5" and Venus.

120 "Santa Maria" (1492)

1971. Air. Famous Ships.
288 **120** 100f. brown, violet & blue 70 35
289 – 150f. violet, brown & grn 1·25 45
290 – 200f. green, blue and red 1·60 75
291 – 250f. red, blue and black 2·25 90
DESIGNS: 150f. "Mayflower" (1620); 200f. Battleship "Potemkin" (1905); 250f. Liner "Normandie" (1935).

121 "Hibiscus rosa-sinensis"

1971. Flowers. Multicoloured.
292 20f. Type **121** 20 10
293 50f. "Euphorbia pulcherrima" 55 15
294 60f. "Adenium obesum" . . 80 20
295 80f. "Allamanda cathartica" 1·25 25
296 100f. "Satanocrater berhautii" . . . . 1·50 35

122 Allegory of Justice

1971. 25th Anniv of Int Court of Justice, The Hague.
297 **122** 160f. chocolate, red & brn 80 35

123 Nat King Cole **124** Statue of Olympic Zeus (by Pheidias)

1971. Air. Famous Negro Musicians. Multicoloured.
298 130f. Type **123** . . . . 1·25 25
299 150f. Erroll Garner . . . . . 1·25 30
300 270f. Louis Armstrong . . . 1·75 45

1971. Air. "The Seven Wonders of the Ancient World".
301 **124** 70f. blue, brown & purple 35 20
302 – 80f. black, brown and blue 40 20
303 – 100f. blue, red and violet 50 25
304 – 130f. black, purple & blue 75 30
305 – 150f. brown, green & blue 1·10 35
306 – 270f. blue, brown & pur 1·60 75
307 – 280f. blue, purple & brn 2·00 85
DESIGNS—VERT: 80f. Pyramid of Cheops, Egypt; 130f. Pharos of Alexandria; 270f. Mausoleum of Halicarnassos; 280f. Colossus of Rhodes. HORIZ: 100f. Temple of Artemis, Ephesus; 150f. Hanging Gardens of Babylon.

125 "Family Life" (carving)

1971. 15th Anniv of Social Security Service.
308 **125** 70f. brown, green and red 40 20

126 Slalom-skiing and Japanese Girl

1972. Air. Winter Olympic Games, Sapporo, Japan.
309 **126** 150f. brown, green & orge 1·00 35
310 – 200f. green, brown and red . . . . 1·50 55
DESIGN: 200f. Ice-hockey and Japanese actor.

127 "Santa Maria della Salute" (Caffi)

1972. Air. U.N.E.S.C.O. "Save Venice" Campaign. Multicoloured.
312 130f. Type **127** 80 35
313 270f. "Rialto Bridge" . . . 1·50 60
314 280f. "St. Mark's Square" (vert) . . . . 1·75 70

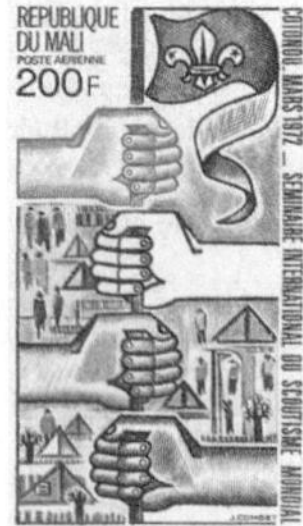

128 Hands clasping Flagpole

1972. Air. Int Scout Seminar, Cotonou, Dahomey.
315 **128** 200f. green, orange & brn 1·75 55

129 Heart and Red Cross Emblems

1972. Air. World Heart Month.
316 **129** 150f. red and blue . . . . 1·00 40

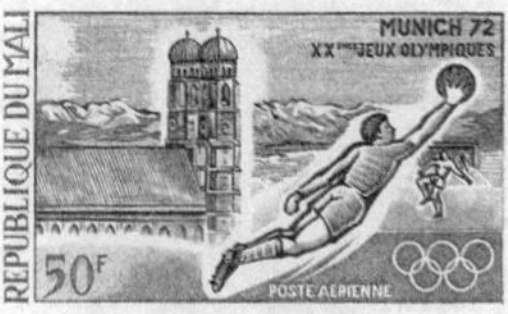

130 Football

1972. Air. Olympic Games, Munich (1st issue). Sports and Munich Buildings.
317 **130** 50f. blue, brown and green 25 20
318 – 150f. blue, brown & green 70 30
319 – 200f. blue, brown & green 80 50
320 – 300f. blue, brown & green 1·25 70
DESIGNS—VERT: 150f. Judo; 200f. Hurdling. HORIZ: 300f. Running.
See also Nos. 357/62.

131 "Apollo 15" and Lunar Rover

1972. Air. History of Transport Development.
322 **131** 150f. red, green and lake 80 40
323 – 250f. red, blue and green 2·00 1·00
DESIGN: 250f. Montgolfier's balloon and Cugnot's steam car.

132 "UIT" on T.V. Screen

1972. World Telecommunications Day.
324 **132** 70f. black, blue and red 40 20

133 Clay Funerary Statue **134** Samuel Morse and Early Telegraph

1972. Mali Archaeology. Multicoloured.
325 30f. Type **133** 20 15
326 40f. Female Figure (wood-carving) 30 20
327 50f. "Warrior" (stone-painting) 40 20
328 100f. Wrought-iron ritual figures . . . . 1·00 35

1972. Death Centenary of Samuel Morse (inventor of telegraph).
329 **134** 80f. purple, green and red 45 20

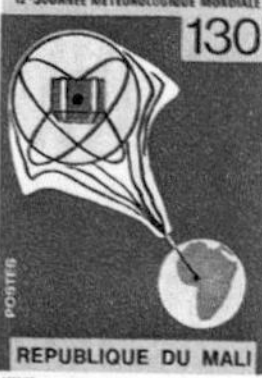

135 "Cinderella" **136** Weather Balloon

1972. Air. Charles Perrault's Fairy Tales.
330 **135** 70f. green, red and brown 45 20
331 – 80f. brown, red and green 50 25
332 – 150f. violet, purple & blue 1·10 35
DESIGNS: 80f. "Puss in Boots"; 150f. "The Sleeping Beauty".

1972. World Meteorological Day.
333 **136** 130f. multicoloured . . . 60 30

137 Astronauts and Lunar Rover

1972. Air. Moon Flight of "Apollo 16".
334 **137** 500f. brown, violet & grn 3·00 1·25

138 Book Year Emblem

1972. Air. International Book Year.
335 **138** 80f. gold, green and blue 40 25

139 Sarakole Dance, Kayes **140** Learning the Alphabet

1972. Traditional Dances. Multicoloured.
336 10f. Type **139** 25 15
337 20f. Malinke dance, Bamako 30 15
338 50f. Hunter's dance, Bougouni 55 20
339 70f. Bambara dance, Segou 70 20
340 80f. Dogon dance, Sanga . . 80 30
341 120f. Targuie dance, Timbukto . . . . 1·40 45

1972. International Literacy Day.
342 **140** 80f. black and green . . . 40 15

141 Statue and Musical Instruments **142** Club Banner

1972. 1st Anthology of Mali Music.
343 **141** 100f. multicoloured . . . 85 30

1972. Air. 10th Anniv of Bamako Rotary Club.
344 **142** 170f. purple, blue and red 1·00 40

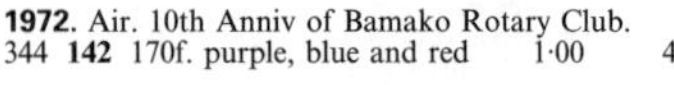

143 Aries the Ram

1972. Signs of the Zodiac.

345 **143** 15f. brown and purple . . 30 20
346 – 15f. black and brown . . 30 20
347 – 35f. blue and red 50 25
348 – 35f. red and green 50 25
349 – 40f. brown and blue . . . 60 30
350 – 40f. brown and purple . . 60 30
351 – 45f. red and blue 70 35
352 – 45f. green and red 70 35
353 – 65f. blue and violet . . . 1·00 35
354 – 65f. brown and violet . . 1·00 35
355 – 90f. blue and mauve . . . 1·60 65
356 – 90f. green and mauve . . 1·60 65

DESIGNS: No. 346, Taurus the Bull; No. 347, Gemini the Twins; No. 348, Cancer the Crab; No. 349, Leo the Lion; No. 350, Virgo the Virgin; No. 351, Libra the Scales; No. 352, Scorpio the Scorpion; No. 353, Sagittarius the Archer; No. 354, Capricornus the Goat; No. 355, Aquarius the Water-carrier; No. 356, Pisces the Fish.

1972. Air. Olympic Games, Munich (2nd issue). Sports and Locations of Games since 1952. As Type **130**.

357 70f. blue, brown and red . . 1·75 40
358 90f. green, red and blue . . . 35 20
359 140f. olive, green and brown 60 20
360 150f. brown, green and red 65 25
361 170f. blue, brown and purple 75 30
362 210f. blue, red and green . . 90 40

DESIGNS—VERT: 70f. Boxing, Helsinki Games (1952); 150f. Weightlifting, Tokyo Games (1964). HORIZ: 90f. Hurdling, Melbourne Games (1956); 140f. 200 metres, Rome Games (1960); 170f. Swimming, Mexico Games (1968); 210f. Throwing the javelin, Munich Games (1972).

1972. Medal Winners, Munich Olympic Games. Nos. 318/20 and 362 optd with events and names, etc.

363 150f. blue, brown and green 70 30
364 200f. blue, brown and green 90 40
365 210f. blue, red and green . . 90 40
366 300f. blue, brown and green 1·25 70

OVERPRINTS: 150f. **JUDO RUSKA 2 MEDAILLES D'OR**; 200f. **STEEPLE KEINO MEDAILLE D'OR**; 210f. **MEDAILLE D'OR 90m. 48**; 300f. **100m. - 200m. BORZOV 2 MEDAILLES D'OR**.

1972. Mali Locomotives (2nd series). As T **106**.

367 10f. blue, green and red . . . 1·60 1·25
368 30f. blue, green and brown 3·25 2·50
369 60f. blue, brown and green 4·00 3·25
370 120f. purple, green and black 6·75 5·25

LOCOMOTIVES: 10f. First Locomotive to arrive at Bamako, 1906; 30f. Steam locomotive, Thies Bamako line, 1920; 60f. Class 40 steam locomotive, Thies–Bamako line, 1927 (inscr "141");. 120f. Alsthom series BB 100 coupled diesel, Dakar–Bamako line, 1947.

146 Emperor Haile Selassie

1972. Air. 80th Birth Anniv of Emperor Haile Selassie.

371 **146** 70f. multicoloured 30 20

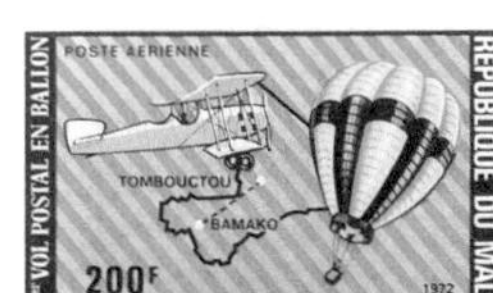

147 Balloon, Breguet 14T Biplane and Map

1972. Air. 1st Mali Airmail Flight by Balloon, Bamako to Timbuktu. Multicoloured.

372 200f. Type **147** . . . . 1·00 45
373 300f. Balloon, Concorde and map . . . . 1·40 60

148 High Jumping

1973. 2nd African Games, Lagos, Nigeria. Mult.

374 70f. Type **148** 30 20
375 270f. Throwing the discus . . 1·25 60
376 280f. Football . . . . 1·40 65

149 14th-century German Bishop

150 Interpol Headquarters, Paris

1973. Air. World Chess Championship, Reykjavik, Iceland.

377 **149** 100f. lt blue, blue & brown . . . . 1·25 35
378 – 200f. red, light red & black . . . . 2·50 75

DESIGN: 200f. 18th-century Indian knight (elephant).

1973. 50th Anniv of International Criminal Police Organization (Interpol).

379 **150** 80f. multicoloured 65 20

151 Emblem and Dove with letter

152 "Fauna Protection" Stamp of 1963

1973. 10th Anniv (1971) of African Postal Union.

380 **151** 70f. multicoloured 35 20

1973. Air. Stamp Day.

381 **152** 70f. orange, red and brown . . . . 1·10 65

153 Astronauts on Moon

155 Handicapped Africans

154 Copernicus

1973. Moon Mission of "Apollo" 17.

382 **153** 250f. brown and blue . . 1·75 65

1973. 500th Birth Anniv of Copernicus.

384 **154** 300f. purple and blue . . 2·25 1·10

1973. "Help the Handicapped".

385 **155** 70f. orange, black and red 35 20

156 Dr. G. A. Hansen

1973. Centenary of Hansen's Identification of the Leprosy Bacillus.

386 **156** 200f. green, black and red 1·60 60

157 Bentley and Alfa Romeo, 1930

1973. 50th Anniv of Le Mans 24-hour Endurance Race.

387 **157** 50f. green, orange and blue 50 15
388 – 100f. green, blue and red 1·00 25
389 – 200f. blue, green and red 2·00 50

DESIGNS: 100f. Jaguar and Talbot, 1953; 200f. Matra and Porsche, 1952.

158 Scouts around Campfire

1973. International Scouting Congress, Addis Ababa and Nairobi.

390 **158** 50f. brown, red and blue 30 15
391 – 70f. brown, red and blue 50 20
392 – 80f. red, brown and green 60 20
393 – 130f. green, blue & brown 85 30
394 – 270f. red, violet and grey 1·75 60

DESIGNS—VERT: 70f. Scouts saluting flag; 130f. Lord Baden-Powell. HORIZ: 80f. Standard-bearers; 270f. Map of Africa and Scouts and Guides in ring.

159 Swimming and National Flags

1973. 1st Afro-American Sports Meeting, Bamako.

395 **159** 70f. green, red and blue 30 20
396 – 80f. green, red and blue 35 25
397 – 330f. blue and red . . . . 1·50 70

DESIGNS—VERT: 80f. Throwing the discus and javelin. HORIZ: 330f. Running.

1973. Pan-African Drought Relief. No. 296 surch **SECHERESSE SOLIDARITE AFRICAINE** and value.

398 200f. on 100f. multicoloured 1·10 65

1973. Air. African Fortnight, Brussels. As T **168a** of Niger.

399 70f. violet, blue and brown 30 20

162 "Perseus" (Cellini)

1973. Air. Famous Sculptures.

400 **162** 100f. green and red . . . 55 25
401 – 150f. purple and red . . . 85 35
402 – 250f. green and red . . . 1·50 65

DESIGNS: 150f. "Pieta" (Michelangelo); 250f. "Victory of Samothrace".

163 Stephenson's "Rocket" (1829) and French Buddicom Locomotive

1973. Air. Famous Locomotives.

403 **163** 100f. black, blue & brown 1·50 45
404 – 150f. multicoloured . . . 1·90 50
405 – 200f. blue, slate and brown . . . . 3·25 80

DESIGNS: 150f. Union Pacific steam locomotive No. 119 (1890) and Santa Fe Railroad steam locomotive "Blue Goose" (1937), U.S.A.; 200f. "Mistral" express (France) and "Hikari" express train (Japan).

164 "Apollo 11" First Landing

1973. Conquest of the Moon.

406 **164** 50f. purple, red and brown 25 20
407 – 75f. grey, blue and red . . 30 20
408 – 100f. slate, brown and blue 75 30
409 – 280f. blue, green and red 1·40 65
410 – 300f. blue, red and green 1·75 80

DESIGNS: 75f. "Apollo 13" Recovery capsule; 100f. "Apollo 14" Lunar trolley; 280f. "Apollo 15" Lunar rover; 300f. "Apollo 17" lift off from Moon.

165 Picasso

166 Pres. John Kennedy

1973. Air. Pablo Picasso (artist). Commem.

411 **165** 500f. multicoloured . . . 3·00 1·25

1973. Air. 10th Death Anniv of Pres. Kennedy.

412 **166** 500f. black, purple & gold 2·50 1·25

1973. Air. Christmas. As T **105** but dated "1973". Multicoloured.

413 100f. "The Annunciation" (V. Carpaccio) (horiz.) . . . 50 25
414 200f. "Virgin of St. Simon" (F. Baroccio) . . . . . . 1·25 50
415 250f. "Flight into Egypt" (A. Solario) . . . . 1·60 70

167 Player and Football

168 Cora

1973. Air. World Football Cup Championship, West Germany.

416 **167** 150f. red, brown and green 90 35
417 – 250f. green, brown & violet . . . . 1·75 60

DESIGN: 250f. Goalkeeper and ball.

1973. Musical Instruments.

419 **168** 5f. brown, red and green 20 10
420 – 10f. brown and blue . . . 25 10
421 – 15f. brown, red and yellow 35 15
422 – 20f. brown and red . . . 40 15
423 – 25f. brown, red and yellow 45 15
424 – 30f. black and blue . . . 60 20
425 – 35f. sepia, brown and red 70 20
426 – 40f. brown and red . . . 75 30

DESIGNS—HORIZ: 10f. Balafon. VERT: 15f. Djembe; 20f. Guitar; 25f. N'Djarka; 30f. M'Bolon; 35f. Dozo N'Goni; 40f. N'Tamani.

169 "Musicians" (mosaic)

1974. Roman Frescoes and Mosaics from Pompeii.
427 **169** 150f. red, brown and grey 75 35
428 – 250f. brown, red & orange 1·25 60
429 – 350f. brown, orange and olive . . . . 1·75 75
DESIGNS—VERT: 250f. "Alexander the Great" (mosaic); 350f. "Bacchante" (fresco).

170 Corncob, Worker and "Kibaru" Newspaper

171 Sir Winston Churchill

1974. 2nd Anniv of Rural Press.
430 **170** 70f. brown and green . . 35 20

1974. Air. Birth Cent of Sir Winston Churchill.
431 **171** 500f. black . . . . 2·50 1·50

172 Chess-pieces on Board

1974. Air. 21st Chess Olympiad, Nice.
432 **172** 250f. indigo, red and blue 3·50 75

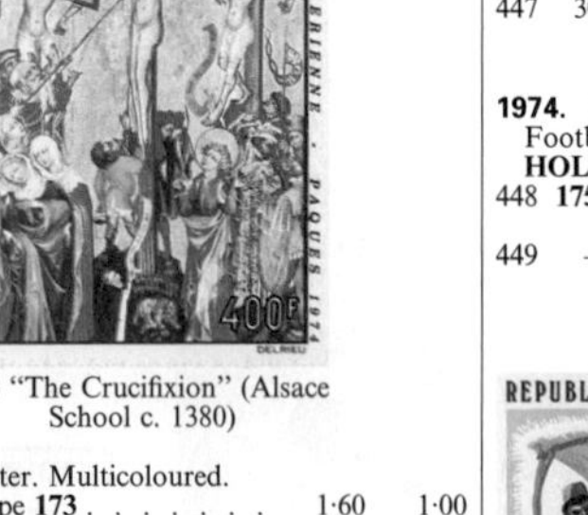

173 "The Crucifixion" (Alsace School c. 1380)

1974. Air. Easter. Multicoloured.
433 400f. Type **173** . . . . 1·60 1·00
434 500f. "The Entombment" (Titian) (horiz) . . . . . . 2·25 1·25

174 Lenin

1974. Air. 50th Death Anniv of Lenin.
435 **174** 150f. purple and violet . . 70 30

175 Goalkeeper and Globe

177 Full-rigged Sailing Ship and Modern Liner

176 Horse-jumping Scenes

1974. World Cup Football Championship, West Germany.
436 **175** 270f. red, green and lilac 1·25 80
437 – 280f. blue, brown and red 1·60 80
DESIGN: 280f. World Cup emblem on football.

1974. Air. World Equestrian Championships, La Baule.
438 **176** 130f. brown, lilac and blue . . . . 1·50 60

1974. Centenary of Universal Postal Union.
439 **177** 80f. purple, lilac & brown 55 25
440 – 90f. orange, grey and blue 40 30
441 – 270f. purple, olive & green . . . . 2·75 1·10
DESIGNS: 90f. Breguet 14T biplane and Douglas DC-8; 270f. Steam and electric mail trains.
See also Nos. 463/4.

178 "Skylab" over Africa

1974. Air. Survey of Africa by "Skylab" Space Station.
442 **178** 200f. indigo, blue & orge 1·00 40
443 – 250f. blue, purple & orge 1·25 60
DESIGN: 250f. Astronaut servicing cameras.

1974. Air. 11th Arab Scout Jamboree, Lebanon. Nos. 391/2 surch **130f. 11e JAMBOREE ARABE AOUT 1974 LIBAN** or **170f. CONGRES PAN-ARABE LIBAN AOUT 1974**.
444 130f. on 70f. brown, red & bl 70 40
445 170f. on 80f. blue, green & red 75 50

1974. Air. 5th Anniv of First Landing on Moon. Nos. 408/9 surch **130f. 1er DEBARQUEMENT SUR LA LUNE 20-VII-69** or **300f. 1er PAS SUR LA LUNE 21-VII-69**.
446 130f. on 100f. slate, brown and blue 70 45
447 300f. on 280f. blue, grn & red 1·40 70

1974. West Germany's Victory in World Cup Football Championship. Nos. 436/7 surch **R.F.A. 2 HOLLANDE 1** and value.
448 **175** 300f. on 270f. red, green and lilac . . . . 1·40 80
449 – 330f. on 280f. blue, brown and red . . . . 1·60 80

182 Weaver

183 River Niger near Gao

1974. Crafts and Craftsmen. Multicoloured.
450 50f. Type **182** 25 15
451 60f. Potter 30 15
452 70f. Smith 40 20
453 80f. Wood-carver 55 20

1974. Mali Views. Multicoloured.
454 10f. Type **183** 15 10
455 20f. "The Hand of Fatma" (rock formation, Hombori) (vert) 15 10
456 40f. Waterfall, Gouina . . . 35 15
457 70f. Hill-dwellings, Dogon (vert) 60 20

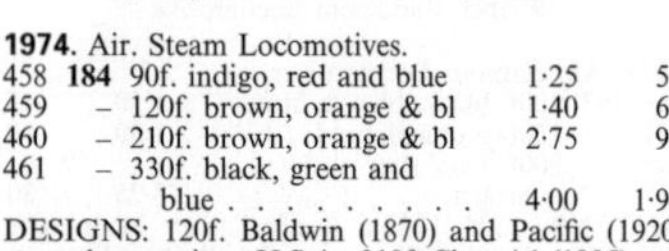

184 Class C No. 3 (1906) and Class P (1939) Steam Locomotives, France

1974. Air. Steam Locomotives.
458 **184** 90f. indigo, red and blue 1·25 50
459 – 120f. brown, orange & bl 1·40 60
460 – 210f. brown, orange & bl 2·75 90
461 – 330f. black, green and blue . . . . 4·00 1·90
DESIGNS: 120f. Baldwin (1870) and Pacific (1920) steam locomotives, U.S.A.; 210f. Class A1 (1925) and Buddicom (1847) steam locomotives; 330f. Hudson steam locomotive, 1938 (U.S.A.) and steam locomotive "Gironde", 1839.

185 Skiing

1974. Air. 50th Anniv of Winter Olympics.
462 **185** 300f. red, blue and green 1·40 80

1974. Berne Postal Convention. Cent, Nos. 439 and 441 surch **9 OCTOBRE 1974** and value.
463 **177** 250f. on 80f. purple, lilac and brown . . . . . . 1·40 80
464 – 300f. on 270f. purple, olive and green . . . . 3·00 1·25

187 Mao Tse-tung and Great Wall of China

1974. 25th Anniv of Chinese People's Republic.
465 **187** 100f. blue, red and green 50 30

188 "The Nativity" (Memling)

1974. Air. Christmas. Multicoloured.
466 290f. Type **188** . . . . 1·25 70
467 310f. "Virgin and Child" (Bourgogne School) . . . 1·50 75
468 400f. "Adoration of the Magi" (Schongauer) . . . 1·90 1·10

189 Raoul Follereau (missionary)

191 Dr. Schweitzer

190 Electric Train and Boeing 707

1974. Air. Raoul Follereau, "Apostle of the Lepers".
469 **189** 200f. blue . . . . 1·25 55
469a 200f. brown . . . . . . 1·75 1·10

1974. Air. Europafrique.
470 **190** 100f. green, brown & blue 2·75 70
471 110f. blue, violet & brown 3·00 70

1975. Birth Centenary of Dr Albert Schweitzer.
472 **191** 150f. turquoise, green & bl 90 40

192 Patients making Handicrafts and Lions International Emblem

1975. 5th Anniv of Samanko (Leprosy rehabilitation village). Multicoloured.
473 90f. Type **192** 50 20
474 100f. View of Samanko . . . 60 25

193 "The Pilgrims at Emmaus" (Champaigne)

1975. Air. Easter. Multicoloured.
475 200f. Type **193** 90 45
476 300f. "The Pilgrims at Emmaus" (Veronese) . . . 1·25 60
477 500f. "Christ in Majesty" (Limoges enamel) (vert) . . 2·25 1·25

194 "Journey to the Centre of the Earth"

1975. Air. 70th Death Anniv of Jules Verne.
478 **194** 100f. green, blue & brown 45 25
479 – 170f. brown, blue & lt brn 75 35
480 – 190f. blue, turquoise & brn . . . . 1·25 55
481 – 220f. brown, purple & blue . . . . 1·50 60
DESIGNS: 170f. Jules Verne and "From the Earth to the Moon"; 190f. Giant octopus–"Twenty Thousand Leagues Under the Sea"; 220f. "A Floating City".

195 Head of "Dawn" (Tomb of the Medici)

1975. Air. 500th Birth Anniv of Michelangelo (artist). Multicoloured.
482 400f. Type **195** . . . . 1·75 1·10
483 500f. "Moses" (marble statue, Rome) . . . . 2·25 1·25

196 Nile Pufferfish

1975. Fishes (1st series).
484 **196** 60f. brown, yellow & grn 80 25
485 – 70f. black, brown and grey 90 35
486 – 80f. multicoloured . . . . 1·10 40
487 – 90f. blue, grey and green 1·60 50
488 – 110f. black and blue . . . 2·25 70
DESIGNS: 70f. Electric catfish; 80f. Deep-sided citharinid; 90f. Lesser tigerfish; 110f. Nile perch.
See also Nos. 544/8.

197 Astronaut

199 Woman with Bouquet

198 Einstein and Equation

1975. Air. Soviet–U.S. Space Co-operation.
489 **197** 290f. red, blue and black 1·10 50
490 – 300f. red, blue and black 1·10 60
491 – 370f. green, purple & black . . . . 1·40 80
DESIGNS: 300f. "America and Russia"; 370f. New York and Moscow landmarks.

1975. Air. 20th Death Anniv of Albert Einstein.
492 **198** 90f. blue, purple & brown 55 30
See also Nos. 504, 507 and 519.

1975. International Women's Year.
493 **199** 150f. red and green . . . 70 35

200 Morris "Oxford", 1913

1975. Early Motor-cars.
494 **200** 90f. violet, brown and blue 60 20
495 – 130f. red, grey and blue 95 25
496 – 190f. deep blue, green and blue . . . . 1·40 40
497 – 230f. brown, blue and red 1·75 45
DESIGNS—MOTOR-CARS: 130f. Franklin "E", 1907; 190f. Daimler, 1900; 230f. Panhard & Levassor, 1895.

201

1975. Air. "Nordjamb 75" World Scout Jamboree, Norway.
498 **201** 100f. blue, brown and lake 55 25
499 – 150f. green, brown & blue 75 30
500 – 290f. lake, brown and blue . . . . 1·40 75
DESIGNS: 150f., 290f. Scouts and emblem (different).

202 Lafayette and Battle Scene

1975. Air. Bicentenary of American Revolution. Mult.
501 290f. Type **202** . . . . 1·50 65
502 300f. Washington and battle scene . . . . 1·50 65
503 370f. De Grasse and Battle of the Chesapeake, 1781 . . . 1·90 95

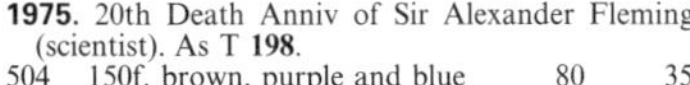
1975. 20th Death Anniv of Sir Alexander Fleming (scientist). As T **198**.
504 150f. brown, purple and blue 80 35

204 Olympic Rings

1975. Air. "Pre-Olympic Year".
505 **204** 350f. violet and blue . . . 1·00 65
506 – 400f. blue . . . . 1·10 80
DESIGNS: 400f. Emblem of Montreal Olympics (1976).

1975. Birth Bicentenary of Andre-Marie Ampere. As T **198**.
507 90f. brown, red and violet . . 45 20

205 Tristater of Carthage

1975. Ancient Coins.
508 **205** 130f. black, blue & purple 50 25
509 – 170f. black, green & brn 70 35
510 – 190f. black, green and red 1·00 65
511 – 260f. black, blue & orange 1·75 1·25
COINS: 170f. Decadrachm of Syracuse; 190f. Tetradrachm of Acanthe; 260f. Didrachm of Eretrie.

1975. Air. "Apollo–Soyuz" Space Link. Nos. 489/91 optd **ARRIMAGE 17 Juil. 1975**.
512 **197** 290f. red, blue and black 1·25 65
513 – 300f. red, blue and black 1·25 65
514 – 370f. green, purple & black . . . . 1·50 95

207 U.N. Emblem and Names of Agencies forming "ONU"

1975. 30th Anniv of United Nations Charter.
515 **207** 200f. blue and green . . . 70 45

208 "The Visitation" (Ghirlandaio)

1975. Air. Christmas. Religious Paintings.
516 290f. Type **208** . . . . 1·40 55
517 300f. "Nativity" (Fra Filippo Lippi School) . . . . . . 1·40 65
518 370f. "Adoration of the Magi" (Velasquez) . . . . 1·60 1·10

1975. Air. 50th Death Anniv of Clement Ader (aviation pioneer). As T **198**.
519 100f. purple, red and blue . . 55 20

209 Concorde in Flight

1976. Air. Concorde's First Commercial Flight.
520 **209** 500f. multicoloured . . . 3·75 1·50

210 Figure-Skating

211 Alexander Graham Bell

1976. Air. Winter Olympic Games, Innsbruck. Multicoloured.
521 120f. Type **210** 50 25
522 420f. Ski-jumping . . . . . 1·50 65
523 430f. Skiing (slalom) . . . . 1·50 75

1976. Telephone Centenary.
524 **211** 180f. blue, brown and light brown 65 35

212 Chameleon

1976. Reptiles. Multicoloured.
525 20f. Type **212** 20 15
526 30f. Lizard 30 15
527 40f. Tortoise 35 20
528 90f. Python 75 25
529 120f. Crocodile . . . . . . 1·25 50

213 Nurse and Patient

1976. Air. World Health Day.
530 **213** 130f. multicoloured . . . 55 25

214 Dr. Adenauer and Cologne Cathedral

1976. Birth Centenary Dr. Konrad Adenauer.
531 **214** 180f. purple and brown 90 40

215 Constructing Orbital Space Station

1976. Air. "The Future in Space".
532 **215** 300f. deep blue, blue and orange . . . . 1·25 60
533 – 400f. blue, red and purple 1·90 90
DESIGN: 400f. Sun and space-ship with solar batteries.

216 American Bald Eagle and Liberty Bell

1976. Air. American Revolution Bicentenary and "Interphil '76" Int Stamp Exn, Philadelphia.
534 **216** 100f. blue, purple & black 70 20
535 – 400f. brown, blue & black 2·50 85
536 – 440f. violet, green & black 2·00 85
DESIGNS—HORIZ: 400f. Warships and American bald eagle. VERT: 440f. Red Indians and American bald eagle.

217 Running

1976. Air. Olympic Games, Montreal.
537 **217** 200f. black, brown and red 70 40
538 – 250f. brown, green & blue 80 50
539 – 300f. black, blue and green . . . . 1·25 60
540 – 400f. black, blue and green . . . . 1·60 90
DESIGNS: 250f. Swimming; 300f. Handball; 440f. Football.

218 Scouts marching

1976. Air. 1st All-African Scout Jamboree, Nigeria.
541 **218** 140f. brown, blue & green 70 35
542 – 180f. brown, green & grey 1·00 40
543 – 200f. violet and brown . . 1·10 50
DESIGNS—HORIZ: 180f. Scouts tending calf. VERT: 200f. Scout surveying camp at dusk.

1976. Fishes (2nd series). As T **196**.
544 100f. black and blue 80 25
545 120f. yellow, brown and green 90 35
546 130f. turquoise, brown & black . . . . 1·10 35
547 150f. yellow, drab and green 1·25 45
548 220f. black, green and brown 2·10 80
DESIGNS: 100f. African bonytongue; 120f. Budgett's upsidedown catfish; 130f. Double-dorsal catfish; 150f. Monod's tilapia; 220f. Big-scaled tetra.

220 Scenes from Children's Book

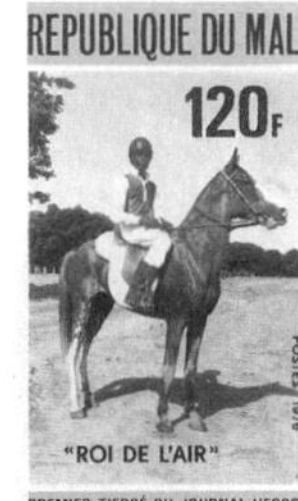

221 "Roi de L'Air"

1976. Literature for Children.
549 **220** 130f. grey, green and red 45 25

1976. 1st Issue of "L'Essor" Newspaper.
550 **221** 120f. multicoloured . . . 1·00 30

222 Fall from Scaffolding

1976. 20th Anniv of National Social Insurance.
551 **222** 120f. multicoloured . . . 35 25

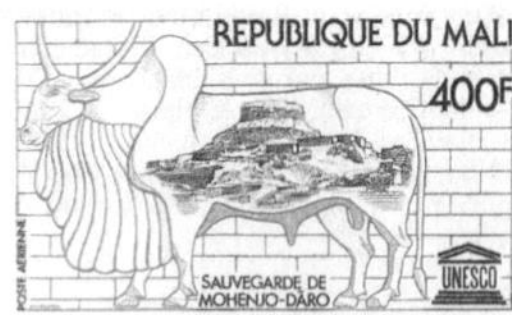

223 Moenjodaro

1976. Air. U.N.E.S.C.O. "Save Moenjodaro" (Pakistan) Campaign.
552 **223** 400f. purple, blue & black . . . 1·75 80
553 – 500f. red, yellow and blue . . . 2·00 1·25
DESIGN: 500f. Effigy, animals and remains.

224 Freighter, Vickers Viscount 800 and Map

1976. Air. Europafrique.
554 **224** 200f. purple and blue . . 1·10 45

225 Cascade of Letters

1976. 25th Anniv of U.N. Postal Administration.
555 **225** 120f. orange, green & lilac 45 25

226 Moto Guzzi "254" (Italy)

1976. Motorcycling.
556 **226** 90f. red, grey and brown 45 20
557 – 120f. violet, blue and black 55 25
558 – 130f. red, grey and green 70 25
559 – 140f. blue, green and grey 90 30
DESIGNS: 120f. B.M.W. "900" (Germany); 130f. Honda "Egli" (Japan); 140f. Motobecane "LT3" (France).

227 "The Nativity" (Taddeo Gaddi)

1976. Air. Christmas. Religious Paintings. Mult.
560 280f. Type **227** . . . . 1·25 50
561 300f. "Adoration of the Magi" (Hans Memling) . . 1·40 60
562 320f. "The Nativity" (Carlo Crivelli) . . . . 1·50 75

228 Muscat Fishing Boat

1976. Ships.
563 **228** 160f. purple, green & blue 75 30
564 – 180f. green, red and blue 75 35
565 – 190f. purple, blue & green 80 40
566 – 200f. green, red and blue 85 40
DESIGNS: 180f. Cochin Chinese junk; 190f. Dunkirk lightship "Ruytingen"; 200f. Nile felucca.

229 Rocket in Flight

1976. Air. Operation "Viking".
567 **229** 500f. blue, red and lake 1·75 1·25
568 – 1000f. lake, blue and deep blue . . . . 3·00 1·90
DESIGN: 1000f. Spacecraft on Mars.

230 Pres. Giscard d'Estaing and Sankore Mosque, Timbuktu

1977. Air. Visit of Pres. Giscard d'Estaing of France.
570 **230** 430f. multicoloured . . . 2·00 80

231 Rocket on Launch-pad, Newton and Apple

1977. Air. 250th Death Anniv of Isaac Newton.
571 **231** 400f. purple, red and green . . . . 2·00 75

232 Prince Philip and Queen Elizabeth II

1977. Air. "Personalities of Decolonization". Mult.
572 180f. Type **232** 65 35
573 200f. General De Gaulle (vert) . . . . 1·10 50
574 250f. Queen Wilhelmina of the Netherlands (vert) . . . 75 55
575 300f. King Baudouin and Queen Fabiola of Belgium 1·10 70
576 480f. Crowning of Queen Elizabeth II (vert) . . . . 2·00 1·25

233 Lindbergh and "Spirit of St. Louis"

1977. Air. 50th Anniv of Lindbergh's Transatlantic Flight.
577 **233** 420f. orange and violet . . 1·90 85
578 – 430f. blue, orange & green 1·90 85
DESIGN: 430f. "Spirit of St. Louis" crossing the Atlantic.

234 Village Indigobird

236 Printed Circuit

235 Louis Braille and Hands reading Book

1977. Mali Birds. Multicoloured.
579 15f. Type **234** 45 10
580 25f. Yellow-breasted barbet 75 10
581 30f. Vitelline masked weaver 75 25
582 40f. Carmine bee eater . . . 1·00 35
583 50f. Senegal parrot . . . . . 1·00 35

1977. 125th Death Anniv of Louis Braille (inventor of "Braille" system of reading and writing for the blind).
584 **235** 200f. blue, red and green 1·10 45

1977. World Telecommunications Day.
585 **236** 120f. red and brown . . . 35 20

236a Chateau Sassenage, Grenoble

1977. Air. 10th Anniv of International French Language Council.
586 **236a** 300f. multicoloured . . . 1·00 50

237 Airship LZ-1 over Lake Constance

1977. Air. History of the Zeppelin.
587 **237** 120f. green, brown & blue 55 25
588 – 130f. deep blue, brown and blue 65 25
589 – 350f. red, blue and deep blue . . . . 1·75 75
590 – 500f. deep blue, green and blue . . . . 2·50 95
DESIGNS: 130f. "Graf Zeppelin" over Atlantic; 350f. Burning of "Hindenburg" at Lakehurst; 500f. Count Ferdinand von Zeppelin and "Graf Zeppelin" at mooring mast.

238 "Anaz imperator"

1977. Insects. Multicoloured.
591 5f. Type **238** 20 15
592 10f. "Sphadromantis viridis" 25 15
593 20f. "Vespa tropica" 25 15
594 35f. "Melolontha melolantha" 30 15
595 60f. Stag beetle 55 20

239 Knight and Rook

1977. Chess Pieces.
596 **239** 120f. black, green & brn 1·10 30
597 – 130f. green, red and black 1·25 30
598 – 300f. green, red and blue 2·75 75
DESIGNS—VERT: 130f. Pawn and Bishop. HORIZ: 300f. King and Queen.

240 Henri Dunant

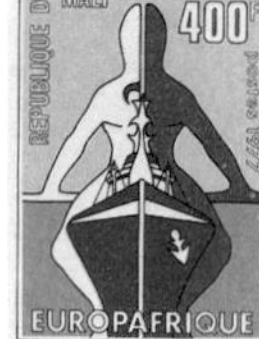

241 Ship

1977. Air. Nobel Peace Prize Winners. Multicoloured.
599 600f. Type **240** (founder of Red Cross) . . . . 2·00 1·00
600 700f. Martin Luther King . . 2·25 1·10

1977. Europafrique.
601 **241** 400f. multicoloured . . . 1·25 75

242 "Head of Horse"

1977. 525th Birth Anniv of Leonardo da Vinci.
602 **242** 200f. brown and black . . 75 50
603 – 300f. brown . . . . . . 1·10 60
604 – 500f. red . . . . 2·00 85
DESIGNS: 300f. "Head of Young Girl"; 500f. Self-portrait.

243 Footballers

245 Dome of the Rock

244 Friendship Hotel

1977. Air. Football Cup Elimination Rounds.
605 – 180f. brown, green & orge 50 30
606 **243** 200f. brown, green & orge 60 35
607 – 420f. grey, green and lilac 1·25 70
DESIGNS—HORIZ: 180f. Two footballers; 420f. Tackling.

1977. Inauguration of Friendship Hotel, Bamako.
608 **244** 120f. multicoloured . . . 35 25

1977. Palestinian Welfare.
609 **245** 120f. multicoloured . . . 55 20
610 180f. multicoloured . . . 70 30

246 Mao Tse-tung and "Comatex" Hall, Bamako

1977. Air. Mao Tse-tung Memorial.
611 **246** 300f. red . . . . 1·25 50

1977. Air. First Commercial Paris–New York Flight by Concorde. Optd **PARIS NEW - YORK 22.11.77.**
612 **209** 500f. multicoloured . . . 7·00 4·50

248 "Adoration of the Magi" (Rubens)

1977. Air. Christmas. Details from "Adoration of the Magi" by Rubens.
613 **248** 400f. multicoloured . . . 1·25 75
614 – 500f. multicoloured . . . 1·60 95
615 – 600f. multicoloured (horiz) 2·00 1·10

249 "Hercules and the Nemean Lion"

1978. 400th Birth Anniv of Peter Paul Rubens. Multicoloured.
616 200f. "Battle of the Amazons" (horiz) 70 35
617 300f. "Return from Labour in the Fields" (horiz) . . . 1·00 55
618 500f. Type **249** . . . . 1·75 95

250 Schubert and Mute Swans

1978. Air. 150th Death Anniv of Franz Schubert (composer). Multicoloured.
619 300f. Schubert and bars of music (vert) . . . . 1·75 60
620 420f. Type **250** . . . . 2·00 85

251 Cook and Shipboard Scene

1978. Air. 250th Birth Anniv of Captain James Cook.
621 **251** 200f. blue, red and violet 1·50 40
622 – 300f. brown, blue & green 3·00 70
DESIGN: 300f. Capt. Cook meeting natives.

252 African and Chained Building

1978. World Anti-Apartheid Year.
623 **252** 120f. violet, brown & blue 40 20
624 – 130f. violet, blue & orange 40 20
625 – 180f. brown, pur & orge 60 30
DESIGNS: 130f. Statue of Liberty and Africans walking to open door; 180f. African children and mule in fenced enclosure.

253 Players and Ball

1978. Air. World Cup Football Championship, Argentina.
626 **253** 150f. red, green and brown 60 30
627 – 250f. red, brown and green . . . . 1·25 45
628 – 300f. red, brown and blue 1·50 50
DESIGNS—VERT: 250f. HORIZ: 300f. Different football scenes.

254 "Head of Christ"

1978. Air. Easter. Works by Durer.
630 **254** 420f. green and brown . . 1·60 75
631 – 430f. blue and brown . . 1·60 75
DESIGN: 430f. "The Resurrection".

255 Red-cheeked Cordon-bleu

1978. Birds. Multicoloured.
632 20f. Type **255** 10 10
633 30f. Masked fire finch 45 10
634 50f. Red-billed fire finch . . . 55 20
635 70f. African collared dove . . 1·00 20
636 80f. White-billed buffalo weaver . . . . 1·40 35

256 C-3 "Trefle"

1978. Air. Birth Centenary of Andre Citroen (automobile pioneer).
637 **256** 120f. brown, lake & green 70 20
638 – 130f. grey, orange and blue 85 25
639 – 180f. blue, green and red 1·25 30
640 – 200f. black, red and lake 1·50 40
DESIGNS: 130f. B-2 "Croisiere Noir" track-laying vehicle, 1924; 180f. B-14 G Saloon, 1927; 200f. Model-11 front-wheel drive car, 1934.

1978. 20th Anniv of Bamako Lions Club. Nos. 473/4 surch **XXe ANNIVERSAIRE DU LIONS CLUB DE BAMAKO 1958-1978** and value.
641 120f. on 90f. Type **192** . . . 45 20
642 130f. on 100f. View of Samanko 55 30

258 Names of 1978 U.P.U. members forming Map of the World

1978. Centenary of U.P.U. Foundation Congress, Paris.
643 **258** 120f. green, orange & mve 45 20
644 – 130f. yellow, red and green 45 20
DESIGN: 130f. Names of 1878 member states across globe.

259 Desert Scene

1978. Campaign against Desertification.
645 **259** 200f. multicoloured . . . 70 35

260 Mahatma Gandhi **262** Dominoes

261 "Dermestes bromius"

1978. 30th Anniv of Gandhi's Assassination.
646 **260** 140f. brown, red and black 85 30

1978. Insects. Multicoloured.
647 15f. Type **261** 20 15
648 25f. "Calosoma sp." 25 15
649 90f. "Lopocerus variegatus" . . 45 20
650 120f. "Coccinella septempunctata" 55 25
651 140f. "Goliathus giganteus" 70 30

1978. Social Games.
652 **262** 100f. black, green and red 40 20
653 – 130f. red, black and blue 85 25
DESIGN: 130f. Bridge hand.

263 Ostrich on Nest (Syrian Manuscript)

1978. Air. Europafrique. Multicoloured.
654 100f. Type **263** 80 25
655 110f. Common zebra (Mansur miniature) 50 30

1978. Air. World Cup Football Championship Finalists. Nos. 626/8 optd with results.
656 **253** 150f. red, green and brown 60 25
657 – 250f. red, brown and green . . . . 1·00 45
658 – 300f. red, brown and blue 1·25 60
OPTS: 150f. **CHAMPION 1978 ARGENTINE**; 250f. **2e HOLLANDE**; 300f. **3e BRESIL 4e ITALIE**.

265 Coronation Coach

1978. Air. 25th Anniv of Coronation of Queen Elizabeth II. Multicoloured.
660 500f. Type **265** . . . . 1·50 70
661 1000f. Queen Elizabeth II . . 2·75 1·40

266 Aristotle and African Animals

1978. 2300th Death Anniv of Aristotle (Greek philosopher).
662 **266** 200f. brown, red and green 90 35

267 Douglas DC-3 and U.S.A. 1918 24c. stamp

1978. Air. History of Aviation.
663 **267** 80f. deep blue, red & blue 35 15
664 – 100f. multicoloured . . . 50 20
665 – 120f. black, blue and red 60 25
666 – 130f. green, red and black 65 30
667 – 320f. violet, blue and red 1·50 65
DESIGNS: 100f. Stampe and Renard SV-4 and Belgium Balloon stamp of 1932; 120f. Clement Ader's Avion III and France Concorde stamp of 1976; 130f. Junkers Ju-52/3m and Germany Biplane stamp of 1919; 320f. Mitsubishi A6M Zero-Sen and Japan Pagoda stamp of 1951.

268 "The Annunciation"

1978. Air. Christmas. Works by Durer.
668 **268** 420f. brown and black . . 1·25 60
669 – 430f. brown and green . . 1·25 60
670 – 500f. black and brown . . 1·60 75
DESIGNS: 430f. "Virgin and Child"; 500f. "Adoration of the Magi".

269 Launch of "Apollo 8" and Moon

1978. Air. 10th Anniv of First Manned Flight around the Moon.
671 **269** 200f. red, green and violet 60 30
672 – 300f. violet, green and red 1·10 50
DESIGN: 300f. "Apollo 8" in orbit around the Moon.

270 U.N. and Human Rights Emblems

1978. 30th Anniv of Declaration of Human Rights.
673 **270** 180f. red, blue and brown 60 35

271 Concorde and Clement Ader's "Eole"

1979. Air. 3rd Anniv of First Commercial Concorde Flight. Multicoloured.
674 120f. Type **271** 70 25
675 130f. Concorde and Wright Flyer I 85 30
676 200f. Concorde and "Spirit of St. Louis" . . . . 1·40 45

1979. Air. "Philexafrique" Stamp Exhibition, Libreville, Gabon (1st issue) and International Stamp Fair, Essen, West Germany. As T **262** of Niger. Multicoloured.
677 200f. Ruff (bird) and Lubeck 1859 ½s. stamp . . . . . . 2·00 90
678 200f. Dromedary and Mali 1965 200f. stamp . . . . . 3·00 1·75
See also Nos. 704/5.

1979. Air. Birth Centenary of Albert Einstein (physicist). No. 492 surch **"1879-1979" 130F**.
679 **198** 130f. on 90f. blue, purple and brown 55 30

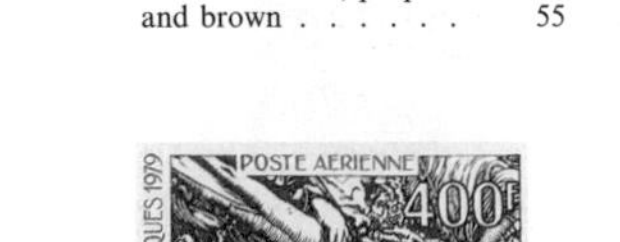

273 "Christ carrying the Cross"

1979. Air. Easter. Works by Durer.
680 **273** 400f. black and turquoise 1·40 60
681 – 430f. black and red . . . 1·40 60
682 – 480f. black and blue . . . 1·60 1·00
DESIGNS: 430f. "Christ on the Cross"; 480f. "The Great Lamentation".

274 Basketball and St. Basil's Cathedral, Moscow
275 African Manatee

1979. Air. Pre-Olympic Year. Multicoloured.
683 420f. Type **274** . . . . 1·50 75
684 430f. Footballer and Kremlin 1·50 75

1979. Endangered Animals. Multicoloured.
685 100f. Type **275** 45 20
686 120f. Chimpanzee 65 30
687 130f. Topi 75 35
688 180f. Gemsbok 90 40
689 200f. Giant eland . . . . . 1·00 55

276 Child and I.Y.C. Emblem

1979. International Year of the Child.
690 **276** 120f. green, red and brown 40 20
691 – 200f. purple and green . . 70 35
692 – 300f. brown, mauve and deep brown . . . . . 1·00 50
DESIGNS: 200f. Girl and scout with birds; 300f. Children with calf.

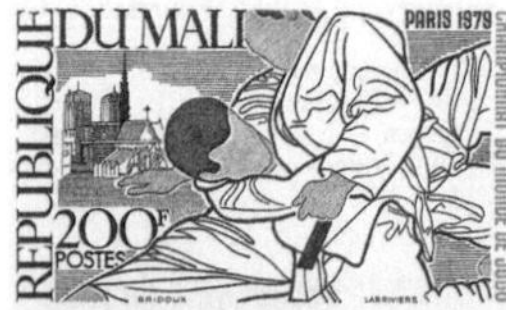

277 Judo

1979. World Judo Championships, Paris.
693 **277** 200f. sepia, red and ochre 80 40

278 Wave Pattern and Human Figures
279 Goat's Head and Lizard Fetishes

1979. World Telecommunications Day.
694 **278** 120f. multicoloured . . . 35 20

1979. World Museums Day. Multicoloured.
695 90f. Type **279** 30 15
696 120f. Seated figures (wood carving) 40 20
697 130f. Two animal heads and figurine (wood carving) . . 50 25

280 Rowland Hill and Mali 1961 25f. stamp
281 Cora Players

1979. Death Centenary of Sir Rowland Hill.
698 **280** 120f. multicoloured . . . 40 20
699 – 130f. red, blue and green 40 20
700 – 180f. black, green and blue 60 30
701 – 200f. black, red and purple 70 35
702 – 300f. blue, deep blue and red . . . . 1·25 50
DESIGNS: 130f. Airship "Graf Zeppelin" and Saxony stamp of 1850; 180f. Concorde and France stamp of 1849; 200f. Stage coach and U.S.A. stamp of 1849; 300f. U.P.U. emblem and Penny Black.

1979.
703 **281** 200f. multicoloured . . . 1·00 40

282 Sankore Mosque and "Adenium obesum"

1979. "Philexafrique" Exhibition, Libreville, Gabon (2nd issue).
704 **282** 120f. multicoloured . . . 90 55
705 – 300f. red, blue and orange 1·90 1·25
DESIGN: 300f. Horseman and satellite.

283 Map of Mali showing Conquest of Desert

1979. Operation "Sahel Vert". Multicoloured.
706 200f. Type **283** 70 30
707 300f. Planting a tree . . . . 1·10 50

284 Lemons
285 Sigmund Freud

1979. Fruit (1st series). Multicoloured.
708 10f. Type **284** 15 10
709 60f. Pineapple 30 15
710 100f. Papaw 50 15
711 120f. Sweet-sops 55 20
712 130f. Mangoes 65 25
See also Nos. 777/81.

1979. 40th Death Anniv of Sigmund Freud (psychologist).
713 **285** 300f. sepia and violet . . 1·25 60

286 Caillie and Camel approaching Fort

1979. 180th Birth Anniv of Rene Caillie (explorer).
714 **286** 120f. sepia, brown & blue 50 20
715 – 130f. blue, green & brown 60 25
DESIGN: 130f. Rene Caillie and map of route across Sahara.

287 "Eurema brigitta"

1979. Butterflies and Moths (1st series). Mult.
716 100f. Type **287** 60 20
717 120f. "Papilio pylades" . . . 75 20
718 130f. "Melanitis leda satyridae" 90 40
719 180f. "Gonimbrasis belina occidentalis" . . . . 1·50 45
720 200f. "Bunaea alcinoe" . . . 1·75 50
See also Nos. 800/4.

288 Mali 1970 300f. Stamp and Modules orbiting Moon

1979. Air. 10th Anniv of First Moon Landing.
721 430f. Type **288** . . . . 1·40 60
722 500f. 1973 250f. stamp and rocket launch . . . . . . 1·60 95

289 Capt. Cook and H.M.S. "Resolution" off Kerguelen Islands

1979. Air. Death Bicent of Captain James Cook.
723 300f. Type **289** . . . . 1·75 80
724 400f. Capt. Cook and H.M.S. "Resolution" off Hawaii 2·50 1·10

290 Menaka Greyhound

1979. Dogs. Multicoloured.
725 20f. Type **290** 30 15
726 50f. Water spaniel 45 15
727 70f. Beagle 60 15
728 80f. Newfoundland 70 20
729 90f. Sheepdog 85 20

291 David Janowski

1979. Air. Chess Grand-masters.
730 **291** 100f. red and brown . . . 85 30
731 – 140f. red, brown and blue 1·25 30
732 – 200f. blue, violet and green . . . . 1·75 50
733 – 300f. brown, ochre and red . . . . 2·25 70
DESIGNS: 140f. Alexander Alekhine; 200f. Willi Schlage; 300f. Efim Bogoljubow.

292 "The Adoration of the Magi" 1511 (detail, Durer)

1979. Air. Christmas. Works by Durer.
734 **292** 300f. brown and orange 1·00 50
735 – 400f. brown and blue . . 1·25 75
736 – 500f. brown and green . . 1·60 95
DESIGNS: 400f. "Adoration of the Magi" (1503); 500f. "Adoration of the Magi" (1511, different).

1979. Air. 20th Anniv of ASECNA (African Air Safety Organization). As T **198** of Malagasy but 36 × 27 mm.
737 120f. multicoloured 40 20

293 Globe, Rotary Emblem and Diesel-electric Train

1980. Air. 75th Anniv of Rotary International. Multicoloured.
738 220f. Type **293** . . . . 2·75 80
739 250f. Globe, Rotary emblem and Douglas DC-10 airliner . . . . 1·00 45
740 430f. Bamako Rotary Club and emblem . . . . 1·40 75

294 African Ass
295 Speed Skating

1980. Protected Animals. Multicoloured.
741 90f. Type **294** 50 20
742 120f. Addax 60 20
743 130f. Cheetahs 75 35

744 140f. Barbary sheep 80 45
745 180f. African buffalo . . . . 1·00 50

1980. Air. Winter Olympic Games, Lake Placid. Multicoloured.
746 200f. Type **295** 70 30
747 300f. Ski jump . . . . 1·10 60

296 Stephenson's "Rocket" (1829) and Mali 30f. Stamp, 1972

1980. Air. 150th Anniv of Liverpool and Manchester Railway.
749 **296** 200f. blue, brown & green 1·25 45
750 – 300f. black, brown & turq 2·00 80
DESIGN: 300f. "Rocket" (1829) and Mali 50f. railway stamp, 1970.

297 Horse Jumping

1980. Air. Olympic Games, Moscow.
751 **297** 200f. green, brown & blue 70 30
752 – 300f. blue, brown & green 1·00 50
753 – 400f. red, green & lt green 1·50 75
DESIGN: 300f. Sailing. 400f. Football.

298 Solar Pumping Station, Koni

1980. Solar Energy. Multicoloured.
755 90f. Type **298** 30 15
756 100f. Solar capture tables, Dire 35 15
757 120f. Solar energy cooker . . 50 20
758 130f. Solar generating station, Dire 55 25

299 Nioro Horse

1980. Horses. Multicoloured.
759 100f. Mopti 50 15
760 120f. Type **299** 65 15
761 130f. Koro 75 20
762 180f. Lake zone horse . . . 90 35
763 200f. Banamba . . . . . . 1·10 40

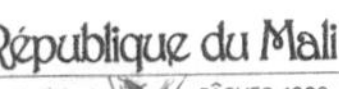

300 "Head of Christ" (Maurice Denis)

1980. Air. Easter.
764 **300** 480f. red and brown . . . 1·60 95
765 – 500f. brown and red . . . 1·60 95
DESIGN: 500f. "Christ before Pilate" (Durer).

301 Kepler and Diagram of Earth's Orbit

1980. Air. 350th Death Anniv of J. Kepler (astronomer).
766 **301** 200f. light blue, blue & red 80 35
767 – 300f. mauve, violet & grn 1·25 55
DESIGN: 300f. Kepler, Copernicus and diagram of solar system.

302 Pluto and Diagram of Orbit

1980. Air. 50th Anniv of Discovery of Planet Pluto.
768 **302** 402f. blue, grey and mauve . . . . 1·90 85

303 "Lunokhod 1" (10th Anniv)

1980. Air. Space Events.
769 **303** 480f. black, red and blue 1·75 85
770 – 500f. grey, blue and red 1·75 85
DESIGN: 500f. "Apollo"–"Soyuz" link-up.

304 Fleming and Laboratory

1980. Sir Alexander Fleming (discoverer of penicillin). Commemoration.
771 **304** 200f. green, sepia & brown . . . . 1·00 35

305 Avicenna, Medical Instruments and Herbs **306** Pilgrim at Mecca

1980. Birth Millenary of Avicenna (Arab physician and philosopher).
772 **305** 120f. blue, red and brown 40 20
773 – 180f. dp brn, turq & brn 60 25
DESIGN: 180f. Avicenna as teacher.

1980. 1400th Anniv of Hegira. Multicoloured.
774 120f. Type **306** 40 15
775 130f. Praying hands 40 20
776 180f. Pilgrims (horiz) 60 30

1980. Fruit (2nd series). As T **284**. Multicoloured.
777 90f. Guavas 45 20
778 120f. Cashews 50 20
779 130f. Oranges 65 25
780 140f. Bananas 75 25
781 180f. Grapefruit 90 35

307 Rochambeau and French Fleet at Rhode Island, 1780

1980. Air. French Support for American Independence.
782 **307** 420f. brown, turq & red 1·75 75
783 – 430f. black, blue and red 1·75 80
DESIGN: 430f. Rochambeau, Washington and Eagle.

308 Dove and U.N. Emblem

1980. 60th Anniv of League of Nations.
784 **308** 200f. blue, red and violet 60 35

309 Scene from "Around the World in 80 Days"

1980. Air. 75th Death Anniv of Jules Verne (writer).
785 **309** 100f. red, green and brown . . . . 10·00 2·75
786 – 100f. brown, chestnut and turquoise . . . . 1·75 30
787 – 150f. green, brn & dp brn 1·25 40
788 – 150f. blue, violet & dp bl 1·25 40
DESIGNS: No. 786, Concorde; No. 787, "From the Earth to the Moon"; No. 788, Astronaut on Moon.

310 Xylophone, Mask and Emblem

1980. 6th Arts and Cultural Festival, Bamako.
789 **310** 120f. multicoloured . . . 40 20

311 Map of Africa and Asia **313** Conference Emblem

1980. 25th Anniv of Afro-Asian Bandung Conference.
790 **311** 300f. green, red and blue 90 55

1980. Air. Olympic Medal Winners. Nos. 751/3 optd.
791 200f. green, brown and blue 70 35
792 300f. blue, brown and green 1·00 55
793 400f. red, green and light green . . . . 1·40 75
OVERPRINTS: 200f. **CONCOURS COMPLET INDIVIDUEL ROMAN (It.) BLINOV (Urss) SALNIKOV (Urss)**; 300f. **FINN RECHARDT (Fin.) MAYRHOFER (Autr.) BALACHOV (Urss)**; 400f. **TCHECOSLOVAQUIE ALLEMAGNE DE L'EST URSS**.

1980. World Tourism Conference, Manila. Mult.
795 120f. Type **313** 35 15
796 180f. Encampment outside fort and Conference emblem 50 30

314 Dam and Rural Scene

1980. 20th Anniv of Independence. Multicoloured.
797 100f. Type **314** 40 15
798 120f. National Assembly Building 40 20
799 130f. Independence Monument (vert) 45 25

1980. Butterflies. (2nd series). As T **287** but dated "1980". Multicoloured.
800 50f. "Uterheisa pulchella" (postage) 40 20
801 60f. "Mylothis chloris pieridae" 50 20
802 70f. "Hypolimnas mishippus" 60 20
803 80f. "Papilio demodocus" . . 75 20
804 420f. "Denaus chrysippus" (48 × 36 mm) (air) . . . . 2·50 1·25

315 Pistol firing Cigarette and Target over Lungs

1980. Anti-smoking Campaign.
805 **315** 200f. multicoloured . . . 75 35

316 Electric Train, Boeing 737 and Globe

1980. Europafrique.
806 **316** 300f. multicoloured . . . 3·75 85

317 Map of West Africa and Agricultural Symbols **318** Gen. de Gaulle and Map of France

1980. 5th Anniv of West African Economic Council. Multicoloured.
807 100f. Type **317** 35 15
808 120f. "Transport" . . . . . 2·50 85
809 130f. "Industry" 45 25
810 140f. "Energy" 50 25

1980. Air. 10th Death Anniv of Gen. Charles de Gaulle. Multicoloured.
811 420f. Type **318** . . . . 1·75 75
812 430f. De Gaulle and Cross of Lorraine . . . . 1·75 75

319 "Hikari" Express Train (Japan) and Mali 1972 10f. Stamp

1980. Air. Locomotives.
813 **319** 120f. blue, green and red 95 20
814 – 130f. green, blue and red 1·25 25
815 – 200f. orange, black & grn 1·60 40
816 – 480f. black, red and green 4·25 95
DESIGNS—HORIZ: 130f. RTG train, U.S.A. and 20f. locomotive stamp of 1970; 200f. "Rembrandt" express, Germany, and 100f. locomotive stamp of 1970. VERT: 480f. TGV 001 turbotrain, France, and 80f. locomotive stamp of 1970.

320 "Flight into Egypt" (Rembrandt)

1980. Air. Christmas. Multicoloured.
817 300f. "St. Joseph showing the infant Jesus to St. Catherine" (Lorenzo Lotto) (horiz) . . . . . . 1·00 55
818 400f. Type **320** . . . . 1·40 80
819 500f. "Christmas Night" (Gauguin) (horiz) . . . . 1·60 90

1980. 5th Anniv of African Posts and Telecommunications Union. As T **292** of Niger.
820 130f. multicoloured 40 20

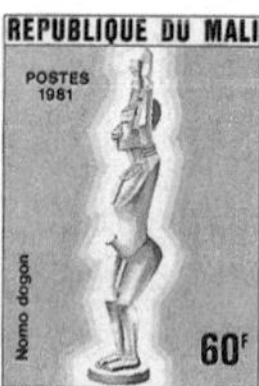

321 Nomo Dogon **323** Mambie Sidibe

322 "Self-portrait" (Blue Period)

1981. Statuettes. Multicoloured.
821 60f. Type **321** 20 15
822 70f. Senoufo fertility symbol 25 15
823 90f. Bamanan fertility statuette 35 15
824 100f. Senoufo captives snuff-box 40 15
825 120f. Dogon fertility statuette 50 20

1981. Birth Bicentenary of Pablo Picasso (artist).
826 **322** 1000f. multicoloured . . . 3·50 1·75

1981. Mali Thinkers and Savants.
827 **323** 120f. brown, buff and red 40 20
828 – 130f. brown, buff & black 40 25
DESIGN: 130f. Amadou Hampate Ba.

324 Mosque and Ka'aba **325** Tackle

1981. 1400th Anniv of Hejira.
829 **324** 120f. multicoloured . . . 40 20
830 180f. multicoloured . . . 60 30

1981. Air. World Cup Football Championship Eliminators. Multicoloured.
831 100f. Type **325** 40 20
832 200f. Heading the ball . . . 85 35
833 300f. Running for ball . . . 1·40 50

326 Kaarta Zebu **327** Crinum de Moore "Crinum moorei"

1981. Cattle. Multicoloured.
835 20f. Type **326** 15 15
836 30f. Peul du Macina sebu . . 15 15
837 40f. Maure zebu 25 15
838 80f. Touareg zebu 50 15
839 100f. N'Dama cow 60 20

1981. Flowers. Multicoloured.
840 50f. Type **327** 30 15
841 100f. Double rose hibiscus "Hibiscus rosa-sinensis" . . 80 15
842 120f. Pervenche "Catharanthus roseus" . . 90 20
843 130f. Frangipani "Plumeria rubra" 90 25
844 180f. Orgueil de Chine "Caesalpinia pulcherrima" 1·40 40

328 Mozart and Musical Instruments

1981. Air. 225th Birth Anniv of Mozart. Mult.
845 420f. Type **328** . . . . 2·00 85
846 430f. Mozart and musical instruments (different) . . 2·00 85

329 "The Fall on the Way to Calvary" (Raphael)

1981. Air. Easter.
847 500f. Type **329** . . . . 1·50 85
848 600f. "Ecce Homo" (Rembrandt) . . . . . . 2·00 1·25

330 Yuri Gagarin

1981. Air. Space Anniversaries and Events.
849 **330** 200f. blue, black and red 85 30
850 – 200f. blue, black & lt blue 85 30
851 – 380f. multicoloured . . . 1·40 55
852 – 430f. violet, black and blue . . . . 1·60 70
DESIGNS—VERT: No. 849, Type **330**: first man in space (20th anniv); No. 850, Alan Shepard, first American in space (20th anniv); No. 851, Saturn and moons (exploration of Saturn). HORIZ: No. 852, Sir William Herschel, and diagram of Uranus (discovery bicentenary).

331 Blind and Sighted Faces **332** Caduceus (Telecommunications and Health)

1981. International Year of Disabled People.
853 **331** 100f. light brown, brown and green 35 15
854 – 120f. violet, blue and purple 45 20
DESIGN: 120f. Mechanical hand and human hand with spanner.

1981. World Telecommunications Day.
855 **332** 130f. multicoloured . . . 40 25

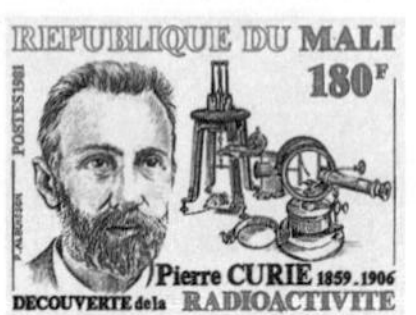

333 Pierre Curie and Instruments

1981. 75th Death Anniv of Pierre Curie (discoverer of radioactivity).
856 **333** 180f. blue, black & orange 90 30

334 Scouts at Well and Dorcas Gazelle

1981. 4th African Scouting Conference, Abidjan. Multicoloured.
857 110f. Type **334** 70 30
858 160f. Scouts signalling and patas monkey . . . . . . 1·25 60
859 300f. Scouts saluting and cheetah (vert) . . . . . . 1·75 85

1981. Air. World Railway Speed Record. No. 816 optd **26 fevrier 1981 Record du monde de vitesse–380 km/h.**
861 480f. black, red and blue . . 3·00 90

336 Columbus, Fleet and U.S. Columbus Stamp of 1892

1981. Air. 475th Death Anniv of Christopher Columbus.
862 **336** 180f. brown, black & blue 90 40
863 – 200f. green, blue & brown 1·10 40
864 – 260f. black, violet and red 1·60 60
865 – 300f. lilac, red and green 1·75 70
DESIGNS—VERT: 200f. "Nina" and 1c. Columbus stamp of Spain; 260f. "Pinta" and 5c. Columbus stamp of Spain. HORIZ: 300f. "Santa Maria" and U.S. 3c. Columbus stamp.

1981. 23rd World Scouting Conference, Dakar. Nos. 857/9 optd **DAKAR 8 AOUT 1981 28e CONFERENCE MONDIALE DU SCOUTISME.**
866 **334** 110f. multicoloured . . . 40 20
867 – 160f. multicoloured . . . 50 30
868 – 300f. multicoloured . . . 1·25 55

338 Space Shuttle after Launching

1981. Air. Space Shuttle. Multicoloured.
870 200f. Type **338** 90 30
871 500f. Space Shuttle in orbit 2·25 75
872 600f. Space Shuttle landing 2·50 1·25

339 "Harlequin on a Horse"

1981. Air. Birth Centenary of Pablo Picasso. Mult.
874 600f. Type **339** . . . . 2·75 1·25
875 750f. "Child with Pigeon" . . 3·25 1·40

340 Prince Charles, Lady Diana Spencer and St. Paul's Cathedral

1981. Air. British Royal Wedding. Multicoloured.
876 500f. Type **340** . . . . 1·25 75
877 700f. Prince Charles, Lady Diana Spencer and coach 1·75 1·10

342 Maure Sheep

1981. Sheep. Multicoloured.
886 10f. Type **342** 15 10
887 25f. Peul sheep 20 10
888 140f. Sahael sheep 50 25
889 180f. Touareg sheep 75 35
890 200f. Djallonke ram 85 35

343 Heinrich von Stephan (founder of U.P.U.), Latecoere 28 and Concorde

1981. Universal Postal Union Day.
891 **343** 400f. red and green . . . 1·60 70

344 Woman drinking from Bowl

1981. World Food Day.
892 **344** 200f. brown, orge & mve 65 30

345 "The Incarnation of the Son of God" (detail, Grunewald)

1981. Air. Christmas. Multicoloured.
893 500f. Type **345** . . . . 1·75 75
894 700f. "The Campori Madonna" (Correggio) . . 2·25 1·25

347 Transport and Hands holding Map of Europe and Africa

1981. Europafrique.
896 **347** 700f. blue, brown & orge 4·75 1·40

348 Guerin, Calmette, Syringe and Bacillus

1981. 60th Anniv of First B.C.G. Inoculation.
897 **348** 200f. brown, violet & blk 85 40

1982. Air. World Chess Championship, Merano. Nos. 731 and 733 optd.
898 140f. red, brown and blue . . 1·25 50
899 300f. brown, ochre and red 2·25 75
OPTS: 140f. **ANATOLI KARPOV VICTOR KORTCHNOI MERANO (ITALIE) Octobre-Novembre 1981**; 300f. **Octobre-Novembre 1981 ANATOLI KARPOV Champion du Monde 1981**.

350 "Nymphaea lotus"

1982. Flowers. Multicoloured.
900 170f. Type **350** 85 35
901 180f. "Bombax costatum" . . 90 35
902 200f. "Parkia biglobosa" . . 1·00 40
903 220f. "Gloriosa simplex" . . 1·25 45
904 270f. "Satanocrater berhautii" . . . . 1·40 50

351 Lewis Carroll and Characters from "Alice" Books

1982. Air. 150th Birth Anniv of Lewis Carroll (Revd. Charles Dodgson).
905 110f. Type **351** . . . . 1·00 25
906 130f. Characters from "Alice" books 75 30
907 140f. Characters from "Alice" books (different) 90 30

352 "George Washington" (Gilbert Stuart)

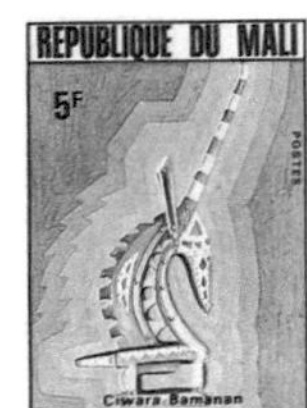

353 Ciwara Bamanan

1982. Air. 250th Birth Anniv of George Washington.
908 **352** 700f. multicoloured . . . 2·00 1·25

1982. Masks. Multicoloured.
909 5f. Type **353** 10 10
910 35f. Kanga Dogon 15 10
911 180f. N Domo Bamanan . . 1·00 40
912 200f. Cimier (Sogoninkum Bamanan) . . . . 1·00 40
913 250f. Kpelie Senoufo . . . . 1·10 45

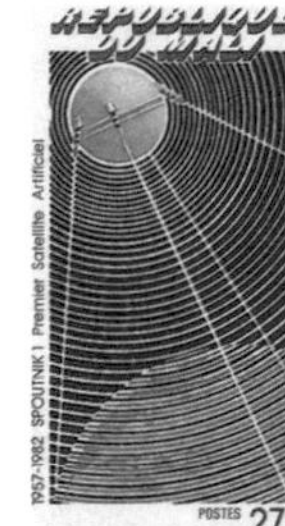

354 Football **355** "Sputnik 1"

1982. Air. World Cup Football Championship, Spain.
914 **354** 220f. multicoloured . . . 80 45
915 – 420f. multicoloured . . . 1·50 90
916 – 500f. multicoloured . . . 1·75 90
DESIGNS: 420f., 500f. Football scenes.

1982. 25th Anniv of First Artificial Satellite.
918 **355** 270f. violet, blue and red 1·25 50

356 Lord Baden-Powell, Tent and Scout Badge

1982. Air. 125th Birth Anniv of Lord Baden-Powell.
919 300f. Type **356** . . . . 1·50 50
920 500f. Saluting scout . . . . 2·25 90

357 "The Transfiguration" (Fra Angelico)

1982. Air. Easter. Multicoloured.
921 680f. Type **357** . . . . 2·00 1·25
922 1000f. "Pieta" (Giovanni Bellini) . . . . 3·00 1·90

358 Doctor giving Child Oral Vaccine **360** "En Bon Ami" (N'Teri)

359 Lions Emblem and Blind Person

1982. Anti-polio Campaign.
923 **358** 180f. multicoloured . . . 80 35

1982. Lions Club Blind Day.
924 **359** 260f. orange, blue and red 1·25 50

1982. Hairstyles. Multicoloured.
925 140f. Type **360** 35 30
926 150f. Tucked-in pony tail . . 60 35
927 160f. "Pour l'Art" 70 45
928 180f. "Bozo Kun" 75 50
929 270f. "Fulaw Kun" . . . . . 1·25 60

361 Arms Stamp of Mali and France

1982. Air. "Philexfrance 82" International Stamp Exhibition, Paris. Multicoloured.
930 180f. Type **361** 60 35
931 200f. Dromedary caravan and 1979 "Philexafrique II" stamp . . . . 1·00 40

362 Fire-engine, 1850

1982. Fire-engines. Multicoloured.
932 180f. Type **362** 95 35
933 200f. Fire-engine, 1921 . . . 1·40 40
934 270f. Fire-engine, 1982 . . . 1·60 50

363 Gobra

1982. Zebu Cattle. Multicoloured.
935 10f. Type **363** 10 10
936 60f. Azaouak 25 15
937 110f. Maure 35 25
938 180f. Toronke 65 35
939 200f. Peul Sambourou . . . 75 40

1982. Air. World Cup Football Championship Winners. Nos. 914/16 optd.
940 **354** 220f. multicoloured . . . 75 45
941 – 420f. multicoloured . . . 1·50 90
942 – 500f. multicoloured . . . 1·75 90
OPTS: 220f. **1 ITALIE 2 RFA 3 POLOGNE**; 420f. **POLOGNE FRANCE 3-2**; 500f. **ITALIE RFA 3-1**.

365 "Urchin with Cherries"

1982. Air. 150th Birth Anniv of Edouard Manet (painter).
944 **365** 680f. multicoloured . . . 2·75 1·25

366 "Virgin and Child" (detail) (Titian)

1982. Air. Christmas. Multicoloured.
945 500f. Type **366** . . . . 1·50 90
946 1000f. "Virgin and Child" (Giovanni Bellini) . . . . 2·75 1·90

367 Wind-surfing **368** Goethe

1982. Introduction of Wind-surfing as Olympic Event. Multicoloured.
947 200f. Type **367** 80 45
948 270f. Wind-surfer . . . . . 1·25 55
949 300f. Wind-surfer (different) 1·40 55

1982. Air. 150th Death Anniv of Goethe (poet).
950 **368** 500f. brown, light brown and black . . . . . . 2·00 90

369 Valentina Tereshkova **370** Transatlantic Balloon "Double Eagle II"

1983. Air. 20th Anniv of Launching of Vostok VI.
951 **369** 400f. multicoloured . . . 1·25 75

1983. Air. Bicentenary of Manned Flight. Mult.
952 500f. Type **370** . . . . 2·00 90
953 700f. Montgolfier balloon . . 2·50 1·25

371 Football

1983. Air. Olympic Games, Los Angeles. Mult.
954 180f. Type **371** 50 30
955 270f. Hurdles 75 40
956 300f. Windsurfing . . . . . 1·10 55

372 "The Transfiguration" (detail)

1983. Air. Easter. Multicoloured.
957 400f. Type **372** . . . . 1·25 75
958 600f. "The Entombment" (detail from Baglioni Retable) . . . . 2·00 1·10

373 Martin Luther King **374** Oua Hairstyle

1983. Celebrities.
959 **373** 800f. brown, blue & pur . . 2·50 1·40
960 – 800f. brown, red & dp red . . 3·00 1·25
DESIGN: No. 960, President Kennedy.

1983. Hairstyles. Multicoloured.
961 180f. Type **374** 60 30
962 200f. Nation (Diamani) . . . 70 30
963 270f. Rond Point 90 40
964 300f. Naamu-Naamu . . . . 1·00 45
965 500f. Bamba-Bamba . . . . 2·50 1·40

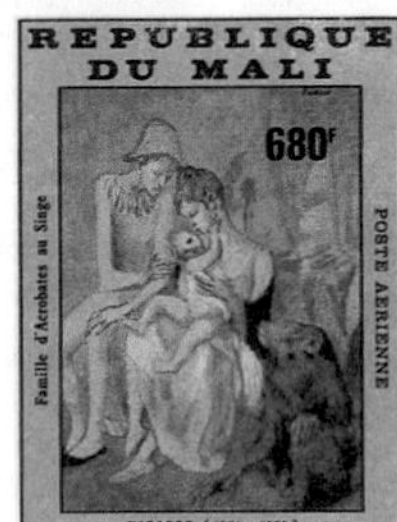

375 "Family of Acrobats with Monkey"

1983. Air. 10th Death Anniv of Picasso.
966 **375** 680f. multicoloured . . . 2·00 1·25

376 Lions Club Emblem and Lions

1983. Air. Lions and Rotary Clubs. Mult.
967 700f. Type **376** . . . . 2·25 2·00
968 700f. Rotary Club emblem, container ship, diesel railcar and Boeing 737 airliner . . . . 6·75 2·25

377 Satellite, Antenna and Telephone

1983. World Communications Year.
969 **377** 180f. multicoloured . . . 55 30

378 Lavoisier and Apparatus **379** Banzoumana Sissoko

1983. Bicent of Lavoisier's Analysis of Water.
970 **378** 300f. green, brown & blue 1·10 50

1983. Mali Musicians. Multicoloured.
971 200f. Type **379** . . . . 1·00 30
972 300f. Batourou Sekou Kouyate . . . . 1·50 45

380 Nicephore Niepce and Camera **381** Space Shuttle "Challenger"

1983. 150th Death Anniv of Nicephore Niepce (pioneer of photography).
973 **380** 400f. blue, green & dp grn 1·75 65

1983. Air. Space Shuttle.
974 **381** 1000f. multicoloured . . . 3·25 1·75

382 Young People and Map of Africa

1983. 2nd Pan-African Youth Festival. Mult.
975 240f. Type **382** 75 40
976 270f. Hands reaching for map of Africa 75 40

383 Mercedes, 1914

1983. Air. Paris–Dakar Rally. Multicoloured.
977 240f. Type **383** . . . . . . 1·40 40
978 270f. Mercedes SSK, 1929 . . 1·50 50
979 500f. Mercedes W 196, 1954 2·50 80

384 Liner and U.P.U. Emblem **385** Pawn and Bishop

1983. U.P.U. Day.
981 **384** 240f. red, black and blue 1·50 50

1983. Air. Chess Pieces.
982 **385** 300f. grey, violet and green . . . . 2·00 60
983 – 420f. green, pink and grey 2·50 85
984 – 500f. blue, dp blue & green . . . . 3·25 1·00
DESIGNS: 420f. Rook and knight; 500f. King and queen.

386 "Canigiani Madonna"

1983. Air. Christmas. 500th Birth Anniv of Raphael. Multicoloured.
986 700f. Type **386** . . . . 2·00 1·00
987 800f. "Madonna of the Lamb" . . . . 2·25 1·25

387 Sahara Goat

1984. Goats. Multicoloured.
988 20f. Type **387** 15 10
989 30f. Billy goat 20 10
990 50f. Billy goat (different) . . 25 15
991 240f. Kaarta goat . . . . . 1·00 40
992 350f. Southern goat . . . . 1·40 75

388 "Leopold Zborowski" (Modigliani)

1984. Air. Birth Centenary of Modigliani (painter).
993 **388** 700f. multicoloured . . . 2·75 1·25

389 Henri Dunant (founder of Red Cross) **390** Sidney Bechet

1984. Air. Celebrities.
994 **389** 400f. deep blue, red & blue . . . . 1·50 65
995 – 540f. deep blue, red & blue . . . . 1·60 85
DESIGN: 540f. Abraham Lincoln.

1984. Air. Jazz Musicians. Multicoloured.
996 470f. Type **390** . . . . 2·50 75
997 500f. Duke Ellington . . . . 2·50 80

391 Microlight Aircraft

1984. Air. Microlight Aircraft. Multicoloured.
998 270f. Type **391** . . . . 1·10 40
999 350f. Lazor Gemini motorized hang-glider . . . 1·40 55

392 Weightlifting

1984. Air. Olympic Games, Los Angeles. Multicoloured.
1000 265f. Type **392** 75 40
1001 440f. Show jumping 90 70
1002 500f. Hurdles . . . . 1·10 80

393 "Crucifixion" (Rubens)

1984. Air. Easter.
1004 **393** 940f. brown & dp brown 3·00 1·50
1005 – 970f. brown and red . . 3·00 1·50
DESIGN—HORIZ: 970f. "The Resurrection" (Mantegna).

1984. Currency revaluation. Various stamps surch. (i) U.P.U. Day (No. 981).
1006 **384** 120f. on 240f. red, black and blue (postage) . . 1·10 50

(ii) Goats (Nos. 988/92)
1007 **387** 10f. on 20f. mult 10 10
1008 – 15f. on 30f. mult 15 10
1009 – 25f. on 50f. mult 20 15
1010 – 125f. on 240f. mult . . . 95 40
1011 – 175f. on 350f. mult . . . 1·75 65

(iii) Paris–Dakar Rally (No. 977)
1012 **383** 120f. on 240f. mult (air) 1·25 40

395 Mercedes "Simplex"

1984. Air. 150th Birth Anniv of Gottlieb Daimler (motor car designer).
1035 **395** 350f. olive, blue and mauve . . . . 2·50 1·10
1036 – 470f. green, violet and plum . . . . 3·25 1·50
1037 – 485f. blue, violet and plum . . . . 3·50 1·75
DESIGNS: 470f. Mercedes-Benz Type "370 S"; 485f. Mercedes-Benz "500 S EC".

396 Farm Workers

1984. Progress in Countryside and Protected Essences. Multicoloured.
1038 5f. Type **396** 10 10
1039 90f. Carpentry 60 30
1040 100f. Tapestry making . . . 70 35
1041 135f. Metal work 80 40
1042 515f. "Borassus flabelifer" 3·25 1·90
1043 1225f. "Vitelaria paradoxa" 7·50 3·75

397 Emblem and Child

1984. United Nations Children's Fund.
1044 **397** 120f. red, brown and green 80 40
1045 – 135f. red, blue and brown 90 50
DESIGN: 135f. Emblem and two children.

398 U.P.U. Emblem, Anchor and Hamburg

1984. Universal Postal Union Congress, Hamburg.
1046 **398** 135f. mauve, green and blue 80 40

1984. Air. Olympic Winners, Los Angeles. No. 1000/1002 optd.
1047 135f. on 265f. Optd **HALTERES 56 KGS / 1. WU (CHINE). 2. LAI (CHINE). 3. KOTAKA (JAPON)** 80 40
1048 220f. on 440f. Optd **DRESSAGE / PAR EQUIPES / 1. RFA 2. SUISSE / 3. SUEDE** . . 1·10 75
1049 250f. on 500f. Optd **ATHLETISME 3000 METRES STEEPLE / 1. KORIR (KENYA). / 2. MAHMOUD (FRANCE). / 3. DIEMER (E-U)** . . . 1·40 1·00

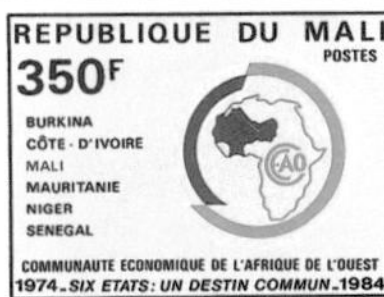

400 Emblem

1984. 10th Anniv of Economic Community of West Africa.
1051 **400** 350f. multicoloured . . . 1·75 1·10

401 Dimetrodon

1984. Prehistoric Animals. Multicoloured.
1052 10f. Type **401** 15 15
1053 25f. Iguanodon (vert) . . . 25 15
1054 30f. Archaeopteryx (vert) . . 35 10
1055 120f. Type **401** . . . . . . 1·50 45
1056 175f. As No. 1053 . . . . . 1·75 70
1057 350f. As No. 1054 . . . . . 3·25 95
1058 470f. Triceratops . . . . . 5·00 2·50

402 "Virgin and Child between St. Joseph and St. Jerome" (detail, Lorenzo Lotto)

1984. Air. Christmas.
1059 **402** 500f. multicoloured . . . 3·00 1·60

1984. Drought Aid. No. 758 surch.
1060 **298** 470f. on 130f. mult . . . 2·75 1·75

404 Horse Galloping

405 "Clitocybe nebularis"

1985. Horses. Multicoloured.
1061 90f. Type **404** 70 35
1062 135f. Beledougou horse . . 1·25 40
1063 190f. Nara horse . . . . . 1·50 70
1064 530f. Trait horse . . . . . 4·50 2·00

1985. Fungi. Multicoloured.
1065 120f. Type **405** . . . . . . 1·75 65
1066 200f. "Lepiota cortinarius" 2·40 1·00
1067 485f. "Agaricus semotus" 6·00 2·40
1068 525f. "Lepiota procera" . . 6·50 2·75

406 Emile Marchoux and Marchoux Institute

1985. Health. Multicoloured.
1069 120f. Type **406** (World Lepers' Day and 40th anniv of Marchoux Institute) (postage) . . . 80 30
1070 135f. Lions' emblem and Samanto Village (15th anniv) 85 35
1071 470f. Laboratory technicians and polio victim (anti-polio campaign) (air) . . 3·50 1·50

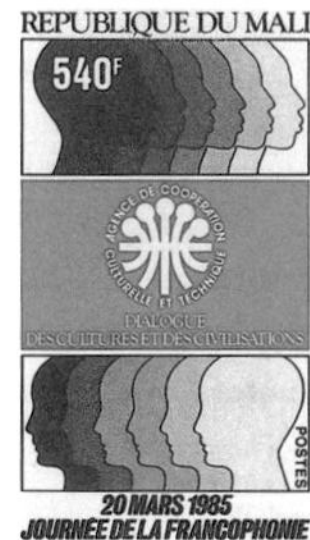

407 Profiles and Emblem

1985. 15th Anniv of Technical and Cultural Co-operation Agency.
1072 **407** 540f. green and brown 3·50 1·90

408 River Kingfisher

1985. Air. Birth Bicentenary of John J. Audubon (ornithologist). Multicoloured.
1073 180f. Type **408** . . . . . . 1·50 55
1074 300f. Great bustard (vert) 2·50 90
1075 470f. Ostrich (vert) . . . . 4·25 1·50
1076 540f. Ruppell's griffon . . . 4·50 2·00

409 National Pioneers Movement Emblem

1985. International Youth Year. Multicoloured.
1077 120f. Type **409** 80 40
1078 190f. Boy leading oxen . . . 1·40 70
1079 500f. Sports motifs and I.Y.Y. emblem . . . . . 3·50 1·75

410 Sud Aviation Caravelle, Boeing 727-200 and Agency Emblem

1985. Air. 25th Anniv of Aerial Navigation Security Agency for Africa and Madagascar (ASECNA).
1080 **410** 700f. multicoloured . . . 4·50 2·50

411 Lion, and Scouts collecting Wood

1985. Air. "Philexafrique" Stamp Exhibition, Lome. Multicoloured.
1081 200f. Type **411** . . . . . . 1·75 1·25
1082 200f. Satellite, dish aerial and globe . . . . 1·75 1·25

412 U.P.U. Emblem, Computer and Reservoir (Development)

1985. "Philexafrique" Stamp Exhibition, Lome, Togo (2nd issue). Multicoloured.
1083 250f. Type **412** . . . . . . 1·75 1·25
1084 250f. Satellite, girls writing and children learning from television (Youth) 1·75 1·25

413 Grey Cat

1986. Cats. Multicoloured.
1085 150f. Type **413** . . . . . . 1·50 60
1086 200f. White cat . . . . . . 2·25 80
1087 300f. Tabby cat . . . . . . 2·50 1·10

414 Hands releasing Doves and Globe

1986. Anti-apartheid Campaign. Multicoloured.
1088 100f. Type **414** 65 40
1089 120f. People breaking chain around world 85 50

415 Comet and Diagram of Orbit

1986. Air. Appearance of Halley's Comet.
1090 **415** 300f. multicoloured . . . 2·25 1·25

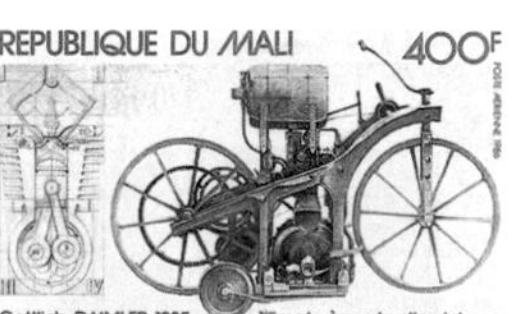

416 Internal Combustion Engine

1986. Air. Centenaries of First Motor Car with Internal Combustion Engine and Statue of Liberty. Multicoloured.
1091 400f. Type **416** . . . . . . 3·00 1·50
1092 600f. Head of statue, and French and American flags . . . . 4·00 2·25

417 Robeson

1986. Air. 10th Death Anniv of Paul Robeson (singer).
1093 **417** 500f. multicoloured . . . 4·00 2·00

418 Women tending Crop

1986. World Communications Day.
1094 **418** 200f. multicoloured . . . 1·50 80

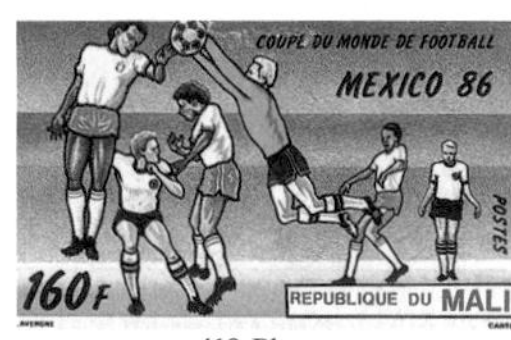

419 Players

1986. World Cup Football Championship, Mexico. Multicoloured.
1095 160f. Type **419** . . . . . . 1·40 65
1096 225f. Player capturing ball 1·90 90

420 Watt

1986. 250th Birth Anniv of James Watt (inventor).
1098 **420** 110f. multicoloured . . . 8·00 3·50

421 Eberth and Microscope

422 Chess Pieces on Board

1986. Air. 60th Death Anniv of Karl Eberth (discoverer of typhoid bacillus).
1099 **421** 550f. multicoloured . . . 4·00 1·90

1986. Air. World Chess Championship, London and Leningrad. Multicoloured.
1100 400f. Type **422** . . . . . . 3·75 1·75
1101 500f. Knight and board . . 4·75 2·25

1986. World Cup Winners. Nos. 1095/6 optd **ARGENTINE 3 R.F.A. 2**.
1102 160f. multicoloured . . . . 1·25 85
1103 225f. multicoloured . . . . 1·60 1·00

424 Head

1986. Endangered Animals. Giant Eland. Mult.
1105 5f. Type **424** 20 10
1106 20f. Standing by dead tree 40 10
1107 25f. Stepping over fallen branch 40 10
1108 200f. Mother and calf . . . 2·25 95

425 Mermoz and "Croix du Sud"

1986. Air. 50th Anniv of Disappearance of Jean Mermoz (aviator). Multicoloured.
1109 150f. Type **425** . . . . . . 1·25 60
1110 600f. CAMS 53 flying boat and monoplane . . . . . 4·25 2·25
1111 625f. Map and seaplane "Comte de la Vaulx" . . 4·50 2·50

1986. 10th Anniv of Concorde's First Commercial Flight. Nos. 674/6 surch **1986–10e Anniversaire du 1er Vol Commercial Supersonique**.
1112 175f. on 120f. Type **271** . . 1·40 80
1113 225f. on 130f. Concorde and Wright Flyer I . . . . . 1·75 1·00
1114 300f. on 200f. Concorde and Lindbergh's "Spirit of St. Louis" . . . . 2·75 1·50

427 Hansen and Follereau

1987. Air. 75th Death Anniv of Gerhard Hansen (discoverer of bacillus) and 10th Death Anniv of Raoul Follereau (leprosy pioneer).
1115 **427** 500f. multicoloured . . . 3·50 1·90

428 Model "A", 1903

1987. 40th Death Anniv of Henry Ford (motor car manufacturer). Multicoloured.

1116 150f. Type **428** . . . . . . 1·50 55
1117 200f. Model "T", 1923 . . . 2·00 75
1118 225f. "Thunderbird", 1968 2·00 95
1119 300f. "Continental", 1963 2·25 1·25

429 Konrad Adenauer 431 Scenes from "The Jazz Singer"

430 Runners and Buddha's Head

1987. Air. 20th Death Anniv of Konrad Adenauer (German statesman).

1120 **429** 625f. stone, brown and red . . . . 4·00 2·25

1987. Air. Olympic Games, Seoul (1988) (1st issue).

1121 **430** 400f. black and brown 2·00 1·40
1122 – 500f. dp green, grn & red . . . . 2·75 1·75

DESIGN: 500f. Footballers.
See also Nos. 1133/4.

1987. Air. 60th Anniv of First Talking Picture.

1123 **431** 550f. red, brn & dp brn 4·00 2·25

432 "Apis florea"

1987. Bees. Multicoloured.

1124 100f. Type **432** 80 50
1125 150f. "Apis dorsata" . . . 1·40 70
1126 175f. "Apis adonsonii" . . . 1·60 80
1127 200f. "Apis mellifera" . . . 1·75 1·00

433 Map, Dove and Luthuli

1987. Air. 20th Death Anniv of Albert John Luthuli (Nobel Peace Prize winner).

1128 **433** 400f. mauve, blue & brn 2·50 1·50

434 Profiles and Lions Emblem

1987. Air. Lions International and Rotary International. Multicoloured.

1129 500f. Type **434** . . . . . . 3·00 1·75
1130 500f. Clasped hands and Rotary emblem . . . . . 3·00 1·75

435 Anniversary Emblem and Symbols of Activities

1988. 30th Anniv of Lions International in Mali.

1131 **435** 200f. multicoloured . . . 1·25 75

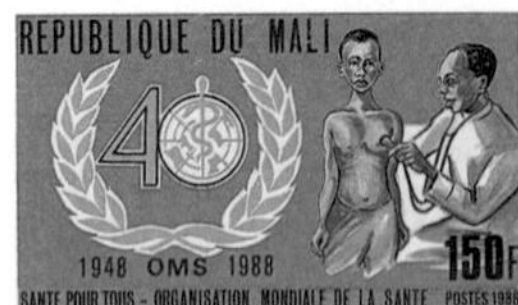

436 Emblem and Doctor examining Boy

1988. 40th Anniv of W.H.O.

1132 **436** 150f. multicoloured . . . 1·10 60

437 Coubertin and Ancient and Modern Athletes

1988. Air. Olympic Games, Seoul (2nd issue). 125th Birth Anniv of Pierre de Coubertin (founder of modern games). Multicoloured.

1133 240f. Type **437** . . . . . . 1·10 90
1134 400f. Stadium, Olympic rings and sports pictograms . . . . 1·90 1·40

438 "Harlequin"

1988. Air. 15th Death Anniv of Pablo Picasso (painter).

1135 **438** 600f. multicoloured . . . 4·25 2·25

439 Concorde and Globe

1988. Air. 15th Anniv of First North Atlantic Crossing by Concorde.

1136 **439** 500f. multicoloured . . . 4·00 2·00

440 Pres. Kennedy 442 Map

1988. 25th Death Anniv of John Fitzgerald Kennedy (American President).

1137 **440** 640f. multicoloured . . . 4·00 2·40

1988. Mali Mission Hospital, Mopti. No. 1132 surch **MISSION MALI HOPITAL de MOPTI 300F** and **MEDECINS DU MONDE** emblem.

1138 **436** 300f. on 150f. mult . . . 2·40 1·75

1988. 25th Anniv of Organization of African Unity.

1139 **442** 400f. multicoloured . . . 2·50 1·25

443 Map, Leaf and Stove

1989. Air. "Improved Stoves: For a Green Mali". Multicoloured.

1140 5f. Type **443** 10 10
1141 10f. Tree and stove 10 10
1142 25f. Type **443** 15 10
1143 100f. As No. 1141 . . . . . 60 35

444 Astronauts on Moon

1989. Air. 20th Anniv of First Manned Moon Landing.

1144 **444** 300f. blue, purple & grn 2·00 1·25
1145 – 500f. purple, blue & brn 3·25 1·75

DESIGN: 500f. Astronauts on Moon (different).

445 Emblem and Crossed Syringes

1989. Vaccination Programme. Multicoloured.

1146 20f. Type **445** 15 10
1147 30f. Doctor vaccinating woman 20 10
1148 50f. Emblem and syringes 40 15
1149 175f. Doctor vaccinating child . . . . 1·40 65

446 Emblem

1989. 25th Anniv of International Law Institute of French-speaking Countries.

1150 **446** 150f. multicoloured . . . 1·10 55
1151 200f. multicoloured . . . 1·40 70

447 Crowd 448 U.P.U. Emblem and Hands holding Envelopes

1989. Air. Bicentenary of French Revolution and "Philexfrance 89" International Stamp Exn, Paris.

1152 **447** 400f. red, blue and purple . . . . 2·50 1·25
1153 – 600f. violet, pur & mve 3·50 2·00

DESIGN: 600f. Marianne and Storming of Bastille.

1989. World Post Day.

1154 **448** 625f. multicoloured . . . 3·50 2·25

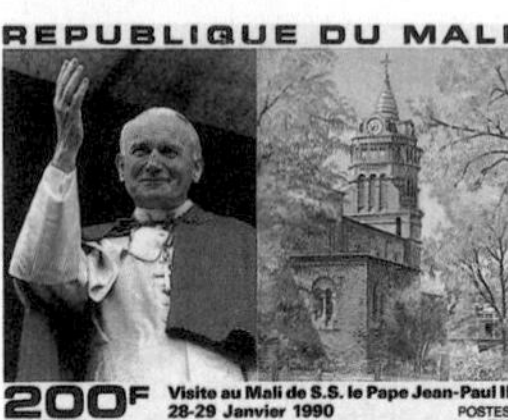

449 Pope and Cathedral

1990. Visit of Pope John Paul II.

1155 **449** 200f. multicoloured . . . 1·60 80

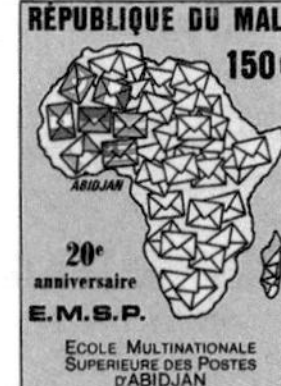

450 Envelopes on Map

1990. 20th Anniv of Multinational Postal Training School, Abidjan.

1156 **450** 150f. multicoloured . . . 1·25 55

451 Footballers

1990. Air. World Cup Football Championship, Italy. Multicoloured.

1157 200f. Type **451** . . . . . . 1·50 75
1158 225f. Footballers (different) 1·75 85

1990. World Cup Result. Nos. 1157/8 optd. Mult.

1160 200f. **ITALIE : 2 / ANGLETERRE : 1** . . . 1·50 85
1161 225f. **R.F.A. : 1 / ARGENTINE : 0** . . . . 1·75 85

453 Pres. Moussa Traore and Bamako Bridge

1990. 30th Anniv of Independence.

1163 **453** 400f. multicoloured . . . 2·50 1·50

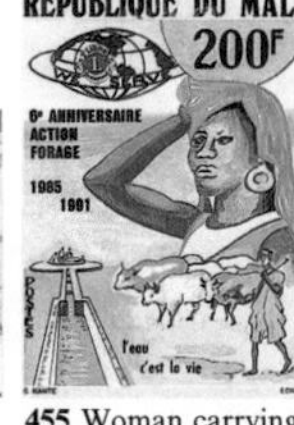

454 Man writing and Adults learning to Read 455 Woman carrying Water and Cattle at Well

1990. International Literacy Year.

1164 **454** 150f. multicoloured . . . 1·25 55
1165 200f. multicoloured . . . 1·50 75

1991. Lions Club (1166) and Rotary International (1167) Projects. Multicoloured.

1166 200f. Type **455** (6th anniv of wells project) . . . . . . 1·40 75
1167 200f. Bamako branch emblem and hand (30th anniv of anti-polio campaign) . . . . 1·40 75

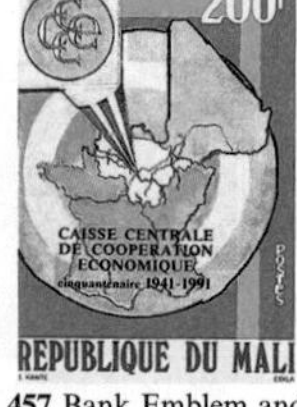

456 Sonrai Dance, Takamba 457 Bank Emblem and Map of France

1991. Dances. Multicoloured.

1168 50f. Type **456** 30 15
1169 100f. Malinke dance, Mandiani 60 30
1170 150f. Bamanan dance, Kono 90 50
1171 200f. Dogon dance, Songho 1·10 75

1991. 50th Anniv of Central Economic Co-operation Bank.

1172 **457** 200f. multicoloured . . . 1·25 75

458 Women with Torch and Banner

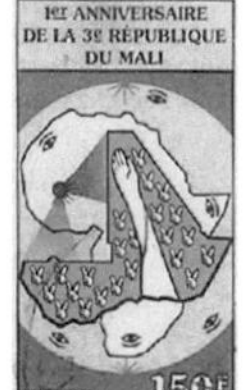

461 Map of Africa

1992. National Women's Movement for the Safeguarding of Peace and National Unity.
1173 **458** 150f. multicoloured . . . 75 40

1992. Various stamps surch.
1174 – 25f. on 470f. mult (No. 1058) (postage) 15 10
1175 **420** 30f. on 110f. mult . . . 18·00 4·50
1176 – 50f. on 300f. mult (No. 1087) 25 15
1177 – 50f. on 1225f. mult (No. 1043) 25 15
1178 – 150f. on 135f. mult (No. 1070) 75 40
1179 – 150f. on 190f. mult (No. 1063) 75 40
1180 – 150f. on 190f. mult (No. 1078) 75 40
1181 **400** 150f. on 350f. mult . . . 75 40
1182 – 150f. on 485f. mult (No. 1067) . . . . . 1·25 50
1183 – 150f. on 525f. mult (No. 1068) . . . . . 1·25 50
1184 – 150f. on 530f. mult (No. 1064) 75 40
1185 **440** 200f. on 640f. mult . . . 1·00 50
1186 – 240f. on 350f. mult (No. 1057) . . . . . 1·90 1·40
1187 **448** 240f. on 625f. mult . . . 1·25 65
1188 **410** 20f. on 700f. mult (air) 10 10
1189 **415** 20f. on 300f. mult . . . 10 10
1190 – 25f. on 470f. mult (No. 1071) 15 10
1191 **408** 30f. on 180f. mult . . . 15 10
1192 – 30f. on 500f. purple, blue and brown (No. 1145) 25 10
1193 – 100f. on 540f. mult (No. 1076) 80 50
1194 **438** 100f. on 600f. mult . . . 50 25
1195 **444** 150f. on 300f. blue, purple and green . . . 75 40
1196 **447** 150f. on 400f. red, blue and purple 75 40
1197 – 200f. on 300f. mult (No. 1074) . . . . . 1·60 1·00
1198 – 240f. on 600f. violet, purple and mauve (No. 1153) . . . . . 1·25 65

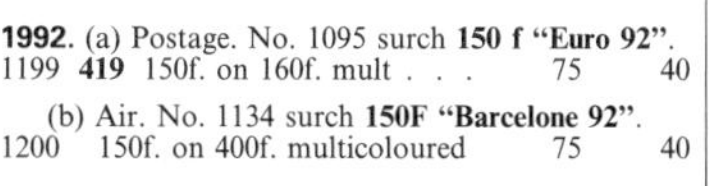

1992. (a) Postage. No. 1095 surch **150 f "Euro 92"**.
1199 **419** 150f. on 160f. mult . . . 75 40

(b) Air. No. 1134 surch **150F "Barcelone 92"**.
1200 150f. on 400f. multicoloured 75 40

1993. 1st Anniv of Third Republic.
1201 **461** 150f. multicoloured . . . 2·00 80

462 Blood, Memorial and Martyrs

463 Polio Victims

1993. 2nd Anniv of Martyrs' Day.
1203 **462** 150f. multicoloured . . . 70 35
1204 160f. multicoloured . . . 75 40

1993. Vaccination Campaign.
1205 **463** 150f. multicoloured . . . 2·00 1·00

464 Lecture on Problem Issues

1993. 35th Anniv of Lions International in Mali.
1207 **464** 200f. multicoloured . . . 90 45
1208 225f. multicoloured . . . 1·00 50

465 Place de la Liberte

466 Figure Skating

1993. Multicoloured, background colour of top panel given.
1209 **465** 20f. blue 10 10
1210 25f. yellow 10 10
1211 50f. pink 35 20
1212 100f. grey 65 20
1213 110f. yellow 65 35
1214 150f. green 90 35
1215 200f. yellow . . . . . . 1·40 55
1216 225f. flesh . . . . 1·40 65
1217 240f. lilac . . . . 1·75 65
1218 260f. lilac . . . . 1·75 65

1994. Winter Olympic Games, Lillehammer. Multicoloured.
1219 150f. Type **466** 35 20
1220 200f. Giant slalom 50 25
1221 225f. Ski jumping 55 30
1222 750f. Speed skating . . . . 1·75 90

467 Juan Schiaffino (Uruguay)

468 Scaphonyx

1994. World Cup Football Championship, U.S.A. Players from Different Teams. Multicoloured.
1224 200f. Type **467** 50 25
1225 240f. Diego Maradona (Argentine Republic) . . 60 30
1226 260f. Paolo Rossi (Italy) . . 65 35
1227 1000f. Franz Beckenbauer (Germany) . . . . 2·40 1·25

1994. Prehistoric Animals. Multicoloured.
1229 5f. Type **468** 10 10
1230 10f. Cynognathus 10 10
1231 15f. Lesothosaurus 10 10
1232 20f. Scutellosaurus 10 10
1233 25f. Ceratosaurus 10 10
1234 30f. Dilophosaurus 10 10
1235 40f. Dryosaurus 10 10
1236 50f. Heterodontosaurus . . 10 10
1237 60f. Anatosaurus 15 10
1238 70f. Saurornithoides 15 10
1239 80f. Avimimus 20 10
1240 90f. Saltasaurus 20 10
1241 300f. Dromaeosaurus . . . 75 40
1242 400f. Tsintaosaurus 95 50
1243 600f. Velociraptor . . . . . 1·50 75
1244 700f. Ouranosaurus . . . . 1·75 90
Nos. 1229/44 were issued together, se-tenant, forming a composite design.

469 "Sternuera castanea"

1994. Insects. Multicoloured.
1246 40f. Type **469** 20 10
1247 50f. "Eudicella gralli" (horiz) 20 10
1248 100f. "Homoderus mellyi" 35 15
1249 200f. "Kraussaria angulifera" (horiz) 60 25

470 Vaccinating Child

1994. Vaccination Campaign.
1250 **470** 150f. green and black . . 35 20
1251 200f. blue and black . . 50 25

471 Feral Rock Pigeons

1994. Birds. Multicoloured.
1252 25f. Type **471** 10 10
1253 30f. Helmeted guineafowl 10 10
1254 150f. South African crowned cranes (vert) 35 20
1255 200f. Red junglefowl (vert) 50 25

472 Family

473 Kirk Douglas in "Spartacus"

1994. International Year of the Family.
1256 **472** 200f. multicoloured . . . 50 25

1994. Film Stars. Multicoloured.
1257 100f. Type **473** (postage) . . 50 15
1258 150f. Elizabeth Taylor in "Cleopatra" 70 20
1259 225f. Marilyn Monroe in "The River of No Return" . . . . 1·10 30
1260 500f. Arnold Swarzenegger in "Conan the Barbarian" 2·50 65
1261 1000f. Elvis Presley in "Loving You" . . . . . 5·25 1·25
1263 200f. Clint Eastwood in "A Mule for Sister Sara" (inscr "SIERRA TORRIDE") (air) . . . . 1·00 25

474 Ella Fitzgerald

1994. Jazz Singers. Multicoloured.
1264 200f. Type **474** 50 25
1265 225f. Lionel Hampton 65 30
1266 240f. Sarah Vaughan . . . 75 30
1267 300f. Count Basie 90 40
1268 400f. Duke Ellington . . . 1·10 50
1269 600f. Miles Davis . . . . . 1·75 75

475 Soldiers caught in Explosion

1994. 50th Anniv of Second World War D-Day Landings. Multicoloured. (a) Villers-Bocage.
1271 200f. Type **475** 75 50
1272 200f. Tank (29 × 47 mm) . . 75 50
1273 200f. Troops beside tank . . 75 50

(b) Beaumont-sur-Sarthe.
1274 300f. Bombers and troops under fire . . . . 1·25 75
1275 300f. Bombers and tanks (29 × 47 mm) . . . . . . 1·25 75
1276 300f. Tank and soldier with machine gun . . . . . . 1·25 75

(c) Utah Beach (wrongly inscr "Utha").
1277 300f. Wounded troops and bow of boat . . . . . . 1·25 75
1278 300f. Troops in boat (29 × 47 mm) . . . . . . 1·25 75
1279 300f. Troops in boats . . . 1·25 75

(d) Air Battle.
1280 400f. Bombers . . . . . . 1·25 75
1281 400f. Aircraft (29 × 47 mm) 1·25 75
1282 400f. Airplane on fire . . . 1·25 75

(e) Sainte-Mere-Eglise.
1283 400f. Troops firing at paratrooper . . . . . . 1·25 75
1284 400f. Church and soldier (29 × 47 mm) . . . . . . 1·25 75
1285 400f. Paratroopers and German troops . . . . . 1·25 75
Nos. 1271/3, 1274/6, 1277/9, 1280/2 and 1283/5 respectively were issued together, se-tenant, forming composite designs.

476 Olympic Rings on National Flag

1994. Centenary of International Olympic Committee (1st issue).
1286 **476** 150f. multicoloured . . . 75 20
1287 200f. multicoloured . . . 1·25 25
See also Nos. 1342/5.

477 Couple holding Condoms

1994. Anti-AIDS Campaign. Multicoloured.
1288 150f. Type **477** 50 20
1289 225f. Nurse treating patient and laboratory worker . . 75 30

478 "Venus of Brassempoury"

1994. Ancient Art. Multicoloured.
1290 15f. Type **478** 10 10
1291 25f. Cave paintings, Tanum 10 10
1292 45f. Prehistoric men painting mural 10 10
1293 50f. Cave paintings, Lascaux (horiz) 10 10
1294 55f. Painting from tomb of Amonherkhopeshef . . . 15 10
1295 65f. God Anubis laying out Pharaoh (horiz) 15 10
1296 75f. Sphinx and pyramid, Mycerinus (horiz) 20 10
1297 85f. Bust of Nefertiti 20 10
1298 95f. Statue of Shibum . . . 25 15
1299 100f. Cavalry of Ur (horiz) 25 15
1300 130f. Head of Mesopotamian harp . . . 30 15
1301 135f. Mesopotamian tablet (horiz) 35 20
1302 140f. Assyrian dignitary . . 35 20
1303 180f. Enamel relief from Babylon (horiz) 45 25
1304 190f. Assyrians hunting . . 45 25
1305 200f. "Mona Lisa of Nimrod" 60 25
1306 225f. Phoenician coins (horiz) 65 30
1307 250f. Phoenician sphinx . . 70 30
1308 275f. Persian archer 75 35
1309 280f. Glass paste mask . . . 80 35

479 "Polyptychus roseus"

1994. Multicoloured. (a) Butterflies and Moths.
1310 20f. Type **479** 10 10
1311 30f. "Elymniopsis bammakoo" 10 10
1312 40f. Silver-striped hawk moth 20 10
1313 150f. Crimson-speckled moth 50 20
1314 180f. Foxy charaxes 60 25
1315 200f. Common dotted border 75 25

(b) Plants.
1316 25f. "Disa kewensis" . . . 10 10
1317 50f. "Angraecum eburneum" 10 10
1318 100f. "Ansellia africana" . . 25 15
1319 140f. Sorghum 35 20
1320 150f. Onion 35 20
1321 190f. Maize 45 25
1322 200f. Clouded agaric 70 25
1323 225f. Parasol mushroom . . 75 30
1324 500f. "Lepiota aspera" . . . 1·40 65

(c) Insects.
1325 225f. Goliath beetle 70 30
1326 240f. Cricket 75 30
1327 350f. Praying mantis . . . . 1·00 45

1994. Winter Olympic Games Medal Winners, Lillehammer. Nos. 1219/22 optd.
1328 150f. **O GRISHSHUK Y. PLATOV RUSSIE** . . 35 20
1329 150f. **Y. GORDEYEVA S. GRINKOV RUSSIE** 35 20
1330 200f. **M. WASMEIER ALLEMAGNE** 50 25
1331 200f. **D. COMPAGNONI ITALIE** 50 25
1332 225f. **T. WEISSFLOG ALLEMAGNE** 55 30
1333 225f. **E. BREDESEN NORVEGE** 55 30
1334 750f. **J.O. KOSS NORVEGE** . . . . . . 1·75 90
1335 750f. **B. BLAIR U.S.A.** . . 1·75 90
A sheetlet also exists containing Nos. 1219/22 each optd with both of the inscriptions for that value.

1994. Results of World Cup Football Championship. Nos. 1224/27 optd **1. BRESIL 2. ITALIE 3. SUEDE.**
1337 200f. multicoloured 80 25
1338 240f. multicoloured 90 30
1339 260f. multicoloured 95 35
1340 1000f. multicoloured . . . . 3·00 1·25

482 Pierre de Coubertin (founder) and Torchbearer
483 Statue and Village

1994. Centenary of International Olympic Committee (2nd issue). Multicoloured.
1342 225f. Type **482** . . . . . . 1·00 30
1343 240f. Coubertin designing Olympic rings . . . . . 1·10 30
1344 300f. Athlete bearing torch and Coubertin (horiz) . . 1·40 40
1345 500f. Olympic rings and Coubertin at desk (horiz) 2·00 65

1994. 20th International Tourism Day. Multicoloured.
1347 150f. Type **483** 75 20
1348 200f. Sphinx, pyramids and Abu Simbel temple (horiz) 1·00 25

484 Reiner Klimker (dressage)

1995. Olympic Games, Atlanta (1996). Multicoloured.
1349 25f. Type **484** 10 10
1350 50f. Kristin Otto (swimming) 10 10
1351 100f. Gunther Winkler (show jumping) 30 10
1352 150f. Birgit Fischer-Schmidt (single kayak) 40 10
1353 200f. Nicole Uphoff (dressage) (vert) 60 20
1354 225f. Renate Stecher (athletics) (vert) 60 20
1355 230f. Michael Gross (swimming) 70 20
1356 240f. Karin Janz (gymnastics) 85 20
1357 550f. Anja Fichtel (fencing) (vert) . . . . 2·00 50
1358 700f. Heide Rosendahl-Ecker (long jump) (vert) 2·50 80

485 Ernst Opik, "Galileo" Probe, Shoemaker-Levy Comet and Jupiter

1995. Anniversaries and Events. Multicoloured.
1359 150f. Type **485** 40 10
1360 200f. Clyde Tombaugh (discoverer of Pluto, 1930) and "Pluto" probe . . . 75 20
1361 500f. Henri Dunant (founder of Red Cross) . . . . . 1·50 40
1362 650f. Astronauts and lunar rover (first manned moon landing, 1969) . . . . . 2·00 40
1363 700f. Emblems of Lions International and Rotary International and child drinking from pump . . . 3·00 40
1364 800f. Gary Kasparov (world chess champion, 1993) . . 4·50 50

486 Agriculture and Fishing (regional integration)

1995. 20th Anniv of Economic Community of West African States. Multicoloured.
1365 150f. Type **486** 50 20
1366 200f. Emblem and handshake (co-operation) (vert) 75 20
1367 220f. Emblem and banknotes (proposed common currency) . . . 90 30
1368 225f. Emblem and doves (peace and security) . . . 1·10 30

487 Emblems of Alliance for Democracy in Mali and Sudanese Union-RDA

1995. 3rd Anniv of New Constitution. Multicoloured.
1369 150f. Type **487** (second round of Presidential election) 40 20
1370 200f. President Alpha Oumar Konare (vert) . . 50 20
1371 225f. Emblems of competing parties (first round of Presidential election) . . . 60 30
1372 240f. Map, flag and initials of parties (multi-party democracy) (vert) 70 30

488 Scout and Viennese Emperor Moth

1995. Scout Jamboree, Netherlands. Designs showing scouts and insects or fungi. Multicoloured.
1373 150f. Type **488** 40 10
1374 225f. Brimstone 60 20
1375 240f. Fig-tree blue 70 20
1376 500f. Clouded agaric . . . . 1·75 40
1377 650f. "Agaricus semotus" 2·00 50
1378 725f. Parasol mushroom . . 2·25 60

489 Paul Harris (founder) and Emblem
490 Imperial Woodpecker ("Campephilus imperialis")

1995. 90th Anniv of Rotary International.
1380 **489** 1000f. multicoloured . . 5·00 1·25

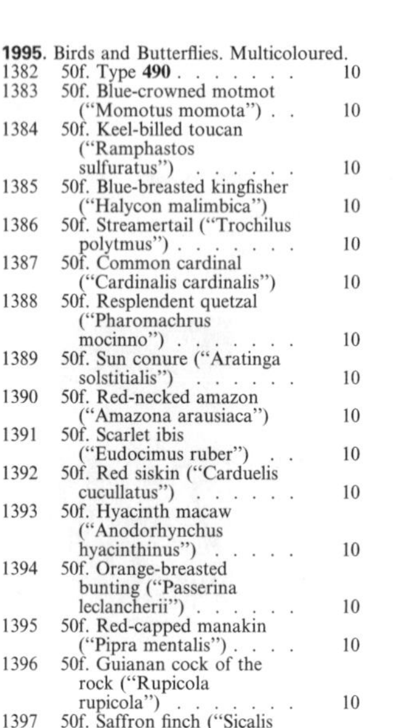
1995. Birds and Butterflies. Multicoloured.
1382 50f. Type **490** 10 10
1383 50f. Blue-crowned motmot ("Momotus momota") . . 10 10
1384 50f. Keel-billed toucan ("Ramphastos sulfuratus") 10 10
1385 50f. Blue-breasted kingfisher ("Halcyon malimbica") 10 10
1386 50f. Streamertail ("Trochilus polytmus") 10 10
1387 50f. Common cardinal ("Cardinalis cardinalis") 10 10
1388 50f. Resplendent quetzal ("Pharomachrus mocinno") 10 10
1389 50f. Sun conure ("Aratinga solstitialis") 10 10
1390 50f. Red-necked amazon ("Amazona arausiaca") 10 10
1391 50f. Scarlet ibis ("Eudocimus ruber") . . 10 10
1392 50f. Red siskin ("Carduelis cucullatus") 10 10
1393 50f. Hyacinth macaw ("Anodorhynchus hyacinthinus") 10 10
1394 50f. Orange-breasted bunting ("Passerina leclancherii") 10 10
1395 50f. Red-capped manakin ("Pipra mentalis") 10 10
1396 50f. Guianan cock of the rock ("Rupicola rupicola") 10 10
1397 50f. Saffron finch ("Sicalis flaveola") 10 10
1398 100f. Black-spotted barbet ("Capito niger") 40 10
1399 100f. Amazon kingfisher ("Chloroceryle amazona") 40 10
1400 100f. Swallow tanager ("Tersina viridis") 40 10
1401 100f. Blue-crowned motmot ("Momotus momota") . . 40 10
1402 100f. Crimson-crested woodpecker ("Campephilus melanoleucos") 40 10
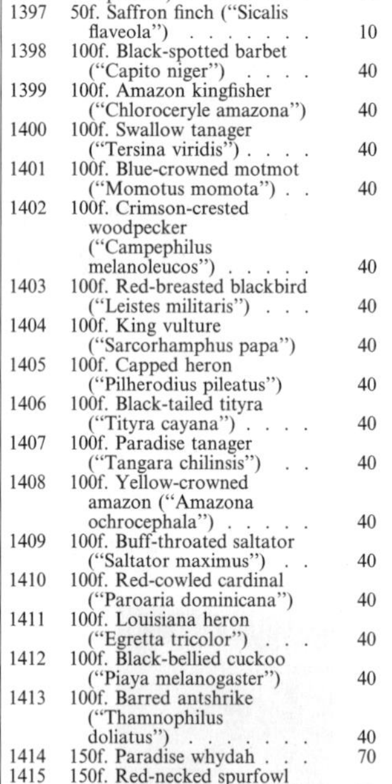
1403 100f. Red-breasted blackbird ("Leistes militaris") . . . 40 10
1404 100f. King vulture ("Sarcorhamphus papa") 40 10
1405 100f. Capped heron ("Pilherodius pileatus") 40 10
1406 100f. Black-tailed tityra ("Tityra cayana") 40 10
1407 100f. Paradise tanager ("Tangara chilensis") . . 40 10
1408 100f. Yellow-crowned amazon ("Amazona ochrocephala") 40 10
1409 100f. Buff-throated saltator ("Saltator maximus") . . 40 10
1410 100f. Red-cowled cardinal ("Paroaria dominicana") 40 10
1411 100f. Louisiana heron ("Egretta tricolor") . . . 40 10
1412 100f. Black-bellied cuckoo ("Piaya melanogaster") 40 10
1413 100f. Barred antshrike ("Thamnophilus doliatus") 40 10
1414 150f. Paradise whydah . . . 70 10
1415 150f. Red-necked spurfowl ("Red-necked Francolin") 70 10
1416 150f. Whale-headed stork (inscr "Shoebill") 70 10
1417 150f. Ruff 70 10
1418 150f. Marabou stork 70 10
1419 150f. Eastern white pelican ("White Pelican") 70 10
1420 150f. Western curlew . . . 70 10
1421 150f. Scarlet ibis 70 10
1422 150f. Great crested grebe . . 70 10
1423 150f. White spoonbill . . . 70 10
1424 150f. African jacana 70 10
1425 150f. African pygmy goose 70 10
1426 200f. Ruby-throated hummingbird 85 15
1427 200f. Grape shoemaker and blue morpho butterflies 85 15
1428 200f. Northern hobby . . . 85 15
1429 200f. Black-mandibled toucan ("Cuvier Toucan") 85 15
1430 200f. Black-necked red cotinga and green-winged macaw 85 15
1431 200f. Green-winged macaws and blue and yellow macaw 85 15
1432 200f. Greater flamingo ("Flamingo") 85 15
1433 200f. Malachite kingfisher 85 15
1434 200f. Bushy-crested hornbill 85 15
1435 200f. Purple swamphen . . 85 15
1436 200f. Striped body 85 15
1437 200f. Painted lady 85 15
Stamps of the same value were issued together, in se-tenant sheetlets, each sheetlet forming a composite design.

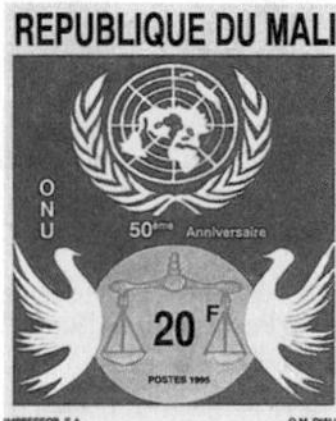

491 Emblem and Scales of Justice

1995. 50th Anniv of U.N.O. Multicoloured.
1439 20f. Type **491** 10 10
1440 170f. Type **491** 70 30
1441 225f. Emblem, doves and men with linked arms (horiz) 80 30
1442 240f. As No. 1441 . . . . . 1·00 50

492 Food Jar

1995. Cooking Utensils. Multicoloured.
1443 5f. Type **492** 20 10
1444 50f. Pestle and mortar . . . 20 10
1445 150f. Bowl (horiz) . . . . . 1·00 10
1446 200f. Grain sack . . . . . 1·10 15

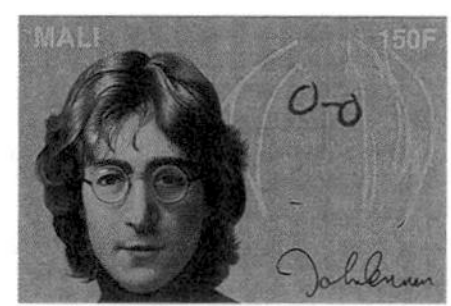

493 Lennon

1995. 15th Death Anniv of John Lennon (musician).
1448 **493** 150f. multicoloured . . . 2·50 10

494 George Barnes

1995. 40th Anniv of Rock Music (1461/6) and Centenary of Motion Pictures (others). Multicoloured. (a) Actors in Western Films.
1449 150f. Type **494** 80 40
1450 150f. William S. Hart . . . 80 40
1451 150f. Tom Mix 80 40
1452 150f. Wallace Beery 80 40
1453 150f. Gary Cooper 80 40
1454 150f. John Wayne 80 40

(b) Leading Ladies and their Directors.
1455 200f. Marlene Dietrich and Josef von Sternberg ("The Blue Angel") . . . . . . 1·00 70
1456 200f. Jean Harlow and George Cukor ("Dinner at Eight") . . . . . . 1·00 70
1457 200f. Mary Astor and John Houston ("The Maltese Falcon") . . . . 1·00 70
1458 200f. Ingrid Bergman and Alfred Hitchcock ("Spellbound") . . . . . 1·00 70
1459 200f. Claudette Colbert and Cecil B. de Mille ("Cleopatra") . . . . . . 1·00 70
1460 200f. Marilyn Monroe and Billy Wilder ("Some Like it Hot") . . . . 1·00 70

(c) Female Singers.
1461 225f. Connie Francis . . . 1·25 70
1462 225f. The Ronettes . . . . 1·25 70
1463 225f. Janis Joplin . . . . . 1·25 70
1464 225f. Debbie Harry . . . . 1·25 70

1465	225f. Cyndi Lauper	1·25	70
1466	225f. Carly Simon	1·25	70
	(d) Musicals.		
1467	240f. Gene Kelly in "Singin' in the Rain"	1·25	70
1468	240f. Cyd Charisse and Fred Astaire in "The Bandwagon"	1·25	70
1469	240f. Liza Minelli in "Cabaret"	1·25	70
1470	240f. Julie Andrews in "The Sound of Music"	1·25	70
1471	240f. Ginger Rogers and Fred Astaire in "Top Hat"	1·25	70
1472	240f. John Travolta and Karen Lynn Gorney in "Saturday Night Fever"	1·25	70

495 Charles de Gaulle (French statesman, 25th death anniv)

1995. Anniversaries. Multicoloured.

1474	150f. Type **495**	50	20
1475	200f. General de Gaulle (50th anniv of liberation of France)	70	20
1476	240f. Enzo Ferrari (car designer, 7th death anniv)	75	30
1477	500f. Ayrton Senna (racing driver, 1st death anniv)	1·50	20
1478	650f. Paul Emile Victor (explorer, 88th birthday)	2·25	30
1479	725f. Paul Harris (founder, 90th anniv of Rotary International)	3·50	40
1480	740f. Michael Schumacher (racing driver, 26th birth anniv) (wrongly dated "1970")	3·50	40
1481	1000f. Jerry Garcia (popular singer, death commemoration)	4·00	50

OFFICIAL STAMPS

O **9** Dogon Mask

O **30** Mali Flag and Emblems

1961.

O26	O **9**	1f. violet	10	10
O27		2f. red	10	10
O28		3f. slate	10	10
O29		5f. turquoise	15	15
O30		10f. brown	20	15
O31		25f. blue	35	15
O32		30f. red	40	20
O33		50f. myrtle	70	25
O34		85f. purple	1·10	65
O35		100f. green	1·40	65
O36		200f. purple	2·75	1·40

1964. Centre and flag mult; frame colour given.

O 90	O **30**	1f. green	10	10
O 91		2f. lavender	10	10
O 92		3f. slate	10	10
O 93		5f. purple	10	10
O 94		10f. blue	15	10
O 95		25f. ochre	20	15
O 96		30f. green	25	15
O 97		50f. orange	35	15
O 98		85f. brown	50	20
O 99		100f. red	65	30
O100		200f. blue	1·50	60

O **341** Arms of Gao

1981. Town Arms. Multicoloured.

O878	5f. Type O **341**	10	10
O879	15f. Tombouctou	10	10
O880	50f. Mopti	20	10
O881	180f. Segou	60	30
O882	200f. Sikasso	80	30
O883	680f. Koulikoro	2·50	95
O884	700f. Kayes	2·75	1·25
O885	1000f. Bamako	4·00	1·50

1984. Nos. O878/85 surch.

O1013	15f. on 5f. Type O **341**	15	10
O1014	50f. on 15f. Tombouctou	30	15
O1015	120f. on 50f. Mopti	70	25
O1016	295f. on 180f. Segou	2·00	90
O1017	470f. on 200f. Sikasso	3·00	1·50
O1018	515f. on 680f. Koulikoro	3·50	1·90
O1019	845f. on 700f. Kayes	6·00	2·50
O1020	1225f. on 1000f. Bamako	7·50	3·75

POSTAGE DUE STAMPS

D **9** Bambara Mask

1961.

D26	D **9**	1f. black	10	10
D27		2f. blue	10	10
D28		5f. mauve	20	10
D29		10f. orange	25	15
D30		20f. turquoise	50	25
D31		25f. purple	65	30

D **28** "Polyptychus roseus"

1964. Butterflies and Moths. Multicoloured.

D83	1f. Type D **28**	10	10
D84	1f. "Deilephila nerii"	10	10
D85	2f. "Bunaea alcinoe"	15	15
D86	2f. "Gynanisa maja"	15	15
D87	3f. "Teracolus eris"	35	30
D88	3f. "Colotis antevippe"	35	30
D89	5f. "Manatha microcera"	35	30
D90	5f. "Charaxes epijasius"	35	30
D91	10f. "Hypokopelates otraeda"	45	35
D92	10f. "Lipaphnaeus leonina"	45	35
D93	20f. "Lobobunaea christyi"	75	70
D94	20f. "Gonimbrasia hecate"	75	70
D95	25f. "Hypolimnas misippus"	1·10	90
D96	25f. "Castopsilia florella"	1·10	90

1984. Nos. D83/96 surch.

D1021	5f. on 1f. Type D **28**	10	10
D1022	5f. on 1f. "Deilephila nerii"	10	10
D1023	10f. on 2f. "Bunaea alcinoe"	10	10
D1024	10f. on 2f. "Gynanisa maja"	10	10
D1025	15f. on 3f. "Teracolus eris"	15	10
D1026	15f. on 3f. "Colotis antevippe"	15	10
D1027	25f. on 5f. "Manatha microcera"	15	15
D1028	25f. on 5f. "Charaxes epijasius"	15	15
D1029	50f. on 10f. "Hypokopelates otraeda"	30	30
D1030	50f. on 10f. "Lipaphnaeus leonina"	30	30
D1031	100f. on 20f. "Lobobunaea christyi"	60	60
D1032	100f. on 20f. "Gonimbrasia hecate"	60	60
D1033	125f. on 25f. "Hypolimnas misippus"	75	75
D1034	125f. on 25f. "Catopsilia florella"	75	75

APPENDIX

The following stamps have either been issued in excess of postal needs or have not been available to the public in reasonable quantities at face value. Such stamps may later be given full listing if there is evidence of regular postal use.

All on gold foil.

1994.

World Cup Football Championship, U.S.A. Air. 3000f.

Film Stars. Air 3000f.

MALTA Pt. 1

An island in the Mediterranean Sea, south of Italy. After a period of self-government under various Constitutions, independence was attained on 21 September 1964. The island became a republic on 13 December 1974.

1860. 12 pence = 1 shilling;
20 shillings = 1 pound.
1972. 10 mils = 1 cent;
100 cents = M£1.

1 **5**

1860. Various frames.

18	**1**	½d. yellow	35·00	35·00
20		½d. green	2·25	50
22	–	1d. red	4·00	35
23	–	2d. grey	5·00	1·50
26	–	2½d. blue	35·00	1·00
27	–	4d. brown	11·00	3·00
28	–	1s. violet	35·00	9·00
30	**5**	5s. red	£110	80·00

6 Harbour of Valletta

7 Gozo Fishing Boat

8 Ancient Maltese Galley

9 Emblematic Figure of Malta

10 Shipwreck of St. Paul

12

1899.

31a	**6**	¼d. brown	1·50	40
79		4d. black	15·00	3·25
32	**7**	4½d. brown	17·00	11·00
58		4½d. orange	4·50	3·50
59	**8**	5d. red	27·00	5·00
60		5d. green	4·25	3·50
34	**9**	2s.6d. olive	40·00	12·00
35	**10**	10s. black	90·00	65·00

1902. No. 26 surch **One Penny**.

36	1d. on 2½d. blue	1·00	1·25

1903.

47b	**12**	½d. green	4·00	10
48		1d. black and red	17·00	20
49		1d. red	2·50	10
50		2d. purple and grey	8·50	2·25
51		2d. grey	3·25	5·50
52		2½d. purple and blue	18·00	60
53		2½d. blue	5·50	2·75
42		3d. grey and purple	1·75	50
54		4d. black and brown	11·00	5·50
55		4d. black and red on yellow	4·00	3·50
44		1s. grey and violet	16·00	7·00
62		1s. black on green	7·50	2·75
63		5s. green and red on yellow	65·00	75·00

13 **15**

17 **18**

1914.

69	**13**	¼d. brown	1·00	10
71		½d. green	2·25	30
73		1d. red	1·50	10
75		2d. grey	9·00	3·50
77		2½d. blue	2·25	50
78		3d. purple on yellow	2·50	8·50
80		6d. purple	11·00	18·00
81a		1s. black on green	12·00	15·00
86	**15**	2s. purple and blue on blue	50·00	30·00
88		5s. green and red on yellow	80·00	95·00
104	**17**	10s. black	£350	£650

1918. Optd **WAR TAX**.

92	**13**	½d. green	1·50	15
93	**12**	3d. grey and purple	1·75	8·00

1921.

100	**18**	2d. grey	4·50	1·75

1922. Optd **SELF-GOVERNMENT**.

114	**13**	¼d. brown	30	75
106		½d. green	1·00	1·75
116		1d. red	1·00	20
117	**18**	2d. grey	2·25	45
118	**13**	2½d. blue	1·10	1·00
108		3d. purple on yellow	3·00	17·00
109		6d. purple	2·50	16·00
110		1s. black on green	3·50	16·00
120	**15**	2s. purple and blue on blue	40·00	85·00
112	**9**	2s.6d. olive	22·00	45·00
113	**15**	5s. green and red on yellow	50·00	80·00
105	**10**	10s. black	£190	£350
121	**17**	10s. black	£140	£200

1922. Surch **One Farthing**.

122	**18**	¼d. on 2d. grey	85	30

22 **23**

1922.

123	**22**	¼d. brown	2·50	60
124		½d. green	2·50	15
125		1d. orange and purple	3·25	20
126		1d. violet	3·25	80
127		1½d. red	4·25	15
128		2d. brown and blue	2·75	1·25
129		2½d. blue	2·75	7·00
130		3d. blue	3·75	1·50
131		3d. black on yellow	3·00	13·00
132		4d. yellow and blue	2·00	2·50
133		6d. green and violet	3·25	2·25
134	**23**	1s. blue and brown	7·00	2·50
135		2s. brown and blue	10·00	10·00
136		2s.6d. purple and black	11·00	15·00
137		5s. orange and blue	21·00	42·00
138		10s. grey and brown	55·00	£150
140	**22**	£1 black and red	95·00	£300

1925. Surch **Two pence halfpenny**.

141	**22**	2½d. on 3d. blue	1·75	3·75

1926. Optd **POSTAGE**.

143	**22**	¼d. brown	70	4·00
144		½d. green	70	15
145		1d. violet	1·00	25
146		1½d. red	1·00	60
147		2d. brown and blue	75	1·00
148		2½d. blue	1·25	80
149		3d. black on yellow	75	80
150		4d. yellow and blue	7·00	17·00
151		6d. green and violet	2·75	3·50
152	**23**	1s. blue and brown	5·50	11·00
153		2s. brown and blue	50·00	£140
154		2s.6d. purple and black	13·00	35·00
155		5s. orange and blue	9·00	35·00
156		10s. grey and brown	7·00	18·00

26

27 Valletta Harbour

28 St. Publius

1926. Inscr "POSTAGE".
157 **26** ¼d. brown 80 15
158 ½d. green 60 15
159 1d. red 3·00 1·00
160 1½d. brown 2·00 10
161 2d. grey 4·50 9·50
162 2½d. blue 4·00 1·00
162a 3d. violet 4·25 2·50
163 4d. black and red 3·25 9·50
164 4½d. violet and yellow 3·50 2·75
165 6d. violet and red 4·25 3·75
166 **27** 1s. black 6·50 4·50
167 **28** 1s.6d. black and green 6·50 13·00
168 – 2s. black and purple 6·50 15·00
169 – 2s.6d. black and red 15·00 48·00
170 – 3s. black and blue 17·00 30·00
171 – 5s. black and green 22·00 60·00
172 – 10s. black and red 55·00 £100
DESIGNS—As Type **27**: 2s. Mdina (Notabile); 5s. Neolithic temple, Mnajdra. As Type **28**: 2s.6d. Gozo boat; 3s. Neptune; 10s. St. Paul.

1928. Air. Optd **AIR MAIL**.
173 **26** 6d. violet and red 1·75 1·00

1928. Optd **POSTAGE AND REVENUE**.
174 **26** ¼d. brown 1·50 10
175 ½d. green 1·50 10
176 1d. red 1·75 3·25
177 1d. brown 4·50 10
178 1½d. brown 2·00 85
179 1½d. red 4·25 10
180 2d. grey 4·25 9·00
181 2½d. blue 2·00 10
182 3d. violet 2·00 80
183 4d. black and red 2·00 1·75
184 4½d. violet and yellow 2·25 1·00
185 6d. violet and red 2·25 1·50
186 **27** 1s. black 5·50 2·50
187 **28** 1s.6d. black and green 6·50 9·50
188 – 2s. black and purple 24·00 55·00
189 – 2s.6d. black and red 17·00 23·00
190 – 3s. black and blue 19·00 30·00
191 – 5s. black and green 29·00 65·00
192 – 10s. black and red 55·00 90·00

1930. As Nos. 157/72, but inscr "POSTAGE & REVENUE".
193 ¼d. brown 60 10
194 ½d. green 60 10
195 1d. brown 60 10
196 1½d. red 70 10
197 2d. grey 1·25 50
198 2½d. blue 2·00 10
199 3d. violet 1·50 20
200 4d. black and red 1·25 4·00
201 4½d. violet and yellow 3·25 1·25
202 6d. violet and red 2·75 1·25
203 1s. black 10·00 14·00
204 1s.6d. black and green 8·50 19·00
205 2s. black and purple 10·00 19·00
206 2s.6d. black and red 17·00 48·00
207 3s. black and blue 27·00 55·00
208 5s. black and green 32·00 65·00
209 10s. black and red 75·00 £160

1935. Silver Jubilee. As T **14a** of Kenya, Uganda and Tanganyika.
210 ½d. black and green 50 50
211 2½d. brown and blue 2·50 4·50
212 6d. blue and olive 7·00 16·00
213 1s. grey and purple 11·00 16·00

1937. Coronation. As T **14b** of Kenya, Uganda and Tanganyika.
214 ½d. green 10 20
215 1½d. red 1·25 65
216 2½d. blue 1·00 80

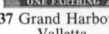

37 Grand Harbour, Valletta

38 H.M.S. "St. Angelo"

39 Verdala Palace

1938. Various designs with medallion King George VI.
217 **37** ¼d. brown 10 10
218 **38** ½d. green 1·75 30
218a ½d. brown 55 30
219 **39** 1d. brown 4·25 40
219a 1d. green 60 10
220 – 1½d. red 1·00 30
220b – 1½d. black 30 15
221 – 2d. black 40 2·00
221a – 2d. red 40 30
222 – 2½d. blue 75 60
222a – 2½d. violet 60 10
223 – 3d. violet 55 80
223a – 3d. blue 30 20
224 – 4½d. olive and brown 50 30
225 – 6d. olive and red 75 30
226 – 1s. black 75 30
227 – 1s.6d. black and olive 7·00 4·00
228 – 2s. green and blue 4·50 4·00
229 – 2s.6d. black and red 8·00 5·50
230 – 5s. black and green 4·50 6·50
231 – 10s. black and red 15·00 15·00
DESIGNS—As Types **38/9**. VERT: 1½d. Hypogeum, Hal Saflieni; 3d. St. John's Co-Cathedral; 6d. Statue of Manoel de Vilhena; 1s. Maltese girl wearing faldetta; 5s. Palace Square, Valletta; 10s. St. Paul. HORIZ: 2d. Victoria and Citadel, Gozo; 2½d. De l'Isle Adam entering Mdina; 4½d. Ruins at Mnajdra; 1s.6d. St. Publius; 2s. Mdina Cathedral; 2s.6d. Statue of Neptune.

1946. Victory. As T **4a** of Pitcairn Islands.
232 1d. green 15 10
233 3d. blue 30 80

1948. Self-government. As 1938 issue optd **SELF-GOVERNMENT 1947**.
234 ¼d. brown 30 20
235 ½d. brown 30 10
236 1d. green 30 10
236a 1d. grey 30 10
237 1½d. black 1·25 10
237b 1½d. green 30 10
238 2d. red 1·25 10
238b 2d. yellow 30 10
239 2½d. violet 80 10
239a 2½d. red 50 1·50
240 3d. blue 1·00 15
240a 3d. violet 50 15
241 4½d. olive and brown 2·00 1·50
241a 4½d. olive and blue 50 90
242 6d. olive and red 3·00 15
243 1s. black 2·75 40
244 1s.6d. black and olive 2·50 50
245 2s. green and blue 5·00 2·50
246 2s.6d. black and red 12·00 2·50
247 5s. black and green 20·00 3·50
248 10s. black and red 20·00 22·00

1949. Silver Wedding. As T **4b/c** of Pitcairn Islands.
249 1d. green 50 10
250 £1 blue 38·00 35·00

1949. U.P.U. As T **4d/g** of Pitcairn Islands.
251 2½d. violet 30 10
252 3d. blue 3·00 1·00
253 6d. red 60 1·00
254 1s. black 60 2·50

53 Queen Elizabeth II when Princess

54 "Our Lady of Mount Carmel" (attrib Palladino)

1950. Visit of Princess Elizabeth.
255 **53** 1d. green 10 15
256 3d. blue 20 20
257 1s. black 65 1·25

1951. 7th Centenary of the Scapular.
258 **54** 1d. green 15 15
259 3d. violet 50 10
260 1s. black 1·10 85

1953. Coronation. As T **4h** of Pitcairn Islands.
261 1½d. black and green 50 10

55 St. John's Co-Cathedral

56 "Immaculate Conception" (Caruana) (altar-piece, Cospicua)

1954. Royal Visit.
262 **55** 3d. violet 30 10

1954. Centenary of Dogma of the Immaculate Conception.
263 **56** 1½d. green 10 10
264 3d. blue 10 10
265 1s. grey 35 20

57 Monument of the Great Siege, 1565

74 "Defence of Malta"

1956.
266 **57** ¼d. violet 20 10
267 – ½d. orange 50 10
314 – 1d. black 50 30
269 – 1½d. green 30 10
270 – 2d. sepia 1·50 10
271 – 2½d. brown 1·50 30
272 – 3d. red 1·50 10
273 – 4½d. blue 2·50 20
274 – 6d. blue 75 10
275 – 8d. ochre 3·50 1·00
276 – 1s. violet 1·00 10
277 – 1s.6d. turquoise 12·00 20
278 – 2s. olive 12·00 2·50
279 – 2s.6d. brown 9·00 2·25
280 – 5s. green 15·00 2·75
281 – 10s. red 38·00 12·00
282 – £1 brown 38·00 25·00
DESIGNS—VERT: ½d. Wignacourt aqueduct horsetrough; 1d. Victory church; 1½d. Second World War memorial; 2d. Mosta Church; 3d. The King's Scroll; 4½d. Roosevelt's Scroll; 8d. Vedette (tower); 1s. Mdina Gate; 1s.6d. "Les Gavroches" (statue); 2s. Monument of Christ the King; 2s.6d. Monument of Grand Master Cottoner; 5s. Grand Master Perellos's monument; 10s. St. Paul (statue); £1 Baptism of Christ (statue). HORIZ: 2½d. Auberge de Castile; 6d. Neolithic Temples at Tarxien.

1957. George Cross Commem. Cross in Silver.
283 **74** 1½d. green 15 10
284 – 3d. red 15 10
285 – 1s. brown 15 10
DESIGNS—HORIZ: 3d. Searchlights over Malta. VERT: 1s. Bombed buildings.

77 Design

81 Sea Raid on Grand Harbour, Valletta

1958. Technical Education in Malta. Inscr "TECHNICAL EDUCATION".
286 **77** 1½d. black and green 10 10
287 – 3d. black, red and grey 10 10
288 – 1s. grey, purple and black 15 10
DESIGNS—VERT: 3d. "Construction". HORIZ: 1s. Technical School, Paola.

1958. George Cross Commem. Cross in first colour outlined in silver.
289 – 1½d. green and black 15 10
290 **81** 3d. red and black 15 10
291 – 1s. mauve and black 15 10
DESIGNS—HORIZ: 1½d. Bombed-out family; 1s. Searchlight crew.

83 Air Raid Casualties

86 Shipwreck of St. Paul (after Palombi)

87 Statue of St. Paul, Rabat, Malta

1959. George Cross Commemoration.
292 **83** 1½d. green, black and gold 20 10
293 – 3d. mauve, black and gold 20 10
294 – 1s. grey, black and gold 70 95
DESIGNS—HORIZ: 3d. "For Gallantry". VERT: 1s. Maltese under bombardment.

1960. 19th Centenary of the Shipwreck of St. Paul. Inscr as in T **86/7**.
295 **86** 1½d. blue, gold and brown 15 10
296 – 3d. purple, gold and blue 15 10
297 – 6d. red, gold and grey 25 10
298 **87** 8d. black and gold 30 50
299 – 1s. purple and gold 25 10
300 – 2s.6d. blue, green and gold 1·00 2·00
DESIGNS—As Type **88**: 3d. Consecration of St. Publius, First Bishop of Malta; 6d. Departure of St. Paul (after Palombi). As Type **87**: 1s. Angel with the "Acts of the Apostles"; 2s.6d. St. Paul with the "Second Epistle to the Corinthians".

92 Stamp of 1860

1960. Centenary of Malta Stamps. Stamp in buff and blue.
301 **92** 1½d. green 25 10
302 3d. red 30 10
303 6d. blue 40 1·00

93 George Cross

1961. George Cross Commemoration.
304 **93** 1½d. black, cream and bistre 15 10
305 – 3d. brown and blue 30 10
306 – 1s. green, lilac and violet 75 1·75
DESIGNS: 3d. and 1s. show George Cross as Type **93** over backgrounds with different patterns.

96 "Madonna Damascena"

100 Bruce, Zammit and Microscope

1962. Great Siege Commemoration.
307 **96** 2d. blue 10 10
308 – 3d. red 10 10
309 – 6d. bronze 25 10
310 – 1s. purple 25 40
DESIGNS: 3d. Great Siege Monument; 6d. Grand Master La Valette; 1s. Assault on Fort St. Elmo.

1963. Freedom from Hunger. As T **20a** of Pitcairn Islands.
311 1s.6d. sepia 1·75 2·50

1963. Cent of Red Cross. As T **20b** of Pitcairn Islands.
312 2d. red on black 25 15
313 1s.6d. red and blue 1·75 4·25

1964. Anti-brucellosis Congress.
316 **100** 2d. brown, black and green 10 10
317 – 1s.6d. black and purple 90 90
DESIGN: 1s.6d. Goat and laboratory equipment.

102 "Nicola Cotoner tending Sick Man" (M. Preti)

1964. 1st European Catholic Doctors' Congress, Valletta. Multicoloured.
318 2d. Type **102** 20 10
319 6d. St. Luke and hospital 50 15
320 1s.6d. Sacra Infermeria, Valletta 1·10 1·90

106 Dove and British Crown

110 Neolithic Era

109 "The Nativity"

1964. Independence.

No.	Type	Description	Unused	Used
321	**106**	2d. olive, red and gold . .	30	10
322	–	3d. brown, red and gold	30	10
323	–	6d. slate, red and gold . .	70	15
324	**106**	1s. blue, red and gold . .	70	15
325	–	1s.6d. blue, red and gold	1·50	1·00
326	–	2s.6d. blue, red and gold	1·50	2·25

DESIGNS: 3d., 1s.6d. Dove and Pope's tiara; 6d., 2s.6d. Dove and U.N. emblem.

1964. Christmas.

No.	Type	Description	Unused	Used
327	**109**	2d. purple and gold . . .	10	10
328		4d. blue and gold	20	15
329		8d. green and gold . . .	45	45

1965. Multicoloured.

No.	Type	Description	Unused	Used
330		½d. Type **110**	10	10
331		1d. Punic era	10	10
332		1½d. Roman era	30	10
333		2d. Proto Christian era . .	10	10
334		2½d. Saracenic era	80	10
335		3d. Siculo Norman era . . .	10	10
336		4d. Knights of Malta . . .	1·00	10
337		4½d. Maltese Navy	1·50	75
337b		5d. Fortifications	30	20
338		6d. French occupation . . .	30	10
339		8d. British rule	70	10
339c		10d. Naval Arsenal	50	1·90
340		1s. Maltese Corps of the British Army	30	10
341		1s.3d. International Eucharistic Congress, 1913	2·00	1·40
342		1s.6d. Self-government, 1921	60	20
343		2s. Gozo Civic Council . .	70	10
344		2s.6d. State of Malta . . .	70	50
345		3s. Independence, 1964 . .	1·75	75
346		5s. HAFMED (Allied Forces, Mediterranean)	6·00	1·00
347		10s. The Maltese Islands (map)	3·00	4·00
348		£1 Patron Saints	3·75	5·00

Nos. 339/48 are larger, 41 × 29 mm from perf to perf, and include portrait of Queen Elizabeth II.

129 "Dante" (Raphael)

131 Turkish Fleet

1965. 700th Birth Anniv of Dante.

No.	Type	Description	Unused	Used
349	**129**	2d. blue	10	10
350		6d. green	25	10
351		2s. brown	1·10	1·50

1965. 400th Anniv of Great Siege. Multicoloured.

No.	Type	Description	Unused	Used
352		2d. Turkish camp	30	10
353		3d. Battle scene	30	10
354		6d. Type **131**	40	10
355		8d. Arrival of relief force . .	70	90
356		1s. Grand Master J. de La Valette's arms	40	10
357		1s.6d. "Allegory of Victory" (from mural by M. Preti)	75	30
358		2s.6d. Victory medal	1·25	3·25

SIZES—As Type **131**: 1s. SQUARE (32½ × 32½ mm): others.

137 "The Three Kings"

1965. Christmas.

No.	Type	Description	Unused	Used
359	**137**	1d. purple and red . . .	10	10
360		4d. purple and blue . . .	30	25
361		1s.3d. slate and purple . .	30	30

138 Sir Winston Churchill

1966. Churchill Commemoration.

No.	Type	Description	Unused	Used
362	**138**	2d. black, red and gold	20	10
363	–	3d. green, olive and gold	20	10
364	**138**	1s. purple, red and gold	30	10
365	–	1s.6d. blue, ultram & gold	40	1·10

DESIGN : 3d., 1s.6d. Sir Winston Churchill and George Cross.

140 Grand Master La Valette

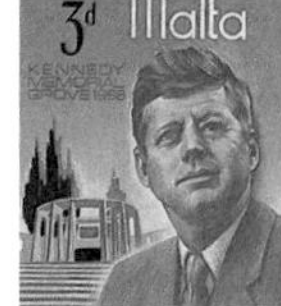

145 Pres. Kennedy and Memorial

1966. 400th Anniv of Valletta. Multicoloured.

No.	Type	Description	Unused	Used
366		2d. Type **140**	10	10
367		3d. Pope Pius V	10	10
368		6d. Map of Valletta	15	10
369		1s. F. Laparelli (architect) . .	15	10
370		2s.6d. G. Cassar (architect)	35	50

1966. Pres. Kennedy Commemoration.

No.	Type	Description	Unused	Used
371	**145**	3d. olive, gold and black	10	10
372		1s.6d. blue, gold and black	10	10

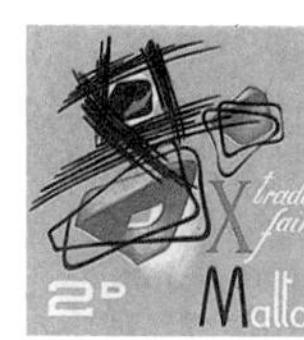

146 "Trade"

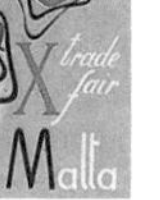

147 "The Child in the Manger"

1966. 10th Malta Trade Fair.

No.	Type	Description	Unused	Used
373	**146**	2d. multicoloured	10	10
374		8d. multicoloured	30	50
375		2s.6d. multicoloured . . .	30	50

1966. Christmas.

No.	Type	Description	Unused	Used
376	**147**	1d. multicoloured	10	10
377		4d. multicoloured	10	10
378		1s.3d. multicoloured . . .	10	10

148 George Cross

149 Crucifixion of St. Peter

1967. 25th Anniv of George Cross Award to Malta.

No.	Type	Description	Unused	Used
379	**148**	2d. multicoloured	10	10
380		4d. multicoloured	10	10
381		3s. multicoloured	15	15

1967. 1900th Anniv of Martyrdom of Saints Peter and Paul.

No.	Type	Description	Unused	Used
382	**149**	2d. brown, orange & black	10	10
383	–	8d. olive, gold and black	15	10
384	–	3s. blue and black	20	15

DESIGNS—As Type **149**: 3s. Beheading of St. Paul. HORIZ (47 × 25 mm): 8d. Open Bible and episcopal emblems.

152 "St. Catherine of Siena"

156 Temple Ruins, Tarxien

1967. 300th Death Anniv of Melchior Gafa (sculptor). Multicoloured.

No.	Type	Description	Unused	Used
385		2d. Type **152**	10	10
386		4d. "St. Thomas of Villanova"	10	10
387		1s.6d. "Baptism of Christ" (detail)	15	10
388		2s.6d. "St. John the Baptist" (from "Baptism of Christ")	15	10

1967. 15th International Historical Architecture Congress, Valletta. Multicoloured.

No.	Type	Description	Unused	Used
389		2d. Type **156**	10	10
390		6d. Facade of Palazzo Falzon, Notabile	10	10
391		1s. Parish Church, Birkirkara	10	10
392		3s. Portal, Auberge de Castille	25	25

160 "Angels"

166 Human Rights Emblem and People

163 Queen Elizabeth II and Arms of Malta

1967. Christmas. Multicoloured.

No.	Type	Description	Unused	Used
393		1d. Type **160**	10	10
394		8d. "Crib"	20	10
395		1s.4d. "Angels"	20	10

1967. Royal Visit.

No.	Type	Description	Unused	Used
396	**163**	2d. multicoloured	10	10
397	–	4d. black, purple and gold	10	10
398	–	3s. multicoloured	20	25

DESIGNS—VERT: 4d. Queen in Robes of Order of St. Michael and St. George. HORIZ: 3s. Queen and outline of Malta.

1968. Human Rights Year. Multicoloured.

No.	Type	Description	Unused	Used
399		2d. Type **166**	10	10
400		6d. Human Rights emblem and people (different) . . .	10	10
401		2s. Type **166** (reversed) . . .	10	10

169 Fair "Products"

170 Arms of the Order of St. John and La Valette

1968. Malta International Trade Fair.

No.	Type	Description	Unused	Used
402	**169**	4d. multicoloured	10	10
403		8d. multicoloured	10	10
404		3s. multicoloured	15	10

1968. 4th Death Cent of Grand Master La Valette. Multicoloured.

No.	Type	Description	Unused	Used
405		1d. Type **170**	10	10
406		8d. "La Valette" (A. de Favray) (vert)	15	10
407		1s.6d. La Valette's tomb (28 × 23 mm)	15	10
408		2s.6d. Angels and scroll bearing date of death (vert)	20	20

174 Star of Bethlehem and Angel waking Shepherds

177 "Agriculture"

1968. Christmas. Multicoloured.

No.	Type	Description	Unused	Used
409		1d. Type **174**	10	10
410		8d. Mary and Joseph with shepherd watching over Cradle	15	10
411		1s.4d. Three Wise Men and Star of Bethlehem	15	20

1968. 6th Food and Agricultural Organization Regional Conference for Europe. Mult.

No.	Type	Description	Unused	Used
412		4d. Type **177**	10	10
413		1s. F.A.O. emblem and coin	10	10
414		2s.6d. "Agriculture" sowing Seeds	10	15

180 Mahatma Gandhi

181 ILO Emblem

1969. Birth Centenary of Mahatma Gandhi.

No.	Type	Description	Unused	Used
415	**180**	1s.6d. brown, black & gold	15	10

1969. 50th Anniv of Int Labour Organization.

No.	Type	Description	Unused	Used
416	**181**	2d. blue, gold & turquoise	10	10
417		6d. sepia, gold and brown	10	10

182 Robert Samut

1969. Birth Centenary of Robert Samut (composer of Maltese National Anthem).

No.	Type	Description	Unused	Used
418	**182**	2d. multicoloured	10	10

183 Dove of Peace, U.N. Emblem and Sea-bed

1969. United Nations Resolution on Oceanic Resources.

No.	Type	Description	Unused	Used
419	**183**	5d. multicoloured	10	10

184 "Swallows" returning to Malta

1969. Maltese Migrants' Convention.

No.	Type	Description	Unused	Used
420	**184**	10d. black, gold and olive	10	10

185 University Arms and Grand Master de Fonseca (founder)

1969. Bicentenary of University of Malta.

No.	Type	Description	Unused	Used
421	**185**	2s. multicoloured	15	20

187 Flag of Malta and Birds

1969. 5th Anniv of Independence.

No.	Type	Description	Unused	Used
422	–	2d. multicoloured	10	10
423	**187**	5d. black, red and gold	10	10
424	–	10d. black, blue and gold	10	10
425	–	1s.6d. multicoloured . . .	20	40
426	–	2s.6d. black, brown & gold	25	50

DESIGNS—SQUARE (31 × 31 mm): 2d. 1919 War Monument. VERT: 10d. "Tourism"; 1s.6d. U.N. and Council of Europe emblems; 2s.6d. "Trade and Industry".

191 Peasants playing Tambourine and Bagpipes

1969. Christmas. Children's Welfare Fund. Multicoloured.

No.	Type	Description	Unused	Used
427		1d.+1d. Type **191**	10	20
428		5d.+1d. Angels playing trumpet and harp	15	20
429		1s.6d.+3d. Choir boys singing	15	45

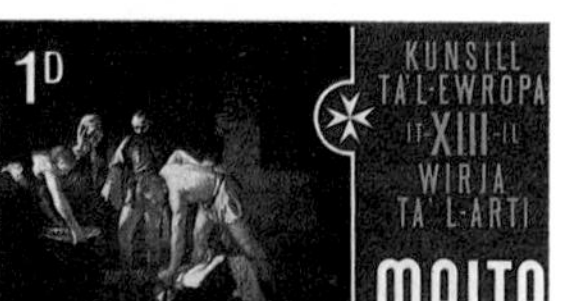

194 "The Beheading of St. John" (Caravaggio)

1970. 13th Council of Europe Art Exn. Mult.

No.	Type	Description	Unused	Used
430		1d. Type **194**	10	10
431		2d. "St. John the Baptist" (M. Preti)	10	10
432		5d. Interior of St. John's Co-Cathedral, Valletta	10	10

433 6d. "Allegory of the Order" (Neapolitan school) 10 10
434 8d. "St. Jerome" (Caravaggio) 15 50
435 10d. Articles from the Order of St. John in Malta . . . 15 10
436 1s.6d. "The Blessed Gerard receiving Godfrey de Bouillon" (A. de Favray) 20 40
437 2s. Cape and Stolone (16th cent) 20 55
SIZES—HORIZ: 1d., 8d. 56 × 30 mm; 2d., 6d. 45 × 32 mm; 10d., 2s. 63 × 21 mm; 1s.6d. 45 × 34 mm. SQUARE: 5d. 39 × 39 mm.

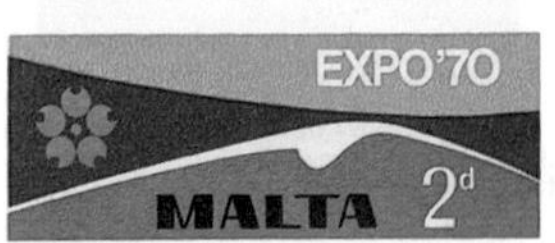

202 Artist's Impression of Fujiyama

1970. World Fair, Osaka.
438 **202** 2d. multicoloured 10 10
439 5d. multicoloured 10 10
440 3s. multicoloured 15 15

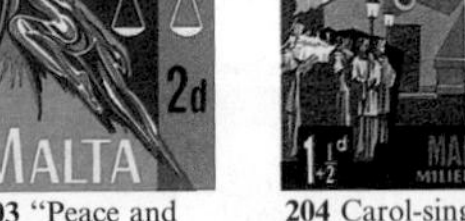

203 "Peace and Justice" 204 Carol-singers, Church and Star

1970. 25th Anniv of United Nations.
441 **203** 2d. multicoloured 10 10
442 5d. multicoloured 10 10
443 2s.6d. multicoloured . . . 15 15

1970. Christmas. Multicoloured.
444 1d.+½d. Type **204** 10 10
445 10d.+2d. Church, star and angels with Infant 15 20
446 1s.6d.+3d. Church, star and nativity scene 20 35

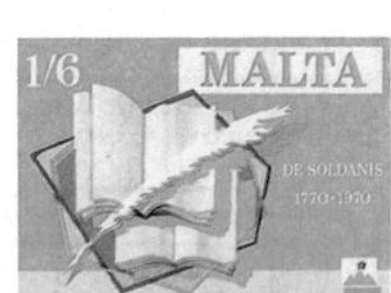

207 Books and Quill

1971. Literary Anniversaries. Multicoloured.
447 1s.6d. Type **207** (De Soldanis (historian) death bicent) . . 10 10
448 2s. Dun Karm (poet), books, pens and lamp (birth cent) 10 15

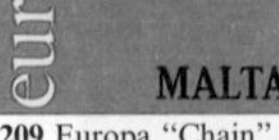

209 Europa "Chain" 211 "Centaurea spathulata"

210 "St. Joseph, Patron of the Universal Church" (G. Cali)

1971. Europa.
449 **209** 2d. orange, black and olive 10 10
450 5d. orange, black and red 10 10
451 1s.6d. orange, blk & slate 45 90

1971. Centenary of Proclamation of St. Joseph as Patron Saint of Catholic Church, and 50th Anniv of Coronation of the Statue of "Our Lady of Victories". Multicoloured.
452 2d. Type **210** 10 10
453 5d. Statue of "Our Lady of Victories" and galley . . . 10 10
454 10d. Type **210** 15 10
455 1s.6d. As 5d. 30 40

1971. National Plant and Bird of Malta. Multicoloured.
456 2s. Type **211** 10 10
457 5d. Blue rock thrush (horiz) 20 10
458 10d. As 5d. 30 15
459 1s.6d. Type **211** . . . . . . 30 1·25

212 Angel

1971. Christmas. Multicoloured.
460 1d.+½d. Type **212** 10 10
461 10d.+2d. Mary and the Child Jesus 15 25
462 1s.6d.+3d. Joseph lying awake 20 40
MS463 131 × 113 mm. Nos. 460/2 75 2·50

213 Heart and W.H.O. Emblem

1972. World Health Day.
464 **213** 2d. multicoloured 10 10
465 10d. multicoloured . . . 15 10
466 2s.6d. multicoloured . . . 40 80

214 Maltese Cross 216 "Communications"

1972. Decimal Currency. Coins. Multicoloured.
467 2m. Type **214** 10 10
468 3m. Bee on honeycomb . . . 10 10
469 5m. Earthen lampstand . . . 10 10
470 1c. George Cross 10 10
471 2c. Classical head 10 10
472 5c. Ritual altar 10 10
473 10c. Grandmaster's galley . . 20 10
474 50c. Great Siege Monument 1·25 1·25
SIZES: 3m., 2c. As Type **214**: 5m., 1c., 5c. 25 × 30 mm; 10c., 50c. 31 × 38 mm.

1972. Nos. 337a, 339 and 341 surch.
475 1c.3 on 5d. multicoloured . . 10 10
476 3c. on 8d. multicoloured . . 15 10
477 5c. on 1s.3d. multicoloured 15 20

1972. Europa.
478 **216** 1c.3 multicoloured 10 10
479 3c. multicoloured 10 10
480 5c. multicoloured 15 35
481 7c.5 multicoloured 20 75

217 Angel

1972. Christmas.
482 **217** 8m.+2m. brown, grey and gold 10 10
483 – 3c.+1c. purple, violet and gold 15 40
484 – 7c.5+1c.5 indigo, blue and gold 20 50
MS485 137 × 113 mm. Nos. 482/4 1·75 4·50
DESIGNS: No. 483, Angel with tambourine; No. 484, Singing angel.
See also Nos. 507/9.

218 Archaeology 219 Europa "Posthorn"

1973. Multicoloured.
486 2m. Type **218** 10 10
487 4m. History 10 10
488 5m. Folklore 10 10
489 8m. Industry 10 10
490 1c. Fishing industry 10 10
491 1c.3 Pottery 10 10
492 2c. Agriculture 10 10
493 3c. Sport 10 10
494 4c. Yacht marina 15 10
495 5c. Fiesta 15 10
496 7c.5 Regatta 25 10
497 10c. Voluntary service . . . 25 10
498 50c. Education . . . . . . 1·25 50
499 £1 Religion . . . . 2·75 2·00
500 £2 Coat of arms (32 × 27 mm) . . . . . . 14·00 17·00
500b £2 National Emblem (32 × 27 mm) . . . . . . 9·00 14·00

1973. Europa.
501 **219** 3c. multicoloured 15 10
502 5c. multicoloured 15 35
503 7c.5 multicoloured 25 65

220 Emblem, and Woman holding Corn 221 Girolamo Cassar (architect)

1973. Anniversaries.
504 **220** 1c.3 multicoloured 10 10
505 – 7c.5 multicoloured 25 40
506 – 10c. multicoloured 30 50
ANNIVERSARIES: 1c.3, 10th anniv of World Food Programme; 7c.5, 25th anniv of W.H.O.; 10c. 25th anniv of Universal Declaration of Human Rights.

1973. Christmas. As T **217**. Multicoloured.
507 8m.+2m. Angels and organ pipes 15 10
508 3c.+1c. Madonna and Child 25 55
509 7c.5+1c.5 Buildings and Star 45 1·25
MS510 137 × 112 mm. Nos. 507/9 4·75 7·50

1973. Prominent Maltese.
511 **221** 1c.3 deep green, green and gold 10 10
512 – 3c. green, blue and gold 15 10
513 – 5c. brown, green and gold 20 15
514 – 7c.5 blue, lt blue & gold 20 30
515 – 10c. deep purple, purple and gold 20 40
DESIGNS: 3c. Giuseppe Barth (ophthalmologist); 5c. Nicolo' Isouard (composer); 7c.5, John Borg (botanist); 10c. Antonio Sciortino (sculptor).

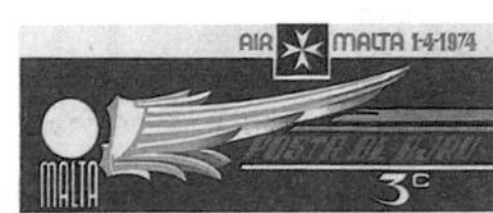

222 "Air Malta" Emblem

1974. Air. Multicoloured.
516 3c. Type **222** 15 10
517 4c. Boeing 720B 15 10
518 5c. Type **222** 20 10
519 7c.5 As 4c. 20 10
520 20c. Type **222** 45 60
521 25c. As 4c. 45 60
522 35c. Type **222** . . . . 60 1·40

223 Prehistoric Sculpture

1974. Europa.
523 **223** 1c.3 blue, black and gold 15 10
524 – 3c. brown, black and gold 20 15
525 – 5c. purple, black and gold 25 50
526 – 7c.5 green, black and gold 35 1·00
DESIGNS—VERT: 3c. Old Cathedral Door, Mdina; 7c.5, "Vetlina" (sculpture by A. Sciortino). HORIZ: 5c. Silver monstrance.

224 Heinrich von Stephan (founder) and Land Transport 225 Decorative Star and Nativity Scene

1974. Centenary of U.P.U.
527 **224** 1c.3 green, blue & orange 30 10
528 – 5c. brown, red and green 30 10
529 – 7c.5 blue, violet and green 35 20
530 – 50c. purple, red and orange . . . . 1·00 1·25
MS531 126 × 91 mm. Nos. 527/30 4·50 7·50
DESIGNS (each containing portrait as Type **224**): 5c. "Washington" (paddle-steamer) and "Royal Viking Star" (liner); 7c.5, Balloon and Boeing 747-100; 50c. U.P.U. Buildings, 1874 and 1974.

1974. Christmas. Multicoloured.
532 8m.+2m. Type **225** 10 10
533 3c.+1c. "Shepherds" 15 20
534 5c.+1c. "Shepherds with gifts" 20 35
535 7c.5+1c.5 "The Magi" . . . 30 45

226 Swearing-in of Prime Minister

1975. Inauguration of Republic.
536 **226** 1c.3 multicoloured 10 10
537 – 5c. red and black 20 10
538 – 25c. multicoloured . . . . 60 1·00
DESIGNS: 5c. National flag; 25c. Minister of Justice, President and Prime Minister.

227 Mother and Child ("Family Life")

1975. International Women's Year.
539 **227** 1c.3 violet and gold . . . 15 10
540 – 3c. blue and gold 15 10
541 **227** 5c. brown and gold . . . 25 15
542 – 20c. brown and gold . . . 80 2·50
DESIGN: 3c., 20c. Office secretary ("Public Life").

228 "Allegory of Malta" (Francesco de Mura)

1975. Europa. Multicoloured.
543 5c. Type **228** 30 10
544 15c. "Judith and Holofernes" (Valentin de Boulogne) . . 50 75
The 15c. is smaller, 47 × 23 mm.

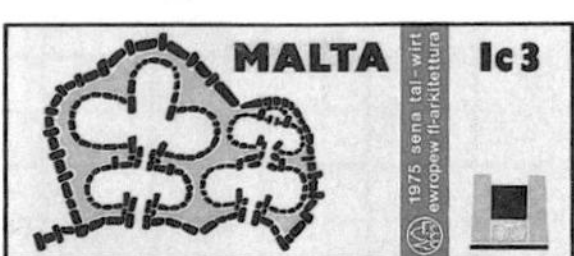

229 Plan of Ggantija Temple

1975. European Architectural Heritage Year.
545 **229** 1c.3 black and red 10 10
546 – 3c. purple, red and brown 20 10
547 – 5c. brown and red 30 25
548 – 25c. green, red and black 1·10 3·00
DESIGNS: 3c. Mdina skyline; 5c. View of Victoria, Gozo; 25c. Silhouette of Fort St. Angelo.

230 Farm Animals 231 "The Right to Work"

1975. Christmas. Multicoloured.
549 8m.+2m. Type **230** 25 25
550 3c.+1c. Nativity scene (50 × 23 mm) 40 75
551 7c.5+1c.5 Approach of the Magi . . . . 45 1·40

1975. 1st Anniv of Republic.
552 **231** 1c.3 multicoloured 10 10
553 – 5c. multicoloured 20 10
554 – 25c. red, blue and black 70 1·10
DESIGNS: 5c. "Safeguarding the Environment"; 25c. National flag.

232 "Festa Tar-Rahal" 233 Water Polo

1976. Maltese Folklore. Multicoloured.
555 1c.3 Type **232** 10 10
556 5c. "L-Imnarja" (horiz) . . . 15 10
557 7c.5 "Il-Karnival" (horiz) . . 35 70
558 10c. "Il-Gimgha L-Kbira" . . 55 1·40

1976. Olympic Games, Montreal. Multicoloured.
559 1c.7 Type **233** 10 10
560 5c. Sailing 25 10
561 30c. Athletics . . . . 85 1·50

234 Lace-making

1976. Europa. Multicoloured.
562 7c. Type **234** 20 35
563 15c. Stone carving 25 60

235 Nicola Cotoner

1976. 300th Anniv of School of Anatomy and Surgery. Multicoloured.
564 2c. Type **235** 10 10
565 5c. Arm 15 10
566 7c. Giuseppe Zammit 20 10
567 11c. Sacra Infermeria 35 65

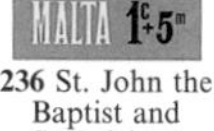

236 St. John the Baptist and St. Michael
237 Jean de la Valette's Armour

1976. Christmas. Multicoloured.
568 1c.+5m. Type **236** 10 20
569 5c.+1c. Madonna and Child 15 60
570 7c.+1c.5 St. Christopher and St. Nicholas 20 80
571 10c.+2c. Complete painting (32 × 27 mm) . . . . . . 30 1·25
Nos. 568/71 show portions of "Madonna and Saints" by Domenico di Michelino.

1977. Suits of Armour. Multicoloured.
572 2c. Type **237** 10 10
573 7c. Aloph de Wignacourt's armour 20 10
574 11c. Jean Jacques de Verdelin's armour 25 50

1977. No. 336 surch **1c7**.
575 1c.7 on 4d. multicoloured . . 25 25

239 "Annunciation"

1977. 400th Birth Anniv of Rubens. Flemish Tapestries. Multicoloured.
576 2c. Type **239** 10 10
577 7c. "Four Evangelists" . . . 25 10
578 11c. "Nativity" 45 45
579 20c. "Adoration of the Magi" 80 1·00
See also Nos. 592/5, 615/18 and 638/9.

240 Map and Radio Aerial
242 "Aid to Handicapped Workers" (detail from Workers' Monument)

241 Ta' L-Isperanza

1977. World Telecommunications Day.
580 **240** 1c. black, green and red 10 10
581 6c. black, blue and red . . 20 10
582 – 8c. black, brown and red . 30 10
583 – 17c. black, mauve and red 60 40
DESIGN—HORIZ: 8, 17c. Map, aerial and airplane tail-fin.

1977. Europa. Multicoloured.
584 7c. Type **241** 30 15
585 20c. Is-Salini . . . . 35 1·00

1977. Maltese Worker Commemoration.
586 **242** 2c. orange and brown . . 10 10
587 – 7c. light brown and brown 15 10
588 – 20c. multicoloured 40 60
DESIGNS—VERT: 7c. "Stoneworker, modern industry and ship-building" (monument detail). HORIZ: 20c. "Mother with Dead Son" and Service Medal.

243 The Shepherds

1977. Christmas. Multicoloured.
589 1c.+5m. Type **243** 10 35
590 7c.+1c. The Nativity 15 55
591 11c.+1c.5 The Flight into Egypt 20 70

1978. Flemish Tapestries. (2nd series). As T **239**. Multicoloured.
592 2c. "The Entry into Jerusalem" 10 10
593 7c. "The Last Supper" (after Poussin) 25 10
594 11c. "The Raising of the Cross" (after Rubens) . . . 30 25
595 25c. "The Resurrection" (after Rubens) 70 80

244 "Young Lady on Horseback and Trooper"

1978. 450th Death Anniv of Albrecht Durer.
596 **244** 1c.7 black, red and blue 10 10
597 – 8c. black, red and grey . . 15 10
598 – 17c. black, red and grey 40 45
DESIGNS: 8c. "The Bagpiper"; 17c. "The Virgin and Child with a Monkey".

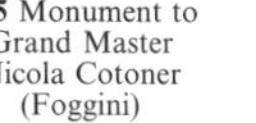

245 Monument to Grand Master Nicola Cotoner (Foggini)
246 Goalkeeper

1978. Europa. Monuments. Multicoloured.
599 7c. Type **245** 15 10
600 25c. Monument to Grand Master Ramon Perellos (Mazzuoli) 35 90

1978. World Cup Football Championship, Argentina. Multicoloured.
601 2c. Type **246** 10 10
602 11c. Players heading ball . . 15 10
603 15c. Tackling 25 35
MS604 125 × 90 mm. Nos. 601/3 2·00 3·25

247 Boeing 707 over Megalithic Temple

1978. Air. Multicoloured.
605 5c. Type **247** 20 10
606 7c. Air Malta Boeing 720B 20 10
607 11c. Boeing 747 taking off from Luqa Airport 35 10
608 17c. Type **247** 45 30
609 20c. As 7c. 60 40
610 75c. As 11c. . . . . 1·75 2·75

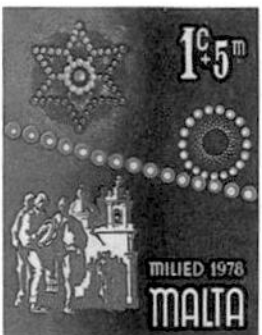

248 Folk Musicians and Village Church
249 Fishing Boat and Aircraft Carrier

1978. Christmas. Multicoloured.
611 1c.+5m. Type **248** 10 10
612 5c.+1c. Choir of Angels . . . 15 20
613 7c.+1c.5 Carol singers . . . 20 35
614 11c.+3c. Folk musicians, church, angels and carol singers (58 × 22 mm) . . . 25 45

1979. Flemish Tapestries (3rd series) showing paintings by Rubens. As T **239**. Multicoloured.
615 2c. "The Triumph of the Catholic Church" 10 10
616 7c. "The Triumph of Charity" 20 10
617 11c. "The Triumph of Faith" 30 25
618 25c. "The Triumph of Truth" 95 80

1979. End of Military Facilities Agreement. Multicoloured.
619 2c. Type **249** 10 10
620 5c. Raising the flag ceremony 10 10
621 7c. Departing soldier and olive sprig 15 10
622 8c. Type **249** 40 40
623 17c. As 5c. 55 60
624 20c. As 7c. 55 60

250 Speronara (fishing boat) and Tail of Air Malta Airliner
251 Children on Globe

1979. Europa. Communications. Multicoloured.
625 7c. Type **250** 20 10
626 25c. Coastal watch tower and radio link towers 40 75

1979. International Year of the Child. Multicoloured.
627 2c. Type **251** 10 10
628 7c. Children flying kites (27 × 33 mm) 15 10
629 11c. Children in circle (27 × 33 mm) 20 35

252 Shells

1979. Marine Life. Multicoloured.
630 2c. Type **252** 10 10
631 5c. Loggerhead turtle 20 10
632 7c. Dolphin (fish) 25 10
633 25c. Noble pen shell . . . . 90 1·25

253 "The Nativity" (detail)

1979. Christmas. Paintings by Giuseppe Cali. Multicoloured.
634 1c.+5m. Type **253** 10 10
635 5c.+1c. "The Flight into Egypt" (detail) 10 15
636 7c.+1c.5 "The Nativity" . . . 15 20
637 11c.+3c. "The Flight into Egypt" 25 50

1980. Flemish Tapestries (4th series). As T **239**. Multicoloured.
638 2c. "The Institution of Corpus Domini" (Rubens) 10 10
639 8c. "The Destruction of Idolatry" (Rubens) 20 20
MS640 114 × 86 mm. 50c. "Grand Master Perelles with St. Jude and St. Simon (unknown Maltese artist) (vert) . . . . 80 1·60

254 Hal Saflieni Hypogeum, Paola
255 Dun Gorg Preca

1980. Int Restoration of Monuments Campaign. Multicoloured.
641 2c.5 Type **254** 10 15
642 6c. Vilhena Palace, Mdina . . 15 20
643 8c. Citadel of Victoria, Gozo (horiz) 20 40
644 12c. Fort St. Elmo, Valletta (horiz) 30 60

1980. Birth Centenary of Dun Gorg Preca (founder of Society of Christian Doctrine).
645 **255** 2c. 5 grey and black . . . 10 10

256 Ruzar Briffa (poet)

1980. Europa.
646 **256** 8c. yellow, brown & green 20 10
647 – 30c. green, brown and lake . . . . 55 1·25
DESIGN: 30c. Nikiol Anton Vassalli (scholar and patriot).

257 "Annunciation"
258 Rook and Pawn

1980. Christmas. Paintings by A. Inglott. Multicoloured.
648 2c.+5m. Type **257** 10 10
649 6c.+1c. "Conception" 20 20
650 8c.+1c.5 "Nativity" 25 40
651 12c.+3c. "Annunciation", "Conception" and "Nativity" (47 × 38 mm) 30 70

1980. 24th Chess Olympiad and International Chess Federation Congress. Multicoloured.
652 2c.5 Type **258** 25 20
653 8c. Bishop and pawn 65 20
654 30c. King, queen and pawn (vert) . . . . 1·00 1·50

259 Barn Owl
260 Traditional Horse Race

1981. Birds. Multicoloured.
655 3c. Type **259** 30 25
656 8c. Sardinian warbler 50 25
657 12c. Woodchat shrike 60 80
658 23c. British storm petrel . . . 1·10 1·75

1981. Europa. Folklore. Multicoloured.
659 8c. Type **260** 20 10
660 30c. Attempting to retrieve flag from end of "gostra" (greasy pole) 40 65

261 Stylized "25"
262 Disabled Artist at Work

1981. 25th Maltese International Trade Fair.
661 **261** 4c. multicoloured 15 15
662 25c. multicoloured 50 60

1981. International Year for Disabled Persons. Multicoloured.
663 3c. Type **262** 20 10
664 35c. Disabled child playing football 90 75

263 Wheat Ear in Conical Flask

264 Megalithic Building

1981. World Food Day.
665 **263** 8c. multicoloured 15 15
666 23c. multicoloured 60 50

1981. History of Maltese Industry. Multicoloured.
667 5m. Type **264** 10 85
668 1c. Cotton production . . . 10 10
669 2c. Early ship-building . . . 85 10
670 3c. Currency minting 30 10
671 5c. "Art" 30 25
672 6c. Fishing . . . . 1·25 25
673 7c. Agriculture . . . . 30 1·50
674 8c. Stone quarrying . . . . . 1·00 35
675 10c. Grape pressing 35 50
676 12c. Modern ship-building . . 2·00 2·25
677 15c. Energy . . . . 70 2·00
678 20c. Telecommunications . . 70 75
679 25c. "Industry" . . . . . . 1·00 2·00
680 50c. Drilling for Water . . . 2·50 2·75
681 £1 Sea transport . . . . . . 7·00 7·50
682 £3 Air transport . . . . . . 12·00 18·00

265 Children and Nativity Scene

266 Shipbuilding

1981. Christmas. Multicoloured.
683 2c.+1c. Type **265** 25 10
684 8c.+2c. Christmas Eve procession (horiz) 35 20
685 20c.+3c. Preaching midnight sermon . . . . 75 1·10

1982. Shipbuilding Industry.
686 **266** 3c. multicoloured 15 10
687 – 8c. multicoloured 30 30
688 – 13c. multicoloured 55 55
689 – 27c. multicoloured . . . . 1·25 1·25
DESIGNS: 8c. to 27c. Differing shipyard scenes.

267 Elderly Man and Has-Serh (home for elderly)

1982. Care of Elderly. Multicoloured.
690 8c. Type **267** 40 20
691 30c. Elderly woman and Has-Zmien (hospital for elderly) 1·40 1·40

268 Redemption of Islands by Maltese, 1428

1982. Europa. Historical Events. Multicoloured.
692 8c. Type **268** 40 20
693 30c. Declaration of rights by Maltese, 1802 . . . . . . 1·00 1·40

269 Stylized Footballer

1982. World Cup Football Championship, Spain.
694 **269** 3c. multicoloured 20 10
695 – 12c. multicoloured 60 55
696 – 15c. multicoloured 70 65
MS697 125 × 90 mm. Nos. 694/6 3·50 4·50
DESIGNS: 12c., 15c. Various stylized footballers.

270 Angel appearing to Shepherds

1982. Christmas. Multicoloured.
698 2c.+1c. Type **270** 15 20
699 8c.+2c. Nativity and Three Wise Men bearing gifts . . 50 60
700 20c.+3c. Nativity scene (45 × 37 mm) . . . . . . 1·00 1·25

271 "Ta Salvo Serafino" (oared brigantine), 1531

1982. Maltese Ships (1st series). Multicoloured.
701 3c. Type **271** 40 10
702 8c. "La Madonna del Rosaria" (tartane), 1740 . . 80 30
703 12c. "San Paulo" (xebec), 1743 . . . . 1·25 55
704 20c. "Ta' Pietro Saliba" (xprunara), 1798 . . . . . 1·60 90
See also Nos. 725/8, 772/5, 792/5 and 809/12.

272 Locomotive "Manning Wardle", 1883

1983. Centenary of Malta Railway. Multicoloured.
705 3c. Type **272** 45 15
706 13c. Locomotive "Black Hawthorn", 1884 . . . . 1·00 1·00
707 27c. Beyer Peacock locomotive, 1895 . . . . . 2·00 3·25

273 Peace Doves leaving Malta

1983. Commonwealth Day. Multicoloured.
708 8c. Type **273** 25 30
709 12c. Tourist landmarks . . . 40 60
710 15c. Holiday beach (vert) . . 45 75
711 23c. Ship-building (vert) . . . 70 1·00

274 Ggantija Megalithic Temples, Gozo

1983. Europa. Multicoloured.
712 8c. Type **274** 40 40
713 30c. Fort St. Angelo . . . . 1·00 2·40

275 Dish Aerials (World Communications Year)

1983. Anniversaries and Events. Multicoloured.
714 3c. Type **275** 45 15
715 7c. Ships' prows and badge (25th anniv of I.M.O. Convention) 70 55
716 13c. Container lorries and badge (30th anniv of Customs Co-operation Council) 90 90
717 20c. Stadium and emblem (9th Mediterranean Games) 1·00 2·25

276 Monsignor Giuseppe de Piro

277 Annunciation

1983. 50th Death Anniv of Monsignor Giuseppe de Piro.
718 **276** 3c. multicoloured 15 15

1983. Christmas. Multicoloured.
719 2c.+1c. Type **277** 35 15
720 8c.+2c. The Nativity 85 60
721 20c.+3c. Adoration of the Magi . . . . 1·60 2·25

278 Workers at Meeting

1983. 40th Anniv of General Workers' Union. Multicoloured.
722 3c. Type **278** 30 10
723 8c. Worker with family . . . 60 40
724 27c. Union H.Q. Building . . 1·60 1·75

1983. Maltese Ships (2nd series). As T **271**. Multicoloured.
725 2c. "Strangier" (full-rigged ship), 1813 . . . . . . 30 25
726 12c. "Tigre" (topsail schooner), 1839 . . . . . 1·25 1·25
727 13c. "La Speranza" (brig), 1844 . . . . 1·25 1·25
728 20c. "Wignacourt" (barque), 1844 . . . . 1·75 2·75

279 Boeing 737

1984. Air. Multicoloured.
729 7c. Type **279** 50 30
730 8c. Boeing 720B 60 35
731 16c. Vickers Vanguard . . . 1·25 70
732 23c. Vickers Viscount . . . . 1·50 70
733 27c. Douglas DC-3 . . . . . 1·75 80
734 38c. Armstrong Whitworth Atalanta "Artemis" . . . 2·25 2·75
735 75c. "Marina" Fiat MF.5 flying boat . . . . 3·25 5·00

280 Bridge

1984. Europa. 25th Anniv of C.E.P.T.
736 **280** 8c. green, black and yellow 35 35
737 30c. red, black and yellow 1·25 1·25

281 Early Policeman

282 Running

1984. 170th Anniv of Malta Police Force. Multicoloured.
738 3c. Type **281** 65 15
739 8c. Mounted police . . . . . 1·50 65
740 11c. Motorcycle policeman 1·75 2·00
741 25c. Policeman and firemen 2·75 3·75

1984. Olympic Games, Los Angeles. Multicoloured.
742 7c. Type **282** 25 30
743 12c. Gymnastics 50 70
744 23c. Swimming . . . . . . 85 1·25

283 "The Visitation" (Pietru Caruana)

284 Dove on Map

1984. Christmas. Paintings from Church of Our Lady of Porto Salvo, Valletta. Multicoloured.
745 2c.+1c. Type **283** 55 65
746 8c.+2c. "The Epiphany" (Rafel Caruana) (horiz) . . 1·00 1·40
747 20c.+3c. "Jesus among the Doctors" (Rafel Caruana) (horiz) . . . . 2·00 4·00

1984. 10th Anniv of Republic. Multicoloured.
748 3c. Type **284** 40 20
749 8c. Fort St. Angelo 75 65
750 30c. Hands . . . . 2·50 4·75

285 1885 ½d. Green Stamp

287 Nicolo Baldacchino (tenor)

286 Boy, and Hands planting Vine

1985. Centenary of Malta Post Office. Mult.
751 3c. Type **285** 45 15
752 8c. 1885 1d. rose 65 45
753 12c. 1885 2½d. blue . . . . . 90 1·40
754 20c. 1885 4d. brown . . . . 1·40 3·00
MS755 165 × 90 mm. Nos. 751/4 3·75 6·50

1985. International Youth Year. Multicoloured.
756 2c. Type **286** 15 15
757 13c. Young people and flowers (vert) 85 60
758 27c. Girl holding flame in hand . . . . 1·75 1·40

1985. Europa. European Music Year. Mult.
759 8c. Type **287** . . . . 2·00 50
760 30c. Francesco Azopardi (composer) . . . . 3·50 5·00

288 Guzeppi Bajada and Manwel Attard (victims)

1985. 66th Anniv of 7 June 1919 Demonstrations. Multicoloured.
761 3c. Type **288** 35 15
762 7c. Karmnu Abela and Wenzu Dyer (victims) . . . 75 40
763 35c. Model of projected Demonstration monument by Anton Agius (vert) . . 2·50 2·75

289 Stylized Birds

1985. 40th Anniv of United Nations Organization. Multicoloured.
764 4c. Type **289** 25 15
765 11c. Arrow-headed ribbons 60 1·25
766 31c. Stylized figures . . . . 1·40 3·25

290 Giorgio Mitrovich (nationalist) (death centenary)

291 The Three Wise Men

1985. Celebrities' Anniversaries. Multicoloured.
767 8c. Type **290** . . . . 1·00 35
768 12c. Pietru Caxaru (poet and administrator) (400th death anniversary) . . . . 1·75 2·50

1985. Christmas. Designs showing details of terracotta relief by Ganni Bonnici. Multicoloured.
769 2c.+1c. Type **291** 55 75
770 8c.+2c. Virgin and Child . . 1·25 1·75
771 20c.+3c. Angels . . . . . . 2·50 4·00

1985. Maltese Ships (3rd series). Steamships. As T **271**. Multicoloured.
772 3c. "Scotia" (paddle-steamer), 1844 . . . . 85 20
773 7c. "Tagliaferro" (screw-steamer), 1822 . . . . . . 1·50 1·00
774 15c. "Gleneagles" (screw-steamer), 1885 . . . . . . 2·25 3·50
775 23c. "L'Isle Adam" (screw-steamer), 1886 . . . . . . 2·75 4·25

292 John XXIII Peace Laboratory and Statue of St. Francis of Assisi

1986. International Peace Year. Multicoloured.
776 8c. Type **292** . . . . 1·25 50
777 11c. Dove and hands holding olive branch (40 × 19 mm) 1·50 2·50
778 27c. Map of Africa, dove and two heads . . . . 3·25 4·75

293 Symbolic Plant and "Cynthia cardui", "Vanessa atalanta" and "Polyommatus icarus"

294 Heading the Ball

1986. Europa. Environmental Conservation. Multicoloured.
779 8c. Type **293** . . . . 1·50 50
780 35c. Island, Neolithic frieze, sea and sun . . . . 2·75 6·00

1986. World Cup Football Championship, Mexico. Multicoloured.
781 3c. Type **294** 60 20
782 7c. Saving a goal . . . . . . 1·25 1·00
783 23c. Controlling the ball . . 4·00 6·50
MS784 125 × 90 mm. Nos. 781/3 7·00 8·50

295 Father Diegu

1986. Maltese Philanthropists. Multicoloured.
785 2c. Type **295** 40 30
786 3c. Adelaide Cini 50 30
787 8c. Alfonso Maria Galea . . 1·25 60
788 27c. Vincenzo Bugeja . . . . 3·25 6·00

296 "Nativity"

1986. Christmas. Paintings by Giuseppe D'Arena. Multicoloured.
789 2c.+1c. Type **296** . . . . . . 1·50 1·75
790 8c.+2c. "Nativity" (detail) (vert) . . . . 3·25 3·50
791 20c.+3c. "Epiphany" . . . . 4·75 7·00

1986. Maltese Ships (4th series). As T **271**. Multicoloured.
792 7c. "San Paul" (freighter), 1921 . . . . 1·25 50
793 10c. "Knight of Malta" (mail steamer), 1930 . . . . . . 1·50 1·75
794 12c. "Valetta City" (freighter), 1948 . . . . . 1·75 2·75
795 20c. "Saver" (freighter), 1959 3·00 4·50

297 European Robin

1987. 25th Anniv of Malta Ornithological Society. Multicoloured.
796 3c. Type **297** . . . . 1·25 50
797 8c. Peregrine falcon (vert) . . 2·50 1·00
798 13c. Hoopoe (vert) . . . . . 3·25 4·00
799 23c. Cory's shearwater . . . 3·75 6·00

298 Aquasun Lido

299 16th-century Pikeman

1987. Europa. Modern Architecture. Multicoloured.
800 8c. Type **298** . . . . 1·25 75
801 35c. Church of St. Joseph, Manikata . . . . 3·50 6·25

1987. Maltese Uniforms (1st series). Multicoloured.
802 3c. Type **299** 75 40
803 7c. 16th-century officer . . . 1·40 90
804 10c. 18th-century standard bearer . . . . 1·60 2·25
805 27c. 18th-century General of the Galleys . . . . 3·50 4·75
See also Nos. 832/5, 851/4, 880/3 and 893/6.

300 Maltese Scenes, Wheat Ears and Sun

1987. Anniversaries and Events. Multicoloured.
806 5c. Type **300** (European Environment Year) . . . . 1·25 50
807 8c. Esperanto star as comet (Centenary of Esperanto) 2·00 60
808 23c. Family at house door (International Year of Shelter for the Homeless) 3·00 3·00

1987. Maltese Ships (5th series). As T **271**. Multicoloured.
809 2c. "Medina" (freighter), 1969 . . . . 70 60
810 11c. "Rabat" (container ship), 1974 . . . . 2·50 2·50
811 13c. "Ghawdex" (passenger ferry), 1979 . . . . 2·75 2·75
812 20c. "Pinto" (car ferry), 1987 3·75 4·00

301 "The Visitation"

1987. Christmas. Illuminated illustrations, score and text from 16th-century choral manuscript. Multicoloured.
813 2c.+1c. Type **301** 65 65
814 8c.+2c. "The Nativity" . . . 2·25 3·00
815 20c.+3c. "The Adoration of the Magi" . . . . 3·75 5·00

302 Dr. Arvid Pardo (U.N. representative)

1987. 20th Anniv of United Nations Resolution on Peaceful Use of the Seabed. Multicoloured.
816 8c. Type **302** . . . . 1·00 75
817 12c. U.N. emblem and sea . . 1·75 3·00
MS818 125 × 90 mm. Nos. 816/17 3·75 4·50

303 Ven. Nazju Falzon (Catholic catechist)

304 "St. John Bosco with Youth" (statue)

1988. Maltese Personalities. Multicoloured.
819 2c. Type **303** 25 30
820 3c. Mgr. Sidor Formosa (philanthropist) 25 30
821 4c. Sir Luigi Preziosi (ophthalmologist) 40 30
822 10c. Fr. Anastasju Cuschieri (poet) 80 85
823 25c. Mgr. Pietru Pawl Saydon (Bible translator) 2·25 3·25

1988. Religious Anniversaries. Multicoloured.
824 10c. Type **304** (death centenary) . . . . 1·00 1·00
825 12c. "Assumption of Our Lady" (altarpiece by Perugino, Ta' Pinu, Gozo) (Marian Year) . . . . . 1·25 1·50
826 14c. "Christ the King" (statue by Sciortino) (75th anniv of International Eucharistic Congress, Valletta) . . . . 1·75 2·50

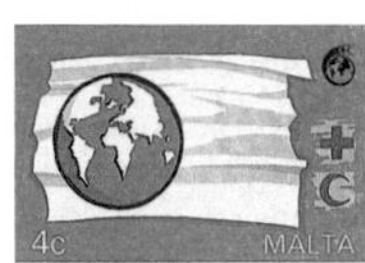

305 Bus, Ferry and Aircraft

306 Globe and Red Cross Emblems

1988. Europa. Transport and Communications. Multicoloured.
827 10c. Type **305** . . . . 1·25 75
828 35c. Control panel, dish aerial and pylons . . . . . 2·75 4·50

1988. Anniversaries and Events. Multicoloured.
829 4c. Type **306** (125th anniv of Int Red Cross) 75 50
830 18c. Divided globe (Campaign for North–South Interdependence and Solidarity) . . . . 2·00 3·00
831 19c. Globe and symbol (40th anniv of W.H.O.) . . . . 2·00 3·00

1988. Maltese Uniforms (2nd series). As T **299**. Multicoloured.
832 3c. Private, Maltese Light Infantry, 1800 . . . . . . 40 30
833 4c. Gunner, Malta Coast Artillery, 1802 . . . . . . 45 35
834 10c. Field Officer, 1st Maltese Provincial Battalion, 1805 1·10 1·25
835 25c. Subaltern, Royal Malta Regiment, 1809 . . . . . 2·50 4·25

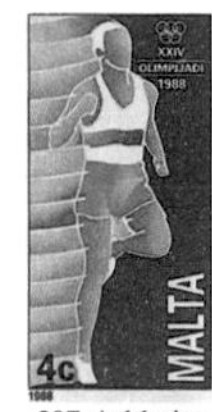

307 Athletics

308 Shepherd with Flock

1988. Olympic Games, Seoul. Multicoloured.
836 4c. Type **307** 30 30
837 10c. Diving 70 80
838 35c. Basketball . . . . 2·00 3·00

1988. Christmas. Multicoloured.
839 3c.+1c. Type **308** 30 30
840 10c.+2c. The Nativity . . . . 85 1·25
841 25c.+3c. Three Wise Men . . 2·00 2·75

309 Commonwealth Emblem

311 Two Boys flying Kite

310 New State Arms

1989. 25th Anniv of Independence. Multicoloured.
842 2c. Type **309** 25 35
843 3c. Council of Europe flag . . 25 35
844 4c. U.N. flag 30 35
845 10c. Workers, hands gripping ring and national flag . . . 75 95
846 12c. Scales and allegorical figure of Justice . . . . . 90 1·40
847 25c. Prime Minister Borg Olivier with Independence constitution (42 × 28 mm) 1·90 3·25

1989.
848 **310** £1 multicoloured . . . . 4·00 4·50

1989. Europa. Children's Games. Multicoloured.
849 10c. Type **311** . . . . 1·25 75
850 35c. Two girls with dolls . . 3·25 4·50

1989. Maltese Uniforms (3rd series). As T **299**. Multicoloured.
851 3c. Officer, Maltese Veterans, 1815 . . . . 45 45
852 4c. Subaltern, Royal Malta Fencibles, 1839 . . . . . 50 50
853 10c. Private, Malta Militia, 1856 . . . . 1·50 1·50
854 25c. Colonel, Royal Malta Fencible Artillery, 1875 . . 2·75 3·75

312 Human Figures and Buildings

1989. Anniversaries and Commemorations. Designs showing logo and stylized human figures. Multicoloured.

855 3c. Type **312** (20th anniv of U.N. Declaration on Social Progress and Development) 30 30
856 4c. Workers and figure in wheelchair (Malta's Ratification of European Social Charter) 35 35
857 10c. Family (40th anniv of Council of Europe) 80 1·25
858 14c. Teacher and children (70th anniv of Malta Union of Teachers) 1·00 1·75
859 25c. Symbolic knights (Knights of the Sovereign Military Order of Malta Assembly) 2·25 3·50

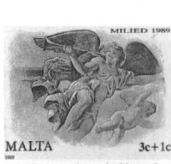

313 Angel and Cherub

315 General Post Office, Auberge d'Italie, Valletta

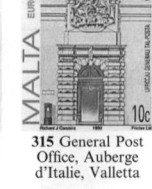

314 Presidents George H. Bush and Mikhail Gorbachev

1989. Christmas. Vault paintings by Mattia Preti from St. John's Co-Cathedral, Valletta.

860 3c.+1c. Type **313** 80 70
861 10c.+2c. Two angels 2·00 2·25
862 20c.+3c. Angel blowing trumpet 2·75 4·00

1989. U.S.A.–U.S.S.R. Summit Meeting, Malta.

863 **314** 10c. multicoloured 1·00 1·25

1990. Europa. Post Office Buildings. Multicoloured.

864 10c. Type **315** 1·00 50
865 35c. Branch Post Office, Zebbug (horiz) 2·50 3·75

316 Open Book and Letters from Different Alphabets (International Literacy Year)

318 St. Paul

317 Samuel Taylor Coleridge (poet) and Government House

1990. Anniversaries and Events. Multicoloured.

866 3c. Type **316** 25 25
867 4c. Count Roger of Sicily and Norman soldiers (900th anniv of Sicilian rule) (horiz) 60 30
868 19c. Communications satellite (25th anniv of I.T.U.) (horiz) 2·25 2·50
869 20c. Football and map of Malta (Union of European Football Association 20th Ordinary Congress, Malta) 2·25 2·50

1990. British Authors. Multicoloured.

870 4c. Type **317** 50 30
871 10c. Lord Byron (poet) and map of Valletta 90 70
872 12c. Sir Walter Scott (novelist) and Great Siege 1·00 95
873 25c. William Makepeace Thackeray (novelist) and Naval Arsenal 2·00 2·25

1990. Visit of Pope John Paul II. Bronze Bas-reliefs.

874 **318** 4c. black, flesh and red 50 1·50
875 – 25c. black, flesh and red 1·50 1·75
DESIGN: 25c. Pope John Paul II.

319 Flags and Football

320 Innkeeper

1990. World Cup Football Championship, Italy. Multicoloured.

876 5c. Type **319** 35 30
877 10c. Football in net 65 1·00
878 14c. Scoreboard and football 1·00 1·75
MS879 123 × 90 mm. Nos. 876/8 3·00 4·00

1990. Maltese Uniforms (4th series). As T **299**. Multicoloured.

880 3c. Captain, Royal Malta Militia, 1889 1·25 55
881 4c. Field officer, Royal Malta Artillery, 1905 1·40 60
882 10c. Labourer, Malta Labour Corps, 1915 2·50 1·50
883 25c. Lieutenant, King's Own Malta Regiment of Militia, 1918 3·75 4·50

1990. Christmas. Figures from Crib by Austin Galea, Marco Bartolo and Rosario Zammit. Multicoloured.

884 3c.+1c. Type **320** 30 50
885 10c.+2c. Nativity (41 × 28 mm) 70 1·25
886 25c.+3c. Shepherd with sheep 1·60 2·50

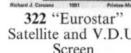

321 1919 10s. Stamp under Magnifying Glass

1991. 25th Anniv of Philatelic Society of Malta.

887 **321** 10c. multicoloured 60 70

322 "Eurostar" Satellite and V.D.U. Screen

324 Interlocking Arrows

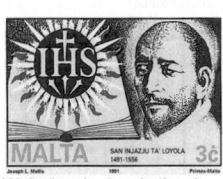

323 St. Ignatius Loyola (founder of Jesuits) (500th birth anniv)

1991. Europa. Europe in Space. Multicoloured.

888 10c. Type **322** 1·00 70
889 35c. "Ariane 4" rocket and projected HOTOL aerospace-plane 2·00 2·75

1991. Religious Commemorations. Multicoloured.

890 3c. Type **323** 30 20
891 4c. Abbess Venerable Maria Adeodata Pisani (185th birth anniversary) (vert) 35 25
892 30c. St. John of the Cross (400th death anniversary) 2·00 2·75

1991. Maltese Uniforms (5th series). As T **299**. Multicoloured.

893 3c. Officer with colour, Royal Malta Fencibles, 1860 30 25
894 10c. Officer with colour, Royal Malta Regiment of Militia, 1903 70 60
895 19c. Officer with Queen's colour, King's Own Malta Regiment, 1968 1·40 1·75
896 25c. Officer with colour, Malta Armed Forces, 1991 1·75 2·00

1991. 25th Anniv of Union Haddiema Maghqudin (public services union).

897 **324** 4c. multicoloured 30 30

325 Western Honey Buzzard

326 Three Wise Men

1991. Endangered Species. Birds. Multicoloured.

898 4c. Type **325** 1·75 2·00
899 4c. Marsh harrier 1·75 2·00
900 10c. Eleonora's falcon 1·75 2·00
901 10c. Lesser kestrel 1·75 2·00

1991. Christmas. Multicoloured.

902 3c.+1c. Type **326** 45 50
903 10c.+2c. Holy Family 1·00 1·25
904 25c.+3c. Two shepherds 2·00 3·00

327 Ta' Hagrat Neolithic Temple

1991. National Heritage of the Maltese Islands. Multicoloured.

905 1c. Type **327** 25 50
906 2c. Cottoner Gate 25 50
907 3c. St. Michael's Bastion, Valletta 25 50
908 4c. Spinola Palace, St. Julian's 25 15
909 5c. Birkirkara Church 30 20
910 10c. Mellieha Bay 60 35
911 12c. Wied iz-Zurrieq 65 40
912 14c. Mgarr harbour, Gozo 75 45
913 20c. Yacht marina 1·10 65
914 50c. Gozo Channel 2·00 1·60
915 £1 "Arab Horses" (sculpture by Antonio Sciortino) 4·25 3·25
916 £2 Independence Monument (Ganni Bonnici) (vert) 8·50 7·00

328 Aircraft Tailfins and Terminal

1992. Opening of Int Air Terminal. Mult.

917 4c. Type **328** 75 30
918 10c. National flags and terminal 1·25 70

329 Ships of Columbus

1992. Europa. 500th Anniv of Discovery of America by Columbus. Multicoloured.

919 10c. Type **329** 1·25 55
920 35c. Columbus and map of Americas 2·50 2·25

330 George Cross and Anti-aircraft Gun Crew

332 Church of the Flight into Egypt

331 Running

1992. 50th Anniv of Award of George Cross to Malta. Multicoloured.

921 4c. Type **330** 1·00 30
922 10c. George Cross and memorial bell 1·50 1·00
923 50c. Tanker "Ohio" entering Grand Harbour 7·00 8·50

1992. Olympic Games, Barcelona. Multicoloured.

924 3c. Type **331** 65 20
925 10c. High jumping 1·25 1·00
926 30c. Swimming 2·50 4·50

1992. Rehabilitation of Historical Buildings.

927 **332** 3c. black, stone and grey 50 30
928 – 4c. black, stone and pink 55 30
929 – 19c. black, stone and lilac 2·25 3·00
930 – 25c. black, stone and green 2·50 3·00
DESIGNS—HORIZ: 4c. St. John's Co-Cathedral; 25c. Auberge de Provence. VERT: 19c. Church of Madonna del Pillar.

333 "The Nativity" (Giuseppe Cali)

1992. Christmas. Religious Paintings by Giuseppe Cali from Mosta Church. Multicoloured.

931 3c.+1c. Type **333** 80 85
932 10c.+2c. "Adoration of the Magi" 2·00 2·25
933 25c.+3c. "Christ with the Elders in the Temple" 3·50 4·25

334 Malta College Building, Valletta

335 Lions Club Emblem

1992. 400th Anniv of University of Malta. Multicoloured.

934 4c. Type **334** 75 25
935 30c. Modern University complex, Tal-Qroqq (horiz) 2·75 4·00

1993. 75th Anniv of International Association of Lions Club. Multicoloured.

936 4c. Type **335** 50 25
937 50c. Eye (Sight First Campaign) 2·75 4·00

336 Untitled Painting by Paul Carbonaro

1993. Europa. Contemporary Art. Mult.

938 10c. Type **336** 1·00 50
939 35c. Untitled painting by Alfred Chircop (horiz) 2·50 4·25

337 Mascot holding Flame

1993. 5th Small States of Europe Games. Multicoloured.

940 3c. Type **337** 20 20
941 4c. Cycling 80 30
942 10c. Tennis 1·50 1·00
943 35c. Yachting 2·75 3·50
MS944 120 × 80 mm. Nos. 940/3 4·00 4·00

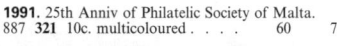

338 Learning First Aid **339** "Papilio machaon"

1993. 50th Anniv of Award of Bronze Cross to Maltese Scouts and Guides. Multicoloured.
945 3c. Type **338** 30 15
946 4c. Bronze Cross 30 20
947 10c. Scout building camp fire 80 80
948 35c. Governor Lord Gort presenting Bronze Cross, 1943 . . . . 2·25 3·25

1993. European Year of the Elderly. Butterflies. Multicoloured.
949 5c. Type **339** 35 20
950 35c. "Vanessa atalanta" . . . 1·75 2·25

340 G.W.U. Badge and Interlocking "50" **341** Child Jesus and Star

1993. 50th Anniv of General Workers Union.
951 **340** 4c. multicoloured 35 40

1993. Christmas. Multicoloured.
952 3c.+1c. Type **341** 30 35
953 10c.+2c. Christmas tree . . . 85 1·10
954 25c.+3c. Star in traditional window . . . . 1·60 2·50

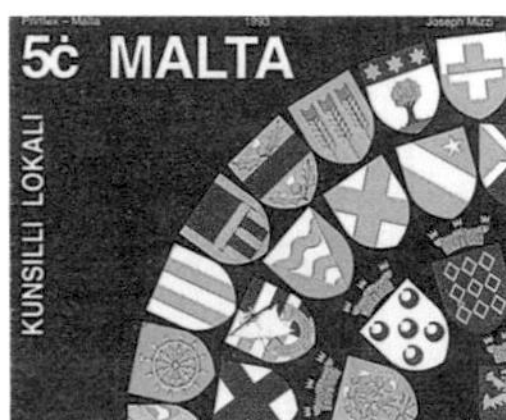

342 Council Arms (face value top left)

1993. Inauguration of Local Community Councils. Sheet 110 × 93 mm, containing T **342** and similar horiz designs showing different Council Arms. Multicoloured.
MS955 5c. Type **342**; 5c. Face value top right; 5c. Face value bottom left; 5c. Face value bottom right 1·50 2·25

343 Symbolic Tooth and Probe **344** Sir Themistocles Zammit (discoverer of Brucella microbe)

1994. 50th Anniv of Maltese Dental Association. Multicoloured.
956 5c. Type **343** 35 30
957 44c. Symbolic mouth and dental mirror . . . . . . 3·00 3·00

1994. Europa. Discoveries. Multicoloured.
958 14c. Type **344** 50 30
959 30c. Bilingually inscribed candelabrum of 2nd century B.C. (deciphering of ancient Phoenician language) . . . . 1·90 3·25

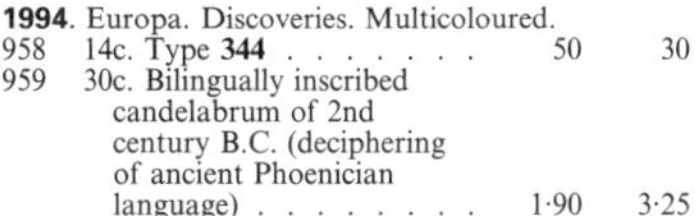

345 Family in Silhouette (International Year of the Family) **346** Football and Map

1994. Anniversaries and Events. Multicoloured.
960 5c. Type **345** 30 20
961 9c. Stylized Red Cross (International recognition of Malta Red Cross Society) 60 50
962 14c. Animals and crops (150th anniv of Agrarian Society) 90 80
963 20c. Worker in silhouette (75th anniv of I.L.O.) . . . 1·25 1·60
964 25c. St. Paul's Anglican Cathedral (155th anniv) (vert) . . . . 1·40 1·75

1994. World Cup Football Championship, U.S.A. Multicoloured.
965 5c. Type **346** 40 20
966 14c. Ball and goal . . . . . 1·00 80
967 30c. Ball and pitch superimposed on map . . 2·50 4·25
MS968 123 × 88 mm. Nos. 965/7 3·75 4·00

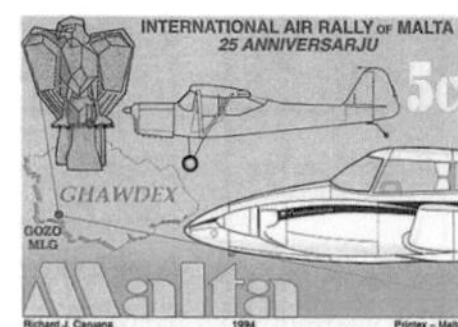

347 Falcon Trophy, Twin Comanche and Auster (25th anniv of Malta International Rally)

1994. Aviation Anniversaries and Events. Multicoloured.
969 5c. Type **347** 50 20
970 14c. Alouette helicopter, display teams and logo (Malta International Airshow) . . . . 1·75 85
971 20c. De Havilland Dove "City of Valetta" and Avro York aircraft with logo (50th anniv of I.C.A.O.) 1·90 1·75
972 25c. Airbus 320 "Nicolas Cottoner" and De Havilland Comet aircraft with logo (50th anniv of I.C.A.O.) . . . . 1·90 1·90

348 National Flags and Astronaut on Moon **350** Helmet-shaped Ewer

349 Virgin Mary and Child with Angels

1994. 25th Anniv of First Manned Moon Landing.
973 **348** 14c. multicoloured . . . . 1·10 1·25

1994. Christmas. Multicoloured.
974 5c. Type **349** 25 10
975 9c.+2c. Angel in pink (vert) 65 70
976 14c.+3c. Virgin Mary and Child (vert) . . . . 90 1·25
977 20c.+3c. Angel in green (vert) 1·60 2·50
Nos. 975/7 are larger, 28 × 41 mm, and depict details from Type **349**.

1994. Maltese Antique Silver Exhibition. Multicoloured.
978 5c. Type **350** 40 20
979 14c. Balsamina 90 80
980 20c. Coffee pot . . . . . . 1·60 1·90
981 25c. Sugar box . . . . 1·90 2·50

351 "60 plus" and Hands touching **352** Hand holding Leaf and Rainbow

1995. Anniversaries and Events. Multicoloured.
982 2c. Type **351** (25th anniv of National Association of Pensioners) 15 15
983 5c. Child's drawing (10th anniv of National Youth Council) 25 20
984 14c. Conference emblem (4th World Conference on Women, Peking, China) . . 70 80
985 20c. Nurse and thermometer (50th anniv of Malta Memorial District Nursing Association) . . . . 1·25 1·40
986 25c. Louis Pasteur (biologist) (death centenary) . . . . . 1·50 1·75

1995. Europa. Peace and Freedom. Multicoloured.
987 14c. Type **352** 75 55
988 30c. Peace doves (horiz) . . . 1·50 2·00

353 Junkers Ju 87B "Stuka" Dive Bombers over Valletta and Anti-aircraft Gun

1995. Anniversaries. Multicoloured.
989 5c. Type **353** (50th anniv of end of Second World War) 25 25
990 14c. Silhouetted people holding hands (50th anniv of United Nations) 70 80
991 35c. Hands holding bowl of wheat (50th anniv of F.A.O.) (vert) . . . . . . 2·00 2·25

354 Light Bulb **356** Pinto's Turret Clock

355 Rock Wall and Girna

1995. Maltese Electricity and Telecommunications. Multicoloured.
992 2c. Type **354** 15 15
993 5c. Symbolic owl and binary codes 25 25
994 9c. Dish aerial 45 50
995 14c. Sun and rainbow over trees 70 80
996 20c. Early telephone, satellite and Moon's surface . . . 1·25 1·50

1995. European Nature Conservation Year. Multicoloured.
997 5c. Type **355** 75 25
998 14c. Maltese wall lizards . . 2·00 80
999 44c. Aleppo pine . . . . . . 3·25 3·00

1995. Treasures of Malta. Antique Maltese Clocks. Multicoloured.
1000 1c. Type **356** 15 60
1001 5c. Michelangelo Sapiano (horologist) and clocks . . 50 25
1002 14c. Arlogg tal-lira clock . . 1·50 80
1003 25c. Sundials . . . . 2·50 3·50

357 Children's Christmas Eve Procession

1995. Christmas. Multicoloured.
1004 5c. Type **357** 25 10
1005 5c.+2c. Children with crib (vert) 30 50
1006 14c.+3c. Children with lanterns (vert) . . . . . 1·00 1·25
1007 25c.+3c. Boy with lantern and balustrade (vert) . . 1·75 2·75
Nos. 1005/7 are 27 × 32 mm and depict details from Type **357**.

358 Silhouetted Children and President's Palace, San Anton

1996. Anniversaries. Multicoloured.
1008 5c. Type **358** (35th anniv of the President's Award) . . 25 25
1009 14c. Nazzareno Camilleri (priest) and St. Patrick's Church, Salesjani (90th birth anniv) 65 65
1010 20c. St. Mary Euphrasia and convent (birth bicentenary) . . . . . . 1·00 1·10
1011 25c. Silhouetted children and fountain (50th anniv of U.N.I.C.E.F.) . . . . 1·25 1·40

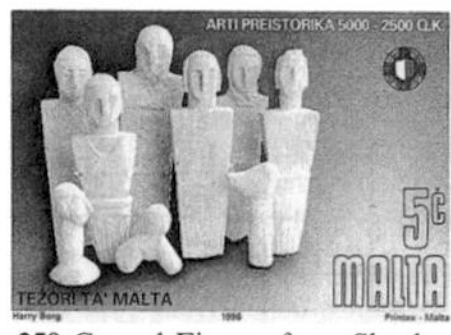

359 Carved Figures from Skorba

1996. Maltese Prehistoric Art Exhibition. Multicoloured.
1012 5c. Type **359** 30 20
1013 14c. Temple carving, Gozo 80 85
1014 20c. Carved figure of a woman, Skorba (vert) . . 1·10 1·25
1015 35c. Ghar Dalam pot (vert) 1·90 2·50

360 Mabel Strickland (politician and journalist) **361** Face and Emblem (United Nations Decade against Drug Abuse)

1996. Europa. Famous Women. Multicoloured.
1016 14c. Type **360** 75 55
1017 30c. Inez Soler (artist, musician and writer) . . . 2·00 2·00

1996. Anniversaries and Events. Multicoloured.
1018 5c. Type **361** 25 25
1019 5c. "Fi" and emblem (50th anniv of Malta Federation of Industry) 25 25
1020 14c. Commemorative plaque and national flag (75th anniv of self-government) 80 80
1021 44c. Guglielmo Marconi and early radio equipment (centenary of radio) . . . 2·25 2·50

362 Judo

1996. Olympic Games, Atlanta. Multicoloured.
1022 2c. Type **362** 10 10
1023 5c. Athletics 30 25
1024 14c. Diving 80 80
1025 25c. Rifle-shooting . . . . 1·40 1·60

363 "Harvest Time" (Cali)

1996. 150th Birth Anniv of Guiseppe Cali (painter). Multicoloured.
1026 5c. Type **363** 30 25
1027 14c. "Dog" (Cali) 80 70
1028 20c. "Countrywoman in a Field" (Cali) (vert) . . . 1·10 1·10
1029 25c. "Cali at his Easel" (Edward Dingli) (vert) . . 1·25 1·25

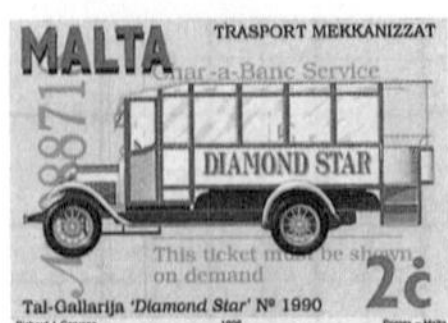

364 Bus No. 1990 "Diamond Star", 1920s

1996. Buses. Multicoloured.
1030 2c. Type **364** 30 10
1031 5c. No. 434 "Tom Mix", 1930s 60 25
1032 14c. No. 1764 "Verdala", 1940s . . . . 1·25 80
1033 30c. No. 3495, 1960s . . . 1·75 2·00

365 Stained Glass Window

1996. Christmas. Multicoloured.
1034 5c. Type **365** 35 10
1035 5c.+2c. Madonna and Child (29×35 mm) 40 50
1036 14c.+3c. Angel facing right (29×35 mm) . . . . . . 80 1·25
1037 25c.+3c. Angel facing left (29×35 mm) . . . . . . 1·25 1·90
Nos. 1035/7 show details from Type **365**.

366 Hompesch Arch and Arms, Zabbar
368 Gahan carrying Door

367 Captain-General of the Galleys' Sedan Chair

1997. Bicentenary of Maltese Cities. Multicoloured.
1038 6c. Type **366** 30 25
1039 16c. Statue, church and arms, Siggiewi 70 70
1040 26c. Seated statue and arms, Zejtun . . . . 1·10 1·10
MS1041 125×90 mm. Nos. 1038/40 3·50 3·50

1997. Treasures of Malta. Sedan Chairs. Multicoloured.
1042 2c. Type **367** 15 15
1043 6c. Cotoner Grandmasters' chair 30 30
1044 16c. Chair from Cathedral Museum, Mdina (vert) . . 70 70
1045 27c. Chevalier D'Arezzo's chair (vert) . . . . 1·10 1·10

1997. Europa. Tales and Legends. Multicoloured.
1046 16c. Type **368** . . . . . . 1·25 75
1047 35c. St. Dimitrius appearing from painting . . . . . . 2·00 1·50

369 Modern Sculpture (Antonio Sciortino)
370 Dr. Albert Laferla

1997. Anniversaries. Multicoloured.
1048 1c. Type **369** 10 15
1049 6c. Joseph Calleia and film reel (horiz) 40 40
1050 6c. Gozo Cathedral (horiz) 40 40
1051 11c. City of Gozo (horiz) . . 60 50
1052 16c. Sculpture of head (Sciortino) 80 70
1053 22c. Joseph Calleia and film camera (horiz) . . . . . 1·00 1·00
ANNIVERSARIES: 1, 16c. 50th death anniv of Antonio Sciortino (sculptor); 6 (No. 1049), 22c. Birth centenary of Joseph Calleia (actor); 6 (No. 1050), 11c. 300th anniv of construction of Gozo Cathedral.

1997. Pioneers of Education. Multicoloured.
1054 6c. Type **370** 30 25
1055 16c. Sister Emilie de Vialar 70 70
1056 19c. Mgr. Paolo Pullicino 80 80
1057 26c. Mgr. Tommaso Gargallo . . . . 1·00 1·10

371 The Nativity

1997. Christmas. Multicoloured.
1058 6c. Type **371** 30 10
1059 6c.+2c. Mary and baby Jesus (vert) 35 50
1060 16c.+3c. Joseph with donkey (vert) . . . . 1·00 1·40
1061 26c.+3c. Shepherd with lamb (vert) . . . . 1·50 2·50
Nos. 1059/61 show details from Type **371**.

372 Plan of Fort and Soldiers in Victoria Lines

1997. Anniversaries. Multicoloured (except 6c.).
1062 2c. Type **372** 20 10
1063 6c. Sir Paul Boffa making speech (black and red) . . 30 25
1064 16c. Plan of fort and gun crew 90 65
1065 37c. Queue of voters . . . . 1·50 2·00
ANNIVERSARIES: 2, 16c. Centenary of Victoria Lines; 6, 37c. 50th anniv of 1947 Self-government Constitution.

373 "Maria Amelia Grognet" (Antonine de Favray)

1998. Treasures of Malta. Costumes and Paintings. Multicoloured.
1066 6c. Type **373** 70 50
1067 6c. Gentleman's waistcoat, c.1790–1810 . . . . . . 70 50
1068 16c. Lady's dinner dress, c.1880 . . . . 1·00 90
1069 16c. "Veneranda, Baroness Abela, and her Grandson" (De Favray) 1·00 90
MS1070 123×88 mm. 26c. City of Valletta from old print (39×47 mm) . . . . 1·60 1·60

374 Grand Master Ferdinand von Hompesch

1998. Bicentenary of Napoleon's Capture of Malta. Multicoloured.
1071 6c. Type **374** 60 70
1072 6c. French fleet 60 70
1073 16c. French landing . . . . 1·10 1·40
1074 16c. General Napoleon Bonaparte . . . . 1·10 1·40

375 Racing Two-man Luzzus
376 Dolphin and Diver

1998. Europa. Sailing Regatta, Grand Harbour. Multicoloured.
1075 16c. Type **375** . . . . . . 1·40 55
1076 35c. Racing four-man luzzus 1·90 2·50

1998. International Year of the Ocean. Multicoloured.
1077 2c. Type **376** 40 25
1078 6c. Diver and sea-urchin . . 65 25
1079 16c. Jacques Cousteau and diver (horiz) . . . . . . 1·60 80
1080 27c. Two divers (horiz) . . 2·00 2·25

377 Goalkeeper saving Goal
378 Ships' Wheels (50th anniv of Int Maritime Organization)

1998. World Cup Football Championship, France. Players and flags. Multicoloured.
1081 6c. Type **377** 70 25
1082 16c. Two players and referee 1·40 70
1083 22c. Two footballers . . . . 1·60 2·00
MS1084 122×87 mm. Nos. 1081/3 2·75 2·75

1998. Anniversaries. Multicoloured.
1085 1c. Type **378** 10 30
1086 6c. Symbolic family (50th anniv of Universal Declaration of Human Rights) 40 25
1087 11c. "GRTU" and cogwheels (50th anniv of General Retailers and Traders Union) 70 40
1088 19c. Mercury (50th anniv of Chamber of Commerce) 1·10 1·40
1089 26c. Aircraft tailfins (25th anniv of Air Malta) . . . 2·00 2·50

379 "Rest on the Flight to Egypt"

1998. Christmas. Paintings by Mattia Preti. Mult.
1090 6c. Type **379** 40 10
1091 6c.+2c. "Virgin and Child with Sts. Anthony and John the Baptist" 50 60
1092 16c.+3c. "Virgin and Child with Sts. Raphael, Nicholas and Gregory" 1·25 1·50
1093 26c.+3c. "Virgin and Child with Sts. John the Baptist and Nicholas" . . . . . 1·75 2·50

380 Fort St. Angelo

1999. 900th Anniv of the Sovereign Military Order of Malta. Multicoloured.
1094 2c. Type **380** 25 10
1095 6c. Grand Master De l'Isle Adam (vert) 50 25
1096 16c. Grand Master La Valette (vert) . . . . 1·00 55
1097 27c. Auberge de Castille et Leon . . . . 1·50 1·60

381 Little Ringed Plover, Ghadira Nature Reserve

1999. Europa. Parks and Gardens. Multicoloured.
1098 16c. Type **381** . . . . . . 1·75 55
1099 35c. River kingfisher, Simar Nature Reserve . . . . . 2·25 2·75

382 Council of Europe Assembly

1999. 50th Anniv of Council of Europe. Mult.
1100 6c. Type **382** 75 25
1101 16c. Council of Europe Headquarters, Strasbourg 1·25 1·25

383 U.P.U. Emblem and Marsamxett Harbour, Valletta

1999. 125th Anniv of Universal Postal Union. Multicoloured.
1102 6c. Type **383** . . . . 1·25 1·40
1103 16c. Nuremberg and "iBRA '99" International Stamp Exhibition emblem . . . 1·50 1·60
1104 22c. Paris and "Philexfrance '99" International Stamp Exhibition emblem . . . 1·60 1·75
1105 27c. Peking and "China '99" International Stamp Exhibition emblem . . . 1·75 1·90
1106 37c. Melbourne and "Australia '99" International Stamp Exhibition emblem . . . 1·90 2·25

384 Couple in Luzzu

1999. Tourism. Multicoloured.
1107 6c. Type **384** 50 25
1108 16c. Tourist taking photograph 95 55
1109 22c. Man sunbathing (horiz) 1·25 1·00
1110 27c. Couple with horse-drawn carriage (horiz) . . 1·90 1·25
1111 37c. Caveman at Ta' Hagrat Neolithic temple (horiz) 2·50 2·75

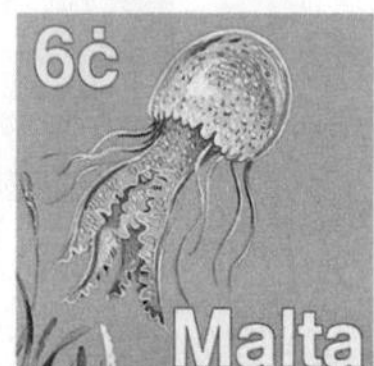

385 Common Jellyfish

1999. Marine Life of the Mediterranean. Mult.
1112 6c. Type **385** 65 65
1113 6c. Peacock wrasse 65 65
1114 6c. Common cuttlefish . . . 65 65
1115 6c. Violet sea-urchin 65 65
1116 6c. Dusky grouper 65 65
1117 6c. Common two-banded seabream 65 65
1118 6c. Star-coral 65 65
1119 6c. Spiny spider crab . . . 65 65
1120 6c. Rainbow wrasse 65 65
1121 6c. Octopus 65 65
1122 6c. Atlantic trumpet triton 65 65
1123 6c. Mediterranean parrotfish 65 65
1124 6c. Long-snouted seahorse 65 65

1125 6c. Deep-water hermit crab . . 65 65
1126 6c. Mediterranean moray . . 65 65
1127 6c. Common starfish 65 65
Nos. 1112/27 were printed together, se-tenant, forming a composite design.

386 Father Mikiel Scerri

1999. Bicentenary of Maltese Uprising against the French. Multicoloured.
1128 6c. Type **386** 70 70
1129 6c. "L-Eroj Maltin" (statue) 70 70
1130 16c. General Belgrand de Vaubois (French commander) . . . . . . 1·25 1·25
1131 16c. Captain Alexander Ball R.N. . . . . 1·25 1·25

387 "Wolfgang Philip Guttenberg interceding with The Virgin" (votive painting)

1999. Mellieha Sanctuary Commemoration. Mult.
1132 **387** 35c. multicoloured . . . 2·00 2·00
MS1133 123 × 88 mm. 6c. "Mellieha Virgin and Child" (rock painting) (vert) 70 80

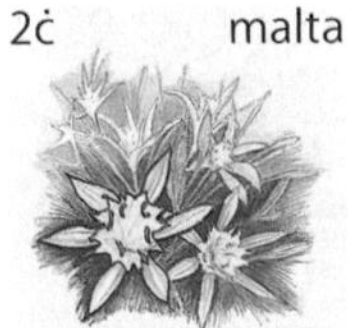

388 Sea Daffodil

1999. Maltese Flowers. Multicoloured.
1134 1c. *Helichrysum melitense* 10 10
1135 2c. Type **388** 10 10
1136 3c. *Cistus creticus* 10 15
1137 4c. Southern dwarf iris . . 10 15
1138 5c. *Papaver rhoeas* 15 20
1139 6c. French daffodil 20 25
1139a 7c. *Vitex angus-castus* . . . 25 30
1140 10c. *Rosa sempervirens* . . 30 35
1141 11c. *Silene colorata* 35 40
1142 12c. *Cynara cardunculus* . . 40 45
1143 16c. Yellow-throated crocus 50 55
1144 19c. *Anthemis arvensis* . . 60 65
1145 20c. *Anacamptis pyramidalis* 65 70
1145a 22c. *Spartium junceum* . . 70 75
1146 25c. Large Star of Bethlehem 80 85
1147 27c. *Borago officinalis* . . . 85 90
1147a 28c. *Crataegus azalorus* . . . 90 95
1147b 37c. *Cercis siliquastrum* . . 1·25 1·40
1147c 45c. *Myrtus communis* . . 1·40 1·50
1148 46c. Wild tulip . . . . . . 1·40 1·50
1149 50c. *Chrysanthemum coronarium* . . . . . . 1·60 1·75
1149a 76c. *Pistacia lentiscus* . . . 2·10 2·25
1150 £1 *Malva sylvestris* . . . . 3·25 3·50
1151 £2 *Adonis microcarpa* . . . 6·25 6·50

389 Madonna and Child

1999. Christmas. Multicoloured.
1152 6c. Type **389** 50 10
1153 6c.+3c. Carol singers . . . 55 55
1154 16c.+3c. Santa Claus . . . 1·40 1·60
1155 26c.+3c. Christmas decorations . . . . 1·75 2·25

390 Parliament Chamber and Symbolic Luzzu

1999. 25th Anniv of Republic. Multicoloured.
1156 6c. Type **390** 40 25
1157 11c. Parliament in session and Council of Europe emblem 60 35
1158 16c. Church and Central Bank of Malta building 80 55
1159 19c. Aerial view of Gozo and emblems . . . . . . 1·10 1·00
1160 26c. Computer and shipyard 1·40 1·60

391 Gift and Flowers

2000. Greetings Stamps. Multicoloured.
1161 3c. Type **391** 25 15
1162 6c. Photograph, envelope and rose 40 25
1163 16c. Flowers and silver heart 80 55
1164 20c. Champagne and pocket watch 95 90
1165 22c. Wedding rings and roses . . . . 1·10 1·10

392 Luzzu and Cruise Liner

2000. Malta during the 20th Century. Multicoloured.
1166 6c. Type **392** 50 25
1167 16c. Street musicians and modern street carnival . . 90 55
1168 22c. Family in 1900 and illuminated quayside . . . 1·25 85
1169 27c. Rural occupations and Citadel, Victoria . . . . 1·75 1·75

393 Footballers and Trophy (Centenary of Malta Football Association)

2000. Sporting Events. Multicoloured.
1170 6c. Type **393** 45 25
1171 16c. Swimming and sailing (Olympic Games, Sydney) 75 55
1172 26c. Judo, shooting and running (Olympic Games, Sydney) . . . . 1·25 1·10
1173 37c. Football (European Championship) . . . . . 1·50 2·00

394 "Building Europe"

2000. Europa.
1174 **394** 16c. multicoloured . . . 1·00 65
1175 46c. multicoloured . . . 2·50 2·50

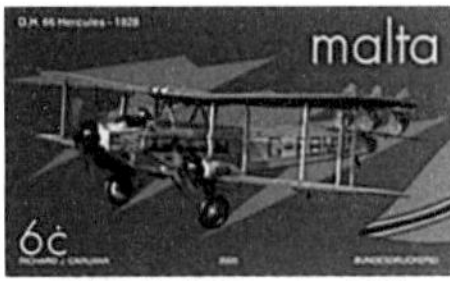

395 D.H.66 Hercules, 1928

2000. Century of Air Transport, 1900–2000. Mult.
1176 6c. Type **395** 75 75
1177 6c. LZ 127 *Graf Zeppelin*, 1933 . . . . 75 75
1178 16c. Douglas DC-3 Dakota of Air Malta Ltd, 1949 1·40 1·40
1179 16c. Airbus A320 of Air Malta . . . . 1·40 1·40
MS1180 122 × 87 mm. Nos. 1176/9 3·25 3·25
Nos. 1176/7 and 1178/9 were each printed together, se-tenant, with the backgrounds forming composite designs.

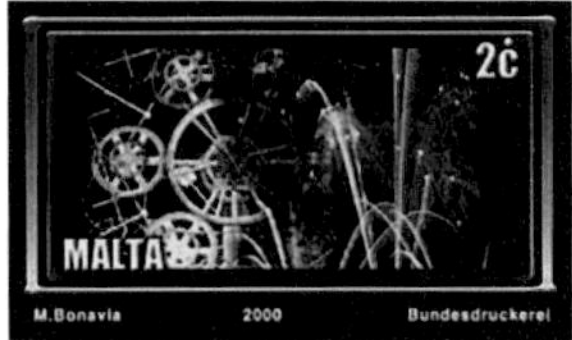

396 Catherine Wheel and Fireworks

2000. Fireworks. Multicoloured.
1181 2c. Type **396** 25 10
1182 6c. Exploding multicoloured fireworks 55 25
1183 16c. Catherine wheel . . . . 1·10 55
1184 20c. Exploding green fireworks . . . . 1·25 1·00
1185 50c. Numbered rockets in rack . . . . 2·75 3·25

397 "Boy walking Dog" (Jean Paul Zammit)

2000. "Stampin' the Future" (Children's stamp design competition winners). Multicoloured.
1186 6c. Type **397** 50 50
1187 6c. "Stars and Woman in Megalithic Temple" (Chiara Borg) 50 50
1188 6c. "Sunny Day" (Bettina Paris) 50 50
1189 6c. "Hands holding Heart" (Roxana Caruana) . . . 50 50

398 Boy's Sermon, Nativity Play and Girl with Doll

2000. Christmas. Multicoloured.
1190 6c. Type **398** 45 10
1191 6c.+3c. Three Wise Men (23 × 27 mm) 55 55
1192 16c.+3c. Family with Father Christmas . . . . 1·25 1·50
1193 26c.+3c. Christmas tree, church and family . . . . 1·75 2·25
MS1194 174 × 45 mm. Nos. 1190/3 3·50 4·00

399 Crocodile Float

2001. Maltese Carnival. Multicoloured.
1195 6c. Type **399** 50 25
1196 11c. King Karnival in procession (vert) 75 40
1197 16c. Woman and children in costumes (vert) 90 55
1198 19c. Horseman carnival float (vert) . . . . 1·10 1·25
1199 27c. Carnival procession . . 1·50 1·75
MS1200 127 × 92 mm. 12c. Old-fashioned clowns; 37c. Women dressed as clowns (both 32 × 32 mm) . . . . 2·50 3·00

400 St. Elmo Lighthouse

401 "The Chicken Seller" (E. Caruana Dingli)

2001. Maltese Lighthouses. Multicoloured.
1201 6c. Type **400** 55 25
1202 16c. Gurdan Lighthouse . . 1·10 70
1203 22c. Delimara Lighthouse 1·50 1·60

2001. Edward Caruana Dingli (painter) Commemoration. Multicoloured.
1204 2c. Type **401** 20 15
1205 4c. "The Village Beau" . . 35 15
1206 6c. "The Faldetta" 50 25
1207 10c. "The Guitar Player" . . 80 60
1208 26c. "Wayside Orange Seller" . . . . 2·00 2·50

402 Nazju Falzon, Gorg Preca and Adeodata Pisani (candidates for Beatification)

2001. Visit of Pope John Paul II. Multicoloured.
1209 6c. Type **402** 75 25
1210 16c. Pope John Paul II and statue of St. Paul . . . . 1·25 1·00
MS1211 123 × 87 mm. 75c. Pope John Paul with Nazju Falzon, Gorg Preca and Adeodata Pisani 3·50 3·50

403 Painted Frog

2001. Europa. Pond Life. Multicoloured.
1212 16c. Type **403** . . . . . . 1·00 65
1213 46c. Red-veined darter (dragonfly) . . . . 2·00 2·50

404 Herring Gull ("Yellow-legged Gull") (*Larus cachinnans*)

2001. Maltese Birds. Multicoloured.
1214 6c. Type **404** 50 50
1215 6c. Common kestrel (*Falco tinnunculus*) 50 50
1216 6c. Golden oriole (*Oriolus oriolus*) 50 50
1217 6c. Chaffinch (*Fringilla coelebs*) and Eurasian goldfinch (*Carduelis carduelis*) 50 50
1218 6c. Blue rock thrush (*Monticola solitarius*) . . 50 50
1219 6c. European bee-eater (*Merops apiaster*) 50 50
1220 6c. House martin (*Delichon urbica*) and barn swallow (*Hirundo rustica*) 50 50
1221 6c. Spanish sparrow (*Passer hispaniolensis*) 50 50
1222 6c. Spectacled warbler (*Sylvia conspicillata*) . . . 50 50
1223 6c. Turtle dove (*Streptopelia turtur*) 50 50
1224 6c. Northern pintail (*Anas acuta*) 50 50
1225 6c. Little bittern (*Ixobrychus minutus*) 50 50
1226 6c. Eurasian woodcock (*Scolopax rusticola*) . . . 50 50
1227 6c. Short-eared owl (*Asio flammeus*) 50 50
1228 6c. Northern lapwing (*Vanellus vanellus*) 50 50
1229 6c. Moorhen (*Gallinula chloropus*) 50 50
Nos 1214/29 were printed together, se-tenant, with the backgrounds forming a composite design.

405 Whistle Flute

407 Man with Net chasing Star

406 Kelb tal-Fenek (Pharaoh Hound)

2001. Traditional Maltese Musical Instruments. Multicoloured.

1230 1c. Type **405** 10 30
1231 3c. Reed pipe 20 30
1232 14c. Maltese bagpipe . . . 65 45
1233 20c. Friction drum . . . . 1·00 1·10
1234 25c. Frame drum . . . . . 1·25 1·50

2001. Maltese Dogs. Multicoloured.

1235 6c. Type **406** 50 25
1236 16c. Kelb tal-Kacca . . . . 1·00 55
1237 19c. Maltese . . . . 1·10 1·10
1238 35c. Kelb tal-But . . . . . 1·75 2·25

2001. Christmas. Multicoloured.

1239 6c.+2c. Type **407** 50 40
1240 15c.+2c. Father and children 1·00 1·10
1241 16c.+2c. Mother and daughter . . . . 1·10 1·25
1242 19c.+3c. Young woman with shopping bags . . . . . 1·25 1·40

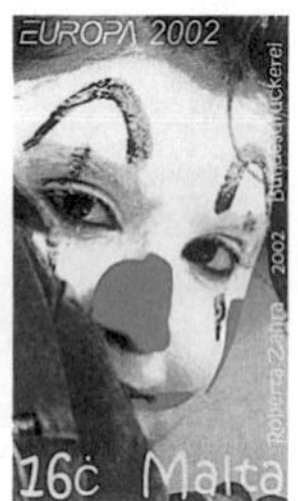

408 *Hippocampus guttulatus*

410 Child's Face painted as Clown

409 Sideboard

2002. Endangered Species. Mediterranean Seahorses. Multicoloured.

1243 6c. Type **408** 50 50
1244 6c. *Hippocampus hippocampus* 50 50
1245 16c. Close-up of *Hippocampus guttulatus* 1·00 1·00
1246 16c. *Hippocampus hippocampus* on seabed . . 1·00 1·00

2002. Antique Furniture. Multicoloured.

1247 2c. Type **409** 20 30
1248 4c. Bureau (vert) 30 20
1249 11c. Inlaid table (vert) . . . 70 40
1250 26c. Cabinet (vert) . . . . 1·25 85
1251 60c. Carved chest . . . . . 2·50 3·25

2002. Europa. Circus.

1252 **410** 16c. multicoloured . . . 1·00 75

411 *Hyles sammuti*

2002. Moths and Butterflies. Multicoloured.

1253 6c. Type **411** 40 40
1254 6c. *Utetheisa pulchella* . . . 40 40
1255 6c. *Ophiusa tirhaca* 40 40
1256 6c. *Phragmatobia fulginosa melitensis* 40 40
1257 6c. *Vanessa cardui* 40 40
1258 6c. *Polyommatus icarus* . . 40 40
1259 6c. *Gonepteryx cleopatra* . . 40 40
1260 6c. *Vanessa atlanta* 40 40
1261 6c. *Eucrostes indigenata* . . 40 40
1262 6c. *Macroglossum stellatarum* 40 40
1263 6c. *Lasiocampa quercus* . . 40 40
1264 6c. *Catocala electa* 40 40
1265 6c. *Maniola jurtina hyperhispulla* 40 40
1266 6c. *Pieris brassicae* 40 40
1267 6c. *Papilio machaon melitensis* 40 40
1268 6c. *Dainaus chrysippus* . . . 40 40

No. 1260 is inscribed "atalania" and 1264 "elocata", both in error.

412 "Kusksu Bil-ful" (bean stew)

2002. Maltese Cookery. Multicoloured.

1269 7c. Type **412** 45 25
1270 12c. "Qaqocc mimli" (stuffed artichoke) 75 50
1271 16c. "Lampuki" (dorada with aubergines) 90 65
1272 27c. "Qaghqd Tal-kavatelli" (chestnut dessert) . . . . 1·50 1·75
MS1273 125 × 90 mm. 75c. "Stuffat Tal-fenek" (rabbit stew) . . . 4·00 4·25

413 *Yavia cryptocarpa* (cactus)

414 Chief Justice Adrian Dingli,

2002. Cacti and Succulents. Multicoloured.

1274 1c. Type **413** 10 30
1275 7c. *Aztekium hintonii* (cactus) (vert) 50 25
1276 28c. *Pseudolithos migiurtinus* (succulent) . . . . 1·50 55
1277 37c. *Pierrebraunia brauniorum* (cactus) (vert) 1·75 1·25
1278 76c. *Euphorbia turbiniformis* (succulent) . . . . 3·50 4·25

2002. Personalities.

1279 **414** 3c. green and black . . . 20 30
1280 – 7c. green and black . . . 45 25
1281 – 15c. brown and agate . . 80 50
1282 – 35c. brown and sepia . . 1·75 1·50
1283 – 50c. light blue and blue 2·00 2·50

DESIGNS: 7c. Oreste Kirkop (opera singer); 15c. Athanasius Kircher (Jesuit scholar); 35c. Archpriest Saverio Cassar; 50c. Emmanuele Vitali (notary).

415 Mary and Joseph in Donkey Cart

2002. Christmas. Multicoloured.

1284 7c. Type **415** 60 25
1285 16c. Shepherds and Kings on a bus . . . . 1·10 55
1286 22c. Holy Family and angels in luzzu (boat) . . . . 1·40 75
1287 37c. Holy Family in horse-drawn carriage . . . . 1·75 1·40
1288 75c. Nativity on Maltese fishing boat . . . . . . 3·25 4·25

416 Vanden Plas Princess Landaulette, 1965

2003. Vintage Cars. Multicoloured.

1289 2c. Type **416** 20 30
1290 7c. Allard "M" type, 1948 45 25
1291 10c. Cadillac Model "B", 1904 . . . . 65 35
1292 26c. Fiat Cinquecento Model "A" Topolino, 1936 . . . . 1·25 1·25
1293 35c. Ford Anglia Super, 1965 . . . . 1·90 2·25

417 Fort St. Elmo

2003. Maltese Military Architecture. Multicoloured.

1294 1c. Type **417** 10 20
1295 4c. Rinella Battery 20 15
1296 11c. Fort St. Angelo 55 40
1297 16c. Section through Reserve Post R15 . . . . 75 60
1298 44c. Fort Tigne . . . . . . 2·25 2·50

418 St. George on Horseback

419 "CISKBEER"

2003. Paintings of St. George.

1299 **418** 3c. multicoloured 10 10
1300 – 7c. multicoloured 20 25
1301 – 14c. multicoloured . . . 45 50
1302 – 19c. multicoloured . . . 65 70
1303 – 27c. multicoloured . . . 85 90

DESIGNS: 7c. to 27c. Various paintings of St. George.

2003. Europa. Poster Art. Multicoloured.

1304 16c. Type **419** 50 55
1305 46c. "CARNIVAL 1939" . . 1·40 1·50

420 Games Mascot with Javelin

2003. Games of Small European States, Malta. Multicoloured.

1306 25c. Type **420** 80 85
1307 50c. Mascot with gun . . . 1·60 1·75
1308 75c. Mascot with ball and net . . . . 2·40 2·50
1309 £1 Mascot with rubber ring at poolside . . . . 3·25 3·50

421 Princess Elizabeth in Malta, c. 1950

2003. 50th Anniv of Coronation. Multicoloured (except No. 1312).

1310 – 12c. black, grey and cinnamon 40 45
1311 – 15c. multicoloured 45 50
1312 – 22c. black, deep grey and grey 70 75
1313 – 60c. black, grey and deep ultramarine . . . . . . 1·90 2·00
MS1314 100 × 72 mm. £1 multicoloured . . . . 3·25 3·50

DESIGNS: 15c. Princess Elizabeth with crowd of children, Malta, c. 1950; 22c. Queen Elizabeth II in evening dress with Duke of Edinburgh, Malta; 60c. Queen Elizabeth II (receiving book) and Duke of Edinburgh, Malta; £1 Queen on walkabout with crowd. 422 Valletta Bastions at Night

2003. Elton John, The Granaries, Floriana. Sheet 125 × 90 mm.

MS1315 422 £1.50 multicoloured 4·75 5·00

No. MS1315 also contains four labels showing different portraits of Elton John.

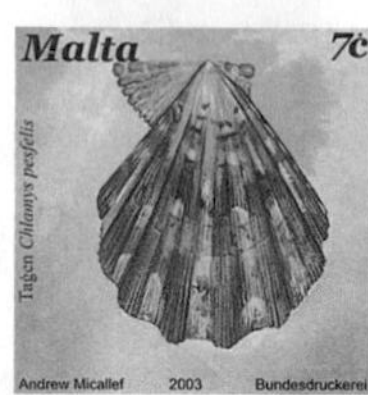

423 *Chlamys pesfelis*

2003. Sea Shells. Multicoloured.

1316 7c. Type **423** 20 25
1317 7c. *Gyroscala lamellose* . . . 20 25
1318 7c. *Phalium granulatum* . . 20 25
1319 7c. *Fusiturris similes* 20 25
1320 7c. *uria lurida* 20 25
1321 7c. *Bolinus brandaris* 20 25
1322 7c. *Charonia tritonis variegate* 20 25
1323 7c. *Clanculus corallinus* . . . 20 25
1324 7c. *Fusinus syracusanus* . . . 20 25
1325 7c. *Pinna nobilis* 20 25
1326 7c. *Acanthocardia tuberculata* 20 25
1327 7c. *Aporrhais pespelecani* . . 20 25
1328 7c. *Haliotis tuberculata lamellose* 20 25
1329 7c. *Tonna galea* 20 25
1330 7c. *Spondylus gaederopus* . . 20 25
1331 7c. *Mitra zonata* 20 25

424 Racing Yachts, Malta–Syracuse Race

2003. Yachting. Multicoloured.

1332 8c. Type **424** 25 30
1333 22c. Yacht, Middle Sea Race (vert) 70 75
1334 35c. Racing yachts, Royal Malta Yacht Club (vert) 1·10 1·25

2003. As Nos. 1139a and 1143 but smaller, 23 × 23 mm. Self-adhesive.

1335 7c. *Vitex agnus-castus* . . . 20 25
1336 16c. *Crocus longiflorus* . . . 50 55

425 Is-Sur ta' San Mikiel, Valletta

2003. Windmills. Each black.

1337 11c. Type **425** 35 40
1338 27c. Ta' Kola, Xaghra (vert) 85 90
1339 45c. Tax-Xarolla, Zurrieq (vert) . . . . 1·40 1·50

426 The Annunciation

2003. Christmas. Multicoloured.

1340 7c. Type **426** 45 50
1341 16c. Holy Family 50 55
1342 22c. The Shepherds following the Star (horiz) 70 75
1343 50c. The Three Kings with gifts (horiz) . . . . . . 1·60 1·75

POSTAGE DUE STAMPS

D 1 D 2

1925. Imperf.

D 1 **D 1** ½d. black . . . . 1·25 7·00
D 2 1d. black . . . . 3·25 3·00
D 3 1½d. black . . . . 3·00 3·75
D 4 2d. black . . . . 7·50 13·00
D 5 2½d. black . . . . 2·75 2·75
D 6 3d. black on grey . . . 9·00 15·00
D 7 4d. black on yellow . . . 5·00 9·50
D 8 6d. black on yellow . . . 5·00 17·00
D 9 1s. black on yellow . . . 7·50 21·00
D10 1s. 6d. black on yellow 14·00 55·00

1925. Perf.

D11 **D 2** ½d. green . . . . 1·25 60
D12 1d. violet . . . . 1·25 45
D13 1½d. brown . . . . . . 1·50 80
D14 2d. grey . . . . 11·00 1·00
D35 2d. brown 85 70
D36 2½d. orange 60 70
D37 3d. blue 60 60
D38 4d. green . . . . 1·00 80
D39 6d. purple . . . . 75 1·50
D40 1s. black . . . . 90 1·50
D41 1s.6d. red . . . . 2·25 7·00

D 3 Maltese Lace D 4

1973.

D42 **D 3** 2m. brown and red . . . 10 10
D43 3m. orange and red . . 10 15
D44 5m. pink and red 15 20
D45 1c. blue and green . . . 30 35
D46 2c. grey and black . . . 40 35
D47 3c. light brown & brown 40 35
D48 5c. dull blue and blue . . 65 70
D49 10c. lilac and plum . . . 85 1·00

1993.

D50 **D 4** 1c. magenta and mauve 15 30
D51 2c. blue and light blue 20 40

D52	5c. green and turquoise	30	45
D53	10c. orange and yellow	45	55

MANAMA Pt. 19

A dependency of Ajman.

100 dirhams = 1 riyal.

1966. Nos. 10, 12, 14 and 18 of Ajman surch **Manama** in English and Arabic and new value.

1	40d. on 40n.p. multicoloured	25	15
2	70d. on 70n.p. multicoloured	50	15
3	1r.50 on 1r.50 multicoloured	1·40	45
4	10r. on 10r. multicoloured	8·25	7·50

1967. Nos. 140/8 of Ajman optd MANAMA in English and Arabic. (a) Postage.

5	15d. blue and brown	10	10
6	30d. brown and black	15	15
7	50d. black and brown	35	35
8	70d. violet and black	60	50
	(b) Air.		
9	1r. green and brown	40	25
10	2r. mauve and black	70	50
11	3r. black and brown	1·10	1·75
12	5r. brown and black	3·50	3·50
13	10r. blue and brown	6·50	6·50

APPENDIX

The following stamps have either been issued in excess of postal needs or have not been available to the public in reasonable quantities at face value. Such stamps may later be given full listing if there is evidence of regular postal use.

1966. New Currency Surcharges. Stamps of Ajman surch **Manama** in English and Arabic and new value.

(a) Nos. 19/20 and 22/4 (Kennedy). 10d. on 10n.p., 15d. on 15n.p., 1r. on 1r., 2r. on 2r., 3r. on 3r.

(b) Nos. 27, 30 and 35/6 (Olympics). 5d. on 5n.p., 25d. on 25n.p., 3r. on 3r., 5r. on 5r.

(c) Nos. 80/2 and 85 (Churchill). 50d. on 50n.p., 75d. on 75n.p., 1r. on 1r., 5r. on 5r.

(d) Nos. 95/8 (Space). Air 50d. on 50n.p., 1r. on 1r., 3r. on 3r., 5r. on 5r.

1967.

World Scout Jamboree, Idaho. Postage 30, 70d., 1r.; Air 2, 3, 4r.

Olympic Games, Mexico (1968). Postage 35, 65, 75d., 1r.; Air 1r.25, 2, 3, 4r.

Winter Olympic Games, Grenoble (1968). Postage 5, 35, 60, 75d.; Air 1, 1r.25, 2, 3r.

Paintings by Renoir and Terbrugghen. Air 35, 65d., 1, 2r. × 3.

1968.

Paintings by Velazquez. Air 1r. × 2, 2r. × 2.

Costumes. Air 30d. × 2, 70d. × 2, 1r. × 2, 2r. × 2.

Olympic Games, Mexico. Postage 1r. × 4; Air 2r. × 4.

Satellites and Spacecraft. Air 30d. × 2, 70d. × 2, 1r. × 2, 2r. × 2, 3r. × 2.

Human Rights Year. Kennedy Brothers and Martin Luther King. Air 1r. × 3, 2r. × 3.

Sports Champions, Famous Footballers. Postage 15, 20, 50, 75d., 1r.; Air 10r.

Heroes of Humanity. Circular designs on gold or silver foil. 60d. × 12.

Olympic Games, Mexico. Circular designs on gold or silver foil. Air 3r. × 8.

Mothers' Day. Paintings. Postage 1r. × 6.

Kennedy Brothers Commem. Postage 2r.; Air 5r.

Cats (1st series). Postage 1, 2, 3d.; Air 2, 3r.

5th Death Anniv of Pres. Kennedy. Air 10r.

Space Exploration. Postage 5, 10, 15, 20, 25d.; Air 15r.

Olympic Games, Mexico. Gold Medals. Postage 2r. × 4; Air 5r. × 4.

Christmas. Air 5r.

1969.

Sports Champions. Cyclists. Postage 1, 2, 5, 10, 15, 20d.; Air 12r.

Sports Champions. German Footballers. Postage 5, 10, 15, 20, 25d.; Air 10r.

Sports Champions. Motor-racing Drivers. Postage 1, 5, 10, 15, 25d.; Air 10r.

Motor-racing Cars. Postage 1, 5, 10, 15, 25d.; Air 10r.

Sports Champions. Boxers. Postage 5, 10, 15, 20d.; Air 10r.

Sports Champions. Baseball Players. Postage 1, 2, 5, 10, 15d.; Air 10r.

Birds. Air 1r. × 11.

Roses. Postage 1r. × 6.

Animals. Air 1r. × 6.

Paintings by Italian Artists. 5, 10, 15, 20d., 10r.

Great Composers. Air 5, 10, 25d., 10r.

Paintings by French Artists. 1r. × 4.

Nude Paintings. Air 2r. × 4.

Kennedy Brothers. Air 2, 3, 10r.

Olympic Games, Mexico. Gold Medal Winners. Postage 1, 2d., 10r.; Air 10d., 5, 10r.

Paintings of the Madonna. Postage 10d.; Air 10r.

Space Flight of "Apollo 9". Optd on 1968 Space Exploration issue. Air 15r.

Space Flight of "Apollo 10". Optd on 1968 Space Exploration issue. Air 15r.

1st Death Anniv of Gagarin. Optd on 1968 Space Exploration issue. 5d.

2nd Death Anniv of Edward White (astronaut). Optd on 1968 Space Exploration issue. 10d.

1st Death Anniv of Robert Kennedy. Optd on 1969 Kennedy Brothers issue. Air 2r.

Olympic Games, Munich (1972). Optd on 1969 Mexico Gold Medal Winners issue. Air 10d., 5, 10r.

Moon Mission of "Apollo 11". Air 1, 2, 3r.

Christmas. Paintings by Brueghel. Postage 1, 2, 4, 5, 10d.; Air 6r.

1970.

"Soyuz" and "Apollo" Space Programmes. Postage 1, 2, 4, 5, 10d.; Air 3, 5r.

Kennedy and Eisenhower Commem. Embossed on gold foil. Air 20r.

Lord Baden-Powell Commem. Embossed on gold foil. Air 20r.

World Cup Football Championship, Mexico. Postage 20, 40, 60, 80d., 1r.; Air 3r.

Brazil's Victory in World Cup Football Championship. Optd on 1970 World Cup issue. Postage 20, 40, 60, 80d., 1r.; Air 3r.

Paintings by Michelangelo. Postage 1, 2, 4, 5, 10d.; Air 6r.

World Fair "Expo 70", Osaka, Japan. Air 25, 50, 75d., 1, 2, 3, 12r.

Paintings by Renoir. Postage 1, 2, 5, 6, 10d.; Air 5, 12r.

Olympic Games, Rome, Tokyo, Mexico and Munich. Postage 15, 30, 50, 70d.; Air 2, 5r.

Winter Olympic Games, Sapporo (1972) (1st issue). Postage 2, 3, 4, 10d.; Air 2, 5r.

Christmas. Flower Paintings by Brueghel. Postage 5, 20, 25, 30, 50d.; Air 60d., 1, 2r.

1971.

Winter Olympic Games, Sapporo (2nd issue). Postage 1, 2, 3, 4, 5, 6, 8, 10, 12, 15, 20, 25, 30, 35, 40, 50d.; Air 75 d, 1, 2, 2r.50.

Roses. Postage 5, 20, 25, 30, 50d.; Air 60d., 1, 2r.

Birds. Postage 5, 20, 25, 30, 50d.; Air 60d., 1, 2r.

Paintings by Modigliani. Air 25, 50, 60, 75d., 1r.50, 3r.

Paintings by Rubens. Postage 1, 2, 3, 4, 5, 10d.; Air 2, 3r.

"Philatokyo '71" Stamp Exhibition, Paintings by Hokusai and Hiroshige. Postage 10, 15, 20, 25, 50, 75d.; Air 1, 2r.

25th Anniv of United Nations. Optd on 1970 Christmas issue. Postage 5, 20, 25, 30, 50d.; Air 60d., 1, 2r.

British Military Uniforms. Postage 5, 20, 25, 30, 50d.; Air 60d., 1, 2r.

Space Flight of "Apollo 14". Postage 15, 25, 50, 60, 70d.; Air 5r.

Space Flight of "Apollo 15". Postage 25, 40, 50, 60d.; Air 1, 6r.

13th World Scout Jamboree, Asagiri, Japan (1st issue). Postage 1, 2, 3, 5, 7, 10, 12, 15, 20, 25, 30, 35, 40, 50, 65, 80d.; Air 1, 1r.25, 1r.50, 2r.

World Wild Life Conservation. Postage 1, 2, 3, 5, 7, 10, 12, 15, 20, 25, 30, 35, 40, 50, 65, 80d.; Air 1r., 1r.25, 1r.50, 2r.

13th World Scout Jamboree, Asagiri, Japan (2nd issue). Stamps. Postage 10, 15, 20, 25, 50, 75d.; Air 1, 2r.

Winter Olympic Games, Sapporo (3rd issue). Postage 1, 2, 3, 4, 5, 10d.; Air 2, 3r.

Cats (2nd series). Postage 15, 25, 40, 60d.; Air 3, 10r.

Lions International Clubs. Optd on 1971 Uniforms issue. Postage 5, 20, 25, 30, 50d.; Air 60d., 1, 2r.

Paintings of Ships. Postage 15, 20, 25, 30, 50d.; Air 60d., 1, 2r.

Great Olympic Champions. Postage 25, 50, 75d., 1r.; Air 5r.

Prehistoric Animals. Postage 15, 20, 25, 30, 50, 60d.; Air 1, 2r.

Footballers. Postage 5, 10, 15, 20, 40d.; Air 5r.

Royal Visit of Queen Elizabeth II to Japan. Postage 10, 20, 30, 40, 50d.; Air 2, 3r.

Fairy Tales. Stories by Hans Andersen. Postage 1, 2, 4, 5, 10d.; Air 3r.

World Fair, Philadelphia (1976). American Paintings. Postage 20, 25, 50, 60, 75d.; Air 3r.

Fairy Tales. Well-known stories. Postage 1, 2, 4, 5, 10d.; Air 3r.

Space Flight of "Apollo 16". Postage 20, 30, 40, 50, 60d.; Air 3, 4r.

Tropical Fishes. Postage 1, 2, 3, 4, 5, 10d.; Air 2, 3r.

European Tour of Emperor Hirohito of Japan. Postage 1, 2, 4, 5, 10d.; Air 6r.

Meeting of Pres. Nixon and Emperor Hirohito of Japan in Alaska. Optd on 1971 Emperor's Tour issue. Air 6r.

2500th Anniv of Persian Empire. Postage 10, 20, 30, 40, 50d.; Air 3r.

Space Flight of "Apollo 15" and Future Developments in Space. Postage 10, 15, 20, 25, 50d.; Air 1, 2r.

1972.

150th Death Anniv (1971) of Napoleon. Postage 10, 20, 30, 40d.; Air 1, 2, 3, 4r.

1st Death Anniv of Gen. de Gaulle. Postage 10, 20, 30, 40d.; Air 1, 2, 3, 4r.

Paintings from the "Alte Pinakothek", Munich. Postage 5, 10, 15, 20, 25d.; Air 5r.

"Tour de France" Cycle Race. Postage 5, 10, 15, 20, 25, 30, 35, 40, 45, 50, 55, 60d.; Air 65, 70, 75, 80, 85, 90, 95d., 1r.

Cats and Dogs. Postage 10, 20, 30, 40, 50d.; Air 1r.

25th Anniv of U.N.I.C.E.F. Optd on 1971 World Scout Jamboree, Asagiri (2nd issue). Postage 10, 15, 20, 25, 50, 75d.; Air 1, 2r.

Past and Present Motorcars. Postage 10, 20, 30, 40, 50d.; Air 1r.

Military Uniforms. 1r. × 11.

The United Arab Emirates Ministry of Communications took over the Manama postal service on 1 August 1972. Further stamps inscribed "Manama" issued after that date were released without authority and had no validity.

MANCHUKUO Pt. 17

Issues for the Japanese puppet Government set up in 1932 under President (later Emperor) Pu Yi.

100 fen = 1 yuan.

1 White Pagoda, Liaoyang

2 Pu Yi, later Emperor Kang-teh

1932. (a) With five characters in top panel as T **1** and **2**.

1	**1**	½f. brown	75	25
2		1f. red	75	10
24		1f. brown	75	10
25		1½f. violet	1·50	75
4		2f. grey	2·25	20
26		2f. blue	3·50	50
27		3f. brown	2·50	10
6		4f. green	50	10
28		4f. brown	18·00	75
7		5f. green	75	15
8		6f. red	3·50	40
9		7f. grey	1·25	20
10		8f. brown	9·00	6·00
11		10f. orange	1·50	15
12	**2**	13f. brown	4·50	4·25
13		15f. red	15·00	75
14		16f. blue	14·00	2·25
15		20f. brown	2·75	40
16		30f. orange	3·25	1·25
17		50f. green	3·75	70
31		1y. violet	8·00	5·50
		(b) With six characters in top panel.		
40	**1**	½f. brown	25	10
41		1f. brown	25	10
42		1½f. violet	65	40
43		3f. brown	40	10
44		5f. blue	8·50	60
45		5f. slate	3·50	40
46		6f. red	1·00	15
47		7f. grey	1·25	40
48		9f. orange	1·25	20
55		10f. blue	4·25	10
56	**2**	13f. brown	3·75	4·25
49		15f. red	2·00	25
50		18f. green	12·00	3·50
51		20f. brown	2·25	20
52		30f. brown	3·35	35
53		50f. green	3·75	30
54		1y. violet	10·00	3·50

3 Map and Flags

6 Emperor's Palace

1933. 1st Anniv of Republic.

19	**3**	1f. orange	1·25	1·00
20	–	2f. green	8·50	7·50
21	**3**	4f. red	1·25	50
22	–	10f. blue	13·00	11·00

DESIGN: 2, 10f. Council Hall, Hsinking.

1934. Enthronement of Emperor.

32	**6**	1½f. brown	1·25	40
33	–	3f. red	1·75	20
34	**6**	6f. green	5·00	3·75
35	–	10f. blue	7·50	3·75

DESIGN: 3f., 10f. Phoenixes.

1934. Stamps of 1932 surch with four Japanese characters.

36	**1**	1f. on 4f. green (No. 6)	3·50	2·25
37		3f. on 4f. green	22·00	18·00
38		3f. on 4f. brown (No. 28)	4·25	2·50
39	**2**	3f. on 16f. blue (No. 14)	6·50	6·50

In No. 38 the left hand upper character of the surcharge consists of three horizontal lines.

12 Orchid Crest of Manchukuo

13 Changpai Mountain and Sacred Lake

1935. China Mail.

64	**12**	2f. green	45	15
65		2½f. violet	35	15
66	**13**	4f. green	1·00	30
67		5f. blue	25	10
68	**12**	8f. yellow	2·25	30
60	**13**	12f. red	4·50	2·25
70		13f. brown	50	15

15 Mt. Fuji

16 Phoenixes

1935. Visit of Emperor Kang-teh to Japan.

71	**15**	1½f. green	1·00	80
72	**16**	3f. orange	1·50	25
73	**15**	6f. red	3·25	3·25
74	**16**	10f. blue	5·00	2·50

17 Symbolic of Accord

19 State Council Building, Hsinking

20 Chengte Palace, Jehol

1936. Japan–Manchukuo Postal Agreement.

75	**17**	1½f. brown	1·75	1·50
76	–	3f. purple	1·50	25
77	**17**	6f. red	6·50	6·50
78	–	10f. blue	5·50	3·50

DESIGN—HORIZ: 3f., 10f. Department of Communications.

1936.

79	**19**	½f. brown	25	15
80		1f. red	25	10
81		1½f. lilac	2·50	2·00
82	A	2f. green	20	10
83	**19**	3f. brown	25	15
84	B	4f. green	20	10
149	**19**	5f. black	10	1·00
86	A	6f. red	75	10
87	B	7f. black	1·00	10
88		9f. red	75	20
89	**20**	10f. blue	40	10
90	B	12f. orange	25	10
91		13f. brown	10·00	20·00
92		15f. red	1·25	30
93	C	18f. green	7·50	7·50
94		19f. green	3·50	1·50
95	A	20f. brown	1·50	35
96	**20**	30f. brown	1·75	30
97	D	38f. blue	13·00	14·00
98		39f. blue	1·00	1·00
99	A	50f. green	2·25	30
154	**20**	1y. purple	45	2·75

DESIGNS: A, Carting soya-beans; B. Peiling Mausoleum; C, Airplane and grazing sheep (domestic and China air mail); D, Nakajima-built Fokker F.VIIb/3m airplane over Sungari River railway bridge (air mail to Japan).

21 Sun rising over Fields

22 Shadowgraph of old and new Hsinking

1937. 5th Anniv of Founding of State.

101	**21**	1½f. red	5·00	6·00
102	**22**	3f. green	1·50	1·75

1937. China Mail. Surch in Chinese characters.

108	**12**	2½f. on 2f. green	2·75	2·00
110	**13**	5f. on 4f. green	2·75	2·50
111		13f. on 12f. brown	9·50	7·00

27 Pouter Pigeon and Hsinking

1937. Completion of Five Year Reconstruction Plan for Hsinking.
112 **27** 2f. purple . . . . 2·00 1·00
113 – 4f. red . . . . 2·00 25
114 **27** 10f. green . . . . 6·50 4·00
115 – 20f. blue . . . . 7·50 5·00
DESIGN: 4, 20f. Flag over Imperial Palace.

29 Manchukuo 30 Japanese Residents Assn. Building

1937. Japan's Relinquishment of Extra-territorial Rights.
116 **29** 2f. red . . . . 1·00 25
117 **30** 4f. green . . . . 2·75 75
118 8f. orange . . . . 3·25 2·00
119 – 10f. blue . . . . 2·75 50
120 – 12f. violet . . . . 3·50 3·00
121 – 20f. brown . . . . 4·75 2·75
DESIGNS—As Type **30**: 10, 20f. Dept. of Communications Bldg. HORIZ: 12f. Ministry of Justice.

32 "Twofold Happiness" 33 Red Cross on Map and Globe

1937. New Year's Greetings.
122 **32** 2f. red and blue . . . . . 3·00 30

1938. Inaug of Manchukuo Red Cross Society.
123 **33** 2f. red . . . . 1·00 1·25
124 4f. green . . . . 1·00 25

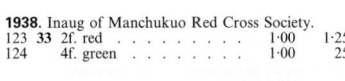

34 Map of Railway Lines 35 "Asia" Express

1939. Completion of 10,000 Kilometres of Manchurian Railways.
125 **34** 2f. blue and orange . . . . 2·75 1·60
126 **35** 4f. deep blue and blue . . 2·75 1·90

36 Manchurian Cranes over Shipmast 37 Census Official and Manchukuo 38 Census Slogans in Chinese and Mongolian

1940. 2nd Visit of Emperor Kang-teh to Japan.
127 **36** 2f. purple 65 35
128 4f. green 95 50

1940. National Census.
129 **37** 2f. brown and yellow . . . 60 1·50
130 **38** 4f. deep green and green 60 1·50

39 Message of Congratulation 40 Dragon Dance

1940. 2600th Anniv of Founding of Japanese Empire.
131 **39** 2f. red . . . . 15 1·50
132 **40** 4f. blue . . . . 15 1·50

41 Recruit (42)

1941. Enactment of Conscription Law.
133 **41** 2f. red . . . . 75 1·50
134 4f. blue . . . . 75 1·50

1942. Fall of Singapore. Stamps of 1936 optd with T **42**.
135 A 2f. green . . . . 1·00 2·00
136 B 4f. green . . . . 1·00 2·00

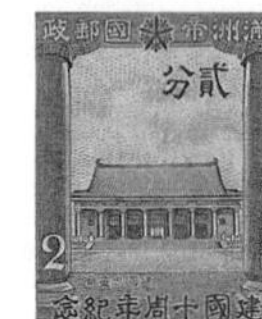

43 Kenkoku Shrine 44 Achievement of Fine Crops

45 Women of Five Races Dancing 46 Map of Manchukuo

1942. 10th Anniv of Founding of State.
137 **43** 2f. red 25 75
138 **44** 3f. orange . . . . 2·25 2·25
139 **43** 4f. lilac 40 75
140 **45** 6f. green . . . . 2·25 2·50
141 **46** 10f. red on yellow . . . . 75 1·50
142 – 20f. blue on yellow . . . . 1·00 1·50
DESIGN—HORIZ: 20f. Flag of Manchukuo.

1942. 1st Anniv of "Greater East Asia War". Stamps of 1936 optd with native characters above date **8.12.8.**
143 **19** 3f. brown . . . . 1·00 1·75
144 A 6f. red . . . . 1·00 1·75

1943. Labour Service Law Proclamation. Stamps of 1936 optd with native characters above heads of pick and shovel.
145 **19** 3f. brown . . . . 1·00 1·75
146 A 6f. red . . . . 1·00 1·75

49 Nurse and Stretcher 50 Furnace at Anshan Plant

1943. 5th Anniv of Manchukuo Red Cross Society.
147 **49** 6f. green . . . . 75 2·50

1943. 2nd Anniv of "Greater East Asia War".
148 **50** 6f. red . . . . 75 2·50

51 Chinese characters 52 Japanese characters 53 "One Heart One Soul"

1944. Friendship with Japan. (a) Chinese characters.
155 **51** 10f. red 25 75
156 40f. green . . . . 75 1·00

(b) Japanese characters.
157 **52** 10f. red 25 75
158 40f. green . . . . 75 1·00

1945. 10th Anniv of Emperor's Edict.
159 **53** 10f. red . . . . 1·25 4·50

MARIANA ISLANDS Pt. 7

A group of Spanish islands in the Pacific Ocean of which Guam was ceded to the U.S.A. and the others to Germany. The latter are now under U.S. Trusteeship.

100 pfennig = 1 mark.

1899. German stamps optd **Marianen**.
7 **8** 3pf. brown . . . . 12·00 22·00
8 5pf. green . . . . 16·00 22·00
9 **9** 10pf. red . . . . 12·00 33·00
10 20pf. blue . . . . 19·00 95·00
11 25pf. orange . . . . 55·00 £130
12 50pf. brown . . . . 65·00 £160

1901. "Yacht" key-type inscr "MARIANEN".
13 N 3pf. brown . . . . 80 1·30
14 5pf. green . . . . 80 2·10
15 10pf. red . . . . 80 3·00
16 20pf. blue . . . . 1·10 4·75
17 25pf. black & red on yellow 1·80 10·50
18 30pf. black & orge on buff 1·80 10·50
19 40pf. black and red . . . . 1·90 11·00
20 50pf. black & pur on buff 1·90 11·50
21 80pf. black and red on rose 2·50 19·00
22 O 1m. red . . . . 4·75 50·00
23 2m. blue . . . . 6·00 90·00
24 3m. black . . . . 8·50 £120
25 5m. red and black £130 £450

MARIENWERDER Pt. 7

A district of E. Prussia where a plebiscite was held in 1920. As a result the district remained part of Germany. After the War of 1939–45 it was returned to Poland and reverted to its original name of Kwidzyn.

100 pfennig = 1 mark.

1

1920.
1 **1** 5pf. green 70 50
2 10pf. red 70 50
3 15pf. grey 70 50
4 20pf. brown 50 45
5 25pf. blue 40 55
6 30pf. orange . . . . 95 1·00
7 40pf. brown 70 70
8 50pf. violet 70 70
9 60pf. brown . . . . 3·25 3·50
10 75pf. brown . . . . 85 1·00
11 1m. brown and green . . . . 1·00 1·00
12 2m. purple . . . . 4·25 3·50
13 3m. red . . . . 4·50 3·75
14 5m. blue and red . . . . . . 15·00 21·00

1920. Stamps of Germany inscr "DEUTSCHES REICH" optd or surch **Commission Interalliee Marienwerder**.
15 **10** 5pf. green . . . . 14·00 28·00
16 20pf. blue . . . . 5·50 17·00
17 50pf. black & purple on buff £350 £700
18 75pf. black and green . . . 3·50 4·75
19 80pf. black and red on rose 70·00 £100
25 **12** 1m. red . . . . 2·75 5·00
21 **24** 1m. on 2pf. grey . . . . . 17·00 35·00
26 **12** 1m.25 green . . . . 2·75 5·50
27 1m.50 brown . . . . 4·00 7·00
22 **24** 2m. on 2½pf. grey . . . . . 8·50 14·00
28 **13** 2m.50 purple . . . . 2·50 5·00
23 **10** 3m. on 3pf. brown . . . . 11·50 14·00
24 **24** 5m. on 7½pf. orange . . . . 7·25 14·00

1920. As T **1**, with inscription at top changed to "PLEBISCITE".
29 5pf. green . . . . 2·50 2·10
30 10pf. red . . . . 2·50 1·70
31 15pf. grey . . . . 10·50 9·75
32 20pf. brown . . . . 1·70 1·40
33 25pf. blue . . . . 12·00 11·00
34 30pf. orange . . . . 1·20 1·00
35 40pf. brown . . . . 1·00 60
36 50pf. violet . . . . 1·50 75
37 60pf. brown . . . . 4·50 3·25
38 75pf. brown . . . . 5·50 5·00
39 1m. brown and green . . . . 1·00 60
40 2m. purple . . . . 1·40 75
41 3m. red . . . . 1·70 1·40
42 5m. blue and red . . . . . . 2·50 2·10

MARSHALL ISLANDS Pts. 7, 22

A group of islands in the Pacific Ocean, a German protectorate from 1885. From 1920 to 1947 it was a Japanese mandated territory and from 1947 part of the United States Trust Territory of the Pacific Islands, using United States stamps. In 1984 it assumed control of its postal services.

A. GERMAN PROTECTORATE

100 pfennig = 1 mark.

1897. Stamps of Germany (a) optd **Marschall-Inseln**.
G1 **8** 3pf. brown £110 £600
G2 5pf. green £425 £375
G3 **9** 10pf. red . . . . 42·00 80·00
G4 20pf. blue . . . . 42·00 70·00

(b) optd **Marshall-Inseln**.
G 5 **8** 3pf. brown . . . . 4·00 4·00
G 6 5pf. green . . . . 9·00 6·00
G 7 **9** 10pf. red . . . . 8·00 10·50
G 8 20pf. blue . . . . 14·00 18·00
G 9 25pf. orange . . . . 35·00 29·00
G10 50pf. brown . . . . 18·00 35·00

1901. "Yacht" key-type inscr "MARSHALL INSELN".
G11 N 3pf. brown . . . . 50 1·40
G12 5pf. green . . . . 55 1·10
G13 10pf. red . . . . 60 3·00
G14 20pf. blue . . . . 90 9·00
G15 25pf. black & red on yell 1·10 11·00
G16 30pf. black & orge on buff 1·10 11·00
G17 40pf. black and red . . . 1·25 11·00
G18 50pf. black & pur on buff 1·90 18·00
G19 80pf. black & red on rose 2·40 28·00
G20 O 1m. red . . . . 3·75 55·00
G21 2m. blue . . . . 5·00 80·00
G22 3m. black . . . . 8·00 £150
G23 5m. red and black £120 £400

B. REPUBLIC

100 cents = 1 dollar.

1 Canoe

1984. Inauguration of Postal Independence. Multicoloured.
1 20c. Type **1** 55 30
2 20c. Fishes and net 55 30
3 20c. Navigational stick-chart . . 55 30
4 20c. Islet with coconut palms 55 30

2 Mili Atoll 3 German Marshall Islands 1900 3pf. Optd Stamp

1984. Maps. Multicoloured.
5 1c. Type **2** 10 10
6 3c. Likiep Atoll 10 10
7 5c. Ebon Atoll 15 10
8 10c. Jaluit Atoll 15 10
9 13c. Ailinginae Atoll 25 15
10 14c. Wotho Atoll 25 15
11 20c. Kwajalein and Ebeye Atolls 30 20
12 22c. Enewetak Atoll 30 20
13 28c. Ailinglaplap Atoll . . . 45 35
14 30c. Majuro Atoll 45 25
15 33c. Namu Atoll 50 40
16 37c. Rongelap Atoll 55 45
16a 39c. Taka and Utirik Atolls 55 45
16b 44c. Ujelang Atoll 65 50
16c 50c. Aur and Maloelap Atolls 80 65
17 $1 Arno Atoll . . . . 1·75 75
18 $2 Wotje and Erikub Atolls 3·25 2·50
19 $5 Bikini Atoll . . . . . . 7·50 6·50
20 $10 Mashallese stick chart (31 × 31 mm) . . . . . . 12·00 10·50

1984. 19th Universal Postal Union Congress Philatelic Salon, Hamburg.
21 **3** 40c. brown, black and yellow 70 50
22 – 40c. brown, black and yellow 70 50
23 – 40c. blue, black and yellow 70 50
24 – 40c. multicoloured 70 50
DESIGNS: No. 22, German Marshall Islands 1901 3pf. "Yacht" stamp; 23, German Marshall Islands 1897 20pf. stamp; 24, German Marshall Islands 1901 5m. "Yacht" stamp.

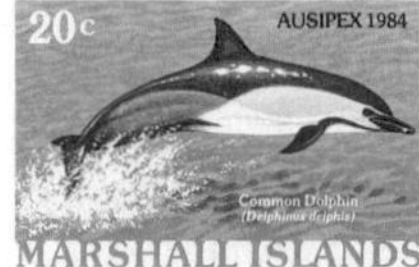

4 Common Dolphin

1984. "Ausipex 84" International Stamp Exhibition, Melbourne. Dolphins. Multicoloured.

25	20c. Type **4**	50	35
26	20c. Risso's dolphin	50	35
27	20c. Spotter dolphins	50	35
28	20c. Bottle-nosed dolphin	50	35

5 Star over Bethlehem and Text

6 Traditional Chief and German and Marshallese Flags

1984. Christmas. Multicoloured.

29	20c. Type **5**	50	30
30	20c. Desert landscape	50	30
31	20c. Two kings on camels	50	30
32	20c. Third king on camel	50	30

1984. 5th Anniv of Constitution. Multicoloured.

33	20c. Type **6**	50	30
34	20c. Pres. Amata Kabua and American and Marshallese flags	50	30
35	20c. Admiral Chester W. Nimitz and Japanese and Marshallese flags	50	30
36	20c. Trygve H. Lie (first Secretary-General of United Nations) and U.N. and Marshallese flags	50	30

7 Leach's Storm Petrel ("Forked-tailed Petrel")

1985. Birth Bicentenary of John J. Audubon (ornithologist). Multicoloured.

37	22c. Type **7** (postage)	85	85
38	22c. Pectoral sandpiper	85	85
39	44c. Brown booby ("Booby Gannet") (air)	1·50	1·50
40	44c. Whimbrel ("Great Esquimaux Curlew")	1·50	1·50

8 Black-spotted Triton

1985. Sea Shells (1st series). Multicoloured.

41	22c. Type **8**	50	35
42	22c. Monodon murex	50	35
43	22c. Diana conch	50	35
44	22c. Great green turban	50	35
45	22c. Rose-branch murex	50	35

See also Nos. 85/9, 131/5 and 220/4.

9 Woman as Encourager and Drum

1985. International Decade for Women. Mult.

46	22c. Type **9**	40	30
47	22c. Woman as Peacemaker and palm branches	40	30
48	22c. Woman as Nurturer and pounding stone	40	30
49	22c. Woman as Benefactress and lesser frigate bird	65	65

Nos. 46/9 were printed together in se-tenant blocks of four within the sheet, each block forming a composite design.

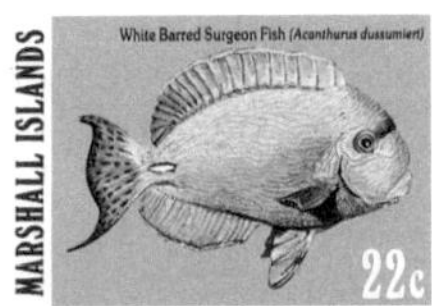

10 Palani ("White Barred Surgeon Fish")

1985. Lagoon Fishes. Multicoloured.

50	22c. Type **10**	60	40
51	22c. Silver-spotted squirrelfish ("White Blotched Squirrel Fish")	60	40
52	22c. Spotted boxfish	60	40
53	22c. Saddle butterflyfish	60	40

11 Basketball

1985. International Youth Year. Multicoloured.

54	22c. Type **11**	40	30
55	22c. Elderly woman recording for oral history project	40	30
56	22c. Islander explaining navigational stick charts	40	30
57	22c. Dancers at inter-atoll music and dance competition	40	30

12 American Board of Commissions for Foreign Missions Stock Certificate

1985. Christmas. "Morning Star I" (first Christian missionary ship to visit Marshall Islands). Multicoloured.

58	14c. Type **12**	15	30
59	22c. Launching of "Morning Star I", 1856	45	30
60	33c. Departure from Honolulu, 1857	70	50
61	44c. Entering Ebon Lagoon, 1857	80	60

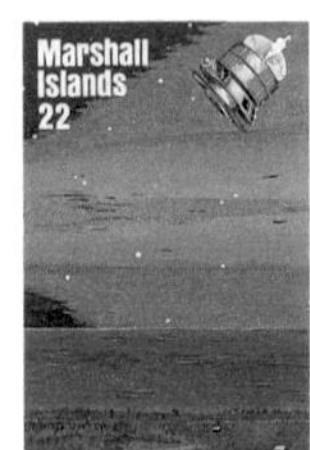

13 "Giotto" and Section of Comet Tail

1985. Appearance of Halley's Comet. Designs showing comet over Roi-Namur Island. Multicoloured.

62	22c. Space shuttle and comet	1·00	55
63	22c. "Planet A" space probe and dish aerial	1·00	55
64	22c. Type **13**	1·00	55
65	22c. "Vega" satellite and buildings on island	1·00	55
66	22c. Sir Edmund Halley, satellite communications ship and airplane	1·00	55

Nos. 62/6 were printed together, se-tenant, forming a composite design.

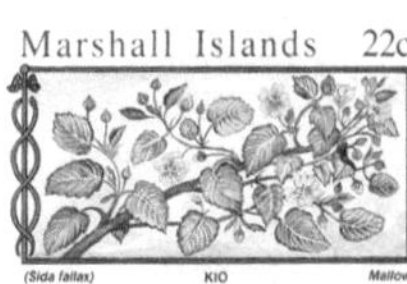

14 Mallow

1985. Medicinal Plants. Multicoloured.

67	22c. Type **14**	45	35
68	22c. Half-flower	45	35
69	22c. "Guettarda speciosa"	45	35
70	22c. Love-vine	45	35

15 Trumpet Triton

1986. World Wildlife Fund. Marine Life. Mult.

71	14c. Type **15**	40	30
72	14c. Giant clam	40	30
73	14c. Small giant clam	40	30
74	14c. Coconut crab	40	30

16 Consolidated PBY-5A Catalina Amphibian

1986. Air. "Ameripex 86" International Stamp Exhibition, Chicago. Mail Planes. Multicoloured.

75	44c. Type **16**	85	65
76	44c. Grumman SA-16 Albatross	85	65
77	44c. Douglas DC-6B	85	65
78	44c. Boeing 727-100	85	65

17 Islanders in Outrigger Canoe

1986. 40th Anniv of Operation Crossroads (atomic bomb tests on Bikini Atoll). Multicoloured.

80	22c. Type **17**	55	35
81	22c. Advance landing of amphibious DUKW from U.S.S. "Sumner"	55	35
82	22c. Loading "L.S.T. 1108" (tank landing ship) for islanders' departure	55	35
83	22c. Man planting coconuts as part of reclamation programme	55	35

1986. Sea Shells (2nd series). As T **8**. Multicoloured.

85	22c. Ramose ("Rose") murex	50	35
86	22c. Orange spider conch	50	35
87	22c. Red-mouth frog shell	50	35
88	22c. Laciniate conch	50	35
89	22c. Giant frog shell	50	35

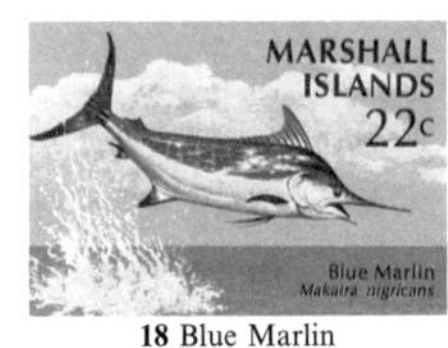

18 Blue Marlin

1986. Game Fishes. Multicoloured.

90	22c. Type **18**	50	40
91	22c. Wahoo	50	40
92	22c. Dolphin	50	40
93	22c. Yellow-finned tuna	50	40

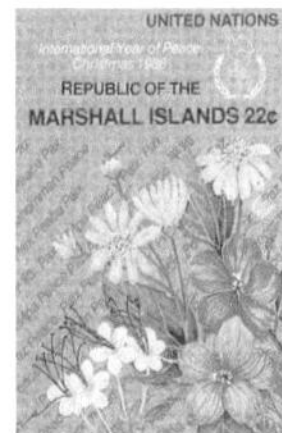

19 Flowers (top left)

1986. International Peace Year. Multicoloured.

94	22c. Type **19** (Christmas) (postage)	50	35
95	22c. Flowers (top right)	50	35
96	22c. Flowers (bottom left)	50	35
97	22c. Flowers (bottom right)	50	35
98	44c. Head of Statue crowned with flowers (24 × 39 mm) (cent of Statue of Liberty) (air)	1·00	70

Nos. 94/7 were issued together, se-tenant, in blocks of four within the sheet, each block forming a composite design of mixed flower arrangement.

20 Girl Scout giving Plant to Patient

1986. Air. 20th Anniv of Marshall Island Girl Scouts and 75th Anniv (1987) of United States Girl Scout Movement. Multicoloured.

99	44c. Type **20**	75	55
100	44c. Giving salute	75	55
101	44c. Girl scouts holding hands in circle	75	55
102	44c. Weaving pandana and palm branch mats	75	55

21 Wedge-tailed Shearwater

1987. Air. Sea Birds. Multicoloured.

103	44c. Type **21**	1·10	1·10
104	44c. Red-footed booby	1·10	1·10
105	44c. Red-tailed tropic bird	1·10	1·10
106	44c. Lesser frigate bird ("Great Frigatebird")	1·10	1·00

22 "James T. Arnold", 1854

1987. Whaling Ships. Multicoloured.

107	22c. Type **22**	60	45
108	22c. "General Scott", 1859	60	45
109	22c. "Charles W. Morgan", 1865	60	45
110	22c. "Lucretia", 1884	60	45

23 Lindbergh's "Spirit of St. Louis" and Congressional Medal of Honour, 1927

1987. Aviators. Multicoloured.

111	33c. Type **23**	70	45
112	33c. Charles Lindbergh and Chance Vought F4U Corsair fighter, Marshall Islands, 1944	70	45
113	39c. William Bridgeman and Consolidated B-24 Liberator bomber, Kwajalein, 1944	80	60
114	39c. Bridgeman and Douglas Skyrocket, 1951	80	60
115	44c. John Glenn and Chance Vought F4U Corsair fighters, Marshall Islands, 1944	1·00	75
116	44c. Glenn and "Friendship 7" space capsule	1·00	75

24 Earhart's Lockheed 10E Electra taking off from Lae, New Guinea

1987. Air. "Capex '87" International Stamp Exhibition, Toronto. 50th Anniv of Amelia Earhart's Round the World Flight Attempt. Multicoloured.

117	44c. Type **24**	90	65
118	44c. U.S. Coastguard cutter "Itasca" waiting off Howland Island for Electra	90	65
119	44c. Islanders and crashed Electra on Mili Atoll	90	65
120	44c. Japanese patrol boat "Koshu" recovering Electra	90	65

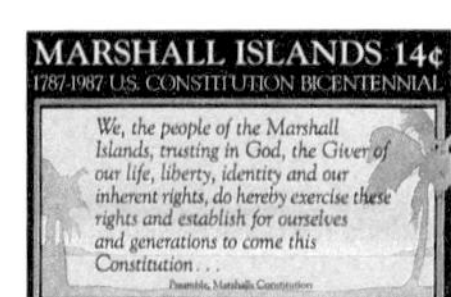

25 "We, the people of the Marshall Islands ..."

1987. Bicentenary of United States of America Constitution. Multicoloured.

122	14c. Type **25**	30	25
123	14c. Marshall Is. and U.S.A. emblems	30	25
124	14c. "We the people of the United States ..."	30	25
125	22c. "All we have and are today as a people ..."	45	25
126	22c. Marshall Is. and U.S.A. flags	45	25
127	22c. "... to establish Justice ..."	45	25
128	44c. "With this Constitution ..."	85	75
129	44c. Marshall Is. stick chart and U.S. Liberty Bell	85	75
130	44c. "... to promote the general Welfare ..."	85	75

The three designs of each value were printed together, se-tenant, the left hand stamp of each strip bearing quotations from the preamble to the Marshall Islands Constitution and the right hand stamp, quotations from the United States Constitution preamble.

1987. Sea Shells (3rd series). As T **8**. Multicoloured.
131 22c. Magnificent cone 50 35
132 22c. Pacific partridge tun . . 50 35
133 22c. Scorpion spider conch 50 35
134 22c. Common hairy triton . . 50 35
135 22c. Arthritic ("Chiragra") spider conch 50 35

26 Planting Coconut

1987. Copra Industry. Multicoloured.
136 44c. Type **26** 70 55
137 44c. Making copra 70 55
138 44c. Bottling extracted coconut oil 70 55

27 "We have seen his star in the east ..."

1987. Christmas. Multicoloured.
139 14c. Type **27** 30 25
140 22c. "Glory to God in the highest; ..." 40 30
141 33c. "Sing unto the Lord a new song ..." 60 40
142 44c. "Praise him in the cymbals and dances; ..." 80 65

28 Reef Heron ("Pacific Reef Heron")

1988. Shore and Water Birds. Multicoloured.
143 44c. Type **28** . . . . 1·10 1·00
144 44c. Bar-tailed godwit . . . 1·10 1·00
145 44c. Blue-faced booby ("Masked Booby") . . . . 1·10 1·00
146 44c. Northern shoveler . . . 1·10 1·00

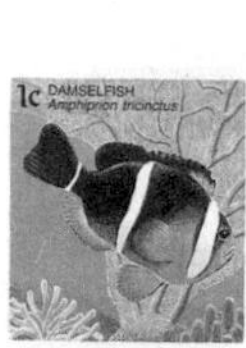

29 Maroon Anemonefish ("Damselfish")

30 Javelin Thrower

1988. Fishes. Multicoloured.
147 1c. Type **29** 10 10
148 3c. Black-faced butterflyfish 10 10
149 14c. Stocky hawkfish 20 10
150 15c. White-spotted puffer ("Balloonfish") 20 10
151 17c. Starry pufferfish ("Trunk Fish") 25 15
152 22c. Moon ("Lyretail") wrasse 30 20
153 25c. Six-banded parrotfish . . 30 20
154 33c. Spotted ("White-spotted") boxfish 40 25
155 36c. Yellow ("Spotted") boxfish 45 30
156 39c. Red-tailed surgeonfish 50 40
157 44c. Forceps ("Long-snouted") butterflyfish . . 55 45
158 45c. Oriental trumpetfish . . 55 45
159 56c. False-eyed pufferfish ("Sharp-nosed Puffer") . . 70 50
160 $1 Yellow seahorse . . . . . 1·50 70
161 $2 Ghost pipefish . . . . . 3·50 1·50
162 $5 Clown triggerfish ("Big-spotted Triggerfish") . . . 7·50 5·50
163 $10 Blue-finned trevally ("Blue Jack") (50 × 28 mm) 15·00 11·00

1988. Olympic Games, Seoul. Multicoloured.
166 15c. Type **30** 35 15
167 15c. Drawing javelin back and star 35 15
168 15c. Javelin drawn back fully (value at left) 35 15
169 15c. Commencing throw (value at right) 35 15
170 15c. Releasing javelin 35 15
171 25c. Runner and star (left half) 45 25
172 25c. Runner and star (right half) 45 25
173 25c. Runner (value at left) . . 45 25
174 25c. Runner (value at right) 45 25
175 25c. Finish of race 45 25

Nos. 166/70 were printed together, se-tenant, forming a composite design of a javelin throw with background of the Marshallese flag. Nos. 171/5 were similarly arranged forming a composite design of a runner and flag.

31 "Casco" sailing through Golden Gate of San Francisco

1988. Centenary of Robert Louis Stevenson's Pacific Voyages. Multicoloured.
176 25c. Type **31** 60 60
177 25c. "Casco" at the Needles of Ua-Pu, Marquesas . . . 60 40
178 25c. "Equator" leaving Honolulu 60 40
179 25c. Chieftain's canoe, Majuro Lagoon 60 40
180 25c. Bronze medallion depicting Stevenson by Augustus St. Gaudens, 1887 . . . . 60 40
181 25c. "Janet Nicoll" (inter-island steamer), Majuro Lagoon 60 40
182 25c. Stevenson's visit to maniap of King Tembinoka of Gilbert Islands 60 40
183 25c. Stevenson in Samoan canoe, Apia Harbour . . . 60 40
184 25c. Stevenson on horse Jack at Valima (Samoan home) 60 40

32 Spanish Ragged Cross Ensign (1516–1785) and Magellan's Ship "Vitoria"

1988. Exploration Ships and Flags. Multicoloured.
185 25c. Type **32** 50 35
186 25c. British red ensign (1707–1800), "Charlotte" and "Scarborough" (transports) 50 35
187 25c. American flag and ensign (1837–45), U.S.S. "Flying Fish" (schooner) and U.S.S. "Peacock" (sloop) 50 35
188 25c. German flag and ensign (1867–1919) and "Planet" (auxiliary schooner) . . . 50 35

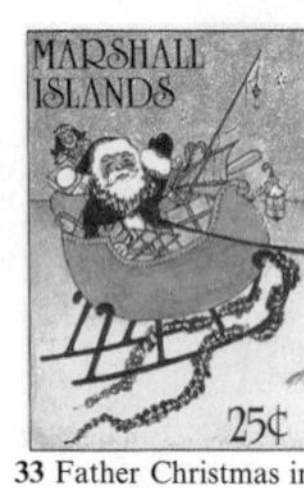

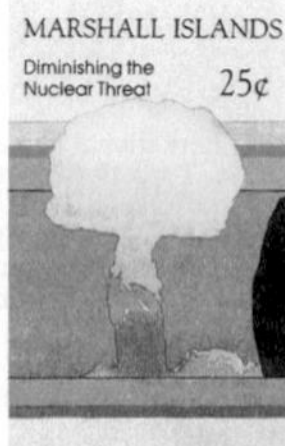

33 Father Christmas in Sleigh

34 Nuclear Test on Bikini Atoll

1988. Christmas. Multicoloured.
189 25c. Type **33** 45 30
190 25c. Reindeer over island with palm huts and trees 45 30
191 25c. Reindeer over island with palm trees 45 30
192 25c. Reindeer and billfish . . 45 30
193 25c. Reindeer over island with outrigger canoe . . . 45 30

1988. 25th Anniv of Assassination of John F. Kennedy (American President). Multicoloured.
194 25c. Type **34** 50 30
195 25c. Kennedy signing Test Ban Treaty 50 30
196 25c. Kennedy 50 30
197 25c. Kennedy using hot-line between Washington and Moscow 50 30
198 25c. Peace Corps volunteers 50 30

35 "SV-5D PRIME" Vehicle Launch from Vandenberg Air Force Base

1988. Kwajalein Space Shuttle Tracking Station. Multicoloured.
199 25c. Type **35** (postage) . . . 45 30
200 25c. Re-entry of "SV-5D" . . 45 30
201 25c. Recovery of "SV-5D" off Kwajalein 45 30
202 25c. Space shuttle "Discovery" over Kwajalein 45 30
203 45c. Shuttle and astronaut over Rongelap (air) 75 55

Nos. 199/202 were printed together, se-tenant, forming a composite design.

36 1918 Typhoon Monument, Majuro

1989. Links with Japan. Multicoloured.
204 45c. Type **36** 80 55
205 45c. Japanese seaplane base and railway, Djarret Islet, 1940s . . . . 1·25 90
206 45c. Japanese fishing boats 1·25 90
207 45c. Japanese skin-divers . . 80 55

37 "Island Woman"

1989. Links with Alaska. Oil Paintings by Claire Fejes. Multicoloured.
208 45c. Type **37** 75 55
209 45c. "Kotzebue, Alaska" . . 75 55
210 45c. "Marshallese Madonna" 75 55

38 Dornier Do-228

1989. Air. Airplanes. Multicoloured.
211 12c. Type **38** 30 20
212 36c. Boeing 737 . . . . . . 55 40
213 39c. Hawker Siddeley H.S. 748 . . . . 65 45
214 45c. Boeing 727 . . . . . . 75 55

1989. Sea Shells (4th series). As T **8**. Mult.
220 25c. Pontifical mitre 55 35
221 25c. Tapestry turban 55 35
222 25c. Flame mouthed ("Bull-mouth") helmet 55 35
223 25c. Prickly Pacific drupe . . 55 35
224 25c. Blood-mouth conch . . 55 35

40 Wandering Tattler

1989. Birds. Multicoloured.
226 45c. Type **40** . . . . 1·10 95
227 45c. Ruddy turnstone . . . . 1·10 95
228 45c. Pacific golden plover . . 1·10 95
229 45c. Sanderling . . . . . . 1·10 95

41 "Bussard" (German cruiser) and 1897 Ship's Post Cancellation

1989. "Philexfrance 89" International Stamp Exhibition, Paris. Marshall Islands Postal History. Multicoloured.
230 25c. Type **41** . . . . 1·50 50
231 25c. First day cover bearing first Marshall Islands stamps and U.S. 10c. stamp . . . . 1·50 50
232 25c. Consolidated PBY-5 Catalina flying boats, floating Fleet Post Office ("L.S.T. 119"), Majuro, and 1944 U.S. Navy cancellation . . . . 1·50 50
233 25c. Nakajima A6M2 "Rufe" seaplane, mailboat off Mili Island and Japanese cancellation . . . . 1·50 50
234 25c. Majuro Post Office . . . 1·50 50
235 25c. Consolidated PBY-5A Catalina amphibian, outrigger canoe and 1951 U.S. civilian mail cancellation . . . . 1·50 50
236 45c. "Morning Star V" (missionary ship) and 1905 Jaluit cancellation . . . . 1·75 55
237 45c. 1906 registered cover with Jaluit cancellation . . 1·75 55
238 45c. "Prinz Eitel Freiderich" (auxiliary cruiser) and 1914 German ship's post cancellation . . . . 1·75 55
239 45c. "Scharnhorst" (cruiser) leading German Asiatic Squadron and 1914 ship's post cancellation . . . . . 1·75 55

Nos. 230/5 were printed together, se-tenant, Nos. 231 and 234 forming a composite design to commemorate the 5th anniversary of Marshall Islands Independent Postal Service.

42 Launch of Apollo "11"

1989. 20th Anniv of First Manned Moon Landing. Multicoloured.
241 25c. Type **42** . . . . 1·00 75
242 25c. Neil Armstrong . . . . 1·00 75
243 25c. Descent of lunar module to moon's surface . . . . 1·00 75
244 25c. Michael Collins . . . . 1·00 75
245 25c. Planting flag on Moon 1·00 75
246 25c. Edwin "Buzz" Aldrin . . 1·00 75

43 Polish Cavalry and German Tanks

1989. History of Second World War. Multicoloured.
(a) 1st issue. Invasion of Poland, 1939.
248 25c. Type **43** 45 35

(b) 2nd issue. Sinking of H.M.S. "Royal Oak", 1939.
249 45c. U-boat and burning battleship 75 55

(c) 3rd issue. Invasion of Finland, 1939.
250 45c. Troops on skis and tanks 75 55

(d) 4th issue. Battle of the River Plate, 1939.
251 45c. H.M.S. "Exeter" (cruiser) 75 55
252 45c. H.M.S. "Ajax" (cruiser) 75 55
253 45c. "Admiral Graf Spee" (German battleship) . . . 75 55
254 45c. H.M.N.Z.S. "Achilles" (cruiser) 75 55

See also Nos. 320/44, 359/84, 409/40, 458/77, 523/48 and 575/95.

44 Angel with Horn

45 Dr. Robert Goddard

1989. Christmas. Multicoloured.
255 25c. Type **44** 70 50
256 25c. Angel singing 70 50
257 25c. Angel with lute 70 50
258 25c. Angel with lyre 70 50

1989. Milestones in Space Exploration. Multicoloured.
259 45c. Type **45** (first liquid fuel rocket launch, 1926) . . . 90 55
260 45c. "Sputnik 1" (first man-made satellite, 1957) . . . 90 55
261 45c. Rocket lifting off (first American satellite, 1958) 90 55
262 45c. Yuri Gagarin (first man in space, 1961) 90 55
263 45c. John Glenn (first American in Earth orbit, 1962) 90 55
264 45c. Valentina Tereshkova (first woman in space, 1963) 90 55
265 45c. Aleksei Leonov (first space walk, 1965) 90 55
266 45c. Edward White (first American space walk, 1965) 90 55
267 45c. "Gemini 6" and "7" (first rendezvous in space, 1965) 90 55
268 45c. "Luna 9" (first soft landing on the Moon, 1966) 90 55
269 45c. "Gemini 8" (first docking in space, 1966) . . 90 55
270 45c. "Venera 4" (first successful Venus probe, 1967) 90 55
271 45c. Moon seen from "Apollo 8" (first manned orbit of Moon, 1968) . . . 90 55
272 45c. Neil Armstrong and U.S. flag (first man on Moon, 1969) 90 55
273 45c. "Soyuz 11" and "Salyut 1" space station (first space station crew, 1971) 90 55
274 45c. Lunar rover of "Apollo 15" (first manned lunar vehicle, 1971) 90 55
275 45c. "Skylab 1" (first American space station, 1973) 90 55
276 45c. "Pioneer 10" and Jupiter (first flight past Jupiter, 1973) 90 55
277 45c. "Apollo" and "Soyuz" craft approaching each other (first international joint space flight, 1975) . . 90 55
278 45c. "Viking 1" on Mars (first landing on Mars, 1976) 90 55
279 45c. "Voyager 1" and Saturn's rings (first flight past Saturn, 1979) 90 55
280 45c. "Columbia" (first space shuttle flight, 1981) 90 55
281 45c. Satellite in outer space (first probe beyond the solar system, 1983) 90 55
282 45c. Astronaut (first untethered space walk, 1984) 90 55
283 45c. Launch of space shuttle "Discovery", 1988 . . . . 90 55

46 White-capped Noddy ("Black Noddy")

1990. Birds. Multicoloured.
284 1c. Type **46** 20 20
285 5c. Red-tailed tropic bird . . 20 20
286 9c. Whimbrel 20 20
287 10c. Sanderling 25 25
288 12c. Black-naped tern 25 25
289 15c. Wandering tattler . . . 30 30
290 20c. Bristle-thighed curlew . . 35 35
291 22c. Greater scaup 40 40
292 23c. Common (inscr "Northern") shoveler . . . 40 40
293 25c. Common (inscr "Brown") noddy 50 50
294 27c. Sooty tern 50 50
295 28c. Sharp-tailed sandpiper 50 50
296 29c. Wedge-tailed shearwater 55 50
297 30c. Pacific golden plover . . 55 55
298 35c. Brown booby 60 60
299 36c. Red-footed booby . . . 65 65
300 40c. White tern 75 75
301 45c. Green-winged (inscr "Common") teal 85 85
302 50c. Great frigate bird . . . 95 95
303 52c. Crested tern (inscr "Great Crested Tern") . . 1·10 1·10
304 65c. Lesser sand plover . . . 1·25 1·25
305 75c. Little tern . . . . 1·50 1·50
306 $1 Reef heron (inscr "Pacific") . . . . 2·25 2·25
307 $2 Blue-faced (inscr "Masked") booby . . . . 4·50 4·50

47 Lodidean (coconut-palm leaf windmill)

1990. Children's Games. Multicoloured.
309 25c. Type **47** 70 55
310 25c. Lejonjon (juggling green coconuts) 70 55
311 25c. Etobobo (coconut leaf musical instrument) 70 55
312 25c. Didmakol (pandanus leaf flying-toy) 70 55

48 Penny Black

1990. 150th Anniv of the Penny Black. Multicoloured.
313 25c. Type **48** 75 75
314 25c. Essay of James Chalmers's cancellation . . 75 75
315 25c. Stamp essay by Robert Sievier 75 75
316 25c. Stamp essay by Charles Whiting 75 75
317 25c. Stamp essay by George Dickinson 75 75
318 25c. "City" medal by William Wyon (struck to commemorate Queen Victoria's first visit to City of London) 75 75

1990. History of Second World War. As T **43**. Multicoloured. (a) 5th issue. Invasions of Denmark and Norway, 1940.
320 25c. German soldier and "Stuka" dive bombers in Copenhagen 45 35
321 25c. Norwegian soldiers, burning building and German column 45 35

(b) 6th issue. Katyn Forest Massacre of Polish Prisoners, 1940.
322 25c. Bound hands and grave (vert) 45 35

(c) 7th issue. Appointment of Winston Churchill as Prime Minister of Great Britain, 1940.
323 45c. Union Jack, Churchill and war scenes 70 50

(d) 8th issue. Invasion of Low Countries, 1940.
324 25c. Bombing of Rotterdam 45 35
325 25c. Invasion of Belgium . . 45 35

(e) 9th issue. Evacuation at Dunkirk, 1940.
326 45c. British bren-gunner on beach 70 50
327 45c. Soldiers queueing for boats 70 50
Nos. 326/7 were issued together, se-tenant, forming a composite design.

(f) 10th issue. German Occupation of Paris, 1940.
328 45c. German soldiers marching through Arc de Triomphe (vert) 70 50

(g) 11th issue. Battle of Mers-el-Kebir, 1940.
329 25c. Vice-Admiral Sir James Somerville, Vice-Admiral Marcel Gensoul and British and French battleships . . 45 35

(h) 12th issue. The Burma Road, 1940.
330 25c. Allied and Japanese forces (vert) 45 35

(i) 13th issue. British Bases and American Destroyers Lend-lease Agreement, 1940.
331 45c. H.M.S. "Georgetown" (formerly U.S.S. "Maddox") 70 50
332 45c. H.M.S. "Banff" (formerly U.S.C.G.C. "Saranac") 70 50
333 45c. H.M.S. "Buxton" (formerly U.S.S. "Edwards") 70 50
334 45c. H.M.S. "Rockingham" (formerly U.S.S. "Swasey") 70 50

(j) 14th issue. Battle of Britain, 1940.
335 45c. Supermarine Spitfire Mk 1A fighters 70 50
336 45c. Hawker Hurricane Mk 1 and Spitfire fighters 70 50
337 45c. Messerschmitt Bf 109E fighters 70 50
338 45c. Junkers Ju 87B-2 "Stuka" dive bomber . . . 70 50
Nos. 335/8 were issued together, se-tenant, forming a composite design.

(k) 15th issue. Tripartite Pact, 1940.
339 45c. Officers' caps of Germany, Italy and Japan (vert) 70 50

(l) 16th issue. Election of Franklin D. Roosevelt for Third United States Presidential Term, 1940.
340 25c. Roosevelt (vert) 45 35

(m) 17th issue. Battle of Taranto, 1940.
341 25c. H.M.S. "Illustrious" (aircraft carrier) 45 35
342 25c. Fairey Swordfish bomber 45 35
343 25c. "Andrea Doria" (Italian battleship) 45 35
344 25c. "Conte di Cavour" (Italian battleship) 45 35
Nos. 341/4 were issued together, se-tenant, forming a composite design.

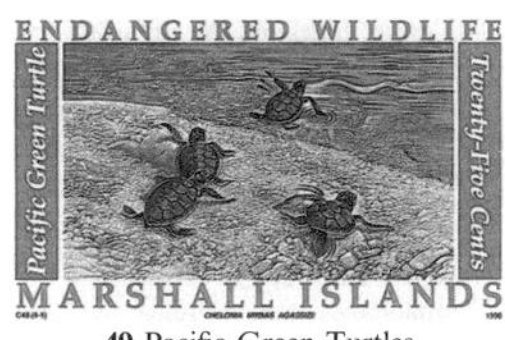

49 Pacific Green Turtles

1990. Endangered Turtles. Multicoloured.
345 25c. Type **49** . . . . 1·10 75
346 25c. Pacific green turtle swimming . . . . 1·10 75
347 25c. Hawksbill turtle hatching 1·10 75
348 25c. Hawksbill turtle swimming . . . . 1·10 75

50 Stick Chart, Outrigger Canoe and Flag

1990. 4th Anniv of Ratification of Compact of Free Association with United States.
349 **50** 25c. multicoloured 75 45

51 Brandenburg Gate, Berlin

1990. Re-unification of Germany.
350 **51** 45c. multicoloured . . . . 1·00 70

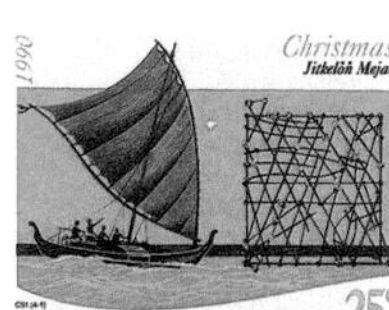

52 Outrigger Canoe and Stick Chart

1990. Christmas. Multicoloured.
351 25c. Type **52** 70 50
352 25c. Missionary preaching and "Morning Star" (missionary ship) 70 50
353 25c. British sailors dancing 70 50
354 25c. Electric guitar and couple dancing 70 50

53 Harvesting Breadfruit

1990. Breadfruit. Multicoloured.
355 25c. Type **53** 70 50
356 25c. Peeling breadfruit . . . 70 50
357 25c. Soaking breadfruit . . . 70 50
358 25c. Kneading dough 70 50

1991. History of Second World War. As T **43**. Multicoloured. (a) 18th issue. Four Freedoms Speech to U.S. Congress by President Franklin Roosevelt, 1941.
359 30c. Freedom of Speech . . . 50 40
360 30c. Freedom from Want . . 50 40
361 30c. Freedom of Worship . . 50 40
362 30c. Freedom from Fear . . 50 40

(b) 19th issue. Battle of Beda Fomm, 1941.
363 30c. Tank battle 50 40

(c) 20th issue. German Invasion of Balkans, 1941.
364 29c. German Dornier DO-17Z bombers over Acropolis, Athens (Greece) (vert) 50 40
365 29c. German tank and Yugoslavian Parliament building (vert) 50 40

(d) 21st issue. Sinking of the "Bismarck" (German battleship), 1941.
366 50c. H.M.S. "Prince of Wales" (battleship) 75 60
367 50c. H.M.S. "Hood" (battle cruiser) 75 60
368 50c. "Bismarck" 75 60
369 50c. Fairey Swordfish torpedo bombers 75 60

(e) 22nd issue. German Invasion of Russia, 1941.
370 30c. German tanks 50 40

(f) 23rd issue. Declaration of Atlantic Charter by United States and Great Britain, 1941.
371 29c. U.S.S. "Augusta" (cruiser) and Pres. Roosevelt of United States (vert) 50 40
372 29c. H.M.S. "Prince of Wales" (battleship) and Winston Churchill (vert) 50 40
Nos. 371/2 were issued together, se-tenant, forming a composite design.

(g) 24th issue. Siege of Moscow, 1941.
373 29c. German tanks crossing snow-covered plain 50 40

(h) 25th issue. Sinking of U.S.S. "Reuben James", 1941.
374 30c. U.S.S. "Reuben James" (destroyer) 50 40
375 30c. German U-boat 562 (submarine) 50 40
Nos. 374/5 were issued together, se-tenant, forming a composite design.

(i) 26th issue. Japanese Attack on Pearl Harbor, 1941.
376 50c. American airplanes (inscr "Peal Harbor") (vert) 75 60
376b As No. 376 but inscr "Pearl Harbor" 75 60
377 50c. Japanese dive bombers (vert) 75 60
378 50c. U.S.S. "Arizona" (battleship) (vert) 75 60
379 50c. "Akagi" (Japanese aircraft carrier) (vert) . . 75 60
Nos. 376/9 were issued together, se-tenant, forming a composite design.

(j) 27th issue. Japanese Capture of Guam, 1941.
380 29c. Japanese troops (vert) 50 40

(k) 28th issue. Fall of Singapore to Japan, 1941.
381 29c. Japanese soldiers with Japanese flag, Union Jack and white flag 50 40

(l) 29th issue. Formation of "Flying Tigers" (American volunteer group), 1941.
382 50c. American Curtiss Tomahawk fighters 75 60
383 50c. Japanese Mitsubishi Ki-21 "Sally" bombers . . 75 60
Nos. 382/3 were issued together, se-tenant, forming a composite design.

(m) 30th issue. Fall of Wake Island to Japan, 1941.
384 29c. American Grumman Wildcat fighters and Japanese Mitsubishi G3M "Nell" bombers over Wake Island 50 40

54 Boeing 747 carrying "Columbia" to Launch Site

1991. Ten Years of Space Shuttle Flights. Multicoloured.
385 50c. Type **54** 90 70
386 50c. Orbital release of Long Duration Exposure Facility from "Challenger", 1984 90 70
387 50c. Shuttle launch at Cape Canaveral 90 70
388 50c. Shuttle landing at Edwards Air Force Base 90 70
Nos. 385/8 were issued together, se-tenant, the backgrounds forming a composite design.

55 "Ixora carolinensis"

1991. Native Flowers. Multicoloured.
389 52c. Type **55** 90 70
390 52c. Glory-bower ("Clerodendum inerme") 90 70
391 52c. "Messerschmidia argentea" 90 70
392 52c. "Vigna marina" 90 70

56 American Bald Eagle and Marshall Islands and U.S. Flags

1991. United States Participation in Operation Desert Storm (campaign to liberate Kuwait).
394 **56** 29c. multicoloured 60 45

57 Red-footed Booby

1991. Birds. Multicoloured.
395 29c. Type **57** 90 40
396 29c. Great frigate bird (facing right) 90 40
397 29c. Brown booby 90 40
398 29c. White tern 90 40
399 29c. Great frigate bird (facing left) 90 40
400 29c. White-capped noddy ("Black Noddy") 90 40

58 Dornier Do-228

1991. Passenger Aircraft. Multicoloured.
402 12c. Type **58** 35 20
403 29c. Douglas DC-8 jetliner 75 50
404 50c. Hawker Siddeley H.S. 748 airliner . . . . 1·25 90
405 50c. Saab 2000 . . . . . . 1·25 90

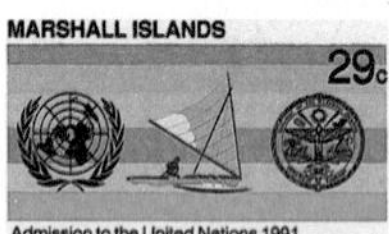

59 U.N. and State Emblems and Outrigger Canoe

1991. Admission of Marshall Islands to the United Nations.
406 **59** 29c. multicoloured 60 45

60 Dove and Glory-bower Flowers

1991. Christmas.
407 **60** 30c. multicoloured 65 50

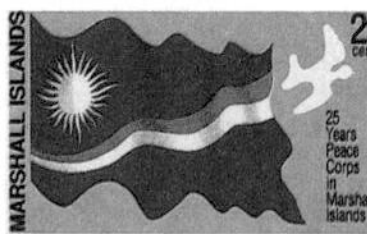

61 State Flag and Dove

1991. 25th Anniv of Peace Corps in Marshall Islands.
408 **61** 29c. multicoloured 55 45

1992. History of Second World War. As T **43**. Multicoloured. (a) 31st issue. Arcadia Conference, Washington D.C., 1942.
409 29c. Pres. Franklin Roosevelt of U.S.A., Winston Churchill of Great Britain, White House and United Nations emblem 50 40

(b) 32nd issue. Fall of Manila to Japan, 1942.
410 50c. Japanese tank moving through Manila 75 60

(c) 33rd issue. Capture of Rabaul by Japan, 1942.
411 29c. Japanese flag, Admiral Yamamoto, General Douglas MacArthur and U.S. flag 50 40

(d) 34th issue. Battle of the Java Sea, 1942.
412 29c. Sinking of the "De Ruyter" (Dutch cruiser) . . 50 40

(e) 35th issue. Capture of Rangoon by Japan, 1942.
413 50c. Japanese tank and soldiers in Rangoon (vert) 75 60

(f) 36th issue. Japanese Landing on New Guinea, 1942.
414 29c. Japanese soldiers coming ashore 50 40

(g) 37th issue. Evacuation of General Douglas MacArthur from Corregidor, 1942.
415 29c. MacArthur 50 40

(h) 38th issue. British Raid on Saint Nazaire, 1942.
416 29c. H.M.S. "Campbeltown" (destroyer) and motor torpedo boat 50 40

(i) 39th issue. Surrender of Bataan, 1942.
417 29c. Prisoners on "death" march (vert) 50 40

(j) 40th issue. Doolittle Raid on Tokyo, 1942.
418 50c. North American B-25 Mitchell bomber taking off from U.S.S. "Hornet" (aircraft carrier) (vert) . . 75 60

(k) 41st issue. Fall of Corregidor to Japan, 1942.
419 29c. Lt.-Gen. Jonathan Wainwright 50 40

(l) 42nd issue. Battle of the Coral Sea, 1942.
420 50c. U.S.S. "Lexington" (aircraft carrier) and Grumman F4F-3 Wildcat fighter (inscr "U.S.S. Lexington") 75 60
420b As No. 420 but additionally inscr with aircraft name 75 60
421 50c. Japanese Aichi D3A 1 "Val" and Nakajima B5N2 "Kate" dive bombers (wrongly inscr 'Mitsubishi A6M2 "Zero" ') 75 60
421a As No. 421 but inscr corrected 75 60
422 50c. American Douglas TBD-1 Devastator torpedo bombers (wrongly inscr "U.S. Douglas SBD Dauntless") 75 60
422a As No. 422 but with inscr corrected 75 60
423 50c. "Shoho" (Japanese aircraft carrier) and Mitsubishi A6M2 Zero-Sen fighters (inscr "Japanese carrier Shoho") 75 60
423a As No. 423 but additionally inscr with aircraft name 75 60

The four designs were issued together, se-tenant, each pair forming a composite design.

(m) 43rd issue. Battle of Midway, 1942.
424 50c. "Akagi" (Japanese aircraft carrier) 75 60
425 50c. U.S.S. "Yorktown" (aircraft carrier) 75 60
426 50c. American Douglas SBD Dauntless dive bombers . . 75 60
427 50c. Japanese Nakajima B5N2 "Kate" dive bombers 75 60

Nos. 424/7 were issued together, se-tenant, forming a composite design.

(n) 44th issue. Destruction of Lidice (Czechoslovakian village), 1942.
428 29c. Cross and memorial at Lidice 50 40

(o) 45th issue. German Capture of Sevastopol, 1942.
429 29c. German siege gun "Dora" (vert) 50 40

(p) 46th issue. Destruction of Convoy PQ-17, 1942.
430 29c. British merchant ship . . 50 40
431 29c. German U-boat 50 40

(q) 47th issue. Marine Landing on Guadalcanal, 1942.
432 29c. American marines landing on beach 50 40

(r) 48th issue. Battle of Savo Island, 1942.
433 29c. Admiral Mikawa of Japan (vert) 50 40

(s) 49th issue. Dieppe Raid, 1942.
434 29c. Soldiers landing at Dieppe 50 40

(t) 50th issue. Battle of Stalingrad, 1942.
435 50c. Heroes monument and burning buildings (vert) . . 75 60

(u) 51st issue. Battle of Eastern Solomon Islands, 1942.
436 29c. Aircraft over U.S.S. "Enterprise" (aircraft carrier) 50 40

(v) 52nd issue. Battle of Cape Esperance, 1942.
437 50c. American cruiser firing guns at night 75 60

(w) 53rd issue. Battle of El Alamein, 1942.
438 29c. Gen. Bernard Montgomery of Great Britain and Gen. Erwin Rommel of Germany . . . 50 40

(x) 54th issue. Battle of Barents Sea, 1942.
439 29c. H.M.S. "Sheffield" (cruiser) 50 40
440 29c. "Admiral Hipper" (German cruiser) 50 40

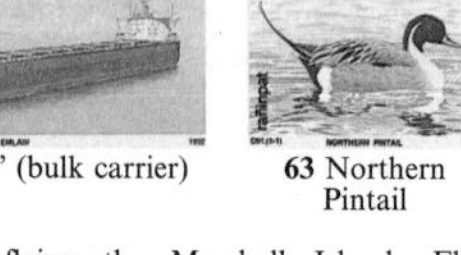

62 "Emlain" (bulk carrier) **63** Northern Pintail

1992. Ships flying the Marshall Islands Flag. Multicoloured.
441 29c. Type **62** 70 50
442 29c. "CSK Valiant" (tanker) 70 50
443 29c. "Ionmeto" (fisheries protection vessel) 70 50
444 29c. "Micro Pilot" (inter-island freighter) 70 50

1992. Nature Protection.
445 **63** 29c. multicoloured 60 45

64 Tipnol (outrigger canoe) **65** Basket Making

1992. Legends of Discovery. Multicoloured.
446 50c. Type **64** 75 75
447 50c. "Santa Maria" (reconstruction of Columbus's flagship) . . . 75 75
448 50c. Constellation Argo Navis 75 75
449 50c. Sailor and tipnol 75 75
450 50c. Christopher Columbus and "Santa Maria" 75 75
451 50c. Astronaut and Argo Navis constellation 75 75

1992. Handicrafts. Multicoloured.
453 29c. Type **65** 50 40
454 29c. Boy holding model outrigger canoe 50 40
455 29c. Man carving boat . . . 50 40
456 29c. Fan making 50 40

66 Christmas Offering

1992. Christmas.
457 **66** 29c. multicoloured 50 40

1993. History of Second World War. As T **43**. Multicoloured. (a) 55th issue. Casablanca Conference, 1943.
458 29c. Pres. Franklin Roosevelt and Winston Churchill . . 50 40

(b) 56th issue. Liberation of Kharkov, 1943.
459 29c. Russian tank in Kharkov 50 40

(c) 57th issue. Battle of the Bismarck Sea, 1943.
460 50c. Japanese Mitsubishi A6M Zero-Sen fighters and "Arashio" (Japanese destroyer) 75 60
461 50c. American Lockheed P-38 Lightnings and Australian Bristol Beaufighter fighters 75 60
462 50c. "Shirayuki" (Japanese destroyer) 75 60
463 50c. American A-20 Havoc and North American B-52 Mitchell bombers 75 60

Nos 460/63 were issued together, se-tenant, forming a composite design.

(d) 58th issue. Interception of Yamamoto, 1943.
464 50c. Admiral Yamamoto . . 75 60

(e) 59th issue. Battle of Kursk, 1943.
465 29c. German "Tiger 1" tank 50 40
466 29c. Soviet "T-34" tank . . . 50 40

Nos. 465/6 were issued together, se-tenant, forming a composite design.

(f) 60th issue. Allied Invasion of Sicily, 1943.
467 52c. Gen. George Patton, Jr 85 60
468 52c. Gen. Bernard Montgomery 85 65
469 52c. Americans landing at Licata 85 65
470 52c. British landing south of Syracuse 85 65

(g) 61st issue. Raids on Schweinfurt, 1943.
471 50c. American Boeing B-17F Flying Fortress bombers and German Messerschmitt Bf 109 fighter 75 60

(h) 62nd issue. Liberation of Smolensk, 1943.
472 29c. Russian soldier and burning buildings (vert) . . 50 40

(i) 63rd issue. Landing at Bougainville, 1943.
473 29c. American Marines on beach at Empress Augusta Bay 50 40

(j) 64th issue. U.S. Invasion of Tarawa, 1943.
474 50c. American Marines . . . 75 60

(k) 65th issue. Teheran Allied Conference, 1943.
475 52c. Winston Churchill of Great Britain, Pres. Franklin Roosevelt of U.S.A. and Josef Stalin of Russia (vert) 85 65

(l) 66th issue. Battle of North Cape, 1943.
476 29c. H.M.S. "Duke of York" (British battleship) 50 40
477 29c. "Scharnhorst" (German battleship) 50 40

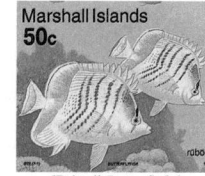

67 Atoll Butterflyfish

1993. Reef Life. Multicoloured.
478 50c. Type **67** 90 60
479 50c. Brick soldierfish 90 60
480 50c. Caerulean damselfish . . 90 60
481 50c. Japanese inflator-filefish 90 60
482 50c. Arc-eyed hawkfish . . . 90 60
483 50c. Powder-blue surgeonfish 90 60

68 "Britannia" (full-rigged ship)

1993. Ships. Multicoloured. (a) Size 35 × 20 mm.
485 10c. "San Jeronimo" (Spanish galleon) 10 10
486 14c. U.S.C.G. "Cape Corwin" (fisheries patrol vessel) 15 10
487 15c. Type **68** 20 15
488 19c. "Micro Palm" (inter-island freighter) 25 15
489 20c. "Eendracht" (Dirk Hartog's ship) 30 15
490 23c. H.M.S "Cornwallis" (sail frigate) 35 20
491 24c. U.S.S. "Dolphin" (schooner) 40 20
492 29c. "Morning Star I" (missionary brigantine) . . 45 25
493 30c. "Rurik" (Otto von Kotzebue's brig) (inscr "Rurick") 50 25
494 32c. "Vitoria" (Magellan's flagship) 55 25
669 32c. As Type **68** 50 40
670 32c. U.S.S. "Dolphin" (schooner) 50 40
671 32c. "Morning Star I" (missionary brigantine) . . 50 40
672 32c. U.S.S. "Lexington" (aircraft carrier) 50 40
673 32c. "Micro Palm" (inter-island freighter) 50 40
674 32c. H.M.S. "Cornwallis" (sail frigate) 50 40

675 32c. H.M.S. "Serpent" (brig) 50 40
676 32c. "Scarborough" (transport) 50 40
677 32c. "San Jeronimo" (Spanish galleon) 50 40
678 32c. "Rurik" (Otto van Kotzebue's brig) (inscr "Rurick") 50 40
679 32c. "Nautilus" (German gunboat) 50 40
680 32c. Fishing vessels 50 40
681 32c. Malmel outrigger canoe 50 40
682 32c. "Eendracht" (Dirk Hartog's ship) 50 40
683 32c. "Nautilus" (brig) 50 40
684 32c. "Nagara" and "Isuzu" (Japanese cruisers) 50 40
685 32c. "Potomac" (whaling ship) 50 40
687 32c. U.S.C.G. "Assateague" (cutter) 50 40
688 32c. "Charles W. Morgan" (whaling ship) 50 40
689 32c. "Victoria" (whaling ship) 50 40
690 32c. U.S.C.G. "Cape Corwin" (fisheries patrol vessel) 50 40
691 32c. "Equator" (schooner) 50 40
692 32c. "Tanager" (inter-island steamer) 50 40
693 32c. "Tole Mour" (hospital schooner) 50 40
495 35c. "Nautilus" (German gunboat) 60 30
496 40c. "Nautilus" (British brig) 65 30
497 45c. "Nagara" and "Isuzu" (Japanese cruisers) 70 35
498 46c. "Equator" (schooner) 75 35
499 50c. U.S.S. "Lexington" (aircraft carrier) 80 40
500 52c. H.M.S. "Serpent" (brig) 85 45
501 55c. "Potomac" (whaling ship) 90 50
502 60c. U.S.C.G. "Assateague" (cutter) 1·00 70
503 75c. "Scarborough" (transport) 1·10 75
504 78c. "Charles W. Morgan" (whaling ship) 1·25 90
505 95c. "Tanager" (inter-island steamer) 1·40 1·00
506 $1 "Tole Mour" (hospital schooner) 1·50 1·10
507 $2.90 Fishing vessels 4·25 2·75
508 $3.00 "Victoria" (whaling ship) 4·50 3·00

(b) Size 46 × 26 mm.

509 $1 Enewetak outrigger canoe 1·50 1·00
510 $2 Jaluit outrigger canoe 4·00 3·00
511 $5 Ailuk outrigger canoe 7·00 5·00
512 $10 Racing outrigger canoes 14·00 10·00

69 Capitol Complex

1993. Inauguration of New Capitol Complex, Majuro. Multicoloured.

513 29c. Type **69** 40 25
514 29c. Parliament building 40 25
515 29c. National seal (vert) 40 25
516 29c. National flag (vert) 40 25

71 Woman with Breadfruit

1993. Marshallese Life in the 1800s. Designs adapted from sketches by Louis Choris. Multicoloured.

518 29c. Type **71** 50 35
519 29c. Canoes and warrior 50 35
520 29c. Chief and islanders 50 35
521 29c. Drummer and dancers 50 35

72 Singing Silent Night

1993. Christmas.

522 **72** 29c. multicoloured 50 35

1994. History of Second World War. As T **43**. Multicoloured. (a) 67th issue. Appointment of Gen. Dwight D. Eisenhower as Commander of Supreme Headquarters, Allied Expeditionary Force, 1944.

523 29c. Eisenhower 50 40

(b) 68th issue. Invasion of Anzio, 1944.

524 50c. Troops landing 70 60

(c) 69th issue. Lifting of Siege of Leningrad, 1944.

525 52c. St. Isaac's Cathedral and soldier with Soviet flag 85 65

(d) 70th issue. U.S. Liberation of Marshall Islands, 1944.

526 29c. Douglas SBD Dauntless dive bombers 50 40

(e) 71st issue. Japanese Defeat at Truk, 1944.

527 29c. Admirals Spruance and Marc Mitscher (vert) 50 40

(f) 72nd issue. U.S. Bombing of Germany, 1944.

528 52c. Boeing B-17 Flying Fortress bombers 85 65

(g) 73rd issue. Allied Liberation of Rome, 1944.

529 50c. Lt.-Gen. Mark Clark and flowers in gun barrel (vert) 75 60

(h) 74th issue. Allied Landings in Normandy, 1944.

530 75c. Airspeed A.S.51 Horsa gliders (inscr "Horsa Gliders") 1·10 80
530b As No. 530 but inscr "Horsa Gliders, Parachute Troops" 1·10 80
531 75c. Hawker Typhoon 1B and North American P-51B Mustang fighters (wrongly inscr "U.S. P51B Mustangs, British Hurricanes") 1·10 80
531a As No. 531 but inscr corrected 1·10 80
532 75c. German gun defences (inscr "German Gun Defenses") 1·10 80
532a As No. 523 but inscr "German Gun Defenses, Pointe du Hoc" 1·10 80
533 75c. Allied amphibious landing 1·10 80

The four designs were issued together, se-tenant, forming a composite design.

(i) 75th issue. V-1 Bombardment of England, 1944.

534 50c. V-1 flying bomb over River Thames 75 60

(j) 76th issue. U.S. Marines Land on Saipan, 1944.

535 29c. U.S. and Japanese troops 50 40

(k) 77th issue. First Battle of the Philippine Sea, 1944.

536 50c. Grumman F6F-3 Hellcat fighter 75 60

(l) 78th issue. U.S. Liberation of Guam, 1944.

537 29c. Naval bombardment 50 40

(m) 79th issue. Warsaw Uprising, 1944.

538 50c. Polish Home Army fighter 75 60

(n) 80th issue. Liberation of Paris, 1944.

539 50c. Allied troops marching along Champs Elysee 75 60

(o) 81st issue. U.S. Marines Land on Peleliu, 1944.

540 29c. Amphibious armoured tracked vehicle 50 40

(p) 82nd issue. General Douglas MacArthur's Return to Philippines, 1944.

541 52c. McArthur and soldiers 85 65

(q) 83rd issue. Battle of Leyte Gulf, 1944.

542 52c. American motor torpedo boat and Japanese warships 85 65

(r) 84th issue. Sinking of the "Tirpitz" (German battleship), 1944.

543 50c. Avro Lancaster bombers 75 60
544 50c. Tirpitz burning 75 60

(s) 85th issue. Battle of the Bulge, 1944.

545 50c. Infantrymen 75 60
546 50c. Tank driver and tanks 75 60
547 50c. Pilot and aircraft 75 60
548 50c. Lt.-Col. Creighton Abrams and Brig.-Gen. Anthony McAuliffe shaking hands 75 60

75 Footballers

76 Neil Armstrong stepping onto Moon

1994. World Cup Football Championship, U.S.A. Multicoloured.

552 50c. Type **75** 1·40 60
553 50c. Footballers (different) 1·40 60

Nos. 552/53 were issued together, se-tenant, forming a composite design.

1994. 25th Anniv of First Manned Moon Landing. Multicoloured.

554 75c. Type **76** 95 70
555 75c. Planting U.S. flag on Moon 95 70
556 75c. Astronauts saluting 95 70
557 75c. Pres. John F. Kennedy and Armstrong 95 70

77 Solar System

1994. The Solar System. Multicoloured.

559 50c. Type **77** 85 65
560 50c. Sun 85 65
561 50c. Moon 85 65
562 50c. Mercury 85 65
563 50c. Venus 85 65
564 50c. Earth 85 65
565 50c. Mars 85 65
566 50c. Jupiter 85 65
567 50c. Saturn 85 65
568 50c. Uranus 85 65
569 50c. Neptune 85 65
570 50c. Pluto 85 65

79 Church and Christmas Tree (Ringo Baso)

1994. Christmas.

573 **79** 29c. multicoloured 50 40

1995. History of Second World War. As T **43**. Multicoloured. (a) 86th issue. Yalta Conference, 1945.

575 32c. Josef Stalin of U.S.S.R., Winston Churchill of Great Britain and Franklin Roosevelt of U.S.A. (vert) 55 45

(b) 87th issue. Allied Bombing of Dresden, 1945.

576 55c. "Europe" (Meissen porcelain statuette), flames and bombers (vert) 90 70

(c) 88th issue. U.S. Marine Invasion of Iwo Jima, 1945.

577 $1 Marines planting flag on Mt. Suribachi (vert) 1·60 1·25

(d) 89th issue. U.S. Capture of Remagen Bridge, Germany, 1945.

578 32c. Troops and tanks crossing bridge (vert) 55 45

(e) 90th issue. U.S. Invasion of Okinawa, 1945.

579 55c. Soldiers throwing grenades (vert) 90 70

(f) 91st issue. Death of Franklin D. Roosevelt, 1945.

580 50c. Funeral cortege 75 60

(g) 92nd issue. U.S. and U.S.S.R. Troops meet at Elbe, 1945.

581 32c. American and Soviet troops 55 45

(h) 93rd issue. Capture of Berlin by Soviet Troops, 1945.

582 60c. Soviet Marshal Georgi Zhukov and Berlin landmarks 95 75

(i) 94th issue. Allied Liberation of Concentration Camps, 1945.

583 55c. Inmates and soldier cutting barbed-wire fence 90 70

(j) 95th issue. V-E (Victory in Europe) Day, 1945.

584 75c. Signing of German surrender, Rheims 1·10 80
585 75c. Soldier kissing girl, Times Square, New York 1·10 80
586 75c. Victory Parade, Red Square, Moscow 1·10 80
587 75c. Royal Family and Churchill on balcony of Buckingham Palace, London 1·10 80

(k) 96th issue. Signing of United Nations Charter, 1945.

588 32c. U.S. President Harry S. Truman and Veterans' Memorial Hall, San Francisco 55 45

(l) 97th issue. Potsdam Conference, 1945.

589 55c. Pres. Harry S. Truman of U.S.A., Winston Churchill and Clement Attlee of Great Britain and Josef Stalin of U.S.S.R. 90 70

(m) 98th issue. Resignation of Winston Churchill, 1945.

590 60c. Churchill leaving 10 Downing Street (vert) 95 75

(n) 99th issue. Dropping of Atomic Bomb on Hiroshima, 1945.

591 $1 Boeing B-29 Superfortress bomber "Enola Gay" and mushroom cloud 1·60 1·25

(o) 100th issue. V-J (Victory in Japan) Day, 1945.

592 75c. Mount Fuji and warships in Tokyo Bay 1·10 80
593 75c. U.S.S. "Missouri" (battleship) 1·10 80
594 75c. Admiral Chester Nimitz signing Japanese surrender watched by Gen. Douglas MacArthur and Admirals William Halsey and Forest Sherman 1·10 80
595 75c. Japanese Foreign Minister Shigemitsu, General Umezu and delegation 1·10 80

Nos. 592/5 were issued together, se-tenant, each pair forming a composite design.

81 Scuba Diver, Meyer's Butterflyfish and Red-tailed Surgeonfish ("Achilles Tang")

1995. Undersea World (1st series). Multicoloured.

596 55c. Type **81** 90 70
597 55c. Moorish idols and scuba diver 90 70
598 55c. Pacific green turtle and anthias ("Fairy Basslet") 90 70
599 55c. Anthias ("Fairy Basslet"), emperor angelfish and orange-finned anemonefish 90 70

Nos. 596/9 were issued together, se-tenant, forming a composite design.

See also Nos. 865/8.

82 U.S.S. "PT 109" (motor torpedo boat)

83 Marilyn Monroe

1995. 35th Anniv of Election of John F. Kennedy as U.S. President. Multicoloured.

600 55c. Type **82** (Second World War command) 80 65
601 55c. Presidential inauguration 80 65
602 55c. Peace corps on agricultural project in Marshall Islands 80 65
603 55c. U.S. airplane and warships superintending removal of Soviet missiles from Cuba 80 65
604 55c. Kennedy signing Nuclear Test Ban Treaty, 1963 80 65
605 55c. Eternal flame on Kennedy's grave, Arlington National Cemetery, Washington D.C. 80 65

1995. 69th Birth Anniv of Marilyn Monroe (actress). Multicoloured.

606 75c. Type **83** 1·10 80
607 75c. Monroe (face value top right) 1·10 80
608 75c. Monroe (face value bottom left) 1·10 80
609 75c. Monroe (face value bottom right) 1·10 80

85 "Mir" (Soviet space station)

86 Siamese and Exotic Shorthair

1995. Docking of Atlantis with "Mir" Space Station (611/12) and 20th Anniv of "Apollo"–"Soyuz" Space Link (613/14). Multicoloured.
611 75c. Type **85** 1·10 80
612 75c. "Atlantis" (U.S. space shuttle) 1·10 80
613 75c. "Apollo" (U.S. spacecraft) 1·10 80
614 75c. "Soyuz" (Soviet spacecraft) 1·10 80
Nos. 611/14 were issued together, se-tenant, forming a composite design.

1995. Cats. Multicoloured.
615 32c. Type **86** 55 45
616 32c. American shorthair tabby and red Persian 55 45
617 32c. Maine coon and Burmese 55 45
618 32c. Himalayan and Abyssinian 55 45

87 Sailfish and Tuna

1995. Pacific Game Fish. Multicoloured.
619 60c. Type **87** 1·00 75
620 60c. Albacores 1·00 75
621 60c. Wahoo 1·00 75
622 60c. Blue marlin 1·00 75
623 60c. Yellow-finned tunas 1·00 75
624 60c. Giant trevally 1·00 75
625 60c. Dolphin (fish) 1·00 75
626 60c. Short-finned mako 1·00 75
Nos. 619/26 were issued together, se-tenant, forming a composite design.

88 Inedel's Magic Kite

91 Shepherds gazing at Sky

1995. Folk Legends (1st series). Multicoloured.
627 32c. Type **88** 60 45
628 32c. Lijebake rescues her granddaughter 60 45
629 32c. Jebro's mother invents the sail 60 45
630 32c. Limajnon escapes to the moon 60 45
See also Nos. 727/30 and 861/4.

1995. Christmas.
633 **91** 32c. multicoloured 45 25

92 Messerschmit Me 262-Ia Schwalbe

93 Rabin

1995. Jet Fighters. Multicoloured.
634 32c. Type **92** 50 40
635 32c. Gloster Meteor F Mk 8 50 40
636 32c. Lockheed F-80 Shooting Star 50 40
637 32c. North American F-86 Sabre 50 40
638 32c. F9F-2 Panther 50 40
639 32c. Mikoyan Gurevich MiG-15 50 40
640 32c. North American F-100 Super Sabre 50 40
641 32c. Convair TF-102A Delta Dagger 50 40
642 32c. Lockheed F-104 Starfighter 50 40
643 32c. Mikoyan Gurevich MiG-21 MT 50 40
644 32c. F8U Crusader 50 40
645 32c. Republic F-105 Thunderchief 50 40
646 32c. Saab J35 Draken 50 40
647 32c. Fiat G-91Y 50 40
648 32c. McDonnell Douglas F-4 Phantom II 50 40
649 32c. Saab JA 37 Viggen 50 40
650 32c. Dassault Mirage F1C 50 40
651 32c. Grumman F-14 Tomcat 50 40
652 32c. F-15 Eagle 50 40
653 32c. General Dynamics F-16 Fighting Falcon 50 40
654 32c. Panavia Tornado F Mk 3 50 40
655 32c. Sukhoi Su-27UB 50 40
656 32c. Dassault Mirage 2000C 50 40
657 32c. Hawker Siddeley Sea Harrier FRS.MK1 50 40
658 32c. F-117 Nighthawk 50 40

1995. Yitzhak Rabin (Israeli Prime Minister) Commemoration.
659 **93** 32c. multicoloured 45 35

95 Blue-grey Noddy

1996. Birds. Multicoloured.
661 32c. Type **95** 70 55
662 32c. Spectacled tern ("Grey-backed Tern") 70 55
663 32c. Blue-faced booby ("Masked Booby") 70 55
664 32c. Black-footed albatross 70 55

96 Cheetah

1996. Big Cats. Multicoloured.
665 55c. Type **96** 90 70
666 55c. Tiger 90 70
667 55c. Lion 90 70
668 55c. Jaguar 90 70

97 5l. Stamp

1996. Centenary of Modern Olympic Games. Designs reproducing 1896 Greek Olympic stamps. Multicoloured.
694 60c. Type **97** 90 70
695 60c. 60l. stamp 90 70
696 60c. 40l. stamp 90 70
697 60c. 1d. stamp 90 70

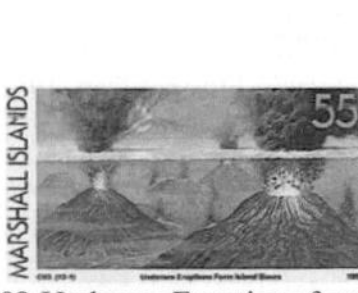

98 Undersea Eruptions form Islands **99** Presley

1996. History of Marshall Islands. Multicoloured.
698 55c. Type **98** 75 60
699 55c. Coral reefs grow around islands 75 60
700 55c. Storm-driven birds carry seeds to atolls 75 60
701 55c. First human inhabitants arrive, 1500 B.C. 75 60
702 55c. Spanish explorers discover islands, 1527 75 60
703 55c. John Marshall charts islands, 1788 75 60
704 55c. German Protectorate, 1885 75 60
705 55c. Japanese soldier on beach, 1914 75 60
706 55c. American soldiers liberate islands, 1944 75 60
707 55c. Evacuation of Bikini Atoll for nuclear testing, 1946 75 60
708 55c. Marshall Islands becomes United Nations Trust Territory, 1947 75 60
709 55c. People and national flag (independence, 1986) 75 60

1996. 40th Anniv of Elvis Presley's First Number One Hit Record "Heartbreak Hotel".
710 **99** 32c. multicoloured 50 40

101 Dean

102 1896 Quadricycle

1996. 65th Birth Anniv of James Dean (actor).
712 **101** 32c. multicoloured 50 40

1996. Centenary of Ford Motor Vehicle Production. Multicoloured.
713 60c. Type **102** 80 60
714 60c. 1903 Model A Roadster 80 60
715 60c. 1909 Model T touring car 80 60
716 60c. 1929 Model A station wagon 80 60
717 60c. 1955 "Thunderbird" 80 60
718 60c. 1964 "Mustang" convertible 80 60
719 60c. 1995 "Explorer" 80 60
720 60c. 1996 "Taurus" 80 60

103 Evacuees boarding "L.S.T. 1108" (tank landing ship)

1996. 50th Anniv of Operation Crossroads (nuclear testing) at Bikini Atoll. Multicoloured.
721 32c.+8c. Type **103** 60 60
722 32c.+8c. U.S. Navy preparation of site 60 60
723 32c.+8c. Explosion of "Able" (first test) 60 60
724 32c.+8c. Explosion of "Baker" (first underwater test) 60 60
725 32c.+8c. Ghost fleet (targets) 60 60
726 32c.+8c. Bikinian family 60 60

1996. Folk Legends (2nd series). As T **88**. Multicoloured.
727 32c. Letao gives gift of fire 50 40
728 32c. Mennin Jobwodda flying on giant bird 50 40
729 32c. Koko chasing Letao in canoe 50 40
730 32c. Mother and girl catching Kouj (octopus) to cook 50 40

104 Pennsylvania Railroad Class K4, U.S.A.

1996. Steam Railway Locomotives. Multicoloured.
731 55c. Type **104** 75 75
732 55c. Big Boy, U.S.A. 75 75
733 55c. Class A4 "Mallard", Great Britain 75 75
734 55c. Class 242, Spain 75 75
735 55c. Class 01 No. 052, Germany 75 75
736 55c. Class 691 No. 031, Italy 75 75
737 55c. "Royal Hudson", Canada 75 75
738 55c. "Evening Star", Great Britain 75 75
739 55c. Class 520, South Australia 75 75
740 55c. Class 232.U.2, France 75 75
741 55c. Class QJ "Advance Forward", China 75 75
742 55c. Class C62 "Swallow", Japan 75 75

105 Stick Chart, Outrigger Canoe and Flag

1996. 10th Anniv of Ratification of Compact of Free Association with U.S.A.
744 **105** $3 multicoloured 4·50 3·50

106 "Madonna and Child with Four Saints" (detail, Rosso Fiorentino)

1996. Christmas.
745 **106** 32c. multicoloured 50 40

107 Curtiss JN-4 "Jenny"

1996. Biplanes. Multicoloured.
746 32c. Type **107** 50 40
747 32c. SPAD XIII 50 40
748 32c. Albatros 50 40
749 32c. De Havilland D.H.4 Liberty 50 40
750 32c. Fokker Dr-1 50 40
751 32c. Sopwith Camel 50 40
752 32c. Martin MB-2 50 40
753 32c. Martin MB-3A Tommy 50 40
754 32c. Curtiss TS-1 50 40
755 32c. P-1 Hawk 50 40
756 32c. Boeing PW-9 50 40
757 32c. Douglas O-2-H 50 40
758 32c. LB-5 Pirate 50 40
759 32c. O2U-1 Corsair 50 40
760 32c. Curtiss F8C Helldiver 50 40
761 32c. Boeing F4B-4 50 40
762 32c. J6B Gerfalcon 50 40
763 32c. Martin BM 50 40
764 32c. FF-1 Fifi 50 40
765 32c. C.R.32 Cricket 50 40
766 32c. Polikarpov I-15 Gull 50 40
767 32c. Fairey Swordfish 50 40
768 32c. Aichi D1A2 50 40
769 32c. Grumman F3F 50 40
770 32c. SOC-3 Seagull 50 40

108 Fan-making

1996. Traditional Crafts. Multicoloured. Self-adhesive gum (780, 782); ordinary or self-adhesive gum (others).
771 32c. Type **108** 50 40
772 32c. Boys sailing model outrigger canoes (country name at right) 50 40
773 32c. Carving canoes 50 40
774 32c. Weaving baskets (country name at right) 50 40
780 32c. As No. 772 but with country name at left 55 45
782 32c. As No. 774 but with country name at left 55 45

110 "Rocking '50s"

1997. 20th Death Anniv of Elvis Presley (entertainer). Different portraits. Multicoloured.
784 32c. Type **110** 55 45
785 32c. "Soaring '60s" 55 45
786 32c. "Sensational '70s" 55 45

111 Kabua **113** St. Andrew

1997. President Amata Kabua Commemoration. Multicoloured.

787 32c. Type **111** 50 40
788 60c. As Type **111** but inscr in English at left and right and in Marshallese at foot 1·00 75

1997. Easter. 140th Anniv of Introduction of Christianity to the Marshall Islands. The Twelve Disciples. Multicoloured.

790 60c. Type **113** 90 70
791 60c. St. Matthew 90 70
792 60c. St. Philip 90 70
793 60c. St. Simon 90 70
794 60c. St. Thaddeus 90 70
795 60c. St. Thomas 90 70
796 60c. St. Bartholomew 90 70
797 60c. St. John 90 70
798 60c. St. James the Lesser . . 90 70
799 60c. St. James the Greater . . 90 70
800 60c. St. Paul 90 70
801 60c. St. Peter 90 70

114 Immigrants arriving at Ellis Island, New York, 1900

1997. The Twentieth Century (1st series). "Decade of New Possibilities, 1900–1909". Multicoloured.

803 60c. Type **114** 90 70
804 60c. Chinese and Dowager Empress Ci Xi, 1900 (Boxer Rebellion) 90 70
805 60c. George Eastman (inventor of box camera) photographing family, 1900 90 70
806 60c. Walter Reed (discoverer of yellow fever transmission by mosquito), 1900 . . . . 90 70
807 60c. Sigmund Freud (pioneer of psychoanalysis) (publication of "Interpretation of Dreams", 1900) 90 70
808 60c. Guglielmo Marconi sending first transatlantic wireless message, 1901 . . 90 70
809 60c. Enrico Caruso (opera singer) (first award of Gold Disc for one million record sales, 1903) 90 70
810 60c. Wright Brothers' Flyer I (first powered flight, Kitty Hawk, 1903) 90 70
811 60c. Albert Einstein and formula (development of Theory of Relativity, 1905) 90 70
812 60c. White ensign and H.M.S. "Dreadnought" (battleship), 1906 . . . . . 90 70
813 60c. San Francisco earthquake, 1906 . . . . . 90 70
814 60c. Mohandas Gandhi and protestors, Johannesburg, South Africa, 1906 . . . . 90 70
815 60c. Pablo Picasso and "Les Demoiselles d'Avignon", 1907 . . . . 90 70
816 60c. First Paris–Peking motor car race, 1907 . . . . . . 90 70
817 60c. Masjik-i-Salaman oil field, Persia, 1908 . . . . 90 70

See also Nos. 872/86, 948/62, 975//89, 1067/81, 1165/79, 1218/32, 1239/55, 1256/70 and 1303/17.

115 Deng Xiaoping

1997. Deng Xiaoping (Chinese statesman) Commemoration.

818 **115** 60c. multicoloured 85 65

116 German Marshall Islands 1899 3pf. Stamp

1997. "Pacific 97" International Stamp Exhibition, San Francisco. Centenary of Marshall Islands Postage Stamps. Multicoloured.

819 50c. Type **116** 70 70
820 50c. German Marshall Islands 1899 5pf. stamp . . 70 70
821 50c. German Marshall Islands 1897 10pf. stamp 70 70
822 50c. German Marshall Islands 1897 20pf. stamp 70 70
823 50c. Unissued German Marshall Islands 25pf. stamp 70 70
824 50c. Unissued German Marshall Islands 50pf. stamp 70 70

117 Curlew on Seashore

1997. The Bristle-thighed Curlew. Multicoloured.

826 16c. Type **117** 30 20
827 16c. Flying 30 20
828 16c. Running 30 20
829 16c. Standing on branch . . 30 20

119 Pacific Arts Festival Canoe, Enewetak

1997. Traditional Outrigger Canoes. Multicoloured.

831 32c. Type **119** 55 45
832 32c. Kor Kor racing canoes 55 45
833 32c. Large voyaging canoe, Jaluit 55 45
834 32c. Sailing canoe, Ailuk . . 55 45

120 Douglas C-54 Skymaster Transport

1997. Aircraft of United States Air Force (1st series). Multicoloured.

835 32c. Type **120** 50 40
836 32c. Boeing B-36 Peacemaker 50 40
837 32c. North American F-86 Sabre jet fighter 50 40
838 32c. Boeing B-47 Stratojet jet bomber 50 40
839 32c. Douglas C-124 Globemaster II transport 50 40
840 32c. Lockheed C-121 Constellation 50 40
841 32c. Boeing B-52 Stratofortress jet bomber 50 40
842 32c. North American F-100 Super Sabre jet fighter . . 50 40
843 32c. Lockheed F-104 Starfighter jet fighter . . . 50 40
844 32c. Lockheed C-130 Hercules transport 50 40
845 32c. Republic F-105 Thunderchief jet fighter . . 50 40
846 32c. KC-135 Stratotanker . . 50 40
847 32c. Convair B-58 Hustler jet bomber 50 40
848 32c. McDonnell Douglas F-4 Phantom II jet fighter . . . 50 40
849 32c. Northrop T-38 Talon trainer 50 40
850 32c. Lockheed C-141 StarLifter jet transport . . 50 40
851 32c. General Dynamics F-111 Aardvark jet fighter . . . 50 40
852 32c. SR-71 "Blackbird" . . . 50 40
853 32c. Lockheed C-5 Galaxy jet transport 50 40
854 32c. A-10 Thunderbolt II bomber 50 40
855 32c. F-15 Eagle fighter . . . 50 40
856 32c. General Dynamics F-16 Fighting Falcon jet fighter 50 40
857 32c. Lockheed F-117 "Nighthawk" Stealth bomber 50 40
858 32c. B-2 Spirit 50 40
859 32c. C-17 Globemaster III transport 50 40

See also Nos. 1272/96.

121 U.S.S. "Constitution"

1997. Bicentenary of Launch of U.S.S. "Constitution" (frigate).

860 **121** 32c. multicoloured 50 40

1997. Folk Legends (3rd series). As T **88**. Multicoloured.

861 32c. The Large Pool of Mejit 55 45
862 32c. The Beautiful Woman of Kwajalein 55 45
863 32c. Sharks and Lowakalle Reef 55 45
864 32c. The Demon of Adrie . . 55 45

1997. Undersea World (2nd series). As T **81**. Multicoloured.

865 60c. Watanabe's angelfish, blue-finned trevallys ("Bluefin Jack"), grey reef shark and scuba diver . . 95 75
866 60c. Scuba diver, anchor and racoon butterflyfish 95 75
867 60c. Lionfish and flame angelfish 95 75
868 60c. Square-spotted anthias ("Fairy Basslet"), anchor, scuba diver with torch and orange-finned anemonefish 95 75

Nos. 865/8 were issued together, se-tenant, forming a composite design.

122 Diana, Princess of Wales, aged 20

1997. Diana, Princess of Wales Commemoration. Multicoloured.

869 60c. Type **122** . . . . 1·00 75
870 60c. Wearing pearl drop earrings (aged 27) . . . . 1·00 75
871 60c. Wearing pearl choker (aged 36) . . . . 1·00 75

123 Flags and Suffragettes

1997. The Twentieth Century (2nd series). "Decade of Revolution and Great War, 1910–1919". Mult.

872 60c. Type **123** 75 55
873 60c. Nobel Prize medal, Ernest Rutherford and diagram of atom, 1911 . . 75 55
874 60c. Sun Yat-Sen (Chinese Revolution, 1911–12) . . . 75 55
875 60c. Sinking of the "Titanic" (liner), 1912 . . . . 75 55
876 60c. Igor Stravinsky (composer) and score of "The Rite of Spring", 1913 75 55
877 60c. Building motor car (introduction of assembly line construction of motor vehicles by Ford Motor Company), 1913 . . . . . 75 55
878 60c. Countess Sophie Chotek and Archduke Franz Ferdinand of Austria, 1914 (assassination in Sarajevo leads to First World War) 75 55
879 60c. Torpedo striking "Lusitania" (liner), 1915 75 55
880 60c. Battle of Verdun, 1916 75 55
881 60c. Patrick Pearse and proclamation of Irish Republic (Easter Rebellion, 1916) 75 55
882 60c. Western wall, Jerusalem (Balfour Declaration of Jewish Homeland, 1917) 75 55
883 60c. "Aurora" (cruiser) signals start of Russian Revolution, 1917 . . . . . 75 55
884 60c. Biplanes and "Red" Baron Manfred von Richthofen (fighter pilot), 1918 . . . . 75 55
885 60c. Armed revolutionaries, Berlin, 1918 . . . . 75 55
886 60c. Meeting of heads of state (Treaty of Versailles, 1919) 75 55

124 Cherub

1997. Christmas. Details of "Sistine Madonna" by Raphael. Multicoloured.

887 32c. Type **124** 45 35
888 32c. Cherub resting head on folded arms 45 35

125 U.S.S. "Alabama" (battleship), 1942

1997. Ships named after U.S. States. Multicoloured.

889 20c. Type **125** 30 20
890 20c. U.S.S. "Alaska" (cruiser), 1869, and junk 30 20
891 20c. U.S.S. "Arizona" (battleship), 1916 . . . . . 30 20
892 20c. U.S.S. "Arkansas" (battleship), 1912 . . . . . 30 20
893 20c. U.S.S. "California" (cruiser), 1974 . . . . . . 30 20
894 20c. U.S.S. "Colorado" (battleship), 1921, and landing craft 30 20
895 20c. U.S.S. "Connecticut" (gunboat), 1776, with fleet 30 20
896 20c. U.S.S. "Delaware" (ship of the line), 1828 . . . . . 30 20
897 20c. U.S.S. "Florida" (cruiser), 1967 . . . . . . 30 20
898 20c. U.S.S. "Georgia" (battleship), 1906 . . . . . 30 20
899 20c. U.S.S. "Honolulu" (cruiser), 1938 . . . . . . 30 20
900 20c. U.S.S. "Idaho" (battleship), 1919 . . . . . 30 20
901 20c. U.S.S. "Illinois" (battleship), 1901 . . . . . 30 20
902 20c. U.S.S. "Indiana" (battleship), 1895 . . . . . 30 20
903 20c. U.S.S. "Iowa" (battleship), 1943 . . . . . 30 20
904 20c. U.S.S. "Kansas" (battleship), 1907 . . . . . 30 20
905 20c. U.S.S. "Kentucky" (battleship), 1900 . . . . . 30 20
906 20c. U.S.S. "Louisiana" (frigate), 1812 . . . . . . 30 20
907 20c. U.S.S. "Maine" (battleship), 1895 . . . . . 30 20
908 20c. U.S.S. "Maryland" (frigate), 1799 . . . . . . 30 20
909 20c. U.S.S. "Massachusetts" (battleship), 1942 . . . . . 30 20
910 20c. U.S.S. "Michigan" (paddle gunboat), 1843 . . 30 20
911 20c. U.S.S. "Minnesota" (corvette), 1857 . . . . . 30 20
912 20c. U.S.S. "Mississippi" (paddle gunboat), 1841, and junk 30 20
913 20c. U.S.S. "Missouri" (battleship), 1944, in Tokyo Bay 30 20
914 20c. U.S.S. "Montana" (battleship), 1908 . . . . . 30 20
915 20c. U.S.S. "Nebraska" (battleship), 1907 . . . . . 30 20
916 20c. U.S.S. "Nevada" (battleship), 1916, at Pearl Harbor 30 20
917 20c. U.S.S. "New Hampshire" (battleship), 1908, and Statue of Liberty 30 20
918 20c. U.S.S. "New Jersey" (battleship), 1943 . . . . . 30 20
919 20c. U.S.S. "New Mexico" (battleship), 1918, in Tokyo Bay 30 20
920 20c. U.S.S. "New York" (frigate), 1800, and felucca 30 20
921 20c. U.S.S. "North Carolina" (battleship), 1941 . . . . . 30 20
922 20c. U.S.S. "North Dakota" (battleship), 1910 . . . . . 30 20
923 20c. U.S.S. "Ohio" (ship of the line), 1838 . . . . . . 30 20
924 20c. U.S.S. "Oklahoma" (battleship), 1916 . . . . . 30 20
925 20c. U.S.S. "Oregon" (battleship), 1896 . . . . . 30 20
926 20c. U.S.S. "Pennsylvania" (battleship), 1905 . . . . . 30 20
927 20c. U.S.S. "Rhode Island" (paddle gunboat), 1861 . . 30 20
928 20c. U.S.S. "South Carolina" (frigate), 1783 . . . . . . 30 20

929 20c. U.S.S. "South Dakota" (battleship), 1942 . . . . . 30 20
930 20c. U.S.S. "Tennessee" (battleship), 1906 . . . . . 30 20
931 20c. U.S.S. "Texas" (battleship), 1914 . . . . . 30 20
932 20c. U.S.S. "Utah" (battleship), 1911 . . . . . 30 20
933 20c. U.S.S. "Vermont" (battleship), 1907 . . . . . 30 20
934 20c. U.S.S. "Virginia" (schooner), 1798 . . . . . 30 20
935 20c. U.S.S. "Washington" (battleship), 1941 . . . . . 30 20
936 20c. U.S.S. "West Virginia" (battleship), 1923 . . . . . 30 20
937 20c. U.S.S. "Wisconsin" (battleship), 1944 . . . . . 30 20
938 20c. U.S.S. "Wyoming" (monitor), 1902 . . . . . 30 20

Dates given are those of either launch or commission.

128 Presley

1998. 30th Anniv of First Television Special by Elvis Presley (entertainer). Multicoloured.

941 32c. Type **128** 45 35
942 32c. Presley in black leather jacket 45 35
943 32c. Presley in white suit in front of "ELVIS" in lights 45 35

129 Chiragra Spider Conch ("Lambis chiragra")

1998. Sea Shells. Multicoloured.

944 32c. Type **129** 50 40
945 32c. Fluted giant clam ("Tridacna squamosa") . . 50 40
946 32c. Adusta murex ("Chicoreus brunneus") . . 50 40
947 32c. Golden cowrie ("Cypraea aurantium") . . 50 40

130 Family listening to Radio

1998. The Twentieth Century (3rd series). "Decade of Optimism and Disillusionment, 1920–1929". Multicoloured.

948 60c. Type **130** 75 55
949 60c. Leaders from Japan, United States, France, Great Britain and Italy (Washington Conference, 1920) 75 55
950 60c. Ludwig Mies van der Rohe (architect), 1922 . . 75 55
951 60c. Mummiform coffin of Tutankhamun (discovery of tomb, 1922) 75 55
952 60c. Workers from U.S.S.R., 1923 (emergence of U.S.S.R. as communist state) 75 55
953 60c. Kemal Ataturk (first president of modern Turkey, 1923) (break-up of Turkish Empire) 75 55
954 60c. Bix Beiderbecke (trumpeter) and flappers (dancers), 1924 (Jazz Age) 75 55
955 60c. Robert Goddard demonstrates first liquid-propelled rocket, 1926 . . 75 55
956 60c. Poster for "The Jazz Singer" (second talking picture, 1926) 75 55
957 60c. Benito Mussolini assumes total power in Italy, 1926 . . . . 75 55
958 60c. Explosive glare and Leonardo da Vinci's "Proportion of Man" (Big Bang Theory of beginning of Universe, 1927) 75 55
959 60c. Sir Alexander Fleming discovers penicillin, 1928 75 55
960 60c. John Logie Baird invents television, 1926 . . . . . 75 55
961 60c. Airship "Graf Zeppelin" above Mt. Fuji, Japan (first round the world flight, 1929) 75 55
962 60c. U.S. stock market crash, 1929 (economic depression) 75 55

131 Pahi Sailing Canoe, Tuamotu Archipelago

1998. Canoes of the Pacific. Multicoloured.

963 32c. Type **131** 45 35
964 32c. Maori war canoe, New Zealand 45 35
965 32c. Wa'a Kaukahi fishing canoe, Hawaii 45 35
966 32c. Amatasi sailing canoe, Samoa 45 35
967 32c. Ndrua sailing canoe, Fiji Islands 45 35
968 32c. Tongiaki voyaging canoe, Tonga 45 35
969 32c. Tipairua travelling canoe, Tahiti 45 35
970 32c. Walap sailing canoe, Marshall Islands 45 35

132 Douglas C-54 Skymaster Transport

1998. 50th Anniv of Berlin Airlift (relief of Berlin during Soviet blockade). Multicoloured.

971 60c. Type **132** 75 55
972 60c. Avro Type 685 York transport 75 55
973 60c. Crowd and building . . 75 55
974 60c. Crowd 75 55

Nos. 971/4 were issued together, se-tenant, forming a composite design.

133 Soup Kitchens, 1930 (depression)

1998. The Twentieth Century (4th series). "Decade of the Great Depression, 1930–1939". Multicoloured.

975 60c. Type **133** 75 55
976 60c. Ernest Lawrence and first cyclotron, 1931 (splitting of atom) 75 55
977 60c. Forced collectivization of farms in Soviet Union, 1932 (Stalin era) 75 55
978 60c. Torchlight Parade celebrates rise of Hitler to power, 1933 (fascism) . . . 75 55
979 60c. Dneproges Dam on Dnepr River, 1933 (harnessing of nature) . . . 75 55
980 60c. Streamlined locomotive "Zephyr" (record-breaking run, Denver to Chicago, 1934) 75 55
981 60c. Douglas DC-3 airliner (first all-metal airliner, 1936) 75 55
982 60c. Pablo Picasso (artist) and "Guernica" (German bombing during Spanish Civil War, 1937) 75 55
983 60c. "Hindenburg" (airship disaster), 1937 (media reporting) 75 55
984 60c. Families fleeing ruins (Japanese assault on Nanjing, 1937) 75 55
985 60c. Neville Chamberlain declares "Peace in our Time", 1938 (appeasement) 75 55
986 60c. Chester Carlson (invention of xerography, 1938) 75 55
987 60c. Jew and Star of David (Kristallnacht (Nazi violence against Jews), 1938) 75 55
988 60c. Junkers "Stuka" bombers over Poland, 1939 (start of Second World War) 75 55
989 60c. Audience (premiere of "Gone with the Wind", 1939) (movies) 75 55

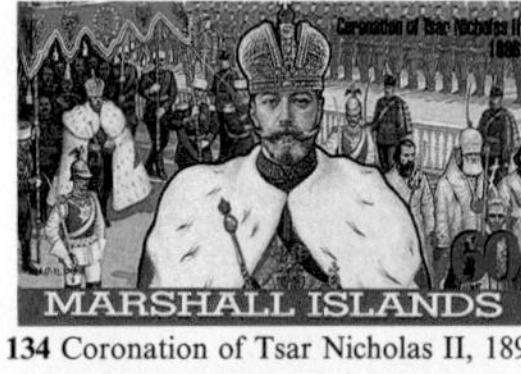

134 Coronation of Tsar Nicholas II, 1896

1998. 80th Death Anniv of Tsar Nicholas II and his Family. Multicoloured.

990 60c. Type **134** 75 55
991 60c. "Varyag" (cruiser) and Tsar (Russo-Japanese war, 1904–05) 75 55
992 60c. Troops firing on crowd, Tsar and October manifesto, 1905 . . . . . 75 55
993 60c. Peasant sowing, Tsar and Rasputin, 1905 . . . . 75 55
994 60c. Mounted troops, Tsar and Nicholas II at strategy meeting, 1915 . . . . . . 75 55
995 60c. Abdication, Tsar and Ipateva House, Ekaterinburg, 1917 . . . . 75 55

135 Babe Ruth

1998. 50th Death Anniv of Babe Ruth (baseball player).

997 **135** 132c. multicoloured . . . 50 40

136 NC-4

1998. Aircraft of United States Navy. Mult.

998 32c. Type **136** 45 35
999 32c. Consolidated PBY-5 Catalina flying boat . . . 45 35
1000 32c. TBD Devastator . . . 45 35
1001 32c. SB2U Vindicator . . . 45 35
1002 32c. Grumman F4F Wildcat fighter 45 35
1003 32c. Vought-Sikorsky OS2U Kingfisher seaplane . . . 45 35
1004 32c. Douglas SBD Dauntless bomber 45 35
1005 32c. Chance Vought F4U Corsair fighter 45 35
1006 32c. Curtiss SB2C Helldiver bomber 45 35
1007 32c. Lockheed PV-1 Ventura bomber 45 35
1008 32c. Grumman TBM Avenger bomber 45 35
1009 32c. Grumman F6F Hellcat fighter 45 35
1010 32c. PB4Y-2 Privateer . . . 45 35
1011 32c. A-1J Skyraider 45 35
1012 32c. McDonnell F2H-2P Banshee 45 35
1013 32c. F9F-2B Panther . . . 45 35
1014 32c. P5M Marlin 45 35
1015 32c. F-8 Crusader 45 35
1016 32c. McDonnell Douglas F-4 Phantom II fighter . . 45 35
1017 32c. A-6 Intruder 45 35
1018 32c. Lockheed P-3 Orion reconnaissance 45 35
1019 32c. Vought A-70 Corsair II 45 35
1020 32c. Douglas A-4 Skyhawk bomber 45 35
1021 32c. S-3 Viking 45 35
1022 32c. F/A-18 Hornet 45 35

137 Classic Six, 1912

1998. Chevrolet Vehicles. Multicoloured.

1023 60c. Type **137** 75 55
1024 60c. Sport Roadster, 1931 75 55
1025 60c. Special Deluxe, 1941 75 55
1026 60c. Cameo Carrier Fleetside, 1955 . . . . . 75 55
1027 60c. Corvette, 1957 . . . . 75 55
1028 60c. Bel Air, 1957 . . . . . 75 55
1029 60c. Camaro, 1967 . . . . 75 55
1030 60c. Chevelle SS 454, 1970 75 55

138 Letter "A" and Pres. Amata Kabua

1998. Marshallese Alphabet and Language. Mult.

1031 33c. Type **138** 45 35
1032 33c. Letter "A" and woman weaving 45 35
1033 33c. Letter "B" and butterfly 45 35
1034 33c. Letter "D" and woman wearing garland of flowers 45 35
1035 33c. Letter "E" and fish . . 45 35
1036 33c. Letter "I" and couple in front of rainbow . . . 45 35
1037 33c. Letter "J" and woven mat 45 35
1038 33c. Letter "K" and Government House . . . 45 35
1039 33c. Letter "L" and night sky 45 35
1040 33c. Letter "L" and red-tailed tropicbird 45 35
1041 33c. Letter "M" and breadfruit 45 35
1042 33c. Letter "M" and arrowroot plant 45 35
1043 33c. Letter "N" and coconut tree 45 35
1044 33c. Letter "N" and wave 45 35
1045 33c. Letter "N" and shark 45 35
1046 33c. Letter "O" and fisherman 45 35
1047 33c. Letter "O" and tattooed woman 45 35
1048 33c. Letter "O" and lionfish 45 35
1049 33c. Letter "P" and visitor's hut 45 35
1050 33c. Letter "R" and whale 45 35
1051 33c. Letter "T" and outrigger sailing canoe . . 45 35
1052 33c. Letter "U" and fire . . 45 35
1053 33c. Letter "U" and whale's fin 45 35
1054 33c. Letter "W" and woven leaf sail 45 35

139 Trust Company of the Marshall Islands Offices, 1998

1998. New Buildings. Multicoloured.

1055 33c. Type **139** 45 35
1056 33c. Embassy of the People's Republic of China, 1996 45 35
1057 33c. Outrigger Marshall Islands Resort, 1996 . . . 45 35

140 Midnight Angel

1998. Christmas.

1058 **140** 33c. multicoloured . . . 45 35

141 Launch of "Friendship 7", 1962

1998. John Glenn's (astronaut) Return to Space. Multicoloured.

1059 60c. Type **141** 75 55
1060 60c. John Glenn, 1962, and Earth 75 55
1061 60c. "Friendship 7" orbiting Earth 75 55
1062 60c. Launch of space shuttle "Discovery", 1998 . . . . 75 55
1063 60c. John Glenn, 1998, and flag 75 55
1064 60c. "Discovery" orbiting Earth, 1998 . . . . . . 75 55

143 British and German Planes over St. Paul's Cathedral (Battle of Britain, 1940)

1998. The Twentieth Century (5th series). "Decade of War and Peace, 1940–1949". Multicoloured.

1067 60c. Type **143** 75 55
1068 60c. Japanese aircraft attack American battleship (Pearl Harbor, 1941) (global warfare) 75 55
1069 60c. Wernher von Braun and missiles (first surface to surface guided missile, 1942) 75 55
1070 60c. The Dorsey Brothers (Big Bands, 1942) 75 55
1071 60c. Soviet worker building weaponry (fight for survival against Germans, 1943) 75 55
1072 60c. Concentration camp prisoners (the Holocaust, 1945) 75 55
1073 60c. Mushroom cloud and skull (first atomic bomb tested, Alamogordo, New Mexico, 1945) 75 55
1074 60c. Families reunited (end of war, 1945) 75 55
1075 60c. Eniac computer and worker (first electronic digital computer goes into operation, 1946) 75 55
1076 60c. American delegate (United Nations, 1946) 75 55
1077 60c. Nuremberg Tribunal (trials of Germans for war crimes 1946) 75 55
1078 60c. George Marshall (U.S. Secretary of State) and Europeans (Marshall Plan, 1947) 75 55
1079 60c. William Shockley, John Bardeen and Walter Brattain (development of transistor, 1948) 75 55
1080 60c. Berlin Airlift, 1948–49 (Cold War) 75 55
1081 60c. Mao Tse-tung proclaiming People's Republic of China, 1949 75 55

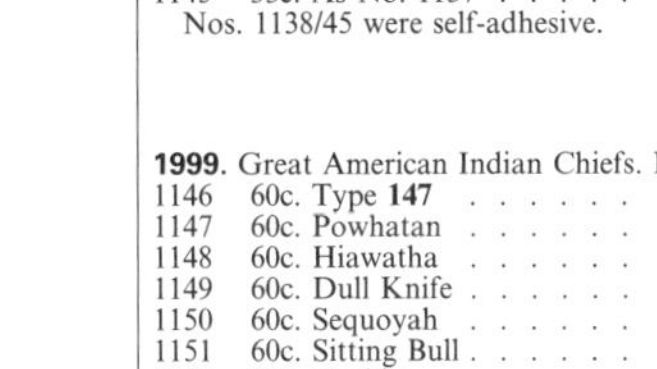

144 Trireme

1998. Warships. Multicoloured.

1082 33c. Type **144** 45 35
1083 33c. Roman galley ("Trireme Romano") 45 35
1084 33c. Viking longship 45 35
1085 33c. Ming treasure ship 45 35
1086 33c. "Mary Rose" (English galleon) 45 35
1087 33c. "Nuestra Senora del Rosario" (Spanish galleon) 45 35
1088 33c. Korean "turtle" ship 45 35
1089 33c. "Brederode" (Dutch ship of the line) 45 35
1090 33c. Venetian galley 45 35
1091 33c. "Santissima Trinidad" (Spanish ship of the line) 45 35
1092 33c. "Ville de Paris" (French ship of the line) 45 35
1093 33c. H.M.S. "Victory" (ship of the line) 45 35
1094 33c. "Bonhomme Richard" (American sail frigate) 45 35
1095 33c. U.S.S. "Constellation" (sail frigate) 45 35
1096 33c. U.S.S. "Hartford" (steam frigate) 45 35
1097 33c. Fijian Ndrua canoe 45 35
1098 33c. H.M.S. "Dreadnought" (battleship) 45 35
1099 33c. H.M.A.S. "Australia" (battle cruiser) 45 35
1100 33c. H.M.S. "Dorsetshire" (cruiser) 45 35
1101 33c. "Admiral Graf Spee" (German battleship) 45 35
1102 33c. "Yamato" (Japanese battleship) 45 35
1103 33c. U.S.S. "Tautog" (submarine) 45 35
1104 33c. "Bismarck" (German battleship) 45 35
1105 33c. U.S.S. "Hornet" (aircraft carrier) 45 35
1106 33c. U.S.S. "Missouri" (battleship) 45 35

146 Pacific Golden Plover ("Lesser Golden Plover") **147** Tecumseh

1999. Birds. Multicoloured.

1108 1c. Type **146** 10 10
1109 3c. Grey-rumped sandpiper ("Siberian (gray-tailed) Tattler") 10 10
1110 5c. Black-tailed godwit 10 10
1113 20c. Common noddy ("Brown Noddy") 25 20
1114 22c. White tern ("Common Fairy Tern") 30 25
1116 33c. Micronesian pigeon 40 30
1117 40c. Franklin's gull 50 40
1118 45c. Rufous-necked sandpiper ("Rufous-necked Stint") 55 40
1119 55c. Long-tailed koel ("Long-tailed Cuckoo") 70 55
1121 75c. Kermadec petrel 95 70
1122 $1 Christmas Island shearwater ("Christmas Shearwater") 1·25 95
1123 $1.20 Purple-capped fruit dove 1·50 1·25
1124 $2 Lesser sand plover ("Mongolian Plover") 2·50 1·90
1125 $3.20 Cattle egret 4·00 3·00
1127 $5 Dunlin 6·25 4·75
1129 $10 Eurasian tree sparrow 12·50 9·50

1999. Canoes of the Pacific. Multicoloured. (a) Size 49 × 30 mm.

1130 33c. Type **131** 40 30
1131 33c. As No. 964 40 30
1132 33c. As No. 965 40 30
1133 33c. As No. 966 but inscr changed to "Tongiaki voyaging canoe, Tonga" 40 30
1134 33c. As No. 967 40 30
1135 33c. As No. 968 but inscr changed to "Amatasi sailing canoe, Samoa" 40 30
1136 33c. As No. 969 40 30
1137 33c. As No. 970 40 30

(b) Size 39 × 24 mm.

1138 33c. Type **131** 40 30
1139 33c. As No. 1131 40 30
1140 33c. As No. 1132 40 30
1141 33c. As No. 1133 40 30
1142 33c. As No. 1134 40 30
1143 33c. As No. 1135 40 30
1144 33c. As No. 1136 40 30
1145 33c. As No. 1137 40 30

Nos. 1138/45 were self-adhesive.

1999. Great American Indian Chiefs. Multicoloured.

1146 60c. Type **147** 75 55
1147 60c. Powhatan 75 55
1148 60c. Hiawatha 75 55
1149 60c. Dull Knife 75 55
1150 60c. Sequoyah 75 55
1151 60c. Sitting Bull 75 55
1152 60c. Cochise 75 55
1153 60c. Red Cloud 75 55
1154 60c. Geronimo 75 55
1155 60c. Chief Joseph 75 55
1156 60c. Pontiac 75 55
1157 60c. Crazy Horse 75 55

148 State Flag

1999.

1158 **148** 33c. multicoloured 40 30

149 Plumeria

1999. Flowers of the Pacific. Multicoloured.

1159 33c. Type **149** 40 30
1160 33c. Vanda 40 30
1161 33c. Ilima 40 30
1162 33c. Tiare 40 30
1163 33c. White ginger 40 30
1164 33c. Hibiscus 40 30

150 Family watching Television

1999. The Twentieth Century (6th series). "Decade of Peril and Progress, 1950–1959". Multicoloured.

1165 60c. Type **150** 75 55
1166 60c. U.N. landing at Inchon, Korea, 1950 (Cold War) 75 55
1167 60c. Vaccination against polio, 1952 75 55
1168 60c. American hydrogen bomb test, Enewetak Atoll, 1952 (Arms race) 75 55
1169 60c. James Watson and Francis Crick (scientists) and DNA double helix, 1953 (unravelling of genetic code) 75 55
1170 60c. Sir Edmund Hillary, Tenzing Norgay and Mt. Everest, 1953 75 55
1171 60c. Coronation of Queen Elizabeth II, Westminster Abbey, 1953 75 55
1172 60c. Singer and dancers, 1954 (rock 'n' roll music) 75 55
1173 60c. Ho Chi Minh and Vietnamese troops celebrating victory over French garrison at Dien Bien Phu, 1954 (end of colonial empires) 75 55
1174 60c. People of different races on bus, 1955 (condemnation of racial discrimination) 75 55
1175 60c. Hungarians firing on Russian tanks, Budapest, 1956 (challenge to Communism) 75 55
1176 60c. Signing of Treaty of Rome, 1957 (European union) 75 55
1177 60c. Launch of Russian sputnik, 1957 (space race) 75 55
1178 60c. De Havilland Comet (first commercial jet airline service, 1958) 75 55
1179 60c. Jack Kilby (inventor) and first microchip, 1959 75 55

152 Presley

1999. Elvis Presley, "Artist of the Century".

1181 **152** 33c. multicoloured 40 30

153 5m. Stamp

1999. "iBRA '99" International Stamp Exhibition, Nuremberg, Germany. Multicoloured.

1182 60c. Type **153** 75 55
1183 60c. 3m. stamp 75 55
1184 60c. 2m. stamp 75 55
1185 60c. 1m. stamp 75 55

154 Magnifying Glass over Committee Members

1999. 20th Anniv of Marshall Islands Constitution.

1186 **154** 33c. multicoloured 40 30

155 Marshall Island Stamps

1999. 15th Anniv of Marshall Islands Postal Service. Multicoloured.

1187 33c. Type **155** 40 30
1188 33c. Butterfly, fish, canoe and flower stamps 40 30
1189 33c. Pres. Amata Kabua, flower and legend stamps 40 30
1190 33c. Stamps and magnifying glass 40 30

Nos. 1187/90 were issued together, se-tenant, forming a composite design.

156 B-10 B

1999. Legendary Aircraft. Multicoloured.

1191 33c. Type **156** 40 30
1192 33c. A-17A Nomad 40 30
1193 33c. Douglas B-18 Bolo bomber 40 30
1194 33c. Boeing B-17F Flying Fortress bomber 40 30
1195 33c. A-20 Havoc 40 30
1196 33c. North American B-25B Mitchell bomber 40 30
1197 33c. Consolidated B-24D Liberator bomber 40 30
1198 33c. North American P-51B Mustang fighter 40 30
1199 33c. Martin B-26 Marauder bomber 40 30
1200 33c. A-26B Invader 40 30
1201 33c. P-59 Airacomet 40 30
1202 33c. KC-97 Stratofreighter 40 30
1203 33c. A-1J Skyraider 40 30
1204 33c. P2V-7 Neptune 40 30
1205 33c. B-45 Tornado 40 30
1206 33c. Boeing B-50 Superfortress 40 30
1207 33c. AJ-2 Savage 40 30
1208 33c. F9F Cougar 40 30
1209 33c. Douglas A-3 Skywarrior jet bomber 40 30
1210 33c. English Electric B-57E Canberra jet bomber 40 30
1211 33c. EB-66 Destroyer 40 30
1212 33c. E-2A Hawkeye 40 30
1213 33c. Northrop F-5E Tiger II jet fighter 40 30
1214 33c. AV-8B Harrier II 40 30
1215 33c. B-1B Lancer 40 30

159 T. H. Maiman and Ruby Crystal Laser, 1960

1999. The Twentieth Century (7th series). "Decade of Upheaval and Exploration 1960–1969". Mult.

1218 60c. Type **159** 75 55
1219 60c. Young couple (birth control pill, 1960) 75 55
1220 60c. Yuri Gagarin (first man in space, 1961) 75 55
1221 60c. John F. Kennedy (President of U.S.A., 1960–63) making speech in Berlin, 1961 (failures of Communism) 75 55
1222 60c. Rachel Carson and endangered species (publication of "Silent Spring", 1962) 75 55
1223 60c. John F. Kennedy and Russian President Nikita Khrushchev (Cuban missile crisis, 1962) 75 55
1224 60c. Pope John XXIII and crowds (Spirit of Ecumenism) 75 55
1225 60c. "Hikari" express train, Japan (new railway record speeds, 1964) 75 55
1226 60c. Chinese workers waving banners (Chinese cultural revolution, 1965) 75 55
1227 60c. Soldier with gun (Arab–Israeli six-day war, 1967) 75 55
1228 60c. Surgeons (first human heart transplants, 1967) 75 55
1229 60c. American soldiers in jungle (Vietnam war) 75 55
1230 60c. Robert F. Kennedy (U.S. presidential candidate) and statue of Abraham Lincoln (political assassinations) 75 55
1231 60c. British Aerospace/Aerospatiale Concorde supersonic jetliner (maiden flight, 1969) 75 55
1232 60c. Neil Armstrong and Buzz Aldrin planting American flag (first men on Moon, 1969) 75 55

161 "Los Reyes" (Alvarao de Menana de Neyra's galleon, 1568)

1999. European Exploration of Marshall Islands. Multicoloured.

1234 33c. Type **161** 40 30
1235 33c. H.M.S. "Dolphin" (Samuel Wallis's frigate, 1767) 40 30
1236 33c. "Scarborough" (John Marshall's transport, 1788) 40 30
1237 33c. "Rurik" (Otto van Kotzebue's brig, 1817) . . 40 30

No. 1236 is wrongly inscribed "Scarsborough" and No. 1237 "Rurick".

162 Nativity

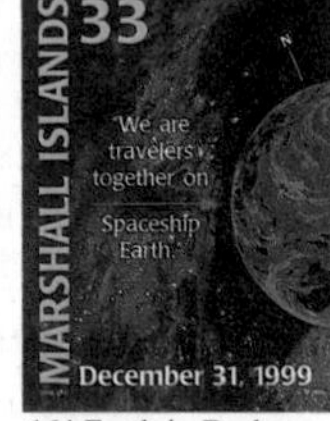

164 Earth in Darkness, December 31, 1999

163 First Scheduled Transatlantic Flight of Boeing 747 Jetliner, 1970

1999. Christmas.

1238 **162** 33c. multicoloured . . . 40 30

1999. The Twentieth Century (8th series). "Decade of Detente and Discovery 1970–1979". Multicoloured.

1239 60c. Type **163** 75 55
1240 60c. Mao Tse Tung and U.S. President Richard Nixon (visit to China, 1972) 75 55
1241 60c. Terrorist with gun (murder of Israeli athletes at Munich Olympics, 1972) 75 55
1242 60c. U.S. "Skylab" and U.S.S.R. "Salyut" space stations orbiting Earth . . 75 55
1243 60c. Cars queueing for petrol (oil crisis, 1973) . . 75 55
1244 60c. Terracotta warriors (discovery of Qin Shi Huang's tomb at Xian, China, 1974) 75 55
1245 60c. Skulls and Cambodians in paddy fields 75 55
1246 60c. "Apollo"–"Soyuz" link-up, 1975 (era of detente) 75 55
1247 60c. "Eagle" (cadet ship) in New York Harbour (bicentenary of U.S. Independence, 1976) . . . 75 55
1248 60c. Computer and family (personal computers reach markets, 1977) 75 55
1249 60c. Scanner and scanned images (diagnostic tools revolutionize medicine, 1977) 75 55
1250 60c. Volkswagen Beetle motor car, 1978 . . . . . 75 55
1251 60c. Pres. Anwar Sadat of Egypt, U.S. President Jimmy Carter and Israeli Prime Minister Menachim Begin, 1978 (peace in Middle East) 75 55
1252 60c. Compact disc, 1979 . . 75 55
1253 60c. Ayatollah Khomeini becomes Iran's leader, 1979 . . . . 75 55

1999. Year 2000. Multicoloured.

1254 33c. Type **164** 40 30
1255 33c. Earth in sunlight, 1 January 2000 . . . . . 40 30

Nos. 1254/5 were issued together, se-tenant, forming a composite design.

165 Lech Walesa and Protestors at Gdansk Shipyard, Poland, 1980

2000. The Twentieth Century (9th series). "Decade of People and Democracy, 1980–1989". Multicoloured.

1256 60c. Type **165** 85 65
1257 60c. Doctor treating AIDS patient, 1981 . . . . . . 85 65
1258 60c. Prince and Princess of Wales (Royal wedding, 1981) 85 65
1259 60c. Man and computer (IBM personal computers introduced 1981) 85 65
1260 60c. British jet fighter and warships (Falkland Islands war, 1982) 85 65
1261 60c. Man using mobile phone (first commercial wireless cellular system, Chicago, 1983) 85 65
1262 60c. Girl playing football (camcorders, 1983) . . . 85 65
1263 60c. Astronauts (space shuttle *Challenger* explodes, 1986) 85 65
1264 60c. Power station and man wearing protective clothing (Chernobyl Nuclear Power Station disaster, 1986) 85 65
1265 60c. Mikhail Gorbachev and workers (era of Glasnost (openness) and Perestroika (restructuring) in U.S.S.R., 1987) 85 65
1266 60c. American B-2 stealth bomber, 1988 . . . . . . 85 65
1267 60c. Aircraft wreckage (bombing of Pan-American flight 103 over Lockerbie, Scotland, 1988) 85 65
1268 60c. *Exxon Valdez* (oil-tanker) and whales (oil spill off Alaskan Coast, 1989) 85 65
1269 60c. Student demonstrators and police in Tiananmen Square, China, 1989 . . . 85 65
1270 60c. German breaking down wall (dismantling of Berlin Wall, 1989) 85 65

167 Boeing P-26A "Peashooter" fighter

2000. Legendary Aircraft (2nd series). Multicoloured.

1272 33c. Type **167** 45 35
1273 33c. Stearman N2S-1 Kaydett biplane 45 35
1274 33c. Seversky P-35A 45 35
1275 33c. Curtiss P-36A Hawk 45 35
1276 33c. Curtiss P-40B Warhawk fighter 45 35
1277 33c. Lockheed P-38 Lightning fighter 45 35
1278 33c. Bell P-39D Airacobra fighter 45 35
1279 33c. Curtiss C-46 Commando airliner . . . 45 35
1280 33c. Republic P-47D Thunderbolt fighter . . . 45 35
1281 33c. Northrop P-61A Black Widow 45 35
1282 33c. Boeing B-29 Superfortress bomber . . 45 35
1283 33c. Grumman F7F-3N Tigercat 45 35
1284 33c. Grumman F8F-2 Bearcat 45 35
1285 33c. North American F-82 Twin Mustang 45 35
1286 33c. Republic F-84G Thunderjet jet fighter . . 45 35
1287 33c. North American FJ-1 Fury 45 35
1288 33c. Fairchild C-119C Flying Boxcar 45 35
1289 33c. Douglas F3D-2 Skynight 45 35
1290 33c. Northrop F-89D Scorpion 45 35
1291 33c. Lockheed F-94B Starfire 45 35
1292 33c. Douglas F4D Skyray 45 35
1293 33c. McDonnell F3H-2 Demon 45 35
1294 33c. McDonnell RF-101A/C Voodoo 45 35
1295 33c. Lockheed U-2F Dragon Lady 45 35
1296 33c. Rockwell OV-10 Bronco 45 35

168 "Masquerade"

2000. Garden Roses. Multicoloured.

1297 33c. Type **168** 45 35
1298 33c. "Tuscany Superb" . . 45 35
1299 33c. "Frau Dagmar Hastrup" 45 35
1300 33c. "Ivory Fashion" . . . 45 35
1301 33c. "Charles de Mills" . . 45 35
1302 33c. "Peace" 45 35

169 Container Ships (political reform in Poland, 1990)

2000. The Twentieth Century (10th series). "Decade of Globalization and Hope, 1990–1999". Multicoloured.

1303 60c. Type **169** 85 65
1304 60c. Fighter planes over burning oil wells, 1991 . . 85 65
1305 60c. Nelson Mandela and F. W. de Klerk (abolition of apartheid, 1991) . . . 85 65
1306 60c. Tim Berners-Lee and computer (creator of World Wide Web, 1991) 85 65
1307 60c. Boris Yeltsin (President of Russian Federation, 1991) 85 65
1308 60c. Yitzhak Rabin, Bill Clinton and Yasir Arafat (signing of Middle East Peace Accord, Washington D.C., 1993) 85 65
1309 60c. High-speed train (inauguration of the "Channel Tunnel" between United Kingdom and France, 1994) 85 65
1310 60c. Family (Bosnian civil war, 1995) 85 65
1311 60c. Athletes (Atlanta Olympic Games, 1996) . . 85 65
1312 60c. Sheep (researchers clone Dolly, 1997) 85 65
1313 60c. Hong Kong and Chinese flag (return of Hong Kong to Chinese rule, 1997) 85 65
1314 60c. Sojourner (roving vehicle) (Mars "Pathfinder" mission, 1997) 85 65
1315 60c. Deaths of Diana, Princess of Wales and Mother Teresa, 1997 . . . 85 65
1316 60c. Rebuilding of German Reichstag, 1999 . . . . 85 65
1317 60c. People of different races (birth of World's sixth billionth inhabitant, 1999) 85 65

170 Panda

2000. Giant Pandas. Multicoloured.

1318 33c. Type **170** 45 35
1319 33c. Adult facing cub . . . 45 35
1320 33c. Adult holding cub . . . 45 35
1321 33c. Two adults 45 35
1322 33c. Moving rock 45 35
1323 33c. Cub beside adult eating bamboo 45 35

171 George Washington

2000. American Presidents. Multicoloured.

1324 1c. Type **171** 10 10
1325 2c. John Adams 10 10
1326 3c. Thomas Jefferson . . . 10 10
1327 4c. James Madison 10 10
1328 5c. James Monroe 10 10
1329 6c. John Quincy Adams . . 10 10
1330 7c. Andrew Jackson 10 10
1331 8c. Martin van Buren . . . 10 10
1332 9c. William Henry Harrison 10 10
1333 10c. John Tyler 15 10
1334 11c. James K. Polk 15 10
1335 12c. Zachary Taylor 15 10
1336 13c. Millard Filmore 20 15
1337 14c. Franklin Pierce 20 15
1338 15c. James Buchanan . . . 20 15
1339 16c. Abraham Lincoln . . . 20 15
1340 17c. Andrew Johnson . . . 25 20
1341 18c. Ulysses S. Grant . . . 25 20
1342 19c. Rutherford B. Hayes 25 20
1343 20c. James A. Garfield . . . 30 25
1344 21c. Chester A. Arthur . . . 30 25
1345 22c. Grover Cleveland . . . 30 25
1346 23c. Benjamin Harrison . . 30 25
1347 24c. The White House . . . 30 25
1348 25c. William McKinley . . 35 25
1349 26c. Theodore Roosevelt . . 35 25
1350 27c. William H. Taft . . . 35 25
1351 28c. Woodrow Wilson . . . 40 30
1352 29c. Warren G. Harding . . 40 30
1353 30c. Calvin Coolidge . . . 40 30
1354 31c. Herbert C. Hoover . . 40 30
1355 32c. Franklin D. Roosevelt 45 35
1356 33c. Harry S. Truman . . . 45 35
1357 34c. Dwight D. Eisenhower 45 35
1358 35c. John F. Kennedy . . . 50 40
1359 36c. Lyndon B. Johnson . . 50 40
1360 37c. Richard M. Nixon . . 50 40
1361 38c. Gerald R. Ford 50 40
1362 39c. James E. Carter 50 40
1363 40c. Ronald W. Reagan . . 55 45
1364 41c. George H. Bush . . . 55 45
1365 42c. William J. Clinton . . 60 45

172 LZ-1 (first Zeppelin airship), 1900

2000. Centenary of Zeppelin Airships. Multicoloured.

1366 33c. Type **172** 45 35
1367 33c. *Graf Zeppelin I*, 1928 45 35
1368 33c. *Hindenburg*, 1936 . . . 45 35
1369 33c. *Graf Zeppelin II*, 1937 45 35

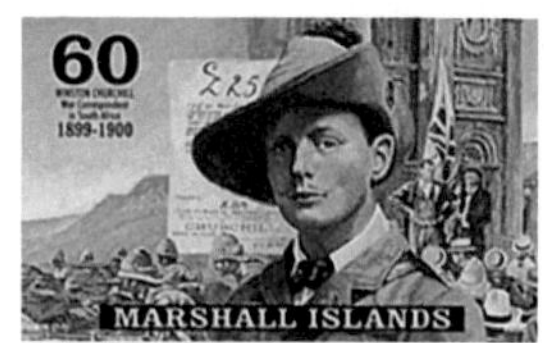

173 Churchill in South Africa as War Correspondent, 1899–1900

2000. 35th Death Anniv of Winston Churchill (British Prime Minister, 1940–45 and 1951–55). Multicoloured.

1370 60c. Type **173** 85 65
1371 60c. Churchill and Clementine Hozier on wedding day, 1908 . . . 85 65
1372 60c. Kaiser Wilhelm II, Churchill and clock tower, Houses of Parliament . . 85 65
1373 60c. Various portraits of Churchill between 1898 and 1960 . . . . 85 65
1374 60c. Wearing naval cap (First Lord of the Admiralty, 1939–40) . . . 85 65
1375 60c. Churchill giving "Victory" sign and St. Paul's Cathedral (Prime Minister, 1940–45) 85 65

174 Cannon, Flag and Soldier preparing to Fire (Army)

2000. 225th Anniv of United States Military Forces. Multicoloured.

1377 33c. Type **174** 45 35
1378 33c. Ship, flag and officer looking through telescope (Navy) 45 35
1379 33c. Ship, cannon and mariner drawing sword (Marines) 45 35

175 Nitijela (elected lower house) Complex

2000. Multicoloured.
1380 33c. Type **175** 45 35
1381 33c. Capitol building . . . 45 35
1382 33c. National Seal and Nitijela Complex (vert) . . 45 35
1383 33c. National Flag and Nitijela Complex (vert) . . 45 35

176 *Half Moon* (Hudson)

2000. Sailing Ships. Multicoloured.
1384 60c. Type **176** 85 65
1385 60c. *Grande Hermine* (Cartier) 85 65
1386 60c. *Golden Hind* (Drake) 85 65
1387 60c. *Matthew* (Cabot) (wrongly inscr "Mathew") 85 65
1388 60c. *Vitoria* (Magellan) (inscr "Victoria") 85 65
1389 60c. *Sao Gabriel* (Vasco da Gama) 85 65

177 As a Young Girl, 1904

2000. "Queen Elizabeth the Queen Mother's Century". Multicoloured.
1390 60c. Type **177** 85 65
1391 60c. Wearing a turquoise hat, 1923 . . . . 85 65
1392 60c. Wearing pearl necklace, 1940 . . . . 85 65
1393 60c. Wearing purple hat, 1990 . . . . 85 65

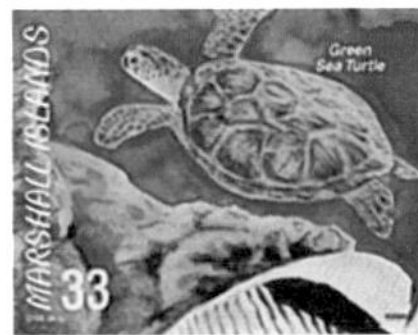
178 Green Sea Turtle

2000. Marine Life. Multicoloured.
1394 33c. Type **178** 45 35
1395 33c. Blue-girdled angelfish 45 35
1396 33c. Clown triggerfish . . . 45 35
1397 33c. Harlequin tuskfish . . . 45 35
1398 33c. Lined butterflyfishes . . 45 35
1399 33c. Whitebonnet anemonefish 45 35
1400 33c. Long-nose filefish . . . 45 35
1401 33c. Emperor angelfish . . . 45 35
Nos. 1394/1401 were issued together, se-tenant, forming the composite design of the reef.

179 Holly Blue Butterfly

2000. Butterflies. Multicoloured.
1402 60c. Type **179** 85 65
1403 60c. Swallowtail butterfly . . 85 65
1404 60c. Clouded yellow butterfly 85 65
1405 60c. Small tortoiseshell butterfly 85 65
1406 60c. Nettle-tree butterfly . . 85 65
1407 60c. Long tailed blue butterfly 85 65
1408 60c. Cranberry blue butterfly 85 65
1409 60c. Small heath butterfly 85 65
1410 60c. Pontic blue butterfly . . 85 65
1411 60c. Lapland fritillary butterfly 85 65
1412 60c. Large blue butterfly . . 85 65
1413 60c. Monarch butterfly . . . 85 65

180 Brandenburg Gate, Berlin and Flag

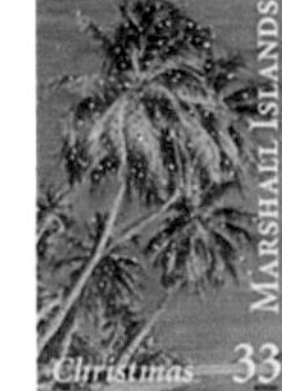
182 Decorated Trees

181 S-44 Submarine, 1925 (½ size illustration)

2000. 10th Anniv of Reunification of Germany.
1414 **180** 33c. multicoloured . . . 45 35

2000. Centenary of United States Submarine Fleet. Multicoloured.
1415 33c. Type **181** 45 35
1416 33c. Gato, 1941 . . . . . . 45 35
1417 33c. Wyoming, 1996 . . . . 45 35
1418 33c. Cheyenne, 1997 . . . . 45 35

2000. Christmas.
1419 **182** 33c. multicoloured . . . 45 35

183 Sun Yat-sen as Young Boy, 1866

2000. 75th Death Anniv of Dr. Sun Yat-sen (President of Republic of China, 1912–25). Multicoloured.
1420 60c. Type **183** 85 65
1421 60c. With family in Honolulu, 1879 and amongst other students in Hong Kong 85 65
1422 60c. As President of Tong Meng Hui, 1905 . . . . 85 65
1423 60c. Empress Dowager (Revolution, 1911) . . . 85 65
1424 60c. As President of Republic of China, 1912 85 65
1425 60c. Flag and various portraits of Sun Yat-sen 85 65

184 Snake (½-size illustration)

2001. New Year. Year of the Snake. Sheet 111 × 88 mm.
1427 **184** 80c. multicoloured . . . 95 55

185 Carnations

2001. Flowers. Multicoloured.
1428 34c. Type **185** 40 25
1429 34c. Violet 40 25
1430 34c. Jonquil 40 25
1431 34c. Sweet pea 40 25
1432 34c. Lily of the Valley . . . 40 25

186 Walap (canoe), Jaluitt

187 Amata Kabua (first President)

2001. Sailing Canoes.
1440 **186** $5 green . . . . 6·00 3·50
1441 – $10 blue . . . . 12·00 7·25
DESIGN: $10 Walap, Enewetak.

2001. Personalities. Multicoloured.
1442 35c. Type **187** 40 25
1443 55c. Robert Reimers (entrepreneur) 65 40
1444 80c. Father Leonard Hacker (humanitarian) 95 55
1445 $1 Dwight Heine (educator) 1·25 75

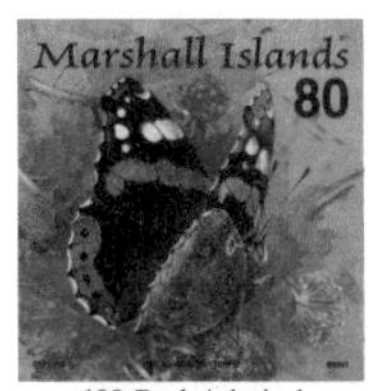
188 Red Admiral

2001. Butterflies. Multicoloured.
1450 80c. Type **188** 95 55
1451 80c. Moroccan orange tip 95 55
1452 80c. Silver-studded blue . . 95 55
1453 80c. Marbled white 95 55
1454 80c. False Apollo 95 55
1455 80c. Ringlet 95 55
1456 80c. Map 95 55
1457 80c. Fenton's wood white 95 55
1458 80c. Grecian copper 95 55
1459 80c. Pale Arctic clouded yellow 95 55
1460 80c. Great banded greyling 95 55
1461 80c. Cardinal 95 55

189 *Tom Thumb*

2001. Fairytales. Multicoloured.
1462 34c. Type **189** 40 25
1463 34c. *Three Little Pigs* . . . 40 25
1464 34c. *Gulliver's Travels* . . . 40 25
1465 34c. *Cinderella* 40 25
1466 34c. *Gallant John* 40 25
1467 34c. *The Ugly Duckling* . . 40 25
1468 34c. *Fisher and the Goldfish* 40 25

190 Pirogues

2001. Racing Watercraft. Multicoloured.
1469 34c. Type **190** 35 20
1470 34c. Windsurfers 35 20
1471 34c. Yachts 35 20
1472 34c. Sailing dinghies 35 20

191 Yuri Alekseyevich Gagarin

2001. 40th Anniv of First Manned Space Flight. Multicoloured.
1473 80c. Type **191** 85 50
1474 80c. Alan Bartlett Shepard 85 50
1475 80c. Virgil Ivan (Gus) Grissom 85 50
1476 80c. Gherman Stepanovich Titov 85 50

192 2000–1 Marshall Island Stamps

2001. Stamp Day.
1477 **192** 34c. multicoloured . . . 35 20

193 Friendship 7 Spacecraft and John Glenn (first USA manned orbit of Earth, 1962)

2001. Space Exploration. Multicoloured.
1478 80c. Type **193** 85 50
1479 80c. First space walk, 1965 85 50
1480 80c. First man on moon, 1969 . . . . 85 50
1481 80c. First space shuttle voyage, 1977 . . . . . . 85 50

MARTINIQUE Pt. 6

An island in the West Indies, now an overseas department using the stamps of France.

100 centimes = 1 franc.

1886. Stamp of French Colonies, "Commerce" type.
(a) Surch **MARTINIQUE** and new value.
3 J 01 on 20c. red on green . . . 10·00 13·50
1 5 on 20c. red on green . . . . 38·00 45·00
4 05 on 20c. red on green . . . 8·25 7·75
2 5c. on 20c. red on green . . . £11000 £11000
6 015 on 20c. red on green . . . 42·00 55·00
5 15 on 20c. red on green . . . £140 £120

(b) Surch **MQE 15 c.**
7 J 15c. on 20c. red on green . . . 65·00 65·00

1888. Stamps of French Colonies, "Commerce" type, surch **MARTINIQUE** and value, thus **01 c.**
10 01c. on 4c. brown on grey . . 8·25 3·00
11 05c. on 4c. brown on grey . . £950 £800
12 05c. on 10c. black and lilac . . 85·00 38·00
13 05c. on 20c. red on green . . 20·00 16·00
14 05c. on 30c. brown on drab 16·00 21·00
15 05c. on 35c. black on yellow 18·00 11·50
16 05c. on 40c. red on yellow . . 50·00 32·00
17 15c. on 4c. brown on grey . . £7250 £6750
18 15c. on 20c. red on green . . £110 60·00
19 15c. on 25c. black on pink . . 10·00 7·25
20 15c. on 75c. red on pink . . . £130 £120

1891. Postage Due stamps of French Colonies surch **TIMBRE-POSTE MARTINIQUE** and value in figures.
21 U 05c. on 5c. black . . . . . 10·00 12·00
25 05c. on 10c. black . . . . . 5·25 5·75
22 05c. on 15c. black . . . . . 6·50 6·00
23 15c. on 20c. black . . . . . 13·00 9·25
24 15c. on 30c. black . . . . . 17·00 9·25

1891. Stamp of French Colonies, "Commerce" type, surch **TIMBRE-POSTE 01c. MARTINIQUE**.
9 01c. on 2c. brown on buff . . . 80 1·00

1892. Stamp of French Colonies, "Commerce" type, surch **1892 MARTINIQUE** and new value.
31 15c. on 25c. black on pink . . 20·00 20·00

1892. "Tablet" key-type inscr "MARTINIQUE", in red (1, 5, 15, 25, 75c., 1f.) or blue (others).
33 D 1c. black on blue . . . . . 1·00 1·00
34 2c. brown on buff . . . . . 1·25 1·40
35 4c. brown on grey . . . . . 1·60 1·75
36 5c. green on green . . . . . 3·50 50
37 10c. black on lilac . . . . . 8·50 70
47 10c. red . . . . 3·75 30
38 15c. blue . . . . 34·00 2·25
48 15c. grey . . . . 11·50 75
39 20c. red on green . . . . . 17·00 7·75
40 25c. black on pink . . . . . 12·00 1·00
49 25c. blue . . . . 14·00 19·00
41 30c. brown on drab . . . . 17·00 12·50
50 35c. black on yellow . . . . 16·00 5·50
42 40c. red on yellow . . . . . 30·00 13·00
43 50c. red on pink . . . . . . 25·00 14·00
51 50c. brown on blue . . . . . 16·00 28·00
44 75c. brown on orange . . . 25·00 17·00
45 1f. green . . . . 24·00 16·00
52 2f. violet on pink . . . . . 80·00 65·00
53 5f. mauve on lilac . . . . . 85·00 80·00

1903. Postage Due stamp of French Colonies surch **TIMBRE POSTE 5 F. MARTINIQUE COLIS POSTAUX**.
53a U 5f. on 60c. brown on buff £450 £475
Despite the surcharge No. 53a was for use on letters as well as parcels.

1904. Nos. 41 and 43 surch **10 c**.
54 10c. on 30c. brown and drab 9·25 12·00
55 10c. on 5f. mauve on lilac . . 8·75 15·00

1904. Surch **1904 0f10**.
56 0f.10 on 30c. brown on drab 14·50 18·00
57 0f.10 on 40c. red on yellow . . 15·00 18·00
58 0f.10 on 50c. red on pink . . 14·50 18·00
59 0f.10 on 75c. brown on orange 11·50 17·00
60 0f.10 on 1f. green . . . . . . 17·00 18·00
61 0f.10 on 5f. mauve on lilac . . £150 £150

13 Martinique Woman

15 Woman and Sugar Cane

14 Fort-de-France

1908.
62 **13** 1c. chocolate and brown . . . 15 20
63 2c. brown and green . . . 15 45
64 4c. brown and purple . . . 40 65
65 5c. brown and green . . . 50 15
87 5c. brown and orange . . . 15 15
66 10c. brown and red . . . . 2·75 15
88 10c. olive and green . . . 1·60 1·00
89 10c. red and purple . . . . 1·25 60
67 15c. red and purple . . . . 1·00 1·10
90 15c. olive and green . . . 15 20
91 15c. red and blue . . . . 2·00 95
68 20c. brown and lilac . . . 2·50 1·40
69 **14** 25c. brown and blue . . . 3·00 45
92 25c. brown and orange . . 35 15
93 30c. brown and red . . . . 2·25 2·75
94 30c. red and carmine . . . 55 2·75
95 30c. brown and light brown . . . . 40 1·00
96 30c. green and blue . . . . 3·00 1·25
71 35c. brown and lilac . . . 1·00 1·50
72 40c. brown and green . . . 1·25 45
73 45c. chocolate and brown . . 2·25 2·50
74 50c. brown and red . . . . 2·75 3·00
97 50c. brown and blue . . . 1·90 2·50
98 50c. green and red . . . . 1·75 20
99 60c. pink and blue . . . . 85 2·75
100 65c. brown and violet . . . 3·00 3·50
75 75c. brown and black . . . 85 3·25
101 75c. blue and deep blue . . 2·00 2·25
102 75c. blue and brown . . . 3·75 3·50
103 90c. carmine and red . . . 7·00 8·50
76 **15** 1f. brown and red . . . . 2·50 3·00
104 1f. blue . . . . 2·25 2·25
105 1f. green and red . . . . . 2·50 2·00
106 1f.10 brown and violet . . 4·50 6·00
107 1f.50 light blue and blue . . 8·00 8·75
77 2f. brown and grey . . . . 4·00 3·25
108 3f. mauve on pink . . . . 12·00 14·00
78 5f. brown and red . . . . 12·00 15·00

1912. Stamps of 1892 surch.
79 05 on 15c. grey 30 25
80 05 on 25c. black on pink . . . 45 3·00
81 10 on 40c. red on yellow . . . 2·25 2·50
82 10 on 5f. mauve on lilac . . . 2·75 4·00

1915. Surch **5c** and red cross.
83 **13** 10c.+5c. brown and red . . 1·90 2·00

1920. Surch in figures.
115 **13** 0,01 on 2c. brown & green 3·00 4·25
109 0,01 on 15c. red and purple 45 30
110 0,02 on 15c. red and purple 45 2·75
84 05 on 1c. chocolate & brn 3·50 3·25
111 0,05 on 15c. red and purple 15 2·75
116 0,05 on 20c. brown and lilac . . . . 3·50 4·25
85 10 on 2c. brown and green 85 80
117 **14** 0,15 on 30c. brown and red 3·50 18·00
86 **13** 25 on 15c. red and purple 2·50 2·75
121 25c. on 15c. red and purple 15 2·75
119 **14** 0,25 on 50c. brown and red £200 £200
120 0,25 on 50c. brown and blue . . . . 4·25 5·00
122 **15** 25c. on 2f. brown and grey 50 2·75
123 25c. on 5f. brown and red 2·00 3·25
112 **14** 60 on 75c. pink and blue 10 40
113 65 on 45c. brown & lt brn 1·75 3·25
114 85 on 75c. brown and black . . . . 2·25 3·50
124 90c. on 75c. carmine and red . . . . 2·75 4·50
125 **15** 1f.25 on 1f. blue . . . . . 75 2·50
126 1f.50 on 1f. ultram & bl . . 2·50 1·75
127 3f. on 5f. green and red . . 3·00 2·50
128 10f. on 5f. red and green 10·50 14·50
129 20f. on 5f. violet & brown 17·00 21·00

1931. "Colonial Exhibition" key-types inscr "MARTINIQUE".
130 E 40c. black and green . . . 4·50 5·50
131 F 50c. black and mauve . . . 4·00 3·00
132 G 90c. black and red . . . 4·50 5·50
133 H 1f.50 black and blue . . . 4·75 5·25

26 Basse Pointe Village

27 Government House, Fort-de-France

28 Martinique Woman

1933.
134 **26** 1c. red on pink . . . . . 15 2·00
135 **27** 2c. blue . . . . 15 2·50
136 3c. purple . . . . 30 2·75
137 **26** 4c. green . . . . 15 2·75
138 **27** 5c. purple 15 35
139 **26** 10c. black on pink 15 30
140 **27** 15c. black on red 15 30
141 **28** 20c. brown 15 30
142 **26** 25c. purple 40 30
143 **27** 30c. green 55 30
144 30c. blue . . . . 45 2·75
145 **28** 35c. green . . . . 60 1·40
146 40c. brown 15 70
147 **27** 45c. brown . . . . 2·75 3·50
148 45c. green . . . . 70 2·25
149 50c. red 70 35
150 **26** 55c. red . . . . 1·50 2·25
151 60c. blue . . . . 40 2·75
152 **28** 65c. red on blue . . . . . 1·00 1·75
153 70c. purple . . . . 1·25 2·25
154 **26** 75c. brown . . . . 2·00 2·00
155 **27** 80c. violet . . . . 1·10 1·75
156 **26** 90c. red . . . . 3·00 80
157 90c. purple . . . . 1·60 1·75
158 **27** 1f. black on green . . . . 1·75 1·10
159 1f. red . . . . 90 2·10
160 **28** 1f.25 violet . . . . 2·50 2·50
161 1f.25 red . . . . 2·00 2·50
162 1f.40 blue . . . . 1·90 2·25
163 **27** 1f.50 blue 95 75
164 1f.60 brown . . . . 2·00 2·25
165 **28** 1f.75 green . . . . 12·00 6·00
166 1f.75 blue . . . . 2·00 1·60
167 **26** 2f. blue on green . . . . 2·50 1·00
168 **28** 2f.25 blue . . . . 2·50 3·00
169 **26** 2f.50 purple . . . . 2·00 2·50
170 **28** 3f. purple . . . . 2·25 1·50
171 5f. red on pink . . . . . 2·50 1·50
172 **26** 10f. blue on blue . . . . 1·75 1·50
173 **27** 20f. red on yellow . . . . 2·25 2·00

30 Belain d'Esnambuc, 1635

31 Schoelcher and Abolition of Slavery, 1848

1935. West Indies Tercentenary.
174 **30** 40c. brown . . . . 3·75 3·50
175 50c. red . . . . 3·75 3·75
176 1f.50 blue . . . . 13·00 16·00
177 **31** 1f.75 red . . . . 16·00 13·00
178 5f. brown . . . . 14·50 16·00
179 10f. green . . . . 11·00 9·75

1937. International Exhibition, Paris. As T **16** of Mauritania.
180 20c. violet . . . . 80 2·75
181 30c. green . . . . 1·10 2·75
182 40c. red . . . . 45 2·25
183 50c. brown and agate . . . . 45 1·60
184 90c. red . . . . 60 3·25
185 1f.50 blue . . . . 75 2·25
MS185a 120×100 mm. 3f. green (as T **16**) Imperf . . . . 7·75 13·50

1938. Int Anti-cancer Fund. As T **22** of Mauritania.
186 1f.75+50c. blue . . . . . . 7·00 14·00

1939. New York World's Fair. As T **28** of Mauritania.
187 1f.25 red . . . . 2·00 3·25
188 2f.25 blue . . . . 2·25 3·25

1939. 150th Anniv of French Revolution. As T **29** of Mauritania.
189 45c.+25c. green and black . . 7·50 11·00
190 70c.+30c. brown and black 7·50 11·00
191 90c.+35c. orange and black 6·75 11·00
192 1f.25+1f. red and black . . . 6·75 11·00
193 2f.25+2f. blue and black . . 6·75 11·00

1944. Mutual Aid and Red Cross Funds. As T **19b** of Oceanic Settlements.
194 5f.+20f. violet . . . . 90 3·50

1945. Eboue. As T **20a** of Oceanic Settlements.
195 2f. black 10 40
196 25f. green . . . . 1·10 2·50

1945. Surch.
197 **27** 1f. on 2c. blue . . . . . . 2·50 1·25
198 **26** 2f. on 4c. olive . . . . . . 50 1·40
199 **27** 3f. on 2c. blue . . . . . . 2·25 90
200 **28** 5f. on 65c. red on blue . . 70 2·00
201 10f. (DIX f.) on 65c. red on blue . . . . 2·50 2·00
202 **27** 20f. (VINGT f.) on 3c. pur 2·50 2·75

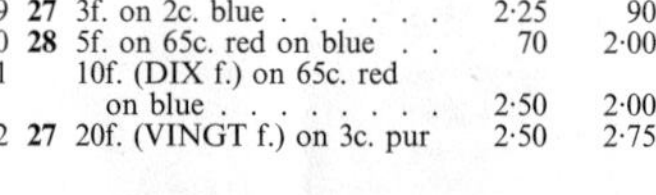

33 Victor Schoelcher

1945.
203 **33** 10c. blue and violet . . . . 15 2·75
204 30c. brown and red . . . . 20 2·00
205 40c. blue and light blue . . 40 2·25
206 50c. red and purple . . . . 40 2·50
207 60c. orange and yellow . . 30 1·75
208 70c. purple and brown . . 95 3·00
209 80c. green and light green 95 2·75
210 1f. blue and light blue . . 30 1·60
211 1f.20 violet and purple . . 90 3·00
212 1f.50 red and orange . . . 55 1·40
213 2f. black and grey . . . . 60 1·25
214 2f.40 red and pink . . . . 1·10 3·25
215 3f. pink and light pink . . 85 1·00
216 4f. ultramarine and blue 70 2·00
217 4f.50 turquoise and green 85 1·25
218 5f. light brown and brown 95 1·50
219 10f. purple and mauve . . 1·10 1·25
220 15f. red and pink . . . . 90 1·50
221 20f. olive and green . . . 60 1·60

1945. Air. As No. 299 of New Caledonia.
222 50f. green . . . . 60 1·75
223 100f. red . . . . 55 2·75

1946. Air. Victory. As T **20b** of Oceanic Settlements.
224 8f. blue . . . . 25 3·25

1946. Air. From Chad to the Rhine. As T **25a** of Madagascar.
225 5f. orange . . . . 80 2·75
226 10f. green . . . . 40 2·75
227 15f. red . . . . 80 3·25
228 20f. brown . . . . 1·00 2·50
229 25f. blue . . . . 55 3·25
230 50f. grey . . . . 1·10 2·25

34 Martinique Woman

39 Mountains and Palms

35 Local Fishing Boats and Rocks

40 West Indians and Latecoere 611 (flying boat)

1947.
231 **34** 10c. lake (postage) . . . . 20 2·50
232 30c. blue . . . . 15 2·50
233 50c. brown . . . . 15 2·75
234 **35** 60c. green . . . . 30 2·75
235 1f. lake . . . . 30 1·00
236 1f.50 violet . . . . 45 2·75
237 – 2f. green . . . . 80 2·25
238 – 2f.50 brown . . . . 80 3·00
239 – 3f. blue . . . . 95 1·50
240 – 4f. brown . . . . 80 2·00
241 – 5f. green . . . . 75 1·50
242 – 6f. mauve 90 50
243 – 10f. blue . . . . 2·00 1·75
244 – 15f. lake . . . . 2·25 2·00
245 – 20f. brown . . . . 1·75 1·90
246 **39** 25f. violet . . . . 1·90 2·00
247 40f. green . . . . 1·90 3·50
248 **40** 50f. purple (air) . . . . . 4·50 4·00
249 – 100f. green . . . . 5·50 6·25
250 – 200f. violet . . . . 32·00 22·00
DESIGNS—HORIZ: As Type **35**: 2f. to 3f. Gathering sugar cane; 4f. to 6f. Mount Pele; 10f. to 20f. Fruit products. As Type **40**—VERT: 100f. Aeroplane over landscape. HORIZ: 200f. Wandering albatross in flight.

POSTAGE DUE STAMPS

1927. Postage Due stamps of France optd **MARTINIQUE**.
D130 D **11** 5c. blue . . . . 25 3·25
D131 10c. brown . . . . . 40 3·75
D132 20c. olive . . . . . . 65 3·75
D133 25c. red . . . . 1·00 4·25
D134 30c. red . . . . 1·25 4·50
D135 45c. green . . . . . . 1·75 4·75
D136 50c. purple . . . . . 2·25 9·00
D137 60c. green . . . . . . 3·25 9·75
D138 1f. red on yellow . . . 4·75 12·00
D139 2f. mauve . . . . . . 6·75 18·00
D140 3f. red . . . . 6·25 21·00

D 29 Fruit

D 43 Map of Martinique

1933.
D174 D **29** 5c. blue on green . . . 35 1·60
D175 10c. brown . . . . . 15 2·75
D176 20c. blue . . . . . . 95 3·00
D177 25c. red on pink . . . 65 3·00
D178 30c. purple . . . . . 65 2·75
D179 45c. red on yellow . . 85 2·50
D180 50c. brown . . . . . 50 3·25
D181 60c. green . . . . . . 1·00 3·25
D182 1f. black on red . . . 85 3·75
D183 2f. purple . . . . . . 90 3·50
D184 3f. blue on blue . . . 1·25 3·75

1947.
D251 D **43** 10c. blue . . . . . . 15 2·75
D252 30c. green . . . . . . 15 2·75
D253 50c. blue . . . . . . 15 3·00
D254 1f. orange . . . . . . 15 3·00
D255 2f. purple . . . . . . 1·25 3·25
D256 3f. purple . . . . . . 1·25 3·25
D257 4f. brown . . . . . . 2·25 3·50
D258 5f. red . . . . 2·25 3·50
D259 10f. black . . . . . . 2·50 4·25
D260 20f. green . . . . . . 3·25 4·25

MAURITANIA Pt. 6; Pt. 13

A French colony extending inland to the Sahara, incorporated in French West Africa from 1945 to 1959. In 1960 Mauritania became an independent Islamic republic.

1906. 100 centimes = 1 franc.
1973. 100 cents = 1 ouguiya (um).

1906. "Faidherbe", "Palms" and "Balay" key-types inscr "MAURITANIE" in blue (10, 40c., 5f.) or red (others).
1 I 1c. grey 90 80
2 2c. brown . . . . 80 1·00
3 4c. brown on blue . . . . 2·50 2·25
4 5c. green . . . . 2·75 2·25
5 10c. pink . . . . 10·00 7·00
6 J 20c. black on blue . . . . 17·00 18·00
7 25c. blue . . . . 9·00 7·50
8 30c. brown on pink . . . . £100 60·00
9 35c. black on yellow . . . 5·75 6·00
10 40c. red on blue . . . . . 8·50 8·25
11 45c. brown on green . . . 8·25 8·25
12 50c. violet . . . . 8·75 8·00
13 75c. green on orange . . . 8·00 6·75
14 K 1f. black on blue . . . . 21·00 19·00
15 2f. blue on pink . . . . . 55·00 70·00
16 5f. red on yellow £130 £110

6 Merchants crossing Desert

1913.
18 **6** 1c. brown and lilac 10 20
19 2c. blue and black . . . . 10 1·25
20 4c. black and violet . . . . 10 1·50
21 5c. green and light green . . 1·75 2·25
37 5c. red and purple . . . . 30 2·50
22 10c. orange and pink . . . 2·50 2·75
38 10c. green and light green . . 10 2·50
39 10c. pink on blue . . . . . 15 2·75
23 15c. black and brown . . . 95 2·75
24 20c. orange and brown . . . 2·00 3·00
25 25c. ultramarine and blue . . 3·00 3·25
40 25c. red and green . . . . 1·75 2·25
26 30c. pink and green . . . . 2·50 3·25
41 30c. orange and red . . . . 2·25 2·50
42 30c. yellow and black . . . 15 2·50
43 30c. light green and green . . 2·75 3·75
27 35c. violet and brown . . . 1·25 3·25
44 35c. light green and green . . 1·00 3·00
28 40c. green and brown . . . 2·50 3·50
29 45c. brown and orange . . . 1·60 2·75
30 50c. pink and lilac . . . . 75 3·25
45 50c. ultramarine and blue . . 1·10 2·75
46 50c. blue and green . . . . 1·90 2·75
47 60c. violet on pink . . . . 1·50 2·75
48 65c. blue and brown . . . . 2·25 3·25

31 75c. brown and blue . . . . 1·50 3·25
49 85c. brown and green . . . . 45 3·00
50 90c. pink and red . . . . . 3·00 3·75
32 1f. black and red . . . . . . 1·60 2·50
51 1f.10 red and mauve . . . . 9·50 15·00
52 1f.25 brown and blue . . . . 3·50 4·00
53 1f.50 blue and light blue . . 1·75 3·00
54 1f.75 red and green . . . . . 2·50 3·25
55 1f.75 ultramarine and blue 1·25 3·25
33 2f. violet and orange . . . . 1·60 3·75
56 3f. mauve on pink . . . . . 1·90 3·75
34 5f. blue and violet . . . . . 3·00 4·25

1915. Surch **5c** and red cross.
35 **6** 10c.+5c. orange and pink . . 1·25 2·25
36 15c.+5c. black and brown . . 95 3·25

1922. Surch in figures and bars (some colours changed).
60 **6** 25c. on 2f. violet and orange 2·75 3·25
57 60 on 75c. violet on pink . . 1·60 2·75
58 65 on 15c. black and brown 3·00 4·25
59 85 on 75c. brown and blue 2·00 4·00
61 90c. on 75c. pink and red . . 3·00 4·00
62 1f.25 on 1f. ultram & blue . . 2·00 3·25
63 1f.50 on 1f. blue & light blue 1·25 3·00
64 3f. on 5f. mauve and brown 9·75 12·00
65 10f. on 5f. green and mauve 9·00 10·50
66 20f. on 5f. orange and blue 5·75 11·00

1931. "Colonial Exhibition" key-types inscr "MAURITANIE".
67 E 40c. green and black . . . . 9·25 13·00
68 F 50c. purple and black . . . 5·00 6·00
69 G 90c. red and black . . . . . 5·00 6·50
70 H 1f.50 blue and black . . . . 5·00 6·50

16 Commerce

22 Pierre and Marie Curie

1937. International Exhibition, Paris.
71 **16** 20c. violet . . . . 45 2·50
72 30c. green . . . . 80 3·25
73 40c. red . . . . 40 3·00
74 50c. brown . . . . 35 1·40
75 90c. red . . . . 30 2·00
76 1f.50 blue . . . . 35 3·25
MS76a 120 × 100 mm. **18** 3f. blue. Imperf . . . . 8·25 10·00

1938. International Anti-cancer Fund.
76b **22** 1f.75+50c. blue . . . . . 3·00 12·50

23 Man on Camel

24 Warriors

25 Encampment

26 Mauritanians

1938.
77 **23** 2c. purple . . . . 15 2·50
78 3c. blue . . . . 10 2·25
79 4c. lilac . . . . 45 2·50
80 5c. red . . . . 10 2·00
81 10c. red . . . . 80 3·00
82 15c. violet . . . . 1·10 2·50
83 **24** 20c. red 35 80
84 25c. blue . . . . 80 2·25
85 30c. purple . . . . 75 2·50
86 35c. green . . . . 60 2·75
87 40c. red . . . . 90 3·00
88 45c. green . . . . 1·75 3·00
89 50c. violet . . . . 55 3·25
90 **25** 55c. lilac . . . . 55 2·50
91 60c. violet . . . . 2·00 3·00
92 65c. green . . . . 45 3·00
93 70c. red . . . . 2·00 3·25
94 80c. blue . . . . 1·50 4·00
95 90c. lilac . . . . 1·10 2·75
96 1f. red . . . . 70 3·50
97 1f. green . . . . 10 2·50
98 1f.25 red . . . . 1·60 3·50
99 1f.40 blue . . . . 2·25 3·25
100 1f.50 violet . . . . . . 1·25 3·00
100a 1f.50 red £110 £100
101 1f.60 brown . . . . . . 3·00 3·50
102 **26** 1f.75 blue . . . . 95 2·00
103 2f. lilac . . . . 85 3·00
104 2f.25 blue . . . . 2·00 3·25
105 2f.50 brown . . . . . . 2·00 3·00
106 3f. green . . . . 75 3·50
107 5f. red . . . . 2·00 3·25
108 10f. purple . . . . 1·25 4·00
109 20f. red . . . . 1·50 3·25

27 Rene Caillie (explorer)

1939. Death Centenary of Caillie.
110 **27** 90c. orange . . . . 30 2·75
111 2f. violet . . . . 40 2·00
112 2f.25 blue . . . . 50 3·50

28

1939. New York World's Fair.
113 **28** 1f.25 red . . . . 1·00 3·25
114 2f.25 blue . . . . 1·10 3·25

29 Storming the Bastille

1939. 150th Anniv of French Revolution.
115 **29** 45c.+25c. green and black 7·75 13·00
116 70c.+30c. brown and black 7·75 13·00
117 90c.+35c. orange and black 7·75 13·00
118 1f.25+1f. red and black . . 8·00 13·00
119 2f.25+2f. blue and black 7·75 13·00

30 Twin-engine Airliner over Jungle

1940. Air.
120 **30** 1f.90 blue . . . . 85 2·75
121 2f.90 red . . . . 35 3·25
122 4f.50 green . . . . 45 3·00
123 4f.90 olive . . . . 1·25 2·25
124 6f.90 orange . . . . . . 80 2·75

1941. National Defence Fund. Surch **SECOURS NATIONAL** and value.
124a +1f. on 50c. (No. 89) . . . 4·75 4·75
124b +2f. on 80c. (No. 94) . . . 8·50 9·50
124c +2f. on 1f.50 (No. 100) . . 8·25 9·50
124d +3f. on 2f. (No. 103) . . . 8·50 9·50

31a Ox Caravan

1942. Marshal Petain issue.
124e **31a** 1f. green . . . . 60 4·00
124f 2f.50 blue . . . . 15 4·00

1942. Air. Colonial Child Welfare Fund. As Nos. 98g/i of Niger.
124g 1f.50+3f.50 green . . . . . 15 3·25
124h 2f.+6f. brown . . . . 15 3·25
124i 3f.+9f. red . . . . 15 3·25

1942. Air. Imperial Fortnight. As No. 98j of Niger.
124j 1f.20+1f.80 blue and red . . 50 3·25

32 Twin-engine Airliner over Camel Caravan

1942. Air. T **32** inscr "MAURITANIE" at foot.
124k **32** 50f. orange and yellow . . 2·00 3·50

1944. Surch.
125 **25** 3f.50 on 65c. green 10 15
126 4f. on 65c. green 15 35
127 5f. on 65c. green 20 65
128 10f. on 65c. green 25 40
129 **27** 15f. on 90c. orange . . . . 75 1·25

ISLAMIC REPUBLIC

35 Flag of Republic

37 Well

38 Slender-billed Gull

1960. Inauguration of Islamic Republic.
130 **35** 25f. bistre, grn & brn on rose . . . . 2·00 2·00

1960. 10th Anniv of African Technical Co-operation Commission. As T **4** of Malagasy Republic.
131 25f. blue and turquoise . . . 2·00 2·00

1960.
132 **37** 50c. purple & brn (postage) 10 10
133 – 1f. bistre, brown and green 10 10
134 – 2f. brown, green and blue 15 10
135 – 3f. red, sepia and turquoise 20 20
136 – 4f. buff and green 20 20
137 – 5f. chocolate, brown and red 15 10
138 – 10f. blue, black and brown 20 15
139 – 15f. multicoloured 40 15
140 – 20f. brown and green . . . 30 15
141 – 25f. blue and green 50 15
142 – 30f. blue, violet and bistre 50 15
143 – 50f. brown and green . . . 80 40
144 – 60f. purple, red and green 1·25 40
145 – 85f. brown, sepia and blue 3·50 1·50
146 – 100f. brn, choc & bl (air) 6·75 2·40
147 200f. myrtle, brown & sepia . . . . 14·00 4·25
148 **38** 500f. sepia, blue and brown 32·00 8·75
DESIGNS—VERT: (As Type **37**) 2f. Harvesting dates; 5f. Harvesting millet; 25, 30f. Seated dance; 50f. "Telmidi" (symbolic figure); 60f. Metalsmith; 85f. Scimitar oryx; 100f. Greater flamingo; 200f. African spoonbill. HORIZ: 3f. Barbary sheep; 4f. Fennec foxes; 10f. Cordwainer; 15f. Fishing-boat; 20f. Nomad school.

39 Flag and Map

43 Campaign Emblem

42 European, African and Boeing 707 Airliners

1960. Proclamation of Independence.
149 **39** 25f. green, brown & chest 50 50

1962. Air. Air Afrique Airline.
150 **42** 100f. green, brown & bistre 1·75 1·10

1962. Malaria Eradication.
151 **43** 25f.+5f. olive 50 50

44 U.N. Headquarters and View of Nouakchott

1962. Admission to U.N.O.
152 **44** 15f. brown, black and blue 20 20
153 25f. brown, myrtle and blue 35 35
154 85f. brown, purple and blue . . . . 1·00 1·00

45 Union Flag

1962. 1st Anniv of Union of African and Malagasy States.
155 **45** 30f. blue 45 45

46 Eagle and Crescent over Nouakchott

1962. 8th Endemic Diseases Eradication Conference, Nouakchott.
156 **46** 30f. green, brown and blue 45 35

47 Diesel Mineral Train

1962.
157 **47** 50f. multicoloured . . . . 3·75 1·25

1962. Air. 1st Anniv of Admission to U.N.O. As T **44** but views from different angles and inscr "1 er ANNIVERSAIRE 27 OCTOBRE 1962".
158 100f. blue, brown & turquoise 1·10 90

49 Map and Agriculture

1962. 2nd Anniv of Independence.
159 **49** 30f. green and purple . . . 45 30

50 Congress Representatives

1962. 1st Anniv of Unity Congress.
160 **50** 25f. brown, myrtle and blue 45 40

51 Globe and Emblem

1962. Freedom from Hunger.
161 **51** 25f.+5f. blue, brown & pur 55 55

52 Douglas DC-3 Airliner over Nouakchott Airport

1963. Air. Creation of National Airline.
162 **52** 500f. myrtle, brown & blue 12·00 4·50

53 Open-cast Mining, Zouerate

1963. Air. Mining Development. Multicoloured.
163 100f. Type **53** . . . . . . 2·50 60
164 200f. Port-Etienne . . . . . 5·25 2·50

54 Striped Hyena

56 "Posts and Telecommunications"

1963. Animals.
165 **54** 50c. black, brown & myrtle 10 10
166 – 1f. black, blue and buff . . 10 10
167 – 1f.50 brown, olive & pur 20 15
168 – 2f. purple, green and red 15 15
169 – 5f. bistre, blue and ochre 25 20
170 – 10f. black and ochre . . . 50 20
171 – 15f. purple and blue . . . 50 20
172 – 20f. bistre, purple and blue 60 20
173 – 25f. ochre, brown & turq 85 25
174 – 30f. bistre, brown and blue 1·50 30
175 – 50f. bistre, brown and green . . . . 2·00 60
176 – 60f. bistre, brown & turq 2·50 90
ANIMALS—HORIZ: 1f. Spotted hyena; 2f. Guinea baboons; 10f. Leopard; 15f. Bongos; 20f. Aardvark; 30f. North African crested porcupine; 60f. Chameleon. VERT: 1f.50, Cheetah; 5f. Dromedaries; 25f. Patas monkeys; 50f. Dorcas gazelle.

1963. Air. African and Malagasy Posts and Telecommunications Union.
177 **56** 85f. multicoloured . . . . 1·00 65

57 "Telstar" Satellite

1963. Air. Space Telecommunications.
178 **57** 50f. brown, purple & green 65 45
179 – 100f. blue, brown and red 1·25 80
180 – 150f. turquoise and brown 2·25 1·50
DESIGNS: 100f. "Syncom" satellite; 150f. "Relay" satellite.

58 "Tiros" Satellite

60 U.N. Emblem, Sun and Birds

59 Airline Emblem

1963. Air. World Meteorological Day.
181 **58** 200f. brown, blue and green . . . . 3·50 1·75

1963. Air. 1st Anniv of "Air Afrique" and DC-8 Service Inauguration.
182 **59** 25f. multicoloured 50 25

1963. Air. 15th Anniv of Declaration of Human Rights.
183 **60** 100f. blue, violet and purple . . . . 1·25 85

61 Cogwheels and Wheat

62 Lichtenstein's Sandgrouse

1964. Air. European-African Economic Convention.
184 **61** 50f. multicoloured . . . . 1·10 70

1964. Air. Birds.
185 **62** 100f. ochre, brown & green 8·50 1·00
186 – 200f. black, brown and blue . . . . 12·00 2·50
187 – 500f. slate, red and green 29·00 7·00
DESIGNS: 200f. Reed cormorant; 500f. Dark chanting goshawk.

63 Temple, Philae

1964. Air. Nubian Monuments Preservation.
188 **63** 10f. brown, black and blue 45 30
189 25f. slate, brown and blue 70 60
190 60f. chocolate, brown & bl 1·50 1·10

64 W.M.O. Emblem. Sun and Lightning

65 Radar Antennae and Sun Emblem

1964. World Meteorological Day.
191 **64** 85f. blue, orange and brown . . . . 1·25 80

1964. International Quiet Sun Years.
192 **65** 25f. red, green and blue . . 35 25

66 Bowl depicting Horse-racing

1964. Air. Olympic Games, Tokyo.
193 **66** 15f. brown and bistre . . . 30 25
194 – 50f. brown and blue . . . 60 50
195 – 85f. brown and red . . . . 1·10 1·00
196 – 100f. brown and green . . 1·50 1·25
DESIGNS—VERT: 50f. Running (vase); 85f. Wrestling (vase). HORIZ: 100f. Chariot-racing (bowl).

67 Flat-headed Grey Mullet

1964. Marine Fauna.
197 **67** 1f. green, blue and brown 25 15
198 – 5f. purple, green and brown 40 15
199 – 10f. green, ochre and blue 50 20
200 – 60f. slate, green and brown 3·50 1·10
DESIGNS—VERT: 5f. Lobster ("Panulirus mauritanicus"); 10f. Lobster ("Panulirus regius"). HORIZ: 60f. Meagre.

68 "Co-operation"

69 Pres. Kennedy

1964. French, African and Malagasy Co-operation.
201 **68** 25f. brown, green & mauve 40 30

1964. Air. 1st Death Anniv of Pres. Kennedy.
202 **69** 100f. multicoloured . . . . 1·75 1·00

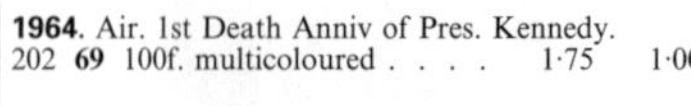

70 "Nymphaea lotus"

1965. Mauritanian Flowers.
203 **70** 5f. green, red and blue . . 25 15
204 – 10f. green, ochre and purple 40 15
205 – 20f. brown, red and sepia 60 20
206 – 45f. turquoise, purple & grn . . . . 1·25 60
FLOWERS—VERT: 10f. "Acacia gommier"; 45f. "Caralluma retrospiciens". HORIZ: 20f. "Adenium obesum".

71 "Hardine"

72 Abraham Lincoln

1965. Musical Instruments and Musicians.
207 **71** 2f. brown, bistre and blue 25 15
208 – 8f. brown, bistre and red 50 15
209 – 25f. brown, black and green 85 20
210 – 40f. black, blue and violet 1·10 35
DESIGNS: 8f. "Tobol" (drums); 25f. "Tidinit" ("Violins"); 40f. Native band.

1965. Death Centenary of Abraham Lincoln.
211 **72** 50f. multicoloured 70 35

73 Early Telegraph and Relay Satellite

1965. Air. Centenary of I.T.U.
212 **73** 250f. green, mauve and blue . . . . 4·25 3·25

74 Palms in the Adrar

1965. "Tourism and Archaeology" (1st series).
213 **74** 1f. green, brown and blue 10 10
214 – 4f. brown, red and blue . . 15 10
215 – 15f. multicoloured 30 20
216 – 60f. sepia, brown and green 90 45
DESIGNS—VERT: 4f. Chinguetti Mosque. HORIZ: 15f. Clay-pits; 60f. Carved doorway, Qualata.
See also Nos. 255/8.

75 "Attack on Cancer" (the Crab)

1965. Air. Campaign against Cancer.
217 **75** 100f. red, blue and ochre 1·50 60

76 Wooden Tea Service

1965. Native Handicrafts.
218 **76** 3f. brown, ochre and slate 15 15
219 – 7f. purple, orange and blue 20 20
220 – 25f. brown, black and red 35 20
221 – 50f. red, green and orange 75 35
DESIGNS—VERT: 7f. Snuff-box and pipe; 25f. Damasquine dagger. HORIZ: 50f. Mederdra chest.

77 Nouakchott Wharf

78 Sir Winston Churchill

1965. Mauritanian Development.
222 – 5f. green and brown . . . 1·75 90
223 **77** 10f. red, turquoise and blue 15 10
224 – 30f. red, brown and purple 3·50 1·10
225 – 85f. violet, lake and blue 1·25 55
DESIGNS—VERT: 5f., 30f. Choum Tunnel. HORIZ: 85f. Nouakchott Hospital.

1965. Air. Churchill Commem.
226 **78** 200f. multicoloured . . . . 2·50 1·25

79 Rocket "Diamant"

1966. Air. French Satellites.
227 **79** 30f. green, red and blue . . 50 25
228 – 60f. purple, blue & turquoise . . . . 1·00 45
229 – 90f. lake, violet and blue 1·50 75
DESIGNS—HORIZ: 60f. Satellite "A 1" and Globe; 90f. Rocket "Scout" and satellite "FR 1".

80 Dr. Schweitzer and Hospital Scene

1966. Air. Schweitzer Commem.
230 **80** 50f. multicoloured . . . . 1·10 50

81 Stafford, Schirra and "Gemini 6"

1966. Air. Space Flights. Multicoloured.

231	50f. Type **81**	60	25
232	100f. Borman, Lovell and "Gemini 7"	1·25	60
233	200f. Beliaiev, Leonov and "Voskhod 2"	2·50	1·25

82 African Woman and Carved Head

1966. World Festival of Negro Arts, Dakar.

234	**82**	10f. black, brown and green	20	10
235	–	30f. purple, black and blue	35	20
236	–	60f. purple, red and orange	75	45

DESIGNS: 30f. Dancers and hands playing cornet; 60f. Cine-camera and village huts.

83 "Dove" over Map of Africa　84 Satellite "D 1"

1966. Air. Organization of African Unity (O.A.U.).

237	**83**	100f. multicoloured	1·00	50

1966. Air. Launching of Satellite "D 1".

238	**84**	100f. plum, brown and blue	1·10	75

85 Breguet 1412 Salon

1966. Air. Early Aircraft.

239	**85**	50f. indigo, blue and bistre	1·00	25
240	–	100f. green, purple and blue	2·00	50
241	–	150f. turquoise, brown & bl	3·00	75
242	–	200f. indigo, blue & purple	4·00	1·25

AIRCRAFT: 100f. Farman Goliath; 150f. Couzinet "Arc en Ciel"; 200f. Latecoere 28-3 seaplane "Comte de la Vaulx".

86 "Acacia ehrenbergiana"

1966. Mauritanian Flowers. Multicoloured.

243	10f. Type **86**	25	15
244	15f. "Schouwia purpurea"	50	15
245	20f. "Ipomaea asarifolia"	65	20
246	25f. "Grewia bicolor"	75	25
247	30f. "Pancratium trianthum"	1·10	25
248	60f. "Blepharis linariifolia"	1·75	55

87 DC-8F and "Air Afrique" Emblem

1966. Air. Inauguration of Douglas DC-8F Air Services.

249	**87**	30f. grey, black and red	75	15

88 "Raft of the Medusa" (after Gericault)

1966. Air. 150th Anniv of Shipwreck of the "Medusa".

250	**88**	500f. multicoloured	9·00	6·50

89 "Myrina silenus"　90 "Hunting" (petroglyph from Tenses, Adrar)

1966. Butterflies. Multicoloured.

251	5f. Type **89**	50	20
252	30f. "Colotis danae"	1·25	40
253	45f. "Hypolimnas misippus"	2·00	60
254	60f. "Danaus chrysippus"	2·75	85

1966. Tourism and Archaeology (2nd series).

255	**90**	2f. chestnut and brown	15	15
256	–	3f. brown and blue	20	20
257	–	30f. green and red	55	25
258	–	50f. brown, green & purple	1·25	80

DESIGNS: 3f. "Fighting" (petroglyph from Tenses, Adrar); 30f. Copper jug (from Le Mreyer, Adrar); 50f. Camel and caravan.

91 Cogwheels and Ears of Wheat

1966. Air. Europafrique.

259	**91**	50f. multicoloured	70	40

92 U.N.E.S.C.O. Emblem

1966. 20th Anniv of U.N.E.S.C.O.

260	**92**	30f. multicoloured	45	20

93 Olympic Village, Grenoble

1967. Publicity for Olympic Games (1968).

261	–	20f. brown, blue and green	30	20
262	**93**	30f. brown, green and blue	40	30
263	–	40f. brown, purple and blue	60	40
264	–	100f. brown, green & black	1·10	70

DESIGNS—VERT: 20f. Old and new buildings, Mexico City; 40f. Ice rink, Grenoble and Olympic torch. HORIZ: 100f. Olympic stadium, Mexico City.

94 South African Crowned Crane　95 Globe, Rockets and Eye

1967. Air. Birds. Multicoloured.

265	100f. Type **94**	3·75	1·10
266	200f. Great egret	8·00	1·50
267	500f. Ostrich	18·00	5·25

1967. Air. World Fair, Montreal.

268	**95**	250f. brown, blue and black	2·25	1·25

96 Prosopis　97 Jamboree Emblem and Scout Kit

1967. Trees.

269	**96**	10f. green, blue and brown	20	10
270	–	15f. green, blue and purple	25	15
271	–	20f. green, purple and blue	30	15
272	–	25f. brown and green	40	20
273	–	30f. brown, green and red	55	25

TREES: 15f. Jujube; 20f. Date palm; 25f. Peltophorum; 30f. Baobab.

1967. World Scout Jamboree, Idaho.

274	**97**	60f. blue, green and brown	85	35
275	–	90f. blue, green and red	1·40	50

DESIGN—HORIZ: 90f. Jamboree emblem and scouts.

98 Weaving　99 Atomic Symbol

1967. Advancement of Mauritanian Women.

276	**98**	5f. red, black and violet	15	10
277	–	10f. black, violet and green	20	10
278	–	20f. black, purple and blue	35	15
279	–	30f. blue, black and brown	45	25
280	–	50f. black, violet and indigo	70	30

DESIGNS—VERT: 10f. Needlework; 30f. Laundering. HORIZ: 20f. Nursing; 50f. Sewing (with machines).

1967. Air. International Atomic Energy Agency.

281	**99**	200f. blue, green and red	2·25	1·10

100 Cattle

1967. Campaign for Prevention of Cattle Plague.

282	**100**	30f. red, blue and green	35	25

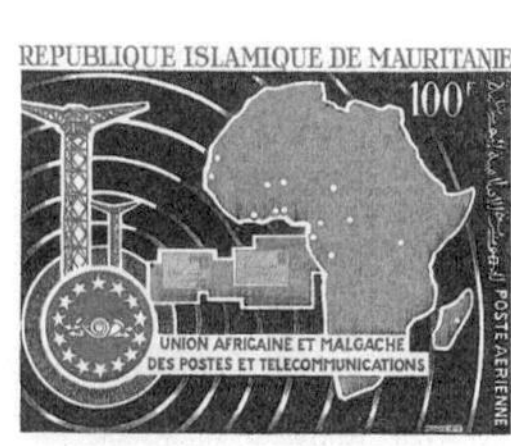
101 Map of Africa, Letters and Pylons

1967. Air. 5th Anniv of U.A.M.P.T.

283	**101**	100f. green, brown & pur	1·00	60

102 "Francois of Rimini" (Ingres)　103 Currency Tokens

1967. Air. Death Centenary of Jean Ingres (painter). Multicoloured.

284	90f. Type **102**	1·25	60
285	200f. "Ingres in his Studio" (Alaux)	2·50	1·25

See also Nos. 306/8.

1967. 5th Anniv of West African Monetary Union.

286	**103**	30f. grey and orange	35	15

104 "Hyphaene thebaica"　105 Human Rights Emblem

1967. Mauritanian Fruits.

287	**104**	1f. brown, green & purple	15	10
288	–	2f. yellow, green & brown	15	10
289	–	3f. olive, green and violet	15	10
290	–	4f. red, green and brown	15	10
291	–	5f. orange, brown & green	20	10

FRUITS—HORIZ: 2f. "Balanites aegyptiaca"; 4f. "Ziziphus lotus". VERT: 3f. "Adansonia digitata"; 5f. "Phoenix dactylifera".

1968. Human Rights Year.

292	**105**	30f. yellow, green & black	30	20
293		50f. yellow, brown & black	55	35

106 Chancellor Adenauer　108 Mosque, Nouakchott

107 Skiing

1968. Air. Adenauer Commemoration.

294	**106**	100f. sepia, brown & blue	1·25	60

1968. Air. Olympic Games, Grenoble and Mexico.

296	**107**	20f. purple, indigo & blue	30	10
297	–	30f. brown, green & plum	35	15
298	–	50f. green, blue and ochre	55	25
299	–	100f. green, red and brown	1·00	50

DESIGNS—VERT: 30f. Horse-vaulting; 50f. Ski-jumping. HORIZ: 100f. Hurdling.

1968. Tourism. Multicoloured.

300	30f. Type **108**	25	20
301	45f. Amogjar Pass	35	20
302	90f. Cavaliers' Tower, Boutilimit	65	35

109 Man and W.H.O. Emblem

1968. Air. 20th Anniv of W.H.O.
303 **109** 150f. blue, purple & brown . . . . 1·50 75

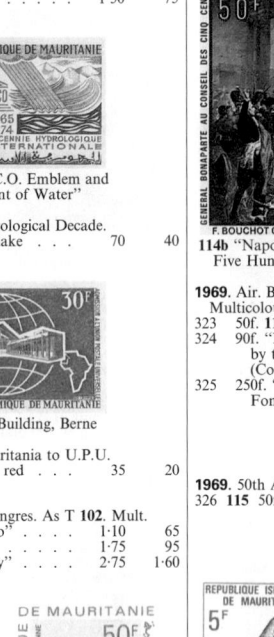

110 U.N.E.S.C.O. Emblem and "Movement of Water"

1968. International Hydrological Decade.
304 **110** 90f. green and lake . . . 70 40

111 U.P.U. Building, Berne

1968. Admission of Mauritania to U.P.U.
305 **111** 30f. brown and red . . . 35 20

1968. Air. Paintings by Ingres. As T **102**. Mult.
306 100f. "Man's Torso" . . . . 1·10 65
307 150f. "The Iliad" . . . . . 1·75 95
308 250f. "The Odyssey" . . . . 2·75 1·60

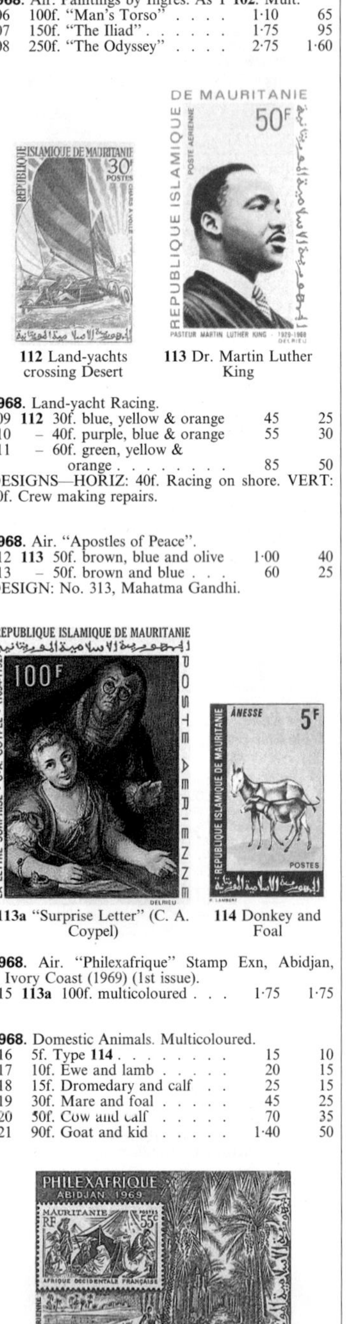

112 Land-yachts crossing Desert

113 Dr. Martin Luther King

1968. Land-yacht Racing.
309 **112** 30f. blue, yellow & orange 45 25
310 – 40f. purple, blue & orange 55 30
311 – 60f. green, yellow & orange 85 50
DESIGNS—HORIZ: 40f. Racing on shore. VERT: 60f. Crew making repairs.

1968. Air. "Apostles of Peace".
312 **113** 50f. brown, blue and olive 1·00 40
313 – 50f. brown and blue . . . 60 25
DESIGN: No. 313, Mahatma Gandhi.

113a "Surprise Letter" (C. A. Coypel)

114 Donkey and Foal

1968. Air. "Philexafrique" Stamp Exn, Abidjan, Ivory Coast (1969) (1st issue).
315 **113a** 100f. multicoloured . . . 1·75 1·75

1968. Domestic Animals. Multicoloured.
316 5f. Type **114** 15 10
317 10f. Ewe and lamb 20 15
318 15f. Dromedary and calf . . 25 15
319 30f. Mare and foal 45 25
320 50f. Cow and calf 70 35
321 90f. Goat and kid . . . . . 1·40 50

114a Forest Scene and Stamp of 1938

1969. Air. "Philexafrique" Stamp Exhibition, Abidjan, Ivory Coast (2nd issue).
322 **114a** 50f. purple, green & brown . . . . 1·10 1·10

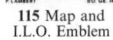

114b "Napoleon at Council of Five Hundred" (Bouchot)

115 Map and I.L.O. Emblem

1969. Air. Birth Bicentenary of Napoleon Bonaparte. Multicoloured.
323 50f. **114b** . . . . 1·50 90
324 90f. "Napoleon's Installation by the Council of State" (Conder) . . . . 2·00 1·25
325 250f. "The Farewell of Fontainebleau" (Vernet) . . 5·00 3·25

1969. 50th Anniv of I.L.O.
326 **115** 50f. multicoloured 50 25

116 Monitor Lizard

117 Date Palm, "Parlatoria blanchardi" and "Pharoscymus anchorage"

1969. Reptiles. Multicoloured.
327 5f. Type **116** 35 20
328 10f. Horned viper 55 30
329 30f. Black-collared cobra . . 1·25 35
330 60f. Rock python . . . . . 2·00 1·10
331 85f. Nile crocodile . . . . . 3·00 1·40

1969. Date-palms. Protection Campaign.
332 **117** 30f. blue, red and green 30 15

118 Camel and Emblem

1969. Air. African Tourist Year.
333 **118** 50f. purple, blue & orange 85 35

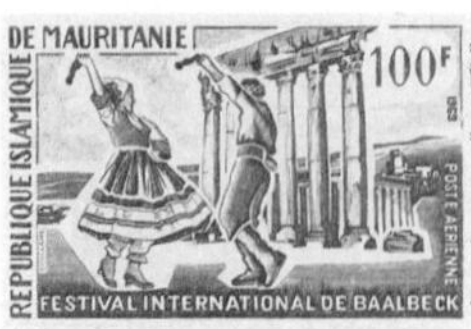

119 Dancers and Baalbek Columns

1969. Baalbek Festival, Lebanon.
334 **119** 100f. brown, red and blue 1·50 55

120 "Apollo 8" and Moon

1969. Air. Moon Flight of "Apollo 8". Embossed on gold foil.
335 **120** 1,000f. gold . . . . . . 14·00 14·00

121 Wolde (marathon)

122a Bank Emblem

122 London-Istanbul Route-Map

1969. Air. Gold Medal Winners, Mexico Olympic Games.
336 **121** 30f. red, brown and blue 25 15
337 – 70f. red, brown and green 50 30
338 – 150f. green, bistre and red 1·25 70
DESIGNS: 70f. Beamon (athletics); 150f. Vera Caslavska (gymnastics).

1969. Air. London–Sydney Motor Rally.
339 **122** 10f. brown, blue & purple 25 10
340 – 20f. brown, blue & purple 50 15
341 – 50f. brown, blue & purple 85 25
342 – 70f. brown, blue & purple 1·10 30
ROUTE—MAPS: 20f. Ankara–Teheran; 50f. Kandahar–Bombay; 70f. Perth–Sydney.

1969. 5th Anniv of African Development Bank. Multicoloured.
344 **122a** 30f. brown, green & blue 30 15

123 Pendant

124 Sea-water Desalination Plant, Nouakchott

1969. Native Handicrafts.
345 **123** 10f. brown and purple . . 20 15
346 – 20f. red, black and blue 40 20
DESIGN—HORIZ: 20f. Rahla headdress.

1969. Economic Development.
347 **124** 10f. blue, purple and red 20 15
348 – 15f. black, lake and blue 25 15
349 – 30f. black, purple and blue 30 20
DESIGNS: 15f. Fishing quay, Nouadhibou; 30f. Meat-processing plant, Kaedi.

125 Lenin

126 "Sternocera interrupta"

1970. Birth Centenary of Lenin.
350 **125** 30f. black, red and blue 30 20

1970. Insects.
351 **126** 5f. black, buff and brown 25 15
352 – 10f. brown, yellow & lake 35 15
353 – 20f. olive, purple & brown 50 25
354 – 30f. violet, green & brown 80 45
355 – 40f. brown, blue and lake 1·50 70
INSECTS: 10f. "Anoplocnemis curvipes"; 20f. "Julodis aequinoctialis"; 30f. "Thermophilum sexmaculatum marginatum"; 40f. "Plocaederus denticornis".

127 Footballers and Hemispheres

128 Japanese Musician, Emblem and Map on Palette

1970. World Cup Football Championship, Mexico.
356 **127** 25f. multicoloured 30 20
357 – 30f. multicoloured 35 20
358 – 70f. multicoloured 70 30
359 – 150f. multicoloured . . . 1·60 75
DESIGNS: 30, 70, 150f. As Type **127**, but with different players.

1970. New U.P.U. Headquarters Building. As T **81** of New Caledonia.
360 30f. red, brown and green . . 35 20

1970. Air. "EXPO 70" World Fair, Osaka, Japan. Multicoloured.
361 50f. Type **128** 50 20
362 75f. Japanese fan 75 35
363 150f. Stylised bird, map and boat . . . . 1·40 80

129 U.N. Emblem and Examples of Progress

1970. Air. 25th Anniv of U.N.O.
364 **129** 100f. green, brown & blue 1·25 60

130 Vladimir Komarov

131 Descent of "Apollo 13"

1970. Air. "Lost Heroes of Space" (1st series).
365 **130** 150f. brown, orge & slate 1·50 70
366 – 150f. brown, blue and slate . . . . 1·50 70
367 – 150f. brown, orge & slate 1·50 70
HEROES: No. 366, Elliott See; 367, Yuri Gagarin.
See also Nos. 376/8.

1970. Air. Space Flight of "Apollo 13".
369 **131** 500f. red, blue and gold 5·00 5·00

132 Woman in Traditional Costume

133 Arms and State House

1970. Traditional Costumes. As T **132**.
370 **132** 10f. orange and brown . . 20 15
371 – 30f. blue, red and brown 40 20
372 – 40f. brown, purple and red 50 30
373 – 50f. blue and brown . . . 70 35
374 – 70f. brown, choc & bl . . 90 45

1970. Air. 10th Anniv of Independence.
375 **133** 100f. multicoloured . . . 1·00 45

1970. Air. "Lost Heroes of Space" (2nd series). As T **130**.
376 150f. brown, blue & turquoise 1·50 70
377 150f. brown, blue & turquoise 1·50 70
378 150f. brown, blue and orange 1·50 70

HEROES: No. 376, Roger Chaffee; No. 377, Virgil Grissom; No. 378, Edward White.

134 Greek Wrestling

1971. Air. "Pre-Olympics Year".
380 **134** 100f. brown, purple & blue . . . . 1·10 75

135 People of Different Races

1971. Racial Equality Year.
381 **135** 30f. plum, blue and brown 30 15
382 – 40f. black, red and blue 35 20
DESIGN—VERT: 40f. European and African hands.

136 Pres. Nasser

1971. Air. Pres. Gamal Nasser of Egypt Commemoration.
383 **136** 100f. multicoloured . . . 85 40

137 Gen. De Gaulle in Uniform

1971. De Gaulle Commem. Multicoloured.
384 40f. Type **137** . . . . 1·25 60
385 100f. De Gaulle as President of France . . . . 2·75 1·40

138 Scout Badge, Scout and Map

1971. Air. 13th World Scout Jamboree, Asagiri, Japan.
387 **138** 35f. multicoloured 40 20
388 40f. multicoloured 50 20
389 100f. multicoloured . . . 1·25 45

139 Diesel Locomotive

1971. Miferma Iron-ore Mines. Multicoloured.
390 35f. Iron ore train . . . . . 2·25 1·00
391 100f. Type **139** . . . . 5·00 2·50
Nos. 390/1 were issued together, se-tenant, forming a composite design.

139a Headquarters, Brazzaville, and Ardin Musicians

1971. Air. 10th Anniv of African and Malagasy Posts and Telecommunications Union.
392 **139a** 100f. multicoloured . . . 1·10 60

140 A.P.U. Emblem and Airmail Envelope

1971. Air. 10th Anniv of African Postal Union.
393 **140** 35f. multicoloured 40 25

141 U.N.I.C.E.F. Emblem and Child

1971. 25th Anniv of U.N.I.C.E.F.
394 **141** 35f. black, brown and blue 35 20

142 "Moslem King" (c. 1218)

1972. Air. Moslem Miniatures. Multicoloured.
395 35f. Type **142** 45 20
396 40f. "Enthroned Prince" (Egypt, c. 1334) 60 25
397 100f. "Pilgrims' Caravan" (Maquamat, Baghdad, 1237) . . . . 1·50 70

1972. Air. U.N.E.S.C.O. "Save Venice" Campaign. As T **127** of Mali. Multicoloured.
398 45f. "Quay and Ducal Palace" (Carlevaris) (vert) 60 25
399 100f. "Grand Canal" (Canaletto) . . . . 1·40 60
400 250f. "Santa Maria della Salute" (Canaletto) . . . . 3·00 1·50

143 Hurdling

1972. Air. Olympic Games, Munich.
401 **143** 75f. purple, orange & grn 55 30
402 100f. purple, blue & brn 75 40
403 200f. purple, lake & green 1·60 70

144 Nurse tending Baby

1972. Mauritanian Red Crescent Fund.
405 **144** 35f.+5f. multicoloured . . 60 60

145 Samuel Morse and Morse Key

1972. World Telecommunications Day. Mult.
406 35f. Type **145** 35 20
407 40f. "Relay" satellite and hemispheres 45 20
408 75f. Alexander Graham Bell and early telephone 70 35

146 Spirifer Shell

1972. Fossil Shells. Multicoloured.
409 25f. Type **146** . . . . 1·00 35
410 75f. Trilobite . . . . 2·75 1·10

147 "Luna 16" and Moon Probe

151 Mediterranean Monk Seal with Young

149 Africans and 500f. Coin

1972. Air. Russian Exploration of the Moon.
411 **147** 75f. brown, blue and green 60 30
412 – 100f. brown, grey & violet 90 50
DESIGN—HORIZ: 100f. "Lunokhod 1".

1972. Air. Gold Medal Winners, Munich. Nos. 401/3 optd as listed below.
413 **143** 75f. purple, orange & grn 60 30
414 100f. purple, blue & brn 80 50
415 200f. purple, lake & green 1·60 1·00
OVERPRINTS: 75f. **110m. HAIES MILBURN MEDAILLE D'OR**; 100f. **400m. HAIES AKII-BUA MEDAILLE D'OR**; 200f. **3,000m. STEEPLE KEINO MEDAILLE D'OR**.

1972. 10th Anniv of West African Monetary Union.
416 **149** 35f. grey, brown and green 30 20

1973. Air. Moon Flight of "Apollo 17". No. 267 surch **Apollo XVII Decembre 1972** and value.
417 250f. on 500f. multicoloured 4·00 2·00

1973. Seals. Multicoloured.
418 40f. Type **151** (postage) . . . 1·50 50
419 135f. Head of Mediterranean monk seal (air) . . . . . 3·00 1·60

152 "Lion and Crocodile" (Delacroix)

1973. Air. Paintings by Delacroix. Mult.
420 100f. Type **152** . . . . 1·50 75
421 250f. "Lion attacking Forest Hog" . . . . 3·25 2·00

153 "Horns of Plenty"

1973. 10th Anniv of World Food Programme.
422 **153** 35f. multicoloured 30 20

154 U.P.U. Monument, Berne, and Globe

1973. World U.P.U. Day.
423 **154** 100f. blue, orange & green 1·00 65

155 Nomad Encampment and Eclipse

1973. Total Eclipse of the Sun.
424 **155** 35f. purple and green . . 35 20
425 – 40f. purple, red and blue 45 20
426 – 140f. purple and red . . . 1·60 75
DESIGNS—VERT: 40f. Rocket and Concorde. HORIZ: 140f. Observation team.

1973. "Drought Relief". African Solidarity. No. 320 surch **SECHERESSE SOLIDARITE AFRICAINE** and value.
428 20um. on 50f. multicoloured 65 45

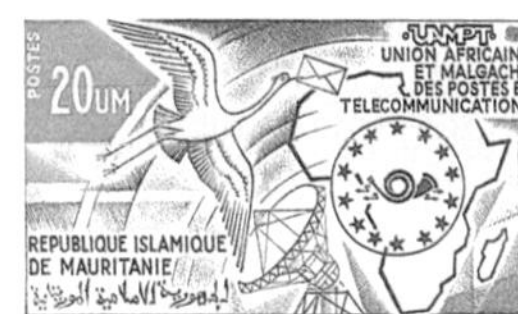

155a Crane with Letter and Union Emblem

1973. 12th Anniv of African and Malagasy Posts and Telecommunications Union.
429 **155a** 20um. brown, lt brn & orge . . . . 1·00 45

157 Detective making Arrest and Fingerprint

1973. 50th Anniv of International Criminal Police Organization (Interpol).
430 **157** 15um. violet, red & brown 1·10 45

1974. Various stamps surch with values in new currency. (a) Postage. (i) Nos. 345/6.
431 **123** 27um. on 10f. brn & pur 1·50 70
432 – 28um. on 20f. red, blk & bl . . . . 1·75 90

(ii) Nos. 351/5.
433 **126** 5um. on 5f. black, buff and brown 70 50
434 – 7um. on 10f. brown, yellow and lake 60 30
435 – 8um. on 20f. olive, purple and brown 70 35

436 – 10um. on 30f. violet, purple and brown . . . 1·00 45
437 – 20um. on 40f. brown, blue and lake . . . . 2·00 1·10

(iii) Nos. 409/10.

438 **146** 5um. on 25f. multicoloured 60 40
439 – 15um. on 75f. mult . . . 1·75 1·00

(iv) No. 418.

440 **151** 8um. on 40f. multicoloured 90 45

(b) Air. (i) Nos. 395/7.

441 **142** 7um. on 35f. mult 40 20
442 – 8um. on 40f. mult 40 20
443 – 20um. on 100f. mult . . . 1·50 70

(ii) No. 419.

444 – 27um. on 135f. mult . . . . 2·25 85

(iii) Nos. 420/1.

445 **152** 20um. on 100f. mult . . . 1·60 70
446 – 50um. on 250f. mult . . . 3·75 2·00

(iv) Nos. 424/6.

447 **155** 7um. on 35f. purple & grn 45 20
448 – 8um. on 40f. pur, red & bl 45 20
449 – 28um. on 140f. pur & red 1·90 70

159 Footballers

161 Sir Winston Churchill

160 Jules Verne and Scenes from Books

1974. Air. World Cup Football Championship, West Germany.

450 **159** 7um. multicoloured . . . 40 20
451 8um. multicoloured . . . 40 20
452 20um. multicoloured . . . 1·10 50

1974. Air. Jules Verne "Prophet of Space Travel" and "Skylab" Flights Commemoration.

454 **160** 70um. silver . . . . . . 4·50 4·50
455 – 70um. silver . . . . . . 4·50 4·50
456 **160** 250um. gold . . . . . . 12·00 12·00
457 – 250um. gold . . . . . . 12·00 12·00

DESIGNS: Nos. 455, 457, "Skylab" in Space.

1974. Air. Birth Centenary of Sir Winston Churchill.

458 **161** 40um. red and purple . . 1·75 95

162 U.P.U. Monument and Globes

1974. Centenary of U.P.U.

459 **162** 30um. red, green & dp grn . . . . 1·25 75
460 50um. red, lt blue & blue 2·00 1·25

163 5 Ouguiya Coin and Banknote

1974. 1st Anniv of Introduction of Ouguiya Currency.

461 **163** 7um. black, green and blue 35 20
462 – 8um. black, mauve and green 40 20
463 – 20um. black, blue and red 1·00 50

DESIGNS: 8um. 10 ouguiya coin and banknote; 20um. 20 ouguiya coin and banknote.

164 Lenin

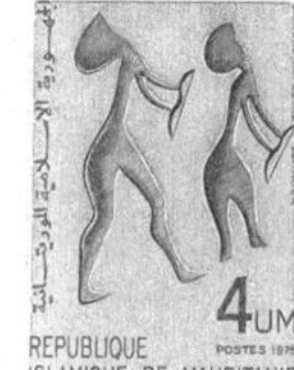

166 Two Hunters

1974. Air. 50th Death Anniv of Lenin.

464 **164** 40um. green and red . . . 2·00 95

1974. Treaty of Berne Centenary. Nos. 459/60 optd **9 OCTOBRE 100 ANS D'UNION POSTALE INTERNATIONALE.**

465 **162** 30um. red, green and deep green . . . . 1·60 80
466 50um. red, light blue and blue . . . . 2·00 1·25

1975. Nos. 287/91 surch in new currency.

467 – 1um. on 5f. orange, brown and green . . . 10 10
468 – 2um. on 4f. red, green and brown 15 15
469 – 3um. on 2f. yellow, green and brown 20 15
470 **104** 10um. on 1f. brown, green and purple 60 20
471 – 12um. on 3f. olive, green and violet 75 30

1975. Rock-carvings, Zemmour.

472 **166** 4um. red and brown . . . 40 15
473 – 5um. purple 45 25
474 – 10um. blue and light blue 80 35

DESIGNS—VERT: 5um. Ostrich. HORIZ: 10um. Elephant.

167 Mauritanian Women

1975. Air. International Women's Year.

475 **167** 12um. purple, brown & bl 50 25
476 – 40um. purple, brown & bl 1·75 85

DESIGNS: 40um. Head of Mauritanian woman.

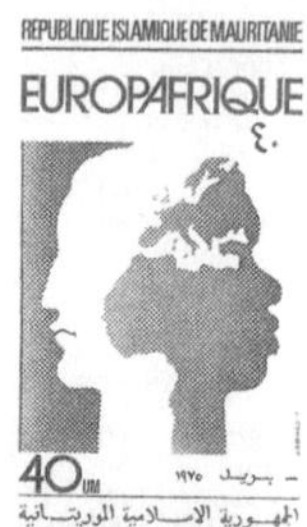

168 Combined European and African Heads

169 Dr. Schweitzer

1975. Europafrique.

477 **168** 40um. brown, red & bistre 1·60 95

1975. Birth Centenary of Dr. Albert Schweitzer.

478 **169** 60um. olive, brown & green . . . . 2·50 1·50

1975. Pan-African Drought Relief. Nos. 301/2 surch **SECHERESSE SOLIDARITE AFRICAINE** and value.

479 15um. on 45f. multicoloured 1·00 50
480 25um. on 90f. multicoloured 1·40 75

171 Akoujt Plant and Man with Camel

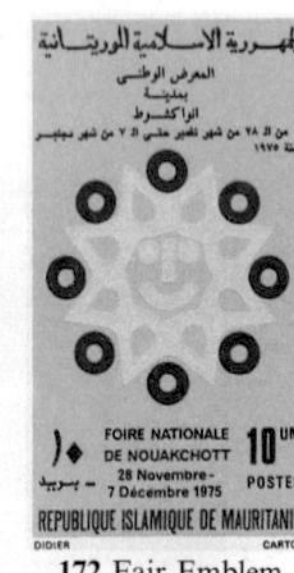

172 Fair Emblem

1975. Mining Industry.

481 **171** 10um. brown, blue & orge 1·25 30
482 – 12um. blue, red and brown . . . . 1·50 40

DESIGN: 12um. Mining operations.

1975. Nouakchott National Fair.

483 **172** 10um. multicoloured . . . 40 25

173 Throwing the Javelin

1975. Air. "Pre-Olympic Year". Olympic Games, Montreal (1976).

484 **173** 50um. red, green & brown 1·60 1·40
485 – 52um. blue, brown and red . . . . 1·75 1·40

DESIGN: 52um. Running.

174 Commemorative Medal

1975. 15th Anniv of Independence. Multicoloured.

486 10um. Type **174** 50 30
487 12um. Map of Mauritania . . 1·60 60

175 "Soyuz" Cosmonauts Leonov and Kubasov

1975. "Apollo–Soyuz" Space Link. Multicoloured.

488 8um. Type **175** (postage) . . 45 20
489 10um. "Soyuz" on launch-pad 55 25
490 20um. "Apollo" on launch-pad (air) 70 45
491 50um. Cosmonauts meeting astronauts . . . . 2·00 1·00
492 60um. Parachute splashdown 2·25 1·25

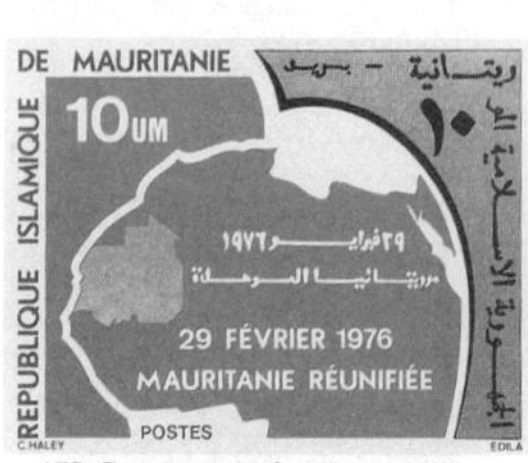

178 Commemorative Text on Map

1976. Reunification of Mauritania.

501 **178** 10um. green, lilac and deep green 45 30

181 Running

1976. Air. Olympic Games, Montreal.

514 **181** 10um. brown, green and violet 40 25
515 – 12um. brown, green and violet 50 35
516 – 52um. brown, green and violet . . . . 1·75 1·25

DESIGNS: 12um. Vaulting (gymnastics); 52um. Fencing.

182 LZ-4 at Friedrichshafen

1976. 75th Anniv of Zeppelin Airship. Mult.

517 5um. Type **182** (postage) . . 25 15
518 10um. "Schwaben" over German Landscape 40 20
519 12um. "Hansa" over Heligoland 50 25
520 20um. "Bodensee" and Doctor H. Durr . . . . . 1·10 50
521 50um. "Graf Zeppelin" over Capitol, Washington (air) 2·25 90
522 60um. "Graf Zeppelin II" crossing Swiss Alps . . . . 3·00 1·25

183 Temple and Bas-relief

1976. U.N.E.S.C.O. "Save Moenjodaro" (Pakistan) Campaign.

524 **183** 15um. multicoloured . . . 80 40

184 Sacred Ibis and Yellow-billed Stork

1976. Air. Mauritanian Birds. Multicoloured.

525 50um. Type **184** . . . . . . 5·00 1·25
526 100um. Marabou storks (horiz) . . . . 8·50 2·75
527 200um. Long-crested and Martial eagles . . . . . . 18·00 5·00

185 Alexander Graham Bell, Early Telephone and Satellite

1976. Telephone Centenary.

528 **185** 10um. blue, lake and red 50 25

176 Foot-soldier of Lauzun's Legion

1976. Bicentenary of American Independence. Mult.

494 8um. Type **176** (postage) . . 60 20
495 10um. "Green Mountain" infantryman 70 20
496 20um. Lauzun Hussars officer (air) 90 40
497 50um. Artillery officer of 3rd Continental Regiment . . . 2·40 1·00
498 60um. Grenadier of Gatinais' Regiment . . . . 3·00 1·25

1976. 10th Anniv of Arab Labour Charter. No. 408 surch **10e ANNIVERSAIRE DE LA CHARTE ARABE DU TRAVAIL** in French and Arabic.

500 12um. on 75f. blue, blk & grn 55 30

186 Mohammed Ali Jinnah

1976. Birth Centenary of Mohammed Ali Jinnah (first Governor-General of Pakistan).
529 **186** 10um. multicoloured . . . 35 20

187 Capsule Assembly

1977. "Viking" Space Mission. Multicoloured.
530 10um. Misson Control (horiz) (postage) 50 15
531 12um. Type **187** 55 20
532 20um. "Viking" in flight (horiz) (air) 80 25
533 50um. "Viking" over Mars (horiz) . . . . 2·00 60
534 60um. Parachute descent . . 2·25 65

188 Bush Hare

1977. Mauritanian Animals. Multicoloured.
536 5um. Type **188** 30 15
537 10um. Golden jackals 65 30
538 12um. Warthogs 90 40
539 14um. Lion and lioness . . . 1·00 50
540 15um. African elephants . . 1·90 80

189 Frederic and Irene Joliot-Curie (Chemistry, 1935)

1977. Nobel Prize-winners. Multicoloured.
541 12um. Type **189** (postage) . . 75 15
542 15um. Emil von Behring and nurse inoculating patient (1901) 75 20
543 14um. George Bernard Shaw and scene from "Androcles and the Lion" (1925) (air) 75 30
544 55um. Thomas Mann and scene from "Joseph and his Brethren" (1929) . . . . . 1·90 60
545 60um. International Red Cross and scene on Western Front (Peace Prize) (1917) . . . . 2·25 70

190 A.P.U. Emblem

1977. 25th Anniv of Arab Postal Union.
547 **190** 12um. multicoloured . . . 45 30

191 Oil Lamp

1977. Pottery from Tegdaoust.
548 **191** 1um. olive, brown and blue 10 10
549 – 2um. mauve, brown & blue 15 10
550 – 5um. orange, brown & blue 25 10
551 – 12um. brown, green and red 55 20
DESIGNS: 2um. Four-handled tureen; 5um. Large jar; 12um. Narrow-necked jug.

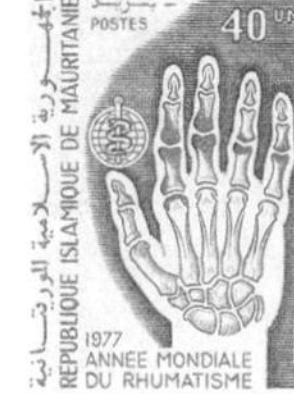

192 Skeleton of Hand

1977. World Rheumatism Year.
552 **192** 40um. orange, brown & grn . . . . 2·00 1·25

193 Holy Kaaba, Mecca

1977. Air. Pilgrimage to Mecca.
553 **193** 12um. multicoloured . . . 60 40

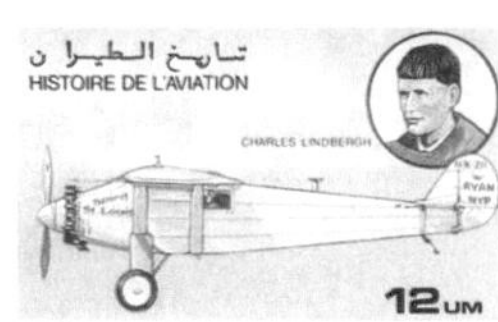

194 Charles Lindbergh and "Spirit of St. Louis"

1977. History of Aviation. Multicoloured.
554 12um. Type **194** 60 15
555 14um. Clement Ader and "Eole" 70 25
556 15um. Louis Bleriot and Bleriot XI 85 25
557 55um. General Italo Balbo and Savoia Marchetti S-55X flying boats . . . . 2·50 70
558 60um. Concorde . . . . . . 2·75 85

195 Dome of the Rock

1977. Palestinian Welfare.
560 **195** 12um. multicoloured . . . 70 30
561 14um. multicoloured . . . 80 35

196 Two Players

1977. World Cup Football Championship—Elimination Rounds. Multicoloured.
562 12um. Type **196** (postage) . . 40 15
563 14um. Sir Alf Ramsey and Wembley Stadium 50 20
564 15um. A "throw-in" 60 20
565 50um. Football and emblems (air) . . . . 2·00 60
566 60um. Eusebio Ferreira . . . 2·40 1·00

197 "Helene Fourment and Her Children" (Rubens)

1977. 400th Birth Anniv of Rubens. Paintings. Multicoloured.
568 12um. Type **197** 50 15
569 14um. "The Marquis of Spinola" 60 20
570 67um. "The Four Philosophers" . . . . . . 2·25 75
571 69um. "Steen Castle and Park" (horiz) . . . . . . 2·50 85

198 Addra Gazelles

1978. Endangered Animals. Multicoloured.
573 5um. Scimitar oryx (horiz) . . 35 15
574 12um. Type **198** 65 25
575 14um. African manatee (horiz) 80 35
576 55um. Barbary sheep . . . . 3·00 1·00
577 60um. African elephant (horiz) . . . . 3·25 1·25
578 100um. Ostrich . . . . . . 4·50 1·75

199 Clasped Hands and President Giscard d'Estaing of France

1978. Air. Franco-African Co-operation. Embossed on foil.
579 **199** 250um. silver . . . . . . 7·00 7·00
580 500um. gold . . . . . . 14·00 14·00

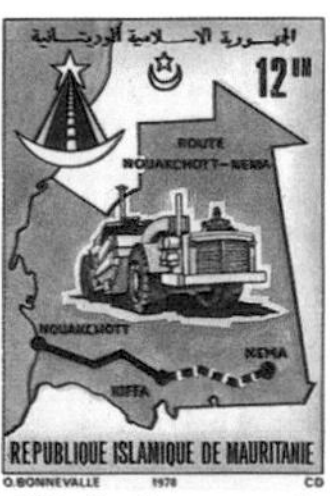

199a Earth-mover and Route Map

200 Footballers

1978. Nouakchott–Nema Highway. Mult.
580a 12um. Type **199a** . . . . . 2·00 1·50
580b 14um. Bulldozer and route map . . . . 2·25 1·75

1978. World Cup Football Championship, Argentina. Multicoloured.
581 12um. Type **200** 40 20
582 14um. World Cup 50 25
583 20um. F.I.F.A. flag and football 85 35

201 Raoul Follereau and St. George fighting Dragon

1978. 25th Anniv of Raoul Follereau Foundation.
585 **201** 12um. brown and green 70 40

202 Emblem and People holding Hands

1978. International Anti-Apartheid Year.
586 – 25um. brown, blue and red 90 60
587 **202** 30um. brown, blue & green . . . . 1·10 70
DESIGN—HORIZ: 25um. Emblem and people behind fence.

203 Charles de Gaulle

1978. Personalities. Multicoloured.
588 12um. Type **203** 90 30
589 14um. King Baudouin of Belgium 90 30
590 55um. Queen Elizabeth II (25th anniv of Coronation) 2·00 90

1978. Air. "Philexafrique" Stamp Exhibition, Libreville (Gabon) (1st issue), and 2nd International Stamp Fair, Essen (West Germany). As T **262** of Niger. Multicoloured.
591 20um. Water rail and Hamburg 1859 ½s. stamp 2·10 1·50
592 20um. Spotted hyena and Mauritania 1967 100f. South African crowned crane stamp . . . . 2·10 1·50
See also Nos. 619/20.

1978. Argentina's Victory in World Cup Football Championship. Nos. 562/6 optd **ARGENTINE–PAYS BAS 3-1** in English and Arabic.
593 **196** 12um. mult (postage) . . 50 25
594 – 14um. multicoloured . . . 55 30
595 – 15um. multicoloured . . . 65 30
596 – 50um. multicoloured (air) 1·75 1·10
597 – 60um. multicoloured . . . 2·25 1·40

205 View of Nouakchott

1978. 20th Anniv of Nouakchott.
599 **205** 12um. multicoloured . . . 45 30

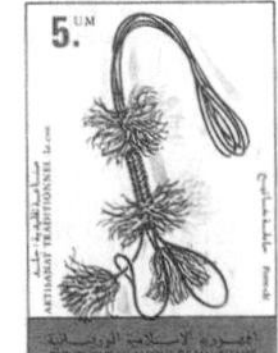

206 Human Rights Emblem

208 Key Chain

207 Wright Flyer I and Clement Ader's Avion III

1978. 30th Anniv of Declaration of Human Rights.
600 **206** 55um. red and blue . . . 1·60 1·25

1979. Air. 75th Anniv of First Powered Flight.
601 **207** 15um. grey, red and blue 1·00 35
602 – 40um. violet, blue & brn 2·00 1·10
DESIGN: 40um. Concorde and Wright Flyer I.

1979. Handicrafts. Multicoloured.
603 5um. Type **208** 25 15
604 7um. Tooth-brush case . . . 30 20
605 10um. Knife sheath 45 25

209 "Market Peasant and Wife"

210 Seated Buddha, Temple of Borobudur

1979. 450th Birth Anniv of Albrecht Durer (artist).
606 **209** 12um. black and red . . . 70 30
607 – 14um. black and red . . . 60 25
608 – 55um. black and red . . . 1·60 75
609 – 60um. black and red . . . 1·90 1·00
DESIGNS: 14um. "Young Peasant and his Wife"; 55um. "Mercenary with Banner"; 60um. "St. George and the Dragon".

1979. U.N.E.S.C.O. Campaign for Preservation of Historic Monuments. Multicoloured.
611 12um. Type **210** 50 30
612 14um. Carthaginian warrior and hunting dog 60 30
613 55um. Erechtheum Caryatid, Acropolis . . . . 1·75 1·25

211 Rowland Hill and Paddle-steamer "Sirius"

1979. Death Centenary of Sir Rowland Hill. Multicoloured.
614 12um. Type **211** 50 25
615 14um. Hill and "Great Republic" (paddle-steamer) 65 25
616 55um. Hill and "Mauretania I" (liner) . . . . 2·00 60
617 60um. Hill and "Stirling Castle" (liner) . . . . . . 2·50 85

212 Satellite over Earth

1979. "Philexafrique" Exhibition, Libreville (2nd issue).
619 – 12um. multicoloured . . . 60 50
620 **212** 30um. red, blue and lilac 1·40 1·25
DESIGN—HORIZ: 12um. Embossed leather cushion cover.

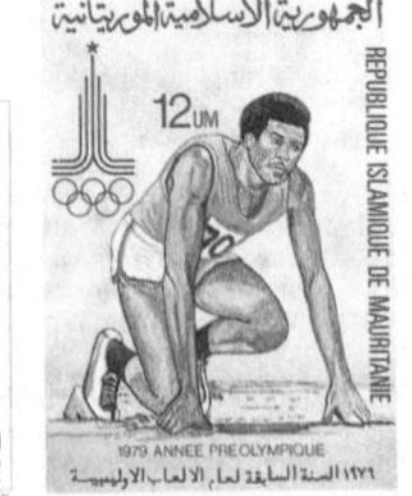

213 Mother and Children

215 Sprinter on Starting-blocks

1979. International Year of the Child. Multicoloured.
621 12um. Type **213** 45 25
622 14um. Mother with sleeping baby 55 35
623 40um. Children playing with ball . . . . 1·50 90

1979. 10th Anniv of "Apollo 11" Moon Landing. Nos. 530/4 optd **ALUNISSAGE APOLLO XI JUILLET 1969**, with Lunar module, or surch also.
624 10um. Mission Control (horiz) (postage) 40 25
625 12um. Type **187** 45 30
626 14um. on 20um. "Viking" in flight (horiz) (air) 60 25
627 50um. "Viking" over Mars (horiz) . . . . 1·60 1·00
628 60um. Parachute descent . . 1·90 1·10

1979. Pre-Olympic Year. Multicoloured.
630 12um. Type **215** 35 15
631 14um. Female runner 40 15
632 55um. Male runner leaving start . . . . 1·50 60
633 60um. Hurdling . . . . . . 1·60 60

215a Skipper

1979. Fishes. Multicoloured.
634a 1um. Type **215a** 10 10
634b 2um. Swordfish 25 15
634c 5um. Tub gurnard 40 20

216 Ice Hockey

1979. Winter Olympic Games, Lake Placid (1980). Ice Hockey. Multicoloured.
635 10um. Type **216** 40 20
636 12um. Saving a goal 45 25
637 14um. Goalkeeper and player 55 25
638 55um. Two players . . . . . 2·00 60
639 60um. Goalkeeper . . . . . 2·25 65
640 100um. Tackle . . . . 3·50 1·25

217 Woman pouring out Tea

1980. Taking Tea.
641 **217** 1um. multicoloured . . . 10 10
642 5um. multicoloured . . . 20 10
643 12um. multicoloured . . . 45 20

218 Koran, World Map and Symbols of Arab Achievements

1980. The Arabs.
644 **218** 12um. multicoloured . . . 40 25
645 15um. multicoloured . . . 50 30

1980. Winter Olympics Medal Winners. Nos. 635/40 optd.
646 10um. **Medaille de bronze SUEDE** 35 20
647 12um. **MEDAILLE DE BRONZE SUEDE** 40 20
648 14um. **Medaille d'argent U.R.S.S.** 45 25
649 55um. **MEDAILLE D'ARGENT U.R.S.S.** . . . 1·50 80
650 60um. **MEDAILLE D'OR ETATS-UNIS** . . . . . . 1·75 90
651 100um. **Medaille d'or ETATS-UNIS** . . . . . . 3·00 1·50

220 Holy Kaaba, Mecca

221 Mother and Child

1980. Pilgrimage to Mecca. Multicoloured.
652 10um. Type **220** 40 20
653 50um. Pilgrims outside Mosque . . . . 1·60 1·10

1980. World Red Cross Societies Day.
654 **221** 20um. multicoloured . . . 70 40

222 Crowd greeting Armed Forces

1980. Armed Forces Festival.
655 **222** 12um. multicoloured . . . 35 20
656 14um. multicoloured . . . 40 25

223 Horse jumping Bar

224 Trees on Map of Mauritania

1980. Olympic Games, Moscow. Multicoloured.
657 10um. Type **223** 30 20
658 20um. Water polo 55 30
659 50um. Horse jumping brick wall (horiz) . . . . 1·40 55
660 70um. Horse jumping stone wall . . . . 1·90 75

1980. Tree Day.
662 **224** 12um. multicoloured . . . 35 20

225 "Rembrandt's Mother"

1980. Paintings by Rembrandt. Multicoloured.
663 10um. "Self-portrait" 30 20
664 20um. Type **225** 75 30
665 50um. "Portrait of a Man in Oriental Costume" . . . . 1·75 55
666 70um. "Titus Lisant" . . . . 2·25 75

226 Footballers

1980. Air. World Cup Football Championship, Spain (1982). Multicoloured.
668 10um. Type **226** 30 20
669 12um. Goalkeeper and players 35 20
670 14um. Goalkeeper catching ball 40 25
671 20um. Fighting for possession 55 30
672 67um. Tackle . . . . 1·90 75

1980. Olympic Medal Winners. Nos. 657/60 optd.
674 10um. **VAINQUEUR KOWALLZYK (POL)** . . 30 20
675 20um. **VAINQUEUR THEURER (AUTR)** . . . 55 30
676 50um. **VAINQUEUR URSS** 1·40 55
677 70um. **VAINQUEUR ROMAN (IT)** . . . . . . 1·90 75

228 "Mastodonte del Giovi", 1853, Italy

1980. Steam Locomotives. Multicoloured.
679 10um. Type **228** 55 15
680 12um. Diesel ore train . . . 60 15
681 14um. Chicago, Milwaukee and St. Paul Railway locomotive No. 810, U.S.A. 75 20
682 20um. Bury steam locomotive, 1837, Great Britain . . . . 1·00 25
683 67um. Locomotive No. 170, France . . . . 3·50 55
684 100um. Berlin–Potsdam line, Germany . . . . 5·25 95

229 Palm Tree, Crescent and Star, Maize and Map

1980. 20th Anniv of Independence.
685 **229** 12um. multicoloured . . . 40 20
686 15um. multicoloured . . . 50 30

230 El Haram Mosque

1981. 15th Century of Hegira. Multicoloured.
687 2um. Type **230** 10 10
688 12um. Medine Mosque . . . 40 20
689 14um. Chinguetti Mosque . . 50 30

231 Space Shuttle in Orbit

1981. Air. Space Shuttle. Multicoloured.
690 12um. Type **231** 40 20
691 20um. Shuttle and space station 85 30
692 50um. Shuttle performing experiment . . . . 1·75 75
693 70um. Shuttle landing . . . . 2·50 1·00

232 "The Harlequin"

1981. Air. Birth Centenary of Pablo Picasso. Multicoloured.
695 12um. Type **232** 50 20
696 20um. "Vase of Flowers" . . 75 30
697 50um. "Three Women at a Fountain" (horiz) . . . . 1·40 75
698 70um. "Dinard Landscape" (horiz) . . . . 2·25 1·00
699 100um. "Le Dejeuner sur l'Herbe" (horiz) . . . . . 3·00 1·50

233 I.Y.D.P. Emblem

1981. International Year of Disabled People.
700 **233** 12um. violet, gold and blue 45 30

234 Open Landau

1981. British Royal Wedding. Multicoloured.
701 14um. Type **234** 40 20
702 18um. Light carriage 45 20
703 77um. Closed coupe . . . . 1·40 1·10

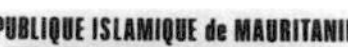

235 George Washington

1981. Bicentenary of Battles of Yorktown and Chesapeake Bay. Multicoloured.
705 14um. Type **235** 45 25
706 18um. Admiral de Grasse . . 55 25
707 63um. Surrender of Cornwallis at Yorktown (horiz) . . . . 1·75 95
708 81um. Battle of Chesapeake Bay (horiz) . . . . 2·25 1·50

236 Columbus and "Pinta"

1981. 450th Death Anniv of Christopher Columbus. Multicoloured.
709 19um. Type **236** . . . . . . 1·00 40
710 55um. Columbus and "Santa Maria" . . . . 2·75 1·10

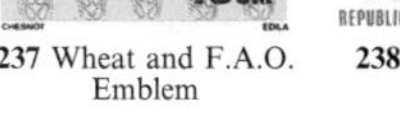

237 Wheat and F.A.O. Emblem

238 Kemal Ataturk

1981. World Food Day.
711 **237** 19um. multicoloured . . . 60 40

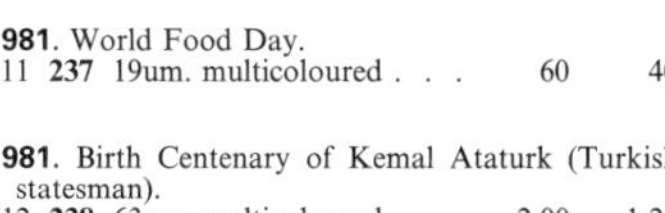

1981. Birth Centenary of Kemal Ataturk (Turkish statesman).
712 **238** 63um. multicoloured . . . 2·00 1·25

239 Eastern White Pelicans

1981. Birds of the Arguin. Multicoloured.
713 2um. Type **239** 40 15
714 18um. Greater flamingoes . . 1·75 80

240 Hand holding Torn Flag

1981. Battle of Karameh Commemoration.
715 **240** 14um. multicoloured . . . 45 30

241 "Dermochelys coiacer"

1981. Turtles. Multicoloured.
716 1um. Type **241** 30 15
717 3um. "Chelonia mydas" . . . 40 15
718 4um. "Eretmochclys imbricata" 50 15

242 Sea Scouts

1982. 75th Anniv of Boy Scout Movement. Multicoloured.
719 14um. Type **242** 55 25
720 19um. Scouts boarding rowing boat 90 35
721 22um. Scouts in rowing boat 1·00 40
722 92um. Scouts in yacht . . . 3·00 1·25

243 Deusenberg, 1921

1982. 75th Anniv of French Grand Prix Motor Race. Multicoloured.
724 7um. Type **243** 50 20
725 12um. Alfa Romeo, 1932 . . 60 20
726 14um. Juan Fangio 75 35
727 18um. Renault, 1979 . . . . 1·00 40
728 19um. Niki Lauda . . . . . 1·00 45

244 A.P.U. Emblem

245 Hexagonal Pattern

1982. 30th Anniv of Arab Postal Union.
730 **244** 14um. orange and brown 45 30

1982. World Telecommunications Day.
731 **245** 21um. multicoloured . . . 65 45

246 Environmental Emblem on Map

1982. 10th Anniv of U.N. Environmental Programme.
732 **246** 14um. blue and light blue 45 30

247 Princess of Wales

1982. 21st Birthday of Princess of Wales. Mult.
733 21um. Type **247** 75 35
734 77um. Princess of Wales (different) . . . . 2·40 1·10

248 Straw Hut

1982. Traditional Houses. Multicoloured.
736 14um. Type **248** 45 30
737 18um. Thatched hut 55 45
738 19um. Tent 60 45

1982. Birth of Prince William of Wales. Nos. 701/3 surch **NAISSANCE ROYALE 1982**.
739 14um. Type **234** 45 35
740 18um. Light carriage 55 40
741 77um. Closed coupe . . . . 2·40 1·25

1982. Air. World Cup Football Championship Results. Nos. 668/72 optd **ITALIE 3 ALLEMAGNE (R.F.A.) 1**.
743 10um. Type **226** 40 25
744 12um. Goalkeeper punching ball 40 30
745 14um. Goalkeeper catching ball 45 30
746 20um. Three players 70 40
747 67um. Tackle . . . . 2·25 1·40

251 Cattle at Collinaire Dam, Hodh El Gharbi

1982. Agricultural Development.
749 14um. Type **251** . . . . . . 1·25 1·10
750 18um. Irrigation canal, Gorgol . . . . 1·75 1·25

252 Desert Rose

1982. Desert Rose.
751 **252** 21um. multicoloured . . . 1·50 1·00

253 Montgolfier Balloon, 1783

1983. Bicent of Manned Flight. Multicoloured.
752 14um. Type **253** 65 20
753 18um. Charles's hydrogen balloon ascent, 1783 (horiz) 65 30
754 19um. Goodyear Aerospace airship 65 30
755 55um. Nieuport 11 "Bebe" biplane (horiz) . . . . . . 1·75 70
756 63um. Concorde (horiz) . . . 3·00 1·00
757 77um. "Apollo 11" on Moon 2·50 1·00
No. 754 is wrongly inscribed "Zeppelin".

254 Ouadane

1983. Protection of Ancient Sites. Multicoloured.
758 14um. Type **254** 40 25
759 18um. Chinguetti 50 30
760 24um. Oualata 70 45
761 30um. Tichitt . . . . 1·00 55

255 Manuscript

256 I.M.O. Emblem

1983. Ancient Manuscripts. Multicoloured.
762 2um. Type **255** 10 10
763 5um. Decorated manuscript 15 15
764 7um. Shield-shaped patterned manuscript 25 20

1983. 25th Anniv of I.M.O.
765 **256** 18um. multicoloured . . . 50 30

257 W.C.Y. Emblem

1983. World Communications Year.
766 **257** 14um. multicoloured . . . 55 30

258 Customs Emblems

1983. 30th Anniv of Customs Co-operation Council.
767 **258** 14um. multicoloured . . . 45 30

259 Pilatre de Rozier and Montgolfier Balloon

260 Grinding Stone

1983. Bicentenary of Manned Flight. Mult.

768 10um. Type **259** (postage) . . 40 20
769 14um. John Wise and balloon "Atlantic" 50 30
770 25um. Charles Renard and Renard and Krebs' airship "La France" (horiz) . . . 85 35
771 100um. Henri Juillot and Lebaudy-Juillot airship "Patrie" (horiz) (air) . . . 3·75 1·25

1983. Prehistoric Grindstones. Multicoloured.

773 10um. Type **260** 50 30
774 14um. Pestle and mortar . . 75 40
775 18um. Grinding dish . . . . 1·00 60

261 Basketball

1983. Pre-Olympic Year. Multicoloured.

776 1um. Type **261** (postage) . . 10 10
777 20um. Wrestling 60 25
778 50um. Show-jumping . . . . 1·50 80
779 77um. Running (air) . . . . 2·25 1·25

262 Lord Baden-Powell (founder of Scout Movement)

1984. Celebrities. Multicoloured.

781 5um. Type **262** (postage) . . 15 10
782 14um. Goethe (poet) 45 20
783 25um. Rubens and detail of painting "The Virgin and Child" 75 45
784 100um. P. Harris (founder of Rotary International) (air) 3·00 1·40

263 Blue-finned Tuna

1984. Fishing Resources. Multicoloured.

786 1um. Type **263** 10 10
787 2um. Atlantic mackerel . . . 15 10
788 5um. European hake 40 15
789 14um. Atlantic horse-mackerel . . . . 1·10 45
790 18um. Building a fishing boat 1·25 55

264 Durer and "Madonna and Child"

1984. Multicoloured.

791 10um. Type **264** (postage) . . 35 20
792 12um. "Apollo 11" and astronaut (15th anniv of first manned Moon landing) 40 25
793 50um. Chess pieces and globe 2·00 80
794 77um. Prince and Princess of Wales (air) . . . . 2·25 1·40

265 Start of Race

1984. Olympic Games, Los Angeles. Multicoloured.

796 14um. Type **265** 40 25
797 18um. Putting the shot (vert) 55 25
798 19um. Hurdling (vert) . . . 55 25
799 44um. Throwing the javelin (vert) . . . . 1·25 65
800 77um. High jumping . . . . 2·00 1·25

266 Feeding Dehydrated Child from Glass

1984. Infant Survival Campaign. Multicoloured.

802 1um. Type **266** 10 10
803 4um. Breast-feeding baby . . 15 10
804 10um. Vaccinating baby . . . 30 20
805 14um. Weighing baby 45 30

267 Aerial View of Complex

1984. Nouakchott Olympic Complex.

806 **267** 14um. multicoloured . . . 50 40

268 Tents and Mosque Courtyard

1984. Pilgrimage to Mecca. Multicoloured.

807 14um. Type **268** 50 30
808 18um. Tents and courtyard (different) 75 40

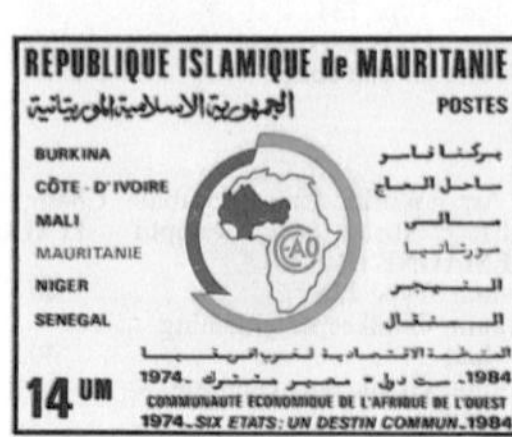

269 Emblem

1984. 10th Anniv of West African Economic Community.

809 **269** 14um. multicoloured . . . 45 30

270 S. van den Berg (windsurfing)

1984. Air. Olympic Games Sailing Gold Medallists. Multicoloured.

810 14um. Type **270** 55 25
811 18um. R. Coutts ("Finn" class) 75 25
812 19um. Spain ("470" class) . . 1·00 25
813 44um. U.S.A. ("Soling" class) 1·90 60

1984. Drought Relief. No. 537 surch **Aide au Sahel 84**.

815 18um. on 10um. multicoloured 70 50

272 Profiles and Emblem

1985. 15th Anniv of Technical and Cultural Co-operation Agency.

816 **272** 18um. blue, deep blue and red 60 45

273 Animal drinking in Water Droplet and Skeletons

1985. Campaign against Drought. Multicoloured.

817 14um. Type **273** . . . . . . 1·10 50
818 18um. Lush trees by river in water droplet and dead trees . . . . 1·10 50

274 Replanting Trees

1985. Anti-desertification Campaign. Multicoloured.

819 10um. Type **274** 35 25
820 14um. Animals fleeing from forest fire . . . . 1·60 85
821 18um. Planting grass to hold sand dunes 65 50

275 Emblem

1985. 30th Anniv (1984) of Arab League.

822 **275** 14um. green and black . . 45 30

276 Map, I.Y.Y. Emblem and Youths

1985. Air. "Philexafrique" Stamp Exhibition, Lome. Multicoloured.

823 40um. Type **276** (International Youth Year) 1·50 1·25
824 40um. Nouadhibou oil refinery . . . . 1·50 1·25

277 Bonaparte's Gulls

1985. Air. Birth Bicentenary of John J. Audubon (ornithologist). Multicoloured.

825 14um. Wester tanager and scarlet tanager . . . . . . 1·25 20
826 18um. Type **277** . . . . . . 1·50 25
827 19um. Blue jays . . . . . . 1·75 35
828 44um. Black skimmer . . . . 4·50 1·40

278 Locomotive "Adler", 1835

1985. Anniversaries. Multicoloured.

830 12um. Type **278** (150th anniv of German railways) . . . 2·25 60
831 18um. Class 10 steam locomotive, 1956 (150th anniv of German railways) 2·50 60
832 44um. Johann Sebastian Bach (composer, 300th birth anniv European Music Year) . . . . 1·60 70
833 77um. Georg Frederick Handel (composer, 300th birth anniv European Music Year) . . . . 2·75 1·25
834 90um. Statue of Liberty (centenary) (vert) . . . . . 2·75 1·40

279 Globe and Emblem

1985. World Food Day.

836 **279** 18um. multicoloured . . . 55 35

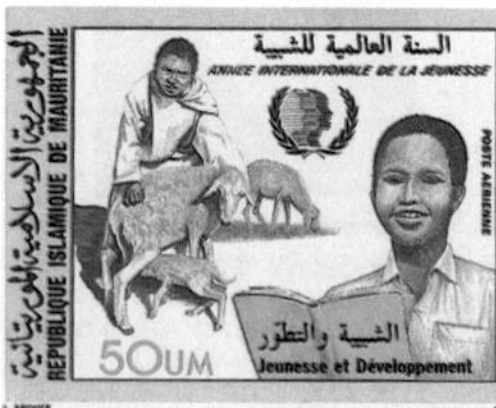

280 Tending Sheep and reading Book

1985. Air. "Philexafrique" Stamp Exhibition, Lome, Togo (2nd issue). Multicoloured.

837 50um. Type **280** . . . . . . 2·00 1·50
838 50um. Dock, iron ore mine and diesel train . . . . . 3·50 90

281 Map showing Industries

1985. 25th Anniv of Independence.

839 **281** 18um. multicoloured . . . 60 40

282 Development

1986. International Youth Year. Multicoloured.
840 18um. Type **282** 60 30
841 22um. Re-afforestation (voluntary work) 70 40
842 25um. Hands reaching from globe to dove (peace) (vert) 75 50

283 Latecoere Seaplane "Comte de la Vaulx" and Map

1986. Air. 55th Anniv (1985) of First Commercial South Atlantic Flight. Multicoloured.
843 18um. Type **283** 75 35
844 50um. Piper Twin Commanche airplanes crossing between maps of Africa and South America 2·00 1·25

284 Toujounine Earth Receiving Station

1986.
845 **284** 25um. multicoloured . . . 90 50

285 Heads of Mother and Pup

1986. World Wildlife Fund. Mediterranean Monk Seal. Multicoloured.
846 2um. Type **285** 50 30
847 5um. Mother and pup on land 75 50
848 10um. Mother and pup swimming . . . . 1·00 75
849 18um. Seal family . . . . . 2·00 1·00

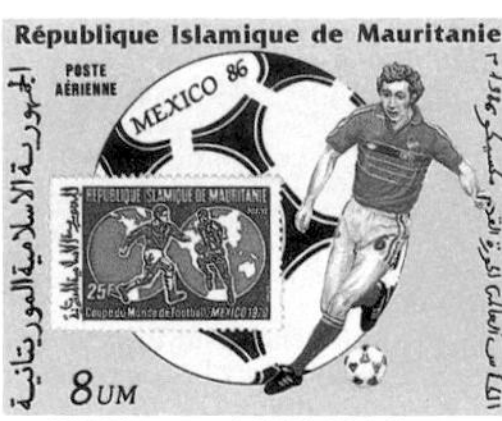

286 Player and 1970 25f. Stamp

1986. Air. World Cup Football Championship, Mexico. Multicoloured.
851 8um. Type **286** 25 10
852 18um. Player and 1970 30f. stamp 60 20
853 22um. Player and 1970 70f. stamp 70 30
854 25um. Player and 1970 150f. stamp 85 35
855 40um. Player and World Cup trophy on "stamp" . . . . 1·25 60

287 Weaving

1986.
857 **287** 18um. multicoloured . . . 60 35

288 Emblem, Boeing 737, Douglas DC-10 and Map

1986. Air. 25th Anniv of Air Afrique.
858 **288** 26um. multicoloured . . . 1·00 40

289 Indian, "Santa Maria" and Route Map

1986. 500th Anniv (1992) of Discovery of America by Christopher Columbus. Multicoloured.
859 2um. Type **289** (postage) . . 10 10
860 22um. Indian, "Nina" and map 65 30
861 35um. Indian, "Pinta" and map . . . . 1·10 50
862 150um. Indian, map and Christopher Columbus (air) 4·50 1·60

290 J. H. Dort, Comet Picture and Space Probe "Giotto"

1986. Appearance of Halley's Comet. Multicoloured.
864 5um. Type **290** (postage) . . 15 10
865 18um. William Huggins (astronomer) and "Ariane" space rocket 60 20
866 26um. E. J. Opik and space probes "Giotto" and "Vega" 80 30
867 80um. F. L. Whipple and "Planet A" space probe (air) . . . . 2·75 1·25

291 Astronauts

1986. "Challenger" Astronauts Commemoration. Multicoloured.
869 7um. Type **291** (postage) . . 20 10
870 22um. Judith Resnik and astronaut 60 30
871 32um. Ellison Onizuka and Ronald McNair . . . . . 1·00 45
872 43um. Christa Corrigan McAuliffe (air) . . . . . . 1·50 60

292 Red Seabream

1986. Fishes and Birds. Multicoloured.
874 4um. Type **292** 30 15
875 22um. White spoonbills . . . 1·75 65
876 32um. Bridled terns . . . . 2·00 1·00
877 98um. Sea-trout . . . . . . 5·50 3·00
See also Nos. 896/900.

293 Arrow through Victim **294** Fisherman

1986. 4th Anniv of Massacre of Palestinian Refugees in Sabra and Shatila Camps, Lebanon.
878 **293** 22um. black, gold and red 80 40

1986. World Food Day.
879 **294** 22um. multicoloured . . . 1·25 40

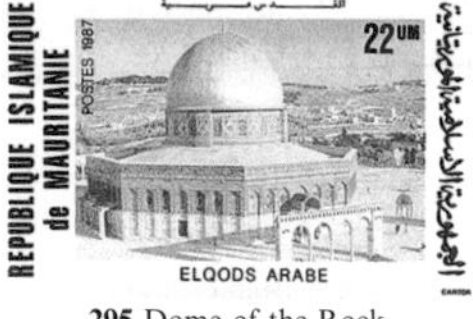

295 Dome of the Rock

1987. "Arab Jerusalem".
880 **295** 22um. multicoloured . . . 80 40

296 Boxing

1987. Air. Olympic Games, Seoul (1988) (1st issue). Multicoloured.
881 30um. Type **296** 80 40
882 40um. Judo . . . . 1·00 55
883 50um. Fencing . . . . 1·25 70
884 75um. Wrestling . . . . . . 2·00 1·10
See also Nos. 902/5.

297 Cordoue Mosque

1987. 1200th Anniv of Cordoue Mosque.
886 **297** 30um. multicoloured . . . 1·00 50

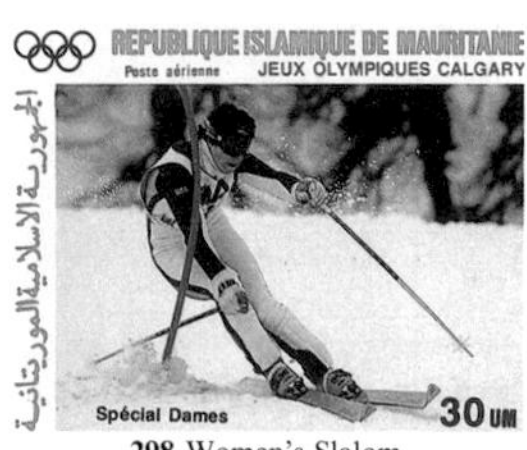

298 Women's Slalom

1987. Air. Winter Olympic Games, Calgary (1988). Multicoloured.
887 30um. Type **298** . . . . . . 1·10 40
888 40um. Men's speed skating 1·40 55
889 50um. Ice hockey . . . . . 1·60 75
890 75um. Women's downhill skiing . . . . 2·50 1·10

299 Adults at Desk

1987. Literacy Campaign. Multicoloured.
892 18um. Type **299** 60 40
893 20um. Adults and children reading 80 50

300 People queueing for Treatment

1987. World Health Day.
894 **300** 18um. multicoloured . . . 70 40

301 Map within Circle

1988. National Population and Housing Census.
895 **301** 20um. multicoloured . . . 60 35

1988. Fishes and Birds. Horiz designs as T **292**. Multicoloured.
896 1um. Small-horned blenny . . 10 10
897 7um. Grey triggerfish 40 15
898 15um. Skipjack tuna 70 30
899 18um. Great cormorants . . 95 65
900 80um. Royal terns . . . . . 4·00 2·75

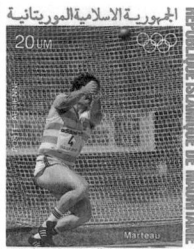

302 People with Candles **303** Hammer Throwing

1988. 40th Anniv of W.H.O.
901 **302** 30um. multicoloured . . . 1·00 40

1988. Air. Olympic Games, Seoul (2nd issue). Multicoloured.
902 20um. Type **303** 50 25
903 24um. Discus 60 30
904 30um. Putting the shot . . . 80 40
905 150um. Javelin throwing . . 4·00 2·10

1988. Winter Olympic Games Gold Medal Winners. Nos. 887/90 optd.
907 30um. Optd **Medaille d'or Vreni Schneider (Suisse)** . . 1·00 50
908 40um. Optd **Medaille d'or 1500m. Andre Hoffman (R.D.A.)** . . . . 1·10 75
909 50um. Optd **Medaille d'or U.R.S.S.** . . . . 1·50 1·00
910 75um. Optd **Medaille d'or Marina Kiehl (R.F.A.)** . . . 2·25 1·50

305 Flags and Globe

1988. 75th Anniv of Arab Scout Movement.
912 **305** 35um. multicoloured . . . 1·50 55

306 Men at Ballot Box

1988. 1st Municipal Elections. Multicoloured.
913 20um. Type **306** 60 30
914 24um. Woman at ballot box 80 40

307 Emblem

308 Ploughing with Oxen

1988. 25th Anniv of Organization of African Unity.
915 **307** 40um. multicoloured . . . 1·25 60

1988. 10th Anniv of International Agricultural Development Fund.
916 **308** 35um. multicoloured . . . 1·10 70

309 Port Activities

1989. 1st Anniv of Nouakchott Free Port.
917 **309** 24um. multicoloured . . . 1·25 65

310 "Heliothis armigera"

311 "Nomadacris septemfasciata"

1989. Plant Pests. Multicoloured.
918 2um. Type **310** 15 15
919 6um. "Aphis gossypii" . . . 20 15
920 10um. "Agrotis ypsilon" . . 35 15
921 20um. "Chilo" sp. 75 30
922 24um. "Plitella xylostella" . . 85 40
923 30um. "Henosepilachna elaterii" . . . . 1·25 55
924 42um. "Trichoplusia ni" . . 1·50 70

1989. Locusts. Multicoloured.
925 5um. Type **311** 15 10
926 20um. Locusts mating . . . 60 30
927 24um. Locusts emerging from chrysallis 70 40
928 40um. Locusts flying . . . . 1·25 75
929 88um. Locust (different) . . . 3·00 1·25

312 Men of Different Races embracing

313 Footballers

1989. "Philexfrance '89" Int Stamp Exn, Paris, and Bicent of French Revolution.
930 **312** 35um. multicoloured . . . 1·10 60

1989. World Cup Football Championship, Italy (1990) (1st issue).
931 **313** 20um. multicoloured . . . 1·00 40
See also Nos. 937/41.

314 Attan'eem Migat, Mecca

1989. Pilgrimage to Mecca.
932 **314** 20um. multicoloured . . . 75 30

315 Emblem 317 Youths

316 Carpet

1989. 25th Anniv of African Development Bank.
933 **315** 37um. black and mauve 1·00 50

1989.
934 **316** 50um. multicoloured . . . 1·50 80

1989. 2nd Anniv of Palestinian "Intifada" Movement.
935 **317** 35um. multicoloured . . . 1·25 50

318 Member Countries' Leaders (½-size illustration)

1990. 1st Anniv of Arab Maghreb Union.
936 **318** 50um. multicoloured . . . 1·50 70

319 Players

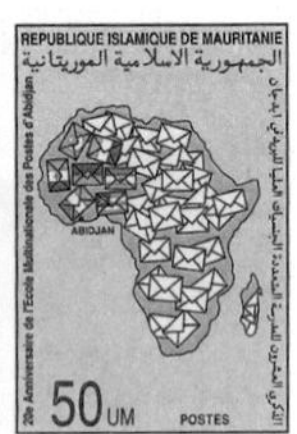
320 Envelopes on Map

1990. Air. World Cup Football Championship, Italy (2nd issue).
937 **319** 50um. multicoloured . . . 1·50 50
938 – 60um. multicoloured . . . 1·90 60
939 – 70um. multicoloured . . . 2·00 75
940 – 90um. multicoloured . . . 2·75 75
941 – 150um. multicoloured . . 4·50 1·25
DESIGNS: 60 to 150um. Show footballers.

1990. 20th Anniv of Multinational Postal Training School, Abidjan.
942 **320** 50um. multicoloured . . . 1·10 50

321 Books and Desk

1990. International Literacy Year.
943 **321** 60um. multicoloured . . . 1·75 1·00

322 Maps and Earth-moving Vehicles

1990. Mineral Resources.
944 **322** 60um. multicoloured . . . 2·75 1·25

323 Dressage

324 Emblem

1990. Olympic Games, Barcelona (1992). Mult.
945 5um. Type **323** (postage) . . 20 15
946 50um. Archery . . . . 1·40 40
947 60um. Throwing the hammer 1·50 50
948 75um. Football . . . . . . 2·00 50
949 90um. Basketball . . . . . . 2·75 65
950 220um. Table tennis (air) . . 6·00 1·40

1990. 2nd Anniv of Declaration of State of Palestine.
952 **324** 85um. multicoloured . . . 1·75 1·10

325 Camp

1990. Integration of Repatriates from Senegal. Multicoloured.
953 50um. Type **325** 90 60
954 75um. Women's sewing group 1·25 1·00
955 85um. Water collection . . . 1·40 1·00

326 Map, Dove and Mandela

1990. Release from South African Prison of Nelson Mandela.
956 **326** 85um. multicoloured . . . 1·60 1·10

327 Downhill skiing

1990. Winter Olympic Games, Albertville (1992). Multicoloured.
957 60um. Type **327** (postage) . . 1·00 60
958 75um. Cross-country skiing 1·50 75
959 90um. Ice hockey . . . . . 1·75 95
960 220um. Figure skating (pairs) (air) . . . . 3·75 2·25

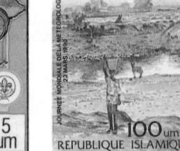

328 Blue Leg 330 Woman carrying Bucket of Water

329 Dish Aerials and Transmitting Tower

1991. Scouts, Fungi and Butterflies. Multicoloured.
962 5um. Type **328** (postage) . . 40 20
963 50um. "Agaricus bitorquis edulis" . . . . 2·50 80
964 60um. "Bunea alcinoe" (butterfly) . . . . 2·25 75
965 90um. "Salamis cytora" (butterfly) . . . . 2·75 1·10
966 220um. "Bronze boletus" . . 6·50 3·00
967 75um. "Cyrestis camillus" (butterfly) (air) . . . . . . 2·50 85

1991. 30th Anniv of Independence. Multicoloured.
968 50um. Type **329** . . . . . . 1·00 65
969 60um. Container ship in dock 2·00 85
970 100um. Workers in field . . . 1·75 1·00

1991. World Meteorological Day.
972 **330** 100um. multicoloured . . 1·75 1·10

331 Health Centre

1991. 20th Anniv of Medecins sans Frontieres (international medical relief organization).
973 **331** 60um. multicoloured . . . 70 45

332 Cats

1991. Domestic Animals. Multicoloured.
974 50um. Type **332** 75 35
975 60um. Basenji dog . . . . . 1·00 45

333 Globe and Stylized Figures

1991. World Population Day.
976 **333** 90um. multicoloured . . . 1·00 60

334 Blind Woman with Sight restored

1991. Anti-blindness Campaign.
977 **334** 50um. multicoloured . . . 55 35

335 Nouakchott Electricity Station

1991. 2nd Anniv of Nouakchott Electricity Station.
978 **335** 50um. multicoloured . . . 55 35

336 Quarrying

1993. Mineral Exploitation, Haoudat. Multicoloured.
979 50um. Type **336** 75 35
980 60um. Dry land 85 40

337 Camel Train

338 Palestinians

1993.

No.	Type	Description	Unused	Used
981	337	50um. multicoloured	55	35
982		60um. multicoloured	65	40

1993. Palestinian "Intifada" Movement. Multicoloured.

No.	Type	Description	Unused	Used
983		50um. Type **338**	55	35
984		60um. Palestinian children by fire (horiz)	65	40

339 Four-man Bobsleighing
340 Soldier Field, Chicago

1993. Winter Olympic Games, Lillehammer. Multicoloured.

No.	Type	Description	Unused	Used
985		10um. Type **339**	10	10
986		50um. Luge	55	35
987		60um. Figure skating	65	40
988		80um. Skiing	85	55
989		220um. Cross-country skiing	2·40	1·50

1994. World Cup Football Championship, U.S.A. Players and Stadiums. Multicoloured.

No.	Type	Description	Unused	Used
991		10um. Type **340**	10	10
992		50um. Foxboro Stadium, Boston	50	30
993		60um. Robert F. Kennedy Stadium, Washington D.C.	65	40
994		90um. Stanford Stadium, San Francisco	95	60
995		220um. Giant Stadium, New York	2·25	1·40

341 Anniversary Emblem and 1962 15f. Stamp

1995. 50th Anniv of U.N.O.

No.	Type	Description	Unused	Used
997	341	60um. multicoloured	60	40

342 Stabilizing Desert
345 Weaving

1995. 50th Anniv of F.A.O. Multicoloured.

No.	Type	Description	Unused	Used
998		50um. Type **342**	50	30
999		60um. Fishermen launching boat	60	40
1000		90um. Planting crops	85	55

1995. Crafts. Multicoloured.

No.	Type	Description	Unused	Used
1006		50um. Type **345**	30	15
1007		60um. Metalwork	35	20

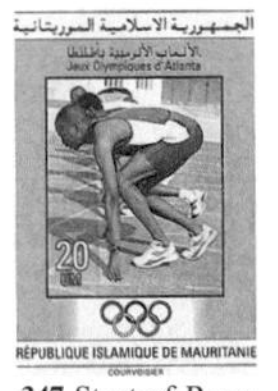

346 Door
347 Start of Race

1995. Tourism. Re-vitalization of Ancient Towns. Multicoloured.

No.	Type	Description	Unused	Used
1008		10um. Type **346**	10	10
1009		20um. Arch and rubble	10	10
1010		40um. Town in desert	25	15
1011		50um. Door in ornate wall	30	15

1996. Olympic Games, Atlanta, U.S.A. Mult.

No.	Type	Description	Unused	Used
1012		20um. Type **347**	10	10
1013		30um. Start of race (horiz)	15	10
1014		40um. Running in lane	25	15
1015		50um. Long-distance race (horiz)	30	15

348 Beaded Locks and Headdress
349 Ball-in-Pot Game

1996. Traditional Hairstyles. Multicoloured.

No.	Type	Description	Unused	Used
1016		50um. Type **348**	30	15
1017		60um. Woman with hair adornments	35	20

1996. Traditional Games. Multicoloured.

No.	Type	Description	Unused	Used
1018		50um. Type **349**	30	15
1019		60um. Strategy game with spherical and conical pieces (horiz)	35	20
1020		90um. Pegs-in-board game (horiz)	50	30

350 Family

1996. 50th Anniv of United Nations Children's Fund. The Rights of the Child. Showing children's drawings. Multicoloured.

No.	Type	Description	Unused	Used
1021		50um. Type **350**	30	15
1022		60um. Boy in wheelchair	35	20

OFFICIAL STAMPS

O 41 Cross of Trarza
O 179

1961.

No.	Type	Description	Unused	Used
O150	O 41	1f. purple and blue	10	10
O151		3f. myrtle and red	10	10
O152		5f. brown and green	10	10
O153		10f. blue and turquoise	20	10
O154		15f. orange and blue	30	15
O155		20f. green and myrtle	35	20
O156		25f. red and orange	40	30
O157		30f. green and purple	45	30
O158		50f. sepia and red	1·00	45
O159		100f. blue and orange	1·60	75
O160		200f. red and green	3·00	1·60

1976.

No.	Type	Description	Unused	Used
O502	O 179	1um. multicoloured	10	10
O503		2um. multicoloured	15	10
O504		5um. multicoloured	20	15
O505		10um. multicoloured	40	20
O506		12um. multicoloured	55	30
O507		40um. multicoloured	1·75	1·00
O508		50um. multicoloured	2·25	1·25

POSTAGE DUE STAMPS

1906. Stamps of 1906 optd **T** in a triangle.

No.	Type	Description	Unused	Used
D18	I	5c. green and red	—	32·00
D19		10c. pink and blue	—	32·00
D20	J	20c. black and red on blue	—	52·00
D21		25c. blue and red	—	52·00
D22		30c. brown & red on pink	—	£120
D23		40c. red on blue	—	£500
D24		50c. violet and red	—	£120
D25	K	1f. black and red on blue	—	£180

1906. "Natives" key-type inscr "MAURITANIE" in blue (10, 30c.) or red (others).

No.	Type	Description	Unused	Used
D25	L	5c. green	1·25	1·10
D26		10c. purple	2·00	1·90
D27		15c. blue on blue	4·00	2·50
D28		20c. black on yellow	4·75	7·75
D29		30c. red on cream	6·75	14·50
D30		50c. violet	10·00	21·00
D31		60c. black on buff	7·25	11·50
D32		1f. black on pink	14·00	23·00

1914. "Figure" key-type inscr "MAURITANIE".

No.	Type	Description	Unused	Used
D35	M	5c. green	10	65
D36		10c. red	15	25
D37		15c. grey	15	1·75
D38		20c. brown	15	2·25
D39		30c. blue	30	2·50
D40		50c. black	30	2·25
D41		60c. orange	20	1·90
D42		1f. violet	35	2·25

1927. Surch in figures.

No.	Type	Description	Unused	Used
D67	M	2f. on 1f. purple	70	4·25
D68		3f. on 1f. brown	65	4·50

D 40 Qualata Motif

D 180

D 55 Ruppell's Griffon

1961.

No.	Type	Description	Unused	Used
D150	D 40	1f. yellow and purple	10	10
D151		2f. grey and red	10	10
D152		5f. pink and red	20	15
D153		10f. green and myrtle	25	15
D154		15f. brown and drab	30	15
D155		20f. blue and red	35	20
D156		25f. red and green	55	35

1963. Birds. Multicoloured.

No.	Type	Description	Unused	Used
D177		50c. Type D **55**	45	15
D178		50c. Common crane	45	15
D179		1f. Eastern white pelican	55	20
D180		1f. Garganey	55	20
D181		2f. Golden oriole	80	25
D182		2f. Variable sunbird	80	25
D183		5f. Great snipe	85	45
D184		5f. Common shoveler	85	45
D185		10f. Vulturine guineafowl	1·40	80
D186		10f. Black stork	1·40	80
D187		15f. Grey heron	1·60	1·25
D188		15f. White stork	1·60	1·25
D189		20f. Paradise whydah	2·10	1·40
D190		20f. Red-legged partridge	2·10	1·40
D191		25f. Little stint	2·75	1·75
D192		25f. Arabian bustard	2·75	1·75

1976.

No.	Type	Description	Unused	Used
D509	D 180	1um. multicoloured	10	10
D510		3um. multicoloured	15	15
D511		10um. multicoloured	35	35
D512		12um. multicoloured	40	40
D513		20um. multicoloured	70	70

APPENDIX

The following stamps have either been issued in excess of postal needs or have not been available to the public in a reasonable quantities at face value. Such stamps may later be given full listing if there is evidence of regular postal use.

1962.

World Refugee Year (1960). Optd on 1960 Definitive issue, 30, 50, 60f.

Olympic Games in Rome (1960) and Tokyo (1964). Surch on 1960 Definitive issue 75f. on 15f., 75f. on 20f.

European Steel and Coal Community and Exploration of Iron-ore in Mauritania. Optd on 1960 Definitive issue. Air 500f.

Malaria Eradication. Optd on 1960 Definitive issue. Air. 100, 200f.

MAURITIUS — Pt. 1

An island in the Indian Ocean, east of Madagascar. Attained self-government on 1 September 1967, and became independent on 12 March 1968.

1847. 12 pence = 1 shilling;
20 shillings = 1 pound.
1878. 100 cents = 1 rupee.

1 ("POST OFFICE")
2 ("POST PAID")

1847. Imperf.

No.	Type	Description	Unused	Used
1	1	1d. red	—	£450000
2		2d. blue	—	£550000

1848. Imperf.

No.	Type	Description	Unused	Used
23	2	1d. red	£1700	£400
25		2d. blue	£2250	£600

3
5

1854. Surch **FOUR-PENCE**. Imperf.

No.	Type	Description	Unused	Used
26	3	4d. green	£1000	£400

1858. No value on stamps. Imperf.

No.	Type	Description	Unused	Used
27	3	(4d.) green	£425	£200
28		(6d.) red	32·00	60·00
29		(9d.) purple	£550	£200

1859. Imperf.

No.	Type	Description	Unused	Used
32	5	6d. blue	£600	38·00
33		6d. black	22·00	42·00
34		1s. red	£2000	45·00
35		1s. green	£500	£120

6
8

1859. Imperf.

No.	Type	Description	Unused	Used
39	6	2d. blue	£1400	£450

1859. Imperf.

No.	Type	Description	Unused	Used
42	8	1d. red	£3750	£800
44		2d. blue	£2000	£450

9
10

1860.

No.	Type	Description	Unused	Used
56	9	1d. purple	65·00	11·00
57		1d. brown	85·00	7·00
60		2d. blue	80·00	8·00
61a		3d. red	50·00	11·00
62		4d. red	80·00	3·25
65		6d. green	£130	4·75
50		6d. grey	£250	90·00
63		6d. violet	£200	27·00
51		9d. purple	£110	38·00
66		9d. green	£130	£200
67	10	10d. red	£250	35·00
70	9	1s. yellow	£180	12·00
53		1s. green	£550	£150
69		1s. blue	£130	21·00
71		5s. mauve	£160	55·00

1862. Perf.

No.	Type	Description	Unused	Used
54	5	6d. black	21·00	60·00
55		1s. green	£1900	£325

HALF PENNY
(11)

HALF PENNY
(13)

1876. Surcharged with T **11**.

No.	Type	Description	Unused	Used
76	9	½d. on 9d. purple	8·50	13·00
77	10	½d. on 10d. red	1·75	18·00

1877. Surch with T **13**.

No.	Type	Description	Unused	Used
79	10	½d. on 10d. red	4·25	29·00

1877. Surch in words.

No.	Type	Description	Unused	Used
80	9	1d. on 4d. red	9·00	14·00
82		1s. on 5s. mauve	£200	£100

1878. Surch.

No.	Type	Description	Unused	Used
83	10	2c. red	7·50	5·00
84	9	4c. on 1d. brown	13·00	5·00
85		8c. on 2d. blue	70·00	1·75
86		13c. on 3d. red	12·00	27·00
87		17c. on 4d. red	£150	2·50
88		25c. on 6d. blue	£200	5·00
89		38c. on 9d. purple	21·00	60·00
90		50c. on 1s. green	85·00	2·75
91		2r.50 on 5s. mauve	13·00	16·00

18
19

1879. Various frames.

No.	Type	Description	Unused	Used
101	18	1c. violet	1·75	50
102		2c. red	30·00	4·75
103		2c. green	2·25	60
104	19	4c. orange	70·00	3·00
105		4c. red	2·75	70
106	–	8c. blue	2·00	1·00
95	–	13c. grey	£120	£160
107	–	15c. brown	4·00	1·25
108	–	15c. blue	5·50	1·00
109	–	16c. brown	4·00	1·25
96	–	17c. red	55·00	5·00
110	–	25c. olive	4·75	2·00
98	–	38c. purple	£150	£225
99	–	50c. green	3·75	2·75

111 – 50c. orange 28·00 8·50
100 – 2r.50 purple 35·00 55·00

1883. No. 96 surch **16 CENTS**.
112 16c. on 17c. red £130 50·00

1883. No. 96 surch **SIXTEEN CENTS**.
115 16c. on 17c. red 75·00 1·50

1885. No. 98 surch **2 CENTS** with bar.
116 2c. on 38c. purple £100 35·00

1887. No. 95 surch **2 CENTS** without bar.
117 2c. on 13c. grey 48·00 85·00

1891. Surch in words with or without bar.
123 18 1c. on 2c. violet 1·25 50
124 – 1c. on 16c. brown (No. 109) 1·25 2·75
118 19 2c. on 4c. red 1·50 60
119 – 2c. on 17c. red (No. 96) 95·00 £100
120 9 2c. on 38c. on 9d. purple (No. 89) 3·00 3·75
121 – 2c. on 38c. purple (No. 98) 4·00 5·00

36

37

1895.
127 36 1c. purple and blue 75 1·50
128 2c. purple and orange 3·00 50
129 3c. purple 70 50
130 4c. purple and green 3·75 50
131 6c. green and red 4·50 4·00
132 18c. green and blue 10·00 3·50

1898. Diamond Jubilee.
133 37 36c. orange and blue 11·00 18·00

1899. Surch in figures and words.
137 – 4c. on 16c. brown (No. 109) 3·25 13·00
134 36 6c. on 18c. (No. 132) 1·00 1·00
156 12c. on 18c. (No. 132) 2·00 5·00
163 37 12c. on 36c. (No. 133) 1·25 1·25
135 15c. on 36c. (No. 133) 1·40 1·75

40 Admiral Mahe de Labourdonnais, Governor of Mauritius 1735–46

42

1899. Birth Bicentenary of Labourdonnais.
136 40 15c. blue 12·00 3·50

1900.
138 36 1c. grey and black 50 10
139 2c. purple 75 20
140 3c. green & red on yellow 3·75 1·25
141 4c. purple & red on yellow 1·50 40
142 4c. green and violet 75 2·00
167a 4c. black and red on blue 3·50 10
144 5c. purple on buff 6·50 50·00
145 5c. purple & black on buff 2·50 2·50
168a 6c. purple and red on red 4·25 10
147 8c. green & black on buff 2·00 7·00
148 12c. black and red 1·75 2·25
149 15c. green and orange 13·00 6·00
171 15c. black & blue on blue 4·00 35
151a 25c. green & red on green 3·50 14·00
174 50c. green on yellow 2·00 2·50
175 42 1r. grey and red 23·00 45·00
154 2r.50 green & blk on blue 18·00 85·00
155 5r. purple and red on red 65·00 85·00

1902. Optd **Postage & Revenue**.
157 36 4c. purple and red on yellow 1·25 20
158 6c. green and red 1·25 2·75
159 15c. green and orange 2·50 75
160 – 25c. olive (No. 110) 3·25 2·75
161 – 50c. green (No. 99) 4·50 3·00
162 – 2r.50 purple (No. 100) 90·00 £130

46

47

1910.
205 46 1c. black 1·00 1·00
206 2c. brown 1·00 10
207 2c. purple on yellow 1·00 30
183 3c. green 3·00 10
184 4c. green and red 3·50 10
210 4c. green 1·00 10
211 4c. brown 2·75 1·50
186 6c. red 2·25 20
213 6c. mauve 1·25 10
187 8c. orange 3·00 1·25
215 10c. grey 2·00 3·25
216 10c. red 4·00 1·50
217 12c. red 1·50 40
218 12c. grey 1·75 3·50
219b 15c. blue 75 25
220 20c. blue 2·00 80
221 20c. purple 8·50 10·00

1910.
185 47 5c. grey and red 2·75 3·00
188 12c. grey 2·25 2·75
190 25c. black & red on yellow 2·00 12·00
191 50c. purple and black 2·25 18·00
192 1r. black on green 6·50 12·00
193 2r.50 black and red on blue 13·00 70·00
194 5r. green and red on yellow 26·00 95·00
195 10r. green and red on green 95·00 £180

48

51

1913.
223 48 1c. black 80 1·25
224 2c. brown 70 10
225 3c. green 70 40
226 4c. green and red 60 30
226c 4c. green 6·00 45
227 5c. grey and red 90 10
228 6c. brown 2·00 60
229 8c. orange 75 10·00
230 10c. red 1·25 20
232b 12c. grey 5·50 20
232 12c. red 30 3·50
233 15c. blue 1·50 20
234 20c. purple 70 40
235 20c. blue 9·50 90
236 25c. black & red on yellow 60 15
237 50c. purple and black 7·50 3·50
238 1r. black on green 3·50 50
239 2r.50 black & red on blue 20·00 7·00
240 5r. green and red on yellow 28·00 70·00
204d 10r. green & red on green 26·00 £110

1924. As T **42** but Arms similar to T **46**.
222 50r. purple and green £700 £1300

1925. Surch with figures, words and bar.
242 46 3c. on 4c. green 3·00 3·75
243 10c. on 12c. red 30 40
244 15c. on 20c. blue 55 20

1935. Silver Jubilee. As T **14a** of Kenya, Uganda and Tanganyika.
245 5c. blue and grey 50 10
246 12c. green and blue 4·50 10
247 20c. brown and blue 5·50 20
248 1r. grey and purple 29·00 42·00

1937. Coronation. As T **14b** of Kenya, Uganda and Tanganyika.
249 5c. violet 40 10
250 12c. red 50 2·00
251 20c. blue 65 10

1938.
252 51 2c. grey 30 10
253 3c. purple and red 2·00 2·00
254b 4c. green 2·00 2·00
255a 5c. violet 3·25 20
256b 10c. red 2·50 20
257 12c. orange 1·00 20
258 20c. blue 1·00 20
259b 25c. purple 6·00 10
260b 1r. brown 19·00 1·25
261a 2r.50 violet 29·00 13·00
262a 5r. olive 27·00 24·00
263a 10r. purple 12·00 24·00

1946. Victory. As T **4a** of Pitcairn Islands.
264 5c. violet 10 40
265 20c. blue 15 20

52 1d. "Post Office" Mauritius and King George VI

1948. Cent of First British Colonial Stamp.
266 52 5c. orange and mauve 10 40
267 12c. orange and green 15 20
268 – 20c. blue 15 10
269 – 1r. blue and brown 15 30
DESIGN: 20c., 1r. As Type **52**, but showing 2d. "Post Office" Mauritius.

1948. Silver Wedding. As T **4b/c** of Pitcairn Islands.
270 5c. violet 10 10
271 10r. mauve 11·00 24·00

1949. U.P.U. As T **4d/g** of Pitcairn Islands.
272 12c. red 50 1·25
273 20c. blue 2·25 2·25
274 35c. purple 60 1·25
275 1r. brown 50 20

55 Aloe Plant

60 Legend of Paul and Virginie

67 Arms of Mauritius

69 Historical Museum, Mahebourg

1950.
276 – 1c. purple 10 50
277 – 2c. red 15 10
278 55 3c. green 60 2·75
279 – 4c. green 20 1·50
280 – 5c. blue 15 10
281 – 10c. red 30 75
282 – 12c. green 1·50 2·25
283 60 20c. blue 1·00 15
284 – 25c. red 1·75 40
285 – 35c. violet 30 10
286 – 50c. green 2·75 50
287 – 1r. brown 5·00 10
288 – 2r.50 orange 12·00 9·50
289 – 5r. brown 14·00 15·00
290 67 10r. blue 14·00 22·00
DESIGNS—HORIZ: 1c. Labourdonnais sugar factory; 2c. Grand Port; 5c. Rempart Mountain; 10c. Transporting cane; 12c. Mauritius dodo and map; 35c. Government House, Reduit; 1r. Timor deer; 2r.50, Port Louis; 5r. Beach scene. VERT: 4c. Tamarind Falls; 25c. Labourdonnais statue; 50c. Pieter Both Mountain.

1953. Coronation. As T **4h** of Pitcairn Islands.
291 10c. black and green 1·25 15

1953. As 1950 but portrait of Queen Elizabeth II. Designs as for corresponding values except where stated.
293 – 2c. red 10 10
294 – 3c. green 30 40
295 – 4c. purple (as 1c.) 10 1·00
296 – 5c. blue 10 10
314 – 10c. green (as 4c.) 15 10
298 69 15c. red 10 10
299 – 20c. red (as 25c.) 15 20
300 – 25c. blue (as 20c.) 1·50 10
301 – 35c. violet 20 10
302 – 50c. green 55 85
315 – 60c. green (as 12c.) 1·75 10
303 – 1r. sepia 30 10
316 – 2r.50 orange 7·50 8·50
305 – 5r. brown 14·00 10·00
306 – 10r. blue 13·00 2·00

70 Queen Elizabeth II and King George III (after Lawrence)

1961. 150th Anniv of British Post Office in Mauritius.
307 70 10c. black and red 10 10
308 20c. ultramarine and blue 30 35
309 35c. black and yellow 40 35
310 1r. purple and green 60 30

1963. Freedom from Hunger. As T **20a** of Pitcairn Islands.
311 60c. violet 40 10

1963. Cent of Red Cross. As T **20b** of Pitcairn Islands.
312 10c. red and black 15 10
313 60c. red and blue 60 20

71 Bourbon White-eye

1965. Birds. Multicoloured.
317 2c. Type **71** (yellow background) 40 15
318 3c. Rodriguez fody ("Rodrigues Fody") (brown background) 1·00 15
319 4c. Mauritius olive white-eye ("Olive White-Eye") 30 15
340 5c. Mascarene paradise flycatcher ("Paradise Flycatcher") 70 15
321 10c. Mauritius fody 30 10
322 15c. Mauritius parakeet ("Parrakeet") (grey background) 2·00 40
323 20c. Mauritius greybird ("Cuckoo-Shrike") (yellow background) 2·00 10
324 25c. Mauritius kestrel ("Kestrel") 2·00 30
341 35c. Pink pigeon 30 15
326 50c. Reunion bulbul ("Mascarene Bul-Bul") 50 40
327 60c. Mauritius blue pigeon (extinct) ("Dutch Pigeon") (yellow background) 60 10
328 1r. Mauritius dodo (extinct) (olive background) 5·50 10
329 2r.50 Rodriguez solitaire (extinct) ("Rodrigues Solitaire") 5·00 6·00
330 5r. Mauritius red rail (extinct) ("Red Rail") 14·00 13·00
331 10r. Broad-billed parrot (extinct) 29·00 24·00
For some values with background colours changed see Nos. 370/5.

1965. Centenary of I.T.U. As T **24a** of Pitcairn Islands.
332 10c. orange and green 20 10
333 60c. yellow and violet 70 20

1965. I.C.Y. As T **24b** of Pitcairn Islands.
334 10c. purple and turquoise 15 10
335 60c. green and violet 30 20

1966. Churchill Commemoration. As T **24c** of Pitcairn Islands.
336 2c. blue 10 2·75
337 10c. green 25 10
338 60c. brown 1·10 20
339 1r. violet 1·25 20

1966. 20th Anniv of U.N.E.S.C.O. As T **25b/d** of Pitcairn Islands.
342 5c. multicoloured 25 30
343 10c. yellow, violet and green 30 10
344 60c. black, purple and orange 1·40 15

86 Red-tailed Tropic Bird

1967. Self-Government. Multicoloured.
345 2c. Type **86** 20 1·75
346 10c. Rodriguez brush warbler 60 10
347 60c. Rose-ringed parakeet (extinct) ("Rodrigues Parakeet") 70 10
348 1r. Grey-rumped swiftlet ("Mauritius Swiftlet") 70 10

1967. Self-Government. Nos. 317/31 optd **SELF GOVERNMENT 1967**.
349 71 2c. multicoloured 10 50
350 – 3c. multicoloured 10 50
351 – 4c. multicoloured 10 50
352 – 5c. multicoloured 10 10
353 – 10c. multicoloured 10 10
354 – 15c. multicoloured 10 30
355 – 20c. multicoloured 15 10
356 – 25c. multicoloured 15 10
357 – 35c. multicoloured 20 10
358 – 50c. multicoloured 30 15
359 – 60c. multicoloured 30 10
360 – 1r. multicoloured 1·50 10
361 – 2r.50 multicoloured 1·00 2·25
362 – 5r. multicoloured 6·00 3·25
363 – 10r. multicoloured 8·00 15·00

91 Flag of Mauritius

1968. Independence. Multicoloured.
364 2c. Type **91** 10 1·50
365 3c. Arms and Mauritius dodo emblem 15 1·50
366 15c. Type **91** 20 10
367 20c. As 3c. 50 10
368 60c. Type **91** 60 10
369 1r. As 3c. 95 10

1968. As Nos. 317/8, 322/3 and 327/8 but background colours changed as below.
370 71 2c. olive 20 2·75
371 – 3c. blue 1·75 5·50
372 – 15c. brown 55 20
373 – 20c. buff 3·50 3·75
374 – 60c. red 1·50 15
375 – 1r. purple 3·25 1·50

93 Dominique rescues Paul and Virginie

1968. Bicentenary of Bernardin de St. Pierre's Visit to Mauritius. Multicoloured.

376 2c. Type **93** . . . . 10 1·25
377 15c. Paul and Virginie crossing the river (vert) . . 35 10
378 50c. Visit of Labourdonnais to Madame de la Tour . . 50 10
379 60c. Meeting of Paul and Virginie in Confidence (vert) 50 10
380 1r. Departure of Virginie for Europe 50 20
381 2r.50 Bernardin de St. Pierre (vert) . . . . 1·50 3·75

99 Black-spotted Emperor

1969. Multicoloured (except 10, 15, 25, 60c.).

382 2c. Type **99** . . . . . . 10 2·50
383 3c. Red reef crab . . . . . 10 3·25
384 4c. Episcopal mitre . . . . 2·00 3·50
385 5c. Black-saddled pufferfish ("Bourse") 30 10
386 10c. Starfish (red, black and flesh) . . . . 2·00 10
387 15c. Sea urchin (brown, black and blue) 30 10
480 20c. Fiddler crab . . . . . 1·25 30
389 25c. Spiny shrimp (red, black and green) . . . . 30 3·50
390 30c. Single harp shells and double harp shell . . . . 1·50 1·75
483 35c. Common paper nautilus . . . . 1·75 15
484 40c. Spanish dancer . . . . 1·00 60
448 50c. Orange spider conch and violet spider conch 45 10
449b 60c. Blue marlin (black, pink and blue) 65 10
487 75c. "Conus clytospira" . . 1·25 1·50
396 1r. Dolphin (fish) 60 10
452 2r.50 Spiny lobster . . . . 2·00 4·50
453 5r. Ruby snapper ("Sacre chien rouge") . . . . . 3·00 2·00
399w 10r. Yellow-edged lyretail ("Croissant queue jaune") 2·00 2·00

117 Gandhi as Law Student

1969. Birth Cent of Mahatma Gandhi. Mult.

400 2c. Type **117** 10 20
401 15c. Gandhi as stretcher-bearer during Zulu Revolt 20 10
402 50c. Gandhi as Satyagrahi in South Africa 20 50
403 60c. Gandhi at No. 10 Downing Street, London 20 10
404 1r. Gandhi in Mauritius, 1901 . . . . 20 10
405 2r.50 Gandhi, the "Apostle of Truth and Non-Violence" 45 2·00
MS406 153 × 153 mm. Nos. 400/5 2·00 7·50

124 Frangourinier Cane-crusher (18th cent)

1969. 150th Anniv of Telfair's Improvements to the Sugar Industry. Multicoloured.

407 2c. Three-roller Vertical Mill 10 20
408 15c. Type **124** 10 10
409 60c. Beau Rivage Factory, 1867 . . . . 10 10
410 1r. Mon Desert-Alma Factory, 1969 . . . . . . 10 10
411 2r.50 Dr. Charles Telfair (vert) . . . . 25 1·25
MS412 159 × 88 mm. Nos. 407/11 1·25 2·25

1970. Expo '70. Nos. 394 and 396 optd **EXPO '70' OSAKA**.

413 60c. black, red and blue . . . 10 10
414 1r. multicoloured 10 10

129 Morne Plage, Mountain and Boeing 707

1970. Inauguration of Lufthansa Flight, Mauritius–Frankfurt. Multicoloured.

415 25c. Type **129** 10 10
416 50c. Boeing 707 and map (vert) 10 10

131 Lenin as a Student

1970. Birth Centenary of Lenin.

417 **131** 15c. green and silver . . . 10 10
418 – 75c. brown 20 20

DESIGN: 75c. Lenin as founder of U.S.S.R.

133 2d. "Post Office" Mauritius and original Post Office

1970. Port Louis, Old and New. Multicoloured.

419 5c. Type **133** 10 10
420 15c. G.P.O. Building (built 1870) 10 10
421 50c. Mail coach (c. 1870) . . 40 10
422 75c. Port Louis Harbour (1970) 55 10
423 2r.50 Arrival of Pierre A. de Suffren (1783) 70 70
MS424 165 × 95 mm. Nos. 419/23 2·75 7·00

138 U.N. Emblem and Symbols

1970. 25th Anniv of U.N.

425 **138** 10c. multicoloured 10 10
426 60c. multicoloured 40 10

139 Rainbow over Waterfall

1971. Tourism. Multicoloured.

427 10c. Type **139** 25 10
428 15c. Trois Mamelles Mountains 25 10
429 60c. Beach scene 35 10
430 2r.50 Marine life . . . . . . 50 1·50

Nos. 427/30 have inscriptions on the reverse.

140 "Crossroads" of Indian Ocean

1971. 25th Anniv of Plaisance Airport. Multicoloured.

431 15c. Type **140** 35 10
432 60c. Boeing 707 and Terminal buildings 60 10
433 1r. Air hostesses on gangway 65 10
434 2r.50 Farman F.190, "Roland Garros" airplane, Choisy Airfield, 1937 . . . . . . 2·00 4·50

141 Princess Margaret Orthopaedic Centre

1971. 3rd Commonwealth Medical Conference. Multicoloured.

435 10c. Type **141** 10 10
436 75c. Operating theatre in National Hospital 20 20

142 Queen Elizabeth II and Prince Philip

1972. Royal Visit. Multicoloured.

455 15c. Type **142** 15 10
456 2r.50 Queen Elizabeth II (vert) . . . . 2·00 2·00

143 Theatre Facade

1972. 150th Anniv of Port Louis Theatre. Multicoloured.

457 10c. Type **143** 10 10
458 1r. Theatre auditorium . . . 40 20

144 Pirate Dhow

1972. Pirates and Privateers. Multicoloured.

459 15c. Type **144** 65 15
460 60c. Treasure chest (vert) . . 1·00 20
461 1r. Lemene and "L'Hirondelle" (vert) . . . 1·25 20
462 2r.50 Robert Surcouf . . . . 4·50 8·00

145 Mauritius University

1973. 5th Anniv of Independence. Multicoloured.

463 15c. Type **145** 10 10
464 60c. Tea development 15 15
465 1r. Bank of Mauritius . . . 15 15

146 Map and Hands

1973. O.C.A.M. Conference. Multicoloured.

466 10c. O.C.A.M. emblem (horiz) 10 10
467 2r.50 Type **146** 40 45

O.C.A.M. = Organisation Commune Africaine Malgache et Mauricienne.

147 W.H.O. Emblem

1973. 25th Anniv of W.H.O.

468 **147** 1r. multicoloured 10 10

148 Meteorological Station, Vacoas

1973. Centenary of I.M.O./W.M.O.

469 **148** 75c. multicoloured 30 70

149 Capture of the "Kent" 1800

1973. Birth Bicentenary of Robert Surcouf (privateer).

470 **149** 60c. multicoloured 50 85

150 P. Commerson

1974. Death Bicentenary (1973) of Philibert Commerson (naturalist).

471 **150** 2r.50 multicoloured . . . 30 40

151 Cow being Milked

1974. 8th F.A.O. Regional Conf for Africa, Mauritius.

472 **151** 60c. multicoloured 20 20

152 Mail Train

1974. Centenary of U.P.U. Multicoloured.

473 15c. Type **152** 40 15
474 1r. New G.P.O., Port Louis 40 20

153 "Cottage Life" (F. Leroy)

1975. Aspects of Mauritian Life. Paintings. Mult.

493 15c. Type **153** 10 10
494 60c. "Milk Seller" (A. Richard) (vert) 25 10
495 1r. "Entrance of Port Louis Market" (Thuillier) 25 10
496 2r.50 "Washerwoman" (Max Boullee) (vert) 80 80

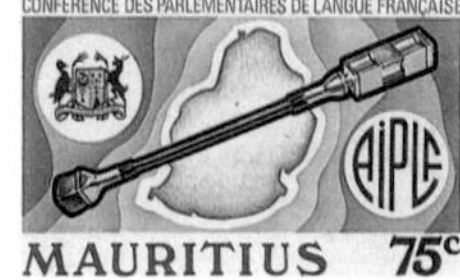

154 Mace across Map

1975. French-speaking Parliamentary Assemblies Conference, Port Louis.

497 **154** 75c. multicoloured . . . . 30 1·25

155 Woman with Lamp ("The Light of the World")

1976. International Women's Year.
498 **155** 2r.50 multicoloured . . . 35 2·00

156 Parched Landscape

1976. Drought in Africa. Multicoloured.
499 50c. Type **156** 15 30
500 60c. Map of Africa and carcass (vert) 15 30

157 "Pierre Loti", 1953–70

1976. Mail Carriers to Mauritius. Multicoloured.
501 10c. Type **157** 70 10
502 15c. "Secunder", 1907 . . . 95 10
503 50c. "Hindoostan", 1842 . . 1·60 15
504 60c. "St. Geran", 1740 . . . 1·75 15
505 2r.50 "Maen", 1638 . . . . 4·00 7·50
MS506 115 × 138 mm. Nos. 501/5 8·50 11·00

158 "The Flame of Hindi carried across the Seas"

1976. 2nd World Hindi Convention. Multicoloured.
507 10c. Type **158** 10 10
508 75c. Type **158** 10 30
509 1r.20 Hindi script . . . . . 20 1·25

159 Conference Logo and Map of Mauritius

160 King Priest and Breastplate

1976. 22nd Commonwealth Parliamentary Association Conference. Multicoloured.
510 1r. Type **159** 25 10
511 2r.50 Conference logo . . . 50 1·75

1976. Moenjodaro Excavations, Pakistan. Mult.
512 60c. Type **160** 45 10
513 1r. House with well and goblet 60 10
514 2r.50 Terracotta figurine and necklace . . . . 1·50 1·00

161 Sega Scene

1977. 2nd World Black and African Festival of Arts and Culture, Nigeria.
515 **161** 1r. multicoloured 30 15

162 The Queen with Sceptre and Rod

1977. Silver Jubilee. Multicoloured.
516 50c. The Queen at Mauritius Legislative Assembly, 1972 15 10
517 75c. Type **162** 20 10
518 5r. Presentation of Sceptre and Rod 55 75

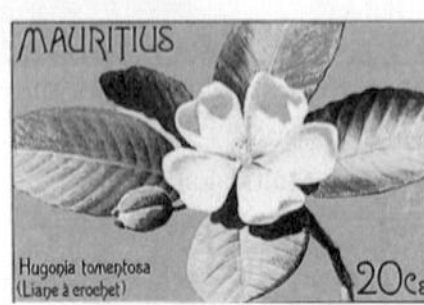

163 "Hugonia tomentosa"

1977. Indigenous Flowers. Multicoloured.
519 20c. Type **163** 20 10
520 1r. "Ochna mauritiana" (vert) 40 10
521 1r.50 "Dombeya acutangula" 50 20
522 5r. "Trochetia blackburniana" (vert) . . . 1·10 1·50
MS523 130 × 130 mm. Nos. 519/22 3·00 6·50

164 De Havilland Twin Otter 200/300

1977. Inaugural International Flight of Air Mauritius. Multicoloured.
524 25c. Type **164** 60 10
525 50c. De Havilland Twin Otter 200/300 and Air Mauritius emblem 80 10
526 75c. Piper Navajo and Boeing 747-100 . . . . 95 20
527 5r. Boeing 707 . . . . 3·00 3·75
MS528 110 × 152 mm. Nos. 524/7 7·50 7·50

165 Portuguese Map of Mauritius, 1519

166 Mauritius Dodo

1978.
529B **165** 10c. multicoloured . . . 75 1·25
530A – 15c. multicoloured . . . 1·50 2·75
531A – 20c. multicoloured . . . 80 2·75
532A – 25c. multicoloured . . . 60 2·00
533B – 35c. multicoloured . . . 1·00 20
534A – 50c. multicoloured . . . 50 75
535A – 60c. multicoloured . . . 60 2·75
536A – 70c. multicoloured . . . 2·75 4·00
537B – 75c. multicoloured . . . 1·75 3·50
538A – 90c. multicoloured . . . 4·00 4·00
539A – 1r. multicoloured . . . 60 50
540A – 1r.20 multicoloured . . 1·75 4·00
541B – 1r.25 multicoloured . . 1·50 20
542A – 1r.50 multicoloured . . 1·00 2·75
543A – 2r. multicoloured . . . 60 70
544A – 3r. multicoloured . . . 60 50
545A – 5r. multicoloured . . . 60 1·75
546A – 10r. multicoloured . . . 1·00 1·00
547A – 15r. multicoloured . . . 1·50 3·00
548A – 25r. green, black & brn 2·00 3·25
DESIGNS—HORIZ: 15c. Dutch Occupation, 1638–1710; 20c. Map by Van Keulen, c. 1700; 50c. Construction of Port Louis, c. 1736; 70c. Map by Bellin, 1763; 90c. Battle of Grand Port, 1810; 1r. Landing of the British, 1810; 1r.20, Government House, c. 1840; 1r.50, Indian immigration, 1835; 2r. Race Course, c. 1870; 3r. Place d'Armes, c. 1880; 5r. Royal Visit postcard, 1901; 10r. Royal College, 1914; 25r. First Mauritian Governor-General and Prime Minister. VERT: 25c. Settlement on Rodriguez, 1691; 35c. French settlers Charter, 1715; 60c. Pierre Poivre, c. 1767; 75c. First coinage, 1794; 1r.25 Lady Gomm's Ball, 1847; 15r. Unfurling of Mauritian flag.

1978. 25th Anniv of Coronation.
549 – 3r. grey, black and blue 25 45
550 – 3r. multicoloured 25 45
551 **166** 3r. grey, black and blue 25 45
DESIGNS: No. 549, Antelope of Bohun; No. 550, Queen Elizabeth II.

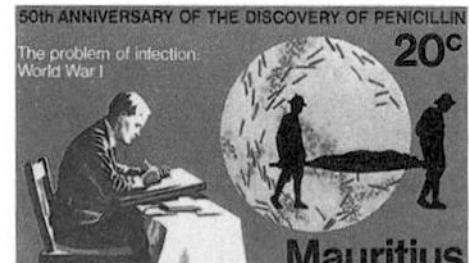

167 Problem of Infection, World War I

1978. 50th Anniv of Discovery of Penicillin.
552 **167** 20c. multicoloured 75 10
553 – 1r. multicoloured . . . . 1·50 10
554 – 1r.50 black, brown & grn 2·25 1·40
555 – 5r. multicoloured . . . . 3·00 6·00
MS556 150 × 90 mm. Nos. 552/5 9·00 9·50
DESIGNS: 1r. First mould growth, 1928; 1r.50, "Penicillium chrysogenum" ("notatum"); 5r. Sir Alexander Fleming.

168 "Papilio manlius" (butterfly)

1978. Endangered Species. Multicoloured.
557 20c. Type **168** . . . . 2·00 30
558 1r. Geckos . . . . 1·00 10
559 1r.50 Greater Mascarene flying fox . . . . 1·25 1·00
560 5r. Mauritius kestrel . . . . 14·00 9·00
MS561 154 × 148 mm. Nos. 557/60 42·00 18·00

169 Ornate Table

171 Father Laval and Crucifix

170 Whitcomb Diesel Locomotive 65H.P., 1949

1978. Bicentenary of Reconstruction of Chateau Le Reduit. Multicoloured.
562 15c. Type **169** 10 10
563 75c. Chateau Le Reduit . . . 10 10
564 3r. Le Reduit gardens 40 45

1979. Railway Locomotives. Multicoloured.
565 20c. Type **170** 20 10
566 1r. "Sir William", 1922 . . . 40 10
567 1r.50 Kitson type 1930 . . . 60 45
568 2r. Garratt type, 1927 . . . . 75 85
MS569 128 × 128 mm. Nos. 565/8 2·00 4·00

1979. Beatification of Father Laval (missionary). Multicoloured.
570 20c. Type **171** 10 10
571 1r.50 Father Laval 10 10
572 5r. Father Laval's tomb (horiz) 35 50
MS573 150 × 96 mm. Nos. 570/2 2·50 3·00

172 Astronaut descending from Lunar Module

173 Great Britain 1855 4d. Stamp and Sir Rowland Hill

1979. 10th Anniv of Moon Landing. Multicoloured. Self-adhesive.
574 20c. Type **172** 30 40
575 3r. Astronaut performing experiment on Moon . . . 80 1·10
576 5r. Astronaut on Moon . . . 3·25 6·00

1979. Death Cent of Sir Rowland Hill. Mult.
577 25c. Type **173** 10 10
578 2r. 1954 60c. definitive . . . 55 55
579 5r. 1847 1d. "POST OFFICE" . . . . 1·00 1·75
MS580 120 × 89 mm. 3r. 1847 2d. "POST OFFICE" . . . . . . 1·10 1·75

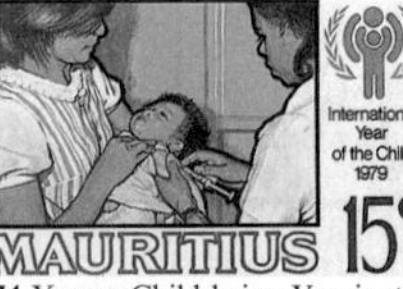

174 Young Child being Vaccinated

1979. International Year of the Child.
581 **174** 15c. multicoloured 10 10
582 – 25c. multicoloured 10 10
583 – 1r. black, blue and light blue 15 10
584 – 1r.50 multicoloured . . . 30 35
585 – 3r. multicoloured . . . . 50 1·10
DESIGNS—HORIZ: 25c. Children playing; 1r.50, Girls in chemistry laboratory; 3r. Boy operating lathe. VERT: 1r. I.Y.C. emblem.

175 The Lienard Obelisk

1980. Pamplemousses Botanical Gardens. Multicoloured.
586 20c. Type **175** 10 10
587 25c. Poivre Avenue 10 10
588 1r. Varieties of Vacoas . . . 20 10
589 2r. Giant water lilies 45 55
590 5r. Mon Plaisir (mansion) . . 80 3·00
MS591 152 × 105 mm. Nos. 586/90 3·50 4·50

176 "Emirne" (French steam packet)

1980. "London 1980" International Stamp Exhibition. Mail-carrying Ships. Multicoloured.
592 25c. Type **176** 25 10
593 1r. "Boissevain" (cargo liner) 40 10
594 2r. "La Boudeuse" (Bougainville's ship) . . . 60 70
595 5r. "Sea Breeze" (English clipper) . . . . 70 2·50

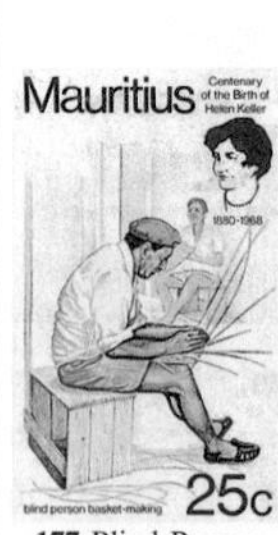

177 Blind Person Basket-making

178 Prime Minister Sir Seewoosagur Ramgoolam

1980. Birth Centenary of Helen Keller (campaigner for the handicapped). Multicoloured.
596 25c. Type **177** 20 10
597 1r. Deaf child under instruction 45 10
598 2r.50 Helen reading braille 70 35
599 5r. Helen at graduation, 1904 1·25 1·25

1980. 80th Birthday and 40th Year in Parliament of Prime Minister Sir Seewoosagur Ramgoolam.
600 **178** 15r. multicoloured . . . . 1·00 1·40

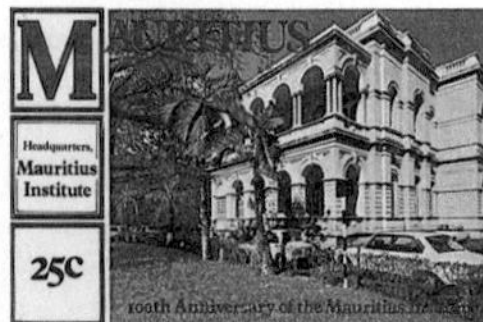

179 Headquarters, Mauritius Institute

1980. Centenary of Mauritius Institute. Mult.
601 25c. Type **179** 15 10
602 2r. Rare copy of Veda . . . 40 20
603 2r.50 Glory of India cone shell 55 25
604 5r. "Le Torrent" (painting by Harpignies) . . . . 65 1·50

180 "Hibiscus liliiflorus"

181 Beau-Bassin/Rose Hill

1981. Flowers. Multicoloured.
605 25c. Type **180** 20 10
606 2r. "Erythrospermum monticolum" 60 65
607 2r.50 "Chasalia boryana" . . 65 1·25
608 5r. "Hibiscus columnaris" . . 1·00 3·25

1981. Coats of Arms of Mauritius Towns. Multicoloured.
609 25c. Type **181** 10 10
610 1r.50 Curepipe 25 20
611 2r. Quatre-Bornes 30 25
612 2r.50 Vacoas/Phoenix 35 30
613 5r. Port Louis 55 75
MS614 130 × 130 mm. Nos. 609/13 1·75 5·00

182 Prince Charles as Colonel-in-Chief, Royal Regiment of Wales

184 Drummer and Piper

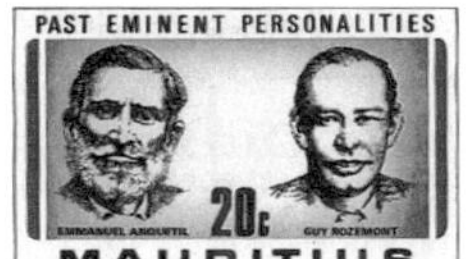
183 Emmanuel Anquetil and Guy Rozemont

1981. Royal Wedding. Multicoloured
615 25c. Wedding bouquet from Mauritius 10 10
616 2r.50 Type **182** 40 15
617 10r. Prince Charles and Lady Diana Spencer 80 90

1981. Famous Politicians and Physician.
618 **183** 20c. black and red 10 10
619 – 25c. black and yellow . . 10 10
620 – 1r.25 black and green . . 30 30
621 – 1r.50 black and red . . . 35 15
622 – 2r. black and blue 45 20
623 – 2r.50 black and brown . . 50 70
624 – 5r. black and blue . . . . 1·50 1·75
DESIGNS: 25c. Remy Ollier and Sookdeo Bissoondoyal; 1r.25, Maurice Cure and Barthelemy Ohsan; 1r.50, Sir Guy Forget and Renganaden Seeneevassen; 2r. Sir Abdul Razak Mohamed and Jules Koenig; 2r.50, Abdoollatiff Mahomed Osman and Dazzi Rama (Pandit Sahadeo); 5r. Sir Thomas Lewis (physician) and electrocardiogram.

1981. Religion and Culture. Multicoloured.
625 20c. Type **184** 10 10
626 2r. Swami Sivananda (vert) 1·00 1·00
627 5r. Chinese Pagoda . . . . 1·25 3·25
The 20c. value commemorates the World Tamil Culture Conference (1980).

185 "Skills"

186 Ka'aba (sacred shrine, Great Mosque of Mecca)

1981. 25th Anniv of Duke of Edinburgh Award Scheme. Multicoloured.
628 25c. Type **185** 10 10
629 1r.25 "Service" 10 10
630 5r. "Expeditions" 20 30
631 10r. Duke of Edinburgh . . . 40 70

1981. Moslem Year 1400 A.H. Commemoration. Multicoloured.
632 25c. Type **186** 30 10
633 2r. Mecca 80 80
634 5r. Mecca and Ka'aba . . . 1·40 2·75

187 Scout Emblem

189 Bride and Groom at Buckingham Palace

188 Charles Darwin

1982. 75th Anniv of Boy Scout Movement and 70th Anniv of Scouting in Mauritius.
635 **187** 25c. lilac and green . . . 10 10
636 – 2r. brown and ochre . . . 40 30
637 – 5r. green and olive . . . 85 1·00
638 – 10r. green and blue . . . 1·25 2·00
DESIGNS: 2r. Lord Baden-Powell and Baden-Powell House; 5r. Grand Howl; 10r. Ascent of Pieter Both.

1982. 150th Anniv of Charles Darwin's Voyage. Multicoloured.
639 25c. Type **188** 20 10
640 2r. Darwin's telescope . . . 40 45
641 2r.50 Darwin's elephant ride 70 55
642 10r. H.M.S. "Beagle" beached for repairs . . . . 1·50 2·75

1982. 21st Birthday of Princess of Wales. Mult.
643 25c. Mauritius coat of arms 10 10
644 2r.50 Princess Diana in Chesterfield, November 1981 . . . . 60 45
645 5r. Type **189** . . . . 75 1·25
646 10r. Formal portrait . . . . 2·75 3·00

190 Prince and Princess of Wales with Prince William

1982. Birth of Prince William of Wales.
647 **190** 2r.50 multicoloured . . . 1·00 50

191 Bois Fandamane Plant

193 Early Wall-mounted Telephone

192 Arms and Flag of Mauritius

1982. Centenary of Robert Koch's Discovery of Tubercle Bacillus. Multicoloured.
648 25c. Type **191** 10 10
649 1r.25 Central market, Port Louis 35 40
650 2r. Bois Banane plant 50 75
651 5r. Platte de Lezard plant . . 60 2·25
652 10r. Dr. Robert Koch . . . 90 3·75

1983. Commonwealth Day. Multicoloured.
653 25c. Type **192** 10 10
654 2r.50 Satellite view of Mauritius 20 30
655 5r. Harvesting sugar cane . . 30 75
656 10r. Port Louis harbour . . . 95 1·50

1983. World Communications Year. Mult.
657 25c. Type **193** 10 10
658 1r.25 Early telegraph apparatus (horiz) 35 20
659 2r. Earth satellite station . . 45 50
660 10r. First hot-air balloon in Mauritius, 1784 (horiz) . . 80 2·75

194 Map of Namibia

195 Fish Trap

1983. Namibia Day. Multicoloured.
661 25c. Type **194** 45 10
662 2r.50 Hand breaking chains 1·50 75
663 5r. Family and settlement . . 2·00 2·25
664 10r. Diamond mining . . . . 4·75 3·75

1983. Fishery Resources. Multicoloured.
665 25c. Type **195** 15 10
666 1r. Fishing boat (horiz) . . . 30 15
667 5r. Game fishing . . . . . . 55 2·25
668 10r. Octopus drying (horiz) 80 4·00

196 Swami Dayananda

197 Adolf von Plevitz

1983. Death Centenary of Swami Dayananda. Multicoloured.
669 25c. Type **196** 10 10
670 35c. Last meeting with father 10 10
671 2r. Receiving religious instruction 50 65
672 5r. Swami demonstrating strength . . . . 70 2·50
673 10r. At a religious gathering 1·00 3·75

1983. 125th Anniv of Arrival in Mauritius of Adolf von Plevitz (social reformer). Multicoloured.
674 25c. Type **197** 10 10
675 1r.25 La Laura, Government school 30 30
676 5r. Von Plevitz addressing Commission of Enquiry, 1872 . . . . 1·00 2·50
677 10r. Von Plevitz with Indian farm workers . . . . . . 1·75 3·75

198 Courtship Chase

1984. The Mauritius Kestrel. Multicoloured.
678 25c. Type **198** 85 30
679 2r. Kestrel in tree (vert) . . . 2·00 1·25
680 2r.50 Young kestrel . . . . 2·25 2·25
681 10r. Head (vert) . . . . . . 3·25 8·50

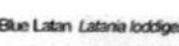

199 Wreck of S.S. "Tayeb"

200 Blue Latan Palm

1984. 250th Anniv of "Lloyd's List" (newspaper). Multicoloured.
682 25c. Type **199** 30 10
683 1r. S.S. "Taher" 95 15
684 5r. East Indiaman "Triton" 3·00 3·25
685 10r. M.S. "Astor" . . . . . 3·50 6·50

1984. Palm Trees. Multicoloured.
686 25c. Type **200** 10 10
687 50c. "Hyophorbe vaughanii" 20 20
688 2r.50 "Tectiphiala ferox" . . 1·50 1·75
689 5r. Round Island bottle-palm 2·25 3·50
690 10r. "Hyophorbe amaricaulis" . . . . 3·50 7·00

201 Slave Girl

203 The Queen Mother on Clarence House Balcony, 1980

202 75th Anniversary Production of "Faust" and Leoville L'Homme

1984. 150th Anniv of Abolition of Slavery and Introduction of Indian Immigrants.
691 **201** 25c. purple, lilac and brown 15 10
692 – 1r. purple, lilac and brown 70 10
693 – 2r. purple and lilac . . . 1·50 1·00
694 – 10r. purple and lilac . . . 7·00 11·00
DESIGNS—VERT: 1r. Slave market. HORIZ: 2r. Indian immigrant family; 10r. Arrival of Indian immigrants.

1984. Centenary of Alliance Francaise (cultural organization). Multicoloured.
695 25c. Type **202** 20 10
696 1r.25 Prize-giving ceremony and Aunauth Beejadbur . . 70 50
697 5r. First headquarters and Hector Clarenc . . . . . 2·00 3·00
698 10r. Lion Mountain and Labourdonnais . . . . . 2·50 5·50

1985. Life and Times of Queen Elizabeth the Queen Mother. Multicoloured.
699 25c. The Queen Mother in 1926 . . . . 50 10
700 2r. With Princess Margaret at Trooping the Colour . . . 1·40 45
701 5r. Type **203** . . . . 1·50 1·60
702 10r. With Prince Henry at his christening (from photo by Lord Snowdon) . . . . . 1·75 3·75
MS703 91 × 73 mm. 15r. Reopening the Stratford Canal, 1964 . . . 5·50 3·75

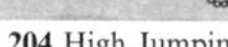
204 High Jumping

205 Adult and Fledgling Pink Pigeons

1985. 2nd Indian Ocean Islands Games. Multicoloured.
704 25c. Type **204** 30 10
705 50c. Javelin-throwing 60 30
706 1r.25 Cycling . . . . 4·00 1·75
707 10r. Wind surfing . . . . . 7·00 12·00

1985. Pink Pigeon. Multicoloured.
708 25c. Type **205** . . . . 3·00 50
709 2r. Pink pigeon displaying at nest . . . . 7·00 1·75
710 2r.50 On nest . . . . 7·50 3·75
711 5r. Pair preening . . . . . . 12·00 12·00

206 Caverne Patates, Rodrigues

1985. 10th Anniv of World Tourism Organization. Multicoloured.
712 25c. Type **206** 50 10
713 35c. Coloured soils, Chamarel 50 40
714 5r. Serpent Island . . . . . 5·00 5·50
715 10r. Coin de Mire Island . . 7·00 11·00

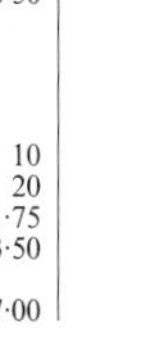

207 Old Town Hall, Port Louis

1985. 250th Anniv of Port Louis. Multicoloured.
716 25c. Type **207** 10 10
717 1r. Al-Aqsa Mosque (180th anniv) 1·50 10
718 2r.50 Vase and trees (250th anniv of settlement of Tamil-speaking Indians) 1·25 1·75
719 10r. Port Louis Harbour 7·00 12·00

208 Edmond Halley and Diagram

1986. Appearance of Halley's Comet. Mult.
720 25c. Type **208** 40 10
721 1r.25 Halley's Comet (1682) and Newton's Reflector 1·10 50
722 3r. Halley's Comet passing Earth 1·60 2·25
723 10r. "Giotto" spacecraft 3·50 7·00

1986. 60th Birthday of Queen Elizabeth II. As T **246a** of Papua New Guinea. Multicoloured.
724 25c. Princess Elizabeth wearing badge of Grenadier Guards, 1942 10 10
725 75c. Investiture of Prince of Wales, 1969 10 10
726 2r. With Prime Minister of Mauritius, 1972 20 25
727 3r. In Germany, 1978 30 40
728 15r. At Crown Agents Head Office, London, 1983 1·25 2·00

209 Maize (World Food Day)

210 "Cryptopus elatus"

1986. International Events. Multicoloured.
729 25c. Type **209** 10 10
730 1r. African Regional Industrial Property Organization emblem (10th anniv) 30 10
731 1r.25 International Peace Year emblem 65 50
732 10r. Footballer and Mauritius Football Association emblem (World Cup Football Championship, Mexico) 5·50 10·00

1986. Orchids. Multicoloured.
733 25c. Type **210** 50 10
734 2r. "Jumellea recta" 1·25 45
735 2r.50 "Angraecum mauritianum" 1·40 60
736 10r. "Bulbophyllum longiflorum" 2·25 3·50

211 Hesketh Bell Bridge

1987. Mauritius Bridges. Multicoloured.
758 25c. Type **211** 25 10
759 50c. Sir Colville Deverell Bridge 35 20
760 2r.50 Cavendish Bridge 70 75
761 5r. Tamarin Bridge 90 2·00
762 10r. Grand River North West Bridge 1·25 2·50

212 Supreme Court, Port Louis

213 Mauritius Dodo Mascot

1987. Bicentenary of the Mauritius Bar. Mult.
763 25c. Type **212** 10 10
764 1r. District Court, Flacq 40 10
765 1r.25 Statue of Justice 50 20
766 10r. Barristers of 1787 and 1987 2·00 2·25

1987. International Festival of the Sea. Mult.
767 25c. Type **213** 50 10
768 1r.50 Yacht regatta (horiz) 1·75 1·00
769 3r. Water skiing (horiz) 2·75 3·50
770 5r. "Svanen" (barquentine) 3·25 7·00

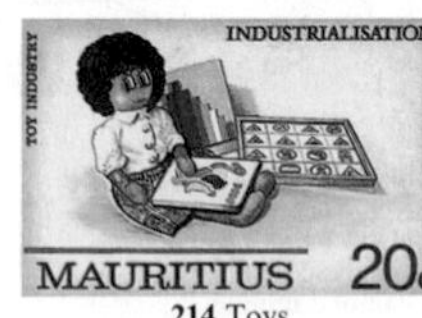

214 Toys

1987. Industrialization. Multicoloured.
771 20c. Type **214** 10 10
772 35c. Spinning factory 10 10
773 50c. Rattan furniture 10 10
774 2r.50 Spectacle factory 85 80
775 10r. Stone carving 2·50 2·75

215 Maison Ouvriere (Int Year of Shelter for the Homeless)

1987. Art and Architecture.
776 **215** 25c. multicoloured 10 10
777 – 1r. black and grey 25 10
778 – 1r.25 multicoloured 30 30
779 – 2r. multicoloured 55 55
780 – 5r. multicoloured 1·00 1·25
DESIGNS: 1r. "Paul et Virginie" (lithograph); 1r.25, Chateau de Rosnay; 2r. "Vieille Ferme" (Boulle); 5r. "Trois Mamelles".

216 University of Mauritius

1988. 20th Anniv of Independence. Mult.
781 25c. Type **216** 10 10
782 75c. Anniversary gymnastic display 20 10
783 2r.50 Hurdlers and aerial view of Sir Maurice Rault Stadium 70 55
784 5r. Air Mauritius aircraft at Sir Seewoosagur Ramgoolam International Airport 1·40 1·60
785 10r. Governor-General Sir Veerasamy Ringadoo and Prime Minister Anerood Jugnauth 2·25 2·75

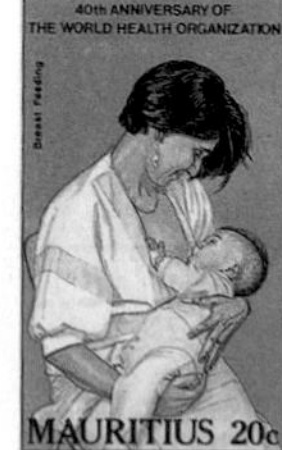

217 Breast Feeding

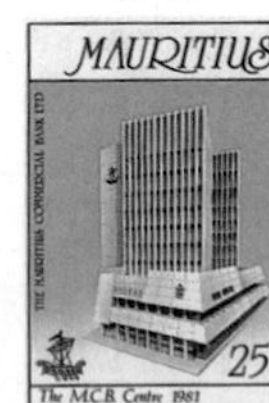

218 Modern Bank Building

1988. 40th Anniv of W.H.O. Multicoloured.
786 20c. Type **217** 15 10
787 2r. Baby under vaccination umbrella and germ droplets 1·25 70
788 3r. Nutritious food 1·40 1·25
789 10r. W.H.O. logo 2·75 3·75

1988. 150th Anniv of Mauritius Commercial Bank Ltd.
790 **218** 25c. black, green and blue 10 10
791 – 1r. black and red 20 10
792 – 1r.25 multicoloured 40 30
793 – 25r. multicoloured 6·50 8·50
DESIGNS—HORIZ: 1r. Mauritius Commercial Bank, 1897; 25r. Fifteen dollar bank note of 1838. VERT: 1r.25, Bank arms.

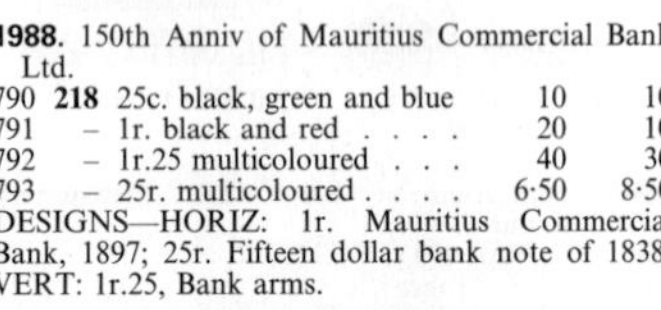

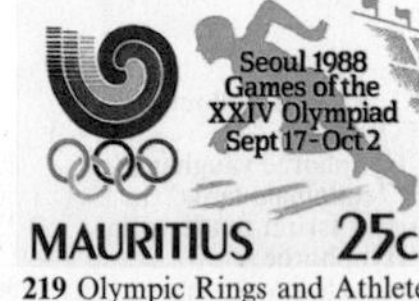

219 Olympic Rings and Athlete

1988. Olympic Games, Seoul. Multicoloured.
794 25c. Type **219** 10 10
795 35c. Wrestling 15 15
796 1r.50 Long distance running 75 60
797 10r. Swimming 2·50 4·00

220 Nature Park

1989. Protection of the Environment. Mult.
798B 15c. Underwater view 15 1·25
799B 20c. As 15c. 15 1·25
800B 30c. Common greenshank ("Greenshank") 1·00 1·25
801B 40c. Type **220** 15 60
810A 50c. Round Island (vert) 15 10
801cB 60c. As 50c. 20 10
811A 75c. Bassin Blanc 20 10
812A 1r. Mangrove (vert) 20 10
802A 1r.50 Whimbrel 1·00 35
813A 2r. Le Morne 30 20
803A 3r. Marine life 50 20
804B 4r. Fern tree (vert) 50 70
814A 5r. Riviere du Poste estuary 60 50
805A 6r. Ecological scenery (vert) 60 50
806B 10r. "Phelsuma ornata" (gecko) on plant (vert) 85 1·40
806aB 15r. Benares waves 1·50 2·50
807B 25r. Migratory birds and map (vert) 3·50 3·50

221 La Tour Sumeire, Port Louis

222 Cardinal Jean Margeot

1989. Bicentenary of the French Revolution.
818 **221** 30c. black, green & yellow 10 10
819 – 1r. black, brown and light brown 25 10
820 – 8r. multicoloured 2·00 2·25
821 – 15r. multicoloured 2·50 3·50
DESIGNS: 1r. Salle de Spectacle du Jardin; 8r. Portrait of Comte de Malartic; 15r. Bicentenary logo.

1989. Visit of Pope John Paul II. Multicoloured.
822 30c. Type **222** 30 10
823 40c. Pope John Paul II and Prime Minister Jugnauth, Vatican, 1988 80 25
824 3r. Mere Marie Magdeleine de la Croix and Chapelle des Filles de Marie, Port Louis, 1864 1·50 1·25
825 6r. St. Francois d'Assise Church, Pamplemousses, 1756 2·25 2·50
826 10r. Pope John Paul II 5·00 6·00

223 Nehru

1989. Birth Centenary of Jawaharlal Nehru (Indian statesman). Multicoloured.
827 40c. Type **223** 1·00 20
828 1r.50 Nehru with daughter, Indira, and grandsons 2·50 85
829 3r. Nehru and Gandhi 4·00 2·75
830 4r. Nehru with Presidents Nasser and Tito 3·25 3·00
831 10r. Nehru with children 5·50 9·00

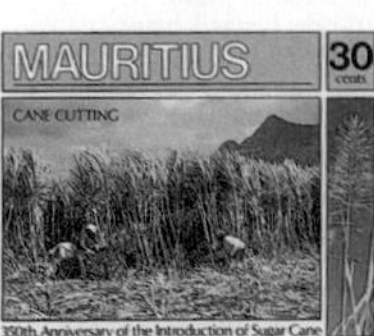

224 Cane Cutting

1990. 350th Anniv of Introduction of Sugar Cane to Mauritius. Multicoloured.
832 30c. Type **224** 15 10
833 40c. Sugar factory, 1867 20 10
834 1r. Mechanical loading of cane 40 10
835 25r. Modern sugar factory 11·00 13·00

225 Industrial Estate

226 Desjardins (naturalist) (150th death anniv)

1990. 60th Birthday of Prime Minister Sir Anerood Jugnauth. Multicoloured.
836 35c. Type **225** 10 10
837 40c. Sir Anerood Jugnauth at desk 10 10
838 1r.50 Mauritius Stock Exchange symbol 40 30
839 4r. Jugnauth with Governor-General Sir Seewoosagur Ramgoolam 1·50 2·25
840 10r. Jugnauth greeting Pope John Paul II 10·00 11·00

1990. Anniversaries. Multicoloured.
841 30c. Type **226** 30 10
842 35c. Logo on TV screen (25th anniv of Mauritius Broadcasting Corporation) (horiz) 30 10
843 6r. Line Barracks (now Police Headquarters) (250th anniv) 4·50 4·75
844 8r. Town Hall, Curepipe (centenary of municipality) (horiz) 3·50 5·50

227 Letters from Alphabets

1990. International Literacy Year. Multicoloured.
845 30c. Type **227** 25 10
846 1r. Blind child reading Braille 1·75 15
847 3r. Open book and globe 3·00 2·25
848 10r. Book showing world map with quill pen 9·50 11·00

1991. 65th Birthday of Queen Elizabeth II and 70th Birthday of Prince Philip. As T **58** of Kiribati. Multicoloured.
849 8r. Queen Elizabeth II 1·40 2·50
850 8r. Prince Philip in Grenadier Guards ceremonial uniform 1·40 2·50

228 City Hall, Port Louis (25th anniv of City status)

1991. Anniversaries and Events. Multicoloured.
851 40c. Type **228** 10 10
852 4r. Colonel Draper (race course founder) (150th death anniv) (vert) 1·75 2·00
853 6r. Joseph Barnard (engraver) and "POST PAID" 2d. stamp (175th birth anniv) (vert) 2·00 2·75
854 10r. Supermarine Spitfire "Mauritius II" (50th anniv of Second World War) 4·50 8·00

229 "Euploea euphon"

1991. "Phila Nippon '91" International Stamp Exn, Tokyo. Butterflies. Multicoloured.
855 40c. Type **229** 60 20
856 3r. "Hypolimnas misippus" (female) 1·90 1·00
857 8r. "Papilio manlius" 3·50 4·25
858 10r. "Hypolimnas misippus" (male) 3·50 4·50

230 Green Turtle, Tromelin

1991. Indian Ocean Islands. Multicoloured.

859 40c. Type **230** 50 20
860 1r. Glossy ibis ("Ibis"), Agalega . . . . 1·50 40
861 2r. Takamaka flowers, Chagos Archipelago . . . 1·60 1·10
862 15r. Violet spider conch sea shell, St. Brandon . . . . 7·00 9·50

231 Pres. Veerasamy Ringadoo and President's Residence

1992. Proclamation of Republic. Multicoloured.

863 40c. Type **231** 10 10
864 4r. Prime Minister Anerood Jugnauth and Government House . . . . 1·00 1·25
865 8r. Children and rainbow . . 2·25 3·75
866 10r. Presidential flag . . . . 4·50 4·75

232 Ticolo (mascot)

233 Bouquet (25th anniv of Fleurir Maurice)

1992. 8th African Athletics Championships, Port Louis. Multicoloured.

867 40c. Type **232** 10 10
868 4r. Sir Anerood Jugnauth Stadium (horiz) . . . . . 75 1·25
869 5r. High jumping (horiz) . . 90 1·40
870 6r. Championships emblem 1·25 1·90

1992. Local Events and Anniversaries. Mult.

871 40c. Type **233** 15 10
872 1r. Swami Krishnanandji Maharaj (25th anniv of arrival) 50 10
873 2r. Boy with dog (humane education) (horiz) . . . . 1·40 75
874 3r. Commission Headquarters (10th anniv of Indian Ocean Commission) (horiz) 1·25 1·00
875 15r. Radio telescope antenna, Bras d'Eau (project inauguration) (horiz) . . . 4·50 7·50

234 Bank of Mauritius Headquarters

235 Housing Development

1992. 25th Anniv of Bank of Mauritius. Mult.

876 40c. Type **234** 10 10
877 4r. Dodo gold coin (horiz) . . 1·75 1·10
878 8r. First bank note issue (horiz) . . . . 2·50 3·25
879 15r. Graph of foreign exchange reserves, 1967–92 (horiz) . . . . 4·50 7·50

1993. 25th Anniv of National Day. Multicoloured.

880 30c. Type **235** 10 10
881 40c. Gross domestic product graph on computer screen 10 10
882 3r. National colours on map of Mauritius 40 60
883 4r. Ballot box 45 75
884 15r. Grand Commander's insignia for Order of Star and Key of the Indian Ocean . . . . 2·00 5·00

236 Bell 206 B JetRanger Helicopter

1993. 25th Anniv of Air Mauritius Ltd. Mult.

885 40c. Type **236** 70 30
886 3r. Boeing 747SP . . . . . . 1·25 1·25
887 4r. Aerospatiale/Aeritalia ATR 42 . . . . 1·40 1·50
888 10r. Boeing 767-200ER . . . 3·00 6·50
MS889 150 × 91 mm. Nos. 885/8 8·50 10·00

1993. No. 811 surch **40cs**.

890 40c. on 75c. Bassin Blanc . . 60 50

238 French Royal Charter, 1715, and Act of Capitulation, 1810

239 "Scotia" (cable ship) and Map of Cable Route

1993. 5th Summit of French-speaking Nations. Multicoloured.

891 1r. Type **238** 75 10
892 5r. Road signs . . . . 2·75 2·25
893 6r. Code Napoleon . . . . . 2·75 3·00
894 7r. Early Mauritius newspapers . . . . 2·75 3·25

1993. Centenary of Telecommunications. Mult.

895 40c. Type **239** 65 20
896 3r. Morse key and code . . . 1·25 90
897 4r. Signal Mountain Earth station . . . . 1·50 1·50
898 8r. Communications satellite 2·75 4·50

240 Indian Mongoose

1994. Mammals. Multicoloured.

899 40c. Type **240** 30 10
900 2r. Indian black-naped hare 1·10 40
901 8r. Pair of crab-eating macaques . . . . 2·75 3·75
902 10r. Adult and infant common tenrec . . . . . 3·00 4·00

241 Dr Edouard Brown-Sequard (physiologist) (death cent)

1994. Anniversaries and Events. Multicoloured.

903 40c. Type **241** 15 10
904 4r. Family in silhouette (International Year of the Family) 45 55
905 8r. World Cup and map of U.S.A. (World Cup Football Championship, U.S.A.) . . . . 1·25 2·25
906 10r. Control tower, SSR International Airport (50th anniv of Civil Aviation Organization) . . . . . . 1·50 2·50

242 "St. Geran" leaving L'Orient for Isle de France, 1744

1994. 250th Anniv of Wreck of "St. Geran" (sailing packet). Multicoloured.

907 40c. Type **242** 25 10
908 5r. In rough seas off Isle de France 75 80
909 6r. Bell and main mast . . . 85 1·25
910 10r. Artifacts from wreck . . 1·40 3·00
MS911 119 × 89 mm. 15r. "St. Geran" leaving L'Orient (vert) . . . . 3·75 5·00

243 Ring-a-ring-a-roses

1994. Children's Games and Pastimes. Children's paintings. Multicoloured.

912 30c. Type **243** 10 10
913 40c. Skipping and ball games 10 10
914 8r. Water sports . . . . . . 1·40 2·25
915 10r. Blind man's buff . . . . 1·40 2·25

244 Nutmeg

245 Mare Longue Reservoir

1995. Spices. Multicoloured.

916 40c. Type **244** 10 10
917 4r. Coriander 55 65
918 5r. Cloves 65 80
919 10r. Cardamom . . . . . . 1·25 2·50

1995. 50th Anniv of End of Second World War. As T **75** of Kiribati, but 35 × 28 mm. Mult.

920 5r. H.M.S. "Mauritius" (cruiser) . . . . 1·75 2·25
921 5r. Mauritian soldiers and map of North Africa . . . 1·75 2·25
922 5r. Consolidated PBY-5 Catalina flying boat, Tombeau Bay . . . . . . 1·75 2·25

1995. Anniversaries. Multicoloured.

923 40c. Type **245** (50th anniv of construction) 15 10
924 4r. Mahebourg to Curepipe road (bicentenary of construction) . . . . . . 1·25 1·40
925 10r. Buildings on fire (centenary of Great Fire of Port Louis) . . . . 2·50 3·25

246 Ile Plate Lighthouse

247 Symbolic Children under U.N.I.C.E.F. Umbrella

1995. Lighthouses. Multicoloured.

926 30c. Type **246** 85 20
927 40c. Pointe aux Caves . . . 85 20
928 8r. Ile aux Fouquets . . . . 3·00 3·25
929 10r. Pointe aux Canonniers 3·50 3·75
MS930 130 × 100 mm. Nos. 926/9 9·00 9·50

1995. 50th Anniv of United Nations. Multicoloured.

931 40c. Type **247** 10 10
932 4r. Hard hat and building construction (I.L.O.) . . . 40 55
933 8r. Satellite picture of cyclone (W.M.O.) . . . . 85 1·40
934 10r. Bread and grain (F.A.O.) 1·00 1·60

248 C.O.M.E.S.A. Emblem

1995. Inauguration of Common Market for Eastern and Southern Africa.

935 **248** 60c. black and pink . . . 10 10
936 4r. black and blue 40 55
937 8r. black and yellow . . . 85 1·40
938 10r. black and green . . . 1·00 1·60

249 "Pachystyla bicolor"

1996. Snails. Multicoloured.

939 60c. Type **249** 15 10
940 4r. "Gonidomus pagodus" . . 65 55
941 5r. "Harmogenanina implicata" 65 65
942 10r. "Tropidophora eugeniae" . . . . 1·10 1·75

250 Boxing

1996. Centenary of Modern Olympic Games. Mult.

943 60c. Type **250** 10 10
944 4r. Badminton 50 50
945 5r. Basketball 80 80
946 10r. Table tennis . . . . . . 1·25 2·00

251 "Zambezia" (freighter)

1996. Ships. Multicoloured.

947 60c. Type **251** 20 10
948 4r. "Sir Jules" (coastal freighter) 65 55
949 5r. "Mauritius" (cargo liner) 75 75
950 10r. "Mauritius Pride" (container ship) . . . . . 1·50 2·25
MS951 125 × 91 mm. Nos. 947/50 2·75 3·50

252 Posting a Letter

1996. 150th Anniv of the Post Office Ordinance. Multicoloured.

952 60c. Type **252** 15 10
953 4r. "B53" duplex postmark 55 55
954 5r. Modern mobile post office 65 65
955 10r. Carriole (19th-century horse-drawn postal carriage) . . . . 1·50 1·75

253 Vavang

1997. Fruits. Multicoloured.

956 60c. Type **253** 10 10
957 4r. Pom zako 45 50
958 5r. Zambos 55 60
959 10r. Sapot negro . . . . . . 1·00 1·50

254 Governor Mahe de la Bourdonnais and Map

1997. Aspects of Mauritius History. Multicoloured.

960 60c. Type **254** 40 15
961 1r. La Perouse and map of Pacific 55 15
962 4r. Governor Sir William Gomm and Lady Gomm's Ball, 1847 . . . . 90 60
963 6r. George Clark discovering skeleton of dodo, 1865 . . 1·40 1·50
964 10r. Professor Brian Abel-Smith and Social Policies report of 1960 . . . . . . 1·50 2·25

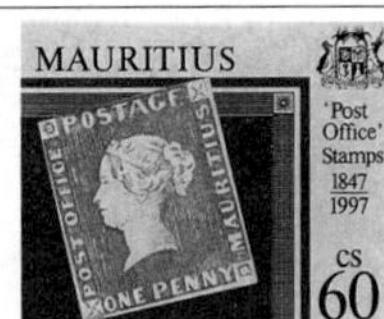

255 1d. "POST OFFICE" Mauritius

1997. 150th Anniv of "POST OFFICE" Stamps. Multicoloured.

965 60c. Type **255** 25 10
966 4r.2d. "POST OFFICE" Mauritius 70 60
967 5r. "POST OFFICE" 1d. and 2d. on gold background . . 1·00 1·25
968 10r. "POST OFFICE" 2d. and 1d. on silver background . . . . . . 1·75 2·50
MS969 127 × 90 mm. 20r. "POST OFFICE" stamps on cover to Bordeaux . . . . 3·00 3·50

256 Wheelwright

1997. Small Businesses. Multicoloured.

970 60c. Type **256** 10 10
971 4r. Laundryman 40 40
972 5r. Shipwright 65 65
973 15r. Quarryman . . . . . . 2·50 3·25

257 "Phelsuma guentheri" (gecko)

1998. Geckos. Multicoloured.

974 1r. Type **257** 20 10
975 6r. "Nactus serpensinsula durrelli" 55 65
976 7r. "Nactus coindemirensis" 65 1·25
977 8r. "Phelsuma edwardnewtonii" . . . . . 75 1·25

258 Steam Train on Viaduct

1998. Inland Transport. Multicoloured.

978 40c. Type **258** 35 10
979 5r. Early lorry 75 55
980 6r. Bus in town street 90 90
981 10r. Sailing barge at wharf 1·75 2·75

259 President Nelson Mandela

1998. State Visit of President Nelson Mandela of South Africa.

982 **259** 25r. multicoloured . . . . 2·50 3·25

260 Count Maurice of Nassau and Dutch Landing

1998. 400th Anniv of Dutch Landing on Mauritius. Multicoloured.

983 50c. Type **260** 20 10
984 1r. Fort Frederik Hendrik and sugar cane 20 10
985 7r. Dutch map of Mauritius (1670) . . . . 1·50 1·75
986 8r. Diagram of landing . . . 1·50 1·75
MS987 105 × 80 mm. 25r. Two Dutch ships . . . . 3·25 3·75

261 Cascade Balfour

1998. Waterfalls. Multicoloured.

988 1r. Type **261** 30 10
989 5r. Rochester Falls 70 55
990 6r. Cascade G.R.S.E. (vert) 80 80
991 10r. 500ft. Cascade (vert) . . 1·50 2·00

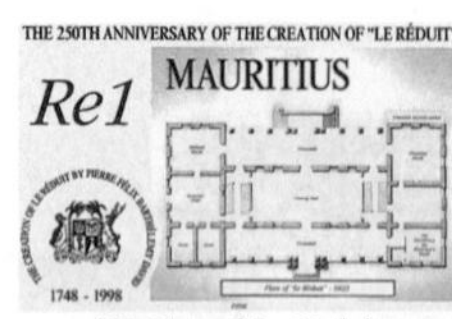

262 Plan of Le Reduit

1998. 250th Anniv of Chateau Le Reduit. Multicoloured.

992 1r. Type **262** 20 10
993 4r. "Le Chateau du Reduit, 1814" (P. Thuillier) 50 45
994 5r. "Le Reduit, 1998" (Hassen Edun) 60 55
995 15r. Commemorative monument . . . . 1·75 2·50

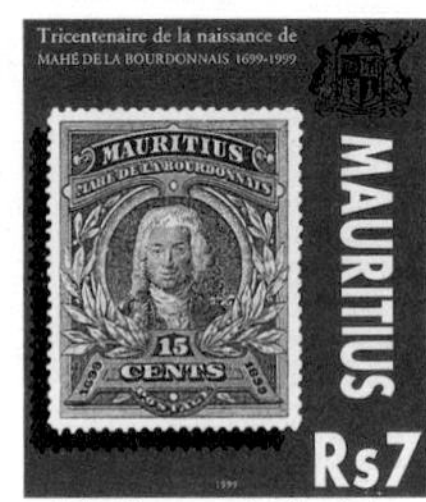

263 Governor Mahe de la Bourdonnais on 15c. Stamp of 1899

1999. 300th Birth Anniv of Governor Mahe de la Bourdonnais.

996 **263** 7r. blue, black and red . . 75 1·00

264 "Clerodendron laciniatum"

1999. Local Plants. Multicoloured.

997 1r. Type **264** 10 10
998 2r. "Senecio lamarckianus" 15 15
999 5r. "Cylindrocline commersonii" 40 55
1000 9r. "Psiadia pollicina" . . . 75 1·50

265 "The Washerwomen" (Herve Masson)

1999. Mauritius through Local Artists' Eyes. Multicoloured.

1001 1r. Type **265** 15 10
1002 3r. "The Casino" (Gaetan de Rosnay) 45 45
1003 4r. "The Four Elements" (Andree Poilly) 55 55
1004 6r. "Going to Mass" (Xavier Le Juge de Segrais) . . . . 75 1·00

266 Old Chimney, Alma

1999. Old Sugar Mill Chimneys. Multicoloured.

1005 1r. Type **266** 15 10
1006 2r. Antoinette 30 15
1007 5r. Belle Mare 65 65
1008 7r. Grande Rosalie . . . . 85 1·25
MS1009 132 × 100 mm. Nos. 1005/8 1·75 2·25

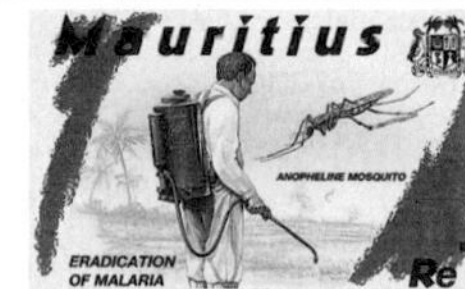

267 Mosquito and Sprayer (Eradication of Malaria)

1999. 20th-century Achievements. Multicoloured.

1010 1r. Type **267** 30 10
1011 2r. Judge's robes, silhouette and airliner (emancipation of women) 60 20
1012 5r. Conference room (international conference centre) 80 75
1013 9r. Spoons full of sugar (development of sugar industry) . . . . 1·40 1·90

268 Crest

2000. 150th Anniv of Mauritius Chamber of Commerce and Industry. Multicoloured.

1014 1r. Type **268** 25 15
1015 2r. Unity, Vision and Service logos 45 20
1016 7r. Francis Channell (First Secretary, 1850–72) . . . 1·10 1·25
1017 15r. Louis Lechelle (First President, 1850) . . . . . 1·75 3·00

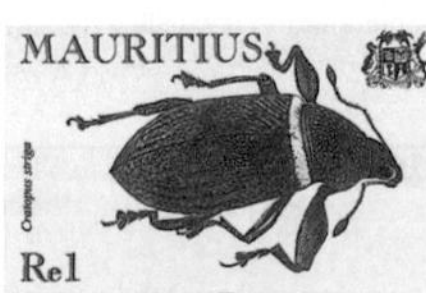

269 "Cratopus striga" (beetle)

2000. Beetles. Multicoloured.

1018 1r. Type **269** 15 10
1019 2r. "Cratopus armatus" . . 25 15
1020 3r. "Cratopus chrysochlorus" 40 25
1021 15r. "Cratopus nigrogranatus" . . . . . 1·50 2·00
MS1022 130 × 100 mm. Nos. 1018/21 2·00 2·25

270 Handball

2000. Olympic Games, Sydney. Multicoloured.

1023 1r. Type **270** 20 10
1024 2r. Archery 35 15
1025 5r. Sailing 70 60
1026 15r. Judo . . . . 1·50 2·00

271 Sir Seewoosagur Ramgoolam greeting Mother Teresa, 1984

2000. Birth Centenary of Sir Seewoosagur Ramgoolam (former Prime Minister). Multicoloured.

1027 1r. Type **271** 70 15
1028 2r. Election as member of Legislative Council, 1948 (vert) 30 15
1029 5r. As a student, 1926 (vert) 70 60
1030 15r. As Prime Minister, 1968 (vert) . . . . 1·50 2·00

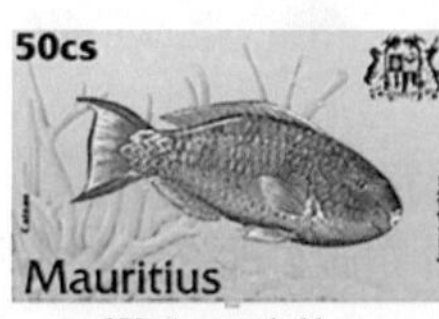

272 *Scarus ghobban*

2000. Fish. Multicoloured.

1031 50c. Type **272** 10 10
1032 1r. *Cephalopholis sonnerati* 10 10
1033 2r. *Naso brevirostris* 10 10
1034 3r. *Lethrinus nebulosus* . . . 10 15
1035 4r. *Centropyge debelius* . . . 15 20
1036 5r. *Amphiprion chrysogaster* 20 25
1037 6r. *Forcipiger flavissimus* . . 25 30
1038 7r. *Acanthurus leucosternon* 30 35
1039 8r. *Pterois volitans* 30 35
1040 10r. *Siderea grisea* 40 45
1041 15r. *Carcharhinus wheeleri* 60 65
1042 25r. *Istiophrous platypterus* 1·00 1·10
MS1043 Three sheets, each 132 × 102 mm. (a) Nos. 1031/3 and 1042. (b) Nos. 1035 and 1038/40. (c) Nos. 1034, 1036/7 and 1041
Set of 3 sheets . . . . 6·50 8·00

273 Affan Tank Wen

275 African Slave and Indian Indentured Labourer

274 Finished Pullover

2000. Famous Mauritians. Multicoloured.

1044 1r. Type **273** 25 10
1045 5r. Alphonse Ravatoni . . . 65 50
1046 7r. Dr. Idrice Goumany . . 90 1·10
1047 9r. Anjalay Coopen . . . . 1·10 1·40

2001. Textile Industry. Multicoloured.

1048 1r. Type **274** 25 10
1049 3r. Computer-aided machinery 45 50
1050 6r. T-shirt folding 80 85
1051 10r. Embroidery machine . . 1·25 1·60

2001. Anti-slavery and Indentured Labour Campaign Commemoration.

1052 **275** 7r. multicoloured . . . . 1·00 1·10

276 *Foetidia mauritiana*

2001. Trees. Multicoloured.

1053 1r. Type **276** 25 10
1054 3r. *Diospyros tessellaria* . . 50 20
1055 5r. *Sideroxylon puberulum* 70 60
1056 15r. *Gastonia mauritiana* . . 1·60 1·90

277 *Geographe* and *Naturaliste* (French corvettes)

2001. Bicentenary of Baudin's Expedition to New Holland (Australia). Multicoloured.

1057 1r. Type **277** 30 10
1058 4r. Capt. Nicholas Baudin and map of voyage . . . 70 35
1059 6r. Mascarene martin (bird) 1·00 85
1060 10r. M. F. Peron and title page of book (vert) . . . 1·40 1·75

278 Hotel School

2001. Mauritius Economic Achievements during the 20th Century. Multicoloured.

1061 2r. Type **278** 25 15
1062 3r. Steel bar milling 30 20
1063 6r. Solar energy panels, Agalega 60 60
1064 10r. Indian Ocean Rim Association for Regional Co-operation . . . . . . 1·25 1·60

279 Gandhi on Mauritius Stamp of 1969 **280** De-husking Coconuts

2001. Centenary of Gandhi's Visit to Mauritius.
1065 **279** 15r. multicoloured . . . 1·75 2·00

2001. Coconut Industry. Multicoloured.
1066 1r. Type **280** 20 10
1067 5r. Shelling coconuts (horiz) 60 40
1068 6r. Drying copra (horiz) . . 70 65
1069 10r. Extracting coconut oil 1·25 1·50

281 New Container Port

2002. 10th Anniv of Republic. Multicoloured.
1070 1r. Type **281** 20 10
1071 4r. Symbols of Mauritius stock exchange 45 35
1072 5r. New reservoir under construction 55 55
1073 9r. Motorway junction . . . 1·10 1·40

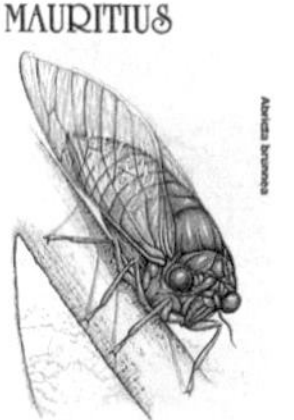

282 *Abricta* **284** Constellation of Orion

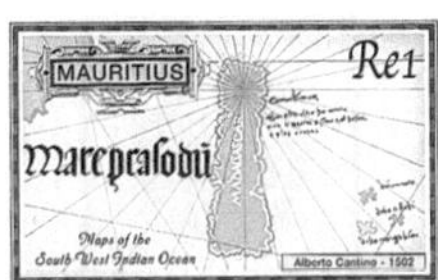

283 Map by Alberto Cantino, 1502

2002. Cicadas. Multicoloured.
1074 1r. Type **282** 15 10
1075 6r. *Fractuosella darwini* . . 60 50
1076 7r. *Distantada thomaseti* . . 70 70
1077 8r. *Dinarobia claudeae* . . . 80 90
MS1078 130 × 100 mm. Nos. 1074/7 2·00 2·25

2002. 16th-century Maps of the South-west Indian Ocean. Multicoloured.
1079 1r. Type **283** 20 10
1080 3r. Map by Jorge Reinel, 1520 . . . . 50 30
1081 4r. Map by Diogo Ribeiro, 1529 . . . . 60 45
1082 10r. Map by Gerard Mercator, 1569 . . . . . 1·40 1·60

2002. Constellations. Multicoloured.
1083 1r. Type **284** 20 10
1084 7r. Sagittarius 70 70
1085 8r. Scorpius 80 85
1086 9r. Southern Cross 90 95

285 African Growth and Opportunity Act Logo **286** Echo Parakeet Chick

2003. 2nd United States/Sub-Saharan Africa Trade and Economic Co-operation Forum.
1087 **285** 1r. red, blue and yellow 15 10
1088 25r. red, ultramarine and blue . . . . 2·10 2·40

2003. Endangered Species. Echo Parakeet. Multicoloured.
1089 1r. Type **286** 20 10
1090 2r. Fledgling 35 15
1091 5r. Female parakeet 70 50
1092 15r. Male parakeet . . . . 1·50 1·60

287 *Trochetia boutoniana*

2003. Trochetias. Multicoloured.
1093 1r. Type **287** 10 10
1094 4r. *Trochetia uniflora* . . . 15 20
1095 7r. *Trochetia triflora* 30 35
1096 9r. *Trochetia parviflora* . . . 40 45

288 Dolphin Emblem (Sixth Indian Ocean Games, Mauritius)

2003. Anniversaries and Events. Multicoloured.
1097 2r. Type **288** 10 10
1098 6r. Crop in field and emblem (150th anniv of Mauritius Chamber of Agriculture) 25 30
1099 9r. Journal of voyage of Bonne Esperance (250th anniv of visit of Abbe de la Caille) 40 45
1100 10r. Sugar cane and emblem (50th anniv of Mauritius Sugar Industry Research Institute) 40 45

289 Batterie de la Pointe du Diable

2003. Fortifications. Multicoloured.
1101 2r. Type **289** 10 10
1102 5r. Donjon St. Louis . . . 20 25
1103 6r. Martello Tower 25 30
1104 12r. Fort Adelaide 50 55

EXPRESS DELIVERY STAMPS

1903. No. 136 surch **EXPRESS DELIVERY 15c.**
E1 **40** 15c. on 15c. blue . . . . . 8·50 23·00

1903. No. 136 surch **EXPRESS DELIVERY (INLAND) 15c.**
E3 **40** 15c. on 15c. blue . . . . . 7·50 3·00

1904. T **42** without value in label. (a) Surch **(FOREIGN) EXPRESS DELIVERY 18 CENTS.**
E5 **42** 18c. green . . . . 1·75 24·00

(b) Surch **EXPRESS DELIVERY (INLAND) 15c.**
E6 **42** 15c. green . . . . 4·25 4·25

POSTAGE DUE STAMPS

D 1

1933.
D 1 **D 1** 2c. black . . . . 1·25 50
D 2 4c. violet 50 65
D 3 6c. red 60 80
D 4 10c. green . . . . 70 1·25
D 5 20c. blue . . . . 50 1·50
D13 50c. purple . . . . . . 75 12·00
D 7 1r. orange . . . . 70 16·00

1982. Nos. 530/1, 535, 540, 542 and 547 surch **POSTAGE DUE** and value.
D14 10c. on 15c. Dutch Occupation, 1638–1710 . . 20 50
D15 20c. on 20c. Van Keulen's map, c. 1700 . . . . . . 30 50
D16 50c. on 60c. Pierre Poivre, c. 1767 (vert) . . . 30 30
D17 1r. on 1r.20 Government House, c. 1840 . . . . . 40 30
D18 1r.50 on 1r.50 Indian immigration, 1835 . . . . 50 75
D19 5r. on 15r. Unfurling Mauritian flag, 1968 . . . 1·00 2·25

MAYOTTE Pt. 6

One of the Comoro Islands adjacent to Madagascar.

In 1974 (when the other islands became an independent state) Mayotte was made an Overseas Department of France, using French stamps. From 1997 it again had its own issues.

100 centimes = 1 franc.

1892. "Tablet" key-type inscr "MAYOTTE".
1 D 1c. black and red on blue . . 1·25 75
2 2c. brown and blue on buff 1·75 1·90
3 4c. brown and blue on grey 2·25 2·25
4 5c. green and red on green 2·50 2·75
5 10c. black and blue on lilac 4·75 4·50
15 10c. red and blue . . . . . 30·00 45·00
6 15c. blue and red . . . . . 10·50 9·50
16 15c. grey and red . . . . . 90·00 75·00
7 20c. red and blue on green 11·00 11·00
8 25c. black and red on pink 6·50 5·50
17 25c. blue and red . . . . . 7·00 8·50
9 30c. brown and blue on drab 14·50 14·50
18 35c. black and red on yellow 4·50 4·00
10 40c. red and blue on yellow 13·50 13·00
19 45c. black on green . . . . 14·00 14·00
11 50c. red and blue on pink 22·00 18·00
20 50c. brown and red on blue 10·50 20·00
12 75c. brown & red on orange 19·00 22·00
13 1f. green and red . . . . . 15·00 19·00
14 5f. mauve and blue on lilac 95·00 10·00

1912. Surch in figures.
21 D 05 on 20c. brown and blue on buff . . . . 1·10 3·75
22 05 on 4c. brown and blue on grey . . . . 1·60 2·25
23 05 on 15c. blue and red . . 1·60 2·00
24 05 on 20c. red and blue on green . . . . 1·50 2·75
25 05 on 25c. black and red on pink . . . . 1·25 2·75
26 05 on 30c. brown and blue on drab . . . . 1·40 3·00
27 10 on 40c. red and blue on yellow . . . . 1·00 2·75
28 10 on 45c. black and red on green . . . . 1·50 1·40
29 10 on 50c. red and blue on pink . . . . 2·75 4·75
30 10 on 75c. brown and red on orange . . . . 1·90 3·75
31 10 on 1f. green and red . . 2·75 3·25

1997. Stamps of France optd **MAYOTTE**. (a) Nos. 2907/10, 2912, 2917, 2924 and 2929/30.
40 **1118** 10c. brown 15 10
41 20c. green 15 10
42 50c. violet 15 10
43 1f. orange 35 15
44 2f. blue 60 35
45 2f.70 green 80 45
46 3f.80 blue . . . . 1·00 55
47 5f. blue . . . . 1·75 70
48 10f. violet . . . . 3·50 1·50

(b) No. 3121. No value expressed.
49 **1118** (–) red 75 55
No. 49 was sold at 3f.

6 Ylang-ylang

1997.
50 **6** 2f.70 multicoloured 85 50

7 Arms

1997.
51 **7** 3f. multicoloured 70 40

8 Terminal Building and Airplane

1997. Air. Inauguration of New Airport.
52 **8** 20f. indigo, red and blue . . 6·00 2·75

9 Le Banga

1997.
53 **9** 3f.80 multicoloured 95 55

10 Dzen-dze (musical instrument)

1997.
54 **10** 5f.20 multicoloured . . . . 1·40 70

1997. Stamps of France optd **MAYOTTE**. (a) On Nos. 3415/20, 3425, 3430 and 3432.
55 **1318** 10c. brown 15 10
56 20c. green 15 10
57 50c. violet 15 10
58 1f. orange 30 15
59 2f. blue 50 35
60 2f.70 green 55 40
62 3f.80 blue 80 55
66 5f. blue . . . . 1·10 65
68 10f. violet . . . . 2·40 1·25

(b) On No. 3407. No value expressed. Ordinary or self-adhesive gum.
69 **1318** (3f.) red 75 35

11 Lemur

1997.
71 **11** 3f. brown and red 80 45

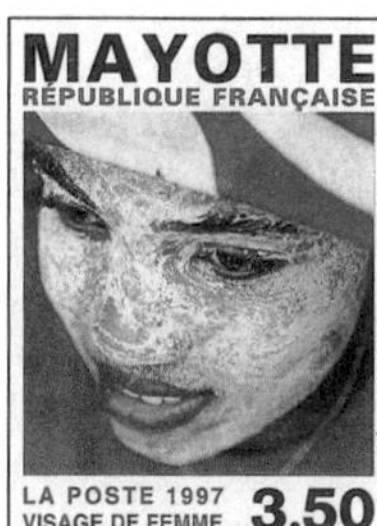

12 Woman's Face

1997.
72 **12** 3f.50 multicoloured 85 55

13 Fishes and Corals

1997. Marine Life.
73 **13** 3f. multicoloured 75 45

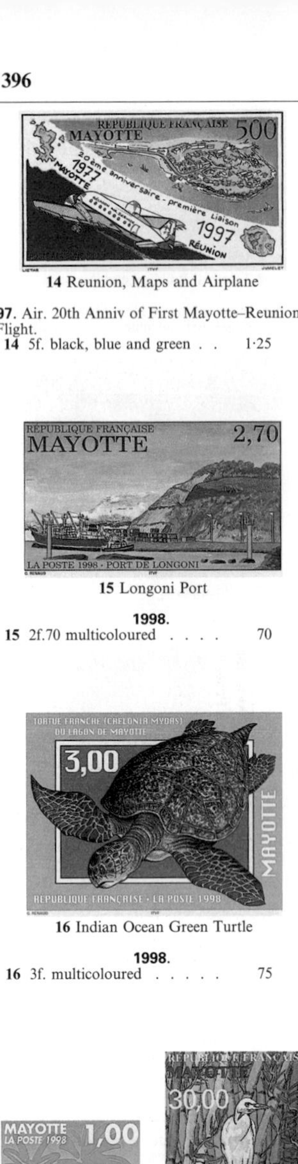

14 Reunion, Maps and Airplane

1997. Air. 20th Anniv of First Mayotte–Reunion Air Flight.
74 **14** 5f. black, blue and green . . 1·25 75

15 Longoni Port

1998.
75 **15** 2f.70 multicoloured 70 40

16 Indian Ocean Green Turtle

1998.
76 **16** 3f. multicoloured 75 45

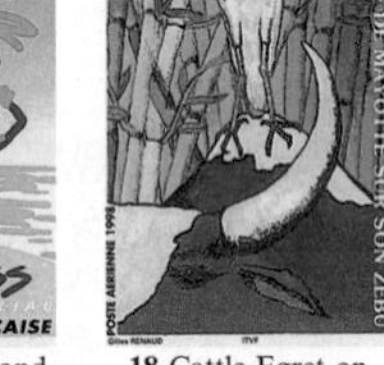

17 Family on Island — 18 Cattle Egret on Zebu's Head

1998. Family Planning.
77 **17** 1f. multicoloured 25 10

1998. Air.
78 **18** 30f. multicoloured . . . . . 7·50 3·75

19 Children in Costume

1998. Children's Carnival.
79 **19** 3f. multicoloured 75 40

20 "Salama Djema II" (ferry)

1998. Mamoudzou–Dzaoudzi Ferry.
80 **20** 3f.80 multicoloured 90 50

21 Tsingoni Mosque — 22 Mariama Salim

1998.
81 **21** 3f. multicoloured 75 40

1998. 2nd Death Anniv of Mariama Salim (women's rights activist).
82 **22** 2f.70 multicoloured 65 35

23 Spreading Nets

1998. Traditional Fishing, Djarifa.
83 **23** 2f. multicoloured 50 25

24 Emperor Angelfish

1998.
84 **24** 3f. multicoloured 70 40

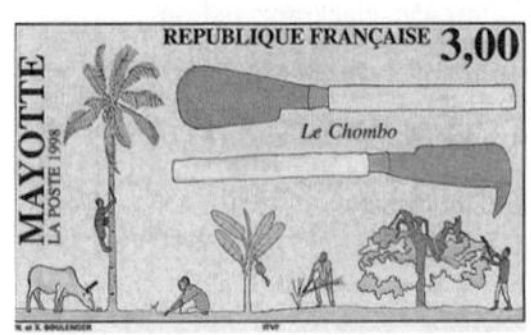

25 Chombos and Workers

1998. The Chombo (agricultural tool).
85 **25** 3f. multicoloured 65 40

26 Map of Mayotte

1999.
86 **26** 3f. multicoloured 65 40

27 Reservoir, Combani

1999.
87 **27** 8f. multicoloured . . . . . 1·90 1·00

28 Coral Hind

1999. Lagoon Fishes. Multicoloured.
88 2f.70 Type **28** 60 30
89 3f. Lionfish (horiz) 70 35
90 5f.20 Regal angelfish (horiz) 1·00 60
91 10f. Powder-blue surgeonfish (horiz) . . . . 2·25 1·10

1999. The Euro (European currency). No. 3553 of France optd **MAYOTTE**.
92 3f. red and blue 75 35

29 Genet

1999.
93 **29** 5f.40 orange, black & stone 1·40 70

30 Baobab Tree

1999.
94 **30** 8f. multicoloured . . . . . 1·90 1·00

1999. "Philexfrance 99" International Stamp Exhibition, Paris. Sheet 150 × 120 mm.
MS95 No. 51 × 4, multicoloured 3·00 3·00

31 Prefecture Building

1999. Dzaoudzi Prefecture.
96 **31** 3f. multicoloured 70 40

32 Pirogues

1999. Pirogues. Sheet 163 × 84 mm containing T **32** and similar multicoloured designs.
MS97 5f. Type **32**; 5f. Two pirogues (vert); 5f. Three pirogues . . . 3·50 3·50

33 Vanilla

1999.
98 **33** 4f.50 multicoloured 95 50

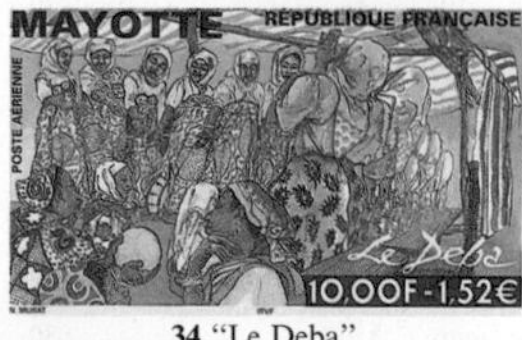

34 "Le Deba"

1999. Air.
99 **34** 10f. multicoloured . . . . . 2·10 1·10

35 Map of Mayotte, Arrow and "2000"

1999. Year 2000.
100 **35** 3f. multicoloured 65 40

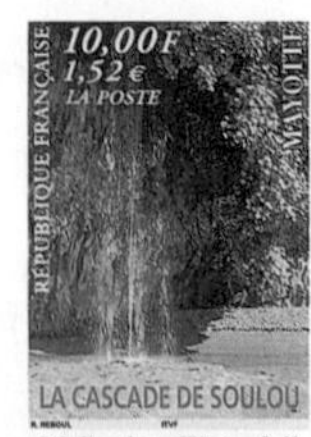

36 Soulou Waterfall

1999.
101 **36** 10f. multicoloured . . . . 2·00 1·10

37 Sailing Boat

2000. Indian Ocean.
102 **37** 3f. multicoloured 65 40

38 Two Whales

2000. Whales.
103 **38** 5f.20 multicoloured . . . . 1·10 60

39 Emblem

2000. District 920 of Inner Wheel (women's section of Rotary International).
104 **39** 5f.20 multicoloured . . . . 1·00 60

40 L'île au Lagon

2000.
105 **40** 3f. multicoloured 65 40

41 Woman wearing Traditional Clothes

2000. Women of Mayotte. Sheet 90 × 70 mm containing T **41** and similar vert design. Multicoloured.
MS106 3f. Type **41**; 5f.20, Women wearing modern clothes . . . 1·60 1·60

42 Tyre Race

2000.
107 **42** 3f. multicoloured 65 40

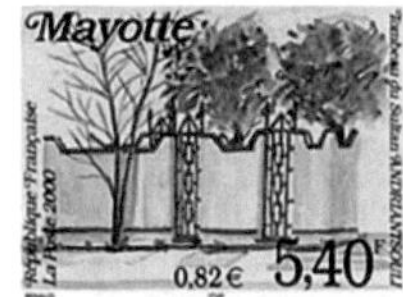

43 Sultan Andriantsouli's Tomb

2000.
108 **43** 5f.40 multicoloured . . . . 1·00 60

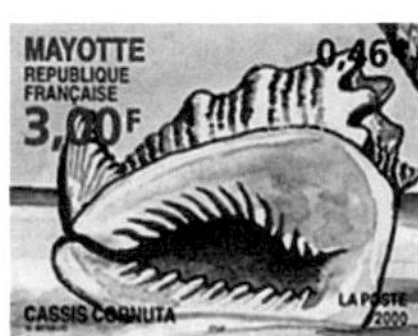

44 Horned Helmet

2000. Shells. Multicoloured.
109 3f. Type **44** 65 40
110 3f. Trumpet triton (*Charonia tritonis*) 65 40
111 3f. Bullmouth helmet (*Cypraecassis rufa*) 65 40
112 3f. Humpback cowrie (*Cyprae mauritiana*) (wrongly inscr "mauritania") and tiger cowrie (*Cyprae tigris*) . . . 65 40

Nos. 109/12 were issued together, se-tenant, with the backgrounds forming a composite design of a beach.

45 M'Dere

2000. 1st Death Anniv of Zena M'Dere.
113 **45** 3f. multicoloured 65 40

46 Distillery

2000. Ylang-ylang Distillery.
114 **46** 2f.70 multicoloured 60 35

47 Building

48 Map of Mayotte

2000. New Hospital.
115 **47** 10f. multicoloured . . . . 2·00 1·10

2001.
116 **48** 2f.70 black and green . . . 60 35

2001. No value expressed. As T **48**.
120 **48** (3f.) black and red 65 40

49 Mother breast-feeding

2001. Breast-feeding.
130 **49** 3f. multicoloured 65 40

50 Pilgrims

2001. Pilgrimage to Mecca.
131 **50** 2f.70 multicoloured 60 35

51 Bush Taxi

2001.
132 **51** 3f. multicoloured 65 40

52 Children playing Football

2001.
133 **52** 3f. multicoloured 60 35

53 Pyjama Cardinalfish

2001.
134 **53** 10f. multicoloured . . . . 2·00 1·25

54 Legionnaire, Map and Market Scene

2001. 25th Anniv of Mayotte Foreign Legion Detachment.
135 **54** 5f.20 multicoloured . . . . 1·00 60

55 Bats in Tree

2001. The Comoro Roussette. Sheet 65 × 90 mm containing T **55** and similar horiz design. Multicoloured.
MS136 3f. Type **55**; 5f.20, Bat in flight . . . . 1·60 1·60

56 Airplanes and Club House

2001. Air. Dzaoudzi Flying Club.
137 **56** 20f. multicoloured . . . . 4·00 2·40

57 Military Personnel and Building

2001. 1st Anniv of Adapted Military Service Units.
138 **57** 3f. multicoloured 60 35

58 *Protea* sp.

2001. Flower and Fruit. Multicoloured.
139 3f. Type **58** 60 35
140 5f.40 Selection of fruit . . . 1·00 60

59 Dziani Dzaha Lake

2001.
141 **59** 5f.20 multicoloured . . . . 1·00 60

60 Mayotte Post Office

2001.
142 **60** 10f. multicoloured . . . . 2·00 1·25

2002. Stamps of France optd **MAYOTTE**. (a) Nos. 3770/85.
143 **1318** 1c. yellow 10 10
144 2c. brown 10 10
145 5c. green 10 10
146 10c. violet 15 10
147 20c. orange 30 15
148 41c. green 55 35
149 50c. blue 70 40
150 53c. green 75 45
151 58c. blue 80 50
152 64c. orange 90 55
153 67c. blue 95 60
154 69c. mauve 95 60
155 €1 turquoise . . . . . 1·40 85
156 €1.02 green . . . . . . 1·40 85
157 €2 violet . . . . 2·75 1·60

(b) No value expressed. No. 3752.
166 41c. red 55 35

No. 166 was sold at the rate for inland letters up to 20 grammes.

61 Arms

2002. Attainment of Department Status within France (11 July 2001).
167 **61** 46c. multicoloured 65 40

62 Runners

2002. Athletics.
168 **62** 41c. multicoloured 55 35

63 Mangroves, Kaweni Basin

2002.
169 **63** €1.52 multicoloured . . . 2·10 1·60

64 Building Facade

66 House and People

65 Women processing Salt (½-size illustration)

2002. 25th Anniv of Mayotte Commune.
170 **64** 46c. multicoloured 65 40

2002. Salt Production at Bandrele.
171 **65** 79c. multicoloured . . . . 1·10 65

2002. National Census.
172 **66** 46c. multicoloured 65 40

67 Sunbird (inscr "Souimanga")

2002. Birds. Sheet 61 × 141 mm containing T **67** and similar horiz designs. Multicoloured.
MS173 46c. Type **67**; 46c. Drongo; 46c. Olive white eye (inscr "Oiseau-lunette"); 46c. Red-headed fody (inscr "Foudy") 2·40 2·40

68 Processing Machinery

2002. Remains of the Sugar Industry.
174 **68** 82c. multicoloured . . . . 1·10 65

69 Mount Choungui

70 Jack Fruit (inscr "Le Jaquier")

2002.
175 **69** 46c. multicoloured 60 35

2002.
176 **70** €1.22 multicoloured . . . 80 50

71 Museum Buildings

2003. Vanilla and Ylang Ylang Eco-museum.

177	**71**	46c. multicoloured	60	35

72 Bananas

2003.

178	**72**	79c. multicoloured	1·00	60

73 Woman with Painted Face

2003. Festival Masks.

179	**73**	46c. multicoloured	60	35

74 Sailfish

2003.

180	**74**	79c. multicoloured	1·00	60

75 Gecko

2003.

181	**75**	50c. multicoloured	65	40

76 Mraha Board and Counters (game)

2003.

182	**76**	€1.52 brown and mauve	2·00	1·20

77 Mtzamboro College

2003.

183	**77**	45c. multicoloured	60	35

78 Ziyara de Pole

2003.

184	**78**	82c. multicoloured	1·10	65

79 Players, Ball and Basket

2003. Basketball.

185	**79**	50c. multicoloured	65	40

80 Dzaoudzi Islet($\frac{1}{2}$-size illustration)

2003.

186	**80**	$1.50 multicoloured	2·00	1·20

81 Women Dancing ("Le Wadaha")

2004.

187	**81**	50c. multicoloured	65	40

MECKLENBURG-SCHWERIN Pt. 7

In northern Germany. Formerly a Grand Duchy, Mecklenburg-Schwerin joined the North German Confederation in 1868.

48 schilling = 1 thaler.

1

2

1856. Imperf.

1a	**1**	$\frac{1}{4}$s. red	£130	£110
1		$\frac{4}{4}$s. red	£130	95·00
2	**2**	3s. yellow	85·00	50·00
4		5s. blue	£200	£250

See note below No. 7.

1864. Roul.

5a	**1**	$\frac{1}{4}$s. red	£2500	£1600
6a		$\frac{1}{4}$s. red	£375	65·00
5		$\frac{4}{4}$s. red	£2250	£1800
6		$\frac{4}{4}$s. red	60·00	60·00
11	**2**	2s. purple	£225	£225
9		3s. yellow	£150	£110
7		5s. bistre	£130	£225

Nos. 1, 1a, 5, 5a have a dotted background, Nos. 6 and 6a a plain background. Prices for Nos. 1a, 5a and 6a are for quarter stamps; prices for Nos. 1, 5 and 6 are for the complete on cover stamp (four quarters) as illustrated in Type **1**.

MECKLENBURG-STRELITZ Pt. 7

In northern Germany. Formerly a Grand Duchy, Mecklenburg-Strelitz joined the North German Confederation in 1868.

30 silbergroschen = 1 thaler.

1

2

1864. Roul. Various frames.

2	**1**	$\frac{1}{4}$sgr. orange	£160	£1700
3		$\frac{1}{3}$sgr. green	65·00	£1200
6		1sch. mauve	£275	£3000
7	**2**	1sgr. red	£140	£170
9		2sgr. blue	32·00	£650
11		3sgr. bistre	32·00	£1200

MEMEL Pt. 7

A seaport and district on the Baltic Sea, formerly part of Germany. Under Allied control after the 1914–18 war, it was captured and absorbed by Lithuania in 1923 and returned to Germany in 1939. From 1945 the area has been part of Lithuania.

1920. 100 pfennig = 1 mark.
1923. 100 centu = 1 litas.

1920. Stamps of France surch **MEMEL** and **pfennig** or **mark** with figure of value.

1	**18**	5pf. on 5c. green	10	20
2		10pf. on 10c. red	10	15
3		20pf. on 25c. blue	10	20
4		30pf. on 30c. orange	10	20
19		40pf. on 20c. brown	10	15
5		50pf. on 35c. violet	10	65
6	**13**	60pf. on 40c. red and blue	20	60
7		80pf. on 45c. green and blue	50	60
8		1m. on 50c. brown and lilac	15	40
9		1m.25 on 60c. violet & blue	95	2·25
10		2m. on 1f. red and green	15	35
11		3m. on 2f. orange and green	9·50	28·00
12		3m. on 5f. blue and buff	11·00	28·00
13		4m. on 2f. orange and green	30	40
14		10m. on 5f. blue and buff	1·75	5·50
15		20m. on 5f. blue and buff	25·00	80·00

1920. Stamps of Germany inscr "DEUTSCHES REICH" optd **Memel- gebiet** or **Memelgebiet**.

25	**10**	5pf. green	30	1·00
26		10pf. red	2·10	6·00
27		10pf. orange	15	40
28	**24**	15pf. brown	2·40	6·00
29	**10**	20pf. blue	30	1·50
30		30pf. black & orange on buff	4·25	10·00
31		30pf. blue	25	3·75
32		40pf. black and red	30	2·40
33		50pf. black & purple on buff	25	85
34		60pf. green	55	1·60
35		75pf. black and green	2·00	6·75
36		80pf. blue	1·20	2·50
37	**12**	1m. red	65	1·40
38		1m.25 green	12·00	31·00
39		1m.50 brown	4·75	11·00
40	**13**	2m. blue	2·30	3·25
41		2m.50 purple	12·50	23·00

1921. Nos. 2/3, 5, 8, 10, 19 and 49 further surch in large figures.

42	**18**	15 on 10pf. on 10c. red	65	80
43		15 on 20pf. on 25c. blue	75	1·00
44		15 on 50pf. on 35c. violet	50	1·00
45		60 on 40pf. on 20c. brown	60	90
46	**13**	75 on 60pf. on 40c. red and blue (49)	1·20	1·60
47		1,25 on 1m. on 50c. brown and lilac	35	1·10
48		5,00 on 2m. on 1f. red and green	1·20	2·00

1921. Surch **MEMEL** and **Pfennig** or **Mark** with figure of value.

60	**18**	5pf. on 5c. orange	30	80
61		10pf. on 10c. red	1·20	2·50
62		10pf. on 10c. green	45	65
63		15pf. on 10c. green	35	1·10
64		20pf. on 20c. brown	5·75	16·00
65		20pf. on 25c. blue	5·75	16·00
66		25pf. on 5c. orange	10	60
67		30pf. on 30c. red	90	2·75
68		35pf. on 35c. violet	35	70
77	**13**	40pf. on 40c. red and blue	30	90
69	**15**	50pf. on 50c. blue	20	55
49	**13**	60pf. on 40c. red and blue	3·50	9·00
71	**15**	75pf. on 15c. green	25	95
70	**18**	75pf. on 35c. violet	25	45
78	**13**	80pf. on 45c. green & blue	20	75
72	**18**	1m. on 25c. blue	30	85
79	**13**	1m. on 40c. red and blue	15	55
73	**18**	$1\frac{1}{4}$m. on 30c. red	30	75
80	**13**	1m.25 on 60c. violet & bl	40	55
81		1m.50 on 45c. green & bl	35	90
82		2m. on 45c. green and blue	50	70
83		2m. on 1f. red and green	25	60
84		$2\frac{1}{4}$m. on 40c. red and blue	50	80
85		$2\frac{1}{2}$m. on 60c. violet and blue	60	1·30
74	**18**	3m. on 5c. orange	20	1·50
86	**13**	3m. on 60c. violet and blue	75	1·40
87		4m. on 45c. green and blue	30	1·00
88		5m. on 1f. red and green	50	1·00
75	**15**	6m. on 15c. green	30	1·60
89	**13**	6m. on 60c. violet and blue	80	95
90		6m. on 2f. orange & green	60	1·40
76	**18**	8m. on 30c. red	55	4·50
91	**13**	9m. on 1f. red and green	45	1·00
92		9m. on 5f. blue and buff	45	1·50
93		10m. on 45c. green & blue	60	1·90
51		10m. on 5f. blue and buff	80	1·70
94		12m. on 40c. red and blue	30	1·20
95		20m. on 40c. red and blue	1·00	2·10
52		20m. on 45c. green & blue	3·50	12·00
96		20m. on 2f. orange & green	50	1·10
97		30m. on 60c. violet & blue	65	2·10
98		30m. on 5f. blue and buff	3·75	8·50
90		40m. on 1f. red and green	35	1·60
100		50m. on 2f. orange & green	9·00	21·00
101		80m. on 2f. orange & green	65	2·00
102		100m. on 5f. blue and buff	1·20	3·75

1921. Air. Nos. 6/8, 10, 13 and 49/50 optd **FLUGPOST** in double-lined letters.

53	**13**	60pf. on 40c. red and blue	30·00	50·00
54		60pf. on 40c. red and blue (No. 49)	3·75	8·00
55		80pf. on 45c. green and blue	2·75	7·00
56		1m. on 50c. brown and lilac	2·50	5·50
57		2m. on 1f. red and green	2·75	6·00
58		3m. on 60c. violet and blue (No. 50)	3·00	7·75
59		4m. on 2f. orange and green	3·75	11·50

1922. Air. Nos. 13, 50, 77/81, 83, 86, 88, 90 and 92 further optd **Flugpost** in script letters.

103	**13**	40pf. on 40c. red and blue (No. 77)	95	1·60
104		80pf. on 45c. green and blue (No. 78)	85	1·60
105		1m. on 40c. red and blue (No. 68)	1·00	1·50
106		1m.25 on 60c. violet and blue (No. 80)	1·00	2·20
107		1m.50 on 45c. green and blue (No. 81)	95	2·40
108		2m. on 1f. red and green (No. 83)	1·30	2·40
110		3m. on 60c. violet and blue (No. 86)	1·30	2·00
111		4m. on 2f. orange and green (No. 13)	1·10	2·20
112		5m. on 1f. red and green (No. 88)	1·20	2·10
113		6m. on 2f. orange and green (No. 90)	1·10	2·30
114		9m. on 5f. blue and buff (No. 92)	1·40	2·20

1922. Air. Surch as in 1921 and optd **FLUGPOST** in ordinary capitals.

115	**13**	40pf. on 40c. red and blue	1·20	5·00
116		1m. on 40c. red and blue	1·20	5·50
117		1m.25 on 60c. violet and blue	1·20	5·25
118		1m.50 on 45c. green and blue	1·20	4·75
119		2m. on 1f. red and green	1·10	7·00
120		3m. on 60c. violet and blue	1·00	6·00
121		4m. on 2f. orange & green	1·20	6·50
122		5m. on 1f. red and green	1·30	6·25
123		6m. on 2f. orange & green	1·20	6·50
124		9m. on 5f. blue and buff	1·40	6·00

1922. Nos. 62, 64 and 69 further surch as in 1921 but with additional surch **Mark** obliterating **Pfennig**.

125	**18**	10m. on 10pf. on 10c. green (No. 62)	80	3·75
126		20m. on 20pf. on 20c. brown (No. 64)	65	1·40
127	**15**	50m. on 50pf. on 50c. blue (No. 69)	2·00	7·50

1923. Nos. 77 and 80 with additional surch.

128	**13**	40m. on 40pf. on 40c. red and blue	1·00	2·10
129		80m. on 1m.25 on 60c. violet and blue	1·00	2·75

1923. Nos. 72 and 82 surch with large figures.

130	**13**	10m. on 2m. on 45c. green and blue	1·70	5·00
131	**18**	25m. on 1m. on 25c. blue	1·80	5·75

LITHUANIAN OCCUPATION

The port and district of Memel was captured by Lithuanian forces in 1923 and incorporated in Lithuania.

1

5

1923. (a) Surch **KLAIPEDA (MEMEL)** and value over curved line and **MARKIU**.

1	**1**	10m. on 5c. blue	40	1·30
2		25m. on 5c. blue	40	1·30
3		50m. on 25c. red	40	1·30
4		100m. on 25c. red	55	1·90
5		400m. on 1l. brown	1·10	3·50

(b) Surch **Klaipeda (Memel)** and value over two straight lines and **Markiu**.

6	**1**	10m. on 5c. blue	75	3·00
7		25m. on 5c. blue	75	3·00
8		50m. on 25c. red	75	3·00
9		100m. on 25c. red	75	3·00

10		400m. on 1l. brown	1·00	4·00
11		500m. on 1l. brown	1·00	4·00

(c) Surch **KLAIPEDA (Memel)** and value over four stars and **MARKIU**.

12	1	10m. on 5c. blue	1·30	5·00
13		20m. on 5c. blue	1·30	5·00
14		25m. on 25c. red	1·30	5·75
15		50m. on 25c. red	1·90	6·50
16		100m. on 1l. brown	2·50	7·75
17		200m. on 1l. brown	2·75	7·75

1923.

18	5	10m. brown	30	55
19		20m. yellow	30	55
20		25m. orange	30	55
21		40m. violet	30	55
22		50m. green	65	1·10
23		100m. red	50	55
24		300m. green	4·50	70·00
25		400m. brown	50	75
26		500m. purple	4·50	70·00
27		1000m. blue	75	1·90

7 Liner, Memel Port — 8 Memel Arms — 9 Memel Lighthouse

1923. Uniting of Memel with Lithuania and Amalgamation of Memel Harbours.

28	7	40m. green	2·75	16·00
29		50m. brown	2·75	16·00
30		80m. green	2·75	16·00
31		100m. red	2·75	16·00
32	8	200m. blue	2·75	16·00
33		300m. brown	2·75	16·00
34		400m. purple	2·75	16·00
35		500m. orange	2·75	16·00
36		600m. green	2·75	16·00
37	9	800m. blue	2·75	16·00
38		1000m. purple	2·75	16·00
39		2000m. red	2·75	16·00
40		3000m. green	2·75	16·00

1923. No. 123 of Memel surch **Klaipeda**, value and large **M** between bars, sideways.

41		100m. on 80 on 1m.25 on 60c.	4·25	15·00
42		400m. on 80 on 1m.25 on 60c.	4·25	15·00
43		500m. on 80 on 1m.25 on 60c.	4·25	15·00

1923. Surch in **CENTU**.

44	5	2c. on 300m. green	5·75	7·75
45		3c. on 300m. green	6·00	9·50
46		10c. on 25m. orange	7·75	7·75
47		15c. on 25m. orange	7·75	7·75
48		20c. on 500m. purple	9·25	17·00
49		30c. on 500m. purple	7·75	7·75
50		50c. on 500m. purple	11·50	21·00

1923. Surch (thin or thick figures) in **CENT.** or **LITAS**.

60	5	2c. on 10m. brown	1·50	6·00
51		2c. on 20m. yellow	3·00	11·50
52		2c. on 50m. green	3·00	9·50
63		3c. on 10m. brown	2·50	7·75
53		3c. on 40m. violet	3·75	9·50
54		3c. on 300m. green	2·75	4·50
55		5c. on 100m. red	3·50	4·50
56		5c. on 300m. green	3·75	9·50
57		10c. on 400m. brown	7·75	13·50
67		15c. on 25m. orange	85·00	£450
58		30c. on 500m. purple	7·75	7·75
68		50c. on 1000m. blue	2·10	7·75
69		1l. on 1000m. blue	4·25	13·50

1923. Surch in **CENT.** or **LITAS**.

70	7	15c. on 40m. green	4·25	14·00
71		30c. on 50m. brown	4·25	7·25
72		30c. on 80m. green	4·25	17·00
73		30c. on 100m. red	4·25	7·25
74	8	50c. on 200m. blue	4·25	14·00
75		50c. on 300m. brown	4·25	7·25
76		50c. on 400m. purple	4·25	12·50
77		50c. on 500m. orange	4·25	7·25
78		1l. on 600m. green	5·00	14·00
79	9	1l. on 800m. blue	5·00	14·00
80		1l. on 1000m. purple	5·00	14·00
81		1l. on 2000m. red	5·00	15·00
82		1l. on 3000m. green	5·00	14·00

1923. Surch in large figures and **Centu** and bars reading upwards.

83	1	10c. on 25m. on 5c. blue (No. 2)	21·00	42·00
84		15c. on 100m. on 25c. red (No. 4)	21·00	£140
85		30c. on 400m. on 1l. brown (No. 5)	7·75	27·00
86		60c. on 50m. on 25c. red (No. 8)	21·00	£170

1923. Surch in large figures and **CENT.** and bars.

87	7	15c. on 50m. brown	£170	£2000
88		25c. on 100m. red	65·00	£1100
89	8	30c. on 300m. brown	£130	£1200
90		60c. on 500m. orange	65·00	£1100

1923. Surch in **Centu** or **Centai** (25c.) between bars.

91	5	15c. on 10m. brown	5·75	25·00
92		15c. on 20m. yellow	2·75	13·50
93		15c. on 25m. orange	2·75	15·00
94		15c. on 40m. violet	2·75	13·50
95		15c. on 50m. green	2·10	11·50
96		15c. on 100m. red	2·10	11·50
97		15c. on 400m. brown	1·90	9·50
98		15c. on 1000m. blue	55·00	£300
99		25c. on 10m. brown	3·50	21·00
100		25c. on 20m. yellow	2·75	13·50
101		25c. on 25m. orange	2·75	15·00
102		25c. on 40m. violet	3·50	21·00
103		25c. on 50m. green	2·10	10·50
104		25c. on 100m. red	1·90	10·50
105		25c. on 400m. brown	1·90	10·50
106		25c. on 1000m. blue	55·00	£350
107		30c. on 10m. brown	5·75	27·00
108		30c. on 20m. yellow	2·75	17·00
109		30c. on 25m. orange	3·75	21·00
110		30c. on 40m. violet	3·00	15·00
111		30c. on 50m. green	2·10	11·50
112		30c. on 100m. red	2·10	11·50
113		30c. on 400m. brown	2·10	11·50
114		30c. on 1000m. blue	55·00	£325

MEXICO Pt. 15

A republic of Central America. From 1864–67 an Empire under Maximilian of Austria.

8 reales = 100 centavos = 1 peso.

1 Miguel Hidalgo y Costilla — 2

1856. With or without optd district name. Imperf.

1c	1	½r. blue	12·50	14·00
8c		½r. black on buff	12·50	17·00
6		1r. orange	11·00	1·60
9b		1r. black on green	2·50	2·75
7b		2r. green	10·50	1·60
10c		2r. black on red	1·40	3·25
4b		4r. red	55·00	75·00
11b		4r. black on yellow	22·00	35·00
12a		4r. red on yellow	50·00	60·00
5c		8r. lilac	75·00	95·00
13a		8r. black on brown	48·00	95·00
14a		8r. green on brown	60·00	80·00

1864. Perf.

15a	2	1r. red	10	
16a		2r. blue	15	
17a		4r. brown	25	
18a		1p. black	95	

3 Arms of Mexico — 4 Emperor Maximilian

1864. Imperf.

30	3	3c. brown	£600	£1200
19a		½r. brown	85·00	£225
31		½r. purple	35·00	28·00
31c		½r. grey	40·00	40·00
32b		1r. blue	8·25	5·00
33		2r. orange	2·50	1·60
34		4r. green	55·00	32·00
35b		8r. red	80·00	48·00

1864. Imperf.

40	4	7c. purple	£225	£2500
36c		7c. grey	32·00	60·00
41		13c. blue	3·75	5·50
42		25c. orange	3·25	5·00
39c		50c. green	11·50	11·50

7 Hidalgo — 8 Hidalgo — 9 Hidalgo

10 Hidalgo — 15 Benito Juarez — 16

1868. Imperf or perf.

67	7	6c. black on brown	4·50	2·50
68		12c. black on green	1·90	60
69		25c. blue on pink	3·50	45
70b		50c. black on yellow	60·00	7·50
71		100c. black on brown	60·00	22·00
76		100c. brown on brown	95·00	28·00

1872. Imperf or perf.

87	8	6c. green	6·25	6·25
88		12c. blue	80	65
94		25c. red	3·50	75
90		50c. yellow	70·00	16·00
91		100c. lilac	48·00	25·00

1874. Various frames. Perf.

102a	9	4c. orange	3·50	6·25
97	10	5c. brown	2·10	1·40
98	9	10c. black	85	50
105		10c. orange	85	50
99	10	25c. blue	35	30
107	9	50c. green	7·00	6·25
108		100c. red	9·50	8·25

1879.

115	15	1c. brown	1·90	1·75
116		2c. violet	1·75	1·50
117		5c. orange	1·25	60
118		10c. blue	1·60	1·25
127a		10c. brown	1·25	
128		12c. brown	3·25	3·25
129		18c. brown	3·75	3·25
130		24c. mauve	3·75	3·25
119		25c. red	4·00	4·75
132		25c. brown	2·10	
120		50c. green	6·25	6·00
134		50c. yellow	35·00	38·00
121		85c. violet	11·00	9·50
122		100c. black	12·50	11·00
137		100c. orange	40·00	48·00

1882.

138	16	2c. green	3·25	2·50
139		3c. red	3·25	2·50
140		6c. blue	2·50	1·90

17 Hidalgo — 18

1884.

141	17	1c. green	1·25	15
142		2c. green	1·90	25
157		2c. red	6·25	1·40
143		3c. green	3·75	80
158		3c. brown	8·75	2·50
144		4c. green	5·00	80
159		4c. red	12·50	7·50
145		5c. green	5·00	60
160		5c. blue	8·75	1·60
146		6c. green	4·50	45
161		6c. brown	10·00	2·50
147		10c. green	4·75	15
162		10c. orange	7·50	45
148		12c. green	8·75	1·25
163		12c. brown	16·00	3·75
149		20c. green	25·00	95
150		25c. green	45·00	1·90
164		25c. blue	55·00	8·75
151		50c. green	40	1·25
152		1p. blue	40	4·75
153		2p. blue	40	8·75
154		5p. blue	£120	80·00
155		10p. blue	£170	95·00

1886.

196	18	1c. green	30	10
209		2c. red	35	10
167		3c. lilac	2·50	1·25
189		3c. red	30	10
198		3c. orange	95	35
168		4c. lilac	4·50	95
211		4c. red	75	50
199		4c. orange	1·10	50
191		5c. blue	20	10
170		6c. lilac	5·00	60
213		6c. red	95	60
200		6c. orange	1·40	35
171		10c. lilac	5·00	15
193		10c. red	10	10
185a		10c. brown	8·75	1·90
201		10c. orange	7·50	35
172		12c. lilac	5·00	3·25
215		12c. red	3·25	3·75
173		20c. lilac	40·00	22·00
194		20c. red	50	20
202		20c. orange	12·50	1·60
174		25c. lilac	16·00	3·75
217		25c. red	95	25
203		25c. orange	4·00	1·10
206		5p. red	£350	£225
207		10p. red	£550	£350

19 Foot Postman — 20 Mounted Postman and Pack Mules — 21 Statue of Cuauhtemoc

22 Mailcoach

23 Steam Mail Train

1895.

253	19	1c. green	20	10
219		2c. red	30	10
220		3c. brown	30	10
221	20	4c. orange	1·50	25
257	21	5c. blue	35	10
223	22	10c. purple	50	10
224	20	12c. olive	8·25	3·75
225	22	15c. blue	4·00	80
226		20c. red	4·00	40
227		50c. mauve	12·00	4·75
228	23	1p. brown	32·00	10·00
229		5p. red	£150	60·00
230		10p. blue	£190	90·00

27 — 28 Juanacatlan Falls

29 Popocatepetl — 30 Cathedral, Mexico

1899. Various frames for T **27**.

266	27	1c. green	80	10
276		1c. purple	60	10
267		2c. red	2·40	10
277		2c. green	80	10
268		3c. brown	1·60	10
278		4c. red	2·50	20
269		5c. blue	2·50	10
279		5c. orange	45	10
270		10c. brown and purple	3·25	15
280		10c. orange and blue	2·50	10
271		15c. purple and lavender	4·25	10
272		20c. blue and red	4·75	15
273a	28	50c. black and purple	19·00	1·25
281		50c. black and red	40·00	3·50
274	29	1p. black and blue	42·00	1·90
275	30	5p. black and red	£130	6·25

32 Josefa Ortiz — 40 Hidalgo at Dolores

1910. Centenary of First Independence Movement.

282	32	1c. purple	10	10
283	–	2c. green	10	10
284	–	3c. brown	25	10
285	–	4c. red	1·25	20
286	–	5c. orange	10	10
287	–	10c. orange and blue	80	10
288	–	15c. lake and slate	4·50	20
289	–	20c. blue and lake	2·50	10
290	40	50c. black and brown	6·25	95
291	–	1p. black and blue	7·50	1·10
292	–	5p. black and red	28·00	2·75

DESIGNS: As Type **32**: 2c. L. Vicario; 3c. L. Rayon; 4c. J. Aldama; 5c. M. Hidalgo; 10c. I. Allende; 15c. E. Gonzalez; 20c. M. Abasolo. As Type **40**: 1p. Mass on Mt. of Crosses; 5p. Capture of Granaditas.

REVOLUTIONARY PROVISIONALS

For full list of the provisional issues made during the Civil War from 1913 onwards, see the Stanley Gibbons Part 15 (Central America) Catalogue.

CONSTITUTIONALIST GENERAL ISSUES

CT 1

1914. "Transitorio".

CT1	CT 1	1c. blue	20	15
CT2		2c. green	30	15
CT3		4c. blue	7·00	1·60
CT4		5c. green	7·00	1·90
CT9		5c. green	10	10
CT5		10c. red	15	15
CT6		20c. brown	25	25
CT7		50c. red	1·60	2·10
CT8		1p. violet	8·75	10·00

The words of value on No. CT4 are 2 × 14 mm and on No. CT9 are 2¼ × 16 mm.

1914. Victory of Torreon. Nos. CT1/7 optd **Victoria de TORREON ABRIL 2-1914**.

CT10	CT 1	1c. blue	95·00	80·00
CT11		2c. green	£110	95·00
CT12		4c. blue	£130	£160
CT13		5c. green	11·50	12·50
CT14		10c. red	60·00	60·00
CT15		20c. brown	£1100	£1100
CT16		50c. red	£1200	£1200

CT 3 CT 4

1914. Handstamped with Type CT **3**. (a) Nos. D282/6.

CT17 D **32** 1c. blue . . . . . . 8·75 10·00
CT18 2c. blue . . . . . . 8·75 10·00
CT19 4c. blue . . . . . . 8·75 10·00
CT20 5c. blue . . . . . . 8·75 10·00
CT21 10c. blue . . . . . . 8·75 10·00

(b) Nos. 282/92.

CT22 **32** 1c. purple 35 30
CT23 – 2c. green 95 80
CT24 – 3c. brown 95 80
CT25 – 4c. red . . . . . . 1·60 1·25
CT26 – 5c. orange 20 10
CT27 – 10c. orange and blue . . 1·90 1·25
CT28 – 15c. lake and slate . . . 3·25 1·90
CT29 – 20c. blue and lake . . . 6·25 3·75
CT30 **40** 50c. black and brown . . 7·50 5·00
CT31 – 1p. black and blue . . . 16·00 6·25
CT32 – 5p. black and red . . . £100 95·00

1914.

CT33 CT **4** 1c. pink . . . . . . 80 12·50
CT34 2c. green . . . . . 80 11·50
CT35 3c. orange . . . . . 80 12·50
CT36 5c. red . . . . . . 60 5·00
CT37 10c. green . . . . . . 60 22·00
CT38 25c. blue . . . . . . 10·00

CT 5

1914. "Denver" issue.

CT39 CT **5** 1c. blue 15 20
CT40 2c. green 15 15
CT41 3c. orange 25 15
CT42 5c. red 25 15
CT43 10c. red 35 40
CT44 15c. mauve . . . . . 60 1·10
CT45 50c. yellow . . . . . 1·25 1·60
CT46 1p. violet . . . . . . 5·25 7·50

1914. Optd **GOBIERNO CONSTITUCIONALISTA**. (a) Nos. 279 and 271/2.

CT50 – 5c. orange . . . . . . 48·00 35·00
CT51 – 15c. purple and lavender 95·00 95·00
CT52 – 20c. blue and red £300 £250

(b) Nos. D282/6.

CT53 D **32** 1c. blue . . . . . . 1·10 1·10
CT54 2c. blue . . . . . . 1·25 1·25
CT55 4c. blue . . . . . . 9·50 9·50
CT56 5c. blue . . . . . . 9·50 9·50
CT57 10c. blue . . . . . . 1·60 1·60

(c) Nos. 282/92.

CT58 **32** 1c. purple 10 10
CT59 – 2c. green 10 10
CT60 – 3c. brown 20 20
CT61 – 4c. red 25 25
CT62 – 5c. orange 10 10
CT63 – 10c. orange and blue . . 10 10
CT64 – 15c. lake and slate . . . 35 30
CT65 – 20c. blue and lake . . . 35 35
CT66 **40** 50c. black and brown . . 1·10 75
CT67 – 1p. black and blue . . . 4·75 3·25
CT68 – 5p. black and red . . . 25·00 19·00

CONVENTIONIST ISSUES

(CV **1**) Villa–Zapata Monogram

1914. Optd with Type CV **1**. (a) Nos. 266/75.

CV 1 **27** 1c. green . . . . . . 60·00
CV 2 2c. red . . . . . . 60·00
CV 3 3c. brown . . . . . . 32·00
CV 4 5c. blue . . . . . . 60·00
CV 5 10c. brown and purple 60·00
CV 6 15c. purple and lavender 60·00
CV 7 20c. blue and red . . . 60·00
CV 8 **28** 50c. black and red . . . £160
CV 9 **29** 1p. black and blue . . . £160
CV10 **30** 5p. black and red . . . £300

(b) Nos. 276/80.

CV11 **27** 1c. purple . . . . . . 60·00
CV12 2c. green . . . . . . 60·00
CV13 4c. red . . . . . . 60·00
CV14 5c. orange . . . . . . 7·75
CV15 10c. orange and blue . . 48·00

(c) Nos. D282/6.

CV16 D **32** 1c. blue . . . . . . 6·00 6·25
CV17 2c. blue . . . . . . 6·00 6·25
CV18 4c. blue . . . . . . 6·00 6·25
CV19 5c. blue . . . . . . 6·00 6·25
CV20 10c. blue . . . . . . 60·00 6·25

(d) Nos. 282/92.

CV21 **32** 1c. purple 40 40
CV22 – 2c. green 45 20

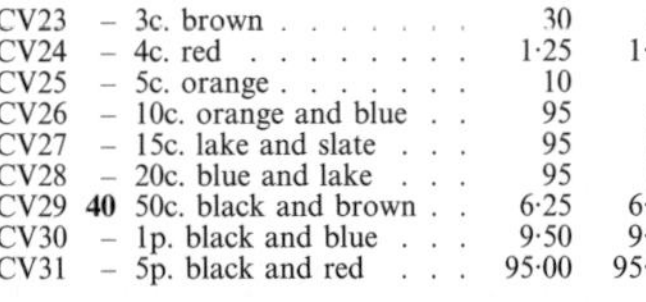

CV23 – 3c. brown 30 30
CV24 – 4c. red . . . . . . 1·25 1·25
CV25 – 5c. orange 10 10
CV26 – 10c. orange and blue . . 95 95
CV27 – 15c. lake and slate . . . 95 95
CV28 – 20c. blue and lake . . . 95 95
CV29 **40** 50c. black and brown . . 6·25 6·25
CV30 – 1p. black and blue . . . 9·50 9·50
CV31 – 5p. black and red . . . 95·00 95·00

CONSTITUTIONALIST PROVISIONAL ISSUES

CT **10** CT **11** Carranza Monogram

1914. Nos. 282/92 handstamped with Type CT **10**.

CT69 **32** 1c. purple . . . . . . 6·00 5·50
CT70 – 2c. green . . . . . . 6·00 5·50
CT71 – 3c. brown . . . . . . 6·00 5·50
CT72 – 4c. red . . . . . . 7·50 7·00
CT73 – 5c. orange 90 90
CT74 – 10c. orange and blue . . 7·00 6·25
CT75 – 15c. lake and slate . . 7·00 6·25
CT76 – 20c. blue and lake . . . 8·75 5·75
CT77 **40** 50c. black and brown . . 19·00 19·00
CT78 – 1p. black and blue . . . 28·00
CT79 – 5p. black and red . . . £100

1915. Optd with Type CT **11**. (a) No. 271.

CT80 – 15c. purple and lavender 50·00 50·00

(b) No. 279.

CT81 – 5c. orange . . . . . . 12·50 12·50

(c) Nos. D282/6.

CT82 D **32** 1c. blue . . . . . . 7·00
CT83 2c. blue . . . . . . 7·00
CT84 4c. blue . . . . . . 7·00
CT85 5c. blue . . . . . . 7·00
CT86 10c. blue . . . . . . 7·00

(d) Nos. 282/92.

CT87 **32** 1c. purple 35 35
CT88 – 2c. green 35 30
CT89 – 3c. brown 35 35
CT90 – 4c. red . . . . . . 1·25 1·25
CT91 – 5c. orange 10 10
CT92 – 10c. orange and blue . . 75 75
CT93 – 15c. lake and slate . . . 75 75
CT94 – 20c. blue and lake . . . 75 75
CT95 **40** 50c. black and brown . . 6·25 6·25
CT96 – 1p. black and blue . . . 9·50 9·50
CT97 – 5p. black and red . . . 95·00 95·00

GENERAL ISSUES.

43 Coat of Arms **44** Statue of Cuauhtemoc **45** Ignacio Zaragoza

1915. Portraits as T **45**. Roul or perf.

293 **43** 1c. violet 10 10
294 **44** 2c. green 20 15
304 **45** 3c. brown 20 15
305 4c. red (Morelos) 20 20
306 5c. orange (Madero) . . . 25 15
307 10c. blue (Juarez) 15 10

46 Map of Mexico **47** Lighthouse, Veracruz

48 Post Office, Mexico City

1915.

299 **46** 40c. grey . . . . . . 2·25 70
433 40c. mauve . . . . . . 1·75 25
300 **47** 1p. grey and brown . . . 35 60
411 1p. grey and blue . . . . 22·00 60
301 **48** 5p. blue and lake . . . . 5·00 5·50
412 5p. grey and green . . . . 1·25 1·50

(49) **50** V. Carranza

1916. Silver Currency. Optd with T **49**. (a) No. 271.

309 – 15c. purple and lavender . . £250 £250

(b) No. 279.

309a – 5c. orange . . . . . . 55·00 55·00

(c) Nos. 282/92.

310 **32** 1c. purple . . . . . . 2·10 3·25
311 – 2c. green 25 15
312 – 3c. brown 25 15
313 – 4c. red . . . . . . 3·75 5·00
314 – 5c. orange 10 10
315 – 10c. orange and blue . . . 60 95
316 – 15c. lake and slate . . . 1·10 1·90
317 – 20c. blue and lake . . . 1·10 1·90
318 **40** 50c. black and brown . . . 5·25 3·25
319 – 1p. black and blue . . . 9·50 4·00
320 – 5p. black and red . . . 95·00 80·00

(d) Nos. CT1/3 and CT5/8.

320b CT **1** 1c. blue . . . . . . 15·00
320c 2c. green . . . . . . 7·50
320d 4c. blue £160
320e 10c. red . . . . . . 1·40
320f 20c. brown . . . . . . 1·90
320g 50c. red . . . . . . 9·50
320h 1p. violet . . . . . . 15·00

(e) Nos. CT39/46.

321 CT **5** 1c. blue . . . . . . 2·40 12·00
322 2c. green . . . . . . 2·40 7·00
323 3c. orange . . . . . . 45 7·00
324 5c. red . . . . . . 45 7·00
325 10c. red . . . . . . 45 3·25
326 15c. mauve . . . . . . 45 7·00
327 50c. yellow . . . . . . 70 8·00
328 1p. violet . . . . . . 6·00 15·00

(f) Nos. CT58/68.

329 **32** 1c. purple . . . . . . 1·60 2·50
330 – 2c. green 35 30
331 – 3c. brown 30 30
332 – 4c. red 30 30
333 – 5c. orange 50 15
334 – 10c. orange and blue . . . 35 30
335 – 15c. lake and slate . . . 40 40
336 – 20c. blue and lake . . . 40 40
337 **40** 50c. black and brown . . . 4·75 3·75
338 – 1p. black and blue . . . 10·00 10·00
339 – 5p. black and red . . . 95·00 85·00

(g) Nos. CV22/9.

340 **32** 1c. purple . . . . . . 7·00 9·50
341 – 2c. green 75 45
342 – 3c. brown . . . . . . 2·00 2·75
343 – 4c. red . . . . . . 8·25 9·50
344 – 5c. orange . . . . . . 2·75 3·75
345 – 10c. orange and blue . . . 7·50 8·75
346 – 15c. lake and slate . . . 7·50 8·75
347 – 20c. blue and lake . . . 7·50 8·75

(h) Nos. CT87/97.

348 **32** 1c. purple . . . . . . 1·60 2·10
349 – 2c. green 30 30
350 – 3c. brown 25 20
351 – 4c. red . . . . . . 3·25 3·75
352 – 5c. orange 40 10
353 – 10c. orange and blue . . . 75 1·25
354 – 15c. lake and slate . . . 60 30
355 – 20c. blue and red . . . 60 55
356 **40** 50c. black and brown . . . 4·75 5·50
357 – 1p. black and blue . . . 7·00 7·50

1916. Carranza's Triumphal Entry into Mexico City.

358 **50** 10c. brown . . . . . . 7·50 8·25
359 10c. blue 60 30

(51)

1916. Optd with T **51**. (a) Nos. D282/6.

360 D **32** 5c. on 1c. blue . . . . 1·60 1·60
361 10c. on 2c. blue . . . . 1·60 1·60
362 20c. on 4c. blue . . . . 1·60 1·60
363 25c. on 5c. blue . . . . 1·60 1·60
364 60c. on 10c. blue 75 75
365 1p. on 1c. blue 75 75
366 1p. on 2c. blue 75 75
367 1p. on 4c. blue 40 40
368 1p. on 5c. blue . . . . 1·60 1·60
369 1p. on 10c. blue . . . . 1·60 1·60

(b) Nos. 282, 286 and 283.

370 **32** 5c. on 1c. purple 10 10
371 10c. on 1c. purple 10 10
372 – 20c. on 5c. orange 10 10
373 – 25c. on 5c. orange 15 15
374 – 60c. on 2c. green . . . . 10·50 12·50

(c) Nos. CT39/40.

375 CT **5** 60c. on 1c. blue . . . . 1·90 3·75
376 60c. on 2c. green . . . . 1·90 3·75

(d) Nos. CT58, CT62 and CT59.

377 **32** 5c. on 1c. purple 10 10
378 – 10c. on 1c. purple 60 60
379 – 25c. on 5c. purple 15 15
380 – 60c. on 2c. green £130 £170

(e) No. CV25.

381 – 25c. on 5c. orange 15 10

(f) Nos. CT87, CT91 and CT88.

382 **32** 5c. on 1c. purple . . . . . 9·50 12·50
383 – 10c. on 1c. purple . . . . 3·25 4·75
385 – 25c. on 5c. orange 50 95
386 – 60c. on 2c. green £140

1916. Nos. D282/6 surch **GPM** and value.

387 D **32** $2.50 on 1c. blue . . . 60 60
388 $2.50 on 2c. blue . . . 6·25 6·25
389 $2.50 on 4c. blue . . . 6·25 6·25
390 $2.50 on 5c. blue . . . 6·25 6·25
391 $2.50 on 10c. blue . . . 6·25 6·25

52a Arms **53** Zaragoza

1916.

392 **52a** 1c. purple 15 15

1917. Portraits. Roul or perf.

393 **53** 1c. violet 25 10
393a 1c. grey 70 20
394 – 2c. green (Vazquez) . . . 35 10
395 – 3c. brown (Suarez) . . . 35 10
396 – 4c. red (Carranza) 60 20
397 – 5c. blue (Herrera) 85 10
398 – 10c. blue (Madero) . . . 1·40 10
399 – 20c. lake (Dominguez) . . 14·00 35
400 – 30c. purple (Serdan) . . . 38·00 60
401 – 30c. black (Serdan) . . . 45·00 60

1919. Red Cross Fund. Surch with cross and premium.

413 5c.+3c. blue (No. 397) . . . 9·00 9·50
414 10c.+5c. blue (No. 398) . . . 11·00 9·50

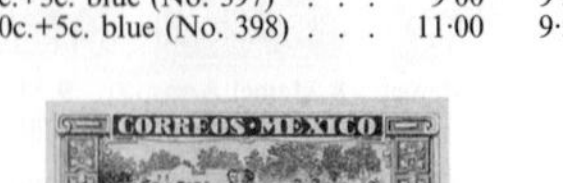

56 Meeting of Iturbide and Guerrero

1921. Centenary of Declaration of Independence.

415 **56** 10c. brown and blue . . . 9·50 1·90
416 – 10p. black and brown . . . 9·50 22·00

DESIGN: 10p. Entry into Mexico City.

58 Golden Eagle

1922. Air.

454 **58** 25c. sepia and lake 50 25
455 25c. sepia and green . . . 55 30
456 50c. red and blue 70 40

59 Morelos Monument **60** Fountain and Aqueduct

61 Pyramid of the Sun, Teotihuacan **62** Castle of Chapultepec

63 Columbus Monument **74** Benito Juarez

64 Juarez Colonnade **65** Monument to Dona Josefa Ortiz de Dominguez

66 Cuauhtemoc Monument **68** Ministry of Communications

69 National Theatre and Palace of Fine Arts

1923. Roul or perf.
436 **59** 1c. brown 25 10
437 **60** 2c. red 15 10
438 **61** 3c. brown 10 10
429 **62** 4c. green 60 10
440 **63** 4c. green 15 10
441 5c. orange 10 10
453 **74** 8c. orange 15 10
423 **64** 10c. brown . . . . 4·75 10
442 **66** 10c. lake 15 10
443 **65** 20c. blue 35 10
426 **66** 30c. green . . . . 35·00 2·50
432 **64** 30c. green 45 10
434 **68** 50c. brown 30 10
435 **69** 1p. blue and lake 50 25

70

72 Sr. Francisco Garcia y Santos

73 Post Office, Mexico City

1926. 2nd Pan-American Postal Congress. Inscr as in T **70/3**.
445 **70** 2c. red . . . . 1·25 35
446 – 4c. green . . . . 1·25 40
447 **70** 5c. orange . . . . 1·25 25
448 – 10c. red . . . . 1·90 25
449 **72** 20c. blue . . . . 1·90 50
450 30c. green . . . . 3·25 1·90
451 40c. mauve . . . . 6·25 1·60
452 **73** 1p. blue and brown . . . . 17·00 3·75
DESIGN—As Type **70**: 4c., 10c. Map of North and South America.

1929. Child Welfare. Optd **Proteccion a la Infancia**.
457 **59** 1c. brown 25 15

77

79 Capt. Emilio Carranza

1929. Obligatory Tax. Child Welfare.
459 **77** 1c. violet 10 10
461 2c. green 20 10
462 5c. brown 15 10

1929. Air. 1st Death Anniv of Carranza (airman).
463 **79** 5c. sepia and green 55 30
464 10c. red and sepia 65 35
465 15c. green and violet . . . 1·90 60
466 20c. black and sepia . . . 60 35
467 50c. black and red . . . . 3·75 1·25
468 1p. sepia and black . . . . 7·75 1·75

80

1929. Air. Perf or roul (10, 15, 20, 50c.), roul (5, 25c.), perf (others).
476a **80** 5c. blue 10 10
477 10c. violet 10 10
478 15c. red 15 10
479 20c. brown 75 10
480 25c. purple 45 40
472 30c. black 10 10
473 35c. blue 15 10
481 50c. red 45 35
474 1p. blue and black . . . 60 30
475 5p. blue and red . . . . 2·50 2·10
476 10p. brown and violet . . 3·75 4·50

81

87

1929. Air. Aviation Week.
482 **81** 20c. violet 60 50
483 40c. green . . . . 55·00 48·00

1930. 2nd Pan-American Postal Congress issue optd **HABILITADO 1930**.
484 **70** 2c. red . . . . 2·10 1·40
485 – 4c. green . . . . 2·10 1·25
486 **70** 5c. orange . . . . 2·10 1·10
487 – 10c. red . . . . 3·75 1·25
488 **72** 20c. blue . . . . 5·00 1·90
489 30c. green . . . . 4·50 2·10
490 40c. mauve . . . . 6·25 4·50
491 **73** 1p. blue and brown . . . . 5·50 3·75

1930. Air. National Tourist Congress. Optd **Primer Congreso Nacional de Turismo. Mexico. Abril 20-27 de 1930.**
492 **80** 10c. violet (No. 477) . . . 1·25 60

1930. Obligatory Tax. Child Welfare. Surch **HABILITADO $0.01**.
494 **77** 1c. on 2c. green 30 15
495 1c. on 5c. brown 60 15

1930. Air. Optd **HABILITADO 1930**.
496 **79** 5c. sepia and green . . . . 3·50 2·75
497 15c. green and violet . . . 5·50 4·75

1930. Air. Optd **HABILITADO Aereo 1930-1931**.
498 **79** 5c. sepia and green . . . . 3·75 4·00
499 10c. red and sepia . . . . 2·10 2·50
500 15c. green and violet . . . 4·00 4·50
501 20c. black and sepia . . . 4·50 3·50
502 50c. black and red . . . . 8·75 6·25
503 1p. sepia and black . . . . 2·50 1·75

1931. Obligatory Tax. Child Welfare. No. CT58 optd **PRO INFANCIA**.
504 **32** 1c. purple 20 15

1931. Fourth Centenary of Puebla.
505 **87** 10c. brown and blue . . . 1·60 25

88

1931. Air. Aeronautic Exhibition.
506 **88** 25c. lake . . . . 2·00 1·60

1931. Nos. 446/52 optd **HABILITADO 1931**.
508 – 4c. green . . . . 35·00
509 **70** 5c. orange . . . . 6·25
510 – 10c. red . . . . 6·25
511 **72** 20c. blue . . . . 6·25
512 30c. green . . . . 11·00
513 40c. mauve . . . . 16·00
514 **73** 1p. blue and brown . . . . 19·00

1931. Air. Surch **HABILITADO Quince centavos**. Perf or rouletted.
516 **80** 15c. on 20c. sepia 20 10

1932. Air. Surch in words and figures. Perf. or roul.
517 **88** 20c. on 25c. lake 30 15
521 **80** 30c. on 20c. sepia 15 10
519 **58** 40c. on 25c. sepia and lake 2·10 1·10
520 40c. on 25c. sepia & green 40·00 40·00
522 **80** 80c. on 25c. (No. 480) . . 90 60

1932. Air. 4th Death Anniv of Emilio Carranza. Optd **HABILITADO AEREO-1932**.
523 **79** 5c. sepia and green . . . . 3·75 3·25
524 10c. red and sepia . . . . 3·25 1·90
525 15c. green and violet . . . 3·75 2·50
526 20c. black and sepia . . . 3·25 1·75
527 50c. black and red . . . . 22·00 22·00

92 Fray Bartolome de las Casas

1933. Roul.
528 **92** 15c. blue 15 10

93 Mexican Geographical and Statistical Society's Arms

94 National Theatre and Palace of Fine Arts

1933. 21st Int Statistical Congress and Centenary of Mexican Geographical and Statistical Society.
529 **93** 2c. green (postage) 75 20
530 5c. brown . . . . 1·10 25
531 10c. blue 35 10
532 1p. violet . . . . 32·00 38·00
533 **94** 20c. violet and red (air) . . 2·10 85
534 30c. violet and brown . . . 4·25 3·75
535 1p. violet and green . . . 42·00 45·00

95 Mother and Child

98 Nevada de Toluca

1934. National University. Inscr "PRO-UNIVERSIDAD".
543 **95** 1c. orange (postage) . . . 10 10
544 – 5c. green . . . . 1·00 15
545 – 10c. lake . . . . 1·25 30
546 – 20c. blue . . . . 5·00 3·25
547 – 30c. black . . . . 8·75 7·50
548 – 40c. brown . . . . 15·00 10·00
549 – 50c. blue . . . . 28·00 32·00
550 – 1p. black and red . . . . 32·00 30·00
551 – 5p. brown and black . . . £120 £160
552 – 10p. violet and brown . . £500 £650
DESIGNS: 5c. Archer; 10c. Festive headdress; 20c. Woman decorating pot; 30c. Indian and Inca Lily; 40c. Potter; 50c. Sculptor; 1p. Gold craftsman; 5p. Girl offering fruit; 10p. Youth burning incense.

553 **98** 20c. orange (air) . . . . . 1·75 1·75
554 – 30c. purple and mauve . . 3·50 4·25
555 – 50c. brown and green . . . 4·00 6·25
556 – 75c. green and black . . . 4·75 8·75
557 – 1p. blue and green . . . . 5·00 6·25
558 – 5p. blue and brown . . . . 26·00 60·00
559 – 10p. red and blue . . . . 80·00 £130
560 – 20p. red and brown . . . £475 £750
DESIGNS—Airplane over: 30c. Pyramids of the Sun and Moon, Teotihuacan; 50c. Mt. Ajusco; 75c. Mts. Ixtaccihuatl and Popocatepetl; 1p. Bridge over R. Papagallo; 5p. Chapultepec Castle entrance; 10p. Orizaba Peak, Mt. Citlaltepetl; 20p. Girl and Aztec calendar stone.

101 Zapoteca Indian Woman

110 Coat of Arms

1934. Pres. Cardenas' Assumption of Office. Designs as Type **101** and **110**. Imprint "OFICINA IMPRESORA DE HACIENDA-MEXICO" at foot of stamp. (a) Postage.
561 – 1c. orange 30 10
562 **101** 2c. green 30 10
563 – 4c. red 45 15
564 – 5c. brown 30 10
565 – 10c. blue 40 10
565a – 10c. violet 80 10
566 – 15c. blue . . . . 2·50 15
567 – 20c. green . . . . 1·25 10
567a – 20c. blue 85 10
568 – 30c. red 35 10
653 – 30c. blue 40 10
569 – 40c. brown 40 10
570 – 50c. black 45 10
571 **110** 1p. red and brown . . . 1·60 10
572 – 5p. violet and orange . . 4·75 55
DESIGNS: 1c. Yalalteca Indian; 4c. Revolution Monument; 5c. Los Remedios Tower; 10c. Cross of Palenque; 15c. Independence Monument, Mexico City; 20c. Independence Monument, Puebla; 30c. "Heroic Children" Monument, Mexico City; 40c. Sacrificial Stone; 50c. Ruins of Mitla, Oaxaca; 5p. Mexican "Charro" (Horseman).

112 Mictlantecuhtli

120 "Peasant admiration"

(b) Air.
573 **112** 5c. black 20 10
574 – 10c. brown 45 10
575 – 15c. green 90 10
576 – 20c. red . . . . 1·90 10
577 – 30c. olive 35 10
577a – 40c. blue 60 10
578 – 50c. green . . . . 1·60 10
579 – 1p. red and green . . . 2·50 10
580 **120** 5p. black and red . . . 4·50 25
DESIGNS—HORIZ: 10c. Temple at Quetzalcoatl; 15c. Aeroplane over Citlaltepetl; 20c. Popocatepetl; 30c. Pegasus; 50c. Uruapan pottery; 1p. "Warrior Eagle". VERT: 40c. Aztec idol.

121 Tractor

122 Arms of Chiapas

1935. Industrial Census.
581 **121** 10c. violet . . . . 2·50 25

1935. Air. Amelia Earhart Flight to Mexico. No. 576 optd **AMELIA EARHART VUELO DE BUENA VOLUNTAD MEXICO 1935**.
581a 20c. red £1900 £2500

1935. Annexation of Chiapas Centenary.
582 **122** 10c. blue 35 15

123 E. Zapata

124 Francisco Madero

1935. 25th Anniv of Revolutionary Plans of Ayala and San Luis Potosi.
583 **123** 10c. violet (postage) . . . 35 10
584 **124** 20c. red (air) 20 10

129 Nuevo Laredo Road

131 Rio Corona Bridge

1936. Opening of Nuevo Laredo Highway (Mexico City–U.S.A.).
591 – 5c. red and green (postage) 15 10
592 – 10c. grey 25 10
593 **129** 20c. green and brown . . 75 50
DESIGNS: As Type **129**: 5c. Symbolical Map of Mexico–U.S.A. road; 10c. Matalote Bridge.

594 – 10c. blue (air) 30 10
595 **131** 20c. orange and violet . . 30 10
596 – 40c. green and blue . . . 40 30
DESIGNS: As Type **131**: 10c. Tasquillo Bridge over Rio Tula; 40c. Guayalejo Bridge.

1936. 1st Congress of Industrial Medicine and Hygiene. Optd **PRIMER CONGRESO NAL. DE HIGIENE Y. MED. DEL TRABAJO**.
597 – 10c. violet (No. 565a) . . . 30 20

1937. As Nos. 561/4, 565a and 576, but smaller. Imprint at foot changed to "TALLERES DE IMP.(RESION) DE EST. (AMPILLAS) Y VALORES-MEXICO".
708 1c. orange (postage) 25 10
709 2c. green 25 10
600 4c. red 40 10
601 5c. brown 35 10
602 10c. violet 25 10
603 20c. red (air) 80 10

134 Blacksmith

1938. Carranza's "Plan of Guadelupe". 25th Anniv. Inscr "CONMEMORATIVO PLAN DE GUADALUPE", etc.
604 **134** 5c. brown & blk (postage) 30 10
605 – 10c. brown 10 10
606 – 20c. orange and brown . . 3·25 50
607 – 20c. blue and red (air) . . 20 10
608 – 40c. red and blue 45 15
609 – 1p. blue and yellow . . . 3·00 1·40

DESIGNS VERT: 10c. Peasant revolutionary; 20c. Preaching revolt. HORIZ: 20c. Horseman; 40c. Biplane; 1p. Mounted horseman.

140 Arch of the Revolution **141** Cathedral and Constitution Square

1938. 16th International Town Planning and Housing Congress, Mexico City. Inscr as in T **140/1**.
610 **140** 5c. brown (postage) . . . 80 30
611 – 5c. olive . . . . 1·60 1·40
612 – 10c. orange . . . . 8·75 7·00
613 – 10c. brown 30 10
614 – 20c. black . . . . 2·10 2·50
615 – 20c. lake . . . . 11·50 9·50
DESIGNS: As Type **140**: 10c. National Theatre; 20c. Independence Column.

616 **141** 20c. red (air) 15 10
617 – 20c. violet . . . . 8·75 6·25
619 – 40c. green . . . . 4·50 3·25
620 – 1p. slate . . . . 4·50 3·25
621 – 1p. light blue . . . . . . 4·50 3·25
DESIGNS: As Type **141**: 40c. Chichen Itza Ruins (Yucatan); 1p. Acapulco Beach.

142 Mosquito and Malaria Victim

1939. Obligatory Tax. Anti-malaria Campaign.
622 **142** 1c. blue 95 10

143 Statue of an Indian **144** Statue of Woman Pioneer and Child

1939. Tulsa Philatelic Convention, Oklahoma.
623 **143** 10c. red (postage) 20 10
624 **144** 20c. brown (air) 50 20
625 40c. green . . . . 1·25 60
626 1p. violet 80 45

145 Mexican Pavilion, World's Fair **146** Morelos Statue on Mexican Pavilion

1939. Air. F. Sarabia non-stop Flight to New York. Optd **SARABIA Vuelo MEXICO-NUEVA YORK**.
626a **146** 20c. blue and red £160 £300

1939. New York World's Fair.
627 **145** 10c. green & blue (postage) 30 10
628 **146** 20c. green (air) 60 25
629 40c. purple . . . . . . 1·60 60
630 1p. brown and red . . . 1·00 50

147 J. de Zumarraga **152** "Building"

154 "Transport"

1939. 400th Anniv of Printing in Mexico.
631 **147** 2c. black (postage) . . . 35 10
632 – 5c. green 35 10
633 – 10c. red 10 10
634 – 20c. blue (air) 10 10
635 – 40c. green 30 10
636 – 1p. red and brown . . . 55 35
DESIGNS: 5c. First printing works in Mexico; 10c. Antonio D. Mendoza; 20c. Book frontispiece; 40c. Title page of first law book printed in America; 1p. Oldest Mexican Colophon.

1939. National Census. Inscr "CENSOS 1939 1940".
637 **152** 2c. red (postage) 60 10
638 – 5c. green 10 10
639 – 10c. brown 10 10
640 **154** 20c. blue (air) . . . . . . 2·50 40
641 – 40c. orange 35 10
642 – 1p. violet and blue . . . 1·75 35
DESIGNS: As Type **152**: 5c. "Agriculture"; 10c. "Commerce". As Type **154**: 40c. "Industry"; 1p. "Seven Censuses".

155 "Penny Black" **156** Roadside Monument

1940. Centenary of First Adhesive Postage Stamps.
643 **155** 5c. yellow & black (postage) 45 25
644 10c. purple 10 10
645 20c. red and blue 15 10
646 1p. red and grey . . . . 4·50 2·50
647 5p. blue and black . . . 23·00 19·00
648 5c. green and black (air) 45 30
649 10c. blue and brown . . . 35 10
650 20c. violet and red . . . 25 10
651 1p. brown and red . . . 2·10 3·25
652 5p. brown and green . . . 25·00 35·00

1940. Opening of Highway from Mexico City to Guadalajara.
654 **156** 6c. green 35 10

159 Original College at Patzcuaro

1940. 4th Centenary of National College of St. Nicholas de Hidalgo.
655 – 2c. violet (postage) . . . 65 25
656 – 5c. red 40 10
657 – 10c. olive 40 10
658 **159** 20c. green (air) 20 10
659 – 40c. orange 25 10
660 – 1p. violet, brown & orange 60 45
DESIGNS—VERT: 2c. V. de Quiroga; 5c. M. Ocampo; 10c. St. Nicholas College Arms; 40c. Former College at Morelia. HORIZ: 1p. Present College at Morelia.

163 Pirate Galleon

1940. 400th Anniv of Campeche. Inscr as in T **163**.
661 – 10c. red & brown (postage) . . . . 1·90 60
662 **163** 20c. brown and red (air) 90 35
663 – 40c. green and black . . . 75 25
664 – 1p. black and blue . . . 3·25 1·90

DESIGNS: 10c. Campeche City Arms; 40c. St. Miguel Castel; 1p. Temple of San Francisco.

165 Helmsman **166** Miguel Hidalgo y Costilla

1940. Inauguration of Pres. Camacho.
665 **165** 2c. orange & black (postage) . . . . 1·00 30
666 5c. blue and brown . . . 3·75 2·10
667 10c. olive and brown . . 1·40 40
668 20c. grey and orange (air) 1·25 60
669 40c. brown and green . . 1·25 95
670 1p. purple and red . . . 2·10 1·25

1940. Compulsory Tax. Dolores Hidalgo Memorial Fund.
671 **166** 1c. red 30 10

168 Javelin throwing **169** Dark Nebula in Orion

1941. National Athletic Meeting.
675 **168** 10c. green . . . . 2·10 25

1942. Inauguration of Astro-physical Observatory at Tonanzintla, Puebla.
676 **169** 2c. blue & violet (postage) 80 50
677 – 5c. blue . . . . 5·50 1·25
678 – 10c. blue and orange . . 5·50 25
679 – 20c. blue and green (air) 7·75 1·90
680 – 40c. blue and red . . . . 7·00 2·50
681 – 1p. black and orange . . 7·00 2·75
DESIGNS: 5c. Solar Eclipse; 10c. Spiral Galaxy of the "Hunting Dog"; 20c. Extra-Galactic Nebula in Virgo; 40c. Ring Nebula in Lyra; 1p. Russell Diagram.

171 Ruins of Chichen-Itza **172** Merida Nunnery

1942. 400th Anniv of Merida. Inscr as in T **171/2**.
682 **171** 2c. brown (postage) . . . 70 30
683 – 5c. red . . . . 1·40 30
684 – 10c. violet 80 10
685 **172** 20c. blue (air) 95 25
686 – 40c. green . . . . 1·40 1·25
687 – 1p. red . . . . 1·60 1·25
DESIGNS–VERT: 5c. Mayan sculpture; 10c. Arms of Merida; 40c. Montejo University Gateway. HORIZ: 1p. Campanile of Merida Cathedral

173 "Mother Earth" **175** Hidalgo Monument

1942. 2nd Inter-American Agricultural Conference.
688 **173** 2c. brown (postage) . . . 40 20
689 – 5c. blue . . . . 1·90 55
690 – 10c. orange 60 25
691 – 20c. green (air) . . . . . 1·25 25
692 – 40c. brown 75 25
693 – 1p. violet . . . . 1·60 1·25

DESIGNS: 5c. Sowing wheat; 10c. Western Hemisphere carrying torch; 20c. Corn; 40c. Coffee; 1p. Bananas.

1942. 400th Anniv of Guadalajara.
694 **175** 2c. brown & blue (postage) 15 15
695 – 5c. red and black 60 25
696 – 10c. blue and red 60 20
697 – 20c. black and green (air) 80 35
698 – 40c. green and olive . . . 1·10 50
699 – 1p. violet and brown . . 80 60
DESIGNS—VERT: 5c. Government Palace; 10c. Guadalajara. HORIZ: 20c. St. Paul's Church, Zapopan; 40c. Sanctuary of Our Lady of Guadalupe; 1p. Arms of Guadalajara.

186 Saltillo Athenaeum, Coahuila

1942. 75th Anniv of Saltillo Athenaeum.
700 **186** 10c. black 90 20

189 Birthplace of Allende **190** "Liberty"

1943. 400th Anniv of San Miguel de Allende.
701 – 2c. blue (postage) 50 15
702 – 5c. brown 55 15
703 – 10c. black . . . . 2·10 50
704 – 20c. green (air) 45 30
705 **189** 40c. purple 60 30
706 – 1p. red . . . . 1·75 1·60
DESIGNS—VERT: 2c. Cupola de las Monjas; 5c. Gothic Church; 10c. Gen. de Allende. HORIZ: 20c. San Miguel de Allende; 1p. Church seen through cloisters.

1944.
707 **190** 12c. brown 20 10

192 Dr. de Castorena **194** "Flight"

1944. 3rd National Book Fair.
732 **192** 12c. brown (postage) . . 40 10
733 – 25c. green (air) 45 10
DESIGN: 25c. Microphone, book and camera.

1944. Air.
734 **194** 25c. brown 30 10

195 Hands clasping Globe

1945. Inter-American Conference.
735 **195** 12c. red (postage) 25 10
736 1p. green 45 10
737 5p. brown . . . . 3·50 2·75
738 10p. black . . . . 6·25 5·00
739 25c. orange (air) 10 10
740 1p. green 15 10
741 5p. blue . . . . 1·50 1·10
742 10p. red . . . . 4·00 3·25
743 20p. blue . . . . 8·75 8·00

196 La Paz Theatre, San Luis Potosi

1945. Reconstruction of La Paz Theatre, San Luis Potosi.
744 **196** 12c. pur & blk (postage) . . 20 10
745 1p. blue and black . . . 30 10
746 5p. red and black . . . . 3·75 3·25
747 10p. green and black . . 8·25 7·50
748 30c. green (air) 10 10
749 1p. purple and green . . . 15 10
750 5p. black and green . . . 1·40 1·25
751 10p. blue and green . . . 2·75 2·10
752 20p. green and black . . 6·00 5·25

197 Fountain of Diana the Huntress **198** Removing Bandage

1945.
753 **197** 3c. violet 40 10

1945. Literacy Campaign.
754 **198** 2c. blue (postage) 15 10
755 6c. orange 20 10
756 12c. blue 20 10
757 1p. olive 25 10
758 5p. red and black . . . . 2·40 1·90
759 10p. green and blue . . . 13·00 12·50
760 30c. green (air) 10 10
761 1p. red 15 10
762 5p. blue . . . . 1·60 1·40
763 10p. red . . . . 2·75 2·75
764 20p. brown and green . . 13·00 12·50

199 Founder of National Post Office **200** O.N.U., Olive Branch and Globe

201 O.N.U. and Flags of United Nations

1946. Foundation of Posts in Mexico in 1580.
765 **199** 8c. black 60 10

1946. United Nations.
766 **200** 2c. olive (postage) 15 10
767 6c. brown 15 10
768 12c. blue 10 10
769 1p. green 30 10
770 5p. red . . . . 3·25 3·25
771 10p. blue . . . . 14·00 12·50
772 **201** 3c. brown (air) 10 10
773 1p. grey 10 10
774 5p. green and brown . . . 70 50
775 10p. brown and sepia . . 2·75 2·50
776 20p. red and slate . . . . 6·75 4·75

202 Zacatecas City Arms **205** Don Genaro Codina and Zacatecas

1946. 400th Anniv of Zacatecas.
777 **202** 2c. brown (postage) . . . 25 10
778 – 12c. blue 15 10
779 – 1p. mauve 30 10
780 – 5p. red . . . . 3·50 1·90
781 – 10p. black and blue . . . 20·00 6·25
DESIGNS: 1p. Statue of Gen. Ortega; 5p. R. L. Velarde (poet); 10p. F. G. Salinas.

782 – 30c. grey (air) 10 10
783 **205** 1p. green and brown . . . 15 10
784 – 5p. green and red . . . . 1·90 1·60
785 – 10p. brown and green . . 7·50 2·75
PORTRAITS: 30c. Fr. Margil de Jesus; 5p. Gen. Enrique Estrada; 10p. D. Fernando Villalpando.

207 Learning Vowels **208** Postman

1946. Education Plan.
786 **207** 1c. sepia 20 10

1947.
787 **208** 15c. blue 15 10

209 Roosevelt and First Mexican Stamp **210** 10c. U.S.A. 1847 and Mexican Eagle

1947. U.S.A. Postage Stamp Centenary.
788 **209** 10c. brown (postage) . . 1·10 60
789 – 15c. green 10 10
790 – 25c. blue (air) 35 20
791 **210** 30c. black 25 10
792 – 1p. blue and red 80 15
DESIGNS: 15c. as Type **209** but vert; 25c., 1p. as Type **210** but horiz.

213 Justo Sierra **214** Ministry of Communications

212 Douglas DC-4

1947.
795 **213** 10p. green and brown (postage) . . . . 65·00 8·50
796 **214** 20p. mauve and green . . 1·10 90
793 – 10p. red and brown (air) 75 80
794 **212** 20p. red and blue . . . . 1·50 1·25
DESIGN—HORIZ: 10p. E. Carranza.

215 Manuel Rincon **217** Vicente Suarez

1947. Battle Centenaries. Portraits of "Child Heroes" etc. Inscr "1er CENTENARIO CHAPULTEPEC ("CHURUBUSCO" or "MOLINO DEL REY") 1847 1947".
797 – 2c. black (postage) . . . 30 10
798 – 5c. red 15 10
799 – 10c. brown 15 10
800 – 15c. green 15 10
801 **215** 30c. olive 20 10
802 – 1p. blue 30 15
803 – 5p. red and blue . . . . 1·25 1·25
DESIGNS—VERT: 2c. Francisco Marquez; 5c. Fernando Montes de Oca; 10c. Juan Escutin; 15c. Agustin Melgar; 1p. Lucas Balderas; 5p. Flag of San Blas Battalion.

804 **217** 25c. violet (air) 15 10
805 – 30c. blue 15 10
806 – 50c. green 25 10
807 – 1p. violet 30 10
808 – 5p. brown and blue . . . 1·25 1·25
DESIGNS—HORIZ: 30c. Juan de la Barrera; 50c. Military Academy; 1p. Pedro Maria Anaya; 5p. Antonio de Leon.

218 Puebla Cathedral **221** Dance of the Half Moons, Puebla

1950. (a) Postage. As T **218**.
835 – 3c. blue 15 10
874 – 5c. brown 25 10
875a – 10c. green 40 10
876a – 15c. green 20 10
877e **218** 20c. blue 30 10
840 – 30c. red 25 10
879 – 30c. brown 35 10
880b – 40c. orange 95 10
1346b – 50c. blue 10 10
1327b – 80c. green 35 10
843 – 1p. brown . . . . . . 2·75 10
1346f – 1p. green 10 10
1011ab – 1p. grey 30 10
1327d – 3p. red 55 10
1012a – 5p. blue and green . . 1·50 60
1013ab – 10p. black and blue . . 2·50 1·25
846 – 20p. violet and green 6·25 6·25
1014 – 20p. violet and black 5·75 4·50
1327e – 50p. orange and green 6·25 4·75
DESIGNS: 3 c, 3p. La Purisima Church, Monterrey; 5c. Modern building, Mexico City; 10c. Convent of the Nativity, Tepoztlan; 15 c, 50p. Benito Juarez; 30c., 80c. Indian dancer, Michoacan; 40c. Sculpture, Tabasco; 50c. Carved head, Veracruz; 1p. Actopan Convent and carved head; 5p. Galleon, Campeche; 10p. Francisco Madero; 20p. Modern building, Mexico City.

(b) Air. As T **221**.
897 – 5c. blue 15 10
898a – 10c. brown 25 15
899a – 20c. red 35 10
850 – 25c. brown 60 10
851 – 30c. olive 15 10
902 – 35c. violet 55 10
1327f – 40c. blue 10 10
904c – 50c. green 35 10
1056 – 80c. red 60 70
906a **221** 1p. grey 45 10
1327h – 1p.60 red 60 10
1327i – 1p.90 red 35 10
907ab – 2p. brown 65 25
908 – 2p.25 purple 60 45
1327j – 4p.30 blue 45 10
1017a – 5p. orange and brown 2·75 35
1327k – 5p.20 lilac 70 25
1327l – 5p.60 green . . . . . 1·40 30
895 – 10p. blue and black 3·75 60
859a – 20p. blue and red . . 5·25 5·75
DESIGNS: 5c., 1p.90 Bay of Acapulco; 10c., 4p.30, Dance of the Plumes, Oaxaca; 20c. Mayan frescoes, Chiapas; 25c., 2p.25, 5p.60, Masks, Michoacan; 30c. Cuauhtemoc; 35c., 2p., 5p.20, Taxco, Guerrero; 40c. Sculpture, San Luis Potosi; 50c., 1p.60, Ancient carvings, Chiapas; 80c. University City, Mexico City; 5p. Architecture, Queretaro; 10p. Hidalgo; 20p. National Music Conservatoire, Mexico City.

222 Arterial Road **224** Diesel Locomotive and Map

1950. Opening of Mexican Section of Pan-American Highway. Inscr "CARRETERA INTERNACIONAL 1950".
860 – 15c. violet (postage) . . . 30 10
861 **222** 20c. blue 20 10
862 – 25c. pink (air) . . . . . 1·60 20
863 – 35c. green 10 10
DESIGNS—HORIZ: 15c. Bridge; 25c. Pres. M. Aleman, bridge and map; 35c. B. Juarez and map.

1950. Inauguration of Mexico–Yucatan Railway.
864 – 15c. purple (postage) . . 1·75 30
865 **224** 20c. red 70 35
866 – 25c. green (air) 70 35
867 – 35c. blue 70 40
DESIGNS—VERT: 15c. Rail-laying. HORIZ: 25c. Diesel trains crossing Isthmus of Tehuantepac; 35c. M. Aleman and railway bridge at Coatzacoalcos.

227 Hands and Globe

1950. 75th Anniv of U.P.U.
868 – 50c. violet (postage) . . . 25 10
869 – 25c. red (air) 55 25
870 **227** 80c. blue 30 20
DESIGNS—HORIZ: 25c. Aztec runner. VERT: 50c. Letters "U.P.U.".

228 Miguel Hidalgo **229**

1953. Birth Bicentenary of Hidalgo.
871 **228** 20c. sepia & blue (postage) . . . . 1·10 10
872 – 25c. lake and blue (air) 35 10
873 **229** 35c. green 35 10
DESIGN: As Type **229**: 25c. Full face portrait.

231 Aztec Athlete **232** View and Mayan Bas-relief

1954. 7th Central American and Caribbean Games.
918 **231** 20c. blue & pink (postage) 55 10
919 **232** 25c. brown and green (air) 35 15
920 – 35c. turquoise and purple 30 10
DESIGN: 35c. Stadium.

233 **234**

1954. Mexican National Anthem Centenary.
921 **233** 5c. lilac and blue (postage) 45 15
922 20c. brown and purple . . 55 10
923 1p. green and red 30 20
924 **234** 25c. blue and lake (air) 45 15
925 35c. purple and blue . . . 20 10
926 80c. green and blue . . . 25 15

235 Torchbearer and Stadium **236** Aztec God and Map

1955. 2nd Pan-American Games, Mexico City. Inscr "II JUEGOS DEPORTIVOS PANAMERICANOS".
927 **235** 20c. green & brn (postage) 40 10
928 **236** 25c. blue and brown (air) 30 10
929 – 35c. brown and red . . . 30 10
DESIGN: As Type **236**: 35c. Stadium and map.

237 Olin Design

238 Feathered Serpent and Mask

1956. Mexican Stamp Centenary.
930 **237** 5c. green & brn (postage) 30 10
931 – 10c. blue and grey . . . 30 10
932 – 30c. purple and red . . . 20 10
933 – 50c. brown and blue . . . 25 10
934 – 1p. black and green . . . 35 10
935 – 5p. sepia and bistre . . . 1·60 1·40
DESIGNS: As Type **237**: 10c. Tohtli bird; 30c. Zochitl flower; 50c. Centli corn; 1p. Mazatl deer; 5p. Teheutli man's head.

937 **238** 5c. black (air) 15 10
938 – 10c. blue 15 10
939 – 50c. purple 10 10
940 – 1p. violet 15 10
941 – 1p.20 mauve 15 10
942 – 5p. turquoise 80 80
DESIGNS: As Type **238**: 10c. Bell tower, coach and Viceroy Enriquez de Almanza; 50c. Morelos and cannon; 1p. Mother, child and mounted horseman; 1p.20, Sombrero and spurs; 5p. Emblems of food and education and pointing hand.

239 Stamp of 1856

1956. Centenary Int Philatelic Exn, Mexico City.
944 **239** 30c. blue and brown . . . 45 15

240 F. Zarco **241** V. Gomez Farias and M. Ocampo

1956. Inscr "CONSTITUYENTE(S) DE 1857".
945 – 25c. brown (postage) 35 10
946 – 45c. blue 15 10
947 – 60c. purple 15 10
1346d **240** 70c. blue 20 10
1327c – 2p.30 blue 55 10
949 **241** 15c. blue (air) 20 10
1327g – 60c. green 15 15
950 – 1p.20 violet and green 35 15
951 **241** 2p.75 purple 50 30
PORTRAITS: As T **240** (postage): 25, 45c., 2p.30, G. Prieto; 60c. P. Arriagan. As T **41** (air): 60c., 1p.20, L. Guzman and I. Ramirez.

242 Paricutin Volcano

1956. Air. 20th International Geological Congress.
952 **242** 50c. violet 30 10

243 Map of Central America and the Caribbean

1956. Air. 4th Inter-American Congress of Caribbean Tourism.
953 **243** 25c. blue and grey 20 10

244 Assembly of 1857 **245** Mexican Eagle and Scales

1957. Centenary of 1857 Constitution.
958 – 30c. gold & lake (postage) 35 10
959 **244** 1p. green and sepia . . . 25 10
960 **245** 50c. brown and green (air) 20 10
961 – 1p. lilac and blue 30 15
DESIGNS—VERT: 30c. Emblem of Constitution. HORIZ: 1p. (Air), "Mexico" drafting the Constitution.

246 Globe, Weights and Dials

1957. Air. Centenary of Adoption of Metric System in Mexico.
962 **246** 50c. black and silver . . . 30 10

247 Train Disaster **248** Oil Derrick

1957. Air. 50th Anniv of Heroic Death of Jesus Garcia (engine driver) at Nacozari.
963 **247** 50c. purple and red . . . 90 25

1958. 20th Anniv of Nationalization of Oil Industry.
964 **248** 30c. black & blue (postage) 25 10
965 – 5p. red and blue . . . . 3·50 2·50
966 – 50c. green and black (air) 10 10
967 – 1p. black and red 20 10
DESIGNS—HORIZ: 50c. Oil storage tank and "AL SERVICIO DE LA PATRIA" ("At the service of the Fatherland"); 1p. Oil refinery at night. VERT: 5p. Map of Mexico and silhouette of oil refinery.

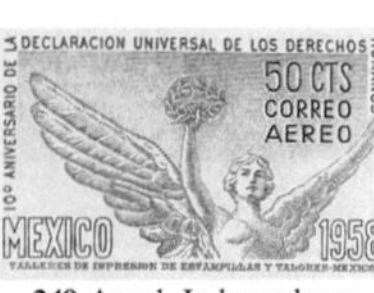

249 Angel, Independence Monument, Mexico City **250** U.N.E.S.C.O. Headquarters, Paris

1958. Air. 10th Anniv of Declaration of Human Rights.
968 **249** 50c. blue 20 10

1959. Inauguration of U.N.E.S.C.O. Headquarters Building, Paris.
969 **250** 30c. black and purple . . 30 10

251 U.N. Headquarters, New York **252** President Carranza

1959. U.N. Economic and Social Council Meeting, Mexico City.
970 **251** 30c. blue and yellow . . . 30 10

1960. "President Carranza Year" (1959) and his Birth Centenary.
971 **252** 30c. pur & grn (postage) 20 10
972 – 50c. violet and salmon (air) 20 10
DESIGN—HORIZ: 50c. Inscription "Plan de Guadalupe Constitucion de 1917" and portrait as Type **252**.

253 Alexander von Humboldt (statue) **254** Alberto Braniff's Voisin "Boxkite" and Bristol Britannia

1960. Death Centenary of Alexander von Humboldt (naturalist).
973 **253** 40c. green and brown . . 20 10

1960. Air. 50th Anniv of Mexican Aviation.
974 **254** 50c. brown and violet . . 40 10
975 1p. brown and green . . . 40 15

255 Francisco I. Madero **257** Dolores Bell

1960. Visit to Mexico of Members of Elmhurst Philatelic Society (American Society of Mexican Specialists). Inscr "HOMENAJE AL COLECCIONISTA".
976 **255** 10p. sepia, green and purple (postage) . . . . 27·00 45·00
977 – 20p. sepia, green and purple (air) . . . . . . 38·00 50·00
DESIGN: As No. 1019a 20p. National Music Conservatoire inscr "MEX. D.F.".

1960. 150th Anniv of Independence.
978 **257** 30c. red & green (postage) 60 10
979 – 1p. sepia and green . . . 25 10
980 – 5p. blue and purple . . . 3·25 3·25
981 – 50c. red and green (air) 15 10
982 – 1p.20 sepia and blue . . . 20 10
983 – 5p. sepia and green . . . 3·50 1·40
DESIGNS—VERT: No. 979, Independence Column; 980, Hidalgo, Dolores Bell and Mexican Eagle. HORIZ: No. 981, Mexican Flag; 982, Eagle breaking chain and bell tolling; 983, Dolores Church.

259 Children at Desk, University and School Buildings **261** Count S. de Revillagigedo

1960. 50th Anniv of Mexican Revolution.
984 – 10c. multicoloured (postage) 30 10
985 – 15c. brown and green . . 1·75 10
986 – 20c. blue and brown . . . 50 10
987 – 30c. violet and sepia . . . 20 10
988 **259** 1p. slate and purple . . . 25 10
989 – 5p. grey and purple . . . 2·10 2·10
990 – 50c. black and blue (air) 20 10
991 – 1p. green and red 20 10
992 – 1p.20 sepia and green . . 20 10
993 – 5p. lt blue, blue & mauve 2·00 90
DESIGNS: No. 984, Pastoral scene (35½ × 45½ mm). As Type **259** VERT: No. 985, Worker and hospital buildings; 986, Peasant, soldier and marine; 987, Power lines and pylons; 989, Coins, banknotes and bank entrance. HORIZ: No. 990, Douglas DC-8 airliner; 991, Riggers on oil derrick; 992, Main highway and map; 993, Barrage.

1960. Air. National Census.
994 **261** 60c. black and lake . . . 35 10

262 Railway Tunnel **263** Mosquito Globe and Instruments

1961. Opening of Chihuahua State Railway.
995 **262** 40c. black & grn (postage) 75 30
996 – 60c. blue and black (air) 75 30
997 – 70c. black and blue . . . 75 30
DESIGNS—HORIZ: 60c. Railway tracks and map of railway; 70c. Railway viaduct.

1962. Malaria Eradication.
998 **263** 40c. brown and blue . . . 25 10

264 Pres. Goulart of Brazil **265** Soldier and Memorial Stone

1962. Visit of President of Brazil.
999 **264** 40c. bistre 65 10

1962. Centenary of Battle of Puebla.
1000 **265** 40c. sepia and green (postage) 25 10
1001 – 1p. olive and green (air) 35 10
DESIGN—HORIZ: 1p. Statue of Gen. Zaragoza.

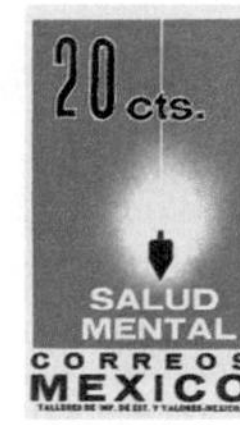

266 Draughtsman and Surveyor **267** Plumb-line

1962. 25th Anniv of National Polytechnic Institute.
1002 **266** 40c. turquoise and blue (postage) 65 10
1003 – 1p. olive and blue (air) 35 10
DESIGN—HORIZ: 1p. Scientist and laboratory assistant.

1962. Mental Health.
1004 **267** 20c. blue and black . . . 90 15

268 Pres. J. F. Kennedy **269** Tower and Cogwheels

1962. Air. Visit of U.S. President.
1005 **268** 80c. blue and red . . . . 1·00 15

1962. "Century 21" Exn ("World's Fair"), Seattle.
1006 **269** 40c. black and green . . 35 10

270 Globe and O.E.A. Emblem **271** Pres. Alessandri of Chile

1962. Inter-American Economic and Social Council.
1007 **270** 40c. sepia and grey (postage) 25 10
1008 – 1p.20 sepia & violet (air) 35 15
DESIGN—HORIZ: 1p.20, Globe, Scroll and O.E.A. emblem.

1962. Visit of President of Chile.
1009 **271** 20c. brown 45 10

272 Balloon over Mexico City **273** "ALALC" Emblem

1962. Air. 1st Mexican Balloon Flight Centenary.
1010 **272** 80c. black and blue . . . 90 25

1963. Air. 2nd "ALALC" Session.
1023 **273** 80c. purple and orange 65 20

274 Pres. Betancourt of Venezuela

275 Petroleum Refinery

1963. Visit of President of Venezuela.
1024 **274** 20c. blue 35 10

1963. Air. 25th Anniv of Nationalization of Mexican Petroleum Industry.
1025 **275** 80c. slate and orange . . 35 10

276 Congress Emblem

277 Campaign Emblem

1963. 19th International Chamber of Commerce Congress, Mexico City.
1026 **276** 40c. brown and black (postage) 45 10
1027 – 80c. black and blue (air) 55 20
DESIGN—HORIZ: 80c. World map and "C.I.C." emblem.

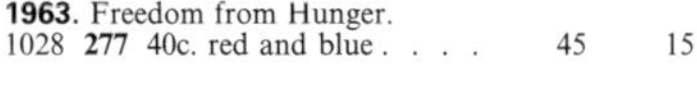

1963. Freedom from Hunger.
1028 **277** 40c. red and blue 45 15

278 Arms and Mountain

279 B. Dominguez

1963. 4th Centenary of Durango.
1029 **278** 20c. brown and blue . . 45 15

1963. Birth Centenary of B. Dominguez (revolutionary).
1030 **279** 20c. olive and green . . 45 15

280 Exhibition Stamp of 1956

281 Pres. Tito

1963. 77th American Philatelic Society Convention, Mexico City.
1031 **280** 1p. brown & bl (postage) 60 45
1032 – 5p. red (air) . . . . . . 1·40 1·00
DESIGN—HORIZ: 5p. EXMEX "stamp" and "postmark".

1963. Air. Visit of President of Yugoslavia.
1033 **281** 2p. green and violet . . 1·10 30

283 Part of U.I.A. Building

284 Red Cross on Tree

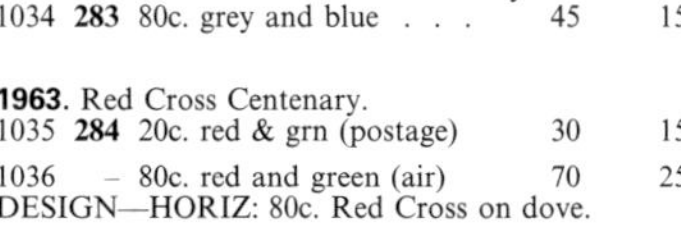

1963. Air. International Architects' Day.
1034 **283** 80c. grey and blue . . . 45 15

1963. Red Cross Centenary.
1035 **284** 20c. red & grn (postage) 30 15
1036 – 80c. red and green (air) 70 25
DESIGN—HORIZ: 80c. Red Cross on dove.

285 Pres. Estenssoro

286 Jose Morelos

1963. Visit of President of Bolivia.
1037 **285** 40c. purple and brown 45 15

1963. 150th Anniv of First Anahuac Congress.
1038 **286** 40c. bronze and green 40 15

287 Don Quixote as Skeleton

288 University Arms

1963. Air. 50th Death Anniv of Jose Posada (satirical artist).
1039 **287** 1p.20 black 75 20

1963. 90th Anniv of Sinaloa University.
1040 **288** 40c. bistre and green . . 45 15

289 Diesel-electric Train

290 "F.S.T.S.E." Emblem

1963. 11th Pan-American Railways Congress, Mexico City.
1041 **289** 20c. brn & blk (postage) 1·25 70
1042 – 1p.20 blue and violet (air) . . . . 1·25 55
DESIGN: 1p.20, Steam and diesel-electric locomotives and horse-drawn tramcar.

1964. 25th Anniv of Workers' Statute.
1075 **290** 20c. sepia and orange . . 30 10

291 Mrs. Roosevelt, Flame and U.N. Emblem

1964. Air. 15th Anniv of Declaration of Human Rights.
1076 **291** 80c. blue and orange . . 50 10

292 Pres. De Gaulle

1964. Air. Visit of President of France.
1077 **292** 2p. blue and brown . . . 1·25 35

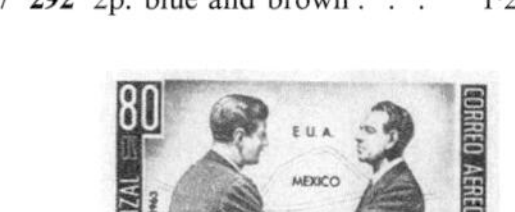

293 Pres. Kennedy and Pres. A. Lopez Mateos

1964. Air. Ratification of Chamizal Treaty (1963).
1078 **293** 80c. black and blue . . . 55 15

294 Queen Juliana and Arms

295 Academy Emblem

1964. Air. Visit of Queen Juliana of the Netherlands.
1079 **294** 20c. bistre and blue . . . 70 15

1964. Centenary of National Academy of Medicine.
1080 **295** 20c. gold and black . . . 30 10

296 Lieut. Jose Azueto and Cadet Virgillo Uribe

1964. Air. 50th Anniv of Heroic Defence of Veracruz.
1081 **296** 40c. green and brown . . 30 10

297 Arms and World Map

298 Colonel G. Mendez

1964. Air. International Bar Assn Conf, Mexico City.
1082 **297** 40c. blue and brown . . 45 10

1964. Centenary of Battle of the Jahuactal Tabasco.
1083 **298** 40c. olive and brown . . 35 10

299 Dr. Jose Rizal

300 Zacatecas

1964. 400 Years of Mexican–Philippine Friendship. Inscr "1564 AMISTAD MEXICANO–FILIPINA 1964".
1084 **299** 20c. blue & grn (postage) 35 10
1085 – 40c. blue and violet . . . 40 10
1086 – 80c. blue & lt blue (air) 1·75 25
1087 – 2p.75 black and yellow 1·75 70
DESIGNS—As Type **299**: VERT: 40c. Legaspi. HORIZ: 80c. "San Pedro" (16th-century Spanish galleon). LARGER (44 × 36 mm): 2p.75, Ancient map of Pacific Ocean.

1964. 50th Anniv of Conquest of Zacatecas.
1088 **300** 40c. green and red . . . 40 10

301 Morelos Theatre, Aguascalientes

302 Andres Manuel del Rio

1965. 50th Anniv of Aguascalientes Convention.
1089 **301** 20c. purple and grey . . 30 10

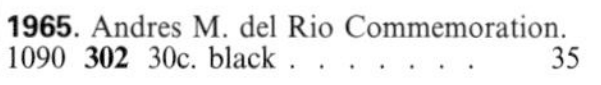

1965. Andres M. del Rio Commemoration.
1090 **302** 30c. black 35 10

303 Netzahualcoyotl Dam

304 J. Morelos (statue)

1965. Air. Inauguration of Netzahualcoyotl Dam.
1091 **303** 80c. slate and purple . . 30 10

1965. 150th Anniv (1964) of First Constitution.
1092 **304** 40c. brown and green . . 40 10

305 Microwave Tower

306 Fir Trees

1965. Air. Centenary of I.T.U.
1093 **305** 80c. blue and indigo . . 40 20
1094 – 1p.20 green and black 45 20
DESIGN: 1p.20, Radio-electric station.

1965. Forest Conservation.
1095 **306** 20c. green and blue . . . 30 10
The inscription "¡CUIDALOS!" means "CARE FOR THEM!".

307 I.C.Y. Emblem

1965. International Co-operation Year.
1096 **307** 40c. brown and green . . 25 10

308 Camp Fire and Tent

1965. Air. World Scout Conference, Mexico City.
1097 **308** 30c. ultramarine and blue 40 20

309 King Baudouin and Queen Fabiola

1965. Air. Visit of Belgian King and Queen.
1098 **309** 2p. blue and green . . . 75 20

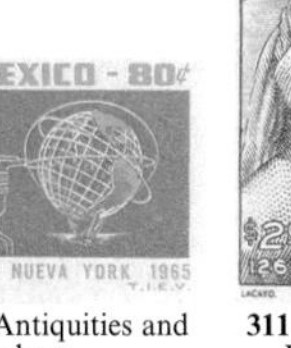

310 Mexican Antiquities and Unisphere

311 Dante (after R. Sanzio)

1965. Air. New York World's Fair.
1099 **310** 80c. green and yellow . . 30 15

1965. Air. Dante's 700th Birth Anniv.
1100 **311** 2p. red . . . . 1·00 55

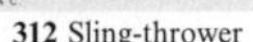

312 Sling-thrower

313 Jose M. Morelos y Pavon (leader of independence movement)

1965. Olympic Games (1968) Propaganda (1st series). Museum pieces.
1101 **312** 20c. blue & olive (postage) 45 10
1102 – 40c. sepia and red . . . 15 10
1103 – 80c. slate and red (air) 35 10
1104 – 1p.20 indigo and blue . . 45 15
1105 – 2p. brown and blue . . . 35 10
DESIGNS—As Type **312**: VERT: 40c. Batsman. HORIZ: 2p. Ball game. HORIZ (36 × 20 mm): 80c. Fieldsman. 1p.20, Scoreboard.

1965. 150th Anniv of Morelos's Execution.
1108 **313** 20c. black and blue . . . 30 10

314 Agricultural Produce

315 Ruben Dario

1966. Centenary of Agrarian Reform Law.
1109 **314** 20c. red 30 10
1110 – 40c. black 40 10
DESIGN: 40c. Emilio Zapata, pioneer of agrarian reform.

1966. Air. 50th Death Anniv of Ruben Dario (Nicaraguan poet).
1111 **315** 1p.20 sepia 55 20

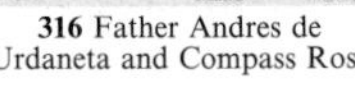

316 Father Andres de Urdaneta and Compass Rose

317 Flag and Postal Emblem

1966. Air. 400th Anniv of Father Andres de Urdaneta's Return from the Philippines.
1112 **316** 2p.75 black 85 45

1966. 9th Postal Union of Americas and Spain Congress (U.P.A.E.), Mexico City.
1113 **317** 40c. blk & grn (postage) 35 10
1114 – 80c. black & mauve (air) 30 15
1115 – 1p.20 black and blue . . 35 15
DESIGNS—VERT: 80c. Flag and posthorn. HORIZ: 1p.20, U.P.A.E. emblem and flag.

318 Friar B. de Las Casas

319 E.S.I.M.E. Emblem and Diagram

1966. 400th Death Anniv of Friar Bartolome de Las Casas ("Apostle of the Indies").
1116 **318** 20c. black on buff . . . 35 10

1966. 50th Anniv of Higher School of Mechanical and Electrical Engineering.
1117 **319** 20c. green and grey . . . 30 10

320 U Thant and U.N. Emblem

321 "1966 Friendship Year"

1966. Air. U.N. Secretary-General U Thant's Visit to Mexico.
1118 **320** 80c. black and blue . . . 30 15

1966. Air. "Year of Friendship" with Central American States.
1119 **321** 80c. green and red . . . 25 10

322 F.A.O. Emblem

323 Running and Jumping

1966. International Rice Year.
1120 **322** 40c. green 30 10

1966. Olympic Games (1968) Propaganda (2nd series).
1121 **323** 20c. black & bl (postage) 55 10
1122 – 40c. black and lake . . . 25 10
1124 – 80c. black & brown (air) 35 10
1125 – 2p.25 black and green 55 25
1126 – 2p.75 black and violet 60 35
DESIGNS: 40c. Wrestling. LARGER (57 × 20 mm): 80c. Obstacle race; 2p.25, American football; 2p.75, Lighting Olympic flame.

324 U.N.E.S.C.O. Emblem

325 Constitution of 1917

1966. Air. 20th Anniv of U.N.E.S.C.O.
1128 **324** 80c. multicoloured . . . 30 10

1967. 50th Anniv of Mexican Constitution.
1129 **325** 40c. black (postage) . . 45 10
1130 – 80c. brown & ochre (air) 35 10
DESIGN: 80c. President V. Carranza.

326 Earth and Satellite

327 Oil Refinery

1967. Air. World Meteorological Day.
1131 **326** 80c. blue and black . . . 30 20

1967. 7th World Petroleum Congress, Mexico City.
1132 **327** 40c. black and blue . . . 30 10

328 Nayarit Indian

329 Degollado Theatre

1967. 50th Anniv of Nayarit State.
1133 **328** 20c. black and green . . 30 10

1967. Cent of Degollado Theatre, Guadalajara.
1134 **329** 40c. brown and mauve . . 10 10

330 Mexican Eagle and Crown

331 School Emblem

1967. Centenary of Triumph over the Empire.
1135 **330** 20c. black and ochre . . 30 10

1967. Air. 50th Anniv of Military Medical School.
1136 **331** 80c. green and yellow . . 35 15

332 Capt. H. Ruiz Gavino

333 Marco Polo

1967. Air. 50th Anniv of 1st Mexican Airmail Flight, Pachuca–Mexico City.
1137 **332** 80c. brown and black . . 30 10
1138 – 2p. brown and black . . 70 20
DESIGN—HORIZ: 2p. De Havilland D.H.6A biplane.

1967. Air. International Tourist Year.
1139 **333** 80c. red and black . . . 20 10

334 Canoeing

335 A. del Valle-Arizpe (writer)

1967. Olympic Games (1968) Propaganda (3rd series).
1140 **334** 20c. black & bl (postage) 20 10
1141 – 40c. black and red . . . 15 10
1142 – 50c. black and green . . 15 10
1143 – 80c. black and violet . . 25 10
1144 – 2p. black and orange . . 40 15
1146 – 80c. black & mauve (air) 15 10
1147 – 1p.20 black and green 15 10
1148 – 2p. black and lemon . . 60 20
1149 – 5p. black and yellow . . 1·00 35
DESIGNS: 40c. Basketball; 50c. Hockey; 80c. (No. 1143), Cycling; 80c. (No. 1146), Diving; 1p.20, Running; 2p. (No. 1144), Fencing; 2p. (No. 1148), Weightlifting; 5p. Football.

1967. Centenary of Fuente Athenaeum, Saltillo.
1151 **335** 20c. slate and brown . . 30 10

336 Hertz and Clark Maxwell

337 P. Moreno

1967. Air. International Telecommunications Plan Conference, Mexico City.
1152 **336** 80c. green and black . . 30 10

1967. 150th Death Anniv of Pedro Moreno (revolutionary).
1153 **337** 40c. black and blue . . . 30 15

338 Gabino Berreda (founder of Preparatory School)

339 Exhibition Emblem

1968. Centenary of National Preparatory and Engineering Schools
1154 **338** 40c. red and blue 35 10
1155 – 40c. blue and black . . . 35 10
DESIGN: No. 1155, Staircase, Palace of Mining.

1968. Air. "Efimex '68" International Stamp Exn, Mexico City.
1156 **339** 80c. green and black . . 25 30
1157 2p. red and black . . 25 30
The emblem reproduces the "Hidalgo" Official stamp design of 1884.

1968. Olympic Games (1968) Propaganda (4th series). Designs as T **334**, but inscr "1968".
1158 20c. black and olive (postage) 25 10
1159 40c. black and purple . . . 25 10
1160 50c. black and green 25 10
1161 80c. black and mauve . . . 25 10
1162 1p. black and brown . . . . 1·50 25
1163 2p. black and grey . . . . 1·75 95
1165 80c. black and blue (air) . . 30 10
1166 1p. black and turquoise . . 35 15
1167 2p. black and yellow 35 20
1168 5p. black and brown 80 70
DESIGNS: 20c. Wrestling; 40c. Various sports; 50c. Water-polo; 80c. (No. 1161), Gymnastics; 80c. (No. 1165), Yachting; 1p. (No. 1162), Boxing; 1p. (No. 1166), Rowing; 2p. (No. 1163), Pistol-shooting; 2p. (No. 1167), Volleyball; 5p. Horse-racing.

340 Dr. Martin Luther King

1968. Air. Martin Luther King Commemorative.
1170 **340** 80c. black and grey . . . 35 15

341 Olympic Flame

342 Emblems of Games

1968. Olympic Games, Mexico. (i) Inaug Issue.
1171 **341** 10p. multicoloured . . . 2·00 1·25

(ii) Games Issue. Multicoloured designs as T **341** (20, 40, 50c. postage and 80c., 1, 2p. air) or as T **342** (others).
1172 20c. Dove of Peace on map (postage) 25 10
1173 40c. Stadium 30 10
1174 50c. Telecommunications Tower, Mexico City . . . 30 10
1175 2p. Palace of Sport, Mexico City . . . . 1·40 25
1176 5p. Cultural symbols of Games . . . . 2·75 80
1178 80c. Dove and Olympic rings (air) 15 10
1179 1p. "The Discus-thrower" 15 10
1180 2p. Olympic medals 45 25
1181 5p. Type **342** . . . . 1·75 85
1182 10p. Line-pattern based on "Mexico 68" and rings . . 1·50 95

343 Arms of Vera Cruz

344 "Father Palou" (M. Guerrero)

1969. 450th Anniv of Vera Cruz.
1185 **343** 40c. multicoloured . . . 30 10

1969. Air. 220th Anniv of Arrival in Mexico of Father Serra (colonizer of California).
1186 **344** 80c. multicoloured . . . 35 10
It was intended to depict Father Serra in this design, but the wrong detail of the painting by Guerrero, which showed both priests, was used.

345 Football and Spectators

1969. Air. World Cup Football Championship (1st issue). Multicoloured.
1187 80c. Type **345** 25 10
1188 2p. Foot kicking ball . . . 35 10
See also Nos. 1209/10.

346 Underground Train

1969. Inauguration of Mexico City Underground Railway System.
1189 **346** 40c. multicoloured . . . 60 20

347 Mahatma Gandhi **348** Footprint on Moon

1969. Air. Birth Centenary of Mahatma Gandhi.
1190 **347** 80c. multicoloured . . . 30 10

1969. Air. 1st Man on the Moon.
1191 **348** 2p. black 30 25

349 Bee and Honeycomb **350** "Flying" Dancers and Los Nichos Pyramid, El Tajin

1969. 50th Anniv of I.L.O.
1192 **349** 40c. brown, blue & yell 20 10

1969. Tourism (1st series). Multicoloured.
1193 40c. Type **350**(postage) . . 25 10
1193a 40c. Puerto Vallarta, Jalisco (vert) 25 10
1194 80c. Acapulco (air) 80 15
1195 80c. Pyramid, Teotihuacan 60 15
1196 80c. "El Caracol" (Maya ruin), Yucatan 60 15
See also Nos. 1200/2 and 1274/7.

351 Red Crosses and Sun **352** "General Allende" (D. Rivera)

1969. Air. 50th Anniv of League of Red Cross Societies.
1197 **351** 80c. multicoloured . . . 30 10

1969. Birth Bicentenary of General Ignacio Allende ("Father of Mexican Independence").
1198 **352** 40c. multicoloured . . . 20 10

353 Dish Aerial **354** Question Marks

1969. Air. Inauguration of Satellite Communications Station, Tulancingo.
1199 **353** 80c. multicoloured . . . 35 10

1969. Tourism (2nd series). As T **350** but dated "1970". Multicoloured.
1200 40c. Puebla Cathedral . . . 40 10
1201 40c. Anthropological Museum, Mexico City . . 40 10
1202 40c. Belaunzaran Street, Guanajuato 40 10

1970. 9th National and 5th Agricultural Census. Multicoloured.
1204 20c. Type **354** 30 10
1205 40c. Horse's head and agricultural symbols . . . 25 10

355 Diagram of Human Eye

1970. 21st International Ophthalmological Congress, Mexico City.
1206 **355** 40c. multicoloured . . . 25 10

356 Cadet Ceremonial Helmet and Kepi **357** Jose Pino Suarez

1970. 50th Anniv of Military College Reorganization.
1207 **356** 40c. multicoloured . . . 20 10

1970. Birth Centenary (1969) of Jose Maria Pino Suarez (statesman).
1208 **357** 40c. multicoloured . . . 20 10

358 Football and Masks **361** Arms of Celaya

360 Composition by Beethoven

1970. Air. World Cup Football Championship (2nd issue). Multicoloured.
1209 80c. Type **358** 30 15
1210 2p. Football and Mexican idols 25 25

1970. Air. Birth Bicentenary of Beethoven.
1212 **360** 2p. multicoloured . . . 50 25

1970. 400th Anniv of Celaya.
1213 **361** 40c. multicoloured . . . 20 10

362 "General Assembly"

1970. Air. 25th Anniv of U.N.O.
1214 **362** 80c. multicoloured . . . 30 10

363 "Eclipse de Sol" **364** "Galileo" (Susterman)

1970. Total Eclipse of the Sun.
1215 **363** 40c. black 20 10

1971. Air. Conquest of Space. Early Astronomers. Multicoloured.
1216 2p. Type **364** 25 10
1217 2p. "Kepler" (unknown artist) 25 10
1218 2p. "Sir Isaac Newton" (Kneller) 25 10

365 "Sister Juana" (M. Cabrera)

1971. Air. Mexican Arts and Sciences (1st series). Paintings. Multicoloured.
1219 80c. Type **365** 40 15
1220 80c. "El Paricutin" (volcano) (G. Murillo) . . 40 15
1221 80c. "Men of Flames" (J. C. Orozco) 40 15
1222 80c. "Self-portrait" (J. M. Velasco) 40 15
1223 80c. "Mayan Warriors" ("Dresden Codex") . . . 40 15
See also Nos. 1243/7, 1284/8, 1323/7, 1351/5, 1390/4, 1417/21, 1523/7, 1540/4, 1650/4, 1688/92, 1834 and 1845.

366 Stamps from Venezuela, Mexico and Colombia

1971. Air. "Philately for Peace". Latin-American Stamp Exhibitions.
1224 **366** 80c. multicoloured . . . 35 15

367 Lottery Balls

1971. Bicentenary of National Lottery.
1225 **367** 40c. black and green . . 25 10

368 "Francisco Clavijero" (P. Carlin)

1971. Air. Return of the Remains of Francisco Javier Clavijero (historian) to Mexico (1970).
1226 **368** 2p. brown and green . . 50 25

369 Vasco de Quiroga and "Utopia" (O'Gorman) **370** "Amado Nervo" (artist unknown)

1971. 500th Birth Anniv of Vasco de Quiroga, Archbishop of Michoacan.
1227 **369** 40c. multicoloured . . . 20 10

1971. Birth Centenary of Amado Nervo (writer).
1228 **370** 80c. multicoloured . . . 20 10

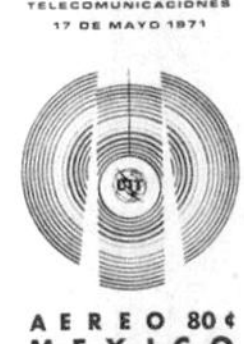

371 I.T.U. Emblem **372** "Mariano Matamoros" (D. Rivera)

1971. Air. World Telecommunications Day.
1229 **371** 80c. multicoloured . . . 25 10

1971. Air. Birth Bicentenary of Mariano Matamoros (patriot).
1230 **372** 2p. multicoloured . . . 45 25

373 "General Guerrero" (O'Gorman) **374** Loudspeaker and Sound Waves

1971. Air. 150th Anniv of Independence from Spain.
1231 **373** 2p. multicoloured . . . 45 25

1971. 50th Anniv of Radio Broadcasting in Mexico.
1232 **374** 40c. black, blue and green 25 10

375 Pres. Cardenas and Banners **376** Stamps of Venezuela, Mexico, Colombia and Peru

1971. 1st Death Anniv of General Lazaro Cardenas.
1233 **375** 40c. black and lilac . . . 25 10

1971. Air. "EXFILIMA 71" Stamp Exhibition Lima, Peru.
1234 **376** 80c. multicoloured . . . 45 15

377 Abstract of Circles **378** Piano Keyboard

1971. Air. 25th Anniv of U.N.E.S.C.O.
1235 **377** 80c. multicoloured . . . 30 15

1971. 1st Death Anniv of Agustin Lara (composer).
1236 **378** 40c. black, blue & yellow 30 10

379 "Mental Patients" **380** City Arms of Monterrey

1971. Air. 5th World Psychiatric Congress, Mexico City.
1237 **379** 2p. multicoloured . . . 25 20

1971. 375th Anniv of Monterrey.
1238 **380** 40c. multicoloured . . . 10 10

381 Durer's Bookplate

1971. Air. 500th Anniv of Albrecht Durer (artist).
1239 **381** 2p. black and brown . . 40 25

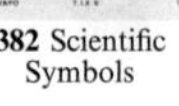

382 Scientific Symbols
383 Emblem of Mexican Cardiological Institute

1972. Air. 1st Anniv of National Council of Science and Technology.
1240 **382** 2p. multicoloured . . . 20 10

1972. World Health Month. Multicoloured.
1241 40c. Type **383** (postage) . . 10 10
1242 80c. Heart specialists (air) 10 10

1972. Air. Mexican Arts and Sciences (2nd series). Portraits. As T **365**.
1243 80c. brown and black . . . 75 15
1244 80c. green and black 75 15
1245 80c. brown and black . . . 75 15
1246 80c. blue and black 75 15
1247 80c. red and black 75 15
PORTRAITS: Nos. 1243, King Netzahualcoyotl of Texcoco (patron of the arts); No. 1244, J. R. de Alarcon (lawyer); No. 1245, J. J. Fernandez de Lizardi (writer); No. 1246, E. G. Martinez (poet); No. 1247, R. L. Velardo (author).

384 Rotary Emblems
385 Indian Laurel and Fruit

1972. Air. 50th Anniv of Rotary Movement in Mexico.
1248 **384** 80c. multicoloured . . . 10 10

1972. Centenary of Chilpancingo as Capital of Guerrero State.
1249 **385** 40c. black, gold and green 10 10

386 Track of Car Tyre

1972. Air. 74th Assembly of International Tourist Alliance, Mexico City.
1250 **386** 80c. black and grey . . . 10 10

387 First issue of "Gaceta De Mexico"
388 Emblem of Lions Organization

1972. 250th Anniv of Publication of "Gaceta De Mexico" (1st newspaper to be published in Latin America).
1251 **387** 40c. multicoloured . . . 10 10

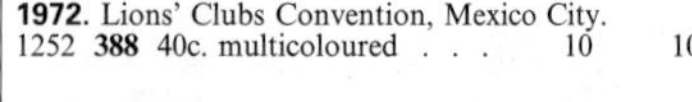

1972. Lions' Clubs Convention, Mexico City.
1252 **388** 40c. multicoloured . . . 10 10

389 "Zaragoza" (cadet sail corvette)
390 "Margarita Maza de Juarez" (artist unknown)

1972. 75th Anniv of Naval Academy, Veracruz.
1253 **389** 40c. multicoloured . . . 60 10

1972. Death Centenary of Pres. Benito Juarez.
1254 **390** 20c. mult (postage) . . . 35 10
1255 – 40c. multicoloured . . . 35 10
1256 – 80c. black and blue (air) 10 10
1257 – 1p.20 multicoloured . . 15 10
1258 – 2p. multicoloured . . . 20 10
DESIGNS: 40c. "Benito Juarez" (D. Rivera); 80c. Page of Civil Register with Juarez signature; 1p.20, "Benito Juarez" (P. Clave); 2p. "Benito Juarez" (J. C. Orozco).

391 "Emperor Justinian I" (mosaic)
392 Atomic Emblem

1972. 50th Anniv of Mexican Bar Association.
1259 **391** 40c. multicoloured . . . 55 10

1972. Air. 16th General Conference of Int Atomic Energy Organization, Mexico City.
1260 **392** 2p. black, blue and grey 15 10

393 Caravel on "Stamp"
394 "Sobre las Olas" (sheet-music cover by O'Brandstetter)

1972. Stamp Day of the Americas.
1261 **393** 80c. violet and brown . . 15 10

1972. Air. 28th International Authors' and Composers' Society Congress, Mexico City.
1262 **394** 80c. brown 15 10

395 "Mother and Child" (G. Galvin)

1972. Air. 25th Anniv of U.N.I.C.E.F.
1263 **395** 80c. multicoloured . . . 50 10

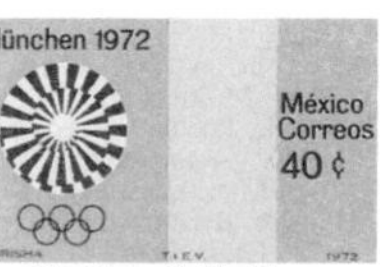

396 "Father Pedro de Gante" (Rodriguez y Arangorti)
397 Olympic Emblems

1972. Air. 400th Death Anniv of Father Pedro de Gante (founder of first school in Mexico).
1264 **396** 2p. multicoloured . . . 25 10

1972. Olympic Games, Munich.
1265 **397** 40c. multicoloured (postage) 10 10
1266 – 80c. multicoloured (air) 15 10
1267 – 2p. black, green and blue 25 10
DESIGNS—HORIZ: 80c. "Football". VERT: 2p. Similar to Type **397**.

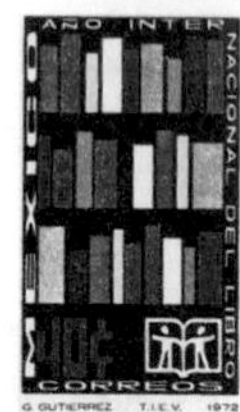

398 Books on Shelves
400 "Footprints on the Americas"

399 Common Snook ("Pure Water")

1972. International Book Year.
1268 **398** 40c. multicoloured . . . 10 10

1972. Anti-pollution Campaign.
1269 **399** 40c. black & bl (postage) 20 10
1270 – 80c. black and blue (air) 15 10
DESIGN—VERT: 80c. Pigeon on cornice ("Pure Air").

1972. Air. Tourist Year of the Americas.
1271 **400** 80c. multicoloured . . . 15 10

401 Stamps of Mexico, Colombia, Venezuela, Peru and Brazil

1973. Air. "EXFILBRA 72" Stamp Exhibition, Rio de Janeiro, Brazil.
1272 **401** 80c. multicoloured . . . 15 10

402 "Metlac Viaduct" (J. M. Velasco)

1973. Centenary of Mexican Railways.
1273 **402** 40c. multicoloured . . . 1·25 25

403 Ocotlan Abbey

1973. Tourism (3rd series). Multicoloured.
1274 40c. Type **403** (postage) . . 20 10
1275 40c. Indian hunting dance, Sonora (vert) 20 10

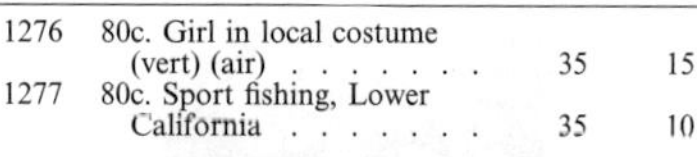

1276 80c. Girl in local costume (vert) (air) 35 15
1277 80c. Sport fishing, Lower California 35 10

404 "God of the Winds"

1973. Air. Centenary of W.M.O.
1278 **404** 80c. black, blue & mauve 35 10

405 Copernicus
406 Cadet

1973. Air. 500th Birth Anniv of Copernicus (astronomer).
1279 **405** 80c. green 15 10

1973. 150th Anniv of Military College.
1280 **406** 40c. multicoloured . . . 10 10

407 "Francisco Madero" (D. Rivera)
408 Antonio Narro (founder)

1973. Birth Centenary of Pres. Francisco Madero.
1281 **407** 40c. multicoloured . . . 10 10

1973. 50th Anniv of "Antonio Narro" Agricultural School, Saltillo.
1282 **408** 40c. grey 10 10

409 San Martin Statue
410 Caryon Molecules

1973. Air. Argentina's Gift of San Martin Statue to Mexico City.
1283 **409** 80c. multicoloured . . . 15 10

1973. Air. "Mexican Arts and Sciences" (3rd series). Astronomers. As T **365** but dated "1973".
1284 80c. green and red 10 10
1285 80c. multicoloured 10 10
1286 80c. multicoloured 10 10
1287 80c. multicoloured 10 10
1288 80c. multicoloured 10 10
DESIGNS: No. 1284, Aztec "Sun" stone; No. 1285, Carlos de Siguenza y Gongora; No. 1286, Francisco Diaz Covarrubias; No. 1287, Joaquin Gallo; No. 1288, Luis Enrique Erro.

1973. 25th Anniv of Chemical Engineering School.
1289 **410** 40c. black, yellow and red 10 10

411 Fist with Pointing Finger
412 "EXMEX 73" Emblem

1974. Promotion of Exports.
1294 **411** 40c. black and green . . 10 10

1974. "EXMEX 73" National Stamp Exhibition, Cuernavaca.
1295 **412** 40c. black (postage) . . 10 10
1296 – 80c. multicoloured (air) 15 10
DESIGN: 80c. Cortes' Palace, Cuernavaca.

413 Manuel Ponce

1974. 25th Death Anniv (1973) of Manuel M. Ponce (composer).
1297 **413** 40c. multicoloured . . . 10 10

414 Gold Brooch, Mochica Culture

1974. Air. Exhibition of Peruvian Gold Treasures, Mexico City.
1298 **414** 80c. multicoloured . . . 15 10

415 C.E.P.A.L. Emblem and Flags **416** Baggage

1974. Air. 25th Anniv of U.N. Economic Commission for Latin America (C.E.P.A.L.).
1299 **415** 80c. multicoloured . . . 15 10

1974. Air. 16th Confederation of Latin American Tourist Organizations (C.O.T.A.L.) Convention, Acapulco.
1300 **416** 80c. multicoloured . . . 15 10

417 Silver Statuette **419** "Dancing Dogs" (Indian statuette)

418 "The Enamelled Saucepan" (Picasso)

1974. 1st International Silver Fair, Mexico City.
1301 **417** 40c. multicoloured . . . 10 10

1974. Air. 1st Death Anniv of Pablo Picasso (artist).
1302 **418** 80c. multicoloured . . . 15 10

1974. 6th Season of Dog Shows.
1303 **419** 40c. multicoloured . . . 10 10

420 Mariano Azuela

1974. Birth Cent (1973) of Mariano Azuela (writer).
1304 **420** 40c. multicoloured . . . 10 10

421 Tepotzotlan Viaduct

1974. National Engineers' Day.
1305 **421** 40c. black and blue . . . 55 15

422 R. Robles (surgeon)

1974. 25th Anniv of W.H.O.
1306 **422** 40c. brown and green . . 10 10

423 U.P.U. Emblem

1974. "Exfilmex 74" Inter-American Stamp Exhibition, Mexico City.
1307 **423** 40c. black and green on yellow (postage) . . . 10 10
1308 80c. black and brown on yellow (air) 15 10

424 Demosthenes

426 Map and Indian Head

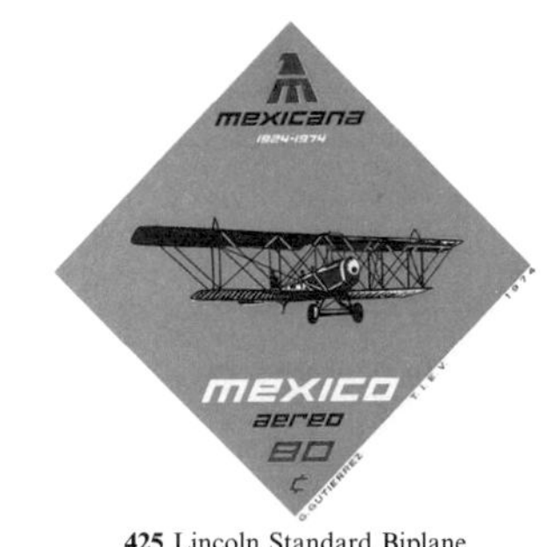

425 Lincoln Standard Biplane

1974. 2nd Spanish-American Reading and Writing Studies Congress, Mexico City.
1309 **424** 20c. green and brown . . 35 10

1974. Air. 50th Anniv of "Mexicana" (Mexican Airlines). Multicoloured.
1310 80c. Type **425** 15 10
1311 2p. Boeing 727-200 jetliner 40 10

1974. 150th Anniv of Union with Chiapas.
1312 **426** 20c. green and brown . . 10 10

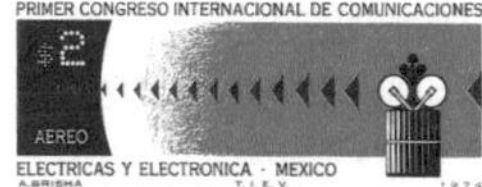

427 "Sonar Waves"

1974. Air. 1st International Electrical and Electronic Communications Congress, Mexico City.
1313 **427** 2p. multicoloured . . . 15 10

428 S. Lerdo de Tejada **429** Manuscript of Constitution

1974. Centenary of Restoration of Senate.
1314 **428** 40c. black and blue . . . 10 10

1974. 150th Anniv of Federal Republic.
1315 **429** 40c. black and green . . 10 10

430 Ball in Play

1974. Air. 8th World Volleyball Championships, Mexico City.
1316 **430** 2p. black, brown & orge 15 10

432 F. C. Puerto **433** Mask, Bat and Catcher's Glove

1974. Air. Birth Centenary of Felipe Carrillo Puerto (politician and journalist).
1318 **432** 80c. brown and green . . 10 10

1974. Air. 50th Anniv of Mexican Baseball League.
1319 **433** 80c. brown and green . . 10 10

434 U.P.U. Monument

1974. Centenary of U.P.U.
1320 **434** 40c. brown and blue (postage) 10 10
1321 – 80c. multicoloured (air) 10 10
1322 – 2p. brown and green . . 20 10

DESIGNS: 80c. Man's face as letter-box, Colonial period; 2p. Heinrich von Stephan, founder of U.P.U.

1974. Air. Mexican Arts and Sciences (4th series). Music and Musicians. As T **365** but dated "1974". Multicoloured.
1323 80c. "Musicians" – Mayan painting, Bonampak . . . 15 10
1324 80c. First Mexican-printed score, 1556 . . . . 15 10
1325 80c. Angela Peralta (soprano and composer) 15 10
1326 80c. "Miguel Lerdo de Tejada" (composer) . . . 15 10
1327 80c. "Silvestre Revueltas" (composer) (bronze by Carlos Bracho) 15 10

435 I.W.Y. Emblem **436** Economic Charter

1975. Air. International Women's Year.
1328 **435** 1p.60 black and red . . 15 10

1975. Air. U.N. Declaration of Nations' Economic Rights and Duties.
1329 **436** 1p.60 multicoloured . . 15 10

437 Jose Maria Mora **439** Dr. M. Jimenez

438 Trans-Atlantic Balsa Raft "Acali"

1975. 150th Anniv of Federal Republic.
1330 **437** 20c. multicoloured . . . 10 10

1975. Air. Trans-Atlantic Voyage of "Acali", Canary Islands to Yucatan (1973).
1331 **438** 80c. multicoloured . . . 50 10

1975. Air. 5th World Gastroenterological Congress.
1332 **439** 2p. multicoloured . . . 15 10

440 Aztec Merchants with Goods ("Codex Florentino")

1975. Centenary (1974) of Mexican Chamber of Commerce.
1333 **440** 80c. multicoloured . . . 10 10

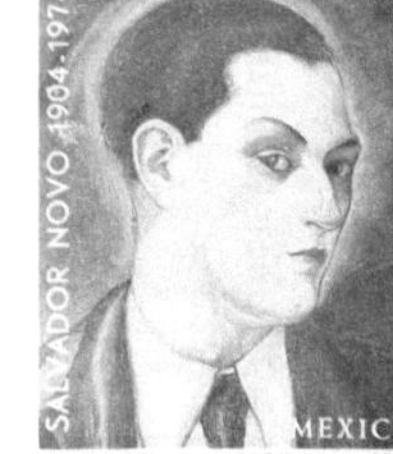

441 Miguel de Cervantes Saavedra (Spanish author) **443** Salvador Novo

442 4-reales Coin of 1675

1975. Air. 3rd International Cervantes Festival, Guanajuato.
1334 **441** 1p.60 red and black . . 15 10

1975. Air. International Numismatics Convention "Mexico 74".
1335 **442** 1p.60 bronze and blue 15 10

1975. Air. 1st Death Anniv of Salvador Novo (poet and writer).
1336 **443** 1p.60 multicoloured . . 15 10

444 "Self-portrait" (Siqueiros)

1975. Air. 1st Death Anniv of David Alfaro Siqueiros (painter).
1337 **444** 1p.60 multicoloured . . 15 10

445 General Juan Aldama (detail from mural by Diego Rivera)

1975. Birth Bicentenary (1974) of General Aldama.
1338 **445** 80c. multicoloured . . . 10 10

446 U.N. and I.W.Y. Emblems

1975. Air. International Women's Year and World Conference.
1339 **446** 1p.60 blue and pink . . 15 10

447 Eagle and Snake ("Codex Duran")

1975. 650th Anniv of Tenochtitlan (now Mexico City). Multicoloured.
1340 80c. Type **447** (postage) . . 10 10
1341 1p.60 Arms of Mexico City (air) 15 10

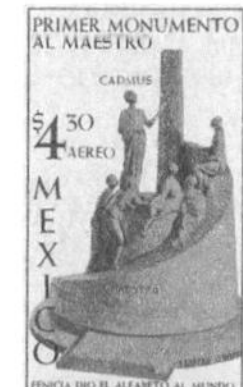

448 Domingo F. Sarmiento (educator and statesman)
449 Teachers' Monument, Mexico City

1975. Air. 1st International Congress of "Third World" Educators, Acapulco.
1342 **448** 1p.60 green and brown 15 10

1975. Air. Mexican–Lebanese Friendship.
1343 **449** 4p.30 green and brown 25 10

450 Games' Emblem

1975. Air. 7th Pan-American Games, Mexico City.
1344 **450** 1p.60 multicoloured . . 15 10

451 Julian Carrillo (composer)
452 Academy Emblem

1975. Birth Centenary of J. Carrillo.
1345 **451** 80c. brown and green . . 10 10

1975. Cent of Mexican Languages Academy.
1346 **452** 80c. yellow and brown 10 10

453 University Building

1975. 50th Anniv of Guadalajara University.
1347 **453** 80c. black, brown & pink 10 10

454 Dr. Atl
455 Road Builders

1975. Air. Atl (Gerardo Murillo, painter and writer). Birth Centenary.
1348 **454** 4p.30 multicoloured . . 25 10

1975. "50 Years of Road Construction" and 15th World Road Congress, Mexico City.
1349 **455** 80c. black & grn (postage) 10 10
1350 – 1p.60 black & blue (air) 15 10
DESIGN: 1p.60, Congress emblem.

1975. Air. Mexican Arts and Sciences (5th series). As T **365**, but dated "1975". Multicoloured.
1351 1p.60 Title page, F. Hernandez' "History of New Spain" 15 10
1352 1p.60 A. L. Herrera (naturalist) 15 10
1353 1p.60 Page from "Badiano Codex" (Aztec herbal) . . 15 10
1354 1p.60 A. Rosenblueth Stearns (neurophysiologist) . . . 15 10
1355 1p.60 A. A. Duges (botanist and zoologist) 15 10

456 Car Engine Parts
457 Aguascalientes Cathedral

1975. Mexican Exports. Multicoloured.
1356 – 5c. blue (postage) . . 35 10
1471 – 20c. black 35 10
1356b – 40c. brown 30 10
1356c **456** 50c. blue 35 10
1472 50c. black 10 10
1473 – 80c. red 10 10
1474 – 1p. violet and yellow 10 10
1358a – 1p. black and orange 10 10
1475 – 2p. blue and turquoise 55 10
1476 – 3p. brown 25 10
1359b – 4p. red and brown . . 25 10
1359e – 5p. brown 10 10
1359ed – 6p. red 10 10
1359ee – 6p. grey 10 10
1359f – 7p. blue 10 10
1359g – 8p. brown 10 10
1359h – 9p. blue 10 10
1479 – 10p. lt green & green 95 45
1360ac – 10p. red 10 10
1360ad – 15p. orange and brown 15 10
1360b – 20p. black 15 10
1360bc – 20p. black and red . . 10 10
1360be – 25p. brown 25 10
1360bh – 35p. yellow and mauve 25 10
1360bk – 40p. yellow and brown 25 10
1360bl – 40p. gold and green 25 10
1360bm – 40p. black 10 10
1360c – 50p. multicoloured . . 1·25 35
1360d – 50p. yellow and blue 35 20
1360da – 50p. red and green . . 35 20
1360db – 60p. brown 30 15
1360dc – 70p. brown 35 20
1360de – 80p. gold and mauve 20 50
1360df – 80p. blue 80 50
1360dg – 90p. blue and green 1·25 55
1360e – 100p. red, green and grey 70 35
1360ea – 100p. brown 10 10
1360f – 200p. yellow, green and grey . . . . . 1·90 30
1360fb – 200p. yellow and green 10 10
1360g – 300p. blue, red and grey 60 60
1360gb – 300p. blue and red . . 15 10
1360h – 400p. bistre, brown and grey 95 35
1360hb – 450p. brown and mauve 20 10
1360i – 500p. green, orange and grey . . . . . 1·90 30
1360ib – 500p. grey and blue 20 10
1360j – 600p. multicoloured 30 10
1360k – 700p. black, red and green 35 10
1360kb – 750p. black, red and green 30 10
1360l – 800p. brown & dp brown 40 10
1360m **456** 900p. black 50 10
1360n – 950p. blue 40 20
1481a – 1000p. black, red and grey 50 20
1360pa – 1000p. red and black 40 10
1360q – 1100p. grey 60 30
1360r – 1300p. red, green and grey 60 30
1360rb – 1300p. red and green 50 25
1360rg – 1400p. black 50 20
1360s – 1500p. brown 55 45
1360t – 1600p. orange 65 30
1360u – 1700p. green and deep green 70 30
1360w – 1900p. blue and green 2·25 75
1481b – 2000p. black and grey 1·25 50
1360xa – 2000p. black 80 55
1360y – 2100p. black, orange and grey 80 55
1360ya – 2100p. black and red 80 55
1360yb – 2200p. red 90 60
1360z – 2500p. blue and grey 95 65
1360za – 2500p. blue 95 65
1630zc – 2800p. black . . . . 1·10 75
1481c – 3000p. green, grey and orange . . . . 1·75 75
1360zf **456** 3600p. black and grey 1·50 1·00
1360zg – 3900p. grey and blue 1·60 1·10
1481d – 4000p. yellow, grey and red . . . . . 2·40 1·25
1360zj – 4800p. red, green and grey . . . . 1·90 1·25
1481e – 5000p. grey, green and orange . . . . 3·00 1·50
1360zn – 6000p. green, yellow and grey . . . . . 2·40 1·60
1360zq – 7200p. multicoloured 3·00 2·00
1361 – 30c. bronze (air) . . . 30 10
1482 – 50c. green and brown 10 10
1361a – 80c. blue 10 10
1483 – 1p.60 black and orange 10 10
1484 – 1p.90 red and green 15 10
1361d – 2p. gold and blue . . 25 10
1485 – 2p.50 red and green 10 10
1361e – 4p. yellow and brown 25 10
1361f – 4p.30 mauve and green 10 20
1361g – 5p. blue and yellow 95 20
1361h – 5p.20 black and red 25 25
1361i – 5p.60 green and yellow 10 30
1488 – 10p. green and light green 55 40
1361j – 20p. black, red and green . . . . . . 2·75 85
1361k – 50p. multicoloured . . 1·60 95
DESIGNS—POSTAGE. 5c., 6, 1600p. Steel tubes; 20c., 40 (1360bm), 1400, 2800p. Laboratory flasks; 40c., 100p. (1360ea) Cup of coffee; 80c., 10 (1360ac), 2200p. Steer marked with beef cuts; 1, 3000p. Electric cable; 2, 90, 1900p. Abalone shell; 3, 60p. Men's shoes; 4p. Ceramic tiles; 5, 1100p. Chemical formulae; 7, 8, 9, 80 (1360df), 2500p. Textiles; 10 (1479), 1700p. Tequila; 15p. Honeycomb; 20 (1360b), 2000p. Wrought iron; 20 (1360bc), 2100p. Bicycles; 25, 70, 1500p. Hammered copper vase; 35, 40 (1360bk/bl), 50 (1360d), 80p. (1360de) Books; 50 (1360c), 600p. Jewellery; 50 (1360da), 4800p. Tomato; 100 (1360e), 1300p. Strawberries; 200, 6000p. Citrus fruit; 300p. Motor vehicles; 400, 450p. Printed circuit; 500 (1360i), 5000p. Cotton boll; 500 (1360ib), 3900p. Valves (petroleum) industry; 700, 750, 7200p. Film; 800p. Construction materials; 1000p. Farm machinery; 4000p. Bee and honeycomb. AIR. 30c. Hammered copper vase; 50c. Electronic components; 80c. Textiles; 1p.60, Bicycles; 1p.90, Valves (petroleum) industry; 2p. Books; 2p.50, Tomato; 4p. Bee and honeycomb; 4p.30, Strawberry; 5p. Motor vehicles; 5p.20, Farm machinery; 5p.60, Cotton boll; 10p. Citrus fruit; 20p. Film; 50p. Cotton.

1975. 400th Anniv of Aguascalientes.
1362 **457** 50c. black and green . . 35 10

458 J. T. Bodet
460 "Death of Cuauhtemoc" (Chavez Morado)

459 "Fresco" (J. C. Orozco)

1975. 1st Death Anniv of Jaime T. Bodet (author and late Director-General of U.N.E.S.C.O.).
1363 **458** 80c. brown and blue . . 10 10

1975. 150th Anniv of Mexican Supreme Court of Justice.
1364 **459** 80c. multicoloured . . . 10 10

1975. 450th Death Anniv of Emperor Cuautemoc.
1365 **460** 80c. multicoloured . . . 10 10

461 Allegory of Irrigation

1976. 50th Anniv of Nat Irrigation Commission.
1366 **461** 80c. deep blue and blue 10 10

462 City Gateway

1976. 400th Anniv of Leon de los Aldamas, Guanajuato.
1367 **462** 80c. yellow and purple 10 10

463 Early Telephone
464 Gold Coin

1976. Air. Telephone Centenary.
1368 **463** 1p.60 black and grey . . 10 10

1976. Air. 4th Int Numismatics Convention.
1369 **464** 1p.60 gold, brown & blk 10 10

465 Tlaloc (Aztec god of rain) and Calles Dam

1976. Air. 12th Int Great Dams Congress.
1370 **465** 1p.60 purple and green 20 10

466 Perforation Gauge

1976. Air. "Interphil '76" International Stamp Exhibition, Philadelphia.
1371 **466** 1p.60 black, red and blue 20 10

467 Rainbow over Industrial Skyline

470 Liberty Bell

1976. Air. U.N. Conf on Human Settlements.
1372 **467** 1p.60 multicoloured . . 20 10

1976. Air. Bicentenary of American War of Independence.
1378 **470** 1p.60 blue and mauve 20 10

471 Forest Fire

1976. Fire Prevention Campaign.
1379 **471** 80c. multicoloured . . . 10 10

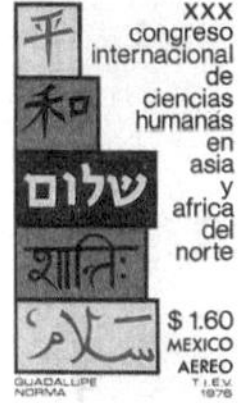

472 Peace Texts

473 Children on TV Screen

1976. Air. 30th International Asian and North American Science and Humanities Congress, Mexico City.
1380 **472** 1p.60 multicoloured . . 15 10

1976. Air. 1st Latin-American Forum on Children's Television.
1381 **473** 1p.60 multicoloured . . 20 10

474 Scout's Hat

475 Exhibition Emblem

1976. 50th Anniv of Mexican Boy Scout Movement.
1382 **474** 80c. olive and brown . . 10 10

1976. "Mexico Today and Tomorrow" Exhibition.
1383 **475** 80c. black, red & turq 10 10

476 New Buildings

477 Dr. R. Vertiz

1976. Inaug of New Military College Buildings.
1384 **476** 50c. brown and ochre . . 10 10

1976. Centenary of Ophthalmological Hospital of Our Lady of the Light.
1385 **477** 80c. brown and black . . 10 10

478 Guadalupe Basilica

1976. Inauguration of Guadalupe Basilica.
1386 **478** 50c. bistre and black . . 10 10

479 "40" and Emblem

1976. 40th Anniv of National Polytechnic Institute.
1387 **479** 80c. black, red and green 10 10

480 Blast Furnace

1976. Inauguration of Lazaro Cardenas Steel Mill, Las Truchas.
1388 **480** 50c. multicoloured . . . 10 10

481 Natural Elements

1976. Air. World Urbanization Day.
1389 **481** 1p.60 multicoloured . . 10 10

1976. Air. Mexican Arts and Sciences (6th series). As T **365** but dated "1976". Multicoloured.
1390 1p.60 black and red 10 10
1391 1p.60 multicoloured 10 10
1392 1p.60 black and yellow . . . 10 10
1393 1p.60 multicoloured 10 10
1394 1p.60 brown and black . . . 10 10
DESIGNS: No. 1390, "The Signal" (Angela Gurria); No. 1391, "The God of Today" (L. Ortiz Monasterio); No. 1392, "The God Coatlicue" (traditional Mexican sculpture); No. 1393, "Tiahuicole" (Manuel Vilar); No. 1394, "The Horseman" (Manuel Tolsa).

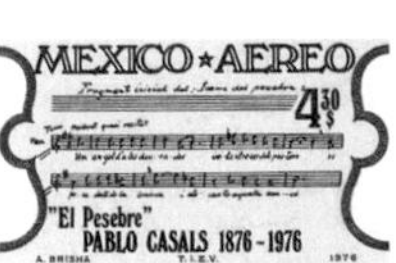

482 Score of "El Pesebre"

1977. Air. Birth Centenary of Pablo Casals (cellist).
1395 **482** 4p.30 blue and brown . . 15 10

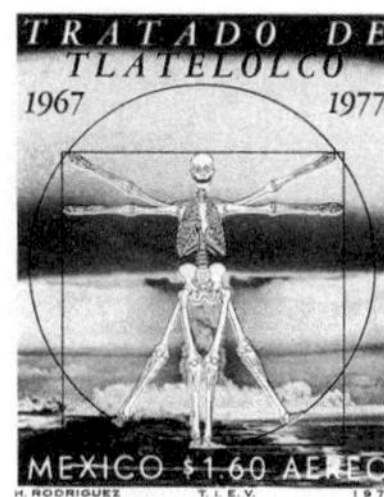

483 "Man's Destruction"

1977. Air. 10th Anniv of Treaty of Tlatelolco.
1396 **483** 1p.60 multicoloured . . 10 10

484 Saltillo Cathedral

485 Light Switch, Pylon and Engineers

1977. 400th Anniv of Founding of Saltillo.
1397 **484** 80c. brown and yellow 10 10

1977. 40 Years of Development in Mexico. Federal Electricity Commission.
1398 **485** 80c. multicoloured . . . 10 10

486 Footballers

1977. Air. 50th Anniv of Mexican Football Federation.
1399 **486** 1p.60 multicoloured . . 10 10
1400 – 4p.30 yellow, blue & blk 15 10
DESIGN: 4p.30, Football emblem.

487 Hands and Scales

1977. Air. 50th Anniv of Federal Council of Reconciliation and Arbitration.
1401 **487** 1p.60 orange, brn & blk 10 10

488 Flags of Spain and Mexico

489 Tlaloc (weather god)

1977. Resumption of Diplomatic Relations with Spain.
1402 **488** 50c. multicoloured (postage) 10 10
1403 80c. multicoloured . . . 10 10
1404 – 1p.60 black and grey (air) 10 10
1405 – 1p.90 red, green & lt grn 10 10
1406 – 4p.30 grey, brown & grn 15 10
DESIGNS: 1p.60, Arms of Mexico and Spain; 1p.90, Maps of Mexico and Spain; 4p.30, President Jose Lopez Portillo and King Juan Carlos.

1977. Air. Centenary of Central Meterological Observatory.
1407 **489** 1p.60 multicoloured . . 10 10

490 Ludwig van Beethoven

491 A. Serdan

1977. Air. 150th Death Anniv of Beethoven.
1408 **490** 1p.60 green and brown 10 10
1409 4p.30 red and blue . . . 15 10

1977. Birth Centenary of Aquiles Serdan (revolutionary martyr).
1410 **491** 80c. black, turq & grn 10 10

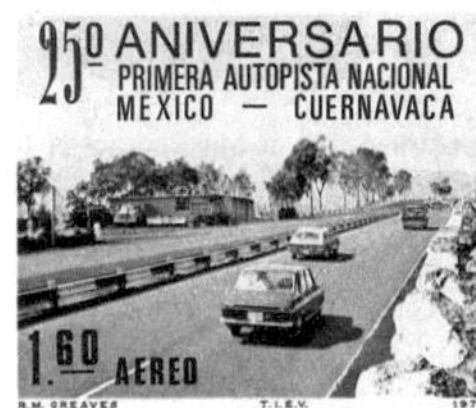

492 Mexico City–Guernavaca Highway

1977. Air. 25th Anniv of First National Highway.
1411 **492** 1p.60 multicoloured . . 10 10

493 Poinsettia

494 Arms of Campeche

1977. Christmas.
1412 **493** 50c. multicoloured . . . 10 10

1977. Air. Bicentenary of Naming of Campeche.
1413 **494** 1p.60 multicoloured . . 10 10

495 Tractor and Dam

1977. Air. U.N. Desertification Conference, Mexico City.
1414 **495** 1p.60 multicoloured . . 10 10

496 Congress Emblem

1977. Air. 20th World Education, Hygiene and Recreation Congress.
1415 **496** 1p.60 multicoloured . . 10 10

497 Freighter "Rio Yaqui"

498 Mayan Dancer

1977. Air. 60th Anniv of National Merchant Marine.
1416 **497** 1p.60 multicoloured . . 60 10

1977. Air. Mexican Arts and Sciences (7th series). Pre-colonial statuettes.
1417 **498** 1p.60 red, black and pink 10 10
1418 – 1p.60 blue, black and light blue 10 10
1419 – 1p.60 grey, black and yellow 10 10
1420 – 1p.60 green, black and turquoise 10 10
1421 – 1p.60 red, black and grey 10 10
DESIGNS: No. 1418, Aztec god of dance; No. 1419, Snake dance; No. 1420, Dancer, Monte Alban; No. 1421, Dancer, Totonaca.

499 Hospital Scene

1978. Air. 35th Anniv of Mexican Social Insurance Institute. Multicoloured.
1422 1p.60 Type **499** 10 10
1423 4p.30 Workers drawing benefits 15 10

500 Moorish Fountain

1978. Air. 450th Anniv of Chiapa de Corzo, Chiapas.
1424 **500** 1p.60 multicoloured . . 10 10

501 Telephones, 1878 and 1978 **502** Oilwell

1978. Centenary of Mexican Telephone.
1425 **501** 80c. red and salmon . . 10 10

1978. 40th Anniv of Nationalization of Oil Resources.
1426 **502** 80c. red and salmon (postage) 10 10
1427 – 1p.60 blue and red (air) 10 10
1428 – 4p.30 black, light blue and blue 55 20
DESIGNS: 1p.60, General I. Cardenas (President, 1938); 4p.30, Oil rig, Gulf of Mexico.

503 Arms of San Cristobal de las Casas

1978. Air. 450th Anniv of San Cristobal de las Casas, Chiapas.
1429 **503** 1p.60 purple, pink and black 10 10

504 Fairchild FC-71 Mail Plane **506** Blood Pressure Gauge and Map of Mexico

505 Globe and Cogwheel

1978. Air. 50th Anniv of First Mexican Airmail Route.
1430 **504** 1p.60 multicoloured . . 20 10
1431 4p.30 multicoloured . . 30 10

1978. Air. World Conference on Technical Co-operation between Underdeveloped Countries. Multicoloured.
1432 1p.60 Type **505** 10 10
1433 4p.30 Globe and cogwheel joined by flags 15 10

1978. Air. World Hypertension Month and World Health Day.
1434 **506** 1p.60 blue and red . . . 10 10
1435 – 4p.30 salmon and blue 15 10
DESIGN: 4p.30, Hand with stethoscope.

507 Kicking Ball **508** Francisco (Pancho) Villa

1978. Air. World Cup Football Championship, Argentina.
1436 **507** 1p.60 bl, lt orge & orge 10 10
1437 – 1p.90 blue, brn & orge 10 10
1438 – 4p.30 blue, grn & orge 15 10
DESIGNS: 1p.90, Saving a goal; 4p.30, Footballer.

1978. Air. Birth Centenary of Francisco Villa (revolutionary leader).
1439 **508** 1p.60 multicoloured . . 10 10

509 Emilio Carranza Stamp of 1929 **510** Woman and Calendar Stone

1978. Air. 50th Anniv of Mexico–Washington Flight by Emilio Carranza.
1440 **509** 1p.60 red and brown . . 10 10

1978. Air. Miss Universe Contest, Acapulco.
1441 **510** 1p.60 black, brn & red 10 10
1442 1p.90 black, brn & grn 10 10
1443 4p.30 black, brn & red 15 10

511 Alvaro Obregon (J. Romero)

1978. Air. 50th Death Anniv of Alvaro Obregon (statesman).
1444 **511** 1p.60 multicoloured . . 10 10

512 Institute Emblem

1978. 50th Anniv of Pan-American Institute for Geography and History.
1445 **512** 80c. blue and black (postage) 10 10
1446 – 1p.60 green and black (air) 10 10
1447 – 4p.30 brown and black 15 10
DESIGNS: 1p.60, 4p.30, Designs as Type **512**, showing emblem.

513 Sun rising over Ciudad Obregon **514** Mayan Statue, Rook and Pawn

1978. Air. 50th Anniv of Ciudad Obregon.
1448 **513** 1p.60 multicoloured . . 10 10

1978. Air. World Youth Team Chess Championship, Mexico City.
1449 **514** 1p.60 multicoloured . . 10 10
1450 4p.30 multicoloured . . 20 10

515 Aristotle **516** Mule Deer

1978. Air. 2300th Death Anniv of Aristotle.
1451 **515** 1p.60 grey, blue and yellow 10 10
1452 – 4p.30 grey, red and yellow 20 10
DESIGN: 4p.30, Statue of Aristotle.

1978. Air. World Youth Team Chess Championship, Mexico City.
1453 1p.60 Type **516** 20 10
1454 1p.60 Ocelot 20 10
See also Nos. 1548/9, 1591/2, 1638/9 and 1683/4.

517 Man's Head and Dove **518** "Dahlia coccinea". ("Dalia" on stamp)

1978. Air. International Anti-Apartheid Year.
1455 **517** 1p.60 grey, red and black 10 10
1456 – 4p.30 grey, lilac and black 15 10
DESIGN: 4p.30, Woman's head and dove.

1978. Mexican Flowers (1st series). Multicoloured.
1457 50c. Type **518** 10 10
1458 80c. "Plumeria rubra" . . . 10 10
See also Nos. 1550/1, 1593/4, 1645/6, 1681/2, 1791/2 and 1913/14.

519 Emblem **520** Dr. Rafael Lucio

1978. Air. 12th World Architects' Congress.
1459 **519** 1p.60 red, black and orange 10 10

1978. Air. 11th International Leprosy Congress.
1460 **520** 1p.60 green 10 10

521 Franz Schubert and "Death and the Maiden" **522** Decorations and Candles

1978. Air. 150th Death Anniv of Franz Schubert (composer).
1461 **521** 4p.30 brown, black and green 15 10

1978. Christmas. Multicoloured.
1462 50c. Type **522** (postage) . . 10 10
1463 1p.60 Children and decoration (air) 10 10

523 Antonio Vivaldi **524** Wright Flyer III

1978. Air. 300th Birth Anniv of Antonio Vivaldi (composer).
1464 **523** 4p.30 red, stone and brown 15 10

1978. Air. 75th Anniv of First Powered Flight.
1465 **524** 1p.60 orange, yell & mve 15 10
1466 – 4p.30 yellow, red & flesh 30 10
DESIGN: 4p.30, Side view of Wright Flyer I.

525 Albert Einstein and Equation

1979. Air. Birth Centenary of Albert Einstein (physicist).
1467 **525** 1p.60 multicoloured . . 10 10

526 Arms of Hermosillo **527** Sir Rowland Hill

1979. Centenary of Hermosillo, Sonora.
1468 **526** 80c. multicoloured . . . 10 10

1979. Air. Death Centenary of Sir Rowland Hill.
1469 **527** 1p.60 multicoloured . . 10 10

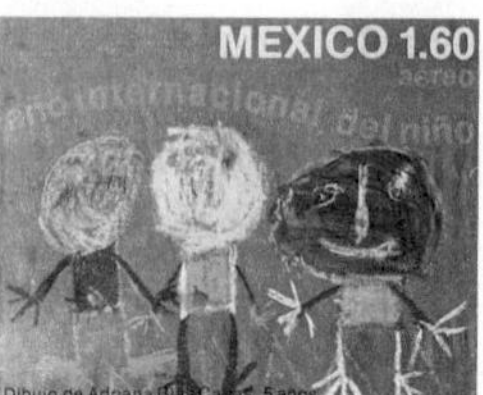

528 "Children" (Adriana Blas Casas)

1979. Air. International Year of the Child.
1470 **528** 1p.60 multicoloured . . 10 10

"MEXICO ELMHURST PHILATELIC SOCIETY INTERNATIONAL" REUNION ANUAL 1979

MEXICO AEREO 1.60

529 Registered Letter from Mexico to Rome, 1880

1979. Air. "Mepsipex 79", Third International Exhibition of Elmhurst Philatelic Society, Mexico City.
1499 **529** 1p.60 multicoloured . . 10 10

530 Football

531 Josefa Ortiz de Dominguez

1979. "Universiada 79", 10th World University Games, Mexico City (1st issue).
1500 **530** 50c. grey, black and blue (postage) 10 10
1501 – 80c. multicoloured . . . 10 10
1502 – 1p. multicoloured . . . 10 10
1504 – 1p.60 multicoloured (air) 10 10
1505 – 4p.30 multicoloured . . 15 10
DESIGNS—VERT: 80c. Aztec ball player; 1p. Wall painting of athletes; 1p.60, Games emblem; 4p.30, Flame and doves.
See also Nos. 1514/19.

1979. 150th Death Anniv of Josefa Ortiz de Dominguez (Mayor of Queretaro).
1507 **531** 80c. pink, black and bright pink 10 10

532 "Allegory of National Culture" (Alfaro Siqueiros)

1979. 50th Anniv of National University's Autonomy. Multicoloured.
1508 80c. Type **532** (postage) . . 10 10
1509 3p. "The Conquest of Energy" (Chavez Morado) 20 10
1510 1p.60 "The Return of Quetzalcoatl" (Chavez Morado) (air) 10 10
1511 4p.30 "Students reaching for Culture" (Alfaro Siqueiros) 15 10

533 Messenger and U.P.U. Emblem

534 Emiliano Zapata (after Diego Rivera)

1979. Air. Centenary of Mexico's Admission to U.P.U.
1512 **533** 1p.60 yellow, black and brown 10 10

1979. Birth Centenary of Emiliano Zapata (revolutionary).
1513 **534** 80c. multicoloured . . . 10 10

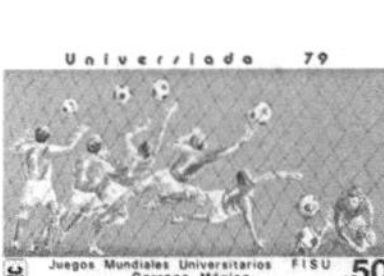

535 Football

536 Tepoztlan, Morelos

1979. "Universiada '79", 10th World University Games, Mexico City (2nd issue). Multicoloured.
1514 50c. Type **535** (postage) . . 10 10
1515 80c. Volleyball 10 10
1516 1p. Basketball 10 10
1518 1p.60 Tennis (air) 10 10
1519 5p.50 Swimming 30 20

1979. Tourism (1st series). Multicoloured.
1526 80c. Type **536** (postage) . . 10 10
1527 80c. Mexacaltitan, Nayarit 10 10
1528 1p.60 Agua Azul waterfall, Chipas (air) 10 10
1529 1p.60 King Coliman statue, Colima 10 10
See also Nos. 1631/4 and 1675/8.

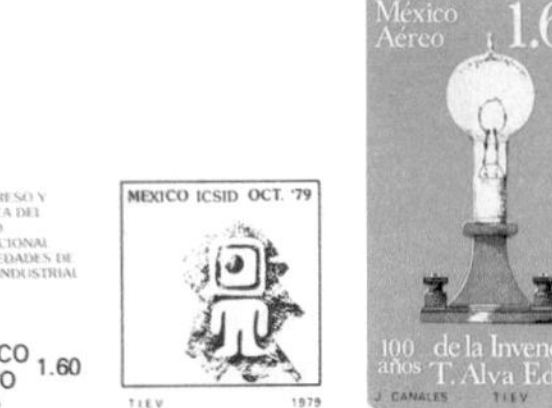
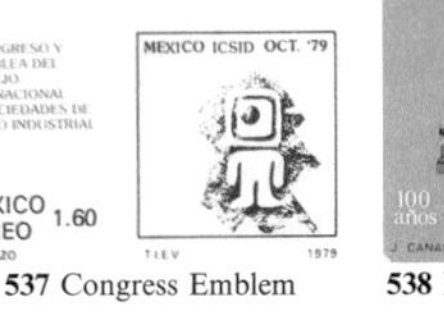

537 Congress Emblem **538** Edison Lamp

1979. Air. 11th Congress and Assembly of International Industrial Design Council.
1530 **537** 1p.60 black, mauve and turquoise 10 10

1979. Air. Centenary of Electric Light.
1531 **538** 1p.60 multicoloured . . 10 10

539 Martin de Olivares (postmaster)

540 Assembly Emblem

1979. 400th Anniv of Royal Proclamation of Mail Services in the New World. Multicoloured.
1532 80c. Type **539** (postage) . . 10 10
1533 1p.60 Martin Enriquez de Almanza (viceroy of New Spain) (air) 10 10
1534 5p.50 King Philip II of Spain 35 20

1979. Air. 8th General Assembly of Latin American Universities Union.
1536 **540** 1p.60 multicoloured . . 10 10

541 Shepherd

542 Moon Symbol from Mexican Codex

1979. Christmas. Multicoloured.
1537 50c. Type **541** (postage) . . 10 10
1538 1p.60 Girl and Christmas tree (air) 10 10

1979. Air. 10th Anniv of First Man on Moon.
1539 **542** 2p.50 multicoloured . . 15 10

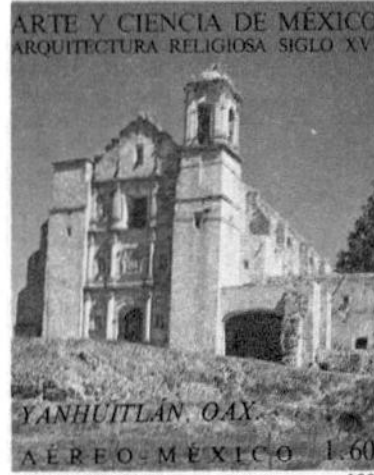

543 Church, Yanhuitlan

1980. Air. Mexican Arts and Sciences (8th series). Multicoloured.
1540 1p.60 Type **543** 10 10
1541 1p.60 Monastery, Yuriria . . 10 10
1542 1p.60 Church, Tlayacapan 10 10
1543 1p.60 Church, Actopan . . 10 10
1544 1p.60 Church, Acolman . . 10 10

544 Steps and Snake's Head

1980. National Pre-Hispanic Monuments (1st series). Multicoloured.
1545 80c. Type **544** (postage) . . 10 10
1546 1p.60 Doble Tlaloc (rain god) (air) 10 10
1547 5p.50 Coyolzauhqui (moon goddess) 35 20
See also Nos. 1565/7 and 1605/7.

1980. Mexican Fauna (2nd series). As T **516**. Multicoloured.
1548 80c. Common turkey (postage) 90 15
1549 1p.60 Greater flamingo (air) 90 40

1980. Mexican Flowers (2nd series). As T **518**. Multicoloured.
1550 80c. "Tajetes erecta" (postage) 15 10
1551 1p.60 "Vanilla planifolia" (air) 25 10

545 Jules Verne

1980. Air. 75th Death Anniv of Jules Verne (author).
1552 **545** 5p.50 brown and black 35 20

546 Skeleton smoking Cigar (after Guadalupe Posada) **547** China Poblana, Puebla

1980. Air. World Health Day. Anti-smoking Campaign.
1553 **546** 1p.60 purple, blue & red 10 10

1980. National Costumes (1st series). Multicoloured.
1554 50c. Type **547** (postage) . . 10 10
1555 80c. Jarocha, Veracruz . . . 10 10
1556 1p.60 Chiapaneca, Chiapas (air) 10 10
See also Nos. 1588/90.

548 Family

549 Cuauhtemoc (last Aztec Emperor)

1980. 10th Population and Housing Census.
1557 **548** 3p. black and silver . . . 20 10

1980. Pre-Hispanic Personalities (1st series). Multicoloured.
1558 80c. Type **549** 10 10
1559 1p.60 Nezahualcoyotl (governor of Tetzcoco) . . 10 10
1560 5p.50 Eight Deer Tiger's Claw (11th Mixtec king) 35 20
See also Nos. 1642/4 and 1846/8.

550 Xipe (Aztec god of medicine) **551** Bronze Medal

1980. 22nd World Biennial Congress of International College of Surgeons, Mexico City.
1561 **550** 1p.60 multicoloured . . 10 10

1980. Olympic Games, Moscow.
1562 **551** 1p.60 bronze, black and turquoise 10 10
1563 – 3p. silver, black and blue 20 10
1564 – 5p.50 gold, black and red 35 20
DESIGNS: 3p. Silver medal; 5p.50, Gold medal.

1980. National Pre-Hispanic Monuments (2nd series). As T **554**. Multicoloured.
1565 80c. Sacred glass 10 10
1566 1p.60 Stone snail 10 10
1567 5p.50 Chac Mool (god) . . 35 20

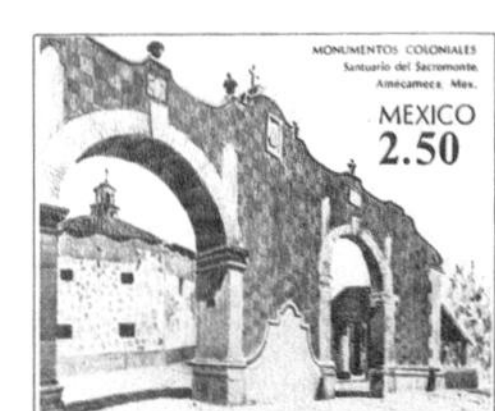

552 Sacromonte Sanctuary, Amecameca

1980. Colonial Architecture (1st series).
1568 **552** 2p.50 grey and black . . 20 10
1569 – 2p.50 grey and black . . 20 10
1570 – 3p. grey and black . . . 25 10
1571 – 3p. grey and black . . . 25 10
DESIGNS—HORIZ: No. 1552, St. Catherine's Convent, Patzcuaro; No. 1554, Hermitage, Cuernavaca. VERT: No. 1553, Basilica, Culiapan.
See also Nos. 1617/20, 1660/3, 1695/8 and 1784/7.

553 Quetzalcoatl (god)

554 Arms of Sinaloa

1980. World Tourism Conference, Manila, Philippines.
1572 **553** 2p.50 multicoloured . . 15 10

1980. 150th Anniv of Sinaloa State.
1573 **554** 1p.60 multicoloured . . 10 10

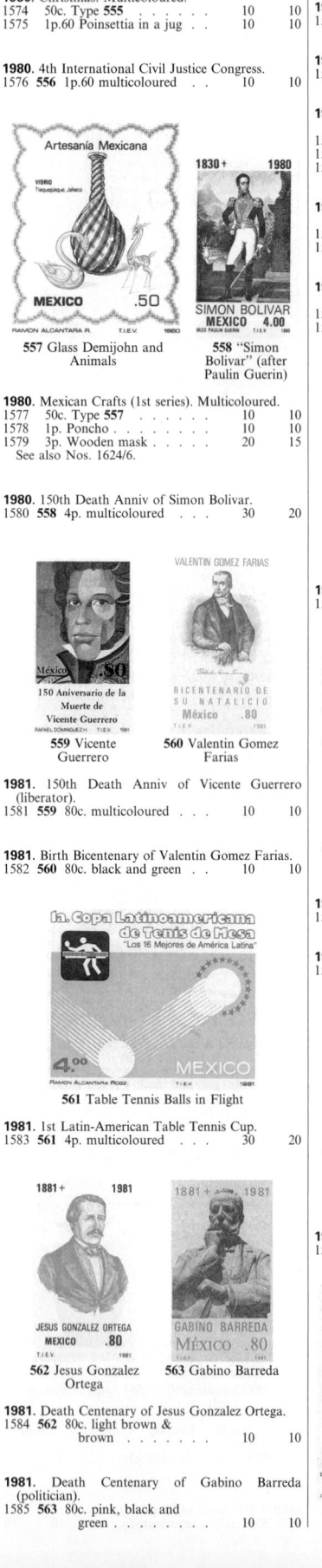

555 Straw Angel 556 Congress Emblem

1980. Christmas. Multicoloured.
1574 50c. Type **555** 10 10
1575 1p.60 Poinsettia in a jug . . 10 10

1980. 4th International Civil Justice Congress.
1576 **556** 1p.60 multicoloured . . 10 10

557 Glass Demijohn and Animals 558 "Simon Bolivar" (after Paulin Guerin)

1980. Mexican Crafts (1st series). Multicoloured.
1577 50c. Type **557** 10 10
1578 1p. Poncho 10 10
1579 3p. Wooden mask 20 15
See also Nos. 1624/6.

1980. 150th Death Anniv of Simon Bolivar.
1580 **558** 4p. multicoloured . . . 30 20

559 Vicente Guerrero 560 Valentin Gomez Farias

1981. 150th Death Anniv of Vicente Guerrero (liberator).
1581 **559** 80c. multicoloured . . . 10 10

1981. Birth Bicentenary of Valentin Gomez Farias.
1582 **560** 80c. black and green . . 10 10

561 Table Tennis Balls in Flight

1981. 1st Latin-American Table Tennis Cup.
1583 **561** 4p. multicoloured . . . 30 20

562 Jesus Gonzalez Ortega 563 Gabino Barreda

1981. Death Centenary of Jesus Gonzalez Ortega.
1584 **562** 80c. light brown & brown 10 10

1981. Death Centenary of Gabino Barreda (politician).
1585 **563** 80c. pink, black and green 10 10

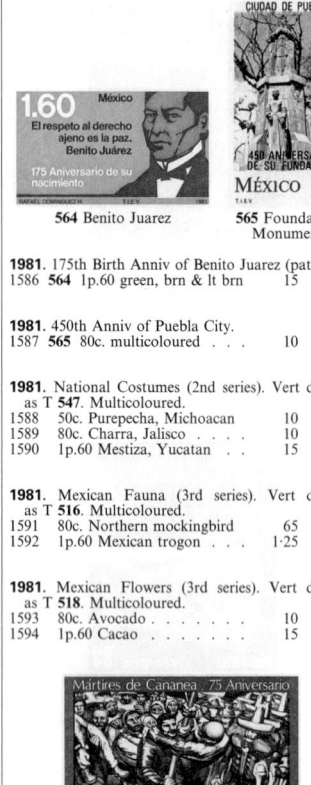

564 Benito Juarez 565 Foundation Monument

1981. 175th Birth Anniv of Benito Juarez (patriot).
1586 **564** 1p.60 green, brn & lt brn 15 10

1981. 450th Anniv of Puebla City.
1587 **565** 80c. multicoloured . . . 10 10

1981. National Costumes (2nd series). Vert designs as T **547**. Multicoloured.
1588 50c. Purepecha, Michoacan 10 10
1589 80c. Charra, Jalisco 10 10
1590 1p.60 Mestiza, Yucatan . . 15 10

1981. Mexican Fauna (3rd series). Vert designs as T **516**. Multicoloured.
1591 80c. Northern mockingbird 65 20
1592 1p.60 Mexican trogon . . . 1·25 40

1981. Mexican Flowers (3rd series). Vert designs as T **518**. Multicoloured.
1593 80c. Avocado 10 10
1594 1p.60 Cacao 15 10

566 "Martyrs of Cananea" (David A. Siqueiros)

1981. 75th Anniv of Martyrs of Cananea.
1595 **566** 1p.60 multicoloured . . 15 10

567 Toy Drummer with One Arm 568 Arms of Queretaro

1981. International Year of Disabled People.
1596 **567** 4p. multicoloured . . . 30 20

1981. 450th Anniv of Queretaro City.
1597 **568** 80c. multicoloured . . . 10 10

569 Mexican Stamp of 1856 and Postal Service Emblem

1981. 125th Anniv of First Mexican Stamp.
1598 **569** 4p. multicoloured . . . 30 20

570 Sir Alexander Fleming 572 St. Francisco Xavier Claver

571 Union Congress Building and Emblem

1981. Birth Centenary of Sir Alexander Fleming (discoverer of penicillin).
1599 **570** 5p. blue and orange . . 35 10

1981. Opening of New Union Congress Building.
1600 **571** 1p.60 green and red . . 10 10

1981. 250th Birth Anniv of St. Francis Xavier Claver.
1601 **572** 80c. multicoloured . . . 10 10

573 "Desislava" (detail of Bulgarian Fresco)

1981. 1300th Anniv of Bulgarian State. Mult.
1602 1p.60 Type **573** 10 10
1603 4p. Horse-headed cup from Thrace 25 20
1604 7p. Madara Horseman (relief) 45 30

1981. Pre-Hispanic Monuments. As T **544**. Multicoloured.
1605 80c. Seated God 10 10
1606 1p.60 Alabaster deer's head 15 10
1607 4p. Jade fish 45 20

574 Pablo Picasso

1981. Birth Centenary of Pablo Picasso (artist).
1608 **574** 5p. deep green and green 35 20

575 Shepherd 576 Wheatsheaf

1981. Christmas. Multicoloured.
1609 50c. Type **575** 10 10
1610 1p.60 Praying girl 15 10

1981. World Food Day.
1611 **576** 4p. multicoloured . . . 25 15

577 Thomas Edison, Lightbulb and Gramophone

1981. 50th Death Anniv of Thomas Edison (inventor).
1612 **577** 4p. stone, brown & green 25 15

578 Co-operation Emblem and Wheat

1981. International Meeting on Co-operation and Development, Cancun.
1613 **578** 4p. blue, grey and black 25 20

579 Globe and Diesel Locomotive

1981. 15th Pan-American Railway Congress.
1614 **579** 1p.60 multicoloured . . 50 25

580 Film Frame

1981. 50th Anniv of Mexican Sound Movies.
1615 **580** 4p. grey, black and green 25 20

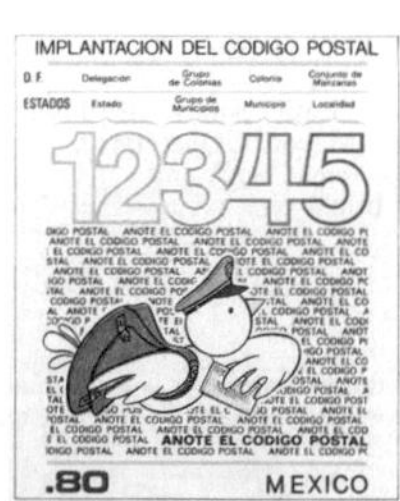

581 Postcode and Bird delivering Letter

1981. Inauguration of Postcodes.
1616 **581** 80c. multicoloured . . . 10 10

1981. Colonial Architecture (2nd series). As T **552**. Multicoloured.
1617 4p. Mascarones House . . . 25 15
1618 4p. La Merced Convent . . 25 15
1619 5p. Chapel of the Third Order, Texcoco 30 20
1620 5p. Father Tembleque Aqueduct, Otumba . . . 30 20

582 "Martyrs of Rio Blanco" (Orozco)

1982. 75th Anniv of Martyrs of Rio Blanco.
1621 **582** 80c. multicoloured . . . 10 10

583 Ignacio Lopez Rayon

1982. 150th Death Anniv of Ignacio Lopez Rayon.
1622 **583** 1p.60 green, red & black 10 10

584 Postal Headquarters

1982. 75th Anniv of Postal Headquarters.
1623 **584** 4p. pink and green . . . 25 20

1982. Mexican Crafts (2nd series). As T **557**. Multicoloured.
1624 50c. "God's Eye" (Huichol art) 10 10
1625 1p. Ceramic snail 10 10
1626 3p. Tiger mask 20 15

585 Postcoded Letter and Bird

1982. Postcode Publicity.
1627 **585** 80c. multicoloured . . . 10 10

586 Dr. Robert Koch and Cross of Lorraine

1982. Centenary of Discovery of Tubercle Bacillus.
1628 **586** 4p. multicoloured . . . 15 10

587 Military Academy

588 Arms of Oaxaca

1982. 50th Anniv of Military Academy.
1629 **587** 80c. yellow, black & gold 10 10

1982. 450th Anniv of Oaxaca City.
1630 **588** 1p.60 multicoloured . . 10 10

1982. Tourism (2nd series). As T **563**. Multicoloured.
1631 80c. Basaseachic Falls, Chihuahua 10 10
1632 80c. Natural rock formation, Pueblo Nuevo, Durango 10 10
1633 1p.60 Mayan City of Edzna, Campeche 10 10
1634 1p.60 La Venta (Olmeca sculpture, Tabasco) . . . 10 10

589 Footballers

1982. World Cup Football Championship, Spain. Multicoloured.
1635 1p.60 Type **589** 10 10
1636 4p. Dribbling 15 10
1637 7p. Tackling 25 15

590 Hawksbill Turtles

1982. Mexican Fauna. Multicoloured.
1638 1p.60 Type **590** 10 10
1639 4p. Grey Whales 15 30

591 Vicente Guerrero

1982. Birth Bicentenary of Vicente Guerrero (independence fighter).
1640 **591** 80c. multicoloured . . . 10 10

592 Symbols of Peace and Communication

1982. Second U.N. Conference on the Exploration and Peaceful Uses of Outer Space, Vienna.
1641 **592** 4p. multicoloured . . . 10 10

1982. Pre-Hispanic Personalities (2nd series). As T **549**. Multicoloured.
1642 80c. Tariacuri 10 10
1643 1p.60 Acamapichtli 10 10
1644 4p. Ten Deer Tiger's breastplate 10 10

593 Pawpaw ("Carica papaya")

1982. Mexican Flora. Multicoloured.
1645 80c. Type **593** 10 10
1646 1p.60 Maize ("Zea mays") 10 10

594 Astrologer

1982. Native Mexican Codices. Florentine Codex. Multicoloured.
1647 80c. Type **594** 10 10
1648 1p.60 Arriving at School . . 10 10
1649 4p. Musicians 10 10

595 Manuel Gamio (anthropologist)

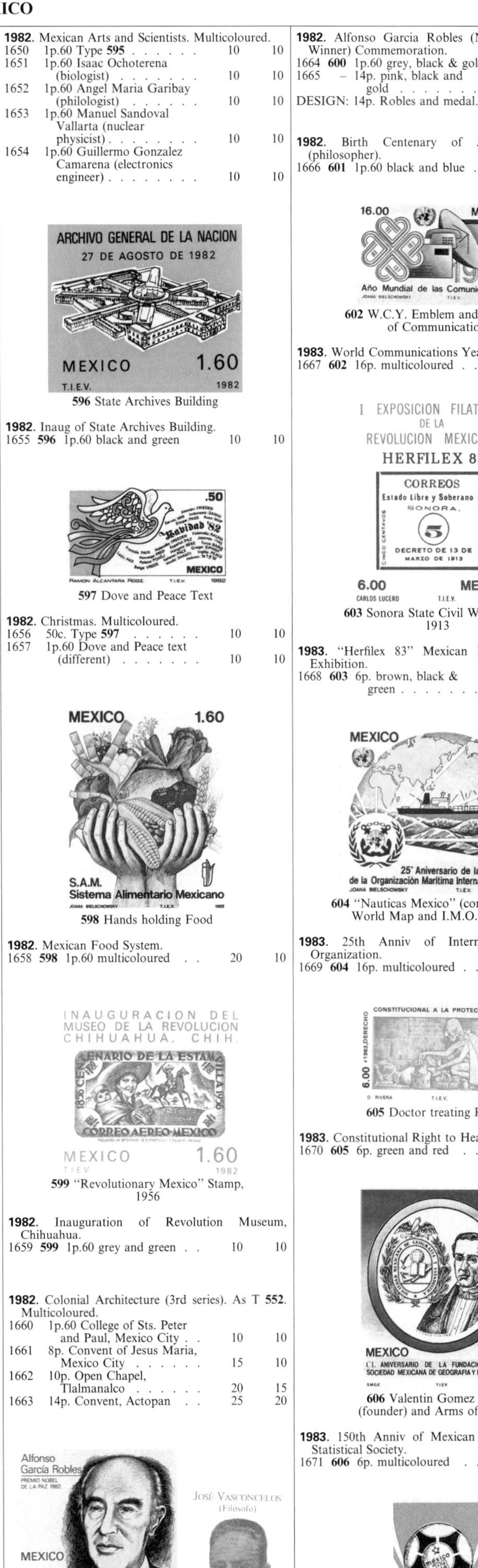

1982. Mexican Arts and Scientists. Multicoloured.
1650 1p.60 Type **595** 10 10
1651 1p.60 Isaac Ochoterena (biologist) 10 10
1652 1p.60 Angel Maria Garibay (philologist) 10 10
1653 1p.60 Manuel Sandoval Vallarta (nuclear physicist) 10 10
1654 1p.60 Guillermo Gonzalez Camarena (electronics engineer) 10 10

596 State Archives Building

1982. Inaug of State Archives Building.
1655 **596** 1p.60 black and green 10 10

597 Dove and Peace Text

1982. Christmas. Multicoloured.
1656 50c. Type **597** 10 10
1657 1p.60 Dove and Peace text (different) 10 10

598 Hands holding Food

1982. Mexican Food System.
1658 **598** 1p.60 multicoloured . . 20 10

599 "Revolutionary Mexico" Stamp, 1956

1982. Inauguration of Revolution Museum, Chihuahua.
1659 **599** 1p.60 grey and green . . 10 10

1982. Colonial Architecture (3rd series). As T **552**. Multicoloured.
1660 1p.60 College of Sts. Peter and Paul, Mexico City . . 10 10
1661 8p. Convent of Jesus Maria, Mexico City 15 10
1662 10p. Open Chapel, Tlalmanalco 20 15
1663 14p. Convent, Actopan . . 25 20

600 Alfonso Garcia Robles and Laurel

601 Jose Vasconcelos

1982. Alfonso Garcia Robles (Nobel Peace Prize Winner) Commemoration.
1664 **600** 1p.60 grey, black & gold 10 10
1665 – 14p. pink, black and gold 25 20
DESIGN: 14p. Robles and medal.

1982. Birth Centenary of Jose Vasconcelos (philosopher).
1666 **601** 1p.60 black and blue . . 10 10

602 W.C.Y. Emblem and Methods of Communication

1983. World Communications Year.
1667 **602** 16p. multicoloured . . . 20 15

603 Sonora State Civil War Stamp, 1913

1983. "Herfilex 83" Mexican Revolution Stamp Exhibition.
1668 **603** 6p. brown, black & green 10 10

604 "Nauticas Mexico" (container ship), World Map and I.M.O. Emblem

1983. 25th Anniv of International Maritime Organization.
1669 **604** 16p. multicoloured . . . 1·25 30

605 Doctor treating Patient

1983. Constitutional Right to Health Protection.
1670 **605** 6p. green and red . . . 10 10

606 Valentin Gomez Farias (founder) and Arms of Society

1983. 150th Anniv of Mexican Geographical and Statistical Society.
1671 **606** 6p. multicoloured . . . 10 10

607 Football

1983. 2nd World Youth Football Championship, Mexico.
1672 **607** 6p. black and green . . 10 10
1673 13p. black and red . . . 15 10
1674 14p. black and blue . . 20 15

1983. Tourism. As T **536**. Multicoloured.
1675 6p. Federal Palace, Queretaro 10 10
1676 6p. Water tank, San Luis Potosi 10 10
1677 13p. Cable car, Zacatecas 15 10
1678 14p. Carved head of Kohunlich, Quintana Roo 20 15

608 Bolivar on Horseback

1983. Birth Bicentenary of Simon Bolivar.
1679 **608** 21p. multicoloured . . . 25 15

609 Angela Peralta **610** Agave

1983. Death Centenary of Angela Peralta (opera singer).
1680 **609** 9p. light brown & brown 10 10

1983. Mexican Flora and Fauna (5th series). Multicoloured.
1681 9p. Type **610** 10 10
1682 9p. Sapodilla 10 10
1683 9p. Swallowtail 30 10
1684 9p. Boa constrictor 10 10

611 Two Candles

1983. Christmas. Multicoloured.
1685 9p. Type **611** 10 10
1686 20p. Three candles 25 15

612 S.C.T. Emblem

1983. Integral Communications and Transport System.
1687 **612** 13p. blue and black . . 15 10

613 Carlos Chavez (musician)

1983. Mexican Arts and Sciences (10th series). Contemporary Artists. Multicoloured.
1688 **613** 9p. brown, light brown and deep brown . . . 10 10
1689 – 9p. brown, light brown and deep brown . . . 10 10
1690 – 9p. deep brown, light brown and brown . . 10 10
1691 – 9p. light brown, deep brown and brown . . 10 10
1692 – 9p. deep brown, stone and brown 10 10
DESIGNS: No. 1689, Francisco Goitia (painter); No. 1690, S. Diaz Miron (poet); No. 1691, Carlos Bracho (sculptor); No. 1692, Fanny Anitua (singer).

614 Orozco (self-portrait)

1983. Birth Centenary of Jose Clemente Orozco (artist).
1693 **614** 9p. multicoloured . . . 10 10

615 Human Rights Emblem

1983. 35th Anniv of Human Rights Declaration.
1694 **615** 20p. deep blue, yellow and blue 25 15

1983. Colonial Architecture (4th series). As T **552**. Each grey and black.
1695 9p. Convent, Malinalco . . 10 10
1696 20p. Cathedral, Cuernavaca 25 15
1697 21p. Convent, Tepeji del Rio 25 15
1698 24p. Convent, Atlatlahucan 30 20

616 Antonio Caso and Books

1983. Birth Centenary of Antonio Caso (philospher).
1699 **616** 9p. blue, lilac and red . . 10 10

617 Joaquin Velazquez

1983. Bicentenary of Royal Legislation on Mining.
1700 **617** 9p. multicoloured . . . 10 10

618 Book and Envelopes

1984. Centenary of First Postal Laws.
1701 **618** 12p. multicoloured . . . 15 10

619 Children dancing around Drops of Anti-Polio Serum

1984. World Anti-polio Campaign.
1702 **619** 12p. multicoloured . . . 15 10

620 Muscovy Duck

1984. Mexican Fauna (6th series). Multicoloured.
1703 12p. Type **620** 70 65
1704 20p. Red-billed whistling duck . . . . 1·40 1·25

621 Xoloitzcuintle Dog

1984. World Dog Show.
1705 **621** 12p. multicoloured . . . 15 10

622 Bank Headquarters

1984. Centenary of National Bank.
1706 **622** 12p. multicoloured . . . 15 10

623 Hands holding Trees **624** Putting the Shot

1984. Protection of Forest Resources.
1707 **623** 20p. multicoloured . . . 20 15

1984. Olympic Games, Los Angeles. Multicoloured.
1708 14p. Type **624** 15 15
1709 20p. Show jumping 20 15
1710 23p. Gymnastics (floor exercise) 25 20
1711 24p. Diving 25 20
1712 25p. Boxing 25 20
1713 26p. Fencing 25 20

625 Mexican and Russian Flags

1984. 60th Anniv of Diplomatic Relations with U.S.S.R.
1715 **625** 23p. multicoloured . . . 25 20

626 Hand holding U.N. emblem

1984. International Population Conference.
1716 **626** 20p. multicoloured . . . 20 15

627 Gen. Mugica

1984. Birth Centenary of General Francisco Mugica (politician).
1717 **627** 14p. brown and black . . 15 15

628 Emblem and Dates **629** Airline Emblem

1984. 50th Anniv of Economic Culture Fund.
1718 **628** 14p. brown, black and red 15 15

1984. 50th Anniv of Aeromexico (state airline).
1719 – 14p. multicoloured . . . 15 15
1720 **629** 20p. black and red . . . 20 15
DESIGN—36 × 44 mm: 14p. "Red Cactus" (sculpture, Sebastian).

630 Palace of Fine Arts

1984. 50th Anniv of Palace of Fine Arts.
1721 **630** 14p. blue, black and brown 15 15

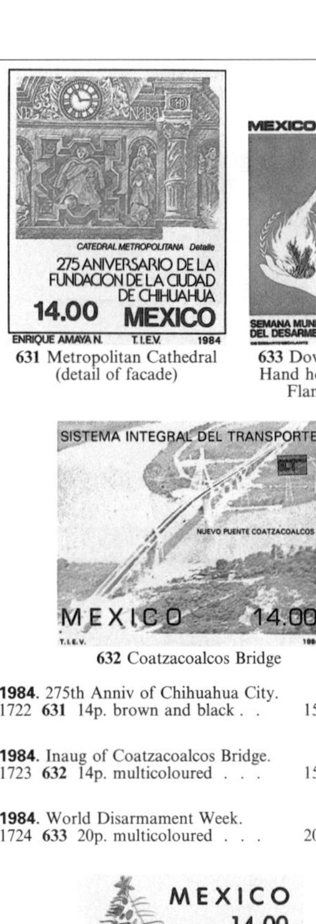

631 Metropolitan Cathedral (detail of facade)

633 Dove and Hand holding Flame

632 Coatzacoalcos Bridge

1984. 275th Anniv of Chihuahua City.
1722 **631** 14p. brown and black . . 15 15

1984. Inaug of Coatzacoalcos Bridge.
1723 **632** 14p. multicoloured . . . 15 15

1984. World Disarmament Week.
1724 **633** 20p. multicoloured . . . 20 15

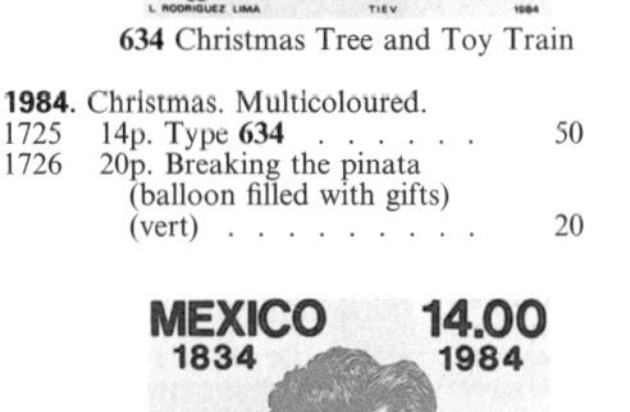

634 Christmas Tree and Toy Train

1984. Christmas. Multicoloured.
1725 14p. Type **634** 50 25
1726 20p. Breaking the pinata (balloon filled with gifts) (vert) 20 15

635 Ignacio Manuel Altamirano

1984. 150th Birth Anniv of Ignacio Manuel Altamirano (politician and journalist).
1727 **635** 14p. red and black . . . 15 15

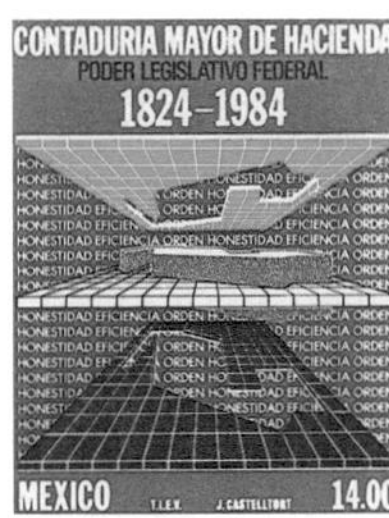

636 Maps, Graph and Text

1984. 160th Anniv of State Audit Office.
1728 **636** 14p. multicoloured . . . 15 15

637 Half a Football and Mexican Colours

1984. Mexico, Site of 1986 World Cup Football Championship. Multicoloured.
1729 20p. Type **637** 20 15
1730 24p. Football and Mexican colours 25 20

638 Romulo Gallegos

639 State Arms and Open Register

1984. Birth Centenary of Romulo Gallegos.
1731 **638** 20p. black and blue . . 20 15

1984. 125th Anniv of Mexican Civil Register.
1732 **639** 24p. blue 25 20

640 Mexican Flag

641 Johann Sebastian Bach

1985. 50th Anniv of National Flag.
1733 **640** 22p. multicoloured . . . 25 20

1985. 300th Birth Anniv of Johann Sebastian Bach (composer).
1734 **641** 35p. red and black . . . 15 30

642 I.Y.Y. Emblem

643 Children and Fruit within Book

1985. International Youth Year.
1735 **642** 35p. purple, gold and black 15 30

1985. Child Survival Campaign.
1736 **643** 36p. multicoloured . . . 15 10

644 Commemorative Medallion

1985. 450th Anniv of State Mint.
1737 **644** 35p. gold, mauve & blue 15 10

645 Victor Hugo, Text and Gateway

1985. Death Centenary of Victor Hugo (novelist).
1738 **645** 35p. grey 15 10

646 Hidalgo 8r. Stamp, 1856

1985. "Mexifil 85" Stamp Exhibition.
1739 **646** 22p. grey, black and purple 10 10
1740 – 35p. grey, black and blue 15 10
1741 – 36p. multicoloured . . . 15 10
DESIGNS: 35p. Carranza 10c. stamp, 1916; 36p. Juarez 50p. stamp, 1975.

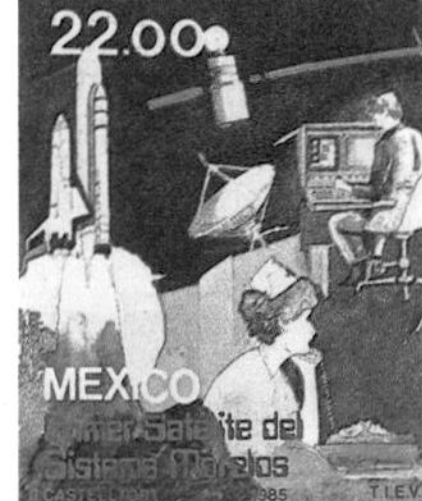

647 Rockets, Satellite, Nurse and Computer Operator

1985. Launching of First Morelos Satellite. Mult.
1743 22p. Type **647** 10 10
1744 36p. Camera, dish aerial, satellite and computers . . 15 10
1745 90p. Camera, dish aerial, satellite, television and couple telephoning . . . 25 20
Nos. 1743/5 were printed together, se-tenant, forming a composite design.

648 Conifer

1985. 9th World Forestry Congress, Mexico.
1747 **648** 22p. brown, black and green 10 10
1748 – 35p. brown, black and green 15 10
1749 – 36p. brown, black and green 15 10
DESIGNS: 35p. Silk-cotton trees; 36p. Mahogany tree.

649 Martin Luis Guzman

1985. Mexican Arts and Sciences (11th series). Contemporary Writers.
1750 **649** 22p. grey and blue . . . 10 10
1751 – 22p. grey and blue . . . 10 10
1752 – 22p. grey and blue . . . 10 10
1753 – 22p. grey and blue . . . 10 10
1754 – 22p. grey and blue . . . 10 10
DESIGNS: No. 1751, Augustin Yanez; 1752, Alfonso Reyes; 1753, Jose Ruben Romero; 1754, Artemio de Valle-Arizpe.

650 Miguel Hidalgo

1985. 175th Anniv of Independence Movement. Each green, black and red.
1755 22p. Type **650** 10 10
1756 35p. Jose Ma. Morelos . . . 10 10
1757 35p. Ignacio Allende 10 10
1758 36p. Leona Vigario 10 10
1759 110p. Vicente Guerrero . . 20 15

651 San Ildefonso

1985. 75th Anniv of National University. Mult.
1761 26p. Type **651** 10 10
1762 26p. Emblem 10 10
1763 40p. Modern building . . . 10 10
1764 45p. 1910 crest and Justo Sierra (founder) 10 10
1765 90p. University crest 15 10

652 Rural and Industrial Landscapes

1985. 25th Anniv of Inter-American Development Bank.
1766 **652** 26p. multicoloured . . . 10 10

653 Guns and Doves

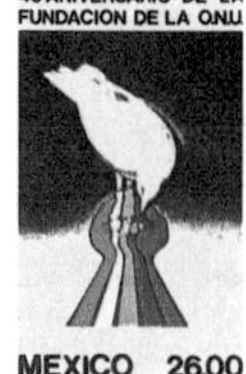

654 Hands and Dove

1985. United Nations Disarmament Week.
1767 **653** 36p. multicoloured . . . 10 10

1985. 40th Anniv of U.N.O.
1768 **654** 26p. multicoloured . . . 10 10

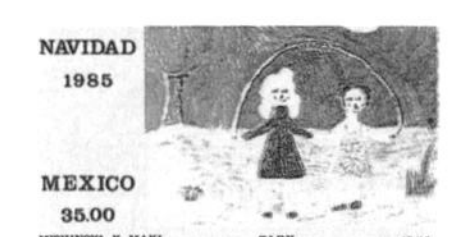

655 "Girls Skipping" (Mishinoya K. Maki)

1985. Christmas. Children's Paintings. Mult.
1769 26p. Disabled and able-bodied children playing (Margarita Salazar) . . . 10 10
1770 35p. Type **655** 10 10

656 Soldadera

1985. 75th Anniv of 1910 Revolution. Each red, black and green.
1771 26p. Type **656** 10 10
1772 35p. Pancho Villa 10 10
1773 40p. Emiliano Zapata . . . 10 10
1774 45p. Venustiano Carranza . . 10 10
1775 110p. Francisco Madero . . 20 15

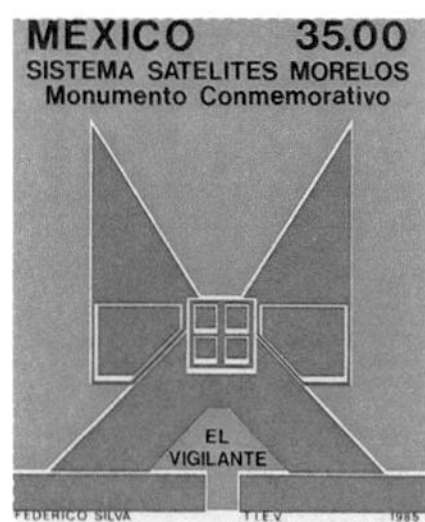

657 "Vigilante" (Federico Silva)

1985. 2nd "Morelos" Telecommunications Satellite Launch.
1777 – 26p. black and blue . . 10 10
1778 **657** 35p. grey, pink and black 10 10
1779 – 45p. multicoloured . . . 10 10
DESIGNS—VERT: 26p. "Cosmonaut" (sculpture by Sebastian). HORIZ: 45p. "Mexican Astronaut" (painting by Cauduro).

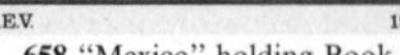
658 "Mexico" holding Book

1985. 25th Anniv of Free Textbooks National Commission.
1781 **658** 26p. multicoloured . . . 10 10

659 Olympic Stadium, University City

1985. World Cup Football Championship, Mexico. Each grey and black.
1782 26p. Type **659** 10 10
1783 45p. Azteca Stadium 10 10

1985. Colonial Architecture (5th series). Vert designs as T **552**. Each brown and black.
1784 26p. Vizcayan College, Mexico City 10 10
1785 35p. Counts of Heras y Soto Palace, Mexico City . . . 10 10
1786 40p. Counts of Calimaya Palace, Mexico City . . . 10 10
1787 45p. St. Carlos Academy, Mexico City 10 10

661 Luis Enrique Erro Planetarium

1986. 50th Anniv of National Polytechnic Institute. Multicoloured.
1788 40p. Type **661** 10 10
1789 65p. National School of Arts and Crafts 10 10
1790 75p. Founders, emblem and "50" 10 10

1986. Mexican Flowers (6th series). As T **518**. Multicoloured.
1791 40p. Calabash 10 10
1792 65p. "Nopalea coccinellifera" (cactus) . . 10 10

663 Doll

1986. World Health Day.
1793 **663** 65p. multicoloured . . . 10 10

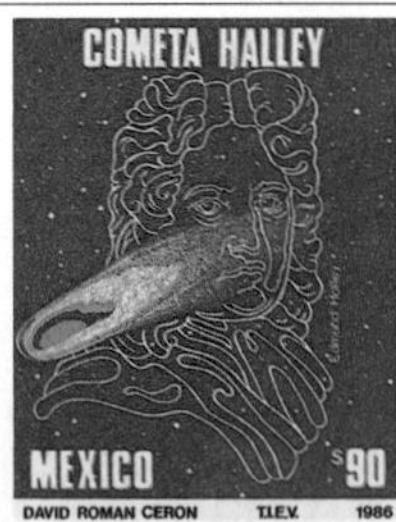

664 Halley and Comet

1986. Appearance of Halley's Comet.
1794 **664** 90p. multicoloured . . . 15 10

665 Emblem

1986. Centenary of Geological Institute.
1795 **665** 40p. multicoloured . . . 10 10

666 "Three Footballers with Berets"

1986. World Cup Football Championship, Mexico (2nd issue). Paintings by Angel Zarraga. Multicoloured.
1796 30p. Type **666** 10 10
1797 40p. "Portrait of Ramon Novaro" 10 10
1798 65p. "Sunday" 10 10
1799 70p. "Portrait of Ernest Charles Gimpel" 10 10
1800 90p. "Three Footballers" . . 15 10

667 Ignacio Allende

1986. 175th Death Annivs of Independence Heroes. Multicoloured.
1802 40p. Type **667** 10 10
1803 40p. Miguel Hidalgo (after J. C. Orozco) 10 10
1804 65p. Juan Aldama 10 10
1805 75p. Mariano Jimenez . . . 10 10

668 Mexican Arms over "FTF"

669 Nicolas Bravo

1986. 50th Anniv of Fiscal Tribunal.
1806 **668** 40p. black, blue and grey 10 10

1986. Birth Bicentenary of Nicolas Bravo (independence fighter).
1807 **669** 40p. multicoloured . . . 10 10

670 "Zapata Landscape"

1986. Paintings by Diego Rivera. Multicoloured.
1808 50p. Type **670** 10 10
1809 80p. "Nude with Arum Lilies" 10 10
1810 110p. "Vision of a Sunday Afternoon Walk on Central Avenue" (horiz) 20 15

671 Guadalupe Victoria

1986. Birth Bicentenary of Guadalupe Victoria (first President).
1811 **671** 50p. multicoloured . . . 10 10

672 People depositing Produce

1986. 50th Anniv of National Depositories.
1812 **672** 40p. multicoloured . . . 10 10

673 Pigeon above Hands holding Posthorn

674 Emblem

1986. World Post Day.
1813 **673** 120p. multicoloured . . 20 15

1986. Foundation of National Commission to Mark 500th Anniv (1992) of Discovery of America.
1814 **674** 50p. black and red . . . 10 10

675 Ministry of Mines

676 Liszt

1986. 15th Pan-American Roads Congress.
1815 **675** 80p. grey and black . . 10 10

1986. 175th Birth Anniv of Franz Liszt (composer).
1816 **676** 100p. brown and black 15 10

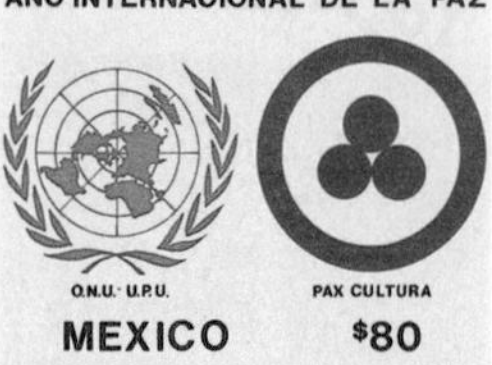

677 U.N. and "Pax Cultura" Emblems

1986. International Peace Year.
1817 **677** 80p. blue, red and black 10 10

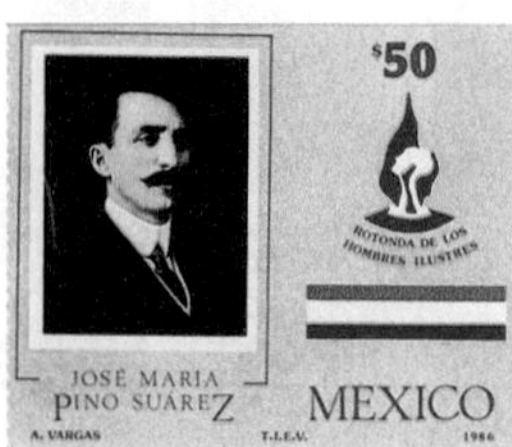

678 Jose Maria Pino Suarez (1st Vice-President of Revolutionary Govt.)

1986. Famous Mexicans buried in The Rotunda of Illustrious Men (1st series).
1818 **678** 50p. multicoloured . . . 10 10
See also Nos. 1823/4, 1838 and 1899.

679 King

680 "Self-portrait"

1986. Christmas. Multicoloured.
1819 50p. Type **679** 10 10
1820 80p. Angel 10 10

1986. Birth Centenary of Diego Rivera (artist).
1821 **680** 80p. multicoloured . . . 10 10

681 Baby receiving Vaccination

682 Perez de Leon College

1987. National Days for Poliomyelitis Vaccination.
1822 **681** 50p. multicoloured . . . 10 10

1987. Famous Mexicans buried in The Rotunda of Illustrious Men (2nd series). As T **678**. Mult.
1823 100p. Jose Maria Iglesias . . 10 10
1824 100p. Pedro Sainz de Baranda 10 10

1987. Centenary of Higher Education.
1825 **682** 100p. multicoloured . . 10 10

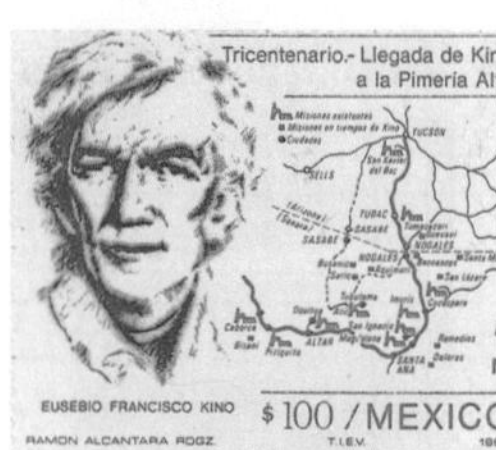

683 Kino and Map

1987. 300th Anniv of Father Eusebio Francisco Kino's Mission to Pimeria Alta.
1826 **683** 100p. multicoloured . . 10 10

684 Baby's Head

1987. Child Immunization Campaign.
1827 **684** 100p. deep blue and blue 10 10

685 Staircase

686 "5th of May, 1862, and the Siege of Puebla" Exhibition Poster, 1887

1987. 50th Anniv of Puebla Independent University.
1828 **685** 200p. grey, pink and black 10 10

1987. 125th Anniv of Battle of Puebla.
1829 **686** 100p. multicoloured . . 10 10

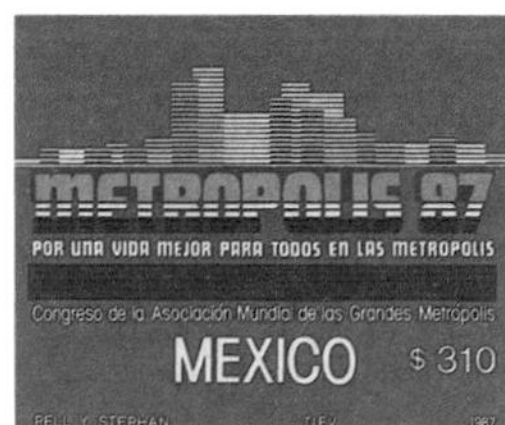

687 Stylized City

1987. "Metropolis 87" World Association of Large Cities Congress.
1830 **687** 310p. red, black and green 45 30

688 Lacquerware Tray, Uruapan, Michoacan

689 Genaro Estrada (author and pioneer of democracy)

1987. Handicrafts. Multicoloured.
1831 100p. Type **688** 10 10
1832 200p. Woven blanket, Santa Ana Chiautempan, Tlaxcala 10 10
1833 230p. Ceramic jar with lid, Puebla, Puebla 15 10

1987. Mexican Arts and Sciences (12th series).
1834 **689** 100p. brown, black and pink 10 10
See also Nos. 1845, 1880 and 1904/5.

690 "Native Traders" (mural, P. O'Higgins)

1987. 50th Anniv of National Foreign Trade Bank.
1835 **690** 100p. multicoloured . . 10 10

691 Diagram of Longitudinal Section through Ship's Hull

1987. 400th Anniv of Publication of First Shipbuilding Manual in America, Diego Garcia de Palacio's "Instrucion Nautica".
1836 **691** 100p. green, blue & brn 10 10

692 Man carrying Sack of Maize Flour

1987. 50th Anniv of National Food Programme.
1837 **692** 100p. multicoloured . . 10 10

1987. Mexicans in Rotunda of Illustrious Men (3rd series). As T **678**. Multicoloured.
1838 100p. Leandro Valle 10 10

693 "Self-portrait with Skull"

1987. Paintings by Saturnino Herran.
1839 **693** 100p. brown and black 15 10
1840 – 100p. multicoloured . . 15 10
1841 – 400p. multicoloured . . 60 50
DESIGNS: No. 1840, "The Offering"; 1841, "Creole with Shawl".

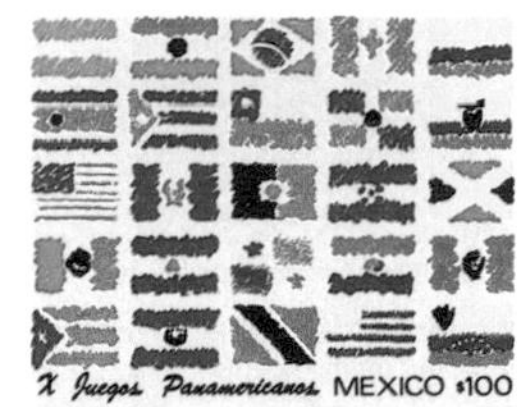

694 Flags of Competing Countries

1987. 10th Pan-American Games, Indianapolis.
1842 **694** 100p. multicoloured . . 10 10
1843 – 200p. black, red and green 10 10
DESIGN: 200p. Running.

695 Electricity Pylon

1987. 50th Anniv of Federal Electricity Commission.
1844 **695** 200p. multicoloured . . 10 10

1987. Mexican Arts and Sciences (13th series). As T **689**. Multicoloured.
1845 100p. J. E. Hernandez y Davalos (author) 10 10

1987. Pre-Hispanic Personalities (3rd series). As T **549**. Multicoloured.
1846 100p. Xolotl (Chichimeca commander) 10 10
1847 200p. Nezahualpilli (leader of Tezcoco tribe) 10 10
1848 400p. Motecuhzoma Ilhuicamina (leader of Tenochtitlan tribe) . . . 45 10

696 Stylized Racing Car

1987. Mexico Formula One Grand Prix.
1849 **696** 100p. multicoloured . . 10 10

697 Mexican Cultural Centre, Mexico City

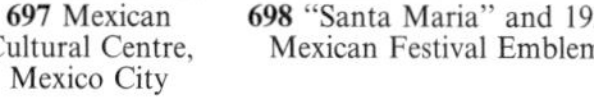

698 "Santa Maria" and 1922 Mexican Festival Emblem

1987. Mexican Tourism.
1850 **697** 100p. multicoloured . . 10 10

1987. 500th Anniv of "Meeting of Two Worlds" (discovery of America by Columbus) (1st issue).
1851 **698** 150p. multicoloured . . 65 20
See also Nos. 1902, 1941, 1979, 2038 and 2062/6.

699 16th-century Spanish Map of Mexico City

1987. 13th International Cartography Conference.
1852 **699** 150p. multicoloured . . 10 10

1987. Mexican Tourism. As T **697**. Multicoloured.
1853 150p. Michoacan 30 10
1854 150p. Garcia Caves, Nuevo Leon 10 10
1855 150p. View of Mazatlan, Sinaloa 10 10

700 Pre Hispanic Wedding Ceremony

1987. Native Codices. Mendocino Codex. Mult.
1856 150p. Type **700** 10 10
1857 150p. Moctezuma's council chamber 10 10
1858 150p. Foundation of Tenochtitlan 10 10

701 Dove with Olive Twig

1987. Christmas.
1859 **701** 150p. mauve 10 10
1860 – 150p. blue 10 10
DESIGN: No. 1860, As T **701** but dove facing left.

702 "Royal Ordinance for the Carriage of Maritime Mail" Title Page

1987. World Post Day.
1861 **702** 150p. green and grey . . 10 10

703 Circle of Flags

1987. 1st Meeting of Eight Latin-American Presidents, Acapulco. Multicoloured.
1863 250p. Type **703** 10 10
1864 500p. Flags and doves . . . 25 10

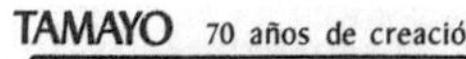

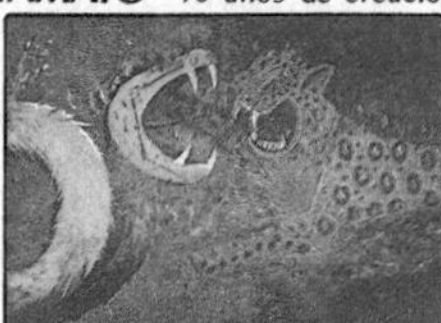

704 "Dualidad 1964"

1987. Rufino Tamayo (painter). "70 Years of Creativity".
1865 **704** 150p. multicoloured . . 10 10

705 Train on Metlac Viaduct

1987. 50th Anniv of Railway Nationalization.
1866 **705** 150p. multicoloured . . 40 15

706 Stradivarius at Work (detail, 19th-century engraving)

1987. 250th Death Anniv of Antonio Stradivarius (violin-maker).
1867 **706** 150p. light violet and violet 10 10

707 Statue of Manuel Crescencio Rejon (promulgator of Yucatan State Constitution)

1988. Constitutional Tribunal, Supreme Court of Justice.
1868 **707** 300p. multicoloured . . 15 10

708 American Manatee

1988. Animals. Multicoloured.
1869 300p. Type **708** 15 10
1870 300p. Mexican mole salamander 15 10

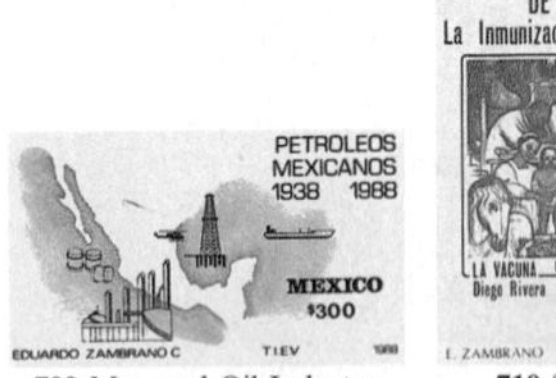

709 Map and Oil Industry Symbols

710 "The Vaccination"

1988. 50th Anniv of Pemex (Nationalized Petroleum Industry).
1871 **709** 300p. blue and black . . 40 10
1872 – 300p. multicoloured . . 15 10
1873 – 500p. multicoloured . . 25 10
DESIGNS:—36×43 mm: No. 1872, PEMEX emblem. 43×36 mm: No. 1873, "50" and oil exploration platform.

1988. World Health Day (1874) and 40th Anniv of W.H.O. (1875). Paintings by Diego Rivera.
1874 **710** 300p. brown and green 15 10
1875 – 300p. multicoloured . . 15 10
DESIGN:—43×36 mm: No. 1875, "The People demand Health".

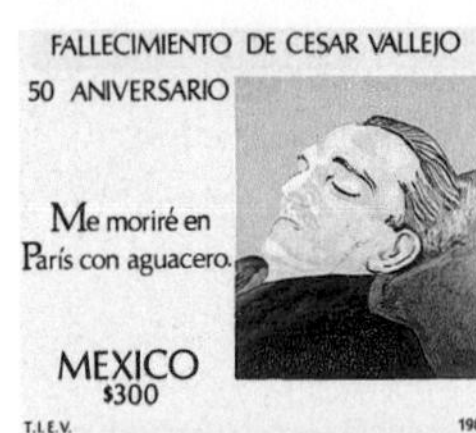

711 "Death Portrait" (Victor Delfin)

1988. 50th Death Anniv of Cesar Vallejo (painter and poet). Multicoloured.
1876 300p. Type **711** 15 10
1877 300p. Portrait by Arnold Belkin and "Hoy me palpo ..." 15 10
1878 300p. Portrait as in T **711** but larger (30×35 mm) 15 10
1879 300p. Portrait as in No. 1877 but larger (23×35 mm) 15 10

1988. Mexican Arts and Sciences (14th series). As T **689**.
1880 300p. brown, black and violet 15 10
DESIGN: 300p. Carlos Pellicer (poet).

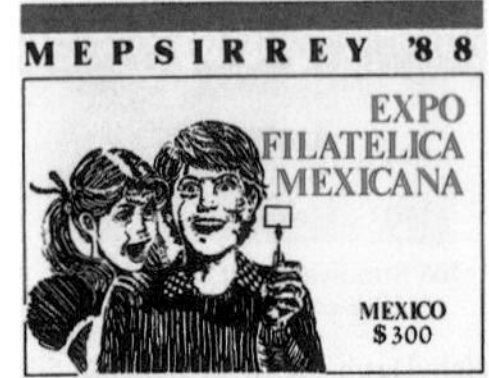

712 Girl and Boy holding Stamp in Tweezers

1988. "Mepsirrey '88" Stamp Exhibition, Monterrey. Multicoloured.
1881 300p. Type **712** 15 10
1882 300p. Envelope with "Monterrey" handstamp 15 10
1883 500p. Exhibition emblem . . 25 10

713 Hernandos Rodriguez Racing Circuit, Mexico City

1988. Mexico Formula One Grand Prix.
1884 **713** 500p. multicoloured . . 25 10

714 Lopez Verlarde and Rose

715 Emblem

1988. Birth Centenary of Ramon Lopez Verlarde (poet). Multicoloured.
1885 300p. Type **714** 15 10
1886 300p. Abstract 15 10

1988. 50th Anniv of Military Sports.
1887 **715** 300p. multicoloured . . 15 10

716 Chrysanthemum, Container Ship and Flags

1988. Centenary of Mexico–Japan Friendship, Trade and Navigation Treaty.
1888 **716** 500p. multicoloured . . 45 10

717 Map

1988. Oceanographical Assembly.
1889 **717** 500p. multicoloured . . 25 10

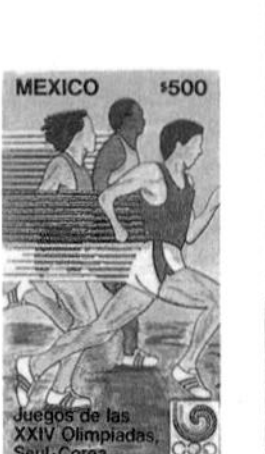

718 Runners

719 Boxer and Flags

1988. Olympic Games, Seoul.
1890 **718** 500p. multicoloured . . 25 10

1988. 25th Anniv of World Boxing Council.
1892 **719** 500p. multicoloured . . 25 10

720 Hospital and Emblem

1988. 125th Anniv of Red Cross.
1893 **720** 300p. grey, red and black 15 10

721 Posada

1988. 75th Death Anniv of Jose Guadalupe Posada (painter).
1894 **721** 300p. black and silver . . 15 10

722 "Danaus plexippus"

1988. Endangered Insects. The Monarch Butterfly. Multicoloured.
1895 300p. Type **722** . . . . . . 1·00 10
1896 300p. Butterflies on wall . . 1·00 10
1897 300p. Butterflies on leaves 1·00 10
1898 300p. Caterpillar, butterfly and chrysalis . . . . . . 1·00 10

1988. Mexicans in Rotunda of Illustrious Persons (4th series). As T **678**. Multicoloured.
1899 300p. Manuel Sandoval Vallarta 15 10

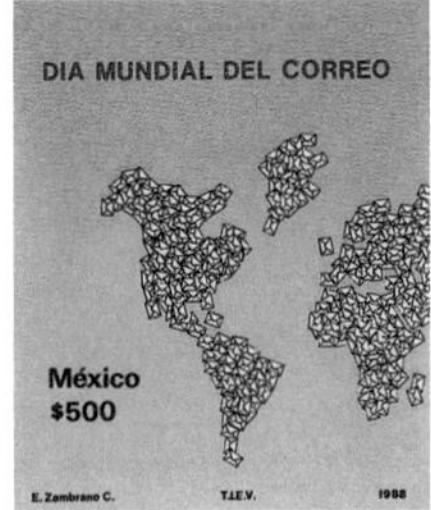

723 Envelopes forming Map

1988. World Post Day.
1900 **723** 500p. black and blue . . 20 10

724 Indian and Monk writing

1988. 500th Anniv of "Meeting of Two Worlds" (2nd issue). Yanhuitian Codex.
1902 **724** 500p. multicoloured . . 20 10

725 Man watering Plant

1988. World Food Day. "Rural Youth".
1903 **725** 500p. multicoloured . . 20 10

1988. Mexican Arts and Sciences (15th series). As T **689**.
1904 300p. black and grey . . . 15 10
1905 300p. brown, black & yellow 15 10
DESIGNS: No. 1904, Alfonso Caso; 1905, Vito Alessio Robles.

726 Act

1988. 175th Anniv of Promulgation of Act of Independence.
1906 **726** 300p. flesh and brown 15 10

727 "Self-portrait 1925"

728 Children and Kites

1988. 25th Death Anniv of Antonio Ruiz (painter). Multicoloured.
1907 300p. Type **727** 15 10
1908 300p. "La Malinche" . . . 15 10
1909 300p. "March Past" 15 10

1988. Christmas. Multicoloured.
1910 300p. Type **728** 15 10
1911 300p. Food (horiz) 15 10

729 Emblem

1988. 50th Anniv of Municipal Workers Trade Union.
1912 **729** 300p. black and brown 15 10

1988. Mexican Flowers (7th series). As T **518**. Multicoloured.
1913 300p. "Mimosa tenuiflora" 15 10
1914 300p. "Ustilago maydis" . . 30 10

731 "50" and Emblem

1989. 50th Anniv of State Printing Works.
1915 **731** 450p. brown, grey and red 20 10

732 Arms and Score of National Anthem

1989. 145th Anniv of Dominican Independence.
1916 **732** 450p. multicoloured . . 20 10

733 Emblem

1989. Centenary of International Boundary and Water Commission.
1917 **733** 1100p. multicoloured . . 50 50

734 Emblem

1989. 10th International Book Fair, Mineria.
1918 **734** 450p. multicoloured . . 20 10

735 Composer at Work

1989. 25th Anniv of Society of Authors and Composers.
1919 **735** 450p. multicoloured . . 20 10

736 People

1989. Anti-AIDS Campaign.
1920 **736** 450p. multicoloured . . 20 10

737 Vicario

738 Statue of Reyes

1989. Birth Bicentenary of Leona Vicario (Independence fighter).
1921 **737** 450p. brown, deep brown and black . . . 20 10

1989. Birth Centenary of Alfonso Reyes (writer).
1922 **738** 450p. multicoloured . . 20 10

739 Speeding Cars

1989. Mexico Formula One Grand Prix.
1923 **739** 450p. multicoloured . . 20 10

740 Sea and Mountains

741 Huehuetcotl (god)

1989. 14th Travel Agents' Meeting, Acapulco.
1924 **740** 1100p. multicoloured . . 50 50

1989. 14th International Congress on Ageing.
1925 **741** 450p. pink, black and stone 20 10

742 Revolutionary and Battle Site

1989. 75th Anniv of Battle of Zacatecas.
1926 **742** 450p. black 20 10

743 Catchers

1989. Baseball Professionals' Hall of Fame. Multicoloured.
1927 550p. Type **743** 20 10
1928 550p. Striker 20 10
Nos. 1927/8 were printed together, se-tenant, forming a composite design.

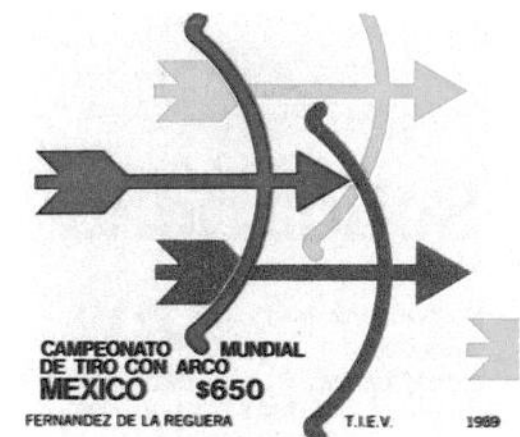

744 Bows and Arrows

1989. World Archery Championships, Switzerland. Multicoloured.
1929 650p. Type **744** 25 10
1920 650p. Arrows and target . . 25 10
Nos. 1929/30 were printed together, se-tenant, forming a composite design.

745 Arms

1989. Centenary of Tijuana.
1931 **745** 1100p. multicoloured . . 50 20

746 Storming the Bastille

1989. Bicentenary of French Revolution.
1932 **746** 1300p. multicoloured . . 60 50

747 Mina

1989. Birth Bicentenary of Francisco Xavier Mina (independence fighter).
1933 **747** 450p. multicoloured . . 20 10

748 Cave Paintings

1989. 25th Anniv of National Anthropological Museum, Chapultepec.
1934 **748** 450p. multicoloured . . 20 10

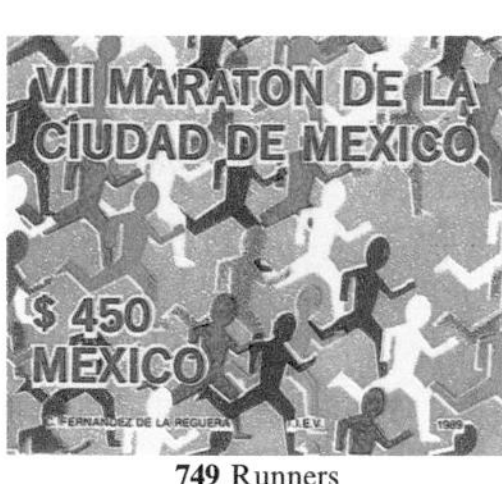

749 Runners

1989. 7th Mexico City Marathon.
1935 **749** 450p. multicoloured . . 20 10

750 Printed Page

1989. 450th Anniv of First American and Mexican Printed Work.
1936 **750** 450p. multicoloured . . 20 10

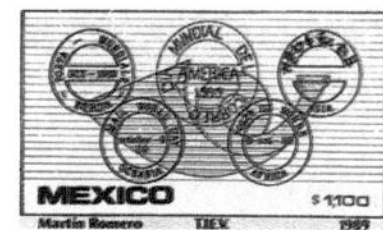

751 Posthorn and Cancellations

1989. World Post Day.
1937 **751** 1100p. multicoloured . . 50 20

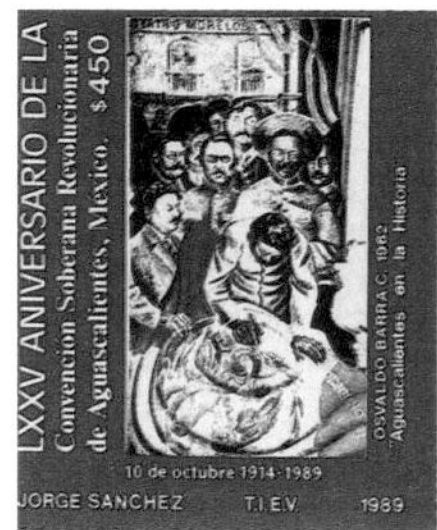

752 "Aguascalientes in History" (Osvaldo Barra)

1989. 75th Anniv of Aguascalientes Revolutionary Convention.
1936 **752** 450p. multicoloured . . 20 10

753 Patterns

1989. America. Pre-Columbian Culture.
1939 450p. Type **753** 20 10
1940 450p. Traditional writing . . 20 10

754 Old and New World Symbols

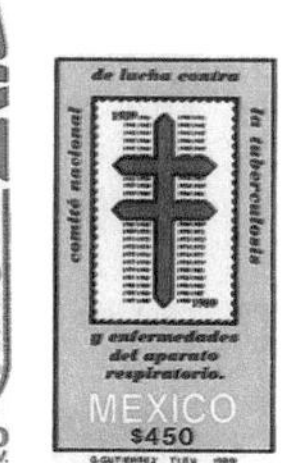

755 Cross of Lorraine

1989. 500th Anniv of "Meeting of Two Worlds" (3rd issue).
1941 **754** 1300p. multicoloured . . 60 25

1989. 50th Anniv of Anti-tuberculosis National Committee.
1942 **755** 450p. multicoloured . . 20 10

756 Mask of God Murcielago

1989.
1943 **756** 450p. green, black & mve 20 10

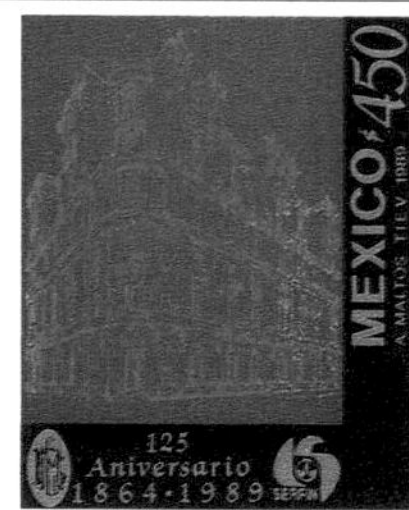

757 Bank

1989. 125th Anniv of Serfin Commercial Bank.
1944 **757** 450p. blue, gold and black 20 10

758 Cortines

759 Man with Sparkler

1989. Birth Centenary of Adolfo Ruiz Cortines (President, 1952–58).
1945 **758** 450p. multicoloured . . 20 10

1989. Christmas. Multicoloured.
1946 450p. Type **759** 20 10
1947 450p. People holding candles (horiz) 20 10

760 Emblem

1989. 50th Anniv of National Institute of Anthropology and History.
1948 **760** 450p. gold, red and black 20 10

761 Steam Locomotive, Diesel Train and Felipe Pescador

1989. 80th Anniv of Nationalization of Railways.
1949 **761** 450p. multicoloured . . 50 15

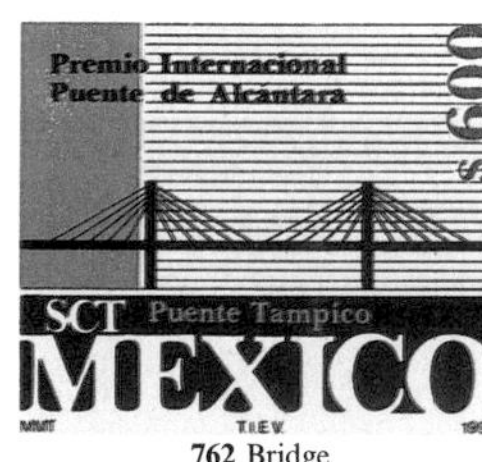

762 Bridge

1990. Opening of Tampico Bridge.
1950 **762** 600p. black, gold and red 20 10

763 Smiling Children

1990. Child Vaccination Campaign.
1951 **763** 700p. multicoloured . . 25 10

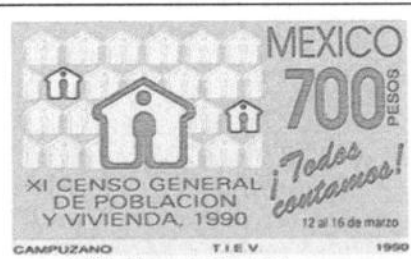

764 People in Houses

1990. 11th General Population and Housing Census.
1952 **764** 700p. green, yell & lt grn 25 10

765 Stamp under Magnifying Glass

1990. 10th Anniv of Mexican Philatelic Association.
1953 **765** 700p. multicoloured . . 25 10

766 Archive

1990. Bicentenary of National Archive.
1954 **766** 700p. blue 25 10

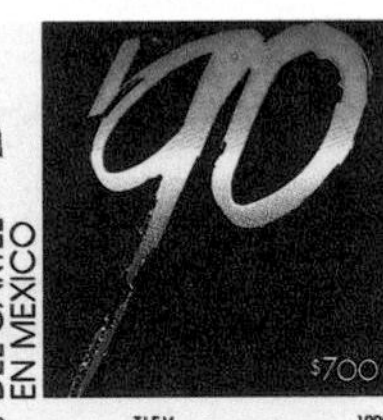

767 Emblem and "90"

1990. 1st International Poster Biennale.
1955 **767** 700p. multicoloured . . 25 10

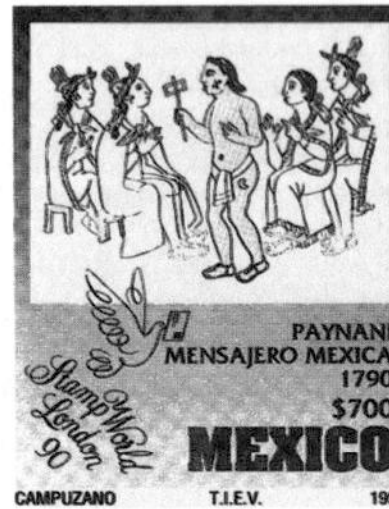

768 Messenger, 1790

1990. "Stamp World London 90" International Stamp Exhibition.
1956 **768** 700p. yellow, red & black 25 10

769 Penny Black

1990. 150th Anniv of the Penny Black.
1957 **769** 700p. black, red and gold 25 10

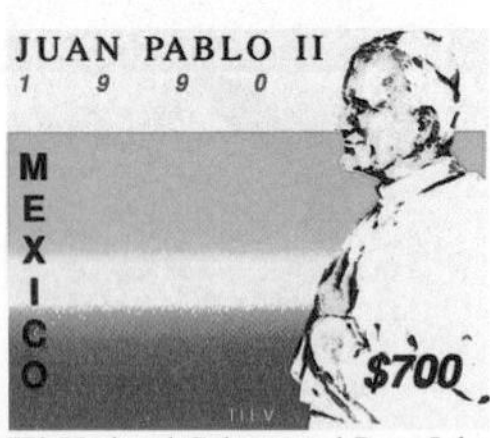

770 National Colours and Pope John Paul II

1990. Papal Visit.
1958 **770** 700p. multicoloured . . 25 10

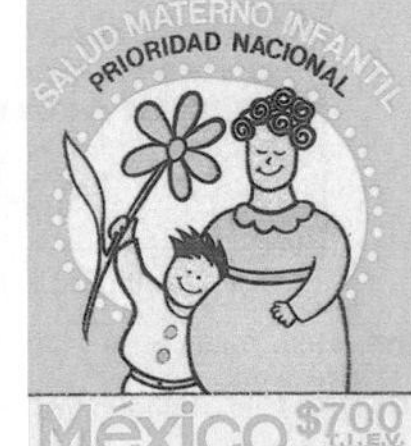

771 Church **772** Mother and Child

1990. 15th Travel Agents' Congress.
1959 **771** 700p. multicoloured . . 25 10

1990. Mother and Child Health Campaign.
1960 **772** 700p. multicoloured . . 25 10

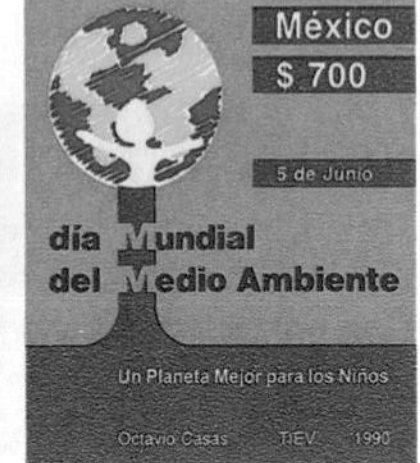

773 Smoke Rings forming Birds **774** Globe as Tree

1990. World Anti-Smoking Day.
1961 **773** 700p. multicoloured . . 25 10

1990. World Environment Day.
1962 **774** 700p. multicoloured . . 25 10

775 Racing Car and Chequered Flag

1990. Mexico Formula One Grand Prix.
1963 **775** 700p. black, red and green 25 10

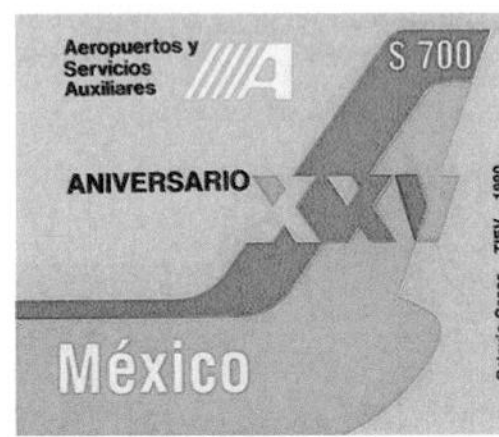

776 Aircraft Tailfin

1990. 25th Anniv of Airports and Auxiliary Services.
1964 **776** 700p. multicoloured . . 25 10

777 Family

1990. United Nations Anti-drugs Decade.
1965 **777** 700p. multicoloured . . 25 10

778 Tree Trunk

1990. Forest Conservation.
1966 **778** 700p. multicoloured . . 25 10

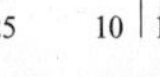

779 Emblem

1990. "Solidarity".
1967 **779** 700p. multicoloured . . 25 10
See also No. 2047.

780 Columns and Native Decoration

1990. World Heritage Site. Oaxaca.
1968 **780** 700p. multicoloured . . 25 10

781 Elegant Tern

1990. Conservation of Rasa Island, Gulf of California.
1969 **781** 700p. grey, black and red 1·10 40

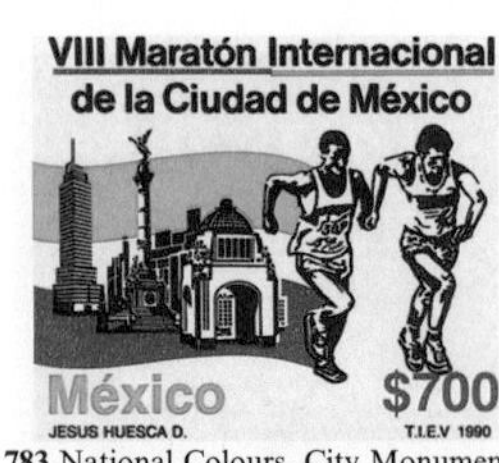

782 Institute Activities

1990. 25th Anniv of Mexican Petroleum Institute.
1970 **782** 700p. blue and black . . 25 10

783 National Colours, City Monuments and Runners

1990. 18th International Mexico City Marathon.
1971 **783** 700p. black, red & green 25 10

784 Facade

1990. 50th Anniv of Colima University.
1972 **784** 700p. multicoloured . . 25 10

785 Abstract

1990. Mexico City Consultative Council.
1973 **785** 700p. multicoloured . . 25 10

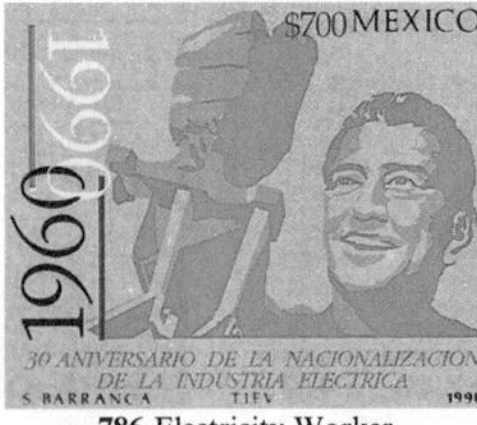

786 Electricity Worker

1990. 30th Anniv of Nationalization of Electricity Industry.
1974 **786** 700p. multicoloured . . 25 10

787 Violin and Bow

1990. 50th Death Anniv of Silvestre Revueltas (violinist).
1975 **787** 700p. multicoloured . . 25 10

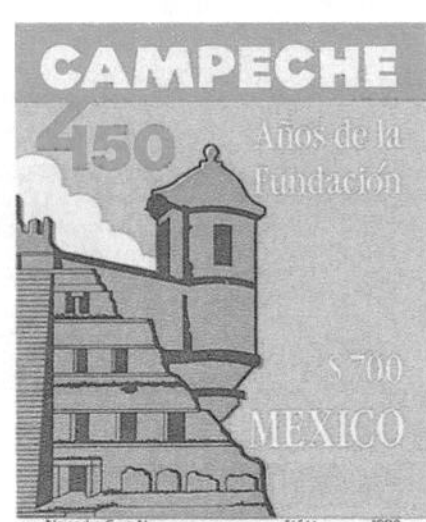

788 Building

1990. 450th Anniv of Campeche.
1976 **788** 700p. multicoloured . . 25 15

789 Crossed Rifle and Pen **790** Emblem

1990. 80th Anniv of San Luis Plan.
1977 **789** 700p. multicoloured . . 25 15

1990. 14th World Supreme Councils Conference.
1978 **790** 1500p. multicoloured . . 55 35

791 Spanish Tower and Mexican Pyramid

1990. 500th Anniv of "Meeting of Two Worlds" (4th issue).
1979 **791** 700p. multicoloured . . 25 15

792 Glass of Beer, Ear of Barley and Hop

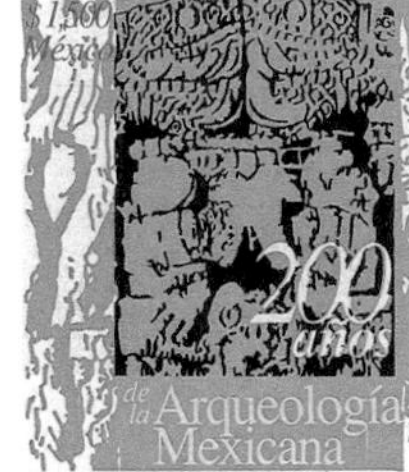

793 Carving

1990. Centenary of Brewing Industry.
1980 **792** 700p. multicoloured . . 25 15

1990. Bicentenary of Archaeology in Mexico.
1981 **793** 1500p. multicoloured . . 55 35

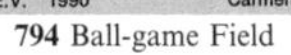

794 Ball-game Field

795 Globe and Poinsettia

1990. 16th Central American and Caribbean Games. Multicoloured.

1982	750p. Type **794**	1·10	20
1983	750p. Amerindian ball-game player	1·10	20
1984	750p. Amerindian ball-game player (different) (horiz)	1·10	20
1985	750p. Yutsil and Balam (mascots) (horiz)	1·10	20

1990. Christmas. Multicoloured.

1986	700p. Type **795**	25	15
1987	700p. Fireworks and candles	25	15

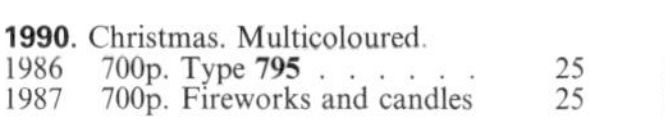

796 Dog (statuette)

1990. 50th Anniv of Mexican Canine Federation.
1988 **796** 700p. multicoloured . . 25 15

797 Microscope, Dolphin and Hand holding Map

1991. 50th Anniv of Naval Secretariat.
1989 **797** 1000p. gold, black & blue 40 25

798 Means of Transport

1991. Accident Prevention.
1990 **798** 700p. multicoloured . . 65 20

799 Products in Bags

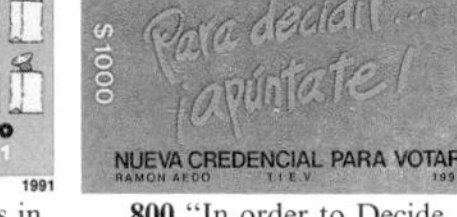

800 "In order to Decide, Register"

1991. 15th Anniv of National Consumer Institute.
1991 **799** 1000p. multicoloured . . 40 25

1991. Electoral Register.
1992 **800** 1000p. orange, grn & blk 40 25

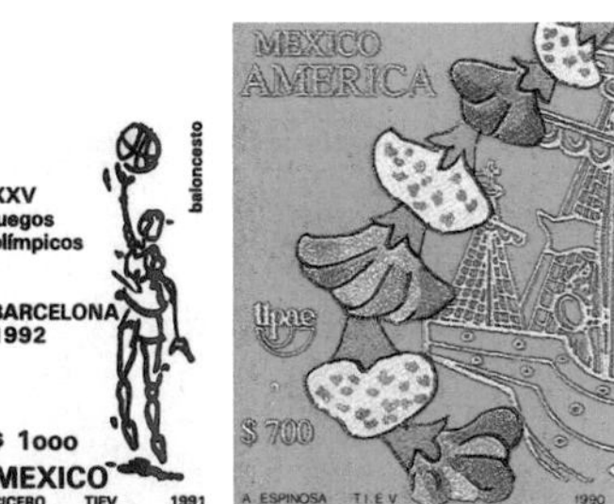

801 Basketball Player

802 Flowers and Caravel

1991. Olympic Games, Barcelona (1992) (1st issue).
1993 **801** 1000p. black and yellow 40 25
See also Nos. 2050, 2057 and 2080/9.

1991. America (1990). Natural World. Mult.

1994	700p. Type **802**	75	20
1995	700p. Right half of caravel, blue and yellow macaw and flowers	75	40

Nos. 1994/5 were issued together, se-tenant, forming a composite design.

803 Children in Droplet

1991. Children's Month. Vaccination Campaign.
1996 **803** 1000p. multicoloured . . 40 25

804 Map

805 Dove and Children

1991. World Post Day (1990).
1997 **804** 1500p. multicoloured . . 55 35

1991. Children's Days for Peace and Development.
1998 **805** 1000p. multicoloured . . 40 25

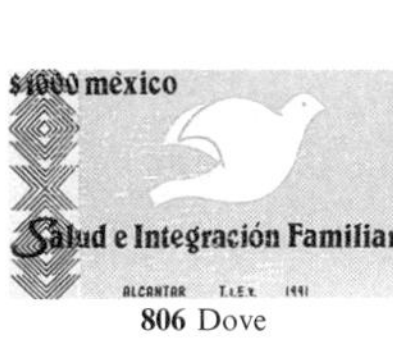

806 Dove

807 Mining

1991. Family Health and Unity.
1999 **806** 1000p. multicoloured . . 40 25

1991. 500th Anniv of Mining.
2000 **807** 1000p. multicoloured . . 40 25

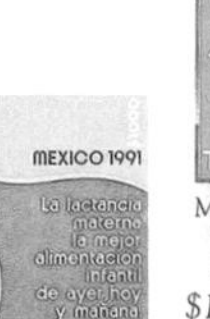

808 Mother feeding Baby

809 Emblem

1991. Breastfeeding Campaign.
2001 **808** 1000p. buff, blue & brn 40 25

1991. 16th Tourism Fair, Acapulco.
2002 **809** 1000p. green & dp green 40 25

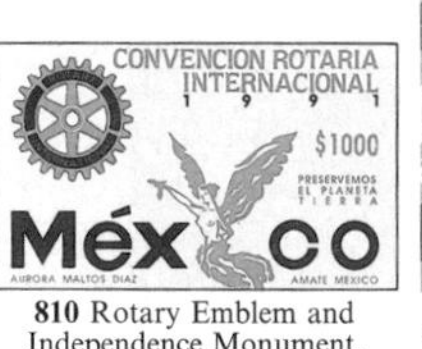

810 Rotary Emblem and Independence Monument, Mexico City

811 "Communication"

1991. Rotary International Convention. "Let us Preserve the Planet Earth".
2003 **810** 1000p. gold and blue . . 40 25

1991. Centenary of Ministry of Transport and Communications (S.C.T.). Multicoloured.

2004	1000p. Type **811**	1·25	50
2005	1000p. Boeing 737 landing	65	25
2006	1000p. Facsimile machine	65	25
2007	1000p. Van	65	25
2008	1000p. Satellites and Earth	65	25
2009	1000p. Railway freight wagons on bridge	1·25	35
2010	1000p. Telephone users	65	25
2011	1000p. Road bridge over road	65	25
2012	1000p. Road bridge and cliffs	65	25
2013	1000p. Stern of container ship and dockyard	1·25	35
2014	1000p. Television camera and presenter	65	25
2015	1000p. Front of truck at toll gate	65	25
2016	1000p. Roadbuilding ("Solidarity")	65	25
2017	1500p. Boeing 737 and control tower	80	35
2018	1500p. Part of fax machine, transmitters and dish aerials on S.C.T. building	80	35
2019	1500p. Satellite (horiz)	80	35
2020	1500p. Diesel and electric trains	1·25	50
2021	1500p. S.C.T. building	80	35
2022	1500p. Road bridge over ravine	80	35
2023	1500p. Bow of container ship and dockyard	1·25	50
2024	1500p. Bus at toll gate	80	35
2025	1500p. Rear of truck and trailer at toll gate	80	35

Nos. 2005/25 were issued together, se-tenant, each block containing several composite designs.

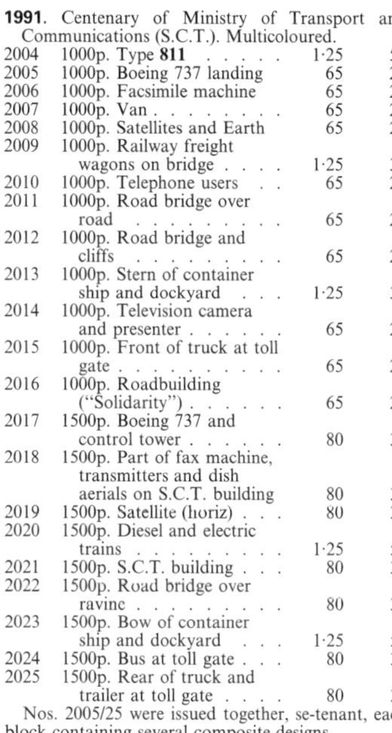

812 Jaguar

1991. Lacandona Jungle Conservation.
2026 **812** 1000p. black, orge & red 40 25

813 Driver and Car

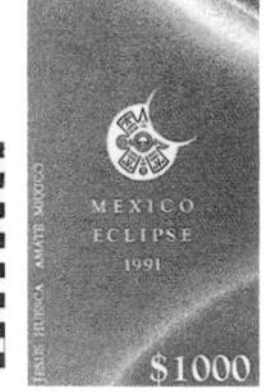

814 Emblem and Left-hand Sections of Sun and Earth

1991. Mexico Formula 1 Grand Prix.
2027 **813** 1000p. multicoloured . . 40 25

1991. Total Eclipse of the Sun. Multicoloured.

2028	1000p. Type **814**	1·00	25
2029	1000p. Emblem and right-hand sections of sun and Earth	1·00	25
2030	1500p. Emblem and centre of sun and Earth showing north and central America	1·50	35

Nos. 2028/30 were issued together, se-tenant, forming a composite design.

815 "Solidarity" (Rufino Tamayo)

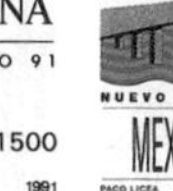

816 Bridge

1991. 1st Latin American Presidential Summit, Guadalajara.
2031 **815** 1500p. black, orge & yell 55 35

1991. Solidarity between Nuevo Leon and Texas.
2032 **816** 2000p. multicoloured . . 1·10 75

817 Runners

819 Emblem

MEXICO $1,500

818 Cogwheel

1991. 9th Mexico City Marathon.
2033 **817** 1000p. multicoloured . . 40 25

1991. 50th Anniv (1990) of National Chambers of Industry and Commerce.
2034 **818** 1500p. multicoloured . . 55 35

1991. 55th Anniv of Federation Fiscal Tribunal.
2035 **819** 1000p. silver and blue . . 40 25

Solidaridad
Unidos para progresar
México $1000
AMATE MEXICO 1991

820 National Colours forming Emblem

1991. "Solidarity—Let us Unite in order to Progress".
2036 **820** 1000p. multicoloured . . 40 25

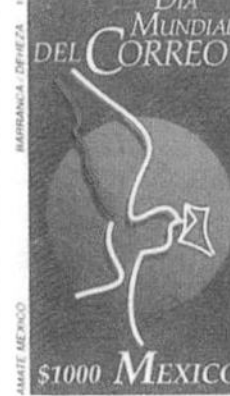

821 Dove with Letter

822 World Map

1991. World Post Day.
2037 **821** 1000p. multicoloured . . 40 25

1991. 500th Anniv of "Meeting of Two Worlds" (5th issue).
2038 **822** 1000p. multicoloured . . 95 25

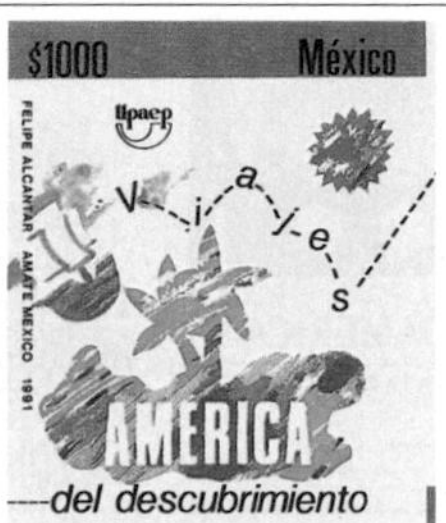

823 Caravel, Sun and Trees

1991. America. Voyages of Discovery. Mult.
2039 1000p. Type **823** 75 25
2040 1000p. Storm cloud, caravel and broken snake 75 25

824 Flowers and Pots

1991. Christmas. Multicoloured.
2041 1000p. Type **824** 40 25
2042 1000p. Children with decoration 40 25

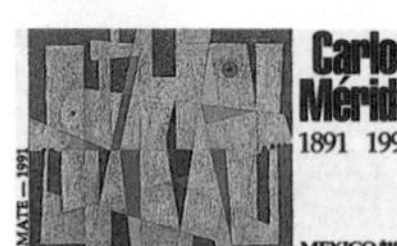

825 Abstract

1991. Carlos Merida (artist) Commemoration.
2043 **825** 1000p. multicoloured . . 40 25

826 Score and Portrait

1991. Death Bicentenary of Wolfgang Amadeus Mozart (composer).
2044 **826** 1000p. multicoloured . . 40 25

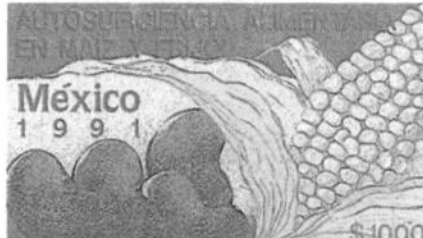

827 Kidney Beans and Maize

1991. Self-sufficiency in Kidney Beans and Maize.
2045 **827** 1000p. multicoloured . . 40 25

828 City Plan

1991. 450th Anniv of Morelia.
2046 **828** 1000p. brown, stone and red 40 25

1991. "Solidarity". As No. 1967 but new value.
2047 **779** 1000p. multicoloured . . 40 25

829 Merida

1992. 450th Anniv of Merida.
2048 **829** 1300p. multicoloured . . 60 40

830 Colonnade

1992. Bicentenary of Engineering Training in Mexico.
2049 **830** 1300p. blue and red . . 60 40

831 Horse Rider

1992. Olympic Games, Barcelona (2nd issue).
2050 **831** 2000p. multicoloured . . 90 60

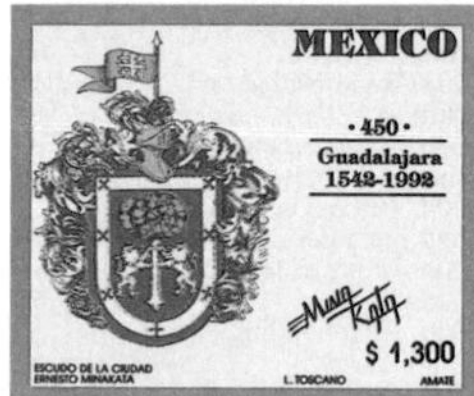

832 City Arms

1992. 450th Anniv of Guadalajara. Multicoloured.
2051 1300p. Type **832** . . . . . 1·10 40
2052 1300p. "Guadalajara Town Hall" (Jorge Navarro) . . 1·10 40
2053 1300p. "Guadalajara Cathedral" (Gabriel Flores) . . . . 1·10 40
2054 1900p. "Founding of Guadalajara" (Rafael Zamarripa) . . . . 1·60 55
2055 1900p. Anniversary emblem (Ignacio Vazquez) . . . . 1·60 55

833 Children and Height Gauge **834** Olympic Torch and Rings

1992. Child Health Campaign.
2056 **833** 2000p. multicoloured . . 90 60

1992. Olympic Games, Barcelona (3rd issue).
2057 **834** 2000p. multicoloured . . 90 60

835 Horse and Racing Car

1992. "500th Anniv of the Wheel and the Horse in America". Mexico Formula 1 Grand Prix.
2058 **835** 1300p. multicoloured . . 60 40

836 Satellite and Map of Americas **837** Human Figure and Cardiograph

1992. "Americas Telecom '92" Telecommunications Exhibition.
2059 **836** 1300p. multicoloured . . 60 40

1992. World Health Day.
2060 **837** 1300p. black, red and blue 60 40

838 Emblem

1992. 60th Anniv of Military Academy.
2061 **838** 1300p. red, yellow & blk 60 40

839 "Inspiration of Christopher Columbus" (Jose Maria Obregon) **840** Complex

1992. 500th Anniv of "Meeting of Two Worlds" (6th issue). "Granada 92" International Stamp Exhibition.
2062 1300p. Type **839** . . . . . 1·00 40
2063 1300p. "Racial Encounter" (Jorge Gonazalez Camarena) . . . . . . 1·00 40
2064 2000p. "Origin of the Sky" (Selden Codex) . . . . . 1·75 60
2065 2000p. "Quetzalcoatl and Tezcatlipoca" (Borhomico Codex) . . . . 1·75 60
2066 2000p. "From Spaniard and Indian, mestizo" . . . . 1·75 60

1992. National Medical Centre.
2068 **840** 1300p. multicoloured . . 60 40

841 Children, Dove and Globe **842** New-born Baby

1992. Children's Rights.
2069 **841** 1300p. multicoloured . . 60 40

1992. Traditional Childbirth.
2070 **842** 1300p. multicoloured . . 60 40

1992. "World Columbian Stamp Expo '92", Chicago. Nos. 2062/6 optd **WORLD COLUMBIAN STAMP EXPO '92 MAY 22-31, 1992 - CHICAGO** and emblem.
2071 1300p. mult (No. 2062) . . 2·00 2·00
2072 1300p. mult (No. 2063) . . 2·00 2·00
2073 2000p. mult (No. 2064) . . 5·00 5·00
2074 2000p. mult (No. 2065) . . 5·00 5·00
2075 2000p. mult (No. 2066) . . 5·00 5·00

845 Arms of Colleges

1992. Bicentenary of Mexico Notary College.
2078 **845** 1300p. multicoloured . . 50 35

846 Trees and Cacti

1992. Tree Day.
2079 **846** 1300p. multicoloured . . 50 35

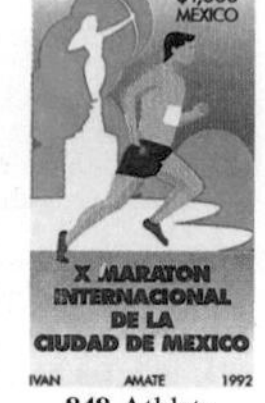

847 Boxing **848** Athlete

1992. Olympic Games, Barcelona (4th issue). Mult.
2080 1300p. Type **847** 80 35
2081 1300p. High jumping . . . 80 35
2082 1300p. Fencing 80 35
2083 1300p. Shooting 80 35
2084 1300p. Gymnastics 80 35
2085 1900p. Rowing . . . . . . 1·60 50
2086 1900p. Running . . . . . . 1·60 50
2087 1900p. Football . . . . . . 1·60 50
2088 1900p. Swimming . . . . . 1·60 50
2089 2000p. Equestrian . . . . . 1·60 55

1992. 10th Mexico City Marathon.
2091 **848** 1300p. multicoloured . . 50 35

849 Emblem

1992. "Solidarity".
2092 **849** 1300p. multicoloured . . 50 35

851 Television, Map and Radio

1992. 50th Anniv of National Chamber of Television and Radio Industry.
2094 **851** 1300p. multicoloured . . 50 35

852 Letter orbiting Globe

1992. World Post Day.
2095 **852** 1300p. multicoloured . . 50 35

853 Satellite above South and Central America and Flags

1992. American Cadena Communications System.
2096 **853** 2000p. multicoloured . . 1·10 55

854 Gold Compass Rose

1992. America. 500th Anniv of Discovery of America by Columbus. Multicoloured.
2097 2000p. Type **854** . . . . . 1·25 55
2098 2000p. Compass rose (different) and fish . . . 1·25 55
Nos. 2097/8 were issued together, se-tenant, forming a composite design.

855 Scroll

1992. 400th Anniv of San Luis Potosi.
2099 **855** 1300p. black and mauve 50 35

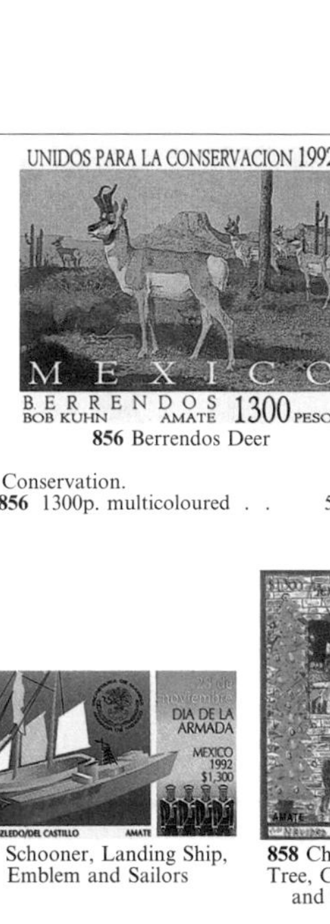

856 Berrendos Deer

1992. Conservation.
2100 **856** 1300p. multicoloured . . 50 35

857 Schooner, Landing Ship, Emblem and Sailors
858 Christmas Tree, Children and Crib

1992. Navy Day.
2101 **857** 1300p. multicoloured . . 50 35

1992. Christmas. Children's Drawings. Mult.
2102 1300p. Type **858** 50 35
2103 2000p. Street celebration (horiz) . . . . 1·25 55

Currency Reform. 1 (new) peso = 1000 (old) pesos.

859 Anniversary Emblem
860 Emblem

1993. 50th Anniv of Mexican Social Security Institute (1st issue).
2104 **859** 1p.50 green, gold & blk 60 40
See also Nos. 2110 and 2152/3.

1993. Centenary of Mexican Ophthalmological Society.
2105 **860** 1p.30 multicoloured . . 50 35

861 Children
862 Society Arms and Founders

1993. Children's Month.
2106 **861** 1p.30 multicoloured . . 50 35

1993. 160th Anniv of Mexican Geographical and Statistical Society.
2107 **862** 1p.30 multicoloured . . 50 35

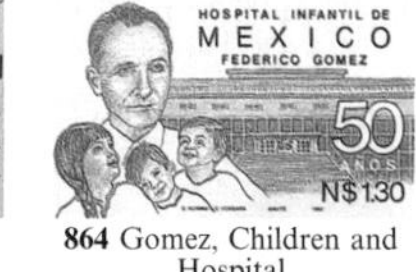

863 1824 Constitution
864 Gomez, Children and Hospital

1993. 150th Death Anniv of Miguel Ramos Arizpe, "Father of Federalism".
2108 **863** 1p.30 multicoloured . . 50 35

1993. 50th Anniv of Federico Gomez Children's Hospital.
2109 **864** 1p.30 multicoloured . . 50 35

865 Doctor with Child

1993. 50th Anniv of Mexican Social Security Institute (2nd issue). Medical Services.
2110 **865** 1p.30 multicoloured . . 50 35

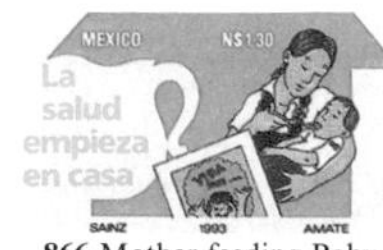

866 Mother feeding Baby

1993. "Health begins at Home".
2111 **866** 1p.30 multicoloured . . 50 35

867 Seal and Map

1993. Upper Gulf of California Nature Reserve.
2112 **867** 1p.30 multicoloured . . 50 35

868 Cantinflas

1993. Mexican Film Stars. Mario Moreno (Cantinflas).
2113 **868** 1p.30 black and blue . . 50 35
See also Nos. 2156/60.

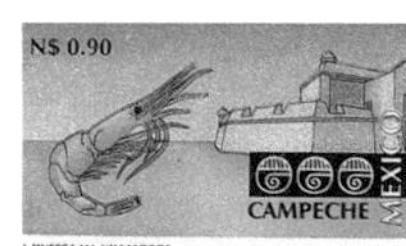

869 Campeche

1993. Tourism. Value expressed as "NS". Mult.
2114 90c. Type **869** 65 25
2115 1p. Guanajuato 70 25
2263 1p.10 As No. 2115 . . . . 70 10
2116 1p.30 Colima 80 35
2264 1p.80 As No. 2124 . . . . 55 20
2265 1p.80 As No. 2118 . . . . 65 20
2266 1p.80 As No. 2116 . . . . 55 20
2267 1p.80 As Type **869** 55 20
2117 1p.90 Michoacan (vert) . . 1·25 50
2118 2p. Coahuila . . . . 1·25 55
2269 2p. As No. 2266 . . . . . 90 20
2119 2p.20 Queretaro . . . . . . 1·60 60
2271 2p.30 As No. 2122 . . . . 70 25
2272 2p.40 As No. 2123 . . . . 80 25
2120 2p.50 Sonora . . . . 2·00 65
2274 2p.70 As No. 2145 . . . . 1·25 25
2121 2p.80 Zacatecas (vert) . . . 2·25 75
2276 3p. Type **869** . . . . . . 1·40 30
2278 3p.40 As No. 2271 . . . . 1·40 35
2122 3p.70 Sinaloa . . . . 3·25 1·25
2280 3p.80 As No. 2272 . . . . 1·25 40
2123 4p.40 Yucatan . . . . . . 3·50 1·50
2124 4p.80 Chiapas . . . . . . 3·75 1·60
2145 6p. Mexico City . . . . . . 4·00 2·00
2290 6p.80 As No. 2120 . . . . 2·50 90
See also Nos. 2410/29.

870 Dr. Maximiliano Ruiz Castaneda

1993. 50th Anniv of Health Service. Multicoloured.
2126 1p.30 Type **870** 50 35
2127 1p.30 Dr. Bernardo Sepulveda Gutierrez . . . 50 35
2128 1p.30 Dr. Ignacio Chavez Sanchez 50 35
2129 1p.30 Dr. Mario Salazar Mallen 50 35
2130 1p.30 Dr. Gustavo Baz Prada 50 35

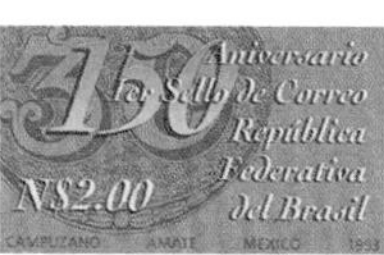

871 Brazil 30r. "Bull's Eye" Stamp
872 Runners

1993. 150th Anniv of First Brazilian Stamps.
2131 **871** 2p. multicoloured . . . 80 55

1993. 11th Mexico City Marathon.
2132 **872** 1p.30 multicoloured . . 1·40 55

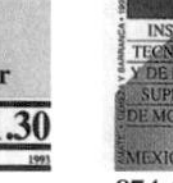

873 Emblem
874 Open Book and Symbols

1993. "Solidarity".
2133 **873** 1p.30 multicoloured . . 50 35

1993. 50th Anniv of Monterrey Institute of Technology and Higher Education. Multicoloured.
2134 1p.30 Type **874** 50 35
2135 2p. Buildings and mountains 80 55
Nos. 2134/5 were issued together, se-tenant, forming a composite design.

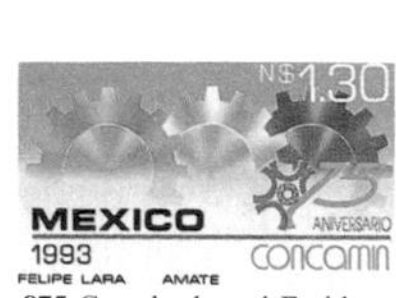
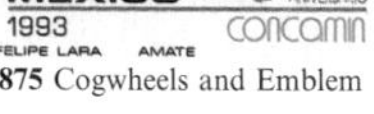

875 Cogwheels and Emblem
876 Torreon

1993. 75th Anniv of Concamin.
2136 **875** 1p.30 multicoloured . . 50 35

1993. Centenary of Torreon.
2137 **876** 1p.30 multicoloured . . 50 35

877 Emblem

1993. "Europalia 93 Mexico" Festival.
2138 **877** 2p. multicoloured . . . 80 55

878 Globe in Envelope
879 Gen. Guadalupe Victoria

1993. World Post Day.
2139 **878** 2p. multicoloured . . . 80 55

1993. 150th Death Anniv of General Manuel Guadalupe Victoria (first President, 1824–28).
2140 **879** 1p.30 multicoloured . . 50 35

880 Emblem
881 Hands protecting Foetus

1993. National Civil Protection System and International Day for Reduction of Natural Disasters.
2141 **880** 1p.30 red, black & yell 50 35

1993. United Nations Decade of International Law.
2142 **881** 2p. multicoloured . . . 80 55

882 Torch Carrier

1993. 20th National Wheelchair Games.
2143 **882** 1p.30 multicoloured . . 50 35

883 Peon y Contreras

1993. 150th Birth Anniv of Jose Peon y Contreras (poet, dramatist and founder of National Romantic Theatre).
2144 **883** 1p.30 violet and black 50 35

884 Horned Guan
885 Presents around Trees

1993. America. Endangered Birds. Multicoloured.
2145 2p. Type **884** . . . . . . 2·50 1·25
2146 2p. Resplendent quetzal on branch (horiz) . . . . . 2·50 1·25

1993. Christmas. Multicoloured.
2147 1p.30 Type **885** 50 35
2148 1p.30 Three wise men (horiz) 50 35

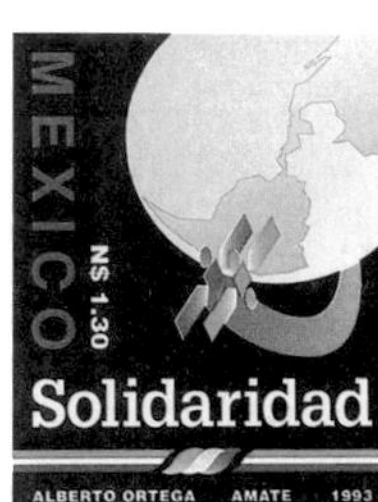

886 Satellites orbiting Earth

1993. "Solidarity".
2149 **886** 1p.30 multicoloured . . 50 35

887 School and Arms

1993. 125th Anniv of National Preparatory School.
2150 **887** 1p.30 multicoloured . . 50 35

888 Emblem on Map

1993. 55th Anniv of Municipal Workers Trade Union.
2151 **888** 1p.30 multicoloured . . 50 35

889 Hands

1993. 50th Anniv of Mexican Social Security Institute (3rd issue). Multicoloured.
2152 1p.30 Type **889** (social security) 50 35
2153 1p.30 Ball, building blocks, child's painting and dummy (day nurseries) . . 50 35

890 Mezcala Solidarity Bridge

1993. Tourism. Multicoloured.
2154 1p.30 Type **890** 50 35
2155 1p.30 Mexico City–Acapulco motorway 50 35

1993. Mexican Film Stars. As T **868**.
2156 1p.30 black and blue . . . 50 35
2157 1p.30 black and orange . . 50 35
2158 1p.30 black and green . . . 50 35
2159 1p.30 black and violet . . . 50 35
2160 1p.30 black and pink . . . 50 35
DESIGNS:—No, 2156, Pedro Armendariz in "Juan Charrasqueado"; 2157, Maria Felix in "The Lover"; 2158, Pedro Infante in "Necesito dinero"; 2159, Jorge Negrete in "It is not enough to be a Peasant"; 2160, Dolores del Rio in "Flor Silvestre".

891 Estefania Castaneda Nunez

1994. 72nd Anniv of Secretariat of Public Education. Educationists. Multicoloured.
2161 1p.30 Type **891** 50 35
2162 1p.30 Lauro Aguirre Espinosa 50 35
2163 1p.30 Rafael Ramirez Castaneda 50 35
2164 1p.30 Moises Saenz Garza 50 35
2165 1p.30 Gregorio Torres Quintero 50 35
2166 1p.30 Jose Vasconcelos . . 50 35
2167 1p.30 Rosaura Zapato Cano 50 35

892 Zapata (after H. Velarde)

893 Emblem and Worker

1994. 75th Death Anniv of Emiliano Zapata (revolutionary).
2168 **892** 1p.30 multicoloured . . 50 35

1994. 75th Anniv of I.L.O.
2169 **893** 2p. multicoloured . . . 80 50

894 Map and Emblem

895 "Earth and Communication" (frieze, detail)

1994. 50th Anniv of National Schools Building Programme Committee.
2170 **894** 1p.30 multicoloured . . 50 35

1994. 3rd Death Anniv of Francisco Zuniga (sculptor).
2171 **895** 1p.30 multicoloured . . 50 35

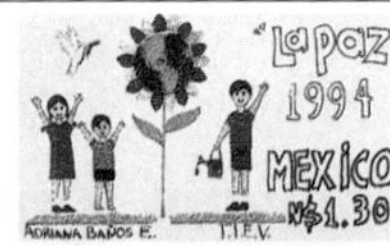

896 Flower and Children

1994. Children's Organization for Peace and Development.
2172 **896** 1p.30 multicoloured . . 50 35

897 Greater Flamingo

1994. DUMAC Nature Protection Organization.
2173 **897** 1p.30 multicoloured . . 1·50 85

898 Children and Silhouette of Absentee

1994. Care and Control of Minors.
2174 **898** 1p.30 black and green 50 35

899 Man and Letters

900 Route Map

1994. 34th World Advertising Congress, Cancun.
2175 **899** 2p. multicoloured . . . 80 35

1994. 50th Anniv of National Association of Importers and Exporters.
2176 **900** 1p.30 multicoloured . . 50 35

901 Head and Emblem

1994. International Telecommunications Day.
2177 **901** 2p. multicoloured . . . 80 55

902 Animals

1994. Yumka Wildlife Centre, Villahermosa.
2178 **902** 1p.30 multicoloured . . 1·25 85

903 Town Centre

904 Mother and Baby

1994. U.N.E.S.C.O. World Heritage Site, Zacatecas.
2179 **903** 1p.30 multicoloured . . 50 35

1994. Friendship Hospital. Mother and Child Health Month.
2180 **904** 1p.30 multicoloured . . 55 45

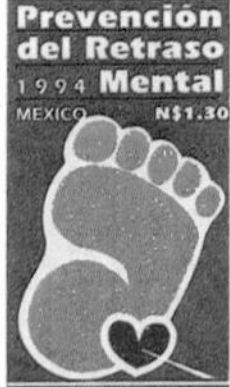

905 Foot and Heart

906 Song and Ornamental Birds

1994. Prevention of Mental Retardation.
2181 **905** 1p.30 multicoloured . . 55 45

1994. Nature Conservation. Multicoloured.
2182 1p.30 Type **906** . . . . . . 1·25 85
2183 1p.30 Game birds (silhouettes) . . . . . . 1·25 85
2184 1p.30 Threatened animals (silhouettes) . . . . . . 1·25 85
2185 1p.30 Animals in danger of extinction (silhouettes) . . 1·25 85
2186 1p.30 Orange-fronted conures . . . . 1·25 85
2187 1p.30 Yellow-tailed oriole 1·25 85
2188 1p.30 Pyrrhuloxias . . . . 1·25 85
2189 1p.30 Loggerhead shrike . . 1·25 85
2190 1p.30 Northern mockingbird 1·25 85
2191 1p.30 Common turkey . . . 1·25 85
2192 1p.30 White-winged dove . . 1·25 85
2193 1p.30 Red-billed whistling duck . . . . 1·25 85
2194 1p.30 Snow goose . . . . . 1·25 85
2195 1p.30 Gambel's quail . . . 1·25 85
2196 1p.30 Peregrine falcon . . . 1·25 85
2197 1p.30 Jaguar 80 50
2198 1p.30 Jaguarundi 80 50
2199 1p.30 Mantled howler monkey 80 50
2200 1p.30 Californian sealions 80 50
2201 1p.30 Pronghorn 80 50
2202 1p.30 Scarlet macaw . . . . 1·25 85
2203 1p.30 Mexican prairie dogs 80 50
2204 1p.30 Wolf 80 50
2205 1p.30 American manatee . . 80 50

907 Player

908 Fish

1994. World Cup Football Championship, U.S.A. Multicoloured.
2206 2p. Type **907** . . . . 1·00 70
2207 2p. Goalkeeper . . . . . . 1·00 70
Nos. 2206/7 were issued together, se-tenant, forming a composite design.

1994. International Fishing Festival, Veracruz.
2208 **908** 1p.30 multicoloured . . 55 45

909 Stylized Figure and Emblem

910 "Butterflies" (Carmen Parra)

1994. 25th Anniv of Juvenile Integration Centres.
2209 **909** 1p.30 multicoloured . . 55 45

1994. 50th Anniv of Diplomatic Relations with Canada.
2210 **910** 2p. multicoloured . . . 90 65

911 Emblems

912 Emblem and Family

1994. 20th Anniv of National Population Council.
2211 **911** 1p.30 multicoloured . . 55 45

1994. International Year of the Family.
2212 **912** 2p. multicoloured . . . 90 60

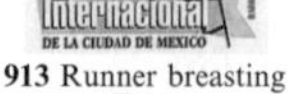

913 Runner breasting Tape

914 Giant Panda

1994. 12th Mexico City International Marathon.
2213 **913** 1p.30 multicoloured . . 55 45

1994. Chapultepec Zoo.
2214 **914** 1p.30 multicoloured . . 80 45

915 Tree

916 Anniversary Emblem

1994. Tree Day.
2215 **915** 1p.30 brown and green 55 45

1994. 60th Anniv of Economic Culture Fund.
2216 **916** 1p.30 multicoloured . . 55 45

917 Statue and Light Rail Transit Train

918 Cathedral and Gardens

1994. 25th Anniv of Mexico City Transport System.
2217 **917** 1p.30 multicoloured . . 65 45

1994. 350th Anniv of Salvatierra City, Guanajuato.
2218 **918** 1p.30 purple, grey and black 55 45

919 State Flag and National Anthem

1994. National Symbols Week.
2219 **919** 1p.30 multicoloured . . 55 45

920 Building and Anniversary Emblem

921 Figures with Flags

1994. 40th Anniv of University City.
2220 **920** 1p.30 multicoloured . . 55 45

1994. 5th Solidarity Week.
2221 **921** 1p.30 black, red and green 55 45

922 Lopez Mateos

923 Palace Facade

1994. 25th Death Anniv of Adolfo Lopez Mateos (President, 1958–64).
2222 **922** 1p.30 multicoloured . . 55 45

1994. 60th Anniv of Palace of Fine Arts.
2223 **923** 1p.30 black and grey . . 55 45

924 Rings and "100"

1994. Centenary of International Olympic Committee.
2224 **924** 2p. multicoloured . . . 90 60

925 Quarter Horse (Juan Rayas)

1994. Horses. Paintings by artists named. Multicoloured.
2225 1p.30 Aztec horse (Heladio Velarde) 80 45
2226 1p.30 Type **925** 80 45
2227 1p.30 Quarter horse (Rayas) (different) 80 45
2228 1p.30 Vaquero on horseback (Velarde) 80 45
2229 1p.30 Aztec horse (Velarde) 80 45
2230 1p.30 Rider with lance (Velarde) 80 45

926 Emblem

927 Saint-Exupery and The Little Prince (book character)

1994. Inauguration of 20 November National Medical Centre.
2231 **926** 1p.30 multicoloured . . 55 45

1994. 50th Death Anniv of Antoine de Saint-Exupery (pilot and writer).
2232 **927** 2p. multicoloured . . . 90 60

928 Man writing Letters to Woman

929 Urban Postman on Bicycle

1994. World Post Day.
2233 **928** 2p. multicoloured . . . 90 60

1994. America. Postal Transport. Multicoloured.
2234 2p. Type **929** 85 50
2235 2p. Rural postman on rail tricycle . . . . 1·40 75
Nos. 2234/5 were issued together, se-tenant, forming a composite design.

930 Couple (Sofia Bassi)

1994. Ancestors' Day.
2236 **930** 1p.30 multicoloured . . 55 45

931 Water Drop and Hand

932 Dr. Mora

1994. National Clean Water Programme.
2237 **931** 1p.30 multicoloured . . 55 45

1994. Birth Bicentenary of Dr. Jose Maria Luis Mora (journalist and politician).
2238 **932** 1p.30 multicoloured . . 55 45

933 Theatre and Soler (actor)

1994. 15th Anniv of Fernando Soler Theatre, Saltillo, Coahuila.
2239 **933** 1p.30 multicoloured . . 55 45

934 Allegory of Flight

935 Museum's Central Pillar

1994. 50th Anniv of I.C.A.O.
2240 **934** 2p. multicoloured . . . 1·10 60

1994. 30th Anniv of National Anthropological Museum.
2241 **935** 1p.30 multicoloured . . 55 45

936 Theatrical Masks

937 Allende

1994. 60th Anniv of National Association of Actors.
2242 **936** 1p.30 multicoloured . . 55 45

1994. 225th Birth Anniv of Ignacio Allende (independence hero).
2243 **937** 1p.30 multicoloured . . 55 45

938 Chapultepec Castle

1994. 50th Anniv of National History Museum.
2244 **938** 1p.30 multicoloured . . 55 45

939 Dome

940 Anniversary Emblem

1994. Centenary of Coahuila School.
2245 **939** 1p.30 multicoloured . . 55 45

1994. 40th Anniv of Pumas University Football Club.
2246 **940** 1p.30 blue and gold . . 55 45

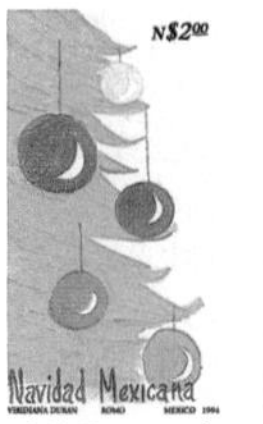

941 Decorated Tree

942 Valley

1994. Christmas. Multicoloured.
2247 2p. Type **941** 80 60
2248 2p. Couple watching shooting star (horiz) . . . 80 60

1994. "Solidarity". Chalco Valley.
2249 **942** 1p.30 multicoloured . . 20 15

943 Ines de la Cruz (after Miguel de Cabrera)

944 X-Ray of Hand and Rontgen

1995. 300th Birth Anniv of Juana Ines de la Cruz (mystic poet).
2250 **943** 1p.80 multicoloured . . 30 20

1995. Centenary of Discovery of X-Rays by Wilhelm Rontgen.
2251 **944** 2p. multicoloured . . . 35 25

945 Ignacio Altamirano

946 Emblem

1995. Teachers' Day.
2252 **945** 1p.80 black, green & bl 30 20

1995. World Telecommunications Day. "Telecommunications and the Environment".
2253 **946** 2p.70 multicoloured . . 70 55

947 Anniversary Emblem

948 Marti

1995. 40th Anniv of National Institute of Public Administration.
2254 **947** 1p.80 green, mve & lilac 30 20

1995. Death Centenary of Jose Marti (Cuban writer and revolutionary).
2255 **948** 2p.70 multicoloured . . 70 55

949 Carranza

950 Kite

1995. 75th Death Anniv of Venustiano Carranza (President 1914–20).
2256 **949** 1p.80 multicoloured . . 30 20

1995. 20th Anniv of National Tourist Organization.
2257 **950** 2p.70 multicoloured . . 70 55

951 Drugs, Skull and Unhappy Face

952 Cardenas del Rio

1995. International Day against Drug Abuse and Trafficking. Multicoloured.
2258 1p.80 Type **951** 85 20
2259 1p.80 Drug addict on swing 85 20
2260 1p.80 Faces behind bars . . 85 20

1995. Birth Centenary of Gen. Lazaro Cardenas del Rio (President 1934–40).
2261 **952** 1p.80 black 30 20

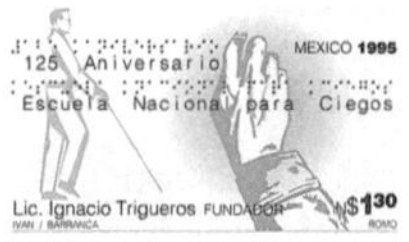

953 Man with White Stick and Hand reading Braille

1995. 125th Anniv of National Blind School. Mult.
2262 **953** 1p.30 brown and black 20 15

954 Northern Pintails

1995. Animals. Multicoloured.
2295 2p.70 Type **954** 90 50
2296 2p.70 Belted kingfisher . . . 90 50
2297 2p.70 Orange tiger 90 50
2298 2p.70 Hoary bat 90 50

955 Runners

956 Envelopes

1995. 13th International Marathon, Mexico City.
2299 **955** 2p.70 multicoloured . . 40 25

1995. 16th Congress of Postal Union of the Americas, Spain and Portugal, Mexico City.
2300 **956** 2p.70 multicoloured . . 40 25

957 Pasteur

958 Hands holding Envelopes

1995. Death Centenary of Louis Pasteur (chemist).
2301 **957** 2p.70 blue, black and green 40 25

1995. World Post Day.
2302 **958** 2p.70 multicoloured . . 40 25

959 Basket of Shopping

960 Anniversary Emblem

1995. World Food Day.
2303 **959** 1p.80 multicoloured . . 30 20

1995. 50th Anniv of F.A.O.
2304 **960** 2p.70 multicoloured . . 40 25

961 Elias Calles **962** Cuauhtemoc

1995. 50th Death Anniv of General Plutarco Elias Calles (President 1924–28).
2305 **961** 1p.80 multicoloured . . 30 20

1995. 500th Birth Anniv of Cuauhtemoc (Aztec Emperor of Tenochtitlan).
2306 **962** 1p.80 multicoloured . . 30 20

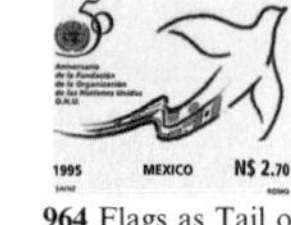

963 National Flag, National Anthem and Constitution **964** Flags as Tail of Dove

1995. National Constitution and Patriotic Symbols Day.
2307 **963** 1p.80 multicoloured . . 30 20

1995. 50th Anniv of U.N.O.
2308 **964** 2p.70 multicoloured . . 40 25

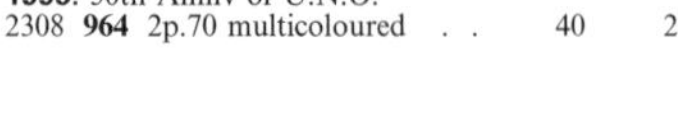

965 Airplane, Streamlined Train and Motor Vehicle

1995. International Passenger Travel Year.
2309 **965** 2p.70 multicoloured . . 80 25

966 "The Holy Family" (Andres de Concha)

1995. 30th Anniv of Museum of Mexican Art in the Vice-regency Period.
2310 **966** 1p.80 multicoloured . . 30 20

967 Pedro Maria Anaya

1995. Generals in Mexican History. Each black, yellow and gold.
2311 1p.80 Type **967** 30 20
2312 1p.80 Felipe Berriozabal . . 30 20
2313 1p.80 Santos Degollado . . 30 20
2314 1p.80 Sostenes Rocha . . . 30 20
2315 1p.80 Leandro Valle 30 20
2316 1p.80 Ignacio Zaragoza . . 30 20

968 Children playing in Garden (Pablo Osorio Gomez) **969** Emblem

1995. Christmas. Children's Drawings. Multicoloured.
2317 1p.80 Type **968** 30 20
2318 2p.70 Adoration of the Wise Men (Oscar Enrique Carrillo) 40 25

1995. 10th Anniv of Mexican Health Foundation.
2319 **969** 1p.80 multicoloured . . 30 20

970 Ocelot **971** Louis Lumiere and Cine-camera

1995. Nature Conservation.
2320 **970** 1p.80 multicoloured . . 30 20

1995. Centenary of Motion Pictures.
2321 **971** 1p.80 black, mauve and blue 30 20

972 Library

1995. National Education Library, Mexico City.
2322 **972** 1p.80 green, blue and yellow 30 20

973 "Proportions of Man" (Leonardo da Vinci) **974** Pedro Vargas

1995. 50th Anniv of National Science and Arts Prize.
2323 **973** 1p.80 multicoloured . . 30 20

1995. Radio Personalities. Multicoloured.
2324 1p.80 Type **974** 85 20
2325 1p.80 Agustin Lara 85 20
2326 1p.80 Aguila Sisters 85 20
2327 1p.80 Tona "La Negra" . . 85 20
2328 1p.80 F. Gabilondo Soler "Cri-Cri" 85 20
2329 1p.80 Emilio Teuro 85 20
2330 1p.80 Gonzalo Curiel . . . 85 20
2331 1p.80 Lola Beltran 85 20

975 Robot Hand holding Optic Fibres

1995. 25th Anniv of Science and Technology Council.
2332 **975** 1p.80 multicoloured . . 30 20

976 Airplane

1996. National Aviation Day. Multicoloured.
2333 1p.80 Type **976** 70 20
2334 1p.80 Squadron 201, 1945 70 20
2335 2p.70 Ley Airport 90 25
2336 2p.70 Modern jetliner and biplane 90 25

977 Child and Caso

1996. Birth Centenary of Dr. Alfonso Caso (anthropologist).
2337 **977** 1p.80 multicoloured . . 30 20

978 Silverio Perez, Carlos Arruza and Manolo Martinez

1996. 50th Anniv of Plaza Mexico (bullring). Matadors. Multicoloured.
2338 1p.80 Type **978** 30 20
2339 2p.70 Roldolfo Gaona, Fermin Espinosa and Lorenzo Garza 40 25

Nos. 2338/9 were issued together, se-tenant, forming a composite design of the bullring.

979 Bag of Groceries

1996. 20th Anniv of Federal Consumer Council.
2340 **979** 1p.80 multicoloured . . 30 20

980 "Treatment of Fracture" (from Sahagun Codex)

1996. 50th Anniv of Mexican Society of Orthopaedics.
2341 **980** 1p.80 multicoloured . . 30 20

981 Rulfo

1996. 10th Death Anniv of Juan Rulfo (writer).
2342 **981** 1p.80 multicoloured . . 30 20

982 Anniversary Emblem and Map of Mexico **983** Healthy Hand reaching for Sick Hand

1996. 60th Anniv of National Polytechnic Institute.
2343 **982** 1p.80 grey, black and red 30 20

1996. United Nations Decade against the Abuse and Illicit Trafficking of Drugs. Multicoloured.
2344 1p.80 Type **983** 60 15
2345 1p.80 Man helping addict out of dark hole 60 15
2346 2p.70 Stylized figures . . . 90 25

984 Gymnastics **985** Cameraman and Film Frames of Couples

1996. Olympic Games, Atlanta, U.S.A. Multicoloured.
2347 1p.80 Type **984** 45 15
2348 1p.80 Hurdling 45 15
2349 2p.70 Football 65 25
2350 2p.70 Running 65 25
2351 2p.70 Show jumping 65 25

1996. Centenary of Mexican Films. Multicoloured.
2352 1p.80 Type **985** 25 15
2353 1p.80 Camera and film frames of individuals . . 25 15

986 Scales

1996. 60th Anniv of Fiscal Tribunal.
2354 **986** 1p.80 multicoloured . . 25 15

987 Runners' Feet

1996. 14th Mexico City International Marathon.
2355 **987** 2p.70 multicoloured . . 40 25

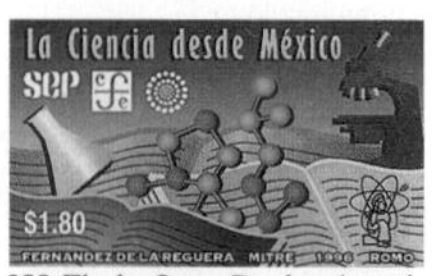

988 Flask, Open Books, Atomic Model and Microscope

1996. Science.
2356 **988** 1p.80 multicoloured . . 25 15

989 "Allegory of Foundation of Zacatecas" (anon)

1996. 450th Anniv of Zacatecas.
2357 **989** 1p.80 multicoloured . . 25 15

990 Rural Education **992** Emblem

1996. 25th Anniv of National Council for the Improvement of Education.
2358 **990** 1p.80 multicoloured . . 25 15

1996. Family Planning Month.
2360 **992** 1p.80 green, mauve and blue 25 15

993 Flag of the "Three Guarantees", 1821

1996. 175th Anniv of Declaration of Independence.
2361 **993** 1p.80 multicoloured . . 25 15

994 Blue Morpho, Monkey, Harpy Eagle and other Birds

1996. Nature Conservation. Multicoloured.
2362 1p.80 Type **994** 55 15
2363 1p.80 Turtle dove, yellow grosbeak with chicks in nest, trogon and hummingbird 55 15

2364 1p.80 Mountains, monarchs (butterflies) in air and American black bear with cub 55 15
2365 1p.80 Fishing buzzard, mule deer, lupins and monarchs (butterflies) on plant . . . 55 15
2366 1p.80 Scarlet macaws, monarchs, toucan, peafowl and spider monkey hanging from tree 55 15
2367 1p.80 Resplendent quetzal, emerald toucanet, bromeliads and tiger-cat 55 15
2368 1p.80 Parrots, white-tailed deer and rabbit by river 55 15
2369 1p.80 Snake, wolf, puma and lizard on rock and blue-capped bird 55 15
2370 1p.80 Coyote, prairie dogs at burrow, quail on branch, deer, horned viper and caracara on cactus . . 55 15
2371 1p.80 Jaguar, euphonias, long-tailed bird, crested bird and bat 55 15
2372 1p.80 "Martucha", peacock, porcupine, butterfly and green snake 55 15
2373 1p.80 Blue magpie, green-headed bird, owl, woodpecker and hummingbird by river . . 55 15
2374 1p.80 Cinnamon cuckoo in tree, fox by river and green macaws in tree . . 55 15
2375 1p.80 Wild sheep by rocks, bird on ocotillo plant, bats, owl, lynx and woodpecker on cactus . . 55 15
2376 1p.80 Ant-eater climbing sloping tree, jaguarundi, bat, orchid and ocellated turkey in undergrowth . . 55 15
2377 1p.80 Ocelot, "grison", coral snake, "temazate", paca and otter by river 55 15
2378 1p.80 Grey squirrel in tree, salamander, beaver, bird, shrew-mole, mountain hen and racoon by river . . . 55 15
2379 1p.80 Butterfly, trogon in red tree, "chachalaca", crested magpie and "tejon" 55 15
2380 1p.80 Bat, "tlalcoyote", "rata ncotoma", "chichimoco", hare, cardinal (bird), lizard, kangaroo rat and tortoise 55 15
2381 1p.80 Beetle on leaf, tapir, tree frog and "tunpache" 55 15
2382 1p.80 Crocodile, insect, cup fungus, boa constrictor and butterfly 55 15
2383 1p.80 Armadillo, "tlacuache", iguana, turkey and butterfly . . . 55 15
2384 1p.80 Turkey, collared peccary, zorilla, lizard, rattlesnake and mouse . . 55 15
2385 1p.80 Cacomistle, "matraca", lark, collared lizard and cacti 55 15

Nos. 2362/85 were issued together, se-tenant, forming a composite design of habitats and wildlife under threat.

995 Bird with Letter in Beak

996 Institute

1996. World Post Day.
2386 **995** 2p.70 multicoloured . . 40 25

1996. 50th Anniv of Salvador Zubiran National Nutrition Institute.
2387 **996** 1p.80 multicoloured . . 25 15

997 Constantino de Tarnava

998 "Portrait of a Woman" (Baltasar de Echave Ibia)

1996. 75th Anniv of Radio Broadcasting in Mexico.
2388 **997** 1p.80 multicoloured . . 25 15

1996. Virreinal Art Gallery. Multicoloured.
2389 1p.80 Type **998** 50 15
2390 1p.80 "Portrait of the Child Joaquin Manuel Fernandez de Santa Cruz" (Nicolas Rodriguez Xuarez) 50 15
2391 1p.80 "Portrait of Dona Maria Luisa Gonzaga Foncerrada y Labarrieta" (Jose Maria Vazquez) . . 50 15
2392 1p.80 "Archangel Michael" (Luis Juarez) 50 15
2393 2p.70 "Virgin of the Apocalypse" (Miguel Cabrera) 65 25

999 Isidro Fabela and Genaro Estrada

1000 Maize

1996. "Precursors of Foreign Policy".
2394 **999** 1p.80 multicoloured . . 25 15

1996. World Food Day.
2395 **1000** 2p.70 multicoloured . . 40 25

1001 Underground Train around Globe

1996. International Metros Conference.
2396 **1001** 2p.70 multicoloured . . 40 25

1002 Star (Elias Martin del Campo)

1996. Christmas. Multicoloured.
2397 1p. Type **1002** 15 10
2398 1p.80 Man with star-shaped bundles on stick (Ehecatl Cabrera Franco) (vert) . . 25 15

1003 Henestrosa

1996. Andres Henestrosa (writer) Commemoration.
2399 **1003** 1p.80 multicoloured . . 25 15

1004 Old and New Institute Buildings

1005 Emblem

1996. 50th Anniv of National Cancer Institute.
2400 **1004** 1p.80 multicoloured . . 25 15

1996. Paisano Programme.
2401 **1005** 2p.70 multicoloured . . 40 25

1006 Painting

1996. Birth Centenary of David Alfaro Siqueiros (painter).
2402 **1006** 1p.80 multicoloured . . 25 15

1007 Dr. Jose Maria Barcelo de Villagran

1996. 32nd National Assembly of Surgeons.
2403 **1007** 1p.80 multicoloured . . 25 15

1008 Black Bears

1996. Nature Conservation.
2404 **1008** 1p.80 multicoloured . . 25 15

1009 Smiling Sun

1010 Library

1996. 50th Anniv of U.N.I.C.E.F.
2405 **1009** 1p.80 multicoloured . . 25 15

1996. 350th Anniv of Palafoxiana Library, Puebla.
2406 **1010** 1p.80 multicoloured . . 25 15

1011 Sphere and Atomic Symbol

1012 Sun's Rays and Earth

1996. National Institute for Nuclear Research.
2407 **1011** 1p.80 multicoloured . . 25 15

1996. World Day for the Preservation of the Ozone Layer.
2408 **1012** 1p.80 multicoloured . . 25 15

1013 Sculpture

1014 Pellicer (after D. Rivera)

1996. 30 Years of Work by Sebastian (sculptor).
2409 **1013** 1p.80 multicoloured . . 25 15

1997. Tourism. As Nos. 2263 etc but with value expressed as "$".
2410 1p. Colima 15 10
2411 1p.80 Chiapas 25 15
2412 2p. Colima 30 20
2413 2p. Guanajuato 30 20
2413a 2p. Coahiula 30 20
2414 2p.30 Chiapas 35 25
2415 2p.50 Quretaro 35 25
2415a 2p.50 Yucatan 35 25
2416 2p.60 Colima 40 25
2417 2p.70 Mexico City 40 25
2418 3p. Type **869** 45 30
2419 3p.10 Coahuila 45 30
2420 3p.40 Sinaloa 50 35
2421 3p.50 Mexico City 50 35
2421a 3p.60 Sonora 50 35
2421b 3p.60 Coahuila 50 35
2421c 3p.70 Campeche 50 35
2422 4p. Michoacan (vert) . . . 60 40
2422a 4p.20 Guanajuato 55 35
2423 4p.40 Yucatan 65 45
2424 4p.90 Sonora 70 45
2425 5p. Queretaro 70 45
2426 5p. Colima 65 45
2426a 5p.30 Michoacan (vert) . . 70 45
2426b 5p.90 Queretaro 80 55
2427 6p. Zacatacas (vert) . . . 85 55
2427a 6p. Sinaloa 85 55
2427b 6p.50 Sinaloa 85 50
2428 7p. Sonora . . . . 1·00 65
2428a 8p. Zacatecas (vert) . . . 1·10 75
2429 8p.50 Mexico City . . . . 1·25 85
2433 10p. Campeche . . . . . 1·40 1·10

1997. Birth Centenary of Carlos Pellicer (lyricist).
2435 **1014** 2p.30 multicoloured . . 35 25

1015 Eloy Blanco (after Oswaldo)

1997. Birth Centenary (1996) of Andres Eloy Blanco (poet).
2436 **1015** 3p.40 multicoloured . . 50 35

1016 Book, Inkwell and Pencil

1017 Tree, Globe and Atomic Cloud

1997. Confederation of American Educationalists' International Summit Conference.
2437 **1016** 3p.40 multicoloured . . 50 35

1997. 30th Anniv of Tlatelolco Treaty (Latin American and Caribbean treaty banning nuclear weapons).
2438 **1017** 3p.40 multicoloured . . 50 35

1019 Felipe Angeles

1020 Woman dancing

1997. Noted Generals. Multicoloured.
2440 2p.30 Type **1019** 35 25
2441 2p.30 Joaquin Amaro Dominguez 35 25
2442 2p.30 Mariano Escobedo . . 35 25
2443 2p.30 Jacinto Trevino Glez 35 25
2444 2p.30 Candido Aguilar Vargas 35 25
2445 2p.30 Francisco Urquizo . . 35 25

1997. International Women's Day.
2446 **1020** 2p.30 multicoloured . . 35 25

1021 "Grammar" (Juan Correa)

1997. 1st International Spanish Language Congress.
2447 **1021** 3p.40 multicoloured . . 50 35

1022 Chavez

1997. Birth Centenary of Dr. Ignacio Chavez.
2448 **1022** 2p.30 multicoloured . . 35 25

1023 State Emblem and Venustiano Carranza (President 1915–20)

1997. 80th Anniv of 1917 Constitution.
2449 **1023** 2p.30 multicoloured . . 35 25

1024 Yanez

1997. 50th Anniv of First Edition of "At the Water's Edge" by Agustin Yanez.
2450 **1024** 2p.30 multicoloured . . 35 25

1025 Mexican Mythological Figures (Luis Nishizawa)

1997. Centenary of Japanese Immigration.
2451 **1025** 3p.40 red, gold and black 50 35

1026 Rafael Ramirez 1027 University

1997. Teachers' Day.
2452 **1026** 2p.30 green and black 35 25

1997. 40th Anniv of Autonomous University of Lower California.
2453 **1027** 2p.30 multicoloured . . 35 25

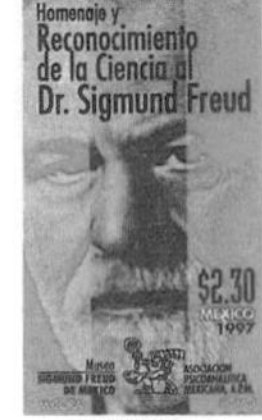
1028 Dove flying Free 1029 Freud

1997. International Day against Illegal Use and Illicit Trafficking of Drugs. Multicoloured.
2454 2p.30 Type **1028** 35 25
2455 3p.40 Dove imprisoned behind bars 50 35
2456 3p.40 Man opening cage . . 50 35
Nos. 2454/6 were issued together, se-tenant, forming a composite design.

1997. 58th Death Anniv of Sigmund Freud (pioneer of psychoanalysis).
2457 **1029** 2p.30 blue, green and violet 35 25

1030 School Arms 1031 Emblem

1997. Centenary of Naval School.
2458 **1030** 2p.30 multicoloured . . 35 25

1997. Introduction of New Social Security Law.
2459 **1031** 2p.30 multicoloured . . 30 20

1032 Globes and Anniversary Emblem

1997. 60th Anniv of National Bank of Foreign Commerce.
2460 **1032** 3p.40 multicoloured . . 40 25

1033 Common Porpoises

1997. Nature Conservation.
2461 **1033** 2p.30 multicoloured . . 30 20

1034 Passenger Airliners, 1947 and 1997

1997. 50th Anniv of Mexican Air Pilots' College.
2462 **1034** 2p.30 multicoloured . . 30 20

1035 Runners

1997. 15th Mexico City Marathon.
2463 **1035** 3p.40 multicoloured . . 40 25

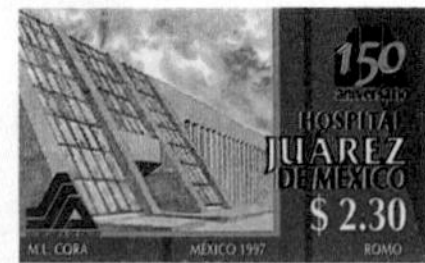
1036 Hospital Entrance

1997. 150th Anniv of Juarez Hospital.
2464 **1036** 2p.30 multicoloured . . 30 20

1037 Battle of Padierna

1997. 150th Anniversaries of Battles. Multicoloured.
2465 2p.30 Type **1037** 30 20
2466 2p.30 Battle of Churubusco 30 20
2467 2p.30 Battle of Molino del Rey 30 20
2468 2p.30 Defence of Chapultepec Fort 30 20

1038 Prieto 1039 Commemorative Cross

1997. Death Centenary of Guillermo Prieto (writer).
2469 **1038** 2p.30 blue 30 20

1997. 150th Anniv of Mexican St. Patrick's Battalion.
2470 **1039** 3p.40 multicoloured . . 40 25

1040 Emblem 1041 Bird carrying Letter

1997. Adolescent Reproductive Health Month.
2471 **1040** 2p.30 multicoloured . . 30 20

1997. World Post Day. Multicoloured.
2472 3p.40 Type **1041** 40 25
2473 3p.40 Heinrich von Stephan (founder of U.P.U.) (horiz) 40 25

1042 Gomez Morin 1043 Hospital

1997. Birth Centenary of Manuel Gomez Morin (politician).
2474 **1042** 2p.30 multicoloured . . 30 20

1997. 50th Anniv of Dr. Manuel Gea Gonzalez General Hospital.
2475 **1043** 2p.30 multicoloured . . 30 20

1044 Emblem 1045 Children celebrating Christmas (Ana Botello)

1997. 75th Anniv of Mexican Bar College of Law.
2476 **1044** 2p.30 red and black . . 30 20

1997. Christmas. Children's Paintings. Multicoloured.
2477 2p.30 Type **1045** 30 20
2478 2p.30 Children playing blind-man's-buff (Adrian Laris) 30 20

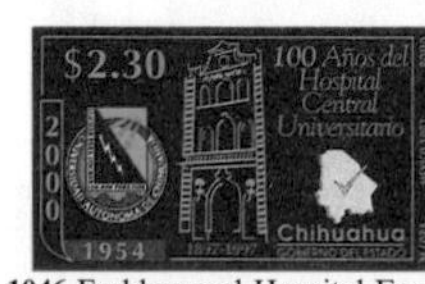
1046 Emblem and Hospital Facade

1997. Centenary of Central University Hospital, Chihuahua.
2479 **1046** 2p.30 multicoloured . . 30 20

1047 Molina and Nobel Medal

1997. Dr. Mario Molina (winner of Nobel Prize for Chemistry, 1995).
2480 **1047** 3p.40 multicoloured . . 40 25

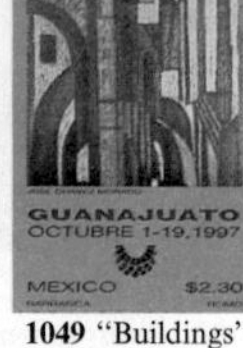
1048 Products and Storage Shelves 1049 "Buildings" (Jose Chavez Morado)

1997. National Chamber of Baking Industry. Multicoloured.
2481 2p.30 Type **1048** 30 20
2482 2p.30 Baker putting loaves in oven 30 20
2483 2p.30 Wedding cake, ingredients and baker . . 30 20
Nos. 2481/3 were issued together, se-tenant, forming a composite design.

1997. 25th Cervantes Festival, Guanajuato.
2484 **1049** 2p.30 multicoloured . . 30 20

1050 Galleon and Map of Loreto, California 1051 Sword and Rifle

1997. 300th Anniv of Loreto.
2485 **1050** 2p.30 multicoloured . . 30 20

1998. 50th Anniv of Military Academy, Puebla.
2486 **1051** 2p.30 multicoloured . . 30 20

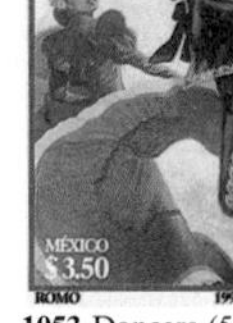
1052 Hands holding Children on Heart 1053 Dancers (5th of May Festival)

1998. International Women's Day.
2487 **1052** 2p.30 multicoloured . . 30 20

1998. Festivals.
2488 **1053** 3p.50 multicoloured . . 45 30

1054 Eiffel Tower, Player and Flag 1055 Sierra

1998. World Cup Football Championship, France. Multicoloured.
2489 2p.30 Type **1054** 30 20
2490 2p.30 Mascot, Eiffel Tower and flag 30 20

1998. 150th Birth Anniv of Justo Sierra (educationist).
2492 **1055** 2p.30 multicoloured . . 30 20

1056 Zubiran

1998. Birth Centenary of Salvador Zubiran (physician).
2493 **1056** 2p.30 multicoloured . . 30 20

1057 Emblem

1998. 50th Anniv of Organization of American States.
2494 **1057** 3p.40 multicoloured . . 40 25

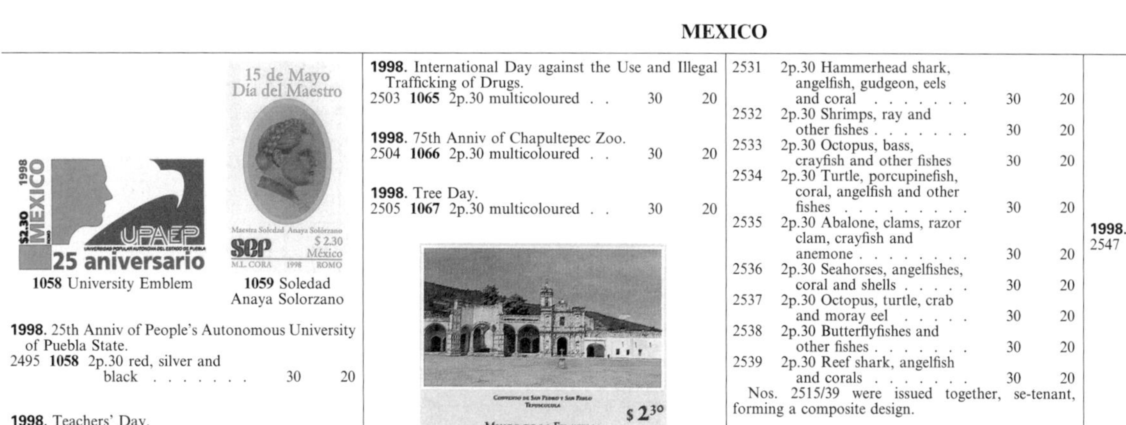

1058 University Emblem **1059** Soledad Anaya Solorzano

1998. 25th Anniv of People's Autonomous University of Puebla State.
2495 **1058** 2p.30 red, silver and black 30 20

1998. Teachers' Day.
2496 **1059** 2p.30 bistre, black and cream 30 20

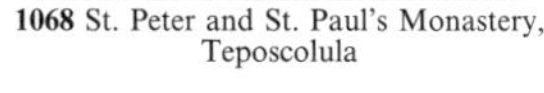

1060 Crops

1998. 250th Anniv of Tamaulipas (formerly New Santander) (1st issue).
2497 **1060** 2p.30 multicoloured . . 30 20
See also Nos. 2548.

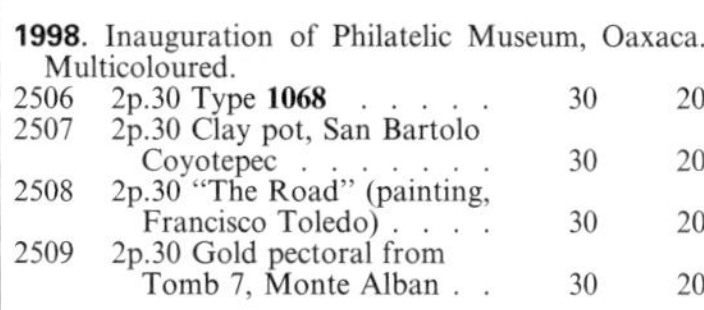

1061 Macuilxochitl

1998. 20th Anniv of Sports Lottery.
2498 **1061** 2p.30 multicoloured . . 30 20

1062 Manila Galleon

1998. Centenary of Philippine Independence.
2499 **1062** 3p.40 multicoloured . . 45 30

1063 Garcia Lorca

1998. Birth Centenary of Federico Garcia Lorca (poet).
2501 **1063** 3p.40 multicoloured . . 40 25

1064 Emblems

1998. 50th Anniv of Universal Declaration of Human Rights.
2502 **1064** 3p.40 green and black 45 30

1065 Open Book and Dove **1067** Tree

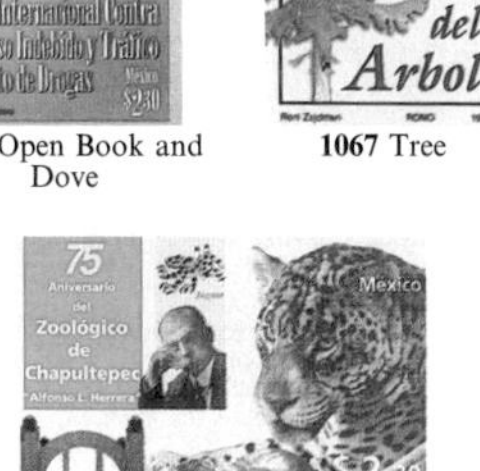

1066 Alfonso Herrera (founder) and Leopard

1998. International Day against the Use and Illegal Trafficking of Drugs.
2503 **1065** 2p.30 multicoloured . . 30 20

1998. 75th Anniv of Chapultepec Zoo.
2504 **1066** 2p.30 multicoloured . . 30 20

1998. Tree Day.
2505 **1067** 2p.30 multicoloured . . 30 20

1068 St. Peter and St. Paul's Monastery, Teposcolula

1998. Inauguration of Philatelic Museum, Oaxaca. Multicoloured.
2506 2p.30 Type **1068** 30 20
2507 2p.30 Clay pot, San Bartolo Coyotepec 30 20
2508 2p.30 "The Road" (painting, Francisco Toledo) 30 20
2509 2p.30 Gold pectoral from Tomb 7, Monte Alban . . 30 20

1069 Juarez

1998. 126th Death Anniv of Benito Juarez (President 1859–64 and 1867–72).
2510 **1069** 2p.30 stone, black and brown 30 20

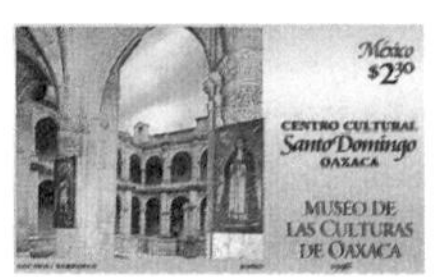

1070 Cultural Museum

1998. St. Dominic's Cultural Centre, Oaxaca. Multicoloured.
2511 2p.30 Type **1070** 30 20
2512 2p.30 Francisco de Burgoa Library 30 20
2513 2p.30 Historical botanic garden 30 20
2514 3p.40 St. Dominic's Monastery (after Teodoro Velasco) 45 30

1071 Frigate Bird, Blue-footed Booby, Whales and Cacti

1998. Marine Life. Multicoloured.
2515 2p.30 Type **1071** 30 20
2516 2p.30 Albatross, humpback whale and seagulls . . . 30 20
2517 2p.30 Tail of whale and swordfish 30 20
2518 2p.30 Fish eagle, flamingo, herons and dolphins . . . 30 20
2519 2p.30 Turtles, flamingoes, cormorant and palm tree 30 20
2520 2p.30 Oystercatcher, turnstone, elephant seal and sealions 30 20
2521 2p.30 Dolphin, turtle, seagulls and swallows . . 30 20
2522 2p.30 Killer whale, dolphins and ray 30 20
2523 2p.30 Flamingoes, pelican, kingfishers and spider . . 30 20
2524 2p.30 Crocodile, roseate spoonbill and tiger heron 30 20
2525 2p.30 Schools of sardines and anchovies 30 20
2526 2p.30 Turtle, squid, gold-finned tunnyfish and shark 30 20
2527 2p.30 Jellyfish, dolphins and fishes 30 20
2528 2p.30 Dolphin (fish), barracudas and haddock 30 20
2529 2p.30 Manatee, fishes, anemone and coral . . . 30 20
2530 2p.30 Seaweed, starfish, coral and fishes 30 20
2531 2p.30 Hammerhead shark, angelfish, gudgeon, eels and coral 30 20
2532 2p.30 Shrimps, ray and other fishes 30 20
2533 2p.30 Octopus, bass, crayfish and other fishes 30 20
2534 2p.30 Turtle, porcupinefish, coral, angelfish and other fishes 30 20
2535 2p.30 Abalone, clams, razor clam, crayfish and anemone 30 20
2536 2p.30 Seahorses, angelfishes, coral and shells 30 20
2537 2p.30 Octopus, turtle, crab and moray eel 30 20
2538 2p.30 Butterflyfishes and other fishes 30 20
2539 2p.30 Reef shark, angelfish and corals 30 20
Nos. 2515/39 were issued together, se-tenant, forming a composite design.

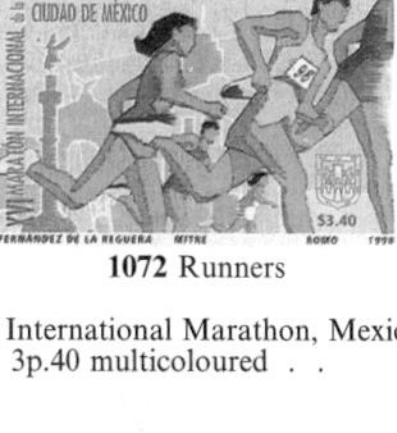

1072 Runners

1998. 16th International Marathon, Mexico City.
2540 **1072** 3p.40 multicoloured . . 45 30

1073 Aztec Deity

1998. World Tourism Day.
2541 **1073** 3p.40 multicoloured . . 45 30

1074 Lucas Alaman (founder)

1998. 175th Anniv of National Archives.
2542 **1074** 2p.30 green, red and black 30 20

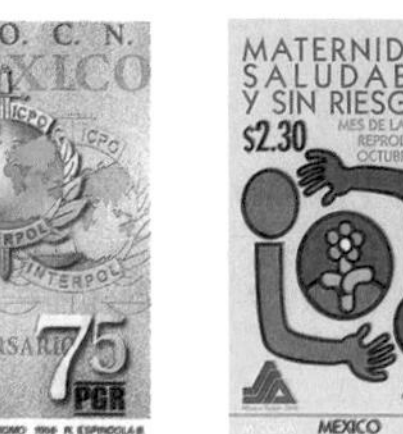

1075 Emblem **1076** Stylized Couple

1998. 75th Anniv of Interpol.
2543 **1075** 3p.40 multicoloured . . 45 30

1998. Healthy Pregnancy Month.
2544 **1076** 2p.30 multicoloured . . 30 20

1077 Painting by Luis Nishizawa

1998.
2545 **1077** 2p.30 multicoloured . . 30 20

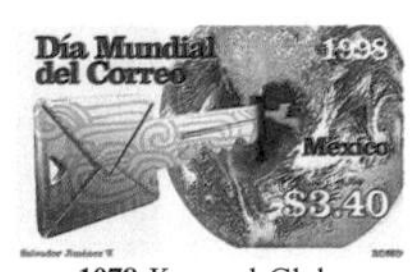

1078 Key and Globe

1998. World Post Day.
2546 **1078** 3p.40 multicoloured . . 45 30

1079 College Campus

1998. 175th Anniv of Military College.
2547 **1079** 2p.30 multicoloured . . 30 20

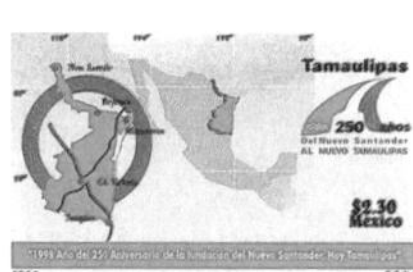

1080 Map

1998. 250th Anniv of Tamaulipas (formerly New Santander) (2nd issue).
2548 **1080** 2p.30 multicoloured . . 30 20

1081 Golden Eagle

1998. Nature Conservation.
2549 **1081** 2p.30 multicoloured . . 30 20

1082 Woman and Potatoes

1998. World Food Day.
2550 **1082** 3p.30 multicoloured . . 45 30

1083 Mexico arrowed on Globe

1998. National Migration Week.
2551 **1083** 2p.30 multicoloured . . 30 20

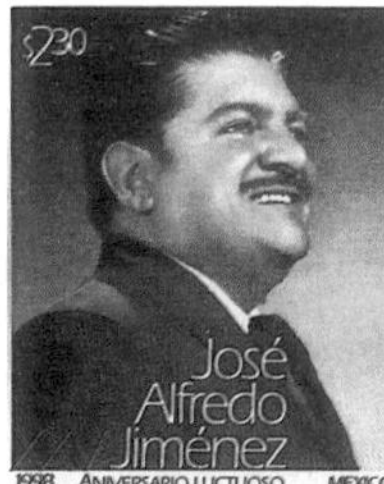

1084 Jimenez

1998. 25th Death Anniv of Jose Alfredo Jimenez (writer).
2552 **1084** 2p.30 multicoloured . . 30 20

1085 Oil Rig and Emblem **1087** Franciscan Monastery, Colima

1086 Mexican Stone Carving and Eiffel Tower

1998. 25th Anniv of Mexican Petroleum Engineers' Association.
2553 **1085** 3p.40 multicoloured . . 45 30

1998. Mexican–French Economic and Cultural Co-operation.
2554 **1086** 3p.40 multicoloured . . 45 30

1998. 475th Anniv of Colima.
2555 **1087** 2p.30 multicoloured . . 30 20

1088 Wise Men approaching Stable

1998. Christmas. Multicoloured. Self-adhesive.
2556 2p.30 Type **1088** 30 20
2557 3p.40 Decorations and pot (vert) 45 30

1089 Woman with Baby

1998. 50th Anniv of National Institute of Indigenous Peoples.
2558 **1089** 2p.30 multicoloured . . 30 20

1090 Eagle holding Statute

1998. 60th Anniv of Federation of Civil Servants' Trade Unions.
2559 **1090** 2p.30 multicoloured . . 30 20

1091 Airplane and Aztec Bird-man

1092 University Arms

1998. 25th Anniv of Latin-American Civil Aviation Commission.
2560 **1091** 3p.40 multicoloured . . 45 30

1998. 125th Anniv of Sinaloa Autonomous University.
2561 **1092** 2p.30 multicoloured . . 30 20

1094 "Satmex 5" and Earth

1999. Launch of "Satmex 5" Satellite.
2563 **1094** 3p. multicoloured . . . 40 25

1095 Maracas Player and Streamers

1096 Couple in Hammock

1999. Veracruz Carnival.
2564 **1095** 3p. multicoloured . . . 40 25

1999. Bicentenary of Acapulco, Guerrero. Mult.
2565 3p. Type **1096** 40 25
2566 4p.20 Diving from cliff . . . 55 30
Nos. 2565/6 were issued together, se-tenant, forming a composite design.

1097 Internet Website

1999. International Women's Day.
2567 **1097** 4p.20 multicoloured . . 55 30

1098 "Mexico" (Jorge Gonzalez Camarena)

1999. 40th Anniv of National Commission for Free Textbooks.
2568 **1098** 3p. multicoloured . . . 40 25

1099 Family Members

1999. 25th Anniv of National Population Council.
2569 **1099** 3p. multicoloured . . . 40 25

1101 Guadalupe Ceniceros de Perez

1999. Teachers' Day.
2571 **1101** 3p. multicoloured . . . 40 25

1102 Pitcher

1999. 75th Anniv of Mexican Baseball League. Each black and grey.
2572 3p. Type **1102** 40 25
2573 3p. Catcher 40 25
2574 3p. Skeletal pitcher 40 25
2575 3p. Pitcher (different) . . . 40 25

1103 10p. Banknote

1999. 115th Anniv of National Bank of Mexico. Multicoloured.
2576 3p. Type **1103** 40 25
2577 3p. Former and current headquarters 40 25

1105 Couple holding Hands

1106 Skyscraper

1999. International Day against Illegal Use and Illicit Trafficking of Drugs.
2579 **1105** 4p.20 multicoloured . . 60 40

1999. 65th Anniv of National Financial Institute.
2580 **1106** 3p. multicoloured . . . 45 30

1107 Tree

1999. Tree Day.
2581 **1107** 3p. multicoloured . . . 45 30

1108 Registration Documents and Fingerprint

1999. 140th Anniv of National Civil Register.
2582 **1108** 3p. multicoloured . . . 45 30

1109 Runner's Feet

1999. 17th International Marathon, Mexico City.
2583 **1109** 4p.20 multicoloured . . 60 40

1110 Children, Flag and Book on Island ("Conoce nuestra Constitucion")

1999. 40th Anniv of National Commission for Free Textbooks (2nd issue). Multicoloured.
2584 3p. Type **1110** 45 30
2585 3p. Children dancing ("Tsuni tsame") 45 30
2586 3p. Bird on flower ("Ciencias naturales") . . 45 30

1111 "Self-portrait"

1999. Birth Centenary of Rufino Tamayo (artist).
2587 **1111** 3p. multicoloured . . . 45 30

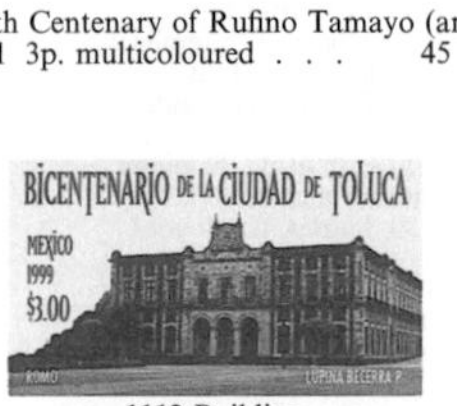

1112 Building

1999. Bicentenary of Toluca City.
2588 **1112** 3p. black and copper 45 30

1113 State Arms, Model Figures and Signature

1999. 175th Anniv of State of Mexico.
2589 **1113** 3p. multicoloured . . . 45 30

1114 "50" and Map of Americas

1999. 50th Anniv of Union of Universities of Latin America.
2590 **1114** 4p.20 multicoloured . . 60 40

1115 Emblem

1999. 40th Anniv of Institute of Security and Social Services of State Workers (I.S.S.S.T.E.).
2591 **1115** 3p. multicoloured . . . 45 30

1116 Map and State Emblem

1999. 25th Anniv of State of Baja California Sur.
2592 **1116** 3p. multicoloured . . . 45 30

1117 Emblem, "25" and Map

1999. 25th Anniv of Mexican Family Planning.
2593 **1117** 3p. multicoloured . . . 45 30

1118 Harpy Eagle

1999. Nature Conservation.
2594 **1118** 3p. multicoloured . . . 45 30

1119 Stone Carving and Arms

1120 U.P.U. Messengers

1999. 25th Anniv of State of Quintana Roo.
2595 **1119** 3p. multicoloured . . . 45 30

1999. 125th Anniv of Universal Postal Union.
2596 **1120** 4p.20 multicoloured . . 60 40

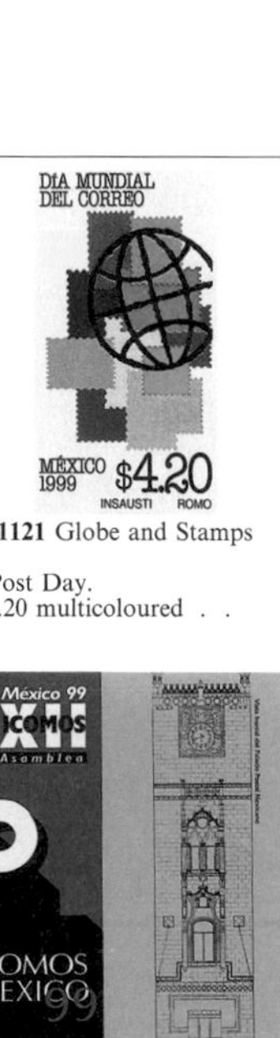

1121 Globe and Stamps

1999. World Post Day.
2597 **1121** 4p.20 multicoloured . . 60 40

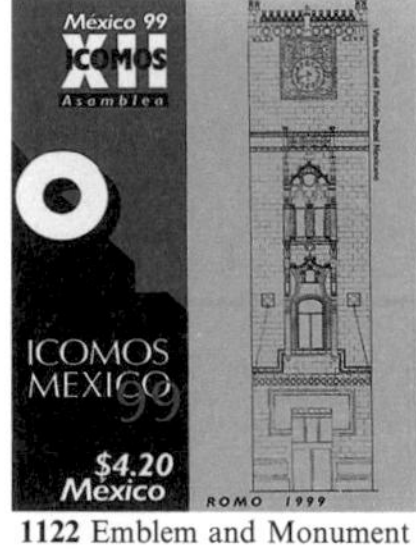

1122 Emblem and Monument

1999. 12th General Assembly of International Council on Monuments and Sites.
2598 **1122** 4p.20 silver, blue and black 60 40

1123 Chavez and Revueltas

1999. Birth Centenaries of Carlos Chavez and Silvestre Revueltas (composers).
2599 **1123** 3p. multicoloured . . . 45 30

1124 Emblem

1126 "Mexico 1999" in Star and Children (Alfredo Carciarreal)

1125 Map, Cave Painting and State Arms

1999. 25th Anniv of Autonomous Metropolitan University.
2600 **1124** 3p. multicoloured . . . 45 30

1999. 150th Anniv of State of Guerrero.
2601 **1125** 3p. multicoloured . . . 45 30

1999. Christmas. Children's Drawings. Multicoloured.
2602 3p. Type **1126** 45 30
2603 4p.20 Christmas decorations (Rodrigo Santiago Salazar) 60 40

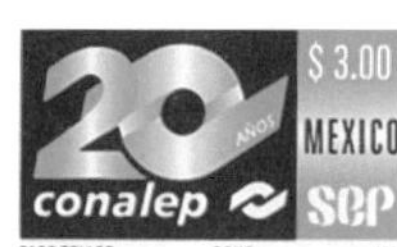

1127 Anniversary Emblem

1999. 20th Anniv of National Commission on Professional Education.
2604 **1127** 3p. green, ultramarine and black 45 30

1128 Humboldt (naturalist)

1999. Bicentenary of Alexander von Humboldt's Exploration of South America.
2605 **1128** 3p. multicoloured . . . 45 30

1130 Emblem and Crowd

1131 Woman ascending Stairs

2000. Census.
2607 **1130** 3p. multicoloured . . . 45 30

2000. International Women's Day.
2608 **1131** 4p.20 multicoloured . . 60 40

1134 Totonaca Temple, El Tajin

2000.
2611 **1134** 3p. multicoloured . . . 45 30

1135 Emblem, Books and Keyboard

2000. 50th Anniv of National Association of Universities and Institutes of Higher Education.
2612 **1135** 3p. multicoloured . . . 45 30

1136 Emblem

2000. 25th Tourism Fair, Acapulco.
2613 **1136** 4p.20 multicoloured . . 60 40

1137 Men in Canoe and Sailing Ship

2000. 500th Anniv of the Discovery of Brazil.
2614 **1137** 4p.20 multicoloured . . 60 40

1138 Luis Alvarez Barret

2000. Teachers' Day.
2615 **1138** 3p. multicoloured . . . 45 30

1139 Flying Cars and Boy with Dog (Alejandro Guerra Millan)

2000. "Stampin the Future". Winning Entries in Children's International Painting Competition. Mult.
2616 3p. Type **1139** 45 30
2617 4p.20 Houses and space ships (Carlos Hernandez Garcia) 60 40

1140 Emblem

2000. 4th Asian–Pacific Telecommunications and Information Industry Economic Co-operation Forum.
2618 **1140** 4p.20 multicoloured . . 60 40

1141 Young Children

1144 Pictograms

2000. International Anti-drugs Day.
2619 **1141** 4p.20 multicoloured . . 60 40

2000. Convive (disabled persons' organization).
2622 **1144** 3p. multicoloured . . . 45 25

1145 Globe and Member Flags

1146 Emblem

2000. 20th Anniv of Association of Latin American Integration.
2623 **1145** 4p.20 multicoloured . . 65 40

2000. 125th Anniv of Restoration of Senate.
2624 **1146** 3p. multicoloured . . . 45 25

1149 Runners crossing Finishing Line

2000. 18th International Marathon, Mexico City.
2627 **1149** 4p.20 multicoloured . . 65 40

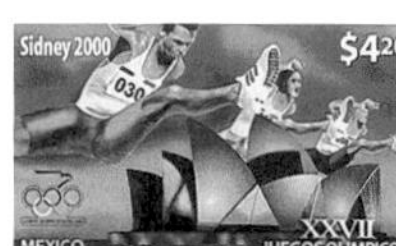

1150 Athletes and Sydney Opera House

2000. Olympic Games, Sydney.
2628 **1150** 4p.20 multicoloured . . 65 40

1151 Emblem and Family

2000. Paisano Programme (support for Mexicans returning home from abroad).
2629 **1151** 4p.20 multicoloured . . 65 40

1152 Emblem

2000. 2nd International U.N.E.S.C.O. World Conference, Colima.
2630 **1152** 4p.20 multicoloured . . 65 40

1153 Profiles

1155 Bird holding Letter

1154 Building and Emblem

2000. Women's Health Month.
2631 **1153** 3p. multicoloured . . . 35 20

2000. 250th Anniv of Ciudad Victoria, Tamaulipas.
2632 **1154** 3p. multicoloured . . . 35 20

2000. World Post Day.
2633 **1155** 4p.20 multicoloured . . 50 30

1156 Emblem

2000. 50th Anniv of National Human Rights Commission.
2634 **1156** 3p. silver and blue . . . 35 20

1157 Doctors and Ambulance

2000. New Millennium. Sheet 223 × 135 mm in shape of flag, containing T **1157** and similar multicoloured designs.
MS2635 3p. Type **1157**; 3p. Posters, doctors and globe (79 × 25 mm); 3p. Children receiving injections; 3p. Poster showing tractor and crowd demonstrating (79 × 25 mm); 4p.20, Modern medical technology (oval- shaped, 39 × 49 mm) . . . . 2·00 1·25

1158 Clouds and Emblem

2000. 50th Anniv of World Meteorological Organization.
2636 **1158** 3p. multicoloured . . . 35 20

1159 Emblem

2000. 50th Anniv of International Diabetes Federation.
2637 **1159** 4p.20 gold and red . . 50 30

1160 Contemporary Art with Sculpture (½-size illustration)

2000. Art. Sheet 223 × 39 mm in shape of flag, containing T **1160** and similar multicoloured designs.
MS2638 3p. Type **1160**; 3p. Photographs (39 × 25 mm); 3p. Opera singer and movie actors; 3p. Dancers (39 × 25 mm); 4p.20 Ballet dancers and musicians (oval-shaped, 39 × 49 mm) . . 2·00 1·25

1161 Samuel Morse, Juan de la Granja and Telegraph Apparatus

2000. 150th Anniv of Telegraph in Mexico.
2639 **1161** 3p. multicoloured . . . 35 20
Samuel Morse invented the telegraph and Morse code system and Juan de la Granja introduced the telegraph to Mexico.

1162 Bunuel

2000. Birth Centenary of Luis Bunuel (film director).
2640 **1162** 3p. silver, black and red 35 20

1163 Lightning

2000. 25th Anniv of Electric Investigation Institute.
2641 **1163** 3p. multicoloured . . . 35 20

1164 Building Customs House, and Bridge

2000. Centenary of Customs.
2642 **1164** 3p. multicoloured . . . 35 20

1165 Star and Girl (Maria Carina Lona Martinez)

2000. Christmas. Children's paintings. Multicoloured.
2643 3p. Type **1165** 35 20
2644 4p.20 Poinsettia (Daniela Escamilla Rodriguez) . . 50 30

1166 Television Set and Emblem

2000. 50th Anniv of Television in Mexico.
2645 **1166** 3p. multicoloured . . . 35 20

1167 Adamo Boari (architect)

2000. Centenary of Commencement of Construction of Postal Headquarters, Mexico City. Sheet 92 × 100 mm, containing T **1167** and similar designs. Multicoloured.
MS2646 3p. multicoloured; 3p. black, brown and red; 3p. multicoloured; 10p. black, brown and red (71 × 39 mm) . . . . 2·10 1·25
DESIGNS: As Type **1167**—3p. Building facade; 3p. Gonzalo Garita y Frontera (engineer). 71 × 39 mm—10p. Completed building.

1168 Coiled Mattress (Manuel Alvarez Bravo)

2000. Photography. Sheet 223 × 135 mm in shape of flag, containing T **1168** and similar multicoloured designs.
MS2647 3p. Type **1168**; 3p. Various portraits (79 × 25 mm); 3p. Roses (Tina Modotti); 3p. Various photographs including a lift, a lake, a 1925 car, a helicopter, a ruined building, a street scene, men in costume and boot heels (79 × 25 mm); 4p.20 Men in gas masks (oval-shaped, 39 × 49 mm) 2·00 1·25

1169 Pyramid of the Niches

2000. El Tajin.
2648 **1169** 3p. multicoloured . . . 35 20

1170 Manatee

2000. Nature Conservation.
2649 **1170** 3p. multicoloured . . . 35 20

1171 Sarabia

2000. Birth Centenary of Francisco Sarabia (aviator).
2650 **1171** 3p. multicoloured . . . 35 20

1172 Telephone Exchange and Fabric Shops (½-size illustration)

2000. Industry. Sheet 223 × 135 mm in shape of flag, containing T **1172** and similar multicoloured designs.
MS2651 3p. Type **1172**; 3p. Tractor and modern farming (39 × 25 mm); 3p. Traditional farming methods and car; 3p. Manufacturing and industrial plant (39 × 25 mm); 4p.20 Globe and industries (oval-shaped, 39 × 49 mm) . . . . 2·00 1·60

1173 Stamps and Post Collection (½-size illustration)

2000. Forms of Communication. Sheet 223 × 135 mm in shape of flag, containing T **1173** and similar multicoloured designs.
MS2652 3p. Type **1173**; 3p. Telephone operators and telegraph clerk (39 × 25 mm); 3p. Old and modern train and station; 3p. Motorway (39 × 25 mm); 4p.20 Globe and satellite and satellite dish (oval-shaped, 39 × 49 mm) 2·00 1·60

2001. Tourism. As Nos. 2410 etc but with face value changed.
2658 6p.50 Queretaro 75 45

1174 Chiapas

2001. Tourism.
2670 **1174** 1p.50 multicoloured . . 20 15
2673 8p.50 multicoloured . . 1·00 60

1175 Emblem, Book and Building

2001. 50th Anniv of National Autonomous University.
2680 **1175** 3p. multicoloured . . . 35 20

1176 Woman

2001. International Women's Day.
2681 **1176** 4p.20 multicoloured . . 50 30

1177 Cement Factory

2001. 53rd Anniv of National Cement Chamber.
2682 **1177** 3p. multicoloured . . . 35 20

1178 Vasconcelos and Ink Pen
1179 People Running and Flames

2001. 42nd Death Anniv of Jose Vasconcelos (lawyer).
2683 **1178** 3p. multicoloured . . . 35 20

2001. 50th Anniv of United Nations High Commissioner for Refugees.
2684 **1179** 4p.20 multicoloured . . 50 30

1180 "Self-portrait wearing Jade Necklace"
1181 Stylized Bird

2001. Frida Kahlo (artist) Commemoration.
2685 **1180** 4p.20 multicoloured . . 50 30
A stamp of similar design was issued by the United States of America.

2001. Anti-drugs Campaign.
2686 **1181** 4p.20 multicoloured . . 50 30

1182 De la Cueva

2001. Birth Centenary of Mario de la Cueva (university director).
2687 **1182** 3p. blue and gold . . . 35 20

1183 Emblem

2001. International Year of Volunteers.
2688 **1183** 4p.20 multicoloured . . 50 30

1184 Women and Flowers (painting)

2001. Rodolfo Morales (artist) Commemoration. Sheet 121 × 60 mm.
MS2689 **1184** 10p. multicoloured 1·10 65

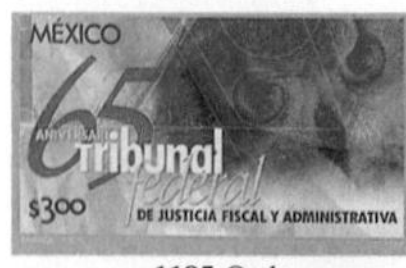
1185 Owl

2001. 65th Anniv of Federal Justice Tribunal.
2690 **1185** 3p. multicoloured . . . 30 20

1186 Emblems and Building

2001. 450th Anniv of University of Mexico.
2691 **1186** 3p. multicoloured . . . 30 20

1187 Adela Formoso
1188 Daniel Villegas

2001. 20th Death Anniv of Adela Formoso de Obregon Santalla (women's rights activist).
2692 **1187** 3p. multicoloured . . . 30 20

2001. 25th Death Anniv of Daniel Cosío Villegas (historian).
2693 **1188** 3p. multicoloured . . . 30 20

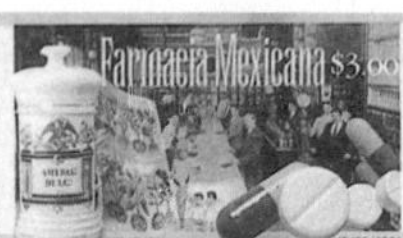
1189 Past and Present Pharmaceutical Drugs

2001.
2694 **1189** 3p. multicoloured . . . 30 20

1190 Girl with Grandfather

2001. Grandparents Day.
2695 **1190** 3p. multicoloured . . . 30 20

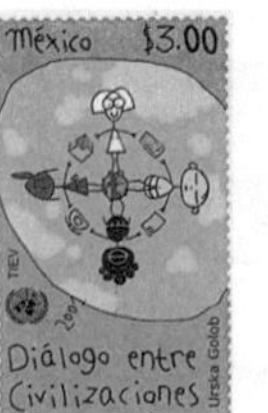
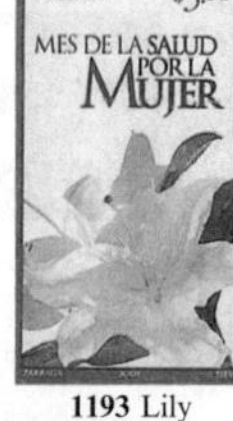
1191 Children encircling Globe
1193 Lily

1192 Envelope as Bicycle

2001. United Nations Year of Dialogue among Civilizations.
2696 **1191** 3p. multicoloured 30 20

2001. Stamp Day.
2697 **1192** 3p. yellow, red and blue 30 20

2001. Women's Health Day.
2698 **1193** 3p. multicoloured 30 20

1194 Eye and People

2001. 25th Anniv of Ophthalmic Institute.
2699 **1194** 4p.20 multicoloured 40 25

1195 Tufted Jay (*Cyanocorax dickeyi*)

2001. Endangered Species.
2700 **1195** 5p.30 multicoloured 50 30

1196 Children (Eunice Gonzalez)

2001. Christmas. Children's Paintings. Multicoloured.
2701 3p. Type **1196** 30 20
2702 4p.20 Candles (Javier Nunez) 40 25

1197 Nurse and Children

2001. Educational Scholarship Fund for Indigenous Children. Sheet 101 × 72 mm. P 14.
MS2703 1197 3p. multicoloured 30 30

1198 Technicians

2001. National Fund for Education. Sheet 101 × 72 mm.
MS2704 1198 3p. multicoloured 30 30

1199 Boy and Girl **1200** Apple

2001. Children's Accident Prevention Campaign.
2705 **1199** 3p. multicoloured 30 20

2001. World Food Day.
2706 **1200** 3p. multicoloured 30 20

EXPRESS LETTER STAMPS

E **55** Express Service Messenger

1919.
E445 E **55** 20c. black and red 35 15

E **95**

1934.
E536 E **95** 10c. blue and red 15 30

E **121** Indian Archer E **222**

1934. New President's Assumption of Office. Imprint "OFICINA IMPRESORA DE HACIENDA–MEXICO".
E581 E **121** 10c. violet 1·00 20

1938. Imprint "TALLERES DE IMP. DE EST. Y VALORES-MEXICO".
E610 E **121** 10c. violet 55 20
E731 20c. orange 25 30

1940. Optd **1940.**
E665 E **55** 20c. black and red 20 15

1950.
E860 E **222** 25c. orange 20 10
E910 – 60c. green 1·10 35
DESIGN: 60c. Hands and letter.

E **244**

E **245**

1956.
E 954 E **244** 35c. purple 25 10
E1065 50c. green 45 10
E 956 E **245** 80c. red 50 80
E1066 1p.20 lilac 1·50 75
E1346p E **244** 2p. orange 20 15
E1346q E **245** 5p. blue 20 60

E **468** Watch Face

1979.
E1373 E **468** 2p. black and orange 10 60

INSURED LETTER STAMPS

IN **125** Safe IN **222** P.O. Treasury Vault

1935. Inscr as in Type IN **125**.
IN583 – 10c. red 1·10 30
IN733 – 50c. blue 75 25
IN734 IN **125** 1p. green 75 35

DESIGNS: 10c. Bundle of insured letters; 50c. Registered mailbag.

1950.
IN911 IN **222** 20c. blue 15 10
IN912 40c. purple 15 10
IN913 1p. green 20 10
IN914 5p. green and blue 65 60
IN915 10p. blue and red 3·00 1·50

IN **469** Padlock

1976.
IN1374 IN **469** 40c. black & turq 10 10
IN1522 1p. black & turq 10 10
IN1376 2p. black and blue 10 10
IN1380 5p. black & turq 10 10
IN1524 10p. black & turq 10 10
IN1525 20p. black & turq 10 10
IN1383 50p. black & turq 95 95
IN1384 100p. black & turq 60 60
The 5, 10, 20p. exist with the padlock either 31 or 32½ mm high.

OFFICIAL STAMPS

O **18** Hidalgo

1884. No value shown.
O156 O **18** Red 30 20
O157 Brown 15 10
O158 Orange 80 15
O159 Green 30 15
O160 Blue 45 35

1894. Stamps of 1895 handstamped **OFICIAL**.
O231 **19** 1c. green 3·75 1·25
O232 2c. red 4·50 1·25
O233 3c. brown 3·75 1·25
O234 **20** 4c. orange 5·50 2·50
O235 **21** 5c. blue 7·50 2·50
O236 **22** 10c. purple 7·00 50
O237 **20** 12c. olive 15·00 6·25
O238 **22** 15c. blue 8·75 3·75
O239 20c. red 8·75 3·75
O240 50c. mauve 19·00 9·50
O241 **23** 1p. brown 48·00 19·00
O242 5p. red £200 95·00
O243 10p. blue £275 £150

1899. Stamps of 1899 handstamped **OFICIAL**.
O276 **27** 1c. green 9·50 60
O286 1c. purple 8·75 95
O277 2c. red 12·50 95
O287 2c. green 8·75 95
O278 3c. brown 12·50 60
O288 4c. red 16·00 45
O279 5c. blue 12·50 1·10
O289 5c. orange 16·00 3·25
O280 10c. brown and purple 16·00 1·40
O290 10c. orange and blue 19·00 95
O281 15c. purple and lavender 16·00 1·40
O282 20c. blue and red 19·00 45
O283 **28** 50c. black and purple 38·00 6·25
O291 50c. black and red 48·00 6·25
O284 **29** 1p. black and blue 80·00 6·25
O285 **30** 5p. black and red 50·00 19·00

1911. Independence stamps optd **OFICIAL**.
O301 **32** 1c. purple 1·25 1·25
O302 – 2c. green 75 45
O303 – 3c. brown 1·25 45
O304 – 4c. red 1·90 45
O305 – 5c. orange 3·25 1·75
O306 – 10c. orange and blue 1·90 45
O307 15c. lake and slate 3·25 2·00
O308 – 20c. blue and lake 2·50 45
O309 **40** 50c. black and brown 8·75 3·75
O310 – 1p. black and blue 15·00 6·25
O311 – 5p. black and red 55·00 32·00

1915. Stamps of 1915 optd **OFICIAL**.
O321 **43** 1c. violet 30 55
O322 **44** 2c. green 30 55
O323 **45** 3c. brown 30 55
O324 4c. red 30 55
O325 5c. orange 30 55
O326 10c. blue 30 55

1915. Stamps of 1915 optd **OFICIAL**.
O318 **46** 40c. grey 4·75 3·25
O455 40c. mauve 3·75 1·90
O319 **47** 1p. grey and brown 3·25 3·75
O456 1p. grey and blue 9·50 6·25
O320 **48** 5p. blue and lake 19·00 16·00
O457 5p. grey and green 55·00 95·00

1916. Nos. O301/11 optd with T **49**.
O358 **32** 1c. purple 1·90
O359 – 2c. green 30
O360 – 3c. brown 35
O361 – 4c. red 2·00
O362 – 5c. orange 35
O363 – 10c. orange and blue 35
O364 – 15c. lake and slate 35
O365 – 20c. blue and lake 40
O366 **40** 50c. black and brown 55·00
O367 – 1p. black and blue 3·25
O368 – 5p. black and red £1600

1918. Stamps of 1917 optd **OFICIAL**.
O424 **53** 1c. violet 1·25 60
O446 1c. grey 30 20
O447 – 2c. green 20 20
O448 – 3c. brown 25 20
O449 – 4c. red 3·75 45
O450 – 5c. blue 20 20
O451 – 10c. blue 30 15
O452 – 20c. lake 2·50 2·50
O454 – 30c. black 3·75 1·40

1923. No. 416 optd **OFICIAL**.
O485 10p. black and brown 60·00 95·00

1923. Stamps of 1923 optd **OFICIAL**.
O471 **59** 1c. brown 20 20
O473 **60** 2c. red 25 25
O475 **61** 3c. brown 55 40
O461 **62** 4c. green 1·90 1·90
O476 **63** 4c. green 40 40
O477 5c. orange 70 65
O489 **74** 8c. orange 3·75 2·50
O479 **66** 10c. lake 55 55
O480 **65** 20c. blue 3·25 2·50
O464 **64** 30c. green 35 25
O467 **68** 50c. brown 55 55
O469 **69** 1p. blue and lake 4·75 4·75

1929. Air. Optd **OFICIAL**.
O501 **80** 5c. blue (roul) 45 25
O502 **81** 20c. violet 55 55
O492 **58** 25c. sepia and lake 6·50 7·50
O490 25c. sepia and green 2·50 3·00

1929. Air. As 1926 Postal Congress stamp optd **HABILITADO Servicio Oficial Aereo**.
O493 **70** 2c. black 26·00 26·00
O494 – 4c. black 26·00 26·00
O495 **70** 5c. black 26·00 26·00
O496 – 10c. black 26·00 26·00
O497 **72** 20c. black 26·00 26·00
O498 30c. black 26·00 26·00
O499 40c. black 26·00 26·00
O500 **73** 1p. black £950 £950

O **85**

1930. Air.
O503 O **85** 20c. grey 2·75 2·75
O504 35c. violet 40 95
O505 40c. blue and brown 50 90
O506 70c. sepia and violet 50 95

1931. Air. Surch **HABILITADO Quince centavos**.
O515 O **85** 15c. on 20c. grey 45 45

1932. Air. Optd **SERVICIO OFICIAL** in one line.
O532 **80** 10c. violet (perf or roul) 30 30
O533 15c. red (perf or roul) 85 85
O534 20c. sepia (roul) 85 85
O531 **58** 50c. red and blue 1·25 1·25

1932. Stamps of 1923 optd **SERVICIO OFICIAL** in two lines.
O535 **59** 1c. brown 15 15
O536 **60** 2c. red 10 10
O537 **61** 3c. brown 95 95
O538 **63** 4c. green 3·25 2·50
O539 5c. red 3·75 2·50
O540 **66** 10c. lake 1·10 75
O541 **65** 20c. blue 4·75 3·25
O544 **64** 30c. green 2·50 95
O545 **46** 40c. mauve 4·75 3·25
O546 **68** 50c. brown 80 95
O547 **69** 1p. blue and lake 95 95

1933. Air. Optd **SERVICIO OFICIAL** in two lines.
O553 **58** 50c. red and blue 1·40 1·25

1933. Air. Optd **SERVICIO OFICIAL** in two lines.
O548 **80** 5c. blue (No. 476a) 30 30
O549 10c. violet (No. 477) 30 30
O550 20c. sepia (No. 479) 30 60
O551 50c. lake (No. 481) 40 95

1934. Optd **OFICIAL**.
O565 **92** 15c. blue 35 35

1938. Nos. 561/71 optd **OFICIAL**.
O622 1c. orange 70 1·25
O623 2c. green 45 45
O624 4c. red 45 45
O625 10c. violet 45 80
O626 20c. blue 55 80
O627 30c. red 70 1·25
O628 40c. brown 70 1·25
O629 50c. black 1·00 1·00
O630 1p. red and brown 2·50 3·75

PARCEL POST STAMPS

P 167 Steam Mail Train

1941.

P732 **P 167** 10c. red . . . . 2·25 55
P733 20c. violet . . . . . . 2·75 70

P 228 Class DE-10 Diesel-electric Locomotive

1951.

P916 **P 228** 10c. pink . . . . . . 1·50 20
P917 20c. violet . . . . . . 2·00 40

POSTAGE DUE STAMPS

D 32

1908.

D282 **D 32** 1c. blue . . . . 1·00 1·00
D283 2c. blue . . . . 1·00 1·00
D284 4c. blue . . . . 1·00 1·00
D285 5c. blue . . . . 1·00 1·00
D286 10c. blue . . . . . . 1·00 1·00

MICRONESIA Pt. 22

A group of islands in the Pacific, from 1899 to 1914 part of the German Caroline Islands. Occupied by the Japanese in 1914 the islands were from 1920 a Japanese mandated territory, and from 1947 part of the United States Trust Territory of the Pacific Islands, using United States stamps. Micronesia assumed control of its postal services in 1984.

100 cents = 1 dollar.

1 Yap

1984. Inauguration of Postal Independence. Maps. Multicoloured.
1 20c. Type **1** 50 40
2 20c. Truk 50 40
3 20c. Pohnpei 50 40
4 20c. Kosrae 50 40

2 Fernandez de Quiros

3 Boeing 727-100

1984.

5 **2** 1c. blue 10 10
6 – 2c. brown 10 10
7 – 3c. blue 10 10
8 – 4c. green 10 10
9 – 5c. brown and olive 10 10
10 – 10c. purple 15 10
11 – 13c. blue 20 10
11a – 15c. red 20 10
12 – 17c. brown 25 10
13 **2** 19c. purple 30 10
14 – 20c. green 30 10
14a – 22c. green 30 15
14b – 25c. orange 30 15
15 – 30c. red 45 15
15a – 36c. blue 50 20
16 – 37c. violet 50 20
16a – 45c. green 60 30
17 – 50c. brown and sepia . . . 80 35
18 – $1 olive . . . . 1·25 85
19 – $2 blue . . . . 2·50 1·50
20 – $5 brown . . . . 6·00 4·50
20a – $10 blue . . . . 12·50 11·00

DESIGNS: 2, 20c. Louis Duperrey; 3, 30c. Fyodor Lutke; 4, 37c. Jules Dumont d'Urville; 5c. Men's house, Yap; 10, 45c. Sleeping Lady (mountains), Kosrae; 13, 15c. Liduduhriap waterfall, Pohnpei; 17, 25c. Tonachau Peak, Truk; 22, 36c. "Senyavin" (full-rigged sailing ship); 50c. Devil mask, Truk; $1 Sokehs Rock, Pohnpei; $2 Outrigger canoes, Kosrae; $5 Stone money, Yap; $10 Official seal.

1984. Air. Multicoloured.
21 28c. Type **3** 55 30
22 35c. Grumman SA-16 Albatros flying boat 70 50
23 40c. Consolidated PBY-5A Catalina amphibian 95 60

4 Truk Post Office

1984. "Ausipex 84" International Stamp Exhibition, Melbourne. Multicoloured.
24 20c. Type **4** (postage) 50 20
25 28c. German Caroline Islands 1919 3pf. yacht stamp (air) 60 40
26 35c. German 1900 20pf. stamp optd for Caroline Islands . . 70 50
27 40c. German Caroline Islands 1915 5m. yacht stamp . . . 80 65

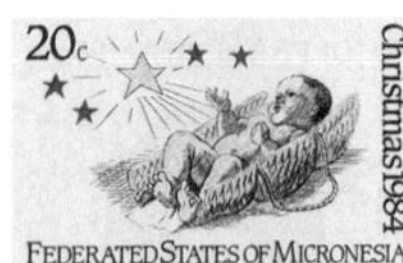

5 Baby in Basket

1984. Christmas. Multicoloured.
28 20c. Type **5** (postage) 55 25
29 28c. Open book showing Christmas scenes (air) . . . 65 40
30 35c. Palm tree decorated with lights 85 50
31 40c. Women preparing food 1·00 65

6 U.S.S. "Jamestown" (warship)

1985. Ships.
32 **6** 22c. black & brown (postage) 65 35
33 – 33c. black and lilac (air) . . 85 50
34 – 39c. black and green . . . . 1·00 75
35 – 44c. black and red . . . . . 1·40 90

DESIGNS: 33c. "L'Astrolabe" (D'Urville's ship); 39c. "La Coquille" (Duperrey's ship); 44c. "Shenandoah" (Confederate warship).

7 Lelu Protestant Church, Kosrae

1985. Christmas.
36 **7** 22c. black and orange (postage) 55 30
37 – 33c. black and violet (air) . . 80 50
38 – 44c. black and green . . . . 1·10 70

DESIGNS: 33c. Dublon Protestant Church; 44c. Pohnpei Catholic Church.

8 "Noddy Tern"

1985. Birth Bicentenary of John J. Audubon (ornithologist). Multicoloured.
39 22c. Type **8** (postage) 80 80
40 22c. "Turnstone" 80 80
41 22c. "Golden Plover" 80 80
42 22c. "Black-bellied Plover" . . 80 80
43 44c. "Sooty Tern" (air) . . . 1·50 1·50

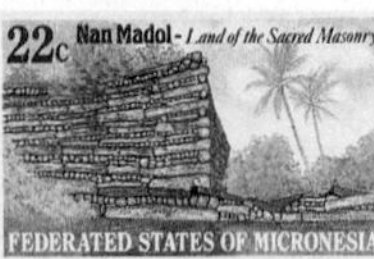

9 Land of Sacred Masonry

1985. Nan Madol, Pohnpei. Multicoloured.
44 22c. Type **9** (postage) 45 25
45 33c. Nan Tauas inner courtyard (air) 60 45
46 39c. Nan Tauas outer wall . . 75 60
47 44c. Nan Tauas burial vault 90 70

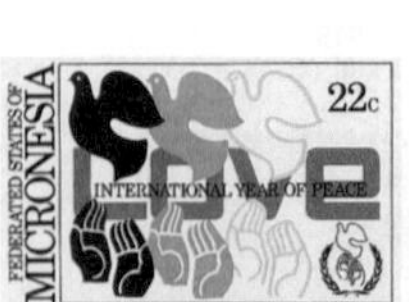

10 Doves, "LOVE" and Hands

12 Bully Hayes

1986. Anniversaries and Events. Multicoloured.
48 22c. Type **10** (International Peace Year) 50 35
49 44c. Halley's comet . . . . . 1·25 80
50 44c. "Trienza" (cargo liner) arriving at jetty (40th anniv of return of Nauruans from Truk) . . . . 1·25 80

1986. Nos. 1/4 surch.
51 22c. on 20c. Type **1** 45 45
52 22c. on 20c. Truk 45 45
53 22c. on 20c. Pohnpei 45 45
54 22c. on 20c. Kosrae 45 45

1986. "Ameripex 86" International Stamp Exhibition, Chicago. Bully Hayes (buccaneer). Multicoloured.
55 22c. Type **12** (postage) 50 30
56 33c. Angelo (crew member) forging Hawaii 5c. blue stamp (air) 65 50
57 39c. "Leonora" sinking off Kosrae 75 60
58 44c. Hayes escaping capture on Kosrae 95 75
59 75c. Cover of book "Bully Hayes, Buccaneer" by Louis Becke . . . . 1·50 1·25

13 "Madonna and Child"

1986. Christmas. "Madonna and Child" Paintings.
61 – 5c. multicoloured (postage) 15 10
62 – 22c. multicoloured 70 30
63 – 33c. multicoloured (air) . . 95 65
64 **13** 44c. multicoloured . . . . . 1·25 1·00

14 Passports on Globe

1986. 1st Micronesian Passport.
65 **14** 22c. blue, black and yellow 50 35

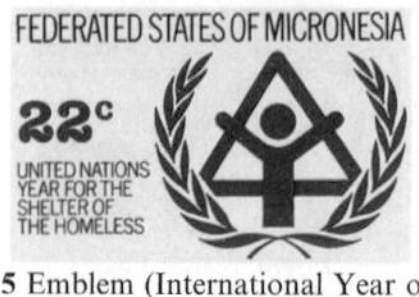

15 Emblem (International Year of Shelter for the Homeless)

1987. Anniversaries and Events.
66 **15** 22c. blue, red and black (postage) 50 40
67 – 33c. green, red and black (air) 75 50
68 – 39c. blue, black and red . . 90 60
69 – 44c. blue, red and black . . 1·25 75

DESIGNS: 33c. Dollar sign (bicentenary of dollar currency); 39c. Space capsule (25th anniv of first American to orbit Earth); 44c. "200 USA" (bicentenary of US constitution).

16 Archangel Gabriel appearing to Mary

1987. Christmas. Multicoloured.
71 22c. Type **16** (postage) 40 30
72 33c. Joseph praying and Mary with baby Jesus (air) 60 45
73 39c. Shepherds with their sheep 75 60
74 44c. Wise men 90 75

17 Spanish Missionary and Flag

1988. Micronesian History. Multicoloured.
75 22c. Type **17** (postage) 50 35
76 22c. Natives producing copra and German flag 50 35
77 22c. School pupils and Japanese flag 50 35
78 22c. General store and U.S. flag 50 35
79 44c. Traditional boatbuilding and fishing skills (air) . . . 1·00 75
80 44c. Welcoming tourists from Douglas DC-10 airliner and divers investigating World War II wreckage . . . . . 1·00 75

18 Ponape White Eye

19 Marathon

1988. Birds. Multicoloured.
81 3c. Type **18** (postage) 10 10
82 14c. Truk monarch 25 10
83 22c. Ponape starling 35 20
84 33c. Truk white eye (air) . . . 55 35
85 44c. Blue-faced parrot finch . . 75 65
86 $1 Yap monarch . . . . . . 1·50 1·40

1988. Olympic Games, Seoul. Multicoloured.
87 25c. Type **19** 45 25
88 25c. Hurdling 45 25
89 45c. Basketball 70 55
90 45c. Volleyball 70 55

20 Girls decorating Tree

1988. Christmas. Multicoloured.
91 25c. Type **20** 45 30
92 25c. Dove with mistletoe in beak and children holding decorations 45 30
93 25c. Boy in native clothing and girl in floral dress sitting at base of tree . . . 45 30
94 25c. Boy in T-shirt and shorts and girl in native clothing sitting at base of tree . . . 45 30

Nos. 91/4 were printed together in blocks of four, se-tenant, forming a composite design.

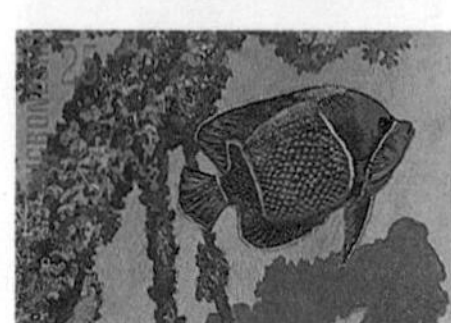
21 Blue-girdled Angelfish

1988. Truk Lagoon, "Micronesia's Living War Memorial". Multicoloured.
95 25c. Type **21** 50 40
96 25c. Jellyfish and shoal of small fishes 50 40
97 25c. Snorkel divers 50 40
98 25c. Two golden trevally (black-striped fishes facing left) 50 40
99 25c. Blackfinned reef shark . 50 40
100 25c. Deck railings of wreck and fishes 50 40
101 25c. Soldierfish (red fish) and damselfish 50 40
102 25c. Damselfish, narrow-banded batfish and aircraft cockpit 50 40
103 25c. Three Moorish idols (fishes with long dorsal fins) 50 40
104 25c. Four pickhandle barracuda and shoal . . . 50 40

105 25c. Spot-banded butterflyfish and damselfish (facing alternate directions) 50 40
106 25c. Three-spotted dascyllus and aircraft propeller 50 40
107 25c. Fox-faced rabbitfish and shoal 50 40
108 25c. Lionfish (fish with spines) 50 40
109 25c. Scuba diver and white-tailed damselfish 50 40
110 25c. Tubular corals 50 40
111 25c. White-tailed damselfish, ornate butterflyfish and brain coral 50 40
112 25c. Pink anemonefish, giant clam and sea plants 50 40

Nos. 95/112 were printed together, se-tenant, in sheetlets of 18 stamps, the backgrounds of the stamps forming an overall design of the remains of a Japanese ship and "Zero" fighter plane on the Lagoon bed colonized by marine life.

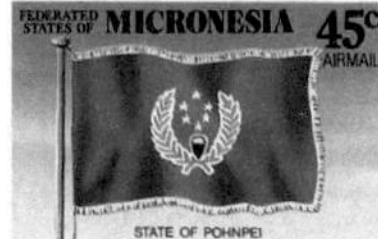

22 Flag of Pohnpei

1989. Air. State Flags. Multicoloured.

113 45c. Type **22** 65 50
114 45c. Truk 65 50
115 45c. Kosrae 65 50
116 45c. Yap 65 50

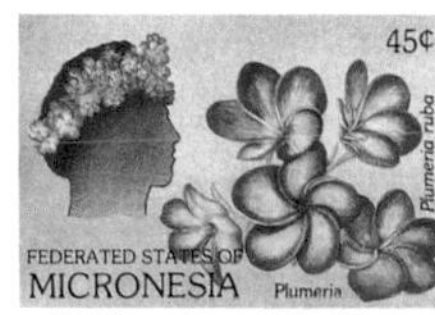

23 Plumeria and Headdress

1989. Mwarmwarms (floral decorations). Mult.

117 45c. Type **23** 65 50
118 45c. Hibiscus and lei 65 50
119 45c. Jasmine and Yap religious mwarmwarm 65 50
120 45c. Bougainvillea and Truk dance mwarmwarm 65 50

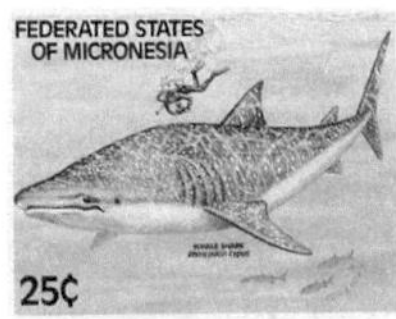

24 Whale Shark

1989. Sharks. Multicoloured.

121 25c. Type **24** 70 40
122 25c. Smooth hammerhead 70 40
123 45c. Tiger shark (vert) 1·10 75
124 45c. Great white shark (vert) 1·10 75

26 "Explorer 1" Satellite over North America

1989. 20th Anniv of First Manned Landing on the Moon. Multicoloured.

126 25c. Bell XS-15 rocket plane 40 30
127 25c. Type **26** 40 30
128 25c. Ed White on space walk during "Gemini 4" mission 40 30
129 25c. "Apollo 18" spacecraft 40 30
130 25c. "Gemini 4" space capsule over South America 40 30
131 25c. Space Shuttle "Challenger" 40 30
132 25c. Italian "San Marco 2" satellite 40 30
133 25c. Russian "Soyuz 19" spacecraft 40 30
134 25c. Neil Armstrong descending ladder to Moon's surface during "Apollo 11" mission 40 30
135 $2.40 Lunar module "Eagle" on Moon (34 × 46 mm) 3·50 2·75

Nos. 126/34 were printed together in se-tenant sheetlets of nine stamps, the backgrounds of the stamps forming an overall design of Earth as viewed from the Moon.

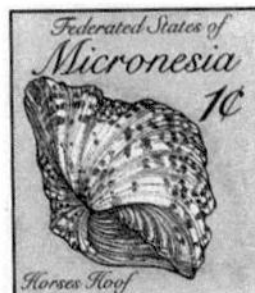

27 Horse's Hoof

1989. Sea Shells. Multicoloured.

136 1c. Type **27** 10 10
137 3c. Rare spotted cowrie 10 10
138 15c. Commercial trochus 20 10
139 20c. General cone 25 10
140 25c. Trumpet triton 30 20
141 30c. Laciniate conch 35 25
142 36c. Red-mouth olive 45 35
143 45c. All-red map cowrie 55 45
144 50c. Textile cone 60 50
145 $1 Orange spider conch 1·40 1·00
146 $2 Golden cowrie 2·75 2·00
147 $5 Episcopal mitre 6·50 4·50

28 Oranges

1989. "World Stamp Expo '89" International Stamp Exhibition, Washington D.C. "Kosrae–The Garden State". Multicoloured.

155 25c. Type **28** 40 30
156 25c. Limes 40 30
157 25c. Tangerines 40 30
158 25c. Mangoes 40 30
159 25c. Coconuts 40 30
160 25c. Breadfruit 40 30
161 25c. Sugar cane 40 30
162 25c. Kosrae house 40 30
163 25c. Bananas 40 30
164 25c. Children with fruit and flowers 40 30
165 25c. Pineapples 40 30
166 25c. Taro 40 30
167 25c. Hibiscus 40 30
168 25c. Ylang ylang 40 30
169 25c. White ginger 40 30
170 25c. Plumeria 40 30
171 25c. Royal poinciana 40 30
172 25c. Yellow allamanda 40 30

29 Angel over Micronesian Village

1989. Christmas. Multicoloured.

173 25c. Type **29** 30 20
174 45c. Truk children dressed as Three Kings 65 50

30 Young Kingfisher and Sokehs Rock, Pohnpei

1990. Endangered Species. Micronesian Kingfisher and Micronesian Pigeon.

175 10c. Type **30** 35 25
176 15c. Adult kingfisher and rain forest, Pohnpei 55 35
177 20c. Pigeon flying over lake at Sleeping Lady, Kosrae 90 65
178 25c. Pigeon perched on leaf, Tol Island, Truk 1·25 1·10

31 Wooden Whale Stamp and "Lyra"

1990. "Stamp World London 90" International Stamp Exhibition. 19th-century British Whaling Ships. Multicoloured.

179 45c. Type **31** 65 45
180 45c. Harpoon heads and "Prudent" 65 45
181 45c. Carved whale bone and "Rhone" 65 45
182 45c. Carved whale tooth and "Sussex" 65 45

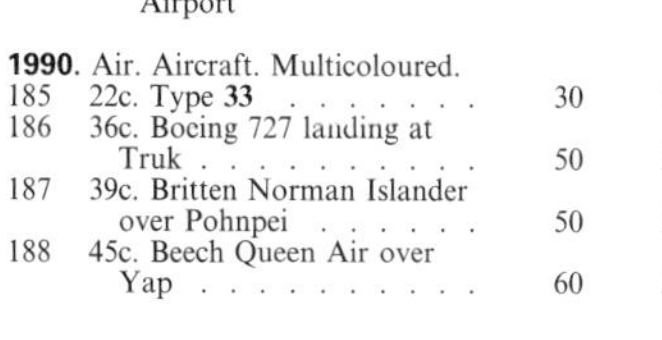

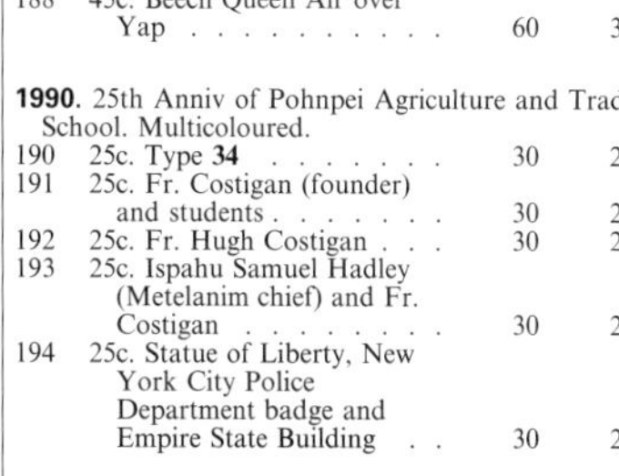

33 Beech 18 over Kosrae Airport **34** School Building

1990. Air. Aircraft. Multicoloured.

185 22c. Type **33** 30 15
186 36c. Boeing 727 landing at Truk 50 30
187 39c. Britten Norman Islander over Pohnpei 50 30
188 45c. Beech Queen Air over Yap 60 35

1990. 25th Anniv of Pohnpei Agriculture and Trade School. Multicoloured.

190 25c. Type **34** 30 20
191 25c. Fr. Costigan (founder) and students 30 20
192 25c. Fr. Hugh Costigan 30 20
193 25c. Ispahu Samuel Hadley (Metelanim chief) and Fr. Costigan 30 20
194 25c. Statue of Liberty, New York City Police Department badge and Empire State Building 30 20

36 Loading Mail Plane at Pohnpei Airport

1990. Pacific Postal Transport. Multicoloured.

196 25c. Type **36** 35 20
197 45c. Launch meeting "Nantaku" (inter-island freighter) in Truk Lagoon to exchange mail, 1940 65 40

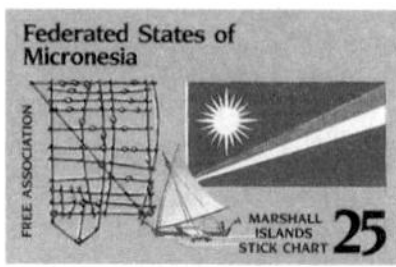

37 Marshallese Stick Chart, Outrigger Canoe and Flag

1990. 4th Anniv of Ratification of Micronesia and Marshall Islands Compacts of Free Association. Multicoloured.

198 25c. Type **37** 45 20
199 25c. Great frigate bird, U.S.S. "Constitution" (frigate), U.S. flag and American bald eagle 55 55
200 25c. Micronesian outrigger canoe and flag 45 20

38 "Caloptilia sp." and New Moon

1990. Moths. Multicoloured.

201 45c. Type **38** 60 50
202 45c. "Anticrates sp." (inscr "Yponomeatidae") and waxing moon 60 50
203 45c. "Cosmopterigidae" family and full moon 60 50
204 45c. "Cosmopteridigae" family and waning moon 60 50

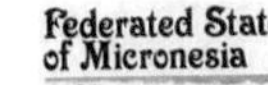

39 Cherub above Roof **41** Hawksbill Turtle returning to Sea

1990. Christmas. "Micronesian Holy Night". Multicoloured.

205 25c. Type **39** 30 20
206 25c. Two cherubs and Star of Bethlehem 30 20
207 25c. Cherub blowing horn 30 20
208 25c. Lambs, goat, pig and chickens 30 20
209 25c. Native wise men offering gifts to Child 30 20
210 25c. Children and dog beside lake 30 20
211 25c. Man blowing trumpet triton 30 20
212 25c. Adults and children on path 30 20
213 25c. Man and children carrying gifts 30 20

Nos. 205/13 were printed together, se-tenant, forming a composite design.

1991. Sea Turtles. Multicoloured.

215 29c. Type **41** 50 30
216 29c. Green turtles swimming underwater 50 30
217 50c. Hawksbill turtle swimming underwater 90 50
218 50c. Leatherback turtle swimming underwater 90 50

42 Boeing E-3 Sentry

1991. Operations Desert Shield and Desert Storm (liberation of Kuwait). Multicoloured.

219 29c. Type **42** 40 25
220 29c. Grumman F-14 Tomcat fighter 40 25
221 29c. U.S.S. "Missouri" (battleship) 40 25
222 29c. Multiple Launch Rocket System 40 25
223 $2.90 Great frigate bird with yellow ribbon and flag of Micronesia (50 × 37 mm) 5·50 5·50

43 "Evening Flowers, Toloas, Truk"

1991. "Phila Nippon '91" International Stamp Exhibition, Tokyo. 90th Birth Anniv (1992) of Paul Jacoulet (artist). Micronesian Ukiyo-e Prints by Jacoulet. Multicoloured.

225 29c. Type **43** 40 25
226 29c. "The Chief's Daughter, Mogomog" 40 25
227 29c. "Yagourouh and Mio, Yap" 40 25
228 50c. "Yap Beauty and Orchids" 70 45
229 50c. "The Yellow-Eyed Boys, Ohlol" 70 45
230 50c. "Violet Flowers, Tomil, Yap" 70 45

44 Sheep and Holy Family

1991. Christmas. Shell Cribs. Multicoloured.

232 29c. Type **44** 40 25
233 40c. Three Kings arriving at Bethlehem 55 35
234 50c. Sheep around manger 65 45

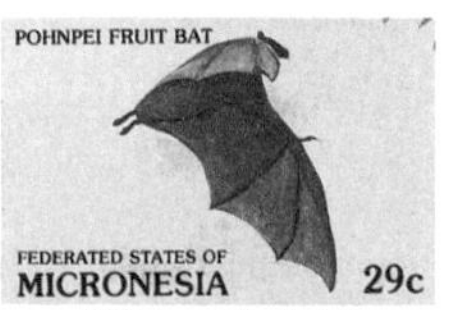

45 Pohnpei Fruit Bat

1991. Pohnpei Rain Forest. Multicoloured.

235 29c. Type **45** 55 55
236 29c. Purple-capped fruit dove 55 55
237 29c. Micronesian kingfisher 55 55
238 29c. Birdnest fern 55 55
239 29c. Caroline swiftlets ("Island Swiftlet") 55 55
240 29c. Ponape white-eye ("Long-billed White-eye") 55 55

241 29c. Common noddy ("Brown Noddy") 55 55
242 29c. Ponape lory ("Pohnpei Lory") 55 55
243 29c. Micronesian flycatcher ("Pohnpei Flycatcher") . . 55 55
244 29c. Truk Island ground dove ("Caroline Ground-Dove") 55 55
245 29c. White-tailed tropic bird 55 55
246 29c. Cardinal honeyeater ("Micronesian Honeyeater") 55 55
247 29c. Ixora 55 55
248 29c. Rufous fantail ("Pohnpei Fantail") 55 55
249 29c. Grey-brown white-eye ("Grey White-eye") 55 55
250 29c. Blue-faced parrot finch 55 55
251 29c. Common Cicadabird ("Cicadabird") 55 55
252 29c. Green skink 55 55

Nos. 235/52 were issued together, se-tenant, forming a composite design.

46 Britten Norman Islander and Outrigger Canoe

47 Volunteers learning Crop Planting

1992. Air. Multicoloured.
253 40c. Type **46** 55 35
254 50c. Boeing 727-200 airliner and outrigger canoe (different) 65 45

1992. 25th Anniv of Presence of United States Peace Corps in Micronesia. Multicoloured.
255 29c. Type **47** 40 25
256 29c. Education 40 25
257 29c. Pres. John Kennedy announcing formation of Peace Corps 40 25
258 29c. Public health nurses . . 40 25
259 29c. Recreation 40 25

48 Queen Isabella of Spain

1992. 500th Anniv of Discovery of America by Christopher Columbus. Multicoloured.
260 29c. Type **48** . . . . 1·10 50
261 29c. "Santa Maria" . . . . 1·10 50
262 29c. Christopher Columbus 1·10 50

49 Flags

1992. 1st Anniv of U.N. Membership.
264 **49** 29c. multicoloured 40 25
265 50c. multicoloured 65 45

50 Bouquet

1992. Christmas.
266 **50** 29c. multicoloured 40 25

51 Edward Rickenbacker (fighter pilot)

1993. Pioneers of Flight (1st series). Pioneers and aircraft. Multicoloured.
267 29c. Type **51** 45 30
268 29c. Manfred von Richthofen (fighter pilot) 45 30
269 29c. Andrei Tupolev (aeronautical engineer) . . 45 30
270 29c. John Macready (first non-stop crossing of U.S.A.) 45 30
271 29c. Sir Charles Kingsford-Smith (first trans-Pacific flight) 45 30
272 29c. Igor Sikorsky (aeronautical engineer) . . 45 30
273 29c. Lord Trenchard ("Father of the Royal Air Force") 45 30
274 29c. Glenn Curtiss (builder of U.S. Navy's first aircraft) 45 30

See also Nos. 322/9, 364/71, 395/402, 418/25, 441/8, 453/60 and 514/21.

52 Big-scaled Soldierfish

1993. Fishes. Multicoloured.
275 10c. Type **52** 15 10
276 19c. Bennett's butterflyfish 25 15
277 20c. Peacock hind ("Peacock Grouper") 25 15
278 22c. Great barracuda . . . 30 20
278a 23c. Yellow-finned tuna . . 30 20
279 25c. Coral hind ("Coral Grouper") 30 20
280 29c. Regal angelfish 40 25
281 30c. Bleeker's parrotfish . . 40 25
282 32c. Saddle butterflyfish (dated "1995") 40 25
283 35c. Picasso triggerfish ("Picassofish") 45 30
284 40c. Mandarin fish 50 35
285 45c. Clown ("Bluebanded") surgeonfish 60 40
285a 46c. Red-tailed surgeonfish ("Achilles Tang") 60 40
286 50c. Undulate ("Orange-striped") triggerfish . . . 65 45
287 52c. Palette surgeonfish . . 70 45
288 55c. Moorish idol 70 45
288a 60c. Skipjack tuna 80 55
289 75c. Oriental sweetlips . . . 95 65
290 78c. Square-spotted anthias ("Square-spot Fairy Basslet") . . . . 1·00 65
290a 95c. Blue-striped ("Blue-lined") snapper . . . . . 1·25 85
291 $1 Zebra moray . . . . . . 1·25 85
292 $2 Fox-faced rabbitfish . . 2·50 1·60
293 $2.90 Masked ("Orangespine") unicornfish . . . . 3·75 2·50
294 $3 Flame angelfish . . . . 3·75 2·50
295 $5 Six-blotched hind ("Cave Grouper") . . . . . . 6·50 4·25

See also Nos. 465/89 and 522/5.

53 "Great Republic"

54 Jefferson

1993. American Clipper Ships. Multicoloured.
301 29c. Type **53** 50 35
302 29c. "Benjamin F. Packard" 50 35
303 29c. "Stag Hound" 50 35
304 29c. "Herald of the Morning" 50 35
305 29c. "Rainbow" and junk . . 50 35
306 29c. "Flying Cloud" 50 35
307 29c. "Lightning" 50 35
308 29c. "Sea Witch" 50 35
309 29c. "Columbia" 50 35
310 29c. "New World" 50 35
311 29c. "Young America" . . . 50 35
312 29c. "Courier" 50 35

1993. 250th Birth Anniv of Thomas Jefferson (U.S. President, 1801–09).
313 **54** 29c. multicoloured 45 25

55 Yap Outrigger Canoe

1993. Traditional Canoes. Multicoloured.
314 29c. Type **55** 50 35
315 29c. Kosrae outrigger canoe 50 35
316 29c. Pohnpei lagoon outrigger canoe 50 35
317 29c. Chuuk war canoe . . . 50 35

56 Ambilos Iehsi

57 Kepirohi Falls

1993. Local Leaders (1st series). Multicoloured.
318 29c. Type **56** (Pohnpei) . . . 45 25
319 29c. Andrew Roboman (Yap) 45 25
320 29c. Joab Sigrah (Kosrae) . . 45 25
321 29c. Petrus Mailo (Chuuk) 45 25

See also Nos. 409/12.

1993. Pioneers of Flight (2nd series). As T **51**. Multicoloured.
322 50c. Lawrence Sperry (inventor of the gyro) . . . 75 50
323 50c. Alberto Santos-Dumont (first powered flight in Europe) 75 50
324 50c. Hugh Dryden (developer of first guided missile) . . 75 50
325 50c. Theodore von Karman (space pioneer) 75 50
326 50c. Orville Wright (first powered flight) 75 50
327 50c. Wilbur Wright (second powered flight) 75 50
328 50c. Otto Lilienthal (first heavier-than-air flight) . . 75 50
329 50c. Sir Thomas Sopwith (aircraft designer) 75 50

1993. Pohnpei Tourist Sites. Multicoloured.
330 29c. Type **57** 40 25
331 50c. Spanish Wall 65 45

See also Nos. 357/9.

58 Female Common ("Great") Eggfly

59 "We Three Kings"

1993. Butterflies. Multicoloured.
333 29c. Type **58** 50 30
334 29c. Female common ("great") eggfly (variant) 50 30
335 50c. Male monarch 90 50
336 50c. Male common ("great") eggfly 90 50

See also Nos. 360/3.

1993. Christmas. Carols. Multicoloured.
337 29c. Type **59** 40 25
338 50c. "Silent Night, Holy Night" 65 45

60 Baby Basket

1993. Yap. Multicoloured.
339 29c. Type **60** 40 25
340 29c. Bamboo raft 40 25
341 29c. Basketry 40 25
342 29c. Fruit bat 40 25
343 29c. Forest 40 25
344 29c. Outrigger canoes 40 25
345 29c. Dioscorea yams 40 25
346 29c. Mangroves 40 25
347 29c. Manta ray 40 25
348 29c. "Cyrtosperma taro" . . 40 25
349 29c. Fish weir 40 25
350 29c. Seagrass, golden rabbitfish and masked rabbitfish 40 25
351 29c. Taro bowl 40 25
352 29c. Thatched house 40 25
353 29c. Coral reef 40 25
354 29c. Lavalava 40 25
355 29c. Dancers 40 25
356 29c. Stone money 40 25

1994. Kosrae Tourist Sites. As T **57** but horiz. Multicoloured.
357 29c. Sleeping Lady (mountains) 40 25
358 40c. Walung 50 35
359 50c. Lelu Ruins 65 45

1994. "Hong Kong '94" International Stamp Exhibition. Designs as Nos. 333/6 but with inscriptions in brown and additionally inscribed "Hong Kong '94 Stamp Exhibition" in English (361/2) or Chinese (others).
360 29c. As No. 333 . . . . . . 50 25
361 29c. As No. 334 . . . . . . 50 25
362 50c. As No. 335 . . . . . . 75 50
363 50c. As No. 336 . . . . . . 75 50

1994. Pioneers of Flight (3rd series). As T **51**. Multicoloured.
364 29c. Octave Chanute (early glider designer) 45 25
365 29c. T. Claude Ryan (founder of first commercial airline) 45 25
366 29c. Edwin (Buzz) Aldrin ("Apollo 11" crew member and second man to step onto moon) 45 25
367 29c. Neil Armstrong (commander of "Apollo 11" and first man on moon) 45 25
368 29c. Frank Whittle (developer of jet engine) 45 25
369 29c. Waldo Waterman (aircraft designer) 45 25
370 29c. Michael Collins ("Apollo 11" crew member) 45 25
371 29c. Wernher von Braun (rocket designer) 45 25

61 Spearfishing

1994. 3rd Micronesian Games. Multicoloured.
372 29c. Type **61** 45 25
373 29c. Basketball 45 25
374 29c. Coconut husking 45 25
375 29c. Tree climbing 45 25

62 Pohnpei

64 "Fagraea berteriana" (Kosrae)

63 People

1994. Traditional Costumes. Multicoloured.
376 29c. Type **62** 45 25
377 29c. Kosrae 45 25
378 29c. Chuuk 45 25
379 29c. Yap 45 25

1994. 15th Anniv of Constitution.
380 **63** 29c. multicoloured 45 25

1994. Native Flowers. Multicoloured.
381 29c. Type **64** 45 25
382 29c. "Pangium edule" (Yap) 45 25
383 29c. "Pittosporum ferrugineum" (Chuuk) . . 45 25
384 29c. "Sonneratia caseolaris" (Pohnpei) 45 25

Nos. 381/4 were issued together, se-tenant, forming a composite design.

65 1985 $10 Definitive under Magnifying Glass

1994. 10th Anniv of Postal Independence. Multicoloured.
385 29c. Type **65** 50 30
386 29c. 1993 traditional canoes block 50 30
387 29c. 1984 postal independence block 50 30
388 29c. 1994 native costumes block 50 30
Nos. 385/8 were issued together, se-tenant, forming a composite design of various Micronesian stamps. Nos. 386/8 are identified by the block in the centre of the design.

66 Players

69 Oriental Cuckoo

68 Iguanodons

1994. World Cup Football Championship, U.S.A. Multicoloured.
389 50c. Type **66** 70 45
390 50c. Ball and players 70 45
Nos. 389/90 were issued together, se-tenant, forming a composite design.

1994. "Philakorea 1994" International Stamp Exhibition, Seoul. Prehistoric Animals. Multicoloured.
392 29c. Type **68** 50 30
393 52c. Iguanodons and coelurosaurs . . . . 1·00 1·00
394 $1 Camarasaurus . . . . . 1·60 1·00
Nos. 392/4 were issued together, se-tenant, forming a composite design.

1994. Pioneers of Flight (4th series). As T **51**. Multicoloured.
395 50c. Yuri Gagarin (first man in space) 75 50
396 50c. Alan Shepard Jr. (first American in space) 75 50
397 50c. William Bishop (fighter pilot) 75 50
398 50c. "Atlas" (first U.S. intercontinental ballistic missile) and Karel Bossart (aerospace engineer) . . . 75 50
399 50c. John Towers (world endurance record, 1912) . . 75 50
400 50c. Hermann Oberth (space flight pioneer) 75 50
401 50c. Marcel Dassault (aircraft producer) 75 50
402 50c. Geoffrey de Havilland (aircraft designer) 75 50

1994. Migratory Birds. Multicoloured.
403 29c. Type **69** 65 65
404 29c. Long-tailed koel ("Long-tailed Cuckoo") 65 65
405 29c. Short-eared owl 65 65
406 29c. Eastern broad-billed roller ("Dollarbird") . . . 65 65

70 Doves

1994. Christmas. Multicoloured.
407 29c. Type **70** 50 30
408 50c. Angels 90 60

1994. Local Leaders (2nd series). As T **56**. Mult.
409 32c. Anron Ring Buas . . . 55 35
410 32c. Belarmino Hatheylul . . 55 35
411 32c. Johnny Moses 55 35
412 32c. Paliknoa Sigrah (King John) 55 35

72 Diver, Coral, Clown Triggerfish and Black-backed Butterflyfish

1995. Chuuk Lagoon. Multicoloured.
414 32c. Type **72** 55 35
415 32c. Black-backed butterflyfish, lionfish, regal angelfish and damselfishes 55 35
416 32c. Diver, thread-finned butterflyfish and damselfishes 55 35
417 32c. Pink anemonefish and damselfishes amongst anemone tentacles 55 35
Nos. 414/17 were issued together, se-tenant, forming a composite design.

1995. Pioneers of Flight (5th series). As T **51**. Multicoloured.
418 32c. Robert Goddard (first liquid-fuelled rocket) . . . 50 30
419 32c. Leroy Grumman (first fighter with retractable landing gear) 50 30
420 32c. Louis-Charles Breguet (aeronautics engineer) . . . 50 30
421 32c. Juan de la Cierva (inventor of autogyro) . . 50 30
422 32c. Hugo Junkers (aircraft engineer) 50 30
423 32c. James Lovell Jr. (astronaut) 50 30
424 32c. Donald Douglas (aircraft designer) 50 30
425 32c. Reginald Mitchell (designer of Spitfire fighter) 50 30

73 West Highland White Terrier

1995. Dogs. Multicoloured.
426 32c. Type **73** 55 35
427 32c. Welsh springer spaniel 55 35
428 32c. Irish setter 55 35
429 32c. Old English sheepdog . . 55 35

74 "Hibiscus tiliaceus"

1995. Hibiscus. Multicoloured.
430 32c. Type **74** 50 30
431 32c. "Hibiscus huegelii" . . . 50 30
432 32c. "Hibiscus trionum" . . 50 30
433 32c. "Hibiscus splendens" . . 50 30
Nos. 430/3 were issued together, se-tenant, forming a composite design.

77 U.S.S. "Portland" (cruiser)

1995. 50th Anniv of End of Second World War. Liberation of Micronesia. Multicoloured.
436 60c. Type **77** (liberation of Chuuk) . . . . 1·00 70
437 60c. U.S.S. "Tillman" (destroyer) (Yap) . . . . . 1·00 70
438 60c. U.S.S. "Soley" (destroyer) (Kosrae) . . . 1·00 70
439 60c. U.S.S. "Hyman" (destroyer) (Pohnpei) . . . 1·00 70

1995. Pioneers of Flight (6th series). As T **51**. Multicoloured.
441 60c. Frederick Rohr (developer of mass-production techniques) . . 90 60
442 60c. Juan Trippe (founder of Pan-American Airways) . . 90 60
443 60c. Konstantin Tsiolkovsky (rocket pioneer) 90 60
444 60c. Count Ferdinand von Zeppelin (airship inventor) 90 60
445 60c. Air Chief Marshal Hugh Dowding (commander of R.A.F. Fighter Command, 1940) 90 60
446 60c. William Mitchell (pioneer of aerial bombing) 90 60
447 60c. John Northrop (aircraft designer) 90 60
448 60c. Frederick Handley Page (producer of first twin-engine bomber) 90 60

79 Poinsettia

80 Rabin

1995. Christmas.
449 **79** 32c. multicoloured 40 25
450 60c. multicoloured 80 55

1995. Yitzhak Rabin (Israeli Prime Minister) Commemoration.
451 **80** 32c. multicoloured 55 35

1995. Pioneers of Flight (7th series). As T **51**. Multicoloured.
453 32c. James Doolittle (leader of America's Second World War bomb raid on Japan) 50 30
454 32c. Claude Dornier (aircraft designer) 50 30
455 32c. Ira Eaker (leader of air effort against occupied Europe during Second World War) 50 30
456 32c. Jacob Ellehammer (first European manned flight) 50 30
457 32c. Henry Arnold (Commander of U.S. air operations during Second World War) 50 30
458 32c. Louis Bleriot (first flight across the English Channel) 50 30
459 32c. William Boeing (founder of Boeing Corporation) . . 50 30
460 32c. Sydney Camm (aircraft designer) 50 30

82 Meeting House

1995. Tourism in Yap. Multicoloured.
461 32c. Type **82** 50 30
462 32c. Stone money 50 30
463 32c. Churu dancing 50 30
464 32c. Traditional canoe . . . 50 30

1995. Fishes. As Nos. 275/95 but face values changed. Multicoloured.
465 32c. Bennett's butterflyfish . . 55 25
466 32c. Regal angelfish 55 25
467 32c. Undulate ("Orange-striped") triggerfish 55 25
468 32c. Zebra moray 55 25
469 32c. Great barracuda 55 25
470 32c. Bleeker's parrotfish . . . 55 25
471 32c. Mandarin fish 55 25
472 32c. Clown ("Blue-banded") surgeonfish 55 25
473 32c. Big-scaled soldierfish . . 55 25
474 32c. Peacock hind ("Peacock Grouper") 55 25
475 32c. Picasso triggerfish ("Picassofish") 55 25
476 32c. Masked ("Orangespine") unicornfish 55 25
477 32c. Red-tailed surgeonfish . . 55 25
478 32c. Coral hind ("Coral Grouper") 55 25
479 32c. Palette surgeonfish . . . 55 25
480 32c. Oriental sweetlips . . . 55 25
481 32c. Fox-faced rabbitfish . . 55 25
482 32c. Saddle butterflyfish (dated "1996") 55 25
483 32c. Moorish idol 55 25
484 32c. Square-spotted anthias ("Square-spot Fairy Basslet") 55 25
485 32c. Flame angelfish 55 25
486 32c. Yellow-finned tuna . . . 55 25
487 32c. Skipjack tuna 55 25
488 32c. Blue-striped ("Blue-lined") snapper 55 25
489 32c. Six-blotched hind ("Cave Grouper") 55 25
See also Nos. 522/5.

83 Necklace Sea Star

1996. Starfishes. Multicoloured.
490 55c. Type **83** 85 55
491 55c. Rhinoceros sea star . . 85 55
492 55c. Blue sea star 85 55
493 55c. Thick-skinned sea star 85 55
Nos. 490/3 were issued together, se-tenant, forming a composite design.

84 10l. Stamp

1996. Centenary of Modern Olympic Games. Designs reproducing 1896 Greek Olympic Issue. Multicoloured.
494 60c. Type **84** . . . . 1·10 70
495 60c. 25l. stamp . . . . . . 1·10 70
496 60c. 20l. stamp . . . . . . 1·10 70
497 60c. 10d. stamp . . . . . . 1·10 70

85 "Palikir"

1996. Patrol Boats. Multicoloured.
498 32c. Type **85** 45 25
499 32c. "Micronesia" 45 25
Nos. 498/9 were issued together, se-tenant, forming a composite design.

87 1896 Quadricycle

1996. Centenary of Ford Motor Vehicle Production. Multicoloured.
501 55c. Type **87** 90 60
502 55c. 1917 Model T Truck . . 90 60
503 55c. 1928 Model A Tudor Sedan 90 60
504 55c. 1932 V-8 Sport Roadster 90 60
505 55c. 1941 Lincoln Continental 90 60
506 55c. 1953 F-100 Truck . . . 90 60
507 55c. 1958 Thunderbird convertible 90 60
508 55c. 1996 Mercury Sable . . 90 60

88 Reza

89 Oranges

1996. Reza (National Police Drug Enforcement Unit's dog).
509 **88** 32c. multicoloured 50 30

1996. Citrus Fruits. Multicoloured.
510 50c. Type **89** 90 60
511 50c. Limes 90 60
512 50c. Lemons 90 60
513 50c. Tangerines 90 60
Nos. 510/13 were issued together, se-tenant, forming a composite design.

1996. Pioneers of Flight (8th series). As T **51**. Multicoloured.
514 60c. Curtis LeMay (commander of Strategic Air Command) 90 60
515 60c. Grover Loening (first American graduate in aeronautical engineering) 90 60
516 60c. Gianni Caproni (aircraft producer) 90 60
517 60c. Henri Farman (founder of Farman Airlines) . . . 90 60
518 60c. Glenn Martin (aircraft producer) 90 60
519 60c. Alliot Verdon Roe (aircraft designer) 90 60
520 60c. Sergei Korolyov (rocket scientist) 90 60
521 60c. Isaac Laddon (aircraft designer) 90 60

1996. 10th Asian International Stamp Exhibition, Taipeh. Fishes. As previous designs but additionally inscr for the exhibition in English (522, 525) or Chinese (523/4).
522 32c. As No. 465 . . . . . . 55 35
523 32c. As No. 468 . . . . . . 55 35

524 32c. As No. 475 . . . . . . 55 35
525 32c. As No. 483 . . . . . . 55 35

90 Wise Men following Star

1996. Christmas.
526 **90** 32c. multicoloured 50 35
527 60c. multicoloured 90 60

91 Outrigger Canoe and State Flag

1996. 10th Anniv of Ratification of Compact of Free Association with U.S.A.
528 **91** $3 multicoloured . . . . . 4·50 3·25

92 Water Buffalo

1997. New Year. Year of the Ox.
529 **92** 32c. multicoloured 50 35

93 Walutahanga, Melanesia **94** Deng Xiaoping

1997. "Pacific 97" International Stamp Exhibition, San Francisco. Sea Goddesses of the Pacific. Multicoloured.
531 32c. Type **93** 50 30
532 32c. Tien-Hou holding lantern, China 50 30
533 32c. Lorop diving in ocean, Micronesia 50 30
534 32c. Oto-Hime with fisherman, Japan 50 30
535 32c. Nomoi holding shell, Micronesia 50 30
536 32c. Junkgowa Sisters in canoe, Australia 50 30

1997. Deng Xiaoping (Chinese statesman) Commemoration. Multicoloured.
537 60c. Type **94** 85 50
538 60c. Facing left (bare-headed) 85 50
539 60c. Facing right 85 50
540 60c. Facing left wearing cap 85 50

95 "Melia azedarach"

1997. Return of Hong Kong to China. Multicoloured.
542 60c. Type **95** 85 50
543 60c. Victoria Peak 85 50
544 60c. "Dendrobium chrysotoxum" 85 50
545 60c. "Bauhinia blakeana" . . 85 50
546 60c. "Cassia surattensis" . . 85 50
547 60c. Sacred lotus ("Nelumbo nucifera") 85 50

96 Tennis

1997. 2nd National Games. Multicoloured.
549 32c. Type **96** 50 30
550 32c. Throwing the discus . . 50 30
551 32c. Swimming 50 30
552 32c. Canoeing 50 30

97 Rapids

1997. Birth Bicentenary of Hiroshige Ando (painter). Designs depicting details from "Whirlpools at Naruto in Awa Province" (Nos. 553/5), "Tail of Genji: Viewing the Plum Blossoms" (Nos. 556/8) and "Snow on the Sumida River" (Nos. 559/61). Multicoloured.
553 20c. Type **97** 30 20
554 20c. Whirlpools (rocky island at left) 30 20
555 20c. Whirlpools (rocky island at right) 30 20
556 50c. Woman on stepping stones 65 40
557 50c. Woman 65 40
558 50c. Woman on balcony of house 65 40
559 60c. House and junks . . . . 1·00 60
560 60c. Two women . . . . . . 1·00 60
561 60c. Woman alighting from junk . . . . 1·00 60
Nos. 553/5, 556/8 and 559/61 respectively, were issued, se-tenant, forming composite designs of the paintings depicted.

98 Presley from High School Graduation Yearbook

1997. 20th Death Anniv of Elvis Presley (entertainer). Multicoloured.
563 50c. Type **98** 85 55
564 50c. With hound dog Nipper (R.C.A. Records mascot) 85 55
565 50c. Wearing red striped shirt in publicity photograph for "Loving You" (film), 1957 85 55
566 50c. Wearing sailor's cap in scene from "Girls, Girls, Girls!" (film), 1963 . . . . 85 55
567 50c. Wearing knitted jacket with collar turned up, 1957 85 55
568 50c. Wearing stetson in scene from "Flaming Star" (film), 1960 . . . . 85 55

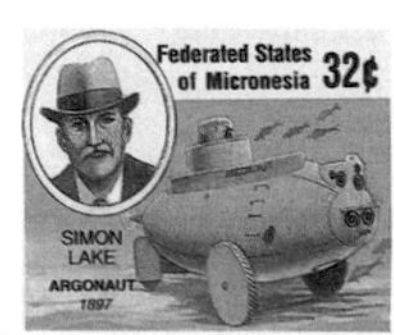

99 Simon Lake and his Submarine "Argonaut", 1897

1997. Ocean Exploration: Pioneers of the Deep. Multicoloured.
569 32c. Type **99** 40 25
570 32c. William Beebe and Otis Barton's bathysphere (record depth, 1934) . . . 40 25
571 32c. Auguste Piccard and his bathyscaphe, 1954 . . . . 40 25
572 32c. Harold Edgerton and his deep sea camera, 1954 . . 40 25
573 32c. Jacques Piccard and U.S. Navy bathyscaphe "Trieste" (designed by Auguste Piccard) (record depth with Don Walsh, 1960) 40 25
574 32c. Edwin Link and diving chamber ("Man-in-Sea" projects, 1962) 40 25
575 32c. Melvin Fisher and diver (discovery of "Atocha" and "Santa Margarita" (Spanish galleons), 1971) 40 25
576 32c. Robert Ballard and submersible "Alvin", 1978 40 25
577 32c. Sylvia Earle and submersible "Deep Rover" (record dive in armoured suit, 1979) 40 25

100 Black-backed Butterflyfish

1997. Butterflyfishes. Multicoloured.
579 50c. Type **100** 75 50
580 50c. Saddle butterflyfish . . . 75 50
581 50c. Thread-finned butterflyfish 75 50
582 50c. Bennett's butterflyfish . . 75 50

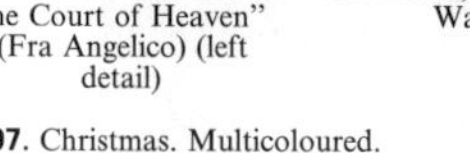
101 "Christ Glorified in the Court of Heaven" (Fra Angelico) (left detail) **102** Diana, Princess of Wales

1997. Christmas. Multicoloured.
583 32c. Type **101** 50 35
584 32c. "Christ Glorified in the Court of Heaven" (right detail) 50 35
585 60c . "A Choir of Angels" (detail, Simon Marmion) 75 50
586 60c. "A Choir of Angels" (different detail) 75 50

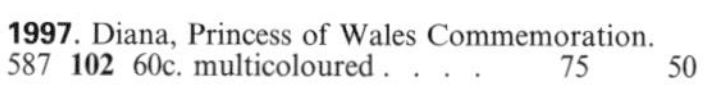
1997. Diana, Princess of Wales Commemoration.
587 **102** 60c. multicoloured 75 50

105 Rabbit

1998. Children's Libraries. The Hundred Acre Wood. Featuring characters from the Winnie the Pooh children's books. Multicoloured.
590 32c. Type **105** 55 35
591 32c. Owl 55 35
592 32c. Eeyore 55 35
593 32c. Kanga and Roo 55 35
594 32c. Piglet 55 35
595 32c. Tigger 55 35
596 32c. Pooh 55 35
597 32c. Christopher Robin . . . 55 35
Nos. 590/7 were issued together, se-tenant, forming a composite design.

106 Player celebrating Goal

1998. World Cup Football Championship, France. Multicoloured.
599 32c. Type **106** 50 30
600 32c. Player in green shirt kicking ball 50 30
601 32c. Player in yellow shirt tackling another player . . 50 30
602 32c. Goalkeeper throwing ball 50 30
603 32c. Player in yellow shirt kicking ball overhead . . . 50 30
604 32c. Goalkeeper in red shirt 50 30
605 32c. Player in yellow shirt with ball between legs . . 50 30
606 32c. Player in red shirt and player on ground 50 30
Nos. 599/606 were issued together, se-tenant, forming a composite design of a pitch.

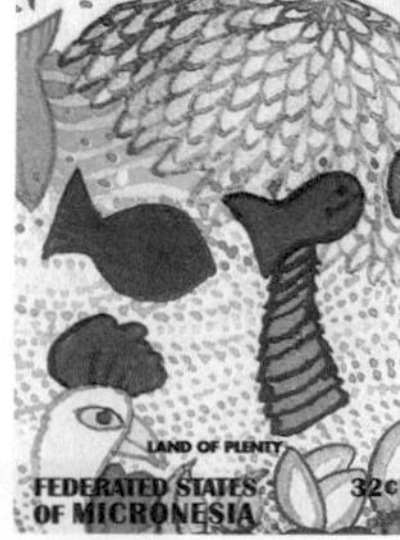

108 Land of Plenty

1998. Old Testament Stories. Multicoloured.
609 32c. Type **108** 50 30
610 32c. Adam and Eve 50 30
611 32c. Serpent of Temptation 50 30
612 40c. Three of Joseph's brothers 60 40
613 40c. Joseph and merchants 60 40
614 40c. Ishmaelites 60 40
615 60c. Rebekah in front of well 80 50
616 60c. Eliezer, Abraham's servant 80 50
617 60c. Angel 80 50

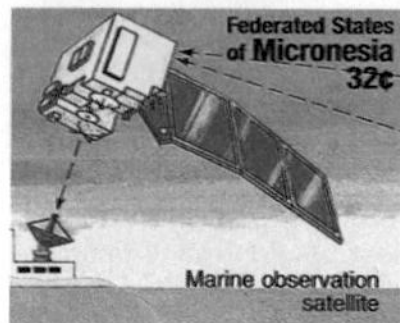

109 Marine Observation Satellite

1998. International Year of the Ocean. Deep Sea Research. Multicoloured.
619 32c. Type **109** 55 35
620 32c. "Natsushima" (support vessel) 55 35
621 32c. "Kaiyo" (research vessel) 55 35
622 32c. Anemone 55 35
623 32c. "Shinkai 2000" (deep-sea research vessel) 55 35
624 32c. Deep-towed research vessel 55 35
625 32c. Tripod fish 55 35
626 32c. Towed deep-survey system 55 35
627 32c. Black smokers 55 35
Nos. 619/27 were issued together, se-tenant, forming a composite design.

110 Grey-brown White-Eye ("Kosrae White-eye") **111** Ribbon-striped ("White-tipped") Soldierfish

1998. Birds. Multicoloured.
629 50c. Type **110** 60 40
630 50c. Truk monarch ("Chuuk Monarch") 60 40
631 50c. Yap monarch 60 40
632 50c. Pohnpei starling 60 40

1998. Fishes. Multicoloured.
634 1c. Type **111** 10 10
635 2c. Red-breasted wrasse . . . 10 10
636 3c. Bicoloured ("Bicolor") angelfish 10 10
637 4c. Falco hawkfish 10 10
638 5c. Convict tang 10 10
639 10c. Square-spotted anthias ("Square-spot Fairy Basslet") 10 10
640 13c. Orange-spotted ("Orangeband") surgeonfish 15 10
641 15c. Multibarred goatfish . . 20 15
642 17c. Masked rabbitfish . . . 20 15
643 20c. White spotted surgeonfish 25 15
644 22c. Blue-girdled angelfish . . 30 20
645 32c. Rectangle triggerfish ("Wedge Picassofish") . . 40 25
646 33c. Black jack 40 25
647 39c. Red parrotfish 50 35
648 40c. Lemon-peel angelfish . . 50 35
649 50c. White-cheeked ("Whitecheek") surgeonfish 60 40
650 55c. Scarlet-finned ("Long-jawed") squirrelfish 65 45
651 60c. Hump-headed ("Humphead") wrasse . . 75 50
652 77c. Onespot snapper 95 65
653 78c. Blue ("Sapphire") damselfish 95 65
654 $1 Blue-finned ("Bluefin") trevally . . . . 1·25 85
655 $3 Whitespot hawkfish . . . 3·75 2·25
656 $3.20 Tan-faced parrotfish . . 4·00 2·75
657 $5 Spotted boxfish ("Trunkfish") . . . . . . 6·25 4·25

658 $10.75 Pink-tailed ("Pinktail") triggerfish 13·50 9·00
659 $11.75 Yellow-faced angelfish (48 × 25 mm) 14·50 9·75

112 Fala being stroked

1998. Fala (Scottish terrier owned by Franklin D. Roosevelt). Multicoloured.
665 32c. Type **112** 40 25
666 32c. Fala and left half of wireless 40 25
667 32c. Fala and right half of wireless 40 25
668 32c. Fala and Roosevelt in car 40 25
669 32c. Fala's seal 40 25
670 32c. Fala 40 25

113 "Eskimo Madonna" (Claire Fejes)

1998. Christmas. Works of Art. Multicoloured.
671 32c. Type **113** 40 25
672 32c. "Madonna" (Man Ray) 40 25
673 32c. "Peasant Mother" (David Siquerios) 40 25
674 60c. "Mother and Child" (Pablo Picasso) 40 25
675 60c. "Gypsy Woman with Baby" (Amedeo Modigliani) 40 25
676 60c. "Mother and Child" (Jose Orozco) 40 25

114 Glenn 115 "Sputnik 1"

1998. John Glenn's (first American to orbit Earth) Return to Space. Multicoloured.
678 60c. Type **114** 75 50
679 60c. Launch of "Friendship 7" 75 50
680 60c. Glenn (bare-headed and in spacesuit) and United States flag on spaceship 75 50
681 60c. Glenn (in spacesuit) and "Friendship" space capsule 75 50
682 60c. Glenn (in spacesuit) and United States flag on pole 75 50
683 60c. Head and shoulders of Glenn in civilian clothes and stars (dated "1992") 75 50
684 60c. "Friendship 7" 75 50
685 60c. John Glenn with President Kennedy 75 50
686 60c. Glenn in overalls 75 50
687 60c. Launch of "Discovery" (space shuttle) 75 50
688 60c. Glenn in cockpit 75 50
689 60c. Head of Glenn in civilian suit 75 50
690 60c. Glenn fastening inner helmet 75 50
691 60c. Glenn with full helmet on 75 50
692 60c. Model of "Discovery" 75 50
693 60c. Head of Glenn smiling (bare-headed) in spacesuit 75 50

1999. Exploration of the Solar System. Multicoloured. (a) Space Achievements of Russia.
695 33c. Type **115** (first artificial satellite, 1957) 40 25
696 33c. Space dog Laika (first animal in space, 1957) (wrongly inscr "Leika") 40 25
697 33c. "Luna 1", 1959 40 25
698 33c. "Luna 3", 1959 40 25
699 33c. Yuri Gagarin (first man in space, 1961) 40 25
700 33c. "Venera 1" probe, 1961 40 25
701 33c. "Mars 1" probe, 1962 40 25
702 33c. Valentina Tereshkova (first woman in space, 1963) 40 25
703 33c. "Voskhod 1", 1964 40 25
704 33c. Aleksei Leonov and "Voskhod 2" (first space walk, 1965) 40 25
705 33c. "Venera 3" probe, 1966 40 25
706 33c. "Luna 10", 1966 40 25
707 33c. "Luna 9" (first landing on moon, 1966) 40 25
708 33c. "Lunokhod 1" moon-vehicle from "Luna 17" (first roving vehicle on Moon, 1970) (wrongly inscr "First robot mission ... Luna 16") 40 25
709 33c. "Luna 16" on Moon's surface (first robot mission, 1970) (wrongly inscr "First roving vehicle ... Luna 17") 40 25
710 33c. "Mars 3", 1971 40 25
711 33c. Leonid Popov, "Soyuz 35" and Valery Ryumin (first long manned space mission, 1980) 40 25
712 33c. Balloon ("Vega 1" Venus-Halley's Comet probe, 1985–86) 40 25
713 33c. "Vega 1" and Halley's Comet, 1986 40 25
714 33c. "Mir" space station 40 25

(b) Achievements of the United States of America
715 33c. "Explorer 1", 1958 40 25
716 33c. Space observatory "OSO-1", 1962 40 25
717 33c. "Mariner 2" Venus probe, 1962 (first scientifically successful planetary mission) 40 25
718 33c. "Mariner 2" Venus probe, 1962 (first scientific interplanetary space discovery) 40 25
719 33c. "Apollo 8" above Moon's surface 40 25
720 33c. Astronaut descending ladder on "Apollo 11" mission (first manned Moon landing, 1969) 40 25
721 33c. Astronaut taking Moon samples, 1969 40 25
722 33c. Lunar Rover of "Apollo 15", 1971 40 25
723 33c. "Mariner 9" Mars probe, 1971 40 25
724 33c. "Pioneer 10" passing Jupiter, 1973 40 25
725 33c. "Mariner 10" passing Mercury, 1974 40 25
726 33c. "Viking 1" on Mars, 1976 40 25
727 33c. "Pioneer 11" passing Saturn, 1979 40 25
728 33c. "STS-1" (first re-usable spacecraft, 1981) 40 25
729 33c. "Pioneer 10" (first man-made object to leave solar system, 1983) 40 25
730 33c. Solar Maximum Mission, 1984 40 25
731 33c. "Cometary Explorer", 1985 40 25
732 33c. "Voyager 2" passing Neptune, 1989 40 25
733 33c. "Galileo" space probe, 1992 40 25
734 33c. "Sojourner" (Mars rover), 1997 40 25

116 Map of the Pacific Ocean

1999. Voyages of the Pacific. Multicoloured.
736 33c. Type **116** 40 25
737 33c. Black-fronted parakeet 40 25
738 33c. Red-tailed tropic bird 40 25
739 33c. Plan of ship's hull 40 25
740 33c. Sketches of winches 40 25
741 33c. Yellow flowers 40 25
742 33c. Full-rigged sailing ship 40 25
743 33c. Three flowers growing from seeds and top of compass rose 40 25
744 33c. Fish (background of ship's planking) 40 25
745 33c. Flag of Yap 40 25
746 33c. Flag of Truk (palm tree) 40 25
747 33c. Flag of Kosrae (four stars) and bottom of compass rose 40 25
748 33c. Sketches of fruit 40 25
749 33c. Three plants and leaves 40 25
750 33c. Fish (leaves at left) 40 25
751 33c. Flag of Pohnpei and equator 40 25
752 33c. Sextant 40 25
753 33c. Red plant 40 25
754 33c. Fish and left side of compass rose 40 25
755 33c. Right side of compass rose and full-rigged sailing ship 40 25

Nos. 736/55 were issued together, se-tenant, forming a composite design.

117 Couple Meeting

1999. "Romance of the Three Kingdoms" (Chinese novel by Luo Guanzhong). Multicoloured.
756 33c. Type **117** 40 25
757 33c. Four men (one with lance) in room 40 25
758 33c. Two riders in combat 40 25
759 33c. Four men watching fifth man walking through room 40 25
760 33c. Captives before man on wheeled throne 40 25
761 50c. Riders approaching castle 40 25
762 50c. Warrior pointing at fire 40 25
763 50c. Opposing warriors riding through thick smoke 40 25
764 50c. Couple kneeling before man on dais 40 25
765 50c. Cauldron on fire 40 25

118 Carriage of Leipzig–Dresden Railway and Caroline Islands 1900 20pf. Stamp

1999. "iBRA" International Stamp Fair, Nuremberg, Germany. Multicoloured.
767 55c. Type **118** 65 45
768 55c. Golsdorf steam railway locomotive and Caroline Islands 1m. "Yacht" stamp 65 45

119 Black Rhinoceros 121 Deep-drilling for Brine Salt

120 "Ghost of O-Iwa"

1999. Earth Day. Multicoloured.
770 33c. Type **119** 40 25
771 33c. Cheetah 40 25
772 33c. Jackass penguin 40 25
773 33c. Blue whale 40 25
774 33c. Red-headed woodpecker 40 25
775 33c. African elephant 40 25
776 33c. Aurrochs 40 25
777 33c. Dodo 40 25
778 33c. Tasmanian wolf 40 25
779 33c. Giant lemur 40 25
780 33c. Quagga 40 25
781 33c. Steller's sea cow 40 25
782 33c. Pteranodon 40 25
783 33c. Shonisaurus 40 25
784 33c. Stegosaurus 40 25
785 33c. Gallimimus 40 25
786 33c. Tyrannosaurus 40 25
787 33c. Archelon 40 25
788 33c. Brachiosaurus 40 25
789 33c. Triceratops 40 25

1999. 150th Death Anniv of Hokusai Katsushika (Japanese artist). Multicoloured.
791 33c. Type **120** 40 25
792 33c. Spotted horse with head lowered 40 25
793 33c. "Abe Nakamaro" 40 25
794 33c. "Ghost of Kasane" 40 25
795 33c. Bay horse with head held up 40 25
796 33c. "The Ghost of Kiku and the Priest Mitazuki" 40 25
797 33c. "Belly Band Float" 40 25
798 33c. Woman washing herself 40 25
799 33c. "Swimmers" 40 25
800 33c. "Eel Climb" 40 25
801 33c. Woman playing lute 40 25
802 33c. "Kimo Ga Imo ni Naru" 40 25

Nos. 792 and 795 are inscribed "Hores Drawings".

1999. New Millennium. Multicoloured. (a) Science and Technology of Ancient China.
804 33c. Type **121** 40 25
805 33c. Chain pump 40 25
806 33c. Magic lantern 40 25
807 33c. Chang Heng's seismograph 40 25
808 33c. Dial and pointer devices 40 25
809 33c. Page of Lui Hui's mathematics treatise (value of Pi) 40 25
810 33c. Porcelain production 40 25
811 33c. Water mill 40 25
812 33c. Relief of horse from tomb of Tang Tai-Tsung (the stirrup) 40 25
813 33c. Page of Lu Yu's tea treatise and detail of Liu Songnian's painting of tea-making 40 25
814 33c. Umbrella 40 25
815 33c. Brandy and whisky production 40 25
816 33c. Page from oldest surviving printed book, woodblock and its print (printing) 40 25
817 33c. Copper plate and its print (paper money) 40 25
818 33c. Woodcut showing gunpowder demonstration 40 25
819 33c. Anji Bridge (segmented arch) (56½ × 36 mm) 40 25
820 33c. Mercator's star map and star diagram on bronze mirror 40 25

(b) People and Events of the Twelfth Century (1100–1150)
821 20c. Holy Roman Emperor Henry IV (death, 1106) 30 20
822 20c. Chastisement of monks of Enryakuji Temple, Kyoto, 1108 30 20
823 20c. Founding of Knights of the Hospital of St. John, 1113 30 20
824 20c. Invention of nautical compass, 1117 30 20
825 20c. Drowning of Prince William, heir of King Henry I of England, 1120 30 20
826 20c. Pope Callixtus II (Treaty of Worms, 1122, between Papacy and Holy Roman Emperor Henry V) 30 20
827 20c. Death of Omar Khayyam (Persian poet), 1126 30 20
828 20c. Death of Duke Guilhem IX, Count of Poitiers and Duke of Aquitaine (earliest known troubadour, 1127) 30 20
829 20c. Coronation of King Roger II of Sicily, 1130 30 20
830 20c. King Stephen and Queen Matilda (start of English civil war, 1135) 30 20
831 20c. Moses Maimonides (philosopher, birth, 1138) 30 20
832 20c. Abelard and Heloise (Church's censure of Abelard, 1140) 30 20
833 20c. Defeat of French and German crusaders at Damascus, 1148 30 20
834 20c. Fall of Mexican city of Tula, 1150s 30 20
835 20c. Completion of Angkor Vat, Cambodia, 1150 30 20
836 20c. Rise of Kingdom of Chimu, Peru, 1150s (56½ × 36 mm) 30 20
837 20c. Honen (Buddhist monk) becomes hermit, 1150 30 20

122 Flowers

1999. Faces of the Millennium: Diana, Princess of Wales. Showing collage of miniature flower photographs. Multicoloured, country panel at left (a) or right (b).
838 50c. Deep red shades (a) 60 40
839 50c. Deep red shades (b) 60 40
840 50c. Deep red shades with violet shades at bottom left (a) 60 40
841 50c. Blackish shades in bottom left corner (b) 40 60

842 50c. Violet shades at left and bottom, pinkish shades at right (a) 60 40
843 50c. Lemon and pink shades (b) 60 40
844 50c. Violet shades (a) 60 40
845 50c. Type **122** (rose in bottom row) (b) 60 40

Nos. 838/45 were issued together, se-tenant, and when viewed as a whole, form a portrait of Diana, Princess of Wales.

123 Face of Woman

1999. Costumes of the World. Multicoloured.
846 33c. Type **123** 30 20
847 33c. Tools for fabric making 30 20
848 33c. Head of African Masai warrior and textile pattern 30 20
849 33c. Head of woman and textile pattern (inscr "French Renaissance costume") 30 20
850 33c. Head of woman in hat with black feathers ("French princess gown 1900–1910") 30 20
851 33c. Head of Micronesian woman in wedding costume 30 20
852 33c. Body of African Masai warrior and head of woman 30 20
853 33c. Body of woman ("Textile patterns of French Renaissance costume") 30 20
854 33c. Body of woman ("1900–1910 French princess gown") 30 20
855 33c. Body and head of two Micronesian women in wedding costumes 30 20
856 33c. Hem of costume and body of woman ("Details of woman costume from African fabrics") 30 20
857 33c. Lower part of dress and head of woman ("French Renaissance costume") 30 20
858 33c. Hem of dress and furled umbrella 30 20
859 33c. Body and legs of two Micronesian women in wedding costumes 30 20
860 33c. Head of woman in Japanese Kabuki costume 30 20
861 33c. Rulers for tailoring 30 20
862 33c. Scissors 30 20
863 33c. Japanese fabrics 30 20
864 33c. Head and body of two women in Japanese Kabuki costumes 30 20
865 33c. Iron 30 20

Nos. 846/65 were issued together, se-tenant, forming several composite designs.

124 "Holy Family with St. John"

1999. Christmas. Paintings by Anthony van Dyck. Multicoloured.
866 33c. Type **124** 30 20
867 60c. "Madonna and Child" 75 50
868 $2 "Virgin and Child with Two Donors" (detail) 2·50 1·60

125 Wright "Flyer I"

1999. Man's First Century of Flight. Multicoloured
870 33c. Type **125** 30 20
871 33c. Bleriot XI and Notre Dame Cathedral, Paris 30 20
872 33c. Fokker D.VII biplane and Brandenburg Gate, Berlin 30 20
873 33c. Dornier Komet I (numbered B 240) and Amsterdam 30 20
874 33c. Charles Lindbergh's Ryan NYP Special "Spirit of St. Louis" and steeple 30 20
875 33c. Mitsubishi A6M Zero-Sen fighter and Mt. Fuji 30 20
876 33c. Boeing B-29 Superfortress bomber and roof of building 30 20
877 33c. Messerschmitt Me 262A jet fighter (swastika on tail) 30 20
878 33c. Chuck Yeager's Bell X-1 rocket plane and Grand Canyon 30 20
879 33c. Mikoyan Gurevich MiG-19 over Russian church 30 20
880 33c. Lockheed U-2 reconnaissance plane over building at night 30 20
881 33c. Boeing 707 jetliner and head of Statue of Liberty, New York 30 20
882 33c. British Aerospace/Aerospatiale Concorde supersonic jetliner and top of Eiffel Tower, Paris 30 20
883 33c. McDonnell Douglas DC-10 jetliner and Sydney Opera House 30 20
884 33c. B-2 Spirit stealth bomber and globe 30 20

Nos. 870/84 were issued together, se-tenant, forming a composite design of the globe.

126 *Oncidium obryzatum*

127 Martin Luther King (civil rights leader)

2000. Orchids. Multicoloured.
886 33c. Type **126** 45 30
887 33c. *Oncidium phalaenopsis* 45 30
888 33c. *Oncidium pulvinatum* 45 30
889 33c. *Paphiodedilum armeniacum* 45 30
890 33c. *Paphiopedilum dayanum* 45 30
891 33c. *Paphiopedilum druryi* 45 30
892 33c. *Baptistonia echinata* 45 30
893 33c. *Bulbophyllum lobbii* 45 30
894 33c. *Cattleya bicolor* 45 30
895 33c. *Cischweinfia dasyandra* 45 30
896 33c. *Cochleanthes discolor* 45 30
897 33c. *Dendrobium bellatulum* 45 30
898 33c. *Esmeralda clarkei* 45 30
899 33c. *Gomesa crispa* 45 30
900 33c. *Masdevallia elephanticeps* 45 30
901 33c. *Maxillaria variabilis* 45 30
902 33c. *Mitoniopsis roezlii* 45 30
903 33c. *Oncidium cavendishianum* 45 30

2000. Personalities of the Twentieth Century. Multicoloured.
905 33c. Type **127** 45 30
906 33c. Dr. Albert Schweitzer (philosopher and missionary) 45 30
907 33c. Pope John Paul II 45 30
908 33c. Sarvepalli Radhakrishnan (philosopher and Indian statesman) 45 30
909 33c. Toyohiko Kagawa (social reformer) 45 30
910 33c. Mahatma Gandhi (Indian leader) 45 30
911 33c. Mother Teresa (nun and missionary) 45 30
912 33c. Khyentse Rinpoche (poet and philosopher) 45 30
913 33c. Desmond Tutu (religious leader) 45 30
914 33c. Chiara Lubich (founder of Focolare movement) 45 30
915 33c. Dalai Lama (religious leader) 45 30
916 33c. Abraham Heschel (theologian) 45 30

129 Mother-of-Pearl (*Salamis parhassus*)

2000. Butterflies. Multicoloured.
918 20c. Type **129** 30 20
919 20c. Blue morpho (*Morpho rhetenor*) 30 20
920 20c. Monarch (*Danaus plexippus*) 30 20
921 20c. *Phyciodes actinote* 30 20
922 20c. *Idea leuconoe* 30 20
923 20c. *Actinote negra sobrina* 30 20
924 55c. Blue triangle (*Graphium sarpedon*) 80 50
925 55c. Swallowtail (*Papilio machaon*) 80 50
926 55c. Cairn's birdwing (*Ornithoptera priamus*) 80 50
927 55c. *Ornithoptera chimaera* 80 50
928 55c. Five-bar swallowtail (*Graphium antiphates*) 80 50
929 55c. *Pachliopta aristolochiae* 80 50

130 Mahatma Gandhi (Indian leader)

131 Mikhail Gorbachev (statesman)

2000. New Millennium. Multicoloured.
931 20c. Type **130** 30 20
932 20c. Poster (Dada Art fair, Berlin, 1920) 30 20
933 20c. Women with American flags (female suffrage, 1930) 30 20
934 20c. Nicola Sacco and Bartolomeo Vanzetti (anarchists) (international controversy over murder conviction, 1921) 30 20
935 20c. Hermann Rorschach (psychiatrist and neurologist) (developed inkblot test, 1921) 30 20
936 20c. George W. Watson (incorporation of I.B.M., 1924) 30 20
937 20c. Leica camera (first commercial 35 mm camera, 1925) 30 20
938 20c. Scientists and John Thomas Scopes (brought to trial for teaching Darwin's theory of evolution, 1925) 30 20
939 20c. Charles Lindbergh (aviator) and Ryan NYP Special Spirit of St. Louis (first solo transatlantic flight, 1927) 30 20
940 20c. "Big Bang" (George Henri Lemaître) (astrophysicist and cosmologist) (formulated "Big Bang" theory, 1927) 30 20
941 20c. Chiang Kai-Shek (Chinese nationalist leader)
942 20c. Werner Heisenberg (theoretical physicist) developed "Uncertainty Principle", 1927 30 20
943 20c. Sir Alexander Fleming (bacteriologist) and microscope (discovery of penicillin, 1928) 30 20
944 20c. Emperor Hirohito of Japan 30 20
945 20c. Car and man (U.S. Stock Market crash causes Great Depression) 30 20
946 20c. Douglas World Cruiser seaplanes and men (round-the-world formation flight, 1924) (59 × 39 mm) 30 20
947 20c. *All Quiet on the Western Front* (novel by Erich Maria Remarque published 1929) 30 20

2000. International Relations in the Twentieth Century. Multicoloured.
948 33c. Type **131** 45 30
949 33c. U.S.S.R. and U.S. flags, Gorbachev and Reagan (end of Cold War) 45 30
950 33c. Ronald Reagan (U.S. President, 1980–88) 45 30
951 33c. Le Duc Tho (Vietnamese politician) 45 30
952 33c. Le Duc Tho and Henry Kissinger (resolution to Vietnam conflict) 45 30
953 33c. Henry Kissinger (U.S. Secretary of State) 45 30
954 33c. Linus Pauling (chemist) 45 30
955 33c. Pauling at protest against nuclear weapons 45 30
956 33c. Peter Benenson (founder of Amnesty International, 1961) 45 30
957 33c. Amnesty International emblem and prisoners 45 30
958 33c. Mahatma Gandhi (Indian leader) 45 30
959 33c. Gandhi fasting 45 30
960 33c. John F. Kennedy (U.S. President, 1960–3) making speech initiating Peace Corps 45 30
961 33c. President Kennedy 45 30
962 33c. Dalai Lama (Tibetan religious leader) praying 45 30
963 33c. Dalai Lama 45 30
964 33c. United Nations Headquarters, New York 45 30
965 33c. Cordell Hull (U.S. Secretary of State 1933–44) (active in creation of United Nations) 45 30
966 33c. Frederick Willem de Klerk (South African politician) 45 30
967 33c. De Klerk and Nelson Mandela (end of Apartheid) 45 30
968 33c. Nelson Mandela 45 30
969 33c. Franklin D. Roosevelt (U.S. President) 45 30
970 33c. Winston Churchill, Roosevelt and Josef Stalin (Soviet leader) (Yalta Conference, 1945) 45 30
971 33c. Winston Churchill (British Prime Minister) 45 30

132 Andrew Carnegie (industrialist)

2000. Philanthropists of the Twentieth Century. Multicoloured.
972 33c. Type **132** 45 30
973 33c. John D. Rockefeller (oil magnate) 45 30
974 33c. Henry Ford (motor manufacturer) 45 30
975 33c. C. J. Walker 45 30
976 33c. James B. Duke 45 30
977 33c. Andrew Mellon (financier) 45 30
978 33c. Charles F. Kettering (engineer) 45 30
979 33c. R. W. Woodruff 45 30
980 33c. Brooke Astor 45 30
981 33c. Howard Hughes (businessman and aviator) 45 30
982 33c. Jesse H. Jones 45 30
983 33c. Paul Mellon 45 30
984 33c. Jean Paul Getty (oil exectutive) 45 30
985 33c. George Soros 45 30
986 33c. Phyllis Wattis 45 30
987 33c. Ted (Robert Edward) Turner (entrepreneur) 45 30

133 Fairies' Bonnets (*Coprinus disseminatus*)

2000. Fungi. Multicoloured.
988 33c. Type **133** 45 30
989 33c. Black Bulgar (*Bulgaria inquinans*) 45 30
990 33c. Amethyst deceiver (*Laccaria amethystina*) (inscr "amethystea") 45 30
991 33c. Common morel (*Morchella esculenta*) 45 30
992 33c. Common bird's nest (*Crucibulum laeve*) 45 30
993 33c. Trumpet agaric (*Clitocybe geotropa*) 45 30
994 33c. Bonnet mycena (*Mycena galericulata*) 45 30
995 33c. Underside of horse mushroom (*Agaricus arvensis*) 45 30
996 33c. Part of *Boletus subtomento* 45 30
997 33c. Oyster mushroom (*Pleurotus ostreatus*) 45 30
998 33c. Fly agaric (*Amanita muscaria*) 45 30
999 33c. Aztec mushroom mandala design 45 30

134 *Freycinetia arborea*

2000. Flowers. Multicoloured.
1001 33c. Type **134** 40 25
1002 33c. Mount Cook lily (*Ranunculus lyallii*) (inscr "lyalli") 40 25
1003 33c. Sun orchid (*Thelymitra nuda*) 40 25
1004 33c. *Bossiaea ensata* 40 25
1005 33c. Swamp hibiscus (*Hibiscus diversifolius*) 40 25
1006 33c. *Gardenia brighamii* 40 25
1007 33c. Elegant brodiaea (Brodiaea elegans) 40 25
1008 33c. Skyrocket (*Ipomopsis aggregata*) 40 25
1009 33c. Hedge bindweed (*Convovulus sepium*) 40 25
1010 33c. Woods' rose (*Rosa woodsii*) 40 25

1011 33c. Swamp rose (*Rosa palustris*) 40 25
1012 33c. Wake robin (*Trillium erectum*) 40 25
MS1013 Two sheets. (a) 95 × 80 mm. $2 Black-eyed susan (*Tetratheca juncea*). (b) 108 × 80 mm. $2 Yellow meadow lily (*Lilium canadense*) Set of 2 sheets . . . 4·75 2·75

FEDERATED STATES OF MICRONESIA
SIAMESE

135 Two Siamese Cats

2000. Cats and Dogs. Multicoloured.
1014 33c. Type **135** 40 25
1015 33c. Red mackerel tabbies 40 25
1016 33c. British shorthair . . . 40 25
1017 33c. Red Persian 40 25
1018 33c. Turkish angora 40 25
1019 33c. Calico 40 25
1020 33c. Afghan hounds 40 25
1021 33c. Yellow labrador retriever 40 25
1022 33c. Greyhound 40 25
1023 33c. German shepherd . . . 40 25
1024 33c. King Charles spaniel 40 25
1025 33c. Jack Russell terrier . . 40 25
MS1026 Two sheets, each 85 × 110 mm. (a) $2 Tortoiseshell and white cat watching bird. (b) $2 Setter and trees Set of 2 sheets 4·75 2·75
Nos. 1014/19 (cats) and 1020/5 (dogs) respectively were issued together, se-tenant, each sheetlet forming a composite design.

136 Henry Taylor (Great Britain) preparing to Dive, 1908, London

2000. Olympic Games, Sydney. Multicoloured.
1027 33c. Type **136** 40 25
1028 33c. Cyclist 40 25
1029 33c. Munich stadium and flag, West Germany . . . 40 25
1030 33c. Ancient Greek wrestlers 40 25

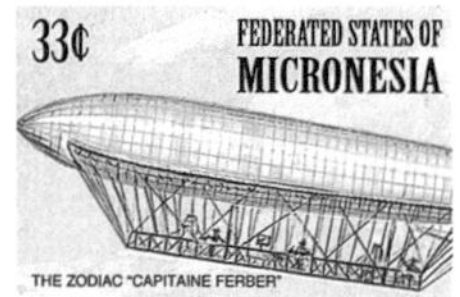

137 Zodiac Airship *Capitaine Ferber*

2000. Centenary of First Zeppelin Flight and Airship Development. Multicoloured.
1031 33c. Type **137** 40 25
1032 33c. Astra airship *Adjutant Reau* 40 25
1033 33c. Airship 1A, Italy . . . 40 25
1034 33c. Astra-Torres No. 14 . . 40 25
1035 33c. Front of Astra-Torres No. 14, Schuttle-Lanz SL3 and front of Siemens-Schukert airship 40 25
1036 33c. Siemens-Schukert airship 40 25
MS1037 Two sheets, each 110 × 85 mm. (a) $2 LZ-130 *Graf Zeppelin II*. (b) $2 Dupuy de Lome airship Set of 2 sheets . . . . 4·75 2·75
Nos. 1031/6 were issued together, se-tenant, forming a composite design.

138 Top of Head

2000. 100th Birthday of Queen Elizabeth the Queen Mother. T **138** and similar vert designs showing collage of miniature flower photographs. Multicoloured, country inscription and face value at left (a) or right (b).
1038 33c. Type **138** 40 25
1039 33c. Top of head (b) 40 25
1040 33c. Eye and temple (a) . . 40 25
1041 33c. Temple (b) 40 25
1042 33c. Cheek (a) 40 25
1043 33c. Cheek (b) 40 25
1044 33c. Chin (a) 40 25
1045 33c. Chin and neck (b) . . . 40 25
Nos. 1038/45 were issued together in se-tenant sheetlets of eight with the stamps arranged in two vertical columns separated by a gutter also containing miniature photographs. When viewed as a whole, the sheetlet forms a portrait of Queen Elizabeth the Queen Mother.

139 Woman Weightlifter and Traditional Cloth

2000. "OLYMPHILEX 2000" International Olympic Stamp Exhibition, Sydney. Sheet 137 × 82 mm, containing T **139** and similar vert designs. Multicoloured.
MS1046 33c. Type **139**; 33c. Woman playing basketball; $1 Male weightlifter . . . . 2·00 1·25

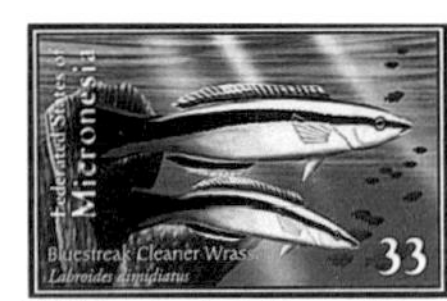

140 Blue-streaked Cleaner Wrasse (*Labroides dimidiatus*)

2000. Coral Reef. Multicoloured.
1047 33c. Type **140** 40 25
1048 33c. Pennant coralfish (*Heniochus acuminatus*) . . 40 25
1049 33c. Chevron butterflyfish (*Chaetodon trifascialis*) . . 40 25
1050 33c. Rock beauty (*Holacanthus tricolor*) . . 40 25
1051 33c. Mandarin fish (*Synchiropus splendidus*) 40 25
1052 33c. Emperor snapper (*Lutjanus sebae*) (wrongly inscr "timorensis") . . . 40 25
1053 33c. Copper-banded butterflyfish (*rostratus*) . . 40 25
1054 33c. Chevron butterflyfish (*Chaetodon trifascialis*) (different) 40 25
1055 33c. Lemon-peel angelfish (*Centropyge flavissimus*) 40 25
1056 33c. Lemon-peel angelfish and harlequin tuskfish (*Choerodon fasciatus*) . . 40 25
1057 33c. Crown triggerfish (*Balistoides conspicillum*) 40 25
1058 33c. Coral hind (*Cephalopholis miniata*) . . 40 25
1059 33c. Pennant coralfish (*Heniochus acuminatus*) (different) 40 25
1060 33c. Scuba diver and six-blotched hind (*Cephalopholis sexmaculata*) 40 25
1061 33c. Common jellyfish (*Aurelia aurita*) 40 25
1062 33c. Palette surgeonfish (*Paracanthurus hepatus*) and common jellyfish . . 40 25
1063 33c. Bicoloured angelfish (*Centropyge bicolor*) . . . 40 25
1064 33c. Thread-finned butterflyfish (*Chaetodon auriga*) and clown anemonefish 40 25
1065 33c. Clown anemonefish (*Amphiprion percula*) . . . 40 25
1066 33c. Three-banded damselfish (*Chrysiptera tricincta*) 40 25
1067 33c. Three-banded damselfish and grey reef shark (*Carcharhinus amblyrhynchs*) (inscr "amblyrhynchos") 40 25
1068 33c. Tail of grey reef shark and starfish (*Luidia ciliaris*) 40 25
MS1069 Two sheets, each 98 × 68 mm. (a) $2 Forceps butterflyfish (*Forcipiger flavissimus*). (b) $2 Emperor angelfish (*Pomacanthus imperator*) Set of 2 sheets . . . . 4·75 2·75
Nos. 1051/59 and 1060/8 respectively were issued, se-tenant, forming a composite design.

141 Back of Head

2000. 80th Birthday of Pope John Paul II. T **141** and similar vert designs showing collage of miniature religious photographs. Multicoloured, country Inscription and face value at left (a) or right (b).
1070 50c. Type **141** 60 35
1071 50c. Forehead (b) 60 35
1072 50c. Ear (a) 60 35
1073 50c. Forehead and eye (b) 60 35
1074 50c. Neck and collar (a) . . 60 35
1075 50c. Nose and cheek (b) . . 60 35
1076 50c. Shoulder (a) 60 35
1077 50c. Hands (b) 60 35
Nos. 1070/7 were issued together in se-tenant sheetlets of eight with the stamps arranged in two vertical columns separated by a gutter also containing miniature photographs. When viewed as a whole, the sheetlet forms a portrait of Pope John Paul II.

142 "The Holy Trinity" (Titian)

2000. Christmas. Multicoloured.
1078 20c. Type **142** 25 10
1079 33c. "Adoration of the Magi" (Diego de Silva y Velasquez) 40 25
1080 60c. "Holy Nereus" (Peter Paul Rubens) 75 45
1081 $3.20 "St. Gregory, St. Maurus, St. Papianus and St. Domitilla" (Rubens) . . . . 4·00 2·40

143 Snake

2001. New Year. Year of the Snake. Two sheets, each 72 × 101 mm, containing horiz design as T **143**. Multicoloured.
MS1082 (a) 60c. Type **143**. (b) 60c. Brown snake . . . . 1·50 90

144 Weepinbell

2001. Pokemon (children's computer game). Showing various Pokemon characters. Multicoloured.
1083 50c. Type **144** 60 35
1084 50c. Snorlax 60 35
1085 50c. Seel 60 35
1086 50c. Hitmonchan 60 35
1087 50c. Jynx 60 35
1088 50c. Pontya 60 35
MS1089 74 × 114 mm. $2 Farfetch'd (37 × 50 mm) . . . . 2·50 1·40

145 Coral Reef

2001. Environmental Protection. Multicoloured.
1090 34c. Type **145** 40 25
1091 34c. Galapagos turtle . . . 40 25
1092 34c. Tasmanian tiger . . . 40 25
1093 34c. Yanomami 40 25
1094 34c. Pelican and Florida Keys 40 25
1095 34c. Bird of prey 40 25
1096 60c. Factory chimneys (Pollution) 75 45
1097 60c. Desert and tree stump (Deforestation) 75 45
1098 60c. Forest (Acid rain) . . . 75 45
1099 60c. Horse, mother and child, tree and Globe (Greenhouse effect) . . . 75 45
MS1100 Two sheets each 110 × 77 mm. (a) $2 Sea bird (visit by Jacques Cousteau); (b) $2 Chimpanzee (Jane Goodall Institute) Set of 2 sheets . . . 4·75 2·75

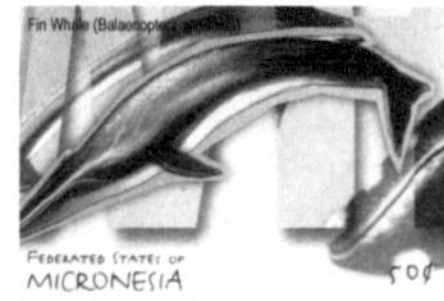

146 Fin Whale (*Balaenoptera physalus*)

2001. Whales of the Pacific. Multicoloured.
1101 50c. Type **146** 60 35
1102 50c. Right whale (*Balaena galacials*) 60 35
1103 50c. Pygmy right whale (*Caperea marginata*) . . . 60 35
1104 50c. Humpback whale (*Megaptera novaeangliae*) (inscr "novaenglaie") . . 60 35
1105 50c. Blue whale (*Balaenoptera musculus*) 60 35
1106 50c. Bowhead whale (*Balaena mysticetus*) . . . 60 35
1107 60c. True's beaked whale (*Mesoplodon mirus*) . . . 75 45
1108 60c. Cuvier's beaked whale (*Ziphius cavirostris*) . . . 75 45
1109 60c. Shepherd's beaked whale (*Tasmacetus shepherdi*) 75 45
1110 60c. Baird's beaked whale (*Berardius bairdii*) 75 45
1111 60c. Northern bottlenose whale (*Hyperodon ampullatus*) 75 45
1112 60c. Pygmy sperm whale (*Kogia breviceps*) 75 45
MS1113 Two sheets each 100 × 70 mm. (a) $2 Killer whale (*Orcinus orca*); (b) $2 Sperm whale (*Physeter macrocephalus*) Set of 2 sheets . . . . 4·75 2·75
Nos. 1101/6 and 1107/12 respectively were issued together, se-tenant, forming a composite design.

147 Three-spotted ("Yellow") Damselfish (*Stegastes planifrons*)

148 "The Courtesan Hinazuru of the Choji-ya" (Chokosai Eisho)

2001. Fishes. Multicoloured.
1114 11c. Type **147** 10 10
1115 34c. Rainbow runner (*Elegatis bipinnulatus*) . . 40 25
1118 70c. Whitelined grouper (*Anyperodon leucogrammicus*) 80 50
1119 80c. Purple queen anthias (*Pseudanthias pascalus*) . . 85 55
1123 $3.50 Eibl's angelfish (*Centropye eibli*) . . . . 4·25 2·50
1127 $12.25 Spotted ("Blue-spotted") boxfish (*Ostracion meleagris*) . . . 14·00 6·00

2001. "PHILANIPPON '01" International Stamp Exhibition, Tokyo. Japanese Art. Multicoloured.
1130 34c. Type **148** 40 25
1131 34c. "The Iris Garden" (Torii Kiyonaga) 40 25
1132 34c. "Girl tying her Hair Ribbon" (Tori Kiyomine) 40 25
1133 34c. "The Courtesan of the Mayuzumi of the Daimonji-ya" (Katsukawa Shuncho) 40 25

1134 34c. "Parody of the Allegory of the Sage Chin Kao Riding a Carp" (Suzuki Harunobo) 40 25
1135 34c. "Bath-house Scene" (Utagawa Toyokuni) . . 40 25
1136 34c. "Dance of Kamisha" (Kitagawa Utamaro) . . . 40 25
1137 34c. "The Courtesan Hinazura at the Keizetsuro" (Kitagawa Utamaro) 40 25
1138 34c. "Toilet Scene" (Kitagawa Utamaro) . . . 40 25
1139 34c. "Applying Lip Rouge" (Kitagawa Utamaro) . . . 40 25
1140 34c. "Beauty reading a Letter" (Kitagawa Utamaro) 40 25
1141 34c. "The Geisha Kamekichi" (Kitagawa Utamaro) 40 25
MS1142 Two sheets each 118 × 88 mm. (a) $2 "Girl seated by a Brook at Sunset" (Suzuki Harunobu). Imperf; (b) $2 "Allegory of Ariwara No Narihira" (Kikugawa Eizan). Imperf Set of 2 sheets . . . . . 4·75 2·75

149 "Oscar Wilde"

2001. Death Centenary of Henri de Toulouse-Lautrec (artist). Multicoloured.
1143 60c. Type **149** 75 45
1144 60c. "Doctor Tapié in a Theatre Corridor" 75 45
1145 60c. "Monsieur Delaporte" 75 45
MS1146 54 × 84 mm. $2 "The Clowness Cha-U-Kao" . . . . 2·40 1·40

150 Queen Victoria **151** Queen Elizabeth

2001. Death Centenary of Queen Victoria. Each black (except **MS**1151 multicoloured).
1147 60c. Type **150** 75 45
1148 60c. Facing right 75 45
1149 60c. Facing left wearing black decorated hat . . . 75 45
1150 60c. Facing forwards . . . 75 45
1151 60c. Holding baby 75 45
1152 60c. Facing left wearing lace headdress 75 45
MS1153 84 × 110 mm. $2 Queen Victoria (37 × 50 mm) . . . . 2·40 1·40

2001. 75th Birthday of Queen Elizabeth II. Each black (except No. 1153 and **MS**1158 multicoloured).
1154 60c. Type **151** 75 45
1155 60c. Wearing blue jacket . . 75 45
1156 60c. As young girl 75 45
1157 60c. As infant 75 45
1158 60c. With dog 75 45
1159 60c. In profile 75 45
MS1160 78 × 108 mm. $2 Princess Elizabeth . . . . 2·40 1·40

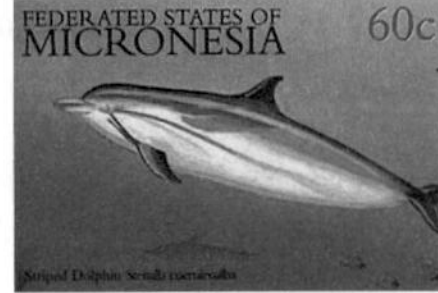

152 Striped Dolphin

2001. Marine Life. Four sheets containing T **152** and similar multicoloured designs.
MS1161 (a) 162 × 153 mm. 60c. × 6, Type **152**; Olive ridley turtle; Goldrim tang; Blue shark; Picasso triggerfish; Polka dot grouper; (b) 152 × 164 mm. 60c. × 6, Loggerhead turtle; Striped marlin; Bicolor cherub; Clown wrasse (*Coris gaimard*) (inscr "gaimardi"); Clown triggerfish; Japanese tang; (c) 96 × 68 mm. $2 Harlequin tusk (50 × 38 mm); (d) 70 × 100 mm. $2 Emperor angelfish (38 × 50 mm) . . . . 17·00 17·00

153 Triceratops

2001. Dinosaurs. Multicoloured.
1162 60c. Type **153** 65 40
1163 60c. Psittacosaurus 65 40
1164 60c. Two Archaeopteryx . . 65 40
1165 60c. Head of Allosaurus . . 65 40
MS1166 Four sheets (a) 103 × 124 mm. 60c. × 6, Tyrannosaurus; Pteranodon; Brachiosaurus; Spinosaurus; Deinonychus; Teratosaurus;(b) 104 × 123 mm. 60c. × 6, Parasaurolophus; Plateosaurus; Archaeopteryx in flight; Allosaurus (different); Torosaurus; Euoplocephalus; (c)68 × 98 mm. $2 Tyrannosaurus (different); (d) 68 × 98 mm. $2 Parasaurolophus (different) (horiz) . . . . . . 17·00 17·00

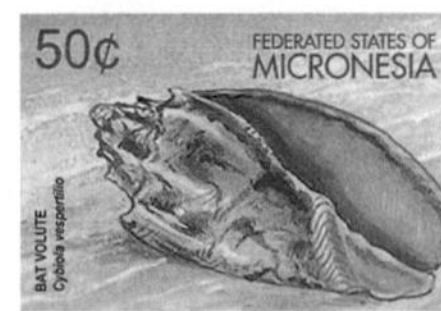

154 *Cymbiola vespertilio* (inscr "Cybiola")

2001. Shells. Four sheets containing T **154** and similar multicoloured designs.
MS1167 (a) 152 × 107 mm. 50c. × 6, Type **154**; Cassis cornuta; *Murex trocheli*; *Cymatium lotorium* (incr "lortrium"); Oliva sericea; *Phos senticosus*; (b) 111 × 145 mm. 50c. × 6; *Oblique nutmeg* (vert); *Cymbiola imperialis* (vert); Pontifical mitre (vert); *Conus eburneus Hwass in Bruguiere* (vert); *Heliacus areola* (inscr "variegated gmelin") (vert); *Corculum cardissa* (vert); (c) 76 × 59 mm. $2 Eyed auger; (d) 76 × 59 mm. $2 Geography cone . . . . 14·50 14·50

155 Malleefowl

2001. Birds. Multicoloured.
1168 5c. Type **155** 10 10
1169 22c. Corncrake 25 15
1170 23c. Hooded merganser . . 25 15
1171 $2.10 Purple gallinule . . . 2·40 1·40
MS1172 Four sheets. (a) 146 × 167 mm. 60c. × 6, Fairy wren; Golden crowned kinglet (*Regulus satrapa*) (inscr " Bebrornis rodericanus"); Flame tempered babbler; Golden headed cisticola (*Cisticola exilis*) (inscr" Orthotomus moreauii"); White browed babbler; White throated dipper (inscr "breasted"); (b) 146 × 167 mm. Logrunner; Common tree creeper (inscr "Eurasian"); Chaffinch (inscr "Goldfinch"); Rufous fantail; Orange bellied flower pecker (inscr "billed"); Goldfinch (inscr "American goldfinch"); (c) 79 × 109 mm. $2 Emperor bird of paradise; (d) 79 × 109 mm. $2 Yellow eyed cuckoo shrike (vert) Set of 4 sheets . . . . 17·00 17·00

156 Alexis Carrel, 1912 (Physiology and Medicine)

2001. Centenary of First Nobel Prize. Four sheets containing T **156** and similar vert designs. Multicoloured.
MS1173 (a) 183 × 29 mm. 60c. × 6, Type **156**; Max Theiler, 1951 (Physiology and Medicine); Niels Finsen, 1903 (Physiology and Medicine); Philip S. Hench, 1950 (Physiology and Medicine); Sune Bergstrom, 1982 (Physiology and Medicine); JohnVane, 1982 (Physiology and Medicine) (b) 183 × 129 mm. 60c. × 6, Bengt Samuelsson, 1982 (Physiology and Medicine); Johannes Fibiger, 1926 (Physiology and Medicine); Theodore Richards, 1914 (Chemistry); Tadeus Reichstein, 1950 (Physiology and Medicine); Frederick Soddy, 1921 (Chemistry)bert Szent-Gyorgi von Nagyrapolt, 1937 (Physiology and Medicine) (c) 106 × 75 mm. Irving Langmuir, 1932 (Chemistry); (d) 106 × 5 mm. Artturi Ilmari Virtanen, 1945 (Chemistry) . . . . 17·00 17·00

157 Sinking of USS *Oklahoma*

2001. 60th Anniv of Attack on Pearl Harbour. Four sheets containing T **157** and similar horiz designs. Multicoloured.
MS1174 (a) 149 × 161 mm. 60c. × 6, Type **157**; Attack on Wheeler airfield; Japanese bomber; USS *Ward* sinking submarine; Bombing of USS *Arizona*; Attack on EWA marine base (b) 149 × 161 mm. 60c. × 6, "Remember Pearl Harbour" poster; Hideki Tojo (Japanese prime minister); Rescuing wounded, Bellows Field; Rescuing crew of USS *Arizona*; Isoroku Yamamoto (Japanese admiral); "Remember Pearl Harbour" poster (different) (c) 80 × 110 mm.; USS*Arizona Memorial*, Hawaii (d) 80 × 110 mm. President F. D. Roosevelt . . . . 17·00 17·00

158 Santa Claus riding Cat

2001. Christmas. Santa Claus. Multicoloured.
1175 22c. Type **158** 25 15
1176 34c. Between decorated trees 35 20
1177 60c. Flying in sleigh 65 40
1178 $1 Riding dog . . . . . . 1·20 70
MS1179 78 × 111 mm. $2 Climbing into chimney (vert) . . . . . 2·25 2·25

159 Horse

2002. Year of the Horse. Sheet containing T **159** and similar vert designs. Each black.
MS1180 60c. × 6, Type **159**; Two horses; Two horses (different); Two horses' heads; Galloping horse . . . . 4·00 4·00
No. **MS**1180 forms a composite design of a herd of horses.

160 Queen Elizabeth II

2002. Golden Jubilee. 50th Anniv of Queen Elizabeth II's Accession to the Throne. Two sheets containing T **160** and similar square designs. Multicoloured.
MS1181 (a) 132 × 100 mm. 80c. × 4, Type **160**; Prince Phillip; Queen Elizabeth wearing white hat; Queen Elizabeth and children; (b) 76 × 109 mm. $2 Queen Elizabeth wearing headscarf . . . . . . 5·75 5·75

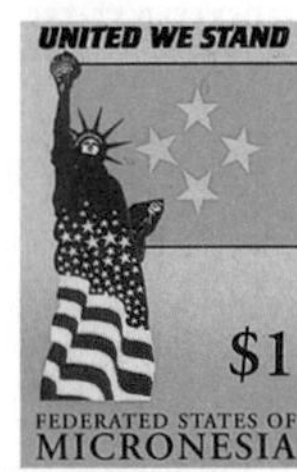

161 Statue of Liberty and American Flag

2002. "United We Stand".
1182 **161** $1 multicoloured . . . . 1·20 70

MIDDLE CONGO Pt. 6

One of three colonies into which Fr. Congo was divided in 1906. Became part of Fr. Equatorial Africa in 1937. Became part of the Congo Republic within the French Community on 28 November 1958.

100 centimes = 1 franc.

1 Leopard in Ambush

2 Bakalois Woman **3** Coconut Palms, Libreville

1907.
1 **1** 1c. olive and brown 50 25
2 2c. violet and brown 55 55
3 4c. blue and brown . . . . . 1·00 1·60
4 5c. green and blue . . . . . 1·25 50
21 5c. yellow and blue . . . . . 1·60 3·00
5 10c. red and blue . . . . . 1·10 80
22 10c. green and light green . . 3·25 4·25
6 15c. purple and pink . . . . 65 2·25
7 20c. brown and blue . . . . 3·00 4·25
8 **2** 25c. blue and green . . . . . 2·50 85
23 25c. green and grey . . . . . 2·50 3·25
9 30c. pink and green . . . . 1·50 3·25
24 30c. red . . . . 95 3·00
10 35c. brown and blue . . . . 2·25 2·50
11 40c. green and brown . . . . 2·75 3·25
12 45c. violet and orange . . . 4·25 6·25
13 50c. green and orange . . . 2·50 3·50
25 50c. blue and green . . . . . 1·60 2·75
14 75c. brown and blue . . . . 6·00 8·00
15 **3** 1f. green and violet . . . . . 9·00 11·00
16 2f. violet and green . . . . . 6·50 10·50
17 5f. blue and pink . . . . . . 38·00 35·00

1916. Surch **5c** and red cross.
20 **1** 10c.+5c. red and blue . . . . 60 2·50

1924. Surch **AFRIQUE EQUATORIALE FRANCAISE** and new value.
26 **3** 25c. on 2f. green and violet 70 2·75
27 25c. on 5f. pink and blue . . 45 80
28 65 on 1f. brown and orange 50 3·00
29 85 on 1f. brown and orange 80 3·00
30 **2** 90 on 75c. scarlet and red . . 2·50 3·00
31 1f.25 on 1f. ultramarine & bl 80 2·50
32 1f.50 on 1f. blue & ultram . . 1·75 2·75
33 3f. on 5f. pink and brown . . 4·00 3·75
34 10f. on 5f. green and red . . 10·00 12·50
35 20f. on 5f. purple and brown 17·00 10·50

1924. Optd **AFRIQUE EQUATORIALE FRANCAISE**.
36 **1** 1c. olive and brown . . . . 15 2·25
37 2c. violet and brown . . . . 20 2·25
38 4c. blue and brown . . . . . 20 2·25
39 5c. yellow and blue . . . . . 40 2·25
40 10c. green and light green . . 80 2·75
41 10c. red and grey . . . . . 55 2·25
42 15c. purple and pink . . . . 1·10 2·25
43 20c. brown and blue . . . . 25 2·75
44 20c. green and light green . . 40 2·75
45 20c. brown and mauve . . . 2·50 2·75
46 **2** 25c. green and grey 50 50
47 30c. red . . . . 55 3·25
48 30c. grey and mauve . . . . 60 1·00
49 30c. deep green and green . . 2·25 3·25

50 35c. brown and blue . . . . 40 3·00
51 40c. green and brown . . . . 55 2·75
52 45c. violet and orange . . . 35 3·00
53 50c. blue and green . . . . . 60 1·25
54 50c. yellow and black 85 30
55 65c. brown and blue . . . . 2·75 4·00
56 75c. brown and blue . . . . 1·25 2·75
57 90c. red and pink . . . . . 3·75 5·00
58 **3** 1f. green and violet . . . . . 1·60 1·75
59 1f.10 mauve and brown . . . 4·00 5·00
60 1f.50 ultramarine and blue 7·25 7·75
61 2f. violet and green . . . . . 1·75 2·25
62 3f. mauve on pink . . . . . 7·50 6·00
63 5f. blue and pink . . . . . . 2·00 2·50

1931. "Colonial Exhibition" key-types inscr "MOYEN CONGO".
65 E 40c. green and black . . . . 4·50 5·50
66 F 50c. mauve and black . . . 2·75 3·75
67 G 90c. red and black . . . . . 2·00 4·00
68 H 1f.50 blue and black . . . . 5·00 4·25

15 Mindouli Viaduct

1933.
69 **15** 1c. brown . . . . 10 2·25
70 2c. blue . . . . 10 2·50
71 4c. olive 20 50
72 5c. red . . . . 50 1·75
73 10c. green . . . . 1·60 2·50
74 15c. purple . . . . 2·00 2·75
75 20c. red on rose . . . . . . 7·75 8·00
76 25c. orange . . . . 1·90 2·75
77 30c. green . . . . 2·50 2·50
78 – 40c. brown . . . . 2·75 3·75
79 – 45c. black on green . . . . 2·75 3·50
80 – 50c. purple . . . . 2·25 45
81 – 65c. red on green . . . . . 2·75 3·25
82 – 75c. black on red . . . . . 10·00 8·50
83 – 90c. red . . . . 2·75 3·25
84 – 1f. red . . . . 1·75 1·50
85 – 1f.25 green . . . . 2·50 2·25
86 – 1f.50 blue . . . . 6·75 3·75
87 – 1f.75 violet . . . . 3·00 2·50
88 – 2f. olive . . . . 2·50 2·25
89 – 3f. black on red . . . . . . 4·00 3·00
90 – 5f. grey . . . . 15·00 16·00
91 – 10f. black . . . . 50·00 26·00
92 – 20f. brown . . . . 30·00 17·00
DESIGNS: 40c. to 1f.50 Pasteur Institute, Brazzaville; 1f.75 to 20f. Government Building, Brazzaville.

POSTAGE DUE STAMPS

1928. Postage Due type of France optd **MOYEN-CONGO A. E. F.**
D64 D **11** 5c. blue . . . . 20 2·50
D65 10c. brown . . . . . . 45 2·75
D66 20c. olive . . . . . . 45 3·00
D67 25c. red . . . . 85 3·25
D68 30c. red . . . . 50 3·00
D69 45c. green . . . . . . 60 3·00
D70 50c. purple . . . . . . 70 3·75
D71 60c. brown on cream . . 95 4·00
D72 1f. red on cream . . . 1·25 3·75
D73 2f. red . . . . 1·60 5·00
D74 3f. violet . . . . 2·75 8·75

D **13** Village

1930.
D75 D **13** 5c. olive and blue . . . 65 2·50
D76 10c. brown and red . . 65 3·00
D77 20c. brown and green . 2·25 4·25
D78 25c. brown and blue . . 2·50 4·50
D79 30c. green and brown . 1·75 7·75
D80 45c. olive and green . . 3·00 6·75
D81 50c. brown and mauve . 3·50 7·75
D82 60c. black and violet . . 4·00 8·00
D83 – 1f. black and brown . . 11·00 16·00
D84 – 2f. brown and mauve . 9·50 18·00
D85 – 3f. brown and red . . . 8·75 16·00
DESIGN: 1 to 3f. "William Guinet" (steamer) on the River Congo.

D **17** "Le Djoue"

1933.
D 93 D **17** 5c. green . . . . . . 25 2·75
D 94 10c. blue on blue . . . 1·25 2·75
D 95 20c. red on yellow . . 2·00 3·00
D 96 25c. red . . . . 2·25 3·25
D 97 30c. red . . . . 2·00 3·50
D 98 45c. purple . . . . . 2·25 3·50
D 99 50c. black . . . . . . 2·50 4·50
D100 60c. black on red . . . 3·00 5·50
D101 1f. red . . . . 2·75 7·25
D102 2f. orange . . . . . . 6·75 11·00
D103 3f. blue . . . . 11·50 15·00

For later issues see **FRENCH EQUATORIAL AFRICA**.

MODENA Pt. 8

A state in Upper Italy, formerly a duchy and now part of Italy. Used stamps of Sardinia after the cessation of its own issues in 1860. Now uses Italian stamps.

100 centesimi = 1 lira.

1 Arms of Este

5 Cross of Savoy

1852. Imperf.
9 **1** 5c. black on green . . . . . 25·00 44·00
3 10c. black on pink . . . . . £325 65·00
4 15c. black on yellow . . . . 40·00 25·00
5 25c. black on buff . . . . . 42·00 29·00
12 40c. black on blue . . . . . 40·00 £120
13 1l. black on white . . . . . 55·00 £2250

1859. Imperf.
18 **5** 5c. green £1300 £600
19 15c. brown £2500 £3500
20 15c. grey £300
21 20c. black £1800 £150
22 20c. lilac . . . . 60·00 £1000
23 40c. red £180 £1200
24 80c. brown £180 £19000

NEWSPAPER STAMPS

1853. As T **1** but in the value tablet inscr "B.G. CEN" and value. Imperf.
N15 **1** 9c. black on mauve . . . . £600 75·00
N16 10c. black on lilac . . . . 55·00 £275

N **4**

1859. Imperf.
N17 N **4** 10c. black £1000 £2000

MOHELI Pt. 6

An island in the Comoro Archipelago adjacent to Madagascar. A separate French dependency until 1914 when the whole archipelago was placed under Madagascar whose stamps were used until 1950. Now part of the Comoro Islands.

100 centimes = 1 franc.

1906. "Tablet" key-type inscr "MOHELI" in blue (2, 4, 10, 20, 30, 40c., 5f.) or red (others).
1 D 1c. black on blue . . . . . 2·25 2·00
2 2c. brown on buff . . . . . 1·25 2·00
3 4c. brown on grey . . . . . 2·25 3·25
4 5c. green . . . . 3·00 2·50
5 10c. red . . . . 2·75 1·90
6 20c. red on green . . . . . 9·75 9·25
7 25c. blue . . . . 9·25 5·25
8 30c. brown on drab . . . . 17·00 7·00
9 35c. black on yellow . . . . 7·00 2·75
10 40c. red on yellow . . . . . 13·50 10·50
11 45c. black on green . . . . 55·00 52·00
12 50c. brown on blue . . . . 23·00 14·00
13 75c. brown on orange . . . 30·00 29·00
14 1f. green . . . . 15·00 20·00
15 2f. violet on pink . . . . . 32·00 42·00
16 5f. mauve on lilac £110 £120

1912. Surch in figures.
17 D 05 on 4c. brown & bl on grey . . . . 2·00 3·25
18 05 on 20c. red & blue on grn 1·90 5·00
19 05 on 30c. brn & bl on drab 1·75 3·75
20 10 on 40c. red & blue on yell 1·90 3·50
21 10 on 45c. blk & red on grn 1·10 2·50
22 10 on 50c. brown & red on bl . . . . 1·75 4·00

MOLDOVA Pt. 10

Formerly Moldavia, a constituent republic of the Soviet Union. Moldova declared its sovereignty within the Union in 1990 and became independent in 1991.

1991. 100 kopeks = 1 rouble.
1993. Kupon (temporary currency).
1993. 100 bani = 1 leu.

1 Arms

2 Codrii Nature Reserve

1991. 1st Anniv of Declaration of Sovereignty. Multicoloured. Imperf.
1 7k. Type **1** 10 10
2 13k. Type **1** 10 10
3 30k. Flag (35 × 23 mm) 15 10

1992.
4 **2** 25k. multicoloured 55 25

3 Arms

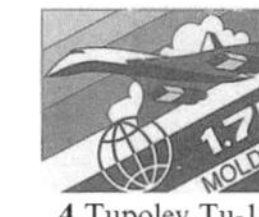
4 Tupolev Tu-144

1992.
5 **3** 35k. green 10 10
6 50k. red 10 10
7 65k. brown 10 10
8 1r. purple 15 10
9 1r.50 blue 25 10

1992. Air.
15 **4** 1r.75 red 10 10
16 2r.50 mauve 15 10
17 7r.75 violet 60 30
18 8r.50 green 80 40
See also Nos. 70/3.

5 European Bee Eater

6 St. Panteleimon's Church

1992. Birds. Multicoloured.
19 50k. Type **5** 20 20
20 65k. Golden oriole 20 20
21 2r.50 Green woodpecker . . . 40 40
22 6r. European roller . . . . . 1·00 1·00
23 7r.50 Hoopoe . . . . 1·25 1·25
24 15r. European cuckoo . . . . 2·75 2·75
See also Nos. 63/9.

1992. Centenary (1991) of St. Panteleimon's Church, Chisinau.
25 **6** 1r.50 multicoloured 15 10

7 Wolf suckling Romulus and Remus

9 High Jumping

1992. Trajan Memorial, Chisinau.
26 **7** 5r. multicoloured 15 10

1992. Various stamps of Russia surch **MOLDOVA** and value.
27 2r.50 on 4k. red (No. 4672) . . 10 10
28 6r. on 3k. red (No. 4671) . . . 10 10
29 8r.50 on 4k. red (No. 4672) . . 30 15
30 10r. on 3k. green (No. 6074) 50 25

1992. Olympic Games, Barcelona. Multicoloured.
31 35k. Type **9** 10 10
32 65k. Wrestling 10 10
33 1r. Archery 10 10
34 2r.50 Swimming 30 15
35 10r. Show jumping . . . . . 1·10 55

1992. Nos. 4669/71 of Russia surch **MOLDOVA**, new value and bunch of grapes.
37 45k. on 2k. mauve 10 10
38 46k. on 2k. mauve 10 10
39 63k. on 1k. green 10 10
40 63k. on 3k. red 10 10
41 70k. on 1k. green 10 10
42 4r. on 1k. green 30 15

1992. Moldovan Olympic Games Medal Winners. Nos. 33/4 optd.
43 1r. Archery (optd **NATALIA VALEEV bronz** and emblem) 40 20
44 2r.50 Swimming (optd **IURIE BASCATOV argint** and emblem) . . . . 1·10 55

13 Moldovan Flag, Statue of Liberty and U.N. Emblem and Building

1992. Admission of Moldova to U.N.O. Mult.
46 1r.30 Type **13** 10 10
47 12r. As Type **13** but with motifs differently arranged 40 20

14 Moldovan Flag and Prague Castle

1992. Admission of Moldova to European Security and Co-operation Conference. Multicoloured.
48 2r.50 Type **14** 15 10
49 25r. Helsinki Cathedral and Moldovan flag 50 25

15 Carpet and Pottery

16 Galleon

1992. Folk Art.
50 **15** 7r.50 multicoloured 25 15

1992. 500th Anniv of Discovery of America by Columbus. Multicoloured.
51 1r. Type **16** 15 10
52 6r. Carrack 80 40
53 6r. Caravel 80 40
MS54 89 × 69 mm. 25r. Christopher Columbus . . . . 3·00 3·00

17 Letter Sorter, Diesel Train, State Flag and U.P.U. Emblem

1992. Admission to U.P.U. Multicoloured.
55 5r. Type **17** 75 40
56 10r. Douglas DC-10 jetliner, computerized letter sorting equipment, state flag and U.P.U. emblem 95 50

18 Aesculapius Snake

1993. Protected Animals. Snakes. Multicoloured.
57 3r. Type **18** 20 10
58 3r. Aesculapius in tree 20 10
59 3r. Aesculapius on path . . . 20 10
60 3r. Aesculapius on rock . . . 20 10
61 15r. Grass snake 75 40
62 25r. Adder . . . . 1·25 60
Nos. 57/60 were issued together, se-tenant, forming a composite design.

1993. Birds. As Nos. 19/24 but with values changed and additional design. Multicoloured.
63 2r. Type **5** 20 20
64 3r. As No. 20 . . . . 20 20
65 5r. As No. 21 . . . . 20 20
66 10r. As No. 22 . . . . 30 20
67 15r. As No. 23 . . . . 40 30

68 50r. As No. 24 . . . . 1·50 1·40
69 100r. Barn swallow . . . . . 3·25 2·75

1993. Air.
70 **4** 25r. red 20 10
71 45r. brown 35 20
72 50r. green 40 20
73 90r. blue 70 35

19 Arms **20** Arms

1993.
74 **19** 2k. blue 10 10
75 3k. purple 10 10
76 6k. green 10 10
77 – 10k. violet and green . . . 10 10
78 – 15k. violet and green . . . 10 10
79 – 20k. violet and grey 10 10
80 – 30k. violet and yellow . . . 15 10
81 – 50k. violet and red 20 10
82 **20** 100k. multicoloured 40 20
83 250k. multicoloured 90 45
DESIGN: 10 to 50k. Similar to Type **19** but with inscription and value at foot differently arranged.

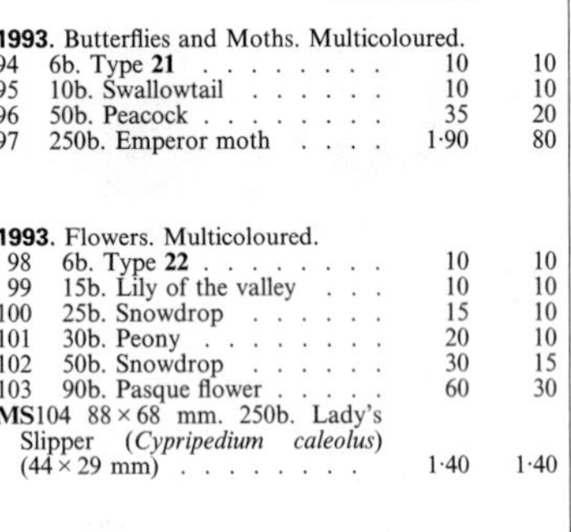

21 Red Admiral **22** "Tulipa bibersteiniana"

1993. Butterflies and Moths. Multicoloured.
94 6b. Type **21** 10 10
95 10b. Swallowtail 10 10
96 50b. Peacock 35 20
97 250b. Emperor moth . . . . 1·90 80

1993. Flowers. Multicoloured.
98 6b. Type **22** 10 10
99 15b. Lily of the valley . . . 10 10
100 25b. Snowdrop 15 10
101 30b. Peony 20 10
102 50b. Snowdrop 30 15
103 90b. Pasque flower 60 30
MS104 88 × 68 mm. 250b. Lady's Slipper (*Cypripedium caleolus*) (44 × 29 mm) . . . . 1·40 1·40

23 Dragos Voda (1352–53) **24** "Story of One Life" (M. Grecu)

1993. 14th-century Princes of Moldavia. Mult.
105 6b. Type **23** 10 10
106 25b. Bogdan Voda I (1359–65) 10 10
107 50b. Latcu Voda (1365–75) 20 10
108 100b. Petru I Musat (1375–91) 45 25
109 150b. Roman Voda Musat (1391–94) 65 35
110 200b. Stefan I (1394–99) . . 90 45

1993. Europa. Contemporary Art. Multicoloured.
111 3b. Type **24** 10 10
112 150b. "Coming of Spring" (I. Vieru) . . . . 1·60 80

25 Biathletes

27 State Arms

1994. Winter Olympic Games, Lillehammer, Norway. Multicoloured.
113 3b. Type **25** 10 10
114 150b. Close-up of biathlete shooting . . . . 1·25 60

1994. No. 4669 of Russia surch **MOLDOVA**, grapes and value.
115 3b. on 1k. green 10 10
116 25b. on 1k. green 10 10
117 50b. on 1k. green 15 10

1994.
118 **27** 1b. multicoloured 10 10
119 10b. multicoloured 10 10
120 30b. multicoloured 10 10
121 38b. multicoloured 15 10
122 45b. multicoloured 15 10
123 75b. multicoloured 30 15
124 1l.50 multicoloured 60 30
125 1l.80 multicoloured 70 35
126 2l.50 mult (24 × 29 mm) . . 95 50
127 4l.50 multicoloured . . . . 1·75 1·25
128 5l.40 multicoloured . . . . 2·00 1·40
129 6l.90 multicoloured . . . . 2·50 1·50
130 7l.20 mult (24 × 29 mm) . . 2·75 1·75
131 13l. mult (24 × 29 mm) . . 5·25 3·50
132 24l. mult (24 × 29 mm) . . 9·25 6·00

28 Launch of "Titan II" Rocket **29** Maria Cibotari (singer)

1994. Europa. Inventions and Discoveries. 25th Anniv of First Manned Moon Landing. Multicoloured.
136 1b. Type **28** 10 10
137 45b. Ed White (astronaut) on space walk ("Gemini 4" flight, 1965) 65 35
138 2l.50 Lunar module landing, 1969 . . . . 2·25 1·25

1994. Entertainers' Death Anniversaries. Mult.
139 3b. Type **29** (45th) 10 10
140 90b. Dumitru Caraciobanu (actor, 14th) 40 20
141 150b. Eugeniu Coca (composer, 40th) 70 35
142 250b. Igor Vieru (actor, 11th) 1·10 55

30 Preparing Stamp Design

1994. Stamp Day.
143 **30** 10b. black, blue and mauve 10 10
144 – 45b. black, mauve and yellow 30 15
145 – 2l. multicoloured . . . . . 1·25 65
DESIGNS: 45b. Printing stamps; 2l. Checking finished sheets.

31 Pierre de Coubertin (founder)

32 Map

1994. Centenary of International Olympic Committee. Multicoloured.
146 60b. Type **31** 20 10
147 1l.50 Rings and "Paris 1994" centenary congress emblem 65 35

1994. Partnership for Peace Programme (co-operation of N.A.T.O. and Warsaw Pact members).
148 – 60b. black, ultram and bl 20 20
149 **32** 2l.50 multicoloured 30 30
DESIGN: 60b. Manfred Worner (Secretary-General of N.A.T.O.) and President Mircea Snegur of Moldova.

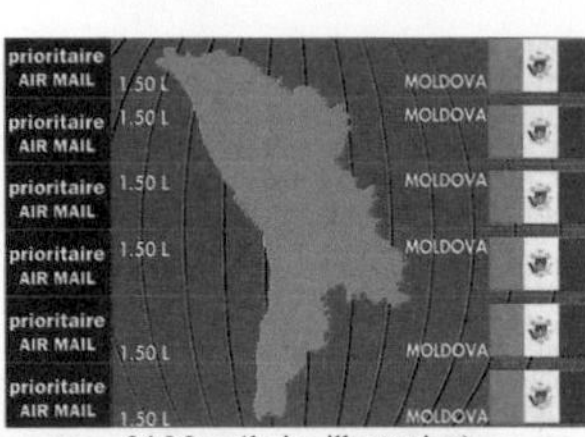

34 Map (½-size illustration)

1994. Air. Self-adhesive. Roul.
152 **34** 1l.50 multicoloured 50 25
153 4l.50 multicoloured . . . . 1·50 75
The individual stamps are peeled directly from the card backing. Each card contains six different designs with the same face value forming the composite design illustrated. Each stamp is a horizontal strip with a label indicating the main class of mail covered by the rate at the left, separated by a vertical line of rouletting. The outer edges of the cards are imperforate.

35 Family

36 Handshake

1994. International Year of the Family. Multicoloured.
154 30b. Type **35** 20 10
155 60b. Mother breast-feeding baby 40 20
156 1l.50 Child drawing . . . . 1·50 90

1994. Preliminary Rounds of European Football Championship, England (1996). Multicoloured.
157 10b. Type **36** 10 10
158 40b. Players competing for ball 25 15
159 2l.40 Goalkeeper making save 1·50 90
MS160 140 × 105 mm. 1l.10 Moldovan and German pennants; 2l.20, German and Moldovan shields on ball; 2l.40, Players 3·00 3·00

37 "Birth of Jesus Christ" (anon)

38 Cracked Green Russula

1994. Christmas. Multicoloured.
161 20b. Type **37** 15 10
162 3l.60 "Birth of Jesus Christ" (Gherasim) . . . . 1·90 1·00

1995. Fungi. Multicoloured.
163 4b. Type **38** 10 10
164 10b. Oak mushroom 25 15
165 20b. Chanterelle 45 25
166 90b. Red-capped scaber stalk 2·10 1·10
167 1l.80 "Leccinum duriusculum" . . . . . . 4·25 2·25

39 Booted Eagle

1995. European Nature Conservation Year. Multicoloured.
168 4b. Type **39** 15 15
169 45b. Roe deer . . . . 1·00 50
170 90b. Wild boar . . . . 2·00 1·10

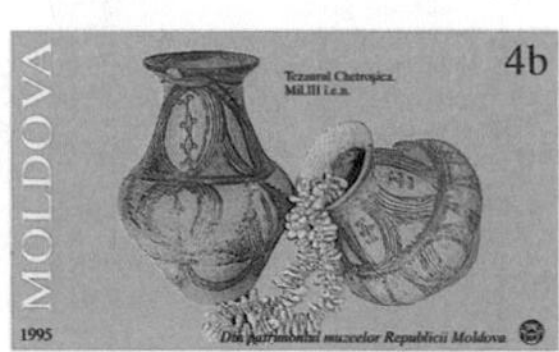

40 Earthenware Urns and Necklace

1995. National Museum Exhibits. Multicoloured.
171 4b. Type **40** 10 10
172 10b.+2b. Representation and skeleton of "Dinotherium gigantissimum" 25 15
173 1l.80+30b. Silver coins . . . 2·75 1·75

41 "May 1945" (Igor Vieru)

1995. Europa. Peace and Freedom. Paintings. Multicoloured.
174 10b. Type **41** 15 10
175 40b. "Peace" (Sergiu Cuciuc) 35 20
176 2l.20 "Spring 1944" (Cuciuc) 2·00 1·10

42 Constantin Stere (writer, 130th birth)

43 Alexandru cel Bun (1400–32)

1995. Anniversaries.
177 **42** 9b. brown and grey . . . 15 10
178 – 10b. purple and grey . . . 15 10
179 – 40b. lilac and grey 55 30
180 – 1l.80 green and grey . . . 2·50 1·50
DESIGNS: 10b. Tamara Ceban (singer, 5th death); 40b. Alexandru Plamadeala (sculptor, 55th death); 1l.80, Lucian Blaga (philosopher, birth centenary).

1995. 15th and 16th-century Princes of Moldavia. Multicoloured.
181 10b. Type **43** 15 10
182 10b. Petru Aron (1451–52 and 1454–57) 15 10
183 10b. Stefan cel Mare (1457–1504) 15 10
184 45b. Petru Rares (1527–38 and 1541–46) 65 35
185 90b. Alexandru Lapusneanu (1552–61 and 1564–68) . . 1·40 70
186 1l.80 Ioan Voda cel Cumplit (1572–74) . . . . 3·00 1·50
MS187 83 × 66 mm. 5l. Stefan del Mare (1457–1504) (24 × 29 mm) 1·40 1·40

44 Soroca Castle

1995. Castles. Multicoloured.
188 10b. Type **44** 15 10
189 20b. Tighina Castle 35 15
190 60b. Alba Castle . . . . . . 1·00 60
191 1l.30 Hotin Castle . . . . . 2·40 1·60

45 Seal in Eye

46 "50" and Emblem

1995. 50th Anniv of U.N.O. Multicoloured.
(a) Ordinary gum. Perf.
192 10b. Type **45** 20 10
193 10b. Airplane in eye 20 10
194 1l.50 Child's face and barbed wire in eye . . . . 3·25 2·00

(b) Self-adhesive. Rouletted.
195 90b. Type **46** 30 15
196 1l.50 Type **46** 45 25

47 "Last Moon of Autumn"

48 Fly Agaric

1995. Centenary of Motion Pictures.
197 **47** 10b. red and black 15 10
198 – 40b. green and black . . . 50 25
199 – 2l.40 blue and black . . . 3·00 2·00

DESIGNS: 40b. "Lautarii"; 2l.40, "Dimitrie Cantemir".

1996. Fungi. Multicoloured.
200 10b. Type **48** 10 10
201 10b. Satan's mushroom . . . 10 10
202 65b. Death cap 65 35
203 1l.30 Clustered woodlover . . 1·25 70
204 2l.40 Destroying angel . . . 2·40 1·25

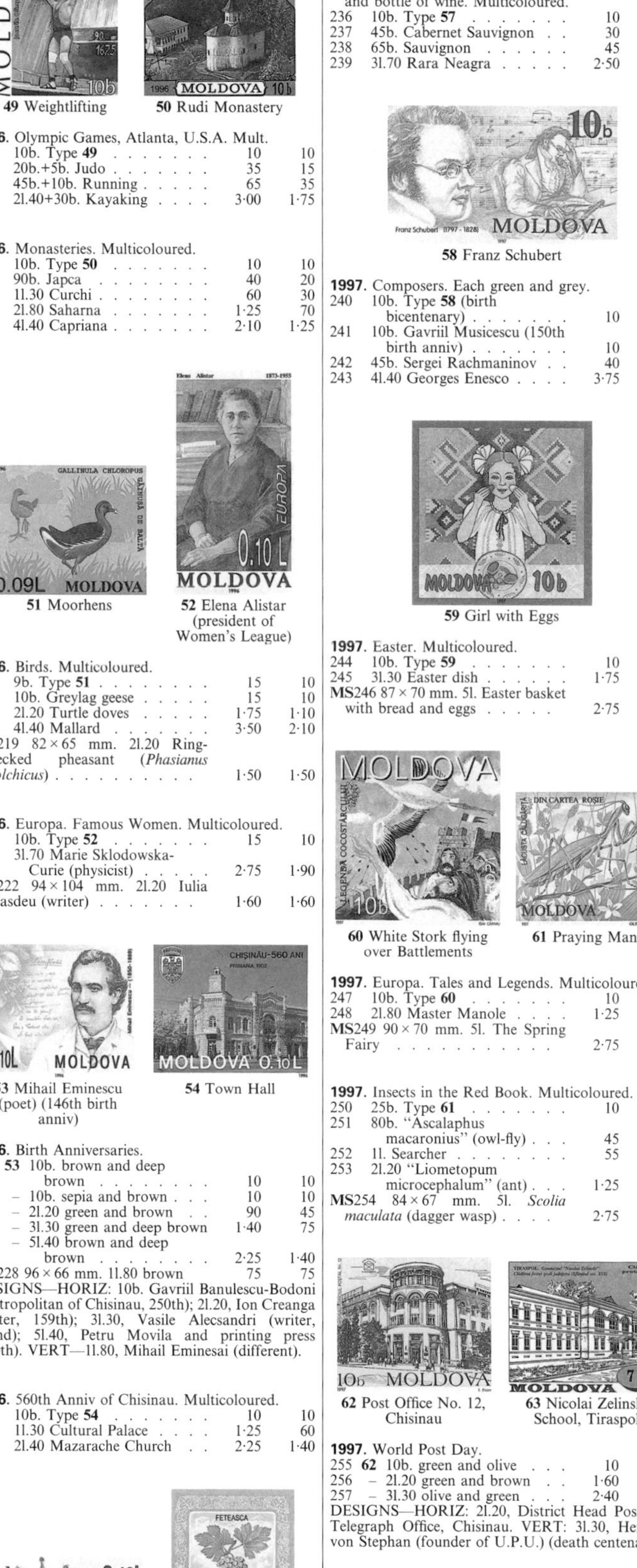

49 Weightlifting **50** Rudi Monastery

1996. Olympic Games, Atlanta, U.S.A. Mult.
205 10b. Type **49** 10 10
206 20b.+5b. Judo 35 15
207 45b.+10b. Running 65 35
208 2l.40+30b. Kayaking . . . . 3·00 1·75

1996. Monasteries. Multicoloured.
210 10b. Type **50** 10 10
211 90b. Japca 40 20
212 1l.30 Curchi 60 30
213 2l.80 Saharna . . . . 1·25 70
214 4l.40 Capriana . . . . 2·10 1·25

51 Moorhens **52** Elena Alistar (president of Women's League)

1996. Birds. Multicoloured.
215 9b. Type **51** 15 10
216 10b. Greylag geese 15 10
217 2l.20 Turtle doves . . . . . 1·75 1·10
218 4l.40 Mallard . . . . 3·50 2·10
MS219 82 × 65 mm. 2l.20 Ring-necked pheasant (*Phasianus colchicus*) . . . . 1·50 1·50

1996. Europa. Famous Women. Multicoloured.
220 10b. Type **52** 15 10
221 3l.70 Marie Sklodowska-Curie (physicist) . . . . . 2·75 1·90
MS222 94 × 104 mm. 2l.20 Iulia Hasdeu (writer) . . . . 1·60 1·60

53 Mihail Eminescu (poet) (146th birth anniv) **54** Town Hall

1996. Birth Anniversaries.
223 **53** 10b. brown and deep brown 10 10
224 – 10b. sepia and brown . . . 10 10
225 – 2l.20 green and brown . . 90 45
226 – 3l.30 green and deep brown 1·40 75
227 – 5l.40 brown and deep brown . . . . 2·25 1·40
MS228 96 × 66 mm. 1l.80 brown 75 75
DESIGNS—HORIZ: 10b. Gavriil Banulescu-Bodoni (Metropolitan of Chisinau, 250th); 2l.20, Ion Creanga (writer, 159th); 3l.30, Vasile Alecsandri (writer, 172nd); 5l.40, Petru Movila and printing press (400th). VERT—1l.80, Mihail Eminesai (different).

1996. 560th Anniv of Chisinau. Multicoloured.
229 10b. Type **54** 10 10
230 1l.30 Cultural Palace . . . . 1·25 60
231 2l.40 Mazarache Church . . 2·25 1·40

55 Carol Singers with Star **57** Feteasca

1996. Christmas. Multicoloured.
232 10b. Type **55** 10 10
233 2l.20+30b. Mother and child at centre of star . . . . . 1·25 60
234 2l.80+50b. Children decorating Christmas tree 1·60 1·00

1996. Moldovan Olympic Games Medal Winners. No. **MS**209 optd **Nicolae JURAVSCHI Victor RENEISCHI – canoe, argint -, Serghei MUREICO – lupt Greco-romame, bronz.**
MS235 123 × 75 mm. 2l.20 mult 2·10 1·40

1997. Moldovan Wines. Each showing a grape variety and bottle of wine. Multicoloured.
236 10b. Type **57** 10 10
237 45b. Cabernet Sauvignon . . 30 15
238 65b. Sauvignon 45 25
239 3l.70 Rara Neagra . . . . . 2·50 1·50

58 Franz Schubert

1997. Composers. Each green and grey.
240 10b. Type **58** (birth bicentenary) 10 10
241 10b. Gavriil Musicescu (150th birth anniv) 10 10
242 45b. Sergei Rachmaninov . . 40 20
243 4l.40 Georges Enesco . . . . 3·75 2·40

59 Girl with Eggs

1997. Easter. Multicoloured.
244 10b. Type **59** 10 10
245 3l.30 Easter dish . . . . . . 1·75 1·10
MS246 87 × 70 mm. 5l. Easter basket with bread and eggs . . . . . 2·75 1·50

60 White Stork flying over Battlements **61** Praying Mantis

1997. Europa. Tales and Legends. Multicoloured.
247 10b. Type **60** 10 10
248 2l.80 Master Manole . . . . 1·25 75
MS249 90 × 70 mm. 5l. The Spring Fairy . . . . 2·75 1·50

1997. Insects in the Red Book. Multicoloured.
250 25b. Type **61** 10 10
251 80b. "Ascalaphus macaronius" (owl-fly) . . . 45 20
252 1l. Searcher 55 30
253 2l.20 "Liometopum microcephalum" (ant) . . . 1·25 70
MS254 84 × 67 mm. 5l. *Scolia maculata* (dagger wasp) . . . . 2·75 2·75

62 Post Office No. 12, Chisinau **63** Nicolai Zelinski School, Tiraspol

1997. World Post Day.
255 **62** 10b. green and olive . . . 10 10
256 – 2l.20 green and brown . . 1·60 80
257 – 3l.30 olive and green . . . 2·40 1·40
DESIGNS—HORIZ: 2l.20, District Head Post and Telegraph Office, Chisinau. VERT: 3l.30, Heinrich von Stephan (founder of U.P.U.) (death centenary).

1997. Protection of Buildings.
258 **63** 7b. black and violet . . . 10 10
259 – 10b. black and purple . . . 10 10
260 – 10b. black and blue . . . 10 10
261 – 90b. black and yellow . . . 50 25
262 – 1l.30 black and blue . . . 75 40
263 – 3l.30 black and grey . . . 1·90 90
DESIGNS: No. 259, Railway station, Tighina; 260, Sts. Constantine and Elena Cathedral, Balti; 261, Church, Causeni; 262, Archangel Michael Cathedral, Cahul; 263, Academy of Art, Chisinau.

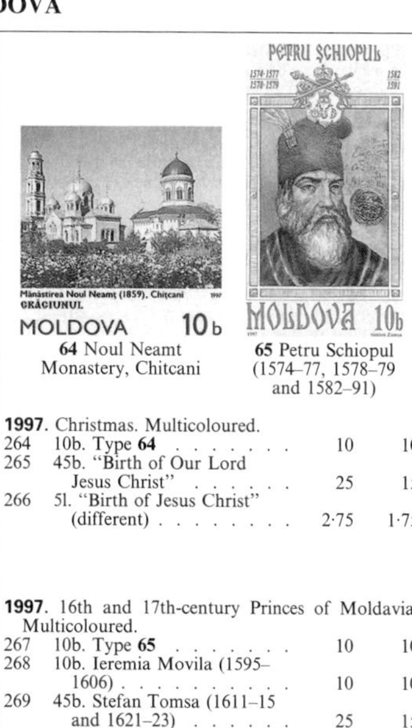

64 Noul Neamt Monastery, Chitcani **65** Petru Schiopul (1574–77, 1578–79 and 1582–91)

1997. Christmas. Multicoloured.
264 10b. Type **64** 10 10
265 45b. "Birth of Our Lord Jesus Christ" 25 15
266 5l. "Birth of Jesus Christ" (different) . . . . 2·75 1·75

1997. 16th and 17th-century Princes of Moldavia. Multicoloured.
267 10b. Type **65** 10 10
268 10b. Ieremia Movila (1595–1606) 10 10
269 45b. Stefan Tomsa (1611–15 and 1621–23) 25 15
270 1l.80 Radu Mihnea (1616–19 and 1623–26) 95 55
271 2l.20 Miron Barnovschi Movila (1626–29 and 1633) 1·10 70
272 2l.80 Bogdan Orbul (1504–1517) . . . . 1·50 90
MS273 93 × 75 mm. 5l. Mihai Viteazul (May–Sept 1600) (25 × 30 mm) . . . . 2·00 2·00

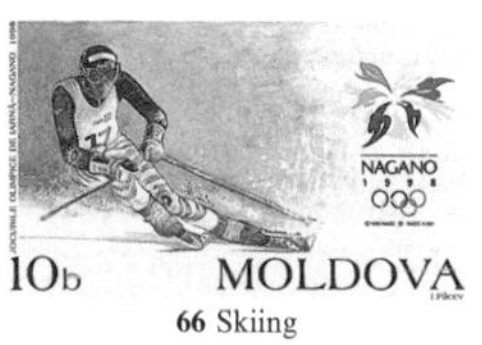

66 Skiing

1998. Winter Olympic Games, Nagano, Japan. Multicoloured.
274 10b. Type **66** 10 10
275 45b. Pairs figure skating . . . 35 15
276 2l.20 Biathlon . . . . 1·75 1·10

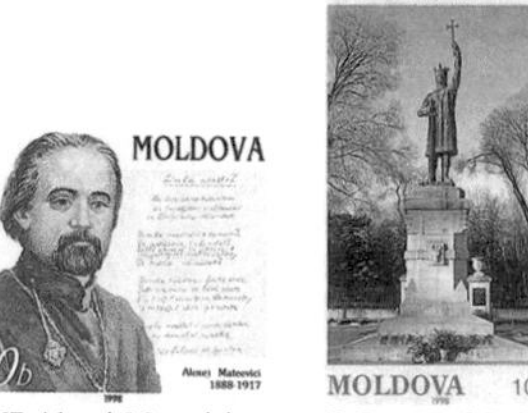

67 Alexei Mateeici **68** Statue of Stefan cel Mare (Alexandru Plamadeala), Chisinau

1998. Anniversaries. Multicoloured.
277 10b. Type **67** (110th birth anniv) 10 10
278 40b. Pantelimon Halippa (115th birth anniv) 20 10
279 60b. Stefan Ciobanu (115th birth anniv) 35 20
280 2l. Constantin Stamati-Ciurea (death centenary) 90 45
MS281 100 × 80 mm. 5l. Nicolae Milescu-Spatarul (290th death anniv) . . . . 2·25 2·25

1998. Art. Multicoloured.
282 10b. Type **68** 10 10
283 60b. "The Resurrection of Christ" (icon) 35 20
284 1l. Modern sculpture (Constantin Brancusi), Targu-Jiu 55 30
285 2l.60 Trajan's Column, Rome 1·25 65

69 Masks and Eye **70** Cherries

1998. Europa. National Festivals. Multicoloured.
286 10b. Type **69** (Eugene Ionescu Theatre Festival) 10 10
287 2l.20 Medallion showing potter (Cermanics Fair) . . 1·10 55
MS288 70 × 58 mm. 5l. Bar of music (Martisor International Music Festival) . . . . 2·25 2·25

1998. Fruits. Multicoloured.
289 7b. Type **70** 10 10
290 10b. Plums 10 10
291 1l. Apples 55 30
292 2l. Pears 90 45

71 Diana, Princess of Wales

1998. Diana, Princess of Wales Commemoration. Sheet 144 × 116 mm containing T **71** and similar horiz designs. Multicoloured.
MS293 10d. Type **71**; 90b. Wearing orange jacket; 1l.80, Wearing burgundy jacket; 2l.20 Wearing jacket with white collar; 5l. Wearing jacket with velvet collar 4·50 4·50

72 Chilia

1998. Medieval Towns.
294 **72** 10b. grey and black . . . 10 10
295 – 60b. brown and black . . . 35 20
296 – 1l. red and black 50 25
297 – 2l. blue and black 95 50
DESIGNS: 60b. Orhei; 1l. Suceava; 2l. Ismail.

73 1858 Moldavia Stamps

1998. 140th Anniv of Stamp Issues for Moldavia. Multicoloured.
298 10b. Type **73** 10 10
299 90b. 1858 Moldavia 54p. and 1928 Rumania 1 and 5l. stamps 40 20
300 2l.20 1858 Moldavia 81p. and Russian stamps . . . . . 1·10 55
301 2l.40 1858 Moldavia 108p. and Moldova 1996 10b. and 1994 45b. stamps . . . 1·25 65

74 Northern Eagle Owl **75** Couple from Vara

1998. Birds. Multicoloured.
302 25b. Type **74** 30 15
303 2l. Demoiselle crane (horiz) 1·25 65

1998. Regional Costumes. Multicoloured.
304 25b. Type **75** 15 10
305 90b. Couple from Vara (different) 60 30
306 1l.80 Couple from Iarna . . 1·25 65
307 2l. Couple from Iarna (different) . . . . 1·40 70

76 Anniversary Emblem and "Proportions of Man" (Leonardo da Vinci)

1998. 50th Anniv of Universal Declaration of Human Rights.
308 **76** 2l.40 multicoloured . . . . 1·60 80

77 Conference Members

1998. 80th Anniv of Union of Bessarabia and Rumania.

309 **77** 90b. brown, blue and black . . . 60 30

78 Mail Coach

1999. Anniversaries. Multicoloured.

310 25b. Type **78** (125th anniv of U.P.U.) 15 10
311 2l.20 Map of Europe and Council of Europe emblem (50th anniv) . . . . 1·50 75

79 Prutul de Jos Park

1999. Europa. Parks and Gardens. Multicoloured.

312 25b. Type **79** 15 10
313 2l.40 Padurea Domneasca Park . . . . 1·60 80
MS314 84 × 65 mm. 5l. Codru Park . . 3·25 3·25

80 Balzac

81 "Aleksandr Pushkin and Constantin Stamati" (B. Lebedev)

1999. Birth Bicent of Honore de Balzac (writer).

315 **80** 90b. multicoloured 60 30

1999. Birth Bicentenary of Aleksandr Pushkin (poet).

316 **81** 65b. brown, deep brown and black 45 25

82 Tranta

1999. National Sports.

317 **82** 25b. green and light green . . 15 10
318 – 1l.80 green and yellow . . 1·25 60
DESIGN: 1l.80, Oina.

83 Neil Armstrong (first man on Moon)

1999. 30th Anniv of First Manned Moon Landing. Multicoloured.

319 25b. Type **83** 15 10
320 25b. Michael Collins (pilot of Command Module) 15 10
321 5l. Edwin Aldrin (pilot of Lunar Module) . . . . . 3·25 1·75

84 Military Merit

85 Embroidered Shirt

1999. Orders and Medals. Multicoloured.

322 25b. Type **84** 15 10
323 25b. For Valour 15 10
324 25b. Civil Merit 15 10
325 90b. Mihai Eminescu Medal . . 60 30
326 1l.10 Order of Gloria Muncii . . 75 40
327 2l.40 Order of Stefan al Mare . 1·60 80
MS328 70 × 50 mm. 5l. Order of the Republic . . . . 3·25 3·25

1999. Crafts. Multicoloured.

329 5b. Inlaid wine flask 10 10
330 25b. Type **85** 15 10
331 95b. Ceramic jugs 60 30
332 1l.80 Wicker table and chairs . 1·25 60

86 Goethe

1999. 250th Birth Anniv of Johann Wolfgang von Goethe (poet).

333 **86** 1l.10 multicoloured 40 20

87 Emblem

88 Metropolitan Varlaam

1999. 10th Anniv of Adoption of Latin Alphabet.

334 **87** 25b. multicoloured 10 10

1999. Patriarchs of the Orthodox Church. Mult.

335 25b. Type **88** 10 10
336 2l.40 Metropolitan Gurie Grosu 80 40

89 Bogdan II (1449–51)

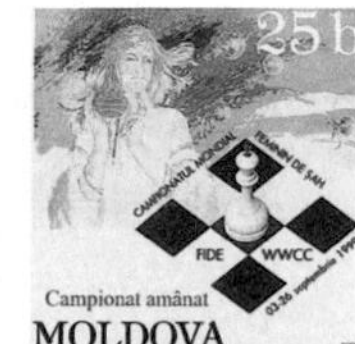

91 Player and Chessboard

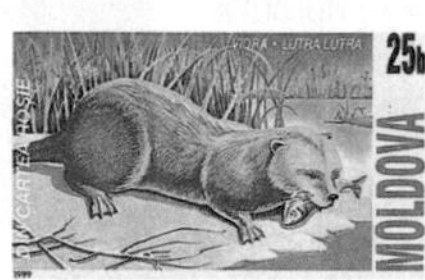

90 European Otter ("Lutra lutra")

1999. 15th to 17th-century Princes of Moldavia. Multicoloured.

337 25b. Type **89** 10 10
338 25b. Bogdan IV (1568–72) . . 10 10
339 25b. Constantin Cantemir (1685–93) 10 10
340 1l.50 Simon Movila (1606–07) 55 25
341 3l. Gheorghe III Duca (1665–66, 1668–72 and 1678–84) 1·00 50
342 3l.90 Ilias Alexandru (1666–68) . . . . 1·25 65
MS343 97 × 78 mm. 5l. Vasile Lupu (1634–53) (25 × 30 mm) . . . . 3·25 3·25

1999. Animals in the Red Book. Multicoloured.

344 25b. Type **90** 10 10
345 1l.80 Beluga ("Huso huso") 65 30
346 3l.60 Greater horseshoe bat ("Rhinolophus ferrumequinum") . . . . . 1·10 55

1999. World Women's Chess Championship, Chisinau. Multicoloured.

347 25b. Type **91** 10 10
348 2l.20+30b. Championship venue and emblem 85 40

92 4th-century B.C. Bronze Helmet and Candle Holder

93 Raluca Eminovici

1999. National History Museum Exhibits. Mult.

349 25b. Type **92** 10 10
350 1l.80 10th-century B.C. ceramic pot 65 30
351 3l.60 Gospel, 1855 . . . . . 1·10 55

2000. 150th Birth Anniv of Mihail Eminescu (poet). Sheet 141 × 111 mm containing T **93** and similar vert designs. Multicoloured.

MS352 . . . . 3·25 3·25

94 Ileana Cosinzeana

2000. Folk Heroes. Multicoloured.

353 25b. Type **94** 10 10
354 1l.50 Fat-Frumos 55 25
355 1l.80 Harap Alb 65 30

95 Henri Coanda (aeronautical engineer)

2000. Birth Anniversaries. Each pink and black.

356 25b. Type **95** (114th anniv) 10 10
357 25b. Toma Ciorba (physician, 136th) 10 10
358 2l. Guglielmo Marconi (physicist, 126th) 70 35
359 3l.60 Norbert Wiener (mathematician, 106th) . . 1·10 55

96 Globe in Palm and Astronaut on Moon

97 "Resurrection" (anon)

2000. The Twentieth Century. Multicoloured.

360 25b. Type **96** (first manned moon landing, 1969) . . . 10 10
361 1l. Model of nuclear fission and hand (use of nuclear energy) 10 10
362 3l. Computer and mouse (development of electronic data processing) 35 15
363 3l.90 P. F. Teoctist (patriarch) and Pope John Paul II (consultation between Eastern and Roman churches) (horiz) 45 20

2000. Easter. Paintings in the National Gallery. Multicoloured.

364 25b. Type **97** 10 10
365 3l. "Resurrection" (anon) . . 35 15

98 "Building Europe"

99 Emblem and Profiles

2000. Europa.

366 **98** 3l. multicoloured 35 15

2000. "EXPO 2000" World's Fair, Hanover, Germany (367) and "WIPA 2000" International Stamp Exhibition, Vienna, Austria (368). Mult.

367 25b. Type **99** 10 10
368 3l.60+30b. Hands holding tweezers and 1994 1b. State Arms stamp 20 10

100 Monastery, Tipova

2000. Churches and Monasteries. Multicoloured.

369 25b. Type **100** 10 10
370 1l.50 St. Nicolas's Church (vert) 15 10
371 1l.80 Palanca Church (vert) 20 10
372 3l. Butucheni Monastery . . 35 15

101 Judo

2000. Olympic Games, Sydney. Multicoloured.

373 25b. Type **101** 10 10
374 1l.80 Wrestling 20 10
375 5l. Weightlifting 55 25

102 Child and Schoolroom

2000. International Teachers' Day.

376 **102** 25b. grey and green . . . 10 10
377 – 3l.60 blue and lilac . . . 40 20
DESIGN: 3l.60, Teacher holding book.

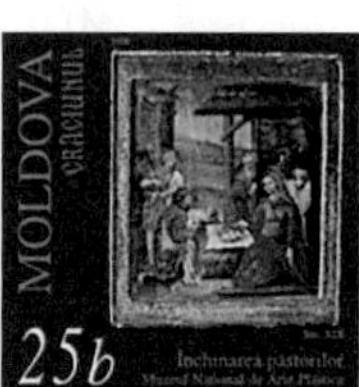

103 Adoration of the Shepherds (icon)

2000. Christmas. Multicoloured.

378 25b. Type **103** 10 10
379 1l.50 The Nativity (icon) . . 15 10
MS380 84 × 66 mm. 5l. Mary and Baby Jesus (icon) (27 × 32 mm) 3·25 3·25

104 Mother and Child

2001. 50th Anniv of United Nations High Commissioner for Refugees.

381 **104** 3l. multicoloured 30 15

105 Corncrake

2001. Endangered Species. The Corncrake. Multicoloured.

382 3l. Type **105** 30 15
383 3l. Singing 30 15
384 3l. In reeds 30 15
385 3l. With chicks 30 15
Nos. 382/5 were issued together, se-tenant, forming a composite design.

106 Yuri Gagarin and *Vostok* (spacecraft)

2001. 40th Anniv of First Manned Space Flight.

386 **106** 1l.80 multicoloured . . . 20 10

107 Maria Dragan

2001. Anniversaries. Multicoloured.
387 25b. Type **107** (singer, 15th death anniv) 10 10
388 1l. Marlene Dietrich (actress, birth centenary) 10 10
389 2l. Ruxandra Lupu (314th death anniv) 20 10
390 3l. Lidia Lipkovski (opera singer, 43rd death anniv) 30 15

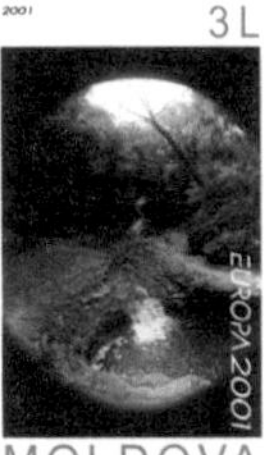

108 Waterfall

110 Stylized Humans (Aliona Valeria Samburic)

109 Prunariu

2001. Europa. Water Resources.
391 **108** 3l. multicoloured 25 15

2001. 20th Anniv of Space Flight by Dumitru Prunariu (first Rumanian cosmonaut).
392 **109** 1l.80 multicoloured . . . 15 10

2001. Winning Entries in Children's Painting Competition. Designs by named artist. Multicoloured.
393 25b. Type **110** 10 10
394 25b. Cars inside house and sun (Ion Sestacovschi) . . 10 10
395 25b. House, balloons and sun (Cristina Mereacre) 10 10
396 1l.80 Abstract painting (Andrei Sestacovschi) . . . 15 10

111 1991 7k. Arms Stamp

112 Tiger (*Panthera tigris*)

2001. 10th Anniv of First Moldovan Stamps. Sheet 100 × 74 mm, containing T **111** and similar multicoloured designs.
MS397 40b. Type **111**; 2l. 1991 13k. Arms stamp; 3l. 30k. 1991 Flag stamp (42 × 25 mm) 45 25

2001. Chisinau Zoo. Multicoloured.
398 40b. Type **112** 10 10
399 1l. Quagga (*Equus quagga*) 10 10
400 1l.50 Brown bear (*Ursus arctos*) 15 10
401 3l. + 30b. *Antilopa nilgau* . . 30 15
MS402 84 × 70 mm. 5l. Lion (*Panthera leo*) 45 25

113 Flag and Buildings

2001. 10th Anniv of Independence.
403 **113** 1l. multicoloured 10 10

114 Cimpoi

116 Nicolai Mavrocordat (1711–15)

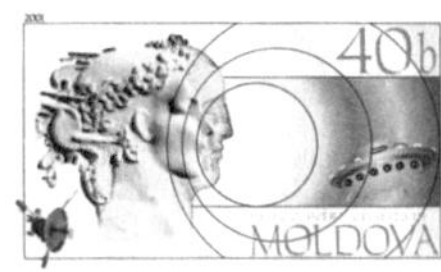

115 Women's Profiles and Space Ship

2001. Musical Instruments. Multicoloured.
404 40b. Type **114** 10 10
405 1l. Fluier 10 10
406 1l.80 Nai 15 10
407 3l. Tar'agot 25 15

2001. United Nations Year of Dialogue among Civilizations. Multicoloured.
408 40b. Type **115** 10 10
409 3l.60 Children encircling globe (vert) 30 15

2001. Rulers. Multicoloured (except **MS**416).
410 40b. Type **116** 10 10
411 40b. Mihai Racovita (1716–26) 10 10
412 40b. Constantin Mavrocordat (1748–49) 10 10
413 40b. Grigore Callimachi (1767–69) 10 10
414 1l. Grigore Alexandru Gnica (1774–77) 10 10
415 3l. Anton Cantemir (1705–7) 25 15
MS416 61 × 88 mm. 5l. Dimitrie Cantemir (1710–11) (black, yellow and red) (horiz) 45 25

117 St. Treime Basilica, Manastirea Saharna

2001. Christmas. Multicoloured.
417 40b. Type **117** 10 10
418 1l. Adormirea Maicii Domnului Basilica, Manastirea Hancu 10 10
419 3l. St. Dumitru Basilica, Orhei 25 15
420 3l.90 Nasterea Domnului Cathedral, Chisinau . . . 35 20

118 Emblem

2001. 10th Anniv of Union of Independent States.
421 **118** 1l.50 multicoloured . . . 15 10

119 Cross Country Sking

2002. Winter Olympic Games, Salt Lake City. Multicoloured.
422 40b. Type **119** 10 10
423 5l. Biathlon 45 25

120 Hora

2002. Traditional Dances. Multicoloured.
424 40b. Type **120** 10 10
425 1l.50 Sirba 15 10

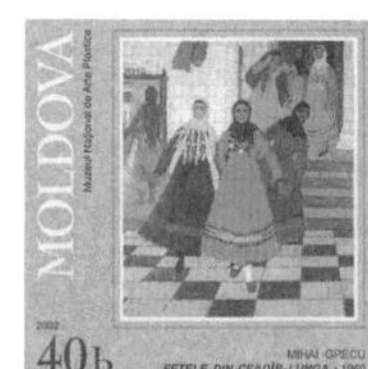

121 "Fetele din Ceadir-lunga" (Mihai Grecu)

2002. Art. Multicoloured.
426 40b. Type **121** 10 10
427 40b. "Meleag Natal" (Eleonora Romanescu) . . 10 10
428 1l.50 "Fata la Fereastra" (Valentina Rusu-Ciobanu) 15 10
429 3l. "In Doi" (Igor Vieru) . . 30 20

122 Entrance to Kishinev Circus

123 Rose

2002. Europa. Circus.
430 **122** 3l. multicoloured 30 20

2002. Botanical Gardens, Kishinev. Sheet 130 × 85 mm containing T **123** and similar vert designs. Multicoloured.
MS431 40b. Type **123**; 40b. Peony; 1l.50 Aster; 3l. Iris 50 30

124 Portrait of Cecilia Gallerani

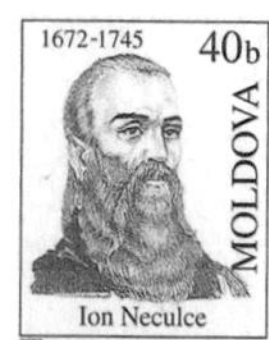

125 Ion Neculce (chronicler) (Lady with an Ermine)

2002. 550th Birth Anniv of Leonardo da Vinci (artist). Sheet 129 × 85 mm containing T **124** and similar vert designs. Multicoloured.
MS432 40b. Type **124**; 1l.50 The Virgin and Child with St. Anne; 3l. Mona Lisa (La Gioconda) . . 50 30

2002. Personalities. All sepia.
433 40b. Type **125** 10 10
434 40b. Nicolae Costin (chronicler) 10 10
435 40b. Grigore Ureche (chronicler) 10 10
436 40b. Nicolae Testemiteanu (rector, Faculty of Medicine, Chisnau University) 10 10
437 1l.50 Sergiu Radautan (rector, Technical Faculty, Chisnau University) . . . 15 10
438 3l.90 Alexandre Dumas (writer) 35 20

126 Vladimir Horse

2002. Horses. Showing horse breeds. Multicoloured.
439 40b. Type **126** 10 10
440 1l.50 Orlov 15 10
441 3l. Arab 30 20

127 Stork, Houses and Man carrying Grapes (Alexandru Catranji)

128 Union Emblem, Member States Presidents and Flags

2002. Children's Paintings. The Post. Multicoloured.
442 40b. Type **127** 10 10
443 1l.50 Birds, flower and globe 15 10
444 2l. Postman and globe . . . 20 15

2002. Union of Independent States Conference, Chisnau. Multicoloured.
445 1l.50 Type **128** 15 10
446 3l.60 Emblem and handshake 35 20

129 Entrance to Underground Warehouse

2002. 50th Anniv of Cricova Wine Factory. Multicoloured.
447 40b. Type **129** 10 10
448 40b. Barrels in warehouse . . 10 10
449 1l.50 Dining hall (vert) . . . 15 10
450 2l. Interior of warehouse . . 20 15
451 3l.60 Glasses and bottles of wine (vert) 35 20

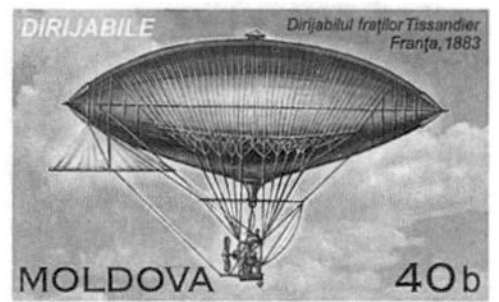

130 Tissandier Brothers' Airship (1883)

2003. Airships. Multicoloured.
452 40b. Type **130** 10 10
453 2l. "Uchebny" (Training Craft) (1908) 20 15
454 5l. LZ 127 "Graf Zeppelin" (1928) (inscr "Count Zeppelin") 50 30

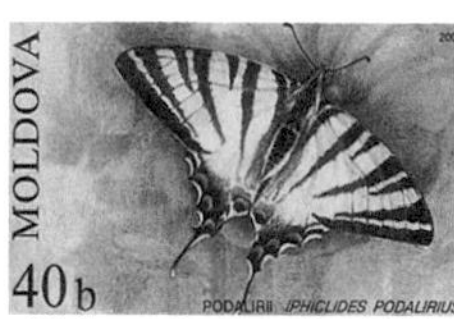

131 Scarce Swallowtail (*Iphiclides podalirius*)

2003. Butterflies and Moths. Multicoloured.
455 40b. Type **131** 10 10
456 2l. Jersey tiger moth (*Callimorpha quadripunctaria*) 20 15
457 3l. Oak hawk moth (*Marumba quercus*) 30 20
458 5l. Meleager's Blue (*Polyommatus daphnis*) . . 50 30
MS459 127 × 82 mm. Nos. 455/8 1·10 1·10

132 Rural Landscape

2003. 10th Anniv of Europa Stamps. Sheet 130 × 85 mm containing T **132** and similar horiz design. Multicoloured.
MS460 1l.50 Type **132**; 5l. Chisinau 60 60

133 Folk Ensemble "JOC"

135 Runner

134 Emblem and Flag

2003. Europa. Poster Art. Multicoloured.
461 3l. Type **133** 30 20
462 5l. Exhibition poster (Mihai Eminescu, 150th birth anniv (Rumanian writer)) 50 30

2003. Red Cross Society of Moldova. Multicoloured.
463 40b. Type **134** 10 10
464 5l. Damaged buildings and Red Cross workers 50 30

2003. European Youth Olympics Festival, Paris. Multicoloured.
465 40b. Type **135** 10 10
466 3l. Cyclists 30 20
467 5l. Gymnast 50 30

POSTAGE DUE STAMPS

D 33 Postal Emblems

1994.
D150 D **33** 30b. brown and green 50 50
D151 40b. green and lilac 65 65
One stamp in the pair was put on insufficiently franked mail, the other stamp on associated documents.

MONACO Pt. 6

A principality on the S. coast of France including the town of Monte Carlo.

1885. 100 centimes = 1 French franc.
2002. 100 cents = 1 euro.

1 Prince Charles III

2 Prince Albert

4 War Widow and Monaco

1885.
1 **1** 1c. olive 22·00 13·00
2 2c. lilac 42·00 19·00
3 5c. blue 50·00 26·00
4 10c. brown on yellow 65·00 26·00
5 15c. red £275 8·50
6 25c. green £500 48·00
7 40c. blue on red 60·00 35·00
8 75c. black on red £225 85·00
9 1f. black on yellow £1400 £400
10 5f. red on green £2500 £1700

1891.
11 **2** 1c. green 50 50
12 2c. purple 55 60
13 5c. blue 38·00 4·25
22 5c. green 35 30
14 10c. brown on yellow 85·00 9·50
23 10c. red 2·50 40
15a 15c. pink £150 6·50
24 15c. brown on yellow 2·50 70
25 15c. green 1·50 2·10
16 25c. green £225 19·00
26 25c. blue 14·00 3·00
17 40c. black on pink 2·50 1·90
18 50c. brown on orange 5·25 3·25
19a 75c. brown on buff 24·00 15·00
20 1f. black on yellow 15·00 8·50
21 5f. red on green £100 70·00
28 5f. mauve £200 £200
29 5f. green 18·00 22·00

1914. Surcharged **+5c.**
30 **2** 10c.+5c. red 5·50 5·00

1919. War Orphans Fund.
31 **4** 2c.+3c. mauve 27·00 23·00
32 5c.+5c. green 15·00 13·00
33 15c.+10c. red 15·00 13·00
34 25c.+15c. blue 32·00 29·00
35 50c.+50c. brown on orange £150 £130
36 1f.+1f. black on yellow £275 £275
37 5f.+5f. red £850 £950

1920. Princess Charlotte's Marriage. Nos. 33/7 optd **20 mars 1920** or surch also.
38 **4** 2c.+3c. on 15c.+10c. red 35·00 35·00
39 2c.+3c. on 25c.+15c. blue 35·00 35·00
40 2c.+3c. on 50c.+50c. brown on orange 35·00 35·00
41 5c.+5c. on 1f.+1f. black on yellow 35·00 35·00
42 5c.+5c.on 5f.+ 5f. red 35·00 35·00
43 15c.+10c. red 22·00 22·00
44 25c.+15c. blue 11·00 10·50
45 50c.+50c. brown on orange 45·00 45·00
46 1f.+1f. black on yellow 60·00 60·00
47 5f.+5f. red £5500 £5500

1921. Princess Antoinette's Baptism. Optd **28 DECEMBRE 1920** or surch also.
48 **2** 5c. green 55 55
49 75c. brown on buff 4·00 5·00
50 2f. on 5f. mauve 30·00 38·00

1922. Surch.
51 **2** 20c. on 15c. green 1·00 1·50
52 25c. on 10c. red 60 80
53 50c. on 1f. black on yellow 4·50 8·00

8 Prince Albert I

9 St. Devote Viaduct

1922.
54 **8** 25c. brown 3·00 3·50
55 – 30c. green 85 1·40
56 – 30c. red 40 40
57 **9** 40c. brown 45 55
58 – 50c. blue 3·50 3·25
59 – 60c. grey 35 30
60 – 1f. black on yellow 25 20
61a – 2f. red 45 40
62 – 5f. brown 28·00 30·00
63 – 5f. green on blue 8·00 8·00
64 – 10f. red 11·00 12·50
DESIGNS:—As Type **9**: 30, 50c. Oceanographic Museum; 60c., 1, 2f. The Rock; 5, 10f. Prince's Palace, Monaco.

12 Prince Louis

13 Prince Louis and Palace

1923.
65 **12** 10c. green 35 45
66 15c. red 50 60
67 20c. brown 30 45
68 25c. purple 25 45
69 **13** 50c. blue 25 45

1924. Surch with new value and bars.
70 **2** 45c. on 50c. brown on orange 50 65
71 75c. on 1f. black on yellow 45 45
72 85c. on 5f. green 30 45

14 15 16

17 St. Devote Viaduct

1924.
73 **14** 1c. grey 10 10
74 2c. brown 10 10
75 3c. mauve 1·90 1·90
76 5c. orange 30 20
77 10c. blue 10 10
78 **15** 15c. green 10 10
79 15c. violet 1·90 1·40
80 20c. mauve 15 10
81 20c. pink 20 10
82 25c. pink 10 10
83 25c. red on yellow 15 15
84 30c. orange 10 10
85 40c. brown 15 10
86 40c. blue on blue 25 20
87 45c. black 50 30
88 **16** 50c. green 15 20
89 **15** 50c. brown on yellow 10 10
90 **16** 60c. brown 10 20
91 **15** 60c. green on green 10 20
92 75c. green on green 20 20
93 75c. red on yellow 30 15
94 75c. black 60 30
95 80c. red on yellow 30 20
96 90c. red on yellow 1·25 95
97 **17** 1f. black on yellow 30 25
98 1f.05 mauve 30 25
99 1f.10 green 7·50 5·25
100 **15** 1f.25 blue on blue 10 25
101 1f.50 blue on blue 3·50 1·25
102 – 2f. brown and mauve 95 60
103 – 3f. lilac and red on yellow 16·00 7·75
104 – 5f. red and green 5·75 4·00
105 – 10f. blue and brown 16·00 15·00
DESIGN—As Type **17**: 2f. to 10f. Monaco.

1926. Surch.
106 **15** 30c. on 25c. pink 25 20
107 50c. on 60c. green on green 90 25
108 **17** 50c. on 1f.05 mauve 70 65
109 50c. on 1f.10 green 9·25 5·00
110 **15** 50c. on 1f.25 blue on blue 90 40
111 1f.25 on 1f. blue on blue 45 40
112 – 1f.50 on 2f. brown and mauve (No. 102) 3·75 3·25

20 Prince Charles III, Louis II and Albert I

1928. International Philatelic Exn, Monte Carlo.
113 **20** 50c. red 1·75 3·75
114 1f.50 blue 1·75 3·75
115 3f. violet 1·75 3·75

20a

21 Palace Entrance

22 St. Devote's Church

23 Prince Louis II

1933.
116 **20a** 1c. plum 10 10
117 2c. green 10 10
118 3c. purple 10 10
119 5c. red 10 10
120 10c. blue 10 10
121 15c. violet 70 1·10
122 **21** 15c. red 75 25
123 20c. brown 75 25
124 A 25c. sepia 1·10 35
125 **22** 30c. green 1·25 35
126 **23** 40c. sepia 2·50 1·50
127 B 45c. brown 2·25 1·40
128 **23** 50c. violet 2·10 85
129 C 65c. green 2·50 60
130 D 75c. blue 3·00 1·60
131 **23** 90c. red 5·25 2·40
132 **22** 1f. brown 21·00 5·75
133 D 1f.25 red 5·00 3·00
134 **23** 1f.50 blue 29·00 7·00
135 A 1f.75 red 27·00 6·75
136 1f.75 red 17·00 9·50
137 B 2f. blue 9·50 3·25
138 **21** 3f. violet 14·50 5·50
139 A 3f.50 orange 38·00 28·00
140 **22** 5f. purple 19·00 11·00
141 A 10f. blue £100 60·00
142 C 20f. black £275 £110
DESIGNS—HORIZ (as Type **21**): A, The Prince's Residence; B, The Rock of Monaco; C, Palace Gardens; D, Fortifications nd Harbour.
For other stamps in Type **20a** see Nos. 249, etc.

1933. Air. Surch with Bleriot XI airplane and **1f50.**
143 1f.50 on 5f. red & grn (No. 104) 21·00 19·00

28 Palace Gardens

1937. Charity.
144 **28** 50c.+50c. green 2·25 2·00
145 – 90c.+90c. red 2·25 2·00
146 – 1f.50+1f.50 blue 5·50 7·50
147 – 2f.+2f. violet 6·50 9·50
148 – 5f.+5f. red 95·00 90·00
DESIGNS—HORIZ: 90c. Exotic gardens; 1f.50, The Bay of Monaco. VERT: 2, 5f. Prince Louis II.

1937. Postage Due stamps optd **POSTES** or surch also.
149 D **18** 5 on 10c. violet 80 1·00
150 10c. violet 80 1·00
151 15 on 30c. bistre 80 1·00
152 20 on 30c. bistre 80 1·00
153 25 on 60c. red 1·00 1·25
154 30c. bistre 2·00 2·25
155 40 on 60c. red 1·75 1·75
156 50 on 60c. red 2·50 3·25
157 65 on 1f. blue 1·90 2·25
158 85 on 1f. blue 4·50 5·00
159 1f. blue 6·00 6·50
160 2f.15 on 2f. red 6·00 6·50
161 2f.25 on 2f. red 15·00 16·00
162 2f.50 on 2f. red 21·00 25·00

30a Prince Louis II

31

1938. National Fete Day. Sheet 100 × 120 mm.
MS163 **30a** 10f. purple 50·00 70·00

1938.
164 **31** 55c. brown 4·50 1·75
165 65c. violet 21·00 17·00
166 70c. brown 15 15
167 90c. violet 15 15
168 1f. red 13·00 6·00
169 1f.25 red 20 20
170 1f.75 blue 13·00 7·75
171 2f.25 blue 20 15

33 Monaco Hospital

1938. Anti-cancer Fund. 40th Anniv of Discovery of Radium.
172 – 65c.+25c. green 8·50 7·75
173 **33** 1f.75+50c. blue 8·50 9·50
DESIGN—VERT: 65c. Pierre and Marie Curie.

34 The Cathedral

38 Monaco Harbour

1939.
174 **34** 20c. mauve 15 15
175 – 25c. brown 30 20
176 – 30c. green 20 20
177 – 40c. red 20 20
178 – 45c. purple 35 20
179 – 50c. green 25 15
180 – 60c. red 20 20
181 – 60c. green 20 50
182 **38** 70c. lilac 35 20
183 75c. green 35 20
184 – 1f. black 20 20
185 – 1f.30 brown 20 20
186 – 2f. purple 20 20
187 – 2f.50 red 18·00 19·00
188 – 2f.50 blue 1·25 1·10
189 **38** 3f. red 40 20
190 **34** 5f. blue 2·25 2·75
191 – 10f. green 95 1·10
192 – 20f. blue 1·10 1·10
DESIGNS—VERT: 25, 40c., 2f. Place St. Nicholas; 30, 60c., 20f. Palace Gateway; 50c., 1f., 1f.30, Palace of Monaco. HORIZ: 45c., 2f.50, 10f. Aerial view of Monaco.

40 Louis II Stadium **41** Lucien

1939. Inauguration of Louis II Stadium, Monaco.
198 **40** 10f. green . . . . 80·00 90·00

1939. National Relief. 16th–18th-century portrait designs and view.
199 **41** 5c.+5c. black . . . . . . 1·50 1·00
200 – 10c.+10c. purple . . . . . 1·50 1·00
201 – 45c.+15c. green . . . . . 5·75 5·00
202 – 70c.+30c. mauve . . . . . 8·75 7·75
203 – 90c.+35c. violet . . . . . 8·75 7·75
204 – 1f.+1f. blue . . . . 22·00 22·00
205 – 2f.+2f. red . . . . 22·00 22·00
206 – 2f.25+1f.25 blue . . . . . 25·00 29·00
207 – 3f.+3f. red . . . . 32·00 42·00
208 – 5f.+5f. red . . . . 55·00 80·00
DESIGNS—VERT: 10c. Honore II; 45c. Louis I; 70c. Charlotte de Gramont; 90c. Antoine I; 1f. Marie de Lorraine; 2f. Jacques I; 2f.25, Louise-Hippolyte; 3f. Honore III. HORIZ: 5f. The Rock of Monaco.

1939. 8th International University Games. As T **40** but inscr "VIIIeme JEUX UNIVERSITAIRES INTERNATIONAUX 1939".
209 40c. green . . . . 90 1·25
210 70c. brown . . . . 1·25 1·50
211 90c. violet . . . . 1·40 2·25
212 1f.25 red . . . . 2·10 3·00
213 2f.25 blue . . . . 3·00 4·50

1940. Red Cross Ambulance Fund. As Nos. 174/92 in new colours surch with Red Cross and premium.
214 **34** 20c.+1f. violet . . . . . . 2·75 2·75
215 – 25c.+1f. green . . . . . . 2·75 2·75
216 – 30c.+1f. red . . . . 2·75 2·75
217 – 40c.+1f. blue . . . . . . 2·75 2·75
218 – 45c.+1f. red . . . . 3·00 3·00
219 – 50c.+1f. brown . . . . . 3·00 3·00
220 – 60c.+1f. green . . . . . 3·00 3·00
221 **38** 75c.+1f. black . . . . . . 3·50 3·50
222 – 1f.+1f. red . . . . 4·00 4·25
223 – 2f.+1f. slate . . . . . . 4·00 4·75
224 – 2f.50+1f. green . . . . . 9·00 10·50
225 **38** 3f.+1f. blue . . . . 11·00 11·00
226 **34** 5f.+1f. black . . . . . . 12·00 13·00
227 – 10f.+5f. blue . . . . . . 24·00 22·00
228 – 20f.+5f. purple . . . . . . 24·00 33·00

44 Prince Louis II

1941.
229 **44** 40c. red 40 40
230 80c. green 40 40
231 1f. violet 10 10
232 1f.20 green 10 10
233 1f.50 red 10 10
234 1f.50 violet 10 10
235 2f. green 10 10
236 2f.40 red 10 10
237 2f.50 blue 70 70
238 4f. blue 10 10

45 **46**

1941. National Relief Fund.
239 **45** 25c.+25c. purple . . . . . 60 1·10
240 **46** 50c.+25c. brown . . . . . 60 1·10
241 75c.+50c. purple . . . . . 1·60 1·50
242 **45** 1f.+1f. blue . . . . 1·60 1·50
243 **46** 1f.50+1f.50 red . . . . . 1·75 2·75
244 **45** 2f.+2f. green . . . . . . 1·75 2·75
245 **46** 2f.50+2f. blue . . . . . . 2·25 3·50
246 **45** 3f.+3f. brown . . . . . . 2·25 3·50
247 **46** 5f.+5f. green . . . . . . 6·25 7·00
248 **45** 10f.+8f. sepia . . . . . . 13·50 14·00

1941. New values and colours.
249 **20a** 10c. black 10 10
250 – 30c. red (as No. 176) . . 20 25
251 **20a** 30c. green 10 10
252 40c. red 10 10
253 50c. violet 10 10
362 **34** 50c. brown 15 25
254 **20a** 60c. blue 10 10
363 – 60c. pink (as No. 175) . . 15 25
255 **20a** 70c. brown 15 10
256 **34** 80c. green 10 20
257 – 1f. brown (as Nos. 178) 10 10
258 **38** 1f.20 blue 15 15
259 – 1f.50 blue (as Nos. 175) 20 20
260 **38** 2f. blue 10 10
261 – 2f. green (as No. 179) . . 20 20
262 – 3f. black (as No. 175) . . 10 10
364 – 3f. purple (as No. 176) . . 40 30
391 – 3f. green (as No. 175) . . 1·25 90
263 **34** 4f. purple 20 40
365 – 4f. green (as No. 175) . . 40 30
264 – 4f.50 violet (as No. 179) 10 25
265 – 5f. green (as No. 176) . . 10 25
392 – 5f. green (as No. 178) . . 30 10
393 – 5f. red (as No. 176) . . . 50 40
266 – 6f. violet (as No. 179) . . 60 30
368 – 8f. brown (as No. 179) . . 1·50 1·75
267 **34** 10f. blue 10 25
370 – 10f. brown (as No. 179) 2·00 1·25
394 **38** 10f. yellow 80 35
268 15f. red 20 25
269 – 20f. brown (as No. 178) 40 25
373 – 20f. red (as No. 178) . . 80 50
270 **38** 25f. green . . . . 1·25 85
374 25f. black . . . . 20·00 12·50
397 – 25f. blue (as No. 176) . . 32·00 12·50
398 – 25f. red (as No. 179) . . 2·00 2·25
399 – 30f. blue (as No. 176) . . 6·00 3·25
400 – 35f. blue (as No. 179) . . 6·50 3·00
401 **34** 40f. red . . . . 6·00 4·00
402 50f. violet . . . . 3·50 85
403 – 65f. violet (as No. 178) . . 12·00 6·00
404 **34** 70f. yellow . . . . 8·75 6·00
405 – 75f. green (as No. 175) . . 20·00 8·00
406 – 85f. red (as No. 175) . . 12·50 5·00
407 – 100f. turquoise (as No. 178) . . . . 12·00 5·50

47 Caudron Rafale over Monaco **48** Propeller and Palace

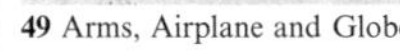

49 Arms, Airplane and Globe **50** Charles II

1942. Air.
271 **47** 5f. green 30 30
272 10f. blue 30 30
273 **48** 15f. brown 40 60
274 – 20f. brown 50 90
275 – 50f. purple . . . . 2·40 3·00
276 **49** 100f. red and purple . . . 2·40 3·00
DESIGNS—VERT: 20f. Pegasus. HORIZ: 50f. Mew gull over Bay of Monaco.

1942. National Relief Fund. Royal Personages.
277 – 2c.+3c. blue 20 30
278 **50** 5c.+5c. red 20 30
279 – 10c.+5c. black 20 30
280 – 20c.+10c. green 20 30
281 – 30c.+30c. purple 20 30
282 – 40c.+40c. red 20 30
283 – 50c.+50c. violet 20 30
284 – 75c.+75c. purple 20 30
285 – 1f.+1f. green 20 30
286 – 1f.50+1f. red 20 30
287 – 2f.50+2f.50 violet . . . . 1·90 3·75
288 – 3f.+3f. blue . . . . 1·90 3·75
289 – 5f.+5f. sepia . . . . . . 2·50 5·25
290 – 10f.+5f. purple . . . . . 3·00 5·25
291 – 20f.+5f. blue . . . . . . 3·00 6·00
PORTRAITS: 2c. Rainier Grimaldi; 10c. Jeanne Grimaldi; 20c. Charles Auguste, Goyon de Matignon; 30c. Jacques I; 40c. Louise-Hippolyte; 50c. Charlotte Grimaldi; 75c. Marie Charles Grimaldi; 1f. Honore III; 1f.50, Honore IV; 2f.50, Honore V; 3f. Florestan I; 5f. Charles III; 10f. Albert I; 20f. Princess Marie-Victoire.

52 Prince Louis II

1943.
292 **52** 50f. violet 45 75

53 St. Devote **54** Blessing the Sea

55 Arrival of St. Devote at Monaco

1944. Charity. Festival of St. Devote.
293 **53** 50c.+50c. brown 20 20
294 – 70c.+80c. blue 20 20
295 – 80c.+70c. green 20 20
296 – 1f.+1f. purple 20 20
297 – 1f.50+1f.50 red 30 45
298 **54** 2f.+2f. purple 40 60
299 – 5f.+2f. violet 45 60
300 – 10f.+40f. blue 45 60
301 **55** 20f.+60f. blue . . . . . . 3·00 5·50
DESIGNS—VERT: 70c., 1f. Various processional scenes; 1f.50, Burning the boat; 10f. Trial scene. HORIZ: 80c. Procession; 5f. St. Devote's Church.

1945. Air. For War Dead and Deported Workers. As Nos. 272/6 (colours changed) surch.
302 1f.+4f. on 10f. red 50 45
303 1f.+4f. on 15f. brown 50 45
304 1f.+4f. on 20f. brown 50 45
305 1f.+4f. on 50f. blue 50 45
306 1f.+4f. on 100f. purple . . . 50 45

57 Prince Louis II **58** Prince Louis II

1946.
361 **57** 30c. black 15 10
389 50c. olive 15 25
390 1f. violet 20 10
307 2f.50 green 30 30
308 3f. mauve 30 30
366 5f. brown 40 30
309 6f. red 30 30
367 6f. purple . . . . 3·50 1·75
310 10f. blue 30 30
369 10f. orange 40 25
371 12f. red . . . . 4·00 2·10
395 12f. slate . . . . 6·00 5·00
396 15f. lake . . . . 6·00 3·50
372 18f. blue . . . . 7·00 5·50
311 **58** 50f. grey . . . . 2·50 1·50
312 100f. red . . . . 3·50 2·25

59 Child Praying **60** Nurse and Baby

1946. Child Welfare Fund.
313 **59** 1f.+3f. green 30 30
314 2f.+4f. red 30 30
315 4f.+6f. blue 30 30
316 5f.+40f. mauve 80 75
317 10f.+60f. red 80 75
318 15f.+100f. blue . . . . . 1·25 1·25

1946. Anti-tuberculosis Fund.
319 **60** 2f.+8f. blue 40 65

1946. Air. Optd **POSTE AERIENNE** over Sud Ouest Cassiopees airplane.
320 **58** 50f. grey . . . . 3·00 4·00
321 100f. red . . . . 4·75 3·25

62 Steamship and Chart

1946. Stamp Day.
322 **62** 3f.+2f. blue 30 40

63

1946. Air.
323 **63** 40f. red 60 75
324 50f. brown . . . . 1·50 90
325 100f. green . . . . 2·50 1·75
326 200f. violet . . . . 2·50 2·00
326a 300f. blue and ultramarine 55·00 50·00
326b 500f. green and deep green . . . . 35·00 30·00
326c 1000f. violet and brown 60·00 55·00

64 Pres. Roosevelt and Palace of Monaco

66 Pres. Roosevelt

1946. President Roosevelt Commemoration.
327 **66** 10c. mauve (postage) . . . 30 25
328 – 30c. blue 30 15
329 **64** 60c. green 30 25
330 – 1f. sepia 80 85
331 – 2f.+3f. green 80 95
332 – 3f. violet . . . . 1·25 1·25

333 – 5f. red (air) 40 50
334 – 10f. black 70 45
335 **66** 15f.+10f. orange . . . . . 1·50 1·25
DESIGNS—HORIZ: 30c., 5f. Rock of Monaco; 2f. Viaduct and St. Devote. VERT: 1, 3, 10f. Map of Monaco.

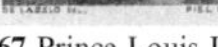

67 Prince Louis II **68** Pres. Roosevelt as a Philatelist

69 Statue of Liberty and New York Harbour

1947. Participation in the Centenary International Philatelic Exhibition, New York. (a) Postage.
336 **67** 10f. blue . . . . 3·25 3·25

(b) Air. Dated "1847 1947"
337 **68** 50c. violet 80 90
338 – 1f.50 mauve 30 40
339 – 3f. orange 40 45
340 – 10f. blue . . . . 2·75 2·75
341 **69** 15f. red . . . . 4·50 4·50
DESIGNS—HORIZ: As Type **68**: 1f.50, G.P.O., New York; 3f. Oceanographic Museum, Monte Carlo. As Type **69**: 10f. Bay of Monaco.

1947. Twenty-fifth Year of Reign of Prince Louis II. Sheet 85 × 98 mm.
MS341a 200f.+300f. brown . . . 22·00 15·00

70 Prince Charles III

1948. Stamp Day.
342 **70** 6f.+4f. green on blue . . . 40 40

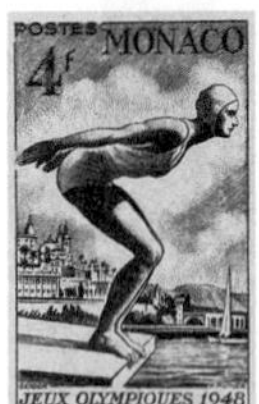

71 Diving **72** Tennis

1948. Olympic Games, Wembley. Inscr "JEUX OLYMPIQUES 1948".
343 – 50c. green (postage) . . . 20 20
344 – 1f. red 20 20
345 – 2f. blue 70 55
346 – 2f.50 red . . . . 1·75 3·50
347 **71** 4f. slate . . . . 1·90 1·75

348 – 5f.+5f. brown (air) . . . . 7·25 7·25
349 – 6f.+9f. violet . . . . . . 12·00 10·00
350 **72** 10f.+15f. red . . . . . . 20·00 18·00
351 – 15f.+25f. blue . . . . . . 24·00 25·00
DESIGNS—HORIZ: 50c. Hurdling; 15f. Yachting. VERT: 1f. Running; 2f. Throwing the discus; 2f.50, Basketball; 5f. Rowing; 6f. Skiing.

75 The Salmacis Nymph **77** F. J. Bosio (wrongly inscr "J. F.")

1948. Death Centenary of Francois Joseph Bosio (sculptor).
352 **75** 50c. green (postage) . . . 40 25
353 – 1f. red 40 25
354 – 2f. blue 80 55
355 – 2f.50 violet . . . . 2·25 1·60
356 **77** 4f. mauve . . . . 2·25 1·90

357 – 5f.+5f. blue (air) . . . . . 12·00 14·00
358 – 6f.+9f. green . . . . . . 12·00 14·00
359 – 10f.+15f. red . . . . . . 13·00 14·00
360 – 15f.+25f. brown . . . . . 16·00 18·00
DESIGNS—VERT: 1, 5f. Hercules struggling with Achelous; 2, 6f. Aristaeus (Garden God); 15f. The Salmacis Nymph (36×48 mm). HORIZ: 2f.50, 10f. Hyacinthus awaiting his turn to throw a quoit.

79 Exotic Gardens **80** "Princess Alice II"

1949. Birth Centenary of Prince Albert I.
375 – 2f. blue (postage) 20 20
376 **79** 3f. green 20 20
377 – 4f. brown and blue 30 25
378 **80** 5f. red 80 85
379 – 6f. violet 50 55
380 – 10f. sepia . . . . 70 1·85
381 – 12f. pink . . . . 1·40 1·40
382 – 18f. orange and brown . . 2·50 2·75

383 – 20f. brown (air) 50 65
384 – 25f. blue 50 65
385 – 40f. green . . . . 95 1·40
386 – 50f. green, brown and black . . . . 1·50 1·75
387 – 100f. red . . . . 5·75 6·50
388 – 200f. orange . . . . . . 11·00 10·50
DESIGNS—HORIZ: 2f. Yacht "Hirondelle I" (1870); 4f. Oceanographic Museum, Monaco; 10f. "Hirondelle II" (1914); 12f. Albert harpooning whale; 18f. Buffalo (Palaeolithic mural); 20f. Constitution Day, 1911; 25f. Paris Institute of Palaeontology; 200f. Coin with effigy of Albert. VERT: 6f. Statue of Albert at tiller; 40f. Anthropological Museum; 50f. Prince Albert I; 100f. Oceanographic Institute, Paris.

82a Princess Charlotte **83** Palace of Monaco and Globe

1949. Red Cross Fund. Sheet 150×172½ mm, containing vert portraits as T **82a**.
MS408 10f.+5f. brown and red; 40f.+5f. green and red; 15f.+5f. red and 25f.+5f. blue and red. Each ×4 . . . . £300 £300
MS409 As **MS**408 but imperf . . £300 £300
DESIGNS: 10, 40f. T **82a**; 15, 25f, Prince Rainier.

1949. 75th Anniv of U.P.U.
410 **83** 5f. green (postage) 30 35
411 10f. orange . . . . 3·50 4·00
412 15f. red 45 55

413 25f. blue (air) 50 55
414 40f. sepia and brown . . . 1·50 1·60
415 50f. blue and green . . . . 2·50 2·75
416 100f. blue and red . . . . 3·50 4·00

84 Prince Rainier III and Monaco Palace **85** Prince Rainier III

1950. Accession of Prince Rainier III.
417 **84** 10c. purple & red (postage) 10 10
418 50c. brown, lt brn & orge 10 10
419 1f. violet 20 25
420 5f. deep green and green 1·60 1·40
421 15f. carmine and red . . . 3·00 3·00
422 25f. blue, green & ultram 3·00 3·75

423 50f. brown and black (air) 4·75 5·25
424 100f. blue, dp brn & brn 7·75 6·75

1950.
425 **85** 50c. violet 20 10
426 1f. brown 20 10
434 5f. green . . . . 6·75 3·75
427 6f. green 95 60
428 8f. green . . . . 4·50 1·75
429 8f. orange . . . . 1·10 70
435 10f. orange . . . . 10·50 5·50
430 12f. blue . . . . 1·10 30
431 15f. red . . . . 2·00 50
432 15f. blue . . . . 1·40 40
433 18f. red . . . . 3·50 1·10

86 Prince Albert I **87** Edmond and Jules de Goncourt

1951. Unveiling of Prince Albert Statue.
436 **86** 15f. blue . . . . 5·75 5·75

1951. 50th Anniv of Goncourt Academy.
437 **87** 15f. purple . . . . 5·75 5·25

88 St. Vincent de Paul **90** St. Peter's Keys and Papal Bull

89 Judgement of St. Devote

1951. Holy Year.
438 **88** 10c. blue, ultramarine & red 20 20
439 – 50c. violet and red 20 20
440 **89** 1f. green and brown . . . 20 25
441 **90** 2f. red and purple 30 45
442 – 5f. green 30 30
443 – 12f. violet 40 45
444 – 15f. red . . . . 3·00 3·00
445 – 20f. brown . . . . 4·50 5·25
446 – 25f. blue . . . . 5·75 7·25
447 – 40f. violet and mauve . . . 7·75 8·25
448 – 50f. brown and olive . . . 9·50 11·00
449 – 100f. brown . . . . 20·00 22·00
DESIGNS—TRIANGULAR: 50c. Pope Pius XII. HORIZ (as Type **90**): 5f. Mosaic. VERT (as Type **90**): 12f. Prince Rainier III in St. Peter's; 15f. St. Nicholas of Patara; 20f. St. Romain; 25f. St. Charles Borromeo; 40f. Coliseum; 50f. Chapel of St. Devote. VERT (as Type **89**): 100f. Rainier of Westphalia.

93 Wireless Mast and Monaco **94** Seal of Prince Rainier III

1951. Monte Carlo Radio Station.
450 **93** 1f. orange, red and blue . . 50 25
451 15f. purple, red and violet 2·50 80
452 30f. brown and blue . . . 11·50 4·50

1951.
453 **94** 1f. violet 60 50
454 5f. black . . . . 2·10 1·40
512 5f. violet . . . . 3·00 70
513 6f. red . . . . 3·50 1·10
455 8f. red . . . . 5·25 3·00
514 8f. brown . . . . 4·00 2·75
456 15f. green . . . . 7·75 5·75
515 15f. blue . . . . 11·50 3·50
457 30f. blue . . . . 15·00 11·50
516 30f. green . . . . 14·50 11·00

1951. Nos. **MS**408/9 surch **1f. on 10f.+5f., 3f. on 15f.+5f., 5f. on 25f. + 5f., 6f. on 40f.+5f.**
MS458 As above £300 £180
MS459 As above imperf £300 £180

95 Gallery of Hercules

1952. Monaco Postal Museum.
460 **95** 5f. chestnut and brown . . 30 35
461 15f. violet and purple . . . 60 35
462 30f. indigo and blue . . . 1·10 40

96 Football

1953. 15th Olympic Games, Helsinki. Inscr "HELSINKI 1952".
463 – 1f. mauve & violet (postage) 20 25
464 **96** 2f. blue and green 20 25
465 – 3f. pale and deep blue . . 20 25
466 – 5f. green and brown . . . 60 30
467 – 8f. red and lake . . . . . 1·50 85
468 – 15f. brown, green and blue 80 70

469 – 40f. black (air) . . . . . . 7·75 6·75
470 – 50f. violet . . . . 9·00 6·75
471 – 100f. green . . . . 13·00 11·00
472 – 200f. red . . . . 17·00 11·50
DESIGNS: 1f. Basketball; 3f. Sailing; 5f. Cycling; 8f. Gymnastics; 15f. Louis II Stadium, Monaco; 40f. Running; 50f. Fencing; 100f. Rifle target and Arms of Monaco; 200f. Olympic torch.

97 "Journal Inedit"

1953. Centenary of Publication of Journal by E. and J. de Goncourt.
473 **97** 5f. green 50 35
474 15f. brown . . . . 2·25 1·25

98 Physalia, Yacht "Princess Alice", Prince Albert, Richet and Portier

1953. 50th Anniv of Discovery of Anaphylaxis.
475 **98** 2f. violet, green and brown 20 20
476 5f. red, lake and green . . 50 20
477 15f. lilac, blue and green 2·25 1·25

99 F. Ozanam **100** St. Jean-Baptiste de la Salle

1954. Death Centenary of Ozanam (founder of St. Vincent de Paul Conferences).
478 **99** 1f. red 20 25
479 – 5f. blue 30 35
480 **99** 15f. black . . . . 1·50 1·25
DESIGN: 5f. Outline drawing of Sister of Charity.

1954. St. J.-B. de la Salle (educationist).
481 **100** 1f. red 20 25
482 – 5f. sepia 30 45
483 **100** 15f. blue . . . . 1·50 1·25
DESIGN: 5f. Outline drawing of De la Salle and two children.

101 **102** **103**

1954. Arms.
484 – 50c. red, black and mauve 10 10
485 – 70c. red, black and blue 10 10
486 **101** 80c. red, black and green 10 10
487 – 1f. red, black and blue . . 10 10
488 **102** 2f. red, black and orange 10 10
489 – 3f. red, black and green 10 10
490 **103** 5f. multicoloured 20 25
DESIGNS—HORIZ: 50c. as Type **101**. VERT: 70c., 1, 3f. as Type **102**.

104 Seal of Prince Rainier III **105** Lambarene

106 Dr. Albert Schweitzer

1954. Precancelled.
491 **104** 4f. red . . . . 1·25 60
492 5f. blue 30 20
493 8f. green . . . . 1·25 80
494 8f. purple 80 45
495 10f. green 20 20
496 12f. violet . . . . 4·00 2·75
497 15f. orange 80 60
498 20f. green . . . . 1·25 80
499 24f. brown . . . . 6·75 3·25
500 30f. blue . . . . 1·40 95
501 40f. brown . . . . 2·00 1·60

502 45f. red . . . . 2·00 1·25
503 55f. blue . . . . 5·00 3·50
See also Nos. 680/3.

1955. 80th Birthday of Dr. Schweitzer (humanitarian).
504 **105** 2f. grn, turq & bl (postage) 20 20
505 **106** 5f. blue and green 70 95
506 – 15f. purple, black and green . . . . 2·10 2·00
507 – 200f. slate, grn & bl (air) 22·00 25·00
DESIGNS—As Type **106**: 15f. Lambarene Hospital. HORIZ (48 × 27 mm): 200f. Schweitzer and jungle scene.

107 Great Cormorants

1955. Air.
508a – 100f. indigo and blue . . 15·00 15·00
509 – 200f. black and blue . . 17·00 9·50
510 – 500f. grey and green . . 29·00 20·00
511a **107** 1,000f. black, turq & grn 70·00 50·00
DESIGNS—As Type **107**: 100f. Roseate tern; 200f. Herring gull; 500f. Wandering albatrosses.

108 Eight Starting Points **109** Prince Rainier III

1955. 25th Monte Carlo Car Rally.
517 **108** 100f. red and brown . . . 60·00 60·00

1955.
518 **109** 6f. purple and green . . . 30 25
519 8f. violet and red 30 25
520 12f. green and red 30 25
521 15f. blue and purple . . . 70 25
522 18f. blue and orange . . . 3·00 25
523 20f. turquoise . . . . . . 1·40 45
524 25f. black and orange . . 70 40
525 30f. sepia and blue . . . 9·75 5·00
526 30f. violet . . . . 3·00 1·75
527 35f. brown . . . . 2·50 1·90
528 50f. lake and green . . . 3·50 1·25
See also Nos. 627/41.

110 "La Maison a Vapeur"

111 "The 500 Millions of the Begum" **113** U.S.S. "Nautilus"

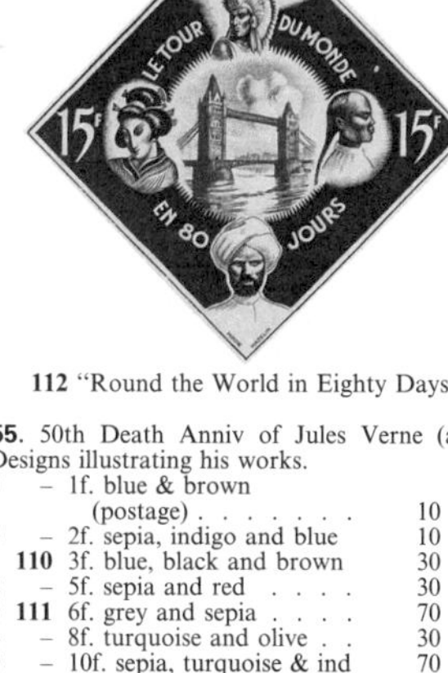

112 "Round the World in Eighty Days"

1955. 50th Death Anniv of Jules Verne (author). Designs illustrating his works.
529 – 1f. blue & brown (postage) 10 10
530 – 2f. sepia, indigo and blue 10 10
531 **110** 3f. blue, black and brown 30 30
532 – 5f. sepia and red 30 30
533 **111** 6f. grey and sepia 70 60
534 – 8f. turquoise and olive . . 30 30
535 – 10f. sepia, turquoise & ind 70 60
536 **112** 15f. red and brown . . . 60 50
537 – 25f. black and green . . . 1·75 1·25
538 **113** 30f. black, purple & turq 4·00 3·25
539 – 200f. indigo and blue (air) 21·00 20·00
DESIGNS—VERT (as Type **111**): 1f. "Five Weeks in a Balloon". HORIZ (as Type **110**): 2f. "A Floating Island"; 10f. "Journey to the Centre of the Earth"; 25f. "20,000 Leagues under the Sea"; 200f. "From the Earth to the Moon". (as Type **111**): 5f. "Michael Strogoff"; 8f. "Le Superbe Orenoque".

114 "The Immaculate Virgin" (F. Brea)

1955. Marian Year.
540 **114** 5f. green, grey and brown 20 20
541 – 10f. green, grey and brown 30 30
542 – 15f. brown and sepia . . 40 40
DESIGNS—As Type **114**: 10f. "Madonna" (L. Brea). As Type **113**: 15f. Bienheureux Rainier.

115 Rotary Emblem

1955. 50th Anniv of Rotary International.
543 **115** 30f. blue and yellow . . . 70 85

116 George Washington

118 President Eisenhower

117 Abraham Lincoln

1956. 5th International Stamp Exhibition, New York.
544 **116** 1f. violet and lilac 10 10
545 – 2f. lilac and purple . . . 20 20
546 **117** 3f. blue and violet 20 20
547 **118** 5f. red 20 20
548 – 15f. brown and chocolate 50 40
549 – 30f. black, indigo and blue . . . . 2·25 1·25
550 – 40f. brown . . . . 3·00 1·50
551 – 50f. red . . . . 3·50 1·50
552 – 100f. green . . . . 3·50 2·50
DESIGNS—As Type **117**: 2f. F. D. Roosevelt. HORIZ (as Type **116**): 15f. Monaco Palace in the 18th century; 30f. Landing of Columbus. (48 × 36 mm): 50f. Aerial view of Monaco Palace in the 18th century; 100f. Louisiana landscape in 18th century. VERT (as Type **118**): 40f. Prince Rainier III.

120

1956. 7th Winter Olympic Games, Cortina d'Ampezzo and 16th Olympic Games, Melbourne.
553 – 15f. brown, green & pur 80 60
554 **120** 30f. red . . . . 1·40 1·40
DESIGN: 15f. "Italia" ski-jump.

1956. Nos. D482/95 with "TIMBRE TAXE" barred out and some surch also. (a) Postage.
555 2f. on 4f. slate and brown . . 30 30
556 2f. on 4f. brown and slate . . 30 30
557 3f. lake and green 30 30
558 3f. green and lake 30 30
559 5f. on 4f. slate and brown . . 50 40
560 5f. on 4f. brown and slate . . 50 40
561 10f. on 4f. slate and brown 70 60
562 10f. on 4f. brown and slate 70 60
563 15f. on 5f. violet and blue . . 1·10 1·40
564 15f. on 5f. blue and violet . . 1·10 1·40
565 20f. violet and blue . . . . . 1·75 2·25
566 20f. blue and violet . . . . . 1·75 2·25
567 25f. on 20f. violet and blue 3·50 2·50
568 25f. on 20f. blue and violet 3·50 2·50
569 30f. on 10f. indigo and blue 5·50 4·00
570 30f. on 10f. blue and indigo 5·50 4·00
571 40f. on 50f. brown and red 7·75 6·00
572 40f. on 50f. red and brown 7·75 6·00
573 50f. on 100f. green and purple . . . . 11·00 8·75
574 50f. on 100f. purple and green . . . . 11·00 8·75
(b) Air. Optd **POSTE AERIENNE** also.
575 100f. on 20f. violet and blue 6·75 7·75
576 100f. on 20f. blue and violet 6·75 7·75

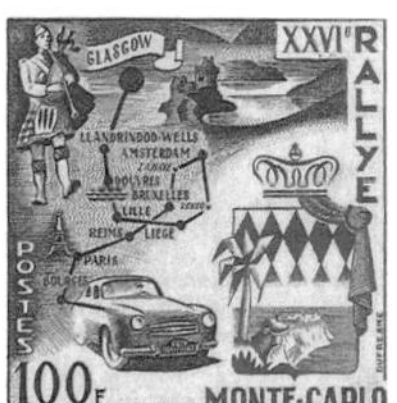

121 Route Map from Glasgow

1956. 26th Monte Carlo Car Rally.
577 **121** 100f. brown and red . . . 17·00 19·00

122 Princess Grace and Prince Rainier III

1956. Royal Wedding.
578 **122** 1f. black & grn (postage) 10 10
579 2f. black and red 10 10
580 3f. black and blue 10 20
581 5f. black and green . . . 20 25
582 15f. black and brown . . 20 40
583 100f. brown & purple (air) 60 40
584 200f. brown and red . . . 60 40
585 500f. brown and grey . . 2·00 1·60

123 Princess Grace **124** Princess Grace with Princess Caroline

1957. Birth of Princess Caroline.
586 **123** 1f. grey 10 10
587 2f. olive 10 10
588 3f. brown 10 10
589 5f. red 20 20
590 15f. pink 20 25
591 25f. blue 60 55
592 30f. violet 60 55
593 50f. red . . . . 1·10 65
594 75f. orange . . . . 2·00 1·60

1958. Birth of Prince Albert.
595 **124** 100f. black . . . . 5·50 4·00

125 Order of St. Charles

126 Route Map from Munich

1958. Centenary of Creation of National Order of St. Charles.
596 **125** 100f. multicoloured . . . 1·50 1·60

1958. 27th Monte Carlo Rally
597 **126** 100f. multicoloured . . . 5·00 5·50

127 Statue of the Holy Virgin and Popes Pius IX and Pius XII

1958. Centenary of Apparition of Virgin Mary at Lourdes.
598 **127** 1f. grey & brown (postage) 10 10
599 – 2f. violet and blue 10 10
600 – 3f. sepia and green . . . 10 10
601 – 5f. blue and sepia 10 10
602 – 8f. multicoloured 20 25
603 – 10f. multicoloured 20 20
604 – 12f. multicoloured 30 25
605 – 20f. myrtle and purple . . 30 25
606 – 35f. myrtle, bistre and brown 40 35
607 – 50f. blue, green and lake 60 55
608 – 65f. turquoise and blue 80 70
609 – 100f. grey, myrtle and blue (air) . . . . 1·40 1·10
610 – 200f. brown and chestnut 1·90 1·75
DESIGNS—VERT (26½ × 36 mm): 2f. St. Bernadette; 3f. St. Bernadette at Bartres; 5f. The Miracle of Bourriette; 20f. St. Bernadette at prayer; 35f. St. Bernadette's canonization. (22 × 36 mm): 8f. Stained-glass window. As Type **127**: 50f. St. Bernadette, Pope Pius XI, Mgr. Laurence and Abbe Peyramale. HORIZ (48 × 36 mm): 10f. Lourdes grotto; 12f. Interior of Lourdes grotto. (36 × 26½ mm): 65f. Shrine of St. Bernadette; (48 × 27 mm): 100f. Lourdes Basilica; 200f. Pope Pius X and subterranean interior of Basilica.

128 Princess Grace and Clinic

1959. Opening of new Hospital Block in "Princess Grace" Clinic, Monaco.
611 **128** 100f. grey, brown & green 2·50 1·50

129 U.N.E.S.C.O. Headquarters, Paris, and Cultural Emblems

1959. Inaug of U.N.E.S.C.O. Headquarters Building.

No.	Type	Description	Unused	Used
612	**129**	25f. multicoloured	20	20
613	–	50f. turquoise, black & ol	30	35

DESIGN: 50f. As Type **129** but with heads of children and letters of various alphabets in place of the emblems.

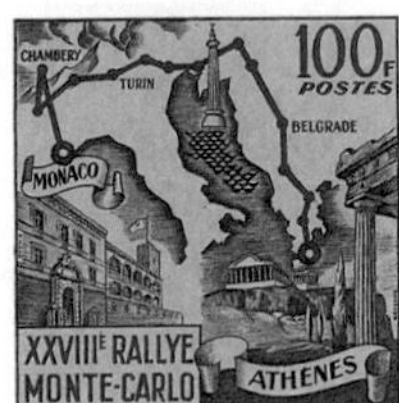

130 Route Map from Athens

1959. 28th Monte Carlo Rally.

No.	Type	Description	Unused	Used
614	**130**	100f. blue, red & grn on bl	4·50	3·50

131 Prince Rainier and Princess Grace

1959. Air.

No.	Type	Description	Unused	Used
615	**131**	300f. violet	9·50	6·75
616		500f. blue	14·50	12·50

See also Nos. 642/3.

132 "Princess Caroline" Carnation

1959. Flowers.

No.	Type	Description	Unused	Used
617	**132**	5f. mauve, green & brown	10	10
618	–	10f. on 3f. pink, green and brown	10	10
619	–	15f. on 1f. yellow & green	20	25
620	–	20f. purple and green	50	40
621	–	25f. on 6f. red, yellow and green	70	65
622	–	35f. pink and green	1·40	1·60
623	–	50f. green and sepia	2·25	1·75
624	–	85f. on 65f. lavender, bronze and green	2·75	2·00
625	–	100f. red and green	4·50	3·00

FLOWERS—As Type **132**: 10f. "Princess Grace" carnation; 100f. "Grace of Monaco" rose. VERT (22 × 36 mm): 15f. Mimosa; 25f. Geranium. HORIZ (36 × 22 mm): 20f. Bougainvillea; 35f. "Laurier" rose; 50f. Jasmine; 85f. Lavender.

(New currency. 100 (old) francs = 1 (new franc.)

133 "Uprooted Tree" **134** Oceanographic Museum

1960. World Refugee Year.

No.	Type	Description	Unused	Used
626	**133**	25c. green, blue and black	20	25

1960. Prince Rainier types with values in new currency.

No.	Type	Description	Unused	Used
627	**109**	25c. blk & orge (postage)	30	10
628		30c. violet	40	10
629		40c. red and brown	40	20
630		45c. brown and grey	40	20
631		50c. red and green	50	25
632		50c. red and brown	50	30
633		60c. brown and green	1·25	40
634		60c. brown and purple	1·60	55
635		65c. blue and brown	9·25	4·00
636		70c. blue and plum	1·00	55
637		85c. green and violet	1·40	90
638		95c. blue	95	85
639		1f.10 blue and brown	2·00	1·60
640		1f.30 brown and red	2·40	1·75
641		2f.30 purple and orange	2·00	65
642	**131**	3f. violet (air)	35·00	14·00
643		5f. blue	35·00	20·00

1960.

No.	Type	Description	Unused	Used
644	–	5c. green, black and blue	15	15
645	**134**	10c. brown and blue	30	25
646	–	10c. blue, violet and green	15	10
647	–	40c. purple, grn & dp grn	55	20
648	–	45c. brown, green and blue	4·50	60
649	–	70c. brown, red and green	40	30
650	–	80c. red, green and blue	1·40	60
651	–	85c. black, brown and grey	6·00	1·90
652	–	90c. red, blue and black	1·50	65
653	–	1f. multicoloured	1·25	30
654	–	1f.15 black, red and blue	2·10	1·25
655	–	1f.30 brown, green & blue	75	55
656	–	1f.40 orange, green & vio	2·25	1·90

DESIGNS—HORIZ: 5c. Palace of Monaco; 10c. (No. 646), Aquatic Stadium; 40, 45, 80c., 1f.40, Aerial view of Palace; 70, 85, 90c., 1f.15, 1f.30, Court of Honour, Monaco Palace; 1f. Palace floodlit.

134a St. Devote

1960. Air.

No.	Type	Description	Unused	Used
668	**134a**	2f. violet, blue and green	1·25	90
669		3f. brown, green and blue	1·90	1·25
670		5f. red	3·50	1·75
671		10f. brown, grey and green	5·00	3·25

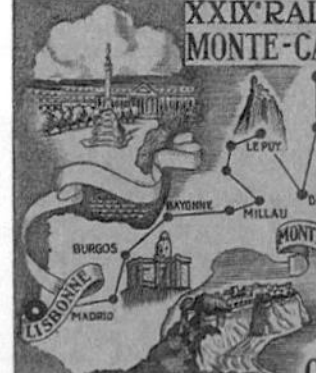

135 Long-snouted Seahorse **136** Route Map from Lisbon

1960. Marine Life and Plants. (a) Marine Life.

No.	Type	Description	Unused	Used
672	–	1c. red and turquoise	10	10
673	–	12c. brown and blue	35	20
674	**135**	15c. green and red	45	20
675	–	20c. multicoloured	55	20

DESIGNS—HORIZ: 1c. "Macrocheira kampferi" (crab); 20c. Lionfish. VERT: 12c. Trapezium horse conch.

(b) Plants.

No.	Type	Description	Unused	Used
676	–	2c. multicoloured	25	10
677	–	15c. orange, brown and olive	60	10
678	–	18c. multicoloured	45	10
679	–	20c. red, olive and brown	45	20

PLANTS—VERT: 2c. "Selenicereus sp."; 15c. "Cereus sp."; 18c. "Aloe ciliaris"; 20c. "Nopalea dejecta".

1960. Prince Rainier Seal type with values in new currency. Precancelled.

No.	Type	Description	Unused	Used
680	**104**	8c. purple	1·40	70
681		20c. green	1·75	85
682		40c. brown	3·50	1·40
683		55c. blue	5·00	2·75

1960. 29th Monte Carlo Rally.

No.	Type	Description	Unused	Used
684	**136**	25c. black, red & bl on bl	1·50	1·50

137 Stamps of Monaco 1885, France and Sardinia, 1860

1960. 75th Anniv of First Monaco Stamp.

No.	Type	Description	Unused	Used
685	**137**	25c. bistre, blue and violet	70	75

138 Aquarium

1960. 50th Anniv of Oceanographic Museum, Monaco.

No.	Type	Description	Unused	Used
686	–	5c. black, blue and purple	30	25
687	**138**	10c. grey, brown and green	40	30
688	–	15c. black, bistre and blue	40	30
689	–	20c. black, blue and mauve	70	40
690	–	25c. turquoise	1·50	1·00
691	–	50c. brown and blue	1·75	1·75

DESIGNS—VERT: 5c. Oceanographic Museum (similar to Type **134**). HORIZ: 15c. Conference Hall; 20c. Hauling-in catch; 25c. Museum, aquarium and underwater research equipment; 50c. Prince Albert, "Hirondelle I" (schooner) and "Princess Alice" (steam yacht).

139 Horse-jumping

1960. Olympic Games.

No.	Type	Description	Unused	Used
692	**139**	5c. brown, red and green	10	10
693	–	10c. brown, blue and green	20	25
694	–	15c. red, brown and purple	20	25
695	–	20c. black, blue and green	2·00	2·25
696	–	25c. purple, turq & grn	70	60
697	–	50c. purple, blue & turq	1·10	90

DESIGNS: 10c. Swimming; 15c. Long-jumping; 20c. Throwing the javelin; 25c. Free-skating; 50c. Skiing.

140 Rally Badge, Old and Modern Cars

1961. 50th Anniv of Monte Carlo Rally.

No.	Type	Description	Unused	Used
698	**140**	1f. violet, red and brown	1·40	1·40

141 Route Map from Stockholm **142** Marine Life

1961. 30th Monte Carlo Rally.

No.	Type	Description	Unused	Used
699	**141**	1f. multicoloured	80	90

1961. World Aquariological Congress. Orange network background.

No.	Type	Description	Unused	Used
700	**142**	25c. red, sepia and violet	20	25

143 Leper in Town of Middle Ages **145** Insect within Protective Hand

144 Semi-submerged Sphinx of Ouadi-es-Saboua

1961. Sovereign Order of Malta.

No.	Type	Description	Unused	Used
701	**143**	25c. black, red and brown	20	25

1961. U.N.E.S.C.O. Campaign for Preservation of Nubian Monuments.

No.	Type	Description	Unused	Used
702	**144**	50c. purple, blue & brown	70	75

1962. Nature Preservation.

No.	Type	Description	Unused	Used
703	**145**	25c. mauve and purple	20	25

146 Chevrolet, 1912

1961. Veteran Motor Cars.

No.	Type	Description	Unused	Used
704	**146**	1c. brown, green and chestnut	10	10
705	–	2c. blue, purple and red	10	10
706	–	3c. purple, black and mauve	10	10
707	–	4c. blue, brown and violet	10	10
708	–	5c. green, red and olive	10	10
709	–	10c. brown, red and blue	10	10
710	–	15c. green and turquoise	20	25
711	–	20c. brown, red and violet	20	25
712	–	25c. violet, red and brown	30	35
713	–	30c. lilac and green	70	80
714	–	45c. green, purple and brown	1·50	1·90
715	–	50c. blue, red and brown	1·50	1·90
716	–	65c. brown, red and grey	2·25	1·75
717	–	1f. blue, red and violet	2·50	2·75

MOTOR CARS: 2c. Peugeot, 1898; 3c. Fiat, 1901; 4c. Mercedes, 1901; 5c. Rolls Royce, 1903;. 10c. Panhard-Lavassor, 1899; 15c. Renault, 1898; 20c. Ford "N", 1906 (wrongly inscr "FORD-S-1908"); 25c. Rochet-Schneider, 1894; 30c. FN-Herstal, 1901; 45c. De Dion Bouton, 1900; 50c. Buick, 1910; 65c. Delahaye, 1901; 1f. Cadillac, 1906.

147 Racing Car and Race Route

1962. 20th Monaco Motor Grand Prix.

No.	Type	Description	Unused	Used
718	**147**	1f. purple	1·25	90

148 Route Map from Oslo

1962. 31st Monte Carlo Rally.

No.	Type	Description	Unused	Used
719	**148**	1f. multicoloured	95	80

149 Louis XII and Lucien Grimaldi

1962. 450th Anniv of Recognition of Monegasque Sovereignty by Louis XII.
720 **149** 25c. black, red and blue 20 25
721 – 50c. brown, lake and blue 30 30
722 – 1f. red, green and brown 50 55
DESIGNS: 50c. Parchment bearing declaration of sovereignty; 1f. Seals of two Sovereigns.

150 Mosquito and Swamp

1962. Malaria Eradication.
723 **150** 1f. green and olive . . . 40 45

151 Sun, Bouquet and "Hope Chest"

1962. National Multiple Sclerosis Society, New York.
724 **151** 20c. multicoloured 20 20

152 Harvest Scene

1962. Europa.
725 **152** 25c. brown, green and blue (postage) 10 10
726 50c. olive and turquoise 20 25
727 1f. olive and purple . . . 40 50
728 – 2f. slate, brown & green (air) 90 90
DESIGN: 2f. Mercury in flight over Europe.

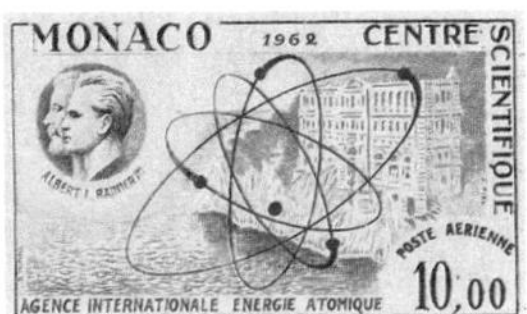

153 Atomic Symbol and Scientific Centre, Monaco

1962. Air. Scientific Centre, Monaco.
729 **153** 10f. violet, brown and blue . . . . 4·75 4·75

154 Yellow Wagtails **155** Galeazzi's Diving Turret

1962. Protection of Birds useful to Agriculture.
730 **154** 5c. yellow, brown & green 10 20
731 – 10c. red, bistre and purple 10 20
732 – 15c. multicoloured 25 20
733 – 20c. sepia, green & mauve 30 30
734 – 25c. multicoloured 40 35
735 – 30c. brown, blue & myrtle 55 45
736 – 45c. brown and violet . . 95 90
737 – 50c. black, olive & turq 1·25 1·10
738 – 85c. multicoloured . . . . 1·75 1·50
739 – 1f. sepia, red and green 2·00 1·75
BIRDS: 10c. European robins; 15c. Eurasian goldfinches; 20c. Blackcaps; 25c. Greater spotted woodpeckers; 30c. Nightingale; 45c. Barn owls; 50c. Common starlings; 85c. Red crossbills; 1f. White storks.

1962. Underwater Exploration.
740 – 5c. black, violet and blue 10 10
741 **155** 10c. blue, violet and brown 10 10
742 – 25c. bistre, green and blue 10 10
743 – 45c. black, blue and green 30 35
744 – 50c. green, bistre and blue 50 55
745 – 85c. blue and turquoise 80 85
746 – 1f. brown, green and blue 1·40 1·25
DESIGNS—HORIZ: 5c. Divers; 25c. Williamson's photosphere (1914) and bathyscaphe "Trieste"; 45c. Klingert's diving-suit (1797) and modern diving-suit; 50c. Diving saucer; 85c. Fulton's "Nautilus" (1800) and modern submarine; 1f. Alexander the Great's diving bell and Beebe's bathysphere.

156 Donor's Arm and Globe **158** Feeding Chicks in Nest

157 "Ring-a-ring o' Roses"

1962. 3rd Int Blood Donors' Congress Monaco.
747 **156** 1f. red, sepia and orange 50 65

1963. U.N. Children's Charter.
748 **157** 5c. red, blue and ochre . . 10 10
749 **158** 10c. green, sepia and blue 10 10
750 – 15c. blue, red and green 10 20
751 – 20c. multicoloured 10 20
752 – 25c. blue, purple & brown 25 25
753 – 50c. multicoloured 50 35
754 – 95c. multicoloured 80 55
755 – 1f. purple, red & turquoise . . . . 1·75 1·10
DESIGNS—As Type **157**: 1f. Prince Albert and Princess Caroline; Children's paintings as Type **158**: HORIZ: 15c. Children on scales; 50c. House and child. VERT: 20c. Sun's rays and children of three races; 25c. Mother and child; 95c. Negress and child.

159 Ship's Figurehead

1963. International Red Cross Centenary.
756 **159** 50c. red, brown & turquoise 30 35
757 – 1f. multicoloured 55 60
DESIGN—HORIZ: 1f. Moynier, Dunant and Dufour.

160 Racing Cars

1963. European Motor Grand Prix.
758 **160** 50c. multicoloured 55 40

161 Emblem and Charter

1963. Founding of Lions Club of Monaco.
759 **161** 50c. blue, bistre and violet 80 65

162 Hotel des Postes and U.P.U. Monument, Berne

1963. Paris Postal Conference Centenary.
760 **162** 50c. lake, green and yellow 30 45

163 "Telstar" Satellite and Globe

1963. 1st Link Trans-Atlantic T.V. Satellite.
761 **163** 50c. brown, green & purple 45 45

164 Route Map from Warsaw

1963. 32nd Monte Carlo Rally.
762 **164** 1f. multicoloured . . . . 1·00 1·10

165 Feeding Chicks

1963. Freedom from Hunger.
763 **165** 1f. multicoloured 50 50

166 Allegory

1963. 2nd Ecumenical Council, Vatican City.
764 **166** 1f. turquoise, green and red 45 45

167 Henry Ford and Ford "A" Car of 1903

1963. Birth Centenary of Henry Ford (motor pioneer).
765 **167** 20c. green and purple . . 25 25

168 H. Garin (winner of 1903 race) cycling through Village

1963. 50th "Tour de France" Cycle Race.
766 **168** 25c. green, brown and blue 30 30
767 – 50c. sepia, green and blue 30 35
DESIGN: 50c. Cyclist passing Desgrange Monument, Col du Galibier, 1963.

169 P. de Coubertin and Discus-thrower

1963. Birth Centenary of Pierre de Coubertin (reviver of Olympic Games).
768 **169** 1f. brown, red and lake 40 60

170 Roland Garros and Morane Saulnier Type I

1963. Air. 50th Anniv of 1st Aerial Crossing of Mediterranean Sea.
769 **170** 2f. sepia and blue . . . . 1·25 90

171 Route Map from Paris **173** "Europa"

172 Children with Stamp Album

1963. 33rd Monte Carlo Rally.
770 **171** 1f. red, turquoise and blue 80 70

1963. "Scolatex" International Stamp Exn, Monaco.
771 **172** 50c. blue, violet and red 20 25

1963. Europa.
772 **173** 25c. brown, red and green 30 25
773 50c. sepia, red and blue 50 50

174 Wembley Stadium

1963. Cent of (English) Football Association.
774 **174** 1c. violet, green and red 10 10
775 – 2c. red, black and green 10 10
776 – 3c. orange, olive and red 10 10
777 – 4c. multicoloured 10 10
Multicoloured horiz designs depicting (a) "Football through the Centuries".
778 10c. "Calcio", Florence (16th cent) 10 10
779 15c. "Soule", Brittany (19th cent) 10 10
780 20c. English military college (after Cruickshank, 1827) 10 10
781 25c. English game (after Overend, 1890) 10 10
(b) "Modern Football".
782 30c. Tackling 20 20
783 50c. Saving goal 50 50
784 95c. Heading ball 70 70
785 1f. Corner kick . . . . . . 1·00 1·00
DESIGNS—As Type **174**: 4c. Louis II Stadium, Monaco. This stamp is optd in commemoration of the Association Sportive de Monaco football teams in the French Championships and in the Coupe de France, 1962–63. HORIZ (36 × 22 mm): 2c. Footballer making return kick; 3c. Goalkeeper saving ball.
Nos. 778/81 and 782/5 were respectively issued together in sheets and arranged in blocks of 4 with a football in the centre of each block.

175 Communications in Ancient Egypt, and Rocket

1964. "PHILATEC 1964" Int Stamp Exn, Paris.
786 **175** 1f. brown, indigo and blue 40 40

176 Reproduction of Rally Postcard Design

1964. 50th Anniv of 1st Aerial Rally, Monte Carlo.
787 **176** 1c. olive, blue & grn (postage) 10 10
788 – 2c. bistre, brown and blue 10 10
789 – 3c. brown, blue and green 10 10
790 – 4c. red, turquoise and blue 10 10
791 – 5c. brown, red and violet 10 10
792 – 10c. violet, brown and blue 10 10
793 – 15c. orange, brown and blue 10 10
794 – 20c. sepia, green and blue 20 10
795 – 25c. brown, blue and red 30 10
796 – 30c. myrtle, purple and blue 40 20
797 – 45c. sepia, turquoise and brown 70 30
798 – 50c. ochre, olive and violet 70 45
799 – 65c. red, slate and turquoise 70 85
800 – 95c. turquoise, red and bistre . . . . 1·25 95
801 – 1f. brown, blue and turquoise . . . . 1·60 1·25
802 – 5f. sepia, blue and brown (air) . . . . 2·40 2·40

DESIGNS: 48 × 27 mm—Rally planes: 2c. Renaux's Farman M.F.7 floatplane; 3c. Espanet's Nieuport 4 seaplane; 4c. Moineau's Breguet HU-3 seaplane; 5c. Roland Garros' Morane Saulnier Type I seaplane; 10c. Hirth's WDD Albatros seaplane; 15c. Prevost's Deperdussin Monocoque Racer. Famous planes and flights: 20c. Vickers-Vimy (Ross Smith: London–Port Darwin, 1919); 25c. Douglas World Cruiser seaplane (U.S. World Flight, 1924); 30c. Savoia Marchetti S-55M flying boat "Santa Maria" (De Pinedo's World Flight, 1925); 45c. Fokker F. VIIa/3m "Josephine Ford" (Flight over North Pole, Byrd and Bennett, 1926); 50c. Ryan NYP Special "Spirit of St. Louis" (1st solo crossing of N. Atlantic, Lindbergh, 1927); 65c. Breguet 19 "Point d'Interrogation" (Paris–New York, Coste and Bellonte, 1930); 95c. Latecoere 28-3 seaplane "Comte de la Vaulx" (Dakar–Natal, first S. Atlantic airmail flight, Mermoz, 1930); 1f. Dornier Do-X flying boat (Germany–Rio de Janeiro, Christiansen, 1930); 5f. Convair B-58 Hustler (New York–Paris in 3 hours, 19' 41" Major Payne, U.S.A.F., 1961).

177 Aquatic Stadium

178 Europa "Flower"

1964. Precancelled.
803 **177** 10c. multicoloured . . . 1·40 90
803a 15c. multicoloured . . . 70 50
804 25c. turquoise, blue & blk 70 50
805 50c. violet, turq & blk 1·40 70

The "1962" date has been obliterated with two bars.

See also Nos. 949/51a and 1227/30.

1964. Europa.
806 **178** 25c. red, green and blue 20 25
807 50c. brown, bistre and blue 35 50

179 Weightlifting

1964. Olympic Games, Tokyo and Innsbruck.
808 **179** 1c. red, brown and blue (postage) 10 10
809 – 2c. red, green and olive 10 10
810 – 3c. blue, brown and red 10 10
811 – 4c. green, olive and red 10 10
812 – 5f. red, brown and blue (air) . . . . 2·00 1·90

DESIGNS: 2c. Judo; 3c. Pole vaulting; 4c. Archery; 5f. Bobsleighing.

180 Pres. Kennedy and Space Capsule

1964. Pres. Kennedy Commemoration.
813 **180** 50c. indigo and blue . . . 40 50

181 Monaco and Television Set

1964. 5th Int Television Festival, Monte Carlo.
814 **181** 50c. brown, blue and red 30 40

182 F. Mistral and Statue

1964. 50th Death Anniv of Frederic Mistral (poet).
815 **182** 1f. brown and olive . . . 40 50

183 Scales of Justice

1964. 15th Anniv of Declaration of Human Rights.
816 **183** 1f. green and brown . . . 40 50

184 Route Map from Minsk

1964. 34th Monte Carlo Rally.
817 **184** 1f. brown, turq & ochre 70 70

185 FIFA Emblem

1964. 60th Anniv of Federation Internationale de Football Association (FIFA).
818 **185** 1f. bistre, blue and red . . 60 65

186 "Syncom 2" and Globe

1965. Centenary of I.T.U.
819 **186** 5c. grn & ultram (postage) 10 10
820 – 10c. chestnut, brown & bl 10 10
821 – 12c. purple, red and grey 10 10
822 – 18c. blue, red and purple 10 20
823 – 25c. violet, bistre & purple 10 20
824 – 30c. bistre, brown & sepia 20 25
825 – 50c. blue and green . . . 30 35
826 – 60c. blue and brown . . . 40 45
827 – 70c. sepia, orange and blue 60 60
828 – 95c. black, indigo and blue 80 80
829 – 1f. brown and blue . . . 95 90
830 – 10f. green, bl & brn (air) 1·60 2·50

DESIGNS—HORIZ (as Type **186**): 10c. "Echo 2"; 18c. "Lunik 3"; 30c. A. G. Bell and telephone; 50c. S. Morse and telegraph; 60c. E. Belin and "belinograph". (48½ × 27 mm): 25c. "Telstar" and Pleumeur-Bodou Station; 70c. Roman beacon and Chappe's telegraph; 95c. Cable ships "Great Eastern" and "Alsace"; 1f. E. Branly, G. Marconi and English Channel. VERT (as Type **186**): 12c. "Relay"; 10f. Monte Carlo television transmitter.

187 Europa "Sprig"

1965. Europa.
831 **187** 30c. brown and green . . 35 25
832 60c. violet and red . . . 1·00 45

188 Monaco Palace (18th cent)

1966. 750th Anniv of Monaco Palace.
833 **188** 10c. violet, green and blue 10 10
834 – 12c. bistre, blue and black 10 10
835 – 18c. green, black and blue 10 10
836 – 30c. brown, black and blue 30 30
837 – 60c. green, blue and bistre 40 55
838 – 1f.30 brown and green . . 90 1·10

DESIGNS (Different views of Palace): 12c. 17th century; 18c. 18th century; 30c. 19th century; 60c. 19th century; 1f.30, 20th century.

189 Dante

1966. 700th Anniv of Dante's Birth.
839 **189** 30c. green, deep green and red 20 25
840 – 60c. blue, turquoise & grn 40 50
841 – 70c. black, green and red 50 60
842 – 95c. blue, violet and purple 70 80
843 – 1f. turquoise, blue & dp bl 70 85

DESIGNS (Scenes from Dante's works): 60c. Dante harassed by the panther (envy); 70c. Crossing the 5th circle; 95c. Punishment of the arrogant; 1f. Invocation of St. Bernard.

190 "The Nativity"

1966. World Association of Children's Friends (A.M.A.D.E.).
844 **190** 30c. brown 20 25

191 Route Map from London

1966. 35th Monte Carlo Rally.
845 **191** 1f. blue, purple and red 60 70

192 Princess Grace with Children

1966. Air. Princess Stephanie's 1st Birthday.
846 **192** 3f. brown, blue and violet 2·00 2·00

193 Casino in 19th Century **194** Europa "Ship"

1966. Centenary of Monte Carlo.
847 – 12c. black, red and blue (postage) 10 10
848 **193** 25c. multicoloured 10 10
849 – 30c. multicoloured 10 10
850 – 40c. multicoloured 25 25
851 – 60c. multicoloured 30 25
852 – 70c. blue and lake 30 35
853 – 95c. black and purple . . 60 60
854 – 1f.30 purple, brown and chestnut 95 80
855 – 5f. lake, ochre and blue (air) . . . . 2·00 2·00

DESIGNS—VERT: 12c. Prince Charles III. HORIZ (as Type **143**): 40c. Charles III Monument; 95c. Massenet and Saint-Saens; 1f.30, Faure and Ravel. (48 × 27 mm): 30c. F. Blanc, originator of Monte Carlo, and view of 1860; 60c. Prince Rainier III and projected esplanade; 70c. Rene Blum and Diaghilev, ballet character from "Petrouchka". (36 × 36 mm): 5f. Interior of Opera House, 1879.

1966. Europa.
856 **194** 30c. orange 20 25
857 60c. green 30 35

195 Prince Rainier and Princess Grace

197 "Learning to Write"

196 Prince Albert I and Yachts "Hirondelle I" and "Princess Alice"

1966. Air.
858 **195** 2f. slate and red 85 40
859 3f. slate and green . . . 1·75 65
860 5f. slate and blue . . . . 2·25 1·00
860a 10f. slate and bistre . . 4·50 2·75
860b 20f. brown and orange 48·00 27·00

1966. 1st International Oceanographic History Congress, Monaco.
861 **196** 1f. lilac and blue 50 60

1966. 20th Anniv of U.N.E.S.C.O.
862 **197** 30c. purple and mauve . . 10 10
863 60c. brown and blue . . . 30 30

198 T.V. Screen, Cross and Monaco Harbour

1966. 10th Meeting of International Catholic Television Association (U.N.D.A.), Monaco.
864 **198** 60c. red, purple & crimson 20 25

199 "Precontinent III"

1966. 1st Anniv of Underwater Research Craft "Precontinent III".
865 **199** 1f. yellow, brown and blue 40 35

200 W.H.O. Building

1966. Inaug of W.H.O. Headquarters, Geneva.
866 **200** 30c. brown, green and blue 15 15
867 60c. brown, red and green 20 15

201 Bugatti, 1931 **202** Dog (Egyptian bronze)

1967. 25th Motor Grand Prix, Monaco. Multicoloured. (a) Postage.
868 1c. Type **201** 10 10
869 2c. Alfa-Romeo, 1932 . . . . 10 10
870 5c. Mercedes, 1936 . . . . . 10 10
871 10c. Maserati, 1948 . . . . . 10 10
872 18c. Ferrari, 1955 . . . . . 20 20
873 20c. Alfa-Romeo, 1950 . . . 10 10
874 25c. Maserati, 1957 . . . . . 20 10
875 30c. Cooper-Climax, 1958 . . 30 20
876 40c. Lotus-Climax, 1960 . . 30 30
877 50c. Lotus-Climax, 1961 . . 50 45
878 60c. Cooper-Climax, 1962 . . 80 45
879 70c. B.R.M., 1963–6 . . . . 90 70
880 1f. Walter Christie, 1907 . . 1·10 90
881 2f.30 Peugeot, 1910 . . . . . 2·00 1·60

(b) Air. Diamond. 50 × 50 mm.
882 3f. black and blue . . . . . 1·40 1·75
DESIGN: 3f. Panhard-Phenix, 1895.

1967. Int Cynological Federation Congress, Monaco.
883 **202** 30c. black, purple & green 35 35

203 View of Monte Carlo

1967. International Tourist Year.
884 **203** 30c. brown, green and blue 20 25

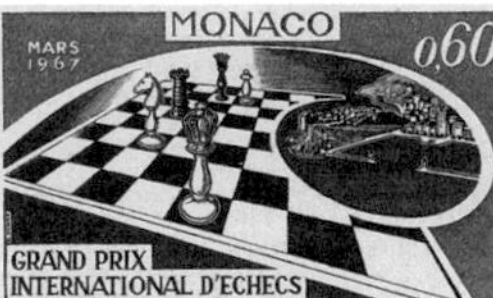

204 Pieces on Chessboard

1967. Int Chess Grand Prix, Monaco.
885 **204** 60c. black, plum and blue 50 40

205 Melvin Jones (founder), Lions Emblem and Monte Carlo

1967. 50th Anniv of Lions International.
886 **205** 60c. blue, ultramarine and brown 30 30

206 Rotary Emblem and Monte Carlo

1967. Rotary International Convention.
887 **206** 1f. bistre, blue and green 40 30

207 Fair Buildings

1967. World Fair, Montreal.
888 **207** 1f. red, slate and blue . . 40 45

208 Squiggle on Map of Europe

1967. European Migration Committee (C.I.M.E.).
889 **208** 1f. brown, bistre and blue 40 30

209 Cogwheels

1967. Europa.
890 **209** 30c. violet, purple and red 30 25
891 60c. green, turq & emer 50 35

210 Dredger and Coastal Chart

1967. 9th Int Hydrographic Congress, Monaco.
892 **210** 1f. brown, blue and green 40 35

211 Marie Curie and Scientific Equipment

1967. Birth Centenary of Marie Curie.
893 **211** 1f. blue, olive and brown 50 40

212 Skiing

1967. Winter Olympic Games, Grenoble.
894 **212** 2f.30 brown, blue & slate 90 90

213 "Prince Rainier I" (E. Charpentier)

1967. Paintings. "Princes and Princesses of Monaco". Multicoloured.
895 1f. Type **213** 40 40
896 1f. "Lucien Grimaldi" (A. di Predis) 55 55
See also Nos. 932/3, 958/9, 1005/6, 1023/4, 1070/1, 1108/9, 1213/14, 1271/2, 1325, 1380/1, 1405/6, 1460/1 and 1531/2.

214 Putting the Shot

1968. Olympic Games, Mexico.
897 **214** 20c. blue, brown and green (postage) 10 10
898 – 30c. brown, blue and plum 10 10
899 – 60c. blue, purple and red 20 25
900 – 70c. red, blue and ochre 30 30
901 – 1f. blue, brown and orange 50 50
902 – 2f.30 olive, blue and lake 1·00 1·25
903 – 3f. blue, violet & grn (air) 1·40 1·25
DESIGNS: 30c. High-jumping; 60c. Gymnastics; 70c. Water-polo; 1f. Greco-Roman wrestling; 2f.30, Gymnastics (different); 3f. Hockey.

215 "St. Martin"

1968. 20th Anniv of Monaco Red Cross.
904 **215** 2f.30 blue and brown . . 80 90

216 "Anemones" (after Raoul Dufy) **217** Insignia of Prince Charles III and Pope Pius IX

1968. Monte Carlo Floral Exhibitions.
905 **216** 1f. multicoloured 50 50

1968. Centenary of "Nullius Diocesis" Abbey.
906 **217** 10c. brown and red . . . 10 10
907 – 20c. red, green and brown 10 10
908 – 30c. brown and blue . . . 20 25
909 – 60c. brown, blue and green 30 30
910 – 1f. indigo, bistre and blue 40 40
DESIGNS—VERT: 20c. "St. Nicholas" (after Louis Brea); 30c. "St. Benedict" (after Simone Martini); 60c. Subiaco Abbey. HORIZ: 1f. Old St. Nicholas' Church (on site of present cathedral).

218 Europa "Key"

1968. Europa.
911 **218** 30c. red and orange . . . 40 25
912 60c. blue and red 70 60
913 1f. brown and green . . . 70 85

219 First Locomotive on Monaco Line, 1868

1968. Centenary of Nice–Monaco Railway.
914 **219** 20c. black, blue and purple 30 30
915 – 30c. black, blue and olive 50 50
916 – 60c. black, blue and ochre 70 70
917 – 70c. black, violet & brown 1·25 1·00
918 – 1f. black, blue and red . . 2·40 1·60
919 – 2f.30 blue, black and red 3·25 2·75
DESIGNS: 30c. Class 220-C steam locomotive, 1898; 60c. Class 230-C steam locomotive, 1910; 70c. Class 231-F steam locomotive, 1925; 1f. Class 241-A steam locomotive, 1932; 2f.30, Class BB 25200 electric locomotive, 1968.

220 Chateaubriand and Combourg Castle

1968. Birth Centenary of Chateaubriand (novelist).
920 **220** 10c. plum, green & myrtle 10 10
921 – 20c. violet, purple and blue 10 10
922 – 25c. brown, violet and blue 10 10
923 – 30c. violet, choc & brn . . 20 20
924 – 60c. brown, green and red 30 20
925 – 2f.30 brown, mauve & bl 85 1·00
Scenes from Chateaubriand's novels: 20c. "Le Genie du Christianisme"; 25c. "Rene"; 30c. "Le Dernier Abencerage"; 60c. "Les Martyrs"; 2f.30, "Atala".

221 Law Courts, Paris, and statues–"La France et la Fidelite"

1968. Birth Centenary of J. F. Bosio (Monegasque sculptor).

926 **221** 20c. brown and purple . . 10 10
927 – 25c. brown and red . . . 10 10
928 – 30c. blue and green . . . 20 10
929 – 60c. green and myrtle . . 40 20
930 – 2f.30 black and slate . . . 70 75

DESIGNS—VERT (26 × 36 mm): 25c. "Henry IV as a Child"; 30c. "J. F. Bosio" (lithograph); 60c. "Louis XIV". HORIZ (as Type **221**): 2f.30, "Napoleon I, Louis XVIII and Charles X".

222 W.H.O. Emblem

1968. 20th Anniv of W.H.O.

931 **222** 60c. multicoloured 30 25

1968. Paintings. "Princes and Princesses of Monaco". As T **213**. Multicoloured.

932 1f. "Prince Charles II" (Mimault) 40 35
933 2f.30 "Princess Jeanne Grimaldi" (Mimault) . . . 70 85

223 The Hungarian March

1969. Death Centenary of Hector Berlioz (composer).

934 **223** 10c. brown, violet and green (postage) 10 10
935 – 20c. brown, olive & mauve 10 10
936 – 25c. brown, blue & mauve 10 10
937 – 30c. black, green and blue 10 20
938 – 40c. red, black and slate 10 20
939 – 50c. brown, slate & purple 20 25
940 – 70c. brown, slate and green 30 25
941 – 1f. black, mauve & brown 30 35
942 – 1f.15 black, blue & turq 50 45
943 – 2f. black, blue & grn (air) 90 90

DESIGNS—HORIZ: 20c. Mephistopheles appears to Faust; 25c. Auerbach's tavern; 30c. Sylphs' ballet; 40c. Minuet of the goblins; 50c. Marguerite's bedroom; 70c. "Forests and caverns"; 1f. The journey to Hell; 1f.15, Heaven; All scenes from Berlioz's "The Damnation of Faust". VERT: 2f. Bust of Berlioz.

224 "St. Elisabeth of Hungary"

1969. Monaco Red Cross.

944 **224** 3f. blue, brown and red 1·10 1·25

225 "Napoleon I" (P. Delaroche)

1969. Birth Bicentenary of Napoleon Bonaparte.

945 **225** 3f. multicoloured . . . . 1·10 1·10

226 Colonnade

1969. Europa.

946 **226** 40c. red and purple . . . 40 30
947 70c. blue, brown and black 60 45
948 1f. ochre, brown and blue 90 65

1969. Precancelled. As T **177**. No date.

949 22c. brown, blue and black 30 30
949a 26c. violet, blue and black 40 25
949b 30c. multicoloured 50 35
950 35c. multicoloured 40 35
950a 45c. multicoloured 60 55
951 70c. black and blue 60 55
951a 90c. green, blue and black 1·10 70

227 "Head of Woman" (Da Vinci)

228 Marine Fauna, King Alfonso XIII of Spain and Prince Albert I of Monaco

1969. 450th Death Anniv of Leonardo da Vinci.

952 **227** 30c. brown 10 10
953 – 40c. red and brown . . . 20 10
954 – 70c. green 30 20
955 – 80c. sepia 40 20
956 – 1f.15 brown 60 40
957 – 3f. brown . . . . 1·40 90

DRAWINGS: 40c. Self-portrait; 70c. "Head of an Old Man"; 80c. "Head of St. Madeleine"; 1f.15, "Man's Head"; 3f. "The Condottiere".

1969. Paintings. "Princes and Princesses of Monaco". As T **213**. Multicoloured.

958 1f. "Prince Honore II" (Champaigne) 30 50
959 3f. "Princess Louise-Hippolyte" (Champaigne) 90 1·00

1969. 50th Anniv of Int Commission for Scientific Exploration of the Mediterranean, Madrid.

960 **228** 40c. blue and black . . . 20 20

229 I.L.O. Emblem

1969. 50th Anniv of I.L.O.

961 **229** 40c. multicoloured 20 25

230 Aerial View of Monaco and T.V. Camera

1969. 10th International Television Festival.

962 **230** 40c. purple, lake and blue 20 20

231 J.C.C. Emblem

1969. 25th Anniv of Junior Chamber of Commerce.

963 **231** 40c. violet, bistre and blue 20 25

232 Alphonse Daudet and Scenes from "Lettres"

1969. Centenary of Daudet's "Lettres de Mon Moulin".

964 **232** 30c. lake, violet and green 10 10
965 – 40c. green, brown and blue 20 20
966 – 70c. multicoloured 30 30
967 – 80c. violet, brown & green 40 30
968 – 1f.15 brown, orange & bl 50 50

DESIGNS (Scenes from the book): 40c. "Installation" (Daudet writing); 70c. "Mule, Goat and Wolf"; 80c. "Gaucher's Elixir" and "The Three Low Masses"; 1f.15, Daudet drinking, "The Old Man" and "The Country Sub-Prefect".

233 Conference Building, Albert I and Rainier III

1970. Interparliamentary Union's Spring Meeting, Monaco.

969 **233** 40c. black, red and purple 20 20

234 Baby Common Seal

1970. Protection of Baby Seals.

970 **234** 40c. drab, blue and purple 40 50

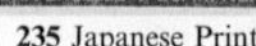

235 Japanese Print **236** Dobermann

1970. Expo 70.

971 **235** 20c. brown, green and red 10 10
972 – 30c. brown, buff and green 20 20
973 – 40c. bistre and violet . . 20 20
974 – 70c. grey and red 50 60
975 – 1f.15 red, green & purple 60 75

DESIGNS—VERT: 30c. Manchurian Cranes (birds); 40c. Shinto temple gateway. HORIZ: 70c. Cherry blossom; 1f.15, Monaco Palace and Osaka Castle.

1970. International Dog Show, Monte Carlo.

976 **236** 40c. black and brown . . 80 85

237 Apollo

1970. 20th Anniv of World Federation for Protection of Animals.

977 **237** 30c. black, red and blue 20 25
978 – 40c. brown, blue and green 40 30
979 – 50c. brown, ochre and blue 60 50
980 – 80c. brown, blue and green . . . . 1·10 90
981 – 1f. brown, bistre and slate 1·60 1·90
982 – 1f.15 brown, green & blue 2·25 2·10

DESIGNS—HORIZ: 40c. Basque ponies; 50c. Common seal. VERT: 80c. Chamois; 1f. White-tailed sea eagles; 1f.15, European otter.

238 "St. Louis" (King of France)

1970. Monaco Red Cross.

983 **238** 3f. green, brown and slate 1·10 1·60

See also Nos. 1022, 1041, 1114, 1189 and 1270.

239 "Roses and Anemones" (Van Gogh)

1970. Monte Carlo Flower Show.

984 **239** 3f. multicoloured . . . . 1·50 2·00

See also Nos. 1042 and 1073.

240 Moon Plaque, Presidents Kennedy and Nixon

1970. 1st Man on the Moon (1969). Multicoloured.

985 40c. Type **240** 40 40
986 80c. Astronauts on Moon . . 60 55

241 New U.P.U. Building and Monument **242** "Flaming Sun"

1970. New U.P.U. Headquarters Building.

987 **241** 40c. brown, black & green 20 20

1970. Europa.

988 **242** 40c. purple 30 25
989 80c. green . . . . 1·10 80
990 1f. blue . . . . 1·60 1·25

243 Camargue Horse

1970. Horses.

991 **243** 10c. slate, olive and blue (postage) 10 10
992 – 20c. brown, olive and blue 20 20
993 – 30c. brown, green and blue 50 30
994 – 40c. grey, brown and slate 70 55
995 – 50c. brown, olive and blue 1·10 80
996 – 70c. brown, orange & grn 2·00 1·25
997 – 85c. blue, green and olive 2·00 1·75
998 – 1f.15 black, green & blue 2·10 2·10
999 – 3f. multicoloured (air) . . 1·50 1·75

HORSES—HORIZ: 20c. Anglo-Arab; 30c. French saddle-horse; 40c. Lippizaner; 50c. Trotter; 70c. English thoroughbred; 85c. Arab; 1f.15, Barbary. DIAMOND (50 × 50 mm): 3f. Rock-drawings of horses in Lascaux grotto.

244 Dumas, D'Artagnan and the Three Musketeers

1970. Death Centenary of Alexandre Dumas (pere) (author).
1000 **244** 30c. slate, brown and blue 20 20

245 Henri Rougier and Voisin "Boxkite"

1970. 60th Anniv of First Mediterranean Flight.
1001 **245** 40c. brown, blue and slate 20 20

246 De Lamartine and scene from "Meditations Poetiques"

1970. 150th Anniv of "Meditations Poetiques" by Alphonse de Lamartine (writer).
1002 **246** 80c. brown, blue & turq 30 30

247 Beethoven

1970. Birth Bicentenary of Beethoven.
1003 **247** 1f.30 brown and red . . 1·60 1·10

1970. 50th Death Anniv of Modigliani. Vert Painting as T **213**. Multicoloured.
1004 3f. "Portrait of Dedie" . . . 2·00 2·00

1970. Paintings. "Princes and Princesses of Monaco". As T **213**.
1005 1f. red and black 30 45
1006 3f. multicoloured . . . . . 90 1·25
PORTRAITS: 1f. "Prince Louis I" (F. de Troy); 3f. "Princess Charlotte de Gramont" (S. Bourdon).

248 Cocker Spaniel **249** Razorbill

1971. International Dog Show, Monte Carlo.
1007 **248** 50c. multicoloured . . . 2·00 1·50
See also Nos. 1036, 1082, 1119, 1218 and 1239.

1971. Campaign Against Pollution of the Sea.
1008 **249** 50c. indigo and blue . . 40 45

250 Hand holding Emblem

1971. 7th Int Blood Donors Federation Congress.
1009 **250** 80c. red, violet and grey 40 45

251 Sextant, Scroll and Underwater Scene

1971. 50th Anniv of Int Hydrographic Bureau.
1010 **251** 80c. brown, green & slate 40 45

252 Detail of Michelangelo Painting ("The Arts")

1971. 25th Anniv of U.N.E.S.C.O.
1011 **252** 30c. brown, blue & violet 10 20
1012 – 50c. blue and brown . . 20 20
1013 – 80c. brown and green . . 30 30
1014 – 1f.30 green 50 50
DESIGNS—VERT: 50c. Alchemist and dish aerial ("Sciences"); 1f.30, Prince Pierre of Monaco (National U.N.E.S.C.O. Commission). HORIZ: 80c. Ancient scribe, book and T.V. screen ("Culture").

253 Europa Chain

1971. Europa.
1015 **253** 50c. red 70 45
1016 80c. blue . . . . 1·25 80
1017 1f.30 green . . . . . . 2·10 1·50

254 Old Bridge, Sospel

1971. Protection of Historic Monuments.
1018 **254** 50c. brown, blue & green 20 20
1019 – 80c. brown, green & grey 30 25
1020 – 1f.30 red, green & brown 50 50
1021 – 3f. slate, blue and olive 1·25 1·10
DESIGNS—HORIZ: 80c. Roquebrune Chateau; 1f.30, Grimaldi Chateau, Cagnes-sur-Mer. VERT: 3f. Roman "Trophy of the Alps", La Turbie.

1971. Monaco Red Cross. As T **238**.
1022 3f. brown, olive and green 1·25 1·40
DESIGN: 3f. St. Vincent de Paul.

1972. Paintings. "Princes and Princesses of Monaco". As T **213**. Multicoloured.
1023 1f. "Prince Antoine I" (Rigaud) 40 45
1024 3f. "Princess Marie de Lorraine" (18th-century French School) . . . . . 1·25 1·40

255 La Fontaine and Animal Fables (350th)

1972. Birth Anniversaries (1971).
1025 **255** 50c. brown, emer & grn 40 30
1026 – 1f.30 purple, black & red 65 60
DESIGN: 1f.30, Baudelaire, nudes and cats (150th).

256 Saint-Saens and scene from Opera, "Samson and Delilah"

1972. 50th Death Anniv (1971) of Camile Saint-Saens.
1027 **256** 90c. brown and sepia . . 40 35

257 Battle Scene

1972. 400th Anniv (1971) of Battle of Lepanto.
1028 **257** 1f. blue, brown and red 40 35

258 "Christ before Pilate" (engraving by Durer)

1972. 500th Birth Anniv (1971) of Albrecht Durer.
1029 **258** 2f. black and brown . . 1·10 1·25

259 "The Cradle" (B. Morisot)

1972. 25th Anniv (1971) of U.N.I.C.E.F.
1030 **259** 2f. multicoloured . . . . 1·10 1·10

260 "Gilles" (Watteau)

1972. 250th Death Anniv (1971) of Watteau.
1031 **260** 3f. multicoloured . . . . 1·60 1·60

261 Santa Claus

1972. Christmas (1971).
1032 **261** 30c. red, blue and brown 10 20
1033 50c. red, green & orange 20 20
1034 90c. red, blue and brown 45 30

262 Class 743 Steam Locomotive, Italy, and TGV 001 Turbotrain, France

1972. 50th Anniv of International Railway Union.
1035 **262** 50c. purple, lilac and red 70 60

1972. Int Dog Show, Monte Carlo. As T **248**.
1036 60c. multicoloured . . . . . 1·60 1·60
DESIGN: 60c. Great Dane.

263 "Pollution Kills"

1972. Anti-pollution Campaign.
1037 **263** 90c. brown, green & black 40 35

264 Ski-jumping

1972. Winter Olympic Games, Sapporo, Japan.
1038 **264** 90c. black, red and green 55 50

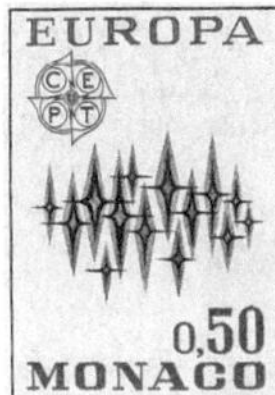

265 "Communications"

1972. Europa.
1039 **265** 50c. blue and orange . . 80 60
1040 90c. blue and green . . . 1·60 1·50

1972. Monaco Red Cross. As T **238**.
1041 3f. brown and purple . . . 1·25 1·40
DESIGN: 3f. St. Francis of Assisi.

1972. Monte Carlo Flower Show. As T **239**.
1042 3f. multicoloured . . . . . 2·40 2·00
DESIGN: 3f. "Vase of Flowers" (Cezanne).

266 "SS. Giovanni e Paolo" (detail, Canaletto)

1972. U.N.E.S.C.O. "Save Venice" Campaign.
1043 **266** 30c. red 20 25
1044 – 60c. violet 30 30
1045 – 2f. blue . . . . 1·25 1·40
DESIGNS—27 × 48 mm: 60c. "S. Pietro di Castello" (F. Guradi). As Type **266**: 2f. "Piazzetta S. Marco" (B. Bellotto).

267 Dressage

1972. Olympic Games, Munich. Equestrian Events.
1046 **267** 60c. brown, blue and lake 40 55
1047 – 90c. lake, brown and blue . . . . 80 1·00
1048 – 1f.10 blue, lake & brown 1·25 1·50
1049 – 1f.40 brown, lake & blue 2·10 2·40
DESIGNS: 90c. Cross country; 1f.10, Show jumping (wall); 1f.40, Show jumping (parallel bars).

268 Escoffier and Birthplace

1972. 125th Birth Anniv of Auguste Escoffier (master chef).
1050 **268** 45c. black and brown . . 20 25

269 Drug Addiction **270** Globe, Birds and Animals

1972. Campaign Against Drugs.
1051 **269** 50c. red, brown & orange 30 25
1052 90c. green, brown & blue 40 45
See also Nos. 1088/91 and 1280/1.

1972. 17th Int Congress of Zoology, Monaco.
1053 **270** 30c. green, brown and red 10 10
1054 – 50c. brown, purple and red 20 20
1055 – 90c. blue, brown and red 40 30
DESIGNS—HORIZ: 50c. VERT: 90c. Similar symbolic design.

271 Bouquet **272** "The Nativity" and Child's face

1972. Monte Carlo Flower Show, 1973 (1st issue). Multicoloured.
1056 30c. Lilies in vase 40 30
1057 50c. Type **271** 70 45
1058 90c. Flowers in vase . . . . 1·25 90
See also Nos. 1073, 1105/7, 1143/4, 1225/6, 1244, 1282/3 and 1316/17.

1972. Christmas.
1059 **272** 30c. grey, blue and purple 10 10
1060 50c. red, purple & brown 20 10
1061 90c. violet, plum & pur 40 30

273 Louis Bleriot and Bleriot XI (Birth cent)

1972. Birth Anniversaries.
1062 **273** 30c. blue and brown . . 20 10
1063 – 50c. blue, turq & new blue 60 60
1064 – 90c. brown and buff . . 80 55
DESIGNS AND ANNIVERSARIES: 50c. Amundsen and polar scene (birth centenary); 90c. Pasteur and laboratory scene (150th birth anniv).

274 "Gethsemane"

1972. Protection of Historical Monuments. Frescoes by J. Canavesio, Chapel of Notre-Dame des Fontaines, La Brigue.
1065 **274** 30c. red 10 10
1066 – 50c. grey 20 25
1067 – 90c. green 40 40
1068 – 1f.40 red 60 55
1069 – 2f. purple . . . . 1·10 80
DESIGNS: 50c. "Christ Outraged"; 90c. "Ascent to Calvary"; 1f.40, "The Resurrection"; 2f. "The Crucifixion".

1972. Paintings. "Princes and Princesses of Monaco". As T **213**. Multicoloured.
1070 1f. "Prince Jacques 1" (N. Largilliere) 40 45
1071 3f. "Princess Louise-Hippolyte" (J. B. Vanloo) 1·25 1·50

275

1973. 25th Anniv of Monaco Red Cross. Sheet 100 × 130 mm.
MS1072 **275** 5f. red . . . . . . 13·00 10·50

1973. Monte Carlo Flower Show (2nd issue). As T **239**.
1073 3f.50 multicoloured . . . . 3·50 3·25
DESIGN: 3f.50, "Bouquet of Flowers".

276 Europa "Posthorn"

1973. Europa.
1074 **276** 50c. orange . . . . . . 2·75 1·25
1075 90c. green . . . . 4·25 2·50

277 Moliere and Characters from "Le Malade Imaginaire"

1973. 300th Death Anniv of Moliere.
1076 **277** 20c. red, brown and blue 35 30

278 Colette, Cat and Books

1973. Birth Anniversaries.
1077 **278** 30c. black, blue and red 70 45
1078 – 45c. multicoloured . . . 1·75 1·25
1079 – 50c. lilac, purple and blue 35 25
1080 – 90c. multicoloured . . . 40 50
DESIGNS AND ANNIVERSARIES—HORIZ: 30c., Type **278** (nature writer, birth cent); 45c. J.-H. Fabre and insects (entomologists, 150th birth anniv); 90c. Sir George Cayley and his "convertiplane" (aviation pioneer, birth bicent). VERT: 50c. Blaise Pascal (philosopher and writer, 350th birth anniv).

279 E. Ducretet, "Les Invalides" and Eiffel Tower

1973. 75th Anniv of Eugene Ducretet's First Hertzian Radio Link.
1081 **279** 30c. purple and brown 20 25

1973. International Dog Show, Monte Carlo. As T **248**. Inscr "1973". Multicoloured.
1082 45c. Alsatian . . . . 7·25 4·25

280 C. Peguy and Chartres Cathedral

1973. Birth Bicentenary of Charles Peguy (writer).
1083 **280** 50c. brown, mauve & grey 30 35

281 Telecommunications Equipment

1973. 5th World Telecommunications Day.
1084 **281** 60c. violet, blue & brown 30 30

282 Stage Characters

1973. 5th World Amateur Theatre Festival.
1085 **282** 60c. lilac, blue and red 30 35

283 Ellis and Rugby Tackle

1973. 150th Anniv of Founding of Rugby Football by William Webb Ellis.
1086 **283** 90c. red, lake and brown 50 50

284 St. Theresa

1973. Birth Centenary of St. Theresa of Lisieux.
1087 **284** 1f.40 multicoloured . . . 60 55

285 Drug Addiction

1973. Campaign Against Drugs.
1088 **285** 50c. red, green and blue 20 25
1089 – 50c. multicoloured . . . 20 25
1090 **285** 90c. violet, green and red 40 45
1091 – 90c. multicoloured . . . 50 50
DESIGN: Nos. 1089, 1091, Children, syringes and addicts.

286 "Institution of the Creche" (Giotto)

1973. 750th Anniv of St. Francis of Assisi Creche.
1092 **286** 30c. purple (postage) . . 30 30
1093 – 45c. red 60 55
1094 – 50c. brown 70 70
1095 – 1f. green . . . . 1·60 1·25
1096 – 2f. brown . . . . 3·00 2·75
1097 – 3f. blue (air) . . . . . . 1·75 1·60
DESIGN—HORIZ: 45c. "The Nativity" (School of F. Lippi); 50c. "The Birth of Jesus Christ" (Giotto). VERT: 1f. "The Nativity" (15th-century miniature); 2f. "The Birth of Jesus" (Fra Angelico); 3f. "The Nativity" (Flemish school).

287 Country Picnic

1973. 50th Anniv of National Committee for Monegasque Traditions.
1098 **287** 10c. blue, green & brown 10 10
1099 – 20c. violet, blue and green 10 10
1100 – 30c. sepia, brown & green 20 25
1101 – 45c. red, violet and purple 40 35
1102 – 50c. black, red and brown 50 40
1103 – 60c. red, violet and blue 50 60
1104 – 1f. violet, blue and brown . . . . 95 1·10
DESIGNS—VERT: 20c. Maypole dance. HORIZ: 30c. "U Bradi" (local dance); 45c. St. Jean fire-dance; 50c. Blessing the Christmas loaf; 60c. Blessing the sea, Festival of St. Devote; 1f. Corpus Christi procession.

1973. Monte Carlo Flower Show, 1974. As T **271**. Multicoloured.
1105 45c. Roses and Strelitzia . . 80 55
1106 60c. Mimosa and myosotis 1·25 90
1107 1f. "Vase of Flowers" (Odilon Redon) . . . . . 2·00 1·60

1973. Paintings. "Princes and Princesses of Monaco". As T **213**. Multicoloured.
1108 2f. "Charlotte Grimaldi" (in day dress, P. Gobert) . . 1·40 1·40
1109 2f. "Charlotte Grimaldi" (in evening dress, P. Gobert) 1·40 1·40

288 Prince Rainier

1974. 25th Anniv of Prince Rainer's Accession. Sheet 100 × 130 mm.
MS1110 **288** 10f. black . . . . . 5·50 5·50

289 U.P.U. Emblem and Symbolic Heads

1974. Centenary of Universal Postal Union.
1111 **289** 50c. purple and brown . . . 30 25
1112 – 70c. multicoloured . . . 40 30
1113 – 1f.10 multicoloured . . . 70 55
DESIGNS: 70c. Hands holding letters; 1f.10, "Countries of the World" (famous buildings).

1974. Monaco Red Cross. As T **238**.
1114 3f. blue, green and purple . . . 1·40 1·25
DESIGN: 3f. St. Bernard of Menthon.

290 Farman, Farman F.60 Goliath and Farman H.F.III

1974. Birth Centenary of Henry Farman (aviation pioneer).
1115 **290** 30c. brown, purple & blue 10 10

291 Marconi, Circuit Plan and Destroyer

1974. Birth Centenary of Guglielmo Marconi (radio pioneer).
1116 **291** 40c. red, deep blue & blue 20 10

292 Duchesne and "Penicillium glaucum"

1974. Birth Centenary of Ernest Duchesne (microbiologist).
1117 **292** 45c. black, blue & purple . . . 30 20

293 Forest and Engine

1974. 60th Death Anniv of Fernand Forest (motor engineer and inventor).
1118 **293** 50c. purple, red and black 30 25

1974. International Dog Show, Monte Carlo. As T **248**, inscr "1974".
1119 60c. multicoloured . . . . . 2·75 2·00
DESIGN: 60c. Schnauzer.

294 Ronsard and Characters from "Sonnet to Helene"

1974. 450th Birth Anniv of Pierre de Ronsard (poet).
1120 **294** 70c. brown and red . . . 40 45

295 Sir Winston Churchill (after bust by O. Nemon)

297 "The King of Rome" (Bosio)

296 Interpol Emblem, and Views of Monaco and Vienna

1974. Birth Centenary of Sir Winston Churchill.
1121 **295** 1f. brown and grey . . . 55 45

1974. 60th Anniv of 1st International Police Judiciary Congress and 50th Anniv of International Criminal Police Organization (Interpol).
1122 **296** 2f. blue, brown and green . . . . 1·10 90

1974. Europa. Sculptures by J. F. Bosio.
1123 **297** 45c. green and brown . . 1·00 75
1124 – 1f.10 bistre and brown . . 1·75 1·40
MS1125 170 × 140 mm. Nos. 1123/5 × 5 . . . . 18·00 17·00
DESIGN: 1f.10, "Madame Elizabeth".

298 "The Box" (A. Renoir)

1974. "The Impressionists". Multicoloured.
1126 1f. Type **298** . . . . 1·40 1·40
1127 1f. "The Dance Class" (E. Degas) . . . . . . 1·40 1·40
1128 2f. "Impression-Sunrise" (C. Monet) (horiz) . . . . 2·75 2·75
1129 2f. "Entrance to Voisins Village" (C. Pissarro) (horiz) . . . . 2·75 2·75
1130 2f. "The Hanged Man's House" (P. Cezanne) (horiz) . . . . 2·75 2·75
1131 2f. "Floods at Port Marly" (A. Sisley) (horiz) . . . . 2·75 2·75

299 Tigers and Trainer

1974. 1st International Circus Festival, Monaco.
1132 **299** 2c. brown, green and blue 10 10
1133 – 3c. brown and purple . . 10 10
1134 – 5c. blue, brown and red . . 10 10
1135 – 45c. brown, black and red 40 35
1136 – 70c. multicoloured . . . 60 45
1137 – 1f.10 brown, green and red . . . . 1·40 75
1138 – 5f. green, blue and brown . . . . 4·00 3·25
DESIGNS—VERT: 3c. Performing horse; 45c. Equestrian act; 1f.10, Acrobats; 5f. Trapeze act. HORIZ: 5c. Performing elephants; 70c. Clowns.

300 Honore II on Medal

1974. 350th Anniv of Monegasque Numismatic Art.
1139 **300** 60c. green and red . . . 40 35

301 Marine Flora and Fauna

1974. 24th Congress of the International Commission for the Scientific Exploration of the Mediterranean. Multicoloured.
1140 45c. Type **301** 80 60
1141 70c. Sea-bed flora and fauna 1·40 90
1142 1f.10 Sea-bed flora and fauna (different) . . . . 2·00 1·40
Nos. 1141/2 are larger, size 52 × 31 mm.

1974. Monte Carlo Flower Show. As T **271**. Multicoloured.
1143 70c. Honeysuckle and violets 70 60
1144 1f.10 Iris and chrysanthemums . . . . 1·00 1·00

302 Prince Rainier III (F. Messina)

303

1974.
1145 **302** 60c. green (postage) . . 70 30
1146 80c. red 80 45
1147 80c. green 40 10
1148 1f. brown . . . . . . 2·00 85
1149 1f. red 50 20
1149a 1f. green 40 20
1149b 1f.10 green 40 20
1150 1f.20 violet . . . . . 4·25 2·00
1150a 1f.20 red 60 20
1150b 1f.20 green 70 20
1151 1f.25 blue . . . . . . 1·00 85
1151a 1f.30 red 70 25
1152 1f.40 red 80 20
1152a 1f.50 black 80 60
1153 1f.60 grey 80 50
1153a 1f.70 blue 90 60
1153b 1f.80 blue . . . . . . 1·40 1·40
1154 2f. mauve . . . . . . 1·50 1·50
1154a 2f.10 brown . . . . . . 1·40 75
1155 2f.30 violet . . . . . 1·75 1·25
1156 2f.50 black . . . . . . 1·75 1·40
1157 9f. violet . . . . 5·00 3·25
1158 **303** 10f. violet (air) . . . . 6·00 2·50
1159 15f. red . . . . 9·00 5·50
1160 20f. blue . . . . 11·00 6·00

304 Coastline, Monte Carlo

305 "Haagocereus chosicensis"

1974.
1161 **304** 25c. blue, green & brown 1·50 45
1162 – 25c. brown, green & blue 30 20
1163 – 50c. brown and blue . . 1·50 45
1164 **304** 65c. blue, brown & green 30 25
1165 – 70c. multicoloured . . . 40 40
1166 **304** 1f.10 brown, green & bl 1·75 65
1167 – 1f.10 black, brown & bl 60 70
1168 – 1f.30 brown, green & bl 60 40
1169 – 1f.40 green, grey & brn 2·00 1·00
1170 – 1f.50 green, blue & black 1·00 90
1171 – 1f.70 brown, green & bl 3·00 2·00
1172 – 1f.80 brown, green & bl 1·10 85
1173 – 2f.30 brown, grey & blue 1·75 1·40
1174 – 3f. brown, grey and green . . . . 4·75 2·00
1175 – 5f.50 brown, green & blue . . . . 6·25 4·25
1176 – 6f.50 brown, blue & grn 3·00 2·40
DESIGNS—VERT: 50c. Palace clock tower; 70c. Botanical gardens; 1f.30, Monaco Cathedral; 1f.40, 1f.50, Prince Albert I statue and Museum; 3f. Fort Antoine. HORIZ: 25c. (1162), 1f.70, "All Saints" Tower; 1f.10 (1167), Palais de Justice; 1f.80, 5f.50, La Condamine; 2f.30, North Galleries of Palace; 6f.50, Aerial view of hotels and harbour.

1975. Plants. Multicoloured.
1180 10c. Type **305** 10 10
1181 20c. "Matucana madisoniarum" 20 20
1182 30c. "Parodia scopaioides" 40 25
1183 85c. "Mediolobivia arachnacantha" . . . . . 1·50 80
1184 1f.90 "Matucana yanganucensis" . . . . . 2·75 2·10
1185 4f. "Echinocereus marksianus" . . . . . . 5·25 3·75

306 "Portrait of a Sailor" (P. Florence)

308 "Prologue"

307 "St. Bernardin de Sienne"

1975. Europa.
1186 **306** 80c. purple . . . . . . 1·10 60
1187 – 1f.20 blue . . . . 1·60 80
MS1188 170 × 130 mm. Nos. 1186/7 × 5 . . . . 18·00 17·00
DESIGN: 1f.20, "St. Devote" (Ludovic Brea).

1975. Monaco Red Cross.
1189 **307** 4f. blue and purple . . . 1·90 1·75

1975. Centenary of "Carmen" (opera by Georges Bizet).
1190 **308** 30c. violet, brown & blk 10 10
1191 – 60c. grey, green and red 20 10
1192 – 80c. green, brown & blk 50 35
1193 – 1f.40 purple, brn & ochre 80 70
DESIGNS—HORIZ: 60c. Lilla Pastia's tavern; 80c. "The Smuggler's Den"; 1f.40, "Confrontation at Seville".

309 Saint-Simon

310 Dr. Albert Schweitzer

1975. 300th Birth Anniv of Louis de Saint-Simon (writer).
1194 **309** 40c. blue 30 25

1975. Birth Centenary of Dr. Schweitzer (Nobel Peace Prize Winner).
1195 **310** 60c. red and brown . . . 50 35

311 "Stamp" and Calligraphy

1975. "Arphila 75" International Stamp Exhibition, Paris.
1196 **311** 80c. brown and orange 50 45

312 Seagull and Sunrise

1975. International Exposition, Okinawa.
1197 **312** 85c. blue, green & orange 60 50

313 Pike smashing Crab

1975. Anti-cancer Campaign.
1198 **313** 1f. multicoloured 60 50

314 Christ with Crown of Thorns

1975. Holy Year.
1199 **314** 1f.15 black, brn & pur 85 60

315 Villa Sauber, Monte Carlo

1975. European Architectural Heritage Year.
1200 **315** 1f.20 green, brown & bl 80 60

316 Woman's Head and Globe

1975. International Women's Year.
1201 **316** 1f.20 multicoloured . . . 80 60

317 Rolls-Royce "Silver Ghost" (1907)

1975. History of the Motor Car.
1202 **317** 5c. blue, green and brown 10 10
1203 – 10c. indigo and blue . . 10 10
1204 – 20c. blue, ultram & black 20 10
1205 – 30c. purple and mauve 40 20
1206 – 50c. blue, purple & mauve 70 50
1207 – 60c. red and green . . . 1·00 70
1208 – 80c. indigo and blue . . 1·75 1·10
1209 – 85c. brown, orange & grn . . . . 2·00 1·50
1210 – 1f.20 blue, red and green 3·00 2·40
1211 – 1f.40 green and blue . . 4·25 2·75
1212 – 5f.50 blue, emerald and green . . . . 9·50 7·00
DESIGNS: 10c. Hispano-Suiza "H.6B" (1926); 20c. Isotta Fraschini "8A" (1928); 30c. Cord "L.29"; 50c. Voisin "V12" (1930); 60c. Duesenberg "SJ" (1933); 80c. Bugatti "57 C" (1938); 85c. Delahaye "135 M" (1940); 1f.20, Cisitalia "Pininfarina" (1945); 1f.40, Mercedes-Benz "300 SL" (1955); 5f.50, Lamborghini "Countach" (1974).

1975. Paintings. "Princes and Princesses of Monaco". As T **213**. Multicoloured.
1213 2f. "Prince Honore III" . . 1·25 85
1214 4f. "Princess Catherine de Brignole" . . . . 2·50 2·40

318 Dog behind Bars

1975. 125th Birth Anniv of Gen. J. P. Delmas de Grammont (author of Animal Protection Code).
1215 **318** 60c. black and brown . . 80 80
1216 – 80c. black and brown . . 1·10 85
1217 – 1f.20 green and purple 1·90 1·50
DESIGNS—VERT: 80c. Cat chased up tree. HORIZ: 1f.20, Horse being ill-treated.

1975. International Dog Show, Monte Carlo. As T **248**, but inscr "1975". Multicoloured.
1218 60c. black and purple . . . 3·50 2·75
DESIGN: 60c. French poodle.

319 Maurice Ravel

1975. Birth Centenaries of Musicians.
1219 **319** 60c. brown and purple 70 55
1220 – 1f.20 black and purple 1·50 1·25
DESIGN: 1f.20, Johann Strauss (the younger).

320 Circus Clown

322 Andre Ampere with Electrical Meter

321 Monaco Florin Coin, 1640

1975. 2nd International Circus Festival.
1221 **320** 80c. multicoloured . . . 80 55

1975. Monaco Numismatics.
1222 **321** 80c. brown and blue . . 50 50
See also Nos. 1275, 1320 and 1448.

1975. Birth Centenary of Andre Ampere (physicist).
1223 **322** 85c. indigo and blue . . 50 50

323 "Lamentations for the Dead Christ"

1975. 500th Birth Anniv of Michelangelo.
1224 **323** 1f.40 olive and black . . 80 80

1975. Monte Carlo Flower Show (1976). As T **271**. Multicoloured.
1225 60c. Bouquet of wild flowers 80 55
1226 80c. Ikebana flower arrangement . . . . . . 1·40 90

1975. Precancelled. Surch.
1227 42c. on 26c. violet, blue and black (No. 949a) . . . . 1·60 1·40
1228 48c. on 30c. multicoloured (No. 949b) . . . . 1·90 1·90
1229 70c. on 45c. multicoloured (No. 950a) . . . . 3·25 2·75
1230 1f.35 on 90c. green, blue and black (No. 951a) . . 4·25 3·75

325 Prince Pierre de Monaco

1976. 25th Anniv of Literary Council of Monaco.
1231 **325** 10c. black 10 10
1232 – 20c. blue and red 20 20
1233 – 25c. blue and red 20 20
1234 – 30c. brown 20 30
1235 – 50c. blue, red and purple 40 30
1236 – 60c. brown, grn & lt brn 50 35
1237 – 80c. purple and blue . . 80 75
1238 – 1f.20 violet, blue & mve 1·60 1·10
COUNCIL MEMBERS—HORIZ: 20c. A. Maurois and Colette; 25c. Jean and Jerome Tharaud; 30c. E. Henriot, M. Pagnol and G. Duhamel; 50c. Ph. Heriat, J. Supervielle and L. Pierard; 60c. R. Dorgeles, M. Achard and G. Bauer; 80c. F. Hellens, A. Billy and Mgr. Grente; 1f.20, J. Giono, L. Pasteur Vallery-Radot and M. Garcon.

326 Dachshunds

1976. International Dog Show, Monte Carlo.
1239 **326** 60c. multicoloured . . . 4·00 3·25

327 Bridge Table and Monte Carlo Coast

1976. 5th Bridge Olympiad, Monte Carlo.
1240 **327** 60c. brown, green and red 50 40

328 Alexander Graham Bell and Early Telephone

1976. Telephone Centenary.
1241 **328** 80c. brown, light brown and grey 50 30

329 Federation Emblem on Globe

1976. 50th Anniv of International Philatelic Federation.
1242 **329** 1f.20 red, blue and green 70 55

330 U.S.A. 2c. Stamp, 1926

1976. Bicent of American Revolution.
1243 **330** 1f.70 black and purple 80 55

331 "The Fritillaries" (Van Gogh)

1976. Monte Carlo Flower Show.
1244 **331** 3f. multicoloured . . . . 7·00 5·00

332 Diving

333 Decorative Plate

1976. Olympic Games, Montreal.
1245 **332** 60c. brown and blue . . 30 30
1246 – 80c. blue, brown & green 40 35
1247 – 85c. blue, green & brown 50 40
1248 – 1f.20 brown, green & bl 70 60
1249 – 1f.70 brown, blue & grn 1·00 1·00
MS1250 150 × 145 mm. Nos. 1245/9 4·00 4·00
DESIGNS—VERT: 80c. Gymnastics; 85c. Hammer-throwing. HORIZ: 1f.20, Rowing; 1f.70, Boxing.

1976. Europa. Monegasque Ceramics. Multicoloured.
1251 80c. Type **333** 70 70
1252 1f.20 Grape-harvester (statuette) . . . . 1·25 1·10
MS1253 170 × 140 mm. Nos. 1251/2 × 5 . . . . 17·00 17·00

334 Palace Clock Tower

335 "St. Louise de Marillac" (altar painting)

1976. Precancelled.
1254 **334** 50c. red 50 45
1255 52c. orange 30 20
1256 54c. green 40 20
1257 60c. green 50 55
1258 62c. mauve 40 40
1259 68c. yellow 50 45
1260 90c. violet 80 80
1261 95c. red 80 65
1262 1f.05 brown 80 60
1263 1f.60 blue . . . . 1·40 1·25
1264 1f.70 turquoise . . . . . 1·40 1·00
1265 1f.85 brown . . . . . . 1·40 1·25

1976. Monaco Red Cross.
1270 **335** 4f. black, purple & green 2·00 1·90

1976. Paintings. "Princes and Princesses of Monaco". As T **213**.
1271 2f. purple . . . . 1·60 1·50
1272 4f. multicoloured . . . . . 3·00 2·10
DESIGNS: 2f. "Prince Honore IV"; 4f. "Princess Louise d'Aumont-Mazarin".

336 St. Vincent-de-Paul

337 Marie de Rabutin Chantal

1976. Centenary of St. Vincent-de-Paul Conference, Monaco.
1273 **336** 60c. black, brown & blue 35 25

1976. 350th Birth Anniv of Marquise de Sevigne (writer).
1274 **337** 80c. black, violet and red 40 30

338 Monaco 2g. "Honore II" Coin, 1640

1976. Monaco Numismatics.
1275 **338** 80c. blue and green . . . 50 40

339 Richard Byrd, "Josephine Ford", Airship "Norge" and Roald Amundsen

1976. 50th Anniv of First Flights over North Pole.
1276 **339** 85c. black, blue and green . . . . 1·25 1·10

340 Gulliver and Lilliputians

1976. 250th Anniv of Jonathan Swift's "Gulliver's Travels".
1277 **340** 1f.20 multicoloured . . . 60 45

341 Girl's Head and Christmas Decorations

1976. Christmas.
1278 **341** 60c. multicoloured . . . 40 25
1279 1f.20 green, orge & pur 60 40

342 "Drug" Dagger piercing Man and Woman
343 Circus Clown

1976. Campaign against Drug Abuse.
1280 **342** 80c. blue, orge & bronze 50 30
1281 1f.20 lilac, purple & brn 70 50

1976. Monte Carlo Flower Show (1977). As T **271**. Multicoloured.
1282 80c. Flower arrangement . . 1·00 75
1283 1f. Bouquet of flowers . . . 1·50 1·25

1976. 3rd International Circus Festival, Monte Carlo.
1284 **343** 1f. multicoloured . . . . 1·40 1·00

344 Schooner "Hirondelle I"

1977. 75th Anniv of Publication of "Career of a Navigator" by Prince Albert I (1st issue). Illustrations by L. Tinayre.
1285 **344** 10c. brown, blue & turq 10 10
1286 – 20c. black, brown & lake 10 20
1287 – 30c. green, blue & orange 20 25
1288 – 80c. black, blue and red 40 40
1289 – 1f. black and brown . . 60 50
1290 – 1f.25 olive, green & violet 80 75
1291 – 1f.40 brown, olive & grn 1·25 1·25
1292 – 1f.90 blue, lt blue & red 2·25 1·60
1293 – 2f.50 brown, blue and turquoise . . . . . . 3·25 2·75
DESIGNS—VERT: 20c. Prince Albert I; 1f. Helmsman; 1f.90, Bringing in the trawl. HORIZ: 30c. Crew-members; 80c. "Hirondelle" in a gale; 1f.25, Securing the lifeboat; 1f.40, Shrimp fishing; 2f.50, Capture of an oceanic sunfish.
See also Nos. 1305/13.

345 Pyrenean Sheep and Mountain Dogs

1977. International Dog Show, Monte Carlo.
1294 **345** 80c. multicoloured . . . 3·75 2·75

346 "Maternity" (M. Cassatt)

1977. World Association of the "Friends of Children".
1295 **346** 80c. deep brown, brown and black 95 70

347 Archers

1977. 10th International Archery Championships.
1296 **347** 1f.10 black, brown & bl 70 50

348 Charles Lindbergh and "Spirit of St. Louis"

1977. 50th Anniv of Lindbergh's Transatlantic Flight.
1297 **348** 1f.90 light blue, light and brown . . . . 1·40 1·10

349 "Harbour, Deauville"

1977. Birth Centenary of Raoul Dufy (painter).
1298 **349** 2f. multicoloured . . . . 3·00 2·50

350 "Portrait of a Young Girl"
351 "L'Oreillon" Tower

1977. 400th Birth Anniv of Peter Paul Rubens (painter).
1299 **350** 80c. orange, brown & blk 50 45
1300 – 1f. red 85 60
1301 – 1f.40 orange and red . . 1·75 1·25
DESIGNS: 1f. "Duke of Buckingham"; 1f.40, "Portrait of a Child".

1977. Europa. Views.
1302 **351** 1f. brown and blue . . . 80 60
1303 – 1f.40 blue, brown and bistre . . . . 1·25 1·10
MS1304 169 × 130 mm. Nos. 1302/3 × 5 . . . . 18·00 18·00
DESIGN: 1f.40, St. Michael's Church, Menton.

1977. 75th Anniv of Publication of "Career of a Navigator" by Prince Albert I (2nd issue). Illustrations by L. Tinayre. As T **344**.
1305 10c. black and blue 10 10
1306 20c. blue 10 15
1307 30c. blue, light blue and green 20 25
1308 80c. brown, black and green 40 35
1309 1f. grey and green 50 50
1310 1f.25 black, brown and lilac 80 75
1311 1f.40 purple, blue and brown . . . . 1·25 1·25
1312 1f.90 black, blue and light blue . . . . 2·10 1·75
1313 3f. blue, brown and green 3·00 2·75
DESIGNS—HORIZ: 10c. "Princess Alice" (steam yacht) at Kiel; 20c. Ship's laboratory; 30c. "Princess Alice" in ice floes; 1f. Polar scene; 1f.25, Bridge of "Princess Alice" during snowstorm; 1f.40, Arctic camp; 1f.90, Ship's steam launch in floating ice; 3f. "Princess Alice" passing iceberg. VERT: 80c. Crewmen in Arctic dress.

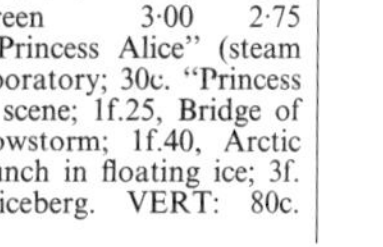

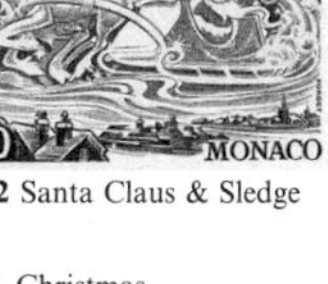
352 Santa Claus & Sledge

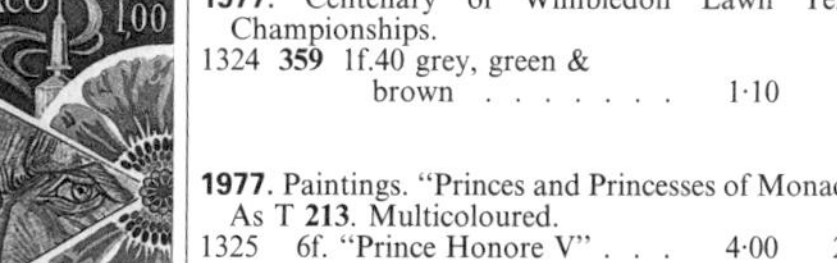
353 Face, Poppy and Syringe

1977. Christmas.
1314 **352** 80c. red, green and blue 40 30
1315 1f.40 multicoloured . . . 60 40

1977. Monte Carlo Flower Show. As T **271**. Mult.
1316 80c. Snapdragons and campanula 80 70
1317 1f. Ikebana . . . . 1·25 1·00

1977. Campaign Against Drug Abuse.
1318 **353** 1f. black, red and violet 50 40

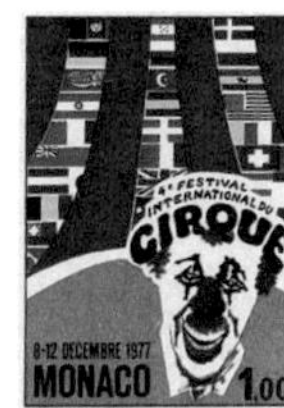
354 Clown and Flags

1977. 4th International Festival of Circus, Monaco.
1319 **354** 1f. multicoloured . . . . 1·40 1·10

355 Gold Coin of Honore II

1977. Monaco Numismatics.
1320 **355** 80c. brown and red . . . 50 45

356 Mediterranean divided by Industry

1977. Protection of the Mediterranean Environment.
1321 **356** 1f. black, green and blue 60 50

357 Dr. Guglielminetti and Road Tarrers

1977. 75th Anniv of First Experiments at Road Tarring in Monaco.
1322 **357** 1f.10 black, bistre and brown 60 45

358 F.M.L.T. Badge and Monte Carlo

1977. 50th Anniv of Monaco Lawn Tennis Federation.
1323 **358** 1f. blue, red and brown 1·00 50

359 Wimbledon and First Championships

1977. Centenary of Wimbledon Lawn Tennis Championships.
1324 **359** 1f.40 grey, green & brown . . . . 1·10 95

1977. Paintings. "Princes and Princesses of Monaco". As T **213**. Multicoloured.
1325 6f. "Prince Honore V" . . . 4·00 2·75

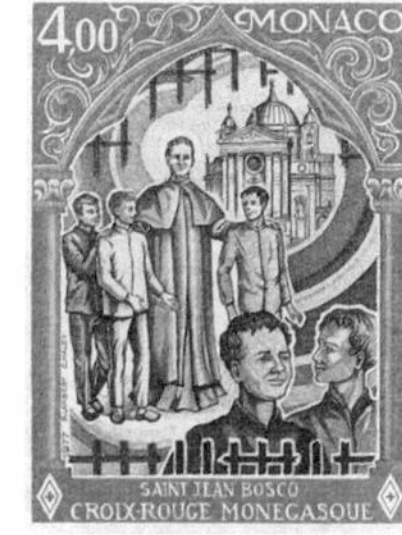
360 St. Jean Bosco

1977. Monaco Red Cross. Monegasque Art.
1326 **360** 4f. green, brown and blue . . . . 1·90 1·75

1978. Precancelled. Surch.
1327 **334** 58c. on 54c. green . . . 50 45
1328 73c. on 68c. yellow . . . 70 60
1329 1f.15 on 1f.05 brown . . 1·00 95
1330 2f. on 1f.85 brown . . . 1·75 1·75

362 Aerial Shipwreck from "L'Ile Mysterieuse"

1978. 150th Birth Anniv of Jules Verne.
1331 **362** 5c. brown, red and olive 10 10
1332 – 25c. turquoise, blue & red 10 10
1333 – 30c. blue, brown & lt blue 20 10
1334 – 80c. black, green & orge 30 30
1335 – 1f. brown, lake and blue 60 50
1336 – 1f.40 bistre, brown and green 80 70
1337 – 1f.70 brown, light blue and blue . . . . . . 1·10 1·25
1338 – 5f.50 violet and blue . . 2·75 2·75
DESIGNS: 25c. The abandoned ship from "L'Ile Mysterieuse"; 30c. The secret of the island from "L'Ile Mysterieuse"; 80c. "Robur the Conqueror"; 1f. "Master Zacharius"; 1f.40, "The Castle in the Carpathians"; 1f.70, "The Children of Captain Grant"; 5f.50, Jules Verne and allegories.

363 Aerial View of Congress Centre

1978. Inauguration of Monaco Congress Centre.
1339 **363** 1f. brown, blue and green 40 40
1340 – 1f.40 blue, brown & grn 60 50
DESIGN: 1f.40, View of Congress Centre from sea.

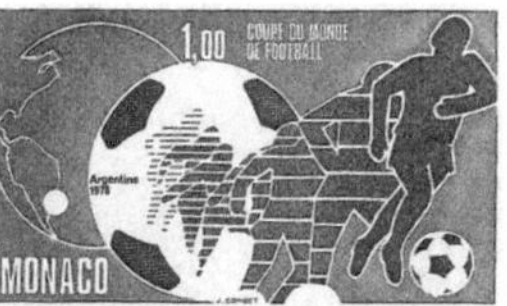
364 Footballers and Globe

1978. World Cup Football Championship, Argentina.
1341 **364** 1f. blue, slate and green 60 55

365 Antonio Vivaldi

366 "Ramoge" (research vessel) and Grimaldi Palace

1978. 300th Birth Anniv of Antonio Vivaldi (composer).
1342 **365** 1f. brown and red . . . 70 70

1978. Environment Protection. "RAMOGE" Agreement.
1343 **366** 80c. multicoloured . . . 40 35
1344 – 1f. red, blue and green 60 40
DESIGN—HORIZ (48×27 mm): 1f. Map of coastline between St. Raphael and Genes.

367 Monaco Cathedral

1978. Europa. Monaco Views.
1345 **367** 1f. green, brown and blue 70 60
1346 – 1f.40 brown, green & bl 1·40 1·00
MS1347 170×143 mm. Nos. 1345/6 ×5 . . . . 18·00 18·00
DESIGN: 1f.40, View of Monaco from the east.

368 Monaco Congress Centre

1978. Precancelled.
1348 **368** 61c. orange 30 25
1349 64c. green 30 25
1350 68c. blue 30 25
1351 78c. purple 40 40
1352 83c. violet 40 40
1353 88c. orange 40 40
1354 1f.25 brown 70 60
1355 1f.30 red 70 60
1356 1f.40 green 70 60
1357 2f.10 blue . . . . 1·00 1·10
1358 2f.25 orange . . . . . . 1·00 1·10
1359 2f.35 mauve . . . . . . 1·10 95

369 "Cinderella"

1978. 350th Birth Anniv of Charles Perrault (writer).
1360 **369** 5c. red, olive and violet 10 10
1361 – 25c. black, brown & mve 10 10
1362 – 30c. green, lake & brown 20 10
1363 – 80c. multicoloured . . . 40 30
1364 – 1f. red, brown and olive 60 55
1365 – 1f.40 mauve, ultramarine and blue 80 65
1366 – 1f.70 green, blue & grey 1·00 85
1367 – 1f.90 multicoloured . . . 1·40 1·10
1368 – 2f.50 blue, orange & grn 1·60 1·50
DESIGNS: 25c. "Puss in Boots"; 30c. "The Sleeping Beauty"; 80c. "Donkey's Skin"; 1f. "Little Red Riding Hood"; 1f.40, "Bluebeard"; 1f.70, "Tom Thumb"; 1f.90, "Riquet with a Tuft"; 2f.50, "The Fairies".

370 "The Sunflowers" (Van Gogh)

372 Girl with Letter

371 Afghan Hound

1978. Monte Carlo Flower Show (1979) and 125th Birth Anniv of Vincent Van Gogh. Multicoloured.
1369 1f. Type **370** . . . . 2·00 1·75
1370 1f.70 "The Iris" (Van Gogh) 3·00 1·90

1978. International Dog Show, Monte Carlo. Multicoloured.
1371 1f. Type **371** . . . . 2·75 1·90
1372 1f.20 Borzoi . . . . 3·25 2·50

1978. Christmas.
1373 **372** 1f. brown, blue and red 50 40

373 Catherine and William Booth

1978. Centenary of Salvation Army.
1374 **373** 1f.70 multicoloured . . . 90 85

374 Juggling Seals

376

375

1978. 5th International Circus Festival, Monaco.
1375 **374** 80c. orange, black & blue 40 45
1376 – 1f. multicoloured 60 55
1377 – 1f.40 brown, mauve and bistre 90 90
1378 – 1f.90 blue, lilac and mauve . . . . 1·60 1·60
1379 – 2f.40 multicoloured . . . 2·50 1·90
DESIGNS—HORIZ: 1f.40, Horseback acrobatics; 1f.90, Musical monkeys; 2f.40, Trapeze. VERT: 1f. Lion tamer.

1978. Paintings. "Princes and Princesses of Monaco". As T **213**. Multicoloured.
1380 2f. "Prince Florestan I" (G. Dauphin) . . . . . . 1·60 1·50
1381 4f. "Princess Caroline Gilbert de la Metz" (Marie Verroust) . . . . 3·00 2·50

1978. 150th Anniv of Henri Dunant (founder of Red Cross). Sheet 100×130 mm.
MS1382 **375** 5f. chocolate, crimson and red . . . . 4·25 4·25

1979. 21st Birthday of Prince Albert. Sheet 80×105 mm.
MS1383 **376** 10f. green and brown 8·00 8·00

377 "Jongleur de Notre-Dame" (Massenet)

1979. Centenary of "Salle Garnier" (Opera House) (1st issue).
1384 **377** 1f. blue, orange & mauve 40 35
1385 – 1f.20 violet, black & turq 60 45
1386 – 1f.50 maroon, grn & turq 70 75
1387 – 1f.70 multicoloured . . . 1·25 1·40
1388 – 2f.10 turquoise and violet . . . . 1·75 1·75
1389 – 3f. multicoloured . . . . 2·50 2·40
DESIGNS—HORIZ: 1f.20, "Hans the Flute Player" (L. Ganne); 1f.50, "Don Quixote" (J. Massenet); 2f.10, "The Child and the Sorcerer" (M. Ravel); 3f. Charles Garnier (architect) and south facade of Opera House. VERT: 1f.70, "L'Aiglon" (A. Honegger and J. Ibert).
See also Nos. 1399/1404.

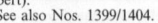

378 Flower, Bird and Butterfly

1979. International Year of the Child. Children's Paintings.
1390 **378** 50c. pink, green and black 25 25
1391 – 1f. slate, green and orange 40 40
1392 – 1f.20 slate, orange & mve 60 60
1393 – 1f.50 yellow, brown & bl 1·00 1·00
1394 – 1f.70 multicoloured . . . 1·25 1·25
DESIGNS: 1f. Horse and Child; 1f.20, "The Gift of Love"; 1f.50, "Peace in the World"; 1f.70, "Down with Pollution".

379 Armed Foot Messenger

1979. Europa.
1395 **379** 1f.20 brown, green & bl 60 45
1396 – 1f.50 brown, turq & bl 70 45
1397 – 1f.70 brown, green & bl 80 75
MS1398 129×149 mm. Nos. 1395/7, each ×2 . . . . 9·00 9·00
DESIGNS: 1f.50, 18th cent felucca; 1f.70, Arrival of first train at Monaco.

380 "Instrumental Music" (G. Boulanger) (detail of Opera House interior)

1979. Centenary of "Salle Garnier" (Opera House) (2nd issue).
1399 – 1f. brown, orange & turq 50 40
1400 – 1f.20 multicoloured . . . 60 50
1401 – 1f.50 multicoloured . . . 1·00 80
1402 – 1f.70 blue, brown and red . . . . 1·40 1·25
1403 – 2f.10 red, violet & black 1·75 1·75
1404 **380** 3f. green, brown and light green . . . . . 2·75 2·50
DESIGNS (as Type **377**)—HORIZ: 1f. "Les Biches" (F. Poulenc); 1f.20, "The Sailors" (G. Auric); 1f.70, "Gaiete Parisienne" (J. Offenbach). VERT: 1f.50, "La Spectre de la Rose" (C. M. Weber) (after poster by Jean Cocteau); 2f.10, "Salome" (R. Strauss).

1979. Paintings. "Princes and Princesses of Monaco". As T **213**. Multicoloured.
1405 3f. "Prince Charles III" (B. Biard) . . . . 1·60 1·40
1406 4f. "Antoinette de Merode" 2·40 1·60

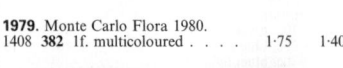

381 St. Pierre Claver

382 "Princess Grace" Orchid

1979. Monaco Red Cross.
1407 **381** 5f. multicoloured . . . . 2·25 2·25

1979. Monte Carlo Flora 1980.
1408 **382** 1f. multicoloured . . . . 1·75 1·40

383 "Princess Grace" Rose

384 Clown balancing on Ball

1979. Monte Carlo Flower Show.
1409 **383** 1f.20 multicoloured . . . 1·60 1·40

1979. 6th International Circus Festival.
1410 **384** 1f.20 multicoloured . . . 70 80

385 Sir Rowland Hill and Penny Black

386 Albert Einstein

1979. Death Centenary of Sir Rowland Hill.
1411 **385** 1f.70 brown, blue & blk 60 55

1979. Birth Centenary of Albert Einstein (physicist).
1412 **386** 1f.70 brown, grey and red 70 55

387 St. Patrick's Cathedral

1979. Centenary of St. Patrick's Cathedral, New York.
1413 **387** 2f.10 black, blue & brn 90 70

388 Nativity Scene

1979. Christmas.
1414 **388** 1f.20 blue, orange & mve 50 55

389 Early Racing Cars

1979. 50th Anniv of Grand Prix Motor Racing.
1415 **389** 1f. multicoloured 70 50

390 Arms of Charles V and Monaco

1979. 450th Anniv of Visit of Emperor Charles V.
1416 **390** 1f.50 brown, blue & blk 60 50

391 Setter and Pointer

1979. International Dog Show, Monte Carlo.
1417 **391** 1f.20 multicoloured . . . 3·00 2·50

392 Spring

1980. Precancels. The Seasons.
1418 **392** 76c. brown and green . . 30 20
1419 88c. olive, emerald & grn 30 20

1420 – 99c. green and brown . . 50 30
1421 – 1f.14 green, emer & brn 30 30
1422 – 1f.60 brown, grey and deep brown 80 60
1423 – 1f.84 lake, grey & brown 80 60
1424 – 2f.65 brown, lt blue & bl 1·40 85
1425 – 3f.05 brown, bl & slate 1·40 85

DESIGNS: 99c., 1f.14, Summer; 1f.60, 1f.84, Autumn; 2f.65, 3f.05, Winter.

394 Paul P. Harris (founder) and View of Chicago

1980. 75th Anniv of Rotary International.
1434 **394** 1f.80 olive, blue & turq 80 65

395 Gymnastics

1980. Olympic Games, Moscow and Lake Placid.
1435 **395** 1f.10 blue, brown & grey 30 25
1436 – 1f.30 red, brown & blue 40 30
1437 – 1f.60 red, blue & brown 50 40
1438 – 1f.80 brown, bis & grn 60 50
1439 – 2f.30 grey, violet & mve 90 75
1440 – 4f. green, blue and brown . . . . 1·40 1·25

DESIGNS: 1f.30, Handball; 1f.60, Pistol-shooting; 1f.80, Volleyball; 2f.30, Ice hockey; 4f. Skiing.

396 Colette (novelist)

1980. Europa. Each black, green and red.
1441 1f.30 Type **396** 40 30
1442 1f.80 Marcel Pagnol (writer) 50 45
MS1443 171 × 143 mm. Nos. 1441/2, each × 5 . . . . 4·75 4·75

397 "La Source"

1980. Birth Bicentenary of Jean Ingres (artist).
1444 **397** 4f. multicoloured . . . . 5·00 3·75

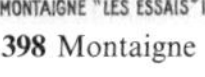

398 Montaigne

399 Guillaume Apollinaire (after G. Pieret)

1980. 400th Anniv of Publication of Montaigne's "Essays".
1445 **398** 1f.30 black, red and blue 55 40

1980. Birth Centenary of Guillaume Apollinaire (poet).
1446 **399** 1f.10 brown 55 40

400 Congress Centre

1980. Kiwanis International European Convention.
1447 **400** 1f.30 black, blue and red 55 40

401 Honore II Silver Ecu, 1649

1980. Numismatics.
1448 **401** 1f.50 black and blue . . 60 55

402 Lhassa Apso and Shih Tzu

1980. International Dog Show, Monte Carlo.
1449 **402** 1f.30 multicoloured . . . 3·50 2·75

403 "The Princess and the Pea"

1980. 175th Birth Anniv of Hans Christian Andersen.
1450 **403** 70c. sepia, red and brown 30 25
1451 – 1f.30 blue, turq & red . . 40 45
1452 – 1f.50 black, blue & turq 70 65
1453 – 1f.60 red, black & brown 80 80
1454 – 1f.80 yellow, brn & turq 1·00 1·00
1455 – 2f.30 brown, pur & vio 1·40 1·25

DESIGNS: 1f.30, "The Little Mermaid"; 1f.50, "The Chimneysweep and Shepherdess"; 1f.60, "The Brave Little Lead Soldier"; 1f.80, "The Little Match Girl"; 2f.30, "The Nightingale".

404 "The Road" (M. Vlaminck)

1980. 75th Anniv of 1905 Autumn Art Exhibition. Multicoloured.
1456 2f. Type **404** . . . . 1·50 1·25
1457 3f. "Woman at Balustrade" (Van Dongen) . . . . . 2·50 1·25
1458 4f. "The Reader" (Henri Matisse) . . . . 3·00 3·00
1459 5f. "Three Figures in a Meadow" (A. Derain) . . 4·50 3·75

1980. Paintings. "Princes and Princesses of Monaco". As T **213**. Multicoloured.
1460 4f. "Prince Albert I" (L. Bonnat) . . . . . . 2·00 1·75
1461 4f. "Princess Marie Alice Heine" (L. Maeterlinck) 2·00 1·75

405 "Sunbirds"

1980. Monaco Red Cross.
1462 **405** 6f. red, bistre and brown 2·50 2·50

406 "MONACO" balanced on Tightrope

1980. 7th International Circus Festival, Monaco.
1463 **406** 1f.30 red, turquoise & blue . . . . 1·40 85

407 Children and Nativity

1980. Christmas.
1464 **407** 1f.10 blue, carmine and red 45 40
1465 2f.30 violet, orange and pink 95 60

1980. Monte Carlo Flower Show, 1981. As T **383**. Multicoloured.
1466 1f.30 "Princess Stephanie" rose 80 60
1467 1f.80 Ikebana . . . . 1·50 1·00

408 "Alcyonium"

409 Fish with Hand for Tail

1980. Marine Fauna. Multicoloured.
1468 5c. "Spirographis spallanzanli" 10 10
1469 10c. "Anemonia sulcata" . . 10 10
1470 15c. "Leptopsammia pruvoit" 10 10
1471 20c. "Pteroides" 10 20
1472 30c. "Paramuricea clavata" (horiz) 30 20
1473 40c. Type **408** 30 20
1474 50c. "Corallium rubrum" . . 40 30
1475 60c. Trunculus murex ("Calliactis parasitica") (horiz) 70 65
1476 70c. "Cerianthus membranaceus" (horiz) 90 80
1477 1f. "Actinia equina" (horiz) 1·00 80
1478 2f. "Protula" (horiz) . . . . 2·00 1·10

1981. "Respect the Sea".
1479 **409** 1f.20 multicoloured . . . 70 55

410 Prince Rainier and Princess Grace

1981. Royal Silver Wedding.
1480 **410** 1f.20 black and green . . 1·00 75
1481 1f.40 black and red . . . 1·40 1·25
1482 1f.70 black and green . . 1·60 1·40
1483 1f.80 black and brown 2·00 1·60
1484 2f. black and blue . . . 3·25 1·90

411 Mozart (after Lorenz Vogel)

412 Palm Cross

1981. 225th Birth Anniv of Wolfgang Amadeus Mozart (composer).
1485 **411** 2f. brown, dp brown & bl . . . . 1·25 85
1486 – 2f.50 blue, brn & dp brn 1·75 1·40
1487 – 3f.50 dp brown, bl & brn 2·75 1·75

DESIGNS—HORIZ: 2f.50, "Mozart at 7 with his Father and Sister" (engraving by Delafoose after drawing by Carmontelle); 3f.50 "Mozart directing Requiem two Days before his Death" (painting by Baude).

1981. Europa. Multicoloured.
1488 **412** 1f.40 green, brown & red 50 40
1489 – 2f. multicoloured 60 55
MS1490 171 × 143 mm. Nos. 1488/9, each × 5 . . . .

DESIGN: 2f. Children carrying palm crosses.

413 Paris Football Stadium, Cup and Footballer

1981. 25th Anniv of European Football Cup.
1491 **413** 2f. black and blue . . . 95 70

414 I.Y.D.P. Emblem and Girl in Wheelchair

1981. International Year of Disabled Persons.
1492 **414** 1f.40 blue and green . . 70 55

415 Palace flying Old Flag, National Flag and Monte Carlo

1981. Centenary of National Flag.
1493 **415** 2f. red, blue and brown 90 65

416 Oceanographic Institute, Paris and Oceanographic Museum, Monaco

1981. 75th Anniv of Oceanographic Institute.
1494 **416** 1f.20 blue, black & brn 60 60

417 Bureau Building and "Faddey Bellingshausen" (hydrographic research ship)

1981. 50th Anniv of Int Hydrographic Bureau.
1495 **417** 2f.50 sepia, brown and light brown . . . . . 1·40 1·25

418 Rough Collies and Shetland Sheepdogs

1981. International Dog Show, Monte Carlo.
1496 **418** 1f.40 multicoloured . . . 3·50 3·25

419 Rainier III and Prince Albert **421** Arctic Scene and Map

1981. (a) 23 × 28 mm.
1497 **419** 1f.40 green (postage) . . 70 20
1498 1f.60 red 95 15
1499 1f.60 green 50 20
1500 1f.70 green 80 25
1501 1f.80 red 60 40
1502 1f.80 green 70 20
1503 1f.90 green . . . . . . 1·40 50
1504 2f. red . . . . 1·25 40
1505 2f. green 85 25
1506 2f.10 red 90 25
1507 2f.20 red 80 40
1508 2f.30 blue . . . . 2·75 2·40
1509 2f.50 brown . . . . . . 1·00 60
1510 2f.60 blue . . . . 1·90 1·75
1511 2f.80 blue . . . . 1·75 1·50
1512 3f. blue . . . . 1·75 1·25
1513 3f.20 blue . . . . 1·75 1·75
1514 3f.40 blue . . . . 2·75 1·60
1515 3f.60 blue . . . . 1·75 1·25
1516 4f. brown . . . . 1·40 75
1517 5f.50 black . . . . . . 1·90 1·40
1518 10f. purple . . . . . . 2·75 1·10
1519 15f. green . . . . 6·50 1·75
1520 20f. blue . . . . 6·50 2·50

(b) 36 × 27 mm.
1521 – 5f. violet (air) . . . . . . 1·60 75
1522 – 10f. red . . . . 3·75 1·50
1523 – 15f. green . . . . 5·00 1·60
1524 – 20f. blue . . . . 6·00 3·00
1525 – 30f. brown . . . . 8·00 4·00
DESIGN: Nos. 1521/5, Double portrait and monograms.

1981. 1st International Congress on Discovery and History of Northern Polar Regions, Rome.
1530 **421** 1f.50 multicoloured . . . 1·25 95

1981. Paintings. "Princes and Princesses of Monaco". Vert designs as T **213**. Multicoloured.
1531 3f. "Prince Louis II" (P.-A. de Laszlo) . . . . 1·60 1·00
1532 5f. "Princess Charlotte" (P.-A. de Laszlo) . . . . . . 3·25 1·90

422 Hercules fighting the Nemean Lion

1981. Monaco Red Cross. The Twelve Labours of Hercules (1st series).
1533 **422** 2f.50+50c. green, brown and red . . . . 1·00 1·25
1534 – 3f.50+50c. blue, green and red . . . . 1·25 1·25
DESIGN: 3f.50, Slaying the Hydra of Lerna.
See also Nos. 1584/5, 1631/2, 1699/1700, 1761/2 and 1794/5.

423 Ettore Bugatti (racing car designer) (Cent) **424** Eglantines and Morning Glory

1981. Birth Anniversaries.
1535 **423** 1f. indigo, blue and red 80 50
1536 – 2f. black, blue and brown 80 75
1537 – 2f.50 brown, black and red . . . . 1·10 80
1538 – 4f. multicoloured . . . . 2·50 2·40
1539 – 4f. multicoloured . . . . 2·50 2·40

DESIGNS: No. 1536, George Bernard Shaw (dramatist, 125th anniv); 1537, Fernand Leger (painter, centenary). LARGER: (37 × 48 mm): 1538, Pablo Picasso (self-portrait) (centenary); 1539, Rembrandt (self-portrait) (375th anniv).

1981. Monte Carlo Flower Show (1982). Mult.
1540 1f.40 Type **424** . . . . . . 1·00 75
1541 2f. "Ikebana" (painting by Ikenobo) . . . . 1·75 1·40

425 "Catherine Deneuve" **426** Tiger, Clown, Acrobat and Elephants

1981. 1st International Rose Show, Monte Carlo.
1542 **425** 1f.80 multicoloured . . . 2·50 1·90

1981. 8th International Circus Festival, Monaco.
1543 **426** 1f.40 violet, mauve & blk 1·90 1·50

427 Praying Children and Nativity

1981. Christmas.
1544 **427** 1f.20 blue, mauve & brn 50 50

428 "Lancia-Stratos" Rally Car

1981. 50th Monte Carlo Rally (1982).
1545 **428** 1f. blue, red & turquoise 90 80

429 Spring

1981. Seasons of the Persimmon Tree. Sheet 143 × 100 mm containing T **429** and similar horiz designs.
MS1546 1f. green, yellow and blue (T **429**); 2f. green and blue (Summer); 3f. red, brown and yellow (Autumn); 4f. brown and red (Winter) . . . . 6·75 6·75

430 "Hoya bella" **431** Spring

1981. Plants in Exotic Garden. Multicoloured.
1547 1f.40 Type **430** . . . . . . 2·50 1·40
1548 1f.60 "Bolivicereus samaipatanus" . . . . . 2·00 1·25
1549 1f.80 "Trichocereus grandiflorus" (horiz) . . . 2·50 1·50
1550 2f. "Argyroderma roseum" 1·25 40
1551 2f.30 "Euphorbia milii" . . 2·00 1·75
1552 2f.60 "Echinocereus fitchii" (horiz) . . . . 2·00 1·75
1553 2f.90 "Rebutia heliosa" (horiz) . . . . 2·00 1·90
1554 4f.10 "Echinopsis multiplex cristata" (horiz) . . . . . 3·00 2·50

1982. Precancels. The Seasons of the Peach Tree.
1555 **431** 97c. mauve and green . . 30 20
1556 – 1f.25 green, orge & mve 50 30
1557 – 2f.03 brown 80 60
1558 – 3f.36 brown and blue . . 1·40 90
DESIGNS: 1f.25, Summer; 2f.03, Autumn; 3f.36, Winter.

432 Common Nutcracker **433** Capture of Monaco Fortress, 1297

1982. Birds from Mercantour National Park.
1559 **432** 60c. black, brown & grn 60 70
1560 – 70c. black and mauve . . 70 70
1561 – 80c. red, black & orange 80 80
1562 – 90c. black, red and blue 1·40 1·25
1563 – 1f.40 brown, black & red 2·40 1·75
1564 – 1f.60 brown, black & blue . . . . 2·75 2·10
DESIGNS—VERT: 70c. Black grouse; 80c. Rock partridge; 1f.60, Golden eagle. HORIZ: 90c. Wallcreeper; 1f.40, Rock ptarmigan.

1982. Europa.
1565 **433** 1f.60 blue, brown and red 50 40
1566 – 2f.30 blue, brown and red 70 45
MS1567 173 × 143 mm. Nos. 1565/6, each × 5 . . . . 6·50 6·50
DESIGN: 2f.30, Signing the Treaty of Peronne, 1641.

434 Old Quarter

1982. Fontvieille.
1568 **434** 1f.40 blue, brown & grn 60 40
1569 – 1f.60 light brown, brown and red 70 60
1570 – 2f.30 purple . . . . . . 1·25 80
DESIGNS: 1f.60, Land reclamation; 2f.30, Urban development.

435 Stadium

1982. Fontvieille Sports Stadium (1st series).
1571 **435** 2f.30 green, brown & blue . . . . 1·00 80
See also No. 1616.

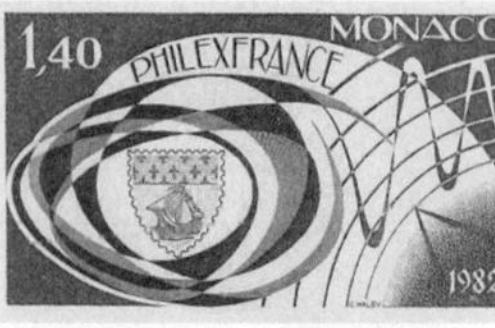

436 Arms of Paris

1982. "Philexfrance" International Stamp Exhibition, Paris.
1572 **436** 1f.40 red, grey and deep red 70 60

437 Old English Sheepdog

1982. International Dog Show, Monte Carlo. Multicoloured.
1573 60c. Type **437** . . . . . . 2·00 1·50
1574 1f. Briard . . . . 2·50 1·90

438 Monaco Cathedral and Arms

1982. Creation of Archbishopric of Monaco (1981).
1575 **438** 1f.60 black, blue and red 60 60

439 St. Francis of Assisi **440** Dr. Robert Koch

1982. 800th Birth Anniv of St. Francis of Assisi.
1576 **439** 1f.40 grey and light grey 70 65

1982. Centenary of Discovery of Tubercle Bacillus.
1577 **440** 1f.40 purple and lilac . . 70 70

441 Lord Baden-Powell **443** St. Hubert (18th-century medallion)

442 Running for Ball

1982. 125th Birth Anniv of Lord Baden-Powell (founder of Boy Scout Movement).
1578 **441** 1f.60 brown and black 1·00 90

1982. World Cup Football Championship, Spain. Sheet 143 × 120 mm containing T **442** and similar square designs, each brown, blue and green.
MS1579 1f. Type **442**; 2f. Kicking ball; 3f. Heading ball; 4f. Goalkeeper . . . . 6·60 6·50

1982. 29th Meeting of International Hunting Council, Monte Carlo.
1580 **443** 1f.60 multicoloured . . . 90 75

444 Books, Reader and Globe

1982. International Bibliophile Association General Assembly, Monte Carlo.
1581 **444** 1f.60 blue, purple & red 60 55

445 "Casino, 1870"

1982. Monaco in the "Belle Epoque" (1st series). Paintings by Hubert Clerissi. Multicoloured.
1582 3f. Type **445** . . . . 1·25 1·10
1583 5f. "Porte d'Honneur, Royal Palace, 1893" . . . . . . 2·50 1·60

See also Nos. 1629/30, 1701/2, 1763/4, 1801/2, 1851/2, 1889/90 and 1965/6.

1982. Monaco Red Cross. The Twelve Labours of Hercules (2nd series). As T **422**.
1584 2f.50+50c. green, red and bright red . . . . 1·25 1·40
1585 3f.50+50c. brown, blue and red . . . . 1·40 1·50
DESIGNS: 2f.50, Capturing the Erymanthine Boar; 3f.50, Shooting the Stymphalian Birds.

446 Nicolo Paganini (violinist and composer, bicent)

447 Vase of Flowers

1982. Birth Anniversaries.
1586 **446** 1f.60 brown and purple 90 60
1587 – 1f.80 red, mauve & brn 1·25 80
1588 – 2f.60 green and red . . . 1·40 1·25
1589 – 4f. multicoloured . . . . 2·75 2·40
1590 – 4f. multicoloured . . . . 2·75 2·40
DESIGNS—VERT: No. 1587, Anna Pavlova (ballerina, centenary); 1588, Igor Stravinsky (composer, centenary). HORIZ (47 × 36 mm): 1589, "In a Boat" (Edouard Manet, 150th anniv); 1590, "The Black Fish" (Georges Braque, centenary).

1982. Monte Carlo Flower Show (1983). Mult.
1591 1f.60 Type **447** . . . . . . 1·40 90
1592 2f.60 Ikebana arrangement 1·75 1·50

448 Bowl of Flowers

449 The Three Kings

1982.
1593 **448** 1f.60 multicoloured . . . 1·40 90

1982. Christmas.
1594 **449** 1f.60 green, blue & orge 50 35
1595 – 1f.80 green, blue & orge 60 35
1596 – 2f.60 green, blue & orge 90 50
MS1597 143 × 105 mm. Nos. 1594/6 2·50 2·50
DESIGNS: 1f.80, The Holy Family; 2f.60, Shepherds and angels.

450 Prince Albert I and Polar Scene

1982. Centenary of First International Polar Year.
1598 **450** 1f.60 brown, green & bl 1·75 1·40

451 Viking Longships off Greenland

1982. Millenary of Discovery of Greenland by Erik the Red.
1599 **451** 1f.60 blue, brown & blk 1·75 1·40

452 Julius Caesar in the Port of Monaco ("Aeneid", Book VI)

1982. 2000th Death Anniv of Virgil (poet).
1600 **452** 1f.80 deep blue, blue and brown . . . . 1·75 1·40

453 Spring

454 Tourism

1983. Precancels. The Seasons of the Apple Tree.
1601 **453** 1f.05 purple, green and yellow 40 50
1602 – 1f.35 light green, deep green and turquoise 50 55
1603 – 2f.19 red, brown & grey 1·00 1·10
1604 – 3f.63 yellow and brown 1·60 1·50
DESIGNS: 1f.35, Summer; 2f.19, Autumn; 3f.63, Winter.

1983. 50th Anniv of Exotic Garden. Mult.
1605 1f.80 Type **454** 90 85
1606 2f. Cactus plants (botanical collections) . . . . 1·25 80
1607 2f.30 Cactus plants (international flower shows) . . . . 1·40 1·40
1608 2f.60 Observatory grotto (horiz) . . . . 1·75 1·50
1609 3f.30 Museum of Prehistoric Anthropology (horiz) . . 2·25 2·00

455 Alaskan Malamute

456 Princess Grace

1983. International Dog Show, Monte Carlo.
1610 **455** 1f.80 multicoloured . . . 4·50 3·75

1983. Princess Grace Commemoration. Sheet 105 × 143 mm.
MS1611 **456** 10f. black . . . . . 7·00 7·00

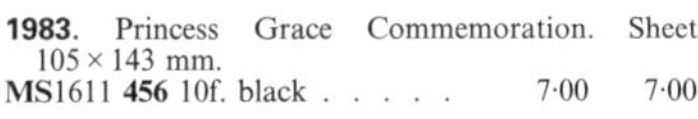

457 St. Charles Borromee and Church

1983. Centenary of St. Charles Church, Monte Carlo.
1612 **457** 2f.60 deep blue, blue and green 95 80

458 Montgolfier Balloon, 1783

459 Franciscan College

1983. Europa.
1613 **458** 1f.80 blue, brown & grey 50 35
1614 – 2f.60 grey, blue & brown 70 60
MS1615 170 × 143 mm. Nos. 1613/14, each × 5 . . . . 7·25 7·25
DESIGN: 2f.60, Space shuttle.

1983. Centenary of Franciscan College, Monte Carlo.
1616 **459** 2f. grey, brown and red 70 60

460 Stadium

1983. Fontvieille Sports Stadium (2nd series).
1617 **460** 2f. green, blue and brown 70 55

461 Early and Modern Cars

1983. Centenary of Petrol-driven Motor Car.
1618 **461** 2f.90 blue, brown & green . . . . 2·00 1·40

462 Blue Whale

1983. International Commission for the Protection of Whales.
1619 **462** 3f.30 blue, light blue and grey . . . . 2·75 2·50

463 Dish Aerial, Pigeon, W.C.Y. Emblem and Satellite

1983. World Communications Year.
1620 **463** 4f. lilac and mauve . . . 1·25 1·10

464 Smoking Moor

466 Circus Performers

465 Johannes Brahms (composer)

1983. Nineteenth Century Automata from the Galea Collection. Multicoloured.
1621 50c. Type **464** 20 20
1622 60c. Clown with diabolo . . 20 20
1623 70c. Smoking monkey . . . 20 20
1624 80c. Peasant with pig . . . 40 40
1625 90c. Buffalo Bill smoking 50 45
1626 1f. Snake charmer 50 45
1627 1f.50 Pianist 80 60
1628 2f. Young girl powdering herself . . . . 1·25 1·00

1983. Monaco in the "Belle Epoque" (2nd series). As T **445**. Multicoloured.
1629 3f. "The Beach, 1902" . . . 2·00 1·60
1630 5f. "Cafe de Paris, 1905" . . 3·25 2·75

1983. Monaco Red Cross. The Twelve Labours of Hercules (3rd series). As T **422**.
1631 2f.50+50c. brn, bl & red . . 1·25 1·00
1632 3f.50+50c. violet, mve & red 1·40 1·25
DESIGNS: 2f.50, Capturing the Hind of Ceryneia; 3f.50, Cleaning the Augean stables.

1983. Birth Anniversaries.
1633 **465** 3f. deep brown, brown and green . . . . . . 1·00 80
1634 – 3f. black, brown and red 1·00 80
1635 – 4f. multicoloured . . . . 2·25 1·90
1636 – 4f. multicoloured . . . . 2·25 1·90
DESIGNS—HORIZ: No. 1633, Type **465** (150th anniv); 1634, Giacomo Puccini (composer) and scene from "Madame Butterfly" (125th anniv). VERT (37 × 48 mm): 1635, "Portrait of a Young Man" (Raphael (artist), 500th anniv); 1636, "Cottin Passage" (Utrillo (artist), centenary).

1983. 9th International Circus Festival, Monaco.
1637 **466** 2f. blue, red and green 1·40 1·25

467 Bouquet

468 Provencale Creche

1983. Monte Carlo Flower Show (1984). Mult.
1638 1f.60 Type **467** . . . . . . 1·00 70
1639 2f.60 Arrangement of poppies . . . . 1·50 1·10

1983. Christmas.
1640 **468** 2f. multicoloured . . . . 1·10 70

469 Nobel Literature Prize Medal

1983. 150th Birth Anniv of Alfred Nobel (inventor of dynamite and founder of Nobel Prizes).
1641 **469** 2f. black, grey and red 90 80

470 O. F. Ozanam (founder) and Paris Headquarters

1983. 150th Anniv of Society of St. Vincent de Paul.
1642 **470** 1f.80 violet and purple 70 50

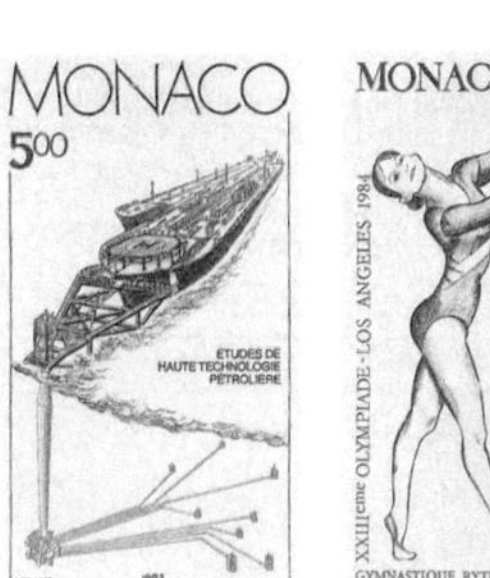
471 "Tazerka" (oil rig) **473** Gymnast will Ball

472 Spring

1983. Oil Industry.
1643 **471** 5f. blue, brown & turq 1·75 1·25

1983. Seasons of the Fig. Sheet 143 × 100 mm containing T **472** and similar horiz designs.
MS1644 1f. green (Type **472**); 2f. green, yellow and red (Summer); 3f. green and (Autumn); 4f. green and red (Winter) . . . . . . 6·75 65

1984. Olympic Games, Los Angeles. Sheet 161 × 143 mm containing T **473** and similar vert designs, each brown, slate and red.
MS1645 2f. Type **473**; 3f. Gymnast with clubs; 4f. Gymnast with ribbon; 5f. Gymnast with hoop 6·25 6·25

474 Skater and Stadium

1984. Winter Olympic Games, Sarajevo.
1646 **474** 2f. blue, green and turquoise 70 55
1647 – 4f. blue, violet and purple . . . . 1·40 1·00
DESIGN: 4f. Skater and snowflake.

475 Bridge

1984. Europa. 25th Anniv of European Post and Telecommunications Conference.
1648 **475** 2f. blue 70 50
1649 3f. green . . . . 1·10 95
MS1650 143 × 170 mm. Nos. 1648/9, each × 4 . . . . 6·25 6·25

476 Balkan Fritillary

478 Sanctuary and Statue of Virgin

477 Auvergne Pointer

1984. Butterflies and Moths in Mercantour National Park. Multicoloured.
1651 1f.60 Type **476** . . . . . . 1·00 1·00
1652 2f. "Zygaena vesubiana" . . 1·50 1·10
1653 2f.80 False mnestra ringlet 1·60 1·40
1654 3f. Small apollo (horiz) . . 1·90 1·60
1655 3f.60 Southern swallowtail (horiz) . . . . 2·75 1·90

1984. International Dog Show, Monte Carlo.
1656 **477** 1f.60 multicoloured . . . 2·50 1·75

1984. Our Lady of Laghet Sanctuary.
1657 **478** 2f. blue, brown and green 70 45

479 Piccard's Stratosphere Balloon "F.N.R.S."

481 Place de la Visitation

480 Concert

1984. Birth Centenary of Auguste Piccard (physicist).
1658 **479** 2f.80 black, green & blue 80 55
1659 – 4f. blue, green & turq . . 1·25 80
DESIGN: 4f. Bathyscaphe.

1984. 25th Anniv of Palace Concerts.
1660 **480** 3f.60 blue and deep blue 1·25 80

1984. Bygone Monaco (1st series). Paintings by Hubert Clerissi.
1661 **481** 5c. brown 10 10
1662 – 10c. red 10 10
1663 – 15c. violet 10 10
1664 – 20c. blue 10 10
1665 – 30c. blue 10 10
1666 – 40c. green 40 20
1667 – 50c. red 10 10
1668 – 60c. blue 10 10
1669 – 70c. orange 50 35
1670 – 80c. green 20 20
1671 – 90c. mauve 30 25
1672 – 1f. blue 30 20
1673 – 2f. black 60 40
1674 – 3f. red . . . . 1·75 80
1675 – 4f. blue . . . . 1·40 75
1676 – 5f. green . . . . 1·40 75
1677 – 6f. green . . . . 2·10 1·10
DESIGNS: 10c. Town Hall; 15c. Rue Basse; 20c. Place Saint-Nicolas; 30c. Quai du Commerce; 40c. Rue des Iris; 50c. Ships in harbour; 60c. St. Charles's Church; 70c. Religious procession; 80c. Olive tree overlooking harbour; 90c. Quayside; 1f. Palace Square; 2f. Fishing boats in harbour; 3f. Bandstand; 4f. Railway station; 5f. Mail coach; 6f. Monte Carlo Opera House.
See also Nos. 2015/27.

482 Spring

1984. Precancels. The Seasons of the Quince.
1678 **482** 1f.14 red and green . . . 40 50
1679 – 1f.47 deep green & green 60 55
1680 – 2f.38 olive, turquoise and green . . . . 1·00 1·00
1681 – 3f.95 green . . . . . . 1·75 1·50
DESIGNS: 1f.47, Summer; 2f.38, Autumn; 3f.95, Winter.

483 Shepherd

485 Bowl of Mixed Flowers

484 Gargantua and Cattle

1984. Christmas. Crib Figures from Provence. Multicoloured.
1682 70c. Type **483** 30 20
1683 1f. Blind man 40 30
1684 1f.70 Happy man 70 50
1685 2f. Spinner 80 70
1686 2f.10 Angel playing trumpet 90 1·10
1687 2f.40 Garlic seller . . . . . 1·10 1·25
1688 3f. Drummer . . . . 1·25 1·25
1689 3f.70 Knife grinder . . . . 1·50 1·25
1690 4f. Elderly couple . . . . . 1·90 1·60

1984. 450th Anniv of First Edition of "Gargantua" by Francois Rabelais.
1691 **484** 2f. black, red and brown 70 50
1692 – 2f. black, red and blue 70 50
1693 – 4f. green . . . . 1·40 1·25
DESIGNS—As T **484**: No. 1692, Panurge's sheep. 36 × 48 mm: 1693, Francois Rabelais.

1984. Monte Carlo Flower Show (1985). Mult.
1694 2f.10 Type **485** . . . . . . 1·00 80
1695 3f. Ikebana arrangement . . 1·60 1·10

486 Television Lights and Emblem

1984. 25th Int Television Festival, Monte Carlo.
1696 **486** 2f.10 blue, grey and mauve 70 55
1697 – 3f. grey, blue and red . . 1·00 80
DESIGN: 3f. "Golden Nymph" (Grand Prix).

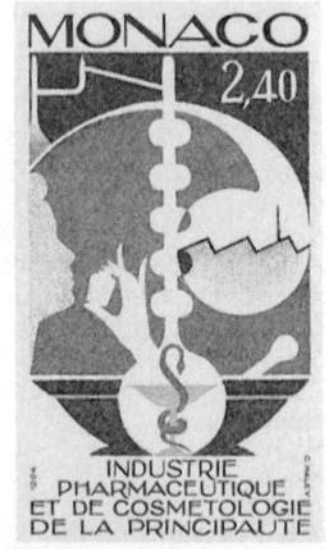
487 Chemical Equipment

488 Clown

1984. Pharmaceutical and Cosmetics Industry.
1698 **487** 2f.40 blue, deep blue and green 80 50

1984. Monaco Red Cross. The Twelve Labours of Hercules (4th series). As T **422**.
1699 3f.+50c. brown, light brown and red . . . . 1·00 1·25
1700 4f.+50c. green, brown and red . . . . 1·40 1·50
DESIGNS: 3f. Killing the Cretan bull; 4f. Capturing the Mares of Diomedes.

1984. Monaco in the "Belle Epoque" (3rd series). Paintings by Hubert Clerissi. As T **445**. Mult.
1701 4f. "Grimaldi Street, 1908" (vert) . . . . 2·25 1·90
1702 5f. "Railway Station, 1910" (vert) . . . . 3·50 2·75

489 "Woman with Chinese Vase"

1984. 150th Birth Anniv of Edgar Degas (artist).
1704 **489** 6f. multicoloured . . . . 3·50 2·50

490 Spring

1985. Precancels. Seasons of the Cherry.
1705 **490** 1f.22 olive, green and blue 40 50
1706 – 1f.57 red, green and yellow 60 55
1707 – 2f.55 orange and brown 1·10 1·10
1708 – 4f.23 purple, green and blue . . . . 1·75 1·60
DESIGNS: 1f.57, Summer; 2f.55, Autumn; 4f.23, Winter.

491 First Stamp

1985. Centenary of First Monaco Stamps.
1709 **491** 1f.70 green 60 40
1710 2f.10 red 70 20
1711 3f. blue . . . . 1·25 65

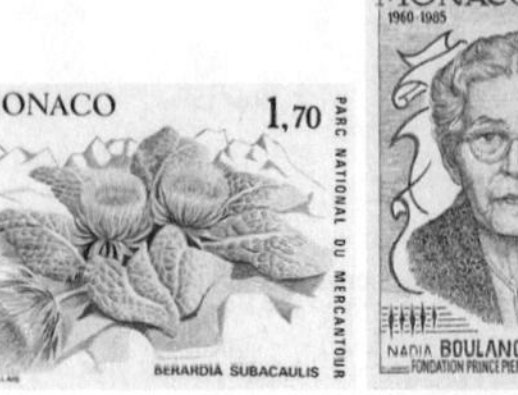
493 "Berardia subacaulis"

495 Nadia Boulanger (composer)

494 Spring

1985. Flowers in Mercantour National Park. Mult.
1724 1f.70 Type **493** 60 45
1725 2f.10 "Saxifraga florulenta" (vert) 70 55
1726 2f.40 "Fritillaria moggridgei" (vert) . . . . 1·00 75
1727 3f. "Sempervivum allionii" (vert) . . . . 1·25 1·10
1728 3f.60 "Silene cordifolia" (vert) . . . . 1·60 1·25
1729 4f. "Primula allionii" . . . 1·95 1·60

1985. Seasons of the Japanese Medlar. Sheet 144 × 100 mm containing T **494** and similar horiz designs.
MS1730 1f. olive and deep olive (Type **494**); 2f. olive, yellow and deep olive (Summer); 3f. olive and deep olive (Autumn); 4f. orange, yellow and olive (Winter) . . . 6·75 6·75

1985. 25th Anniv of First Musical Composition Competition.
1731 **495** 1f.70 brown 70 50
1732 – 2f.10 blue 90 90
DESIGN: 2f.10, Georges Auric (composer).

496 Stadium and Runners

1985. Inauguration of Louis II Stadium, Fontvieille, and Athletics and Swimming Championships.
1733 **496** 1f.70 brown, red and violet 50 40
1734 – 2f.10 blue, brown and green 85 50
DESIGN: 2f.10, Stadium and swimmers.

497 Prince Antoine I

1985. Europa.
1735 **497** 2f.10 blue 70 50
1736 – 3f. red 90 85
MS1737 170 × 143 mm. Nos. 1735/6, each × 5 . . . . 9·25 9·25
DESIGN: 3f. John-Baptiste Lully (composer).

498 Museum, "Hirondelle I" (schooner) and "Denise" (midget submarine)

1985. 75th Anniv of Oceanographic Museum.
1738 **498** 2f.10 black, green and blue 70 65

499 Boxer

1985. International Dog Show, Monte Carlo.
1739 **499** 2f.10 multicoloured . . . 1·90 1·50

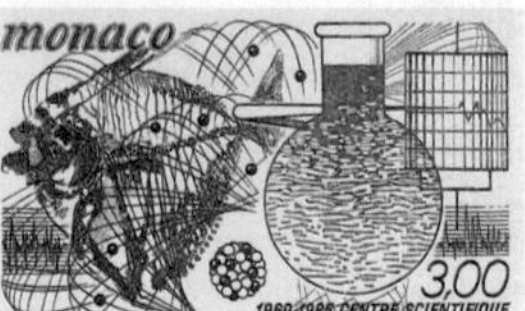
500 Scientific Motifs

1985. 25th Anniv of Scientific Centre.
1740 **500** 3f. blue, black and violet 1·00 70

501 Children and Hands holding Seedling and Emblem

1985. International Youth Year.
1741 **501** 3f. brown, green and light brown . . . . . 1·00 70

502 Regal Angelfish **503** Catamaran

1985. Fishes in Oceanographic Museum Aquarium (1st series). Multicoloured.
1742 1f.80 Type **502** 90 80
1743 1f.90 Type **502** . . . . . . 1·50 80
1744 2f.20 Powder blue surgeonfish 90 75
1745 3f.20 Red-tailed butterflyfish 1·25 1·25
1746 3f.40 As No. 1745 . . . . . 2·75 1·90
1747 3f.90 Clown triggerfish . . . 1·90 1·75
1748 7f. Fishes in aquarium (36 × 48 mm) . . . . . . 3·25 2·75
See also Nos. 1857/62.

1985. Monaco–New York Sailing Race. Sheet 143 × 105 mm containing T **503** and similar vert designs. Each black, blue and turquoise.
MS1749 4f. Type **503**; 4f. Single hull yacht; 4f. Trimaran . . . . . 5·00 5·00

504 Rome Buildings and Emblem

1985. "Italia '85" International Stamp Exhibition, Rome.
1750 **504** 4f. black, green and red 1·25 85

505 Clown **506** Decorations

1985. 11th International Circus Festival, Monaco.
1751 **505** 1f.80 multicoloured . . . 1·25 85

1985. Christmas.
1752 **506** 2f.20 multicoloured . . . 80 45

507 Ship and Marine Life **508** Arrangement of Roses, Tulips and Jonquil

1985. Fish Processing Industry.
1753 **507** 2f.20 blue, turquoise and brown 70 45

1985. Monte Carlo Flower Show (1986). Mult.
1754 2f.20 Type **508** 90 80
1755 3f.20 Arrangement of chrysanthemums and heather . . . . 1·50 1·40

509 Globe and Satellite

1985. European Telecommunications Satellite Organization.
1756 **509** 3f. black, blue and violet 1·00 1·00

510 Sacha Guitry (actor, centenary)

1985. Birth Anniversaries.
1757 **510** 3f. orange and brown . . 1·00 95
1758 – 4f. blue, brown and mauve . . . . 1·25 1·10
1759 – 5f. turquoise, blue and grey . . . . 1·50 1·25
1760 – 6f. blue, brown and black . . . . 1·90 1·50
DESIGNS: 4f. Wilhelm and Jacob Grimm (folklorists, bicentenaries); 5f. Frederic Chopin and Robert Schumann (composers, 175th annivs); 6f. Johann Sebastian Bach and Georg Friedrich Handel (composers, 300th annivs).

1985. Monaco Red Cross. The Twelve Labours of Hercules (5th series). As T **422**.
1761 3f.+70c. green, deep red and red . . . . 1·00 90
1762 4f.+80c. brown, blue & red 1·25 1·25
DESIGNS: 3f. The Cattle of Geryon; 4f. The Girdle of Hippolyte.

1985. Monaco in the "Belle Epoque" (4th series). As T **445**, showing paintings by Hubert Clerissi. Multicoloured.
1763 4f. "Port of Monaco, 1912" 2·00 1·25
1764 6f. "Avenue de la Gare 1920" . . . . 2·50 2·00

511 Prince Charles III **512** Spring

1985. Centenary of First Monaco Stamps (2nd issue). Sheet 142 × 71 mm containing T **511** and similar vert designs. Each blue and black.
MS1765 5f. Type **511**; 5f. Prince Albert I; 5f. Prince Louis II; 5f. Prince Rainier III . . . . . . 6·25 6·25

1986. Precancels. Seasons of the Hazel Tree.
1766 **512** 1f.28 brown, green & bl 40 50
1767 – 1f.65 green, brown & yell 60 55
1768 – 2f.67 grey, brown and deep brown . . . . . 1·00 1·10
1769 – 4f.44 green and brown 1·60 1·60
DESIGNS: 1f.65, Summer; 2f.67, Autumn; 4f.44, Winter.

513 Ancient Monaco

1986. 10th Anniv of "Annales Monegasques" (historical review).
1770 **513** 2f.20 grey, blue and brown 70 45

514 Scotch Terriers

1986. International Dog Show, Monte Carlo.
1771 **514** 1f.80 multicoloured . . . 3·00 2·10

515 Mouflon

1986. Mammals in Mercantour National Park. Multicoloured.
1772 2f.20 Type **515** 80 40
1773 2f.50 Ibex 90 60
1774 3f.20 Chamois . . . . . . 1·25 1·00
1775 3f.90 Alpine marmot (vert) 1·90 1·25
1776 5f. Arctic hare (vert) . . . . 2·25 1·75
1777 7f.20 Stoat (vert) . . . . . 2·75 2·25

516 Research Vessel "Ramoge"

1986. Europa. Each green, blue and red.
1778 2f.20 Type **516** 70 50
1779 3f.20 Underwater nature reserve, Larvotto beach 1·10 75
MS1780 171 × 144 mm. Nos. 1778/79, each × 5 . . . . 10·00 10·00

517 Prince Albert I and National Council Building

1986. Anniversaries and Events.
1781 **517** 2f.50 brown and green 80 80
1782 – 3f.20 brown, red and black . . . . 1·40 1·25
1783 – 3f.90 purple and red . . 1·75 1·75
1784 – 5f. green, red and blue 1·60 1·50
DESIGNS—HORIZ: 2f.50, Type **517** (75th anniv of First Constitution); 3f.20, Serge Diaghilev and dancers (creation of new Monte Carlo ballet company); 3f.90, Henri Rougier and Turcat-Mery car (75th Anniv of first Monte Carlo Rally). VERT: 5f. Flags and Statue of Liberty (centenary).

518 Chicago and Flags

1986. "Ameripex '86" International Stamp Exhibition, Chicago.
1785 **518** 5f. black, red and blue 1·60 1·10

519 Player and Mayan Figure

1986. World Cup Football Championship, Mexico. Sheet 100 × 143 mm containing T **519** and similar vert design. Each black, red and blue.
MS1786 5f. Type **519**; 7f. Goalkeeper and Mayan figures 5·75 5·75

520 Comet, Telescopes and 1532 Chart by Apian

1986. Appearance of Halley's Comet.
1787 **520** 10f. blue, brown & green 3·00 2·50

521 Monte Carlo and Congress Centre

1986. 30th International Insurance Congress.
1788 **521** 3f.20 blue, brown & grn 1·00 80

522 Christmas Tree Branch and Holly **523** Clown's Face and Elephant on Ball

1986. Christmas. Multicoloured.
1789 1f.80 Type **522** 60 25
1790 2f.50 Christmas tree branch and poinsettia 80 40

1986. 12th International Circus Festival, Monaco.
1791 **523** 2f.20 multicoloured . . . 1·10 95

524 Posy of Roses and Acidanthera **525** Making Plastic Mouldings for Car Bodies

1986. Monte Carlo Flower Show (1987). Mult.
1792 2f.20 Type **524** . . . . . . 1·00 65
1793 3f.90 Lilies and beech in vase . . . . 1·60 1·50

1986. Monaco Red Cross. The Twelve Labours of Hercules (6th series). As T **422**.
1794 3f.+70c. green, yell & red 1·25 1·25
1795 4f.+80c. blue, brown & red 1·40 1·50
DESIGNS: 3f. The Golden Apples of the Hesperides; 4f. Capturing Cerberus.

1986. Plastics Industry.
1796 **525** 3f.90 turquoise, red and grey . . . . 1·25 80

526 Scenes from "Le Cid" (Pierre Corneille)

1986. Anniversaries.
1797 **526** 4f. deep brown & brown 1·25 1·00
1798 – 5f. brown and blue . . . 1·50 1·10
DESIGNS: 4f. Type **526** (350th anniv of first performance); 5f. Franz Liszt (composer) and bible (175th birth anniv).

527 Horace de Saussure, Mont Blanc and Climbers

1986. Bicentenary of First Ascent of Mont Blanc by Dr. Paccard and Jacques Balmat.
1799 **527** 5f.80 blue, red and black 1·75 1·50

528 "The Olympic Diver" (Emma de Sigaldi)

1986. 25th Anniv of Unveiling of "The Olympic Diver" (statue).
1800 **528** 6f. multicoloured . . . . 1·75 1·40

1986. Monaco in the "Belle Epoque" (5th series). Paintings by Hubert Clerissi. As T **445**. Mult.
1801 6f. "Bandstand and Casino, 1920" (vert) . . . . . . 2·50 1·90
1802 7f. "Avenue du Beau Rivage, 1925" (vert) . . . 4·25 3·25

1986. Seasons of the Strawberry Tree. Sheet 143 × 100 mm containing T **529** and similar horiz designs.
MS1803 3f. red and olive (T **529**); 4f. olive, lake and red (Summer); 5f. lake, olive and brown-red (Autumn); 6f. olive and red (Winter) . . . . 8·25 8·25

530 Spring

1987. Precancels. Seasons of the Chestnut.
1804 **530** 1f.31 green, yellow & brn 40 35
1805 – 1f.69 green and brown 60 45
1806 – 2f.74 brown, yellow & bl 1·00 85
1807 – 4f.56 brown, grn & grey 1·60 1·40
DESIGNS: 1f.69, Summer; 2f.74, Autumn; 4f.56, Winter.

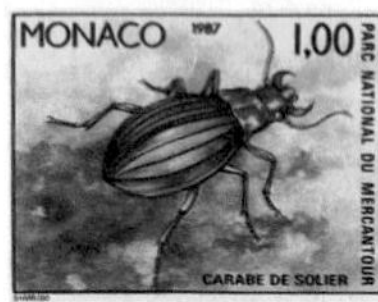

531 Golden Hunter

1987. Insects in Mercantour National Park. Multicoloured.
1808 1f. Type **531** 40 35
1809 1f.90 Golden wasp (vert) . . 70 65
1810 2f. Green tiger beetle . . . 90 90
1811 2f.20 Brown aeshna (vert) 1·25 80
1812 3f. Leaf beetle . . . . . . 1·75 1·50
1813 3f.40 Grasshopper (vert) . . 2·50 1·90

532 St. Devote Church

1987. Centenary of St. Devote Parish Church.
1814 **532** 1f.90 brown 70 45

533 Dogs

1987. International Dog Show, Monte Carlo.
1815 **533** 1f.90 grey, black & brn 1·40 1·00
1816 – 2f.70 black and green . . 2·00 1·75
DESIGN: 2f.70, Poodle.

534 Stamp Album

1987. Stamp Day.
1817 **534** 2f.20 red, purple and mauve 70 45

535 Louis II Stadium, Fontvieille **536** Cathedral

1987. Europa. Each blue, green and red.
1818 2f.20 Type **535** 70 55
1819 3f.40 Crown Prince Albert Olympic swimming pool 1·25 85
MS1820 143 × 71 mm. Nos. 1818/19, each × 5 . . . . 10·50 10·50

1987. Centenary of Monaco Diocese.
1821 **536** 2f.50 green 70 50

537 Spring

1987. Seasons of the Vine. Sheet 142 × 100 mm containing T **537** and similar horiz designs.
MS1822 3f. green and brown (Type **537**); 4f. green and brown (Summer); 5f. violet, brown and green (Autumn); 6f. orange-brown (Winter) . . . . 8·75 8·75

538 Lawn Tennis

1987. 2nd European Small States Games, Monaco.
1823 **538** 3f. black, red and purple 1·50 1·40
1824 – 5f. blue and black . . . 1·90 1·60
DESIGN: 5f. Sailing dinghies and windsurfer.

539 "Red Curly Tail" (Alexander Calder)

1987. "Monte Carlo Sculpture 1987" Exhibition.
1825 **539** 3f.70 multicoloured . . . 1·50 95

540 Prince Rainier III **542** Festival Poster (J. Ramel)

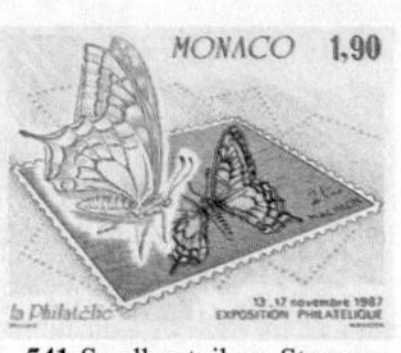

541 Swallowtail on Stamp

1987. 50th Anniv of Monaco Stamp Issuing Office.
1826 **540** 4f. blue . . . . 1·25 1·25
1827 – 4f. red . . . . 1·25 1·25
1828 – 8f. black . . . . 2·75 2·75
DESIGNS: No. 1827, Prince Louis II. (47 × 37 mm): 1828, Villa Miraflores.

1987. International Stamp Exhibition.
1829 **541** 1f.90 deep green and green 60 40
1830 2f.20 purple and red . . 70 45
1831 2f.50 purple and mauve 80 55
1832 3f.40 deep blue and blue 1·25 75

1987. 13th International Circus Festival, Monaco (1988).
1833 **542** 2f.20 multicoloured . . . 1·40 95

543 Christmas Scenes

1987. Christmas.
1834 **543** 2f.20 red 85 45

544 Strawberry Plants and Campanulas in Bowl

1987. Monte Carlo Flower Show (1988). Mult.
1835 2f.20 Type **544** 80 60
1836 3f.40 Ikebana arrangement of water lilies and dog roses (horiz) . . . . . . 1·40 1·10

545 Obverse and Reverse of Honore V 5f. Silver Coin

1987. 150th Anniv of Revival of Monaco Coinage.
1837 **545** 2f.50 black and red . . . 80 55

546 Graph, Factory, Electron Microscope and Printed Circuit

1987. Electro-Mechanical Industry.
1838 **546** 2f.50 blue, green and red 95 65

547 St. Devote

1987. Monaco Red Cross. St. Devote, Patron Saint of Monaco (1st series). Multicoloured.
1839 4f. Type **547** . . . . 1·25 80
1840 5f. St. Devote and her nurse 1·50 1·10
See also Nos. 1898/9, 1956/7, 1980/1, 2062/3 and 2101/2.

1987. 50th Anniv of Monaco Stamp Issuing Office (2nd issue). Sheet 140 × 70 mm containing T **540** and other designs. Each purple.
MS1841 4f. Type **540**; 4f. As No. 1827; 8f. As No. 1828 . . 6·00 6·00

548 Oceanographic Museum and I.A.E.A. Headquarters, Vienna

1987. 25th Anniv of International Marine Radioactivity Laboratory, Monaco.
1842 **548** 5f. black, brown and blue . . . . 1·50 1·25

549 Jouvet

1987. Birth Centenary of Louis Jouvet (actor).
1843 **549** 3f. black . . . . 1·00 95

550 River Crossing

1987. Bicentenary of First Edition of "Paul and Virginia" by Bernardin de Saint-Pierre.
1844 **550** 3f. green, orange and blue . . . . 1·00 85

551 Marc Chagall (painter)

1987. Anniversaries.
1845 **551** 4f. black and red . . . . 1·25 1·10
1846 – 4f. purple, red and brown . . . . 1·25 1·10
1847 – 4f. red, blue and brown 1·25 1·10
1848 – 4f. green, brown & purple . . . . 1·25 1·10
1849 – 5f. blue, brown and green . . . . 1·60 1·25
1850 – 5f. brown, green and blue . . . . 1·60 1·25
DESIGNS: No. 1845, Type **551** (birth centenary); 1846, Chapel of Ronchamp and Charles Edouard Jeanneret (Le Corbusier) (architect, birth centenary); 1847, Sir Isaac Newton (mathematician) and diagram (300th anniv of publication of "Principia Mathematica"); 1848, Key and Samuel Morse (inventor, 150th Anniv of Morse telegraph); 1849, Wolfgang Amadeus Mozart and scene from "Don Juan" (opera, bicentenary of composition); 1850, Hector Berlioz (composer) and scene from "Mass for the Dead" (150th anniv of composition).

1987. Monaco in the "Belle Epoque" (6th series). As T **445** showing paintings by Hubert Clerissi. Multicoloured.
1851 6f. "Main Ramp to Palace Square, 1925" (vert) . . . 2·50 1·60
1852 7f. "Monte Carlo Railway Station, 1925" (vert) . . . 3·25 2·75

552 Coat of Arms **553** Spanish Hogfish

1987.
1853 **552** 2f. multicoloured 65 35
1854 2f.20 multicoloured . . . 65 30

1988. Fishes in Oceanographic Museum Aquarium (2nd series). Multicoloured.
1857 2f. Type **553** 80 65
1858 2f.20 Copper-banded butterflyfish . . . . . . 1·10 50
1859 2f.50 Harlequin filefish . . . 1·40 95
1860 3f. Blue boxfish . . . . . . 1·40 75
1861 3f.70 Lionfish . . . . 2·10 1·60
1862 7f. Moon wrasse (horiz) . . 3·00 1·75

554 Spring **556** Dachshunds

555 Cross-country Skiing

1988. Precancels. Seasons of the Pear Tree. Multicoloured.
1863 1f.36 Type **554** 40 50
1864 1f.75 Summer 60 65
1865 2f.83 Autumn . . . . 1·10 1·10
1866 4f.72 Winter . . . . 1·60 1·60
See also Nos. 1952/5.

1988. Winter Olympic Games, Calgary. Sheet 143 × 93 mm containing T **555** and similar horiz design. Each black, lilac and blue.
MS1867 4f. Type **555**; 6f. Shooting 11·00 11·00

1988. European Dachshunds Show, Monte Carlo.
1868 **556** 3f. multicoloured . . . . 1·75 1·60

557 Children of different Races around Globe

1988. 25th Anniv of World Association of Friends of Children.
1869 **557** 5f. green, brown and blue . . . . 1·60 1·60

558 Satellite Camera above Man with World as Brain **560** Jean Monnet (statesman)

559 Coxless Four

1988. Europa. Transport and Communications. Each black, brown and red.
1870 2f.20 Type **558** . . . . . . 1·10 70
1871 3f.60 Atlantique high speed mail train and aircraft propeller . . . . 1·75 1·40
MS1872 170 × 143 mm. Nos. 1870/1, each × 5 . . . . 13·50 13·50

1988. Centenary of Monaco Nautical Society (formerly Regatta Society).
1873 **559** 2f. blue, green and red 80 55

1988. Birth Centenaries.
1874 **560** 2f. black, brown and blue . . . . 1·75 1·25
1875 – 2f. black and blue . . . 1·75 1·25
DESIGN: No. 1875, Maurice Chevalier (entertainer).

561 "Leccinum rotundifoliae"

1988. Fungi in Mercantour National Park. Multicoloured.
1876 2f. Type **561** 70 60
1877 2f.20 Crimson wax cap . . . 90 60
1878 2f.50 "Pholiota flammans" 1·00 1·25
1879 2f.70 "Lactarius lignyotus" 1·25 1·40
1880 3f. Goaty smell (vert) . . . 1·40 1·60
1881 7f. "Russula olivacea" (vert) 2·75 3·25

562 Nansen **563** Church and "Miraculous Virgin"

1988. Centenary of First Crossing of Greenland by Fridtjof Nansen (Norwegian explorer).
1882 **562** 4f. violet . . . . 1·75 1·40

1988. Restoration of Sanctuary of Our Lady of Laghet.
1883 **563** 5f. multicoloured . . . . 1·50 1·25

564 Anniversary Emblem

1988. 40th Anniv of W.H.O.
1884 **564** 6f. red and blue . . . . 1·75 1·40

565 Anniversary Emblem

1988. 125th Anniv of Red Cross.
1885 **565** 6f. red, grey and black 1·75 1·25

566 Congress Centre

1988. 10th Anniv of Monte Carlo Congress Centre.
1886 **566** 2f. green 70 75
1887 – 3f. red . . . . 90 1·10
DESIGN: 3f. Auditorium.

567 Tennis

1988. Olympic Games, Seoul. New Women's Disciplines. Sheet 143 × 100 mm containing T **567** and similar horiz designs. Each brown, black and blue.
MS1888 2f. Type **567**; 3f. Table tennis; 5f. "470" dinghy; 7f. Cycling . . . . 9·00 9·00

1988. Monaco in the "Belle Epoque" (7th series). Paintings by Hubert Clerissi. As T **445**. Mult.
1889 6f. "Steam packet in Monte Carlo Harbour, 1910" . . 2·50 1·90
1890 7f. "Place de la Gare, 1910" 2·75 2·50

568 Festival Poster (J. Ramel) **569** Star Decoration

1988. 14th International Circus Festival, Monaco (1989).
1891 **568** 2f. multicoloured . . . . 1·00 55

1988. Christmas.
1892 **569** 2f. multicoloured 80 60

570 Arrangement of Fuchsias, Irises, Roses and Petunias **571** Models

1988. Monte Carlo Flower Show (1989).
1893 **570** 3f. multicoloured . . . . 1·40 85

1988. Ready-to-Wear Clothing Industry.
1894 **571** 3f. green, orange & black 90 75

572 Lord Byron (bicentenary)

1988. Writers' Birth Anniversaries.
1895 **572** 3f. black, brown and blue 90 80
1896 – 3f. purple and blue . . . 90 80
DESIGN: No. 1896, Pierre de Marivaux (300th anniv).

573 Spring

1988. Seasons of the Olive Tree. Sheet 143 × 100 mm containing T **573** and similar horiz designs.
MS1897 3f. deep olive, yellow and olive (Type **573**); 4f. deep olive and olive (Summer); 5f. deep olive and olive (Autumn); 6f. deep olive and olive (Winter) . . . . 11·00 11·00

1988. Monaco Red Cross. St. Devote, Patron Saint of Monaco (2nd series). As T **547**. Multicoloured.
1898 4f. Roman governor Barbarus arriving at Corsica . . . . 1·25 80
1899 5f. St. Devote at the Roman senator Eutychius's house 1·90 1·25

574 "Le Nain and his Brothers" (Antoine Le Nain)

1988. Artists' Birth Anniversaries.
1900 **574** 5f. brown, olive and red 1·90 1·40
1901 – 5f. black, green and blue 1·90 1·40
DESIGNS: No. 1900, Type **574** (400th anniv): 1901, "The Great Archaeologists" (bronze statue, Giorgio de Chirico) (centenary).

575 Sorcerer

1989. Rock Carvings in Mercantour National Park. Multicoloured.
1902 2f. Type **575** 65 45
1903 2f.20 Oxen in yoke 75 55
1904 3f. Hunting implements . . 1·00 85
1905 3f.60 Tribal chief . . . . . 1·40 1·10
1906 4f. Puppet (vert) . . . . . 1·60 1·25
1907 5f. Jesus Christ (vert) . . . 2·00 1·40

576 Rue des Spelugues **577** Prince Rainier

1989. Old Monaco (1st series). Multicoloured.
1908 2f. Type **576** 60 45
1909 2f.20 Place Saint Nicolas . . 70 55
See also Nos. 1969/70 and 2090/1.

1989.
1910 **577** 2f. blue and azure . . . 70 20
1911 2f.10 blue and azure . . 70 25
1912 2f.20 brown and pink . . 90 30
1913 2f.20 blue and azure . . 70 20
1914 2f.30 brown and pink . . 80 30
1915 2f.40 blue and azure . . 70 25
1916 2f.50 brown and pink . . 80 30
1917 2f.70 blue 70 65
1918 2f.80 brown and pink . . 85 35
1919 3f. brown and pink . . . 85 25
1920 3f.20 blue and cobalt . . 1·10 75
1922 3f.40 blue and cobalt . . 1·40 95
1923 3f.60 blue and cobalt . . 1·60 1·25
1924 3f.70 blue and cobalt . . 1·10 70
1925 3f.80 purple and lilac . . 1·50 50
1926 3f.80 blue and cobalt . . 95 45
1927 4f. purple and lilac . . . 1·00 95
1930 5f. brown and pink . . . 1·50 65
1932 10f. deep green and green . . . . 2·25 90
1934 15f. blue and grey . . . 3·75 1·25
1936 20f. red and pink . . . 4·50 1·75
1938 25f. black and grey . . . 6·00 2·10
1940 40f. brown and pink . . 8·00 4·25
See also Nos. 2388/90.

578 Yorkshire Terrier

1989. International Dog Show, Monte Carlo.
1941 **578** 2f.20 multicoloured . . . 90 65

579 Magician, Dove and Cards

1989. 5th Grand Prix of Magic, Monte Carlo.
1942 **579** 2f.20 black, blue and red 90 55

580 Nuns and Monks around "Our Lady of Misericorde"

1989. 350th Anniv of Archiconfrerie de la Misericorde.
1943 **580** 3f. brown, black and red . . . 90 60

581 Charlie Chaplin (actor) and Film Scenes

1989. Birth Centenaries.
1944 – 3f. green, blue and mauve . . . . 1·00 95
1945 **581** 4f. purple, green and red . . 1·50 1·25
DESIGN: 3f. Jean Cocteau (writer and painter), scene from "The Double-headed Eagle" and frescoes in Villefrance-sur-Mer chapel.

582 Spring

1989. Seasons of the Pomegranate. Sheet 144 × 100 mm containing T **582** and similar horiz designs.
MS1946 3f. red, green and (Type **582**); 4f. brown, green and red (Summer); 5f. green, red and brown (Autumn); 6f. brown and green (Winter) . . . . 8·00 8·00

583 Boys playing Marbles

1989. Europa. Children's Games. Each mauve, brown and grey.
1947 2f.20 Type **583** 70 60
1948 3f.60 Girls skipping . . . . 1·10 1·00
MS1949 171 × 143 mm. Nos. 1947/8, each × 5 . . . . 10·50 10·50

584 Prince Rainier

1989. 40th Anniv of Reign of Prince Rainier. Sheet 100 × 130 mm.
MS1950 **584** 20f. lilac . . . . . 8·25 8·25

585 "Lliberty"

1989. "Philexfrance 89" International Stamp Exhibition, Paris. Sheet 143 × 105 mm containing T **585** and similar vert designs.
MS1951 5f. blue (Type **585**); 5f. black ("Equality"); 5f. red ("Fraternity") . . . . 5·75 5·75

1989. Precancels. As Nos. 1863/6 but values changed. Multicoloured.
1952 1f.39 Type **554** 40 50
1953 1f.79 Summer 60 65
1954 2f.90 Autumn . . . . 1·40 1·10
1955 4f.84 Winter . . . . 1·90 1·60

1989. Monaco Red Cross. St. Devote, Patron Saint of Monaco (3rd series). As T **547**. Multicoloured.
1956 4f. St. Devote beside the dying Eutychius . . . . . 1·25 85
1957 5f. Barbarus condemns St. Devote to torture for refusing to make a sacrifice to the gods . . . 1·60 1·10

586 "Artist's Mother" (Philibert Florence)

1989. Artists' 150th Birth Anniversaries.
1958 **586** 4f. brown . . . . 1·60 1·40
1959 – 6f. multicoloured . . . . 2·00 1·60
1960 – 8f. multicoloured . . . . 2·75 2·00
DESIGNS—HORIZ: 6f. "Molesey Regatta" (Alfred Sisley). VERT: 8f. "Farmyard at Auvers" (Paul Cezanne).

587 Poinsettia, Christmas Roses and Holly

1989. Christmas.
1961 **587** 2f. multicoloured . . . . 1·60 70

588 Map and Emblem

1989. Centenary of Interparliamentary Union.
1962 **588** 4f. black, green and red . . 1·50 80

589 Princess Grace (founder)

1989. 25th Anniv of Princess Grace Foundation. Sheet 133 × 104 mm containing T **589** and similar vert design. Each blue.
MS1963 5f. Type **589**; 5f. Princess Caroline (Foundation president) . . . 7·00 7·00

590 Monaco Palace, White House, Washington, and Emblem

1989. 20th U.P.U. Congress, Washington D.C.
1964 **590** 6f. blue, brown and black . . . . 1·60 1·25

1989. Monaco in the "Belle Epoque" (8th series). Paintings by Hubert Clerissi. As T **445**. Mult.
1965 7f. "Barque in Monte Carlo Harbour, 1915" (vert) . . 2·50 1·90
1966 8f. "Gaming Tables, Casino, 1915" (vert) . . . . . . 2·75 2·50

591 World Map

1989. 10th Anniv of Monaco Aide et Presence (welfare organization).
1967 **591** 2f.20 brown and red . . 1·50 1·10

592 Clown and Horses

593 Phalaenopsis "Princess Grace"

1989. 15th International Circus Festival, Monte Carlo.
1968 **592** 2f.20 multicoloured . . . 1·60 1·40

1990. Old Monaco (2nd series). Paintings by Claude Rosticher. As T **576**. Multicoloured.
1969 2f.10 La Rampe Major . . 70 45
1970 2f.30 Town Hall Courtyard 80 50

1990. International Garden and Greenery Exposition, Osaka, Japan. Multicoloured.
1971 2f. Type **593** 75 55
1972 3f. Iris "Grace Patricia" . . 1·00 70
1973 3f. "Paphiopedilum" "Prince Rainier III" . . . . . . 1·00 75
1974 4f. "Cattleya" "Principessa Grace" . . . . 1·40 80
1975 5f. Rose "Caroline of Monaco" . . . . 2·25 1·50

594 Bearded Collie

1990. International Dog Show, Monte Carlo.
1976 **594** 2f.30 multicoloured . . . 1·25 1·00

595 Noghes and Racing Car

1990. Birth Centenary of Antony Noghes (founder of Monaco Grand Prix and Monte Carlo Rally).
1977 **595** 3f. red, lilac and black . . . 1·10 75

596 Cyclist and Lancia Rally Car

1990. Centenary of Automobile Club of Monaco (founded as Cycling Racing Club).
1978 **596** 4f. blue, brown & purple 1·50 1·25

597 Telephone, Satellite and Dish Aerial

1990. 125th Anniv of I.T.U.
1979 **597** 4f. lilac, mauve and blue 1·25 1·25

1990. Monaco Red Cross. St. Devote, Patron Saint of Monaco (4th series). As T **547**. Multicoloured.
1980 4f. St. Devote being flogged 1·25 1·00
1981 5f. Placing body of St. Devote in fishing boat 1·75 1·25

598 Sir Rowland Hill and Penny Black

1990. 150th Anniv of Penny Black.
1982 **598** 5f. blue and black . . . 2·00 1·50

599 "Post Office, Place de la Mairie"

1990. Europa. Post Office Buildings. Paintings by Hubert Clerissi. Multicoloured.
1983 2f.30 Type **599** 70 50
1984 3f.70 "Post Office, Avenue d'Ostende" . . . . 1·25 85
MS1985 170 × 145 mm. Nos. 1983/4, each × 4 . . . . 9·50 9·50

600 Ball, Player and Trophy

1990. World Cup Football Championship, Italy. Sheet 142 × 100 mm containing T **600** and similar horiz designs.
MS1986 5f. green, black and red; (Type **600**); 5f. black, red and green (Players); 5f. black and green (Pitch, ball and map of Italy); 5f. red, green and black (Pitch, players and stadium) . . 11·00 11·00

601 Anatase

1990. Minerals in Mercantour National Park. Mult.
1987 2f.10 Type **601** 60 35
1988 2f.30 Albite 70 45
1989 3f.20 Rutile . . . . 1·00 85
1990 3f.80 Chlorite . . . . 1·40 85

1991 4f. Brookite (vert) . . . . . 1·75 1·40
1992 6f. Quartz (vert) . . . . . 2·50 1·90

602 Powerboat

603 Pierrot writing (mechanical toy)

1990. World Offshore Powerboat Racing Championship.
1993 **602** 2f.30 brown, red & blue 90 60

1990. Philatelic Round Table.
1994 **603** 3f. blue . . . . 1·00 60

604 Christian Samuel Hahnemann (founding of homeopathy)

1990. Bicentenaries.
1995 **604** 3f. purple, green & black 1·00 75
1996 – 5f. chestnut, brown & bl 1·75 1·25
DESIGN: 5f. Jean-Francois Champollion (Egyptologist) and hieroglyphics (birth bicentenary).

605 Monaco Heliport, Fontvieille

1990. 30th International Civil Airports Association Congress, Monte Carlo.
1997 **605** 3f. black, red and brown 90 50
1998 – 5f. black, blue and brown . . . . 1·75 1·25
DESIGN: 5f. Aerospatiale Ecureuil helicopters over Monte Carlo Congress Centre.

606 Petanque Player **608** Miller on Donkey

607 Spring

1990. 26th World Petanque Championship.
1999 **606** 6f. blue, brown & orange 2·00 1·25

1990. Precancels. Seasons of the Plum Tree. Multicoloured.
2000 1f.46 Type **607** 45 35
2001 1f.89 Summer 65 45
2002 3f.06 Autumn . . . . 1·25 85
2003 5f.10 Winter . . . . 1·90 1·40

1990. Christmas. Crib figures from Provence. Multicoloured.
2004 2f.30 Type **608** 80 40
2005 3f.20 Woman carrying faggots . . . . 1·00 70
2006 3f.80 Baker . . . . 1·40 95
See also Nos. 2052/4, 2097/9, 2146/8 and 2191/3.

609 Spring

1990. Seasons of the Lemon Tree. Sheet 143 × 100 mm containing T **609** and similar horiz designs. Multicoloured.
MS2007 3f. Type **609**; 4f. Summer; 5f. Autumn; 6f. Winter . . . . 7·50 7·50

610 Pyotr Ilich Tchaikovsky (composer) **611** Clown playing Concertina

1990. 150th Birth Anniversaries.
2008 **610** 5f. blue and green . . . 1·75 1·10
2009 – 5f. bistre and blue . . . 1·75 1·10
2010 – 7f. multicoloured . . . . 3·50 3·00
DESIGNS—As T **610**: No. 2009, "Cathedral" (Auguste Rodin, sculptor). 48 × 37 mm: "The Magpie" (Claude Monet, painter).

1991. 16th International Circus Festival, Monte Carlo.
2011 **611** 2f.30 multicoloured . . . 95 75
See also No. 2069.

1991. Bygone Monaco (2nd series). Paintings by Hubert Clerissi. As T **481**.
2015 20c. purple 10 10
2017 40c. green 10 10
2018 50c. red 10 10
2019 60c. blue 20 10
2020 70c. green 20 10
2021 80c. blue 20 20
2022 90c. lilac 20 20
2023 1f. blue 30 20
2024 2f. red 50 25
2025 3f. black 80 30
2027 7f. grey and black . . . . . 1·60 80
DESIGNS: 20c. Rock of Monaco and Fontvieille; 40c. Place du Casino; 50c. Place de la Cremaillere and railway station; 60c. National Council building; 70c. Palace and Rampe Major; 80c. Avenue du Beau Rivage; 90c. Fishing boats, Fontvieille; 1f. Place d'Armes; 2f. Marche de la Condamine; 3f. Yacht; 7f. Oceanographic Museum.

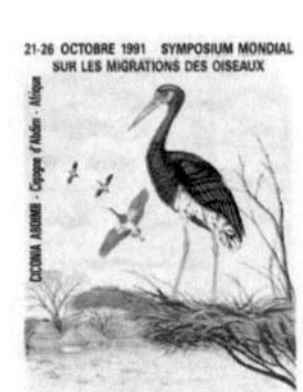

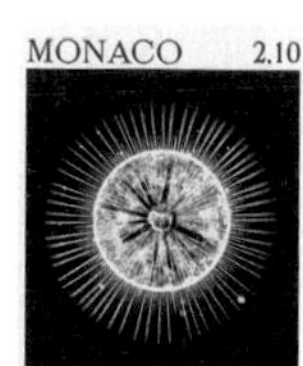

612 Abdim's Stork **613** Phytoplankton

1991. International Symposium on Bird Migration. Multicoloured.
2029 2f. Type **612** 70 55
2030 3f. Broad-tailed hummingbirds 90 80
2031 4f. Garganeys . . . . . . 1·40 1·10
2032 5f. Eastern broad-billed roller . . . . 1·75 1·50
2033 6f. European bee eaters . . 2·25 1·90

1991. Oceanographic Museum (1st series).
2034 **613** 2f.10 multicoloured . . . 95 55
See also Nos. 2095/6.

614 Schnauzer

1991. International Dog Show, Monte Carlo.
2035 **614** 2f.50 multicoloured . . . 1·25 85

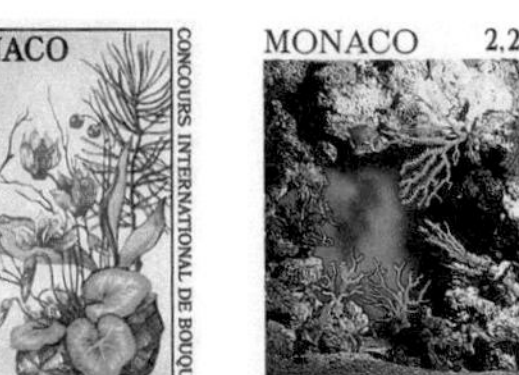

615 Cyclamen, Lily-of-the-Valley and Pine Twig in Fir-cone **616** Corals

1991. Monte Carlo Flower Show.
2036 **615** 3f. multicoloured . . . . 1·10 65

1991. "Joys of the Sea" Exhibition. Multicoloured.
2037 2f.20 Type **616** 85 65
2038 2f.40 Coral necklace 95 75

617 Control Room, "Eutelsat" Satellite and Globe

1991. Europa. Europe in Space. Each blue, black and green.
2039 2f.30 Type **617** 85 50
2040 3f.20 Computer terminal, "Inmarsat" satellite, research ship transmitting signal and man with receiving equipment . . . 1·10 70
MS2041 143 × 171 mm. Nos. 2039/40, each × 5 . . . . 9·50 9·50

618 Cross-country Skiers and Statue of Skiers by Emma de Sigaldi

1991. 1992 Olympic Games. (a) Winter Olympics, Albertville.
2042 **618** 3f. green, blue and olive 1·00 1·10
2043 – 4f. green, blue and olive 1·40 1·40

(b) Olympic Games, Barcelona.
2044 – 3f. green, lt brown & brown . . . . 1·00 1·25
2045 – 5f. black, brown and green 1·50 1·75
DESIGNS: No. 2043, Right-hand part of statue and cross-country skiers; 2044, Track, relay runners and left part of statue of relay runners by Emma de Sigaldi; 2045, Right part of statue, view of Barcelona and track.

619 Head of "David" (Michelangelo), Computer Image and Artist at Work **620** Prince Pierre, Open Book and Lyre

1991. 25th International Contemporary Art Prize.
2046 **619** 4f. green, dp green & lilac . . . . 1·40 95

1991. 25th Anniv of Prince Pierre Foundation.
2047 **620** 5f. black, blue and brown . . . . 1·50 1·25

621 Tortoises

1991. Endangered Species. Hermann's Tortoise. Multicoloured.
2048 1f.25 Type **621** 85 70
2049 1f.25 Head of tortoise . . . 85 70
2050 1f.25 Tortoise in grass . . . 85 70
2051 1f.25 Tortoise emerging from among plants . . . 85 70

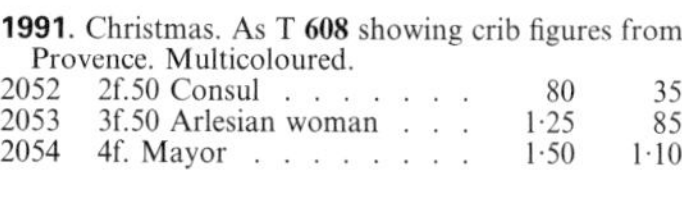

1991. Christmas. As T **608** showing crib figures from Provence. Multicoloured.
2052 2f.50 Consul 80 35
2053 3f.50 Arlesian woman . . . 1·25 85
2054 4f. Mayor . . . . 1·50 1·10

622 Norway Spruce

1991. Conifers in Mercantour National Park. Multicoloured.
2055 2f.50 Type **622** 85 30
2056 3f.50 Silver fir . . . . . . 1·25 65
2057 4f. "Pinus uncinata" . . . . 1·25 80
2058 5f. Scots pine (vert) . . . . 1·50 1·00
2059 6f. Arolla pine . . . . . . 1·75 1·25
2060 7f. European larch (vert) . . 2·00 1·50

623 Spring

1991. Seasons of the Orange Tree. Sheet 142 × 101 mm containing T **623** and similar horiz designs.
MS2061 3f. orange, green and brown (Type **623**); 4d. green and brown (Summer); 5f. green, orange and brown (Autumn); 6f. green and olive-brown (Winter) . . . . . 7·50 7·50

1991. Monaco Red Cross. St. Devote, Patron Saint of Monaco (5th series). As T **547**. Multicoloured.
2062 4f.50 Fishing boat carrying body caught in storm . . 1·50 80
2063 5f.50 Dove guiding boatman to port of Monaco . . . 1·75 1·10

624 "Portrait of Claude Monet"

1991. 150th Birth Anniv of Auguste Renoir (painter).
2064 **624** 5f. multicoloured . . . . 1·60 1·25

625 Prince Honore II of Monaco

1991. 350th Anniv of Treaty of Peronne (giving French recognition of sovereignty of Monaco). Paintings by Philippe de Champaigne. Mult.
2065 6f. Type **625** . . . . 2·10 1·60
2066 7f. King Louis XIII of France . . . . 2·50 1·75

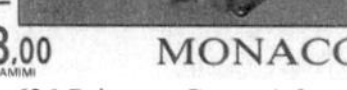

626 Princess Grace (after R. Samini) **627** 1891 Stamp Design

1991. 10th Anniv of Princess Grace Theatre.
2067 **626** 8f. multicoloured . . . . 3·25 2·40

1991. Centenary of Prince Albert Stamps. Sheet 114 × 72 mm.
MS2068 **627** 10f. red; 10f. green; 10f. lilac . . . . 9·50 9·50

1992. 16th International Circus Festival, Monte Carlo. As No. 2011 but value and dates changed.
2069 **611** 2f.50 multicoloured . . . 95 75
The 1991 Festival was cancelled.

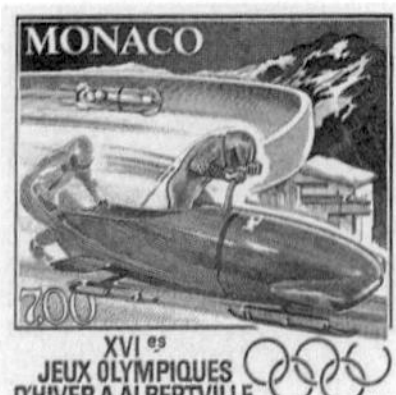

628 Two-man Bobsleighs

1992. Winter Olympic Games, Albertville (7f.), and Summer Games, Barcelona (8f.).
2070 **628** 7f. blue, turquoise & blk . . . 2·10 1·40
2071 – 8f. purple, blue and green . . . . 2·50 1·50
DESIGN: 8f. Football.

629 Spring

1992. Exotic Gardens. Seasons of the Prickly Pear. Sheet 142 × 100 mm containing T **629** and similar horiz designs. Multicoloured.
MS2072 3f. Type **629**; 4f. Summer; 5f. Autumn; 6f. Winter . . . . 8·00 8·00

630 Spring

1992. Precancels. Seasons of the Walnut Tree. Mult.
2073 1f.60 Type **630** 50 60
2074 2f.08 Summer 60 70
2075 2f.98 Autumn . . . . 1·10 1·10
2076 5f.28 Winter . . . . 1·75 1·75

631 Golden Labrador

1992. International Dog Show, Monte Carlo.
2077 **631** 2f.20 multicoloured . . . 1·25 80

632 Racing along Seafront

1992. 50th Monaco Grand Prix.
2078 **632** 2f.50 black, purple & bl 85 55

633 Mixed Bouquet

1992. 25th Monte Carlo Flower Show.
2079 **633** 3f.40 multicoloured . . . 1·40 85

634 Ford Sierra Rally Car

1992. 60th Monte Carlo Car Rally.
2080 **634** 4f. black, green and red 1·50 1·10

635 Rough-toothed Dolphin (*Steno bredanensis*)

1992. Mediterranean Dolphins. Sheet 142 × 100 mm containing T **635** and similar horiz designs. Multicoloured.
MS2081 4f. Type **635** 5f. Common dolphin (*Delphinus delphis*); 6f. Bottle-nosed dolphin (*Tursiops truncates*); 7f. Striped dolphin (*Stenella coeruleoalba*) . . . . 10·00 10·00

636 "Pinta" off Palos

1992. Europa. 500th Anniv of Discovery of America by Columbus. Multicoloured.
2082 2f.50 Type **636** 80 65
2083 3f.40 "Santa Maria" in the Antilles . . . . 1·40 1·10
2084 4f. "Nina" off Lisbon . . . 1·50 1·25
MS2085 140 × 170 mm. Nos. 2082/4, each × 2 . . . . 7·50 7·50

637 Produce

1992. "Ameriflora" Horticultural Show, Columbus, Ohio. Multicoloured.
2086 4f. Type **637** . . . . 1·25 95
2087 5f. Vase of mixed flowers . . 1·60 1·50

638 Prince Rainier I and Fleet (detail of fresco by E. Charpentier, Spinola Palace, Genoa)

1992. Columbus Exhibition, Genoa (6f.), and "Expo '92" World's Fair, Seville (7f.).
2088 **638** 6f. brown, red and blue 2·00 1·40
2089 – 7f. brown, red and blue 2·10 1·60
DESIGN: 7f. Monaco pavilion.

1992. Old Monaco (3rd series). Paintings by Claude Rosticher. As T **576**. Multicoloured.
2090 2f.20 La Porte Neuve (horiz) 75 25
2091 2f.50 La Placette Bosio (horiz) 85 25

639 "Christopher Columbus"

1992. "Genova '92" International Thematic Stamp Exhibition. Roses. Multicoloured.
2092 3f. Type **639** . . . . 1·25 1·00
2093 4f. "Prince of Monaco" . . 1·40 1·10

640 Lammergeier

1992.
2094 **640** 2f.20 orange, blk & grn 85 80

1992. Oceanographic Museum (2nd series). As T **613**. Multicoloured.
2095 2f.20 "Ceratium ranipes" . . 85 60
2096 2f.50 "Ceratium hexacanthum" 95 70

1992. Christmas. As T **608** showing crib figures from Provence. Multicoloured.
2097 2f.50 Basket-maker 85 30
2098 3f.40 Fishwife . . . . . . 1·25 65
2099 5f. Rural constable . . . . 1·75 1·40

641 "Seabus" (projected tourist submarine)

1992.
2100 **641** 4f. blue, red and brown 1·40 1·25

642 Burning Boat Ceremony, St. Devote's Eve

1992. Monaco Red Cross. St. Devote, Patron Saint of Monaco (6th series).
2101 **642** 6f. red, blue and brown 1·75 1·10
2102 – 8f. purple, orange and red . . . . 2·40 1·60
DESIGN: 8f. Procession of reliquary, St. Devote's Day.

643 Athletes, Sorbonne University and Coubertin

1992. Centenary of Pierre de Coubertin's Proposal for Revival of Olympic Games.
2103 **643** 10f. blue . . . . 3·00 1·90

644 Baux de Provence and St. Catherine's Chapel

1992. Titles of Princes of Monaco. Marquis of Baux de Provence.
2104 **644** 15f. multicoloured . . . 4·25 2·75

645 1856 40c. Sardinian Stamp **646** Clown and Tiger

1992. Stamp Museum. Sheet 115 × 72 mm containing T **645** and similar vert design.
MS2105 10f. red and black (Type **645**); 10f. green and black (1860 1c. French stamp) . . . 7·00 7·00

1993. 17th Int Circus Festival, Monte Carlo.
2106 **646** 2f.50 multicoloured . . . 85 55

647 Short-toed Eagles

1993. Birds of Prey in Mercantour National Park.
2107 **647** 2f. chestnut, brown and orange 65 50
2108 – 3f. indigo, orange & blue 1·10 65
2109 – 4f. brown, ochre and blue . . . . 1·25 1·10
2110 – 5f. brown, chestnut and green . . . . 1·60 1·40
2111 – 6f. brown, mauve & grn 1·90 1·60
DESIGNS—HORIZ: 3f. Peregrine falcon. VERT: 4f. Eagle owl; 5f. Western honey buzzard; 6f. Tengmalm's owl.

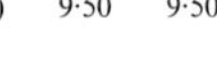
648 Fin Wale (*Balaenoptera physalus*)

1993. Mediterranean Whales. Sheet 143 × 100 mm containing T **648** and similar horiz designs. Multicoloured.
MS2112 4f. Type **648**; 5f. Minke whale (*Balaenoptera acutorostrata*); 6f. Sperm whale (Physeter catodon); 7f. Cuvier's beaked whale (Ziphius cavirostris) 9·50 9·50

649 Spring

1993. Seasons of the Almond. Sheet 142 × 100 mm containing T **649** and similar horiz designs. Multicoloured.
MS2113 5f. Type **649**; 5f. Summer; 5f. Autumn; 5f. Winter . . . . 8·25 8·25

650 Mixed Bouquet **652** Fire Fighting and Rescue

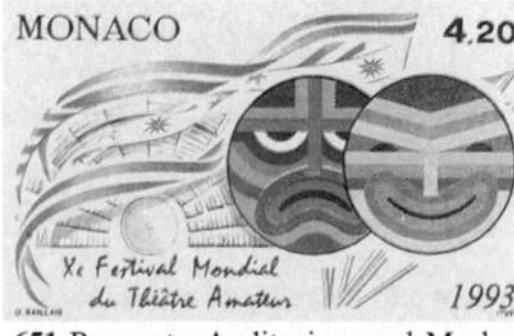

651 Pennants, Auditorium and Masks

1993. Monte Carlo Flower Show.
2114 **650** 3f.40 multicoloured . . . 1·10 75

1993. 10th International Amateur Theatre Festival.
2115 **651** 4f.20 multicoloured . . . 1·40 75

1993. World Civil Protection Day.
2116 **652** 6f. black, red and green 1·90 1·40

653 Newfoundland

1993. International Dog Show, Monte Carlo.
2117 **653** 2f.20 multicoloured . . . 90 70

654 Golfer

1993. 10th Monte Carlo Open Golf Tournament.
2118 **654** 2f.20 multicoloured . . . 70 65

655 Princess Grace **656** Mirror and Candelabra

1993. 10th Death Anniv (1992) of Princess Grace.
2119 **655** 5f. blue . . . . 1·50 1·25

1993. 10th Antiques Biennale.
2120 **656** 7f. multicoloured . . . . 2·10 1·40

657 "Echinopsis multiplex" **658** Monte Carlo Ballets

1993. Cacti.
2121 **657** 2f.50 green, purple & yell 70 60
2122 – 2f.50 green and purple 70 60
2123 – 2f.50 green, purple & yell 70 60
2124 – 2f.50 green and yellow 70 60
DESIGNS: No. 2122, "Zygocactus truncatus"; 2123, "Echinocereus procumbens"; 2124, "Euphorbia virosa".
See also Nos. 2154/66.

1993. Europa. Contemporary Art.
2125 **658** 2f.50 black, brn & pink 70 50
2126 – 4f.20 grey and brown . . 1·25 95
MS2127 143 × 172 mm. Nos. 2125/6, each × 3 . . . . 6·75 6·75
DESIGN: 4f.20, "Evolution" (sculpture, Emma de Sigaldi).

659 **660** State Arms and Olympic Rings

1993. Admission to United Nations Organization. Sheet 115 × 72 mm.
MS2128 10f. blue (T **659**); 10f. brown (T **577**); 10f. red and brown (state arms) . . . . 9·50 9·50

1993. 110th International Olympic Committee Session, Monaco.
2129 **660** 2f.80 red, brown & blue 80 85
2130 – 2f.80 blue, lt blue & red 80 85
2131 – 2f.80 brown, blue & red 80 85
2132 – 2f.80 blue, lt blue & red 80 85
2133 – 2f.80 brown, blue & red 80 85
2134 – 2f.80 blue, lt blue & red 80 85
2135 – 2f.80 brown, blue & red 80 85
2136 **660** 2f.80 blue, lt blue & red 80 85
2137 – 4f.50 multicoloured . . . 1·25 1·40
2138 – 4f.50 black, yellow & bl 1·25 1·40
2139 – 4f.50 red, yellow & blue 1·25 1·40
2140 – 4f.50 black, yellow & bl 1·25 1·40
2141 – 4f.50 red, yellow & blue 1·25 1·40
2142 – 4f.50 black, yellow & bl 1·25 1·40
2143 – 4f.50 red, yellow & blue 1·25 1·40
2144 – 4f.50 red, yellow & blue 1·25 1·40
DESIGNS: 2130, Bobsleighing; 2131, Skiing; 2132, Yachting; 2133, Rowing; 2134, Swimming; 2135, Cycling; 2136, 2144, Commemorative inscription; 2138, Gymnastics (rings exercise); 2139, Judo; 2140, Fencing; 2141, Hurdling; 2142, Archery; 2143, Weightlifting.

661 Examining 1891 1c. Stamp

1993. Centenary of Monaco Philatelic Union.
2145 **661** 2f.40 multicoloured . . . 70 45

1993. Christmas. Crib figures from Provence. As T **608**. Multicoloured.
2146 2f.80 Donkey 80 35
2147 3f.70 Shepherd holding lamb 1·00 90
2148 4f.40 Ox lying down in barn 1·25 1·25

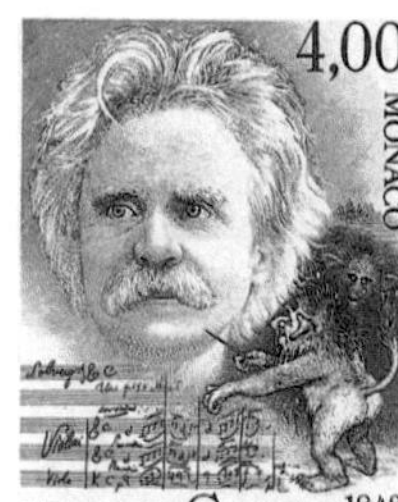

662 Grieg, Music and Trolls

1993. 150th Birth Anniv of Edvard Grieg (composer).
2149 **662** 4f. blue . . . . 1·60 1·10

663 Abstract Lithograph **664** Monaco Red Cross Emblem

1993. Birth Centenary of Joan Miro (painter and sculptor).
2150 **663** 5f. multicoloured . . . . 1·60 1·40

1993. Monaco Red Cross.
2151 **664** 5f. red, yellow and black 1·40 1·10
2152 – 6f. red and black . . . . 1·90 1·60
DESIGN: 6f. Crosses inscribed with fundamental principles of the International Red Cross.

665 "St. Joseph the Carpenter"

1993. 400th Birth Anniv of Georges de la Tour (painter).
2153 **665** 6f. multicoloured . . . . 1·75 1·40

1994. Cacti. As Nos. 2121/4 but values changed and additional designs.
2153a – 10c. green, orange and red 10 10
2154 **657** 20c. green, purple and yellow 10 10
2155 – 30c. green and purple 10 10
2156 – 40c. green and yellow 10 10
2157 – 50c. green, red and olive 10 10
2158 – 60c. green, red and yellow 20 25
2159 – 70c. green, red and blue 20 25
2160 – 80c. green, orange and red 20 25
2162 – 1f. green, brown and yellow 25 25
2164 – 2f. green, red and yellow 50 45
2165 – 2f.70 green, red and yellow 70 50
2166 – 4f. green, purple and yellow . . . . 1·00 60
2166a – 4f. green, red and yellow 80 70
2167 – 5f. green, mauve and brown . . . . 1·25 85
2167a – 6f. brown, green and red . . . . 1·50 1·25
2167b – 7f. green, brown and red . . . . 1·90 1·50
DESIGNS: 10c. "Bromelia brevifolia"; 30c. "Zygocactus truncatus"; 40c. "Euphorbia virosa"; 50c. "Selenicereus grandiflorus"; 60c. "Opuntia basilaris"; 70c. "Aloe plicatilis"; 80c. "Opuntia hybride"; 1f. "Stapelia flavirostris"; 2f. "Aporocactus flagelliformis"; 2f.70, "Opuntia dejecta"; 4f. (2166), "Echinocereus procumbens"; 4f. (2166a), "Echinocereus blanckii"; 5f. "Cereus peruvianus"; 6f. "Euphorbia milii; 7f. "Stapelia variegata.

666 Festival Poster **667** Artist/Poet

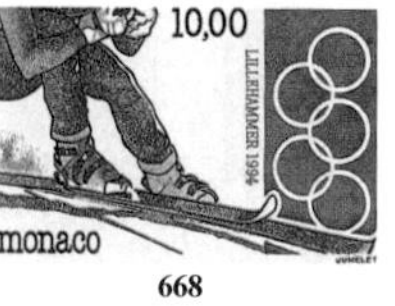

668

1994. 18th Int Circus Festival, Monte Carlo.
2168 **666** 2f.80 multicoloured . . . 95 70

1994. Mechanical Toys.
2169 **667** 2f.80 blue 70 75
2170 – 2f.80 red 70 75
2171 – 2f.80 purple 70 75
2172 – 2f.80 green 70 75
DESIGNS: No. 2170, Bust of Japanese woman; 2171, Shepherdess with sheep; 2172, Young Parisienne.

1994. Mediterranean Whales and Dolphins. Sheet 143 × 100 mm containing horiz designs as T **648**. Multicoloured.
MS2173 4f. Killer whale (*Orcinus orca*); 5f. Risso's dolphin (*Grampus griseus*); 6f. False killer whale (*Pseudorca crassidens*); 7f. Long-finned pilot whale (*Globicephala melas*) . . . . . 8·50 8·50

1994. Winter Olympic Games, Lillehammer, Norway. Sheet 123 × 80 mm containing T **668** and similar horiz design. Each blue and red.
MS2174 10f. Type **668**; 10f. Bobsleighing . . . . 7·50 7·50

669 King Charles Spaniels

1994. International Dog Show, Monte Carlo.
2175 **669** 2f.40 multicoloured . . . 95 45

670 Couple, Leaves and Pollution **671** Iris

1994. Monaco Committee of Anti-tuberculosis and Respiratory Diseases Campaign.
2176 **670** 2f.40+60c. mult 85 75

1994. Monte Carlo Flower Show.
2177 **671** 4f.40 multicoloured . . . 1·40 85

672 Levitation Trick

1994. 10th Monte Carlo Magic Grand Prix.
2178 **672** 5f. blue, black and red 1·50 95

673 Ingredients and Dining Table overlooking Harbour

1994. 35th Anniv of Brotherhood of Cordon d'Or French Chefs.
2179 **673** 6f. multicoloured . . . . 1·75 1·25

674 Isfjord, Prince Albert I, Map of Spitzbergen and "Princess Alice II"

1994. Europa. Discoveries made by Prince Albert I. Each black, blue and red.
2180 2f.80 Type **674** 85 70
2181 4f.50 Oceanographic Museum, Grimaldi's spookfish and "Eryoneicus alberti" (crustacean) . . . . . . 1·40 1·10
MS2182 155 × 130 mm. Nos. 2180/1, each × 3 . . . . 7·50 7·50

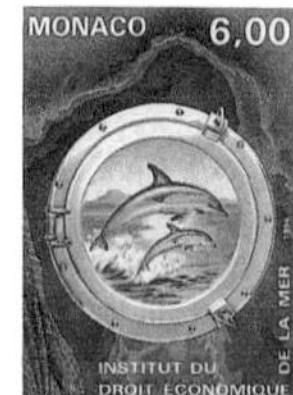

675 Olympic Flag and Sorbonne University **676** Dolphins through Porthole

1994. Centenary of International Olympic Committee.
2183 **675** 3f. multicoloured 95 75

1994. Economic Institute of the Rights of the Sea Conference, Monaco.
2184 **676** 6f. multicoloured . . . . 1·75 1·50

677 Family around Tree of Hearts **678** Footballer's Legs and Ball

1994. International Year of the Family.
2185 **677** 7f. green, orange and blue . . . . 1·90 1·50

1994. World Cup Football Championship, U.S.A.
2186 **678** 8f. red and black . . . . 2·25 1·50

679 Athletes and Villa Miraflores

1994. Inauguration of New Seat of International Amateur Athletics Federation.
2187 **679** 8f. blue, purple and bistre . . . . 2·10 2·00

680 De Dion Bouton, 1903

1994. Vintage Car Collection of Prince Rainier III.

2188 **680** 2f.80 black, brown and mauve 85 80

681 Emblem and Monte Carlo

682 Emblem and Korean Scene

1994. 1st Association of Postage Stamp Catalogue Editors and Philatelic Publications Grand Prix.

2189 **681** 3f. multicoloured 95 55

1994. 21st Universal Postal Union Congress, Seoul.

2190 **682** 4f.40 black, blue and red 1·40 85

1994. Christmas. As T **608** showing crib figures from Provence. Multicoloured.

2191 2f.80 Virgin Mary 70 60
2192 4f.50 Baby Jesus . . . . . 1·25 85
2193 6f. Joseph . . . . 1·60 1·10

683 Prince Albert I

684 Three Ages of Voltaire (writer, 300th anniv)

1994. Inaug of Stamp and Coin Museum (1st issue). Coins.

2194 **683** 3f. stone, brown and red 85 65
2195 – 4f. grey, brown and red 1·25 95
2196 – 7f. stone, brown and red 1·90 1·50
MS2197 115 × 73 mm. 10f. × 3, As Nos. 2194/6 . . . . 9·75 9·75

DESIGNS: 4f. Arms of House of Grimaldi; 7f. Prince Rainier III.

See also Nos. **MS**2225; 2265/7 and 2283/**MS**6.

1994. Birth Anniversaries.

2198 **684** 5f. green . . . . 1·50 1·10
2199 – 6f. brown and purple . . 1·75 1·40

DESIGN—HORIZ: 6f. Sarah Bernhardt (actress, 150th anniv).

685 Heliport and Helicopter

1994. 50th Anniv of International Civil Aviation Organization.

2200 **685** 5f. green, black and blue 1·40 1·00
2201 – 7f. brown, black and red 1·90 1·60

DESIGN: 7f. Harbour and helicopter.

686 Spring

1994. 1st European Stamp Salon, Flower Gardens, Paris. Seasons of the Apricot. Sheet 142 × 100 mm containing T **686** and similar horiz designs. Multicoloured.

MS2202 6f. Type **686**; 7f. Summer; 8f. Autumn; 9f. Winter . . . . 9·75 9·75

687 Blood Vessels on Woman (anti-cancer)

1994. Monaco Red Cross. Health Campaigns.

2203 **687** 6f. blue, black and red 1·60 1·10
2204 – 8f. green, black and red 2·10 1·60

DESIGN: 8f. Tree and woman (anti-AIDS).

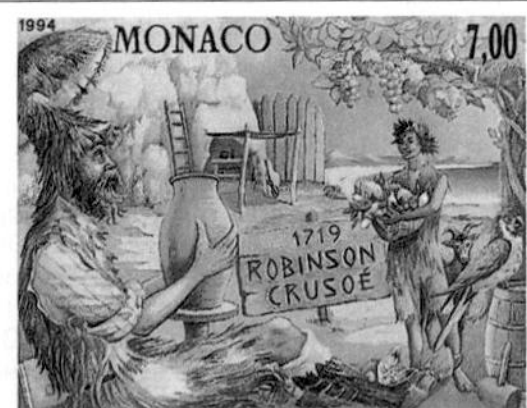

688 Robinson Crusoe and Friday

1994. Anniversaries. Multicoloured.

2205 7f. Type **688** (275th anniv of publication of "Robinson Crusoe" by Daniel Defoe) 2·10 1·50
2206 9f. "The Snake Charmer" (150th birth anniv of Henri Rousseau, painter) 2·50 1·75

689 Clown playing Trombone

690 Crown Prince Albert

1995. 19th Int Circus Festival, Monte Carlo.

2207 **689** 2f.80 multicoloured . . . 70 65

1995. 35th Television Festival, Monte Carlo.

2208 **690** 8f. brown . . . . 2·00 2·00

691 Fontvieille

1995. European Nature Conservation Year.

2209 **691** 2f.40 multicoloured . . . 60 45

692 American Cocker Spaniel

1995. International Dog Show, Monte Carlo.

2210 **692** 4f. multicoloured . . . . 1·00 1·00

693 Parrot Tulips

1995. Monte Carlo Flower Show.

2211 **693** 5f. multicoloured . . . . 1·50 1·00

694 "Acer palmatum"

1995. European Bonsai Congress.

2212 **694** 6f. multicoloured . . . . 1·50 85

695 Alfred Nobel (founder of Nobel Prizes) and Dove

1995. Europa. Peace and Freedom. Multicoloured.

2213 2f.80 Type **695** 75 70
2214 5f. Roses, broken chain and watchtower . . . . 1·40 1·00

696 Emblem of Monagasque Disabled Children Association

1995. Int Special Olympics, New Haven, U.S.A.

2215 **696** 3f. multicoloured 75 55

697 Emblem

1995. Rotary International Convention, Nice.

2216 **697** 4f. blue . . . . 1·10 1·00

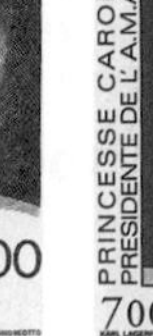

699 Jean Giono

701 Princess Caroline (President)

700 Saint Hubert (patron saint of hunting)

1995. Writers' Birth Centenaries.

2218 **699** 5f. lilac, brown and green . . . . 1·40 90
2219 – 6f. brown, violet and green . . . . 1·50 1·10

DESIGN: 6f. Marcel Pagnol.

1995. General Assembly of International Council for Hunting and Conservation of Game.

2220 **700** 6f. blue . . . . 1·50 1·40

1995. World Association of Friends of Children General Assembly, Monaco.

2221 **701** 7f. blue . . . . 1·60 1·40

702 Athletes and Medal

1995. International Amateur Athletics Federation Grand Prix, Monaco.

2222 **702** 7f. mauve, purple and grey . . . . 1·75 1·40

703 "Trophee des Alpes" (Hubert Clerissi)

1995. 2000th Anniv of Emperor Augustus Monument, La Turbie.

2223 **703** 8f. multicoloured . . . . 1·90 1·75

704 Prince Pierre (after Philip Laszlo de Lombos)

706 St. Antony (wooden statue)

705 1974 60c. Honore II Stamp

1995. Birth Centenary of Prince Pierre of Monaco.

2224 **704** 10f. purple . . . . . . 2·50 1·75

1995. Inauguration of Stamp and Coin Museum (2nd issue). Sheet 135 × 89 mm containing T **705** and similar designs.

MS2225 10f. red, brown and blue (T **706**); 10f. blue and brown (entrance of museum) (*vert*); 10f. blue (1051 30f. first museum stamp) . . . . 9·50 9·50

1995. 800th Birth Anniv of St. Antony of Padua.

2226 **706** 2f.80 multicoloured . . . 65 55

707 United Nations Charter and Peacekeeping Soldiers

1995. 50th Anniv of U.N.O.

2227 **707** 2f.50 multicoloured . . . 65 55
2228 – 2f.50 multicoloured . . . 65 55
2229 – 2f.50 multicoloured . . . 65 55
2230 – 2f.50 blue, black and brown 65 55
2231 – 3f. black, brown and blue 75 75
2232 – 3f. multicoloured 75 75
2233 – 3f. multicoloured 75 75
2234 – 3f. multicoloured 75 75
MS2235 112 × 151 mm. 3f. As No. 2227; 3f. As No. 2228; 3f. As No. 2229; 3f. As No. 2230; 4f.50, As No. 2231; 4f.50, As No. 2232; 4f.50, As No. 2233; 4f.50, As No. 2234 . . . . 11·00 11·00

DESIGNS: No. 2228, Wheat ears, boy and arid ground; 2229, Children from different nationalities; 2230, Head of Colossus, Abu Simbel Temple; 2231, United Nations meeting; 2232, Growing crops and hand holding seeds; 2233, Figures and alphabetic characters; 2234, Lute and U.N.E.S.C.O. headquarters, Paris.

Nos. 2228 and 2232 commemorate the F.A.O., Nos. 2229 and 2233 International Year of Tolerance, Nos. 2230 and 2234 U.N.E.S.C.O.

708 Rose "Grace de Monaco" **709** Balthazar

1995. Flowers. Multicoloured.

2236	3f. Type **708**	65	50
2237	3f. Fuchsia "Lakeland Princess"	65	50
2238	3f. Carnation "Centenaire de Monte-Carlo"	65	50
2239	3f. Fuchsia "Grace"	65	50
2240	3f. Rose "Princesse de Monaco"	65	50
2241	3f. Alstroemeria "Gracia"	65	50
2242	3f. Lily "Princess Gracia"	65	50
2243	3f. Carnation "Princesse Caroline"	65	50
2244	3f. Rose "Stephanie de Monaco"	65	50
2245	3f. Carnation "Prince Albert"	65	50
2246	3f. Sweet pea "Grace de Monaco"	65	50
2247	3f. Gerbera "Gracia"	65	50

1995. Christmas. Crib Figures from Provence of the Three Wise Men. Multicoloured.

2248	3f. Type **709**	75	55
2249	5f. Gaspard	1·25	75
2250	6f. Melchior	1·50	1·10

710 Tree, Bird, Seahorse and Association Emblem

1995. 20th Anniv of Monaco Association for Nature Protection.

2251	**710** 4f. green, black and red	90	70

711 Rontgen and X-Ray of Hand

1995. Centenary of Discovery of X-Rays by Wilhelm Rontgen.

2252	**711** 6f. black, yellow and green	1·40	75

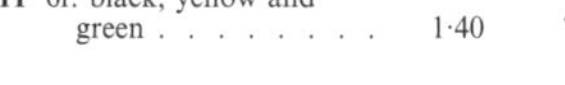

712 First Screening to Paying Public, Paris, December 1895

1995. Centenary of Motion Pictures.

2253	**712** 7f. blue	1·60	85

713 Allegory of Anti-leprosy Campaign

1995. Monaco Red Cross. Multicoloured.

2254	7f. Type **713**	1·75	1·40
2255	8f. Doctors Prakash and Mandakini Amte (anti-leprosy campaign in India)	1·90	1·75

714 First Car with Tyres

1995. Centenary of Invention of Inflatable Tyres.

2256	**714** 8f. purple and claret	1·90	1·40

715 "Spring"

1995. 550th Birth Anniv of Sandro Botticelli (artist).

2257	**715** 15f. blue	3·75	3·50

716 Poster **718** Rhododendron

717 Illusion

1996. 20th International Circus Festival, Monte Carlo.

2258	**716** 2f.40 multicoloured	70	55

1996. Magic Festival, Monte Carlo.

2259	**717** 2f.80 black	85	55

1996. Monte Carlo Flower Show.

2260	**718** 3f. multicoloured	85	55

719 Wire-haired Fox Terrier

1996. International Dog Show, Monte Carlo.

2261	**719** 4f. multicoloured	1·25	95

720 "Chapel" (Hubert Clerissi)

1996. 300th Anniv of Chapel of Our Lady of Mercy.

2262	**720** 6f. multicoloured	1·75	1·60

721 Prince Albert I of Monaco (½-size illustration)

1996. Centenary of Oceanographic Expeditions. Multicoloured.

2263	3f. Type **721**	85	55
2264	4f.50 King Carlos I of Portugal	1·40	85

722 Prince Rainier III (after F. Messina) **723** Princess Grace

1996. Inauguration of Stamp and Coin Museum (2nd issue). 1974 Prince Rainier design.

2265	**722** 10f. violet	2·00	1·40
2266	15f. brown	3·25	1·75
2267	20f. blue	4·00	2·40

1996. Europa. Famous Women.

2268	**723** 3f. brown and red	85	60

724 Fishes, Sea and Coastline

1996. 20th Anniv of Ramoge Agreement on Environmental Protection of Mediterranean.

2269	**724** 3f. multicoloured	85	60

725 Saint Nicolas (detail of altarpiece by Louis Brea)

1996. 20th Anniv of Annales Monegasques (historical review). Sheet 180 × 100 mm containing T **725**. and similar vert designs. Each brown.

MS2270	3f. Type **725**; 3f. hector Berlioz (composer); 4f. Guillaume Apollinaire (poet and art critic); 4f. Niccolo Machiavelli (statesman); 5f. Jean-Baptiste Bosio (painter); 5f. Sidonie Colette (writer); 6f. Francois-Joseph Bosio (sculptor); 6f. Michel Eyqúem de Montaigne (writer and philosopher)	11·50	11·50

726 Chinese Acrobatics Group in Monaco

1996. Monaco–Chinese Diplomatic Relations. Sheet 100 × 60 mm containing T **726** and similar horiz design. Multicoloured.

MS2271	5f. Type **726**; 5f. Fuling Tomg, Peking	3·50	3·50

727 Code and Monaco **728** Throwing the Javelin

1996. Introduction of International Dialling Code "377".

2272	**727** 3f. blue	85	60
2273	3f.80 red	1·10	85

1996. Olympic Games, Atlanta. Multicoloured.

2274	3f. Type **728**	85	80
2275	3f. Baseball	85	80
2276	4f.50 Running	1·40	1·40
2277	4f.50 Cycling	1·40	1·40

729 Children of Different Races with Balloon **730** Angel and Star

1996. 50th Anniv of U.N.I.C.E.F.

2278	**729** 3f. brown, blue and lilac	85	70

1996. Christmas. Multicoloured.

2279	3f. Type **730**	85	60
2280	6f. Angels heralding	1·50	1·25

731 Planet and Neptune, God of the Sea (after Roman mosaic, Sousse)

1996. Anniversaries.

2281	**731** 4f. red, blue and black	1·00	95
2282	– 5f. blue and red	1·25	1·10

DESIGNS—4f. Type **731** (150th anniv of discovery of planet Neptune by Johann Galle); 5f. Rene Descartes (after Franz Hals) (philosopher and scientist, 400th birth anniv).

732 Coins and Press

1996. Inauguaration of Stamp and Coin Museum (3rd issue).

2283	**732** 5f. brown and blue	1·25	1·40
2284	– 5f. brown and purple	1·25	1·40
2285	– 10f. blue and brown	3·00	2·75
MS2286	130 × 80 mm. Nos. 2283/5	6·50	6·50

DESIGNS—As T **733**: 5f. Stamp press and engraver. 48 × 37 mm: 10f. Museum entrance.

733 Camille Corot (bicentenary)

1996. Artists' Birth Anniversaries. Self-portraits. Multicoloured.

2287	6f. Type **733**	1·50	1·40
2288	7f. Francisco Goya (250th anniv)	1·75	1·75

734 Allegory

1996. Monaco Red Cross. Anti-tuberculosis Campaign. Multicoloured.

2289	7f. Type **734**	1·75	1·25
2290	8f. Camille Guerin and Albert Calmette (developers of vaccine)	2·00	1·40

735 Spring

1996. Seasons of the Blackberry. Sheet 143 × 100 mm containing T **735** and similar horiz designs. Multicoloured.
MS2291 4f. Type **735**; 5f. Summer; 6f. Autumn; 7f. Winter . . . . 7·50 7·50

736 "Gloria" (cadet barque), Club, Motorboat and "Tuiga" (royal yacht)

1996. Monaco Yacht Club.
2292 **736** 3f. multicoloured 80 65

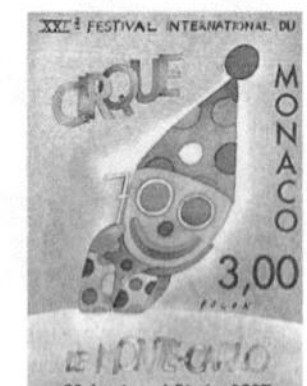

737 Seal of Prince Rainier III **738** Clown

1996. 700th Anniv of Grimaldi Dynasty (1st issue).
2293 **737** 2f.70 red, brown and blue 80 55
See also Nos. 2302/14 and 2326/38.

1996. 21st International Circus Festival, Monte Carlo (1997).
2294 **738** 3f. multicoloured 80 55

739 Old and New Racing and Rally Cars

1996. Motor Sport.
2295 **739** 3f. multicoloured 80 55

740 Pictures, Engraving Tools and "Stamps"

1996. 60th Anniv of Stamp Issuing Office (2296) and "Monaco 97" International Stamp Exhibition, Monte Carlo (2297). Each brown, mauve and blue.
2296 3f. Type **740** 80 55
2297 3f. Stamp, magnifying glass and letters 80 55
Nos. 2296/7 were issued together, se-tenant, forming a composite design featuring the Grand Staircase of the Prince's Palace.

741 Double Red Camellia

1996. Monte Carlo Flower Show (1997).
2298 **741** 3f.80 multicoloured . . . 1·00 70

742 Afghan Hound

1996. International Dog Show, Monte Carlo.
2299 **742** 4f.40 multicoloured . . . 1·40 1·25

743 Award **744** Giant Bellflower and Carob Pods and Leaves

1996. 37th Television Festival, Monte Carlo (1997).
2300 **743** 4f.90 multicoloured . . . 1·25 1·10

1996.
2301 **744** 5f. multicoloured . . . . 1·40 1·10

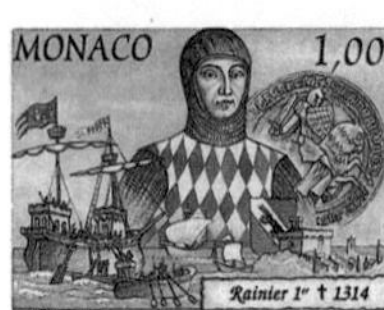

745 Rainier I, Battle of Zerikzee, Arms of his wife Andriola Grillo and Chateau de Cagnes

1997. 700th Anniv of Grimaldi Dynasty (2nd issue). The Seigneurs. Multicoloured.
2302 1f. Type **745** 35 35
2303 1f. Seal of Charles I, Battle of Crecy, Chateau de Roquebrune and Rocher fortifications 35 35
2304 1f. Siege of Rocher by Boccanegra, seal of Rainier II, arms of his two wives Ilaria del Caretto and Isabelle Asinari, Vatican and Papal Palace, Avignon . . 35 35
2305 2f. Defeat of combined fleets of Venice and Florence and Jean I on horseback and with his wife Pomelline Fregoso 55 60
2306 2f. Claudine, acclamation by crowd of her husband Lambert, seals of Lambert and his father Nicolas and strengthening of Monaco Castle 55 60
2307 7f. Statue of Francois Grimaldi disguised as Franciscan monk and clashes between Ghibellines and Guelphs at Genoa . . . . 1·90 1·75
2308 7f. Honore I flanked by Pope Paul III and Duke of Savoy and Battle of Lepanto . . . . 1·90 1·75
2309 7f. Charles II, flags of Genoa and Savoy and attack on Rocher by Capt. Cartier . . . . . . 1·90 1·75
2310 7f. Hercule I, flags of Savoy, Nice and Provence, assassination of Hercule and acclamation of his infant son Honore II . . 1·90 1·75
2311 9f. Catalan aiding Doge of Venice in war against Aragon, exercising "Right of the Sea" and entrusting education of his heiress Claudine to his wife Pomelline . . . . 2·75 2·75
2312 9f. Jean II with his wife Antoinette of Savoy, retable in Chapel of St. Nicholas and assassination of Jean by his brother Lucien . . . . 2·75 2·75
2313 9f. Lucien and siege of Monaco by Genoa . . . 2·75 2·75
2314 9f. Seal of Augustin, Treaty of Tordesillas, visit by King Charles V and Augustin as bishop with his nephew and heir Honore . . . . 2·75 2·75
MS2315 **737** 150 × 80 mm. 2 × 2f.70 red; 2 × 2f.70 brown; 2 × 2f.70 blue; 2 × 2f.70 red, brown and blue . . . . 7·50 7·50

746 Tennis Match and Players

1997. Centenary of Monaco Tennis Championships.
2316 **746** 4f.60 multicoloured . . . 1·25 95

747 Prince Rainier, Trophy and Stamp and Coin Museum

1997. Award to Prince Rainier of International Philately Grand Prix (made to "Person who has Contributed Most to Philately") by Association of Catalogue Editors.
2317 **747** 4f.60 multicoloured . . . 1·25 1·10

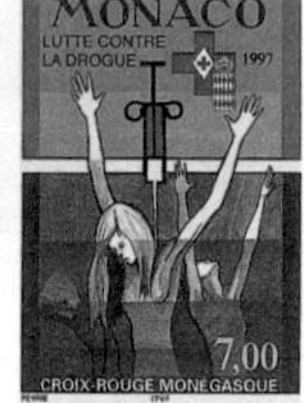

748 Images of St.Devote (patron saint) **749** Syringe and Drug Addicts

1997. Europa. Tales and Legends.
2318 **748** 3f. orange and brown . . 80 70
2319 – 3f. blue 80 70
DESIGN: No. 2319, Hercules.

1997. Monaco Red Cross. Anti-drugs Campaign.
2320 **749** 7f. black, blue and red 2·00 1·40

750 First Stamps of United States and Monaco 1996 15f. Stamp

1997. "Pacific 97" International Stamp Exhibiton, San Francisco. 150th Anniv of First United States Stamps.
2321 **750** 4f.90 multicoloured . . . 1·40 1·10

751 Winter and Summer Uniforms, 1997

1997. The Palace Guard. Multicoloured.
2322 3f. Type **751** 80 65
2323 3f.50 Uniforms of 1750, 1815, 1818, 1830 and 1853 1·00 70
2324 5f.20 Uniforms of 1865, 1870, 1904, 1916 and 1935 1·40 1·10

1997. Victory of Marcelo M. Rios at Monaco Tennis Championships. No. 2316 optd **M. RIOS**.
2325 **746** 4f.60 multicoloured . . . 1·40 1·25

1997. 700th Anniv of Grimaldi Dynasty (3rd issue). The Princes. As T **745**. Multicoloured.
2326 1f. Honore II 35 35
2327 1f. Louis I 35 35
2328 1f. Antoine I 35 35
2329 2f. Jacques I 65 65
2330 7f. Charles III . . . . . . 1·90 1·90
2331 7f. Albert I . . . . 1·90 1·90
2332 7f. Louis II . . . . 1·90 1·90
2333 7f. Rainier III . . . . . . 1·90 1·90
2334 9f. Louise-Hippolyte . . . . 2·50 2·50
2335 9f. Honore IV (wrongly inscr "Honore III") . . . 2·50 2·50
2336 9f. Honore III (wrongly inscr "Honore IV") . . . 2·50 2·50
2337 9f. Honore V . . . . 2·50 2·50
2338 9f. Florestan I . . . . . . 2·50 2·50

753 Club Badge, Ball as Globe and Stadium

1997. Monaco, Football Champion of France, 1996–97
2339 **753** 3f. multicoloured 80 75

754 Magic Wand, Hands and Stars

1997. 13th Magic Grand Prix, Monte Carlo.
2340 **754** 4f.40 black and gold . . 1·25 1·10

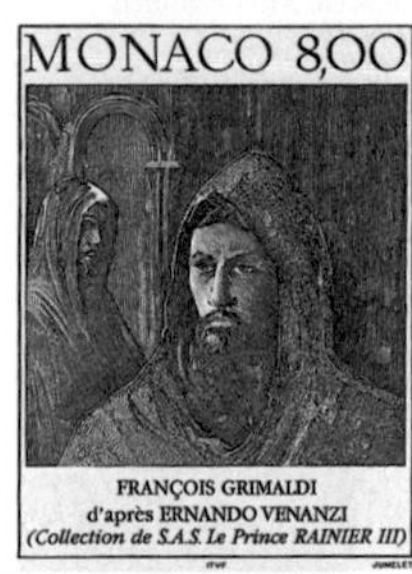

755 "Francois Grimaldi" (Ernando Venanzi)

1997. Paintings. Multicoloured.
2341 8f. Type **755** . . . . 2·10 1·75
2342 9f. "St. Peter and St. Paul" (Peter Paul Rubens) . . . 2·25 2·25

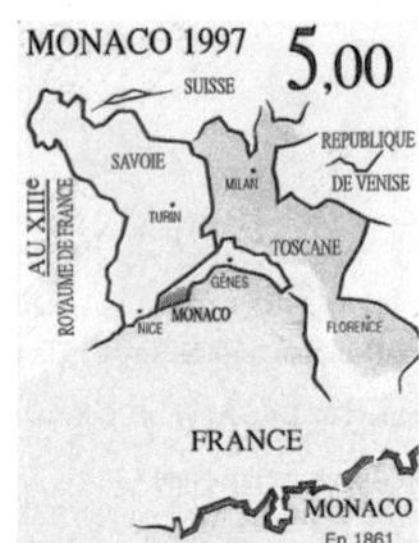

756 Monaco in 13th Century and 1861

1997. 700th Anniv of Grimaldi Dynasty (4th issue). Geographical Evolution of Monaco. Sheet 120 × 145 mm containing T **756** and similar vert designs. Multicoloured.
MS2343 5f. Type **756**; 5f. Monaco from 15th--19th centuries; 5f. Left half of Monaco; 5f. Right half of Monaco . . . . 7·00 7·00
The bottom two stamps of the miniature sheet form a composite design of present-day Monaco with a map showing dates at which the territory was expanded.

757 Map of Europe and Blue Whales

1997. 49th Session of International Whaling Commission, Monaco.
2344 **757** 6f.70 multicoloured . . . 1·40 1·25

1997. Election of 1995 Botticelli Stamp as Most Beautiful Stamp in the World. Sheet 115 × 100 mm.
MS2345 **715** 15f. blue . . . . . 5·25 5·25

758 Princess Charlotte

1997. 20th Death Anniv of Princess Charlotte.
2346 **758** 3f.80 brown . . . . . . 1·00 1·00

759 Dancer of Russian Ballet and Kremlin, Moscow

761 Diamond-Man (Ribeiro)

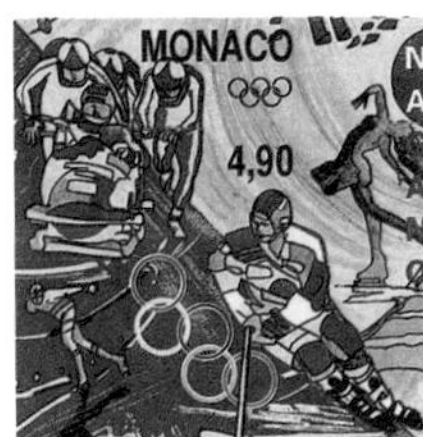
760 Trees in Monaco

1997. "Moskva 97" International Stamp Exhbition, Moscow.
2347 **759** 5f. multicoloured . . . . 1·25 1·25

1997. 10th Anniv of Marcel Korenlein Arboretum.
2348 **760** 9f. multicoloured . . . . 2·50 2·25

1997. Winning Entries in Schoolchildren's Drawing Competition.
2349 **761** 4f. multicoloured . . . . 1·00 90
2350 – 4f.50 blue, ultramarine and red . . . . 1·25 1·00
DESIGN—HORIZ: 4f.50, Flying diamonds (Testa).

762 Four-man Bobsleighing, Speed and Figure Skating and Ice Hockey

1997. Winter Olympic Games, Nagano, Japan (1998). Multicoloured.
2351 4f.90 Type **762** . . . . . . 1·40 1·40
2352 4f.90 Alpine skiing, biathlon, two-man bobsleighing and ski-jumping . . . . 1·40 1·40
Nos. 2351/2 were issued together, se-tenant, forming a composite design.

763 Albert I (statue) (½-size illustration)

1997. 150th Birth Anniv of Prince Albert I (1st issue).
2353 **763** 8f. multicoloured . . . . 2·10 2·10
See also No. 2368.

764 Clown and Horse

765 Pink Campanula and Carob Plant

1997. 22nd International Circus Festival, Monte Carlo (1998).
2354 **764** 3f. multicoloured 80 75

1997. Monte Carlo Flower Show (1998).
2355 **765** 4f.40 multicoloured . . . 1·25 1·10

766 "The Departure of Marcus Attilius Regulus for Carthage"

768 Baseball Hat, Television Controller, Ballet Shoe and Football Boot

767 Pope Innocent IV

1997. 250th Birth Anniv of Louis David (painter).
2356 **766** 5f.20 green and red . . . 1·40 1·25

1997. 750th Anniv of Creation of Parish of Monaco by Papal Bull.
2357 **767** 7f.50 brown and blue . . 1·90 1·85

1998. 38th Television Festival.
2358 **768** 4f.50 multicoloured . . . 1·10 1·00

769 Past and Present Presidents

1998. 50th Anniv of Monaco Red Cross.
2359 **769** 5f. brown and red . . . 1·40 1·40

770 Boxer and Dobermann

1998. International Dog Show, Monte Carlo.
2360 **770** 2f.70 multicoloured . . . 80 70

771 White Doves and Laurel Wreath

1998. 30th Meeting of Academy of Peace and International Security.
2361 **771** 3f. green and blue . . . 80 70

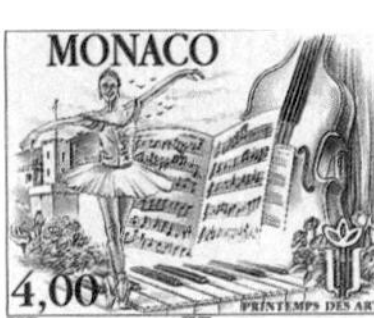
772 Ballet Dancer, Piano Keys, Music Score and Violin

1998. 15th Spring Arts Festival.
2362 **772** 4f. multicoloured . . . . 1·00 65

773 Pierre and Marie Curie

1998. Centenary of Discovery of Radium.
2363 **773** 6f. blue and mauve . . . 1·60 1·50

774 Caravel and Globe

1998. "Expo '98" World's Fair, Lisbon. International Year of the Ocean.
2364 **774** 2f.70 multicoloured . . . 80 75

775 St. Devote (stained glass window, Palace Chapel) (½-size illustration)

1998. Europa (1st issue). National Festivals.
2365 **775** 3f. multicoloured 80 70
See also No. 2372.

776 Monte Carlo

777 Kessel

1998. Junior Chamber of Commerce European Conference, Monte Carlo.
2366 **776** 3f. multicoloured 80 75

1998. Birth Centenary of Joseph Kessel (writer).
2367 **777** 3f.90 multicoloured . . . 1·00 1·00

778 Prince Albert I at different Ages (½-size illustration)

1998. 150th Birth Anniv of Prince Albert I (2nd issue).
2368 **778** 7f. brown . . . . 1·75 1·60

779 Garnier and Monte Carlo Casino

780 Trophy and Monte Carlo

1998. Death Centenary of Charles Garnier (architect).
2369 **779** 10f. multicoloured . . . 2·75 2·25

1998. 10th World Music Awards, Monte Carlo.
2370 **780** 10f. multicoloured . . . 2·75 2·50

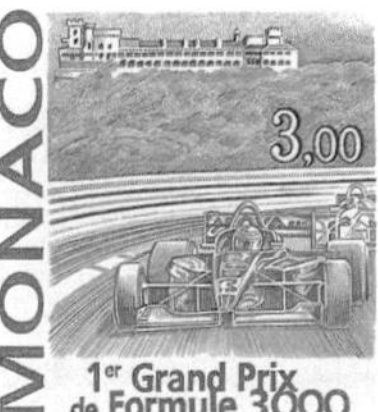
781 Racing Cars

1998. 1st Formula 3000 Grand Prix, Monte Carlo.
2371 **781** 3f. red and black 85 45

782 Prince Rainier III, Prince Albert and Royal Palace (½-size illustration)

1998. Europa (2nd issue). National Festivals.
2372 **782** 3f. multicoloured 85 70

783 Porcelain Teapot and Figure of Francois Grimaldi

1998. Fine Arts. Multicoloured.
2373 8f. Type **783** . . . . 2·00 1·90
2374 9f. Fine-bound books and illustration . . . . 2·25 1·40

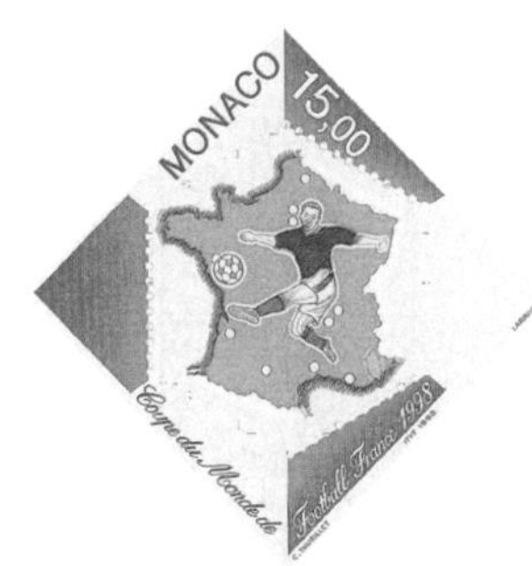
784 Player on Map of France

1998. World Cup Football Championship, France.
2375 **784** 15f. multicoloured . . . 4·25 4·00

785 Modern and Old Motor Cars and Ferrari

1998. Birth Centenary of Enzio Ferrari (motor manufacturer).
2376 **785** 7f. multicoloured . . . . 1·90 1·75

786 Gershwin, Trumpeter, Dancers and Opening Bars of "Rhapsody in Blue"

1998. Birth Cent of George Gershwin (composer).
2377 **786** 7f.50 ultramarine, blue and black . . . . . . 1·90 1·75

787 Int Marine Pollution College and Marine Environment Laboratory

1998. Int Marine Pollution Conference, Monaco.
2378 **787** 4f.50 multicoloured . . . 1·40 1·10

788 Venue

1998. Post Europ (successor to C.E.P.T.) Plenary Assembly, Monaco.
2379 **788** 5f. multicoloured . . . . 1·40 1·10

789 Belem Tower, Lisbon, and Palace, Monaco

1998. "Expo '98" World's Fair and Stamp Exhibition, Lisbon.
2380 **789** 6f.70 multicoloured . . . 1·75 1·75

790 Sportsmen

1998. 30th Anniv of International Association against Violence in Sport.
2381 **790** 4f.20 multicoloured . . . 1·10 1·00

791 Magician

1998. "Magic Stars" Magic Festival, Monte Carlo.
2382 **791** 3f.50 gold and red . . . 90 90

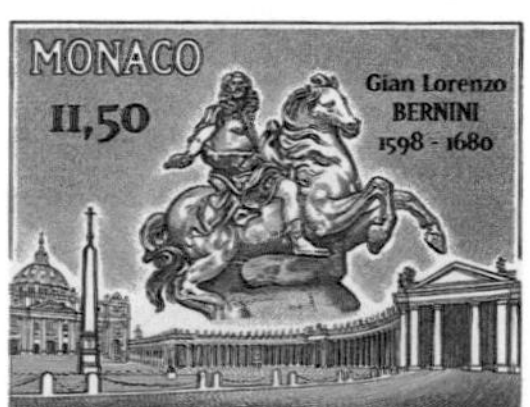

792 Statue and Vatican Colonnade

1998. 400th Birth Anniv of Giovanni Lorenzo Bernini (architect and sculptor).
2383 **792** 11f.50 blue and brown 3·00 3·25

793 Milan Cathedral **794** Christmas Tree Decoration

1998. "Italia 98" Int Stamp Exhibition, Milan.
2384 **793** 4f.90 green and red . . . 1·25 1·25

1998. Christmas. Multicoloured.
2385 3f. Type **794** 80 65
2386 6f.70 "The Nativity" (detail of icon) (horiz) . . . . . 1·75 1·75
MS2387 86×95 mm. 15f. "Virgin and Child" (detail of icon) (36×49 mm) . . . . 5·25 5·25

1998. As Nos. 1910 etc but no value expressed.
2388 **577** (2f.70) turquoise & blue 60 25
2389 (3f.) red and pink . . . 60 25
2390 (3f.80) blue and cobalt 80 40

795 Lion

1998. 23rd International Circus Festival, Monte Carlo (1999).
2391 **795** 2f.70 multicoloured . . . 70 55

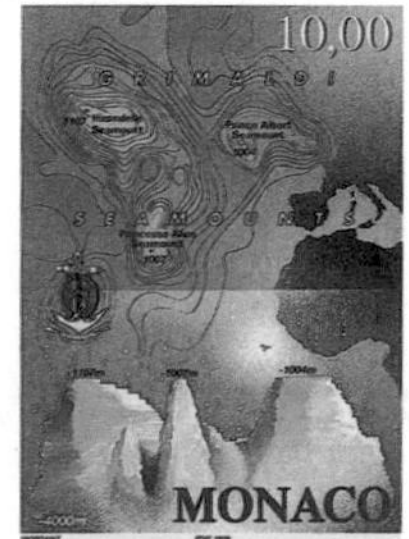

796 Map and Elevation of Seamounts

1998. Grimaldi Seamounts.
2392 **796** 10f. multicoloured . . . 2·50 2·00

797 Prince's Arms and Monogram

1998. 50th Anniv (1999) of Accession of Prince Rainier III (1st issue). Sheet 100×130 mm.
MS2393 **797** 25f. gold and red . . 6·25 6·25
See also No. **MS**2417.

798 1860 Cover and Stamp and Coin Museum

1999. "Monaco 99" International Stamp Exhibition.
2394 **798** 3f. multicoloured 80 50
MS2395 160×111 mm. No. 2394 ×4 . . . . 3·50 3·50

799 Festival Poster

1999. 39th Television Festival.
2396 **799** 3f.80 multicoloured . . . 1·00 60

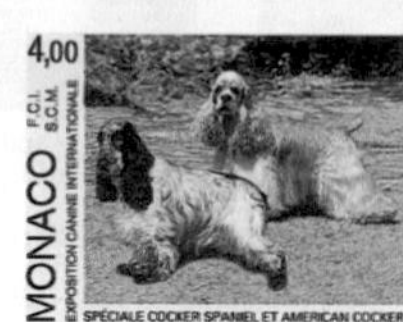

800 Cocker Spaniel and American Cocker

1999. International Dog Show, Fontvieille.
2397 **800** 4f. multicoloured . . . . 1·00 65

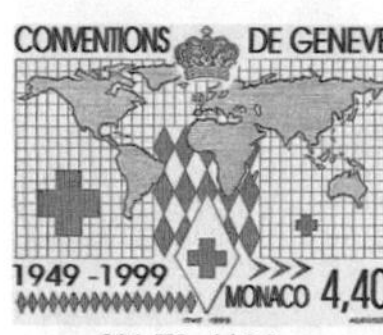

801 World Map

1999. 50th Anniv of Geneva Conventions.
2398 **801** 4f.40 red, brown and black . . . . 1·10 60

802 Arrangement of Flowers named after Grimaldi Family Members

1999. Monte Carlo Flower Show.
2399 **802** 4f.50 multicoloured . . . 1·10 60

803 Children and Heart

1999. 20th Anniv of Monaco Aid and Presence.
2400 **803** 6f.70 multicoloured . . . 1·75 1·00
No. 2400 is also denominated in euros.

804 Palace and Centre

1999. 20th Anniv of Congress Centre Auditorium.
2401 **804** 2f.70 multicoloured . . . 70 50

DENOMINATION. From No. 2402 Monaco stamps are denominated both in francs and in euros. As no cash for the latter was in circulation until 2002, the catalogue continues to use the franc value.

805 Globe and Piano Keys

1999. 10th Piano Masters, Monte Carlo.
2402 **805** 4f.60 multicoloured . . . 1·25 65

806 Rose "Jubile du Prince de Monaco" **808** Olympic Rings and Trophy

807 Williams's Bugatti (winner of first race) and Michael Schumacher's Car (winner of 1999 race)

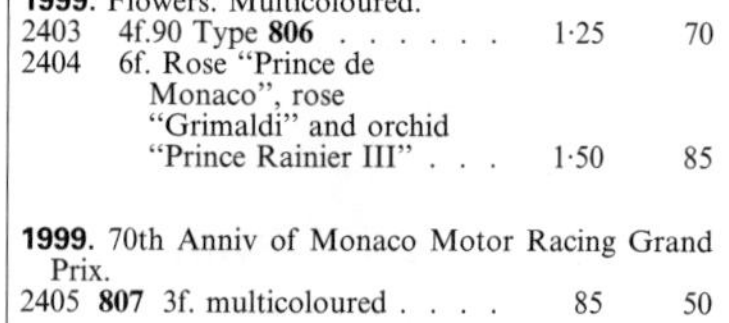

1999. Flowers. Multicoloured.
2403 4f.90 Type **806** . . . . . . 1·25 70
2404 6f. Rose "Prince de Monaco", rose "Grimaldi" and orchid "Prince Rainier III" . . . 1·50 85

1999. 70th Anniv of Monaco Motor Racing Grand Prix.
2405 **807** 3f. multicoloured 85 50

1999. 3rd Association of Postage Stamp Catalogue Editors and Philatelic Publications Grand Prix.
2406 **808** 4f.40 multicoloured . . . 1·10 75

809 Riders jumping over Monte Carlo (½-size illustration)

1999. 5th International Show Jumping Competition, Monte Carlo.
2407 **809** 5f.20 red, black and blue 1·40 95

810 Footballer, Runner and Palace (½-size illustration)

1999. 75th Anniv of Monaco Sports Association. Multicoloured.
2408 7f. Type **810** . . . . 1·75 1·10
2409 7f. Boxer, footballer, harbour, runner and handballer . . . . 1·75 1·10

811 Architect's Drawing of Forum

1999. Construction of Grimaldi Forum (congress and exhibition centre).
2410 **811** 3f. multicoloured 80 50

812 Facade and Construction

1999. Centenary of Laying of First Stone of Oceanographic Museum.
2411 **812** 5f. multicoloured . . . . 1·25 1·10

813 Eiffel Tower on Map of France, 1849 20c. "Ceres" Stamp and Emblem **814** Casino and Rock

1999. "Philexfrance 99" International Stamp Exhibition, Paris (1st issue). 150th Anniv of First French Stamps.
2412 **813** 2f.70 multicoloured . . . 70 55
See also No. 2423.

1999. Europa. Parks and Gardens. Multicoloured.
2413 3f. Type **814** 70 60
2414 3f. Fontvieille (48×27 mm) 70 60

815 Fontvieille in 1949, Line Graph and Underground Station in 1999 (½-size illustration)

1999. 50 Years of the Economy. Multicoloured.
2415 5f. Type **815** (second sector) 1·25 1·10
2416 5f. Le Larvotto in 1949, line graph and Grimaldi Forum in 1999 (third sector) . . . . 1·25 1·10

816 Definitive Stamps, 2950—89 (½-size illustration)

1999. 50th Anniv of Accession of Prince Rainier III (2nd issue). Two sheets, 100 × 130 mm (a) or 119 × 145 mm (b).
MS2417 Two sheets. (a) 20f. blue and gold (as Type **584** but with monogram superimposed); (b) 30f. multicoloured (Type **816**) . . . 12·50 12·50

817 Honore de Balzac

818 Emblem and Chinese Drawing

1999. Writers' Birth Bicentenaries.
2418 **817** 4f.50 blue and scarlet . . 1·10 70
2419 – 5f.20 brown, blue and red . . . . 1·25 85
DESIGN: 5f.20, Sophie Rostopchine, Comtesse de Segur.

1999. 125th Anniv of Universal Postal Union.
2420 **818** 3f. blue, red and yellow 70 55

819 Iris "Rainier III" and Rose "Rainier III"

821 Emblem and Monaco 1885 and French 1878 Stamps

820 Anniversary Emblem

1999. Flowers.
2421 **819** 4f. multicoloured 90 75

1999. 50th Anniv of Monaco's Admission to United Nations Educational, Scientific and Educational Organization.
2422 **820** 4f.20 multicoloured . . . 1·00 80

1999. "Philexfrance 99" International Stamp Exhibition, Paris (2nd issue).
2423 **821** 7f. black, blue and mauve . . . . 1·60 1·50

822 Athletes

1999. 10th Sportel (sport and television) Congress, Fontvieille.
2424 **822** 10f. multicoloured . . . 2·25 2·00

823 Maltese Cross, Knights and Valletta

1999. 900th Anniv of Sovereign Military Order of Malta and 25th Anniv of National Association of the Order.
2425 **823** 11f.50 red, brown and blue . . . . 2·50 2·50

824 1999 Postcard of Monaco, 1989 Definitive Design and Obverse of Jubilee Coin

1999. Postcard, Coin and Stamp Exhibition, Fontvieille (1st issue).
2426 **824** 3f. multicoloured 70 55
See also No. 2429.

1999. "Magic Stars" Magic Festival, Monte Carlo. As No. 2382 but face value and date changed.
2427 **791** 4f.50 gold and red . . . 1·10 90

825 Fontvielle Project, Stage 2

1999. Achievements and Projects. Sheet 150 × 100 mm containing T **825** and similar multicoloured designs.
MS2428 4f. Type **825**; 9f. New harbour mole; 9f. Grimaldi Forum (congress centre); 19f. Underground train, harbour and station (76 × 36 mm) . . . . . 10·50 10·50

826 1949 Postcard of Monaco, Reverse of Jubilee Coin and 1950 Definitive

1999. Postcard, Coin and Stamp Exhibition, Fontvieille (2nd issue).
2429 **826** 6f.50 multicoloured . . . 1·60 1·40

827 Pierrot juggling "2000"

828 "Madonna and Child" (Simone Cantarini)

1999. 24th International Circus Festival, Monte Carlo (2000).
2430 **827** 2f.70 multicoloured . . . 65 55

1999. Christmas.
2431 **828** 3f. multicoloured 75 55

829 Blessing and Holy Door, St. Peter's Cathedral, Rome

1999. Holy Year 2000.
2432 **829** 3f.50 multicoloured . . . 80 65

830 Mixed Arrangement

831 Emblem

1999. 33rd Monte Carlo Flower Show.
2433 **830** 4f.50 multicoloured . . . 1·10 90

1999. "Monaco 2000" International Stamp Exhibitions.
2434 **831** 3f. multicoloured 75 55

832 Bust of Napoleon (Antonio Canova)

833 Festival Emblem

2000. 30th Anniv of Napoleonic Museum.
2435 **832** 4f.20 multicoloured . . . 1·00 80

2000. 40th Television Festival, Monte Carlo.
2436 **833** 4f.90 multicoloured . . . 1·10 95

834 St. Peter and St. James the Major

2000. The Twelve Apostles. Multicoloured.
2437 **834** 4f. blue, orange and gold 80 75
2438 – 5f. red and gold . . . . 1·00 95
2439 – 6f. violet and gold . . . 1·25 1·10
2440 – 7f. brown and gold . . . 1·50 1·40
2441 – 8f. green and gold . . . 1·75 1·50
2442 – 9f. red, orange and gold 1·90 1·75
DESIGNS: 5f. St. John and St. Andrew; 6f. St. Philip and St. Bartholomew; 7f. St. Matthew and St. Thomas; 8f. St. James the Minor and St. Jude; 9f. St. Simon and St. Mathias.

835 Golden Labrador and Golden Retriever

2000. International Dog Show, Monte Carlo.
2443 **835** 6f.50 multicoloured . . . 1·60 1·40

836 Man's Head, Drawings and Key (Adami)

2000. Monaco and the Sea. Multicoloured.
2444 6f.55 Type **836** . . . . . . 1·50 1·40
2445 6f.55 "Monaco" above sea (Arman) . . . . 1·50 1·40
2446 6f.55 Abstract designs (Cane) . . . . 1·50 1·40
2447 6f.55 Hand touching sun in sky (Folon) . . . . . . 1·50 1·40
2448 6f.55 Angel sleeping and boats (Fuchs) . . . . . . 1·50 1·40
2449 6f.55 Harbour (E. de Sigaldi) . . . . 1·50 1·40
2450 6f.55 Views of harbour on silhouettes of yachts (Sosno) . . . . 1·50 1·40
2451 6f.55 Waves and floating ball (Verkade) . . . . . 1·50 1·40

837 Olympic Rings on Globe and Flags

2000. Olympic Games, Sydney, Australia.
2452 **837** 7f. multicoloured . . . . 1·50 1·40

838 "Building Europe"

839 Racing Cars

2000. Europa. Multicoloured.
2453 3f. Type **838** 75 70
2454 3f. Map of Europe and Post Europ member countries' flags (56 × 37 mm) 75 70

2000. 2nd Historic Vehicles Grand Prix.
2455 **839** 4f.40 multicoloured . . . 90 80

840 Monaco Pavilion and Emblem

2000. "EXPO 2000" World's Fair, Hanover.
2456 **840** 5f. multicoloured . . . . 1·00 95

841 Sts. Mark, Matthew, John and Luke

2000. The Four Evangelists.
2457 **841** 20f. black, flesh and green . . . . 4·25 4·25

842 St. Stephen and Emblem

843 Golfer

2000. "WIPA 2000" International Stamp Exhibition, Vienna.
2458 **842** 4f.50 black, blue and red 90 85

2000. Pro-celebrity Golf Tournament, Monte Carlo.
2459 **843** 4f.40 multicoloured . . . 90 85

844 Fencing

2000. Olympic Games, Sydney. Multicoloured.
2460 2f.70 Type **844** 65 35
2461 4f.50 Rowing 90 55

845 Humber Beeston and Woman with Parasol, 1911

2000. Motor Cars and Fashion. Motor cars from the Royal Collection. Multicoloured.
2462 3f. Type **845** 65 45
2463 6f.70 Jaguar 4-cylinder and woman, 1947 . . . . . . 1·50 85
2464 10f. Rolls Royce Silver Cloud and woman wearing swing coat, 1956 2·00 1·25
2465 15f. Lamborghini Countach and woman wearing large hat, 1986 . . . . 3·25 1·60

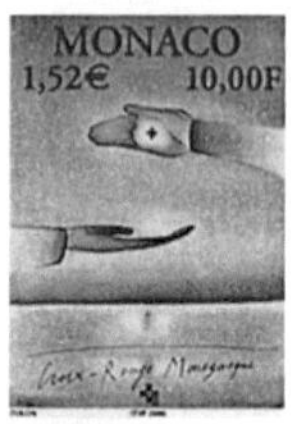

846 Entrance to Museum **847** Open Hands and Emblem

2000. Philatelic Rarities Exhibition (1999), Stamp and Coin Museum, Monte Carlo.
2466 **846** 3f.50 multicoloured . . . 75 65

2000. Monaco Red Cross.
2467 **847** 10f. multicoloured . . . 2·10 1·90

848 Magnifying Glass, Stamps and Exhibition Hall **849** Magician

2000. "WORLD STAMP USA" International Exhibition, Anaheim, California.
2468 **848** 4f.40 multicoloured . . . 95 55

2000. "Magic Stars" Magic Festival, Monte Carlo.
2469 **849** 4f.60 multicoloured . . . 95 55

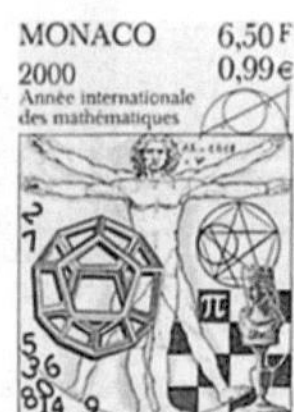

850 Da Vinci's "Man" and Mathematical Symbols

2000. World Mathematics Year.
2470 **850** 6f.50 brown . . . . . . 1·40 65

851 Right-hand Section of Screen

2000. Holy Year. Restoration of Altar Screen, Monaco Cathedral. Sheet 120 × 100 mm containing T **851** and similar design.
MS2471 10f. Type **851**; 20f. Left-hand and central sections (53 × 52 mm) . . . . 6·75 6·75

852 Shark and Museum Facade

2000. Opening of New Aquarium, Oceanographical Museum.
2472 **852** 3f. multicoloured 65 35

853 Cathedral and Statue of Bear

2000. "ESPANA 2000" International Stamp Exhibition, Madrid.
2473 **853** 3f.80 multicoloured . . . 85 45

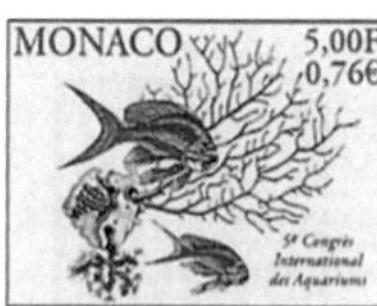

854 Fishes and Corals

2000. 5th International Congress on Aquaria (5f.) and 25th Anniv of Monaco Nature Protection Association (9f.). Multicoloured.
2474 5f. Type **854** . . . . 1·10 55
2475 9f. Starfish, water plant and fish . . . . 1·90 95

855 Museum Facade and Plants

2000. 50th Anniv of Observatory Cave and 40th Anniv of Anthropological Museum.
2476 **855** 5f.20 purple, green and brown . . . . 1·00 55

856 Fresco, Oceanography Museum (½-size illustration)

2000. International Aquariological Congress.
2477 **856** 7f. multicoloured . . . . 1·50 65

857 18th-century Crib **858** Princess Stephanie (President)

2000. Christmas.
2478 **857** 3f. multicoloured 65 25

2000. Motor Cars and Fashion. Motor cars from the Royal Collection. As T **845**. Multicoloured.
2479 5f. Ferrari Formula 1 racing car and woman in racing clothes, 1989 . . . . . . 1·10 55
2480 6f. Fiat 600 "Jolly" and woman wearing swimming costume, 1955 . . . . . 1·25 65
2481 8f. Citroen C4F "Autochenille" and woman wearing coat and hat, 1929 . . . . 1·75 85

2000. Association for Help and Protection of Disabled Children (A.M.A.P.E.I.).
2482 **858** 11f.50 blue and red . . . 2·40 1·10

859 Exhibition Poster

2000. "Monaco 2000" Stamp Exhibition, Sheet 150 × 90 mm containing two examples of T **859**.
MS2483 20f. × 2 multicoloured 4·50 4·50

860 Warrior kneeling **861** Museum Building

2000. Terracotta Warrior Exhibition, Grimaldi Forum (2001).
2484 **860** 2f.70 black and red . . . 65 25

2000. 50th Anniv of Postal Museum.
2485 **861** 3f. multicoloured 65 25

862 Arms **863** Iris "Princess Caroline of Monaco"

2000. Self-adhesive.
2486 **862** (3f.) black and red . . . 65 25

2000. 34th Monte Carlo Flower Show.
2487 **863** 3f.80 multicoloured . . . 85 35

864 Sardinian 1851 5c., 20c. and 40c. Stamps

2000. 150th Anniv (2001) of First Sardinian Stamp.
2488 **864** 6f.50 blue, red and black 1·40 65

865 Seahorse, Marine Life and Life Belt

2000. 25th Anniv (2001) of the Ramoge Agreement on Environmental Protection of Mediterranean.
2489 **865** 6f.70 multicoloured . . . 1·50 65

866 Breitling Orbiter and 1984 2f.80 Stamp **867** Clown with Seal balancing Ball

2000. 1st Non-Stop Balloon Circumnavigation of Globe (1999). Award to Bertrand Picard of International Philately Grand Prix by Association of Catalogue Editors.
2490 **866** 9f. multicoloured . . . . 1·90 95

2000. 25th International Circus Festival, Monte Carlo (2001). Different poster designs by artist named. Multicoloured (except No. 2492).
2491 2f.70 Type **867** 65 35
2492 6f. Clown playing guitar (Hodge) (black, red and blue) . . . . 1·25 65
2493 6f. Clown resting head (Knie) . . . . 1·25 65
2494 6f. Tiger and circus tent (P. Merot) . . . . 1·25 65
2495 6f. Lions, horses and trapeze artists (Poulet) . . . . . 1·25 65
2496 6f. Monkey and circus tents (T. Mordant) . . . . . . 1·25 65

868 Player kicking Ball

2000. Monaco, Football Champion of France, 1999–2000.
2497 **868** 4f.50 multicoloured . . . 1·00 45

869 Sea Mammals and Mediterranean Sea

2000. Mediterranean Sea Marine Mammals Sanctuary.
2498 **869** 5f.20 multicoloured . . . 1·10 55

870 Nativity Scene (½-size illustration)

2000. Christmas.
2499 **870** 10f. multicoloured . . . 2·00 1·10

871 Poster **873** Flower Arrangement

872 Leonberger and Newfoundland Dogs

2001. 41st Television Festival, Monte Carlo.
2500 **871** 3f.50 multicoloured . . . 70 50

2001. International Dog Show, Monte Carlo.
2501 **872** 6f.50 multicoloured . . . 1·25 95

2001. Flower Show, Genoa.
2502 **873** 6f.70 multicoloured . . . 1·25 95

874 Monaco Palace

875 Princess Caroline and Portrait of Prince Pierre of Monaco (founder)

2001. Europa. Water Resources. Multicoloured.
2503 3f. Type **874** 60 45
2504 3f. Undercover washing area 60 45

2001. 50th Anniv of Literary Council of Monaco.
2505 **875** 2f.70 black, brown and green 50 25

876 Malraux

877 Town Hall

2001. Birth Centenary of Andre Malraux (writer).
2506 **876** 10f. black and red . . . 1·90 1·40

2001. "BELGICA 2001" International Stamp Exhibition, Brussels.
2507 **877** 4f. blue and red 75 60

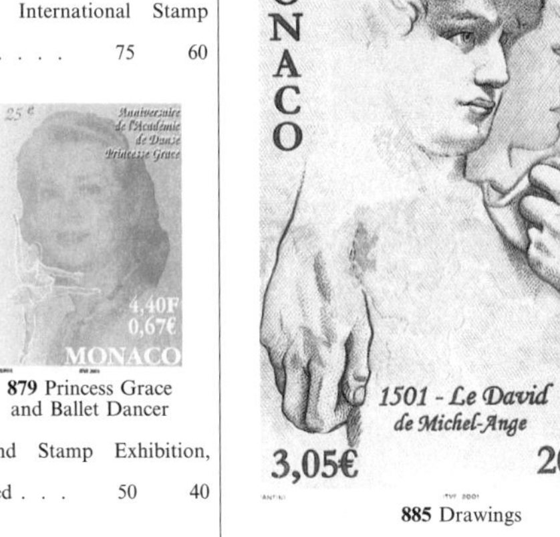

878 Coins, Stamp and Book

879 Princess Grace and Ballet Dancer

2001. Postcard, Coin and Stamp Exhibition, Fontvielle.
2508 **878** 2f.70 multicoloured . . . 50 40

2001. 25th Anniv of Princess Grace Dance Academy.
2509 **879** 4f.40 multicoloured . . . 85 65

880 Model

2001. Naval Museum, Fontvielle.
2510 **880** 4f.50 multicoloured . . . 85 65

881 Petanque Balls

2001. World Petanque Championships.
2511 **881** 5f. multicoloured 75 70

882 Fireplace, Throne Room

2001. Royal Palace (1st series). Multicoloured.
2512 3f. Type **882** 60 40
2513 4f.50 Blue Room 85 65
2514 6f.70 York Chamber . . . . 1·25 95
2515 15f. Throne room ceiling fresco . . . . 3·00 2·25
See also Nos. 2541/3.

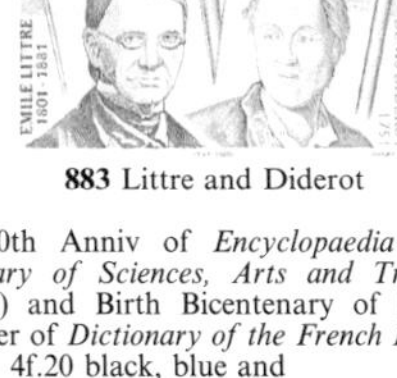

883 Littre and Diderot

2001. 250th Anniv of *Encyclopaedia or Critical Dictionary of Sciences, Arts and Trades* (Denis Diderot) and Birth Bicentenary of Emile Littre (compiler of *Dictionary of the French Language*).
2516 **883** 4f.20 black, blue and green 80 60

884 Medal and Steam Yacht

2001. 30th Anniv of Prince Albert Oceanography Prize.
2517 **884** 9f. blue . . . . 1·75 1·25

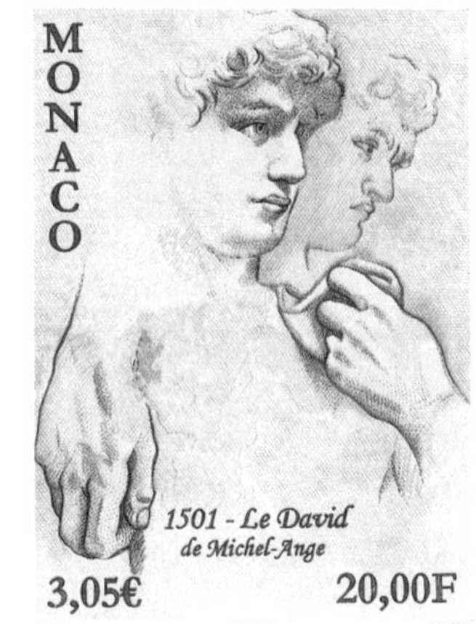

885 Drawings

2001. 500th Anniv of David (sculpture, Michaelangelo).
2518 **885** 20f. multicoloured . . . 3·75 3·00

886 Alfred Nobel (prize fund founder)

888 Virgin and Child

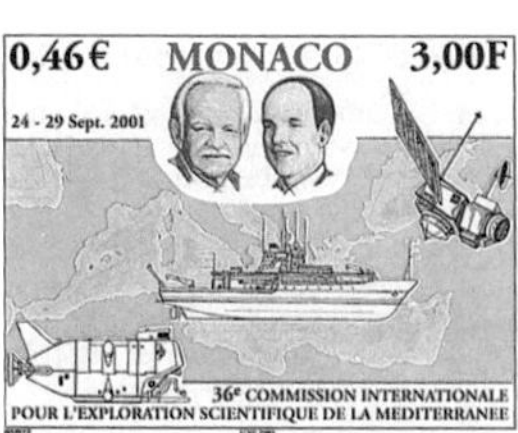

887 Prince Rainer, Prince Albert, Map, Satellite, Ship, and Submarine

2001. Centenary of the Nobel Prize. Multicoloured.
2519 5f. Type **886** 95 70
2520 8f. Henri Dunant (founder of Red Cross and winner of Peace Prize, 1901) . . 1·50 1·10
2521 11f.50 Enrico Fermi (physicist and winner of Physics Prize, 1938) . . . 2·25 1·75

2001. 36th International Commission for Scientific Exploration of the Mediterranean Meeting.
2522 **887** 3f. multicoloured 60 45

2001. Christmas.
2523 **888** 3f. multicoloured 60 45

889 Garden Tiger Moth (*Artica caja*)

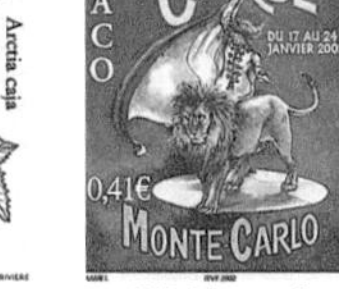

890 Lion and Ringmaster

2002. Flora and Fauna.
2524 **889** 1c. black, red and sepia 10 10
2525 – 2c. multicoloured 10 10
2526 – 5c. multicoloured 10 10
2527 – 10c. black, green and yellow 15 10
2528 – 20c. red, yellow and black 25 20
2529 – 41c. multicoloured . . . 65 45
2530 – 50c. multicoloured . . . 60 45
2531 – €1 multicoloured . . . 1·25 1·00
2532 – €2 multicoloured . . . 2·50 2·00
2533 – €5 brown, green and black . . . . 6·25 4·75
2534 – €10 green, red and black . . . . 12·50 9·50
DESIGNS—VERT: 5c. Blue trumpet vine (*Thunbergia grandiflora*); 41c. *Helix aspera*; 50c. Foxy charaxes (*Charaxes jasius*); €2 Red thorn apple (*Datura sanguinea*); €5 Crested tit (*Parus crisatus*). HORIZ: 2c. *Luria lurida*; 10c. Great tit (*Parus major*); 20c. Common barberfish (*Anthias anthias*); €1 Zoned mitre (*Mitra zonata*); €10 Common snipefish (*Macroramphosus scolopax*).

2002. 26th International Circus Festival, Monte Carlo.
2540 **890** 41c. multicoloured . . . 50 40

891 Crystal Gallery

2002. Royal Palace (2nd series). Multicoloured.
2541 41c. Type **891** 50 40
2542 46c. Throne room (horiz) 60 45
2543 58c. Landscape painting in Crystal Gallery (horiz) . . 75 60

892 Rocking Horse of Flowers

2002. 35th Monte Carlo Flower Show.
2544 **892** 53c. multicoloured . . . 65 50

893 Old and Modern Rally Cars

2002. Motoring Events in Monaco. Sheet 124 × 95 mm, containing T **893** and similar vert design. Multicoloured.
MS2545 €1.07, Type **893** (70th Monte Carlo car rally); €1.22, Old racing car (Historic Vehicles third Grand Prix) and modern Formula 1 racing car (60th Monaco Grand Prix) . . . . . 3·25 2·40

894 Skiers, Ice Skater and Ice Hockey Player

2002. Winter Olympic Games, Salt Lake City, U.S.A. Multicoloured.
2546 23c. Type **894** 35 25
2547 23c. Bobsleigh, luge and skiers (face value, emblem and country inscription at right) 35 25
Nos. 2446/7 were issued together, se-tenant, forming a composite design.

895 Exhibition Cases and Prince Albert I

2002. Anniversaries. Multicoloured.
2548 64c. Type **895** (centenary of Prehistoric Anthropology Museum) 90 65
2549 67c. Title page, Prince Albert I and ship (centenary of publication of "La Carriere d'un Navigateur" (memoirs) by Prince Albert I) 95 70

896 Mazarin (painting, Phillippe de Champaigne)

2002. 400th Birth Anniv of Jules Mazarin (cardinal to Louis XIV).
2550 **896** 69c. multicoloured . . . 1·00 75

897 Bust of Napoleon Bonaparte and Medal

2002. Bicentenary of Legion d'Honneur.
2551 **897** 70c. multicoloured . . . 1·00 75

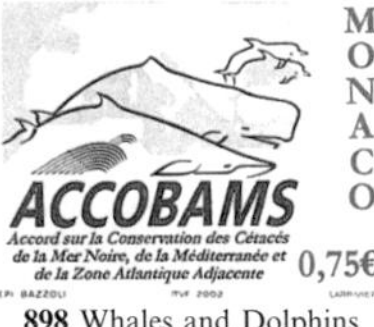

898 Whales and Dolphins

2002. 1st Meeting of Signatories to Agreement on the Conservation of Cetaceans of the Black Sea, Mediterranean Sea and Contiguous Atlantic Area (ACCOBAMS), Monaco.
2552 **898** 75c. multicoloured . . . 1·80 80

899 Da Vinci

2002. 550th Birth Anniv of Leonardo da Vinci (artist).
2553 **899** 76c. multicoloured . . . 1·10 80

900 St. Bernard and Bouvier

2002. International Dog Show, Monte Carlo.
2554 **900** 99c. multicoloured . . . 1·40 1·00

901 Police Officers and Badge

2002. Centenary of Police Force.
2555 **901** 53c. multicoloured . . . 75 55

902 Map of Europe and Flag

2002. 25th Anniv of European Academy of Postal Studies.
2556 **902** 58c. multicoloured . . . 85 60

903 Circus and Globe **904** Emblem

2002. Europa. Circus. Multicoloured.
2557 46c. Type **903** 65 45
2558 46c. "JOURS DE CIRQUE" and performers 65 45

2002. 20th International Swimming Competition.
2559 **904** 64c. multicoloured . . . 95 65

905 Tarmac Roads

2002. Centenary of First Tarmac Roads.
2560 **905** 41c. red, black and brown 60 45

906 Exhibition Hall and Displays **907** Emblem

2002. "Monacophil 2002" International Stamp Exhibition.
2561 **906** 46c. green, violet and red 65 45

2002. 42nd Television Festival, Monte Carlo.
2562 **907** 70c. multicoloured . . . 1·00 75

908 Footballers and Globe

2002. World Cup Football Championship, Japan and South Korea.
2563 **908** 75c. green, blue and red 1·10 80

909 Obverse of 1, 2 and 5 cent Coins and Reverse

2002. Coins.
2564 **909** 46c. copper, red and black 65 45
2565 – 46c. gold, red and black 65 45
2566 – €1.50 multicoloured . . 2·10 1·50
2567 – €1.50 multicoloured . . 2·10 1·50
DESIGNS: Type **909**; 46c. Obverse of 10, 20 and 50 cent coins and reverse; €1.50, Obverse and reverse of 1 euro coin; €1.50, Obverse and reverse of 2 euro coin.

910 Debussy, Pelleas and Melisande

2002. Centenary of First Performance of Claude Debussy's Opera "Pelleas and Melisande".
2568 **910** 69c. green, blue and red 1·00 75

911 Saint Devote, Boat and Dove

2002. Monaco Red Cross.
2569 **911** €1.02 red, greenish blue and black . . . . . . 1·50 1·10

912 Aerial View of Monaco

2002. International Year of Mountains.
2570 **912** €1.37 multicoloured . . 2·00 1·50

913 Hugo **914** Dumas

2002. Birth Bicentenary of Victor Hugo (writer). Each blue, brown and red.
2571 50c. Type **913** 70 50
2572 57c. Scenes from his books 80 60
Nos. 2571/2 were issued together, se-tenant, forming a composite design.

2002. Birth Bicentenary of Alexandre Dumas (writer). Multicoloured.
2573 61c. Type **914** 90 65
2574 61c. Scenes from his books 90 65
Nos. 2573/4 were issued together, se-tenant, forming a composite design.

915 Princess Grace **916** Star-shaped Flower

2002. 26th Publication of "Annales Monegasques" (archives).
2575 **915** €1.75 multicoloured . . 2·50 1·80

2002. Christmas.
2576 **916** 50c. multicoloured . . . 70 50

917 Frame from Film and Melies **918** Magician

2002. Centenary of "Le Voyage dans la Lune" (film by Georges Melies).
2577 **917** 76c. multicoloured . . . 1·10 80

2002. "Magic Stars" Magic Festival, Monte Carlo.
2578 **918** €1.52 multicoloured . . 2·20 1·60

919 1949 Mercedes 220A Cabriolet

2002. Motor Cars from the Royal Collection. Multicoloured.
2579 46c. Type **919** 65 45
2580 69c. 1956 Rolls Royce Silver Cloud . . . . 1·75 75
2581 €1.40 1974 Citroen DS 21 2·00 1·50

920 Spring

2002. Royal Palace (3rd series). Frescoes. Sheet 120 × 100 mm containing T **920** and similar horiz designs showing the Four Seasons. Multicoloured.
MS2582 50c. Type **920**; €1 Summer; €1.50, Autumn; €2 Winter 7·00 5·25

921 Footballer and Golden Ball **923** Flower Arrangement

922 Exhibition Poster

2002. Award of International Philatelic Grand Prix to Luis Figo (footballer and 2001 Golden Ball winner). Centenary of Real Madrid Football Club.
2583 **921** 91c. multicoloured . . . 1·80 30

2002. "MonacoPhil 2002" Stamp Exhibition (2nd issue). Sheet 120 × 82 mm, containing T **922** and similar vert design. Multicoloured. Imperf.
MS2584 €3 Type **922**; €3 Exhibition emblem . . . . . . 8·50 6·50

2002. 36th Monte Carlo Flower Show.
2585 **923** 67c. multicoloured . . . 95 70

924 Princesses Caroline and Stephanie (presidents)

2002. 40th Anniv of "Association Mondiale des Amis de l'Enfance" (children's society).
2586 **924** €1.25 multicoloured . . 1·80 1·30

925 St. George (statue) **926** Prince Louis II, Flag, Arch and Building

2002. 1700th Anniv of St. George's Martyrdom.
2587 **925** 53c. multicoloured . . . 75 55

2002. Bicentenary of Saint-Cyr Imperial Military School.
2588 **926** 61c. multicoloured . . . 90 65

927 Clown **928** Crossed Pennants and Part of Yacht and Crew

2003. 27th International Circus Festival, Monte Carlo.
2589 **927** 59c. multicoloured . . . 80 60

2003. 50th Anniv of Monaco Yacht Club.
2590 **928** 46c. multicoloured . . . 60 45

929 Children

2003. 15th Premiere Rampe (children's circus) Festival.
2591 **929** €2.82 multicoloured . . 3·75 2·75

930 Team Members pushing Bobsleigh

2003. 10th World Bobsleigh Pushing Championship.
2592 **930** 80c. multicoloured . . . 1·00 75

931 Dove, Globe and Prince Albert I **932** Leaves, Spectator, Tennis Court and Player

2003. Centenary of Monaco International Peace Institute.
2593 **931** €1.19 multicoloured 1·60 1·20

2003. Tennis Masters Championship, Monte Carlo.
2594 **932** €1.30 multicoloured . . 1·75 1·30

MONACO
0,79€
Exposition Canine Internationale
ROUGH COLLIE

933 Rough Collie

2003. International Dog Show, Monte Carlo.
2595 **933** 79c. multicoloured . . . 1·00 75

934 Anniversary Emblem

2003. 40th Anniv of Monaco Junior Chamber of Commerce.
2596 **934** 41c. multicoloured . . . 55 40

935 Club Grounds

2003. 75th Anniv of Monte Carlo Country Club.
2597 **935** 46c. multicoloured . . . 60 45

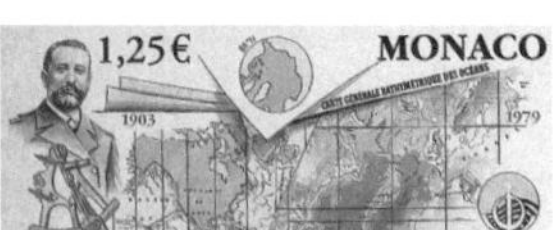

936 Prince Albert I, Sextant, Maps and Emblem (½-size illustration)

2003. Centenary of First General Bathymetric Chart of the Oceans. Multicoloured.
2598 €1.25 Type **936** . . . . . 1·60 1·20
2599 €1.25, Buildings and maps 1·60 1·20
Nos. 2598/9 were issued together, se-tenant, forming a composite design.

937 Girl on Diving Board (Jean-Gabriel Domergue) **938** Castle, Coin and Ship

2003. Europa. Poster Art. Multicoloured.
2600 50c. Type **937** 65 50
2601 50c. Monte-Carlo (Alphonse Mucha) 65 50

2003. Postcard Coin and Stamp Exhibition, Fontvielle.
2602 **938** 45c. multicoloured . . . 60 45

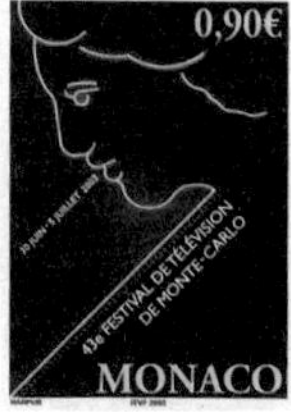

939 Face **940** Bronze Statuette

2003. 43rd International Television Festival.
2603 **939** 90c. multicoloured . . . 1·20 90

2003. 15th Biannual Antique Dealers Meeting.
2604 **940** €1.80 multicoloured . . 2·40 1·80

941 Roald Amundsen and Polar Scene

2003. Centenaries. Multicoloured.
2605 90c. Type **941** (1st crossing of North Pole) . . . . . 1·20 90
2606 €1.80 Wright brothers and *Kitty Hawk* (1st powered flight) . . . . 2·40 1·80

942 Hector Berlioz **944** Hand holding Pipette and DNA Double Helix (50th anniv of discovery)

943 Woman's Head (Francois Boucher) (300th anniv)

2003. Composers Birth Anniversaries.
2607 **942** 75c. black and red . . . 1·00 75
2608 – €1.60 blue, sepia and red . . . . 2·10 1·60
DESIGNS—VERT: Type **942** (bicentenary). HORIZ: €1.60 Aram Khatchaturian (centenary).

2003. Artists' Birth Anniversaries.
2609 **943** €1.30 multicoloured . . 1·75 1·30
2610 – €3 mauve and black . . 4·00 3·00
2611 – €3.60 brown and black 4·75 3·50
DESIGNS: €1.30, Type **943**; €3 Vincent Van Gogh (150th anniv); €3.60, Girolamo Francesco Maria Mazzola (Le Parmigianino) (500th anniv).

2003. Scientific Anniversaries.
2612 **944** 58c. black, blue and red 80 50
2613 – €1.11 chestnut, blue and red . . . . 1·40 1·10
DESIGNS: Type **944**; Alexander Fleming (75th anniv of discovery of penicillin).

945 Nostradamus **946** Magician

2003. 500th Birth Anniv of Michel de Nostre-Dame (Nostradamus) (astrologer).
2614 **945** 70c. multicoloured . . . 40 30

2003. "Magic Stars" Magic Festival, Monte Carlo.
2615 **946** 75c. multicoloured . . . 1·00 75

947 Marie and Pierre Curie

2003. Centenary of Award of Nobel Prize for Physics to Antoine Henri Becquerel and Pierre and Marie Curie.
2616 **947** €1.20 multicoloured . . 1·60 1·20

948 St. Devote kneeling before Cross **950** Star-shaped Flower

949 Edmund Hilary and Mount Everest

2003. 1700th (2004) Anniv of Arrival of St. Devote (patron saint) in Monaco (1st series) . Each blue, black and red.
2617 45c. Type **948** 60 45
2618 45c. St. Devote facing Barbarus 60 45
2619 45c. Boat carrying St. Devote's body 60 45
2620 45c. St. Devote (statue) . . 60 45
See also No. 2626/30.

2003. 50th Anniv of First Ascent of Mount Everest.
2621 **949** €1 multicoloured . . . 1·30 1·00

2003. Christmas.
2622 **950** 50c. multicoloured . . . 65 50

951 Lion and Lion Tamer **952** Exhibition Poster

2003. MonacoPhil 2004 Stamp Exhibition (December 2004).
2623 **951** 50c. multicoloured . . . 65 50

2003. 28th International Circus Festival (January 2004), Monte Carlo.
2624 **952** 70c. multicoloured . . . 95 70

953 Tram and Buildings

2004. Centenary of Beausoleil Municipality.
2625 **953** 75c. multicoloured . . . 1·00 75

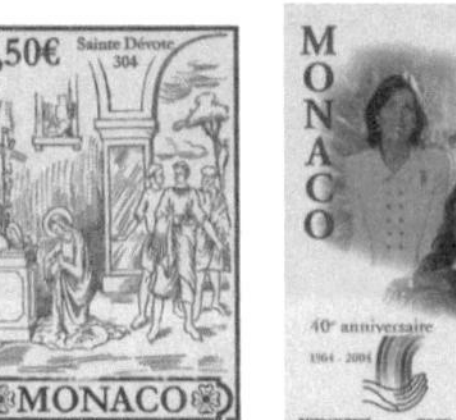

954 St. Devote kneeling before Alta **955** Princesses Grace and Caroline

2004. 1700th Anniv of St. Devote's Arrival (2nd series).
2626 **954** 50c. red and brown . . . 65 50
2627 – 75c. orange and brown (horiz) . . . . 1·00 75
2628 – 90c. brown and deep brown (horiz) . . . . 1·20 90
2629 – €1 brown and deep brown . . . . 1·30 1·00
2630 – €4 purple and brown (horiz) . . . . 5·75 4·25
DESIGNS: 75c. Before Barbarus; 90c. Martyrdom; €1 Boat carrying St. Devote's body; €4 Arrival in Monaco.

2004. 40th Anniv of Princess Grace Foundation.
2640 **955** 50c. multicoloured . . . 65 50

956 Princess Grace and Shamrock Leaf

2004. 20th Anniv of Princess Grace Irish Library.
2641 **956** €1.11 green and brown 1·50 1·10

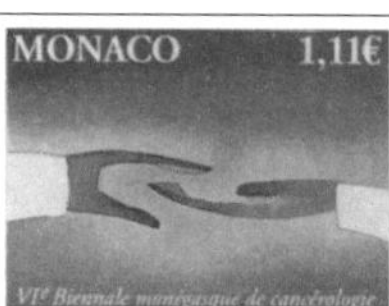

957 Hands

2004. 6th Biennial Oncological Meeting.
2642 **957** €1.11 multicoloured . . 1·50 1·10

958 Princess Grace (statue) (Daphne du Barry) **959** Garden

2004.
2643 **958** €1.45 multicoloured . . 2·00 1·50

2004. 20th Anniv of Princess Grace Rose Garden.
2644 **959** €1.90 multicolured . . . 2·50 1·90

POSTAGE DUE STAMPS

D 3 D 4 D 18

1906.
D 29a **D 3** 1c. green 30 45
D 30 5c. green 40 55
D 31a 10c. red 30 55
D 32 10c. brown £350 £110
D 33 15c. purple on cream 1·75 1·40
D113 20c. bistre on buff . . 30 30
D 34 30c. blue 30 55
D114 40c. mauve 30 30
D 35 50c. brown on buff . . 3·00 3·25
D115 50c. green 30 30
D116 60c. black 30 50
D117 60c. mauve . . . . . 15·00 19·00
D118 1f. purple on cream . . 25 25
D119 2f. red . . . . 60 1·00
D120 3f. red . . . . 60 1·00
D121 5f. blue 60 75

1910.
D36 **D 4** 1c. olive 20 40
D37 10c. lilac 30 40
D38 30c. bistre £150 £150

1919. Surch.
D39 **D 4** 20c. on 10c. lilac . . . . 3·00 4·50
D40 40c. on 30c. bistre . . . 3·00 5·50

1925.
D106 **D 18** 1c. olive 30 35
D107 10c. violet 20 45
D108 30c. bistre 30 55
D109 60c. red 45 65
D110 1f. blue . . . . 60·00 55·00
D111 2f. red . . . . 70·00 75·00

1925. Surch **1 franc a percevoir**.
D112 **D 3** 1f. on 50c. brown on buff 60 70

D 64 D 65

1946.
D327 **D 64** 10c. black 10 10
D328 30c. violet 10 10
D329 50c. blue 10 10
D330 1f. green 20 20
D331 2f. brown 20 25
D332 3f. mauve 20 25
D333 4f. red 30 35
D334 **D 65** 5f. brown 30 25
D335 10f. blue 50 25
D336 20f. turquoise 50 55
D337 50f. red and mauve . . 40·00 48·00
D338 100f. red and green . . 7·50 8·00

D 99 Buddicom Locomotive, 1843

1953.

D478	–	1f. red and green	10	10
D479	–	1f. green and red	10	10
D480	–	2f. turquoise and blue	10	10
D481	–	2f. blue and turquoise	10	10
D482	D 99	3f. lake and green	10	10
D483	–	3f. green and lake	10	10
D484	–	4f. slate and brown	25	25
D485	–	4f. brown and slate	25	25
D486	–	5f. violet and blue	45	45
D487	–	5f. blue and violet	45	45
D488	–	10f. indigo and blue	5·00	6·50
D489	–	10f. blue and indigo	5·00	6·50
D490	–	20f. violet and blue	2·00	3·00
D491	–	20f. blue and violet	2·00	3·00
D492	–	50f. brown and red	5·00	7·50
D493	–	50f. red and brown	5·00	7·50
D494	–	100f. green and purple	8·50	12·00
D495	–	100f. purple and green	8·50	12·00

TRIANGULAR DESIGNS: Nos. D478, Pigeons released from mobile loft; D479, Sikorsky S-51 helicopter; D480, Brig; D481, "United States" (liner); D483, Streamlined steam locomotive; D484, Santos-Dumont's monoplane No. 20 Demoiselle; D485, De Havilland Comet 1 airliner; D486, Old motor car; D487, "Sabre" racing-car; D488, Leonardo da Vinci's flying machine; D489, Postal rocket; D490, Mail balloon, Paris, 1870; D491, Airship "Graf Zeppelin"; D492, Postilion; D493, Motor cycle messenger; D494, Mail coach; D495, Railway mail van.

D 140 18th-century Felucca

1960.

D698	D 140	1c. brown, green & bl	55	55
D699	–	2c. sepia, blue & grn	10	10
D700	–	5c. purple, blk & turq	10	10
D701	–	10c. black, green & bl	10	10
D702	–	20c. purple, grn & bl	1·25	1·25
D703	–	30c. brown, bl & grn	80	80
D704	–	50c. blue, brn & myrtle	1·25	1·50
D705	–	1f. brown, myrtle & bl	1·75	1·75

DESIGNS: 2c. Paddle-steamer "La Palmaria"; 5c. Arrival of first railway train at Monaco; 10c. 15th–16th-century armed messenger; 20c. 18th-century postman; 30c. "Charles III" (paddle-steamer); 50c. 17th-century courier; 1f. Mail coach (19th-century).

D 393 Prince's Seal

D 492 Coat of Arms

1980.

D1426	D 393	5c. red and brown	10	10
D1427		10c. orange and red	10	10
D1428		15c. violet and red	10	10
D1429		20c. green and red	10	10
D1430		30c. blue and red	20	20
D1431		40c. bistre and red	20	20
D1432		50c. violet and red	30	30
D1433		1f. grey and blue	65	65
D1434		2f. brown and black	80	75
D1435		3f. red and green	1·25	1·00
D1436		4f. green and red	1·75	1·50
D1437		5f. brown and mauve	2·10	1·60

1985.

D1712	D 492	5c. multicoloured	10	10
D1713		10c. multicoloured	10	10
D1714		15c. multicoloured	10	10
D1715		20c. multicoloured	10	10
D1716		30c. multicoloured	10	10
D1717		40c. multicoloured	10	20
D1718		50c. multicoloured	10	20
D1719		1f. multicoloured	30	45
D1720		2f. multicoloured	60	65
D1721		3f. multicoloured	1·00	1·25
D1722		4f. multicoloured	1·25	1·40
D1723		5f. multicoloured	1·75	2·00

MONGOLIA Pt. 10

A republic in Central Asia between China and Russia, independent since 1921.

1924. 100 cents = 1 dollar (Chinese).
1926. 100 mung = 1 tugrik.

1 Eldev-Otchir Symbol

2 Soyombo Symbol

1924. Inscr in black.
1 **1** 1c. brown, pink and grey on bistre . . . . 4·00 4·00
2 2c. brown, blue and red on brown . . . . 5·00 3·50
3 5c. grey, red and yellow . . . 25·00 20·00
4 10c. blue and brown on blue 9·00 7·00
5 20c. grey, blue and white on blue . . . . 18·00 10·00
6 50c. red and orange on pink 30·00 18·00
7 $1 bistre, red and white on yellow . . . . 45·00 28·00
Stamps vary in size according to the face value.

1926. Fiscal stamps as T **2** optd **POSTAGE** in frame in English and Mongolian.
8 **2** 1c. blue . . . . 10·00 10·00
9 2c. buff . . . . 10·00 10·00
10 5c. purple . . . . 14·00 12·00
11 10c. green . . . . 18·00 15·00
12 20c. brown . . . . 20·00 17·00
13 50c. brown and yellow . . . £175 £160
14 $1 brown and pink £400 £325
15 $5 red and olive £600
Stamps vary in size according to the face value.

4 State Emblem: Soyombo Symbol

5 State Emblem: Soyombo Symbol

1926. New Currency.
16 **4** 5m. black and lilac . . . . . 4·50 4·50
17 20m. black and blue . . . . 4·00 4·00

1926.
18 **5** 1m. black and yellow . . . . 1·40 80
19 2m. black and brown . . . . 1·60 90
20 5m. black and lilac (A) . . . 2·50 1·40
28 5m. black and lilac (B) . . . 13·00 9·50
21 10m. black and blue . . . . 1·60 1·10
30 20m. black and blue . . . . 14·00 8·00
22 25m. black and green . . . . 4·00 1·75
23 40m. black and yellow . . . 5·75 2·00
24 50m. black and brown . . . 7·00 3·25
25 1t. black, green and brown 18·00 6·50
26 3t. black, yellow and red . . 38·00 30·00
27 5t. black, red and purple . . 60·00 48·00
In (A) the Mongolian numerals are in the upper and in (B) in the lower value tablets.
These stamps vary in size according to the face value.

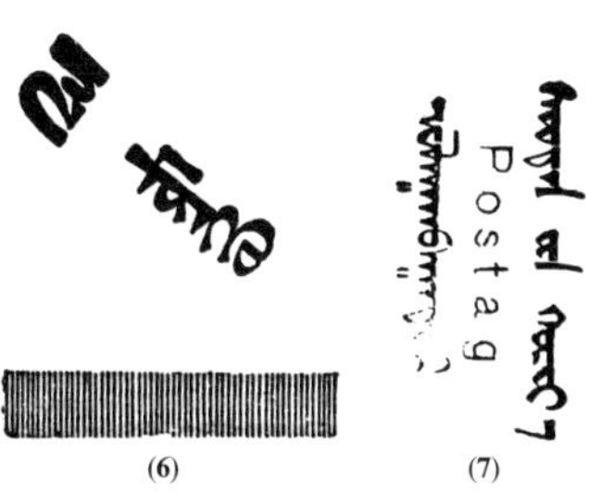
(6) (7)

1930. Surch as T **6**.
32 **5** 10m. on 1m. black & yellow 25·00 25·00
33 20m. on 2m. black & brown 35·00 30·00
34 25m. on 40m. black & yellow 40·00 35·00

1931. Optd with T **7**.
35 **2** 1c. blue . . . . 17·00 8·00
36 2c. buff . . . . 18·00 6·00
37 5c. purple . . . . 25·00 6·00
38 10c. green . . . . 20·00 6·00
39 20c. brown . . . . 32·00 8·50
40 50c. brown and yellow . . . — —
41 $1 brown and pink . . . . . — —

1931. Surch **Postage** and value in **menge**.
43 **2** 5m. on 5c. purple . . . . . 25·00 8·00
44 10m. on 10c. green . . . . . 38·00 20·00
45 20m. on 20c. brown . . . . 50·00 25·00

9 Govt Building, Ulan Bator

11 Sukhe Bator

12 Lake and Mountain Scenery

1932.
46 – 1m. brown . . . . 1·75 1·00
47 – 2m. red . . . . 1·75 1·00
48 – 5m. blue 50 30
49 **9** 10m. green 50 30
50 – 15m. brown 50 30
51 – 20m. red 50 30
52 – 25m. violet 75 30
53 **11** 40m. black 75 40
54 – 50m. blue 50 30
55 **12** 1t. green 90 50
56 – 3t. violet . . . . 2·00 1·25
57 – 5t. brown . . . . 12·00 7·50
58 – 10t. blue . . . . 20·00 13·00
DESIGNS—As Type **9**: 1m. Weavers; 5m. Machinist. As Type **11**: 2m. Telegraphist; 15m. Revolutionary soldier carrying flag; 20m. Mongols learning Latin alphabet; 25m. Soldier; 50m. Sukhe Bator's monument. As Type **12**: 3t. Sheep-shearing; 5t. Camel caravan; 10t. Lassoing wild horses (after painting by Sampilon).

13 Mongol Man

14 Camel Caravan

1943. Network background in similar colour to stamps.
59 **13** 5m. green . . . . 3·50 3·50
60 – 10m. blue . . . . 6·00 3·75
61 – 15m. red . . . . 7·00 5·00
62 **14** 20m. brown . . . . 11·00 9·00
63 – 25m. brown . . . . 11·00 11·00
64 – 30m. red . . . . 12·00 12·00
65 – 45m. purple . . . . 17·00 17·00
66 – 60m. green . . . . 28·00 28·00
DESIGNS—VERT: 10m. Mongol woman; 15m. Soldier; 30m. Arms of the Republic; 45m. Portrait of Sukhe Bator, dated 1894–1923. HORIZ: 25m. Secondary school; 60m. Pastoral scene.

15 Marshal Kharloin Choibalsan

17 Victory Medal

16 Choibalsan and Sukhe Bator

1945. 50th Birthday of Choibalsan.
67 **15** 1t. black . . . . 9·00 8·00

1946. 25th Anniv of Independence. As T **16/17**.
68 – 30m. bistre . . . . 4·50 3·50
69 **16** 50m. purple . . . . 5·50 4·00
70 – 60m. brown . . . . 5·50 5·50
71 – 60m. black . . . . 8·00 5·50
72 **17** 80m. brown . . . . 7·50 7·50
73 – 1t. blue . . . . 11·00 12·00
74 – 2t. brown . . . . 14·00 16·00
DESIGNS—VERT: (21½ × 32 mm): 30m. Choibalsan, aged four. As Type **17**: 60m. (No. 71), Choibalsan when young man; 1t. 25th Anniversary Medal; 2t. Sukhe Bator. HORIZ: As Type **16**: 60m. (No. 70), Choibalsan University.

17a Flags of Communist Bloc

1951. Struggle for Peace.
75 **17a** 1t. multicoloured . . . . . 7·50 7·50

17b Lenin (after P. Vasilev)

1951. Honouring Lenin.
76 **17b** 3t. multicoloured . . . . . 17·00 17·00

18 State Shop

19 Sukhe Bator

1951. 30th Anniv of Independence.
77 – 15m. green on azure . . . . 3·25 3·25
78 **18** 20m. orange . . . . 3·25 3·25
79 – 20m. multicoloured . . . . 3·75 3·75
80 – 25m. blue on azure . . . . 3·75 3·75
81 – 30m. multicoloured . . . . 4·25 4·25
82 – 40m. violet on pink . . . . 4·50 4·50
83 – 50m. brown on azure . . . 9·00 9·00
84 – 60m. black on pink . . . . 8·00 8·00
85 **19** 2t. brown . . . . 15·00 15·00
DESIGNS—HORIZ: (As Type **18**): 15m. Alti Hotel; 40m. State Theatre, Ulan Bator; 50m. Pedagogical Institute. 55½ × 26 mm: 25m. Choibalsan University. VERT: (As Type **19**): 20m. (No. 79); 30m. Arms and flag; 60m. Sukhe Bator Monument.

20 Schoolchildren

1952. Culture.
86 – 5m. brown on pink . . . . 2·00 1·75
87 **20** 10m. blue on pink . . . . . 2·50 2·50
DESIGN: 5m. New houses.

21 Choibalsan in National Costume

22 Choibalsan and Farm Worker

1953. 1st Death Anniv of Marshal Choibalsan. As T **21/22**.
88 **21** 15m. blue . . . . 2·50 2·75
89 **22** 15m. green . . . . 2·50 2·75
90 **21** 20m. green . . . . 5·00 6·00
91 **22** 20m. sepia . . . . 2·50 2·50
92 – 20m. blue . . . . 2·50 2·50
93 – 30m. sepia . . . . 3·25 3·25
94 – 50m. brown . . . . 3·25 3·25
95 – 1t. red . . . . 4·00 4·00
96 – 1t. purple . . . . 4·00 4·00
97 – 2t. red . . . . 4·00 4·00
98 – 3t. purple . . . . 5·00 5·00
99 – 5t. red . . . . 19·00 19·00
DESIGNS: As Type **21**: 1t. (96); 2t. Choibalsan in uniform. 33 × 48 mm: 3, 5t. Busts of Choibalsan and Sukhe Bator. 33 × 46 mm: 50m., 1t. (95), Choibalsan and young pioneer. 48 × 33 mm: 20m. (92); 30m. Choibalsan and factory hand.

23 Arms of the Republic

23a Lenin

1954.
100 **23** 10m. red . . . . 6·50 4·00
101 20m. red . . . . 13·00 5·00
102 30m. red . . . . 6·00 4·50
103 40m. red . . . . 7·00 4·50
104 60m. red . . . . 6·50 4·50

1955. 85th Birth Anniv of Lenin.
105 **23a** 2t. blue . . . . 3·75 2·00

23b Flags of the Communist Bloc

24 Sukhe Bator and Choibalsan

1955. Struggle for Peace.
106 **23b** 60m. multicoloured . . . 1·25 65

1955.
107 **24** 30m. green 30 20
108 – 30m. blue 50 20
109 – 30m. red 40 20
110 – 40m. purple . . . . 1·00 40
111 – 50m. brown . . . . 1·00 45
112 – 1t. multicoloured . . . . . 2·75 1·25
DESIGNS—HORIZ: 30m. blue, Lake Khobsogol; 50m. Choibalsan University. VERT: 30m. red, Lenin Statue, Ulan Bator; 40m. Sukhe Bator and dog; 1t. Arms and flag of the Republic.

24a Steam Train linking Ulan Bator and Moscow

25 Arms of the Republic

1956. Mongol–Soviet Friendship. Multicoloured.
113 1t. Type **24a** . . . . 25·00 13·00
114 2t. Flags of Mongolia and Russia . . . . 4·50 2·75

1956.
115 **25** 20m. brown 50 30
116 30m. brown 65 35
117 40m. blue 80 45
118 60m. green . . . . 1·00 65
119 1t. red . . . . 1·60 80

26 Hunter and Golden Eagle

27 Arms

27a Wrestlers

1956. 35th Anniv of Independence.
120 **26** 30m. brown . . . . . . 25·00 21·00
121 **27** 30m. blue . . . . 5·00 4·00
122 **27a** 60m. green . . . . 15·00 15·00
123 – 60m. orange . . . . . . 15·00 15·00
DESIGN: As Type **26**: 60m. (No. 123), Children. Also inscr "xxxv".

28 29

1958. With or without gum.
124 **28** 20m. red . . . . 1·50 1·00

1958. 13th Mongol People's Revolutionary Party Congress. With or without gum.
125 **29** 30m. red and salmon . . . 3·00 2·25

1958. As T **27a** but without "xxxv". With or without gum.
126 50m. brown on pink . . . . 5·00 3·75

30 Dove and Globe

1958. 4th Congress of International Women's Federation, Vienna. With or without gum.
127 **30** 60m. blue . . . . 3·25 2·00

31 Ibex **32** Yak

1958. Mongolian Animals. As T **31/2**.
128 – 30m. pale blue . . . . . . 6·50 2·10
129 – 30m. turquoise . . . . . . 4·50 2·10
130 **31** 30m. green . . . . 3·00 1·50
131 30m. turquoise . . . . . . 3·00 1·00
132 **32** 60m. bistre . . . . 3·50 2·00
133 60m. orange . . . . 3·50 1·25
134 – 1t. blue . . . . 5·00 2·50
135 – 1t. light blue . . . . 4·00 1·75
136 – 1t. red . . . . 5·00 3·25
137 – 1t. red . . . . 4·00 2·00
DESIGNS—VERT: 30m. (Nos. 128/9), Dalmatian pelicans. HORIZ: 1t. (Nos. 134/5), Yak, facing right; 1t. (Nos. 136/7), Bactrian camels.

33 Goat **34** "Tulaga"

1958. Mongolian Animals.
138 **33** 5m. sepia and yellow . . . 15 10
139 – 10m. sepia and green . . . 20 10
140 – 15m. sepia and lilac . . . 35 10
141 – 20m. sepia and blue . . . 35 10
142 – 25m. sepia and red . . . 40 10
143 – 30m. purple and mauve . . 50 10
144 **33** 40m. green 50 10
145 – 50m. brown and salmon . . 60 20
146 – 60m. blue 80 20
147 – 1t. bistre and yellow . . . 1·75 50
ANIMALS: 10, 30m. Ram; 15, 60m. Stallion; 20, 50m. Bull; 25m., 1t. Bactrian camel.

1959.
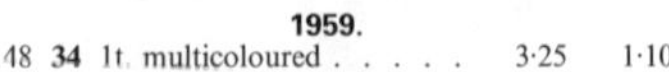
148 **34** 1t. multicoloured . . . . . 3·25 1·10

35 Taming a Wild Horse

1959. Mongolian Sports. Centres and inscriptions multicoloured: frame colours given below.
149 **35** 5m. yellow and orange . . 20 10
150 – 10m. purple 20 10
151 – 15m. yellow and green . . 20 10
152 – 20m. lake and red 25 10
153 – 25m. blue 40 15
154 – 30m. yellow, green & turq 55 15
155 – 70m. red and yellow . . . 70 30
156 – 80m. purple . . . . 1·10 60
DESIGNS: 10m. Wrestlers; 15m. Introducing young rider; 20m. Archer; 25m. Galloping horseman; 30m. Archery contest; 70m. Hunting a wild horse; 80m. Proclaiming a champion.

36 Child Musician

1959. Mongolian Youth Festival (1st issue).
157 **36** 5m. purple and blue . . . 20 10
158 – 10m. brown and green . . 25 10
159 – 20m. green and purple . . 25 10
160 – 25m. blue and green . . . 50 25
161 – 40m. violet and myrtle . . 95 40
DESIGNS—VERT: 10m. Young wrestlers; 20m. Youth on horse; 25m. Artists in national costume. HORIZ: 40m. Festival parade.

37 Festival Badge **38** Kalmuck Script

1959. Mongolian Youth Festival (2nd issue).
162 **37** 30m. purple and blue . . . 30 20

1959. Mongolists' Congress. Designs as T **38** incorporating "MONGOL" in various scripts.
163 – 30m. multicoloured . . . . 5·00 5·00
164 – 40m. red, blue and yellow 5·00 5·00
165 **38** 50m. multicoloured . . . . 7·00 7·00
166 – 60m. red, blue and yellow 11·00 11·00
167 – 1t. yellow, turquoise & orge . . . . 14·00 14·00
SCRIPTS ($29\frac{1}{2}\times42\frac{1}{2}$ mm): 30m. Stylized Ulghur; 40m. Soyombo; 60m. Square (Pagspa). ($21\frac{1}{2}\times31$ mm): 1t. Cyrillic.

39 Military Monument **40** Herdswoman and Lamb

1959. 20th Anniv of Battle of Khalka River.
168 – 40m. red, brown and yellow 55 15
169 **39** 50m. multicoloured 55 15
DESIGN: 40m. Mounted horseman with flag (emblem), inscr "AUGUST 1959 HALHIN GOL".

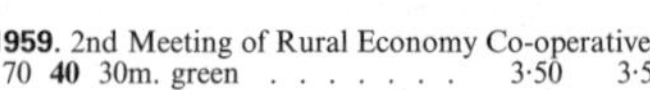
1959. 2nd Meeting of Rural Economy Co-operatives.
170 **40** 30m. green . . . . 3·50 3·50

41 Sable

1959. Mongolian Fauna.
171 **41** 5m. purple, yellow and blue 15 10
172 – 10m. multicoloured 55 10
173 – 15m. black, green and red 45 10
174 – 20m. purple, blue and red 55 15
175 – 30m. myrtle, purple & grn 50 15
176 – 50m. black, blue and green 1·10 30
177 – 1t. black, green and red . . 1·75 40
ANIMALS—HORIZ: (58 × 21 mm): 10m. Common pheasants; 20m. European otter; 50m. Saiga; 1t. Siberian musk deer. As Type **41**: 15m. Muskrat; 30m. Argali.

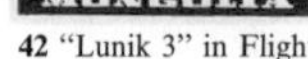

42 "Lunik 3" in Flight **44** "Flower" Emblem

43 Motherhood Badge

1959. Launching of "Lunik 3" Rocket.
178 **42** 30m. yellow and violet . . 65 25
179 – 50m. red, green and blue 80 35
DESIGN—HORIZ: 50m. Trajectory of "Lunik 3" around the Moon.

1960. International Women's Day.
180 **43** 40m. bistre and blue . . . 40 15
181 **44** 50m. yellow, green and blue 70 20

45 Lenin **46** Larkspur

1960. 90th Birth Anniv of Lenin.
182 **45** 40m. red 40 15
183 50m. violet 60 30

1960. Flowers.
184 **46** 5m. blue, green and bistre 10 10
185 – 10m. red, green and orange 10 10
186 – 15m. violet, green and bistre 10 10
187 – 20m. yellow, green and olive 15 10
188 – 30m. violet, green & emer 15 10
189 – 40m. orange, green & violet 35 15
190 – 50m. violet, green and blue 45 20
191 – 1t. mauve, green & lt green 80 40
FLOWERS: 10m. Tulip; 15m. Jacob's ladder; 20m. Asiatic globe flower; 30m. Clustered bellflower; 40m. Grass of Parnassus; 50m. Meadow cranesbill; 1t. "Begonia vansiana".

47 Horse-jumping

1960. Olympic Games. Inscr "ROMA 1960" or "ROMA MCMLX". Centres in greenish grey.
192 **47** 5m. red, black & turquoise 10 10
193 – 10m. violet and yellow . . 10 10
194 – 15m. turquoise, black & red 10 10
195 – 20m. red and blue 10 10
196 – 30m. ochre, black and green 10 10
197 – 50m. blue and turquoise 15 10
198 – 70m. green, black and violet 25 20
199 – 1t. mauve and green . . . 35 25
DESIGNS—DIAMOND SHAPED: 10m. Running; 20m. Wrestling; 50m. Gymnastics; 1t. Throwing the discus. As Type **47**: 15m. Diving; 30m. Hurdling; 70m. High-jumping.

48

1960. Red Cross.
200 **48** 20m. red, yellow and blue 70 25

49 Newspapers

1960. 40th Anniv of Mongolian Newspaper "Unen" ("Truth").
201 **49** 20m. buff, green and red 15 10
202 30m. red, yellow and green 20 15

50 Hoopoe

1961. Mongolian Songbirds.
203 – 5m. mauve, black and green 75 10
204 **50** 10m. red, black and green 85 10
205 – 15m. yellow, black & green 1·00 10
206 – 20m. green, black and bistre . . . . 1·25 15
207 – 50m. blue, black and red 1·75 30
208 – 70m. yellow, black & mauve . . . . 2·00 50
209 – 1t. mauve, orange and black . . . . 2·40 70
BIRDS: As Type **50**: 15m. Golden oriole; 20m. Black-billed capercaillie. Inverted triangulars: 5m. Rose-coloured starling; 50m. Eastern broad-billed roller; 70m. Tibetan sandgrouse; 1t. Mandarin.

51 Foundry Worker **52** Patrice Lumumba

1961. 15th Anniv of World Federation of Trade Unions.
210 **51** 30m. red and black 15 10
211 – 50m. red and violet 20 10
DESIGN—HORIZ: 50m. Hemispheres.

1961. Patrice Lumumba (Congolese politician) Commemoration.
212 **52** 30m. brown . . . . 1·50 1·00
213 50m. purple . . . . 2·00 1·25

53 Bridge **54** Yuri Gagarin with Capsule

1961. 40th Anniv of Independence (1st issue). Mongolian Modernization.
214 **53** 5m. green 10 10
215 – 10m. blue 10 10
216 – 15m. red 10 10
217 – 20m. brown 10 10
218 – 30m. blue 15 10
219 – 50m. green 25 15
220 – 1t. violet 50 30

DESIGNS: 10m. Shoe-maker; 15m. Store at Ulan Bator; 30m. Government Building, Ulan Bator; 50m. Machinist; 1t. Ancient and modern houses. (59 × 20½ mm): 20m. Choibalsan University.
See also Nos. 225/**MS**32a, 233/**MS**241c, **MS**241d, 242/8 and 249/56.

1961. World's First Manned Space Flight. Mult.
221 20m. Type **54** 15 10
222 30m. Gagarin and globe (horiz) 30 10
223 50m. Gagarin in capsule making parachute descent 30 20
224 1t. Globe and Gagarin (horiz) 50 35

55 Postman with Reindeer

1961. 40th Anniv of Independence (2nd issue). Mongolian Postal Service.
225 **55** 5m. red, brown and blue (postage) 15 10
226 – 15m. violet, brown & bistre 30 10
227 – 20m. blue, black and green 20 10
228 – 25m. violet, bistre and green 30 15
229 – 30m. green, black & lav . . 5·00 1·25
MS229a 115 × 90 mm. 5, 10, 15 and 50m. in designs of Nos. 226/9 but new colours . . . . 7·00 5·50

230 – 10m. orange, black and green (air) 35 10
231 – 50m. black, pink and green 1·00 25
232 – 1t. multicoloured . . . . . 1·10 35
MS232a 115 × 90 mm. 20, 25, 30m., 1t. in designs of Nos. 225, 230/2 but new colours . . . . 3·50 3·50
DESIGNS: Postman with—10m. Horses; 15m. Camels; 20m. Yaks; 25m. "Sukhe Bator" (lake steamer); 30m. Diesel mail train; 50m. Ilyushin Il-14M mail plane over map; 1t. Postal emblem.

56 Rams

1961. 40th Anniv of Independence (3rd issue). Animal Husbandry.
233 **56** 5m. black, red and blue . . 10 10
234 – 10m. black, green & purple 10 10
235 – 15m. black, red and green 10 10
236 – 20m. sepia, blue and brown 10 10
237 – 25m. black, yellow & green 15 10
238 – 30m. black, red and violet 15 10
239 – 40m. black, green and red 25 15
240 – 50m. black, brown and blue 30 25
241 – 1t. black, violet and olive 55 40
MS241a 105 × 150 mm. 5, 15 and 40m. in designs of Nos. 241, 237 and 234 but new colours . . . 50 50
MS241b 105 × 150 mm. 25, 50m. and 1t. in designs of Nos. 236, 239 and 240, but new colours 50 50
MS241c 105 × 150 mm. 25, 50m. and 1t. in designs of Nos. 235, 239 and 233 but new colours 50 50
DESIGNS: 10m. Oxen; 15m. Camels; 20m. Pigs and poultry; 25m. Angora goats; 30m. Mongolian horses; 40m. Ewes; 50m. Cows; 1t. Combine-harvester.

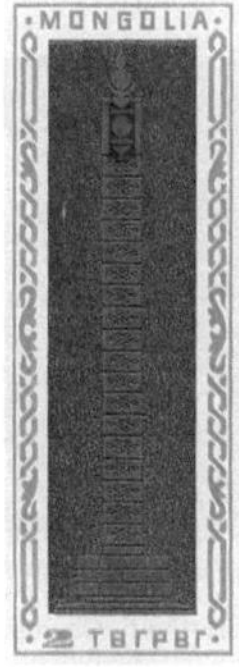

56a

1961. 40th Anniv of Independence (4th issue). Sheet 118 × 128 mm. Imperf.
MS241d 2t. gold, red and blue (pair separated by label) . . . . . . 1·00 1·00

57 Children Wrestling

1961. 40th Anniv of Independence (5th issue). Mongolian Sports.
242 **57** 5m. multicoloured 10 10
243 – 10m. sepia, red and green 10 10
244 – 15m. purple blue and yellow 10 10
245 – 20m. red, black and green 1·10 30
246 – 30m. purple, green & lav 15 10
247 – 50m. indigo, orange & blue 30 20
248 – 1t. purple, blue and grey 35 20
DESIGNS: 10m. Horse-riding; 15m. Children on camel and pony; 20m. Falconry; 30m. Skiing; 50m. Archery; 1t. Dancing.

58 Young Mongol

1961. 40th Anniv of Independence (6th issue). Mongolian Culture.
249 **58** 5m. purple and green . . . 10 10
250 – 10m. blue and red 10 10
251 – 15m. brown and blue . . . 10 10
252 – 20m. green and violet . . . 15 10
253 – 30m. red and blue 20 15
254 – 50m. violet and bistre . . . 40 20
255 – 70m. green and mauve . . 45 25
256 – 1t. red and blue 65 60
DESIGNS—HORIZ. 10m. Mongol chief; 70m. Orchestra; 1t. Gymnast. VERT: 15m. Sukhe Bator Monument; 20m. Young singer; 30m. Young dancer; 50m. Dombra-player.

59 Mongol Arms **60** Congress Emblem

1961. Arms multicoloured; inscr in blue; background colours given.
257 **59** 5m. salmon 10 10
258 10m. lilac 10 10
259 15m. brown 10 10
260 20m. turquoise 10 10
261 30m. ochre 10 10
262 50m. mauve 15 10
263 70m. olive 20 10
264 1t. orange 30 15

1961. 5th World Federation of Trade Unions Congress, Moscow.
265 **60** 30m. red, yellow and blue 15 10
266 50m. red, yellow and sepia 20 10

61 Dove, Map and Globe

1962. Admission of Mongolia to U.N.O.
267 **61** 10m. multicoloured 10 10
268 – 30m. multicoloured 15 10
269 – 50m. multicoloured 20 15
270 – 60m. multicoloured 30 20
271 – 70m. multicoloured 35 30
DESIGNS: 30m. U.N. Emblem and Mongol Arms; 50m. U.N. and Mongol flags; 60m. U.N. Headquarters and Mongolian Parliament building; 70m. U.N. and Mongol flags, and Assembly.

62 Football, Globe and Flags

1962. World Cup Football Championship, Chile. Multicoloured.
272 10m. Type **62** 10 10
273 30m. Footballers, globe and ball 10 10
274 50m. Footballers playing in stadium 20 15
275 60m. Goalkeeper saving goal 25 20
276 70m. Stadium 50 30

63 D. Natsagdorj **64** Torch and Handclasp

1962. 3rd Congress of Mongolian Writers.
277 **63** 30m. brown 15 10
278 50m. green 20 10

1962. Afro-Asian People's Solidarity.
279 **64** 20m. multicoloured 15 10
280 30m. multicoloured 20 10

65 Flags of Mongolia and U.S.S.R. **67** Victory Banner

1962. Mongol–Soviet Friendship.
281 **65** 30m. multicoloured 15 10
282 50m. multicoloured 20 10

1962. Malaria Eradication. Nos. 184/91 optd with Campaign emblem and **LUTTE CONTRE LE PALUDISME**.
283 **46** 5m. 20 20
284 – 10m. 20 20
285 – 15m. 20 20
286 – 20m. 20 20
287 – 30m. 30 30
288 – 40m. 30 30
289 – 50m. 50 50
290 – 1t. 80 80

1962. 800th Birth Anniv of Genghis Khan.
291 **67** 20m. multicoloured . . . . 5·50 5·50
292 – 30m. multicoloured . . . . 5·50 5·50
293 – 50m. black, brown and red 12·00 12·00
294 – 60m. buff, blue and brown 12·00 12·00
DESIGNS: 30m. Engraved lacquer tablets; 50m. Obelisk; 60m. Genghis Khan.

68 Eurasian Perch

1962. Fishes. Multicoloured.
295 5m. Type **68** 10 10
296 10m. Burbot 20 10
297 15m. Arctic grayling 30 10
298 20m. Short-spined seascorpion 40 15
299 30m. Estuarine zander . . . 60 20
300 50m. Siberian sturgeon . . . 95 30
301 70m. Waleck's dace . . . . 1·25 45
302 1t.50 Yellow-winged bullhead 2·25 70

69 Sukhe Bator

1963. 70th Birth Anniv of Sukhe Bator.
303 **69** 30m. blue 15 10
304 60m. lake 20 10

70 Dog "Laika" and "Sputnik 2"

1963. Space Flights. Multicoloured.
305 5m. Type **70** 10 10
306 15m. Rocket blasting off . . 15 10
307 25m. "Lunik 2" (1959) . . . 15 10
308 70m. Nikolaev and Popovich 30 25
309 1t. Rocket "Mars" (1962) . . 40 35
SIZES: As Type **70**: 70m., 1t. VERT: (21 × 70 mm): 15m., 25m.

71 Children packing Red Cross Parcels

1963. Red Cross Centenary Multicoloured.
310 20m. Type **71** 10 10
311 30m. Blood transfusion . . . 15 10
312 50m. Doctor treating child 20 15
313 60m. Ambulance at street accident 25 15
314 1t.30 Centenary emblem . . . 40 20

72 Karl Marx **73** Woman

1963. 145th Birth Anniv of Karl Marx.
315 **72** 30m. blue 15 10
316 60m. lake 20 10

1963. 5th World Congress of Democratic Women, Moscow.
317 **73** 30m. multicoloured 15 10

74 Peacock

1963. Mongolian Butterflies. Multicoloured.
318 5m. Type **74** 30 10
319 10m. Brimstone 35 10
320 15m. Small tortoiseshell . . . 35 15
321 20m. Apollo 55 20
322 30m. Swallowtail 85 25
323 60m. Damon blue . . . . . 1·25 50
324 1t. Poplar admiral . . . . . 1·75 65

75 Globe and Scales of Justice

1963. 15th Anniv of Declaration of Human Rights.

325 **75** 30m. red, blue and brown . . . 15 20
326 60m. black, blue and yellow 25 10

76 Shaggy Ink Cap

1964. Fungi. Multicoloured.

327 5m. Type **76** 25 10
328 10m. Woolly milk cap . . . 35 10
329 15m. Field mushroom . . . 45 15
330 20m. Milk-white russula . . . 50 20
331 30m. Granulated boletus . . 75 30
332 50m. "Lactarius scrobiculatus" . . . . . . 1·00 45
333 70m. Saffron milk cap . . . 1·40 65
334 1t. Variegated boletus . . . . 1·90 85

77 Lenin when a Young Man — **77a** Cross-country Skier

1964. 60th Anniv of London Bolshevik (Communist) Party.

335 **77** 30m. red and brown . . . 45 10
336 50m. ultramarine and blue 50 10

1964. 9th Winter Olympic Games, Innsbruck. Sheet 86 × 72 mm.

MS336a **77a** 4t. black . . . . . 1·00 1·00

78 Gymnastics

1964. Olympic Games, Tokyo. Multicoloured.

337 5m. Type **78** 10 10
338 10m. Throwing the javelin . . 10 10
339 15m. Wrestling 10 10
340 20m. Running 10 10
341 30m. Horse-jumping 10 10
342 50m. High-diving 20 15
343 60m. Cycling 25 20
344 1t. Emblem of Tokyo Games 40 30
MS344a 87 × 77 mm. 4t. black, green and red (Wrestlers–Horiz 38 × 28 mm) . . . . 1·00 1·00

79 Congress Emblem

1964. 4th Mongolian Women's Congress.

345 **79** 30m. multicoloured 20 10

80 "Lunik 1"

1964. Space Research. Multicoloured.

346 5m. Type **80** 10 10
347 10m. "Vostoks 1 and 2" . . 10 10
348 15m. "Tiros" (vert) 10 10
349 20m. "Cosmos" (vert) . . . 10 10
350 30m. "Mars Probe" (vert) . . 10 10
351 60m. "Luna 4" (vert) 20 15
352 80m. "Echo 2" 30 20
353 1t. Radio telescope 35 25

81 Horseman and Flag

1964. 40th Anniv of Mongolian Constitution.

354 **81** 25m. multicoloured 20 10
355 50m. multicoloured 30 10

81a Austrian and Mongolian stamps encircling Globe

1965. "WPIA" Stamp Exhibition, Vienna. Sheet 90 × 130 mm.

MS355a **81a** 4t. red . . . . . . 1·00 1·00

82 Marine Exploration

1965. International Quiet Sun Year. Multicoloured.

356 5m. Type **82** (postage) . . . 40 10
357 10m. Weather balloon . . . 15 10
358 60m. Northern Lights 60 20
359 80m. Geomagnetic emblems 70 25
360 1t. Globe and I.Q.S.Y. emblem . . . . 1·10 50
361 15m. Weather satellite (air) 40 10
362 20m. Antarctic exploration 3·00 55
363 30m. Space exploration . . . 55 15

83 Horses Grazing

1965. Mongolian Horses. Multicoloured.

364 5m. Type **83** 15 10
365 10m. Hunting with golden eagles 50 20
366 15m. Breaking-in wild horse 20 10
367 20m. Horses racing 20 10
368 30m. Horses jumping 25 10
369 60m. Hunting wolves 30 25
370 80m. Milking a mare 40 30
371 1t. Mare and colt 70 40

84 Farm Girl with Lambs

1965. 40th Anniv of Mongolian Youth Movement.

372 **84** 5m. orange, bistre and green 10 10
373 – 10m. bistre, blue and red 10 10
374 – 20m. ochre, red and violet 20 15
375 – 30m. lilac, brown and green 30 20
376 – 50m. orange, buff and blue 55 35

DESIGNS: 10m. Young drummers; 20m. Children around campfire; 30m. Young wrestlers; 50m. Emblem.

85 Chinese Perch

1965. Mongolian Fishes. Multicoloured.

377 5m. Type **85** 25 10
378 10m. Lenok 25 10
379 15m. Siberian sturgeon . . . 30 15
380 20m. Taimen 45 15
381 30m. Banded catfish 75 20
382 60m. Amur catfish . . . . . 1·10 20
383 80m. Northern pike . . . . 1·25 40
384 1t. Eurasian perch . . . . . 1·75 60

86 Marx and Lenin — **87** I.T.U. Emblem and Symbols

1965. Organization of Socialist Countries' Postal Administrations Conference, Peking.

385 **86** 10m. black and red 15 10

1965. Air. I.T.U. Centenary.

386 **87** 30m. blue and bistre . . . 15 10
387 50m. red, bistre and blue 20 10
MS387a 86 × 130 mm. 4t. blue, black and gold (Communications satellite, 38 × 51mm) . . . . . 1·00 1·00

88 Sable

1966. Mongolian Fur Industry.

388 **88** 5m. purple, black & yellow 10 10
389 – 10m. brown, black and grey 10 10
390 – 15m. brown, black and blue 35 10
391 – 20m. multicoloured 20 10
392 – 30m. brown, black & mauve 25 10
393 – 60m. brown, black & green 40 25
394 – 80m. multicoloured 60 40
395 – 1t. blue, black and olive . . 1·40 50

DESIGNS (Fur animals): HORIZ: 10m. Red fox; 30m. Pallas's cat; 60m. Beech marten. VERT: 15m. European otter; 20m. Cheetah; 80m. Stoat; 1t. Woman in fur coat.

89 W.H.O. Building

1966. Inauguration of W.H.O. Headquarters, Geneva.

396 **89** 30m. blue, gold and green 15 10
397 50m. blue, gold and red . . 25 10

90 Footballers

91

1966. World Cup Football Championship. Multicoloured.

398 10m. Type **90** 10 10
399 30m. Footballers (different) 10 10
400 60m. Goalkeeper saving goal 15 15
401 80m. Footballers (different) 30 20
402 1t. World Cup flag 50 35
MS403 **91** 4t. brown and grey . . 1·00 1·00

92 Sukhe Bator and Parliament Buildings, Ulan Bator

1966. 15th Mongolian Communist Party Congress.

404 **92** 30m. multicoloured 20 10

93 Wrestling — **95** State Emblem

94 "Luna 10", Globe and Moon

1966. World Wrestling Championships, Toledo (Spain). Similar wrestling designs.

405 **93** 10m. black, mauve & purple 10 10
406 – 30m. black, mauve and grey 10 15
407 – 60m. black, mauve & brown 20 15

408 – 80m. black, mauve and lilac	30	20
409 – 1t. black, mauve & turq	40	20

1966. Air. "Luna 10" Commemoration. Sheet 84 × 130 mm.

MS410 **94** 4t. multicoloured	2·40	2·40

1966. 45th Anniv of Independence. Mult.

411 30m. Type **95**	1·25	50
412 50m. Sukhe Bator, emblems of agriculture and industry (horiz)	2·75	75

96 "Physochlaena physaloides"

1966. Flowers. Multicoloured.

413 5m. Type **96**	10	10
414 10m. Onion	15	10
415 15m. Red lily	20	10
416 20m. "Thermopsis lanceolata"	25	10
417 30m. "Amygdalus mongolica"	40	20
418 60m. Bluebeard	50	30
419 80m. "Piptanthus mongolicus"	60	40
420 1t. "Iris bungei"	85	55

1966. 60th Birth Anniv of D. Natsagdorj. Nos. 277/8 optd **1906 1966**.

420a **63** 30m. brown	6·50	6·50
420b 50m. green	6·50	6·50

97 Child with Dove

1966. Children's Day. Multicoloured.

421 10m. Type **97**	10	10
422 15m. Children with reindeer (horiz)	10	10
423 20m. Boys wrestling	10	10
424 30m. Boy riding horse (horiz)	20	10
425 60m. Children on camel	30	15
426 80m. Shepherd boy with sheep (horiz)	35	15
427 1t. Boy archer	70	40

98 "Proton 1"

1966. Space Satellites. Multicoloured.

428 5m. "Vostok 2" (vert)	10	10
429 10m. Type **98**	10	10
430 15m. "Telstar 1" (vert)	10	10
431 20m. "Molniya 1" (vert)	10	10
432 30m. "Syncom 3" (vert)	10	10
433 60m. "Luna 9" (vert)	20	15
434 80m. "Luna 12" (vert)	30	20
435 1t. Mars and photographs taken by "Mariner 4"	35	25

99 Tarbosaurus

1966. Prehistoric Animals. Multicoloured.

436 5m. Type **99**	20	10
437 10m. Talararus	20	10
438 15m. Protoceratops	30	15
439 20m. Indricotherium	30	15
440 30m. Saurolophus	50	20
441 60m. Mastodon	75	30
442 80m. Mongolotherium	90	45
443 1t. Mammuthus	1·00	70

100 Congress Emblem

101 Sukhe Bator and Mongolian and Soviet Soldiers

1967. 9th International Students' Union Congress.

444 **100** 30m. ultramarine and blue	15	10
445 50m. blue and pink	25	15

1967. 50th Anniv of October Revolution.

446 **101** 40m. multicoloured	25	20
447 – 60m. multicoloured	35	25

DESIGN: 60m. Lenin, and soldiers with sword.

102 Vietnamese Mother and Child

1967. Help for Vietnam.

448 **102** 30m.+20m. brown, red and blue	20	10
449 50m.+30m. brown, blue and red	30	15

103 Figure Skating

1967. Winter Olympic Games, Grenoble. Mult.

450 5m. Type **103**	10	10
451 10m. Speed skating	10	10
452 15m. Ice hockey	10	10
453 20m. Skijumping	15	10
454 30m. Bob sleighing	15	10
455 60m. Figure skating (pairs)	30	25
456 80m. Downhill skiing	40	30
MS457 92 × 92 mm. 4t. Figure skating (different)	1·00	1·00

104 Bactrian Camel and Calf

1968. Young Animals. Multicoloured.

458 5m. Type **104**	15	10
459 10m. Yak	15	10
460 15m. Lamb	20	10
461 20m. Foal	30	10
462 30m. Calf	30	10
463 60m. Bison	40	15
464 80m. Roe deer	55	30
465 1t. Reindeer	80	40

105 Prickly Rose

ДЭХБ
20 ЖИЛ
WHO
(**106**)

1968. Mongolian Berries.

466 **105** 5m. ultramarine on blue	15	10
467 – 10m. brown on buff	15	10
468 – 15m. emerald on green	20	10
469 – 20m. red on cream	20	10
470 – 30m. red on pink	25	10
471 – 60m. brown on orange	45	20
472 – 80m. turquoise on blue	60	25
473 – 1t. red on cream	80	40

DESIGNS: 10m. Blackcurrant; 15m. Gooseberry; 20m. Crab-apple; 30m. Strawberry; 60m. Redcurrant; 80m. Cowberry; 1t. Sea buckthorn.

1968. 20th Anniv of World Health Organization. Nos. 396/7 optd with T **106**.

474 **89** 30m. blue, gold and green	2·50	2·50
475 50m. blue, gold and red	2·50	2·50

107 Human Rights Emblem

1968. Human Rights Year.

476 **107** 30m. green and blue	15	10

108 "Das Kapital"

1968. 150th Birth Anniv of Karl Marx. Mult.

477 30m. Type **108**	15	10
478 50m. Karl Marx	25	15

109 "Portrait of Artist Sharab" (A. Sangatzohyo)

1968. Mongolian Paintings. Multicoloured.

479 5m. Type **109**	15	10
480 10m. "On Remote Roads" (A. Sangatzohyo)	20	10
481 15m. "Camel Calf" (B. Avarzad)	30	10
482 20m. "The Milk" (B. Avarzad)	40	15
483 30m. "The Bowman" (B. Gombosuren)	55	30
484 80m. "Girl Sitting on a Yak" (A. Sangatzohyo)	95	55
485 1t.40 "Cagan Dara Ekke" (Janaivajara)	1·90	1·00
MS486 120 × 86 mm. 4t. "Meeting" (A. Sangatzohyo) (horiz)	4·25	4·25

110 Volleyball

1968. Olympic Games, Mexico. Multicoloured.

487 5m. Type **110**	10	10
488 10m. Wrestling	10	10
489 15m. Cycling	10	10
490 20m. Throwing the javelin	10	10
491 30m. Football	10	10
492 60m. Running	20	15
493 80m. Gymnastics	30	20
494 1t. Weightlifting	35	25
MS495 92 × 92 mm. 4t. Horse-jumping	1·00	1·00

111 Hammer and Spade

112 Gorky

1968. 7th Anniv of Darkhan Town.

496 **111** 50m. orange and blue	15	10

1968. Birth Centenary of Maksim Gorky (writer).

497 **112** 60m. ochre and blue	15	10

113 "Madonna and Child" (Boltraffio)

1968. 20th Anniv (1966) of U.N.E.S.C.O. Paintings by European Masters in National Gallery, Budapest. Multicoloured.

498 5m. Type **113**	20	10
499 10m. "St. Roch healed by an angel" (Moretto of Brescia)	25	10
500 15m. "Madonna and Child with St. Anne" (Macchietti)	35	10
501 20m. "St. John on Patmos" (Cano)	45	15
502 30m. "Young lady with viola da gamba" (Kupetzky)	50	15
503 80m. "Study of a head" (Amerling)	80	50
504 1t.40 "The death of Adonis" (Furini)	1·60	75
MS505 80 × 120 mm. 4t. "Portrait of a Lady" (Renoir)	4·25	4·25

114 Paavo Nurmi (running)

1969. Olympic Games' Gold-medal Winners. Multicoloured.

506 5m. Type **114**	10	10
507 10m. Jesse Owens (running)	10	10
508 15m. F. Blankers-Koen (hurdling)	10	10
509 20m. Laszlo Papp (boxing)	10	10
510 30m. Wilma Rudolph (running)	10	10
511 60m. Boris Sahlin (gymnastics)	20	10
512 80m. D. Schollander (swimming)	25	15
513 1t. A. Nakayama (ring exercises)	35	25

115 Bayit Costume (woman)

1969. Mongolian Costumes. Multicoloured.

515 5m. Type **115**	10	10
516 10m. Torgut (man)	15	10
517 15m. Sakhchin (woman)	20	10
518 20m. Khalka (woman)	30	10
519 30m. Daringanga (woman)	35	15
520 60m. Mingat (woman)	50	20
521 80m. Khalka (man)	65	25
522 1t. Barga (woman)	1·10	40

116 Emblem and Helicopter Rescue

1969. 30th Anniv of Mongolian Red Cross.
523 **116** 30m. red and blue 60 20
524 – 50m. red and violet . . . 50 25
DESIGN: 50m. Shepherd and ambulance.

117 Yellow Lion's-foot

1969. Landscapes and Flowers. Multicoloured.
525 5m. Type **117** 15 10
526 10m. Variegated pink 15 10
527 15m. Superb pink 25 10
528 20m. Meadow cranesbill . . 25 10
529 30m. Mongolian pink 45 15
530 60m. Asiatic globe flower . . 50 15
531 80m. Long-lipped larkspur 70 30
532 1t. Saxaul 85 40

118 "Bullfight" (O. Tsewegdjaw)

1969. 10th Anniv of Co-operative Movement. Paintings in National Gallery, Ulan Bator. Mult.
533 5m. Type **118** 10 10
534 10m. "Colts Fighting" (O. Tsewegdjaw) 10 10
535 15m. "Horse-herd" (A. Sengetsohyo) 20 10
536 20m. "Camel Caravan" (D. Damdinsuren) 20 10
537 30m. "On the Steppe" (N. Tsultem) 35 15
538 60m. "Milking Mares" (O. Tsewegdjaw) 40 15
539 80m. "Off to School" (B. Avarzad) 50 30
540 1t. "After Work" (G. Odon) 80 40
MS541 121 × 85 mm. 4t. "Horse-herd" (D. Damdinsuren) (60 × 40 mm) . . . . 2·75 2·75

119 Astronaut and Module on Moon

1969. Air. First Man on the Moon. Sheet 86 × 121 mm.
MS542 **119** 4t. multicoloured . . 2·50 2·50

120 Army Crest

БНМАУ-ыг
тунхагласны
45
жилийн ой
1969—XI—26
(121)

1969. 30th Anniv of Battle of Khalka River.
543 **120** 50m. multicoloured . . . 15 10

1969. 45th Anniv of Mongolian People's Republic. Nos. 411/12 optd with T **121**.
544 **95** 30m. multicoloured . . . . 3·75 3·75
545 – 50m. multicoloured . . . . 5·25 5·25

122 "Sputnik 3"

1969. Exploration of Space. Multicoloured.
546 5m. Type **122** 10 10
547 10m. "Vostok 1" 10 10
548 15m. "Mercury 7" 10 10
549 20m. Space-walk from "Voskhod 2" 10 10
550 30m. "Apollo 8" in Moon orbit 15 10
551 60m. Space-walk from "Soyuz 5" 30 20
552 80m. "Apollo 12" and Moon landing 40 30
MS553 108 × 77 mm. 4t. "Apollo 12" . . . . 1·00 1·00

123 Wolf

1970. Wild Animals. Multicoloured.
554 5m. Type **123** 20 10
555 10m. Brown bear 40 10
556 15m. Lynx 50 10
557 20m. Wild boar 50 10
558 30m. Elk 55 20
559 60m. Bobak marmot 65 20
560 80m. Argali 75 35
561 1t. "Hun Hunter and Hound" (tapestry) 90 50

124 "Lenin Centenary" (silk panel, Cerenhuu)

1970. Birth Centenary of Lenin. Multicoloured.
562 20m. Type **124** 15 10
563 50m. "Mongolians meeting Lenin" (Sangatzohyo) (horiz) 20 10
564 1t. "Lenin" (Mazhig) 35 15

125 "Fairy Tale" Pavilion

1970. "EXPO 70" World Trade Fair, Osaka, Japan. Multicoloured.
565 1t.50 Type **125** 50 45
MS566 111 × 81 mm. 4t. Matsushita Pavilion and "Time Capsule" (51 × 38 mm) . . . . 3·50 3·50

126 Footballers

1970. World Cup Football Championship, Mexico.
567 **126** 10m. multicoloured . . . 10 10
568 – 20m. multicoloured . . . 10 10
569 – 30m. multicoloured . . . 10 10
570 – 50m. multicoloured . . . 10 10
571 – 60m. multicoloured . . . 15 10
572 – 1t. multicoloured 30 20
573 – 1t.30 multicoloured . . . 35 25
MS574 122 × 95 mm 4t. multicoloured (50 × 37 mm) . . 1·00 1·00
DESIGNS: Nos. 568/**MS**574, Different football scenes.

127 Common Buzzard

1970. Birds of Prey. Multicoloured.
575 10m. Type **127** 75 15
576 20m. Tawny owls . . . . . 1·00 15
577 30m. Northern goshawk . . 1·25 20
578 50m. White-tailed sea eagle 1·90 30
579 60m. Peregrine falcon . . . . 1·90 60
580 1t. Common kestrels . . . . 2·10 65
581 1t.30 Black kite . . . . . . 2·50 80

128 Soviet Memorial, Berlin-Treptow

1970. 25th Anniv of Victory in Second World War.
582 **128** 60m. multicoloured . . . 15 10

129 Mongol Archery

1970. Mongolian Traditional Life. Multicoloured.
583 10m. Type **129** 30 15
584 20m. Bodg-gegeen's Palace, Ulan Bator 30 15
585 30m. Mongol horsemen . . . 30 20
586 40m. "The White Goddess-Mother" 30 25
587 50m. Girl in National costume 65 45
588 60m. "Lion's Head" (statue) 75 45
589 70m. Dancer's mask 85 65
590 80m. Gateway, Bogd-gegeen's Palace . . . . 1·00 1·00

130 Frogmen boarding "Apollo 13"

1970. Safe Return of "Apollo 13" Spacecraft. Sheet 110 × 80 mm.
MS591 **130** 4t. multicoloured . . 1·00 1·00

131 I.E.Y. and U.N. Emblems with Flag

1970. International Education Year.
592 **131** 60m. multicoloured . . . 35 15

132 Horseman, "50" and Sunrise

1970. 50th Anniv of National Press.
593 **132** 30m. multicoloured . . . 25 10

133 "Vostok 3" and "4"

1971. Space Research. Multicoloured.
594 10m. Type **133** 10 10
595 20m. Space-walk from "Voskhod 2" 10 10
596 30m. "Gemini 6" and "7" . . 10 10
597 50m. Docking of "Soyuz 4" and "5" 10 10
598 60m. "Soyuz 6", "7" and "8" 15 10
599 80m. "Apollo 11" and lunar module 20 15
600 1t. "Apollo 13" damaged . . 25 20
601 1t.30 "Luna 16" 30 25
MS602 120 × 90 mm. 4t. Satellite communications station, Ulan Bator . . . . 2·10 2·10
No. 594 is incorrectly inscribed "Vostok 2-3". The date refers to flight of "Vostoks 3" and "4".

134 Sukhe Bator addressing Meeting

1971. 50th Anniv of Revolutionary Party. Mult.
603 30m. Type **134** 10 10
604 60m. Horseman with flag . . 15 10
605 90m. Sukhe Bator with Lenin 25 15
606 1t.20 Mongolians with banner 40 25

135 "Lunokhod 1"

1971. Exploration of the Moon. Sheet 114 × 95 mm containing T **135** and similar vert design. Multicoloured.
MS607 2t. × 2 (a) Type **135**; (b) "Apollo 14" module on Moon 1·90 1·90

136 Tsam Mask

1971. Mongol Tsam Masks.
608 **136** 10m. multicoloured . . . 15 10
609 – 20m. multicoloured . . . 25 10
610 – 30m. multicoloured . . . 30 10
611 – 50m. multicoloured . . . 35 15
612 – 60m. multicoloured . . . 45 20
613 – 1t. multicoloured 80 30
614 – 1t.30 multicoloured . . . 1·00 50
DESIGNS: Nos. 609/14, Different dance masks.

137 Banner and Party Emblems

1971. 16th Revolutionary Party Congress.

615 **137**	60m. multicoloured	15	10

138 Steam Locomotive

1971. "50 Years of Transport Development". Multicoloured.

616	20m. Type **138**	70	10
617	30m. Diesel locomotive	70	10
618	40m. Russian "Urals" lorry	65	15
619	50m. Russian "Moskovich 412" car	75	15
620	60m. Polikarpov Po-2 biplane	90	25
621	80m. Antonov An-24B airliner	1·10	40
622	1t. Lake steamer "Sukhe Bator"	2·00	70

139 Soldier

1971. 50th Anniv of People's Army and Police. Multicoloured.

623	60m. Type **139**	10	10
624	1t.50 Policeman and child	40	15

140 Emblem and Red Flag

1971. 50th Anniv of Revolutionary Youth Organization.

625 **140**	60m. multicoloured	20	10

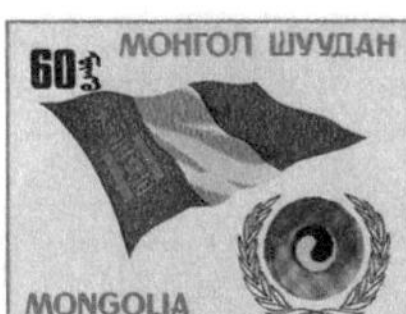

141 Mongolian Flag and Year Emblem

1971. Racial Equality Year.

626 **141**	60m. multicoloured	15	10

142 "The Old Man and the Tiger"

1971. Mongolian Folk Tales. Multicoloured.

627	10m. Type **142**	20	10
628	20m. "The Boy Giant-killer"	20	10
629	30m. Cat and mice	20	10
630	50m. Mongolians riding on eagle	25	10
631	60m. Girl on horseback ("The Wise Bride")	40	15
632	80m. King and courtiers with donkey	55	20
633	1t. Couple kneeling before empty throne ("Story of the Throne")	80	25
634	1t.30 "The Wise Bird"	95	40

143 Yaks

1971. Livestock Breeding. Multicoloured.

635	20m. Type **143**	20	10
636	30m. Bactrian camels	20	10
637	40m. Sheep	25	10
638	50m. Goats	40	10
639	60m. Cattle	50	20
640	80m. Horses	60	25
641	1t. Pony	95	45

144 Cross-country Skiing

1972. Winter Olympic Games, Sapporo, Japan. Multicoloured.

642	10m. Type **144**	10	10
643	20m. Bobsleighing	10	10
644	30m. Figure skating	10	10
645	50m. Slalom skiing	10	10
646	60m. Speed skating	15	10
647	80m. Downhill skiing	20	15
648	1t. Ice hockey	25	15
649	1t.30 Pairs figure skating	30	20
MS650	110 × 90 mm. 4t. Ski jumping (50 × 38 mm)	1·00	1·00

145 "Horse-breaking" (A. Sengatzohyo)

1972. Paintings by Contemporary Artists from the National Gallery, Ulan Bator. Multicoloured.

651	10m. Type **145**	15	10
652	20m. "Black Camel" (A. Sengatzohyo)	20	10
653	30m. "Jousting" (A. Sengatzohyo)	25	10
654	50m. "Wrestling Match" (A. Sengatzohyo)	30	10
655	60m. "Waterfall" (A. Sengatzohyo)	40	10
656	80m. "Old Musician" (U. Yadamsuren)	50	20
657	1t. "Young Musician" (U. Yadamsuren)	60	25
658	1t.30 "Ancient Prophet" (B. Avarzad)	85	40

146 "Apollo 16"

1972. Air. "Co-operation in Space Exploration". Sheet 111 × 90 mm.

MS659 **146**	4t. multicoloured	2·75	2·75

147 "Calosoma fischeri" (ground beetle)

1972. Beetles. Multicoloured.

660	10m. Type **147**	20	10
661	20m. "Mylabris mongolica" (blister beetle)	25	10
662	30m. "Sternoplax zichyi" (mealworm beetle)	30	10
663	50m. "Rhaebus komarovi" (snout weevil)	40	15
664	60m. "Meloe centripubens" (oil beetle)	55	15
665	80m. "Eodorcadion mongolicum" (longhorn beetle)	75	25
666	1t. "Platyope maongolica" (mealworm beetle)	90	30
667	1t.30 "Lixus nigrolineatus" (weevil)	1·40	50

148 Przhevalsli's Wild Horse

1972. Air. Centenary of Discovery of Wild Horse Species by Nikolai Przhevalski. Sheet 115 × 90 mm.

MS668 **148**	4t. multicoloured	7·00	6·00

149 Satellite and Dish Aerial ("Telecommunications")

1972. Air. National Achievements. Multicoloured.

669	20m. Type **149**	10	10
670	30m. Horse-herd ("Livestock Breeding")	20	10
671	40m. Diesel train and Tupolev Tu-144 jetliner ("Transport")	95	10
672	50m. Corncob and farm ("Agriculture")	25	15
673	60m. Ambulance and hospital ("Public Health")	60	15
674	80m. Actors ("Culture")	60	20
675	1t. Factory ("Industry")	65	30

150 Globe, Flag and Dish Aerial

1972. Air. World Telecommunications Day.

676 **150**	60m. multicoloured	25	15

151 Running

1972. Olympic Games, Munich. Multicoloured.

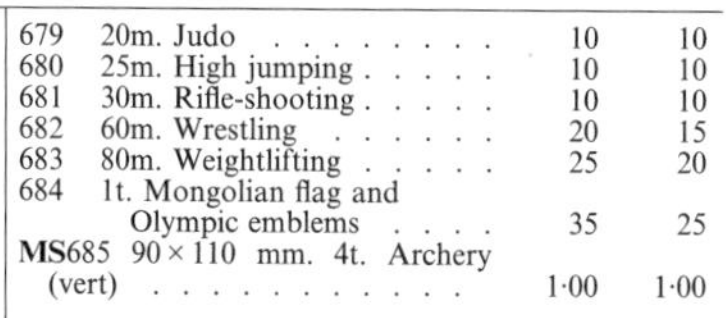

677	10m. Type **151**	10	10
678	15m. Boxing	10	10
679	20m. Judo	10	10
680	25m. High jumping	10	10
681	30m. Rifle-shooting	10	10
682	60m. Wrestling	20	15
683	80m. Weightlifting	25	20
684	1t. Mongolian flag and Olympic emblems	35	25
MS685	90 × 110 mm. 4t. Archery (vert)	1·00	1·00

152 E.C.A.F.E. Emblem

1972. 25th Anniv of E.C.A.F.E.

686 **152**	60m. blue, gold and red	20	10

153 Mongolian Racerunner

1972. Reptiles. Multicoloured.

687	10m. Type **153**	20	10
688	15m. Radde's toad	25	10
689	20m. Halys viper	35	10
690	25m. Toad-headed agama	40	15
691	30m. Asiatic grass frog	55	15
692	60m. Plate-tailed geckol	70	25
693	80m. Steppe ribbon snake	85	35
694	1t. Mongolian agama	1·25	55

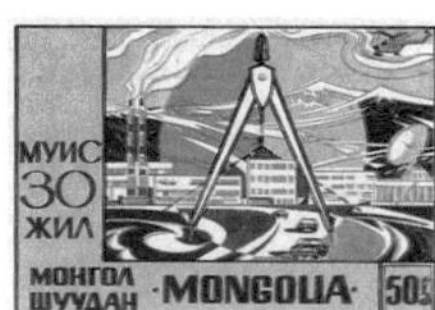

154 "Technical Knowledge"

1972. 30th Anniv of Mongolian State University. Multicoloured.

695	50m. Type **154**	15	10
696	60m. University building	20	10

155 "Madonna and Child with St. John the Baptist and a Holy Woman" (Bellini)

1972. Air. U.N.E.S.C.O. "Save Venice" Campaign. Paintings. Multicoloured.

697	10m. Type **155**	15	10
698	20m. "The Transfiguration" (Bellini) (vert)	20	10
699	30m. "Blessed Virgin with the Child" (Bellini) (vert)	25	10
700	50m. "Presentation of the Christ in the Temple" (Bellini)	40	15
701	60m. "St. George" (Bellini) (vert)	50	20
702	80m. "Departure of Ursula" (detail, Carpaccio) (vert)	65	35
703	1t. "Departure of Ursula" (different detail, Carpaccio)	85	45
MS704	90 × 111 mm. 3t.+1t. As No. 703	4·00	4·00

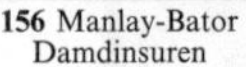

156 Manlay-Bator Damdinsuren

157 Spassky Tower, Moscow Kremlin

1972. National Heroes. Multicoloured.

705 10m. Type **156** 10 10
706 20m. Ard Ayus in chains (horiz) 20 10
707 50m. Hatan-Bator Magsarzhav 30 15
708 60m. Has-Bator on the march (horiz) 40 20
709 1t. Sukhe Bator 70 30

1972. 50th Anniv of U.S.S.R.

710 **157** 60m. multicoloured . . . 25 15

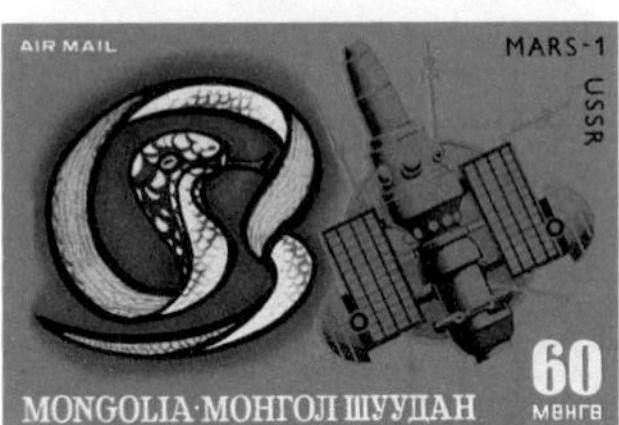

158 Snake and "Mars 1"

1972. Air. Animal Signs of the Mongolian Calendar and Progress in Space Exploration. Multicoloured.

711 60m. Type **158** 70 25
712 60m. Horse and "Apollo 8" (square) 70 25
713 60m. Sheep and "Electron 2" (square) 70 25
714 60m. Monkey and "Explorer 6" 70 25
715 60m. Dragon and "Mariner 2" 70 25
716 60m. Pig and "Cosmos 110" (square) 70 25
717 60m. Dog and "Ariel 2" (square) 70 25
718 60m. Cockerel and "Venus 1" 70 25
719 60m. Hare and "Soyuz 5" . . 70 25
720 60m. Tiger and "Gemini 7" (square) 70 25
721 60m. Ox and "Venus 4" (square) 70 25
722 60m. Rat and "Apollo 15" lunar rover 70 25

The square designs are size 40 × 40 mm.

159 Swimming Gold Medal (Mark Spitz, U.S.A.)

1972. Gold Medal Winners, Munich Olympic Games. Multicoloured.

723 5m. Type **159** 10 10
724 10m. High jumping (Ulrike Meyfarth, West Germany) 10 10
725 20m. Gymnastics (Savao Kato, Japan) 10 10
726 30m. Show jumping (Andras Balczo, Hungary) 10 10
727 60m. Running (Lasse Viren, Finland) 25 15
728 80m. Swimming (Shane Gould, Australia) 35 20
729 1t. Putting the shot (Anatoli Bondarchuk, U.S.S.R.) . . 40 25
MS730 111 × 91 mm. 4t. Wrestling silver medal (Khorloo Baianmunk, Mongolia) . . . . 1·00 1·00

160 Monkey on Cycle

1973. Mongolian Circus (1st series). Mult.

731 5m. Type **160** 10 10
732 10m. Seal with ball 15 10
733 15m. Bear on mono-wheel . . 20 10
734 20m. Acrobat on camel . . . 25 10
735 30m. Acrobat on horse . . . 40 10
736 50m. Clown playing flute . . 50 20
737 60m. Contortionist 60 25
738 1t. New Circus Hall, Ulan Bator 80 40

See also Nos. 824/30.

161 Mounted Postman

162 Sukhe Bator receiving Traditional Gifts

1973.

739 **161** 50m. brown (postage) . . 60 10
740 – 60m. green . . . . 2·50 15
741 – 1t. purple . . . . 1·00 20
742 – 1t.50 blue (air) . . . . . 1·75 25

DESIGNS: 60m. Diesel train; 1t. Mail truck; 1t.50, Antonov An-24 airliner.

1973. 80th Birth Anniv of Sukhe Bator. Mult.

743 10m. Type **162** 10 10
744 20m. Holding reception . . . 10 10
745 50m. Leading army 20 10
746 60m. Addressing council . . 25 10
747 1t. Giving audience (horiz) 45 20

163 W.M.O. Emblem and Meteorological Symbols

1973. Air. Centenary of World Meteorological Organization.

748 **163** 60m. multicoloured . . . 30 10

164 "Copernicus" (anon)

1973. 500th Birth Anniv of Nicholas Copernicus (astronomer). Multicoloured.

749 50m. Type **164** 15 10
750 60m. "Copernicus in his Observatory" (J. Matejko) (55 × 35 mm) 25 10
751 1t. "Copernicus" (Jan Matejko) 35 15
MS752 151 × 115 mm. As Nos. 749/51 but face values 1, 2 and 1t. respectively . . . . . 1·90 1·90

165 "Tulaga" Stamp of 1959

1973. "IBRA 73" International Stamp Exhibition, Munich. Sheet 81 × 116 mm.

MS753 **165** 4t. multicoloured . . 2·25 2·25

Нэгдлийн Холбооны IV Их
Хурал 1973–6–11

(166)

1973. 4th Agricultural Co-operative Congress, Ulan Bator. No. 538 optd with T **166**.

754 60m. multicoloured . . . . .

167 Marx and Lenin

1973. 9th Organization of Socialist States Postal Ministers Congress, Ulan Bator.

755 **167** 60m. multicoloured . . . 30 10

168 Russian Stamp and Emblems

1973. Air. Council for Mutual Economic Aid Posts and Telecommunications Conference, Ulan Bator. Multicoloured.

756 30m. Type **168** . . . . . . 1·25 30
757 30m. Mongolia 45 20
758 30m. Bulgaria 45 20
759 30m. Hungary 45 20
760 30m. Czechoslovakia 45 20
761 30m. German Democratic Republic 45 20
762 30m. Cuba 45 20
763 30m. Rumania 45 20
764 30m. Poland . . . . 1·25 30

169 Common Shelduck

1973. Aquatic Birds. Multicoloured.

765 5m. Type **169** 50 10
766 10m. Black-throated diver . . 70 10
767 15m. Bar-headed geese . . . 1·10 15
768 30m. Great crested grebe . . 1·50 25
769 50m. Mallard . . . . 2·00 50
770 60m. Mute swan . . . . . . 2·40 50
771 1t. Greater scaups . . . . . 2·75 70

170 Siberian Weasel

1973. Small Fur Animals. Multicoloured.

772 5m. Type **170** 20 10
773 10m. Siberian chipmunk . . 20 10
774 15m. Siberian flying squirrel 20 10
775 20m. Eurasian badger 25 15
776 30m. Eurasian red squirrel . . 35 15
777 60m. Wolverine 70 30
778 80m. American mink 85 45
779 1t. Arctic hare . . . . 1·25 60

171 Launching "Soyuz" Spacecraft

1973. Air. "Apollo" and "Soyuz" Space Programmes. Multicoloured.

780 5m. Type **171** 10 10
781 10m. "Apollo 8" 10 10
782 15m. "Soyuz 4" and "5" linked 10 10
783 20m. "Apollo 11" module on Moon 10 10
784 30m. "Apollo 14" after splashdown 10 10
785 50m. Triple flight by "Soyuz 6", "7" and "8" 20 15
786 60m. "Apollo 16" lunar rover 25 15
787 1t. "Lunokhod 1" 40 30
MS788 110 × 91 mm. 4t. Proposed "Soyuz" and "Apollo" link-up 1·00 1·00

172 Global Emblem

1973. 15th Anniv of Review "Problems of Peace and Socialism".

789 **172** 60m. red, gold and blue 25 10

173 Alpine Aster

1973. Mongolian Flowers. Multicoloured.

790 5m. Type **173** 10 10
791 10m. Mongolian catchfly . . 20 10
792 15m. "Rosa davurica" . . . 25 10
793 20m. Mongolian dandelion 30 15
794 30m. "Rhododendron dahuricum" 45 25
795 50m. "Clematis tangutica" . . 55 40
796 60m. Siberian primrose . . . 65 45
797 1t. Pasque flower 85 75

174 Poplar Admiral

1974. Butterflies and Moths. Multicoloured.

798	5m. Type **174**	30	10
799	10m. Hebe tiger moth	35	10
800	15m. Purple tiger moth	40	10
801	20m. Rosy underwing	55	10
802	30m. "Isoceras kaszabi" (moth)	70	15
803	50m. Spurge hawk moth	1·00	30
804	60m. Garden tiger moth	1·10	40
805	1t. Clouded buff	1·50	50

175 "Hebe Namshil" (L. Merdorsh)

1974. Mongolian Opera and Drama. Multicoloured.

806	15m. Type **175**	15	10
807	20m. "Sive Hiagt" (D. Luvsansharav) (horiz)	15	10
808	25m. "Edre" (D. Namdag)	20	10
809	30m. "The Three Khans of Sara-gol" (horiz)	25	15
810	60m. "Amarsana" (B. Damdinsuren)	40	20
811	80m. "Edre" (different scene)	55	25
812	1t. "Edre" (different scene)	85	55

176 Comecon Headquarters, Moscow

1974. Air. 25th Anniv of Communist Council for Mutual Economic Aid ("Comecon").

813	**176** 60m. multicoloured	30	20

177 Government Building and Sukhe Bator Monument, Ulan Bator

1974. 50th Anniv of Renaming of Capital as Ulan Bator.

814	**177** 60m. multicoloured	20	10

178 Mongolian 10c. Stamp of 1924

1974. Air. 50th Anniv of First Mongolian Stamps. Sheet 130 × 85 mm.

MS815	**178** 4t. multicoloured	3·00	3·00

179 Mounted Courier

1974. Air. Centenary of U.P.U (1st issue). Multicoloured.

816	50m. Type **179**	1·50	40
817	50m. Reindeer mail sledge	1·50	40
818	50m. Mail coach	1·50	40
819	50m. Balloon post	2·00	40
820	50m. Lake steamer "Sukhe Bator" and Polikarpov Po-2 biplane	2·25	40
821	50m. Diesel train and P.O. truck	2·25	40
822	50m. Rocket in orbit	1·50	40
MS823	100 × 90 mm. 4t. "UPU" over globe (24 × 45 mm)	14·00	14·00

See also 883/**MS**890.

180 Performing Horses

1974. Mongolian Circus (2nd series). Multicoloured.

824	10m. Type **180** (postage)	10	10
825	20m. Juggler (vert)	15	10
826	30m. Elephant on ball (vert)	20	10
827	40m. Performing yak	30	15
828	60m. Acrobats (vert)	45	20
829	80m. Trick cyclist (vert)	60	25
830	1t. Contortionist (vert) (air)	70	35

181 "Training a Young Horse"

1974. International Children's Day. Drawings by Lhamsurem. Multicoloured.

831	10m. Type **181**	10	10
832	20m. "Boy with Calf"	15	10
833	30m. "Riding untamed Horse"	20	10
834	40m. "Boy with Foal"	25	10
835	60m. "Girl dancing with Doves"	30	15
836	80m. "Wrestling"	35	25
837	1t. "Hobby-horse Dance"	60	30

182 Archer on Foot

1974. "Nadam" Sports Festival. Multicoloured.

838	10m. Type **182**	10	10
839	20m. "Kazlodanie" (Kazakh mounted game)	15	10
840	30m. Mounted archer	20	10
841	40m. Horse-racing	25	10
842	60m. Bucking horse-riding	30	15
843	80m. Capturing wild horse	35	25
844	1t. Wrestling	60	30

183 Giant Panda

1974. Bears. Multicoloured.

845	10m. Brown bear	25	10
846	20m. Type **183**	25	10
847	30m. Giant Panda	45	15
848	40m. Brown bear	45	20
849	60m. Sloth bear	70	30
850	80m. Asiatic black bear	80	50
851	1t. Brown bear	1·50	65

184 Red Deer

1974. Games Reserves. Fauna. Multicoloured.

852	10m. Type **184**	15	10
853	20m. Eurasian beaver	30	10
854	30m. Leopard	40	15
855	40m. Herring gull	85	35
856	60m. Roe deer	80	30
857	80m. Argali	85	35
858	1t. Siberian musk deer	1·25	55

185 Detail of Buddhist Temple, Palace of Bogdo Gegen

1974. Mongolian Architecture. Multicoloured.

859	10m. Type **185**	10	10
860	15m. Buddhist temple (now museum)	10	10
861	30m. "Charity" Temple, Ulan Bator	20	10
862	50m. Yurt (tent)	30	20
863	80m. Arbour in court-yard	50	30

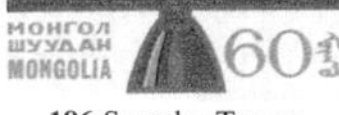

186 Spassky Tower, Moscow, and Sukhe Bator Statue, Ulan Bator

187 Proclamation of the Republic

1974. Brezhnev's Visit to Mongolia.

864	**186** 60m. multicoloured	30	10

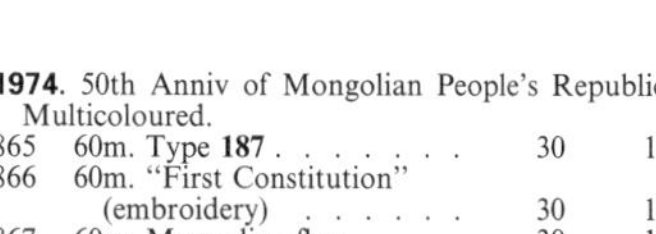

1974. 50th Anniv of Mongolian People's Republic. Multicoloured.

865	60m. Type **187**	30	10
866	60m. "First Constitution" (embroidery)	30	10
867	60m. Mongolian flag	30	10

188 Gold Decanter

1974. Goldsmiths' Treasures of the 19th Century. Multicoloured.

868	10m. Type **188**	15	10
869	20m. Silver jug	20	10
870	30m. Night lamp	25	10
871	40m. Tea jug	35	20
872	60m. Candelabra	45	20
873	80m. Teapot	60	30
874	1t. Silver bowl on stand	80	40

189 Northern Lapwing

1974. Protection of Water and Nature Conservation. Multicoloured.

875	10m. Type **189** (postage)	40	10
876	20m. Lenok (fish)	45	10
877	30m. Marsh marigolds	40	15
878	40m. Dalmatian pelican	80	25
879	60m. Eurasian perch	75	25
880	80m. Sable	75	25
881	1t. Hydrologist with jar of water (air)	80	30
MS882	83 × 117 mm. 4t. Wild roses (60 × 60 mm)	3·25	3·25

190 U.S. Mail Coach

1974. Centenary of U.P.U. Multicoloured.

883	10m. Type **190**	15	10
884	20m. French postal cart	20	10
885	30m. Changing horses, Russian mail and passenger carriage	35	15
886	40m. Swedish postal coach with caterpillar tracks	45	20
887	50m. First Hungarian mail van	50	25
888	60m. German Daimler-Benz mail van and trailer	65	40
889	1t. Mongolian postal courier	95	55
MS890	111 × 90 mm. 4t. UPU emblem	6·25	6·25

191 Red Flag

193 Mongolian Woman

192 "Zygophyllum xanthoxylon" (½-size illustration)

1975. 30th Anniv of Victory.
891 **191** 60m. multicoloured . . . 30 10

1975. 12th International Botanical Conference. Rare Medicinal Plants. Multicoloured.
892 10m. Type **192** 20 10
893 20m. "Incarvillea potaninii" 30 10
894 30m. "Lancea tibetica" . . . 45 15
895 40m. "Jurinea mongolica" . . 45 20
896 50m. "Saussurea involucrata" 55 20
897 60m. "Allium mongolicum" 65 30
898 1t. "Adonis mongolica" . . . 1·25 40

1975. International Women's Year.
899 **193** 60m. multicoloured . . . 30 10

194 "Soyuz" on Launch-pad

1975. Air. Joint Soviet–American Space Project. Multicoloured.
900 10m. Type **194** 20 10
901 20m. Launch of "Apollo" . . 15 10
902 30m. "Apollo" and "Soyuz" spacecraft 30 10
903 40m. Docking manoeuvre . . 35 20
904 50m. Spacecraft docked together 50 20
905 60m. "Soyuz" in orbit . . . 60 30
906 1t. "Apollo" and "Soyuz" spacecraft and communications satellite 95 40
MS907 102 × 83 mm. 4t. "Soyuz" and "Apollo" crewmen . . . . 3·00 3·00

195 Child and Lamb

1975. International Children's Day. Multicoloured.
908 10m. Type **195** 10 10
909 20m. Child riding horse . . . 20 10
910 30m. Child with calf 20 10
911 40m. Child and "orphan camel" 25 15
912 50m. "The Obedient Yak" 30 20
913 60m. Child riding on swan 35 25
914 1t. Two children singing . . 55 40
See also Nos. 979/85.

196 Pioneers tending Tree

Тээвэр—50
1975—7—15
(197)

1975. 50th Anniv of Mongolian Pioneer Organization. Multicoloured.
915 50m. Type **196** 20 10
916 60m. Children's study circle 30 10
917 1t. New emblem of Mongolian pioneers . . . 40 20

1975. 50th Anniv of Public Transport. Nos. 616/22 optd with T **197**.
918 **138** 20m. multicoloured . . . 2·50 2·50
919 – 30m. multicoloured . . . 2·50 2·50
920 – 40m. multicoloured . . . 1·90 1·90
921 – 50m. multicoloured . . . 1·90 1·90
922 – 60m. multicoloured . . . 2·50 2·50
923 – 80m. multicoloured . . . 3·00 3·00
924 – 1t. multicoloured . . . . 3·75 3·75

198 Argali

1975. Air. South Asia Tourist Year.
925 **198** 1t.50 multicoloured . . . 90 40

199 Golden Eagle attacking Red Fox

1975. Hunting Scenes. Multicoloured.
926 10m. Type **199** 50 10
927 20m. Lynx-hunting (vert) . . 45 10
928 30m. Hunter stalking bobak marmots 50 15
929 40m. Hunter riding on reindeer (vert) 60 20
930 50m. Shooting wild boar . . 60 25
931 60m. Wolf in trap (vert) . . . 75 35
932 1t. Hunters with brown bear 1·00 50

200 Haite's Bullhead

1975. Fishes. Multicoloured.
933 10m. Type **200** 25 10
934 20m. Flat-headed asp 40 10
935 30m. Altai osman 45 15
936 40m. Tench 55 20
937 50m. Hump-backed whitefish 80 25
938 60m. Mongolian redfin . . . 95 30
939 1t. Goldfish . . . . 1·60 60

201 "Morin Hur" (musical instrument)

1975. Mongolian Handicrafts. Multicoloured.
940 10m. Type **201** 10 10
941 20m. Saddle 15 10
942 30m. Headdress 20 10
943 40m. Boots 30 15
944 50m. Cap 40 15
945 60m. Pipe and tobacco pouch 45 20
946 1t. Fur hat 75 30

202 Revolutionary with Banner

1975. 70th Anniv of 1905 Russian Revolution.
947 **202** 60m. multicoloured . . . 25 10

203 "Taming a Wild Horse"

1975. Mongolian Paintings. Multicoloured.
948 10m. Type **203** 10 10
949 20m. "Camel Caravan" (horiz) 25 10
950 30m. "Man playing Lute" . . 35 10
951 40m. "Woman adjusting Headdress" (horiz) 40 15
952 50m. "Woman in ceremonial Costume" 40 25
953 60m. "Woman fetching Water" 50 30
954 1t. "Woman playing Yaga" (musical instrument) . . . 75 40
MS955 110 × 90 mm. 4t. "Warrior on horse-back" . . . . 3·00 2·75

204 Ski Jumping

1975. Winter Olympic Games, Innsbruck. Multicoloured.
956 10m. Type **204** 10 10
957 20m. Ice hockey 10 10
958 30m. Slalom skiing 10 10
959 40m. Bobsleighing 15 10
960 50m. Rifle shooting (biathlon) 20 10
961 60m. Speed skating 20 15
962 1t. Figure skating 35 25
MS963 110 × 70 mm. 4t. Skier carrying torch . . . . 1·00 1·00

205 "House of Young Technicians"

1975. Public Buildings.
964 **205** 50m. blue 40 10
965 – 60m. green 50 15
966 – 1t. brown 70 25
DESIGNS: 60m. Hotel, Ulan Bator; 1t. "Museum of the Revolution".

206 "Molniya" Satellite

1976. Air. 40th Anniv of Mongolian Meteorological Office.
967 **206** 60m. blue and yellow . . 40 15

207 Mongolian Girl

208 "The Wise Musician" (Sharav)

1976. Air. 30th Anniv of United Nations Educational, Scientific and Cultural Organization. Sheet 100 × 86 mm.
MS968 **207** 4t. multicoloured . . 3·25 3·00

1976. Air "Interphil 76" International Stamp Exhibition, Philadelphia. Sheet 97 × 70 mm.
MS969 **208** 4t. multicoloured . . 2·75 2·50

209 "National Economy" Star

1976. 17th Mongolian People's Revolutionary Party Congress, Ulan Bator.
970 **209** 60m. multicoloured . . . 30 10

210 Archery

1976. Olympic Games, Montreal. Multicoloured.
971 10m. Type **210** 10 10
972 20m. Judo 10 10
973 30m. Boxing 10 10
974 40m. Gymnastics 15 10
975 60m. Weightlifting 20 15
976 80m. High jumping 25 20
977 1t. Rifle shooting 35 25
MS978 105 × 78 mm. 4t. Wrestling 1·00 1·00

1976. Int Children's Day. As T **195**. Mult.
979 10m. Gobi Desert landscape 15 10
980 20m. Horse-taming 20 10
981 30m. Horse-riding 25 10
982 40m. Pioneers' camp 35 10
983 60m. Young musician 50 20
984 80m. Children's party 70 25
985 1t. Mongolian wrestling . . . 90 30

211 Cavalry Charge

1976. 55th Anniv of Revolution. Multicoloured.
986 60m. Type **211** (postage) . . 40 10
987 60m. Man and emblem (vert) 40 10
988 60m. "Industry and Agriculture" (air) 40 10

212 "Sukhe Bator" Star

1976. Mongolian Orders and Awards. Sheet 116 × 77 mm.
MS989 **212** 4t. multicoloured . . 1·00 1·00

213 Osprey

1976. Protected Birds. Multicoloured.
990 10m. Type **213** . . . . 1·50 40
991 20m. Griffon vulture . . . . 1·00 20
992 30m. Lammergeier . . . . . 1·40 25
993 40m. Marsh harrier . . . . . 1·75 25
994 60m. Cinerous vulture . . . 2·00 40
995 80m. Golden eagle . . . . . 2·50 45
996 1t. Tawny eagle . . . . . . 2·75 55

214 "Rider on Wild Horse"

1976. Paintings by O. Tsewegdjaw. Multicoloured.
997 10m. Type **214** 15 10
998 20m. "The First Nadam" (game on horse-back) (horiz) 20 10
999 30m. "Harbour on Khobsogol Lake" (horiz) 55 15
1000 40m. "Awakening the Steppe" (horiz) 45 20
1001 80m. "Wrestling" (horiz) . . 60 25
1002 1t. "The Descent" (yak hauling timber) . . . . . 1·10 50

215 "Industrial Development"

1976. Mongolian–Soviet Friendship.
1003 **215** 60m. multicoloured . . . 1·25 20

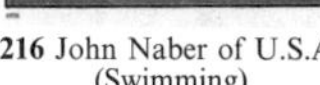

216 John Naber of U.S.A. (Swimming)

217 Tablet on Tortoise

1976. Olympic Games, Montreal. Gold Medal Winners. Multicoloured.
1004 10m. Type **216**(postage) . . 10 10
1005 20m. Nadia Comaneci of Rumania (gymnastics) . . 10 10
1006 30m. Kornelia Ender of East Germany (swimming) 10 10
1007 40m. Mitsuo Tsukahara of Japan (gymnastics) . . . 15 10
1008 60m. Gregor Braun of West Germany (cycling) 20 15
1009 80m. Lasse Viren of Finland (running) 25 20
1010 1t. Nikolai Andrianov of U.S.S.R. (gymnastics) . . 35 25
MS1011 103 × 78 mm. 4t. Zeveg Oidov of Mongolia (wrestling) (air) . . . . 1·00 1·00

1976. Archaeology.
1012 **217** 50m. brown and blue . . 80 15
1013 – 60m. black and green . . 1·10 15
DESIGN: 60m. 6th-century stele.

218 R-1 Biplane

1976. Aircraft. Multicoloured.
1014 10m. Type **218** 20 10
1015 20m. Polikarpov R-5 biplane 30 10
1016 30m. Kalinin K-5 monoplane 40 10
1017 40m. Polikarpov Po-2 biplane 45 15
1018 60m. Polikarpov I-16 jet fighter 60 25
1019 80m. Yakovlev Ya-6 Air 6 monoplane 75 35
1020 1t. Junkers F-13 monoplane 95 40

219 Dancers in Folk Costume

1977. Mongolian Folk Dances. Multicoloured.
1021 10m. Type **219** 25 10
1022 20m. Dancing girls in 13th-century costume . . 35 10
1023 30m. West Mongolian dance 45 10
1024 40m. "Ekachi" dance . . . 50 15
1025 60m. "Bielge" ("Trunk") dance 80 20
1026 80m. "Hodak" dance . . . 95 30
1027 1t. "Dojarka" dance . . . . 1·10 45

220 Gravitational Effects on "Pioneer"

1977. 250th Death Anniv of Sir Isaac Newton (mathematician). Multicoloured.
1028 60m. Type **220** (postage) . . 25 15
1029 60m. Apple tree (25 × 32 mm) 25 15
1030 60m. Planetary motion and sextant 25 15
1031 60m. Sir Isaac Newton (25 × 32 mm) 25 15
1032 60m. Spectrum of light . . . 25 15
1033 60m. Attraction of Earth . . 25 15
1034 60m. Laws of motion of celestial bodies (25 × 32 mm) 25 15
1035 60m. Space-walking (air) . . 25 15
1036 60m. "Pioneer 10" and Jupiter 25 15

221 Natsagdorj, Mongolian Scenes and Extract from poem "Mother" (½-size illustration)

1977. Natsagdorj (poet) Commem. Mult.
1037 60m. Type **221** 40 25
1038 60m. Border stone, landscape and extract from poem "My Homeland" 40 25

222 Horse Race

1977. Horses. Multicoloured.
1039 10m. Type **222** 25 10
1040 20m. Girl on white horse . . 30 10
1041 30m. Rangeman on brown horse 40 10
1042 40m. Tethered horses . . . 55 20
1043 60m. White mare with foal 70 20
1044 80m. Brown horse with shepherd . . . . 1·00 30
1045 1t. White horse . . . . . . 1·25 45

223 "Mongolemys elegans"

1977. Prehistoric Animals. Multicoloured.
1046 10m. Type **223** 30 10
1047 20m. "Embolotherium ergiliense" 45 10
1048 30m. "Psittacosaurus mongoliensis" 55 15
1049 40m. Enthelodon 70 20
1050 60m. "Spirocerus kiakhtensis" . . . . . . 1·00 25
1051 80m. Hipparion . . . . . . 1·40 40
1052 1t. "Bos primigenius" . . . 1·60 55

224 Netherlands 5c. Stamp, 1852, and Mongolian $1 Fiscal Stamp, 1926

1977. "Amphilx 77" International Stamp Exhibition, Amsterdam. Sheet 100 × 76 mm.
MS1053 **224** 4t. multicoloured . . 1·00 1·00

225 Child feeding Lambs

1977. Children's Day and 1st Balloon Flight in Mongolia. Multicoloured.
1054 10m.+5m. Type **225**(postage) 30 15
1055 20m.+5m. Boy playing flute and girl dancing 45 15
1056 30m.+5m. Girl chasing butterflies 55 20
1057 40m.+5m. Girl with ribbon 60 25
1058 60m.+5m. Girl with flowers 70 40
1059 80m.+5m. Girl with bucket 90 50
1060 1t.+5m. Boy going to school 1·25 60
MS1061 83 × 72 mm. 4t.+50m. Children in balloon (air) . . . 5·50 5·00

226 Industrial Plant and Transport

1977. Erdenet (New Town).
1062 **226** 60m. multicoloured . . . 1·25 20

227 Trade Unions Emblem

1977. Air. 11th Mongolian Trade Unions Congress.
1063 **227** 60m. multicoloured . . . 1·00 15

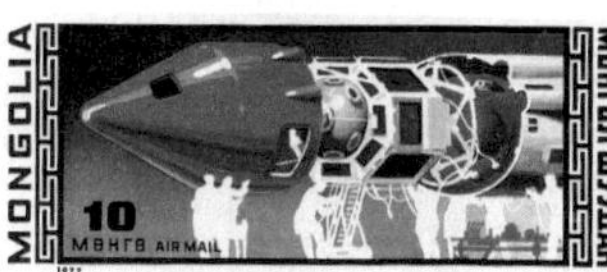

228 Mounting Bell-shaped Gear on Rocket (½-size illustration)

1977. Air. 11th Anniv of "Intercosmos" Co-operation. Multicoloured.
1064 10m. Type **228** 10 10
1065 20m. Launch of "Intercosmos 3" 10 10
1066 30m. Research ship "Kosmonavt Yury Gargarin" 40 15
1067 40m. Observation of lunar eclipse 15 10
1068 60m. Earth station's multiple antennae 15 15
1069 80m. Magnetosphere examination, Van Allen Zone 20 20
1070 1t. Meteorological satellites 30 25
MS1071 126 × 90 mm. 4t. Satellite linked to "Intercosmos" countries on globe (58 × 36 mm) . . . . 1·00 1·00

229 Fire-fighters' Bucket Chain

1977. Mongolian Fire-fighting Services. Multicoloured.
1072 10m. Type **229** 10 10
1073 20m. Horse-drawn hand pump 10 10
1074 30m. Horse-drawn steam pump 10 10
1075 40m. Fighting forest fire . . 15 10
1076 60m. Mobile foam extinguisher 20 15
1077 80m. Modern fire engine . . 25 20
1078 1t. Mil Mi-8 helicopter spraying fire 35 25

230 "Molniya" Satellite and Dish Aerial on TV Screen

1977. 40th Anniv of Technical Institute.
1079 **230** 60m. blue, black and grey 30 10

231 Black-veined White

1977. Butterflies and Moths. Multicoloured.
1080 10m. Type **231** 20 10
1081 20m. Lappet moth 35 10
1082 30m. Lesser clouded yellow 50 20
1083 40m. Dark tussock moth . . 70 20
1084 60m. Lackey moth . . . . 1·00 25
1085 80m. Clouded buff . . . . 1·40 35
1086 1t. Scarce copper . . . . . 1·60 50

232 Lenin Museum

1977. Inauguration of Lenin Museum, Ulan Bator.
1087 **232** 60m. multicoloured . . . 40 20

233 Cruiser "Aurora" and Soviet Flag

1977. 60th Anniv of Russian Revolution. Mult.

1088 50m. Type **233** 60 15
1089 60m. Dove and globe (horiz) 50 15
1090 1t.50 Freedom banner around the globe (horiz) 75 35

234 Giant Pandas

1977. Giant Pandas. Multicoloured.

1091 10m. Eating bamboo shoot (vert) 20 10
1092 20m. Type **234** 35 10
1093 30m. Female and cub in washtub (vert) 45 15
1094 40m. Male and cub with bamboo shoot 60 20
1095 60m. Female and cub (vert) 80 30
1096 80m. Family (horiz) . . . . 1·40 50
1097 1t. Male on hind legs (vert) 1·60 65

235 "Helene Fourment and her Chiildren"

1977. 400th Birth Anniv of Peter Paul Rubens (artist). Sheet 78 × 104 mm.

MS1098 **235** 4t. multicoloured . . 3·25 3·25

236 Montgolfier Brothers' Balloon

1977. Air. Airships and Balloons. Multicoloured.

1099 20m. Type **236** 10 10
1100 30m. Airship "Graf Zeppelin" over North Pole 10 10
1101 40m. Airship "Osoaviakhim" over the Arctic 20 10
1102 50m. Soviet Airship "Sever" 30 15
1103 60m. Aereon 340 airship . . 40 20
1104 80m. Nestrenko's planned airship 45 20
1105 1t.20 "Flying Crane" airship 70 35
MS1106 104 × 75 mm. 4t. Russian Zeppelin stamp of 1931 and statue of Sukhe Bator (46 × 31 mm) 2·00 2·00

237 Ferrari "312-T2"

1978. Racing Cars. Multicoloured.

1107 20m. Type **237** 25 10
1108 30m. Ford McLaren "M-23" 30 10
1109 40m. Soviet experimental car 40 20
1110 50m. Japanese Mazda . . . 50 20
1111 60m. Porsche "936-Turbo" 60 25
1112 80m. Model of Soviet car 65 25
1113 1t.20 American rocket car "Blue Flame" 95 40

238 Variegated Boletus (½-size illustration)

1978. Mushrooms. Multicoloured.

1114 20m. Type **238** 50 15
1115 30m. The charcoal burner 75 20
1116 40m. Red cap 80 25
1117 50m. Brown birch bolete . . 1·00 30
1118 60m. Yellow swamp russula 1·25 35
1119 80m. "Lactarius resimus" 1·50 50
1120 1t.20 "Flammula spumosa" 2·00 75

239 Aleksandr Mozhaisky and his Monoplane, 1884

1978. Air. History of Aviation. Multicoloured.

1121 20m. Type **239** 10 10
1122 30m. Henri Farman and Farman H.F.III biplane 10 10
1123 40m. Geoffrey de Havilland and De Havilland FE-1 biplane 20 10
1124 50m. Charles Lindbergh and "Spirit of St. Louis" . . . 30 15
1125 60m. Shagdarsuren, Demberel, biplane and glider 40 20
1126 80m. Chkalov, Baidukov, Belyakov and Tupolev ANT-25 airliner 45 25
1127 1t.20 A. N. Tupolev and Tupolev Tu-154 jetliner 70 35
MS1128 110 × 75 mm. 4t. Wright Brothers and Wright Flyer III 2·00 2·00

240 Footballers and View of Rio de Janeiro

1978. World Cup Football Championship, Argentina. Multicoloured.

1129 20m. Type **240**(postage) . . 10 10
1130 30m. Footballers and Old Town Tower, Berne . . . 10 10
1131 40m. Footballers and Stockholm Town Hall . . 15 10
1132 50m. Footballers and University of Chile . . . 20 10
1133 60m. Footballers, Houses of Parliament and Tower of London 30 15
1134 80m. Footballers and Theatre Degolladeo of Guadalajara, Mexico . . 35 15
1135 1t.20 Footballers and Munich Town Hall . . . 45 25
MS1136 105 × 70 mm. 4t. Footballers (44 × 38 mm) (air) 1·50 1·50

241 Mongolian Youth and Girl

1978. Mongolian Youth Congress, Ulan Bator.

1137 **241** 60m. multicoloured . . . 35 15

242 Eurasian Beaver and 1954 Canadian Beaver Stamp

1978. "CAPEX '78". International Stamp Exhibition, Toronto. Multicoloured.

1138 20m. Type **242**(postage) . . 20 10
1139 30m. Tibetan sandgrouse and Canada S.G. 620 . . 50 35
1140 40m. Black-throated diver and Canada S.G. 495 . . 65 40
1141 50m. Argali and Canada S.G. 449 . . . . 70 15
1142 60m. Brown bear and Canada S.G. 447 . . . . 80 15
1143 80m. Elk and Canada S.G. 448 . . . . 90 25
1144 1t.20 Herring gull and Canada S.G. 474 . . . . 1·90 75
MS1145 100 × 80 mm. 4t. Mongolian 1969 stamp and Canadian 1971 stamp depicting paintings (58 × 36 mm) (air) . . . . . . 3·75 3·75

243 Marx, Engels and Lenin

1978. 20th Anniv of Review "Problems of Peace and Socialism".

1146 **243** 60m. red, gold and black 35 15

244 Map of Cuba, Liner, Tupolev Tu-134 Jetliner and Emblem (½-size illustration)

1978. Air. 11th World Youth Festival, Havana.

1147 **244** 1t. multicoloured 90 20

245 "Open-air Repose"

1978. 20th Anniv of Philatelic Co-operation between Mongolia and Hungary. Paintings by P. Angalan. Multicoloured.

1148 1t.50 Type **245** 40 40
1149 1t.50 "Winter Night" . . . 40 40
1150 1t.50 "Saddling" 40 40

246 A. Gubarev, V. Remek and Exhibition Emblem

1978. Air. "PRAGA 1978" International Stamp Exhibition, Prague. Sheet 103 × 88 mm.

MS1151 **246** 4t. multicoloured . . 1·00 1·00

247 Butterfly Dog

1978. Dogs. Multicoloured.

1152 10m. Type **247** 20 10
1153 20m. Black Mongolian sheepdog 25 10
1154 30m. Puli (Hungarian sheepdog) 35 15
1155 40m. St. Bernard 40 20
1156 50m. German shepherd dog 55 25
1157 60m. Mongolian watchdog 65 25
1158 70m. Semoyedic spitz . . . 75 35
1159 80m. Laika (space dog) . . 90 35
1160 1t.20 Black and white poodles and cocker spaniel . . . . 1·10 55

248 Open Book showing Scenes from Mongolian Literary Works

1978. 50th Anniv of Mongolian Writers' Association.

1161 **248** 60m. blue and red . . . 35 15

249 "Dressed Maja" (Goya, 150th death anniv)

1978. Painters' Anniversaries.

1162 **249** 1t.50 multicoloured . . . 1·25 1·25
1163 – 1t.50 multicoloured . . . 1·25 1·25
1164 – 1t.50 multicoloured . . . 1·25 1·25
MS1165 105 × 132 mm. 4t. black and stone . . . . 3·00 3·00

DESIGNS: As T **249**—No.1163, "Ta Matete" (Gauguin, 75th death Anniv); 1164, "Bridge at Arles" (Van Gogh, 125th birth anniv). 49 × 49 mm—4t. "Melancoly" (Durer, 450th death anniv).

250 Young Bactrian Camel

1978. Bactrian Camels. Multicoloured.

1166 20m. Camel with Foal . . . 25 15
1167 30m. Type **250** 30 15
1168 40m. Two camels 45 20
1169 50m. Woman leading loaded camel 55 25
1170 60m. Camel in winter coat 70 30
1171 80m. Camel-drawn water waggon 90 45
1172 1t.20 Camel racing . . . . 1·25 60

251 Flags of COMECON Countries

1979. 30th Anniv of Council of Mutual Economic Assistance.

1173 **251** 60m. multicoloured . . . 35 15

252 Children riding Camel

1979. International Year of the Child. Multicoloured.

1174 10m.+5m. Type **252** 20 15
1175 30m.+5m. Children feeding chickens 30 15
1176 50m.+5m. Children with deer 45 15
1177 60m.+5m. Children picking flowers 55 20

1178 70m.+5m. Children watering tree 65 25
1179 80m.+5m. Young scientists 75 35
1180 1t.+5m. Making music and dancing . . . . 1·00 50
MS1181 78 × 99 mm. 4t.+50m. Girl on horse . . . . 3·75 3·50
See also No. **MS**1449.

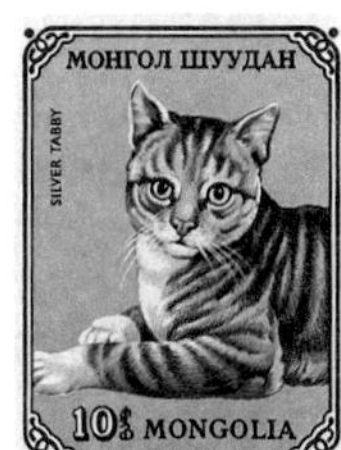

253 Silver Tabby

1978. Domestic Cats. Multicoloured.
1182 10m. Type **253** 20 10
1183 30m. White Persian 35 15
1184 50m. Red Persian 55 15
1185 60m. Blue-cream Persian . . 70 20
1186 70m. Siamese 80 30
1187 80m. Smoke Persian 90 35
1188 1t. Birman . . . . 1·25 50

254 "Potaninia mongolica"

1979. Flowers. Multicoloured.
1189 10m. Type **254** 20 10
1190 30m. "Sophora alopecuroides" 30 10
1191 50m. "Halimodendron halodendron" 35 15
1192 60m. "Myosotis asiatica" . . 50 20
1193 70m. "Scabiosa comosa" . . 50 30
1194 80m. "Leucanthemum sibiricum" 60 30
1195 1t. "Leontopodium ochroleucum" 80 45

255 Finland v. Czechoslovakia

1979. World Ice Hockey Championships, Moscow. Multicoloured.
1196 10m. Type **255** 10 10
1197 30m. West Germany v. Sweden 10 10
1198 50m. U.S.A. v. Canada . . 15 10
1199 60m. Russia v. Sweden . . . 15 10
1200 70m. Canada v. Russia . . 20 15
1201 80m. Swedish goalkeeper . . 20 15
1202 1t. Czechoslovakia v. Russia 30 20

256 Lambs (Sanzhid)

1979. Agriculture Paintings. Multicoloured.
1203 10m. Type **256** 10 10
1204 30m. "Milking camels" (Budbazar) 20 10
1205 50m. "Aircraft bringing help" (Radnabazar) . . . 40 15
1206 60m. "Herdsmen" (Budbazar) 40 15
1207 70m. "Milkmaids" "Nanzadsguren) (vert) . . 55 30
1208 80m. "Summer Evening" (Sanzhid) 75 40
1209 1t. "Country Landscape" (Tserendondog) 90 50
MS1210 86 × 70 mm. 4t. "After Rain" (Khaidav) . . . . . . 3·50 3·50

257 First Mongolian and Bulgarian Stamps

1979. Death Centenary of Sir Rowland Hill, and "Philaserdica 79" International Stamp Exn, Sofia. Each black, grey and brown.
1211 1t. Type **257** . . . . 1·50 1·00
1212 1t. American mail coach . . 1·50 1·00
1213 1t. Travelling post office, London–Birmingham railway . . . . 2·00 1·25
1214 1t. Paddle-steamer "Hindoostan" . . . . . 1·75 1·00

258 Stephenson's "Rocket"

1979. Development of Railways. Multicoloured.
1215 10m. Type **258** 30 10
1216 20m. Locomotive "Adler", 1835, Germany 35 10
1217 30m. Steam locomotive, 1860, U.S.A. 45 10
1218 40m. Class KB4 steam locomotive, 1931, Mongolia 55 15
1219 50m. Class Er steam locomotive, 1936, Mongolia 60 20
1220 60m. Diesel train, 1970, Mongolia 70 25
1221 70m. "Hikari" express train, 1963, Japan 90 30
1222 80m. Monorail aerotrain "Orleans", France 95 40
1223 1t.20 Experimental jet train "Rapidity", Russia . . . 1·10 50

259 Flags of Mongolia and Russia

262 East German Flag, Berlin Buildings and "Soyuz 31"

260 Pallas's Cat

1979. 40th Anniv of Battle of Khalka River.
1224 **259** 60m. gold, red and yellow 30 20
1225 – 60m. red, yellow and blue 30 20
DESIGN: No. 1225, Ribbons, badge and military scene.

1979. Wild Cats. Multicoloured.
1226 10m. Type **260** 15 10
1227 30m. Lynx 30 15
1228 50m. Tiger 55 25
1229 60m. Snow leopard 65 25
1230 70m. Leopard 75 35
1231 80m. Cheetah 80 35
1232 1t. Lion . . . . 1·25 50

1979. 30th Anniv of German Democratic Republic (East Germany).
1234 **262** 60m. multicoloured . . . 35 10

263 Demoiselle Crane

1979. Air. Protected Birds. Multicoloured.
1235 10m. Type **263** 40 25
1236 30m. Barred warbler 60 25
1237 50m. Ruddy shelduck . . . 70 35
1238 60m. Azure-winged magpie 85 50
1239 70m. Goldfinch 85 50
1240 80m. Great tit 95 65
1241 1t. Golden oriole . . . . . 1·40 75

264 "Venus 5" and "6"

1979. Air. Space Research. Multicoloured.
1242 10m. Type **264** 10 10
1243 30m. "Mariner 5" 10 10
1244 50m. "Mars 3" 15 10
1245 60m. "Viking 1" and "2" 15 10
1246 70m. "Luna 1", "2" and "3" 20 15
1247 80m. "Lunokhod 2" 20 15
1248 1t. "Apollo 15" Moon-rover 30 20
MS1249 83 × 77 mm. 4t. Armstrong and Aldrin on Moon . . . . . 1·00 75

265 Cross-country Skiing

1980. Winter Olympic Games, Lake Placid. Multicoloured.
1250 20m. Type **265** 10 10
1251 30m. Biathlon 10 10
1252 40m. Ice hockey 15 10
1253 50m. Ski jumping 15 10
1254 60m. Slalom 20 15
1255 80m. Speed skating 20 15
1256 1t.20 Four-man bobsleigh 30 20
MS1257 90 × 105 mm. 4t. Ice skating 1·00 1·00

266 "Andrena scita" (mining bee)

1980. Air. Wasps and Bees. Multicoloured.
1258 20m. Type **266** 10 10
1259 30m. "Paravespula germanica" (wasp) . . . 10 10
1260 40m. "Perilampus ruficornis" (parasitic wasp) 20 10
1261 50m. Buff-tailed bumble bee 30 15
1262 60m. Honey bee 40 20
1263 80m. "Stilbum cyanurum" (cuckoo wasp) 45 25
1264 1t.20 "Parnopes grandior" (cuckoo wasp) 70 35

1980. "London 1980" International Stamp Exhibition. Sheet 95 × 64 mm.
MS1265 **117** 4t. multicoloured . . 1·00 1·00

267 Weightlifting

1980. Olympic Games, Moscow. Multicoloured.
1266 20m. Type **267** 10 10
1267 30m. Archery 10 10
1268 40m. Gymnastics 15 10
1269 50m. Running 15 10
1270 60m. Boxing 20 15
1271 80m. Judo 20 15
1272 1t.20 Cycling 30 20
MS1273 91 × 84 mm. 4t. Wrestling 1·00 1·00

268 Zlin Z-526 AFs Akrobat Special

1980. Air. World Acrobatic Championship, Oshkosh, Wisconsin. Multicoloured.
1274 20m. Type **268** 10 10
1275 30m. Socata RF-6B Sportsman (inscr "RS-180") 15 10
1276 40m. Grumman A-1 Yankee 20 10
1277 50m. MJ-2 Tempete 30 15
1278 60m. Pitts S-2A biplane (inscr "Pits") 35 20
1279 80m. Hirth Acrostar 45 25
1280 1t.20 Yakovlev Yak-50 . . . 65 35
MS1281 89 × 68 mm. 4t. Yakolev Yak-52 (49 × 42 mm) . . . . . 2·00 2·00

269 Swimming

1980. Olympic Medal Winners. Multicoloured.
1282 20m. Type **269**(postage) . . 10 10
1283 30m. Fencing 10 10
1284 50m. Judo 10 10
1285 60m. Athletics 15 10
1286 80m. Boxing 20 10
1287 1t. Weightlifting 25 15
1288 1t.20 Kayak-canoe 30 20
MS1289 112 × 95 mm. 4t. Wrestling (silver medal, J. Davaazhav of Mongolia) (air) . . . . 1·00 1·00

270 Sukhe Bator

271 Gubarev

1980. Mongolian Politicians.
1290 **270** 60m. brown 15 10
1291 – 60m. blue 15 10
1292 – 60m. turquoise 15 10
1293 – 60m. bronze 15 10
1294 – 60m. green 15 10
1295 – 60m. red 15 10
1296 – 60m. brown 15 10
DESIGNS—VERT: No. 1291, Marshal Choibalsan; 1292, Yu. Tsedenbal aged 13; 1293, Tsedenbal as soldier, 1941; 1294, Pres. Tsedenbal in 1979; 1295, Tsedenbal with children. HORIZ: No. 1296, Tsedenbal and President Brezhnev of Russia.
See also **MS**1522.

1980. "Intercosmos" Space Programme. Multicoloured.
1297 40m. Type **271** 10 10
1298 40m. Czechoslovak stamp showing Gubarev and Remek 10 10

1299 40m. P. Klimuk 10 10
1300 40m. Polish stamp showing M. Hermaszewski 10 10
1301 40m. V. Bykovsky 10 10
1302 40m. East German stamp showing S. Jahn 10 10
1303 40m. N. Rukavishnikov . . 10 10
1304 40m. Bulgarian stamp showing G. Ivanov . . . 10 10
1305 40m. V. Kubasov 10 10
1306 40m. Hungarian stamp showing Kubasov and B. Farkas 10 10

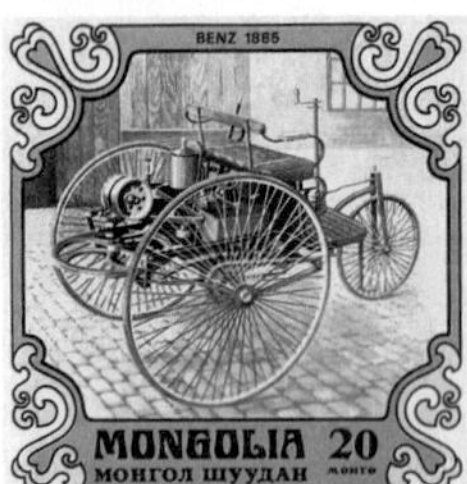

272 Benz, 1885

1980. Classic Cars. Multicoloured.
1307 20m. Type **272** 25 10
1308 30m. "President" Czechoslovakia, 1897 . . 30 10
1309 40m. Armstrong Siddeley, 1904 . . . . 35 25
1310 50m. Russo-Balt, 1909 . . . 45 20
1311 60m. Packard, 1909 . . . . 50 20
1312 80m. Lancia, 1911 . . . . . 70 30
1313 1t.60 "Marne" taxi, 1914 . . 1·60 60
MS1314 70 × 90 mm. 4t. "NAMI-1", Russia, 1927 . . . . 4·25 4·25

273 Adelie Penguin **274** Kepler

1980. Antarctic Exploration. Multicoloured.
1315 20m. Type **273** . . . . . . 1·25 20
1316 30m. Blue whales 70 15
1317 40m. Wandering albatross and Jacques Cousteau's ship "Calypso" and bathysphere . . . . . . 1·90 40
1318 50m. Weddell seals and mobile research station . . 90 20
1319 60m. Emperor penguins . . 2·75 45
1320 70m. Great skuas . . . . . 3·25 60
1321 80m. Killer whales . . . . 1·75 50
1322 1t.20 Adelie penguins, research station, Ilyushin Il-18B airplane and tracked vehicle . . . . . 5·00 1·00
MS1323 90 × 120 mm. 4t. Map of Antarctica during carbon age (*circular*, 43 mm diameter) . . 6·25 5·00

1980. Air. 350th Death Anniv of Johannes Kepler (astronomer). Sheet 98 × 78 mm.
MS1324 **274** 4t. black and yellow 1·00 1·00

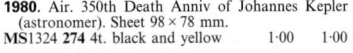

275 "Yurta Picture"

1980. 50th Anniv of Gombosuren (painter). Sheet 80 × 98 mm containing T **275** and similar horiz design. Multicoloured.
MS1325 2t. Type **275**; 2t. "Old-time Market" . . . . 1·00 1·00

276 "The Shepherd speaking the Truth"

1980. Nursery Tales. Multicoloured.
1326 20m. Type **276** 10 10
1327 30m. Children under umbrella and rainbow ("Above them the Sky is always clear") 10 10
1328 40m. Children on sledge and skis ("Winter's Joys") . . 10 10
1329 50m. Girl watching boy playing flute ("Little Musicians") 15 10
1330 60m. Boys giving girl leaves ("Happy Birthday") . . . 15 10
1331 80m. Children with flowers and briefcase ("First Schoolday") 20 15
1332 1t.20 Girls dancing ("May Day") 35 25
MS1333 79 × 89 mm. Children and squirrels ("The Wonder-working Squirrels" . . . . 1·00 1·00

277 Soldier

1981. 60th Anniv of Mongolian People's Army.
1334 **277** 60m. multicoloured . . . 40 15

278 Economy Emblems within Party Initials

1981. 60th Anniv of Mongolian Revolutionary People's Party.
1335 **278** 60m. gold, red and black 30 15

279 Motocross

1981. Motor Cycle Sports. Multicoloured.
1336 10m. Type **279** 10 10
1337 20m. Tour racing 10 10
1338 30m. Ice racing 10 10
1339 40m. Road racing 15 10
1340 50m. Motocross (different) 15 10
1341 60m. Road racing (different) 20 10
1342 70m. Speedway 20 10
1343 80m. Sidecar racing 25 15
1344 1t.20 Road racing (different) 40 20

280 Cosmonauts entering Space Capsule

1981. Soviet–Mongolian Space Flight. Mult.
1345 20m. Type **280** 10 10
1346 30m. Rocket and designer S. P. Korolev 10 10
1347 40m. "Vostok 1" and Yuri Gagarin 10 10
1348 50m. "Soyuz"–"Salyut" space station 15 10
1349 60m. Spectral photography 15 10
1350 80m. Crystal and space station 20 15
1351 1t.20 Space complex, Moscow Kremlin and Sukhe Bator statue, Ulan Bator 35 25
MS1352 70 × 80 mm. 4t. Cosmonauts Dzhanibekov and Gurragchaa (31 × 42 mm) . . . 1·00 1·00

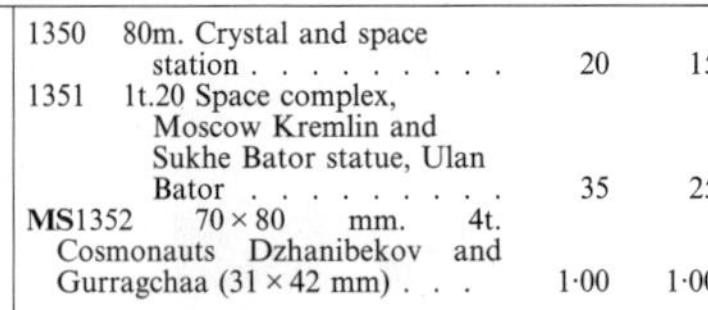

281 Ulan Bator Buildings and 1961 Mongolian Stamp

1981. Stamp Exhibitions.
1353 **281** 1t. multicoloured . . . . 2·25 1·00
1354 – 1t. multicoloured . . . . 1·75 80
1355 – 1t. black, blue and magenta . . . . . . 1·75 80
1356 – 1t. multicoloured . . . . 2·25 1·00
DESIGNS: No. 1353, Type **281** (Mongolian stamp exhibition); 1354, Wurttemberg stamps of 1947 and 1949 and view of Old Stuttgart ("Naposta '81" exhibition); 1355, Parliament building and sculpture, Vienna, and Austrian stamp of 1933 ("WIPA 1981" exhibition); 1356, Japanese stamp of 1964, cherry blossom and girls in Japanese costume ("Japex '81" exhibition, Tokyo).

282 Star and Industrial and Agricultural Scenes

1981. 18th Mongolian Revolutionary People's Party Congress.
1357 **282** 60m. multicoloured . . . 30 10

283 Sukhe Bator Statue, Ulan Bator

1981. 60th Anniv of Mongolian Revolutionary People's Party (2nd issue). Sheet 70 × 90 mm.
MS1358 **283** 4t. multicoloured . . 1·00 1·00

284 Sheep Farming

1981. "Results of the People's Economy". Multicoloured.
1359 20m. Type **284** 10 10
1360 30m. Transport . . . . . . 1·25 15
1361 40m. Telecommunications 60 15
1362 50m. Public health service 20 10
1363 60m. Agriculture 30 10
1364 80m. Electrical industry . . 35 15
1365 1t.20 Housing 50 20

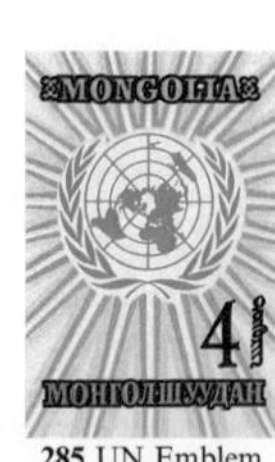

285 UN Emblem **287** Arms of Mongolia and Russia

286 Pharaonic Ship (15th century B.C.)

1981. 20th Anniv of United Nations Membership. Sheet 70 × 90 mm.
MS1366 **285** 4t. multicoloured . . 1·00 1·00

1981. Sailing Ships. Multicoloured.
1367 10m. Type **286** 15 10
1368 20m. Mediterranean sailing ship (9th century) 20 10
1369 40m. Hanse kogge (12th century) (vert) 30 10
1370 50m. Venetian felucca (13th century) (vert) 40 15
1371 60m. Columbus's "Santa Maria" (vert) 45 25
1372 80m. Cook's H.M.S. "Endeavour" (vert) . . . 50 30
1373 1t. "Poltava" (Russian ship of the line) (vert) 70 35
1374 1t.20 American schooner (19th century) (vert) . . . 80 40

1981. Soviet–Mongolian Friendship Pact.
1375 **287** 60m. red, blue and gold 35 10

288 "Hendrickje in Bed"

1981. 375th Birth Anniv of Rembrandt (artist). Multicoloured.
1376 20m. "Flora" 20 10
1377 30m. Type **288** 25 15
1378 40m. "Young Woman with Earrings" 45 20
1379 50m. "Young girl in the Window" 50 25
1380 60m. "Hendrickje like Flora" 60 30
1381 80m. "Saskia with Red Flower" 80 35
1382 1t.20 "The Holy Family with Drape" (detail) . . . 1·10 45
MS1383 68 × 85 mm. 4t. "Self-portrait with Saskia" . . . . . 3·75 3·75

289 Billy Goat (pawn)

1981. Mongolian Chess Pieces. Multicoloured.
1384 20m. Type **289** 20 10
1385 40m. Horse-drawn cart (rook) 30 15
1386 50m. Camel (bishop) 40 20
1387 60m. Horse (knight) 60 25
1388 80m. Lion (queen) 75 30
1389 1t.20 Man with dog (king) 1·10 40
MS1390 90 × 70 mm. 4t. Chess game (illustration of Mongolian folk tale) . . . . 2·50 2·50

290 White-tailed Sea Eagle and German 1m. "Zeppelin" Stamp

1981. Air. 50th Anniv of "Graf Zeppelin" Polar Flight. Multicoloured.
1391 20m. Type **290** 75 25
1392 30m. Arctic fox and German 2m. "Zeppelin" stamp 40 15
1393 40m. Walrus and German 4m. "Zeppelin" stamp 50 15
1394 50m. Polar bear and Russian 30k. "Zeppelin" stamp 60 15
1395 60m. Snowy owl and Russian 35k. "Zeppelin" stamp 1·90 70
1396 80m. Atlantic puffin and Russian 1r. "Zeppelin" stamp 2·25 90
1397 1t.20 Northern sealion and Russian 2r. "Zeppelin" stamp 1·50 30
MS1398 93 × 77 mm. 4t. *Graf Zeppelin* and Russian ice-breaker *Malygin* (36 × 51 mm) 5·00 4·00

291 Circus Camel and Circus Building, Ulan Bator

1981. Mongolian Sport and Art. Multicoloured.
1399 10m. Type **291** 10 10
1400 20m. Horsemen and stadium (National holiday cavalcade) 15 10
1401 40m. Wrestling and Ulan Bator stadium 25 15
1402 50m. Archers and stadium 35 20
1403 60m. Folk singer-dancer and House of Culture 45 20
1404 80m. Girl playing jatga (folk instrument) and Ulan Bator Drama Theatre 60 30
1405 1t. Ballet dancers and Opera House 90 40
1406 1t.20 Exhibition Hall and statue of man on bucking horse 1·10 65

292 Mozart and scene from "The Magic Flute"

1981. Composers. Multicoloured.
1407 20m. Type **292** 15 10
1408 30m. Beethoven and scene from "Fidelio" 20 10
1409 40m. Bartok and scene from "The Miraculous Mandarin" 20 10
1410 50m. Verdi and scene from "Aida" 30 15
1411 60m. Tchaikovsky and scene from "The Sleeping Beauty" 35 15
1412 80m. Dvorak and score of "New World" symphony 45 25
1413 1t.20 Chopin, piano, score and quill pens 60 30

293 "Mongolian Women in Everyday Life" (detail, Davaakhuu)

294 Gorbatko

1981. International Decade for Women. Mult.
1414 20m. Type **293** 25 10
1415 30m. "Mongolian Women in Everyday Life" (different detail) 35 15
1416 40m. "National Day" (detail, Khishigbaiar) 40 20
1417 50m. "National Day" (detail) (different) 50 25
1418 60m. "National Day" (detail) (different) 60 35

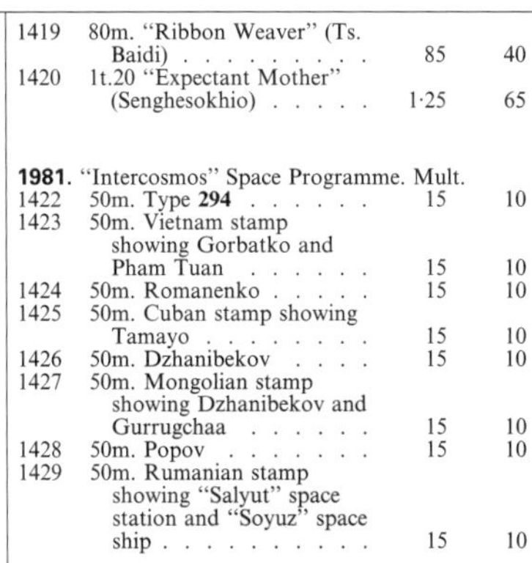
1419 80m. "Ribbon Weaver" (Ts. Baidi) 85 40
1420 1t.20 "Expectant Mother" (Senghesokhio) 1·25 65

1981. "Intercosmos" Space Programme. Mult.
1422 50m. Type **294** 15 10
1423 50m. Vietnam stamp showing Gorbatko and Pham Tuan 15 10
1424 50m. Romanenko 15 10
1425 50m. Cuban stamp showing Tamayo 15 10
1426 50m. Dzhanibekov 15 10
1427 50m. Mongolian stamp showing Dzhanibekov and Gurrugchaa 15 10
1428 50m. Popov 15 10
1429 50m. Rumanian stamp showing "Salyut" space station and "Soyuz" space ship 15 10

295 Karl von Drais Bicycle, 1816

1982. History of the Bicycle. Multicoloured.
1430 10m. Type **295** 10 10
1431 20m. Macmillan bicycle, 1838 10 10
1432 40m. First American pedal bicycle by Pierre Lallament, 1866 15 10
1433 50m. First European pedal bicycle by Ernest Michaux 20 10
1434 60m. "Kangaroo" bicycle, 1877 20 10
1435 80m. Coventry Rotary Tandem, 1870s 30 10
1436 1t. Chain-driven bicycle, 1878 35 15
1437 1t.20 Modern bicycle 40 20
MS1438 95 × 90 mm. 4t Modern road racers (43 × 43 mm) 1·50 1·50

296 Footballers (Brazil, 1950)

1982. World Cup Football Championship, Spain. Multicoloured.
1439 10m. Type **296**(postage) 10 10
1440 20m. Switzerland, 1954 10 10
1441 40m. Sweden, 1958 15 10
1442 50m. Chile, 1962 20 10
1443 60m. England, 1966 20 10
1444 80m. Mexico, 1970 30 10
1445 1t. West Germany, 1974 35 15
1446 1t.20 Argentina, 1978 40 20
MS1447 90 × 70 mm. 4t. Spain, 1982 (air) (44 × 44 mm) 1·50 1·50

297 Trade Union Emblem and Economic Symbols

299 Dimitrov

298 Children with Deer

1982. 12th Mongolian Trade Unions Congress.
1448 **297** 60m. multicoloured 1·00 30

1982. "Philefrance 82" International Stamp Exhibition, Paris. Sheet 105 × 68 mm.
MS1449 **298** 4t. multicoloured 1·00 1·00
For 50m.+5m. as Type **298** but larger, see No. 1176.

1982. Birth Centenary of Georgi Dimitrov (Bulgarian statesman).
1450 **299** 60m. black, grey and gold 35 10

300 Chicks

1982. Young Animals. Multicoloured.
1451 10m. Type **300** 10 10
1452 20m. Colt 10 10
1453 30m. Lamb 15 10
1454 40m. Roe deer fawn 20 10
1455 50m. Bactrian camel 20 10
1456 60m. Kid 25 10
1457 70m. Calf 30 15
1458 1t.20 Wild piglet 40 20

301 Coal-fired Industry

1982. Coal Mining.
1459 **301** 60m. multicoloured 35 10

302 Emblem

304 Revsomol Emblem within "Flower"

303 Siberian Pine

1982. 18th Revsomol Youth Congress.
1460 **302** 60m. multicoloured 35 10

1982. Trees. Multicoloured.
1461 20m. Type **303** 10 10
1462 30m. Siberian fir 10 10
1463 40m. Poplar 20 10
1464 50m. Siberian larch 20 10
1465 60m. Scots pine 25 10
1466 80m. Birch 30 15
1467 1t.20 Spruce 50 25

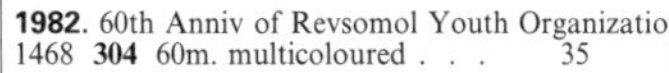
1982. 60th Anniv of Revsomol Youth Organization.
1468 **304** 60m. multicoloured 35 10

305 World Map and Satellite

1982. Air. I.T.U. Delegates' Conference, Nairobi.
1469 **305** 60m. multicoloured 45 15

306 Japanese "Iseki-6500" Tractor

1982. Tractors. Multicoloured.
1470 10m. Type **306** 10 10
1471 20m. West German "Deutz-DX230" 10 10
1472 40m. British "Bonser" 15 10
1473 50m. American "International-884" 20 10
1474 60m. French Renault "TX 145-14" 20 10
1475 80m. Russian "Belarus-611" 25 10
1476 1t. Russian "K-7100" 30 15
1477 1t.20 Russian "DT-75" 40 20

307 Hump-backed Whitefish and Lake Hevsgel

1982. Landscapes and Animals. Multicoloured.
1478 20m. Type **307** 50 15
1479 30m. Zavkhan Highlands and sheep 30 10
1480 40m. Lake Hovd and Eurasian beaver 40 10
1481 50m. Lake Uvs and horses 50 15
1482 60m. Bajankhongor Steppe and goitred gazelle 60 20
1483 80m. Bajan-Elgii Highlands and rider with golden eagle 65 20
1484 1t.20 Gobi Desert and bactrian camels 1·00 50

308 "Sputnik 1"

1982. Air. Second U.N. Conference on the Exploration and Peaceful Uses of Outer Space. Multicoloured.
1485 60m. Type **308** 15 10
1486 60m. "Sputnik 2" and Laika (first dog in space) 15 10
1487 60m. "Vostok 1" and Yuri Gagarin (first man in space) 15 10
1488 60m. "Venera 8" 15 10
1489 60m. "Vostok 6" and V. Tereshkova (first woman in space) 15 10
1490 60m. Aleksei Leonov and space walker 15 10
1491 60m. Neil Armstrong and astronaut on Moon's surface 15 10
1492 60m. V. Dzhanibekov, Jean-Loup Chretien and "Soyuz T-6" 15 10
MS1493 88 × 70 mm. 4t. "Soyuz" and "Salyut" coupling (49 × 33 mm) 1·00 1·00

309 Montgolfier Brothers' Balloon, 1783

1982. Air. Bicentenary of Manned Flight. Mult.

1494	20m. Type **309**	10	10
1495	30m. Jean-Pierre Blanchard and John Jeffries crossing the channel, 1785	15	10
1496	40m. Charles Green's flight to Germany in balloon "Royal Vauxhall", 1836	20	10
1497	50m. Salomon Andree's North Pole flight in balloon "Ornen", 1897	25	10
1498	60m. First Gordon Bennett balloon race, Paris, 1906	30	15
1499	80m. First stratosphere flight by Auguste Piccard in balloon "F.N.R.S.", Switzerland, 1931	40	20
1500	1t.20 Stratosphere balloon USSR-VR-62 flight, 1933	55	25
MS1501	78 × 98 mm. 4t. First Mongolian balloon flight, 1977	2·00	2·00

310 Sorcerer tells Mickey Mouse to clean up Quarters

1983. Drawings from "The Sorcerer's Apprentice" (section of Walt Disney's film "Fantasia"). Mult.

1502	25m. Type **310**	20	10
1503	35m. Mickey notices Sorcerer has left his cap behind	30	15
1504	45m. Mickey puts cap on and commands broom to fetch water	35	20
1505	55m. Broom carrying water	40	25
1506	65m. Mickey sleeps while broom continues to fetch water, flooding the room	50	30
1507	75m. Mickey uses axe on broom to try to stop it	55	35
1508	85m. Each splinter becomes a broom which continues to fetch water	65	40
1509	1t.40 Mickey, clinging to Sorcerer's Book of Spells, caught in whirlpool	1·00	55
1510	2t. Mickey handing cap back to Sorcerer	1·40	75
MS1511	127 × 102 mm. 7t. Mickey dreaming himself to be Master of the Universe	5·00	4·50

311 Foal with Mother

1983. "The Foal and the Hare" (folk tale). Mult.

1512	10m. Type **311**	10	10
1513	20m. Foal wanders off alone	15	10
1514	30m. Foal finds sack	25	15
1515	40m. Foal unties sack	30	15
1516	50m. Wolf jumps out of sack	40	20
1517	60m. Hare appears as wolf is about to eat foal	45	25
1518	70m. Hare tricks wolf into re-entering sack	50	30
1519	80m. Hare ties up sack with wolf inside	60	35
1520	1t.20 Hare and foal look for foal's mother	90	50
MS1521	121 × 94 mm. 7t. Boy with foal (58 × 58 mm). Imperf	5·00	4·50

311a Tank Monument, Ulan Bator

1983. Air. 40th Anniv of Formation of "Revolutionary Mongolia" Tank Regiment of Soviet Army. Sheet 110 x 75 mm.

MS1522 **311a** 4t. multicoloured

1983. 90th Birth Anniv of Sukhe Bator. Sheet 65 × 72 mm containing designs as T **270** but smaller, 25 × 32 mm.

MS1523	**270** 4t. purple	1·00	1·00

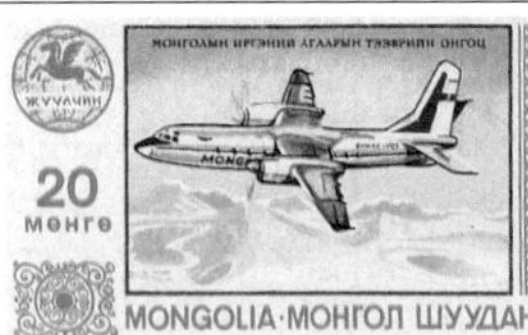

312 Antonov An-24B Aircraft

1983. Tourism. Multicoloured.

1524	20m. Type **312**	20	10
1525	30m. Skin tent	10	10
1526	40m. Roe deer	15	10
1527	50m. Argali	25	10
1528	60m. Imperial eagle	85	40
1529	80m. Khan Museum, Ulan Bator	40	20
1530	1t.20 Sukhe Bator statue, Ulan Bator	55	25

313 Rose

1983. Flowers. Multicoloured.

1531	20m. Type **313**	10	10
1532	30m. Dahlia	15	10
1533	40m. Marigold	20	10
1534	50m. Narcissus	25	10
1535	60m. Viola	30	10
1536	80m. Tulip	40	15
1537	1t.20 Sunflower	50	25

314 Border Guard

1983. 50th Anniv of Border Guards.

1538	**314** 60m. multicoloured	40	10

315 Boy riding Buffalo

1983. "Brasiliana 83" International Stamp Exhibition, Rio de Janeiro. Sheet 135 × 88 mm.

MS1539	**325** 4t. multicoloured	1·00	1·00

316 Karl Marx

1983. Death Centenary of Karl Marx.

1540	**316** 60m. red, gold and blue	35	10

317 Agriculture

1983. 18th Communist Party Congress Five Year Plan. Multicoloured.

1541	10m. Type **317**	10	10
1542	20m. Power industry	10	10
1543	30m. Textile industry	10	10
1544	40m. Science in industry and agriculture	15	10
1545	60m. Improvement of living standards	20	10
1546	80m. Communications	2·00	50
1547	1t. Children (education)	40	20

318 Young Inventors

1983. Children's Year. Multicoloured.

1548	10m. Type **318**	15	10
1549	20m. In school	25	10
1550	30m. Archery	40	15
1551	40m. Shepherdess playing flute	50	20
1552	50m. Girl with deer	65	30
1553	70m. Collecting rocks and mushrooms	2·25	50
1554	1t.20 Girl playing lute and boy singing	1·25	60

319 Skating

1983. 10th Anniv of Children's Fund. Mult.

1555	20m. Type **319**	10	10
1556	30m. Shepherds	10	10
1557	40m. Tree-planting	15	10
1558	50m. Playing by the sea	20	10
1559	60m. Carrying water	25	15
1560	80m. Folk dancing	30	20
1561	1t.20 Ballet	55	25
MS1562	93 × 110 mm. 4t. Christmas	1·50	1·00

320 Pallas's Pika

1983. Small Mammals. Multicoloured.

1563	20m. Type **320**	35	20
1564	30m. Long-eared jerboa	45	25
1565	40m. Eurasian red squirrel	55	30
1566	50m. Daurian hedgehog	65	40
1567	60m. Harvest mouse	80	45
1568	80m. Eurasian water shrew	1·25	70
1569	1t.20 Siberian chipmunk	1·75	95

321 "Sistine Madonna"

1983. 500th Birth Anniv of Raphael (artist). Sheet 102 × 138 mm.

MS1570	**321** 4t. multicoloured	2·00	2·00

322 Bobsleighing

1984. Winter Olympic Games, Sarajevo. Mult.

1571	20m. Type **322**	10	10
1572	30m. Cross-country skiing	10	10
1573	40m. Ice hockey	10	10
1574	50m. Speed skating	15	10
1575	60m. Ski jumping	15	10
1576	80m. Ice dancing	20	15
1577	1t.20 Biathlon (horiz)	35	25
MS1578	133 × 105 mm. 4t. Ski jumping (horiz)	1·00	1·00

323 Mail Van

1984. World Communications Year. Multicoloured.

1579	10m. Type **323**	10	10
1580	20m. Earth receiving station	10	10
1581	40m. Airliner	40	15
1582	50m. Central Post Office, Ulan Bator	25	10
1583	1t. Transmitter	40	15
1584	1t.20 Diesel train	3·50	1·25
MS1585	90 × 110 mm. 4t. Aerials (41 × 22 mm)	1·75	1·75

324 "Ausipex 84" Emblem and Tupolev Tu-154

1984. "Espana 84", Madrid and "Ausipex 84", Melbourne, International Stamp Exhibitions. Sheet 104 × 90 mm.

MS1586	**324** 4t. multicoloured	2·00	2·00

325 Cycling

326 Flag, Rocket and Coastal Scene

1984. Olympic Games, Los Angeles. Multicoloured.

1587	20m. Gymnastics (horiz)	10	10
1588	30m. Type **325**	10	10
1589	40m. Weightlifting	10	10
1590	50m. Judo	10	10
1591	60m. Archery	15	10
1592	80m. Boxing	20	15
1593	1t.20 High jumping (horiz)	35	25
MS1594	105 × 85 mm. 4t. Wrestling (horiz)	1·00	1·00

1984. 25th Anniv of Cuban Revolution.

1595	**326** 60m. multicoloured	25	10

327 1924 1c. Stamp

1984. 60th Anniv of Mongolian Stamps. Sheet 90 × 110 mm.
MS1596 **327** 4t. multicoloured . . 1·50 1·50

328 Douglas DC-10

329 Speaker, Radio and Transmitter

1984. Air. Civil Aviation. Multicoloured.

No.	Description		
1597	20m. Type **328**	10	10
1598	30m. Airbus Industrie A300B2	20	10
1599	40m. Concorde supersonic jetliner	25	10
1600	50m. Boeing 747-200	30	15
1601	60m. Ilyushin Il-62M	30	20
1602	80m. Tupolev Tu-154	50	25
1603	1t.20 Ilyushin Il-86	60	35
MS1604	110 × 90 mm. 4t. Yakovlev Yak-42	2·00	2·00

1984. 50th Anniv of Mongolian Broadcasting.
1605 **329** 60m. multicoloured . . . 60 20

330 Silver and Gold Coins

1984. 60th Anniv of State Bank.
1606 **330** 60m. multicoloured . . . 25 10

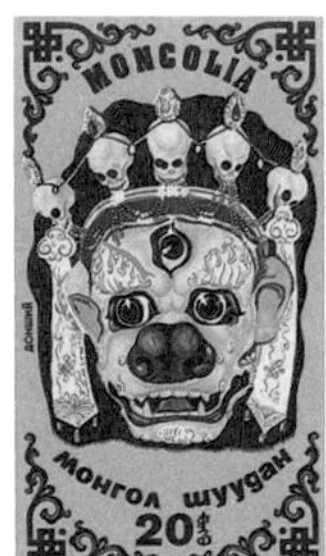
331 Donshy Mask

333 Sukhe Bator Statue

332 Golden Harp

1984. Traditional Masks. Multicoloured.

No.	Description		
1607	20m. Type **331**	10	10
1608	30m. Zamandi	25	10
1609	40m. Ulaan-Yadam	30	10
1610	50m. Lkham	45	15
1611	60m. Damdinchoizhoo	55	20
1612	80m. Ochirvaan	75	25
1613	1t.20 Namsrai	1·25	40
MS1614	90 × 110 mm. 4t. Ulaanzhamsran	3·50	3·50

1984. Scenes from Walt Disney's "Mickey and the Beanstalk" (cartoon film). Multicoloured.

No.	Description		
1615	25m. Type **332**	20	10
1616	35m. Mickey holding box of magic beans	30	15
1617	45m. Mickey about to eat bean	40	20
1618	55m. Mickey looking for magic bean	50	25
1619	65m. Goofy, Mickey and Donald at top of beanstalk	55	30
1620	75m. Giant holding Mickey	60	35
1621	85m. Giant threatening Mickey	80	40
1622	140m. Goofy, Mickey and Donald cutting down beanstalk	1·40	65
1623	2t. Goofy and Donald rescuing golden harp	1·60	75
MS1624	126 × 101 mm. 7t. Mickey, Goofy, Donald and giant plants (50 × 37 mm)	5·50	4·50

1984. 60th Anniv of Ulan Bator City.
1625 **333** 60m. multicoloured . . . 60 20

334 Arms, Flag and Landscape

335 Rider carrying Flag

1984. 60th Anniv of Mongolian People's Republic.
1626 **334** 60m. multicoloured . . . 60 20

1984. 60th Anniv of Mongolian People's Revolutionary Party.
1627 **335** 60m. multicoloured . . . 35 10

336 Collie

1984. Dogs. Multicoloured.

No.	Description		
1628	20m. Type **336**	10	10
1629	30m. German shepherd	25	10
1630	40m. Papillon	35	10
1631	50m. Cocker spaniel	50	15
1632	60m. Terrier puppy (diamond-shaped)	60	20
1633	80m. Dalmatians (diamond-shaped)	75	25
1634	1t.20 Mongolian shepherd	1·25	40

337 Gaetan Boucher (speed skating)

1984. Winter Olympic Gold Medal Winners. Multicoloured.

No.	Description		
1635	20m. Type **337**	10	10
1636	30m. Eirik Kvalfoss (biathlon)	10	10
1637	40m. Marja-Liisa Hamalainen (cross-country skiing)	10	10
1638	50m. Max Julen (slalom)	15	10
1639	60m. Jens Weissflog (ski jumping) (vert)	15	10
1640	80m. W. Hoppe and D. Schauerhammer (two-man bobsleigh) (vert)	20	15
1641	1t.20 J. Valova and O. Vassiliev (pairs figure skating) (vert)	35	25
MS1642	110 × 90 mm. 4t. Russia (ice hockey)	1·00	1·00

338 Four Animals and Tree

1984. "The Four Friendly Animals" (fairy tale). Multicoloured.

No.	Description		
1643	10m. Type **338**	15	10
1644	20m. Animals discussing who was the oldest	20	10
1645	30m. Monkey and elephant beside tree	20	10
1646	40m. Elephant as calf and young tree	25	10
1647	50m. Monkey and young tree	40	15
1648	60m. Hare and young tree	50	20
1649	70m. Dove and sapling	55	20
1650	80m. Animals around mature tree	70	30
1651	1t.20 Animals supporting each other so that dove could reach fruit	95	40
MS1652	103 × 84 mm. 4t. Dove passing fruit to other animals (vert)	3·75	3·75

339 Fawn

1984. Red Deer. Multicoloured.

No.	Description		
1653	50m. Type **339**	40	20
1654	50m. Stag	40	20
1655	50m. Adults and fawn by river	40	20
1656	50m. Doe in woodland	40	20

340 Flag and Pioneers

342 Black Stork

341 Shar Tarlan

1985. 60th Anniv of Mongolian Pioneer Organization.
1657 **340** 60m. multicoloured . . . 40 15

1985. Cattle. Multicoloured.

No.	Description		
1658	20m. Type **341**	10	10
1659	30m. Bor khalium	20	10
1660	40m. Sarlag	30	10
1661	50m. Dornod talin bukh	45	15
1662	60m. Char tarlan	55	20
1663	80m. Nutgiin uulderiin unee	65	20
1664	1t.20 Tsagaan tolgoit	1·10	35
MS1665	90 × 110 mm. 4t. Girl with calf (vert)	3·25	3·25

1985. Birds. Multicoloured.

No.	Description		
1666	20m. Type **342**	30	45
1667	30m. White-tailed sea eagle	40	45
1668	40m. Great white crane	55	45
1669	50m. Heude's parrotbill	85	90
1670	60m. Hooded crane	1·00	90
1671	80m. Japanese white-naped crane	1·25	1·25
1672	1t.20 Rough-legged buzzard	2·10	2·25
MS1673	125 × 70 mm. 4t. Brandt's cormorant (*Phalacrocorax penicillatus*) (47 × 39 mm)	4·00	4·00

343 Footballers

344 Monument

1985. World Junior Football Championship, U.S.S.R.

No.	Description		
1674	**343** 20m. multicoloured	10	10
1675	– 30m. multicoloured	10	10
1676	– 40m. multicoloured	15	10
1677	– 50m. multicoloured	20	10
1678	– 60m. multicoloured	25	10
1679	– 80m. multicoloured	30	15
1680	– 1t.20 multicoloured	50	25
MS1681	110 × 90 mm. 4t. multicoloured (horiz)	1·00	1·00

DESIGNS: 30m. to 4t., Different footballing scenes.

1985. 40th Anniv of Victory in Europe.
1682 **344** 60m. multicoloured . . . 30 10

345 Snow Leopards

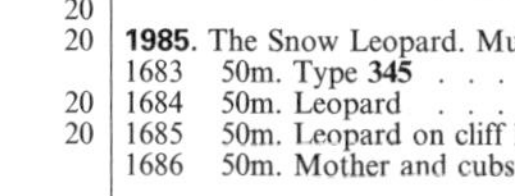

1985. The Snow Leopard. Multicoloured.

No.	Description		
1683	50m. Type **345**	40	20
1684	50m. Leopard	40	20
1685	50m. Leopard on cliff ledge	40	20
1686	50m. Mother and cubs	40	20

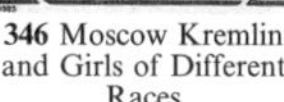
346 Moscow Kremlin and Girls of Different Races

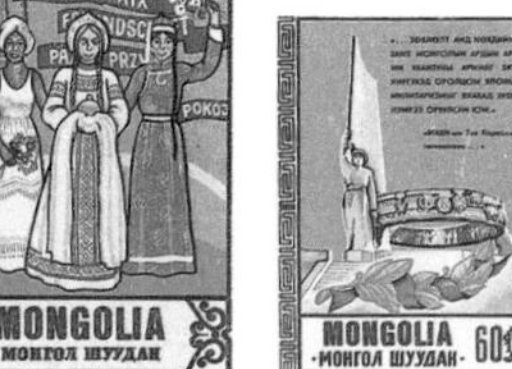
347 Monument

1985. 12th World Youth and Students' Festival, Moscow.
1687 **346** 60m. multicoloured . . . 30 10

1985. 40th Anniv of Victory in Asia.
1688 **347** 60m. multicoloured . . . 35 10

348 "Rosa dahurica"

1985. Plants. Multicoloured.

No.	Description		
1689	20m. Type **348**	10	10
1690	30m. False chamomile	20	10
1691	40m. Dandelion	30	10
1692	50m. "Saxzitraga nirculus"	45	15
1693	60m. Cowberry	55	20
1694	80m. "Sanguisorba officinalis"	65	20
1695	1t.20 "Plantago major"	1·10	35
MS1696	90 × 110 mm. 4t. Sea buckthorn (*Hippophae rhamnoides*) (wrongly inscr "Hippopae thamnoides")	3·25	3·25

See also Nos. 1719/25.

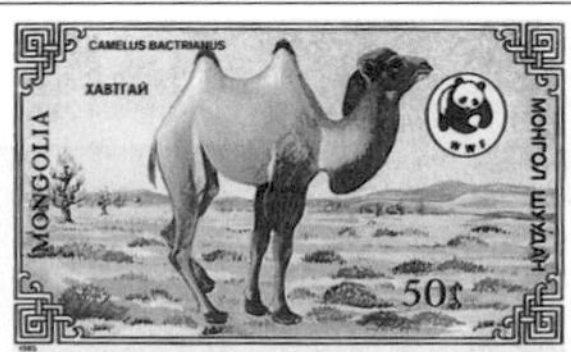

349 Camel

1985. The Bactrian Camel. Multicoloured.
1697 50m. Type **349** 40 20
1698 50m. Adults and calf . . . 40 20
1699 50m. Calf 40 20
1700 50m. Adult 40 20

350 "Soyuz" Spacecraft

1985. Space. Multicoloured.
1701 20m. Type **350** 10 10
1702 30m. "Kosmos" satellite . . 10 10
1703 40m. "Venera-9" satellite . . 10 10
1704 50m. "Salyut" space station 15 10
1705 60m. "Luna-9" landing vehicle 15 10
1706 80m. "Soyuz" rocket on transporter . . . . 1·10 50
1707 1t.20 Dish aerial receiving transmission from "Soyuz" 30 15
MS1708 110 × 90 mm. 4t. Cosmonauts on space walk . . 1·00 1·00

351 Horseman

1985. "Italia '85" International Stamp Exhibition, Rome. Sheet 110 × 90 mm.
MS1709 **351** 4t. multicoloured . . 1·00 1·00

352 U.N. and Mongolian Flags and U.N. Headquarters, New York **354** Congress Emblem

353 "Tricholoma mongolica"

1985. 40th Anniv of U.N.O.
1710 **352** 60m. multicoloured . . . 30 10

1985. Fungi. Multicoloured.
1711 20m. Type **353** 20 10
1712 30m. Chanterelle 25 10
1713 40m. Honey fungus 30 10
1714 50m. Caesar's mushroom . . 55 15
1715 70m. Chestnut mushroom 80 20
1716 80m. Red-staining mushroom 90 25
1717 1t.20 Cep . . . . 1·40 35

1986. 19th Mongolian Revolutionary People's Party Congress.
1718 **354** 60m. multicoloured . . . 25 10

1986. Plants. As T **348**. Multicoloured.
1719 20m. "Valeriana officinalis" 10 10
1720 30m. "Hyoscymus niger" . . 20 10
1721 40m. "Ephedra sinica" . . . 30 10
1722 50m. "Thymus gobica" . . 45 15
1723 60m. "Paeonia anomalia" 55 20
1724 80m. "Achilea millefolium" 65 25
1725 1t.20 "Rhododendron adamsii" . . . . 1·10 35

355 Scene from Play

1986. 80th Birth Anniv of D. Natsagdorj (writer).
1726 **355** 60m. multicoloured . . . 25 10

356 Thalmann **357** Man wearing Patterned Robe

1986. Birth Centenary of Ernst Thalmann (German politician).
1727 **356** 60m. multicoloured . . . 25 10

1986. Costumes. Multicoloured.
1728 60m. Type **357** 25 10
1729 60m. Man in blue robe and fur-lined hat with ear flaps 25 10
1730 60m. Woman in black and yellow dress and bolero 25 10
1731 60m. Woman in pink dress patterned with stars . . . 25 10
1732 60m. Man in cream robe with fur cuffs 25 10
1733 60m. Man in brown robe and mauve and yellow tunic 25 10
1734 60m. Woman in blue dress with black, yellow and red overtunic 25 10

358 Footballers

1986. World Cup Football Championship, Mexico.
1735 **358** 20m. multicoloured . . . 10 10
1736 – 30m. multicoloured . . . 10 10
1737 – 40m. multicoloured . . . 10 10
1738 – 50m. multicoloured . . . 15 10
1739 – 60m. multicoloured . . . 15 10
1740 – 80m. multicoloured . . . 20 15
1741 – 1t.20 multicoloured . . . 35 25
MS1742 110 × 90 mm. 4t. multicoloured (horiz) . . . . . 1·00 1·00
DESIGNS: 30m. to 4t., Different footballing scenes.

359 Mink

1986. Mink. Multicoloured.
1743 60m. Type **359** 45 15
1744 60m. Mink on rock 45 15
1745 60m. Mink on snow-covered branch 45 15
1746 60m. Two mink 45 15
See also Nos. 1771/4, 1800/3, 1804/7, 1840/3 and 1844/7.

360 "Neptis coenobita" **361** Sukhe Bator Statue

1986. Butterflies and Moths. Multicoloured.
1747 20m. Type **360** 10 10
1748 30m. "Colias tycha" 15 10
1749 40m. "Leptidea amurensis" 20 10
1750 50m. "Oeneis tarpenledevi" 30 15
1751 60m. "Mesoacidalia charlotta" 40 20
1752 80m. Eyed hawk moth . . . 45 25
1753 1t.20 Large tiger moth . . . 75 40

1986. 65th Anniv of Independence.
1754 **361** 60m. multicoloured . . . 25 10

362 Yak and Goats Act

1986. Circus. Multicoloured.
1755 20m. Type **362** 10 10
1756 30m. Acrobat 10 10
1757 40m. Yak act 15 10
1758 50m. Acrobats (vert) 20 10
1759 60m. High wire act (vert) . . 25 15
1760 80m. Fire juggler on camel (vert) 30 15
1761 1t.20 Acrobats on camel-drawn cart (vert) 50 25

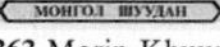

363 Morin Khuur **364** Flag and Emblem

1986. Musical Instruments. Multicoloured.
1762 20m. Type **363** 10 10
1763 30m. Bishguur (wind instrument) 20 10
1764 40m. Ever buree (wind) . . 30 10
1765 50m. Shudarga (string) . . . 45 15
1766 60m. Khiil (string) 55 20
1767 80m. Janchir (string) (horiz) 65 25
1768 1t.20 Jatga (string) (horiz) 1·10 35

1986. International Peace Year.
1770 **364** 10m. multicoloured . . . 50 20

1986. Przewalski's Horse. As T **359**. Mult.
1771 50m. Horses grazing on sparsely grassed plain . . 45 15
1772 50m. Horses grazing on grassy plain 45 15
1773 50m. Adults with foal . . . 45 15
1774 50m. Horses in snow . . . 45 15

365 Temple

1986. Ancient Buildings. Multicoloured.
1775 60m. Type **365** 60 20
1776 60m. Temple with light green roof and white doors 60 20
1777 60m. Temple with porch . . 60 20
1778 60m. White building with three porches 60 20

366 Redhead ("Aythya americana")

1986. Birds. Multicoloured.
1779 60m. Type **366** 85 55
1780 60m. Ruffed grouse ("Bonasa umbellus") . . 85 55
1781 60m. Tundra swan ("Olor columbianus") 85 55
1782 60m. Water pipit ("Anthus spinoletta") 85 55

367 Alfa Romeo "RL Sport", 1922

1986. Cars. Multicoloured.
1783 20m. Type **367** 10 10
1784 30m. Stutz "Bearcat", 1912 15 10
1785 40m. Mercedes "Simplex", 1902 . . . . 20 10
1786 50m. Tatra "11", 1923 . . . 25 10
1787 60m. Ford Model "T", 1908 30 15
1788 80m. Vauxhall, 1905 . . . . 40 20
1789 1t.20 Russo-Balt "K", 1913 60 30
MS1790 110 × 90 mm. 4t. As No. 1789 . . . . 2·00 2·00

368 Wilhelm Steinitz and Curt von Bardeleben Game, 1895

1986. World Chess Champions. Multicoloured.
1791 20m. Type **368** 10 10
1792 30m. Emanuel Lasker and Harry Pilsberi game, 1895 15 10
1793 40m. Alexander Alekhine and Richard Retti game, 1925 . . . . 20 10
1794 50m. Mikhail Botvinnik and Capablanca game, 1938 25 10
1795 60m. Anatoly Karpov and Wolfgang Untsiker game, 1975 . . . . 30 15
1796 80m. Nona Gaprindashvili and Lasarevich game, 1961 . . . . 40 20
1797 1t.20 Maia Chirburdanidze and Irina Levitina game, 1984 . . . . 60 30
MS1798 110 × 100 mm. 4t. Players around International Chess Federation emblem . . . . . 2·00 2·00

369 "Vega 2" Spacecraft and Comet

1986. Appearance of Halley's Comet. Sheet 110 × 90 mm.
MS1799 **369** 4t. multicoloured . . 1·00 1·00

1986. Saiga Antelope. As T **359**. Multicoloured.
1800 60m. Male 45 15
1801 60m. Female with calf . . . 45 15
1802 60m. Male and female . . . 45 15
1803 60m. Male and female in snow 45 15

1986. Pelicans. As T **359**. Multicoloured.
1804 60m. Dalmatian pelican ("Pelecanus crispus") . . 1·10 55
1805 60m. Dalmatian pelican preening . . . . 1·10 55

1806 60m. Eastern white pelican ("Pelecanus onocrotalus") 1·10 55
1807 60m. Eastern white pelicans in flight 1·10 55

370 Siamese Fighting Fish

1987. Aquarium Fishes. Multicoloured.
1808 20m. Type **370** 10 10
1809 30m. Goldfish 15 10
1810 40m. Glowlight rasbora 25 10
1811 50m. Acara 35 10
1812 60m. Platy 40 15
1813 80m. Green swordtail 55 20
1814 1t.20 Freshwater angelfish (vert) 95 30
MS1815 111 × 91 mm. 4t. Sail-finned tetra (*Crenuchus spilurus*) (53 × 32 mm) 3·00 3·00

371 Lassoing Horse

1987. Traditional Equestrian Sports. Mult.
1816 20m. Type **371** 10 10
1817 30m. Breaking horse 15 10
1818 40m. Mounted archer 20 10
1819 50m. Race 25 10
1820 60m. Horseman snatching flag from ground 35 15
1821 80m. Tug of war 40 20
1822 1t.20 Racing wolf 70 25

372 Grey-headed Woodpecker
373 Butterfly Hunting

1987. Woodpeckers. Multicoloured.
1823 20m. Type **372** 30 20
1824 30m. Wryneck 45 25
1825 40m. Great spotted woodpecker 75 25
1826 50m. White-backed woodpecker 1·10 35
1827 60m. Lesser spotted woodpecker 1·25 35
1828 80m. Black woodpecker 1·75 50
1829 1t.20 Three-toed woodpecker 3·25 85
MS1830 85 × 105 mm. 4t. Pryer's woodpecker (*Saphopipo noguchi*) 3·00 3·00

1987. Children's Activities. Multicoloured.
1831 20m. Type **373** 10 10
1832 30m. Feeding calves 10 10
1833 40m. Drawing on ground in chalk 15 10
1834 50m. Football 20 10
1835 60m. Go-carting 25 15
1836 80m. Growing vegetables 30 15
1837 1t.20 Playing string instrument 45 25

374 Industry and Agriculture

1987. 13th Congress and 60th Anniv of Mongolian Trade Union.
1838 **374** 60m. multicoloured 1·00 30

375 Women in Traditional Costume
376 Flags of Member Countries

1987. 40th Anniv of Mongol–Soviet Friendship.
1839 **375** 60m. multicoloured 40 10

1987. Argali. As T **359**. Multicoloured.
1840 60m. On grassy rock (full face) 45 15
1841 60m. On rock (three-quarter face) 45 15
1842 60m. Family 45 15
1843 60m. Close-up of head and upper body 45 15

1987. Swans. As T **359**. Multicoloured.
1844 60m. Mute Swan ("Cygnus olor") in water 85 55
1845 60m. Mute swan on land 85 55
1846 60m. Tundra swan ("Cygnus bewickii") 85 55
1847 60m. Tundra swan, ("Cygnus gunus") and mute swan 85 55

1987. 25th Anniv of Membership of Council for Mutual Economic Aid.
1848 **376** 60m. multicoloured 35 10

377 Sea Buckthorn
378 Couple in Traditional Costume

1987. Fruits. Multicoloured.
1849 20m. Type **377** 10 10
1850 30m. Blackcurrants 10 10
1851 40m. Redcurrants 15 10
1852 50m. Redcurrants 20 10
1853 60m. Raspberries 25 15
1854 80m. "Padus asiatica" 30 15
1855 1t.20 Strawberries 45 25
MS1856 90 × 110 mm. 4t. Child with apple (29 × 51 mm) 1·50 1·50

1987. Folk Art. Multicoloured.
1857 20m. Type **378** 10 10
1858 30m. Gold-inlaid baton and pouch 15 10
1859 40m. Gold and jewelled ornaments 20 10
1860 50m. Bag and dish 30 10
1861 60m. Earrings 35 15
1862 80m. Pipe, pouch and bottle 45 20
1863 1t.20 Decorative headdress 65 25

379 Dancer

1987. Dances.
1864 **379** 20m. multicoloured 10 10
1865 – 30m. multicoloured 15 10
1866 – 40m. multicoloured 20 10
1867 – 50m. multicoloured 30 10
1868 – 60m. multicoloured 35 15
1869 – 80m. multicoloured 45 20
1870 – 1t.20 multicoloured 65 25
DESIGNS: 30m. to 1t.20, Different dances.

380 Lute Player
381 Scottish Fold

1987. Hafnia 87 International Stamp Exhibition, Copenhagen. Sheet 90 × 114 mm.
MS1871 **380** 4t. multicoloured 1·50 1·50

1987. Cats. Multicoloured.
1872 20m. Type **381** 10 10
1873 30m. Grey 15 10
1874 40m. Oriental 20 10
1875 50m. Abyssinian (horiz) 30 10
1876 60m. Manx (horiz) 35 15
1877 80m. Black shorthair (horiz) 45 20
1878 1t.20 Spotted (horiz) 65 25
MS1879 91 × 111 mm. 4t. Tabby shorthair 1·50 1·50

382 Mil Mi-V12

1987. Helicopters. Multicoloured.
1880 20m. Type **382** 10 10
1881 30m. Westland WG-30 15 10
1882 40m. Bell 206L LongRanger II 20 10
1883 50m. Kawasaki-Hughes 369HS 25 10
1884 60m. Kamov Ka-32 30 10
1885 80m. Mil Mi-17 35 15
1886 1t.20 Mil Mi-10K 60 25

383 City Scene
384 Kremlin, Lenin and Revolutionaries

1987. 19th Mongolian People's Revolutionary Party Congress. Multicoloured.
1887 60m. Type **383** 25 10
1888 60m. Clothing and mining industries 1·00 25
1889 60m. Agriculture 25 10
1890 60m. Family 25 10
1891 60m. Workers, factories and fields 25 10
1892 60m. Building construction 25 10
1893 60m. Scientist 25 10

1987. 70th Anniv of Russian October Revolution.
1894 **384** 60m. multicoloured 35 10

385 Seven with One Blow

1987. Walt Disney Cartoons. Multicoloured (a) "The Brave Little Tailor" (Grimm Brothers).
1895 25m. Type **385** 10 10
1896 35m. Brought before the King 20 10
1897 45m. Rewards for bravery 25 10

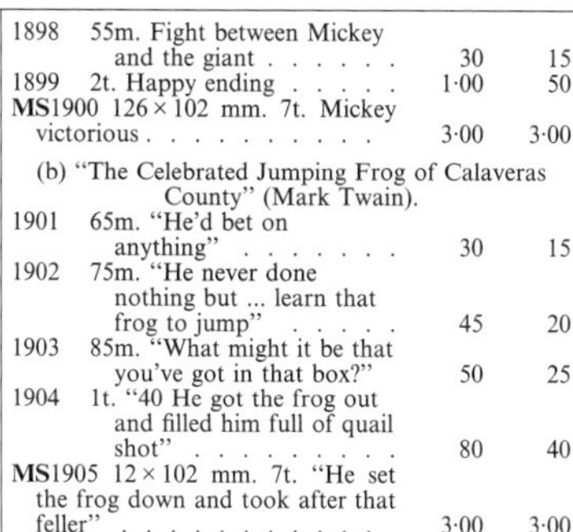

1898 55m. Fight between Mickey and the giant 30 15
1899 2t. Happy ending 1·00 50
MS1900 126 × 102 mm. 7t. Mickey victorious 3·00 3·00

(b) "The Celebrated Jumping Frog of Calaveras County" (Mark Twain).
1901 65m. "He'd bet on anything" 30 15
1902 75m. "He never done nothing but ... learn that frog to jump" 45 20
1903 85m. "What might it be that you've got in that box?" 50 25
1904 1t. "40 He got the frog out and filled him full of quail shot" 80 40
MS1905 12 × 102 mm. 7t. "He set the frog down and took after that feller" 3·00 3·00

386 Head

1987. The Red Fox. Multicoloured.
1906 60m. Type **386** 45 15
1907 60m. Vixen and cubs 45 15
1908 60m. Stalking 45 15
1909 60m. In the snow 45 15

387 "Mir" Space Station

1987. Intercosmos XX. Sheet 118 × 97 mm.
MS1910 **387** 4t. multicoloured 1·00 1·00

388 Bobsleighing
389 Sukhe Bator

1988. Air. Winter Olympic Games, Calgary. Mult.
1911 20m. Type **388** 10 10
1912 30m. Ski jumping 10 10
1913 40m. Skiing 15 10
1914 50m. Biathlon 20 10
1915 60m. Speed skating 25 10
1916 80m. Figure skating 30 15
1917 1t.20 Ice hockey 50 25
MS1918 91 × 110 mm. 4t. Cross-country skiing 1·40 1·40

1988. 95th Birth Anniv of Sukhe Bator.
1919 **389** 60m. multicoloured 40 10

390 "Invitation"

1988. Roses. Multicoloured.
1920 20m. Type **390** 10 10
1921 30m. "Meilland" 10 10
1922 40m. "Pascali" 15 10
1923 50m. "Tropicana" 20 10
1924 60m. "Wendy Cussons" 25 10
1925 80m. "Rosa sp." (wrongly inscr "Blue Moon") 30 15
1926 1t.20 "Diorama" 50 25
MS1927 97 × 117 mm. 4t. Red rose 1·40 1·40

391 "Ukhaant Ekhner"

1988. Puppets. Multicoloured.
1928 20m. Type **391** 10 10
1929 30m. "Altan Everte Mungun Turuut" 10 10
1930 40m. "Aduuchyn Khuu" . . 15 10
1931 50m. "Suulenkhuu" 20 10
1932 60m. "Khonchyn Khuu" . . 25 10
1933 80m. "Argat Byatskhan Baatar" 30 15
1934 1t.20 "Botgochyn Khuu" . . 50 25

392 "Tatra 11" Car, 1923

1988. "Praga 88" International Stamp Exhibition, Prague. Sheet 110 × 90 mm.
MS1935 **392** 4t. multicoloured . .

393 Judo

394 Marx

1988. Olympic Games, Seoul. Multicoloured.
1936 20m. Type **393** 10 10
1937 30m. Archery 10 10
1938 40m. Weightlifting 15 10
1939 50m. Gymnastics 20 10
1940 60m. Cycling 25 10
1941 80m. Running 30 15
1942 1t.20 Wrestling 50 25
MS1943 90 × 110 mm. 4t. Boxing 1·40 1·40

1988. 170th Birth Anniv of Karl Marx.
1944 **394** 60m. multicoloured . . . 50 20

395 Couple and Congress Banner

396 "Kosmos"

1988. 19th Revsomol Youth Congress.
1945 **395** 60m. multicoloured . . . 1·00 30

1988. Spacecraft and Satellites. Multicoloured.
1946 20m. Type **396** 10 10
1947 30m. "Meteor" 10 10
1948 40m. "Salyut"–"Soyuz" space complex 10 10
1949 50m. "Prognoz-6" 15 10
1950 60m. "Molniya-1" 15 10
1951 80m. "Soyuz" 20 15
1952 1t.20 "Vostok" 35 20
MS1953 96 × 115 mm. 4t. Satellite scanning areas of Earth . . . 3·00 3·00

397 Buddha

398 Emblem

1988. Religious Sculptures.
1954 **397** 20m. multicoloured . . . 10 10
1955 – 30m. multicoloured . . . 10 10
1956 – 40m. multicoloured . . . 20 10
1957 – 50m. multicoloured . . . 25 10
1958 – 60m. multicoloured . . . 30 10
1959 – 70m. multicoloured . . . 35 10
1960 – 80m. multicoloured . . . 40 15
1961 – 1t.20 multicoloured . . . 65 25
DESIGNS: 30m. to 1t.20, Different buddhas.

1988. 30th Anniv of Problems of "Peace and Socialism" (magazine).
1962 **398** 60m. multicoloured . . . 50 10

399 Eagle

1988. White-tailed Sea Eagle. Multicoloured.
1963 60m. Type **399** 90 60
1964 60m. Eagle on fallen branch and eagle landing 90 60
1965 60m. Eagle on rock 90 60
1966 60m. Eagle (horiz) 90 60

400 Ass

1988. Asiatic Wild Ass. Multicoloured.
1967 60m. Type **400** 40 15
1968 60m. Head of ass 40 15
1969 60m. Two adults 40 15
1970 60m. Mare and foal 40 15

401 Athlete

403 U.S.S.R. (ice hockey)

402 "Mongolian Camp" (H. Jargalsuren)

1988. Traditional Sports. Multicoloured.
1971 10m. Type **401** 10 10
1972 20m. Horseman 15 10
1973 30m. Archery 20 10
1974 40m. Wrestling 25 10
1975 50m. Archery (different) . . 35 15
1976 70m. Horsemen (national holiday cavalcade) 60 30
1977 1t.20 Horsemen, wrestlers and archers 95 45

1988. Childrens' Fund. Sheet 115 × 95 mm.
MS1978 **402** 4t. multicoloured . . 1·00 1·00

1988. Winter Olympic Games Gold Medal Winners. Multicoloured.
1979 1t.50 Type **403** 30 10
1980 1t.50 Bonnie Blair (speed skating) 30 10
1981 1t.50 Alberto Tomba (slalom) 30 10
1982 1t.50 Matti Nykanen (ski jumping) (horiz) 30 10
MS1983 110 × 87 mm. 4t. Katarina Witt (figure skating) (horiz) . . 1·00 1·00

404 Brown Goat

1988. Goats. Multicoloured.
1984 20m. Type **404** 10 10
1985 30m. Black goat 10 10
1986 40m. White long-haired goats 15 10
1987 50m. Black long-haired goat 20 10
1988 60m. White goat 25 10
1989 80m. Black short-haired goat 30 15
1990 1t.20 Nanny and kid . . . 50 25
MS1991 95 × 116 mm. 4t. Head of goat (vert) . . . . 1·40 1·40

405 Emblem

1989. 60th Anniv of Mongolian Writers' Association.
1992 **405** 60m. multicoloured . . . 40 10

406 Beaver gnawing Trees

1989. Eurasian Beaver. Multicoloured.
1993 60m. Type **406** 40 15
1994 60m. Beaver with young . . 40 15
1995 60m. Beavers beside tree stump and in water . . . 40 15
1996 60m. Beaver rolling log . . 40 15

407 Dancers

1989. Ballet.
1997 **407** 20m. multicoloured . . . 10 10
1998 – 30m. multicoloured . . . 10 10
1999 – 40m. multicoloured (vert) 15 10
2000 – 50m. multicoloured . . . 20 10
2001 – 60m. multicoloured . . . 25 10
2002 – 80m. multicoloured (vert) 30 15
2003 – 1t.20 multicoloured (vert) 50 25
DESIGNS: 30m. to 1t.20, Different dancing scenes.

408 "Ursus pruinosus"

1989. Bears. Multicoloured.
2004 20m. Type **408** 10 10
2005 30m. Brown bear 20 10
2006 40m. Asiatic black bear . . 30 15
2007 50m. Polar bear 40 20
2008 60m. Brown bear 55 25
2009 80m. Giant panda 70 35
2010 1t.20 Brown bear . . . . . 1·10 55
MS2011 110 × 90 mm. 4t. Giant panda (different) . . . . . . 3·00 3·00

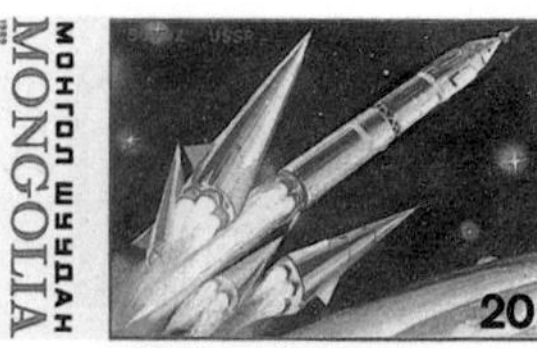

409 "Soyuz" Spacecraft

1989. Space. Multicoloured.
2012 20m. Type **409** 10 10
2013 30m. "Apollo"–"Soyuz" link 15 10
2014 40m. "Columbia" space shuttle (vert) 20 10
2015 50m. "Hermes" spacecraft 30 15
2016 60m. "Nippon" spacecraft (vert) 45 20
2017 80m. "Energy" rocket (vert) 65 30
2018 1t.20 "Buran" space shuttle (vert) 95 45
MS2019 110 × 88 mm. 4t. German "Sanger" project . . . . . . 2·50 2·50

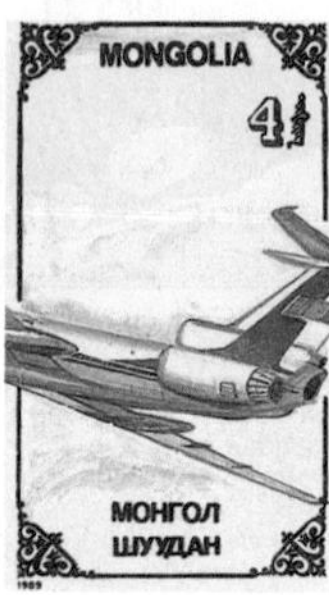

410 Tupolev Tu-154

1989. "Philexfrance 89", Paris (1st issue). and "Bulgaria '89", Sofia, International Stamp Exhibitions. Sheet 90 × 110 mm.
MS2020 **410** 4t. multicoloured . . 2·00 2·00
See also **MS**2034.

411 Nehru

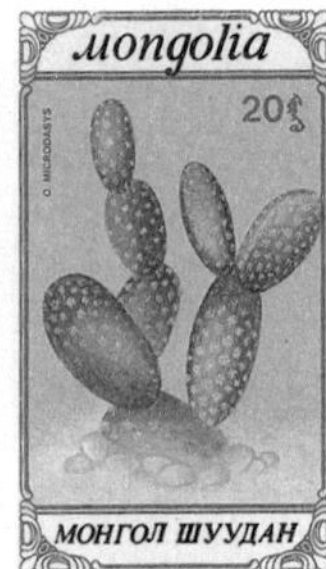

412 "Opuntia microdasys"

1989. Birth Centenary of Jawaharial Nehru (Indian statesman).
2021 **411** 10m. multicoloured . . . 50 15

1989. Cacti. Multicoloured.
2022 20m. Type **412** 10 10
2023 30m. "Echinopsis multipiex" 10 10
2024 40m. "Rebutia tephracanthus" 15 10
2025 50m. "Brasilicactus haselbergii" 20 10
2026 60m. "Gymnocalycium mihanovichii" 25 10
2027 80m. "C. strausii" 30 15
2028 1t.20 "Horridocactus tuberisvicatus" 50 25
MS2029 90 × 110 mm. 4t. *Astrophytum ornatum* . . . . . 1·40 1·40

1989. 800th Anniv of Coronation of Genghis Khan. Nos. 291/4 optd **CHINGGIS KHAN CROWNATION 1189**.
2030 **67** 20m. multicoloured . . . 2·75 2·75
2031 – 30m. multicoloured . . . 4·25 4·25
2032 – 50m. black, brown and red . . . . 6·50 6·50
2033 – 60m. buff, blue and brown . . . . 8·50 8·50

414 Concorde

1989. "Philexfrance 89" International Stamp Exhibition, Paris (2nd issue). Sheet 130 × 55 mm containing T **414** and similar horiz designs. Multicoloured.
MS2034 20m. Type **414**; 60m. French TGV express train; 1t.20, Sukhe Bator statue . . . . . 4·50 4·50

415 Citroen "BX"

1989. Motor Cars. Multicoloured.
2035 20m. Type **415** 10 10
2036 30m. Volvo "760 GLF" . . 10 10
2037 40m. Honda "Civic" 60 25
2038 50m. Volga 20 10
2039 60m. Ford "Granada" . . . 25 10
2040 80m. Baz "21099" 30 15
2041 1t.20 Mercedes "190" . . . 50 20
MS2042 110 × 90 mm. 4t. As No. 2038 . . . . 1·50 1·50

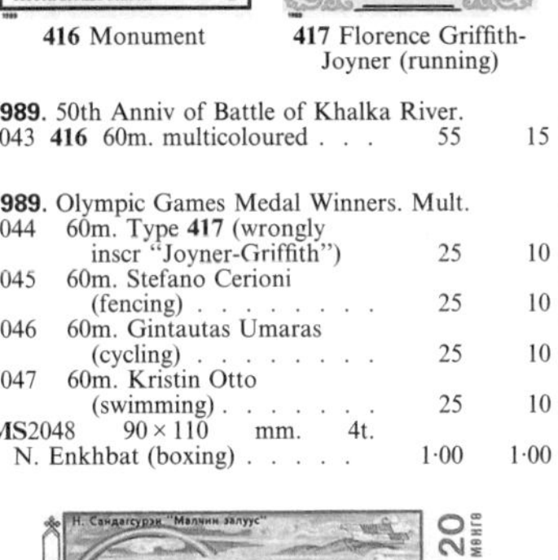

416 Monument 417 Florence Griffith-Joyner (running)

1989. 50th Anniv of Battle of Khalka River.
2043 **416** 60m. multicoloured . . . 55 15

1989. Olympic Games Medal Winners. Mult.
2044 60m. Type **417** (wrongly inscr "Joyner-Griffith") 25 10
2045 60m. Stefano Cerioni (fencing) 25 10
2046 60m. Gintautas Umaras (cycling) 25 10
2047 60m. Kristin Otto (swimming) 25 10
MS2048 90 × 110 mm. 4t. N. Enkhbat (boxing) . . . . . 1·00 1·00

418 "Malchin Zaluus" (N. Sandagsuren)

1989. 30th Anniv of Co-operative Movement. Paintings. Multicoloured.
2049 20m. Type **418** 10 10
2050 30m. "Tsaatny Tukhai Dursamkh" (N. Sandagsuren) (vert) 20 10
2051 40m. "Uul Shig Tushigtei" (D. Amgalan) 30 15
2052 50m. "Goviin Egshig" (D. Amgalan) 40 20
2053 60m. "Tsagaan Sar" (Ts. Dagvanyam) 55 25
2054 80m. "Tumen Aduuny Bayar" (M. Butemkh) (vert) 65 30
2055 1t.20 "Bilcheer Deer" (N. Tsultem) . . . . . . 1·10 50
MS2056 110 × 90 mm. 4t. "Naadam" (detail, Ts. Dagvanyam) . . . . 4·00 4·00

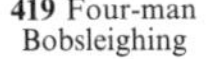

419 Four-man Bobsleighing 420 Victory Medal

1989. Ice Sports. Multicoloured.
2057 20m. Type **419** 10 10
2058 30m. Luge 10 10
2059 40m. Figure skating 15 10
2060 50m. Two-man bobsleighing 20 10
2061 60m. Ice dancing 25 10
2062 80m. Speed skating 30 15
2063 1t.20 Ice speedway 50 25
MS2064 90 × 110 mm. 4t. Ice hockey 1·40 1·40

1989. Orders. Designs showing different badges and medals. Multicoloured, background colour given.
2065 **420** 60m. blue 25 10
2066 – 60m. orange 25 10
2067 – 60m. mauve 25 10
2068 – 60m. violet 25 10
2069 – 60m. green 25 10
2070 – 60m. blue 25 10
2071 – 60m. red 25 10

1989. "World Stamp Expo 89" International Stamp Exhibition, Washington D.C. No. **MS**2034 optd **WORLD STAMP EXPO'89, WASHINGTON DC, WASHINGTON DC** and logo on the margin.
MS2072 130 × 55 mm. 20m. multicoloured; 60m. multicoloured; 1t.20, multicoloured . . . . 4·50 4·50

422 Chu Lha 423 Sukhe Bator Statue

1989. Buddhas. Multicoloured.
2073 20m. Damdin Sandub . . . 10 10
2074 30m. Pagwa Lama 20 10
2075 40m. Type **422** 30 15
2076 50m. Agwanglobsan 40 20
2077 60m. Dorje Dags Dan . . . 55 25
2078 80m. Wangchikdorje 65 30
2079 1t.20 Buddha . . . . 1·10 50
MS2080 74 × 89 mm. 4t. Migjid Jang-Rasek . . . . 3·00 3·00

1990. New Year.
2081 **423** 10m. multicoloured . . . 75 35

424 Newspapers and City 425 Emblem

1990. 70th Anniv of "Khuvisgalt Khevlel" (newspaper).
2082 **424** 60m. multicoloured . . . 65 30

1990. 20th Mongolian People's Revolutionary Party Congress.
2083 **425** 60m. multicoloured . . . 50 25

426 Male Character

1990. "Mandukhai the Wise" (film).
2084 **426** 20m. multicoloured . . . 20 10
2085 – 30m. multicoloured . . . 30 15
2086 – 40m. multicoloured . . . 45 20
2087 – 50m. multicoloured . . . 55 30
2088 – 60m. multicoloured . . . 75 35
2089 – 80m. multicoloured . . . 90 45
2090 – 1t.20 multicoloured . . . 1·25 65
MS2091 83 × 105 mm. 4t. multicoloured (vert) . . . . . 4·00 40
DESIGNS: 30m. to 4t., Different characters from the film.

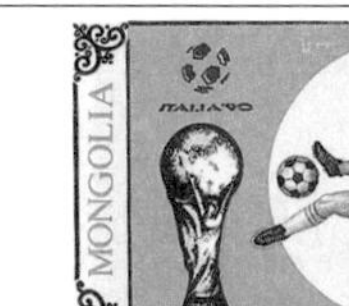

427 Trophy and Players

1990. World Cup Football Championship, Italy.
2092 **427** 20m. multicoloured . . . 10 10
2093 – 30m. multicoloured . . . 10 10
2094 – 40m. multicoloured . . . 10 10
2095 – 50m. multicoloured . . . 15 10
2096 – 60m. multicoloured . . . 15 10
2097 – 80m. multicoloured . . . 20 10
2098 – 1t.20 multicoloured . . . 35 20
MS2099 89 × 110 mm. 4t. multicoloured (Trophy) (vert) 1·00 1·00
DESIGNS: 30m. to 4t., Trophy and different players.

428 Lenin

1990. 120th Birth Anniv of Lenin.
2100 **428** 60m. black, red and gold 65 30

429 Mother with Fawn

1990. Siberian Musk Deer. Multicoloured.
2101 60m. Type **429** 65 30
2102 60m. Deer in wood 65 30
2103 60m. Deer on river bank . . 65 30
2104 60m. Deer in winter landscape 65 30

430 Clock Tower, Houses of Parliament, London

1990. "Stamp World London '90" International Stamp Exhibition (1st issue) Sheet 91 × 105 mm.
MS2105 **430** 4t. multicoloured . . 2·00 2·00
See also Nos. **MS**2107 and 2191/**MS**2200.

1990. 800th Anniv (1989) of Coronation of Genghis Khan (2nd issue). Sheet 116 × 142 mm.
MS2106 **431** 7t. multicoloured . . 3·00 3·00

431 Genghis Khan

1990. "Stamp World London '90" International Stamp Exhibition (2nd issue). No. **MS**2106 optd with Penny Black and **Stamp World London 90** in margin.
MS2107 **431** 7t. multicoloured . . 3·00 2·00

433 Russian Victory Medal 434 Crane

1990. 45th Anniv of End of Second World War.
2108 **433** 60m. multicoloured . . . 65 30

1990. The Japanese White-naped Crane. Mult.
2109 60m. Type **434** 70 70
2110 60m. Crane feeding (horiz) 70 70
2111 60m. Cranes flying (horiz) 70 70
2112 60m. Crane on river bank 70 70

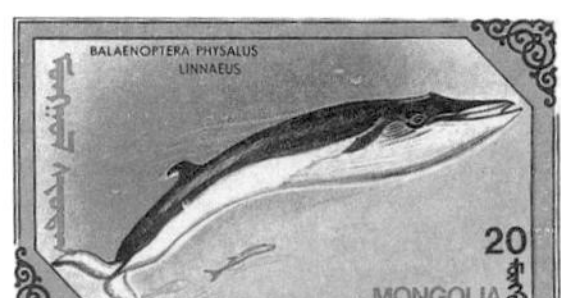

435 Fin Whale

1990. Marine Mammals. Multicoloured.
2113 20m. Type **435** 15 10
2114 30m. Humpback whale . . 30 15
2115 40m. Narwhal 40 20
2116 50m. Risso's dolphin . . . 50 25
2117 60m. Bottle-nosed dolphin 60 30
2118 80m. Atlantic white-sided dolphin 85 40
2119 1t.20 Bowhead whale . . . 1·10 55
MS2120 90 × 110 mm. 4t. Dall's porpoise (vert) . . . . 3·50 3·50

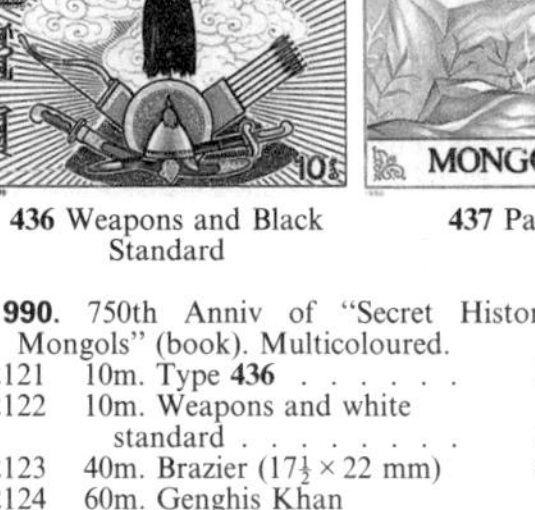

436 Weapons and Black Standard 437 Panda

1990. 750th Anniv of "Secret History of the Mongols" (book). Multicoloured.
2121 10m. Type **436** 10 10
2122 10m. Weapons and white standard 10 10
2123 40m. Brazier (17½ × 22 mm) 40 20
2124 60m. Genghis Khan (17½ × 22 mm) 60 30
2125 60m. Horses galloping . . . 60 30
2126 60m. Tartar camp 60 30
2127 80m. Men kneeling to ruler 75 35
2128 80m. Court 75 35

1990. The Giant Panda. Multicoloured.
2129 10m. Type **437** 15 10
2130 20m. Panda eating bamboo 25 10
2131 30m. Adult eating bamboo, and cub 40 20
2132 40m. Panda on tree branch (horiz) 45 25
2133 50m. Adult and cub resting (horiz) 55 25
2134 60m. Panda and mountains (horiz) 75 35
2135 80m. Adult and cub playing (horiz) 85 45
2136 1t.20 Panda on snow-covered river bank (horiz) 1·60 80
MS2137 94 × 114 mm. 4t. Panda holding bamboo shoots (vert) 4·25 4·25

438 Chasmosaurus

1990. Prehistoric Animals. Multicoloured.
2138 20m. Type **438** 15 10
2139 30m. Stegosaurus 25 10
2140 40m. Probactrosaurus . . . 35 15
2141 50m. Opisthocoelicaudia . . 55 25
2142 60m. Iguanodon (vert) . . . 65 30

2143 80m. Tarbosaurus 90 45
2144 1t.20 Mamenchisaurus (after Mark Hallett) (60 × 22 mm) . . . . . . 1·10 55
MS2145 110 × 90 mm. 4t. Allosaurus attacking herd of Brachiosaurus (after John Gurche) . . . . . 3·50 3·50

439 Lighthouse, Alexandria, Egypt

440 Kea

1990. Seven Wonders of the World. Mult.
2146 20m. Type **439** 15 10
2147 30m. Pyramids of Egypt (horiz) 25 10
2148 40m. Statue of Zeus, Olympia 35 20
2149 50m. Colossus of Rhodes 55 25
2150 60m. Mausoleum, Halicarnassus 65 35
2151 80m. Temple of Artemis, Ephesus (horiz) 90 45
2152 1t.20 Hanging Gardens of Babylon . . . . 1·10 55
MS2153 89 × 110 mm. 4t. Map and pyramids . . . . 3·50 3·50

1990. Parrots. Multicoloured.
2154 20m. Type **440** 20 20
2155 30m. Hyacinth macaw . . . 35 35
2156 40m. Australian king parrot 50 50
2157 50m. Grey parrot 65 65
2158 60m. Kakapo 75 75
2159 80m. Alexandrine parakeet 1·10 1·10
2160 1t.20 Scarlet macaw . . . . 1·25 1·25
MS2161 84 × 104 mm. 4t. Electus parrot . . . . 3·00 3·00

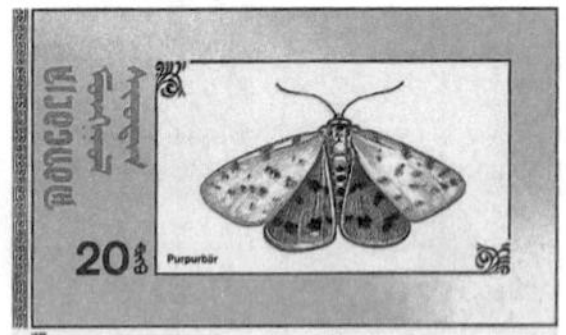
441 Purple Tiger Moth

1990. Moths and Butterflies. Multicoloured.
2162 20m. Type **441** 15 10
2163 30m. Viennese emperor moth 25 10
2164 40m. Comma 40 20
2165 50m. Magpie moth 50 25
2166 60m. Chequered moth . . . 60 30
2167 80m. Swallowtail 85 45
2168 1t.20 Orange-tip . . . . .
MS2169 90 × 110 mm. 4t. Striped hawk moth (vert). Perf or imperf 3·50 1·75

442 Jetsons in Flying Saucer

1991. The Jetsons (cartoon characters). Mult.
2170 20m. Type **442** 10 10
2171 25m. Family walking on planet, and dragon (horiz) 15 10
2172 30m. Jane, George, Elroy and dog Astro 20 10
2173 40m. George, Judy, Elroy and Astro crossing river 25 10
2174 50m. Flying in saucer (horiz) 30 15
2175 60m. Jetsons and Cosmo Spacely (horiz) 35 20
2176 70m. George and Elroy flying with jetpacks . . . 45 20
2177 80m. Elroy (horiz) 50 25
2178 1t.20 Judy and Astro watching Elroy doing acrobatics on tree 75 40
MS2179 Two sheets, each 102 × 127 mm. (a) 7t. Elroy with hands in pocket; (b) 7t. Elroy jumping . . . . 6·00 6·00

443 Dino and Bam-Bam meeting Mongolian Boy with Camel

1991. The Flintstones (cartoon characters). Mult.
2180 25m. Type **443** 10 10
2181 35m. Bam-Bam and Dino posing with boy (vert) . . 15 10
2182 45m. Mongolian mother greeting Betty Rubble, Wilma Flintstone and children 20 10
2183 55m. Barney Rubble and Fred riding dinosaurs . . 25 10
2184 65m. Flintstones and Rubbles by river 30 15
2185 75m. Bam-Bam and Dino racing boy on camel . . . 40 20
2186 85m. Fred, Barney and Bam-Bam with Mongolian boy 55 25
2187 1t.40 Flintstones and Rubbles in car 90 45
2188 2t. Fred and Barney taking refreshments with Mongolian . . . . 1·40 70
MS2189 Two sheets, each 126 × 101 mm. (a) 7t. Wilma, Betty and Bam-Bam; (b) 7t. Bam-Bam and Pebbles riding Dino . . . 6·00 6·00

444 Party Emblem

445 Black-capped Chickadee

1991. 70th Anniv of Mongolian People's Revolutionary Party.
2190 **444** 60m. multicoloured . . . 50 25

1991. "Stamp World London 90" International Stamp Exhibition. Multicoloured.
2191 25m. Type **445** 15 15
2192 35m. Common cardinal . . 20 20
2193 45m. Crested shelduck . . . 30 30
2194 55m. Mountain bluebird . . 35 35
2195 65m. Northern oriole . . . 45 45
2196 75m. Bluethroat (horiz) . . 50 50
2197 85m. Eastern bluebird . . . 65 65
2198 1t.40 Great reed warbler . . 1·25 1·25
2199 2t. Golden eagle . . . . . 1·60 1·60
MS2200 Two sheets. (a) 94 × 76 mm. 7t. Ring-necked pheasant (*horiz*); (b) 76 x 94 mm. 7t. Great scaup 6·00 6·00

446 Black Grouse

1991. Birds. Multicoloured.
2201 20m. Type **446** 25 25
2202 30m. Common shelduck . . 35 35
2203 40m. Common pheasant . . 45 45
2204 50m. Long-tailed duck . . . 60 60
2205 60m. Hazel grouse 65 65
2206 80m. Red-breasted merganser . . . . 1·00 1·00
2207 1t.20 Goldeneye . . . . . . 1·75 1·75
MS2208 96 × 115 mm. 4t. Green-winged teal (*Anas crecca*) (vert) 4·00 4·00

447 Emblem

448 Superb Pink

1991. 70th Anniv of Mongolian People's Army.
2209 **447** 60m. multicoloured . . . 50 25

1991. Flowers. Multicoloured.
2210 20m. Type **448** 15 10
2211 30m. "Gentiana pneumonanthe" (wrongly inscr "puenmonanthe") 25 10
2212 40m. Dandelion 40 20
2213 50m. Siberian iris 55 25
2214 60m. Turk's-cap lily 65 30
2215 80m. "Aster amellus" . . . 90 45
2216 1t.20 Thistle . . . . 1·25 60
MS2217 95 × 115 mm. 4t. Bellflower (*Campanula persicifolia*) . . . 3·50 3·50

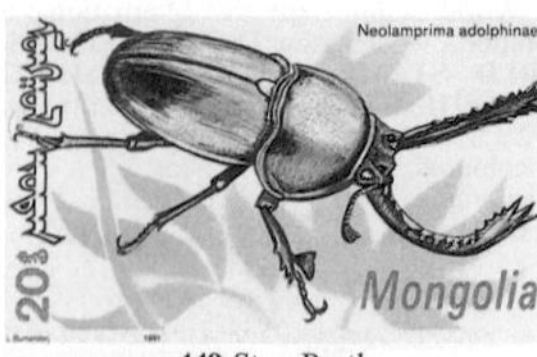

449 Stag Beetle

1991. Beetles. Multicoloured.
2218 20m. Type **449** 15 10
2219 30m. "Chelorrhina polyphemus" 25 10
2220 40m. "Coptolabrus coelestis" 40 20
2221 50m. "Epepeotes togatus" 55 25
2222 60m. Tiger beetle 65 30
2223 80m. "Macrodontia cervicornis" 90 45
2224 1t.20 Hercules beetle . . . . 1·25 60
MS2225 95 × 115 mm. 4t. *Cercopis sanguinolenta* (vert) . . . . . 3·50 3·50

450 Defend

1991. Buddhas. Multicoloured.
2226 20m. Type **450** 15 10
2227 30m. Badmasanhava 25 10
2228 40m. Avalokitecvara 35 15
2229 50m. Buddha 50 25
2230 60m. Mintugwa 60 30
2231 80m. Shyamatara 70 35
2232 1t.20 Samvara . . . . . . 1·10 55
MS2233 95 × 116 mm. 4t. Lamidhatara . . . . 3·00 3·00

451 Zebras

1991. African Wildlife. Multicoloured.
2234 20m. Type **451** 15 10
2235 30m. Cheetah (wrongly inscr "Cheetan") 25 10
2236 40m. Black rhinoceros . . . 40 20
2237 50m. Giraffe (vert) 55 25
2238 60m. Gorilla 65 35
2239 80m. Elephants 90 45
2240 1t.20 Lion (vert) . . . . . 1·25 60
MS2241 95 × 116 mm. 4t. Gazelle (vert) . . . . 3·50 3·50

452 Communications

1991. Meiso Mizuhara Stamp Exhibition, Ulan Bator.
2242 **452** 1t.20 multicoloured . . . 2·00 60

453 Scotch Bonnet

1991. Fungi. Multicoloured.
2243 20m. Type **453** 15 10
2244 30m. Oak mushroom . . . 20 10
2245 40m. "Hygrophorus marzuelus" 30 15
2246 50m. Chanterelle 40 20
2247 60m. Field mushroom . . . 55 25
2248 80m. Bronze boletus 70 35
2249 1t.20 Caesar's mushroom . . 1·25 60
2250 2t. "Tricholoma terreum" 2·10 1·00
MS2251 95 × 80 mm. 4t. *Mitrophora hybrida* (31 × 39 mm) . . . . . 4·50 4·50

454 Emblem

1991. 70th Anniv of Revolution. Sheet 84 × 109 mm.
MS2252 **454** 4t. multicoloured . . 1·00 1·00

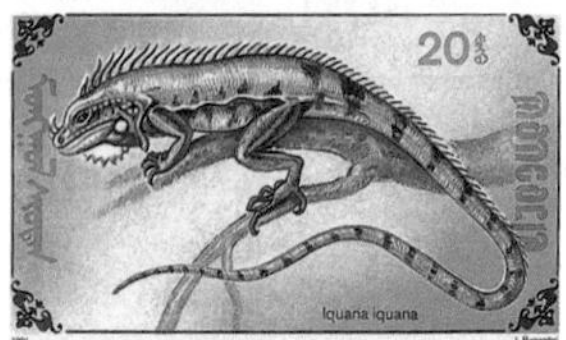

455 Green Iguana

1991. Reptiles. Multicoloured.
2253 20m. Type **455** 15 10
2254 30m. Flying gecko 30 15
2255 40m. Frilled lizard 40 20
2256 50m. Common cape lizard 55 25
2257 60m. Common basilisk . . . 65 30
2258 80m. Common tegu 90 45
2259 1t.20 Marine iguana . . . . 1·50 50
MS2260 75 × 96 mm. 4t. Bengal monitor lizard (Varanus bengalensis) (32 × 54 mm) . . . 3·75 3·75

456 Warrior

1991. Masked Costumes. Multicoloured.
2261 35m. Type **456** 20 10
2262 45m. Mask with fangs . . . 30 15
2263 55m. Bull mask 40 20
2264 65m. Dragon mask 55 25
2265 85m. Mask with beak . . . 65 30
2266 1t.40 Old man . . . . . . 1·25 60
2267 2t. Gold mask with earrings 1·50 75
MS2268 90 × 110 mm. 4t. Lion mask 4·00 4·00

457 German Shepherd

1991. Dogs. Multicoloured.
2269 20m. Type **457** 15 10
2270 30m. Dachshund (vert) . . . 30 15
2271 40m. Yorkshire terrier (vert) 40 20
2272 50m. Standard poodle . . . 50 25
2273 60m. Springer spaniel . . . 70 35
2274 80m. Norfolk terrier 90 45
2275 1t.20 Keeshund . . . . . . 1·50 75
MS2276 110 × 90 mm. 4t. Herding dog (54 × 32 mm) . . . . . . 3·75 3·75

458 Siamese

1991. Cats. Multicoloured.
2277 20m. Type **458** 15 10
2278 30m. Black and white longhaired (vert) 30 15
2279 40m. Ginger red 40 20
2280 50m. Tabby (vert) 50 30
2281 60m. Red and white (vert) 70 35
2282 80m. Maine coon (vert) . . 90 45
2283 1t.20 Blue-eyed white persian (vert) . . . . . . 1·50 65
MS2284 101 × 91 mm. 4t. Tortoiseshell and white . . . . 3·75 3·75

459 Pagoda **460** "Zegris fausti"

1991. "Phila Nippon '91" International Stamp Exhibition, Tokyo. Multicoloured.
2285 1t. Type **459** 30 10
2286 2t. Japanese woman 55 25
2287 3t. Mongolian woman . . . 85 40
2288 4t. Temple . . . . 1·40 65

(b) No. **MS**2233 optd **PHILA NIPPON'91** and logos in the margin.
MS2288a 95 × 115 mm. 4t. multicoloured . . . . 1·60 1·00

1991. Butterflies and Flowers. Multicoloured.
2289 20m. Type **460** 10 10
2290 25m. Yellow roses 15 10
2291 30m. Apollo 20 10
2292 40m. Purple tiger moth . . 25 10
2293 50m. "Pseudochazara regeli" 30 15
2294 60m. "Colotis fausta" . . . 35 15
2295 70m. Red rose 40 20
2296 80m. Margueritas 50 25
2297 1t.20 Lily 75 35

1991. "Expo '90" International Garden and Greenery Exhibition, Osaka. Nos. 2289/97 optd **EXPO '90** and symbol.
2298 20m. multicoloured 10 10
2299 25m. multicoloured 15 10
2300 30m. multicoloured 20 10
2301 40m. multicoloured 25 10
2302 50m. multicoloured 30 15
2303 60m. multicoloured 35 15
2304 70m. multicoloured 40 20
2305 80m. multicoloured 50 25
2306 1t.20 multicoloured 75 35

(b) Two sheets, each 94 × 77 mm, containing horiz design as T **460**. Multicoloured.
MS2307 Two sheets. (a) 7t. Cactus; (b) 7t. Butterfly . . . . 9·00 9·00

462 Poster for 1985 Digital Stereo Re-issue

1991. 50th Anniv (1990) of Original Release of Walt Disney's "Fantasia" (cartoon film). Mult.
2308 1t.70 Type **462** 15 10
2309 2t. 1940 poster for original release 20 10
2310 2t.30 Poster for 1982 digital re-issue 25 10
2311 2t.60 Poster for 1981 stereo re-issue 35 15
2312 4t.20 Poster for 1969 "Psychedelic Sixties" release 60 30
2313 10t. 1941 poster for original release . . . . 1·50 75
2314 15t. Mlle. Upanova (sketch by Campbell Grant) . . . 2·00 90
2315 16t. Mickey as the Sorcerer's Apprentice (original sketch) . . . . 2·40 1·25
MS2316 Four sheets, each 127 × 102 mm. (a) 30t. "Russian Dance" (50 × 37 mm); (b) 30t. Stravinsky's "Rite of Spring" (48 × 35 mm); (c) 30t."The Sorcerer's Apprentice"; (d) 30t. "Chinese Dance" (50 × 36 mm) 15·00 15·00

463 Speed Skating

1992. Winter Olympic Games, Albertville. Mult.
2317 60m. Type **463** 10 10
2318 80m. Ski jumping 10 10
2319 1t. Ice hockey 15 10
2320 1t.20 Ice skating 15 10
2321 1t.50 Biathlon (horiz) . . . 15 10
2322 2t. Skiing (horiz) 20 15
2323 2t.40 Two-man bobsleigh (horiz) 25 15
MS2324 90 × 110 mm. 8t. Four-man bobsleigh (32 × 54 mm) . . . . 1·00 1·00

464 Zeppelin

1992. 75th Death Anniv of Count Ferdinand von Zeppelin (airship pioneer). Sheet 78 × 102 mm.
MS2325 **464** 16t. multicoloured 2·00 2·00

465 Elk

1992. The Elk. Multicoloured.
2326 3t. Type **465** 70 30
2327 3t. Female with young (horiz) 70 30
2328 3t. Adult male (horiz) . . . 70 30
2329 3t. Female 70 30

466 Steam Locomotive, Darjeeling–Himalaya Railway, India

1992. Multicoloured. (a) Railways of the World.
2330 3t. Type **466** 70 25
2331 3t. The "Royal Scot", Great Britain 70 25
2332 6t. Steam train on bridge over River Kwai, Burma–Siam Railway . . . . . . 1·60 60
2333 6t. Baltic steam locomotive No. 767, Burma . . . . 1·60 60
2334 8t. Baldwin steam locomotive, Thailand . . 2·10 70
2335 8t. Western Railways steam locomotive, Pakistan . . . 2·10 70
2336 16t. Class P36 locomotive, Russia . . . . 4·50 1·50
2337 16t. Shanghai–Peking express, China . . . . . 4·50 1·50
MS2338 Two sheets, each 112 × 83 mm. (a) 30t. "Hikari" express train, Japan (56 × 41 mm); (b) 30t. TGV express train, France (56 × 41 mm) . . . . 9·00 9·00

(b) "Orient Express". Black and gold (**MS**2347a) or multicoloured (others).
2339 3t. 1931 advertising poster 70 25
2340 3t. 1928 advertising poster 70 25
2341 6t. Dawn departure . . . . 1·60 60
2342 6t. The "Golden Arrow" leaving Victoria Station, London . . . . 1·60 60
2343 8t. Standing in station, Yugoslavia . . . . 2·10 70
2344 8t. Train passing through mountainous landcape, early 1900s . . . . 2·10 70
2345 16t. "Fleche d'Or" approaching Etaples . . . 4·50 1·50
2346 16t. Arrival in Istanbul . . 4·50 1·50
MS2347 Two sheets, each 113 × 84 mm. (a) 30t. Crowded railway platform; (b) Pullman Car Company arms; 30t. Compagnie Internationale des Wogons-Lits et des Grands Express Europeens arms . . . . 11·00 11·00

467 Columbus **468** Black-billed Magpie

1992. 500th Anniv of Discovery of America by Columbus (1st issue). World Columbian Stamp "Expo '92", Chicago and "Genova '92" International Thematic Stamp Exhibition. Sheet 100 x 70 mm containing T **467** and similar vert design. Multicoloured.
MS2348 30t. Type **467**; 30t. *Santa Maria* . . . . 5·50 5·50
See also Nos. 2370/**MS**2377.

1992. Multicoloured. (a) Birds.
2349 3t. Type **468** 40 20
2350 3t. Northern eagle owl . . . 40 20
2351 6t. Relict gull (horiz) . . . 80 40
2352 6t. Redstart (horiz) 80 40
2353 8t. Demoiselle crane . . . . 1·10 55
2354 8t. Black stork (horiz) . . . 1·10 55
2355 16t. Rough-legged buzzard 2·25 1·10
2356 16t. Golden eagle (horiz) . . 2·25 1·10
MS2357 Two sheets, each 115 × 90 mm. (a) 30t. Mallards swimming and in flight (50 × 37); (b) 30t. Red-breasted goose (50 × 37 mm) . . . . 8·00 8·00

(b) Butterflies and Moths.
2358 3t. Scarce swallowtail (horiz) 40 20
2359 3t. Small tortoiseshell . . . 40 20
2360 6t. "Thyria jacobaeae" (value at right) (horiz) . . 80 40
2361 6t. Peacock (value at left) (horiz) 80 40
2362 8t. Camberwell beauty (value at left) (horiz) . . . 1·10 55
2363 8t. Red admiral (value at right) (horiz) . . . . . 1·10 55
2364 16t. "Hyporhaia audica" (horiz) . . . . 2·25 1·10
2365 16t. Large tortoiseshell (flying over river) (horiz) 2·25 1·10
MS2366 Two sheets. (a) 114 × 90 mm. 30t. Swallowtail (50 × 37 mm); (b) 113 × 90 mm. 30t. Purple tiger moth (50 × 37 mm) . . . . 8·00 8·00

469 Bugler

1992. Celebrities and Events. Five sheets containing T **469** and similar horiz designs. Multicoloured.
MS2367 Five sheets (a) 120 × 80 mm. 30t. Mother Teresa of Calcutta (winner of Nobel Peace Prize, 1979); (b) 120 × 80 mm. 30t. Pope John Paul II celebrating Mass; (c) 115 × 89 mm. 30t. President Punsalmaagiyn Ochirbat of Mongolia and President George Bush of U.S.A.; (d) 120 × 80 mm. 30t. Type **469** (17th World Scout Jamboree, Korea (1991)); (e) 120 × 80 mm. 30t. Type **469** (18th World Scout Jamboree, Netherlands (1995)) . . . . . 16·00 16·00

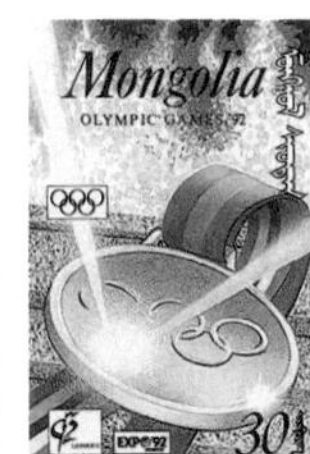

470 Genghis Khan **471** Gold Medal

1992. 830th Birth Anniv of Genghis Khan. Sheet 100 × 120 mm.
MS2368 **470** 16t. multicoloured 5·00 5·00

1992. Olympic Games, Barcelona (1st issue), "Granada '92" International Thematic Stamp Exhibition and "Expo '92" World's Fair, Seville. Sheet 100 × 70 mm containing T **471** and similar vert design. Multicoloured.
MS2369 30t. Type **471**; 30t. Olympic torch . . . . 9·00 9·00
See also Nos. 2379/**MS**2388.

472 Fleet

1992. 500th Anniv of Discovery of America by Columbus (2nd issue). Multicoloured.
2370 3t. Type **472** 15 10
2371 7t. Amerindians' canoe approaching "Santa Maria" 25 10
2372 10t. "Pinta" 35 15
2373 16t. "Santa Maria" in open sea (vert) 55 25
2374 30t. "Santa Maria" passing coastline . . . . 1·10 50
2375 40t. Dolphins and "Santa Maria" . . . . 1·50 75
2376 50t. "Nina" . . . . 1·90 90
MS2377 Two sheets, each 94 × 115 mm. (a) 80t. Christopher Columbus (37 × 49 mm); (b) 80t. iSanta Mariai (37 × 49 mm) . . 7·50 7·50

1992. Mongolian Stamp Exhibition, Taiwan. No. **MS**1449 optd **MONGOLIAN STAMP EXHIBTION 1992 – TAIWAN** in margin.
MS2378 105 × 68 mm. **298** 4t. multicoloured . . . . 3·00 3·00

474 Long Jumping

1992. Olympic Games, Barcelona. Multicoloured.
2379 3t. Type **474** 10 10
2380 6t. Gymnastics (pommel exercise) 10 10
2381 8t. Boxing 10 10
2382 16t. Wrestling 10 10
2383 20t. Archery (vert) 10 10
2384 30t. Cycling 10 10
2385 40t. Show jumping 15 10
2386 50t. High jumping 20 10
2387 60t. Weightlifting 20 10
MS2388 Two sheets, each 100 × 82 mm. (a) 80t. Throwing the javelin (38 × 26 mm); (b) 80t. Judo (38 × 26 mm) . . . . . . 1·00 1·00

1993. Birth Centenary of Sukhe Bator. No. **MS**1523 optd **1893 – 1993** in the margin.
MS2389 65 × 72 mm. **270** 4t. purple 3·00 3·00

Eight designs, each 200t. and embossed on both gold and silver foil and accompanied by matching miniature sheets, were issued in 1993 in limited printings, depicting animals, sports or transport.

476 Black Grouse

1993. Birds. Multicoloured.
2390 3t. Type **476** 10 10
2391 8t. Moorhen 30 15
2392 10t. Golden-crowned kinglet 40 20
2393 16t. River kingfisher 60 30
2394 30t. Red-throated diver . . 1·10 50
2395 40t. Grey heron . . . . . . 1·50 75

2396 50t. Hoopoe . . . . 1·90 90
2397 60t. Blue-throated niltava 2·25 1·10
MS2398 Two sheets, each 115 × 90 mm. (a) 80t. Great crested grebe (*Podiceps cristatus*) (45 × 35 mm); (b) 80t. Griffon vulture (*Gyps fulvus*) (48 × 35 mm) 7·00 7·00

477 Orange-tip

1993. Butterflies and Moths. Multicoloured.
2399 3t. Type **477** 10 10
2400 8t. Peacock 30 15
2401 10t. High brown fritillary . . 40 20
2402 16t. "Limenitis reducta" . . 60 30
2403 30t. Common burnet . . . 1·10 50
2404 40t. Common blue . . . . 1·50 75
2405 50t. Apollo . . . . 1·90 90
2406 60t. Great peacock . . . . 2·25 1·10
MS2407 Two sheets, each 115 × 90 mm. (a) 80t. Poplar admiral (*Limenitis populi*) (49 × 37 mm); (b) 80t. Scarce copper (Heodes virgaureae) (49 × 37 mm) . . . . 7·00 7·00

1993. No. 1221 surch **XXX 15Ter**.
2408 15t. on 70m. multicoloured 2·75 1·00

479 Nicolas Copernicus (astronomer)

1993. "Polska'93" International Stamp Exhibition, Poznan. Multicoloured.
2409 30t. Type **479** (520th birth anniv) . . . . 2·00 90
2410 30t. Frederic Chopin (composer) . . . . 2·00 90
2411 30t. Pope John Paul II . . . 2·00 90
MS2412 Two sheets, each 98 × 122 mm. (a) 80t. Type **479**; (b) 80t. As No. 2411 . . . . . . 11·00 11·00

1993. No. 263 surch **8-Ter**.
2413 8t. on 70m. multicoloured 40 20

481 Sun Yat-sen (Chinese statesman)

1993. "Taipei '93" International Stamp Exhibition. Two sheets each containing vert design as T **481**. Multicoloured.
MS2414 Two sheets, each 100 × 124 mm. (a) 80t. Type **481**; (b) 80t. Genghis Khan (portrait as in Type **431**) . . . . 1·25 75

482 Hologram of Airship

1993. Airship Flight over Ulan Bator.
2415 **482** 80t. multicoloured . . . 1·00 50

483 Buddha

1993. "Bangkok 1993" International Stamp Exhibition. Multicoloured.
2416 50t. Buddha on throne . . . 55 25
2417 100t. Buddha (different) . . 1·10 50
2418 150t. Type **483** . . . . . . 1·60 80
2419 200t. Multi-armed Buddha 2·25 1·10
MS2420 90 × 125 mm. 300t. Buddha with right hand raised . . . . 3·00 3·00

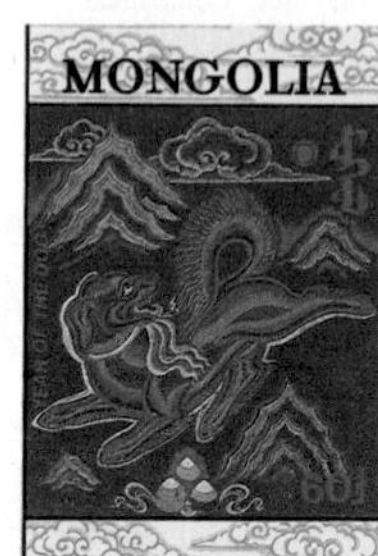

484 Clouds, Mountains and Dog

1994. New Year. Year of the Dog. Multicoloured.
2421 60t. Type **484** 45 20
2422 60t. Dog reclining between mountains and waves (horiz) 45 20

485 Uruguay (1930, 1950)

1994. World Cup Football Championship, U.S.A. Previous Winners. Multicoloured.
2423 150t. Type **485** 30 15
2424 150t. Italy (1934) 30 15
2425 150t. German Federal Republic (1954) 30 15
2426 150t. Brazil (1958) 30 15
2427 150t. Argentina (1978, 1986) 30 15
2428 200t. Italy (1938) 40 20
2429 200t. Brazil (1962) 40 20
2430 200t. German Federal Republic (1974) 40 20
2431 250t. Brazil (1970) 50 25
2432 250t. Italy (1982) 50 25
2433 250t. German Federal Republic (1990) 50 25
MS2434 Five sheets. (a) 167 × 120 mm. Nos. 2427 and 2431/3; (b) 118 × 93 mm. Nos. 2423 and 2427; (c) 118 × 93 mm. Nos. 2424, 2428 and 2432; (d) 118 × 93 mm. Nos. 2425, 2430 and 2433; (e) 118 × 93 mm. Nos. 2426, 2429 and 2431 . . 16·00 16·00

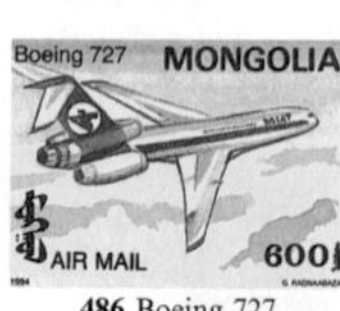

486 Boeing 727

1994. Air. "Hong Kong '94" International Stamp Exhibition. Sheet 96 × 69 mm.
MS2435 **486** 600t. multicoloured 4·00 2·00

487 Pres. Punsalmaagin Ochirbat

1994. 1st Direct Presidential Election. Sheet 86 × 91 mm.
MS2436 **487** 150t. multicoloured 90 50

488 Biathlon

1994. Winter Olympic Games, Lillehammer, Norway. Multicoloured.
2437 50t. Type **488** 30 15
2438 60t. Two-man bobsleigh . . 35 15
2439 80t. Skiing 45 20
2440 100t. Ski jumping 60 30
2441 120t. Ice skating 70 35
2442 200t. Speed skating . . . . 1·25 60
MS2443 100 × 125 mm. 400t. Ice hockey . . . . 3·75 3·75

489 Dalai Lama

1994. Award of Nobel Peace Prize to Dalai Lama. Sheet 85 × 104 mm.
MS2444 **489** 400t. multicoloured 5·00 5·00

490 Lammergeier

1994. Wildlife. Multicoloured.
2445 60t. Type **490** 45 20
2446 60t. Grey-headed woodpecker on tree trunk 45 20
2447 60t. Japanese white-naped cranes 45 20
2448 60t. Western marsh harrier 45 20
2449 60t. Golden oriole on branch 45 20
2450 60t. Bank swallows 45 20
2451 60t. Montagu's harrier perched on rock 45 20
2452 60t. Pallid harriers in flight 45 20
2453 60t. Squirrel on branch . . 45 20
2454 60t. Dragonfly 45 20
2455 60t. Black stork 45 20
2456 60t. Northern pintail . . . 45 20
2457 60t. Spotted nutcracker standing on rock 45 20
2458 60t. Marmot 45 20
2459 60t. Ladybird on flower . . 45 20
2460 60t. Clutch of eggs in ground nest 45 20
2461 60t. Grasshopper 45 20
2462 60t. Butterfly 45 20
Nos. 2445/62 were issued together, se-tenant, forming a composite design.

491 Command Module **492** Flowers

1994. 25th Anniv of First Manned Moon Landing. Multicoloured.
2463 200t. Type **491** 65 30
2464 200t. Earth, astronaut in chair and shuttle wing . . 65 30
2465 200t. Shuttle approaching Earth 65 30
2466 200t. Astronaut on Moon 65 30
MS2467 105 × 130 mm. Nos. 2463/6 2·40 1·25

1994.
2468 **492** 10t. green and black . . 10 10
2469 – 18t. purple and black . . 10 10
2470 – 22t. blue and black . . . 15 10
2471 – 44t. purple and black . . 25 10
DESIGNS: 18, 44t. Argali; 22t. Airplane.

493 Korean Empire 1884 5m. Stamp

1994. "Philakorea 1994" International Stamp Exhibition, Seoul. Multicoloured.
2472 600t. Type **493** . . . . . . 2·25 1·00
2473 600t. Mongolia 1924 1c. stamp . . . . 2·25 1·00
2474 600t. Mongolia 1966 Children's Day 15 m. stamp (47 × 34 mm) . . . 2·25 1·00
2475 600t. South Korea 1993 New Year 110 w. stamp (47 × 34 mm) . . . . . . 2·25 1·00
MS2476 94 × 76 mm. 600t. Korean man in traditional dress (34 × 47 mm) . . . . 2·50 2·50

494 Butterfly

1994. "Singpex '94" National Stamp Exhibtion, Singapore. Year of the Dog. Multicoloured.
2477 300t. Type **494** . . . . . . 1·00 50
MS2478 105 × 78 mm. 400t. Dog 3·50 3·50

495 1924 20c. Stamp

1994. 70th Anniv of First Mongolian Stamp. Sheet 91 × 111 mm.
MS2479 **495** 400t. multicoloured 3·50 3·50

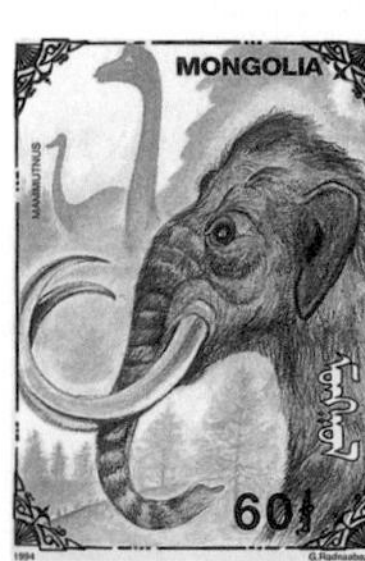

496 Mammoth

1994. Prehistoric Animals. Multicoloured.
2480 60t. Type **496** 35 15
2481 80t. Stegosaurus 50 25
2482 100t. Talararus (horiz) . . . 75 35
2483 120t. Gorythosaurus (horiz) 90 45
2484 200t. Tyrannosaurus (horiz) 1·50 75
MS2485 124 × 99 mm. 400t. Triceratops (horiz) . . . . . . 3·75 2·00

497 National Flags

1994. Mongolia–Japan Friendship and Co-operation.
2486 **497** 20t. multicoloured . . . 15 10

498 Boar and Mountains

1995. New Year. Year of the Pig. Multicoloured.

2487	200t. Type **498**	65	30
2488	200t. Boar reclining amongst clouds (vert)	65	30

499 Dancer

1995. Tsam Religious Mask Dance.

2489	**499**	20t. multicoloured . . .	10	10
2490	–	50t. multicoloured . . .	20	10
2491	–	60t. multicoloured . . .	30	15
2492	–	100t. multicoloured . . .	50	25
2493	–	120t. multicoloured . . .	60	30
2494	–	150t. multicoloured . . .	65	30
2495	–	200t. multicoloured . . .	95	40
MS2496		92 × 133 mm. 400t. multicoloured	3·00	3·00

DESIGNS: 50t. to 400t. Different masked characters.

500 Saiga

1995. The Saiga. Multicoloured.

2497	40t. Type **500**	20	10
2498	50t. Male and female . . .	30	15
2499	70t. Male running	45	20
2500	200t. Head and neck of male	1·00	50

501 Garden Tiger Moth

1995. "Hong Kong '95" Stamp and Collecting Fair. Sheet 104 × 100 mm containing T **501** and similar square design plus two labels. Multicoloured.

MS2501	200t. Type **501**; 200t. Dandelion and anemone . . .	4·00	4·00

502 Yellow Oranda

1995. Goldfish. Multicoloured.

2502	20t. Type **502**	20	10
2503	50t. Red and white veil-tailed wen-yu	35	15
2504	60t. Brown oranda red-head	45	20
2505	100t. Pearl-scaled	80	30
2506	120t. Red lion-head	1·00	45
2507	150t. Brown oranda	1·40	55
2508	200t. Red and white oranda with narial	1·90	75
MS2509	136 × 110 mm. 400t. Red and white goldfish (49 × 37 mm)	3·25	3·25

See also No. **MS**2510.

1995. "Singapore '95" International Stamp Exhibition. As No. **MS**2509 but with exhibition embelm in the margin.

MS2510	136 × 110 mm. 400t. multicoloured	3·25	3·25

503 Bishop

1995. X-Men (comic strip). Designs showing characters. Multicoloured.

2511	30t. Type **503**	10	10
2512	50t. Beast	15	10
2513	60t. Rogue	25	10
2514	70t. Gambit	30	15
2515	80t. Cyclops	40	20
2516	100t. Storm	50	25
2517	200t. Professor X	95	45
2518	250t. Wolverine	1·25	60
MS2519	168 × 171 mm. 250t. Wolverine (horiz); 250t. Magneto (horiz)	3·50	3·50

504 Trygve Lie (1946—52)

1995. 50th Anniv of United Nations Organization. Sheet 125 × 115 mm containing T **504** and similar vert designs showing Secretaries-General and various views of the New York Headquarters complex. Multicoloured.

MS2520	60t. Type **504**; 60t. Dag Hammarskjold (1953–61); 60t. U. Thant (1961–71); 60t. Kurt Waldheim (1972–81); 60t. Javier Perez de Cuellar (1982–91); 60t. Boutros Boutros Ghali (from 1992)	4·00	4·00

505 Presley

1995. 60th Birth Anniv of Elvis Presley (entertainer). Multicoloured.

2521	60t. Type **505**	30	15
2522	80t. Wearing cap	35	15
2523	100t. Holding microphone	45	20
2524	120t. Wearing blue and white striped T-shirt . . .	60	30
2525	150t. With guitar and microphone	70	35
2526	200t. On motor bike with girl	85	40
2527	250t. On surfboard	1·10	50
2528	300t. Pointing with left hand	1·50	70
2529	350t. Playing guitar and girl clapping	1·90	85
MS2530	Two sheets. (a) 139 × 91 mm. 400t. Playing guitar; (b) 139 × 94 mm. 400t. Wearing army uniform with Priscilla Presley	12·00	12·00

Nos. 2521/9 were issued together, se-tenant, forming a composite design.

See also No. **MS**2543.

506 Monroe smiling

1995. 70th Birth Anniv (1996) of Marilyn Monroe (actress). Multicoloured.

2531	60t. Type **506**	30	15
2532	80t. Wearing white dress . .	35	15
2533	100t. Pouting	45	20
2534	120t. With naval officer and cello player	60	30
2535	150t. Wearing off-the-shoulder blouse	70	35
2536	200t. Using telephone and wearing magenta dress . .	85	40
2537	250t. Man kissing Monroe's shoulder	1·10	50
2538	300t. With white fur collar	1·50	70
2539	350t. With Clark Gable . .	1·90	85
MS2540	Two sheets. (a) 139 × 90 mm. 300t. Wearing black lace dress; (b) 137 × 106 mm. 300t. Lying on tiger skin rug	7·50	7·50

Nos. 2531/9 were issued together, se-tenant, forming a composite design.

Seel also No. **MS**2544.

507 Rat sitting between Mountains

1996. New Year. Year of the Rat. Multicoloured.

2541	150t. Type **507**	70	35
2542	200t. Rat crouching between mountains and waves (horiz)	85	40

1996. 70th Birth Anniv of Marilyn Monroe (actress) (2nd issue). Two sheets containing vert designs as T **506**.

MS2544	Two sheets. (a) 100 × 136 mm. 200t. Close-up of Monroe; (b) 146 × 112 mm. 300t. Close-up of Monroe and in scene from *Niagara*	6·50	6·50

1996. Mongolian–Chinese Friendship. Sheet 97 × 133 mm containing T **508** and similar vert designs. Multicoloured.

MS2545	. . . .	7·25	7·25

1996. "China '96" International Stamp Exhibition, Peking. As No. **MS**2545 but with each stamp additionally bearing either the exhibition emblem or a mascot holding the emblem.

MS2546	65t. × 4 multicoloured	7·25	7·25

509 Mongolian 1924 2c. Stamp

510 Cycling

1996. "Capex '96" International Stamp Exhibition, Toronto. Sheet 116 × 90 mm containing T **509** and similar design. Multicoloured.

MS2547	350t. Type **509**; 400t. Canadian 1851 3d. stamp (36 × 26 mm)	7·00	7·00

1996. Olympic Games, Atlanta, U.S.A. Mult.

2548	30t. Type **510**	10	10
2549	60t. Shooting	10	10
2550	80t. Weightlifting	15	10
2551	100t. Boxing	20	10
2552	120t. Archery (vert)	25	10
2553	150t. Rhythmic gymnastics (vert)	30	15
2554	200t. Hurdling (vert)	40	20
2555	350t. Show jumping	70	35
2556	400t. Wrestling	80	40
MS2557	Two sheets, each 130 × 93 mm. (a) 500t. Basketball (37 × 53 mm); (b) 600t. Judo (51 × 39 *mm*)	5·00	5·00
MS2558	Two sheets. As No. **MS**2557 but additionally inscr in top margin " Centenary International Olympic Games 1896—1996"	5·00	5·00

Since the above, further issues have appeared inscribed either "Mongolia" or "Mongol Post". It has so far proved impossible to discover the dates on which these stamps were issued and, indeed, if any of them were available for postal purposes in Mongolia.

MONG-TSEU (MENGTSZ) Pt. 17

An Indo-Chinese P.O. in Yunnan province, China, closed in 1922.

1903. 100 centimes = 1 franc.
1919. 100 cents = 1 piastre.

Stamps of Indo-China surcharged.

1903. "Tablet" key-type surch **MONGTZE** and value in Chinese.

1	D	1c. black and red on buff . .	5·75	8·75
2		2c. brown and blue on buff	3·50	5·50
3		4c. brown and blue on grey	5·75	8·25
4		5c. green and red	3·75	4·75
5		10c. red and blue	5·75	11·00
6		15c. grey and red	9·25	11·00
7		20c. red and blue on green	11·00	17·00
8		25c. blue and red	10·50	11·50
9		25c. black and red on pink	£500	£500
10		30c. brown & blue on drab	8·25	16·00
11		40c. red and blue on yellow	60·00	65·00
12		50c. red and blue on pink	£275	£275
13		50c. brown and red on blue	£100	£100
14		75c. brown and red on orge	£120	£100
15		1f. green and red	£120	£100
16		5f. mauve and blue on lilac	£120	£100

1906. Surch **Mong-Tseu** and value in Chinese.

17	**8**	1c. green	80	3·50
18		2c. purple on yellow	90	3·75
19		4c. mauve on blue	75	3·75
20		5c. green	1·25	4·25
21		10c. pink	1·25	5·00
22		15c. brown on blue	1·40	5·00
23		20c. red on green	4·75	5·75
24		25c. blue	6·00	6·25
25		30c. brown on cream	8·00	11·00
26		35c. black on yellow	6·25	7·75
27		40c. black on grey	2·00	10·00
28		50c. brown	11·50	20·00
29	D	75c. brown & red on orange	45·00	45·00
30	**8**	1f. green	16·00	20·00
31		2f. brown on yellow	48·00	50·00
32	D	5f. mauve and blue on lilac	£100	£110
34	**8**	10f. red on green	90·00	90·00

1908. Surch **MONGTSEU** and value in Chinese.

35	**10**	1c. black and brown	1·10	80
36		2c. black and brown	1·40	95
37		4c. black and blue	1·90	1·90
38		5c. black and green	1·90	80
39		10c. black and red	1·75	2·75
40		15c. black and violet	2·75	3·25
41	**11**	20c. black and violet	4·00	5·25
42		25c. black and blue	3·75	7·75
43		30c. black and brown . . .	4·00	4·75
44		35c. black and green	5·00	4·75
45		40c. black and brown . . .	3·50	4·50
46		50c. black and red	5·00	5·50
47	**12**	75c. black and orange . . .	9·25	12·50
48	–	1f. black and red	13·50	12·00
49	–	2f. black and green	15·00	18·00
50	–	5f. black and blue	£100	£110
51	–	10f. black and violet	£100	£110

1919. Nos. 35/51 further surch in figures and words.

52	**10**	$\frac{2}{5}$ c. on 1c. black and brown	1·25	3·00
53		$\frac{4}{5}$ c. on 2c. black and brown	1·25	3·00
54		$1\frac{3}{5}$ c. on 4c. black and blue	1·75	2·75
55		2c. on 5c. black and green	2·00	3·00
56		4c. on 10c. black and red	3·00	3·25
57		6c. on 15c. black and violet	2·50	3·25
58	**11**	8c. on 20c. black and violet	5·00	5·00
59		10c. on 25c. black and blue	4·25	4·00
60		12c. on 30c. black & brown	3·50	4·00
61		14c. on 35c. black & green	3·00	3·75
62		16c. on 40c. black & brown	3·00	4·00
63		20c. on 50c. black and red	3·50	4·00
64	**12**	30c. on 75c. black & orange	4·00	4·75
65	–	40c. on 1f. black and red . .	7·50	9·50
66	–	80c. on 2f. black and green	6·00	6·50
67	–	2p. on 5f. black and blue . .	£120	£120
68	–	4p. on 10f. black and violet	18·00	26·00

MONTENEGRO Pt. 3

Formerly a monarchy on the Adriatic Sea, now part of Yugoslavia. In Italian and German occupation during 1939–45 war.

1874. 100 novcic = 1 florin.
1902. 100 heller = 1 krone.
1907. 100 para = 1 krone (1910 = 1 perper).

1 Prince Nicholas

Прослава
1493 1893
Штампарије
(2)

1874.

45	**1**	1n. blue	40	45
38		2n. yellow	2·00	2·00
51		2n. green	20	15
39		3n. green	50	50
52		3n. red	20	15
40		5n. red	50	50
53		5n. orange	45	20
19		7n. mauve	35·00	30·00
41		7n. pink	50	50
54		7n. grey	35	45
42		10n. blue	50	50
55		10n. purple	30	45
56		15n. brown	30	45

46 20n. brown 25 25
7 25n. purple £250 £275
44 25n. brown 50 2·75
57 25n. blue 30 45
47 30n. brown 40 45
48 50n. blue 40 45
49 1f. green 1·25 2·75
50 2f. red 1·25 4·00

1893. 400th Anniv of Introduction of Printing into Montenegro. Optd with T 2.
81 **1** 2n. yellow 24·00 2·75
82 3n. green 1·50 1·50
83 5n. red 1·25 1·25
84 7n. pink 1·00 1·00
86 10n. blue 1·75 1·75
87 15n. bistre 1·50 1·50
89 25n. brown 1·90 1·90

3 Monastery near Cetinje, Royal Mausoleum

1896. Bicentenary of Petrovich Niegush Dynasty.
90 **3** 1n. brown and blue 30 1·00
91 2n. yellow and purple 30 1·00
92 3n. green and brown 30 1·00
93 5n. brown and green 30 1·00
94 10n. blue and yellow 30 1·00
95 15n. green and blue 30 1·00
96 20n. blue and green 40 1·25
97 25n. yellow and blue 40 1·25
98 30n. brown and purple 45 1·25
99 50n. blue and red 50 1·50
100 1f. blue and pink 90 1·75
101 2f. black and brown 1·00 1·50

УСТАВ
Constitution
1905
Никољдан

4 (5) 7

1902.
102 **4** 1h. blue 30 30
103 2h. mauve 30 30
104 5h. green 30 20
105 10h. red 30 30
106 25h. blue 30 50
107 50h. green 40 50
108 1k. brown 35 35
109 2k. brown 50 50
110 5k. brown 75 1·50

1905. Granting of Constitution. Optd with T **5**.
111 **4** 1h. blue 15 20
112 2h. mauve 15 20
113 5h. green 15 20
114 10h. red 50 50
124a 25h. blue 15 25
125a 50h. green 15 25
126a 1k. brown 15 25
127a 2k. brown 15 25
119 5k. orange 75 2·50

1907. New Currency.
129 **7** 1pa. yellow 15 20
130 2pa. black 15 20
131 5pa. green 1·00 10
132 10pa. red 1·50 10
133 15pa. blue 20 15
134 20pa. orange 20 20
135 25pa. blue 20 1·25
136 35pa. brown 25 15
137 50pa. lilac 45 35
138 1k. red 45 60
139 2k. green 45 60
140 5k. red 90 2·00

9 King Nicholas when a Youth
10 King Nicholas and Queen Milena

11 Prince Nicholas
12 Nicholas I

1910. Proclamation of Kingdom and 50th Anniv of Reign of Prince Nicholas.
141 **9** 1pa. black 35 15
142 **10** 2pa. purple 35 15
143 – 5pa. green 30 15
144 – 10pa. red 30 15
145 – 15pa. blue 30 15
146 **10** 20pa. olive 65 15
147 – 25pa. blue 65 15
148 – 35pa. brown 85 85
149 – 50pa. violet 65 35
150 – 1per. lake 65 35
151 – 2per. green 85 50
152 **11** 5per. blue 1·25 1·00
DESIGNS: As Type **9**: 5, 10, 25, 35pa. Nicholas I in 1910; 15pa. Nicholas I in 1878; 50pa., 1, 2per. Nicholas I in 1890.

1913.
153 **12** 1pa. orange 15 15
154 2pa. purple 15 15
155 5pa. green 15 15
156 10pa. red 15 15
157 15pa. blue 20 20
158 20pa. brown 20 20
159 25pa. blue 20 20
160 35pa. red 50 50
161 50pa. blue 25 25
162 1per. brown 25 25
163 2per. purple 65 65
164 5per. green 65 65

ITALIAN OCCUPATION

Montenegro
Црна Гора
17-IV-41-XIX
(1)

ЦРНА ГОРА
(2)

1941. Stamps of Yugoslavia optd with T **1**. (a) Postage. On Nos. 414, etc.
1 **99** 25p. black 30 65
2 1d. green 30 65
3 1d.50 red 30 65
4 2d. mauve 30 65
5 3d. brown 30 65
6 4d. blue 30 65
7 5d. blue 1·50 4·75
8 5d.50 violet 1·50 4·75
9 6d. blue 1·50 4·75
10 8d. brown 1·75 5·50
11 12d. violet 1·50 4·75
12 16d. purple 1·50 4·75
13 20d. blue 90·00 £140
14 30d. pink 40·00 65·00

(b) Air. On Nos. 360/7.
15 **80** 50p. brown 8·00 6·00
16 – 1d. green 2·00 5·00
17 – 2d. blue 2·00 5·50
18 – 2d.50 red 3·00 6·00
19 **80** 5d. violet 22·00 45·00
20 – 10d. red 22·00 45·00
21 – 20d. green 22·00 50·00
22 – 30d. blue 22·00 48·00

1941. Stamps of Italy optd with T **2**. (a) On Postage stamps of 1929.
28 **98** 5c. brown 15 50
29 – 10c. brown 15 50
30 – 15c. green 15 50
31 **99** 20c. red 15 50
32 – 25c. green 15 50
33 **103** 30c. brown 15 50
34 50c. violet 15 50
35 – 75c. red 15 50
36 – 1l.25 blue 15 50

(b) On Air stamp of 1930.
37 **110** 50c. brown 15 50

1942. Nos. 416 etc of Yugoslavia optd **Governatorato del Montenegro Valore LIRE**.
43 **99** 1d. green 75 1·40
44 1d.50 red 25·00 30·00
45 3d. brown 75 1·40
46 4d. blue 75 1·40
47 5d.50 violet 75 1·40
48 6d. blue 75 1·40
49 8d. brown 75 1·40
50 12d. violet 75 1·40
51 16d. purple 75 1·40

1942. Air. Nos. 360/7 of Yugoslavia optd **Governatorato del Montenegro Valore in Lire**.
52 **80** 0.50l. brown 2·50 3·50
53 – 1l. green 2·50 3·50
54 – 2l. blue 2·50 3·50
55 – 2.50l. red 2·50 3·50
56 **80** 5l. violet 2·50 3·50
57 – 10l. brown 2·50 3·50
58 – 20l. green 65·00 £100
59 – 30l. blue 20·00 32·00

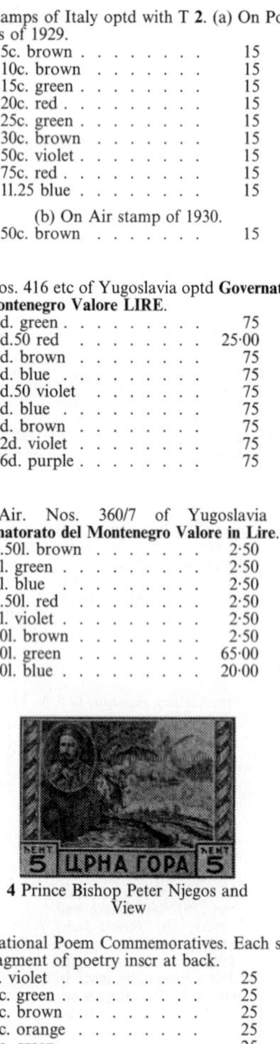
4 Prince Bishop Peter Njegos and View

1943. National Poem Commemoratives. Each stamp has fragment of poetry inscr at back.
60 **4** 5c. violet 25 75
61 – 10c. green 25 75
62 – 15c. brown 25 75
63 – 20c. orange 25 75
64 – 25c. green 25 75
65 – 50c. mauve 25 75
66 – 1l.25 blue 25 75
67 – 2l. green 1·00 2·00
68 – 5l. red on buff 2·50 6·00
69 – 20l. purple on grey 5·00 13·00
DESIGNS—HORIZ: 10c. Meadow near Mt. Lovcen; 15c. Country Chapel; 20c. Chiefs Meeting; 25, 50c. Folk Dancing; 1l.25, Taking the Oath; 2l. Moslem wedding procession; 5l. Watch over wounded standard-bearer. VERT: 20l. Portrait of Prince Bishop Peter Njegos.

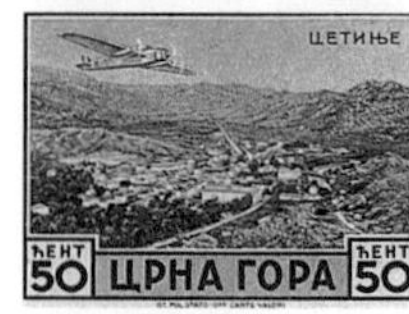

5 Cetinje

1943. Air. With Junkers G31 airplane (2, 20l.) or Fokker F.VIIa/3m airplane (others).
70 **5** 50c. brown 35 1·25
71 – 1l. blue 35 1·25
72 – 2l. mauve 35 1·25
73 – 5l. green 70 2·50
74 – 10l. purple on buff 4·00 9·00
75 – 20l. blue on pink 6·25 16·00
DESIGNS—HORIZ: 1l. Coastline; 2l. Budva; 5l. Mt. Lovcen; 10l. Lake of Scutari. VERT: 20l. Mt. Durmitor.

GERMAN OCCUPATION

1943. Nos. 419/20 of Yugoslavia surch **Deutsche Militaer-Verwaltung Montenegro** and new value in lire.
76 **99** 50c. on 3d. brown 3·00 24·00
77 1l. on 3d. brown 3·00 24·00
78 1l.50 on 3d. brown 3·00 24·00
79 2l. on 3d. brown 4·50 45·00
80 4l. on 3d. brown 4·50 45·00
81 5l. on 4d. blue 5·00 45·00
82 8l. on 4d. blue 9·75 90·00
83 10l. on 4d. blue 14·00 £150
84 20l. on 4d. blue 30·00 £325

1943. Appointment of National Administrative Committee. Optd **Nationaler Verwaltungsausschuss 10.XI.1943**. (a) Postage. On Nos. 64/8.
85 25c. green 5·75 £190
86 50c. mauve 5·75 £190
87 1l.25 blue 5·75 £190
88 2l. green 5·75 £190
89 5l. red on buff £160 £2250

(b) Air. On Nos. 70/4.
90 **5** 50c. brown 9·50 £190
91 1l. blue 9·50 £190
92 2l. mauve 9·50 £190
93 5l. green 9·50 £190
94 10l. purple on buff £2000 £16000

1944. Refugees Fund. Surch **Flüchtlingshilfe Montenegro** and new value in German currency. (a) On Nos. 419/20 of Yugoslavia.
95 **99** 0.15+0.85Rm. on 3d. 7·75 £170
96 0.15+0.85Rm. on 4d. 7·75 £170

(b) On Nos. 46/9.
97 – 0.15+0.85Rm. on 25c. 7·75 £170
98 – 0.15+1.35Rm. on 50c. 7·75 £170
99 – 0.25+1.75Rm. on 1l.25 7·75 £170
100 – 0.25+1.75Rm. on 2l. 7·75 £170

(c) Air. On Nos. A52/4.
101 **5** 0.15+0.85Rm. on 50c. 7·75 £180
102 – 0.25+1.25Rm. on 1l. 7·75 £180
103 – 0.50+1.50Rm. on 2l. 7·75 £180

1944. Red Cross. Surch **+Crveni krst Montenegro** and new value in German currency. (a) On Nos. 419/20 of Yugoslavia.
104 **99** 0.50+2.50Rm. on 3d. 6·50 £170
105 0.50+2.50Rm. on 4d. 6·50 £170

(b) On Nos. 64/5.
106 – 0.15+0.85Rm. on 25c. 6·50 £170
107 – 0.15+1.35Rm. on 50c. 6·50 £170

(c) Air. On Nos. 70/2.
108 **5** 0.25+1.75Rm. on 50c. 6·50 £170
109 – 0.25+2.75Rm. on 1l. 6·50 £170
110 – 0.50+2Rm. on 2l. 6·50 £170

ACKNOWLEDGEMENT OF RECEIPT STAMPS

A 3

A 4

1895.
A90 **A 3** 10n. blue and red 85 1·00

1902.
A111 **A 4** 25h. orange and red 75 75

1905. Optd with T **5**.
A120 **A 4** 25h. orange and red 60 60

1907. As T **7**, but letters "A" and "R" in top corners.
A141 **7** 25p. olive 50 65

1913. As T **12**, but letters "A" and "R" in top corners.
A169 **12** 25p. olive 40 70

POSTAGE DUE STAMPS

D 3

D 4

D 8

1894.
D90 **D 3** 1n. red 2·25 1·40
D91 2n. green 50 20
D92 3n. orange 50 20
D93 5n. green 50 20
D94 10n. purple 50 30
D95 20n. blue 50 30
D96 30n. green 50 30
D97 50n. pale green 50 30

1902.
D111 **D 4** 5h. orange 20 20
D112 10h. green 30 30
D113 25h. purple 30 30
D114 50h. green 30 30
D115 1k. grey 35 35

1905. Optd with T **5**.
D120 **D 4** 5h. orange 35 50
D121 10h. olive 50 1·00
D122 25h. purple 35 50
D123 50h. green 35 50
D124 1k. pale green 50 75

1907.
D141 **D 8** 5p. brown 25 35
D142 10p. violet 25 35
D143 25p. red 25 35
D144 50p. green 25 35

1913. As T **12** but inscr "НОРТОМАРКА" at top.
D165 5p. grey 75 75
D166 10p. lilac 50 50
D167 25p. blue 50 50
D168 50p. red 65 65

ITALIAN OCCUPATION

1941. Postage Due stamps of Yugoslavia optd **Montenegro Upha 17-IV-41-XIX**.
D23 **D 56** 50p. violet 50 1·00
D24 1d. mauve 50 1·00
D25 2d. blue 50 1·00
D26 5d. orange 30·00 50·00
D27 10d. brown 3·00 6·00

1942. Postage Due stamps of Italy optd **UPHATOPA**.
D38 **D 141** 10c. blue 15 1·25
D39 20c. red 15 1·25
D40 30c. orange 15 1·25
D41 50c. violet 15 1·25
D42 1l. orange 25 1·25

MONTSERRAT Pt. 1

One of the Leeward Is., Br. W. Indies. Used general issues for Leeward Is. concurrently with Montserrat stamps until 1 July 1956, when Leeward Is. stamps were withdrawn.

1876. 12 pence = 1 shilling;
20 shillings = 1 pound.
1951. 100 cents = 1 West Indian dollar.

1876. Stamps of Antigua as T **1** optd **MONTSERRAT**.
8c 1d. red 17·00 14·00
2 6d. green 65·00 42·00

3

1880.
7 **3** ½d. green 1·00 8·00
9 2½d. brown £225 65·00
10 2½d. blue 22·00 20·00
5 4d. blue £140 40·00
12 4d. mauve 5·00 3·00

4 Device of the Colony

5

1903.
24a **4** ½d. green 80 1·25
15 1d. grey and red 75 40
26a 2d. grey and brown 2·25 1·25
17 2½d. grey and blue 1·50 1·75
28a 3d. orange and purple 9·50 2·50
29a 6d. purple and olive 10·00 5·50
30 1s. green and purple 10·00 7·00
21 2s. green and brown 25·00 17·00

22 2s.6d. green and black . . . 19·00 38·00
33 **5** 5s. black and red . . . . . 95·00 £110

1908.
36 **4** 1d. red . . . . 1·40 30
38 2d. grey . . . . 1·75 15·00
39 2½d. blue . . . . 2·25 3·50
40 3d. purple on yellow . . . . 1·00 18·00
43 6d. purple . . . . 6·50 50·00
44 1s. black on green . . . . . 8·50 45·00
45 2s. purple and blue on blue 30·00 55·00
46 2s.6d. black and red on blue 30·00 70·00
47 **5** 5s. red and green on yellow 50·00 70·00

1914. As T **5**, but portrait of King George V.
48 5s. red and green on yellow . . 65·00 90·00

8

10 Plymouth

1916.
63 **8** ½d. brown . . . . 15 5·50
64 ½d. green 30 30
50 1d. red . . . . 1·00 75
65 1d. violet 30 60
67 1½d. yellow . . . . 1·75 9·50
68 1½d. red . . . . 30 3·75
69 1½d. brown . . . . 2·00 50
70 2d. grey . . . . 50 2·00
71a 2½d. blue 60 90
72 2½d. yellow . . . . 1·25 19·00
74 3d. purple on yellow . . . . 1·10 4·75
73 3d. blue . . . . 60 16·00
75 4d. black and red on yellow 60 12·00
76 5d. purple and olive . . . . 3·75 10·00
77 6d. purple . . . . 3·00 7·50
78 1s. black on green . . . . . 3·00 7·00
79 2s. purple and blue on blue 7·00 15·00
80 2s.6d. black and red on blue 12·00 50·00
81 3s. green and violet . . . . 12·00 19·00
82 4s. black and red . . . . . 15·00 38·00
83 5s. green and red on yellow 26·00 45·00

1917. Optd **WAR STAMP**.
60 **8** ½d. green . . . . 10 1·50
62 1½d. black and orange . . . 10 30

1932. 300th Anniv of Settlement of Montserrat.
84 **10** ½d. green . . . . 75 8·00
85 1d. red . . . . 75 5·50
86 1½d. brown . . . . 1·25 2·50
87 2d. grey . . . . 1·50 16·00
88 2½d. blue . . . . 1·25 15·00
89 3d. orange . . . . 1·50 17·00
90 6d. violet . . . . 2·25 28·00
91 1s. olive . . . . 12·00 38·00
92 2s.6d. purple . . . . 48·00 70·00
93 5s. brown £100 £160

1935. Silver Jubilee. As T **14a** of Kenya, Uganda and Tanganyika.
94 1d. blue and red . . . . . . 85 3·25
95 1½d. blue and grey . . . . . 1·50 2·75
96 2½d. brown and blue . . . . 2·25 3·25
97 1s. grey and purple . . . . . 3·00 14·00

1937. Coronation. As T **14b** of Kenya, Uganda and Tanganyika.
98 1d. red . . . . 30 1·25
99 1½d. brown 40 30
100 2½d. blue . . . . 40 1·25

11 Carr's Bay

1938. King George VI.
101a **11** ½d. green 15 20
102a – 1d. red 50 30
103a – 1½d. purple 50 50
104a – 2d. orange . . . . 1·50 70
105a – 2½d. blue 50 30
106a **11** 3d. brown . . . . 2·00 40
107a – 6d. violet . . . . 2·50 60
108a **11** 1s. red . . . . 2·25 30
109a – 2s.6d. blue . . . . . . 17·00 2·50
110a **11** 5s. red . . . . 21·00 3·00
111 – 10s. blue . . . . 13·00 19·00
112 **11** £1 black . . . . 13·00 27·00
DESIGNS: 1d., 1½d., 2½d. Sea Island cotton; 2d., 6d., 2s.6d., 10s. Botanic station.

1946. Victory. As T **4a** of Pitcairn Islands.
113 1½d. purple 10 10
114 3d. brown 10 10

1949. Silver Wedding. As T **4b/c** of Pitcairn Islands.
115 2½d. blue 10 10
116 5s. red . . . . 4·75 8·50

1949. U.P.U. As T **4d/g** of Pitcairn Islands.
117 2½d. blue . . . . 15 1·00
118 3d. brown . . . . 1·75 50
119 6d. purple 30 50
120 1s. purple 30 50

1951. Inauguration of B.W.I. University College. As T **15a/b** of Leeward Islands.
121 3c. black and purple . . . . 20 1·00
122 12c. black and violet . . . . 20 1·00

14 Government House

1951.
123 **14** 1c. black . . . . 10 2·00
124 – 2c. green 15 70
125 – 3c. brown 30 70
126 – 4c. red 30 80
127 – 5c. violet 30 70
128 – 6c. brown 30 30
129 – 8c. blue . . . . 1·00 20
130 – 12c. blue and brown . . . 50 30
131 – 24c. red and green . . . . 1·25 30
132 – 60c. black and red . . . . 6·50 3·25
133 – $1.20 green and blue . . . 6·50 6·00
134 – $2.40 black and green . . . 8·00 12·00
135 – $4.80 black and purple . . 17·00 16·00
DESIGNS: 2c., $1.20, Sea Island cotton: cultivation; 3c. Map; 4c., 24c. Picking tomatoes; 5c., 12c. St. Anthony's Church; 6c., $4.80, Badge; 8c., 60c. Sea Island cotton: ginning; $2.40, Government House (portrait on right).

1953. Coronation. As T **4h** of Pitcairn Islands.
136 2c. black and green 60 40

1953. As 1951 but portrait of Queen Elizabeth II.
136a ½c. violet (As 3c.) (I) . . . 50 10
136b ½c. violet (II) 80 10
137 1c. black 10 10
138 2c. green 15 10
139 3c. brown (I) 50 10
139a 3c. brown (II) . . . . 80 2·00
140 4c. red 30 20
141 5c. violet 30 75
142 6c. brown (I) 30 10
142a 6c. brown (II) 55 15
143 8c. blue . . . . 1·00 10
144 12c. blue and brown . . . . 1·50 10
145 24c. red and green . . . . . 1·50 20
145a 48c. olive and purple (As 2c.) . . . . 12·00 2·75
146 60c. black and red . . . . . 8·00 2·25
147 $1.20 green and blue . . . . 15·00 7·00
148 $2.40 black and green . . . 13·00 13·00
149 $4.80 black and purple (I) 5·00 10·00
149a $4.80 black and purple (II) 16·00 7·50
I. Inscr "Presidency". II. Inscr "Colony".

18a Federation Map

1958. Inauguration of British Caribbean Federation.
150 **18a** 3c. green 55 20
151 6c. blue 75 60
152 12c. red 90 15

1963. Freedom from Hunger. As T **20a** of Pitcairn Islands.
153 12c. violet 30 15

1963. Cent of Red Cross. As T **20b** of Pitcairn Islands.
154 4c. red and black 15 20
155 12c. red and blue 35 50

20 Shakespeare and Memorial Theatre, Stratford-upon-Avon

1964. 400th Birth Anniv of Shakespeare.
156 **20** 12c. blue 10 10

1965. Cent of I.T.U. As T **24a** of Pitcairn Islands.
158 4c. red and violet 15 10
159 48c. green and red 30 20

21 Pineapple

1965. Multicoloured.
160 1c. Type **21** 10 10
161 2c. Avocado 10 10
162 3c. Soursop 10 10
163 4c. Pepper 10 10
164 5c. Mango 10 10
165 6c. Tomato 10 10
166 8c. Guava 10 10
167 10c. Ochro 10 10
168 12c. Lime 15 40
169 20c. Orange 30 10
170 24c. Banana 20 10
171 42c. Onion 75 60
172 48c. Cabbage . . . . 2·00 75
173 60c. Pawpaw . . . . 3·00 1·10
174 $1.20 Pumpkin . . . . 2·00 5·00
175 $2.40 Sweet potato . . . . . 6·00 8·50
176 $4.80 Egg plant . . . . . . 6·00 11·00

1965. I.C.Y. As T **24b** of Pitcairn Islands.
177 2c. purple and turquoise . . 10 20
178 12c. green and lavender . . . 25 10

1966. Churchill Commem. As T **24c** of Pitcairn Islands.
179 1c. blue . . . . 10 1·25
180 2c. green 10 10
181 24c. brown 50 10
182 42c. violet 60 60

23 Queen Elizabeth II and Duke of Edinburgh

1966. Royal Visit.
183 **23** 14c. black and blue 75 15
184 24c. black and mauve . . . 1·25 15

24 W.H.O. Building

1966. Inauguration of W.H.O. Headquarters, Geneva.
185 **24** 12c. black, green and blue 15 25
186 60c. black, pur & ochre . . 35 75

1966. 20th Anniv of U.N.E.S.C.O. As T **25b/d** of Pitcairn Islands.
187 4c. multicoloured 10 10
188 60c. yellow, violet and olive 35 10
189 $1.80 black, purple and orange . . . . 1·40 70

25 Sailing Dinghies

1967. International Tourist Year. Multicoloured.
190 5c. Type **25** 15 10
191 15c. Waterfall near Chance Mountain (vert) 20 10
192 16c. Fishing, skin diving and swimming 25 70
193 24c. Playing golf . . . . . . 1·60 45

1968. Nos. 168, 170, 172, 174/6 surch.
194 15c. on 12c. Lime 20 15
195 25c. on 24c. Banana 25 15
196 50c. on 48c. Cabbage 45 15
197 $1 on $1.20 Pumpkin 80 40
198 $2.50 on $2.40 Sweet potato 1·00 4·25
199 $5 on $4.80 Egg plant . . . 1·10 4·25

27 Sprinting

1968. Olympic Games, Mexico.
200 **27** 15c. mauve, green and gold 10 10
201 – 25c. blue, orange and gold 15 10
202 – 50c. green, red and gold . . 25 10
203 – $1 multicoloured 35 30
DESIGNS—HORIZ: 25c. Weightlifting; 50c. Gymnastics. VERT: $1 Sprinting and Aztec pillars.

31 Alexander Hamilton

1968. Human Rights Year. Multicoloured.
204 5c. Type **31** 10 10
205 15c. Albert T. Marryshow . . 10 10
206 25c. William Wilberforce . . 10 10
207 50c. Dag Hammarskjold . . . 10 10
208 $1 Dr. Martin Luther King . 25 30

32 "The Two Trinities" (Murillo)

34 Map showing CARIFTA Countries

1968. Christmas.
209 **32** 5c. multicoloured 10 10
210 – 15c. multicoloured 10 10
211 **32** 25c. multicoloured 10 10
212 – 50c. multicoloured 25 20
DESIGN: 15, 50c. "The Adoration of the Kings" (detail, Botticelli).

1969. 1st Anniv of CARIFTA (Caribbean Free Trade Area). Multicoloured.
223 15c. Type **34** 10 10
224 20c. Type **34** 10 10
225 35c. "Strength in Unity" (horiz) 10 20
226 50c. As 35c. (horiz) 15 20

36 Telephone Receiver and Map of Montserrat

41 King Caspar before the Virgin and Child (detail) (Norman 16th-cent stained glass window)

40 Dolphin (fish)

1969. Development Projects. Multicoloured.
227 15c. Type **36** 10 10
228 25c. School symbols and map 10 10
229 50c. Hawker Siddeley H.S.748 aircraft and map 15 20
230 $1 Electricity pylon and map 25 75

1969. Game Fish. Multicoloured.
231 5c. Type **40** 35 10
232 15c. Atlantic sailfish 50 10
233 25c. Blackfin tuna 60 10
234 40c. Spanish mackerel . . . 80 55

1969. Christmas. Paintings multicoloured; frame colours given.
235 **41** 15c. black, gold and violet 10 10
236 25c. black and red 10 10
237 – 50c. black, blue and orange 15 15
DESIGN—HORIZ: 50c. "Nativity" (Leonard Limosin).

43 "Red Cross Sale"

1970. Centenary of British Red Cross. Mult.
238 3c. Type **43** 10 25
239 4c. School for deaf children 10 25
240 15c. Transport services for disabled 10 20
241 20c. Workshop 10 60

44 Red-footed Booby

1970. Birds. Multicoloured.
242 1c. Type **44** 10 10
243 2c. American kestrel (vert) 15 15
244 3c. Magnificent frigate bird (vert) 15 15
245 4c. Great egret (vert) . . . 1·00 15
299a 5c. Brown pelican (vert) . . 60 55

247	10c. Bananaquit (vert)	40	10
248	15c. Smooth-billed ani	30	15
249	20c. Red-billed tropic bird	35	15
250	25c. Montserrat oriole	50	50
251	50c. Green-throated carib (vert)	5·00	1·50
252	$1 Antillean crested hummingbird	6·50	1·00
253	$2.50 Little blue heron (vert)	5·50	12·00
254	$5 Purple-throated carib	7·50	16·00
254c	$10 Forest thrush	15·00	15·00

45 "Madonna and Child with Animals" (Brueghel the Elder, after Durer)

1970. Christmas. Multicoloured.

255	5c. Type **45**	10	10
256	15c. "The Adoration of the Shepherds" (Domenichino)	10	10
257	20c. Type **45**	10	10
258	$1 As 15c.	35	1·50

46 War Memorial

1970. Tourism. Multicoloured.

259	5c. Type **46**	10	10
260	15c. Plymouth from Fort St. George	10	10
261	25c. Carr's Bay	15	15
262	50c. Golf Fairway	1·00	2·25
MS263	135 × 109 mm. Nos. 259/62	2·50	2·25

47 Girl Guide and Badge

48 "Descent from the Cross" (Van Hemessen)

1970. Diamond Jubilee of Montserrat Girl Guides. Multicoloured.

264	10c. Type **47**	10	10
265	15c. Brownie and badge	10	10
266	25c. As 15c.	15	15
267	40c. Type **47**	20	80

1971. Easter. Multicoloured.

268	5c. Type **48**	10	10
269	15c. "Noli me tangere" (Orcagna)	10	10
270	20c. Type **48**	10	10
271	40c. As 15c.	15	85

49 D.F.C. and D.F.M. in Searchlights

50 "The Nativity with Saints" (Romanino)

1971. Golden Jubilee of Commonwealth Ex-Services League. Multicoloured.

272	10c. Type **49**	10	10
273	20c. M.C., M.M. and jungle patrol	15	10
274	40c. D.S.C., D.S.M. and submarine action	15	15
275	$1 V.C. and soldier attacking bunker	30	70

1971. Christmas. Multicoloured.

276	5c. Type **50**	10	10
277	15c. "Choir of Angels" (Simon Marmion)	10	10
278	20c. Type **50**	10	10
279	$1 As 15c.	35	40

51 Piper Apache

1971. 14th Anniv of Inauguration of L.I.A.T. (Leeward Islands Air Transport). Multicoloured.

280	5c. Type **51**	10	10
281	10c. Beech 50 Twin Bonanza	15	15
282	15c. De Havilland Heron	30	15
283	20c. Britten Norman Islander	35	15
284	40c. De Havilland Twin Otter 100	50	45
285	75c. Hawker Siddeley H.S.748	1·40	2·25
MS286	203 × 102 mm. Nos. 280/5	7·00	13·00

52 "Chapel of Christ in Gethsemane", Coventry Cathedral

1972. Easter. Multicoloured.

287	5c. Type **52**	10	10
288	10c. "The Agony in the Garden" (Bellini)	10	10
289	20c. Type **52**	10	10
290	75c. As 10c.	35	85

53 Lizard

54 "Madonna of the Chair" (Raphael)

1972. Reptiles. Multicoloured.

291	15c. Type **53**	15	10
292	20c. Mountain chicken (frog)	20	10
293	40c. Iguana (horiz)	35	20
294	$1 Tortoise (horiz)	1·00	1·00

1972. Christmas. Multicoloured.

303	10c. Type **54**	10	10
304	35c. "Virgin and Child with Cherub" (Fungai)	15	10
305	50c. "Madonna of the Magnificat" (Botticelli)	20	30
306	$1 "Virgin and Child with St. John and an Angel" (Botticelli)	30	65

55 Lime, Tomatoes and Pawpaw

1972. Royal Silver Wedding. Multicoloured, background colour given.

307	**55** 35c. pink	10	10
308	$1 blue	20	20

56 "Passiflora herbertiana"

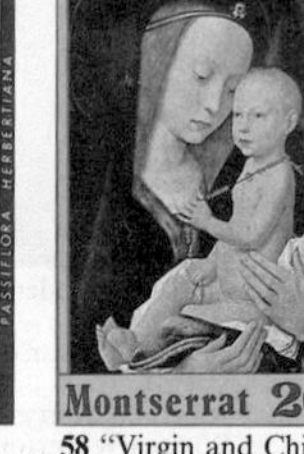

58 "Virgin and Child" (School of Gerard David)

57 Montserrat Monastery, Spain

1973. Easter. Passion-flowers. Multicoloured.

309	20c. Type **56**	20	10
310	35c. "P. vitifolia"	25	10
311	75c. "P. amabilis"	35	75
312	$1 "P. alata-caerulea"	50	80

1973. 480th Anniv of Columbus's Discovery of Montserrat. Multicoloured.

313	10c. Type **57**	15	10
314	35c. Columbus sighting Montserrat	30	15
315	60c. "Santa Maria" off Montserrat	70	60
316	$1 Island badge and map of voyage	80	70
MS317	126 × 134 mm. Nos. 313/16	9·00	13·00

1973. Christmas. Multicoloured.

318	20c. Type **58**	15	10
319	35c. "The Holy Family with St. John" (Jordaens)	20	10
320	50c. "Virgin and Child" (Bellini)	25	30
321	90c. "Virgin and Child with Flowers" (Dolci)	50	70

58a Princess Anne and Captain Mark Phillips

1973. Royal Wedding. Multicoloured, background colour given.

322	**58a** 35c. green	10	10
323	$1 blue	20	20

59 Steel Band

1974. 25th Anniv of University of West Indies. Multicoloured.

324	20c. Type **59**	15	10
325	35c. Masqueraders (vert)	15	10
326	60c. Student weaving (vert)	25	45
327	$1 University Centre, Montserrat	30	55
MS328	130 × 89 mm. Nos. 324/7	1·75	6·00

60 Hands with Letters

1974. Centenary of U.P.U.

329	**60** 1c. multicoloured	10	10
330	– 2c. red, orange and black	10	10
331	**60** 3c. multicoloured	10	10
332	– 5c. orange, red and black	10	10
333	**60** 50c. multicoloured	20	20
334	– $1 blue, green and black	40	65

DESIGN: 2, 5c., $1 Figures from U.P.U. Monument.

1974. Various stamps surch.

335	2c. on $1 mult (No. 252)	30	2·50
336	5c. on 50c. mult (No. 333)	30	60
337	10c. on 60c. mult (No. 326)	65	1·75
338	20c. on $1 mult (No. 252)	30	2·25
339	35c. on $1 blue, green and black (No. 334)	40	1·25

62 Churchill and Houses of Parliament

1974. Birth Cent of Sir Winston Churchill. Mult.

340	35c. Type **62**	15	10
341	70c. Churchill and Blenheim Palace	20	20
MS342	81 × 85 mm. Nos. 340/1	50	70

63 Carib "Carbet"

1975. Carib Artefacts. Self-adhesive or ordinary gum.

343	**63** 5c. brown, yellow and black	10	10
344	– 20c. black, brown & yellow	10	10
345	– 35c. black, yellow & brown	15	10
346	– 70c. yellow, brown & black	45	40

DESIGNS: 20c. "Caracoli"; 35c. Club or mace; 70c. Carib canoe.

64 One-Bitt Coin

1975. Local Coinage, 1785–1801.

351	**64** 5c. black, blue and silver	10	10
352	– 10c. black, pink and silver	15	10
353	– 35c. black, green and silver	20	15
354	– $2 black, red and silver	70	1·50
MS355	142 × 142 mm. Nos. 351/4	1·25	2·75

DESIGNS: 10c. Eighth dollar; 35c. Quarter dollar; $2 One dollar.

65 1d. and 6d. Stamps of 1876

1976. Centenary of First Montserrat Postage Stamp.

356	**65** 5c. red, green and black	15	10
357	– 10c. yellow, red and black	20	10
358	– 40c. multicoloured	40	40
359	– 55c. mauve, green and black	50	50
360	– 70c. multicoloured	60	70
361	– $1.10 green, blue and black	80	1·00
MS362	170 × 159 mm. Nos. 356/61	2·50	5·50

DESIGNS: 10c. G.P.O. and bisected 1d. stamp; 40c. Bisects on cover; 55c. G.B. 6d. used in Montserrat and local 6d. of 1876; 70c. Stamps for 2½d. rate, 1876; $1.10, Packet boat "Antelope" and 6d. stamp.

66 "The Trinity"

69 Mary and Joseph

68 White Frangipani

1976. Easter. Paintings by Orcagna. Multicoloured.
363 15c. Type **66** 10 10
364 40c. "The Resurrection" 15 15
365 55c. "The Ascension" 15 15
366 $1.10 "Pentecost" 30 40
MS367 160×142 mm. Nos. 363/6 1·25 2·25

1976. Nos. 244, 246 and 247 surch.
368 2c. on 5c. multicoloured 10 1·25
369 30c. on 10c. multicoloured 30 30
370 45c. on 3c. multicoloured 40 50

1976. Flowering Trees. Multicoloured.
371 1c. Type **68** 10 10
372 2c. Cannon-ball tree 10 10
373 3c. Lignum vitae 10 10
374 5c. Malay apple 15 10
375 10c. Jacaranda 30 10
376 15c. Orchid tree 50 10
377 20c. Manjak 30 10
378 25c. Tamarind 60 75
379 40c. Flame of the forest 30 30
380 55c. Pink cassia 40 40
381 70c. Long john 40 30
382 $1 Saman 50 80
383 $2.50 Immortelle 75 1·50
384 $5 Yellow poui 1·10 2·25
385 $10 Flamboyant 1·50 4·25

1976. Christmas. Multicoloured.
386 5c. Type **69** 10 10
387 20c. The Shepherds 10 10
388 55c. Mary and Jesus 15 15
389 $1.10 The Magi 30 50
MS390 95×135 mm. Nos. 386/9 60 2·25

70 Hudson River Review, 1976

1976. Bicent of American Revolution. Mult.
391 15c. Type **70** 65 20
392 40c. "Raleigh" (American frigate), 1777* 1·00 40
393 75c. H.M.S. "Druid" (frigate), 1777* 1·00 40
394 $1.25 Hudson River Review (different detail) 1·40 60
MS395 95×145 mm. Nos. 391/4 3·25 2·75
*The date is wrongly given on the stamps as "1776".
Nos. 391 and 394 and 392/3 respectively were issued in se-tenant pairs, each pair forming a composite design.

71 The Crowning

1977. Silver Jubilee. Multicoloured.
396 30c. Royal Visit, 1966 10 10
397 45c. Cannons firing salute 15 10
398 $1 Type **71** 25 50

72 "Ipomoea alba" **75** The Stable at Bethlehem

73 Princess Anne laying Foundation Stone of Glendon Hospital

1977. Flowers of the Night. Multicoloured.
399 15c. Type **72** 15 10
400 40c. "Epiphyllum hookeri" (horiz) 25 30
401 55c. "Cereus hexagonus" (horiz) 25 30
402 $1.50 "Cestrum nocturnum" 60 1·40
MS403 126×130 mm. Nos. 399/402 1·25 3·50

1977. Development. Multicoloured.
404 20c. Type **73** 30 10
405 40c. "Statesman" (freighter) in Plymouth Port 35 15
406 55c. Glendon Hospital 35 20
407 $1.50 Jetty at Plymouth Port 1·00 1·50
MS408 146×105 mm. Nos. 404/7 1·75 3·00

1977. Royal Visit. Nos. 380/1 and 383 surch **$1.00 SILVER JUBILEE 1977 ROYAL VISIT TO THE CARIBBEAN**.
409 $1 on 55c. Pink cassia 25 45
410 $1 on 70c. Long john 25 45
411 $1 on $2.50 Immortelle 25 45

1977. Christmas. Multicoloured.
412 5c. Type **75** 10 10
413 40c. The Three Kings 10 10
414 55c. Three Ships 15 10
415 $2 Three Angels 40 2·00
MS416 119×115 mm. Nos. 412/15 1·00 2·25

76 Four-eyed Butterflyfish

1978. Fish. Multicoloured.
417 30c. Type **76** 55 10
418 40c. French angelfish 60 15
419 55c. Blue tang 70 15
420 $1.50 Queen triggerfish 1·10 1·25
MS421 152×102 mm. Nos. 417/20 3·50 3·00

77 St. Paul's Cathedral

1978. 25th Anniv of Coronation. Multicoloured.
422 40c. Type **77** 10 10
423 55c. Chichester Cathedral 10 10
424 $1 Lincoln Cathedral 20 25
425 $2.50 Llandaff Cathedral 40 50
MS426 130×102 mm. Nos. 422/5 70 1·25

78 "Alpinia speciosa" **79** Private, 21st (Royal North British Fusiliers), 1786

1978. Flowers. Multicoloured.
427 40c. Type **78** 20 10
428 55c. "Allamanda cathartica" 20 15
429 $1 "Petrea volubilis" 35 45
430 $2 "Hippeastrum puniceum" 55 80

1978. Military Uniforms (1st series). British Infantry Regiments. Multicoloured.
431 30c. Type **79** 15 15
432 40c. Corporal, 86th (Royal County Down), 1831 20 15
433 55c. Sergeant, 14th (Buckinghamshire), 1837 25 15
434 $1.50 Officer, 55th (Westmorland), 1784 50 80
MS435 140×89 mm. Nos. 431/4 1·25 2·75
See also Nos. 441/5.

80 Cub Scouts

1979. 50th Anniv of Boy Scout Movement on Montserrat. Multicoloured.
436 40c. Type **80** 20 10
437 55c. Scouts with signalling equipment 20 15
438 $1.25 Camp fire (vert) 35 60
439 $2 Oath ceremony (vert) 45 1·00
MS440 120×110 mm. Nos. 436/9 1·25 2·25

1979. Military Uniforms (2nd series). As T **79**. Multicoloured.
441 30c. Private, 60th (Royal American), 1783 15 15
442 40c. Private, 1st West India, 1819 20 15
443 55c. Officer, 5th (Northumberland), 1819 20 15
444 $2.50 Officer, 93rd (Sutherland Highlanders), 1830 60 1·25
MS445 139×89 mm. Nos. 441/4 1·25 2·50

81 Child reaching out to Adult

1979. International Year of the Child.
446 **81** $2 black, brown and flesh 50 55
MS447 85×99 mm. No. 446 50 1·10

82 Sir Rowland Hill with Penny Black and Montserrat 1876 1d. Stamp

1979. Death Cent of Sir Rowland Hill and Cent of U.P.U. Membership. Multicoloured.
448 40c. Type **82** 20 10
449 55c. U.P.U. emblem and notice announcing Leeward Islands entry into Union 20 15
450 $1 1883 letter following U.P.U. membership 30 50
451 $2 Great Britain Post Office Regulations Notice and Sir Rowland Hill 40 1·50
MS452 135×154 mm. Nos. 448/51 1·00 2·25

83 Plume Worm

1979. Marine Life. Multicoloured.
453 40c. Type **83** 30 15
454 55c. Sea fans 40 20
455 $2 Sponge and coral 1·00 2·50

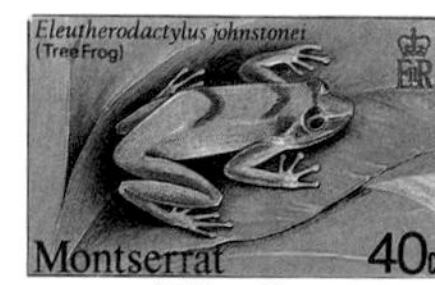

84 Tree Frog

1980. Reptiles and Amphibians. Mult.
456 40c. Type **84** 15 15
457 55c. Tree lizard 15 15
458 $1 Crapaud 30 50
459 $2 Wood slave 50 1·00

85 "Marquess of Salisbury" and 1838 Handstamps

1980. "London 1980" Int Stamp Exhibition. Mult.
460 40c. Type **85** 20 15
461 55c. Hawker Siddeley H.S.748 aircraft and 1976 55c. definitive 25 25
462 $1.20 "La Plata" (liner) and 1903 5s. stamp 30 45
463 $1.20 "Lady Hawkins" (packet steamer) and 1932 Tercentenary 5s. commemorative 30 45
464 $1.20 "Avon I" (paddle-steamer) and Penny Red stamp with "A 08" postmark 30 45
465 $1.20 Aeronca Champion 17 airplane and 1953 $1.20 definitive 30 45
MS466 115×110 mm. Nos. 460/5 1·25 2·50

1980. 75th Anniv of Rotary International. No. 383 optd **75th Anniversary of Rotary International**.
467 $2.50 Immortelle 55 85

87 Greek, French and U.S.A. Flags

1980. Olympic Games, Moscow. Multicoloured.
468 40c. Type **87** 20 60
469 55c. Union, Swedish and Belgian flags 20 60
470 70c. French, Dutch and U.S.A. flags 25 75
471 $1 German, Union and Finnish flags 30 75
472 $1.50 Australian, Italian and Japanese flags 35 1·00
473 $2 Mexican, West German and Canadian flags 40 1·00
474 $2.50 "The Discus Thrower" (sculpture, Miron) 40 1·10
MS475 150×100 mm. Nos. 468/74 1·50 3·50

1980. Nos. 371, 373, 376 and 379 surch.
476 5c. on 3c. Lignum vitae 10 10
477 35c. on 1c. Type **68** 15 15
478 35c. on 3c. Lignum vitae 15 15
479 35c. on 15c. Orchid tree 15 15
480 55c. on 40c. Flame of the forest 15 15
481 $5 on 40c. Flame of the forest 60 2·00

89 "Lady Nelson", 1928

1980. Mail Packet Boats (1st series). Mult.
482 40c. Type **89** 30 15
483 55c. "Chignecto", 1913 30 15
484 $1 "Solent II", 1878 50 65
485 $2 "Dee", 1841 70 1·25
See also Nos. 615/19.

90 "Heliconius charithonia" **91** Atlantic Spadefish

1981. Butterflies. Multicoloured.
486 50c. Type **90** 50 40
487 65c. "Pyrgus oileus" 60 45
488 $1.50 "Phoebis agarithe" 70 85
489 $2.50 "Danaus plexippus" 1·00 1·10

1981. Fishes. Multicoloured.
555 5c. Type **91** 20 10
556 10c. Hogfish and neon goby 25 10
492 15c. Creole wrasse 80 30
493 20c. Three-spotted damselfish 70 10
559 25c. Sergeant major 35 20
560 35c. Fin-spot wrasse 45 30
496 45c. Schoolmaster 80 40
497 55c. Striped parrotfish 1·10 45
498 65c. Bigeye 80 60
564 75c. French grunt 75 55
565 $1 Rock beauty 85 65
501 $2 Blue chromis 1·50 1·10
502 $3 Royal gramma ("Fairy basslet") and blueheads 1·50 1·75
503 $5 Cherub angelfish 1·50 2·75
504 $7.50 Long-jawed squirrelfish 2·00 4·75
570 $10 Caribbean long-nosed butterflyfish 2·00 6·00

92 Fort St. George

1981. Montserrat National Trust. Multicoloured.
506 50c. Type **92** 25 20
507 65c. Bird sanctuary, Fox's Bay 45 35
508 $1.50 Museum 50 65
509 $2.50 Bransby Point Battery, c. 1780 . . . . . 60 1·10

1981. Royal Wedding. Royal Yachts. As T **26/27** of Kiribati. Multicoloured.
510 90c. "Charlotte" 25 25
511 90c. Prince Charles and Lady Diana Spencer 85 85
512 $3 "Portsmouth" 60 60
513 $3 As No. 511 . . . . 1·50 1·50
514 $4 "Britannia" 75 75
515 $4 As No. 511 . . . . 1·75 1·75
MS516 120 × 109 mm. $5 As No. 511 1·00 1·00

93 H.M.S. "Dorsetshire" and Fairey Firefly Seaplane

1981. 50th Anniv of Montserrat Airmail Service. Multicoloured.
519 50c. Type **93** 30 30
520 65c. Beech 50 Twin Bonanza 40 30
521 $1.50 De Havilland Dragon Rapide "Lord Shaftesbury" 60 1·50
522 $2.50 Hawker Siddeley H.S.748 and maps of Montserrat and Antigua 80 2·75

94 Methodist Church, Bethel
95 Rubiaceae ("Rondeletia buxifolia")

1981. Christmas. Churches. Multicoloured.
523 50c. Type **94** 15 15
524 65c. St. George's Anglican Church, Harris 15 15
525 $1.50 St. Peter's Anglican Church, St. Peter's 30 60
526 $2.50 St. Patrick's R.C. Church, Plymouth . . . . 50 1·00
MS527 176 × 120 mm. Nos. 523/6 1·40 3·00

1982. Plant Life. Multicoloured.
528 50c. Type **95** 20 30
529 65c. Boraginaceae ("Heliotropium ternatum") (horiz) 25 40
530 $1.50 Simarubaceae ("Picramnia pentandra") 50 85
531 $2.50 Ebenaceae ("Diospyrus revoluta") (horiz) . . . . 70 1·25

96 Plymouth

1982. 350th Anniv of Settlement of Montserrat by Sir Thomas Warner.
532 **96** 40c. green 20 30
533 55c. red 20 35
534 65c. brown 25 50
535 75c. grey 25 60
536 85c. blue 25 75
537 95c. orange 25 80
538 $1 violet 25 80
539 $1.50 olive . . . . 30 1·25
540 $2 claret . . . . 35 1·50
541 $2.50 brown . . . . 40 1·50
The design of Nos. 532/41 is based on the 1932 Tercentenary set.

97 Catherine of Aragon, Princess of Wales, 1501
98 Local Scout

1982. 21st Birthday of Princess of Wales. Mult.
542 75c. Type **97** 15 15
543 $1 Coat of Arms of Catherine of Aragon . . . 15 15
544 $5 Diana, Princess of Wales 80 1·25

1982. 75th Anniv of Boy Scout Movement. Mult.
545 $1.50 Type **98** 50 50
546 $2.20 Lord Baden-Powell . . 60 75

99 Annunciation

1982. Christmas. Multicoloured.
547 35c. Type **99** 15 15
548 75c. Shepherds' Vision . . . 25 35
549 $1.50 The Stable 45 85
550 $2.50 Flight into Egypt . . . 55 1·10

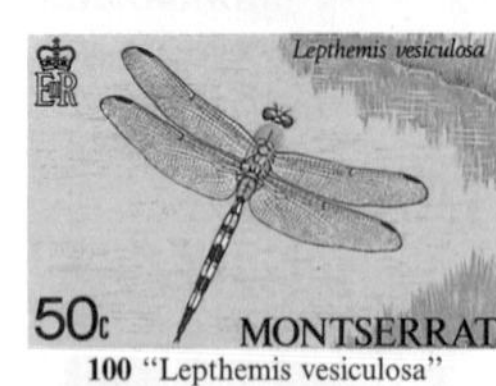

100 "Lepthemis vesiculosa"

1983. Dragonflies. Multicoloured.
551 50c. Type **100** 55 20
552 65c. "Orthemis ferruginea" 65 25
553 $1.50 "Triacanthagyna trifida" . . . . 1·25 1·50
554 $2.50 "Erythrodiplax umbrata" . . . . 1·75 3·00

101 Blue-headed Hummingbird
102 Montserrat Emblem

1983. Hummingbirds. Multicoloured.
571 35c. Type **101** . . . . 1·50 35
572 75c. Green-throated carib . . 1·75 85
573 $2 Antillean crested hummingbird . . . . . . 2·75 2·75
574 $3 Purple-throated carib . . 3·00 3·75

1983.
575 **102** $12 blue and red . . . . 3·50 5·00
576 $30 red and blue . . . . 6·50 12·00

1983. Various stamps surch. (a) Nos. 491, 494, 498/9 and 501.
577 40c. on 25c. Sergeant major (No. 494) 30 35
578 70c. on 10c. Hogfish and neon goby (No. 491) . . . 45 50
579 90c. on 65c. Bigeye (No. 498) 55 70
580 $1.15 on 75c. French grunt (No. 499) 65 80
581 $1.50 on $2 Blue chromis (No. 501) . . . . 85 1·00
(b) Nos. 512/15.
582 70c. on $3 "Portsmouth" . . 50 1·00
583 70c. on $3 Prince Charles and Lady Diana Spencer . . . 1·50 2·75
584 $1.15 on $4 "Britannia" . . . 65 1·50
585 $1.15 on $4 As No. 583 . . . 1·75 3·25

104 Montgolfier Balloon, 1783
106 Statue of Discus Thrower

105 Boys dressed as Clowns

1983. Bicentenary of Manned Flight. Mult.
586 35c. Type **104** 15 15
587 75c. De Havilland Twin Otter 200/300 (horiz) 25 30
588 $1.50 Lockheed Vega V (horiz) 40 75
589 $2 Beardmore airship R.34 (horiz) . . . . 60 1·25
MS590 109 × 145 mm. Nos. 586/9 1·25 2·75

1983. Christmas. Carnival. Multicoloured.
591 55c. Type **105** 10 10
592 90c. Girls dressed as silver star bursts 15 20
593 $1.15 Flower girls 20 35
594 $2 Masqueraders 35 80

1984. Olympic Games, Los Angeles. Mult.
595 90c. Type **106** 30 35
596 $1 Olympic torch 35 45
597 $1.25 Los Angeles Olympic stadium 40 50
598 $2.50 Olympic and American flags . . . . 65 1·00
MS599 110 × 110 mm. Nos. 595/8 1·50 2·25

107 Cattle Egret

1984. Birds of Montserrat. Multicoloured.
600 5c. Type **107** 30 50
601 10c. Carib grackle 30 50
602 15c. Moorhen ("Common Gallinule") 30 50
603 20c. Brown booby 40 50
604 25c. Black-whiskered vireo 40 50
605 40c. Scaly-breasted thrasher 60 60
606 55c. Laughing gull 75 30
607 70c. Glossy ibis 90 50
608 90c. Green-backed heron ("Green Heron") . . . . . 1·00 60
609 $1 Belted kingfisher (vert) . . 1·25 70
610 $1.15 Bananaquit (vert) . . . 1·50 1·40
611 $3 American kestrel ("Sparrow Hawk") (vert) 3·25 5·50
612 $5 Forest thrush (vert) . . . 4·50 7·50
613 $7.50 Black-crowned night heron (vert) . . . . . . 5·00 13·00
614 $10 Bridled quail dove (vert) 5·50 13·00

1984. Mail Packet Boats (2nd series). As T **89**. Multicoloured.
615 55c. "Tagus II", 1907 . . . . 20 40
616 90c. "Cobequid", 1913 . . . 30 50
617 $1.15 "Lady Drake", 1942 40 70
618 $2 "Factor", 1948 . . . . . 60 1·75
MS619 152 × 100 mm. Nos. 615/18 1·50 5·00
No. **MS**619 also commemorates the 250th anniversary of "Lloyd's List" (newspaper).

108 Hermit Crab and West Indian Top Shell

1984. Marine Life. Multicoloured.
620 90c. Type **108** . . . . 1·50 1·00
621 $1.15 Rough file shell . . . . 1·75 1·40
622 $1.50 True tulip . . . . . . 2·50 3·25
623 $2.50 Queen or pink conch 3·25 5·00

109 "Bull Man"

1984. Christmas. Carnival Costumes. Mult.
624 55c. Type **109** 50 25
625 $1.15 Masquerader Captain 1·50 1·25
626 $1.50 "Fantasy" Carnival Queen . . . . 1·75 2·50
627 $2.30 "Ebony and Ivory" Carnival Queen . . . . . 2·50 4·25

110 Mango
111 "Oncidium urophyllum"

1985. National Emblems. Multicoloured.
628 $1.15 Type **110** 30 60
629 $1.50 Lobster claw . . . . . 40 1·00
630 $3 Montserrat oriole . . . . 60 2·75

1985. Orchids of Montserrat. Multicoloured.
631 90c. Type **111** 40 55
632 $1.15 "Epidendrum difforme" 40 80
633 $1.50 "Epidendrum ciliare" 45 1·25
634 $2.50 "Brassavola cucullata" 55 2·75
MS635 120 × 140 mm. Nos. 631/4 3·75 6·50

112 Queen Elizabeth the Queen Mother
115 Black-throated Blue Warbler

113 Cotton Plants

1985. Life and Times of Queen Elizabeth the Queen Mother. Various vertical portraits.
636 **112** 55c. multicoloured 25 45
637 – 55c. multicoloured 25 45
638 – 90c. multicoloured 25 55
639 – 90c. multicoloured 25 55
640 – $1.15 multicoloured . . . 25 60
641 – $1.15 multicoloured . . . 25 60
642 – $1.50 multicoloured . . . 30 70
643 – $1.50 multicoloured . . . 30 70
MS644 85 × 113 mm. $2 multicoloured; $2 multicoloured 65 1·90
Each value was issued in pairs showing a floral pattern across the bottom of the portraits which stops short of the left-hand edge on the first stamp and of the right-hand edge on the second.

1985. Montserrat Sea Island Cotton Industry. Multicoloured.
645 90c. Type **113** 25 45
646 $1 Operator at carding machine 25 50
647 $1.15 Threading loom . . . 25 65
648 $2.50 Weaving with hand loom . . . . 50 2·75
MS649 148 × 103 mm. Nos. 645/8 3·00 3·75

1985. Royal Visit. Nos. 514/15, 543, 587/8 and 640/1 optd **CARIBBEAN ROYAL VISIT 1985** or surch also.
650 75c. multicoloured (No. 587) 3·00 2·50
651 $1 multicoloured (No. 543) 4·50 3·50
652 $1.15 multicoloured (No. 640) 4·25 6·50
653 $1.15 multicoloured (No. 641) 4·25 6·50
654 $1.50 multicoloured (No. 588) 7·00 7·00
655 $1.60 on $4 mult (No. 514) 2·00 4·25
656 $1.60 on $4 mult (No. 515) 17·00 22·00
No. 656 shows a new face value only, "CARIBBEAN ROYAL VISIT 1985" being omitted from the surcharge.

1985. Leaders of the World. Birth Bicentenary of John J. Audubon (ornithologist). Designs showing original paintings. Multicoloured.
657 15c. Type **115** 15 40
658 15c. Palm warbler 15 40
659 30c. Bobolink 15 40
660 30c. Lark sparrow 15 40
661 55c. Chipping sparrow . . . 20 40
662 55c. Northern oriole 20 40
663 $2.50 American goldfinch . . 40 1·40
664 $2.50 Blue grosbeak . . . . 40 1·40

116 Herald Angel appearing to Goatherds

1985. Christmas. Designs showing Caribbean Nativity. Multicoloured.
665 70c. Type **116** 15 15
666 $1.15 Three Wise Men following Star 25 40
667 $1.50 Carol singing around War Memorial, Plymouth 30 85
668 $2.30 Praying to "Our Lady of Montserrat", Church of Our Lady, St. Patrick's Village . . . . 45 2·00

117 Lord Baden-Powell

1986. 50th Anniv of Montserrat Girl Guide Movement. Multicoloured.
669 20c. Type **117** 15 60
670 20c. Girl Guide saluting . . . 15 60
671 75c. Lady Baden-Powell . . . 25 75
672 75c. Guide assisting in old people's home 25 75
673 90c. Lord and Lady Baden-Powell 30 75
674 90c. Guides serving meal in old people's home 30 75
675 $1.15 Girl Guides of 1936 . . 40 80
676 $1.15 Two guides saluting . . 40 80

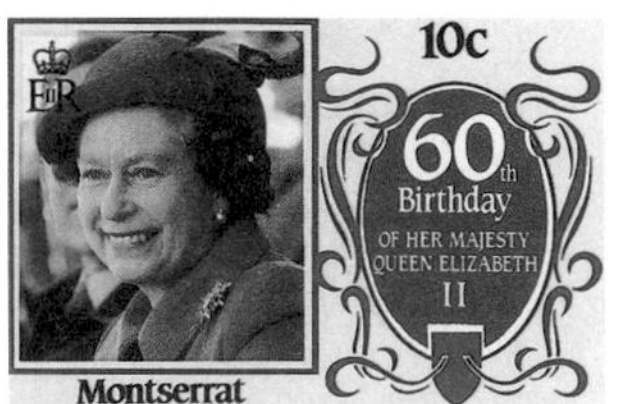

117a Queen Elizabeth II

1986. 60th Birthday of Queen Elizabeth II. Multicoloured.
677 10c. Type **117a** 10 10
678 $1.50 Princess Elizabeth in 1928 . . . . 25 50
679 $3 In Antigua, 1977 . . . . 40 1·25
680 $6 In Canberra, 1982 (vert) 65 2·25
MS681 85 × 115 mm. $8 Queen with bouquet . . . . 3·25 5·50

118 King Harold and Halley's Comet, 1066 (from Bayeux Tapestry)

1986. Appearance of Halley's Comet. Mult.
682 35c. Type **118** 20 25
683 50c. Comet of 1301 (from Giotto's "Adoration of the Magi") 25 30
684 70c. Edmond Halley and Comet of 1531 . . . . . . 25 40
685 $1 Comets of 1066 and 1910 25 40
686 $1.15 Comet of 1910 . . . . 30 50
687 $1.50 E.S.A. "Giotto" spacecraft and Comet . . . 30 80
688 $2.30 U.S. space telescope and Comet . . . . 40 1·75
689 $4 Computer reconstruction of 1910 Comet . . . . . . 50 3·25
MS690 Two sheets, each 140 × 115 mm. (a) 40c. Type **118**; $1.75, As No. 683; $2 As No. 684; $3 As No. 685. (b) 55c. As No. 686; 60c. As No. 687; 80c. As No. 688; $5 As No. 689 Set of 2 sheets . . . . 2·75 9·00

118a Prince Andrew

1986. Royal Wedding (1st issue). Multicoloured.
691 70c. Type **118a** 25 40
692 70c. Miss Sarah Ferguson . . 25 40
693 $2 Prince Andrew wearing stetson (horiz) 40 90
694 $2 Miss Sarah Ferguson on skiing holiday (horiz) . . . 40 90
MS695 115 × 85 mm. $10 Duke and Duchess of York on Palace balcony after wedding (horiz) 3·00 4·75
See also Nos. 705/8.

119 "Antelope" being attacked by "L'Atalante"

1986. Mail Packet Sailing Ships. Mult.
696 90c. Type **119** . . . . 2·00 1·50
697 $1.15 "Montagu" (1810) . . 2·25 2·00
698 $1.50 "Little Catherine" being pursued by "L'Etoile" (1813) . . . . . 2·75 2·75
699 $2.30 "Hinchingbrook I" (1813) . . . . 3·50 5·00
MS700 165 × 123 mm. Nos. 696/9 10·00 11·00

120 Radio Montserrat Building, Dagenham

1986. Communications. Multicoloured.
701 70c. Type **120** . . . . 1·00 70
702 $1.15 Radio Gem dish aerial, Plymouth . . . . 1·00 1·50
703 $1.50 Radio Antilles studio, O'Garro's . . . . 1·75 2·25
704 $2.30 Cable and Wireless building, Plymouth . . . . 2·25 4·25

1986. Royal Wedding (2nd issue). Nos. 691/4 optd **Congratulations to T.R.H. The Duke & Duchess of York**.
705 70c. Prince Andrew . . . . . 70 1·25
706 70c. Miss Sarah Ferguson . . 70 1·25
707 $2 Prince Andrew wearing stetson (horiz) . . . . . . 1·25 1·75
708 $2 Miss Sarah Ferguson on skiing holiday (horiz) . . . 1·25 1·75

121a Statue of Liberty **123** Christmas Rose

122 Sailing and Windsurfing

1986. Centenary of Statue of Liberty. Vert views of Statue as T **121a** in separate miniature sheets. Multicoloured.
MS709 Three sheets, each 85 × 115 mm. $3; $4.50; $5 Set of 3 sheets . . . . 3·75 9·00

1986. Tourism. Multicoloured.
710 70c. Type **122** 40 70
711 $1.15 Golf . . . . 70 1·50
712 $1.50 Plymouth market . . . 70 2·00
713 $2.30 Air Recording Studios 80 3·00

1986. Christmas. Flowering Shrubs. Mult.
714 70c. Type **123** 70 40
715 $1.15 Candle flower 95 85
716 $1.50 Christmas tree kalanchoe . . . . 1·50 1·50
717 $2.30 Snow on the mountain 2·00 4·50
MS718 150 × 110 mm. Nos. 714/17 7·50 8·00

124 Tiger Shark

1987. Sharks. Multicoloured.
719 40c. Type **124** . . . . 1·50 55
720 90c. Lemon shark . . . . . 2·50 1·50
721 $1.15 Great white shark . . . 2·75 2·00
722 $3.50 Whale shark . . . . . 5·50 8·00
MS723 150 × 102 mm. Nos. 719/22 12·00 14·00

1987. Nos. 601, 603, 607/8 and 611 surch.
724 5c. on 70c. Glossy ibis . . . 50 2·25
725 $1 on 20c. Brown booby . . 1·75 1·00
726 $1.15 on 10c. Carib grackle 2·00 1·40
727 $1.50 on 90c. Green-backed heron . . . . 2·25 2·50
728 $2.30 on $3 American kestrel (vert) . . . . 3·25 7·50

1987. "Capex '87" International Stamp Exhibition, Toronto. No. **MS**690 optd with **CAPEX 87** logo.
MS729 Two sheets. As No. **MS**690 Set of 2 sheets . . . . 4·00 10·00
No. **MS**729 also carries an overprint commemorating the exhibition on the lower sheet margins.

127 "Phoebis trite" **128** "Oncidium variegatum"

1987. Butterflies. Multicoloured.
730 90c. Type **127** . . . . 2·00 1·10
731 $1.15 "Biblis hyperia" . . . 2·50 1·60
732 $1.50 "Polygonus leo" . . . 3·00 2·50
733 $2.50 "Hypolimnas misippus" 4·50 6·50

1987. Christmas. Orchids. Multicoloured.
734 90c. Type **128** 60 45
735 $1.15 "Vanilla planifolia" (horiz) 85 55
736 $1.50 "Gongora quinquenervis" . . . . . . 1·10 1·10
737 $3.50 "Brassavola nodosa" (horiz) . . . . 2·00 5·00
MS738 100 × 75 mm. $5 "Oncidium lanceanum" (horiz) . . . . . 10·00 12·00

1987. Royal Ruby Wedding. Nos. 601, 604/5 and 608 surch **40th Wedding Anniversary HM Queen Elizabeth II HRH Duke of Edinburgh. November 1987.** and value.
739B 5c. on 90c. Green-backed heron 30 40
740B $1.15 on 10c. Carib grackle 1·00 1·00
741B $2.30 on 25c. Black-whiskered vireo . . . . . 1·75 2·25
742B $5 on 40c. Scaly-breasted thrasher . . . . 3·50 5·00

130 Free-tailed Bat **131** Magnificent Frigate Bird

1988. Bats. Multicoloured.
743 55c. Type **130** 80 40
744 90c. "Chiroderma improvisum" (fruit bat) . . 1·25 90
745 $1.15 Fisherman bat . . . . 1·60 1·50
746 $2.30 "Brachyphylla cavernarum" (fruit bat) . . 3·00 5·50
MS747 133 × 110 mm. $2.50 Funnel-eared bat . . . . 6·50 8·00

1988. Easter. Birds. Multicoloured.
748 90c. Type **131** 60 45
749 $1.15 Caribbean elaenia . . . 80 75
750 $1.50 Glossy ibis . . . . . . 1·00 1·50
751 $3.50 Purple-throated carib 2·00 4·00
MS752 100 × 75 mm. $5 Brown pelican . . . . 2·50 3·50

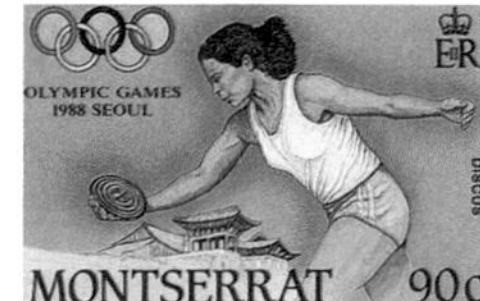

132 Discus throwing

1988. Olympic Games, Seoul. Multicoloured.
753 90c. Type **132** 70 50
754 $1.15 High jumping 80 55
755 $3.50 Athletics . . . . 2·00 3·25
MS756 103 × 77 mm. $5 Rowing 3·00 3·00

133 Golden Tulip

1988. Sea Shells. Multicoloured.
757 5c. Type **133** 30 50
758 10c. Little knobbed scallop 40 50
759 15c. Sozoni's cone 40 50
760 20c. Globular coral shell . . 50 50
761 25c. American or common sundial 50 50
762 40c. King helmet 60 50
763 55c. Channelled turban . . . 80 50
764 70c. True tulip . . . . 1·00 75
765 90c. Music volute . . . . . 1·25 75
766 $1 Flame auger . . . . . . 1·40 80
767 $1.15 Rooster-tail conch . . 1·50 90
768 $1.50 Queen or pink conch 1·60 1·40
769 $3 Teramachi's slit shell . . . 2·50 4·25
770 $5 Common or Florida crown conch . . . . 3·50 6·50
771 $7.50 Beau's murex . . . . . 4·50 11·00
772 $10 Atlantic trumpet triton 5·50 11·00

134 University Crest

1988. 40th Anniv of University of West Indies.
773 **134** $5 multicoloured . . . . 2·40 3·50

1988. Princess Alexandra's Visit. Nos. 763, 766 and 769/70 surch **HRH PRINCESS ALEXANDRA'S VISIT NOVEMBER 1988** and new value.
774 40c. on 55c. Channelled turban 45 45
775 90c. on $1 Flame auger . . . 70 80
776 $1.15 on $3 Teramachi's slit shell 85 95
777 $1.50 on $5 Common or Florida crown conch . . . 1·10 1·50

136 Spotted Sandpiper

1988. Christmas. Sea Birds. Multicoloured.
778 90c. Type **136** 70 55
779 $1.15 Ruddy turnstone . . . 85 70
780 $3.50 Red-footed booby . . . 2·00 3·75
MS781 105 × 79 mm. $5 Audubon's shearwater . . . . 2·75 4·00

137 Handicapped Children in Classroom

1988. 125th Anniv of International Red Cross.
782 **137** $3.50 multicoloured . . . 1·50 2·25

138 Drum Major in Ceremonial Uniform

1989. 75th Anniv (1986) of Montserrat Defence Force. Uniforms. Multicoloured.
783 90c. Type **138** 70 50
784 $1.15 Field training uniform 85 75
785 $1.50 Cadet in ceremonial uniform . . . . 1·25 1·75
786 $3.50 Gazetted Police Officer in ceremonial uniform . . 2·50 3·75
MS787 102 × 76 mm. $5 Island Girl Guide Commissioner and brownie 3·50 4·25

139 Amazon Lily

1989. Easter. Lilies. Multicoloured.

788	90c. Type **139**	50	50
789	$1.15 Salmon blood lily (vert)	70	70
790	$1.50 Amaryllis (vert)	85	1·25
791	$3.50 Amaryllis (vert)	1·90	3·00
MS792	103 × 77 mm. $5 Resurrection lily (vert)	4·25	6·50

140 "Morning Prince" (schooner), 1942

1989. Shipbuilding in Montserrat. Mult.

793	90c. Type **140**	1·00	60
794	$1.15 "Western Sun" (inter-island freighter)	1·50	1·10
795	$1.50 "Kim G" (inter-island freighter) under construction	1·75	2·25
796	$3.50 "Romaris" (inter-island ferry), c. 1942	3·00	5·00

141 The Scarecrow

1989. 50th Anniv of "The Wizard of Oz" (film). Multicoloured.

797	90c. Type **141**	40	45
798	$1.15 The Lion	55	60
799	$1.50 The Tin Man	70	85
800	$3.50 Dorothy	1·60	2·50
MS801	113 × 84 mm. $5 Characters from film (horiz)	2·40	3·75

1989. Hurricane Hugo Relief Fund. Nos. 795/6 surch **Hurricane Hugo Relief Surcharge $2.50**.

802	$1.50+$2.50 "Kim G" (inter-island freighter under construction)	2·75	4·00
803	$3.50+$2.50 "Romaris" (inter-island ferry), c. 1942	3·00	5·00

143 "Apollo 11" above Lunar Surface

1989. 20th Anniv of First Manned Landing on Moon. Multicoloured.

804	90c. Type **143**	35	40
805	$1.15 Astronaut alighting from lunar module "Eagle"	45	50
806	$1.50 "Eagle" and astronaut conducting experiment	60	80
807	$3.50 Opening "Apollo 11" hatch after splashdown	1·40	2·50
MS808	101 × 76 mm. $5 Astronaut on Moon	4·75	6·00

144 "Yamato" (Japanese battleship)

1990. World War II Capital Ships. Multicoloured.

809	70c. Type **144**	2·75	70
810	$1.15 U.S.S."Arizona" at Pearl Harbor	3·25	95
811	$1.50 "Bismarck" (German battleship) in action	4·00	2·75
812	$3.50 H.M.S. "Hood" (battle cruiser)	6·00	9·00
MS813	118 × 90 mm. $5 "Bismarck" and map of North Atlantic	12·00	12·00

145 The Empty Tomb

1990. Easter. Stained glass windows from St. Michael's Parish Church, Bray, Berkshire. Multicoloured.

814	$1.15 Type **145**	2·00	2·25
815	$1.50 The Ascension	2·00	2·25
816	$3.50 The Risen Christ with Disciples	2·75	3·25
MS817	65 × 103 mm. $5 The Crucifixion	4·50	6·00

1990. "Stamp World London '90" International Stamp Exhibition. Nos. 460/4 surch **Stamp World London 90**, emblem and value.

818	70c. on 40c. Type **85**	60	60
819	90c. on 55c. Hawker Siddeley H.S.748 aircraft and 1976 55c. definitive	80	80
820	$1 on $1.20 "La Plata" (liner) and 1903 5s. stamp	90	90
821	$1.15 on $1.20 "Lady Hawkins" (packet steamer) and 1932 Tercentenary 5s. commemorative	1·10	1·10
822	$1.50 on $1.20 "Avon I" (paddle-steamer) and Penny Red stamp with "A 08" postmark	1·50	2·00

147 General Office, Montserrat and 1884 ½d. Stamp

1990. 150th Anniv of the Penny Black. Mult.

823	90c. Type **147**	65	65
824	$1.15 Sorting letters and Montserrat 1d. stamp of 1876 (vert)	85	90
825	$1.50 Posting letters and Penny Black (vert)	1·25	1·75
826	$3.50 Postman delivering letters and 1840 Twopence Blue	3·00	4·50
MS827	102 × 75 mm. $5 Montserrat soldier's letter of 1836 and Penny Black	8·50	10·00

148 Montserrat v. Antigua Match

1990. World Cup Football Championship, Italy. Multicoloured.

828	90c. Type **148**	65	55
829	$1.15 U.S.A. v. Trinidad match	85	75
830	$1.50 Montserrat team	1·25	1·50
831	$3.50 West Germany v. Wales match	2·25	3·50
MS832	77 × 101 mm. $5 World Cup trophy (vert)	6·00	7·50

149 Spinner Dolphin

1990. Dolphins. Multicoloured.

833	90c. Type **149**	1·50	85
834	$1.15 Common dolphin	1·75	1·25
835	$1.50 Striped dolphin	2·50	2·50
836	$3.50 Atlantic spotted dolphin	3·75	5·00
MS837	103 × 76 mm. $5 Atlantic white-sided dolphin	8·50	9·50

150 Spotted Goatfish

1991. Tropical Fishes. Multicoloured.

838	90c. Type **150**	1·50	95
839	$1.15 Cushion star	1·75	1·25
840	$1.50 Rock beauty	2·50	2·75
841	$3.50 French grunt	3·75	5·50
MS842	103 × 76 mm. $5 Buffalo trunkfish	5·50	7·00

1991. Nos. 760/1, 768 and 771 surch.

843	5c. on 20c. Globular coral shell	65	1·75
844	5c. on 25c. American or common sundial	65	1·75
845	$1.15 on $1.50 Queen or pink conch	2·75	3·25
846	$1.15 on $7.50 Beau's murex	2·75	3·25

152 Duck

1991. Domestic Birds. Multicoloured.

847	90c. Type **152**	60	60
848	$1.15 Hen and chicks	80	90
849	$1.50 Red junglefowl ("Rooster")	1·10	1·50
850	$3.50 Helmeted guineafowl	2·40	3·50

153 "Panaeolus antillarum"

1991. Fungi.

851	**153**	90c. grey	1·25	1·00
852	–	$1.15 red	1·50	1·25
853	–	$1.50 brown	2·25	2·25
854	–	$2 purple	2·50	3·25
855	–	$3.50 blue	3·75	5·00

DESIGNS: $1.15, "Cantharellus cinnabarinus"; $1.50, "Gymnopilus chrysopellus"; $2 "Psilocybe cubensis"; $3.50, "Leptonia caeruleocapitata".

154 Red Water Lily **155** Tree Frog

1991. Lilies. Multicoloured.

856	90c. Type **154**	65	65
857	$1.15 Shell ginger	75	85
858	$1.50 Early day lily	1·00	1·60
859	$3.50 Anthurium	2·50	3·75

1991. Frogs and Toad. Multicoloured.

860	$1.15 Type **155**	3·25	1·25
861	$2 Crapaud toad	4·50	4·50
862	$3.50 Mountain chicken (frog)	7·50	8·00
MS863	110 × 110 mm. $5 Tree frog, crapaud toad and mountain chicken (76½ × 44 mm)	11·00	12·00

156 Black British Shorthair Cat

1991. Cats. Multicoloured.

864	90c. Type **156**	1·50	90
865	$1.15 Seal point Siamese	1·75	1·10
866	$1.50 Silver tabby Persian	2·25	2·25
867	$2.50 Birman temple cat	3·00	3·75
868	$3.50 Egyptain mau	4·00	5·00

157 Navigational Instruments

1992. 500th Anniv of Discovery of America by Columbus. Multicoloured.

869	$1.50 Type **157**	1·25	1·50
870	$1.50 Columbus and coat of arms	1·25	1·50
871	$1.50 Landfall on the Bahamas	1·25	1·50
872	$1.50 Petitioning Queen Isabella	1·25	1·50
873	$1.50 Tropical birds	1·25	1·50
874	$1.50 Tropical fruits	1·25	1·50
875	$3 Ships of Columbus (81 × 26 mm)	1·75	2·00

158 Runner with Olympic Flame

1992. Olympic Games, Barcelona. Multicoloured.

876	$1 Type **158**	90	60
877	$1.15 Montserrat, Olympic and Spanish flags	1·25	90
878	$2.30 Olympic flame on map of Montserrat	2·25	2·75
879	$3.60 Olympic events	2·75	4·25

159 Tyrannosaurus

1992. Death Centenary of Sir Richard Owen (zoologist). Multicoloured.

880	$1 Type **159**	2·00	1·25
881	$1.15 Diplodocus	2·25	1·40
882	$1.50 Apatosaurus	2·75	2·75
883	$3.45 Dimetrodon	5·50	8·00
MS884	114 × 84 mm. $4.60, Sir Richard Owen and dinosaur bone (vert)	8·50	10·00

160 Male Montserrat Oriole

1992. Montserrat Oriole. Multicoloured.

885	$1 Type **160**	1·10	1·10
886	$1.15 Male and female orioles	1·40	1·40
887	$1.50 Female oriole with chicks	1·75	2·00
888	$3.60 Map of Montserrat and male oriole	3·50	5·00

161 "Psophus stridulus" (grasshopper)

1992. Insects. Multicoloured.

889	5c. Type **161**	30	40
890	10c. "Gryllus campestris" (field cricket)	35	40
891	15c. "Lepthemis vesiculosa" (dragonfly)	40	40
892	20c. "Orthemis ferruginea" (red skimmer)	45	45
893	25c. "Gerris lacustris" (pond skater)	45	45
894	40c. "Byctiscus betulae" (leaf weevil)	60	50
895	55c. "Atta texana" (leaf-cutter ants)	60	40
896	70c. "Polistes fuscatus" (paper wasp)	70	60
897	90c. "Sparmopolius fulvus" (bee fly)	80	60
898	$1 "Chrysopa carnea" (lace wing)	1·25	65
899	$1.15 "Phoebis philea" (butterfly)	2·00	90
900	$1.50 "Cynthia cardui" (butterfly)	2·25	1·75
901	$3 "Utetheisa bella" (moth)	3·00	4·25

902 $5 "Alucita pentadactyla" (moth) . . . . 4·25 6·00
903 $7.50 "Anartia jatropha" (butterfly) . . . . 5·50 8·50
904 $10 "Heliconius melpomene" (butterfly) . . . . 5·50 8·50

162 Adoration of the Magi

1992. Christmas. Multicoloured.
905 $1.15 Type **162** . . . . . . 2·00 75
906 $4.60 Appearance of angel to shepherds . . . . 4·50 6·50

163 $1 Coin and $20 Banknote

164 Columbus meeting Amerindians

1993. East Caribbean Currency. Multicoloured.
907 $1 Type **163** 90 70
908 $1.15 10c. and 25c. coins with $10 banknote . . . . . . 1·25 85
909 $1.50 5c. coin and $5 banknote . . . . 1·75 2·00
910 $3.60 1c. and 2c. coins with $1 banknote . . . . 4·00 6·00

1993. Organization of East Caribbean States. 500th Anniv of Discovery of America by Columbus. Multicoloured.
911 $1 Type **164** . . . . 1·10 90
912 $2 Ships approaching island 2·00 2·75

165 Queen Elizabeth II on Montserrat with Chief Minister W. H. Bramble, 1966

1993. 40th Anniv of Coronation. Multicoloured.
913 $1.15 Type **165** . . . . . . 1·50 75
914 $4.60 Queen Elizabeth II in State Coach, 1953 . . . . 4·50 5·50

1993. 500th Anniv of Discovery of Montserrat. As Nos. 869/75, some with new values, each showing "500th ANNIVERSARY DISCOVERY OF MONTSERRAT" at foot and with additional historical inscr across the centre.
915 $1.15 mult (As Type **157**) . . 1·75 2·00
916 $1.15 multicoloured (As No. 870) . . . . 1·75 2·00
917 $1.15 multicoloured (As No. 871) . . . . 1·75 2·00
918 $1.50 multicoloured (As No. 872) . . . . 2·00 2·25
919 $1.50 multicoloured (As No. 873) . . . . 2·00 2·25
920 $1.50 multicoloured (As No. 874) . . . . 2·00 2·25
921 $3.45 multicoloured (As No. 875) . . . . 2·75 3·50

Additional inscriptions: No. 915, "PRE-COLUMBUS CARIB NAME OF ISLAND ALLIOUGANA"; 916, "COLUMBUS NAMED ISLAND SANTA MARIA DE MONTSERRATE"; 917, "COLUMBUS SAILED ALONG COASTLINE 11th NOV. 1493"; 918, "ISLAND OCCUPIED BY FRENCH BRIEFLY IN 1667"; 919, "ISLAND DECLARED ENGLISH BY TREATY OF BREDA 1667"; 920, "AFRICAN SLAVES BROUGHT IN DURING 1600's"; 921, "IRISH CATHOLICS FROM ST. KITTS AND VIRGINIA SETTLED ON ISLAND BETWEEN 1628–1634".

166 Boeing Sentry, 1993

1993. 75th Anniv of Royal Air Force. Mult.
922 15c. Type **166** 45 20
923 55c. Vickers Valiant B Mk 1, 1962 . . . . 65 40
924 $1.15 Handley Page Hastings C Mk 2, 1958 . . . . . . 1·25 75
925 $3 Lockheed Ventura, 1943 2·50 4·25
MS926 117 × 78 mm. $1.50 Felixstowe F5, 1921; $1.50 Armstrong Whitworth Atlas, 1934; $1.50 Fairey Gordon, 1935; $1.50 Boulton & Paul Overstrand, 1936 . . . . 4·50 6·00

167 Ground Beetle

1994. Beetles. Multicoloured.
927 $1 Type **167** 65 65
928 $1.15 Click beetle 80 80
929 $1.50 Harlequin beetle . . . 1·25 1·50
930 $3.45 Leaf beetle . . . . . . 3·00 4·50
MS931 68 × 85 mm. $4.50 Scarab beetle . . . . 3·50 4·00

168 "Gossypium barbadense"

1994. Flowers. Multicoloured.
932 90c. Type **168** . . . . 1·25 80
933 $1.15 "Hibiscus sabdariffa" 1·50 1·00
934 $1.50 "Hibiscus esculentus" 1·75 1·75
935 $3.50 "Hibiscus rosa-sinensis" 3·75 6·00

169 Coaching Young Players and Logo

1994. World Cup Football Championship, U.S.A. Multicoloured.
936 90c. Type **169** . . . . 1·90 2·25
937 $1 United States scoring against England, 1950 . . 1·90 2·25
938 $1.15 Rose Bowl stadium, Los Angeles, and trophy 1·90 2·25
939 $3.45 German players celebrating with trophy, 1990 . . . . 3·00 3·50
MS940 114 × 85 mm. $2 Jules Rimet (founder) and Jules Rimet Trophy; $2 Bobby Moore (England) holding trophy, 1966; $2 Lew Jaschin (U.S.S.R.); $2 Sepp Herberger (Germany) and German players celebrating, 1990 7·00 9·00

170 Elasmosaurus

1994. Aquatic Dinosaurs. Multicoloured.
941 $1 Type **170** . . . . 2·25 2·25
942 $1.15 Plesiosaurus . . . . . 2·25 2·25
943 $1.50 Nothosaurus . . . . . 2·75 2·75
944 $3.45 Mosasaurus . . . . . 3·50 4·25

1994. Space Anniversaries. Nos. 804/7 variously surch or optd, each including **Space Anniversaries**.
945 40c. on 90c. Type **143** . . . 1·50 80
946 $1.15 Astronaut alighting from lunar module "Eagle" 2·25 1·50
947 $1.50 "Eagle" and astronaut conducting experiment . . 2·75 2·75
948 $2.30 on $3.50 Opening "Apollo 11" hatch after splashdown . . . . 4·25 6·00

Surcharges and overprints: No. 945, **Juri Gagarin First man in space April 12, 1961**; 946, **First Joint US Soviet Mission July 15, 1975**; 947 **25th Anniversary First Moon Landing Apollo XI – July 20, 1994**; 948, **Columbia First Space Shuttle April 12, 1981**.

172 1969 Festival Logo

1994. 25th Anniv of Woodstock Music Festival. Multicoloured.
949 $1.15 Type **172** . . . . . . 1·00 1·00
950 $1.50 1994 anniversary festival logo . . . . 1·25 1·25

173 Sea Fan

1995. Marine Life. Multicoloured.
951 $1 Type **173** 60 50
952 $1.15 Sea lily 70 60
953 $1.50 Sea pen . . . . 90 1·00
954 $3.45 Sea fern . . . . 2·00 3·00
MS955 88 × 96 mm. $4.50 Sea rose 3·00 4·00

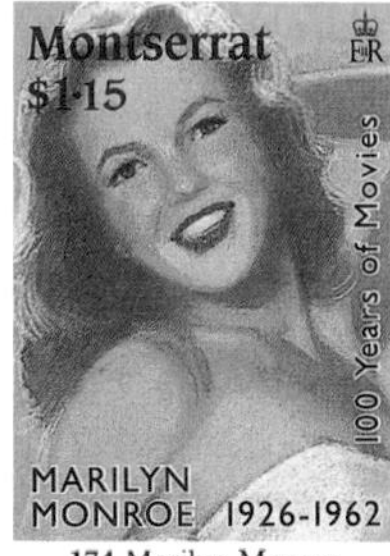

174 Marilyn Monroe

1995. Centenary of Cinema. Portraits of Marilyn Monroe (film star). Multicoloured.
956 $1.15 Type **174** . . . . . . 90 1·00
957 $1.15 Puckering lips . . . . 90 1·00
958 $1.15 Laughing in brown evening dress and earrings 90 1·00
959 $1.15 Wearing red earrings 90 1·00
960 $1.15 In brown dress without earrings . . . . 90 1·00
961 $1.15 With white boa . . . . 90 1·00
962 $1.15 In red dress . . . . . 90 1·00
963 $1.15 Wearing white jumper 90 1·00
964 $1.15 Looking over left shoulder . . . . 90 1·00
MS965 102 × 132 mm. $6 With Elvis Presley (50 × 56 mm) . . . . . 4·50 5·50

175 Jesse Owens (U.S.A.)

177 Ears of Wheat ("Food")

176 Atmospheric Sounding Experiments using V2 Rockets

1995. 5th International Amateur Athletic Federation Games, Göteborg. Sheet 181 × 103 mm, containing T **175** and similar vert designs.
MS966 $1.50 black and pink (Type **175**); $1.50 black and orange (Eric Lemming (Sweden)); $1.50 black and yellow (Rudolf Harbig (Germany)); $1.50 black and green (young Montserrat athletes) . . . . 4·50 6·00

1995. 50th Anniv of End of Second World War. Scientific Achievements. Multicoloured.
967 $1.15 Type **176** . . . . . . 80 1·00
968 $1.15 American space shuttle "Challenger" . . . . . . 80 1·00
969 $1.15 Nuclear experiment, Chicago, 1942 . . . . . . 80 1·00
970 $1.15 Calder Hall Atomic Power Station, 1956 . . . 80 1·00
971 $1.50 Radar-equipped Ju 88G 7a nightfighter . . . . . . 1·25 1·50
972 $1.50 Boeing E6 A.W.A.C.S. aircraft . . . . 1·25 1·50
973 $1.50 Gloster G.41 Meteor Mk III jet fighter . . . . 1·25 1·50
974 $1.50 Concorde (airliner) . . 1·25 1·50

1995. 50th Anniv of United Nations. Multicoloured.
975 $1.15 Type **177** 90 75
976 $1.50 Open book ("Education") . . . . . . 1·25 1·00
977 $2.30 P.T. class ("Health") 1·75 2·25
978 $3 Dove ("Peace") . . . . . 2·25 3·50
MS979 105 × 75 mm. $6 Scales ("Justice") . . . . 3·75 6·00

178 Headquarters Building

1995. 25th Anniv of Montserrat National Trust. Multicoloured.
980 $1.15 Type **178** 80 75
981 $1.50 17th-century cannon, Bransby Point . . . . . . 1·25 1·00
982 $2.30 Impression of Galways Sugar Mill (vert) . . . . . 2·25 2·50
983 $3 Great Alps Falls (vert) . . 4·00 5·00

1995. 25th Anniv of Air Recording Studios. No. 713 surch **air 25TH ANNIVERSARY 1970 - 1995**.
984 $2.30+$5 Air Recording Studios . . . . 4·25 5·50

The $5 premium on No. 984 was for relief following a volcanic eruption.

180 Bull Shark

1996. Scavengers of the Sea. Multicoloured.
985 $1 Type **180** 80 70
986 $1.15 Sea mouse 90 80
987 $1.50 Bristleworm . . . . . 1·25 1·50
988 $3.45 Prawn "Xiphocaris" . . 2·50 3·50
MS989 69 × 95 mm. $4.50 Man of war fish . . . . 3·00 4·00

181 Marconi and Radio Equipment, 1901

1996. Centenary of Radio. Multicoloured.
990 $1.15 Type **181** 90 80
991 $1.50 Marconi's steam yacht "Elettra" . . . . 1·25 1·00
992 $2.30 Receiving first Transatlantic radio message, Newfoundland, 1901 . . . . 1·75 2·25
993 $3 Imperial Airways airplane at Croydon Airport, 1920 2·25 3·50
MS994 74 × 105 mm. $4.50 Radio telescope, Jodrell Bank . . . . 3·00 4·00

182 Paul Masson (France) (Cycling)

1996. Olympic Games, Atlanta. Gold Medal Winners of 1896. Multicoloured.
995 $1.15 Type **182** 80 80
996 $1.50 Robert Garrett (U.S.A.) (Discus) 1·00 1·00
997 $2.30 Spyridon Louis (Greece) (Marathon) 1·50 1·75
998 $3 John Boland (Great Britain) (Tennis) 2·00 3·25

183 James Dean

1996. James Dean (film star) Commemoration. Multicoloured.
999 $1.15 Type **183** 80 95
1000 $1.15 Wearing stetson facing right 80 95
1001 $1.15 Wearing blue sweater 80 95
1002 $1.15 Wearing black sweater 80 95
1003 $1.15 Full face portrait wearing stetson 80 95
1004 $1.15 Wearing fawn jacket 80 95
1005 $1.15 Wearing red wind-cheater 80 95
1006 $1.15 Smoking a cigarette 80 95
1007 $1.15 In open-necked shirt and green jumper 80 95
MS1008 169 × 133 mm. $6 As No. 1000 (51 × 57 mm) 4·50 6·00

184 Leprechaun

185 Blue and Green Teddybears

1996. Mythical Creatures. Multicoloured.
1009 5c. Type **184** 10 30
1010 10c. Pegasus 10 30
1011 15c. Griffin 15 30
1012 20c. Unicorn 20 30
1013 25c. Gnomes 25 30
1014 40c. Mermaid 40 40
1015 55c. Cockatrice 50 40
1016 70c. Fairy 65 40
1017 90c. Goblin 80 50
1018 $1 Faun 90 55
1019 $1.15 Dragon 1·00 65
1020 $1.50 Giant 1·25 85
1021 $3 Elves 2·00 2·50
1022 $5 Centaur 3·25 3·75
1023 $7.50 Phoenix 4·75 6·00
1024 $10 Erin 5·50 6·50

1996. Jerry Garcia and the Grateful Dead (rock group) Commemoration. Multicoloured.
1025 $1.15 Type **185** 1·00 1·00
1026 $1.15 Green and yellow teddybears 1·00 1·00
1027 $1.15 Brown and pink teddybears 1·00 1·00
1028 $6 Jerry Garcia (37 × 50 mm) 5·50 5·50
Nos. 1025/7 were printed together, se-tenant, forming a composite design.

186 Turkey Vulture

1997. Scavengers of the Sky. Multicoloured.
1029 $1 Type **186** 75 70
1030 $1.15 American crow 90 70
1031 $1.50 Great skua 1·25 1·50
1032 $3.45 Black-legged kittiwake ("Kittiwake") 2·25 3·75
MS1033 74 × 95 mm. $4.50 King vulture 3·00 4·00

1997. "HONG KONG '97" International Stamp Exhibition. Nos. 1025/7 optd **HONG KONG '97**.
1034 $1.15 Type **185** 70 1·00
1035 $1.15 Green and yellow teddybears 70 1·00
1036 $1.15 Brown and pink teddybears 70 1·00

1997. "PACIFIC '97" International Stamp Exhibition, San Francisco. Nos. 999/1007 optd **PACIFIC 97 World Philatelic Exhibition San Francisco, California 29 May - 8 June**.
1037 $1.15 Type **183** 80 95
1038 $1.15 Wearing stetson facing right 80 95
1039 $1.15 Wearing blue sweater 80 95
1040 $1.15 Wearing black sweater 80 95
1041 $1.15 Full-face portrait wearing stetson 80 95
1042 $1.15 Wearing fawn jacket 80 95
1043 $1.15 Wearing red wind-cheater 80 95
1044 $1.15 Smoking a cigarette 80 95
1045 $1.15 In open-necked shirt and green jumper 80 95

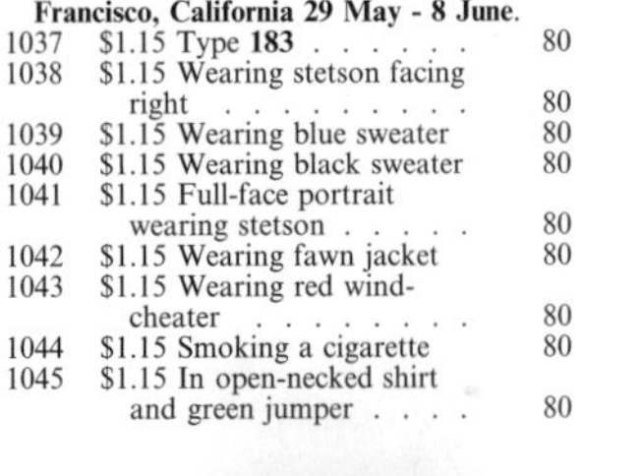

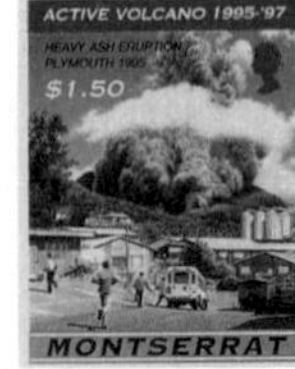

189 Heavy Ash Eruption over Plymouth, 1995

1997. Eruption of Soufriere Volcano. Mult.
1046 $1.50 Type **189** 1·10 1·25
1047 $1.50 Burning rock flow entering sea 1·10 1·25
1048 $1.50 Double venting at Castle Peak 1·10 1·25
1049 $1.50 Mangrove cuckoo 1·10 1·25
1050 $1.50 Lava flow at night, 1996 1·10 1·25
1051 $1.50 Antillean crested hummingbird 1·10 1·25
1052 $1.50 Ash cloud over Plymouth 1·10 1·25
1053 $1.50 Lava spine, 1996 1·10 1·25
1054 $1.50 Burning rock flows forming new land 1·10 1·25

190 Elvis Presley

1997. Rock Legends. Multicoloured.
1055 $1.15 Type **190** 1·50 1·40
1056 $1.15 Jimi Hendrix 1·50 1·40
1057 $1.15 Jerry Garcia 1·50 1·40
1058 $1.15 Janis Joplin 1·50 1·40

191 Untitled Painting by Frama

1997. Frama Exhibition at Guggenheim Museum, New York.
1059 **191** $1.50 multicoloured 1·00 1·25

1997. No. 1028 surch **$1.50**.
1060 $1.50 on $6 Jerry Garcia (37 × 50 mm) 1·00 1·25

193 Prickly Pear

194 Eva and Juan Peron (Argentine politicians)

1998. Medicinal Plants. Multicoloured.
1061 $1 Type **193** 65 50
1062 $1.15 Pomme coolie 70 55
1063 $1.50 Aloe 85 90
1064 $3.45 Bird pepper 1·75 2·50

1998. Famous People of the 20th Century. Mult.
1065 $1.15 Type **194** 1·00 1·10
1066 $1.15 Pablo Picasso (painter) 1·00 1·10
1067 $1.15 Wernher von Braun (space scientist) 1·00 1·10
1068 $1.15 David Ben Gurion (Israeli statesman) 1·00 1·10
1069 $1.15 Jean Henri Dunant (founder of Red Cross) 1·00 1·10
1070 $1.15 Dwight Eisenhower (President of U.S.A.) 1·00 1·10
1071 $1.15 Mahatma Gandhi (leader of Indian Independence movement) 1·00 1·10
1072 $1.15 King Leopold III and Queen Astrid of Belgium 1·00 1·10
1073 $1.15 Grand Duchess Charlotte and Prince Felix of Luxembourg 1·00 1·10
1074 $1.50 Charles Augustus Lindbergh (pioneer aviator) 1·00 1·10
1075 $1.50 Mao Tse-tung (Chinese communist leader) 1·00 1·10
1076 $1.50 Earl Mountbatten (last Viceroy of India) 1·00 1·10
1077 $1.50 Konrad Adenauer (German statesman) 1·00 1·10
1078 $1.50 Anne Frank (Holocaust victim) 1·00 1·10
1079 $1.50 Queen Wilhelmina of the Netherlands 1·00 1·10
1080 $1.50 King George VI of Great Britain 1·00 1·10
1081 $1.50 King Christian X of Denmark 1·00 1·10
1082 $1.50 King Haakon VII and Crown Prince Olav of Norway 1·00 1·10
1083 $1.50 King Alfonso XIII of Spain 1·00 1·10
1084 $1.50 King Gustavus V of Sweden 1·00 1·10
MS1085 115 × 63 mm. $3 John F. Kennedy (Resident of U.S.A.) (50 × 32 mm) 1·75 2·50

195 Jerry Garcia

1998. Rock Music Legends. Multicoloured. (a) Jerry Garcia.
1086 $1.15 In long-sleeved blue shirt 90 1·10
1087 $1.15 With drum kit in background 90 1·10
1088 $1.15 Type **195** 90 1·10
1089 $1.15 Wearing long-sleeved black t-shirt 90 1·10
1090 $1.15 Close-up with left hand in foreground 90 1·10
1091 $1.15 With purple and black background 90 1·10
1092 $1.15 Holding microphone 90 1·10
1093 $1.15 In short-sleeved blue t-shirt 90 1·10
1094 $1.15 In sunglasses with cymbal in background 90 1·10

(b) Bob Marley. Predominant colour for each design given.
1095 $1.15 Pointing (green) 90 1·10
1096 $1.15 Wearing neck chain (green) 90 1·10
1097 $1.15 Singing into microphone (green) 90 1·10
1098 $1.15 Singing with eyes closed (yellow) 90 1·10
1099 $1.15 Facing audience (yellow) 90 1·10
1100 $1.15 In striped t-shirt with fingers on chin (red) 90 1·10
1101 $1.15 In Rastafarian hat (red) 90 1·10
1102 $1.15 In striped t-shirt with hand closed (red) 90 1·10
MS1103 152 × 101 mm. $5 Jerry Garcia (50 × 75 mm) 2·75 3·50

196 Ash Eruption from Soufriere Hills Volcano

1998. Total Eclipse of the Sun. Multicoloured.
1104 $1.15 Type **196** 1·75 1·50
1105 $1.15 Volcano emitting black cloud 1·75 1·50
1106 $1.15 Village below volcano 1·75 1·50
1107 $1.15 Lava flow and wrecked house 1·75 1·50
MS1108 152 × 102 mm. $6 Solar eclipse (vert) 6·00 6·50

197 Princess Diana on Wedding Day, 1981

1998. Diana, Princess of Wales Commemoration. Multicoloured.
1109 $1.15 Type **197** 1·50 70
1110 $1.50 Accepting bouquet from children 1·75 1·10
1111 $3 At Royal Ascot 3·00 4·00
MS1112 133 × 100 mm. $6 Diana and "Princess of Wales" rose (50 × 37 mm) 5·50 5·50

1998. 19th World Scout Jamboree, Chile. Nos. 669/72 optd **19th WORLD JAMBOREE MONDIAL CHILE 1999** and emblem.
1113 20c. Type **117** 30 40
1114 20c. Girl Guide saluting 30 40
1115 75c. Lady Baden-Powell 70 1·00
1116 75c. Guide assisting in old people's home 70 1·00

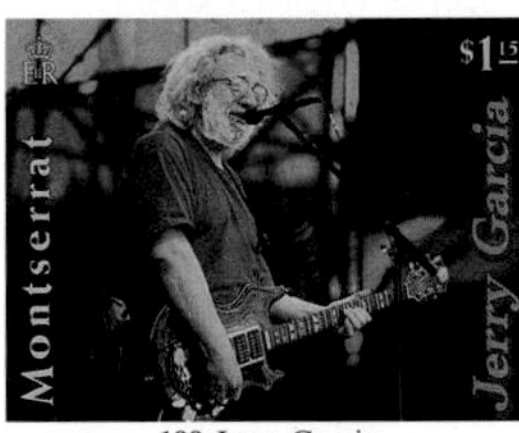

199 Jerry Garcia

1999. Jerry Garcia (rock musician) Commem. Mult.
1117 $1.15 Type **199** 90 1·00
1118 $1.15 In front of drum kit (violet background) 90 1·00
1119 $1.15 Singing into microphone 90 1·00
1120 $1.15 Playing guitar, facing right (vert) 90 1·00
1121 $1.15 Singing with eyes closed (vert) 90 1·00
1122 $1.15 Singing in white spotlight (vert) 90 1·00
1123 $1.15 In front of drum kit (green background) 90 1·00
1124 $1.15 In long-sleeved black shirt 90 1·00
1125 $1.15 In red shirt 90 1·00
1126 $1.15 In short-sleeved black t-shirt (without frame) (vert) 90 1·00
1127 $1.15 In blue t-shirt (oval frame) (vert) 90 1·00
1128 $1.15 In short-sleeved black t-shirt (oval frame) (vert) 90 1·00
MS1129 Two sheets. (a) 115 × 153 mm. $6 Jerry Garcia in concert (50 × 75 mm). (b) 153 × 115 mm. $6 Singing into microphone (75 × 50 mm) Set of 2 sheets 7·00 8·00

1999. "iBRA '99" International Stamp Exhibition, Nuremberg. Nos. 975/6 optd **iBRA INTERNATIONALE BRIEFMARKEN WELTAUSSTELLUNG NURNBERG 27.4.-4.5.99.**
1130 $1.15 Type **177** 1·50 1·50
1131 $1.50 Open book ("Education") 1·75 2·25

201 Mango

1999. Tropical Caribbean Fruits. Multicoloured.
1132 $1.15 Type **201** 75 70
1133 $1.50 Breadfruit 90 85
1134 $2.30 Papaya 1·40 1·60
1135 $3 Lime 1·75 2·25
1136 $6 Akee 3·50 5·00
MS1137 134 × 95 mm. Nos. 1132/6 8·50 10·00

202 Yorkshire Terrier

1999. Dogs. Each black.
1138 70c. Type **202** . . . . . . 1·10 65
1139 $1 Welsh corgi . . . . . . 1·25 75
1140 $1.15 King Charles spaniel 1·40 85
1141 $1.50 Poodle . . . . 1·50 1·25
1142 $3 Beagle . . . . 2·75 4·00
MS1143 133 × 95 mm. Nos. 1138/42 8·00 8·50

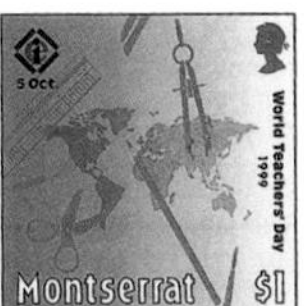

203 Pupil's Equipment and World Map

1999. World Teachers' Day. Multicoloured.
1144 $1 Type **203** . . . . 1·25 70
1145 $1.15 Teacher and class . . 1·25 80
1146 $1.50 Emblems of vocational training . . . . 1·50 1·25
1147 $5 Scientific equipment . . . 5·00 6·50

204 Great Hammerhead Shark

1999. Endangered Species. Great Hammerhead Shark. Multicoloured.
1148 50c. Type **204** 50 60
1149 50c. Two hammerhead sharks among fish 50 60
1150 50c. Two hammerhead sharks on sea-bed 50 60
1151 50c. Three hammerhead sharks 50 60

205 Flowers

2000. New Millennium.
1152 **205** $1.50 multicoloured . . 1·50 1·50

206 Alfred Valentine

2000. West Indies Cricket Tour and 100th Test Match at Lord's. Multicoloured.
1153 $1 Type **206** . . . . 1·50 60
1154 $5 George Headley batting 3·00 4·00
MS1155 119 × 101 mm. $6 Lord's Cricket Ground (horiz) . . . . 5·50 6·00

207 Spitfire Squadron taking-off

2000. "The Stamp Show 2000" International Stamp Exhibition, London. 60th Anniv of Battle of Britain. Multicoloured.
1156 70c. Type **207** . . . . . . 1·00 50
1157 $1.15 Overhauling Hurricane Mk I . . . . 1·25 65
1158 $1.50 Hurricane MK I attacking . . . . 1·50 1·25
1159 $5 Flt. Lt. Frank Howell's Spitfire Mk IA . . . . . 3·50 5·00
MS1160 110 × 87 mm. $6 Hawker Hurricane . . . . 4·50 5·50

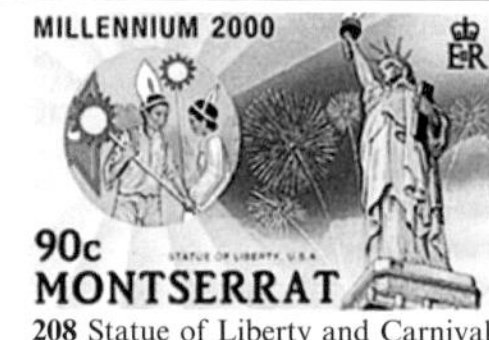

208 Statue of Liberty and Carnival Scene

2000. New Millennium. Landmarks. Each including carnival scene. Multicoloured.
1161 90c. Type **208** 75 50
1162 $1.15 Great Wall of China 95 60
1163 $1.50 Eiffel Tower . . . . . 1·25 1·25
1164 $3.50 Millennium Dome . . 2·50 3·50

209 Queen Elizabeth the Queen Mother and W.H. Bramble Airport

2000. Queen Elizabeth the Queen Mother's 100th Birthday. Each showing different portrait. Mult.
1165 70c. Type **209** 85 40
1166 $1.15 Government House 1·25 65
1167 $3 Court House . . . . . . 2·50 2·75
1168 $6 War Memorial Clock Tower . . . . 4·50 5·50
MS1169 120 × 75 mm. Nos. 1165/8 8·00 9·00

210 Three Wise Men following Star **211** Golden Swallow

2000. Christmas. Multicoloured.
1170 $1 Type **210** . . . . 1·00 55
1171 $1.15 Cavalla Hill Methodist Church . . . . 1·10 65
1172 $1.50 Shepherds with flocks 1·25 85
1173 $3 Mary and Joseph arriving at Bethlehem . . 2·25 2·75
MS1174 105 × 75 mm. $6 As $3 4·50 5·50

2001. Caribbean Birds. Multicoloured.
1175 $1 Type **211** . . . . 1·25 65
1176 $1.15 Crested quail dove (horiz) . . . . 1·40 75
1177 $1.50 Red-legged thrush (horiz) . . . . 1·50 1·10
1178 $5 Fernandina's flicker . . . 4·25 5·50
MS1179 95 × 68 mm. $8 St. Vincent amazon (horiz) . . . . 7·00 8·00

212 Edward Stanley Gibbons, Charles J. Phillips and 391 Strand Shop

2001. Famous Stamp Personalities. Multicoloured.
1180 $1 Type **212** . . . . 1·10 60
1181 $1.15 John Lister and Montserrat stamps . . . 1·25 70
1182 $1.50 Theodore Champion and French postilion . . 1·40 1·10
1183 $3 Thomas De La Rue and De La Rue's stand at Great Exhibition, 1851 . . 2·75 3·50
MS1184 95 × 68 mm. $8 Sir Rowland Hill and Bruce Castle 5·50 6·50

213 Princess Elizabeth at International Horse Show, 1950

2001. Queen Elizabeth II's 75th Birthday. Mult.
1185 90c. Type **213** 90 55
1186 $1.15 Queen Elizabeth II, 1986 . . . . 1·10 70
1187 $1.50 Queen Elizabeth II, 1967 . . . . 1·25 1·25
1188 $5 Queen Elizabeth, 1976 4·00 4·75
MS1189 90 × 68 mm. $6 Queen Elizabeth, 2000 . . . . 7·00 7·50

214 Look Out Village

2001. Reconstruction. Multicoloured.
1190 70c. Type **214** 70 50
1191 $1 St. John's Hospital . . . 90 65
1192 $1.15 Tropical Mansions Suites Hotel . . . . . . 1·00 70
1193 $1.50 Montserrat Secondary School . . . . 1·25 1·10
1194 $3 Golden Years Care Home . . . . 2·75 3·50

215 West Indian Cherry

2001. Caribbean Fruits. Multicoloured.
1195 5c. Type **215** 10 10
1196 10c. Mammee apple 10 10
1197 15c. Lime 10 10
1198 20c. Grapefruit 10 15
1199 25c. Orange 10 15
1200 40c. Passion fruit 15 20
1201 55c. Banana 20 25
1202 70c. Pawpaw 30 35
1203 90c. Pomegranate 35 40
1204 $1 Guava 40 45
1205 $1.15 Mango 45 50
1206 $1.50 Sugar apple 60 65
1207 $3 Cashew . . . . 1·20 1·30
1208 $5 Soursop . . . . 2·00 2·10
1209 $7.50 Watermelon . . . . . 3·00 3·25
1210 $10 Pineapple . . . . 4·00 4·25

216 Common Long-tail Skipper (butterfly)

2001. Caribbean Butterflies. Multicoloured.
1211 $1 Type **216** 90 60
1212 $1.15 Straight-line sulphur 1·00 70
1213 $1.50 Giant hairstreak . . . 1·25 1·10
1214 $3 Monarch . . . . 2·00 2·75
MS1215 115 × 115 mm. $10 Painted Lady . . . . 7·00 8·00
The overall design of No. **MS**1215 is butterfly-shaped

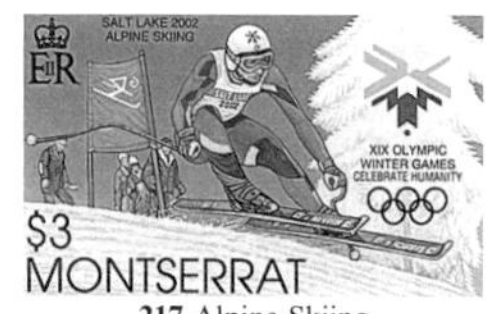

217 Alpine Skiing

2002. Winter Olympic Games, Salt Lake City. Mult.
1216 $3 Type **217** . . . . 2·25 2·50
1217 $5 Four man bobsleigh . . 3·25 3·75

218 Sergeant Major (fish)

2002. Fishes of the Caribbean. Multicoloured.
1218 $1 Type **218** 90 55
1219 $1.15 Mutton snapper . . . 1·00 60
1220 $1.50 Lantern bass . . . . 1·25 1·00
1221 $5 Shy Hamlet . . . . . . 4·75 5·50
MS1222 102 × 70 mm. $8 Queen angelfish . . . . 7·00 7·50

2002. Queen Elizabeth the Queen Mother Commemoration. Nos. 1165/8 optd **Life and Death of Her Majesty Queen Elizabeth The Queen Mother 1900 2002.**
1223 70c. Type **209** 70 40
1224 $1.15 Government House 1·00 60
1225 $3 Court House . . . . . . 2·75 2·75
1226 $6 War Memorial Clock Tower . . . . 4·75 5·50

220 *Allamanda cathartica*

2002. Wild Flowers. Multicoloured.
1227 70c. Type **220** 30 35
1228 $1.15 *Lantana camara* . . . 45 50
1229 $1.50 *Leonotis nepetifolia* . . 60 65
1230 $5 *Plumeria rubra* . . . . . 2·00 2·25
MS1231 105 × 75 mm. $8 *Alpinia purpurata* . . . . 3·25 3·50

221 Queen Elizabeth II wearing Imperial State Crown and Coronation Robes
223 Prince William

222 *Wright Flyer II* (blue)

2003. 50th Anniv of Coronation. Two sheets containing vert designs as T **221**. Multicoloured.
MS1232 153 × 85 mm. $3 Type **221**; $3 St. Edward's Crown; $3 Queen wearing diadem and blue sash 3·75 4·00
MS1233 105 × 75 mm. $6 Queen wearing Imperial State Crown and Coronation robes . . . . . . 2·40 2·50

2003. Centenary of Powered Flight. Multicoloured.
MS1234 116 × 125 mm. $2 Type **222**; $2 Wright *Flyer II* (brown); $2 Orville and Wilbur Wright; $2 Wright *Flyer I* . . . . 2·40 2·50
MS1235 106 × 76 mm. $6 Wright *Flyer II* . . . . 2·40 2·50

2003. 21st Birthday of Prince William of Wales. Different portraits. Multicoloured.
MS1236 155 × 85 mm. $3 Type **223**; $3 Prince William (frame incomplete at bottom left); $3 Prince William (frame complete at bottom left) . . . . 3·75 4·00
MS1237 106 × 76 mm. $6 Prince William . . . . 2·40 2·50

224 Piping Frog

2003. Animals of the Caribbean. Multicoloured.
MS1238 145 × 90 mm. $1.50 Type **224**; $1.50 Land hermit crab; $1.50 Spix's pinche; $1.50 Dwarf Ggecko; $1.50 Green sea turtle; $1.50 Small Indian mongoose 3·75 9·00
MS1239 92 × 66 mm. $6 Sally lightfoot crab . . . . 2·40 2·50

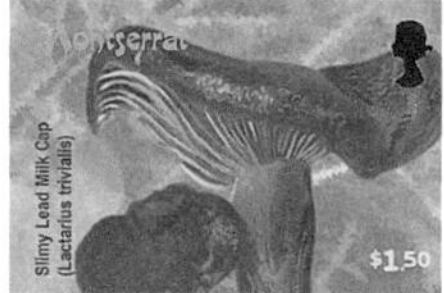

225 *Lactarius trivialis*

2003. Mushrooms of the World. Multicoloured.
MS1240 145 × 90 mm. $1.50 Type **225**; $1.50 *Gomphidius roseus*; $1.50 *Lycoperdon pyriforme*; $1.50 *Hygrophorus coccineus*; $1.50 *Russula xerampelina*; $1.50 *Gomphus floccosus* . . . . 3·75 4·00
MS1241 92 × 66 mm. $6 *Amanita muscaria* . . . . 2·40 2·50

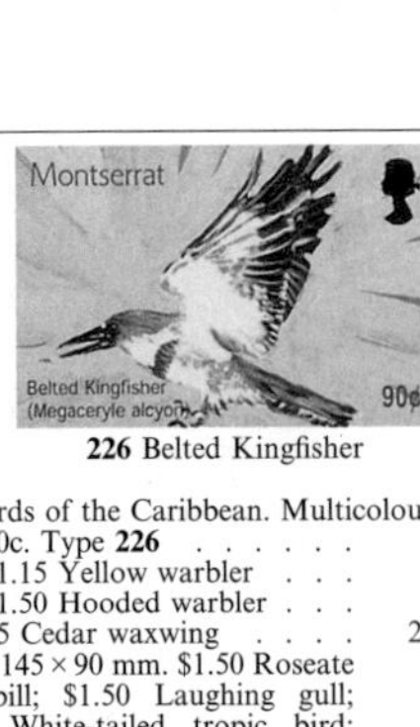

226 Belted Kingfisher

2003. Birds of the Caribbean. Multicoloured.
1242 90c. Type **226** 35 35
1243 $1.15 Yellow warbler 45 50
1244 $1.50 Hooded warbler 60 65
1245 $5 Cedar waxwing 2·00 2·10
MS1246 145 × 90 mm. $1.50 Roseate spoonbill; $1.50 Laughing gull; $1.50 White-tailed tropic bird; $1.50 Bare-eyed thrush; $1.50 Glittering-throated emerald; $1.50 Carib grackle ("Lesser Antillean Grackle") 3·75 4·00
MS1247 92 × 68 mm. $6 Bananaquit 2·40 2·50

OFFICIAL STAMPS

1976. Various stamps, some already surch, optd **O.H.M.S.**
O1 5c. multicoloured (No. 246) † 65
O2 10c. multicoloured (No. 247) † 75
O3 30c. on 10c. mult (No. 369) † 1·50
O4 45c. on 3c. mult (No. 370) † 2·00
O5 $5 multicoloured (No. 254) † £100
O6 $10 multicoloured (No. 254a) † £550

These stamps were issued for use on mail from the Montserrat Philatelic Bureau. They were not sold to the public, either unused or used.

1976. Nos. 372, 374/82, 384/5 and 476 optd **O.H.M.S.** or surch also.
O17 5c. Malay apple † 10
O28 5c. on 3c. Lignum vitae † 20
O18 10c. Jacaranda † 10
O19 15c. Orchid tree † 10
O20 20c. Manjak † 10
O21 25c. Tamarind † 15
O33 30c. on 15c. Orchid tree † 30
O34 35c. on 2c. Cannon-ball tree † 30
O35 40c. Flame of the forest † 40
O22 55c. Pink cassia † 35
O23 70c. Long john † 45
O24 $1 Saman † 60
O39 $2.50 on 40c. Flame of the forest † 2·00
O25 $5 Yellow poui † 1·50
O16 $10 Flamboyant † 3·75

1981. Nos. 490/4, 496, 498, 500, 502/3 and 505 optd **O.H.M.S.**
O42 5c. Type **91** 10 10
O43 10c. Hogfish and neon goby 10 10
O44 15c. Creole wrasse 10 10
O45 20c. Three-spotted damselfish 15 15
O46 25c. Sergeant major 15 15
O47 45c. Schoolmaster 25 20
O48 65c. Bigeye 35 30
O49 $1 Rock beauty 65 65
O50 $3 Royal gramma ("Fairy basslet") and blueheads 1·50 1·75
O51 $5 Cherub angelfish 2·00 2·25
O52 $10 Caribbean long-nosed butterflyfish 3·00 2·25

1983. Nos. 510/15 surch **O.H.M.S.** and value.
O53 45c. on 90c. "Charlotte" 20 30
O54 45c. on 90c. Prince Charles and Lady Diana Spencer 60 1·00
O55 75c. on $3 "Portsmouth" 25 35
O56 75c. on $3 Prince Charles and Lady Diana Spencer 90 1·40
O57 $1 on $4 "Britannia" 35 50
O58 $1 on $4 Prince Charles and Lady Diana Spencer 1·00 1·50

1983. Nos. 542/4 surch **O.H.M.S.**
O59 70c. on 75c. Type **97** 60 40
O60 $1 Coat of Arms of Catherine of Aragon 70 50
O61 $1.50 on $5 Diana, Princess of Wales 1·00 80

1985. Nos. 600/12 and 614 optd **O H M S.**
O62 5c. Type **107** 1·25 1·00
O63 10c. Carib grackle 1·25 1·00
O64 15c. Moorhen 1·50 1·00
O65 20c. Brown booby 1·50 70
O66 25c. Black-whiskered vireo 1·50 70
O67 40c. Scaly-breasted thrasher 2·00 70
O68 55c. Laughing gull 2·25 70
O69 70c. Glossy ibis 2·50 90
O70 90c. Green-backed heron 2·75 90
O71 $1 Belted kingfisher 2·75 90
O72 $1.15 Bananaquit 3·00 90
O73 $3 American kestrel 4·50 2·50
O74 $5 Forest thrush 5·50 2·50
O75 $10 Bridled quail dove 7·00 2·50

1989. Nos. 757/70 and 772 optd **O H M S.**
O76 5c. Type **133** 40 60
O77 10c. Little knobbed scallop 40 60
O78 15c. Sozoni's cone 50 60
O79 20c. Globular coral shell 55 50
O80 25c. American or common sundial 55 50
O81 40c. King helmet 60 55
O82 55c. Channelled turban 70 50
O83 70c. True tulip shell 90 75
O84 90c. Music volute 1·00 90
O85 $1 Flame auger 1·00 80
O86 $1.15 Rooster-tail conch 1·25 85
O87 $1.50 Queen or pink conch 1·40 1·40
O88 $3 Teramachi's slit shell 2·00 2·50
O89 $5 Common or Florida crown conch 3·25 3·25
O90 $10 Atlantic trumpet triton 5·50 5·50

1989. Nos. 578 and 580/1 surch **OHMS.**
O91 70c. on 10c. Hogfish and neon goby 2·00 1·75
O92 $1.15 on 75c. French grunt 2·50 1·75
O93 $1.50 on $2 Blue chromis 2·75 3·00

1992. Nos. 838/41, 847/50, 856/9 surch or optd **OHMS.**
O 94 70c. on 90c. Type **150** 1·40 1·40
O 95 70c. on 90c. Type **152** 1·40 1·40
O 96 70c. on 90c. Type **154** 1·40 1·40
O 97 70c. on $3.50 French grunt 1·40 1·40
O 98 $1 on $3.50 Helmeted guineafowl 1·50 1·50
O 99 $1 on $3.50 Anthurium 1·50 1·50
O100 $1.15 Cushion star 1·50 1·50
O101 $1.15 Hen and chicks 1·50 1·50
O102 $1.15 Shell ginger 1·50 1·50
O103 $1.50 Rock beauty 1·60 1·60
O104 $1.50 Red junglefowl 1·60 1·60
O105 $1.50 Early day lily 1·60 1·60

1993. Nos. 889/902 and 904 optd **OHMS.**
O106 5c. Type **161** 60 80
O107 10c. "Gryllus campestris" (field cricket) 60 80
O108 15c. "Lepthemis vesiculosa" (dragonfly) 70 80
O109 20c. "Orthemis ferruginea" (red skimmer) 70 60
O110 25c. "Gerris lacustris" (pond skater) 70 60
O111 40c. "Byctiscus betulae" (leaf weevil) 85 40
O112 55c. "Atta texana" (leaf-cutter ants) 90 40
O113 70c. "Polistes fuscatus" (paper wasp) 1·00 70
O114 90c. "Sparmopolius fulvus" (bee fly) 1·10 70
O115 $1 "Chrysopa carnea" (lace wing) 1·25 70
O116 $1.15 "Phoebis philea" (butterfly) 2·00 1·50
O117 $1.50 "Cynthia cardui" (butterfly) 2·25 2·25
O118 $3 "Utetheisa bella" (moth) 3·00 3·50
O119 $5 "Alucita pentadactyla" (moth) 3·75 4·25
O120 $10 "Heliconius melpomene" (butterfly) 6·00 6·50

1997. Nos. 1009/22 and 1024 optd **O.H.M.S.**
O121 5c. Type **184** 15 50
O122 10c. Pegasus 25 50
O123 15c. Griffin 35 50
O124 20c. Unicorn 35 50
O125 25c. Gnomes 35 50
O126 40c. Mermaid 50 50
O127 55c. Cockatrice 60 50
O128 70c. Fairy 70 55
O129 90c. Goblin 90 60
O130 $1 Faun 1·00 60
O131 $1.15 Dragon 1·25 65
O132 $1.50 Giant 1·40 85
O133 $3 Elves 2·50 2·75
O134 $5 Centaur 4·00 4·25
O135 $10 Erin 6·00 6·50

2002. Nos. 1195/1208 and 1210 optd **OHMS.**
O137 5c. Type **215** 10 10
O138 10c. Mammee apple 10 10
O139 15c. Lime 10 10
O140 20c. Grapefruit 10 15
O141 25c. Orange 10 15
O142 40c. Passion fruit 15 20
O143 55c. Banana 20 25
O144 70c. Pawpaw 30 35
O145 90c. Pomegranate 35 40
O146 $1 Guava 40 45
O147 $1.15 Mango 45 50
O148 $1.50 Sugar apple 60 65
O149 $3 Cashew 1·20 1·30
O150 $5 Soursop 2·00 2·10
O151 $10 Pineapple 4·00 4·25

MOROCCO Pt. 13

An independent kingdom, established in 1956, comprising the former French and Spanish International Zones.

A. NORTHERN ZONE

100 centimes = 1 peseta.

1 Sultan of Morocco

2 Polytechnic

1956.
1 **1** 10c. brown 10 10
2 – 15c. brown 10 10
3 **2** 25c. violet 10 10
4 – 50c. green 25 25
5 **1** 80c. green 90 90
6 – 2p. lilac 7·50 7·50
7 **2** 3p. blue 15·00 15·00
8 – 10p. green 31·00 31·00

DESIGNS—HORIZ: 15c., 2p. Villa Sanjurjo harbour. VERT: 50c., 10p. Cultural Delegation building, Tetuan.

3 Lockheed Super Constellation over Lau Dam

1956. Air.
9 **3** 25c. purple 20 15
10 – 1p.40 mauve 90 60
11 **3** 3p.40 red 1·90 1·50
12 – 4p.80 purple 3·50 2·50

DESIGN: 1p.40, 4p.80, Lockheed Super Constellation over Rio Nekor Bridge.

1957. 1st Anniv of Independence. As T **7** but with Spanish inscriptions and currency.
13 80c. green 65 50
14 1p.50 olive 1·90 1·40
15 3p. red 4·25 3·25

1957. As T **5** but with Spanish inscriptions and currency.
16 30c. indigo and blue 10 10
17 70c. purple and brown 20 10
18 80c. purple 1·60 40
19 1p.50 lake and green 50 15
20 3p. green 75 50
21 7p. red 5·25 1·50

1957. Investiture of Prince Moulay el Hassan. As T **9** but with Spanish inscriptions and currency.
22 80c. blue 65 25
23 1p.50 green 1·60 80
24 3p. red 4·75 2·50

1957. Nos. 17 and 19 surch.
25 15c. on 70c. purple and brown 75 75
26 1p.20 on 1p.50 lake and green 1·40 1·40

1957. 30th Anniv of Coronation of Sultan Sidi Mohammed ben Yusuf. As T **10** but with Spanish inscription and currency.
27 1p.20 green and black 65 50
28 1p.80 red and black 90 75
29 3p. violet and black 1·60 1·50

B. SOUTHERN ZONE

100 centimes = 1 franc.

5 Sultan of Morocco

6 Classroom

1956.
30 **5** 5f. indigo and blue 20 10
31 10f. sepia and brown 15 10
32 15f. lake and green 25 10
33 25f. purple 1·10 10
34 30f. green 1·90 10
35 50f. red 3·00 15
36 70f. brown and sepia 4·25 60

1956. Education Campaign.
37 – 10f. violet and purple 1·90 1·25
38 – 15f. lake and red 2·40 1·50
39 **6** 20f. green and turquoise 2·50 2·50
40 – 30f. red and lake 4·50 2·75
41 – 50f. blue and indigo 7·50 5·00

DESIGNS: 10f. Peasants reading book; 15f. Two girls reading; 30f. Child reading to old man; 50f. Child teaching parents the alphabet.

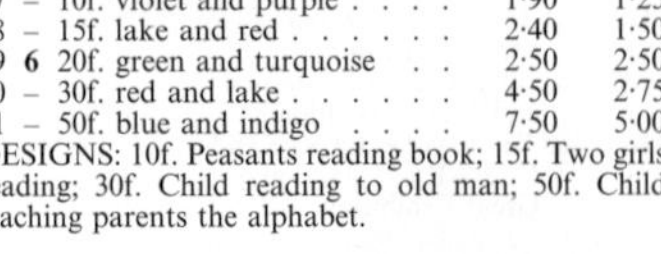

7 Sultan of Morocco

8 Emblem over Casablanca

1957. 1st Anniv of Independence.
42 **7** 15f. green 1·60 1·25
43 25f. olive 2·25 1·25
44 30f. red 4·00 1·90

1957. Air. International Fair, Casablanca.
45 **8** 15f. green and red 1·25 1·00
46 25f. turquoise 2·25 1·40
47 30f. brown 2·75 1·75

9 Crown Prince Moulay el Hassan

10 King Mohammed V

1957. Investiture of Crown Prince Moulay el Hassan.
48 **9** 15f. blue 1·50 95
49 25f. green 1·75 1·25
50 30f. red 2·75 1·60

1957. 30th Anniv of Coronation of King Mohammed V.
51 **10** 15f. green and black 95 50
52 25f. red and black 1·50 1·00
53 30f. violet and black 1·60 1·10

C. ISSUES FOR THE WHOLE OF MOROCCO

1958. 100 centimes = 1 franc.
1962. 100 francs = 1 dirham.

11 Moroccan Pavilion

1958. Brussels International Exhibition.
54 **11** 15f. turquoise 25 20
55 25f. red 25 25
56 30f. blue 35 30

12 King Mohammed V and U.N.E.S.C.O. Headquarters, Paris

1958. Inauguration of U.N.E.S.C.O. Headquarters Building, Paris.
57 **12** 15f. green 25 20
58 25f. lake 25 25
59 30f. blue 35 30

13 Ben-Smine Sanatorium

14 King Mohammed V on Horseback

1959. "National Aid".
60 **13** 50f. bistre, green and red 70 35

1959. King Mohammed V's 50th Birthday.
61 **14** 15f. lake 65 30
62 25f. blue 95 35
63 45f. green 1·10 45

15 Princess Lalla Amina

16

1959. Children's Week.
64 **15** 15f. blue 25 20
65 25f. green 30 25
66 45f. purple 60 30

1960. Meeting of U.N. African Economic Commission, Tangier.
67 **16** 45f. green, brown and violet 1·10 50

+10f

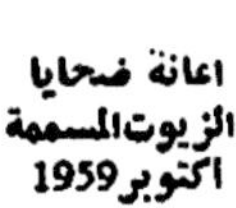

(17) 18 Arab Refugees

1960. Adulterated Cooking Oil Victims Relief Fund. Surch as T **17**.
68 **5** 5f.+10f. indigo and blue . . . 35 30
69 10f.+10f. sepia and brown . . 70 45
70 15f.+10f. lake and green . . 1·25 95
71 25f.+15f. purple . . . . . . 1·40 1·10
72 30f.+20f. green . . . . . . 2·25 2·00

1960. World Refugee Year.
73 **18** 15f. black, green and ochre 25 20
74 – 45f. green and black 65 35
DESIGNS: 45f. "Uprooted tree" and Arab refugees.

19 Marrakesh 20 Lantern

1960. 900th Anniv of Marrakesh.
75 **19** 100f. green, brown and blue 1·40 95

1960. 1100th Anniv of Karaouiyne University.
76 **20** 15f. purple 60 50
77 – 25f. blue 65 55
78 – 30f. brown . . . . 1·25 60
79 – 35f. black . . . . 1·60 80
80 – 45f. green . . . . 2·25 1·40
DESIGNS: 25f. Fountain; 30f. Minaret; 35f. Frescoes; 45f. Courtyard.

21 Arab League Centre and King Mohammed V

1960. Inauguration of Arab League Centre, Cairo.
81 **21** 15f. black and green 20 20

اسبوع التضامن
1380
1960
+5f

(22) 23 Wrestling

1960. Solidarity Fund. Nos. 458/9 (Mahakma, Casablanca) of French Morocco surch as T **22**.
82 **106** 15f.+3f. on 18f. myrtle . . 55 55
83 +5f. on 20f. lake 80 80

1960. Olympic Games.
84 **23** 5f. purple, green and violet 10 10
85 – 10f. chocolate, blue & brown 15 10
86 – 15f. brown, blue and green 20 15
87 – 20f. purple, blue and bistre 25 20
88 – 30f. brown, violet and red 30 25
89 – 40f. brown, blue and violet 60 25
90 – 45f. blue, green and purple 75 35
91 – 70f. black, blue and brown 1·40 45
DESIGNS: 10f. Gymnastics; 15f. Cycling; 20f. Weightlifting; 30f. Running; 40f. Boxing; 45f. Sailing; 70f. Fencing.

24 Runner 25 Post Office and Letters

1961. 3rd Pan-Arab Games, Casablanca.
92 **24** 20f. green 20 15
93 30f. lake 65 20
94 50f. blue 75 60

1961. African Postal and Telecommunications Conference, Tangier.
95 **25** 20f. purple and mauve . . . 35 30
96 – 30f. turquoise and green . . 45 35
97 – 90f. ultramarine and blue 85 60
DESIGNS—VERT: 30f. Telephone operator. HORIZ: 90f. Sud Aviation Caravelle mail plane over Tangier.

26 King Mohammed V and African Map 27 Lumumba and Congo Map

1962. 1st Anniv of African Charter of Casablanca.
98 **26** 20f. purple and buff 20 20
99 30f. indigo and blue 25 25

1962. Patrice Lumumba Commemoration.
100 **27** 20f. black and bistre . . . 20 20
101 30f. black and brown . . . 30 25

28 King Hassan II 29 "Pupils of the Nation"

1962. Air.
102 **28** 90f. black 75 15
103 1d. red 90 15
104 2d. blue . . . . 1·10 45
105 3d. green . . . . 2·25 1·10
106 5d. violet . . . . 4·50 1·60

1962. Children's Education.
107 **29** 20f. blue, red and green . . 35 25
108 30f. sepia, brown and green 40 35
109 90f. blue, purple and green 90 50

1962. Arab League Week. As T **76** of Libya.
110 20f. brown 20 15

30 King Hassan II 31 Scout with Banner

1962.
111 **30** 1f. olive 10 10
112 2f. violet 10 10
113 5f. sepia 10 10
114 10f. brown 10 10
115 15f. turquoise 15 10
116 20f. purple (18 × 22 mm) 20 10
116a 20f. purple (17½ × 23½ mm) 30 10
116b 25f. red 20 10
117 30f. green 25 10
117a 35f. slate 65 10
117b 40f. blue 65 10
118 50f. purple 80 10
118a 60f. purple . . . . 1·10 10
119 70f. blue . . . . 1·25 10
120 80f. lake . . . . 2·10 15

1962. 5th Arab Scout Jamboree, Rabat.
121 **31** 20f. purple and blue . . . 20 15

32 Campaign Emblem and Swamp 33 Aquarium, Brown Trout and Fish

1962. Malaria Eradication Campaign.
122 **32** 20f. blue and green 20 15
123 – 50f. lake and green 35 25
DESIGN—VERT: 50f. Sword piercing mosquito.

1962. Casablanca Aquarium. Multicoloured.
124 20f. Type **33** 85 25
125 30f. Aquarium and Mediterranean moray . . . 90 25

فيضانات
1963
20 + 5

34 Mounted Postman and 1912 Sherifian Stamp (35)

1962. First National Philatelic Exhibition, Rabat, and Stamp Day.
126 **34** 20f. green and brown . . . 75 35
127 – 30f. black and red 90 40
128 – 50f. bistre and blue . . . . 1·25 50
DESIGNS: 30f. Postman and circular postmark; 50f. Sultan Hassan I and octagonal postmark. (Both stamps commemorate 70th anniv of Sherifian post.)

1963. Flood Relief Fund. Surch as T **35**.
129 **5** 20+5f. on 5f. indigo & bl . . 90 85
130 30+10f. on 50f. red . . . . 1·00 85

36 King Moulay Ismail 37 Ibn Batota (voyager)

1963. 300th Anniv of Meknes.
131 **36** 20f. sepia 25 20

1963. "Famous Men of Maghreb".
132 **37** 20f. purple 45 20
133 – 20f. black 45 20
134 – 20f. myrtle 25 25
134a **37** 40f. blue 30 10
PORTRAITS: No. 133, Ibn Khaldoun (historian); 134, Al Idrissi (geographer).

38 Sugar Beet and Refinery 39 Isis (bas relief)

1963. Freedom from Hunger.
135 **38** 20f. black, brown and green 25 20
136 – 50f. black, brown and blue 65 35
DESIGN—VERT: 50f. Fisherman and tuna.

1963. Nubian Monuments Preservation.
137 – 20f. black and grey 20 15
138 **39** 30f. violet 25 25
139 – 50f. purple 60 35
DESIGNS—HORIZ: 20f. Heads of Colossi, Abu Simbel; 50f. Philae Temple.

40 Agadir before Earthquake

1963. Reconstruction of Agadir.
140 **40** 20f. red and blue 35 35
141 30f. red and blue 45 35
142 – 50f. red and blue 80 40
DESIGNS: 30f. is optd with large red cross and date of earthquake, 29th February, 1960; 50f. Reconstructed Agadir.

41 Plan of new Agadir Hospital 42 Emblems of Morocco and Rabat

1963. Centenary of International Red Cross.
143 **41** 30f. multicoloured 50 20

1963. Opening of Parliament.
144 **42** 20f. multicoloured 45 20

43 Hands breaking Chain 44 National Flag

1963. 15th Anniv of Declaration of Human Rights.
145 **43** 20f. brown, sepia and green 45 20

1963. Evacuation of Foreign Troops from Morocco.
146 **44** 20f. red, green and black 25 25

45 "Moulay Abdurrahman" (after Delacroix)

1964. 3rd Anniv of King Hassan's Coronation.
147 **45** 1d. multicoloured . . . . 2·75 1·90

46 Map, Chart and W.M.O. Emblem

1964. World Meteorological Day. Multicoloured.
148 20f. African weather map (vert) (postage) 25 20
149 30f. Type **46** 40 35
150 90f. Globe and weather vane (vert) (air) 90 45

47 Fair Entrance

1964. Air. 20th Anniv of Casablanca Int Fair.
151 **47** 1d. red, drab and blue . . 95 60

48 Moroccan Pavilion at Fair

1964. Air. New York World's Fair.
152 **48** 1d. multicoloured . . . . 1·25 65

49 Children Playing in the Sun — 50 Olympic Torch

1964. Postal Employees' Holiday Settlements.
153 **49** 20f. multicoloured 25 20
154 – 30f. multicoloured 35 25
DESIGN: 30f. Boy, girl and holiday settlement.

1964. Olympic Games, Tokyo.
155 **50** 20f. green, violet and red 25 25
156 30f. purple, blue and green 35 30
157 50f. red, blue and green . . 75 35

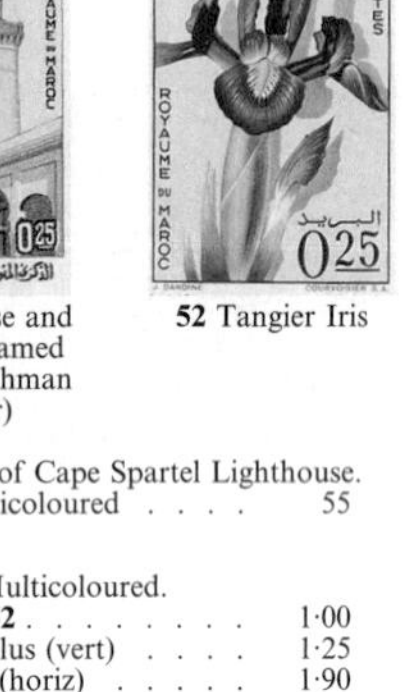

51 Lighthouse and Sultan Mohamed ben Abdurrahman (founder) — **52** Tangier Iris

1964. Centenary of Cape Spartel Lighthouse.
158 **51** 25f. multicoloured 55 45

1965. Flowers. Multicoloured.
159 25f. Type **52** . . . . 1·00 45
160 40f. Gladiolus (vert) . . . . 1·25 55
161 60f. Caper (horiz) . . . . . 1·90 1·40

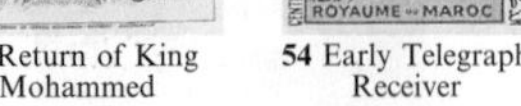

53 Return of King Mohammed — **54** Early Telegraph Receiver

1965. 10th Anniv of Return of King Mohammed V from Exile.
162 **53** 25f. green 50 20

1965. Centenary of I.T.U. Multicoloured.
163 25f. Type **54** 20 20
164 40f. "TIROS" weather satellite 35 30

55 I.C.Y. Emblem — **59** Corn

1965. International Co-operation Year.
165 **55** 25f. black and green . . . 25 20
166 60f. lake 40 35

1965. Sea Shells. As T **52**. Mult, background colours given.
167 25f. violet 55 25
168 25f. blue 55 25
169 25f. yellow 55 25
SEASHELLS: No. 167, Knobbed triton ("Charonia nodifera"); 168, Smooth callista ("Pitaria chione"); 169, "Cymbium tritonis".

1965. Shellfish. As T **52**. Multicoloured.
170 25f. Helmet crab 70 50
171 40f. Mantis shrimp . . . . . 1·60 95
172 1d. Royal prawn (horiz) . . . 2·25 1·40

1965. Orchids. As T **52**. Multicoloured.
173 25f. "Ophrys speculum" (vert) 60 45
174 40f. "Ophrys fusca" (vert) . . 95 50
175 60f. "Ophrys tenthredinifera" (horiz) . . . . 1·75 1·25

1966. Agricultural Products (1st issue).
176 **59** 25f. black and ochre . . . 20 15
See also Nos. 188/9 and 211.

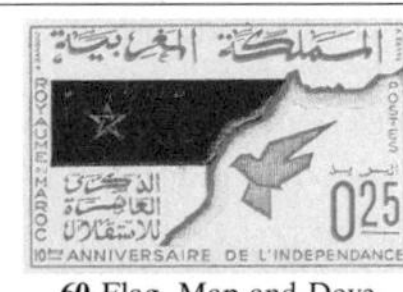

60 Flag, Map and Dove

1966. 10th Anniv of Independence.
177 **60** 25f. red and green 20 15

61 King Hassan II and Crown

1966. 5th Anniv of King Hassan's Coronation.
178 **61** 25f. blue, green and red . . 20 15

62 Cross-country Runner

1966. 53rd "Cross des Nations" (Cross-country Race).
179 **62** 25f. green 20 15

63 W.H.O. Building

1966. Inaug of W.H.O. Headquarters, Geneva.
180 **63** 25f. black and purple . . . 20 15
181 – 40f. black and blue 25 20
DESIGN: 40f. W.H.O. Building (different view).

64 King Hassan and Parachutist — **65** Brooch

1966. 10th Anniv of Royal Armed Forces.
182 **64** 25f. black and gold 60 25
183 – 40f. black and gold 60 25
DESIGN: 40f. Crown Prince Hassan kissing hand of King Mohammed.

1966. Palestine Week. As No. 110 but inscr "SEMAINE DE LA PALESTINE" at foot and dated "1966".
184 25f. blue 20 15

1966. Red Cross Seminar. Moroccan Jewellery. Multicoloured.
185 25f.+5f. Type **65** 90 45
186 40f.+10f. Pendant . . . . . 1·25 55
See also Nos. 203/4, 246/7, 274/5, 287/8, 303/4, 324/5, 370/1, 397/8, 414/15, 450/1 and 493.

66 Rameses II, Abu Simbel — **67** Class XDd Diesel Train

1966. Air. 20th Anniv of U.N.E.S.C.O.
187 **66** 1d. red and yellow . . . . 1·25 75

1966. Agricultural Products (2nd and 3rd issue). As T **59**.
188 40f. multicoloured 25 10
189 60f. multicoloured 35 20
DESIGNS—VERT: 40f. Citrus fruits. HORIZ: 60f. Olives.

1966. Moroccan Transport. Multicoloured.
190 25f. Type **67** (postage) . . . 1·50 60
191 40f. Liner "Maroc" 80 40
192 1d. Tourist coach 95 60
193 3d. Sud Aviation Caravelle of Royal Air Maroc (48 × 27½ mm) (air) . . . . 4·50 1·90

68 Twaite Shad

1967. Fishes. Multicoloured.
194 25f. Type **68** . . . . 1·10 25
195 40f. Plain bonito . . . . . . 1·40 30
196 1d. Bluefish . . . . 3·00 1·40

69 Hilton Hotel, Ancient Ruin and Map

1967. Opening of Hilton Hotel, Rabat.
197 **69** 25f. black and blue 20 15
198 1d. purple and blue 50 20

70 Ait Aadel Dam

1967. Inauguration of Ait Aadel Dam.
199 **70** 25f. grey, blue and green 25 15
200 40f. bistre and blue 65 20

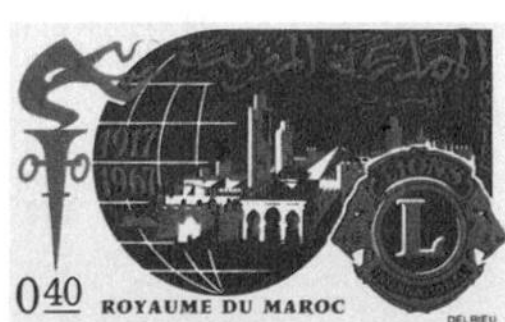

71 Moroccan Scene and Lions Emblem

1967. 50th Anniv of Lions International.
201 **71** 40f. blue and gold 50 20
202 1d. green and gold . . . . 1·00 25

1967. Moroccan Red Cross. As T **65**. Mult.
203 60f.+5f. Necklace 95 95
204 1d.+10f. Two bracelets . . . 1·90 1·90

72 Three Hands and Pickaxe — **73** I.T.Y. Emblem

1967. Communal Development Campaign.
205 **72** 25f. green 20 15

1967. International Tourist Year.
206 **73** 1d. blue and cobalt 80 35

74 Arrow and Map — **75** Horse-jumping

1967. Mediterranean Games, Tunis.
207 **74** 25f. multicoloured 25 20
208 40f. multicoloured 30 20

1967. International Horse Show.
209 **75** 40f. multicoloured 30 20
210 1d. multicoloured 75 35

1967. Agricultural Products (4th issue). As T **59**.
211 40f. mult (Cotton plant) . . . 65 15

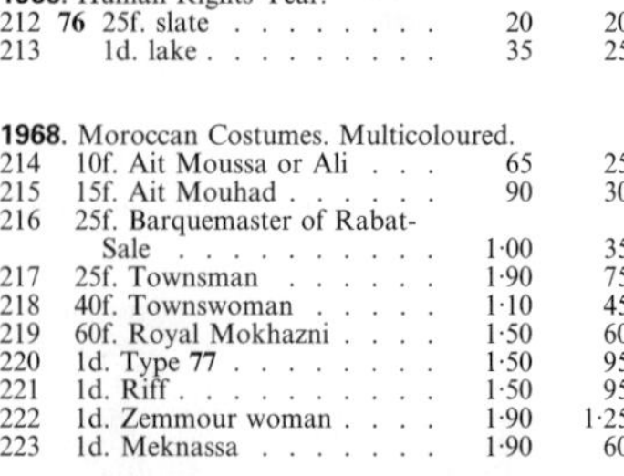

76 Human Rights Emblem — **77** Msouffa Woman

1968. Human Rights Year.
212 **76** 25f. slate 20 20
213 1d. lake 35 25

1968. Moroccan Costumes. Multicoloured.
214 10f. Ait Moussa or Ali . . . 65 25
215 15f. Ait Mouhad 90 30
216 25f. Barquemaster of Rabat-Sale . . . . 1·00 35
217 25f. Townsman . . . . . . 1·90 75
218 40f. Townswoman . . . . . 1·10 45
219 60f. Royal Mokhazni . . . . 1·50 60
220 1d. Type **77** . . . . 1·50 95
221 1d. Riff . . . . 1·50 95
222 1d. Zemmour woman . . . . 1·90 1·25
223 1d. Meknassa . . . . 1·90 60

78 King Hassan — **79** Red Crescent Nurse and Child

1968.
224 **78** 1f. multicoloured 10 10
225 2f. multicoloured 10 10
226 5f. multicoloured 10 10
227 10f. multicoloured 10 10
228 15f. multicoloured 10 10
229 20f. multicoloured 10 10
230 25f. multicoloured 15 10
231 30f. multicoloured 15 10
232 35f. multicoloured 45 10
233 40f. multicoloured 45 10
234 50f. multicoloured 50 10
235 60f. multicoloured 50 10
236 70f. multicoloured . . . . 4·00 90
237 75f. multicoloured . . . . 1·00 15
238 80f. multicoloured 70 20
239 – 90f. multicoloured . . . . 1·40 20
240 – 1d. multicoloured . . . . 2·00 20
241 – 2d. multicoloured . . . . 2·50 35
242 – 3d. multicoloured . . . . 5·00 80
243 – 5d. multicoloured . . . . 8·75 2·50
Nos. 239/43 bear a similar portrait of King Hassan, but are larger, 26½ × 40½ mm.

1968. 20th Anniv of W.H.O.
244 **79** 25f. brown, red and blue 20 10
245 40f. brown, red and slate 25 15

1968. Red Crescent. Moroccan Jewellery. As T **65**. Multicoloured.
246 25f. Pendant brooch 80 40
247 40f. Bracelet . . . . 1·25 50

80 Rotary Emblem, Conference Building and Map

1968. Rotary Int District Conf, Casablanca.
248 **80** 40f. gold, blue and green 65 20
249 1d. gold, ultramarine and blue 75 30

81 Belt Pattern — **82** Princess Lalla Meryem

1968. "The Belts of Fez". Designs showing ornamental patterns.
250 **81** 25f. multicoloured . . . . 1·90 70
251 – 40f. multicoloured . . . . 2·25 1·25
252 – 60f. multicoloured . . . . 3·50 1·75
253 – 1d. multicoloured . . . . 6·00 3·25

1968. World Children's Day. Multicoloured.
254 25f. Type **82** 25 20
255 40f. Princess Lalla Asmaa . . 65 25
256 1d. Crown Prince Sidi Mohammed . . . . 1·10 55

83 Wrestling

1968. Olympic Games, Mexico. Multicoloured.
257 15f. Type **83** 15 15
258 20f. Basketball 15 15
259 25f. Cycling 50 15
260 40f. Boxing 60 15
261 60f. Running 75 15
262 1d. Football . . . . 1·25 45

84 Silver Crown

85 Costumes of Zagora, South Morocco

1968. Ancient Moroccan Coins.
263 **84** 20f. silver and purple . . . 55 20
264 – 25f. gold and purple . . . 80 25
265 – 40f. silver and green . . . 1·40 65
266 – 60f. gold and red . . . . . 1·60 65
COINS: 25f. Gold dinar; 40f. Silver dirham; 60f. Gold piece.
See also Nos. 270/1.

1969. Traditional Women's Costumes. Mult.
267 15f. Type **85** (postage) . . . 1·25 75
268 25f. Ait Adidou costumes . . 1·90 1·10
269 1d. Ait Ouaouzguit costumes (air) . . . . 2·50 1·25

1969. 8th Anniv of Coronation of Hassan II. As T **84** (silver coins).
270 1d. silver and blue . . . . . 4·25 1·60
271 5d. silver and violet . . . . 10·00 6·00
COINS: 1d. One dirham coin of King Mohammed V; 5d. One dirham coin of King Hassan II.

86 Hands "reading" Braille on Map

1969. Protection of the Blind Week.
272 **86** 25f.+10f. multicoloured . . 45 15

87 "Actor"

89 King Hassan II

1969. World Theatre Day.
273 **87** 1d. multicoloured 45 25

1969. 50th Anniv of League of Red Cross Societies. Moroccan Jewellery as T **65**. Mult.
274 25f.+5f. Bracelets 90 45
275 40f.+10f. Pendant . . . . . 1·25 55

1969. King Hassan's 40th Birthday.
276 **89** 1d. multicoloured . . . . 1·25 35

(90)

91 Mahatma Gandhi

1969. Islamic Summit Conf, Rabat (1st issue). No. 240 optd with T **90**.
278 1d. multicoloured . . . . . 5·00 4·00

1969. Birth Centenary of Mahatma Gandhi.
279 **91** 40f. brown and lavender 60 15

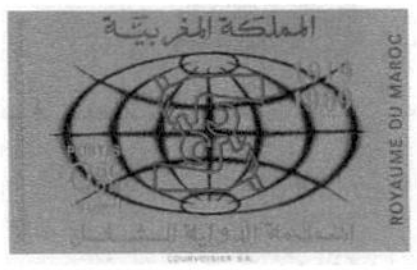

92 I.L.O. Emblem

1969. 50th Anniv of I.L.O.
280 **92** 50f. multicoloured 50 20

93 King Hassan on Horseback

1969. Islamic Summit Conference, Rabat (2nd issue).
281 **93** 1d. multicoloured . . . . 1·10 35

94 "Spahi Horseman" (Haram al Glaoui)

1970. Moroccan Art.
282 **94** 1d. multicoloured . . . . 1·10 30

1970. Flood Victims Relief Fund. Nos. 227/8 surch.
283 **78** 10f.+25f. multicoloured . . 3·50 3·50
284 15f.+25f. multicoloured . . 3·50 3·50

96 Drainage System, Fez

97 "Dance of the Guedra" (P. Beaubrun)

1970. 50th Congress of Public and Municipal Health Officials, Rabat.
285 **96** 60f. multicoloured 35 20

1970. Folklore Festival, Marrakesh.
286 **97** 40f. multicoloured 75 20

1970. Red Crescent. Moroccan Jewellery as T **65**. Multicoloured.
287 25f.+5f. Necklace . . . . . 1·00 65
288 50f.+10t. Pendant . . . . . 1·50 1·40

1970. Population Census. No. 189 surch **1970 0,25** and Arabic inscr.
290 25f. on 60f. multicoloured . . 50 10

99 Dish Aerial, Souk el Arba des Sehoul Communications Station

100 Ruddy Shelduck

1970. 17th Anniv of Revolution.
291 **99** 1d. multicoloured 80 35

1970. Nature Protection. Wild Birds. Mult.
292 25f. Type **100** 75 45
293 40f. Houbara bustard . . . . 1·75 65

101 I.E.Y. Emblem and Moroccan with Book

1970. International Education Year.
294 **101** 60f. multicoloured 65 20

102 Symbols of U.N.

1970. 25th Anniv of U.N.O.
295 **102** 50f. multicoloured 55 15

103 League Emblem, Map and Laurel

1970. 25th Anniv of Arab League.
296 **103** 50f. multicoloured 50 15

104 Olive Grove and Extraction Plant

1970. World Olive-oil Production Year.
297 **104** 50f. black, brown & green 55 15

105 Es Sounna Mosque

1971. Restoration of Es Sounna Mosque, Rabat.
298 **105** 60f. multicoloured 60 15

106 "Heart" within Horse

107 King Hassan II and Dam

1971. European and North African Heart Week.
299 **106** 50f. multicoloured 50 20

1971. 10th Anniv of King Hassan's Accession.
300 **107** 25f. multicoloured 45 10

108 Palestine on Globe

1971. Palestine Week.
302 **108** 25f.+10f. multicoloured 25 20

1971. Red Crescent, Moroccan Jewellery. As T **65**. Multicoloured.
303 25f.+5f. "Arrow-head" brooch 75 50
304 40f.+10f. Square pendant . . 1·10 90

109 Hands holding Peace Dove

1971. Racial Equality Year.
305 **109** 50f. multicoloured 50 15

110 Musical Instrument

1971. Protection of the Blind Week.
306 **110** 40f.+10f. multicoloured 60 20

111 Children at Play

112 Shah Mohammed Reza Pahlavi of Iran

1971. International Children's Day.
307 **111** 40f. multicoloured 45 15

1971. 2,500th Anniv of Persian Empire.
308 **112** 1d. multicoloured 70 30

113 Aerial View of Mausoleum

1971. Mausoleum of Mohammed V. Multicoloured.
309 25f. Type **113** 15 15
310 50f. Tomb of Mohammed V 20 20
311 1d. Interior of Mausoleum (vert) 80 50

114 Football and Emblem

1971. Mediterranean Games, Izmir, Turkey. Mult.
312 40f. Type **114** 55 15
313 60f. Athlete and emblem . . 70 20

115 A.P.U. Emblem

1971. 25th Anniv of Founding of Arab Postal Union at Sofar Conference.
314 **115** 25f. red, blue & light blue 15 10

116 Sun and Landscape

1971. 50th Anniv of Sherifian Phosphates Office.
315 **116** 70f. multicoloured 55 20

117 Torch and Book Year Emblem

118 Lottery Symbol

1972. International Book Year.
316 **117** 1d. multicoloured 65 25

1972. Creation of National Lottery.
317 **118** 25f. gold, black and brown 15 10

119 Bridge of Sighs

120 Mizmar (double-horned flute)

1972. U.N.E.S.C.O. "Save Venice" Campaign. Multicoloured.
318 25f. Type **119** 15 15
319 50f. St. Mark's Basilica (horiz) 20 15
320 1d. Lion of St. Marks (horiz) 65 20

1972. Protection of the Blind Week.
321 **120** 25f.+10f. multicoloured 60 20

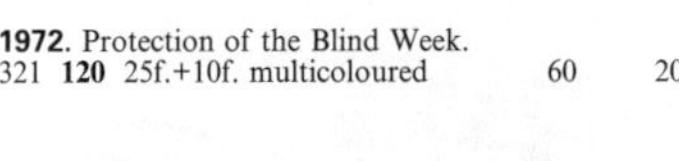

121 Bridge and Motorway

1972. 2nd African Highways Conference, Rabat.
322 **121** 75f. multicoloured 75 20

122 Moroccan Stamp of 1969, and Postmark

1972. Stamp Day.
323 **122** 1d. multicoloured 65 20

1972. Red Crescent. Moroccan Jewellery. As T **65**. Multicoloured.
324 25f.+5f. Jewelled bangles . . 75 75
325 70f.+10f. Filigree pendant . . 1·10 1·10

123 "Betrothal of Imilchil" (Tayeb Lahlou)

124 Dove on African Map

1972. Folklore Festival, Marrakesh.
326 **123** 60f. multicoloured 90 35

1972. 9th Organization of African Unity Summit Conference, Rabat.
327 **124** 25f. multicoloured 15 15

125 Polluted Beach

1972. U.N. Environmental Conservation Conf, Stockholm.
328 **125** 50f. multicoloured 50 20

126 Running

127 "Sonchus pinnatifidus"

1972. Olympic Games, Munich.
329 **126** 25f. red, pink and black 15 15
330 – 50f. violet, lilac and black 20 15
331 – 75f. green, yellow & black 60 20
332 – 1d. blue, lt blue & black 75 25
DESIGNS: 50f. Wrestling; 75f. Football; 1d. Cycling.

1972. Moroccan Flowers (1st series). Mult.
333 25f. Type **127** 45 15
334 40f. "Amberboa crupinoides" 55 15
See also Nos. 375/6.

128 Sand Gazelle

129 Rabat Carpet

1972. Nature Protection. Fauna. Multicoloured.
335 25f. Type **128** 75 25
336 40f. Barbary sheep . . . . . 1·00 60

1972. Moroccan Carpets (1st series). Mult.
337 50f. Type **129** . . . . 1·00 35
338 75f. Rabat carpet with "star-shaped" centre . . . . . . 1·50 50
See also Nos. 380/1, 406/7, 433/4, 485/7 and 513.

130 Mother and Child with U.N. Emblem

132 Global Weather Map

131 "Postman" and "Stamp"

1972. International Children's Day.
339 **130** 75f. blue, yellow and green 35 30

1973. Stamp Day.
340 **131** 25f. multicoloured 15 10

1973. Centenary of W.M.O.
341 **132** 70f. multicoloured 70 20

133 King Hassan and Arms

1973.

342	**133**	1f. multicoloured	10	10
343		2f. multicoloured	10	10
344		5f. multicoloured	10	10
345		10f. multicoloured . . .	10	10
346		15f. multicoloured . . .	10	10
347		20f. multicoloured . . .	10	10
348		25f. multicoloured . . .	10	10
349		30f. multicoloured . . .	15	10
350		35f. multicoloured . . .	15	10
351		40f. multicoloured . . .	5·00	70
352		50f. multicoloured . . .	50	10
353		60f. multicoloured . . .	60	15
354		70f. multicoloured . . .	25	15
355		75f. multicoloured . . .	30	15
356		80f. multicoloured . . .	60	20
357		90f. multicoloured . . .	75	15
358		1d. multicoloured . . .	2·00	20
359		2d. multicoloured . . .	4·25	55
360		3d. multicoloured . . .	6·25	1·25
361		5d. multicoloured (brown background)	4·25	1·25
361a		5d. multicoloured (pink background)	4·00	90

مناظرة
السياحة
1973

(134)

1973. Nat Tourist Conf. Nos. 324/5 surch with T **134**.
362 **65** 25f. on 5f. multicoloured 2·50 2·50
363 70f. on 10f. multicoloured 2·50 2·50
On No. 363 the Arabic text is arranged in one line.

135 Tambours

1973. Protection of the Blind Week.
364 **135** 70f.+10f. multicoloured 75 55

136 Kaaba, Mecca, and Mosque, Rabat

1973. Prophet Mohammed's Birthday.
365 **136** 25f. multicoloured 15 10

137 Roses and M'Gouna

1973. M'Gouna Rose Festival.
366 **137** 25f. multicoloured 45 10

138 Handclasp and Torch

139 Folk-dancers

1973. 10th Anniv of Organization of African Unity.
367 **138** 70f. multicoloured 30 15

1973. Folklore Festival, Marrakesh. Multicoloured.
368 50f. Type **139** 50 15
369 1d. Folk-musicians 75 25

1973. Red Crescent. Moroccan Jewellery. As T **65**. Multicoloured.
370 25f.+5f. Locket . . . . . . 1·00 50
371 70f.+10f. Bracelet inlaid with pearls . . . . 1·10 60

140 Solar System

141 Microscope

1973. 500th Birth Anniv of Nicholas Copernicus.
372 **140** 70f. multicoloured 60 20

1973. 25th Anniv of W.H.O.
373 **141** 70f. multicoloured 55 20

142 Interpol Emblem and Fingerprint

1973. 50th Anniv of International Criminal Police Organization (Interpol).
374 **142** 70f. multicoloured 30 25

1973. Moroccan Flowers (2nd series). As T **127**. Multicoloured.
375 25f. "Chrysanthemum carinatum" (horiz) 75 35
376 1d. "Amberboa muricata" . . 1·25 55

143 Striped Hyena

1973. Nature Protection. Multicoloured.
377 25f. Type **143** 95 40
378 50f. Eleonora's falcon (vert) 3·00 1·00

144 Map and Arrows

1973. Meeting of Maghreb Committee for Co-ordination of Posts and Telecommunications, Tunis.
379 **144** 25f. multicoloured 15 10

1973. Moroccan Carpets (2nd series). As T **129**. Multicoloured.
380 25f. Carpet from the High Atlas . . . . 1·00 25
381 70f. Tazenakht carpet . . . . 1·50 50

ﺍﻟﻤﺆﺗﻤﺮ ﺍﻻﺳﻼﻣﻲ - ﻻﻫﻮﺭ
1394

145 Golf Club and Ball (146)

1974. International "Hassan II Trophy" Golf Grand Prix, Rabat.
382 **145** 70f. multicoloured . . . . 1·25 60

1974. Islamic Summit Conference, Lahore, Pakistan. No. 281 optd with T **146**.
383 1d. multicoloured . . . . . 2·75 1·60

147 Human Rights Emblem
148 Vanadinite

1974. 25th Anniv (1973) of Declaration of Human Rights.
384 **147** 70f. multicoloured 50 20

1974. Moroccan Mineral Sources. Multicoloured.
385 25f. Type **148** 95 50
386 70f. Erythrine . . . . 1·90 1·00

149 Marrakesh Minaret
150 U.P.U. Emblem and Congress Dates

1974. 173rd District of Rotary International Annual Conference, Marrakesh.
387 **149** 70f. multicoloured 70 20

1974. Centenary of U.P.U.
388 **150** 25f. black, red and green 15 10
389 – 1d. multicoloured 70 25
DESIGN—HORIZ: 1d. Commemorative scroll.

151 Drummers and Dancers

1974. 15th Folklore Festival, Marrakesh. Mult.
390 25f. Type **151** 35 15
391 70f. Juggler with woman . . 1·25 30

152 Environmental Emblem and Scenes

154 Flintlock Pistol

1974. World Environmental Day.
392 **152** 25f. multicoloured 20 15

1974. Red Crescent. Moroccan Firearms. Mult.
397 25f.+5f. Type **154** 75 75
398 70f.+10f. Gunpowder box . . 1·10 1·10

155 Stamps, Postmark and Magnifying Glass

ﺍﻻﺣﺼﺎﺀ ﺍﻟﻔﻼﺣﻲ
1,00
(156)

1974. Stamp Day.
399 **155** 70f. multicoloured 60 20

1974. No. D393 surch with T **156**.
400 1d. on 5f. orange, green & blk . . . . 1·90 1·25

157 World Cup Trophy

158 Erbab (two-string fiddle)

1974. World Cup Football Championship, West Germany.
401 **157** 1d. multicoloured 85 65

1974. Blind Week.
402 **158** 70f.+10f. multicoloured 1·00 50
See also No. 423.

160 Double-spurred Francolin

162 Jasmine

1974. Moroccan Animals. Multicoloured.
404 25f. Type **160** 55 30
405 70f. Leopard (horiz) 95 40

1974. Moroccan Carpets (3rd series). As T **129**. Multicoloured.
406 25f. Zemmour carpet 65 10
407 1d. Beni M'Guild carpet . . 1·25 50

1975. Flowers (1st series). Multicoloured.
408 25f. Type **162** 50 10
409 35f. Orange lilies 60 10
410 70f. Poppies 85 35
411 90f. Carnations . . . . . . 1·10 50
See also Nos. 417/20.

163 Aragonite

165 "The Water-carrier" (Feu Taieb-Lalou)

1975. Minerals. Multicoloured.
412 50f. Type **163** 75 40
413 1d. Agate . . . . 1·50 75
See also Nos. 543 and 563/4.

1975. Red Crescent. Moroccan Jewellery. As T **65**. Multicoloured.
414 25f.+5f. Pendant 75 75
415 70f.+10f. Earring . . . . . . 1·10 1·00

1975. "Moroccan Painters".
416 **165** 1d. multicoloured . . . . 1·10 30

1975. Flowers (2nd series). As T **162**. Mult.
417 10f. Daisies 10 10
418 50f. Pelargoniums 60 10
419 60f. Orange blossom 75 30
420 1d. Pansies . . . . 1·10 60

166 Collector with Stamp Album

167 Dancer with Rifle

1975. Stamp Day.
421 **166** 40f. multicoloured 20 10

1975. 16th Nat Folklore Festival, Marrakesh.
422 **167** 1d. multicoloured 65 30

1975. Blind Week. As T **158**. Multicoloured.
423 1d. Mandolin 85 25

168 "Animals in Forest" (child's drawing)

1975. Children's Week.
424 **168** 25f. multicoloured 15 10

169 Games Emblem and Athletes

1975. 7th Mediterranean Games, Algiers.
425 **169** 40f. multicoloured 45 10

170 Waldrapp

1975. Fauna. Multicoloured.
426 40f. Type **170** . . . . 2·50 50
427 1d. Caracal (vert) . . . . . 1·50 75
See also Nos. 470/1.

1975. "Green March" (1st issue). Nos. 370/1 optd **1975** and Arabic inscr.
428 25f. (+ 5f.) multicoloured . . 2·50 2·50
429 70f. (+ 10f.) multicoloured . . 2·50 2·50
The premiums on the stamps are obliterated.

172 King Mohammed V greeting Crowd

1975. 20th Anniv of Independence. Mult.
430 40f. Type **172** 15 10
431 1d. King Hassan (vert) . . . 75 45
432 1d. King Hassan V wearing fez (vert) 75 45

1975. Moroccan Carpets (4th series). As T **129**. Multicoloured.
433 25f. Ouled Besseba carpet . . 60 35
434 1d. Ait Ouaouzguid carpet 90 45
See also Nos. 485/7 and 513.

173 Marchers crossing Desert

174 Fez Coin of 1883/4

1975. "Green March" (2nd issue).
435 **173** 40f. multicoloured 15 10

1976. Moroccan Coins (1st series). Multicoloured.
436 5f. Type **174** 10 10
437 15f. Rabat silver coin 1774/5 10 10
438 35f. Sabta coin, 13/14th centuries 75 35
439 40f. Type **174** 50 10
440 50f. As No. 437 . . . . . . 75 35
441 65f. As No. 438 . . . . . . 75 50
442 1d. Sabta coin, 12/13th centuries . . . . 1·10 60
See also Nos. 458/67a.
For Nos. 439/40 in smaller size, see Nos. 520/b.

175 Interior of Mosque

1976. Millennium of Ibn Zaidoun Mosque. Mult.
443 40f. Type **175** 15 10
444 65f. Interior archways (vert) 50 15

176 Moroccan Family

1976. Family Planning.
445 **176** 40f. multicoloured 15 10

177 Bou Anania College, Fez

1976. Moroccan Architecture.
446 **177** 1d. multicoloured 70 20

178 Temple Sculpture

1976. Borobudur Temple Preservation Campaign. Multicoloured.
447 40f. Type **178** 15 15
448 1d. View of Temple 60 20

179 Dome of the Rock, Jerusalem

1976. 6th Anniv of Islamic Conference.
449 **179** 1d. multicoloured 70 20

1976. Red Crescent. Moroccan Jewellery. As T **65**. Multicoloured.
450 40f. Jewelled purse 15 10
451 1d. Jewelled pectoral 65 25

180 George Washington, King Hassan I, Statue of Liberty and Mausoleum of Mohammed V

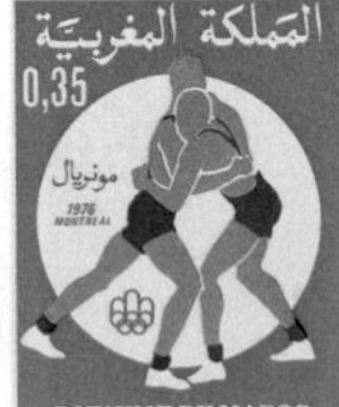

181 Wrestling

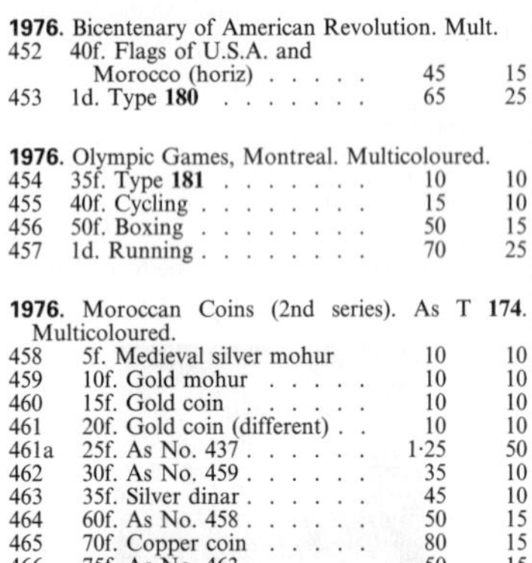

1976. Bicentenary of American Revolution. Mult.
452 40f. Flags of U.S.A. and Morocco (horiz) 45 15
453 1d. Type **180** 65 25

1976. Olympic Games, Montreal. Multicoloured.
454 35f. Type **181** 10 10
455 40f. Cycling 15 10
456 50f. Boxing 50 15
457 1d. Running 70 25

1976. Moroccan Coins (2nd series). As T **174**. Multicoloured.
458 5f. Medieval silver mohur 10 10
459 10f. Gold mohur 10 10
460 15f. Gold coin 10 10
461 20f. Gold coin (different) . . 10 10
461a 25f. As No. 437 . . . . . . 1·25 50
462 30f. As No. 459 . . . . . . 35 10
463 35f. Silver dinar 45 10
464 60f. As No. 458 . . . . . . 50 15
465 70f. Copper coin 80 15
466 75f. As No. 463 . . . . . . 50 15
466a 80f. As No. 460 . . . . . . 2·50 75
467 2d. As No. 465 . . . . . . 60 35
467a 3d. As No. 461 . . . . . . 3·75 1·25

182 Early and Modern Telephones with Dish Aerial

1976. Telephone Centenary.
468 **182** 1d. multicoloured 70 25

183 Gold Medallion

1976. Blind Week.
469 **183** 50f. multicoloured 50 10

1976. Birds. As T **170**. Multicoloured.
470 40f. Dark chanting goshawk (vert) . . . . 2·25 75
471 1d. Purple swamphen (vert) 3·50 1·40

185 King Hassan, Emblems and Map

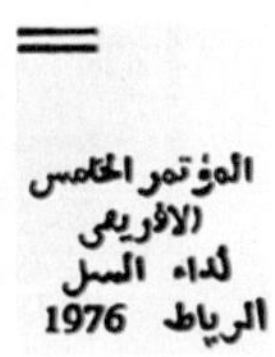

الموتمر الخامس
الافريقي
لداء السل
1976 الرباط

(186)

1976. 1st Anniv of "Green March".
472 **185** 40f. multicoloured 45 10

1976. Fifth African Tuberculosis Conference. Nos. 414/15 optd with T **186**.
473 25f. multicoloured . . . . . 1·90 1·90
474 70f. multicoloured . . . . . 2·25 2·25

187 Globe and Peace Dove

188 African Nations Cup

1976. Conference of Non-Aligned Countries, Colombo.
475 **187** 1d. red, black and blue 30 20

1976. African Nations Football Championship.
476 **188** 1d. multicoloured 65 20

189 Letters encircling Globe

1977. Stamp Day.
477 **189** 40f. multicoloured 40 10

موسم حب الملوك
1977
0,40

190 "Aeonium arboreum" 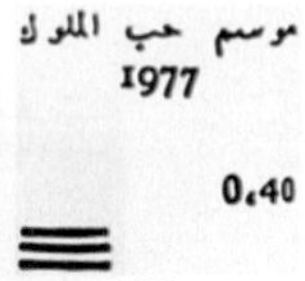 (192)

191 Ornamental Candle Lamps

1977. Flowers. Multicoloured.
478 40f. Type **190** 30 10
479 50f. "Malope trifida" (24 × 38 mm) 95 30
480 1d. "Hesperolaburnum platyclarpum" . . . . . . 1·10 30

1977. Procession of the Candles, Sale.
481 **191** 40f. multicoloured 45 10

1977. Cherry Festival. No. D394 surch with T **192**.
482 40f. on 10f. Cherries 75 30

193 Map and Emblem

1977. 5th Congress. Organization of Arab Towns.
483 **193** 50f. multicoloured 15 10

194 A.P.U. Emblem

1977. 25th Anniv of Arab Postal Union.
484 **194** 1d. multicoloured 60 20

1977. Moroccan Carpets (5th series). As T **129**. Multicoloured.
486 40f. Ait Haddou carpet . . . 40 20
487 1d. Henbel rug, Sale 95 30

195 Zither

196 Mohammed Ali Jinnah

1977. Blind Week.
488 **195** 1d. multicoloured 85 25

1977. Birth Centenary of Mohammed Ali Jinnah.
489 **196** 70f. multicoloured 50 20

197 Marcher with Flag

1977. 2nd Anniv of "Green March".
490 **197** 1d. multicoloured 60 20

198 Assembly Hall

1977. Opening of House of Representatives.
491 **198** 1d. multicoloured 65 20

199 Silver Brooch

200 Bowl with Funnel

1977. Red Crescent.
493 **199** 1d. multicoloured . . . . 1·25 60

1978. Moroccan Copperware. Multicoloured.
494 40f. Type **200** 35 10
495 1d. Bowl with cover 70 20

201 Development Emblem

202 Decorative Pot with Lid

1978. Sahara Development. Multicoloured.
496 40f. Type **201** 35 10
497 1d. Fishes in net and camels at oasis (horiz) 60 20

1978. Blind Week. Multicoloured.
498 1d. Type **202** 90 30
499 1d. Decorative jar 90 30

203 Map and Red Cross within Red Crescent

1978. 10th Conference of Arab Red Crescent and Red Cross Societies.
500 **203** 1d. red and black 65 20

204 View of Fez

205 Dome of the Rock

1978. Rotary International Meeting, Fez.
501 **204** 1d. multicoloured 65 20

1978. Palestine Welfare.
502 **205** 5f. multicoloured 10 10
503 10f. multicoloured 10 10

206 Flautist and Folk Dancers

208 Yacht

207 Sugar Field and Crushing Plant

1978. National Folklore Festival, Marrakesh.
504 **206** 1d. multicoloured 55 20

1978. Sugar Industry.
505 **207** 40f. multicoloured 15 10

1978. World Sailing Championships.
506 **208** 1d. multicoloured 60 20

209 Tree, Tent and Scout Emblem

211 Human Rights Emblem

210 Moulay Idriss

1978. Pan-Arab Scout Festival, Rabat.
507 **209** 40f. multicoloured 15 10

1978. Moulay Idriss Great Festival.
508 **210** 40f. multicoloured 15 10

1978. 30th Anniv of Declaration of Human Rights.
509 **211** 1d. multicoloured 65 20

212 Houses in Agadir

214 Decorated Pot

213 Player, Football and Cup

1979. Southern Moroccan Architecture (1st series). Multicoloured.
510 40f. Type **212** 15 10
511 1d. Old fort at Marrakesh . . 60 15
See also Nos. 536 and 562.

1979. Mohammed V Football Cup.
512 **213** 40f. multicoloured 15 10

1979. Moroccan Carpets (6th series). As T **129**. Multicoloured.
513 40f. Marmoucha carpet . . . 40 15

1979. Blind Week.
514 **214** 1d. multicoloured 65 20

215 "Procession from a Mosque" **216** Coffee Pot and Heater

1979. Paintings by Mohamed Ben Ali Rbati. Mult.
515 40f. Type **215** 15 10
516 1d. "Religious Ceremony in a Mosque" (horiz) 55 20

1979. Red Cresent. Brassware. Multicoloured.
517 40f. Engraved circular boxes 25 15
518 1d. Type **216** 85 30

217 Costumed Girls **218** Curved Dagger in Jewelled Sheath

1979. National Folklore Festival, Marrakesh.
519 **217** 40f. multicoloured 15 10

1979. Moroccan Coins. As T **174**, but smaller, $17\frac{1}{2} \times 22\frac{1}{2}$ mm.
520 40f. multicoloured 10 10
520b 50f. multicoloured 10 10

1979. Ancient Weapons.
521 **218** 1d. black and yellow . . . 75 20

219 King Hassan II **221** King Hassan II

220 Festival Emblem

1979. King Hassan's 50th Birthday.
522 **219** 1d. multicoloured 70 20

1979. 4th Arab Youth Festival, Rabat.
523 **220** 1d. multicoloured 70 20

1979. "25th Anniv of Revolution of King and People".
524 **221** 1d. multicoloured 30 20

222 World Map superimposed on Open Book

1979. 50th Anniv of Int Bureau of Education.
525 **222** 1d. brown and yellow . . 60 20

223 Pilgrims in Wuquf, Arafat

1979. Pilgrimage to Mecca.
526 **223** 1d. multicoloured 70 20

استرجاع اقليم وادى الذهب
1979_8_14

(224)

1979. Recovery of Oued Eddahab Province. Design as No. 497, with face value amended (40f.), optd with T **224**.
527 40f. multicoloured 15 10
528 1d. multicoloured 65 20

225 Centaurium **226** Children around Globe

1979. Flowers. Multicoloured.
529 40f. Type **225** 15 10
530 1d. "Leucanthemum catanance" 55 20

1979. International Year of the Child.
531 **226** 40f. multicoloured 60 25

227 European Otter **228** Traffic Signs

1979. Wildlife. Multicoloured.
532 40f. Type **227** 50 15
533 1d. Moussier's redstart . . . 1·60 50

1980. Road Safety. Multicoloured.
534 40f. Type **228** 15 10
535 1d. Children at crossing . . . 30 20

229 Fortress

1980. South Moroccan Architecture (2nd series).
536 **229** 1d. multicoloured 55 20

230 Copper Bowl with Lid **231** Pot

1980. Red Crescent. Multicoloured.
537 50f. Type **230** 50 15
538 70f. Copper kettle and brazier 60 20

1980. Blind Week.
539 **231** 40f. multicoloured 15 10

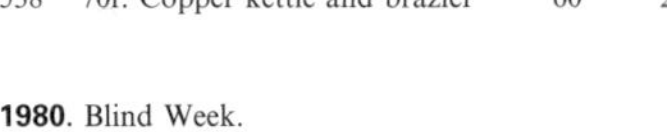

232 Mechanized Sorting Office, Rabat

1980. Stamp Day.
540 **232** 40f. multicoloured 15 10

233 World Map and Rotary Emblem **234** Leather Bag and Cloth

1980. 75th Anniv of Rotary International.
541 **233** 1d. multicoloured 55 20

1980. 4th Textile and Leather Exhibition, Casablanca.
542 **234** 1d. multicoloured 55 20

1980. Minerals (2nd series). As T **163**. Mult.
543 40f. Gypsum 85 10

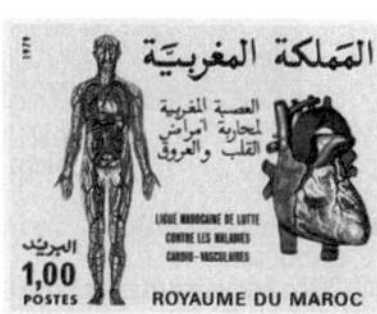
235 Peregrine Falcon **236** Diagram of Blood Circulation and Heart

1980. Hunting with Falcon.
544 **235** 40f. multicoloured . . . . 1·25 65

1980. Campaign against Cardiovascular Diseases.
545 **236** 1d. multicoloured 65 20

237 Decade Emblem and Human Figures **238** Harnessed Horse

1980. Decade for Women.
546 **237** 40f. mauve and blue . . . 15 10
547 – 1d. multicoloured 55 20
DESIGN: 1d. Decade and United Nations emblems.

1980. Ornamental Harnesses. Multicoloured.
548 40f. Harnessed horse (different) 15 10
549 1d. Type **238** 75 20

239 Satellite orbiting Earth and Dish Aerial **241** Conference Emblem

240 Light Bulb and Fuel Can

1980. World Meteorological Day.
550 **239** 40f. multicoloured 15 10

1980. Energy Conservation. Multicoloured.
551 40f. Type **240** 15 10
552 1d. Hand holding petrol pump 55 20

1980. World Tourism Conference, Manila.
553 **241** 40f. multicoloured 15 10

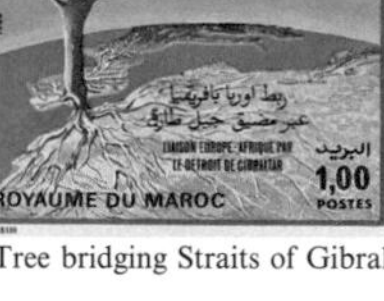
242 Tree bridging Straits of Gibraltar

1980. European–African Liaison over the Straits of Gibraltar.
554 **242** 1d. multicoloured 60 20

243 Flame and Marchers

1980. 5th Anniv of "The Green March".
555 **243** 1d. multicoloured 60 20

244 Holy Kaaba, Mecca **245** "Senecio antheuphorbium"

1980. 1400th Anniv of Hegira. Multicoloured.
556 40f. Type **244** 15 10
557 1d. Mosque, Mecca 60 20

1980. Flowers. Multicoloured.
558 40f. Type **245** 60 10
559 1d. "Periploca laevigata" . . 1·25 50

246 Painting by Aherdan **247** Nejjarine Fountain, Fez

1980. Paintings.
560 – 40f. bistre and brown . . 15 10
561 **246** 1d. multicoloured 60 20
DESIGN: 40f. Composition of bird and feathers.

1981. Moroccan Architecture (3rd series).
562 **247** 40f. multicoloured 10 10

1981. Minerals (3rd series). Vert designs as T **163**. Multicoloured.
563 40f. Onyx 95 35
564 1d. Malachite-azurite . . . . 1·60 75

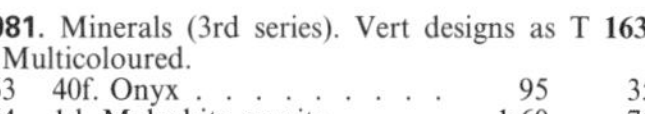

248 King Hassan II

1981. 25th Anniv of Independence. Mult.
565 60f. Type **248** 35 10
566 60f. Map, flags, broken chains and "25" 35 10
567 60f. King Mohammed V. . . 35 10

249 King Hassan II

1981. 20th Anniv of King Hassan's Coronation.
568 **249** 1d.30 multicoloured . . . 50 25

250 "Source" (Jillali Gharbaoul)

1981. Moroccan Painting.
569 **250** 1d.30 multicoloured . . . 75 25

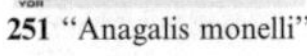

251 "Anagalis monelli" **252** King Hassan as Major General

1981. Flowers. Multicoloured.
570 40f. Type **251** 20 10
571 70f. "Bubonium intricatum" 40 15

1981. 25th Anniv of Moroccan Armed Forces.
572 **252** 60f. lilac, gold and green 35 10
573 – 60f. multicoloured 35 10
574 – 60f. lilac, gold and green 35 10
DESIGNS: No. 573, Army badge; 574, King Mohammed V (founder).

253 Caduceus (Telecommunications and Health) **254** Plate with Pattern

1981. World Telecommunications Day.
575 **253** 1d.30 multicoloured . . . 70 20

1981. Blind Week. Multicoloured.
576 50f. Type **254** 10 10
577 1d.30 Plate with ship pattern 60 20

255 Musicians and Dancers **256** "Seboula" Dagger

1981. 22nd National Folklore Festival, Marrakesh.
578 **255** 1d.30 multicoloured . . . 85 25

1981. Ancient Weapons.
579 **256** 1d.30 multicoloured . . . 75 20

257 Pestle and Mortar **258** Hands holding I.Y.D.P. Emblem

1981. Red Crescent. Moroccan Copperware. Mult.
580 60f. Type **257** 25 15
581 1d.30 Tripod brazier 80 25

1981. International Year of Disabled People.
582 **258** 60f. multicoloured 35 10

259 "Iphiclides feisthamelii Lotteri" **260** King Hassan and Marchers

1981. Butterflies (1st series). Multicoloured.
583 60f. Type **259** 50 25
584 1d.30 "Zerynthina rumina africana" . . . . 1·25 60
See also Nos. 609/10.

1981. 6th Anniv of "Green March".
585 **260** 1d.30 multicoloured . . . 70 20

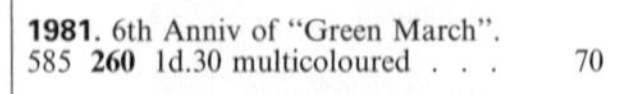

261 Town Buildings and Congress Emblem

1981. 10th International Twinned Towns Congress, Casablanca.
586 **261** 1d.30 multicoloured . . . 20 20

262 Dome of the Rock **264** Terminal Building and Runway

1981. Palestinian Solidarity Day.
587 **262** 60f. multicoloured 35 10

1981. 12th Arab Summit Conference, Fez. Nos. 502/3 surch **1981 0,40**.
588 **205** 40f. on 5f. multicoloured 4·00 4·00
588a 40f. on 10f. multicoloured . . . . 2·75 2·75

1981. 1st Anniv of Mohammed V Airport.
589 **264** 1d.30 multicoloured . . . 70 20

265 Al Massira Dam **266** King Hassan II

1981. Al Massira Dam.
590 **265** 60f. multicoloured 35 10

1981.
591 **266** 5f. red, blue and gold . . 10 10
592 10f. red, yellow and gold 10 10
593 15f. red, green and gold 10 10
594 20f. red, pink and gold 10 10
595 25f. red, lilac and gold 10 10
596 30f. blue, lt blue & gold 10 10
597 35f. blue, yellow and gold 10 10
598 40f. blue, green and gold 10 10
599 50f. blue, pink and gold 10 10
600 60f. blue, lilac and gold 10 10
601 65f. blue, lilac and gold 10 10
602 70f. violet, yellow and gold 10 10
603 75f. violet, green and gold 15 15
604 80f. violet, pink and gold 15 15
605 90f. violet, lilac and gold 15 15
605a 1d.25 red, mauve & gold 20 15
605b 4d. brown, yell & gold 1·10 55
See also Nos. 624/9, 718/22, 759/61, 866, 895/6 and 930.

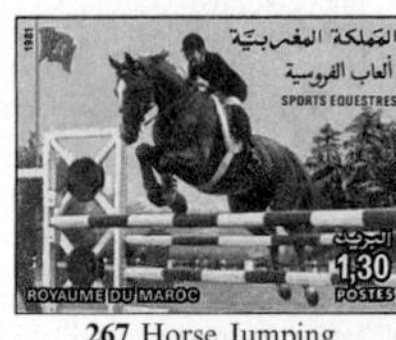

267 Horse Jumping

1981. Equestrian Sports.
606 **267** 1d.30 multicoloured . . . 1·25 25

268 Ait Quaquzguit

1982. Carpets (1st series). Multicoloured.
607 50f. Type **268** 10 10
608 1d.30 Ouled Besseba 60 30
See also Nos. 653/4.

1982. Butterflies and Moths (2nd series). As T **259**. Multicoloured.
609 60f. "Celerio oken lineata" 70 25
610 1d.30 "Mesoacidalia aglaja lyauteyi" . . . . 1·50 55

269 Tree and Emblem **270** Jug

1982. World Forestry Day.
611 **269** 40f. multicoloured 10 10

1982. Blind Week.
612 **270** 1d. multicoloured 50 25

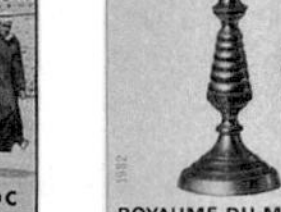

271 Dancers **272** Candlestick

1982. Popular Art.
613 **271** 1d.40 multicoloured . . . 60 35

1982. Red Crescent.
614 **272** 1d.40 multicoloured . . . 60 35

273 Painting by M. Mezian **274** Buildings and People on Graph

1982. Moroccan Painting.
615 **273** 1d.40 multicoloured . . . 60 35

1982. Population and Housing Census.
616 **274** 60f. multicoloured 15 15

275 Dr. Koch, Lungs and Apparatus **276** I.T.U. Emblem

1982. Centenary of Discovery of Tubercle Bacillus.
617 **275** 1d.40 multicoloured . . . 75 35

1982. I.T.U. Delegates' Conference, Nairobi.
618 **276** 1d.40 multicoloured . . . 60 35

277 Wheat, Globe, Sea and F.A.O. Emblem

1982. World Food Day.
619 **277** 60f. multicoloured 15 15

278 Class XDd Diesel Locomotive (1956) and Route Map

1982. Unity Railway.
620 **278** 1d.40 multicoloured . . . 1·25 70

279 A.P.U. Emblem

1982. 30th Anniv of Arab Postal Union.
621 **279** 1d.40 multicoloured . . . 40 15

280 Dome of the Rock and Map of Palestine **281** Red Coral

1982. Palestinian Solidarity.
622 **280** 1d.40 multicoloured . . . 40 15

1982. Red Coral of Al Hoceima.
623 **281** 1d.40 multicoloured . . . 70 25

1983. Size 25 × 32 mm but inscribed "1982".
624 **266** 1d. red, blue and gold . . 25 10
625 1d.40 brown, lt brown & gold 35 10
626 2d. red, green and gold 45 15
627 3d. brown, yellow and gold 65 25
628 5d. brown, green and gold 1·40 50
629 10d. brown, orange and gold . . . . 2·75 90

282 Moroccan Stamps **283** King Hassan II

1983. Stamp Day.
630 **282** 1d.40 multicoloured . . . 60 20

1983.
631 **283** 1d.40 multicoloured . . . 25 20
632 2d. multicoloured 35 30
633 3d. multicoloured 80 50
634 5d. multicoloured . . . . 1·40 45
635 10d. multicoloured . . . 2·75 1·10

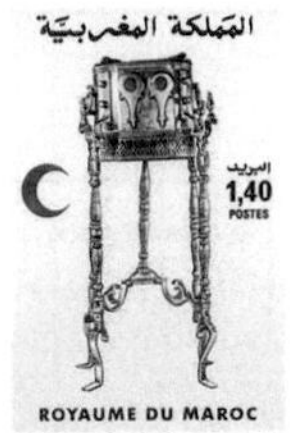

284 Decorated Pot **286** Ornamental Stand

285 Musicians

1983. Blind Week.
636 **284** 1d.40 multicoloured . . . 60 20

1983. Popular Arts.
637 **285** 1d.40 multicoloured . . . 75 20

1983. Red Crescent.
638 **286** 1d.40 multicoloured . . . 75 20

287 Commission Emblem

1983. 25th Anniv of Economic Commission for Africa.
639 **287** 1d.40 multicoloured . . . 55 20

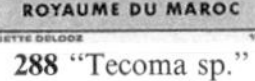

288 "Tecoma sp." **290** Games Emblem and Stylized Sports

289 King Hassan II, Map and Sultan of Morocco

1983. Flowers. Multicoloured.
640 60c. Type **288** 10 10
641 1d.40 "Strelitzia sp." 75 20

1983. 30th Anniv of Revolution.
642 **289** 80c. multicoloured 20 20

1983. 9th Mediterranean Games, Casablanca.
644 **290** 80c. blue, silver and gold 20 20
645 – 1d. multicoloured 20 20
646 – 2d. multicoloured 60 30
DESIGNS—VERT: 1d. Games emblem. HORIZ: 2d. Stylized runner.

291 Ploughing

1983. Touiza.
648 **291** 80c. multicoloured 20 20

292 Symbol of "Green March" **293** Palestinian formed from Map and Globe

1983. 8th Anniv of "Green March".
649 **292** 80f. multicoloured 20 15

1983. Palestinian Welfare.
650 **293** 80f. multicoloured 20 15

294 Ouzoud Waterfall **295** Children's Emblem

1983. Ouzoud Waterfall.
651 **294** 80f. multicoloured 20 15

1983. Children's Day. Multicoloured.
652 **295** 2d. multicoloured 70 30

1983. Carpets (2nd series). As T **268**. Mult.
653 60f. Zemmouri 10 10
654 1d.40 Zemmouri (different) 55 20

296 Transport and W.C.Y. Emblem

1983. World Communications Year.
655 **296** 2d. multicoloured . . . . 1·75 70

297 Views of Jerusalem and Fez

1984. Twinned Towns.
656 **297** 2d. multicoloured 95 20

298 Fennec Fox

1984. Animals. Multicoloured.
657 80f. Type **298** 30 25
658 2d. Lesser Egyptian jerboa 60 35

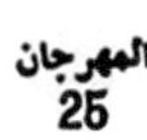

299 Map of League Members and Emblem (**300**)

1984. 39th Anniv of League of Arab States.
659 **299** 2d. multicoloured 70 20

1984. 25th National Folklore Festival, Marrakesh. No. 578 optd with T **300**.
660 **255** 1d.30 multicoloured . . . 75 15

301 "Metha viridis" **303** Lidded Container

302 Decorated Bowl

1984. Flowers. Multicoloured.
661 80f. Type **301** 20 15
662 2d. Aloe 75 30

1984. Blind Week.
663 **302** 80f. multicoloured 20 15

1984. Red Crescent.
664 **303** 2d. multicoloured 75 30

304 Sports Pictograms **305** Dove carrying Children

1984. Olympic Games, Los Angeles.
665 **304** 2d. multicoloured 75 30

1984. International Child Victims' Day.
666 **305** 2d. multicoloured 70 30

306 U.P.U. Emblem and Ribbons **307** Hands holding Ears of Wheat

1984. Universal Postal Union Day.
667 **306** 2d. multicoloured 40 30

1984. World Food Day.
668 **307** 80f. multicoloured 20 15

308 Stylized Bird, Airplane and Emblem **309** Inscribed Scroll

1984. 40th Anniv of I.C.A.O.
669 **308** 2d. multicoloured 40 30

1984. 9th Anniv of "Green March".
670 **309** 80f. multicoloured 20 15

311 Flag and Dome of the Rock **312** Emblem and People

1984. Palestinian Welfare.
672 **311** 2d. multicoloured 60 25

1984. 36th Anniv of Human Rights Declaration.
673 **312** 2d. multicoloured 60 25

313 Aidi **314** Weighing Baby

1984. Dogs. Multicoloured.
674 80f. Type **313** 50 10
675 2d. Sloughi . . . . 1·10 25

1985. Infant Survival Campaign.
676 **314** 80f. multicoloured 15 10

315 Children playing in Garden **316** Sherifian Mail Postal Cancellation, 1892

1985. 1st Moroccan S.O.S. Children's Village.
677 **315** 2d. multicoloured 60 25

1985. Stamp Day.
678 **316** 2d. grey, pink and black 60 25
See also Nos. 698/9, 715/16, 757/8, 778/9, 796/7, 818/19, 841/2, 877/8, 910/11 and 924/5.

317 Emblem, Birds, Landscape and Fish **318** Musicians

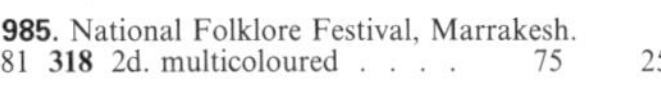

1985. World Environment Day.
680 **317** 80f. multicoloured 20 10

1985. National Folklore Festival, Marrakesh.
681 **318** 2d. multicoloured 75 25

319 Decorated Plate **320** Bougainvillea

1985. Blind Week.
682 **319** 80f. multicoloured 15 10

1985. Flowers. Multicoloured.
683 80f. Type **320** 60 10
684 2d. "Hibiscus rosasinensis" 1·25 50

321 Woman in Headdress **323** Map and Emblem

322 Musicians and Dancers

1985. Red Crescent.
685 **321** 2d. multicoloured . . . . 1·25 50

1985. National Folklore Festival, Marrakesh.
686 **322** 2d. multicoloured 95 25

1985. 6th Pan-Arab Games.
687 **323** 2d. multicoloured 95 25

324 Emblem on Globe **325** Emblem

1985. 40th Anniv of U.N.O.
688 **324** 2d. multicoloured 60 25

1986. International Youth Year.
689 **325** 2d. multicoloured 60 25

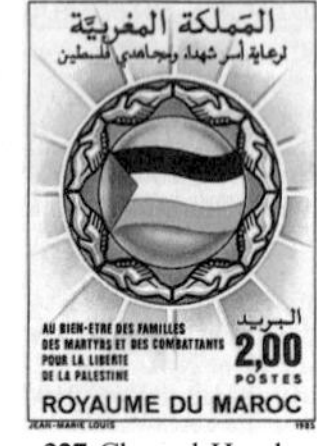

326 Medal **327** Clasped Hands around Flag

1985. 10th Anniv of "Green March".
690 **326** 2d. multicoloured 60 25

1985. Palestinian Welfare.
691 **327** 2d. multicoloured 60 25

328 "Euphydryas desfontainii" **329** Arms

1985. Butterflies (1st series). Multicoloured.
692 80f. Type **328** 45 30
693 2d. "Colotis evagore" . . . . 1·40 90
See also Nos. 713/14.

1986. 25th Anniv of King Hassan's Coronation. Multicoloured.
694 80f. Type **329** 15 10
695 2d. King Hassan II (horiz) 60 25

330 Emblem **331** Vase

1986. 26th International Military Medicine Congress.
697 **330** 2d. multicoloured 60 25

1986. Stamp Day. As T **316**.
698 80f. orange and black 15 10
699 2d. green and black 60 25
DESIGNS: 80f. Sherifian postal seal of Maghzen-Safi; 2d. Sherifian postal seal of Maghzen-Safi (different).

1986. Blind Week.
700 **331** 1d. multicoloured 15 10

332 Footballer and Emblem

1986. World Cup Football Championship, Mexico. Multicoloured.
701 1d. Type **332** 50 10
702 2d. Cup, pictogram of footballer and emblem . . 1·00 25

333 Copper Coffee Pot **334** "Warionia saharae"

1986. Red Crescent.
703 **333** 2d. multicoloured . . . . 1·25 50

1986. Flowers. Multicoloured.
704 1d. Type **334** 60 10
705 2d. "Mandragora autumnalis" . . . . 1·25 50

335 Emblem **336** Dove and Olive Branch

1986. 18th Parachute Championships.
706 **335** 2d. multicoloured 90 25

1986. International Peace Year.
707 **336** 2d. multicoloured 60 25

337 Horsemen **338** Book

1986. Horse Week.
708 **337** 1d. light brown, pink and brown 60 10

1986. 11th Anniv of "Green March".
709 **338** 1d. multicoloured 15 10

339 Stylized People and Wheat **340** Marrakesh

1986. Fight against Hunger.
710 **339** 2d. multicoloured 60 25

1986. Aga Khan Architecture Prize.
711 **340** 2d. multicoloured 60 25

341 Hands holding Wheat

الملتقى العالمي الاول
لخطباء الجمعة

(342)

1986. "1,000,000 Hectares of Grain".
712 **341** 1d. multicoloured 15 10

1986. Butterflies (2nd series). As T **328**. Mult.
713 1d. "Elphinstonia charlonia" 65 35
714 2d. "Anthocharis belia" . . . 90 85

1987. Stamp Day. As T **316**.
715 1d. blue and black 15 10
716 2d. red and black 60 25
DESIGNS: 1d. Circular postal cancellation of Tetouan; 2d. Octagonal postal cancellation of Tetouan.

1987. Air. 1st World Reunion of Friday Preachers. Optd with T **342**.
717 **283** 2d. multicoloured 90 60

1987. Size 25 × 32 mm but inscr "1986".
718 **266** 1d.60 red, brown and gold 25 20
719 2d.50 red, grey and gold 60 25
720 6d.50 red, brown and gold 1·50 35
721 7d. red, brown and gold 1·75 45
722 8d.50 red, lilac and gold 2·00 50

343 Sidi Muhammad ben Yusuf addressing Crowd

1987. 40th Anniv of Tangier Conference. Each blue, silver and black.
723 1d. Type **343** 15 10
724 1d. King Hassan II making speech 15 10

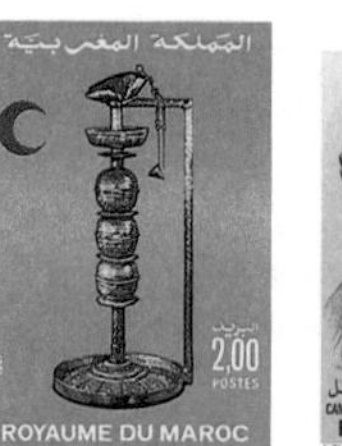

344 Copper Lamp **345** Woman with Baby and Packet of Salt being emptied into Beaker

1987. Red Crescent.
726 **344** 2d. multicoloured 60 25

1987. U.N.I.C.E.F. Child Survival Campaign.
727 **345** 1d. multicoloured 15 10

346 Decorated Pottery Jug **347** "Zygophyllum fontanesii"

1987. Blind Week.
728 **346** 1d. multicoloured 15 10

1987. Flowers. Multicoloured.
729 1d. Type **347** 15 10
730 2d. "Otanthus maritimus" . . 60 25

348 Arabesque from Door, Dar Batha Palace, Fez **349** Map and King Hassan giving Blood

1987. Bicentenary of Diplomatic Relations with United States of America.
731 **348** 1d. blue, red and black 15 10

1987. Blood Transfusion Service.
732 **349** 2d. multicoloured 95 25

350 Woman from Melhfa **351** Emblem and Irrigated Field

1987. Sahara Costumes. Multicoloured.
733 1d. Type **350** 15 10
734 2d. Man from Derraa 60 25

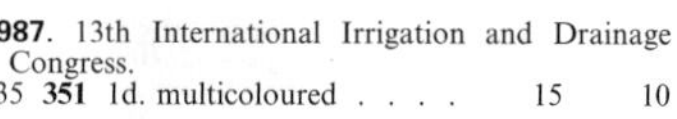

1987. 13th International Irrigation and Drainage Congress.
735 **351** 1d. multicoloured 15 10

352 Baby on Hand and Syringe **353** Azurite

1987. United Nations Children's Fund Child Survival Campaign.
736 **352** 1d. multicoloured 15 10

1987. Mineral Industries Congress, Marrakesh. Multicoloured.
737 1d. Type **353** 50 10
738 2d. Wulfenite . . . . 1·00 50

354 "12" on Scroll

1987. 12th Anniv of "Green March".
739 **354** 1d. multicoloured 15 10

355 Activities **356** Desert Sparrow

1987. Armed Forces Social Services Month.
740 **355** 1d. multicoloured 15 10

1987. Birds. Multicoloured.
741 1d. Type **356** . . . . 1·10 45
742 2d. Barbary partridge . . . . 2·00 95

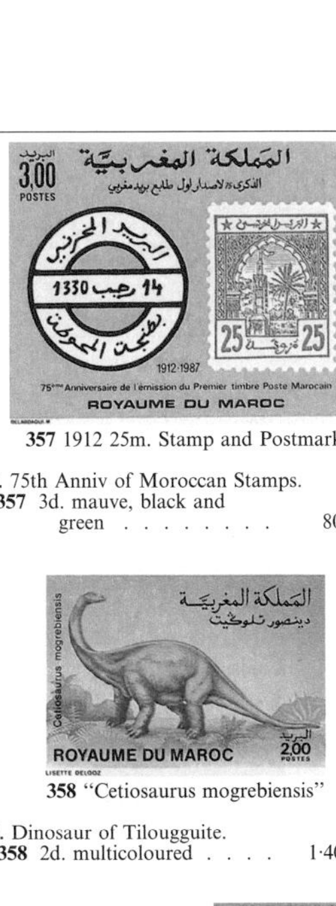

357 1912 25m. Stamp and Postmark

1987. 75th Anniv of Moroccan Stamps.
743 **357** 3d. mauve, black and green 80 40

358 "Cetiosaurus mogrebiensis"

1988. Dinosaur of Tilougguite.
744 **358** 2d. multicoloured . . . . 1·40 50

359 King Mohammed V **360** Map and Player in Arabesque Frame

1988. International Conf on King Mohammed V, Rabat.
745 **359** 2d. multicoloured 60 25

1988. 16th African Nations Cup Football Competition.
746 **360** 3d. multicoloured 75 40

361 Boy with Horse

1988. Horse Week.
747 **361** 3d. multicoloured . . . . 1·50 60

362 Pottery Flask **363** Anniversary Emblem

1988. Blind Week.
748 **362** 3d. multicoloured 75 35

1988. 125th Anniv of Red Cross.
749 **363** 3d. black, red and pink 75 35

364 "Citrullus colocynthis" **365** Breastfeeding Baby

1988. Flowers. Multicoloured.
750 3d.60 Type **364** 90 45
751 3d.60 "Calotropis procera" 90 45

1988. U.N.I.C.E.F. Child Survival Campaign.
752 **365** 3d. multicoloured 95 35

366 Olympic Medals and Rings **367** Greater Bustard

1988. Olympic Games, Seoul.
753 **366** 2d. multicoloured 30 25

1988. Birds. Multicoloured.
754 3d.60 Type **367** . . . . . . 1·90 80
755 3d.60 Greater flamingo . . . 1·90 80

368 "13" on Scroll

اتحاد المغرب العربى

مراكش – فبراير 89

(370)

369 Housing of the Ksours and Csbaha

1988. 13th Anniv of "Green March".
756 **368** 2d. multicoloured 60 25

1988. Stamp Day. As T **316**.
757 3d. brown and black 95 35
758 3d. violet and black 95 35
DESIGNS: No. 757, Octagonal postal cancellation of Maghzen el Jadida; 758, Circular postal cancel-lation of Maghzen el Jadida.

1988. Size 25 × 32 mm but inscr "1988".
759 **266** 1d.20 blue, lilac and gold 15 10
760 3d.60 red and gold . . . 75 20
761 5d.20 brown, bis & gold 1·25 30

1989. Architecture.
762 **369** 2d. multicoloured 60 25

1989. Union of Arab Maghreb. No. 631 optd with T **370**.
763 **283** 1d.40 multicoloured . . . 50 15

371 King and Bishop with Chess Symbols

1989. 25th Anniv of Royal Moroccan Chess Federation.
764 **371** 2d. multicoloured 85 25

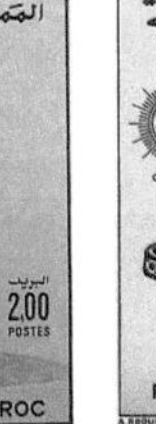

372 Copper Vase **373** Ceramic Vase

1989. Red Crescent.
765 **372** 2d. multicoloured 60 25

1989. Blind Week.
766 **373** 2d. multicoloured 60 25

374 King Hassan **375** "Cerinthe major"

1989. 60th Birthday of King Hassan II. Mult.
767 2d. Type **374** 75 25
768 2d. King Hassan in robes . . 75 25

1989. Flowers. Multicoloured.
770 2d. Type **375** 75 25
771 2d. "Narcissus papyraceus" 75 25

376 Telephone Handset linking Landmarks

1989. World Telecommunications Day.
772 **376** 2d. multicoloured 60 25

377 Gender Symbols forming Globe, Woman and Eggs

1989. 1st World Fertility and Sterility Congress.
773 **377** 2d. multicoloured 75 25

378 Desert Wheatear

1989. Birds. Multicoloured.
774 2d. Type **378** 50 50
775 3d. Shore lark . . . . 1·75 75

379 House of Representatives

1989. Centenary of Interparliamentary Union.
776 **379** 2d. multicoloured 60 25

380 Scroll

1989. 14th Anniv of "Green March".
777 **380** 3d. multicoloured 70 35

1990. Stamp Day. As T **316**.
778 2d. orange and black 60 20
779 3d. green and black 70 35
DESIGNS: 2d. Round postal cancellation of Casablanca; 3d. Octagonal postal cancellation of Casablanca.

381 Flags forming Map

1990. 1st Anniv of Union of Arab Maghreb.
780 **381** 2d. multicoloured 65 20

382 Oil Press

1990. 3rd World Olive Year. Multicoloured.
782 2d. Type **382** 60 15
783 3d. King Hassan and olives 85 25

383 Decorated Pot

1990. Blind Week.
784 **383** 2d. multicoloured 55 15

384 Silver Teapot

1990. Red Crescent.
785 **384** 2d. multicoloured 60 15

385 Arabic Script and Open Book **386** Turtle Dove

1990. International Literacy Year.
786 **385** 3d. green, yellow and black 80 25

1990. Birds. Multicoloured.
787 2d. Type **386** . . . . 1·10 35
788 3d. Hoopoe (horiz) . . . . . 1·90 65

387 "15" on Scroll **388** "35", Sun's Rays and Flag

1990. 15th Anniv of "Green March".
789 **387** 3d. multicoloured 80 25

1990. 35th Anniv of Independence.
790 **388** 3d. multicoloured 80 25

389 Dam

1990.
791 **389** 3d. multicoloured 80 25

390 Emblem

392 Projects and Emblem

391 Morse Code Apparatus

1990. 10th Anniv of Royal Academy of Morocco.
792 **390** 3d. multicoloured 85 25

1990. 20th Anniv of National Postal Museum. Multicoloured.
793 2d. Type **391** 60 15
794 3d. Horse-drawn mail wagon, 1913 . . . . 85 25

1991. Stamp Day. As T **316**.
796 2d. red and black 60 15
797 3d. blue and black 85 25
DESIGNS: 2d. Round postal cancellation of Rabat; 3d. Octagonal postal cancellation of Rabat.

1991. 40th Anniv of United Nations Development Programme.
798 **392** 3d. turquoise, yellow & blk 85 25

393 King Hassan

394 Mining

1991. 30th Anniv of Enthronement of King Hassan II. Multicoloured.
799 3d. Type **393** 85 25
800 3d. King Hassan in robes . . 85 25

1991. 70th Anniv of Mineral Exploitation by Sherifian Phosphates Office.
802 **394** 3d. multicoloured 85 25

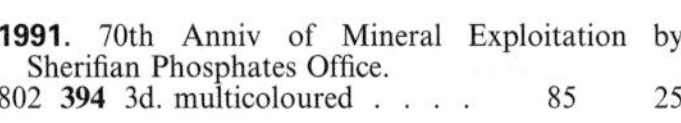

395 Kettle on Stand

396 Lantern

1991. Blind Week.
803 **395** 3d. multicoloured 85 25

1991. Red Crescent.
804 **396** 3d. multicoloured 85 25

397 "Cynara humilis"

398 Man

1991. Flowers. Multicoloured.
805 3d. Type **397** 85 25
806 3d. "Pyrus mamorensis" . . 85 25

1991. Ouarzazate Costumes. Multicoloured.
807 3d. Type **398** 85 20
808 3d. Woman 85 20

1991. Inscribed "1991".
809 **266** 1d.35 red, green and gold 20 10

399 Road

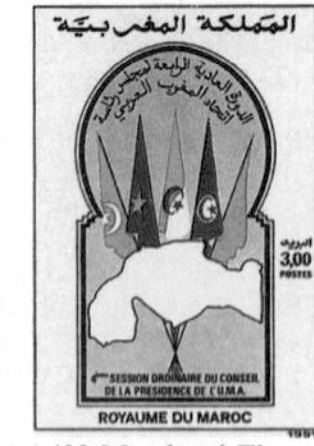

400 Members' Flags and Map

1991. 19th World Roads Congress, Marrakesh.
810 **399** 3d. multicoloured 85 20

1991. 4th Ordinary Session of Arab Maghreb Union Presidential Council, Casablanca.
811 **400** 3d. multicoloured 85 20

401 "16" on Scroll

402 White Stork

1991. 16th Anniv of "Green March".
812 **401** 3d. multicoloured 85 20

1991. Birds. Multicoloured.
813 3d. Type **402** . . . . 1·50 50
814 3d. European bee eater . . . 1·50 50

403 Figures and Blood Splash

405 Zebra and Map of Africa

404 Emblem

1991. World AIDS Day.
815 **403** 3d. multicoloured 85 20

1991. 20th Anniv of Islamic Conf Organization.
816 **404** 3d. multicoloured 85 20

1991. African Tourism Year.
817 **405** 3d. multicoloured 85 20

1992. Stamp Day. As T **316**.
818 3d. green and black 85 20
819 3d. violet and black 85 20
DESIGNS: No. 818, Circular postal cancellation of Essaouira; No. 819, Octagonal postal cancellation of Essaouira.

406 Satellites around Earth

407 Bottle

1992. International Space Year.
820 **406** 3d. multicoloured 85 20

1992. Blind Week.
821 **407** 3d. multicoloured 85 20

408 Brass Jug

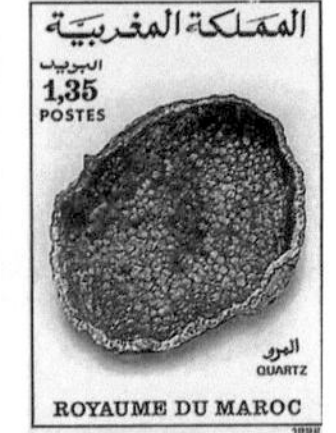

409 Quartz

1992. Red Crescent.
822 **408** 3d. multicoloured 85 50

1992. Minerals. Multicoloured.
823 1d.35 Type **409** 45 10
824 3d.40 Calcite . . . . 1·10 60

410 Woman

411 "Campanula afra"

1992. Tata Costumes. Multicoloured.
825 1d.35 Type **410** 20 10
826 3d.40 Man . . . . 1·10 60

1992. Flowers. Multicoloured.
827 1d.35 Type **411** 20 10
828 3d.40 "Thymus broussonetii" 1·10 60

412 Olympic Rings and Torch

414 La Koutoubia, La Giralda (cathedral bell-tower) and Exhibition Emblem

413 Map of Africa and Methods of Transport and Communication

1992. Olympic Games, Barcelona.
829 **412** 3d.40 multicoloured . . . 1·10 20

1992. Decade of Transport and Communications in Africa.
830 **413** 3d.40 multicoloured . . . 3·00 1·00

1992. "Expo '92" World's Fair, Seville.
831 **414** 3d.40 multicoloured . . . 1·10 50

415 Columbus's Fleet and Route Map

1992. 500th Anniv of Discovery of America by Columbus.
832 **415** 3d.40 multicoloured . . . 1·25 50

416 Pin-tailed Sandgrouse

1992. Birds. Multicoloured.
833 3d. Type **416** . . . . 1·10 40
834 3d. Griffon vulture ("Gyps fulvus") (vert) . . . . . . 1·10 40

417 "17" on Scroll

1992. 17th Anniv of "Green March".
835 **417** 3d.40 multicoloured . . . 1·10 20

418 Postal Messenger, Route Map and Cancellations

1992. Centenary of Sherifian Post. Multicoloured.
836 1d.35 Type **418** 20 10
837 3d.40 Postal cancellation, "100" on scroll and Sultan Mulay al-Hassan . . . . . 1·10 50

419 Conference Emblem

1992. International Nutrition Conference, Rome.
839 **419** 3d.40 multicoloured . . . 1·10 50

420 Douglas DC-9 Airliners on Runway

422 Satellite orbiting Earth

421 Dishes

1992. Al Massira Airport, Agadir.
840 **420** 3d.40 multicoloured . . . 1·10 20

1993. Stamp Day. As T **316**.
841 1d.70 green and black . . . 25 10
842 3d.80 orange and black . . . 1·10 50
DESIGNS: 1d.70, Round postal cancellation of Tangier; 3d.80, Octagonal postal cancellation of Tangier.

1993. Blind Week.
843 **421** 4d.40 multicoloured . . . 1·25 25

1993. World Meteorological Day.
844 **422** 4d.40 multicoloured . . . 1·25 25

423 Kettle on Stand **424** Emblem

1993. Red Crescent.
845 **423** 4d.40 multicoloured . . . 1·25 25

1993. World Telecommunications Day.
846 **424** 4d.40 multicoloured . . . 60 25

425 Woman extracting Argan Oil **426** Prince Sidi Mohammed

1993. Argan Oil. Multicoloured.
847 1d.70 Type **425** 25 10
848 4d.80 Branch and fruit of argan tree 70 30

1993. 30th Birthday of Prince Sidi Mohammed.
849 **426** 4d.80 multicoloured . . . 70 30

427 King Hassan and Mosque **428** Canopy, Sceptres, Flag and "40" on Sun

1993. Inauguration of King Hassan II Mosque.
850 **427** 4d.80 multicoloured . . . 70 30

1993. 40th Anniv of Revolution.
851 **428** 4d.80 multicoloured . . . 70 30

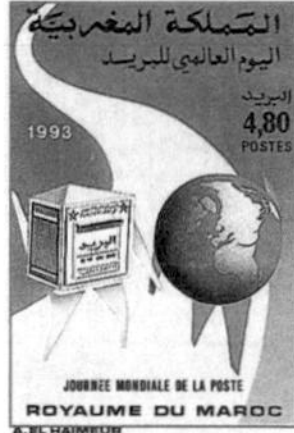

429 Post Box and Globe **430** Emblem

1993. World Post Day.
852 **429** 4d.80 multicoloured . . . 70 30

1993. Islamic Summer University.
853 **430** 4d.80 multicoloured . . . 70 30

431 "18" on Scroll **433** Flags, Scroll and "50"

432 Marbled Teal

1993. 18th Anniv of "Green March".
854 **431** 4d.80 multicoloured . . . 70 30

1993. Waterfowl. Multicoloured.
855 1d.70 Type **432** 25 10
856 4d.80 Red-knobbed coot . . 70 30

1994. 50th Anniv of Istaqlal (Independence) Party.
857 **433** 4d.80 multicoloured . . . 70 30

434 House **435** Decorated Vase

1994. Signing of Uruguay Round Final Act of General Agreement on Tariffs and Trade, Marrakesh.
858 **434** 1d.70 multicoloured . . . 25 10
859 – 4d.80 multicoloured . . . 70 30
DESIGN: 4d.80, Mosque.

1994. Blind Week.
861 **435** 4d.80 multicoloured . . . 70 30

436 Copper Vessel **437** Couple

1994. Red Crescent.
862 **436** 4d.80 multicoloured . . . 70 30

1994. National Congress on Children's Rights. Children's Drawings. Multicoloured.
863 1d.70 Type **437** 25 10
864 4d.80 Couple under sun . . . 70 30

438 Ball, Moroccan and U.S.A. Flags, Pictogram and Trophy

1994. World Cup Football Championship, U.S.A.
865 **438** 4d.80 multicoloured . . . 70 30

1994. Size 25 × 32 mm but inscr "1994".
866 **266** 1d.70 red, blue and gold 25 10

439 King Hassan II and Arms

1994. 65th Birthday of King Hassan II. Mult.
867 1d.70 Type **439** 25 10
868 4d.80 King Hassan II (vert) 70 30

440 "100" and Rings **441** Saint-Exupery, Route Map and Biplane

1994. Centenary of International Olympic Committee.
869 **440** 4d.80 multicoloured . . . 70 30

1994. 50th Death Anniv of Antoine de Saint-Exupery (writer and pilot).
870 **441** 4d.80 multicoloured . . . 70 30

442 "Chamaeleon gummifer"

1994. Flowers. Multicoloured.
871 1d.70 Type **442** 25 10
872 4d.80 "Pancratium maritimum" (vert) 70 30

443 Slender-billed Curlew

1994. Birds. Multicoloured.
873 1d.70 Type **443** 25 10
874 4d.80 Audouin's gull 70 30

444 Scroll and March **445** Decorated Vase

1994. 19th Anniv of "Green March". Mult.
875 1d.70 Type **444** 25 10
876 4d.80 Marchers and Moroccan coastline 70 30

1994. Stamp Day. As T **316**.
877 1d.70 blue and black 25 10
878 4d.80 red and black 70 30
DESIGNS: 1d.70, Round postal cancellation of Marrakesh; 4d.80, Octagonal postal cancellation of Marrakesh.

1995. Blind Week.
879 **445** 4d.80 multicoloured . . . 70 30

446 Anniversary Emblem **447** Copper Vessel

1995. 50th Anniv of League of Arab States.
880 **446** 4d.80 multicoloured . . . 70 30

1995. Red Crescent.
881 **447** 4d.80 multicoloured . . . 70 30

448 "Malva hispanica" **449** European Roller

1995. Flowers. Multicoloured.
882 2d. Type **448** 30 10
883 4d.80 "Phlomis crinita" . . . 70 30

1995. Birds. Multicoloured.
884 1d.70 Type **449** 25 10
885 4d.80 Eurasian goldfinch . . 70 30

450 Anniversary Emblem, Building and Map

1995. 50th Anniv of F.A.O.
886 **450** 4d.80 multicoloured . . . 70 30

451 "50" and Flags

1995. 50th Anniv of U.N.O. Multicoloured.
887 1d.70 Type **451** 25 10
888 4d.80 U.N. emblem, doves and map 70 30

452 "20" on Scroll **453** "40", National Flag and Crown

1995. 20th Anniv of "Green March". Mult.
889 1d.70 Type **452** 25 10
890 4d.80 National flag, book and medal 70 30

1995. 40th Anniv of Independence.
891 **453** 4d.80 multicoloured . . . 70 30

1995. Stamp Day. As T **316**.
893 1d.70 bistre and black . . . 25 10
894 4d.80 lilac and black 70 30
DESIGNS: 1d.70, Round postal cancellation of Meknes; 4d.80, Octagonal cancellation of Meknes.

1996. Size 25 × 32 mm but inscr "1996".
895 **266** 5d.50 brown, red and gold 80 35
896 20d. brown, blue and gold 2·75 1·10

454 National Arms **455** Decorated Vase

1996. 35th Anniv of Enthronement of King Hassan II. Multicoloured.
897 2d. Type **454** 30 15
898 5d.50 King Hassan II 80 35

1996.
900 **455** 5d.50 multicoloured . . . 80 35

456 Leather Flask **457** "Cleonia lusitanica"

1996.
901 **456** 5d.50 multicoloured . . . 80 35

1996. Flowers. Multicoloured.
902 2d. Type **457** 30 15
903 5d.50 "Tulipa sylvestris" . . 80 35

458 King Hassan II wearing Military Uniform **459** Emblem and Runners

1996. 40th Anniv of Royal Armed Forces. Mult.
904 2d. Type **458** 30 15
905 5d.50 King Hassan II and globe 80 35

1996. Centenary of Modern Olympic Games. Olympic Games, Atlanta, U.S.A.
906 **459** 5d.50 multicoloured . . . 70 30

460 Osprey

461 "21" on Scroll

1996. Birds. Multicoloured.
907 2d. Type **460** 25 10
908 5d.50 Little egret 70 30

1996. 21st Anniv of "Green March".
909 **461** 5d.50 multicoloured . . . 70 30

1996. Stamp Day. As T **316**.
910 2d. orange and black 25 10
911 5d.50 green and black . . . 70 30
DESIGNS: 2d. Round postal cancellation of Maghzen-Fes; 5d.50, Octagonal postal cancellation of Maghzen-Fes.

462 Rainbow and Emblem

1996. 50th Anniv of U.N.I.C.E.F.
912 **462** 5d.50 multicoloured . . . 70 30

463 Terracotta Vessel

1997.
913 **463** 5d.50 multicoloured . . . 70 30

464 Lupin

465 King Mohammed V

1997. Flowers. Multicoloured.
914 2d. Type **464** 25 10
915 5d.50 Milk thistle 70 30

1997. 50th Anniv of Tangier Talks (determining future status of Tangier).
916 2d. Type **465** 25 10
917 2d. King Hassan II 25 10

466 Map in Open Book and Quill

468 Copper Door Knocker

467 Ibn Battuta and Globe

1997. World Book Day.
918 **466** 5d.50 multicoloured . . . 70 30

1997. International Conference on Ibn Battuta (explorer).
919 **467** 5d.50 multicoloured . . . 70 30

1997.
920 **468** 5d.50 multicoloured . . . 70 30

469 Demoiselle Crane

470 "22" on Scroll

1997. Birds. Multicoloured.
921 2d. Type **469** 25 10
922 5d.50 Blue tit 70 30

1997. 22nd Anniv of "Green March".
923 **470** 5d.50 multicoloured . . . 70 30

1997. Stamp Day. As T **316**.
924 2d. blue and black 25 10
925 5d.50 red and black 70 30
DESIGNS: 2d. Round postal cancellation of Maghzen-Larache; 5d.50, Octagonal postal cancellation of Maghzen-Larache.

471 Flask

1998. Moroccan Pottery.
926 **471** 6d. multicoloured 75 30

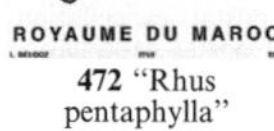

472 "Rhus pentaphylla"

473 Route Map and Emblem

1998. Plants. Multicoloured.
927 2d.30 Type **472** 30 15
928 6d. "Orchis papilionacea" . . 75 30

1998. 26th International Road Haulage Union Congress, Marrakesh.
929 **473** 6d. multicoloured 75 30

1998. Size 25 × 32 mm but inscr "1998".
930 **266** 2d.30 red, green and gold 30 15

474 Sconce

475 Players and Ball

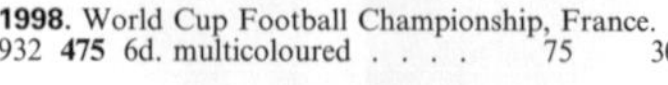

1998. Moroccan Copperware.
931 **474** 6d. multicoloured 75 30

1998. World Cup Football Championship, France.
932 **475** 6d. multicoloured 75 30

476 Emblem, Rainbow, World Map and Hands

1998. International Year of the Ocean.
933 **476** 6d. multicoloured 75 30

477 King Mohammed V and King Hassan II

1998. 45th Anniv of Revolution.
934 **477** 6d. multicoloured 75 30

478 Globe and Letter

479 Nightingale

1998. World Stamp Day.
935 **478** 6d. multicoloured 75 30

1998. Birds. Multicoloured.
936 2d.30 Type **479** 30 15
937 6d. Ostrich 75 30

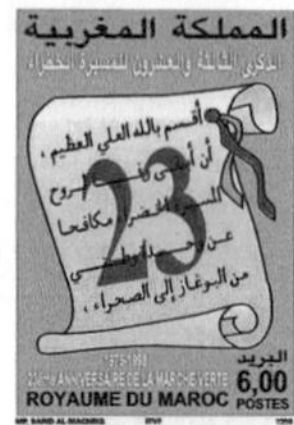

480 Scroll

481 Arabic Script

1998. 23rd Anniv of "Green March".
938 **480** 6d. multicoloured 75 30

1998. 40th Anniv of Code of Civil Liberties.
939 **481** 6d. multicoloured 75 30

482 Anniversary Emblem

483 Mask and Globe

1998. 50th Anniv of Universal Declaration of Human Rights.
940 **482** 6d. multicoloured 75 30

1999. World Theatre Day.
941 **483** 6d. multicoloured 75 30

484 *Eryngium triquetrum*

1999. Flowers. Multicoloured.
942 2d.30 Type **484** 30 15
943 6d. Mistletoe 75 30

485 Bab Mansour Laalej

1999.
944 **485** 6d. multicoloured 75 30

486 King Hassan II on Throne

1999. 70th Birthday of King Hassan II. Mult.
945 2d.30 Type **486** 30 15
946 6d. King Hassan wearing robes 75 30

487 Necklace

1999. Moroccan Jewellery.
948 **487** 6d. multicoloured 75 30

488 Hands holding Globe and Water falling on Tree

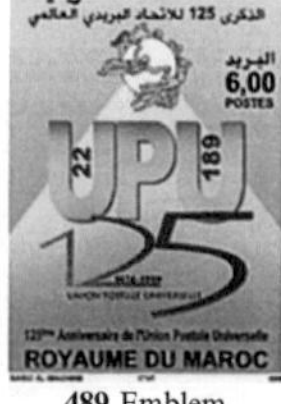

489 Emblem

1999. World Environment Day.
949 **488** 6d. multicoloured 75 30

1999. 125th Anniv of Universal Postal Union.
950 **489** 6d. multicoloured 75 30

490 Obverse and Reverse of Medal

1999. F.A.O. Agriculture Medal.
951 **490** 6d. multicoloured 75 30

491 Stylized People

1999. Solidarity Week.
952 **491** 6d. blue, yellow and black 75 30

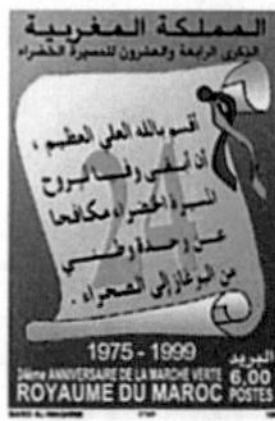

492 "24" on Scroll

1999. 24th Anniv of "Green March".
953 **492** 6d. multicoloured 75 30

493 Zebra Seabream

1999. Fishes. Multicoloured.
954 2d.30 Type **493** 30 15
955 6d. Opah 75 30

494 Stork on Nest (A. Slaoui)

1999. "Year of Morocco in France". Paintings. Multicoloured.

956	6d. Type **494**	75	30
957	6d. Women sitting on mat (Afif Bennani)	75	30
958	6d. Guitar (Abdelkader Rhorbal)	75	30
959	6d. View of harbour (A. Slaoui)	75	30

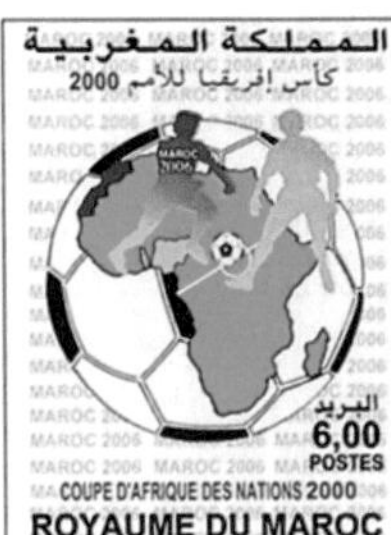

495 Players and Globe

2000. African Nations' Cup Football Championship.
960 **495** 6d. multicoloured 75 30

496 Globe and "2000"

2000. New Year
961 **496** 6d. multicoloured 75 30

497 Beach and Calendar

2000. 40th Anniv of the Reconstruction of Agadir.
962 **497** 6d.50 multicoloured . . . 80 35

498 Emblem and Building

2000. 25th Anniv of Islamic Development Bank.
963 **498** 6d.50 multicoloured . . . 80 35

499 Stylized People

2000. National Disabled Persons Day.
964 **499** 6d.50 multicoloured . . . 80 35

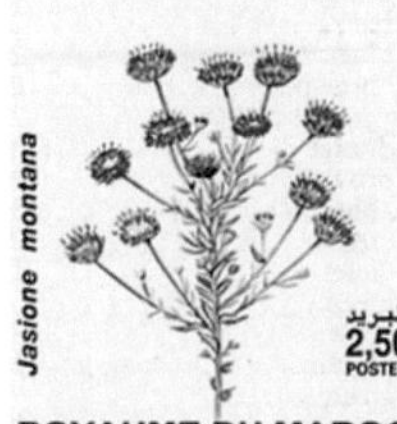

500 *Jasione montana*

2000. Flowers. Multicoloured.

965	2d.50 Type **500**	30	10
966	6d.60 *Pistorica breviflora*	80	30

501 Emblem

2000. 50th Anniv of World Meteorological Organization.
967 **501** 6d.50 multicoloured . . . 80 30

502 People dancing

2000. National Festival of Popular Arts, Marrakesh.
968 **502** 6d.50 multicoloured . . . 80 30

503 Open Book and White Dove

2000. International Year of Culture and Peace.
969 **503** 6d.50 multicoloured . . . 80 30

COLLOQUE INTERNATIONAL SUR HASSAN II Du 6 au 9 - 7 - 2000
6,50

(**504**)

505 King Mohammed VI

2000. Air. International Conference on Hassan II. No. 631 optd with T **504**.
970 6d.50 on 1d.40 multicoloured 80 30

2000. 1st Anniv of Enthronement of King Mohammed VI. Multicoloured.

971	2d.50 Type **505**	30	10
972	6d.50 King Mohammed VI	80	30

506 Ruins, Volubis and Performers

2000. Mediterranean Song and Dance Festival.
974 **506** 6d.50 multicoloured . . . 80 30

507 Emblem and Olympic Torch

508 Emblem, House and Children

2000. Olympic Games, Sydney.
975 **507** 6d.50 multicoloured . . . 80 30

2000. 50th Anniv of S.O.S. Children's Villages.
976 **508** 6d.50 multicoloured . . . 80 30

509 Quill, Globe and Emblem

511 "25" on Scroll

510 Emblem

2000. International Teachers' Day.
977 **509** 6d.50 multicoloured . . . 80 30

2000. King Mohammed VI Solidarity Foundation.
978 **510** 6d.50 blue, yellow and black 80 30

2000. 25th Anniv of "Green March". Mult.

979	2d.50 Type **511**	30	10
980	6d.50 "25" and text	80	30

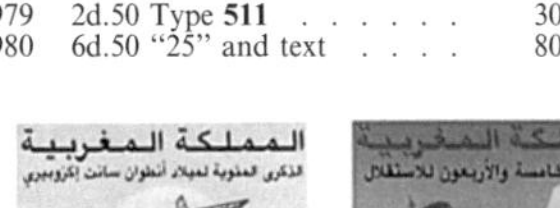

512 St. Exupery and Plane

513 "45" and National Flag

2000. Birth Centenary of Antonie de Saint.-Exupery (author).
981 **512** 6d.50 multicoloured . . . 80 30

2000. 45th Anniv of Independence.
982 **513** 6d.50 multicoloured . . . 80 30

514 Mediterranean Cardinalfish (*Apogon imberbis*)

2000. Fishes. Multicoloured.

983	2d.50 Type **514**	30	10
984	6d.50 Cadenat's rockfish (*Scorpaena loppei*)	80	30

515 El Bab el Gharbi

2001.
985 **515** 6d.50 multicoloured . . . 80 30

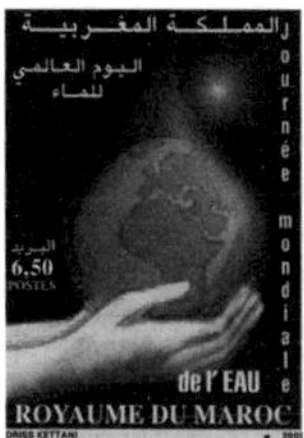

516 Hands holding Globe

517 King Mohammed VI enclosed in Droplet of Water

2001. International Water Day.
986 **516** 6d.50 multicoloured . . . 80 30

2001. 45th Anniv of Armed Forces. Multicoloured.

987	2d.50 Type **517**	30	10
988	6d.50 King Mohammed VI (different)	80	30

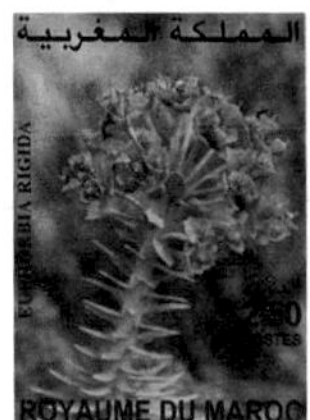

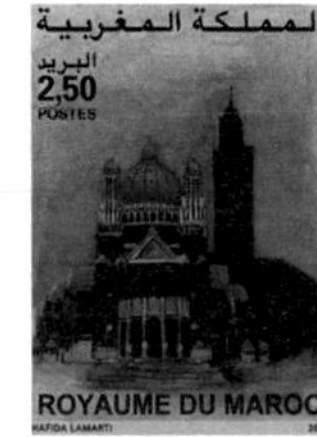

518 Spurge (*Euphorbia rigida*)

519 Koekelberg Basilica, Brussels

2001. Flowers. Multicoloured.

989	2d.50 Type **518**	30	10
990	6d.50 Horned poppy (*Glaucium flavum*)	80	30

2001. Religious Buildings.

991	2d.50 Type **519**	30	10
992	6d.50 Hassan II Mosque, Casablanca	80	30

Stamps of a similar design were issued by Belgium.

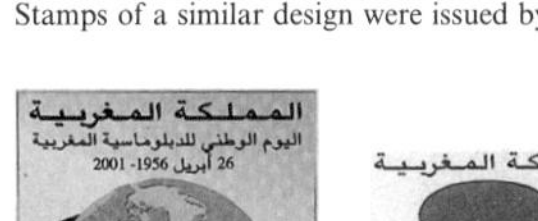

520 Globe and Dove

521 King Mohammed VI

2001. National Diplomacy Day.
993 **520** 6d.50 multicoloured . . . 80 30

2001. 2nd Anniv of Enthronement of King Mohammed VI. Multicoloured.

994	2d.50 Type **521**	30	10
995	6d. Smiling facing left	70	30
996	6d.50 Wearing decorated tie (crown upper left)	80	30
997	10d. King Mohammed VI (horiz)	1·20	50

522 Black-bellied Angler

523 Postal Seal, Kasir el Kabir (*Lophus budegassa*)

2001. Marine Life. Multicoloured.
998 2d.50 Type **522** 30 10
999 6d.50 Monk seal (*Monachus monachus*) (horiz) 80 10

2001. Stamp Day.
1000 **523** 2d.50 bistre and black 30 10
1001 – 6d.50 lilac and black . . 80 10
DESIGN: 6d.50 Octagonal seal.

524 Hands holding Globe

525 Palm Trees

2001. 7th Conference Session of Signatory States to United Nations Framework Convention on Climatic Change, Marrakech.
1002 **524** 6d.50 multicoloured . . 80 30

2001. World Day to Combat Desertification.
1003 **525** 6d.50 multicoloured . . 80 30

526 Flags and Marchers

2001. 26th Anniv of "Green March".
1004 **526** 6d.50 multicoloured . . 80 30

527 King Mohammed VI and Children

2001. King Mohammed VI Solidarity Foundation.
1005 **527** 6d.50 multicoloured . . 80 30
1006 – 6d.50 ultramarine, lemon and black (28 × 28 mm) 80 30
DESIGN: As No. 978 but inscr "2001".

528 Wallace Fountain, Paris

529 Hands holding Globe

2001. Moroccan—French Cultural Heritage. Multicoloured.
1007 2d.50 Type **528** 30 10
1008 6d.50 Nejjarine fountain, Fez 80 30
Stamps of the same design were issued by France.

2001. United Nations Year of Dialogue among Civilizations.
1009 **529** 6d.50 multicoloured . . 80 30

POSTAGE DUE STAMPS

D 53

1965.
D162 **D 53** 5f. green . . . . . . 3·00 1·25
D163 10f. brown 50 25
D164 20f. red 50 25
D165 30f. sepia . . . . . . 1·25 50

D 153 Peaches

1974.
D393 – 5f. orange, grn & blk 10 10
D394 – 10f. green, red & blk 10 10
D395 – 20f. green and black 50 10
D396 **D 153** 30f. orge, grn & blk 60 35
D397 – 40f. green and black 15 10
D398 – 60f. orge, grn & blk 20 15
D399 – 80f. orge, grn & blk 50 20
D399a – 1d. multicoloured 20 15
D400 – 1d.20 multicoloured 50 15
D401 – 1d.60 multicoloured 60 20
D402 – 2d. multicoloured 55 25
D403 – 5d. multicoloured 65 30
DESIGNS: 60f., 1d.60, Peaches. VERT: 5f. Oranges; 10f., 1d.20, Cherries; 20f. Raisins; 40f. Grapes; 80f. Oranges; 1, 5d. Apples; 2d. Strawberries.

MOROCCO AGENCIES Pt. 1

Stamps used at British postal agencies in Morocco, N. Africa, the last of which closed on 30 April 1957.

I. GIBRALTAR ISSUES OVERPRINTED.

For use at all British Post Offices in Morocco.
All British P.O.s in Morocco were under the control of the Gibraltar P.O. until 1907 when control was assumed by H.M. Postmaster-General.

1898. Stamps of Gibraltar (Queen Victoria) optd **Morocco Agencies**.
9 **7** 5c. green 50 75
10 10c. red . . . . 2·00 30
11 20c. olive . . . . 6·50 70
3 20c. olive and brown . . . . 7·50 1·75
4 25c. blue . . . . 3·75 60
5 40c. brown . . . . 6·00 3·25
14 50c. lilac . . . . 9·00 3·50
7 1p. brown and blue . . . . 17·00 27·00
8 2p. black and red . . . . . 21·00 27·00

1903. Stamps of Gibraltar (King Edward VII) optd **Morocco Agencies**.
24 **8** 5c. light green and green . . 8·50 3·00
18 10c. purple on red . . . . . 8·00 40
26 20c. green and red . . . . . 4·75 29·00
20 25c. purple and black on blue 8·00 30
28 50c. purple and violet . . . . 7·00 42·00
29 1p. black and red . . . . . 28·00 80·00
30 2p. black and blue . . . . . 15·00 35·00

II. BRITISH CURRENCY.

On sale at British P.O.s throughout Morocco, including Tangier, until 1937.

PRICES. Our prices for used stamps with these overprints are for examples used in Morocco. These stamps could also be used in the United Kingdom, with official sanction, from the summer of 1950 onwards, and with U.K. postmarks are worth about 50 per cent less.
Stamps of Great Britain optd **MOROCCO AGENCIES**.

1907. King Edward VII.
31 **83** ½d. green . . . . 2·25 8·50
32 1d. red . . . . 9·50 5·50
33 – 2d. green and red . . . . . 9·50 5·50
34 – 4d. green and brown . . . . 3·75 4·00
35 – 4d. orange . . . . 10·00 11·00
36 – 6d. purple . . . . 15·00 19·00
37 – 1s. green and red . . . . . 26·00 17·00
38 – 2s.6d. purple . . . . 75·00 £110

1914. King George V.
55 **105** ½d. green . . . . 1·50 50
43 **104** 1d. red 85 20
44 **105** 1½d. brown . . . . . . 3·00 12·00
45 **106** 2d. orange . . . . . . 3·50 60
58 **104** 2½d. blue . . . . 2·25 5·00
46 **106** 3d. violet . . . . 1·25 35
47 4d. green . . . . 3·00 1·25
60b **107** 6d. purple . . . . 1·00 60
49 **108** 1s. brown . . . . 5·50 1·25
53 **109** 2s.6d. brown . . . . . 38·00 25·00
74 5s. red . . . . 23·00 £100

1935. Silver Jubilee.
62 **123** ½d. green . . . . 1·25 6·50
63 1d. red . . . . 1·25 6·50
64 1½d. brown . . . . 2·25 10·00
65 2½d. blue . . . . 2·50 2·50

1935. King George V.
66 **119** 1d. red . . . . 3·25 13·00
67 **118** 1½d. brown . . . . 3·25 16·00
68 **120** 2d. orange . . . . 1·25 7·00
69 **119** 2½d. blue . . . . 1·75 4·25
70 **120** 3d. violet 50 30
71 4d. green 50 30
72 **122** 1s. brown . . . . 80 3·00

1936. King Edward VIII.
75 **124** 1d. red 10 30
76 2½d. blue 10 15

In 1937 unoverprinted Great Britain stamps replaced overprinted **MOROCCO AGENCIES** issues as stocks became exhausted. In 1949 overprinted issues reappeared and were in use at Tetuan (Spanish Zone), the only remaining British P.O. apart from that at Tangier.

1949. King George VI.
77 **128** ½d. green . . . . 1·75 7·00
94 ½d. orange . . . . 2·00 1·00
78 1d. red . . . . 2·75 9·00
95 1d. blue . . . . 2·00 1·40
79 1½d. brown . . . . 2·75 8·50
96 1½d. green . . . . 2·00 2·75
80 2d. orange . . . . 3·00 9·00
97 2d. brown . . . . 2·25 4·00
81 2½d. blue . . . . 3·25 10·00
98 2½d. red . . . . 2·00 4·25
82 3d. violet . . . . 1·50 1·75
83 **129** 4d. green . . . . 50 1·25
84 5d. brown . . . . 3·00 15·00
85 6d. purple . . . . 1·50 1·50
86 **130** 7d. green . . . . 50 16·00
87 8d. red . . . . 3·00 6·50
88 9d. olive . . . . 50 11·00
89 10d. blue . . . . 50 6·50
90 11d. plum . . . . 70 7·00
91 1s. brown . . . . 2·75 6·00
92 **131** 2s.6d. green . . . . 16·00 35·00
93 5s. red . . . . 28·00 60·00

1951. Pictorials.
99 **147** 2s.6d. green . . . . . . 13·00 21·00
100 – 5s. red (No. 510) . . . . 13·00 22·00

1952. Queen Elizabeth II.
101 **154** ½d. orange 10 10
102 1d. blue . . . . 15 1·60
103 1½d. green 15 20
104 2d. brown . . . . 20 1·75
105 **155** 2½d. red . . . . 15 1·00
106 4d. blue . . . . 1·25 3·50
107 **156** 5d. brown 65 60
108 6d. purple . . . . 85 3·50
109 **158** 8d. mauve 70 70
110 **159** 1s. bistre 70 60

III. SPANISH CURRENCY.

Stamps surcharged in Spanish currency were sold at British P.O.s throughout Morocco until the establishment of the French Zone and the Tangier International Zone, when their use was confined to the Spanish Zone.
Stamps of Great Britain surch **MOROCCO AGENCIES** and value in Spanish currency.

1907. King Edward VII.
112 **83** 5c. on ½d. green . . . . . 7·00 20
113 10c. on 1d. red . . . . . 11·00 10
114a – 15c. on 1½d. purple and green . . . . 2·50 20
115 – 20c. on 2d. green and red 2·25 20
116a **83** 25c. on 2½d. blue . . . . 1·50 20
117 – 40c. on 4d. green & brown . . . . 1·00 2·75
118a – 40c. on 4d. orange . . . 1·00 60
119a – 50c. on 5d. purple and blue . . . . 1·75 3·00
120a – 1p. on 10d. purple and red . . . . 22·00 12·00
121 – 3p. on 2s.6d. purple . . . 21·00 25·00
122 – 6p. on 5s. red . . . . . . 35·00 45·00
123 – 12p. on 10s. blue . . . . 75·00 75·00

1912. King George V.
126 **101** 5c. on ½d. green . . . . . 3·00 20
127 **102** 10c. on 1d. red . . . . . 1·00 10

1914. King George V.
128 **105** 3c. on ½d. green . . . . . 1·00 4·25
129 5c. on ½d. green 60 10
130 **104** 10c. on 1d. red . . . . . 1·25 10
131 **105** 15c. on 1½d. brown . . . 1·00 10
132 **106** 20c. on 2d. orange . . . 1·00 25
133 **104** 25c. on 2½d. blue . . . . 1·75 25
148 **106** 40c. on 4d. green . . . . 2·00 2·25
135 **108** 1p. on 10d. blue . . . . 2·75 6·00
142 **109** 3p. on 2s.6d. brown . . . 23·00 75·00
136 6p. on 5s. red . . . . . 29·00 48·00
138 12p. on 10s. blue £100 £160

1935. Silver Jubilee.
149 **123** 5c. on ½d. green . . . . . 1·00 80
150 10c. on 1d. red . . . . . 2·75 2·25
151 15c. on 1½d. brown . . . 5·50 17·00
152 25c. on 2½d. blue . . . . 3·50 2·25

1935. King George V.
153 **118** 5c. on ½d. green . . . . . 1·00 18·00
154 **119** 10c. on 1d. red . . . . . 2·50 9·00
155 **118** 15c. on 1½d. brown . . . 5·50 3·25
156 **120** 20c. on 2d. orange . . . 50 25
157 **119** 25c. on 2½d. blue . . . . 1·25 4·25
158 **120** 40c. on 4d. green . . . . 50 3·00
159 **122** 1p. on 10d. blue . . . . 5·50 30

1936. King Edward VIII.
160 **124** 5c. on ½d. green 10 10
161 10c. on 1d. red . . . . . 50 2·00
162 15c. on 1½d. brown . . . 10 15
163 25c. on 2½d. blue 10 10

1937. Coronation.
164 **126** 15c. on 1½d. brown . . . 60 50

1937. King George VI.
165 **128** 5c. on ½d. green . . . . . 1·00 30
182 5c. on ½d. orange . . . . 2·00 3·50
166 10c. on 1d. red 80 10
183 10c. on 1d. blue . . . . . 3·25 6·50
167 15c. on 1½d. brown . . . 1·00 25
184 15c. on 1½d. green . . . . 1·75 15·00
168 25c. on 2½d. blue . . . . 1·75 1·00
185 25c. on 2½d. red . . . . 1·75 7·50
169 **129** 40c. on 4d. green . . . . 30·00 13·00
186 40c. on 4d. blue . . . . . 60 9·00
170 **130** 70c. on 7d. green . . . . 1·50 13·00
171 1p. on 10d. blue . . . . 2·25 3·50

1940. Stamp Centenary.
172 **134** 5c. on ½d. green . . . . . 30 2·25
173 10c. on 1d. red . . . . . 3·50 2·25
174 15c. on 1½d. brown . . . 60 2·25
175 25c. on 2½d. blue 70 75

1948. Silver Wedding.
176 **137** 25c. on 2½d. blue . . . . 1·00 30
177 **138** 45p. on £1 blue . . . . . 17·00 22·00

1948. Olympic Games.
178 **139** 25c. on 2½d. blue . . . . 50 1·00
179 **140** 30c. on 3d. violet . . . . 50 1·00
180 – 60c. on 6d. purple . . . . 50 1·00
181 – 1p.20 on 1s. brown . . . 60 1·00

1954. Queen Elizabeth II.
189 **154** 5c. on ½d. orange . . . . 15 2·50
188 10c. on 1d. blue . . . . . 50 1·00
190 **155** 40c. on 4d. blue . . . . . 70 1·75

IV. FRENCH CURRENCY.

Stamps surch in French currency were sold at British P.O.s in the French Zone.
Stamps of Great Britain surch **MOROCCO AGENCIES** and value in French currency.

1917. King George V.
191 **105** 3c. on ½d. green . . . . . 1·00 2·50
192 5c. on ½d. green 40 20
203 **104** 10c. on 1d. red . . . . . 30 1·75
194 **105** 15c. on 1½d. brown . . . 2·50 20
205 **104** 25c. on 2½d. blue . . . . 1·25 50
206 **106** 40c. on 4d. green 60 80
207 **107** 50c. on 5d. brown . . . . 1·25 10
198 **108** 75c. on 9d. green . . . . 1·00 75
209 90c. on 9d. green . . . . 15·00 7·00
210 1f. on 10d. blue . . . . 1·00 10
211 1f.50 on 1s. brown . . . 9·50 2·25
200 **109** 3f. on 2s.6d. brown . . . 7·50 1·50
226 6f. on 5s. red . . . . . . 6·00 21·00

1935. Silver Jubilee.
212 **123** 5c. on ½d. green 15 15
213 10c. on 1d. red . . . . . 2·50 50
214 15c. on 1½d. brown . . . 35 50
215 25c. on 2½d. blue 30 25

1935. King George V.
216 **118** 5c. on ½d. green . . . . . 50 5·00
217 **119** 10c. on 1d. red 35 30
218 **118** 15c. on 1½d. brown . . . 4·75 5·50
219 **119** 25c. on 2½d. blue 30 15
220 **120** 40c. on 4d. green 30 15
221 **121** 50c. on 5d. brown 30 15
222 **122** 90c. on 9d. olive . . . . 35 1·75
223 1f. on 10d. blue 30 30
224 1f.50 on 1s. brown . . . 75 3·25

1936. King Edward VIII.
227 **124** 5c. on ½d. green 10 15
228 15c. on 1½d. brown . . . 10 15

1937. Coronation.
229 **126** 15c. on 1½d. brown . . . 30 20

1937. King George VI.
230 **128** 5c. on ½d. green . . . . . 2·25 2·25

V. TANGIER INTERNATIONAL ZONE.

This Zone was established in 1924 and the first specially overprinted stamps issued in 1927.

PRICES. Our note re U.K. usage (at beginning of Section II) also applies to **TANGIER** optd stamps.

Stamps of Great Britain optd **TANGIER**.

1927. King George V.
231 **105** ½d. green . . . . 2·75 20
232 **104** 1d. red . . . . 3·00 25

233 105 1½d. brown 5·50 3·50
234 106 2d. orange 3·25 20

1934. King George V.
235 118 ½d. green 1·25 1·60
236 119 1d. red 3·75 2·50
237 118 1½d. brown 50 20

1935. Silver Jubilee optd **TANGIER TANGIER**.
238 123 ½d. green 1·25 4·50
239 1d. red 13·50 14·00
240 1½d. brown 1·25 1·00

1936. King Edward VIII.
241 124 ½d. green 10 20
242 1d. red 10 10
243 1½d. brown 15 10

1937. Coronation optd **TANGIER TANGIER**.
244 126 1½d. brown 50 30

1937. King George VI.
245 128 ½d. green 2·25 1·25
280 ½d. orange 85 1·50
246 1d. red 6·00 1·00
281 1d. blue 1·00 3·00
247 1½d. brown 2·25 25
282 1½d. green 1·00 14·00
261 2d. orange 5·00 5·50
283 2d. brown 1·00 2·50
262 2½d. blue 1·75 5·00
284 2½d. red 1·00 5·50
263 3d. violet 70 1·25
264 129 4d. green 11·00 10·00
285 4d. blue 3·00 3·00
265 5d. brown 3·75 18·00
266 6d. purple 70 30
267 130 7d. green 1·25 12·00
268 8d. red 3·75 10·00
269 9d. olive 1·25 12·00
270 10d. blue 1·25 12·00
271 11d. plum 1·25 10·00
272 1s. brown 1·25 2·50
273 131 2s.6d. green 4·50 12·00
274 5s. red 13·00 38·00
275 – 10s. blue (No. 478a) 40·00 £100

1940. Stamp Centenary.
248 134 ½d. green 30 4·50
249 1d. red 45 50
250 1½d. brown 2·00 4·50

1946. Victory.
253 135 2½d. blue 50 50
254 3d. violet 50 1·75

1948. Silver Wedding.
255 137 2½d. blue 50 15
256 138 £1 blue 20·00 25·00

1948. Olympic Games.
257 139 2½d. blue 1·00 1·75
258 140 3d. violet 1·00 1·75
259 – 6d. purple 1·00 1·75
260 – 1s. brown 1·00 1·00

1949. U.P.U.
276 143 2½d. blue 70 2·50
277 144 3d. violet 70 1·50
278 – 6d. purple 70 1·00
279 – 1s. brown 70 3·00

1951. Pictorial stamps.
286 147 2s.6d. green 9·50 5·00
287 – 5s. red (No. 510) 15·00 17·00
288 – 10s. blue (No. 511) 20·00 17·00

1952. Queen Elizabeth II.
313 154 ½d. orange 10 30
314 1d. blue 20 40
291 1½d. green 10 30
292 2d. brown 20 60
293 155 2½d. red 10 80
294 3d. lilac 20 1·00
320 4d. blue 65 2·00
296 157 5d. brown 60 1·00
297 6d. purple 45 15
298 7d. green 80 2·75
299 158 8d. mauve 60 1·50
300 9d. olive 1·40 75
301 10d. blue 1·40 2·75
302 11d. purple 1·40 3·25
303 159 1s. brown 50 70
304 1s.3d. green 65 4·00
305 1s.6d. blue 1·00 1·75

1953. Coronation.
306 161 2½d. red 40 30
307 – 4d. blue 1·00 30
308 163 1s.3d. green 1·00 1·25
309 – 1s.6d. blue 1·00 1·00

1955. Pictorials.
310 166 2s.6d. brown 3·50 8·00
311 – 5s. red 4·50 15·00
312 – 10s. blue 16·00 21·00

1957. Cent of British Post Office in Tangier. Queen Elizabeth II stamps optd **1857-1957 TANGIER**.
323 154 ½d. orange 10 10
324 1d. blue 10 10
325 1½d. green 10 10
326 2d. brown 10 10
327 155 2½d. red 15 1·00
328 3d. lilac 15 40
329 4d. blue 30 20
330 157 5d. brown 30 35
331 6d. purple 30 35
332 7d. green 30 35
333 158 8d. mauve 30 1·00
334 9d. olive 30 30
335 10d. blue 30 30
336 11d. plum 30 30
337 159 1s. bistre 30 30
338 1s.3d. green 45 4·25
339 1s.6d. blue 50 1·60
340 166 2s.6d. brown 2·00 3·75
341 – 5s. red (No. 596a) 2·75 5·50
342 – 10s. blue (No. 597a) 3·75 7·00

MORVI Pt. 1

A state of India, Bombay district. Now uses Indian stamps.

12 pies = 1 anna.

1 Maharaja Lakhdirji

3 Maharaja Lakhdirji

1931.
8 1 3p. red 3·50 10·00
9b 6p. green 4·00 10·00
5 ½a. blue 2·50 13·00
6 1a. brown 3·25 23·00
10 1a. blue 3·25 10·00
7 2a. brown 4·00 32·00
11 2a. violet 10·00 30·00

1934.
16 3 3p. red 1·25 3·25
17 6p. green 75 2·50
14 1a. brown 1·10 10·00
19 2a. violet 2·50 16·00

MOSUL Pt.1

Stamps used by Indian forces in Mesopotamia (now Iraq) at the close of the 1914–18 war.

12 pies = 1 anna; 16 annas = 1 rupee.

1919. Turkish Fiscal stamps surch **POSTAGE I.E.F. 'D'** and value in annas.
1 ½a. on 1pi. green and red 2·25 1·90
2 1a. on 20pa. black on red 1·40 1·75
4 2½a. on 1pi. mauve and yellow 1·50 1·50
5 3a. on 20pa. green 1·60 4·00
6 3a. on 20pa. green and orange 35·00 55·00
7 4a. on 1pi. violet 3·00 3·50
8 8a. on 10pa. red 4·00 5·00

MOZAMBIQUE Pt. 9; Pt. 13; Pt. 1

Former Overseas Province of Portugal in East Africa, granted independence in 1975. The Republic of Mozambique joined the Commonwealth on 12 November 1995.

1876. 1000 reis = 1 milreis.
1913. 100 centavos = 1 escudo.
1980. 100 centavos = 1 metical.

1876. "Crown" key-type inscr "MOCAMBIQUE".
1 P 5r. black 50 40
11 10r. yellow 1·60 1·40
19 10r. green 40 30
3 20r. bistre 50 30
20 20r. red £100 75·00
4a 25r. red 25 15
21 25r. lilac 1·10 60
14 40r. blue 4·00 2·50
22 40r. buff 75 65
6 50r. green 35·00 11·00
23 50r. blue 40 30
7 100r. lilac 40 25
8 200r. orange 1·25 70
9 300r. brown 95 65

1886. "Embossed" key-type inscr "PROVINCIA DE MOCAMBIQUE".
30 Q 5r. black 50 35
32 10r. green 45 35
34 20r. red 50 35
48 25r. lilac 3·25 1·75
37 40r. brown 45 30
38 50r. blue 70 35
40 100r. brown 50 30
42 200r. violet 1·10 75
43 300r. orange 1·40 45

1893. No. 37 surch **PROVISORIO 5 5**.
53 Q 5 on 40r. brown 32·00 23·00

1894. "Figures" key-type inscr "MOCAMBIQUE".
56 R 5r. orange 30 20
57 10r. mauve 30 20
58 15r. brown 35 25
59 20r. lilac 35 20
65 25r. green 30 15
60 50r. blue 1·10 25
67 75r. pink 65 45
61 80r. green 1·10 65
62 100r. brown on buff 70 50
68 150r. red on pink 3·00 1·60
64 200r. blue on blue 1·10 90
69 300r. blue on brown 1·60 1·25

1895. "Embossed" key-type of Mozambique optd **1195 CENTENARIO ANTONINO 1895**.
71 Q 5r. black 2·25 1·60
72 10r. green 2·25 1·75
73 20r. red 2·40 2·00
74 25r. purple 2·40 2·00
75 40r. brown 2·40 2·25
76 50r. blue 2·40 2·25
77 100r. brown 2·40 2·25
78 200r. lilac 7·50 5·50
79 300r. orange 7·50 5·50

1897. No. 69 surch **50 reis**.
82 R 50r. on 300r. blue on brown 60·00 45·00

1898. Nos. 34 and 37 surch **MOCAMBIQUE** and value.
84 Q 2½r. on 20r. red 7·00 5·50
85 5r. on 40r. brown 6·00 5·50

1898. "King Carlos" key type inscr "MOCAMBIQUE". Name and value in red (500r.) or black (others).
86 S 2½r. grey 15 15
87 5r. red 15 15
88 10r. green 15 15
89 15r. brown 1·50 75
138 15r. green 50 40
90 20r. lilac 50 25
91 25r. green 50 25
139 25r. red 40 15
92 50r. blue 55 30
140 50r. brown 1·25 85
141 65r. blue 3·00 3·00
93 75r. pink 2·50 1·50
142 75r. purple 1·00 85
94 80r. mauve 2·50 1·50
95 100r. blue on blue 1·25 65
143 115r. brown on pink 3·00 2·50
144 130r. brown on yellow 3·00 2·50
96 150r. brown on yellow 2·25 1·50
97 200r. purple on pink 1·00 70
98 300r. blue on pink 2·00 1·25
145 400r. blue on cream 4·50 3·25
99 500r. black on blue 4·75 3·00
100 700r. mauve on yellow 5·50 3·50

1902. Various types surch.
146 S 50r. on 65r. blue 1·10 1·00
101 R 65r. on 10r. mauve 95 85
102 65r. on 15r. brown 95 85
105 Q 65r. on 20r. red 1·40 1·00
106 R 65r. on 20r. lilac 95 85
108 Q 65r. on 40r. brown 1·25 1·25
110 65r. on 200r. violet 1·50 1·00
111 V 115r. on 2½r. brown 95 90
113 Q 115r. on 5r. black 65 55
114 R 115r. on 5r. orange 90 75
115 115r. on 25r. green 95 85
117 Q 115r. on 50r. blue 60 50
120 130r. on 25r. mauve 70 45
121 R 130r. on 75r. red 95 90
122 130r. on 100r. brn on buff 2·25 2·25
123 130r. on 150r. red on pink 1·00 1·00
124 130r. on 200r. blue on bl 2·00 2·00
126 Q 130r. on 300r. orange 75 45
128 400r. on 10r. green 1·75 1·60
129 R 400r. on 50r. blue 60 50
130 400r. on 80r. green 60 50
132 Q 400r. on 100r. brown 12·50 8·50
133 R 400r. on 300r. bl on brn 60 50

1902. "King Carlos" key-type of Mozambique optd **PROVISORIO**.
134 S 15r. brown 75 45
135 25r. green 75 45
136 50r. blue 1·25 95
137 75r. pink 2·10 1·25

1911. "King Carlos" key-type of Mozambique optd **REPUBLICA**.
147 S 2½r. grey 10 15
148 5r. orange 15 15
149 10r. green 40 25
150 15r. green 15 10
151 20r. lilac 40 20
152 25r. red 15 10
153 50r. brown 15 15
154 75r. purple 30 25
155 100r. blue on blue 30 25
156 115r. brown on pink 40 30
157 130r. brown on yellow 40 30
158 200r. purple on pink 75 50
159 400r. blue on yellow 70 45
160 500r. black on blue 70 45
161 700r. mauve on yellow 70 45

1912. "King Manoel" key-type inscr "MOCAMBIQUE" with opt **REPUBLICA**.
162 T 2½r. lilac 15 10
163 5r. black 15 10
164 10r. green 15 10
165 20r. red 35 25
166 25r. brown 15 10
167 50r. blue 20 15
168 75r. brown 20 15
169 100r. brown on green 20 15
170 200r. green on orange 45 40
171 300r. black on blue 45 40
172 500r. brown and green 90 80

1913. Surch **REPUBLICA MOCAMBIQUE** and value on "Vasco da Gama" issues. (a) Portuguese Colonies.
173 ¼c. on 2½r. green 45 30
174 ½c. on 5r. red 40 30
175 1c. on 10r. purple 35 30
176 2½c. on 25r. green 35 30
177 5c. on 50r. blue 40 30
178 7½c. on 75r. brown 70 55
179 10c. on 100r. brown 50 45
180 15c. on 150r. brown 45 40

(b) Macao.
181 ¼c. on ½a. green 60 50
182 ½c. on 1a. red 55 50
183 1c. on 2a. purple 55 45
184 2½c. on 4a. green 55 45
185 5c. on 8a. blue 1·50 1·25
186 7½c. on 12a. brown 85 75
187 10c. on 16a. brown 60 50
188 15c. on 24a. brown 55 45

(c) Timor.
189 ¼c. on ½a. green 60 50
190 ½c. on 1a. red 60 50
191 1c. on 2a. purple 55 45
192 2½c. on 4a. green 55 45
193 5c. on 8a. blue 90 70
194 7½c. on 12a. brown 65 50
195 10c. on 16a. brown 50 45
196 15c. on 24a. brown 45 35

1914. "Ceres" key-type inscr "MOCAMBIQUE".
197 U ¼c. green 10 10
198 ½c. black 10 10
199 1c. green 10 10
200 1½c. brown 10 10
201 2c. red 10 10
270 2c. grey 10 10
202 2½c. violet 10 10
255 3c. orange 10 10
256 4c. pink 10 10
257 4½c. grey 10 10
203 5c. blue 10 10
275 6c. mauve 10 10
259 7c. blue 10 10
260 7½c. brown 10 10
278 8c. grey 10 10
279 10c. red 10 10
280 12c. brown 10 10
281 12c. green 10 10
283 15c. purple 10 10
284 20c. green 15 15
285 24c. blue 15 15
286 25c. brown 20 20
209 30c. brown on green 70 50
287 30c. green 15 15
295 30c. lilac on pink 70 55
210 40c. brown on pink 75 60
288 40c. turquoise 40 15
211 50c. orange on orange 1·40 1·10
289 50c. mauve 15 10
297 60c. brown on pink 70 55
290 60c. blue 45 25
291 60c. pink 45 25
298 80c. brown on blue 65 45
293 80c. red 45 25
299 1e. green on blue 1·10 65
264 1e. pink 50 40
301 1e. blue 70 45
300 2e. mauve on pink 80 50
302 2e. purple 40 30
303 5e. brown 4·50 1·90
304 10e. pink 6·75 2·50
305 20e. green 18·00 8·25

1915. Provisional issues of 1902 optd **REPUBLICA**.
226 S 50r. blue (No. 136) 30 20
227 50r. on 65r. blue 30 25
213 75r. pink (No. 137) 70 40
228 V 115r. on 2½r. brown 30 25
216 Q 115r. on 5r. black 9·00 8·50
229 R 115r. on 5r. orange 30 25
230 115r. on 25r. green 30 25
231 130r. on 75r. red 30 25
220 130r. on 100r. brown on buff 55 45
232 130r. on 150r. red on pink 30 25
233 130r. on 200r. blue on bl 30 25
223 400r. on 50r. blue 65 60
224 400r. on 80r. green 65 60
225 400r. on 300r. blue on brn 65 60

1918. Charity Tax stamp surch **2½ CENTAVOS**. Roul or perf.
248 C 16 2½c. on 5c. red 40 25

1920. Charity Tax stamps surch. (a) **CORREIOS** and value in figures.
306 C 15 1c. on 1c. green 30 30
307 C 16 1½c. on 5c. red 30 25

(b) **SEIS CENTAVOS**.
308 C 16 6c. on 5c. red 40 30

1921. "Ceres" stamps of 1913 surch.
309 U 10c. on ¼c. black 70 60
310 30c. on 1½c. brown 70 60
316 50c. on 4c. pink 55 35
311 60c. on 2½c. violet 90 70
328 70c. on 2e. purple 30 20
329 1e.40 on 2e. purple 35 20

1922. "Ceres" key-type of Lourenco Marques surch.
312 U 10c. on ¼c. black 50 45
314 30c. on 1½c. brown 50 45

1922. Charity Tax stamp surch **2$00**.
315 C 16 $2 on 5c. red 60 35

1924. 4th Death Centenary of Vasco da Gama. "Ceres" key-type of Mozambique optd **Vasco da Gama 1924**.
317 U 80c. pink 50 35

1925. Nos. 129 and 130 surch **Republica 40 C.**
318 R 40c. on 400r. on 50r. 35 25
319 40c. on 400r. on 80r. 35 30

1929. "Due" key-type inscr "MOCAMBIQUE" optd **CORREIOS**.
320 W 50c. lilac 55 45

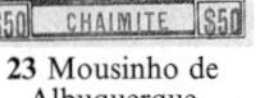

23 Mousinho de Albuquerque

25 "Portugal" and Camoens' "The Lusiads"

1930. Albuquerque's Victories Commemorative. Vignette in grey.
321 **23** 50c. lake and red (Macontene) . . . . . . 2·75 2·50
322 50c. orge & red (Mujenga) 2·75 2·50
323 50c. mve & brn (Coolela) 2·25 1·90
324 50c. grey and green (Chaimite) . . . . . . 2·75 2·50
325 50c. bl & ind (Ibrahimo) 2·25 1·90
326 50c. blue and black (Mucuto-muno) . . . . 2·25 1·90
327 50c. vio & lilac (Naguema) 2·25 1·90
The above were for compulsory use throughout Mozambique in place of ordinary postage stamps on certain days in 1930 and 1931. They are not listed among the Charity Tax stamps as the revenue was not applied to any charitable fund.

1938. Value in red (1, 15c., 1e.40) or black (others).
330 **25** 1c. brown 10 10
331 5c. brown 10 10
332 10c. purple 10 10
333 15c. black 10 10
334 20c. grey 10 10
335 30c. green 10 10
336 35c. green . . . . 2·50 1·40
337 40c. red 10 10
338 45c. blue 20 20
339 50c. brown 15 10
340 60c. green 20 15
341 70c. brown 20 15
342 80c. green 20 15
343 85c. red 55 40
344 1e. purple 25 15
345 1e.40 blue . . . . 3·75 1·25
346 1e.75 blue . . . . 2·40 1·10
347 2e. lilac 65 25
348 5e. green . . . . 1·25 30
349 10e. brown . . . . 2·75 50
350 20e. orange . . . . 12·50 80

1938. As 1938 issue of Macao. Name and value in black.
351 **54** 1c. green (postage) 10 10
352 5c. brown 10 10
353 10c. red 10 10
354 15c. purple 10 10
355 20c. grey 10 10
356 – 30c. purple 15 10
357 – 35c. green 20 15
358 – 40c. brown 20 15
359 – 50c. mauve 20 10
360 – 60c. black 20 10
361 – 70c. violet 25 15
362 – 80c. orange 25 15
363 – 1e. red 30 15
364 – 1e.75 blue 90 30
365 – 2e. red 90 30
366 – 5e. green . . . . 2·25 30
367 – 10e. blue . . . . 4·50 60
368 – 20e. brown . . . . 11·00 1·00
369 **56** 10c. red (air) 10 10
370 20c. violet 10 10
371 50c. orange 15 10
372 1e. blue 20 10
373 2e. red 40 15
374 3e. green 60 20
375 5e. brown . . . . 1·00 35
376 9e. red . . . . 1·90 45
377 10e. mauve . . . . 3·00 60
DESIGNS: 30 to 50c. Mousinho de Albuquerque; 60c. to 1e. Dam; 1e.75 to 5e. Henry the Navigator; 10, 20e. Afonso de Albuquerque.

1938. No. 338 surch **40 centavos**.
378 **25** 40c. on 45c. blue . . . . . 1·75 1·50

26a Route of President's Tour

27 New Cathedral, Lourenco Marques

1938. President Carmona's 2nd Colonial Tour.
379 **26a** 80c. violet on mauve . . . 3·25 1·40
380 1e.75 blue on blue . . . . 10·00 3·50
381 3e. green on green . . . . 15·00 6·50
382 20e. brown on cream . . 70·00 30·00

1944. 400th Anniv of Lourenco Marques.
383 **27** 50c. brown . . . . 1·60 60
384 – 50c. green . . . . 1·60 60
385 – 1e.75 blue . . . . 11·00 2·10
386a – 20e. black . . . . 6·75 60
DESIGNS—HORIZ: 1e.75, Lourenco Marques Central Railway Station; 20e. Town Hall, Lourenco Marques.
See also No. 405.

1946. Nos. 354, 364 and 375 surch.
387 10c. on 15c. purple (postage) 40 30
388 60c. on 1e.75 blue 60 35
389 3e. on 5e. brown (air) . . . . 4·00 1·75

1947. No. 386a surch.
390 2e. on 20e. black . . . . . . 1·25 1·10

30 Lockheed L.18 Lodestar

1946. Air. Values in black.
391 **30** 1e.20 red . . . . 1·00 65
392 1e.60 blue . . . . 1·50 80
393 1e.70 purple . . . . 2·10 1·20
394 2e.90 brown . . . . 3·75 1·40
395 3e. green . . . . 2·75 1·60

1947. Air. Optd **Taxe percue**. Values in red (50c.) or black (others).
397 **30** 50c. black 40 30
398 1e. pink 50 30
399 3e. green 80 40
400 4e.50 green . . . . 1·40 55
401 5e. red . . . . 2·00 80
402 10e. blue . . . . 5·50 1·90
403 20e. violet . . . . 13·50 5·25
404 50e. orange . . . . 30·00 12·00

1948. As T **27** but without commemorative inscr.
405 4e.50 red . . . . 1·25 40

31 Antonio Enes

33 Lourenco Marques

1948. Birth Centenary of Antonio Enes.
406 **31** 50c. black and cream . . . 1·00 20
407 5e. purple and cream . . . 4·25 80

1948.
408 – 5c. brown 55 15
409 – 10c. purple . . . . 1·10 15
410 – 20c. brown 55 15
411 – 30c. purple 55 15
412 – 40c. green 55 15
413 **33** 50c. grey 55 15
414 – 60c. purple 70 15
415 **33** 80c. violet 55 15
416 – 1e. red 75 15
417 – 1e.20 grey . . . . 4·50 45
418 – 1e.50 violet 75 20
419 – 1e.75 blue . . . . 2·10 25
420 – 2e. brown . . . . 1·25 15
421 – 2e.50 blue . . . . 4·75 20
422 – 3e. green . . . . 2·00 20
423 – 3e.50 green . . . . 3·50 20
424 – 5e. green . . . . 3·00 20
425 – 10e. brown . . . . 7·25 35
426 – 15e. red . . . . 18·00 1·50
427 – 20e. orange . . . . 32·00 1·75
DESIGNS—VERT: 5, 30c. Gogogo Peak; 20, 40c. Zumbo River; 60c., 3e.50, Nhanhangare Waterfall. HORIZ: 10c., 1e.20, Railway bridge over River Zambesi at Sena; 1, 5e. Gathering coconuts; 1e.50, 2e. River Pungue at Beira; 1e.75, 3e. Polana beach, Lourenco Marques; 2e.50, 10e. Bird's eye view of Lourenco Marques; 15, 20e. Malema River.

1949. Honouring the Statue of Our Lady of Fatima. As T **62** of Macao.
428 50c. blue . . . . 5·25 90
429 1e.20 mauve . . . . 10·50 1·75
430 4e.50 green . . . . 40·00 6·25
431 20e. brown . . . . 75·00 9·25

35 Aircraft and Globe

36 Clown Triggerfish

1949. Air.
432 **35** 50c. brown 55 25
433 1e.20 violet . . . . 1·10 50
434 4e.50 blue . . . . 2·50 90
435 5e. green . . . . 4·50 1·10
436 20e. brown . . . . 13·00 2·50

1949. 75th Anniv of U.P.U. As T **64** of Macao.
437 4e.50 blue . . . . 1·50 60

1950. Holy Year. As Nos. 425/6 of Macao.
438 1e.50 orange 65 30
439 3e. blue 90 45

1951. Fishes. Multicoloured.
440 5c. Type **36** 35 15
441 10c. Thread-finned butterflyfish 25 15
442 15c. Racoon butterflyfish . . 85 25
443 20c. Lionfish 35 15
444 30c. Pearl puffer 35 15
445 40c. Golden filefish 25 15
446 50c. Spot-cheeked surgeonfish 25 15
447 1e. Pennant coralfish (vert) 35 15
448 1e.50 Seagrass wrasse . . . 35 15
449 2e. Sombre sweetlips . . . 35 15
450 2e.50 Blue-striped snapper . . 1·00 20
451 3e. Convict tang . . . . . 1·00 20
452 3e.50 Starry triggerfish . . . 1·10 15
453 4e. Cornetfish . . . . . . 1·75 25
454 4e.50 Vagabond butterflyfish 2·50 20
455 5e. Sail-backed mailcheek . . 2·50 15
456 6e. Dusky batfish (vert) . . . 2·50 15
457 8e. Moorish idol (vert) . . . 4·25 35
458 9e. Triangulate boxfish . . . 4·25 30
459 10e. Eastern flying gurnard 10·50 1·50
460 15e. Red-toothed triggerfish 70·00 10·50
461 20e. Picasso triggerfish . . . 35·00 4·50
462 30e. Long-horned cowfish . . 42·00 6·50
463 50e. Spotted cowfish . . . . 65·00 14·00

1951. Termination of Holy Year. As T **69** of Macao.
464 5e. red and orange . . . . . 1·90 90

37 Victor Cordon (colonist)

39 Liner and Lockheed Constellation Airliner

1951. Birth Centenary of Cordon.
465 **37** 1e. brown and light brown 1·25 30
466 5e. black and blue . . . . 6·00 85

1952. 1st Tropical Medicine Congress, Lisbon. As T **71** of Macao.
467 3e. orange and blue . . . . 1·25 35
DESIGN: 3e. Miguela Bombarda Hospital.

1952. 4th African Tourist Congress.
468 **39** 1e.50 multicoloured . . . . 1·25 35

40 Missionary

41 Citrus Butterfly

1953. Missionary Art Exhibition.
469 **40** 10c. red and lilac 10 10
470 1e. red and green 70 20
471 5e. black and blue . . . . 1·40 40

1953. Butterflies and Moths. Multicoloured.
472 10c. Type **41** 10 10
473 15c. "Amphicallia thelwalli" 10 10
474 20c. Forest queen 10 10
475 30c. Western scarlet 10 10
476 40c. Black-barred red-tip . . 10 10
477 50c. Mocker swallowtail . . . 10 10
478 80c. "Nudaurelia hersilia dido" 15 15
479 1e. African moon moth . . . 15 10
480 1e.50 Large striped swallowtail 15 10
481 2e. "Athletes ethica" . . . . 4·50 30
482 2e.30 African monarch . . . 3·00 25
483 2e.50 Green swallowtail . . . 7·50 25
484 3e. "Arniocera ericata" . . . 95 10
485 4e. Apollo moth 50 10
486 4e.50 Peach moth 50 10
487 5e. "Metarctica lateritia" . . 50 10
488 6e. "Xanthospilopteryx mozambica" 55 15
489 7e.50 White bear . . . . . . 3·00 30
490 10e. Flame-coloured charaxes 7·50 1·00
491 20e. Fervid tiger moth . . . 11·00 1·00

42 Stamps

43 Map of Mozambique

1953. Philatelic Exhibition, Lourenco Marques.
492 **42** 1e. multicoloured . . . . . 1·25 30
493 3e. multicoloured . . . . . 3·25 1·10

1953. Portuguese Postage Stamp Centenary. As T **75** of Macao.
494 50c. multicoloured 50 35

1954. 4th Centenary of Sao Paulo. As T **76** of Macao.
495 3e.50 multicoloured 30 20

1954. Multicoloured map; Mozambique territory in colours given.
496 **43** 10c. lilac 10 10
497 20c. yellow 10 10
498 50c. blue 10 10
499 1e. yellow 10 10
500 2e.30 white 65 35
501 4e. orange 65 25
502 10e. green . . . . 1·90 25
503 20e. brown . . . . 2·75 35

44 Arms of Beira

45 Mousinho de Albuquerque

1954. 1st Philatelic Exhibition, Manica and Sofala.
504 **44** 1e.50 multicoloured 35 20
505 3e.50 multicoloured 90 35

1955. Birth Centenary of M. de Albuquerque.
506 **45** 2e. brown and grey 50 30
507 – 2e.50 multicoloured . . . . 1·10 55
DESIGN: 2e.50, Equestrian statue of Albuquerque.

46 Arms and Inhabitants

47 Beira

1956. Visit of President to Mozambique. Multicoloured. Background in colours given.
508 **46** 1e. cream 25 15
509 2e.50 blue 65 30

1957. 50th Anniv of Beira.
510 **47** 2e.50 multicoloured 65 25

1958. 6th International Congress of Tropical Medicine. As T **79** of Macao.
511 1e.50 multicoloured . . . . . 1·25 70
DESIGN: 1e.50, "Strophanthus grandiflorus" (plant).

1958. Brussels International Exn. As T **78** of Macao.
512 3e.50 multicoloured 25 15

48 Caravel

49 "Arts and Crafts"

1960. 500th Death Anniv of Prince Henry the Navigator.
513 **48** 5e. multicoloured 45 20

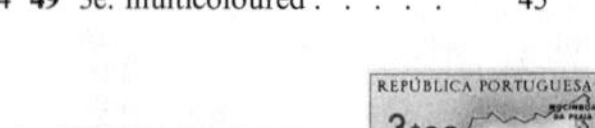

1960. 10th Anniv of African Technical Co-operation Commission.
514 **49** 3e. multicoloured 45 20

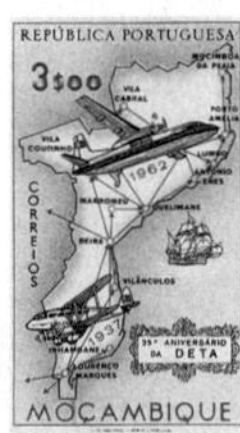

50 Arms of Lourenco Marques

51 Fokker F.27 Friendship and De Havilland D.H.89 Dragon Rapide over Route Map

1961. Arms. Multicoloured.
515 5c. Type **50** 15 10
516 15c. Chibuto 15 10
517 20c. Nampula 15 10
518 30c. Inhambane 15 10

519 50c. Mozambique (city) . . . 15 10
520 1e. Matola 30 15
521 1e.50 Quelimane 30 15
522 2e. Mocuba 50 15
523 2e.50 Antonio Enes . . . . . 1·10 15
524 3e. Cabral 50 15
525 4e. Manica 50 20
526 4e.50 Pery 50 15
527 5e. St. Tiago de Tete 60 20
528 7e.50 Porto Amelia 80 35
529 10e. Chinde . . . . 1·40 35
530 20e. Joao Belo . . . . . . 2·75 50
531 50e. Beira . . . . 4·50 1·25

1962. Sports. As T **82** of Macao. Multicoloured.
532 50c. Water-skiing 10 10
533 1e. Wrestling 75 20
534 1e.50 Gymnastics 35 15
535 2e.50 Hockey 60 15
536 4e.50 Netball 90 40
537 15e. Outboard speedboat racing . . . . 1·60 90

1962. Malaria Eradication. Mosquito design as T **83** of Macao. Multicoloured.
538 2e.50 "Anopheles funestus" 50 30

1962. 25th Anniv of D.E.T.A. (Mozambique Airline).
539 **51** 3e. multicoloured 45 20

52 Lourenco Marques in 1887 and 1962

53 Oil Refinery, Sonarep

1962. 75th Anniv of Lourenco Marques.
540 **52** 1e. multicoloured 40 20

1962. Air. Multicoloured.
541 1e.50 Type **53** 50 10
542 2e. Salazar Academy 30 10
543 3e.50 Aerial view of Lourenco Marques Port . . 40 15
544 4e.50 Salazar Barrage 35 15
545 5e. Trigo de Morais Bridge and Dam 40 15
546 20e. Marcelo Caetano Bridge and Dam . . . . 1·10 50
Each design includes an airplane in flight.

54 Arms of Mozambique and Statue of Vasco da Gama

55 Nef, 1430

1963. Bicentenary of City of Mozambique.
547 **54** 3e. multicoloured 35 20

1963. 10th Anniv of T.A.P. Airline. As T **52** of Portuguese Guinea.
548 2e.50 multicoloured 35 15

1963. Evolution of Sailing Ships. Multicoloured.
549 10c. Type **55** 10 10
550 20c. Caravel, 1436 (vert) . . 10 10
551 30c. Lateen-rigged caravel, 1460 (vert) 15 10
552 50c. Vasco da Gama's ship "Sao Gabriel", 1497 (vert) 30 10
553 1e. Don Manuel's nau, 1498 (vert) 55 10
554 1e.50 Galleon, 1530 (vert) . . 40 15
555 2e. Nau "Flor de la Mer", 1511 (vert) 40 15
556 2e.50 Caravel "Redonda", 1519 . . . . 45 15
557 3e.50 Nau, 1520 (vert) . . . 45 15
558 4e. Portuguese Indies galley, 1521 . . . . 50 20
559 4e.50 Galleon "Santa Tereza", 1639 (vert) . . . 50 20
560 5e. Nau "N. Senhora da Conceicao", 1716 (vert) . . 10·00 30
561 6e. Warship "N. Senhora do Bom Sucesso", 1764 . . . 80 25
562 7e.50 Bomb launch, 1788 . . 90 35
563 8e. Naval brigantine "Lebre", 1793 . . . . 90 35
564 10e. Corvette "Andorinha", 1799 . . . . 95 35
565 12e.50 Naval schooner "Maria Teresa", 1820 . . . 1·25 60
566 15e. Warship "Vasco da Gama", 1841 . . . . . . 1·60 60
567 20e. Sail frigate "Don Fernando II e Gloria", 1843 (vert) . . . . 2·00 75
568 30e. Cadet barque "Sagres I", 1924 (vert) . . . . 3·50 1·25

1964. Centenary of National Overseas Bank. As T **84** of Macao but view of Bank building, Lourenco Marques.
569 1e.50 multicoloured 20 15

56 Pres. Tomas

57 State Barge of Joao V, 1728

1964. Presidential Visit.
570 **56** 2e.50 multicoloured 15 10

1964. Portuguese Marine, 18th and 19th Centuries. Multicoloured.
571 15c. Type **57** 10 10
572 35c. State barge of Jose I, 1753 . . . . 10 10
573 1e. Barge of Alfandega, 1768 35 10
574 1e.50 Oarsman of 1780 (vert) 30 15
575 2e.50 State barge "Pinto da Fonseca", 1780 . . . . . 20 10
576 5e. State barge of Carlota Joaquina, 1790 . . . . . 25 20
577 9e. Don Miguel's state barge, 1831 . . . . 60 40

1965. I.T.U. Centenary. As T **85** of Macao.
578 1e. multicoloured 30 20

1966. 40th Anniv of Portuguese National Revolution. As T **86** of Macao, but showing different building. Multicoloured.
579 1e. Beira railway station and Antonio Enes Academy . . 85 50

58 Arquebusier, 1560

59 Luis de Camoens (poet)

1967. Portuguese Military Uniforms. Mult.
580 20c. Type **58** 10 10
581 30c. Arquebusier, 1640 . . . 10 10
582 40c. Infantryman, 1777 . . . 15 10
583 50c. Infantry officer, 1777 . . 15 10
584 80c. Drummer, 1777 . . . . 35 20
585 1e. Infantry sergeant, 1777 30 10
586 2e. Infantry major, 1784 . . 30 15
587 2e.50 Colonial officer, 1788 40 15
588 3e. Infantryman, 1789 . . . 40 20
589 5e. Colonial bugler, 1801 . . 50 30
590 10e. Colonial officer, 1807 . . 70 30
591 15e. Infantryman, 1817 . . . 85 55

1967. Centenary of Military Naval Association. As T **88** of Macao. Multicoloured.
592 3e. A. Coutinho and paddle-gunboat "Tete" 35 15
593 10e. J. Roby and paddle-gunboat "Granada" . . . 65 35

1967. 50th Anniv of Fatima Apparitions. As T **89** of Macao.
594 50c. "Golden Crown" . . . 15 10

1968. 500th Birth Anniv of Pedro Cabral (explorer). As T **90** of Macao.
595 1e. Erecting the Cross at Porto Sequro (horiz) . . . 10 10
596 1e.50 First mission service in Brazil (horiz) 20 10
597 3e. Church of Grace, Santarem 40 15

1969. Birth Centenary of Admiral Gago Coutinho. As T **91** of Macao.
598 70c. Admiral Gago Coutinho Airport, Lourenco Marques (horiz) 25 10

1969. 400th Anniv of Camoens' Visit to Mozambique. Multicoloured.
599 15c. Type **59** 10 10
600 50c. Nau of 1553 (horiz) . . 15 10
601 1e.50 Map of Mozambique, 1554 . . . . 20 15
602 2e.50 Chapel of Our Lady of Baluarte (horiz) 25 20
603 5e. Part of the "Lusiad" (poem) 40 30

1969. 500th Birth Anniv of Vasco da Gama (explorer). As T **92** of Macao. Multicoloured.
604 1e. Route map of Da Gama's Voyage to India (horiz) . . 15 10

1969. Centenary of Overseas Administrative Reforms. As T **93** of Macao.
605 1e.50 multicoloured 15 10

1969. 500th Birth Anniv of King Manoel I. As T **95** of Macao. Multicoloured.
606 80c. Illuminated arms (horiz) 15 10

1970. Birth Centenary of Marshal Carmona. As T **96** of Macao. Multicoloured.
607 5e. Portrait in ceremonial dress 25 15

60 Fossilized Fern

1971. Rocks, Minerals and Fossils. Mult.
608 15c. Type **60** 15 10
609 50c. "Lytodiscoides conduciensis" (fossilized snail) 20 10
610 1e. Stibnite 20 10
611 1e.50 Pink beryl 20 10
612 2e. Endothiodon and fossil skeleton 25 10
613 3e. Tantalocolumbite 30 10
614 3e.50 Verdelite 40 15
615 4e. Zircon 50 30
616 10e. Petrified tree-stump . . . 1·25 65

1972. 400th Anniv of Camoens' "The Lusiads" (epic poem). As T **98** of Macao. Multicoloured.
617 4e. Mozambique Island in 16th century . . . . 1·25 30

1972. Olympic Games, Munich. As T **99** of Macao. Multicoloured.
618 3e. Hurdling and swimming 15 10

1972. 50th Anniv of 1st Flight, Lisbon–Rio de Janeiro. As T **100** of Macao. Multicoloured.
619 1e. Fairey IIID seaplane "Santa Cruz" at Recife . . 15 10

61 Racing Dinghies

1973. World Championships for "Vauriens" Class Yachts, Lourenco Marques.
620 **61** 1e. multicoloured 15 10
621 – 1e.50 multicoloured 15 10
622 – 3e. multicoloured 30 20
DESIGNS: Nos. 621/2 similar to Type **61**.

1973. Centenary of I.M.O./W.M.O. As T **102** of Macao.
623 2e. multicoloured 20 20

62 Dish Aerials

1974. Inauguration of Satellite Communications Station Network.
624 **62** 50c. multicoloured 20 20

63 Bird with "Flag" Wings

1975. Implementation of Lusaka Agreement.
625 **63** 1c. multicoloured 10 10
626 1e.50 multicoloured 10 10
627 2e. multicoloured 15 10
628 3e.50 multicoloured 25 15
629 6e. multicoloured 65 30

1975. Independence. Optd **INDEPENDENCIA 25 JUN 75**.
631 **43** 10c. multicoloured (postage) 50 50
632 – 40c. mult (No. 476) 10 10
633 **62** 50c. multicoloured 20 15
634 **61** 1e. multicoloured 30 25
635 – 1e.50 mult (No. 621) 85 75
636 – 2e. multicoloured (No. 623) 2·40 2·40
637 – 2e.50 mult (No. 535) 35 30
638 – 3e. multicoloured (No. 618) 40 35
639 – 3e. multicoloured (No. 622) 45 40
640 – 3e.50 mult (No. 614) . . . 2·40 2·40
641 – 4e.50 mult (No. 536) . . . 2·75 1·50
642 – 7e.50 mult (No. 489) . . . 80 30
643 – 10e. mult (No. 616) . . . . 1·40 35
644 – 15e. mult (No. 537) . . . . 1·75 1·50
645 **43** 20e. multicoloured . . . . 4·75 4·25
646 – 3e.50 multicoloured (No. 543) (air) 35 25
647 – 4e.50 mult (No. 544) . . . 40 25
648 – 5e. multicoloured (No. 545) 1·25 50
649 – 20e. mult (No. 546) . . . . 2·00 4·25

66 Workers, Farmers and Children

67 Farm Worker

1975. "Vigilance, Unity, Work". Multicoloured.
650 20c. Type **66** 10 10
651 30c. Type **66** 10 10
652 50c. Type **66** 10 10
653 2e.50 Type **66** 15 10
654 4e.50 Armed family, workers and dancers 25 15
655 5e. As No. 654 . . . . . . 35 15
656 10e. As No. 654 . . . . . . 95 30
657 50e. As No. 654 . . . . . . 4·25 2·10

1976. Women's Day.
659 **67** 1e. black and green 10 10
660 – 1e.50 black and brown . . 10 10
661 – 2e.50 black and blue . . . 15 10
662 – 10e. black and red 90 40
DESIGNS: 1e.50, Teaching; 2e.50, Nurse; 10e. Mother.

1976. Pres. Kaunda's First Visit to Mozambique. Optd **PRESIDENTE KENNETH KAUNDA PREMEIRA VISITA 20/4/1976**.
663 **63** 2e. multicoloured 15 10
664 3e.50 multicoloured 25 15
665 6e. multicoloured 50 30

69 Arrival of President Machel

70 Mozambique Stamp of 1876 and Emblem

1976. 1st Anniv of Independence. Mult.
666 50c. Type **69** 10 10
667 1e. Proclamation ceremony 10 10
668 2e.50 Signing ceremony . . . 15 10
669 7e.50 Soldiers on parade . . 40 20
670 20e. Independence flame . . 1·50 1·10

1976. Stamp Centenary.
671 **70** 1e.50 multicoloured 10 10
672 6e. multicoloured 30 20

1976. "FACIM" Industrial Fair. Optd **FACIM 1976**.
673 **66** 2e.50 multicoloured 30 15

72 Weapons and Flag

73 Thick-tailed Bush baby

1976. Army Day.
674 **72** 3e. multicoloured 20 10

1977. Animals. Multicoloured.
675 50c. Type **73** 15 10
676 1e. Ratel (horiz) 15 10
677 1e.50 Temminck's ground pangolin 20 10
678 2e. Steenbok (horiz) 20 10
679 2e.50 Diademed monkey . . 25 10
680 3e. Hunting dog (horiz) . . . 25 10

681 4e. Cheetah (horiz) 35 10
682 5e. Spotted hyena 50 15
683 7e.50 Warthog (horiz) . . . 1·00 25
684 8e. Hippopotamus (horiz) . . 1·10 30
685 10e. White rhinoceros (horiz) 1·10 30
686 15e. Sable antelope . . . . . 1·60 65

74 Congress Emblem

75 "Women" (child's drawing)

1977. 3rd Frelimo Congress, Maputo. Mult.
687 3e. Type **74** 15 10
688 3e.50 Macheje Monument (site of 2nd Congress) (34 × 24 mm) 20 10
689 20e. Maputo Monument (23 × 34 mm) . . . . . . 1·40 50

1977. Mozambique Women's Day.
690 **75** 5e. multicoloured 25 10
691 15e. multicoloured 65 25

76 Labourer and Farmer

77 Crowd with Arms and Crops

1977. Labour Day.
692 **76** 5e. multicoloured 25 10

1977. 2nd Anniv of Independence.
693 **77** 50c. multicoloured 10 10
694 1e.50 multicoloured 10 10
695 3e. multicoloured 15 10
696 15e. multicoloured 60 25

78 "Encephalartos ferox"

79 "Chariesthes bella"

1978. Stamp Day. Nature Protection. Mult.
697 1e. Type **78** 10 10
698 10e. Nyala 50 20

1978. Beetles. Multicoloured.
699 50c. Type **79** 10 10
700 1e. "Tragocephalus variegata" 10 10
701 1e.50 "Monochamus leuconotus" 10 10
702 3e. "Prosopocera lactator" 25 10
703 5e. "Dinocephalus ornatus" 40 10
704 10e. "Tragiscoschema nigroscriptus" 60 20

80 Violet-crested Turaco

81 Mother and Child

1978. Birds. Multicoloured.
705 50c. Type **80** 35 15
706 1e. Lilac-breasted roller . . . 45 15
707 1e.50 Red-headed weaver . . 45 15
708 2e.50 Violet starling 50 25
709 3e. Peters's twin-spot . . . . 1·00 35
710 15e. European bee eater . . . 2·50 70

1978. Global Eradication of Smallpox.
711 **81** 15e. multicoloured 45 25

82 "Crinum delagoense"

83 First Stamps of Mozambique and Canada

1978. Flowers. Multicoloured.
712 50c. Type **82** 10 10
713 1e. "Gloriosa superba" . . . 10 10
714 1e.50 "Eulophia speciosa" . . 10 10
715 3e. "Erithrina humeana" . . 15 10
716 5e. "Astripomoea malvacea" 80 15
717 10e. "Kigelia africana" . . . 1·00 60

1978. "CAPEX '78" International Stamp Exhibition, Toronto.
718 **83** 15e. multicoloured 45 25

84 Mozambique Flag

85 Boy with Books

1978. 3rd Anniv of Independence. Multicoloured.
719 1e. Type **84** 10 10
720 1e.50 Coat of Arms 10 10
721 7e.50 People and Constitution 25 15
722 10e. Band and National Anthem 30 20

1978. 11th World Youth Festival, Havana. Mult.
724 2e.50 Type **85** 10 10
725 3e. Soldiers 15 10
726 7e.50 Harvesting wheat . . . 25 20

86 Czechoslovakian 50h. Stamp, 1919

1978. "PRAGA '78" International Stamp Exhibition.
727 **86** 15e. blue, ochre and red . . 45 30

87 Football

1978. Stamp Day. Sports. Multicoloured.
729 50c. Type **87** 10 10
730 1e.50 Putting the shot 10 10
731 3e. Hurdling 15 10
732 7e.50 Basketball 35 20
733 12e.50 Swimming 45 35
734 25e. Roller-skate hockey . . 1·25 60

88 U.P.U. Emblem and Dove

1979. Membership of U.P.U.
735 **88** 20e. multicoloured . . . . 1·00 45

89 Eduardo Mondlane

1979. 10th Death Anniv of Eduardo Mondlane (founder of FRELIMO). Multicoloured.
736 1e. Soldier handing gourd to woman 10 10
737 3e. FRELIMO soldiers . . . 15 10
738 7e.50 Children learning to write 30 20
739 12e.50 Type **89** 40 30

90 Shaded Silver

91 I.Y.C. Emblem

1979. Domestic Cats. Multicoloured.
740 50c. Type **90** 10 10
741 1e.50 Manx cat 10 10
742 2e.50 British blue 15 10
743 3e. Turkish cat 20 10
744 12e.50 Long-haired tabby . . 85 55
745 20e. African wild cat . . . . 1·50 90

1979. Obligatory Tax. International Year of the Child.
746 **91** 50c. red 15 10

92 Wrestling

1979. Olympic Games, Moscow (1980). Mult.
747 1e. Type **92** 10 10
748 2e. Running 10 10
749 3e. Horse jumping 15 10
750 5e. Canoeing 15 10
751 10e. High jump 30 20
752 15e. Archery 50 40

93 Flowers

1979. International Year of the Child. Mult.
754 50c. Type **93** 10 10
755 1e.50 Dancers 10 10
756 3e. In the city 15 10
757 5e. Working in the country 15 10
758 7e.50 Houses 25 15
759 12e.50 Transport . . . . . . 1·50 50

94 Flight from Colonialism

1979. 4th Anniv of Independence. Multicoloured.
760 50c. Type **94** 10 10
761 2e. Eduardo Mondlane (founder of FRELIMO) . . 10 10
762 3e. Armed struggle, death of Mondlane 15 10
763 7e.50 Final fight for liberation 25 15
764 15e. President Samora Machel proclaims victory 45 35

95 Golden Scorpionfish

1979. Tropical Fish. Multicoloured.
766 50c. Type **95** 10 10
767 1e.50 Golden trevally 15 10
768 2e.50 Brick goby 20 10
769 3e. Clown surgeonfish . . . 25 15
770 10e. Lace goby 60 25
771 12e.50 Yellow-edged lyretail 95 40

96 Quartz

1979. Minerals. Multicoloured.
772 1e. Type **96** 10 10
773 1e.50 Beryl 10 10
774 2e.50 Magnetite 15 10
775 5e. Tourmaline 30 10
776 10e. Euxenite 60 20
777 20e. Fluorite . . . . 1·40 45

97 Soldier handing out Guns

1979. 15th Anniv of Fight for Independence.
778 **97** 5e. multicoloured 25 15

98 Locomotive No. 1, 1914

1979. Early Locomotives. Multicoloured.
779 50c. Type **98** 15 10
780 1e.50 Gaza Railway locomotive No. 1, 1898 . . 20 10
781 3e. Cape Government Railway 1st Class locomotive, 1878 . . . . . 45 10
782 7e.50 Delagoa Bay Railway locomotive No. 9, 1892 . . 75 20
783 12e.50 Locomotive No. 41, 1896 . . . . 1·25 30
784 15e. Trans Zambesia Railway Class D steam locomotive 1·40 35

99 Dalmatian

1979. Dogs. Multicoloured.
785 50c. Basenji (vert) 10 10
786 1e.50 Type **99** 15 10
787 3e. Boxer 15 10
788 7e.50 Blue gascon pointer . . 35 15
789 12e.50 English cocker spaniel 85 25
790 15e. Pointer . . . . 1·25 30

100 "Papilio nireus"

1979. Stamp Day. Butterflies. Multicoloured.
791 1e. Type **100** 10 10
792 1e.50 "Amauris ochlea" . . . 10 10
793 2e.50 "Pinacopterix eriphia" 15 10
794 5e. "Junonia hierta" 35 10
795 10e. "Nephronia argia" . . . 1·00 20
796 20e. "Catacroptera cloanthe" 2·10 90

101 "Dermacentor circumguttatus cunhasilvai" and African Elephant

1980. Ticks. Multicoloured.
797 50c. Type **101** 20 10
798 1e.50 "Dermacentor rhinocerinos" and black rhinoceros 30 10
799 2e.50 "Amblyomma hebraeum" and giraffe . . 40 15
800 3e. "Amblyomma pomposum" and eland . . 50 15
801 5e. "Amblyomma theilerae" and cow 60 15
802 7e.50 "Amblyomma eburneum" and African buffalo 85 30

102 Ford "Hercules" Bus, 1950

1980. Road Transport. Multicoloured.
803 50c. Type **102** 10 10
804 1e.50 Scania "Marco-Polo" bus, 1978 . . . . 10 10
805 3e. Bussing Nag Bus, 1936 15 10
806 5e. Ikarus articulated bus, 1978 . . . . 20 10
807 7e.50 Ford Taxi, 1929 . . . 40 15
808 12e.50 Fiat "131" Taxi, 1978 80 20

103 Soldier and Map of Southern Africa

1980. Zimbabwe Independence.
809 **103** 10e. blue and brown . . . 40 15

104 Marx, Engels and Lenin

1980. International Workers' Day.
810 **104** 10e. multicoloured 40 15

105 "Market" (Moises Simbine)

1980. "London 1980" International Stamp Exhibition. Multicoloured.
811 50c. "Heads" (Malangatana) 10 10
812 1e.50 Type **105** 10 10
813 3e. "Heads with Helmets" (Malangatana) 15 10
814 5e. "Women with Goods" (Machiana) 20 10
815 7e.50 "Crowd with Masks" (Malangatana) 25 15
816 12e.50 "Man and Woman with Spear" (Mankeu) . . 50 25

106 Telephone

1980. World Telecommunications Day.
817 **106** 15e. multicoloured 60 25

107 Mueda Massacre 108 Crowd waving Tools

1980. 20th Anniv of Mueda Massacre.
818 **107** 15e. green, brown and red 60 25

1980. 5th Anniv of Independence.
819 – 1e. black and red 10 10
820 **108** 2e. multicoloured 10 10
821 – 3e. multicoloured 15 10
822 – 4e. multicoloured 20 10
823 – 5e. black, yellow and red 20 10
824 – 10e. multicoloured 40 15
DESIGNS—As T **108**: 1e. Crowd, doctor tending patient, soldier and workers tilling land; 3e. Crowd with flags and tools; 4e. Stylized figures raising right hand; 5e. Hand grasping flags, book and plants; 10e. Figures carrying banners each with year date. 55 × 37 mm: 30e. Soldiers.

109 Gymnastics

1980. Olympic Games, Moscow. Multicoloured.
826 50c. Type **109** 10 10
827 1e.50 Football 10 10
828 2e.50 Running 10 10
829 3e. Volleyball 20 10
830 10e. Cycling 40 15
831 12e.50 Boxing 45 20

110 Narina's Trogon

1980. Birds. Multicoloured.
832 1m. Type **110** 35 10
833 1m.50 South African crowned crane 40 10
834 2m.50 Red-necked spurfowl 45 10
835 5m. Ostrich 85 20
836 7m.50 Spur-winged goose . . 1·00 25
837 12m.50 African fish eagle . . 1·40 35

111 Family and Census Officer

1980. First General Census.
838 **111** 3m.50 multicoloured . . . 25 10

112 Animals fleeing from Fire

1980. Campaign against Bush Fires.
839 **112** 3m.50 multicoloured . . . 25 10

113 Common Harp

1980. Stamp Day. Shells. Multicoloured.
840 1m. Type **113** 10 10
841 1m.50 Arthritic spider conch 15 10
842 2m.50 Venus comb murex . . 20 10
843 5m. Clear sundial 40 15
844 7m.50 Ramose murex 50 20
845 12m.50 Diana conch . . . . 1·10 35

114 Pres. Machel, Electricity Pylons, Aircraft and Lorry

1981. "Decade for Victory over Underdevelopment".
846 **114** 3m.50 blue and red . . . 2·00 75
847 – 7m.50 brown and green 25 15
848 – 12m.50 mauve and blue 50 30
DESIGNS: 7m.50, Pres. Machel and armed forces on parade; 12m.50, Pres. Machel and classroom scenes.

115 Footballer and *Athletic de Bilbao* Stadium

1981. World Cup Football Championship, Spain (1982). Multicoloured.
849 1m. Type **115** 10 10
850 1m.50 Valencia, C.F. 10 10
851 2m.50 Oviedo C.F. 10 10
852 5m. R. Betis Balompie . . . 20 10
853 7m.50 Real Zaragoza 25 15
854 12m.50 R.C.D. Espanol . . . 50 25

116 Giraffe 117 Chitende

1981. Protected Animals. Multicoloured.
856 50c. Type **116** 10 10
857 1m.50 Topi 10 10
858 2m.50 Aardvark 10 10
859 3m. African python 10 10
860 5m. Loggerhead turtle . . . 20 15
861 10m. Marabou stork . . . . 1·10 45
862 12m.50 Saddle-bill stork . . . 1·40 55
863 15m. Kori bustard . . . . . 1·90 65

1981. Musical Instruments. Multicoloured.
864 50c. Type **117** 10 10
865 2m. Pankwe (horiz) 10 10
866 2m.50 Kanyembe 10 10
867 7m. Nyanga (horiz) 30 20
868 10m. Likuti and M'Petheni (horiz) 70 25

118 Disabled Persons making Baskets

1981. International Year of Disabled People.
869 **118** 5m. multicoloured 25 15

119 De Havilland Dragon Rapide

1981. Air. Mozambique Aviation History. Mult.
870 50c. Type **119** 10 10
871 1m.50 Junkers Ju 52/3m . . . 10 10
872 3m. Lockheed Super Electra 20 15
873 7m.50 De Havilland Dove . . 35 30
874 10m. Douglas DC-3 . . . . 50 35
875 12m.50 Fokker Friendship 75 50

120 Controlled Killing, Marromeu

1981. World Hunting Exhibition, Plovdiv. Mult.
876 2m. Type **120** 30 15
877 5m. Traditional hunting Cheringoma 20 15
878 6m. Tourist hunting, Save . . 40 30
879 7m.60 Marksmanship, Gorongosa 40 20
880 12m.50 African elephants, Gorongosa . . . . 1·50 60
881 20m. Trap, Cabo Delgado . . 80 50

121 50 Centavos Coin 122 Sunflower

1981. 1st Anniv of New Currency. Mult.
883 50c. Type **121** 10 10
884 1m. One metical coin 10 10
885 2m.50 Two meticals 50 coin 10 10
886 5m. Five meticals coin . . . 20 15
887 10m. Ten meticals coin . . . 50 25
888 20m. Twenty meticals coin 1·40 55

1981. Agricultural Resources.
890 **122** 50c. orange and red . . . 10 10
891 – 1m. black and red 10 10
892 – 1m.50 blue and red . . . 10 10
893 – 2m.50 yellow and red . . 10 10
894 – 3m.50 green and red . . . 15 10
895 – 4m.50 grey and red . . . 15 10
896 – 10m. blue and red 40 15
897 – 12m.50 brown and red . . 50 20
898 – 15m. brown and red . . . 60 25
899 – 25m. green and red . . . 1·40 40
900 – 40m. orange and red . . . 2·00 60
901 – 60m. brown and red . . . 2·75 1·00
DESIGNS: 1m. Cotton; 1m.50, Sisal; 2m.50, Cashew; 3m.50, Tea; 4m.50, Sugar cane; 10m. Castor oil; 12m.50, Coconut; 15m. Tobacco; 25m. Rice; 40m. Maize; 60m. Groundnut.

123 Archaeological Excavation, Manyikeni

1981. Archaeological Excavation. Mult.
902 1m. Type **123** 10 10
903 1m.50 Hand-axe (Massingir Dam) 10 10
904 2m.50 Ninth century bowl (Chibuene) 10 10
905 7m.50 Ninth century pot (Chibuene) 30 20
906 12m.50 Gold beads (Manyikeni) 50 30
907 20m. Gong (Manyikeni) . . . 80 50

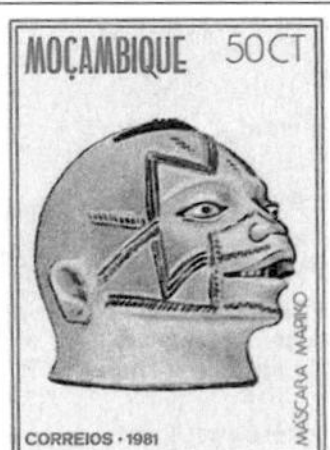

124 Mapiko Mask

1981. Sculptures. Multicoloured.

908	50c. Type **124**	10	10
909	1m. Woman who suffers	10	10
910	2m.50 Woman with a child	10	10
911	3m.50 The man who makes fire	15	10
912	5m. Chietane	20	15
913	12m.50 Chietane (different)	70	30

125 Broken Loaf on Globe

1981. World Food Day.

914	**125**	10m. multicoloured	45	25

126 Tanker "Matchedje"

1981. Mozambique Ships. Multicoloured.

915	50c. Type **126**	15	15
916	1m.50 Tug "Macuti"	15	15
917	3m. Trawler "Vega 7"	25	15
918	5m. Freighter "Linde"	35	25
919	7m.50 Freighter "Pemba"	55	30
920	12m.50 Dredger "Rovuma"	95	55

127 "Portunus pelagicus"

1981. Crustaceans. Multicoloured.

921	50c. Type **127**	10	10
922	1m.50 "Scylla serrata"	10	10
923	3m. "Penacus indicus"	15	10
924	7m.50 "Palinurus delagoae"	35	20
925	12m.50 "Lysiosquilla maculata"	55	35
926	15m. "Panulirus ornatus"	80	45

128 "Hypoxis multiceps" **129** Telex Tape, Telephone and Globe

1981. Flowers. Multicoloured.

927	1m. Type **128**	10	10
928	1m.50 "Pelargonium luridun"	10	10
929	2m.50 "Caralluma melanathera"	10	10
930	7m.50 "Ansellia gigantea"	35	20
931	12m.50 "Stapelia leendertsiae"	60	35
932	25m. "Adenium multiflorum"	1·50	70

1982. 1st Anniv of Mozambique Post and Telecommunications. Multicoloured.

933	6m. Type **129**	35	20
934	15m. Winged envelope and envelope forming railway wagon	3·00	1·50

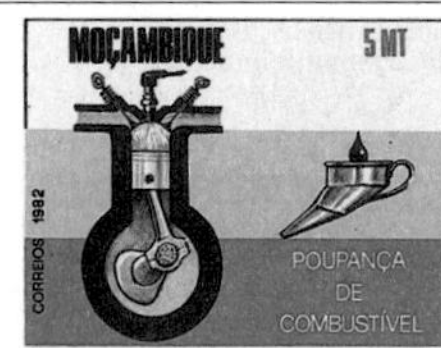

130 Diagram of Petrol Engine

1982. Fuel Saving. Multicoloured.

935	5m. Type **130**	30	15
936	7m.50 Speeding car	45	25
937	10m. Loaded truck	60	35

131 Sea-snake

1982. Reptiles. Multicoloured.

938	50c. Type **131**	20	10
939	1m.50 "Naja mossambica mossambica"	10	10
940	3m. "Thelotornis capensis mossambica"	20	15
941	6m. "Dendroaspis polylepis polylepis"	35	25
942	15m. "Dispholidus typus"	80	50
943	20m. "Bitis arietans arietans"	1·50	75

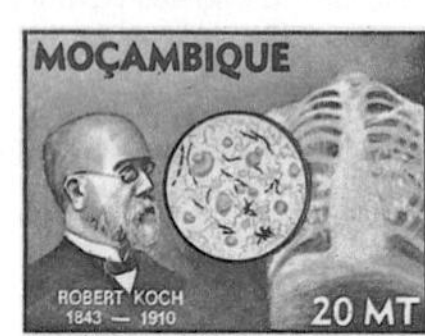

132 Dr. Robert Koch, Bacillus and X-Ray

1982. Centenary of Discovery of Tubercle Bacillus.

944	**132**	20m. multicoloured	1·75	1·00

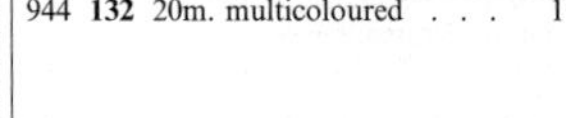

133 Telephone Line **134** Player with Ball

1982. International Telecommunications Union. Plenipotentiary Conference.

945	**133**	20m. multicoloured	1·00	75

1982. World Cup Football Championship, Spain. Multicoloured.

946	1m.50 Type **134**	10	10
947	3m.50 Player heading ball	25	15
948	7m. Two players fighting for ball	40	20
949	10m. Player receiving ball	60	30
950	20m. Goalkeeper	1·25	1·00

135 Political Rally **137** "Vangueria infausta"

1982. 25th Anniv of FRELIMO. Multicoloured.

953	4m. Type **135**	25	15
954	8m. Agriculture	45	25
955	12m. Marching workers	70	35

1982. Fruits. Multicoloured.

956	1m. Type **137**	10	10
957	2m. "Mimusops caffra"	10	10
958	4m. "Sclerocarya caffra"	25	15
959	8m. "Strychnos spinosa"	45	25
960	12m. "Salacia kraussi"	70	40
961	32m. "Trichilia emetica"	1·90	85

138 "Sputnik I"

1982. 25th Anniv of First Artificial Satellite. Multicoloured.

962	1m. Type **138**	10	10
963	2m. First manned space flight	10	10
964	4m. First walk in space	25	15
965	8m. First manned flight to the Moon	45	25
966	16m. "Soyuz"–"Apollo" mission	1·25	70
967	20m. "Intercosmos" rocket	1·50	70

139 Vigilantes

1982. People's Surveillance Day.

968	**139**	4m. multicoloured	25	15

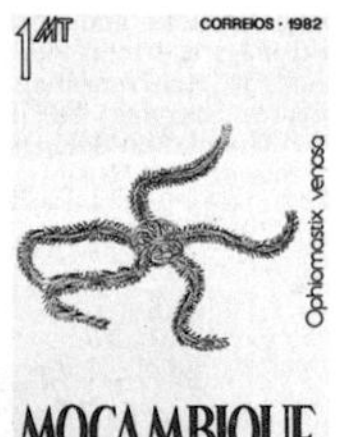

140 Caique **141** "Ophiomostix venosa"

1982. Traditional Boats. Multicoloured.

969	1m. Type **140**	10	10
970	2m. Machua	15	10
971	4m. Calaua (horiz)	30	15
972	8m. Chitatarro (horiz)	60	25
973	12m. Cangaia (horiz)	80	35
974	16m. Chata (horiz)	1·75	60

1982. Starfishes and Sea Urchins. Multicoloured.

975	1m. Type **141**	10	10
976	2m. "Protoreaster lincki"	10	10
977	4m. "Tropiometra carinata"	15	10
978	8m. "Holothuria scabra"	35	20
979	12m. "Prionocidaris baculosa"	60	35
980	16m. "Colobocentrotus atnatus"	80	40

142 Soldiers defending Mozambique

1983. 4th Frelimo Party Congress. Multicoloured.

981	4m. Type **142**	15	10
982	8m. Crowd waving voting papers	30	20
983	16m. Agriculture, industry and education	65	40

143 "Codium duthierae"

1983. Seaweeds. Multicoloured.

984	1m. Type **143**	10	10
985	2m. "Halimeda cunata"	10	10
986	4m. "Dictyota liturata"	15	10
987	8m. "Endorachne binghamiae"	40	20
988	12m. "Laurencia flexuosa"	60	30
989	20m. "Acrosorium sp."	1·25	55

144 Diving and Swimming

1983. Olympic Games, Los Angeles (1st issue). Multicoloured.

990	1m. Type **144**	10	10
991	2m. Boxing	10	10
992	4m. Basketball	20	10
993	8m. Handball	35	20
994	12m. Volleyball	55	30
995	16m. Running	65	40
996	20m. Yachting	1·25	65

See also Nos. 1029/34.

145 Mallet Type Locomotive

1983. Steam Locomotives. Multicoloured.

998	1m. Type **145**	10	10
999	2m. Baldwin, 1915–45	20	10
1000	4m. Class 141-148, 1950	40	15
1001	8m. Baldwin, 1926	75	25
1002	16m. Henschel Garratt type, 1956	1·40	50
1003	32m. Natal Government Class H, 1899–1903	3·00	1·00

146 O.A.U. Emblem

1983. 20th Anniv of Organization of African Unity.

1004	**146**	4m. multicoloured	20	15

147 Four-toed Elephant-shrew **150** "Communications"

148 Aiding Flood Victims

1983. Mozambique Mammals. Multicoloured.

1005	1m. Type **147**	10	10
1006	2m. Four-striped grass mouse	15	10
1007	4m. Vincent's bush squirrel	25	15
1008	8m. Hottentot mole-rat	50	25
1009	12m. Natal red hare	75	40
1010	16m. Straw-coloured fruit bat	1·25	75

1983. 2nd Anniv of Mozambique Red Cross. Multicoloured.

1011	4m. Type **148**	20	10
1012	8m. Red Cross lorry	40	20
1013	16m. First aid demonstration	75	40
1014	32m. Agricultural worker performing first aid	1·90	75

1983. World Communications Year.

1016	**150**	8m. multicoloured	1·50	75

151 Line Fishing

1983. Fishery Resources. Multicoloured.

1017	50c. Type **151**	10	10
1018	2m. Chifonho (basket trap)	10	10
1019	4m. Spear fishing	25	15
1020	8m. Gamboa (fence trap) . .	40	25
1021	16m. Mono (basket trap) . .	1·50	40
1022	20m. Lema (basket trap) . .	1·60	55

152 Kudu Horn **153** Swimming

1983. Stamp Day. Multicoloured.

1023	50c. Type **152**	10	10
1024	1m. Drum communication	10	10
1025	4m. Postal runners	20	15
1026	8m. Mail canoe	40	40
1027	16m. Mail van	75	40
1028	20m. Steam mail train . . .	3·25	1·50

1984. Olympic Games, Los Angeles (2nd issue). Multicoloured.

1029	50c. Type **153**	10	10
1030	4m. Football	20	10
1031	8m. Hurdling	35	20
1032	16m. Basketball	90	50
1033	32m. Handball	1·90	80
1034	60m. Boxing	3·00	1·75

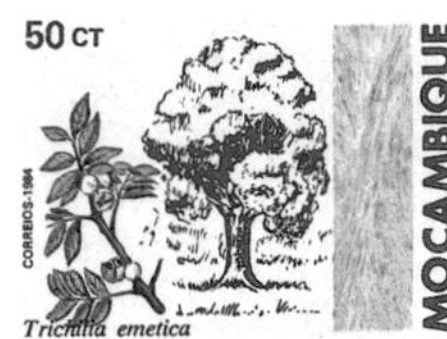

154 "Trichilia emetica"

1984. Indigenous Trees. Multicoloured.

1035	50c. Type **154**	10	10
1036	2m. "Brachystegia spiciformis"	10	10
1037	4m. "Androstachys johnsonii"	20	10
1038	8m. "Pterocarpus angolensis"	35	20
1039	16m. "Milletia stuhlmannii"	80	40
1040	50m. "Dalbergia melanoxylon"	2·75	1·75

155 Dove with Olive Sprig

1984. Nkomati South Africa–Mozambique Non-aggression Pact.

1041	**155** 4m. multicoloured . . .	25	10

156 State Arms

1984. Emblems of the Republic. Multicoloured.

1042	4m. Type **156**	20	10
1043	8m. State Flag	40	20

157 Makway Dance

1984. "Lubrapex '84" Portuguese–Brazilian Stamp Exhibition, Lisbon. Traditional Mozambican dances. Multicoloured.

1044	4m. Type **157**	20	10
1045	8m. Mapiko dance	40	20
1046	16m. Wadjaba dance . . .	1·40	50

158 Nampula Museum and Statuette of Woman with Water Jug

1984. Museums. Multicoloured.

1047	50c. Type **158**	10	10
1048	4m. Natural History Museum and secretary bird	35	10
1049	8m. Revolution Museum and soldier carrying wounded comrade	35	20
1050	16m. Colonial History Museum and cannon . .	65	40
1051	20m. National Numismatic Museum and coins . . .	1·25	65
1052	30m. St. Paul's Palace and antique chair	1·50	95

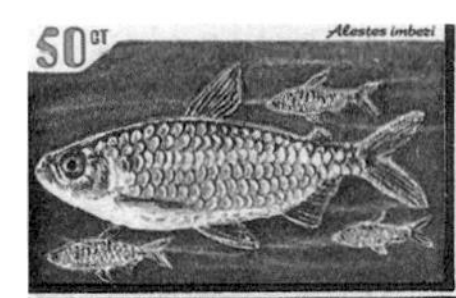

159 Imber's Tetra

1984. Fishes. Multicoloured.

1053	50c. Type **159**	10	10
1054	4m. Purple labeo	25	10
1055	12m. Brown squeaker . . .	75	35
1056	16m. Blue-finned notho . .	95	55
1057	40m. Slender serrate barb	2·50	1·40
1058	60m. Barred minnow . . .	3·75	1·90

160 Badge and Laurels **162** Knife and Club

161 Rural Landscape and Emblem

1984. International Fair, Maputo.

1059	**160** 16m. multicoloured . . .	70	50

1984. 20th Anniv of African Development Bank.

1060	**161** 4m. multicoloured . . .	30	10

1984. Traditional Weapons. Multicoloured.

1061	50c. Type **162**	10	10
1062	4m. Axes	20	10
1063	8m. Spear and shield . . .	35	15
1064	16m. Bow and arrow . . .	75	35
1065	32m. Rifle	1·90	95
1066	50m. Assegai and arrow . .	2·75	1·90

163 Workers and Emblem

1984. 1st Anniv of Organization of Mozambican Workers.

1067	**163** 4m. multicoloured . . .	20	10

164 Barue 1902 Postmark

1984. Stamp Day. Postmarks. Multicoloured.

1068	4m. Type **164**	15	10
1069	8m. Zumbo postmark and King Carlos 15r. Mozambique "key type" stamp	35	20
1070	12m. Mozambique Company postmark and 1935 airmail stamp . . .	55	30
1071	16m. Macequece postmark and 1937 2e. Mozambique Company stamp	70	40

165 Keeper and Hive **166** Shot-putter and Emblem

1985. Bee-keeping. Multicoloured.

1072	4m. Type **165**	15	10
1073	8m. Worker bee	45	20
1074	16m. Drone	1·25	40
1075	20m. Queen bee	1·75	60

1985. "Olymphilex 85" Olympic Stamps Exhibition, Lausanne.

1076	**166** 16m. blue, black and red	75	35

167 Forecasting Equipment and Desert

1985. World Meteorology Day.

1077	**167** 4m. multicoloured . . .	35	10

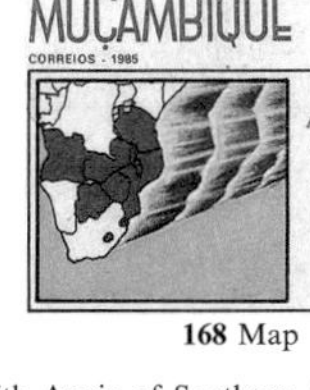

168 Map

1985. 5th Anniv of Southern African Development Co-ordination Conference. Multicoloured.

1078	4m. Type **168**	15	10
1079	8m. Map and pylon	45	20
1080	16m. Industry and transport	2·50	1·25
1081	32m. Member states' flags	1·90	95

169 Battle of Mujenga, 1896

1985. 10th Anniv of Independence. Mult.

1082	1m. Type **169**	10	10
1083	4m. Attack on Barue by Macombe, 1917	25	10
1084	8m. Attack on Massangano, 1868	55	20
1085	16m. Battle of Marracuene, 1895, and Gungunhana	1·50	50

170 U.N. Building, New York and Flag

1985. 40th Anniv of U.N.O.

1086	**170** 16m. multicoloured . . .	80	50

171 Mathacuzana

1985. Traditional Games and Sports. Multicoloured.

1087	50c. Type **171**	10	10
1088	4m. Mudzobo	20	10
1089	8m. Muravarava (board game)	40	20
1090	16m. N'tshuwa	90	50

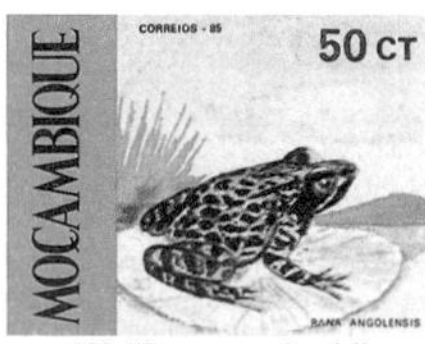

172 "Rana angolensis"

1985. Frogs and Toads. Multicoloured.

1091	50c. Type **172**	10	10
1092	1m. "Hyperolius pictus" . .	10	10
1093	4m. "Ptychadena porosissima"	15	10
1094	8m. "Afrixalus formasinii"	50	20
1095	16m. "Bufo regularis" . . .	95	50
1096	32m. "Hyperolius marmoratus"	2·40	95

174 "Aloe ferox" **176** Comet and "Giotto" Space Probe

175 Mozambique Company 1918 10c. Stamp

1985. Medicinal Plants. Multicoloured.

1099	50c. Type **174**	10	10
1100	1m. "Boophone disticha"	10	10
1101	3m.50 "Gloriosa superba"	15	10
1102	4m. "Cotyledon orbiculata"	15	10
1103	8m. "Homeria breyniana"	55	20
1104	50m. "Haemanthus coccineus"	3·75	1·90

1985. Stamp Day. Multicoloured.

1105	1m. Type **175**	1·25	75
1106	4m. Nyassa Co. 1911 25r. stamp	15	10
1107	8m. Mozambique Co. 1918 ½c. stamp	50	20
1108	16m. Nyassa Co. 1924 1c. Postage Due stamp . . .	1·25	50

1986. Appearance of Halley's Comet.

1109	**176** 4m. blue and light blue	20	10
1110	– 8m. violet and light violet	50	20
1111	– 16m. multicoloured . . .	95	50
1112	– 30m. multicoloured . . .	2·00	95

DESIGNS: 8m. Comet orbits; 16m. Small and large telescopes, comet and space probe; 30m. Comet, stars and globe.

177 Vicente

1986. World Cup Football Championship, Mexico. Multicoloured.

1113	3m. Type **177**	15	10
1114	4m. Coluna	20	10
1115	8m. Costa Pereira	40	20
1116	12m. Hilario	65	35
1117	16m. Matateu	95	50
1118	50m. Eusebio	3·25	1·90

178 Dove and Emblem

179 "Amanita muscaria"

1986. International Peace Year.

1119 **178** 16m. multicoloured . . . 85 45

1986. Fungi. Multicoloured.

1120	4m. Type **179**	50	20
1121	8m. "Lactarius deliciosus"	95	30
1122	16m. "Amanita phaloides"	2·00	65
1123	30m. "Tricholoma nudum"	4·25	1·25

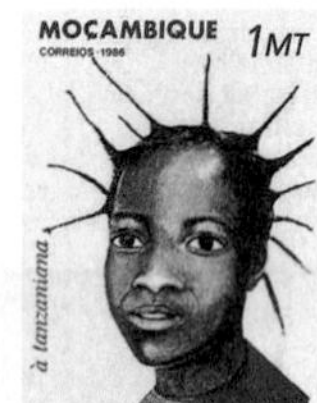

181 Spiky Style

1986. Women's Hairstyles. Multicoloured.

1125	1m. Type **181**	10	10
1126	4m. Beaded plaits	25	10
1127	8m. Plaited tightly to head	50	20
1128	16m. Plaited tightly to head with ponytail	1·25	55

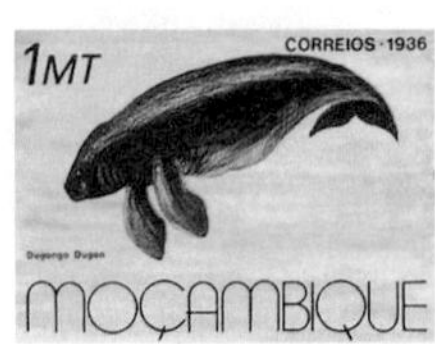

182 Dugong

1986. Marine Mammals. Multicoloured.

1129	1m. Type **182**	10	10
1130	8m. Common dolphin	35	20
1131	16m. "Neobalena marginata"	1·25	85
1132	50f. Fin whale	4·25	2·75

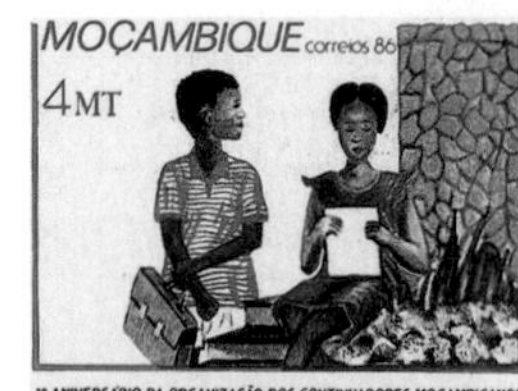

183 Children Studying

1986. 1st Anniv of Continuadores Youth Organization.

1133 **183** 4m. multicoloured . . . 30 15

184 50m. Notes

1986. Savings. Multicoloured.

1134	4m. Type **184**	25	10
1135	8m. 100m. notes	50	20
1136	16m. 500m. notes	1·40	50
1137	30m. 1000m. notes	2·75	1·25

185 Quelimane Post Office

1986. Stamp Day. Post Offices. Multicoloured.

1138	3m. Type **185**	20	10
1139	4m. Maputo	30	10
1140	8m. Beira	65	20
1141	16m. Nampula	1·40	50

186 Pyrite

1987. Minerals. Multicoloured.

1142	4m. Type **186**	30	10
1143	8m. Emerald	60	20
1144	12m. Agate	85	40
1145	16m. Malachite	1·40	50
1146	30m. Garnet	2·50	1·25
1147	50m. Amethyst	4·25	2·00

187 Crowd beneath Flag

1987. 10th Anniv of Mozambique Liberation Front.

1148 **187** 4m. multicoloured . . . 30 15

188 Little Libombos Dam

1987.

1149 **188** 16m. multicoloured . . . 1·40 60

189 Children being Vaccinated

1987. World Health Day. Vaccination Campaign.

1150 **189** 50m. multicoloured . . . 1·90 1·50

190 Common Grenadier

191 Football

1987. Birds. Multicoloured.

1151	3m. Type **190**	25	15
1152	4m. Woodland kingfisher	30	20
1153	8m. White-fronted bee eater	65	40
1154	12m. Lesser seedcracker	1·10	60
1155	16m. African broad-billed roller	1·25	90
1156	30m. Neergaard's sunbird	2·50	1·60

1987. Olympic Games, Seoul (1988) (1st issue). Multicoloured.

1157	12m.50 Type **191**	10	10
1158	25m. Running	20	10
1159	50m. Handball	40	20
1160	75m. Chess	1·25	30
1161	100m. Basketball	1·25	35
1162	200m. Swimming	2·00	65

See also Nos. 1176/81.

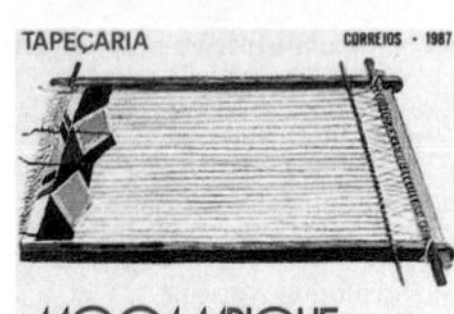

193 Work on Loom

1987. Weaving. Multicoloured.

1164	20m. Type **193**	15	10
1165	40m. Triangle and diamond design	40	10
1166	80m. "Eye" design	70	20
1167	200m. Red carpet	2·00	60

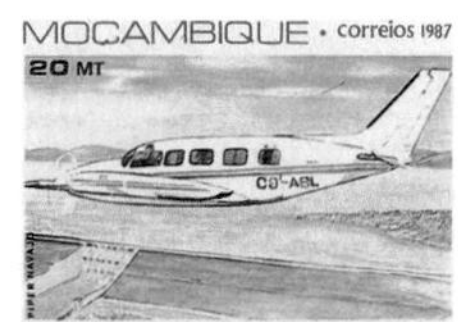

194 Piper "Navajo"

1987. Air. History of Aviation in Mozambique. Multicoloured.

1168	20m. Type **194**	15	10
1169	40m. De Havilland Hornet moth	25	10
1170	80m. Boeing 737	50	20
1171	120m. Beechcraft King Air	75	20
1172	160m. Piper Aztec	1·00	35
1173	320m. Douglas DC-10	2·00	75

195 Early Plan

1987. Centenary of Maputo as City.

1174 **195** 20m. multicoloured . . . 20 15

1987. No. 895 surch **4,00 MT**.

1175 4m. on 4m.50 grey and red 15 10

197 Javelin throwing

198 "Boophane disticha"

1988. Olympic Games, Seoul (2nd issue). Mult.

1176	10m. Type **197**	10	10
1177	20m. Baseball	10	10
1178	40m. Boxing	10	10
1179	80m. Hockey	40	10
1180	100m. Gymnastics	50	15
1181	400m. Cycling	1·50	75

1988. Flowers. Multicoloured.

1182	10m. "Heamanthus nelsonii"	10	10
1183	20m. "Crinum polyphyllum"	15	10
1184	40m. Type **198**	15	10
1185	80m. "Cyrtanthus contractus"	35	10
1186	100m. "Nerine angustifolia"	50	15
1187	400m. "Cyrtanthus galpinnii"	2·00	75

199 Man refusing Cigarette

1988. 40th Anniv of W.H.O. Anti-smoking Campaign.

1188 **199** 20m. multicoloured . . . 20 10

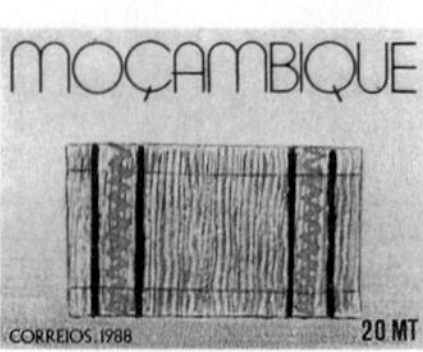

201 Mat

1988. Basketry. Multicoloured.

1190	20m. Type **201**	10	10
1191	25m. Basket with lid	10	10
1192	80m. Basket with handle	20	10
1193	100m. Fan	30	10
1194	400m. Dish	1·50	1·00
1195	500m. Conical basket	1·90	1·40

203 Percheron

1988. Horses. Multicoloured.

1197	20m. Type **203**	15	10
1198	40m. Arab	20	10
1199	80m. Pure blood	40	10
1200	100m. Pony	50	15

204 Machel

1988. 2nd Death Anniv of Samora Machel (President 1975–86).

1201 **204** 20m. multicoloured . . . 15 10

205 Inhambane

1988. Ports. Multicoloured.

1202	20m. Type **205**	15	10
1203	50m. Quelimane (vert)	40	10
1204	75m. Pemba	50	10
1205	100m. Beira	55	20
1206	250m. Nacali (vert)	1·10	50
1207	500m. Maputo	2·75	1·25

206 Mobile Post Office

1988. Stamp Day. Multicoloured.

1208	20m. Type **206**	10	10
1209	40m. Posting box (vert)	15	10

207 Maize **208** Mondlane

1989. 5th FRELIMO Congress. Multicoloured.
1210 25m. Type **207** 10 10
1211 50m. Hoe 10 10
1212 75m. Abstract 10 10
1213 100m. Cogwheels 20 10
1214 250m. Right-half of cogwheel 50 25
Nos. 1210/14 were printed together, se-tenant, forming a composite design.

1989. 20th Anniv of Assassination of Pres. Mondlane.
1215 **208** 25m. black, gold and red 15 10

209 "Storming the Bastille" (Thevenin)

1989. Bicentenary of French Revolution. Mult.
1216 100m. Type **209** 25 10
1217 250m. "Liberty guiding the People" (Delacroix) . . . 60 35

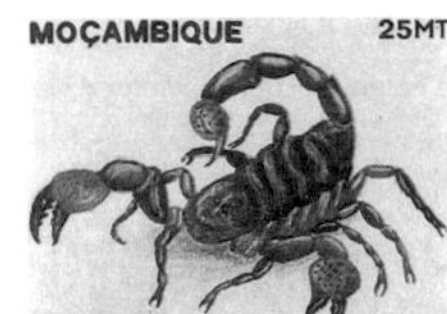

210 "Pandinus sp."

1989. Venomous Animals. Multicoloured.
1219 25m. Type **210** 10 10
1220 50m. Egyptian cobra . . . 10 10
1221 75m. "Bombus sp." (bee) . . 15 10
1222 100m. "Paraphysa sp." (spider) 25 10
1223 250m. Marble cone 90 40
1224 500m. Lionfish . . . . . . 1·90 70

211 "Acropora pulchra"

1989. Corals. Multicoloured.
1225 25m. Type **211** 10 10
1226 50m. "Eunicella papilosa" 15 10
1227 100m. "Dendrophyla migrantus" 30 10
1228 250m. "Favia fragum" . . . 50 35

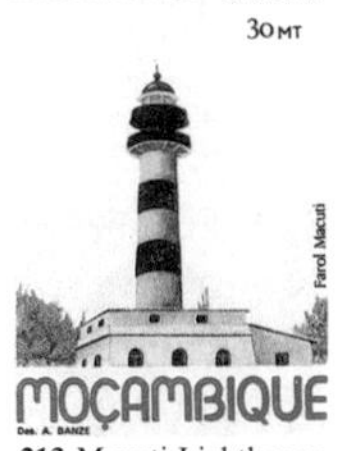

212 Footballers **213** Macuti Lighthouse

1989. World Cup Football Championship, Italy (1990). Designs showing various footballing scenes.
1229 **212** 30m. multicoloured . . . 10 10
1230 – 60m. multicoloured . . . 15 10
1231 – 125m. multicoloured . . 30 10
1232 – 200m. multicoloured . . 50 25
1233 – 250m. multicoloured . . 65 35
1234 – 500m. multicoloured . . 1·50 70

1989. Lighthouses. Multicoloured.
1235 30m. Type **213** 15 10
1236 60m. Pinda 15 10
1237 125m. Cape Delgado . . . 30 10
1238 200m. Goa Island 60 25
1239 250m. Caldeira Point . . . 80 35
1240 500m. Vilhena . . . . . . 1·50 70

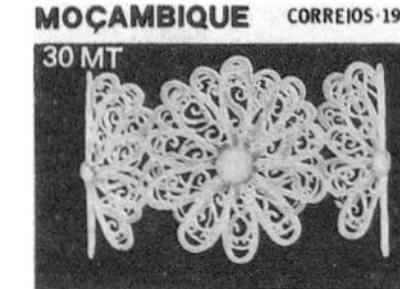

214 Bracelet

1989. Silver Filigree Work.
1241 **214** 30m. grey, red and black 10 10
1242 – 60m. grey, blue and black 15 10
1243 – 125m. grey, red and black 25 10
1244 – 200m. grey, blue & black 40 25
1245 – 250m. grey, purple & blk 55 35
1246 – 500m. grey, green & blk 1·25 70
DESIGNS: 60m. Flower belt; 125m. Necklace; 200m. Casket; 250m. Spoons; 500m. Butterfly.

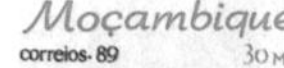

215 Flag and Soldiers **216** Rain Gauge

1989. 25th Anniv of Fight for Independence.
1247 **215** 30m. multicoloured . . . 15 10

1989. Meteorological Instruments. Multicoloured.
1248 30m. Type **216** 10 10
1249 60m. Radar graph 15 10
1250 125m. Sheltered measuring instruments 30 10
1251 200m. Computer terminal 55 25

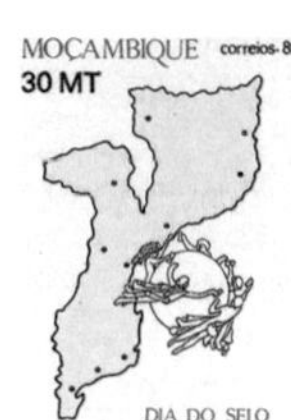

218 Map and U.P.U. Emblem **219** Railway Map

1989. Stamp Day.
1253 **218** 30m. multicoloured . . . 15 10
1254 – 60m. black, green and red 15 10
DESIGN: 60m. Map and Mozambique postal emblem.

1990. 10th Anniv of Southern Africa Development Co-ordination Conference.
1255 **219** 35m. multicoloured . . . 1·00 50

220 Cloth and Woman wearing Dress

1990. Traditional Dresses. Designs showing women wearing different dresses and details of cloth used.
1256 **220** 42m. multicoloured . . . 10 10
1257 – 90m. multicoloured . . . 15 10
1258 – 150m. multicoloured . . 20 10
1259 – 200m. multicoloured . . 25 15
1260 – 400m. multicoloured . . 55 40
1261 – 500m. multicoloured . . 65 50

221 Sena Fortress, Sofala

1990. Fortresses.
1262 **221** 45m. blue and black . . 10 10
1263 – 90m. blue and black . . 15 10
1264 – 150m. multicoloured . . 20 10
1265 – 200m. multicoloured . . 30 15
1266 – 400m. red and black . . 55 40
1267 – 500m. red and black . . 70 40
DESIGNS: 90m. Sto. Antonio, Ibo Island; 150m. S. Sebastiao, Mozambique Island; 200m. S. Caetano, Sofala; 400m. Our Lady of Conception, Maputo; 500m. S. Luis, Tete.

223 Obverse and Reverse of 50m. Coin

1990. 15th Anniv of Bank of Mozambique.
1269 **223** 100m. multicoloured . . 20 10

224 Statue of Eduardo Mondlane (founder of FRELIMO)

1990. 15th Anniv of Independence. Mult.
1270 42m.50 Type **224** 10 10
1271 150m. Statue of Samora Machel (President, 1975–86) 25 15

225 White Rhinoceros

1990. Endangered Animals. Multicoloured.
1272 42m.50 Type **225** 15 10
1273 100m. Dugong 20 10
1274 150m. African elephant . . 35 15
1275 200m. Cheetah 40 15
1276 400m. Spotted-necked otter 70 40
1277 500m. Hawksbill turtle . . . 85 50

226 "Dichrostachys cinerea" **227** Pillar Box waving to Kurika

1990. Environmental Protection. Plants. Mult.
1278 42m.50 Type **226** 10 10
1279 100m. Forest fire 20 10
1280 150m. Horsetail tree 25 10
1281 200m. Mangrove 30 15
1282 400m. "Estrato herbaceo" (grass) 65 40
1283 500m. Pod mahogany . . . 80 50

1990. Kurika (post mascot) at Work. Mult.
1284 42m.50 Type **227** 15 10
1285 42m.50 Hand cancelling envelopes 15 10
1286 42m.50 Leaping across hurdles 15 10
1287 42m.50 Delivering post to chicken 15 10

228 "10" and Posts Emblem **229** Bird-of-Paradise Flower

1991. 10th Anniv of National Posts and Telecommunications Enterprises, Mozambique.
1288 **228** 50m. blue, red and black 15 10
1289 – 50m. brown, green & black 15 10
DESIGN: No. 1289, "10" and telecommunications emblem.

1991. Flowers. Multicoloured.
1290 50m. Type **229** 15 10
1291 125m. Flamingo lily 25 15
1292 250m. Calla lily 50 30
1293 300m. Canna lily 55 35

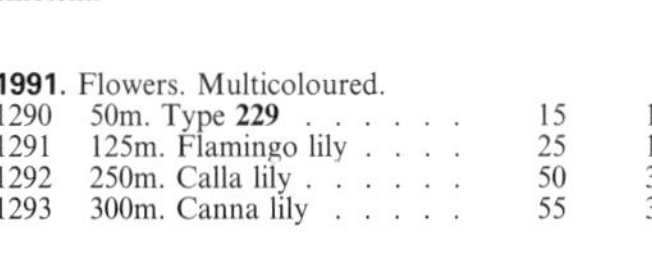

230 Two Hartebeest **231** Mpompine

1991. Lichtenstein's Hartebeest. Multicoloured.
1294 50m. Type **230** 15 10
1295 100m. Alert hartebeest . . . 20 10
1296 250m. Hartebeest grazing . . 1·50 70
1297 500m. Mother feeding young 2·10 1·40

1991. Maputo Drinking Fountains. Mult.
1298 50m. Type **231** 10 10
1299 125m. Chinhambanine . . . 15 10
1300 250m. S. Pedro-Zaza . . . 25 10
1301 300m. Xipamanine 35 15

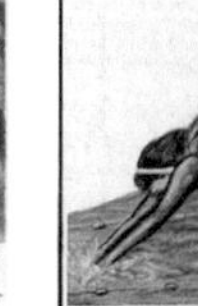

232 Painting by Samate **233** Diving

1991. Paintings by Mozambican Artists. Mult.
1302 180m. Type **232** 15 10
1303 250m. Malangatana Ngwenya 20 15
1304 560m. Malangatana Ngwenya (different) . . . 40 30

1991. Olympic Games, Barcelona (1992). Mult.
1305 10m. Type **233** 10 10
1306 50m. Roller hockey 15 10
1307 100m. Tennis 20 10
1308 200m. Table tennis 30 10
1309 500m. Running 50 20
1310 1000m. Badminton . . . . 1·10 40

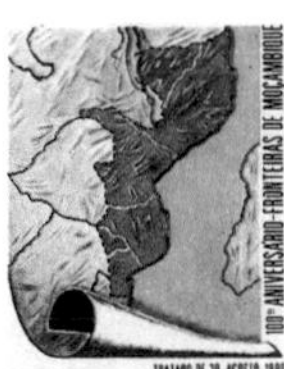

234 Proposed Boundaries in 1890 Treaty **236** Skipping

1991. Centenary of Settling of Mozambique Borders. Multicoloured.
1311 600m. Type **234** 50 25
1312 800m. Frontiers settled in English–Portuguese 1891 treaty 75 35

1991. Stamp Day. Children's Games. Mult.
1314 40m. Type **236** 10 10
1315 150m. Spinning top 10 10
1316 400m. Marbles 20 10
1317 900m. Hopscotch 45 20

237 "Christ" **238** "Rhisophora mucronata"

1992. Stained Glass Windows. Multicoloured.
1318 40m. Type **237** 10 10
1319 150m. "Faith" 10 10
1320 400m. "IC XC" 20 10
1321 900m. Window in three sections 45 20

1992. Marine Flowers. Multicoloured.
1322 300m. Type **238** 15 10
1323 600m. "Cymodocea ciliata" 30 15
1324 1000m. "Sophora inhambanensis" 85 25

239 Spears

240 Amethyst Sunbird

1992. "Lubrapex 92" Brazilian–Portuguese Stamp Exhibition, Lisbon. Weapons. Multicoloured.
1325 100m. Type **239** 10 10
1326 300m. Tridents 15 10
1327 500m. Axe 25 10
1328 1000m. Dagger 85 25

1992. Birds. Multicoloured.
1329 150m. Type **240** 30 30
1330 200m. Mosque swallow . . 30 30
1331 300m. Red-capped robin chat 45 30
1332 400m. Lesser blue-eared glossy starling 60 30
1333 500m. Grey-headed bush shrike . . . . 1·50 30
1334 800m. African golden oriole 2·25 70

241 Emblem

242 Phiane

1992. 30th Anniv of Eduardo Mondlane University.
1335 **241** 150m. green and brown 10 10

1992. "Genova '92" International Thematic Stamp Exn. Musical Instruments. Multicoloured.
1336 200m. Type **242** 10 10
1337 300m. Xirupe (rattle) . . . 15 10
1338 500m. Ngulula (drum) . . . 25 10
1339 1500m. Malimba (drum) . . 75 35

243 Children Eating

244 Parachutist

1992. International Nutrition Conference, Rome.
1341 **243** 450m. multicoloured . . 20 10

1992. Parachuting. Multicoloured.
1342 50m. Type **244** 10 10
1343 400m. Parachutist and buildings 20 10
1344 500m. Airplane dropping parachutists 25 10
1345 1500m. Parachutist (different) . . . . 1·10 1·10

1992. No. 890 surch **50MT**.
1346 **122** 50m. on 50c. orge & red 10 10

246 Order of Peace and Friendship

1993. Mozambique Decorations. Multicoloured.
1347 400m. Type **246** 20 10
1348 800m. Bagamoyo Medal . . 40 20
1349 1000m. Order of Eduardo Mondlane 50 25
1350 1500m. Veteran of the Struggle for National Liberation Medal 70 35

247 Tree Stumps and Girl carrying Wood

1993. Pollution. Multicoloured.
1351 200m. Type **247** 10 10
1352 750m. Chimneys smoking 35 15
1353 1000m. Tanker sinking . . . 50 25
1354 1500m. Car exhaust fumes 70 35

248 Lion (Gorongosa Park, Sofala)

1993. National Parks. Multicoloured.
1355 200m. Type **248** 10 10
1356 800m. Giraffes (Banhine Park, Gaza) 40 20
1357 1000m. Dugongs (Bazoruto Park, Inhambane) 50 25
1358 1500m. Ostriches (Zinave Park, Inhambane) . . . . 1·75 75

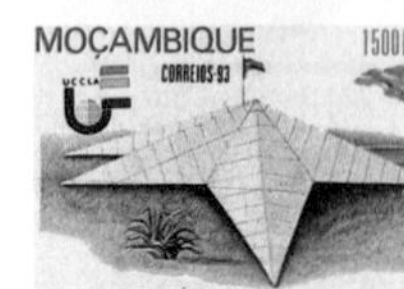

249 Heroes Monument, Maputo

1993. "Brasiliana 93" International Stamp Exhibition, Rio de Janeiro.
1359 **249** 1500m. multicoloured . . 55 25

250 Conference Emblem

251 "Cycas cercinalis"

1993. National Culture Conference, Maputo.
1360 **250** 200m. multicoloured . . 10 10

1993. Forest Plants. Multicoloured.
1361 200m. Type **251** 10 10
1362 250m. "Cycas revoluta" . . 10 10
1363 900m. "Encephalartos ferox" 25 10
1364 2000m. "Equisetum ramosissimum" 50 25

252 "Anacardium occidentale"

254 Mozambique Rough-scaled Sand Lizard

1994. Medicinal Plants. Multicoloured.
1365 200m. Type **252** 10 10
1366 250m. "Sclerocarya caffra" 10 10
1367 900m. "Annona senegalensis" 25 10
1368 2000m. "Crinum delagoense" 50 25

1994. Various stamps surch.
1369 50m. on 7m.50 mult (No. 905) 10 10
1370 50m. on 7m.50 mult (No. 924) 10 10
1371 50m. on 7m.50 mult (No. 930) 10 10
1372 100m. on 10m. blue and red (No. 896) 10 10
1373 100m. on 12m.50 mult (No. 931) 10 10
1374 200m. on 12m.50 brown and red (No. 897) 10 10
1375 250m. on 12m.50 mult (No. 925) 10 10

1994. "Philakorea 1994" International Stamp Exhibition, Seoul. Reptiles. Multicoloured.
1376 300m. Type **254** 10 10
1377 500m. Olive loggerhead turtle 10 10
1378 2000m. Northern coppery snake 40 20
1379 3500m. Marshall's chameleon 75 35

255 Crop-spraying

1994. 50th Anniv of I.C.A.O. Multicoloured.
1381 300m. Type **255** 10 10
1382 500m. Airport 10 10
1383 2000m. Air transport . . . 40 20
1384 3500m. Aircraft maintenance 75 35

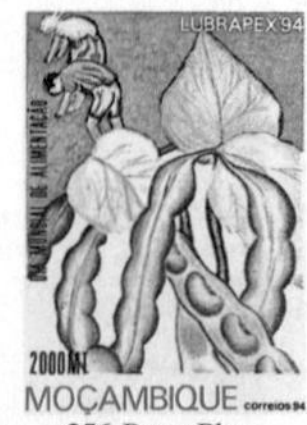

256 Bean Plant

257 Queue of Voters

1994. "Lubrapex'94" Portuguese–Brazilian Stamp Exhibition. World Food Day.
1385 **256** 2000m. multicoloured . . 40 20

1994. 1st Multiparty Elections.
1386 **257** 900m. multicoloured . . 20 10

258 Document and Handshake

259 Couple using Drugs

1994. 20th Anniv of Lusaka Accord (establishing independence).
1387 **258** 1500m. multicoloured . . 30 15

1994. Anti-drugs Campaign. Multicoloured.
1388 500m. Type **259** 10 10
1389 1000m. Couple, syringe, cigarette and skeleton . . 20 10
1390 2000m. Addict 40 20
1391 5000m. Sniffer dog capturing man with drugs 1·00 50

260 Basket

261 Dress and Cloak

1995. Baskets and Bags. Multicoloured.
1392 250m. Type **260** 10 10
1393 300m. Bag with two handles 10 10
1394 1200m. Circular bag with one handle 20 10
1395 5000m. Bag with flap . . . 85 40

1995. Women's Costumes. Multicoloured.
1396 250m. Type **261** 10 10
1397 300m. Blouse and calf-length skirt 10 10
1398 1200m. Blouse and ankle-length skirt 20 10
1399 5000m. Strapless top and skirt 85 40

262 State Arms

263 Bushbaby

1995. Investiture (1994) of President Joaquim Chissano. Multicoloured.
1400 900m. Type **262** 15 10
1401 2500m. National flag . . . 45 20
1402 5000m. Pres. Chissano . . . 85 40

Nos. 1400/2 were issued together, se-tenant, the commemorative inscription at the foot extending across the strip.

1995. Mammals. Multicoloured.
1403 500m. Type **263** 10 10
1404 2000m. Greater kudu (horiz) 25 10
1405 3000m. Bush pig (horiz) . . 40 20
1406 5000m. Bushbuck 65 30

1995. Various stamps surch.
1407 250m. on 12m.50 multicoloured (No. 931) 10 10
1408 300m. on 10m. blue and red (No. 896) 10 10
1409 500m. on 12m.50 multicoloured (No. 925) 10 10
1410 900m. on 12e.50 multicoloured (No. 771) 10 10
1411 1000m. on 12m.50 multicoloured (No. 837) 15 10
1412 1500m. on 16m. multicoloured (No. 1064) 20 10
1413 2000m. on 16m. multicoloured (No. 995) 25 10
1414 2500m. on 12m. multicoloured (No. 880) 35 15

265 Family carrying Foodstuffs

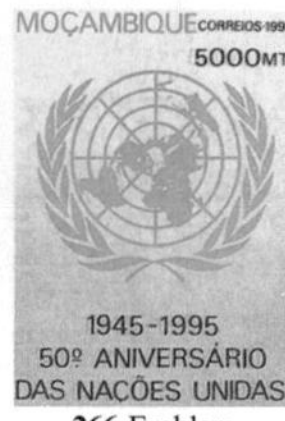

266 Emblem

1995. 50th Anniv of F.A.O.
1415 **265** 5000m. multicoloured . . 65 30

1995. 50th Anniv of United Nations Organization.
1416 **266** 5000m. blue and black 65 30

267 Child wearing Blue Cloak

1995. 20th Anniv of U.N.I.C.E.F. in Mozambique.
1417 **267** 5000m. multicoloured . . 60 65

268 Player scoring Goal

1996. Football. Multicoloured.
1418 1000m. Type **268** 25 15
1419 2000m. Goalkeeper holding ball 40 25
1420 4000m. Referee admonishing players 60 70
1421 6000m. Two players tackling for ball 75 75

269 Mask

270 "Mae Africa" (De Malangatana)

1996. Local Masks.
1422 **269** 1000m. multicoloured . . 10 15
1423 – 2000m. multicoloured . . 20 25
1424 – 4000m. multicoloured . . 40 45
1425 – 6000m. multicoloured . . 60 65
DESIGNS: 2000 to 6000m. Different masks.

1996. 15th Anniv of Mozambique Red Cross.
1426 **270** 5000m. multicoloured . . 50 55

271 African Elephant

272 Mine Field

1996. Wild Animals. Multicoloured.
1427 1000m. Type **271** 65 30
1428 2000m. White rhinoceros . . 85 55
1429 4000m. Leopard 90 90
1430 6000m. Pel's fishing owl . . 1·75 1·50

1996. Land Mine Clearance Campaign. Mult.
1431 2000m. Type **272** 30 25
1432 6000m. Warning sign . . . 75 65
1433 8000m. Soldier with mine detector 90 90
1434 10000m. Soldier lifting mine 1·25 1·25

273 City Street

274 5r. Stamp of 1876 and Magnifying Glass

1996. "Keeping the City Clean".
1435 **273** 2000m. multicoloured . . 30 25

1996. 120th Anniv of Mozambique Stamps.
1436 **274** 2000m. multicoloured . . 30 25

275 Mitumbui

1997. Local Boats. Multicoloured.
1437 2000m. Type **275** 20 25
1438 6000m. Muterere 60 65
1439 8000m. Lancha 80 85
1440 10000m. Dhow . . . . . . 1·00 1·10

276 Village Scene

1997. International Children's Day.
1441 **276** 2000m. multicoloured . . 30 25

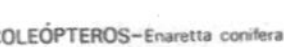

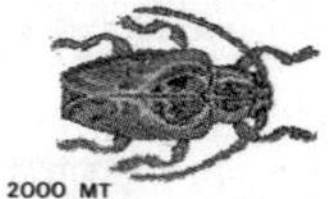

277 "Enaretta conitera"

1997. Beetles. Multicoloured.
1442 2000m. Type **277** 30 25
1443 6000m. "Zographus hieroglyphicus 70 65
1444 8000m. "Tragiscoschema bertolonii" 90 90
1445 10000m. "Tragocephala ducalis" . . . . 1·25 1·25
MS1446 97 × 105 mm. Nos. 1442/5 2·50 2·75

No. **MS**1446 also commemorates the "LUBRAPEX 97" International Stamp Exhibition, Brazil.

278 Yellow-billed Stork

280 Sun and Globe

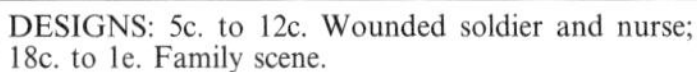

279 Abstract Patterns

1997. Aquatic Birds. Multicoloured.
1447 2000m. Type **278** 50 25
1448 4000m. Black-winged stilt 70 45
1449 8000m. Long-toed stint (horiz) . . . . 1·25 1·10
1450 10000m. Eastern white pelican . . . . 1·40 1·40

1997. Centenary of Joao Ferreira dos Santos Group.
1451 **279** 2000m. multicoloured . . 30 25

1997. Protection of Ozone Layer.
1452 **280** 2000m. multicoloured . . 30 25

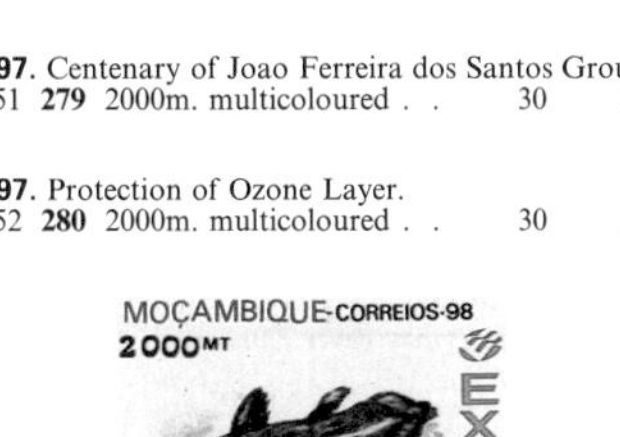

282 Coelacanth

1998. "EXPO '98" International Stamp Exhibition, Lisbon.
1454 **282** 2000m. multicoloured . . 55 25

283 Woman with Food Products

1998. Food Production.
1455 **283** 2000m. multicoloured . . 30 25

CHARITY TAX STAMPS

The notes under this heading in Portugal also apply here.

C **15** Arms of Portugal and Mozambique and Allegorical Figures

C **16** Prow of Galley of Discoveries and Symbols of Declaration of War

1916. War Tax Fund. Imperf, roul or perf.
C234 C **15** 1c. green 35 25
C235 C **16** 5c. red 35 30

C **18** "Charity"

C **22** Society's Emblem

1920. 280th Anniv of Restoration of Portugal. Wounded Soldiers and Social Assistance Funds.
C309 C **18** ¼c. green 70 70
C310 ½c. black 75 70
C311 1c. brown 75 70
C312 2c. brown 75 75
C313 3c. lilac 75 75
C314 4c. green 75 75
C315 – 5c. green 85 75
C316 – 6c. blue 85 75
C317 – 7½c. brown 85 75
C318 – 8c. yellow 85 75
C319 – 10c. lilac 85 85
C320 – 12c. pink 85 85
C321 – 18c. red 85 85
C322 – 24c. brown . . . . . 1·10 85
C323 – 30c. green . . . . . 1·10 85
C324 – 40c. red . . . . . . 1·10 85
C325 – 50c. yellow . . . . . 1·10 85
C326 – 1e. blue . . . . . . 1·10 85

DESIGNS: 5c. to 12c. Wounded soldier and nurse; 18c. to 1e. Family scene.

1925. Marquis de Pombal stamps of Portugal, but inscr "MOCAMBIQUE".
C327 C **73** 15c. brown 15 15
C328 – 15c. brown 15 15
C329 C **75** 15c. brown 15 15

1925. Red Cross. Surch **50 CENTAVOS**.
C330 C **22** 50c. yellow and grey 55 40

1926. Surch **CORREIOS** and value.
C337 C **22** 5c. yellow and red . . 75 60
C338 10c. yellow and green 75 60
C339 20c. yellow and grey 75 60
C340 30c. yellow and blue 75 60
C331 40c. yellow and grey 80 75
C341 40c. yellow and violet 75 60
C332 50c. yellow and grey 80 75
C342 50c. yellow and red . . 75 60
C333 60c. yellow and grey 80 75
C343 60c. yellow and brown 75 60
C334 80c. yellow and grey 80 75
C344 80c. yellow and blue 75 60
C335 1e. yellow and grey . . 90 75
C345 1e. yellow and green 75 60
C336 2e. yellow and grey . . 90 75
C346 2e. yellow and brown 75 60

C **25**

1928. Surch **CORREIOS** and value in black, as in Type C **25**.
C347 C **25** 5c. yellow and green 1·10 1·00
C348 10c. yellow and blue 1·10 1·00
C349 20c. yellow and black 1·10 1·00
C350 30c. yellow and red . . 1·10 1·00
C351 40c. yellow and purple 1·10 1·00
C352 50c. yellow and red . . 1·10 1·00
C353 60c. yellow and brown 1·10 1·00
C354 80c. yellow and brown 1·10 1·00
C355 1e. yellow and grey . . 1·10 1·00
C356 2e. yellow and red . . 1·10 1·00

C **27** C **29** Pelican

C **28** "Charity"

1929. Value in black.
C357 C **27** 40c. purple and blue 85 85
C358 40c. violet and red . . 85 85
C359 40c. violet and green 85 85
C360 40c. red and brown . . 85 85
C361 (No value) red & green . . . . 1·10 1·10
C362 40c. blue and orange 1·10 1·10
C363 40c. blue and brown 85 85
C364 40c. purple and green 1·10 1·00
C365 40c. black and yellow 1·10 1·10
C366 40c. black and brown 1·10 1·10

1942.
C383 C **28** 50c. pink and black . . 2·00 90

1943. Inscr "Colonia de Mocambique". Value in black.
C390 C **29** 50c. red . . . . 1·50 75
C389 50c. blue . . . . . . 1·50 75
C386 50c. violet . . . . . 1·50 75
C387 50c. brown . . . . . 1·50 75
C393 50c. green . . . . . 1·50 75

1952. Inscr "Provincia de Mocambique". Value in black.
C514 C **29** 30c. yellow 45 35
C515 50c. orange 45 35
C469 50c. green 75 40
C470 50c. brown 75 40

1957. No. C470 surch **$30**.
C511 C **29** 30c. on 50c. brown . . 45 25

C **56** Women and Children

C **58** Telegraph Poles and Map

1963.
C569 C **56** 30c. black, green & red 15 15
C570 50c. black, bistre & red 20 15
C571 50c. black, pink & red 20 15
C572 50c. black, green & red 20 15
C573 50c. black, blue & red 20 15
C574 50c. black, buff & red 20 15
C575 50c. black, grey & red 20 15
C576 50c. black, yell & red 20 15
C577 1e. grey, black and red 50 25
C578 1e. black, buff and red 15 10
C578a 1e. black, mauve & red 15 10

1965. Mozambique Telecommunications Improvement.
C579 C **58** 30c. black, pink & vio 10 10
C580 – 50c. black, brown & blue 10 10
C581 – 1e. black, orange & green 20 20

DESIGN—19½ × 36 mm: 50c., 1e. Telegraph linesman.

A 2e.50 in Type C **58** was also issued for compulsory use on telegrams.

NEWSPAPER STAMPS

1893. "Embossed" key-type of Mozambique surch.

(a) **JORNAES 2½ 2½**.
N53 Q 2½r. on 40r. brown . . . . 9·50 7·50

(b) **JORNAES 2½ REIS**.
N54 Q 2½r. on 40r. brown . . . . 45·00 30·00
N57 5r. on 40r. brown . . . . 28·00 24·00

1893. "Newspaper" key-type inscribed "MOCAMBIQUE".
N58 V 2½r. brown 25 20

POSTAGE DUE STAMPS

1904. "Due" key-type inscr "MOCAMBIQUE".
D146 W 5r. green 15 15
D147 10r. grey 15 15
D148 20r. brown 15 15
D149 30r. orange 30 20
D150 50r. brown 30 20
D151 60r. brown . . . . . . 1·25 75
D152 100r. mauve . . . . . . 1·25 75
D153 130r. blue 70 65
D154 200r. red . . . . 1·25 65
D155 500r. violet . . . . . . 1·25 65

1911. "Due" key-type of Mozambique optd **REPUBLICA**.
D162 W 5r. green 15 15
D163 10r. grey 15 15
D164 20r. brown 20 15
D165 30r. orange 20 15
D166 50r. brown 20 15
D167 60r. brown 30 20
D168 100r. mauve 30 20
D169 130r. blue 50 40
D170 200r. red 65 60
D171 500r. lilac 65 60

1917. "Due" key-type of Mozambique, but currency changed.
D246 W ½c. green 15 15
D247 1c. grey 15 15
D248 2c. brown 15 15
D249 3c. orange 15 15
D250 5c. brown 15 15
D251 6c. brown 15 15
D252 10c. mauve 15 15
D253 13c. blue 30 25
D254 20c. red 30 25
D255 50c. lilac 30 25

1918. Charity Tax stamps optd **PORTEADO**.
D256 C **15** 1c. green 50 40
D257 C **16** 5c. red 50 40

1922. "Ceres" key-type of Lourenco Marques (¼, 1½c.) and of Mozambique (1, 2½, 4c.) surch **PORTEADO** and value and bar.
D316 U 5c. on ¼c. black 55 40
D318 6c. on 1c. green 60 40
D317 10c. on 1½c. brown . . . 55 40

D319 20c. on 2½c. violet . . . 60 40
D320 50c. on 4c. pink 60 40

1924. "Ceres" key-type of Mozambique surch **Porteado** and value.
D321 U 20c. on 30c. green 35 30
D323 50c. on 60c. blue 55 40

1925. Marquis de Pombal charity tax designs as Nos. C327/9, optd **MULTA**.
D327 C **73** 30c. brown 15 15
D328 – 30c. brown 15 15
D329 C **75** 30c. brown 15 15

1952. As Type D **70** of Macao, but inscr "MOCAMBIQUE".
D468 10c. multicoloured 10 10
D469 30c. multicoloured 10 10
D470 50c. multicoloured 10 10
D471 1e. multicoloured 20 20
D472 2e. multicoloured 20 20
D473 5e. multicoloured 25 25

MOZAMBIQUE COMPANY Pt. 9

The Mozambique Company was responsible from 1891 until 1942 for the administration of Manica and Sofala territory in Portuguese East Africa. Now part of Mozambique.

1899. 1000 reis = 1 milreis.
1913. 100 centavos = 1 escudo.

1892. "Embossed" key-type inscr "PROVINCA DE MOCAMBIQUE" optd **COMPA. DE MOCAMBIQUE**.
10 Q 5r. black 70 40
2 10r. green 75 60
3 20r. red 95 60
4 25r. mauve 75 60
5 40r. brown 75 60
6 50r. blue . . . . 1·00 70
7 100r. brown . . . . 1·00 70
8 200r. violet . . . . 1·30 1·00
9 300r. orange . . . . 1·30 65

2

1895. Value in black or red (500, 1000r.).
33 **2** 2½r. yellow 30 25
114 2½r. grey . . . . 1·00 60
17 5r. orange 30 25
36 10r. mauve 45 30
115 10r. green 75 55
39 15r. brown 45 30
116 15r. green . . . . 1·00 60
20 20r. lilac 30 25
45 25r. green 45 30
117 25r. red . . . . 1·00 60
46 50r. blue 45 30
118 50r. brown . . . . 1·00 75
109 65r. blue 60 50
48 75r. red 45 30
119 75r. mauve . . . . 2·10 95
50 80r. green 45 30
52 100r. brown on buff . . . . 1·20 70
120 100r. blue on blue . . . . 2·10 1·50
110 115r. pink on pink . . . . 1·70 1·30
121 115r. brown on pink . . . . 2·75 1·90
111 130r. green on pink . . . . 1·70 1·30
122 130r. brown on yellow . . . 3·00 1·90
54 150r. orange on pink . . . 1·20 70
55 200r. blue on blue 95 90
123 200r. lilac on pink . . . . 3·00 2·00
56 300r. blue on brown . . . . 1·20 90
112 400r. black on blue . . . . 1·70 1·30
124 400r. blue on yellow . . . . 3·75 3·25
58 500r. black . . . . 1·20 90
125 500r. black on blue . . . . 3·75 3·25
126 700r. mauve on buff . . . . 3·75 3·50
59 1000r. mauve . . . . 1·30 90

1895. Surch **PROVISORIO 25**.
77 **2** 25 on 80r. green . . . . . . 21·00 24·00

1895. No. 6 optd **PROVISORIO**.
78 Q 50r. blue . . . . 4·00 3·50

1898. Vasco da Gama. Optd **1498 Centenario da India 1898**.
80 **2** 2½r. yellow . . . . 1·20 95
81 5r. orange . . . . 1·60 1·20
82 10r. mauve . . . . 1·60 1·20
84 15r. brown . . . . 3·00 1·90
86 20r. lilac . . . . 3·00 1·90
87 25r. green . . . . 3·00 1·90
99 50r. blue . . . . 2·10 1·70
89 75r. red . . . . 5·50 3·50
91 80r. green . . . . 3·75 2·75
101 100r. brown on buff . . . . 4·00 3·50
102 150r. orange on pink . . . 4·00 3·50
94 200r. blue on blue . . . . . 6·25 4·25
104 300r. blue on brown . . . . 7·50 5·00

1899. Surch **25 PROVISORIO**.
105 **2** 25 on 75r. red . . . . . . 3·25 2·75

1900. Surch **25 Reis** and bar.
106 **2** 25r. on 5r. orange . . . . . 2·50 1·50

1900. Perforated through centre and surch **50 REIS**.
108 **2** 50r. on half of 20r. lilac . . 1·20 95

1911. Optd **REPUBLICA**.
145 **2** 2½r. grey 40 35
147 5r. orange 40 35
148 10r. green 40 35
150 15r. green 25 20
151 20r. lilac 40 35
153 25r. red 40 35
155 50r. brown 40 35
156 75r. mauve 40 35
157 100r. blue on blue 40 35
159 115r. brown on pink 75 55
160 130r. brown on yellow . . . 75 55
161 200r. lilac on pink 75 55
162 400r. blue on yellow 75 55
163 500r. black on blue 75 55
164 700r. mauve on yellow . . . 1·20 70

1916. Surch **REPUBLICA** and value in figures.
166 **2** ¼c. on 2½r. grey 25 20
168 ½c. on 5r. orange 25 20
170 1c. on 10r. green 30 30
173 1½c. on 15r. green 30 30
175 2c. on 20r. lilac 30 30
178 2½c. on 25r. red 30 30
180 5c. on 50r. brown 30 30
181 7½c. on 75r. mauve 65 45
182 10c. on 100r. blue on blue 60 30
183 11½c. on 115r. brown on pink . . . . 1·40 65
184 13c. on 130r. brown on yell 1·40 65
185 20c. on 200r. lilac on pink 1·50 60
186 40c. on 400r. blue on yellow 1·50 60
187 50c. on 500r. black on blue 1·70 75
188 70c. on 700r. mauve on yell 1·70 90

1917. Red Cross Fund. Stamps of 1911 (optd **REPUBLICA**) optd with red cross and **31.7.17.**
189 **2** 2½r. grey . . . . 5·50 4·50
190 10r. green . . . . 5·50 4·50
191 20r. lilac . . . . 6·50 5·50
192 50r. brown . . . . 21·00 14·50
193 75r. mauve . . . . 48·00 44·00
194 100r. blue on blue . . . . . 55·00 55·00
195 700r. mauve on yellow . . . 75·00 75·00

1918. Stamps of 1911 (optd **REPUBLICA**) surch with new value.
196 **2** ¼c. on 700r. mauve on yellow . . . . 1·50 1·30
197 2½c. on 500r. black on blue 1·50 1·30
198 5c. on 400r. blue on yellow 1·50 1·30

14 Native Village

15 Ivory

1918.
199 **14** ¼c. green and brown . . . 15 15
233 ¼c. black and green 25 25
200 **15** ½c. black 15 15
201 – 1c. black and green 15 15
202 – 1½c. green and black . . . 15 15
203 – 2c. black and red 15 15
235 – 2c. black and grey 25 25
204 – 2½c. black and lilac 15 15
236 – 3c. black and orange . . . 35 30
205 – 4c. brown and green . . . 15 15
237 – 4c. black and red 35 30
227 **14** 4½c. black and grey 20 15
206 – 5c. black and blue 25 15
207 – 6c. blue and purple 30 25
238 – 6c. black and mauve . . . 40 30
228 – 7c. black and blue 75 25
208 – 7½c. green and orange . . . 35 30
239 – 8c. black and lilac 75 60
210 – 10c. black and red 45 30
229 – 12c. black and brown . . . 65 45
241 – 12c. black and green . . . 65 45
242 – 15c. black and red 60 55
212 – 20c. black and green . . . 20 15
213 – 30c. black and brown . . . 40 30
244 – 30c. black and green . . . 75 65
214 – 40c. black and green . . . 30 20
246 – 40c. black and blue . . . . 1·00 75
215 – 50c. black and orange . . . 40 30
247 – 50c. black and mauve . . . 1·20 1·00
230 – 60c. brown and red 75 50
231 – 80c. brown and blue . . . 1·75 80
248 – 80c. black and red . . . . 1·20 1·00
216 – 1e. black and green 70 50
249 – 1e. black and blue . . . . 1·20 1·00
232 – 2e. violet and red . . . . 2·25 80
250 – 2e. black and lilac . . . . 3·00 1·30
DESIGNS—HORIZ: 1, 3c. Maize field; 2c. Sugar factory; 5c., 2e. Beira; 20c. Law Court; 40c. Mangrove swamp. VERT: 1½c. India-rubber; 2½c. River Buzi; 4c. Tobacco bushes; 6c. Coffee bushes; 7, 15c. Steam train, Amatongas Forest; 7½c. Orange tree; 8, 12c. Cotton plants; 10, 80c. Sisal plantation; 30c. Coconut palm; 50, 60c. Cattle breeding; 1e. Mozambique Co's Arms.

1920. Pictorial issue surch in words.
217 ¼c. on 30c. (No. 213) . . . . 3·50 3·25
218 ½c. on 1e. (No. 216) . . . . 3·50 3·25
219 1½c. on 2½c. (No. 204) . . . 2·30 1·40
220 1½c. on 5c. (No. 206) . . . . 2·30 1·40
221 2c. on 2½c. (No. 204) . . . . 2·30 1·40
222 4c. on 20c. (No. 212) . . . . 2·75 2·20
223 4c. on 40c. (No. 214) . . . . 2·75 2·20
224 6c. on 8c. (No. 239) . . . . 3·75 2·20
225 6c. on 50c. (No. 215) . . . . 3·75 2·20

33

36 Tea

1925.
251 **33** 24c. black and blue . . . . 1·60 1·20
252 – 25c. blue and brown . . . 1·60 1·20
253 **33** 85c. black and red . . . . 1·30 85
254 – 1e.40 black and blue . . . 1·30 85
255 – 5e. blue and brown . . . . 2·00 75
256 **36** 10e. black and red . . . . 3·50 1·00
257 – 20e. black and green . . . 4·00 1·50
DESIGNS—VERT: 25c., 1e.40, Beira; 5e. Tapping rubber. HORIZ: 20e. River Zambesi.

38 Ivory

1931.
258 **38** 45c. blue . . . . 2·50 1·40
259 – 70c. brown . . . . 1·30 85
DESIGN—VERT: 70c. Gold mining.

40 Zambesi Bridge

1935. Opening of River Zambesi Railway Bridge at Sena.
260 **40** 1e. black and blue . . . . 2·75 1·90

41 Armstrong-Whitworth Atalanta Airliner over Beira

1935. Inauguration of Blantyre–Beira–Salisbury Air Route.
261 **41** 5c. black and blue 75 50
262 10c. black and red 75 50
263 15c. black and red 75 50
264 20c. black and green . . . 75 50
265 30c. black and green . . . 75 50
266 40c. black and blue . . . . 1·00 65
267 45c. black and blue . . . . 1·00 65
268 50c. black and purple . . . 1·00 65
269 60c. brown and red . . . . 1·70 1·00
270 80c. black and red . . . . 1·70 1·00

42 Armstrong-Whitworth Atalanta Airliner over Beira

1935. Air.
271 **42** 5c. black and blue 20 20
272 10c. black and red 20 20
273 15c. black and red 20 20
274 20c. black and green . . . 20 20
275 30c. black and green . . . 20 20
276 40c. black and green . . . 20 20
277 45c. black and blue 20 20
278 50c. black and purple . . . 20 20
279 60c. brown and red 20 20
280 80c. black and red 20 20
281 1e. black and blue 20 20
282 2e. black and lilac 50 45
283 5e. blue and brown 85 70
284 10e. black and red . . . . 1·10 85
285 20e. black and green . . . 2·20 1·00

43 Coastal Dhow

46 Palms at Beira

45 Crocodile

1937.
286 – 1c. lilac and green 20 20
287 – 5c. green and blue 20 20
288 **43** 10c. blue and red 20 20
289 – 15c. black and red 20 20
290 – 20c. blue and green 25 20
291 – 30c. blue and green 25 20
292 – 40c. black and blue 25 20
293 – 45c. brown and blue . . . 25 20
294 **45** 50c. green and violet . . . 25 20
295 – 60c. blue and red 25 20
296 – 70c. green and brown . . . 25 20
297 – 80c. green and red 35 25
298 – 85c. black and red 35 30
299 – 1e. black and blue 35 30
300 **46** 1e.40 green and blue . . . 75 30
301 – 2e. brown and lilac . . . . 1·20 35
302 – 5e. blue and brown 75 35
303 – 10e. black and red . . . . 1·20 60
304 – 20e. purple and green . . . 1·80 1·10
DESIGNS—VERT: 21 × 29 mm—1c. Giraffe; 20c. Common zebra; 70c. Native woman. 23 × 31 mm—10e. Old Portuguese gate, Sena; 20e. Arms. HORIZ: 29 × 21 mm—5c. Native huts; 15c. S. Caetano fortress, Sofala; 60c. Leopard; 80c. Hippopotami. 37 × 22 mm—5e. Railway bridge over River Zambesi. TRIANGULAR: 30c. Python; 40c. White rhinoceros; 45c. Lion; 85c. Vasco da Gama's flagship "Sao Gabriel"; 1e. Native in dugout canoe; 2e. Greater kudu.

1939. President Carmona's Colonial Tour. Optd **28-VII-1939 Visita Presidencial**.
305 – 30c. (No. 291) . . . . . . 1·20 90
306 – 40c. (No. 292) . . . . . . 1·20 90
307 – 45c. (No. 293) . . . . . . 1·20 90
308 **45** 50c. green and violet . . . 1·20 90
309 – 85c. (No. 298) . . . . . . 1·20 90
310 – 1e. (No. 299) . . . . . . 2·10 1·10
311 – 2e. (No. 301) . . . . . . 2·50 1·90

49 King Afonso Henriques

51 "Don John IV" after Alberto de Souza

1940. 800th Anniv of Portuguese Independence.
312 **49** 1e.75 light blue and blue 1·90 90

1940. Tercentenary of Restoration of Independence.
313 **51** 40c. black and blue 50 35
314 50c. green and violet . . . 50 35
315 60c. blue and red 50 35
316 70c. green and brown . . . 50 35
317 80c. green and red 50 35
318 1e. black and blue 50 35

CHARITY TAX STAMPS

The notes under this heading in Portugal also apply here.

1932. No. 236 surch **Assistencia Publica 2 Ctvos. 2.**
C260 2c. on 3c. black and orange 1·50 1·10

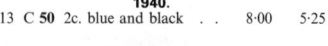

C 41 "Charity"

C 50

1934.
C261 C **41** 2c. black and mauve 1·60 1·10

1940.
C313 C **50** 2c. blue and black . . 8·00 5·25

C 52

1941.
C319 C **52** 2c. red and black . . . 8·00 5·25

NEWSPAPER STAMPS

1894. "Newspaper" key-type inscr "MOCAMBIQUE" optd **COMPA. DE MOCAMBIQUE**.
N15 V 2½r. brown 75 60

POSTAGE DUE STAMPS

D 9 D 32

1906.
D114 **D 9** 5r. green 50 40
D115 10r. grey 50 40
D116 20r. brown 50 40
D117 30r. orange 80 60
D118 50r. brown 80 60
D119 60r. brown . . . . . . 3·50 3·50
D120 100r. mauve . . . . . 1·10 1·00
D121 130r. blue . . . . . . 7·00 3·75
D122 200r. red . . . . . . 1·80 1·30
D123 500r. lilac . . . . . . 3·00 2·40

1911. Optd **REPUBLICA**.
D166 **D 9** 5r. green 25 25
D167 10r. grey 30 30
D168 20r. brown 30 30
D169 30r. orange 30 30
D170 50r. brown 30 30
D171 60r. brown 60 45
D172 100r. mauve 60 45
D173 130r. blue . . . . . . 1·30 1·20
D174 200r. red . . . . . . 1·60 1·30
D175 500r. lilac . . . . . . 1·80 1·60

1916. Currency changed.
D189 **D 9** ½c. green 25 25
D190 1c. grey 25 25
D191 2c. brown 25 25
D192 3c. orange 25 25
D193 5c. brown 25 25
D194 6c. brown 40 40
D195 10c. mauve 70 70
D196 13c. blue . . . . . . 1·30 1·30
D197 20c. red . . . . . . 1·30 1·30
D198 50c. lilac . . . . . . 2·00 2·00

1919.
D217 **D 32** ½c. green 10 10
D218 1c. black 10 10
D219 2c. brown 10 10
D220 3c. orange 10 10
D221 5c. brown 15 10
D222 6c. brown 20 20
D223 10c. red 20 20
D224 13c. blue 25 25
D225 20c. red 25 20
D226 50c. grey 30 30

MUSCAT Pt. 1

Independent Sultanate in Eastern Arabia with Indian and, subsequently, British postal administration.

12 pies = 1 anna; 16 annas = 1 rupee.

(2)

1944. Bicentenary of Al-Busaid Dynasty. Stamps of India (King George VI) optd as T **2**.
1 **100a** 3p. slate . . . . 30 6·00
2 ½a. mauve . . . . 30 6·00
3 9p. green . . . . 30 6·00
4 1a. red . . . . 30 6·00
5 **101** 1½a. plum . . . . 30 6·00
6 2a. red . . . . 60 6·00
7 3a. violet . . . . 1·00 6·00
8 3½a. blue . . . . 1·00 6·00
9 **102** 4a. brown . . . . 1·00 6·00
10 6a. green . . . . 1·25 6·00
11 8a. violet . . . . 1·25 6·00
12 12a. red . . . . 1·25 6·00
13 – 14a. purple (No. 277) . . 4·00 9·50
14 **93** 1r. slate and brown . . . 1·50 10·00
15 2r. purple and brown . . 3·00 16·00

OFFICIAL STAMPS

1944. Bicentenary of Al-Busaid Dynasty. Official stamps of India optd as T **2**.
O 1 **O 20** 3p. slate . . . . 50 11·00
O 2 ½a. purple . . . . . . 50 11·00
O 3 9p. green . . . . 50 11·00
O 4 1a. red . . . . 50 11·00
O 5 1½a. violet . . . . . . 50 11·00
O 6 2a. orange . . . . . . 70 11·00
O 7 2½a. violet . . . . . . 3·50 11·00
O 8 4a. brown . . . . 1·75 11·00
O 9 8a. violet . . . . 3·75 13·00
O10 **93** 1r. slate and brown (No. O138) . . . . . 2·50 21·00

For later issues see **BRITISH POSTAL AGENCIES IN EASTERN ARABIA**.

MUSCAT AND OMAN Pt. 19

Independent Sultanate in Eastern Arabia. The title of the Sultanate was changed in 1971 to Oman.

1966. 64 baizas = 1 rupee.
1970. 1000 baizas = 1 rial saidi.

12 Sultan's Crest **14** Nakhal Fort

1966.
94 **12** 3b. purple 10 10
95 5b. brown 10 10
96 10b. brown 10 10
97 A 15b. black and violet . . . 20 15
98 20b. black and blue . . . 30 20
99 25b. black and orange . . 35 20
100 **14** 30b. mauve and blue . . . 45 30
101 B 50b. green and brown . . . 70 40
102 C 1r. blue and orange . . . . 1·40 75
103 D 2r. brown and green . . . 2·75 1·50
104 E 5r. violet and red . . . . . 6·75 4·50
105 F 10r. red and violet . . . . 11·00 9·50
DESIGNS—VERT: 21¼ × 25¼ mm: A, Crest and Muscat harbour. HORIZ (as Type **14**): B, Samail Fort; C, Sohar Fort; D, Nizwa Fort; E, Matrah Fort; F, Mirani Fort.

15 Mina el Fahal

1969. 1st Oil Shipment (July 1967). Multicoloured.
106 20b. Type **15** 80 40
107 25b. Storage tanks 70 50
108 40b. Desert oil-rig . . . . . 1·10 85
109 1r. Aerial view from "Gemini 4" . . . . 2·75 2·00

1970. Designs as issue of 1966, but inscribed in new currency.
110 **12** 5b. purple 10 10
111 10b. brown 10 10
112 20b. brown 20 10
113 A 25b. black and violet . . . 25 15
114 30b. black and blue . . . 35 20
115 40b. black and orange . . 45 25
116 **14** 50b. mauve and blue . . . 50 30
117 B 75b. green and brown . . . 75 50
118 C 100b. blue and orange . . . 1·10 65
119 D ¼r. brown and green . . . 3·00 1·90
120 E ½r. violet and red . . . . . 6·00 3·75
121 F 1r. red and violet . . . . . 11·00 7·75

For later issues see **OMAN**.

MYANMAR Pt. 21

Formerly known as Burma.

100 pyas = 1 kyat.

81 Fountain, National Assembly Park (½-size illustration)

1990. State Law and Order Restoration Council.
312 **81** 1k. multicoloured . . . . 1·10 70

1990. As Nos. 258/61 of Burma but inscr "UNION OF MYANMAR".
313 15p. deep green and green . . 15 15
314 20p. black, brown and blue 00 00
315 50p. violet and brown . . . 50 25
316 1k. violet, mauve and black 1·00 70

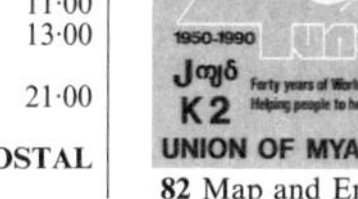

82 Map and Emblem

83 Nawata Ruby

1990. 40th Anniv of United Nations Development Programme.
322 **82** 2k. blue, yellow and black 2·20 1·40

1991. Gem Emporium.
323 **83** 50p. multicoloured . . . . 1·00 70

84 "Grandfather giving Sword to Grandson" (statuette, Nan Win)

85 Emblem

1992. 44th Anniv of Independence. Multicoloured.
324 50p. Warrior defending personification of Myanmar and map (poster, Khin Thein) 50 45
325 2k. Type **84** . . . . 2·30 1·70

1992. National Sports Festival.
326 **85** 50p. multicoloured 60 45

86 Campaign Emblem

87 Fish, Water Droplet and Leaf

1992. Anti-AIDS Campaign.
327 **86** 50p. red 50 45

1992. International Nutrition Conference, Rome.
328 **87** 50p. multicoloured 35 15
329 1k. multicoloured 60 45
330 3k. multicoloured . . . . 1·70 1·30
331 5k. multicoloured . . . . 3·00 2·20

88 Statue

89 Hintha (legendary bird)

1993. National Convention for Drafting of New Constitution.
332 **88** 50p. multicoloured 25 15
333 3k. multicoloured . . . . 1·70 1·30

1993. Statuettes. Multicoloured.
334 5k. Type **89** . . . . 2·75 2·30
335 10k. Lawkanat . . . . 5·75 4·75

90 Horseman aiming Spear at Target

1993. Festival of Traditional Equestrian Sports, Sittwe.
336 **90** 3k. multicoloured . . . . 1·70 1·30

91 Tree, Globe and Figures

92 Association Emblem

1994. World Environment Day.
337 **91** 4k. multicoloured . . . . 2·30 1·70

1994. 1st Anniv of Union Solidarity and Development Association.
338 **92** 3k. multicoloured . . . . 1·50 1·10

93 City and Emblem

1995. 50th Anniv of Armed Forces Day.
339 **93** 50p. multicoloured 45 45

94 Cross through Poppy Head

95 Camera and Film

1995. International Day against Drug Abuse.
340 **94** 2k. multicoloured . . . . 1·60 1·20

1995. 60th Anniv of Myanmar Film Industry.
341 **95** 50p. multicoloured 45 45

96 Figures around Emblem

97 Convocation Hall

1995. 50th Anniv of United Nations Organization.
342 **96** 4k. multicoloured . . . . 3·00 3·00

1995. 60th Anniv of Yangon University.
343 **97** 50p. multicoloured 45 45
344 2k. multicoloured . . . . 1·50 1·50

98 Punt

1996. Visit Myanmar Year. Multicoloured.
345 50p. Type **98** 35 35
346 4k. Karaweik Hall . . . . . 2·75 2·75
347 5k. Mandalay Palace . . . . 3·50 3·50

99 Four-man Canoe

1996. International Letter Writing Week. "Unity equals Success". Multicoloured.
348 2k. Type **99** . . . . 1·40 1·40
349 5k. Human pyramid holding flag aloft (vert) . . . . . 3·50 3·50

100 Breastfeeding

101 Emblem and Map of Myanmar

1996. 50th Anniv of U.N.I.C.E.F. Multicoloured.
350 1k. Type **100** 70 70
351 2k. Nurse inoculating child 1·40 1·40
352 4k. Children outside school 2·75 2·75

1997. 30th Anniv of Association of South-East Asian Nations.
353 **101** 1k. multicoloured 85 85
354 2k. multicoloured . . . . 1·70 1·70

102 Throne **103** Xylophone

1998. 50th Anniv of Independence.
355 **102** 2k. multicoloured . . . . 1·60 1·60

1998. Musical Instruments. Multicoloured.
356 5k. Type **103** . . . . 4·00 4·00
357 10k. Mon brass gongs . . . 7·75 7·75
358 20k. Rakhine auspicious drum . . . . 13·00 13·00
359 30k. Myanmar harp . . . . 19·00 19·00
360 50k. Shan pot drum . . . . 31·00 31·00
361 100k. Kachin brass gong . . 44·00 44·00

104 Emblem **105** Dove and U.P.U. Emblem

1999. Asian and Pacific Decade of Disabled Persons. Seventh Far East and South Pacific Region Disabled Games.
365 **104** 2k. multicoloured . . . . 1·70 1·70
366 5k. multicoloured . . . . 3·50 3·50

1999. 125th Anniv of Universal Postal Union.
367 **105** 2k. multicoloured . . . . 1·50 1·50
368 5k. multicoloured . . . . 3·25 3·25

106 People linking Hands around Map of Myanmar **107** Weathervane

2000. 52nd Anniv of Independence.
369 **106** 2k. multicoloured . . . . 1·50 1·50

2000. World Meteorological Day. 50th Anniv of World Meteorological Organization.
370 **107** 2k. black and blue . . . 1·70 1·70
371 – 5k. multicoloured . . . . 4·00 4·00
372 – 10k. multicoloured . . . 7·50 7·50
DESIGNS—HORIZ: 5k. Emblem and globe; 10k. Emblem and symbols for rain and sunshine.

108 Royal Palace Gate, Burma and Great Wall of China (½-size illustration)

2000. 50th Anniv of Burma–China Relations.
373 **108** 5k. multicoloured . . . . 4·00 4·00

109 Burning Poppy Heads and Needles

2000. Anti-drugs Campaign.
374 **109** 2k. multicoloured . . . . 1·50 1·50

110 Television Set and Map of Myanmar

2001. 53rd Anniv of Independence.
375 **110** 2k. multicoloured . . . . 1·50 1·50

111 National Flag and Globe

2002. 54th Anniv of Independence. Multicoloured.
376 2k. Type **111** 50 50
377 30k. As No. 376 but inscriptions and face value in English . . . . 8·25 8·25

112 Flag and Statue

2003. 55th Anniv of Independence. Multicoloured.
378 2k. Type **112** 50 50
379 30k. As No. 378 but inscriptions and face value in English . . . . 8·25 8·25

113 Black Orchid

2004. Flora. Multicoloured.
380 30k. Type **113** . . . . 5·25 5·25
381 30k. Mango . . . . 5·25 5·25

NABHA Pt. 1

A "Convention" state in the Punjab, India.

12 pies = 1 anna; 16 annas = 1 rupee.

Stamps of India optd **NABHA STATE**.

1885. Queen Victoria. Vert opt.
1 **23** ½a. turquoise . . . . 3·50 4·50
2 – 1a. purple . . . . 42·00 £150
3 – 2a. blue . . . . 17·00 45·00
4 – 4a. green (No. 96) . . . . . 75·00 £190
5 – 8a. mauve £300
6 – 1r. grey (No. 79) £325

1885. Queen Victoria. Horiz opt.
36 **40** 3p. red 50 20
14 **23** ½a. turquoise 30 10
15 – 9p. red . . . . 1·50 3·00
17 – 1a. purple . . . . 1·75 80
18 – 1a.6p. brown . . . . 1·50 3·00
20 – 2a. blue . . . . 2·00 1·50
22 – 3a. orange . . . . 3·00 2·00
12 – 4a. green (No. 69) . . . . . 35·00 £170
24 – 4a. green (No. 96) . . . . . 5·00 2·25
26 – 6a. brown (No. 80) . . . . 2·50 3·00
27 – 8a. mauve . . . . 2·50 2·00
28 – 12a. purple on red . . . . 3·50 4·00
29 – 1r. grey (No. 101) . . . . . 11·00 4·50
30 **37** 1r. green and red . . . . 10·00 4·25
31 **38** 2r. red and orange £110 £225
32 3r. brown and green £110 £300
33 5r. blue and violet £110 £425

1903. King Edward VII.
37 3p. grey 75 15
38 ½a. green (No. 122) . . . . . 1·00 60
39 1a. red (No. 123) . . . . . 1·60 70
40a 2a. lilac . . . . 2·75 35
40b 2½a. blue . . . . 18·00 85·00
41 3a. orange . . . . 1·00 40
42 4a. olive . . . . 2·50 1·75
43 6a. bistre . . . . 2·50 15·00
44 8a. mauve . . . . 9·00 20·00
45 12a. purple on red . . . . . 3·50 20·00
46 1r. green and red . . . . . 9·00 12·00

1907. As last, but inscr "INDIA POSTAGE & REVENUE".
47 ½a. green (No. 149) . . . . . 1·50 1·25
48 1a. red (No. 150) . . . . . . 1·00 70

1913. King George V. Optd in two lines.
49a **55** 3p. grey 25 35
50 **56** ½a. green 35 15
51 **57** 1a. red . . . . 1·00 10
59 1a. brown . . . . 4·75 2·50
52 **59** 2a. lilac 60 60
53 **62** 3a. orange 50 35
54 **63** 4a. olive . . . . 65 1·25
55 **64** 6a. bistre . . . . 85 4·75
56a **65** 8a. mauve . . . . 3·00 3·25
57 **66** 12a. red . . . . 1·90 20·00
58 **67** 1r. brown and green . . . 8·00 4·50

1928. King George V. Optd in one line.
60 **55** 3p. grey . . . . 1·40 15
61 **56** ½a. green 70 20
73 **79** ½a. green 50 40
61a **80** 9p. green . . . . 10·00 10·00
62 **57** 1a. brown . . . . 1·50 15
74 **81** 1a. brown 40 30
63 **82** 1¼a. mauve . . . . 1·75 5·50
64 **70** 2a. lilac . . . . 2·50 35
65 **61** 2½a. orange . . . . 80 8·00
66 **62** 3a. blue . . . . 2·75 1·10
75 **57** 3a. red . . . . 4·00 13·00
76 **63** 4a. olive . . . . 4·25 3·50
67 **71** 4a. green . . . . 3·00 1·75
71 **67** 2r. red and orange . . . . 26·00 95·00
72 5r. blue and purple . . . . 70·00 £275

1938. King George VI. Nos. 247/63.
77 **91** 3p. slate . . . . 7·00 70
78 ½a. brown . . . . 6·00 1·00
79 9p. green . . . . 19·00 4·00
80 1a. red . . . . 2·75 70
81 **92** 2a. red . . . . 1·25 6·00
82 – 2a.6p. violet . . . . 1·25 9·00
83 – 3a. green . . . . 1·40 5·00
84 – 3a.6p. blue . . . . 1·40 19·00
85 – 4a. brown . . . . 7·00 7·00
86 – 6a. green . . . . 3·00 20·00
87 – 8a. violet . . . . 2·25 20·00
88 – 12a. red . . . . 2·50 20·00
89 **93** 1r. slate and brown . . . . 11·00 26·00
90 2r. purple and brown . . . 25·00 90·00
91 5r. green and blue . . . . 35·00 £170
92 10r. purple and red . . . . 55·00 £350
93 15r. brown and green . . . £170 £650
94 25r. slate and purple £140 £650

1942. King George VI. Optd **NABHA** only.
95 **91** 3p. slate . . . . 35·00 4·00
105 **100a** 3p. slate . . . . 1·00 1·00
96 **91** ½a. brown . . . . 75·00 5·00
106 **100a** ½a. mauve . . . . 3·00 1·10
97 **91** 9p. green . . . . 11·00 13·00
107 **100a** 9p. green . . . . 2·50 1·10
98 **91** 1a. red . . . . 11·00 2·75
108 **100a** 1a. red . . . . 1·00 3·25
109 **101** 1a.3p. brown . . . . . . 1·00 2·75
110 1½a. violet . . . . 2·00 2·00
111 2a. red . . . . 1·10 4·00
112 3a. violet . . . . 3·50 3·75
113 3½a. blue . . . . 15·00 48·00
114 **102** 4a. brown . . . . 1·75 1·00
115 6a. green . . . . 10·00 45·00
116 8a. violet . . . . 9·00 35·00
117 12a. purple . . . . 6·00 48·00

OFFICIAL STAMPS

Stamps of Nabha optd **SERVICE**.

1885. Nos. 1/3 (Queen Victoria).
O1 ½a. turquoise . . . . 3·25 1·00
O2 1a. purple 60 20
O3 2a. blue . . . . 70·00 £130

1885. Nos. 14/30 (Queen Victoria).
O 6 ½a. turquoise 40 10
O 8 1a. purple . . . . 1·25 25
O 9 2a. blue . . . . 2·25 1·00
O11 3a. orange . . . . 24·00 75·00
O13 4a. green (No. 4) . . . . . 3·00 1·25
O15 6a. brown . . . . 18·00 28·00
O17 8a. mauve . . . . 2·75 1·00
O18 12a. purple on red . . . . . 6·50 18·00
O19 1r. grey . . . . 35·00 £250
O20 1r. green and red . . . . . 30·00 75·00

1903. Nos. 37/46 (King Edward VII).
O25 3p. grey . . . . 1·40 20·00
O26 ½a. green 80 35
O27 1a. red 70 10
O29 2a. lilac . . . . 1·75 40
O30 4a. olive . . . . 1·60 50
O32 8a. mauve . . . . 1·40 1·50
O34 1r. green and red . . . . . 1·60 2·25

1907. Nos. 47/8 (King Edward VII inscr "INDIA POSTAGE & REVENUE").
O35 ½a. green 75 50
O36 1a. red 75 30

1913. Nos. 54 and 58 (King George V).
O37 **63** 4a. olive . . . . 10·00 55·00
O38 **67** 1r. brown and green . . . 55·00 £400

1913. Official stamps of India (King George V) optd **NABHA STATE**.
O39a **55** 3p. grey . . . . 70 7·50
O40 **56** ½a. green 40 15
O41 **57** 1a. red 30 10
O42 **59** 2a. purple 50 50
O43 **63** 4a. olive 50 50
O44 **65** 8a. mauve . . . . 1·00 1·50
O46 **67** 1r. brown and green . . . 4·25 2·75

1932. Stamps of India (King George V) optd **NABHA STATE SERVICE**.
O47 **55** 3p. grey 10 15
O48 **81** 1a. brown 15 15
O49 **63** 4a. olive . . . . 21·00 2·50
O50 **65** 8a. mauve . . . . 1·00 2·00

1938. Stamps of India (King George VI) optd **NABHA STATE SERVICE**.
O53 **91** 9p. green . . . . 3·50 3·75
O54 1a. red . . . . 15·00 90

1943. Stamps of India (King George VI) optd **NABHA**.
O55 O **20** 3p. slate . . . . 80 1·10
O56 ½a. brown 90 30
O57 ½a. purple . . . . 3·50 70
O58 9p. green . . . . 1·25 20
O59 1a. red 60 20
O61 1½a. violet 70 40
O62 2a. orange . . . . 2·00 1·10
O64 4a. brown . . . . 3·50 3·00
O65 8a. violet . . . . 5·50 17·00

1943. Stamps of India (King George VI) optd **NABHA SERVICE**.
O66 **93** 1r. slate and brown . . . 8·50 35·00
O67 2r. purple and brown . . 27·00 £160
O68 5r. green and blue £170 £500

NAGORNO-KARABAKH Pt. 10

The mountainous area of Nagorno-Karabakh, mainly populated by Armenians, was declared an Autonomous Region within the Azerbaijan Soviet Socialist Republic on 7 July 1923.

Following agitation for union with Armenia in 1988 Nagorno-Karabakh was placed under direct U.S.S.R. rule in 1989. On 2 September 1991 the Regional Soviet declared its independence and this was confirmed by popular vote on 10 December. By 1993 fighting between Azerbaijan forces and those of Nagorno-Karabakh, supported by Armenia, led to the occupation of all Azerbaijan territory separating Nagorno-Karabakh from the border with Armenia. A ceasefire under Russian auspices was signed on 18 February 1994.

1993. 100 kopeks = 1 rouble.
1995. 100 louma = 1 dram.

1 National Flag

1993. Inscr "REPUBLIC OF MOUNTAINOUS KARABAKH".
1 **1** 1r. multicoloured 20 20
2 – 3r. blue, purple and brown . . 60 60
3 – 15r. red and blue . . . . . . 3·00 3·00
MS4 80 × 80 mm. 20r. brown, ultramarine and red . . . . . 4·00 4·00
MS5 60 × 80 mm. 20r. brown, ultramarine and red (imperf) 4·00 4·00
DESIGNS: 3r. President Arthur Mkrtchian; 15r. "We are Our Mountains" (sculpture of man and woman); 20r. Gandzasar Monastery.

Ա Բ Գ
(**2** "A") (**2a** "P") (**2b** "K")

1995. Nos. 1 and 3 surch in Armenian script as T **2/2b**.
6 **2** (50d.) on 1r. multicoloured 1·25 1·25
7 **2a** (100d.) on 15r. red and blue 2·25 2·25
8 **2b** (200d.) on 15r. red and blue 4·75 4·75

3 Dadiwank Monastery

1996. 5th Anniv of Independence. Multicoloured.

9 50d. Type **3** 50 50
10 100d. Parliament Building, Stepanakert 90 90
11 200d. "We are Our Mountains" (sculpture of man and woman) . . . . . 1·60 1·60
MS12 110 × 82 mm. 50d. Map and flag; 100d. As No. 10; 200d. As No. 11; 500d. Republic coat-of-arms (colours of national flag extend diagonally across the miniature sheet from bottom left to top right with the order incorrectly shown as orange, blue and red) . . . . 2·75 2·75

4 Boy playing Drum and Fawn (Erna Arshakyan)

1997. Festivals. Multicoloured.

13 50d. Type **4** (New Year) . . . 35 35
14 200d. Madonna and Child with angels (Mihran Akopyan) (Christmas) (vert) 1·75 1·75

5 Eagle and Demonstrator with Flag

1998. 10th Anniv of Karabakh Movement.

15 **5** 250d. multicoloured 75 75

6 Parliament Summer Palace

1998. 5th Anniv of Liberation of Shushi. Mult.

16 100d. Type **6** 30 30
17 250d. Church of the Saviour (vert) 75 75
MS18 124 × 92 mm. 750d. Type **6** 2·25 2·25

NAKHICHEVAN Pt. 10

An autonomous province of Azerbaijan, separated from the remainder of the republic by Armenian territory. Nos. 1 and 2 were issued during a period when the administration of Nakhichevan was in dispute with the central government.

100 qopik = 1 manat.

1 President Aliev

1993. 70th Birthday of President H. Aliev of Nakhichevan.

1 **1** 5m. black and red . . . . . . 3·75 3·75
2 – 5m. multicoloured . . . . . . 3·75 3·75
MS3 110 × 90 mm. Nos.1/2 . . . 8·00 8·00
DESIGN: No. 2, Map of Nakhichevan.

NAMIBIA Pt. 1

Formerly South West Africa, which became independent on 21 March 1990.

1990. 100 cents = 1 rand.
1993. 100 cents = 1 Namibia dollar.

141 Pres. Sam Nujoma, Map of Namibia and National Flag

1990. Independence. Multicoloured.

538 18c. Type **141** 20 15
539 45c. Hands releasing dove and map of Namibia (vert) 50 75
540 60c. National flag and map of Africa . . . . 1·00 1·50

142 Fish River Canyon

1990. Namibia Landscapes. Multicoloured.

541 18c. Type **142** 25 20
542 35c. Quiver-tree forest, Keetmanshoop 50 35
543 45c. Tsaris Mountains . . . 60 55
544 60c. Dolerite boulders, Keetmanshoop 70 65

143 Stores on Kaiser Street, c. 1899

1990. Centenary of Windhoek. Multicoloured.

545 18c. Type **143** 20 20
546 35c. Kaiser Street, 1990 . . . 30 35
547 45c. City Hall, 1914 . . . . 40 65
548 60c. City Hall, 1990 . . . . 50 1·00

144 Maizefields

145 Gypsum

1990. Farming. Multicoloured.

549 20c. Type **144** 15 20
550 35c. Sanga bull 30 35
551 50c. Damara ram 40 45
552 65c. Irrigation in Okavango 50 60

1991. Minerals. As Nos. 519/21 and 523/33 of South West Africa, some with values changed and new design (5r.), inscr "Namibia" as T **145**. Multicoloured.

553 1c. Type **145** 10 10
554 2c. Fluorite 15 10
555 5c. Mimetite 20 10
556 10c. Azurite 30 10
557 20c. Dioptase 35 10
558 25c. Type **139** 35 15
559 30c. Tsumeb lead and copper complex 50 20
560 35c. Rosh Pinah zinc mine 50 20
561 40c. Diamonds 65 25
562 50c. Uis tin mine 65 25
563 65c. Boltwoodite 65 35
564 1r. Rossing uranium mine . . 70 50
565 1r.50 Wulfenite . . . . . . 1·10 70
566 2r. Gold . . . . 1·50 1·10
567 5r. Willemite (vert as T **145**) 3·00 2·75

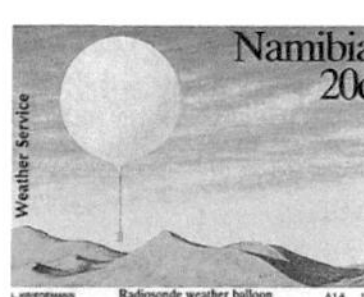

146 Radiosonde Weather Balloon

1991. Centenary of Weather Service. Mult.

568 20c. Type **146** 20 20
569 35c. Sunshine recorder . . . 35 30
570 50c. Measuring equipment . . 45 50
571 65c. Meteorological station, Gobabeb 50 60

147 Herd of Zebras

1991. Endangered Species. Mountain Zebra. Mult.

572 20c. Type **147** . . . . 1·10 60
573 25c. Mare and foal . . . . . 1·25 70
574 45c. Zebras and foal . . . . 2·00 1·75
575 60c. Two zebras . . . . . . 2·50 3·00

148 Karas Mountains

1991. Mountains of Namibia. Multicoloured.

576 20c. Type **148** 20 20
577 25c. Gamsberg Mountains . . 30 30
578 45c. Mount Brukkaros . . . 45 70
579 60c. Erongo Mountains . . . 65 1·00

149 Bernabe de la Bat Camp

1991. Tourist Camps. Multicoloured.

580 20c. Type **149** 45 30
581 25c. Von Bach Dam Recreation Resort 55 45
582 45c. Gross Barmen Hot Springs 85 65
583 60c. Namutoni Rest Camp 1·00 1·00

150 Artist's Pallet

1992. 21st Anniv of Windhoek Conservatoire. Multicoloured.

584 20c. Type **150** 20 15
585 25c. French horn and cello 25 20
586 45c. Theatrical masks 50 60
587 60c. Ballet dancers 65 90

151 Mozambique Mouthbrooder

1992. Freshwater Angling. Multicoloured.

588 20c. Type **151** 45 20
589 25c. Large-mouthed yellowfish 50 20
590 45c. Common carp 95 50
591 60c. Sharp-toothed catfish . . 1·10 65

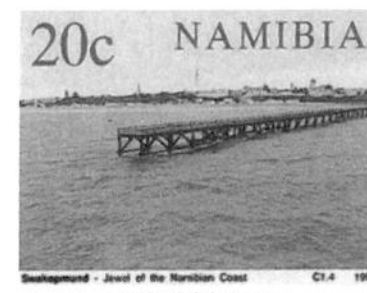

152 Old Jetty

1992. Centenary of Swakopmund. Mult.

592 20c. Type **152** 25 25
593 25c. Recreation centre . . . 25 25
594 45c. State House and lighthouse 80 60
595 60c. Sea front 85 75
MS596 118 × 93 mm. Nos. 592/5 2·75 2·75

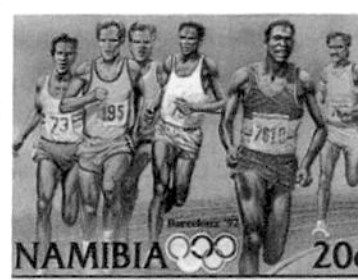

153 Running

154 Wrapping English Cucumbers

1992. Olympic Games, Barcelona. Mult.

597 20c. Type **153** 25 20
598 25c. Map of Namibia, Namibian flag and Olympic rings 30 20
599 45c. Swimming 50 40
600 60c. Olympic Stadium, Barcelona 65 55
MS601 115 × 75 mm. Nos. 597/600 (sold at 2r.) . . . . 2·25 2·75

1992. Integration of the Disabled. Mult.

602 20c. Type **154** 20 15
603 25c. Weaving mats 20 15
604 45c. Spinning thread 40 30
605 60c. Preparing pot plants . . 55 50

155 Elephants in Desert

1993. Namibia Nature Foundation. Rare and Endangered Species. Multicoloured.

606 20c. Type **155** 40 20
607 25c. Sitatunga in swamp . . 30 20
608 45c. Black rhinoceros 65 50
609 60c. Hunting dogs 65 60
MS610 217 × 59 mm. Nos. 606/9 (sold at 2r.50) . . . . 3·50 3·50

156 Herd of Simmentaler Cattle

1993. Centenary of Simmentalar Cattle in Namibia. Multicoloured.

611 20c. Type **156** 35 10
612 25c. Cow and calf 35 15
613 45c. Bull 70 40
614 60c. Cattle on barge 95 75

157 Sand Dunes, Sossusvlei

1993. Namib Desert Scenery. Multicoloured.

615 30c. Type **157** 25 20
616 40c. Blutkuppe 25 20
617 65c. River Kuiseb, Homeb 40 45
618 85c. Desert landscape 60 65

158 Smiling Child

1993. S.O.S. Child Care in Namibia. Mult.

619 30c. Type **158** 20 20
620 40c. Family 25 20
621 65c. Modern house 45 55
622 85c. Young artist with mural 65 80

159 "Charaxes jasius"

160 White Seabream

1993. Butterflies. Multicoloured.

707 5c. Type **159** 50 50
624 10c. "Acraea anemosa" . . . 20 20
625 20c. "Papilio nireus" 30 10
626 30c. "Junonia octavia" . . . 30 10
627 40c. "Hypolimnus misippus" 30 10
708 50c. "Physcaeneura panda" 60 40
629 65c. "Charaxes candiope" . . 40 30
630 85c. "Junonia hierta" 50 40
631 90c. "Colotis cellmene" . . . 50 40
632 $1 "Cacyreus dicksoni" . . . 55 35
633 $2 "Charaxes bohemani" . . 80 80
634 $2.50 "Stugeta bowkeri" . . 80 1·10
635 $5 "Byblia anvatara" . . . . 1·25 1·75
See also No. 648.

1994. Coastal Angling. Multicoloured.

636 30c. Type **160** 25 25
637 40c. Kob 25 25
638 65c. West coast steenbras . . 40 40
639 85c. Galjoen 60 60
MS640 134 × 89 mm. Nos. 636/9 (sold at $2.50) . . . . 2·00 2·50

161 Container Ship at Wharf

1994. Incorporation of Walvis Bay Territory into Namibia. Multicoloured.

641	30c. Type **161**	40	30
642	65c. Aerial view of Walvis Bay	60	80
643	85c. Map of Namibia	95	1·25

162 "Adenolobus pechuelii"

163 Yellow-billed Stork

1994. Flowers. Multicoloured.

644	35c. Type **162**	25	25
645	40c. "Hibiscus elliottiae"	25	25
646	65c. "Pelargonium cortusifolium"	40	40
647	85c. "Hoodia macrantha"	50	60

1994. Butterflies. As T **159**, but inscr "STANDARDISED MAIL". Multicoloured.

648	(–) "Graphium antheus"	25	20

No. 648 was initially sold at 35c., but this was subsequently increased to reflect changes in postal rates.

1994. Storks. Multicoloured.

649	35c. Type **163**	55	30
650	40c. Abdim's stork	55	30
651	80c. African open-bill stork	90	50
652	$1.10 White stork	1·00	65

164 Steam Railcar, 1908

1994. Steam Locomotives. Multicoloured.

653	35c. Type **164**	45	30
654	70c. Krauss side-tank locomotive No. 106, 1904	70	50
655	80c. Class 24 locomotive, 1948	75	55
656	$1.10 Class 7C locomotive, 1914	1·10	80

165 Cape Cross Locomotive No. 84 "Prince Edward", 1895

1995. Cent of Railways in Namibia. Mult.

657	35c. Type **165**	65	25
658	70c. Steam locomotive, German South West Africa	90	35
659	80c. South African Railways Class 8 steam locomotive	95	40
660	$1.10 Trans-Namib Class 33-400 diesel-electric locomotive	1·40	55
MS661	101 × 94 mm. Nos. 657/60	3·50	1·75

166 National Arms

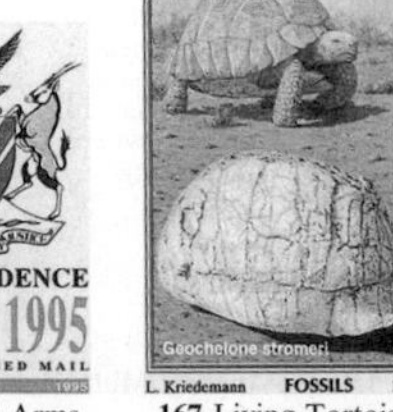

167 Living Tortoise and "Geochelone stromeri" (fossil)

1995. 5th Anniv of Independence.

662	**166** (–) multicoloured	40	30

No. 662 is inscribed "STANDARDISED MAIL" and was initially sold for 35c., but this was subsequently increased to reflect changes in postal rates.

1995. Fossils. Multicoloured.

663	40c. Type **167**	70	25
664	80c. Ward's diamond bird and "Diamantornis wardi" (fossil eggs)	1·00	80
665	90c. Hyraxes and "Prohyrax hendeyi" skull	1·10	90
666	$1.20 Crocodiles and "Crocodylus lloydi" skull	1·40	1·50

168 Martii Rautanen and Church

169 Ivory Buttons

1995. 125th Anniv of Finnish Missionaries in Namibia. Multicoloured.

667	40c. Type **168**	25	20
668	80c. Albin Savola and hand printing press	50	50
669	90c. Karl Weikkolin and wagon	60	65
670	$1.20 Dr. Selma Rainio and Onandjokwe Hospital	85	95

1995. Personal Ornaments. Multicoloured.

671	40c. Type **169**	20	20
672	80c. Conus shell pendant	45	45
673	90c. Cowrie shell headdress	55	55
674	$1.20 Shell button pendant	85	95

169a Warthog

1995. "Singapore '95" International Stamp Exhibition. Sheet 110 × 52 mm, containing design as No. 359b of South West Africa.

MS675	**169a** $1.20 multicoloured	1·10	1·25

170 U.N. Flag

1995. 50th Anniv of the United Nations.

676	**170** 40c. blue and black	20	20

171 Bogenfels Arch

1996. Tourism. Multicoloured.

677	(–) Type **171**	15	15
678	90c. Ruacana Falls	30	30
679	$1 Epupa Falls	30	30
680	$1.30 Herd of wild horses	35	50

No. 677 is inscribed "Standardised Mail" and was initially sold at 45c.

172 Sister Leoni Kreitmeier and Dobra Education and Training Centre

1996. Centenary of Catholic Missions in Namibia. Multicoloured.

681	50c. Type **172**	20	20
682	95c. Father Johann Malinowski and Heirachabis Mission	30	40
683	$1 St. Mary's Cathedral, Windhoek	30	40
684	$1.30 Archbishop Joseph Gotthardt and early church, Ovamboland	35	80

172a Caracal

1996. "CAPEX '96" International Stamp Exhibition, Toronto. Sheet 105 × 45 mm, containing design as No. 358c of South West Africa.

MS685	**172a** $1.30 multicoloured	85	90

173 Children and U.N.I.C.E.F. Volunteer

1996. 50th Anniv of U.N.I.C.E.F. Multicoloured.

686	(–) Type **173**	15	15
687	$1.30 Girls in school	60	60

No. 686 is inscribed "STANDARD POSTAGE" and was initially sold at 50c.

174 Boxing

1996. Centennial Olympic Games, Atlanta. Mult.

688	(–) Type **174**	15	15
689	90c. Cycling	50	40
690	$1 Swimming	30	40
691	$1.30 Running	40	70

No. 688 is inscribed "Standard Postage" and was initially sold at 50c.

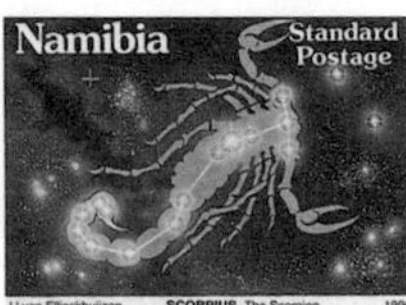

175 Scorpius

1996. Stars in the Namibian Sky. Multicoloured.

692	(–) Type **175**	15	15
693	90c. Sagittarius	30	30
694	$1 Southern Cross	35	30
695	$1.30 Orion	40	50
MS696	100 × 80 mm. No. 694	1·50	1·75

No. 692 is inscribed "Standard Postage" and was initially sold at 50c.

See also No. **MS**706.

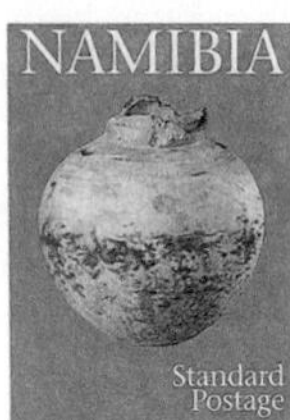

176 Urn-shaped Pot

1996. Early Pottery. Multicoloured.

697	(–) Type **176**	15	15
698	90c. Decorated storage pot	30	40
699	$1 Reconstructed cooking pot	30	40
700	$1.30 Storage pot	35	70

No. 697 is inscribed "Standard Postage" and was initially sold at 50c.

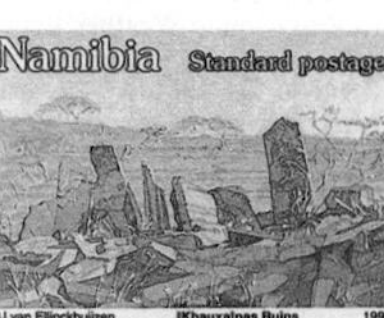

177 Khauxa!nas Ruins

1997. Khaux!nas Ruins.

701	**177** (–) multicoloured	35	20
702	– $1 multicoloured	80	50
703	– $1.10 multicoloured	90	90
704	– $1.50 multicoloured	1·25	1·75

DESIGNS: $1 to $1.50, Different views.

No. 701 is inscribed "Standard postage" and was initially sold at 50c.

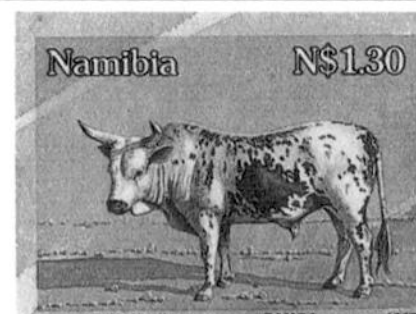

178 Ox

1997. "HONG KONG '97" International Stamp Exhibition and Chinese New Year ("Year of the Ox"). Sheet 103 × 67 mm.

MS705	**178** $1.30 multicoloured	1·10	1·10

1997. Support for Organised Philately. No. **MS**696 with margin additionally inscr "Reprint February 17 1997. Sold in aid of organised philately N$3.50".

MS706	$1 Southern Cross (sold at $3.50)	1·75	2·00

179 Heinrich von Stephan

180 Cinderella Waxbill

1997. Death Centenary of Heinrich von Stephan (founder of U.P.U.).

709	**179** $2 multicoloured	1·40	1·40

1997. Waxbills. Multicoloured.

710	50c. Type **180**	20	20
711	60c. Black-cheeked waxbill	20	20

181 Helmeted Guineafowl

1997. Greetings Stamp.

712	**181** $1.20 multicoloured	30	35

For similar designs see Nos. 743/6.

182 Jackass Penguins Calling

1997. Endangered Species. Jackass Penguin. Mult.

713	(–) Type **182**	25	30
714	$1 Incubating egg	40	40
715	$1.10 Adult with chick	50	50
716	$1.50 Penguins swimming	55	60
MS717	101 × 92 mm. As Nos. 713/16, but without WWF symbol (sold at $5)	1·50	1·50

No. 713 is inscribed "STANDARD POSTAGE" and was initially sold at 50c.

183 Caracal

1997. Wildcats. Multicoloured.

718	(–) Type **183**	20	20
719	$1 "Felis lybic"	40	30
720	$1.10 Serval	50	40
721	$1.50 Black-footed cat	60	55
MS722	100 × 80 mm. $5 As No. 721	2·00	2·25

No. **MS**722 was sold in aid of organised philately in Southern Africa.

No. 718 is inscribed "STANDARD POSTAGE" and was initially sold at 50c.

184 "Catophractes alexandri"

1997. Greeting Stamps. Flowers and Helmeted Guineafowl. Multicoloured.
723 (–) Type **184** 60 60
724 (–) "Crinum paludosum" . . 60 60
725 (–) "Gloriosa superba" . . . 60 60
726 (–) "Tribulus zeyheri" . . . 60 60
727 (–) "Aptosimum pubescens" 60 60
728 50c. Helmeted guineafowl raising hat 10 10
729 50c. Holding bouquet 10 10
730 50c. Ill in bed 10 10
731 $1 With heart round neck . . 15 20
732 $1 With suitcase and backpack 15 20
Nos. 723/7 are inscribed "Standard Postage" and were initially sold at 50c. each.

185 Collecting Bag

1997. Basket Work. Multicoloured.
733 50c. Type **185** 20 20
734 90c. Powder basket 30 30
735 $1.20 Fruit basket 35 35
736 $2 Grain basket 70 75

186 Veterinary Association Coat of Arms

1997. 50th Anniv of Namibian Veterinary Association.
737 **186** $1.50 multicoloured . . . 50 50

187 Head of Triceratops

1997. Youth Philately. Dinosaurs. Sheet 82 × 56 mm.
MS738 **187** $5 multicoloured . . 1·50 1·75

188 German South West Africa Postman
189 False Mopane

1997. World Post Day.
739 **188** (–) multicoloured 20 20
No. 739 is inscribed "STANDARD POSTAGE" and was initially sold at 50c.

1997. Trees. Multicoloured.
740 (–) Type **189** 15 20
741 $1 Ana tree 30 40
742 $1.10 Shepherd's tree 35 55
743 $1.50 Kiaat 50 70
No. 740 is inscribed "STANDARD POSTAGE" and was initially sold at 50c.

1997. Christmas. As T **181**, showing Helmeted Guineafowl, each with festive frame. Mult.
744 (–) Guineafowl facing right 15 20
745 $1 Guineafowl in grass . . . 30 30
746 $1.10 Guineafowl on rock . . 35 40
747 $1.50 Guineafowl in desert 50 55
MS748 110 × 80 mm. $5 Helmeted guineafowl (vert) . . . . . . 2·25 2·25
No. 744 is inscribed "standard postage" and was initially sold at 50c.

190 Flame Lily
191 John Muafangejo

1997. Flora and Fauna. Multicoloured.
749 5c. Type **190** 10 10
750 10c. Bushman poison . . . 10 10
751 20c. Camel's foot 10 10
752 30c. Western rhigozum . . . 10 10
753 40c. Blue-cheeked bee-eater 10 10
754 50c. Laughing dove 10 10
755 (–) Peach-faced lovebird ("Roseyfaced Lovebird") 10 10
756 60c. Lappet-faced vulture . . 10 10
757a 90c. Southern yellow-billed hornbill ("Yellow-billed Hornbill") 15 20
758a $1 Lilac-breasted roller . . . 15 20
759a $1.10 Hippopotamus . . . 15 20
760 $1.20 Giraffe 20 25
761 (–) Leopard 20 25
762 $1.50 Elephant 25 30
763 $2 Lion 35 40
764 $4 Buffalo 65 70
765 $5 Black rhinoceros 85 90
766 $10 Cheetah . . . . 1·70 1·80
No. 755 is inscribed "standard postage" and was initially sold at 50c.; No. 761 is inscribed "postcard rate" and was initially sold at $1.20.
Nos. 755, 758 and 761 exist with ordinary or self-adhesive gum.

1997. 10th Death Anniv of John Muafangejo (artist).
770 **191** (50c.) multicoloured . . . 75 30
No. 770 is inscribed "STANDARD POSTAGE" and was initially sold at 50c.

192 Gabriel B. Taapopi

1998. Gabriel B. Taapopi (writer) Commemoration.
771 **192** (–) silver and brown . . . 75 30
No. 771 is inscribed "STANDARD POSTAGE" and was initially sold at 50c.

193 Year of the Tiger

1998. International Stamp and Coin Exhibition, 1997, Shanghai. Sheets 165 × 125 mm or 97 × 85 mm, containing multicoloured designs as T **193**. (a) Lunar New Year.
MS772 165 × 125 mm. $2.50 × 6. Type **193**; Light green tiger and circular symbol; Yellow tiger and head symbol; Blue tiger and square symbol; Emerald tiger and square symbol; Mauve tiger and triangular symbol (61 × 29 mm) 2·50 3·25
MS773 97 × 85 mm. $6 Symbolic tiger designs (71 × 40 mm) . . 1·25 1·40

(b) Chinese Calendar.
MS774 165 × 125 mm. $2.50 × 6. Various calendar symbols (24 × 80 mm) . . . . 2·50 3·25
MS775 97 × 85 mm. $6 Soft toy tigers (71 × 36 mm) . . . . . 1·25 1·40

(c) 25th Anniv of Shanghai Communique.
MS776 165 × 125 mm. $3.50 × 4. Pres. Nixon's visit to China, 1972; Vice Premier Deng Xiaoping's visit to U.S.A., 1979; Pres. Reagan's visit to China, 1984; Pres. Bush's visit to China, 1989 (61 × 32 mm) . . . . 2·50 3·00
MS777 97 × 85 mm. $6 China–U.S.A. Communique, 1972 (69 × 36 mm) . . . . 1·25 1·40

(d) Pres. Deng Xiaoping's Project for Unification of China.
MS778 165 × 125 mm. $3.50 × 4. Beijing as national capital; Return of Hong Kong; Return of Macao; Links with Taiwan (37 × 65 mm) 2·50 3·00
MS779 97 × 85 mm. $6 Reunified China (71 × 41 mm) . . . . . 1·25 1·40

(e) Return of Macao to China, 1999.
MS780 Two sheets, each 165 × 120 mm. (a) $4.50 × 3 Carnival dragon and modern Macao (44 × 33 mm). (b) $4.50 × 3 Ruins of St. Paul's Church, Macao (62 × 29 mm) Set of 2 sheets . . 4·00 5·50
MS781 Two sheets, each 97 × 85 mm. (a) $6 Carnival dragon and modern Macao (62 × 32 mm). (b) $6 Deng Xiaoping and ruins of St. Paul's Church, Macao (71 × 36 mm) Set of 2 sheets . . . . 2·00 2·75

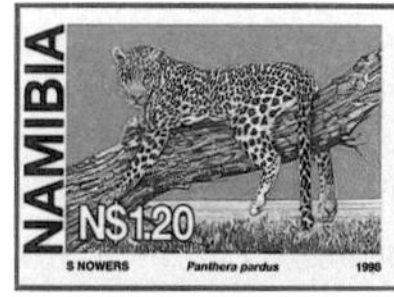

194 Leopard

1998. Large Wild Cats. Multicoloured.
782 $1.20 Type **194** 50 25
783 $1.90 Lioness and cub . . . 70 55
784 $2 Lion 70 60
785 $2.50 Cheetah 80 90
MS786 112 × 98 mm. Nos. 782/5 2·50 2·50

195 Narra Plant
196 Collecting Rain Water

1998. Narra Cultivation.
787 **195** $2.40 multicoloured . . . 50 60

1998. World Water Day.
788 **196** (–) multicoloured 50 30
No. 788 is inscribed "STANDARD POSTAGE" and was initially sold at 50c. On 1 April 1998 the standard postage rate was increased to 55c.

1998. Diana, Princess of Wales Commemoration. Sheet 145 × 70 mm, containing vert designs as T **91** of Kiribati. Multicoloured.
MS789 $1 Princess Diana wearing protective mask; $1 Wearing Red Cross badge; $1 Wearing white shirt; $1 Comforting crippled child 1·60 1·75

197 White-faced Scops Owl ("Whitefaced Owl")

1998. Owls of Namibia. Multicoloured.
790 55c. Black-tailed tree rat (20 × 24 mm) 10 10
791 $1.50 Type **197** 25 30
792 $1.50 African barred owl ("Barred Owl") 25 30
793 $1.90 Spotted eagle owl . . . 30 35
794 $1.90 Barn owl (61 × 24 mm) 30 35
See also No. **MS**850.

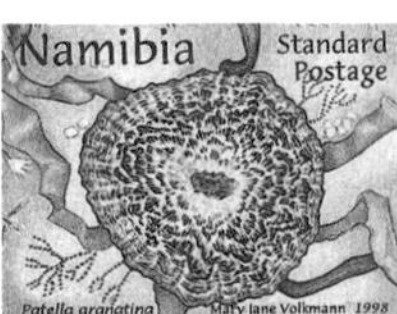

198 "Patella ganatina" (Limpet)

1998. Shells. Multicoloured.
795 (–) Type **198** 35 10
796 $1.10 "Cymatium cutaceum africanum" (Triton) . . . 70 30
797 $1.50 "Conus mozambicus" (Cone) 90 65
798 $6 "Venus verrucosa" (Venus clam) . . . . 2·75 3·50
MS799 109 × 84 mm. Nos. 795/8 3·75 3·75
No. 795 is inscribed "Standard Postage" and was initially sold at 55c.

199 Underwater Diamond Excavator

1998. Marine Technology. Sheet 70 × 90 mm.
MS800 **199** $2.50 multicoloured 1·25 1·25

200 "Chinga" (cheetah)

1998. Wildlife Conservation. "Racing for Survival" (Olympic sprinter Frank Frederiks v cheetah). Sheet 108 × 80 mm.
MS801 **200** $5 multicoloured . . 1·25 1·40

201 Namibian Beach

1998. World Environment Day. Multicoloured.
802 (–) Type **201** 10 10
803 $1.10 Okavango sunset . . . 20 25
804 $1.50 Sossusvlei 30 35
805 $1.90 African Moringo tree 40 45
No. 802 is inscribed "STANDARD POSTAGE" and was initially sold at 55c.

202 Two Footballers
203 Chacma Baboon

1998. World Cup Football Championship, France. Sheet 80 × 56 mm.
MS806 **202** $5 multicoloured . . 1·25 1·40

1998. Animals with their Young. Sheet 176 × 60 mm, containing T **203** and similar vert designs.
MS807 $1.50, Type **203**; $1.50, Blue Wildebeest; $1.50, Meercat (suricate); $1.50, African Elephant; $1.50, Burchell's Zebra 1·75 1·90

204 Carmine Bee Eater

1998. Wildlife of the Caprivi Strip. Multicoloured.
808 60c. Type **204** 25 25
809 60c. Sable antelope (40 × 40 mm) 25 25
810 60c. Lechwe (40 × 40 mm) . . 25 25
811 60c. Woodland waterberry . . 25 25
812 60c. Nile monitor (40 × 40 mm) 25 25
813 60c. African jacana 25 25
814 60c. African fish eagle . . . 25 25
815 60c. Woodland kingfisher . . 25 25
816 60c. Nile crocodile (55 × 30 mm) 25 25
817 60c. Black mamba (32 × 30 mm) 25 25
Nos. 808/17 were printed together, se-tenant, with the backgrounds forming a composite design.

205 Black Rhinoceros and Calf

1998. "ILSAPEX '98" International Stamp Exhibition, Johannesburg. Sheet 103 × 68 mm.
MS818 **205** $5 multicoloured . . 1·40 1·50

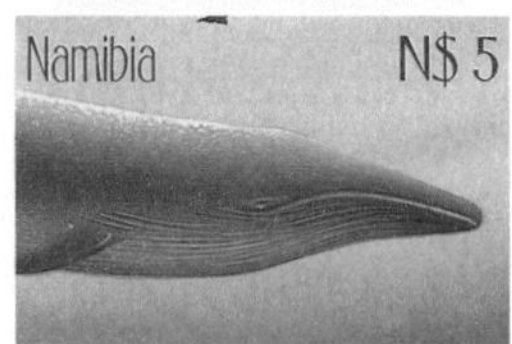

206 Blue Whale

1998. Whales of the Southern Oceans (joint issue with Norfolk Island and South Africa). Sheet 103 × 70 mm.
MS819 **206** $5 multicoloured . . 1·60 1·75

207 Damara Dik-dik 208 Yoka perplexed

1999. "Fun Stamps for Children". Animals. Mult.
820 $1.80 Type **207** . . . . . . 1·25 1·25
821 $2.65 Striped tree squirrel (26 × 36 mm) . . . . . . 2·25 2·25

1999. "Yoka the Snake" (cartoon). Multicoloured. Self-adhesive.
822 $1.60 Type **208** 35 40
823 $1.60 Yoka under attack (33 × 27 mm) 35 40
824 $1.60 Yoka caught on branch 35 40
825 $1.60 Yoka and wasps (33 × 27 mm) 35 40
826 $1.60 Yoka and footprint . . 35 40
827 $1.60 Yoka and tail of red and white snake 35 40
828 $1.60 Mouse hunt (33 × 27 mm) 35 40
829 $1.60 Snakes entwined . . . 35 40
830 $1.60 Red and white snake singing 35 40
831 $1.60 Yoka sulking (33 × 27 mm) 35 40

209 "Windhuk" (liner)

1999. "Windhuk" (liner) Commemoration. Sheet 110 × 90 mm.
MS832 **209** $5.50 multicoloured 90 95

210 Zogling Glider, 1928

1999. Gliding in Namibia. Multicoloured.
833 $1.60 Type **210** 25 30
834 $1.80 Schleicher glider, 1998 30 35

211 Yoka the Snake with Toy Zebra

1999. "iBRA '99" International Stamp Exhibition, Nuremberg. Sheet 110 × 84 mm.
MS835 **211** $5.50 multicoloured 90 95

212 Greater Kestrel

1999. Birds of Prey. Multicoloured.
836 60c. Type **212** 50 25
837 $1.60 Common kestrel ("Rock Kestrel") 75 55
838 $1.80 Red-headed falcon ("Red-necked Falcon") . . 75 65
839 $2.65 Lanner falcon . . . . 1·25 1·40

213 Wattled Crane

1999. Wetland Birds. Multicoloured.
840 $1.60 Type **213** 25 30
841 $1.80 Variegated sandgrouse ("Burchell's Sandgrouse") 30 35
842 $1.90 White-collared pratincole ("Rock Pratincole") 30 35
843 $2.65 Eastern white pelican 40 45

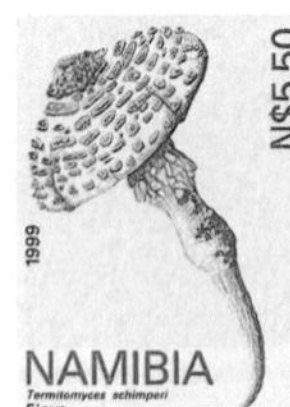

214 "Termitomyces schimperi" (fungus) 216 Johanna Gertze

215 "Eulophia hereroensis" (orchid)

1999. "PhilexFrance '99" International Stamp Exhibition, Paris. Sheet 79 × 54 mm.
MS844 **214** $5.50 multicoloured 90 95

1999. "China '99" International Philatelic Exhibition, Beijing. Orchids. Multicoloured.
845 $1.60 Type **215** 25 30
846 $1.80 "Ansellia africana" . . 30 35
847 $2.65 "Eulophia leachii" . . 40 45
848 $3.90 "Eulophia speciosa" . . 65 70
MS849 72 × 72 mm. $5.50 "Eulophia walleri" 90 95

1999. Winning entry in 5th Stamp World Cup, France. Sheet 120 × 67 mm, design as No. 794, but with changed face value. Multicoloured.
MS850 $11 Barn owl (61 × 24 mm) 1·80 1·90

1999. Johanna Gertze Commemoration.
851 **216** $20 red, pink and blue . . 3·25 3·50

217 Sunset over Namibia

1999. New Millennium. Multicoloured.
852 $2.20 Type **217** 35 40
853 $2.40 Sunrise over Namibia 35 40
MS854 77 × 54 mm. $9 Globe (hologram) (37 × 44 mm) . . . 1·50 1·60

218 South African Shelduck

2000. Ducks of Namibia. Multicoloured.
855 $2 Type **218** 35 40
856 $2.40 White-faced whistling duck 35 40
857 $3 Comb duck ("Knobbilled duck") 50 55
858 $7 Cape shoveler . . . . . . 1·20 1·30
No. 858 is inscribed "Cape shoveller" in error.

2000. Nos. 749/52 surch with **standard postage** (859) or new values (others).
859 (–) on 5c. Type **190** 10 15
860 $1.80 on 30c. Western rhigozum 30 35
861 $3 on 10c. Bushman poison 50 55
862 $6 on 20c. Camel's foot . . . 1·00 1·10
No. 859 was initially sold at 65c. The other surcharges show face values.

220 Namibian Children

2000. 10th Anniv of Independence. Multicoloured.
863 65c. Type **220** 10 15
864 $3 Namibian flag 50 55

221 Actor playing Jesus wearing Crown of Thorns

2000. Easter Passion Play. Multicoloured.
865 $2.10 Type **221** 35 40
866 $2.40 On the way to Calvary 35 40

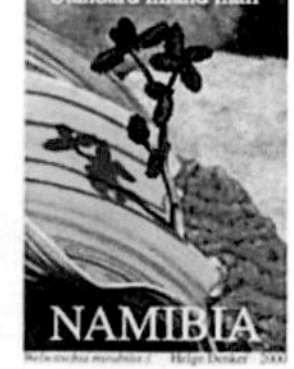

222 Tenebrionid Beetle 223 *Welwitschia mirabilis*

2000. "The Stamp Show 2000" International Stamp Exhibition, London. Wildlife of Namibian Dunes. Sheet 165 × 73 mm, containing T **222** and similar multicoloured designs.
MS867 $2 Type **222**; $2 Namib golden mole; $2 Brown hyena; $2 Shovel-snouted lizard (49 × 30 mm); $2 Dune lark (25 × 36 mm); $6 Namib side-winding adder (25 × 36 mm) . . 2·75 3·00

2000. *Welwitschia mirabilis* (prehistoric plant). Multicoloured.
868 (–) Type **223** 10 15
869 $2.20 *Welwitschia mirabilis* from above 35 40
870 $3 Seed pods 50 55
871 $4 Flats covered by *Welwitschia mirabilis* . . . 65 70
No. 868 is inscribed "Standard inland mail" and was originally sold for 65c.

224 High Energy Stereoscopic System Telescopes

2000. High Energy Stereoscopic System Telescopes Project. Namibian Khomas Highlands. Sheet 100 × 70 mm.
MS872 **224** $11 multicoloured . . 1·80 1·90

225 Jackal-berry Tree

2000. Trees with Nutritional Value. Multicoloured.
873 (–) Type **225** 10 15
874 $2 Sycamore fig 35 40
875 $2.20 Bird plum 35 40
876 $7 Marula . . . . 1·20 1·30
No. 873 is inscribed "Standard inland mail" and was originally sold for 65c.

226 Yoka and Nero the Elephant

2000. "Yoka the Snake" (cartoon) (2nd series). Sheet 103 × 68 mm.
MS877 **226** $11 multicoloured . . 1·80 1·90

227 Striped Anemone 229 Wood-burning Stove

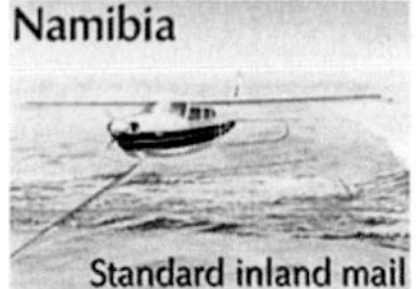

228 Cessna 210 Turbo Aircraft

2001. Sea Anemone. Multicoloured.
878 (–) Type **227** 10 15
879 $2.45 Violet-spotted anemone 40 45
880 $3.50 Knobbly anemone . . 60 65
881 $6.60 False plum anemone 1·10 1·20
No. 878 is inscribed "Standard inland mail" and was originally sold for 70c.

2001. Civil Aviation. Multicoloured.
882 (–) Type **228** 10 15
883 $2.20 Douglas DC-6B airliner 35 40
884 $2.50 Pitts S2A bi-plane . . . 40 45
885 $13.20 Bell 407 helicopter . . 2·20 2·30
No. 882 is inscribed "Standard inland mail" and was originally sold for 70c.

2001. Renewable Energy Sources. Multicoloured.
886 (–) Type **229** 15 20
887 (–) Biogas digester 15 20
888 (–) Solar cooker 15 20
889 (–) Re-cycled tyre 15 20
890 (–) Solar water pump 15 20
891 $3.50 Solar panel above traditional hut 60 65
892 $3.50 Solar street light . . . 60 65
893 $3.50 Solar panels on hospital building 60 65
894 $3.50 Solar telephone 60 65
895 $3.50 Wind pump 60 65
Nos. 886/95 were printed together, se-tenant, with the backgrounds forming a composite design.
Nos. 886/90 are inscribed "Standard Mail" and were originally sold for $1 each.

230 Ruppell's Parrot 231 Plaited Hair, Mbalantu

2001. Flora and Fauna from the Central Highlands. Multicoloured.
896 (–) Type **230** 15 20
897 (–) Flap-necked chameleon (40 × 30 mm) 15 20
898 (–) Klipspringer (40 × 30 mm) 15 20
899 (–) Rockrunner (40 × 30 mm) 15 20
900 (–) Pangolin (40 × 40 mm) 15 20
901 $3.50 Camel thorn (55 × 30 mm) 60 65
902 $3.50 Berg aloe (40 × 30 mm) 60 65
903 $3.50 Kudu (40 × 40 mm) . . 60 65
904 $3.50 Rock agama (40 × 40 mm) 60 65
905 $3.50 Armoured ground cricket (40 × 30 mm) . . . 60 65
Nos. 896/905 were printed together, se-tenant, with the backgrounds forming a composite design.
Nos. 896/900 are inscribed "Standard Mail" and were originally sold for $1 each.

2002. Traditional Women's Hairstyles and Headdresses. Multicoloured.
906 (–) Type **231** 15 20
907 (–) Cloth headdress, Damara 15 20
908 (–) Beaded hair ornaments, San 15 20

909 (–) Leather ekori headdress, Herero 15 20
910 (–) Bonnet, Baster 15 20
911 (–) Seed necklaces, Mafue 15 20
912 (–) Thihukeka hairstyle, Mbukushu 15 20
913 (–) Triangular cloth headdress, Herero 15 20
914 (–) Goat-skin headdress, Himba 15 20
915 (–) Horned headdress, Kwanyama 15 20
916 (–) Headscarf, Nama 15 20
917 (–) Plaits and oshikoma, Ngandjera/Kwaluudhi 15 20

Nos. 906/17 are inscribed "STANDARD MAIL" and were originally sold for $1 each.

232 African Hoopoe

2002. Birds. Multicoloured.
918 (–) Type **232** 15 20
919 $2.20 Paradise flycatcher 35 40
920 $2.60 Swallowtailed bee eater 40 45
921 $2.80 Malachite kingfisher 45 50

No. 918 is inscribed "Standard Mail" and was originally sold for $1.

NANDGAON Pt. 1

A state of central India. Now uses Indian stamps.

12 pies = 1 anna; 16 annas = 1 rupee.

1

2 (½a.)

1891. Imperf.
1 **1** ½a. blue 5·00 £150
2 2a. pink 22·00 £450

1893. Imperf.
3 **2** ½a. green 11·00 75·00
6 1a. red 48·00 £110
4 2a. red 9·50 75·00

OFFICIAL STAMPS

1893. Optd **M.B.D.** in oval.
O1 **1** ½a. blue £350
O4 **2** ½a. green 5·50 9·50
O5 1a. red 8·50 32·00
O6 2a. red 8·00 20·00

NAPLES Pt. 8

A state on the S.W. coast of Central Italy, formerly part of the Kingdom of Sicily, but now part of Italy.

200 tornesi = 100 grano = 1 ducato.

1 Arms under Bourbon Dynasty

4 Cross of Savoy

1858. The frames differ in each value. Imperf.
8 **1** ½t. blue £150000 £10000
1a ½g. red £2250 £475
2 1g. red £450 40·00
3 2g. red £275 12·00
4a 5g. red £4500 £9500
5a 10g. red £5000 £32000
6a 20g. red £6500 £1300
7a 50g. red £10000 £3000

1860. Imperf.
9 **4** ½t. blue £38000 £3750

NATAL Pt. 1

On the east coast of S. Africa. Formerly a British Colony, later a province of the Union of S. Africa.

12 pence = 1 shilling;
20 shillings = 1 pound.

1

1857. Embossed stamps. Various designs.
1 **1** 1d. blue — £1100
2 1d. red — £1700
3 1d. buff — £1000
4 – 3d. red — £400
5 – 6d. green — £1100
6 – 9d. blue — £7000
7 – 1s. buff — £5500

The 3d., 6d., 9d. and 1s. are larger. Beware of reprints.

6

7

1859.
19 **6** 1d. red 90·00 27·00
12 3d. blue £110 32·00
13 6d. grey £170 50·00
24 6d. violet 50·00 28·00

1867.
25 **7** 1s. green £140 28·00

1869. Variously optd **POSTAGE** or **Postage**.
50 **6** 1d. red 90·00 40·00
82 1d. yellow 70·00 70·00
53 3d. blue £150 42·00
83 6d. violet 55·00 6·50
84 **7** 1s. green 80·00 6·00

1870. Optd **POSTAGE** in a curve.
59 **7** 1s. green 75·00 10·00
108 1s. orange 40·00 1·00

1870. Optd **POSTAGE** twice, reading up and down.
60 **6** 1d. red 75·00 13·00
61 3d. blue 80·00 13·00
62 6d. violet £160 25·00

1873. Optd **POSTAGE** once, reading up.
63 **7** 1s. brown £190 19·00

23

28

16

1874. Queen Victoria. Various frames.
97a **23** ½d. green 2·75 75
99 – 1d. red 3·00 10
107 – 2d. olive 2·75 1·40
113 **28** 2½d. blue 5·00 75
68 – 3d. blue £100 19·00
101 – 3d. grey 3·75 1·25
102 – 4d. brown 4·50 75
103 – 6d. lilac 4·00 1·00
73 **16** 5s. red 70·00 28·00

1877. No. 99 surch ½ **HALF**.
85 ½d. on 1d. red 26·00 65·00

POSTAGE POSTAGE.

Half-penny Half-Penny

(21) (29)

1877. Surch as T **21**.
91 **6** ½d. on 1d. yellow 8·00 13·00
92 1d. on 6d. violet 50·00 9·00
93 1d. on 6d. red 95·00 40·00

1885. Surch in words.
104 ½d. on 1d. red (No. 99) 16·00 11·00
105 2d. on 3d. grey (No. 101) 18·00 5·50
109 2½d. on 4d. brown (No. 102) 10·00 10·00

1895. No. 23 surch with T **29**.
114 **6** ½d. on 6d. violet 1·75 3·75

1895. No. 99 surch **HALF**.
125 HALF on 1d. red 2·00 1·50

31

32

1902.
127 **31** ½d. green 2·50 20
128 1d. red 6·50 15
129 1½d. green and black 3·00 2·25
130 2d. red and olive 1·75 25
131 2½d. blue 1·25 3·00
132 3d. purple and grey 1·00 1·25
152 4d. red and brown 2·75 1·25
134 5d. black and orange 2·00 2·75
135 6d. green and purple 2·00 2·00
136 1s. red and blue 2·75 2·50
137 2s. green and violet 48·00 9·00
138 2s.6d. purple 40·00 12·00
139 4s. red and yellow 65·00 70·00
140 **32** 5s. blue and red 26·00 9·50
141 10s. red and purple 65·00 26·00
142 £1 black and blue £170 55·00
143 £1.10s. green and violet £375 95·00
162 £1.10s. orange and purple £1100 £1800
144 £5 mauve and black £2500 £600
145 £10 green and orange £6500 £2500
145b £20 red and green £14000 £6500

1908. As T **31/2** but inscr "POSTAGE POSTAGE".
165 **31** 6d. purple 4·50 2·75
166 1s. black on green 6·00 2·00
167 2s. purple and blue on blue 15·00 3·00
168 2s.6d. black and red on blue 25·00 3·00
169 **32** 5s. green and red on yellow 19·00 22·00
170 10s. green and red on green 65·00 70·00
171 £1 purple and black on red £250 £225

OFFICIAL STAMPS

1904. Optd **OFFICIAL**.
O1 **31** ½d. green 3·00 35
O2 1d. red 3·50 70
O3 2d. red and olive 22·00 10·00
O4 3d. purple and grey 12·00 4·00
O5 6d. green and purple 42·00 55·00
O6 1s. red and blue £130 £190

NAURU Pt. 1

An island in the W. Pacific Ocean, formerly a German possession and then administered by Australia under trusteeship. Became a republic on 31 January 1968.

1916. 12 pence = 1 shilling;
20 shillings = 1 pound.
1966. 100 cents = 1 Australian dollar.

1916. Stamps of Gt. Britain (King George V) optd **NAURU**.
1 **105** ½d. green 2·25 7·50
2 **104** 1d. red 1·75 6·00
15 **105** 1½d. brown 24·00 42·00
4 **106** 2d. orange 2·00 13·00
6 **104** 2½d. blue 2·75 7·00
7 **106** 3d. violet 2·00 3·75
8 4d. green 2·00 8·50
9 **107** 5d. brown 2·25 9·50
10 6d. purple 4·00 10·00
11 **108** 9d. black 8·50 23·00
12 1s. brown 7·00 19·00
25 **109** 2s.6d. brown 75·00 £110
22 5s. red £100 £140
23 10s. blue £250 £325

4

6

1924.
26A **4** ½d. brown 1·75 2·75
27B 1d. green 2·50 3·00
28B 1½d. red 1·00 1·50
29B 2d. orange 2·25 8·00
30dB 2½d. blue 3·00 4·00
31cB 3d. blue 3·50 13·00
32B 4d. green 4·25 13·00
33B 5d. brown 4·00 4·00
34B 6d. violet 4·00 5·00
35A 9d. brown 9·50 19·00
36B 1s. red 6·50 2·75
37B 2s.6d. green 28·00 35·00
38B 5s. purple 38·00 50·00
39B 10s. yellow 95·00 £120

1935. Silver Jubilee. Optd **HIS MAJESTY'S JUBILEE. 1910-1935**.
40 **4** 1½d. red 75 80
41 2d. orange 1·50 4·25
42 2½d. blue 1·50 1·50
43 1s. red 5·00 3·50

1937. Coronation.
44 **6** 1½d. red 45 1·75
45 2d. orange 45 2·75
46 2½d. blue 45 1·75
47 1s. purple 65 1·75

8 Anibare Bay

18 "Iyo" ("calophyllum")

21 White Tern

1954.
48 – ½d. violet 20 60
49a **8** 1d. green 20 40
50 – 3½d. red 1·75 75
51 – 4d. blue 2·00 1·50
52 – 6d. orange 70 20
53 – 9d. red 60 20
54 – 1s. purple 30 30
55 – 2s.6d. green 2·75 1·00
56 – 5s. mauve 9·00 2·25

DESIGNS—HORIZ: ½d. Nauruan netting fish; 3½d. Loading phosphate from cantilever; 4d. Great frigate bird; 6d. Canoe; 9d. Domaneab (meeting house); 2s.6d. Buada Lagoon. VERT: 1s. Palm trees; 5s. Map of Nauru.

1963.
57 – 2d. multicoloured 75 2·25
58 – 3d. multicoloured 40 35
59 **18** 5d. multicoloured 40 75
60 – 8d. black and green 2·00 80
61 – 10d. black 40 30
62 **21** 1s.3d. blue, black and green 1·75 4·50
63 – 2s.3d. blue 3·25 55
64 – 3s.3d. multicoloured 1·75 2·75

DESIGNS—VERT (As Type **21**): 2d. Micronesian pigeon. (26 × 29 mm): 10d. Capparis (flower). HORIZ (As Type **18**): 3d. Poison nut (flower); 8d. Black lizard; 2s.3d. Coral pinnacles; 3s.3d. Nightingale reed warbler ("Red Warbler").

22 "Simpson and his Donkey"

1965. 50th Anniv of Gallipoli Landing.
65 **22** 5d. sepia, black and green 15 10

24 Anibare Bay

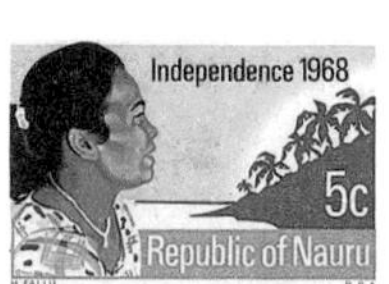

27 "Towards the Sunrise"

1966. Decimal Currency. As earlier issues but with values in cents and dollars as in T **24**. Some colours changed.
66 **24** 1c. blue 15 10
67 – 2c. purple (as No. 48) 15 40
68 – 3c. green (as No. 50) 30 2·00
69 – 4c. multicoloured (as T **18**) 20 10
70 – 5c. blue (as No. 54) 25 60
71 – 7c. black & brn (as No. 60) 30 10
72 – 8c. green (as No. 61) 20 10
73 – 10c. red (as No. 51) 40 10
74 – 15c. bl, blk and grn (as T **21**) 60 2·00
75 – 25c. brown (as No. 63) 30 1·00
76 – 30c. mult (as No. 58) 45 30
77 – 35c. mult (as No. 64) 75 35
78 – 50c. mult (as No. 57) 1·50 80
79 – $1 mauve (as No. 56) 75 1·00

The 25c. is as No. 63 but larger, 27½ × 25 mm.

1968. Nos. 66/79 optd **REPUBLIC OF NAURU**.
80 **24** 1c. blue 10 30
81 – 2c. purple 10 10

82 – 3c. green 15 10
83 – 4c. multicoloured 15 10
84 – 5c. blue 10 10
85 – 7c. black and brown 25 10
86 – 8c. green 15 10
87 – 10c. red 60 15
88 – 15c. blue, black and green 1·25 2·50
89 – 25c. brown 20 15
90 – 30c. multicoloured 55 15
91 – 35c. multicoloured . . . . . 1·25 30
92 – 50c. multicoloured . . . . . 1·25 35
93 – $1 purple 75 50

1968. Independence.
94 **27** 5c. multicoloured 10 10
95 – 10c. black, green and blue 10 10
DESIGN: 10c. Planting seedling, and map.

29 Flag of Independent Nauru

1969.
96 **29** 15c. yellow, orange and blue 50 15

30 Island, "C" and Stars

1972. 25th Anniv of South Pacific Commission.
97 **30** 25c. multicoloured 30 30

1973. 5th Anniv of Independence. No. 96 optd **Independence 1968-1973.**
98 **29** 15c. yellow, orange and blue 20 30

32 Denea

33 Artefacts and Map

1973. Multicoloured.
99 1c. Ekwenababae 40 20
100 2c. Kauwe iud 45 20
101 3c. Rimone 45 20
102 4c. Type **32** 45 40
103 5c. Erekogo 45 40
104 7c. Racoon butterflyfish ("Ikimago") (horiz) 50 80
105 8c. Catching flying fish (horiz) 30 20
106 10c. Itsibweb (ball game) (horiz) 30 20
107 15c. Nauruan wrestling . . . 35 20
108 20c. Snaring great frigate birds ("Frigate Birds") . . 70 70
109 25c. Nauruan girl 40 30
110 30c. Catching common noddy birds ("Noddy Birds") (horiz) 60 40
111 50c. Great frigate birds ("Frigate Birds") (horiz) 80 75
112 $1 Type **33** 80 75

34 Co-op Store

1973. 50th Anniv of Nauru Co-operative Society. Multicoloured.
113 5c. Type **34** 20 30
114 25c. Timothy Detudamo (founder) 20 15
115 50c. N.C.S. trademark (vert) 45 55

35 Phosphate Mining

1974. 175th Anniv of First Contact with the Outside World. Multicoloured.
116 7c. M.V. "Eigamoiya" (bulk carrier) 65 90
117 10c. Type **35** 50 25
118 15c. Fokker Fellowship "Nauru Chief" 65 30
119 25c. Nauruan chief in early times 50 35
120 35c. Capt. Fearn and 18th-century frigate (70 × 22 mm) . . . . . . 2·25 2·50
121 50c. 18th-century frigate off Nauru (70 × 22 mm) . . . 1·25 1·40
The ship on the 35c. and 50c. is wrongly identified as the "Hunter" (snow).

36 Map of Nauru

37 Rev. P. A. Delaporte

1974. Centenary of U.P.U. Multicoloured.
122 5c. Type **36** 15 20
123 8c. Nauru Post Office 15 20
124 20c. Nauruan postman . . . 15 10
125 $1 U.P.U. Building and Nauruan flag 40 60
MS126 157 × 105 mm. Nos. 122/5. Imperf . . . . 2·00 5·50

1974. Christmas and 75th Anniv of Rev. Delaporte's Arrival.
127 **37** 15c. multicoloured 20 20
128 20c. multicoloured 30 30

38 Map of Nauru, Lump of Phosphate Rock and Albert Ellis

1975. Phosphate Mining Anniversaries. Mult.
129 5c. Type **38** 25 40
130 7c. Coolies and mine 35 40
131 15c. Electric phosphate train, barges and ship . . . . . 1·00 1·40
132 25c. Modern ore extraction 1·25 1·50
ANNIVERSARIES: 5c. 75th anniv of discovery; 7c. 70th anniv of Mining Agreement; 15c. 55th anniv of British Phosphate Commissioners; 25c. 5th anniv of Nauru Phosphate Corporation.

39 Micronesian Outrigger

41 "Our Lady" (Yaren Church)

40 New Civic Centre

1975. South Pacific Commission Conf, Nauru (1st issue). Multicoloured.
133 20c. Type **39** 75 40
134 20c. Polynesian double-hull 75 40
135 20c. Melanesian outrigger . . 75 40
136 20c. Polynesian outrigger . . 75 40

1975. South Pacific Commission Conf, Nauru (2nd issue). Multicoloured.
137 30c. Type **40** 15 15
138 50c. Domaneab (meeting-house) 30 30

1975. Christmas. Stained-glass Windows. Mult.
139 5c. Type **41** 15 30
140 7c. "Suffer little children" (Orro Church) 15 30
141 15c. As 7c. 20 60
142 25c. Type **41** 25 80

42 Flowers floating towards Nauru

1976. 30th Anniv of Islanders' Return from Truk. Multicoloured.
143 10c. Type **42** 10 10
144 14c. Nauru encircled by garland 15 10
145 25c. Nightingale reed warbler and maps 85 25
146 40c. Return of the islanders 45 35

43 3d. and 9d. Stamps of 1916

1976. 60th Anniv of Nauruan Stamps. Mult.
147 10c. Type **43** 15 15
148 15c. 6d. and 1s. stamps . . . 15 15
149 25c. 2s.6d. stamp 20 25
150 50c. 5s. "Specimen" stamp 25 35

44 "Pandanus mei" and "Enna G" (cargo liner)

1976. South Pacific Forum, Nauru. Mult.
151 10c. Type **44** 25 20
152 20c. "Tournefortia argentea" with Boeing 737 and Fokker Fellowship aircraft 40 30
153 30c. "Thespesia populnea" and Nauru Tracking Station 40 30
154 40c. "Cordia subcordata" and produce 40 35

45 Nauruan Choir

46 Nauru House and Coral Pinnacles

1976. Christmas. Multicoloured.
155 15c. Type **45** 10 10
156 15c. Nauruan choir 10 10
157 20c. Angel in white dress . . 15 15
158 20c. Angel in red dress . . . 15 15

1977. Opening of Nauru House, Melbourne. Mult.
159 15c. Type **46** 15 15
160 30c. Nauru House and Melbourne skyline 25 25

47 Cable Ship "Anglia"

48 Father Kayser and First Catholic Church

1977. 75th Anniv of First Trans-Pacific Cable and 20th Anniv of First Artificial Earth Satellite.
161 **47** 7c. multicoloured 20 10
162 – 15c. blue, grey and black 30 15
163 – 20c. blue, grey and black 30 20
164 – 25c. multicoloured 30 20
DESIGNS: 15c. Tracking station, Nauru; 20c. Stern of "Anglia"; 25c. Dish aerial.

1977. Christmas. Multicoloured.
165 15c. Type **48** 10 10
166 25c. Congregational Church, Orro 15 15
167 30c. Catholic Church, Arubo 15 15

49 Arms of Nauru

1978. 10th Anniv of Independence.
168 **49** 15c. multicoloured 20 15
169 60c. multicoloured 35 30

1978. Nos. 159/60 surch.
170 **46** 4c. on 15c. multicoloured 45 1·50
171 5c. on 15c. multicoloured 45 1·50
172 – 8c. on 30c. multicoloured 45 1·50
173 – 10c. on 30c. multicoloured 45 1·50

51 Collecting Shellfish

1978.
174 **51** 1c. multicoloured 50 30
175 – 2c. multicoloured 50 30
176 – 3c. multicoloured . . . . . 2·00 1·00
177 – 4c. brown, blue and black 50 30
178 – 5c. multicoloured . . . . . 2·25 1·00
179 – 7c. multicoloured . . . . . 30 1·50
180 – 10c. multicoloured 30 20
181 – 15c. multicoloured 40 30
182 – 20c. grey, black and blue 30 30
183 – 25c. multicoloured 30 30
184 – 30c. multicoloured . . . . 1·75 45
185 – 32c. multicoloured . . . . 2·75 1·25
186 – 40c. multicoloured . . . . 1·75 2·25
187 – 50c. multicoloured . . . . 1·50 1·25
188 – $1 multicoloured . . . . . 55 1·00
189 – $2 multicoloured . . . . . 60 1·00
190 – $5 grey, black and blue . . 1·10 2·25
DESIGNS: 2c. Coral outcrop; 3c. Reef scene; 4c. Girl with fish; 5c. Reef heron; 7c. Catching fish, Buada Lagoon; 10c. Ijuw Lagoon; 15c. Girl framed by coral; 20c. Pinnacles, Anibare Bay reef; 25c. Pinnacle at Meneng; 30c. Head of great frigate bird; 32c. White-capped noddy birds in coconut palm; 40c. Wandering tattler; 50c. Great frigate birds on perch; $1 Old coral pinnacles at Topside; $2 New pinnacles at Topside; $5 Blackened pinnacles at Topside.

52 A.P.U. Emblem

53 Virgin and Child

1978. 14th General Assembly of Asian Parliamentarians' Union. Nauru.
191 **52** 15c. multicoloured 20 25
192 – 20c. black, blue and gold 20 25
DESIGN: 20c. As Type **52**, but with different background.

1978. Christmas. Multicoloured.
193 7c. Type **53** 10 10
194 15c. Angel in sunrise scene (horiz) 10 10
195 20c. As 15c. 15 15
196 30c. Type **53** 20 20

54 Baden-Powell and Cub Scout

1978. 70th Anniv of Boy Scout Movement. Mult.
197 20c. Type **54** 20 15
198 30c. Scout 25 20
199 50c. Rover Scout 35 30

55 Wright Flyer I over Nauru

1979. Flight Anniversaries. Multicoloured.
200 10c. Type **55** 20 15
201 15c. Fokker F.VIIa/3m "Southern Cross" superimposed on nose of Boeing 737 . . . . 30 20
202 15c. "Southern Cross" and Boeing 737 (front view) . . 30 20
203 30c. Wright Flyer I over Nauru airfield 55 30
ANNIVERSARIES: Nos. 200, 203, 75th anniv of powered flight; 201/2, 50th anniv of Kingsford-Smith's Pacific flight.

56 Sir Rowland Hill and Marshall Islands 10pf. stamp of 1901

1979. Death Cent of Sir Rowland Hill. Mult.
204 5c. Type **56** 15 10
205 15c. Sir Rowland Hill and "Nauru" opt on G.B. 10s. "Seahorse" stamp of 1916–23 . . . . 25 20
206 60c. Sir Rowland Hill and Nauru 60c. 10th anniv of Independence stamp, 1978 55 40
MS207 159 × 101 mm. Nos. 204/6 85 1·25

57 Dish Antenna, Transmitting Station and Radio Mast

1979. 50th Anniv of International Consultative Radio Committee. Multicoloured.
208 7c. Type **57** 15 10
209 32c. Telex operator 35 25
210 40c. Radio operator 40 25

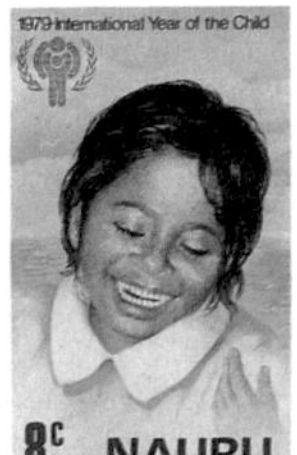

58 Smiling Child

1979. International Year of the Child.
211 **58** 8c. multicoloured 10 10
212 – 15c. multicoloured 15 15
213 – 25c. multicoloured 20 20
214 – 32c. multicoloured 20 20
215 – 50c. multicoloured 25 25
DESIGNS: 15c. to 50c. Smiling children.

59 Ekwenababae (flower), Scroll inscribed "Peace on Earth" and Star

1979. Christmas. Multicoloured.
216 7c. Type **59** 10 10
217 15c. "Thespia populnea" (flower), scroll inscribed "Goodwill towards Men" and star 10 10
218 20c. Denea (flower), scroll inscribed "Peace on Earth" and star 10 10
219 30c. Erekogo (flower), scroll inscribed "Goodwill toward Men" and star 20 20

60 Dassault Bregeut Mystere Falcon 50 over Melbourne

1980. 10th Anniv of Air Nauru. Multicoloured.
220 15c. Type **60** 35 15
221 20c. Fokker F.28 Fellowship over Tarawa 40 15
222 25c. Boeing 727-100 over Hong Kong 40 15
223 30c. Boeing 737 over Auckland 40 15

61 Steam Locomotive

1980. 10th Anniv of Nauru Phosphate Corporation. Multicoloured.
224 8c. Type **61** 10 10
225 32c. Electric locomotive . . . 20 20
226 60c. Diesel-hydraulic locomotive 35 35
MS227 168 × 118 mm. Nos. 224/6 1·00 2·50
No. **MS**227 also commemorates the "London 1980" International Stamp Exhibition.

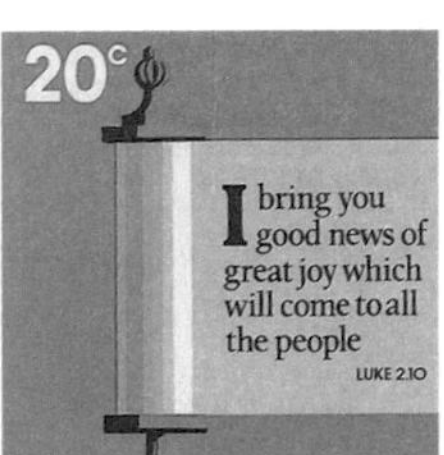

62 Verse 10 from Luke, Chapter 2 in English

1980. Christmas. Verses from Luke, Chapter 2. Multicoloured.
228 20c. Type **62** 10 10
229 20c. Verse 10 in Nauruan . . 10 10
230 30c. Verse 14 in English . . . 15 15
231 30c. Verse 14 in Nauruan . . 15 15
See also Nos. 248/51.

63 Nauruan, Australia, Union and New Zealand Flags on Aerial View of Nauru

1980. 20th Anniv of U.N. Declaration on the Granting of Independence to Colonial Countries and Peoples. Multicoloured.
232 25c. Type **63** 15 15
233 50c. U.N. Trusteeship Council (72 × 23 mm) . . . 15 15
234 50c. Nauru independence ceremony, 1968 (72 × 23 mm) 25 25

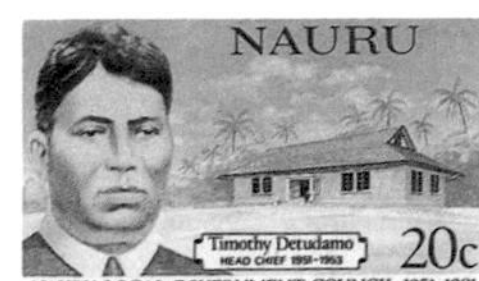

64 Timothy Detudamo

1981. 30th Anniv of Nauru Local Government Council. Head Chiefs. Multicoloured.
235 20c. Type **64** 15 15
236 30c. Raymond Gadabu 15 15
237 50c. Hammer DeRobart . . 25 25

65 Casting Net by Hand

1981. Fishing. Multicoloured.
238 8c. Type **65** 15 10
239 20c. Outrigger canoe 25 15
240 32c. Outboard motor boat . . 35 20
241 40c. Trawler 35 25
MS242 167 × 116 mm. No. 241 × 4 2·25 2·00
No. **MS**242 was issued to commemorate the "WIPA 1981" International Stamp Exhibition, Vienna.

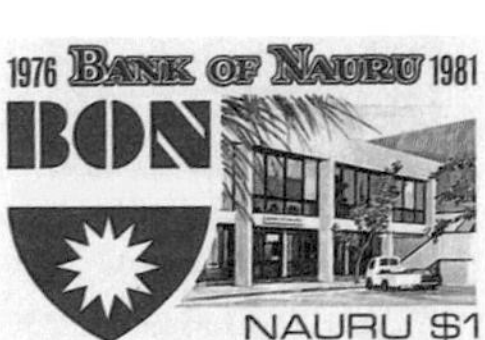

66 Bank of Nauru Emblem and Building

1981. 5th Anniv of Bank of Nauru.
243 **66** $1 multicoloured 60 60

67 Inaugural Speech

1981. U.N. Day. E.S.C.A.P. (United Nations Economic and Social Commission for Asia and the Pacific) Events. Multicoloured.
244 15c. Type **67** 15 15
245 20c. Presenting credentials . . 15 15
246 25c. Unveiling plaque 20 20
247 30c. Raising U.N. flag . . . 25 25

1981. Christmas. Bible Verses. Designs as T **62**. Multicoloured.
248 20c. Matthew 1, 23 in English 15 15
249 20c. Matthew 1, 23 in Nauruan 15 15
250 30c. Luke 2, 11 in English . . 20 20
251 30c. Luke 2, 11 in Nauruan 20 20

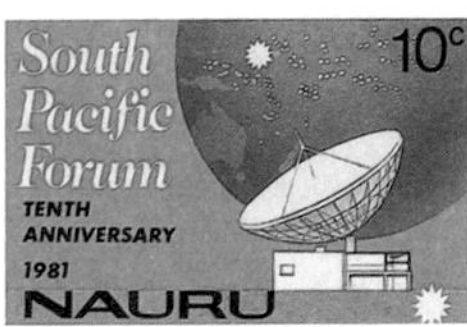

68 Earth Satellite Station

1981. 10th Anniv of South Pacific Forum. Mult.
252 10c. Type **68** 20 15
253 20c. "Enna G" (cargo liner) 25 20
254 30c. Boeing 737 airliner . . . 25 25
255 40c. Local produce 25 30

69 Nauru Scouts leaving for 1935 Frankston Scout Jamboree

1982. 75th Anniv of Boy Scout Movement. Mult.
256 7c. Type **69** 15 15
257 8c. Two Nauru scouts on "Nauru Chief", 1935 (vert) 15 15
258 15c. Nauru scouts making pottery, 1935 (vert) 15 20
259 20c. Lord Huntingfield addressing Nauru scouts, Frankston Jamboree, 1935 20 25
260 25c. Nauru cub and scout, 1982 . . . . 20 30
261 40c. Nauru cubs, scouts and scouters, 1982 . . . . . . 30 45
MS262 152 × 114 mm. Nos. 256/61. Imperf . . . . 1·25 2·25
No. **MS**262 also commemorates Nauru's participation in the "Stampex" National Stamp Exhibition, London.

70 100 kw Electricity Generating Plant under Construction (left side)

1982. Ocean Thermal Energy Conversion. Mult.
263 25c. Type **70** 60 30
264 25c. 100 kw Electricity Generating Plant under construction (right side) . . 60 30
265 40c. Completed plant (left) 80 40
266 40c. Completed plant (right) 80 40
Nos. 263/4 and 265/6 were each issued as horizontal se-tenant pairs, forming composite designs.

71 S.S. "Fido"

1982. 75th Anniv of Phosphate Shipments. Mult.
267 5c. Type **71** 40 10
268 10c. Steam locomotive "Nellie" 50 20
269 30c. Class "Clyde" diesel locomotive 60 50
270 60c. M.V. "Eigamoiya" (bulk carrier) 65 80
MS271 165 × 107 mm. $1 "Eigamoiya", "Rosie-D" and "Kolle-D" (bulk carriers) (67 × 27 mm) . . . . 1·50 2·25
No. **MS**271 was issued to commemorate "ANPEX 82" National Stamp Exhibition, Brisbane.

72 Queen Elizabeth II on Horseback

1982. Royal Visit. Multicoloured.
272 20c. Type **72** 30 20
273 50c. Prince Philip, Duke of Edinburgh 40 45
274 $1 Queen Elizabeth II and Prince Philip (horiz) . . . 45 1·00

73 Father Bernard Lahn

1982. Christmas. Multicoloured.
275 10c. Type **73** 20 35
276 30c. Reverend Itubwa Amram 20 50
277 40c. Pastor James Aingimen 25 80
278 50c. Bishop Paul Mea . . . 30 1·10

74 Speaker of the Nauruan Parliament

75 Nauru Satellite Earth Station

1983. 15th Anniv of Independence. Mult.
279 15c. Type **74** 20 20
280 20c. Family Court in session 25 25
281 30c. Law Courts building (horiz) 25 25
282 50c. Parliamentary chamber (horiz) 40 40

1983. World Communications Year. Mult.
283 5c. Type **75** 20 10
284 10c. Omni-directional range installation 20 15
285 20c. Emergency short-wave radio 25 25
286 25c. Radio Nauru control room 40 30
287 40c. Unloading air mail . . . 90 45

76 Return of Exiles from Truk on M.V. "Trienza", 1946

1983. Angam Day. Multicoloured.
288 15c. Type **76** 20 25
289 20c. Mrs. Elsie Agio (exile community leader) (vert) (25 × 41 mm) 20 25
290 30c. Child on scales (vert) (25 × 41 mm) 35 40
291 40c. Nauruan children (vert) (25 × 41 mm) 45 50

77 "The Holy Virgin, Holy Child and St. John" (School of Raphael)

78 S.S. "Ocean Queen"

1983. Christmas. Multicoloured.
292 5c. Type **77** 10 10
293 15c. "Madonna on the Throne, surrounded by Angels" (School of Sevilla) 20 15
294 50c. "The Mystical Betrothal of St. Catherine with Jesus" (School of Veronese) (horiz) 60 40

1984. 250th Anniv of "Lloyd's List" (newspaper). Multicoloured.
295 20c. Type **78** 30 20
296 25c. M.V "Enna G" 35 25
297 30c. M.V "Baron Minto" . . 40 30
298 40c. Sinking of M.V. "Triadic", 1940 . . . . . 50 45

79 1974 U.P.U. $1 Stamp

1984. Universal Postal Union Congress, Hamburg.
299 **79** $1 multicoloured . . . . . 70 1·25

80 "Hypolimnas bolina" (female)

1984. Butterflies. Multicoloured.
300 25c. Type **80** 35 40
301 30c. "Hypolimnas bolina" (male) 35 55
302 50c. "Danaus plexippus" . . 40 85

81 Coastal Scene

1984. Life in Nauru. Multicoloured.
303 1c. Type **81** 10 40
304 3c. Nauruan woman (vert) 15 40
305 5c. Modern trawler 40 50
306 10c. Golfer on the links . . . 90 50
307 15c. Excavating phosphate (vert) 90 65
308 20c. Surveyor (vert) 65 55
309 25c. Air Nauru Boeing 727 airliner 80 55
310 30c. Elderly Nauruan (vert) 50 50
311 40c. Loading hospital patient onto Boeing 727 aircraft 90 55
312 50c. Skin-diver with fish (vert) . . . . 1·00 80
313 $1 Tennis player (vert) . . . 2·50 3·25
314 $2 Anabar Lagoon . . . . . 2·50 3·75

82 Buada Chapel

1984. Christmas. Multicoloured.
315 30c. Type **82** 40 50
316 40c. Detudamo Memorial Church 50 65
317 50c. Candle-light service, Kayser College (horiz) . . 60 70

83 Air Nauru Boeing 737 Jet on Tarmac

1985. 15th Anniv of Air Nauru. Multicoloured.
318 20c. Type **83** 50 35
319 30c. Stewardesses on Boeing 737 aircraft steps (vert) . . 60 60
320 40c. Fokker F.28 Fellowship over Nauru 75 75
321 50c. Freight being loaded onto Boeing 727 (vert) . . 85 85

84 Open Cut Mining

1985. 15th Anniv of Nauru Phosphate Corporation. Multicoloured.
322 20c. Type **84** . . . . 1·00 60
323 25c. Diesel locomotive hauling crushed ore . . . 2·00 1·00
324 30c. Phosphate drying plant 1·75 1·00
325 50c. Early steam locomotive 2·50 1·75

85 Mother and Baby on Beach **86** Adult Common Noddy with Juvenile

1985. Christmas. Multicoloured.
326 50c. Beach scene . . . . . . 1·50 2·25
327 50c. Type **85** . . . . 1·50 2·25
Nos. 326/7 were printed together, se-tenant, forming a composite design.

1985. Birth Bicentenary of John J. Audubon (ornithologist). Common ("Brown") Noddy. Mult.
328 10c. Type **86** 35 35
329 20c. Adult and immature birds in flight 50 70
330 30c. Adults in flight 65 85
331 50c. "Brown Noddy" (John J. Audubon) . . . . 80 1·10

87 Douglas Motor Cycle

1986. Early Transport on Nauru. Multicoloured.
332 15c. Type **87** 80 70
333 20c. Primitive lorry 95 95
334 30c. German-built steam locomotive, 1910 . . . . . 1·50 1·50
335 40c. "Baby" Austin car . . . 1·75 1·75

88 Island and Bank of Nauru

1986. 10th Anniv of Bank of Nauru. Children's Paintings. Multicoloured.
336 20c. Type **88** 20 30
337 25c. Borrower with notes and coins 25 35
338 30c. Savers 30 40
339 40c. Customers at bank counter 35 55

89 "Plumeria rubra"

1986. Flowers. Multicoloured.
340 20c. Type **89** 40 70
341 25c. "Tristellateia australis" 50 85
342 30c. "Bougainvillea cultivar" 60 1·00
343 40c. "Delonix regia" . . . . 75 1·25

90 Carol Singers

1986. Christmas. Multicoloured.
344 20c. Type **90** 40 30
345 $1 Carol singers and hospital patient . . . . 1·60 3·50

91 Young Girls Dancing

1987. Nauruan Dancers. Multicoloured.
346 20c. Type **91** 80 80
347 30c. Stick dance . . . . . . 1·00 1·25
348 50c. Boy doing war dance (vert) . . . . 1·75 2·50

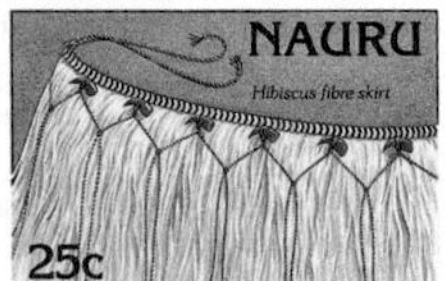

92 Hibiscus Fibre Skirt

1987. Personal Artefacts. Multicoloured.
349 25c. Type **92** 75 75
350 30c. Headband and necklets 85 85
351 45c. Decorative necklets . . . 1·10 1·10
352 60c. Pandanus leaf fan . . . 1·60 1·60

93 U.P.U. Emblem and Air Mail Label **94** Open Bible

1987. World Post Day.
353 **93** 40c. multicoloured . . . . 1·50 1·25
MS354 122 × 82 mm. $1 U.P.U. emblem and map of Pacific showing mail routes (114 × 74 mm) 2·50 3·25

1987. Centenary of Nauru Congregational Church.
355 **94** 40c. multicoloured . . . . 1·50 1·75

95 Nauruan Children's Party

1987. Christmas. Multicoloured.
356 20c. Type **95** 75 50
357 $1 Nauruan Christmas dinner 2·75 3·25

96 Loading Phosphate on Ship

1988. 20th Anniv of Independence. Mult.
358 25c. Type **96** . . . . 1·00 1·00
359 40c. Tomano flower (vert) . . 1·50 1·50
360 55c. Great frigate bird (vert) 2·25 2·25
361 $1 Arms of Republic (35 × 35 mm) . . . . . . 2·50 3·50

97 Map of German Marshall Is. and 1901 5m. Yacht Definitive

1988. 80th Anniv of Nauru Post Office. Mult.
362 30c. Type **97** 75 75
363 50c. Letter and post office of 1908 . . . . 1·00 1·25
364 70c. Nauru Post Office and airmail letter . . . . . . 1·25 1·50

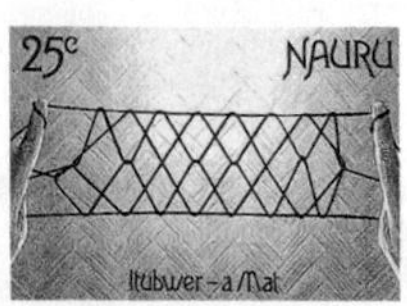

98 "Itubwer" (mat)

1988. String Figures. Multicoloured.
365 25c. Type **98** 35 35
366 40c. "Etegerer – the Pursuer" 50 60
367 55c. "Holding up the Sky" 65 70
368 80c. "Manujie's Sword" . . . 1·00 1·75

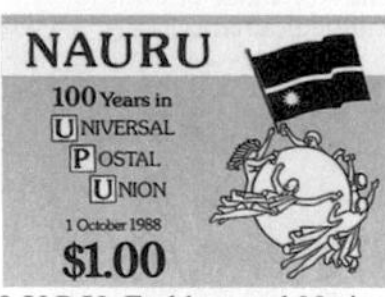

99 U.P.U. Emblem and National Flag

1988. Cent of Nauru's Membership of U.P.U.
369 **99** $1 multicoloured . . . . . 1·25 1·25

100 "Hark the Herald Angels"

1988. Christmas. Designs showing words and music from "Hark the Herald Angels Sing".
370 **100** 20c. black, red and yellow 60 30
371 – 60c. black, red and mauve 1·40 1·25
372 – $1 black, red and green 2·25 2·25

101 Logo (15th anniv of Nauru Insurance Corporation) **102** Mother and Baby

1989. Anniversaries and Events. Multicoloured.
373 15c. Type **101** 30 30
374 50c. Logos (World Telecommunications Day and 10th anniv of Asian-Pacific Telecommunity) . . 75 85
375 $1 Photograph of island scene (150 years of photography) . . . . . . 1·75 2·00
376 $2 Capitol and U.P.U. emblem (20th U.P.U. Congress, Washington) . . 2·75 4·50

1989. Christmas. Multicoloured.
377 20c. Type **102** 50 30
378 $1 Children opening presents 2·25 3·25

103 Eigigu working while Sisters play **104** Early Mining by Hand

1989. 20th Anniv of First Manned Landing on Moon. Legend of "Eigigu, the Girl in the Moon". Multicoloured.
379 25c. Type **103** . . . . 3·00 2·75
380 30c. Eigigu climbing tree . . 3·25 3·00
381 50c. Eigigu stealing toddy from blind woman . . . . 6·00 5·50
382 $1 Eigigu on Moon . . . . 8·00 7·50

1990. 20th Anniv of Nauru Phosphate Corporation. Multicoloured.
383 50c. Type **104** 75 75
384 $1 Modern mining by excavator . . . . 1·25 2·00

105 Sunday School Class **106** Eoiyepiang laying Baby on Mat

1990. Christmas. Multicoloured.
385 25c. Type **105** . . . . 90 1·25
386 25c. Teacher telling Christmas story . . . . . 90 1·25
Nos. 385/6 were printed together, se-tenant, forming a composite design.

1990. Legend of "Eoiyepiang, the Daughter of Thunder and Lightning". Multicoloured.
387 25c. Type **106** . . . . 1·50 60
388 30c. Eoiyepiang making floral decoration . . . . 1·75 70
389 50c. Eoiyepiang left on snow-covered mountain . . . . 2·25 2·00
390 $1 Eoiyepiang and warrior 3·25 3·50

107 Oleander

1991. Flowers. Multicoloured.

391	15c. Type **107**	10	15
392	20c. Lily	15	20
393	25c. Passion flower	20	25
394	30c. Lily (different)	25	30
395	35c. Caesalpinia	30	35
396	40c. Clerodendron	35	40
397	45c. "Baubina pinnata"	40	45
398	50c. Hibiscus (vert)	40	45
399	75c. Apocymaceae	65	70
400	$1 Bindweed (vert)	85	90
401	$2 Tristellateia (vert)	1·70	1·80
402	$3 Impala lily (vert)	2·50	2·75

108 Jesus Christ and Children (stained glass window)

1991. Christmas. Sheet 124 × 82 mm.
MS403 **108** $2 multicoloured . . 4·00 4·50

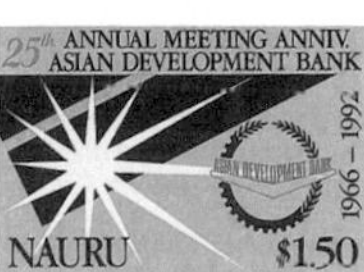

109 Star and Symbol of Asian Development Bank

1992. 25th Annual Meeting of Asian Development Bank.
404 **109** $1.50 multicoloured . . . 2·00 2·50

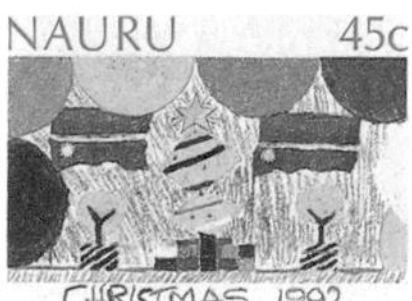

110 Gifts under Christmas Tree

1992. Christmas. Children's Paintings. Mult.

405	45c. Type **110**	75	75
406	60c. Father Christmas in sleigh	1·00	1·50

111 Hammer DeRoburt

112 Running, Constitution Day Sports

1993. 25th Anniv of Independence and Hammer DeRoburt (former President) Commemoration.
407 **111** $1 multicoloured . . . . 2·50 3·00

1993. 15th Anniv of Constitution Day. Mult.

408	70c. Type **112**	1·40	1·40
409	80c. Part of Independence Proclamation	1·40	1·40

113 Great Frigate Birds, Flying Fish and Island

1993. 24th South Pacific Forum Meeting, Nauru. Multicoloured.

410	60c. Type **113**	1·40	1·50
411	60c. Red-tailed tropic bird, great frigate bird, dolphin and island	1·40	1·50
412	60c. Racoon butterflyfish ("Ikimago"), coral and sea urchins	1·40	1·50
413	60c. Three different types of fish with corals	1·40	1·50
MS414	140 × 130 mm. Nos. 410/13	7·00	8·00

Nos. 410/13 were printed together, se-tenant, forming a composite design.

114 "Peace on Earth, Goodwill to Men" and Star

1993. Christmas. Multicoloured.

415	55c. Type **114**	85	85
416	65c. "Hark the Herald Angels Sing" and star	90	90

115 Girls with Dogs

1994. "Hong Kong '94" International Stamp Exhibition. Chinese New Year ("Year of the Dog"). Multicoloured.

417	$1 Type **115**	1·50	2·00
418	$1 Boys with dogs	1·50	2·00
MS419	100 × 75 mm. Nos. 417/18	3·00	3·75

1994. "Singpex '94" National Stamp Exhibition, Singapore. No. **MS**419 optd "SINGPEX '94" and emblem in gold on sheet margin.
MS420 100 × 75 mm. Nos. 417/18 . . . 3·00 3·75

116 Weightlifting

117 Peace Dove and Star over Island

1994. 15th Commonwealth Games, Victoria, Canada.
421 **116** $1.50 multicoloured . . . 1·40 2·00

1994. Christmas. Multicoloured.

422	65c. Type **117**	90	90
423	75c. Star over Bethlehem	1·00	1·00

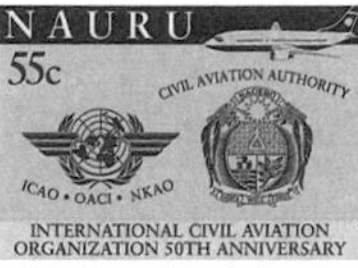

118 Air Nauru Airliner and Emblems

1994. 50th Anniv of I.C.A.O. Multicoloured.

424	55c. Type **118**	50	55
425	65c. Control tower, Nauru International Airport	60	65
426	80c. D.V.O.R. equipment	70	1·00
427	$1 Crash tenders	90	1·10
MS428	165 × 127 mm. Nos. 424/7	4·00	4·50

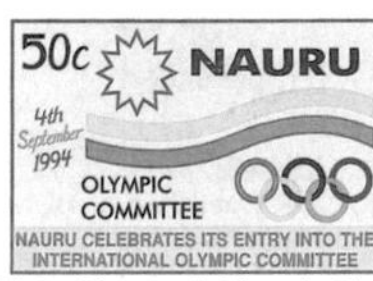

119 Emblem and Olympic Rings

1994. Nauru's Entry into Int Olympic Committee.
429 **119** 50c. multicoloured 50 50

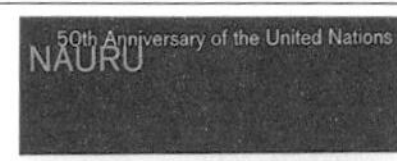

120 Nauruan Flag

1995. 50th Anniv of United Nations (1st issue). Multicoloured.

430	75c. Type **120**	1·40	1·40
431	75c. Arms of Nauru	1·40	1·40
432	75c. Outrigger canoe on coastline	1·40	1·40
433	75c. Airliner over phosphate freighter	1·40	1·40
MS434	110 × 85 mm. Nos. 430/3	4·50	5·50

Nos. 430/3 were printed together, se-tenant, forming a composite design.
See also Nos. 444/5.

121 Signing Phosphate Agreement, 1967

1995. 25th Anniv of Nauru Phosphate Corporation. Multicoloured.

435	60c. Type **121**	80	1·00
436	60c. Pres. Bernard Dowiyogo and Prime Minister Keating of Australia shaking hands	80	1·00
MS437	120 × 80 mm. $2 Excavating phosphate	2·75	3·25

1995. International Stamp Exhibitions. No. 309 surch.

438	50c. on 25c. multicoloured (surch **at Beijing**)	1·40	1·40
439	$1 on 25c. multicoloured (surch **at Jakarta**)	1·40	1·75
440	$1 on 25c. multicoloured (surch **at Singapore**)	1·40	1·75

123 Sea Birds (face value at top right)

1995. Olympic Games, Atlanta. Sheet 140 × 121 mm, containing T **123** and similar vert designs. Multicoloured.
MS441 60c.+15c. Type **123**; 60c.+15c. Sea brids (face value at top left); 60c.+15c. Four dolphins; 60c.+15c. Pair of dolphins . . 4·00 4·50
The premiums on No. **MS**441 were for Nauru sport development.

124 Children playing on Gun

1995. 50th Anniv of Peace. Multicoloured

442	75c. Type **124**	1·75	2·00
443	$1.50 Children making floral garlands	1·75	2·00

125 Nauru Crest, Coastline and U.N. Anniversary Emblem

126 Young Girl praying

1995. 50th Anniv of United Nations (2nd issue). Multicoloured.

444	75c. Type **125**	90	1·00
445	$1.50 Aerial view of Nauru and U.N. Headquarters, New York	1·60	2·00

1995. Christmas. Multicoloured.

446	60c. Type **126**	90	1·00
447	70c. Man praying	90	1·00

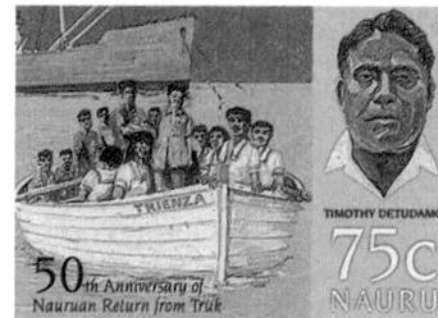

127 Returning Refugees and Head Chief Timothy Detudamo

1996. 50th Anniv of Nauruans' Return from Truk.

448 **127**	75c. multicoloured	90	1·00
449	$1.25 multicoloured	1·60	2·00
MS450	120 × 80 mm. Nos. 448/9	3·00	3·50

128 Nanjing Stone Lion

1996. "CHINA '96" 9th Asian International Stamp Exhibition, Peking. Sheet 130 × 110 mm.
MS451 **128** 45c. multicoloured 80 1·00

129 Symbolic Athlete

1996. Centenary of Modern Olympic Games. Mult.

452	40c. Type **129**	90	70
453	50c. Symbolic weightlifter	1·00	90
454	60c. Weightlifter (horiz)	1·10	1·00
455	$1 Athlete (horiz)	1·50	2·00

130 The Nativity and Angel

1996. Christmas. Multicoloured.

456	50c. Type **130**	60	60
457	70c. Angel, world map and wild animals	80	1·00

131 Dolphin (fish)

1997. Endangered Species. Fishes. Multicoloured.

458	20c. Type **131**	85	85
459	30c. Wahoo	90	90
460	40c. Sailfish	1·00	1·00
461	50c. Yellow-finned tuna	1·10	1·10

132 Statue of Worshipper with Offering

133 Princess Elizabeth and Lieut. Philip Mountbatten, 1947

1997. "HONG KONG '97" International Stamp Exhibition. Statues of different worshippers (1c. to 15c.) or Giant Buddha of Hong Kong (25c.).
462 **132** 1c. multicoloured 20 20
463 – 2c. multicoloured 20 20
464 – 5c. multicoloured 25 25
465 – 10c. multicoloured 30 30
466 – 12c. multicoloured 30 30
467 – 15c. multicoloured 30 30
468 – 25c. multicoloured 40 40

1997. Golden Wedding of Queen Elizabeth and Prince Philip.
469 **133** 80c. black and gold . . . 90 1·00
470 – $1.20 multicoloured . . . 1·40 1·60
MS471 150 × 110 mm. Nos. 469/70 (sold at $3) . . . . 3·00 3·50
DESIGN: $1.20, Queen Elizabeth and Prince Philip, 1997.

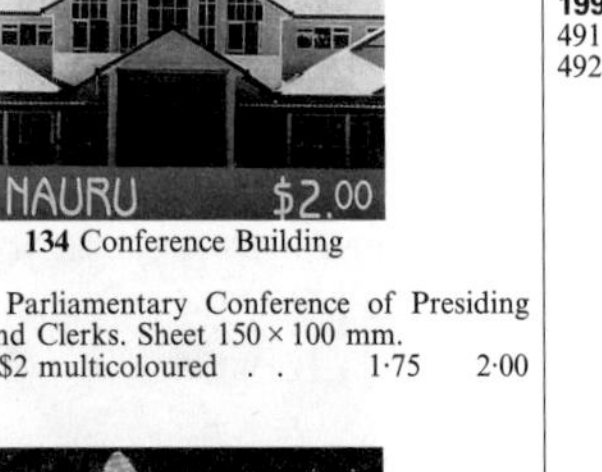

134 Conference Building

1997. 28th Parliamentary Conference of Presiding Officers and Clerks. Sheet 150 × 100 mm.
MS472 **134** $2 multicoloured . . 1·75 2·00

135 Commemorative Pillar

1997. Christmas. 110th Anniv of Nauru Congregational Church. Multicoloured.
473 60c. Type **135** 60 55
474 80c. Congregational Church 80 90

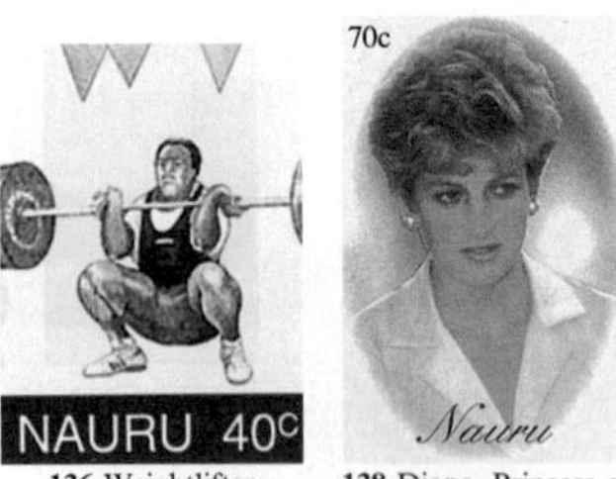

136 Weightlifter **138** Diana, Princess of Wales

137 Juan Antonio Samaranch and Aerial View

1998. Commonwealth, Oceania and South Pacific Weightlifting Championships, Nauru. Sheet 180 × 100 mm, containing T **136** and similar vert designs showing weightlifters.
MS475 40c., 60c., 80c., $1.20 multicoloured . . . . 2·25 2·75

1998. Visit of International Olympic Committee President.
476 **137** $2 multicoloured . . . . 1·75 2·00

1998. Diana, Princess of Wales Commemoration. Multicoloured.
477 70c. Type **138** 55 60
478 70c. Wearing white shirt . . 55 60
479 70c. With tiara 55 60
480 70c. In white jacket 55 60
481 70c. Wearing pink hat . . . 55 60
482 70c. In white suit 55 60

139 Gymnastics

140 Sqn. Ldr. Hicks (Composer of Nauru's National Anthem) conducting

1998. 16th Commonwealth Games, Kuala Lumpur, Malaysia. Multicoloured.
483 40c. Type **139** 40 40
484 60c. Athletics 55 60
485 70c. Sprinting 65 70
486 80c. Weightlifting 70 80
MS487 153 × 130 mm. Nos. 483/6 1·90 2·40

1998. 30th Anniv of Independence. Multicoloured.
488 $1 Type **140** 85 80
489 $2 Sqn. Ldr. Hicks and score 1·75 2·25
MS490 175 × 110 mm. Nos. 488/9 2·50 3·00

141 Palm Trees, Fish, Festive Candle and Flower

1998. Christmas. Multicoloured.
491 85c. Type **141** . . . . 80 1·00
492 95c. Flower, present, fruit and island scene . . . . . 85 1·00

142 18th-century Frigate

1998. Bicentenary of First Contact with the Outside World. Multicoloured.
493 $1.50 Type **142** . . . . . . 1·50 1·75
494 $1.50 Capt. John Fearn . . . 1·50 1·75
MS495 173 × 131 mm. Nos. 493/4 3·00 3·50
No. 493 is wrongly identified as "Hunter" (snow).

143 H.M.A.S. "Melbourne" (cruiser)

1999. "Australia '99" World Stamp Exhibition, Melbourne. Ships. Sheet 101 × 120 mm, containing T **143** and similar multicoloured designs.
MS496 70c. Type **143**; 80c. H.M.A.S. "D'Amantina" (frigate); 90c. "Alcyone" (experimental ship); $1 "Rosie-D" (bulk carrier); $1.10 Outrigger canoe (80 × 30 mm) . . . . 4·25 4·75

1999. 30th Anniv of First Manned Landing on Moon. As T **98a** of Kiribati. Multicoloured.
497 70c. Neil Armstrong (astronaut) 65 70
498 80c. Service and lunar module on way to Moon 70 80
499 90c. Aldrin and "Apollo 11" on Moon's surface . . . . 85 1·00
500 $1 Command module entering Earth's atmosphere . . . . 90 1·25
MS501 90 × 80 mm. $2 Earth as seen from Moon (circular, 40 mm diam) . . . . 1·90 2·40

144 Emblem and Forms of Transport

1999. 125th Anniv of Universal Postal Union.
502 **144** $1 multicoloured . . . . 1·00 1·25

145 Killer Whale

146 Girl holding Candle

1999. "China '99" International Philatelic Exhibition, Beijing. Sheet 185 × 85 mm, containing T **145** and similar vert design. Multicoloured.
MS503 50c. Type **145**; 50c. Swordfish . . . . 1·00 1·40

1999. Christmas. Multicoloured.
504 65c. Type **146** 70 75
505 70c. Candle and Christmas tree 80 85

147 Nauruan Woman in Traditional Dress and Canoes

2000. New Millennium. Multicoloured.
506 70c. Type **147** . . . . 1·00 1·00
507 $1.10 Aspects of modern Nauru . . . . 1·75 1·75
508 $1.20 Woman holding globe and man at computer . . . 1·75 1·75
MS509 149 × 88 mm. Nos. 506/8 3·00 3·75

148 Power Plant

2000. Centenary of Phosphate Discovery. Mult.
510 $1.20 Type **148** . . . . . . 1·25 1·25
511 $1.80 Phosphate train . . . . 2·00 2·00
512 $2 Albert Ellis and phosphate sample . . . . 2·00 2·25
MS513 79 × 131 mm. Nos. 510/12 4·50 5·50

149 Queen Mother in Royal Blue Hat and Coat **150** Running and Sydney Opera House

2000. 100th Birthday of Queen Elizabeth the Queen Mother. Sheet 150 × 106 mm, containing T **149** and similar horiz designs, each including photograph of Queen Mother as a child. Multicoloured.
MS514 150 × 106 mm. $1 Type **149**; $1.10 In lilac hat and coat; $1.20 In turquoise hat and coat; $1.40 In greenish blue hat and coat with maple leaf brooch . . . . . . 4·50 5·00

2000. Olympic Games, Sydney. Multicoloured.
515 90c. Type **150** 85 85
516 $1 Basketball . . . . 1·00 90
517 $1.10 Weightlifting and cycling . . . . 1·25 1·10
518 $1.20 Running and Olympic Torch . . . . 1·25 1·40

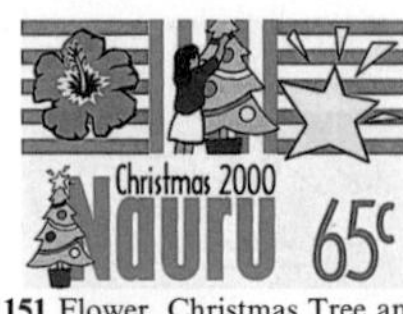

151 Flower, Christmas Tree and Star

2000. Christmas. Multicoloured.
519 65c. Type **151** 60 70
520 75c. Decorations, toy engine and palm tree 65 75
MS521 134 × 95 mm. Nos. 519/20 1·50 2·00

152 Noddy and Part of Island

2001. 32nd Pacific Islands Forum, Nauru. Multicoloured.
522 90c. Type **152** . . . . 1·25 1·40
523 $1 Frigate bird in flight and part of island . . . . . . 1·40 1·50
524 $1.10 Two frigate birds and part of island . . . . . . 1·50 1·60
525 $2 Frigate bird and Nauru airport . . . . 2·25 2·50
MS526 145 × 130 mm. Nos. 522/5 5·50 6·50
Nos. 522/5 were printed together, se-tenant, forming a composite view of Nauru.

153 Princess Elizabeth in A.T.S. Uniform, 1946

2002. Golden Jubilee.
527 **153** 70c. black, mauve and gold . . . . 1·10 1·25
528 – 80c. multicoloured . . . . 1·10 1·25
529 – 90c. black, mauve and gold . . . . 1·25 1·40
530 – $1 multicoloured . . . . 1·25 1·40
MS531 162 × 95 mm. Nos. 527/30 and $4 multicoloured . . . . . 7·00 8·00
DESIGNS—HORIZ: 80c. Queen Elizabeth in multicoloured hat; 90c. Princess Elizabeth at Cheltenham Races, 1951; $1 Queen Elizabeth in evening dress, 1997. VERT (38 x 51 mm)—$4 Queen Elizabeth after Annigoni.
Designs as Nos. 527/30 in No. **MS**531 omit the gold frame around each stamp and the "Golden Jubilee 1952–2002" inscription.

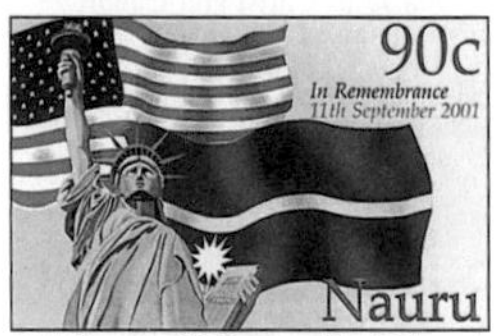

154 Statue of Liberty with U.S. and Nauru Flags

2002. In Remembrance. Victims of Terrorist Attacks on U.S.A. (11 September 2001).
532 **154** 90c. multicoloured 75 80
533 $1 multicoloured 85 90
534 $1.10 multicoloured . . . 95 1·10
535 $2 multicoloured . . . . 1·60 1·75

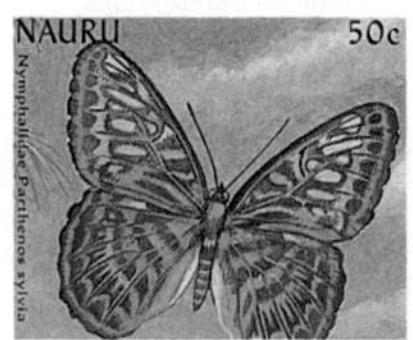

155 *Parthenos sylvia*

2002. Butterflies of the Pacific. Multicoloured.
536 50c. Type **155** 75 75
537 50c. *Delias madetes* 75 75
538 50c. *Danaus philene* 75 75
539 50c. *Arhopala hercules* . . . 75 75
540 50c. *Paipilio canopus* 75 75
541 50c. *Danaus schenkii* 75 75
542 50c. *Pairthenos tigrina* . . . 75 75
543 50c. *Mycalesis phidon* 75 75
544 50c. *Vindula sapor* 75 75
MS545 85 × 60 mm. $2 *Graphium agamemnon* . . . . 2·50 2·75
Nos. 536/44 were printed together, se-tenant, forming a composite design.

156 Queen Elizabeth in London, 1940

2002. Queen Elizabeth the Queen Mother Commemoration.
546 **156** $1.50 black, gold and purple . . . . 2·00 2·25
547 – $1.50 multicoloured . . . 2·00 2·25
MS548 145 × 70 mm. Nos. 546/7 4·00 4·50
DESIGNS: No. 547, Queen Mother in Norwich, 1990.
Designs as Nos. 546/7 in No. **MS**548 omit the "1900--2002" inscription and the coloured frame.

157 Turntable Ladder and Burning Building

2002. International Firefighters. Multicoloured.
549 20c. Type **157** 35 25
550 50c. Firefighting tug and burning ship 70 55
551 90c. Fighting a forest fire . . 1·10 85
552 $1 Old and new helmets . . . 1·25 90
553 $1.10 Steam-driven pump and modern fire engine . . . . 1·25 95
554 $2 19th-century and present day hose teams . . . . . 2·00 2·50
MS555 110 × 90 mm. $5 Airport fire engine . . . . 5·50 6·00

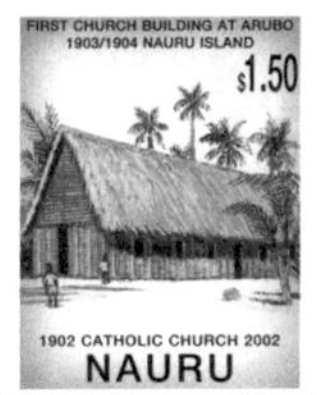

158 First Catholic Church, Arubo

2002. Centenary of Catholic Church on Nauru.
556 **158** $1.50 brown and black . . 1·40 1·60
557 – $1.50 violet and black . . 1·40 1·60
558 – $1.50 blue and black . . . 1·40 1·60
559 – $1.50 green and black . . 1·40 1·60
560 – $1.50 blue and black . . . 1·40 1·60
561 – $1.50 red and black . . . 1·40 1·60
DESIGNS: No. 557, Father Friedrich Gründl (first missionary); 558, Sister Stanisla; 559, Second Catholic church, Ibwenape; 560, Brother Kalixtus Bader (lay brother); 561, Father Alois Kayser (missionary).

159 "Holy Family with dancing Angels" (Van Dyck)

2002. Christmas. Religious Art. Multicoloured.
562 15c. Type **159** 30 25
563 $1 "Holy Virgin with Child" (Cornelis Bloemaert after Lucas Cangiasius) . . . . 1·10 75
564 $1.20 "Holy Family with Cat" (Rembrandt) . . . . 1·25 90
565 $3 "Holy Family with St. John" (Pierre Brebiette after Raphael) . . . . . . 3·00 3·50

160 Bubble Tentacle Sea Anemone and Fire Anemonefish ("Red-and-Black Anemone Fish")

2003. Endangered Species. Sea Anemones and Anemonefish. Multicoloured.
566 15c. Type **160** 35 25
567 $1 Leathery sea anemone and orange-finned anemonefish 1·25 75
568 $1.20 Magnificent sea anemone and pink anemonefish . . . . 1·40 1·00
569 $3 Merten's sea anemone and yellow-tailed anemonefish ("Clark's Anemone Fish") 3·25 3·75

161 Santos-Dumont's *Ballon No. 6* flying around Eiffel Tower, 1901

2003. Centenary of Powered Flight. Airships. Multicoloured.
570 50c. Type **161** 50 55
571 50c. USS *Shenandoah* 50 55
572 50c. Airship R101, 1929 . . . 50 55
573 50c. British Beardmore Airship R34, 1919 (first double crossing of North Atlantic) 50 55
574 50c. Zeppelin LZ-1 (first flight, 1900) 50 55
575 50c. Airship USS *Los Angeles* moored to airship tender USS *Patoka* 50 55
576 50c. Goodyear C-71 airship 50 55
577 50c. LZ-130 *Graf Zeppelin II* 50 55
578 50c. Zeppelin airship over Alps 50 55
MS579 150 × 100 mm. $2 LZ-127 *Graf Zeppelin* over Mount Fuji; $2 LZ-127 *Graf Zeppelin* over San Francisco;$2 LZ-127 *Graf Zeppelin* exchanging mail with Soviet ice breaker over Franz Josef Land . . . . 5·00 5·25

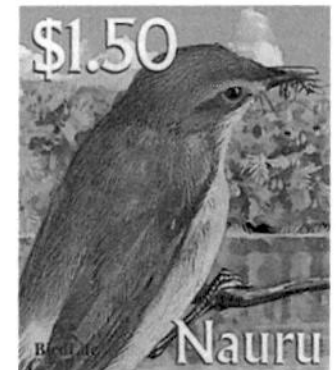

162 Nightingale Reed Warbler

2003. Bird Life International. Nightingale Reed Warbler ("Nauru Reed Warbler"). Multicoloured.
580 $1.50 Type **162** . . . . . . 1·30 1·40
581 $1.50 Nightingale reed warbler on reeds (horiz) . . 1·30 1·40
MS582 175 × 80 mm. $1.50 Head (horiz); Type **162**; $1.50 Singing; $1.50 No. 581; $1.50 Adult and nestlings (horiz) . . . . 5·00 5·25

NAWANAGAR Pt. 1

A state of India, Bombay District. Now uses Indian stamps.

6 docra = 1 anna.

1 (1 docra) **2** (2 docra)

1877. Imperf or perf.
1 **1** 1doc. blue . . . . 50 23·00

1880. Imperf.
6ab **2** 1doc. lilac . . . . 3·00 6·50
8 c 2doc. green . . . . 3·75 9·00
9 b 3doc. yellow . . . . 5·00 10·00

4 (1 docra)

1893. Imperf or perf.
13 **4** 1doc. black . . . . 1·25 5·00
14 2doc. green . . . . 1·40 5·50
15b 3doc. yellow . . . . 1·40 9·00

NEAPOLITAN PROVINCES Pt. 8

Temporary issues for Naples and other parts of S. Italy which adhered to the new Kingdom of Italy in 1860.

200 tornesi = 100 grano = 1 ducato.

1

1861. Embossed. Imperf.
2 **1** ½t. green . . . . 9·25 £140
5 ½g. brown £130 £150
9 1g. black . . . . £325 19·00
10 2g. blue . . . . 80·00 9·50
15 5g. red . . . . £140 90·00
18 10g. orange £100 £170
19 20g. yellow £425 £1600
23 50g. slate . . . . 23·00 £7000

NEGRI SEMBILAN Pt. 1

A state of the Federation of Malaya, incorporated in Malaysia in 1963.

100 cents = 1 dollar (Straits or Malayan).

1891. Stamp of Straits Settlements optd **Negri Sembilan**.
1 **5** 2c. red . . . . 3·00 5·00

2 Tiger **3**

1891.
2 **2** 1c. green . . . . 3·00 1·00
3 2c. red . . . . 3·25 7·50
4 5c. blue . . . . 30·00 40·00

1896.
5 **3** 1c. purple and green . . . . 9·50 5·00
6 2c. purple and brown . . . . 35·00 £110
7 3c. purple and red . . . . . 14·00 1·00
8 5c. purple and yellow . . . . 8·50 8·00
9 8c. purple and blue . . . . . 29·00 16·00
10 10c. purple and orange . . . 27·00 14·00
11 15c. green and violet . . . . 42·00 75·00
12 20c. green and olive . . . . 65·00 38·00
13 25c. green and red . . . . . 70·00 90·00
14 50c. green and black . . . . 70·00 65·00

1898. Surch in words and bar.
15 **3** 1c. on 15c. green and violet 95·00 £180
16 **2** 4c. on 1c. green . . . . . . 2·00 15·00
17 **3** 4c. on 3c. purple and red . . 3·00 16·00
18 **2** 4c. on 5c. blue . . . . 1·25 15·00

1898. Surch in words only.
19 **3** 4c. on 8c. purple and blue . . 4·75 4·25

6 Arms of Negri Sembilan **7** Arms of Negri Sembilan

1935.
21 **6** 1c. black . . . . 1·00 20
22 2c. green . . . . 1·00 20
23 2c. orange . . . . 4·25 65·00
24 3c. green . . . . 8·00 8·00
25 4c. orange . . . . 1·00 10
26 5c. brown . . . . 1·75 10
27 6c. red . . . . 15·00 2·50
28 6c. grey . . . . 4·75 75·00
29 8c. grey . . . . 2·00 10
30 10c. purple . . . . 1·00 10
31 12c. blue . . . . 1·90 50
32 15c. blue . . . . 10·00 50·00
33 25c. purple and red . . . . 1·25 70
34 30c. purple and orange . . . 3·50 2·00
35 40c. red and purple . . . . 2·00 2·00
36 50c. black on green . . . . 4·50 2·25
37 $1 black and red on blue . . 4·00 3·50
38 $2 green and red . . . . . 32·00 16·00
39 $5 green and red on green . . 21·00 60·00

1948. Silver Wedding. As T **4b/c** of Pitcairn Islands.
40 10c. violet 15 50
41 $5 green . . . . 19·00 28·00

1949.
42 **7** 1c. black 20 10
43 2c. orange 20 10
44 3c. green 20 30
45 4c. brown 20 10
46a 5c. purple 30 45
47 6c. grey . . . . 1·00 10
48 8c. red 50 75
49 8c. green . . . . 1·75 1·60
50 10c. mauve 20 10
51 12c. red . . . . 1·75 2·75
52 15c. blue . . . . 3·00 10
53 20c. black and green 50 75
54 20c. blue . . . . 1·00 10
55 25c. purple and orange . . . 50 10
56 30c. red and purple . . . . 1·25 2·50
57 35c. red and purple . . . . 1·00 1·00
58 40c. red and purple . . . . 1·50 4·75
59 50c. black and blue . . . . 2·25 20
60 $1 blue and purple . . . . 3·75 2·25
61 $2 green and red . . . . . 12·00 17·00
62 $5 green and brown . . . . 50·00 45·00

1949. U.P.U. As T **4d/g** of Pitcairn Islands.
63 10c. purple 20 10
64 15c. blue . . . . 1·40 2·75
65 25c. orange . . . . 30 2·25
66 50c. black . . . . 60 3·25

1953. Coronation. As T **4h** of Pitcairn Islands.
67 10c. black and purple . . . . 1·25 50

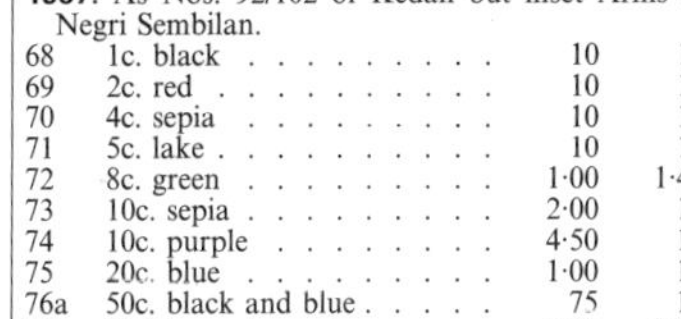

1957. As Nos. 92/102 of Kedah but inset Arms of Negri Sembilan.
68 1c. black 10 10
69 2c. red 10 10
70 4c. sepia 10 10
71 5c. lake 10 10
72 8c. green . . . . 1·00 1·40
73 10c. sepia . . . . 2·00 10
74 10c. purple . . . . 4·50 10
75 20c. blue . . . . 1·00 10
76a 50c. black and blue 75 10
77 $1 blue and purple . . . . 1·50 2·00
78 $2 green and red . . . . . 7·50 16·00
79 $5 brown and green . . . . 11·00 17·00

8 Tuanku Munawir

1961. Installation of Tuanku Munawir as Yang di-Pertuan Besar of Negri Sembilan.
80 **8** 10c. multicoloured 30 70

9 "Vanda hookeriana"

1965. As Nos. 115/21 of Kedah but with Arms of Negri Sembilan inset and inscr "NEGERI SEMBILAN" as in T **6**.
81 **9** 1c. multicoloured . . . . . . 10 1·60
82 – 2c. multicoloured . . . . . . 10 1·60
83 – 5c. multicoloured 40 10
84 – 6c. multicoloured 40 60
85 – 10c. multicoloured 40 10
86 – 15c. multicoloured 80 10
87 – 20c. multicoloured . . . . . 1·25 1·00
The higher values used in Negri Sembilan were Nos. 20/7 of Malaysia (National Issues).

10 Negri Sembilan Crest and Tuanku Ja'afar

1968. Installation of Tuanku Ja'afar as Yang di-Pertuan Besar of Negri Sembilan.
88 **10** 15c. multicoloured 15 70
89 50c. multicoloured . . . . . 30 1·40

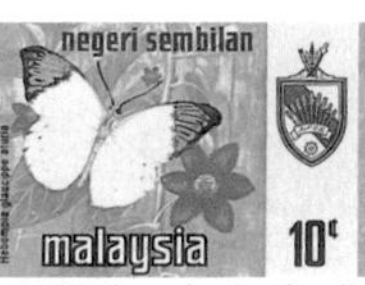

11 "Hebomoia glaucippe"

1971. Butterflies. As Nos. 124/30 of Kedah but with Arms of Negri Sembilan inset as T **11** and inscr "negeri sembilan".
91 – 1c. multicoloured . . . . . 40 2·00
92 – 2c. multicoloured . . . . . 70 2·00
93 – 5c. multicoloured . . . . . 1·00 20
94 – 6c. multicoloured . . . . . 1·00 2·00
95 **11** 10c. multicoloured . . . . . 1·00 10
96 – 15c. multicoloured . . . . . 1·40 10
97 – 20c. multicoloured . . . . . 1·40 50
The higher values in use with this issue were Nos. 64/71 of Malaysia (National Issues).

12 "Hibiscus rosa-sinensis" **13** Oil Palm

1979. Flowers. As Nos. 135/41 of Kedah but with Arms of Negri Sembilan and inscr "negeri sembilan" as in T **12**.
103 1c. "Rafflesia hasseltii" . . . 10 1·25
104 2c. "Pterocarpus indicus" . . . 10 1·25
105 5c. "Lagerstroemia speciosa" 15 40
106 10c. "Durio zibethinus" . . . 20 10
107 15c. Type **12** 20 10
108 20c. "Rhododendron scortechinii" 25 10
109 25c. "Etlingera elatior" (inscr "Phaeomeria speciosa") . . 45 25

1986. As Nos. 152/8 of Kedah but with Arms of Negri Sembilan and inscr "NEGERI SEMBILAN" as T **13**.
117 1c. Coffee 10 10
118 2c. Coconuts 10 10
119 5c. Cocoa 10 10
120 10c. Black pepper 10 10
121 15c. Rubber 10 10
122 20c. Type **13** 10 10
123 30c. Rice 10 10

NEPAL Pt. 21

An independent kingdom in the Himalayas N. of India.

1861. 16 annas = 1 rupee.
1907. 64 pice = 1 rupee.
1954. 100 paisa = 1 rupee.

1 (1a.) Crown and Kukris — 2 (½a.) Bow and Arrow and Kukris — 3 Siva Mahadeva (2p.)

1881. Imperf or pin-perf.

34	2	½a. black	2·75	1·80
35		½a. orange	£375	£190
42	1	1a. blue	6·75	2·00
14		1a. green	48·00	48·00
16c		2a. violet	37·00	37·00
40		2a. brown	11·00	4·50
41		4a. green	7·50	7·50

1907. Various sizes.

57	3	2p. brown	35	35
58		4p. green	1·10	75
59		8p. red	75	50
60		16p. purple	11·00	2·75
61		24p. orange	11·00	1·80
62		32p. blue	15·00	2·20
63		1r. red	30·00	18·00
50		5r. black and brown	26·00	12·00

5 Swayambhunath Temple, Katmandu

7 Guheswari Temple, Patan

8 Sri Pashupati (Siva Mahadeva)

1949.

64	5	2p. brown	90	75
65	–	4p. green	90	75
66	–	6p. pink	1·80	75
67	–	8p. red	1·80	1·10
68	–	16p. purple	1·80	1·10
69	–	20p. blue	3·75	1·80
70	7	24p. red	3·00	1·10
71	–	32p. blue	5·50	1·80
72	8	1r. orange	30·00	18·00

DESIGNS—As Type **5**: 4p. Pashupatinath Temple, Katmandu; 6p. Tri-Chundra College; 8p. Mahabuddha Temple. 26 × 30 mm: 16p. Krishna Mandir Temple, Patan. As Type **7**: 20p. View of Katmandu; 32p. The twenty-two fountains, Balaju.

9 King Tribhuvana

10 Map of Nepal

1954. (a) Size 18 × 22 mm.

73	9	2p. brown	1·80	35
74		4p. green	6·00	1·10
75		6p. red	1·50	35
76		8p. lilac	1·10	35
77		12p. orange	11·00	1·80
		(b) Size 25½ × 29½ mm.		
78	9	16p. brown	1·50	35
79		20p. red	3·00	1·10
80		24p. purple	2·50	1·10
81		32p. blue	3·75	1·10
82		50p. mauve	30·00	5·50
83		1r. red	44·00	8·75
84		2r. orange	37·00	7·50
		(c) Size 30 × 18 mm.		
85	10	2p. brown	1·50	75
86		4p. green	6·00	1·10
87		6p. red	15·00	1·80
88		8p. lilac	1·10	75
89		12p. orange	15·00	1·80
		(d) Size 38 × 21½ mm.		
90	10	16p. brown	1·80	75
91		20p. red	3·00	75
92		24p. purple	2·20	75
93		32p. blue	5·50	1·50
94		50p. mauve	30·00	5·50
95		1r. red	48·00	7·50
96		2r. orange	37·00	7·50

11 Mechanization of Agriculture

13 Hanuman Dhoka, Katmandu

1956. Coronation.

97	11	4p. green	6·00	6·00
98	–	6p. red and yellow	3·75	3·00
99	–	8p. violet	3·00	1·50
100	13	24p. red	6·00	6·00
101	–	1r. red	£110	95·00

DESIGNS—As Type **11**: 8p. Processional elephant. As Type **13**: 6p. Throne; 1r. King and Queen and mountains.

15 U.N. Emblem and Nepalese Landscape

16 Nepalese Crown

1956. 1st Anniv of Admission into U.N.O.

102	15	12p. blue and brown	7·50	6·00

1957. (a) Size 18 × 22 mm.

103	16	2p. brown	75	75
104		4p. green	1·10	75
105		6p. red	75	75
106		8p. violet	75	75
107		12p. red	4·00	1·10
		(b) Size 25½ × 29½ mm.		
108	16	16p. brown	5·50	1·80
109		20p. red	8·75	2·50
110		24p. mauve	5·50	2·20
111		32p. blue	7·50	2·50
112		50p. pink	15·00	5·50
113		1r. salmon	37·00	11·00
114		2r. orange	22·00	7·50

17 Gaunthali carrying Letter

18 Temple of Lumbini

1958. Air. Inauguration of Nepalese Internal Airmail Service.

115	17	10p. blue	1·90	1·90

1958. Human Rights Day.

116	18	6p. yellow	1·50	1·50

19 Nepalese Map and Flag

1959. 1st Nepalese Elections.

117	19	6p. red and green	50	45

20 Spinning Wheel

21 King Mahendra

1959. Cottage Industries.

118	20	2p. brown	45	45

1959. Admission of Nepal to U.P.U.

119	21	12p. blue	50	45

22 Vishnu

23 Nyatopol Temple, Bhaktapur

1959.

120	22	1p. brown	15	15
121	–	2p. violet	15	15
122	–	4p. blue	50	35
123	–	6p. pink	50	15
124	–	8p. brown	35	15
125	–	12p. grey	50	15
126	23	16p. violet and brown	50	15
127		20p. red and blue	1·80	75
128	23	24p. red and green	1·80	75
129		32p. blue and lilac	1·10	75
130		50p. green and red	1·80	75
131	–	1r. blue and brown	16·00	6·00
132	–	2r. blue and purple	15·00	6·25
133	–	5r. red and violet	60·00	55·00

DESIGNS—As Type **22**. HORIZ: 2p. Krishna; 8p. Siberian musk deer; 12p. Indian rhinoceros. VERT: 4p. Himalayas; 6p. Gateway, Bhaktapur Palace. As Type **23**. VERT: 1r., 2r. Himalayan monal pheasant; 5r. Satyr tragopan.

24 King Mahendra opening Parliament

1959. Opening of 1st Nepalese Parliament.

134	24	6p. red	1·10	1·10

25 Sri Pashupatinath — 26 Children, Pagoda and Mt. Everest

1959. Renovation of Sri Pashupatinath Temple, Katmandu.

135	25	4p. green (18 × 25 mm)	75	75
136		8p. red (21 × 28½ mm)	1·50	75
137		1r. blue (24½ × 33½ mm)	8·75	6·00

1960. Children's Day.

137a	26	6p. blue	15·00	11·00

27 King Mahendra

28 Mt. Everest

1960. King Mahendra's 41st Birthday.

138	27	1r. purple	1·60	1·10

See also Nos. 163/4a.

1960. Mountain Views.

139	–	5p. brown and purple	35	15
140	28	10p. purple and blue	50	20
141	–	40p. brown and violet	1·30	80

DESIGNS: 5p. Machha Puchhre; 40p. Manaslu (wrongly inscr "MANSALU").

29 King Tribhuvana

30 Prince Gyanendra cancelling Children's Day Stamps of 1960

1961. 10th Democracy Day.

142	29	10p. orange and brown	15	15

1961. Children's Day.

143	30	12p. orange	37·00	37·00

31 King Mahendra — 32 Campaign Emblem and House

1961. King Mahendra's 42nd Birthday.

144	31	6p. green	35	35
145		12p. blue	50	50
146		50p. red	1·10	1·10
147		1r. brown	1·80	1·80

1962. Malaria Eradication.

148	32	12p. blue	35	35
149	–	1r. orange and red	1·10	1·10

DESIGN: 1r. Emblem and Nepalese flag.

33 King Mahendra on Horseback — 34 Bhana Bhakta Acharya

1962. King Mahendra's 43rd Birthday.

150	33	10p. blue	20	20
151		15p. brown	35	35
152		45p. brown	75	75
153		1r. grey	1·10	1·10

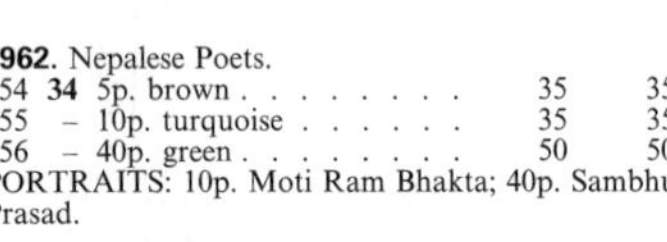

1962. Nepalese Poets.

154	34	5p. brown	35	35
155	–	10p. turquoise	35	35
156	–	40p. green	50	50

PORTRAITS: 10p. Moti Ram Bhakta; 40p. Sambhu Prasad.

35 King Mahendra

36 King Mahendra

1962.

157	35	1p. red	15	10
158		2p. blue	15	10
158a		3p. grey	50	35
159		5p. brown	15	10
160	36	10p. purple	15	15
161		40p. brown	35	35
162		75p. green	11·00	11·00
162a	35	75p. green	1·50	75
163	27	2r. red	1·50	1·50
164		5r. green	3·00	3·00
164a		10r. violet	11·00	8·75

No. 162a is smaller, 17½ × 20 mm.

37 Emblems of Learning

1963. U.N.E.S.C.O. "Education for All" Campaign.

165	37	10p. black	35	15
166		15p. brown	50	35
167		50p. blue	90	75

38 Hands holding Lamps

1963. National Day.

168	38	5p. blue	15	15
169		10p. brown	15	15
170		50p. purple	75	50
171		1r. green	1·50	75

39 Campaign Symbols

40 Map of Nepal and Open Hand

1963. Freedom from Hunger.

172	39	10p. orange	35	15
173		15p. blue	50	35

174 50p. green 1·10 75
175 1r. brown 1·50 1·30

1963. Rastruya Panchayat.
176 **40** 10p. green 15 15
177 15p. purple 35 35
178 50p. grey 95 50
179 1r. blue 1·50 90

41 King Mahendra

42 King Mahendra and Highway Map

1963. King Mahendra's 44th Birthday.
180 **41** 5p. violet 15 15
181 10p. brown 35 15
182 15p. green 50 35

1964. Inauguration of East–West Highway.
183 **42** 10p. orange and blue 15 15
184 15p. orange and blue 35 20
185 50p. brown and green 60 35

43 King Mahendra at Microphone

44 Crown Prince Birendra

1964. King Mahendra's 45th Birthday.
186 **43** 1p. brown 15 15
187 2p. grey 20 20
188 2r. brown 1·10 1·10

1964. Crown Prince's 19th Birthday.
189 **44** 10p. green 90 75
190 15p. brown 90 75

45 Flag, Kukris, Rings and Torch

46 Nepalese Family

1964. Olympic Games, Tokyo.
191 **45** 10p. blue, red and pink 95 75

1965. Land Reform.
192 – 2p. black and green 35 35
193 – 5p. brown and green 35 35
194 – 10p. purple and grey 35 35
195 **46** 15p. brown and yellow 50 50
DESIGNS: 2p. Farmer ploughing; 5p. Ears of wheat; 10p. Grain elevator.

47 Globe and Letters

48 King Mahendra

1965. Introduction of International Insured and Parcel Service.
196 **47** 15p. violet 35 35

1965. King Mahendra's 46th Birthday.
197 **48** 50p. purple 90 75

49 Four Martyrs

50 I.T.U. Emblem

1965. "Nepalese Martyrs".
198 **49** 15p. green 20 15

1965. I.T.U. Centenary.
199 **50** 15p. black and purple 50 35

51 I.C.Y. Emblem

52 Devkota (poet)

1965. International Co-operation Year.
200 **51** 1r. multicoloured 1·10 90

1965. Devkota Commemoration.
201 **52** 15p. brown 35 30

54 Flag and King Mahendra

1966. Democracy Day.
202 **54** 15p. red and blue 75 50

55 Siva Parvati and Pashuvati Temple

1966. Maha Siva-Ratri Festival.
203 **55** 15p. violet 45 35

56 "Stamp" Emblem

1966. Nepalese Philatelic Exhibition, Katmandu.
204 **56** 15p. orange and green 50 35

57 King Mahendra

58 Queen Mother

1966. King Mahendra's 47th Birthday.
205 **57** 15p. brown and yellow 45 30

1966. Queen Mother's 60th Birthday.
206 **58** 15p. brown 35 35

59 Queen Ratna

60 Flute-player and Dancer

1966. Children's Day.
207 **59** 15p. brown and yellow 45 35

1966. Krishna Anniv.
208 **60** 15p. violet and yellow 45 35

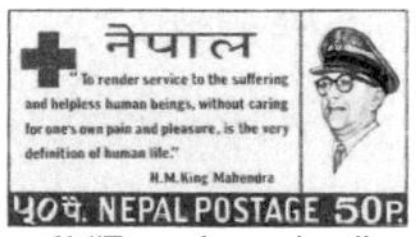

61 "To render service..."

1966. 1st Anniv of Nepalese Red Cross.
209 **61** 50p. red and green 4·50 1·50

62 W.H.O. Building on Flag

63 Paudyal

1966. Inaug of W.H.O. Headquarters, Geneva.
210 **62** 1r. violet 2·20 1·50

1966. Leknath Paudyal (poet) Commemoration.
211 **63** 15p. blue 45 35

64 Rama and Sita

65 Buddha

1967. Rama Navami, 2024, birthday of Rama.
212 **64** 15p. brown and yellow 45 35

1967. Buddha Jayanti, birthday of Buddha.
213 **65** 75p. purple and orange 35 35

66 King Mahendra addressing Nepalese

1967. King Mahendra's 48th Birthday.
214 **66** 15p. brown and blue 45 35

67 Queen Ratna and Children

68 Ama Dablam (mountain)

1967. Children's Day.
215 **67** 15p. brown and cream 45 35

1967. International Tourist Year.
216 **68** 5p. violet (postage) 35 35
217 – 65p. brown 75 75
218 – 1r.80 red and blue (air) 1·80 1·50
DESIGNS—38 × 20 mm: 65p. Bhaktapur Durbar Square. 35½ × 25½ mm: 1r.80, Plane over Katmandu.

69 Open-air Class

1967. Constitution Day. "Go to the Village" Educational Campaign.
219 **69** 15p. multicoloured 45 35

70 Crown Prince Birendra, Campfire and Scout Emblem

1967. Diamond Jubilee of World Scouting.
220 **70** 15p. blue 75 50

71 Prithvi Narayan Shah (founder of Kingdom)

72 Arms of Nepal

1968. Bicentenary of the Kingdom.
221 **71** 15p. blue and red 75 50

1968. National Day.
222 **72** 15p. blue and red 75 50

73 W.H.O. Emblem and Nepalese Flag

1968. 20th Anniv of W.H.O.
223 **73** 1r.20 blue, red and yellow 3·00 2·20

74 Sita and Janaki Temple

1968. Sita Jayanti.
224 **74** 15p. brown and violet 50 35

75 King Mahendra, Mountains and Himalayan Monal Pheasant

1968. King Mahendra's 49th Birthday.
225 **75** 15p. multicoloured 65 35

76 Garuda and Airline Emblem

1968. Air. 10th Anniv of Royal Nepalese Airlines.
226 **76** 15p. brown and blue 35 35
227 – 65p. blue 75 75
228 – 2r.50 blue and orange 2·50 2·20
DESIGNS—DIAMOND (25½ × 25½ mm): 65p. Route-map. As Type **76**: 2r.50, Convair Metropolitan airliner over Mount Dhaulagiri.

77 Flag, Queen Ratna and Children

78 Human Rights Emblem and Buddha

1968. Children's Day and Queen Ratna's 41st Birthday.
229 **77** 5p. red, yellow and green 35 30

1968. Human Rights Year.
230 **78** 1r. red and green 3·00 2·20

79 Crown Prince Birendra and Dancers

1968. Crown Prince Birendra's 24th Birthday, and National Youth Festival.
231 **79** 25p. blue 75 50

80 King Mahendra, Flags and U.N. Building, New York

81 Amsu Varma (7th-century ruler)

1969. Nepal's Election to U.N. Security Council.
232 **80** 1r. multicoloured . . . . . 1·10 90

1969. Famous Nepalese.
233 **81** 15p. violet and green . . . 50 1·50
234 – 25p. turquoise 75 75
235 – 50p. brown 95 95
236 – 1r. purple and brown . . . 1·10 90
DESIGNS—VERT: 25p. Ram Shah (17th-century King of Gurkha); 50p. Bhimsen Thapa (19th-century Prime Minister). HORIZ: 1r. Bal Bhadra Kunwar (19th-century warrior).

82 I.L.O. Emblem

1969. 50th Anniv of I.L.O.
237 **82** 1r. brown and mauve . . . 5·50 3·75

83 King Mahendra

85 Queen Ratna, and Child with Toy

84 King Tribhuvana and Queens

1969. King Mahendra's 50th Birthday.
238 **83** 25p. multicoloured 45 45

1969. 64th Birth Anniv of King Tribhuvana.
239 **84** 25p. brown and yellow . . 45 45

1969. National Children's Day.
240 **85** 25p. mauve and brown . . 45 45

86 Rhododendron

87 Durga, Goddess of Victory

1969. Flowers. Multicoloured.
241 25p. Type **86** 60 50
242 25p. Narcissus 60 50
243 25p. Marigold 60 50
244 25p. Poinsettia 60 50

1969. Durga Pooja Festival.
245 **87** 15p. black and orange . . 35 35
246 50p. violet and brown . . 80 80

88 Crown Prince Birendra and Princess Aishwarya

1970. Royal Wedding.
247 **88** 25p. multicoloured 45 20

89 Produce, Cow and Landscape

1970. Agricultural Year.
248 **89** 25p. multicoloured 45 35

90 King Mahendra, Mt. Everest and Nepalese Crown

1970. King Mahendra's 51st Birthday.
249 **90** 50p. multicoloured 75 50

91 Lake Gosainkunda

1970. Nepalese Lakes. Multicoloured.
250 5p. Type **91** 35 35
251 25p. Lake Phewa Tal 50 50
252 1r. Lake Rara Daha 90 90

92 A.P.Y. Emblem

1970. Asian Productivity Year.
253 **92** 1r. blue 90 75

93 Queen Ratna and Children's Palace, Taulihawa

1970. National Children's Day.
254 **93** 25p. grey and brown . . . 45 35

94 New Headquarters Building

1970. New U.P.U. Headquarters, Berne.
255 **94** 2r.50 grey and brown . . . 1·00 80

95 U.N. Flag

1970. 25th Anniv of United Nations.
256 **95** 25p. blue and purple . . . 45 35

96 Durbar Square, Patan

1970. Tourism. Multicoloured.
257 15p. Type **96** 35 15
258 25p. Boudhanath Stupa (temple) (vert) 50 35
259 1r. Mt. Gauri Shankar . . . 90 75

97 Statue of Harihar, Valmiki Ashram

98 Torch within Spiral

1971. Nepalese Religious Art.
260 **97** 25p. black and brown . . . 45 30

1971. Racial Equality Year.
261 **98** 1r. red and blue . . . . . 1·10 80

99 King Mahendra taking Salute

1971. King Mahendra's 52nd Birthday.
262 **99** 15p. purple and blue . . . 45 30

100 Sweta Bhairab

1971. Bhairab Statues of Shiva.
263 **100** 15p. brown and chestnut 35 35
264 – 25p. brown and green . . 35 35
265 – 50p. brown and blue . . . 75 75
DESIGNS: 25p. Mahankal Bhairab; 50p. Kal Bhairab.

101 Child presenting Queen Ratna with Garland

1971. National Children's Day.
266 **101** 25p. multicoloured . . . 45 30

102 Iranian and Nepalese Flags on Map of Iran

1971. 2,500th Anniv of Persian Empire.
267 **102** 1r. multicoloured . . . . 1·10 75

103 Mother and Child

1971. 25th Anniv of U.N.I.C.E.F.
268 **103** 1r. blue . . . . 1·10 75

104 Mt. Everest

1971. Tourism. Himalayan Peaks.
269 **104** 25p. dp brown, brn and bl 35 15
270 – 1r. black, brown and blue 75 50
271 – 1r.80 green, brown & blue 1·30 95
DESIGNS: 1r. Mt. Kanchenjunga; 1r.80, Mt. Annapurna I.

105 Royal Standard

106 Araniko and White Dagoba, Peking

1972. National Day.
272 **105** 25p. black and red . . . 45 30

1972. Araniko (13th-century architect) Commem.
273 **106** 15p. brown and blue . . . 20 20

107 Open Book

1972. International Book Year.
274 **107** 2p. brown and buff . . . 15 15
275 5p. black and brown . . . 15 15
276 1r. black and blue 90 75

108 Human Heart

1972. World Heart Month.
277 **108** 25p. red and green . . . 45 35

109 King Mahendra

110 King Birendra

1972. 1st Death Anniv of King Mahendra.
278 **109** 25p. brown and black . . 45 30

1972. King Birendra's 28th Birthday.
279 **110** 50p. purple and brown . . 50 45

111 Northern Border Costumes

112 Sri Baburam Acharya

1973. National Costumes. Multicoloured.
280 25p. Type **111** 35 15
281 50p. Hill-dwellers 45 35
282 75p. Katmandu Valley . . . 60 45
283 1r. Inner Terai 90 60

1973. 85th Birth Anniv of Sri Baburam Acharya (historian).
284 **112** 25p. grey and red 15 10

113 Nepalese Family

1973. 25th Anniv of W.H.O.
285 **113** 1r. blue and orange . . . 90 75

114 Birthplace of Buddha, Lumbini

1973. Tourism. Multicoloured.
286 25p. Type **114** 35 15
287 75p. Mt. Makalu 50 35
288 1r. Castle, Gurkha 75 75

115 Transplanting Rice

1973. 10th Anniv of World Food Programme.
289 **115** 10p. brown and violet . . 15 15

116 Interpol H.Q., Paris

1973. 50th Anniv of International Criminal Police Organization (Interpol).
290 **116** 25p. blue and brown . . . 35 20

117 Shri Shom Nath Sigdyal

118 Cow

1973. 1st Death Anniv of Shri Shom Nath Sigdyal (scholar).
291 **117** 1r.25 violet 90 75

1973. Domestic Animals. Multicoloured.
292 2p. Type **118** 15 15
293 3r.25 Yak . . . . 1·60 1·10

119 King Birendra

1974. King Birendra's 29th Birthday.
294 **119** 5p. brown and black . . . 15 15
295 15p. brown and black . . 20 15
296 1r. brown and black . . . 75 50

120 Text of National Anthem

121 King Janak seated on Throne

1974. National Day.
297 **120** 25p. purple 35 15
298 – 1r. green 50 45
DESIGN: 1r. Anthem musical score.

1974. King Janak Commemoration.
299 **121** 2r.50 multicoloured . . . 1·80 1·50

122 Emblem and Village

1974. 25th Anniv of SOS Children's Village International.
300 **122** 25p. blue and red 35 35

123 Football

124 W.P.Y. Emblem

1974. Nepalese Games. Multicoloured.
301 2p. Type **123** 15 15
302 2r.75 Baghchal (diagram) . . 1·10 90

1974. World Population Year.
303 **124** 5p. blue and brown . . . 20 15

125 U.P.U. Monument, Berne

126 Red Lacewing

1974. Centenary of U.P.U.
304 **125** 1r. black and green . . . 75 50

1974. Nepalese Butterflies. Multicoloured.
305 10p. Type **126** 15 15
306 15p. Leaf butterfly 45 20
307 1r.25 Leaf butterfly (underside) . . . . 1·10 75
308 1r.75 Red-breasted jezebel . . 1·30 1·10

127 King Birendra

128 Muktinath

1974. King Birendra's 30th Birthday.
309 **127** 25p. black and green . . 20 20

1974. "Visit Nepal" Tourism. Multicoloured.
310 25p. Type **128** 35 15
311 1r. Peacock window, Bhaktapur (horiz) 75 45

129 Guheswari Temple

1975. Coronation of King Birendra. Multicoloured.
312 25p. Type **129** 35 15
313 50p. Lake Rara (37 × 30 mm) 35 15
314 1r. Throne and sceptre (46 × 26 mm) 50 35
315 1r.25 Royal Palace, Katmandu (46 × 26 mm) 1·10 50
316 1r.75 Pashupatinath Temple (25 × 31 mm) 75 75
317 2r.75 King Birendra and Queen Aishwarya (46 × 25 mm) . . . . . . 1·10 90

130 Tourism Year Emblem

1975. South Asia Tourism Year. Multicoloured.
319 2p. Type **130** 15 15
320 25p. Temple stupa (vert) . . 35 35

131 Tiger

1975. Wildlife Conservation. Multicoloured.
321 2p. Type **131** 35 35
322 5p. Swamp deer (vert) . . . 35 35
323 1r. Lesser panda 75 75

132 Queen Aishwarya and I.W.Y. Emblem

1975. International Women's Year.
324 **132** 1r. multicoloured 50 35

133 Rupse Falls

134 King Birendra

1975. Tourism. Multicoloured.
325 2p. Mt. Ganesh Himal (horiz) 15 15
326 25p. Type **133** 15 15
327 50p. Kumari ("Living Goddess") 50 35

1975. King Birendra's 31st Birthday.
328 **134** 25p. violet and mauve . . 20 15

136 Flag and Map

138 Flags of Nepal and Colombo Plan

137 Transplanting Rice

1976. Silver Jubilee of National Democracy Day.
330 **136** 2r.50 red and blue 90 75

1976. Agriculture Year.
331 **137** 25p. multicoloured . . . 20 15

1976. 25th Anniv of Colombo Plan.
332 **138** 1r. multicoloured 50 45

139 Running

140 "Dove of Peace"

1976. Olympic Games, Montreal.
333 **139** 3r.25 black and blue . . . 1·50 1·10

1976. 5th Non-aligned Countries' Summit Conf.
334 **140** 5r. blue, yellow and black 1·90 1·30

141 Lakhe Dance

1976. Nepalese Dances. Multicoloured.
335 10p. Type **141** 15 15
336 15p. Maruni dance 15 15
337 30p. Jhangad dance 35 20
338 1r. Sebru dance 50 35

142 Nepalese Lily

143 King Birendra

1976. Flowers. Multicoloured.
339 30p. Type **142** 50 15
340 30p. "Meconopsis grandis" 50 15
341 30p. "Cardiocrinum giganteum" (horiz) 50 15
342 30p. "Megacodon stylophorus" (horiz) . . . 50 15

1976. King Birendra's 32nd Birthday.
343 **143** 5p. green 15 10
344 30p. dp brown, brn & yell 20 15

144 Liberty Bell

1976. Bicentenary of American Revolution.
345 **144** 10r. multicoloured . . . . 2·75 2·40

145 Kaji Amarsingh Thapa

1977. Kaji Amarsingh Thapa (19th-century warrior) Commemoration.
346 **145** 10p. green and brown . . 15 15

146 Terracotta Figurine and Kapilavastu

1977. Tourism.
347 **146** 30p. violet 15 15
348 – 5r. green and brown . . . 1·50 1·10
DESIGN: 5r. Ashokan pillar, Lumbini.

147 Great Indian Hornbill

1977. Birds. Multicoloured.
349 5p. Type **147** 45 20
350 15p. Cheer pheasant (horiz) 80 20
351 1r. Green magpie (horiz) . . 1·30 50
352 2r.30 Spiny babbler . . . . 2·40 75

148 Tukuche Himal and Police Flag

1977. 1st Anniv of Ascent of Tukuche Himal by Police Team.
353 **148** 1r.25 multicoloured . . . 20 15

149 Map of Nepal and Scout Emblem

150 Dhanwantari, the Health-giver

1977. 25th Anniv of Scouting in Nepal.
354 **149** 3r.50 multicoloured . . . 45 30

1977. Health Day.
355 **150** 30p. green 20 15

151 Map of Nepal and Flags

152 King Birendra

1977. 26th Consultative Committee Meeting of Colombo Plan, Katmandu.
356 **151** 1r. multicoloured 35 20

1977. King Birendra's 33rd Birthday.
357 **152** 5p. brown 15 15
358 1r. brown 35 35

153 General Post Office, Katmandu, and Seal

1978. Centenary of Nepalese Post Office.
359 **153** 25p. brown and agate . . 15 15
360 – 75p. brown and agate . . 35 35

DESIGN: 75p. General Post Office, Katmandu, and early postmark.

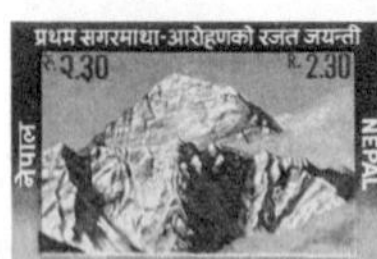

154 South-west Face of Mt. Everest

1978. 25th Anniv of First Ascent of Mt. Everest.
361 **154** 2r.30 grey and brown . . 90 50
362 – 4r. blue and green . . . . 1·30 1·10
DESIGN: 4r. South face of Mt. Everest.

155 Sun, Ankh and Landscape

1978. World Environment Day.
363 **155** 1r. green and orange . . . 35 20

156 Queen Mother Ratna 157 Rapids, Tripsuli River

1978. Queen Mother's 50th Birthday.
364 **156** 2r.30 green 75 50

1978. Tourism. Multicoloured.
365 10p. Type **157** 15 10
366 50p. Window, Nara Devi, Katmandu 20 15
367 1r. Mahakali dance (vert) . . 45 35

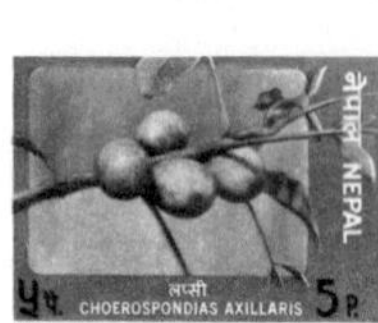

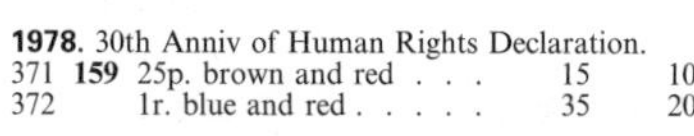

158 Lapsi ("Choerospondias axillaris") 159 Lamp and U.N. Emblem

1978. Fruits. Multicoloured.
368 5p. Type **158** 20 10
369 1r. Katus (vert) 50 35
370 1r.25 Rudrakshya 75 45

1978. 30th Anniv of Human Rights Declaration.
371 **159** 25p. brown and red . . . 15 10
372 1r. blue and red 35 20

160 Wright Flyer I and Boeing 727-100 161 King Birendra

1978. Air. 75th Anniv of First Powered Flight.
373 **160** 2r.30 blue and brown . . 90 75

1978. King Birendra's 34th Birthday.
374 **161** 30p. blue and brown . . . 15 10
375 2r. brown and violet . . . 60 45

162 Red Machchhindranath and Kamroop and Patan Temples

1979. Red Machchhindranath (guardian deity) Festival.
376 **162** 75p. brown and green . . 35 20

163 "Buddha's Birth" (carving, Maya Devi Temple) 164 Planting a Sapling

1979. Lumbini Year.
377 **163** 1r. yellow and brown . . 35 20

1979. Tree Planting Festival.
378 **164** 2r.30 brown, green & yellow 90 75

165 Chariot of Red Machchhindranath 166 Nepalese Scouts and Guides

1979. Bhoto Jatra (Vest Exhibition) Festival.
379 **165** 1r.25 multicoloured . . . 45 35

1979. International Year of the Child.
380 **166** 1r. brown 45 35

167 Mount Pabil 168 Great Grey Shrike

1979. Tourism.
381 **167** 30p. green 15 15
382 – 50p. red and blue 15 15
383 – 1r.25 multicoloured . . . 45 45
DESIGNS: 50p. Yajnashala, Swargadwari. 1r.25, Shiva-Parbati (wood carving, Gaddi Baithak Temple).

1979. International World Pheasant Association Symposium, Katmandu. Multicoloured.
384 10p. Type **168** (postage) . . . 20 15
385 10r. Fire-tailed sunbird . . . 5·50 3·50
386 3r.50 Himalayan monal pheasant (horiz) (air) . . . 1·90 1·60

169 Lichchhavi Coin (obverse) 170 King Birendra

1979. Coins.
387 **169** 5p. orange and brown . . 15 15
388 – 5p. orange and brown . . 15 15
389 – 15p. blue and indigo . . . 15 15
390 – 15p. blue and indigo . . . 15 15
391 – 1r. blue and deep blue . . 45 45
392 – 1r. blue and deep blue . . 45 45
DESIGNS: No. 388, Lichchhavi coin (reverse); 389, Malla coin (obverse); 390, Malla coin (reverse); 391, Prithvi Narayan Shah coin (obverse); 392, Prithvi Narayan Shah coin (reverse).

1979. King Birendra's 35th Birthday. Mult.
393 25p. Type **170** 15 10
394 2r.30 Reservoir 75 50

171 Samyak Pooja Festival

1980. Samyak Pooja Festival, Katmandu.
395 **171** 30p. brown, grey & purple 15 15

172 Sacred Basil

1980. Herbs. Multicoloured.
396 5p. Type **172** 15 10
397 30p. Valerian 20 10
398 1r. Nepalese pepper 35 20
399 2r.30 Himalayan rhubarb . . 75 50

173 Gyandil Das 174 Everlasting Flame and Temple, Shirsasthan

1980. Nepalese Writers.
400 **173** 5p. lilac and brown . . . 10 10
401 – 30p. purple and brown . . 15 10
402 – 1r. green and blue 30 20
403 – 2r.30 blue and green . . . 60 50
DESIGNS: 30p. Siddhidas Amatya; 1r. Pahalman Singh Swanr; 2r.30, Jay Prithvi Bahadur Singh.

1980. Tourism. Multicoloured.
404 10p. Type **174** 10 10
405 1r. Godavari Pond 35 20
406 5r. Mount Dhaulagiri . . . . 1·20 90

175 Bhairab Dancer 176 King Birendra

1980. World Tourism Conf, Manila, Philippines.
407 **175** 25r. multicoloured . . . . 5·25 4·00

1980. King Birendra's 36th Birthday.
408 **176** 1r. multicoloured 35 20

177 I.Y.D.P. Emblem and Nepalese Flag

1981. International Year of Disabled Persons.
409 **177** 5r. multicoloured . . . . 1·50 1·10

178 Nepal Rastra Bank 179 One Anna Stamp of 1881

1981. 25th Anniv of Nepal Rastra Bank.
410 **178** 1r.75 multicoloured . . . 45 35

1981. Nepalese Postage Stamp Centenary.
411 **179** 10p. blue, brown and black 15 10
412 – 40p. purple, brown & blk 15 10
413 – 3r.40 green, brown & blk 90 75
DESIGNS: 40p. 2a. stamp of 1881; 3r.40, 4a. stamp of 1881.

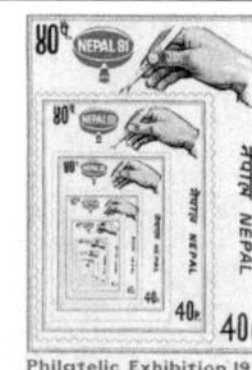

180 Nepalese Flag and Association Emblem 181 Hand holding Stamp

1981. 70th Council Meeting of International Hotel Association, Katmandu.
415 **180** 1r.75 multicoloured . . . 45 35

1981. "Nepal 81" Stamp Exhibition, Katmandu.
416 **181** 40p. multicoloured . . . 15 10

182 King Birendra 183 Image of Hrishikesh, Ridi

1981. King Birendra's 37th Birthday.
417 **182** 1r. multicoloured 30 20

1981. Tourism. Multicoloured.
418 5p. Type **183** 10 10
419 25p. Tripura Sundari Temple, Baitadi 10 10
420 2r. Mt. Langtang Lirung . . 45 20

184 Academy Building 185 Balakrishna Sama

1982. 25th Anniv of Royal Nepal Academy.
421 **184** 40p. multicoloured . . . 15 15

1982. 1st Death Anniv of Balakrishna Sama (writer).
422 **185** 1r. multicoloured 20 20

186 "Intelsat V" and Dish Aerial 187 Mount Nuptse

1982. Sagarmatha Satellite Earth Station, Balambu.
423 **186** 5r. multicoloured . . . . 1·30 75

1982. 50th Anniv of Union of International Alpinist Associations. Multicoloured.
424 25p. Type **187** 15 15
425 2r. Mount Lhotse (31 × 31 mm) 50 35
426 3r. Mount Everest (39 × 31 mm) . . . . . . 1·10 50
Nos. 424/6 were issued together, se-tenant, forming a composite design.

188 Games Emblem and Weights 189 Indra Sarobar Lake

1982. 9th Asian Games, New Delhi.
427 **188** 3r.40 multicoloured . . . 90 75

1982. Kulekhani Hydro-electric Project.
428 **189** 2r. multicoloured 50 35

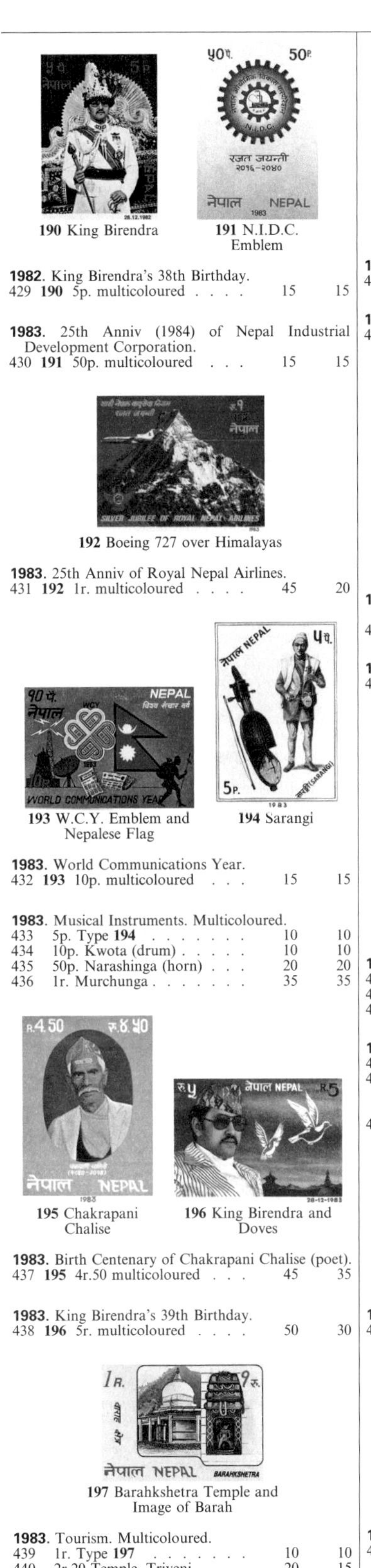

190 King Birendra

191 N.I.D.C. Emblem

1982. King Birendra's 38th Birthday.
429 **190** 5p. multicoloured 15 15

1983. 25th Anniv (1984) of Nepal Industrial Development Corporation.
430 **191** 50p. multicoloured . . . 15 15

192 Boeing 727 over Himalayas

1983. 25th Anniv of Royal Nepal Airlines.
431 **192** 1r. multicoloured 45 20

193 W.C.Y. Emblem and Nepalese Flag

194 Sarangi

1983. World Communications Year.
432 **193** 10p. multicoloured . . . 15 15

1983. Musical Instruments. Multicoloured.
433 5p. Type **194** 10 10
434 10p. Kwota (drum) 10 10
435 50p. Narashinga (horn) . . . 20 20
436 1r. Murchunga 35 35

195 Chakrapani Chalise

196 King Birendra and Doves

1983. Birth Centenary of Chakrapani Chalise (poet).
437 **195** 4r.50 multicoloured . . . 45 35

1983. King Birendra's 39th Birthday.
438 **196** 5r. multicoloured 50 30

197 Barahkshetra Temple and Image of Barah

1983. Tourism. Multicoloured.
439 1r. Type **197** 10 10
440 2r.20 Temple, Triveni 20 15
441 6r. Mount Cho-oyu 50 35

198 Auditing Accounts

1984. 25th Anniv of Auditor General.
442 **198** 25p. multicoloured . . . 50 45

199 Antenna and Emblem

1984. 20th Anniv of Asia-Pacific Broadcasting Union.
443 **199** 5r. multicoloured . . . . 1·30 1·10

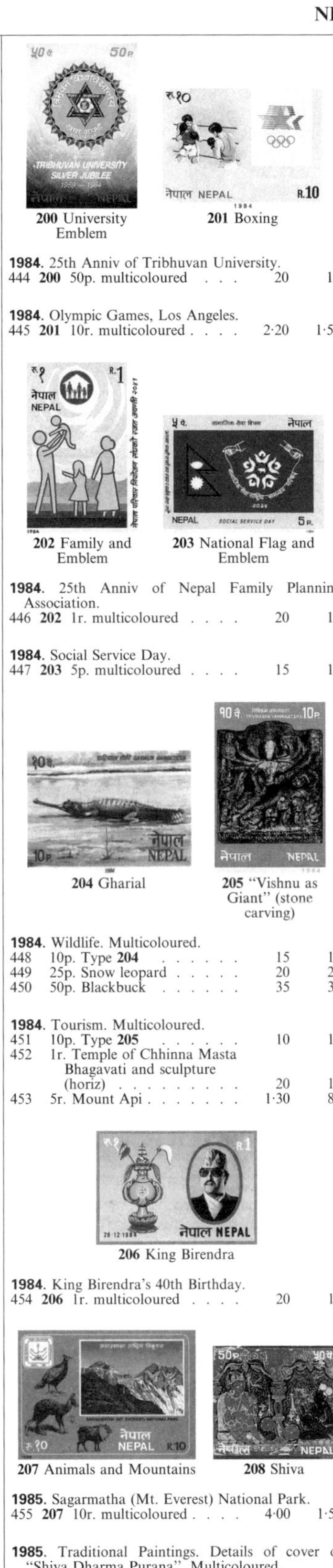

200 University Emblem

201 Boxing

1984. 25th Anniv of Tribhuvan University.
444 **200** 50p. multicoloured . . . 20 15

1984. Olympic Games, Los Angeles.
445 **201** 10r. multicoloured . . . . 2·20 1·50

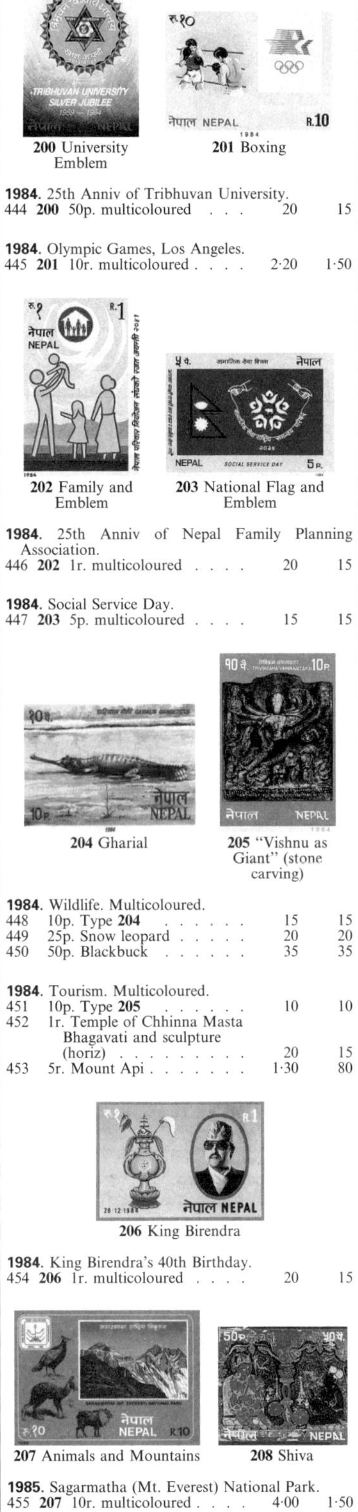

202 Family and Emblem

203 National Flag and Emblem

1984. 25th Anniv of Nepal Family Planning Association.
446 **202** 1r. multicoloured 20 15

1984. Social Service Day.
447 **203** 5p. multicoloured 15 15

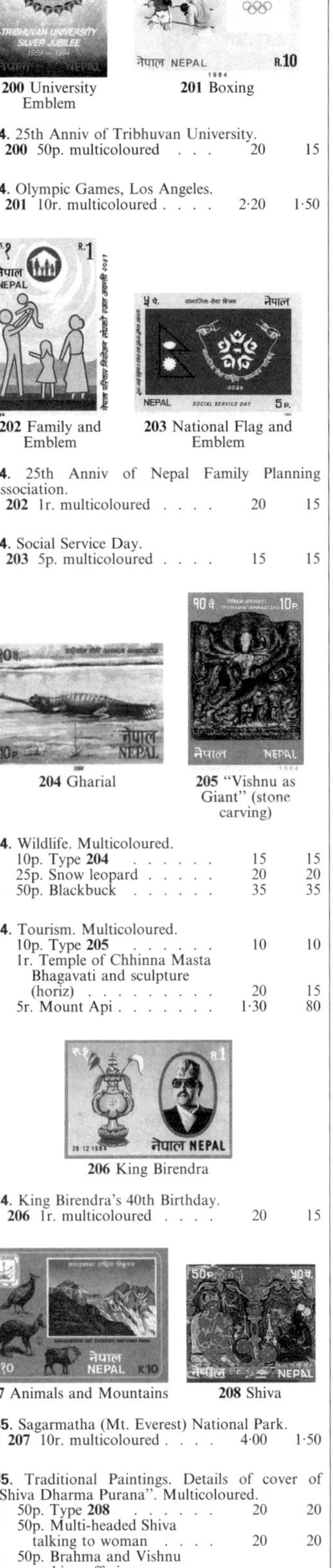

204 Gharial

205 "Vishnu as Giant" (stone carving)

1984. Wildlife. Multicoloured.
448 10p. Type **204** 15 15
449 25p. Snow leopard 20 20
450 50p. Blackbuck 35 35

1984. Tourism. Multicoloured.
451 10p. Type **205** 10 10
452 1r. Temple of Chhinna Masta Bhagavati and sculpture (horiz) 20 15
453 5r. Mount Api . . . . 1·30 80

206 King Birendra

1984. King Birendra's 40th Birthday.
454 **206** 1r. multicoloured 20 15

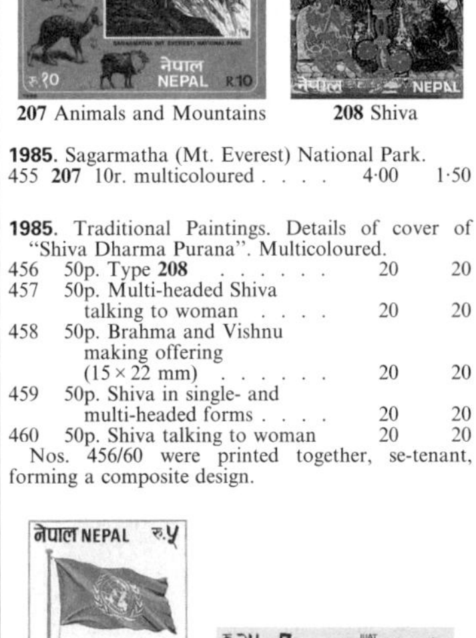

207 Animals and Mountains

208 Shiva

1985. Sagarmatha (Mt. Everest) National Park.
455 **207** 10r. multicoloured . . . . 4·00 1·50

1985. Traditional Paintings. Details of cover of "Shiva Dharma Purana". Multicoloured.
456 50p. Type **208** 20 20
457 50p. Multi-headed Shiva talking to woman 20 20
458 50p. Brahma and Vishnu making offering (15 × 22 mm) 20 20
459 50p. Shiva in single- and multi-headed forms 20 20
460 50p. Shiva talking to woman 20 20
Nos. 456/60 were printed together, se-tenant, forming a composite design.

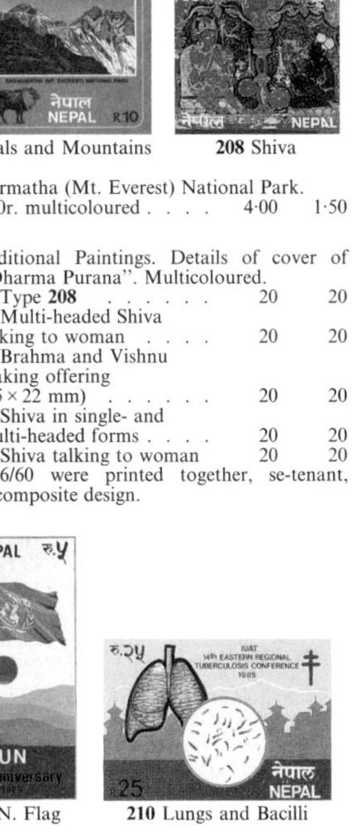

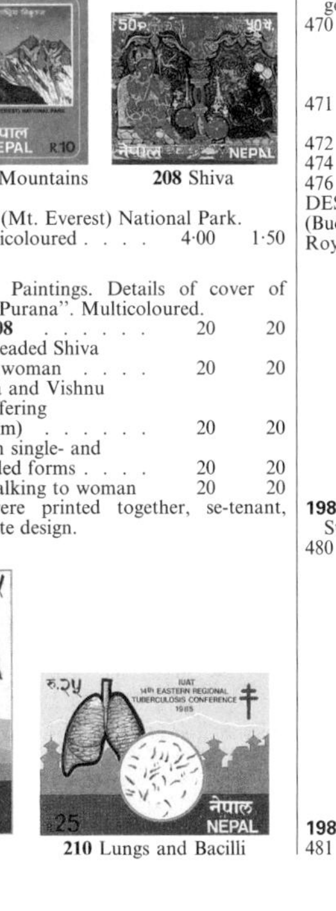

209 U.N. Flag

210 Lungs and Bacilli

1985. 40th Anniv of U.N.O.
461 **209** 5r. multicoloured . . . . 1·10 75

1985. 14th Eastern Regional Tuberculosis Conf, Katmandu.
462 **210** 25r. multicoloured . . . . 5·25 3·75

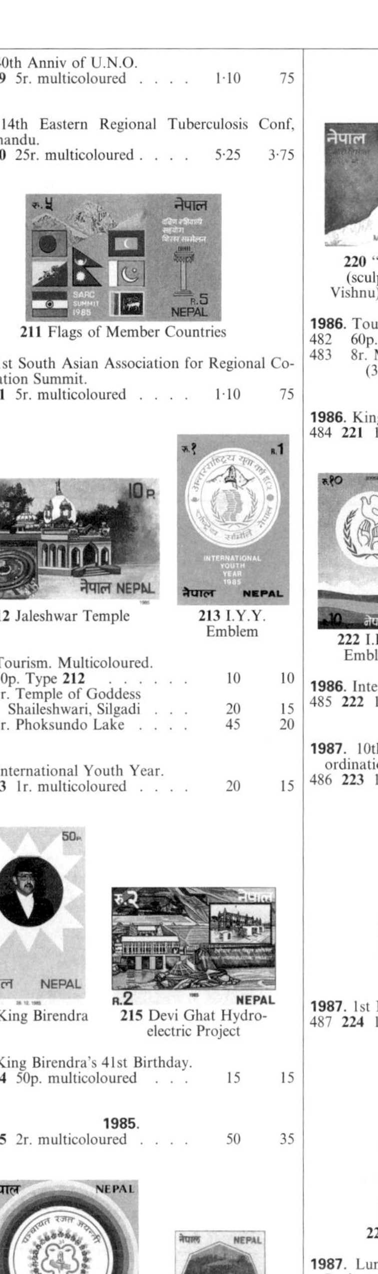

211 Flags of Member Countries

1985. 1st South Asian Association for Regional Co-operation Summit.
463 **211** 5r. multicoloured . . . . 1·10 75

212 Jaleshwar Temple

213 I.Y.Y. Emblem

1985. Tourism. Multicoloured.
464 10p. Type **212** 10 10
465 1r. Temple of Goddess Shaileshwari, Silgadi . . . 20 15
466 2r. Phoksundo Lake 45 20

1985. International Youth Year.
467 **213** 1r. multicoloured 20 15

214 King Birendra

215 Devi Ghat Hydro-electric Project

1985. King Birendra's 41st Birthday.
468 **214** 50p. multicoloured . . . 15 15

1985.
469 **215** 2r. multicoloured 50 35

216 Emblem

217 Royal Crown

1986. 25th Anniv of Panchayat System (partyless government).
470 **216** 4r. multicoloured 90 75

1986.
471 **217** 5p. brown and deep brown 10 10
472 – 10p. blue 15 15
474 – 50p. blue 20 20
476 – 1r. brown and ochre . . . 15 10
DESIGNS: 10p. Mayadevi Temple of Lumbini (Buddha's birthplace); 50p. Pashupati Temple; 1r. Royal Crown.

218 Pharping Hydro-electric Station

1986. 75th Anniv of Pharping Hydro-electric Power Station.
480 **218** 15p. multicoloured . . . 15 15

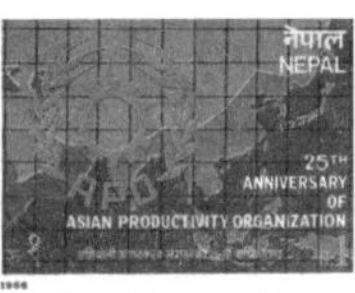

219 Emblem and Map

1986. 25th Anniv of Asian Productivity Organization.
481 **219** 1r. multicoloured 20 15

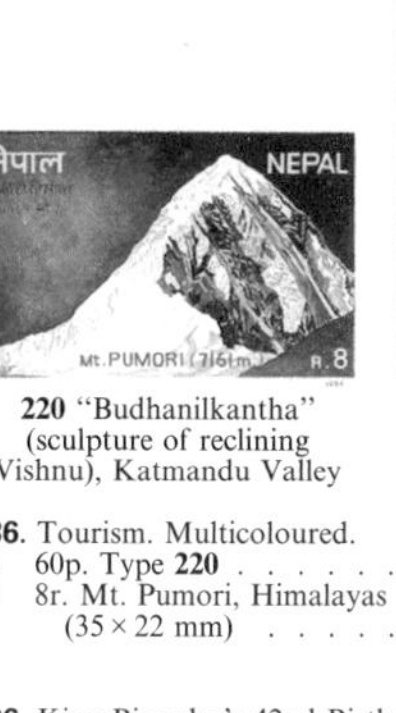

220 "Budhanilkantha" (sculpture of reclining Vishnu), Katmandu Valley

221 King Birendra

1986. Tourism. Multicoloured.
482 60p. Type **220** 15 10
483 8r. Mt. Pumori, Himalayas (35 × 22 mm) . . . . . . 1·50 1·10

1986. King Birendra's 42nd Birthday.
484 **221** 1r. multicoloured 20 15

222 I.P.Y. Emblem

223 National Flag and Council Emblem

1986. International Peace Year.
485 **222** 10r. multicoloured . . . . 1·60 1·30

1987. 10th Anniv of National Social Service Co-ordination Council.
486 **223** 1r. multicoloured 20 15

224 Emblem and Forest

1987. 1st Nepal Scout Jamboree, Katmandu.
487 **224** 1r. brown, orange and blue 45 15

225 Ashokan Pillar and Maya Devi

1987. Lumbini (Buddha's Birthplace) Development Project.
488 **225** 4r. multicoloured 75 50

226 Emblem

227 Emblem

1987. 3rd South Asian Association for Regional Co-operation Summit, Katmandu.
489 **226** 60p. gold and red 15 15

1987. 25th Anniv of Rastriya Samachar Samiti (news service).
490 **227** 4r. purple, blue and red 75 50

228 Kashthamandap, Katmandu

229 Gyawali

1987.
491 **228** 25p. multicoloured . . . 15 15

1987. 89th Birth Anniv of Surya Bikram Gyawali.
492 **229** 60p. multicoloured . . . 15 15

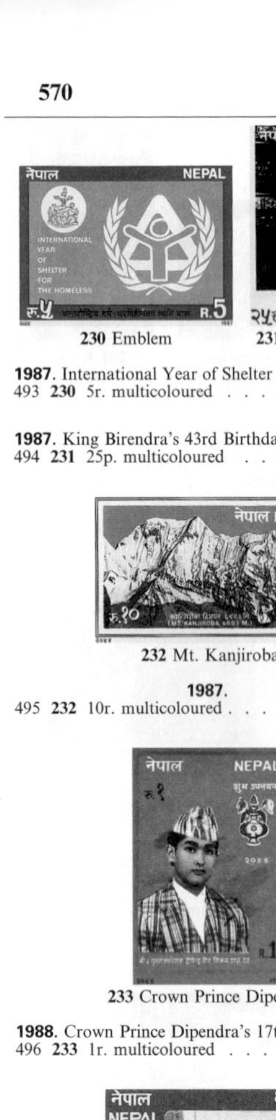

230 Emblem **231** King Birendra

1987. International Year of Shelter for the Homeless.
493 **230** 5r. multicoloured 90 75

1987. King Birendra's 43rd Birthday.
494 **231** 25p. multicoloured . . . 15 15

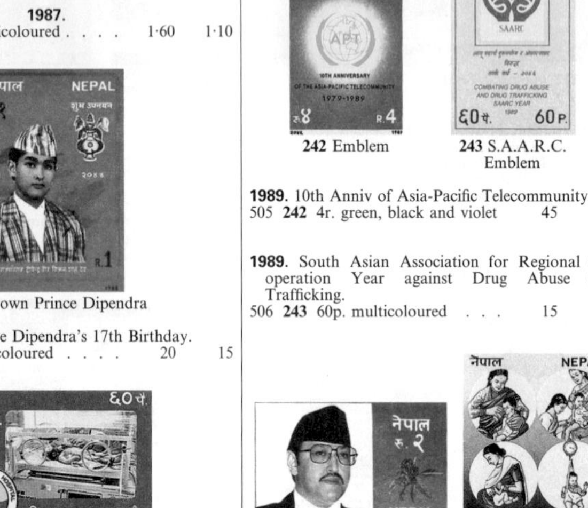

232 Mt. Kanjiroba

1987.
495 **232** 10r. multicoloured . . . . 1·60 1·10

233 Crown Prince Dipendra

1988. Crown Prince Dipendra's 17th Birthday.
496 **233** 1r. multicoloured 20 15

234 Baby in Incubator

1988. 25th Anniv of Kanti Children's Hospital, Katmandu.
497 **234** 60p. multicoloured . . . 15 15

235 Swamp Deer **236** Laxmi, Goddess of Wealth

1988. 12th Anniv of Royal Shukla Phanta Wildlife Reserve.
498 **235** 60p. multicoloured . . . 35 15

1988. 50th Anniv of Nepal Bank Ltd.
499 **236** 2r. multicoloured 35 20

237 Queen Mother **238** Hands protecting Blood Droplet

1988. 60th Birthday of Queen Mother.
500 **237** 5r. multicoloured 90 75

1988. 25th Anniv of Nepal Red Cross Society.
501 **238** 1r. red and brown 20 15

239 Temple and Statue

1988. Temple of Goddess Bindhyabasini, Pokhara.
502 **239** 15p. multicoloured . . . 15 15

240 King Birendra **241** Temple

1988. King Birendra's 44th Birthday.
503 **240** 4r. multicoloured 75 45

1989. Pashupati Area Development Trust.
504 **241** 1r. multicoloured 20 15

242 Emblem **243** S.A.A.R.C. Emblem

1989. 10th Anniv of Asia-Pacific Telecommunity.
505 **242** 4r. green, black and violet 45 30

1989. South Asian Association for Regional Co-operation Year against Drug Abuse and Trafficking.
506 **243** 60p. multicoloured . . . 15 15

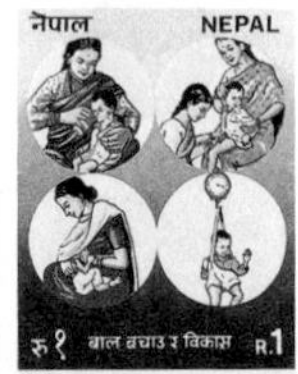

244 King Birendra **245** Child Survival Measures

1989. King Birendra's 45th Birthday.
507 **244** 2r. multicoloured 35 15

1989. Child Survival Campaign.
508 **245** 1r. multicoloured 15 15

246 Lake Rara

1989. Rara National Park.
509 **246** 4r. multicoloured 45 30

247 Mt. Amadablam

1989.
510 **247** 5r. multicoloured 75 35

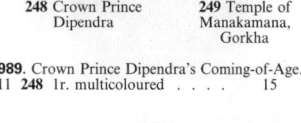

248 Crown Prince Dipendra **249** Temple of Manakamana, Gorkha

1989. Crown Prince Dipendra's Coming-of-Age.
511 **248** 1r. multicoloured 15 15

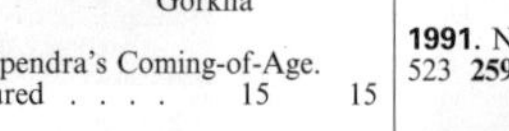

1990.
512 **249** 60p. black and violet . . 15 15

250 Emblem and Children **251** Emblem

1990. 25th Anniv of Nepal Children's Organization.
513 **250** 1r. multicoloured 15 15

1990. Centenary of Bir Hospital.
514 **251** 60p. red, blue and yellow 15 15

252 Emblem **253** Goddess and Bageshwori Temple, Nepalgunj

1990. 20th Anniv of Asian–Pacific Postal Training Centre, Bangkok.
515 **252** 4r. multicoloured 50 30

1990. Tourism. Multicoloured.
516 1r. Type **253** 15 15
517 5r. Mt. Saipal (36 × 27 mm) 60 35

254 Leisure Activities

1990. South Asian Association for Regional Co-operation Girls' Year.
518 **254** 4r.60 multicoloured . . . 25 15

255 King Birendra **256** Koirala

1990. King Birendra's 46th Birthday.
519 **255** 2r. multicoloured 20 15

1990. 76th Birth Anniv of Bisweswar Prasad Koirala (Prime Minister, 1959–60).
520 **256** 60p. black, orange and red 10 10

257 Indian Rhinoceros and Lake **258** Flower and Crowd

1991. Royal Chitwan National Park.
521 **257** 4r. multicoloured 75 35

1991. 1st Anniv of Abrogation of Ban on Political Parties.
522 **258** 1r. multicoloured 15 15

259 Official and Villagers **260** Federation and Jubilee Emblems

1991. National Population Census.
523 **259** 60p. multicoloured . . . 15 15

1991. 25th Anniv of Federation of Nepalese Chambers of Commerce and Industry.
524 **260** 3r. multicoloured 35 20

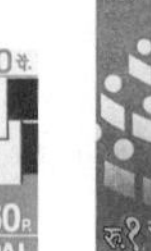

261 Crosses **262** Delegates

1991. 25th Anniv (1990) of Nepal Junior Red Cross.
525 **261** 60p. red and grey 10 10

1991. 1st Session of Revived Parliament.
526 **262** 1r. multicoloured 15 15

263 King Birendra making Speech

1991. Constitution Day.
527 **263** 50p. multicoloured . . . 10 10

264 Rama and Janaki (statues) and Vivaha Mandap **266** King Birendra

265 Mt. Kumbhakarna

1991. 5th Anniv of Rebuilt Vivaha Mandap Pavilion, Janaki Temple.
528 **264** 1r. multicoloured 15 15

1991. Tourism.
529 **265** 4r.60 multicoloured . . . 50 30

1991. King Birendra's 47th Birthday.
530 **266** 8r. multicoloured 90 50

267 Houses **268** Glass magnifying Society Emblem

1991. South Asian Association for Regional Co-operation Year of Shelter.
531 **267** 9r. multicoloured 90 60

1992. 25th Anniv (1991) of Nepal Philatelic Society.
532 **268** 4r. multicoloured 45 30

269 Rainbow over River and Trees

1992. Environmental Protection.
533 **269** 60p. multicoloured . . . 15 15

270 Nutrition, Education and Health Care

1992. Rights of the Child.
534 **270** 1r. multicoloured 15 15

271 Thakurdwara Temple, Bardiya

272 Bank Emblem

1992. Temples. Multicoloured.
535 75p. Type **271** (postage) . . . 10 10
536 1r. Namo Buddha Temple, Kavre 10 10
537 2r. Narijhowa Temple, Mustang 15 10
538 11r. Dantakali Temple, Bijayapur (air) . . . . . . 1·00 65

1992. 25th Anniv of Agricultural Development Bank.
539 **272** 40p. brown and green . . 15 15

273 Pin-tailed Green Pigeon

1992. Birds. Multicoloured.
540 1r. Type **273** 10 10
541 3r. Bohemian waxwing 30 15
542 25r. Rufous-tailed desert (inscr "Finch") lark . . . 2·20 1·50

274 King Birendra exchanging Swords with Goddess Sree Bhadrakali

275 Pandit Kulchandra Gautam

1992. King Birendra's 48th Birthday.
543 **274** 7r. multicoloured 60 35

1992. Poets. Multicoloured, frame colour given in brackets.
544 1r. Type **275** 15 10
545 1r. Chittadhar Hridaya (drab) 15 10
546 1r. Vidyapati (stone) 15 10
547 1r. Teongsi Sirijunga (grey) 15 10

276 Shooting and Marathon

277 Golden Mahseer

1992. Olympic Games, Barcelona.
548 **276** 25r. multicoloured . . . . 2·20 1·50

1993. Fishes. Multicoloured.
549 25p. Type **277** 10 10
550 1r. Marinka 10 10
551 5r. Indian eel 20 10
552 10r. False loach 35 20

278 Antibodies attacking Globe

279 Tanka Prasad Acharya (Prime Minister, 1956–57)

1993. World AIDS Day.
554 **278** 1r. multicoloured 15 15

1993. Death Anniversaries. Multicoloured.
555 25p. Type **279** (1st anniv) . . 10 10
556 1r. Sungdare Sherpa (mountaineer) (4th anniv) 10 10
557 7r. Siddhi Charan Shrestha (poet) (1st anniv) 50 30
558 15r. Falgunanda (religious leader) (44th anniv) . . . . 1·10 75

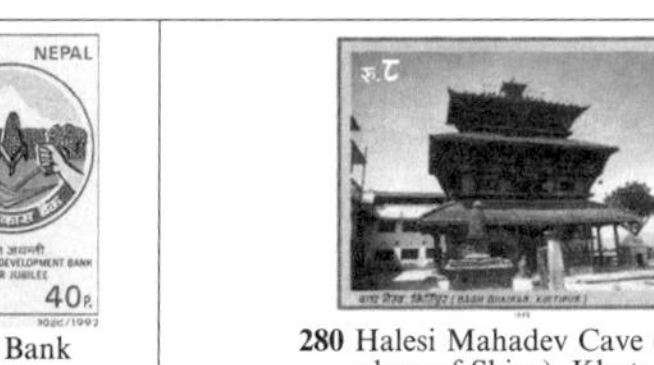

280 Halesi Mahadev Cave (hiding place of Shiva), Khotang

1993. Holy Places. Multicoloured.
559 1r.50 Type **280** 10 10
560 5r. Devghat (gods' bathing place), Tanahun 35 20
561 8r. Bagh Bairab Temple, Kirtipur 60 35

281 Tushahiti Fountain, Sundari Chowk, Patan

282 King Birendra

1993. Tourism. Multicoloured.
562 5r. Type **281** 35 20
563 8r. White-water rafting . . . 60 35

1993. King Birendra's 49th Birthday.
564 **282** 10r. multicoloured 75 45

283 Monument

284 Mt. Everest

1994.
565 **283** 20p. brown 10 10
566 – 25p. red 10 10
567 – 30p. green 10 10
568 **284** 1r. multicoloured 15 15
569 – 5r. multicoloured 35 20
DESIGNS—20 × 22 mm: 25p. State arms. 22 × 20 mm: 30p. Lumbini. 25 × 15 mm: 5r. Map of Nepal, crown and state arms and flag.

285 Pasang Sherpa

1994. 1st Death Anniv of Pasang Sherpa (mountaineer).
570 **285** 10r. multicoloured 75 45

286 Cigarette, Lungs and Crab's Claws

287 Postal Delivery

1994. Anti-smoking Campaign.
571 **286** 1r. multicoloured 15 15

1994.
572 **287** 1r.50 multicoloured . . . 15 15

288 Khuda

1994. Weapons. Multicoloured.
573 5r. Kukris (three swords and two scabbards) 35 20
574 5r. Type **288** 35 20
575 5r. Dhaal (swords and shield) 35 20
576 5r. Katari (two daggers) . . . 35 20

289 Workers and Emblem

1994. 75th Anniv of I.L.O.
577 **289** 15r. gold, blue & ultram 1·10 75

290 Landscape

1994. World Food Day.
578 **290** 25r. multicoloured . . . . 1·80 1·20

291 "Dendrobium densiflorum"

292 Family

1994. Orchids. Multicoloured.
579 10r. Type **291** 75 45
580 10r. "Coelogyne flaccida" . . 75 45
581 10r. "Cymbidium devonianum" 75 45
582 10r. "Coelogyne corymbosa" 75 45

1994. International Year of the Family.
583 **292** 9r. emerald, green and red 65 45

293 Emblem and Airplane

294 "Russula nepalensis"

1994. 50th Anniv of I.C.A.O.
584 **293** 11r. blue, gold and deep blue 80 50

1994. Fungi. Multicoloured.
585 7r. Type **294** 50 30
586 7r. Morels ("Morchella conica") 50 30
587 7r. Caesar's mushroom ("Amanita caesarea") . . . 50 30
588 7r. "Cordyceps sinensis" . . 50 30

295 Dharanidhar Koirala (poet)

1994. Celebrities. Multicoloured.
589 1r. Type **295** 10 10
590 2r. Narayan Gopal Guruwacharya (singer) . . 15 10
591 6r. Bahadur Shah (vert) . . . 45 30
592 7r. Balaguru Shadananda . . 50 30

296 King Birendra, Flag, Map and Crown

1994. King Birendra's 50th Birthday (1st issue).
593 **296** 9r. multicoloured 65 45
See also No. 621.

297 Lake Tilicho, Manang

1994. Tourism. Multicoloured.
594 9r. Type **297** 65 45
595 11r. Taleju Temple, Katmandu (vert) 80 50

298 Health Care

1994. Children's Activities. Multicoloured.
596 1r. Type **298** 10 10
597 1r. Classroom 10 10
598 1r. Playground equipment . . 10 10
599 1r. Stamp collecting 10 10

299 Singhaduarbar

300 Crab on Lungs

1995.
600 **299** 10p. green 10 10
601 – 50p. blue 10 10
DESIGN—VERT: 50p. Pashupati.

1995. Anti-cancer Campaign.
602 **300** 2r. multicoloured 15 15

301 Chandra Man Singh Maskey (artist)

302 Bhakti Thapa (soldier)

1995. Celebrities. Multicoloured.
603 3r. Type **301** 20 15
604 3r. Parijat (writer) 20 15
605 3r. Bhim Nidhi Tiwari (writer) 20 15
606 3r. Yuddha Prasad Mishra (writer) 20 15

1995. Celebrities. Multicoloured.
607 15p. Type **302** 10 10
608 1r. Madan Bhandari (politician) 10 10
609 4r. Prakash Raj Kaphley (human rights activist) . . 10 15

303 Gaur ("Bos gaurus")

1995. "Singapore '95" International Stamp Exhibition. Mammals. Multicoloured.
610 10r. Type **303** 75 45
611 10r. Lynx ("Felis lynx") . . . 75 45
612 10r. Assam macaque ("Macaca assamensis") . . 75 45
613 10r. Striped hyena ("Hyaena hyaena") 75 45

304 Anniversary Emblem

1995. 50th Anniv of F.A.O.
614 **304** 7r. multicoloured 50 30

305 Figures around Emblem

306 Bhimeswor Temple, Dolakha

1995. 50th Anniv of U.N.O.
615 **305** 50r. multicoloured . . . . 3·75 2·40

1995. Tourism. Multicoloured.
616 1r. Type **306** 10 10
617 5r. Ugra Tara Temple, Dadeldhura (horiz) 35 20
618 7r. Mt. Nampa (horiz) . . . 50 30
619 18r. Nrity Aswora (traditional Pauba painting) (27 × 39 mm) . . . . . . 1·30 90
620 20r. Lumbini (Buddha's birthplace) (28 × 28 mm) 1·50 95

307 King Birendra

309 King Birendra

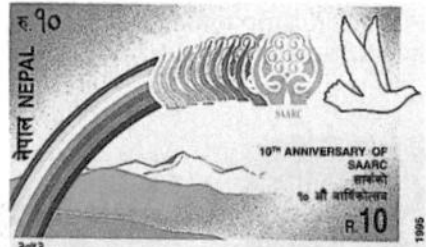

308 Anniversary Emblem

1995. King Birendra's 50th Birthday (1994) (2nd issue).
621 **307** 1r. multicoloured 15 15

1995. 10th Anniv of South Asian Association for Regional Co-operation.
622 **308** 10r. multicoloured 75 45

1995. King Birendra's 51st Birthday.
623 **309** 12r. multicoloured 90 60

310 Karnali Bridge

1996.
624 **310** 7r. multicoloured 50 30

311 State Arms

312 Kaji Kalu Pande (soldier and royal adviser)

1996.
625 **311** 25p. red 15 15

1996. Political Figures. Multicoloured.
626 75p. Type **312** 10 10
627 1r. Pushpa Lal Shrestha (Nepal Communist Party General-Secretary) 10 10
628 5r. Suvarna Shamsher Rana (founder of Nepal Democratic Congress Party) 35 20

313 Hem Raj Sharma (grammarian)

314 Runner and Track

1996. Writers. Multicoloured.
629 1r. Type **313** 10 10
630 3r. Padma Prasad Bhattarai (Sanskrit scholar) 20 15
631 5r. Bhawani Bhikshu (novelist) 35 20

1996. Olympic Games, Atlanta.
632 **314** 7r. multicoloured 50 30

315 Kasthamandap, Katmandu

316 Hindu Temple, Arjundhara

1996. Temples.
633 **315** 10p. red and black . . . 10 10
634 50p. black and red . . . 10 10
635 – 1r. red and blue 10 10
DESIGN—VERT: 1r. Nyata Pola temple, Bhaktapur.

1996. Tourism. Multicoloured.
636 1r. Type **316** 10 10
637 2r. Durbar, Nuwakot 15 10
638 8r. Gaijatra Festival, Bhaktapur 65 45
639 10r. Lake Beganas, Kaski . . 90 60

317 Krishna Peacock

318 Ashoka Pillar

1996. Butterflies and Birds. Multicoloured.
640 5r. Type **317** 45 30
641 5r. Great barbet ("Great Himalayan Barbet") . . . 45 30
642 5r. Sarus crane 45 30
643 5r. Northern jungle queen . . 45 30
Nos. 640/3 were issued together, se-tenant, forming a composite design.

1996. Centenary of Rediscovery of Ashoka Pillar, Lumbini (birthplace of Buddha).
644 **318** 12r. multicoloured . . . . 1·00 65

319 King Birendra

1996. King Birendra's 52nd Birthday.
645 **319** 10r. multicoloured 60 60

320 Mt. Annapurna South and Mt. Annapurna I

1996. The Himalayas.
646 18r. Type **320** . . . . 1·10 75
647 18r. Mt. Machhapuchhre and Mt. Annapurna III . . . . 1·10 75
648 18r. Mt. Annapurna IV and Mt. Annapurna II . . . . 1·10 75
Nos. 646/8 were issued together, se-tenant, forming a composite design.

321 King Birendra before Throne

1997. Silver Jubilee of King Birendra's Accession.
649 **321** 2r. multicoloured 15 15

322 Mountains and National Flags

323 Postal Emblem

1997. 40th Anniv of Nepal–Japan Diplomatic Relations.
650 **322** 18r. multicoloured . . . . 1·30 90

1997.
651 **323** 2r. red and brown 15 15

324 Campaign Emblem

1997. National Tourism Year.
652 **324** 2r. red and blue 15 10
653 – 10r. multicoloured 75 45
654 – 18r. multicoloured . . . . 1·30 90
655 – 20r. multicoloured . . . . 1·50 95
DESIGNS—HORIZ: 10r. Upper Mustang mountain peak; 18r. Rafting, River Sunkoshi. VERT: 20r. Changunarayan.

325 Chepang Couple

326 National Flags and Handshake

1997. Ethnic Groups. Multicoloured.
656 5r. Type **325** 35 20
657 5r. Gurung couple 35 20
658 5r. Rana Tharu couple . . . 35 20

1997. 50th Anniv of Nepal United States Diplomatic Relations.
659 **326** 20r. multicoloured . . . . 1·50 95

327 Riddhi Bahadur Malla (writer)

328 "Jasminum gracile"

1997. Celebrities. Multicoloured.
660 2r. Type **327** 15 10
661 2r. Dr. K. I. Singh (politician) 15 10

1997. Flowers. Multicoloured.
662 40p. Type **328** 10 10
663 1r. China aster 10 10
664 2r. "Manglietia insignis" . . 15 10
665 15r. "Luculia gratissima" . . 1·20 75

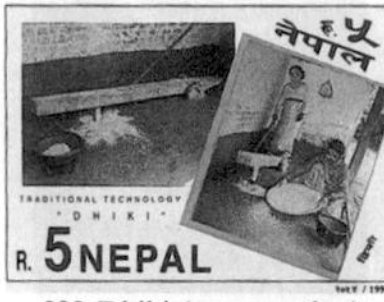

329 Dhiki (corn crusher)

1997. Traditional Technology. Multicoloured.
666 5r. Type **329** . . . . 35 2·20
667 5r. Janto (mill stone) . . . . 35 2·20
668 5r. Kol (oil mill) (vert) . . . 35 2·20
669 5r. Okhal (implement for pounding rice) (vert) . . . 35 2·20

330 King Birendra

331 Sunrise, Shree Antudanda, Ilam

1997. King Birendra's 53rd Birthday.
670 **330** 10r. multicoloured 75 45

1998. Tourism. Multicoloured.
671 2r. Type **331** 15 10
672 10r. Maitidevi Temple, Katmandu 75 45
673 18r. Great Renunciation Gate, Kapilavastu . . . . 1·30 90
674 20r. Mt. Cholatse, Solukhumbu (vert) . . . . 1·50 95

332 Ram Prasad Rai (nationalist)

1998. Personalities.
675 **332** 75p. black and brown . . 10 10
676 – 1r. black and mauve . . . 15 15
677 – 2r. black and green . . . 20 15
678 – 2r. black and blue 20 15
679 – 5r.40 black and red . . . 35 20
DESIGNS: No. 676, Imansing Chemjong (Kiranti language specialist); 677, Tulsi Meher Shrestha (social worker); 678, Maha Pundit Dadhi Ram Marasini (poet); 679, Mahananda Sapkota (educationalist and writer).

333 Match Scenes

1998. World Cup Football Championship, France.
680 **333** 12r. multicoloured 90 60

334 Ganesh Man Singh

1998. 1st Death Anniv of Ganesh Man Singh (politician).
681 **334** 5r. multicoloured 35 20

335 World Map and Nepalese Soldiers

1998. 40 Years of Nepalese Army Involvement in United Nations Peace Keeping Missions.
682 **335** 10r. multicoloured 75 45

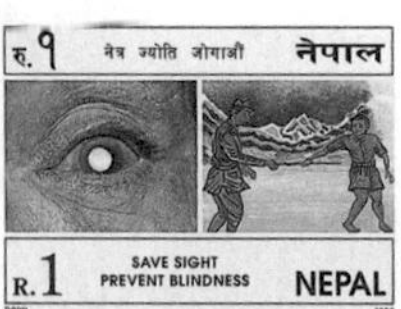

336 Cataract and Guiding of Blind Man

1998. Cataract Awareness Campaign.
683 **336** 1r. multicoloured 15 15

337 King Cobra

1998. Snakes. Multicoloured.
684 1r.70 Type **337** 10 10
685 2r. Golden tree snake 15 10
686 5r. Asiatic rock python 35 20
687 10r. Karan's pit viper 75 45

338 Dove and Profile

1998. 50th Anniv of Universal Declaration of Human Rights.
688 **338** 10r. multicoloured 75 45

339 Disabled Persons **340** King Birendra

1998. Asian and Pacific Decade of Disabled Persons.
689 **339** 10r. multicoloured 75 45

1998. King Birendra's 54th Birthday.
690 **340** 2r. multicoloured 15 15

341 Dam and Power House

1998. River Marsyangdi Hydro-electric Power Station.
691 **341** 12r. multicoloured 90 60

342 Hospital and Emblem

1999. 25th Anniv of Nepal Eye Hospital.
692 **342** 2r. multicoloured 15 15

343 Kalika Bhagawati Temple, Baglung

1999. Tourism. Multicoloured.
693 2r. Type **343** 15 10
694 2r. Chandan Nath Temple, Jumla (vert) 15 75
695 12r. Bajrayogini Temple, Sankhu (vert) 1·10 75
696 15r. Mt. Everest 1·30 90
697 15r. Ashokan Pillar, Lumbini, and English translation of its inscription (39 × 27 mm) 1·30 90

344 Four-horned Antelope **346** U.P.U. Emblem and Cockerel

345 Him Kanchha (mascot) and Games Emblem

1999. Mammals. Multicoloured.
698 10r. Type **344** 90 60
699 10r. Argali (Ovis ammon) 90 60

1999. 8th South Asian Sports Federation Games, Katmandu.
700 **345** 10r. multicoloured 90 60

1999. 125th Anniv of Universal Postal Union.
701 **346** 15r. multicoloured 1·30 15

347 Ramnarayan Mishra (revolutionary, 1922–67)

1999. Personalities.
702 **347** 1r. green and black 10 10
703 – 1r. brown and black 10 10
704 – 1r. blue and black 10 10
705 – 2r. red and black 15 10
706 – 2r. blue and black 15 10
707 – 2r. buff and black 15 10
DESIGNS: No. 703, Master Mitrasen (writer, 1895–1946); 704, Bhupi Sherchan (poet, 1935–89); 705, Rudraraj Pandey (writer, 1901–87); 706, Gopalprasad Rimal (writer, 1917–73); 707, Mangaladevi Singh (revolutionary, 1924–96).

348 Sorathi Dance

1999. Local Dances. Multicoloured.
708 5r. Type **348** 45 30
709 5r. Bhairav dance 45 30
710 5r. Jhijhiya dance 45 30

349 Children working and writing

1999. Nepal's involvement in International Programme on the Elimination of Child Labour.
711 **349** 12r. multicoloured 1·10 75

350 King Birendra

1999. King Birendra's 55th Birthday.
712 **350** 5r. multicoloured 45 30

351 Headquarters

2000. 60th Anniv of Radio Nepal.
713 **351** 2r. multicoloured 15 15

352 Queen Aishwarya **353** Front Page of Newspaper and Emblem

2000. Queen Aishwarya's 50th Birthday.
714 **352** 15r. multicoloured 1·30 1·30

2000. Centenary of *Gorkhapatra* (newspaper).
715 **353** 10r. multicoloured 80 80

354 Tchorolpa Glacial Lake, Dolakha

2000. Tourist Sights. Multicoloured.
716 12r. Type **354** 1·00 1·00
717 15r. Dakshinkali Temple, Kathmandu 1·30 1·30
718 18r. Mount Annapurna (50th anniv of first ascent) 1·50 1·50

355 Ranipokhari Pagoda, Kathmandu

2000.
719 **355** 50p. black and orange 10 10
720 1r. black and blue 10 10
721 2r. black and brown 15 15

356 Soldier and Child

2000. 50th Anniv of Geneva Convention.
725 **356** 5r. multicoloured 45 45

357 Runners

2000. Olympic Games, Sydney.
726 **357** 25r. multicoloured 2·20 2·20

358 Hridayachandra Singh Pradhan (writer) **359** Indian Rhinoceros (male)

2000. Personalities.
727 **358** 2r. black and yellow 15 15
728 – 2r. black and brown 15 15
729 – 5r. black and blue 45 45
730 – 5r. black and red 45 45
DESIGNS: No. 728, Thir Barn Malla (revolutionary); 729, Krishna Prasad Koirala (social reformer); 730, Manamohan Adhikari (polititian).

2000. Wildlife. Multicoloured.
731 10r. Type **359** 90 90
732 10r. Indian rhinoceros (*Rhinoceros unicornis*) (female) 90 90
733 10r. Lesser adjutant stork (*Leptoptilos javanicus*) 90 90
734 10r. Bengal florican (*Houbaropsis bengalensis*) 90 90

360 Orchid (*Dactylorhiza hatagirea*) **361** King Birendra

2000. Flowers. Multicoloured.
735 5r. Type **360** 45 45
736 5r. *Mahonia napaulensis* (horiz) 45 45
737 5r. *Talauma hodgsonii* (horiz) 45 45

2000. King Birendra's 56th Birthday.
738 **361** 5r. multicoloured 45 45

362 King Tribhuvana and Crowd

2001. 50th Anniv of Constitutional Monarchy.
739 **362** 5r. multicoloured 45 45

363 Crowd and Emblem

2001. Population Census.
740 **363** 2r. multicoloured 15 15

364 Khaptad Baba (religious leader) **365** Asiatic Coinwort (*Centella asiatica*)

2001. Personalities.
741 **364** 2r. pink and black 15 15
742 – 2r. mauve and black 15 15
743 – 2r. magenta and black 15 15
744 – 2r. red and black 15 15
745 – 2r. blue and black 15 15
DESIGNS: No. 742, Bhikkhu Pragyananda Mahathera (Buddhist writer and teacher); 743, Guru Prasad Mainali (author); 744, Tulsi Lal Amatya Politician); 745, Madan Lal Agrawal (industrialist).

2001. Plants. Multicoloured.
746 5r. Type **365** 45 45
747 15r. *Bergenia ciliata* 1·50 1·50
748 30r. Himalayan yew (*Taxus baccata wallichania*) 3·00 3·00

366 Pipal Tree (*Ficus religiosa*) **367** Tents

2001.
749 **366** 10r. multicoloured 90 90

2001. 50th Anniv of United Nations High Commissioner for Refugees.
750 **367** 20r. multicoloured 1·80 1·80

368 National Flag **369** Amargadi Fort

2001.
751 **368** 10p. red and blue 15 15

2001. Tourism. Multicoloured.
752 2r. Type **369** 15 15
753 5r. Hiranyavarna Mahavihar (Golden Temple) (vert) 45 45
754 15r. Jugal mountain range 1·30 1·30

370 King Birendra

2001. 57th Birth Anniv of King Birendra.
755 **370** 15r. multicoloured . . . . 1·30 1·30

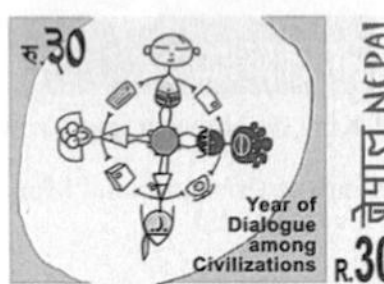

371 Children encircling Globe

2001. United Nations Year of Dialogue among Civilizations.
756 **371** 30r. multicoloured . . . . 2·50 2·50

372 Scout Emblem

2002. 50th Anniv of Nepalese Scouts.
757 **372** 2r. chestnut and olive . . 20 20

373 World Cup Emblem and Footballer

2002. World Cup Football Championships, Japan and South Korea.
758 **373** 15r. multicoloured . . . . 1·30 1·30

374 King Gyanendra

375 King Birendra and Queen Aishwarya

2002. 1st Anniv of Accession of King Gyanendra.
759 **374** 5r. multicoloured 45 45

2002. King Birendra and Queen Aishwarya Commemoration.
760 **375** 10r. multicoloured 45 45

376 "Aryabalokiteshwor"

377 Family encircled by Barbed Wire (Siddhimuni Shakya)

2002. Paintings. Multicoloured.
761 5r. Type **376** 45 45
762 5r. "Moti (pearl)" (King Birendra) (horiz) 45 45

2002. Social Awareness.
763 **377** 1r. black and brown . . . 10 10
764 – 2r. black and lilac 15 15
DESIGNS: Type **377** (integration of untouchables); 2r. Children leaving for school (treatment of girls).

378 Leaf Beetle

379 Valley and Mountains

2002. Insects. Multicoloured.
765 3r. Type **378** 30 30
766 5r. Short horn grasshopper 45 45

2002. International Year of Mountains.
767 **379** 5r. multicoloured 45 45

380 Pathibhara Devisthan, Taplejung

2002. Tourism. Multicoloured.
768 5r. Type **380** 45 45
769 5r. Galeshwor Mahadevsthan, Myagdi 45 45
770 5r. Ramgram Stupa, Nawalparasi 45 45
771 5r. Mt. Nilgiri, Mustang . . 45 45

381 Dayabor Singh Kansakar (philanthropist)

383 Anniversary Emblem

382 Members Flags and Organization Emblem

2002. Personalities. Multicoloured.
772 2r. Type **381** 15 15
773 25r. Ekai Kawaguchi (first Japanese to visit Nepal) . . 2·20 2·20

2002. South Asian Association for Regional Co-operation (SAARC) Charter Day.
774 **382** 15r. multicoloured . . . . 1·30 1·30

2003. 50th Anniv of Chamber of Commerce.
775 **383** 5r. multicoloured 10 10

384 FNCCI Emblem

2003. Industry and Commerce Day.
776 **384** 5r. multicoloured 10 10

385 Mt. Everest

2003. 50th Anniv of the First Ascent of Mount Everest.
777 **385** 25r. multicoloured 40 20

386 Babu Chiri Sherpa

2003. Babu Chiri Sherpa (mountaineer) Commemoration.
778 **386** 5r. multicoloured 10 10

387 King Gyanendra

2003. 57th Birth Anniv of King Gyanendra.
779 **387** 5r. multicoloured 10 10

388 Tea Garden

2003. Eastern Nepal Tea Gardens.
780 **388** 25r. multicoloured 40 20

389 Dilli Raman Regmi

2003. 2nd Death Anniv of Dilli Raman Regmi (politician and historian).
781 **389** 5r. brown and black . . . 10 10

390 Gopal Das Shrestha

2003. 5th Death Anniv of Gopal Das Shrestha (journalist).
782 **390** 5r. green and black . . . 10 10

391 Container, Crane and Emblem

2003. Export Year.
783 **391** 25r. multicoloured 40 20

392 Sankhadhar Sakhwaa (statue) and Celebrating Crowd

2003. Sankhadhar Sakhwaa (founder of Nepal calender).
784 **392** 5r. multicoloured 10 10

393 Ganesh (statue), Kageshwar

394 Lotus

2003. Tourist Sights. Multicoloured.
785 5r. Type **393** 10 10
786 5r. Hydroelectric dam on Kali Gandaki river (horiz) 10 10
787 30r. Buddha (statue), Swayambhu (horiz) 50 25

2003. Flowers. Multicoloured.
788 10r. Type **394** 20 10
789 10r. Picrorhiza 20 10
790 10r. Himalayan rhubarb . . 20 10
791 10r. Jasmine 20 10

OFFICIAL STAMPS

O **25** Nepalese Arms and Soldiers

काज सरकारी
(O **28**)

1960. (a) Size 30 × 18 mm.
O135 O **25** 2p. brown 10 10
O136 4p. green 15 10
O137 6p. red 15 10
O138 8p. violet 15 15
O139 12p. orange 20 20

(b) Size 38 × 27 mm.
O140 O **25** 16p. brown 35 30
O141 24p. red 50 45
O142 32p. purple 60 60
O143 50p. blue . . . . . . 1·10 1·00
O144 1r. red . . . . 2·20 1·90
O145 2r. orange . . . . . . 4·50 4·00

1960. Optd as Type O **28**.
O146 **27** 1r. purple 90

1961. Optd with Type O **28**.
O148 **35** 1p. red 15 15
O149 2p. blue 15 15
O150 5p. brown 20 20
O151 **36** 10p. purple 10 10
O152 40p. brown 15 15
O153 75p. green 20 20
O154 **27** 2r. red 60 60
O155 5r. green . . . . 1·60 1·60

NETHERLANDS Pt. 4

A kingdom in the N.W. of Europe on the North Sea.

1852. 100 cents = 1 gulden (florin).
2002. 100 cents = 1 euro.

1

3 King William III

4

1852. Imperf.
1 **1** 5c. blue . . . . £225 30·00
2 10c. red . . . . £225 27·00
3b 15c. orange £600 £100

1864. Perf.
8 **3** 5c. blue . . . . £200 16·00
9 10c. red . . . . £300 7·50
10 15c. orange . . . . £500 90·00

1867.
17d **4** 5c. blue . . . . 85·00 2·40
18c 10c. red . . . . £150 3·00
19c 15c. brown . . . . £650 30·00
20 20c. green . . . . £600 23·00
15 25c. purple £2250 £100
22 50c. gold £2750 £160

5

6

1869.
58 **5** ½c. brown . . . . 24·020 4·00
53 1c. black . . . . £190 70·00
59 1c. green . . . . 11·50 2·40
55a 1½c. red . . . . £130 80·00
56a 2c. yellow . . . . 42·00 12·00
62 2½c. mauve . . . . £500 70·00

1872.
80 **6** 5c. blue . . . . 9·00 30
81 7½c. brown . . . . 38·00 17·00
82 10c. red . . . . 60·00 1·60
83 12½c. grey . . . . 65·00 2·40
84 15c. brown . . . . £375 5·00
85 20c. green . . . . £450 5·00
86 22½c. green . . . . 80·00 45·00
87 25c. lilac . . . . £575 4·00
97 50c. bistre . . . . £750 10·00
90 1g. violet . . . . £500 40·00
75 – 2g.50 blue and red £950 £110
No. 75 is similar to Type **6** but larger and with value and country scrolls transposed.

8

9 Queen Wilhelmina

1876.

133 **8** ½c. red . . . . 3·00 10
134 1c. green . . . . 9·50 10
137 2c. yellow . . . . 38·00 2·75
139 2½c. mauve . . . . 15·00 30

1891.

147a **9** 3c. orange . . . . 8·75 2·00
148a 5c. blue . . . . 5·00 25
149b 7½c. brown . . . . 17·00 5·25
150b 10c. red . . . . 25·00 1·40
151b 12½c. grey . . . . 25·00 1·50
152a 15c. brown . . . . 50·00 4·00
153b 20c. green . . . . 65·00 3·00
154a 22½c. green . . . . 32·00 11·50
155 25c. mauve . . . . £110 5·25
156a 50c. bistre . . . . £500 16·00
159 – 50c. brown and green . . . 75·00 9·50
157 **9** 1g. violet . . . . £550 65·00
160 – 1g. green and brown . . . £190 19·00
161 – 2g.50 blue and red £450 £140
165 – 5g. red and green £700 £400
Nos. 159, 160, 161 and 165 are as Type **9** but larger and with value and country scrolls transposed.

11 **12**

13 **14**

1898. Nos. 174 and 176 also exist imperf.

167 **12** ½c. lilac 60 20
168 1c. red . . . . 1·10 15
170 1½c. blue . . . . 3·00 35
171 2c. brown . . . . 4·50 20
172 2½c. green . . . . 3·75 20
173 **13** 3c. orange . . . . 17·00 3·50
174 3c. green . . . . 1·50 15
175 4c. purple . . . . 1·50 90
176 4½c. mauve . . . . 3·75 3·75
177b 5c. red . . . . 1·75 15
178 7½c. brown 75 20
179 10c. grey . . . . 7·50 15
180 12½c. blue . . . . 4·00 25
181 15c. brown . . . . 95·00 3·50
182 15c. red and blue . . . . . 7·50 15
183 17½c. mauve . . . . 50·00 12·00
184 17½c. brown and blue . . . 18·00 90
185 20c. green £120 70
186 20c. grey and green . . . 12·00 45
187 22½c. green and brown . . 11·50 50
188 25c. blue and pink . . . . 11·50 30
189 30c. purple and mauve . . 25·00 50
190 40c. orange and green . . 38·00 90
191 50c. red and green . . . £110 95
192 50c. violet and grey . . . 65·00 90
193 60c. green and olive . . . 38·00 1·10
194a **11** 1g. green . . . . 50·00 75
195b 2½g. lilac . . . . 95·00 3·50
196a 5g. red . . . . £225 5·50
197 10g. red £750 £700

1906. Society for the Prevention of Tuberculosis.

208 **14** 1c. (+1c.) red . . . . . . 18·00 10·00
209 3c. (+3c.) green . . . . . 32·00 22·00
210 5c. (+5c.) violet . . . . . 30·00 15·00

15 Admiral M. A. de Ruyter **16** William I

1907. Birth Tercentenary of Admiral de Ruyter.

211 **15** ½c. blue . . . . 2·10 1·40
212 1c. red . . . . 4·00 2·50
213 2½c. red . . . . 7·00 2·50

1913. Independence Centenary.

214 **16** 2½c. green on green 90 85
215 – 3c. yellow on cream . . . 1·40 1·25
216 – 5c. red on buff . . . . . 1·40 90
217 – 10c. grey . . . . 4·25 2·40
218 **16** 12½c. blue on blue . . . . 3·25 2·25
219 – 20c. brown . . . . 12·50 10·00
220 – 25c. blue . . . . 15·00 8·75
221 – 50c. green . . . . 32·00 28·00
222 **16** 1g. red . . . . 48·00 20·00
223 – 2½g. lilac . . . . £120 48·00
224 – 5g. yellow on cream . . . £250 40·00
225 – 10g. orange £750 £750

DESIGNS: 3c., 20c., 2½g. William II; 5c., 25c., 5g. William III; 10c., 50c., 10g. Queen Wilhelmina.

1919. Surch **Veertig Cent** (40c.) or **Zestig Cent** (60c.).

234 **13** 40c. on 30c. purple & mve 32·00 3·75
235 60c. on 30c. purple & mve 32·00 3·50

1920. Surch in figures.

238 **13** 4c. on 4½c. mauve . . . . 5·25 1·75
236 **11** 2.50 on 10g. red £140 £120
237 – 2.50 on 10g. red (No. 225) £150 £110

23 **24**

1921. Air.

239 **23** 10c. red . . . . 1·75 1·40
240 15c. green . . . . 6·25 2·25
241 60c. blue . . . . 19·00 20

1921.

242 **24** 5c. green . . . . 8·75 20
243 12½c. red . . . . 20·00 3·25
244 20c. blue . . . . 26·00 25

25 Lion in Dutch Garden and Orange Tree (emblematical of Netherlands) **26** **27**

1923.

248 **25** 1c. violet 65 65
249 2c. orange . . . . 6·00 20
250 **26** 2½c. green . . . . 2·10 70
251 **27** 4c. blue . . . . 1·50 60

1923. Surch.

252 **12** 2c. on 1c. red 60 20
253 2c. on 1½c. blue 60 25
254 **13** 10c. on 3c. green . . . . 5·00 20
255 10c. on 5c. red . . . . . 10·00 55
256 10c. on 12½c. blue . . . . 8·25 60
257a 10c. on 17½c. brown & blue . . . 4·50 4·00
258a 10c. on 22½c. olive & brown . . . 4·50 4·00

30 **31**

1923. 25th Anniv of Queen's Accession.

259 **31** 2c. green 30 10
260 **30** 5c. green 40 25
261 **31** 7½c. red 50 25
262 10c. red 40 10
263 20c. blue . . . . 4·25 80
264 25c. yellow . . . . 7·50 1·60
265b 35c. orange . . . . 8·00 3·50
266a 50c. black . . . . 18·00 50
267 **30** 1g. red . . . . 35·00 7·25
268 2½g. black £250 £200
269 5g. blue £225 £170

1923. Surch **DIENST ZEGEL PORTEN AAN TEEKEN RECHT** and value.

270 **13** 10c. on 3c. green . . . . . 1·25 1·10
271 1g. on 17½c. brown & blue 80·00 17·00

33

1923. Culture Fund.

272 **33** 2c. (+5c.) blue on pink . . 20·00 17·00
273 – 10c. (+5c.) red on pink . . 20·00 17·00
DESIGN: 10c. Two women.

35 Carrier Pigeon **36** Queen Wilhelmina

1924.

304C **35** ½c. grey 45 30
305A 1c. red 20 10
306C 1½c. mauve 40 10
424a 1½c. grey 20 10
425 2c. orange 20 10
426a 2½c. green . . . . 1·60 20
427 3c. green 20 10
427a 4c. blue 20 10
428 **36** 5c. green 20 10
429 6c. brown 20 10
279A 7½c. yellow 60 10
313A 7½c. violet . . . . . . 4·00 10
314A 7½c. red 30 10
279cA 9c. red and black . . . 1·60 1·50
281A 10c. red . . . . 1·75 10
317A 10c. blue . . . . 2·75 10
282A 12½c. red . . . . 2·10 40
319A 12½c. blue 35 10
320A 15c. blue . . . . 7·25 20
321C 15c. yellow 85 60
322C 20c. blue . . . . 5·50 2·50
434 21c. brown . . . . . . 25·00 90
324B 22½c. brown . . . . . . 6·75 2·40
434a 22½c. orange . . . . . 15·00 18·00
435 25c. green . . . . . . 5·00 15
326A 27½c. grey . . . . . . 4·50 20
437 30c. violet . . . . . . 6·00 20
286cA 35c. brown . . . . . . 35·00 7·00
437a 40c. brown . . . . . . 9·50 20
330A 50c. green . . . . . . 5·50 20
289A 60c. violet . . . . . . 30·00 95
331A 60c. black . . . . . . 23·00 1·00
301 1g. blue (23 × 29 mm) 8·75 50
302 2½g. red (23 × 29 mm) 90·00 5·25
303 5g. black (23 × 29 mm) £180 2·75
For further stamps in Type **35**, see Nos. 546/57.

1924. International Philatelic Exn, The Hague.

290 **36** 10c. green . . . . 38·00 38·00
291 15c. black . . . . 42·00 42·00
292 35c. red . . . . 38·00 38·00

37 **38**

1924. Dutch Lifeboat Centenary.

293 **37** 2c. brown . . . . 4·00 3·00
294 **38** 10c. brown on yellow . . . 7·00 2·50

39 **40** Arms of South Holland

1924. Child Welfare.

295 **39** 2c. (+2c.) green . . . . . 2·10 2·10
296 7½c. (+3½c.) brown . . . . 5·75 6·25
297 10c. (+2½c.) red . . . . . 4·50 1·75

1925. Child Welfare. Arms as T **40**.

298A – 2c. (+2c.) green and yellow 90 85
299A – 7½c. (+3½c.) violet and blue . . . . 4·50 4·75
300A **40** 10c. (+2½c.) red and yellow . . . . 3·50 60
ARMS: 2c. North Brabant; 7½c. Gelderland.
See also Nos. 350/3A and 359/62A.

1926. Child Welfare. Arms as T **40**.

350A 2c. (+2c.) red and silver . . 55 50
351A 5c. (+3c.) green and blue 1·60 1·40
352A 10c. (+3c.) red and green 2·40 30
353A 15c. (+3c.) yellow and blue 6·25 5·75
ARMS: 2c. Utrecht; 5c. Zeeland; 10c. North Holland; 15c. Friesland.

46 Queen Wilhelmina **47** Red Cross Allegory

1927. 60th Anniv of Dutch Red Cross Society.

354a **46** 2c. (+2c.) red . . . . . . 3·25 2·40
355 – 3c. (+2c.) green . . . . . 6·29 9·00
356 – 5c. (+3c.) blue . . . . . 1·10 1·10
357a – 7½c. (+3½c.) blue . . . . 5·50 2·25
358 **47** 15c. (+5c.) red and blue 9·75 10·00
PORTRAITS: 2c. King William III; 3c. Queen Emma; 5c. Henry, Prince Consort.

1927. Child Welfare. Arms as T **40**.

359A 2c. (+2c.) red and lilac . . 45 45
360A 5c. (+3c.) green and yellow 1·75 1·60
361A 7½c. (+3½c.) red and black 4·00 40
362A 15c. (+3c.) blue and brown 6·00 5·50
ARMS: 2c. Drente; 5c. Groningen; 7½c. Limburg; 15c. Overyssel.

48 Sculler **49** Footballer

1928. Olympic Games, Amsterdam.

363 **48** 1½c.+1c. green . . . . . . 2·25 1·60
364 – 2c.+1c. purple . . . . . 3·00 2·00
365 **49** 3c.+1c. green . . . . . . 2·50 2·40
366 – 5c.+1c. blue . . . . . . 3·00 1·60
367 – 7½c.+2½c. orange . . . . 3·00 1·90
368 – 10c.+2c. red . . . . . . 8·00 6·00
369 – 15c.+2c. blue . . . . . 8·00 4·50
370 – 30c.+3c. sepia . . . . . 25·00 24·00
DESIGNS—HORIZ: 2c. Fencing. VERT: 5c. Sailing; 7½c. Putting the shot; 10c. Running; 15c. Show-jumping; 30c. Boxing.

50 Lieut. Koppen

1928. Air.

371 **50** 40c. red 60 60
372 – 75c. green 60 60
DESIGN: 75c. Van der Hoop.

52 J. P. Minckelers **53** Mercury

1928. Child Welfare.

373 **52** 1½c.+1½c. violet 60 50
374 – 5c.+3c. green . . . . . . 1·90 70
375a – 7½c.+2½c. red . . . . . . 3·50 35
376a – 12½c.+3½c. blue . . . . . 10·00 7·50
PORTRAITS: 5c. Boerhaave; 7½c. H. A. Lorentz; 12½c. G. Huygens.

1929. Air.

377 **53** 1½g. black . . . . 2·75 1·60
378 4½g. red . . . . 1·60 3·00
379 7½g. green . . . . 25·00 4·00

1929. Surch **21**.

380 **36** 21c. on 22½c. brown . . . 21·00 1·40

55 "Friendship and Security" **56** Rembrandt and "De Staalmeesters"

1929. Child Welfare.

381A **55** 1½c. (+1½c.) grey . . . . 2·25 50
382C 5c. (+3c.) green . . . . . 3·75 80
383A 6c. (+4c.) red . . . . . 2·25 35
384A 12½c. (+3½c.) blue . . . . 15·00 13·00

1930. Rembrandt Society.

385 **56** 5c. (+5c.) green . . . . . 8·00 7·50
386 6c. (+5c.) black . . . . . 5·50 3·75
387 12½c. (+5c.) blue . . . . . 8·50 8·50

57 Spring **58** **59** Queen Wilhelmina

1930. Child Welfare.

388A **57** 1½c. (+1½c.) red . . . . 1·60 50
389A – 5c. (+3c.) green . . . . . 2·75 65
390A – 6c. (+4c.) purple . . . . 2·40 40
391A – 12½c. (+3½c.) blue . . . . 19·00 9·50
DESIGNS (allegorical): 5c. Summer; 6c. Autumn; 12½c. Winter.

1931. Gouda Church Restoration Fund.

392 **58** 1½c.+1½c. green . . . . . 17·50 15·00
393 – 6c.+4c. red . . . . . . 21·00 18·00
DESIGN: No. 393, Church facade.

1931.

395 – 70c. blue and red (postage) . . . . 30·00 45
395b – 80c. green and red . . . £110 3·25
394 **59** 36c. red and blue (air) . . 12·50 75
DESIGNS: 70c. Portrait and factory; 80c. Portrait and shipyard.

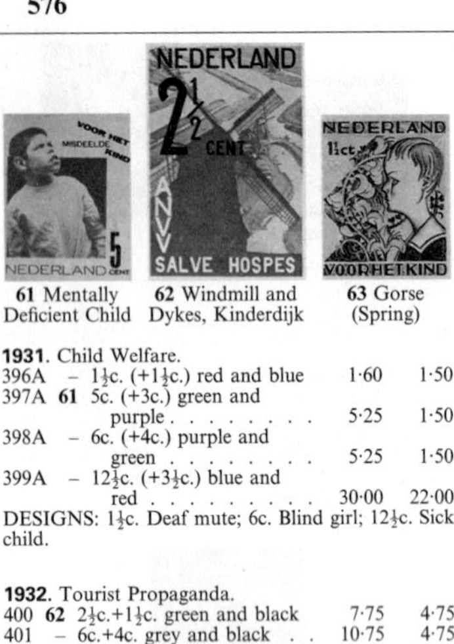

61 Mentally Deficient Child **62** Windmill and Dykes, Kinderdijk **63** Gorse (Spring)

1931. Child Welfare.
396A – 1½c. (+1½c.) red and blue 1·60 1·50
397A **61** 5c. (+3c.) green and purple 5·25 1·50
398A – 6c. (+4c.) purple and green 5·25 1·50
399A – 12½c. (+3½c.) blue and red 30·00 22·00
DESIGNS: 1½c. Deaf mute; 6c. Blind girl; 12½c. Sick child.

1932. Tourist Propaganda.
400 **62** 2½c.+1½c. green and black 7·75 4·75
401 – 6c.+4c. grey and black 10·75 4·75
402 – 7½c.+3½c. red and black 30·00 15·00
403 – 12½c.+2½c. blue and black 35·00 22·00
DESIGNS: 6c. Aerial view of Town Hall, Zierikzee; 7½c. Bridges at Schipluiden and Moerdijk; 12½c. Tulips.

1932. Child Welfare.
404A **63** 1½c. (+1½c.) brown & yell 2·50 45
405A – 5c. (+3c.) blue and red 3·25 80
406A – 6c. (+4c.) green and orange 2·50 40
407A – 12½c. (+3½c.) blue & orange 27·00 22·00
DESIGNS: Child and: 5c. Cornflower (Summer); 6c. Sunflower (Autumn); 12½c. Christmas rose (Winter).

64 Arms of House of Orange

65 Portrait by Goltzius

1933. 4th Birth Centenary of William I of Orange. T **64** and portraits of William I inscr "1533", as T **65**.
408 **64** 1½c. black 60 30
409 **65** 5c. green 1·75 30
410 – 6c. purple 2·75 15
411 – 12½c. blue 16·00 3·00
DESIGNS: 6c. Portrait by Key; 12½c. Portrait attributed to Moro.

68 Dove of Peace

69 Projected Monument at Den Helder

70 "De Hoop" (hospital ship)

1933. Peace Propaganda.
412 **68** 12½c. blue 8·75 35

1933. Seamen's Fund.
413 **69** 1½c. (+1½c.) red 3·25 1·60
414 **70** 5c. (+3c.) green and red 10·25 3·00
415 – 6c. (+4c.) green 16·00 2·40
416 – 12½c. (+3½c.) blue 23·00 17·00
DESIGNS: 6c. Lifeboat; 12½c. Seaman and Seamen's Home.

73 Pander S.4 Postjager

1933. Air. Special Flights.
417 **73** 30c. green 75 70

74 Child and Star of Epiphany

75 Princess Juliana

1933. Child Welfare.
418A **74** 1½c. (+1½c.) orange and grey 1·60 50
419A 5c. (+3c.) yellow and brown 2·25 65
420A 6c. (+4c.) gold and green 3·25 60
421A 12½c. (+3½c.) silver and blue 25·00 17·00

1934. Crisis stamps.
438 – 5c. (+4c.) purple 12·50 3·00
439 **75** 6c. (+5c.) blue 10·50 4·25
DESIGN: 5c. Queen Wilhelmina.

76 Dutch Warship

77 Dowager Queen Emma

1934. Tercentenary of Curacao.
440 – 6c. black 3·25 15
441 **76** 12½c. blue 22·00 2·50
DESIGN: 6c. Willemstad Harbour.

1934. Anti-T.B. Fund.
442 **77** 6c. (+2c.) blue 12·50 1·50

78 Destitute child

79 H. D. Guyot

1934. Child Welfare.
443 **78** 1½c. (+1½c.) brown 1·60 50
444 5c. (+3c.) red 2·50 1·00
445 6c. (+4c.) green 2·50 30
446 12½c. (+3½c.) blue 25·00 16·00

1935. Cultural and Social Relief Fund.
447 **79** 1½c. (+1½c.) red 1·75 1·60
448 – 5c. (+3c.) brown 4·50 5·00
449 – 6c. (+4c.) green 5·50 85
450 – 12½c. (+3½c.) blue 27·00 5·75
PORTRAITS: 5c. A. J. M. Diepenbrock; 6c. F. C. Donders; 12½c. J. P. Sweelinck.
See also Nos. 456/9, 469/72, 478/82 and 492/6.

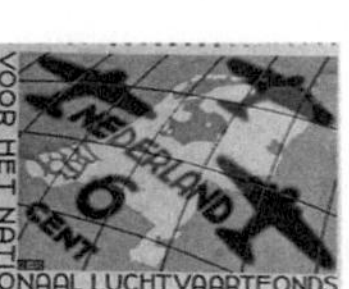

80 Aerial Map of Netherlands

81 Child picking Fruit

1935. Air Fund.
451 **80** 6c. (+4c.) brown 27·00 9·25

1935. Child Welfare.
452 **81** 1½c. (+1½c.) red 65 45
453 5c. (+3c.) green 1·60 1·40
454 6c. (+4c.) brown 1·60 40
455 12½c. (+3½c.) blue 23·00 8·25

1936. Cultural and Social Relief Fund. As T **79**.
456 1½c. (+1½c.) sepia 90 1·00
457 5c. (+3c.) green 4·25 3·50
458 6c. (+4c.) red 3·75 55
459 12½c. (+3½c.) blue 14·00 3·25
PORTRAITS: 1½c. H. Kamerlingh Onnes; 5c. Dr. A. S. Talma; 6c. Mgr. Dr. H. J. A. M. Schaepman; 12½c. Desiderius Erasmus.

83 Pallas Athene

1936. Tercentenary of Utrecht University Foundation.
460 **83** 6c. red 1·75 25
461 – 12½c. blue 5·50 8·75
DESIGN: 12½c. Gisbertus Voetius.

84 Child Herald

85 Scout Movement

1936. Child Welfare.
462 **84** 1½c. (+1½c.) slate 60 35
463 5c. (+3c.) green 2·25 75
464 6c. (+4c.) brown 2·00 30
465 12½c. (+3½c.) blue 15·00 4·25

1937. Scout Jamboree.
466 – 1½c. black and green 20 15
467 **85** 6c. brown and black 1·50 15
468 – 12½c. black and blue 4·50 1·25
DESIGNS: 1½c. Scout Tenderfoot Badge; 12½c. Hermes.

1937. Cultural and Social Relief Fund. Portraits as T **79**.
469 1½c.+1½c. sepia 60 60
470 5c.+3c. green 5·50 4·00
471 6c.+4c. purple 1·25 40
472 12½c.+3½c. blue 8·25 1·00
PORTRAITS: 1½c. Jacob Maris; 5c. F. de la B. Sylvius; 6c. J. van den Vondel; 12½c. A. van Leeuwenhoek.

86 "Laughing Child" by Frans Hals

87 Queen Wilhelmina

1937. Child Welfare.
473 **86** 1½c. (+1½c.) black 20 15
474 3c. (+2c.) green 1·60 1·10
475 4c. (+2c.) red 65 50
476 5c. (+3c.) green 60 15
477 12½c. (+3½c.) blue 7·50 1·25

1938. Cultural and Social Relief Fund. As T **79**.
478 1½c.+1½c. sepia 40 50
479 3c.+2c. green 65 35
480 4c.+2c. red 2·00 2·10
481 5c.+3c. green 2·50 35
482 12½c.+3½c. blue 9·25 1·10
PORTRAITS: 1½c. M. van St. Aldegonde; 3c. O. G. Heldring; 4c. Maria Tesselschade; 5c. Rembrandt; 12½c. H. Boerhaave.

1938. 40th Anniv of Coronation.
483 **87** 1½c. black 20 15
484 5c. red 30 15
485 12½c. blue 3·75 1·50

88 Carrion Crow

89 Boy with Flute

1938. Air. Special Flights.
486 **88** 12½c. blue and grey 65 65
790a 25c. blue and grey 4·00 1·75

1938. Child Welfare.
487 **89** 1½c.+1½c. black 20 30
488 3c.+2c. brown 50 40
489 4c.+2c. green 90 85
490 5c.+3c. red 45 20
491 12½c.+3½c. blue 10·00 2·00

1939. Cultural and Social Relief Fund. As T **79**.
492 1½c.+1½c. brown 65 60
493 2½c.+2½c. green 3·50 2·75
494 3c.+3c. red 90 1·25
495 5c.+3c. green 2·75 35
496 12½c.+3½c. blue 6·75 1·10
PORTRAITS: 1½c. M. Maris; 2½c. Anton Mauve; 3c. Gerardus van Swieten; 5c. Nicolas Beets; 12½c. Pieter Stuyvesant.

91 St. Willibrord's landing in the Netherlands

92 Replica of Locomotive "De Arend"

93 Child and Cornucopia

1939. 12th Death Centenary of St. Willibrord.
497 **91** 5c. green 75 15
498 – 12½c. blue 5·50 3·00
DESIGN: 12½c. St. Willibrord as Bishop of Utrecht.

1939. Centenary of Netherlands Railway.
499 **92** 5c. green 80 15
500 – 12½c. blue 8·25 4·25
DESIGN: 12½c. Electric railcar.

1939. Child Welfare.
501 **93** 1½c.+1½c. black 20 25
502 2½c.+2½c. green 5·50 3·00
503 3c.+3c. red 75 30
504 5c.+3c. green 1·10 25
505 12½c.+3½c. blue 4·50 1·50

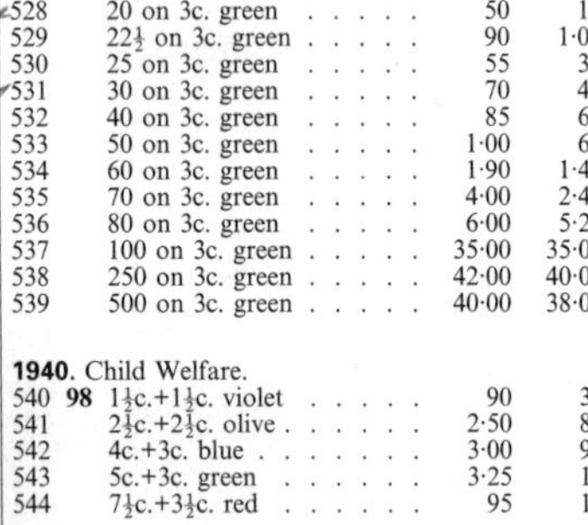

94 Queen Wilhelmina **95** Vincent Van Gogh **98** Girl with Dandelion

1940.
506 **94** 5c. green 30 10
506a 6c. brown 70 15
507 7½c. red 30 10
508 10c. purple 30 10
509 12½c. blue 30 10
510 15c. blue 30 10
510a 17½c. blue 1·25 85
511 20c. violet 65 15
512 22½c. olive 1·25 1·00
513 25c. red 50 15
514 30c. ochre 1·00 40
515 40c. green 2·00 85
515a 50c. orange 8·00 65
515b 60c. purple 8·00 2·50

1940. Cultural and Social Relief Fund.
516 **95** 1½c.+1½c. brown 2·00 50
517 – 2½c.+2½c. green 6·00 1·10
518 – 3c.+3c. red 3·50 1·10
519 – 5c.+3c. green 7·50 40
520 – 12½c.+3½c. blue 6·75 85
PORTRAITS: 1½c. E. J. Potgieter; 3c. Petrus Camper; 5c. Jan Steen; 12½c. Joseph Scaliger.
See also Nos. 558/62 and 656/60.

1940. As No. 519, colour changed. Surch.
521 7½c.+2½c. on 5c.+3c. red 65 40

1940. Surch with large figures and network.
522 **35** 2½ on 3c. red 3·00 40
523 5 on 3c. green 20 15
524 7½ on 3c. red 20 10
525 10 on 3c. green 20 15
526 12½ on 3c. blue 40 30
527 17½ on 3c. green 70 65
528 20 on 3c. green 50 15
529 22½ on 3c. green 90 1·00
530 25 on 3c. green 55 35
531 30 on 3c. green 70 45
532 40 on 3c. green 85 65
533 50 on 3c. green 1·00 65
534 60 on 3c. green 1·90 1·40
535 70 on 3c. green 4·00 2·40
536 80 on 3c. green 6·00 5·25
537 100 on 3c. green 35·00 35·00
538 250 on 3c. green 42·00 40·00
539 500 on 3c. green 40·00 38·00

1940. Child Welfare.
540 **98** 1½c.+1½c. violet 90 30
541 2½c.+2½c. olive 2·50 85
542 4c.+3c. blue 3·00 95
543 5c.+3c. green 3·25 15
544 7½c.+3½c. red 95 15

1941.
546 **35** 5c. green 10 10
547 7½c. red 10 10
548 10c. violet 80 15
549 12½c. blue 30 30
550 15c. blue 80 35
551 17½c. red 15 15
552 20c. violet 85 15
553 22½c. olive 15 25
554 25c. lake 35 30
555 30c. brown 3·00 30
556 40c. green 15 30
557 50c. brown 15 15

1941. Cultural and Social Relief Fund. As T **95** but inscr "ZOMERZEGEL 31.12.46".
558 1½c.+1½c. brown 85 30
559 2½c.+2½c. green 85 30
560 4c.+3c. red 85 30
561 5c.+3c. green 85 30
562 7½c.+3½c. purple 85 30
PORTRAITS: 1½c. Dr. A. Mathijsen; 2½c. J. Ingenhousz; 4c. Aagje Deken; 5c. Johan Bosboom; 7½c. A. C. W. Staring.

100 "Titus Rembrandt"

101 Legionary

1941. Child Welfare.
563 **100** 1½c.+1½c. black 50 30
564 2½c.+2½c. olive 50 30

565 4c.+3c. blue 50 30
566 5c.+3c. green 50 30
567 7½c.+3½c. red 50 30

1942. Netherlands Legion Fund.
568 **101** 7½c.+2½c. red 75 60
569 – 12½c.+87½c. blue 6·25 6·00
MS569a 155×110 mm. No. 568 (block of ten) £110 70·00
MS569b 96×97 mm. No. 569 (block of ten) 90·00 80·00
DESIGN—HORIZ: 12½c. Legionary with similar inscription.

1943. 1st European Postal Congress. As T **26** but larger (21×27½ mm) surch **EUROPEESCHE P T T VEREENIGING 19 OCTOBER 1942 10 CENT.**
570 **26** 10c. on 2½c. yellow 20 25

103 Seahorse
104 Michiel A. de Ruyter 

1943. Old Germanic Symbols.
571 **103** 1c. black 10 10
572 – 1½c. red 10 10
573 – 2c. blue 10 10
574 – 2½c. green 10 10
575 – 3c. red 10 10
576 – 4c. brown 10 10
577 – 5c. olive 10 10
DESIGNS—VERT: 1½c. Triple crowned tree; 2½c. Birds in ornamental tree; 4c. Horse and rider. HORIZ: 2c. Swans; 3c. Trees and serpentine roots; 5c. Prancing horses.

1943. Dutch Naval Heroes.
578 **104** 7½c. red 10 10
579 – 10c. green 15 10
580 – 12½c. blue 15 15
581 – 15c. violet 15 15
582 – 17½c. grey 15 15
583 – 20c. brown 15 15
584 – 22½c. red 15 20
585 – 25c. purple 45 55
586 – 30c. blue 15 20
587 – 40c. grey 15 15
PORTRAITS: 10c. Johan Evertsen; 12½c. Maarten H. Tromp; 15c. Piet Hein; 17½c. Wilhelm Joseph van Gent; 20c. Witte de With; 22½c. Cornelis Evertsen; 25c. Tjerk Hiddes de Fries; 30c. Cornelis Tromp; 40c. Cornelis Evertsen the younger.

105 Mail Cart
106 Child and Doll's House 

1943. Stamp Day.
589 **105** 7½c.+7½c. red 15 15

1944. Child Welfare and Winter Help Funds. Inscr "WINTERHULP" (1½c. and 7½c.) or "VOLKSDIENST" (others).
590 **106** 1½c.+3½c. black 15 20
591 – 4c.+3½c. brown 15 20
592 – 5c.+5c. green 15 20
593 – 7½c.+7½c. red 15 20
594 – 10c.+40c. blue 15 20
DESIGNS: 4c. Mother and child; 5c., 10c. Mother and children; 7½c. Child and wheatsheaf.

107 Infantryman
111 Queen Wilhelmina 

1944.
595 **107** 1½c. black 10 10
596 – 2½c. green 10 10
597 – 3c. brown 10 10
598 – 5c. blue 10 10
599 **111** 7½c. red 10 10
600 10c. orange 10 10
601 12½c. blue 10 10
602 15c. red 1·40 1·25
603 17½c. green 1·10 1·10
604 20c. violet 50 30
605 22½c. red 1·10 90
606 25c. brown 1·75 1·40
607 30c. green 30 20
608 40c. purple 2·10 1·90
609 50c. mauve 1·40 1·00
DESIGNS—HORIZ: 2½c. "Nieuw Amsterdam" (liner); 3c. Airman. VERT: 5c. "De Ruyter" (cruiser). The above set was originally for use on Netherlands warships serving with the Allied Fleet, and was used after liberation in the Netherlands.

112 Lion and Dragon
113 

1945. Liberation.
610 **112** 7½c. orange 20 15

1945. Child Welfare.
611 **113** 1½c.+2½c. grey 30 30
612 2½c.+3½c. green 30 30
613 5c.+5c. brown 30 30
614 7½c.+4½c. red 30 30
615 12½c.+5½c. blue 30 30

114 Queen Wilhelmina
115 Emblem of Abundance 

1946.
616 **114** 1g. blue 1·75 50
617 2½g. red £130 10·50
618 5g. green £130 27·00
619 10g. violet £130 26·00

1946. War Victims' Relief Fund.
620 **115** 1½c.+3½c. black 50 30
621 2½c.+5c. green 60 55
622 5c.+10c. violet 60 55
623 7½c.+15c. red 50 30
624 12½c.+37½c. blue 95 55

116 Princess Irene
117 Boy on Roundabout 

1946. Child Welfare.
625 **116** 1½c.+1½c. brown 60 55
626 – 2½c.+1½c. green 60 55
627 **116** 4c.+2c. red 70 55
628 – 5c.+2c. brown 70 55
629 – 7½c.+2½c. red 60 15
630 – 12½c.+7½c. blue 60 55
PORTRAITS: 2½c., 5c. Princess Margriet; 7½c., 12½c. Princess Beatrix.

1946. Child Welfare.
631 **117** 2c.+2c. violet 60 45
632 4c.+2c. green 60 45
633 7½c.+2½c. red 60 45
634 10c.+5c. purple 70 15
635 20c.+5c. blue 95 65

118 Numeral
119 Queen Wilhelmina 
122 Children 

1946.
636 **118** 1c. red 10 10
637 2c. blue 10 10
638 2½c. orange 7·50 1·60
638a 3c. brown 10 10
639 4c. green 35 10
639a 5c. orange 10 10
639c 6c. grey 35 15
639d 7c. red 15 10
639f 8c. mauve 15 10

1947.
640 **119** 5c. green 1·10 10
641 6c. black 40 10
642 6c. blue 60 10
643 7½c. red 40 20
644 10c. purple 70 10
645 12½c. red 70 40
646 15c. violet 8·25 10
647 20c. blue 8·75 10
648 22½c. green 70 65
649 25c. blue 16·00 10
650 30c. orange 16·00 25
651 35c. blue 16·00 55
652 40c. brown 19·00 55
653 – 45c. blue 22·00 12·00
654 – 50c. brown 14·50 30
655 – 60c. red 18·00 2·25

Nos. 653/5 are as Type **119** but have the inscriptions in colour on white ground.

1947. Cultural and Social Relief Fund. As T **95** but inscr "ZOMERZEGEL ... 13.12.48".
656 2c.+2c. red 85 45
657 4c.+2c. green 1·40 65
658 7½c.+2½c. violet 1·90 85
659 10c.+5c. brown 1·75 35
660 20c.+5c. blue 1·40 65
PORTRAITS: 2c. H. van Deventer; 4c. P. C. Hooft; 7½c. Johan de Witt; 10c. J. F. van Royen; 20c. Hugo Grotius.

1947. Child Welfare.
661 **122** 2c.+2c. brown 15 15
662 – 4c.+2c. green 1·10 55
663 – 7½c.+2½c. brown 1·10 85
664 – 10c.+5c. lake 1·25 15
665 **122** 20c.+5c. blue 1·40 85
DESIGN: 4c. to 10c. Baby.

124 Ridderzaal, The Hague
125 Queen Wilhelmina 

1948. Cultural and Social Relief Fund.
666 **124** 2c.+2c. brown 1·90 45
667 – 6c.+4c. green 2·00 55
668 – 10c.+5c. red 1·40 30
669 – 20c.+5c. blue 2·00 85
BUILDINGS: 6c. Palace on the Dam; 10c. Kneuterdijk Palace; 20c. Nieuwe Kerk, Amsterdam.

1948. Queen Wilhelmina's Golden Jubilee.
670 **125** 10c. red 15 10
671 20c. blue 2·25 1·90

126 Queen Juliana
127 Boy in Canoe 

1948. Coronation.
672 **126** 10c. brown 1·60 10
673 20c. blue 2·00 50

1948. Child Welfare.
674 **127** 2c.+2c. green 15 15
675 – 5c.+3c. green 2·25 70
676 – 6c.+4c. grey 1·25 15
677 – 10c.+5c. red 50 15
678 – 20c.+8c. blue 2·25 1·00
DESIGNS: 5c. Girl swimming; 6c. Boy on toboggan; 10c. Girl on swing; 20c. Boy skating.

128 Terrace near Beach

1949. Cultural and Social Relief Fund.
679 **128** 2c.+2c. yellow and blue 2·00 20
680 – 5c.+3c. yellow and blue 3·50 1·90
681 – 6c.+4c. green 3·00 45
682 – 10c.+5c. yellow and blue 3·75 10
683 – 20c.+5c. blue 3·50 1·90
DESIGNS: 5c. Hikers in cornfield; 6c. Campers by fire; 10c. Gathering wheat; 20c. Yachts.

129 Queen Juliana
130 Queen Juliana 
131 Hands reaching for Sunflower 

1949.
684 **129** 5c. green 65 10
685 6c. blue 40 10
686 10c. orange 40 10
687 12c. red 1·90 1·75
688 15c. green 5·75 40
689 20c. blue 4·25 10
690 25c. brown 12·50 10
691 30c. violet 8·75 10
692 35c. blue 23·00 15
693 40c. purple 40·00 30
694 45c. orange 1·90 80
695 45c. violet 55·00 55
696 50c. green 10·00 25
697 60c. brown 15·00 20
697a 75c. red 70·00 1·25
698 **130** 1g. red 4·00 15
699 2½g. brown £250 2·00
700a 5g. brown £450 3·50
701 10g. violet £300 15·00

1949. Red Cross and Indonesian Relief Fund.
702 **131** 2c.+3c. yellow and grey 95 30
703 6c.+4c. yellow and red 60 35
704 10c.+5c. yellow and blue 3·75 25
705 30c.+10c. yellow & brn 9·50 3·00

132 Posthorns and Globe
133 "Autumn" 

1949. 75th Anniv of U.P.U.
706 **132** 10c. lake 95 10
707 20c. blue 9·50 2·25

1949. Child Welfare Fund. Inscr "VOOR HET KIND".
708 **133** 2c.+3c. brown 40 15
709 – 5c.+3c. red 6·50 1·90
710 – 6c.+4c. green 3·50 40
711 – 10c.+5c. grey 40 15
712 – 20c.+7c. blue 5·50 1·50
DESIGNS: 5c. "Summer"; 6c. "Spring"; 10c. "Winter"; 20c. "New Year".

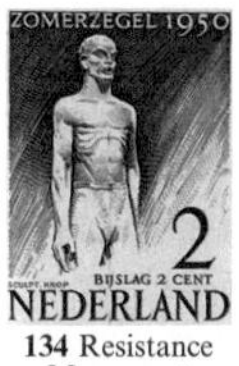

134 Resistance Monument
135 Section of Moerdijk Bridge 

1950. Cultural and Social Relief Fund. Inscr "ZOMERZEGEL 1950".
713 **134** 2c.+2c. brown 2·00 1·10
714 – 4c.+2c. green 11·50 10·50
715 – 5c.+3c. grey 8·75 3·25
716 – 6c.+4c. violet 4·50 65
717 **135** 10c.+5c. slate 6·00 35
718 – 20c.+5c. blue 17·00 14·00
DESIGNS—VERT: 4c. Sealing dykes; 5c. Rotterdam skyscraper. HORIZ: 6c. Harvesting; 20c. "Overijssel" (canal freighter).

1950. Surch with bold figure **6**.
719 **119** 6c. on 7½c. red 2·25 15

137 Good Samaritan and Bombed Church
138 Janus Dousa 

1950. Bombed Churches Rebuilding Fund.
720 **137** 2c.+2c. olive 7·25 1·75
721 5c.+3c. brown 10·50 10·25
722 6c.+4c. green 7·25 3·00
723 10c.+5c. red 17·50 65
724 20c.+5c. blue 32·00 29·00

1950. 375th Anniv of Leyden University.
725 **138** 10c. olive 4·25 15
726 – 20c. blue 4·25 1·25
PORTRAIT: 20c. Jan van Hout.

139 Baby and Bees
140 Bergh Castle 

1950. Child Welfare. Inscr "VOOR HET KIND".
727 **139** 2c.+3c. red 30 15
728 – 5c.+3c. olive 10·00 3·75
729 – 6c.+4c. green 3·50 65
730 – 10c.+5c. purple 40 15
731 – 20c.+7c. blue 10·50 9.00.
DESIGNS: 5c. Boy and fowl; 6c. Girl and birds; 10c. Boy and fish; 20c. Girl, butterfly and frog.

1951. Cultural and Social Relief Fund. Castles.
732 – 2c.+2c. violet 2·50 1·25
733 **140** 5c.+3c. red 8·75 5·50
734 – 6c.+4c. sepia 3·00 55
735 – 10c.+5c. green 6·00 30
736 – 20c.+5c. blue 8·50 7·50
DESIGNS—HORIZ: 2c. Hillenraad; 6c. Hernen. VERT: 10c. Rechteren; 20c. Moermond.

141 Girl and Windmill

142 Gull

1951. Child Welfare.
737 **141** 2c.+3c. green 60 15
738 – 5c.+3c. blue . . . . . . 7·50 4·25
739 – 6c.+4c. brown . . . . . 5·50 65
740 – 10c.+5c. lake 35 15
741 – 20c.+7c. blue . . . . . . 7·50 6·50
DESIGNS: Each shows boy or girl: 5c. Crane; 6c. Fishing nets; 10c. Factory chimneys; 20c. Flats.

1951. Air.
742 **142** 15g. brown £275 £125
743 25g. black £275 £125

143 Jan van Riebeeck

1952. Tercentenary of Landing in South Africa and Van Riebeeck Monument Fund.
744 **143** 2c.+3c. violet . . . . . . 5·50 3·75
745 6c.+4c. green . . . . . . 6·25 4·50
746 10c.+5c. red . . . . . . 7·25 4·50
747 20c.+5c. blue . . . . . . 5·50 3·50

144 Miner

145 Wild Rose

1952. 50th Anniv of State Mines, Limburg.
748 **144** 10c. blue . . . . 2·25 10

1952. Cultural and Social Relief Fund. Floral designs inscr "ZOMERZEGEL 1952".
749 **145** 2c.+2c. green and red . . 70 50
750 – 5c.+3c. yellow and green 2·50 2·75
751 – 6c.+4c. green and red . . 2·25 1·00
752 – 10c.+5c. green & orange 1·90 35
753 – 20c.+5c. green and blue 10·50 8·50
FLOWERS: 5c. Marsh marigold; 6c. Tulip; 10c. Marguerite; 20c. Cornflower.

146 Radio Masts

147 Boy feeding Goat

1952. Netherlands Stamp Centenary and Centenary of Telegraph Service.
754 – 2c. violet 50 10
755 **146** 6c. red 60 15
756 – 10c. green 50 10
757 – 20c. slate . . . . 7·50 1·90
DESIGNS: 2c. Telegraph poles and steam train; 10c. Postman delivering letters, 1852; 20c. Postman delivering letters, 1952.

1952. International Postage Stamp Exn, Utrecht ("ITEP"). Nos. 754/7 but colours changed.
757a – 2c. brown . . . . 20·00 15·00
757b **146** 6c. blue . . . . 20·00 15·00
757c – 10c. lake . . . . 20·00 15·00
757d – 20c. blue . . . . 20·00 15·00
Nos. 757a/d were sold only in sets at the Exhibition at face plus 1g. entrance fee.

1952. Child Welfare.
758 **147** 2c.+3c. black and olive 20 20
759 – 5c.+3c. black and pink . . 3·00 1·25
760 – 6c.+4c. black and green 2·50 45
761 – 10c.+5c. black & orange 15 15
762 – 20c.+7c. black and blue 7·50 6·00
DESIGNS: 5c. Girl riding donkey; 6c. Girl playing with dog; 10c. Boy and cat; 20c. Boy and rabbit.

1953. Flood Relief Fund. Surch **19 53 10c +10 WATERSNOOD**.
763 **129** 10c.+10c. orange 65 15

149 Hyacinth

150 Red Cross

1953. Cultural and Social Relief Fund.
764 **149** 2c.+2c. green and violet 70 40
765 – 5c.+3c. green & orange 2·10 1·75
766 – 6c.+4c. yellow and green 2·00 55
767 – 10c.+5c. green and red . . 3·25 15
768 – 20c.+5c. green and blue 13·15 12·00
FLOWERS: 5c. African marigold; 6c. Daffodil; 10c. Anemone; 20c. Dutch iris.

1953. Red Cross Fund. Inscr "RODE KRUIS".
769 **150** 2c.+3c. red and sepia . . 95 45
770 – 6c.+4c. red and brown . . 3·75 2·50
771 – 7c.+5c. red and olive . . 1·10 45
772 – 10c.+5c. red 65 15
773 – 25c.+8c. red and blue . . 8·25 5·00
DESIGNS: 6c. Man with lamp; 7c. Rescue worker in flooded area; 10c. Nurse giving blood transfusion; 25c. Red Cross flags.

151 Queen Juliana

152 Queen Juliana

1953.
775 **151** 10c. brown 15 10
776 12c. turquoise 15 10
777 15c. red 15 10
777b 18c. turquoise 15 10
778 20c. purple 15 10
778b 24c. olive 25 20
779 25c. blue 25 10
780a 30c. orange 40 10
781 35c. brown 70 10
781a 37c. turquoise 50 15
782 40c. slate 40 10
783 45c. red 40 10
784 50c. green 55 10
785 60c. brown 65 10
785a 62c. red . . . . 3·00 2·50
785b 70c. blue 65 10
786 75c. purple 65 10
786a 80c. violet 65 10
786b 85c. green . . . . . . 1·10 10
786c 95c. brown . . . . . . 1·40 25
787 **152** 1g. red . . . . 1·90 20
788 2½g. green . . . . . . 8·75 15
789 5g. black . . . . . . 3·75 30
790 10g. blue . . . . . . 17·50 1·75

153 Girl with Pigeon

154 M. Nijhoff (poet)

1953. Child Welfare. Inscr "VOOR HET KIND".
791 – 2c.+3c. blue and yellow 15 15
792 – 5c.+3c. lake and green . . 3·25 2·25
793 **153** 7c.+5c. brown and blue 3·75 85
794 – 10c.+5c. lilac and bistre 15 15
795 – 25c.+8c. turq & pink . . 11·00 10·00
DESIGNS: 2c. Girl, bucket and spade; 5c. Boy and apple; 10c. Boy and tjalk (sailing boat); 25c. Girl and tulip.

1954. Cultural and Social Relief Fund.
796 **154** 2c.+3c. blue . . . . . . 1·90 1·60
797 – 5c.+3c. brown . . . . . 2·75 1·75
798 – 7c.+5c. red . . . . . . 3·75 1·40
799 – 10c.+5c. green . . . . . 7·25 60
800 – 25c.+8c. purple . . . . 10·50 11·00
PORTRAITS: 5c. W. Pijper (composer); 7c. H. P. Berlage (architect); 10c. J. Huizinga (historian); 25c. Vincent van Gogh (painter).

155 St. Boniface

156 Boy and Model Glider

1954. 1200th Anniv of Martyrdom of St. Boniface.
801 **155** 10c. blue . . . . 2·75 10

1954. National Aviation Fund.
802 **156** 2c.+2c. green . . . . . . 1·40 1·00
803 – 10c.+4c. blue . . . . . 3·50 65
PORTRAIT: 10c. Dr. A. Plesman (aeronautical pioneer).

157 Making Paperchains

158 Queen Juliana

1954. Child Welfare.
804 **157** 2c.+3c. brown 15 15
805 – 5c.+3c. olive . . . . . . 1·75 1·50
806 – 7c.+5c. blue . . . . . . 1·60 55
807 – 10c.+5c. red 15 15
808 – 25c.+8c. blue . . . . . . 9·25 5·75
DESIGNS—VERT: 5c. Girl brushing her teeth; 7c. Boy and toy boat; 10c. Nurse and child. HORIZ: 25c. Invalid boy drawing in bed.

1954. Ratification of Statute for the Kingdom.
809 **158** 10c. red . . . . 1·00 15

159 Factory, Rotterdam

160 "The Victory of Peace"

1955. Cultural and Social Relief Fund.
810 **159** 2c.+3c. brown . . . . . 1·25 1·10
811 – 5c.+3c. green . . . . . . 1·40 95
812 – 7c.+5c. red . . . . 1·25 95
813 – 10c.+5c. blue . . . . . . 2·10 20
814 – 25c.+8c. brown . . . . . 11·50 9·50
DESIGNS—HORIZ: 5c. Post Office, The Hague; 10c. Town Hall, Hilversum; 25c. Office Building, The Hague. VERT: 7c. Stock Exchange, Amsterdam.

1955. 10th Anniv of Liberation.
815 **160** 10c. red . . . . 1·60 15

161 Microscope and Emblem of Cancer

162 "Willem van Loon" (D. Dircks)

1955. Queen Wilhelmina Anti-cancer Fund.
816 **161** 2c.+3c. black and red . . 60 55
817 5c.+3c. green and red . . 1·60 1·25
818 7c.+5c. purple and red . . 1·40 65
819 10c.+5c. blue and red . . 90 15
820 25c.+8c. olive and red . . 5·75 5·75

1955. Child Welfare Fund.
821 **162** 2c.+3c. green 45 15
822 – 5c.+3c. red . . . . 2·25 95
823 – 7c.+5c. brown . . . . . 4·00 80
824 – 10c.+5c. blue 40 15
825 – 25c.+8c. lilac . . . . . . 9·25 7·75
PORTRAITS: 5c. "Portrait of a Boy" (J. A. Backer); 7c. "Portrait of a Girl" (unknown); 10c. "Philips Huygens" (A. Hanneman); 25c. "Constantin Huygens" (A. Hanneman).

163 "Farmer"

1956. Cultural and Social Relief Fund and 350th Birth Anniv of Rembrandt. Details from Rembrandt's paintings.
826 **163** 2c.+3c. slate . . . . . . 2·75 2·50
827 – 5c.+3c. olive . . . . . . 1·75 1·40
828 – 7c.+5c. brown . . . . . 4·25 4·00
829 – 10c.+5c. green . . . . . 12·50 65
830 – 25c.+8c. brown . . . . . 18·00 16·00
PAINTINGS: 5c. "Young Tobias with Angel"; 7c. "Persian wearing Fur Cap"; 10c. "Old Blind Tobias"; 25c. Self-portrait, 1639.

164 Yacht

165 Amphora

1956. 16th Olympic Games, Melbourne.
831 **164** 2c.+3c. black and blue . . 75 65
832 – 5c.+3c. black and yellow 1·25 95
833 **165** 7c.+5c. black and brown 1·40 95
834 – 10c.+5c. black and grey 2·75 55
835 – 25c.+8c. black and green 6·50 5·75
DESIGNS: As Type **164**: 5c. Runner; 10c. Hockey player; 25c. Water polo player.

1956. Europa. As T **110** of Luxembourg.
836 10c. black and lake . . . . . 2·25 10
837 25c. black and blue . . . . . 50·00 1·60

167 "Portrait of a Boy" (Van Scorel)

1956. Child Welfare Fund. 16th-century Dutch Paintings.
838 **167** 2c.+3c. grey and cream 40 10
839 – 5c.+3c. olive and cream 1·25 1·10
840 – 7c.+5c. purple & cream 3·50 1·50
841 – 10c.+5c. red and cream 40 15
842 – 25c.+8c. blue and cream 7·25 3·75
PAINTINGS: 5c. "Portrait of a Boy"; 7c. "Portrait of a Girl"; 10c. "Portrait of a Girl"; 25c. "Portrait of Eechie Pieters".

168 "Curacao" (trawler) and Fish Barrels

169 Admiral M. A. de Ruyter

1957. Cultural and Social Relief Fund. Ships.
843 – 4c.+3c. blue . . . . . . 1·25 1·00
844 – 6c.+4c. lilac . . . . . . 2·25 1·90
845 – 7c.+5c. red . . . . . . 1·90 1·25
846 **168** 10c.+8c. green . . . . . 3·75 35
847 – 30c.+8c. brown . . . . . 4·75 4·25
DESIGNS: 4c. "Gaasterland" (freighter); 6c. Coaster; 7c. "Willem Barendsz" (whale factory ship) and whale; 30c. "Nieuw Amsterdam" (liner).

1957. 350th Birth Anniv of M. A. de Ruyter.
848 **169** 10c. orange 70 15
849 – 30c. blue . . . . 4·75 1·90
DESIGN: 30c. De Ruyter's flagship, "De Zeven Provincien".

170 Blood Donors' Emblem

171 "Europa" Star

1957. 90th Anniv of Netherlands Red Cross Society and Red Cross Fund.
850 **170** 4c.+3c. blue and red . . . 1·10 1·10
851 – 6c.+4c. green and red . . 1·40 1·25
852 – 7c.+5c. red and green . . 1·40 1·25
853 – 10c.+8c. red and ochre . . 1·25 15
854 – 30c.+8c. red and blue . . 2·75 2·50
DESIGNS: 6c. "J. Henry Dunant" (hospital ship); 7c. Red Cross; 10c. Red Cross emblem; 30c. Red Cross on globe.

1957. Europa.
855 **171** 10c. black and blue . . . 60 10
856 30c. green and blue . . . 7·00 1·50

172 Portrait by B. J. Blommers

173 Walcheren Costume

1957. Child Fund Welfare. 19th- and 20th-Century Paintings by Dutch Masters.
857 **172** 4c.+4c. red 40 15
858 – 6c.+4c. green . . . . . . 2·50 1·90
859 – 8c.+4c. sepia . . . . . 3·25 1·90
860 – 12c.+9c. purple 40 15
861 – 30c.+9c. blue . . . . . 8·25 6·75
PORTRAITS: Child paintings by: W. B. Tholen (6c.); J. Sluyters (8c.); M. Maris (12c.); C. Kruseman (30c.).

1958. Cultural and Social Relief Fund. Provincial Costumes.
862 **173** 4c.+4c. blue 70 55
863 – 6c.+4c. ochre . . . . . . 1·60 1·00
864 – 8c.+4c. red . . . . 4·75 1·60

865 – 12c.+9c. brown . . . . . 1·75 20
866 – 30c.+9c. lilac . . . . . . 7·50 6·25
COSTUMES: 6c. Marken; 8c. Scheveningen; 12c. Friesland; 30c. Volendam.

1958. Surch **12 C**.
867 **151** 12c. on 10c. brown . . . 1·25 10

1958. Europa. As T **119a** of Luxembourg.
868 12c. blue and red 20 10
869 30c. red and blue . . . . . 1·00 65

176 Girl on Stilts and Boy on Tricycle

177 Cranes

1958. Child Welfare Fund. Children's Games.
870 **176** 4c.+4c. blue 20 15
871 – 6c.+4c. red . . . . 2·50 1·75
872 – 8c.+4c. green . . . . . . 1·75 1·00
873 – 12c.+9c. red 20 15
874 – 30c.+9c. blue . . . . . . 6·00 4·75
DESIGNS: 6c. Boy and girl on scooter; 8c. Boys playing leap-frog; 12c. Boys on roller-skates; 30c. Girl skipping and boy in toy car.

1959. 10th Anniv of N.A.T.O. As T **123** of Luxembourg (N.A.T.O. emblem).
875 12c. blue and yellow 20 10
876 30c. blue and red . . . . . 1·00 60

1959. Cultural and Social Relief Fund. Prevention of Sea Encroachment.
877 – 4c.+4c. blue on green . . 1·40 1·25
878 – 6c.+4c. brown on grey . . 95 90
879 – 8c.+4c. violet on blue . . 2·25 1·40
880 **177** 12c.+9c. green on yell . . 4·25 20
881 – 30c.+9c. black on red . . 6·50 6·00
DESIGNS: 4c. Tugs and caisson; 6c. Dredger; 8c. Labourers making fascine mattresses; 30c. Sand-spouter and scoop.

1959. Europa. As T **123a** of Luxembourg.
882 12c. red 20 10
883 30c. green . . . . 3·60 3·25

178 Silhouette of Douglas DC-8 Airliner and World Map

179 Child in Play-pen

1959. 40th Anniv of K.L.M. (Royal Dutch Airlines).
884 **178** 12c. blue and red 20 10
885 – 30c. blue and green . . . 1·60 1·25
DESIGN: 30c. Silhouette of Douglas DC-8 airliner.

1959. Child Welfare Fund.
886 **179** 4c.+4c. blue and brown 20 15
887 – 6c.+4c. brown and green 1·75 1·40
888 – 8c.+4c. blue and red . . . 2·75 1·75
889 – 12c.+9c. red, black and blue 20 10
890 – 30c.+9c. turquoise and yellow . . . . 4·25 3·50
DESIGNS: 6c. Boy as "Red Indian" with bow and arrow; 8c. Boy feeding geese; 12c. Traffic warden escorting children; 30c. Girl doing homework.

180 Refugee Woman

181 White Water-lily

1960. World Refugee Year.
891 **180** 12c.+8c. purple 35 15
892 30c.+10c. green . . . . . 3·50 2·25

1960. Cultural and Social Relief Fund. Flowers.
893 – 4c.+4c. red, green and grey 95 60
894 – 6c.+4c. yellow, green and salmon . . . . 1·40 1·25
895 **181** 8c.+4c. multicoloured . . 3·25 1·90
896 – 12c.+8c. red, green and buff . . . . 2·75 30
897 – 30c.+10c. blue, green and yellow . . . . 6·00 5·00
FLOWERS—VERT: 4c. "The Princess" tulip; 6c. Gorse; 12c. Poppy; 30c. Blue sea-holly.

182 J. van der Kolk

183 Marken Costume

1960. World Mental Health Year.
898 **182** 12c. red 85 15
899 – 30c. blue (J. Wier) . . . . 6·50 2·40

1960. Europa. As T **113a** of Norway.
900 12c. yellow and red 20 10
901 30c. yellow and blue . . . . 3·00 1·90

1960. Child Welfare Fund. Costumes. Mult portraits.
902 **183** 4c.+4c. slate 35 15
903 – 6c.+4c. ochre . . . . . . 2·40 1·25
904 – 8c.+4c. turquoise . . . . 5·00 1·75
905 – 12c.+9c. violet 30 10
906 – 30c.+9c. grey . . . . . . 7·25 5·75
DESIGNS: Costumes of: 6c. Volendam; 8c. Bunschoten; 12c. Hindeloopen; 30c. Huizen.

184 Herring Gull

185 Doves

1961. Cultural and Social Relief Fund. Beach and Meadow Birds.
907 **184** 4c.+4c. slate and yellow 1·25 1·25
908 – 6c.+4c. sepia and brown 1·40 1·40
909 – 8c.+4c. brown and olive 1·10 2·00
910 – 12c.+8c. black and blue 2·40 40
911 – 30c.+10c. black & green 3·00 2·75
BIRDS—HORIZ: 6c. Oystercatcher; 12c. Pied avocet. VERT: 8c. Curlew; 30c. Northern lapwing.

1961. Europa.
912 **185** 12c. brown 10 10
913 30c. turquoise 30 30

186 St. Nicholas

187 Queen Juliana and Prince Bernhard

1961. Child Welfare.
914 **186** 4c.+4c. red 20 15
915 – 6c.+4c. blue . . . . . . 1·25 90
916 – 8c.+4c. bistre . . . . . 1·25 1·00
917 – 12c.+9c. green 20 10
918 – 30c.+9c. orange . . . . . 3·50 3·00
DESIGNS: 6c. Epiphany; 8c. Palm Sunday; 12c. Whitsuntide; 30c. Martinmas.

1962. Silver Wedding.
919 **187** 12c. red 20 10
920 30c. green . . . . 1·40 75

188 Detail of "The Repast of the Officers of the St. Jorisdoelen" after Frans Hals

189 Telephone Dial

1962. Cultural, Health and Social Welfare Funds.
921 – 4c.+4c. green . . . . . . 1·10 90
922 – 6c.+4c. black 90 90
923 – 8c.+4c. purple . . . . . 1·40 1·25
924 – 12c.+8c. bistre . . . . . 1·40 40
925 **188** 30c.+10c. blue . . . . . 1·60 1·40
DESIGNS—HORIZ: 4c. Roman cat (sculpture). VERT: 6c. "Pleuroceras spinatus" (ammonite); 8c. Pendulum clock (after principle of Huygens); 12c. Ship's figurehead.

1962. Completion of Netherlands Automatic Telephone System. Inscr "1962".
926 **189** 4c. red and black 20 10
927 – 12c. drab and black . . . 55 10
928 – 30c. ochre, blue and black 2·25 1·60
DESIGNS—VERT: 12c. Diagram of telephone network. HORIZ: 30c. Arch and telephone dial.

190 Europa "Tree"

191 "Polder" Landscape (reclaimed area)

1962. Europa.
929 **190** 12c. black, yellow & bistre 10 10
930 30c. black, yellow and blue . . . . 1·00 1·25

1962.
935 – 4c. deep blue and blue . . 10 10
937 **191** 6c. deep green and green 40 15
938 – 10c. deep purple and purple 10 10
DESIGNS: 4c. Cooling towers, State mines, Limburg; 10c. Delta excavation works.

192 Children cooking Meal

193 Ears of Wheat

1962. Child Welfare.
940 **192** 4c.+4c. red 20 15
941 – 6c.+4c. bistre 95 55
942 – 8c.+4c. blue . . . . . . 1·60 1·40
943 – 12c.+9c. green 20 10
944 – 30c.+9c. lake . . . . . . 2·75 2·50
DESIGNS—Children: 6c. Cycling; 8c. Watering flowers; 12c. Feeding poultry; 30c. Making music.

1963. Freedom from Hunger.
945 **193** 12c. ochre and blue . . . 20 10
946 30c. ochre and red . . . 1·25 1·00

194 "Gallery" Windmill

195

1963. Cultural, Health and Social Welfare Funds. Windmill types.
947 **194** 4c.+4c. blue . . . . . . 1·10 1·00
948 – 6c.+4c. violet . . . . . . 1·10 1·00
949 – 8c.+4c. green . . . . . . 1·40 1·40
950 – 12c.+8c. brown . . . . . 1·40 30
951 – 30c.+10c. red . . . . . . 1·75 1·90
WINDMILLS—VERT: 6c. North Holland polder; 12c. "Post"; 30c. "Wip". HORIZ: 8c. South Holland polder.

1963. Paris Postal Conference Centenary.
952 **195** 30c. blue, green & blk . . 1·40 1·25

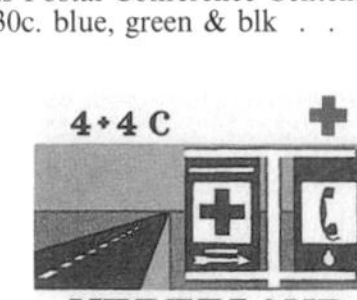

196 Wayside First Aid Post

1963. Red Cross Fund and Centenary (8c.).
953 **196** 4c.+4c. blue and red . . . 40 40
954 – 6c.+4c. violet and red . . 35 30
955 – 8c.+4c. red and black . . 1·10 80
956 – 12c.+9c. brown and red . 20 10
957 – 30c.+9c. green and red . . 1·60 1·40
DESIGNS: 6c. "Books" collection-box; 8c. Crosses; 12c. "International Aid" (Negro children at meal); 30c. First aid party tending casualty.

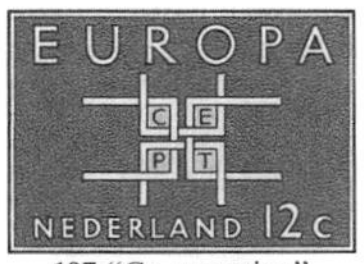

197 "Co-operation"

198 "Auntie Luce sat on a goose ..."

1963. Europa.
958 **197** 12c. orange and brown . . 20 10
959 30c. orange and green . . 1·40 1·10

1963. Child Welfare.
960 **198** 4c.+4c. ultramarine & bl 20 15
961 – 6c.+4c. green and red . . 70 65
962 – 8c.+4c. brown & green . . 95 60
963 – 12c.+9c. violet & yellow 20 10
964 – 30c.+8c. blue and pink . . 1·60 1·40
DESIGNS (Nursery rhymes): 6c. "In the Hague there lives a count ..."; 8c. "One day I passed a puppet's fair ..."; 12c. "Storky, storky, Billy Spoon ..."; 30c. "Ride on a little pram ...".

199 William, Prince of Orange, landing at Scheveningen

200 Knights' Hall, The Hague

1963. 150th Anniv of Kingdom of the Netherlands.
965 **199** 4c. black, bistre and blue 10 10
966 – 5c. black, red and green 20 10
967 – 12c. bistre, blue and black 10 10
968 – 30c. red and black 75 60
DESIGNS: 12c. Triumvirate: Van Hogendorp, Van Limburg, and Van der Duyn van Maasdam; 30c. William I taking oath of allegiance.

1964. 500th Anniv of 1st States-General Meeting.
969 **200** 12c. black and olive . . . 20 10

201 Guide Dog for the Blind

1964. Cultural, Health and Social Welfare Funds. Animals.
970 **201** 5c.+5c. red, black and olive 60 45
971 – 8c.+5c. brown, black and red 40 30
972 – 12c.+9c. black, grey and bistre 60 20
973 – 30c.+9c. multicoloured . . 70 65
DESIGNS: 8c. Three red deer; 12c. Three kittens; 30c. European bison and calf.

202 University Arms

203 Signal No. 144, Amersfoort Station

1964. 350th Anniv of Groningen University.
974 **202** 12c. slate 10 10
975 – 30c. brown 25 25
DESIGN: 30c. "AG" monogram.

1964. 125th Anniv of Netherlands Railways.
976 **203** 15c. black and green . . . 20 10
977 – 40c. black and yellow . . 75 70
DESIGN: 40c. Class ELD-4 electric train.

204 Bible and Dove

1964. 150th Anniv of Netherlands Bible Society.
978 **204** 15c. brown 20 10

205 Europa "Flower"

206 Young Artist

1964. Europa.
979 **205** 15c. green 20 10
980 20c. brown 40 40

1964. 20th Anniv of "BENELUX". As T **150a** of Luxembourg, but smaller 35×22 mm.
981 15c. violet and flesh 20 10

1964. Child Welfare.
982 **206** 7c.+3c. blue and green . . 50 45
983 – 10c.+5c. red, pink and green 40 40
984 – 15c.+10c. yellow, black and bistre 20 10
985 – 20c.+10c. red, sepia and mauve 60 45
986 – 40c.+15c. green & blue . 1·00 80
DESIGNS: 10c. Ballet-dancing; 15c. Playing the recorder; 20c. Masquerading; 40c. Toy-making.

207 Queen Juliana
208 "Killed in Action" (Waalwijk) and "Destroyed Town" (Rotterdam) (monuments)

1964. 10th Anniv of Statute for the Kingdom.
987 **207** 15c. green 20 10

1965. "Resistance" Commemoration.
988 **208** 7c. black and red 20 10
989 – 15c. black and olive . . . 20 10
990 – 40c. black and red 95 85
MONUMENTS: 15c. "Docker" (Amsterdam) and "Killed in Action" (Waalwijk); 40c. "Destroyed Town" (Rotterdam) and "Docker" (Amsterdam).

209 Medal of Knight (Class IV)
210 I.T.U. Emblem and "Lines of Communication"

1965. 150th Anniv of Military William Order.
991 **209** 1g. grey . . . . 1·60 65

1965. Centenary of I.T.U.
992 **210** 20c. blue and drab . . . 20 25
993 40c. brown and blue . . . 60 45

211 Veere

1965. Cultural, Health and Social Welfare Funds.
994 **211** 8c.+6c. black and yellow 35 25
995 – 10c.+6c. black & turq . . 50 40
996 – 18c.+12c. black & brn . . 40 25
997 – 20c.+10c. black & blue . . 50 40
998 – 40c.+10c. black & green 55 45
DESIGNS: (Dutch towns): 10c. Thorn; 18c. Dordrecht; 20c. Staveren; 40c. Medemblik.

212 Europa "Sprig"

1965. Europa.
999 **212** 18c. black, red and brown 20 10
1000 20c. black, red and blue 30 30

213 Girl's Head

1965. Child Welfare. Multicoloured.
1001 8c.+6c. Type **213** 20 15
1002 10c.+6c. Ship 50 50
1003 18c.+12c. Boy (vert) 20 15
1004 20c.+10c. Duck-pond . . . 65 55
1005 40c.+10c. Tractor . . . . 1·90 75
MS1006 143 × 124 mm. Nos. 1001 (5) and 1003 (6) . . . . 26·00 21·00

214 Marines of 1665 and 1965
215 "Help them to a safe Haven" (Queen Juliana)

1965. Tercentenary of Marine Corps.
1007 **214** 18c. blue and red 20 10

1966. Intergovernmental Committee for European Migration (I.C.E.M.) Fund.
1008 **215** 10c.+7c. yellow & blk . . 50 35
1009 40c.+20c. red & black 40 25
MS1010 117 × 44 mm. Nos. 1008 and 1009 (2) . . . . 3·50 1·10

216 Writing Materials
217 Aircraft in Flight

1966. Cultural, Health and Social Welfare Funds. Gysbert Japicx Commem and 200th Anniv of Netherlands Literary Society. Multicoloured.
1011 10c.+5c. Type **216** 40 40
1012 12c.+8c. Part of MS, Japicx's poem "Wobbelke" 40 40
1013 20c.+10c. Part of miniature, "Knight Walewein" . . . 55 40
1014 25c.+10c. Initial "D" and part of MS, novel, "Ferguut" 70 55
1015 40c.+20c. 16th-century printery (woodcut) . . . 55 55

1966. Air (Special Flights).
1016 **217** 25c. multicoloured . . . 20 45

218 Europa "Ship"
219 Infant

1966. Europa.
1017 **218** 20c. green and yellow . . 20 10
1018 40c. deep blue and blue 35 25

1966. Child Welfare.
1019 **219** 10c.+5c. red and blue . . 20 15
1020 – 12c.+8c. green and red 20 15
1021 – 20c.+10c. blue and red 20 15
1022 – 25c.+10c. purple & bl . . 95 85
1023 – 40c.+20c. red & green 90 80
MS1024 132 × 125 mm. Nos. 1019 × 4, 1020 x 5, 1021 × 3 2·75 2·25
DESIGNS: 12c. Young girl; 20c. Boy in water; 25c. Girl with moped; 40c. Young man with horse.

220 Assembly Hall

1967. 125th Anniv of Delft Technological University.
1025 **220** 20c. sepia and yellow . . 20 10

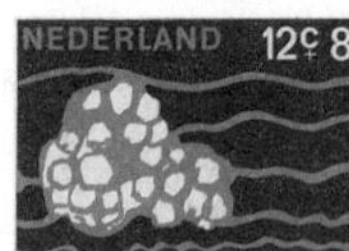

221 Common Northern Whelk Eggs

1967. Cultural, Health and Social Welfare Funds. Marine Fauna.
1026 **221** 12c.+8c. brown & grn 30 30
1027 – 15c.+10c. blue, light blue and deep blue 30 30
1028 – 20c.+10c. mult 30 25
1029 – 25c.+10c. brown, purple and bistre 60 55
1030 – 45c.+20c. mult 80 65
DESIGNS: 15c. Common northern whelk; 20c. Common blue mussel; 25c. Jellyfish; 45c. Crab.

222 Cogwheels
223 Netherlands 5c. Stamp of 1852

1967. Europa.
1031 **222** 20c. blue and light blue 40 10
1032 45c. purple & light purple . . . . 1·10 80

1967. "Amphilex 67" Stamp Exn, Amsterdam.
1035 **223** 20c. blue and black . . . 2·25 1·90
1036 – 25c. red and black . . . 2·25 1·90
1037 – 75c. green and black . . 2·25 1·90
DESIGNS: 25c. Netherlands 10c. stamp of 1864; 75c. Netherlands 20c. stamp of 1867.
Nos. 1035/7 were sold at the exhibition and at post offices at 3g.70, which included entrance fee to the exhibition.

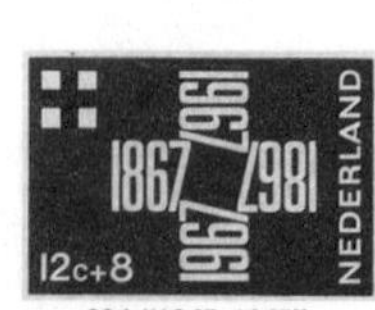

224 "1867–1967"
225 "Porcupine Lullaby"

1967. Centenary of Dutch Red Cross.
1038 12c.+8c. blue and red . . . 30 30
1039 15c.+10c. red 50 40
1040 20c.+10c. olive and red . . 30 20
1041 25c.+10c. green and red . . 50 50
1042 45c.+20c. grey and red . . . 70 65
DESIGNS: 12c. Type **224**; 15c. Red crosses; 20c. "NRK" ("Nederlandsche Rood Kruis") in the form of a cross; 25c. Maltese cross and "red" crosses; 45c. "100" in the form of a cross.

1967. Child Welfare. Multicoloured.
1043 12c.+8c. Type **225** 20 20
1044 15c.+10c. "The Whistling Kettle" 20 20
1045 20c.+10c. "Dikkertje Dap" (giraffe) 20 20
1046 25c.+10c. "The Flower-seller" . . . . 1·25 80
1047 45c.+20c. "Pippeloentje" (bear) . . . . 1·10 85
MS1048 150 × 108 mm. Nos. 1043 (3), 1044 (4), 1045 (3) . . . . 4·00 3·75

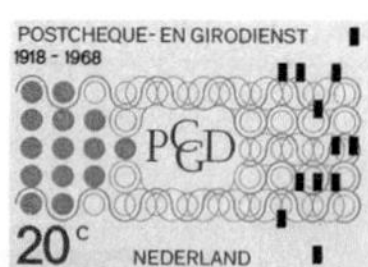

226 "Financial Automation"

1968. 50th Anniv of Netherlands Postal Cheque and Clearing Service.
1049 **226** 20c. red, black and yellow 20 10

227 St. Servatius' Bridge, Maastricht

1968. Cultural, Health and Social Welfare Funds. Dutch Bridges.
1050 **227** 12c.+8c. green . . . . . 1·40 95
1051 – 15c.+10c. brown 70 65
1052 – 20c.+10c. red 50 25
1053 – 25c.+10c. blue 55 55
1054 – 45c.+20c. blue 90 85
BRIDGES: 15c. Magere ("Narrow"), Amsterdam; 20c. Railway, Culemborg; 25c. Van Brienenoord, Rotterdam; 45c. Oosterschelde, Zeeland.

228 Europa "Key"

1968. Europa.
1055 **228** 20c. blue 30 10
1056 45c. red 95 80

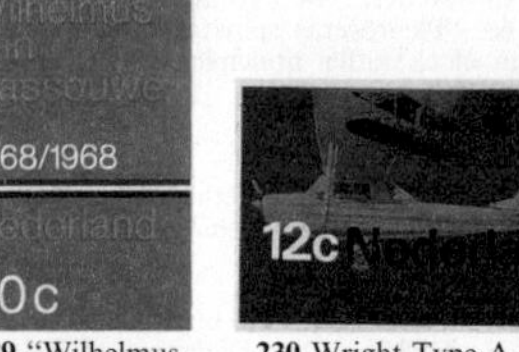

229 "Wilhelmus van Nassouwe"
230 Wright Type A and Cessna 150F

1968. 400th Anniv of Dutch National Anthem, "Wilhelmus".
1057 **229** 20c. multicoloured . . . 20 10

1968. Dutch Aviation Anniversaries.
1058 12c. black, red and mauve 20 10
1059 20c. black, emerald and green 20 10
1060 45c. black, blue and green 1·25 1·10
DESIGNS AND EVENTS: 12c. T **230** (60th anniv (1967) of Royal Netherlands Aeronautical Assn); 20c. Fokker F.II and Fellowship aircraft (50th anniv (1969) of Royal Netherlands Aircraft Factories "Fokker"); 45c. De Havilland D.H.9B biplane and Douglas DC-9 airliner (50th anniv (1969) of Royal Dutch Airlines "KLM").

231 "Goblin"

1968. Child Welfare.
1061 **231** 12c.+8c. pink, black and green 20 15
1062 – 15c.+10c. pink, blue and black 20 15
1063 – 20c.+10c. blue, green and black 20 15
1064 – 25c.+10c. red, yellow and black . . . . . . 1·60 1·10
1065 – 45c.+20c. yellow, orange and black . . . . . 1·60 1·25
MS1066 106½ × 151 mm. Nos. 1061 (3), 1062 (2), 1063 (3) . . . . 9·00 9·00
DESIGNS: 15c. "Giant"; 20c. "Witch"; 25c. "Dragon"; 45c. "Sorcerer".

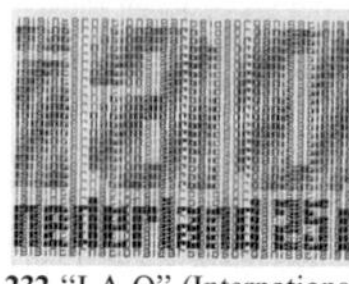

232 "I A O" (Internationale Arbeidsorganisatie)

1969. 50th Anniv of I.L.O.
1067 **232** 25c. red and black . . . 60 10
1068 45c. blue and black . . . 1·00 90

233 Queen Juliana
234 Villa, Huis ter Heide (1915)

1969. (a) Type **233**.
1069 **233** 25c. red . . . . 1·40 20
1069c 30c. brown 15 20
1070a 35c. blue 20 10
1071a 40c. red 30 10
1072a 45c. blue 30 10
1073a 50c. purple 25 10
1073c 55c. red 20 10
1074a 60c. blue 20 10
1075 70c. brown 50 10
1076 75c. green 60 10
1077 80c. red 65 10
1077a 90c. grey 65 10

(b) Size 22 × 33 mm.
1078 – 1g. green 70 10
1079 – 1g.25 lake 95 10
1080 – 1g.50 brown . . . . . . 1·10 10
1081 – 2g. mauve . . . . 1·40 10
1082 – 2g.50 blue . . . . 1·75 10
1083 – 5g. grey . . . . 3·50 10
1084 – 10g. blue . . . . 7·00 1·10
DESIGN: 1g.to 10g. similar to Type **233**.

1969. Cultural, Health and Social Welfare Funds. 20th-century Dutch Architecture.
1085 **234** 12c.+8c. black & brn . . 70 70
1086 – 15c.+10c. black, red and blue 70 70
1087 – 20c.+10c. black & vio . . 70 70
1088 – 25c.+10c. brown & grn 70 30
1089 – 45c.+20c. black, blue and yellow 70 70
DESIGNS: 15c. Private House, Utrecht (1924); 20c. Open-air School, Amsterdam (1930); 25c. Orphanage, Amsterdam (1960); 45c. Congress Building, The Hague (1969).

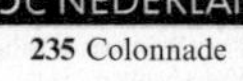

235 Colonnade
236 Stylized "Crab" (of Cancer)

1969. Europa.
1090 **235** 25c. blue 40 10
1091 45c. red . . . . 1·40 1·10

1969. 20th Anniv of Queen Wilhelmina Cancer Fund.
1092 **236** 12c.+8c. violet 65 60
1093 25c.+10c. orange 95 40
1094 45c.+20c. green . . . . 1·75 1·50

1969. 25th Anniv of "BENELUX" Customs Union. As T **186** of Luxembourg.
1095 25c. multicoloured 30 10

238 Erasmus
239 Child with Violin

1969. 500th Birth Anniv of Desiderius Erasmus.
1096 **238** 25c. purple on green . . 30 10

1969. Child Welfare.
1097 – 12c.+8c. black, yellow and blue 20 15
1098 **239** 15c.+10c. black and red 20 15
1099 – 20c.+10c. black, yellow and red . . . . 1·75 1·40
1100 – 25c.+10c. black, red and yellow 20 15
1101 – 45c.+20c. black, red and green . . . . 2·00 1·75
MS1102 150 × 99 mm. Nos. 1097 (4), 1098 (4), 1100 (2) . . . . . . 10·00 9·00
DESIGNS—VERT: 12c. Child with recorder; 20c. Child with drum. HORIZ: 25c. Three choristers; 45c. Two dancers.

240 Queen Juliana and "Sunlit Road"

1969. 25th Anniv of Statute for the Kingdom.
1103 **240** 25c. multicoloured . . . 30 10

241 Prof. E. M. Meijers (author of "Burgerlijk Wetboek")

1970. Introduction of New Netherlands Civil Code ("Burgerlijk Wetboek").
1104 **241** 25c. ultramarine, green and blue 30 10

242 Netherlands Pavilion
243 "Circle to Square"

1970. Expo 70 World Fair, Osaka, Japan.
1105 **242** 25c. grey, blue and red 30 15

1970. Cultural, Health and Social Welfare Funds.
1106 **243** 12c.+8c. black on yell . . 1·10 1·25
1107 – 15c.+10c. black on silver 1·10 1·25
1108 – 20c.+10c. black . . . . 1·10 1·25
1109 – 25c.+10c. black on bl . . 1·10 75
1110 – 45c.+20c. white on grey 1·10 1·25
DESIGNS: 15c. Parallel planes in cube; 20c. Overlapping scales; 25c. Concentric circles in transition; 45c. Spirals.

244 "V" Symbol

245 "Flaming Sun"

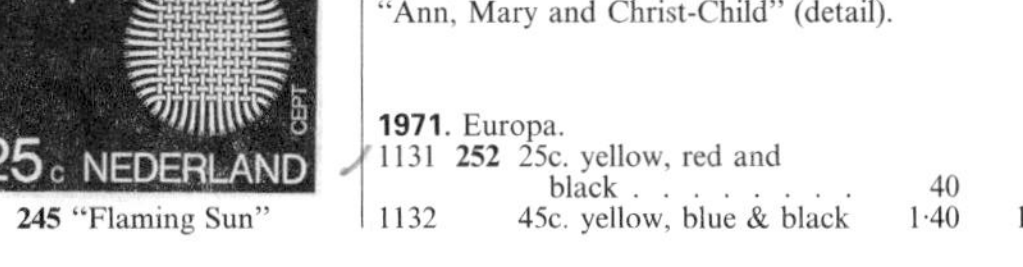

1970. 25th Anniv of Liberation.
1111 **244** 12c. red, blue and brown 40 10

1970. Europa.
1112 **245** 25c. red 40 10
1113 45c. blue . . . . 1·60 1·00

246 "Work and Co-operation"
247 Globe on Plinth

1970. Inter-Parliamentary Union Conference.
1114 **246** 25c. green, black and grey 60 10

1970. 25th Anniv of United Nations.
1115 **247** 45c. black, violet & blue 1·00 85

248 Human Heart
249 Toy Block

1970. Netherlands Heart Foundation.
1116 **248** 12c.+8c. red, black and yellow 70 75
1117 25c.+10c. red, black and mauve 70 65
1118 45c.+20c. red, black and green 70 60

1970. Child Welfare. "The Child and the Cube".
1119 **249** 12c.+8c. blue, violet and green 20 15
1120 – 15c.+10c. green, blue and yellow . . . . 1·40 1·40
1121 **249** 20c.+10c. mauve, red and violet . . . . . 1·40 1·40
1122 – 25c.+10c. red, yellow and mauve 20 15
1123 **249** 45c.+20c. grey, cream and black . . . . . 1·75 1·60
MS1124 126 × 145 mm. Nos. 1119 (9), 1122 (2) . . . . 18·00 16·00
DESIGN: 15c., 25c. As Type **249**, but showing underside of block.

250 "Fourteenth Census 1971"

1971. 14th Netherlands Census.
1125 **250** 15c. purple 20 10

251 "50 years of Adult University Education"
252 Europa Chain

1971. Cultural, Health and Social Welfare Funds. Other designs show 15th-century wooden statues by unknown artists.
1126 **251** 15c.+10c. black, red and yellow . . . . 1·40 1·40
1127 – 20c.+10c. black and green on green . . . . 1·25 1·00
1128 – 25c.+10c. black and orange on orange . . 1·25 60
1129 – 30c.+15c. black and blue on blue . . . . 1·40 1·40
1130 – 45c.+20c. black and red on pink . . . . 1·40 1·40
STATUES: 20c. "Apostle Paul"; 25c. "Joachim and Ann"; 30c. "John the Baptist and Scribes"; 45c. "Ann, Mary and Christ-Child" (detail).

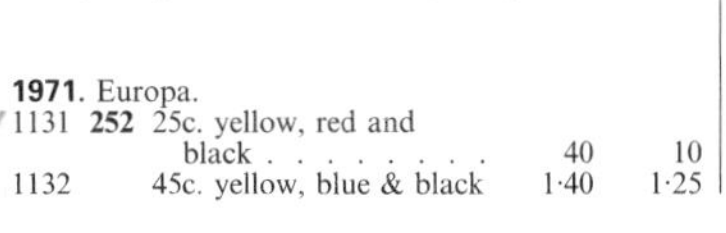

1971. Europa.
1131 **252** 25c. yellow, red and black 40 10
1132 45c. yellow, blue & black 1·40 1·25

253 Carnation Symbol of Prince Bernhard Fund
254 "The Good Earth"

1971. Prince Bernhard's 60th Birthday.
1133 **253** 15c. yellow, grey & black 20 15
1134 – 20c. multicoloured . . . 65 40
1135 – 25c. multicoloured . . . 30 15
1136 – 45c.+20c. black, purple and yellow . . . . . 2·50 2·25
DESIGNS—HORIZ: 20c. Panda symbol of World Wildlife Fund. VERT: 25c. Prince Bernhard; 45c. Statue, Borobudur Temple, Indonesia.

1971. Child Welfare.
1137 **254** 15c.+10c. red, purple and black 20 15
1138 – 20c.+10c. mult 30 20
1139 – 25c.+10c. mult 20 20
1140 – 30c.+15c. blue, violet and black . . . . . . 1·10 65
1141 – 45c.+20c. blue, green and black . . . . . . 1·90 1·40
MS1142 100 × 145 mm. Nos. 1137 (6), 1138 and 1139 (2) . . . . 12·00 11·50
DESIGNS—VERT: 20c. Butterfly; 45c. Reflecting water. HORIZ: 25c. Sun waving; 30c. Moon winking.

255 Delta Map
256 "Fruits"

1972. Delta Sea-Defences Plan.
1143 **255** 20c. multicoloured . . . 20 10

1972. Cultural, Health and Social Welfare Funds. "Floriade Flower Show" (20c., 25c.) and "Holland Arts Festival" (30c., 45c.). Multicoloured.
1144 20c.+10c. Type **256** . . . . 1·10 90
1145 25c.+10c. "Flower" . . . . 1·10 90
1146 30c.+15c. "Sunlit Landscape" . . . . . . 1·10 65
1147 45c.+25c. "Music" . . . . 1·10 90

257 "Communications"
258 "There is more to be done in the world than ever before" (Thorbecke)

1972. Europa.
1148 **257** 30c. brown and blue . . 95 10
1149 45c. brown and orange 1·40 1·10

1972. Death Centenary of J. R. Thorbecke (statesman).
1150 **258** 30c. black and blue . . . 70 15

259 Netherlands Flag
260 Hurdling

1972. 400th Anniv of Netherlands Flag.
1151 **259** 20c. multicoloured . . . 50 20
1152 25c. multicoloured . . . 1·25 15

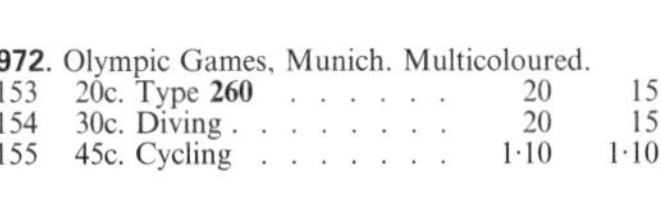

1972. Olympic Games, Munich. Multicoloured.
1153 20c. Type **260** 20 15
1154 30c. Diving 20 15
1155 45c. Cycling . . . . 1·10 1·10

261 Red Cross
262 Prince Willem-Alexander

1972. Netherlands Red Cross.
1156 **261** 5c. red 20 15
1157 – 20c.+10c. red and pink 55 55
1158 – 25c.+10c. red & orange 95 85
1159 – 30c.+15c. red & black 70 55
1160 – 45c.+25c. red and blue 1·00 90
DESIGNS: 20c. Accident services; 25c. Blood transfusion; 30c. Refugee relief; 45c. Child care.

1972. Child Welfare. Multicoloured.
1161 25c.+15c. Type **262** 20 15
1162 30c.+10c. Prince Johan Friso (horiz) 70 65
1163 35c.+15c. Prince Constantin (horiz) 70 15
1164 50c.+20c. The Three Princes (horiz) . . . . 2·40 2·00
MS1165 126 × 109 mm. Nos. 1161 × 4 and 1163 × 3 . . . . . . 8·00 7·00

263 Tulips in Bloom
264 "De Zeven Provincien" (De Ruyter's flagship)

1973. Tulip Exports.
1166 **263** 25c. multicoloured . . . 65 10

1973. Cultural, Health and Social Welfare Funds. Dutch Ships. Multicoloured.
1167 25c.+15c. Type **264** 95 90
1168 30c.+10c. "W.A. Scholten" (steamship) (horiz) 95 90
1169 35c.+15c. "Veendam" (liner) (horiz) . . . . 1·10 75
1170 50c.+20c. Fishing boat (from etching by R. Nooms) . . . . 1·25 1·25

265 Europa "Posthorn"
266 Hockey-players

1973. Europa.
1171 **265** 35c. light blue and blue 55 10
1172 50c. blue and violet . . . 95 85

1973. Events and Anniversaries. Multicoloured.
1173 25c. Type **266** 40 25
1174 30c. Gymnastics . . . . . 2·00 60
1175 35c. Dish aerial (vert) . . . 50 15
1176 50c. Rainbow 85 75
EVENTS—VERT: 25c. 75th anniv of Royal Netherlands Hockey Association; 30c. World Gymnastics Championships, Rotterdam. HORIZ: 35c. Opening of Satellite Station, Burum; 50c. Centenary of World Meteorological Organization.

267 Queen Juliana

268 "Co-operation"

1973. Silver Jubilee of Queen Juliana's Accession.
1177 **267** 40c. multicoloured . . . 50 15

1973. International Development Co-operation.
1178 **268** 40c. multicoloured . . . 95 10

269 "Chess" 270 Northern Goshawk

1973. Child Welfare.
1179 **269** 25c.+15c. red, yellow and black 40 20
1180 – 30c.+10c. green, mauve and black . . . . . . 1·60 65
1181 – 40c.+20c. yellow, green and black 40 15
1182 – 50c.+20c. blue, yellow and black . . . . . . 1·60 2·00
MS1183 74 × 144 mm. Nos. 1179 × 2, 1180 and 1181 × 3 . . . 11·50 11·00
DESIGNS: 30c. "Noughts and crosses"; 40c. "Maze"; 50c. "Dominoes".

1974. "Nature and Environment". Multicoloured.
1184 25c. Type **270** . . . . . . 1·10 55
1185 25c. Tree . . . . 1·10 55
1186 25c. Fisherman and frog . . 1·10 55
Nos. 1184/6 were issued together, se-tenant, forming a composite design.

271 Bandsmen (World Band Contest, Kerkrade) 272 Football on Pitch

1974. Cultural, Health and Social Welfare Funds.
1187 **271** 25c.+15c. mult 95 85
1188 – 30c.+10c. mult 95 85
1189 – 40c.+20c. brown, black and red 95 65
1190 – 50c.+20c. purple, black and red 95 85
DESIGNS: 30c. Dancers and traffic-lights ("Modern Ballet"); 40c. Herman Heijermans; 50c. "Kniertje" (character from Heijermans' play "Op hoop van zegan"). The 40c. and 50c. commemorate the 50th death anniv of the playwright.

1974. Sporting Events.
1191 **272** 25c. multicoloured . . . 20 15
1192 – 40c. yellow, red & mauve 35 15
DESIGNS AND EVENTS—HORIZ: 25c. (World Cup Football Championship, West Germany). VERT: 40c. Hand holding tennis ball (75th anniv of Royal Dutch Lawn Tennis Association).

273 Netherlands Cattle 274 "BENELUX" (30th Anniv of Benelux (Customs Union))

1974. Anniversaries. Multicoloured.
1193 25c. Type **273** . . . . . . 8·75 1·90
1194 25c. "Cancer" 95 20
1195 40c. "Suzanna" (lifeboat) seen through binoculars 70 20
EVENTS AND ANNIVERSARIES: No. 1193, Cent of Netherlands Cattle Herdbook Society; 1194, 25th anniv of Queen Wilhelmina Cancer Research Fund; 1195, 150th anniv of Dutch Lifeboat Service.

1974. International Anniversaries.
1196 **274** 30c. green, turquoise & blue 30 15
1197 – 45c. deep blue, silver & blue 50 15
1198 – 45c. yellow, blue & black 50 15
DESIGNS—VERT: No. 1197, NATO emblem (25th anniv); 1198, Council of Europe emblem (25th anniv).

275 Hands with Letters 276 Boy with Hoop

1974. Centenary of Universal Postal Union.
1199 **275** 60c. multicoloured . . . 55 45

1974. 50th Anniv of Child Welfare Issues. Early Photographs.
1200 **276** 30c.+15c. brown & blk 20 15
1201 – 35c.+20c. brown 55 55
1202 – 45c.+20c. black 55 25
1203 – 60c.+20c. black . . . . 1·25 1·40
MS1204 75 × 145 mm. Nos. 1200 × 4 and 1201/2 . . . . 4·75 4·50
DESIGNS: 35c. Child and baby; 45c. Two young girls; 60c. Girl sitting on balustrade.

277 Amsterdam 278 St. Hubertus Hunting Lodge, De Hoge Veluwe National Park

1975. Anniversaries. Multicoloured.
1205 30c. Type **277** 30 30
1206 30c. Synagogue and map . . 30 30
1207 35c. Type **277** 40 15
1208 45c. "Window" in human brain 35 45
ANNIVERSARIES: Nos. 1205, 1207, Amsterdam (700th anniv); 1206, Portuguese-Israelite Synagogue, Amsterdam (300th anniv); 1208, Leyden University and university education (400th anniv).

1975. Cultural, Health and Social Welfare Funds. National Monument Year. Preserved Monuments. Multicoloured.
1209 35c.+20c. Type **278** 55 55
1210 40c.+15c. Bergijnhof (Beguinage), Amsterdam (vert) 55 55
1211 50c.+20c. "Kuiperspoort" (Cooper's gate), Middelburg (vert) 70 55
1212 60c.+20c. Orvelte village, Drenthe 95 85

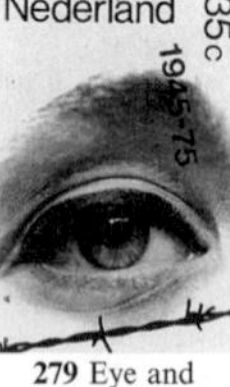

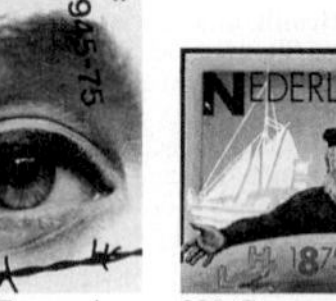

279 Eye and Barbed Wire 280 Company Emblem and "Stad Middelburg" (schooner)

1975. 30th Anniv of Liberation.
1213 **279** 35c. black and red . . . 35 10

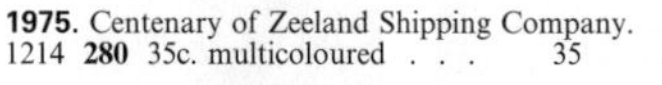

1975. Centenary of Zeeland Shipping Company.
1214 **280** 35c. multicoloured . . . 35 15

281 Dr. Albert Schweitzer crossing Lambarene River

1975. Birth Centenary of Dr. Schweitzer (medical missionary).
1215 **281** 50c. multicoloured . . . 40 10

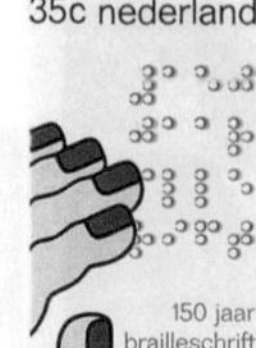

282 Man and Woman on "Playing-card" 283 Braille Reading

1975. International Events. Multicoloured.
1216 35c. Type **282** (Int Women's Year) 35 15
1217 50c. Metric scale (Metre Convention cent) (horiz) 40 10

1975. 150th Anniv of Invention of Braille.
1218 **283** 35c. multicoloured . . . 35 15

284 Dutch 25c. Coins 285 "Four Orphans" (C. Simons), Torenstraat Orphanage, Medemblik

1975. Savings Campaign.
1219 **284** 50c. grey, green and blue 40 10

1975. Child Welfare. Historic Ornamental Stones. Multicoloured.
1220 35c.+15c. Type **285** 20 15
1221 40c.+15c. "Milkmaid" Kooltuin Alkmaar . . . 50 50
1222 50c.+25c. "Four Sons of Aymon seated on Beyaert", Herengracht . . 40 20
1223 60c.+25c. "Life at the Orphanage", Molenstraat Orphanage, Gorinchem 1·00 75
MS1224 145 × 75 mm. Nos. 1220 × 3 and 1222 × 2 . . . . 3·25 3·00

286 18th-century Lottery Ticket 287 Numeral

1976. 250th Anniv of National Lottery.
1225 **286** 35c. multicoloured . . . 35 15

1976. (a) Ordinary gum.
1226 **287** 5c. grey 10 10
1227 10c. blue 10 10
1228 25c. violet 20 10
1229 40c. brown 40 10
1230 45c. blue 40 10
1231 50c. mauve 40 10
1232 55c. green 65 10
1233 60c. yellow 70 10
1234 65c. brown . . . . . . 1·00 10
1235 70c. violet 85 10
1236 80c. mauve . . . . . . 1·50 10

(b) Self-adhesive gum.
1237 **287** 5c. grey 10 10
1238 10c. blue 10 10
1239 25c. violet 15 10

288 West European Hedgehog

1976. Cultural, Health and Social Welfare Funds. Nature Protection (40, 75c.) and Anniversaries. Multicoloured.
1241 40c.+20c. Type **288** 60 45
1242 45c.+20c. Open book (vert) 60 45
1243 55c.+20c. People and organization initials . . . 65 30
1244 75c.+25c. Frog and spawn (vert) 85 80
ANNIVERSARIES: No. 1242, 175th anniv of Primary education and centenary of Agricultural education; 1243, 75th anniv of Social Security Bank and legislation.

289 Admiral Michiel de Ruyter (statue)

1976. 300th Death Anniv of Admiral Michiel de Ruyter.
1245 **289** 55c. multicoloured . . . 40 15

290 Guillaume Groen van Prinsterer

1976. Death Centenary of Guillaume Groen van Prinsterer (statesman).
1246 **290** 55c. multicoloured . . . 40 15

291 Detail of 18th-century Calendar

1976. Bicentenary of American Revolution.
1247 **291** 75c. multicoloured . . . 55 35

292 Long-distance Marchers 293 The Art of Printing

1976. Sport and Recreation Anniversaries. Mult.
1248 40c. Type **292** 30 25
1249 55c. Runners "photo-finish" 65 25
ANNIVERSARIES: 40c. 60th Nijmegen Long-distance March; 55c. Royal Dutch Athletics Society (75th anniv).

1976. Anniversaries.
1250 **293** 45c. red and blue 30 25
1251 – 55c.+25c. mult 50 45
DESIGNS AND EVENTS: 45c. Type **293** (75th anniv of Netherlands Printers' organization); 55c. Rheumatic patient "Within Care" (50th anniv of Dutch Anti-Rheumatism Association).

294 Dutch Tjalk and Reclaimed Land 295 Queen Wilhelmina 4$\frac{1}{2}$c. Stamp, 1919

1976. Zuider Zee Project—Reclamation and Urbanization. Multicoloured.
1252 **294** 40c. blue, olive and red 30 15
1253 – 75c. yellow, red and blue 55 45
DESIGN: 75c. Duck flying over reclaimed land.

1976. "Amphilex '77" International Stamp Exhibition, Amsterdam (1977) (1st series). Stamp Portraits of Queen Wilhelmina. Multicoloured.
1254 – 55c.+55c. blue, deep grey and grey 95 80
1255 **295** 55c.+55c. purple, deep grey and grey 95 80
1256 – 55c.+55c. brown, deep grey and grey 95 80
1257 – 75c.+75c. turquoise, deep grey and grey 95 80
1258 – 75c.+75c. blue, deep grey and grey 95 80
DESIGNS: No. 1254, 5c. stamp, 1891; 1256, 25c. stamp, 1924; 1257, 15c. stamp, 1940; 1258, 25c. stamp, 1947.
See also Nos. 1273/6.

296 "Football" (J. Raats)

1976. Child Welfare. Children's Paintings. Mult
1259 40c.+20c. Type **296** 30 25
1260 45c.+20c. "Boat" (L. Jacobs) 30 30
1261 55c.+20c. "Elephant" (M. Lugtenburg) 40 15
1262 75c.+25c. "Caravan" (A. Seeleman) 70 85
MS1263 145 × 75 mm. Nos. 1259/61 × 2 . . . . 2·25 2·00

297 Ballot-paper and Pencil

1977. National Events. Multicoloured.
1264 40c. "Energy" (vert) 30 10
1265 45c. Type **297** 40 15
EVENTS: 40c. "Be wise with energy" campaign; 45c. Elections to Lower House of States-General.
See also No. 1268.

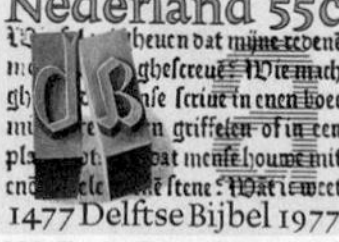

298 Spinoza 299 Early Type Faces and "a" on Bible Script

1977. 300th Death Anniv of Barach (Benedictus) de Spinoza (philosopher).

1266 **298** 75c. multicoloured . . . 55 35

1977. 500th Anniv of Printing of "Delft Bible".

1267 **299** 55c. multicoloured . . . 45 35

1977. Elections to Lower House of States-General. As T **297** but also inscribed "25 MEI '77".

1268 45c. multicoloured 40 20

300 Altar of Goddess Nehalennia **301** "Kaleidoscope"

1977. Cultural, Health and Social Welfare Funds. Roman Archaeological Discoveries.

1269 – 40c.+20c. mult 40 30

1270 **300** 45c.+20c. black, stone and green 50 30

1271 – 55c.+20c. black, blue and red 50 30

1272 – 75c.+25c. black, grey and yellow 65 50

DESIGNS: 40c. Baths, Heerlen; 55c. Remains of Zwammerdam ship; 75c. Parade helmet.

1977. "Amphilex 1977" International Stamp Exhibition, Amsterdam (2nd series). As T **295**.

1273 55c.+45c. grn, brn & grey 55 35

1274 55c.+45c. blue, brn & grey 55 45

1275 55c.+45c. blue, brn & grey 55 45

1276 55c.+45c. red, brn & grey 55 35

MS1277 100×72 mm. Nos. 1273 and 1276 . . . . 90 75

DESIGNS: No. 1273, Queen Wilhelmina 1g. stamp, 1898; 1274, Queen Wilhelmina 20c. stamp, 1923; 1275, Queen Wilhelmina 12½c. stamp, 1938; 1276, Queen Wilhelmina 10c. stamp, 1948.

1977. Bicentenary of Netherlands Society for Industry and Commerce.

1278 **301** 55c. multicoloured . . . 45 10

302 Man in Wheelchair and Maze of Steps **303** Risk of Drowning

1977. Anniversaries.

1279 **302** 40c. brown, green & blue 30 15

1280 – 45c. multicoloured . . . 30 20

1281 – 55c. multicoloured . . . 40 10

DESIGNS—HORIZ: 40c. Type **302** (50th anniv of A.V.O. Nederland); 45c. Diagram of water current (50th anniv of Delft Hydraulic Laboratory). VERT: 55c. Teeth (centenary of dentists' training in Netherlands).

1977. Child Welfare. Dangers to Children. Mult.

1282 40c.+20c. Type **303** 35 20

1283 45c.+20c. Medicine cabinet (poisons) 35 20

1284 55c.+20c. Balls in road (traffic) 35 20

1285 75c.+25c. Matches (fire) . . 65 65

MS1286 75×144 mm. Nos. 1282/4 ×2 . . . . 2·40 1·40

304 "Postcode" **305** Makkum Dish

1978. Introduction of Postcodes.

1287 **304** 40c. red and blue 30 10

1288 45c. red and blue 30 10

1978. Cultural, Health and Social Welfare Funds. Multicoloured.

1289 40c.+20c. Anna Maria van Schurman (writer) 40 30

1290 45c.+20c. Passage from letter by Belle de Zuylen (Mme. de Charriere) . . . 50 30

1291 55c.+20c. Delft dish 50 30

1292 75c.+25c. Type **305** 65 50

306 "Human Rights" Treaty **307** Chess

1978. European Series.

1293 **306** 45c. grey, black and blue 30 15

1294 – 55c. black, stone and orange 45 10

DESIGN: 55c. Haarlem Town Hall (Europa).

1978. Sports.

1295 **307** 40c. multicoloured . . . 30 15

1296 – 45c. red and blue 30 20

DESIGN: 45c. The word "Korfbal".

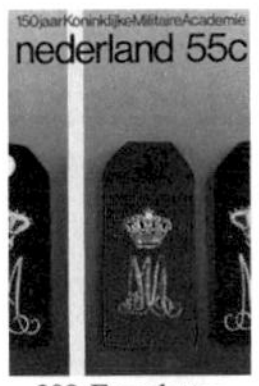

308 Kidney Donor **309** Epaulettes

1978. Health Care. Multicoloured.

1297 **308** 40c. black, blue and red 30 20

1298 – 45c. multicoloured . . . 30 20

1299 – 55c.+25c. red, grey and black 50 45

MS1300 144×50 mm. No. 1299 ×3 1·10 1·10

DESIGNS—VERT: 45c. Heart and torch. HORIZ: 55c. Red crosses on world map.

1978. 150th Anniv of Royal Military Academy, Breda.

1301 **309** 55c. multicoloured . . . 40 10

310 Verkade as Hamlet

1978. Birth Centenary of Eduard Rutger Verkade (actor and producer).

1302 **310** 45c. multicoloured . . . 30 20

311 Boy ringing Doorbell

1978. Child Welfare. Multicoloured.

1303 40c.+20c. Type **311** 40 20

1304 45c.+20c. Child reading . . 50 20

1305 55c.+20c. Boy writing (vert) 50 20

1306 75c.+25c. Girl and blackboard 65 65

MS1307 144×75 mm. Nos. 1303/5 ×2 . . . . 2·40 2·00

312 Clasped Hands and Arrows **313** Names of European Community Members

1979. 400th Anniv of Treaty of Utrecht.

1308 **312** 55c. blue 40 20

1979. First Direct Elections to European Assembly.

1309 **313** 45c. red, blue and black 30 15

314 Queen Juliana

1979. Queen Juliana's 70th Birthday.

1310 **314** 55c. multicoloured . . . 40 15

315 Fragment of "Psalmen Trilogie" (J. Andriessen) **316** Netherlands Stamps and Magnifying Glass

1979. Cultural, Health and Social Welfare Funds.

1311 **315** 40c.+20c. grey and red 40 30

1312 – 45c.+20c. grey and red 50 30

1313 – 55c.+20c. mult 50 25

1314 – 75c.+25c. mult 65 45

DESIGNS AND EVENTS: 150th anniv of Musical Society; 45c. Choir. Restoration of St. John's Church, Gouda (stained glass windows); 55c. Mary (detail, "Birth of Christ"); 75c. William of Orange (detail, "Relief of Leyden").

1979. Europa and 75th Anniv of Scheveningen Radio. Multicoloured.

1315 55c. Type **316** 40 15

1316 75c. Liner and Morse Key 55 40

317 Map of Chambers of Commerce **318** Action Shot of Football Match

1979. 175th Anniv of First Dutch Chamber of Commerce, Maastricht.

1317 **317** 45c. multicoloured . . . 30 20

1979. Anniversaries. Multicoloured.

1318 45c. Type **318** (centenary of organized football) . . . 30 20

1319 55c. Women's suffrage meeting (60th anniv of Women's suffrage) (vert) 40 15

319 Porch of Old Amsterdam Theatre

1979. 300th Death Annivs of Joost van den Vondel (poet) and Jan Steen (painter). Multicoloured.

1320 40c. Type **319** 30 20

1321 45c. "Gay Company" (detail) (Jan Steen) . . . 30 20

320 Hindustani Girl on Father's Shoulder (The Right to Love)

1979. Child Welfare. International Year of the Child

1322 **320** 40c.+20c. grey, red and yellow 40 20

1323 – 45c.+20c. grey, red and black 50 20

1324 – 55c.+20c. grey, black and yellow 50 20

1325 – 75c.+25c. black, blue and red 65 65

MS1326 144×75 mm. Nos. 1322/4, each ×2 . . . . 2·40 2·00

DESIGNS—HORIZ: 45c. Chilean child from refugee camp (The Right to Medical Care). VERT: 55c. Senegalese boy from Sahel area (The Right to Food); 75c. Class from Albert Cuyp School, Amsterdam (The Right to Education).

321 A. F. de Savornin Lohman **322** Dunes

1980. Dutch Politicians. Multicoloured.

1327 45c. Type **321** (Christian Historical Union) 30 20

1328 50c. P. J. Troelstra (Socialist Party) 30 20

1329 60c. P. J. Oud (Liberal Party) 50 20

1980. Cultural, Health and Social Welfare Funds. Multicoloured.

1330 45c.+20c. Type **322** 50 30

1331 50c.+20c. Country estate (vert) 50 30

1332 60c.+25c. Lake District . . 55 30

1333 80c.+35c. Moorland 70 50

323 Avro Type 683 Lancaster dropping Food Parcels **324** Queen Beatrix and New Church, Amsterdam

1980. 35th Anniv of Liberation. Multicoloured.

1334 45c. Type **323** 40 20

1335 60c. Anne Frank (horiz) . . 50 10

1980. Installation of Queen Beatrix.

1336 **324** 60c. blue, red and yellow 1·00 30

1337 65c. blue, red and yellow 1·40 10

325 Young Stamp Collectors **326** "Flight"

1980. "Jupostex 1980" Stamp Exhibition, Eindhoven, and Dutch Society of Stamp Dealers Show, The Hague.

1338 **325** 50c. multicoloured . . . 40 30

1980. Air. (Special Flights).

1339 **326** 1g. blue and black . . . 80 65

327 Bridge Players and Cards **328** Road Haulage

1980. Sports Events. Multicoloured.

1340 50c. Type **327** (Bridge Olympiad, Valkenburg) 40 20

1341 60c.+25c. Sportswoman in wheelchair (Olympics for the Disabled, Arnhem and Veenendaal) 55 40

1980. Transport.

1342 **328** 50c. multicoloured . . . 40 15

1343 – 60c. blue, brown & black 50 15

1344 – 80c. multicoloured . . . 65 30

DESIGNS: 60c. Rail transport; 80c. Motorized canal barge.

329 Queen Wilhelmina

1980. Europa.

1345 **329** 60c. black, red and blue 50 10

1346 – 80c. black, red and blue 65 30

DESIGN: 80c. Sir Winston Churchill.

330 Abraham Kuyper (first rector) and University Seal

1980. Centenary of Amsterdam Free University.

1347 **330** 50c. multicoloured . . . 40 15

331 "Pop-up" Book **332** Saltmarsh

1980. Child Welfare. Multicoloured.
1348 45c.+20c. Type **331** 40 20
1349 50c.+20c. Child flying on a book (vert) 50 40
1350 60c.+30c. Boy reading "Kikkerkoning" (vert) . . 55 10
1351 80c.+30c. Dreaming in a book 65 65
MS1352 144 × 75 mm. Nos. 1348 × 2 and 1350 × 3 . . . . 2·40 1·00

1981. Cultural, Health and Social Welfare Funds. Multicoloured.
1353 45c.+20c. Type **332** 40 30
1354 55c.+25c. Dyke 50 30
1355 60c.+25c. Drain 55 30
1356 65c.+30c. Cultivated land 65 30

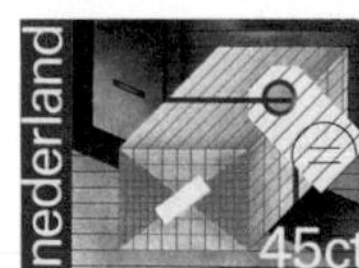

333 Parcel (Parcel Post)

1981. P.T.T. Centenaries. Multicoloured.
1357 45c. Type **333** 40 15
1358 55c. Telephone, dish aerial and telephone directory page (public telephone service) 45 15
1359 65c. Savings bank books, deposit transfer card and savings bank stamps (National Savings Bank) 50 10
MS1360 145 × 75 mm. Nos. 1357/9 1·25 90

334 Huis ten Bosch Royal Palace, The Hague

1981.
1361 **334** 55c. multicoloured . . . 45 15

335 Carillon

1981. Europa. Multicoloured.
1362 45c. Type **335** 40 20
1363 65c. Barrel organ 50 15

336 Council of State Emblem and Maps of 1531 and 1981

1981. 450th Anniv of Council of State.
1364 **336** 65c. orange, deep orange and red 50 10

337 Marshalling Yard, Excavator and Ship's Screw

1981. Industrial and Agricultural Exports. Mult.
1365 45c. Type **337** 40 15
1366 55c. Inner port, cast-iron component and weighing machine 45 20
1367 60c. Airport, tomato and lettuce 50 40
1368 65c. Motorway interchange, egg and cheese 50 10

338 "Integration in Society"

1981. Child Welfare. Integration of Handicapped Children. Multicoloured.
1369 45c.+25c. Type **338** 40 10
1370 55c.+20c. "Integration in the Family" (vert) 50 50
1371 60c.+25c. Child vaccinated against polio (Upper Volta project) (vert) . . . 55 50
1372 65c.+30c. "Integration among Friends" 65 10
MS1373 144 × 76 mm. Nos. 1369 × 3 and 1372 × 2 . . . . 2·40 1·75

339 Queen Beatrix **340** Agnieten Chapel and Banners

1981.
1374 **339** 65c. brown and black . . 55 10
1375 70c. lilac and black . . . 70 10
1376 75c. pink and black . . 70 10
1377 90c. green and black . . 1·10 10
1378 1g. lilac and black . . . 70 15
1379 1g.20 bistre and black 1·25 20
1380 1g.40 green and black . . 1·75 20
1381 1g.50 lilac and black . . 1·10 20
1382 2g. bistre and black . . 1·40 15
1383 2g.50 orange and black 1·75 30
1384 3g. blue and black . . . 2·10 20
1385 4g. green and black . . . 3·00 20
1386 5g. blue and black . . . 3·75 20
1387 6g.50 lilac and black . . 5·75 20
1388 7g. blue and black . . . 4·75 30
1389 7g.50 green and black . . 5·75 50
For this design but on uncoloured background see Nos. 1594/1605.

1982. 350th Anniv of University of Amsterdam.
1395 **340** 65c. multicoloured . . . 50 10

341 Skater **342** Apple Blossom

1982. Centenary of Royal Dutch Skating Association.
1396 **341** 45c. multicoloured . . . 40 20

1982. Cultural, Health and Social Welfare Funds. Multicoloured.
1397 50c.+20c. Type **342** 50 30
1398 60c.+25c. Anemones 55 30
1399 65c.+25c. Roses 55 30
1400 70c.+30c. African violets . . 65 55

343 Stripes in National Colours

1982. Bicentenary of Netherlands–United States Diplomatic Relations.
1401 **343** 50c. red, blue and black 40 20
1402 65c. red, blue and black 55 15

344 Sandwich Tern and Eider **345** Zebra Crossing

1982. Waddenzee. Multicoloured.
1403 50c. Type **344** 40 20
1404 70c. Barnacle Geese 55 10

1982. 50th Anniv of Dutch Road Safety Organization.
1405 **345** 60c. multicoloured . . . 50 30

NEDERLAND 60c

346 Ground Plan of Enkhuizen Fortifications **347** Aerial view of Palace and Liberation Monument

1982. Europa. Multicoloured.
1406 50c. Type **346** 40 20
1407 70c. Part of ground plan of Coevorden fortifications 55 10

1982. Royal Palace, Dam Square, Amsterdam. Mult.
1408 50c. Facade, ground plan and cross-section of palace 40 10
1409 60c. Type **347** 50 10

348 Great Tits and Child **349** Touring Club Activities

1982. Child Welfare. Child and Animal. Mult.
1410 50c.+30c. Type **348** 40 15
1411 60c.+20c. Child arm-in-arm with cat 50 15
1412 65c.+20c. Child with drawing of rabbit 65 45
1413 70c.+30c. Child with palm cockatoo 70 70
MS1414 75 × 144 mm. Nos. 1410 × 4 and 1411 . . . . 2·50 2·10

1983. Centenary of Royal Dutch Touring Club.
1415 **349** 70c. multicoloured . . . 60 10

350 Johan van Oldenbarnevelt (statesman) (after J. Houbraken) **351** Newspaper

1983. Cultural, Health and Social Welfare Funds.
1416 **350** 50c.+20c. pink, blue and black 50 40
1417 – 60c.+25c. mult 65 40
1418 – 65c.+25c. mult 70 55
1419 – 70c.+30c. grey, black and gold 70 55
DESIGNS: 60c. Willem Jansz Blaeu (cartographer) (after Thomas de Keijser); 65c. Hugo de Groot (statesman) (after J. van Ravesteyn); 70c. "Saskia van Uylenburch" (portrait of his wife by Rembrandt).

1983. Europa. Multicoloured.
1420 50c. Type **351** (75th anniv of Netherlands Newspaper Publishers Association) 40 20
1421 70c. European Communications Satellite and European Telecommunication Satellites Organization members' flags 55 10

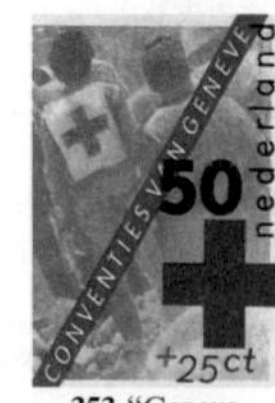

352 "Composition 1922" (P. Mondriaan) **353** "Geneva Conventions"

1983. De Stijl Art Movement. Multicoloured.
1422 50c. Type **352** 40 15
1423 65c. Contra construction from "Maison Particuliere" (C. van Eesteren and T. van Doesburg) 50 30

1983. Red Cross.
1424 **353** 50c.+25c. mult 50 45
1425 – 60c.+20c. mult 55 45
1426 – 65c.+25c. mult 65 45
1427 – 70c.+30c. grey, black and red 70 65
DESIGNS: 60c. Red Cross and text "charity, independence, impartiality"; 65c. "Socio-medical work"; 70c. Red Cross and text "For Peace".

354 Luther's Signature **355** Child looking at Donkey and Ox through Window

1983. 500th Birth Anniv of Martin Luther (Protestant Reformer).
1428 **354** 70c. multicoloured . . . 55 10

1983. Child Welfare. Child and Christmas. Mult.
1429 50c.+10c. Type **355** 50 45
1430 50c.+25c. Child riding flying snowman 55 15
1431 60c.+30c. Child in bed and star 65 70
1432 70c.+30c. Children dressed as the three kings 70 15
MS1433 144 × 75 mm. Nos. 1430 × 4 and 1432 × 2 . . . . 3·00 3·00

356 Parliament

1984. Second Elections to European Parliament.
1434 **356** 70c. multicoloured . . . 50 10

357 Northern Lapwings **358** St. Servaas

1984. Cultural, Health and Social Welfare Funds. Pasture Birds. Multicoloured.
1435 50c.+20c. Type **357** 50 40
1436 60c.+25c. Ruffs 55 40
1437 65c.+25c. Redshanks (vert) 65 55
1438 70c.+30c. Black-tailed godwits (vert) 70 55

1984. 1600th Death Anniv of St. Servaas (Bishop of Tongeren and Maastricht).
1439 **358** 60c. multicoloured . . . 50 15

359 Bridge

1984. Europa. 25th Anniv of European Post and Telecommunications Conference.
1440 **359** 50c. deep blue and blue 40 15
1441 70c. green and light green 55 10

360 Eye and Magnifying Glass

1984. Centenary of Organized Philately in the Netherlands and "Filacento" International Stamp Exhibition, The Hague. Multicoloured.
1442 50c.+20c. Type **360** 55 45
1443 60c.+25c. 1909 cover . . . 65 55
1444 70c.+30c. Stamp club meeting, 1949 . . . . . . 65 65
MS1445 144 × 50 mm. Nos. 1442/4 2·50 2·00

361 William of Orange (after Adriaen Thomaszoon Key)

1984. 400th Death Anniv of William of Orange.
1446 **361** 70c. multicoloured . . . 55 15

362 Giant Pandas and Globe

363 Graph and Leaf

1984. World Wildlife Fund.
1447 **362** 70c. multicoloured . . . 70 15

1984. 11th International Small Business Congress, Amsterdam.
1448 **363** 60c. multicoloured . . . 50 20

364 Violin Lesson

365 Sunny, First Dutch Guide-Dog

1984. Child Welfare. Strip Cartoons. Mult.
1449 50c.+25c. Type **364** 40 30
1450 60c.+20c. At the dentist . . 70 55
1451 65c.+20c. The plumber . . . 85 75
1452 70c.+30c. The king and money chest 65 30
MS1453 75 × 144 mm. Nos. 1449 × 4 and 1452 × 2 . . . . 3·50 3·50

1985. 50th Anniv of Royal Dutch Guide-Dog Fund.
1454 **365** 60c. black, ochre and red 50 20

366 Plates and Cutlery on Place-mat

367 Saint Martin's Church, Zaltbommel

1985. Tourism. Multicoloured.
1455 50c. Type **366** (centenary of Travel and Holidays Association) 40 20
1456 70c. Kroller-Muller museum emblem, antlers and landscape (50th anniv of De Hoge Veluwe National Park) 55 10

1985. Cultural, Health and Social Welfare Funds. Religious Buildings. Multicoloured.
1457 50c.+20c. Type **367** 55 45
1458 60c.+25c. Winterswijk synagogue and Holy Ark (horiz) 65 55
1459 65c.+25c. Bolsward Baptist church 70 55
1460 70c.+30c. Saint John's Cathedral, 's-Hertogen-bosch (horiz) 70 40

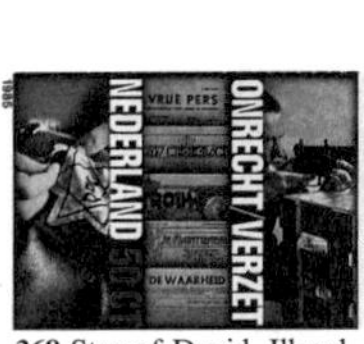

368 Star of David, Illegal Newspapers and Rifle Practice (Resistance Movement)

369 Piano Keyboard

1985. 40th Anniv of Liberation.
1461 **368** 50c. black, stone and red 45 20
1462 – 60c. black, stone and blue 50 15
1463 – 65c. black, stone & orge 55 45
1464 – 70c. black, stone & green 55 20
DESIGNS: 60c. Bombers over houses, "De Vliegende Hollander" (newspaper) and soldier (Allied Forces); 65c. Soldiers and civilians, "Parool" (newspaper) and American war cemetery, Margraten (Liberation); 70c. Women prisoners, prison money and Burma Railway (Dutch East Indies).

1985. Europa. Music Year. Multicoloured.
1465 50c. Type **369** 40 20
1466 70c. Organ 55 10

370 National Museum, Amsterdam (centenary)

1985. Anniversaries and Events. Multicoloured.
1467 50c. Type **370** 40 20
1468a 60c. Teacher with students (bicentenary of Amsterdam Nautical College) 50 25
1469 70c. Ship's mast and rigging ("Sail '85", Amsterdam) 55 10

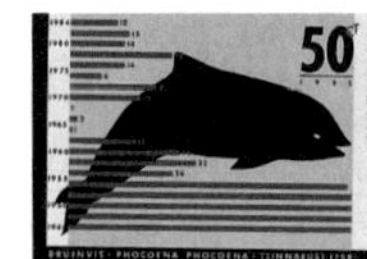

371 Porpoise and Graph

1985. Endangered Animals.
1470 **371** 50c. black, blue and red 40 20
1471 – 70c. black, blue and red 55 15
DESIGN: 70c. Seal and PCB molecule structure.

372 Ignition Key and Framed Photograph ("Think of Me")

1985. Child Welfare. Road Safety. Multicoloured.
1472 50c.+25c. Type **372** 55 20
1473 60c.+20c. Child holding target showing speeds . . 55 65
1474 65c.+20c. Girl holding red warning triangle 65 75
1475 70c.+30c. Boy holding "Children Crossing" sign 90 20
MS1476 132 × 80 mm. Nos. 1472 × 4 and 1475 × 2 . . . . 3·50 3·50

373 Penal Code Extract

1986. Centenary of Penal Code.
1477 **373** 50c. black, yellow & purple 40 15

374 Surveyor with Pole and N.A.P. Water Gauge

1986. 300th Anniv of Height Gauging Marks at Amsterdam.
1478 **374** 60c. multicoloured . . . 45 15

375 Windmill, Graph and Cloudy Sky

1986. Inaug of Windmill Test Station, Sexbierum.
1479 **375** 70c. multicoloured . . . 55 10

376 Scales

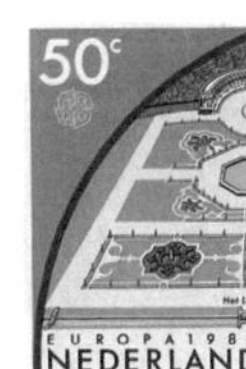

377 Het Loo Palace Garden, Apeldoorn

1986. Cultural, Health and Social Welfare Funds. Antique Measuring Instruments. Multicoloured.
1480 50c.+20c. Type **376** 55 35
1481 60c.+25c. Clock (vert) . . . 55 35
1482 65c.+25c. Barometer (vert) 65 65
1483 70c.+30c. Jacob's staff . . . 70 85

1986. Europa. Multicoloured.
1484 50c. Type **377** 40 20
1485 70c. Tree with discoloured crown 50 10

378 Cathedral

379 Drees at Binnenhof, 1947

1986. Utrecht Events.
1486 **378** 50c. multicoloured . . . 50 30
1487 – 60c. blue, pink and black 55 30
1488 – 70c. multicoloured . . . 70 20
DESIGNS—VERT: 50c. Type **378** (completion of interior restoration); 60c. German House (75th anniv of Heemschut Conservation Society). HORIZ: 70c. Extract from foundation document (350th anniv of Utrecht University).

1986. Birth Centenary of Dr. Willem Drees (politician).
1489 **379** 55c. multicoloured . . . 55 20

380 Draughts as Biscuits in Saucer

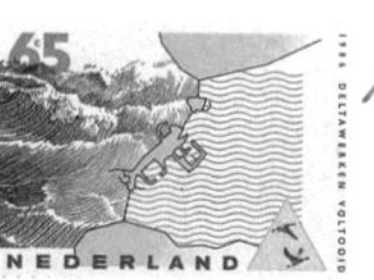

381 Map of Flood Barrier

1986. 75th Anniversary of Royal Dutch Draughts Association (1490) and Royal Dutch Billiards Association (1491). Multicoloured.
1490 75c. Type **380** 65 65
1491 75c. Player in ball preparing to play 20 20

1986. Delta Project Completion. Multicoloured.
1492 65c. Type **381** 55 30
1493 75c. Flood barrier 65 20

382 Children listening to Music (experiencing)

383 Engagement Picture

1986. Child Welfare. Child and Culture.
1494 55c.+25c. Type **382** 70 65
1495 65c.+35c. Boy drawing (achieving) 75 45
1496 75c.+35c. Children at theatre (understanding) 85 20
MS1497 150 × 72 mm. Nos. 1494, 1495 × 2 and 1496 × 2 . . . . 3·50 3·00

1987. Golden Wedding of Princess Juliana and Prince Bernhard.
1498 **383** 75c. orange, black and gold 70 20

384 Block of Flats and Hut

1987. International Year of Shelter for the Homeless (65c.) and Centenary of Netherlands Salvation Army (75c.). Multicoloured.
1499 65c. Type **384** 55 30
1500 75c. Army officer, meeting and tramp 65 20

385 Eduard Douwes Dekker (Multatuli) and De Harmonie Club

1987. Writers' Death Annivs. Multicoloured.
1501 55c. Type **385** (centenary) 50 30
1502 75c. Constantijn Huygens and Scheveningseweg, The Hague (300th anniv) . . . 1·00 20

386 Steam Pumping Station, Nijerk

1987. Cultural Health and Social Welfare Funds. Industrial Buildings.
1503 **386** 55c.+30c. red, grey and black 90 80
1504 – 65c.+35c. grey, black and blue . . . . . . 1·00 80
1505 – 75c.+35c. grey, yellow and black . . . . . . 1·10 65
DESIGNS: 65c. Water tower, Deventer; 75c. Brass foundry, Joure.

387 Dance Theatre, Scheveningen (Rem Koolhaas)

1987. Europa. Architecture. Multicoloured.
1506 55c. Type **387** 50 30
1507 75c. Montessori School, Amsterdam (Herman Hertzberger) 65 20

388 Auction at Broek op Langedijk

1987. Centenary of Auction Sales (55, 75c.) and 150th Anniv of Groningen Agricultural Society (65c.). Multicoloured.
1508 55c. Type **388** 50 30
1509 65c. Groningen landscape and founders' signatures 70 30
1510 75c. Auction sale and clock 70 20

389 Telephone Care Circles

390 Map of Holland

1987. Dutch Red Cross. Multicoloured.
1511 55c.+30c. Type **389** 70 70
1512 65c.+35c. Red cross and hands (Welfare work) . . 80 60
1513 75c.+35c. Red cross and drip (Blood transfusion) 90 50

1987. 75th Anniv of Netherlands Municipalities Union.
1514 **390** 75c. multicoloured . . . 65 20

391 Noordeinde Palace, The Hague

392 Woodcutter

1987.
1515 **391** 65c. multicoloured . . . 55 10

1987. Child Welfare. Child and Profession. Mult.
1516 55c.+25c. Type **392** 65 70
1517 65c.+35c. Woman sailor . . 80 50
1518 75c.+35c. Woman pilot . . 90 30
MS1519 150 × 72 mm. Nos. 1516, 1517 × 2 and 1518 × 2 . . . . 3·50 3·25

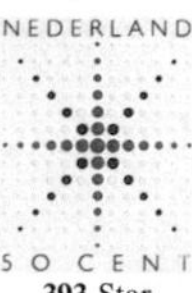

393 Star

394 "Narcissus cyclamineus" "Peeping Tom" and Extract from "I Call You Flowers" (Jan Hanlo)

1987. Christmas.

1520 **393** 50c. red, blue and green . . . 65 25
1521 50c. yellow, red and blue . . . 65 25
1522 50c. red, blue and yellow . . . 65 20
1523 50c. yellow, red and green 65 20
1524 50c. blue, green and red . . . 65 20

The first colour described is that of the St. George's Cross.

1988. "Filacept" European Stamp Exhibition, The Hague (1st issue). Flowers. Multicoloured.

1525 55c.+55c. Type **394** 90 85
1526 75c.+70c. "Rosa gallica" "Versicolor" and "Roses" (Daan van Golden) . . . 1·10 1·10
1527 75c.+70c. Sea holly and 1270 map of The Hague . . . 1·10 1·10

See also No. **MS**1542.

395 Quagga

1988. Cultural, Health and Social Welfare Funds. 150th Anniv of Natura Artis Magistra Zoological Society. Multicoloured.

1528 55c.+30c. Type **395** 65 70
1529 65c.+35c. American manatee . . 85 85
1530 75c.+35c. Orang-utan (vert) . . 90 50

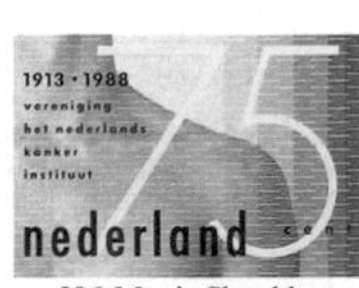

396 Man's Shoulder

397 Traffic Scene with Lead Symbol crossed Through

1988. 75th Anniv of Netherlands Cancer Institute.

1531 **396** 75c. multicoloured . . . 60 20

1988. Europa. Transport. Multicoloured.

1532 55c. Type **397** (lead-free petrol) 50 20
1533 75c. Cyclists reflected in car wing mirror (horiz) . . . 85 20

398 Pendulum, Prism and Saturn

1988. 300th Anniv of England's Glorious Revolution. Multicoloured.

1534 65c. Type **398** 55 20
1535 75c. Queen Mary, King William III and 17th-century warship . . 70 20

399 "Cobra Cat" (Appel)

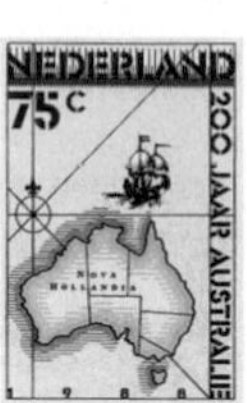

400 Sailing Ship and Map of Australia

1988. 40th Anniv of Founding of Cobra Painters Group. Multicoloured.

1536 55c. Type **399** 65 65
1537 65c. "Kite" (Corneille) . . . 65 65
1538 75c. "Stumbling Horse" (Constant) 70 35

1988. Bicentenary of Australian Settlement.

1539 **400** 75c. multicoloured . . . 70 20

401 Statue of Erasmus, Rotterdam

402 "Rain"

1988. 75th Anniv of Erasmus University, Rotterdam (1540) and Centenary of Concertgebouw Concert Hall and Orchestra (1541).

1540 **401** 75c. deep green and green 65 20
1541 – 75c. violet 65 20

DESIGN: No. 1541, Violin and Concertgebouw concert hall.

1988. "Filacept" European Stamp Exhibition, The Hague (2nd issue). Flowers. Sheet 144 × 62 mm.

MS1542 Nos. 1525/7 . . . . . . 3·50 3·25

1988. Child Welfare. Centenary of Royal Netherlands Swimming Federation. Children's drawings. Multicoloured.

1543 55c.+25c. Type **402** 65 55
1544 65c.+35c. "Getting Ready for the Race" 85 50
1545 75c.+35c. "Swimming Test" . . 85 35
MS1546 150 × 72 mm. Nos. 1543, 1544 × 2 and 1545 × 2 . . . . 3·50 3·50

403 Stars

1988. Christmas.

1547 **403** 50c. multicoloured . . . 55 10

404 Postal and Telecommunications Services

1989. Privatization of Netherlands PTT.

1548 **404** 75c. multicoloured . . . 70 20

405 "Solidarity"

406 Members' Flags

1989. Trade Unions. Multicoloured.

1549 55c. Type **405** 50 20
1550 75c. Talking mouths on hands 65 20

1989. 40th Anniv of N.A.T.O.

1551 **406** 75c. multicoloured . . . 65 20

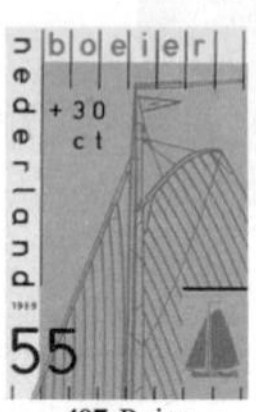

407 Boier

408 Boy with Homemade Telephone

1989. Cultural, Health and Social Welfare Funds. Old Sailing Vessels.

1552 **407** 55c.+30c. green & blk . . 70 75
1553 – 65c.+35c. blue & black . . 85 75
1554 – 75c.+35c. brown & blk . . 1·00 75

DESIGNS: 65c. Fishing smack; 75c. Clipper.

1989. Europa. Children's Games. Multicoloured.

1555 55c. Type **408** 50 20
1556 75c. Girl with homemade telephone 75 20

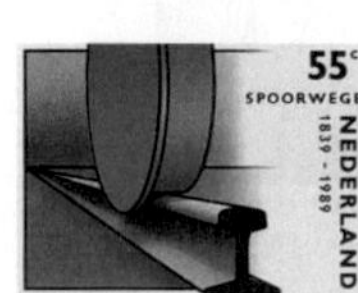

409 Wheel on Rail

410 Boy with Ball and Diagram of Goal Scored in European Championship

1989. 150th Anniv of Netherlands' Railways. Mult.

1557 55c. Type **409** 50 30
1558 65c. Steam, electric and diesel locomotives 50 30
1559 75c. Diesel train, station clock and "The Kiss" (sculpture by Rodin) . . . 55 20

1989. Centenary of Royal Dutch Football Assn.

1560 **410** 75c. multicoloured . . . 55 20

411 Map

412 Right to Housing

1989. 150th Anniv of Division of Limburg between Netherlands and Belgium.

1561 **411** 75c. multicoloured . . . 55 20

1989. Child Welfare. 30th Anniv of Declaration of Rights of the Child. Multicoloured.

1562 55c.+25c. Type **412** 65 65
1563 65c.+35c. Right to food . . 70 55
1564 75c.+35c. Right to education . 85 30
MS1565 150 × 72 mm. Nos. 1562, 1563 × 2 and 1564 × 2 . . . . 3·50 3·50

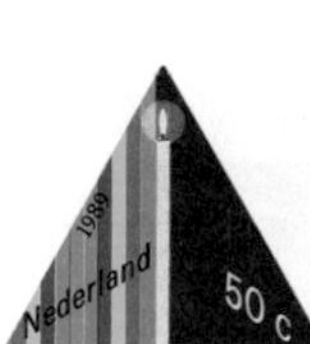

413 Candle

414 "Arms of Leiden" (tulip) and Plan of Gardens in 1601

1989. Christmas.

1566 **413** 50c. multicoloured . . . 55 10

1990. 400th Anniv of Hortus Botanicus (botanical gardens), Leiden.

1567 **414** 65c. multicoloured . . . 50 30

415 Pointer on Graduated Scale

416 "Self-portrait" (detail)

1990. Centenary of Labour Inspectorate.

1568 **415** 75c. multicoloured . . . 65 20

1990. Death Centenary of Vincent van Gogh (painter). Multicoloured.

1569 55c. Type **416** 60 20
1570 75c. "Green Vineyard" (detail) 70 20

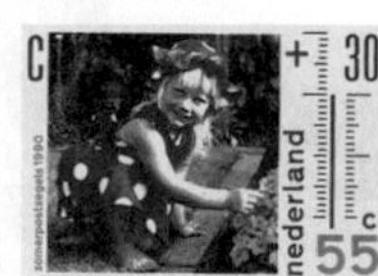

417 Summer's Day

1990. Cultural, Health and Social Welfare Funds. The Weather. Multicoloured.

1571 55c.+30c. Type **417** 70 65
1572 65c.+35c. Clouds and isobars (vert) 90 75
1573 75c.+35c. Satellite weather picture (vert) . . . . . . 1·00 70

418 Zuiderkerk Ruins

1990. 50th Anniv of German Bombing of Rotterdam.

1574 **418** 55c. deep brown, brown and black 50 30
1575 – 65c. multicoloured . . . 60 20
1576 – 75c. multicoloured . . . 65 20

DESIGNS: 65c. City plan as stage; 75c. Girder and plans for future construction.

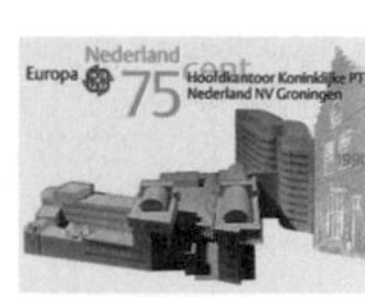
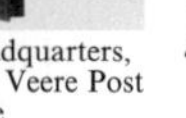

419 Postal Headquarters, Groningen, and Veere Post Office

420 Construction of Indiaman and Wreck of "Amsterdam"

1990. Europa. Post Office Buildings.

1577 – 55c. grey, mauve & brn . . 50 30
1578 **419** 75c. blue, green and grey . 65 20

DESIGN: 55c. As Type **419** but inscr "Postkantoor Veere".

1990. 3rd Anniv of Dutch East India Company Ships Association (replica ship project) (1579) and "Sail 90", Amsterdam (1580). Multicoloured.

1579 65c. Type **420** 60 35
1580 75c. Crew manning yards on sailing ship 65 20

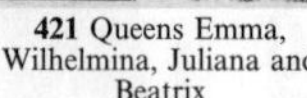

421 Queens Emma, Wilhelmina, Juliana and Beatrix

422 Flames, Telephone Handset and Number

1990. Netherlands Queens of the House of Orange.

1581 **421** 150c. multicoloured . . . 1·40 65

1990. Introduction of National Emergency Number.

1582 **422** 65c. multicoloured . . . 60 30

423 Girl riding Horse

424 Falling Snow

1990. Child Welfare. Hobbies. Multicoloured.

1583 55c.+25c. Type **423** 65 60
1584 65c.+35c. Girl at computer . . 85 50
1585 75c.+35c. Young philatelist . . 90 40
MS1586 150 × 71 mm. Nos. 1583, 1584 × 2 and 1585 × 2 . . . . 4·25 3·50

1990. Christmas.

1587 **424** 50c. multicoloured . . . 45 10

425 Industrial Chimneys, Exhaust Pipes and Aerosol Can (Air Pollution)

1991. Environmental Protection. Multicoloured.

1588 55c. Type **425** 60 30
1589 65c. Outfall pipes and chemicals (sea pollution) . . 65 30
1590 75c. Agricultural chemicals, leaking drums and household landfill waste (soil pollution) 70 20

426 German Raid on Amsterdam Jewish Quarter and Open Hand

1991. 50th Anniv of Amsterdam General Strike.
1591 **426** 75c. multicoloured . . . 65 20

427 Princess Beatrix and Prince Claus on Wedding Day

428 Queen Beatrix

1991. Royal Silver Wedding Anniversary. Mult.
1592 75c. Type **427** 70 20
1593 75c. Queen Beatrix and Prince Claus on horseback 70 20

1991. (a) Ordinary gum.
1594 **428** 75c. deep green & green 1·40 30
1595 80c. brown & lt brown 50 10
1597 90c. blue 65 20
1598 1g. violet 70 20
1599 1g.10 blue 85 20
1600 1g.30 blue and violet 90 20
1601 1g.40 green and olive 90 15
1601a 1g.50 green . . . . . . 5·50 1·60
1602 1g.60 purple and mauve 1·00 20
1603 2g. brown . . . . . . 1·10 20
1603a 2g.50 purple . . . . . 2·50 85
1604 3g. blue . . . . 2·00 20
1605 5g. red . . . . 1·75 20
1706 7g.50 violet . . . . . . 5·25 1·40
1708 10g. green . . . . . . 6·75 65

(b) Self-adhesive gum.
1606 **428** 1g. violet . . . . 1·00 80
1607 1g.10 blue . . . . . . 1·10 90
1608 1g.45 green . . . . . . 1·25 1·10
1609 2g.50 purple . . . . . 2·50 2·10
1609a 5g. red . . . . 5·25 4·50

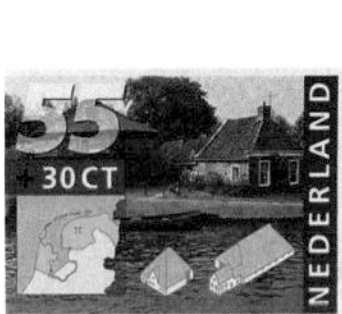
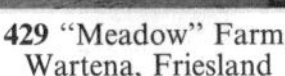
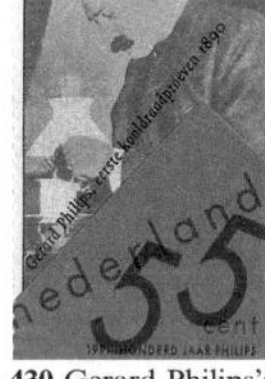

429 "Meadow" Farm, Wartena, Friesland

430 Gerard Philips's Experiments with Carbon Filaments

1991. Cultural, Health and Social Welfare Funds. Traditional Farmhouses. Multicoloured.
1610 55c.+30c. Type **429** 85 80
1611 65c.+35c. "T-house" farm, Kesteren, Gelderland . . 90 80
1612 75c.+35c. "Courtyard" farm, Nuth, Limburg . . 1·00 80

1991. 75th Anniv of Netherlands Standards Institute (65c.) and Centenary of Philips Organization (others). Multicoloured.
1615 55c. Type **430** 60 35
1616 65c. Wiring to Standard NEN 1010 (horiz) 65 20
1617 75c. Laser beams reading video disc 70 20

431 Man raising Hat to Space

432 Sticking Plaster over Medal

1991. Europa. Europe in Space. Multicoloured.
1618 55c. Type **431** 55 40
1619 75c. Ladders stretching into space 70 20

1991. 75th Anniv of Nijmegen International Four Day Marches.
1620 **432** 80c. multicoloured . . . 65 20

433 Jacobus Hendericus van't Hoff

1991. Dutch Nobel Prize Winners (1st series). Multicoloured.
1621 60c. Type **433** (chemistry, 1901) 60 35
1622 70c. Pieter Zeeman (physics, 1902) 65 30
1623 80c. Tobias Michael Carel Asser (peace, 1911) . . . 70 20
See also Nos. 1690/2 and 1773/5.

434 Children and Open Book

1991. Centenary (1992) of Public Libraries in the Netherlands.
1624 **434** 70c. drab, black & mauve 65 25
1625 – 80c. multicoloured . . . 70 20
DESIGN: 80c. Books on shelf.

435 Girls with Doll and Robot

436 "Greetings Cards keep People in Touch"

1991. Child Welfare. Outdoor Play. Multicoloured.
1626 60c.+30c. Type **435** 70 40
1627 70c.+35c. Bicycle race . . . 1·00 90
1628 80c.+40c. Hide and seek . . 90 40
MS1629 144 × 75 mm. Nos. 1626 × 4 and 1638 × 2 . . . . 5·00 4·50

1991. Christmas.
1630 **436** 55c. multicoloured . . . 45 10

437 Artificial Lightning, Microchip and Oscilloscope

1992. 150th Anniv of Delft University of Technology.
1631 **437** 60c. multicoloured . . . 55 30

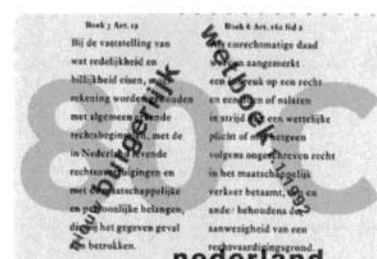

438 Extract from Code

1992. Implementation of Property Provisions of New Civil Code.
1632 **438** 80c. multicoloured . . . 70 20

439 Volleyball

1992. Winter Olympic Games, Albertville and Summer Games, Barcelona. Sheet 125 × 72 mm containing T **439** and similar vert designs. Multicoloured.
MS1633 80c. Type **439**; 80c. Putting the shot and rowing; 80c. Speed skating and rowing; 80c. Hockey 3·25 2·75

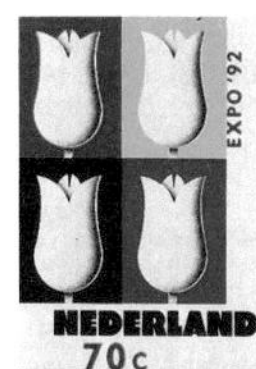

440 Tulips ("Mondrian does not like Green")

1992. "Expo '92" World's Fair, Seville. Mult.
1634 70c. Type **440** 65 30
1635 80c. "Netherland Expo '92" 70 20

441 Tasman's Map of Staete Landt (New Zealand)

1992. 350th Anniv of Discovery of Tasmania and New Zealand by Abel Tasman.
1636 **441** 70c. multicoloured . . . 65 30

442 Yellow and Purple Flowers

443 Geometric Planes

1992. Cultural, Health and Social Welfare Funds. "Floriade" Flower Show, Zoetermeer. Mult.
1637 60c.+30c. Water lilies . . . 90 80
1638 70c.+35c. Orange and purple flowers . . . . . 1·10 90
1639 80c.+40c. Type **442** . . . . 1·25 65

1992. 150th Anniv of Royal Association of Netherlands Architects (60c.) and Inauguration of New States General Lower House (80c.). Mult.
1643 60c. Type **443** 55 30
1644 80c. Atrium and blue sky (symbolizing sending of information into society) 70 20

444 Globe and Columbus

445 Moneta (Goddess of Money)

1992. Europa. 500th Anniv of Discovery of America by Columbus.
1645 **444** 60c. multicoloured . . . 65 30
1646 – 80c. black, mauve & yellow 85 20
DESIGN—VERT: 80c. Galleon.

1992. Centenary of Royal Netherlands Numismatics Society.
1647 **445** 70c. multicoloured . . . 65 25

446 Teddy Bear wearing Stethoscope

447 List of Relatives and Friends

1992. Centenary of Netherlands Paediatrics Society.
1648 **446** 80c. multicoloured . . . 70 20

1992. 50th Anniv of Departure of First Deportation Train from Westerbork Concentration Camp.
1649 **447** 70c. multicoloured . . . 65 25

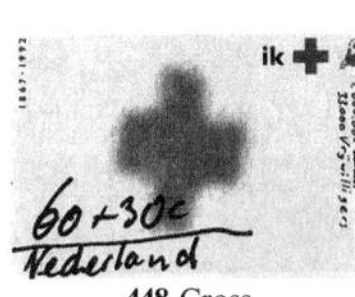

448 Cross

1992. 125th Anniv of Netherlands Red Cross. Multicoloured.
1650 60c.+30c. Type **448** 90 80
1651 70c.+35c. Supporting injured person . . . . 1·10 90
1652 80c.+40c. Red cross on dirty bandage . . . . 1·25 65

449 "United Europe" and European Community Flag

450 Queen Beatrix on Official Birthday, 1992, and at Investiture

1992. European Single Market.
1656 **449** 80c. multicoloured . . . 70 20

1992. $12\frac{1}{2}$ Years since Accession to the Throne of Queen Beatrix.
1657 **450** 80c. multicoloured . . . 70 20

451 Saxophone Player

452 Poinsettia

1992. Child Welfare. Child and Music. Mult.
1658 60c.+30c. Type **451** 85 50
1659 70c.+35c. Piano player . . . 90 60
1660 80c.+40c. Double bass player . . . . 1·00 75
MS1661 144 × 75 mm. Nos. 1658 × 3, 1659 × 2 and 1660 . . . 4·50 4·25

1992. Christmas.
1662 **452** 55c. multicoloured (centre of flower silver) 45 10
1663 55c. multicoloured (centre red) 45 10

453 Cycling

1993. Centenary of Netherlands Cycle and Motor Industry Association.
1664 **453** 70c. multicoloured . . . 65 35
1665 – 80c. brown, grey & yell 70 20
DESIGN: 80c. Car.

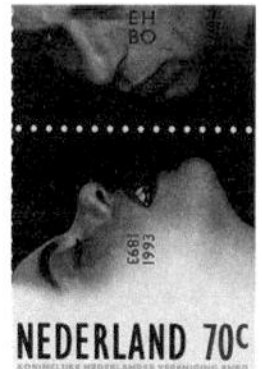

454 Collages

455 Mouth to Mouth Resuscitation

1993. Greetings Stamps. Multicoloured.
1666 70c. Type **454** 60 20
1667 70c. Collages (different) . . 60 20

1993. Anniversaries. Multicoloured.
1668 70c. Type **455** (centenary of Royal Netherlands First Aid Association) 65 35
1669 80c. Pests on leaf (75th anniv of Wageningen University of Agriculture) 70 20
1670 80c. Lead driver and horses (bicentenary of Royal Horse Artillery) 70 20

456 Emblems

1993. 150th Anniv of Royal Dutch Notaries Association. Each red and violet.
1671 80c. Type **456** ("150 Jaar" reading up) 70 20
1672 80c. As Type **456** but emblems inverted and "150 Jaar" reading down 70 20
Nos. 1671/2 were issued together in horizontal tete-beche pairs, each pair forming a composite design.

457 Large White

458 Elderly Couple

1993. Butterflies. Multicoloured.
1673 70c. Pearl-bordered fritillary 70 35
1674 80c. Large tortoiseshell . . . 80 20

1675 90c. Type **457** 90 80
MS1676 104 × 71 mm. 160c. Common blue . . . . 1·90 1·90

1993. Cultural, Health and Social Welfare Funds. Senior Citizens' Independence.
1677 70c.+35c. Type **458** . . . . 1·10 1·10
1678 70c.+35c. Elderly man . . . 1·10 1·10
1679 80c.+40c. Elderly woman with dog . . . . 1·25 85

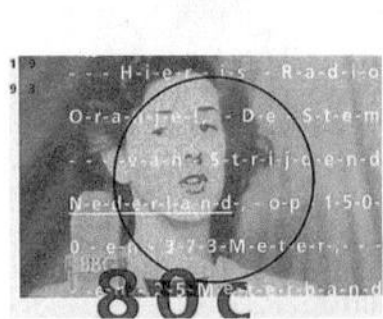

459 Broadcaster

460 Sports Pictograms

1993. Radio Orange (Dutch broadcasts from London during Second World War). Mult.
1683 80c. Type **459** 70 20
1684 80c. Man listening to radio in secret 70 20

1993. 2nd European Youth Olympic Days. Mult.
1685 70c. Type **460** 70 30
1686 80c. Sports pictograms (different) 80 20

461 "The Embodiment of Unity" (Wessel Couzijn)

462 Johannes Diderik van der Waals (Physics, 1910)

1993. Europa. Contemporary Art. Multicoloured.
1687 70c. Type **461** 70 35
1688 80c. Architectonic sculpture (Per Kirkeby) 80 20
1689 160c. Sculpture (Naum Gabo) (vert) . . . . . . 1·40 1·10

1993. Dutch Nobel Prize Winners (2nd series).
1690 **462** 70c. blue, black and red 65 30
1691 – 80c. mauve, black & red 70 20
1692 – 90c. multicoloured . . . 90 75
DESIGNS: 80c. Willem Einthoven (medicine, 1924); 90c. Christiaan Eijkman (medicine, 1929).

463 Pen and Pencils

1993. Letter Writing Campaign. Multicoloured.
1693 80c. Type **463** 65 20
1694 80c. Envelope 65 20

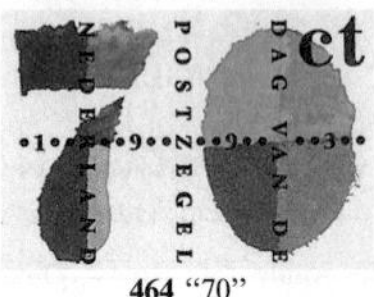

464 "70"

1993. Stamp Day (70c.) and Netherlands PTT (80c.). Multicoloured.
1695 70c. Type **464** 65 30
1696 80c. Dish aerial and dove carrying letter 70 20

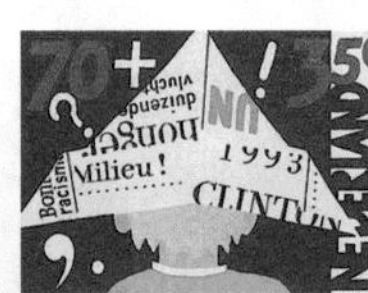

465 Child in Newspaper Hat

1993. Child Welfare. Child and the Media. Mult.
1697 70c.+35c. Type **465** 90 65
1698 70c.+35c. Elephant using headphones 90 65
1699 80c.+40c. Television . . . . 1·10 50
MS1700 143 × 75 mm. Nos. 1697/99, each × 2 . . . . 5·75 4·00

466 Candle

1993. Christmas. Multicoloured.
1711 55c. Type **466** 45 10
1712 55c. Fireworks 45 10
Both designs have a number of punched holes.

467 "Composition"

1994. 50th Death Anniv of Piet Mondriaan (artist). Multicoloured.
1713 70c. "The Red Mill" (detail) 65 30
1714 80c. Type **467** 70 20
1715 90c. "Broadway Boogie Woogie" (detail) 90 60

468 Barnacle Goose

1994. "Fepapost 94" European Stamp Exhibition, The Hague. Multicoloured.
1716 70c.+60c. Type **468** . . . . 1·00 85
1717 80c.+70c. Bluethroat . . . . 1·10 1·25
1718 90c.+80c. Garganey . . . . 1·25 1·10

469 Downy Rose

1994. Wild Flowers. Multicoloured.
1719 70c. Type **469** 65 30
1720 80c. Daisies 70 20
1721 90c. Wood forgetmenot . . 90 75
MS1722 71 × 50 mm. 160c. Orange lily . . . . 1·90 1·75

470 Airplane

1994. 75th Aircraft Industry Anniversaries.
1723 **470** 80c. blue and black . . . 70 20
1724 – 80c. grey, red and black 70 20
1725 – 80c. multicoloured . . . 70 20
DESIGNS: No. 1723, Type **470** (KLM (Royal Dutch Airlines)); 1724, Plan and outline of aircraft and clouds (Royal Netherlands Fokker Aircraft Industries); 1725, Airplane and clouds (National Aerospace Laboratory).

471 Woman using Telephone

472 Eisinga's Planetarium

1994. Cultural, Health and Social Welfare Funds. Senior Citizens' Security. Multicoloured.
1726 70c.+35c. Type **471** 90 90
1727 80c.+40c. Man using telephone . . . . 1·10 1·10
1728 90c.+35c. Man using telephone (different) . . . 1·25 1·10

1994. Anniversaries. Multicoloured.
1732 80c. Type **472** (250th birth anniv of Eise Eisinga) . . 70 20
1733 90c. Astronaut and boot print on Moon surface (25th anniv of first manned Moon landing) 1·10 65

473 Players Celebrating

1994. World Cup Football Championship, U.S.A.
1734 **473** 80c. multicoloured . . . 70 30

474 Stock Exchange

1994. Quotation of Netherlands PTT (KPN) on Stock Exchange.
1735 **474** 80c. multicoloured . . . 70 20

475 Road Sign, Car and Bicycle

1994. Anniversaries and Events. Multicoloured.
1736 70c. Type **475** (centenary of provision of road signs by Netherlands Motoring Association) 65 40
1737 80c. Equestrian sports (World Equestrian Games, The Hague) . . . 70 20

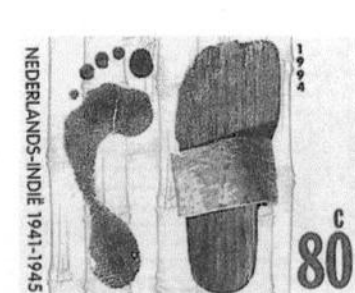

476 Footprint and Sandal

1994. Second World War. Multicoloured.
1738 80c. Type **476** (war in Netherlands Indies, 1941–45) 70 20
1739 90c. Soldier, children and aircraft dropping paratroops (50th anniv of Operation Market Garden (Battle of Arnhem)) (vert) 90 60

477 Brandaris Lighthouse, Terschelling

1994. Lighthouses. Multicoloured.
1740 70c. Type **477** 65 40
1741 80c. Ameland (vert) 70 20
1742 90c. Vlieland (vert) 90 75

1994. "Fepapost '94" European Stamp Exhibition, The Hague (2nd issue). Sheet 144 × 62 mm.
MS1743 Nos. 1716/18 plus 3 labels 3·30 3·50

478 Decorating

479 Star and Christmas Tree

1994. Child Welfare. "Together". Multicoloured.
1744 70c.+35c. Type **478** 90 65
1745 80c.+40c. Girl on swing knocking fruit off tree (vert) . . . . 1·10 60
1746 90c.+35c. Girl helping boy onto playhouse roof (vert) 1·10 1·10

1994. Christmas. Multicoloured.
1748 55c. Type **479** 45 10
1749 55c. Candle and star 45 10

480 Flying Cow

1995.
1750 **480** 100c. multicoloured . . . 1·10 30

481 "Prayer" (detail)

1995. Anniversary and Events.
1751 **481** 80c. multicoloured . . . 70 30
1752 – 80c. multicoloured . . . 70 30
1753 – 80c. black and red . . . 70 30
DESIGNS—VERT: No. 1751, Type **481** (50th death anniv of Hendrik Werkman (graphic designer); 1752, "Mesdag Panorama" (detail) (re-opening of Mesdag Museum). HORIZ: No. 1753, Mauritius 1847 2d. "POST OFFICE" stamp (purchase of remaining mint example in private hands by PTT Museum).

482 Joriz Ivens (documentary maker)

1995. Year of the Film (centenary of motion pictures). Multicoloured.
1754 70c. Type **482** 65 30
1755 80c. Scene from "Turkish Delight" 70 20

483 Mahler and Score of 7th Symphony

1995. Mahler Festival, Amsterdam.
1756 **483** 80c. black and blue . . . 70 30

484 Dates and Acronym

1995. Centenaries. Multicoloured.
1757 80c. Type **484** (Netherlands Institute of Chartered Accountants) 70 20
1758 80c. Builders, bricklayer's trowel and saw (Netherlands Association of Building Contractors) 70 20

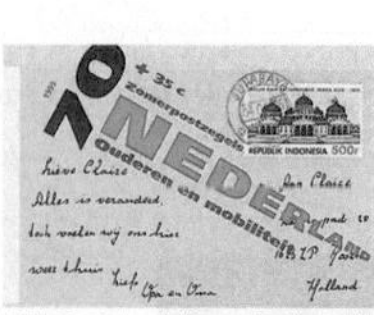

485 Postcard from Indonesia

486 "40 45"

1995. Cultural, Health and Social Welfare Funds. Mobility of the Elderly. Multicoloured.
1759 70c.+35c. Type **485** 90 85
1760 80c.+40c. Couple reflected in mirror . . . . 1·10 85
1761 100c.+45c. Couple with granddaughter at zoo . . 1·25 1·25
MS1762 144 × 75 mm. Nos. 1759 × 2, 1760 × 3 and 1761 . . . 7·25 6·50

1995. 50th Anniversaries. Multicoloured.
1763 80c. Type **486** (end of Second World War) . . . 70 30
1764 80c. "45 95" (liberation) . . 70 30
1765 80c. "50" (U.N.O.) 70 30

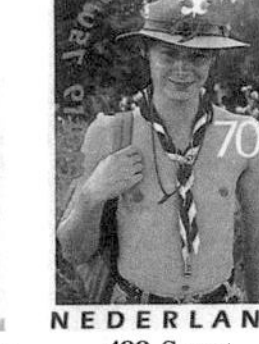

487 Birthday Cake and Signs of the Zodiac
488 Scout

1995. Birthday Greetings.
1766 **487** 70c. multicoloured . . . 1·75 30

1995. Events. Multicoloured.
1767 70c. Type **488** (World Scout Jamboree, Dronten) . . . 70 30
1768 80c. Amsterdam harbour ("Sail '95" and finish of Tall Ships Race) (horiz) 70 20

489 Common Kestrel
490 Petrus Debye (Chemistry, 1936)

1995. Birds of Prey. Multicoloured.
1769 70c. Type **489** 65 30
1770 80c. Face of hen harrier (horiz) 70 20
1771 100c. Red kite (horiz) . . . 90 75
MS1772 72 × 50 mm. 160c. Honey buzzard . . . . 1·90 1·75

1995. Dutch Nobel Prize Winners (3rd series). Multicoloured.
1773 80c. Type **490** 70 20
1774 80c. Frederik Zernike (Physics, 1953) 70 20
1775 80c. Jan Tinbergen (Economics, 1969) 70 20

491 Eduard Jacobs and Jean-Louis Pisuisse

1995. Centenary of Dutch Cabaret. Multicoloured.
1776 70c. Type **491** 70 30
1777 80c. Wim Kan and Freek de Jonge . . . . 1·10 20

492 "The Schoolteacher" (Leonie Ensing)
493 Children with Stars

1995. Child Welfare. "Children and Fantasy". Children's Computer Drawings. Multicoloured.
1778 70c.+35c. "Dino" (Sjoerd Stegeman) (horiz) 85 85
1779 80c.+40c. Type **492** . . . . 1·00 85
1780 100c.+50c. "Children and Colours" (Marcel Jansen) (horiz) . . . . 1·25 1·40
MS1781 144 × 74 mm. Nos. 1778 × 2, 1779 × 3 and 1780 . . . 5·25 4·50

1995. Christmas. Self-adhesive.
1782 **493** 55c. red, yellow and black 60 10
1783 – 55c. blue, yellow and black 60 10
DESIGN: No. 1783, Children looking at star through window.

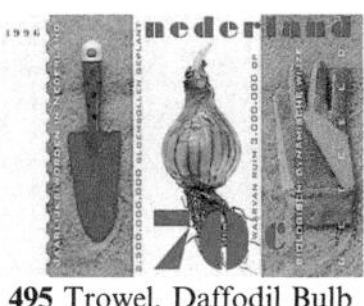

494 "Woman in Blue reading a Letter"
495 Trowel, Daffodil Bulb and Glove

1996. Johannes Vermeer Exhibition, Washington and The Hague. Details of his Paintings. Mult.
1784 70c. "Lady writing a Letter with her Maid" 65 40
1785 80c. "The Love Letter" . . 70 30
1786 100c. Type **494** . . . . . . 1·10 90
MS1787 144 x 75 mm. Nos. 1784/6 2·50 2·25

1996. Spring Flowers. Multicoloured.
1788 70c. Type **495** 65 40
1789 80c. Tulips "kissing" woman 70 20
1790 100c. Snake's-head fritillary (detail of painting, Charles Mackintosh) . . . 1·75 85
MS1791 72 × 50 mm. 160c. Crocuses 1·75 1·50

496 Putting up "MOVED" sign
497 Swimming

1996. Change of Address Stamp.
1792 **496** 70c. multicoloured . . . 1·00 40
For 80c. self-adhesive version of this design see No. 1826.

1996. Cultural, Health and Social Welfare Funds. The Elderly in the Community. Multicoloured.
1793 70c.+35c. Type **497** 85 80
1794 80c.+40c. Grandad bottle-feeding baby . . . . . . 1·00 90
1795 100c.+50c. Playing piano . . 1·40 1·25
MS1796 144 × 75 mm. Nos. 1793 × 2, 1794 × 3 and 1795 . . . 6·00 6·50

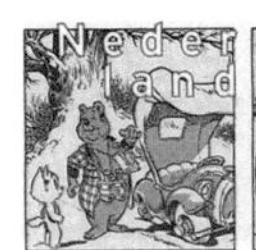
498 Beside Car

1996. Heer Bommel (cartoon character). Sheet 108 × 50 mm containing T **498** and similar horiz design. Multicoloured.
MS1797 70c. Type **498**; 80c. Reading letter . . . . 1·75 1·50

499 Cycling

1996. Tourism. Multicoloured.
1798 70c. Type **499** 65 10
1799 70c. Paddling in sea 65 20
1800 80c. Traditional architecture, Amsterdam 70 20
1801 100c. Windmills, Zaanse Schand Open-Air Museum 85 30

500 Parade in Traditional Costumes

1996. Bicentenary of Province of North Brabant.
1802 **500** 80c. multicoloured . . . 70 20

501 Lighting Olympic Torch
502 Erasmus Bridge

1996. Sporting Events. Multicoloured.
1803 70c. Type **501** (Olympic Games, Atlanta) 65 20
1804 80c. Flag and cyclists (Tour de France cycling championship) 70 20
1805 100c. Player, ball and Wembley Stadium (European Football Championship, England) 85 55
1806 160c. Olympic rings and athlete on starting block (Olympic Games, Atlanta) 1·25 55

1996. Bridges and Tunnels. Multicoloured.
1807 80c. Type **502** 65 20
1808 80c. Wijker Tunnel (horiz) 65 20
1809 80c. Martinus Nijhoff Bridge (horiz) 65 20

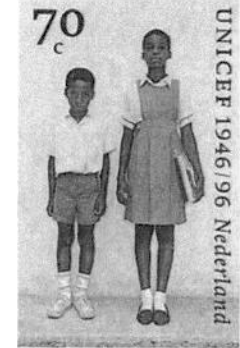

503 Children in School Uniforms
504 Bert and Ernie

1996. 50th Anniv of U.N.I.C.E.F. Multicoloured.
1810 70c. Type **503** 65 20
1811 80c. Girl carrying platter on head 65 20

1996. Sesame Street (children's television programme). Multicoloured.
1812 70c. Type **504** 65 20
1813 80c. Bears holding Big Bird's foot 60 15

505 Petrus Plancius
506 Books and Baby

1996. 16th-century Voyages of Discovery.
1814 **505** 70c. black, yellow and red 60 40
1815 – 80c. multicoloured . . . 65 20
1816 – 80c. multicoloured . . . 65 20
1817 – 100c. multicoloured . . . 65 65
DESIGNS: No. 1815, Cornelis de Houtman; 1816, Willem Barentsz; 1817, Mahu en De Cordes.

1996. Child Welfare. Multicoloured.
1818 70c.+35c. Type **506** 65 75
1819 80c.+40c. Animals and boy 90 85
1820 80c.+40c. Tools and girl . . 90 60
MS1821 75 × 144 mm. Nos. 1818/20, each × 2 . . . . 5·25 4·50

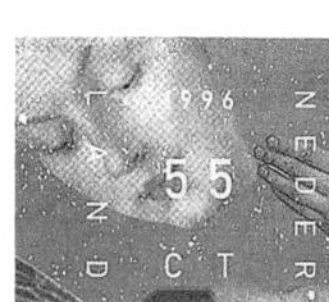

507 Woman's Face and Hand

1996. Christmas. Multicoloured. Self-adhesive.
1822 55c. Type **507** 50 20
1823 55c. Woman's eyes and man shouting 50 20
1824 55c. Bird's wing, hands and detail of man's face . . . 50 20
1825 55c. Men's faces and bird's wing 50 20
Nos. 1822/5 were issued together, se-tenant, forming a composite design.

1997. Change of Address Stamp. Self-adhesive.
1826 **496** 80c. multicoloured . . . 60 30
No. 1826 was intended for use by people moving house.

508 Numeral on Envelope with Top Flap

1997. Business Stamps. Multicoloured. Self-adhesive.
1827 80c. Type **508** 50 20
1828 160c. Numeral on envelope with side flap . . . . . . 1·00 40

509 Skaters

1997. 15th Eleven Cities Skating Race.
1829 **509** 80c. multicoloured . . . 65 20

510 Heart

1997. Greetings Stamps.
1830 **510** 80c. multicoloured . . . 50 30
The price quoted for No. 1830 is for an example with the heart intact. The heart can be scratched away to reveal different messages.

511 Pony

1997. Nature and the Environment. Multicoloured.
1831 80c. Type **511** 65 20
1832 100c. Cow 90 65
MS1833 72 × 50 mm. 160c. Sheep 1·60 1·40

512 Suske, Wiske, Lambik and Aunt Sidonia

1997. Suske and Wiske (cartoon by Willy Vandersteen). Multicoloured.
1834 80c. Type **512** 50 20
MS1835 108 × 50 mm. 80c. Wilbur; 80c. Type **512** . . . . 1·60 1·40

513 Rosebud

1997. Cultural, Health and Social Welfare Funds. The Elderly and their Image. Multicoloured.
1836 80c.+40c. Type **513** 90 80
1837 80c.+40c. Rose stem 90 80
1838 80c.+40c. Rose 90 80
MS1839 144 × 75 mm. Nos. 1836/8, each × 2 . . . . 5·50 5·00

514 Birthday Cake

1997. Greetings Stamps. Multicoloured.
1840 80c. Type **514** 50 20
1841 80c. Cup of coffee, glasses of wine, candles, writing letter, and amaryllis . . . 50 20
See also No. 1959.

515 "REKENKAMER ..." (550th anniv of Court of Audit)
516 Clasped Hands over Red Cross

1997. Anniversaries.
1842 **515** 80c. multicoloured . . . 65 25
1843 – 80c. red, yellow and black 65 25
1844 – 80c. red, black and blue 65 25
DESIGNS—50th anniv of Marshall Plan (post-war American aid for Europe): No. 1843, Map of Europe; 1844, Star and stripes.

1997. Red Cross.
1845 **516** 80c.+40c. mult . . . . . 1·10 1·10

517 "eu" and Globe

1997. European Council of Ministers' Summit, Amsterdam.
1846 **517** 100c. multicoloured . . . 1·00 40

518 Children playing in Boat

1997. Water Activities. Multicoloured.
1847 80c. Type **518** 60 25
1848 1g. Skutsje (sailing barges) race, Friesland 80 40

519 "vernuft"

1997. Anniversaries. Multicoloured.
1849 **519** 80c. ultramarine and blue 60 25
1850 – 80c. ultramarine and blue 60 25
1851 – 80c. multicoloured . . . 60 30
1852 – 80c. multicoloured . . . 60 25
DESIGNS: No. 1849, Type **519** (150th anniv of Royal Institute of Engineers); 1850, "adem" (centenary of Netherlands Asthma Centre, Davos, Switzerland); 1851, Flower (centenary of Florens College (horticultural college) and 125th anniv of Royal Botanical and Horticultural Society); 1852, Pianist accompanying singer (birth bicentenary of Franz Schubert (composer)).

520 "Nederland80"

1997. Youth. Multicoloured.
1853 **520** 80c. red and blue 50 25
1854 – 80c. multicoloured . . . 50 25
DESIGN: No. 1854, "NEDERLAND80" in style of computer games giving appearance of three-dimensional block on race track.

521 Stork with Bundle

1997. New Baby Stamp. Self-adhesive gum.
1855 **521** 80c. multicoloured . . . 50 30
See also Nos. 1960, 2120 amd 2189.

522 "Little Red Riding Hood"

523 Heads and Star

1997. Child Welfare. Fairy Tales. Multicoloured.
1856 80c.+40c. Type **522** . . . . 1·00 65
1857 80c.+40c. Man laying loaves on ground ("Tom Thumb") . . . . 1·00 65
1858 80c.+40c. Woodman with bottle ("Genie in the Bottle") . . . . 1·00 65
MS1859 144 × 75 mm. Nos. 1856/8, each × 2 . . . . 6·00 4·75

1997. Christmas. Multicoloured, colour of background given.
1860 **523** 55c. yellow 50 25
1861 55c. blue 50 25
1862 – 55c. orange 50 25
1863 – 55c. red 50 25
1864 – 55c. green 50 25
1865 **523** 55c. green 50 25
DESIGN: Nos. 1862/4, Heads and heart.

524 Light across Darkness

525 Cow and "Ship" Tiles

1998. Bereavement Stamp.
1866 **524** 80c. blue 50 35

1998. Delft Faience.
1867 **525** 100c. multicoloured . . . 65 35
1868 – 160c. blue . . . . 1·00 90
DESIGN: 160c. Ceramic tile showing boy standing on head.

526 Strawberries in Bloom (Spring)

527 Handshake

1998. The Four Seasons. Multicoloured.
1869 80c. Type **526** 65 65
1870 80c. Strawberry, flan and strawberry plants (Summer) 65 65
1871 80c. Bare trees and pruning diagram (Winter) 65 65
1872 80c. Orchard and apple (Autumn) 65 65

1998. Anniversaries. Multicoloured.
1873 80c. Type **527** (350th anniv of Treaty of Munster) . . 60 40
1874 80c. Statue of Johan Thorbecke (politician) (150th anniv of Constitution) 60 40
1875 80c. Child on swing (50th anniv of Declaration of Human Rights) 60 40

528 Bride and Groom

529 Shopping List

1998. Wedding Stamp. Self-adhesive gum.
1876 **528** 80c. multicoloured . . . 50 35
See also No. 1961.

1998. Cultural, Health and Social Welfare Funds. Care and the Elderly.
1877 80c.+40c. Type **529** . . . . 1·00 95
1878 80c.+40c. Sweet . . . . . . 1·00 95
1879 80c.+40c. Training shoe . . 1·00 95
MS1880 144 × 75 mm. Nos. 1877/9, each × 2 . . . . 6·00 5·50

530 Letters blowing in Wind

1998. Letters to the Future.
1881 **530** 80c. multicoloured . . . 60 40

531 Customers

1998. Centenary of Rabobank.
1882 **531** 80c. yellow, green and blue 60 40

532 Goalkeeper catching Boot

1998. Sport. Multicoloured.
1883 80c. Type **532** (World Cup Football Championship, France) 50 40
1884 80c. Family hockey team (centenary of Royal Netherlands Hockey Federation) (35 × 24 mm) 60 30

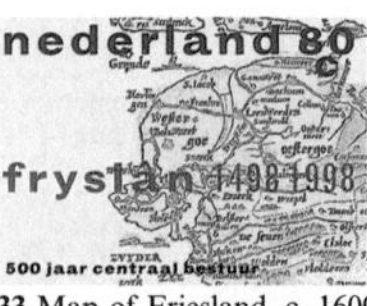
533 Map of Friesland, c. 1600

1998. 500th Anniv of Central Administration of Friesland.
1885 **533** 80c. multicoloured . . . 60 40

534 River Defences

1998. Bicentenary of Directorate-General of Public Works and Water Management. Multicoloured.
1886 80c. Type **534** 60 40
1887 1g. Sea defences 80 55

535 "tnt post groep"

1998. Separation of Royal Netherlands PTT into TNT Post Groep and KPN NV (telecommunications).
1888 **535** 80c. black, blue and red 60 45
1889 – 80c. black, blue and green 60 45
DESIGN: No. 1889, "kpn nv".
Nos. 1888/9 were issued together, se-tenant, forming a composite design of the complete "160".

536 Books and Keyboard

1998. Cultural Anniversaries. Multicoloured.
1890 80c. Type **536** (bicentenary of National Library) . . . 60 40
1891 80c. Maurits Escher (graphic artist, birth centenary) looking at his mural "Metamorphose" in The Hague Post Office (vert) 60 40
1892 80c. Simon Vestdijk (writer, birth centenary) and page from "Fantoches" (vert) 60 40

537 Queen Wilhelmina

1998. Royal Centenaries. Sheet 144 × 75 mm containing T **537** and similar vert design. Multicoloured.
MS1893 80c. Type **537** (coronation); 80c. Gilded Coach . . . . . . 1·60 1·40

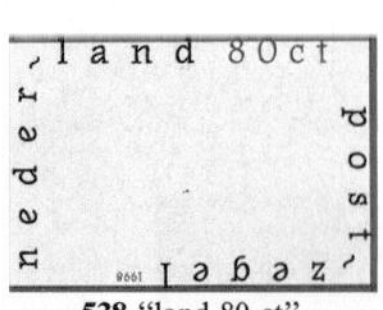
538 "land 80 ct"

1998. Greetings Stamps. Multicoloured. Self-adhesive.
1894 80c. Type **538** (top of frame red) 70 50
1895 80c. "80 ct post" (top of frame mauve) 70 50
1896 80c. Type **538** (top of frame orange) 70 50
1897 80c. "80 ct post" (top of frame orange) 70 50
1898 80c. Type **538** (top of frame yellow) 70 50

The part of the frame used for identification purposes is above the face value.
Nos. 1894/8 were only available in sheetlets of ten stamps and 20 labels (five stamps and ten labels on each side of the card). It was intended that the sender should insert the appropriate greetings label into the rectangular space on each stamp before use.

539 Rabbits

1998. Domestic Pets. Multicoloured.
1899 80c. Type **539** 60 45
1900 80c. Drent partridge dog . . 50 45
1901 80c. Kittens 50 40

540 Cathy and Jeremy writing a Letter

1998. 25th Anniv of Jack, Jacky and the Juniors (comic strip characters).
1902 80c. Type **540** 50 40
MS1903 108 × 50 mm. 80c. Type **540**; 80c. Posting letter 1·40 1·25

541 St. Nicholas on Horseback

1998. Child Welfare. Celebrations. Multicoloured.
1904 80c.+40c. Type **541** . . . . 1·00 70
1905 80c.+40c. Making birthday cake . . . . 1·00 70
1906 80c.+40c. Carnival parade 1·00 70
MS1907 144 × 75 mm. Nos. 1904/6, each × 2 . . . . 6·00 4·75

542 Hare and Snowball

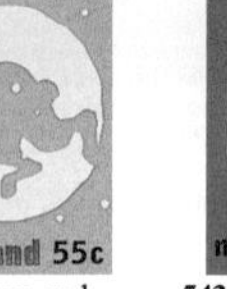
543 House and Tree on Snowball

1998. Christmas. Self-adhesive.
1908 **542** 55c. blue, red and black 75 35
1909 – 55c. multicoloured . . . 75 35
1910 – 55c. blue, red and black 75 35
1911 – 55c. multicoloured . . . 75 35
1912 – 55c. blue, red and black 75 35
1913 – 55c. green, blue and red 75 35
1914 – 55c. green, blue and red 75 35
1915 – 55c. green, blue and red 75 35
1916 – 55c. green, blue and red 75 35
1917 – 55c. green, blue and red 75 35
1918 – 55c. blue, green and red 75 35
1919 – 55c. red, green and black 75 35
1920 – 55c. blue, green and red 75 35
1921 – 55c. green, red and black 75 35
1922 – 55c. blue, green and red 75 35
1923 – 55c. blue, green and red 75 35
1924 – 55c. blue, green and red 75 35
1925 – 55c. blue, green and red 75 35
1926 – 55c. blue, green and red 75 35
1927 – 55c. blue, green and red 75 35
DESIGNS: No. 1909, House and snowball; 1910, Dove and snowball; 1911, Christmas tree and snowball; 1912, Reindeer and snowball; 1913, Hare; 1914, House; 1915, Dove; 1916, Christmas tree; 1917, Reindeer; 1918, House and hare; 1919, House and heart; 1920, Dove and house; 1921, Christmas tree and house; 1922, House and reindeer; 1923, Christmas tree and hare; 1924, Christmas tree and house; 1925, Christmas tree and dove; 1926, Christmas tree and heart; 1927, Christmas tree and reindeer.

1999. Make-up Rate Stamp.
1928 **543** 25c. red and black . . . 25 20

544 Euro Coin

1999. Introduction of the Euro (European currency).
1929 **544** 80c. multicoloured . . . 60 30

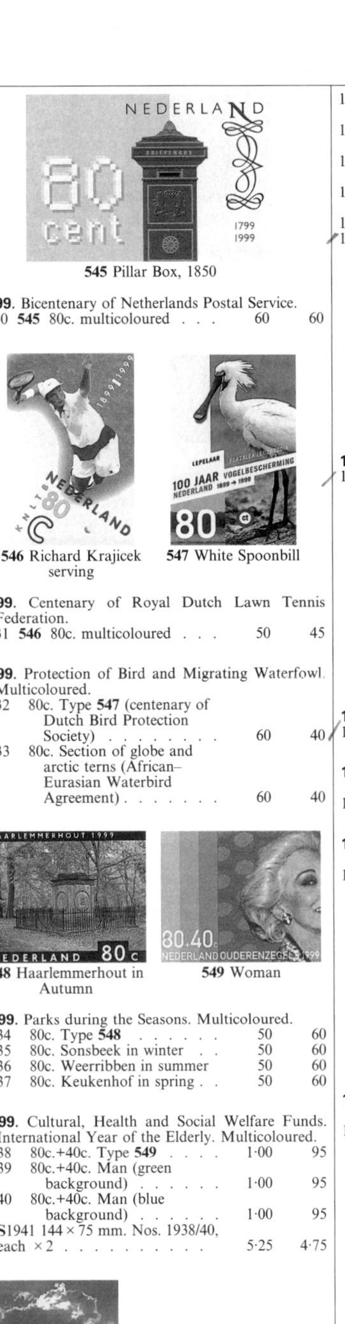

545 Pillar Box, 1850

1999. Bicentenary of Netherlands Postal Service.
1930 **545** 80c. multicoloured . . . 60 60

546 Richard Krajicek serving
547 White Spoonbill

1999. Centenary of Royal Dutch Lawn Tennis Federation.
1931 **546** 80c. multicoloured . . . 50 45

1999. Protection of Bird and Migrating Waterfowl. Multicoloured.
1932 80c. Type **547** (centenary of Dutch Bird Protection Society) 60 40
1933 80c. Section of globe and arctic terns (African–Eurasian Waterbird Agreement) 60 40

548 Haarlemmerhout in Autumn
549 Woman

1999. Parks during the Seasons. Multicoloured.
1934 80c. Type **548** 50 60
1935 80c. Sonsbeek in winter . . 50 60
1936 80c. Weerribben in summer 50 60
1937 80c. Keukenhof in spring . . 50 60

1999. Cultural, Health and Social Welfare Funds. International Year of the Elderly. Multicoloured.
1938 80c.+40c. Type **549** . . . . 1·00 95
1939 80c.+40c. Man (green background) . . . . . . 1·00 95
1940 80c.+40c. Man (blue background) . . . . . . 1·00 95
MS1941 144 × 75 mm. Nos. 1938/40, each × 2 . . . . 5·25 4·75

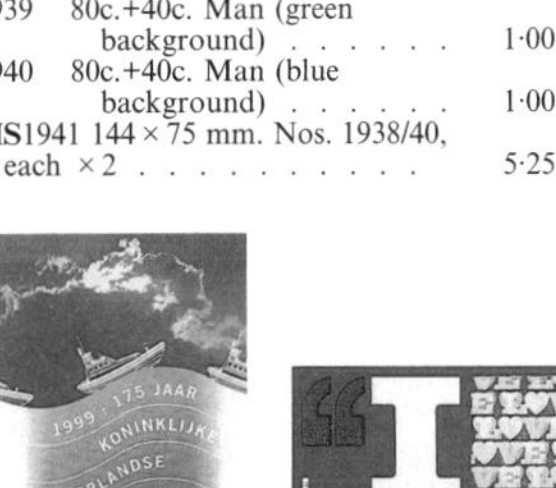

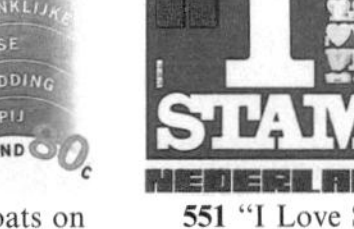

550 Lifeboats on Rough Sea
551 "I Love Stamps"

1999. Water Anniversaries. Multicoloured.
1942 80c. Type **550** (175th Anniv of Royal Netherlands Lifeboat Association) . . 60 45
1943 80c. Freighters in canal (150th Anniv of Royal Association of Ships' Masters "Schuttevaer") 60 45

1999.
1944 **551** 80c. blue and red 50 50
1945 – 80c. red and blue 50 50
DESIGN: No. 1945, "Stamps love Me".

552 "The Goldfinch" (Carel Fabritius)

1999. 17th-century Dutch Art. Multicoloured. Self-adhesive gum (1g.).
1946 80c. Type **552** 70 65
1947 80c. "Self-portrait" (Rembrandt) 70 65
1948 80c. "Self-portrait" (Judith Leyster) 70 65
1949 80c. "St. Sebastian" (Hendrick ter Brugghen) 70 65
1950 80c. "Beware of Luxury" (Jan Steen) 70 65
1951 80c. "The Sick Child" (Gabriel Metsu) 70 65
1952 80c. "Gooseberries" (Adriaen Coorte) 70 65
1953 80c. "View of Haarlem" (Jacob van Ruisdael) . . 70 65
1954 80c. "Mariaplaats, Utrecht" (Pieter Saenredam) . . . 70 65
1955 80c. "Danae" (Rembrandt) 70 65
1956 1g. "The Jewish Bride" (Rembrandt) 65 55

553 "80" on Computer Screen

1999. Ordinary or self-adhesive gum.
1957 **553** 80c. multicoloured . . . 50 40

554 Amaryllis, Coffee Cup, Candles, Letter Writing and Wine Glasses

1999. Greetings Stamp. Self-adhesive.
1959 **554** 80c. multicoloured . . . 50 40

1999. New Baby Stamp. As No. 1855 but ordinary gum.
1960 **521** 80c. multicoloured . . . 50 50

1999. Wedding Stamp. As No. 1876 but ordinary gum.
1961 **528** 80c. multicoloured . . . 50 50

555 Victorian Heavy Machinery and Modern Computer

1999. Centenary of Confederation of Netherlands Industry and Employers.
1962 **555** 80c. multicoloured . . . 60 50

556 Tintin and Snowy wearing Space Suits

1999. 70th Anniv of Tintin (comic strip character by Herge). Scenes from "Explorers on the Moon". Multicoloured.
1963 80c. Type **556** 50 50
MS1964 108 × 50 mm. 80c. Tintin, Snowy and Captain Haddock in moon buggy; 80c .Type **556** . . 1·60 1·40

557 Pillar Box, 1850

1999. Bicentenary of Netherlands Postal Service (2nd issue). Sheet 144 × 75 mm.
MS1965 **557** 5g. red, black and blue 4·00 3·50

558 Digger (completion of Afsluitdijk, 1932)

1999. The Twentieth Century. Multicoloured.
1966 80c. Type **558** . . . . . . 1·10 80
1967 80c. Space satellite . . . . 1·10 80
1968 80c. Berlage Commodity Exchange, Amsterdam (inauguration, 1903) . . . 1·10 80
1969 80c. Empty motorway (car-free Sundays during oil crisis, 1973–74) . . . . . 1·10 80
1970 80c. Old man (Old Age Pensions Act, 1947) . . . 1·10 80
1971 80c. Delta Flood Project, 1953–97 . . . . 1·10 80
1972 80c. Players celebrating (victory of Netherlands in European Cup Football Championship, 1998) . . 1·10 80
1973 80c. Four riders on one motor cycle (liberation and end of Second World War, 1945) . . . . 1·10 80
1974 80c. Woman posting vote (Women's Franchise, 1919) . . . . 1·10 80
1975 80c. Ice skaters (eleven cities race) . . . . 1·10 80

559 Pluk van de Pettevlet on Fire Engine

1999. Child Welfare. Characters created by Fiep Westendorp. Multicoloured.
1976 80c.+40c. Type **559** . . . . 1·00 75
1977 80c.+40c. Otje drinking through straw . . . . . 1·00 75
1978 80c.+40c. Jip and Janneke with cat . . . . 1·00 75
MS1979 144 × 75 mm. Nos. 1976/8, each × 2 . . . . 6·00 4·75

560 Father Christmas (Robin Knegt)
561 "25"

1999. Christmas. Winning entries in design competition. Multicoloured.
1980 55c. Type **560** 50 25
1981 55c. Angel singing (Davinia Bovenlander) (vert) . . . 50 25
1982 55c. Dutch doughnuts in box (Henk Drenth) . . . 50 25
1983 55c. Moon wearing Christmas hat (Lizet van den Berg) (vert) 50 25
1984 55c. Father Christmas carrying sacks (Noortje Kruse) 50 25
1985 55c. Clock striking midnight (Hucky de Haas) (vert) . . 50 25
1986 55c. Ice skater (Marleen Bos) 50 25
1987 55c. Human Christmas tree (Mariette Strik) (vert) . . 50 25
1988 55c. Woman wearing Christmas tree earrings (Saskia van Oversteeg) . . 50 25
1989 55c. Woman vacuuming pine needles (Frans Koenis) (vert) 50 25
1990 55c. Angel with harp and music score (Evelyn de Zeeuw) 50 25
1991 55c. Hand balancing candle, star, hot drink, hat and Christmas tree on fingers (Aafke van Ewijk) (vert) 50 25
1992 55c. Christmas tree (Daan Roepman) (vert) 50 25
1993 55c. Cat wearing crown (Sjoerd van der Zee) (vert) 50 25
1994 55c. Bird flying over house (Barbara Vollers) . . . 50 25
1995 55c. Baby with angel wings (Rosmarijn Schmink) (vert) 50 25
1996 55c. Dog wearing Christmas hat (Casper Heijstek and Mirjam Cnosser) 50 25
1997 55c. Angel flying (Patricia van der Neut) (vert) . . . 50 25
1998 55c. Nativity (Marco Cockx) 50 25
1999 55c. Christmas tree with decorations (Matthias Meiling) (vert) 50 25

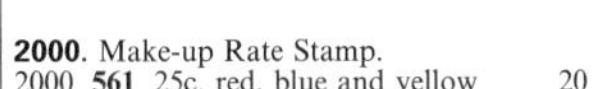

2000. Make-up Rate Stamp.
2000 **561** 25c. red, blue and yellow 20 25

562 1 Guilder Coin, Margaret of Austria (Regent of Netherlands) (after Bernard van Orley) and "Coronation of Charles V" (Juan de la Coate)

2000. 500th Birth Anniv of Charles V, Holy Roman Emperor. Multicoloured.
2001 80c. Type **562** 60 50
2002 80c. Map of the Seventeen Provinces, "Charles V after the Battle of Muehlberg" (Titian) and Margaret of Parma (Regent of Netherlands) (after Antonius Mohr) . . 60 50

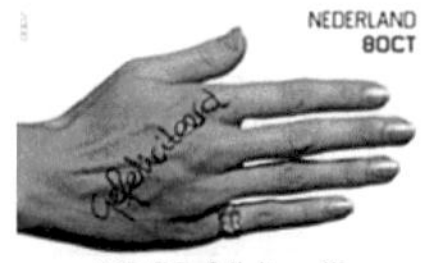

563 "Gefeliciteerd" ("Congratulations")

2000. Greetings stamps. Showing greetings messages on hands. Multicoloured.
2003 80c. Type **563** 60 55
2004 80c. "Succes met je nieuwe baan" ("Good luck with your new job") 60 55
2005 80c. "gefeliciteerd met je huis" ("Congratulations on your new home") . . 60 55
2006 80c. "PROFICIAT" ("Congratulations") . . . 60 55
2007 80c. "Succes" ("Hope you have success") 60 55
2008 80c. "Veel geluk samen" ("Good luck together") 60 55
2009 80c. "Proficiat met je diploma" ("Congratulations on passing your exam") . . . 60 55
2010 80c. "Geluk" ("Good luck") 60 55
2011 80c. "Van Harte" ("Cordially") 60 55
2012 80c. "GEFELICITEERD MET JE RUBEWIUS!" ("Congratulations on passing your driving test!") 60 55

564 Players celebrating
565 Man and Woman passing Ball

2000. European Football Championship, Netherlands and Belgium. Multicoloured.
2013 80c. Type **564** 50 30
2014 80c. Football 50 30

2000. Cultural, Health and Social Welfare Funds. Senior Citizens. Multicoloured.
2015 80c.+40c. Type **565** 90 60
2016 80c.+40c. Woman picking apples 90 60
2017 80c.+40c. Woman wearing swimming costume . . . 90 60
MS2018 144 × 74 mm. Nos. 2015/17, each × 2 . . . . 6·25 5·25

566 "Feigned Sadness" (C. Troost)

2000. Bicentenary of the Rijksmuseum, Amsterdam. Multicoloured. (a) Ordinary gum.
2019 80c. Type **566** 60 55
2020 80c. "Harlequin and Columbine" (porcelain figurine) (J. J. Kandler) 60 55
2021 80c. "Ichikawa Ebizo IV" (woodcut) (T. Sharaku) 60 55
2022 80c. "Heavenly Beauty" (sandstone sculpture) . . 60 55
2023 80c. "St. Vitus" (wood sculpture) 60 55
2024 80c. "Woman in Turkish Costume" (J. E. Liotard) 60 55
2025 80c. "J. van Speyk" (J. Schoemaker Doyer) . . 60 55
2026 80c. "King Saul" (engraving) (L. van Leyden) 60 55
2027 80c. "L'Amour Menacant" (marble sculpture) (E. M. Falconet) 60 55
2028 80c. "Sunday" (photograph) (C. Ariens) 60 55

(b) Self-adhesive.
2029 80c. "The Nightwatch" (Rembrandt) 60 55

567 "80" and "Doe Maar" Record Cover

2000. Doe Maar (Dutch pop group). Multicoloured.
2030 80c. Type **567** 50 45
2031 80c. "80" and song titles . . 50 45

568 "Dutch Landscape" (Jeroen Krabb)

2000. Priority Mail. Contemporary Art. Self-adhesive.
2033 **568** 110c. multicoloured . . . 60 50

569 "The Nightwatch" (Rembrandt)

2000. Priority Mail. Self-adhesive.
2034 **569** 110c. multicoloured . . . 65 65

570 *Libertad* (full-rigged cadet ship)

2000. "Sail Amsterdam 2000". Sailing Ships. Multicoloured.
2036 80c. Type **570** 45 20
2037 80c. *Amerigo Vespucci* (cadet ship) and figurehead . . . 45 20
2038 80c. *Dar Mlodziezy* (full-rigged cadet ship) and sail 45 20
2039 80c. *Europa* (cadet ship) and wheel 45 20
2040 80c. *Kruzenshtern* (cadet barque) and bell 45 20
2041 80c. *Sagres II* (cadet barque) and sail 45 20
2042 80c. *Alexander von Humboldt* (barque) and sail 45 20
2043 80c. *Sedov* (cadet barque) and sailors dropping sail 45 20
2044 80c. *Mir* (square-rigged training ship) 45 20
2045 80c. *Oosterschelde* (schooner) and rope . . . 45 20

571 Roller Skating

2000. Sjors and Sjimmie (comic strip characters by Frans Piet). Multicoloured.
2046 80c. Type **571** 45 20
2047 80c. In car 45 20
2049 80c. Listening to radio . . . 45 20
2050 80c. Swinging on rope . . . 45 20
MS2048 108 × 50 mm. 80c. As No. 2049; 80c. As No. 2047 . . 1·10 90

2000. Bereavement Stamp. As No. 1866 but self-adhesive.
2051 **524** 80c. blue 45 20

572 Green Dragonfly

2000. Endangered Species. Multicoloured.
2052 80c. Type **572** 45 20
2053 80c. Weather loach 45 20

573 Canal Boat

2000. 150th Anniv (2002) of Netherlands Stamps (1st issue). Sheet 108 × 50 mm containing T **573** and similar horiz design. Multicoloured.
MS2054 80c. Type **573**; 80c. Mail carriage . . . .
See also Nos. **MS**2138 and **MS**2250.

574 Children wearing Monster Hats

575 Couple with Christmas Tree

2000. Child Welfare. Multicoloured. (a) Self-adhesive gum.
2055 80c.+40c. Type **574** 65 40
2056 80c.+40c. Boy sailing bath-tub 65 40
2057 80c.+40c. Children brewing magical stew 65 40

(b) Ordinary gum.
MS2058 80c.+40c. Type **574**; 80c.+40c. Ghostly games; 80c. + 40c. Girl riding crocodile; 80c.+40c. As No. 2056; 80c.+40c. As No. 2057; 80c.+40c. Children playing dragon . . . . 4·75 2·75

2000. Christmas. Multicoloured.
2059 60c. Type **575** 35 15
2060 60c. Children making snow balls 35 15
2061 60c. Couple dancing 35 15
2062 60c. Man playing French horn 35 15
2063 60c. Man carrying Christmas tree 35 15
2064 60c. Man carrying young child 35 15
2065 60c. Woman reading book 35 15
2066 60c. Couple kissing 35 15
2067 60c. Man playing piano . . 35 15
2068 60c. Woman watching from window 35 15
2069 60c. Woman sitting in chair 35 15
2070 60c. Man sitting beside fire 35 15
2071 60c. Snowman flying 35 15
2072 60c. Couple in street 35 15
2073 60c. Child playing violin . . 35 15
2074 60c. Children on sledge . . 35 15
2075 60c. Man writing letter . . . 35 15
2076 60c. Woman carrying plate of food 35 15
2077 60c. Family 35 15
2078 60c. Woman sleeping . . . 35 15

576 Moon

577 Whinchat

2001. Make-up Rate Stamp.
2079 **576** 20c. multicoloured . . . 15 10

2001. Centenary of Royal Dutch Nature Society. Multicoloured.
2080 80c. Type **577** 45 20
2081 80c. Family in rowing boat 45 20
2082 80c. Fox 45 20
2083 80c. Couple bird watching 45 20
2084 80c. Flowers 45 20

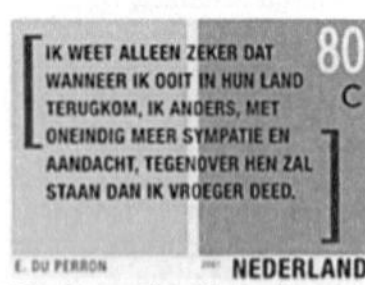

578 Poem (by E. du Perron)

2001. "Between Two Cultures". National Book Week. Multicoloured.
2085 80c. Type **578** 45 20
2086 80c. Men in street 45 20
2087 80c. Poem (by Hafid Bouazza) 45 20
2088 80c. Woman and young men 45 20
2089 80c. Poem (by Adriaan van Dis) 45 20
2090 80c. Profiles of two women 45 20
2091 80c. Poem (by Kader Abdolah) 45 20
2092 80c. Two young girls 45 20
2093 80c. Poem (by Ellen Ombre) 45 20
2094 80c. Boy carrying map . . . 45 20

579 Rotterdam Bridge

2001. Priority Mail. Rotterdam, European City of Culture. Self-adhesive gum.
2095 **579** 110c. multicoloured . . . 65 25

580 Emergency Rescuers

2001. International Year of Volunteers. Sheet 108 × 50 mm. containing Type **580** and similar horiz design. Multicoloured.
MS2096 80c. Type **MS**508, 80c. Animal rescuers . . . . 1·10 1·10

581 Chess Board

2001. Birth Centenary of Machgielis "Professor Max" Euwe (chess player). Sheet 108 × 50 mm containing T **581** and similar horiz design. Multicoloured.
MS2097 80c. Type **581**; 80c. Euwe and chess pieces . . . . 1·10 1·10

582 Helen's Flower (*Helenium rubinzwerg*)

2001. Flowers. Multicoloured. (a) Self-adhesive gum.
2098 80c.+40c. Type **582** 65 40
2099 80c.+40c. Russian hollyhock (*Alcea rugosa*) 65 40
2100 80c.+40c. Persian cornflower (*Centaurea dealbata*) . . . 65 40

(b) Ordinary gum.
MS2101 144 × 75 mm. 80c.+40c. *Caryopteris* "Heavenly Blue"; 80c.+40c. Type **582**; 80c.+40c. As No. 2099; 80c.+40c. Spurge (*Euphorbia schillingii*); 80c.+40c. As No. 2100; 80c.+40c. Hooker inula (*Inula hookeri*) . . . . . 4·75 4·00

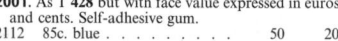

583 "Autumn" (detail) (L. Gestel)

2001. Art Nouveau. Multicoloured.
2102 80c. Type **583** . . . 45 20
2103 80c. Book cover by C. Lebeau for *De Stille Kracht* . . . 45 20
2104 80c. Burcht Federal Council Hall, Amsterdam (R. N. Roland Holst and H. P. Berlage) 45 20
2105 80c. "O Grave Where is Thy Victory" (painting) (J. Throop) . . . 45 20
2106 80c. Vases by C. J. van der Hoef from Amphora factory 45 20
2107 80c. Capital from staircase of Utrecht building (J. Mendes da Costa) 45 20
2108 80c. Illustration of common peafowl from *The Happy Owls* (T. van Hoytema) 45 20
2109 80c. "The Bride" (detail) (painting) (J. Thorn Prikker) 45 20
2110 80c. Factory-printed cotton fabric (M. Duco Crop) 45 20
2111 80c. Dentz van Schaik room (L. Zyl) 45 20

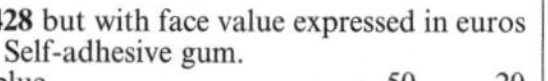

2001. As T **428** but with face value expressed in euros and cents. Self-adhesive gum.
2112 85c. blue 50 20

584 Sky and Landscape

2001. Self-adhesive gum.
2113 **584** 85c. multicoloured . . . 50 20

585 Arrows

2001. Business Coil Stamp. Self-adhesive gum.
2114 **585** 85c. purple and silver . . 50 20

586 Reclaimed Land

2001. Multicoloured. Self-adhesive gum.
2115 85c. Type **586** (postage) . . 50 20
2116 1g.20 Beach (priority mail) 65 25
2117 1g.65 Town and canal . . . 90 35

587 House carrying Suitcase

2001. Greetings Stamps. Self-adhesive gum.
2118 **587** 85c. black and yellow . . 50 20
2119 – 85c. red, yellow and gold 50 20
2120 – 85c. multicoloured . . . 50 20
2121 – 85c. multicoloured . . . 50 20
DESIGNS: No. 2118, Type **587** (change of address stamp); 2119, Couple (wedding stamp); 2120, As Type **521** (new baby); 2121, As Type **524** (bereavement stamp).

588 Tom and Jerry

589 "Veel Geluk" ("Good Luck")

2001. Cartoon Characters. Multicoloured.
2122 85c. Type **588** 50 20
2123 85c. Fred Flintstone and Barney Rubble 50 20
2124 85c. Johnny Bravo 50 20
2125 85c. Dexter posting letter . . 50 20
2126 85c. Powerpuff Girls 50 20

2001. Greetings Stamps. Multicoloured. Self-adhesive gum.
2127 85c. Type **589** 50 20
2128 85c. "Gefeliciteerd!" ("Congratulations!") . . . 50 20
2129 85c. "Veel Geluk" with envelope flap (horiz) . . . 50 20
2130 85c. "Gefeliciteerd!" with envelope flap (horiz) . . . 50 20
2131 85c. "Proficiat" ("Congratulations") . . . 50 20
2132 85c. "Succes !" ("Success") 50 20
2133 85c. "Van Harte ..." ("Cordially ...") 50 20
2134 85c. "Proficiat" with envelope flap (horiz) . . . 50 50
2135 85c. "Succes !" with envelope flap (horiz) . . . 50 20
2136 85c. "Van Harte ..." with envelope flap (horiz) . . . 50 20

590 Guilder Coins

591 Waaigat Canal and Williamstad, Curacao (J. E. Heemskerk after G. C. W. Voorduin)

2001. Replacement of the Guilder. Self-adhesive.
2137 **590** 12g.75 silver . . . . . . 7·00 3·00

2001. 150th Annivs of Netherlands Stamps (2002) (2nd issue) and of Royal Institute foe Linguistics and Anthropology. Sheet 108 × 50 mm containing T **591** and similar horiz design. Multicoloured.
MS2138 85c. Type **591**; 85c. Pangka sugar refinery, Java (J.C. Grieve after A. Salm) . . . . 1·40 1·40

592 Magnifier, Target Mark and Dots

2001. Centenary of Royal Dutch Printers' Association. Sheet 108 × 50 mm containing T **592** and similar horiz design. Multicoloured.
MS2139 85c. Type **592**; 85c. Magnifier, computer zoom symbol and colour palette . . . . . . 1·40 1·40

593 Computer Figure and River

2001. Child Welfare. Multicoloured. (a) Self-adhesive gum.
2140 85c.+40c. Type **593** . . . . 1·25 1·00

(b) Ordinary gum.
MS2141 146 × 76 mm. 85c.+40c. Figure and printer; 85c.+40c. Road, car and figure; 85c.+40c. Post box, blocks and droplets; 85c.+40c. Post box, figure and stairs; 85c.+40c. Type **593**; 85c.+40c. Figure swinging on rope and log in river . . . . 5·50 5·50

594 Clock and Grapes **595** "12"

2001. Christmas. Multicoloured. Self-adhesive gum.
2142 60c. Type **594** 35 15
2143 60c. Stars and bun 35 15
2144 60c. Steeple and buns . . . 35 15
2145 60c. Cherub and coins . . . 35 15
2146 60c. Champagne bottle . . . 35 15
2147 60c. Wreath around chimney . 35 15
2148 60c. Tower 35 15
2149 60c. Christmas tree bauble . 35 15
2150 60c. Playing card with Christmas tree as sign . . 35 15
2151 60c. Cake seen through window 35 15
2152 60c. Decorated Christmas tree 35 15
2153 60c. Father Christmas . . . 35 15
2154 60c. Sign displaying hot drink 35 15
2155 60c. Candles seen through window 35 15
2156 60c. Illuminated roof-tops . 35 15
2157 60c. Reindeer 35 15
2158 60c. Snowman 35 15
2159 60c. Parcel 35 15
2160 60c. Bonfire 35 15
2161 60c. Children on toboggan . 35 15

2002. Make-up Rate Stamp. (a) Self-adhesive gum.
2162 **595** 2c. red 15 10
2166 12c. green 15 10

(b) Ordinary gum.
2169 **595** 2c. red 15 10
2170 5c. mauve 10 10
2171 10c. blue 15 10

596 Queen Beatrix **597** Arrows

2002. Queen Beatrix. Self-adhesive gum.
2175 **596** 25c. brown and green . . 35 15
2176 39c. blue and pink . . . 50 20
2177 40c. blue and brown . . 50 20
2178 50c. pink and green . . 65 25
2179 55c. mauve and brown . 75 45
2181 65c. green and violet . . 85 35
2182 70c. deep green and green 95 60
2183 78c. blue and brown . . 1·00 40
2185 €1 green and blue . . . 1·25 50
2187 €3 mauve and green . . 3·75 1·50

2002. Business Coil Stamps. Self-adhesive gum.
2195 **597** 39c. purple and silver . . 50 20
2196 78c. blue and gold . . . 1·00 40

598 Prince Willem-Alexander and Máxima Zorreguieta

2002. Marriage of Prince Willem-Alexander and Maxima Zorreguieta. Sheet 145 × 75 mm, containing T **598** and similar horiz design.
MS2197 **598** 39c. black, silver and orange; 39c. multicoloured . . 1·25 1·25
DESIGN: 39c. "Willem-Alexander Maxima" and "222".

599 Sky and Landscape

2002. Self-adhesive gum.
2198 **599** 39c. multicoloured . . . 55 25

600 Couple **601** "Veel Geluk" ("Good Luck")

2002. Greetings Stamps. Face values in euros. Self-adhesive gum.
2199 – 39c. black and yellow . . 55 25
2200 **600** 39c. red, yellow and gold 55 25
2201 – 39c. multicoloured . . . 55 25
2202 – 39c. blue 55 25
DESIGNS: No. 2199, As Type **587** (change of address stamp); 2200, Type **600** (wedding stamp); 2201, As Type **521** (new baby); 2202, As Type **524** (bereavement stamp).

2001. Greetings Stamps. Face values in euros. Multicoloured. Self-adhesive gum.
2203 39c. Type **601** 55 25
2204 39c. "Gefeliciteerd!" ("Congratulations!") . . . 55 25
2205 39c. "Veel Geluk" ("Good Luck") (horiz) 55 25
2206 39c. "Gefeliciteerd!" with envelope flap (horiz) . . . 55 25
2207 39c. "Proficiat" ("Congratulations") . . . 55 25
2208 39c. "Succes !" ("Success") 55 25
2209 39c. "Van Harte..." ("Cordially ...") 55 25
2210 39c. "Proficiat" with envelope flap (horiz) . . . 55 25
2211 39c. "Succes !" with envelope flap (horiz) . . . 55 25
2212 39c. "Van Harte..." with envelope flap (horiz) . . . 55 25

602 Reclaimed Land

2002. Landscapes. Face values in euros. Multicoloured. Self-adhesive gum.
2213 39c. Type **603** (postage) . . 55 25
2214 54c. Beach (priority mail) 70 30
2215 75c. Town and canal . . . 1·00 40

603 Water Lily **604** Flowers and Red Crosses

2002. "Floriade 2002" International Horticultural Exhibition, Harlemmermeer. Flowers. Multicoloured.
2216 39c. + 19c. Type **603** . . . 80 50
2217 39c. + 19c. Dahlia 80 50
2218 39c. + 19c. Japanese cherry blossom 80 50
2219 39c. + 19c. Rose 80 50
2220 39c. + 19c. Orchid 80 50
2221 39c. + 19c. Tulip 80 50
Nos. 2216/21 were printed on paper impregnated with perfume which was released when the stamps were scratched.

2002. Red Cross. 10th Annual Blossom Walk.
2222 **604** 39c. + 19c. multicoloured 80 50

605 Langnek

2002. 50th Anniv of Efteling Theme Park. Multicoloured. Self-adhesive gum.
2223 39c. Type **605** 55 25
2224 39c. Pardoes de Tovernar . . 55 25
2225 39c. Droomvlucht Elfje . . 55 25
2226 39c. Kleine Boodschap . . . 55 25
2227 39c. Holle Bolle Gijs 55 25

606 "West Indies Landscape" (Jan Mostaert)

2002. Landscape Paintings. Showing paintings and enlarged detail in foreground. Multicoloured.
2228 39c. Type **606** 55 25
2229 39c. "Riverbank with Cows" (Aelbert Cuyp) 55 25
2230 39c. "Cornfield" (Jacob van Ruisdael) 55 25
2231 39c. "Avenue at Middelharnis" (Meindert Hobbema) 55 25
2232 39c. "Italian Landscape with Umbrella Pines" (Hendrik Voogd) 55 25
2233 39c. "Landscape in Normandy" (Andreas Schelfhout) 55 25
2234 39c. "Landscape with Waterway" (Jan Toorop) 55 25
2235 39c. "Landscape" (Jan Sluijters) 55 25
2236 39c. "Kismet" (Michael Raedecker) 55 25
2237 39c. "Untitled" (Robert Zandvliet) 55 25

607 Circus Performers **608** Circles

2002. Priority Mail. Europa. Circus. Multicoloured.
2238 54c. Type **607** 70 30
2239 54c. Lions and Big Top . . 70 30

2002. Business Coil Stamp. Self-adhesive gum.
2240 **608** 39c. deep blue, blue and red 55 25
2241 78c. green, light green and red . . . . . . 1·10 45

609 Dutch East Indiaman and 1852 Stamps

2002. 150th Anniv of Netherlands Stamps. 400th Anniv of Dutch East India Company (V. O. C.). Sheet 108 × 50 mm, containing T **609** and similar horiz design. Multicoloured.
MS2250 Type **609**; 39c. Two Dutch East Indiamen and stamps of 1852 . . . . 1·10 45

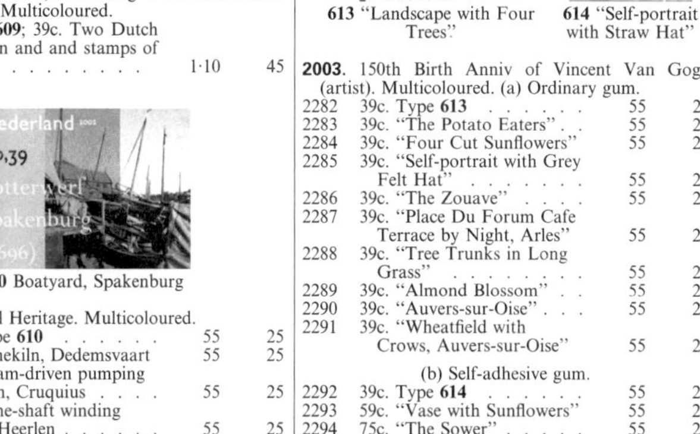

610 Boatyard, Spakenburg

2002. Industrial Heritage. Multicoloured.
2251 39c. Type **610** 55 25
2252 39c. Limekiln, Dedemsvaart 55 25
2253 39c. Steam-driven pumping station, Cruquius 55 25
2254 39c. Mine-shaft winding gear, Heerlen 55 25
2255 39c. Salt drilling tower, Hengelo 55 25
2256 39c. Windmill, Weidum . . 55 25
2257 39c. Brick-works, Zevenaar 55 25
2258 39c. "Drie Hoefijzers" brewery, Breda 55 25
2259 39c. Water-treatment plant, Tilburg 55 25
2260 39c. "Nodding-donkey" oil pump, Schoonebeck . . . 55 25

611 Cat and Child

2002. Child Welfare. Sheet 147 × 76 mm, containing T **611** and similar horiz designs. Multicoloured.
MS2261 Type **611**, 39c.+19c. Blue figure and upper part of child with green head; 39c.+19c. Child and ball; 39c.+19c. Child with yellow head and raised arms; 39c.+19c. Child with brown head and left arm raised; 39c.+19c. Dog and child . . . . 4·00 2·20

612 Woman and Child

2002. Christmas. Multicoloured. Self-adhesive gum.
2262 29c. Type **612** 40 15
2263 29c. Seated man facing left 40 15
2264 29c. Profile with raised collar 40 15
2265 29c. Stream and figure wearing scarf 40 15
2266 29c. Woman, tree and snowflakes 40 15
2267 29c. Snowflakes and man wearing knee-length coat beside grasses 40 15
2268 29c. Snowflakes, man, and gate and stream 40 15
2269 29c. Snowflakes, windmill, stream and woman . . . 40 15
2270 29c. Seated man facing right 40 15
2271 29c. Willow tree and profile of child facing left 40 15
2272 29c. Man leaning against tree 40 15
2273 29c. Man with hands in pockets 40 15
2274 29c. Seated couple 40 15
2275 29c. Fir tree and man's profile facing left 40 15
2276 29c. Man carrying child on shoulders 40 15
2277 29c. Profile of boy facing right 40 15
2278 29c. Standing child facing left 40 15
2279 29c. Snowflakes, sea and upper part of man with raised collar 40 15
2280 29c. Sea behind man wearing hat and glasses 40 15
2281 29c. Figure with out-stretched arms 40 15
Nos. 2262/81 were issued together, se-tenant, the stamps arranged in strips of five, each strip forming a composite design.

613 "Landscape with Four Trees" **614** "Self-portrait with Straw Hat"

2003. 150th Birth Anniv of Vincent Van Gogh (artist). Multicoloured. (a) Ordinary gum.
2282 39c. Type **613** 55 25
2283 39c. "The Potato Eaters" . . 55 25
2284 39c. "Four Cut Sunflowers" 55 25
2285 39c. "Self-portrait with Grey Felt Hat" 55 25
2286 39c. "The Zouave" 55 25
2287 39c. "Place Du Forum Cafe Terrace by Night, Arles" 55 25
2288 39c. "Tree Trunks in Long Grass" 55 25
2289 39c. "Almond Blossom" . . 55 25
2290 39c. "Auvers-sur-Oise" . . . 55 25
2291 39c. "Wheatfield with Crows, Auvers-sur-Oise" 55 25

(b) Self-adhesive gum.
2292 39c. Type **614** 55 25
2293 59c. "Vase with Sunflowers" 55 25
2294 75c. "The Sower" 55 25

615 North Pier, Ijmuiden

2003. 50th Anniv of Floods in Zeeland, North Brabant and South Holland. Designs showing photographs from national archives. Each grey and black.

2295 39c. Type **615** 55 25
2296 39c. Hansweert Lock . . . 55 55
2297 39c. Building dam, Wieringermeer 55 25
2298 39c. Ijsselmeer Dam 55 25
2299 39c. Breached dyke, Willemstad 55 25
2300 39c. Repairing dyke, Stavenisse 55 25
2301 39c. Building dam, Zandkreek 55 25
2302 39c. Building dam, Grevelingen 55 25
2303 39c. Flood barrier, Oosterschelde 55 25
2304 39c. Floods, Roermond . . 55 25

616 See-through Register (security feature)

2003. 300th Anniv of Joh. Enschede (printers). Multicoloured.

2305 39c. Type **616** 55 25
2306 39c. Fleischman's musical notation 55 25

No. 2305 has the remaining symbols of the see-through register printed on the back over the gum. This forms a complete design when held up to the light.

No. 2305 was embossed with a notional barcode and No. 2306 with a security device.

617 Alstroemeria

2003. Flower Paintings. Multicoloured.

2307 39c.+19c. Type **617** 80 50
2308 39c.+19c. Sweet pea 80 50
2309 39c.+19c. Pansies 80 50
2310 39c.+19c. Trumpet vine . . 80 50
2311 39c.+19c. Lychnis 80 50
2312 39c.+19c. Irises 80 50

618 Oystercatcher

619 "39"

2003. Fauna of the Dutch Shallows. Winning Entry in Stamp Design Competition. Multicoloured.

MS2313 Two sheets, each 140×82 mm. (a) 39c. ×4, Type **618**; Spoonbill (horiz); Eider duck: Grey seal (horiz) (b) 59c. ×4, Herring gull; Curlew (horiz); Seals and gull; Crab (horiz) . . 5·25 5·25

MS2313 (b) were issued with "PRIORITY/ Prioritaire" label attached at either upper or lower edge.

2003. Greetings Stamps. Two sheets, each 122×170 mm, containing T **619** and similar vert designs. Multicoloured.

MS2314 (a) 39c. ×10, Type **619** (blue) (green) (purple) (pink) (orange) (yellow) (olive) (turquoise) (red) (brown); (b) 39c. ×10, Flowers; Flag; Present; Champagne glass; Medal; Guitar; Balloons; Cut-out figures; Slice of cake; Garland . . . . 10·50 10·50

Nos. **MS**2314a/b were each issued with a se-tenant label attached at left showing either Marjolein Bastin (artist); Paint tubes and splashes (painting, Marjolein Bastin); Humberto Tan (television presenter); Figures symbolising Red Cross; Daphne Deckers (presenter and actress); Fan-mail; Prime Minister Jan Balkenende; Palm top computer; Sien Diels (Sesame Street presenter); Tommie (character from Sesame Street) (**MS**2314a) or a girl (**MS**2314b). The labels could be personalised by the addition of a photograph for an inclusive fee of €12 for the first sheet and €5.95 for subsequent sheets bearing the same design.

620 Coffee Cup

2003. 250th Anniv of Douwe Egberts (coffee and tea retailers). Multicoloured.

2315 39c. Type **620** 55 10
2316 39c. As No. 2315 but with colours reversed 55 10

Nos. 2315/16 were impregnated with the scent of coffee which was released when the stamps were rubbed.

621 Airplane, Ship and Trucks

2003. Land, Air and Water. Winning Entry in Stamp Design Competition. Multicoloured.

2318 39c. Cat, bird, fish and envelope 55 10

622 Nelson Mandela and Child

2003. 85th Birth Anniv of Nelson Mandela (President of South Africa). Multicoloured.

2319 39c. Type **622** 55 10
2320 39c. Children (Nelson Mandela's Children's Fund) 55 10

623 "For You from Me"

2003. Self-adhesive gum.

2321 **623** 39c. multicoloured . . . 55 10

624 Children Kissing

625 "39"

2003. Winning Entries in Stamp Design Competition. Sheet 108×151 mm containing T **624** and similar horiz designs. Multicoloured.

MS2322 39c. ×10, Type **624**; Traditional costume; Cat; Puppies; Child; Bride and groom; 2CV cars; Motorcycle; Peacock butterfly; Flowers . . . . 5·50 5·50

2003. Company Stamp. Self adhesive.

2323 **626** 39c. multicoloured . . . 55 10

626 Coloured Squares

2003. Stamp Day. 75th Anniv of Netherlands Association of Stamp Dealers (NVPH).

2324 **626** 39c. multicoloured . . . 55 10

627 Notepad, Radio and Ballet Shoes

2003. Child Welfare. Sheet 147×76 mm containing T **627** and similar horiz designs. Multicoloured.

MS2325 39c.+19c. ×6, Type **627**; Masks and open book; Microphone, music notation and paint brush; Violin, pencil, football and television; Drum and light bulbs; Trumpet, light bulbs, hat and earphones . . . . . . 5·00 5·00

MARINE INSURANCE STAMPS

M 22

1921.

M238 M **22** 15c. green . . . . . 9·25 45·00
M239 60c. red . . . . . . 11·00 55·00
M240 75c. brown . . . . . 12·50 65·00
M241 – 1g.50 blue . . . . . 65·00 £500
M242 – 2g.25 brown £110 £700
M243 – 4½g. black £180 £850
M244 – 7½g. red £250 £1200

DESIGNS (inscr "DRIJVENDE BRANDKAST"): 1g.50, 2g.25, "Explosion"; 4½g., 7½g. Lifebelt.

OFFICIAL STAMPS

1913. Stamps of 1898 optd **ARMENWET**.

O214 **12** 1c. red . . . . 3·50 3·00
O215 1½c. blue . . . . 95 2·25
O216 2c. brown . . . . 6·25 7·00
O217 2½c. green . . . . 16·00 12·50
O218 **13** 3c. green . . . . 3·50 1·25
O219 5c. red . . . . 3·50 4·75
O220 10c. grey . . . . 35·00 40·00

POSTAGE DUE STAMPS

D 8

D 9

1870.

D76 D **8** 5c. brown on yellow . . 55·00 11·75
D77 10c. purple on blue . . . £110 15·00

For same stamps in other colours, see Netherlands Indies, Nos. D1/5.

1881.

D174 D **9** ½c. black and blue . . . 40 40
D175 1c. black and blue . . . 1·25 40
D176 1½c. black and blue . . 65 50
D177 2½c. black and blue . . 1·75 40
D178 3c. black and blue . . . 1·60 1·00
D179 4c. black and blue . . . 1·60 1·60
D180 5c. black and blue . . . 9·75 40
D181 6½c. black and blue . . 35·00 32·00
D182 7½c. black and blue . . 1·75 60
D183 10c. black and blue . . 28·00 50
D184 12½c. black and blue . . 23·00 1·25
D185 15c. black and blue . . 28·00 95
D186 20c. black and blue . . 24·00 6·25
D187 25c. black and blue . . 35·00 60
D188 1g. red and blue . . . 90·00 29·00

No. D188 is inscribed "EEN GULDEN".

1906. Surch.

D213 D **9** 3c. on 1g. red and blue 28·00 28·00
D215 4 on 6½c. black and blue . . . . 4·50 5·50
D216 6½ on 20c. black & blue 3·75 4·50
D214 50c. on 1g. red & blue £125 £125

1907. De Ruyter Commemoration. stamps surch **PORTZEGEL** and value.

D217A **15** ½c. on 1c. red . . . . . 1·25 1·25
D218A 1c. on 1c. red 70 70
D219A 1½c. on 1c. red 70 70
D220A 2½c. on 1c. red . . . . 1·60 1·60
D221A 5c. on 2½c. red . . . . 1·60 70
D222A 6½c. on 2½c. red . . . . 3·00 3·00
D223A 7½c. on ½c. blue . . . . 1·90 1·40
D224A 10c. on ½c. blue . . . . 1·90 95
D225A 12½c. on ½c. blue . . . 4·50 4·50
D226A 15c. on 2½c. red . . . . 6·25 3·75
D227A 25c. on ½c. blue . . . . 8·25 7·50
D228A 50c. on ½c. blue . . . . 40·00 35·00
D229A 1g. on ½c. blue . . . . 60·00 48·00

1912. Re-issue of Type D **9** in one colour.

D230 D **9** ½c. blue 40 40
D231 1c. blue 40 40
D232 1½c. blue . . . . 2·00 1·75
D233 2½c. blue 60 40
D234 3c. blue . . . . 1·10 70
D235 4c. blue 55 55
D236 4½c. blue . . . . 5·00 4·75
D237 5c. blue 65 55
D238 5½c. blue . . . . 4·75 4·50
D239 7c. blue . . . . 2·25 2·25
D240 7½c. blue . . . . 3·25 1·60
D241 10c. blue . . . . 1·10 55
D242 12½c. blue 55 55
D453 15c. blue 55 55
D244 20c. blue 55 40
D245 25c. blue . . . . 65·00 95
D246 50c. blue 55 40

D 25

D 121

1921.

D442 D **25** 3c. blue 75 20
D445 6c. blue 40 40
D446 7c. blue 55 55
D447 7½c. blue 55 50
D448 8c. blue 70 40
D449 9c. blue 65 65
D450 11c. blue . . . . . . 9·50 3·25
D247 12c. blue 50 40
D455 25c. blue 50 40
D456 30c. blue 50 40
D458 1g. red 70 40

1923. Surch in white figures in black circle.

D272 D **9** 1c. on 3c. blue 70 70
D273 2½c. on 7c. blue . . . . 1·10 55
D274 25c. on 1½c. blue . . . 8·25 70
D275 25c. on 7½c. blue . . . 9·25 55

1924. Stamps of 1898 surch **TE BETALEN PORT** and value in white figures in black circle.

D295 **13** 4c. on 3c. green . . . . 1·40 1·25
D296 **12** 5c. on 1c. red 70 40
D297 10c. on 1½c. blue . . . . 1·10 50
D298 **13** 12½c. on 5c. red . . . . 1·25 50

1947.

D656 D **121** 1c. blue 20 20
D657 3c. blue 20 25
D658 4c. blue . . . . . . 9·25 95
D659 5c. blue 20 20
D660 6c. blue 40 40
D661 7c. blue 25 25
D662 8c. blue 25 25
D663 10c. blue 25 20
D664 11c. blue 50 50
D665 12c. blue 95 85
D666 14c. blue 95 70
D667 15c. blue 40 20
D668 16c. blue 85 85
D669 20c. blue 35 25
D670 24c. blue . . . . . . 1·25 1·25
D671 25c. blue 40 25
D672 26c. blue . . . . . . 1·40 1·60
D673 30c. blue 60 20
D674 35c. blue 70 20
D675 40c. blue 70 20
D676 50c. blue 95 25
D677 60c. blue . . . . . . 1·00 50
D678 85c. blue . . . . . . 15·00 55
D679 90c. blue . . . . . . 3·00 65
D680 95c. blue . . . . . . 3·00 65
D681 1g. red . . . . 2·25 20
D682 1g.75 red . . . . . . 5·50 35

For stamps as Types D **121**, but in violet, see under Surinam.

INTERNATIONAL COURT OF JUSTICE

Stamps specially issued for use by the Headquarters of the Court of International Justice. Nos. J1 to J36 were not sold to the public in unused condition.

1934. Optd **COUR PER- MANENTE DE JUSTICE INTER- NATIONALE**.

J1 **35** 1½c. mauve . . . . — 55
J2 2½c. green . . . . — 55
J3 **36** 7½c. red . . . . — 95
J4 **68** 12½c. blue . . . . — 25·00
J7 **36** 12½c. blue . . . . — 18·00
J5 15c. yellow . . . . — 1·25
J6 3c. purple . . . . — 2·25

1940. Optd **COUR PER- MANANTE DE JUSTICE INTER- NATIONALE**.

J 9 **94** 7½c. red . . . . — 9·25
J10 12½c. blue . . . . — 9·25
J11 15c. blue . . . . — 9·25
J12 30c. bistre . . . . — 9·25

1947. Optd **COUR INTERNATIONALE DE JUSTICE**.

J13 **94** 7½c. red . . . . — 1·10
J14 10c. purple . . . . — 1·10
J15 12½c. blue . . . . — 1·10
J16 20c. violet . . . . — 1·10
J17 25c. red . . . . — 1·10

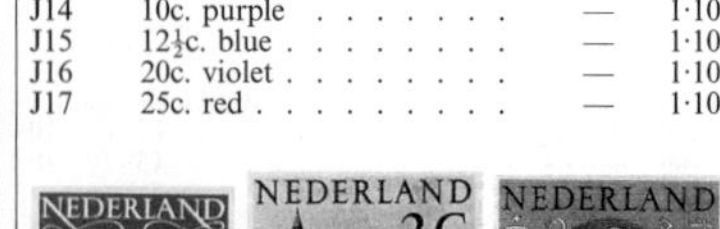

J 3

J 4 Peace Palace, The Hague

J 5 Queen Juliana

1950.

J18 J **3** 2c. blue . . . . — 8·25
J19 4c. green . . . . — 8·25

1951.

J20 J **4** 2c. lake . . . . — 60
J21 3c. blue . . . . — 60
J22 4c. green . . . . — 60
J23 5c. brown . . . . — 60
J24 J **5** 6c. mauve . . . . — 2·10
J25 J **4** 6c. green . . . . — 90
J26 7c. red . . . . — 90
J27 J **5** 10c. green . . . . — 20
J28 12c. red . . . . — 1·75

J29 15c. red . . . . — 20
J30 20c. blue . . . . — 25
J31 25c. brown . . . . — 25
J32 30c. purple . . . . — 40
J33 **J 4** 40c. blue . . . . — 35
J34 45c. red . . . . — 50
J35 50c. mauve . . . . — 55
J36 **J 5** 1g. grey . . . . — 65

J 6 Olive Branch and Peace Palace, The Hague

1989.
J37 **J 6** 5c. black and yellow . . . 15 15
J38 10c. black and blue . . . 15 15
J39 25c. black and red 20 20
J41 50c. black and green . . . 35 40
J42 55c. black and mauve . . . 40 35
J43 60c. black and bistre . . . 40 45
J44 65c. black and green . . . 40 45
J45 70c. black and blue . . . 45 50
J46 75c. black and yellow . . 45 60
J47 80c. black and green . . . 50 65
J49 1g. black and orange . . . 65 75
J50 1g.50 black and blue . . . 95 1·25
J51 1g.60 black and brown . . 1·00 1·25
J54 – 5g. multicoloured . . . . 3·50 3·75
J56 – 7g. multicoloured . . . . 4·25 5·00
DESIGNS: 5, 7g. Olive branch and column.

NETHERLANDS ANTILLES Pt. 4

Curacao and other Netherlands islands in the Caribbean Sea. In December 1954 these were placed on an equal footing with Netherlands under the Crown.

100 cents = 1 gulden.

48 Spanish Galleon

49 Alonso de Ojeda

1949. 450th Anniv of Discovery of Curacao.
306 **48** 6c. green . . . . 3·25 2·00
307 **49** 12½c. red . . . . 4·00 3·25
308 **48** 15c. blue . . . . 4·00 2·50

50 Posthorns and Globe

51 Leap-frog

1949. 75th Anniv of U.P.U.
309 **50** 6c. red . . . . 4·00 2·75
310 25c. blue . . . . 4·00 1·25

1950. As numeral and portrait types of Netherlands but inscr "NED. ANTILLEN".
325 **118** 1c. brown 10 10
326 1½c. blue 10 10
327 2c. orange 10 10
328 2½c. green 90 20
329 3c. violet 20 10
329a 4c. green 60 35
330 5c. red 10 10
310a **129** 5c. yellow 20 10
311 6c. purple . . . . . . 1·40 10
311a 7½c. brown . . . . . . 5·50 10
312a 10c. red . . . . 1·60 1·60
313 12½c. green . . . . . . 2·50 20
314a 15c. blue 30 10
315a 20c. orange 40 25
316 21c. black . . . . 2·50 1·60
316a 22½c. green . . . . . . 6·25 10
317a 25c. violet 50 35
318 27½c. brown . . . . . . 7·25 1·50
319a 30c. sepia . . . . 1·10 70
319b 40c. blue 55 45
320 50c. olive . . . . 11·00 10
321 **130** 1½g. green . . . . 45·00 25
322 2½g. brown . . . . . . 50·00 1·60
323 5g. red . . . . 65·00 11·00
324 10g. purple . . . . . . £200 65·00

1951. Child Welfare.
331 **51** 1½c.+1c. violet . . . . . 7·25 1·10
332 – 5c.+2½c. brown . . . . . 9·50 3·25
333 – 6c.+2½c. blue . . . . . . 9·50 3·75
334 – 12½c.+5c. red . . . . . . 11·00 4·25
335 – 25c.+10c. turquoise . . . . 10·50 3·25
DESIGNS: 5c. Kite-flying; 6c. Girl on swing; 12½c. Girls playing "Oranges and Lemons"; 25c. Bowling hoops.

52 Gull over Ship

54 Fort Beekenburg

1952. Seamen's Welfare Fund. Inscr "ZEEMANSWELVAREN".
336 **52** 1½c.+1c. green . . . . . . 7·25 1·25
337 – 6c.+4c. brown . . . . . . 9·00 3·25
338 – 12½c.+7c. mauve . . . . . 9·00 3·50
339 – 15c.+10c. blue . . . . . . 11·00 4·25
340 – 25c.+15c. red . . . . . . 10·50 4·25
DESIGNS: 6c. Sailor and lighthouse; 12½c. Sailor on ship's prow; 15c. Tanker in harbour; 25c. Anchor and compass.

1953. Netherlands Flood Relief Fund. No. 321 surch **22½ Ct. +7½ Ct. WATERSNOOD NEDERLAND 1953.**
341 **130** 22½c.+7½c. on 1½g. green 1·25 1·25

1953. 250th Anniv of Fort Beekenburg.
342 **54** 22½c. brown . . . . 5·00 50

55 Aruba Beach

1954. 3rd Caribbean Tourist Assn Meeting.
343 **55** 15c. blue and buff . . . . 5·00 2·75

1954. Ratification of Statute of the Kingdom. As No. 809 of Netherlands.
344 **158** 7½c. green 90 85

56 "Anglo" Flower

1955. Child Welfare.
345 **56** 1½c.+1c. bl, yell & turq . . 1·75 80
346 – 7½c.+5c. red, yellow & vio 3·75 2·25
347 – 15c.+5c. red, grn & olive 3·75 2·40
348 – 22½c.+7½c. red, yell & bl 3·75 2·25
349 – 25c.+10c. red, yell & grey 3·75 2·40
FLOWERS: 7½c. White Cayenne; 15c. "French" flower; 22½c. Cactus; 25c. Red Cayenne.

57 Prince Bernhard and Queen Juliana

1955. Royal Visit.
350 **57** 7½c.+2½c. red 20 20
351 22½c.+7½c. blue . . . . . 1·10 1·10

59 Oil Refinery

1955. 21st Meeting of Caribbean Commission.
352 – 15c. blue, green and brown 3·75 2·40
353 **59** 25c. blue, green and brown 4·50 2·75
DESIGN (rectangle, 36 × 25 mm): 15c. Aruba Beach.

60 St. Anne Bay

1956. 10th Anniv of Caribbean Commission.
354 **60** 15c. blue, red and black . . 35 35

61 Lord Baden-Powell

1957. 50th Anniv of Boy Scout Movement.
355 **61** 6c.+1½c. yellow 60 55
356 7½c.+2½c. green 60 55
357 15c.+5c. red 60 55

62 "Dawn of Health"

1957. 1st Caribbean Mental Health Congress, Aruba.
358 **62** 15c. black and yellow . . . 35 35

63 Saba

1957. Tourist Publicity. Multicoloured.
359 7½c. Type **63** 45 45
360 15c. St. Maarten 45 45
361 25c. St. Eustatius 45 45

64 Footballer

65 Curacao Intercontinental Hotel

1957. 8th Central American and Caribbean Football Championships.
362 **64** 6c.+2½c. orange 95 75
363 – 7½c.+5c. red . . . . . . 1·40 1·10
364 – 15c.+5c. green . . . . . . 1·40 1·10
365 – 22½c.+7½c. blue . . . . . 1·40 90
DESIGNS—HORIZ: 7½c. Caribbean map. VERT: 15c. Goalkeeper saving ball; 22½c. Footballers with ball.

1957. Opening of Curacao Intercontinental Hotel.
366 **65** 15c. blue 35 35

66 Map of Curacao

67 American Kestrel

1957. International Geophysical Year.
367 **66** 15c. deep blue and blue . . 75 75

1958. Child Welfare. Bird design inscr "VOOR HET KIND". Multicoloured.
368 2½c.+1c. Type **67** 50 30
369 7½c.+1½c. Yellow oriole . . . 95 80
370 15c.+2½c. Scaly-breasted ground doves . . . . . . 1·10 1·00
371 22½c.+2½c. Brown-throated conure . . . . 1·25 90

68 Greater Flamingoes (Bonaire)

1958. Size 33½ × 22 mm.
372 **68** 6c. pink and green . . . 1·90 15
373 A 7½c. yellow and brown . . 20 15
374 8c. yellow and blue . . . 20 15
375 B 10c. yellow and grey . . . 20 15
376 C 12c. grey and green . . . 20 15
377 D 15c. blue and green . . . 20 15
377a 15c. lilac and green . . . 15 10
378 E 20c. grey and red 20 15
379 A 25c. green and blue . . . 30 15
380 D 30c. green and brown . . 30 15
381 E 35c. pink and grey . . . 35 15
382 C 40c. green and mauve . . 50 15
383 B 45c. blue and violet . . . 50 15
384 **68** 50c. pink and brown . . . 50 15
385 E 55c. green and red 55 25
386 **68** 65c. pink and green . . . 65 30
387 D 70c. orange and purple . . 1·25 50
388 **68** 75c. pink and violet . . . 70 50
389 B 85c. green and brown . . 80 70
390 E 90c. orange and blue . . 90 90
391 C 95c. yellow and orange . . 1·10 1·00
392 D 1g. grey and red . . . . 1·00 15
393 A 1½g. brown and violet . . 1·40 20
394 C 2½g. yellow and blue . . . 2·40 40
395 B 5g. mauve and brown . . 5·00 75
396 **68** 10g. pink and blue . . . 9·00 5·00
DESIGNS: A. Dutch Colonial houses (Curacao); B. Mountain and palms (Saba); C. Town Hall (St. Maarten); D. Church tower (Aruba); E. Memorial obelisk (St. Eustatius).

For larger versions of some values see Nos. 653/6.

69

1958. 50th Anniv of Netherlands Antilles Radio and Telegraph Administration.
397 **69** 7½c. lake and blue 20 20
398 15c. blue and red 35 35

70 Red Cross Flag and Antilles Map

71 Aruba Caribbean Hotel

1958. Neth. Antilles Red Cross Fund. Cross in red.
399 **70** 6c.+2c. brown 30 30
400 7½c.+2½c. green 55 55
401 15c.+5c. yellow 55 55
402 22½c.+7½c. blue 55 55

1959. Opening of Aruba Caribbean Hotel.
403 **71** 15c. multicoloured 35 35

72 Zeeland

1959. Curacao Monuments Preservation Fund. Multicoloured.
404 6c.+1½c. Type **72** . . . . . 1·25 90
405 7½c.+2½c. Saba Island . . . 1·25 90
406 15c.+5c. Molenplein (vert) . . 1·25 90
407 22½c.+7½c. Scharloobrug . . 1·25 90
408 25c.+7½c. Brievengat . . . . 1·25 90

73 Water-distillation Plant

74 Antilles Flag

1959. Inauguration of Aruba Water-distillation Plant.
409 **73** 20c. light blue and blue . . 50 50

1959. 5th Anniv of Ratification of Statute of the Kingdom.
410 **74** 10c. red, blue and light blue 50 35
411 20c. red, blue and yellow 50 35
412 25c. red, blue and green . . 50 35

75 Fokker F.XVIII "De Snip" over Caribbean

76 Mgr. Niewindt

1959. 25th Anniv of K.L.M. Netherlands–Curacao Air Service. Each yellow, deep blue and blue.
413 10c. Type **75** 50 35
414 20c. Fokker F.XVIII "De Snip" over globe 50 35

415 25c. Douglas DC-7C "Seven Seas" over Handelskade (bridge), Willemstad . . . 50 15
416 35c. Douglas DC-8 at Aruba Airport 50 55

1960. Death Centenary of Mgr. M. J. Niewindt.
417 **76** 10c. purple 55 45
418 20c. violet 55 55
419 25c. olive 55 55

77 Flag and Oil-worker

78 Frogman

1960. Labour Day.
420 **77** 20c. multicoloured 45 45

1960. Princess Wilhelmina Cancer Relief Fund. Inscr "KANKERBESTRIJDING".
421 **78** 10c.+2c. blue . . . . . . 1·40 1·10
422 – 20c.+3c. multicoloured . . 1·40 1·40
423 – 25c.+5c. red, blue & blk 1·40 1·40
DESIGNS—HORIZ: 20c. Queen angelfish; 25c. Big-scaled soldierfish.

79 Child on Bed

1961. Child Welfare. Inscr "voor het kind".
424 6c.+2c. black and green . . . 35 30
425 10c.+3c. black and red . . . 35 30
426 20c.+6c. black and yellow . . 35 30
427 25c.+8c. black and orange . . 35 30
DESIGNS: 6c. Type **79**; 10c. Girl with doll; 20c. Boy with bucket; 25c. Children in classroom.

80 Governor's Salute to the American Naval Brig "Andrew Doria" at St. Eustatius

1961. 185th Anniv of 1st Salute to the American Flag.
428 **80** 20c. multicoloured 65 65

1962. Royal Silver Wedding. As T **187** of Netherlands.
429 10c. orange 30 30
430 25c. blue 30 30

81 Jaja (nursemaid) and Child

82 Knight and World Map

1962. Cultural Series.
431 – 6c. brown and yellow . . . 35 30
432 – 10c. multicoloured 35 30
433 – 20c. multicoloured 35 35
434 **81** 25c. brown, green and black 35 35
MS435 108 × 134 mm. Nos. 431/4 1·90 1·90
DESIGNS: 6c. Corn-masher; 10c. Benta player; 20c. Petji kerchief.

1962. 5th International Candidates Chess Tournament, Curacao.
436 **82** 10c.+5c. green 95 70
437 20c.+10c. red 95 70
438 25c.+10c. blue 95 70

1963. Freedom from Hunger. No. 378 surch **TEGEN DE HONGER** wheat sprig and **+10c.**
439 20c.+10c. grey and red . . . 55 55

84 Family Group

1963. 4th Caribbean Mental Health Congress, Curacao.
440 **84** 20c. buff and blue 30 30
441 – 25c. red and blue 30 30
DESIGN: 25c. Egyptian Cross emblem.

85 "Freedom"

1963. Centenary of Abolition of Slavery in Dutch West Indies.
442 **85** 25c. brown and yellow . . 35 30

86 Hotel Bonaire

1963. Opening of Hotel Bonaire.
443 **86** 20c. brown 35 30

87 Child and Flowers

88 Test-tube and Flask

1963. Child Welfare. Child Art. Multicoloured.
444 5c.+2c. Type **87** 35 30
445 6c.+3c. Children and flowers (horiz) 35 30
446 10c.+5c. Girl with ball (horiz) 35 30
447 20c.+10c. Men with flags (horiz) 35 30
448 25c.+12c. Schoolboy 35 30

1963. 150th Anniv of Kingdom of the Netherlands. As No. 968 of Netherlands, but smaller, 26 × 27 mm.
449 25c. green, red and black . . 35 30

1963. Chemical Industry, Aruba.
450 **88** 20c. red, light green and green 45 45

89 Winged Letter

1964. 35th Anniv of 1st U.S.–Curacao Flight. Multicoloured.
451 20c. Type **89** 35 35
452 25c. Route map, Sikorsky S-38 flying boat and Boeing 707 . . . . 35 35

90 Trinitaria

1964. Child Welfare. Multicoloured.
453 6c.+3c. Type **90** 30 30
454 10c.+5c. Magdalena 30 30
455 20c.+10c. Yellow keiki . . . 30 30
456 25c.+11c. Bellisima 30 30

91 Caribbean Map

1964. 5th Caribbean Council Assembly.
457 **91** 20c. yellow, red and blue 35 30

92 "Six Islands"

93 Princess Beatrix

1964. 10th Anniv of Statute for the Kingdom.
458 **92** 25c. multicoloured 35 30

1965. Visit of Princess Beatrix.
459 **93** 25c. red 35 35

94 I.T.U. Emblem and Symbols

1965. Centenary of I.T.U.
460 **94** 10c. deep blue and blue . . 20 20

95 "Asperalla" (tanker) at Curacao

1965. 50th Anniv of Curacao's Oil Industry. Multicoloured.
461 10c. Catalytic cracking plant (vert) 30 20
462 20c. Type **95** 30 20
463 25c. Super fractionating plant (vert) 30 30

96 Flag and Fruit Market, Curacao

1965.
464 **96** 1c. blue, red and green . . 10 10
465 – 2c. blue, red and yellow . . 10 10
466 – 3c. blue, red and cobalt . . 10 10
467 – 4c. blue, red and orange 10 10
468 – 5c. blue, red and blue . . . 20 10
469 – 6c. blue, red and pink . . 20 10
DESIGNS (Flag and): 2c. Divi-divi tree; 3c. Lace; 4c. Greater flamingoes; 5c. Church; 6c. Lobster. Each is inscr with a different place-name.

97 Cup Sponges

1965. Child Welfare. Marine Life. Multicoloured.
470 6c.+3c. Type **97** 20 20
471 10c.+5c. Cup sponges (diff) 20 20
472 20c.+10c. Sea anemones on star coral 30 20
473 25c.+11c. Basket sponge, blue chromis and "Brain" coral 35 30

98 Marine and Seascape

99 Budgerigars and Wedding Rings

1965. Tercentenary of Marine Corps.
474 **98** 25c. multicoloured 20 20

1966. Intergovernmental Committee for European Migration (I.C.E.M.) Fund. As T **215** of Netherlands.
475 35c.+15c. bistre and brown 30 30

1966. Marriage of Crown Princess Beatrix and Herr Claus von Amsberg.
476 **99** 25c. multicoloured 30 20

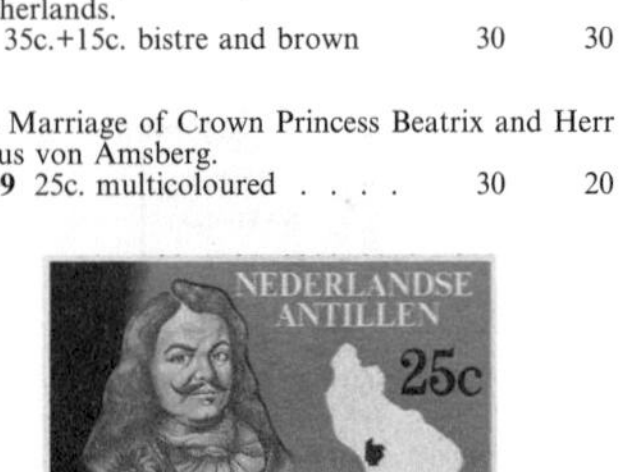

100 Admiral de Ruyter and Map

1966. 300th Anniv of Admiral de Ruyter's Visit to St. Eustatius.
477 **100** 25c. ochre, violet and blue 20 20

101 "Grammar"

102 Cooking

1966. 25 Years of Secondary Education.
478 **101** 6c. black, blue and yellow 20 20
479 – 10c. black, red and green 20 20
480 – 20c. black, blue and yellow 30 20
481 – 25c. black, red and green 30 20
DESIGNS: The "Free Arts", figures representing: 10c. "Rhetoric" and "Dialect"; 20c. "Arithmetic" and "Geometry"; 25c. "Astronomy" and "Music".

1966. Child Welfare. Multicoloured.
482 6c.+3c. Type **102** 20 20
483 10c.+5c. Nursing 20 20
484 20c.+10c. Metal-work fitting 30 20
485 25c.+11c. Ironing 30 20

103 "Gelderland" (cruiser)

1967. 60th Anniv of Royal Netherlands Navy League.
486 **103** 6c. bronze and green . . 20 20
487 – 10c. ochre and yellow . . 20 20
488 – 20c. brown and sepia . . 30 20
489 – 25c. blue and indigo . . . 30 20
SHIPS: 10c. "Pioneer" (schooner); 20c. "Oscilla" (tanker); 25c. "Santa Rosa" (liner).

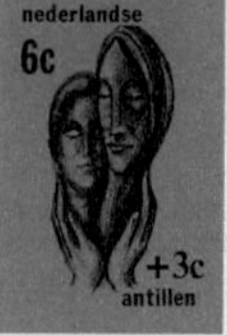

104 M. C. Piar

105 "Heads in Hands"

1967. 150th Death Anniv of Manuel Piar (patriot).
490 **104** 20c. brown and red . . . 30 20

1967. Cultural and Social Relief Funds.
491 **105** 6c.+3c. black and blue . . 20 20
492 10c.+5c. black & mauve 20 20
493 20c.+10c. purple 30 20
494 25c.+11c. blue 30 20

106 "The Turtle and the Monkey"

107 Olympic Flame and Rings

1967. Child Welfare. "Nanzi" Fairy Tales. Mult.
495 6c.+3c. "Princess Long Nose" (vert) 20 20
496 10c.+5c. Type **106** 20 20

497 20c.+10c. "Nanzi (spider) and the Tiger" 30 20
498 25c.+11c. "Shon Arey's Balloon" (vert) 90 70

1968. Olympic Games, Mexico. Multicoloured.
499 10c. Type **107** 30 30
500 20c. "Throwing the discus" (statue) 30 30
501 25c. Stadium and doves 30 30

108 "Dance of the Ribbons"

1968. Cultural and Social Relief Funds.
502 **108** 10c.+5c. multicoloured 20 20
503 15c.+5c. multicoloured 20 20
504 20c.+10c. multicoloured 30 20
505 25c.+10c. multicoloured 30 20

109 Boy with Goat

1968. Child Welfare Fund. Multicoloured.
506 6c.+3c. Type **109** 20 20
507 10c.+5c. Girl with dog 20 20
508 20c.+10c. Boy with cat 30 20
509 25c.+11c. Girl with duck 30 20

110 Fokker Friendship 500

111 Radio Pylon, "Waves" and Map

1968. Dutch Antillean Airlines.
510 **110** 10c. blue, black and yellow 30 30
511 – 20c. blue, black and brown 30 30
512 – 25c. blue, black and pink 30 30
DESIGNS: 20c. Douglas DC-9; 25c. Fokker Friendship 500 in flight and Douglas DC-9 on ground.

1969. Opening of Broadcast Relay Station, Bonaire.
513 **111** 25c. green, dp blue & blue 30 30

112 "Code of Laws"

113 "Carnival"

1969. Centenary of Netherlands Antilles Court of Justice.
514 **112** 20c. green, gold & lt green 30 30
515 – 25c. multicoloured 30 30
DESIGN: 25c. "Scales of Justice".

1969. Cultural and Social Relief Funds. Antilles' Festivals. Multicoloured.
516 10c.+5c. Type **113** 35 35
517 15c.+5c. "Harvest Festival" 35 35
518 20c.+10c. "San Juan Day" 35 35
519 25c.+10c. "New Years' Day" 35 35

114 I.L.O. Emblem, "Koenoekoe" House and Cacti

1969. 50th Anniv of I.L.O.
520 **114** 10c. black and blue 20 20
521 25c. black and red 30 20

115 Boy playing Guitar

118 St. Anna Church, Otrabanda, Curacao

117 Radio Station, Bonaire

1969. Child Welfare.
522 **115** 6c.+3c. violet & orange 30 30
523 – 10c.+5c. green & yellow 35 35
524 – 20c.+10c. red and blue 35 35
525 – 25c.+11c. brown & pink 40 40
DESIGNS: 10c. Girl playing recorder; 20c. Boy playing "marimula"; 25c. Girl playing piano.

1969. 15th Anniv of Statute of the Kingdom. As T **240** of the Netherlands, but inscr "NEDERLANDSE ANTILLEN".
526 25c. multicoloured 30 30

1970. 5th Anniv of Trans-World Religious Radio Station, Bonaire. Multicoloured.
527 10c. Type **117** 20 20
528 15c. Trans-World Radio emblem 20 20

1970. Churches of the Netherlands Antilles. Mult.
529 10c. Type **118** 35 30
530 20c. "Mikve Israel-Emanuel" Synagogue, Punda, Curacao (horiz) 35 30
531 25c. Pulpit Fort Church Curacao 35 30

119 "The Press"

120 Mother and Child

1970. Cultural and Social Relief Funds. "Mass-media". Multicoloured.
532 10c.+5c. Type **119** 50 50
533 15c.+5c. "Films" 50 50
534 20c.+10c. "Radio" 50 50
535 25c.+10c. "Television" 50 50

1970. Child Welfare. Multicoloured.
536 6c.+3c. Type **120** 50 50
537 10c.+5c. Child with piggy-bank 50 50
538 20c.+10c. Children's Judo 50 50
539 25c.+11c. "Pick-a-back" 50 50

121 St. Theresia's Church, St. Nicolaas, Aruba

122 Lions Emblem

1971. 40th Anniv of St. Theresia Parish, Aruba.
540 **121** 20c. multicoloured 30 30

1971. 25th Anniv of Curacao Lions Club.
541 **122** 25c. multicoloured 35 35

123 Charcoal Stove

125 Admiral Brion

1971. Cultural and Social Relief Funds. Household Utensils. Multicoloured.
542 10c.+5c. Type **123** 55 55
543 15c.+5c. Earthenware water vessel 55 55
544 20c.+10c. Baking oven 55 55
545 25c.+10c. Kitchen implements 55 55

1971. Prince Bernhard's 60th Birthday. Design as No. 1135 of Netherlands.
546 45c. multicoloured 55 55

1971. 150th Death Anniv of Admiral Pedro Luis Brion.
547 **125** 40c. multicoloured 35 35

126 Bottle Doll

127 Queen Emma Bridge, Curacao

1971. Child Welfare. Home-made Toys. Mult.
548 15c.+5c. Type **126** 65 65
549 20c.+10c. Simple cart 65 65
550 30c.+15c. Spinning-tops 65 65

1971. Views of the Islands. Multicoloured.
551 1c. Type **127** 10 10
552 2c. The Bottom, Saba 10 10
553 3c. Greater flamingoes, Bonaire 10 10
554 4c. Distillation plant, Aruba 10 10
555 5c. Fort Amsterdam, St. Maarten 20 10
556 6c. Fort Oranje, St. Eustatius 20 10

128 Ship in Dock

129 Steel Band

1972. Inauguration of New Dry Dock Complex, Willemstad, Curacao.
557 **128** 30c. multicoloured 35 35

1972. Cultural and Social Relief Funds. Folklore. Multicoloured.
558 15c.+5c. Type **129** 70 70
559 20c.+10c. "Seu" festival 70 70
560 30c.+15c. "Tambu" dance 70 70

130 J. E. Irausquin

131 Dr. M. F. da Costa Gomez

1972. 10th Death Anniv of Juan Enrique Irausquin (Antilles statesman).
561 **130** 30c. red 35 35

1972. 65th Birth Anniv of Moises F. da Costa Gomez (statesman).
562 **131** 30c. black and green 35 35

132 Child playing with Earth

133 Pedestrian Crossing

1972. Child Welfare. Multicoloured.
563 15c.+5c. Type **132** 75 75
564 20c.+10c. Child playing in water 75 75
565 30c.+15c. Child throwing ball into the air 75 75

1973. Cultural and Social Relief Funds. Road Safety.
566 **133** 12c.+6c. multicoloured 80 80
567 – 15c.+7c. grn, orge & red 80 80
568 – 40c.+20c. multicoloured 80 80
DESIGNS: 15c. Road-crossing patrol; 40c. Traffic lights.

134 William III (portrait from stamp of 1873)

135 Map of Aruba, Curacao and Bonaire

1973. Stamp Centenary.
569 **134** 15c. violet, mauve and gold 35 25
570 – 20c. multicoloured 50 35
571 – 30c. multicoloured 50 35
DESIGNS: 20c. Antilles postman; 30c. Postal Service emblem.

1973. Inauguration of Submarine Cable and Microwave Telecommunications Link. Multicoloured.
572 15c. Type **135** 50 45
573 30c. Six stars ("The Antilles") 50 45
574 45c. Map of Saba, St. Maarten and St. Eustatius 50 45
MS575 145 × 50 mm. Nos. 572/4 2·25 1·75

136 Queen Juliana

137 Jan Eman

1973. Silver Jubilee of Queen Juliana's Reign.
576 **136** 15c. multicoloured 55 55

1973. 16th Death Anniv of Jan Eman (Aruba statesman).
577 **137** 30c. black and green 35 35

138 "1948–1973"

139 L. B. Scott

1973. Child Welfare Fund. 25th Anniv of 1st Child Welfare Stamps.
578 **138** 15c.+5c. light green, green and blue 70 70
579 – 20c.+10c. brown, green and blue 70 70
580 – 30c.+15c. violet, blue and light blue 70 70
MS581 108 × 75 mm. Nos. 578 × 2, 579 × 2 3·50 3·25
DESIGNS: No. 579, Three Children; 580, Mother and child.

1974. 8th Death Anniv of Lionel B. Scott (St. Maarten statesman).
582 **139** 30c. multicoloured 35 35

140 Family Meal

141 Girl combing Hair

1974. Family Planning Campaign. Multicoloured.
583 6c. Type **140** 20 20
584 12c. Family at home 30 30
585 15c. Family in garden 35 30

1974. Cultural and Social Relief Funds. "The Younger Generation". Multicoloured.
586 12c.+6c. Type **141** 1·00 90
587 15c.+7c. "Pop dancers" 1·00 90
588 40c.+20c. Group drummer 1·00 90

142 Desulphurisation Plant

1974. 50th Anniv of Lago Oil Co, Aruba. Mult.
589 15c. Type **142** 30 30
590 30c. Fractionating towers . . 35 35
591 45c. Lago refinery at night 55 55

143 U.P.U. Emblem **144** "A Carpenter outranks a King"

1974. Centenary of Universal Postal Union.
592 **143** 15c. gold, green and black 50 45
593 30c. gold, blue and black 50 45

1974. Child Welfare. Children's Songs. Mult.
594 15c.+5c. Type **144** 80 80
595 20c.+10c. Footprints ("Let's Do a Ring-dance") 80 80
596 30c.+15c. "Moon and Sun" 80 80

145 Queen Emma Bridge **146** Ornamental Ventilation Grid

1975. Antillean Bridges. Multicoloured.
597 20c. Type **145** 45 45
598 30c. Queen Juliana Bridge . . 45 45
599 40c. Queen Wilhelmina Bridge 55 55

1975. Cultural and Social Welfare Funds.
600 **146** 12c.+6c. multicoloured . . 70 70
601 – 15c.+7c. brown & stone 70 70
602 – 40c.+20c. multicoloured 70 70
DESIGNS: 15c. Knight accompanied by buglers (tombstone detail); 40c. Foundation stone.

147 Sodium Chloride Molecules

1975. Bonaire Salt Industry. Multicoloured.
603 15c. Type **147** 50 35
604 20c. Salt incrustation and blocks 50 45
605 40c. Map of salt area (vert) 55 45

148 Fokker F.XVIII "De Snip" and Old Control Tower

1975. 40th Anniv of Aruba Airport. Mult.
606 15c. Type **148** 35 25
607 30c. Douglas DC-9-30 and modern control tower . . . 50 35
608 40c. Tail of Boeing 727-200 and "Princess Beatrix" Airport buildings 50 45

149 I.W.Y. Emblem

1975. International Women's Year. Multicoloured.
609 6c. Type **149** 20 20
610 12c. "Social Development" 35 25
611 20c. "Equality of Sexes" . . 50 35

150 Children making Windmill

1975. Child Welfare. Multicoloured.
612 15c.+5c. Type **150** 70 70
613 20c.+10c. Child modelling clay 70 70
614 30c.+15c. Children drawing pictures 70 70

151 Beach, Aruba **152** J. A. Abraham (statesman)

1976. Tourism. Multicoloured.
615 40c. Type **151** 55 55
616 40c. Fish Kiosk, Bonaire . . 55 55
617 40c. "Table Mountain", Curacao 55 55

1976. Abraham Commemoration.
618 **152** 30c. purple on brown . . 45 45

153 Dyke Produce **154** Arm holding Child

1976. Agriculture, Animal Husbandry and Fisheries. Multicoloured.
619 15c. Type **153** 35 25
620 35c. Cattle 55 45
621 45c. Fishes 55 50

1976. Child Welfare. "Carrying the Child".
622 **154** 20c.+10c. multicoloured 70 65
623 – 25c.+12c. multicoloured 70 65
624 – 40c.+18c. multicoloured 70 65
DESIGNS—HORIZ: 25c. VERT: 40c. Both similar to Type **154** showing arm holding child.

155 "Andrew Doria" (naval brig) receiving Salute **156** Carnival Costume

1976. Bicentenary of American Revolution. Multicoloured.
625 25c. Flags and plaque, Fort Oranje 70 45
626 40c. Type **155** 70 45
627 55c. Johannes de Graaff, Governor of St. Eustatius 70 70

1977. Carnival.
628 – 25c. multicoloured 55 50
629 **156** 35c. multicoloured 55 50
630 – 40c. multicoloured 55 50
DESIGNS: 25c., 40c. Women in Carnival costumes.

157 Tortoise (Bonaire) **158** "Ace" Playing Card

1977. Rock Paintings. Multicoloured.
631 25c. Bird (Aruba) 50 35
632 35c. Abstract (Curaca) . . . 50 45
633 40c. Type **157** 55 45

1977. Sixth Central American and Caribbean Bridge Championships. Multicoloured.
634 **158** 20c.+10c. red and black 50 35
635 – 25c.+12c. multicoloured 50 50
636 – 40c.+18c. multicoloured 65 65
MS637 75 × 108 mm. Nos. 634/5 × 2
DESIGNS—VERT: 25c. "King" playing card. HORIZ: 40c. Bridge hand.

158 "Ace" Playing Card

1977. "Amphilex 77" International Stamp Exhibition, Amsterdam. Sheet 175 × 105 mm.
MS638 Nos. 634/6 but with green backgrounds . . . . 3·50 3·25

159 "Cordia sebestena" **160** Bells outside Main Store

1977. Flowers. Multicoloured.
639 25c. Type **159** 50 35
640 40c. "Albizzia lebbeck" (vert) 55 40
641 55c. "Tamarindus indica" . . 65 65

1977. 50th Anniv of Spritzer and Fuhrmann (jewellers). Multicoloured.
642 20c. Type **160** 50 35
643 40c. Globe basking in sun . . 55 50
644 55c. Antillean flag and diamond ring 65 65

161 Children with Toy Animal

1977. Child Welfare. Multicoloured.
645 15c.+15c. Type **161** 25 20
646 20c.+10c. Children with toy rabbit 50 50
647 25c.+12c. Children with toy cat 55 55
648 40c.+18c. Children with toy beetle 65 55
MS649 108 × 75 mm. Nos. 646 × 2, 648 × 2 . . . . 2·40 2·10

162 "The Unspoiled Queen" (Saba)

1977. Tourism. Multicoloured.
650 25c. Type **162** 20 10
651 35c. "The Golden Rock" (St. Eustatius) 25 20
652 40c. "The Friendly Island" (St. Maarten) 25 25

1977. As Nos. 378, 381/2 and 385, but larger, (39 × 22 mm).
653 E 20c. grey and red . . . . . 1·60 65
654 35c. pink and brown . . . 3·50 3·00
655 C 40c. green and mauve . . . 55 35
656 E 55c. green and red 75 50

163 19th-century Chest **164** Water-skiing

1978. 150th Anniv of Netherlands Antilles' Bank. Multicoloured.
657 **163** 15c. blue and light blue 20 10
658 – 20c. orange and gold . . 20 20
659 – 40c. green and deep green 25 25
DESIGNS: 20c. Bank emblem; 40c. Strong-room door.

1978. Sports Funds. Multicoloured.
660 15c.+5c. Type **164** 20 20
661 20c.+10c. Yachting 20 20
662 25c.+12c. Football 20 20
663 40c.+18c. Baseball 35 30

165 "Erythrina velutina" **166** "Polythysana rubrescens"

1978. Flora of Netherlands Antilles. Multicoloured.
664 15c. "Delconix regia" 20 20
665 25c. Type **165** 25 20
666 50c. "Gualacum officinale" (horiz) 35 35
667 55c. "Gilricidia sepium" (horiz) 50 50

1978. Butterflies. Multicoloured.
668 15c. Type **166** 20 20
669 25c. "Caligo sp." 25 20
670 35c. "Prepona praeneste" . . 35 35
671 40c. "Morpho sp." 50 45

167 "Conserve Energy" (English) **168** Red Cross

1978. Energy Conservation.
672 **167** 15c. orange and black . . 20 20
673 – 20c. green and black . . . 25 20
674 – 40c. red and black 50 40
DESIGNS: As No. 672 but text in Dutch (20c.) or in Papiamento (40c.).

1978. 150th Birth Anniv of Henri Dunant (founder of Red Cross).
675 **168** 55c.+25c. red and blue . . 25 25
MS676 144 × 50 mm. No. 675 × 3 2·10 2·10

169 Curacao from Sea, and Punched Tape **170** Boy Rollerskating

1978. 70th Anniv of Antilles Telecommunications Corporation (Landsradio). Multicoloured.
677 20c. Type **169** 25 25
678 40c. Ship's bridge, punched tape and radio mast . . . 35 35
679 55c. Satellite and aerial (vert) 55 55

1978. Child Welfare. Multicoloured.
680 15c.+5c. Type **170** 50 35
681 20c.+10c. Boy and girl flying kite 55 45
682 25c.+12c. Boy and girl playing marbles 55 50
683 40c.+18c. Girl riding bicycle 65 55
MS684 75 × 108 mm. Nos. 680/1 × 2 1·60 1·40

171 Ca'i Awa (pumping station) **172** Aruba Coat of Arms (float)

1978. 80th Death Anniv of Leonard Burlington Smith (entrepreneur and U.S. Consul).
685 **171** 25c. multicoloured 20 20
686 – 35c. black, greenish yellow and yellow 25 25
687 – 40c. multicoloured 50 25
DESIGNS—VERT: 35c. Leonard Burlington Smith. HORIZ: 40c. Opening ceremony of Queen Emma Bridge, 1888.

1979. 25th Aruba Carnival. Multicoloured.
688 40c.+10c. Float representing heraldic fantasy 50 35
689 75c.+20c. Type **172** 70 70

173 Goat and P.A.H.O. Emblem **174** Yacht and Sun

1979. 12th Inter-American Ministerial Meeting on Foot and Mouth Disease and Zoonosis Control, Curacao. Multicoloured.
690 50c. Type **173** 35 35
691 75c. Horse and conference emblem 45 45
692 150c. Cows, flag and Pan-American Health Organization (P.A.H.O.) and W.H.O. emblems . . . 1·00 1·00
MS693 143 × 50 mm. As Nos. 690/2 but background colours changed 2·00 2·00

1979. 12th International Sailing Regatta, Bonaire. Multicoloured.
694 15c.+5c. Type **174** 20 20
695 35c.+25c. Yachts 35 35
696 40c.+15c. Yacht and globe (horiz) 50 45
697 55c.+25c. Yacht, sun and flamingo 65 50
MS698 124 × 72 mm. Nos. 694/7 1·60 1·60

175 Corps Members **176** "Melochia tomentosa"

1979. 50th Anniv of Curacao Volunteer Corps.
699 **175** 15c.+10c. blue, red and ultramarine 20 20
700 – 40c.+20c. blue, violet and gold 55 55
701 – 1g. multicoloured 70 65
DESIGNS: 40c. Sentry in battle dress and emblem; 1g. Corps emblem, flag and soldier in ceremonial uniform.

1979. Flowers. Multicoloured.
702 25c. "Casearia tremula" . . . 30 20
703 40c. "Cordia cylindrostachya" 35 35
704 1g.50 Type **176** . . . . . . 1·10 1·10

177 Girls reading Book **178** Dove and Netherlands Flag

1979. International Year of the Child.
705 **177** 20c.+10c. multicoloured 25 25
706 – 25c.+12c. multicoloured 35 35
707 – 35c.+15c. violet, brown and black 55 45
708 – 50c.+20c. multicoloured 65 65
MS709 75 × 108 mm. Nos. 705 and 707, each × 2 . . . . 1·50 1·40
DESIGNS: 25c. Toddler and cat; 35c. Girls carrying basket; 50c. Boy and girl dressing-up.

1979. 25th Anniv of Statute of the Kingdom. Multicoloured.
710 65c. Type **178** 65 55
711 1g.50 Dove and Netherlands Antilles flag . . . . 1·10 1·10

179 Map of Aruba and Foundation Emblem

1979. 30th Anniv of Aruba Cultural Centre Foundation. Multicoloured.
712 95c. Type **179** 80 80
713 1g. Foundation headquarters 90 90

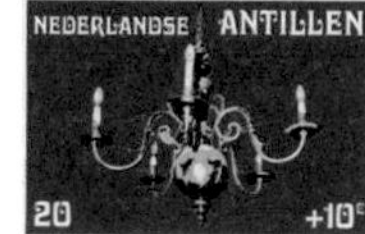

180 Brass Chandelier

1980. 210th Anniv of Fort Church, Curacao.
714 **180** 20c.+10c. yellow, black and brown 25 25
715 – 50c.+25c. multicoloured 55 55
716 – 100c. multicoloured . . . 80 80
DESIGNS: 50c. Pipe organ; 100c. Cupola tower, 1910.

181 Rotary Emblem and Cogwheel

1980. 75th Anniv of Rotary International. Multicoloured.
717 45c. Rotary emblem 35 35
718 50c. Globe and cogwheels . . 50 35
719 85c. Type **181** 70 70
MS720 120 × 75 mm. Nos. 717/19 1·50 1·50

182 Savings Box

1980. 75th Anniv of Post Office Savings Bank. Multicoloured.
721 25c. Type **182** 25 20
722 150c. Savings box (different) 1·25 1·25

183 Queen Juliana Accession Stamp

1980. Accession of Queen Beatrix.
723 **183** 25c. red, green and gold 20 20
724 – 60c. green, red and gold 50 45
DESIGN: 60c. 1965 Royal Visit stamp.

184 Sir Rowland Hill **185** Gymnastics (beam exercise)

1980. "London 1980" International Stamp Exhibition.
725 **184** 45c. black and green . . . 35 35
726 – 60c. black and red 50 50
727 – 1g. red, black and blue . . 90 90
MS728 160 × 90 mm. 45c. black and red; 60c. black and blue; 1g. red, black and green . . . . 1·90 1·90
DESIGNS: 60c. "London 1980" logo; 1g. Airmail label.

1980. Sports Funds.
729 **185** 25c.+10c. red and black 25 25
730 – 30c.+15c. yellow & blk . . 35 35
731 – 45c.+20c. light green, green and black 55 50
732 – 60c.+25c. pink, orange and black 70 65
MS733 75 × 144 mm. Nos. 729 and 732, each × 3 . . . . 2·75 2·50
DESIGNS: 30c. Gymnastics (horse vaulting); 45c. Volleyball; 60c. Basketball.

186 White-fronted Dove

1980. Birds. Multicoloured.
734 25c. Type **186** 25 25
735 60c. Tropical mockingbird . . 65 55
736 85c. Bananaquit 90 70

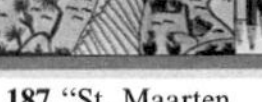

187 "St. Maarten Landscape" **188** Rudolf Theodorus Palm

1980. Child Welfare. Children's Drawings. Multicoloured.
737 25c.+10c. Type **187** 35 25
738 30c.+15c. "Bonaire House" 50 50
739 40c.+20c. "Child writing on Board" 55 55
740 60c.+25c. "Dancing Couple" (vert) 70 65
MS741 149 × 108 mm. Nos. 737 and 740, each × 3 plus four labels 3·00 2·75

1981. Birth Centenary (1980) of Rudolf Theodorus Palm (musician).
742 **188** 60c. brown and yellow . . 55 55
743 – 1g. buff and blue . . . . 1·00 90
DESIGN: 1g. Musical score and hands playing piano.

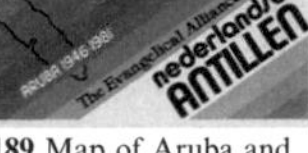

189 Map of Aruba and TEAM Emblem **190** Boy in Wheelchair

1981. 50th Anniv of Evangelical Alliance Mission (TEAM) in Antilles. Multicoloured.
744 30c. Type **189** 25 25
745 50c. Map of Curacao and emblem 55 45
746 1g. Map of Bonaire and emblem . . . . 1·00 90

1981. International Year of Disabled Persons. Multicoloured.
747 25c.+10c. Blind woman . . . 35 35
748 30c.+15c. Type **190** 50 45
749 45c.+20c. Child in walking frame 70 70
750 60c.+25c. Deaf girl 80 80

191 Tennis **192** Gateway

1981. Sports Funds. Multicoloured.
751 30c.+15c. Type **191** 55 45
752 50c.+20c. Swimming 70 70
753 70c.+25c. Boxing . . . . . . 1·00 90
MS754 100 × 72 mm. Nos. 751/3 2·25 2·10

1981. 125th Anniv of St. Elisabeth's Hospital. Multicoloured.
755 60c. Type **192** 55 55
756 1g.50 St. Elisabeth's Hospital 1·40 1·40

193 Marinus van der Maarel (promoter) **194** Mother and Child

1981. 50th Anniv (1980) of Antillean Boy Scouts Association. Multicoloured.
757 45c.+20c. Wolf Cub and leader 80 80
758 70c.+25c. Type **193** . . . . 1·10 1·10
759 1g.+50c. Headquarters, Ronde Klip . . . . 1·60 1·60
MS760 144 × 50 mm. Nos. 757/9 3·50 3·50

1981. Child Welfare. Multicoloured.
761 35c.+15c. Type **194** 45 45
762 45c.+20c. Boy and girl . . . 65 65
763 55c.+25c. Child with cat . . 80 80
764 85c.+40c. Girl with teddy bear . . . . 1·25 1·25
MS765 75 × 108 mm. Nos. 761 and 763, each × 2 . . . . 2·50 2·50

195 "Jatropha gossypifolia" **196** Pilot Gig approaching Ship

1981. Flowers. Multicoloured.
766 45c. "Cordia globosa" . . . 40 35
767 70c. Type **195** 75 70
768 100c. "Croton flavens" . . . 90 90

1982. Centenary of Pilotage Service. Mult.
769 70c. Type **196** 90 90
770 85c. Modern liner and map of Antilles . . . . 1·10 1·00
771 1g. Pilot boarding ship . . . 1·25 1·10

197 Fencing **198** Holy Ark

1982. Sports Funds.
772 **197** 35c.+15c. mauve and violet 70 65
773 – 45c.+20c. blue and deep blue 90 80
774 – 70c.+35c. multicoloured 1·40 1·25
775 – 85c.+40c. brown and deep brown . . . . 1·60 1·40
MS776 144 × 50 mm. No. 774 × 2 plus label . . . . 3·25 3·75
DESIGNS: 45c. Judo; 70c. Football; 85c. Cycling.

1982. 250th Anniv of Dedication of Mikve Israel-Emanuel Synagogue, Curacao. Mult.
777 75c. Type **198** . . . . . . 1·00 80
778 85c. Synagogue facade . . . 1·10 80
779 150c. Tebah (raised platform) 1·60 1·40

199 Peter Stuyvesant (Governor) and Flags of Netherlands, Netherlands Antilles and United States **200** Airport Control Tower

1982. Bicentenary of Netherlands–United States Diplomatic Relations.
780 **199** 75c. multicoloured . . . . 1·10 90

1982. International Federation of Air Traffic Controllers.
782 – 35c. black, ultramarine and blue 55 35
783 **200** 75c. black, green and light green . . . . 1·00 80
784 – 150c. black, orange and salmon . . . . 1·60 1·40
DESIGNS: 35c. Radar plot trace; 150c. Radar aerials.

201 Mail Bag **202** Brown Chromis

1982. "Philexfrance 82" International Stamp Exhibition, Paris. Multicoloured.
785 45c. Exhibition emblem . . . 65 50
786 85c. Type **201** . . . . 1·00 60
787 150c. Netherlands Antilles and French flags . . . . . 1·60 1·40
MS788 125 × 64 mm. Nos. 785/7 3·25 2·75

1982. Fishes. Multicoloured.
789 35c. Type **202** 70 45
790 75c. Spotted trunkfish . . . 1·25 90
791 85c. Blue tang . . . . 1·40 1·10
792 100c. French angelfish . . . 1·50 1·10

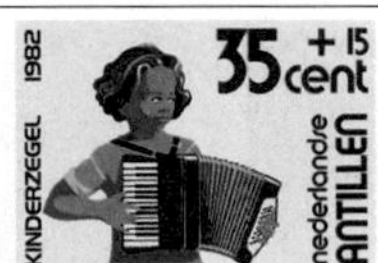

203 Girl playing Accordion

1982. Child Welfare. Multicoloured.
793 35c.+15c. Type **203** 80 65
794 75c.+35c. Boy playing guitar 1·40 1·25
795 85c.+40c. Boy playing violin 1·60 1·40
MS796 144 × 50 mm. Nos. 793/5 4·00 3·50

204 Saba House

1982. Cultural and Social Relief Funds. Local Houses. Multicoloured.
797 35c.+15c. Type **204** 90 65
798 75c.+35c. Aruba House . . . 1·50 1·25
799 85c.+40c. Curacao House . . 1·75 1·40
MS800 72 × 100 mm. Nos. 797/9 4·50 3·25

205 High Jumping

1983. Sports Funds. Multicoloured.
801 35c.+15c. Type **205** 70 55
802 45c.+20c. Weightlifting . . . 1·10 90
803 85c.+40c. Wind-surfing . . . 1·60 1·40

206 Natural Bridge, Aruba

207 W.C.Y. Emblem and Means of Communication

1983. Tourism. Multicoloured.
804 35c. Type **206** 65 55
805 45c. Lac Bay, Bonaire . . . 70 65
806 100c. Willemstad, Curacao 1·40 1·25

1983. World Communications Year.
807 **207** 1g. multicoloured . . . . 1·40 1·25
MS808 100 × 72 mm. No. 807 . . 1·50 1·25

208 "Curacao" (paddle-steamer) and Post Office Building

209 Mango ("Mangifera indica")

1983. "Brasiliana 83" International Stamp Exhibition, Rio de Janeiro. Multicoloured.
809 45c. Type **208** 80 70
810 55c. Brazil flag, exhibition emblem and Netherlands Antilles flag and postal service emblem 90 80
811 100c. Governor's Palace, Netherlands Antilles, and Sugarloaf Mountain, Rio de Janeiro . . . . 1·50 1·40
MS812 100 × 72 mm. Nos. 809/11 3·25 2·75

1983. Flowers. Multicoloured.
813 45c. Type **209** 90 70
814 55c. "Malpighia punicifolia" 1·00 80
815 100c. "Citrus aurantifolia" 1·60 1·40

210 Boy and Lizard

1983. Child Welfare. Multicoloured.
816 45c.+20c. Type **210** . . . . 1·10 90
817 55c.+25c. Girl watching ants 1·25 1·10
818 100c.+50c. Girl feeding donkey . . . . 2·10 1·90
MS819 100 × 72 mm. Nos. 816/18 4·50 4·00

211 Aruba Water Jar

212 Saba

1983. Cultural and Social Relief Funds. Pre-Columbian Pottery.
820 **211** 45c.+20c. light blue, blue and black . . . . . . 1·25 1·00
821 – 55c.+25c. pink, red and black . . . . 1·40 1·25
822 – 85c.+40c. stone, green and black . . . . 1·60 1·40
823 – 100c.+50c. light brown, brown and black . . . 2·10 2·00
DESIGNS: 55c. Aruba decorated bowl; 85c. Curacao human figurine; 100c. Fragment of Curacao female figurine.

1983. Local Government Buildings. Multicoloured.
824 20c. Type **212** 25 25
825 25c. St. Eustatius 25 25
826 30c. St. Maarten 35 35
827 35c. Aruba . . . . 2·40 45
828 45c. Bonaire 55 55
829 55c. Curacao 70 65
830 60c. Type **212** 65 65
831 65c. As No. 825 . . . . . . 70 70
832 70c. Type **212** 65 45
833 75c. As No. 826 . . . . . . 90 90
834 85c. As No. 827 . . . . . . 3·00 1·10
835 85c. As No. 828 . . . . . . 80 55
836 90c. As No. 828 . . . . . . 1·10 1·10
837 95c. As No. 829 . . . . . . 1·25 1·25
838 1g. Type **212** . . . . . . 1·25 1·10
839 1g.50 As No. 825 . . . . . 1·50 1·40
841 2g.50 As No. 826 . . . . . 2·50 1·75
842 5g. As No. 828 . . . . . . 5·50 3·50
843 10g. As No. 829 . . . . . . 9·50 6·00
844 15g. Type **212** . . . . . . 14·00 9·50

213 Note-taking, Typesetting and Front Page of "Amigoe"

1984. Centenary of "Amigoe de Curacao" (newspaper). Multicoloured.
845 45c. Type **213** 70 65
846 55c. Printing press and newspapers 80 70
847 85c. Reading newspaper . . . 1·40 1·25

214 W.I.A. and I.C.A.O. Emblems

1984. 40th Anniv of I.C.A.O.
848 **214** 25c. multicoloured 45 35
849 – 45c. violet, blue and black 90 65
850 – 55c. multicoloured . . . . 1·00 75
851 – 100c. multicoloured . . . 1·60 1·25
DESIGNS: 45c. I.C.A.O. anniversary emblem; 55c. A.L.M. and I.C.A.O. emblems; 100c. Fokker F.XIII airplane "De Snip".

215 Fielder

1984. Sports Funds. 50th Anniv of Curacao Baseball Federation. Multicoloured.
852 25c.+10c. Type **215** 90 65
853 45c.+20c. Batter . . . . . . 1·40 1·10
854 55c.+25c. Pitcher . . . . . . 1·60 1·40
855 85c.+40c. Running for base 1·90 1·60
MS856 144 × 50 mm. Nos. 852/5 5·75 4·25

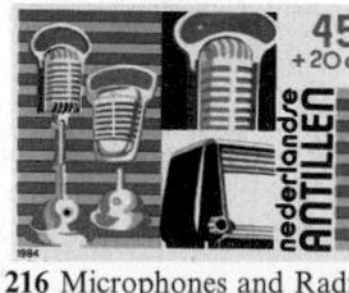

216 Microphones and Radio

1984. Cultural and Social Relief Funds. Radio and Gramophone. Multicoloured.
857 45c.+20c. Type **216** . . . . 1·40 1·10
858 55c.+25c. Gramophones and record . . . . 1·90 1·40
859 100c.+50c. Gramophone with horn . . . . 2·10 1·90

217 Bonnet-maker

1984. Centenary of Curacao Chamber of Commerce and Industry. Multicoloured.
860 45c. Type **217** . . . . . . 1·25 90
861 55c. Chamber emblem . . . 1·25 90
862 1g. "Southward" (liner) passing under bridge . . . 1·75 1·40
No. 861 is an inverted triangle.

218 Black-faced Grassquit

219 Eleanor Roosevelt and Val-Kill, Hyde Park, New York

1984. Birds. Multicoloured.
863 45c. Type **218** . . . . 1·00 80
864 55c. Rufous-collared sparrow 1·25 1·40
865 150c. Blue-tailed emerald . . 1·90 1·90

1984. Birth Centenary of Eleanor Roosevelt.
866 **219** 45c. multicoloured 80 65
867 – 85c. black, gold and bistre 1·25 1·10
868 – 100c. black, yellow and red . . . . 1·10 1·25
DESIGNS: 85c. Portrait in oval frame; 100c. Eleanor Roosevelt with children.

220 Child Reading

221 Adult Flamingo and Chicks

1984. Child Welfare. Multicoloured.
869 45c.+20c. Type **220** . . . . 1·10 1·00
870 55c.+25c. Family reading . . 1·40 1·40
871 100c.+50c. Family in church 1·90 1·90
MS872 100 × 72 mm. Nos. 869/71 4·50 4·50

1985. Greater Flamingoes. Multicoloured.
873 25c. Type **221** 70 55
874 45c. Young flamingoes . . . 1·10 75
875 55c. Adult flamingoes . . . . 1·10 90
876 100c. Flamingoes in various flight positions . . . . . . 1·90 1·40

222 Symbols of Entered Apprentice

223 Players with Ball

1985. Bicentenary of De Vergenoeging Masonic Lodge, Curacao. Multicoloured.
877 45c. Type **222** . . . . 1·00 70
878 55c. Symbols of the Fellow Craft . . . . 1·10 1·00
879 100c. Symbols of the Master Mason . . . . 1·90 1·60

1985. Sports Funds. Football. Multicoloured.
880 10c.+5c. Type **223** 55 35
881 15c.+5c. Dribbling ball . . . 55 45
882 45c.+20c. Running with ball 1·10 1·00
883 55c.+25c. Tackling . . . . . 1·40 1·25
884 85c.+40c. Marking player with ball . . . . 1·90 1·75

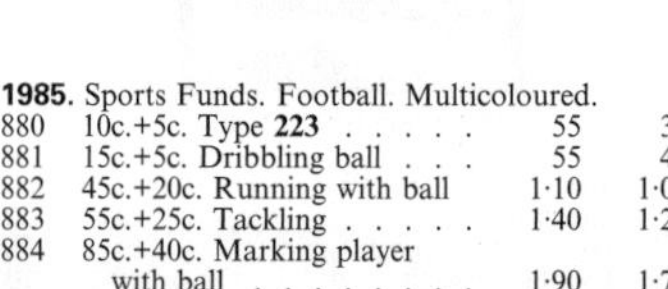

224 Boy using Computer

1985. Cultural and Social Welfare Funds. International Youth Year. Multicoloured.
885 45c.+20c. Type **224** . . . . 1·25 1·10
886 55c.+25c. Girl listening to records . . . . 1·50 1·40
887 100c.+50c. Boy break-dancing . . . . 2·25 2·10

225 U.N. Emblem

1985. 40th Anniv of U.N.O.
888 **225** 55c. multicoloured . . . . 1·00 90
889 1g. multicoloured . . . . 1·50 1·40

226 Pierre Lauffer and Poem

227 Eskimo

1985. Papiamentu (Creole language). Multicoloured.
890 45c. Type **226** 55 55
891 55c. Wave inscribed "Papiamentu" 75 75

1985. Child Welfare. Multicoloured.
892 5c.+5c. Type **227** 35 20
893 10c.+5c. African child . . . 50 25
894 25c.+10c. Chinese girl 70 50
895 45c.+20c. Dutch girl . . . . 1·10 90
896 55c.+25c. Red Indian girl . . 1·25 1·10
MS897 100 × 72 mm. Nos. 894/6 3·25 2·50

228 "Calotropis procera"

229 Courthouse

1985. Flowers. Multicoloured.
898 5c. Type **228** 35 20
899 10c. "Capparis flexuosa" . . 35 20
900 20c. "Mimosa distachya" . . 55 35
901 45c. "Ipomoea nil" 90 65
902 55c. "Heliotropium ternatum" . . . . 1·10 70
903 150c. "Ipomoea incarnata" 1·90 1·60

1986. 125th Anniv of Curacao Courthouse. Multicoloured.
904 5c. Type **229** 25 20
905 15c. States room (vert) . . . 35 20
906 25c. Court room 55 35
907 55c. Entrance (vert) 90 70

230 Sprinting

231 Girls watching Artist at work

1986. Sports Funds. Multicoloured.
908 15c.+5c. Type **230** 90 45
909 25c.+10c. Horse racing . . . 1·10 70
910 45c.+20c. Motor racing . . . 1·40 1·00
911 55c.+25c. Football . . . . . 1·50 1·25

1986. Curacao Youth Care Foundation. Multicoloured.
912 30c.+15c. Type **231** 90 65
913 45c.+20c. Children watching sculptor at work . . . . . 1·10 80
914 55c.+25c. Children watching potter at work . . . . . . 1·40 1·10

232 Chained Man

1986. 25th Anniv of Amnesty International. Multicoloured.

915 45c. Type **232** 80 55
916 55c. Dove behind bars . . . 90 65
917 100c. Man behind bars . . . 1·40 1·10

233 Post Office Mail Box **234** Boy playing Football

1986. Mail Boxes. Multicoloured.

918 10c. Type **233** 20 20
919 25c. Street mail box on pole 35 25
920 45c. Street mail box in brick column 65 55
921 55c. Street mail box 80 65

1986. Child Welfare. Multicoloured.

922 20c.+10c. Type **234** 55 50
923 25c.+15c. Girl playing tennis 70 55
924 45c.+20c. Boy practising judo 90 80
925 55c.+25c. Boy playing baseball . . . . 1·10 1·00
MS926 75 × 72 mm. Nos. 924/5 2·10 1·75

235 Brothers' First House and Mauritius Vliegendehond **236** Engagement Picture

1986. Centenary of Friars of Tilburg Mission. Multicoloured.

927 10c. Type **235** 30 20
928 45c. St. Thomas College and Mgr. Ferdinand E. C. Kieckens 75 55
929 55c. St. Thomas College courtyard and Fr. F.S. de Beer 85 70

1987. Golden Wedding of Princess Juliana and Prince Bernhard.

930 **236** 1g.35 orange, blk & gold 2·10 1·60
MS931 50 × 72 mm. No. 930 . . 3·00 1·40

237 Map **238** Girls playing Instruments

1987. 150th Anniv of Maduro Holding Inc. Multicoloured.

932 70c. Type **237** 70 65
933 85c. Group activities 90 80
934 1g.55 Saloman Elias Levy Maduro (founder) . . . . 1·60 1·60

1987. Cultural and Social Relief Funds.

935 **238** 35c.+15c. multicoloured 70 65
936 – 45c.+25c. light green, green and blue . . . . 1·10 80
937 – 85c.+40c. multicoloured 1·40 1·25

DESIGNS: 45c. Woman pushing man in wheelchair. 85c. Bandstand.

239 Map and Emblem

1987. 50th Anniv of Curacao Rotary Club. Multicoloured.

938 15c. Type **239** 20 20
939 50c. Zeelandia country house (meeting venue) 65 55
940 65c. Emblem on map of Curacao 75 70

240 Octagon (house where Bolivar's sisters lived)

1987. 175th Anniv of Simon Bolivar's Exile on Curacao (60, 80c.) and 50th Anniv of Bolivarian Society (70, 90c.). Multicoloured.

941 60c. Type **240** 70 65
942 70c. Society headquarters, Willemstad, Curacao . . . 80 70
943 80c. Room in Octagon . . . 1·00 90
944 90c. Portraits of Manuel Carlos Piar, Simon Bolivar and Pedro Luis Brion . . . 1·10 1·00

241 Baby

1987. Child Welfare. Multicoloured.

945 40c.+15c. Type **241** . . . . 1·00 70
946 55c.+25c. Child . . . . . . 1·25 1·00
947 115c.+50c. Youth . . . . . 1·75 1·50
MS948 144 × 50 mm. Nos. 945/7 4·25 1·40

242 White-tailed Tropic Birds

1987. 25th Anniv of Netherlands Antilles National Parks Foundation. Multicoloured.

949 70c. Type **242** 70 65
950 85c. White-tailed deer 90 80
951 155c. Iguana . . . . 1·60 1·50

243 Printing Press and Type

1987. 175th Anniv of "De Curacaosche Courant" (periodical and printing shop). Multicoloured.

952 55c. Type **243** 70 55
953 70c. Keyboard and modern printing press 85 65

244 William Godden (founder)

1988. 75th Anniv of Curacao Mining Company. Multicoloured.

954 40c. Type **244** 70 45
955 105c. Phosphate processing plant . . . . 1·50 1·10
956 155c. Tafelberg (source of phosphate) . . . . 2·25 1·60

245 Flags, Minutes and John Horris Sprockel (first President) **246** Bridge through "100"

1988. 50th Anniv of Netherlands Antilles Staten (legislative body). Multicoloured.

957 65c. Type **245** 70 70
958 70c. Ballot paper and schematic representation of extension of voting rights 90 70
959 155c. Antilles and Netherlands flags and birds representing five Antilles islands and Aruba . . . . 1·60 1·40

1988. Cultural and Social Relief Funds. Centenary of Queen Emma Bridge, Curacao. Mult.

960 55c.+25c. Type **246** . . . . 1·10 65
961 115c.+55c. Willemstad harbour (horiz) . . . . . 1·75 1·40
962 190c.+60c. Leonard B. Smith (engineer) and flags (horiz) 2·75 2·50

247 Broken Chain

1988. 125th Anniv of Abolition of Slavery. Mult.

963 155c. Type **247** . . . . . . 1·50 1·40
964 190c. Breach in slave wall . . 1·75 1·40

248 Flags and Map **249** Charles Hellmund (Bonaire councillor)

1988. 3rd Inter-American Foundation of Cities "Let us Build Bridges" Conference, Curacao. Multicoloured.

965 80c. Type **248** . . . . 1·00 70
966 155c. Bridge and globe . . . 1·40 1·25

1988. Celebrities. Multicoloured.

967 55c. Type **249** 65 45
968 65c. Atthelo Maud Edwards-Jackson (founder of Saba Electric Company) 70 50
969 90c. Nicolaas Debrot (Governor of Antilles, 1962–69) . . . . 1·10 90
970 120c. William Charles de la Try Ellis (lawyer and politician) . . . . 1·25 1·10

250 Child watching Television **251** "Cereus hexagonus"

1988. Child Welfare. Multicoloured.

971 55c.+25c. Type **250** . . . . 1·00 65
972 65c.+30c. Boy with radio . . 1·10 90
973 115c.+55c. Girl using computer . . . . 1·60 1·40
MS974 118 × 67 mm. Nos. 971/3 3·25 2·50

1988. Cacti. Multicoloured.

975 55c. Type **251** 70 50
976 115c. Melocactus . . . . . . 1·25 90
977 125c. "Opuntia wentiana" . . 1·25 1·10

252 Magnifying Glass over 1936 and 1980 Stamps **253** Crested Bobwhite

1989. Cultural and Social Relief Funds. 50th Anniv of Curacao Stamp Association. Multicoloured.

978 30c.+10c. Type **252** 80 45
979 55c.+20c. Picking up stamp with tweezers (winning design by X. Rico in drawing competition) . . . 1·10 80
980 80c.+30c. Barn owl and stamp album . . . . . . 1·25 1·00

Nos. 978/80 were printed together, se-tenant, forming a composite design.

1989. 40th Anniv of Curacao Foundation for Prevention of Cruelty to Animals. Multicoloured.

981 65c. Type **253** 90 70
982 115c. Dogs and cats . . . . 1·25 1·10

254 "Sun Viking" in Great Bay Harbour, St. Maarten **255** Paula Clementina Dorner (teacher)

1989. Tourism. Cruise Liners. Multicoloured.

983 70c. Type **254** 90 70
984 155c. "Eugenio C" entering harbour, St. Annabay, Curacao . . . . 1·60 1·10

1989. Celebrities. Multicoloured.

985 40c. Type **255** 65 45
986 55c. John Aniseto de Jongh (pharmacist and politician) 70 50
987 90c. Jacobo Jesus Maria Palm (musician) . . . . . 1·00 80
988 120c. Abraham Mendes Chumaceiro (lawyer and social campaigner) . . . . 1·25 1·10

256 Boy and Girl under Tree **257** Hand holding "7"

1989. Child Welfare. Multicoloured.

989 40c.+15c. Type **256** 90 65
990 65c.+30c. Two children playing on shore . . . . . 1·10 90
991 115c.+35c. Adult carrying child . . . . 1·60 1·40
MS992 92 × 62 mm. 155c.+75c. Children playing on shore . . 3·25 2·50

1989. 40th Anniv of Queen Wilhelmina Foundation for Cancer Care. Multicoloured.

993 30c. Type **257** 55 45
994 60c. Seated figure and figure receiving radiation treatment 80 70
995 80c. Figure exercising and Foundation emblem . . . 1·00 70

1989. "World Stamp Expo '89" International Stamp Exhibition, Washington, D.C. Sheet 112 × 65 mm containing multicoloured designs as previous issues but with changed values.

MS996 70c. As No. 625; 155c. Type **199**; 250c. Type **80** . . . 5·00 4·50

258 Fireworks **259** "Tephrosia cinerea"

1989. Christmas. Multicoloured.

997 30c. Type **258** 50 35
998 100c. Christmas tree decorations . . . . 1·10 90

1990. Flowers. Multicoloured.

999 30c. Type **259** 35 35
1000 55c. "Erithalis fruticosa" . . 65 55
1001 65c. "Evolvulus antillanus" 70 65
1002 70c. "Jacquinia arborea" . . 80 70
1003 125c. "Tournefortia onaphalodes" . . . . . . 1·40 1·40
1004 155c. "Sesuvium portulacastrum" . . . . 1·90 1·40

260 Girl Guides **261** Nun with Child, Flag and Map

1990. Cultural and Social Relief Funds. Mult.

1005 30c.+10c. Type **260** (60th anniv) 70 50
1006 40c.+15c. Totolika (care of mentally handicapped organization) (17th anniv) 90 70
1007 155c.+65c. Boy scout (60th anniv) . . . . 2·50 2·50

1990. Centenary of Arrival of Dominican Nuns in Netherlands Antilles. Multicoloured.

1008 10c. Type **261** 20 20
1009 55c. St. Rose Hospital and St. Martin's Home, St. Maarten 65 50
1010 60c. St. Joseph School, St. Maarten 70 65

262 Goal Net, Ball and Shield

263 Carlos Nicolaas-Perez (philologist and poet)

1990. Multicoloured.
1011 65c.+30c. Type **262** (65th anniv of Sport Unie Brion Trappers football club) . . 1·10 1·00
1012 115c.+55c. Guiding addict from darkness towards sun (anti-drugs campaign) 1·75 1·75

1990. Meritorious Antilleans. Multicoloured.
1013 40c. Type **263** 50 35
1014 60c. Evert Kruythoff (writer) 70 65
1015 80c. John de Pool (writer) 90 80
1016 150c. Joseph Sickman Corsen (poet and composer) . . . . 1·75 1·60

264 Queen Emma

265 Isla Refinery

1990. Dutch Queens of the House of Orange. Multicoloured.
1017 100c. Type **264** . . . . . . 1·40 1·10
1018 100c. Queen Wilhelmina . . 1·40 1·10
1019 100c. Queen Juliana . . . . 1·40 1·10
1020 100c. Queen Beatrix . . . . 1·40 1·10
MS1021 77 × 64 mm. 250c. Queens Emma, Wilhelmina, Juliana and Beatrix (35 × 24 mm) . . . . .

1990. 75th Anniv of Oil Refining on Curacao.
1022 **265** 100c. multicoloured . . . 1·25 1·25

266 Flower and Bees

267 Parcels

1990. Child Welfare. International Literacy Year. Designs illustrating letters of alphabet. Multicoloured.
1023 30c.+5c. Type **266** 65 45
1024 55c.+10c. Dolphins and sun 1·00 70
1025 65c.+15c. Donkey with bicycle . . . . 1·10 90
1026 100c.+20c. Goat dreaming of house . . . . 1·50 1·75
1027 115c.+25c. Rabbit carrying food on yoke . . . . . . 1·75 1·50
1028 155c.+55c. Lizard, moon and cactus . . . . 2·75 2·40

1990. Christmas. Multicoloured.
1029 30c. Type **267** (25th anniv of Curacao Lions Club's Good Neighbour project) 55 35
1030 100c. Mother and child . . 1·40 1·10

268 Flag, Map and Distribution of Mail

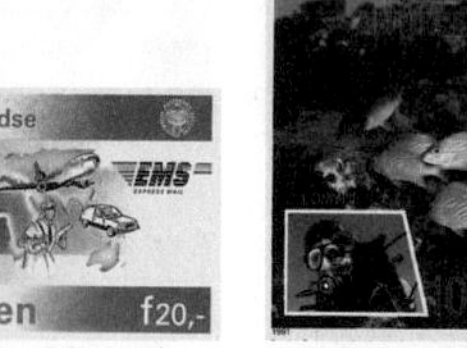
269 Scuba Diver and French Grunt

1991. 6th Anniv of Express Mail Service.
1031 **268** 20g. multicoloured . . . 23·00 22·00

1991. Fishes. Multicoloured.
1032 10c. Type **269** 35 20
1033 40c. Spotted trunkfish . . . 65 45
1034 55c. Copper sweepers . . . 85 70
1035 75c. Skindiver and yellow goatfishes . . . . 1·10 90
1036 100c. Black-barred soldier-fishes . . . . 1·50 1·25

270 Children and Stamps

1991. Cultural and Social Relief Funds. Mult.
1037 30c.+10c. Type **270** (12th anniv of Philatelic Club of Curacao) 70 55
1038 65c.+25c. St. Vincentius Brass Band (50th anniv) 1·25 1·10
1039 155c.+55c. Games and leisure pursuits (30th anniv of FESEBAKO) (Curacao community centres) . . . . 2·75 2·50

271 "Good Luck"

272 Westpoint Lighthouse, Curacao

1991. Greetings Stamps. Multicoloured.
1040 30c. Type **271** 35 35
1041 30c. "Thank You" 35 35
1042 30c. Couple and family ("Love You") 35 35
1043 30c. Song birds ("Happy Day") 35 35
1044 30c. Greater flamingo and medicines ("Get Well Soon") 35 35
1045 30c. Flowers and balloons ("Happy Birthday") . . . 35 35

1991. Lighthouses. Multicoloured.
1046 30c. Type **272** 50 45
1047 70c. Willems Toren, Bonaire 80 80
1048 115c. Klein Curacao lighthouse . . . . 1·60 1·60

273 Peter Stuyvesant College

1991. 50th Anniv of Secondary Education in Netherlands Antilles (65c.) and "Espamer '91" Spain–Latin America Stamp Exhibition, Buenos Aires (125c.). Multicoloured.
1049 65c. Type **273** 70 70
1050 125c. Dancers of Netherlands Antilles, Argentina and Portugal (vert) . . . . 1·40 1·40

274 Octopus with Letters and Numbers

275 Nativity

1991. Child Welfare. Multicoloured.
1051 40c.+15c. Type **274** 90 70
1052 65c.+30c. Parents teaching arithmetic . . . . 1·40 1·25
1053 155c.+65c. Bird and tortoise with clock . . . . 2·75 2·75
MS1054 118 × 67 mm. 55c.+25c. Owl with letters and national flag; 100c. + 35c. Books and bookworms; 115c.+50c. Dragon, ice-cream cone and icicles. Imperf . . . 4·50 4·00

1991. Christmas. Multicoloured.
1055 30c. Type **275** 35 35
1056 100c. Angel appearing to shepherds . . . . 1·10 1·10

276 Joseph Alvarez Correa (founder) and Headquarters of S.E.L. Maduro and Sons

277 Fawn

1991. 75th Anniv of Maduro and Curiel's Bank. Multicoloured.
1057 30c. Type **276** 65 50
1058 70c. Lion rampant (bank's emblem) and "75" . . . 1·10 90
1059 155c. Isaac Haim Capriles (Managing Director, 1954–74) and Scharloo bank branch . . . . . . 1·90 1·75

1992. The White-tailed Deer. Multicoloured.
1060 5c. Type **277** (postage) . . . 20 20
1061 10c. Young adults 25 20
1062 30c. Stag 50 35
1063 40c. Stag and hind in water 65 45
1064 200c. Stag drinking (air) . . 2·40 2·40
1065 355c. Stag calling . . . . . 4·25 4·00

278 Windsurfer

279 The Alhambra, Grenada

1992. Cultural and Social Relief Funds. Olympic Games, Barcelona. Multicoloured.
1066 30c.+10c. Type **278** (award of silver medal to Jan Boersma, 1988 Games) . . 74 55
1067 55c.+25c. Globe, national flag and Olympic rings . . 1·10 90
1068 115c.+55c. Emblem of National Olympic Committee (60th anniv) 2·10 2·00
Nos. 1066/8 were issued together, se-tenant, forming a composite design.

1992. "Granada '92" International Stamp Exhibition (250c.) and "Expo '92" World's Fair, Seville (500c.). Sheet 92 × 52 mm containing T **279** and similar horiz design. Multicoloured.
MS1069 250c. Type **279**; 500c. Carthusian Monastery, Seville, and Columbus . . . . 10·00 9·00

280 "Santa Maria"

1992. "World Columbian Stamp Expo '92", Chicago. Multicoloured.
1070 250c. Type **280** . . . . . . 3·00 2·75
1071 500c. Chart and Columbus 5·75 5·50

281 View of Dock and Town

282 Angela de Lannoy-Willems

1992. Curacao Port Container Terminal. Mult.
1072 80c. Type **281** 90 90
1073 125c. Crane and ship . . . 1·40 1·40

1992. Celebrities.
1074 **282** 30c. black, brown & grn 35 35
1075 – 40c. black, brown & blue 55 45
1076 – 55c. black, brown & orge 70 65
1077 – 70c. black, brown and red 80 70
1078 – 100c. black, brown & blue . . . . 1·10 1·10
DESIGNS: 30c. Type **282** (first woman Member of Parliament); 40c. Lodewijk Daniel Gerharts (entrepreneur on Bonaire); 55c. Cyrus Wilberforce Wathey (entrepreneur on St. Maarten); 70c. Christian Winkel (Deputy Governor of Antilles); 100c. Mother Joseph (founder of Roosendaal Congregation (Franciscan welfare sisterhood)).

283 Spaceship

284 Queen Beatrix and Prince Claus

1992. Child Welfare. Multicoloured.
1079 30c.+10c. Type **283** 55 45
1080 70c.+30c. Robot . . . . . 1·10 1·10
1081 100c.+40c. Extra-terrestrial being . . . . 1·60 1·50
MS1082 94 × 54 mm. 155c.+70c. Martian . . . . 3·25 2·75

1992. 12½ Years since Accession to the Throne of Queen Beatrix (100c.) and Royal Visit to Netherlands Antilles (others). Designs showing photos of previous visits to the Antilles. Multi.
1083 70c. Type **284** 80 80
1084 100c. Queen Beatrix signing book . . . . 1·10 1·10
1085 175c. Queen Beatrix and Prince Claus with girl . . 1·90 1·90

285 Crib

286 Hibiscus

1992. Christmas. Multicoloured.
1086 30c. Type **285** 50 35
1087 100c. Mary and Joseph searching for lodgings (vert) . . . . 1·40 1·10

1993. Flowers. Multicoloured.
1088 75c. Type **286** 80 80
1089 90c. Sunflower . . . . . . 1·00 1·00
1090 175c. Ixora . . . . 1·90 1·90
1091 195c. Rose . . . . 2·25 2·25

287 De Havilland Twin Otter and Flight Paths

288 Pekingese

1993. Anniversaries. Multicoloured.
1092 65c. Type **287** (50th anniv of Princess Juliana International Airport, St. Maarten) 70 70
1093 75c. Laboratory worker and National Health Laboratory (75th anniv) 80 80
1094 90c. De Havilland Twin Otter on runway at Princess Juliana International Airport . . 1·00 1·00
1095 175c. White and yellow cross (50th anniv of Princess Margriet White and Yellow Cross Foundation for District Nursing) . . . . 1·90 1·90

1993. Dogs. Multicoloured.
1096 65c. Type **288** 80 70
1097 90c. Standard poodle . . . 1·10 1·00
1098 100c. Pomeranian . . . . . 1·25 1·10
1099 175c. Papillon . . . . . . 2·00 1·90

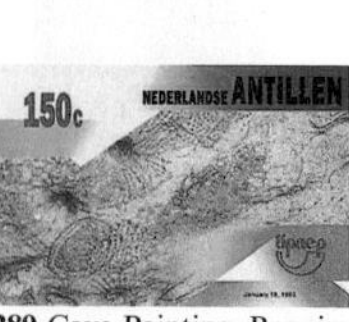
289 Cave Painting, Bonaire

290 "Sun and Sea"

1993. "Brasiliana '93" International Stamp Exhibition, Rio de Janeiro, and Admittance of Antilles to Postal Union of the Americas, Spain and Portugal. Multicoloured.
1100 150c. Type **289** . . . . . . 1·60 1·60
1101 200c. Exhibition emblem and Antilles flag . . . . 2·10 2·10
1102 250c. Globe and hand signing U.P.A.E.P. agreement . . . . 2·75 2·75

1993. "Carib-Art" Exhibition, Curacao. Multicoloured.
1103 90c. Type **290** . . . . . . 1·00 1·00
1104 150c. "Heaven and Earth" 1·60 1·60

291 "Safety in the Home"

1993. Child Welfare. Child and Danger. Mult.
1105 65c.+25c. Type **291** . . . . 1·10 1·00
1106 90c.+35c. Child using seat belt ("Safety in the Car") (vert) . . . . 1·40 1·40
1107 175c.+75c. Child wearing armbands ("Safety in the Water") . . . . 2·75 2·75
MS1108 168 × 79 mm. 35c.+15c. × 5, Child writing in exercise book ("Danger of Failing at School") 4·00 2·75

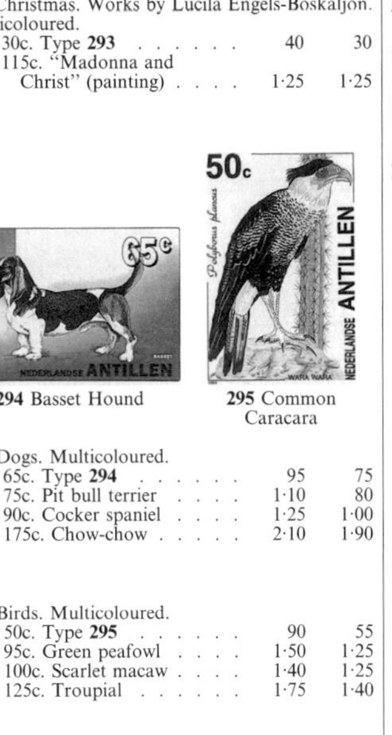

292 Consulate, Curacao **293** "Mother and Child" (mosaic)

1993. Bicentenary of United States Consul General to the Antilles. Multicoloured.
1109 65c. Type **292** 80 70
1110 90c. Arms of Netherlands Antilles and U.S.A . . . 1·10 1·00
1111 175c. American bald eagle 2·00 1·90

1993. Christmas. Works by Lucila Engels-Boskaljon. Multicoloured.
1112 30c. Type **293** 40 30
1113 115c. "Madonna and Christ" (painting) . . . . 1·25 1·25

294 Basset Hound **295** Common Caracara

1994. Dogs. Multicoloured.
1114 65c. Type **294** 95 75
1115 75c. Pit bull terrier . . . . 1·10 80
1116 90c. Cocker spaniel . . . . 1·25 1·00
1117 175c. Chow-chow . . . . . 2·10 1·90

1994. Birds. Multicoloured.
1118 50c. Type **295** 90 55
1119 95c. Green peafowl . . . . 1·50 1·25
1120 100c. Scarlet macaw . . . . 1·40 1·25
1121 125c. Troupial . . . . . . 1·75 1·40

296 Joseph Husurell Lake **297** Players' Legs

1994. Celebrities. Multicoloured.
1122 65c. Type **296**(founder of United People's Liberation Front) 70 70
1123 75c. Efrain Jonckheer (politician and diplomat) 90 80
1124 100c. Michiel Martinus Romer (teacher) . . . . . 1·10 1·10
1125 175c. Carel Nicolaas Winkel (social reformer) . . . . 2·00 1·90

1994. World Cup Football Championship, U.S.A. Multicoloured.
1126 90c. Type **297** . . . . . . 1·10 1·00
1127 150c. Foot and ball . . . . 1·75 1·60
1128 175c. Referee's whistle and cards . . . . 2·00 1·90

298 Chair and Hammer

299 Birds and Dolphin

1994. 75th Anniv of International Labour Organization. Multicoloured.
1129 90c. Type **298** . . . . . . 1·25 1·10
1130 110c. Heart and "75" . . . 1·40 1·25
1131 200c. Tree . . . . 2·50 2·50

1994. Nature Protection. Multicoloured.
1132 10c. Type **299** 30 30
1133 35c. Dolphin, magnificent frigate bird, brown pelican and troupial 50 50
1134 50c. Coral, iguana, lobster and fish 65 65
1135 125c. Fish, turtle, queen conch, greater flamingoes and American wigeons . . 1·60 1·60
MS1136 84 × 70 mm. Nos. 1132/5 3·50 3·25

300 1945 7½c. Netherlands Stamp

301 Mother and Child

1994. "Fepapost '94" European Stamp Exhibition, The Hague. Multicoloured.
1137 2g.50 Type **300** . . . . . . 2·75 2·50
1138 5g. Curacao 1933 6c. stamp 5·50 5·25
MS1139 96 × 55 mm. Nos. 1137/8 9·50 8·25

1994. Child Welfare. International Year of the Family. Multicoloured.
1140 35c.+15c. Type **301** 60 50
1141 65c.+25c. Father and daughter reading together 1·25 1·10
1142 90c.+35c. Grandparents . . 2·10 2·00
MS1143 86 × 51 mm. 175c.+75c. I.Y.F. emblem . . . . 3·50 2·75

302 Dove in Hands

1994. Christmas. Multicoloured.
1144 30c. Type **302** 50 35
1145 115c. Globe and planets in hands . . . . 1·50 1·25

303 Carnival and Houses

304 Handicapped and Able-bodied Children

1995. Carnival. Multicoloured.
1146 125c. Type **303** . . . . . . 1·50 1·40
1147 175c. Carnival and harbour 2·10 1·90
1148 250c. Carnival and rural house . . . . 3·00 2·75

1995. 50th Anniv of Mgr. Verriet Institute (for the physically handicapped). Multicoloured.
1149 65c. Type **304** 80 70
1150 90c. Cedric Virginie (wheelchair-bound bookbinder) . . . . . . 1·10 1·00

305 Dobermann

1995. Dogs. Multicoloured.
1151 75c. Type **305** . . . . . . 1·10 85
1152 85c. German shepherd . . . 1·25 1·00
1153 100c. Bouvier . . . . 1·40 1·10
1154 175c. St. Bernard . . . . . 2·40 1·90

306 Bonaire

1995. Flags and Arms of the Constituent Islands of the Netherlands Antilles. Multicoloured.
1155 10c. Type **306** 20 10
1156 35c. Curacao 50 35
1157 50c. St. Maarten 70 55
1158 65c. Saba 90 70
1159 75c. St. Eustatius (also state flag and arms) . . . . . 1·00 80
1160 90c. Island flags and state arms . . . . 1·10 1·00

307 Monument to Slave Revolt of 1795

309 Sealpoint Siamese

1995. Cultural and Social Relief Funds. Bicentenary of Abolition of Slavery in the Antilles (1161/2) and Children's Drawings on Philately (1163/4). Multicoloured.
1161 30c.+10c. Type **307** 55 50
1162 45c.+15c. Magnificent frigate bird and slave bell 70 65
1163 65c.+25c. "Stamps" from Curacao and Bonaire (Nicole Wever and Sabine Anthonio) . . . . 1·10 1·00
1164 75c.+35c. "Stamps" from St. Maarten, St. Eustatius and Saba (Chad Jacobs, Martha Hassell and Dion Humphreys) . . . . . . 1·25 1·10

1995. Hurricane Relief Fund. Nos. 831, 833 and 838 surch **ORKAAN LUIS** and premium.
1165 65c.+65c. multicoloured . . 1·60 1·50
1166 75c.+75c. multicoloured . . 1·75 1·60
1167 1g.+1g. multicoloured . . . 2·40 2·10

1995. Cats. Multicoloured.
1168 25c. Type **309** 50 30
1169 60c. Maine coon 90 65
1170 65c. Silver Egyptian mau . . 1·00 75
1171 90c. Angora . . . . 1·25 1·00
1172 150c. Blue smoke Persian 2·00 1·60

310 Helping Elderly Woman across Road

1995. Child Welfare. Children and Good Deeds. Multicoloured.
1173 35c.+15c. Type **310** 60 55
1174 65c.+25c. Reading newspaper to blind person 1·10 1·00
1175 90c.+35c. Helping younger brother . . . . 1·40 1·25
1176 175c.+75c. Giving flowers to the sick . . . . 2·75 2·50

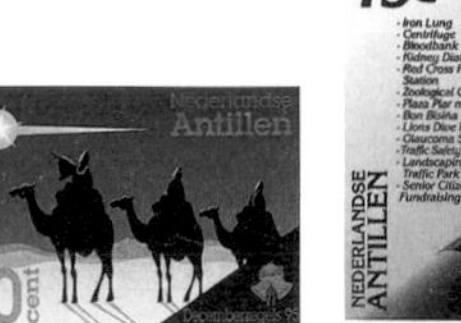

311 Wise Men on Camels **312** Serving the Community

1995. Christmas. Multicoloured.
1177 30c. Type **311** 50 35
1178 115c. Fireworks over houses 1·40 1·25

1996. 50th Anniv of Curacao Lions Club. Multicoloured.
1179 75c. Type **312** . . . . . . 1·10 80
1180 105c. Anniversary emblem 1·40 1·25
1181 250c. Handshake . . . . . 3·25 2·75

313 Disease on Half of Leaf **314** Dish Aerial and Face

1996. 60th Anniv of Capriles Psychiatric Clinic, Otrabanda on Rif. Multicoloured.
1182 60c. Type **313** 70 65
1183 75c. Tornado and sun over house . . . . 1·10 80

1996. Centenary of Guglielmo Marconi's Patented Wireless Telegraph. Multicoloured.
1184 85c. Type **314** . . . . . . 1·00 90
1185 175c. Dish aerial and morse transmitter . . . . 2·10 1·90

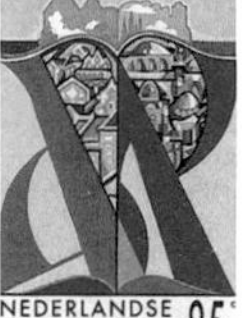

315 Letters and Buildings

316 Gulf Fritillary

1996. Translation of Bible into Papiamentu (Creole language). Multicoloured.
1186 85c. Type **315** . . . . . . 1·00 90
1187 225c. Bible and alphabets 2·75 2·40

1996. "Capex '96" International Stamp Exhibition, Toronto, Canada. Butterflies. Multicoloured.
1188 5c. Type **316** 20 10
1189 110c. "Callithea philotima" 1·25 1·10
1190 300c. Clipper . . . . 3·50 3·25
1191 750c. "Euphaedra francina" 8·75 8·25
MS1192 132 × 75 mm. Nos. 1189/90 5·75 4·50

317 Mary Johnson-Hassell (introducer of drawn-thread work to Saba, 57th death)

1996. Anniversaries.
1193 **317** 40c. orange and black on grey 60 50
1194 – 50c. green and black on grey 70 55
1195 – 75c. red and black on grey . . . . 1·00 80
1196 – 80c. blue and black on grey . . . . 1·10 1·00
DESIGNS: 40c. Type **317** (introducer of drawn-thread work to Saba); 50c. Cornelius Marten (Papa Cornes) (pastor to Bonaire); 75c. Phelippi Chakutoe (union leader); 85c. Chris Engels (physician, artist, author and fencing champion).

318 Shire

1996. Horses. Multicoloured.
1197 110c. Type **318** . . . . . . 1·50 1·25
1198 225c. Shetland ponies . . . 2·75 2·50
1199 275c. British thoroughbred 2·25 3·00
1200 350c. Przewalski mare and foal . . . . 4·50 4·00

319 Street Child and Shanty Town

320 Straw Hat with Poinsettias and Gifts

1996. Child Welfare. 50th Anniv of U.N.I.C.E.F. Multicoloured.
1201 40c.+15c. Type **319** 70 65
1202 75c.+25c. Asian child weaver . . . . 1·25 1·10
1203 110c.+45c. Child in war zone of former Yugoslavia (vert) . . . . 1·90 1·75
1204 225c.+100c. Impoverished Caribbean mother and child (vert) . . . . 3·75 3·50

1996. Christmas. Multicoloured. Self-adhesive.
1205 35c. Type **320** 60 35
1206 150c. Father Christmas . . 2·00 1·60

321 Emblem

322 Deadly Galerina

1997. Cultural and Social Relief Funds.
1207 **321** 40c.+15c. black and yellow 70 65
1208 – 75c.+30c. blue, mauve and black . . . . . . 1·25 1·10

1209 – 85c.+40c. red and black 1·60 1·50
1210 – 110c.+50c. black, green and red 1·90 1·90

DESIGNS: 40c. Type **321** (50th anniv of Curacao Foundation for Care and Resettlement of Ex-prisoners); 75c. Emblem (60th anniv (1996) of General Union of Public Servants (ABVO)); 85c. Flag of Red Cross (65th anniv of Curacao division); 110c. National Red Cross emblem (65th anniv of Curacao division).

1997. Fungi. Multicoloured.
1211 40c. Type **322** 60 50
1212 50c. Destroying angel 75 55
1213 75c. Cep 1·10 80
1214 175c. Fly agaric 2·25 1·90

323 Budgerigars

1997. Birds. Multicoloured.
1215 5c. Type **323** 25 10
1216 25c. Sulphur-crested cockatoo 70 30
1217 50c. Yellow-shouldered Amazon 95 55
1218 75c. Purple heron 1·10 80
1219 85c. Ruby topaz hummingbird 1·40 90
1220 100c. South African crowned crane 1·60 1·10
1221 110c. Vermilion flycatcher 1·75 1·10
1222 125c. Greater flamingo 1·75 1·40
1223 200c. Osprey 2·50 2·25
1224 225c. Keel-billed toucan 3·00 2·50

324 Parrots ("Love") **325** "Correspondence"

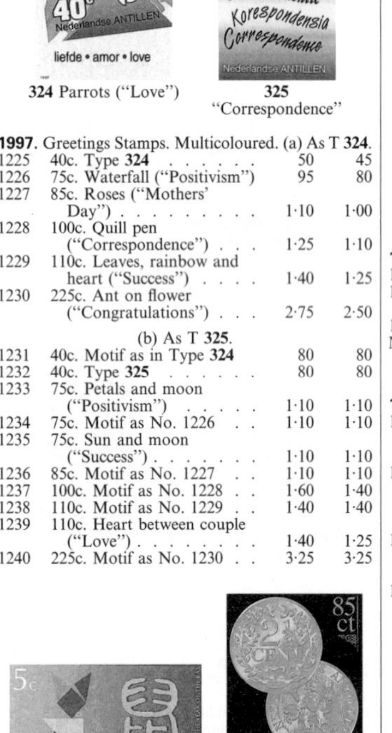

1997. Greetings Stamps. Multicoloured. (a) As T **324**.
1225 40c. Type **324** 50 45
1226 75c. Waterfall ("Positivism") 95 80
1227 85c. Roses ("Mothers' Day") 1·10 1·00
1228 100c. Quill pen ("Correspondence") 1·25 1·10
1229 110c. Leaves, rainbow and heart ("Success") 1·40 1·25
1230 225c. Ant on flower ("Congratulations") 2·75 2·50

(b) As T **325**.
1231 40c. Motif as in Type **324** 80 80
1232 40c. Type **325** 80 80
1233 75c. Petals and moon ("Positivism") 1·10 1·10
1234 75c. Motif as No. 1226 1·10 1·10
1235 75c. Sun and moon ("Success") 1·10 1·10
1236 85c. Motif as No. 1227 1·10 1·10
1237 100c. Motif as No. 1228 1·60 1·40
1238 110c. Motif as No. 1229 1·40 1·40
1239 110c. Heart between couple ("Love") 1·40 1·25
1240 225c. Motif as No. 1230 3·25 3·25

326 Rat

327 $2\frac{1}{2}$ Cent Coin (Plaka)

1997. "Pacific '97" International Stamp Exhibition, San Francisco. Chinese Zodiac. Designs showing Tangram (puzzle) representations and Chinese symbols for each animal. Multicoloured.
1241 5c. Type **326** 15 10
1242 5c. Ox 15 10
1243 5c. Tiger 15 10
1244 40c. Rabbit 60 50
1245 40c. Dragon 60 50
1246 40c. Snake 60 50
1247 75c. Horse 1·00 80
1248 75c. Goat 1·00 80
1249 75c. Monkey 1·00 80
1250 100c. Rooster 1·25 1·10
1251 100c. Dog 1·25 1·10
1252 100c. Pig 1·25 1·10
MS1253 145 × 150 mm. Nos. 1241/52 10·50 10·50

1997. Coins. Obverse and reverse of coins. Multicoloured.
1254 85c. Type **327** 1·25 1·00
1255 175c. 5 cent (Stuiver) 2·10 2·00
1256 225c. $2\frac{1}{2}$ gulden (Fuerte) 3·25 2·50

328 Score of "Atras de Nos" and Salsa Drummer

1997. Child Welfare. The Child and Music. Multicoloured.
1257 40c.+15c. Type **328** 65 60
1258 75c.+25c. Score of "For Elise" and pianist 1·10 1·00
1259 110c.+45c. Score of "Blues for Alice" and flautist 1·90 1·75
1260 225c.+100c. Score of "Yesterday" and guitarist 2·75 2·50

329 Nampu Grand Bridge, Shanghai

330 Worshippers (detail of mural by Marcolino Maas in Church of the Holy Family, Willemstad, Curacao)

1997. "Shanghai 1997" International Stamp and Coin Exhibition, China. Multicoloured.
1261 15c. Type **329** 20 20
1262 40c. Giant panda 70 55
1263 75c. Tiger (New Year) (vert) 1·10 90
MS1264 108 × 78 mm. 90c. The Bund, Shanghai 2·10 1·60

1997. Christmas and New Year. Multicoloured.
1265 35c. Type **330** 60 40
1266 150c. Popping champagne cork and calendar (New Year) 2·00 1·60

331 Partial Eclipse

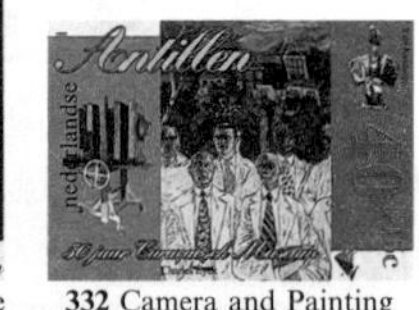

332 Camera and Painting

1998. Total Solar Eclipse, Curacao. Multicoloured.
1267 85c. Type **331** 1·10 1·00
1268 110c. Close-up of sun in total eclipse 1·60 1·25
1269 225c. Total eclipse 3·00 2·76
MS1270 85 × 52 mm. 750c. Hologram of stages of the eclipse 11·00 11·00

1998. Cultural and Social Relief Funds. Mult.
1271 40c.+15c. Type **332** (50th anniv of Curacao Museum) 70 65
1272 40c.+15c. Desalination plant and drinking water (70 years of seawater desalination) 70 65
1273 75c.+25c. Mangrove roots and shells (Lac Cai wetlands, Bonaire) (vert) 1·40 1·10
1274 85c.+40c. Lake and underwater marine life (Little Bonaire wetlands) (vert) 1·75 1·60

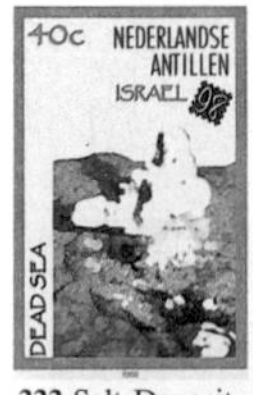

333 Salt Deposit, Dead Sea

334 Superior, 1923, and Elias Moreno Brandao

1998. "Israel 98" International Stamp Exhibition, Tel Aviv. Multicoloured.
1275 40c. Type **333** 45 45
1276 75c. Zion Gate, Jerusalem 90 80
1277 110c. Masada 1·25 1·10
MS1278 58 × 91 mm. 225c. Mikve Israel-Emanuel Synagogue, Curacao 3·00 3·00

1998. 75th Anniv of E. Moreno Brandao and Sons (car dealers). Chevrolet Motor Cars. Multicoloured.
1279 40c. Type **334** 1·60 1·00
1280 55c. Roadster, 1934 1·75 1·40
1281 75c. Styleline deluxe sedan, 1949 2·10 1·75
1282 110c. Bel Air convertible, 1957 3·25 2·50
1283 225c. Corvette Stingray coupe, 1963 5·50 5·25
1284 500c. Chevelle SS-454 2-door hardtop, 1970 13·50 12·00

335 State Flag and Arms

336 Christina Flanders (philanthropic worker)

1998. 50th Anniv of Netherlands Antilles Advisory Council. Multicoloured.
1285 75c. Type **335** 90 80
1286 85c. Gavel 1·00 95

1998. Death Anniversaries. Multicoloured.
1287 40c. Type **336** (second anniv) 50 45
1288 75c. Abraham Jesurun (writer and first president of Curacao Chamber of Commerce, 80th anniv) 95 80
1289 85c. Capt. Gerrit Newton (seaman and shipyard manager, 50th anniv (1999)) 1·00 95
1290 110c. Eduardo Adriana (sportsman, first anniv) 1·40 1·10

337 Ireland Pillar Box

338 Globe and New Post Emblem

1998. Postboxes (1st series). Multicoloured.
1291 15c. Type **337** 25 15
1292 40c. Nepal postbox 60 45
1293 75c. Uruguay postbox 1·00 80
1294 85c. Curacao postbox 1·00 1·00
See also Nos. 1413/16.

1998. Privatization of Postal Services.
1295 **338** 75c. black, blue and red 90 80
1296 – 110c. multicoloured 1·40 1·10
1297 – 225c. multicoloured 2·50 2·40

DESIGNS—VERT: 110c. Tree and binary code. HORIZ: 225c. 1949 25c. U.P.U. stamp, reproduction of No. 1296 and binary code.

339 Black Rhinoceros

1998. Endangered Species. Multicoloured.
1298 5c. Type **339** 40 10
1299 75c. White-tailed hawk (vert) 1·10 80
1300 125c. White-tailed deer 1·75 1·40
1301 250c. Tiger ("Tigris") (vert) 3·25 2·75

340 Short-finned Mako ("Mako Shark")

1998. Fishes. Multicoloured.
1302 275c. Type **340** 3·75 3·00
1303 350c. Manta ray 4·50 3·75

341 1950 5c. Stamp

342 Child with Family Paper Chain

1998. "70th Anniv of Dutch Stamp Dealers Club" Stamp Exhibition, The Hague. Multicoloured.
1304 225c. Type **341** 2·50 60
1305 500c. 1950 Queen Juliana 15c. stamp 5·50 5·50
MS1306 72 × 50 mm. 500c. Curacao 1922 $12\frac{1}{2}$c. stamp 6·25 6·25

1998. Child Welfare. Universal Rights of the Child. Multicoloured.
1307 40c.+15c. Type **342** (right to name and nationality) 65 60
1308 75c.+25c. Children eating water melons (right to health care) 1·10 1·00
1309 110c.+45c. Children painting (right of handicapped children to special care) 1·90 1·75
1310 225c.+100c. Children playing with can telephones (right to freedom of expression) 3·75 3·50

343 Former Office, Curacao

1998. 60th Anniv of PriceWaterhouseCoopers (accountancy firm). Multicoloured.
1311 75c. Type **343** 1·50 85
1312 225c. Modern office, Curacao 3·00 2·40

344 "Christmas Tree" (Theodora van Ierland)

345 Avila Beach Hotel and Dr. Pieter Maal (founder)

1998. Christmas. Children's Paintings. Multicoloured.
1313 35c. Type **344** 40 50
1314 150c. "Post in mail box" (Anna Sordam) 1·75 1·60

1999. 50th Anniv of Avila Beach Hotel. Mult.
1315 75c. Type **345** 1·00 80
1316 110c. Beach and flamboyant tree 1·40 1·25
1317 225c. Mesquite tree 2·75 2·40

346 Rabbit and Great Wall of China

347 Girls hugging and Wiri

1999. "China 1999" International Stamp Exhibition, Peking. Year of the Rabbit. Multicoloured.
1318 75c. Type **346** 60 80
1319 225c. Rabbit and Jade Pagoda (vert) 2·75 2·40
MS1320 88 × 53 mm. 225c. Rabbit (vert) 3·00 3·00

1999. 50th Anniv of Government Correctional Institute. Musical instruments. Multicoloured.
1321 40c. Type **347** 60 45
1322 75c. Institute building and bamba 1·00 80
1323 85c. Boy at lathe and triangle (horiz) 1·00 90

348 Launch of Ship

349 Godett

1999. 500th Anniv of First Written Record (by Amerigo Vespucci) of Curacao. Multicoloured.
1324 75c. Type **348** 1·10 80
1325 110c. Otrobanda, 1906 1·50 1·25
1326 175c. Nos. 1324/5 and anniversary emblem 2·25 2·00

1327 225c. Fort Beeckenburg, Caracasbaai . . . . . . 2·75 2·40
1328 500c. 1949 12½c. stamp and sailing ship . . . . 5·75 5·50

1999. Fourth Death Anniv of Wilson Godett (politician).
1329 **349** 75c. multicoloured . . . 1·10 80

350 Amerindians and Old Map

1999. The Millennium. Multicoloured. (a) Size 35½ × 35½ mm. Ordinary gum.
1330 5c. Type **350** (arrival of Alonso de Ojeda, Amerigo Vespucci and Juan de la Cosa, 1499) . . 40 40
1331 10c. Dutch ship, indian and soldier on horseback (Dutch conquest, 1634) 40 40
1332 40c. Flags of constituent islands of Netherlands Antilles, Autonomy Monument in Curacao and document granting autonomy, 1954 . . . . . 60 60
1333 75c. Telephone and Curacao 1873 25c. King William III stamp (installation of telephones on Curacao, 1892) . . . 1·00 1·00
1334 85c. Fokker F.XVIII airplane "De Snip" (first Amsterdam–Curacao flight, 1934) . . . . . . 1·10 1·10
1335 100c. Oil refinery, Curacao (inauguration, 1915) . . . 1·10 1·10
1336 110c. Dish aerial, undersea fibre optic cable and dolphins (telecommunications) . . 1·40 1·40
1337 125c. Curacao harbour, bridge and bow of cruise liner (tourism) . . . . . 1·75 1·75
1338 225c. Ka'i orgel (musical instrument) and couple in folk costume (culture) . . 2·75 2·75
1339 350c. Brown-throated conure, common caracara, yellow-shouldered amazon and greater flamingoes (nature) . . . . 4·25 4·25

(b) Size 29 × 29 mm. Self-adhesive.
1340 5c. Type **350** 40 40
1341 10c. As No. 1331 . . . . . 40 40
1342 40c. As No. 1332 . . . . . 60 60
1343 75c. As No. 1333 . . . . . 1·00 1·00
1344 85c. As No. 1334 . . . . . 1·10 1·10
1345 100c. As No. 1335 . . . . 1·10 1·10
1346 110c. As No. 1336 . . . . 1·40 1·40
1347 125c. As No. 1337 . . . . 1·75 1·75
1348 225c. As No. 1338 . . . . 2·75 2·75
1349 350c. As No. 1339 . . . . 4·25 4·25

351 Ijzerstraat, Otrobanda

1999. Cultural and Social Relief Funds. Willemstad, World Heritage Site. Multicoloured.
1350 40c.+15c. Type **351** 70 65
1351 75c.+30c. Oldest house in Punda (now Postal Museum) (vert) . . . . . 1·40 1·10
1352 110c.+50c. "The Bridal Cake" (now Central National Archives), Scharloo . . . . 2·00 1·75

352 St. Paul's Roman Catholic Church, Saba

1999. Tourist Attractions. Multicoloured.
1357 150c. Type **352** . . . . . . 2·40 1·60
1359 250c. Greater flamingoes, Bonaire . . . . 3·25 2·75
1361 500c. Courthouse, St. Maarten . . . . . . 6·00 5·50

353 Basketball

1999. Child Welfare. Sports. Multicoloured.
1370 40c.+15c. Type **353** . . . . 1·00 65
1371 75c.+25c. Golf . . . . . . 1·60 1·10
1372 110c.+45c. Fencing . . . . 2·10 1·60
1373 225c.+100c. Tennis . . . . 4·25 3·50

354 *Saintpaulia ionantha*

1999. Flowers. Multicoloured.
1374 40c. Type **354** 80 80
1375 40c. *Gardenia jasminioides* 80 80
1376 40c. Allamanda 80 80
1377 40c. Bougainvillea 80 80
1378 75c. Strelitzia . . . . 1·00 1·00
1379 75c. Cymbidium . . . . . 1·00 1·00
1380 75c. Phalaenopsis . . . . . 1·00 1·00
1381 75c. *Cassia fistula* . . . . . 1·00 1·00
1382 110c. Doritaenopsis . . . . 1·60 1·60
1383 110c. Guzmania . . . . . . 1·60 1·60
1384 225c. *Catharanthus roseus* 2·75 2·75
1385 225c. *Caralluma hexagona* 2·75 2·75

355 Children wearing Hats

356 Man, Baby and Building Blocks (Fathers' Day)

1999. Christmas. Multicoloured.
1386 35c. Type **355** 50 40
1387 150c. Clock face and islands 1·90 1·60

2000. Greetings Stamps. Multicoloured.
1388 40c. Type **356** 55 50
1389 40c. Women and globe (Mothers' Day) 55 50
1390 40c. Hearts and flowers (Valentine's Day) 55 50
1391 75c. Puppy and present ("Thank You") 95 90
1392 110c. Butterfly and vase of flowers (Special Occasions) . . . . 1·10 1·00
1393 150c. As No. 1389 . . . . 2·25 2·10
1394 150c. As No. 1390 . . . . 2·25 2·10
1395 225c. Hands and wedding rings (Anniversary) . . . 2·75 2·75

357 Dragon

2000. Chinese Year of the Dragon. Multicoloured.
1396 110c. Type **357** . . . . . . 1·10 1·00
MS1397 50 × 85 mm. 225c. Chinese dragons . . . . 3·00 3·00

358 Red Eyed Tree Frog

2000. Endangered Animals. Multicoloured.
1398 40c. Type **358** . . . . . . 1·00 1·00
1399 75c. King penguin (vert) . . 1·60 1·60
1400 85c. Killer whale (vert) . . . 1·60 1·60
1401 100c. African elephant (vert) 1·60 1·60
1402 110c. Chimpanzee (vert) . . 1·60 1·60
1403 225c. Tiger . . . . 3·00 3·00

359 Children playing

360 Space Shuttle Launch

2000. Cultural and Social Relief Funds. Mult.
1404 75c.+30c. Type **359** . . . . 1·00 95
1405 110c.+50c. Schoolchildren performing science experiments . . . . . . 2·10 2·00
1406 225c.+100c. Teacher giving lesson (vert) . . . . . . 3·75 3·75

2000. "World Stamp Expo 2000", Anaheim, California. Space Exploration. Multicoloured.
1407 75c. Type **360** . . . . . . 1·40 1·00
1408 225c. Astronaut, Moon and space station . . . . . . 3·00 3·00
MS1409 100 × 70 mm. 225c. Futuristic space station . . . . 3·25 3·25

361 Cycling

362 People

2000. Olympic Games, Sydney. Multicoloured.
1410 75c. Type **361** . . . . . . 1·10 1·10
1411 225c. Athletics . . . . . . 3·00 3·00
MS1412 50 × 72 mm. 225c. Swimming . . . . 2·75 2·75

2000. Postboxes (2nd series). As T **337**. Multicoloured.
1413 110c. Mexico postbox . . . 1·40 1·40
1414 175c. Dubai postbox . . . . 2·25 2·25
1415 350c. Great Britain postbox 4·25 4·25
1416 500c. United States of America postbox . . . . 6·00 6·00

2000. Social Insurance Bank. Multicoloured.
1417 75c. Type **362** . . . . . . 1·00 1·00
1418 110c. Adult holding child's hand (horiz) . . . . . . 1·40 1·40
1419 225c. Anniversary emblem 3·25 3·25

363 Child reaching towards Night Sky

364 Angels and Score of *Jingle Bells* (carol)

2000. Child Welfare. Multicoloured.
1420 40c.+15c. Type **363** . . . . 1·00 1·00
1421 75c.+25c. Children using Internet (horiz) . . . . . 1·60 1·60
1422 110c.+45c. Children playing with toy boat (horiz) . . 2·40 2·40
1423 225c.+100c. Children consulting map . . . . . 4·00 4·00

2000. Christmas. Multicoloured.
1424 40c. Type **364** 70 70
1425 150c. Seasonal messages in different languages (horiz) 2·10 2·10

365 Red King Snake

366 Forest

2001. Chinese Year of the Snake. Multicoloured.
1426 110c. Type **365** . . . . . . 1·40 1·40
MS1427 87 × 53 mm. 225c. Indian cobra (*Naja naja*) (vert) . . . . 3·50 3·50

2001. "HONG KONG 2001" World Stamp Exhibition. Landscapes. Multicoloured.
1428 25c. Type **366** 55 55
1429 40c. Palm trees and waterfall 75 75
1430 110c. Spinner dolphins (*Stenella longirostris*) . . . 1·25 1·25

367 Persian Shaded Golden Cat

368 *Mars* (Dutch ship of the line)

2001. Cats and Dogs. Multicoloured.
1431 55c. Type **367** . . . . . . 1·10 1·10
1432 75c. Burmese bluepoint cat and kittens . . . . 1·40 1·40
1433 110c. American wirehair . . 1·75 1·75
1434 175c. Golden retriever dog 2·10 2·10
1435 225c. German shepherd dog 3·00 3·00
1436 750c. British shorthair silver tabby . . . . 9·00 9·00

2001. Ships. Multicoloured.
1437 110c. Type **368** . . . . . . 1·40 1·40
1438 275c. *Alphen* (frigate) . . . 3·50 3·50
1439 350c. *Curacao* (paddle-steamer) (horiz) . . . . . 4·50 4·50
1440 500c. *Pioneer* (schooner) (horiz) . . . . 6·25 6·25

369 Pen and Emblem

370 Fedjai riding Bicycle

2001. 5th Anniv of Caribbean Postal Union. Multicoloured.
1441 75c. + 25c. Type **369** . . . 75 75
1442 110c. + 45c. Emblem . . . 1·10 1·10
1443 225c. + 100c. Silhouettes encircling globe . . . . . 2·40 2·40

2001. Fedjai (cartoon postman) (1st series). Multicoloured.
1444 5c. Type **370** 10 10
1445 40c. Fedjai and children . . 30 25
1446 75c. Fedjai and post box containing bird's nest and chicks 55 45
1447 85c. Fedjai and elderly woman 60 50
1448 100c. Barking dog and Fedjai sitting on postbox 75 60
1449 110c. Fedjai and boy reading comic 80 65
See also Nos. 1487/90.

371 Cave Entrance and Area Map

372 Streamertail (*Trochilus polytmus*)

2001. Kueba Boza (Muzzle Cave). Multicoloured.
1450 85c. Type **371** 60 50
1451 110c. *Leptonycteris nivalis cursoae* (bat) 80 65
1452 225c. *Glosophaga elongata* (bat) . . . . 1·60 1·25

2001. Birds. Multicoloured.
1453 10c. Type **372** 10 10
1454 85c. Eastern white pelican (*Pelecanus onocrotalus*) . . 60 50
1455 110c. Gouldian finch (*Erythrura gouldiae*) . . . 80 65
1456 175c. Painted bunting (*Passerina ciris*) . . . . . 1·25 1·00
1457 250c. Atlantic puffin (*Fratercula artica*) . . . . 1·90 1·50
1458 350c. American darter (*Anhinga anhinga*) . . . . 2·50 2·00

373 Chapel Facade and Map of St. Maarten Island

2001. 150th Anniv of Philipsburg Methodist Chapel. Multicoloured.
1459 75c. Type **373** 55 45
1460 110c. Rainbow, open Bible and map of St. Maarten 80 65

374 Boy feeding Toddler

2001. Child Welfare. Youth Volunteers. Multicoloured.
1461 40c. + 15c. Type **374** . . . 40 35
1462 75c. + 25c. Girls dancing (vert) 75 60
1463 110c. + 45c. Boy and elderly woman (vert) . . . . . . 1·10 90

375 Children of Different Nations

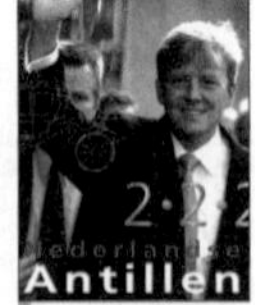

376 Prince Willem-Alexander

2001. Christmas. Multicoloured.
1464 40c. Type **375** 30 25
1465 150c. Children and Infant Jesus (vert) . . . . 1·10 90

2002. Wedding of Crown Prince Willem-Alexander to Maxima Zorreguieta. Multicoloured.
1466 75c. Type **376** 55 45
1467 110c. Princess Maxima . . . 80 65
MS1468 75 × 72 mm. 2g.25, Prince Willem-Alexander facing left; 2g.75, Princess Maxima facing left 3·75 3·75

377 Horse

378 Blue-tailed Emerald (*Chlorostilbon mellisugus*) and Passion Flower (*Passiflora foetida*)

2002. Chinese New Year. Year of the Horse. Multicoloured.
1469 25c. Type **377** 20 15
MS1470 52 × 86 mm. 95c. Horse's head 75 75

2002. Flora and Fauna. Multicoloured.
1471 50c. Type **378** 35 30
1472 95c. Lineated anole (*Anolis lineatus*) and *Cordia sebestena* (flower) (horiz) 65 55
1473 120c. Dragonfly (*Odonata*) (horiz) 90 75
1474 145c. Hermit crab (*Coenobita clypeatus*) (horiz) . . . . 1·10 90
1475 285c. Paper wasp (*Polistes versicolor*) . . . . 2·10 1·75

379 Flambeau (*Dryas julia*)

380 Flags as Football

2002. Butterflies. Multicoloured.
1480 25c. Type **379** 20 15
1481 145c. Monarch (*Danaus plexippus*) (horiz) . . . . 1·10 90
1482 400c. *Mechanitis polymnia* (horiz) . . . . 2·75 2·25
1483 500c. *Pyrrhopygopsis socrates* (wrongly inscr "Pyrhapygopsis socrates") (horiz) . . . . 3·50 2·75

2002. World Cup Football Championship, Japan and South Korea. Multicoloured.
1484 95c. + 35c. Type **380** . . . 95 75
1485 145c. + 55c. Player and globe as football . . . . 1·50 1·25
1486 240c. + 110c. Player and ball . . . . 2·50 2·00

381 Fedjai skipping

2002. Fedjai (cartoon postman) (2nd series). Multicoloured.
1487 10c. Type **381** 10 10
1488 55c. Fedjai and dog in rubbish bin (vert) 40 35
1489 95c. Fedjai presenting envelope on tray (vert) . . 70 55
1490 240c. Fedjai helping elderly woman across road (vert) 90 70

382 Man

383 *Wingfieldara casseta*

2002. "The Potato Eaters" (Vincent Van Gogh). Amphilex 2002 International Stamp Exhibition, Amsterdam. Designs showing parts of painting. Multicoloured.
1491 70c. Type **382** 40 30
1492 95c. Man (different) 60 50
1493 145c. Woman facing front 90 70
1494 240c. Woman facing left . . 1·40 1·10
MS1495 98 × 75 mm. 500c. As No. 1494 but design enlarged (horiz) . . . . 3·00 3·00

2002. Orchids. Multicoloured.
1496 95c. Type **383** 60 50
1497 285c. *Cymbidium Magna Charta* . . . . 1·70 1·40
1498 380c. *Brassolaeliocattleya* . . 2·25 1·80
1499 750c. *Miltonia spectabilis* . . 4·50 3·50

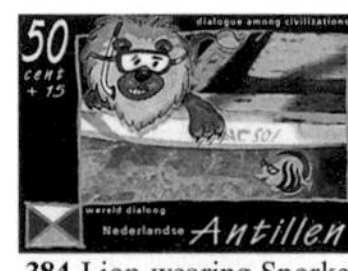

384 Lion wearing Snorkel

2001. Child Welfare. Multicoloured.
1500 50c.+15c. Type **384** 40 40
1501 95c.+35c. Kangaroo 80 80
1502 145c.+55c. Goat and penguin . . . . 1·20 1·20
1503 240c.+100c. Lizard and toucan . . . . 3·40 3·40

385 Christmas Trees

2002. Christmas. T **385** and similar horiz design. Multicoloured.
1504 95c. Type **385** 60 50
1505 240c. Lanterns . . . . . . 1·40 1·10

386 Savanna Hawk (*Buteogallus meridionalis*)

387 Goat's Head

2002. Birds. Multicoloured.
1506 5c. Type **386** 10 10
1507 20c. Black-spotted barbet (*Capito niger*) 15 10
1508 30c. Scarlet macaw (*Ara macao*) 20 15
1509 35c. Great jacamar (*Jacamerops aurea*) . . . 20 15
1510 70c. White-necked jacobin (*Florisuga mellivora*) . . . 40 30
1511 85c. Crimson fruit-crow (*Haematoderis militaris*) (inscr "Heamatoderus") 55 45
1512 90c. Peach-fronted conure (*Aratinga aurea*) 55 45
1513 95c. Green oropendula (*Psarocolius viridis*) . . . 60 50
1514 100c. Eastern meadowlark (*Stumella magna*) (horiz) 60 50
1515 145c. Sun conure (*Aratinga solstitalis*) (horiz) 85 70
1516 240c. White-tailed toucan (*Trogon virdis*) . . . . . 1·40 1·10
1517 285c. Red-billed toucan (*Ramphastos tucanus*) . . 1·70 1·40

2003. New Year. Year of the Goat.
1518 **387** 25c. multicoloured . . . 15 10
MS1519 86 × 52 mm. 96c. black, red and grey 30 30
DESIGN: 95c. Rearing goat.

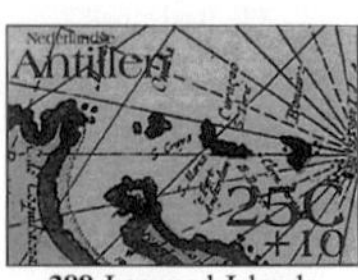

388 Leeward Islands

2003. Cultural and Social Relief Funds. Sheet 150 × 61 mm containing T **388** and similar multicoloured designs showing maps.
MS1520 25c.+10c. Type **388**; 30c.+15c. Windward Islands (vert); 55c.+25c. Curacao and Bonaire; 85c.+35c. St. Marten, Saba and St. Eustatius (vert); 95c +40c. Caribbean . . . . 2·25 2·25

389 *Rhetus arcius*

390 Trumpet

2003. Butterflies. Multicoloured.
1521 5c. Type **389** 10 10
1522 10c. *Evenus teresina* (horiz) 10 10
1523 25c. *Bhutanitis thaidina* (horiz) 15 10
1524 30c. *Semomesia capanea* (horiz) 20 15
1525 45c. *Papilio machaon* (horiz) 25 20
1526 55c. *Papilio multicaudata* . . 30 25
1527 65c. *Graphium weiskei* . . . 40 30
1528 95c. *Aneyluris formosissima venahalis* 60 50
1529 100c. *Euphaedra neophron* (horiz) 60 50
1530 145c. *Ornithoptera goliath Samson* (horiz) 85 70
1531 275c. *Aneyluris colubra* . . . 1·60 1·30
1532 350c. *Papilio lorquinianus* . . 2·10 1·70

2003. Musical Instruments. Sheet 125 × 61 mm containing T **390** and similar vert designs. Multicoloured.
MS1533 20c. Type **390**; 75c. Drums; 145c. Tenor saxophone; 285c. Double bass . . . . 1·50 1·50

391 Early Banknote

2003. 300th Anniv of Joh. Enschede (printers). Two sheets containing T **391** and similar vert designs. Multicoloured.
MS1534 (a) 120 × 61 mm. 70c. Type **391**; 95c. 1873 stamp; 145c. Revenue stamp; 240c. 1967 banknote (b) 85 × 52 mm. 550c. Johan Enschede building, Haarlem . . . . 6·50 6·50

POSTAGE DUE STAMPS

1952. As Type D **121** of Netherlands but inscr "NEDERLANDSE ANTILLEN".
D336 1c. green 10 10
D337 2½c. green 65 65
D338 5c. green 20 10
D339 6c. green 55 50
D340 7c. green 55 50
D341 8c. green 55 50
D342 9c. green 55 50
D343 10c. green 30 20
D344 12½c. green 30 20
D345 15c. green 35 30
D346 20c. green 35 50
D347 25c. green 55 10
D348 30c. green . . . . 1·25 1·50
D349 35c. green . . . . 1·60 1·50
D350 40c. green . . . . 1·25 1·50
D351 45c. green . . . . 1·50 1·50
D352 50c. green . . . . 1·25 1·25

PROVINCIAL STAMPS

The following stamps, although only valid for postage throughout Netherlands, were only available from Post Offices within the province depicted and from the Philatelic Bureau.

V 1 Freisland

2002. Multicoloured.
V 1 39c. Type **V 1** 55 25
V 2 39c. Drenthe 55 25
V 3 39c. North Holland 55 25
V 4 39c. Gelderland 55 25
V 5 39c. North Brabant 55 25
V 6 39c. Groningen 55 25
V 7 39c. South Holland 55 25
V 8 39c. Utrecht 55 25
V 9 39c. Limburg 55 25
V10 39c. Zeeland 55 25
V11 39c. Flevoland 55 25
V12 39c. Overijssel 55 25

NETHERLANDS INDIES Pt. 4

A former Dutch colony, consisting of numerous settlements in the East Indies, of which the islands of Java and Sumatra and parts of Borneo and New Guinea are the most important. Renamed Indonesia in 1948, Independence was granted during 1949. Netherlands New Guinea remained a Dutch possession until 1962 when it was placed under U.N. control, being incorporated with Indonesia in 1963.

100 cents = 1 gulden.

1 King William III

2

1864. Imperf.
1 **1** 10c. red £325 £100

1868. Perf.
2 **1** 10c. red £1000 £180

1870. Perf.
27 **2** 1c. green . . . . 5·50 3·50
28 2c. purple . . . . £100 90·00
29 2c. brown . . . . 8·00 4·50
30 2½c. buff . . . . 45·00 23·00
12 5c. green . . . . 65·00 7·00
32 10c. brown . . . . 18·00 1·10
40 12½c. drab . . . . 5·25 2·50
34 15c. brown . . . . 23·00 2·50
5 20c. blue . . . . £110 3·50
36 25c. purple . . . . 24·00 1·40
44 30c. green . . . . 40·00 4·50
17 50c. red . . . . 27·00 3·25
38 2g.50 green and purple . . . 90·00 16·00

5

6 Queen Wilhelmina

1883.
87 **5** 1c. green . . . . 1·40 20
88 2c. brown . . . . 1·40 20
89 2½c. buff . . . . 1·40 70
90 3c. purple . . . . 1·75 20
86 5c. green . . . . 45·00 26·00
91 5c. blue . . . . 14·00 20

1892.
94 **6** 10c. brown . . . . 7·00 40
95 12½c. grey . . . . 12·00 24·00
96 15c. brown . . . . 17·00 1·60
97 20c. blue . . . . 38·00 1·60
98 25c. purple . . . . 32·00 1·60
99 30c. green . . . . 48·00 2·00
100 50c. red . . . . 35·00 1·60
101 2g.50 blue and brown . . . £130 38·00

1900. Netherlands stamps of 1898 surch **NED.-INDIE** and value.
111 **13** 10c. on 10c. lilac . . . . . 2·40 40
112 12½c. on 12½c. blue . . . . 3·00 80
113 15c. on 15c. brown . . . . 4·00 80
114 20c. on 20c. green . . . . 20·00 80
115 25c. on 25c. blue and pink 17·00 80
116 50c. on 50c. red and green 32·00 1·10
117 **11** 2½g. on 2½g. lilac . . . . . 50·00 19·00

1902. Surch.
118 **5** ½ on 2c. brown 50 35
119 2½ on 3c. purple 55 50

11

12

13

1902.

120	11	½c. lilac	60	30
121		1c. olive	60	30
122		2c. brown	4·00	35
123		2½c. green	2·40	20
124		3c. orange	2·75	1·25
125		4c. blue	17·00	9·00
126		5c. red	6·00	20
127		7½c. grey	4·00	35
128	12	10c. slate	1·60	20
129		12½c. blue	2·00	20
130		15c. brown	9·75	2·10
131		17½c. bistre	4·00	30
132		20c. grey	2·00	1·50
133		20c. olive	27·00	25
134		22½c. olive and brown	4·75	30
135		25c. mauve	11·50	30
136		30c. brown	32·00	30
137		50c. red	25·00	30
138	13	1g. lilac	60·00	40
206		1g. lilac on blue	42·00	4·75
139		2½g. grey	70·00	1·60
207		2½g. grey on blue	60·00	26·00

1902. No. 130 optd with horiz bars.

140		15c. brown	2·00	70

1905. No. 132 surch **10 cent.**

141		10c. on 20c. grey	2·75	1·25

1908. Stamps of 1902 optd **JAVA**.

142		½c. lilac	35	20
143		1c. olive	60	30
144		2c. brown	2·50	2·50
145		2½c. green	1·50	20
146		3c. orange	1·10	1·00
147		5c. red	2·50	20
148		7½c. grey	2·00	1·75
149		10c. slate	1·00	20
150		12½c. blue	2·10	70
151		15c. brown	3·25	3·00
152		17½c. bistre	1·75	65
153		20c. olive	10·00	70
154		22½c. olive and brown	4·75	2·75
155		25c. mauve	4·75	30
156		30c. brown	28·00	2·50
157		50c. red	19·00	70
158		1g. lilac	45·00	3·00
159		2½g. grey	65·00	50·00

1908. Stamps of 1902 optd **BUITEN BEZIT**.

160		½c. lilac	45	35
161		1c. olive	55	35
162		2c. brown	1·90	2·50
163		2½c. green	1·10	20
164		3c. orange	1·00	1·10
165		5c. red	3·10	50
166		7½c. grey	3·00	2·50
167		10c. slate	1·10	20
168		12½c. blue	9·75	2·25
169		15c. brown	4·50	2·50
170		17½c. bistre	2·10	1·75
171		20c. olive	8·75	2·10
172		22½c. olive and brown	6·25	4·50
173		25c. mauve	7·00	35
174		30c. brown	15·00	2·10
175		50c. red	7·00	80
176		1g. lilac	55·00	4·50
177		2½g. grey	85·00	55·00

19

20

1912.

208	19	½c. lilac	30	20
209		1c. green	30	20
210		2c. brown	55	20
264		2c. grey	55	20
211		2½c. green	1·40	20
265		2½c. pink	70	20
212		3c. brown	55	20
266		3c. green	1·10	20
213		4c. blue	1·10	20
267		4c. green	1·10	20
268		4c. bistre	9·00	4·00
214		5c. pink	1·25	20
269		5c. green	1·10	20
270		5c. blue	70	20
215		7½c. brown	70	20
271		7½c. bistre	70	20
216	20	10c. red	1·10	20
272	19	10c. lilac	1·75	20
217	20	12½c. blue	1·25	20
273		12½c. red	1·25	35
274		15c. blue	7·00	30
218		17½c. brown	1·25	20
219		20c. green	2·10	20
275		20c. blue	2·10	20
276		20c. orange	12·50	20
220		22½c. orange	2·10	75
221		25c. mauve	2·10	20
222		30c. grey	2·10	20
277		32½c. violet and orange	2·10	30
278		35c. brown	7·25	55
279		40c. green	2·75	20

21

1913.

223	21	50c. green	4·75	20
280		60c. blue	6·00	20
281		80c. orange	4·75	35
224		1g. brown	4·00	20
283		1g.75 lilac	20·00	1·75
225		2½g. pink	16·00	1·25

1915. Red Cross. Stamps of 1912 surch **+5 cts.** and red cross.

243		1c.+5c. green	5·50	5·50
244		5c.+5c. pink	5·50	5·50
245		10c.+5c. red	7·00	7·00

1917. Stamps of 1902, 1912 and 1913 surch.

246		½c. on 2½c. (No. 211)	35	35
247		1c. on 4c. (No. 213)	35	55
250		12½c. on 17½c. (No. 218)	30	20
251		12½c. on 22½c. (No. 220)	35	20
248		17½c. on 22½c. (No. 134)	1·75	70
252		20c. on 22½c. (No. 220)	35	20
249		30c. on 1g. (No. 138)	6·25	1·75
253		32½c. on 50c. (No. 223)	1·00	20
254		40c. on 50c. (No. 223)	3·50	50
255		60c. on 1g. (No. 224)	5·75	35
256		80c. on 1g. (No. 224)	6·25	80

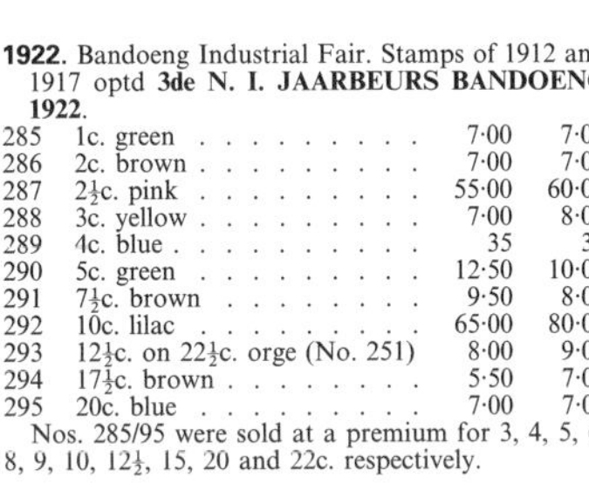

1922. Bandoeng Industrial Fair. Stamps of 1912 and 1917 optd **3de N. I. JAARBEURS BANDOENG 1922.**

285		1c. green	7·00	7·00
286		2c. brown	7·00	7·00
287		2½c. pink	55·00	60·00
288		3c. yellow	7·00	8·00
289		4c. blue	35	35
290		5c. green	12·50	10·00
291		7½c. brown	9·50	8·00
292		10c. lilac	65·00	80·00
293		12½c. on 22½c. orge (No. 251)	8·00	9·00
294		17½c. brown	5·50	7·00
295		20c. blue	7·00	7·00

Nos. 285/95 were sold at a premium for 3, 4, 5, 6, 8, 9, 10, 12½, 15, 20 and 22c. respectively.

33

36 Fokker F.VIIa

1923. Queen's Silver Jubilee.

296	33	5c. green	35	35
297		12½c. red	35	35
298		20c. blue	70	35
299		50c. orange	2·50	90
300		1g. purple	4·25	60
301		2½g. grey	38·00	32·00
302		5g. brown	£120	£110

1928. Air. Stamps of 1912 and 1913 surch **LUCHTPOST**, Fokker F.VII airplane and value.

303		10c. on 12½c. red	1·25	1·25
304		20c. on 25c. mauve	2·75	2·75
305		40c. on 80c. orange	2·10	2·10
306		75c. on 1g. sepia	1·10	1·10
307		1½g. on 2½g. red	7·25	7·25

1928. Air.

308	36	10c. purple	35	35
309		20c. brown	90	75
310		40c. red	1·10	75
311		75c. green	2·40	35
312		1g.50 orange	4·25	75

1930. Air. Surch **30** between bars.

313	36	30c. on 40c. red	1·10	40

38 Watch-tower

40 M. P. Pattist in Flight

1930. Child Welfare. Centres in brown.

315	–	2c. (+1c.) mauve	1·10	1·00
316	38	5c. (+2½c.) green	4·50	3·50
317	–	12½c. (+2½c.) red	3·50	70
318	–	15c. (+5c.) blue	5·00	5·25

DESIGNS—VERT: 2c. Bali Temple. HORIZ: 12½c. Minangkabau Compound; 15c. Buddhist Temple, Borobudur.

1930. No. 275 surch **12½**.

319		12½c. on 20c. blue	80	20

1931. Air. 1st Java–Australia Mail.

320	40	1g. brown and blue	15·00	12·50

41

1931. Air.

321	41	30c. red	2·75	35
322		4½g. blue	9·00	2·75
323		7½g. green	11·50	3·50

42 Ploughing

1931. Lepers' Colony.

324	42	2c. (+1c.) brown	2·50	2·00
325	–	5c. (+2½c.) green	4·00	4·00
326	–	12½c. (+2½c.) red	3·25	65
327	–	15c. (+5c.) blue	7·75	6·75

DESIGNS: 5c. Fishing; 12½c. Native actors; 15c. Native musicians.

1932. Air. Surch **50** on Fokker F.VIIa/3m airplane.

328	36	50c. on 1g.50 orange	3·25	55

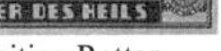
44 Plaiting Rattan

45 William of Orange

1932. Salvation Army. Centres in brown.

329	–	2c. (+1c.) purple	55	55
330	44	5c. (+2½c.) green	3·00	2·25
331	–	12½c. (+2½c.) red	90	35
332	–	15c. (+5c.) blue	4·25	3·50

DESIGNS: 2c. Weaving; 12½c. Textile worker; 15c. Metal worker.

1933. 400th Birth Anniv of William I of Orange.

333	45	12½c. red	1·60	40

46 Rice Cultivation

47 Queen Wilhelmina

1933.

335	46	1c. violet	30	20
397		2c. purple	10	40
337		2½c. bistre	30	20
338		3c. green	30	20
339		3½c. grey	30	20
340		4c. green	90	20
401		5c. blue	10	10
342		7½c. violet	1·10	20
343		10c. red	2·00	20
403	47	10c. red	20	10
334		12½c. brown	8·00	35
345		12½c. red	55	20
404		15c. blue	10	10
405		20c. purple	35	10
348		25c. green	2·10	20
349		30c. blue	3·50	20
350		32½c. bistre	9·00	8·25
408		35c. violet	5·00	1·50
352		40c. green	2·75	20
353		42½c. yellow	2·75	35
354		50c. blue	5·00	35
355		60c. blue	5·50	70
356		80c. red	7·00	1·10
357		1g. violet	8·75	35
358		1g.75 green	18·00	10·00
414		2g. green	25·00	12·50
359		2g.50 purple	21·00	1·75
415		5g. bistre	24·00	6·25

The 50c. to 5g. are larger, 30 × 30 mm.

48 Pander S.4 Postjager

1933. Air. Special Flights.

360	48	30c. blue	1·50	1·50

49 Woman and Lotus Blossom

53 Cavalryman and Wounded Soldier

1933. Y.M.C.A. Charity.

361	49	2c. (+1c.) brown & purple	70	45
362	–	5c. (+2½c.) brown and green	2·40	2·00
363	–	12½c. (+2½c.) brown & orge	2·75	30
364	–	15c. (+5c.) brown and blue	3·25	2·75

DESIGNS: 5c. Symbolizing the sea of life; 12½c. Y.M.C.A. emblem; 15c. Unemployed man.

1934. Surch.

365	36	2c. on 10c. purple	35	50
366		2c. on 20c. brown	35	30
367	41	2c. on 30c. red	35	65
368	36	42½c. on 75c. green	4·75	35
369		42½c. on 1g.50 orange	4·75	50

1934. Anti-tuberculosis Fund. As T **77** of Netherlands.

370		12½c. (+2½c.) brown	1·75	55

1935. Christian Military Home.

371	–	2c. (+1c.) brown and purple	1·75	1·25
372	53	5c. (+2½c.) brown and green	3·50	3·50
373	–	12½c. (+2½c.) brown & orge	3·50	30
374	–	15c. (+5c.) brown and blue	5·25	5·25

DESIGNS: 2c. Engineer chopping wood; 12½c. Artilleryman and volcano victim; 15c. Infantry bugler.

54 Dinner-time

55 Boy Scouts

1936. Salvation Army.

375	54	2c. (+1c.) purple	1·25	70
376		5c. (+2½c.) blue	1·50	1·25
377		7½c. (+2½c.) violet	1·50	1·60
378		12½c. (+2½c.) orange	1·50	40
379		15c. (+5c.) blue	2·50	2·40

Nos. 376/9 are larger, 30 × 27 mm.

1937. Scouts' Jamboree.

380	55	7½c. (+2½c.) green	1·00	95
381		12½c. (+2½c.) red	1·00	55

1937. Nos. 222 and 277 surch in figures.

382		10c. on 30c. slate	2·50	30
383		10c. on 32½c. violet and orange	2·75	35

59 Sifting Rice

62 Douglas DC-2 Airliner

1937. Relief Fund. Inscr "A.S.I.B.".

385	59	2c. (+1c.) sepia and orange	1·40	80
386	–	3½c. (+1½c.) grey	1·40	90
387	–	7½c. (+2½c.) green & orange	1·50	1·10
388	–	10c. (+2½c.) red and orange	1·50	30
389	–	20c. (+5c.) blue	1·40	1·40

DESIGNS: 3½c. Mother and children; 7½c. Ox-team ploughing rice-field; 10c. Ox-team and cart; 20c. Man and woman.

1938. 40th Anniv of Coronation. As T **87** of Netherlands.

390		2c. violet	10	10
391		10c. red	10	10
392		15c. blue	1·40	70
393		20c. red	70	35

1938. Air Service Fund. 10th Anniv of Royal Netherlands Indies Air Lines.

394	62	17½c. (+5c.) brown	90	90
395	–	20c. (+5c.) slate	90	90

DESIGN: 20c. As Type **62**, but reverse side of airliner.

63 Nurse and Child

1938. Child Welfare. Inscr "CENTRAAL MISSIE-BUREAU".
416 **63** 2c. (+1c.) violet 80 55
417 – 3½c. (+1½c.) green . . . . 1·25 1·10
418 – 7½c. (+2½c.) red 90 90
419 – 10c. (+2½c.) red . . . . . 1·00 30
420 – 20c. (+5c.) blue . . . . . 1·25 1·10
DESIGNS—(23 × 23 mm): Nurse with child suffering from injuries to eye (3½c.), arm (7½c.), head (20c.) and nurse bathing a baby (10c.).

63a Group of Natives

64 European Nurse and Patient

1939. Netherlands Indies Social Bureau and Protestant Church Funds.
421 – 2c. (+1c.) violet 30 30
422 – 3½c. (+1½c.) green 35 30
423 **63a** 7½c. (+2½c.) brown . . . 30 30
424 – 10c. (+2½c.) red . . . . . 1·60 1·00
425 **64** 10c. (+2½c.) red . . . . . 1·60 90
426 – 20c. (+5c.) blue 55 50
DESIGNS—VERT: 2c. as Type **63a** but group in European clothes. HORIZ: 3½c., 10c. (No. 424) as Type **64**, but Native nurse and patient.

1940. Red Cross Fund. No. 345 surch **10+5 ct** and cross.
428 **47** 10c.+5c. on 12½c. red . . . 3·50 55

68 Queen Wilhelmina

69 Netherlands Coat of Arms

1941. As T **94** of Netherlands but inscr "NED. INDIE" and T **68**.
429 – 10c. red 55 35
430 – 15c. blue . . . . 2·50 1·75
431 – 17½c. orange . . . . 1·00 70
432 – 20c. mauve . . . . 30·00 32·00
433 – 25c. green . . . . 40·00 42·00
434 – 30c. brown . . . . 4·50 1·40
435 – 35c. purple £160 £350
436 – 40c. green . . . . 12·00 3·50
437 – 50c. red . . . . 3·50 75
438 – 60c. blue . . . . 3·00 75
439 – 80c. red . . . . 3·00 75
440 – 1g. violet . . . . 3·00 75
441 – 2g. green . . . . 16·00 1·75
442 – 5g. bistre £300 £600
443 – 10g. green . . . . 42·00 18·00
444 **68** 25g. orange £250 £140
Nos 429/36 measure 18 × 23 mm, Nos. 431/43 20½ × 26 mm.

1941. Prince Bernhard Fund for Dutch Forces.
453 **69** 5c.+5c. blue and orange . . 75 15
454 10c.+10c. blue and red . . . 75 15
455 1g.+1g. blue and grey . . . 16·00 10·75

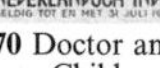
70 Doctor and Child

71 Wayangwong Dancer

1941. Indigent Mohammedans' Relief Fund.
456 **70** 2c. (+1c.) green . . . . . 1·10 55
457 – 3½c. (+1½c.) brown . . . . 5·25 2·75
458 – 7½c. (+2½c.) violet . . . . 4·50 3·50
459 – 10c. (+2½c.) red . . . . . 1·75 35
460 – 15c. (+5c.) blue . . . . . 13·00 7·00
DESIGNS: 3½c. Native eating rice; 7½c. Nurse and patient; 10c. Nurse and children; 15c. Basket-weaver.

1941.
461 – 2c. red 30 15
462 – 2½c. purple 55 15
463 – 3c. green 55 35
464 **71** 4c. green 50 35
465 – 5c. blue 10 10
466 – 7½c. violet 55 10
DESIGNS (dancers): 2c. Menari; 2½c. Nias; 3c. Legon; 5c. Padjoge; 7½c. Dyak.
See also Nos. 514/16.

72 Paddyfield

73 Queen Wilhelmina

1945.
467 **72** 1c. green 55 15
468 – 2c. mauve 55 30
469 – 2½c. purple 55 15
470 – 5c. blue 35 15
471 – 7½c. olive 75 15
472 **73** 10c. brown 35 15
473 15c. blue 35 15
474 17½c. red 35 15
475 20c. purple 35 15
476 30c. grey 35 15
477 – 60c. grey 75 15
478 – 1g. green . . . . 1·10 15
479 – 2½g. orange . . . . . . 3·50 70
DESIGNS: As Type **72**: 2c. Lake in W. Java; 2½c. Medical School, Batavia; 5c. Seashore; 7½c. Douglas DC-2 airplane over Bromo Volcano. (30 × 30 mm): 60c. to 2½g. Portrait as Type **73** but different frame.

76 Railway Viaduct near Soekaboemi

81 Queen Wilhelmina

1946.
484 **76** 1c. green 30 20
485 – 2c. brown 30 20
486 – 2½c. red 30 20
487 – 5c. blue 30 20
488 – 7½c. blue 30 20
DESIGNS: 2c. Power station; 3c. Minangkabau house; 5c. Tondano scene (Celebes); 7½c. Buddhist Stupas, Java.

1947. Surch in figures.
502 – 3c. on 2½c. red (No. 486) . . 30 20
503 – 3c. on 7½c. blue (No. 488) . 30 20
504 **76** 4c. on 1c. green 30 20
505 – 45c. on 60c. blue (No. 355) . 1·40 95
No. 505 has three bars.

1947. Optd **1947**.
506 **47** 12½c. red 35 20
507 25c. green 35 20
508 – 40c. green (No. 436) . . . 55 20
509 **47** 50c. blue 75 30
510 80c. red . . . . 1·10 65
511 – 2g. green (No. 441) . . . . 4·00 55
512 – 5g. brown (No. 442) . . . 10·75 6·75

1948. Relief for Victims of the Terror. Surch **PELITA 15+10 Ct.** and lamp.
513 **47** 15c.+10c. on 10c. red . . . 30 30

1948. Dancers. As T **71**.
514 3c. red (Menari) 35 20
515 4c. green (Legon) 35 20
516 7½c. brown (Dyak) 70 65

1948.
517 **81** 15c. orange 90 70
518 20c. blue 35 35
519 25c. green 35 35
520 40c. green 35 35
521 45c. mauve 55 70
522 50c. lake 50 35
523 80c. red 55 35
524 1g. violet 50 35
525 10g. green . . . . 30·00 12·50
526 25g. orange . . . . 60·00 50·00
Nos. 524/6 are larger, 21 × 26 mm.

1948. Queen Wilhelmina's Golden Jubilee. As T **81** but inscr "1898 1948".
528 15c. orange 40 30
529 20c. blue 40 30

1948. As T **126** of Netherlands.
530 15c. red 50 35
531 20c. blue 50 35

MARINE INSURANCE STAMPS

1921. As Type M **22** of the Netherlands, but inscribed "NED. INDIE".
M257 15c. green . . . . 9·00 28·00
M258 60c. red . . . . 9·00 45·00
M259 75c. brown . . . . 9·00 48·00
M260 1g.50 blue . . . . 27·00 £225
M261 2g.25 brown . . . . . . 32·00 £275
M262 4½g. black . . . . 60·00 £550
M263 7½g. red . . . . 75·00 £600

OFFICIAL STAMPS

1911. Stamps of 1892 optd **D** in white on a black circle.
O178 **6** 10c. brown . . . . 2·40 1·40
O179 12½c. grey . . . . 4·00 5·25
O180 15c. bistre . . . . 4·00 3·50
O181 20c. blue . . . . 3·50 2·10
O182 25c. mauve . . . . 13·00 9·75
O183 50c. red . . . . 3·00 2·00
O184 2g.50 blue and brown . . 55·00 55·00

1911. Stamps of 1902 (except No. O185) optd **DIENST**.
O186 ½c. lilac 35 70
O187 1c. olive 35 35
O188 2c. brown 35 35
O185 2½c. yellow (No. 91) . . . 90 1·90
O189 2½c. green . . . . 1·75 1·75
O190 3c. orange 55 50
O191 4c. blue 35 35
O192 5c. red . . . . 1·10 90
O193 7½c. grey . . . . 2·75 2·75
O194 10c. slate 35 35
O195 12½c. blue . . . . 2·50 2·50
O196 15c. brown 90 90
O197 15c. brown (No. 140) . . . 35·00
O198 17½c. bistre . . . . 3·50 2·75
O199 20c. olive 90 55
O200 22½c. olive and brown . . . 3·50 3·50
O201 25c. mauve . . . . 2·10 1·90
O202 30c. brown . . . . 1·10 65
O203 50c. red . . . . 14·00 9·00
O204 1g. lilac . . . . 3·50 1·60
O205 2½g. grey . . . . 32·00 35·00

POSTAGE DUE STAMPS

1874. As Postage Due stamps of Netherlands. Colours changed.
D56 D **8** 5c. yellow £300 £250
D57 10c. green on yellow . . . £110 90·00
D59 15c. orange on yellow . . 22·00 18·00
D60 20c. green on blue . . . . 35·00 14·50

1882. As Type D **10** of Netherlands.
D63b 2½c. black and red . . . . 55 1·10
D64b 5c. black and red . . . . 55 1·10
D65 10c. black and red . . . . 4·50 5·00
D70 15c. black and red . . . . 4·50 4·50
D71c 20c. black and red . . . . 90·00 55
D76b 30c. black and red . . . . 3·50 4·50
D72b 40c. black and red . . . . 2·50 1·25
D73b 50c. black and pink . . . 1·40 1·60
D67 75c. black and red . . . . 1·10 1·40

1892. As Type D **9** of Netherlands.
D102 2½c. black and pink . . . 1·10 35
D103 5c. black and pink . . . . 3·50 30
D104b 10c. black and pink . . . 4·50 2·50
D105 15c. black and pink . . . 15·00 2·50
D106b 20c. black and pink . . . 5·50 2·00
D107 30c. black and pink . . . 23·00 8·00
D108 40c. black and pink . . . 20·00 3·00
D109 50c. black and pink . . . 12·50 1·25
D110 75c. black and pink . . . 25·00 5·50

1913. As Type D **9** of Netherlands.
D226 1c. orange . . . . 10 1·75
D489 1c. violet 75 90
D227 2½c. orange 10 10
D527 2½c. brown . . . . 1·10 1·25
D228 3½c. orange . . . . 10 1·75
D491 3½c. blue 70 90
D229 5c. orange 10 10
D230 7½c. orange 10 10
D493 7½c. green 90 90
D231 10c. orange 10 10
D494 10c. mauve 90 90
D232 12½c. orange . . . . . . 2·75 10
D448 15c. orange . . . . 1·90 1·25
D234 20c. orange 20 10
D495 20c. blue . . . . 90 1·10
D235 25c. orange 20 10
D496 25c. yellow . . . . 90 1·10
D236 30c. orange 20 20
D497 30c. brown . . . . 1·10 1·10
D237 37½c. orange . . . . . . 18·00 14·50
D238 40c. orange 20 20
D498 40c. green . . . . 1·10 1·25
D239 50c. orange . . . . 2·10 10
D499 50c. yellow . . . . 1·50 1·50
D240 75c. orange . . . . 2·75 20
D500 75c. blue . . . . 1·50 1·50
D241 1g. orange . . . . 5·00 7·25
D452 1g. blue . . . . 1·40 90
D501 100c. green . . . . 1·50 1·50

1937. Surch **20**.
D384 D **5** 20c. on 37½c. red . . . 90 50

1946. Optd **TE BETALEN PORT** or surch also.
D480 2½c. on 10c. red (No. 429) . 90 90
D481 10c. red (No. 429) . . . . 2·00 2·00
D482 20c. mauve (No. 432) . . . 5·50 5·50
D483 40c. green (No. 436) . . . 45·00 45·00

For later issues see **INDONESIA**.

NETHERLANDS NEW GUINEA Pt. 4

The Western half of the island of New Guinea was governed by the Netherlands until 1962, when control was transferred to the U.N. (see West New Guinea). The territory later became part of Indonesia as West Irian (q.v.).

100 cents = 1 gulden.

1950. As numeral and portrait types of Netherlands but inscr "NIEUW GUINEA".
1 **118** 1c. grey 25 20
2 2c. orange 25 20
3 2½c. olive 50 20
4 3c. mauve . . . . 1·90 1·40
5 4c. green . . . . 1·90 1·25
6 5c. blue . . . . 3·25 20
7 7½c. brown 50 20
8 10c. violet . . . . 1·90 20
9 12½c. red . . . . 1·90 1·60
10 **129** 15c. brown . . . . 2·25 75
11 20c. blue 90 20
12 25c. red 90 20
13 30c. blue . . . . 11·00 20
14 40c. green . . . . 1·50 20
15 45c. brown . . . . 5·00 75
16 50c. orange . . . . 1·10 20
17 55c. grey . . . . 10·00 55
18 80c. purple . . . . 10·50 3·25
19 **130** 1g. red . . . . 11·50 20
20 2g. brown . . . . 9·00 1·40
21 5g. green . . . . 12·50 1·25

1953. Netherlands Flood Relief Fund. Nos. 6, 10 and 12 surch **hulp nederland 1953** and premium.
22 **118** 5c.+5c. blue . . . . 9·00 9·00
23 **129** 15c.+10c. brown . . . . . 9·00 9·00
24 25c.+10c. red . . . . 9·00 9·00

5 Lesser Bird of Paradise

6 Queen Juliana

1954.
25 **5** 1c. yellow and red 15 15
26 5c. yellow and brown 20 20
27 – 10c. brown and blue 20 20
28 – 15c. brown and yellow . . . 25 20
29 – 20c. brown and green . . . . 1·10 65
DESIGN: 10, 15, 20c. Greater bird of paradise.

1954.
30 **6** 25c. red 25 25
31 30c. blue 25 25
32 40c. orange . . . . 2·25 2·25
33 45c. green . . . . 75 1·25
34 55c. turquoise 55 25
35 80c. grey 90 35
36 85c. brown . . . . 1·25 50
37 1g. purple . . . . 4·75 2·25

1955. Red Cross. Nos. 26/8 surch with cross and premium.
38 **5** 5c.+5c. yellow and sepia . . 1·25 1·10
39 – 10c.+10c. brown and blue . . 1·25 1·10
40 – 15c.+10c. brown and lemon . 1·25 1·10

8 Child and Native Hut

10 Papuan Girl and Beach Scene

1956. Anti-leprosy Fund.
41 – 5c.+5c. green . . . . 1·10 1·00
42 **8** 10c.+5c. purple . . . . . . 1·10 1·00
43 – 25c.+10c. blue . . . . 1·10 1·00
44 **8** 30c.+10c. buff . . . . . . 1·10 1·00
DESIGN: 5c., 25c. Palm-trees and native hut.

1957. Child Welfare Fund.
51 **10** 5c.+5c. lake . . . . 1·10 1·00
52 – 10c.+5c. green . . . . . . 1·10 1·00
53 **10** 25c.+10c. brown . . . . . 1·10 1·00
54 – 30c.+10c. blue . . . . . . 1·10 1·00
DESIGN: 10c., 30c. Papuan child and native hut.

11 Red Cross and Idol

12 Papuan and Helicopter

1958. Red Cross Fund.
55 **11** 5c.+5c. multicoloured . . . 1·10 1·10
56 – 10c.+5c. multicoloured . . . 1·10 1·10
57 **11** 25c.+10c. multicoloured . . 1·10 1·10
58 – 30c.+10c. multicoloured . . 1·10 1·10
DESIGN: 10c., 30c. Red Cross and Asman-Papuan bowl in form of human figure.

1959. Stars Mountains Expedition, 1959.
59 **12** 55c. brown and blue . . . . 1·25 90

13 Blue-crowned Pigeon

14 "Tecomanthe dendrophila"

1959.

60 **13** 7c. purple, blue and brown 35 35
61 12c. purple, blue and green 35 35
62 17c. purple and blue 35 35

1959. Social Welfare. Inscr "SOCIALE ZORG".
63 **14** 5c.+5c. red and green . . . 75 65
64 – 10c.+5c. purple, yellow and olive 75 65
65 – 25c.+10c. yellow, green and red 75 65
66 – 30c.+10c. green and violet 75 65
DESIGNS: 10c. "Dendrobium attennatum Lindley"; 25c. "Rhododendron zoelleri Warburg"; 30c. "Boea cf. urvillei".

1960. World Refugee Year. As T **180** of Netherlands.
67 25c. blue 65 65
68 30c. ochre 65 65

16 Paradise Birdwing

1960. Social Welfare Funds. Butterflies.
69 **16** 5c.+5c. multicoloured . . . 90 90
70 – 10c.+5c. bl, blk & salmon 90 90
71 – 25c.+10c. red, sepia & yell 90 90
72 – 30c.+10c. multicoloured . . 90 90
BUTTERFLIES: 10c. Large green-banded blue; 25c. Red lacewing; 30c. Catops owl butterfly.

17 Council Building, Hollandia

1961. Opening of Netherlands New Guinea Council.
73 **17** 25c. turquoise 25 35
74 30c. red 25 35

18 "Scapanes australis" 19 Children's Road Crossing

1961. Social Welfare Funds. Beetles.
75 **18** 5c.+5c. multicoloured . . . 50 35
76 – 10c.+5c. multicoloured . . . 50 35
77 – 25c.+10c. multicoloured . . 50 35
78 – 30c.+10c. multicoloured . . 50 35
BEETLES: 10c. Brenthid weevil; 25c. "Neolamprima adolphinae" (stag beetle); 30c. "Aspidomorpha aurata" (leaf beetle).

1962. Road Safety Campaign. Triangle in red.
79 **19** 25c. blue 25 35
80 – 30c. green (Adults at road crossing) 25 35

1962. Silver Wedding of Queen Juliana and Prince Bernhard. As T **187** of Netherlands.
81 55c. brown 35 50

21 Shadow of Palm on Beach

1962. 5th South Pacific Conference, Pago Pago. Multicoloured.
82 25c. Type **21** 25 40
83 30c. Palms on beach 25 40

22 Lobster

1962. Social Welfare Funds. Shellfish. Multicoloured.
84 5c.+5c. Crab (horiz) 20 20
85 10c.+5c. Type **22** 20 20
86 25c.+10c. Spiny lobster . . . 25 25
87 30c.+10c. Shrimp (horiz) . . . 25 35

POSTAGE DUE STAMPS

1957. As Type D **121** of Netherlands but inscr "NEDERLANDS NIEUW GUINEA".
D45 1c. red 20 25
D46 5c. red . . . . 75 1·25
D47 10c. red . . . . 1·90 2·40
D48 25c. red . . . . 2·75 1·10
D49 40c. red . . . . 2·75 1·25
D50 1g. blue . . . . 3·50 4·50

For later issues see **WEST NEW GUINEA** and **WEST IRIAN**.

NEVIS Pt. 1

One of the Leeward Islands, Br. W. Indies. Used stamps of St. Kitts–Nevis from 1903 until June 1980 when Nevis, although remaining part of St. Kitts–Nevis, had a separate postal administration.

1861. 12 pence = 1 shilling;
20 shillings = 1 pound.
1980. 100 cents = 1 dollar.

1 2 5

(The design on the stamps refers to a medicinal spring on the Island).

1861. Various frames.
15 **1** 1d. red . . . . 20·00 15·00
6 **2** 4d. red . . . . £100 60·00
12 4d. orange . . . . £100 21·00
7 – 6d. lilac . . . . £100 50·00
20 – 1s. green . . . . 85·00 £100

1879.

25 **5** ½d. green . . . . 4·75 13·00
23 1d. mauve . . . . 70·00 32·00
27a 1d. red . . . . 9·00 9·00
28 2½d. brown . . . . £100 48·00
29 2½d. blue . . . . 17·00 16·00
30 4d. blue . . . . £300 50·00
31 4d. grey . . . . 9·00 3·50
32 6d. green £375 £350
33 6d. brown . . . . 22·00 60·00
34 1s. violet £100 £180

1883. Half of No. 23 surch **NEVIS. ½d.**
35 **5** ½d. on half 1d. mauve . . . £850 45·00

1980. Nos. 394/406 of St. Christopher, Nevis and Anguilla with "St. Christopher" and "Anguilla" obliterated.
37 5c. Radio and T.V. station . . 10 10
38 10c. Technical college 10 10
39 12c. T.V. assembly plant . . . 10 30
40 15c. Sugar cane harvesting . . 10 10
41 25c. Crafthouse (craft centre) 10 10
42 30c. "Europa" (liner) 20 15
43 40c. Lobster and sea crab . . 15 40
44 45c. Royal St. Kitts Hotel and golf course 80 70
45 50c. Pinney's Beach, Nevis . . 15 30
46 55c. New runway at Golden Rock 60 15
47 $1 Picking cotton 15 30
48 $5 Brewery 30 75
49 $10 Pineapples and peanuts . . 40 1·00

7a Queen Elizabeth the Queen Mother

1980. 80th Birthday of Queen Elizabeth the Queen Mother.
50 **7a** $2 multicoloured 20 30

8 Nevis Lighter 9 Virgin and Child

1980. Boats. Multicoloured.
51 5c. Type **8** 10 10
52 30c. Local fishing boat 15 10
53 55c. "Caona" (catamaran) . . 15 10
54 $3 "Polynesia" (cruise schooner) (39 × 53 mm) . . 40 40

1980. Christmas. Multicoloured.
55 5c. Type **9** 10 10
56 30c. Angel 10 10
57 $2.50 The Wise Men 20 30

10 Charlestown Pier 11 New River Mill

1981. Multicoloured.
58A 5c. Type **10** 10 10
59A 10c. Court House and Library 10 10
60A 15c. Type **11** 10 10
61A 20c. Nelson Museum 10 10
62A 25c. St. James' Parish Church 15 15
63A 30c. Nevis Lane 15 15
64A 40c. Zetland Plantation . . . 20 20
65A 45c. Nisbet Plantation . . . 20 25
66A 50c. Pinney's Beach 25 25
67A 55c. Eva Wilkin's Studio . . 25 30
68A $1 Nevis at dawn 30 45
69A $2.50 Ruins of Fort Charles 35 80
70A $5 Old Bath House . . . . 40 1·00
71A $10 Beach at Nisbet's . . . 50 2·00

1981. Royal Wedding. Royal Yachts. As T **26/27** of Kiribati. Multicoloured.
72 55c. "Royal Caroline" 15 15
73 55c. Prince Charles and Lady Diana Spencer 40 40
74 $2 "Royal Sovereign" 30 30
75 $2 As No. 73 . . . . 80 1·25
76 $5 "Britannia" 45 80
77 $5 As No. 73 . . . . 1·00 2·00
MS78 120 × 109 mm. $4.50 As No. 73 . . . . 1·10 1·25

12 "Heliconius charithonia"

1982. Butterflies (1st series). Multicoloured.
81 5c. Type **12** 10 10
82 30c. "Siproeta stelenes" . . . 20 10
83 55c. "Marpesia petreus" . . . 25 15
84 $2 "Phoebis agarithe" 60 80
See also Nos. 105/8.

13 Caroline of Brunswick, Princess of Wales, 1793

1982. 21st Birthday of Princess of Wales. Mult.
85 30c. Type **13** 10 10
86 55c. Coat of arms of Caroline of Brunswick 15 15
87 $5 Diana, Princess of Wales 1·25 1·25

1982. Birth of Prince William of Wales. Nos. 85/7 optd **ROYAL BABY**.
88 30c. As Type **13** 10 10
89 55c. Coat of arms of Caroline of Brunswick 15 15
90 $5 Diana, Princess of Wales 60 1·00

14 Cyclist

1982. 75th Anniv of Boy Scout Movement. Multicoloured.
91 5c. Type **14** 20 10
92 30c. Athlete 25 10
93 $2.50 Camp cook 50 65

15 Santa Claus

1982. Christmas. Children's Paintings. Mult.
94 15c. Type **15** 10 10
95 30c. Carollers 10 10
96 $1.50 Decorated house and local band (horiz) 15 25
97 $2.50 Adoration of the Shepherds (horiz) 25 40

16 Tube Sponge 19 Montgolfier Balloon, 1783

17 H.M.S. "Boreas" off Nevis

1983. Corals (1st series). Multicoloured.
98 15c. Type **16** 10 10
99 30c. Stinging coral 15 10
100 55c. Flower coral 15 10
101 $3 Sea rod and red fire sponge 50 80
MS102 82 × 115 mm. Nos. 98/101 1·40 2·50
See also Nos. 423/6.

1983. Commonwealth Day. Multicoloured.
103 55c. Type **17** 15 10
104 $2 Capt. Horatio Nelson and H.M.S. "Boreas" at anchor 45 60

1983. Butterflies (2nd series). As T **12**. Mult.
105 30c. "Pyrgus oileus" 20 10
106 55c. "Junonia evarete" (vert) 20 10
107 $1.10 "Urbanus proteus" (vert) 30 40
108 $2 "Hypolimnas misippus" 40 75

1983. Nos. 58 and 60/71 optd **INDEPENDENCE 1983**.
109B 5c. Type **10** 10 10
110B 15c. Type **11** 10 10
111B 20c. Nelson Museum . . . 10 10
112B 25c. St. James' Parish Church 10 15
113B 30c. Nevis Lane 15 15
114B 40c. Zetland Plantation . . 15 20
115B 45c. Nisbet Plantation . . . 15 25
116B 50c. Pinney's Beach 15 25
117B 55c. Eva Wilkin's Studio . . 15 30
118B $1 Nevis at dawn 15 30
119B $2.50 Ruins of Fort Charles 25 45
120B $5 Old Bath House 30 55
121B $10 Beach at Nisbet's . . . 40 70

1983. Bicentenary of Manned Flight. Mult.
122 10c. Type **19** 10 10
123 45c. Sikorsky S-38 flying boat (horiz) 15 10
124 50c. Beech 50 Twin Bonanza (horiz) 15 10
125 $2.50 Hawker Siddeley Sea Harrier (horiz) . . . . . . 30 1·25
MS126 118 × 145 mm. Nos. 122/5 75 1·25

20 Mary praying over Holy Child

1983. Christmas. Multicoloured.
127 5c. Type **20** 10 10
128 30c. Shepherds with flock . . 10 10
129 55c. Three Angels 10 10
130 $3 Boy with two girls 30 60
MS131 135 × 149 mm. Nos. 127/30 85 2·00

21 "County of Oxford" (1945)

1983. Leaders of the World. Railway Locomotives (1st series). The first in each pair shows technical drawings and the second the locomotive at work.

132 **21** 55c. multicoloured 10 20
133 – 55c. multicoloured 10 20
134 – $1 red, blue and black . . 10 20
135 – $1 multicoloured 10 20
136 – $1 purple, blue and black 10 20
137 – $1 multicoloured 10 20
138 – $1 red, black and yellow 10 20
139 – $1 multicoloured 10 20
140 – $1 multicoloured 10 20
141 – $1 multicoloured 10 20
142 – $1 yellow, black and blue 10 20
143 – $1 multicoloured 10 20
144 – $1 yellow, black and purple 10 20
145 – $1 multicoloured 10 20
146 – $1 multicoloured 10 20
147 – $1 multicoloured 10 20

DESIGNS: Nos. 132/3, "County of Oxford", Great Britain (1945); 134/5, "Evening Star", Great Britain (1960); 136/7, Stanier Class 5 No. 44806, Great Britain (1934); 138/9, "Pendennis Castle", Great Britain (1924); 140/1, "Winston Churchill", Great Britain (1946); 142/3, "Mallard", Great Britain (1938) (inscr "1935" in error); 144/5, "Britannia", Great Britain (1951); 146/7, "King George V", Great Britain.

See also Nos. 219/26, 277/84, 297/308, 352/9 and 427/42.

22 Boer War

1984. Leaders of the World. British Monarchs (1st series). Multicoloured.

148 5c. Type **22** 10 10
149 5c. Queen Victoria 10 10
150 50c. Queen Victoria at Osborne House 10 30
151 50c. Osborne House 10 30
152 60c. Battle of Dettingen . . . 10 30
153 60c. George II 10 30
154 75c. George II at the Bank of England 10 30
155 75c. Bank of England 10 30
156 $1 Coat of Arms of George II 10 30
157 $1 George II (different) . . . 10 30
158 $3 Coat of Arms of Queen Victoria 20 50
159 $3 Queen Victoria (different) 20 50

See also Nos. 231/6.

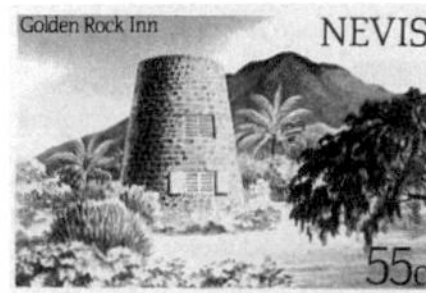

23 Golden Rock Inn

1984. Tourism (1st series). Multicoloured.

160 55c. Type **23** 25 20
161 55c. Rest Haven Inn 25 20
162 55c. Cliffdwellers Hotel . . . 25 20
163 55c. Pinney's Beach Hotel . . 25 20

See also Nos. 245/8.

24 Early Seal of Colony

1984.

164 **24** $15 red . . . . 1·10 4·00

25 Cadillac

1984. Leaders of the World Automobiles (1st series). As T **25**. The first design in each pair shows technical drawings and the second paintings.

165 1c. yellow, black and mauve 10 10
166 1c. multicoloured 10 10
167 5c. blue, mauve and black . . 10 10
168 5c. multicoloured 10 10
169 15c. multicoloured 10 15
170 15c. multicoloured 10 15
171 35c. mauve, yellow and black 10 25
172 35c. multicoloured 10 25
173 45c. blue, mauve and black 10 25
174 45c. multicoloured 10 25
175 55c. multicoloured 10 25
176 55c. multicoloured 10 25
177 $2.50 mauve, black and yellow 20 40
178 $2.50 multicoloured 20 40
179 $3 blue, yellow and black . . 20 40
180 $3 multicoloured 20 40

DESIGNS: No. 165/6, Cadillac "V16 Fleetwood Convertible" (1932); 167/8, Packard "Twin Six Touring Car" (1916); 169/70, Daimler "2 Cylinder" (1886); 171/2, Porsche "911 S Targa" (1970); 173/4, Benz "Three Wheeler" (1885); 175/6, M.G. "TC" (1947); 177/8, Cobra "Roadster 289" (1966); 179/80, Aston Martin "DB6 Hardtop" (1966).

See also Nos. 203/10, 249/64, 326/37, 360/371 and 411/22.

26 Carpentry

1984. 10th Anniv of Culturama Celebrations. Multicoloured.

181 30c. Type **26** 10 10
182 55c. Grass mat and basket making 10 10
183 $1 Pottery firing 15 25
184 $3 Culturama Queen and dancers 40 55

27 Yellow Bell

29 C. P. Mead

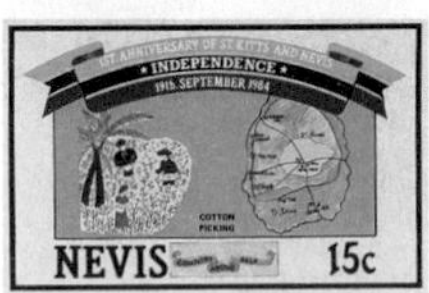

28 Cotton-picking and Map

1984. Flowers. Multicoloured.

185A 5c. Type **27** 10 10
186A 10c. Plumbago 10 10
187A 15c. Flamboyant 10 10
188B 20c. Eyelash orchid 60 30
189A 30c. Bougainvillea 10 15
190B 40c. Hibiscus 30 30
191A 50c. Night-blooming cereus 15 20
192A 55c. Yellow mahoe 15 25
193A 60c. Spider-lily 15 25
194A 75c. Scarlet cordia 20 30
195A $1 Shell-ginger 20 40
196A $3 Blue petrea . . . . . . 30 1·10
197A $5 Coral hibiscus . . . . . 50 2·00
198A $10 Passion flower . . . . 80 3·50

1984. 1st Anniv of Independence of St. Kitts–Nevis. Multicoloured.

199 15c. Type **28** 10 10
200 55c. Alexander Hamilton's birthplace 10 10
201 $1.10 Local agricultural produce 20 40
202 $3 Nevis Peak and Pinney's Beach . . . . 50 1·00

1984. Leaders of the World. Automobiles (2nd series). As T **25**. The first in each pair shows technical drawings and the second paintings.

203 5c. black, blue and brown . . 10 10
204 5c. multicoloured 10 10
205 30c. black, turquoise and brown 15 15
206 30c. multicoloured 15 15
207 50c. black, drab and brown 15 15
208 50c. multicoloured 15 15
209 $3 black, brown and green 30 45
210 $3 multicoloured 30 45

DESIGNS: Nos. 203/4, Lagonda "Speed Model" touring car (1929); 205/6, Jaguar "E-Type" 4.2 litre (1967); 207/8, Volkswagen "Beetle" (1947); 209/10, Pierce Arrow "V12" (1932).

1984. Leaders of the World. Cricketers (1st series). As T **29**. The first in each pair shows a head portrait and the second the cricketer in action. Multicoloured.

211 5c. Type **29** 10 10
212 5c. C. P. Mead 10 10
213 25c. J. B. Statham 20 30
214 25c. J. B. Statham 20 30
215 55c. Sir Learie Constantine 30 40
216 55c. Sir Learie Constantine 30 40
217 $2.50 Sir Leonard Hutton . . 50 1·25
218 $2.50 Sir Leonard Hutton . . 50 1·25

See also Nos. 237/4.

1984. Leaders of the World. Railway Locomotives (2nd series). As T **21**. The first in each pair shows technical drawings and the second the locomotive at work.

219 5c. multicoloured 10 10
220 5c. multicoloured 10 10
221 10c. multicoloured 10 10
222 10c. multicoloured 10 10
223 60c. multicoloured 15 25
224 60c. multicoloured 15 25
225 $2 multicoloured 50 70
226 $2 multicoloured 50 70

DESIGNS: Nos. 219/20, Class EF81 electric locomotive, Japan (1968); 221/22, Class 5500 electric locomotive, France (1927); 223/4, Class 240P, France (1940); 225/6, "Hikari" express train, Japan (1964).

30 Fifer and Drummer from Honeybees Band

1984. Christmas. Local Music. Multicoloured.

227 15c. Type **30** 15 10
228 40c. Guitar and "barhow" players from Canary Birds Band 25 10
229 60c. Shell All Stars steel band 30 10
230 $3 Organ and choir, St. John's Church, Fig Tree . . . . 1·25 1·00

1984. Leaders of the World. British Monarchs (2nd series). As T **22**. Multicoloured.

231 5c. King John and Magna Carta 10 10
232 5c. Barons and King John . . 10 10
233 55c. King John 10 15
234 55c. Newark Castle 10 15
235 $2 Coat of arms 25 40
236 $2 King John (different) . . 25 40

1984. Leaders of the World. Cricketers (2nd series). As T **29**. The first in each pair listed shows a head portrait and the second the cricketer in action. Multicoloured.

237 5c. J. D. Love 10 10
238 5c. J. D. Love 10 10
239 15c. S. J. Dennis 10 15
240 15c. S. J. Dennis 10 15
241 55c. B. W. Luckhurst 15 20
242 55c. B. W. Luckhurst 15 20
243 $2.50 B. L. D'Oliveira . . . 40 60
244 $2.50 B. L. D'Oliveira . . . 40 60

1984. Tourism (2nd series). As T **23**. Multicoloured.

245 $1.20 Croney's Old Manor Hotel 15 25
246 $1.20 Montpelier Plantation Inn 15 25
247 $1.20 Nisbet's Plantation Inn 15 25
248 $1.20 Zetland Plantation Inn 15 25

1985. Leaders of the World. Automobiles (3rd series). As T **25**. The first in each pair shows technical drawings and the second the paintings.

249 1c. black, green and light green 10 10
250 1c. multicoloured 10 10
251 5c. black, blue and light blue 10 10
252 5c. multicoloured 10 10
253 10c. black, green and light green 10 10
254 10c. multicoloured 10 10
255 50c. black, green and brown 10 10
256 50c. multicoloured 10 10
257 60c. black, green and blue . . 10 10
258 60c. multicoloured 10 10
259 75c. black, red and orange 10 10
260 75c. multicoloured 10 10
261 $2.50 black, green and blue 20 30
262 $2.50 multicoloured 20 30
263 $3 black, green and light green 20 30
264 $3 multicoloured 20 30

DESIGNS: Nos. 249/50, Delahaye "Type 35 Cabriolet" (1935); 251/2, Ferrari "Testa Rossa" (1958); 253/4, Voisin "Aerodyne" (1934); 255/6, Buick "Riviera" (1963); 257/8, Cooper "Climax" (1960); 259/60, Ford "999" (1904); 261/2, MG "M-Type Midget" (1930); 263/4, Rolls-Royce "Corniche" (1971).

31 Broad-winged Hawk

1985. Local Hawks and Herons. Multicoloured.

265 20c. Type **31** . . . . 1·25 20
266 40c. Red-tailed hawk . . . . 1·40 30
267 60c. Little blue heron . . . . 1·40 40
268 $3 Great blue heron (white phase) . . . . 2·75 1·90

32 Eastern Bluebird

1985. Leaders of the World. Birth Bicentenary of John J. Audubon (ornithologist) (1st issue). Multicoloured.

269 5c. Type **32** 10 10
270 5c. Common cardinal 10 10
271 55c. Belted kingfisher 20 55
272 55c. Mangrove cuckoo . . . 20 55
273 60c. Yellow warbler 20 55
274 60c. Cerulean warbler 20 55
275 $2 Burrowing owl . . . . . . 60 1·25
276 $2 Long-eared owl . . . . . 60 1·25

See also Nos. 285/92.

1985. Leaders of the World. Railway Locomotives (3rd series). As T **21**. The first in each pair showing technical drawings and the second the locomotive at work.

277 1c. multicoloured 10 10
278 1c. multicoloured 10 10
279 60c. multicoloured 20 20
280 60c. multicoloured 20 20
281 90c. multicoloured 25 25
282 90c. multicoloured 25 25
283 $2 multicoloured 40 60
284 $2 multicoloured 40 60

DESIGNS: Nos. 277/8, Class "Wee Bogie", Great Britain (1882); 279/80, "Comet", Great Britain (1851); 281/2, Class 8H No. 6173, Great Britain (1908); 283/4, Class A No. 23, Great Britain (1866).

1985. Leaders of the World. Birth Bicentenary of John J. Audubon (ornithologist) (2nd issue). As T **32**. Multicoloured.

285 1c. Painted bunting 10 10
286 1c. Golden-crowned kinglet 10 10
287 40c. Common flicker 25 40
288 40c. Western tanager 25 40
289 60c. Varied thrush 25 45
290 60c. Evening grosbeak . . . 25 45
291 $2.50 Blackburnian warbler 50 80
292 $2.50 Northern oriole 50 80

33 Guides and Guide Headquarters

1985. 75th Anniv of Girl Guide Movement. Multicoloured.

293 15c. Type **33** 10 10
294 60c. Girl Guide uniforms of 1910 and 1985 (vert) . . . 15 25
295 $1 Lord and Lady Baden-Powell (vert) 20 40
296 $3 Princess Margaret in Guide uniform (vert) . . . 50 1·25

1985. Leaders of the World. Railway Locomotives (4th series). As T **21**. The first in each pair shows technical drawings and the second the locomotive at work.

297 5c. multicoloured 10 10
298 5c. multicoloured 10 10
299 30c. multicoloured 10 15
300 30c. multicoloured 10 15
301 60c. multicoloured 10 20
302 60c. multicoloured 10 20
303 75c. multicoloured 10 25
304 75c. multicoloured 10 25
305 $1 multicoloured 10 25
306 $1 multicoloured 10 25
307 $2.50 multicoloured 20 60
308 $2.50 multicoloured 20 60

DESIGNS: Nos. 297/8, "Snowdon Ranger" (1878); 299/300, Large Belpaire locomotive, Great Britain (1904); 301/2, Class "County" No. 3821, Great Britain (1904); 303/4, "L'Outrance", France (1877); 305/6, Class PB-15, Australia (1899); 307/8, Class 64, Germany (1928).

34 The Queen Mother at Garter Ceremony

35 Isambard Kingdom Brunel

1985. Leaders of the World. Life and Times of Queen Elizabeth the Queen Mother. Various vertical portraits.

309 **34** 45c. multicoloured 10 15
310 – 45c. multicoloured 10 15
311 – 75c. multicoloured 10 20
312 – 75c. multicoloured 10 20
313 – $1.20 multicoloured 15 35

314 – $1.20 multicoloured 15 35
315 – $1.50 multicoloured 20 40
316 – $1.50 multicoloured 20 40
MS317 85 × 114 mm. $2 multicoloured; $2 multicoloured 50 1·40

Each value was issued in pairs showing a floral pattern across the bottom of the portraits which stops short of the left-hand edge on the first stamp and of the right-hand edge on the second.

1985. 150th Anniv of Great Western Railway. Designs showing railway engineers and their achievements. Multicoloured.

318 25c. Type **35** 15 35
319 25c. Royal Albert Bridge, 1859 15 35
320 50c. William Dean 20 45
321 50c. Locomotive "Lord of the Isles", 1895 20 45
322 $1 Locomotive "Lode Star", 1907 25 65
323 $1 G. J. Churchward 25 65
324 $2.50 Locomotive "Pendennis Castle", 1924 35 80
325 $2.50 C. B. Collett 35 80

Nos. 318/19, 320/1, 322/3 and 324/5 were printed together se-tenant, each pair forming a composite design.

1985. Leaders of the World. Automobiles (4th series). As T **25**. The first in each pair shows technical drawings and the second paintings.

326 10c. black, blue and red 10 10
327 10c. multicoloured 10 10
328 35c. black, turquoise and blue 10 25
329 35c. multicoloured 10 25
330 75c. black, green and brown 10 40
331 75c. multicoloured 10 40
332 $1.15 black, brown and green 15 45
333 $1.15 multicoloured 15 45
334 $1.50 black, blue and red 15 50
335 $1.50 multicoloured 15 50
336 $2 black, lilac and violet 20 60
337 $2 multicoloured 20 60

DESIGNS: Nos. 326/7, Sunbeam "Coupe de l'Auto" (1912); 328/9, Cisitalia "Pininfarina Coupe" (1948); 330/1, Porsche "928S" (1980); 332/3, MG "K3 Magnette" (1933); 334/5, Lincoln "Zephyr" (1937); 336/7, Pontiac 2 Door (1926).

1985. Royal Visit. Nos. 76/7, 83, 86, 92/3, 98/9 and 309/10 optd **CARIBBEAN ROYAL VISIT 1985** or surch also.

338 **16** 15c. multicoloured 75 1·25
339 – 30c. multicoloured (No. 92) 1·75 1·75
340 – 30c. multicoloured (No. 99) 75 1·25
341 – 40c. on 55c. mult (No. 86) 1·75 2·00
342 **34** 45c. multicoloured 1·50 3·25
343 – 45c. multicoloured (No. 310) 1·50 3·25
344 – 55c. multicoloured (No. 83) 1·50 1·25
345 – $1.50 on $5 multicoloured (No. 76) 2·25 3·00
346 – $1.50 on $5 multicoloured (No. 77) 13·00 17·00
347 – $2.50 mult (No. 93) 2·25 3·50

36 St. Paul's Anglican Church, Charlestown

1985. Christmas. Churches of Nevis (1st series). Multicoloured.

348 10c. Type **36** 15 10
349 40c. St. Theresa Catholic Church, Charlestown 35 30
350 60c. Methodist Church, Gingerland 40 50
351 $3 St. Thomas Anglican Church, Lowland 80 2·75

See also Nos. 462/5.

1986. Leaders of the World. Railway Locomotives (5th series). As T **21**. The first in each pair shows technical drawings and the second the locomotive at work.

352 30c. multicoloured 15 25
353 30c. multicoloured 15 25
354 75c. multicoloured 25 50
355 75c. multicoloured 25 50
356 $1.50 multicoloured 40 70
357 $1.50 multicoloured 40 70
358 $2 multicoloured 50 80
359 $2 multicoloured 50 80

DESIGNS: Nos. 352/3, "Stourbridge Lion", U.S.A. (1829); 354/5, EP-2 Bi-Polar electric locomotive, U.S.A. (1919); 356/7, Gas turbine No. 59, U.S.A. (1953); 358/9 Class FL9 diesel locomotive No. 2039, U.S.A. (1955).

1986. Leaders of the World. Automobiles (5th series). As T **25**. The first in each pair showing technical drawings and the second paintings.

360 10c. black, brown and green 10 10
361 10c. multicoloured 10 10
362 60c. black, orange and red 15 25
363 60c. multicoloured 15 25
364 75c. black, light brown and brown 15 25
365 75c. multicoloured 15 25
366 $1 black, light grey and grey 15 30
367 $1 multicoloured 15 30
368 $1.50 black, yellow and green 20 35
369 $1.50 multicoloured 20 35
370 $3 black, light blue and blue 30 65
371 $3 multicoloured 30 65

DESIGNS: Nos. 360/1, Adler "Trumpf" (1936); 362/3, Maserati "Tipo 250F" (1957); 364/5, Oldsmobile "Limited" (1910); 366/7, Jaguar "C-Type" (1951); 368/9, ERA "1.5L B Type" (1937); 370/1, Chevrolet "Corvette" (1953).

37 Supermarine Spitfire Prototype, 1936

1986. 50th Anniv of Spitfire (fighter aircraft). Multicoloured.

372 $1 Type **37** 20 50
373 $2.50 Supermarine Spitfire Mk 1A in Battle of Britain, 1940 30 75
374 $3 Supermarine Spitfire Mk XII over convoy, 1944 30 75
375 $4 Supermarine Spitfire Mk XXIV, 1948 30 1·25
MS376 114 × 86 mm. $6 Supermarine Seafire Mk III on escort carrier H.M.S. "Hunter" 1·10 3·75

38 Head of Amerindian

39 Brazilian Player

1986. 500th Anniv (1992) of Discovery of America by Columbus (1st issue). Multicoloured.

377 75c. Type **38** 75 1·00
378 75c. Exchanging gifts for food from Amerindians 75 1·00
379 $1.75 Columbus's coat of arms 1·25 2·00
380 $1.75 Breadfruit plant 1·25 2·00
381 $2.50 Columbus's fleet 1·25 2·25
382 $2.50 Christopher Columbus 1·25 2·25
MS383 95 × 84 mm. $6 Christopher Columbus (different) 6·00 9·50

The two designs of each value were printed together, se-tenant, each pair forming a composite design showing charts of Columbus's route in the background.

See also Nos. 546/54, 592/600, 678/84 and 685/6.

1986. 60th Birthday of Queen Elizabeth II. As T **117a** of Montserrat. Multicoloured.

384 5c. Queen Elizabeth in 1976 10 10
385 75c. Queen Elizabeth in 1953 15 25
386 $2 In Australia 20 60
387 $8 In Canberra, 1982 (vert) 75 2·00
MS388 85 × 115 mm. $10 Queen Elizabeth II 4·50 7·50

1986. World Cup Football Championship, Mexico. Multicoloured.

389 1c. Official World Cup mascot (horiz) 10 10
390 2c. Type **39** 10 10
391 5c. Danish player 10 10
392 10c. Brazilian player (different) 10 10
393 20c. Denmark v Spain 20 20
394 30c. Paraguay v Chile 30 30
395 60c. Italy v West Germany 40 55
396 75c. Danish team (56 × 36 mm) 40 65
397 $1 Paraguayan team (56 × 36 mm) 50 70
398 $1.75 Brazilian team (56 × 36 mm) 60 1·25
399 $3 Italy v England 75 1·90
400 $6 Italian team (56 × 36 mm) 1·10 3·00
MS401 Five sheets, each 85 × 115 mm. (a) $1.50 As No. 398. (b) $2 As No. 393. (c) $2 As No. 400. (d) $2.50 As No. 395. (e) $4 As No. 394 Set of 5 sheets 12·00 15·00

40 Clothing Machinist

1986. Local Industries. Multicoloured.

402 15c. Type **40** 20 15
403 40c. Carpentry/joinery workshop 45 30
404 $1.20 Agricultural produce market 1·25 1·50
405 $3 Fishing boats landing catch 2·50 3·25

1986. Royal Wedding. As T **118a** of Montserrat. Multicoloured.

406 60c. Prince Andrew in midshipman's uniform 15 25
407 60c. Miss Sarah Ferguson 15 25
408 $2 Prince Andrew on safari in Africa (horiz) 40 60
409 $2 Prince Andrew at the races (horiz) 40 60
MS410 115 × 85 mm. $10 Duke and Duchess of York on Palace balcony after wedding (horiz) 2·50 5·00

See also Nos. 454/7.

1986. Automobiles (6th series). As T **25**. The first in each pair showing technical drawings and the second paintings.

411 15c. multicoloured 10 10
412 15c. multicoloured 10 10
413 45c. black, light blue and blue 20 25
414 45c. multicoloured 20 25
415 60c. multicoloured 20 30
416 60c. multicoloured 20 30
417 $1 black, light green and green 25 40
418 $1 multicoloured 25 40
419 $1.75 black, lilac and deep lilac 30 50
420 $1.75 multicoloured 30 50
421 $3 multicoloured 50 90
422 $3 multicoloured 50 90

DESIGNS: Nos. 411/12, Riley "Brooklands Nine" (1930); 413/14, Alfa Romeo "GTA" (1966); 415/16, Pierce Arrow "Type 66" (1913); 417/18, Willys-Knight "66A" (1928); 419/20, Studebaker "Starliner" (1953); 421/2, Cunningham "V-8" (1919).

41 Gorgonia

41a Statue of Liberty and World Trade Centre, Manhattan

1986. Corals (2nd series). Multicoloured.

423 15c. Type **41** 25 15
424 60c. Fire coral 55 55
425 $2 Elkhorn coral 90 2·00
426 $3 Vase sponge and feather star 1·10 2·50

1986. Railway Locomotives (6th series). As T **21**. The first in each pair showing technical drawings and the second the locomotive at work.

427 15c. multicoloured 10 10
428 15c. multicoloured 10 10
429 45c. multicoloured 15 25
430 45c. multicoloured 15 25
431 60c. multicoloured 20 30
432 60c. multicoloured 20 30
433 75c. multicoloured 20 40
434 75c. multicoloured 20 40
435 $1 multicoloured 20 50
436 $1 multicoloured 20 50
437 $1.50 multicoloured 25 60
438 $1.50 multicoloured 25 60
439 $2 multicoloured 30 65
440 $2 multicoloured 30 65
441 $3 multicoloured 35 80
442 $3 multicoloured 35 80

DESIGNS: Nos. 427/8, Connor Single Class, Great Britain (1859); 429/30, Class P2 "Cock o' the North", Great Britain (1934); 431/2, Class 7000 electric locomotive, Japan (1926); 433/4, Class P3, Germany (1897); 435/6, "Dorchester", Canada (1836); 436/7, Class "Centennial" diesel locomotive, U.S.A. (1969); 439/40, "Lafayette", U.S.A. (1837); 441/2, Class C-16 No. 222, U.S.A. (1882).

1986. Centenary of Statue of Liberty. Multicoloured.

443 15c. Type **41a** 20 15
444 25c. Sailing ship passing statue 30 20
445 40c. Statue in scaffolding 30 25
446 60c. Statue (side view) and scaffolding 30 30
447 75c. Statue and regatta 40 40
448 $1 Tall Ships parade passing statue (horiz) 40 45
449 $1.50 Head and arm of statue above scaffolding 40 60
450 $2 Ships with souvenir flags (horiz) 55 80
451 $2.50 Statue and New York waterfront 60 90
452 $3 Restoring statue 80 1·25
MS453 Four sheets, each 85 × 115 mm. (a) $3.50 Statue at dusk. (b) $4 Head of Statue. (c) $4.50 Statue and lightning. (d) $5 Head and torch at sunset Set of 4 sheets 3·50 11·00

1986. Royal Wedding (2nd issue). Nos. 406/9 optd **Congratulations to T.R.H. The Duke & Duchess of York**.

454 60c. Prince Andrew in midshipman's uniform 15 40
455 60c. Miss Sarah Ferguson 15 40
456 $2 Prince Andrew on safari in Africa (horiz) 40 1·00
457 $2 Prince Andrew at the races (horiz) 40 1·00

42 Dinghy sailing

1986. Sports. Multicoloured.

458 10c. Type **42** 20 10
459 25c. Netball 35 15
460 $2 Cricket 3·00 2·50
461 $3 Basketball 3·75 3·00

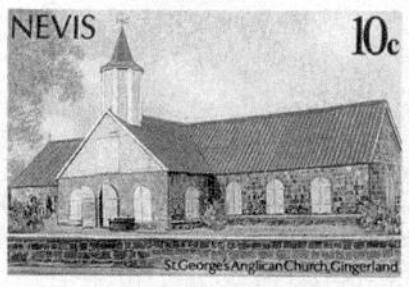

43 St. George's Anglican Church, Gingerland

44 Constitution Document, Quill and Inkwell

1986. Christmas. Churches of Nevis (2nd series). Multicoloured.

462 10c. Type **43** 15 10
463 40c. Trinity Methodist Church, Fountain 30 25
464 $1 Charlestown Methodist Church 60 65
465 $5 Wesleyan Holiness Church, Brown Hill 2·75 4·00

1987. Bicentenary of U.S. Constitution and 230th Birth Anniv of Alexander Hamilton (U.S. statesman). Multicoloured.

466 15c. Type **44** 10 10
467 40c. Alexander Hamilton and Hamilton House 20 25
468 60c. Alexander Hamilton 25 35
469 $2 Washington and his Cabinet 90 1·40
MS470 70 × 82 mm. $5 Model ship "Hamilton" on float, 1788 6·50 7·50

1987. Victory of "Stars and Stripes" in America's Cup Yachting Championship. No. 54 optd **America's Cup 1987 Winners 'Stars & Stripes'**.

471 $3 Windjammer S.V. "Polynesia" 1·10 1·60

46 Fig Tree Church

1987. Bicentenary of Marriage of Horatio Nelson and Frances Nisbet. Multicoloured.

472 15c. Type **46** 15 10
473 60c. Frances Nisbet 40 30
474 $1 H.M.S. "Boreas" (frigate) 1·25 1·00
475 $3 Captain Horatio Nelson 2·50 3·25
MS476 102 × 82 mm. $3 As No. 473; $3 No. 475 5·00 6·50

47 Queen Angelfish

1987. Coral Reef Fishes. Multicoloured.

477 60c. Type **47** 35 60
478 60c. Blue angelfish 35 60
479 $1 Stoplight parrotfish (male) 40 80
480 $1 Stoplight parrotfish (female) 40 80
481 $1.50 Red hind 45 90
482 $1.50 Rock hind 45 90

483 $2.50 Coney (bicoloured phase) 50 1·50
484 $2.50 Coney (red-brown phase) 50 1·50
Nos. 478, 480, 482 and 484 are inverted triangles.

48 "Panaeolus antillarum"

50 Hawk-wing Conch

49 Rag Doll

1987. Fungi (1st series). Multicoloured.
485 15c. Type **48** 80 30
486 50c. "Pycnoporus sanguineus" 1·50 80
487 $2 "Gymnopilus chrysopellus" 2·75 3·25
488 $3 "Cantharellus cinnabarinus" 3·25 4·50
See also Nos. 646/53.

1987. Christmas. Toys. Multicoloured.
489 10c. Type **49** 10 10
490 40c. Coconut boat 20 25
491 $1.20 Sandbox cart 55 60
492 $5 Two-wheeled cart 1·75 4·00

1988. Sea Shells and Pearls. Multicoloured.
493 15c. Type **50** 20 15
494 40c. Rooster-tail conch 30 20
495 60c. Emperor helmet 50 40
496 $2 Queen or pink conch 1·60 2·00
497 $3 King helmet 1·75 2·25

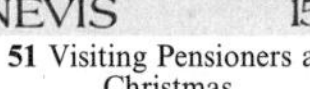
51 Visiting Pensioners at Christmas

52 Athlete on Starting Blocks

1988. 125th Anniv of International Red Cross. Multicoloured.
498 15c. Type **51** 10 10
499 40c. Teaching children first aid 15 20
500 60c. Providing wheelchairs for the disabled 25 35
501 $5 Helping cyclone victim 2·10 3·50

1988. Olympic Games, Seoul. Multicoloured.
502 10c. Type **52** 10 35
503 $1.20 At start 50 85
504 $2 During race 85 1·25
505 $3 At finish 1·25 1·50
MS506 137 × 80 mm. As Nos. 502/5, but each size 24 × 36 mm 2·75 3·75
Nos. 502/5 were printed together, se-tenant, each strip forming a composite design showing an athlete from start to finish of race.

53 Outline Map and Arms of St. Kitts–Nevis

54 Poinsettia

1988. 5th Anniv of Independence.
507 **53** $5 multicoloured 2·10 3·00

1988. 300th Anniv of Lloyd's of London. As T **167a** of Malawi. Multicoloured.
508 15c. House of Commons passing Lloyd's Bill, 1871 20 10
509 60c. "Cunard Countess" (liner) (horiz) 1·10 65
510 $2.50 Space shuttle deploying satellite (horiz) 2·25 3·00
511 $3 "Viking Princess" (cargo liner) on fire, 1966 2·25 3·00

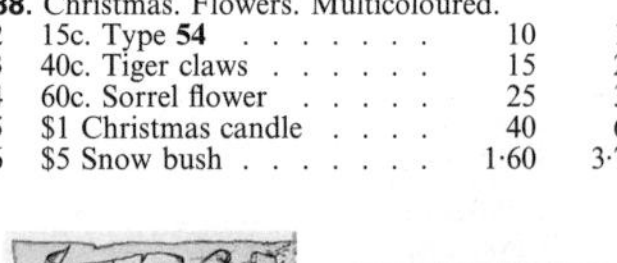

1988. Christmas. Flowers. Multicoloured.
512 15c. Type **54** 10 10
513 40c. Tiger claws 15 20
514 60c. Sorrel flower 25 30
515 $1 Christmas candle 40 60
516 $5 Snow bush 1·60 3·75

55 British Fleet off St. Kitts

56 Cicada

1989. "Philexfrance 89" International Stamp Exhibition, Paris. Battle of Frigate Bay, 1782. Multicoloured.
517 50c. Type **55** 1·25 1·40
518 $1.20 Battle off Nevis 1·50 1·75
519 $2 British and French fleets exchanging broadsides 1·75 2·00
520 $3 French map of Nevis, 1764 2·25 2·50
Nos. 517/19 were printed together, se-tenant, forming a composite design.

1989. "Sounds of the Night". Multicoloured.
521 10c. Type **56** 20 15
522 40c. Grasshopper 40 35
523 60c. Cricket 55 50
524 $5 Tree frog 3·75 5·50
MS525 135 × 81 mm. Nos. 521/4 5·50 7·00

1989. 20th Anniv of First Manned Landing on Moon. As T **51a** of Kiribati. Multicoloured.
526 15c. Vehicle Assembly Building, Kennedy Space Centre 15 10
527 40c. Crew of "Apollo 12" (30 × 30 mm) 20 20
528 $2 "Apollo 12" emblem (30 × 30 mm) 1·00 1·75
529 $3 "Apollo 12" astronaut on Moon 1·40 2·00
MS530 100 × 83 mm. $6 Aldrin undertaking lunar seismic experiment 2·50 3·50

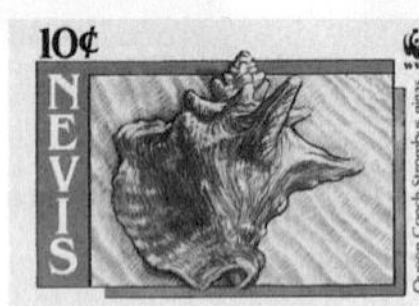
57 Queen or Pink Conch feeding

1990. Queen or Pink Conch. Multicoloured.
531 10c. Type **57** 60 30
532 40c. Queen or pink conch from front 90 40
533 60c. Side view of shell 1·25 90
534 $1 Black and flare 1·60 2·00
MS535 72 × 103 mm. $5 Underwater habitat 3·50 4·50

58 Wyon Medal Portrait

59

1990. 150th Anniv of the Penny Black.
536 **58** 15c. black and brown 15 10
537 – 40c. black and green 30 25
538 – 60c. black 45 55
539 – $4 black and blue 2·50 3·75
MS540 114 × 84 mm. $5 black, red and brown 4·00 5·00
DESIGNS: 40c. Engine-turned background; 60c. Heath's engraving of portrait; $4 Essay with inscriptions; $5 Penny Black.
No. **MS**540 also commemorates "Stamp World London 90" International Stamp Exhibition.

1990. 500th Anniv of Regular European Postal Services.
541 **59** 15c. brown 20 15
542 – 40c. green 35 25
543 – 60c. violet 55 65
544 – $4 blue 2·75 3·75
MS545 110 × 82 mm. $5 red, brown and grey 4·00 5·00
Nos. 541/5 commemorate the Thurn and Taxis postal service and the designs are loosely based on those of the initial 1852–58 series.

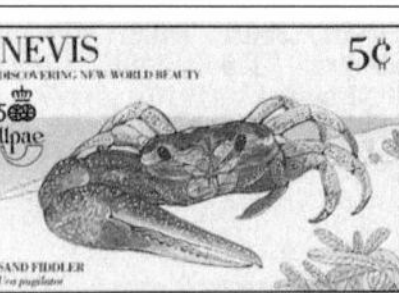
60 Sand Fiddler

1990. 500th Anniv (1992) of Discovery of America by Columbus (2nd issue). New World Natural History—Crabs. Multicoloured.
546 5c. Type **60** 10 20
547 15c. Great land crab 15 15
548 20c. Blue crab 15 15
549 40c. Stone crab 30 30
550 60c. Mountain crab 45 45
551 $2 Sargassum crab 1·40 1·75
552 $3 Yellow box crab 1·75 2·25
553 $4 Spiny spider crab 2·25 3·00
MS554 Two sheets, each 101 × 70 mm. (a) $5 Sally Lightfoot. (b) $5 Wharf crab Set of 2 sheets 9·00 10·00

1990. 90th Birthday of Queen Elizabeth the Queen Mother. As T **198a** of Lesotho.
555 $2 black, mauve and buff 1·40 1·60
556 $2 black, mauve and buff 1·40 1·60
557 $2 black, mauve and buff 1·40 1·60
MS558 90 × 75 mm. $6 brown, mauve and black 3·50 4·25
DESIGNS: No. 555, Duchess of York with corgi; 556, Queen Elizabeth in Coronation robes, 1937; 557, Duchess of York in garden; **MS**558, Queen Elizabeth in Coronation robes, 1937 (different).

61 MaKanaky, Cameroons

62 "Cattleya deckeri"

1990. World Cup Football Championship, Italy. Star Players. Multicoloured.
559 10c. Type **61** 40 10
560 25c. Chovanec, Czechoslovakia 45 15
561 $2.50 Robson, England 2·75 3·25
562 $5 Voller, West Germany 3·75 5·50
MS563 Two sheets, each 90 × 75 mm. (a) $5 Maradona, Argentina. (b) $5 Gordillo, Spain Set of 2 sheets 6·75 8·00

1990. Christmas. Native Orchids. Mult.
564 10c. Type **62** 55 20
565 15c. "Epidendrum ciliare" 55 20
566 20c. "Epidendrum fragrans" 65 20
567 40c. "Epidendrum ibaguense" 85 25
568 60c. "Epidendrum latifolium" 1·10 50
569 $1.20 "Maxillaria conferta" 1·40 1·75
570 $2 "Epidendrum strobiliferum" 1·75 2·75
571 $3 "Brassavola cucullata" 2·00 3·00
MS572 102 × 71 mm. $5 "Rodriguezia lanceolata" 7·00 8·00

1991. 350th Death Anniv of Rubens. As T **250** of Maldive Islands, showing details from "The Feast of Achelous". Multicoloured.
573 10c. Two jugs (vert) 55 15
574 40c. Woman at table (vert) 1·00 30
575 60c. Two servants with fruit (vert) 1·25 45
576 $4 Achelous (vert) 3·25 5·50
MS577 101 × 71 mm. $5 "The Feast of Achelous" 4·50 5·50

63 "Agraulis vanillae"

1991. Butterflies. Multicoloured.
578B 5c. Type **63** 20 50
579A 10c. "Historis odius" 40 50
580B 15c. "Marpesia corinna" 20 20
581B 20c. "Anartia amathea" 30 30
582B 25c. "Junonia evarete" 30 30
583B 40c. "Heliconius charithonia" 40 30
584B 50c. "Marpesia petreus" 70 35
585A 60c. "Dione juno" 75 50
586B 75c. "Heliconius doris" 80 60
586cB 80c. As 60c. 80 60
587A $1 "Hypolimnas misippus" 90 80
588A $3 "Danaus plexippus" 2·00 2·75
589A $5 "Heliconius sara" 2·75 4·00
590A $10 "Tithorea harmonia" 5·00 8·00
591A $20 "Dryas julia" 9·50 13·00

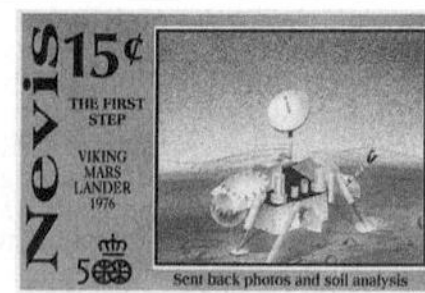
64 "Viking Mars Lander", 1976

1991. 500th Anniv of Discovery of America by Columbus (1992) (3rd issue). History of Exploration. Multicoloured.
592 15c. Type **64** 20 20
593 40c. "Apollo 11", 1969 30 25
594 60c. "Skylab", 1973 45 45
595 75c. "Salyut 6", 1977 55 55
596 $1 "Voyager 1", 1977 65 65
597 $2 "Venera 7", 1970 1·25 1·60
598 $4 "Gemini 4", 1965 2·50 3·25
599 $5 "Luna 3", 1959 2·75 3·25
MS600 Two sheets, each 105 × 76 mm. (a) $6 Bow of "Santa Maria" (vert). (b) $6 Christopher Columbus (vert) Set of 2 sheets 8·00 9·00

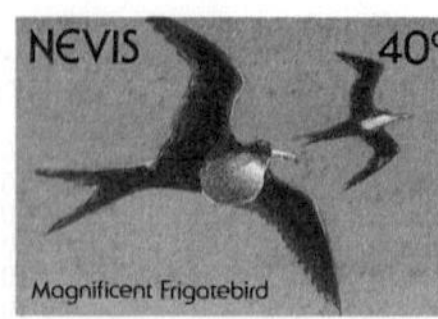
65 Magnificent Frigate Bird

1991. Island Birds. Multicoloured.
601 40c. Type **65** 80 65
602 40c. Roseate tern 80 65
603 40c. Red-tailed hawk 80 65
604 40c. Zenaida dove 80 65
605 40c. Bananaquit 80 65
606 40c. American kestrel 80 65
607 40c. Grey kingbird 80 65
608 40c. Prothonotary warbler 80 65
609 40c. Blue-hooded euphonia 80 65
610 40c. Antillean crested hummingbird 80 65
611 40c. White-tailed tropic bird 80 65
612 40c. Yellow-bellied sapsucker 80 65
613 40c. Green-throated carib 80 65
614 40c. Purple-throated carib 80 65
615 40c. Red-billed whistling duck ("Black-bellied tree-duck") 80 65
616 40c. Ringed kingfisher 80 65
617 40c. Burrowing owl 80 65
618 40c. Ruddy turnstone 80 65
619 40c. Great blue heron 80 65
620 40c. Yellow-crowned night-heron 80 65
MS621 76 × 59 mm. $6 Great egret 10·00 11·00
Nos. 601/20 were printed together, se-tenant, forming a composite design.

1991. 65th Birthday of Queen Elizabeth II. As T **210** of Lesotho. Multicoloured.
622 15c. Queen Elizabeth at polo match with Prince Charles 40 20
623 40c. Queen and Prince Philip on Buckingham Palace balcony 50 35
624 $2 In carriage at Ascot, 1986 1·75 1·75
625 $4 Queen Elizabeth II at Windsor polo match, 1989 3·00 3·75
MS626 68 × 90 mm. $5 Queen Elizabeth and Prince Philip 4·25 5·00

1991. 10th Wedding Anniv of Prince and Princess of Wales. As T **210** of Lesotho. Multicoloured.
627 10c. Prince Charles and Princess Diana 75 20
628 50c. Prince of Wales and family 80 30
629 $1 Prince William and Prince Harry 1·25 1·00
630 $5 Prince and Princess of Wales 4·25 4·00
MS631 68 × 90 mm. $5 Prince and Princess of Wales in Hungary, and young princes at Christmas 6·00 6·00

1991. "Phila Nippon '91" International Stamp Exhibition, Tokyo. Japanese Railway Locomotives. As T **257** of Maldive Islands. Mult.
632 10c. Class C62 steam locomotive 80 30
633 15c. Class C56 steam locomotive (horiz) 90 30
634 40c. Class C55 streamlined steam locomotive (horiz) 1·40 50
635 60c. Class 1400 steam locomotive (horiz) 1·50 80
636 $1 Class 485 diesel rail car 1·75 1·00
637 $2 Class C61 steam locomotive 2·75 2·50
638 $3 Class 485 diesel train (horiz) 3·00 3·00
639 $4 Class 7000 electric train (horiz) 3·25 3·75
MS640 Two sheets, each 108 × 72 mm. (a) $5 Class D51 steam locomotive (horiz). (b) $5 "Hikari" express train (horiz) Set of 2 sheets 8·50 9·00

1991. Christmas. Drawings by Albrecht Durer. As T **211** of Lesotho.
641 10c. black and green 15 10
642 40c. black and orange 30 25

643 60c. black and blue 35 30
644 $3 black and mauve 1·40 2·75
MS645 Two sheets, each 96×124 mm. (a) $6 black. (b) $6 black Set of 2 sheets 5·50 6·25
DESIGNS: 10c. "Mary being Crowned by an Angel"; 40c. "Mary with the Pear"; 60c. "Mary in a Halo"; $3 "Mary with Crown of Stars and Sceptre"; $6 (**MS**645a) "The Holy Family" (detail); $6 (**MS**645b) "Mary at the Yard Gate" (detail).

66 "Marasmius haemtocephalus"
67 Monique Knol (cycling), Netherlands

1991. Fungi (2nd series). Multicoloured.
646 15c. Type **66** 30 20
647 40c. "Psilocybe cubensis" 40 30
648 60c. "Hygrocybe acutoconica" 50 40
649 75c. "Hygrocybe occidentalis" 60 60
650 $1 "Boletellus cubensis" 70 70
651 $2 "Gymnopilus chrysopellus" 1·25 1·50
652 $4 "Cantharellus cinnabarinus" 2·25 2·75
653 $5 "Chlorophyllum molybdites" 2·25 2·75
MS654 Two sheets, each 70×58 mm. (a) $6 "Psilocybe cubensis", "Hygrocybe acutoconica" and "Boletellus cubensis" (horiz). (b) $6 "Hygrocybe occidentalis", "Marasmius haematocephalus" and "Gymnopilus chrysopellus" (horiz) Set of 2 sheets 9·00 9·50

1992. 40th Anniv of Queen Elizabeth II's Accession. As T **214** of Lesotho. Multicoloured.
655 10c. Charlestown from the sea 50 10
656 40c. Charlestown square 70 25
657 $1 Mountain scenery 1·25 60
658 $5 Early cottage 3·25 3·75
MS659 Two sheets, each 74×97 mm. (a) $6 Queen or pink conch on beach. (b) $6 Nevis sunset Set of 2 sheets 8·50 9·00

1992. Olympic Games, Barcelona. Gold Medal Winners of 1988. Multicoloured.
660 20c. Type **67** 75 30
661 25c. Roger Kingdom (hurdles), U.S.A. 50 30
662 50c. Yugoslavia (men's waterpolo) 75 50
663 80c. Anja Fichtel (foil), West Germany 90 70
664 $1 Said Aouita (mid-distance running), Morocco 1·00 80
665 $1.50 Yuri Sedykh (hammer throw), U.S.S.R. 1·25 1·40
666 $3 Shushunova (women's gymnastics), U.S.S.R. 2·25 2·75
667 $5 Valimir Artemov (men's gymnastics), U.S.S.R. 2·50 3·25
MS668 Two sheets, each 103×73 mm. (a) $6 Niam Suleymanoglu (weightlifting), Turkey. (b) $6 Florence Griffith-Joyner (women's 100 metres), U.S.A. Set of 2 sheets 5·50 7·00
No. 660 is inscribed "France" in error.

68 "Landscape" (Mariano Fortuny i Marsal)
69 Early Compass and Ship

1992. "Granada '92" International Stamp Exhibition, Spain. Spanish Paintings. Multicoloured.
669 20c. Type **68** 40 30
670 25c. "Dona Juana la Loca" (Francisco Pradilla Ortiz) (horiz) 40 30
671 50c. "Idyll" (Fortuny i Marsal) 60 50
672 80c. "Old Man Naked in the Sun" (Fortuny i Marsal) 80 70
673 $1 "The Painter's Children in the Japanese Salon" (detail) (Fortuny i Marsal) 90 80
674 $2 "The Painter's Children in the Japanese Salon" (different detail) (Fortuny i Marsal) 1·40 1·40
675 $3 "Still Life: Sea Bream and Oranges" (Luis Eugenio Melendez) (horiz) 2·25 2·75
676 $5 "Still Life: Box of Sweets, Pastry and Other Objects" (Melendez) 2·75 3·50
MS677 Two sheets, each 121×95 mm. (a) $6 "Bullfight" (Fortuny i Marsal) (111×86 mm). (b) $6 "Moroccans" (Fortuny i Marsal) (111×86 mm). Imperf Set of 2 sheets 5·50 6·50

1992. 500th Anniv of Discovery of America by Columbus (4th issue) and "World Columbian Stamp Expo '92", Chicago. Multicoloured.
678 20c. Type **69** 75 25
679 50c. Manatee and fleet 1·25 50
680 80c. Green turtle and "Santa Maria" 1·50 80
681 $1.50 "Santa Maria" and arms 2·25 1·75
682 $3 Queen Isabella of Spain and commission 2·50 3·25
683 $5 Pineapple and colonists 3·00 4·50
MS684 Two sheets, each 101×70 mm. (a) $6 British storm petrel and town (horiz). (b) $6 Peppers and carib canoe (horiz) Set of 2 sheets 10·00 12·00

1992. 500th Anniv of Discovery of America by Columbus (5th issue). Organization of East Caribbean States. As Nos. 911/12 of Montserrat. Multicoloured.
685 $1 Columbus meeting Amerindians 50 50
686 $2 Ships approaching island 1·25 1·40

1992. Postage Stamp Mega Event, New York. Sheet 100×70 mm, containing multicoloured design as T **219** of Lesotho.
MS687 $6 Empire State Building 4·50 5·00

70 Minnie Mouse
71 Care Bear and Butterfly

1992. Mickey's Portrait Gallery. Mult.
688 10c. Type **70** 50 20
689 15c. Mickey Mouse 50 20
690 40c. Donald Duck 70 30
691 80c. Mickey Mouse, 1930 90 70
692 $1 Daisy Duck 1·00 80
693 $2 Pluto 1·75 1·50
694 $4 Goofy 2·75 3·00
695 $5 Goofy, 1932 2·75 3·00
MS696 Two sheets. (a) 102×128 mm. $6 Mickey in armchair (horiz). (b) 128×102 mm. $6 Mickey and Minnie in airplane (horiz) Set of 2 sheets 10·00 11·00

1992. Christmas. Religious Paintings. As T **218** of Lesotho. Multicoloured.
697 20c. "The Virgin and Child between Two Saints" (Giovanni Bellini) 40 15
698 40c. "The Virgin and Child surrounded by Four Angels" (Master of the Castello Nativity) 55 25
699 50c. "Virgin and Child surrounded by Angels with St. Frediano and St. Augustine" (detail) (Filippo Lippi) 60 30
700 80c. "The Virgin and Child between St. Peter and St. Sebastian" (Bellini) 85 70
701 $1 "The Virgin and Child with St. Julian and St. Nicholas of Myra" (Lorenzo di Credi) 1·00 80
702 $2 "St. Bernadino and a Female Saint presenting a Donor to Virgin and Child" (Francesco Bissolo) 1·75 1·50
703 $4 "Madonna and Child with Four Cherubs" (ascr Barthel Bruyn) 2·75 3·50
704 $5 "The Virgin and Child" (Quentin Metsys) 3·00 3·50
MS705 Two sheets, each 76×102 mm. (a) $6 "Virgin and Child surrounded by Two Angels" (detail) (Perugino). (b) $6 "Madonna and Child with the Infant, St. John and Archangel Gabriel" (Sandro Botticelli) Set of 2 sheets 7·00 8·00
No. 699 is inscribed "Fillipo Lippi" in error.

1993. Ecology. Multicoloured.
706 80c. Type **71** 60 60
MS707 71×101 mm. $2 Care Bear on beach 2·25 2·50

1993. Bicentenary of the Louvre, Paris. As T **221** of Lesotho. Multicoloured.
708 $1 "The Card Cheat" (left detail) (La Tour) 85 85
709 $1 "The Card Cheat" (centre detail) (La Tour) 85 85
710 $1 "The Card Cheat" (right detail) (La Tour) 85 85
711 $1 "St. Joseph, the Carpenter" (La Tour) 85 85
712 $1 "St. Thomas" (La Tour) 85 85
713 $1 "Adoration of the Shepherds" (left detail) (La Tour) 85 85
714 $1 "Adoration of the Shepherds" (right detail) (La Tour) 85 85
715 $1 "Mary Magdalene with a Candle" (La Tour) 85 85
MS716 70×100 mm. $6 "Archangel Raphael leaving the Family of Tobius" (Rembrandt) (52×85 mm) 4·25 4·75

1993. 15th Death Anniv of Elvis Presley (singer). As T **280** of Maldive Islands. Multicoloured.
717 $1 Elvis Presley 1·10 85
718 $1 Elvis with guitar 1·10 85
719 $1 Elvis with microphone 1·10 85

72 Japanese Launch Vehicle H-11
73 "Plumeria rubra"

1993. Anniversaries and Events. Mult.
720 15c. Type **72** 60 30
721 50c. Airship "Hindenburg" on fire, 1937 (horiz) 1·00 65
722 75c. Konrad Adenauer and Charles de Gaulle (horiz) 65 65
723 80c. Red Cross emblem and map of Nevis (horiz) 1·25 80
724 80c. "Resolute" (yacht), 1920 1·25 80
725 80c. Nelson Museum and map of Nevis (horiz) 1·25 80
726 80c. St. Thomas's Church (horiz) 70 80
727 $1 Blue whale (horiz) 2·00 1·25
728 $3 Mozart 3·00 2·75
729 $3 Graph and U.N. emblems (horiz) 1·75 2·25
730 $3 Lions Club emblem 1·75 2·25
731 $5 Soviet "Energia" launch vehicle SL-17 3·25 3·75
732 $5 Lebaudy-Juillot airship No. 1 "La Jaune" (horiz) 3·25 3·75
733 $5 Adenauer and Pres. Kennedy (horiz) 3·25 3·75
MS734 Five sheets. (a) 104×71 mm. $6 Astronaut. (b) 104×71 mm. $6 Zeppelin LZ-5, 1909 (horiz). (c) 100×70 mm. $6 Konrad Adenauer (horiz). (d) 75×103 mm. $6 "America 3" (yacht), 1992 (horiz). (e) 98×66 mm. $6 Masked reveller from "Don Giovanni" (horiz) Set of 5 sheets 18·00 19·00
ANNIVERSARIES AND EVENTS—Nos. 720, 731, **MS**734a, International Space Year; 721, 732, **MS**734b, 75th death anniv of Count Ferdinand von Zeppelin (airship pioneer); 722, 733, **MS**734c, 25th death anniv of Konrad Adenauer (German statesman); 723, 50th anniv of St. Kitts–Nevis Red Cross; 724, **MS**734d, Americas Cup Yachting Championship; 725, Opening of Nelson Museum; 726, 150th anniv of Anglican Diocese of North-eastern Caribbean and Aruba; 727, Earth Summit '92, Rio; 728, **MS**734e, Death bicent of Mozart; 729, International Conference on Nutrition, Rome; 730, 75th anniv of International Association of Lions Clubs.

1993. West Indian Flowers. Multicoloured.
735 10c. Type **73** 75 30
736 25c. "Bougainvillea" 90 30
737 50c. "Allamanda cathartica" 1·10 50
738 80c. "Anthurium andraeanum" 1·50 70
739 $1 "Ixora coccinea" 1·75 75
740 $2 "Hibiscus rosa-sinensis" 2·75 2·25
741 $4 "Justicia brandegeeana" 4·00 4·75
742 $5 "Antigonon leptopus" 4·00 4·75
MS743 Two sheets, each 100×70 mm. (a) $6 "Lantana camara". (b) $6 "Petrea volubilis" Set of 2 sheets 7·50 8·50

74 Antillean Blue (male)

1993. Butterflies. Multicoloured.
744 10c. Type **74** 60 40
745 25c. Cuban crescentspot (female) 75 40
746 50c. Ruddy daggerwing 1·00 50
747 80c. Little yellow (male) 1·25 75
748 $1 Atala 1·25 90
749 $1.50 Orange-barred giant sulphur 2·00 2·25
750 $4 Tropic queen (male) 3·25 4·50
751 $5 Malachite 3·25 4·50
MS752 Two sheets, each 76×105 mm. (a) $6 Polydamus swallowtail (male). (b) $6 West Indian buckeye Set of 2 sheets 10·00 11·00

1993. 40th Anniv of Coronation. As T **224** of Lesotho.
753 10c. multicoloured 15 20
754 80c. brown and black 45 55
755 $2 multicoloured 1·10 1·40
756 $4 multicoloured 2·00 2·25
MS757 71×101 mm. $6 multicoloured 3·00 3·50
DESIGNS—38×47 mm: 10c. Queen Elizabeth II at Coronation (photograph by Cecil Beaton); 80c. Queen wearing Imperial State Crown; $2 Crowning of Queen Elizabeth II; $4 Queen and Prince Charles at polo match. $28\frac{1}{2}\times42\frac{1}{2}$ mm: $6 "Queen Elizabeth II, 1977" (detail) (Susan Crawford).

75 Flag and National Anthem
76 "Annunciation of Mary"

1993. 10th Anniv of Independence of St. Kitts–Nevis. Multicoloured.
758 25c. Type **75** 1·25 25
759 80c. Brown pelican and map of St. Kitts–Nevis 1·50 1·00

1993. World Cup Football Championship 1994, U.S.A. As T **278** of Maldive Islands. Mult.
760 10c. Imre Garaba (Hungary) and Michel Platini (France) (horiz) 70 30
761 25c. Diego Maradona (Argentina) and Giuseppe Bergomi (Italy) (horiz) 85 30
762 50c. Luis Fernandez (France) and Vasily Rats (Russia) (horiz) 1·10 45
763 80c. Victor Munez (Spain) (horiz) 1·50 65
764 $1 Preben Elkjaer (Denmark) and Andoni Goicoechea (Spain) (horiz) 1·75 85
765 $2 Elzo Coelho (Brazil) and Jean Tigana (France) (horiz) 2·75 2·25
766 $3 Pedro Troglio (Argentina) and Sergei Alejnikov (Russia) (horiz) 3·00 3·25
767 $5 Jan Karas (Poland) and Antonio Luiz Costa (Brazil) (horiz) 3·75 4·75
MS768 Two sheets. (a) 100×70 mm. $5 Belloumi (Algeria) (horiz). (b) 70×100 mm. $5 Trevor Steven (England) Set of 2 sheets 11·00 11·00

1993. Christmas. Religious Paintings by Durer. Black, yellow and red (Nos. 769/73 and 776) or multicoloured (others).
769 20c. Type **76** 50 15
770 40c. "The Nativity" (drawing) 70 30
771 50c. "Holy Family on a Grassy Bank" 80 30
772 80c. "The Presentation of Christ in the Temple" 1·00 55
773 $1 "Virgin in Glory on the Crescent" 1·25 70
774 $1.60 "The Nativity" (painting) 2·00 2·25
775 $3 "Madonna and Child" 2·50 3·25
776 $5 "The Presentation of Christ in the Temple" (detail) 3·25 4·75
MS777 Two sheets, each 105×130 mm. (a) $6 "Mary, Child and the Long-tailed Monkey" (detail) (Durer). (b) $6 "The Rest on the Flight into Egypt" (detail) (Jean-Honure Fragonard) (horiz) Set of 2 sheets 8·50 9·50

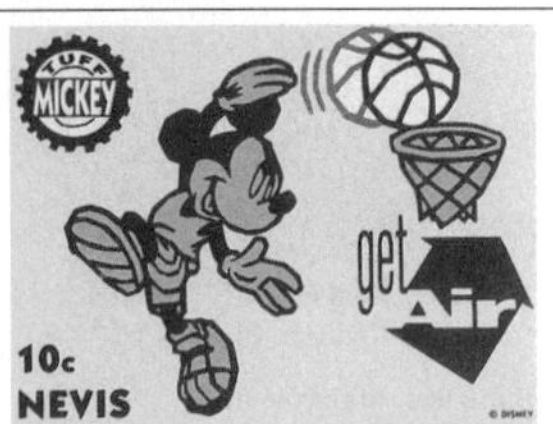

77 Mickey Mouse playing Basketball

1994. Sports and Pastimes. Walt Disney cartoon characters. Multicoloured (except No. **MS**786a).

778 10c. Type **77** 40 30
779 25c. Minnie Mouse sunbathing (vert) 50 20
780 50c. Mickey playing volleyball 70 40
781 80c. Minnie dancing (vert) . . 80 60
782 $1 Mickey playing football 1·00 70
783 $1.50 Minnie hula hooping (vert) . . . . 1·75 2·00
784 $4 Minnie skipping (vert) . . 2·75 3·50
785 $5 Mickey wrestling Big Pete 2·75 3·50
MS786 Two sheets, each (a) 127 × 102 mm. $6 Mickey, Donald Duck and Goofy in tug of war (black, red and green). (b) 102 × 127 mm. $6 Mickey using Test your Strength machine Set of 2 sheets . . . . 9·00 10·00

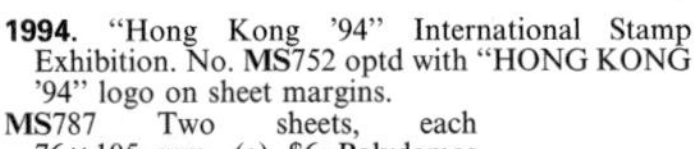

1994. "Hong Kong '94" International Stamp Exhibition. No. **MS**752 optd with "HONG KONG '94" logo on sheet margins.

MS787 Two sheets, each 76 × 105 mm. (a) $6 Polydamas swallowtail (male). (b) $6 West Indian buckeye Set of 2 sheets 7·50 8·00

1994. Hummel Figurines. As T **256** of Maldive Islands. Multicoloured.

788 5c. Girl with umbrella . . . 15 40
789 25c. Boy holding beer mug and parsnips 45 15
790 50c. Girl sitting in tree . . . 65 35
791 80c. Boy in hat and scarf . . 85 60
792 $1 Boy with umbrella . . . . 1·00 70
793 $1.60 Girl with bird . . . . 1·75 1·75
794 $2 Boy on sledge . . . . . . 2·00 2·00
795 $5 Boy sitting in apple tree 2·75 3·75
MS796 Two sheets, each 94 × 125 mm. (a) Nos. 788 and 792/4. (b) Nos. 789/91 and 795 Set of 2 sheets . . . . 6·50 7·50

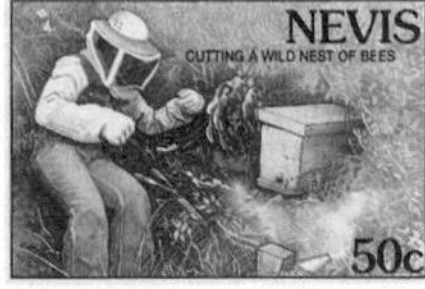

79 Beekeeper collecting Wild Nest

1994. Beekeeping. Multicoloured.

797 50c. Type **79** 65 30
798 80c. Beekeeping club 90 40
799 $1.60 Extracting honey from frames . . . . 1·75 1·75
800 $3 Keepers placing queen in hive . . . . 2·75 3·75
MS801 100 × 70 mm. $6 Queen and workers in hive and mechanical honey extractor . . . . 5·00 5·50

80 Blue Point Himalayan

1994. Persian Cats. Multicoloured.

802 80c. Type **80** . . . . 1·00 90
803 80c. Black and white Persian 1·00 90
804 80c. Cream Persian . . . . . 1·00 90
805 80c. Red Persian . . . . . . 1·00 90
806 80c. Persian . . . . 1·00 90
807 80c. Persian black smoke . . 1·00 90
808 80c. Chocolate smoke Persian 1·00 90
809 80c. Black Persian . . . . . 1·00 90
MS810 Two sheets, each 100 × 70 mm. (a) $6 Silver tabby Persian. (B) $6 Brown tabby Persian Set of 2 sheets . . . . 10·00 11·00

81 Black Coral

83 Symbol 1. Turtles and Cloud

82 Striped Burrfish

1994. Endangered Species. Black Coral.

811 **81** 25c. multicoloured 60 75
812 – 40c. multicoloured 70 80
813 – 50c. multicoloured 70 80
814 – 80c. multicoloured 80 90

DESIGNS: 40c. to 80c. Different forms of coral.

1994. Fishes. Multicoloured.

815 10c. Type **82** 50 50
816 50c. Flame-backed angelfish 55 55
817 50c. Reef bass 55 55
818 50c. Long-finned damselfish ("Honey Gregory") 55 55
819 50c. Saddle squirrelfish . . . 55 55
820 50c. Cobalt chromis 55 55
821 50c. Genie's neon goby . . . 55 55
822 50c. Slender-tailed cardinalfish 55 55
823 50c. Royal gramma 55 55
824 $1 Blue-striped grunt 75 75
825 $1.60 Blue angelfish . . . . 1·00 1·25
826 $3 Cocoa damselfish . . . . 1·50 1·75
MS827 Two sheets, each 100 × 70 mm. (a) $6 Blue marlin. (b) $6 Sailfish (vert) Set of 2 sheets 8·00 8·50

Nos. 816/23 were printed together, se-tenant, forming a composite design.

No. 824 is inscribed "BLUESRIPED GRUNT" in error.

1994. "Philakorea '94" International Stamp Exhibition, Seoul. Longevity symbols. Multicoloured.

828 50c. Type **83** 35 50
829 50c. Symbol 2. Manchurian cranes and bamboo 35 50
830 50c. Symbol 3. Deer and bamboo 35 50
831 50c. Symbol 4. Turtles and Sun 35 50
832 50c. Symbol 5. Manchurian cranes under tree 35 50
833 50c. Symbol 6. Deer and tree 35 50
834 50c. Symbol 7. Turtles and rock 35 50
835 50c. Symbol 8. Manchurian cranes above tree 35 50

84 Twin-roofed House with Veranda

1994. Island Architecture. Multicoloured.

836 25c. Type **84** 70 20
837 50c. Two-storey house with outside staircase 95 30
838 $1 Government Treasury . . 1·40 1·10
839 $5 Two-storey house with red roof . . . . 4·00 6·00
MS840 102 × 72 mm. $6 Raised bungalow with veranda . . . . 3·75 5·00

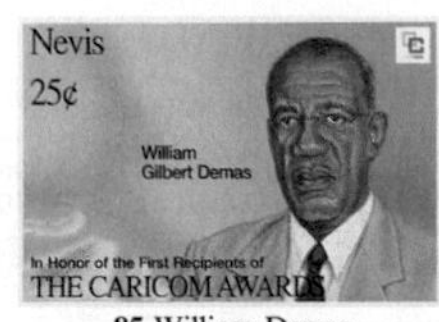

85 William Demas

1994. First Recipients of Order of Caribbean Community. Multicoloured.

841 25c. Type **85** 30 10
842 50c. Sir Shridath Ramphal 50 45
843 $1 Derek Walcott . . . . . 2·25 1·25

86 "The Virgin Mary as Queen of Heaven" (detail) (Jan Provost)

88 Rufous-breasted Hermit

87 Mickey and Minnie Mouse

1994. Christmas. Religious Paintings. Multicoloured.

844 20c. Type **86** 20 10
845 40c. "The Virgin Mary as Queen of Heaven" (different detail) (Provost) 35 25
846 50c. "The Virgin Mary as Queen of Heaven" (different detail) (Provost) 40 30
847 80c. "Adoration of the Magi" (detail) (Circle of Van der Goes) 60 40
848 $1 "Adoration of the Magi" (different detail) (Circle of Van der Goes) 70 50
849 $1.60 "Adoration of the Magi" (different detail) (Circle of Van der Goes) 1·25 1·50
850 $3 "Adoration of the Magi" (different detail) (Circle of Van der Goes) . . . . . . 2·00 2·50
851 $5 "The Virgin Mary as Queen of Heaven" (different detail) (Provost) 3·00 3·75
MS852 Two sheets, each 96 × 117 mm. (a) $5 "The Virgin Mary as Queen of Heaven" (different detail) (Provost). (b) $6 "Adoration of the Magi" (different detail) (Circle of Van der Goes) Set of 2 sheets . . . . . 8·00 8·50

1995. Disney Sweethearts (1st series). Walt Disney Cartoon Characters. Multicoloured.

853 10c. Type **87** 20 20
854 25c. Donald and Daisy Duck 35 20
855 50c. Pluto and Fifi 50 35
856 80c. Clarabelle Cow and Horace Horsecollar 70 50
857 $1 Pluto and Figaro 85 65
858 $1.50 Polly and Peter Penguin . . . . 1·25 1·50
859 $4 Prunella Pullet and Hick Rooster . . . . 2·50 3·25
860 $5 Jenny Wren and Cock Robin . . . . 2·50 3·25
MS861 Two sheets, each 133 × 107 mm. (a) $6 Daisy Duck (vert). (b) $6 Minnie Mouse (vert) Set of 2 sheets . . . . 8·00 8·50

See also Nos. 998/1007.

1995. Birds. Multicoloured.

862 50c. Type **88** 50 50
863 50c. Purple-throated carib . . 50 50
864 50c. Green mango 50 50
865 50c. Bahama woodstar . . . 50 50
866 50c. Hispaniolan emerald . . 50 50
867 50c. Antillean crested hummingbird 50 50
868 50c. Green-throated carib . . 50 50
869 50c. Antillean mango 50 50
870 50c. Vervain hummingbird 50 50
871 50c. Jamaican mango 50 50
872 50c. Cuban emerald 50 50
873 50c. Blue-headed hummingbird 50 50
874 50c. Hooded merganser . . . 50 50
875 80c. Green-backed heron . . 75 50
876 $2 Double-crested cormorant 1·25 1·40
877 $3 Ruddy duck . . . . . . 1·50 1·75
MS878 Two sheets, each 100 × 70 mm. (a) $6 Black skimmer. (b) $6 Snowy plover Set of 2 sheets . . . . 8·00 8·50

No. 870 is inscribed "VERVIAN" in error.

89 Pointer

1995. Dogs. Multicoloured.

879 25c. Type **89** 30 20
880 50c. Old Danish pointer . . . 50 50
881 80c. Irish setter 65 65
882 80c. Weimaraner 65 65
883 80c. Gordon setter 65 65
884 80c. Brittany spaniel 65 65
885 80c. American cocker spaniel 65 65
886 80c. English cocker spaniel 65 65
887 80c. Labrador retriever . . . 65 65
888 80c. Golden retriever 65 65
889 80c. Flat-coated retriever . . 65 65
890 $1 German short-haired pointer 75 75
891 $2 English setter . . . . . . 1·40 1·40
MS892 Two sheets, each 72 × 58 mm. (a) $6 German shepherds. (b) $6 Bloodhounds Set of 2 sheets . . . . 8·00 8·50

"POINTER" is omitted from the inscription on No. 890. No. **MS**892a is incorrectly inscribed "SHEPHARD".

90 "Schulumbergera truncata"

92 Oriental and African People

91 Scouts backpacking

1995. Cacti. Multicoloured.

893 40c. Type **90** 30 20
894 50c. "Echinocereus pectinatus" 40 25
895 80c. "Mammillaria zeilmanniana alba" 65 40
896 $1.60 "Lobivia hertriehiana" 1·10 1·25
897 $2 "Hammatocactus setispinus" . . . . 1·40 1·50
898 $3 "Astrophytum myriostigma" . . . . . . 1·60 2·00
MS899 Two sheets, each 106 × 76 mm. (a) $6 "Opuntia robusta". (b) $6 "Rhipsalidopsis gaertneri" Set of 2 sheets . . . 7·00 7·50

1995. 18th World Scout Jamboree, Netherlands. Multicoloured.

900 $1 Type **91** . . . . 1·00 1·10
901 $2 Scouts building aerial rope way . . . . 1·50 1·75
902 $4 Scout map reading . . . . 2·00 2·25
MS903 101 × 71 mm. $6 Scout in canoe (vert) . . . . 4·00 4·50

Nos. 900/2 were printed together, se-tenant, forming a composite design.

1995. 50th Anniv of End of Second World War in Europe. As T **317** of Maldive Islands. Multicoloured.

904 $1.25 Clark Gable and aircraft . . . . 1·00 1·00
905 $1.25 Audie Murphy and machine-gunner . . . . . 1·00 1·00
906 $1.25 Glenn Miller playing trombone . . . . 1·00 1·00
907 $1.25 Joe Louis and infantry 1·00 1·00
908 $1.25 Jimmy Doolittle and U.S.S. "Hornet" (aircraft carrier) . . . . 1·00 1·00
909 $1.25 John Hersey and jungle patrol . . . . 1·00 1·00
910 $1.25 John F. Kennedy in patrol boat . . . . 1·00 1·00
911 $1.25 James Stewart and bombers . . . . 1·00 1·00
MS912 101 × 71 mm. $6 Jimmy Doolittle (vert) . . . . 3·50 4·00

1995. 50th Anniv of United Nations. Each lilac and black.

913 $1.25 Type **92** 55 80
914 $1.60 Asian people . . . . . 75 1·10
915 $3 American and European people . . . . 1·40 1·60
MS916 105 × 75 mm. $6 Pres. Nelson Mandela of South Africa . . . 3·00 3·50

Nos. 913/15 were printed together, se-tenant, forming a composite design.

1995. 50th Anniv of F.A.O. As T **92**. Multicoloured.

917 40c. Woman wearing yellow headdress 15 60
918 $2 Babies and emblem . . . 85 1·25
919 $3 Woman wearing blue headdress . . . . 1·25 1·60
MS920 105 × 80 mm. $6 Man carrying hoe . . . . 2·50 3·50

Nos. 917/19 were printed together, se-tenant, forming a composite design.

No. **MS**920 is inscribed "1945–1955" in error.

93 Rotary Emblem on Nevis Flag

1995. 90th Anniv of Rotary International. Multicoloured.
921 $5 Type **93** . . . . 2·50 3·25
MS922 95 × 66 mm. $6 Rotary emblem and beach . . . . . . 3·00 3·75

1995. 95th Birthday of Queen Elizabeth the Queen Mother. As T **321** of Maldive Islands.
923 $1.50 brown, light brown and black . . . . 2·00 1·75
924 $1.50 multicoloured . . . . 2·00 1·75
925 $1.50 multicoloured . . . . 2·00 1·75
926 $1.50 multicoloured . . . . 2·00 1·75
MS927 102 × 127 mm. $6 multicoloured . . . . 6·00 6·00
DESIGNS: No. 923, Queen Elizabeth the Queen Mother (pastel drawing); 924, Wearing pink hat; 925, At desk (oil painting); 926, Wearing blue hat; **MS**927, Wearing tiara.
No. **MS**927 was also issued additionally inscribed "IN MEMORIAM 1900–2002" on margin.

1995. 50th Anniv of End of Second World War in the Pacific. United States Aircraft. As T **317** of Maldive Islands. Multicoloured.
928 $2 Grumman F4F Wildcat 1·40 1·40
929 $2 Chance Vought F4U-1A Corsair . . . . 1·40 1·40
930 $2 Vought SB2U Vindicator 1·40 1·40
931 $2 Grumman F6F Hellcat . . 1·40 1·40
932 $2 Douglas SDB Dauntless 1·40 1·40
933 $2 Grumman TBF-1 Avenger 1·40 1·40
MS934 108 × 76 mm. $6 Chance Vought F4U-1A Corsair on carrier flight deck . . . . . . 4·50 5·50

94 Emil von Behring (1901 Medicine)

1995. Centenary of Nobel Trust Fund. Past Prize Winners. Multicoloured.
935 $1.25 Type **94** 75 85
936 $1.25 Wilhelm Rontgen (1901 Physics) 75 85
937 $1.25 Paul Heyse (1910 Literature) 75 85
938 $1.25 Le Duc Tho (1973 Peace) 75 85
939 $1.25 Yasunari Kawabata (1968 Literature) 75 85
940 $1.25 Tsung-dao Lee (1957 Physics) 75 85
941 $1.25 Werner Heisenberg (1932 Physics) 75 85
942 $1.25 Johannes Stark (1919 Physics) 75 85
943 $1.25 Wilhelm Wien (1911 Physics) 75 85
MS944 101 × 71 mm. $6 Kenzaburo Oe (1994 Literature) . . . . . 3·25 3·75

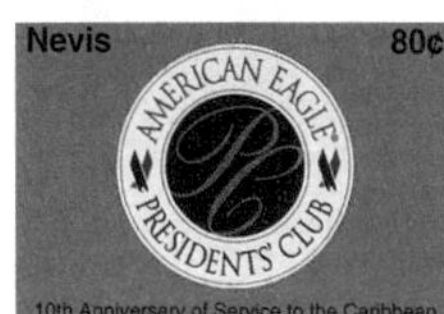

95 American Eagle Presidents' Club Logo

1995. 10th Anniv of American Eagle Air Services to the Caribbean. Sheet 70 × 100 mm, containing T **95** and similar horiz design. Multicoloured.
MS945 80c. Type **95**; $3 Aircraft over Nevis beach . . . . . . 2·40 2·50

96 Great Egrets

1995. Marine Life. Multicoloured.
946 50c. Type **96** 55 55
947 50c. 17th-century galleon . . 55 55
948 50c. Galleon and marlin . . 55 55
949 50c. Herring gulls 55 55
950 50c. Nassau groupers 55 55
951 50c. Spotted eagleray 55 55
952 50c. Leopard shark and hammerhead 55 55
953 50c. Hourglass dolphins . . . 55 55
954 50c. Spanish hogfish 55 55
955 50c. Jellyfish and seahorses 55 55
956 50c. Angelfish and buried treasure 55 55
957 50c. Hawksbill turtle 55 55
958 50c. Common octopus . . . 55 55
959 50c. Moray eel 55 55
960 50c. Queen angelfish and butterflyfish 55 55
961 50c. Ghost crab and sea star 55 55
MS962 Two sheets. (a) 106 × 76 mm. $5 Nassau grouper. (b) 76 × 106 mm. $5 Queen angelfish (vert) Set of 2 sheeets . . . . 7·00 7·00
No. **MS**962 also commemorates the "Singapore '95" International Stamp Exhibition.
Nos. 946/61 were printed together, se-tenant, forming a composite design.

97 SKANTEL Engineer

1995. 10th Anniv of SKANTEL (telecommunications company). Multicoloured.
963 $1 Type **97** 60 50
964 $1.50 SKANTEL sign outside Nevis office . . . . 80 1·25
MS965 76 × 106 mm. $5 St. Kitts SKANTEL office (horiz) . . . 3·00 3·50

98 "Rucellai Madonna and Child" (detail) (Duccio)

1995. Christmas. Religious Paintings by Duccio di Buoninsegna. Multicoloured.
966 20c. Type **98** 20 15
967 50c. "Angel form the Rucellai Madonna" (detail) 40 25
968 80c. "Madonna and Child" (different) 60 40
969 $1 "Angel from the Annunciation" (detail) . . 75 60
970 $1.60 "Madonna and Child" (different) . . . . 1·25 1·50
971 $3 "Angel from the Rucellai Madonna" (different) . . 1·90 2·75
MS972 Two sheets, each 102 × 127 mm. (a) $5 "Nativity with the Prophets Isaiah and Ezekiel" (detail). (b) $6 "The Crevole Madonna" (detail) Set of 2 sheets . . . . 6·50 7·50

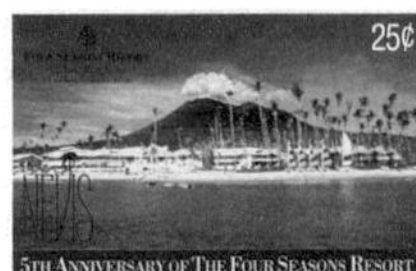

99 View of Nevis Four Seasons Resort

1996. 5th Anniv of Four Seasons Resort, Nevis. Multicoloured.
973 25c. Type **99** 15 20
974 50c. Catamarans, Pinney's Beach 25 30
975 80c. Robert Trent Jones II Golf Course 40 45
976 $2 Prime Minister Simeon Daniel laying foundation stone . . . . 1·00 1·40
MS977 76 × 106 mm. $6 Sunset over resort . . . . 3·00 3·50

100 Rat, Plant and Butterfly

1996. Chinese New Year ("Year of the Rat"). Multicoloured.
978 $1 Type **100** 50 60
979 $1 Rat with prickly plant . . 50 60
980 $1 Rat and bee 50 60
981 $1 Rat and dragonfly 50 60
MS982 74 × 104 mm. Nos. 978/81 2·25 2·50
MS983 74 × 104 mm. $3 Rat eating 2·00 2·25

101 Ancient Greek Boxers

1996. Olympic Games, Atlanta. Previous Medal Winners. Multicoloured.
984 25c. Type **101** 25 20
985 50c. Mark Spitz (U.S.A.) (Gold – swimming, 1972) 35 30
986 80c. Siegbert Horn (East Germany) (Gold – single kayak slalom, 1972) . . . 50 45
987 $1 Jim Thorpe on medal (U.S.A.), 1912 (vert) . . . 60 70
988 $1 Glenn Morris on medal (U.S.A.), 1936 (vert) . . . 60 70
989 $1 Bob Mathias on medal (U.S.A.), 1948 and 1952 (vert) 60 70
990 $1 Rafer Johnson on medal (U.S.A.), 1960 (vert) . . . 60 70
991 $1 Bill Toomey (U.S.A.), 1968 (vert) 60 70
992 $1 Nikolay Avilov (Russia), 1972 (vert) 60 70
993 $1 Bruce Jenner (U.S.A.), 1976 (vert) 60 70
994 $1 Daley Thompson (Great Britain), 1980 and 1984 (vert) 60 70
995 $1 Christian Schenk (East Germany), 1988 (vert) . . 60 70
996 $3 Olympic Stadium and Siegestor Arch, Munich (vert) . . . . 1·60 2·00
MS997 Two sheets, each 105 × 75 mm. (a) $5 Willi Holdorf (West Germany) (Gold – decathlon, 1964) (vert). (b) $5 Hans-Joachim Walde (West Germany) (Silver – decathlon, 1968) (vert) Set of 2 sheets . . 6·50 7·00

1996. Disney Sweethearts (2nd series). As T **87**. Walt Disney Cartoon Characters. Multicoloured.
998 $2 Pocahontas and John Smith . . . . 1·75 1·50
999 $2 Mowgli and the Girl . . 1·75 1·50
1000 $2 Belle and the Beast . . . 1·75 1·50
1001 $2 Cinderella and Prince Charming . . . . 1·75 1·50
1002 $2 Pinocchio and the Dutch Girl . . . . 1·75 1·50
1003 $2 Grace Martin and Henry Coy . . . . 1·75 1·50
1004 $2 Snow White and the Prince . . . . 1·75 1·50
1005 $2 Aladdin and Jasmine . . 1·75 1·50
1006 $2 Pecos Bill and Slue Foot Sue . . . . 1·75 1·50
MS1007 Two sheets, each 110 × 130 mm. (a) $6 Sleeping Beauty and Prince Phillip (vert). (b) $6 Ariel and Eric Set of 2 sheets . . . . 9·00 10·00

102 Qian Qing Gong, Peking

1996. "CHINA '96" 9th Asian International Stamp Exhibition, Peking. Peking Pagodas. Multicoloured.
1008 $1 Type **102** 50 60
1009 $1 Temple of Heaven . . . 50 60
1010 $1 Zhongnanhai 50 60
1011 $1 Da Zing Hall, Shehyang Palace 50 60
1012 $1 Temple of the Sleeping Buddha 50 60
1013 $1 Huang Qiong Yu, Altar of Heaven 50 60
1014 $1 The Grand Bell Temple 50 60
1015 $1 Imperial Palace 50 60
1016 $1 Pu Tuo Temple 50 60
MS1017 104 × 74 mm. $6 Summer Palace of Emperor Wan Yan-liang (vert) . . . . 3·00 3·50

1996. 70th Birthday of Queen Elizabeth II. As T **334** of Maldive Islands. Multicoloured.
1018 $2 Queen Elizabeth II . . . 1·25 1·40
1019 $2 Wearing evening dress 1·25 1·40
1020 $2 In purple hat and coat 1·25 1·40
MS1021 125 × 103 mm. $6 Taking the salute at Tropping the Colour 4·00 4·25

103 Children reading Book

1996. 50th Anniv of U.N.I.C.E.F. Multicoloured.
1022 25c. Type **103** 30 20
1023 50c. Doctor and child . . . 60 30
1024 $4 Children . . . . 2·75 3·50
MS1025 75 × 105 mm. $6 Young girl (vert) . . . . 3·00 3·50

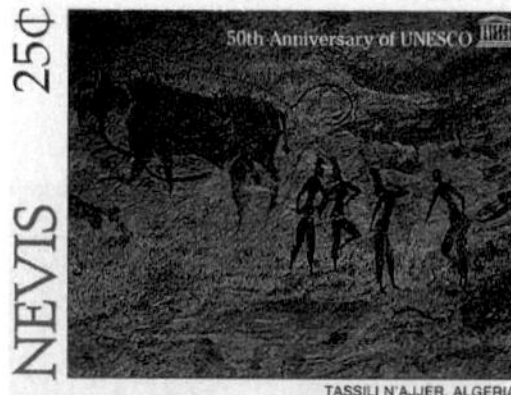

104 Cave Paintings, Tassili n'Ajjer, Algeria

1996. 50th Anniv of U.N.E.S.C.O. Multicoloured.
1026 25c. Type **104** 55 25
1027 $2 Temple, Tikai National Park, Guatemala (vert) . . 1·40 1·50
1028 $3 Temple of Hera, Samos, Greece . . . . 1·75 2·25
MS1029 106 × 76 mm. $6 Pueblo, Taos, U.S.A. . . . . 3·00 3·50

105 American Academy of Ophthalmology Logo

1996. Centenary of American Academy of Ophthalmology.
1030 **105** $5 multicoloured . . . . 3·25 3·50

106 "Rothmannia longiflora"

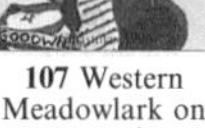

107 Western Meadowlark on Decoration

1996. Flowers. Multicoloured.
1031 25c. Type **106** 25 20
1032 50c. "Gloriosa simplex" . . 35 30
1033 $1 "Monodora myristica" 60 70
1034 $1 Giraffe 60 70
1035 $1 "Adansonia digitata" . . 60 70
1036 $1 "Ansellia gigantea" . . . 60 70
1037 $1 "Geissorhiza rochensis" 60 70
1038 $1 "Arctotis venusta" . . . 60 70
1039 $1 "Gladiotus cardinalis" 60 70
1040 $1 "Eucomis bicolor" . . . 60 70
1041 $1 "Protea obtusifolia" . . 60 70
1042 $2 "Catharanthus roseus" 1·10 1·25
1043 $3 "Plumbago auriculata" 1·60 1·90
MS1044 75 × 105 mm. $5 "Strelitzia reginae" . . . . 2·50 3·00

1996. Christmas. Birds. Multicoloured.
1045 25c. Type **107** 30 20
1046 50c. Bird (incorrectly inscr as "American goldfinch") with decorations (horiz) 45 30
1047 80c. Santa Claus, sleigh and reindeer (horiz) 60 45
1048 $1 American goldfinch on stocking 70 55
1049 $1.60 Northern mockingbird ("Mockingbird") with snowman decoration . . . 1·00 1·10
1050 $5 Yellow-rumped cacique and bauble . . . . 2·75 3·50
MS1051 Two sheets. (a) 106 × 76 mm. $6 Blue and yellow macaw ("Macaw") (horiz). (b) 76 × 106 mm. $6 Vermilion flycatcher (horiz) Set of 2 sheets 6·00 6·75
No. 1048 is inscribed "WESTERN MEADOWLARK" and No. 1050 "YELLOW-RUMPED CAIEQUE", both in error.

108 Ox (from "Five Oxen" by Han Huang)

1997. Chinese New Year ("Year of the Ox"). T **108** and similar oxen from the painting by Han Huang. Sheet 230 × 93 mm.
MS1052 50c., 80c., $1.60, $2 multicoloured . . . . 3·25 3·50
The fifth ox appears on a small central label.

109 Giant Panda eating Bamboo Shoots

110 Elquemedo Willett

1997. "HONG KONG '97" International Stamp Exhibition. Giant Pandas. Multicoloured.
1053 $1.60 Type **109** . . . . . . 1·25 1·25
1054 $1.60 Head of panda . . . 1·25 1·25
1055 $1.60 Panda with new-born cub . . . . 1·25 1·25
1056 $1.60 Panda hanging from branch . . . . 1·25 1·25
1057 $1.60 Panda asleep on tree 1·25 1·25
1058 $1.60 Panda climbing trunk 1·25 1·25
MS1059 73 × 103 mm. $5 Panda with cub . . . . 2·50 3·00

1997. Nevis Cricketers. Multicoloured.
1060 25c. Type **110** 30 25
1061 80c. Stuart Williams 70 50
1062 $2 Keith Arthurton . . . . 1·25 1·50
MS1063 Two sheets, each 106 × 76 mm. (a) $5 Willett, Arthurton and Williams as part of the 1990 Nevis team (horiz). (b) $5 Williams and Arthurton as part of the 1994 West Indies team Set of 2 sheets . . . . 5·00 5·25

111 Crimson-speckled Moth

1997. Butterflies and Moths. Multicoloured.
1064 10c. Type **111** 15 20
1065 25c. Purple emperor 25 20
1066 50c. Regent skipper 35 30
1067 80c. Provence burnet moth 60 45
1068 $1 Common wall butterfly 60 70
1069 $1 Red-lined geometrid . . 60 70
1070 $1 Boisduval's autumnal moth 60 70
1071 $1 Blue pansy 60 70
1072 $1 Common clubtail 60 70
1073 $1 Tufted jungle king . . . 60 70
1074 $1 Lesser marbled fritillary 60 70
1075 $1 Peacock royal 60 70
1076 $1 Emperor gum moth . . . 60 70
1077 $1 Orange swallow-tailed moth 60 70
1078 $4 Cruiser butterfly . . . . 2·25 2·50
MS1079 Two sheets. (a) 103 × 73 mm. $5 Great purple. (b) 73 × 103 mm. $5 Jersey tiger moth Set of 2 sheets . . . . 5·00 5·75
No. 1073 is inscribed "TUFTED JUNGLE QUEEN" in error.

112 Boy with Two Pigeons

1997. 300th Anniv of Mother Goose Nursery Rhymes. Sheet 72 × 102 mm.
MS1080 **112** $5 multicoloured . . 2·50 3·00

113 Paul Harris and Literacy Class

1997. 50th Death Anniv of Paul Harris (founder of Rotary International). Multicoloured.
1081 $2 Type **113** . . . . 1·00 1·25
MS1082 78 × 108 mm. $5 Football coaching session, Chile . . . . 2·50 3·00

1997. Golden Wedding of Queen Elizabeth and Prince Philip. As T **350** of Maldive Islands. Multicoloured.
1083 $1 Queen Elizabeth II . . . 80 80
1084 $1 Royal Coat of Arms . . 80 80
1085 $1 Queen Elizabeth wearing red hat and coat with Prince Philip 80 80
1086 $1 Queen Elizabeth in blue coat and Prince Philip . . 80 80
1087 $1 Caernarvon Castle . . . 80 80
1088 $1 Prince Philip in R.A.F. uniform 80 80
MS1089 100 × 70 mm. $5 Queen Elizabeth at Coronation . . . 2·50 3·00

1997. "Pacific '97" International Stamp Exhibition, San Francisco. Death Centenary of Heinrich von Stephan. As T **351** of Maldive Islands.
1090 $1.60 green . . . . 90 1·10
1091 $1.60 brown . . . . 90 1·10
1092 $1.60 blue . . . . 90 1·10
MS1093 82 × 118 mm. $5 sepia 2·50 3·00
DESIGNS: No. 1090, Russian reindeer post, 1859; 1091, Von Stephan and Mercury; 1092, "City of Cairo" (paddle-steamer), Mississippi, 1800s; **MS**1093, Von Stephan and Bavarian postal messenger, 1640.

1997. Birth Bicentenary of Hiroshige (Japanese painter). "One Hundred Famous Views of Edo". As T **352** of Maldive Islands. Multicoloured.
1094 $1.60 "Scattered Pines, Tone River" . . . . 1·25 1·25
1095 $1.60 "Mouth of Nakagawa River" . . . . 1·25 1·25
1096 $1.60 "Niijuku Ferry" . . . 1·25 1·25
1097 $1.60 "Horie and Nekozane" . . . . 1·25 1·25
1098 $1.60 "Konodai and the Tone River" . . . . . . 1·25 1·25
1099 $1.60 "Maple Trees, Tekona Shrine and Bridge, Mama" . . . . 1·25 1·25
MS1100 Two sheets, each 102 × 127 mm. (a) $6 "Mitsumata Wakarenofuchi". (b) $6 "Moto-Hachiman Shrine, Sunamura" Set of 2 sheets . . . . 7·00 7·50

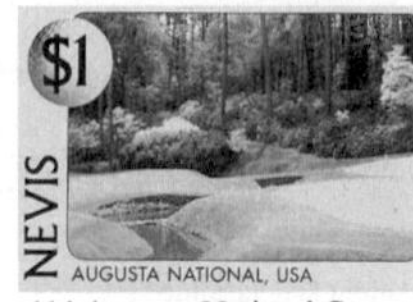

114 Augusta National Course, U.S.A.

1997. Golf Courses of the World. Multicoloured.
1101 $1 Type **114** 70 70
1102 $1 Cabo del Sol, Mexico . . 70 70
1103 $1 Cypress Point, U.S.A. . . 70 70
1104 $1 Lost City, South Africa 70 70
1105 $1 Moscow Country Club, Russia 70 70
1106 $1 New South Wales, Australia 70 70
1107 $1 Royal Montreal, Canada 70 70
1108 $1 St. Andrews, Scotland . . 70 70
1109 $1 Four Seasons Resort, Nevis 70 70

115 "Cantharellus cibarius"

116 Diana, Princess of Wales

1997. Fungi. Multicoloured.
1110 25c. Type **115** 30 20
1111 50c. "Stropharia aeruginosa" 40 30
1112 80c. "Suillus hiteus" 60 65
1113 80c. "Amanita muscaria" . . 60 65
1114 80c. "Lactarius rufus" . . . 60 65
1115 80c. "Amanita rubescens" 60 65
1116 80c. "Armillaria mellea" . . 60 65
1117 80c. "Russula sardonia" . . 60 65
1118 $1 "Boletus edulis" 65 70
1119 $1 "Pholiota lenta" 65 70
1120 $1 "Cortinarius bolaris" . . 65 70
1121 $1 "Coprinus picaceus" . . 65 70
1122 $1 "Amanita phalloides" . . 65 70
1123 $1 "Cystolepiota aspera" . . 65 70
1124 $3 "Lactarius turpis" . . . 1·75 2·00
1125 $4 "Entoloma clypeatum" 2·25 2·50
MS1126 Two sheets, each 98 × 68 mm. (a) $5 "Galerina mutabilis". (b) $5 "Gymnopilus junonius" Set of 2 sheets . . . 6·00 6·50
Nos. 1112/17 and 1118/23 respectively were printed together, se-tenant, with the backgrounds forming composite designs.

1997. Diana, Princess of Wales Commemoration. Multicoloured.
1127 $1 Type **116** . . . . 1·00 90
1128 $1 Wearing white blouse . . 1·00 90
1129 $1 In wedding dress, 1981 1·00 90
1130 $1 Wearing turquoise blouse 1·00 90
1131 $1 Wearing tiara . . . . . 1·00 90
1132 $1 Wearing blue blouse . . 1·00 90
1133 $1 Wearing pearl necklace 1·00 90
1134 $1 Wearing diamond drop earrings . . . . 1·00 90
1135 $1 Wearing sapphire necklace and earrings . . 1·00 90

117 Victoria Govt Class S Pacific Locomotive, Australia

1997. Trains of the World. Multicoloured.
1136 10c. Type **117** 35 20
1137 50c. Express steam locomotive, Japan 55 30
1138 80c. L.M.S. steam-turbine locomotive, Great Britain 75 45
1139 $1 Electric locomotive, Switzerland 90 55
1140 $1.50 "Mikado" steam locomotive, Sudan . . . . 1·25 1·40
1141 $1.50 "Mohammed Ali el Kebir" steam locomotive, Egypt . . . . 1·25 1·40
1142 $1.50 Southern Region steam locomotive "Leatherhead" . . . . . 1·25 1·40
1143 $1.50 Great Southern Railway Drumm battery-powered railcar, Ireland 1·25 1·40
1144 $1.50 Pacific locomotive, Germany . . . . 1·25 1·40
1145 $1.50 Canton–Hankow Railway Pacific locomotive, China . . . . 1·25 1·40
1146 $2 L.M.S. high-pressure locomotive, Great Britain 1·60 1·75
1147 $3 Great Northern Railway "Kestrel", Ireland . . . . 2·00 2·25
MS1148 Two sheets, each 71 × 48 mm. (a) $5 L.M.S. high-pressure locomotive. (b) $5 G.W.R. "King George V" Set of 2 sheets . . . . 7·00 7·50

118 "Selection of Angels" (detail) (Durer)

1997. Christmas. Paintings. Multicoloured.
1149 20c. Type **118** 30 15
1150 25c. "Selection of Angels" (different detail) (Durer) 35 20
1151 50c. "Andromeda and Perseus" (Rubens) 55 30
1152 80c. "Harmony" (detail) (Raphael) 75 45
1153 $1.60 "Harmony" (different detail) (Raphael) . . . . 1·40 1·50
1154 $5 "Holy Trinity" (Raphael) 3·50 4·50
MS1155 Two sheets, each 114 × 104 mm. (a) $5 "Study Muse" (Raphael) (horiz). (b) $5 "Ezekiel's Vision" (Raphael) (horiz) Set of 2 sheets . . . . 6·50 7·00

119 Tiger (semi-circular character at top left)

1998. Chinese New Year ("Year of the Tiger"). Multicoloured.
1156 80c. Type **119** 30 35
1157 80c. Oblong character at bottom right 30 35
1158 80c. Circular character at top left 30 35
1159 80c. Square character at bottom right 30 35
MS1160 67 × 97 mm. $2 Tiger (vert) 80 85

120 Social Security Board Emblem

121 Soursop

1998. 20th Anniv of Social Security Board. Multicoloured.
1161 30c. Type **120** 10 15
1162 $1.20 Opening of Social Security building, Charlestown (horiz) . . . 50 55
MS1163 100 × 70 mm. $6 Social Security staff (59 × 39 mm) . . 2·40 2·50

1998. Fruits. Multicoloured.
1164A 5c. Type **121** 10 10
1165A 10c. Carambola 10 10
1166A 25c. Guava 10 15
1167A 30c. Papaya 10 15
1168A 50c. Mango 20 25
1169A 60c. Golden apple 25 30
1170A 80c. Pineapple 30 35
1171A 90c. Watermelon 35 40
1172A $1 Bananas 40 45
1173A $1.80 Orange 75 80
1174A $3 Honeydew . . . . . . 1·20 1·30
1175A $5 Cantelope . . . . . . 2·00 2·10
1176A $10 Pomegranate . . . . 4·00 4·25
1177A $20 Cashew . . . . 8·00 8·25

122 African Fish Eagle ("Fish Eagle")

1998. Endangered Species. Multicoloured.
1178 30c. Type **122** 10 15
1179 80c. Summer tanager at nest 30 35
1180 90c. Orang-Utan and young 35 40
1181 $1 Young chimpanzee . . . 40 45
1182 $1 Keel-billed toucan . . . 40 45
1183 $1 Chaco peccary 40 45
1184 $1 Spadefoot toad and insect 40 45
1185 $1 Howler monkey 40 45
1186 $1 Alaskan brown bear . . 40 45
1187 $1 Koala bears 40 45
1188 $1 Brown pelican 40 45
1189 $1 Iguana 40 45
1190 $1.20 Tiger cub 50 55
1191 $2 Cape pangolin 80 85
1192 $3 Hoatzin . . . . 1·20 1·30
MS1193 Two sheets, each 69 × 99 mm. (a) $5 Young mandrill. (b) $5 Polar bear cub Set of 2 sheets . . . . 4·00 4·25
No. 1185 is inscribed "MOWLER MONKEY" and No. 1192 "MOATZIN", both in error.

123 Chaim Topol (Israeli actor)

1998. "Israel 98" International Stamp Exn, Tel-Aviv.
1194 **123** $1.60 multicoloured . . 65 70

124 Boeing 747 200B (U.S.A.)

1998. Aircraft. Multicoloured.
1195 10c. Type **124** 10 10
1196 90c. Cessna 185 Skywagon (U.S.A.) 35 40
1197 $1 Northrop B-2 A (U.S.A.) 40 45
1198 $1 Lockheed SR-71A (U.S.A.) 40 45
1199 $1 Beechcraft T-44A (U.S.A.) 40 45
1200 $1 Sukhoi Su-27UB (U.S.S.R.) 40 45
1201 $1 Hawker Siddeley Harrier GR. Mk1 (Great Britain) 40 45
1202 $1 Boeing E-3A Sentry (U.S.A.) 40 45
1203 $1 Convair B-36H (U.S.A.) 40 45
1204 $1 IAI KFIR C2 (Israel) . . 40 45

1205 $1.80 McDonnell Douglas DC-9 SO (U.S.A.) 75 80
1206 $5 Airbus A-300 B4 (U.S.A.) 2·00 2·10
MS1207 Two sheets, each 76 × 106 mm. (a) $5 Lockheed F-117A (U.S.A.) (56 × 42 mm). (b) $5 Concorde (Great Britain) (56 × 42 mm) Set of 2 sheets 4·00 4·25

125 Anniversary Logo

127 Prime Minister Kennedy Simmonds receiving Constitutional Instruments from Princess Margaret, 1983

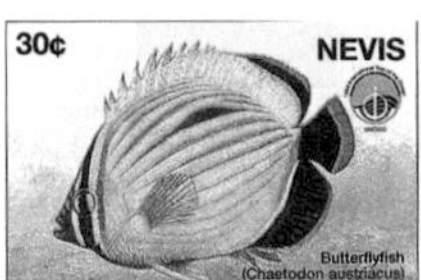

126 Butterflyfish

1998. 10th Anniv of "Voice of Nevis" Radio.
1208 **125** 20c. vio, lt vio & blk 10 15
1209 – 30c. multicoloured 10 15
1210 – $1.20 multicoloured 50 55
MS1211 110 × 85 mm. $5 multicoloured 2·00 2·10
DESIGNS: 30c. Evered Herbert (Station Manager); $1.20, V.O.N. studio; $5 Merritt Herbert (Managing Director).

1998. International Year of the Ocean. Multicoloured.
1212 30c. Type **126** 10 15
1213 80c. Bicolor cherub 30 35
1214 90c. Copperbanded butterfly-fish (vert) 35 40
1215 90c. Forcepsfish (vert) 35 40
1216 90c. Double-saddled butterfly-fish (vert) 35 40
1217 90c. Blue surgeonfish (vert) 35 40
1218 90c. Orbiculate batfish (vert) 35 40
1219 90c. Undulated triggerfish (vert) 35 40
1220 90c. Rock beauty (vert) 35 40
1221 90c. Flamefish (vert) 35 40
1222 90c. Queen angelfish (vert) 35 40
1223 $1 Pyjama cardinal fish 40 45
1224 $1 Wimplefish 40 45
1225 $1 Long-nosed filefish 40 45
1226 $1 Oriental sweetlips 40 45
1227 $1 Blue-spotted boxfish 40 45
1228 $1 Blue-stripe angelfish 40 45
1229 $1 Goldrim tang 40 45
1230 $1 Blue chromis 40 45
1231 $1 Common clownfish 40 45
1232 $1.20 Silver badgerfish 50 55
1233 $2 Asfur angelfish 80 85
MS1234 Two sheets. (a) 76 × 106 mm. $5 Red-faced batfish (vert). (b) 106 × 76 mm. $5 Longhorned cowfish (vert) Set of 2 sheets 4·00 4·25
Nos. 1214/22 and 1223/31 respectively were printed together, se-tenant, with the backgrounds forming composite designs.
No. 1223 is inscribed "Pygama" in error.

1998. 15th Anniv of Independence.
1235 **127** $1 multicoloured 40 45

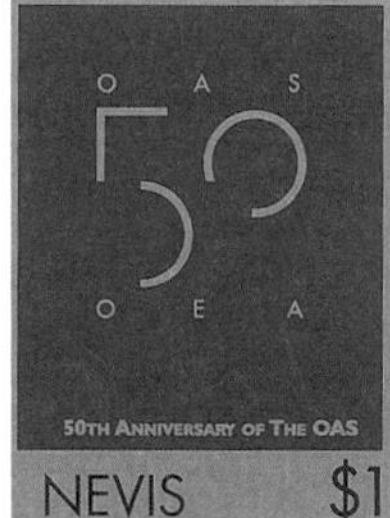

128 Stylized "50"

1998. 50th Anniv of Organization of American States.
1236 **128** $1 blue, light blue and black 40 45

129 365 "California"

1998. Birth Centenary of Enzo Ferrari (car manufacturer). Multicoloured.
1237 $2 Type **129** 1·60 1·60
1238 $2 Pininfarina's P6 1·60 1·60
1239 $2 250 LM 1·60 1·60
MS1240 104 × 70 mm. $5 212 "Export Spyder" (91 × 34 mm) 4·50 4·75

130 Scouts of Different Nationalities

1998. 19th World Scout Jamboree, Chile. Multicoloured.
1241 $3 Type **130** 1·20 1·30
1242 $3 Scout and Gettysburg veterans, 1913 1·20 1·30
1243 $3 First black scout troop, Virginia, 1928 1·20 1·30

131 Gandhi in South Africa, 1914

133 Princess Diana

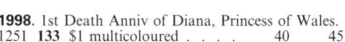

132 Panavia Tornado F3

1998. 50th Death Anniv of Mahatma Gandhi. Multicoloured.
1244 $1 Type **131** 40 45
1245 $1 Gandhi in Downing Street, London 40 45

1998. 80th Anniv of Royal Air Force. Multicoloured.
1246 $2 Type **132** 80 85
1247 $2 Panavia Tornado F3 firing Skyflash missile 80 85
1248 $2 Tristar Mk1 Tanker refuelling Tornado GR1 80 85
1249 $2 Panavia Tornado GR1 firing AIM-9L missile 80 85
MS1250 Two sheets, each 91 × 68 mm. (a) $5 Bristol F2B Fighter and two peregrine falcons (birds). (b) $5 Wessex helicopter and EF-2000 Eurofighter Set of 2 sheets 4·00 4·25

1998. 1st Death Anniv of Diana, Princess of Wales.
1251 **133** $1 multicoloured 40 45

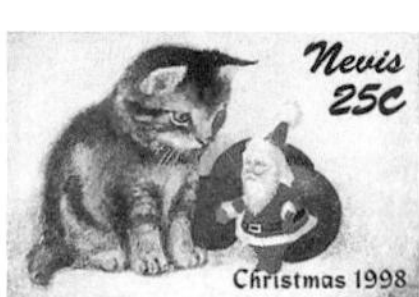

134 Kitten and Santa Claus Decoration

1998. Christmas. Multicoloured.
1252 25c. Type **134** 10 15
1253 60c. Kitten playing with bauble 25 30
1254 80c. Kitten in Christmas stocking (vert) 30 35
1255 90c. Fox Terrier puppy and presents 35 40
1256 $1 Angel with swallows 40 45
1257 $3 Boy wearing Santa hat (vert) 1·20 1·30
MS1258 Two sheets. (a) 71 × 102 mm. $5 Two dogs. (b) 102 × 71 mm. $5 Family with dog (vert) Set of 2 sheets 4·00 4·25

135 Mickey Mouse

1998. 70th Birthday of Mickey Mouse. Walt Disney cartoon characters playing basketball. Mult.
1259 $1 Type **135** 85 85
1260 $1 Donald Duck bouncing ball 85 85
1261 $1 Minnie Mouse in green kit 85 85
1262 $1 Goofy wearing purple 85 85
1263 $1 Huey in green baseball cap 85 85
1264 $1 Goofy and Mickey 85 85
1265 $1 Mickey bouncing ball 85 85
1266 $1 Huey, Dewey and Louie 85 85
1267 $1 Mickey, in purple, shooting ball 85 85
1268 $1 Goofy in yellow shorts and vest 85 85
1269 $1 Minnie in purple 85 85
1270 $1 Mickey in yellow vest and blue shorts 85 85
1271 $1 Minnie in yellow 85 85
1272 $1 Donald spinning ball on finger 85 85
1273 $1 Donald and Mickey 85 85
1274 $1 Dewey shooting for goal 85 85
MS1275 Four sheets. (a) 127 × 105 mm. $5 Minnie wearing purple bow (horiz). (b) 105 × 127 mm. $5 Minnie wearing green bow (horiz). (c) 105 × 127 mm. $6 Mickey in yellow vest (horiz). (d) 105 × 127 mm. $6 Mickey in purple vest (horiz) Set of 4 sheets 15·00 15·00

136 Black Silver Fox Rabbits

1999. Chinese New Year ("Year of the Rabbit"). Multicoloured.
1276 $1.60 Type **136** 85 70
1277 $1.60 Dutch rabbits (brown with white "collar") 85 70
1278 $1.60 Dwarf rabbits (brown) 85 70
1279 $1.60 Netherlands Dwarf rabbits (white with brown markings) 85 70
MS1280 106 × 76 mm. $5 Dwarf albino rabbit and young (57 × 46 mm) 2·00 2·10

137 Laurent Blanc (France)

1999. Leading Players of 1998 World Cup Football Championship, France. Multicoloured.
1281 $1 Type **137** 40 45
1282 $1 Dennis Bergkamp (Holland) 40 45
1283 $1 Davor Sukor (Croatia) 40 45
1284 $1 Ronaldo (Brazil) 40 45
1285 $1 Didier Deschamps (France) 40 45
1286 $1 Patrick Kluivert (Holland) 40 45
1287 $1 Rivaldo (Brazil) 40 45
1288 $1 Zinedine Zidane (France) 40 45
MS1289 121 × 96 mm. $5 Zinedine Zidane (France) 2·00 2·10
Nos. 1281/8 were printed together, se-tenant, with the backgrounds forming a composite design.

138 Kritosaurus

1999. "Australia '99" World Stamp Exhibition, Melbourne. Prehistoric Animals. Multicoloured.
1290 30c. Type **138** 10 15
1291 60c. Oviraptor 25 30
1292 80c. Eustreptospondylus 30 35
1293 $1.20 Tenontosaurus 50 55
1294 $1.20 Edmontosaurus 50 55
1295 $1.20 Avimimus 50 55
1296 $1.20 Minmi 50 55
1297 $1.20 Segnosaurus 50 55
1298 $1.20 Kentrosaurus 50 55
1299 $1.20 Deinonychus 50 55
1300 $1.20 Saltasaurus 50 55
1301 $1.20 Compsognathus 50 55
1302 $1.20 Hadrosaurus 50 55
1303 $1.20 Tuojiangosaurus 50 55
1304 $1.20 Euoplocephalus 50 55
1305 $1.20 Anchisaurus 50 55
1306 $2 Ouranosaurus 80 85
1307 $3 Muttaburrasaurus 1·20 1·30
MS1308 Two sheets, each 110 × 85 mm. (a) $5 Triceratops. (b) $5 Stegosaurus Set of 2 sheets 4·00 4·25
Nos. 1294/9 and 1300/5 respectively were printed together, se-tenant, with the backgrounds forming composite designs.

139 Emperor Haile Selassie of Ethiopia

1999. Millennium Series. Famous People of the Twentieth Century. World Leaders. Multicoloured.
1309 90c. Type **139** 35 40
1310 90c. Haile Selassie and Ethiopian warriors (56 × 41 mm) 35 40
1311 90c. David Ben-Gurion, woman soldier and ancient Jewish prophet (56 × 41 mm) 35 40
1312 90c. David Ben-Gurion (Prime Minister of Israel) 35 40
1313 90c. President Franklin D. Roosevelt of U.S.A. and Mrs. Roosevelt 35 40
1314 90c. Franklin and Eleanor Roosevelt campaigning (56 × 41 mm) 35 40
1315 90c. Mao Tse-tung and the Long March, 1934 (56 × 41 mm) 35 40
1316 90c. Poster of Mao Tse-tung (founder of People's Republic of China) 35 40
MS1317 Two sheets. (a) 76 × 105 mm. $5 President Nelson Mandela of South Africa. (b) 105 × 76 mm. $5 Mahatma Gandhi (leader of Indian Independence movement) Set of 2 sheets 4·00 4·25

140 Malachite Kingfisher

1999. Birds. Multicoloured.
1318 $1.60 Type **140** 65 70
1319 $1.60 Lilac-breasted roller 65 70
1320 $1.60 Swallow-tailed bee eater 65 70
1321 $1.60 Jay ("Eurasian Jay") 65 70
1322 $1.60 Black-collared apalis 65 70
1323 $1.60 Grey-backed camaroptera 65 70
1324 $1.60 Yellow warbler 65 70
1325 $1.60 Common yellowthroat 65 70
1326 $1.60 Painted bunting 65 70
1327 $1.60 Belted kingfisher 65 70
1328 $1.60 American kestrel 65 70
1329 $1.60 Northern oriole 65 70
MS1330 Two sheets, each 76 × 106 mm. (a) $5 Bananaquit. (b) $5 Groundscraper thrush (vert) Set of 2 sheets 4·00 4·25

141 "Phaius" hybrid

142 Miss Sophie Rhys-Jones and Prince Edward

1999. Orchids. Multicoloured.
1331 20c. Type **141** 10 15
1332 25c. "Cuitlauzina pendula" 10 15
1333 50c. "Bletilla striata" 20 25
1334 80c. "Cymbidium" "Showgirl" 30 35
1335 $1 "Cattleya intermedia" 40 45
1336 $1 "Cattleya" "Sophia Martin" 40 45

1337 $1 "Phalaenopsis" "Little Hal" 40 45
1338 $1 "Laeliocattleya alisal" "Rodeo" 40 45
1339 $1 "Laelia lucasiana fournieri" 40 45
1340 $1 "Cymbidium" "Red Beauty" 40 45
1341 $1 "Sobralia" sp. 40 45
1342 $1 "Promenaea xanthina" 40 45
1343 $1 "Cattleya pumpernickel" 40 45
1344 $1 "Odontocidium artur elle" 40 45
1345 $1 "Neostylis lou sneary" 40 45
1346 $1 "Phalaenopsis aphrodite" 40 45
1347 $1 "Arkundina graminieolia" 40 45
1348 $1 "Cymbidium" "Hunter's Point" 40 45
1349 $1 "Rhynchostylis coelestis" 40 45
1350 $1 "Cymbidium" "Elf's Castle" 40 45
1351 $1.60 "Zygopetalum crinitium" (horiz) 65 70
1352 $3 "Dendrobium nobile" (horiz) 1·20 1·30
MS1353 Two sheets, each 106 × 81 mm. (a) $5 "Spathoglottis plicata" (horiz). (b) $5 "Arethusa bulbosa" Set of 2 sheets 4·00 4·25

1999. Royal Wedding. Multicoloured.
1354 $2 Type **142** 80 85
1355 $2 Miss Sophie Rhys-Jones at Ascot 80 85
1356 $2 Miss Sophie Rhys-Jones smiling 80 85
1357 $2 Prince Edward smiling 80 85
1358 $2 Miss Sophie Rhys-Jones wearing black and white checked jacket 80 85
1359 $2 Prince Edward and Miss Sophie Rhys-Jones wearing sunglasses 80 85
1360 $2 Miss Sophie Rhys-Jones wearing black hat and jacket 80 85
1361 $2 Prince Edward wearing red-striped tie 80 85
MS1362 Two sheets, each 83 × 66 mm. (a) $5 Prince Edward and Miss Sophie Rhys-Jones smiling (horiz). (b) $5 Prince Edward kissing Miss Sophie Rhys-Jones (horiz) Set of 2 sheets 4·00 4·25

1999. "iBRA '99" International Stamp Exhibition, Nuremberg. As T **262** of Lesotho. Multicoloured.
1363 30c. "Beuth" (railway locomotive) and Baden 1851 1k. stamp 10 15
1364 80c. "Beuth" and Brunswick 1852 1sgr. stamp 30 35
1365 90c. "Kruzenshtern" (cadet barque) and Bergedorf 1861 ½s. and 1s. stamps 35 40
1366 $1 "Kruzenshtern" and Bremen 1855 3gr. stamp 40 45
MS1367 134 × 90 mm. $5 1912 First Bavarian air flight label 2·00 2·10

1999. 150th Death Anniv of Katsushika Hokusai (Japanese artist). As T **263** of Lesotho. Mult.
1368 $1 "Women returning Home at Sunset" (women by lake) 40 45
1369 $1 "Blind Man" (without beard) 40 45
1370 $1 "Women returning Home at Sunset" (women descending hill) 40 45
1371 $1 "Young Man on a White Horse" 40 45
1372 $1 "Blind Man" (with beard) 40 45
1373 $1 "Peasant crossing a Bridge" 40 45
1374 $1.60 "Poppies" (one flower) 65 70
1375 $1.60 "Blind Man" (with beard) 65 70
1376 $1.60 "Poppies" (two flowers) 65 70
1377 $1.60 "Abe No Nakamaro gazing at the Moon from a Terrace" 65 70
1378 $1.60 "Blind Man" (without beard) 65 70
1379 $1.60 "Cranes on a Snowy Pine" 65 70
MS1380 Two sheets, each 74 × 103 mm. (a) $5 "Carp in a Waterfall". (b) $5 "Rider in the Snow" Set of 2 sheets 4·00 4·25

1999. "PhilexFrance '99" International Stamp Exhibition, Paris. Two sheets, each 106 × 81 mm, containing horiz designs as T **372** of Maldive Islands. Multicoloured.
MS1381 (a) $5 First Class carriage, 1837. (b) $5 "141.R" Mixed Traffic steam locomotive Set of 2 sheets 4·00 4·25

143 Steelband

1999. 25th Culturama Festival. Multicoloured.
1382 30c. Type **143** 10 15
1383 80c. Clowns 30 35
1384 $1.80 Masqueraders with band 75 80
1385 $5 Local string band 2·00 2·10
MS1386 91 × 105 mm. $5 Carnival dancers (50 × 37 mm) 2·00 2·10

1999. "Queen Elizabeth the Queen Mother's Century". As T **267** of Lesotho.
1387 $2 black and gold 80 85
1388 $2 multicoloured 80 85
1389 $2 black and gold 80 85
1390 $2 multicoloured 80 85
MS1391 153 × 157 mm. $6 multicoloured 2·40 2·50
DESIGNS: No. 1387, Lady Elizabeth Bowes-Lyon on Wedding Day, 1923; 1388, Duchess of York with Princess Elizabeth, 1926; 1389, King George VI and Queen Elizabeth during Second World War; 1390, Queen Mother in 1983. 37 × 49 mm: No. **MS**1391, Queen Mother in 1957.

No. **MS**1391 was also issued with the embossed gold coat of arms at bottom left replaced by the inscription "Good Health and Happiness to Her Majesty the Queen Mother on her 101st Birthday".

144 "The Adoration of the Magi" (Durer)

146 Boris Yeltsin (President of Russian Federation, 1991)

145 Flowers forming Top of Head

1999. Christmas. Religious Paintings. Multicoloured.
1392 30c. Type **144** 10 15
1393 90c. "Canigiani Holy Family" (Raphael) 35 40
1394 $1.20 "The Nativity" (Durer) 50 55
1395 $1.80 "Madonna and Child surrounded by Angels" (Rubens) 75 80
1396 $3 "Madonna and Child surrounded by Saints" (Rubens) 1·20 1·30
MS1397 76 × 106 mm. $5 "Madonna and Child by a Window" (Durer) (horiz) 2·00 2·10

1999. Faces of the Millennium: Diana, Princess of Wales. Showing collage of miniature flower photographs. Multicoloured.
1398 $1 Type **145** (face value at left) 40 45
1399 $1 Top of head (face value at right) 40 45
1400 $1 Ear (face value at left) 40 45
1401 $1 Eye and temple (face value at right) 40 45
1402 $1 Cheek (face value at left) 40 45
1403 $1 Cheek (face value at right) 40 45
1404 $1 Blue background (face value at left) 40 45
1405 $1 Chin (face value at right) 40 45
Nos. 1398/1405 were printed together, se-tenant, and when viewed as a sheetlet, forms a portrait of Diana, Princess of Wales.

2000. New Millennium. People and Events of Eighteenth Century (1700–49). As T **268** of Lesotho. Multicoloured.
1406 30c. Jonathan Swift ("Gulliver's Travels", 1726) 10 15
1407 30c. Emperor Kangxi of China 10 15
1408 30c. Bartolommeo Cristofori (invention of piano, 1709) 10 15
1409 30c. Captain William Kidd hanging on gibbet, 1701 10 15
1410 30c. William Herschel (astronomer) 10 15
1411 30c. King George I of Great Britain, 1714 10 15
1412 30c. Peter the Great of Russia (trade treaty with China, 1720) 10 15
1413 30c. "Death" (bubonic plague in Austria and Germany, 1711) 10 15
1414 30c. "Standing Woman" (Kaigetsudo Dohan (Japanese artist)) 10 15
1415 30c. Queen Anne of England, 1707 10 15
1416 30c. Anders Celcius (invention of centigrade thermometer, 1742) 10 15
1417 30c. Vitus Bering (discovery of Alaska and Aleutian Islands, 1741) 10 15
1418 30c. Edmund Halley (calculation of Halley's Comet, 1705) 10 15
1419 30c. John Wesley (founder of Methodist Church, 1729) 10 15
1420 30c. Sir Isaac Newton (publication of "Optick Treatise", 1704) 10 15
1421 30c. Queen Anne (Act of Union between England and Scotland, 1707) (59 × 39 mm) 10 15
1422 30c. Johann Sebastian Bach (composition of "The Well-tempered Klavier", 1722) 10 15
No. 1418 is inscribed "cometis" in error.

2000. New Millennium. People and Events of Twentieth Century (1990–99). Multicoloured.
1423 50c. Type **146** 20 25
1424 50c. American soldiers and burning oil wells (Gulf War, 1991) 20 25
1425 50c. Soldiers (Bosnian Civil War, 1992) 20 25
1426 50c. Pres. Clinton, Yitzchak Rabin and Yasser Arafat (Oslo Accords, 1993) 20 25
1427 50c. Prime Ministers John Major and Albert Reynolds (Joint Declaration on Northern Ireland, 1993) 20 25
1428 50c. Frederik de Klerk and Nelson Mandela (end of Apartheid, South Africa, 1994) 20 25
1429 50c. Cal Ripkin (record number of consecutive baseball games, 1995) 20 25
1430 50c. Kobe from air (earthquake, 1995) 20 25
1431 50c. Mummified Inca girl preserved in ice, 1995 20 25
1432 50c. NASA's "Sojourner" on Mars, 1997 20 25
1433 50c. Dr. Ian Wilmat and cloned sheep, 1997 20 25
1434 50c. Death of Princess Diana, 1997 20 25
1435 50c. Fireworks over Hong Kong on its return to China, 1997 20 25
1436 50c. Mother with septuplets, 1998 20 25
1437 50c. Guggenheim Museum, Bilbao, 1998 20 25
1438 50c. "2000" and solar eclipse, 1999 (59 × 39 mm) 20 25
1439 50c. Pres. Clinton (impeachment in 1999) 20 25
No. 1423 incorrectly identifies his office as "Prime Minister".

147 Dragon

2000. Chinese New Year ("Year of the Dragon"). Multicoloured.
1440 $1.60 Type **147** 65 70
1441 $1.60 Dragon with open claws (face value bottom left) 65 70
1442 $1.60 Dragon holding sphere (face value bottom right) 65 70
1443 $1.60 Dragon looking up (face value bottom left) 65 70
MS1444 76 × 106 mm. $5 Dragon (37 × 50 mm) 2·00 2·10

148 Spotted Scat

2000. Tropical Fish. Showing fish in spotlight. Multicoloured.
1445 30c. Type **148** 10 15
1446 80c. Delta topsail platy ("Platy Variatus") 30 35
1447 90c. Emerald betta 35 40
1448 $1 Sail-finned tang 40 45
1449 $1 Black-capped basslet ("Black-capped Gramma") 40 45
1450 $1 Sail-finned snapper ("Majestic Snapper") 40 45
1451 $1 Purple fire goby 40 45
1452 $1 Clown triggerfish 40 45
1453 $1 Forceps butterflyfish ("Yellow Long-nose") 40 45
1454 $1 Clown wrasse 40 45
1455 $1 Yellow-headed jawfish 40 45
1456 $1 Oriental sweetlips 40 45
1457 $1 Royal gramma 40 45
1458 $1 Thread-finned butterflyfish 40 45
1459 $1 Yellow tang 40 45
1460 $1 Bicoloured angelfish 40 45
1461 $1 Catalina goby 40 45
1462 $1 Striped mimic blenny ("False Cleanerfish") 40 45
1463 $1 Powder-blue surgeonfish 40 45
1464 $4 Long-horned cowfish 1·60 1·70
MS1465 Two sheets, each 97 × 68 mm. (a) $5 Clown killifish. (b) $5 Twin-spotted wrasse ("Clown Coris") Set of 2 sheets 4·00 4·25
Nos. 1448/55 and 1456/63 were each printed together, se-tenant, the backgrounds forming composite designs.

149 Miniature Pinscher

2000. Dogs of the World. Multicoloured.
1466 10c. Type **149** 10 10
1467 20c. Pyrenean mountain dog 10 15
1468 30c. Welsh springer spaniel 10 15
1469 80c. Alaskan malamute 30 35
1470 90c. Beagle (horiz) 35 40
1471 90c. Bassett hound (horiz) 35 40
1472 90c. St. Bernard (horiz) 35 40
1473 90c. Rough collie (horiz) 35 40
1474 90c. Shih tzu (horiz) 35 40
1475 90c. American bulldog (horiz) 35 40
1476 $1 Irish red and white setter (horiz) 40 45
1477 $1 Dalmatian (horiz) 40 45
1478 $1 Pomeranian (horiz) 40 45
1479 $1 Chihuahua (horiz) 40 45
1480 $1 English sheepdog (horiz) 40 45
1481 $1 Samoyed (horiz) 40 45
1482 $2 Bearded collie 80 85
1483 $3 American cocker spaniel 1·20 1·30
MS1484 Two sheets. (a) 76 × 106 mm. $5 Leonberger dog. (b) 106 × 76 mm. $5 Longhaired miniature dachshund (horiz) Set of 2 sheets 4·00 4·25

2000. 18th Birthday of Prince William. As T **278** of Lesotho. Multicoloured.
1485 $1.60 Prince William shaking hands 65 70
1486 $1.60 Wearing ski outfit 65 70
1487 $1.60 At airport 65 70
1488 $1.60 Wearing blue shirt and jumper 65 70
MS1489 100 × 80 mm. $5 At official engagement (38 × 50 mm) 2·00 2·10

150 "Mariner 9"

2000. "EXPO 2000" World Stamp Exhibition, Anaheim, U.S.A. Exploration of Mars. Multicoloured.
1490 $1.60 Type **150** 65 70
1491 $1.60 "Mars 3" 65 70
1492 $1.60 "Mariner 4" 65 70
1493 $1.60 "Planet B" 65 70
1494 $1.60 "Mars Express Lander" 65 70
1495 $1.60 "Mars Express" 65 70
1496 $1.60 "Mars 4" 65 70
1497 $1.60 "Mars Water" 65 70
1498 $1.60 "Mars 1" 65 70
1499 $1.60 "Viking" 65 70
1500 $1.60 "Mariner 7" 65 70
1501 $1.60 "Mars Surveyor" 65 70
MS1502 Two sheets, each 106 × 76 mm. (a) $5 "Mars Observer" (horiz). (b) $5 "Mars Climate Orbiter" Set of 2 sheets 4·00 4·25
Nos. 1490/5 and 1496/1501 were each printed together, se-tenant, with the backgrounds forming composite designs.

2000. 50th Anniv of Berlin Film Festival. As T **272** of Lesotho showing actors, directors and film scenes with awards. Multicoloured.
1503 $1.60 "Rani Radovi", 1969 65 70
1504 $1.60 Salvatore Giuliano (director), 1962 65 70
1505 $1.60 "Schonzeit fur Fuches", 1966 65 70
1506 $1.60 Shirley Maclaine (actress), 1971 65 70

1507	$1.60 Simone Signoret (actress), 1971	65	70
1508	$1.60 Tabejad Bijad (director), 1974	65	70
MS1509	97 × 103 mm. $5 "Komissar", 1988	2·00	2·25

2000. 175th Anniv of Stockton and Darlington Line (first public railway). As T **273** of Lesotho. Multicoloured.

1510	$3 Locomotion No. 1, 1875, and George Stephenson	1·20	1·30
1511	$3 Original drawing of Richard Trevithick's locomotive, 1804	1·20	1·30

2000. 250th Death Anniv of Johann Sebastian Bach (German composer). Sheet 76 × 88 mm, containing vert design as T **274** of Lesotho. Multicoloured.

MS1512	$5 Johann Sebastian Bach	2·00	2·10

151 Albert Einstein

2000. Election of Albert Einstein (mathematical physicist) as *Time Magazine* "Man of the Century". Showing portraits with photographs in background. Multicoloured.

1513	$2 Type **151**	80	85
1514	$2 Riding bicycle	80	85
1515	$2 Standing on beach	80	85

2000. Centenary of First Zeppelin Flight. As T **276** of Lesotho.

1516	$3 green, purple and black	1·20	1·30
1517	$3 green, purple and black	1·20	1·30
1518	$3 green, purple and black	1·20	1·30
MS1519	116 × 76 mm. $5 green, mauve and black	2·00	2·10

DESIGNS: (38 × 24 mm)—No. 1516, LZ-129 *Hindenburg*, 1929; 1517, LZ-1, 1900; 1518, LZ-11 *Viktoria Luise*. (50 × 37 mm)—No. **MS**1519, LZ-127 *Graf Zeppelin*, 1928.

No. 1516 is inscribed "Hindenberg" in error.

2000. Olympic Games, Sydney. As T **277** of Lesotho. Multicoloured.

1520	$2 Gisela Mauermeyer (discus), Berlin (1936)	80	85
1521	$2 Gymnast on uneven bars	80	85
1522	$2 Wembley Stadium, London (1948) and Union Jack	80	85
1523	$2 Ancient Greek horseman	80	85

2000. West Indies Cricket Tour and 100th Test Match at Lord's. As T **206** of Montserrat. Multicoloured.

1524	$2 Elquemeda Willett	80	85
1525	$3 Keith Arthurton	1·20	1·30
MS1526	121 × 104 mm. $5 Lord's Cricket Ground (horiz)	2·00	2·10

152 King Edward III of England

2000. Monarchs of the Millennium.

1527	**152** $1.60 black, stone and brown	65	70
1528	– $1.60 multicoloured	65	70
1529	– $1.60 multicoloured	65	70
1530	– $1.60 black, stone and brown	65	70
1531	– $1.60 black, stone and brown	65	70
1532	– $1.60 purple, stone and brown	65	70
MS1533	115 × 135 mm. $5 multicoloured	2·00	2·10

DESIGNS: No. 1528, Emperor Charles V (of Spain); 1529, King Joseph II of Hungary; 1530, Emperor Henry II of Germany; 1531, King Louis IV of France; 1532, King Ludwig II of Bavaria; **MS**1533, King Louis IX of France.

153 Member of The Angels

154 Bob Hope in Ranger Uniform, Vietnam

2000. Famous Girl Pop Groups. Multicoloured.

1534	90c. Type **153**	35	40
1535	90c. Member of The Angels with long hair	35	40
1536	90c. Member of The Angels with chin on hand	35	40
1537	90c. Member of The Dixie Cups (record at left)	35	40
1538	90c. Member of The Dixie Cups with shoulder-length hair	35	40
1539	90c. Member of The Dixie Cups with short hair and slide	35	40
1540	90c. Member of The Vandellas (record at left)	35	40
1541	90c. Member of The Vandellas ("Nevis" clear of hair)	35	40
1542	90c. Member of The Vandellas ("is" of "Nevis" on hair)	35	40

Each horizontal row depicts a different group with Nos. 1534/6 having green backgrounds, Nos. 1537/9 yellow and Nos. 1540/2 mauve.

2000. Bob Hope (American entertainer).

1543	**154** $1 black, grey and mauve	40	45
1544	– $1 Indian red, grey and mauve	40	45
1545	– $1 black, grey and mauve	40	45
1546	– $1 multicoloured	40	45
1547	– $1 black, grey and mauve	40	45
1548	– $1 multicoloured	40	45

DESIGNS: No. 1544, On stage with Sammy Davis Jnr.; 1545, With wife Dolores; 1546, Playing golf; 1547, Making radio broadcast; 1548, Visiting Great Wall of China.

155 David Copperfield

157 Beach Scene and Logo

156 Mike Wallace

2000. David Copperfield (conjurer).

1549	**155** $1.60 multicoloured	65	70

2000. Mike Wallace (television journalist). Sheet 120 × 112 mm.

MS1550	**156** $5 multicoloured	2·00	2·10

2000. 2nd Caribbean Beekeeping Congress. No. **MS**801 optd **2nd Caribbean Beekeeping Congress August 14–18, 2000** on top margin.

MS1551	100 × 70 mm. $6 Queen and workers in hive and mechanical honey extractor	2·40	2·50

2000. "Carifesta VII" Arts Festival. Multicoloured.

1552	30c. Type **157**	10	15
1553	90c. Carnival scenes	35	40
1554	$1.20 Stylized dancer with streamers	50	55

158 Golden Elegance Oriental Lily

2000. Caribbean Flowers. Multicoloured.

1555	30c. Type **158**	10	15
1556	80c. Frangipani	30	35
1557	90c. Star of the March	35	40
1558	90c. Tiger lily	35	40
1559	90c. Mont Blanc lily	35	40
1560	90c. Torch ginger	35	40
1561	90c. Cattleya orchid	35	40
1562	90c. St. John's wort	35	40
1563	$1 Culebra	40	45
1564	$1 Rubellum lily	40	45
1565	$1 Silver elegance oriental lily	40	45
1566	$1 Chinese hibiscus	40	45
1567	$1 Tiger lily (different)	40	45
1568	$1 Royal poincia	40	45
1569	$1.60 Epiphyte	65	70
1570	$1.60 Enchantment lily	65	70
1571	$1.60 Glory lily	65	70
1572	$1.60 Purple granadilla	65	70
1573	$1.60 Jacaranda	65	70
1574	$1.60 Shrimp plant	65	70
1575	$1.60 Garden zinnia	65	70
1576	$5 Rose elegance lily	2·00	2·10
MS1577	Two sheets. (a) 75 × 90 mm. $5 Bird of paradise (plant). (b) 90 × 75 mm. $5 Dahlia Set of 2 sheets	4·00	4·25

Nos. 1557/62, 1563/8 and 1569/74 were each printed together, se-tenant, with the backgrounds forming composite designs.

159 Aerial View of Resort

2000. Re-opening of Four Seasons Resort. Mult.

1578	30c. Type **159**	10	15
1579	30c. Palm trees on beach	10	15
1580	30c. Golf course	10	15
1581	30c. Couple at water's edge	10	15

160 "The Coronation of the Virgin" (Velazquez)

2000. Christmas. Religious Paintings. Multicoloured.

1582	30c. Type **160**	10	15
1583	80c. "The Immaculate Conception" (Velazquez)	30	35
1584	90c. "Madonna and Child" (Titian) (horiz)	35	40
1585	$1.20 "Madonna and Child with St. John the Baptist and St. Catherine" (Titian) (horiz)	50	55
MS1586	108 × 108 mm. $6 "Madonna and Child with St. Catherine" (Titian) (horiz)	2·40	2·50

Nos. 1584/5 are both inscribed "Titien" in error.

161 Snake coiled around Branch

2001. Chinese New Year. "Year of the Snake". Multicoloured.

1587	$1.60 Type **161**	65	70
1588	$1.60 Snake in tree	65	70
1589	$1.60 Snake on path	65	70
1590	$1.60 Snake by rocks	65	70
MS1591	70 × 100 mm. $5 Cobra at foot of cliff	2·00	2·10

162 Charlestown Methodist Church

2001. Leeward Islands District Methodist Church Conference. Multicoloured.

1592	50c. Type **162**	20	25
1593	50c. Jessups Methodist Church	20	25
1594	50c. Clifton Methodist Church	20	25
1595	50c. Trinity Methodist Church	20	25
1596	50c. Combermere Methodist Church	20	25
1597	50c. New River Methodist Church	20	25
1598	50c. Gingerland Methodist Church	20	25

163 Two Giraffes

2001. Wildlife from "The Garden of Eden". Multicoloured.

1599	$1.60 Type **163**	65	70
1600	$1.60 Rainbow boa constrictor	65	70
1601	$1.60 Suffolk sheep and mountain cottontail hare	65	70
1602	$1.60 Bluebuck antelope	65	70
1603	$1.60 Fox	65	70
1604	$1.60 Box turtle	65	70
1605	$1.60 Pileated woodpecker ("Red-crested Woodpecker") and unicorn	65	70
1606	$1.60 African elephant	65	70
1607	$1.60 Siberian tiger	65	70
1608	$1.60 Greater flamingo and Adam and Eve	65	70
1609	$1.60 Hippopotamus	65	70
1610	$1.60 Harlequin frog	65	70
MS1611	Four sheets, each 84 × 69 mm. (a) $5 Keel-billed toucan ("Toucan") (vert). (b) $5 American bald eagle. (c) $5 Koala bear (vert). (d) $5 Blue and yellow macaw (vert) Set of 4 sheets	8·00	8·25

Nos. 1599/1604 and 1605/10 were each printed together, se-tenant, with the backgrounds forming composite designs.

164 Zebra

2001. Butterflies of Nevis. Multicoloured.

1612	30c. Type **164**	10	15
1613	80c. Julia	30	35
1614	$1 Ruddy dagger	40	45
1615	$1 Common morpho	40	45
1616	$1 Banded king shoemaker	40	45
1617	$1 Figure of eight	40	45
1618	$1 Grecian shoemaker	40	45
1619	$1 Mosaic	40	45
1620	$1 White peacock	40	45
1621	$1 Hewitson's blue hairstreak	40	45
1622	$1 Tiger pierid	40	45
1623	$1 Gold drop helicopsis	40	45
1624	$1 Cramer's mesene	40	45
1625	$1 Red-banded pereute	40	45
1626	$1.60 Small flambeau	65	70
1627	$5 Purple mort bleu	2·00	2·10
MS1628	Two sheets, each 72 × 100 mm. (a) $5 Common mechanitis. (b) $5 Hewitson's pierella Set of 2 sheets	4·00	4·25

165 *Clavulinopsis corniculata*

2001. Caribbean Fungi. Multicoloured.

1629	20c. Type **165**	10	15
1630	25c. *Cantharellus cibarius*	10	15
1631	50c. *Chlorociboria aeruginascens*	20	25
1632	80c. *Auricularia auricula-judae*	30	35
1633	$1 *Entoloma incanum*	40	45
1634	$1 *Entoloma nitidum*	40	45
1635	$1 *Stropharia cyanea*	40	45
1636	$1 *Otidea onotica*	40	45
1637	$1 *Aleuria aurantia*	40	45
1638	$1 *Mitrula paludosa*	40	45
1639	$1 *Gyromitra esculenta*	40	45
1640	$1 *Helvella crispa*	40	45
1641	$1 *Morcella semilibera*	40	45
1642	$2 *Peziza vesiculosa*	80	85
1643	$3 *Mycena acicula*	1·20	1·30
MS1644	Two sheets, each 110 × 85 mm. (a) $5 *Russula sardonia*. (b) $5 *Omphalotus olearius* Set of 2 sheets	4·00	4·25

166 Early Life of Prince Shotoku

2001. "Philanippon 01" International Stamp Exhibition, Tokyo. Prince Shotoku Pictorial Scroll. Multicoloured.
1645 $2 Type **166** 80 85
1646 $2 With priests and nuns, and preaching 80 85
1647 $2 Subduing the Ezo . . . 80 85
1648 $2 Playing with children . . 80 85
1649 $2 Passing through gate . . 80 85
1650 $2 Battle against Mononobe-no-Moriya . . 80 85
1651 $2 Yumedono Hall 80 85
1652 $2 Watching dog and deer 80 85

167 Prince Albert

168 Queen Elizabeth II wearing Blue Hat

2001. Death Centenary of Queen Victoria. Multicoloured.
1653 $1.20 Type **167** 50 55
1654 $1.20 Queen Victoria at accession 50 55
1655 $1.20 Queen Victoria as a young girl 50 55
1656 $1.20 Victoria Mary Louisa, Duchess of Kent (Queen Victoria's mother) 50 55
1657 $1.20 Queen Victoria in old age 50 55
1658 $1.20 Albert Edward, Prince of Wales as a boy 50 55
MS1659 97 × 70 mm. $5 Queen Victoria at accession . . . . . 2·00 2·10

2001. Queen Elizabeth II's 75th Birthday. Multicoloured.
1660 90c. Type **168** 35 40
1661 90c. Wearing tiara 35 40
1662 90c. Wearing yellow hat . . 35 40
1663 90c. Wearing grey hat . . . 35 40
1664 90c. Wearing red hat . . . 35 40
1665 90c. Bare-headed and wearing pearl necklace . . 35 40
MS1666 95 × 107 mm. $5 Wearing blue hat . . . . 2·00 2·25

169 Christmas Candle (flower)

171 Maracana Football Stadium, Brazil 1950

170 Flag of Antigua & Barbuda

2001. Christmas. Flowers. Multicoloured.
1667 30c. Type **169** 10 15
1668 90c. Poinsettia (horiz) . . . 35 40
1669 $1.20 Snowbush (horiz) . . 50 55
1670 $3 Tiger claw . . . . 1·20 1·30

2001. Flags of the Caribbean Community. Multicoloured.
1671 90c. Type **170** 35 40
1672 90c. Bahamas 35 40
1673 90c. Barbados 35 40
1674 90c. Belize 35 40
1675 90c. Dominica 35 40
1676 90c. Grenada 35 40
1677 90c. Guyana 35 40
1678 90c. Jamaica 35 40
1679 90c. Montserrat 35 40
1680 90c. St. Kitts & Nevis . . . 35 40
1681 90c. St. Lucia 35 40
1682 90c. Surinam 35 40
1683 90c. St. Vincent and the Grenadines 35 40
1684 90c. Trinidad & Tobago . . 35 40

No. 1675 shows the former flag of Dominica, superseded in 1990.

2001. World Cup Football Championship, Japan and Korea (2002). Multicoloured.
1685 $1.60 Type **171** 65 70
1686 $1.60 Ferenc Puskas (Hungary), Switzerland 1954 . . . . 65 70
1687 $1.60 Luiz Bellini (Brazil), Sweden 1958 . . . . . . 65 70
1688 $1.60 Mauro (Brazil), Chile 1962 . . . . 65 70
1689 $1.60 West German cap, England 1966 . . . . . . 65 70
1690 $1.60 Pennant, Mexico 1970 65 70
1691 $1.60 Passarella (Argentina), Argentina 1978 . . . . . 65 70
1692 $1.60 Dino Zoff (Italy), Spain 1982 . . . . 65 70
1693 $1.60 Azteca Stadium, Mexico 1986 . . . . . . 65 70
1694 $1.60 San Siro Stadium, Italy 1990 . . . . 65 70
1695 $1.60 Dennis Bergkamp (Holland), U.S.A. 1994 65 70
1696 $1.60 Stade de France, France 1998 . . . . . . 65 70
MS1697 Two sheets, each 88 × 75 mm. (a) $5 Detail of Jules Rimet Trophy, Uruguay 1930. (b) $5 Detail of World Cup Trophy, Japan/Korea 2002 Set of 2 sheets 4·00 4·25
Nos. 1685 and 1687 are inscribed "Morocana" and "Luis" respectively, both in error.

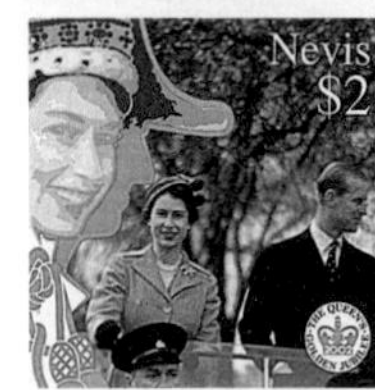

172 Queen Elizabeth and Duke of Edinburgh in reviewing Car

2002. Golden Jubilee. Multicoloured.
1698 $2 Type **172** 80 85
1699 $2 Prince Philip 80 85
1700 $2 Queen Elizabeth wearing yellow coat and hat . . . 80 85
1701 $2 Queen Elizabeth and horse at polo match . . . 80 85
MS1702 76 × 108 mm. $5 Queen Elizabeth with Prince Philip in naval uniform . . . . 2·00 2·10

173 Chestnut and White Horse

2002. Chinese New Year ("Year of the Horse"). Paintings by Ren Renfa. Multicoloured.
1703 $1.60 Type **173** 65 70
1704 $1.60 Bay horse 65 70
1705 $1.60 Brown horse 65 70
1706 $1.60 Dappled grey horse 65 70

174 Beechey's Bee

2002. Fauna. Multicoloured.
1707 $1.20 Type **174** 50 55
1708 $1.20 Banded king shoemaker butterfly . . . 50 55
1709 $1.20 Streaked sphinx caterpillar 50 55
1710 $1.20 Hercules beetle . . . 50 55
1711 $1.20 South American palm weevil 50 55
1712 $1.20 Giant katydid 50 55
1713 $1.60 Roseate spoonbill . . . 65 70
1714 $1.60 White-tailed tropicbird 65 70
1715 $1.60 Ruby-throated tropicbird 65 70
1716 $1.60 Black skimmer . . . 65 70
1717 $1.60 Black-necked stilt . . 65 70
1718 $1.60 Mourning dove 65 70
1719 $1.60 Sperm whale and calf 65 70
1720 $1.60 Killer whale 65 70
1721 $1.60 Minke whales 65 70
1722 $1.60 Fin whale 65 70
1723 $1.60 Blaineville's beaked whale 65 70
1724 $1.60 Pygmy sperm whale 65 70
MS1725 Three sheets, each 105 × 78 mm. (a) $5 Click beetle. (b) $5 Royal tern. (c) $5 Humpback whale (vert) . . . . 4·00 4·25
Nos. 1707/12 (insects), 1713/18 (birds) and 1719/24 (whales) were each printed together, se-tenant, with the backgrounds forming composite designs.

175 Mount Assiniboine, Canada

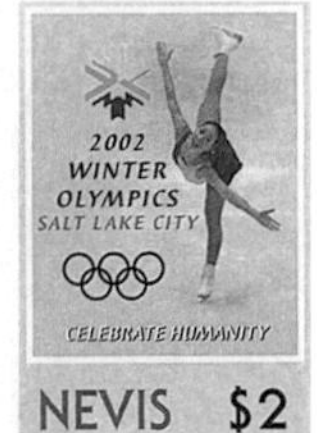

177 Women's Figure Skating

176 Horse-riders on Beach

2002. International Year of Mountains. Multicoloured.
1726 $2 Type **175** 80 85
1727 $2 Mount Atitlan, Guatemala 80 85
1728 $2 Mount Adams, U.S.A. 80 85
1729 $2 The Matterhorn, Switzerland 80 85
1730 $2 Mount Dhaulagiri, Nepal 80 85
1731 $2 Mount Chamlang, Nepal 80 85
MS1732 106 × 125 mm. $5 Mount Kvaenangen, Norway . . . . 2·00 2·10
Nos. 1727 and 1729 are inscribed "ATAILAN" and "MATTHERORN", both in error.

2002. Year of Eco Tourism. Multicoloured.
1733 $1.60 Type **176** 65 70
1734 $1.60 Windsurfing 65 70
1735 $1.60 Pinney's Beach . . . 65 70
1736 $1.60 Hikers by beach . . . 65 70
1737 $1.60 Robert T. Jones Golf Course 65 70
1738 $1.60 Scuba diver and fish 65 70
MS1739 115 × 90 mm. $5 Snorkel diver on reef . . . . 2·00 2·10

2002. Winter Olympic Games, Salt Lake City. Multicoloured.
1740 $2 Type **177** 80 85
1741 $2 Aerial skiing 80 85
MS1742 88 × 119 mm. Nos. 1740/1 1·60 1·70

178 Two Scout Canoes in Mist

179 U.S. Flag as Statue of Liberty with Nevis Flag

2002. 20th World Scout Jamboree, Thailand. Multicoloured.
1743 $2 Type **178** 80 85
1744 $2 Canoe in jungle 80 85
1745 $2 Scout on rope-ladder . . 80 85
1746 $2 Scouts with inflatable boats 80 85
MS1747 105 × 125 mm. $5 Scout painting . . . . 2·00 2·10

2002. "United We Stand". Support for Victims of 11 September 2001 Terrorist Attacks.
1748 **179** $2 multicoloured 80 85

180 "Nevis Peak with Windmill" (Eva Wilkin)

2002. Art. Mmulticoloured (except Nos. 1750/1).
1749 $1.20 Type **180** 50 55
1750 $1.20 "Nevis Peak with ruined Windmill" (Eva Wilkin) (brown and black) 50 55
1751 $1.20 "Fig Tree Church" (Eva Wilkin) (brown and black) 50 55
1752 $1.20 "Nevis Peak with Blossom" (Eva Wilkin) 50 55
1753 $2 "Golden Pheasants and Loquat" (Kano Shoei) (30 × 80 mm) 80 85
1754 $2 "Flowers and Birds of the Four Seasons" (Winter) (Ikeda Koson) (30 × 80 mm) 80 85
1755 $2 "Pheasants and Azaleas" (Kano Shoei) (30 × 80 mm) 80 85
1756 $2 "Flowers and Birds of the Four Seasons" (Spring) (Ikeda Koson) (different) (30 × 80 mm) 80 85
1757 $3 "White Blossom" (Shikibu Terutada) (38 × 62 mm) . . . . . . 1·20 1·30
1758 $3 "Bird and Flowers" (Shikibu Terutada) (38 × 62 mm) . . . . . . 1·20 1·30
1759 $3 "Bird and Leaves" (Shikibu Terutada) (38 × 62 mm) . . . . . . 1·20 1·30
1760 $3 "Red and White Flowers" (Shikibu Terutada) (38 × 62 mm) 1·20 1·30
1761 $3 "Bird on Willow Tree" (Yosa Buson) (62 × 38 mm) . . . . . . 1·20 1·30
1762 $3 "Bird on Peach Tree" (Yosa Buson) (62 × 38 mm) . . . . . . 1·20 1·30
MS1763 Two sheets, each 105 × 105 mm. (a) $5 "Golden Pheasants among Rhododendrons" (Yamamoto Baiitsu) (38 × 62 mm). (b) $5 "Musk Cat and Camellias" (Uto Gyoshi) (62 × 38 mm) . . . . 4·00 4·25
Nos. 1757/62 were printed together, se-tenant, with the backgrounds forming a composite design.

181 "Madonna and Child Enthroned with Saints" (Pietro Perugino)

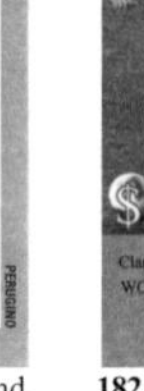

182 Claudio Reyna (U.S.A.) and Torsten Frings (Germany)

2002. Christmas. Religious Art. Multicoloured.
1764 30c. Type **181** 10 15
1765 80c. "Adoration of the Magi" (Domenico Ghirlandaio) 30 35
1766 90c. "San Zaccaria Altarpiece" (Giovanni Bellini) 35 40
1767 $1.20 "Presentation at the Temple" (Bellini) 50 55
1768 $5 "Madonna and Child" (Simone Martini) . . . . 2·00 2·10
MS1769 102 × 76 mm. $6 "Maesa" (Martini) . . . . 2·40 2·50

2002. World Cup Football Championship, Japan and Korea. Multicoloured.
1770 $1.20 Type **182** 50 55
1771 $1.20 Michael Ballack (Germany) and Eddie Pope (U.S.A.) 50 55
1772 $1.20 Sebastian Kehl (Germany) and Brian McBride (U.S.A.) 50 55
1773 $1.20 Carlos Puyol (Spain) and Eul Yong Lee (South Korea) 50 55
1774 $1.20 Jin Cheul Choi (South Korea) and Gaizka Mendieta (Spain) 50 55
1775 $1.20 Juan Valeron (Spain) and Jin Cheul Choi (South Korea) 50 55
1776 $1.60 Emile Heskey (England) and Edmilson (Brazil) 65 70
1777 $1.60 Rivaldo (Brazil) and Sol Campbell (England) 65 70
1778 $1.60 Ronaldinho (Brazil) and Nicky Butt (England) 65 70
1779 $1.60 Ilhan Mansiz (Turkey) and Omar Daf (Senegal) 65 70
1780 $1.60 Hasan Sas (Turkey) and Pape Bouba Diop (Senegal) 65 70
1781 $1.60 Lamine Diata (Senegal) and Hakan Sukur (Turkey) 65 70
MS1782 Four sheets, each 82 × 82 mm. (a) $3 Sebastian Kehl (Germany); $3 Frankie Hejduk (U.S.A.). (b) $3 Hong Myung Bo (South Korea); $3 Gaizka Mendieta (Spain). (c) $3 David Beckham (England) and Roque Junior (Brazil); $3 Paul Scholes (England) and Rivaldo (Brazil). (d) $3 Alpay Ozalan (Turkey); $3 Khalilou Fadiga (Senegal) . . 9·75 10·00
No. 1780 is inscribed "Papa" in error.

183 Ram and Two Ewes

2003. Chinese New Year ("Year of the Ram").
1783 **183** $2 multicoloured 80 85

184 Marlene Dietrich

2003. Famous People of the 20th Century. (a) 10th Death Anniv of Marlene Dietrich. Multicoloured.
MS1784 127 × 165 mm. $1.60 × 2 Type **184**; $1.60 × 2 Wearing white coat and black hat; $1.60 × 2 Holding cigarette . . . . . . 4·00 4·25
MS1785 76 × 51 mm. $5 Marlene Dietrich . . . . 2·00 2·10

(b) 25th Death Anniv of Elvis Presley. Sheet 154 × 151 mm. Multicoloured.
MS1786 $1.60 × 6 Elvis Presley 4·00 4·25

(c) Life and Times of President John F. Kennedy. Two sheets, each 126 × 141 mm.
MS1787 $2 Taking Oath of Office, 1961 (black, brown and rose); $2 Watching swearing in of Cabinet Officers (black, brown and rose); $2 With Andrei Gromyko (Soviet Foreign Minister), 1963 (multicoloured); $2 Making speech during Cuban Missile Crisis, 1962 (black, violet and rose) . . . . 3·25 3·50
MS1788 $2 Robert and Ted Kennedy (brothers) (slate, violet and rose); $2 John F. Kennedy (slate, violet and rose); $2 John as boy with brother Joe Jnr (maroon, black and rose); $2 With Robert Kennedy in Rose Garden of White House (multicoloured) . . . . 2·40 2·50

(d) 75th Anniv of First Solo Transatlantic Flight. Two sheets, each 142 × 126 mm. Multicoloured
MS1789 $2 Ryan Airlines crew attaching wing to fuselage of NYP Special *Spirit of St. Louis*; $2 Charles Lindbergh with Donald Hall and Mr. Mahoney (president of Ryan Airlines); $2 Lindbergh planning flight; $2 Donald Hall (chief engineer of Ryan Airlines) working on plans of aircraft . . 3·25 3·50
MS1790 $2 Donald Hall and drawing of *Spirit of St. Louis*; $2 Charles Lindbergh; $2 *Spirit of St. Louis* being towed from factory; $2 *Spirit of St. Louis* at Curtis Field before flight . . . 3·25 3·50

185 Princess Diana

2003. 5th Death Anniv of Diana, Princess of Wales. Multicoloured.
MS1791 203 × 150 mm. $2 Type **185**; $2 Wearing white dress and four strings of pearls; $2 Wearing black sleeveless dress; $2 Wearing black and white hat . . . . 3·25 3·50
MS1792 95 × 116 mm. $5 Wearing pearl and sapphire choker . . 2·00 2·20

186 Abraham Lincoln Bear

2003. Centenary of the Teddy Bear. Multicoloured.
MS1793 137 × 152 mm. $2 Type **186**; $2 Napolean bear; $2 Henry VIII bear; $2 Charlie Chaplin bear 3·25 3·50
MS1794 100 × 70 mm. $5 Baseball bear . . . . 2·00 2·10

2003. Centenary of Tour de France Cycle Race. As T **429** of Maldives showing past winners. Multicoloured.
MS1795 160 × 100 mm. $2 Gustave Garrigou (1911); $2 Odile Defraye (1912); $2 Philippe Thys (1913); $2 Philippe Thys (1914) . . . . . 3·25 3·50
MS1796 100 × 70 mm. $5 Francois Faber . . . . 2·00 2·10

187 Cadillac 355-C V8 Sedan (1933)

2003. Centenary of General Motors Cadillac. Multicoloured.
MS1797 120 × 170 mm. $2 Type **187**; $2 Eldorado (1953); $2 Coupe Deville (1977); $2 Seville Elegante (1980) . . . . 3·25 3·50
MS1798 84 × 120 mm. $5 Cadillac (1954) . . . . 2·00 2·10

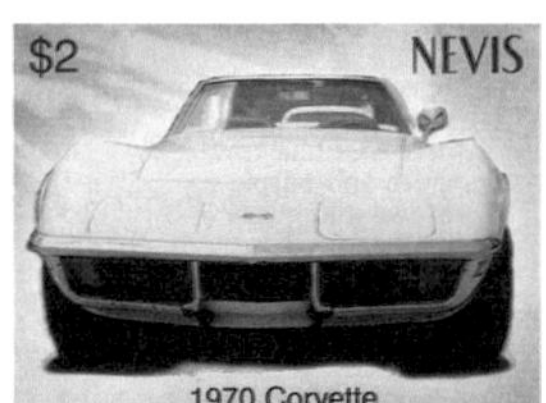

188 Corvette (1970)

2003. 50th Anniv of General Motors Chevrolet Corvette. Multicoloured.
MS1799 120 × 140 mm. $2 Type **188**; $2 Corvette (1974); $2 Corvette (1971); $2 Corvette (1973) . . 3·25 3·50
MS1800 120 × 85 mm. $5 C5 Corvette (1997) . . . . 2·00 2·10

189 Queen Elizabeth II on Coronation Day

190 Prince William

2003. 50th Anniv of Coronation. Multicoloured.
MS1801 156 × 93 mm. $3 Type **189**; $3 Queen wearing Imperial State Crown (red background); $3 Wearing Imperial State Crown (in recent years) . . . . 3·75 4·00
MS1802 106 × 76 mm. $5 Wearing tiara and blue sash . . . . . 2·00 2·10

2003. 21st Birthday of Prince William of Wales. Multicoloured.
MS1803 147 × 86 mm. $3 Type **190**; $3 Wearing jacket and blue and gold patterned tie; $3 Wearing fawn jumper . . . . 3·75 4·00
MS1804 98 × 68 mm. $5 Prince William . . . . 2·00 2·10

2003. Centenary of Powered Flight. A. V. Roe (aircraft designer) Commemoration. As T **430** of Maldives. Multicoloured.
MS1805 177 × 96 mm. $1.80 A. V. Roe's Triplane I, 1909; $1.80 Avro Type D biplane, 1911; $1.80 Avro Type F, 1912; $1.80 Avro 504 3·00 3·25
MS1806 106 × 76 mm. $5 Avro No. 561, 1924 . . . . 2·00 2·10

191 *Phalaenopsis joline*

2003. Orchids, Marine Life and Butterflies. Multicoloured.
1807 20c. Type **191** 10 15
1808 30c. Nassau grouper (fish) 10 15
1809 30c. *Perisama bonplandii* (butterfly) (horiz) 10 15
1810 80c. Acropora (coral) . . . 30 35
1811 90c. Doubletooth soldierfish (horiz) 35 40
1812 90c. *Danaus Formosa* (butterfly) (horiz) 35 40
1813 $1 *Amauris vasati* (butterfly) (horiz) 40 45
1814 $1.20 Vanda thonglor (orchid) 50 55
1815 $2 Potinara (orchid) (horiz) 80 85
1816 $3 *Lycaste aquila* (orchid) (horiz) . . . . 1·20 1·30
1817 $3 *Lycorea ceres* (butterfly) (horiz) . . . . 1·20 1·30
1818 $5 American manatee (horiz) . . . . 2·00 2·10
MS1819 136 × 116 mm. $2 *Brassolaelia cattleya*; $2 *Cymbidium claricon*; $2 *Calanthe restita*; $2 *Odontoglossum crispum* (orchids) (all horiz) . . . . . 3·25 3·50
MS1820 116 × 136 mm. $2 Lionfish; $2 Copper-banded butterflyfish; $2 Honeycomb grouper; $2 Blue tang (all horiz) . . . . 3·25 3·50
MS1821 136 × 116 mm. $2 *Kallima rumia*; $2 *Nessaea ancaeus*; $2 *Callicore cajetani*; $2 *Hamadryas guatemalena* (butterflies) (all horiz) 3·25 3·50
MS1822 Three sheets, each 96 × 66 mm. (a) $5 *Odontioda brocade* (orchid). (b) $5 Blue-striped grunt (fish). (c) $5 *Euphaedra medon* (butterfly) (all horiz) . . . . 6·00 6·25

192 "Madonna of the Magnificat" (Botticelli)

2003. Christmas. Multicoloured.
1823 30c. Type **192** 10 15
1824 90c. "Madonna with the Long Neck" (detail) (Parmigianino) 35 40
1825 $1.20 "Virgin and Child with St. Anne" (detail) (Da Vinci) 50 55
1826 $5 "Madonna and Child and Scenes from the Life of St. Anne" (detail) (Filippo Lippi) . . . . . 2·00 2·10
MS1827 96 × 113 mm. $6 "The Conestabile Madonna" (Raphael) 2·40 2·50

OFFICIAL STAMPS

1980. Nos. 40/49 optd **OFFICIAL**.
O 1 15c. Sugar cane being harvested 10 10
O 2 25c. Crafthouse (craft centre) 10 10
O 3 30c. "Europa" (liner) 10 10
O 4 40c. Lobster and sea crab . . 15 15
O 5 45c. Royal St. Kitts Hotel and golf course 20 20
O 6 50c. Pinney's Beach, Nevis 15 20
O 7 55c. New runway at Golden Rock 15 20
O 8 $1 Picking cotton 15 25
O 9 $5 Brewery 45 55
O10 $10 Pineapples and peanuts 70 90

1981. Nos. 60/71 optd **OFFICIAL**.
O11 15c. New River Mill 10 10
O12 20c. Nelson Museum 10 10
O13 25c. St. James' Parish Church 10 15
O14 30c. Nevis Lane 15 15
O15 40c. Zetland Plantation . . . 15 20
O16 45c. Nisbet Plantation . . . 20 25
O17 50c. Pinney's Beach 20 25
O18 55c. Eva Wilkin's Studio . . 25 30
O19 $1 Nevis at dawn 30 30
O20 $2.50 Ruins of Fort Charles 40 50
O21 $5 Old Bath House 50 65
O22 $10 Beach at Nisbet's . . . 80 1·00

1983. Nos. 72/7 optd or surch **OFFICIAL**.
O23 45c. on $2 "Royal Sovereign" 10 15
O24 45c. on $2 Prince Charles and Lady Diana Spencer 20 25
O25 55c. "Royal Caroline" . . . 10 15
O26 55c. Prince Charles and Lady Diana Spencer . . . 25 25
O27 $1.10 on $5 "Britannia" . . 20 25
O28 $1.10 on $5 Prince Charles and Lady Diana Spencer 55 60

1985. Nos. 187/98 optd **OFFICIAL**.
O29 15c. Flamboyant 20 20
O30 20c. Eyelash orchid 30 30
O31 30c. Bougainvillea 30 40
O32 40c. Hibiscus sp 30 40
O33 50c. Night-blooming cereus 35 40
O34 55c. Yellow mahoe 35 45
O35 60c. Spider-lily 40 50
O36 75c. Scarlet cordia 45 55
O37 $1 Shell-ginger 60 60
O38 $3 Blue petrea . . . . . . 1·25 1·75
O39 $5 Coral hibiscus . . . . . 2·00 2·25
O40 $10 Passion flower . . . . . 3·00 2·50

1993. Nos. 578/91 optd **OFFICIAL**.
O41 5c. Type **63** 55 75
O42 10c. "Historis odius" 60 75
O43 15c. "Marpesia corinna" . . 70 60
O44 20c. "Anartia amathea" . . 70 40
O45 25c. "Junonia evarete" . . . 70 40
O46 40c. "Heliconius charithonia" 85 45
O47 50c. "Marpesia petreus" . . 85 45
O48 75c. "Heliconius doris" . . . 1·25 60
O49 80c. "Dione juno" . . . . . 1·25 50
O50 $1 "Hypolimnas misippus" 1·25 80
O51 $3 "Danaus plexippus" . . . 2·50 2·75
O52 $5 "Heliconius sara" . . . . 3·50 4·00
O53 $10 "Tithorea harmonia" . . 6·50 7·00
O54 $20 "Dryas julia" . . . . . 12·00 13·00

1999. Nos. 1166/77 optd **OFFICIAL**.
O55 25c. Guava 10 15
O56 30c. Papaya 10 15
O57 50c. Mango 20 25
O58 60c. Golden apple 25 30
O59 80c. Pineapple 30 35
O60 90c. Watermelon 35 40
O61 $1 Bananas 40 45
O62 $1.80 Orange 75 80
O63 $3 Honeydew . . . . 1·20 1·30
O64 $5 Cantaloupe . . . . . . 2·00 2·10
O65 $10 Pomegranate . . . . . 4·00 4·25
O66 $20 Cashew . . . . 8·00 8·25

NEW BRUNSWICK Pt. 1

An eastern province of the Dominion of Canada, whose stamps are now used.

1851. 12 pence = 1 shilling;
20 shilling = 1 pound.
1860. 100 cents = 1 dollar.

1 Royal Crown and Heraldic Flowers of the United Kingdom

1851.
2 **1** 3d. red £2000 £350
4 6d. yellow £4500 £700
5 1s. mauve £13000 £4000

2 Locomotive 3 Queen Victoria

1860.
8 2 1c. purple . . . . 38·00 38·00
10 3 2c. orange . . . . 19·00 19·00
13 – 5c. brown £4500
14 – 5c. green . . . . 17·00 13·00
17 – 10c. red . . . . 38·00 40·00
18 – 12½c. blue . . . . 50·00 40·00
19 – 17c. black . . . . 38·00 48·00
DESIGNS—VERT: 5c. brown, Charles Connell; 5c. green, 10c. Queen Victoria; 17c. King Edward VII when Prince of Wales. HORIZ: 12½c. Steamship.

NEW CALEDONIA Pt. 6

A French Overseas Territory in the S. Pacific, E. of Australia, consisting of New Caledonia and a number of smaller islands.

100 centimes = 1 franc.

1 Napoleon III

1860. Imperf.
1 1 10c. black £250

Nos. 5/30 are stamps of French Colonies optd or surch.

1881. "Peace and Commerce" type surch **N C E** and new value. Imperf.
5 H 05 on 40c. red on yellow . . 14·00 20·00
8a 5 on 40c. red on yellow . . 12·50 12·50
9 5 on 75c. red . . . . 35·00 35·00
6 25 on 35c. black on orange £200 £200
7 25 on 75c. red £275 £275

1886. "Peace and Commerce" (imperf) and "Commerce" types surch **N.C.E. 5c.**
10 J 5c. on 1f. green . . . . . . 17·00 19·00
11 H 5c. on 1f. green £7500 £8500

1891. "Peace and Commerce" (imperf) and "Commerce" types surch **N.-C.E. 10 c.** in ornamental frame.
13 H 10c. on 40c. red on yellow 26·00 22·00
14 J 10c. on 40c. red on yellow 12·50 13·50

1892. "Commerce" type surch **N.-C.E. 10 centimes** in ornamental frame.
15 J 10c. on 30c. brown on drab 10·50 11·00

1892. Optd **NLLE CALEDONIE.** (a) "Peace and Commerce" type. Imperf.
16 H 20c. red on green £250 £275
17 35c. black on orange . . . . 50·00 60·00
19 1f. green £200 £200

(b) "Commerce" type.
20 J 5c. green on green . . . . . 14·50 9·00
21 10c. black on lilac . . . . . £120 65·00
22 15c. blue . . . . 85·00 42·00
23 20c. red on green . . . . . . £100 60·00
24 25c. brown on yellow . . . . 21·00 6·25
25 25c. black on pink . . . . . £100 10·00
26 30c. brown on drab . . . . 75·00 65·00
27 35c. black on orange £200 £150
29 75c. red on pink £190 £120
30 1f. green £120 £120

1892. "Tablet" key-type inscr "NLLE CALEDONIE ET DEPENDANCES".
31 D 1c. black and red on blue . . 30 15
32 2c. brown and blue on buff 40 55
33 4c. brown and blue on grey 1·10 3·50
55 5c. green and red . . . . . 2·75 25
34 10c. black and blue on lilac 4·00 2·75
56 10c. red and blue . . . . . 5·00 50
35 15c. blue and red . . . . . 16·00 1·40
57 15c. grey and red . . . . . 8·75 30
36 20c. red and blue on green 6·50 8·50
37 25c. black and red on pink 10·00 2·00
58 25c. blue and red . . . . . 10·50 4·50
38 30c. brown and blue on drab 10·00 8·50
39 40c. red and blue on yellow 16·00 9·25
40 50c. red and blue on pink 60·00 23·00
59 50c. brown and red on blue 35·00 85·00
60 50c. brown and blue on blue 38·00 42·00
41 75c. brown & red on orange 22·00 18·00
42 1f. green and red . . . . . 16·00 17·00

1892. Surch **N-C-E** in ornamental scroll and new value. (a) "Peace and Commerce" type. Imperf.
44 H 10 on 1f. green £4500 £3250

(b) "Commerce" type.
45 J 5 on 20c. red on green . . . 27·00 7·00
46 5 on 75c. red on pink . . . . 16·00 9·25
48 10 on 1f. green . . . . 13·00 8·00

1899. Stamps of 1892 surch (a) **N-C-E** in ornamental scroll and **5**.
50 D 5 on 2c. brown & bl on buff 10·00 12·50
51 5 on 4c. brown & bl on grey 1·25 3·25

(b) **N.C.E.** and **15** in circle.
52 D 15 on 30c. brown and blue on drab . . . . 2·50 5·00
53 15 on 75c. brown and red on orange . . . . 10·00 10·50
54 15 on 1f. green and red . . 32·00 25·00

1902. Surch **N.-C.E.** and value in figures.
61 D 5 on 30c. brown and blue on drab . . . . 3·50 7·75
62 15 on 40c. red and blue on yellow . . . . 3·50 7·00

1903. 50th Anniv of French Annexation. Optd **CINQUANTENAIRE 24 SEPTEMBRE 1853 1903** and eagle.
63 D 1c. black and red on blue . . 70 1·10
64 2c. brown and blue on buff 2·50 2·25
65 4c. brown and blue on grey 4·50 4·50
66 5c. green and red . . . . . 3·00 3·25
69 10c. black and blue on lilac 3·50 5·25
70 15c. grey and red . . . . . 9·25 4·50
71 20c. red and blue on green 15·00 12·00
72 25c. black and red on pink 17·00 17·00
73 30c. brown and blue on drab 26·00 21·00
74 40c. red and blue on yellow 38·00 21·00
75 50c. red and blue on pink 60·00 40·00
76 75c. brown & blue on orange . . . . 85·00 £110
77 1f. green and red £110 £100

1903. Nos. 64 etc further surch with value in figures within the jubilee opt.
78 D 1 on 2c. brown & bl on buff 60 75
79 2 on 4c. brown & bl on grey 2·50 3·00
80 4 on 5c. green and red . . . 90 2·50
82 10 on 15c. grey and red . . 45 1·00
83 15 on 20c. red and blue on green . . . . 50 2·50
84 20 on 25c. black and red on pink . . . . 2·75 4·00

15 Kagu 16

17 "President Felix Faure" (barque)

1905.
85 15 1c. black on green 25 30
86 2c. brown 25 25
87 4c. blue on orange 40 55
88 5c. green 40 55
112 5c. blue 25 35
113 10c. green 60 60
114 10c. red . . . . 1·25 70
90 15c. lilac 60 50
91 16 20c. brown 15 25
92 25c. blue on green . . . . 1·10 35
115 25c. red on yellow 35 20
93 30c. brown on orange . . . 30 1·60
116 30c. red . . . . 1·25 3·50
117 30c. orange . . . . 50 1·25
94 35c. black on yellow . . . 40 1·25
95 40c. red on green . . . . 1·60 2·25
96 45c. red . . . . 1·40 2·75
97 50c. red on orange . . . . 3·25 3·50
118 50c. blue . . . . 70 1·00
119 50c. grey 30 95
120 65c. blue . . . . 90 2·75
98 75c. olive . . . . 35 2·75
121 75c. blue . . . . 1·50 2·25
122 75c. violet . . . . 80 2·75
99 17 1f. blue on green . . . . 1·25 2·75
123 1f. blue . . . . 2·00 3·25
100 2f. red on blue . . . . . . 3·50 3·75
101 5f. black on orange . . . . 8·50 9·25

1912. Stamps of 1892 surch.
102 D 05 on 15c. grey and red . . 45 1·50
103 05 on 20c. red and blue on green . . . . 25 1·75
104 05 on 30c. brown and blue on drab . . . . 25 2·50
105 10 on 40c. red and blue on yellow . . . . 75 1·60
106 10 on 50c. brown and blue on blue . . . . 1·60 2·25

1915. Surch **NCE 5** and red cross.
107 15 10c.+5c. red . . . . 1·25 1·90

1915. Surch **5c** and red cross.
109 15 10c.+5c. red . . . . 1·40 3·00
110 15c.+5c. lilac . . . . . . 20 2·75

1918. Surch **5 CENTIMES.**
111 15 5c. on 15c. lilac . . . . . 1·60 3·25

1922. Surch **0 05.**
124 15 0.05 on 15c. lilac 50 50

1924. Types **15/17** (some colours changed) surch.
125 15 25c. on 15c. lilac . . . . . 40 2·50
126 17 25c. on 2f. red on blue . . 55 2·25
127 25c. on 5f. black on orange 70 3·00
128 16 60 on 75c. green . . . . . 25 2·00
129 65 on 45c. purple . . . . 55 3·75
130 85 on 45c. purple . . . . 1·10 4·25
131 90 on 75c. red . . . . . . 25 3·00
132 17 1f.25 on 1f. blue . . . . . 45 3·25
133 1f.50 on 1f. blue on blue 80 3·50
134 3f. on 5f. mauve . . . . . 1·50 3·75
135 10f. on 5f. green on mauve 2·75 10·00
136 20f. on 5f. red on yellow 10·00 20·00

22 Pointe des Paletuviers

23 Chief's Hut

24 La Perouse, De Bougainville and "L'Astrolabe"

1928.
137 22 1c. blue and purple . . . . 10 1·90
138 2c. green and brown . . . 10 1·75
139 3c. blue and red . . . . . 15 2·50
140 4c. blue and orange . . . 15 2·25
141 5c. brown and blue . . . . 15 1·25
142 10c. brown and lilac . . . 20 60
143 15c. blue and brown . . . 20 50
144 20c. brown and red . . . . 20 1·40
145 25c. brown and green . . . 25 15
146 23 30c. deep green and green 20 1·25
147 35c. mauve and black . . . 50 20
148 40c. green and red . . . . 15 2·75
149 45c. red and blue . . . . 1·50 3·25
150 45c. green and deep green 2·50 3·00
151 50c. brown and mauve . . 25 25
152 55c. red and blue . . . . 2·50 1·10
153 60c. red and blue . . . . 20 2·75
154 65c. blue and brown . . . 35 1·25
155 70c. brown and mauve . . 1·75 3·00
156 75c. drab and blue . . . . 1·10 2·25
157 80c. green and purple . . . 1·50 2·50
158 85c. brown and green . . . 2·50 2·00
159 90c. pink and red . . . . 1·75 2·75
160 90c. red and brown . . . . 2·00 1·50
161 24 1f. pink and drab . . . . 5·50 1·60
162 1f. carmine and red . . . . 85 2·50
163 1f. green and red . . . . . 1·00 2·75
164 1f.10 brown and green . . 10·00 17·00
165 1f.25 green and brown . . 2·25 3·00
166 1f.25 carmine and red . . . 70 3·00
167 1f.40 red and blue . . . . 1·25 2·75
168 1f.50 light blue and blue 50 2·25
169 1f.60 brown and green . . 2·25 3·25
170 1f.75 orange and blue . . . 2·00 2·75
171 1f.75 blue and ultramarine 2·25 3·00
172 2f. brown and orange . . . 75 50
173 2f.25 blue and ultramarine 2·25 3·00
174 2f.50 brown . . . . 70 2·50
175 3f. brown and mauve . . . 70 2·25
176 5f. brown and blue . . . . 55 2·25
177 10f. brown & pur on pink 1·90 2·75
178 20f. brown & red on yellow 2·50 3·75

1931. "Colonial Exhibition" key-types.
179 E 40c. green and black . . . 5·25 6·00
180 F 50c. mauve and black . . . 5·25 6·00
181 G 90c. red and black . . . . 5·25 6·00
182 H 1f.50 blue and black . . . 5·25 5·00

1932. Paris–Noumea Flight. Optd with Couzinet 33 airplane and **PARIS-NOUMEA Verneilh-Deve-Munch 5 Avril 1932.**
183 23 40c. olive and red £350 £375
184 50c. brown and mauve . . £350 £375

1933. 1st Anniv of Paris–Noumea Flight. Optd **PARIS-NOUMEA Premiere liaison aerienne 5 Avril 1932** and Couzinet 33 airplane.
185 22 1c. blue and purple . . . . 8·00 12·00
186 2c. green and brown . . . 8·50 12·00
187 4c. blue and orange . . . 7·75 12·00
188 5c. brown and blue . . . . 7·50 12·00
189 10c. brown and lilac . . . 8·25 12·00
190 15c. blue and brown . . . 7·50 11·50
191 20c. brown and red . . . . 7·50 12·00
192 25c. brown and green . . . 8·50 12·00
193 23 30c. deep green and green 8·00 12·00
194 35c. mauve and black . . . 7·25 12·00
195 40c. green and red . . . . 8·50 9·75
196 45c. red and blue . . . . 7·75 12·00
197 50c. brown and mauve . . 7·00 12·00
198 70c. brown and mauve . . 8·00 14·00
199 75c. drab and blue . . . . 8·75 11·00
200 85c. brown and green . . . 8·00 11·00
201 90c. pink and red . . . . 8·00 11·50
202 24 1f. pink and drab . . . . 10·50 14·00
203 1f.25 green and brown . . 10·50 13·50
204 1f.50 light blue and blue 10·00 13·50
205 1f.75 orange and blue . . . 8·00 9·75
206 2f. brown and orange . . . 10·00 16·00
207 3f. brown and mauve . . . 10·00 15·00
208 5f. brown and blue . . . . 12·50 16·00
209 10f. brown & pur on pink 8·00 16·00
210 20f. brown & red on yellow 8·25 16·00

1937. International Exhibition, Paris. As Nos. 168/73 of St.-Pierre et Miquelon.
211 20c. violet . . . . 55 3·50
212 30c. green . . . . 70 3·50
213 40c. red . . . . 35 3·00
214 50c. brown and blue . . . . 3·00 4·00
215 90c. red . . . . 2·00 2·75
216 1f.50 blue . . . . 2·50 4·50
MS216a 120 × 100 mm. 3f. sepia 13·00 18·00
DESIGNS—HORIZ: 30c. Sailing ships; 40c. Berber, Negress and Annamite; 90c. France extends torch of civilization; 1f.50, Diane de Poitiers. VERT: 50c. Agriculture.

27 Breguet Saigon Flying Boat over Noumea

1938. Air.
217 27 65c. violet . . . . 50 3·25
218 4f.50 red . . . . 2·00 2·75
219 7f. green . . . . 35 2·50
220 9f. blue . . . . 3·00 4·00
221 20f. orange . . . . 2·00 2·75
222 50f. black . . . . 2·50 4·50

1938. Int Anti-cancer Fund. As T **22** of Mauritania.
223 1f.75+50c. blue . . . . . . 5·75 18·00

1939. New York World's Fair. As T **28** of Mauritania.
224 1f.25 red . . . . 65 3·50
225 2f.25 blue . . . . 70 2·00

1939. 150th Anniv of French Revolution. As T **29** of Mauritania.
226 45c.+25c. green and black (postage) . . . . 10·00 13·50
227 70c.+30c. brown and black 9·50 13·50
228 90c.+35c. orange and black 8·75 13·50
229 1f.25+1f. red and black . . 10·00 13·50
230 2f.25+2f. blue and black . . 10·50 13·50
231 4f.50+4f. black and orange (air) . . . . 7·75 45·00

1941. Adherence to General de Gaulle. Optd **France Libre.**
232 22 1c. blue and purple . . . . 8·25 24·00
233 2c. green and brown . . . 10·50 23·00
234 3c. blue and red . . . . . 8·50 23·00
235 4c. blue and orange . . . 8·00 23·00
236 5c. brown and blue . . . . 7·00 23·00
237 10c. brown and lilac . . . 7·50 32·00
238 15c. blue and brown . . . 20·00 32·00
239 20c. brown and red . . . . 15·00 22·00
240 25c. brown and green . . . 15·00 22·00
241 23 30c. deep green and green 14·00 22·00
242 35c. mauve and black . . . 14·50 22·00
243 40c. green and red . . . . 19·00 22·00
244 45c. green and deep green 18·00 24·00
245 50c. brown and mauve . . 15·00 24·00
246 55c. red and blue . . . . 19·00 30·00
247 60c. red and blue . . . . 15·00 24·00
248 65c. blue and brown . . . 21·00 30·00
249 70c. brown and mauve . . 15·00 30·00
250 75c. drab and blue . . . . 19·00 30·00
251 80c. green and purple . . . 19·00 24·00
252 85c. brown and green . . . 18·00 27·00
253 90c. pink and red . . . . 18·00 27·00
254 24 1f. carmine and red . . . . 17·00 27·00
255 1f.25 green and brown . . 14·50 27·00
256 1f.40 red and blue . . . . 14·50 27·00
257 1f.50 light blue and blue 17·00 27·00
258 1f.60 brown and green . . 17·00 27·00
259 1f.75 orange and blue . . . 19·00 27·00
260 2f. brown and orange . . . 21·00 27·00
261 2f.25 blue and ultramarine 17·00 27·00
262 2f.50 brown . . . . 22·00 30·00
263 3f. brown and mauve . . . 18·00 30·00
264 5f. brown and blue . . . . 18·00 30·00
265 10f. brown & pur on pink 20·00 36·00
266 20f. brown & red on yellow 21·00 40·00

29 Kagu

30 Fairey FC-1 Airliner

1942. Free French Issue. (a) Postage.

267 **29** 5c. brown . . . . 30 1·75
268 10c. blue . . . . 30 1·75
269 25c. green . . . . 30 1·25
270 30c. red . . . . 30 2·75
271 40c. green . . . . 35 1·50
272 80c. purple . . . . 30 1·50
273 1f. mauve 90 80
274 1f.50 red 75 35
275 2f. black . . . . 1·10 50
276 2f.50 blue . . . . 1·50 1·75
277 4f. violet . . . . 1·00 40
278 5f. yellow 50 85
279 10f. brown 50 60
280 20f. green . . . . 1·10 1·90

(b) Air.

281 **30** 1f. orange . . . . 25 2·25
282 1f.50 red . . . . 30 2·75
283 5f. purple . . . . 60 2·00
284 10f. black . . . . 65 2·75
285 25f. blue . . . . 60 1·90
286 50f. green . . . . 75 1·25
287 100f. red . . . . 1·40 2·25

1944. Mutual Aid and Red Cross Funds. As T **19b** of Oceanic Settlements.
288 5f.+20f. red . . . . 1·00 3·25

1945. Eboue. As T **20a** of Oceanic Settlements.
289 2f. black . . . . 40 2·50
290 25f. green . . . . 1·60 3·25

1945. Surch.
291 **29** 50c. on 5c. brown 45 50
292 60c. on 5c. brown . . . . 45 3·00
293 70c. on 5c. brown . . . . 65 3·00
294 1f.20 on 5c. brown . . . . 30 2·50
295 2f.40 on 25c. green . . . . 1·60 3·00
296 3f. on 25c. green . . . . . 1·40 2·00
297 4f.50 on 25c. green . . . . 1·40 2·75
298 15f. on 2f.50 blue . . . . 2·00 1·10

1946. Air. Victory. As T **20b** of Oceanic Settlements.
299 8f. blue . . . . 25 3·00

1946. Air. From Chad to the Rhine. As T **25a** of Madagascar.
300 **35** 5f. black . . . . 80 2·50
301 – 10f. red . . . . 55 2·50
302 – 15f. blue . . . . 55 3·50
303 – 20f. brown . . . . 75 3·50
304 – 25f. green . . . . 60 3·75
305 – 50f. purple . . . . 70 4·25
DESIGNS: 5f. Legionaries by Lake Chad; 10f. Battle of Koufra; 15f. Tank Battle, Mareth; 20f. Normandy Landings; 25f. Liberation of Paris; 50f. Liberation of Strasbourg.

36 Two Kagus
37 Sud Est Languedoc Airliners over Landscape

1948. (a) Postage.
306 **36** 10c. purple and yellow . . 20 2·75
307 30c. purple and green . . . 20 2·75
308 40c. purple and brown . . 20 2·75
309 – 50c. purple and pink . . . 15 25
310 – 60c. brown and yellow . . 1·50 2·50
311 – 80c. green and light green 1·50 2·75
312 – 1f. violet and orange . . . 20 25
313 – 1f.20 brown and blue . . . 50 2·75
314 – 1f.50 blue and yellow . . . 40 1·25
315 – 2f. brown and green . . . 30 35
316 – 2f.40 red and purple . . . 70 2·75
317 – 3f. violet and orange . . . 2·50 75
318 – 4f. indigo and blue 75 25
319 – 5f. violet and red 75 30
320 – 6f. brown and yellow . . . 65 65
321 – 10f. blue and orange . . . 60 40
322 – 15f. red and blue 75 55
323 – 20f. violet and yellow . . . 75 60
324 – 25f. blue and orange . . . 1·75 95

(b) Air.
325 – 50f. purple and orange . . 2·50 3·75
326 **37** 100f. blue and green . . . 7·25 4·25
327 – 200f. brown and yellow . . 6·50 7·25
DESIGNS—As T **36**: HORIZ: 50c. to 80c. Ducos Sanatorium; 1f.50, Porcupine Is; 2f. to 4f. Nickel foundry; 5f. to 10f. "The Towers of Notre Dame" Rocks. VERT: 15f. to 25f. Chief's hut. As T **37**: HORIZ: Sud Est Languedoc airliner over- 50f. St. Vincent Bay; 200f. Noumea.

38 People of Five Races, Bomber and Globe

1949. Air. 75th Anniv of U.P.U.
328 **38** 10f. multicoloured . . . . 1·75 8·50

39 Doctor and Patient **40**

1950. Colonial Welfare Fund.
329 **39** 10f.+2f. purple & brown 2·25 6·75

1952. Military Medal Centenary.
330 **40** 2f. red, yellow and green 3·00 5·25

41 Admiral D'Entrecasteaux

1953. French Administration Centenary. Inscr "1853 1953".
331 **41** 1f.50 lake and brown . . . 2·75 3·00
332 – 2f. blue and turquoise . . 1·90 1·50
333 – 6f. brown, blue and red . . 4·00 3·25
334 – 13f. blue and green . . . . 4·25 3·50
DESIGNS: 2f. Mgr. Douarre and church; 6f. Admiral D'Urville and map; 13f. Admiral Despointes and view.

42 Normandy Landings, 1944

1954. Air. 10th Anniv of Liberation.
335 **42** 3f. blue and deep blue . . 8·25 8·25

43 Towers of Notre-Dame (rocks)

44 Coffee

45 Transporting Nickel

1955.
336 **43** 2f.50c. blue, green and sepia (postage) . . . . . 80 1·60
337 3f. blue, brown and green 3·00 3·25
338 **44** 9f. deep blue and blue . . 90 40
339 **45** 14f. blue and brown (air) 1·00 1·10

46 Dumbea Barrage

47 "Xanthostemon"

1956. Economic and Social Development Fund.
340 **46** 3f. green and blue 70 45

1958. Flowers.
341 **47** 4f. multicoloured . . . . . 1·25 1·40
342 – 15f. red, yellow and green 2·75 1·60
DESIGN: 15f. Hibiscus.

48 "Human Rights"

49 Zebra Lionfish

1958. 10th Anniv of Declaration of Human Rights.
343 **48** 7f. red and blue . . . . . 85 1·10

1959.
344 **49** 1f. brown and grey 45 25
345 – 2f. blue, purple and green 1·60 1·60
346 – 3f. red, blue and green . . 60 75
347 – 4f. purple, red and green 2·50 2·75
348 – 5f. bistre, blue and green 2·50 2·25
349 – 10f. multicoloured . . . . 1·25 40
350 – 26f. multicoloured . . . . 2·25 4·75
DESIGNS—HORIZ: 2f. Outrigger canoes racing; 3f. Harlequin tuskfish; 5f. Sail Rock, Noumea; 26f. Fluorescent corals. VERT: 4f. Fisherman with spear. 10f. Blue sea lizard and "Spirographe" (coral).

49a The Carved Rock, Bourail

1959. Air.
351 – 15f. green, brown and red 4·00 2·75
352 – 20f. brown and green . . 9·50 4·75
353 – 25f. black, blue and purple . . . . 9·50 3·75
354 – 50f. brown, green and blue . . . . 6·25 5·50
355 – 50f. brown, green and blue . . . . 7·75 4·00
356 – 100f. brown, green & blue 36·00 9·50
357 **49a** 200f. brown, green & blue 16·00 14·00
DESIGNS—HORIZ: 15f. Fisherman with net; 20f. New Caledonia nautilus; 25f. Underwater swimmer shooting bump-headed unicornfish; 50f. (No. 355), Isle of Pines; 100f. Corbeille de Yate. VERT: 50f. (No. 354), Yate barrage.

49b Napoleon III
49c Port-de-France, 1859

1960. Postal Centenary.
358 **15** 4f. red 75 90
359 – 5f. brown and lake . . . 65 1·50
360 – 9f. brown and turquoise 75 2·00
361 – 12f. black and blue . . . 70 2·50
362 **49b** 13f. blue . . . . 1·40 2·75
363 **49c** 19f. red, green & turquoise . . . . 1·75 1·75
364 – 33f. red, green and blue 2·25 3·25
MS364a 150 × 80 mm. Nos. 358, 362 and 364 . . . . 9·50 9·50
DESIGNS—As Type **49c**: HORIZ: 5f. Girl operating cheque-writing machine; 12f. Telephone receiver and exchange building; 33f. As Type **49c** but without stamps in upper corners. VERT: 9f. Letter-box on tree.

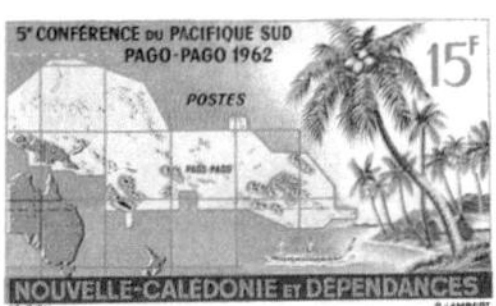

49d Map of Pacific and Palms

1962. 5th South Pacific Conference, Pago-Pago.
365 **49d** 15f. multicoloured . . . . 1·60 2·50

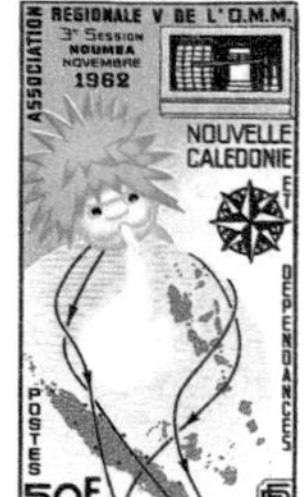

49e Map and Symbols of Meteorology

1962. 3rd Regional Assembly of World Meteorological Association, Noumea.
366 **49e** 50f. multicoloured . . . . 6·25 8·00

50 "Telstar" Satellite and part of Globe

1962. Air. 1st Transatlantic TV Satellite Link.
367 **50** 200f. turquoise, brown & bl . . . . 18·00 15·00

51 Emblem and Globe

1963. Freedom from Hunger.
368 **51** 17f. blue and purple . . . 2·25 2·50

52 Relay-running

53 Centenary Emblem

1963. 1st South Pacific Games, Suva, Fiji.
369 **52** 1f. red and green . . . . . 70 1·75
370 – 7f. brown and blue . . . . 1·00 2·00
371 – 10f. brown and green . . . 2·00 2·00
372 – 27f. blue and deep purple 4·50 4·00
DESIGNS: 7f. Tennis; 10f. Football; 27f. Throwing the javelin.

1963. Red Cross Centenary.
373 **53** 37f. red, grey and blue . . 6·75 6·75

54 Globe and Scales of Justice

54a "Bikkia fritillarioides"

1963. 15th Anniv of Declaration of Human Rights.
374 **54** 50f. red and blue . . . . . 9·25 9·00

1964. Flowers. Multicoloured.
375 1f. "Freycinettia" . . . . . 1·50 1·60
376 2f. Type **54a** . . . . 55 1·90
377 3f. "Xanthostemon francii" 1·40 2·25
378 4f. "Psidiomyrtus locellatus" 2·75 1·75
379 5f. "Callistemon suberosum" 3·25 2·75
380 7f. "Montrouziera sphaeroidea" (horiz) . . . 5·75 3·00
381 10f. "Ixora collina" (horiz) 5·75 3·00
382 17f. "Deplanchea speciosa" 5·75 4·75

54b "Ascidies polycarpa" **54c** "Philately"

1964. Corals and Marine Animals from Noumea Aquarium.
383 **54b** 7f. red, brown and blue (postage) . . . . 1·75 2·50
384 – 10f. red and blue . . . . 2·50 2·50
385 – 17f. red, green and blue 5·50 2·25
388 – 13f. bistre, black and orange (air) . . . . . 4·25 2·75
389 – 15f. green, olive and blue 6·25 3·00
390 – 25f. blue and green . . . 10·50 5·75
386 – 27f. multicoloured . . . . 6·00 4·50
387 – 37f. multicoloured . . . . 10·00 6·75
DESIGNS—As T **54b**: VERT: 10f. "Alcyonium catalai" (coral). HORIZ: 17f. "Hymenocera elegans" (crab). 48 × 28 mm: 27f. Palette surgeonfish; 37f. "Phyllobranchus" (sea slug). 48 × 27 mm: 13f. Twin-spotted wrasse (young); 15f. Twin-spotted wrasse (subadult); 25f. Twin-spotted wrasse (adult).

1964. "PHILATEC 1964" Int Stamp Exn, Paris.
391 **54c** 40f. brown, green & violet 7·00 9·25

54d Houailou Mine

1964. Air. Nickel Production at Houailou.
392 **54d** 30f. multicoloured . . . . 4·25 4·25

54e Ancient Greek Wrestling

1964. Air. Olympic Games, Tokyo.
393 **54e** 10f. sepia, mauve & green 20·00 21·00

55 Weather Satellite **56** "Syncom" Communications Satellite, Telegraph Poles and Morse Key

1965. Air. World Meteorological Day.
394 **55** 9f. multicoloured . . . . . 4·50 3·75

1965. Air. Centenary of I.T.U.
395 **56** 40f. purple, brown and blue . . . . 10·00 11·50

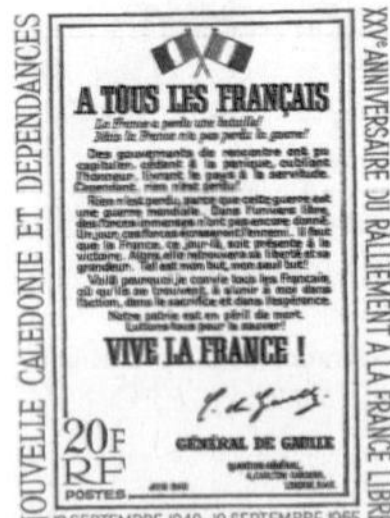
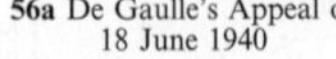

56a De Gaulle's Appeal of 18 June 1940 **56b** Amedee Lighthouse

1965. 25th Anniv of New Caledonia's Adherence to the Free French.
396 **56a** 20f. black, red and blue 10·00 9·50

1965. Inauguration of Amedee Lighthouse.
397 **56b** 8f. bistre, blue and green 1·40 2·00

56c Rocket "Diamant"

1966. Air. Launching of 1st French Satellite.
398 **56c** 8f. lake, blue and turquoise . . . . 5·25 3·25
399 – 12f. lake, blue & turquoise 4·50 4·50
DESIGN: 12f. Satellite "A1".

56d Games Emblem

1966. Publicity for 2nd South Pacific Games, Noumea.
400 **56d** 8f. black, red and blue . . 1·75 2·25

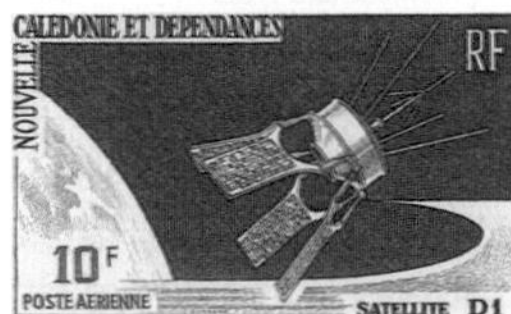

56e Satellite "D1"

1966. Air. Launching of Satellite "D1".
401 **56e** 10f. brown, blue and buff 2·00 2·50

57 Noumea, 1866 (after Lebreton)

1966. Air. Centenary of Renaming of Port-de-France as Noumea.
402 **57** 30f. slate, red and blue . . 5·00 5·00

58 Red-throated Parrot Finch **59** U.N.E.S.C.O. Allegory

1966. Birds. Multicoloured.
403 1f. Type **58** (postage) . . . . 3·00 2·50
404 1f. New Caledonian grass warbler . . . . 2·25 1·75
405 2f. New Caledonian whistler 2·75 1·75
406 3f. New Caledonian pigeon ("Notou") . . . . 4·00 2·75
407 3f. White-throated pigeon ("Collier blanc") . . . . . 3·00 2·25
408 4f. Kagu . . . . 3·00 2·25
409 5f. Horned parakeet . . . . 6·75 3·00
410 10f. Red-faced honeyeater . . 10·00 3·75
411 15f. New Caledonian friarbird . . . . 8·25 3·50
412 30f. Sacred kingfisher . . . . 11·50 6·50
413 27f. Horned parakeet (diff) (air) . . . . 6·75 4·25
414 37f. Scarlet honeyeater . . . 11·50 7·25
415 39f. Emerald dove . . . . . 14·50 5·00
416 50f. Cloven-feathered dove 19·00 19·00
417 100f. Whistling kite . . . . . 34·00 13·00
Nos. 413/14 are 26 × 45½ mm; Nos. 415/17 are 27½ × 48 mm.

1966. 20th Anniv of U.N.E.S.C.O.
418 **59** 16f. purple, ochre and green . . . . 2·75 2·50

60 High Jumping

1966. South Pacific Games, Noumea.
419 **60** 17f. violet, green and lake 3·25 1·25
420 – 20f. green, purple and lake 4·75 2·75
421 – 40f. green, violet and lake 5·75 4·00
422 – 100f. purple, turq & lake 12·00 7·50
MS423 149 × 99 mm. Nos. 419/22 35·00 35·00
DESIGNS: 20f. Hurdling; 40f. Running; 100f. Swimming.

61 Lekine Cliffs

1967.
424 **61** 17f. grey, green and blue 2·50 1·25

62 Ocean Racing Yachts

1967. Air. 2nd Whangarei–Noumea Yacht Race.
425 **62** 25f. red, blue and green . . 7·25 5·00

63 Magenta Stadium

1967. Sport Centres. Multicoloured.
426 10f. Type **63** . . . . 2·75 2·00
427 20f. Ouen-Toro swimming pool . . . . 4·00 1·60

64 New Caledonian Scenery

1967. International Tourist Year.
428 **64** 30f. multicoloured . . . . 5·75 3·50

65 19th-century Postman

1967. Stamp Day.
429 **65** 7f. red, green and turquoise 2·75 2·50

66 "Papilio montrouzieri"

1967. Butterflies and Moths.
430 **66** 7f. blue, black and green (postage) . . . . 3·00 2·50
431 – 9f. blue, brown and mauve 4·25 2·25
432 – 13f. violet, purple & brown 5·00 3·00
433 – 15f. yellow, purple and blue . . . . 8·25 4·00
434 – 19f. orange, brown and green (air) . . . . 7·25 3·25
435 – 29f. purple, red and blue 10·00 6·50
436 – 85f. brown, red and yellow 23·00 12·00
BUTTERFLIES—As T **66**: 9f. "Polyura clitarchus"; 13f. Common eggfly (male), and 15f. (female). 48 × 27 mm: 19f. Orange tiger; 29f. Silver-striped hawk moth; 85f. "Dellas elipsis".

67 Garnierite (mineral), Factory and Jules Garnier

1967. Air. Centenary of Garnierite Industry.
437 **67** 70f. multicoloured . . . . 9·75 7·50

67a Lifou Island

1967. Air.
438 **67a** 200f. multicoloured . . . 19·00 12·50

67b Skier and Snow-crystal

1967. Air. Winter Olympic Games, Grenoble.
439 **67b** 100f. brown, blue & green 18·00 12·50

68 Bouquet, Sun and W.H.O. Emblem **69** Human Rights Emblem

1968. 20th Anniv of W.H.O.
440 **68** 20f. blue, red and violet . . 3·00 2·00

1968. Human Rights Year.
441 **69** 12f. red, green and yellow 1·75 2·50

70 Ferrying Mail Van across Tontouta River

1968. Stamp Day.
442 **70** 9f. brown, blue and green 2·50 2·75

71 Geography Cone **72** Dancers

1968. Sea Shells.
443 – 1f. brn, grey & grn (postage) . . . . 2·25 2·00
444 – 1f. purple and violet . . . 2·00 2·00
445 – 2f. purple, red and blue . . 2·25 2·25
446 – 3f. brown and green . . . 2·25 1·90
447 – 5f. red, brown and violet 2·75 85
448 **71** 10f. brown, grey and blue 2·75 2·00
449 – 10f. yellow, brown and red 3·75 2·00
450 – 10f. black, brown & orange 3·25 2·25
451 – 15f. red, grey and green . . 6·00 3·00
452 – 21f. brown, sepia and green 6·50 2·75
453 – 22f. red, brown & blue (air) . . . . 6·25 3·25
454 – 25f. brown and red . . . . 4·00 3·50
455 – 33f. brown and blue . . . 8·00 4·50
456 – 34f. violet, brown & orange 7·75 3·50
457 – 39f. brown, grey and green 7·50 3·75
458 – 40f. black, brown and red 7·00 4·00
459 – 50f. red, purple and green 7·25 5·00
460 – 60f. brown and green . . . 16·00 8·00
461 – 70f. brown, grey and violet 17·00 8·00
462 – 100f. brown, black and blue . . . . 30·00 18·00
DESIGNS—VERT: 1f. (No. 443) Swan conch ("Strombus epidromis"); 1f. (No. 444) Scorpion conch ("Lambis scorpius"); 3f. Common spider conch; 10f. (No. 450) Variable conch ("Strombus variabilis"). 27 × 48 mm: 22f. Laciniate cone; 25f. Orange spider conch; 34f. Vomer conch; 50f. Chiragra spider conch. 36 × 22 mm: 2f. Snipe's-bill murex; 5f. Troschel's murex; 10f. (No. 449) Sieve cowrie; 15f. "Murex sp."; 21f. Mole cowrie. 48 × 27 mm: 33f. Eyed cowrie; 39f. Lienardi's cone; 40f. Cabrit's cone; 60f. All-red map cowrie; 70f. Scarlet cone; 100f. Adusta murex.

1968. Air.
463 **72** 60f. red, blue and green . . 11·00 7·25

73 Rally Car

1968. 2nd New Caledonian Motor Safari.
464 **73** 25f. blue, red and green . . 5·25 3·50

74 Caudron C-60 "Aiglon" and Route Map

1969. Air. Stamp Day. 30th Anniv of 1st Noumea–Paris Flight by Martinet and Klein.
465 **74** 29f. red, blue and violet . . 4·50 2·50

75 Concorde in Flight

1969. Air. 1st Flight of Concorde.
466 **75** 100f. green and light green 26·00 27·00

76 Cattle-dip

1969. Cattle-breeding in New Caledonia.
467 **76** 9f. brown, green and blue (postage) . . . . 2·50 2·25
468 – 25f. violet, brown and green . . . . 4·25 2·75
469 – 50f. purple, red & grn (air) 7·00 4·50
DESIGNS: 25f. Branding. LARGER 48 × 27 mm; 50f. Stockman with herd.

77 Judo

1969. 3rd South Pacific Games, Port Moresby, Papua New Guinea.
470 **77** 19f. purple, bl & red (post) 3·00 1·50
471 – 20f. black, red and green 4·00 2·75
472 – 30f. black and blue (air) . . 6·00 3·50
473 – 39f. brown, green and black . . . . 9·50 4·50
DESIGNS—HORIZ: 20f. Boxing; 30f. Diving (38 × 27 mm). VERT: 39f. Putting the shot (27 × 48 mm).

1969. Air. Birth Bicentenary of Napoleon Bonaparte. As T **114b** of Mauritania. Multicoloured.
474 40f. "Napoleon in Coronation Robes" (Gerard) (vert) . . . . . . 26·00 16·00

78 Douglas DC-4 over Outrigger Canoe

1969. Air. 20th Anniv of Regular Noumea–Paris Air Service.
475 **78** 50f. green, brown and blue 8·00 5·00

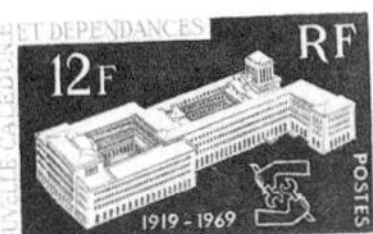

79 I.L.O. Building Geneva

1969. 50th Anniv of I.L.O.
476 **79** 12f. brown, violet & salmon . . . . 2·25 2·50

80 "French Wings around the World"

1970. Air. 10th Anniv of French "Around the World" Air Service.
477 **80** 200f. brown, blue and violet . . . . 26·00 10·50

81 New U.P.U. Building, Berne

1970. Inauguration of New U.P.U. Headquarters Building, Berne.
478 **81** 12f. red, grey and brown 2·75 2·25

82 Packet Steamer "Natal", 1883

1970. Stamp Day.
479 **82** 9f. black, green and blue 5·25 3·25

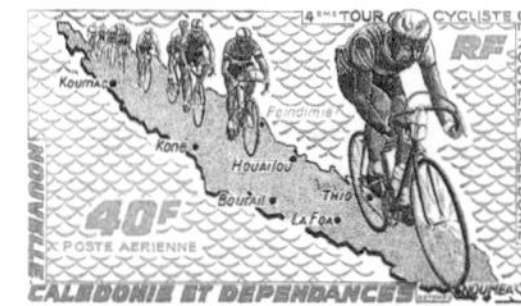

83 Cyclists on Map

1970. Air. 4th "Tour de Nouvelle Caledonie" Cycle Race.
480 **83** 40f. brown, blue & lt blue 6·25 4·00

84 Mt. Fuji and Japanese "Hikari" Express Train

1970. Air. "EXPO 70" World Fair, Osaka, Japan. Multicoloured.
481 20f. Type **84** . . . . 4·25 2·75
482 45f. "EXPO" emblem, map and Buddha . . . . 6·00 3·00

85 Racing Yachts

1971. Air. One Ton Cup Yacht Race Auckland, New Zealand.
483 **85** 20f. green, red and black 4·50 2·25

86 Steam Mail Train, Dumbea

1971. Stamp Day.
484 **86** 10f. black, green and red 4·00 2·75

87 Ocean Racing Yachts

1971. 3rd Whangarei–Noumea Ocean Yacht Race.
485 **87** 16f. turquoise, green and blue . . . . 5·25 3·25

88 Lieut.-Col. Broche and Theatre Map

1971. 30th Anniv of French Pacific Battalion's Participation in Second World War Mediterranean Campaign.
486 **88** 60f. multicoloured . . . . 8·75 6·00

89 Early Tape Machine 90 Weightlifting

1971. World Telecommunications Day.
487 **89** 19f. orange, purple and red 3·75 2·50

1971. 4th South Pacific Games, Papeete, French Polynesia.
488 **90** 11f. brown & red (postage) 2·75 2·75
489 – 23f. violet, red and blue . . 4·00 1·10
490 – 25f. green and red (air) . . 4·00 3·50
491 – 100f. blue, green and red 8·25 5·00
DESIGNS—VERT: 23f. Basketball. HORIZ: 48 × 27 mm: 25f. Pole-vaulting; 100f. Archery.

91 Port de Plaisance, Noumea

1971. Air.
492 **91** 200f. multicoloured . . . . 25·00 12·50

92 De Gaulle as President of French Republic, 1970

93 Publicity Leaflet showing De Havilland Gipsy Moth "Golden Eagle"

1971. 1st Death Anniv of General De Gaulle.
493 **92** 34f. black and purple . . . 8·50 3·75
494 – 100f. black and purple . . 17·00 10·00
DESIGN: 100f. De Gaulle in uniform, 1940.

1971. Air. 40th Anniv of 1st New Caledonia to Australia Flight.
495 **93** 90f. brown, blue and orange . . . . 13·00 7·25

94 Downhill Skiing

1972. Air. Winter Olympic Games, Sapporo, Japan.
496 **94** 50f. green, red and blue . . 4·50 4·25

95 St. Mark's Basilica, Venice

1972. Air. U.N.E.S.C.O. "Save Venice" Campaign.
497 **95** 20f. brown, green and blue 4·75 3·00

96 Commission Headquarters, Noumea

1972. Air. 25th Anniv of South Pacific Commission.
498 **96** 18f. multicoloured . . . . 3·00 2·50

97 Couzinet 33 "Le Biarritz" and Noumea Monument

1972. Air. 40th Anniv of 1st Paris–Noumea Flight.
499 **97** 110f. black, purple & green 3·00 2·75

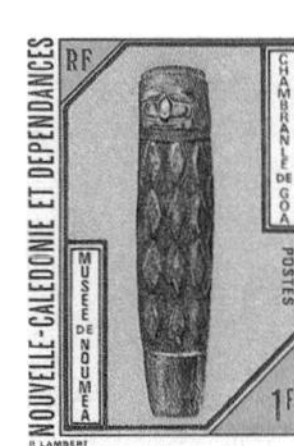

98 Pacific Island Dwelling 99 Goa Door-post

1972. Air. South Pacific Arts Festival, Fiji.
500 **98** 24f. brown, blue and orange . . . . 4·50 3·00

1972. Exhibits from Noumea Museum.
501 **99** 1f. red, green & grey (post) 1·75 1·75
502 – 2f. black, green & deep grn 1·60 1·75
503 – 5f. multicoloured . . . . . 2·25 2·00
504 – 12f. multicoloured . . . . 4·00 2·75
505 – 16f. multicoloured (air) . . 3·25 2·75
506 – 40f. multicoloured . . . . 5·00 3·00
DESIGNS: 2f. Carved wooden pillow; 5f. Monstrance; 12f. Tchamba mask; 16f. Ornamental arrowheads; 40f. Portico, chief's house.

100 Hurdling over "H" of "MUNICH"

1972. Air. Olympic Games, Munich.
507 **100** 72f. violet, purple and blue . . . . 11·00 6·25

101 New Head Post Office Building, Noumea

1972. Air.
508 **101** 23f. brown, blue and green . . . . 4·00 2·50

102 J.C.I. Emblem

1972. 10th Anniv of New Caledonia Junior Chamber of Commerce.
509 **102** 12f. multicoloured . . . . 2·75 2·50

103 Forest Scene

1973. Air. Landscapes of the East Coast. Multicoloured.
510 11f. Type **103** . . . . 2·75 2·25
511 18f. Beach and palms (vert) 4·25 2·75
512 21f. Waterfall and inlet (vert) 5·25 3·00
See also Nos. 534/6.

104 Moliere and Characters

1973. Air. 300th Death Anniv of Moliere (playwright).
513 **104** 50f. multicoloured . . . . 7·50 4·50

105 Tchamba Mask

1973.
514 **105** 12f. purple (postage) . . . 4·25 3·00
515 – 23f. blue (air) . . . . . . 9·25 7·00
DESIGN: 23f. Concorde in flight.

106 Liner "El Kantara" in Panama Canal

1973. 50th Anniv of Marseilles–Noumea Shipping Service via Panama Canal.
516 **106** 60f. black, brown & green 9·75 6·50

107 Globe and Allegory of Weather

1973. Air. Centenary of World Meteorological Organization.
517 **107** 80f. multicoloured . . . . 9·50 4·75

108 DC-10 in Flight

1973. Air. Inauguration of Noumea–Paris DC-10 Air Service.
518 **108** 100f. green, brown & blue 11·50 6·25

109 Common Egg Cowrie

1973. Marine Fauna from Noumea Aquarium. Multicoloured.
519 8f. Black-wedged butterflyfish (daylight) . . . . 2·75 2·25
520 14f. Black-wedged butterflyfish (nocturnal) . . 3·25 2·75
521 3f. Type **109** (air) . . . . . 2·25 2·00
522 32f. Orange-spotted surgeonfish (adult and young) . . . . 7·00 3·50
523 32f. Green-lined paper bubble ("Hydatina") . . . . . . 4·50 3·25
524 37f. Pacific partridge tun ("Dolium perdix") . . . . 6·00 3·25

111 Office Emblem

1973. 10th Anniv of Central Schools Co-operation Office.
532 **111** 20f. blue, yellow and green . . . . 2·75 2·50

112 New Caledonia Mail Coach, 1880

1973. Air. Stamp Day.
533 **112** 15f. multicoloured . . . . 3·50 2·00

1974. Air. Landscapes of the West Coast. As T **103**. Multicoloured.
534 8f. Beach and palms (vert) . . 2·50 2·25
535 22f. Trees and mountain . . 3·25 2·50
536 26f. Trees growing in sea . . 3·75 2·75

113 Centre Building

1974. Air. Opening of Scientific Studies Centre, Anse-Vata, Noumea.
537 **113** 50f. multicoloured . . . . 4·50 3·00

114 "Bird" embracing Flora

1974. Nature Conservation.
538 **114** 7f. multicoloured . . . . 1·90 1·90

115 18th-century French Sailor

1974. Air. Discovery and Reconnaissance of New Caledonia and Loyalty Islands.
539 – 20f. violet, red and blue 3·25 2·50
540 – 25f. green, brown and red 3·25 2·75
541 **115** 28f. brown, blue and green . . . . 3·25 2·75
542 – 30f. blue, brown and red 4·00 3·00
543 – 36f. red, brown and blue 6·25 3·75
DESIGNS—HORIZ: 20f. Captain Cook, H.M.S. "Endeavour" and map of Grand Terre island; 25f. La Perouse, "L'Astrolabe" and map of Grand Terre island (reconnaissance of west coast); 30f. Entrecasteaux, ship and map of Grand Terre island (reconnaissance of west coast); 36f. Dumont d'Urville, "L'Astrolabe" and map of Loyalty Islands.

116 "Telecommunications"

1974. Air. Centenary of U.P.U.
544 **116** 95f. orange, purple & grey 8·25 5·00

117 "Art"

1974. Air. "Arphila 75" International Stamp Exhibition, Paris (1975) (1st issue).
545 **117** 80f. multicoloured . . . . 6·00 4·00
See also No. 554.

118 Hotel Chateau-Royal

1974. Air. Inauguration of Hotel Chateau Royal, Noumea.
546 **118** 22f. multicoloured . . . . 3·00 3·25

118a Animal Skull, Burnt Tree and Flaming Landscape

1975. "Stop Bush Fires".
547 **118a** 20f. multicoloured . . . 1·90 2·25

119 "Cricket"

1975. Air. Tourism. Multicoloured.
548 3f. Type **119** . . . . 2·25 2·00
549 25f. "Bougna" ceremony . . 3·25 2·25
550 31f. "Pilou" native dance . . 4·00 2·50

120 "Calanthe veratrifolia"

121 Global "Flower"

1975. New Caledonian Orchids. Multicoloured.
551 8f. Type **120** (postage) . . . 2·50 2·00
552 11f. "Lyperanthus gigas" . . 2·75 2·25
553 42f. "Eriaxis rigida" (air) . . 6·25 3·50

1975. Air. "Arphila 75" International Stamp Exhibition, Paris (2nd issue).
554 **121** 105f. purple, green & blue 9·50 5·00

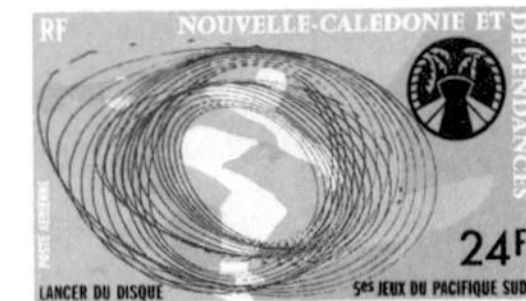

122 Throwing the Discus

1975. Air. 5th South Pacific Games, Guam.
555 24f. Type **122** . . . . 3·25 2·50
556 50f. Volleyball . . . . 4·50 3·00

123 Festival Emblem **124** Birds in Flight

1975. "Melanesia 2000" Festival, Noumea.
557 **123** 12f. multicoloured . . . . 1·90 1·90

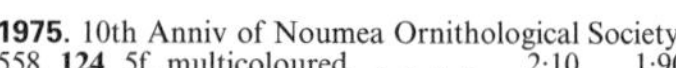

1975. 10th Anniv of Noumea Ornithological Society.
558 **124** 5f. multicoloured . . . . 2·10 1·90

125 Pres. Pompidou **127** Brown Booby

126 Concordes

1975. Pompidou Commemoration.
559 **125** 26f. grey and green . . . 3·00 2·50

1976. Air. First Commercial Flight of Concorde.
560 **126** 147f. blue and red . . . . 18·00 11·00

1976. Ocean Birds. Multicoloured.
561 1f. Type **127** . . . . 1·25 2·00
562 2f. Blue-faced booby . . . . 1·50 1·90
563 8f. Red-footed booby (vert) 2·75 2·50

128 Festival Emblem

1976. South Pacific Festival of Arts, Rotorua, New Zealand.
564 **128** 27f. multicoloured . . . . 3·00 2·50

129 Lion and Lions' Emblem

130 Early and Modern Telephones

1976. 15th Anniv of Lions Club, Noumea.
565 **129** 49f. multicoloured . . . . 5·00 3·50

1976. Air. Telephone Centenary.
566 **130** 36f. multicoloured . . . . 3·75 2·75

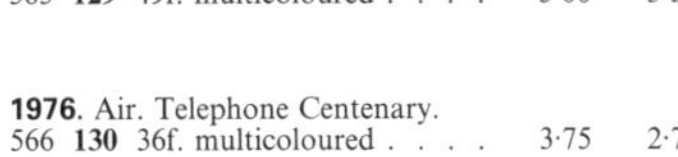

131 Capture of Penboscht

1976. Air. Bicent of American Revolution.
567 **131** 24f. purple and brown . . 3·00 2·75

132 Bandstand

1976. "Aspects of Old Noumea". Multicoloured.
568 25f. Type **132** . . . . 2·25 2·25
569 30f. Monumental fountain (vert) . . . . 2·50 3·25

133 Athletes

1976. Air. Olympic Games, Montreal.
570 **133** 33f. violet, red and purple 3·50 2·75

134 "Chick" with Magnifier

1976. Air. "Philately in Schools", Stamp Exhibition, Noumea.
571 **134** 42f. multicoloured . . . . 4·50 3·00

135 Dead Bird and Trees

1976. Nature Protection.
572 **135** 20f. multicoloured . . . . 2·25 2·25

136 South Pacific Heads

1976. 16th South Pacific Commission Conference.
573 **136** 20f. multicoloured . . . . 2·75 2·25

137 Old Town Hall, Noumea

1976. Air. Old and New Town Halls, Noumea. Mult.
574 75f. Type **137** . . . . 6·50 4·50
575 125f. New Town Hall . . . . 11·00 5·00

138 Water Carnival

1977. Air. Summer Festival, Noumea.
576 **138** 11f. multicoloured . . . . 3·50 1·90

139 "Pseudophyllanax imperialis" (cricket)

1977. Insects.
577 **139** 26f. emerald, green & brn 2·75 2·75
578 – 31f. brown, sepia & green 3·75 2·50
DESIGN: 31f. "Agrianome fairmairei" (long-horn beetle).

140 Miniature Roadway

1977. Air. Road Safety.
579 **140** 50f. multicoloured . . . . 4·25 2·75

141 Earth Station

1977. Earth Satellite Station, Noumea.
580 **141** 29f. multicoloured . . . . 2·75 2·25

142 "Phajus daenikeri"

1977. Orchids. Multicoloured.
581 22f. Type **142** . . . . 2·75 2·25
582 44f. "Dendrobium finetianum" . . . . 4·25 3·00

143 Mask and Palms

1977. La Perouse School Philatelic Exn.
583 **143** 35f. multicoloured . . . . 2·75 2·75

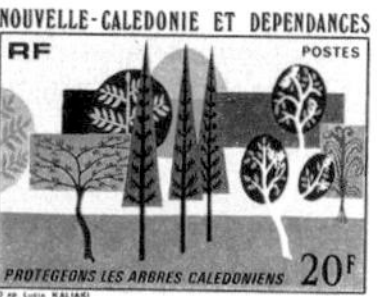

144 Trees

1977. Nature Protection.
584 **144** 20f. multicoloured . . . . 1·75 2·25

145 Palm Tree and Emblem

1977. French Junior Chambers of Commerce Congress.
585 **145** 200f. multicoloured . . . 12·00 9·00

146 Young Bird

1977. Great Frigate Birds. Multicoloured.
586 16f. Type **146** (postage) . . . 1·50 2·25
587 42f. Adult male bird (horiz) (air) . . . . 4·50 3·50

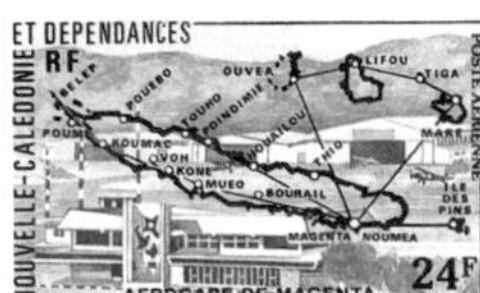

147 Magenta Airport and Map of Internal Air Network

1977. Air. Airports. Multicoloured.
588 24f. Type **147** . . . . 2·75 2·25
589 57f. La Tontout International Airport, Noumea . . . . 4·50 3·25

1977. Air. 1st Commercial Flight of Concorde, Paris–New York. Optd **22.11.77 PARIS NEW-YORK**.
590 **126** 147f. blue and red . . . . 19·00 16·00

149 Horse and Foal

1977. 10th Anniv of S.E.C.C. (Horse-breeding Society).
591 **149** 5f. brown, green and blue 2·25 1·90

150 "Moselle Bay" (H. Didonna)

1977. Air. Views of Old Noumea (1st series).
592 **150** 41f. multicoloured . . . . 4·50 3·25
593 – 42f. purple and brown . . 4·50 3·25
DESIGN—49 × 27 mm: 42f. "Settlers Valley" (J. Kreber).

151 Black-naped Tern

1978. Ocean Birds. Multicoloured.
594 22f. Type **151** . . . . 2·00 2·25
595 40f. Sooty tern . . . . 4·00 3·25

152 "Araucaria montana"

153 "Halityle regularis"

1978. Flora. Multicoloured.
596 16f. Type **152** (postage) . . . 2·00 2·00
597 42f. "Amyema scandens" (horiz) (air) . . . . 3·75 2·50

1978. Noumea Aquarium.
598 **153** 10f. multicoloured . . . . 2·25 1·75

154 Turtle

1978. Protection of the Turtle.
599 **154** 30f. multicoloured . . . . 2·50 2·50

155 New Caledonian Flying Fox

1978. Nature Protection.
600 **155** 20f. multicoloured . . . . 2·50 2·25

156 "Underwater Carnival"

1978. Air. Aubusson Tapestry.
601 **156** 105f. multicoloured . . . 6·75 4·00

157 Pastor Maurice Leenhardt

1978. Birth Centenary of Pastor Maurice Leenhardt.
602 **157** 37f. sepia, green & orange 3·00 2·75

158 Hare chasing "Stamp" Tortoise

1978. School Philately (1st series).
603 **158** 35f. multicoloured . . . . 4·00 3·00

159 Heads, Map, Magnifying Glass and Cone Shell

1978. Air. Thematic Philately at Bourail.
604 **159** 41f. multicoloured . . . . 3·25 2·75

160 Candles

161 Footballer and League Badge

1978. 3rd New Caledonian Old People's Day.
605 **160** 36f. multicoloured . . . . 2·50 2·25

1978. 50th Anniv of New Caledonian Football League.
606 **161** 26f. multicoloured . . . . 2·50 2·25

162 "Fauberg Blanchot" (after Lacouture)

1978. Air. Views of Old Noumea.
607 **162** 24f. multicoloured . . . . 2·00 2·25

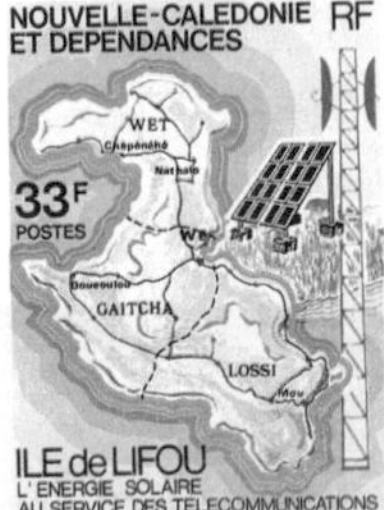
163 Map of Lifou, Solar Energy Panel and Transmitter Mast

1978. Telecommunications through Solar Energy.
608 **163** 33f. multicoloured . . . . 2·75 2·50

164 Petroglyph, Mere Region

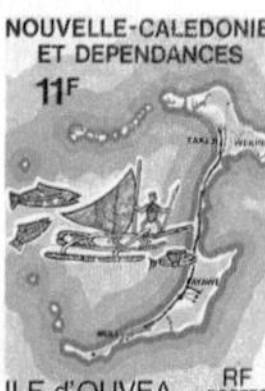
165 Ouvea Island and Outrigger Canoe

1979. Archaeological Sites.
609 **164** 10f. red . . . . 1·90 1·25

1979. Islands. Multicoloured.
610 11f. Type **165** . . . . 2·25 1·75
611 31f. Mare Island and ornaments (horiz) . . . . 1·75 1·10
See also Nos. 629 and 649.

166 Satellite Orbit of Earth

167 19th-century Barque and Modern Container Ship

1979. Air. 1st World Survey of Global Atmosphere.
612 **166** 53f. multicoloured . . . . 3·25 2·75

1979. Air. Centenary of Chamber of Commerce and Industry.
613 **167** 49f. mauve, blue & brown 3·25 2·50

168 Child's Drawing

1979. Air. International Year of the Child.
614 **168** 35f. multicoloured . . . . 3·25 2·50

169 House at Artillery Point

1979. Views of Old Noumea.
615 **169** 20f. multicoloured . . . . 2·25 1·75

170 Skipjack Tuna

1979. Air. Sea Fishes (1st series). Multicoloured.
616 29f. Type **170** . . . . 2·75 2·25
617 30f. Black marlin . . . . . . 2·75 2·25
See also Nos. 632/3 and 647/8.

171 L. Tardy de Montravel (founder) and View of Port-de-France (Noumea)

1979. Air. 125th Anniv of Noumea.
618 **171** 75f. multicoloured . . . . 4·75 3·25

172 The Eel Queen (Kanaka legend)

173 Auguste Escoffier

1979. Air. Nature Protection.
619 **172** 42f. multicoloured . . . . 3·75 3·00

1979. Auguste Escoffier Hotel School.
620 **173** 24f. brown, green and turquoise . . . . 2·25 2·25

174 Games Emblem and Catamarans

1979. 6th South Pacific Games, Fiji.
621 **174** 16f. multicoloured . . . . 2·25 1·10

175 Children of Different Races, Map and Postmark

1979. Air. Youth Philately.
622 **175** 27f. multicoloured . . . . 2·25 2·00

176 Aerial View of Centre

1979. Air. Overseas Scientific and Technical Research Office (O.R.S.T.O.M.) Centre, Noumea.
623 **176** 25f. multicoloured . . . . 2·50 2·25

177 "Agathis ovata"

1979. Trees. Multicoloured.
624 5f. Type **177** . . . . 1·60 1·90
625 34f. "Cyathea intermedia" . . 2·50 2·25

178 Rodeo Riding

1979. Pouembout Rodeo.
626 **178** 12f. multicoloured . . . . 2·25 1·75

179 Hill, 1860 10c. Stamp and Post Office

1979. Air. Death Centenary of Sir Rowland Hill.
627 **179** 150f. black, brown & orge 7·75 4·50

180 "Bantamia merleti"

1980. Noumea Aquarium. Fluorescent Corals (1st issue).
628 **180** 23f. multicoloured . . . . 2·50 1·75
See also No. 646.

1980. Islands. As T **165**. Multicoloured.
629 23f. Map of Ile des Pins and ornaments (horiz) . . . . 1·90 1·25

181 Outrigger Canoe

1980. Air.
630 **181** 45f. blue, turq & indigo 2·75 2·25

182 Globe, Rotary Emblem, Map and Carving

1980. Air. 75th Anniv of Rotary International.
631 **182** 100f. multicoloured . . . 5·50 3·25

1980. Air. Sea Fishes (2nd series). As T **170**. Multicoloured.
632 34f. Angler holding dolphin (fish) . . . . 2·25 1·90
633 39f. Fishermen with sailfish (vert) . . . . 2·75 2·00

183 "Hibbertia virotii"

184 High Jumper, Magnifying Glass, Albums and Plimsoll

1980. Flowers. Multicoloured.
634 11f. Type **183** . . . . 1·60 85
635 12f. "Grevillea meisneri" . . 1·60 1·40

1980. School Philately.
636 **184** 30f. multicoloured . . . . 1·90 1·50

185 Scintex Super Emeraude Airplane and Map

1980. Air. Coral Sea Air Rally.
637 **185** 31f. blue, green and brown . . . . 2·00 1·90

186 Sailing Canoe

1980. Air. South Pacific Arts Festival, Port Moresby.
638 **186** 27f. multicoloured . . . . 1·90 1·75

187 Road Signs as Road-users

1980. Road Safety.
639 **187** 15f. multicoloured . . . . 1·60 1·10

188 "Parribacus caledonicus"

1980. Noumea Aquarium. Marine Animals (1st series). Multicoloured.
640 5f. Type **188** . . . . 1·00 30
641 8f. "Panulirus versicolor" . . 1·25 1·10
See also Nos. 668/9.

189 Kiwanis Emblem

1980. Air. 10th Anniv of Noumea Kiwanis Club.
642 **189** 50f. multicoloured . . . . 2·75 2·25

190 Sun, Tree and Solar Panel

1980. Nature Protection. Solar Energy.
643 **190** 23f. multicoloured . . . . 1·90 1·60

191 Old House, Poulou

1980. Air. Views of Old Noumea (4th series).
644 **191** 33f. multicoloured . . . . 1·90 1·75

192 Charles de Gaulle **193** Manta Ray

1980. Air. 10th Death Anniv of Charles de Gaulle (French statesman).
645 **192** 120f. green, olive and blue 8·00 4·25

1981. Air. Noumea Aquarium. Fluorescent Corals (2nd series). As T **180**. Multicoloured.
646 60f. "Trachyphyllia geoffroyi" . . . . 3·00 2·00

1981. Sea Fishes (3rd series). Multicoloured.
647 23f. Type **193** . . . . 1·75 1·50
648 25f. Grey reef shark . . . . 1·75 1·50

1981. Islands. As T **165**. Multicoloured.
649 26f. Map of Belep Archipelago and diver (horiz) . . . . 1·75 1·40

194 "Xeronema moorei"

1981. Air. Flowers. Multicoloured.
650 38f. Type **194** . . . . 2·00 1·50
651 51f. "Geissois pruinosa" . . 2·00 1·75

195 Yuri Gagarin and "Vostok 1"

1981. Air. 20th Anniv of First Men in Space. Multicoloured.
652 64f. Type **195** . . . . 2·75 2·50
653 155f. Alan Shepard and "Freedom 7" . . . . . . 6·75 4·25
MS654 149 × 119 mm. As Nos. 652/3 but colours changed (sold at 225f.) 13·00 13·50

196 Liberation Cross, "Zealandia" (troopship) and Badge

1981. Air. 40th Anniv of Departure of Pacific Battalion for Middle East.
655 **196** 29f. multicoloured . . . . 2·75 1·75

197 Rossini's Volute **198** Sail Corvette "Constantine"

1981. Shells. Multicoloured.
656 1f. Type **197** . . . . 95 1·00
657 2f. Clouded cone . . . . . . 90 1·10
658 13f. Stolid cowrie (horiz) . . 1·75 1·25

1981. Ships (1st series).
659 **198** 10f. blue, brown and red 1·50 1·25
660 – 25f. blue, brown and red 2·00 1·75
DESIGN: 25f. Paddle-gunboat "Le Phoque", 1853.
See also Nos. 680/1 and 725/6.

199 "Echinometra mathaei"

1981. Air. Water Plants. Multicoloured.
661 38f. Type **199** . . . . 1·90 1·60
662 51f. "Prionocidaris verticillata" . . . . 2·50 1·75

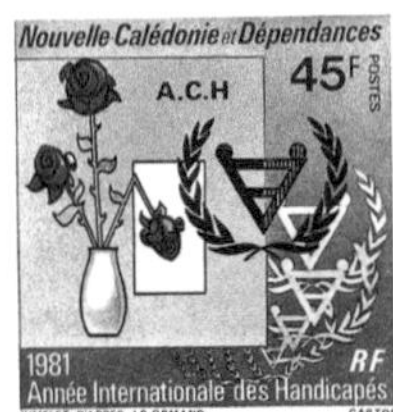

200 Broken-stemmed Rose and I.Y.D.P. Emblems

1981. International Year of Disabled Persons.
663 **200** 45f. multicoloured . . . . 2·75 1·90

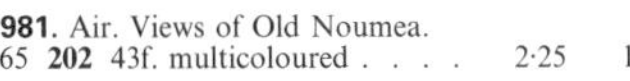
201 25c. Surcharged Stamp of 1881 **202** Latin Quarter

1981. Air. Stamp Day.
664 **201** 41f. multicoloured . . . . 2·25 1·75

1981. Air. Views of Old Noumea.
665 **202** 43f. multicoloured . . . . 2·25 1·75

203 Trees and Unicornfish **204** Victor Roffey and "Golden Eagle"

1981. Nature Protection.
666 **203** 28f. blue, green and brown . . . . 1·75 1·75

1981. Air. 50th Anniv of First New Caledonia–Australia Airmail Flight.
667 **204** 37f. black, violet and blue 2·00 1·60

1982. Noumea Aquarium. Marine Animals (2nd series). As T **188**. Multicoloured.
668 13f. "Calappa calappa" . . . 1·00 1·40
669 25f. "Etisus splendidus" . . . 1·50 90

205 "La Rousette"

1982. Air. New Caledonian Aircraft (1st series).
670 **205** 38f. brown, red and green 1·90 1·50
671 – 51f. brown, orange & grn 2·25 1·75
DESIGN: 51f. "Le Cagou".
See also Nos. 712/13.

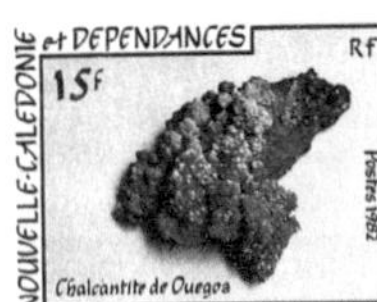

206 Chalcantite, Ouegoa

1982. Rocks and Minerals (1st series). Multicoloured.
672 15f. Type **206** . . . . 1·90 1·25
673 30f. Anorthosite, Blue River 2·50 1·75
See also Nos. 688/9.

207 De Verneilh, Deve and Munch (air crew), Couzinet 33 "Le Biarritz" and Route Map

1982. Air. 50th Anniv of First Flight from Paris to Noumea.
674 **207** 250f. mauve, blue and black . . . . 9·75 5·00

208 Scout and Guide Badges and Map

1982. Air. 50th Anniv of New Caledonian Scout Movement.
675 **208** 40f. multicoloured . . . . 2·00 1·75

209 "The Rat and the Octopus" (Canaque legend)

1982. "Philexfrance 82" International Stamp Exhibition, Paris.
676 **209** 150f. blue, mauve and deep blue . . . . . . 5·25 4·00

210 Footballer, Mascot and Badge

1982. Air. World Cup Football Championship, Spain.
677 **210** 74f. multicoloured . . . . 3·00 1·75

211 Savanna Trees at Niaoulis **212** Islanders, Map and Kagu

1982. Flora. Multicoloured.
678 20f. Type **211** . . . . 1·75 1·40
679 29f. "Melaleuca quinquenervia" (horiz) . . 2·00 1·10

1982. Ships (2nd series). As T **198**.
680 44f. blue, purple and brown 1·90 1·75
681 59f. blue, light brown and brown . . . . 2·50 1·90
DESIGNS: 44f. Naval transport barque "Le Cher"; 59f. Sloop "Kersaint", 1902.

1982. Air. Overseas Week.
682 **212** 100f. brown, green & blue 2·50 2·25

213 Ateou Tribal House **214** Grey's Fruit Dove

1982. Traditional Houses.
683 **213** 52f. multicoloured . . . . 2·75 2·00

1982. Birds. Multicoloured.
684 32f. Type **214** . . . . 1·75 1·75
685 35f. Rainbow lory . . . . . 1·75 1·75

215 Canoe

1982. Central Education Co-operation Office.
686 **215** 48f. multicoloured . . . . 2·50 1·75

216 Bernheim and Library

1982. Bernheim Library, Noumea.
687 **216** 36f. brown, purple & blk 1·90 1·50

1983. Air. Rocks and Minerals (2nd series). As T **206**. Multicoloured.
688 44f. Paya gypsum (vert) . . . 2·25 1·90
689 59f. Kone silica (vert) . . . . 2·75 2·00

217 "Dendrobium oppositifolium"

1983. Orchids. Multicoloured.
690 10f. Type **217** . . . . 1·10 60
691 15f. "Dendrobium munificum" . . . . 1·25 1·00
692 29f. "Dendrobium fractiflexum" . . . . . . 1·75 90

218 W.C.Y. Emblem, Map of New Caledonia and Globe

1983. Air. World Communications Year.
693 **218** 170f. multicoloured . . . 6·25 3·75

219 "Crinum asiaticum"

1983. Flowers. Multicoloured.
694 1f. Type **219** 45 55
695 2f. "Xanthostemon aurantiacum" . . . . . . 45 1·00
696 4f. "Metrosideros demonstrans" (vert) . . . 45 55

220 Wall Telephone and Noumea Post Office, 1890

1983. 25th Anniv of Post and Telecommunications Office. Multicoloured.
697 30f. Type **220** . . . . 1·75 75
698 40f. Telephone and Noumea Post Office, 1936 . . . . . 1·90 1·25
699 50f. Push-button telephone and Noumea Post Office, 1972 . . . . 2·50 1·40
MS700 114 × 94 mm. As Nos. 697/9 but colours changed . . . . . 11·00 12·00

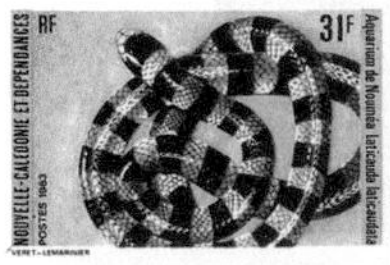

221 "Laticaudata laticaudata"

224 Volleyball

223 Bangkok Temples

1983. Noumea Aquarium. Sea Snakes. Multicoloured.
701 31f. Type **221** . . . . 1·75 1·25
702 33f. "Laticauda colubrina" 2·00 1·40

1983. Air. New Caledonian Aircraft (2nd series). As T **205**. Each red, mauve & brown.
712 46f. Mignet HM14 "Pou du Ciel" . . . . 2·00 1·75
713 61f. Caudron C-600 "Aiglon" 2·50 1·90

1983. Air. "Bangkok 1983" International Stamp Exhibition.
714 **223** 47f. multicoloured . . . . 2·00 1·90

1983. 7th South Pacific Games, Western Samoa.
715 **224** 16f. purple, blue and red 1·75 1·40

225 Oueholle

1983. Air.
716 **225** 76f. multicoloured . . . . 2·75 2·25

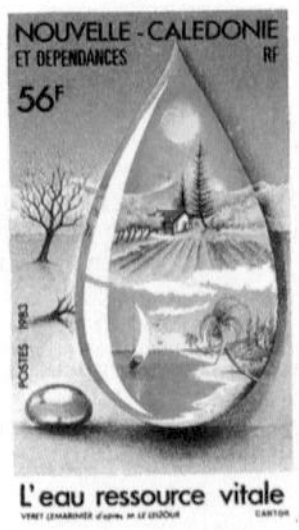

226 Desert and Water Drop showing Fertile Land

227 Barn Owl

1983. Water Resources.
717 **226** 56f. multicoloured . . . . 2·75 1·50

1983. Birds of Prey. Multicoloured.
718 34f. Type **227** . . . . 1·90 1·90
719 37f. Osprey . . . . 3·25 2·25

228 "Young Man on Beach" (R. Mascart)

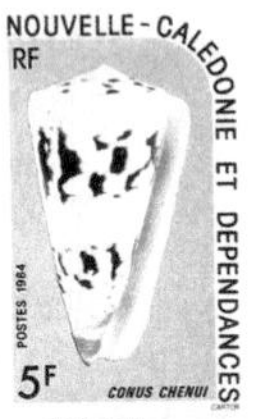

229 "Conus chenui"

1983. Air. Paintings. Multicoloured.
720 100f. Type **228** . . . . . . 4·00 3·00
721 350f. "Man with Guitar" (P. Nielly) . . . . 13·00 6·25

1984. Sea Shells (1st series). Multicoloured.
722 5f. Type **229** . . . . 1·10 1·00
723 15f. Molucca cone . . . . . 1·25 1·00
724 20f. "Conus optimus" . . . 1·75 1·40
See also Nos. 761/2 and 810/11.

230 "St. Joseph" (freighter)

1984. Ships (3rd series). Each black, red and blue.
725 18f. Type **230** . . . . 1·60 1·40
726 31f. "Saint Antoine" (freighter) . . . . 1·75 1·40

231 Yellow-tailed Anemonefish

1984. Air. Noumea Aquarium. Fishes. Multicoloured.
727 46f. Type **231** . . . . 2·25 1·75
728 61f. Bicoloured angelfish . . 2·75 2·25

232 Arms of Noumea

233 "Araucaria columnaris"

1984.
729 **232** 35f. multicoloured . . . . 1·75 1·40

1984. Air. Trees. Multicoloured.
730 51f. Type **233** . . . . 2·50 1·75
731 67f. "Pritchardiopsis jeanneneyi" . . . . 2·50 1·90

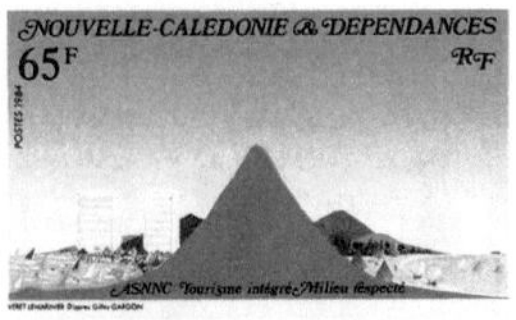

234 Tourist Centres

1984. Nature Protection.
732 **234** 65f. multicoloured . . . . 2·75 1·90

235 Swimming

1984. Air. Olympic Games, Los Angeles. Multicoloured.
733 50f. Type **235** . . . . 2·50 2·00
734 83f. Windsurfing . . . . . . 3·00 2·50
735 200f. Marathon . . . . . . 7·75 5·50

236 "Diplocaulobium ou-hinnae"

1984. Orchids. Multicoloured.
736 16f. Type **236** . . . . 1·60 1·40
737 38f. "Acianthus atepalus" . . 2·00 1·90

237 Royal Exhibition Hall, Melbourne

1984. Air. "Ausipex 84" International Stamp Exhibition, Melbourne.
738 **237** 150f. green, brown & mve 6·25 4·50
MS739 143 × 104 mm. **237** 150f. mauve and violet . . . . . . 7·00 7·25

238 School and Arrow Sign-post

239 Anchor, Rope and Stars

1984. Centenary of Public Education.
740 **238** 59f. multicoloured . . . . 2·25 1·75

1984. Air. Armed Forces Day.
741 **239** 51f. multicoloured . . . . 2·00 1·75

240 "Women looking for Crabs" (Mme. Bonnet de Larbogne)

1984. Air. Art. Multicoloured.
742 120f. Type **240** . . . . . . 4·50 3·00
743 300f. "Cook discovering New Caledonia" (tapestry by Pilioko) . . . . 10·50 7·25

241 Kagu

1985.
744 **241** 1f. blue 45 45
745 2f. green 45 45
746 3f. orange 50 45
747 4f. green 50 45
748 5f. mauve 45 50
749 35f. red . . . . 1·00 70
750 38f. red 95 80
751 40f. red . . . . 1·25 60
For similar design but with "& DEPENDANCES" omitted, see Nos. 837/43.

1985. Sea Shells (2nd series). As T **229**. Multicoloured.
761 55f. Bubble cone . . . . . . 2·00 1·90
762 72f. Lambert's cone . . . . 2·75 2·25

243 Weather Station transmitting Forecast to Boeing 737 and Trawler

1985. World Meteorology Day.
763 **243** 17f. multicoloured . . . . 1·25 1·25

244 Map and Hands holding Red Cross

1985. International Medicines Campaign.
764 **244** 41f. multicoloured . . . . 2·00 1·40

245 Electronic Telephone Exchange

1985. Inaug of Electronic Telephone Equipment.
765 **245** 70f. multicoloured . . . . 2·75 1·90

246 Marguerite la Foa Suspension Bridge

1985. Protection of Heritage.
766 **246** 44f. brown, red and blue 2·00 1·60

247 Kagu with Magnifying Glass and Stamp

1985. "Le Cagou" Stamp Club.
767 **247** 220f. multicoloured . . . 6·00 4·50
MS768 120 × 100 mm. No. 767 (sold at 230f.) . . . . 8·00 8·25

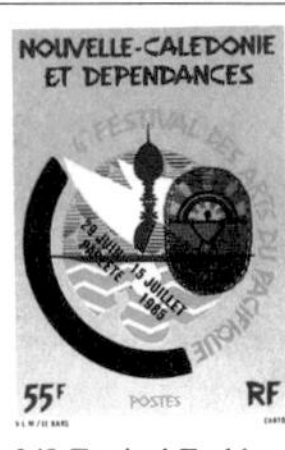

248 Festival Emblem

1985. 4th Pacific Arts Festival, Papeete. Mult.
769 55f. Type **248** . . . . 2·50 90
770 75f. Girl blowing trumpet triton . . . . 2·75 2·25

249 Flowers, Barbed Wire and Starving Child

1985. International Youth Year.
771 **249** 59f. multicoloured . . . . 2·25 1·60

250 "Amedee Lighthouse" (M. Hosken)
251 Tree and Seedling

1985. Electrification of Amedee Lighthouse.
772 **250** 89f. multicoloured . . . . 3·25 2·25

1985. "Planting for the Future".
773 **251** 100f. multicoloured . . . 3·50 2·25

252 De Havilland Dragon Rapide and Route Map

1985. Air. 30th Anniv of First Regular Internal Air Service.
774 **252** 80f. multicoloured . . . . 2·75 2·25

253 Hands and U.N. Emblem

1985. 40th Anniv of U.N.O.
775 **253** 250f. multicoloured . . . 8·00 4·50

254 School, Map and "Nautilus"

1985. Air. Jules Garnier High School.
776 **254** 400f. multicoloured . . . 13·00 7·25

255 Purple Swamphen

1985. Birds. Multicoloured.
777 50f. Type **255** . . . . 1·50 1·75
778 60f. Island thrush . . . . . 1·75 2·00

256 Aircraft Tail Fins and Eiffel Tower

1986. Air. 30th Anniv of Scheduled Paris–Noumea Flights.
779 **256** 72f. multicoloured . . . . 2·75 2·00

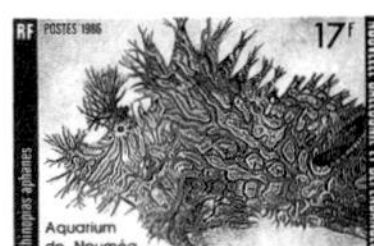

257 Merlet Scorpionfish

1986. Noumea Aquarium. Multicoloured.
780 10f. Emperor angelfish . . . 75 1·10
781 17f. Type **257** . . . . 90 1·25

258 Kanumera Bay, Isle of Pines

1986. Landscapes (1st series). Multicoloured.
782 50f. Type **258** . . . . 2·00 1·60
783 55f. Inland village . . . . . 2·25 1·60
See also Nos. 795/6 and 864/5.

259 "Bavayia sauvagii"

1986. Geckos. Multicoloured.
784 20f. Type **259** . . . . 1·50 1·25
785 45f. "Rhacodactylus leachianus" . . . .

260 Players and Azteca Stadium

1986. World Cup Football Championship, Mexico.
786 **260** 60f. multicoloured . . . . 1·90 2·00

261 Vivarium, Nou Island

1986. Air. Protection of Heritage.
787 **261** 230f. deep brown, blue and brown . . . . . . 7·25 5·00

262 Pharmaceutical Equipment

1986. 120th Anniv of First Pharmacy.
788 **262** 80f. multicoloured . . . . 2·75 2·25

263 "Coelogynae licastioides"

1986. Orchids. Multicoloured.
789 44f. Type **263** . . . . 2·00 1·60
790 58f. "Calanthe langei" . . . 2·50 1·90

264 Black-backed Magpie

1986. "Stampex 86" National Stamp Exhibition, Adelaide.
791 **264** 110f. multicoloured . . . 3·25 3·75

265 Aerospatiale/Aeritalia ATR 42 over New Caledonia

1986. Air. Inaugural Flight of ATR 42.
792 **265** 18f. multicoloured . . . . 1·25 1·25

266 Emblem and 1860 Stamp
267 Arms of Mont Dore

1986. Air. "Stockholmia 86" International Stamp Exhibition.
793 **266** 108f. black, red and lilac 3·50 3·00

1986.
794 **267** 94f. multicoloured . . . . 3·25 2·25

1986. Landscapes (2nd series). As T **258**. Multicoloured.
795 40f. West coast (vert) . . . . 1·75 1·40
796 76f. South . . . . 2·75 2·00

268 Wild Flowers
269 Club Banner

1986. Association for Nature Protection.
797 **268** 73f. multicoloured . . . . 2·75 2·00

1986. 25th Anniv of Noumea Lions Club.
798 **269** 350f. multicoloured . . . 10·00 8·25

270 "Moret Bridge" (Alfred Sisley)

1986. Paintings. Multicoloured.
799 74f. Type **270** . . . . 2·75 2·00
800 140f. "Hunting Butterflies" (Berthe Morisot) . . . . . 4·75 3·25

271 Emblem and Sound Waves
272 "Challenge France"

1987. Air. 25th Anniv of New Caledonia Amateur Radio Association.
801 **271** 64f. multicoloured . . . . 2·00 1·90

1987. America's Cup Yacht Race. Multicoloured.
802 30f. Type **272** . . . . 2·00 1·60
803 70f. "French Kiss" . . . . . 2·75 2·25

273 "Anona squamosa" and "Graphium gelon"

1987. Plants and Butterflies. Multicoloured.
804 46f. Type **273** . . . . 2·25 1·75
805 54f. "Abizzia granulosa" and "Polyura gamma" . . . . 2·50 1·90

274 Peaceful Landscape, Earphones and Noisy Equipment

1987. Air. Nature Protection. Campaign against Noise.
806 **274** 150f. multicoloured . . . 5·25 3·00

275 Isle of Pines Canoe

1987. Canoes. Each brown, green and blue.
807 72f. Type **275** . . . . 2·50 2·00
808 90f. Ouvea canoe . . . . . 3·00 2·25

276 Town Hall

1987. New Town Hall, Mont Dore.
809 **276** 92f. multicoloured . . . . 3·25 2·25

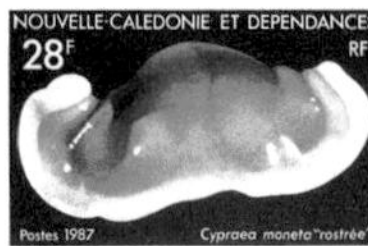

277 Money Cowrie

1987. Sea Shells (3rd series). Multicoloured.
810 28f. Type **277** . . . . 1·50 1·40
811 36f. Martin's cone . . . . . 1·90 1·60

278 Games Emblem
279 Emblem

1987. 8th South Pacific Games, Noumea (1st issue).
812 **278** 40f. multicoloured . . . . 1·75 1·60
See also Nos. 819/21.

1987. 13th Soroptimists International Convention, Melbourne.
813 **279** 270f. multicoloured . . . 8·75 6·00

280 New Caledonia White-Eye

1987. Birds. Multicoloured.
814 18f. Type **280** . . . . 1·10 1·25
815 21f. Peregrine falcon (vert) 1·10 1·25

281 Flags on Globe

1987. 40th Anniv of South Pacific Commission.
816 **281** 200f. multicoloured . . . 6·75 4·00

282 Globe and Magnifying Glass on Map of New Caledonia

1987. Schools Philately.
817 **282** 15f. multicoloured . . . . 1·25 1·10

283 Cricketers

1987. Air. French Cricket Federation.
818 **283** 94f. multicoloured . . . . 3·25 2·50

284 Golf

1987. 8th South Pacific Games, Noumea (2nd issue). Multicoloured.
819 20f. Type **284** . . . . 1·25 1·10
820 30f. Rugby football . . . . . 1·60 1·25
821 100f. Long jumping . . . . 3·25 2·25

285 Arms of Dumbea

287 University

286 Route Map, "L'Astrolabe", "La Boussole" and La Perouse

1988. Air.
822 **285** 76f. multicoloured . . . . 2·75 2·00

1988. Bicentenary of Disappearance of La Perouse's Expedition.
823 **286** 36f. blue, brown and red 1·75 1·40

1988. French University of South Pacific, Noumea and Papeete.
824 **287** 400f. multicoloured . . . 12·50 8·25

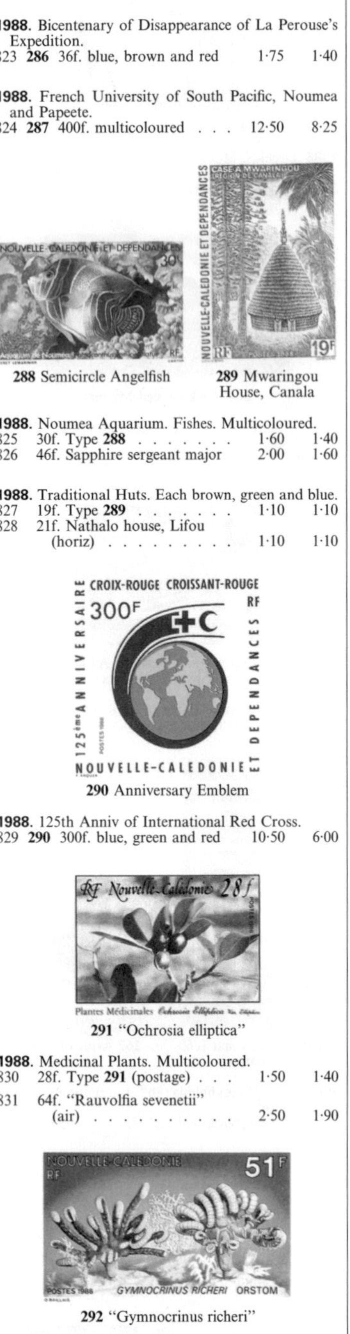

288 Semicircle Angelfish

289 Mwaringou House, Canala

1988. Noumea Aquarium. Fishes. Multicoloured.
825 30f. Type **288** . . . . 1·60 1·40
826 46f. Sapphire sergeant major 2·00 1·60

1988. Traditional Huts. Each brown, green and blue.
827 19f. Type **289** . . . . 1·10 1·10
828 21f. Nathalo house, Lifou (horiz) . . . . 1·10 1·10

290 Anniversary Emblem

1988. 125th Anniv of International Red Cross.
829 **290** 300f. blue, green and red 10·50 6·00

291 "Ochrosia elliptica"

1988. Medicinal Plants. Multicoloured.
830 28f. Type **291** (postage) . . . 1·50 1·40
831 64f. "Rauvolfia sevenetii" (air) . . . . 2·50 1·90

292 "Gymnocrinus richeri"

1988.
832 **292** 51f. multicoloured . . . . 2·25 1·75

293 Furnished Room and Building Exterior

1988. Bourail Museum and Historical Association.
833 **293** 120f. multicoloured . . . 3·50 3·00

294 La Perouse sighting Phillip's Fleet in Botany Bay

1988. "Sydpex 88" Stamp Exhibition, Sydney. Multicoloured.
834 42f. Type **294** . . . . 2·00 1·75
835 42f. Phillip sighting "La Boussole" and "L'Astrolabe" . . . . . 2·00 1·75
MS836 175 × 120 mm. Nos. 834/5 (sold at 120f.) . . . . 2·50 2·50

295 Kagu

297 Laboratory Assistant, Noumea Institute and Pasteur

296 Table Tennis

1988.
837 **295** 1f. blue 75 10
838 2f. green 80 30
839 3f. orange 75 30
840 4f. green 75 10
841 5f. mauve 75 30
842 28f. orange . . . . 1·10 55
843 40f. red . . . . 1·40 40

1988. Olympic Games, Seoul.
846 **296** 150f. multicoloured . . . 4·75 3·00

1988. Centenary of Pasteur Institute, Paris.
847 **297** 100f. red, black and blue 3·25 2·50

298 Georges Baudoux

1988. Writers.
848 **298** 72f. brown, green and purple (postage) . . . . 2·75 1·90
849 – 73f. brown, bl & blk (air) 2·75 2·00
DESIGN: 73f. Jean Mariotti.

299 Map and Emblems

1988. Air. Rotary International Anti-Polio Campaign.
850 **299** 220f. multicoloured . . . 6·25 5·00

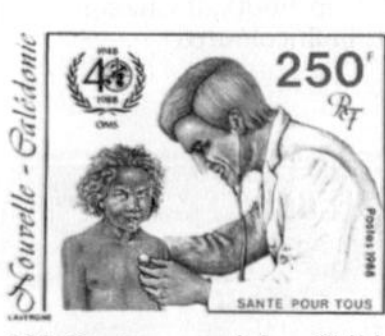

300 Doctor examining Child

1988. 40th Anniv of W.H.O.
851 **300** 250f. multicoloured . . . 8·00 4·50

301 "Terre des Hommes" (L. Bunckley)

1988. Paintings. Multicoloured.
852 54f. Type **301** . . . . 2·50 1·90
853 92f. "Latin Quarter" (Marik) 3·50 2·50

302 Arms of Koumac

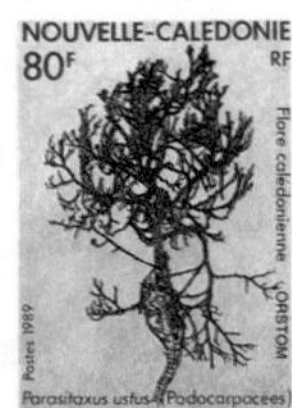

303 "Parasitaxus ustus"

1989.
854 **302** 200f. multicoloured . . . 5·75 4·00

1989. Flowers. Multicoloured.
855 80f. Type **303** . . . . 2·50 2·00
856 90f. "Tristaniopsis guillainii" (horiz) . . . . 2·75 2·25

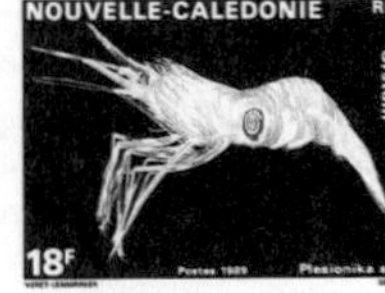

304 "Plesionika sp."

1989. Marine Life. Multicoloured.
857 18f. Type **304** . . . . 1·40 1·10
858 66f. Sail-backed scorpionfish 2·25 1·90
859 110f. Cristiate latiaxis . . . . 3·50 2·75

305 "Liberty"

306 Canoe and Diamond Decoration

1989. Bicentenary of French Revolution and "Philexfrance 89" International Stamp Exhibition, Paris. Multicoloured.
860 40f. Type **305** (postage) . . . 1·75 1·40
861 58f. "Equality" (air) . . . . 2·25 1·75
862 76f. "Fraternity" . . . . . . 2·75 2·00
MS863 155 × 110 mm. 180f. "Liberty" "Equality" and "Fraternity" (92 × 51 mm) . . 4·75 5·00

1989. Landscapes (3rd series). As T **258**. Mult.
864 180f. Ouaieme ferry (post) . . 5·75 3·25
865 64f. "The Broody Hen" (rocky islet), Hienghene (air) . . . . 2·50 1·75

1989. Bamboo Decorations by C. Ohlen. Each black, bistre and orange.
866 70f. Type **306** (postage) . . . 2·75 1·90
867 44f. Animal design (air) . . . 1·75 1·60

307 "Hobie Cat 14" Yachts

1989. 10th World "Hobie Cat" Class Catamaran Championship, Noumea.
868 **307** 350f. multicoloured . . . 10·50 6·50

308 Book Title Pages and Society Members

1989. 20th Anniv of Historical Studies Society.
869 **308** 74f. black and brown . . 2·75 2·00

309 Fort Teremba

1989. Protection of Heritage.
870 **309** 100f. green, brown & blue . . . 3·25 2·25

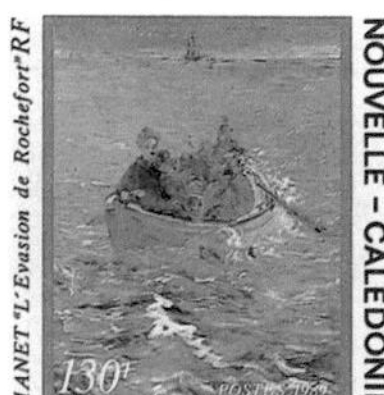

310 "Rochefort's Escape" (Edouard Manet)

1989. Paintings. Multicoloured.
871 130f. Type **310** . . . . . . 4·50 3·00
872 270f. "Self-portrait" (Gustave Courbet) . . . . 8·25 5·50

311 Fr. Patrick O'Reilly

1990. Writers.
873 **311** 170f. black and mauve . . 5·25 3·25

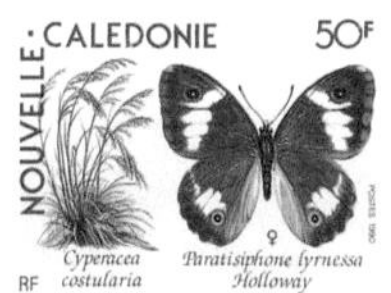

312 Grass and Female Butterfly

1990. "Cyperacea costularia" (grass) and "Paratisiphone lyrnessa" (butterfly). Multicoloured.
874 50f. Type **312** (postage) . . . 1·90 1·60
875 18f. Grass and female butterfly (different) (air) . . 1·10 1·10
876 94f. Grass and male butterfly 3·00 2·25

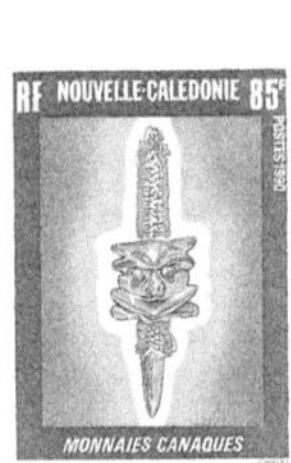

313 "Maize" Stem with Face

RF NOUVELLE-CALEDONIE 230 F
EXPOSITION DE JADE ET DE NACRE
314 Exhibit

1990. Kanaka Money.
877 **313** 85f. olive, orange & green 3·00 1·90
878 – 140f. orange, black & grn 4·50 2·75
DESIGN: 140f. "Rope" stem with decorative end.

1990. Jade and Mother-of-pearl Exhibition.
879 **314** 230f. multicoloured . . . 7·25 4·50

315 Ocellate Nudibranch

1990. Noumea Aquarium. Sea Slugs. Multicoloured.
880 10f. Type **315** . . . . 75 1·00
881 42f. "Chromodoris kuniei" (vert) . . . . 1·60 1·40

316 Head of "David" (Michelangelo) and Footballers

1990. World Cup Football Championship, Italy.
882 **316** 240f. multicoloured . . . 7·00 4·25

317 De Gaulle

Nouvelle-Calédonie 40F
Pétroglyphe, Site de Neounda
318 Neounda Site

1990. Air. 50th Anniv of De Gaulle's Call to Resist.
883 **317** 160f. multicoloured . . . 4·75 3·50

1990. Petroglyphs.
884 **318** 40f. brown, green and red (postage) . . . . 1·50 1·40
885 – 58f. black, brown and blue (air) . . . . 2·00 1·75
DESIGN—HORIZ: 58f. Kassducou site.

319 Map and Pacific International Meeting Centre

1990.
886 **319** 320f. multicoloured . . . 8·00 4·25

320 New Zealand Cemetery, Bourail

321 Kagu

1990. Air. "New Zealand 1990" International Stamp Exhibition, Auckland. Multicoloured.
887 80f. Type **320** . . . . 2·75 2·25
888 80f. Brigadier William Walter Dove . . . . 2·75 2·25
MS889 140 × 100 mm. 150f. Kagu, brown kiwi and maps of New Caledonia and New Zealand 5·00 5·00

1990.
890 **321** 1f. blue 45 45
891 2f. green 45 45
892 3f. yellow 45 45
893 4f. green 45 45
894 5f. violet 45 45
895 9f. grey 50 50
896 12f. red 50 50
897 40f. mauve 75 75
898 50f. red 80 80
899 55f. red 85 85
The 5 and 55f. exist both perforated with ordinary gum and imperforate with self-adhesive gum.
For design with no value expressed see No. 994.

322 "Munidopsis sp"

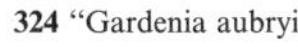
324 "Gardenia aubryi"

323 Emblem

1990. Air. Deep Sea Animals. Multicoloured.
900 30f. Type **322** . . . . 1·10 1·25
901 60f. "Lyreidius tridentatus" 1·75 1·60

1990. Air. 30th South Pacific Conference, Noumea.
902 **323** 85f. multicoloured . . . . 2·25 2·00

1990. Flowers. Multicoloured.
903 105f. Type **324** . . . . . . 3·00 2·25
904 130f. "Hibbertia baudouinii" 3·50 2·75

325 De Gaulle

1990. Air. Birth Centenary of Charles de Gaulle (French statesman).
905 **325** 410f. blue . . . . 12·00 5·00

326 "Mont Dore, Mountain of Jade" (C. Degroiselle)

1990. Air. Pacific Painters. Multicoloured.
906 365f. Type **326** (postage) . . 10·00 6·00
907 110f. "The Celieres House" (M. Petron) (air) . . . . . 3·25 2·75

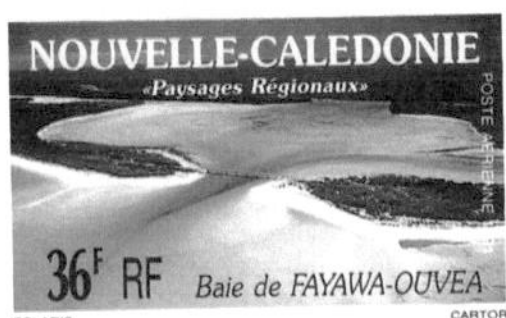

327 Fayawa-Ouvea Bay

1991. Air. Regional Landscapes. Multicoloured.
908 36f. Type **327** . . . . . . 1·60 1·40
909 90f. Coastline of Mare . . . 2·75 2·00

328 Louise Michel and Classroom

1991. Writers.
910 **328** 125f. mauve and blue . . 3·75 2·50
911 – 125f. blue and brown . . 3·75 2·50
DESIGN: No. 911, Charles B. Nething and photographer.

329 Houailou Hut

330 Northern Province

1991. Melanesian Huts. Multicoloured.
912 12f. Type **329** . . . . 1·10 1·00
913 35f. Hienghene hut . . . . . 1·50 1·25

1991. Provinces. Multicoloured.
914 45f. Type **330** . . . . 1·75 1·60
915 45f. Islands Province . . . . 1·75 1·60
916 45f. Southern Province . . . 1·75 1·60

331 "Dendrobium biflorum"

1991. Orchids. Multicoloured.
917 55f. Type **331** . . . . 2·00 1·60
918 70f. "Dendrobium closterium" . . . . 2·25 1·75

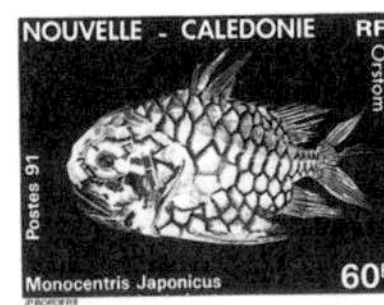

332 Japanese Pineconefish

1991. Fishes. Multicoloured.
919 60f. Type **332** . . . . 2·25 1·60
920 100f. Japanese bigeye . . . . 3·00 2·25

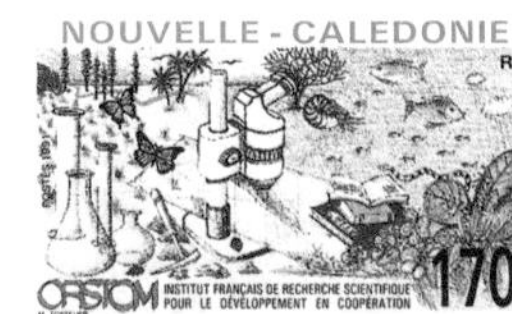

333 Research Equipment and Sites

1991. French Scientific Research Institute for Development and Co-operation.
921 **333** 170f. multicoloured . . . 5·00 2·75

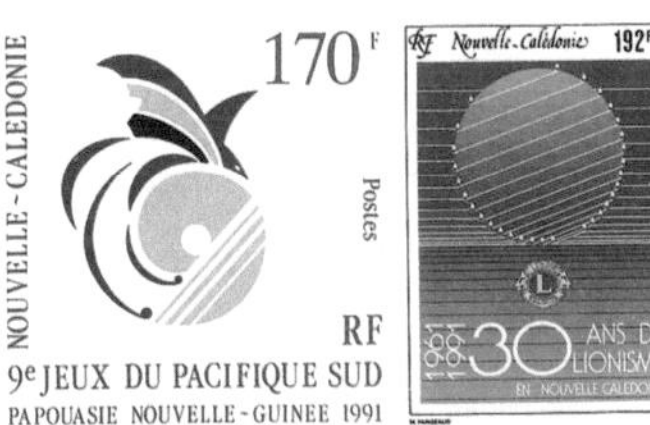

334 Emblem **336** Emblems

335 Map and Dragon

1991. 9th South Pacific Games, Papua New Guinea.
922 **334** 170f. multicoloured . . . 5·00 2·75

1991. Centenary of Vietnamese Settlement in New Caledonia.
923 **335** 300f. multicoloured . . . 8·25 5·00

1991. 30th Anniv of Lions International in New Caledonia.
924 **336** 192f. multicoloured . . . 5·50 3·00

337 Map, "Camden" (missionary brig), Capt. Robert Clark Morgan and Trees

1991. 150th Anniv of Discovery of Sandalwood.
925 **337** 200f. blue, turquoise & grn . . . . 5·50 3·25

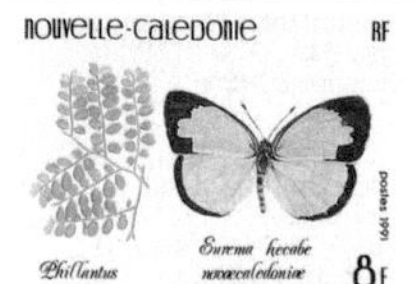
338 "Phillantus" and Common Grass Yellow

1991. "Phila Nippon '91" International Stamp Exhibition, Tokyo. Plants and Butterflies. Mult.
926 8f. Type **338** . . . . 85 1·00
927 15f. "Pipturus incanus" and "Hypolimnas octocula" . . 1·10 1·00
928 20f. "Stachytarpheta urticaefolia" and meadow argos . . . . 1·25 1·10
929 26f. "Malaisia scandens" and "Cyrestis telamon" . . . . 1·40 1·10
MS930 100 × 122 mm. 75f. *Cyrestis telamon*; 75f. *Hypolimnas octocula*; 75f. *Eurema hecabe*; 75f. *Precis villida* (all vert) . . . . 9·00 9·25

339 Nickel Processing Plant and Dam

1991. 50th Anniv of Central Economic Co-operation Bank. Multicoloured.
931 76f. Type **339** . . . . 2·50 1·90
932 76f. Housing and hotels . . . 2·50 1·90

340 "Caledonian Cricket" (Marcel Moutouh)

1991. Air. Pacific Painters. Multicoloured.
933 130f. Type **340** . . . . . . 3·75 2·25
934 435f. "Saint Louis" (Janine Goetz) . . . . 12·00 7·25

341 Blue River (½-size illustration)

1992. Air. Blue River National Park.
935 **341** 400f. multicoloured . . . 7·00 5·00
MS936 127 × 91 mm. No. 935 (sold at 450f.) . . . . 7·25 6·50

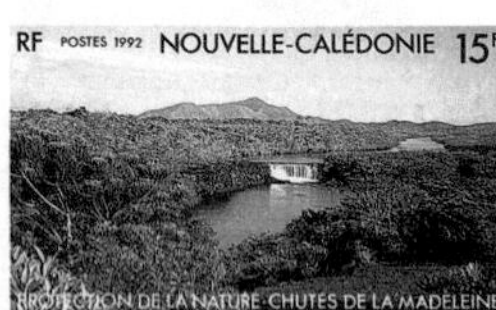
342 La Madeleine Falls

1992. Nature Protection.
937 **342** 15f. multicoloured 30 30
MS938 122 × 88 mm. No. 937 (sold at 150f.) . . . . 2·50 2·75

343 Lapita Pot

345 "Pinta"

344 Barqueta Bridge

1992. Air. Noumea Museum.
939 **343** 25f. black and orange . . 40 35

1992. Air. "Expo '92" World's Fair, Seville.
940 **344** 10f. multicoloured 20 25

1992. Air. "World Columbian Stamp Expo '92", Chicago. Multicoloured.
941 80f. Type **345** . . . . 1·25 1·10
942 80f. "Santa Maria" . . . . . 1·25 1·10
943 80f. "Nina" . . . . 1·25 1·10
MS944 160 × 70 mm. 110f. Eric the Red and longship; 110f. Christopher Columbus and arms; 110f. Amerigo Vespucci (sold at 360f.) . . . . 5·00 5·00

346 Manchurian Crane and Kagu within "100"

1992. Centenary of Arrival of First Japanese Immigrants. Multicoloured, background colours given.
945 **346** 95f. yellow . . . . 1·75 1·25
946 95f. grey . . . . 1·75 1·25

347 Synchronised Swimming

1992. Olympic Games, Barcelona.
947 **347** 260f. multicoloured . . . 3·50 2·50

348 Bell Airacobra, Grumman F4F Wildcat, Barrage Balloon, Harbour and Nissen Huts

1992. 50th Anniv of Arrival of American Forces in New Caledonia.
948 **348** 50f. multicoloured 80 60

349 "Wahpa" (Paul Mascart)

1992. Air. Pacific Painters.
949 **349** 205f. multicoloured . . . 3·00 1·75

350 Australian Cattle Dog

352 "Amalda fuscolingua"

351 Entrecasteaux and Fleet

1992. Air. Canine World Championships.
950 **350** 175f. multicoloured . . . 2·50 1·75

1992. Air. Navigators. Bicentenary of Landing of Admiral Bruni d'Entrecasteaux on West Coast of New Caledonia.
951 **351** 110f. orange, blue & green 1·75 1·10

1992. Air. Shells. Multicoloured.
952 30f. Type **352** 60 45
953 50f. "Cassis abbotti" 85 65

353 Deole

1992. Air. "La Brousse en Folie" (comic strip) by Bernard Berger. Multicoloured.
954 80f. Type **353** . . . . 1·25 85
955 80f. Tonton Marcel . . . . . 1·25 85
956 80f. Tathan . . . . 1·25 85
957 80f. Joinville . . . . 1·25 85

354 Lagoon

1993. Lagoon Protection.
958 **354** 120f. multicoloured . . . 2·40 1·60

355 Harbour (Gaston Roullet)

1993. Air. Pacific Painters.
959 **355** 150f. multicoloured . . . 2·25 1·50

356 Symbols of New Caledonia

1993. School Philately. "Tourism my Friend".
960 **356** 25f. multicoloured 45 35

357 Still and Plantation

1993. Air. Centenary of Production of Essence of Niaouli.
966 **357** 85f. multicoloured . . . . 1·25 90

358 Planets and Copernicus

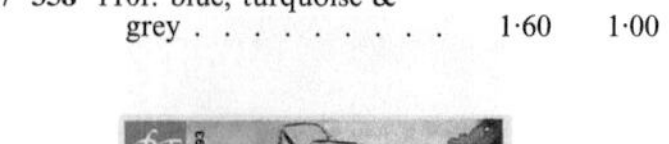

1993. Air. "Polska '93" International Stamp Exhibition, Poznan. 450th Death Anniv of Nicolas Copernicus (astronomer).
967 **358** 110f. blue, turquoise & grey . . . . 1·60 1·00

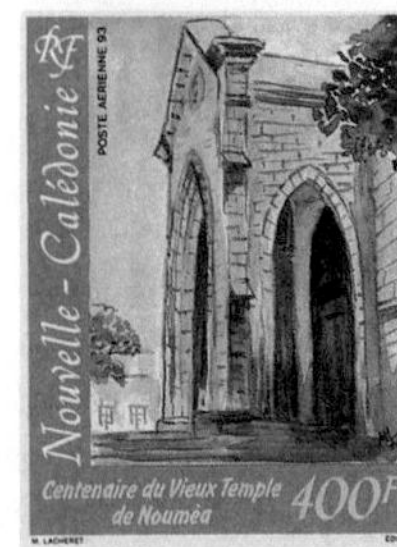
359 Noumea Temple

1993. Air. Centenary of First Protestant Church in Noumea.
968 **359** 400f. multicoloured . . . 6·00 4·00

1993. No. 898 surch **55F**.
969 **321** 55f. on 50f. red . . . . . 1·00 75

361 Malabou

1993. Air. Regional Landscapes.
970 **361** 85f. multicoloured . . . . 1·25 85

362 Locomotive and Bridge

1993. Air. Centenary of Little Train of Thio.
971 **362** 115f. red, green and lilac 1·75 1·10

363 Rochefort

364 "Megastylis paradoxa"

1993. Air. 80th Death Anniv of Henri Rochefort (journalist).
972 **363** 100f. multicoloured . . . 1·60 1·00

1993. Air. "Bangkok 1993" International Stamp Exhibition, Thailand. Multicoloured.
973 30f. Type **364** 70 40
974 30f. "Vanda coerulea" . . . 70 40
MS975 120 × 90 mm. 140f. Exhibition centre (51 × 39 mm) 3·00 3·00

365 Route Map and Boeing 737-300/500

1993. Air. 10th Anniv of Air Cal (national airline).
976 **365** 85f. multicoloured . . . . 1·60 1·25

366 "Francois Arago" (cable ship)

1993. Air. Centenary of New Caledonia–Australia Telecommunications Cable.
977 **366** 200f. purple, blue & turq . . . 4·00 2·40

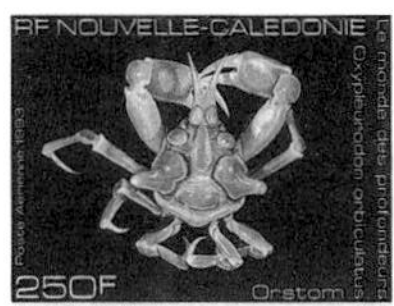

367 "Oxypleurodon orbiculatus"

1993. Air. Deep-sea Life.
978 **367** 250f. multicoloured . . . 4·50 2·75

368 Aircraft, Engine and Hangar

1993. Air. 25th Anniv of Chamber of Commerce and Industry's Management of La Tontouta Airport, Noumea.
979 **368** 90f. multicoloured . . . . 1·75 1·10

369 First Christmas Mass, 1843 (stained glass window, Balade church)

1993. Air. Christmas.
980 **369** 120f. multicoloured . . . 2·10 1·40

370 Bourail

1993. Town Arms. Multicoloured.
981 70f. Type **370** . . . . 1·60 1·25
982 70f. Noumea . . . . 1·60 1·25
983 70f. Canala . . . . 1·60 1·25
984 70f. Kone . . . . 1·60 1·25
985 70f. Paita . . . . 2·75 1·40
986 70f. Dumbea . . . . 1·60 1·25
987 70f. Koumac . . . . 1·60 1·25
988 70f. Ponerihouen . . . . . . 1·60 1·25
989 70f. Kaamoo Hyehen . . . . 1·60 1·25
990 70f. Mont Dore . . . . . . 2·50 1·40
991 70f. Thio . . . . 1·60 1·25
992 70f. Kaala-Gomen . . . . . 1·60 1·25
993 70f. Touho . . . . 1·60 1·25

1994. No value expressed
994 **321** (60f.) red . . . . 1·10 40

371 Dog, Exhibition Emblem and Chinese Horoscope Signs (New Year)

1994. Air. "Hong Kong '94" International Stamp Exhibition. Multicoloured.
995 60f. Type **371** . . . . 1·40 90
MS996 161 × 120 mm. 105f. Giant panda (51 × 39 *mm*);105f. Kagu (51 × 39 mm) . . . . 4·50 4·50

372 Airbus Industrie A340

1994. Air 1st Paris–Noumea Airbus Flight. Self-adhesive.
997 **372** 90f. multicoloured . . . . 2·10 1·40

1994. "Philexjeunes '94" Youth Stamp Exhibition, Grenoble. No. 960 optd **PHILEXJEUNES'94 GRENOBLE 22–24 AVRIL**.
998 **356** 25f. multicoloured 50 40

374 Photograph of Canala Post Office and Post Van

1994. 50th Anniv of Noumea–Canala Postal Service.
999 **374** 15f. brown, green and blue 50 40

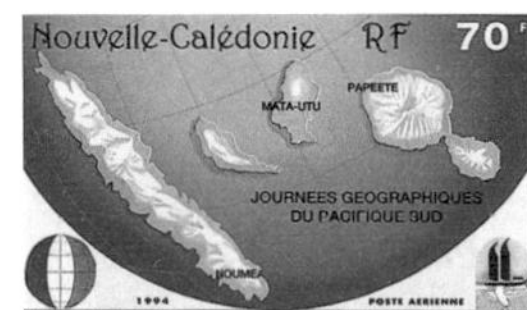

375 Pacific Islands on Globe

1994. Air. South Pacific Geographical Days.
1000 **375** 70f. multicoloured . . . 1·40 95

376 Post Office, 1859

1994. Postal Administration Head Offices. Mult.
1001 30f. Type **376** 60 50
1002 60f. Posts and Telecommunications Office, 1936 . . . . . . 1·40 80
1003 90f. Ministry of Posts and Telecommunications, 1967 1·90 1·40
1004 120f. Ministry of Posts and Telecommunications, 1993 2·50 1·75

377 "The Mask Wearer"

1994. Pacific Sculpture.
1005 **377** 60f. multicoloured . . . 1·40 70

378 "Legend of the Devil Fish" (Micheline Neporon)

1994. Air. Pacific Painters.
1006 **378** 120f. multicoloured . . . 2·25 1·50

379 "Chambeyronia macrocarpa" **380** Podtanea Pot

1994.
1007 **379** 90f. multicoloured . . . 1·90 1·25

1994. Air. Noumea Museum.
1008 **380** 95f. multicoloured . . . 1·90 1·40

381 Trophy, U.S. Flag and Ball

1994. Air. World Cup Football Championship, U.S.A.
1009 **381** 105f. multicoloured . . . 2·00 1·60

1994. No. D707 with "Timbre Taxe" obliterated by black bar.
1010 D **222** 5f. multicoloured . . 10·00 2·50

382 Timor Deer

1994. Bourail Fair.
1011 **382** 150f. multicoloured . . . 3·00 1·75

383 Korean Family

1994. Air. "Philakorea 1994" International Stamp Exhibition, Seoul. Multicoloured.
1012 60f. Type **383** . . . . 1·25 70
MS1013 110 × 110 mm. 35f. Containers, peppers and emblem (36 × 37 mm); 35f. Carafe, celery, cannage and garlic (36 × 37 mm); 35f. Container and turnips (36 × 37 mm); 35f. Jug, seafood and lemon (36 × 37 mm) . . . 3·50 3·50

384 "L'Atalante" (oceanographic research vessel)

1994. Air. ZoNeCo (evaluation programme of Economic Zone).
1014 **384** 120f. multicoloured . . . 2·40 1·75

385 "Nivose"

1994. Attachment of the "Nivose" (French surveillance frigate) to New Caledonia. Multicoloured.
1015 30f. Type **385** 70 50
1016 30f. Aircraft over frigate . . 70 50

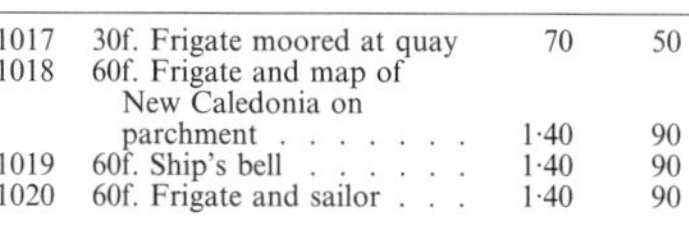
1017 30f. Frigate moored at quay 70 50
1018 60f. Frigate and map of New Caledonia on parchment . . . . 1·40 90
1019 60f. Ship's bell . . . . . . 1·40 90
1020 60f. Frigate and sailor . . . 1·40 90

386 Driving Cattle

1994. Air. 1st European Stamp Salon, Flower Gardens, Paris. Multicoloured.
1021 90f. Aerial view of island . . 1·75 1·25
1022 90f. Type **386** . . . . . . 1·75 1·25

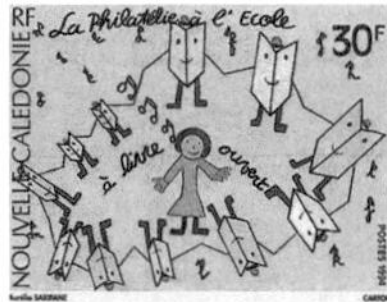

387 Paper Darts around Girl

1994. School Philately.
1023 **387** 30f. multicoloured . . . 60 40

388 Jaques Nervat

1994. Writers.
1024 **388** 175f. multicoloured . . . 3·50 2·00

389 Satellite transmitting to Globe and Computer Terminal

1994. Air. 50th Anniv of Overseas Scientific and Technical Research Office.
1025 **389** 95f. multicoloured . . . 2·25 1·40

390 Emblem and Temple

1994. Air. 125th Anniv of Freemasonary in New Caledonia.
1026 **390** 350f. multicoloured . . . 7·00 3·50

391 Thiebaghi Mine

1994. Air.
1027 **391** 90f. multicoloured . . . 1·90 1·25

392 Place des Cocotiers, Noumea

1994. Christmas.
1028 **392** 30f. multicoloured . . . 70 60

No. 1028 covers any one of five stamps which were issued together in horizontal se-tenant strips, the position of the bell, tree and monument differing on each stamp. The strip is stated to produce a three-dimensional image without use of a special viewer.

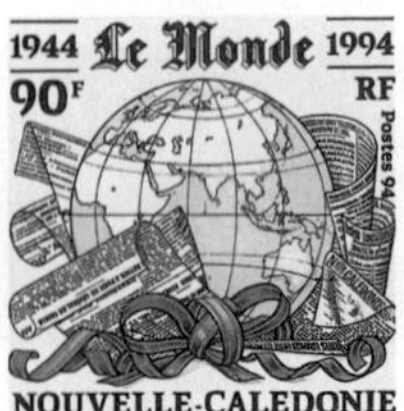

393 Globe and Newspapers

1994. 50th Anniv of "Le Monde" (newspaper).
1029 **393** 90f. multicoloured . . . 2·25 1·75

394 1988 100f. Pasteur Institute Stamp

1995. Death Centenary of Louis Pasteur (chemist).
1030 **394** 120f. multicoloured . . . 2·25 1·50

395 Pictorial Map

1995. Air. Tourism.
1031 **395** 90f. multicoloured . . . 1·90 1·25

396 Profile of De Gaulle (Santucci) and Cross of Lorraine

1995. 25th Death Anniv of Charles de Gaulle (French President, 1959–69).
1032 **396** 1000f. deep blue, blue and gold . . . . . . 18·00 15·00

397 Emblem

1995. Pacific University Teachers' Training Institute.
1033 **397** 100f. multicoloured . . . 1·90 1·40

398 "Sylviornis neocaledoniae"

1995.
1034 **398** 60f. multicoloured . . . 1·60 1·25

399 Swimming, Cycling and Running

1995. Triathlon.
1035 **399** 60f. multicoloured . . . 1·40 90

400 Tent and Trees

1995. 50th Anniv of Pacific Franc.
1036 **400** 10f. multicoloured . . . 30 30

No. 1036 covers any one of four stamps which were issued together in horizontal se-tenant strips, the position of the central motif rotating slightly in a clockwise direction from the left to the right-hand stamp. The strip is stated to produce a three-dimensional image without use of a special viewer.

401 Bourbon Palace (Paris), Map of New Caledonia and Chamber

1995. 50th Anniversaries. Multicoloured.
1037 60f. Type **401** (first representation of New Caledonia at French National Assembly) . . . 1·40 70
1038 90f. National emblems, De Gaulle and Allied flags (end of Second World War) . . . . 1·90 1·25
1039 90f. U.N. Headquarters, New York (U.N.O.) . . . 1·90 1·25

402 "Sebertia acuminata"

1995.
1040 **402** 60f. multicoloured . . . 1·50 80

403 Common Noddy

1995. "Singapore'95" International Stamp Exhibition. Sea Birds. Multicoloured.
1041 5f. Type **403** 10 15
1042 10f. Silver gull 20 25
1043 20f. Roseate tern 40 45
1044 35f. Osprey 80 60
1045 65f. Red-footed booby . . . 1·25 1·25
1046 125f. Great frigate bird . . 2·25 1·75
MS1047 130 × 100 mm. Nos. 1041/6 5·50 3·50

404 Golf

1995. 10th South Pacific Games.
1048 **404** 90f. multicoloured . . . 1·75 1·40

405 "The Lizard Man" (Dick Bone)

1995. Pacific Sculpture.
1049 **405** 65f. multicoloured . . . 1·25 90

406 Venue

1995. Air. 35th South Pacific Conference.
1050 **406** 500f. multicoloured . . . 8·00 5·50

407 Silhouette of Francis Carco

1995. Writers.
1051 **407** 95f. multicoloured . . . 1·75 1·40

408 Ouare

1995. Air. Kanak Dances. Multicoloured.
1052 95f. Type **408** . . . . . . 1·75 1·25
1053 100f. Pothe . . . . 1·75 1·25

409 Saw-headed Crocodilefish

1995. World of the Deep.
1054 **409** 100f. multicoloured . . . 2·00 1·40

410 "Mekosuchus inexpectatus"

1996. Air.
1055 **410** 125f. multicoloured . . . 2·40 1·60

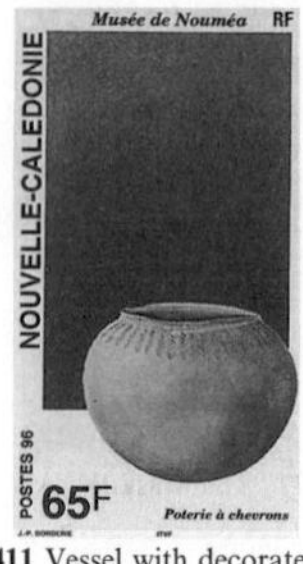

411 Vessel with decorated Rim

1996. Noumea Museum.
1056 **411** 65f. multicoloured . . . 1·25 90

412 "Captaincookia margaretae"

1996. Flowers. Multicoloured.
1057 65f. Type **412** . . . . . . 1·25 80
1058 95f. "Ixora cauliflora" . . . 1·75 1·25

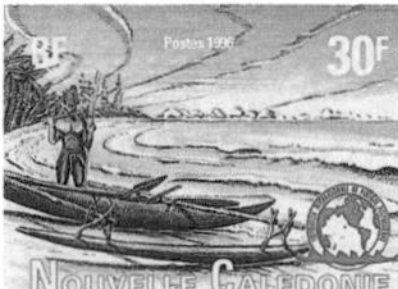

413 Pirogue on Beach

1996. World Pirogue Championships, Noumea. Multicoloured.
1059 30f. Type **413** 60 40
1060 65f. Pirogue leaving shore 1·40 70
1061 95f. Double-hulled pirogue 1·75 1·10
1062 125f. Sports pirogue . . . . 2·25 1·90

Nos. 1059/62 were issued together, se-tenant, forming a composite design.

414 Red Batfish

1996. "China'96" International Stamp Exhibition, Peking. Deep Sea Life. Multicoloured.
1063 25f. Type **414** 50 40
1064 40f. "Perotrochus deforgesi" (slit shell) 70 50
1065 65f. "Mursia musorstomia" (crab) . . . . 1·25 80
1066 125f. Sea lily . . . . 2·50 1·60

415 "Sarcolchilus koghiensis"

1996. "Capex'96" International Stamp Exhibition, Toronto, Canada. Orchids. Multicoloured.
1067 5f. Type **415** 10 10
1068 10f. "Phaius robertsii" . . . 20 10
1069 25f. "Megastylis montana" 40 35
1070 65f. "Dendrobium macrophyllum" . . . . . 1·10 85
1071 95f. "Dendrobium virotii" 1·75 1·25
1072 125f. "Ephemerantha comata" . . . . 2·00 1·50

416 Indonesian Couple beneath Tree

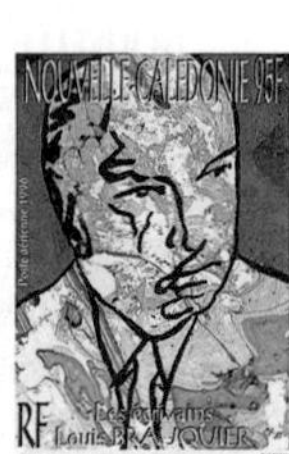

417 Louis Brauquier

1996. Air. Centenary of Arrival of First Indonesian Immigrants.
1073 **416** 130f. multicoloured . . . 2·25 1·75

1996. Air. Writers.
1074 **417** 95f. multicoloured . . . 1·75 1·25

1996. 50th Anniv of U.N.I.C.E.F. No. 1023 optd **unicef** and emblem.
1075 **387** 30f. multicoloured . . . 60 50

419 Dish Aerial

1996. Air. Anniversaries. Multicoloured.
1076 95f. Type **419** (20th anniv of New Caledonia's first Earth Station) . . . . . 1·75 1·25
1077 125f. Guglielmo Marconi (inventor) and telegraph masts (centenary of radio-telegraphy) . . . . 2·40 1·25

420 Tribal Dance

1996. Air. 7th South Pacific Arts Festival.
1078 **420** 100f. multicoloured . . . 1·75 1·40

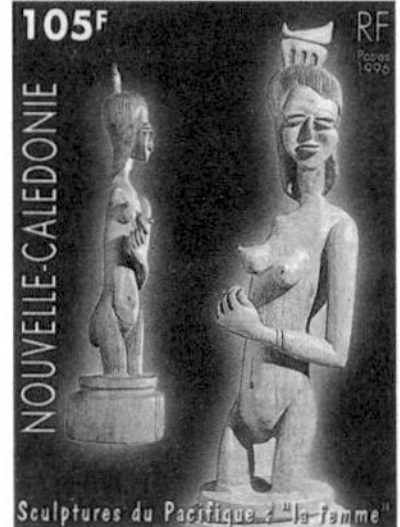
421 "The Woman" (Elija Trijikone)

1996. Sculptures of the Pacific.
1079 **421** 105f. multicoloured . . . 2·00 1·40

422 Ordination, St. Joseph's Cathedral,Noumea

1996. 50th Anniv of Ordination of First Priests in New Caledonia.
1080 **422** 160f. multicoloured . . . 3·00 2·00

423 "Man" (Paula Boi)

1996. Pacific Painters.
1081 **423** 200f. multicoloured . . . 3·50 2·50

424 Gaica Dance

1996.
1082 **424** 500f. multicoloured . . . 8·50 5·50

425 Great Reef

1996. Air. 50th Autumn Stamp Show, Paris. Multicoloured.
1083 95f. Type **425** . . . . . . 1·75 1·25
1084 95f. Mount Koghi . . . . . 1·75 1·25

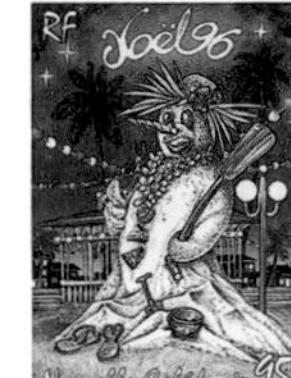
426 Decorated Sandman

1996. Christmas.
1085 **426** 95f. multicoloured . . . 1·75 90

427 Horned Tortoises

1997. Air.
1086 **427** 95f. multicoloured . . . 1·75 1·40

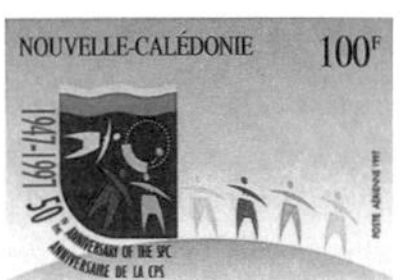
428 Emblem

1997. Air. 50th Anniv of South Pacific Commission.
1087 **428** 100f. multicoloured . . . 1·75 1·25

429 Junk, Hong Kong, Ox and Flag

1997. Air. "Hong Kong '97" International stamp exhibiton. Year of the Ox. Multicoloured.
1088 95f. Type **429** . . . . 1·75 1·25
MS1089 121 × 91 mm. 75f. Farmer ploughing with ox (39 × 29 mm); 75f. Cattle grazing (39 × 29 mm) 3·50 3·50

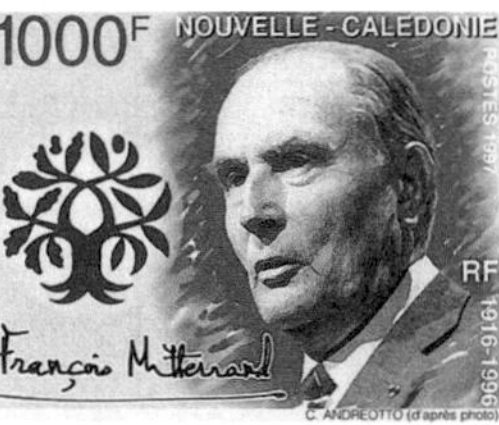
430 Mitterrand

1997. 1st Death Anniv of Francois Mitterrand (French President, 1981–95).
1090 **430** 1000f. multicoloured . . 16·00 12·00

431 Windmill ("Letters from My Windmill") 432 Lapita Pot with Geometric Pattern

1997. Death Centenary of Alphonse Daudet (writer). Multicoloured.
1091 65f. Type **431** . . . . . . 1·40 90
1092 65f. Boy sitting by wall ("The Little Thing") . . . 1·40 90
1093 65f. Hunter in jungle ("Tartarinde Tarascon") 1·40 90
1094 65f. Daudet at work . . . . 1·40 90
MS1095 100 × 120 mm. Nos. 1091/4 5·00 5·00

1997. Air. Melanesian Pottery in Noumea Museum. Multicoloured.
1096 95f. Type **432** . . . . . . 1·75 1·25
1097 95f. Lapita pot with "face" design . . . . 1·75 1·25

433 French Parliament Building and Lafleur

1997. Appointment of Henri Lafleur as First New Caledonian Senator in French Parliament.
1098 **433** 105f. multicoloured . . . 2·00 1·50

434 Cotton Harlequin Bug

1997. Insects. Multicoloured.
1099 65f. Type **434** . . . . . . 1·50 1·25
1100 65f. "Kanakia gigas" . . . 1·50 1·25
1101 65f. "Aenetus cohici" (moth) 1·50 1·25

435 Iekawe

1997. 5th Death Anniv of Jacques Ieneic Iekawe (first Melanesian Prefect).
1102 **435** 250f. multicoloured . . . 4·00 3·00

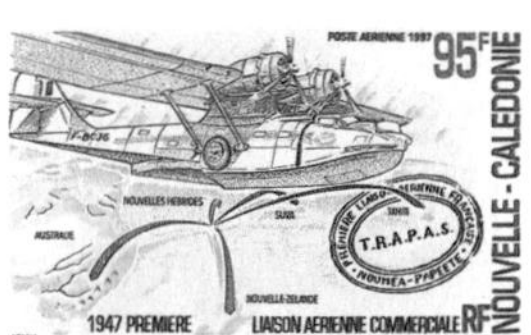
436 Consolidated Catalina Flying Boat and South Pacific Routes Map

1997. Air. 50th Anniv of Establishment by TRAPAS of First Commercial Air Routes in South Pacific. Multicoloured.
1103 95f. Type **436** . . . . . . 1·50 1·25
1104 95f. TRAPAS emblem, seaplane and New Caledonia domestic flight routes . . . . 1·50 1·25

437 Kagu 438 Cup and Harness Racing

1997.
1105 **437** 5f. violet 10 10
1107 30f. orange 50 40
1113 95f. blue . . . . 1·50 60
1114 100f. blue . . . . 1·00 80

No. 1114 also comes self-adhesive.
See also No. 1128.

1997. Equestrian Sports. Multicoloured.
1118 65f. Type **438** . . . . . . 1·25 80
1119 65f. Cup and horse racing 1·25 80

439 Port de France (engraving)

1997.
1120 **439** 95f. multicoloured . . . 1·50 1·00

440 "Marianne", Voter and Tiki 441 Seahorses

1997. 50th Anniv of First Elections of Melanesian Representatives to French Parliament.
1121 **440** 150f. multicoloured . . . 2·40 1·75

1997. 5th Indo-Pacific Fishes Conference.
1122 **441** 100f. multicoloured . . . 1·50 1·00

442 Hammerhead Shark Dance Mask (Ken Thaiday)

1997. Pacific Art and Culture. Multicoloured.
1123 100f. Type **442** . . . . . . 1·50 1·10
1124 100f. Painting of traditional Melanesian images by Yvette Bouquet . . . . . 1·50 1·10
1125 100f. "Doka" (figurines by Frank Haikiu) . . . . . 1·50 1·10

443 Father Christmas surfing to Earth

1997. Christmas. Multicoloured.
1126 95f. Type **443** . . . . . . 1·40 1·00
1127 100f. Dolphin with "Meilleurs Voeux" banner 1·40 1·00

1998. As Nos. 1107/13 but with no value expressed. Ordinary or self-adhesive gum.
1128 **437** (70f.) red . . . . 1·00 40

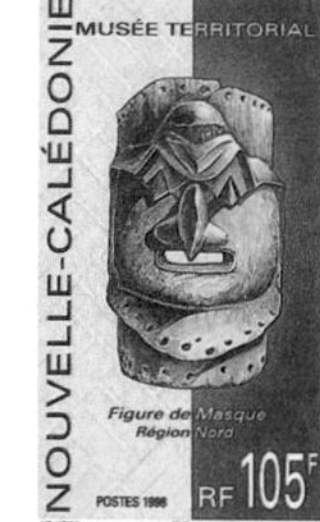
444 "Lentinus tuber-regium" 445 Mask from Northern Region

1998. Edible Mushrooms. Multicoloured.
1130 70f. Type **444** . . . . . . 1·00 80
1131 70f. "Morchella anteridiformis" . . . . . 1·00 80
1132 70f. "Volvaria bombycina" 1·00 80

1998. Territorial Museum. Multicoloured.
1133 105f. Type **445** . . . . . . 1·50 1·00
1134 110f. Section of door frame from Central Region . . . 1·50 1·00

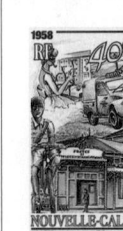

446 Painting by Gauguin

1998. 150th Birth Anniv of Paul Gauguin (painter).
1135 **446** 405f. multicoloured . . . 5·00 3·75

447 Player

1998. World Cup Football Championship, France.
1136 **447** 100f. multicoloured . . . 1·40 95

448 "Mitimitia"

1998. Tjibaou Cultural Centre. Multicoloured.
1137 30f. Type **448** 40 30
1138 70f. Jean-Marie Tjibaou (politician) and Centre . . 90 70
1139 70f. Detail of a Centre building (Renzo Piano) (vert) 90 70
1140 105f. "Man Bird" (Mathias Kauage) (vert) . . . . . 1·40 95

449 Broken Chains and Slaves

1998. 150th Anniv of Abolition of Slavery.
1141 **449** 130f. brown, blue and purple . . . . 1·60 1·25

450 Dogs watching Postman delivering Letter

1998. Stamp Day.
1142 **450** 70f. multicoloured . . . 85 65

451 Vincent Bouquet

1998. 50th Anniv of Election of First President of Commission of Chiefs.
1143 **451** 110f. multicoloured . . . 1·40 95

452 Noumea Fantasia, 1903

1998. 100 Years of Arab Presence.
1144 **452** 80f. multicoloured . . . 95 70

453 Departure

1998. "Portugal 98" International Stamp Exhibition, Lisbon. 500th Anniv of Vasco da Gama's Voyage to India via Cape of Good Hope. Multicoloured.
1145 100f. Type **453** . . . . . . 1·40 95
1146 100f. Fleet at Cape of Good Hope . . . . 1·40 95
1147 100f. Vasco da Gama meeting Indian king . . . 1·40 95
1148 100f. Vasco da Gama in armorial shield flanked by plants . . . . 1·40 95
MS1149 160 × 130 mm. 70f. Route map (39 × 51 mm; 70f. Vasco da Gama (39 × 51 mm); 70f. *Sao Gabriel* (flagship) and fleet (39 × 51 mm) . . . . 3·50 3·50

454 Kagu

455 Liberty Trees

1998. Endangered Species. The Kagu. Multicoloured.
1150 5f. Type **454** 10 10
1151 10f. Kagu by branch . . . 10 10
1152 15f. Two kagus 20 15
1153 70f. Two kagus, one with wings outspread 80 60

1998. 50th Anniv of Universal Declaration of Human Rights.
1154 **455** 70f. green, black and blue 85 65

456 "Prison, Nou Island" (engraving)

1998.
1155 **456** 155f. multicoloured . . . 1·90 1·40

457 View of Island

1998. Regional Scenes. Multicoloured.
1156 100f. Type **457** . . . . . . 1·40 95
1157 100f. View of sea . . . . . 1·40 95

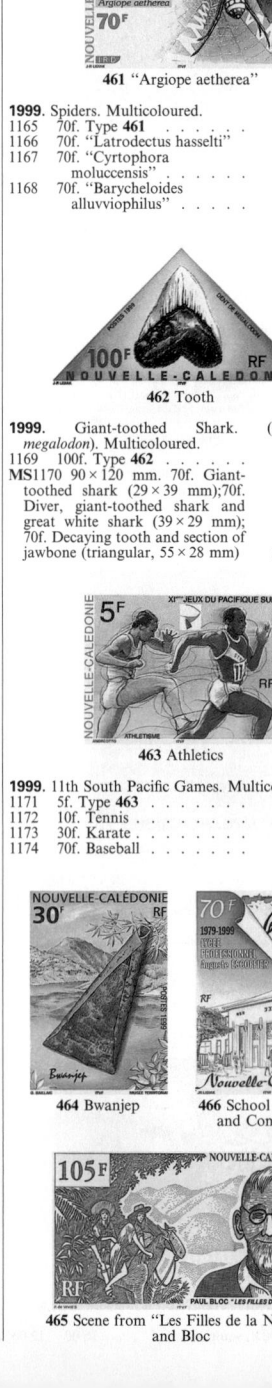

458 Switchboard, Post Van, Postman on Bicycle and Post Office (1958)

459 Marine Life forming Christmas Tree ("Merry Christmas")

1998. 40th Anniv of Posts and Telecommunications Office. Multicoloured.
1158 70f. Type **458** 75 55
1159 70f. Automatic service machine, woman with mobile phone, dish aerial, motor cycle courier and post office (1998) 75 55

1998. Greetings stamps. Multicoloured.
1160 100f. Type **459** . . . . . . 1·10 80
1161 100f. Treasure chest ("Best Wishes") . . . . 1·10 80
1162 100f. Fish ("Good Holiday") . . . . 1·10 80
1163 100f. Fishes and reefs ("Happy Birthday") . . . 1·10 80

460 Map, Memorial and "Monique"

1998. 20th Anniv of Erection of Memorial to the Victims of the "Monique" (inter-island freighter) Disaster.
1164 **460** 130f. multicoloured . . . 1·40 1·00

461 "Argiope aetherea"

1999. Spiders. Multicoloured.
1165 70f. Type **461** 75 55
1166 70f. "Latrodectus hasselti" 75 55
1167 70f. "Cyrtophora moluccensis" 75 55
1168 70f. "Barycheloides alluvviophilus" 75 55

462 Tooth

1999. Giant-toothed Shark. (*Carcharodon megalodon*). Multicoloured.
1169 100f. Type **462** . . . . . . 1·10 80
MS1170 90 × 120 mm. 70f. Giant-toothed shark (29 × 39 mm);70f. Diver, giant-toothed shark and great white shark (39 × 29 mm); 70f. Decaying tooth and section of jawbone (triangular, 55 × 28 mm) 3·00 2·00

463 Athletics

1999. 11th South Pacific Games. Multicoloured.
1171 5f. Type **463** 10 10
1172 10f. Tennis 10 10
1173 30f. Karate 30 55
1174 70f. Baseball 75 55

464 Bwanjep

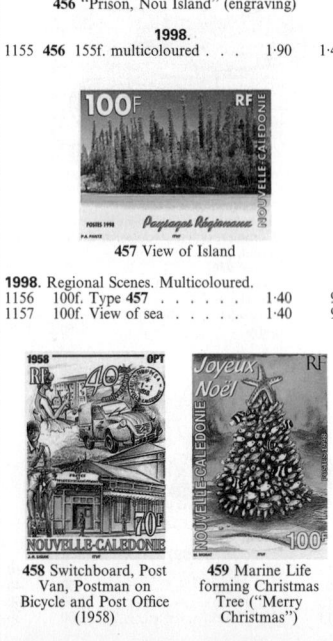

466 School Building and Computer

465 Scene from "Les Filles de la Neama" and Bloc

1999. Traditional Musical Instruments. Mult.
1175 30f. Type **464** 30 25
1176 70f. Bells 75 55
1177 100f. Flutes . . . . 1·10 80

1999. 29th Death Anniv of Paul Bloc (writer).
1178 **465** 105f. blue, green & purple . . . . 1·10 80

1999. 20th Anniv of Auguste Escoffier Commercial and Hotelier Professional School. Multicoloured.
1179 70f. Type **466** 75 55
1180 70f. School building and chef's hat 75 55

467 Unloading Supplies, Helicopters and Map

1999. Humanitarian Aid.
1181 **467** 135f. multicoloured . . . 1·40 1·00

468 10c. Napoleon III Stamp, 1860

1999. 140th Anniv (2000) of First New Caledonian Stamp and "Philexfrance 99" International Stamp Exhibition, Paris.
1182 **468** 70f. multicoloured . . . 75 55
MS1183 155 × 110 mm. 100f. black (two 1860 10c. stamps) (recess) (36 × 29 mm); 100f. multicoloured (1860 10c. stamp) (thermography)(36 × 29 mm); 100f. Close-up of Napoleon's head (litho) (36 × 29 mm);100f. gold and black (1860 10c. stamp) (embossing); 700f. 1997 Kagu design and hologram of Napoleon's head (44 × 35 mm) 12·50 12·50

469 Food Platter

1999. Hotels and Restaurants. Multicoloured.
1184 5f. Type **469** 10 10
1185 30f. Seafood platter 30 25
1186 70f. Hotel cabins by lake . . 75 55
1187 100f. Modern hotel and swimming pool . . . . . 1·00 80

470 Eiffel Tower, Lighthouse with 1949 and 1999 Aircraft

1999. Air. 50th Anniv of First Paris–Noumea Scheduled Flight.
1188 **470** 100f. multicoloured . . . 1·00 80

471 Paintings (½-size illustration)

1999.
1189 **471** 70f. multicoloured . . . 75 55

472 Aji Aboro (Kanak dance)

1999.
1190 **472** 70f. multicoloured . . . 75 55

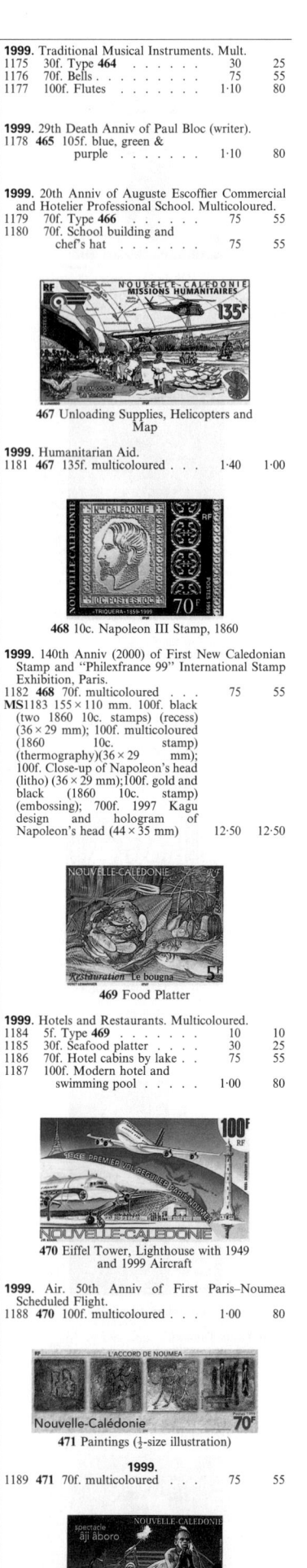

473 Chateau Hagen

1999. Historic Monuments of South Province.
1191 **473** 155f. multicoloured . . . 1·60 1·10

474 Children protecting Tree

1999. Nature Protection: "Don't touch my Tree".
1192 **474** 30f. multicoloured . . . 30 25

475 Children around Tree

1999. Greetings Stamps. Multicoloured.
1193 100f. Type **475** ("Merry Christmas") . . . . . . 1·00 85
1194 100f. Children with flowers and star ("Best Wishes 2000") . . . . 1·00 85
1195 100f. Children and Year 2000 cake ("Happy Birthday") . . . . 1·00 85
1196 100f. Children looking in pram ("Congratulations") 1·00 85

476 Amedee Lighthouse

2000.
1197 **476** 100f. multicoloured . . . 1·00 80

477 *L'Emile Renouf* (four-masted steel barque)

2000. Centenary of Loss of *Emile Renouf* on Durand Reef, Insel Mare.
1198 **477** 135f. multicoloured . . . 1·40 1·00

478 Painted Shells (Gilles Subileau)

2000. Pacific Painters.
1199 **478** 155f. multicoloured . . . 1·60 1·10

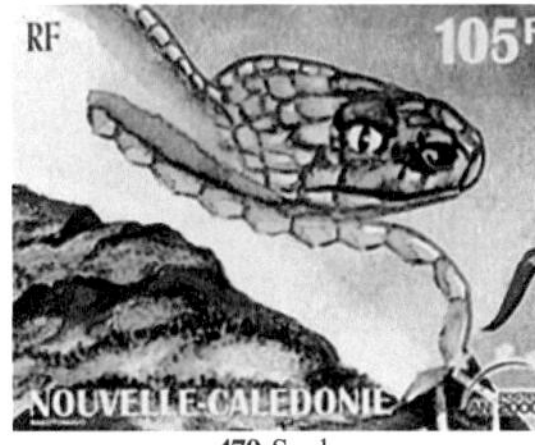

479 Snake

2000. Chinese New Year. Year of the Dragon. Sheet 121 × 90 mm containing T **479** and similar horiz design. Multicoloured.
MS1200 105f. Type **479**; 105f. Dragon . . . . 2·40 2·40

480 Prawn

2000. Noumia Aquarium. Multicoloured.
1201 70f. Type **480** 75 55
1202 70f. Fluorescent corals . . . 75 55
1203 70f. Hump-headed wrasse (*Cheilinus undulatus*) . . . 75 55

481 Lockheed P-38 Lightning Fighter

2000. Air. Birth Centenary of Antoine de Saint-Exupery (writer and pilot).
1204 **481** 130f. multicoloured . . . 1·40 1·00

482 Aerial View

2000. Mangrove Swamp, Voh.
1205 **482** 100f. multicoloured . . . 1·00 80

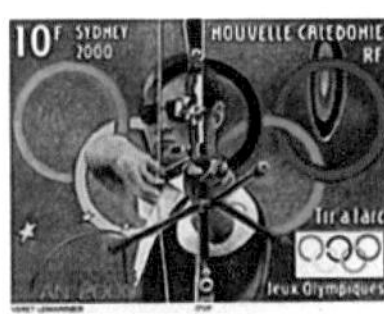

483 Archery

2000. Olympic Games, Sydney. Multicoloured.
1206 10f. Type **483** 10 10
1207 30f. Boxing 30 35
1208 80f. Cycling 85 70
1209 100f. Fencing . . . . 1·00 80

484 Museum Exhibit

2000. Museum of New Caledonia. Multicoloured.
1210 90f. Type **484** 90 75
1211 105f. Museum exhibit . . . 1·10 85

485 Library Building and Lucien Bernheim

2000. Bernheim Library, Noumea.
1212 **485** 500f. brown, blue and green . . . . 5·00 4·25

486 Painting

2000. Eighth Pacific Arts Festival, Kanaky, New Caledonia. Sheet 120 × 90 mm containing T **486** and similar horiz designs. Multicoloured.
MS1213 70f. Type **486**; 70f. Human figures; 70f. Stylized faces and fish; 70f. Stylized faces and fishes on coloured squares . . . . . . 3·00 3·00

487 Henri Dunant (founder), Baby and Patients with Volunteers

2000. Red Cross.
1214 **487** 100f. multicoloured . . . 1·00 80

488 Canoeist

2000. Regional Landscapes. Multicoloured.
1215 100f. Type **488** . . . . . . 1·00 80
1216 100f. Speedboat near island 1·00 80
1217 100f. Sunset and man on raft . . . . 1·00 80

489 Queen Hortense

490 Boy on Roller Skates (Kevyn Pamoiloun)

2000.
1218 **489** 110f. red, green and blue 1·10 85

2000. "Philately at School". Entries in Children's Painting Competition. Multicoloured.
1219 70f. Type **490** 75 55
1220 70f. People using airborne vehicles (Lise-Marie Samanich) 75 55
1221 70f. Aliens (Alexandre Mandin) 75 55

491 Kagu Parents ("Congratulations")

2000. Greetings Stamps. Multicoloured.
1222 100f. Type **491** . . . . . . 1·00 80
1223 100f. Kagu on deck chair ("Happy Holidays") . . . 1·00 80
1224 100f. Kagu with bunch of flowers ("Best Wishes") 1·00 80

492 The Nativity

2000. Christmas.
1225 **492** 100f. multicoloured . . . 1·00 80

493 Snakes

2001. Chinese New Year. Year of the Snake. Multicoloured.
1226 100f. Type **493** . . . . . . 1·00 80
MS1227 130 × 91 mm. 70f. Snake and Pacific island; 70f. Snake and Chinese symbols . . . . 1·50 1·50

494 *France II* (barque)

2001. Reconstruction of *France II* .
1228 **494** 110f. multicoloured . . . 1·10 90

495 Two Nautili

2001. Noumea Aquarium. The New Calendonia Nautilus. Multicoloured.
1229 100f. Type **495** . . . . . . 1·00 80
1230 100f. Section through nautilus . . . . 1·00 80
1231 100f. Two nautili (different) 1·00 80

496 New Caledonian Crow, Tools and Emblem

2001. Association for the Protection of New Caledonian Nature (ASNNC).
1232 **496** 70f. multicoloured . . . 70 60

497 Humpback Whale and Calf

2001. Operation Cetaces (marine mammal South Pacific study programme). Multicoloured.
1233 100f. Type **497** . . . . . . 1·00 80
1234 100f. Whales leaping . . . . 1·00 80

498 "Guards of Gaia" (statue) (I.Waia)

2001. Ko Neva 2000 Prize Winner.
1235 **498** 70f. multicoloured . . . 70 60

499 "Vision of Oceania" (J. Lebars)

2001.
1236 **499** 110f. multicoloured . . . 1·10 90

500 Profiles

2001. Year of Communication.
1237 **500** 265f. multicoloured . . . 2·75 2·25

501 Air International Caledonie Airbus A310-300

2001. Air. First Anniv of Noumea–Osaka Passenger Service.
1238 **501** 110f. multicoloured . . . 1·10 90

502 "The Solitary Boatman" (Marik)

2001. Pacific Painters.
1239 **502** 110f. multicoloured . . . 1·10 90

503 Observation Capsule on Coral Reef

2001.
1240 **503** 135f. multicoloured . . . 1·40 1·25

504 Qanono Church, Lifou

2001.
1241 **504** 500f. multicoloured . . . 5·00 4·00

505 Fernande Leriche (educator and author)

507 Kite Surfer

506 Cyclists

2001.
1242 **505** 155f. brown, red and blue . . . . 1·60 1·25

2001. 1st Olympic Gold Medal for New Caledonian Sportsman.
1243 **506** 265f. multicoloured . . . 2·75 2·25

2001.
1244 **507** 100f. multicoloured . . . 1·00 80

508 Children on Book

2001. School Philately.
1245 **508** 70f. multicoloured . . . 70 60

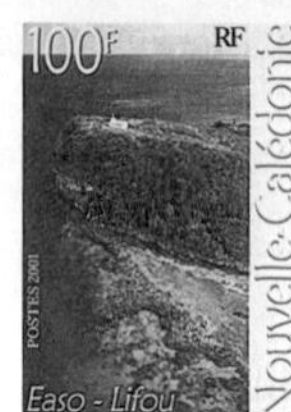
509 Easo

2001. Lifou Island. Multicoloured.
1246 100f. Type **509** . . . . . . 1·00 80
1247 100f. Jokin . . . . 1·00 80

510 Father Christmas

2001. Christmas. Multicoloured.
1248 100f. Type **510** . . . . . . 1·00 80
1249 100f. Bat with spotted wings and "Meilleurs Voeux" 1·00 80
1250 100f. Bat with party hat and red nose and "Vive la Fete" . . . . 1·00 80

511 Horse and Sea Horse

2002. Chinese New Year. Year of the Horse. Multicoloured.
1251 100f. Type **511** . . . . . . 1·25 1·00
MS1252 190 × 30 mm. 70f. Horse's head; 70f. Sea horse . . . . . 1·75 1·40

512 Two Flying Foxes

2002. St. Valentine's Day.
1253 **512** 100f. multicoloured . . . 1·25 1·00

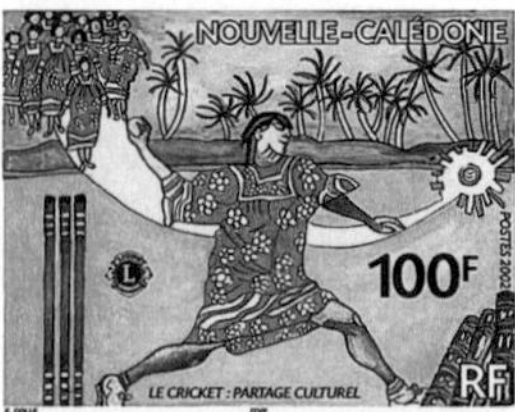
513 Cricketer in Traditional Dress

2002. Cricket.
1254 **513** 100f. multicoloured . . . 1·25 1·00

514 Ancient Axe

2002.
1255 **514** 505f. multicoloured . . . 6·00 5·00

515 Hobie 16 Catamaran

2002. Hobie 16 Catamaran World Championship.
1256 **515** 70f. multicoloured . . . 85 70

516 Loggerhead Turtle (*Caretta caretta*)

2002. Noumea Aquarium. Sheet 185 × 120 mm in shape of turtle containing T **516** and similar horiz designs. Multicoloured.
MS1257 30f. Type **516**; 30f. Green sea turtle (*Chelonia mydas*); 70f. Hawksbill turtle (*Eretmochelys imbricata*) (inscr "imbricat"); 70f. Leatherback sea turtle (*Dermochelys coriacea*) . . . . 2·40 2·00

517 Player

2002. World Cup Football Championship 2002, Japan and South Korea.
1258 **517** 100f. multicoloured . . . 1·25 1·00

518 Coffee Bean Plant

2002. Coffee Production. Multicoloured.
1259 70f. Type **518** 85 70
1260 70f. Coffee production process 85 70
1261 70f. Cafe and cup of coffee 85 70

519 *Alcmene* (French corvette)

2002. Exploration of Coast of New Caledonia by *Alcmene*.
1262 **519** 210f. multicoloured . . . 2·60 2·10

520 Emma Piffault (statue)

521 Circus School

2002. Emma Piffault Commemoration.
1263 **520** 10f. multicoloured . . . 15 10

2002.
1264 **521** 70f. multicoloured . . . 85 70

522 Telescope and Caillard

2002. 90th Birth Anniv of Edmond Caillard (astronomer).
1265 **522** 70f. multicoloured . . . 85 70

523 Face in Landscape, Couple, Ship and Birds

2002. Jean Mariotti (writer).
1266 **523** 70f. multicoloured . . . 85 70

524 Adult Sperm Whale and Calf

2002. New Caledonia–Norfolk Island Joint Issue. Operation Cetaces (marine mammal study). Multicoloured.
1267 100f. Type **524** . . . . . . 1·25 1·00
1268 100f. Sperm whale attacked by giant squid . . . . . 1·25 1·00
Stamps of similar designs were issued by Norfolk Islands.

525 Coral Snake Musicians

2002. Christmas.
1269 **525** 100f. multicoloured . . . 1·25 1·00

526 Central Mountain Chain

2002. International Year of Mountains. Litho.
1270 **526** 100f. multicoloured . . . 1·25 1·00

527 Powder Store, Bourail Military Post (½-size illustration)

2002.
1271 **527** 1000f. multicoloured . . 12·00 9·50

528 "Life and Death" (Adrian Trohmae)

2002. Pacific Painters.
1272 **528** 100f. multicoloured . . . 1·25 85

529 Couple enclosed in Heart

2003. St. Valentine's Day.
1273 **529** 100f. multicoloured . . . 1·10 90

530 Goat's Head

2003. Chinese New Year. Year of the Goat.
1274 **530** 100f. multicoloured . . . 1·10 90

531 Kagu 532 1903 Stamp

2003. (a) With face value.
1275 **531** 10f. green 10 10
1276 15f. agate 15 10
1277 30f. orange 35 30

(b) No value expressed. Ordinary or self-adhesive gum.
1278 (70f.) scarlet 80 65

2003. Centenary of First Kagu Stamp.
1290 **532** 70f. multicoloured . . . 80 65

533 High-finned Grouper (*Epinephelus maculates*)

2003. Noumea Aquarium. Groupers. Multicoloured.
1291 70f. Type **533** 80 85
1292 70f. Purple-spotted grouper (*Plectropomus leopardus*) 80 85
1293 70f. Hump-back grouper (*Cromileptes altivelis*) . . 80 65

534 School Building

2003. Grand Noumea High School.
1294 **534** 70f. multicoloured . . . 80 65

535 Shooting

2003. 12th South Pacific Games, Suva. Multicoloured.
1295 5f. Type **535** 10 10
1296 30f. Rugby 35 30
1297 70f. Tennis 80 65

536 Adult Sea Cow and Calf (½-size illustration)

2003. Sea Cow (*Dugong dugon*). Operation Cetaces (marine mammal study). Multicoloured.
1298 100f. Type **536** . . . . . . 1·10 90
1299 100f. Adult and calf grazing (40 × 30 mm) . . . . . . 1·10 90
Nos. 1298/9 were printed together, se-tenant, forming a composite design.

537 "The Harvest"

2003. Death Centenary of Paul Gauguin (artist) (1st issue).
1300 **537** 100f. multicoloured . . . 1·10 90
See also No. **MS**1303.

538 Governor Feillet

2003. Death Centenary of Governor Feillet (first governor).
1301 **538** 100f. black and green . . 1·10 90

539 Aircalin Airbus A330–200

2003. 20th Anniv of Aircalin.
1302 **539** 100f. multicoloured . . . 1·10 90

540 Tahitian Heads (sketch)

2003. Death Centenary of Paul Gauguin (artist) (2nd issue). Sheet 130 × 90 mm containing T **540** and similar vert design. Multicoloured.
MS1303 100f. Type **540**; 100f. Still-life with Maori statue . . . . 2·20 2·20
Stamps of a similar design were issued by Wallis et Futuna.

OFFICIAL STAMPS

O 49 Ancestor Pole O 110 Carved Wooden Pillow (Noumea Museum)

1958. Inscr "OFFICIEL".
O344 **O 49** 1f. yellow 45 85
O345 3f. green 70 90
O346 4f. purple 85 60
O347 5f. blue . . . . 60 1·10
O348 9f. black . . . . . . 1·10 1·25
O349 A 10f. violet . . . . . . 2·75 90
O350 13f. green . . . . . . 1·50 2·50
O351 15f. blue . . . . . . 2·00 1·60
O352 24f. mauve . . . . . 3·00 2·00
O353 26f. orange . . . . . 1·90 4·00
O354 B 50f. green . . . . . . 2·00 4·00
O355 100f. brown . . . . . 9·00 10·00
O356 200f. red . . . . . . 9·75 23·00
DESIGNS: A, B, Different idols.

1973.
O525 **O 110** 1f. green, blk & yell 1·90 1·75
O526 2f. red, black & grn 1·75 1·75
O527 3f. green, blk & brn 1·90 1·75
O528 4f. green, black & bl 1·90 1·75
O529 5f. green, blk & mve 2·00 1·75
O530 9f. green, black & bl 2·25 2·25
O531 10f. green, blk & orge 2·25 2·00
O532 11f. grn, blk & mve 2·00 1·75
O533 12f. green, blk & turq 2·25 2·25
O534 15f. green, blk & lt grn . . . . 2·00 1·75
O535 20f. green, blk & red 2·00 1·75
O536 23f. green, blk & red 2·25 2·25
O537 24f. green, blk & bl 2·00 2·00
O538 25f. green, blk & grey 2·25 2·25
O539 26f. green, blk & yell 2·25 2·00
O540 29f. red, black & grn 2·50 2·25
O541 31f. red, black & yell 2·25 2·25
O542 35f. red, black & yell 2·25 2·25
O543 36f. green, blk & mve 2·25 2·25
O544 38f. red, black & brn 2·25 2·25
O545 40f. red, black & bl 2·25 2·25
O546 42f. green, blk & brn 2·25 2·25
O547 50f. green, blk & bl 2·50 2·25
O548 58f. blue, blk & grn 2·75 2·25
O549 65f. red, black & mve 2·75 2·25
O550 76f. red, black & yell 3·25 2·50
O551 100f. green, blk & red 4·00 3·00
O552 200f. green, blk & yell 7·25 4·25

PARCEL POST STAMPS

1926. Optd **Colis Postaux** or surch also.
P137 **17** 50c. on 5f. green on mauve . . . . 35 3·25
P138 1f. blue . . . . 65 3·75
P139 2f. red on blue . . . . . 1·00 4·25

1930. Optd **Colis Postaux**.
P179 **23** 50c. brown and mauve . . 60 3·00
P180 **24** 1f. pink and drab . . . . 60 3·50
P181 2f. brown and orange . . 80 4·00

POSTAGE DUE STAMPS

1903. Postage Due stamps of French Colonies optd **CINQUANTENAIRE 24 SEPTEMBRE 1853 1903** and eagle. Imperf.
D78 U 5c. blue . . . . 1·75 1·10
D79 10c. brown . . . . 7·00 6·25
D80 15c. green . . . . 19·00 4·00
D81 30c. red . . . . 12·50 11·50
D82 50c. purple . . . . . . 60·00 10·00
D83 60c. brown on buff . . . . £200 55·00
D84 1f. pink . . . . 27·00 10·00
D85 2f. brown £750 £800

D 18 Outrigger Canoe D 25 Sambar Stag D 38

1906.
D102 **D 18** 5c. blue on blue . . . 15 45
D103 10c. brown on buff . . 40 2·75
D104 15c. green . . . . . . 45 2·25
D105 20c. black on yellow 50 1·60
D106 30c. red . . . . 55 2·50
D107 50c. blue on cream . . 90 3·25
D108 60c. green on blue . . 75 3·00
D109 1f. green on cream . . 95 3·75

1926. Surch.
D137 **D 18** 2f. on 1f. mauve . . . 1·00 5·00
D138 3f. on 1f. brown . . . 1·00 5·00

1928.
D179 **D 25** 2c. brown and blue . . 15 2·25
D180 4c. green and red . . . 25 2·25
D181 5c. grey and orange 35 2·75
D182 10c. blue and mauve 20 1·00
D183 15c. red and olive . . 25 2·75
D184 20c. olive and red . . 1·50 3·25
D185 25c. blue and brown 25 3·00
D186 30c. olive and green 20 3·25
D187 50c. red and brown . . 2·00 3·75
D188 60c. red and mauve . . 3·00 3·50
D189 1f. green and blue . . 2·50 3·00
D190 2f. olive and red . . . 3·50 3·25
D191 3f. brown and violet 3·00 4·50

1948.
D328 **D 38** 10c. mauve . . . . . 15 2·50
D329 30c. brown . . . . . 20 3·00
D330 50c. green . . . . . . 25 3·00
D331 1f. brown . . . . . . 25 3·00
D332 2f. red . . . . 60 3·00
D333 3f. brown . . . . . . 35 3·00
D334 4f. blue . . . . 60 3·00
D335 5f. red . . . . 50 3·25
D336 10f. green . . . . . . 1·00 3·50
D337 20f. blue . . . . . . 1·10 3·00

D 222 New Caledonian Flying Fox

1983.
D703 **D 223** 1f. multicoloured . . 10 10
D704 2f. multicoloured . . 10 10
D705 3f. multicoloured . . 10 10
D706 4f. multicoloured . . 20 20
D707 5f. multicoloured . . 20 20
D708 10f. multicoloured . . 20 20
D709 20f. multicoloured . . 40 40
D710 40f. multicoloured . . 80 80
D711 50f. multicoloured . . 90 90

NEWFOUNDLAND Pt. 1

An island off the east coast of Canada. A British Dominion merged since 1949 with Canada, whose stamps it now uses.

1857. 12 pence = 1 shilling;
20 shillings = 1 pound.
1866. 100 cents = 1 dollar.

1 2

3 Royal Crown and Heraldic Flowers of the United Kingdom

1857. Imperf.

No.	Type	Description	Unused	Used
1	1	1d. purple	£100	£170
10	2	2d. red	£325	£475
11	3	3d. green	75·00	£150
12	2	4d. red	£2500	£850
13	1	5d. brown	90·00	£325
14	2	6d. red	£3000	£600
7		6½d. red	£2250	£2750
8		8d. red	£250	£450
9		1s. red	£14000	£5000

The frame design of Type **2** differs for each value.

1861. Imperf.

No.	Type	Description	Unused	Used
16	1	1d. brown	£180	£325
17	2	2d. lake	£180	£425
18		4d. lake	32·00	95·00
19	1	5d. brown	70·00	£325
20	2	6d. lake	23·00	£100
21		6½d. lake	75·00	£450
22		8d. lake	85·00	£600
23		1s. lake	38·00	£300

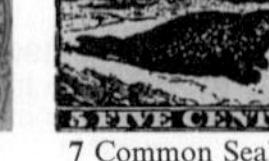

6 Codfish — **7** Common Seal on Ice-floe

8 Prince Consort — **9** Queen Victoria

10 Schooner — **11** Queen Victoria

1866. Perf (2c. also roul).

No.	Type	Description	Unused	Used
31	6	2c. green	80·00	35·00
26	7	5c. brown	£500	£170
32	8	10c. black	£190	40·00
33	9	12c. brown	48·00	48·00
29	10	13c. orange	£100	80·00
30	11	24c. blue	35·00	38·00

12 King Edward VII when Prince of Wales — **14** Queen Victoria

1868. Perf or roul.

No.	Type	Description	Unused	Used
34	12	1c. purple	55·00	50·00
36	14	3c. orange	£250	£100
42		3c. blue	£275	4·25
38	7	5c. black	£250	£110
43		5c. blue	£180	3·50
39	14	6c. red	8·50	19·00

19 Newfoundland Dog — **15** King Edward VII when Prince of Wales

16 Codfish — **17**

18 Common Seal on Ice-floe

20 Atlantic Brigantine — **21** Queen Victoria

1880.

No.	Type	Description	Unused	Used
49	19	½c. red	12·00	7·50
59		½c. black	9·50	5·00
44a	15	1c. brown	27·00	9·00
50a		1c. green	6·00	3·25
46	16	2c. green	50·00	24·00
51		2c. orange	17·00	5·00
47	17	3c. blue	85·00	6·00
52		3c. brown	65·00	1·50
59a	18	5c. blue	70·00	3·75
54	20	10c. black	55·00	55·00

1890.

No.	Type	Description	Unused	Used
55	21	3c. grey	29·00	2·00

This stamp on pink paper was stained by sea-water.

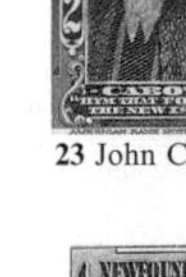

22 Queen Victoria — **23** John Cabot

24 Cape Bonavista — **25** Caribou-hunting

1897. 400th Anniv of Discovery of Newfoundland and 60th Year of Queen Victoria's Reign. Dated "1497 1897".

No.	Type	Description	Unused	Used
66	22	1c. green	2·50	6·50
67	23	2c. red	2·25	2·75
68	24	3c. blue	3·50	1·00
69	25	4c. olive	9·50	4·00
70	–	5c. violet	13·00	3·00
71	–	6c. brown	9·50	3·25
72	–	8c. orange	21·00	9·00
73	–	10c. brown	42·00	7·50
74	–	12c. blue	35·00	6·50
75	–	15c. red	20·00	18·00
76	–	24c. violet	25·00	21·00
77	–	30c. blue	48·00	70·00
78	–	35c. red	60·00	60·00
79	–	60c. black	17·00	13·00

DESIGNS—As Type **24**: 5c. Mining; 6c. Logging; 8c. Fishing; 10c. Cabot's ship, the "Matthew"; 15c. Seals; 24c. Salmon-fishing; 35c. Iceberg. As Type **23**: 12c. Willow/red grouse; 30c. Seal of the Colony; 60c. Henry VII.

1897. Surch **ONE CENT** and bar.

No.	Type	Description	Unused	Used
80	21	1c. on 3c. grey	50·00	22·00

39 Prince Edward, later Duke of Windsor — **40** Queen Victoria

1897. Royal portraits.

No.	Type	Description	Unused	Used
83	39	½c. olive	2·25	1·50
84	40	1c. red	3·25	3·50
85a	–	1c. green	9·00	20
86	–	2c. orange	4·00	4·50
87	–	2c. red	16·00	40
88	–	3c. orange	20·00	30
89	–	4c. violet	25·00	4·50
90	–	5c. blue	42·00	3·00

DESIGNS: 2c. King Edward VII when Prince of Wales; 3c. Queen Alexandra when Princess of Wales; 4c. Queen Mary when Duchess of York; 5c. King George V when Duke of York.

45 Map of Newfoundland — **46** King James I

47 Arms of Colonisation Co. — **49** "Endeavour" (immigrant ship), 1610

1908.

No.	Type	Description	Unused	Used
94	45	2c. lake	27·00	1·00

1910. Dated "1610 1910".

No.	Type	Description	Unused	Used
109	46	1c. green	1·75	30
107	47	2c. red	5·00	40
97	–	3c. olive	6·00	16·00
98	49	4c. violet	15·00	14·00
108	–	5c. blue	8·00	2·75
111	–	6c. purple	18·00	45·00
112	–	8c. bistre	48·00	70·00
102	–	9c. green	42·00	80·00
103	–	10c. grey	55·00	£100
115	–	12c. brown	60·00	60·00
105	–	15c. black	65·00	£100

DESIGNS—HORIZ: 5c. Cupids; 8c. Mosquito; 9c. Logging camp, Red Indian Lake; 10c. Paper mills, Grand Falls. VERT: 3c. John Guy; 6c. Sir Francis Bacon; 12c. King Edward VII; 15c. King George V. (Cupids and Mosquito are places).

57 Queen Mary — **58** King George V

67 Seal of Newfoundland

1911. Coronation.

No.	Type	Description	Unused	Used
117	57	1c. green	9·00	30
118	58	2c. red	4·50	20
119	–	3c. brown	21·00	22·00
120	–	4c. purple	19·00	26·00
121	–	5c. blue	7·00	1·50
122	–	6c. grey	13·00	25·00
123	–	8c. blue	55·00	75·00
124	–	9c. blue	19·00	45·00
125	–	10c. green	29·00	40·00
126	–	12c. plum	25·00	45·00
127	67	15c. lake	20·00	45·00

PORTRAITS—VERT (As Type **57/8**): 3c. Duke of Windsor when Prince of Wales; 4c. King George VI when Prince Albert; 5c. Princess Mary, the Princess Royal; 6c. Duke of Gloucester when Prince Henry; 8c. Duke of Kent when Prince George; 9c. Prince John; 10c. Queen Alexandra; 12c. Duke of Connaught.

68 Caribou

1919. Newfoundland Contingent, 1914–18.

No.	Type	Description	Unused	Used
130	68	1c. green	3·75	20
131		2c. red	3·75	85
132		3c. brown	7·00	20
133		4c. mauve	7·50	70
134		5c. blue	9·00	1·25
135		6c. grey	7·00	40·00
136		8c. purple	11·00	45·00
137		10c. green	7·00	4·25
138		12c. orange	18·00	60·00
139		15c. blue	15·00	60·00
140		24c. brown	22·00	28·00
141		36c. olive	15·00	29·00

DESIGNS—Each inscr with the name of a different action: 1c. Suvla Bay; 3c. Gueudecourt; 4c. Beaumont Hamel; 6c. Monchy; 10c. Steenbeck; 15c. Langemarck; 24c. Cambrai; 36c. Combles. The 2, 5, 8 and 12c. are inscribed "Royal Naval Reserve-Ubique".

1919. Air. Hawker Flight. No. 132a optd **FIRST TRANS- ATLANTIC AIR POST April, 1919.**

No.	Type	Description	Unused	Used
142	68	3c. brown	£15000	£8000

1919. Air. Alcock and Brown Flight. Surch **Trans-Atlantic AIR POST, 1919. ONE DOLLAR.**

No.	Type	Description	Unused	Used
143		$1 on 15c. red (No. 75)	£110	£110

1920. Surch in words between bars.

No.	Type	Description	Unused	Used
144		2c. on 30c. blue (No. 77)	4·50	19·00
146		3c. on 15c. red (No. 75)	21·00	17·00
147		3c. on 35c. red (No. 78)	8·50	13·00

1921. Air. Optd **AIR MAIL to Halifax, N.S. 1921.**

No.	Type	Description	Unused	Used
148a		35c. red (No. 78)	80·00	80·00

73 Twin Hills, Tor's Cove — **75** Statue of Fighting Newfoundlander, St. John's

1923.

No.	Type	Description	Unused	Used
149	73	1c. green	1·75	20
150	–	2c. red	1·00	10
151	75	3c. brown	1·50	10
152	–	4c. purple	1·00	30
153	–	5c. blue	2·50	1·75
154	–	6c. grey	4·50	8·50
155	–	8c. purple	6·00	3·50
156	–	9c. green	18·00	29·00
157	–	10c. violet	6·50	3·50
158	–	11c. olive	3·75	17·00
159	–	12c. lake	3·25	10·00
160	–	15c. blue	3·25	19·00
161	–	20c. brown	10·00	12·00
162	–	24c. brown	45·00	75·00

DESIGNS—HORIZ: 2c. South-west Arm, Trinity; 6c. Upper Steadies, Humber River; 8c. Quidi Vidi, near St. John's; 9c. Caribou crossing lake; 11c. Shell Bird Island; 12c. Mount Moriah, Bay of Islands; 20c. Placentia. VERT: 4c. Humber River; 5c. Coast at Trinity; 10c. Humber River Canon; 15c. Humber River, near Little Rapids; 24c. Topsail Falls.

1927. Air. Optd **Air Mail DE PINEDO 1927.**

No.	Type	Description	Unused	Used
163		60c. black (No. 79)	£28000	£7500

88 Newfoundland and Labrador — **89** S.S. "Caribou"

90 King George V and Queen Mary — **91** Duke of Windsor when Prince of Wales

1928. Publicity issue.

No.	Type	Description	Unused	Used
164	88	1c. green	2·25	1·25
180	89	2c. red	1·75	40
181	90	3c. brown	1·00	20
201	91	4c. mauve	2·00	1·25
183	–	5c. grey	7·00	3·25
184a	–	6c. blue	2·25	17·00
170	–	8c. brown	3·75	28·00
171	–	9c. green	2·00	15·00
185	–	10c. violet	4·25	3·50
173	–	12c. lake	2·00	21·00
174a	–	14c. purple	6·00	8·50
175	–	15c. blue	3·75	28·00
176a	–	20c. black	2·75	7·00
177	–	28c. green	28·00	48·00
178	–	30c. brown	6·00	17·00

DESIGNS—HORIZ: 5c. Express train; 6c. Newfoundland Hotel, St. John's; 8c. Heart's Content; 10c. War Memorial, St. John's; 15c. Vickers Vimy aircraft; 20c. Parliament House, St. John's. VERT: 9, 14c. Cabot Tower, St. John's; 12, 28c. G.P.O., St. John's; 30c. Grand Falls, Labrador.

1929. Surch **THREE CENTS**.

No.	Type	Description	Unused	Used
188		3c. on 6c. (No. 154)	1·00	5·50

1930. Air. No. 141 surch **Trans-Atlantic AIR MAIL By B. M. "Columbia" September 1930 Fifty Cents.**

No.	Type	Description	Unused	Used
191	68	50c. on 36c. olive	£5500	£450

103 Westland Limousine III and Dog-team

104 Vickers Vimy Biplane and early Sailing Packet

105 Routes of historic Trans-Atlantic Flights

1931. Air.

192	**103**	15c. brown	7·50	14·00
193	**104**	50c. green	32·00	55·00
194	**105**	$1 blue	50·00	95·00

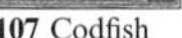

107 Codfish

108 King George V

110 Duke of Windsor when Prince of Wales

111 Reindeer

112 Queen Elizabeth II when Princess

121 Corner Brook Paper Mills

1932.

209	**107**	1c. green	2·75	30
276		1c. grey	20	1·00
210	**108**	2c. red	1·50	20
223		2c. green	1·25	10
211	–	3c. brown	1·50	20
212	**110**	4c. lilac	6·00	2·00
224		4c. red	3·00	40
213	**111**	5c. purple	5·00	1·75
225c		5c. violet	70	30
214	**112**	6c. blue	4·00	14·00
226	–	7c. lake	2·75	3·75
282	**121**	8c. red	2·00	2·75
215	–	10c. brown	70	65
216	–	14c. black	4·25	5·50
217	–	15c. purple	1·25	2·00
218	–	20c. green	1·00	1·00
228	–	24c. blue	1·00	3·25
219	–	25c. grey	2·00	2·25
220	–	30c. blue	38·00	35·00
289	–	48c. brown	4·00	7·00

DESIGNS—VERT: 3c. Queen Mary; 7c. Queen Mother when Duchess of York. HORIZ: 10c. Salmon; 14c. Newfoundland dog; 15c. Harp seal; 20c. Cape Race; 24c. Loading iron ore, Bell Island; 25c. Sealing fleet; 30, 48c. Fishing fleet.

1932. Air. Surch **TRANS-ATLANTIC WEST TO EAST Per Dornier DO-X May, 1932. One Dollar and Fifty Cents**.

221	**105**	$1.50 on $1 blue	£200	£225

1933. Optd **L. & S. Post.** ("Land and Sea") between bars.

229	**103**	15c. brown	3·75	12·00

124 Put to Flight

1933. Air.

230	**124**	5c. brown	18·00	18·00
231	–	10c. yellow	14·00	32·00
232	–	30c. blue	32·00	45·00
233	–	60c. green	50·00	£100
234	–	75c. brown	50·00	£100

DESIGNS: 10c. Land of Heart's Delight; 30c. Spotting the herd; 60c. News from home; 75c. Labrador.

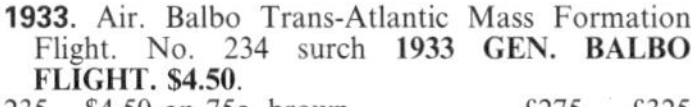

1933. Air. Balbo Trans-Atlantic Mass Formation Flight. No. 234 surch **1933 GEN. BALBO FLIGHT. $4.50**.

235		$4.50 on 75c. brown	£275	£325

130 Sir Humphrey Gilbert

131 Compton Castle, Devon

1933. 350th Anniv of Annexation. Dated "1583 1933".

236	**130**	1c. black	1·00	1·50
237	**131**	2c. green	1·50	70
238	–	3c. brown	2·25	1·25
239	–	4c. red	80	50
240	–	5c. violet	2·00	80
241	–	7c. blue	14·00	17·00
242	–	8c. orange	8·00	15·00
243	–	9c. blue	7·00	14·00
244	–	10c. brown	4·00	10·00
245	–	14c. black	15·00	30·00
246w	–	15c. red	7·50	21·00
247	–	20c. green	14·00	19·00
248	–	24c. purple	15·00	23·00
249	–	32c. black	7·50	50·00

DESIGNS—VERT: 3c. Gilbert coat of arms; 5c. Anchor token; 14c. Royal Arms; 15c. Gilbert in the "Squirrel"; 24c. Queen Elizabeth I; 32c. Gilbert's statue at Truro. HORIZ: 4c. Eton College; 7c. Gilbert commissioned by Elizabeth; 8c. Fleet leaving Plymouth, 1583; 9c. Arrival at St. John's; 10c. Annexation, 5 August, 1583; 20c. Map of Newfoundland.

1935. Silver Jubilee. As T **14a** of Kenya, Uganda and Tanganyika.

250		4c. red	1·00	1·75
251		5c. violet	1·25	2·50
252		7c. blue	1·75	7·00
253		24c. olive	5·00	12·00

1937. Coronation. As T **14b** of Kenya, Uganda and Tanganyika.

254		2c. green	1·00	3·00
255		4c. red	1·60	3·50
256		5c. purple	3·00	4·00

144 Atlantic Cod

155 King George VI

1937. Coronation.

257	**144**	1c. grey	3·00	30
258e	–	3c. brown	6·00	3·50
259	–	7c. blue	2·50	1·25
260	–	8c. red	2·00	3·50
261	–	10c. black	4·50	8·50
262	–	14c. black	1·40	2·75
263	–	15c. red	12·00	4·25
264f	–	20c. green	2·50	9·00
265	–	24c. blue	2·50	2·75
266	–	25c. black	2·75	2·25
267	–	48c. purple	8·50	6·00

DESIGNS: 3c. Map of Newfoundland; 7c. Rein-deer; 8c. Corner Brook Paper Mills; 10c. Atlantic salmon; 14c. Newfoundland dog; 15c. Harp seal; 20c. Cape Race; 24c. Bell Island; 25c. Sealing fleet; 48c. The Banks fishing fleet.

1938.

277	**155**	2c. green	30	75
278	–	3c. red	30	30
270	–	4c. blue	2·25	60
271	–	7c. blue	1·00	4·75

DESIGNS: 3c. Queen Mother; 4c. Queen Elizabeth II, aged 12; 7c. Queen Mary.

159 King George VI and Queen Elizabeth

1938. Royal Visit.

272	**159**	5c. blue	3·25	1·00

1939. Surch in figures and triangles.

273	**159**	2c. on 5c. blue	2·50	50
274		4c. on 5c. blue	2·00	1·00

161 Grenfell on the "Strathcona" (after painting by Gribble)

1941. 50th Anniv of Sir Wilfred Grenfell's Labrador Mission.

275	**161**	5c. blue	30	1·00

162 Memorial University College

1942.

290	**162**	30c. red	1·00	2·75

163 St. John's

165 Queen Elizabeth II when Princess

1943. Air.

291	**163**	7c. blue	50	1·00

1946. Surch **TWO CENTS**.

292	**162**	2c. on 30c. red	30	1·00

1947. 21st Birthday of Princess Elizabeth.

293	**165**	4c. blue	30	1·00

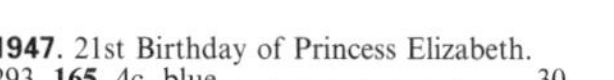

166 Cabot off Cape Bonavista

1947. 450th Anniv of Cabot's Discovery of Newfoundland.

294	**166**	5c. violet	20	1·00

POSTAGE DUE STAMPS

D 1

1939.

D1	**D 1**	1c. green	2·25	9·00
D2		2c. red	13·00	7·50
D3		3c. blue	5·00	23·00
D4		4c. orange	9·00	17·00
D5		5c. brown	5·50	26·00
D6		10c. purple	7·00	18·00

NEW GUINEA Pt. 1

Formerly a German Colony, part of the island of New Guinea. Occupied by Australian forces during the 1914–18 war and subsequently joined with Papua and administered by the Australian Commonwealth under trusteeship. After the Japanese defeat in 1945 Australian stamps were used until 1952 when the combined issue appeared for Papua and New Guinea (q.v.). The stamps overprinted "N.W. PACIFIC ISLANDS" were also used in Nauru and other ex-German islands.

12 pence = 1 shilling;
20 shillings = 1 pound.

1914. "Yacht" key-types of German New Guinea surch **G.R.I.** and value in English currency.

16	N	1d. on 3pf. brown	45·00	55·00
17		1d. on 5pf. green	18·00	30·00
18		2d. on 10pf. red	24·00	40·00
19		2d. on 20pf. blue	28·00	45·00
5		2½d. on 10pf. red	65·00	£140
6		2½d. on 20pf. blue	75·00	£150
22		3d. on 25pf. blk & red on yell	£110	£150
23		3d. on 30pf. blk & orge on buff	90·00	£130
24		4d. on 40pf. black and red	£100	£160
25		5d. on 50pf. black & pur on buff	£160	£190
26		8d. on 80pf. blk & red on rose	£325	£400
12	O	1s on 1m. red	£1600	£2250
13		2s. on 2m. blue	£1700	£2500
14		3s. on 3m. black	£3250	£4250
15		5s. on 5m. red and black	£7000	£8500

Nos. 3/4 surch **1**.

31	N	"1" on 2d. on 10pf. red	£14000	£14000
32		"1" on 2d. on 20pf. blue	£13000	£8500

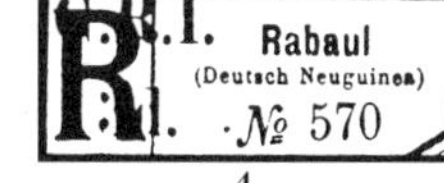

4

1914. Registration labels with names of various towns surch **G.R.I. 3d**.

33	**4**	3d. black and red	£180	£200

1914. "Yacht" key-types of German Marshall Islands surch **G.R.I.** and value in English currency.

50	N	1d. on 3pf. brown	50·00	85·00
51		1d. on 5pf. green	50·00	55·00
52		2d. on 10pf. red	17·00	26·00
53		2d. on 20pf. blue	18·00	30·00
64g		2½d. on 10pf. red	£7500	
64h		2½d. on 20pf. blue	£1100	
54		3d. on 25pf. black and red on yellow	£275	£375
55		3d. on 30pf. black and orange on buff	£300	£400
56		4d. on 40pf. black and red	£100	£130
57		5d. on 50pf. black and purple on buff	£140	£180
58		8d. on 80pf. black and red on rose	£400	£500
59	O	1s. on 1m. red	£1900	£3250
60		2s. on 2m. blue	£1200	£2000
61		3s. on 3m. black	£3500	£5000
62		5s. on 5m. red and black	£7000	£9000

1915. Nos. 52 and 53 surch **1**.

63	N	"1" on 2d. on 10pf. red	£140	£170
64		"1" on 2d. on 20pf. blue	£3000	£2250

1915. Stamps of Australia optd **N. W. PACIFIC ISLANDS**.

102	**3**	½d. green	1·50	3·50
103		1d. red	3·25	1·60
120		1d. violet	1·75	6·50
94	**1**	2d. grey	5·50	15·00
121	**3**	2d. orange	6·00	2·75
122		2d. red	9·00	3·75
74	**1**	2½d. blue	2·75	16·00
96		3d. olive	5·50	11·00
70	**3**	4d. orange	4·00	15·00
123		4d. violet	20·00	40·00
124		4d. blue	11·00	60·00
105		5d. brown	2·25	12·00
110	**1**	6d. blue	4·50	14·00
89		9d. violet	16·00	21·00
90		1s. green	11·00	24·00
115		2s. brown	21·00	38·00
116		5s. grey and yellow	60·00	65·00
84		10s. grey and pink	£110	£160
99		£1 brown and blue	£250	£400

1918. Nos. 105 and 90 surch **One Penny**.

100	**3**	1d. on 5d. brown	90·00	80·00
101	**1**	1d. on 1s. green	90·00	75·00

12 Native Village

14 Raggiana Bird of Paradise (Dates either side of value)

1925.

125	**12**	½d. orange	2·50	7·00
126		1d. green	2·50	5·50
126a		1½d. red	3·25	2·75
127		2d. red	2·50	4·50
128		3d. blue	4·50	4·00
129		4d. olive	13·00	21·00
130b		6d. brown	4·50	48·00
131		9d. purple	13·00	45·00
132		1s. green	15·00	27·00
133		2s. lake	30·00	48·00
134		5s. brown	48·00	65·00
135		10s. red	£100	£180
136		£1 grey	£190	£300

1931. Air. Optd with biplane and **AIR MAIL**.

137	**12**	½d. orange	1·50	6·50
138		1d. green	1·60	5·00
139		1½d. red	1·25	5·00
140		2d. red	1·25	7·00
141		3d. blue	1·75	13·00
142		4d. olive	1·25	9·00
143		6d. brown	1·75	14·00
144		9d. purple	3·00	17·00
145		1s. green	3·00	17·00
146		2s. lake	7·00	42·00
147		5s. brown	20·00	65·00
148		10s. red	75·00	£100
149		£1 grey	£140	£250

1931. 10th Anniv of Australian Administration. Dated "1921–1931".

150	**14**	1d. green	4·00	1·50
151		1½d. red	5·00	10·00
152		2d. red	5·00	4·25
153		3d. blue	5·00	4·75
154		4d. olive	6·50	20·00
155		5d. green	5·00	20·00
156		6d. brown	5·00	19·00
157		9d. violet	8·50	19·00
158		1s. grey	6·00	15·00
159		2s. lake	10·00	30·00
160		5s. brown	42·00	55·00
161		10s. red	85·00	£130
162		£1 grey	£190	£250

1931. Air. Optd with biplane and **AIR MAIL**.

163	**14**	½d. orange	3·25	3·25
164		1d. green	4·00	4·75
165		1½d. red	3·75	10·00
166		2d. red	3·75	3·00
167		3d. blue	6·00	6·50
168		4d. olive	6·00	6·00
169		5d. green	6·00	11·00
170		6d. brown	7·00	26·00
171		9d. violet	8·00	15·00

172 1s. grey 7·50 15·00
173 2s. lake 16·00 48·00
174 5s. brown 42·00 70·00
175 10s. red 60·00 £120
176 £1 grey £110 £250

1932. As T **14**, but without dates.
177 1d. green 2·00 20
178 1½d. red 2·00 11·00
179 2d. red 2·00 20
179a 2½d. green 6·50 21·00
180 3d. blue 2·50 80
180a 3½d. red 13·00 11·00
181 4d. olive 2·50 6·00
182 5d. green 2·50 70
183 6d. brown 4·00 3·25
184 9d. violet 9·50 22·00
185 1s. grey 4·50 10·00
186 2s. lake 4·00 17·00
187 5s. brown 27·00 45·00
188 10s. red 48·00 70·00
189 £1 grey 95·00 £100

1932. Air. T **14**, but without dates, optd with biplane and **AIR MAIL**.
190 ½d. orange 60 1·50
191 1d. green 1·25 1·50
192 1½d. mauve 1·75 7·50
193 2d. red 1·75 30
193a 2½d. green 6·00 2·50
194 3d. blue 3·25 3·00
194a 3½d. red 4·50 3·25
195 4d. olive 4·50 10·00
196 5d. green 7·00 7·50
197 6d. brown 4·50 15·00
198 9d. violet 6·00 9·00
199 1s. grey 6·00 9·00
200 2s. lake 10·00 45·00
201 5s. brown 48·00 55·00
202 10s. red 80·00 80·00
203 £1 grey 75·00 55·00

16 Bulolo Goldfields

18 King George VI

1935. Air.
204 **16** £2 violet £225 £130
205 £5 green £550 £400

1935. Silver Jubilee. Nos. 177 and 179 optd **HIS MAJESTY'S JUBILEE. 1910–1935.**
206 1d. green 75 50
207 2d. red 1·75 50

1937. Coronation.
208 **18** 2d. red 50 75
209 3d. blue 50 1·50
210 5d. green 50 1·50
211 1s. purple 50 75

1939. Air. As T **16** but inscr "AIR MAIL POSTAGE".
212 ½d. orange 3·75 7·00
213 1d. green 3·25 4·50
214 1½d. red 4·00 9·50
215 2d. red 8·00 3·50
216 3d. blue 13·00 18·00
217 4d. olive 14·00 8·50
218 5d. green 12·00 3·75
219 6d. brown 25·00 18·00
220 9d. violet 25·00 24·00
221 1s. green 25·00 19·00
222 2s. red 65·00 48·00
223 5s. brown £130 95·00
224 10s. pink £375 £250
225 £1 olive £100 £110

OFFICIAL STAMPS

1915. Nos. 16 and 17 optd **O. S.**
O1 N 1d on 3pf. brown 26·00 75·00
O2 1d. on 3pf. green 80·00 £140

1925. Optd **O S.**
O22 **12** 1d. green 1·00 4·50
O23 1½d. red 5·50 17·00
O24 2d. red 1·75 3·75
O25 3d. blue 3·50 7·25
O26 4d. olive 4·50 8·50
O27a 6d. brown 7·00 35·00
O28 9d. purple 4·00 35·00
O29 1s. green 5·50 35·00
O30 2s. lake 28·00 60·00

1931. Optd **O S.**
O31 **14** 1d. green 6·00 13·00
O32 1½d. red 7·00 12·00
O33 2d. red 10·00 7·00
O34 3d. blue 6·50 6·00
O35 4d. olive 5·50 8·50
O36 5d. green 10·00 12·00
O37 6d. brown 14·00 17·00
O38 9d. violet 16·00 28·00
O39 1s. grey 16·00 28·00
O40 2s. lake 40·00 70·00
O41 5s. brown £100 £170

1932. T **14**, but without dates, optd **O S.**
O42 1d. green 7·00 8·00
O43 1½d. red 8·00 12·00
O44 2d. red 8·00 3·25
O45 2½d. green 3·25 6·00
O46 3d. blue 8·00 25·00
O47 3½d. red 3·25 9·00
O48 4d. olive 8·00 19·00
O49 5d. green 7·00 19·00
O50 6d. brown 13·00 42·00
O51 9d. violet 12·00 42·00
O52 1s. grey 16·00 29·00
O53 2s. lake 35·00 75·00
O54 5s. brown £120 £170

For later issues see **PAPUA NEW GUINEA**.

NEW HEBRIDES Pt. 1

A group of islands in the Pacific Ocean, E. of Australia, under joint administration of Gt. Britain and France. The Condominium ended in 1980, when the New Hebrides became independent as the Republic of Vanuatu.

1908. 12 pence = 1 shilling;
20 shillings = 1 pound.
1938. 100 gold centimes = 1 gold franc.
1977. 100 centimes = 1 New Hebrides franc.

BRITISH ADMINISTRATION

1908. Stamps of Fiji optd. (a) **NEW HEBRIDES. CONDOMINIUM.** (with full points).
1a **23** ½d. green 40 7·00
2 1d. red 50 40
5 2d. purple and orange 60 70
6 2½d. purple and blue on blue 60 70
7 5d. purple and green 80 2·00
8 6d. purple and red 70 1·25
3 1s. green and red 19·00 3·75

(b) **NEW HEBRIDES CONDOMINIUM** (without full points).
10 **23** ½d. green 3·50 24·00
11 1d. red 10·00 8·50
12 2d. grey 60 3·00
13 2½d. blue 65 4·25
14 5d. purple and green 1·25 5·50
15 6d. purple and deep purple 1·00 5·00
16 1s. black and green 1·00 7·50

3 Weapons and Idols

1911.
18 **3** ½d. green 85 1·75
19 1d. red 3·75 2·00
20 2d. grey 8·00 4·00
21 2½d. blue 3·00 5·50
24 5d. green 4·50 7·00
25 6d. purple 3·00 5·00
26 1s. black on green 2·75 13·00
27 2s. purple on blue 22·00 22·00
28 5s. green on yellow 35·00 48·00

1920. Surch. (a) On T **3**.
40 **3** 1d. on ½d. green 4·00 22·00
30 1d. on 5d. green 7·00 60·00
31 1d. on 1s. black on green 1·25 13·00
32 1d. on 2s. purple on blue 1·00 10·00
33 1d. on 5s. green on yellow 1·00 10·00
41 3d. on 1d. red 4·00 11·00
42 5d. on 2½d. blue 7·50 21·00

(b) On No. F16 of French New Hebrides.
34 **3** 2d. on 40c. red on yellow 1·00 18·00

5

1925.
43 **5** ½d. (5c.) black 1·25 12·00
44 1d. (10c.) green 1·00 11·00
45 2d. (20c.) grey 1·75 2·50
46 2½d. (25c.) brown 1·00 13·00
47 5d. (50c.) blue 3·00 2·75
48 6d. (60c.) purple 3·50 12·00
49 1s. (1f.25) black on green 3·25 19·00
50 2s. (2f.50) purple on blue 6·00 22·00
51 5s. (6f.25) green on yellow 6·00 25·00

6 Lopevi Islands and Outrigger Canoe

1938.
52 **6** 5c. green 2·50 4·00
53 10c. orange 1·25 2·00
54 15c. violet 3·50 4·00
55 20c. red 1·60 2·50
56 25c. brown 1·60 2·50
57 30c. blue 2·25 2·50
58 40c. olive 4·50 6·00
59 50c. purple 1·60 2·50
60 1f. red on green 4·00 8·50
61 2f. blue on green 30·00 17·00
62 5f. red on yellow 70·00 48·00
63 10f. violet on blue £200 75·00

1949. U.P.U. As T **4d/g** of Pitcairn Islands.
64 10c. orange 30 75
65 15c. violet 30 75
66 30c. blue 30 75
67 50c. purple 40 75

7 Outrigger Sailing Canoes

1953.
68 **7** 5c. green 60 20
69 10c. red 60 10
70 15c. yellow 60 10
71 20c. blue 60 10
72 – 25c. olive 60 10
73 – 30c. brown 60 10
74 – 40c. sepia 60 10
75 – 50c. violet 1·00 10
76 – 1f. orange 5·00 1·00
77 – 2f. purple 5·00 8·00
78 – 5f. red 7·00 22·00
DESIGNS: 25c. to 50c. Native carving; 1f. to 5f. Two natives outside hut.

1953. Coronation. As T **4h** of Pitcairn Islands.
79 10c. black and red 60 50

10 "San Pedro y San Paulo" (Quiros) and Map

1956. 50th Anniv of Condominium. Inscr "1906 1956".
80 **10** 5c. green 15 10
81 10c. red 15 10
82 – 20c. blue 10 10
83 – 50c. lilac 15 15
DESIGN: 20, 50c. "Marianne", "Talking Drum" and "Britannia".

12 Port Villa; Iririki Islet

1957.
84 **12** 5c. green 40 1·00
85 10c. red 30 10
86 15c. yellow 50 1·00
87 20c. blue 40 10
88 – 25c. olive 45 10
89 – 30c. brown 45 10
90 – 40c. sepia 45 10
91 – 50c. violet 45 10
92 – 1f. orange 1·00 1·00
93 – 2f. mauve 4·00 3·00
94 – 5f. black 9·00 4·75
DESIGNS: 25c. to 50c. River scene and spear fisherman; 1f. to 5f. Woman drinking from coconut.

1963. Freedom from Hunger. As T **20a** of Pitcairn Islands.
95 60c. green 50 15

1963. Centenary of Red Cross. As T **20b** of Pitcairn Islands, but with British and French cyphers in place of the Queen's portrait.
96 15c. red and black 20 10
97 45c. red and blue 35 20

17 Cocoa Beans

1963.
98 – 5c. red, brown and blue 1·00 50
99 **17** 10c. brown, buff and green 15 10
100 – 15c. bistre, brown and violet 15 10
101 – 20c. black, green and blue 55 10
102 – 25c. violet, brown and red 50 70
103 – 30c. brown, bistre and violet 75 10
104 – 40c. red and blue 80 1·40
105 – 50c. green, yellow and blue 60 10
129 – 60c. red and blue 40 15
106 – 1f. red, black and green 2·00 3·25
107 – 2f. black, purple and green 2·00 1·75
108 – 3f. multicoloured 10·00 6·00
109 – 5f. blue, deep blue and black 10·00 21·00
DESIGNS: 5 c Exporting manganese, Forari; 15c. Copra; 20c. Fishing from Palikulo Point; 25c. Picasso triggerfish; 30c. New Caledonian nautilus shell; 40, 60c. Lionfish; 50c. Clown surgeonfish; 1f. Cardinal honeyeater (bird); 2f. Buff-bellied flycatcher; 3f. Thicket warbler; 5f. White-collared kingfisher.

1965. Centenary of I.T.U. As T **24a** of Pitcairn Islands, but with British and French cyphers in place of the Queen's portrait.
110 15c. red and drab 20 10
111 60c. blue and red 35 20

1965. I.C.Y. As T **24b** of Pitcairn Islands, but with British and French cyphers in place of the Queen's portrait.
112 5c. purple and turquoise 15 10
113 55c. green and lavender 20 20

1966. Churchill Commemoration. As T **24c** of Pitcairn Islands, but with British and French cyphers in place of the Queen's portrait.
114 5c. blue 20 10
115 15c. green 40 10
116 25c. brown 50 10
117 30c. violet 50 10

1966. World Cup Football Championship. As T **25** of Pitcairn Islands, but with British and French cyphers in place of the Queen's portrait.
118 20c. multicoloured 30 15
119 40c. multicoloured 70 15

1966. Inauguration of W.H.O. Headquarters, Geneva. As T **24** of Montserrat, but with British and French cyphers in place of the Queen's portrait.
120 25c. black, green and blue 15 10
121 60c. black, purple and ochre 40 20

1966. 20th Anniv of U.N.E.S.C.O. As T **25b/d** of Pitcairn Islands, but with British and French cyphers in place of the Queen's portrait.
122 15c. multicoloured 25 10
123 30c. yellow, violet and olive 65 10
124 45c. black, purple and orange 75 15

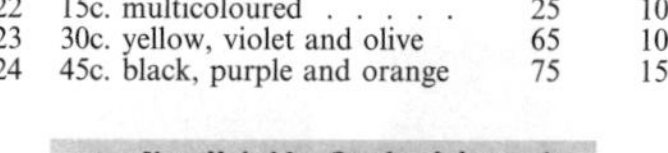

36 The Coast Watchers

1967. 25th Anniv of Pacific War. Multicoloured.
125 15c. Type **36** 15 10
126 25c. Map of war zone, U.S. marine and Australian soldier 40 20
127 60c. H.M.A.S. "Canberra" (cruiser) 45 30
128 1f. Boeing B-17 "Flying Fortress" 45 60

40 Globe and Hemispheres

1968. Bicent of Bougainville's World Voyage.
130 **40** 15c. green, violet and red 15 10
131 – 25c. olive, purple and blue 30 10
132 – 60c. brown, purple & green 35 10
DESIGNS: 25c. Ships "La Boudeuse" and "L'Etoile", and map; 60c. Bougainville, ship's figure-head and bougainvillea flowers.

43 Concorde and Vapour Trails

1968. Anglo-French Concorde Project.
133 **43** 25c. blue, red and blue 35 20
134 – 60c. red, black and blue 40 25
DESIGN: 60c. Concorde in flight.

45 Kauri Pine

1969. Timber Industry.
135 **45** 20c. multicoloured 10 10

46 Cyphers, Flags and Relay Runner receiving Baton

1969. 3rd South Pacific Games, Port Moresby. Multicoloured.
136 25c. Type **46** 10 10
137 1f. Runner passing baton . . 20 20

48 Diver on Platform

52 General Charles de Gaulle

51 U.P.U. Emblem and Headquarters Building

1969. Pentecost Island Land Divers. Mult.
138 15c. Type **48** 10 10
139 25c. Diver jumping 10 10
140 1f. Diver at end of fall . . . 20 20

1970. New U.P.U. Headquarters Building.
141 **51** 1f.05 slate, orange & purple 15 15

1970. 30th Anniv of New Hebrides' Declaration for the Free French Government.
142 **52** 65c. multicoloured 35 70
143 1f.10 multicoloured 45 70

1970. No. 101 surch **35**.
144 35c. on 20c. black, green and blue 30 30

54 "The Virgin and Child" (Bellini)

57 Kauri Pine, Cone and Arms of Royal Society

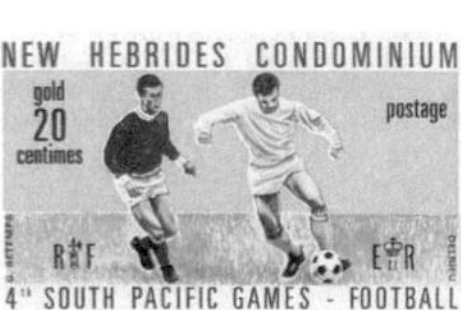

56 Football

1970. Christmas. Multicoloured.
145 15c. Type **54** 10 10
146 50c. "The Virgin and Child" (Cima) 20 20

1971. Death of General Charles de Gaulle. Nos. 142/3 optd **1890-1970 IN MEMORIAM 9-11-70**.
147 **52** 65c. multicoloured 15 10
148 1f.10 multicoloured 15 20

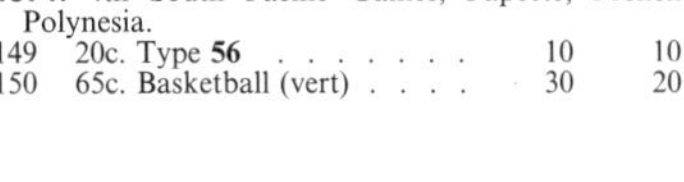

1971. 4th South Pacific Games, Papeete, French Polynesia.
149 20c. Type **56** 10 10
150 65c. Basketball (vert) 30 20

1971. Royal Society's Expedition to New Hebrides.
151 **57** 65c. multicoloured 20 15

58 "The Adoration of the Shepherds" (detail, Louis le Nain)

60 Ceremonial Headdress, South Malekula

59 De Havilland Drover 3

1971. Christmas. Multicoloured.
152 25c. Type **58** 10 10
153 50c. "The Adoration of the Shepherds" (detail, Tintoretto) 30 60

1972. Aircraft. Multicoloured.
154 20c. Type **59** 30 15
155 25c. Short S25 Sandringham 4 flying boat 30 15
156 30c. De Havilland Dragon Rapide 30 15
157 65c. Sud Aviation SE 210 Caravelle . . . . 75 1·25

1972. Multicoloured.
158 5c. Type **60** 10 20
159 10c. Baker's pigeon 25 20
160 15c. Gong and carving, North Ambrym 15 20
161 20c. Red-headed parrot finch 40 25
162 25c. Graskoin's cowrie (shell) 40 25
163 30c. Red-lip olive (shell) . . . 50 30
164 35c. Chestnut-bellied kingfisher 65 40
165 65c. Pretty conch (shell) . . . 75 60
166 1f. Gong (North Malekula) and carving (North Ambrym) . . . . 50 1·00
167 2f. Palm lorikeet . . . . . . 3·50 4·50
168 3f. Ceremonial headdress, South Malekula (different) 1·50 6·00
169 5f. Great green turban (shell) 4·00 13·00

61 "Adoration of the Kings" (Spranger)

63 "Dendrobium teretifolium"

1972. Christmas. Multicoloured.
170 25c. Type **61** 10 10
171 70c. "The Virgin and Child in a Landscape" (Provoost) 20 20

1972. Royal Silver Wedding. As T **98** of Gibraltar, but with Royal and French cyphers in background.
172 35c. violet 15 10
173 65c. green 20 10

1973. Orchids. Multicoloured.
174 25c. Type **63** 25 10
175 30c. "Ephemerantha comata" 25 10
176 35c. "Spathoglottis petri" . . 30 10
177 65c. "Dendrobium mohlianum" 60 55

64 New Wharf at Vila

65 Wild Horses

1973. Opening of New Wharf at Villa. Mult.
178 25c. Type **64** 20 10
179 70c. As Type **64** but horiz . . 40 30

1973. Tanna Island. Multicoloured.
180 35c. Type **65** 30 15
181 70c. Yasur Volcano 55 20

66 Mother and Child

1973. Christmas. Multicoloured.
182 35c. Type **66** 10 10
183 70c. Lagoon scene 20 20

67 Pacific Pigeon

1974. Wild Life. Multicoloured.
184 25c. Type **67** 60 25
185 35c. "Lyssa curvata" (moth) 60 60
186 70c. Green sea turtle 60 70
187 1f.15 Grey-headed flying fox 80 1·50

1974. Royal Visit. Nos. 164 and 167 optd **ROYAL VISIT 1974**.
188 35c. multicoloured 40 10
189 2f. multicoloured 60 40

69 Old Post Office

1974. Inaug of New Post Office, Vila. Mult.
190 35c. Type **69** 15 50
191 70c. New Post Office 15 60

70 Capt. Cook and Map

1974. Bicent of Discovery. Multicoloured.
192 35c. Type **70** . . . . 1·25 2·00
193 35c. William Wales and beach landing . . . . . . 1·25 2·00
194 35c. William Hodges and island scene . . . . 1·25 2·00
195 1f.15 Capt. Cook, map and H.M.S. "Resolution" (59 × 34 mm) . . . . . . 2·50 3·50

71 U.P.U. Emblem and Letters

1974. Centenary of U.P.U.
196 **71** 70c. multicoloured 30 70

72 "Adoration of the Magi" (Velazquez)

74 Canoeing

73 Charolais Bull

1974. Christmas. Multicoloured.
197 35c. Type **72** 10 10
198 70c. "The Nativity" (Gerard van Honthorst) 20 20

1975.
199 **73** 10f. brown, green and blue 7·00 18·00

1975. World Scout Jamboree, Norway. Mult.
200 25c. Type **74** 15 10
201 35c. Preparing meal 15 10
202 1f. Map-reading 35 15
203 5f. Fishing . . . . 1·25 2·50

75 "Pitti Madonna" (Michelangelo)

77 Telephones of 1876 and 1976

76 Concorde in British Airways Livery

1975. Christmas. Michelangelo's Sculptures. Mult.
204 35c. Type **75** 10 10
205 70c. "Bruges Madonna" . . 15 10
206 2f.50 "Taddei Madonna" . . 70 50

1976. 1st Commercial Flight of Concorde.
207 **76** 5f. multicoloured . . . . . 4·00 5·00

1976. Centenary of Telephone. Multicoloured.
208 25c. Type **77** 15 10
209 70c. Alexander Graham Bell 30 10
210 1f.15 Satellite and Noumea Earth Station 50 50

78 Map of the Islands

1976. Constitutional Changes. Multicoloured.
211 25c. Type **78** 40 15
212 1f. View of Santo (horiz) . . 75 60
213 2f. View of Vila (horiz) . . . 1·10 2·00
Nos. 212/13 are smaller, 36 × 26 mm.

79 "The Flight into Egypt" (Lusitano)

80 Royal Visit, 1974

1976. Christmas. Multicoloured.
214 35c. Type **79** 10 10
215 70c. "Adoration of the Shepherds" 15 10
216 2f.50 "Adoration of the Magi" 45 50

Nos. 215/16 show retables by the Master of Santos-o-Novo.

1977. Silver Jubilee. Multicoloured.
217 35c. Type **80** 10 10
218 70c. Imperial State Crown 15 10
219 2f. The Blessing 30 65

1977. Currency change. Nos. 158/69 and 199 surch.
233 5f. on 5c. Type **60** 50 15
234 10f. on 10c. Baker's pigeon 50 15
222 15f. on 15c. Gong and carving 60 1·50
223 20f. on 20c. Red-headed parrot finch 1·25 55
224 25f. on 25c. Gaskoin's cowrie (shell) 1·75 2·00
225 30f. on 30c. Red-lip olive (shell) 1·75 1·10
226 35f. on 35c. Chestnut-bellied kingfisher 1·75 1·25
239 40f. on 65c. Pretty conch (shell) 1·50 55
228 50f. on 1f. Gong and carving 1·00 1·75
229 70f. on 2f. Palm lorikeet 5·50 75
230 100f. on 3f. Ceremonial headdress 1·00 3·75
231 200f. on 5f. Great green turban (shell) 5·00 14·00
241 500f. on 10f. Type **73** 19·00 14·00

89 Island of Erromango and Kauri Pine

90 "Tempi Madonna" (Raphael)

1977. Islands. Multicoloured.
242 5f. Type **89** 30 10
243 10f. Territory map and copra-making 40 30
244 15f. Espiritu Santo and cattle 30 30
245 20f. Efate and Vila P.O. 30 25
246 25f. Malekula and headdresses 40 40
247 30f. Aobe, Maewo and pigs' tusks 45 50
248 35f. Pentecost and land diver 50 65
249 40f. Tanna and John Frum Cross 70 60
250 50f. Shepherd Is. and canoe 1·00 40
251 70f. Banks Is. and dancers 1·75 4·00
252 100f. Ambrym and idols 1·75 90
253 200f. Aneityum and baskets 1·75 2·50
254 500f. Torres Is. and archer fisherman 4·00 7·50

1977. Christmas. Multicoloured.
255 10f. Type **90** 20 45
256 15f. "The Flight into Egypt" (Gerard David) 30 60
257 30f. "Virgin and Child" (Batoni) 40 90

91 Concorde over New York

1978. Concorde Commemoration.
258 10f. Type **91** 1·00 75
259 20f. Concorde over London 1·25 1·00
260 30f. Concorde over Washington 1·60 1·40
261 40f. Concorde over Paris 1·90 1·60

92 White Horse of Hanover

93 "Madonna and Child"

1978. 25th Anniv of Coronation.
262 **92** 40f. brown, blue and silver 15 30
263 – 40f. multicoloured 15 30
264 – 40f. brown, blue and silver 15 30

DESIGNS: No. 263, Queen Elizabeth II; 264, Gallic Cock.

1978. Christmas. Paintings by Durer. Mult.
265 10f. Type **93** 10 10
266 15f. "The Virgin and Child with St. Anne" 10 10
267 30f. "Madonna of the Siskin" 15 10
268 40f. "Madonna of the Pear" 20 15

1979. 1st Anniv of Internal Self-Government. Surch **166°E 11.1.79 FIRST ANNIVERSARY INTERNAL SELF-GOVERNMENT** and new value.
269 **78** 10f. on 25f. multicoloured (blue background) 10 10
270 40f. on 25f. multicoloured (green background) 20 20

95 1938 5c. Stamp and Sir Rowland Hill

96 Chubwan Mask

1979. Death Centenary of Sir Rowland Hill. Mult.
271 10f. Type **95** 10 10
272 20f. 1969 25c. Pentecost Island Land Divers commemorative 20 10
273 40f. 1925 2d. (20c.) 25 20
MS274 143 × 94 mm. Nos. 272 and F286 75 90

1979. Arts Festival. Multicoloured.
275 5f. Type **96** 10 10
276 10f. Nal-Nal clubs and spears 10 10
277 20f. Ritual puppet 15 10
278 40f. Neqatmalow headdress 25 15

97 "Native Church" (Metas Masongo)

1979. Christmas and International Year of the Child. Children's Drawings. Multicoloured.
279 5f. Type **97** 10 10
280 10f. "Priest and Candles" (Herve Rutu) 10 10
281 20f. "Cross and Bible" (Mark Deards) (vert) 10 10
282 40f. "Green Candle and Santa Claus" (Dev Raj) (vert) 15 15

98 White-bellied Honeyeater

1980. Birds. Multicoloured.
283 10f. Type **98** 50 10
284 20f. Scarlet robin 70 10
285 30f. Yellow-fronted white-eye 90 45
286 40f. Fan-tailed cuckoo 1·00 70

POSTAGE DUE STAMPS

1925. Optd **POSTAGE DUE**.
D1 **5** 1d. (10c.) green 30·00 1·00
D2 2d. (20c.) grey 35·00 1·00
D3 3d. (30c.) red 35·00 2·50
D4 5d. (50c.) blue 40·00 4·50
D5 10d. (1c.) red on blue 45·00 5·50

1938. Optd **POSTAGE DUE**.
D 6 **6** 5c. green 24·00 38·00
D 7 10c. orange 24·00 38·00
D 8 20c. red 28·00 55·00
D 9 40c. olive 35·00 65·00
D10 1f. red on green 45·00 75·00

1953. Nos. 68/9, 71, 74 and 76 optd **POSTAGE DUE**.
D11 **7** 5c. green 4·00 13·00
D12 10c. red 1·75 10·00
D13 20c. blue 5·00 19·00
D14 – 40c. sepia (No. 74) 7·00 29·00
D15 – 1f. orange (No. 76) 4·50 29·00

1957. Optd **POSTAGE DUE**.
D16 **12** 5c. green 30 1·50
D17 10c. red 30 1·50
D18 20c. blue 75 1·75
D19 – 40c. sepia (No. 90) 1·00 2·50
D20 – 1f. orange (No. 92) 1·25 3·25

FRENCH ADMINISTRATION

1908. Stamps of New Caledonia optd **NOUVELLES HEBRIDES**.
F1 **15** 5c. green 4·75 4·75
F2 10c. red 6·00 3·50
F3 **16** 25c. blue on green 6·00 2·25
F4 50c. red on green 7·00 4·75
F5 **17** 1f. blue on green 17·00 20·00

1910. Nos. F1/5 further optd **CONDOMINIUM**.
F 6 **15** 5c. green 2·75 3·00
F 7 10c. red 2·75 1·25
F 8 **16** 25c. blue on green 2·25 3·75
F 9 50c. red on orange 6·50 9·75
F10 **17** 1f. blue on green 14·00 22·00

The following issues are as stamps of British Administration but are inscr "NOUVELLES HEBRIDES" except where otherwise stated.

1911.
F11 **3** 5c. green 1·00 2·75
F12 10c. red 50 75
F13 20c. grey 1·00 2·25
F25 25c. blue 1·25 5·50
F15 30c. brown on yellow 6·50 5·25
F16 40c. red on yellow 1·40 3·75
F17 50c. olive 2·00 4·00
F18 75c. orange 7·00 23·00
F19 1f. red on blue 2·50 3·00
F20 2f. violet 8·50 22·00
F21 5f. red on green 12·00 35·00

1920. Surch in figures.
F34 5c. on 40c. red on yellow (No. F16) 27·00 95·00
F32a 5c. on 50c. red on orange (No. F4) £450 £450
F33 5c. on 50c. red on orange (No. F9) 2·40 11·00
F38 10c. on 5c. green (No. F11) 1·00 5·00
F33a 10c. on 25c. blue on green (No. F8) 50 1·50
F35 20c. on 30c. brown on yellow (No. F26) 11·00 65·00
F39 30c. on 10c. red (No. F12) 1·00 2·50
F41 50c. on 25c. blue (No. F25) 2·50 24·00

1921. Stamp of New Hebrides (British) surch **10c.**
F37 10c. on 5d. green (No. 24) 11·00 50·00

1925.
F42 **5** 5c. (½d.) black 75 10·00
F43 10c. (1d.) green 1·00 9·00
F44 20c. (2d.) grey 1·75 2·75
F45 25c. (2½d.) brown 1·50 9·00
F46 30c. (3d.) red 1·50 8·00
F47 40c. (4d.) red on yellow 1·50 8·00
F48 50c. (5d.) blue 1·50 1·75
F49 75c. (7½d.) brown 1·50 13·00
F50 1f. (10d.) red on blue 1·50 2·50
F51 2f. (1s.8d.) violet 2·50 24·00
F52 5f. (4d.) red on green 3·50 24·00

1938.
F53 **6** 5c. green 2·25 5·00
F54 10c. orange 1·75 1·40
F55 15c. violet 1·50 3·25
F56 20c. red 1·90 3·00
F57 25c. brown 4·50 3·50
F58 30c. blue 4·50 4·00
F59 40c. olive 1·50 8·00
F60 50c. purple 1·50 2·50
F61 1f. red on green 2·00 4·50
F62 2f. blue on green 27·00 28·00
F63 5f. red on yellow 50·00 45·00
F64 10f. violet and blue £200 £180

1941. Free French Issue. As last, optd **France Libre**.
F65 **6** 5c. green 2·00 24·00
F66 10c. orange 3·25 23·00
F67 15c. violet 5·50 38·00
F68 20c. red 16·00 30·00
F69 25c. brown 19·00 40·00
F70 30c. blue 19·00 35·00
F71 40c. olive 17·00 38·00
F72 50c. purple 17·00 35·00
F73 1f. red on green 18·00 35·00
F74 2f. blue on green 16·00 35·00
F75 5f. red on yellow 16·00 35·00
F76 10f. violet on blue 16·00 35·00

1949. 75th Anniv of U.P.U.
F77 10c. orange 2·50 4·75
F78 15c. violet 3·75 8·50
F79 30c. blue 5·50 11·00
F80 50c. purple 6·50 14·00

1953.
F81 **7** 5c. green 2·00 2·75
F82 10c. red 3·00 2·75
F83 15c. yellow 3·00 3·00
F84 20c. blue 3·00 2·75
F85 – 25c. olive 1·25 2·75
F86 – 30c. brown 1·25 3·00
F87 – 40c. sepia 1·75 3·00
F88 – 50c. violet 1·25 2·75
F89 – 1f. orange 9·50 7·50
F90 – 2f. purple 16·00 45·00
F91 – 5f. red 18·00 85·00

1956. 50th Anniv of Condominium.
F92 **10** 5c. green 1·00 2·00
F93 10c. red 1·00 2·25
F94 – 20c. blue 65 2·50
F95 – 50c. violet 1·00 2·50

1957.
F 96 **12** 5c. green 40 2·25
F 97 10c. red 1·25 2·25
F 98 15c. yellow 1·50 2·75
F 99 20c. blue 1·40 2·00
F100 – 25c. olive 1·25 1·75
F101 – 30c. brown 1·40 1·75
F102 – 40c. sepia 2·00 1·25
F103 – 50c. violet 2·00 1·60
F104 – 1f. orange 5·50 4·00
F105 – 2f. mauve 11·00 21·00
F106 – 5f. black 28·00 48·00

F 7 Emblem and Globe

1963. Freedom from Hunger.
F107 F **7** 60c. green and brown 10·00 16·00

F **8** Centenary Emblem

F **9** "Syncom" Communications Satellite, Telegraph Poles and Morse Key

1963. Centenary of Red Cross.
F108 F **8** 15c. red, grey and orange 7·25 8·25
F109 45c. red, grey and bistre 9·75 24·00

1963.
F110 – 5c. lake, brown and blue 55 65
F111 – 10c. brown, buff and green* 2·00 2·50
F112 – 10c. brown, buff and green 75 1·60
F113 **18** 15c. bistre, brown and violet 6·00 1·25
F114 – 20c. black, green and blue* 2·25 3·75
F115 – 20c. black, green and blue 1·50 1·60
F116 – 25c. violet, brown and red 70 1·10
F117 – 30c. brown, bistre and violet 7·50 1·25
F118 – 40c. red and blue 3·25 7·50
F119 – 50c. green, yellow and turquoise 8·50 1·60
F120 – 60c. red and blue 1·75 1·90
F121 – 1f. red, black and green 2·00 4·00
F122 – 2f. black, brown and olive 17·00 8·00
F123 – 3f. multicoloured* 10·50 26·00
F124 – 3f. multicoloured 8·50 11·00
F125 – 5f. blue, indigo and black 24·00 28·00

The stamps indicated by an asterisk have "RF" wrongly placed on the left.

1965. Centenary of I.T.U.
F126 F **9** 15c. blue, green and brown 5·75 8·25
F127 60c. red, grey and green 11·00 27·00

1965. I.C.Y. As Nos. 112/13.
F128 5c. purple and turquoise 2·50 6·00
F129 55c. green and lavender 9·50 12·00

1966. Churchill Commem. As Nos. 114/17.
F130 5c. multicoloured 2·10 4·00
F131 15c. multicoloured 3·00 1·90
F132 25c. multicoloured 3·50 5·50
F133 30c. multicoloured 4·25 6·00

1966. World Cup Football Championship. As Nos. 118/19.
F134 20c. multicoloured 1·90 4·25
F135 40c. multicoloured 3·50 4·25

1966. Inauguration of W.H.O. Headquarters, Geneva. As Nos. 120/1.
F136 25c. black, green and blue 2·50 3·50
F137 60c. black, mauve and ochre 3·50 7·50

1966. 20th Anniv of U.N.E.S.C.O. As Nos. 122/4.
F138 15c. multicoloured 1·50 2·25
F139 30c. yellow, violet and olive 2·25 3·50
F140 45c. black, purple and orange 2·25 4·25

1967. 25th Anniv of Pacific War. As Nos. 125/8.
F141 15c. multicoloured 1·25 1·50
F142 25c. multicoloured 1·60 3·00

F143	60c. multicoloured	1·75	2·50
F144	1f. multicoloured	2·00	2·75

1968. Bicentenary of Bougainville's World Voyage. As Nos. 130/2.

F145	15c. green, violet and red	55	1·10
F146	25c. olive, purple and blue	65	1·25
F147	60c. brown, purple and green	1·10	1·50

1968. Anglo-French Concorde Project. As Nos. 133/4.

F148	25c. blue, red and violet	1·90	2·40
F149	60c. red, black and blue	2·25	4·25

1969. Timber Industry. As No. 135.

F150	20c. multicoloured	45	1·00

1969. 3rd South Pacific Games, Port Moresby, Papua New Guinea. As Nos. 136/7.

F151	25c. multicoloured	50	1·40
F152	1f. multicoloured	1·50	2·00

1969. Land Divers of Pentecost Island. As Nos. 138/40.

F153	15c. multicoloured	55	1·25
F154	25c. multicoloured	45	1·25
F155	1f. multicoloured	1·10	2·00

1970. Inauguration of New U.P.U. Headquarters Building, Berne. As No. 141.

F156	1f.05 slate, orange & purple	1·00	2·75

1970. New Hebrides' Declaration for the Free French Government. As Nos. 142/3.

F157	65c. multicoloured	1·75	2·00
F158	1f.10 multicoloured	2·00	2·25

1970. No. F115 surch **35**.

F159	35c. on 20c. black, green and blue	65	1·75

1970. Christmas. As Nos. 145/6.

F160	15c. multicoloured	25	1·00
F161	50c. multicoloured	45	1·25

1971. Death of General Charles de Gaulle. Nos. F157/8 optd **1890-1970 IN MEMORIAM 9-11-70**.

F162	65c. multicoloured	1·00	1·50
F163	1f.10 multicoloured	1·50	2·00

1971. 4th South Pacific Games, Papeete, French Polynesia. As Nos. 149/50.

F164	20c. multicoloured	75	1·00
F165	65c. multicoloured	1·00	1·50

1971. Royal Society Expedition to New Hebrides. As No. 151.

F166	65c. multicoloured	1·00	1·50

1971. Christmas. As Nos. 152/3.

F167	25c. multicoloured	50	75
F168	50c. multicoloured	60	1·25

1972. Aircraft. As Nos. 154/7.

F169	20c. multicoloured	1·00	1·60
F170	25c. multicoloured	1·00	1·60
F171	30c. multicoloured	1·10	1·60
F172	65c. multicoloured	2·75	5·00

1972. As Nos. 158/69.

F173	5c. multicoloured	85	1·40
F174	10c. multicoloured	1·90	1·75
F175	15c. multicoloured	90	1·25
F176	20c. multicoloured	2·50	1·50
F177	25c. multicoloured	1·90	1·60
F178	30c. multicoloured	1·90	1·50
F179	35c. multicoloured	3·00	1·50
F180	65c. multicoloured	2·40	2·00
F181	1f. multicoloured	2·40	2·75
F182	2f. multicoloured	15·00	13·50
F183	3f. multicoloured	7·50	17·00
F184	5f. multicoloured	10·00	30·00

1972. Christmas. As Nos. 170/1.

F185	25c. multicoloured	45	1·00
F186	70c. multicoloured	65	1·50

1972. Royal Silver Wedding. As Nos. 172/3.

F187	35c. multicoloured	50	50
F188	65c. multicoloured	60	1·25

1973. Orchids. As Nos. 174/7.

F189	25c. multicoloured	2·75	1·40
F190	30c. multicoloured	2·75	1·60
F191	35c. multicoloured	2·75	1·60
F192	65c. multicoloured	4·75	5·00

1973. Opening of New Wharf at Vila. As Nos. 178/9.

F193	25c. multicoloured	80	1·10
F194	70c. multicoloured	1·10	2·25

1973. Tanna Island. As Nos. 180/1.

F195	35c. multicoloured	2·25	2·25
F196	70c. multicoloured	3·25	3·25

1973. Christmas. As Nos. 182/3.

F197	35c. multicoloured	50	1·00
F198	70c. multicoloured	75	2·75

1974. Wild Life. As Nos. 184/7.

F199	25c. multicoloured	4·50	3·25
F200	35c. multicoloured	5·75	2·40
F201	70c. multicoloured	6·00	4·75
F202	1f.15 multicoloured	7·50	11·00

1974. Royal Visit of Queen Elizabeth II. Nos. F179 and F182 optd **VISITE ROYALE 1974**.

F203	35c. Chestnut-bellied kingfisher	3·00	90
F204	2f. Green palm lorikeet	6·50	8·25

1974. Inauguration of New Post Office, Vila. As Nos. 190/1.

F205	35c. multicoloured	1·00	2·00
F206	70c. multicoloured	1·00	2·00

1974. Bicent of Discovery. As Nos. 192/5.

F207	35c. multicoloured	4·00	5·75
F208	35c. multicoloured	4·00	5·75
F209	35c. multicoloured	4·00	5·75
F210	1f.15 multicoloured	8·50	12·00

1974. Centenary of U.P.U. As No. 196.

F210a	70c. blue, red and black	1·40	3·00

1974. Christmas. As Nos. 197/8.

F211	35c. multicoloured	40	75
F212	70f. multicoloured	60	1·25

1975. Charolais Bull. As No. 199.

F213	10f. brown, green and blue	30·00	45·00

1975. World Scout Jamboree, Norway. As Nos. 200/3.

F214	25c. multicoloured	70	50
F215	35c. multicoloured	75	60
F216	1f. multicoloured	1·25	1·25
F217	5f. multicoloured	6·50	10·00

1975. Christmas. As Nos. 204/6.

F218	35c. multicoloured	35	50
F219	70c. multicoloured	55	90
F220	2f.50 multicoloured	1·90	3·00

1976. 1st Commercial Flight of Concorde. As No. 207, but Concorde in Air France livery.

F221	5f. multicoloured	13·00	12·00

1976. Centenary of Telephone. As Nos. 208/10.

F222	25c. multicoloured	60	50
F223	70c. multicoloured	1·50	1·50
F224	1f.15 multicoloured	1·75	2·75

1976. Constitutional Changes. As Nos. 211/13.

F225	25c. multicoloured	60	50
F226	1f. multicoloured	1·50	1·25
F227	2f. multicoloured	2·50	2·75

1976. Christmas. Paintings. As Nos. 214/16.

F228	35c. multicoloured	30	30
F229	70c. multicoloured	50	50
F230	2f.50 multicoloured	1·75	3·00

1977. Silver Jubilee. As Nos. F217/9.

F231	35c. multicoloured	30	20
F232	70c. multicoloured	55	35
F233	2f. multicoloured	55	65

1977. Currency change. Nos. F173/84 and F213, surch.

F234	5f. on 5c. multicoloured	1·00	1·25
F235	10f. on 10c. multicoloured	2·50	1·25
F236	15f. on 15c. multicoloured	1·25	1·25
F237	20f. on 20c. multicoloured	3·00	1·50
F238	25f. on 25c. multicoloured	2·50	1·75
F239	30f. on 30c. multicoloured	2·50	2·25
F240	35f. on 35c. multicoloured	4·25	2·25
F241	40f. on 65c. multicoloured	3·25	3·00
F242	50f. on 1f. multicoloured	2·50	3·00
F243	70f. on 2f. multicoloured	7·50	4·00
F244	100f. on 3f. multicoloured	3·50	6·00
F245	200f. on 5f. multicoloured	13·00	25·00
F246	500f. on 10f. multicoloured	23·00	45·00

1977. Islands. As Nos. 242/54.

F256	5f. multicoloured	1·25	1·75
F257	10f. multicoloured	1·00	1·75
F258	15f. multicoloured	2·00	1·75
F259	20f. multicoloured	2·00	1·75
F260	25f. multicoloured	2·00	1·75
F261	30f. multicoloured	2·00	1·75
F262	35f. multicoloured	2·75	1·75
F263	40f. multicoloured	1·50	2·25
F264	50f. multicoloured	2·75	2·25
F265	70f. multicoloured	5·50	4·50
F266	100f. multicoloured	4·50	4·00
F267	200f. multicoloured	6·00	12·00
F268	500f. multicoloured	10·00	18·00

1977. Christmas. As Nos. 255/7.

F269	10f. multicoloured	30	30
F270	15f. multicoloured	50	50
F271	30f. multicoloured	80	1·40

1978. Concorde. As Nos. 258/61.

F272	10f. multicoloured	2·50	1·50
F273	20f. multicoloured	2·75	1·75
F274	30f. multicoloured	3·25	2·25
F275	40f. multicoloured	3·75	3·50

1978. Coronation. As Nos. 262/4.

F276	40f. brown, blue and silver	25	70
F277	40f. multicoloured	25	70
F278	40f. brown, blue and silver	25	70

1978. Christmas. As Nos. 265/8.

F279	10f. multicoloured	15	30
F280	15f. multicoloured	20	35
F281	30f. multicoloured	30	70
F282	40f. multicoloured	35	85

1979. Internal Self-Government. As T **37** surch **166°E PREMIER GOUVERNEMENT AUTONOME 11.1.78. 11.1.79** and new value.

F283	10f. on 25f. multicoloured (blue background)	90	1·00
F284	40f. on 25f. multicoloured (green background)	1·60	1·75

1979. Death Centenary of Sir Rowland Hill. As Nos. 271/3.

F285	10f. multicoloured	35	50
F286	20f. multicoloured	35	60
F287	40f. multicoloured	40	1·00

1979. Arts Festival. As Nos. 275/8.

F288	5f. multicoloured	30	60
F289	10f. multicoloured	30	60
F290	20f. multicoloured	40	80
F291	40f. multicoloured	60	1·25

1979. Christmas and International Year of the Child. As Nos. 279/82.

F292	5f. multicoloured	85	60
F293	10f. multicoloured	1·00	60
F294	20f. multicoloured	1·10	80
F295	40f. multicoloured	1·90	2·00

1980. Birds. As Nos. 283/6.

F296	10f. multicoloured	1·10	1·75
F297	20f. multicoloured	1·40	2·00
F298	30f. multicoloured	1·75	2·75
F299	40f. multicoloured	1·90	3·25

POSTAGE DUE STAMPS

1925. Nos. F32 etc, optd **CHIFFRE TAXE**.

FD53	5	10c. (1d.) green	50·00	3·00
FD54		20c. (2d.) grey	55·00	3·00
FD55		30c. (3d.) red	55·00	3·00
FD56		50c. (5d.) blue	48·00	3·00
FD57		1f. (10d.) red on blue	48·00	3·00

1938. Optd **CHIFFRE TAXE**.

FD65	6	5c. green	14·00	50·00
FD66		10c. orange	17·00	50·00
FD67		20c. red	23·00	55·00
FD68		40c. olive	48·00	£110
FD69		1f. red on green	48·00	£130

1941. Free French Issue. As last optd **France Libre**.

FD77	6	5c. green	13·00	35·00
FD78		10c. orange	13·00	35·00
FD79		20c. red	13·00	35·00
FD80		40c. olive	17·00	35·00
FD81		1f. red on green	16·00	35·00

1953. Optd **TIMBRE-TAXE**.

FD92	7	5c. green	8·00	20·00
FD93		10c. red	6·50	19·00
FD94		20c. blue	20·00	29·00
FD95	–	40c. sepia (No. F87)	13·00	27·00
FD96	–	1f. orange (No. F89)	17·00	48·00

1957. Optd **TIMBRE-TAXE**.

FD107	12	5c. green	90	9·00
FD108		10c. red	1·40	9·00
FD109		20c. blue	2·75	13·00
FD110	–	40c. sepia (No. F102)	6·50	26·00
FD111	–	1f. orange (No. F104)	5·50	32·00

For later issues see **VANUATU**.

NEW REPUBLIC Pt. 1

A Boer republic originally part of Zululand. It was incorporated with the South African Republic in 1888 and annexed to Natal in 1903.

12 pence = 1 shilling;
20 shillings = 1 pound.

1

1886. On yellow or blue paper.

1	1	1d. black	†	£3000
2		1d. violet	11·00	13·00
73		2d. violet	9·00	9·00
74		3d. violet	14·00	14·00
75		4d. violet	14·00	14·00
81		6d. violet	8·50	8·50
82		9d. violet	9·00	9·00
83		1s. violet	9·00	9·00
77		1s.6d. violet	15·00	15·00
85		2s. violet	19·00	17·00
86		2s.6d. violet	25·00	25·00
87		3s. violet	45·00	45·00
88		4s. violet	12·00	12·00
89		5s. violet	14·00	14·00
90		5s.6d. violet	13·00	13·00
91		7s.6d. violet	15·00	18·00
92		10s. violet	13·00	13·00
93		10s.6d. violet	17·00	17·00
44		12s. violet	£300	
23		13s. violet	£400	
94		£1 violet	48·00	48·00
25		30s. violet	£100	

Some stamps are found with Arms embossed in the paper, and others with the Arms and without a date above "ZUID-AFRIKA".

NEW SOUTH WALES Pt. 1

A S.E. state of the Australian Commonwealth, whose stamps it now uses.

12 pence = 1 shilling;
20 shillings = 1 pound.

1 Seal of the Colony

8

1850. Imperf.

11	1	1d. red	£2500	£275
25		2d. blue	£2000	£130
42		3d. green	£2500	£225

1851. Imperf.

47	8	1d. red	£900	£110
83		1d. orange	£200	19·00
86		2d. blue	£140	8·50
87		3d. green	£250	29·00
76		6d. brown	£1600	£250
79		8d. yellow	£4000	£600

16

11

1854. Imperf.

109	16	1d. red	£160	22·00
112		2d. blue	£140	9·00
115		3d. green	£800	80·00
88	11	5d. green	£1000	£600
90		6d. grey	£450	35·00
96		6d. brown	£500	35·00
98		8d. orange	£4000	£950
100		1s. red	£800	70·00

For these stamps perforated, see No. 134 etc.

24

1860. Perf.

195	16	1d. red	48·00	17·00
134		2d. blue	£100	10·00
226e		3d. green	6·00	80
329	11	5d. green	7·50	1·25
143		6d. brown	£300	45·00
165		6d. violet	65·00	4·75
218		8d. orange	£110	17·00
168		1s. red	95·00	7·50
297c	24	5s. purple	48·00	13·00

26

28

1862. Queen Victoria. Various frames.

207	26	1d. red	8·00	70
210	28	2d. blue	11·00	65
230c	–	4d. brown	35·00	1·50
234	–	6d. lilac	48·00	1·25
310	–	10d. lilac	14·00	6·00
237	–	1s. black	65·00	3·50

1871. As No. 310, surch **NINEPENCE**.

236d	9d. on 10d. brown	8·00	7·00

42

1885.

238b	**42**	5s. green and lilac	£425	90·00
277b		10s. red and violet	£200	50·00
240a		£1 red and lilac	£3250	

45 View of Sydney

46 Emu

52 Capt. Arthur Phillip, 1st Governor, and Lord Carrington, Governor in 1888

55 Allegorical Figure of Australia

1888. Cent of New South Wales.

253	**45**	1d. mauve	4·50	65
254	**46**	2d. blue	8·00	30
338	–	4d. brown	10·00	3·50
256	–	6d. red	22·00	3·50
297fb	–	6d. green	23·00	9·00
342	–	6d. yellow	12·00	2·25
257	–	8d. purple	19·00	3·75
347	–	1s. brown	24·00	1·75
263	–	5s. violet	£150	29·00
350b	**52**	20s. blue	£160	60·00

DESIGNS—As Type **45**: 4d. Capt. Cook; 6d. Queen Victoria and Arms; 8d. Superb lyrebird; 1s. Kangaroo. As Type **52**: 5s. Map of Australia.

1890.

265	**55**	2½d. blue	4·00	50

1891. Types as 1862, but new value and colours, surch in words.

266	**26**	½d. on 1d. grey	3·00	4·00
267a	–	7½d. on 6d. brown	5·00	3·00
268d	–	12½d. on 1s. red	11·00	10·00

58

62

63

64

66 Superb Lyrebird

67

1892.

272	**58**	½d. grey	2·25	20
298		½d. green	1·00	40
300	**62**	1d. red	1·25	10
335	**63**	2d. blue	2·00	10
296	**64**	2½d. violet	9·00	1·25
303		2½d. blue	3·50	70
352	**67**	9d. brown and blue	9·50	1·75
349a	**66**	2s.6d. green	32·00	18·00

60

1897. Diamond Jubilee and Hospital Charity.

280	**60**	1d. (1s.) green and brown	40·00	40·00
281	–	2½d. (2s.6d.) gold & blue	£170	£170

DESIGN—VERT: 2½d. Two female figures.

OFFICIAL STAMPS

1879–92. Various issues optd **O S.**

A. Issues of 1854 to 1871

O20b	**26**	1d. red	8·50	1·40
O21c	**28**	2d. blue	8·00	1·00
O25c	**16**	3d. green	5·00	3·75
O27a	–	4d. brown (No. 230e)	13·00	3·50
O28	**11**	5d. green	13·00	15·00
O31	–	6d. lilac (No. 234)	20·00	6·00
O32b	**11**	8d. orange	22·00	10·00
O11	–	9d. on 10d. (No. 236d)	£475	
O18a	–	10d. lilac (No. 310)	£170	£100
O33	–	1s. black (No. 237)	25·00	8·00
O18	**24**	5s. purple	£200	8·50

B. Fiscal stamps of 1885.

O37	**24**	10s. red and violet	£2000	£800
O38		£1 red and violet	£8500	£5000

C. Issue of 1888 (Nos. 253/346b).

O39		1d. mauve	2·75	65
O40		2d. blue	4·50	40
O41		4d. brown	11·00	3·75
O42		6d. red	8·50	5·50
O43		8d. purple	26·00	12·00
O44		1s. brown	20·00	4·00
O49a		5s. violet	£170	70·00
O48		20s. blue	£1900	£800

D. Issues of 1890 and 1892

O58a	**58**	½d. grey	5·00	16·00
O55	**26**	½d. on 1d. grey	55·00	55·00
O54	**55**	2½d. blue	9·00	8·00
O56	–	7½d. on 6d. (No. 283)	35·00	40·00
O57	–	12½d. on 1s. (No. 284c)	60·00	70·00

POSTAGE DUE STAMPS

D 1

1891.

D 1	**D 1**	½d. green	4·00	3·50
D 2b		1d. green	8·00	1·50
D 3		2d. green	12·00	2·00
D 4		3d. green	22·00	5·00
D 5		4d. green	14·00	2·00
D 6		6d. green	25·00	5·50
D 7		8d. green	75·00	17·00
D 8		5s. green	£130	45·00
D 9a		10s. green	£250	£130
D10b		20s. green	£250	£170

REGISTRATION STAMPS

15

1856.

102	**15**	(6d.) red and blue (Imp)	£800	£170
106		(6d.) orange and blue (Imp)	£950	£180
127		(6d.) red and blue (Perf)	85·00	19·00
120		(6d.) orange and blue (Perf)	£375	60·00

NEW ZEALAND Pt. 1

A group of islands in the south Pacific Ocean. A Commonwealth Dominion.

1855. 12 pence = 1 shilling;
20 shillings = 1 pound.
1967. 100 cents = 1 dollar.

1  3

1855. Imperf.
35 **1** 1d. red £375 £225
34 1d. orange £450 £200
39 2d. blue £325 75·00
40 3d. lilac £350 £140
43 6d. brown £800 90·00
45 1s. green £1000 £275

1862. Perf.
110 **1** 1d. orange £130 30·00
132 1d. brown £110 32·00
114 2d. blue £130 19·00
133 2d. orange £100 25·00
117 3d. lilac £100 30·00
119 4d. red £2250 £250
120 4d. yellow £160 £100
122 6d. brown £180 25·00
136 6d. blue £120 50·00
125 1s. green £160 90·00

1873.
151 **3** ½d. pink 10·00 1·40

5  6  7  8  9  10  11

1874. Inscr "POSTAGE".
180 **5** 1d. lilac 45·00 4·00
181 **6** 2d. red 45·00 2·50
154 **7** 3d. brown £100 55·00
182 **8** 4d. purple £140 42·00
183 **9** 6d. blue 80·00 10·00
184 **10** 1s. green £120 38·00
185 **11** 2s. red £325 £275
186 5s. grey £350 £275

13  16  19  F 4

1882. Inscr "POSTAGE & REVENUE".
236 **13** ½d. black 4·00 15
237 **10** 1d. red 4·00 10
238 **9** 2d. mauve 11·00 40
239 **16** 2½d. blue 48·00 3·75
198 **10** 3d. yellow 45·00 7·00
222 **6** 4d. green 50·00 3·75
200 **19** 5d. black 48·00 13·00
224b **8** 6d. brown 55·00 7·50
202 **9** 8d. blue 65·00 45·00
226 **7** 1s. brown 80·00 7·00

1882.
F 90 **F 4** 2s. blue 25·00 4·00
F 99 2s.6d. brown 27·00 4·50
F100 3s. mauve 70·00 6·00
F102 5s. green 70·00 8·50
F 87 10s. brown £130 18·00
F 77 £1 red £170 50·00

The above are revenue stamps authorised for use as postage stamps as there were no other postage stamps available in these denominations. Other values in this and similar types were mainly used for revenue purposes.

23 Mount Cook or Aorangi
24 Lake Taupo and Mount Ruapehu 
26 Lake Wakatipu and Mount Earnslaw 
25 Pembroke Peak, Milford Sound 
28 Sacred Huia Birds 
29 White Terrace, Rotomahana 
30 Otira Gorge and Mount Ruapehu 
31 Brown Kiwi 
32 Maori War Canoe 
33 Pink Terrace, Rotomahana 
34 Kea and Kaka 
35 Milford Sound 

1898.
246 **23** ½d. purple 6·00 1·00
302 ½d. green 5·50 60
247 **24** 1d. blue and brown 5·00 30
248 **25** 2d. red 26·00 20
249 **26** 2½d. blue (A)* 8·00 29·00
320 2½d. blue (B)* 15·00 3·50
309 **28** 3d. brown 26·00 1·50
252 **29** 4d. red 13·00 18·00
311a **30** 5d. brown 26·00 5·00
254 **31** 6d. green 50·00 32·00
265 6d. red 35·00 4·00
325 **32** 8d. blue 27·00 11·00
326 **33** 9d. purple 27·00 8·00
268a **34** 1s. orange 50·00 4·00
328 **35** 2s. green 70·00 24·00
329 – 5s. red £170 £200

DESIGN—As Type **30**: 5s. Mount Cook.
*Type A of 2½d. is inscr "WAKITIPU", Type B "WAKATIPU".

40 Commemorative of the New Zealand Contingent in the South African War

1900.
274 **29** 1d. red 13·00 10
275b **40** 1½d. brown 9·50 4·00
319 **25** 2d. purple 5·50 1·75
322d **24** 4d. blue and brown 4·00 2·50

The 1d., 2d. and 4d. are smaller than the illustrations of their respective types.

42  **44** Maori Canoe "Te Arawa"

1901.
303 **42** 1d. red 3·00 10

1906. New Zealand Exhibition, Christchurch. Inscr "COMMEMORATIVE SERIES OF 1906".
370 **44** ½d. green 22·00 30·00
371 – 1d. red 16·00 16·00
372 – 3d. brown and blue 48·00 75·00
373 – 6d. red and green £170 £250

DESIGNS: 1d. Maori art; 3d. Landing of Cook; 6d. Annexation of New Zealand.

50  **51** King Edward VII  **53** Dominion

1907.
386 **50** 1d. red 22·00 1·75
383 **28** 3d. brown 35·00 15·00
376 **31** 6d. red 40·00 8·00
385 **34** 1s. orange £110 24·00

These are smaller in size than the 1898 and 1901 issues. Type **50** also differs from Type **42** in the corner ornaments.

1909.
387 **51** ½d. green 4·25 50
405 **53** 1d. red 1·75 10
388 **51** 2d. mauve 9·50 6·50
389 3d. brown 23·00 1·25
390a 4d. orange 6·00 6·50
391a 5d. brown 17·00 3·00
392 6d. red 40·00 1·25
393 8d. blue 10·00 1·50
394 1s. red 48·00 2·75

1913. Auckland Industrial Exhibition. Optd **AUCKLAND EXHIBITION, 1913**.
412 **51** ½d. green 13·00 48·00
413 **53** 1d. red 19·00 40·00
414 **51** 3d. brown £130 £250
415 6d. red £160 £300

62 King George V

1915.
446 **62** ½d. green 1·00 30
416 1½d. grey 3·50 1·75
438 1½d. brown 2·25 20
417a 2d. violet 7·00 35·00
439 2d. yellow 2·25 20
419 2½d. blue 3·25 5·00
449 3d. brown 7·50 65
421 4d. yellow 4·25 50·00
422e 4d. violet 7·00 50
423 4½d. green 12·00 23·00
424 5d. blue 6·50 1·00
425 6d. red 8·00 50
426 7½d. brown 10·00 23·00
427 8d. blue 11·00 50·00
428 8d. brown 18·00 1·50
429 9d. green 17·00 2·75
430c 1s. orange 14·00 50

1915. No. 446 optd **WAR STAMP** and stars.
452 **62** ½d. green 2·00 50

64 "Peace" and Lion  **65** "Peace" and Lion

1920. Victory. Inscr "VICTORY" or dated "1914 1919" (6d.).
453 **64** ½d. green 3·00 2·50
454 **65** 1d. red 4·50 60
455 – 1½d. orange 3·00 50
456 – 3d. brown 12·00 14·00
457 – 6d. violet 13·00 17·00
458 – 1s. orange 20·00 48·00

DESIGNS—HORIZ (As Type **65**): 1½d. Maori chief. (As Type **64**): 3d. Lion; 1s. King George V. VERT (As Type **64**): 6d. "Peace" and "Progress".

1922. No. 453 surch **2d. 2d. TWOPENCE**.
459 **64** 2d. on ½d. green 3·50 1·40

69 New Zealand  **70** Exhibition Buildings

1923. Restoration of Penny Postage.
460 **69** 1d. red 3·00 60

1925. Dunedin Exhibition.
463 **70** ½d. green on green 3·00 11·00
464 1d. red on rose 3·50 5·50
465 4d. mauve on mauve 30·00 70·00

71  **73** Nurse

1926.
468 **71** 1d. red 75 20
469 – 2s. blue 50·00 23·00
470 – 3s. mauve 85·00 £140

The 2s. and 3s. are larger, 21 × 25 mm.

1929. Anti-T.B. Fund.
544 **73** 1d.+1d. red 11·00 18·00

1930. Inscr "HELP PROMOTE HEALTH".
545 **73** 1d.+1d. red 20·00 32·00

74 Smiling Boy **F 6** "Arms" Type

75 New Zealand Lake Scenery

1931. Health Stamps.
546 **74** 1d.+1d. red 75·00 75·00
547 2d.+1d. blue 75·00 60·00

1931. Air.
548 **75** 3d. brown 24·00 15·00
549 4d. purple 24·00 19·00
550 7d. orange 27·00 9·00

1931. Air. Surch **FIVE PENCE**.
551 **75** 5d. on 3d. green 10·00 8·00

1931. Various frames.
F191 **F 6** 1s.3d. yellow 10·00 2·00
F192 1s.3d. yellow and black 2·00 1·25
F193 2s.6d. brown 8·50 70
F194 4s. red 16·00 1·25
F195 5s. green 18·00 1·00
F196 6s. red 32·00 3·25
F197 7s. blue 32·00 5·50
F198 7s.6d. grey 60·00 50·00
F153 8s. violet 28·00 32·00
F154 9s. orange 30·00 29·00
F201 10s. red 32·00 2·25
F156 12s.6d. purple £130 £130
F202 15s. green 42·00 19·00
F203 £1 pink 28·00 3·75
F159 25s. blue £325 £425
F205w 30s. brown £225 £100
F161 35s. yellow £2500 £2750
F206 £2 violet 85·00 22·00
F207 £2 10s. red £250 £275
F208w £3 green £130 48·00
F165 £3 10s. red £1300 £1200
F210 £4 blue £140 £120
F167 £4 10s. grey £1000 £1100
F211w £5 blue £170 45·00

77 Hygeia Goddess of Health — **78** The Path to Health

1932. Health Stamp.
552 **77** 1d.+1d. red . . . . 20·00 27·00

1933. Health Stamp.
553 **78** 1d.+1d. red . . . . 13·00 17·00

1934. Air. Optd **TRANS-TASMAN AIR MAIL "FAITH IN AUSTRALIA."**.
554 **75** 7d. blue . . . . 35·00 40·00

80 Crusader

1934. Health Stamp.
555 **80** 1d.+1d. red . . . . 11·00 17·00

81 Collared Grey Fantail — **83** Maori Woman — **86** Maori Girl

85 Mt. Cook — **87** Mitre Peak

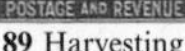

89 Harvesting — **91** Maori Panel

93 Capt. Cook at Poverty Bay

1935.
556 **81** ½d. green . . . . 1·50 1·00
557 – 1d. red . . . . 1·75 75
558a **83** 1½d. brown . . . . . . 6·00 7·00
580 – 2d. orange 30 10
581c **85** 2½d. brown and grey . . 50 4·00
561 **86** 3d. brown . . . . . . 12·00 2·75
583d **87** 4d. black and brown . . 1·00 10
584c – 5d. blue . . . . 2·00 1·50
585c **89** 6d. red . . . . 1·25 10
586d – 8d. brown . . . . . . 3·75 70
631 **91** 9d. red and black . . . 3·50 3·00
588 – 1s. green . . . . 2·50 60
589e **93** 2s. olive . . . . 5·50 1·50
590c – 3s. chocolate and brown 3·50 2·25
DESIGNS—As Type **81**: 1d. Brown kiwi; 2d. Maori carved house; 1s. Parson bird. As Type **87**: 8d. Tuatara lizard. As Type **85**: 5d. Swordfish; 3s. Mt. Egmont.

95 Bell Block Aerodrome

1935. Air.
570 **95** 1d. red . . . . 1·00 70
571 3d. violet . . . . 5·00 3·00
572 6d. blue . . . . 9·50 3·00

96 King George V and Queen Mary

1935. Silver Jubilee.
573 **96** ½d. green . . . . 75 1·00
574 1d. red . . . . 1·00 80
575 6d. orange . . . . 17·00 26·00

97 "The Key to Health" — **99** N.Z. Soldier at Anzac Cove

1935. Health Stamp.
576 **97** 1d.+1d. red . . . . 2·50 2·75

1936. Charity. 21st Anniv of "Anzac" Landing at Gallipoli.
591 **99** ½d.+½d. green . . . . . . 60 1·75
592 1d.+1d. red . . . . 60 1·40

100 Wool

1936. Congress of British Empire Chambers of Commerce, Wellington. Inscr as in T **100**.
593 **100** ½d. green 30 30
594 – 1d. red (Butter) 30 20
595 – 2½d. blue (Sheep) . . . . 1·25 8·00
596 – 4d. violet (Apples) . . . 1·00 5·50
597 – 6d. brown (Exports) . . . 2·50 4·50

105 Health Camp

1936. Health Stamp.
598 **105** 1d.+1d. red . . . . . . 1·75 3·75

106 King George VI and Queen Elizabeth

1937. Coronation.
599 **106** 1d. red 30 10
600 2½d. blue . . . . 80 2·50
601 6d. orange . . . . 1·10 2·25

107 Rock climbing — **108** King George VI

1937. Health Stamp.
602 **107** 1d.+1d. red . . . . . . 2·50 3·50

1938.
603 **108** ½d. green . . . . 6·50 10
604 ½d. orange 20 40
605 1d. red . . . . 5·00 10
606 1d. green 20 10
607 1½d. brown . . . . . . 26·00 2·50
608 1½d. red 20 60
680 2d. orange 15 10
609 3d. blue 20 10
681 4d. purple 70 50
682 5d. grey 50 90
683 6d. red 50 10
684 8d. violet 65 50
685 9d. brown . . . . 1·75 50
686b – 1s. brown and red . . . 50 80
687 – 1s.3d. brown and blue . . 1·25 1·25
688 – 2s. orange and green . . 3·75 2·50
689 – 3s. brown and grey . . . 3·50 3·50
The shilling values are larger, 22×25½ mm, and "NEW ZEALAND" appears at the top.

109 Children playing — **110** Beach Ball

1938. Health Stamp.
610 **109** 1d.+1d. red . . . . . . 6·50 3·00

1939. Health Stamps. Surch.
611 **110** 1d. on ½d.+½d. green . . 4·75 4·50
612 2d. on 1d.+1d. red . . . 4·75 4·50

1939. Surch in bold figures.
F212 **F 6** 3/6 on 3s.6d. green . . . 20·00 7·00
F214 5/6 on 5s.6d. lilac . . . 48·00 18·00
F215 11/- on 11s. yellow . . . 75·00 48·00
F216 22/- on 22s. red £275 £130
F186 35/- on 35s. orange . . . £450 £225

112 "Endeavour", Chart of N.Z. and Captain Cook

1940. Centenary of Proclamation of British Sovereignty. Inscr "CENTENNIAL OF NEW ZEALAND 1840 1940".
613 – ½d. green 30 10
614 **112** 1d. brown and red . . . 2·75 10
615 – 1½d. blue and mauve . . 30 60
616 – 2d. green and brown . . 1·50 10
617 – 2½d. green and blue . . 2·00 1·00
618 – 3d. purple and red . . . 3·75 1·00
619 – 4d. brown and red . . . 13·00 1·50
620 – 5d. blue and brown . . . 7·00 3·75
621 – 6d. green and violet . . 11·00 1·25
622 – 7d. black and red . . . 1·50 4·00
623 – 8d. black and red . . . 11·00 3·00
624 – 9d. green and orange . . 7·50 2·00
625 – 1s. green and deep green 13·00 3·75
DESIGNS—HORIZ (as T **112**): ½d. Arrival of the Maoris, 1350; 1½d. British Monarchs; 2d. Abel Tasman with "Heemskerk" and chart; 3d. Landing of immigrants, 1840; 4d. Road, rail, ocean and air transport; 6d. "Dunedin" and "frozen mutton" sea route to London; 7, 8d. Maori council; 9d. Gold mining methods, 1861 and 1940. (25×21 mm): 5d. H.M.S. "Britomart" at Akaroa, 1840. VERT (21×25 mm): 2½d. Treaty of Waitangi. (As T **112**): 1s. Giant kauri tree.

1940. Health Stamps.
626 **110** 1d.+½d. green . . . . . . 14·00 16·00
627 2d.+1d. orange . . . . . 14·00 16·00

1941. Surch.
628 **108** 1d. on ½d. green . . . . 1·75 10
629 2d. on 1½d. brown . . . 1·75 10

1941. Health Stamps. Optd **1941**.
632 **110** 1d.+½d. green . . . . . . 50 2·25
633 2d.+1d. orange . . . . . 50 2·25

125 Boy and Girl on Swing

1942. Health Stamps.
634 **125** 1d.+½d. green . . . . . . 30 1·25
635 2d.+1d. orange . . . . . 30 1·25

126 Princess Margaret

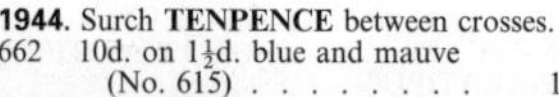

1943. Health Stamps.
636 **126** 1d.+½d. green . . . . . . 20 1·50
637 – 2d.+1d. brown 20 25
DESIGN: 2d. Queen Elizabeth II as Princess.

1944. Surch **TENPENCE** between crosses.
662 10d. on 1½d. blue and mauve (No. 615) 15 20

129 Queen Elizabeth II as Princess and Princess Margaret — **130** Peter Pan Statue, Kensington Gardens

1944. Health Stamps.
663 **129** 1d.+½d. green 30 40
664 2d.+1d. blue 30 30

1945. Health Stamps.
665 **130** 1d.+½d. green and buff . . 15 20
666 2d.+1d. red and buff . . 15 20

131 Lake Matheson — **132** King George VI and Parliament House, Wellington

133 St. Paul's Cathedral — **139** "St. George" (Wellington College War Memorial window)

1946. Peace Issue.
667 **131** ½d. green and brown . . . 20 65
668 **132** 1d. green 10 10
669 **133** 1½d. red 10 50
670 – 2d. purple 15 10
671 – 3d. blue and grey 30 15
672 – 4d. green and orange . . 20 20
673 – 5d. green and blue . . . 40 65
674 – 6d. brown and red . . . 15 30
675 **139** 8d. black and red 15 30
676 – 9d. blue and black . . . 15 30
677 – 1s. grey 15 40
DESIGNS—As Type **132**: 2d. The Royal Family. As Type **131**: 3d. R.N.Z.A.F. badge and airplanes; 4d. Army badge, tank and plough; 5d. Navy badge, H.M.N.Z.S. "Achilles" (cruiser) and "Dominion Monarch" (liner); 6d. N.Z. coat of arms, foundry and farm; 9d. Southern Alps and Franz Josef Glacier. As T **139**: 1s. National Memorial campanile.

142 Soldier helping Child over Stile — **145** Statue of Eros

1946. Health Stamps.
678 **142** 1d.+½d. green and orange 15 15
679 2d.+1d. brown & orange 15 15

1947. Health Stamps.
690 **145** 1d.+½d. green 15 15
691 2d.+1d. red 15 15

146 Port Chalmers, 1848

1948. Centenary of Otago. Various designs inscr "CENTENNIAL OF OTAGO".
692 **146** 1d. blue and green . . . 25 35
693 – 2d. green and brown . . . 25 35
694 – 3d. purple 30 60
695 – 6d. black and red 30 60
DESIGNS—HORIZ: 2d. Cromwell, Otago; 6d. Otago University. VERT: 3d. First Church, Dunedin.

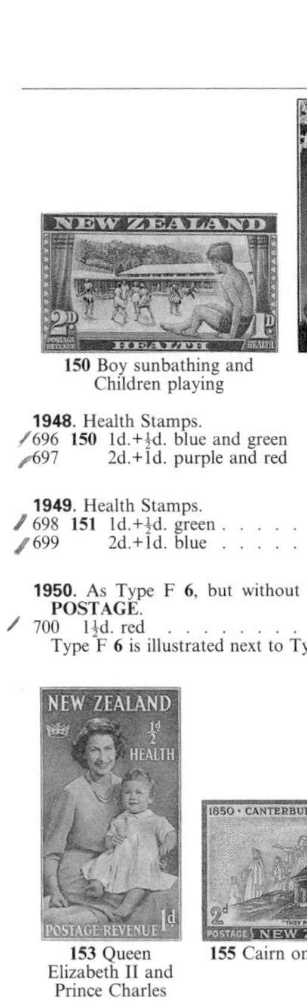

150 Boy sunbathing and Children playing

151 Nurse and Child

1948. Health Stamps.

696	**150**	1d.+½d. blue and green	15	20
697		2d.+1d. purple and red	15	20

1949. Health Stamps.

698	**151**	1d.+½d. green	25	20
699		2d.+1d. blue	25	20

1950. As Type F **6**, but without value, surch **1½d. POSTAGE.**

700		1½d. red	40	30

Type F **6** is illustrated next to Type **74**.

153 Queen Elizabeth II and Prince Charles

155 Cairn on Lyttleton Hills

1950. Health Stamps.

701	**153**	1d.+½d. green	25	20
702		2d.+1d. purple	25	20

1950. Centenary of Canterbury, N.Z.

703	–	1d. green and blue	35	55
704	**155**	2d. red and orange	35	55
705	–	3d. deep blue and blue	35	75
706	–	6d. brown and blue	45	75
707	–	1s. purple and blue	45	1·00

DESIGNS—VERT: 1d. Christchurch Cathedral; 3d. John Robert Godley. HORIZ: 6d. Canterbury University College; 1s. Aerial view of Timaru.

159 "Takapuna" class Yachts

1951. Health Stamps.

708	**159**	1½d.+½d. red and yellow	20	1·00
709		2d.+1d. green and yellow	25	25

160 Princess Anne

161 Prince Charles

1952. Health Stamps.

710	**160**	1½d.+½d. red	15	30
711	**161**	2d.+1d. brown	15	20

1952. Surch in figures.

712	**108**	1d. on ½d. orange	30	90
713		3d. on 1d. green	10	10

164 Queen Elizabeth II

166 Westminster Abbey

165 Coronation State Coach

1953. Coronation.

714	–	2d. blue	30	30
715	**164**	3d. brown	30	10
716	**165**	4d. red	1·25	2·50
717	**166**	8d. grey	80	1·60
718	–	1s.6d. purple and blue	2·00	2·75

DESIGNS—As Type **165**: 2d. Queen Elizabeth II and Buckingham Palace; 1s.6d. St. Edward's Crown and Royal Sceptre.

168 Girl Guides

169 Boy Scouts

1953. Health Stamps.

719	**168**	1½d.+½d. blue	15	10
720	**169**	2d.+1d. green	15	40

170 Queen Elizabeth II

171 Queen Elizabeth II and Duke of Edinburgh

1953. Royal Visit.

721	**170**	3d. purple	10	10
722	**171**	4d. blue	10	60

172

173

174 Queen Elizabeth II

1953. Small figures of value.

723	**172**	½d. black	15	30
724		1d. orange	15	10
725		1½d. red	20	10
726		2d. green	20	10
727		3d. red	20	10
728		4d. blue	40	50
729		6d. purple	70	1·60
730		8d. red	60	60
731	**173**	9d. brown and green	60	60
732		1s. black and red	65	10
733		1s.6d. black and blue	1·25	60
733c		1s.9d. black and orange	7·00	1·50
733d	**174**	2s.6d. brown	18·00	8·00
734		3s. green	12·00	30
735		5s. red	17·00	4·50
736		10s. blue	40·00	19·00

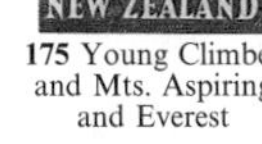

175 Young Climber and Mts. Aspiring and Everest

176 Maori Mail-carrier

177 Queen Elizabeth II

179 Children's Health Camps Federation Emblem

1954. Health Stamps.

737	**175**	1½d.+½d. brown and violet	15	30
738		2d.+1d. brown and blue	15	30

1955. Centenary of First New Zealand Stamps. Inscr "1855–1955".

739	**176**	2d. brown and green	10	10
740	**177**	3d. red	10	10
741	–	4d. black and blue	60	1·00

DESIGN—HORIZ (As Type **176**): 4d. Douglas DC-3 airliner.

1955. Health Stamps.

742	**179**	1½d.+½d. brown and chestnut	10	60
743		2d.+1d. red and green	10	35
744		3d.+1d. brown and red	15	10

180

183 Takahe

181 "The Whalers of Foveaux Strait"

1955. As 1953 but larger figures of value and stars omitted from lower right corner.

745	**180**	1d. orange	50	10
746		1½d. brown	60	60
747		2d. green	40	10
748b		3d. red	50	10
749		4d. blue	1·00	80
750		6d. purple	10·00	20
751		8d. brown	6·50	8·00

1956. Southland Centennial.

752	**181**	2d. green	30	15
753	–	3d. brown	10	10
754	**183**	8d. violet and red	1·25	1·75

DESIGN—As Type **181**: 3d. Allegory of farming.

184 Children picking Apples

185 New Zealand Lamb and Map

1956. Health Stamps.

755	**184**	1½d.+½d. brown	15	70
756		2d.+1d. green	15	55
757		3d.+1d. red	15	15

1957. 75th Anniv of First Export of N.Z. Lamb.

758	**185**	4d. blue	50	1·00
759	–	8d. red	75	1·25

DESIGN—HORIZ: 8d. Lamb, sailing ship "Dunedin" and "Port Brisbane" (refrigerated freighter).

187 Sir Truby King

188 Life-savers in Action

1957. 50th Anniv of Plunket Society.

760	**187**	3d. red	10	10

1957. Health Stamps.

761	**188**	2d.+1d. black and green	15	70
762	–	3d.+1d. blue and red	15	10
MS762b		Two sheets, each 112 × 96 mm, with Nos. 761 and 762 in blocks of 6 (2 × 3) Per pair	9·00	23·00

DESIGN: 3d. Children on seashore.

1958. Surch.

763a	**180**	2d. on 1½d. brown	15	10
808		2½d. on 3d. red	25	15

192 Boys' Brigade Bugler

193 Sir Charles Kingsford-Smith and Fokker F.IIa/3m Southern Cross

1958. Health Stamps.

764	–	2d.+1d. green	20	40
765	**192**	3d.+1d. blue	20	40
MS765a		Two sheets, each 104 × 124 mm, with Nos. 764/5 in blocks of 6 (3 × 2) Per pair	7·00	16·00

DESIGN: 2d. Girls' Life Brigade cadet.

1958. 30th Anniv of 1st Air Crossing of Tasman Sea.

766	**193**	6d. blue	50	75

194 Seal of Nelson

1958. Centenary of City of Nelson.

767	**194**	3d. red	10	10

195 "Pania" Statue, Napier

196 Australian Gannets on Cape Kidnappers

1958. Centenary of Hawke's Bay Province.

768	**195**	2d. green	10	10
769	**196**	3d. blue	20	10
770	–	8d. brown	55	1·50

DESIGN—As Type **195**: 8d. Maori sheep-shearer.

197 "Kiwi", Jamboree Badge

198 Careening H.M.S. "Endeavour" at Ship Cove

1959. Pan-Pacific Scout Jamboree, Auckland.

771	**197**	3d. brown and red	30	10

1959. Centenary of Marlborough Province. Inscr as in T **198**.

772	**198**	2d. green	30	10
773	–	3d. blue	30	10
774	–	8d. brown	1·00	2·25

DESIGNS: 3d. Shipping wool, Wairau Bar, 1857; 8d. Salt industry, Grassmere.

201 Red Cross Flag

1959. Red Cross Commemoration.

775	**201**	3d.+1d. red and blue	20	10

202 Grey Teal

204 "The Explorer"

1959. Health Stamps.

776	**202**	2d.+1d. yellow, olive and red	50	65
777	–	3d.+1d. black, pink and blue	50	65
MS777c		Two sheets, each 95×109 mm, with Nos. 776/7 in blocks of 6 (3×2) Per pair	8·00	21·00

DESIGN: 3d. New Zealand stilt.

1960. Centenary of Westland Province.

778	**204**	2d. green	20	10
779	–	3d. salmon	20	10
780	–	8d. black	70	3·00

DESIGNS: 3d. "The Gold Digger"; 8d. "The Pioneer Woman".

207 Manuka (Tea Tree)

215 Timber Industry

219 Taniwha (Maori Rock Drawing)

225 Sacred Kingfisher

1960.

781	**207**	½d. green and red	10	10
782	–	1d. multicoloured	10	10
783	–	2d. multicoloured	10	10
784	–	2½d. multicoloured	1·00	10
785	–	3d. multicoloured	30	10
786	–	4d. multicoloured	40	10
787	–	5d. multicoloured	1·25	10
788	–	6d. lilac, green and turquoise	50	10
788d	–	7d. red, green and yellow	50	1·40
789	–	8d. multicoloured	40	10
790	–	9d. red and blue	40	10
791	**215**	1s. brown and green	30	10
792b	–	1s.3d. red, sepia and blue	1·75	25
793	–	1s.6d. olive and brown	75	10
794	–	1s.9d. brown	10·00	15
795	–	1s.9d. multicoloured	5·50	1·00
796	**219**	2s. black and buff	2·50	10
797	–	2s.6d. yellow and brown	1·75	1·00
798	–	3s. sepia	23·00	75
799	–	3s. bistre, blue and green	3·25	1·75
800	–	5s. myrtle	3·00	80
801	–	10s. blue	5·50	3·25
802	–	£1 mauve	12·00	7·50

DESIGNS—VERT (as Type **207**): 1d. Karaka; 2d. Kowhai Ngutu-kaka (Kaka Beak); 2½d. Titoki (plant); 3d. Kowhai; 4d. Puarangi (Hibiscus); 5d. Matua tikumu (Mountain daisy); 6d. Pikiarero (Clematis); 7d. Koromiko; 8d. Rata. (As T **215**): 1s.3d. Rainbow trout; 1s.6d. Tiki. (As T **219**): 5s. Sutherland Falls; £1 Pohutu Geyser. HORIZ (as T **215**): 9d. National flag; 1s.9d. Aerial top-dressing. (As Type **219**): 2s.6d. Butter-making; 3s. Tongariro National Park and Chateau; 10s. Tasman Glacier.

1960. Health Stamps.

803	**225**	2d.+1d. sepia and blue	50	75
804	–	3d.+1d. purple & orange	50	75
MS804b		Two sheets, each 95×107 mm, with Nos. 803/4 in blocks of 6 Per pair	26·00	35·00

DESIGN: 3d. New Zealand pigeon.

227 "The Adoration of the Shepherds" (Rembrandt)

228 Great Egret

1960. Christmas.

805	**227**	2d. red & brown on cream	15	10

1961. Health Stamps.

806	**228**	2d.+1d. black and purple	50	70
807	–	3d.+1d. sepia and green	50	70
MS807a		Two sheets, each 97×121 mm, with Nos. 806/7 in blocks of 6 (3×2) Per pair	26·00	28·00

DESIGN: 3d. New Zealand falcon.

232 "Adoration of the Magi" (Durer)

236 Tieke Saddleback

233 Morse Key and Port Hills, Lyttleton

1961. Christmas.

809	**232**	2½d. multicoloured	10	10

1962. Telegraph Centenary.

810	**233**	3d. sepia and green	10	10
811	–	8d. black and red	90	90

DESIGN: 8d. Modern teleprinter.

1962. Health Stamps.

812	–	2½d.+1d. multicoloured	50	70
813	**236**	3d.+1d. multicoloured	50	70
MS813b		Two sheets, each 96×101 mm, with Nos. 812/13 in blocks of 6 (3×2) Per pair	45·00	50·00

DESIGN: 2½d. Red-fronted parakeet.

237 "Madonna in Prayer" (Sassoferrato)

238 Prince Andrew

1962. Christmas.

814	**237**	2½d. multicoloured	10	10

1963. Health Stamps.

815	**238**	2½d.+1d. blue	30	70
816	–	3d.+1d. red	30	10
MS816a		Two sheets, each 93×100 mm, with Nos. 815/16 in blocks of 6 (3×2) Per pair	23·00	35·00

DESIGN: 3d. Prince Andrew (different).

240 "The Holy Family" (Titian)

1963. Christmas.

817	**240**	2½d. multicoloured	10	10

241 Steam Locomotive "Pilgrim" (1863) and Class DG Diesel Locomotive

1963. Centenary of New Zealand Railway. Inscr as in T **241**. Multicoloured.

818	3d. Type **241**	40	10
819	1s.9d. Diesel express and Mt. Ruapehu	1·50	1·50

243 "Commonwealth Cable"

1963. Opening of COMPAC (Trans-Pacific Telephone Cable).

820	**243**	8d. multicoloured	50	1·25

244 Road Map and Car Steering-wheel

1964. Road Safety Campaign.

821	**244**	3d. black, yellow and blue	30	10

245 Silver Gulls

1964. Health Stamps. Multicoloured.

822	2½d.+1d. Type **245**	40	50
823	3d.+1d. Little penguin	40	50
MS823b	Two sheets, each 171×84 mm, with Nos. 822/3 in blocks of 8 (4×2) Per pair	48·00	55·00

246 Rev. S. Marsden taking first Christian Service at Rangihoua Bay, 1814

1964. Christmas.

824	**246**	2½d. multicoloured	10	10

1964. Surch **7D POSTAGE**.

825	F **6**	7d. on (–) red	50	1·50

248 Anzac Cove

1965. 50th Anniv of Gallipoli Landing.

826	**248**	4d. brown	10	10
827	–	5d. green and red	10	60

DESIGN: 5d. Anzac Cove and poppy.

249 I.T.U. Emblem and Symbols

250 Sir Winston Churchill

1965. Centenary of I.T.U.

828	**249**	9d. blue and brown	55	35

1965. Churchill Commemoration.

829	**250**	7d. black, grey and blue	30	50

251 Wellington Provincial Council Building

252 Kaka

1965. Centenary of Government in Wellington.

830	**251**	4d. multicoloured	20	10

1965. Health Stamps. Multicoloured.

831	3d.+1d. Type **252**	40	65
832	4d.+1d. Collared grey fantail	40	65
MS832b	Two sheets, each 100×109 mm, with Nos. 831/2 in blocks of 6 (3×2) Per pair	38·00	45·00

254 I.C.Y. Emblem

255 "The Two Trinities" (Murillo)

1965. International Co-operation Year.

833	**254**	4d. red and olive	20	10

1965. Christmas.

834	**255**	3d. multicoloured	10	10

256 Arms of New Zealand

1965. 11th Commonwealth Parliamentary Conf. Multicoloured.

835	4d. Type **256**	25	20
836	9d. Parliament House, Wellington, and Badge	65	1·25
837	2s. Wellington from Mt. Victoria	4·50	6·50

259 "Progress" Arrowhead

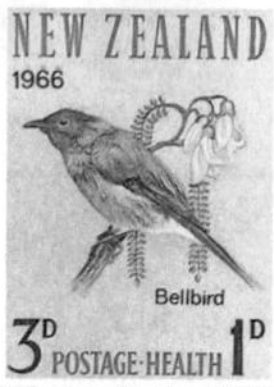

260 New Zealand Bell Bird

1966. 4th National Scout Jamboree, Trentham.

838	**259**	4d. gold and green	15	10

1966. Health Stamps. Multicoloured.

839	3d.+1d. Type **260**	40	75
840	4d.+1d. Weka rail	40	75
MS841	Two sheets, each 107×91 mm. Nos. 839/40 in blocks of 6 (3×2) Per pair	22·00	48·00

262 "The Virgin with Child" (Maratta)

263 Queen Victoria and Queen Elizabeth II

1966. Christmas.

842	**262**	3d. multicoloured	10	10

1967. Centenary of New Zealand Post Office Savings Bank.

843	**263**	4d. black, gold and purple	10	10
844	–	9d. multicoloured	10	20

DESIGN: 9d. Half-sovereign of 1867 and commemorative dollar coin.

265 Manuka (Tea Tree)

268 Running with Ball

1967. Decimal Currency. Designs as earlier issues, but with values inscr in decimal currency as T **265**.

845	**265**	½c. blue, green and red	10	10
846	–	1c. mult (No. 782)	10	10
847	–	2c. mult (No. 783)	10	10
848	–	2½c. mult (No. 785)	10	10
849	–	3c. mult (No. 786)	10	10
850	–	4c. mult (No. 787)	30	10
851	–	5c. lilac, olive and green (No. 788)	50	25
852	–	6c. mult (No. 788d)	50	60
853	–	7c. mult (No. 789)	60	60
854	–	8c. red and blue (No. 790)	60	30

855 **215** 10c. brown and green . . . 60 30
856 – 15c. green and brown (No. 793) . . . . . 1·75 1·00
857 **219** 20c. black and buff . . 1·25 10
858 – 25c. yellow and brown (No. 797) . . . . . 1·50 2·00
859 – 30c. yellow, green and blue (No. 799) . . . 1·50 25
860 – 50c. green (No. 800) . . 2·00 50
861 – $1 blue (No. 801) . . . 9·00 70
862 – $2 mauve (No. 802) . . 4·00 6·00
F219a **F 6** $4 violet . . . . 2·50 1·50
F220a $6 green . . . . 3·00 3·00
F221a $8 blue . . . . 5·00 4·50
F222a $10 blue . . . . 6·00 3·75
For 15c. in different colours, see No. 874.

1967. Health Stamps. Rugby Football.
867 **268** 2½c.+1c. multicoloured . . 15 15
868 – 3c.+1c. multicoloured . . 15 15
MS869 Two sheets. (a) 76×130 mm (867). (b) 130×76 mm (868). Containing blocks of six Per pair 23·00 38·00
DESIGN—HORIZ: 3c. Positioning for place-kick.

271 Brown Trout **273** Forest and Timber

1967.
870 – 7c. multicoloured . . . . 1·50 90
871 **271** 7½c. multicoloured 50 70
872 – 8c. multicoloured 75 70
873 **273** 10c. multicoloured 50 10
874 – 15c. green, deep green and red (as No. 793) . . . 1·00 1·00
875 – 18c. multicoloured . . . . 1·00 55
876 – 20c. multicoloured . . . . 1·00 20
877 – 25c. multicoloured . . . . 1·75 2·00
878 – 28c. multicoloured 60 10
879 – $2 black, ochre and blue (as No. 802) . . . 13·00 13·00
DESIGNS: 7c. "Kaitia" (trawler) and catch; 8c. Apples and orchard; 18c. Sheep and the "Woolmark"; 20c. Consignments of beef and herd of cattle; 25c. Dairy farm, Mt. Egmont and butter consignment. VERT: 28c. Fox Glacier, Westland National Park.
No. 871 was originally issued to commemorate the introduction of the brown trout into New Zealand.
No. 874 is slightly larger than No. 793, measuring 21×25 mm, and the inscr and numerals differ in size.

278 "The Adoration of the Shepherds" (Poussin) **279** Mount Aspiring, Aurora Australis and Southern Cross

1967. Christmas.
880 **278** 2½c. multicoloured 10 10

1967. Cent of Royal Society of New Zealand.
881 **279** 4c. multicoloured 25 20
882 – 8c. multicoloured 25 80
DESIGN: 8c. Sir James Hector (founder).

281 Open Bible **282** Soldiers and Tank

1968. Centenary of Maori Bible.
883 **281** 3c. multicoloured 10 10

1968. New Zealand Armed Forces. Multicoloured.
884 4c. Type **282** 25 15
885 10c. Airmen, Fairey Firefly and English Electric Canberra aircraft 35 70
886 28c. Sailors and H.M.N.Z.S. "Achilles", 1939, and H.M.N.Z.S. "Waikato", 1968 . . . . 50 2·50

285 Boy breasting Tape and Olympic Rings

1968. Health Stamps. Multicoloured.
887 2½c.+1c. Type **285** 20 15
888 3c.+1c. Girl swimming and Olympic rings 20 15
MS889 Two sheets, each 145×95 mm. Nos. 887/8 in blocks of 6 Per pair . . . . 16·00 42·00

287 Placing Votes in Ballot Box **288** Human Rights Emblem

1968. 75th Anniv of Universal Suffrage in New Zealand.
890 **287** 3c. ochre, green and blue 10 10

1968. Human Rights Year.
891 **288** 10c. red, yellow and green 10 30

289 "Adoration of the Holy Child" (G. van Honthorst)

1968. Christmas.
892 **289** 2½c. multicoloured 10 10

290 I.L.O. Emblem

1969. 50th Anniv of Int Labour Organization.
893 **290** 7c. black and red 15 30

291 Supreme Court Building, Auckland

1969. Centenary of New Zealand Law Society.
894 **291** 3c. multicoloured 10 10
895 – 10c. multicoloured 20 60
896 – 18c. multicoloured . . . . 30 1·50
DESIGNS—VERT: 10c. Law Society's coat of arms; 18c. "Justice" (from Memorial Window in University of Canterbury, Christchurch).

295 Student being conferred with Degree

1969. Centenary of Otago University. Mult.
897 3c. Otago University (vert) 10 10
898 10c. Type **295** 20 25

296 Boys playing Cricket

1969. Health Stamps.
899 **296** 2½c.+1c. multicoloured . . 40 65
900 – 3c.+1c. multicoloured . . 40 65
901 – 4c.+1c. brown and ultramarine . . . . . . 40 2·00
MS902 Two sheets, each 144×84 mm. Nos. 899/900 in blocks of 6 Per pair . . . . . 16·00 48·00
DESIGNS—HORIZ: 3c. Girls playing cricket. VERT: 4c. Dr. Elizabeth Gunn (founder of first Children's Health Camp).

299 Oldest existing House in New Zealand, and Old Stone Mission Store, Kerikeri

1969. Early European Settlement in New Zealand, and 150th Anniv of Kerikeri. Multicoloured.
903 4c. Type **299** 20 25
904 6c. View of Bay of Islands 30 1·75

301 "The Nativity" (Federico Fiori Barocci) **306** Girl, Wheat Field and C.O.R.S.O. Emblem

302 Captain Cook, Transit of Venus and "Octant"

1969. Christmas.
905 **301** 2½c. multicoloured 10 10

1969. Bicentenary of Captain Cook's Landing in New Zealand.
906 **302** 4c. black, red and blue . . 75 35
907 – 6c. green, brown and black . . . . 1·00 2·50
908 – 18c. brown, green and black . . . . 1·75 2·50
909 – 28c. red, black and blue 2·75 4·00
MS910 109×90 mm. Nos. 906/9 18·00 35·00
DESIGNS: 6c. Sir Joseph Banks (naturalist) and outline of H.M.S. "Endeavour"; 18c. Dr. Daniel Solander (botanist) and his plant; 28c. Queen Elizabeth II and Cook's chart, 1769.

1969. 25th Anniv of C.O.R.S.O. (Council of Organizations for Relief Services Overseas). Multicoloured.
911 7c. Type **306** . . . . 35 1·10
912 8c. Mother feeding her child, dairy herd and C.O.R.S.O. emblem (horiz) . . . . . . 35 1·25

308 "Cardigan Bay" (champion trotter)

1970. Return of "Cardigan Bay" to New Zealand.
913 **308** 10c. multicoloured 30 30

309 "Vanessa gonerilla" (butterfly) **310** Queen Elizabeth II and New Zealand Coat of Arms

1970.
914 – ½c. multicoloured . . . 10 20
915 **309** 1c. multicoloured . . . 10 10
916 – 2c. multicoloured . . . 10 10
917 – 2½c. multicoloured . . . 30 20
918 – 3c. multicoloured . . . 15 10
919 – 4c. multicoloured . . . 15 10
920 – 5c. multicoloured . . . 30 10
921 – 6c. black, green and red 30 65
922 – 7c. multicoloured . . . 50 1·00
923 – 7½c. multicoloured . . . 75 1·50
924 – 8c. multicoloured . . . 50 1·00
925 **310** 10c. multicoloured . . . 50 15
926 – 15c. black, flesh and brown 75 50
927 – 18c. green, brown & black 75 50
928 – 20c. black and brown . . 75 15
929 – 23c. multicoloured . . . 60 30
930b – 25c. multicoloured . . . 50 40
931 – 30c. multicoloured . . . 50 15
932 – 50c. multicoloured . . . 50 20
933 – $1 multicoloured . . . . 1·25 1·25
934 – $2 multicoloured . . . . 2·50 1·75

DESIGNS—VERT (as T **309**): ½c. "Lycaena salustius" (butterfly); 2c. "Argyrophenga antipodum" (butterfly); 2½c. "Nyctemera annulata (moth); 3c. "Detunda egregia" (moth); 4c. Charagia virescens" (moth); 5c. Scarlet wrasse ("Scarlet parrot fish"); 6c. Big-bellied sea horses; 7c. Leather-jacket (fish); 7½c. Intermediate halfbeak ("Garfish"); 8c. John Dory (fish). (As T **310**): 18c. Maori club; 25c. Hauraki Gulf Maritime Park; 30c. Mt. Cook National Park. HORIZ (as T **310**): 15c. Maori fish hook; 20c. Maori tattoo pattern; 23c. Egmont National Park; 50c. Abel Tasman National Park; $1 Geothermal power; $2 Agricultural technology.

311 Geyser Restaurant **312** U.N. H.Q. Building

1970. World Fair, Osaka. Multicoloured.
935 7c. Type **311** 20 75
936 8c. New Zealand Pavilion . . 20 75
937 18c. Bush Walk 40 75

1970. 25th Anniv of United Nations.
938 **312** 3c. multicoloured 10 10
939 – 10c. red and yellow . . . 20 20
DESIGN: 10c. Tractor on horizon.

313 Soccer **314** "The Virgin adoring the Child" (Correggio)

1970. Health Stamps. Multicoloured.
940 2½c.+1c. Netball (vert) . . . 25 70
941 3c.+1c. Type **313** 25 70
MS942 Two sheets. (a) 102×125 mm (940). (b) 125×102 mm (941). Containing blocks of six Per pair . . . . 18·00 45·00

1970. Christmas.
943 **314** 2½c. multicoloured 10 10
944 – 3c. multicoloured 10 10
945 – 10c. black, orange & silver 30 75
DESIGNS—VERT: 3c. Stained glass window, Invercargill Presbyterian Church "The Holy Family". HORIZ: 10c. Tower of Roman Catholic Church, Seckburn.

316 Chatham Islands Lily

1970. Chatham Islands. Multicoloured.
946 1c. Type **316** 10 35
947 2c. Shy albatross 30 40

317 Country Women's Institute Emblem

1971. 50th Annivs of Country Women's Institutes and Rotary International in New Zealand. Multicoloured.
948 4c. Type **317** 10 10
949 10c. Rotary emblem and map of New Zealand 20 60

318 "Rainbow II" (yacht)

1971. One Ton Cup Racing Trophy. Mult.
950 5c. Type **318** 25 25
951 8c. One Ton Cup . . . . . 25 1·50

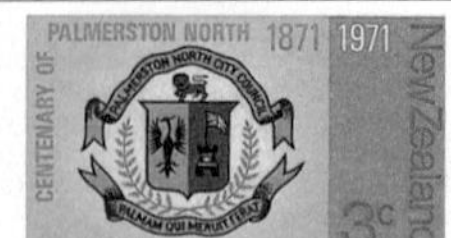

319 Civic Arms of Palmerston North

1971. City Centenaries. Multicoloured.
952 3c. Type **319** 10 10
953 4c. Arms of Auckland . . . 10 15
954 5c. Arms of Invercargill . . . 15 1·10

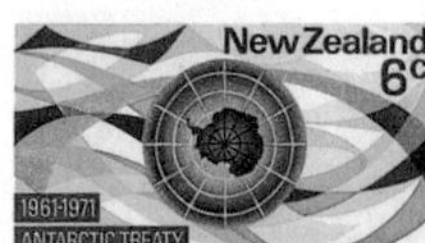

320 Antarctica on Globe

1971. 10th Anniv of Antarctic Treaty.
955 **320** 6c. multicoloured . . . . 1·00 1·50

321 Child on Swing

323 Satellite-tracking Aerial

1971. 25th Anniv of U.N.I.C.E.F.
956 **321** 7c. multicoloured . . . . 50 1·00

1971. No. 917 surch **4c.**
957 4c. on 2½c. multicoloured . . 15 10

1971. Opening of Satellite Earth Station.
958 **323** 8c. black, grey and red . . 50 1·50
959 – 10c. black, green and violet . . . . 50 1·00
DESIGN: 10c. Satellite.

324 Girls playing Hockey

1971. Health Stamps. Multicoloured.
960 3c.+1c. Type **324** 45 65
961 4c.+1c. Boys playing hockey 45 65
962 5c.+1c. Dental health . . . 1·10 2·00
MS963 Two sheets, each 122 × 96 mm. Nos. 960/1 in blocks of six Per pair . . . . 19·00 45·00

325 "Madonna bending over the Crib" (Maratta)

1971. Christmas. Multicoloured.
964 3c. Type **325** 10 10
965 4c. "The Annunciation" (stained-glass window) . . 10 10
966 10c. "The Three Kings" . . . 70 1·25
Nos. 965/6 are smaller, size 21½ × 38 mm.

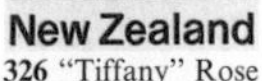

326 "Tiffany" Rose

327 Lord Rutherford and Alpha Particles

1971. 1st World Rose Convention, Hamilton. Mult.
967 2c. Type **326** 15 30
968 5c. "Peace" 35 35
969 8c. "Chrysler Imperial" . . . 60 1·10

1971. Birth Centenary of Lord Rutherford (scientist). Multicoloured.
970 1c. Type **327** 20 50
971 7c. Lord Rutherford and formula . . . . 55 1·75

328 Benz (1895)

329 Coat of Arms of Wanganui

1972. International Vintage Car Rally. Mult.
972 3c. Type **328** 20 10
973 4c. Oldsmobile (1904) 20 10
974 5c. Ford "Model T" (1914) 20 10
975 6c. Cadillac Service car (1915) 25 45
976 8c. Chrysler (1924) . . . . . 55 2·00
977 10c. Austin "7" (1923) . . . 55 1·50

1972. Anniversaries.
978 **329** 3c. multicoloured 15 10
979 – 4c. orange, brown & black 15 10
980 – 5c. multicoloured 25 10
981 – 8c. multicoloured . . . . 40 1·10
982 – 10c. multicoloured . . . . 40 1·10
DESIGNS AND EVENTS—VERT: 3c. Type **329** (centenary of Wanganui Council); 5c. De Havilland D.H.89 Dragon Rapide and Boeing 737 (25th anniv of National Airways Corp); 8c. French frigate and Maori palisade (bicentenary of landing by Marion du Fresne). HORIZ: 4c. Postal Union symbol (10th anniv of Asian–Oceanic Postal Union); 10c. Stone cairn (150th anniv of New Zealand Methodist Church).

330 Black Scree Cotula

331 Boy playing Tennis

1972. Alpine Plants. Multicoloured.
983 4c. Type **330** 30 10
984 6c. North Island edelweiss . . 40 40
985 8c. Haast's buttercup 60 85
986 10c. Brown Mountain daisy 70 1·25

1972. Health Stamps.
987 **331** 3c.+1c. grey and brown 30 50
988 – 4c.+1c. brown, grey and yellow 30 50
MS989 Two sheets, each 107 × 123 mm. Nos. 987/8 in blocks of six Per pair . . . . 18·00 40·00
DESIGN: No. 988, Girl playing tennis.

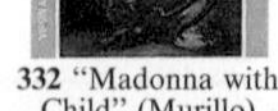

332 "Madonna with Child" (Murillo)

333 Lake Waikaremoana

1972. Christmas. Multicoloured.
990 3c. Type **332** 10 10
991 5c. "The Last Supper" (stained-glass window, St. John's Church, Levin) 15 10
992 10c. Pohutukawa flower . . . 35 70

1972. Lake Scenes. Multicoloured.
993 6c. Type **333** . . . . 75 1·00
994 8c. Lake Hayes . . . . . . 85 1·00
995 18c. Lake Wakatipu . . . . 1·25 2·00
996 23c. Lake Rotomahana . . . 1·40 2·25

334 Old Pollen Street

1973. Commemorations.
997 **334** 3c. multicoloured 10 10
998 – 4c. multicoloured 15 10
999 – 5c. multicoloured 15 15
1000 – 6c. multicoloured 50 50
1001 – 8c. grey, blue and gold 35 50
1002 – 10c. multicoloured . . . 50 80
DESIGNS AND EVENTS: 3c. (centenary of Thames Borough); 4c. Coalmining and pasture (centenary of Westport Borough); 5c. Cloister (centenary of Canterbury University); 6c. Forest, birds and lake (50th anniv of Royal Forest and Bird Protection Society); 8c. Rowers (Success of N.Z. rowers in 1972 Olympics); 10c. Graph and people (25th anniv of E.C.A.F.E.).

335 Class W Locomotive

1973. New Zealand Steam Locomotives. Mult.
1003 3c. Type **335** 30 10
1004 4c. Class X 30 10
1005 5c. Class Ab 30 10
1006 10c. Class Ja No. 1274 . . . 1·75 1·40

336 "Maori Woman and Child"

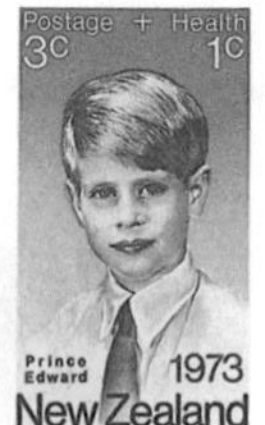

337 Prince Edward

1973. Paintings by Frances Hodgkins. Mult.
1027 5c. Type **336** 30 15
1028 8c. "Hilltop" . . . . 45 1·10
1029 10c. "Barn in Picardy" . . . 60 90
1030 18c. "Self-portrait Still Life" 90 2·25

1973. Health Stamps.
1031 **337** 3c.+1c. green & brown 30 50
1032 4c.+1c. red and brown 30 50
MS1033 Two sheets, each 96 × 121 mm, with Nos. 1031/2 in blocks of 6 (3 × 2) Per pair . . 16·00 35·00

338 "Tempi Madonna" (Raphael)

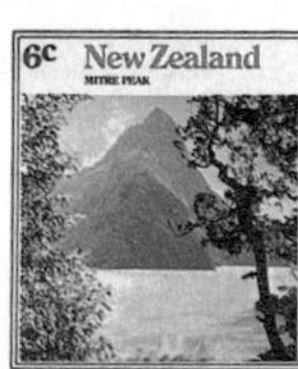

339 Mitre Peak

1973. Christmas. Multicoloured.
1034 3c. Type **338** 10 10
1035 5c. "Three Kings" (stained-glass window, St. Theresa's Church, Auckland) 10 10
1036 10c. Family entering church 25 50

1973. Mountain Scenery. Multicoloured.
1037 6c. Type **339** 55 80
1038 8c. Mt. Ngauruhoe . . . . 65 1·25
1039 18c. Mt. Sefton (horiz) . . . 80 2·50
1040 23c. Burnett Range (horiz) 1·00 2·75

340 Hurdling

341 Queen Elizabeth II

1974. 10th British Commonwealth Games, Christchurch.
1041 **340** 4c. multicoloured 10 10
1042 – 5c. black and violet . . . 10 10
1043 – 10c. multicoloured . . . 20 15
1044 – 18c. multicoloured . . . 15 50
1045 – 23c. multicoloured . . . 20 80
DESIGNS: 5c. Ball-player (4th Paraplegic Games, Dunedin); 10c. Cycling; 18c. Rifle-shooting; 23c. Bowls.

1974. New Zealand Day. Sheet 131 × 74 mm, containing T **341** and similar horiz designs, size 37 × 20 mm. Multicoloured.
MS1046 4c. × 5 Treaty House, Waitangi; Signing Waitangi Treaty; Type **341**; Parliament Buildings extensions; Children in class . . . . 70 2·50

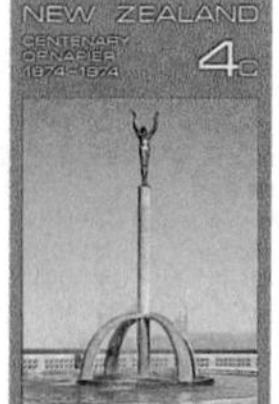

342 "Spirit of Napier" Fountain

344 Children, Cat and Dog

343 Boeing Seaplane, 1919

1974. Centenaries of Napier and U.P.U. Mult.
1047 4c. Type **342** 10 10
1048 5c. Clock Tower, Berne . . 20 30
1049 8c. U.P.U. Monument, Berne . . . . 55 1·60

1974. History of New Zealand Airmail Transport. Multicoloured.
1050 3c. Type **343** 25 10
1051 4c. Lockheed 10 Electra "Kauha", 1937 . . . . . 30 10
1052 5c. Bristol Type 170 Freighter Mk 31, 1958 . . 30 30
1053 23c. Short S.30 modified "G" Class flying boat "Aotearoa", 1940 . . . . 1·40 2·00

1974. Health Stamps.
1054 **344** 3c.+1c. multicoloured . . 20 50
1055 – 4c.+1c. multicoloured . . 25 50
1056 – 5c.+1c. multicoloured . . 1·00 1·50
MS1057 145 × 123 mm. No. 1055 in block of ten . . . . 21·00 38·00
Nos. 1055/6 are similar to Type **344**, showing children with pets.

345 "The Adoration of the Magi" (Konrad Witz)

346 Great Barrier Island

1974. Christmas. Multicoloured.
1058 3c. Type **345** 10 10
1059 5c. "The Angel Window" (stained glass window, Old St. Pauls Church, Wellington) 10 10
1060 10c. Madonna lily 30 90

1974. Offshore Islands. Multicoloured.
1061 6c. Type **346** 25 40
1062 8c. Stewart Island . . . . . 40 1·25
1063 18c. White Island . . . . . 50 1·50
1064 23c. The Brothers . . . . . 55 1·75

347 Crippled Child

1975. Anniversaries and Events. Multicoloured.
1065 3c. Type **347** 10 10
1066 5c. Farming family 10 10
1067 10c. I.W.Y. symbols 15 65
1068 18c. Medical School Building, Otago University . . . . 40 1·75
COMMEMORATIONS: 3c. 40th anniv of New Zealand Crippled Children Society; 5c. 50th anniv of Women's Division, Federated Farmers of New Zealand; 10c. International Women's Year; 18c. Centenary of Otago Medical School.

348 Scow "Lake Erie"

1975. Historic Sailing Ships.
1069 **348** 4c. black and red 30 10
1070 – 5c. black and blue . . . 30 10
1071 – 8c. black and yellow . . 40 60
1072 – 10c. black and yellow . . 45 60
1073 – 18c. black and brown . . 75 2·25
1074 – 23c. black and lilac . . . 85 2·25
SHIPS: 5c. Schooner "Herald"; 8c. Brigantine "New Zealander"; 10c. Topsail schooner "Jessie Kelly"; 18c. Barque "Tory"; 23c. Full-rigged clipper "Rangitiki".

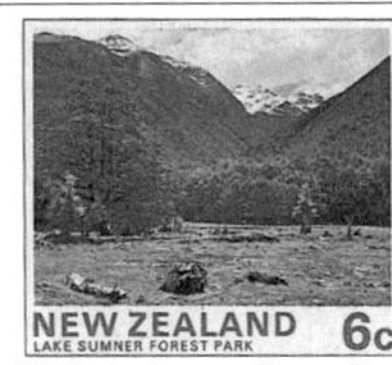

349 Lake Sumner Forest Park

1975. Forest Park Scenes. Multicoloured.
1075 6c. Type **349** 30 60
1076 8c. North-west Nelson . . . 40 1·00
1077 18c. Kaweka . . . . 65 1·75
1078 23c. Coromandel . . . . . 90 1·75

350 Girl feeding Lamb **351** "Virgin and Child" (Zanobi Machiavelli)

1975. Health Stamps. Multicoloured.
1079 3c.+1c. Type **350** 15 30
1080 4c.+1c. Boy with hen and chicks 15 30
1081 5c.+1c. Boy with duck and duckling . . . . 40 1·50
MS1082 123 × 146 mm. No. 1080 × 10 . . . . 15·00 38·00

1975. Christmas. Multicoloured.
1083 3c. Type **351** 10 10
1084 5c. "Cross in Landscape" (stained-glass window, Greendale Church) (horiz) 10 10
1085 10c. "I saw three ships" (carol) (horiz) 35 65

352 "Sterling Silver" **353** Queen Elizabeth II (photograph by W. Harrison)

353a Maripi (knife) **353b** Rainbow Abalone or Paua

1975. (a) Garden Roses. Multicoloured.
1086 1c. Type **352** 10 10
1087 2c. "Lilli Marlene" 10 20
1088 3c. "Queen Elizabeth" . . 60 10
1089 4c. "Super Star" 10 60
1090 5c. "Diamond Jubilee" . . 10 10
1091a 6c. "Cresset" . . . . . . 40 1·00
1092a 7c. "Michele Meilland" . . 40 10
1093a 8c. "Josephine Bruce" . . 30 10
1094 9c. "Iceberg" 30 60

(b) Type **353**.
1094ab 10c. multicoloured . . . 30 10

(c) Maori Artefacts.
1095 **353a** 11c. brown, yellow & black 30 80
1096 – 12c. brown, yellow & black 30 50
1097 – 13c. brown, mauve & black . . . . 40 1·00
1098 – 14c. brown, yellow & black 30 20
DESIGNS: 12c. Putorino (flute); 13c. Wahaika (club); 14c. Kotiate (club).

(d) Sea Shells. Multicoloured.
1099 20c. Type **353b** 15 20
1100 30c. Toheroa clam 25 50
1101 40c. Old woman or coarse dosinia 30 35
1102 50c. New Zealand or spiny murex 40 45
1103 $1 New Zealand scallop . . 70 1·00
1104 $2 Circular saw . . . . . . 1·00 1·75

(e) Building. Multicoloured.
1105 $5 "Beehive" (section of Parliamentary Buildings, Wellington) (22 × 26 mm) 2·00 1·50

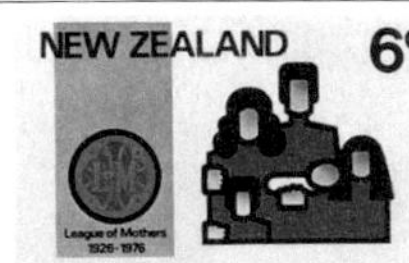

354 Family and League of Mothers Badge

1976. Anniversaries and Metrication. Mult.
1110 6c. Type **354** 10 10
1111 7c. Weight, temperature, linear measure and capacity 10 10
1112 8c. "William Bryon" (immigrant ship), mountain and New Plymouth 15 10
1113 10c. Two women shaking hands and Y.W.C.A. badge 15 50
1114 25c. Map of the world showing cable links . . . 30 1·25
ANNIVERSARIES: 6c. 50th anniv of League of Mothers; 7c. Metrication; 8c. Centenary of New Plymouth; 10c. 50th anniv of New Zealand Y.W.C.A.; 25c. Link with International Telecommunications Network.

355 Gig

1976. Vintage Farm Transport. Multicoloured.
1115 6c. Type **355** 15 40
1116 7c. Thornycroft lorry . . . 15 10
1117 8c. Scandi wagon 30 15
1118 9c. Traction engine 20 40
1119 10c. Wool wagon 20 40
1120 25c. Cart . . . . 65 2·25

356 Purakaunui Falls **357** Boy and Pony

1976. Waterfalls. Multicoloured.
1121 10c. Type **356** 25 10
1122 14c. Marakopa Falls 40 95
1123 15c. Bridal Veil Falls . . . 45 1·10
1124 16c. Papakorito Falls . . . 55 1·25

1976. Health Stamps. Multicoloured.
1125 7c.+1c. Type **357** 20 30
1126 8c.+1c. Girl and calf 20 30
1127 10c.+1c. Girls and bird . . 40 90
MS1128 96 × 121 mm. Nos. 1125/7 × 2 . . . . 3·00 6·00

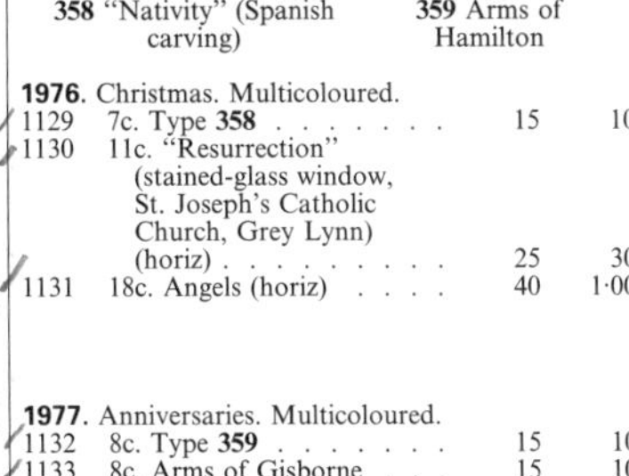

358 "Nativity" (Spanish carving) **359** Arms of Hamilton

1976. Christmas. Multicoloured.
1129 7c. Type **358** 15 10
1130 11c. "Resurrection" (stained-glass window, St. Joseph's Catholic Church, Grey Lynn) (horiz) 25 30
1131 18c. Angels (horiz) . . . . 40 1·00

1977. Anniversaries. Multicoloured.
1132 8c. Type **359** 15 10
1133 8c. Arms of Gisborne . . . 15 10
1134 8c. Arms of Masterton . . . 15 10
1135 10c. A.A. emblem 15 40
1136 10c. Arms of the Royal Australasian College of Surgeons 15 40
ANNIVERSARIES: No. 1132, Cent of Hamilton; 1133, Cent of Gisborne; 1134, Cent of Masterton; 1135, 75th anniv of Automobile Association in New Zealand; 1136, 50th anniv of R.A.C.S.

360 Queen Elizabeth II **361** Physical Education and Maori Culture

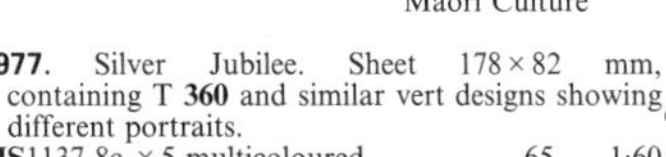

1977. Silver Jubilee. Sheet 178 × 82 mm, containing T **360** and similar vert designs showing different portraits.
MS1137 8c. × 5 multicoloured . . 65 1·60

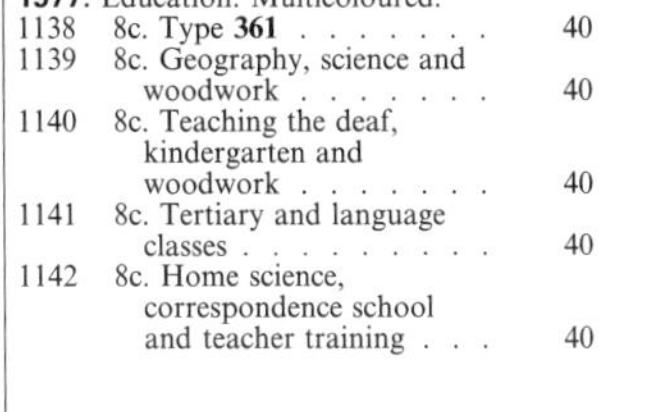

1977. Education. Multicoloured.
1138 8c. Type **361** 40 70
1139 8c. Geography, science and woodwork 40 70
1140 8c. Teaching the deaf, kindergarten and woodwork 40 70
1141 8c. Tertiary and language classes 40 70
1142 8c. Home science, correspondence school and teacher training . . . 40 70

1977. Nos. 918/19 surch.
1143 7c. on 3c. "Detunda egregia" (moth) 40 70
1144 8c. on 4c. "Charagia virescens" (moth) 40 70

363 Karitane Beach

1977. Seascapes. Multicoloured.
1145 10c. Type **363** 15 10
1146 16c. Ocean Beach, Mount Maunganui 30 30
1147 18c. Piha Beach 30 30
1148 30c. Kaikoura Coast 35 40

364 Girl with Pigeon **365** "The Holy Family" (Correggio)

1977. Health Stamps. Multicoloured.
1149 7c.+2c. Type **364** 20 50
1150 8c.+2c. Boy with frog . . . 25 55
1151 10c.+2c. Girl with butterfly 45 1·00
MS1152 97 × 120 mm. Nos. 1149/51 × 2 . . . . 1·75 6·50
Stamps from No. **MS**1152 are without white border and together form a composite design.

1977. Christmas. Multicoloured.
1153 7c. Type **365** 15 10
1154 16c. "Madonna and Child" (stained-glass window, St. Michael's and All Angels, Dunedin) (vert) 25 25
1155 23c. "Partridge in a Pear Tree" (vert) . . . . . . 40 1·25

366 Merryweather Manual Pump, 1860

1977. Fire Fighting Appliances. Multicoloured.
1156 10c. Type **366** 15 10
1157 11c. 2-wheel hose, reel and ladder, 1880 . . . . 15 25
1158 12c. Shand Mason steam fire engine, 1873 . . . . 20 30
1159 23c. Chemical fire engine, 1888 . . . . 30 90

367 Town Clock and Coat of Arms, Ashburton **368** Students and Ivey Hall, Lincoln College

1978. Centenaries.
1160 **367** 10c. multicoloured . . . 15 10
1161 – 10c. multicoloured . . . 15 10
1162 – 12c. red, yellow and black 15 15
1163 – 20c. multicoloured . . . 20 30
DESIGNS—VERT: No. 1161, Mount Egmont (cent of Stratford); 1162, Early telephone (cent of telephone in New Zealand). HORIZ: No. 1163, Aerial view of Bay of Islands (cent of Bay of Islands County).

1978. Land Resources and Centenary of Lincoln College of Agriculture. Multicoloured.
1164 10c. Type **368** 15 10
1165 12c. Sheep grazing 15 30
1166 15c. Fertiliser ground spreading 15 30
1167 16c. Agricultural Field Days 15 40
1168 20c. Harvesting grain . . . 20 40
1169 30c. Dairy farming 30 90

369 **370** Maui Gas Drilling Platform

1978. Coil Stamps.
1170 **369** 1c. purple 10 65
1171 2c. orange 10 65
1172 5c. brown 10 65
1173 10c. blue 30 80

1978. Resources of the Sea. Multicoloured.
1174 12c. Type **370** 15 15
1175 15c. Trawler 15 20
1176 20c. Map of 200 mile fishing limit 20 30
1177 23c. Humpback whale and bottle-nosed dolphins . . 25 35
1178 35c. Kingfish, snapper, grouper and squid 40 60

371 First Health Charity Stamp **372** "The Holy Family" (El Greco)

1978. Health Stamps.
1179 **371** 10c.+2c. black, red and gold 30 35
1180 – 12c.+2c. multicoloured 30 40
MS1181 97 × 124 mm. Nos. 1179/80 × 3 . . . . . . 1·25 4·00
DESIGNS: 10c. Type **371** (50th anniv of Health Stamps); 12c. Heart Operation (National Heart Foundation).

1978. Christmas. Multicoloured.
1182 7c. Type **372** 10 10
1183 16c. All Saint's Church, Howick (horiz) 25 35
1184 23c. Beach scene (horiz) . . 30 50

373 Sir Julius Vogel **374** Riverlands Cottage, Blenheim

1979. Statesmen. Designs each brown and drab.

1185	10c. Type **373**	25	50
1186	10c. Sir George Grey	25	50
1187	10c. Richard John Seddon	25	50

1979. Architecture (1st series).

1188	**374** 10c. black, light blue and blue	10	10
1189	– 12c. black, light green and green	15	25
1190	– 15c. black and grey	20	40
1191	– 20c. black, brown and sepia	25	40

DESIGNS: 12c. The Mission House, Waimate North; 15c. "The Elms", Tauranga; 20c. Provincial Council Buildings, Christchurch.

See also Nos. 1217/20 and 1262/5.

375 Whangaroa Harbour

1979. Small Harbours. Multicoloured.

1192	15c. Type **375**	15	10
1193	20c. Kawau Island	20	40
1194	23c. Akaroa Harbour (vert)	20	50
1195	35c. Picton Harbour (vert)	30	70

376 Children with Building Bricks

1979. International Year of the Child.

1196	**376** 10c. multicoloured	15	10

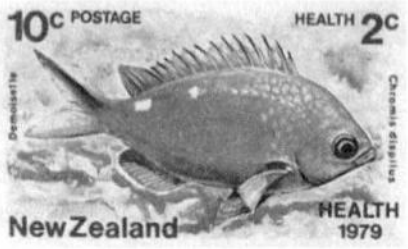

377 Two-spotted Chromis

1979. Health Stamps. Marine Life. Multicoloured.

1197	10c.+2c. Type **377**	30	60
1198	10c.+2c. Sea urchin	30	60
1199	12c.+2c. Red goatfish and underwater cameraman (vert)	30	60
MS1200	144 × 72 mm. Nos. 1197/9, each × 2	1·25	2·75

1979. Nos. 1091a/3a and 1094ab surch.

1201	4c. on 8c. "Josephine Bruce"	10	50
1202	14c. on 10c. Type **353**	30	10
1203	17c. on 6c. "Cresset"	30	1·00
1203a	20c. on 7c. "Michele Meilland"	30	10

379 "Madonna and Child" (sculpture, Ghiberti)

380 Chamber, House of Representatives

1979. Christmas. Multicoloured.

1204	10c. Type **379**	15	10
1205	25c. Christ Church, Russell	30	50
1206	35c. Pohutukawa (tree)	40	70

1979. 25th Commonwealth Parliamentary Conf, Wellington. Multicoloured.

1207	14c. Type **380**	15	10
1208	20c. Mace and Black Rod	20	30
1209	30c. "Beehive" wall hanging	30	75

381 1855 1d. Stamp

1980. Anniversaries and Events.

1210	**381** 14c. black, red and yellow	20	30
1211	– 14c. black, blue & yellow	20	30
1212	– 14c. black, green & yellow	20	30
1213	– 17c. multicoloured	20	30
1214	– 25c. multicoloured	25	35
1215	– 30c. multicoloured	25	40
MS1216	146 × 96 mm. Nos. 1210/12 (as horiz strip) (sold at 52c.)	1·00	4·00

DESIGNS: No. 1211, 1855 2d. stamp; 1212, 1855 1s. stamp (125th anniv of New Zealand stamps); 1213, Geyser, wood-carving and building (Centenary of Rotorua (town)); 1214, "Earina autumnalis" and "Thelymitra venosa" (International Orchid Conference, Auckland); 1215, Ploughing and Golden Plough Trophy (World Ploughing Championships, Christchurch).

382 Ewelme Cottage, Parnell

1980. Architecture (2nd series). Multicoloured.

1217	14c. Type **382**	15	10
1218	17c. Broadgreen, Nelson	15	25
1219	25c. Courthouse, Oamaru	20	35
1220	30c. Government Buildings, Wellington	25	40

383 Auckland Harbour

1980. Large Harbours. Multicoloured.

1221	25c. Type **383**	20	20
1222	30c. Wellington Harbour	25	30
1223	35c. Lyttelton Harbour	25	35
1224	50c. Port Chalmers	30	1·10

384 Surf-fishing

385 "Madonna and Child with Cherubim" (sculpture, Andrea della Robbia)

1980. Health Stamps. Fishing. Multicoloured.

1225	14c.+2c. Type **384**	30	85
1226	14c.+2c. Wharf-fishing	30	85
1227	17c.+2c. Spear-fishing	30	55
MS1228	148 × 75 mm. Nos. 1225/7, each × 2	1·60	3·25

1980. Christmas. Multicoloured.

1229	10c. Type **385**	15	10
1230	25c. St. Mary's Church, New Plymouth	25	25
1231	35c. Picnic scene	40	1·00

386 Te Heu Heu (chief)

387 Lt. Col. the Hon. W. H. A. Feilding and Borough of Feilding Crest (cent)

1980. Maori Personalities. Multicoloured.

1232	15c. Type **386**	15	10
1233	25c. Te Hau (chief)	20	20
1234	35c. Te Puea (princess)	25	10
1235	45c. Ngata (politician)	35	20
1236	60c. Te Ata-O-Tu (warrior)	40	50

1981. Commemorations.

1237	**387** 20c. multicoloured	20	20
1238	– 25c. orange and black	25	25

DESIGN AND COMMEMORATION: 25c. I.Y.D. emblem and cupped hands (International Year of the Disabled).

388 The Family at Play

389 Kaiauai River

1981. "Family Life". Multicoloured.

1239	20c. Type **388**	15	10
1240	25c. The family young and old	20	20
1241	30c. The family at home	20	35
1242	35c. The family at church	25	45

1981. River Scenes. Multicoloured.

1243	30c. Type **389**	20	25
1244	35c. Mangahao	20	30
1245	40c. Shotover (horiz)	25	40
1246	60c. Cleddau (horiz)	35	65

390 St. Paul's Cathedral

1981. Royal Wedding. Multicoloured.

1247	20c. Type **390**	30	30
1248	20c. Prince Charles and Lady Diana Spencer	30	30

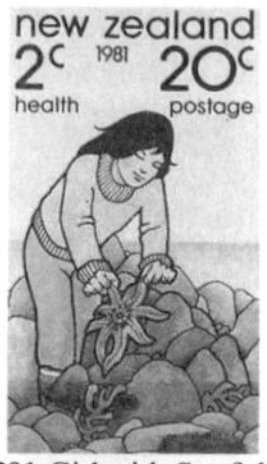

391 Girl with Starfish

392 "Madonna suckling the Child" (painting, d'Oggiono)

1981. Health Stamps. Children playing by the Sea. Multicoloured.

1249	20c.+2c. Type **391**	25	65
1250	20c.+2c. Boy fishing	25	65
1251	25c.+2c. Children exploring rock pool	25	35
MS1252	100 × 125 mm. Nos. 1249/51, each × 2	1·25	3·00

Nos. 1249/50 were printed together, se-tenant, forming a composite design.

The stamps from No. MS1252 were printed together, se-tenant, in horizontal strips, each forming a composite design.

1981. Christmas. Multicoloured.

1253	14c. Type **392**	15	10
1254	30c. St. John's Church, Wakefield	20	25
1255	40c. Golden tainui (flower)	35	35

393 Tauranga Mission House

394 Map of New Zealand

1981. Commemorations. Multicoloured.

1256	20c. Type **393**	20	10
1257	20c. Water tower, Hawera	20	10
1258	25c. Cat	25	35
1259	30c. "Dunedin" (refrigerated sailing ship)	25	40
1260	35c. Scientific research equipment	25	45

COMMEMORATIONS: No. 1256, Centenary of Tauranga (town); 1257, Centenary of Hawera (town); 1258, Centenary of S.P.C.A. (Society for the Prevention of Cruelty to Animals in New Zealand); 1259, Centenary of frozen meat exports; 1260, International Year of Science.

1982.

1261	**394** 24c. green and blue	30	10

395 Alberton, Auckland

1982. Architecture (3rd series). Multicoloured.

1262	20c. Type **395**	15	15
1263	25c. Caccia Birch, Palmerston North	15	25
1264	30c. Railway station, Dunedin	40	30
1265	35c. Post Office, Ophir	25	40

396 Kaiteriteri Beach, Nelson (Summer)

1982. New Zealand Scenes. Multicoloured.

1266	35c. Type **396**	20	30
1267	40c. St. Omer Park, Queenstown (Autumn)	25	35
1268	45c. Mt. Ngauruhoe, Tongariro National Park (Winter)	25	40
1269	70c. Wairarapa farm (Spring)	40	60

397 Labrador

398 "Madonna with Child and Two Angels" (painting by Piero di Cosimo)

1982. Health Stamps. Dogs. Multicoloured.

1270	24c.+2c. Type **397**	80	1·00
1271	24c.+2c. Border collie	80	1·00
1272	30c.+2c. Cocker spaniel	80	1·00
MS1273	98 × 125 mm. Nos. 1270/2, each × 2	4·25	6·50

1982. Christmas. Multicoloured.

1274	18c. Type **398**	15	10
1275	35c. Rangiatea Maori Church, Otaki	25	30
1276	45c. Surf life-saving	40	40

399 Nephrite

399a Grapes

399b Kokako

400 Old Arts Building, Auckland University

1982. (a) Minerals. Multicoloured.

1277	1c. Type **399**	10	10
1278	2c. Agate	10	10
1279	3c. Iron pyrites	10	10
1280	4c. Amethyst	10	10
1281	5c. Carnelian	10	10
1282	9c. Native sulphur	20	10

(b) Fruits. Multicoloured.

1283	10c. Type **399a**	50	10
1284	20c. Citrus fruit	35	10
1285	30c. Nectarines	30	10
1286	40c. Apples	35	10
1287	50c. Kiwifruit	40	10

(c) Native Birds. Multicoloured.

1288	30c. Kakapo	60	25
1289	40c. Mountain ("Blue") duck	60	35
1290	45c. New Zealand falcon	1·25	35
1291	60c. New Zealand teal	2·25	1·00
1292	$1 Type **399b**	1·00	30
1293	$2 Chatham Island robin	1·00	50

1294 $3 Stitchbird . . . . 1·25 1·40
1295 $4 Saddleback . . . . . . 1·50 2·00
1296 $5 Takahe . . . . 3·50 3·00
1297 $10 Little spotted kiwi . . . 5·00 6·00

1983. Commemorations. Multicoloured.
1303 24c. Salvation Army Centenary logo 20 10
1304 30c. Type **400** 20 40
1305 35c. Stylized kangaroo and kiwi 20 40
1306 40c. Rainbow trout 25 55
1307 45c. Satellite over Earth . . 25 55

COMMEMORATIONS: 24c. Salvation Army centenary; 30c. Auckland University centenary; 35c. Closer Economic Relationship agreement with Australia; 40c. Centenary of introduction of rainbow trout into New Zealand; 45c. World Communications Year.

401 Queen Elizabeth II

1983. Commonwealth Day. Multicoloured.
1308 24c. Type **401** 20 10
1309 35c. Maori rock drawing . . 30 50
1310 40c. Woolmark and woolscouring symbols . . 30 80
1311 45c. Coat of arms 30 80

402 "Boats, Island Bay" (Rita Angus)

403 Mt. Egmont

1983. Paintings by Rita Angus. Multicoloured.
1312 24c. Type **402** 25 10
1313 30c. "Central Otago Landscape" 30 45
1314 35c. "Wanaka Landscape" 35 50
1315 45c. "Tree" 50 70

1983. Beautiful New Zealand. Multicoloured.
1316 35c. Type **403** 25 35
1317 40c. Cooks Bay 30 40
1318 45c. Lake Matheson (horiz) 30 45
1319 70c. Lake Alexandrina (horiz) 50 70

404 Tabby

405 "The Family of the Holy Oak Tree" (Raphael)

1983. Health Stamps. Cats. Multicoloured.
1320 24c.+2c. Type **404** 60 75
1321 24c.+2c. Siamese 60 75
1322 30c.+2c. Persian . . . . . 85 1·00
MS1323 100 × 126 mm. Nos. 1320/2, each × 2 . . . . 2·50 3·00

1983. Christmas. Multicoloured.
1324 18c. Type **405** 15 10
1325 35c. St. Patrick's Church, Greymouth 30 45
1326 45c. "The Glory of Christmas" 35 80

406 Geology

1984. Antarctic Research. Multicoloured.
1327 24c. Type **406** 35 10
1328 40c. Biology 45 40
1329 58c. Glaciology . . . . . . 60 1·50
1330 70c. Meteorology 70 85
MS1331 126 × 110 mm. Nos. 1327/30 1·90 3·50

407 "Mountaineer", Lake Wakatipu

1984. New Zealand Ferry Boats. Multicoloured.
1332 24c. Type **407** 20 10
1333 40c. "Waikana", Otago . . 25 45
1334 58c. "Britannia", Waitemata 30 1·40
1335 70c. "Wakatere", Firth of Thames 45 85

408 Mount Hutt

1984. Ski-slope Scenery. Multicoloured.
1336 35c. Type **408** 20 25
1337 40c. Coronet Park 25 30
1338 45c. Turoa 25 30
1339 70c. Whakapapa 40 75

409 Hamilton's Frog

1984. Amphibians and Reptiles. Multicoloured.
1340 24c. Type **409** 30 30
1341 24c. Great Barrier skink . . 30 30
1342 30c. Harlequin gecko . . . 30 35
1343 58c. Otago skink 45 70
1344 70c. Gold-striped gecko . . 60 75

410 Clydesdales ploughing

1984. Health Stamps. Horses. Multicoloured.
1345 24c.+2c. Type **410** 50 75
1346 24c.+2c. Shetland ponies . . 50 75
1347 30c.+2c. Thoroughbreds . . 50 75
MS1348 148 × 75 mm. Nos. 1345/7, each × 2 . . . . 2·25 3·25

411 "Adoration of the Shepherds" (Lorenzo di Credi)

1984. Christmas. Multicoloured.
1349 18c. Type **411** 15 10
1350 35c. Old St. Paul's, Wellington (vert) 30 30
1351 45c. "The Joy of Christmas" (vert) 40 70

412 Mounted Riflemen, South Africa, 1901

1984. New Zealand Military History. Mult.
1352 24c. Type **412** 25 10
1353 40c. Engineers, France, 1917 35 45
1354 58c. Tanks of 2nd N.Z. Divisional Cavalry, North Africa, 1942 . . . . . . 50 1·50
1355 70c. Infantryman in jungle kit, and 25-pounder gun, Korea and South-East Asia, 1950–72 . . . . . 60 90
MS1356 122 × 106 mm. Nos. 1352/5 1·25 2·25

413 St. John Ambulance Badge

1985. Centenary of St. John Ambulance in New Zealand.
1357 **413** 24c. black, gold and red 20 15
1358 30c. black, silver and blue 25 45
1359 40c. black and grey . . . 30 1·10

The colours of the badge depicted are those for Bailiffs and Dames Grand Cross (24c.), Knights and Dames of Grace (30c.) and Officer Brothers and Sisters (40c.).

414 Nelson Horse Tram, 1862

1985. Vintage Trams. Multicoloured.
1360 24c. Type **414** 40 10
1361 30c. Graham's Town steam tram, 1871 . . . . 50 60
1362 35c. Dunedin cable car, 1881 . . . . 50 70
1363 40c. Auckland electric tram, 1902 . . . . 50 70
1364 45c. Wellington electric tram, 1904 . . . . 60 90
1365 58c. Christchurch electric tram, 1905 . . . . 70 1·75

415 Shotover Bridge

416 Queen Elizabeth II (from photo by Camera Press)

1985. Bridges of New Zealand. Multicoloured.
1366 35c. Type **415** 40 60
1367 40c. Alexandra Bridge . . . 45 60
1368 45c. South Rangitikei Railway Bridge (vert) . . 50 1·25
1369 70c. Twin Bridges (vert) . . 60 1·25

1985. Multicoloured, background colours given.
1370 **416** 25c. red 50 10
1371 35c. blue 90 10

417 Princess of Wales and Prince William

418 The Holy Family in the Stable

1985. Health Stamps. Designs showing photographs by Lord Snowdon. Multicoloured.
1372 25c.+2c. Type **417** . . . . . 90 1·25
1373 25c.+2c. Princess of Wales and Prince Henry . . . . 90 1·25
1374 35c.+2c. Prince and Princess of Wales with Princes William and Henry . . . 90 1·25
MS1375 118 × 84 mm. Nos. 1372/4, each × 2 . . . . 4·25 6·00

1985. Christmas. Multicoloured.
1376 18c. Type **418** 20 10
1377 40c. The shepherds 45 85
1378 50c. The angels . . . . . . 45 1·00

419 H.M.N.Z.S. "Philomel" (1914–47)

1985. New Zealand Naval History. Multicoloured.
1379 25c. Type **419** 70 15
1380 45c. H.M.N.Z.S. "Achilles" (1936–46) . . . . 1·10 1·40
1381 60c. H.M.N.Z.S. "Rotoiti" (1949–65) . . . . 1·40 2·00
1382 75c. H.M.N.Z.S. "Canterbury" (from 1971) 1·75 2·25
MS1383 124 × 108 mm. Nos. 1379/82 4·50 5·25

420 Police Computer Operator

1986. Centenary of New Zealand Police. Designs showing historical aspects above modern police activities. Multicoloured.
1384 25c. Type **420** 35 55
1385 25c. Detective and mobile control room 35 55
1386 25c. Policewoman and badge 35 55
1387 25c. Forensic scientist, patrol car and policeman with child 35 55
1388 25c. Police College, Porirua, "Lady Elizabeth II" (patrol boat) and dog handler 35 55

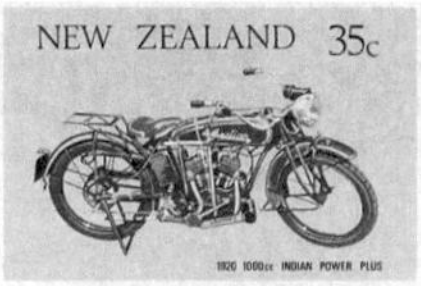

421 Indian "Power Plus" 1000cc Motor Cycle (1920)

1986. Vintage Motor Cycles. Multicoloured.
1389 35c. Type **421** 40 45
1390 45c. Norton "CS1" 500cc (1927) 45 65
1391 60c. B.S.A. "Sloper". 500cc (1930) . . . . 55 1·50
1392 75c. Triumph "Model H" 550cc (1915) . . . . . . 60 1·75

422 Tree of Life

1986. International Peace Year. Multicoloured.
1393 25c. Type **422** 30 30
1394 25c. Peace dove 30 30

423 Knights Point

424 "Football" (Kylie Epapara)

1986. Coastal Scenery. Multicoloured.
1395 55c. Type **423** 55 65
1396 60c. Becks Bay 55 80
1397 65c. Doubtless Bay . . . . 60 1·25
1398 80c. Wainui Bay . . . . . 75 1·25
MS1399 124 × 99 mm. No. 1398 (sold at $1.20) . . . . 1·40 1·25

1986. Health Stamps. Children's Paintings (1st series). Multicoloured.
1400 30c.+3c. Type **424** 40 65
1401 30c.+3c. "Children at Play" (Philip Kata) 40 65
1402 45c.+3c. "Children Skipping" (Mia Flannery) (horiz) 50 65
MS1403 144 × 81 mm. Nos. 1400/2, each × 2 . . . . 2·25 2·75

See also Nos. 1433/5.

425 "A Partridge in a Pear Tree" **426** Conductor and Orchestra

1986. Christmas. "The Twelve Days of Christmas" (carol). Multicoloured.
1404 25c. Type **425** 20 10
1405 55c. "Two turtle doves" 45 55
1406 65c. "Three French hens" 50 1·00

1986. Music in New Zealand.
1407 **426** 30c. multicoloured 25 10
1408 – 60c. black, blue & orange 45 70
1409 – 80c. multicoloured 70 1·75
1410 – $1 multicoloured 80 1·25
DESIGNS: 60c. Cornet and brass band; 80c. Piper and Highland pipe band; $1 Guitar and country music group.

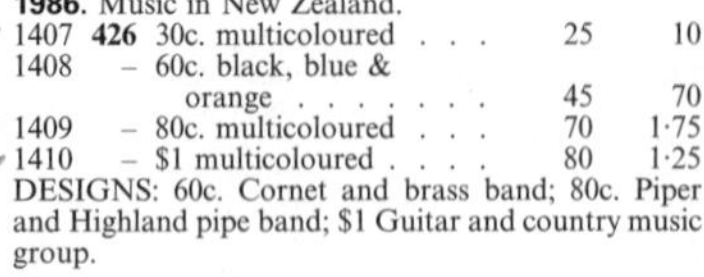

427 Jetboating **428** Southern Cross Cup

1987. Tourism. Multicoloured.
1411 60c. Type **427** 50 50
1412 70c. Sightseeing flights 60 60
1413 80c. Camping 70 75
1414 85c. Windsurfing 70 85
1415 $1.05 Mountaineering 90 1·10
1416 $1.30 River rafting 1·10 1·40

1987. Yachting Events. Designs showing yachts. Multicoloured.
1417 40c. Type **428** 35 15
1418 80c. Admiral's Cup 70 80
1419 $1.05 Kenwood Cup 85 1·25
1420 $1.30 America's Cup 1·10 1·40

429 Hand writing Letter and Postal Transport

1987. New Zealand Post Ltd Vesting Day. Mult.
1421 40c. Type **429** 1·00 1·50
1422 40c. Posting letter, train and mailbox 1·00 1·50

430 Avro Type 626 and Wigram Airfield, 1937

1987. 50th Anniv of Royal New Zealand Air Force. Multicoloured.
1423 40c. Type **430** 65 15
1424 70c. Curtiss Kittyhawk I over World War II Pacific airstrip 90 1·75
1425 80c. Short S25 Sunderland flying boat and Pacific lagoon 1·00 1·75
1426 85c. Douglas A-4F Skyhawk and Mt. Ruapehu 1·10 1·60
MS1427 115 × 105 mm. Nos. 1423/6 5·00 6·00

431 Urewera National Park and Fern Leaf **432** "Kite Flying" (Lauren Baldwin)

1987. Centenary of National Parks Movement. Multicoloured.
1428 70c. Type **431** 70 55
1429 80c. Mt. Cook and buttercup 75 60
1430 85c. Fiordland and pineapple shrub 80 65
1431 $1.30 Tongariro and tussock 1·40 95
MS1432 123 × 99 mm. No. 1431 (sold at $1.70) 1·25 1·75

1987. Health Stamps. Children's Paintings (2nd series). Multicoloured.
1433 40c.+3c. Type **432** 80 1·50
1434 40c.+3c. "Swimming" (Ineke Schoneveld) 80 1·50
1435 60c.+3c. "Horse Riding" (Aaron Tylee) (vert) 1·25 1·50
MS1436 100 × 117 mm. Nos. 1433/5, each × 2 5·00 7·00

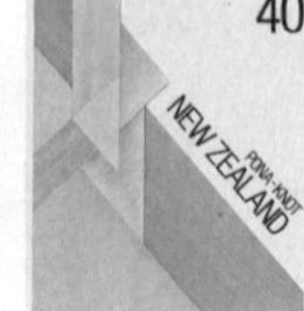

433 "Hark the Herald Angels Sing" **434** Knot ("Pona")

1987. Christmas. Multicoloured.
1437 35c. Type **433** 45 10
1438 70c. "Away in a Manger" 90 70
1439 85c. "We Three Kings of Orient Are" 1·10 85

1987. Maori Fibre-work. Multicoloured.
1440 40c. Type **434** 35 10
1441 60c. Binding ("Herehere") 45 55
1442 80c. Plait ("Whiri") 60 1·25
1443 85c. Cloak weaving ("Korowai") with flax fibre ("Whitau") 65 1·40

435 "Geothermal"

1988. Centenary of Electricity. Each shows radiating concentric circles representing energy generation.
1444 **435** 40c. multicoloured 30 20
1445 – 60c. black, red and brown 40 45
1446 – 70c. multicoloured 50 70
1447 – 80c. multicoloured 55 60
DESIGNS: 60c. "Thermal"; 70c. "Gas"; 80c. "Hydro".

436 Queen Elizabeth II and 1882 Queen Victoria 1d. Stamp

1988. Centenary of Royal Philatelic Society of New Zealand. Multicoloured.
1448 40c. Type **436** 35 75
1449 40c. As Type **436**, but 1882 Queen Victoria 2d. 35 75
MS1450 107 × 160 mm. $1 "Queen Victoria" (Chalon) (vert) 3·00 3·50

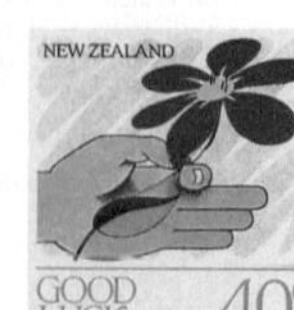

437 "Mangopare" **438** "Good Luck"

1988. Maori Rafter Paintings. Multicoloured.
1451 40c. Type **437** 40 45
1452 40c. "Koru" 40 45
1453 40c. "Raupunga" 40 45
1454 60c. "Koiri" 55 75

1988. Greetings Stamps. Multicoloured.
1455 40c. Type **438** 70 85
1456 40c. "Keeping in touch" 70 85
1457 40c. "Happy birthday" 70 85
1458 40c. "Congratulations" (41 × 27 mm) 70 85
1459 40c. "Get well soon" (41 × 27 mm) 70 85

439 Paradise Shelduck **440** Milford Track

1988. Native Birds. Multicoloured.
1459a 5c. Sooty crake 10 30
1460 10c. Double-banded plover 10 30
1461 20c. Yellowhead 20 30
1462 30c. Grey-backed white-eye ("Silvereye") 30 30
1463 40c. Brown kiwi 35 40
1463b 45c. Rock wren 80 80
1464 50c. Sacred kingfisher 50 60
1465 60c. Spotted cormorant ("Spotted shag") 50 65
1466 70c. Type **439** 70 1·00
1467 80c. Victoria penguin ("Fiordland Crested Penguin") 1·00 1·00
1467a 80c. New Zealand falcon 2·00 1·40
1468 90c. New Zealand robin 1·25 1·50
The 40 and 45c. also exist self-adhesive.

1988. Scenic Walking Trails. Multicoloured.
1469 70c. Type **440** 50 60
1470 80c. Heaphy Track 55 75
1471 85c. Copland Track 60 80
1472 $1.30 Routeburn Track 90 1·25
MS1473 124 × 99 mm. No. 1472 (sold at $1.70) 1·50 1·50

441 Kiwi and Koala at Campfire

1988. Bicentenary of Australian Settlement.
1474 **441** 40c. multicoloured 40 35
A stamp in a similar design was also issued by Australia.

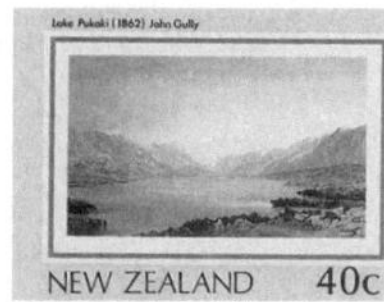

442 Swimming **443** "O Come All Ye Faithful"

1988. Health Stamps. Olympic Games, Seoul. Mult.
1475 40c.+3c. Type **442** 40 70
1476 60c.+3c. Athletics 60 1·10
1477 70c.+3c. Canoeing 70 1·10
1478 80c.+3c. Show-jumping 90 1·40
MS1479 120 × 90 mm. Nos. 1475/8 3·25 4·50

1988. Christmas. Carols. Designs showing illuminated verses. Multicoloured.
1480 35c. Type **443** 30 30
1481 70c. "Hark the Herald Angels Sing" 50 65
1482 80c. "Ding Dong Merrily on High" 50 85
1483 85c. "The First Nowell" 55 95

444 "Lake Pukaki" (John Gully)

1988. New Zealand Heritage (1st issue). "The Land". Designs showing 19th-century paintings. Multicoloured.
1484 40c. Type **444** 35 20
1485 60c. "On the Grass Plain below Lake Arthur" (William Fox) 45 45
1486 70c. "View of Auckland" (John Hoyte) 55 70
1487 80c. "Mt. Egmont from the Southward" (Charles Heaphy) 60 70
1488 $1.05 "Anakiwa, Queen Charlotte Sound" (John Kinder) 80 1·10
1489 $1.30 "White Terraces, Lake Rotomahana", (Charles Barraud) 95 1·40
See also Nos. 1505/10, 1524/9, 1541/6, 1548/53 and 1562/7.

445 Brown Kiwi

1988.
1490 **445** $1 green 2·00 3·25
1490b $1 red 2·00 2·75
1490c $1 blue 1·00 1·40
2090 $1 violet 75 80
2090a $1.10 gold 80 85
2090b £1.50 brown 1·10 1·20
See also Nos. **MS**1745, **MS**1786 and **MS**2342.

446 Humpback Whale and Calf

1988. Whales. Multicoloured.
1491 60c. Type **446** 80 85
1492 70c. Killer whales 1·00 1·10
1493 80c. Southern right whale 1·10 1·25
1494 85c. Blue whale 1·25 1·50
1495 $1.05 Southern bottlenose whale and calf 1·50 2·00
1496 $1.30 Sperm whale 1·60 2·00
Although inscribed "ROSS DEPENDENCY" Nos. 1491/6 were available from post offices throughout New Zealand.

447 Clover **448** Katherine Mansfield

1989. Wild Flowers. Multicoloured.
1497 40c. Type **447** 40 20
1498 60c. Lotus 50 65
1499 70c. Montbretia 60 1·25
1500 80c. Wild ginger 70 1·25

1989. New Zealand Authors. Multicoloured.
1501 40c. Type **448** 30 25
1502 60c. James K. Baxter 40 50
1503 70c. Bruce Mason 50 70
1504 80c. Ngaio Marsh 55 70

449 Moriori Man and Map of Chatham Islands

1989. New Zealand Heritage (2nd issue). The People.
1505 **449** 40c. multicoloured 45 25
1506 – 60c. brown, grey and deep brown 60 75
1507 – 70c. green, grey and deep green 65 90
1508 – 80c. blue, grey and deep blue 75 90
1509 – $1.05 grey, light grey and black 1·00 1·60
1510 – $1.30 red, grey and brown 1·25 2·00
DESIGNS: 60c. Gold prospector; 70c. Settler ploughing; 80c. Whaling; $1.05, Missionary preaching to Maoris; $1.30, Maori village.

450 White Pine (Kahikatea) **451** Duke and Duchess of York with Princess Beatrice

1989. Native Trees. Multicoloured.
1511 80c. Type **450** 75 80
1512 85c. Red pine (Rimu) 80 85

1513	$1.05 Totara	1·00	1·10
1514	$1.30 Kauri	1·25	1·40
MS1515	102 × 125 mm. No. 1514 (sold at $1.80)	1·75	1·75

1989. Health Stamps. Multicoloured.

1516	40c.+3c. Type **451**	80	1·50
1517	40c.+3c. Duchess of York with Princess Beatrice	80	1·50
1518	80c.+3c. Princess Beatrice	1·40	1·75
MS1519	120 × 89 mm. Nos. 1516/18, each × 2	5·50	7·50

452 One Tree Hill, Auckland through Bedroom Window

1989. Christmas. Designs showing Star of Bethlehem. Multicoloured.

1520	35c. Type **452**	40	15
1521	65c. Shepherd and dog in mountain valley	75	70
1522	80c. Star over harbour	95	1·10
1523	$1 Star over globe	1·25	1·40

453 Windsurfing

1989. New Zealand Heritage (3rd issue). The Sea. Multicoloured.

1524	40c. Type **453**	50	25
1525	60c. Fishes of many species	85	70
1526	65c. Striped marlin and game fishing launch	90	85
1527	80c. Rowing boat and yachts in harbour	1·00	90
1528	$1 Coastal scene	1·25	1·10
1529	$1.50 "Rotoiti" (container ship) and tug	1·90	2·25

454 Games Logo

1989. 14th Commonwealth Games, Auckland. Mult.

1530	40c. Type **454**	40	35
1531	40c. Goldie (games kiwi mascot)	40	35
1532	40c. Gymnastics	40	35
1533	50c. Weightlifting	50	55
1534	65c. Swimming	65	70
1535	80c. Cycling	80	90
1536	$1 Lawn bowling	1·00	1·25
1537	$1.80 Hurdling	1·75	1·90
MS1538	Two sheets, each 105 × 92 mm, with different margin designs. (a) Nos. 1530/1 (horiz pair). (b) Nos. 1530/1 (vert pair) Set of 2 sheets	5·00	3·50

455 Short S.30 modified "G" Class Flying Boat "Aotearoa" and Boeing 747-200

1990. 50th Anniv of Air New Zealand.

1539	**455** 80c. multicoloured	1·40	1·10

456 Chief Kawiti signing Treaty

458 *Thelymitra pulchella*

457 Maori Voyaging Canoe

1990. 150th Anniv of Treaty of Waitangi. Sheet 80 × 118 mm, containing T **456** and similar multicoloured design.

MS1540	40c. Type **456**; 40c. Chief Hone Heke (first signatory) and Lieut-Governor Hobson (horiz)	3·25	3·75

1990. New Zealand Heritage (4th issue). The Ships. Multicoloured.

1541	40c. Type **457**	60	25
1542	50c. H.M.S. "Endeavour" (Cook), 1769	85	80
1543	60c. "Tory" (barque), 1839	95	1·00
1544	80c. "Crusader" (full-rigged immigrant ship), 1871	1·40	1·50
1545	$1 "Edwin Fox" (full-rigged immigrant ship), 1873	1·60	1·50
1546	$1.50 "Arawa" (steamer), 1884	2·00	3·00

1990. "New Zealand 1990" International Stamp Exhibition, Auckland. Native Orchids. Sheet 179 × 80 mm, containing T **458** and similar vert designs. Multicoloured.

MS1547	40c. Type **458**; 40c. "Corybas macranthus"; 40c. "Dendrobium cunninghamii"; 40c. "Pterostylis banksii"; 80c. "Aporostylis bifolia" (sold at $4.90)	4·50	4·50

The stamps in No. **MS**1547 form a composite design.

459 Grace Neill (social reformer) and Maternity Hospital, Wellington

1990. New Zealand Heritage (5th issue). Famous New Zealanders. Multicoloured.

1548	40c. Type **459**	55	30
1549	50c. Jean Batten (pilot) and Percival P.3 Gull Six aircraft	65	85
1550	60c. Katherine Sheppard (suffragette) and 19th-century women	85	1·50
1551	80c. Richard Pearse (inventor) and early flying machine	1·10	1·50
1552	$1 Lt.-Gen. Sir Bernard Freyberg and tank	1·25	1·50
1553	$1.50 Peter Buck (politician) and Maori pattern	1·50	2·50

460 Akaroa

461 Jack Lovelock (athlete) and Race

1990. 150th Anniv of European Settlements. Mult.

1554	80c. Type **460**	75	75
1555	$1 Wanganui	95	95
1556	$1.50 Wellington	1·40	2·25
1557	$1.80 Takapuna Beach, Auckland	1·60	2·25
MS1558	125 × 100 mm. No. 1557 (sold at $2.30)	3·50	3·50

1990. Health Stamps. Sportsmen (1st series). Mult.

1559	40c.+5c. Type **461**	50	85
1560	80c.+5c. George Nepia (rugby player) and match	75	1·40
MS1561	115 × 96 mm. Nos. 1559/60, each × 2	2·75	3·75

See also Nos. 1687/8.

462 Creation Legend of Rangi and Papa

1990. New Zealand Heritage (6th issue). The Maori. Multicoloured.

1562	40c. Type **462**	40	30
1563	50c. Pattern from Maori feather cloak	55	80
1564	60c. Maori women's choir	60	90
1565	80c. Maori facial tattoos	75	1·00
1566	$1 War canoe prow (detail)	90	1·25
1567	$1.50 Maori haka	1·40	2·75

463 Queen Victoria **464** Angel

1990. 150th Anniv of the Penny Black. Sheet 169 × 70 mm, containing T **463** and similar vert designs.

MS1568	40c. × 6 blue (Type **463**, King Edward VII, King George V, King Edward VIII, King George VI, Queen Elizabeth II)	4·00	5·00

1990. Christmas.

1569	**464** 40c. purple, blue & brn	40	10
1570	– $1 purple, green & brown	80	50
1571	– $1.50 purple, red & brown	1·40	2·50
1572	– $1.80 purple, red & brown	1·60	2·50

DESIGNS: $1 to $1.80, Different angels.

465 Antarctic Petrel

466 Coopworth Ewe and Lambs

1990. Antarctic Birds. Multicoloured.

1573	40c. Type **465**	80	30
1574	50c. Wilson's storm petrel	90	75
1575	60c. Snow petrel	1·10	1·25
1576	80c. Southern fulmar	1·25	1·25
1577	$1 Bearded penguin ("Chinstrap Penguin")	1·40	1·25
1578	$1.50 Emperor penguin	1·60	3·00

Although inscribed "Ross Dependency" Nos. 1573/8 were available from post offices throughout New Zealand.

1991. New Zealand Farming and Agriculture. Sheep Breeds. Multicoloured.

1579	40c. Type **466**	40	20
1580	60c. Perendale	55	75
1581	80c. Corriedale	70	85
1582	$1 Drysdale	85	90
1583	$1.50 South Suffolk	1·25	2·50
1584	$1.80 Romney	1·50	2·50

467 Moriori, Royal Albatross, Nikau Palm and Artefacts

469 Tuatara on Rocks

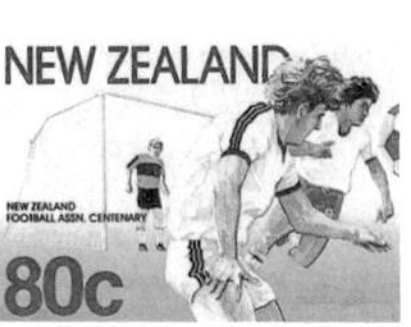

468 Goal and Footballers

1991. Bicentenary of Discovery of Chatham Islands. Multicoloured.

1585	40c. Type **467**	75	50
1586	80c. Carvings, H.M.S. "Chatham", Moriori house of 1870, and Tommy Solomon	1·50	2·00

1991. Centenary of New Zealand Football Association. Multicoloured.

1587	80c. Type **468**	1·40	1·75
1588	80c. Five footballers and referee	1·40	1·75

Nos. 1587/8 were printed together, se-tenant, forming a composite design.

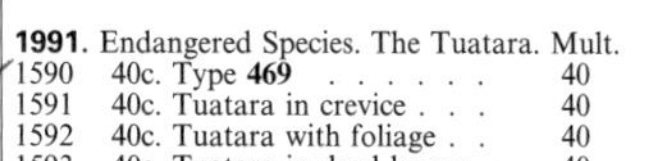

1991. Endangered Species. The Tuatara. Mult.

1590	40c. Type **469**	40	60
1591	40c. Tuatara in crevice	40	60
1592	40c. Tuatara with foliage	40	60
1593	40c. Tuatara in dead leaves	40	60

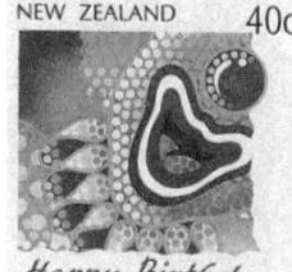

470 Clown **471** Cat at Window

1991. "Happy Birthday". Multicoloured.

1594	40c. Type **470**	75	85
1595	40c. Balloons	75	85
1596	40c. Party hat	75	85
1597	40c. Birthday present (41 × 27 mm)	75	85
1598	40c. Birthday cake (41 × 27 mm)	75	85
1599	45c. Type **470**	75	85
1600	45c. As No. 1595	75	85
1601	45c. As No. 1596	75	85
1602	45c. As No. 1597	75	85
1603	45c. As No. 1598	75	85

1991. "Thinking of You". Multicoloured.

1604	40c. Type **471**	75	85
1605	40c. Cat playing with slippers	75	85
1606	40c. Cat with alarm clock	75	85
1607	40c. Cat in window (41 × 27 mm)	75	85
1608	40c. Cat at door (41 × 27 mm)	75	85
1609	45c. Type **471**	75	85
1610	45c. As No. 1605	75	85
1611	45c. As No. 1606	75	85
1612	45c. As No. 1607	75	85
1613	45c. As No. 1608	75	85

472 Punakaiki Rocks

1991. Scenic Landmarks. Multicoloured.

1614	40c. Type **472**	40	30
1615	50c. Moeraki Boulders	55	55
1616	80c. Organ Pipes	85	85
1617	$1 Castle Hill	95	95
1618	$1.50 Te Kaukau Point	1·50	1·60
1619	$1.80 Ahuriri River Clay Cliffs	1·75	1·90

473 Dolphins Underwater

1991. Health Stamps. Hector's Dolphin. Mult.

1620	45c.+5c. Type **473**	90	1·25
1621	80c.+5c. Dolphins leaping	1·25	2·00
MS1622	115 × 100 mm. Nos. 1620/1, each × 2	5·00	6·50

474 Children's Rugby

475 "Three Shepherds"

1991. World Cup Rugby Championship. Mult.

1623	80c. Type **474**	1·00	1·25
1624	$1 Women's rugby	1·10	1·00
1625	$1.50 Senior rugby	1·75	2·75
1626	$1.80 "All Blacks" (national team)	2·00	2·75
MS1627	113 × 90 mm. No. 1626 (sold at $2.40)	4·00	5·00

1991. Christmas. Multicoloured.

1628	45c. Type **475**	55	80
1629	45c. Two Kings on camels	55	80
1630	45c. Mary and Baby Jesus	55	80
1631	45c. King with gift	55	80
1632	65c. Star of Bethlehem	70	80
1633	$1 Crown	85	95
1634	$1.50 Angel	1·40	2·25

476 "Dodonidia helmsii"

1991. Butterflies. Multicoloured.
1640 $1 Type **476** . . . . 1·75 80
1641 $2 "Zizina otis oxleyi" . . . 2·50 1·75
1642 $3 "Vanessa itea" . . . . . 3·00 3·00
1643 $4 "Lycaena salustius" . . . 2·25 2·40
1644 $5 "Bassaris gonerilla" . . . 2·75 3·00

479 Yacht "Kiwi Magic", 1987

1992. New Zealand Challenge for America's Cup. Multicoloured.
1655 45c. Type **479** 45 20
1656 80c. Yacht "New Zealand", 1988 . . . . 80 70
1657 $1 Yacht "America", 1851 95 85
1658 $1.50 "America's Cup" Class yacht, 1992 . . . . 1·60 1·60

480 "Heemskerk"

1992. Great Voyages of Discovery. Mult.
1659 45c. Type **480** 55 25
1660 80c. "Zeehan" . . . . . . 90 1·10
1661 $1 "Santa Maria" . . . . . 1·25 1·10
1662 $1.50 "Pinta" and "Nina" 1·50 2·50
Nos. 1659/60 commemorate the 350th anniv of Tasman's discovery of New Zealand and Nos. 1661/2 the 500th anniv of discovery of America by Columbus.

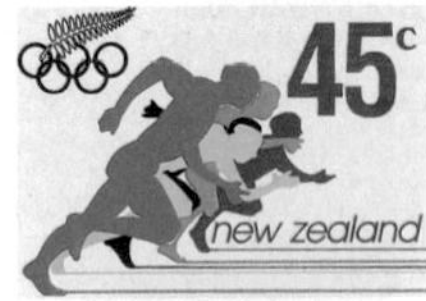

481 Sprinters

1992. Olympic Games, Barcelona (1st issue).
1663 **481** 45c. multicoloured . . . 50 50
See also Nos. 1670/3.

482 Weddell Seal and Pup

1992. Antarctic Seals. Multicoloured.
1664 45c. Type **482** 70 30
1665 50c. Crabeater seals swimming 80 60
1666 65c. Leopard seal and Adelie penguins . . . . . 1·00 1·25
1667 80c. Ross seal . . . . . . 1·25 1·25
1668 $1 Southern elephant seal and harem . . . . 1·40 1·25
1669 $1.80 Hooker's sea lion and pup . . . . 2·25 3·25
Although inscribed "ROSS DEPENDENCY" Nos. 1664/9 were available from post offices throughout New Zealand.

483 Cycling

1992. Olympic Games, Barcelona (2nd issue). Multicoloured.
1670 45c. Type **483** 65 35
1671 80c. Archery 90 70
1672 $1 Equestrian three-day eventing . . . . 1·00 85
1673 $1.50 Sailboarding . . . . 1·50 1·40
MS1674 125×100 mm. Nos. 1670/3 3·50 4·00

484 Ice Pinnacles, Franz Josef Glacier

1992. Glaciers. Multicoloured.
1675 45c. Type **484** 40 25
1676 50c. Tasman Glacier 50 45
1677 80c. Snowball Glacier, Marion Plateau 70 70
1678 $1 Brewster Glacier 85 85
1679 $1.50 Fox Glacier . . . . . 1·40 1·60
1680 $1.80 Franz Josef Glacier 1·50 1·60

485 "Grand Finale" Camellia

486 Tree and Hills

1992. Camellias. Multicoloured.
1681 45c. Type **485** 60 25
1682 50c. "Showa-No-Sakae" . . 70 60
1683 80c. "Sugar Dream" 90 80
1684 $1 "Night Rider" . . . . . 1·10 85
1685 $1.50 "E.G. Waterhouse" 1·50 2·75
1686 $1.80 "Dr. Clifford Parks" 1·75 3·00

1992. Health Stamps. Sportsmen (2nd series). As T **461**. Multicoloured.
1687 45c.+5c. Anthony Wilding (tennis player) and match 1·00 1·25
1688 80c.+5c. Stewie Dempster (cricketer) and batsman 1·00 1·50
MS1689 115×96 mm. Nos. 1687/8, each×2 . . . . 4·50 5·50

1992. Landscapes. Multicoloured.
1690 45c. Type **486** 60 65
1691 45c. River and hills 60 65
1692 45c. Hills and mountain . . 60 65
1693 45c. Glacier 60 65
1694 45c. Hills and waterfall . . 60 65
1695 45c. Tree and beach 60 65
1696 45c. Estuary and cliffs . . . 60 65
1697 45c. Fjord 60 65
1698 45c. River delta 60 65
1699 45c. Ferns and beach . . . 60 65

487 Reindeer over Houses

488 1920s Fashions

1992. Christmas. Multicoloured.
1700 45c. Type **487** . . . . . . 90 1·00
1701 45c. Santa Claus on sleigh over houses . . . . . . 90 1·00
1702 45c. Christmas tree in window . . . . 90 1·00
1703 45c. Christmas wreath and children at window . . . 90 1·00
1704 65c. Candles and fireplace 1·10 90
1705 $1 Family going to church 1·40 1·00
1706 $1.50 Picnic under Pohutukawa tree . . . . 2·00 2·75

1992. New Zealand in the 1920s. Multicoloured.
1707 45c. Type **488** 50 20
1708 50c. Dr. Robert Jack and early radio announcer . . 55 65
1709 80c. "All Blacks" rugby player, 1924 . . . . . . 85 1·00
1710 $1 Swaggie and dog . . . . 95 1·00
1711 $1.50 Ford "Model A" car and young couple . . . . 1·75 2·25
1712 $1.80 Amateur aviators and biplane . . . . 2·00 2·75

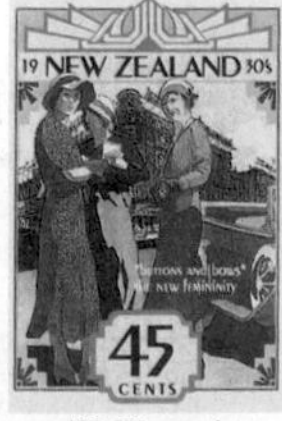

489 "Old Charley" Toby Jug

490 Women's Fashions of the 1930s

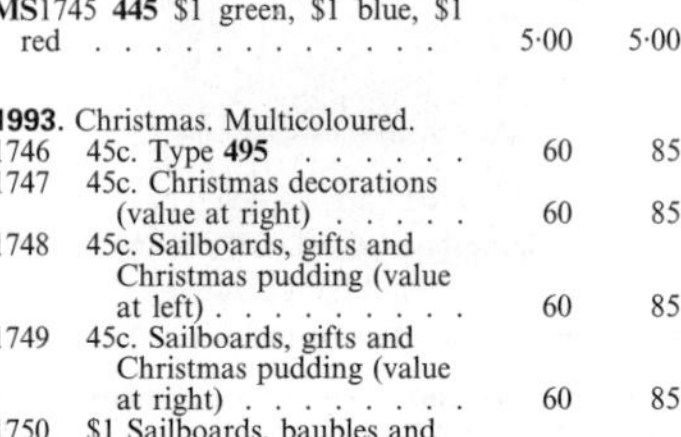

1993. Royal Doulton Ceramics Exhibition, New Zealand. Multicoloured.
1713 45c. Type **489** 50 20
1714 50c. "Bunnykins" nursery plate 55 60
1715 80c. "Maori Art" tea set . . 85 85
1716 $1 "Ophelia" handpainted plate . . . . 1·00 90
1717 $1.50 "St. George" figurine 1·60 2·50
1718 $1.80 "Lambeth" salt-glazed stoneware vase . . . . . 1·90 2·50
MS1719 125×100 mm. No. 1718 1·60 2·50

1993. New Zealand in the 1930s. Multicoloured.
1720 45c. Type **490** 50 25
1721 50c. Unemployed protest march 55 75
1722 80c. "Phar Lap" (racehorse) 85 95
1723 $1 State housing project . . 1·00 1·00
1724 $1.50 Boys drinking free school milk . . . . 1·75 3·00
1725 $1.80 Cinema queue . . . . 1·90 2·75

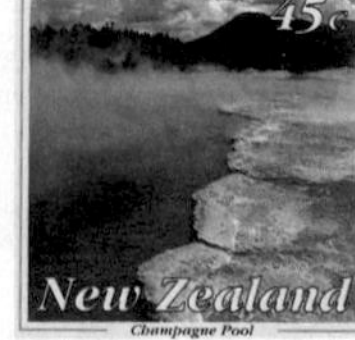

491 Women signing Petition

492 Champagne Pool

1993. Centenary of Women's Suffrage. Mult.
1726 45c. Type **491** 50 20
1727 80c. Aircraft propeller and woman on tractor . . . . 1·00 85
1728 $1 Housewife with children 1·00 95
1729 $1.50 Modern women . . . 1·60 2·00

1993. Thermal Wonders, Rotorua. Multicoloured.
1730 45c. Type **492** 60 25
1731 50c. Boiling mud 60 40
1732 80c. Emerald pool 85 70
1733 $1 Hakereteke Falls 95 80
1734 $1.50 Warbrick Terrace . . 1·50 1·75
1735 $1.80 Pohutu Geyser . . . 1·60 1·75
See also No. **MS**1770.

493 Yellow-eyed Penguin, Hector's Dolphin and New Zealand Fur Seal

1993. Endangered Species Conservation. Mult.
1736 45c. Type **493** 85 95
1737 45c. Taiko (bird), Mount Cook lily and mountain duck ("Blue Duck") . . . 85 95
1738 45c. Giant snail, rock wren and Hamilton's frog . . . 85 95
1739 45c. Kaka (bird), New Zealand pigeon and giant weta 85 95
1740 45c. Tusked weta (23×28 mm) 85 95

494 Boy with Puppy

495 Christmas Decorations (value at left)

1993. Health Stamps. Children's Pets. Mult.
1741 45c.+5c. Type **494** 60 90
1742 80c.+5c. Girl with kitten . . 90 1·50
MS1743 115×96 mm. Nos. 1741/2, each×2 . . . . 2·75 4·25

1993. "Taipei '93" Asian International Stamp Exhibition, Taiwan. (a) No. **MS**1743 optd **TAIPEI '93** and emblem on sheet margin. Mult.
MS1744 Nos. 1741/2, each×2 . . 12·00 13·00

(b) Sheet 125×100 mm, containing Nos. 1490/c.
MS1745 **445** $1 green, $1 blue, $1 red . . . . 5·00 5·00

1993. Christmas. Multicoloured.
1746 45c. Type **495** 60 85
1747 45c. Christmas decorations (value at right) 60 85
1748 45c. Sailboards, gifts and Christmas pudding (value at left) 60 85
1749 45c. Sailboards, gifts and Christmas pudding (value at right) 60 85
1750 $1 Sailboards, baubles and Christmas cracker . . . . 1·50 1·25
1751 $1.50 Sailboards, present and wreath . . . . 2·00 3·25

496 Rainbow Abalone or Paua

497 Sauropod

1993. Marine Life. Multicoloured.
1752 45c. Type **496** 95 95
1753 45c. Green mussels 95 95
1754 45c. Tarakihi 95 95
1755 45c. Salmon 95 95
1756 45c. Southern blue-finned tuna, yellow-finned tuna and kahawai 95 95
1757 45c. Rock lobster 95 95
1758 45c. Snapper 95 95
1759 45c. Grouper 95 95
1760 45c. Orange roughy 95 95
1761 45c. Squid, hoki and black oreo 95 95

1993. Prehistoric Animals. Multicoloured.
1762 45c. Type **497** 60 45
1763 45c. Carnosaur and sauropod (30×25 mm) . . 75 60
1764 80c. Pterosaur . . . . . . 1·10 85
1765 $1 Ankylosaur . . . . . . 1·25 95
1766 $1.20 Mauisaurus . . . . . 1·50 2·50
1767 $1.50 Carnosaur . . . . . 1·60 2·50
MS1768 125×100 mm. $1.50 No. 1767 . . . . 1·75 1·75

1993. "Bangkok '93" International Stamp Exhibition, Thailand. (a) No. **MS**1768 optd **BANGKOK '93** and emblem on sheet margin. Multicoloured.
MS1769 $1.50 No. 1767 . . . . 1·60 2·00

(b) Sheet 115×100 mm, containing No. 1735.
MS1770 $1.80 multicoloured . . 2·75 3·75

498 Soldiers, National Flag and Pyramids

499 Bungy Jumping

1993. New Zealand in the 1940s. Multicoloured.
1771 45c. Type **498** 80 25
1772 50c. Aerial crop spraying . . 85 60
1773 80c. Hydro-electric scheme 1·10 80
1774 $1 Marching majorettes . . 1·40 90
1775 $1.50 American troops . . . 1·90 2·00
1776 $1.80 Crowd celebrating victory . . . . 2·00 2·25

1994. Tourism. Multicoloured.
1777 45c. Type **499** 50 25
1778 45c. White water rafting (25×25 mm) 50 55
1779 80c. Trout fishing 70 70
1780 $1 Jet boating (horiz) . . . 80 80
1781 $1.50 Tramping . . . . . . 1·40 2·00
1782 $1.80 Heli-skiing . . . . . 1·90 2·00
See also No. **MS**1785.

500 "New Zealand Endeavour" (yacht)

503 Rock and Roll Dancers

501 Mt. Cook and New Zealand Symbols

1994. Round the World Yacht Race.
1783 **500** $1 multicoloured 1·40 1·60

1994.
1784 **501** $20 blue and gold 14·50 15·00

1994. "Hong Kong '94" International Stamp Exhibition. Multicoloured.
MS1785 95 × 115 mm. $1.80 No. 1782 3·50 3·50
MS1786 100 × 125 mm. $1 × 3 As Nos. 1490/c 4·50 4·50

1994. New Zealand in the 1950s. Multicoloured.
1787 45c. Type **503** 45 25
1788 80c. Sir Edmund Hillary on Mt. Everest 75 75
1789 $1 Aunt Daisy (radio personality) 85 85
1790 $1.20 Queen Elizabeth II during 1953 royal visit 1·25 1·25
1791 $1.50 Children playing with Opo the dolphin 1·60 2·00
1792 $1.80 Auckland Harbour Bridge 1·90 2·00

504 Mt. Cook and Mt. Cook Lily ("Winter")

1994. The Four Seasons. Multicoloured.
1793 45c. Type **504** 45 25
1794 70c. Lake Hawea and Kowhai ("Spring") 65 65
1795 $1.50 Opononi Beach and Pohutukawa ("Summer") 1·40 1·40
1796 $1.80 Lake Pukaki and Puriri ("Autumn") 1·75 1·75

505 Rainbow Abalone or Paua Shell

506 Maui pulls up Te Ika

1994. New Zealand Life. Multicoloured.
1797 45c. Type **505** (25 × 20 mm) 40 45
1798 45c. Pavlova dessert (35 × 20 mm) 40 45
1799 45c. Hokey pokey ice cream (25 × 20 mm) 40 45
1800 45c. Fish and chips (35 × 20 mm) 40 45
1801 45c. Jandals (30 × 20 mm) 40 45
1802 45c. Bush shirt (25 × 30½ mm) 40 45
1803 45c. Buzzy Bee (toy) (35 × 30½ mm) 40 45
1804 45c. Gumboots and black singlet (25 × 30½ mm) 40 45
1805 45c. Rugby boots and ball (35 × 30½ mm) 40 45
1806 45c. Kiwifruit (30 × 30½ mm) 40 45
See also Nos. 2318/27.

1994. Maori Myths. Multicoloured.
1807 45c. Type **506** 50 25
1808 80c. Rona snatched up by Marama 85 85
1809 $1 Maui attacking Tuna 1·00 1·00
1810 $1.20 Tane separating Rangi and Papa 1·40 2·00
1811 $1.50 Matakauri slaying the Giant of Wakatipu 1·50 2·00
1812 $1.80 Panenehu showing crayfish to Tangaroa 1·75 2·00

507 1939 2d. on 1d.+1d. Health Stamp and Children playing with Ball

508 Astronaut on Moon (hologram)

1994. Health Stamps. 75th Anniv of Children's Health Camps. Multicoloured.
1813 45c.+5c. Type **507** 50 80
1814 45c.+5c. 1949 1d.+½d. stamp and nurse holding child 50 80
1815 45c.+5c. 1969 4c.+1c. stamp and children reading 50 80
1816 80c.+5c. 1931 2d.+1d. stamp and child in cap 75 1·00
MS1817 130 × 90 mm. Nos. 1813/16 2·00 3·25

1994. 25th Anniv of First Manned Moon Landing.
1818 **508** $1.50 multicoloured 2·00 2·25

509 "people reaching people"

1994. Self adhesive.
1818ab **509** 40c. multicoloured 60 55
1819 45c. multicoloured 80 65

510 African Elephants

1994. Stamp Month. Wild Animals. Multicoloured.
1820 45c. Type **510** 80 80
1821 45c. White rhinoceros 80 80
1822 45c. Lions 80 80
1823 45c. Common zebras 80 80
1824 45c. Giraffe and calf 80 80
1825 45c. Siberian tiger 80 80
1826 45c. Hippopotamuses 80 80
1827 45c. Spider monkey 80 80
1828 45c. Giant panda 80 80
1829 45c. Polar bear and cub 80 80

1994. "Philakorea '94" International Stamp Exhibition, Seoul. Multicoloured.
MS1830 125 × 100 mm. Nos. 1459a/65 6·50 6·00
MS1831 125 × 100 mm. Nos. 1820, 1822, 1824/5 and 1828/9 3·75 4·50

511 Children with Crib

512 Batsman

1994. Christmas. Multicoloured.
1832 45c. Father Christmas and children (30 × 25 mm) 45 40
1833 45c. Type **511** 45 20
1834 70c. Man and toddler with crib 65 80
1835 80c. Three carol singers 70 85
1836 $1 Five carol singers 90 90
1837 $1.50 Children and candles 1·25 2·00
1838 $1.80 Parents with child 1·60 2·00
MS1839 125 × 100 mm. Nos. 1833/6 2·75 2·75

1994. Centenary of New Zealand Cricket Council.
(a) Horiz designs, each 30 × 25 mm. Multicoloured.
1840 45c. Bathers catching balls 55 70
1841 45c. Child on surf board at top 55 70
1842 45c. Young child with rubber ring at top 55 70
1843 45c. Man with beach ball at top 55 70
1844 45c. Woman with cricket bat at right 55 70
1845 45c. Boy in green cap with bat 55 70
1846 45c. Man in spotted shirt running 55 70
1847 45c. Woman in striped shorts with bat 55 70
1848 45c. Boy in wet suit with surf board at right 55 70
1849 45c. Sunbather with newspaper at right 55 70

(b) T **512** and similar vert designs. Multicoloured.
1850 45c. Type **512** 60 40
1851 80c. Bowler 1·00 80
1852 $1 Wicket keeper 1·25 1·00
1853 $1.80 Fielder 2·00 1·75

1995. "POST X '95" Postal History Exhibition, Auckland. Sheet 130 × 90 mm, containing No. 1297 and a reproduction of No. 557 optd "SPECIMEN".
MS1854 $10 multicoloured 17·00 17·00

513 Auckland

1995. New Zealand by Night. Multicoloured.
1855 45c. Type **513** 55 25
1856 80c. Wellington 85 65
1857 $1 Christchurch 1·00 85
1858 $1.20 Dunedin 1·25 1·40
1859 $1.50 Rotorua 1·40 1·60
1860 $1.80 Queenstown 1·60 1·60
See also No. **MS**1915.

514 The 15th Hole, Waitangi

515 New Zealand Pigeon and Nest

1995. New Zealand Golf Courses. Multicoloured.
1861 45c. Type **514** 65 30
1862 80c. The 6th hole, New Plymouth 1·00 90
1863 $1.20 The 9th hole, Rotorua 1·50 2·50
1864 $1.80 The 5th hole, Queenstown 2·40 3·00

1995. Environment. Multicoloured.
1865 45c. Type **515** 65 65
1866 45c. Planting sapling 65 65
1867 45c. Dolphins and whales 65 65
1868 45c. Thunderstorm 65 65
1869 45c. Backpackers 65 65
1870 45c. Animal pests 65 65
1871 45c. Noxious plants 65 65
1872 45c. Undersized fish and shellfish 65 65
1873 45c. Pollution from factories 65 65
1874 45c. Family at picnic site 65 65

516 Teacher with Guitar and Children

517 Map of Australasia and Asia

1995. Maori Language Year. Multicoloured.
1875 45c. Type **516** 50 20
1876 70c. Singing group 75 75
1877 80c. Mother and baby 85 85
1878 $1 Women performing traditional welcome 1·10 1·10
1879 $1.50 Grandfather reciting family genealogy 1·75 2·25
1880 $1.80 Tribal orator 2·00 2·25

1995. Meetings of Asian Development Bank Board of Governors and International Pacific Basin Economic Council, Auckland. Multicoloured.
1881 $1 Type **517** 1·25 1·00
1882 $1.50 Map of Australasia and Pacific 1·75 2·75

518 "Black Magic" (yacht)

1995. New Zealand's Victory in 1995 America's Cup.
1883 **518** 45c. multicoloured 55 55

519 Boy on Skateboard

1995. Health Stamps. Children's Sports. Mult.
1884 45c.+5c. Type **519** 75 1·25
1885 80c.+5c. Girl on bicyle 1·75 1·75
MS1886 130 × 90 mm. Nos. 1884/5, each × 2 4·00 5·00

1995. "Stampex '95" National Stamp Exhibition, Wellington. No. **MS**1886 additionally inscr with "Stampex '95" and emblem on sheet margin. Mult.
MS1887 130 × 90 mm. Nos. 1884/5, each × 2 5·50 6·50

520 Lion Red Cup and Players

1995. Centenary of Rugby League. Multicoloured.
1888 45c. Trans Tasman test match (30 × 25 mm) 60 60
1889 45c. Type **520** 50 20
1890 $1 Children's rugby and mascot 1·25 1·10
1891 $1.50 George Smith, Albert Baskerville and early match 2·00 2·50
1892 $1.80 Courtney Goodwill Trophy and match against Great Britain 2·25 2·50
MS1893 125 × 100 mm. No. 1892 3·00 3·00

521 Sheep and Lamb

522 Archangel Gabriel

1995. Farmyard Animals. Multicoloured.
1894 40c. Type **521** 75 75
1895 40c. Deer 75 75
1896 40c. Mare and foal 75 75
1897 40c. Cow with calf 75 75
1898 40c. Goats and kid 75 75
1899 40c. Common turkey 75 75
1900 40c. Ducks 75 75
1901 40c. Red junglefowl 75 75
1902 40c. Sow with piglets 75 75
1903 40c. Border collie 75 75
1904 45c. As Type **521** 75 75
1905 45c. As No. 1895 75 75
1906 45c. As No. 1896 75 75
1907 45c. As No. 1897 75 75
1908 45c. As No. 1898 75 75
1909 45c. As No. 1899 75 75
1910 45c. As No. 1900 75 75
1911 45c. As No. 1901 75 75
1912 45c. As No. 1902 75 75
1913 45c. As No. 1903 75 75

1995. "Singapore '95" International Stamp Exhibition. Multicoloured.
MS1914 170 × 70 mm. Nos. 1909/13 3·25 4·00
MS1915 148 × 210 mm. Nos. 1855/60 9·50 10·00
No. **MS**1915 also includes the "JAKARTA '95" logo.

1995. Christmas. Stained Glass Windows from St. Mary's Anglican Church, Merivale (Nos. 1916/18), The Lady Chapel of St. Luke's Anglican Church, Christchurch (Nos. 1919/22) or St. John the Evangelist Church, Cheviot (No. 1923). Multicoloured. (a) As T **522**.
1916 40c. Type **522** 70 25
1917 45c. Type **522** 70 25
1918 70c. Virgin Mary 1·00 90
1919 80c. Shepherds 1·10 1·00
1920 $1 Virgin and Child 1·40 1·10
1921 $1.50 Two Wise Men 2·25 2·75
1922 $1.80 Wise Man kneeling 2·50 2·75

(b) Smaller design, 25 × 30 mm.
1923 40c. Angel with trumpet 60 50

523 Face and Nuclear Disarmament Symbol

524 Mt. Cook

1995. Nuclear Disarmament.
1924 **523** $1 multicoloured 1·00 1·00

1995. New Zealand Scenery. Multicoloured.
1925 5c. Type **524** 10 10
1926 10c. Champagne Pool 10 10
1927 20c. Cape Reinga 15 20
1928 30c. Mackenzie Country 20 25
1929 40c. Mitre Peak (vert) 30 35
1930 50c. Mt. Ngauruhoe 35 40
1931 60c. Lake Wanaka (vert) 45 50
1932 70c. Giant kauri tree (vert) 50 55
1933 80c. Doubtful Sound (vert) 60 65
1934 90c. Waitomo Limestone Cave (vert) 65 70
1934a 90c. Rangitoto Island 65 70
1934b $1 Taiaroa Head (27 × 22 mm) 75 80
1934c $1.10 Kaikoura Coast (27 × 22 mm) 80 85
1934d $1.30 Lake Camp, South Canterbury (27 × 22 mm) 95 1·00
1934e $2 Great Barrier Island (27 × 22 mm) 1·50 1·60

1934f $3 Cape Kidnappers (27 × 22 mm) . . . . . 2·20 2·30
1935 $10 Mt. Ruapehu (38 × 32 mm) . . . . . 7·25 7·50

For similar self-adhesive designs see Nos. 1984b/91b.

For miniature sheets containing some of these designs see Nos. **MS**1978, **MS**1998, **MS**2005, **MS**2328 and **MS**2401.

525 Dame Kiri te Kanawa (opera singer)

526 National Flags, Peace Dove and "50"

1995. Famous New Zealanders. Multicoloured.

1936 40c. Type **525** 75 40
1937 80c. Charles Upham, V.C. (war hero) . . . . 1·00 85
1938 $1 Barry Crump (author) . . 1·25 1·00
1939 $1.20 Sir Brian Barratt-Boyes (surgeon) . . . . . 1·75 1·25
1940 $1.50 Dame Whina Cooper (Maori leader) . . . . . 1·75 1·75
1941 $1.80 Sir Richard Hadlee (cricketer) . . . . 2·75 2·25

1995. 50th Anniv of United Nations.

1942 **526** $1.80 multicoloured . . 2·75 2·50

527 Fern and Globe

1995. Commonwealth Heads of Government Meeting, Auckland. Multicoloured.

1943 40c. Type **527** 75 40
1944 $1.80 Fern and New Zealand flag . . . . . . 3·50 2·75

528 "Kiwi"

1996. Famous Racehorses. Multicoloured.

1945 40c. Type **528** 55 25
1946 80c. "Rough Habit" 95 95
1947 $1 "Blossom Lady" . . . . 1·25 1·25
1948 $1.20 "Il Vicolo" . . . . . 1·60 1·60
1949 $1.50 "Horlicks" . . . . . 1·75 2·00
1950 $1.80 "Bonecrusher" . . . . 2·50 2·50
MS1951 Seven sheets, each 162 × 110 mm. (a) No. 1945. (b) No. 1946. (c) No. 1947. (d) No. 1948. (e) No. 1949. (f) No. 1950. (g) Nos. 1945/50 Set of 7 sheets . . . . 16·00 19·00

529 Kete (basket)

530 Southern Black-backed Gulls

1996. Maori Crafts. Multicoloured.

1952 40c. Type **529** 50 25
1953 80c. Head of Taiaha (spear) 90 90
1954 $1 Taniko (embroidery) . . 1·25 1·25
1955 $1.20 Pounamu (greenstone) 1·50 1·75
1956 $1.50 Hue (gourd) . . . . . 1·75 2·50
1957 $1.80 Korowai (feather cloak) . . . . 2·00 2·50

See also No. **MS**2049.

1996. Marine Life. Multicoloured. Self-adhesive or ordinary gum.

1968 40c. Type **530** 50 55
1969 40c. Children, sea cucumber and spiny starfish 50 55
1970 40c. Yacht, gull and common shrimps 50 55
1971 40c. Gaudy nudibranch . . 50 55
1972 40c. Large rock crab and clingfish 50 55
1973 40c. Snake skin chiton and red rock crab 50 55
1974 40c. Estuarine triplefin and cat's-eye shell 50 55
1975 40c. Cushion star and sea horses 50 55
1976 40c. Blue-eyed triplefin and Yaldwyn's triplefin . . . 50 55
1977 40c. Common octopus . . . 50 55

1996. "SOUTHPEX '96" Stamp Show, Invercargill. Sheet 100 × 215 mm, containing No. 1929 × 10.

MS1978 40c. × 10 multicoloured 5·50 5·50

531 Fire and Ambulance Services

532 Mt. Egmont, Taranaki

1996. Rescue Services. Multicoloured.

1979 40c. Type **531** 50 40
1980 80c. Civil Defence 90 90
1981 $1 Air-sea rescue . . . . . 1·10 1·10
1982 $1.50 Air ambulance and rescue helicopter . . . . 1·60 2·50
1983 $1.80 Mountain rescue and Red Cross . . . . 2·25 2·50

1996. New Zealand Scenery. Self-adhesive. Mult.

1983a 10c. Champagne Pool . . 10 10
1984b 40c. Type **532** 25 30
1985 40c. Piercy Island, Bay of Islands 25 30
1986 40c. Tory Channel, Marlborough Sounds . . 30 35
1987 40c. "Earnslaw" (ferry), Lake Wakatipu 25 30
1988 40c. Lake Matheson . . . 25 30
1989 40c. Fox Glacier 25 30
1990 80c. Doubtful Sound (as No. 1933) 60 65
1991 $1 Pohutukawa tree (33 × 22 mm) 70 70
1991b $1.10 Kaikoura Coast . . 80 85

533 Yellow-eyed Penguin

534 Baby in Car Seat

1996. Marine Wildlife. Multicoloured.

1992 40c. Type **533** 50 50
1993 80c. Royal albatross (horiz) 90 90
1994 $1 Great egret (horiz) . . . 1·10 1·10
1995 $1.20 Flukes of sperm whale (horiz) . . . . 1·40 1·60
1996 $1.50 Fur seals . . . . . . 1·60 2·00
1997 $1.80 Bottlenose dolphin . . 2·00 2·00

See also Nos. **MS**1999 and **MS**2037.

1996. "CHINA '96" 9th International Stamp Exhibition, Peking. Multicoloured.

MS1998 180 × 80 mm. Nos. 1926/8 and 1930 . . . . 1·75 2·00
MS1999 140 × 90 mm. Nos. 1994 and 1996 . . . . 2·75 3·00

No. **MS**1999 also shows designs as Nos. 1992/3, 1995 and 1997, but without face values.

1996. Health Stamps. Child Safety. Multicoloured. Self-adhesive (2003) or ordinary (others) gum.

2000 40c.+5c. Type **534** 50 75
2003 40c.+5c. Type **534** (21½ × 38 mm) 50 75
2001 80c.+5c. Child and adult on zebra crossing . . . . . 90 1·25
MS2002 130 × 90 mm. Nos. 2000/1, each × 2 . . . . 2·75 2·75

Stamps from No. **MS**2002 are slightly larger with "NEW ZEALAND" and the face values redrawn.

1996. "CAPEX '96" International Stamp Exhibition, Toronto. (a) No. **MS**2002 optd **CAPEX '96** and emblem on sheet margin. Mult.

MS2004 Nos. 2000/1, each × 2 . . 3·25 2·75

(b) Sheet 180 × 80 mm, containing Nos. 1931/4.

MS2005 $3 multicoloured . . . . 3·25 3·25

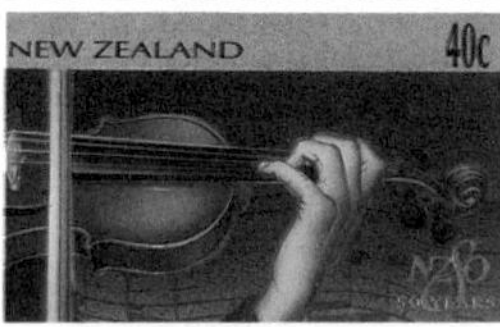

535 Violin

1996. 50th Anniv of New Zealand Symphony Orchestra. Multicoloured.

2006 40c. Type **535** 40 40
2007 80c. French horn . . . . . 1·00 1·50

536 Swimming

537 "Hinemoa"

1996. Centennial Olympic Games, Atlanta. Mult.

2008 40c. Type **536** 50 25
2009 80c. Cycling . . . . 1·25 1·00
2010 $1 Running . . . . 1·25 1·00
2011 $1.50 Rowing . . . . 1·75 3·00
2012 $1.80 Dinghy racing . . . . 2·00 3·00
MS2013 120 × 80 mm. Nos. 2008/12 6·00 6·50

1996. Centenary of New Zealand Cinema. Mult.

2014 40c. Type **537** 50 40
2015 80c. "Broken Barrier" . . . 1·00 1·00
2016 $1.50 "Goodbye Pork Pie" 1·75 2·50
2017 $1.80 "Once Were Warriors" . . . . 1·75 2·50

538 Danyon Loader (swimmer) and Blyth Tait (horseman)

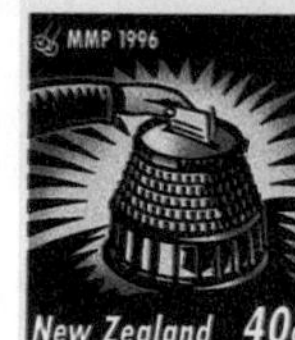

539 Beehive Ballot Box

1996. New Zealand Olympic Gold Medal Winners, Atlanta.

2018 **538** 40c. multicoloured . . . 50 50

1996. New Zealand's First Mixed Member Proportional Representation Election.

2019 **539** 40c. black, red and yellow 50 50

540 King following Star

1996. Christmas. Multicoloured. (a) Size 35 × 35 mm.

2020 40c. Type **540** 50 20
2021 70c. Shepherd and Baby Jesus 80 80
2022 80c. Angel and shepherd . . 90 90
2023 $1 Mary, Joseph and Baby Jesus . . . . 1·25 1·00
2024 $1.50 Mary and Joseph with donkey . . . . 2·00 2·50
2025 $1.80 The Annunciation . . 2·00 2·25

(b) Size 30 × 24 mm. Self-adhesive.

2026 40c. Angels with trumpets 50 80
2027 40c. King with gift 70 50

541 Adzebill

1996. Extinct Birds. Multicoloured. (a) Size 40 × 28 mm.

2028 40c. Type **541** 60 40
2029 80c. South Island whekau ("Laughing Owl") . . . . 1·25 1·25
2030 $1 Piopio . . . . 1·25 1·10
2031 $1.20 Huia . . . . 1·50 1·75
2032 $1.50 Giant eagle . . . . . 1·75 2·50
2033 $1.80 Giant moa . . . . . 2·00 2·50
MS2034 105 × 92 mm. No. 2033 2·00 2·00

(b) Size 30 × 24 mm. Self-adhesive.

2035 40c. Stout-legged wren . . . 70 50

1996. "TAIPEI '96" 10th Asian International Stamp Exhibition, Taiwan. (a) No. **MS**2034 overprinted with "TAIPEI '96" logo on sheet margin. Multicoloured.

MS2036 105 × 92 mm. No. 2033 2·75 2·75

(b) Sheet 140 × 90 mm, containing Nos. 1993 and 1997. Multicoloured.

MS2037 Nos. 1993 and 1997 . . 2·75 2·75

No. **MS**2037 also shows designs as Nos. 1992 and 1994/6, but without face values.

542 Seymour Square, Blenheim

543 Holstein Friesian Cattle

1996. Scenic Gardens. Multicoloured.

2038 40c. Type **542** 50 25
2039 80c. Pukekura Park, New Plymouth . . . . 1·00 1·00
2040 $1 Wintergarden, Auckland 1·25 1·10
2041 $1.50 Botanic Garden, Christchurch . . . . . . 1·75 2·25
2042 $1.80 Marine Parade Gardens, Napier . . . . 1·90 2·25

1997. Cattle Breeds. Multicoloured.

2043 40c. Type **543** 70 40
2044 80c. Jersey . . . . 1·40 1·00
2045 $1 Simmental . . . . 1·60 1·00
2046 $1.20 Ayrshire . . . . . . 1·90 1·60
2047 $1.50 Angus . . . . 1·90 2·00
2048 $1.80 Hereford . . . . . . 2·25 2·00

1997. "HONG KONG '97" International Stamp Exhibition. Multicoloured.

MS2049 130 × 110 mm. Nos. 1952/3 and 1956 . . . . 3·00 3·00
MS2050 101 × 134 mm. Nos. 2044/5 and 2047 . . . . 3·50 3·50

No. **MS**2050 is also inscribed for the Chinese New Year ("Year of the Ox").

544 James Cook and Sextant

1997. Millennium Series (1st issue). Discoverers of New Zealand. Multicoloured.

2051 40c. Type **544** 80 45
2052 80c. Kupe and ocean-going canoe . . . . 1·00 90
2053 $1 Carved panel depicting Maui (vert) . . . . 1·25 1·00
2054 $1.20 Anchor and "St. Jean Baptiste" (Jean de Surville) (vert) . . . . . 1·75 1·60
2055 $1.50 Dumont d'Urville, crab and "Lastrolabe" . . 2·00 2·00
2056 $1.80 Abel Tasman and illustration from journal 2·00 2·00

See also Nos. 2140/5, 2216/21, 2239/44, 2304/9 and 2310.

545 Rippon Vineyard, Central Otago

1997. New Zealand Vineyards. Multicoloured.

2057 40c. Type **545** 60 25
2058 80c. Te Mata Estate, Hawke's Bay . . . . . . 1·00 90
2059 $1 Cloudy Bay Vineyard, Marlborough . . . . . . 1·25 1·00
2060 $1.20 Pegasus Bay Vineyard, Waipara . . . . 1·50 1·75
2061 $1.50 Milton Vineyard, Gisborne . . . . 1·75 2·50
2062 $1.80 Goldwater Estate, Waiheke Island . . . . . 1·90 2·50
MS2063 Seven sheets, each 150 × 110 mm. (a) No. 2057. (b) No. 2058. (c) No. 2059. (d) No. 2060. (e) No. 2061. (f) No. 2062. (g) Nos. 2057/62 Set of 7 sheets . . . . 13·00 14·00

See also No. **MS**2081.

546 Cottage Letterbox

1997. Curious Letterboxes. Multicoloured. Self-adhesive.
2064 40c. Type **546** 50 50
2065 40c. Owl letterbox 50 50
2066 40c. Blue whale letterbox . . 50 50
2067 40c. "Kilroy is Back" letterbox 50 50
2068 40c. Nesting box letterbox 50 50
2069 40c. Piper letterbox 50 50
2070 40c. Diver's helmet letterbox 50 50
2071 40c. Aircraft letterbox . . . 50 50
2072 40c. Water tap letterbox . . 50 50
2073 40c. Indian palace letterbox 50 50

547 "The Promised Land", 1948 (Colin McCahon)

1997. Contemporary Paintings by Colin McCahon. Multicoloured.
2074 40c. Type **547** 50 35
2075 $1 "Six Days in Nelson and Canterbury", 1950 . . . 1·10 90
2076 $1.50 "Northland Panels" (detail), 1958 . . . . . . 1·75 2·25
2077 $1.80 "Moby Dick is sighted off Muriwai Beach", 1972 2·25 2·25

548 Carrier Pigeon (based on 1899 "Pigeon-gram" local stamp)

1997. Centenary of Great Barrier Island Pigeon Post.
2078 **548** 40c. red 50 70
2079 80c. blue . . . . 90 1·40
See also Nos. **MS**2080 and **MS**2122.

1997. "Pacific '97" International Stamp Exhibition, San Francisco. Multicoloured.
MS2080 137 × 120 mm. Nos. 2078/9, each × 2 . . . . 2·50 2·50
MS2081 140 × 100 mm. Nos. 2057, 2059 and 2061 . . . . . . 3·00 3·00
No. **MS**2080 is in a triangular format.

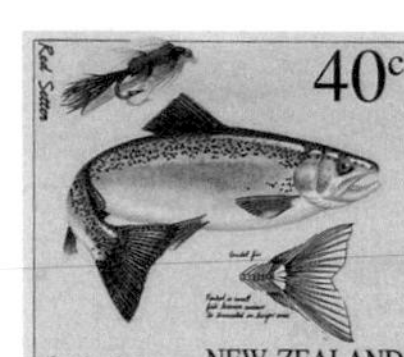

549 Rainbow Trout and Red Setter Fly

1997. Fly Fishing. Multicoloured.
2082 40c. Type **549** 40 35
2083 $1 Sea-run brown trout and grey ghost fly 90 90
2084 $1.50 Brook charr and twilight beauty fly . . . . 1·40 2·50
2085 $1.80 Brown trout and Hare and Cooper fly . . . . . 1·60 2·50
See also No. **MS**2172.

550 "Beach Scene" (Fern Petrie)

1997. Children's Health. Children's paintings. Mult. (a) Ordinary gum.
2086 40c.+5c. Type **550** 45 75
2087 80c.+5c. "Horse-riding on the Waterfront" (Georgia Dumergue) . . . . 80 1·25
MS2088 130 × 90 mm. Nos. 2086/7 and 40c.+ 5c. As No. 2089 (25 × 36 mm) . . . . 1·75 1·75

(b) Self-adhesive.
2089 40c.+5c. "Picking Fruit" (Anita Pitcher) 60 60

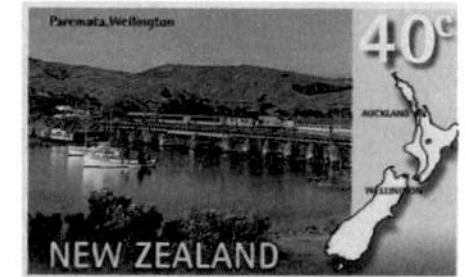

551 The "Overlander" at Paremata, Wellington

1997. Scenic Railway Services. Multicoloured.
2091 40c. Type **551** 50 35
2092 80c. The "Tranz Alpine" in the Southern Alps 90 80
2093 $1 The "Southerner" at Canterbury . . . . 1·00 90
2094 $1.20 The "Coastal Pacific" on the Kaikoura Coast 1·40 2·00
2095 $1.50 The "Bay Express" at Central Hawke's Bay . . 1·60 2·25
2096 $1.80 The "Kaimai Express" at Tauranga Harbour . . 1·75 2·25
See also No. **MS**2173.

552 Samuel Marsden's "Active", Bay of Islands

553 Huhu Beetle

1997. Christmas. Multicoloured. (a) Ordinary gum.
2097 40c. Type **552** 45 20
2098 70c. Revd. Marsden preaching 75 65
2099 80c. Marsden and Maori chiefs 85 75
2100 $1 Maori family . . . . . 1·00 90
2101 $1.50 Handshake and cross 1·60 2·00
2102 $1.80 Pohutukawa (flower) and Rangihoua Bay . . . 1·75 2·00

(b) Smaller design, 29 × 24 mm. Self-adhesive.
2103 40c. Memorial cross, Pohutukawa and Bay of Islands 40 40

1997. Insects. Multicoloured. Self-adhesive.
2104 40c. Type **553** 50 50
2105 40c. Giant land snail . . . 50 50
2106 40c. Giant weta 50 50
2107 40c. Giant dragonfly 50 50
2108 40c. Peripatus 50 50
2109 40c. Cicada 50 50
2110 40c. Puriri moth 50 50
2111 40c. Veined slug 50 50
2112 40c. Katipo 50 50
2113 40c. Flax weevil 50 50

554 "Rosa rugosa"

555 Queen Elizabeth II and Prince Philip

1997. New Zealand–China Joint Issue. Roses. Mult.
2114 40c. Type **554** 50 50
2115 40c. "Aotearoa" 50 50
MS2116 115 × 95 mm. 80c. Nos. 2114/15 . . . . 1·00 1·00

1997. Golden Wedding of Queen Elizabeth and Prince Philip.
2117 **555** 40c. multicoloured . . . 50 50

556 Cartoon Kiwi on Busy-bee

1997. New Zealand Cartoons. "Kiwis Taking on the World". Multicoloured.
2118 40c. Type **556** 60 25
2119 $1 "Let's have 'em for Breakfast" . . . . 1·10 80
2120 $1.50 Kiwi dinghy winning race . . . . 1·40 1·75
2121 $1.80 "CND" emblem cut in forest . . . . 1·75 1·75

1997. "Aupex '97" National Stamp Exhibtion, Auckland. Sheet 140 × 120 mm. Multicoloured.
MS2122 Nos. 2078/9, each × 2 . . 2·10 2·10
No. **MS**2122 is in a triangular format.

1997. International Stamp and Coin Exhibition 1997, Shanghai. Sheet as No. **MS**2116, but redrawn to include "Issued by New Zealand Post to commemorate the International Stamp and Coin Expo. Shanghai, China. 19–23 November 1997" inscr in English and Chinese with additional die-stamped gold frame and logo.
MS2123 115 × 95 mm. Nos. 2114/15 70 70

557 Modern Dancer

1998. Performing Arts. Multicoloured.
2124 40c. Type **557** 50 25
2125 80c. Trombone player . . . 85 75
2126 $1 Opera singer . . . . . . 1·50 85
2127 $1.20 Actor . . . . 1·50 1·50
2128 $1.50 Singer . . . . 1·75 2·50
2129 $1.80 Ballet dancer . . . . 2·25 2·50
MS2130 Seven sheets, each 150 × 110 mm. (a) No. 2124. (b) No. 2125. (c) No. 2126. (d) No. 2127. (e) No. 2128. (f) No. 2129. (g) Nos. 2124/9 Set of 7 sheets . . . . 15·00 18·00

558 Museum of New Zealand

1998. Opening of Museum of New Zealand, Wellington. Multicoloured.
2131 40c. Type **558** 30 35
2132 $1.80 Museum, spotted cormorant and silver gull 1·40 1·40

559 Domestic Cat

560 Maoris and Canoe

1998. Cats. Multicoloured.
2133 40c. Type **559** 40 35
2134 80c. Burmese 75 80
2135 $1 Birman 85 80
2136 $1.20 British blue . . . . . 1·00 1·40
2137 $1.50 Persian . . . . 1·25 1·75
2138 $1.80 Siamese . . . . 1·75 2·00

1998. Chinese New Year ("Year of the Tiger"). Multicoloured.
MS2139 100 × 135 mm. Nos. 2133, 2135 and 2138 . . . . 3·00 3·00

1998. Millennium Series (2nd issue). Immigrants. Multicoloured.
2140 40c. Type **560** 35 25
2141 80c. 19th-century European settlers and immigrant ship 75 65
2142 $1 Gold miners and mine 1·00 80
2143 $1.20 Post 1945 European migrants and liner . . . 1·25 1·10
2144 $1.50 Pacific islanders and church . . . . 1·40 1·60
2145 $1.80 Asian migrant and jumbo jet . . . . 1·60 1·60

561 "With Great Respect to the Mehmetcik" Statue, Gallipoli

562 Mother and Son Hugging

1998. Joint Issue New Zealand–Turkey. Memorial Statues. Multicoloured.
2146 40c. Type **561** 40 35
2147 $1.80 "Mother with Children", National War Memorial, Wellington . . 1·25 1·40

1998. "Stay in Touch" Greetings Stamps. Mult. Self-adhesive.
2148 40c. Type **562** 25 30
2149 40c. Couple on beach . . . 25 30
2150 40c. Boys striking hands . . 25 30
2151 40c. Grandmother and grandson 25 30
2152 40c. Young boys in pool (horiz) 25 30
2153 40c. "I'LL MISS YOU ... PLEASE WRITE" (horiz) 25 30
2154 40c. Symbolic couple and clouds (horiz) 25 30
2155 40c. Young couple kissing (horiz) 25 30
2156 40c. Couple sat on sofa (horiz) 25 30
2157 40c. Maoris rubbing noses (horiz) 25 30

563 Mount Cook or Aorangi

565 Girl wearing Lifejacket

564 "Wounded at Cassino"

1998. Centenary of 1898 Pictorial Stamps. Designs as T **23/26** and **28/35** with modern face values as T **563**.
2158 **563** 40c. brown 50 50
2159 **24** 40c. blue and brown . . 50 50
2160 **25** 40c. brown 50 50
2161 **28** 40c. brown 50 50
2162 **29** 40c. red 50 50
2163 **31** 40c. green 50 50
2164 **32** 40c. blue 50 50
2165 **34** 40c. orange 50 50
2166 **26** 80c. blue (inscr "LAKE WAKITIPU") (35 × 23 mm) 85 75
2167 80c. blue (inscr "LAKE WAKATIPU") (35 × 23 mm) 85 75
2168 **30** $1 brown (23 × 35 mm) 95 85
2169 **33** $1.20 brown (35 × 23 mm) . . . . 1·00 1·60
2170 **35** $1.50 green (35 × 23 mm) 1·25 1·75
2171 – $1.80 red (as No. 329) (23 × 35 mm) . . . . 1·40 1·75
See also Nos. **MS**2188 and **MS**2214.

1998. "Israel '98" World Stamp Exhibition, Tel Aviv. Multicoloured.
MS2172 112 × 90 mm. Nos. 2082 and 2085 . . . . 2·50 2·75
MS2173 125 × 100 mm. Nos. 2092/3 and 2095 . . . . 4·00 4·00

1998. Paintings by Peter McIntyre. Multicoloured.
2174 40c. Type **564** 35 30
2175 $1 "The Cliffs of Rangitikei" 85 75
2176 $1.50 "Maori Children, King Country" . . . . . 1·25 1·40
2177 $1.80 "The Anglican Church, Kakahi" . . . . 1·40 1·50
See also No. **MS**2215.

1998. Children's Health. Water Safety. Mult. (a) Ordinary gum.
2178 40c.+5c. Type **565** 40 50
2179 80c.+5c. Boy learning to swim 60 75
MS2180 125 × 90 mm. Nos. 2178/9, each × 2 . . . . 2·00 2·00

(b) Smaller design, 25 × 37 mm. Self-adhesive.
2181 40c.+5c. Type **565** 30 50

566 Sunrise near Cambridge

1998. Scenic Skies. Multicoloured.
2182 40c. Type **566** 40 20
2183 80c. Clouds over Lake Wanaka 75 65
2184 $1 Sunset over Mount Maunganui 85 75
2185 $1.20 Rain clouds over South Bay, Kaikoura . . 1·00 1·10
2186 $1.50 Sunset near Statue of Wairaka, Whakatane Harbour . . . . 1·40 1·25
2187 $1.80 Cloud formation above Lindis Pass . . . . 1·60 1·75
See also No. **MS**2245.

1998. "TARAPEX '98" National Stamp Exhibition, New Plymouth.
MS2188 90 × 80 mm. Nos. 2166/7 1·60 1·75

567 Virgin Mary and Christ Child
568 Lemon and Mineral Water Bottle, Paeroa

1998. Christmas. Multicoloured. (a) Ordinary gum.
2189 40c. Type **567** 35 15
2190 70c. Shepherds approaching the stable 55 55
2191 80c. Virgin Mary, Joseph and Christ Child 65 65
2192 $1 Magi with gift of gold 80 80
2193 $1.50 Three magi . . . . . 1·25 1·40
2194 $1.80 Angel and shepherds 1·40 1·50

(b) Smaller design, 24 × 29 mm. Self-adhesive.
2195 40c. Type **567** 35 30

1998. Town Icons. Multicoloured. Self-adhesive.
2196 40c. Type **568** 35 35
2197 40c. Carrot, Ohakune . . . 35 35
2198 40c. Brown Trout, Gore (25 × 36 mm) 35 35
2199 40c. Crayfish, Kaikoura (25 × 36 mm) 35 35
2200 40c. Sheep-shearer, Te Kuiti (25 × 36 mm) 35 35
2201 40c. "Pania of the Reef" (Maori legend), Napier (25 × 36 mm) 35 35
2202 40c. Paua Shell, Riverton (24 × 29 mm) 35 35
2203 40c. Kiwifruit, Te Puke (24 × 29 mm) 35 35
2204 40c. Border Collie, Lake Tekapo (24 × 29 mm) . . 35 35
2205 40c. "Big Cow", Hawera (24 × 29 mm) 35 35

569 Moonfish
571 "Fuchsia excorticata"

570 Wellington in 1841 and 1998

1998. International Year of the Ocean. Mult.
2206 40c. Type **569** 35 50
2207 40c. Mako shark 35 50
2208 40c. Yellowfin tuna 35 50
2209 40c. Giant squid 35 50
2210 80c. Striped marlin 60 70
2211 80c. Porcupine fish 60 70
2212 80c. Eagle ray 60 70
2213 80c. Sandager's wrasse . . . 60 70

Nos. 2206/9 and 2210/13 respectively were printed together, se-tenant, forming composite designs.
See also Nos. **MS**2246 and **MS**2277.

1998. "Italia '98" International Philatelic Exhibition, Milan. Multicoloured.
MS2214 90 × 80 mm. Nos. 2167 and 2170 . . . . 3·00 3·25
MS2215 112 × 90 mm. Nos. 2176/7 2·00 2·25

1998. Millennium Series (3rd issue). Urban Transformations. Multicoloured.
2216 40c. Type **570** 70 30
2217 80c. Auckland in 1852 and 1998 . . . . 95 55
2218 $1 Christchurch in 1851 and 1998 . . . . 1·10 70
2219 $1.20 Westport in 1919 and 1998 . . . . 1·40 1·25
2220 $1.50 Tauranga in 1880 and 1998 . . . . 1·60 1·50
2221 $1.80 Dunedin in 1862 and 1998 . . . . 1·75 1·75

1999. Flowering Trees of New Zealand. Mult.
2222 40c. Type **571** 40 20
2223 80c. "Solanum laciniatum" 65 55
2224 $1 "Sophora tetraptera" . . 75 70
2225 $1.20 "Carmichaelia stevensonii" . . . . . . 85 1·00
2226 $1.50 "Olearia angustfolia" 1·25 1·60
2227 $1.80 "Metrosideros umbellata" . . . . 1·40 1·60
See also No. **MS**2286.

572 Civic Theatre, Auckland
573 Labrador Puppy and Netherland Dwarf Rabbit

1999. Art Deco Architecture. Multicoloured.
2228 40c. Type **572** 50 20
2229 $1 Masonic Hotel, Napier 2·00 80
2230 $1.50 Medical and Dental Chambers, Hastings . . . 1·40 1·60
2231 $1.80 Buller County Chambers, Westport . . . 1·40 1·60

1999. Popular Pets. Multicoloured.
2232 40c. Type **573** 40 30
2233 80c. Netherland dwarf rabbit 80 55
2234 $1 Tabby kitten and Netherland dwarf rabbit 90 70
2235 $1.20 Lamb . . . . 1·25 1·25
2236 $1.50 Welsh pony . . . . . 1·40 1·50
2237 $1.80 Two budgerigars . . . 1·50 1·60
MS2238 100 × 135 mm. Nos. 2232/4 1·75 1·75
No. **MS**2238 also commemorates the Chinese New Year ("Year of the Rabbit").
See also No. **MS**2287.

574 Toy Fire Engine and Marbles

1999. Millennium Series (4th issue). Nostalgia. Multicoloured.
2239 40c. Type **574** 40 30
2240 80c. Commemorative tin of biscuits and cereal packet 70 55
2241 $1 Tram, tickets and railway crockery 85 70
2242 $1.20 Radio and "Woman's Weekly" magazine . . . 1·00 1·25
2243 $1.50 Coins, postcards and stamps . . . . 1·25 1·40
2244 $1.80 Lawn mower and seed packets . . . . 1·40 1·60

1999. "Australia '99" World Stamp Exhibition, Melbourne. Multicoloured.
MS2245 130 × 70 mm. Nos. 2182 and 2187 . . . . 1·90 1·90
MS2246 130 × 90 mm. Nos. 2206/7 and 2210/11 . . . . 2·00 2·00

575 Hunter Building, Victoria University
576 Auckland Blues Player kicking Ball

1999. Centenary of Victoria University, Wellington.
2247 **575** 40c. multicoloured . . . 30 30

1999. New Zealand U-Bix Rugby Super 12 Championship. Multicoloured. Ordinary or self-adhesive gum.
2248 40c. Type **576** 40 40
2249 40c. Auckland Blues player being tackled 40 40
2250 40c. Chiefs player being tackled 40 40
2251 40c. Chiefs lineout jump . . . 40 40
2252 40c. Wellington Hurricanes player being tackled . . . 40 40
2253 40c. Wellington Hurricanes player passing ball . . . 40 40
2254 40c. Canterbury Crusaders lineout jump 40 40
2255 40c. Canterbury Crusaders player kicking ball . . . 40 40
2256 40c. Otago Highlanders player diving for try . . . 40 40
2257 40c. Otago Highlanders player running with ball 40 40

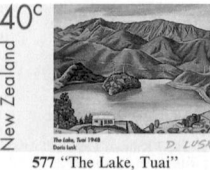

577 "The Lake, Tuai"

1999. Paintings by Doris Lusk. Multicoloured.
2268 40c. Type **577** 35 30
2269 $1 "The Pumping Station" 80 70
2270 $1.50 "Arcade Awning, St. Mark's Square, Venice (2)" . . . . 1·10 1·25
2271 $1.80 "Tuam St. II" . . . . 1·25 1·40
See also No. **MS**2276.

578 "A Lion in the Meadow" (Margaret Mahy)

1999. Children's Health. Children's Books. Mult. (a) Ordinary gum.
2272 40c.+5c. Type **578** 55 55
2273 80c.+5c. "Greedy Cat" (Joy Cowley) 70 70
MS2274 130 × 90 mm. 40c. + 5c. Type **578**; 40c. + 5c. As No. 2275 (37 × 25 mm); 80c. + 5c. No. 2273 1·40 1·40

(b) Smaller design, 37 × 25 mm. Self-adhesive.
2275 40c.+5c. "Hairy Maclary's Bone" (Lynley Dodd) (37 × 25 mm) 50 50

1999. "PhilexFrance '99" International Stamp Exhibiton, Paris. Multicoloured.
MS2276 112 × 90 mm. Nos. 2268 and 2271 . . . . 1·75 1·75
MS2277 130 × 90 mm. Nos. 2208/9 and 2212/13 . . . . 2·00 2·00

579 "APEC"

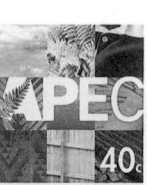

1999. 10th Asia-Pacific Economic Co-operation Meeting, New Zealand.
2278 **579** 40c. multicoloured . . . 30 30

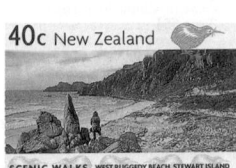

580 West Ruggedy Beach, Stewart Island

1999. Scenic Walks. Multicoloured.
2279 40c. Type **580** 35 30
2280 80c. Ice lake, Butler Valley, Westland 60 55
2281 $1 Tonga Bay, Abel Tasman National Park 75 70
2282 $1.20 East Matakitaki Valley, Nelson Lakes National Park 85 90
2283 $1.50 Great Barrier Island 1·10 1·25
2284 $1.80 Mt. Egmont, Taranaki 1·40 1·40
MS2285 Seven sheets, each 150 × 110 mm. (a) No. 2279. (b) No. 2280. (c) No. 2281. (d) No. 2282. (e) No. 2283. (f) No. 2284. (g) Nos. 2279/84 Set of 7 sheets . . . . 9·50 10·00
See also No. **MS**2295.

1999. "China '99" International Stamp Exhibition, Peking. Multicoloured.
MS2286 112 × 90 mm. Nos. 2222/3 1·00 1·00
MS2287 100 × 135 mm. Nos. 2232 and 2234 . . . . 1·00 1·00

581 Baby Jesus with Animals

1999. Christmas. Multicoloured. (a) Ordinary gum.
2288 40c. Type **581** 30 15
2289 80c. Virgin Mary praying 65 55
2290 $1.10 Mary and Joseph on way to Bethlehem 80 75
2291 $1.20 Angel playing harp . . 85 80
2292 $1.50 Three shepherds . . . 1·10 1·25
2293 $1.80 Three wise men with gifts . . . . 1·40 1·40

(b) Smaller design, 23 × 28 mm. Self-adhesive.
2294 40c. Type **581** 30 30

1999. "Palmpex '99" National Stamp Exhibition, Palmerston North. Sheet 130 × 90 mm, containing No. 2284. Multicoloured.
MS2295 $1.80, Mt. Egmont, Taranaki . . . . 1·40 1·40

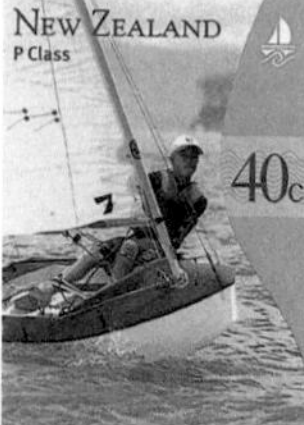

582 "P" Class Dinghy

1999. Yachting. Multicoloured. (a) Size 28 × 39 mm. Ordinary gum.
2296 40c. Type **582** 35 15
2297 80c. Laser dinghy 60 55
2298 $1.10 18ft skiff 80 75
2299 $1.20 Hobie catamaran . . 85 80
2300 $1.50 Racing yacht . . . . 1·10 1·25
2301 $1.80 Cruising yacht . . . . 1·25 1·40
MS2302 125 × 100 mm. Nos. 2296/301 . . . . 4·50 5·00

(b) Size 23 × 28 mm. Self-adhesive.
2303 40c. Optimist dinghy 30 30

583 Group of Victorian Women (female suffrage, 1893)

1999. Millenium Series (5th issue). New Zealand Achievements. Multicoloured.
2304 40c. Type **583** 40 15
2305 80c. Richard Pearse's aircraft (powered flight, 1903) 75 55
2306 $1.10 Lord Rutherford (splitting the atom, 1919) 85 85
2307 $1.20 Boat on lake (invention of jet boat, 1953) 90 90
2308 $1.50 Sir Edmund Hillary (conquest of Everest, 1953) . . . . 1·40 1·50
2309 $1.80 Protesters and warship (nuclear free zone, 1987) 1·40 1·60

584 Sunrise and World Map

2000. Millennium Series (6th issue).
2310 **584** 40c. multicoloured . . . 65 30

585 Araiteuru (North Island sea guardian)

586 Chilly Bin (cool box)

2000. Chinese New Year ("Year of the Dragon"). Maori Spirits and Guardians. Multicoloured.

2311 40c. Type **585** 35 15
2312 80c. Kurangaituku (giant bird woman) 60 55
2313 $1.10 Te Hoata and Te Pupu (volcanic taniwha sisters) 80 75
2314 $1.20 Patupaiarehe (mountain fairy tribe) . . 85 80
2315 $1.50 Te Ngarara-huarau (giant first lizard) . . . . 1·10 1·25
2316 $1.80 Tuhirangi (South Island sea guardian) . . . 1·25 1·40
MS2317 125 × 90 mm. Nos. 2315/16 2·50 2·50

2000. New Zealand Life (2nd series). Each including a cartoon kiwi. Multicoloured. Self-adhesive.

2318 40c. Type **586** 35 35
2319 40c. Pipis (seafood delicacy) 35 35
2320 40c. "Lilo" 35 35
2321 40c. Chocolate fish 35 35
2322 40c. Bach or Crib (holiday home) 35 35
2323 40c. Barbeque 35 35
2324 40c. Ug (fur-lined) boots . . 35 35
2325 40c. Anzac biscuits 35 35
2326 40c. Hot dog 35 35
2327 40c. Meat pie 35 35

2000. "The Stamp Show 2000" International Stamp Exhibition, London. Sheet 110 × 80 mm, containing Nos. 1934b and 1934e/f. Multicoloured.

MS2328 $1 Taiaroa Head; $2 Great Barrier Island; $3 Cape kidnappers . . . . 4·00 4·50

587 Volkswagen Beetle

2000. "On The Road". Motor Cars.

2329 **587** 40c. brown and black . . 35 30
2330 – 80c. blue and black . . . 60 55
2331 – $1.10 brown and black 80 80
2332 – $1.20 green and black . . 85 85
2333 – $1.50 brown and black 1·10 1·25
2334 – $1.80 lilac and black . . 1·25 1·40
MS2335 Seven sheets, each 150 × 110 mm. (a) No. 2329. (b) No. 2330. (c) No. 2331. (d) No. 2332. (e) No. 2333. (f) No. 2334. (g) Nos. 2329/34 Set of 7 sheets . . . . 11·00 12·00

DESIGNS: 80c. Ford Zephyr Mk I; $1.10, Morris Mini Mk II; $1.20, Holden HQ Kingswood; $1.50, Honda Civic; $1.80, Toyota Corolla.

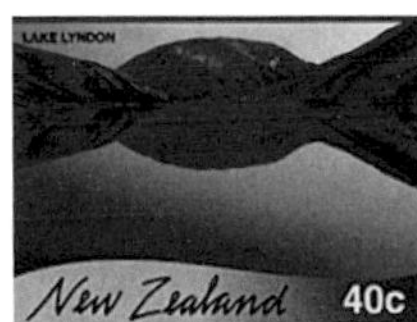

588 Lake Lyndon, Canterbury

2000. Scenic Reflections. Multicoloured.

2336 40c. Type **588** 50 30
2337 80c. Lion (cruising launch) on Lake Wakatipu . . . 85 55
2338 $1.10 Eruption of Mount Ruapehu . . . . 1·00 80
2339 $1.20 Rainbow Mountain Scenic Reserve, Rotorua 1·10 85
2340 $1.50 Tairua Harbour, Coromandel Peninsula . . 1·40 1·50
2341 $1.80 Lake Alexandrina . . 1·50 1·50

See also No. **MS**2368.

2000. "EXPO 2000" World Stamp Exhibition, Anaheim, U.S.A. Sheet 132 × 78 mm, containing Nos. 1490, 1490b/c and 2090/a.

MS2342 $1 red; $1 blue; $1 violet; $1 green; $1.10 gold . . . . . . 3·00 3·25

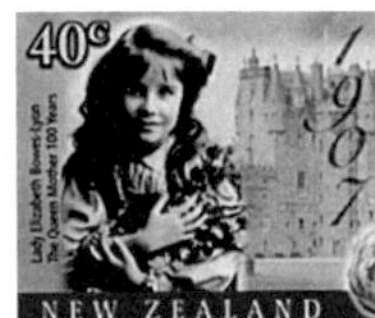

589 Lady Elizabeth Bowes-Lyon and Glamis Castle, 1907

2000. Queen Elizabeth the Queen Mother's 100th Birthday. Multicoloured.

2343 40c. Type **589** 60 30
2344 $1.10 Fishing in New Zealand, 1966 . . . . . 1·10 70
2345 $1.80 Holding bunch of daisies, 1997 . . . . . . 1·75 1·60
MS2346 115 × 60 mm. Nos. 2343/5 2·40 2·40

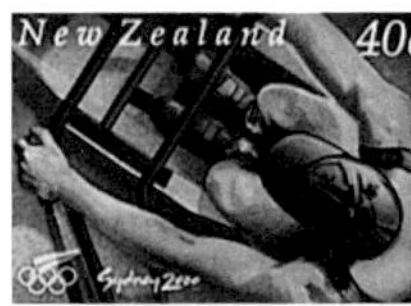

590 Rowing

2000. Olympic Games, Sydney, and other Sporting Events. Multicoloured.

2347 40c. Type **590** 35 30
2348 80c. Show jumping 65 55
2349 $1.10 Cycling 80 80
2350 $1.20 Triathlon 85 85
2351 $1.50 Bowling . . . . . . 1·10 1·25
2352 $1.80 Netball . . . . 1·25 1·40

Nos. 2351/2 omit the Olympic logo.

591 Virgin Mary and Baby Jesus

2000. Christmas. Multicoloured. (a) Ordinary gum.

2353 40c. Type **591** 35 30
2354 80c. Mary and Joseph on way to Bethlehem 60 55
2355 $1.10 Baby Jesus in manger 85 80
2356 $1.20 Archangel Gabriel . . 95 90
2357 $1.50 Shepherd with lamb 1·25 1·40
2358 $1.80 Three Wise Men . . . 1·40 1·60

(b) Self-adhesive. Size 30 × 25 mm.

2359 40c. Type **591** 25 30

592 Geronimo (teddy bear)

2000. Children's Health. Teddy Bears and Dolls. Multicoloured. (a) Ordinary gum.

2360 40c.+5c. Type **592** 45 50
2361 80c.+5c. Antique French doll and wooden Schoenhut doll 70 80
2362 $1.10 Chad Valley bear . . 75 70
2363 $1.20 Poppy (doll) 80 80
2364 $1.50 Swanni (large bear) and Dear John (small bear) . . . . 90 1·25
2365 $1.80 Lia (doll) and bear . . 1·10 1·25
MS2366 100 × 60 mm. 40c. + 5c. Type **592**; 80c. + 5c. As No. 2361 1·00 1·00

(b) Self-adhesive. Size 29 × 24 mm.

2367 40c.+5c. Type **592** 35 40

2000. "CANPEX 2000" National Stamp Exhibition, Christchurch. Sheet 95 × 80 mm, containing Nos. 2336 and 2341. Multicoloured.

MS2368 40c. Type **588**; $1.80 Lake Alexandrina . . . . 1·40 1·50

593 Lesser Kestrel

2000. Threatened Birds. Multicoloured.

2369 40c. Type **593** 50 30
2370 40c. Yellow-fronted parakeet 50 30
2371 80c. New Zealand stilt ("Black Stilt") 70 55
2372 $1.10 Fernbird ("Stewart Island Fernbird") 75 70
2373 $1.20 Kakapo . . . . 90 1·00
2374 $1.50 Weka rail ("North Island Weka") . . . . . 1·10 1·25
2375 $1.80 Brown kiwi ("Okarito Brown Kiwi") . . . . . 1·25 1·25

Nos. 2369 and 2375 form a joint issue with France. See also No. **MS**2393.

594 *Sonoma* (mail ship) at Quay

2001. Moving the Mail in the 20th Century.

2376 **594** 40c. purple and red . . . 30 35
2377 – 40c. green 30 35
2378 – 40c. agate 30 35
2379 – 40c. blue 30 35
2380 – 40c. brown 30 35
2381 – 40c. purple 30 35
2382 – 40c. black and cinnamon 30 35
2383 – 40c. multicoloured . . . 30 35
2384 – 40c. mauve 30 35
2385 – 40c. multicoloured . . . 30 35

DESIGNS: No. 2377, Stagecoach crossing river; 2378, Early postal lorry; 2379, Paddle steamer on River Wanganui; 2380, Railway T.P.O.; 2381, Loading mail through nose door of aircraft; 2382, Postwoman with bicycle; 2383, Loading lorry by fork-lift truck; 2384, Aircraft at night; 2385, Computer mouse.

See also No. **MS**2424.

595 Green Turtle

2001. Chinese New Year ("Year of the Snake"). Marine Reptiles. Multicoloured.

2386 40c. Type **595** 45 30
2387 80c. Leathery turtle 70 55
2388 90c. Loggerhead turtle . . . 75 60
2389 $1.30 Hawksbill turtle . . . 1·10 1·10
2390 $1.50 Banded sea-snake . . 1·25 1·25
2391 $2 Yellow-bellied sea-snake 1·40 1·40
MS2392 125 × 90 mm. Nos. 2390/1 2·10 2·25

2001. "Hong Kong 2001" Stamp Exhibition. Sheet 100 × 80 mm, containing Nos. 2374/5. Multicoloured.

MS2393 $1.50, North Island weka; $1.80, Okarito brown kiwi . . 1·90 2·00

596 Camellia

2001. Garden Flowers. Multicoloured.

2394 40c. Type **596** 30 25
2395 80c. Siberian iris 60 55
2396 90c. Daffodil 65 60
2397 $1.30 Chrysanthemum . . . 85 1·10
2398 $1.50 Sweet pea . . . . . . 90 1·25
2399 $2 Petunia . . . . 1·10 1·25
MS2400 95 × 125 mm. Nos. 2394/9 4·00 4·25

2001. Invercargill "Stamp Odyssey 2001" National Stamp Exhibition. Sheet 133 × 81 mm, containing Nos. 1934a/d. Multicoloured.

MS2401 90c. Rangitoto Island; $1 Taiaroa Head; $1.10, Kaikoura Coast; $1.30, Lake Camp, South Canterbury . . . . 2·50 2·75

597 Greenstone Amulet

2001. Art from Nature. Multicoloured.

2402 40c. Type **597** 35 30
2403 80c. Oamaru stone sculpture 65 55
2404 90c. Paua ornament 70 60
2405 $1.30 Kauri ornament . . . 95 1·10
2406 $1.50 Flax basket . . . . . 1·10 1·25
2407 $2 Silver-dipped fern frond 1·25 1·25

Nos. 2402/7 were each printed in sheets of 25 (5 × 5) in which the stamps were included in four different orientations so that four blocks of 4 in each sheet showed the complete work of art.

598 Douglas DC-3

2001. Aircraft. Multicoloured.

2408 40c. Type **598** 35 30
2409 80c. Fletcher FU24 Topdresser 65 55
2410 90c. De Havilland DH82A Tiger Moth 70 60
2411 $1.30 Fokker FVIIb/3m Southern Cross . . . . . 90 1·10
2412 $1.50 De Havilland DH100 Vampire . . . . 1·00 1·25
2413 $2 Boeing & Westervelt seaplane . . . . 1·25 1·25

599 Parcel

2001. Greetings Stamps. Multicoloured.

2414 40c. Type **599** 25 30
2415 40c. Trumpet 25 30
2416 40c. Heart and ribbon . . . 25 30
2417 40c. Balloons 25 30
2418 40c. Flower 25 30
2419 90c. Photo frame 60 65
2420 90c. Fountain pen and letter 60 65
2421 90c. Candles on cake . . . 60 65
2422 90c. Star biscuits 60 65
2423 90c. Candle and flowers . . 60 65

2001. "Belgica 2001" International Stamp Exhibition, Brussels. Sheet 180 × 90 mm, containing Nos. 2376/85. Multicoloured.

MS2424 40c. × 10, Nos. 2376/85 3·00 3·50

600 Bungy Jumping, Queenstown

2001. Tourism Centenary. Multicoloured. (a) Size 38 × 32 mm. Ordinary gum.

2425 40c. Type **600** 25 30
2426 80c. Maori Canoe on Lake Rotoiti 45 50
2427 90c. Sightseeing from Mount Alfred 55 60
2428 $1.30 Fishing on Glenorchy river 75 80
2429 $1.50 Sea-kayaking in Abel Tasman National Park . . 85 90
2430 $2 Fiordland National Park 1·10 1·25

(b). Size 30 × 25 mm. Self-adhesive.

2431 40c. Type **600** 25 30
2432 90c. Sightseeing from Mount Alfred 55 60
2433 $1.50 Sea-kayaking in Abel Tasman National Park . . 85 90

2001. "Philanippon '01" International Stamp Exhibition, Tokyo. Sheet 90 × 82 mm, containing Nos. 2429/30. Multicoloured.

MS2434 $1.50 Sea-kayaking in Abel Tasman National Park; $2 Fiordland National Park . . . 2·25 2·40

601 Family cycling

2001. Children's Health. Cycling. Multicoloured. (a) Size 39 × 29 mm. Ordinary gum.

2435 40c. + 5c. Type **601** 25 30
2436 90c. + 5c. Mountain bike stunt 55 60
MS2437 Circular, 100 mm diameter. Nos. 2435/6 . . . . 1·00 1·10

(b) Size 29 × 23½. Self-adhesive.

2438 40c. + 5c. Boy on bike . . . 25 30

602 "When Christ was born of Mary free"

2001. Christmas. Carols. Multicoloured. (a) Size 29 × 34 mm. Ordinary gum.

2439 40c. Type **602** 30 30
2440 80c. "Away in a manger" . . 55 50
2441 90c. "Joy to the world" . . . 60 55
2442 $1.30 "Angels we have heard on high" 85 80
2443 $1.50 "O holy night" 95 90
2444 $2 "While shepherds watched" . . . . 1·25 1·25

(b) Size 21 × 26 mm. Self-adhesive.

2445 40c. Type **602** 35 30

603 Queen Elizabeth II at State Opening of Parliament, 1954

605 Gandalf (Sir Ian McKellen) and Saruman (Christopher Lee)

604 Rockhopper Penguins

2001. Queen Elizabeth II's 75th Birthday. Multicoloured (except 40c.).

2446 40c. Type **603** (black and silver) 35 30
2447 80c. Queen Elizabeth II on walkabout, 1970 . . . . 55 50
2448 90c. Queen Elizabeth II wearing Maori cloak, 1977 . . . . 60 55
2449 $1.30 Queen Elizabeth II with bouquet, 1986 . . . 85 80
2450 $1.50 Queen Elizabeth II at Commonwealth Games, 1990 . . . . 95 90
2451 $2 Queen Elizabeth II, 1997 1·25 1·25

2001. New Zealand Penguins. Multicoloured.

2452 40c. Type **604** 40 30
2453 80c. Little penguin ("Little Blue Penguin") 60 50
2454 90c. Snares Island penguins ("Snares Crested Penguins") 65 55
2455 $1.30 Big-crested penguins ("Erect-crested Penguins") 90 80
2456 $1.50 Victoria penguins ("Fiordland Crested Penguins") . . . . 1·10 90
2457 $2 Yellow-eyed penguins . . 1·40 1·25

2001. Making of *The Lord of the Rings* Film Trilogy (1st issue): *The Fellowship of the Ring*. Multicoloured. (a) Designs 24 × 50 mm or 50 × 24 mm.

2458 40c. Type **605** 25 30
2459 80c. The Lady Galadriel (Cate Blanchett) 45 50
2460 90c. Sam Gamgee (Sean Austin) and Frodo Baggins (Elijah Wood) (horiz) 50 55
2461 $1.30 Guardian of Rivendell 75 80
2462 $1.50 Strider (Viggo Mortensen) 85 90
2463 $2 Boromir (Sean Bean) (horiz) . . . . 1·10 1·25

(b) Designs 26 × 37 mm or 37 × 26 mm. Self-adhesive.

2464 40c. Type **605** 25 30
2465 80c. The Lady Galadriel (Cate Blanchett) 45 50
2466 90c. Sam Gamgee (Sean Austin) and Frodo Baggins (Elijah Wood) (horiz) 50 55
2467 $1.30 Guardian of Rivendell 75 80
2468 $1.50 Strider (Viggo Mortensen) 85 90
2469 $2 Boromir (Sean Bean) (horiz) . . . . 1·10 1·25

See also No. **MS**2490 and 2652/63.

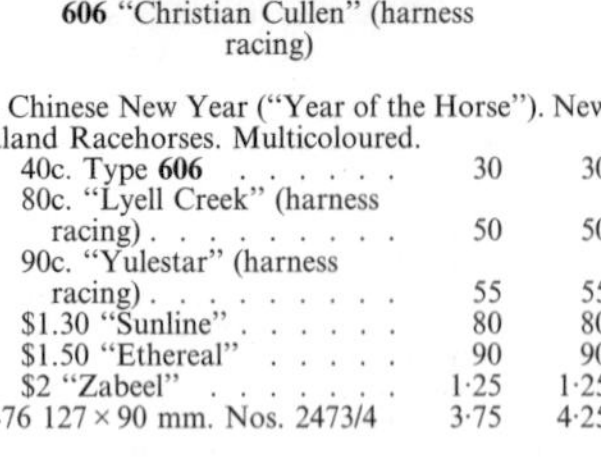

606 "Christian Cullen" (harness racing)

2002. Chinese New Year ("Year of the Horse"). New Zealand Racehorses. Multicoloured.

2470 40c. Type **606** 30 30
2471 80c. "Lyell Creek" (harness racing) 50 50
2472 90c. "Yulestar" (harness racing) 55 55
2473 $1.30 "Sunline" 80 80
2474 $1.50 "Ethereal" 90 90
2475 $2 "Zabeel" . . . . 1·25 1·25
MS2476 127 × 90 mm. Nos. 2473/4 3·75 4·25

607 *Hygrocybe rubrocarnosa*

608 War Memorial Museum, Auckland

2002. Fungi. Multicoloured.

2477 40c. Type **607** 45 30
2478 80c. *Entoloma hochstetteri* 75 50
2479 90c. *Aseroe rubra* 85 60
2480 $1.30 *Hericium coralloides* 1·10 1·10
2481 $1.50 *Thaxterogaster porphyreus* . . . . . . 1·25 1·40
2482 $2 *Ramaria aureorhiza* . . . 1·60 1·60
MS2483 114 × 104 mm. Nos. 2477/82 5·50 5·50

2002. Architectural Heritage. Multicoloured.

2484 40c. Type **608** 35 30
2485 80c. Stone Store, Kerikeri (25 × 30 mm) 60 50
2486 90c. Arts Centre, Christchurch (50 × 30 mm) 65 55
2487 $1.30 Government Buildings, Wellington (50 × 30 mm) 95 80
2488 $1.50 Dunedin Railway Station (25 × 30 mm) . . 1·10 90
2489 $2 Sky Tower, Auckland . . 1·25 1·25

2002. "Northpex 2002" Stamp Exhibition. Sheet 130 × 95 mm, containing Nos. 2458, 2461 and 2463. Multicoloured.

MS2490 40c. Gandalf (Sir Ian Mckellen) and Saruman (Christopher Lee); $1.30 Guardian of Rivendell; $2 Boromir (Sean Bean) (horiz) . . . . 3·50 3·50

No. **MS**2490 was sold at face value.

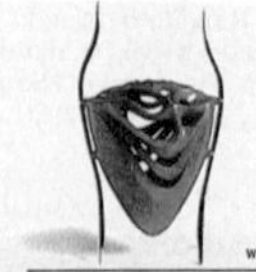

609 "Starfish Vessel" (wood sculpture) (Graeme Priddle)

2002. Artistic Crafts. Joint Issue with Sweden. Multicoloured.

2491 40c. Type **609** 35 30
2492 40c. Flax basket (Willa Rogers) (37 × 29 mm) . . 35 30
2493 80c. "Catch II" (clay bowl) (Raewyn Atkinson) . . . 55 50
2494 90c. "Vessel Form" (silver brooch) (Gavin Hitchings) 60 55
2495 $1.30 Glass towers from "Immigration" series (Emma Camden) 85 85
2496 $1.50 "Pacific Rim" (clay vessel) (Merilyn Wiseman) 95 1·10
2497 $2 Glass vase (Ola and Maria Höglund) (37 × 29 mm) . . . . . . 1·25 1·40

Nos. 2492 and 2497 are additionally inscribed "JOINT ISSUE WITH SWEDEN".

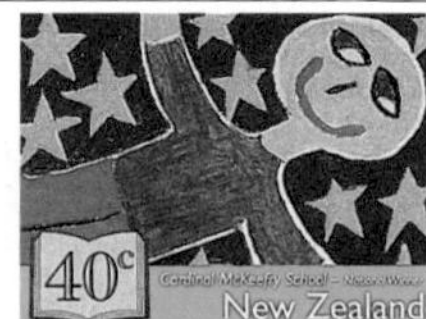

610 *Brodie* (Anna Poland, Cardinal McKeefry School) (National Winner)

2002. Children's Book Festival. Stamp Design Competition. Designs illustrating books. Multicoloured.

2498 40c. Type **610** 30 35
2499 40c. *The Last Whale* (Hee Su Kim, Glendowie Primary School) 30 35
2500 40c. *Scarface Claw* (Jayne Bruce, Rangiora Borough School) 30 35
2501 40c. *Which New Zealand Bird?* (Teigan Stafford-Bush, Ararimu School) . . 30 35
2502 40c. *Which New Zealand Bird?* (Hazel Gilbert, Gonville School) 30 35
2503 40c. *The Plight of the Penguin* (Gerard Mackle, Temuka High School) . . 30 35
2504 40c. *Scarface Claw* (Maria Rodgers, Salford School) 30 35
2505 40c. *Knocked for Six* (Paul Read, Ararimu School) 30 35
2506 40c. *Grandpa's Shorts* (Jessica Hitchings, Ashleigh Bree, Malyna Sengdara and Aniva Kini, Glendene Primary School) 30 35
2507 40c. *Which New Zealand Bird?* (Olivia Duncan, Takapuna Intermediate School) 30 35
MS2508 230 × 90 mm. Nos. 2498/507 2·75 3·25

611 Queen Elizabeth the Queen Mother, 1992

2002. Queen Elizabeth the Queen Mother Commemoration.

2509 **611** $2 multicoloured . . . . 1·60 1·60

612 Tongaporutu Cliffs, Taranaki

2002. Coastlines. Multicoloured. (a) Size 38 × 29 mm. Ordinary gum.

2510 40c. Type **612** 25 30
2511 80c. Lottin Point, East Cape 50 55
2512 90c. Curio Bay, Catlins . . 60 65
2513 $1.30 Kaikoura Coast . . . 85 90
2514 $1.50 Meybille Bay, West Coast . . . . 95 1·00
2515 $2 Papanui Point, Raglan 1·25 1·40

(b) Size 28 × 21 mm. Self-adhesive.

2516 40c. Type **612** 25 30
2517 90c. Curio Bay, Catlins . . 60 65
2518 $1.50 Meybille Bay, West Coast . . . . 95 1·00

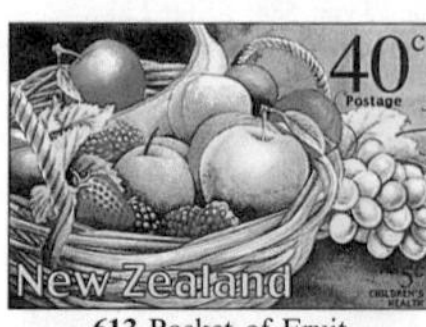

613 Basket of Fruit

2002. Children's Health. Healthy Eating. Multicoloured. (a) Ordinary gum.

2519 40c.+5c. Type **613** 50 55
2520 90c.+5c. Selection of vegetables 75 80
MS2521 90 × 75 mm. Nos. 2519/20 and as No. 2522 (22 × 26 mm) 1·75 2·00

(b) Self-adhesive.

2522 40c.+5c. Fruit and vegetables (22 × 26 mm) 30 35

2002. "Amphilex 2002" International Stamp Exhibition, Amsterdam. Sheet 130 × 95 mm, containing Nos. 2462/3. Multicoloured.

MS2523 $1.50 Strider (Viggo Mortensen); $2 Boromir (Sean Bean) (horiz) . . . . 1·25 1·40

No. **MS**2523 was sold at face value.

614 St. Werenfried, Tokaanu

2002. Christmas. Church Interiors. Multicoloured. (a) Size 35 × 35 mm. Ordinary gum.

2524 40c. Type **614** 25 30
2525 80c. St. David's, Christchurch 50 55
2526 90c. Orthodox Church of Transfiguration of Our Lord, Masterton 60 65
2527 $1.30 Cathedral of the Holy Spirit, Palmerston North 85 90
2528 $1.50 St. Paul's Cathedral, Wellington . . . . 95 1·00
2529 $2 Cathedral of the Blessed Sacrament, Christchurch 1·25 1·40

(b) Size 25 × 30 mm. Self-adhesive.

2530 40c. St. Werenfried, Tokaanu 25 30

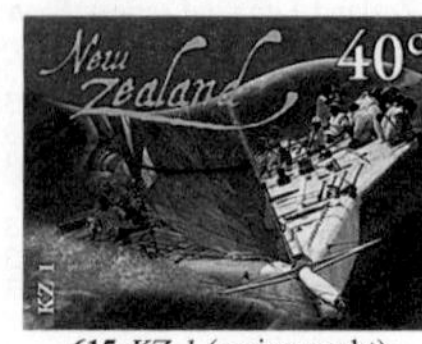

615 *KZ 1* (racing yacht)

2002. Racing and Leisure Craft. Multicoloured.

2531 40c. Type **615** 30 35
2532 80c. *High 5* (ocean racing yacht) 65 55
2533 90c. *Gentle Spirit* (sports fishing and diving boat) 75 70
2534 $1.30 *North Star* (luxury motor cruiser) . . . . . 1·00 1·00
2535 $1.50 *Ocean Runner* (powerboat) . . . . . . 1·25 1·40
2536 $2 *Salperton* (ocean-going yacht) . . . . 1·40 1·50
MS2537 140 × 80 mm. Nos. 2531/6 4·75 5·00

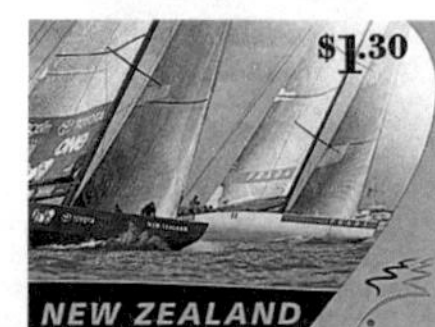

616 *Black Magic* (New Zealand) and *Luna Rossa* (Italy)

2002. America's Cup, 2003 (1st issue). Scenes from 2000 final, between New Zealand and Italy. Multicoloured.

2538 $1.30 Type **616** 85 90
2539 $1.50 Aerial view of race . . 95 1·00
2540 $2 Yachts turning . . . . . 1·25 1·40
MS2541 140 × 80 mm. Nos. 2538/40 4·50 4·75

See also Nos. 2562/5.

2002. "Stampshow 02" International Stamp Exhibition, Melbourne. No. **MS**2541 with "Stampshow 02" emblem and inscription on the margin. Multicoloured.

MS2542 140 × 80 mm. Nos. 2538/40 3·00 3·25

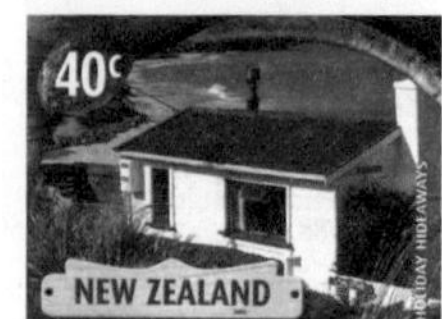

617 Green-roofed Holiday Cottage and Paua Shell

2002. Holiday Homes. Multicoloured.

2543 40c. Type **617** 30 35
2544 40c. Red-roofed cottage and sunflower 30 35
2545 40c. White-roofed cottage and life-belt 30 35
2546 40c. Cottage with orange door, boat and fishing fly 30 35
2547 40c. Blue-roofed cottage and fish 30 35
2548 40c. Cottage and caravan 30 35

618 "The Nativity" (15th-cent painting in style of Di Baldese)

2002. New Zealand–Vatican City Joint Issue.
2549 **618** $1.50 multicoloured . . 1·25 1·40

2002. Making of *The Lord of the Rings* Film Trilogy (2nd issue): The Two Towers. As T **605**. Multicoloured. (a) Designs 50 × 24 mm or 24 × 50 mm. Ordinary gum.
2550 40c. Aragorn (Viggo Mortenson) and Eowyn (Miranda Otto) (horiz) . . 25 30
2551 80c. Orc raider (horiz) . . . 50 55
2552 90c. Gandalf the White (Sir Ian McKellen) 60 65
2553 $1.30 Easterling warriors (horiz) 85 90
2554 $1.50 Frodo (Elijah Wood) 95 1·00
2555 $2 Eowyn, Shield Maiden of Rohan (Miranda Otto) (horiz) . . . . 1·25 1·40

(b) Designs 37 × 26 mm or 26 × 37 mm. Self-adhesive.
2556 40c. Strider (Viggo Mortenson) and Eowyn (Miranda Otto) (horiz) . . 25 30
2557 80c. Orc raider (horiz) . . . 50 55
2558 90c. Gandalf the White (Sir Ian McKellen) 60 65
2559 $1.30 Easterling warriors (horiz) 85 90
2560 $1.50 Frodo (Elijah Wood) 95 1·00
2561 $2 Eowyn, Shield Maiden of Rohan (Miranda Otto) (horiz) . . . . 1·25 1·40

2003. America's Cup (2nd issue). The Defence. As T **616**. Multicoloured.
2562 40c. Aerial view of Team New Zealand yacht . . . 25 30
2563 80c. Two Team New Zealand yachts 50 55
2564 90c. Team New Zealand yacht tacking 60 65
MS2565 140 × 80 mm. Nos. 2562/4 1·40 1·50

619 Shepherd with Flock in High Country

2003. Chinese New Year ("Year of the Sheep"). Sheep Farming. Multicoloured.
2566 40c. Type **619** 35 30
2567 90c. Mustering the sheep . . 65 55
2568 $1.30 Sheep in pen with sheep dog . . . . 1·10 1·10
2569 $1.50 Sheep shearing . . . 1·25 1·40
2570 $2 Sheep shearing (different) 1·50 1·60
MS2571 125 × 85 mm. Nos. 2568 and 2570 . . . . 2·50 2·75

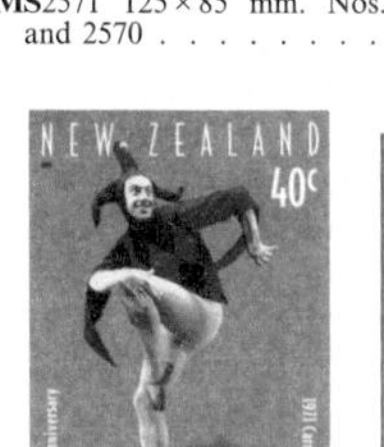

620 Jon Trimmer in *Carmina Burana*

621 Officer, Forest Rangers, 1860s

2003. 50th Anniv of Royal New Zealand Ballet. Scenes from past productions. Multicoloured.
2572 40c. Type **620** 35 30
2573 90c. *Papillon* (horiz) 75 65
2574 $1.30 *Cinderella* . . . . . . 1·10 1·10
2575 $1.50 *FrENZy* . . . . . . 1·25 1·40
2576 $2 *Swan Lake* (horiz) . . . 1·50 1·60

2003. New Zealand Military Uniforms. Multicoloured.
2577 40c. Type **621** 40 40
2578 40c. Lieutenant, Napier Naval Artillery Volunteers, 1890s 40 40
2579 40c. Officer, 2nd Regt, North Canterbury Mounted Rifles, 1900–10 40 40
2580 40c. Mounted Trooper, New Zealand Mounted Rifles, South Africa 1899–1902 40 40
2581 40c. Staff Officer, New Zealand Division, France, 1918 . . . . 40 40
2582 40c. Petty Officer, Royal New Zealand Navy, 1914–18 . . . . 40 40
2583 40c. Rifleman, New Zealand Rifle Brigade, France, 1916–18 . . . . 40 40
2584 40c. Sergeant, New Zealand Engineers, 1939–45 . . . 40 40
2585 40c. Matron, Royal New Zealand Navy Hospital, 1940s 40 40
2586 40c. Private, New Zealand Women's Auxiliary Army Corps, Egypt, 1942 . . . 40 40
2587 40c. Pilot serving with R.A.F. Bomber Command, Europe, 1943 40 40
2588 40c. Fighter Pilot, No. 1 (Islands) Group, Royal New Zealand Air Force, Pacific, 1943 . . . . . . 40 40
2589 40c. Driver, Women's Auxiliary Air Force, 1943 40 40
2590 40c. Gunner, 16th Field Regt, Royal New Zealand Artillery, Korea, 1950–53 40 40
2591 40c. Acting Petty Officer, H.M.N.Z.S. *Tamaki*, 1957 40 40
2592 40c. Scouts, New Zealand Special Air Service, Malaya, 1955–57 . . . . 40 40
2593 40c. Canberra Pilot serving with R.A.F. Far East Command, Malaya, 1960 40 40
2594 40c. Infantrymen, 1st Bn, Royal New Zealand Infantry Regt, South Vietnam, 1960s 40 40
2595 40c. Infantryman, New Zealand Bn, UNTAET, East Timor, 2000 . . . . 40 40
2596 40c. Monitor, Peace Monitoring Group, Bougainville, 2001 . . . . 40 40
Nos. 2577/96 were printed together, se-tenant, with detailed descriptions of the designs printed on the reverse.

622 Ailsa Mountains

2003. New Zealand Landscapes. Each including the fern symbol after the country inscr. Multicoloured.
2597 50c. Type **622** 30 35
2598 $1 Coromandel 65 70
2599 $1.50 Arrowtown . . . . . 95 1·00
2600 $2 Tongariro National Park 1·25 1·40
2601 $5 Castlepoint Lighthouse 3·25 3·50
No. 2599 also comes self-adhesive.

623 Sir Edmund Hillary and Mount Everest

2003. 50th Anniv of Conquest of Everest. Multicoloured.
2616 40c. Type **623** 30 35
2617 40c. Climbers reaching summit and Tenzing Norgay 30 35

624 Buckingham Palace

2003. 50th Anniv of Coronation. As Nos. 714/18 (Coronation issue of 1953) but face values in decimal currency as T **624**.
2618 **624** 40c. ultramarine 30 35
2619 – 90c. brown 65 70
2620 – $1.30 red . . . . 95 1·30
2621 – $1.50 blue . . . . 1·10 1·20
2622 – $2 violet and ultramarine 1·50 1·60
DESIGNS—VERT: (as T **164**)—90c. Queen Elizabeth II; $1.50, Westminster Abbey. HORIZ: (as T **624**)—$1.30, Coronation State Coach; $2 St. Edward's Crown and Royal Sceptre.

625 New Zealand vs. South Africa Match, 1937

2003. Centenary of New Zealand Test Rugby. Multicoloured.
2623 40c. Type **625** 40 35
2624 90c. New Zealand vs. Wales match, 1963 . . . . . . 65 70
2625 $1.30 New Zealand vs. Australia, 1985 . . . . . 95 1·00
2626 $1.50 New Zealand vs. France, 1986 . . . . . . 1·10 1·20
2627 $1.50 All Blacks jersey . . . 1·10 1·20
2628 $2 New Zealand vs. England, 1997 . . . . . 1·50 1·60
MS2629 100 × 180 mm. Nos. 2623/8 4·75 5·00

626 Papaaroha, Coromandel Peninsula

2003. New Zealand Waterways. Multicoloured.
2630 40c. Type **626** 30 35
2631 90c. Waimahana Creek, Chatham Islands 65 70
2632 $1.30 Blue Lake, Central Otago . . . . 95 1·00
2633 $1.50 Waikato River . . . . 1·10 1·20
2634 $2 Hooker River, Canterbury . . . . 1·50 1·60

627 Boy on Swing

2003. Children's Health. Playgrounds. Multicoloured. (a) Size 39 × 29 mm. Ordinary gum.
2635 40c.+5c. Type **627** 35 40
2636 90c.+5c. Girls playing hopscotch 70 75
MS2637 88 × 90 mm. Nos. 2635/6 and 40c.+5c. Girl on climbing frame . . . . 1·70 1·80

(b) Size 24 × 29 mm. Self-adhesive.
2638 40c.+5c. Girl on climbing frame 35 40

628 Benz Velo (1895)

2003. Veteran Vehicles. Multicoloured.
2639 40c. Type **628** 30 35
2640 90c. Oldsmobile (1903) . . . 65 70
2641 $1.30 Wolseley (1911) . . . 95 1·00
2642 $1.50 Talbot (1915) . . . . 1·10 1·20
2643 $2 Model T Ford (1915) . . 1·50 1·60

629 Christ Child in Crib

630 Hamadryas Baboon

2003. Christmas Decorations. Multicoloured. (a) Size 30 × 30 mm. Ordinary gum.
2644 40c. Type **629** 30 35
2645 90c. Silver and gold bird . . 65 70
2646 $1.30 Silver candle . . . . 95 1·00
2647 $1.50 Bells . . . . 1·10 1·20
2648 $2 Angel . . . . 1·50 1·60

(b) Size 21 × 26 mm. Self-adhesive.
2649 40c. Type **629** 30 35
2650 $1 Filigree metalwork decoration with baubles 75 80

2003. "Bangkok 2003" World Philatelic Exhibition. Sheet, 110 × 80 mm, containing Nos. 2572/3 and 2576.
MS2651 40c. Type **620**; 90c. *Papillon* (horiz); $2 *Swan Lake* (horiz) 1·70 1·80

2003. Making of The Lord of the Rings Film Trilogy (3rd issue): *The Return of the King*. As T **605**. Multicoloured. (a) Designs 24 × 49 mm or 49 × 50 mm. Ordinary gum.
2652 40c. Legolas 30 35
2653 80c. Frodo Baggins 60 65
2654 90c. Merry and Pippin (horiz) 65 70
2655 $1.30 Aragorn . . . . . . 95 1·00
2656 $1.50 Gandalf the White . . 1·10 1·20
2657 $2 Gollum (horiz) . . . . . 1·50 1·60

(b) Designs 24 × 35 mm or 35 × 24 mm. Self-adhesive.
2658 40c. Legolas 30 35
2659 80c. Frodo Baggins 60 65
2660 90c. Merry and Pippin (horiz) 65 70
2661 $1.30 Aragorn . . . . . . 95 1·00
2662 $1.50 Gandalf the White . . 1·10 1·20
2663 $2 Gollum (horiz) . . . . . 1·50 1·60

2003. "Welpex 2003" National Stamp Exhibition, Wellington. Sheet 120 × 100 mm, containing Nos. 2626/8.
MS2664 $1.50 New Zealand vs. France, 1986; $1.50 All Blacks jersey; $2 New Zealand vs. England, 1997 . . . . 3·75 4·00

2004. New Zealand Zoo Animals. Multicoloured. (a) Ordinary gum. Size 29 × 39 mm.
2665 40c. Type **630** 30 35
2666 90c. Malayan sun bear . . . 65 70
2667 $1.30 Red panda . . . . . 95 1·00
2668 $1.50 Ring-tailed lemur . . 1·10 1·20
2669 $2 Spider monkey . . . . . 1·50 1·60
MS2670 125 × 90 mm. Nos. 2668/9 1·60 1·90
No. **MS**2670 commemorates Chinese New Year, "Year of the Monkey".

(b) Self-adhesive. Size 24 × 29 mm.
2671 40c. Type **631** 30 35

2004. Hong Kong 2004 International Stamp Exhibition. Sheet, 110 × 80 mm, containing Nos. 2627/8.
MS2672 $1.50 All Blacks jersey; $2 New Zealand vs. England, 1997 2·50 2·75

631 New Zealand Team

2004. Rugby Sevens. Multicoloured.
2673 40c. Type **631** 30 35
2674 90c. Hong Kong team . . . 65 70
2675 $1.50 Hong Kong Stadium 1·10 1·20
2676 $2 Westpac Stadium, Wellington . . . . 1·50 1·60
MS2677 125 × 85 mm. Nos. 2673/6 3·50 3·75
Stamps of the same design were issued by Hong Kong.

632 Parliament Building, Auckland, 1854

2004. 150th Anniv of First Official Parliament in New Zealand.
2678 **632** 40c. purple and black . . 30 35
2679 – 90c. lilac and black . . . 65 70
2680 – $1.30 grey and black . . 95 1·00
2681 – $1.50 blue and black . . 1·10 1·20
2682 – $2 green and black . . . 1·50 1·60
MS2683 186 × 65 mm. Nos. 2678/82 4·50 4·75
DESIGNS: 90c. Parliament Buildings, Wellington, 1865; $1.30 Parliament Buildings, Wellington, 1899; $1.50 Parliament House, Wellington, 1918; $2 The Beehive, Wellington, 1977.

EXPRESS DELIVERY STAMPS

E 1

1903.
E1 **E 1** 6d. red and violet . . . . 38·00 23·00

E 2 Express Mail Delivery Van

1939.
E6 **E 2** 6d. violet . . . . 1·50 1·75

LIFE INSURANCE DEPARTMENT

1

3 Castlepoint Lighthouse

1891.
L13 **L 1** ½d. purple . . . . 55·00 3·75
L14 1d. blue . . . . 55·00 75
L15 2d. brown . . . . 75·00 3·50
L 4 3d. brown . . . . £170 22·00

L 5 6d. green . . . . £275 60·00
L 6 1s. pink £500 £120

1905. Similar type but "V.R." omitted.
L24 ½d. green . . . . 14·00 2·00
L22 1d. blue . . . . £160 30·00
L38 1d. red . . . . 3·25 2·00
L26 1½d. black . . . . 40·00 8·00
L27 1½d. brown . . . . 1·50 2·75
L21 2d. brown . . . . £1000 90·00
L28 2d. purple . . . . 48·00 28·00
L29 2d. yellow . . . . 5·50 2·00
L30 3d. brown . . . . 45·00 26·00
L35 3d. red . . . . 18·00 23·00
L41 6d. pink . . . . 13·00 35·00

1947. Lighthouses.
L42 L 3 ½d. green and orange . . . 1·50 70
L43 – 1d. olive and blue . . . . 1·75 1·25
L44 – 2d. blue and black . . . . 1·00 1·00
L45 – 2½d. black and blue . . . . 9·50 13·00
L46 – 3d. mauve and blue . . . . 3·25 1·00
L47 – 4d. brown and orange . . . 4·25 1·75
L48 – 6d. brown and blue . . . . 4·00 2·50
L49 – 1s. brown and blue . . . . 4·00 3·25
LIGHTHOUSES—HORIZ: 1d. Taiaroa; 2d. Cape Palliser; 6d. The Brothers. VERT: 2½d. Cape Campbell; 3d. Eddystone; 4d. Stephens Island; 1s. Cape Brett.

1967. Decimal currency. Stamps of 1947–65 surch.
L50a 1c. on 1d. (No. L43) . . . . 1·00 4·25
L51 2c. on 2½d. (No. L45) . . . . 9·50 14·00
L52 2½c. on 3d. (No. L46) . . . . 1·50 4·50
L53 3c. on 4d. (No. L47) . . . . 4·50 5·50
L54 5c. on 6d. (No. L48) . . . . 75 6·00
L55a 10c. on 1s. (No. L49) . . . . 75 4·00

13 Moeraki Point Lighthouse

1969.
L56 L 13 ½c. yellow, red and violet . . 65 1·75
L57 – 2½c. blue, green and buff . . 50 1·25
L58 – 3c. stone, yellow & brn . . 50 75
L59 – 4c. green, ochre and blue . . 50 1·00
L60 – 8c. multicoloured . . . . . 40 2·75
L61 – 10c. multicoloured . . . . 40 2·75
L62 – 15c. multicoloured . . . . 40 2·00
DESIGNS—HORIZ: 2½c. Puysegur Point Lighthouse; 4c. Cape Egmont Lighthouse. VERT: 3c. Baring Head Lighthouse; 8c. East Cape; 10c. Farewell Spit; 15c. Dog Island Lighthouse.

1978. No. L57 surch **25c.**
L63 25c. on 2½c. blue, green and buff 75 1·75

17

1981.
L64 L 17 5c. multicoloured 10 10
L65 10c. multicoloured 10 10
L66 20c. multicoloured 15 15
L67 30c. multicoloured 25 25
L68 40c. multicoloured 30 30
L69 50c. multicoloured 30 35

OFFICIAL STAMPS

1891. Optd **O.P.S.O.**
O 1 3 ½d. pink . . . . — £500
O 2 13 ½d. black . . . . — £225
O13 23 ½d. green . . . . — £225
O 4 10 1d. pink . . . . — £225
O19 42 1d. red . . . . — £250
O 6 9 2d. mauve . . . . — £375
O 8 16 2½d. blue . . . . — £275
O14 26 2½d. blue (A) . . . . . . — £450
O21 2½d. blue (B) . . . . . . — £325
O22 28 3d. brown . . . . — £450
O16 24 4d. blue and brown . . . — £425
O11 19 5d. black . . . . — £425
O17a 30 5d. brown . . . . — £425
O12 8 6d. brown (No. 224b) . . . — £600
O18 32 8d. blue . . . . — £550
O23 34 1s. red . . . . — £900
O24 35 2s. green . . . . — £1400

Optd **OFFICIAL.**

1907. Pictorials.
O59 23 ½d. green . . . . 9·00 60
O61a 25 2d. purple . . . . 8·50 1·60
O63 28 3d. brown . . . . 45·00 1·75
O64 31 6d. red . . . . £140 20·00
O65 34 1s. orange . . . . 85·00 15·00
O66 35 2s. green . . . . 70·00 75·00
O67 – 5s. red (No. 329) £150 £170

1907. "Universal" type.
O60b 42 1d. red . . . . 10·00 50

1908.
O70 50 1d. red . . . . 65·00 2·75
O72 31 6d. red (No. 254) . . . . . £130 35·00

1910. King Edward VII etc.
O73 51 ½d. green . . . . 5·00 30
O78 53 1d. red . . . . 3·25 10
O74 51 3d. brown . . . . 14·00 80
O75 6d. red . . . . 19·00 5·50
O76 8d. blue . . . . 12·00 18·00
O77 1s. orange . . . . 48·00 15·00

1913. Queen Victoria.
O82 F 4 2s. blue . . . . 48·00 45·00
O83 5s. green . . . . 75·00 90·00
O84 £1 red £550 £550

1915. King George V.
O 96 62 ½d. green . . . . 1·50 10
O 90 1½d. grey . . . . 5·00 90
O 91 1½d. brown . . . . 5·00 30
O 98 2d. yellow . . . . 2·50 50
O 99 3d. brown . . . . 5·00 50
O101 4d. violet . . . . 14·00 3·75
O102 6d. red . . . . 5·00 75
O103 8d. brown . . . . 65·00 £150
O104 9d. green . . . . 40·00 38·00
O105b 1s. orange . . . . 7·00 2·00

1927. King George V.
O111 71 1d. red . . . . 2·00 20
O112 2s. blue . . . . 70·00 £100

1933. "Arms".
O113 F 6 5s. green £250 £300

Optd **Official.**

1936. "Arms".
O133 F 6 5s. green . . . . 40·00 6·00

1936. As 1935.
O120 81 ½d. green . . . . 7·50 4·50
O115 – 1d. red (No. 557) . . . . . 3·75 1·25
O122 83 1½d. brown . . . . 21·00 4·75
O123 – 2d. orange (No. 580) . . . 3·75 10
O124a 85 2½d. brown and grey . . . 14·00 21·00
O125 86 3d. brown . . . . 48·00 3·50
O126c 87 4d. black and brown . . . 4·50 1·00
O127c 89 6d. red . . . . 10·00 30
O128a – 8d. brown (No. 586b) . . . 8·50 16·00
O130 91 9d. red and black . . . . 20·00 22·00
O131b – 1s. green (No. 588) . . . . 24·00 1·50
O132d 93 2s. olive . . . . 42·00 7·50

1938. King George VI.
O134 108 ½d. green . . . . 19·00 2·25
O135 ½d. orange . . . . 1·60 3·50
O136 1d. red . . . . 19·00 15
O137 1d. green . . . . 3·00 10
O138 1½d. brown . . . . 75·00 18·00
O139 1½d. red . . . . 9·00 6·00
O152 2d. orange . . . . 2·25 10
O140 3d. blue . . . . 3·00 10
O153 4d. purple . . . . 4·25 2·50
O154 6d. red . . . . 13·00 50
O155 8d. violet . . . . 8·00 6·50
O156 9d. brown . . . . 9·00 6·50
O157a – 1s. brown and red (No. 686b) . . . . 8·50 9·00
O158 – 2s. orange and green (No. 688) . . . . 27·00 16·00

1940. Centenary stamps.
O141 ½d. green . . . . 2·50 35
O142 1d. brown and red . . . . . 5·00 10
O143 1½d. blue and mauve . . . . 3·50 2·00
O144 2d. green and brown . . . . 5·00 10
O145 2½d. green and blue . . . . 4·75 2·75
O146 3d. purple and red . . . . . 8·00 1·00
O147 4d. brown and red . . . . . 40·00 1·50
O148 6d. green and violet . . . . 25·00 1·50
O149 8d. black and red . . . . . 30·00 17·00
O150 9d. olive and red . . . . . 11·00 5·00
O151 1s. green . . . . 48·00 3·00

O 6 Queen Elizabeth II

1954.
O159 O 6 1d. orange 75 40
O160 1½d. brown . . . . 3·75 5·00
O161 2d. green 50 40
O162 2½d. olive . . . . 3·50 1·50
O163 3d. red 70 10
O164 4d. blue . . . . 1·25 65
O165 9d. red . . . . 7·00 2·25
O166 1s. purple . . . . 1·00 10
O167 3s. slate . . . . 30·00 48·00

1959. Surch.
O169 O 6 2½d. on 2d. green . . . . 1·00 1·50
O168 6d. on 1½d. brown . . . . 50 1·10

POSTAGE DUE STAMPS

D 1 D 2

1899.
D 9 D 1 ½d. red and green . . . . . 3·00 16·00
D10 1d. red and green . . . . 12·00 2·00
D15 2d. red and green . . . . 45·00 6·00
D12 3d. red and green . . . . 13·00 3·50
D16 4d. red and green . . . . 32·00 9·00
D 6 5d. red and green . . . . 22·00 24·00
D 7 6d. red and green . . . . 29·00 28·00
D 2 8d. red and green . . . . 60·00 75·00
D 8 10d. red and green . . . 70·00 85·00
D 3 1s. red and green . . . . 65·00 85·00
D 4 2s. red and green £120 £140

1902.
D18 D 2 ½d. red and green . . . . 1·75 2·00
D30 1d. red and green . . . . 3·75 80
D22a 2d. red and green . . . . 5·50 2·00
D36 3d. red and green . . . . 15·00 42·00

D 3

1939.
D41 D 3 ½d. green . . . . 5·00 5·00
D42 1d. red . . . . 2·75 50
D46 2d. blue . . . . 8·00 1·40
D47aw 3d. brown . . . . 9·00 9·00

NICARAGUA Pt. 15

A republic of Central America, independent since 1821.

1862. 100 centavos = 1 peso (paper currency).
1912. 100 centavos de cordoba = 1 peso de cordoba (gold currency).
1925. 100 centavos = 1 cordoba.

2 Volcanoes 5

1862. Perf or roul.
13 2 1c. brown . . . . 1·50 75
4 2c. blue . . . . 2·25 75
14 5c. black . . . . 6·00 1·25
18 10c. red . . . . 2·25 1·40
19 25c. green . . . . 2·25 2·40

1882.
20 5 1c. green 15 20
21 2c. red 15 20
22 5c. blue 15 15
23 10c. violet 15 60
24 15c. yellow . . . . 30 1·50
25 20c. grey . . . . 50 3·00
26 50c. violet . . . . 70 6·00

6 Steam Locomotive and Telegraph Key 7

1890.
27 6 1c. brown 25 30
28 2c. red 25 30
29 5c. blue 25 20
30 10c. grey 25 25
31 20c. red . . . . 25 1·75
32 50c. violet . . . . 25 5·50
33 1p. brown . . . . 40 7·75
34 2p. green . . . . 40 10·00
35 5p. red . . . . 50 19·00
36 10p. orange . . . . 50 27·00

1891.
37 7 1c. brown 15 30
38 2c. red 15 30
39 5c. blue 15 25
40 10c. grey 15 35
41 20c. lake . . . . 15 1·75
42 50c. violet . . . . 15 3·00
43 1p. sepia . . . . 15 4·50
44 2p. green . . . . 15 5·00
45 5p. red . . . . 15 12·00
46 10p. orange . . . . 15 15·00

8 First Sight of the New World

1892. Discovery of America.
47 8 1c. brown 15 25
48 2c. red 15 25
49 5c. blue 15 20
50 10c. grey 15 25
51 20c. red . . . . 15 1·75
52 50c. violet . . . . 15 4·25
53 1p. brown . . . . 15 4·25
54 2p. green . . . . 15 5·00
55 5p. red . . . . 15 14·00
56 10p. orange . . . . 15 18·00

9 Volcanoes 10

1893.
57 9 1c. brown 15 25
58 2c. red 15 25
59 5c. blue 15 20
60 10c. grey 15 25
61 20c. brown . . . . 15 1·40
62 50c. violet . . . . 15 3·50
63 1p. brown . . . . 15 4·25
64 2p. green . . . . 15 5·00
65 5p. red . . . . 15 11·00
66 10p. orange . . . . 15 14·00

1894.
67 10 1c. brown 15 25
68 2c. red 15 25
69 5c. blue 15 20
70 10c. grey 15 25
71 20c. red . . . . 15 1·50
72 50c. violet . . . . 15 3·50
73 1p. brown . . . . 15 4·25
74 2p. green . . . . 15 7·50
75 5p. brown . . . . 15 9·00
76 10p. orange . . . . 15 12·00

11 12 Map of Nicaragua 13 Arms of Republic of Central America

1895.
77 11 1c. brown 15 20
78 2c. red 15 20
79 5c. blue 15 15
80 10c. grey 15 20
81 20c. red 15 70
82 50c. violet . . . . 15 3·00
83 1p. brown . . . . 15 4·50
84 2p. green . . . . 15 4·75
85 5p. red . . . . 15 9·25
86 10p. orange . . . . 15 14·50

1896. Date "1896".
90 12 1c. violet 15 75
91 2c. green 15 50
92 5c. red 15 35
93 10c. blue 30 65
94 20c. brown . . . . 1·75 3·50
95 50c. grey . . . . 35 4·75
96 1p. black . . . . 35 6·50
97 2p. red . . . . 35 9·00
98 5p. blue . . . . 35 9·00

1897. As T **12**, dated "1897".
99 12 1c. violet 25 35
100 2c. green 25 35
101 5c. red 25 20
102 10c. blue . . . . 3·75 65
103 20c. brown . . . . 1·50 2·75
104 50c. grey . . . . 5·25 5·75
105 1p. black . . . . 5·25 8·75
106 2p. red . . . . 11·50 11·00
107 5p. blue . . . . 11·50 25·00

1898.
108 13 1c. brown 20 20
109 2c. grey 20 20
110 4c. lake 20 30
122 5c. olive . . . . 15·00 15
112 10c. purple . . . . 8·75 40
113 15c. blue . . . . 25 1·00
114 20c. blue . . . . 6·00 1·00
115 50c. yellow . . . . 6·00 5·75
116 1p. blue . . . . 30 9·50
117 2p. brown . . . . 11·00 13·00
118 5p. orange . . . . 15·00 19·00

14 — 15 Mt. Momotombo

1899.

126	**14**	1c. green	10	25
127		2c. brown	10	25
128		4c. red	20	25
129		5c. blue	15	25
130		10c. orange	15	25
131		15c. brown	15	40
132		20c. green	20	70
133		50c. red	15	1·75
134		1p. orange	15	5·00
135		2p. violet	15	12·00
136		5p. blue	15	14·50

1900.

137	**15**	1c. red	35	10
138		2c. orange	65	15
139		3c. green	75	20
140		4c. olive	95	25
184		5c. red	1·50	45
185		5c. blue	1·50	45
142		6c. red	19·00	5·50
186		10c. mauve	1·50	45
144		15c. blue	10·00	35
145		20c. brown	9·00	30
146		50c. lake	9·00	1·60
147		1p. yellow	20·00	6·75
148		2p. red	8·00	75
149		5p. black	14·00	2·50

1901. Surch **1901** and value.

151	**15**	2c. on 1p. yellow	11·00	8·50
169		3c. on 6c. red	8·00	5·00
163		4c. on 6c. red	7·00	4·00
173		5c. on 1p. yellow	11·50	5·75
168		10c. on 2p. red	8·00	1·75
152		10c. on 5p. black	14·00	11·00
153		20c. on 2p. red	22·00	20·00
176		20c. on 5p. black	6·00	3·75

1901. Postage Due stamps of 1900 optd **1901 Correos**.

177	D **16**	1c. red	60	30
178		2c. orange	45	30
179		5c. blue	55	45
180		10c. violet	55	45
181		20c. brown	75	1·00
182		30c. green	70	1·00
183		50c. lake	70	1·00

1902. Surch **1902** and value.

187	**15**	15c. on 2c. orange	4·00	1·50
188		30c. on 1c. red	1·50	4·25

27 Pres. Santos Zelaya — 37 Arms

1903. 10th Anniv of Revolution against Sacaza and 1st election of Pres. Zelaya.

189	**27**	1c. black and green	25	45
190		2c. black and red	50	45
191		5c. black and blue	25	45
192		10c. black and orange	25	70
193		15c. black and lake	45	1·40
194		20c. black and violet	45	1·40
195		50c. black and olive	45	3·00
196		1p. black and brown	45	3·50

1904. Surch **15 Centavos**.

200	**15**	15c. on 10c. mauve	5·75	3·00

1904. Surch **Vale**, value and wavy lines.

203	**15**	5c. on 10c. mauve	1·90	50
204		15c. on 10c. mauve	60	40

1905. No. 186 surch **5 CENTS**.

205	**15**	5c. on 10c. mauve	75	50

1905.

206	**37**	1c. green	20	15
207		2c. red	20	15
208		3c. violet	25	20
280		3c. orange	25	15
209		4c. orange	25	20
281		4c. violet	25	15
282		5c. blue	25	15
211		6c. grey	45	30
283		6c. brown	1·75	1·10
212		10c. brown	55	20
284		10c. lake	60	10
213		15c. olive	55	25
285		15c. black	60	10
214		20c. lake	45	25
286		20c. olive	60	10
215		50c. orange	1·75	1·40
287		50c. green	70	35
216		1p. black	90	90
288		1p. yellow	70	35
217		2p. green	90	1·25
289		2p. red	70	35
218		5p. violet	1·00	1·50

1906. Surch **Vale** (or **VALE**) and value in one line.

292	**37**	2c. on 3c. orange	90	75
293		5c. on 20c. olive	30	25
247		10c. on 2c. red	1·10	45
223		10c. on 3c. violet	30	15
248		10c. on 4c. orange	1·25	55
291		10c. on 15c. black	30	25
250		10c. on 20c. lake	1·90	85
252		10c. on 50c. orange	1·40	45
234		10c. on 2p. green	12·00	7·00
235		10c. on 5p. violet	60·00	42·00
226		15c. on 1c. green	30	20
229		20c. on 2c. red	40	25
230		20c. on 5c. blue	45	35
236		35c. on 6c. grey	1·60	1·60
232		50c. on 6c. grey	45	35
238		1p. on 5p. violet	25·00	14·50

51 — 50 — 64

1908. Fiscal stamps as T **51** optd **CORREO–1908** or surch **VALE** and value also.

260	**51**	1c. on 5c. yellow	35	20
261		2c. on 5c. yellow	35	25
262		4c. on 5c. yellow	65	30
256		5c. yellow	45	35
257		10c. blue	35	20
263		15c. on 50c. green	45	30
264		35c. on 50c. green	2·50	65
258		1p. brown	20	1·40
259		2p. grey	20	1·50

1908. Fiscal stamps as T **50** optd **CORREOS–1908** or surch **VALE** and value also.

268	**50**	2c. orange	2·10	1·00
269		4c. on 2c. orange	1·00	65
270		5c. on 2c. orange	1·10	45
271		10c. on 2c. orange	1·10	25

1909. Surch **CORREOS–1909 VALE** and value.

273	**51**	1c. on 50c. green	2·25	95
274		2c. on 50c. green	4·00	1·75
275		4c. on 50c. green	4·00	1·75
276		5c. on 50c. green	2·25	1·10
277		10c. on 50c. green	65	40

1910. Surch **Vale** and value in two lines.

296	**37**	2c. on 3c. orange	65	35
300		2c. on 4c. violet	25	15
301		5c. on 20c. olive	25	15
302		10c. on 15c. black	30	15
303		10c. on 50c. green	20	15
299		10c. on 1p. yellow	65	35
305		10c. on 2p. red	45	35

1911. Surch **Correos 1911** (or **CORREOS 1911**) and value.

307	**51**	2c. on 5p. blue	25	30
312		5c. on 2p. grey	90	70
308		5c. on 10p. pink	55	30
309		10c. on 25c. lilac	30	20
310		10c. on 2p. grey	30	20
311		35c. on 1p. brown	30	25

1911. Surch **VALE POSTAL de 1911** and value.

313	**51**	5c. on 25c. lilac	90	70
314		5c. on 50c. green	3·00	3·00
315		5c. on 5p. blue	4·00	4·00
317		5c. on 50p. red	3·00	3·00
318		10c. on 50c. green	70	45

1911. Railway tickets as T **64**, with fiscal surch on the front, further surch for postal use. (a) Surch **vale CORREO DE 1911** and value on back.

319	**64**	2c. on 5c. on 2nd class blue	55	65
320		05c. on 5c. on 2nd class blue	30	40
321		10c. on 5c. on 2nd class blue	30	40
322		15c. on 10c. on 1st class red	40	50

(b) Surch **vale CORREO DE 1911** and value on front.

322c	**64**	2c. on 5c. on 2nd class blue	8·00	8·00
322d		05c. on 5c. on 2nd class blue	£170	£170
322e		10c. on 5c. on 2nd class blue	80·00	80·00
322f		15c. on 10c. on 1st class red	22·00	22·00

(c) Surch **CORREO** and value on front.

323	**64**	2c. on 10c. on 1st class red	80	80
324		20c. on 10c. on 1st class red	4·00	4·00
325		50c. on 10c. on 1st class red	7·50	7·50

(d) Surch **Correo Vale 1911** and value on front.

326	**64**	2c. on 10c. on 1st class red	15	15
328		5c. on 5c. on 2nd class blue	90	80
327		5c. on 10c. on 1st class red	20	1·25
330		10c. on 10c. on 1st class red	70	50

(e) Surch **Vale CORREO DE 1911** and value on back.

331	**64**	5c. on 10c. on 1st class red	18·00	
332		10c. on 10c. on 1st class red	7·00	

(f) Surch **CORREO Vale 10 cts. 1911** and bar obliterating **oficial** on front.

333	**64**	10c. on 10c. on 1st class red	1·25	1·00

70 — 71

1912.

337	**70**	1c. green	25	15
338		2c. red	25	15
339		3c. brown	25	15
340		4c. purple	25	15
341		5c. black and blue	25	15
342		6c. brown	25	70
343		10c. brown	25	15
344		15c. violet	25	15
345		20c. brown	25	15
346		25c. black and green	25	15
347	**71**	35c. brown and green	1·10	1·10
348	**70**	50c. blue	65	30
349		1p. orange	90	1·40
350		2p. green	90	1·75
351		5p. black	1·60	2·10

1913. Surch **Vale 15 cts Correos 1913**.

352	**71**	15c. on 35c. brown & green	30	20

1913. Surch **VALE 1913** and value in "centavos de cordoba". A. On stamps of 1912 issue.

353	**70**	½c. on 3c. brown	35	25
354		½c. on 15c. violet	20	15
355		½c. on 1p. orange	20	15
356		1c. on 3c. brown	55	45
357		1c. on 4c. purple	20	15
358		1c. on 50c. blue	20	15
359		1c. on 5p. black	20	15
360		2c. on 4c. purple	25	20
361		2c. on 20c. brown	2·25	2·75
362		2c. on 25c. black & green	25	15
363	**71**	2c. on 35c. brown & green	20	35
364	**70**	2c. on 50c. blue	20	90
365		2c. on 2p. green	15	15
366		3c. on 6c. brown	15	10

B. On Silver Currency stamps of 1912 (Locomotive type).

367	Z **1**	½c. on 2c. red	3·25	2·50
368		1c. on 3c. brown	2·10	1·60
369		1c. on 4c. red	2·10	1·60
370		1c. on 6c. red	2·10	1·60
371		1c. on 20c. blue	2·10	1·60
372		1c. on 25c. black & green	2·10	1·60
384		2c. on 1c. green	25·00	19·00
373		2c. on 25c. black & green	11·25	8·50
374		5c. on 35c. black & green	2·10	1·60
375		5c. on 50c. olive	2·10	1·60
376		6c. on 1p. orange	2·10	1·60
377		10c. on 2p. brown	2·10	1·60
378		1p. on 5p. green	2·10	1·60

1914. No. 352 surch with new value and **Cordoba** and thick bar over old surch.

385	**71**	½c. on 15c. on 35c.	15	10
386		1c. on 15c. on 35c.	20	15

1914. Official stamps of 1913 surch with new value and thick bar through "OFICIAL".

387	**70**	1c. on 25c. blue	30	20
388	**71**	1c. on 35c. blue	30	20
389	**70**	1c. on 1p. blue	20	15
391		2c. on 50c. blue	30	15
392		2c. on 2p. blue	20	15
393		5c. on 5p. blue	20	15

79 National Palace, Managua — 80 Leon Cathedral

1914. Various frames.

394	**79**	½c. blue	50	15
395		1c. green	50	15
396	**80**	2c. orange	50	15
397	**79**	3c. brown	80	25
398	**80**	4c. red	80	25
399	**79**	5c. grey	30	10
400	**80**	6c. sepia	5·25	3·25
401		10c. yellow	55	15
402	**79**	15c. violet	3·50	1·40
403	**80**	20c. grey	6·50	3·25
404	**79**	25c. orange	85	20
405	**80**	50c. blue	85	25

See also Nos. 465/72, 617/27 and 912/24.

1915. Surch **VALE 5 cts. de Cordoba 1915**.

406	**80**	5c. on 6c. sepia	1·10	35

1918. Stamps of 1914 surch **Vale centavos de cordoba**.

407	**80**	½c. on 6c. sepia	2·00	75
408		½c. on 10c. yellow	1·40	25
409	**79**	½c. on 15c. violet	1·40	45
410		½c. on 25c. orange	3·00	85
411	**80**	½c. on 50c. blue	1·40	25
440		1c. on 2c. orange	90	20
413	**79**	1c. on 3c. brown	1·50	25
414	**80**	1c. on 6c. sepia	7·00	2·10
415		1c. on 10c. yellow	13·00	4·75
416	**79**	1c. on 15c. violet	2·40	55
418	**80**	1c. on 20c. grey	1·40	25
420	**79**	1c. on 25c. orange	2·40	70
421	**80**	1c. on 50c. blue	7·75	2·25
422		2c. on 4c. red	1·75	25
423		2c. on 6c. sepia	13·00	4·75
424		2c. on 10c. yellow	13·00	2·50
425		2c. on 20c. grey	7·00	2·10
426	**79**	2c. on 25c. orange	3·00	30
427	**80**	5c. on 6c. sepia	5·00	2·50
428	**79**	5c. on 15c. violet	1·75	45

1919. Official stamps of 1915 surch **Vale centavo de cordoba** and with bar through "OFICIAL".

444	**80**	½c. on 2c. blue	30	15
445		½c. on 4c. blue	70	15
446	**79**	1c. on 3c. blue	70	25
432		1c. on 25c. blue	1·10	20
433	**80**	2c. on 50c. blue	1·10	20
443a		10c. on 20c. blue	1·00	40

1921. Official stamps of 1913 optd **Particular** and wavy lines through "OFICIAL".

441	**70**	1c. blue	90	45
442		5c. blue	90	35

1921. No. 399 surch **Vale medio centavo**.

447	**79**	½c. on 5c. black	35	15

1921. Official stamp of 1915 optd **Particular R de C** and bars.

448	**79**	1c. blue	3·50	1·00

1921. Official stamps of 1915 surch **Vale un centavo R de C** and bars.

449	**79**	1c. on 5c. blue	95	35
450	**80**	1c. on 6c. blue	50	20
451		1c. on 10c. blue	65	20
452	**79**	1c. on 15c. blue	1·10	20

90 — 91 Jose C. del Valle

1921. Fiscal stamps as T **23** surch **R de C Vale** and new value.

453	**90**	1c. on 1c. red and black	10	10
454		1c. on 2c. green and black	10	10
455		1c. on 4c. orange and black	10	10
456		1c. on 15c. blue and black	10	10

No. 456 is inscr "TIMBRE TELEGRAFICO".

1921. Independence Centenary.

457	–	½c. black and blue	30	25
458	**91**	1c. black and green	30	25
459	–	2c. black and red	30	25
460	–	5c. black and violet	30	25
461	–	10c. black and orange	20	25
462	–	25c. black and yellow	30	25
463	–	50c. black and violet	30	25

DESIGNS: ½c. Arce; 2c. Larreinaga; 5c. F. Chamorro; 10c. Jerez; 25c. J. P. Chamorro; 50c. Dario.

1922. Surch **Vale un centavo R. de C.**

464	**80**	1c. on 10c. yellow	10	10

1922. As Nos. 394, etc, but colours changed.

465	**79**	½c. green	15	10
466		1c. violet	15	10
467	**80**	2c. red	15	10
468	**79**	3c. olive	25	15
469	**80**	6c. brown	15	15
470	**79**	15c. brown	25	15
471	**80**	20c. brown	35	15
472		1cor. brown	65	35

Nos. 465/72 are size 27 × 22¾ mm.

For later issues of these types, see Nos. 617/27 and 912/24.

1922. Optd **R. de C.**

473	**79**	1c. violet	10	10

1922. Independence issue of 1921 surch **R. de C. Vale un centavo**.

474	**91**	1c. on 1c. black and green	55	45
475	–	1c. on 5c. black and violet	55	55
476	–	1c. on 10c. black and orange	55	30
477	–	1c. on 25c. black and yellow	55	25
478	–	1c. on 50c. black and violet	25	20

94 — 99 F. Hernandez de Cordoba

1922. Surch **Nicaragua R. de C. Vale un cent.**
479 **94** 1c. yellow 10 10
480 1c. mauve 10 10
481 1c. blue 10 10

1922. Surch **Vale 0.01 de Cordoba** in two lines.
482 **80** 1c. on 10c. yellow 70 25
483 2c. on 10c. yellow 70 20

1923. Surch **Vale 2 centavos de cordoba** in three lines.
484 **79** 1c. on 5c. black 70 15
485 **80** 2c. on 10c. yellow 70 15

1923. Optd **Sello Postal.**
486 – ½c. black and blue (No. 457) . . . . 5·50 4·25
487 **91** 1c. black and green . . . . 1·40 70

1923. Independence issue of 1921 surch **R. de C. Vale un centavo de cordoba.**
488 1c. on 2c. black and red . . 30 30
489 1c. on 5c. black and violet . . 35 15
490 1c. on 10c. black and orange 15 15
491 1c. on 25c. black and yellow 25 25
492 1c. on 50c. black and violet 15 10

1923. Fiscal stamp optd **R. de C.**
493 **90** 1c. red and black 15 10

1924. Optd **R. de C. 1924** in two lines.
494 **79** 1c. violet 15 15

1924. 400th Anniv of Foundation of Leon and Granada.
495 **99** 1c. green 90 25
496 2c. red 90 25
497 5c. blue 65 25
498 10c. brown 65 45

1925. Optd **R. de C. 1925** in two lines.
499 **79** 1c. violet 15 10

1927. Optd **Resello 1927.**
525 **79** ½c. green 10 10
528 1c. violet (No. 466) 10 10
555 1c. violet (No. 473) 15 10
532 **80** 2c. red 15 10
533 **79** 3c. green 20 10
537 **80** 4c. red . . . . 9·50 8·00
539 **79** 5c. grey 55 20
542 **80** 6c. brown . . . . 7·75 6·50
543 10c. yellow 25 15
545 **79** 15c. brown 55 25
547 **80** 20c. brown 25 15
549 **79** 25c. orange 30 15
551 **80** 50c. blue 30 15
553 1cor. brown 35 15

1928. Optd **Resello 1928.**
559 **79** ½c. green 20 15
560 1c. violet 10 10
561 **80** 2c. red 15 10
562 **79** 3c. green 15 10
563 **80** 4c. red 15 10
564 **79** 5c. grey 15 10
565 **80** 6c. brown 15 10
566 10c. yellow 20 10
567 **79** 15c. brown 25 20
568 **80** 20c. brown 35 20
569 **79** 25c. orange 55 20
570 **80** 50c. blue 90 10
571 1cor. brown 75 25

1928. Optd **Correos 1928.**
574 **79** ½c. green 15 10
575 1c. violet 10 10
576 3c. olive 55 20
577 **80** 4c. red 25 10
578 **79** 5c. grey 20 10
579 **80** 6c. brown 30 15
580 10c. yellow 35 15
581 **79** 15c. brown . . . . 1·00 15
582 **80** 20c. brown . . . . 1·00 15
583 **79** 25c. orange . . . . 1·00 20
584 **80** 50c. blue . . . . 1·00 20
585 1cor. brown . . . . 3·00 1·50

1928. No. 577 surch **Vale 2 cts.**
586 **80** 2c. on 4c. red 90 25

1928. Fiscal stamp as T **90**, but inscr "TIMBRE TELEGRAFICO" and surch **Correos 1928 Vale** and new value.
587 **90** 1c. on 5c. blue and black 25 15
588 2c. on 5c. blue and black 25 15
589 3c. on 5c. blue and black 25 15

1928. Obligatory Tax. No. 587 additionally optd **R. de T.**
590 **90** 1c. on 5c. blue and black 45 10

1928. As Nos. 465/72 but colours changed.
591 **79** ½c. red 30 15
592 1c. orange 30 15
593 **80** 2c. green 30 15
594 **79** 3c. purple 30 20
595 **80** 4c. brown 30 20
596 **79** 5c. yellow 30 15
597 **80** 6c. blue 30 20
598 10c. blue 65 20
599 **79** 15c. red 85 35
600 **80** 20c. green 85 35
601 **79** 25c. purple . . . . 16·00 3·75
602 **80** 50c. brown . . . . 1·90 70
603 1cor. violet . . . . 3·75 1·75
See also Nos. 617/27 and 912/24.

106

1928.
604 **106** 1c. purple 20 10
647 1c. red 25 10
For 1c. green see No. 925.

1929. Optd **R. de C.**
605 **79** 1c. orange 10 10
628 1c. olive 15 10

1929. Optd **Correos 1929.**
606 **79** ½c. green 20 15

1929. Optd **Correos 1928.**
607 **99** 10c. brown 55 45

1929. Fiscal stamps as T **90**, but inscr "TIMBRE TELEGRAFICO". A. Surch **Correos 1929 R. de C. C$ 0.01** vert.
613 **90** 1c. on 5c. blue and black 10 15

B. Surch **Correos 1929** and value.
611 **90** 1c. on 10c. green and black 20 15
612 2c. on 5c. blue and black 20 10

C. Surch **Correos 1929** and value vert and **R. de C.** or **R. de T.** horiz.
608 **90** 1c. on 5c. blue and black (R. de T.) 20 15
609 2c. on 5c. blue and black (R. de T.) 15 15
610 2c. on 5c. blue and black (R. de C.) . . . . 13·00 70

1929. Air. Optd **Correo Aereo 1929. P.A.A.**
614 **79** 25c. sepia . . . . 1·40 1·40
615 25c. orange . . . . 1·00 1·00
616 25c. violet 90 70

1929. As Nos. 591/603 but colours changed.
617 **79** 1c. green 10 10
618 3c. blue 25 15
619 **80** 4c. blue 25 15
620 **79** 5c. brown 30 15
621 **80** 6c. drab 30 15
622 10c. brown 45 15
623 **79** 15c. red 65 20
624 **80** 20c. orange 80 25
625 **79** 25c. violet 20 10
626 **80** 50c. green 35 15
627 1cor. yellow . . . . 2·75 90
See also Nos. 912/24.

112 Mt. Momotombo

1929. Air.
629 **112** 15c. purple 25 10
630 20c. green 70 45
631 25c. olive 50 30
632 50c. sepia 80 45
633 1cor. red . . . . 1·10 55
See also Nos. 926/30.

1930. Air. Surch **Vale** and value.
634 **112** 15c. on 25c. olive 40 30
635 20c. on 25c. olive 60 45

114 G.P.O. Managua

1930. Opening of the G.P.O., Managua.
636 **114** ½c. sepia 80 60
637 1c. red 80 60
638 2c. orange 65 45
639 3c. orange . . . . 1·00 90
640 4c. yellow . . . . 1·00 90
641 5c. olive . . . . 1·60 1·10
642 6c. green . . . . 1·60 1·10
643 10c. black . . . . 1·60 1·00
644 25c. blue . . . . 3·25 2·40
645 50c. blue . . . . 5·25 3·50
646 1cor. violet . . . . 15·00 7·25

1931. Optd **1931** and thick bar obliterating old overprint "1928".
648 **99** 10c. brown (No. 607) . . . 45 90

1931. No. 607 surch **C$ 0.02.**
649 **99** 2c. on 10c. brown 55 45

1931. Optd **1931** and thick bar.
650 **99** 2c. on 10c. brown (No. 498) . . . . 55 1·75

1931. Air. Nos. 614/16 surch **1931 Vale** and value.
651 **79** 15c. on 25c. sepia . . . . 90·00 90·00
652 15c. on 25c. orange . . . . 45·00 45·00
653 15c. on 25c. violet . . . . 9·00 9·00
654 20c. on 25c. violet . . . . 9·00 9·00

1931. Optd **1931.**
656 **79** ½c. green 35 10
657 1c. olive 35 10
665 1c. orange (No. 605) . . . 10 10
658 **80** 2c. red 35 10
659 **79** 3c. blue 35 15
660 5c. yellow . . . . 2·10 1·40
661 5c. sepia 65 20
662 15c. orange 70 45
663 25c. sepia . . . . 9·00 3·75
664 25c. violet . . . . 3·50 1·50

1931. Air. Surch **1931** and value.
667 **80** 15c. on 25c. olive . . . . 4·75 4·75
668 15c. on 50c. sepia . . . . 36·00 36·00
669 15c. on 1cor. red . . . . . 90·00 90·00
666 15c. on 20c. on 25c. olive (No. 635) . . . . 7·50 7·50

120 G.P.O. before and after the Earthquake

1932. G.P.O. Reconstruction Fund.
670 **120** ½c. green (postage) . . . 90 90
671 1c. brown . . . . 1·25 1·25
672 2c. red 90 90
673 3c. blue 90 90
674 4c. blue 90 90
675 5c. brown . . . . 1·40 1·40
676 6c. brown . . . . 1·40 1·40
677 10c. brown . . . . 2·25 1·50
678 15c. red . . . . 3·50 2·25
679 20c. orange . . . . 2·10 2·10
680 25c. violet . . . . 2·25 2·25
681 50c. green . . . . 2·25 2·25
682 1cor. yellow . . . . . . 4·50 4·50
683 15c. mauve (air) 90 75
684 20c. green . . . . 1·10 1·10
685 25c. brown . . . . 5·50 5·50
686 50c. brown . . . . 7·00 7·00
687 1cor. red . . . . 10·50 10·50

1932. Air. Surch **Vale** and value.
688 **112** 30c. on 50c. sepia . . . . 1·40 1·40
689 35c. on 50c. sepia . . . . 1·40 1·40
690 40c. on 1cor. red . . . . 1·60 1·60
691 55c. on 1cor. red . . . . 1·60 1·60
For similar surcharges on these stamps in different colours see Nos. 791/4 and 931/4.

1932. Air. International Air Mail Week. Optd **Semana Correo Aereo Internacional 11–17 Septiembre 1932.**
692 **112** 15c. violet . . . . 40·00 40·00

1932. Air. Inauguration of Inland Airmail Service. Surch **Inauguracion Interior 12 Octubre 1932 Vale C$0.08.**
693 **112** 8c. on 1cor. red . . . . . 13·00 13·00

1932. Air. Optd **Interior–1932** or surch **Vale** and value also.
705 **120** 25c. brown . . . . 4·75 4·75
706 32c. on 50c. brown . . . 5·50 5·50
707 40c. on 1cor. red . . . . 4·25 4·25

1932. Air. Nos. 671, etc, optd **Correo Aereo Interior** in one line and **1932**, or surch **Vale** and value also.
694 **120** 1c. brown . . . . 12·00 12·00
695 2c. red . . . . 12·00 12·00
696 3c. blue . . . . 5·50 5·50
697 4c. blue . . . . 5·50 5·50
698 5c. brown . . . . 5·50 5·50
699 6c. brown . . . . 5·50 5·50
700 8c. on 10c. brown . . . . 5·25 5·25
701 16c. on 20c. orange . . . 5·25 5·25
702 24c. on 25c. violet . . . . 5·25 5·25
703 50c. green . . . . 5·25 5·25
704 1cor. yellow . . . . . . 5·50 5·50

1932. Air. Surch **Correo Aereo Interior–1932** in two lines and **Vale** and value below.
710 **80** 1c. on 2c. red 40 40
711 **79** 2c. on 3c. blue 40 40
712 **80** 3c. on 4c. blue 40 40
713 **79** 4c. on 5c. sepia 40 40
714 **80** 5c. on 6c. brown 40 40
715 6c. on 10c. brown 40 40
716 **79** 8c. on 15c. orange 40 40
717 **80** 16c. on 20c. orange 40 40
718 **79** 24c. on 25c. violet 85 60
719 25c. on 25c. violet 85 60
720 **80** 32c. on 50c. green 85 75
721 40c. on 50c. green 95 85
722 50c. on 1cor. yellow . . . 1·25 1·25
723 100c. on 1cor. yellow . . . 2·50 2·50

127 Wharf, Port San Jorge

128 La Chocolata Cutting

1932. Opening of Rivas Railway.
726 **127** 1c. yellow (postage) . . . 19·00
727 – 2c. red . . . . 19·00
728 – 5c. sepia . . . . 19·00
729 – 10c. brown . . . . 19·00
730 – 15c. yellow . . . . 19·00
731 **128** 15c. violet (air) . . . . . 25·00
732 – 20c. green . . . . 25·00
733 – 25c. brown . . . . 25·00
734 – 50c. sepia . . . . 25·00
735 – 1cor. red . . . . 25·00
DESIGNS—HORIZ: 2c. El Nacascolo Halt; 5c. Rivas Station; 10c. San Juan del Sur; 15c. (No. 730), Arrival platform at Rivas; 20c. El Nacascolo; 25c. La Cuesta cutting; 50c. San Juan del Sur quay; 1cor. El Estero.

1932. Surch **Vale** and value in words.
736 **79** 1c. on 3c. blue 35 15
737 **80** 2c. on 4c. blue 30 15

130 Railway Construction

1932. Opening of Leon–Sauce Railway.
739 – 1c. yellow (postage) . . . 19·00
740 – 2c. red . . . . 19·00
741 – 5c. sepia . . . . 19·00
742 **130** 10c. brown . . . . 19·00
743 – 15c. yellow . . . . 19·00
744 – 15c. violet (air) . . . . . 25·00
745 – 20c. green . . . . 25·00
746 – 25c. brown . . . . 25·00
747 – 50c. sepia . . . . 25·00
748 – 1cor. red . . . . 25·00
DESIGNS—HORIZ: 1c. El Sauce; 2c., 15c. (No. 744), Bridge at Santa Lucia; 5c. Santa Lucia; 15c. (No. 743), Santa Lucia cutting; 20c. Santa Lucia River Halt; 25c. Malpaicillo Station; 50c. Railway panorama; 1cor. San Andres.

1933. Surch **Resello 1933 Vale** and value in words.
749 **79** 1c. on 3c. blue 20 15
750 1c. on 5c. sepia 20 15
751 **80** 2c. on 10c. brown 20 15

133 Flag of the Race

1933. 441st Anniv of Columbus' Departure from Palos. Roul.
753 **133** ½c. green (postage) . . . 95 95
754 1c. green 80 80
755 2c. red 80 80
756 3c. red 80 80
757 4c. orange 80 80
758 5c. yellow 95 95
759 10c. brown 95 95
760 15c. brown 95 95
761 20c. blue 95 95
762 25c. blue 95 95
763 30c. violet . . . . 2·40 2·40
764 50c. purple . . . . 2·40 2·40
765 1cor. brown . . . . . . 2·40 2·40
766 1c. brown (air) 90 90
767 2c. purple 90 90
768 4c. violet . . . . 1·50 1·40

769 5c. blue 1·40 1·40
770 6c. blue 1·40 1·40
771 8c. brown 45 45
772 15c. brown 45 45
773 20c. yellow 1·40 1·40
774 25c. orange 1·40 1·40
775 50c. red 1·40 1·40
776 1cor. green 9·00 9·00

(134) (Facsimile signatures of R. E. Deshon, Minister of Transport and J. R. Sevilla, P.M.G.)

1933. Optd with T **134**.
777 **79** ½c. green 30 15
778 1c. green 15 10
779 **80** 2c. red 40 15
780 **79** 3c. blue 15 10
781 **80** 4c. blue 20 15
782 **79** 5c. brown 20 10
783 **80** 6c. drab 25 20
784 10c. brown 25 15
785 **79** 15c. red 30 20
786 **80** 20c. orange 40 30
787 **79** 25c. violet 45 25
788 **80** 50c. green 75 50
789 1cor. yellow 4·00 1·60

1933. No. 605 optd with T **134**.
790 **79** 1c. orange 25 15

1933. Air. Surch **Vale** and value.
791 **112** 30c. on 50c. orange 35 15
792 35c. on 50c. blue 45 20
793 40c. on 1cor. yellow 70 15
794 55c. on 1cor. green 70 30

135 Lake Xolotlan

1933. Air. International Airmail Week.
795 **135** 10c. brown 90 90
796 15c. violet 75 75
797 25c. red 85 85
798 50c. blue 90 90

Correo Aéreo Interior Vale C$ 0.50

(136)

1933. Air. Inland service. Colours changed. Surch as T **136** and optd with T **134**.
799 **80** 1c. on 2c. green 15 15
800 **79** 2c. on 3c. olive 15 15
801 **80** 3c. on 4c. red 15 15
802 **79** 4c. on 5c. blue 15 15
803 **80** 5c. on 6c. blue 15 15
804 6c. on 10c. sepia 15 10
805 **79** 8c. on 15c. brown 20 15
806 **80** 16c. on 20c. brown 20 15
807 **79** 24c. on 25c. red 15 15
808 25c. on 25c. orange 30 30
809 **80** 32c. on 50c. violet 30 25
810 40c. on 50c. green 40 25
811 50c. on 1cor. yellow 40 30
812 1cor. on 1cor. red 95 80

1933. Obligatory Tax. As No. 647 optd with T **134**. Colour changed.
813 **106** 1c. orange 25 15

1934. Air. Surch **Servicio Centroamericano Vale 10 centavos**.
814 **112** 10c. on 20c. green 35 35
815 10c. on 25c. olive 35 35
See also No. 872.

1935. Optd **Resello 1935**. (a) Nos. 778/9.
816 **79** 1c. green 10 10
817 **80** 2c. red 15 10

(b) No. 813 but without T **134** opt.
818 **106** 1c. orange 15 10

1935. No. 783 surch **Vale Medio Centavo**.
819 **80** ½c. on 6c. brown 35 15

1935. Optd with T **134** and **RESELLO – 1935** in a box.
820 **79** ½c. green 20 15
821 **80** ½c. on 6c. brown (No. 819) 15 10
822 **79** 1c. green 25 10
823 **80** 2c. red 55 10
824 2c. red (No. 817) 30 10
825 **79** 3c. blue 30 15
826 **80** 4c. blue 30 15
827 **79** 5c. brown 25 10
828 **80** 6c. drab 30 10
829 10c. brown 55 20
830 **79** 15c. red 15 10
831 **80** 20c. orange 90 25
832 **79** 25c. violet 30 15
833 **80** 50c. green 35 25
834 1cor. yellow 45 35

1935. Obligatory Tax. No. 605 optd with **RESELLO – 1935** in a box.
835 **79** 1c. orange 25·00

1935. Obligatory Tax. Optd **RESELLO – 1935** in a box. (a) No. 813 without T **134** opt.
836 **106** 1c. orange 25 15

(b) No. 818.
868 **106** 1c. orange 20 15

1935. Air. Nos. 799/812 optd with **RESELLO – 1935** in a box.
839 **80** 1c. on 2c. green 10 10
840 **79** 2c. on 3c. olive 20 20
879 **80** 3c. on 4c. red 15 15
880 **79** 4c. on 5c. blue 15 15
881 **80** 5c. on 6c. blue 15 15
882 6c. on 10c. sepia 15 15
883 **79** 8c. on 15c. brown 15 15
884 **80** 16c. on 20c. brown 15 15
847 **79** 24c. on 25c. red 35 30
848 25c. on 25c. orange 25 25
849 **80** 32c. on 50c. violet 20 20
850 40c. on 50c. green 30 25
851 50c. on 1cor. yellow 45 35
852 1cor. on 1cor. red 85 40

1935. Air. Optd with **RESELLO – 1935** in a box. (a) Nos. 629/33.
853 **112** 15c. purple 30 10
873 20c. green 40 30
855 25c. green 40 35
856 50c. sepia 40 35
857 1cor. red 65 35

(b) Nos. 791/4.
858 **112** 30c. on 50c. orange 40 35
859 35c. on 50c. blue 40 25
860 40c. on 1cor. yellow 40 35
861 55c. on 1cor. green 40 30

(c) Nos. 814/5.
862 **112** 10c. on 20c. green £300 £300
863 10c. on 25c. olive 60 50

1935. Optd with **RESELLO – 1935** in a box.
864 **79** ½c. green (No. 465) 15 10
865 1c. green (No. 617) 20 10
866 **80** 2c. red (No. 467) 55 10
867 **79** 3c. blue (No. 618) 20 15

1936. Surch **Resello 1936 Vale** and value.
869 **79** 1c. on 3c. blue (No. 618) 15 10
870 2c. on 5c. brown (No. 620) 15 10

1936. Air. Surch **Servicio Centroamericano Vale diez centavos** and **RESELLO – 1935** in a box.
871 **112** 10c. on 25c. olive 30 30

1936. Obligatory Tax. No. 818 optd **1936**.
874 **106** 1c. orange 50 20

1936. Obligatory Tax. No. 605 optd with T **134** and **1936**.
875 **79** 1c. orange 50 20

1936. Air. No. 622 optd **Correo Aereo Centro-Americano Resello 1936**.
876 **80** 10c. brown 20 20

1936. Air. Nos. 799/800 and 805 optd **Resello 1936**.
885 **80** 1c. on 2c. green 25 20
886 **79** 2c. on 3c. olive 10 10
887 8c. on 15c. brown 25 25

1936. Optd with or without T **37**, surch **1936 Vale** and value.
888 **79** ½c. on 15c. red 20 15
889 **80** 1c. on 4c. blue 25 15
890 **79** 1c. on 5c. brown 25 20
891 **80** 1c. on 6c. drab 45 20
892 **79** 1c. on 15c. red 25 20
893 **80** 1c. on 20c. orange 20 15
895 2c. on 10c. brown 30 20
896 **79** 2c. on 15c. red 60 50
897 **80** 2c. on 20c. orange 55 45
898 **79** 2c. on 25c. violet 35 20
900 **80** 2c. on 50c. green 35 25
901 2c. on 1cor. yellow 35 30
902 3c. on 4c. blue 40 30

1936. Optd **Resello 1936**.
903 **79** 3c. blue (No. 618) 35 25
904 5c. brown (No. 620) 30 15
905 **80** 10c. brown (No. 784) 30 20

1936. Air. Surch **1936 Vale and value**.
906 **112** 15c. on 50c. brown 30 25
907 15c. on 1cor. red 30 25

1936. Fiscal stamps surch **RECONSTRUCCION COMUNICACIONES 5 CENTAVOS DE CORDOBA** and further surch **Vale dos centavos Resello 1936**.
908 **90** 1c. on 5c. green 25 10
909 2c. on 5c. green 25 10

1936. Obligatory Tax. Fiscal stamps surch **RECONSTRUCCION COMUNICACIONES 5 CENTAVOS DE CORDOBA** and further surch. (a) **1936 R. de C. Vale Un Centavo**.
910 **90** 1c. on 5c. green 15 10

(b) **Vale un centavo R. de C. 1936**.
911 **90** 1c. on 5c. green 20 10

1937. Colours changed. Size 27 × 22¾ mm.
912 **79** ½c. black 15 10
913 1c. red 15 10
914 **80** 2c. blue 15 10
915 **79** 3c. brown 15 10
916 **80** 4c. yellow 20 10
917 **79** 5c. red 15 10
918 **80** 6c. violet 20 10
919 10c. green 20 10
920 **79** 15c. green 15 10
921 **80** 20c. brown 30 10
922 **79** 25c. orange 30 10
923 **80** 50c. brown 35 15
924 1cor. blue 40 25

1937. Obligatory Tax. Colour changed.
925 **106** 1c. green 15 10

1937. Air. Colours changed.
926 **112** 15c. orange 20 10
927 20c. red 20 15
928 25c. black 25 15
929 50c. violet 45 15
930 1cor. orange 65 15

1937. Air. Surch **Vale** and value. Colours changed.
931 **112** 30c. on 50c. red 30 10
932 35c. on 50c. olive 35 10
933 40c. on 1cor. green 35 15
934 55c. on 1cor. blue 35 30

1937. Air. Surch **Servicio Centroamericano Vale Diez Centavos**.
949 **112** 10c. on 1cor. red 30 15

1937. Air. No. 805 (without T **134**) optd **1937**.
950 **79** 8c. on 15c. brown 50 15

142 Baseball Player

1937. Obligatory Tax. For 1937 Central American Olympic Games. Optd with ball in red under "OLIMPICO".
951 **142** 1c. red 35 15
952 1c. yellow 35 15
953 1c. blue 35 15
953a 1c. green 35 15

1937. Nos. 799/809 optd **Habilitado 1937**.
954 **80** 1c. on 2c. green 10 10
955 **79** 2c. on 3c. olive 10 10
956 **80** 3c. on 4c. red 10 10
957 **79** 4c. on 5c. blue 10 10
958 **80** 5c. on 6c. blue 10 10
959 6c. on 10c. brown 10 10
960 **79** 8c. on 15c. brown 10 10
961 **80** 16c. on 20c. brown 20 20
962 **79** 24c. on 25c. red 20 20
963 25c. on 25c. orange 20 25
964 **80** 32c. on 50c. violet 20 25

144 Presidential Palace, Managua

1937. Air. Inland.
965 **144** 1c. red 15 10
966 2c. blue 15 10
967 3c. olive 15 10
968 4c. black 15 10
969 5c. purple 20 10
970 6c. brown 20 10
971 8c. violet 20 10
972 16c. orange 35 25
973 24c. yellow 35 15
974 25c. green 50 25

145 Nicaragua

1937. Air. Abroad.
975 **145** 10c. green 25 10
976 15c. blue 25 10
977 20c. yellow 30 25
978 25c. violet 30 25
979 30c. red 40 25
980 50c. orange 60 25
981 1cor. olive 65 45

146 Presidential Palace

1937. Air. Abroad. 150th Anniv of U.S. Constitution.
982 – 10c. blue and green 1·10 70
983 **146** 15c. blue and orange 1·10 70
984 – 20c. blue and red 80 65
985 – 25c. blue and brown 80 65
986 – 30c. blue and green 80 65
987 – 35c. blue and yellow 35 25
988 – 40c. blue and green 55 40
989 – 45c. blue and purple 55 40
990 – 50c. blue and mauve 55 40
991 – 55c. blue and green 2·25 1·25
992 – 75c. blue and green 55 30
993 – 1cor. red and blue 75 30
DESIGNS: 10c. Children's Park, Managua; 20c. S. America; 25c. C. America; 30c. N. America; 35c. Lake Tiscapa; 40c. Pan-American motor-road; 45c. Priniomi Park; 50c. Piedrecitas Park; 55c. San Juan del Sur; 75c Rio Tipitapa; 1cor. Granade landscape.

146b Diriangen

1937. Air. Day of the Race.
993a **146b** 1c. green (inland) 15 10
993b 4c. lake 15 10
993c 5c. violet 25 15
993d 8c. blue 15 10

993e 10c. brown (abroad) 20 10
993f 15c. blue 20 10
993g 20c. pink 30 15

147 Letter Carrier

1937. 75th Anniv of Postal Administration.
994 **147** ½c. green 15 10
995 – 1c. mauve 15 10
996 – 2c. brown 15 10
997 – 3c. violet 65 20
998 – 5c. blue 65 20
999 – 7½c. red 2·50 75
DESIGNS: 1c. Mule transport; 2c. Diligence; 3c. Yacht; 5c. Packet steamer; 7½c. Steam mail train.

147a Gen. Tomas Martinez

1938. Air. 75th Anniv of Postal Administration.
999a **147a** 1c. blk & orge (inland) 25 20
999b 5c. black and violet 25 20
999c 8c. black and blue 30 30
999d 16c. black and brown 40 35

999e – 10c. blk & grn (abroad) 30 25
999f – 15c. black and blue 40 35
999g – 25c. black and violet 25 25
999h – 50c. black and red 40 30
DESIGNS: 10c. to 50c. Gen. Anastasio Somoza.

1938. Surch **1938** and **Vale**, new value in words and **Centavos**.
1000 **79** 3c. on 25c. orange 10 10
1001 **80** 5c. on 50c. brown 10 10
1002 6c. on 1 cor. blue 15 15

149 Dario Park

150 Lake Managua

151 President Somoza

1939.
1003 **149** 1½c. green (postage) 10 10
1004 2c. red 10 10
1005 3c. blue 10 10
1006 6c. brown 10 10
1007 7½c. green 10 10
1008 10c. brown 15 10
1009 15c. orange 15 10
1010 25c. violet 15 15
1011 50c. green 30 20
1012 1cor. yellow 60 45

1013 **150** 2c. blue (air: inland) 15 15
1014 3c. olive 15 15
1015 8c. mauve 15 15
1016 16c. orange 25 15
1017 24c. yellow 25 15
1018 32c. green 35 15
1019 50c. red 40 15

1020 **151** 10c. brown (air: abroad) 15 10
1021 15c. blue 15 10
1022 20c. yellow 15 20
1023 25c. violet 15 15
1024 30c. red 20 20
1025 50c. orange 30 20
1026 1cor. olive 45 35

1939. Nos. 920/1. Surch **Vale un Centavo 1939**.
1027 **79** 1c. on 15c. green 10 10
1028 **80** 1c. on 20c. brown 10 10

153 Will Rogers and Managua Airport

1939. Air. Will Rogers Commemorative. Inscr "WILL ROGERS/1931/1939".
1029 **153** 1c. green 10 10
1030 – 2c. red 10 10
1031 – 3c. blue 10 10
1032 – 4c. blue 15 10
1033 – 5c. red 10 10
DESIGNS: 2c. Rogers at Managua; 3c. Rogers in P.A.A. hut; 4c. Rogers and U.S. Marines; 5c. Rogers and street in Managua.

156 Senate House and Pres. Somoza

1940. Air. President's Visit to U.S.A. (a) Inscr "AEREO INTERIOR".
1034 – 4c. brown 15 10
1035 **156** 8c. brown 10 10
1036 – 16c. green 15 10
1037 **156** 20c. mauve 30 15
1038 – 32c. red 20 20

(b) Inscr "CORREO AEREO INTERNACIONAL".
1039 – 25c. blue 20 15
1040 – 30c. black 20 10
1041 **156** 50c. red 25 40
1042 – 60c. green 30 35
1043 – 65c. brown 30 20
1044 – 90c. olive 40 35
1045 – 1cor. violet 60 30
DESIGNS: 4c., 16c., 25c., 30c., 65c., 90c. Pres. Somoza addressing Senate; 32c., 60c., 1cor. Portrait of Pres. Somoza between symbols of Nicaragua and New York World's Fair.

158 L. S. Rowe, Statue of Liberty and Union Flags

1940. Air. 50th Anniv of Pan-American Union.
1046 **158** 1cor.25 multicoloured 40 35

159 First Issue of Nicaragua and Sir Rowland Hill

1941. Air. Centenary of First Adhesive Postage stamps.
1047 **159** 2cor. brown 2·25 75
1048 3cor. blue 7·00 80
1049 5cor. red 20·00 2·10

1941. Surch **Servicio ordinario Vale Diez Centavos de Cordoba**.
1050 **153** 10c. on 1c. green 15 10

161 Rube Dario

1941. 25th Death Anniv of Ruben Dario (poet).
1051 **161** 10c. red (postage) 20 15

1052 20c. mauve (air) 25 15
1053 35c. green 30 20
1054 40c. orange 35 25
1055 60c. blue 40 35

1943. Surch **Servicio Ordinario Vale Diez Centavos**
1056 **153** 10c. on 1c. green 10 10

162 "V" for Victory 163 Red Cross

164 Red Cross Workers and Wounded

1943. Victory.
1057 **162** 10c. red and violet (postage) 10 10
1058 30c. red and brown 15 10

1059 40c. red and green (air) 15 10
1060 60c. red and blue 20 10

1944. Air. 80th Anniv of Int Red Cross Society.
1061 **163** 25c. red 40 15
1062 – 50c. bistre 65 35
1063 **164** 1cor. green 1·25 1·00
DESIGN—VERT: 50c. Two Hemispheres.

165 Columbus and Lighthouse 166 Columbus's Fleet and Lighthouse

1945. Honouring Columbus's Discovery of America and Erection of Columbus Lighthouse near Trujillo City, Dominican Republic.
1064 **165** 4c. black & green (postage) 15 10
1065 6c. black and orange 20 10
1066 8c. black and red 20 15
1067 10c. black and blue 30 15

1068 **166** 20c. grey and green (air) 60 20
1069 35c. black and red 95 25
1070 75c. pink and green 1·75 55
1071 90c. blue and red 2·00 85
1072 1cor. blue and black 2·25 50
1073 2cor.50 red and blue 6·00 2·50

168 Roosevelt as a Stamp Collector

1946. President Roosevelt Commemorative Inscr "HOMENAJE A ROOSEVELT".
1074 **168** 4c. green & black (postage) 15 15
1075 – 8c. violet and black 20 20
1076 – 10c. blue and black 30 25
1077 – 16c. red and black 40 30
1078 – 32c. brown and black 50 25
1079 – 50c. grey and black 50 25

1080 – 25c. orange & black (air) 20 10
1081 – 75c. red and black 25 20
1082 – 1cor. green and black 30 30
1083 – 3cor. violet and black 2·25 2·25
1084 – 5cor. blue and black 3·00 3·00
DESIGNS—portraying Roosevelt. HORIZ: 8c., 25c. with Churchill at the Atlantic Conference; 16c., 1cor. with Churchill, De Gaulle and Giraud at the Casablanca Conference; 32c., 3cor. with Churchill and Stalin at the Teheran Conference. VERT: 10c., 75c. Signing Declaration of War against Japan; 50c., 5cor. Head of Roosevelt

171 Managua Cathedral

172 G.P.O., Managua

1947. Managua Centenary. Frames in black.
1085 **171** 4c. red (postage) 10 10
1086 – 5c. blue 15 10
1087 – 6c. green 20 15
1088 – 10c. olive 20 15
1089 – 75c. brown 30 25

1090 – 5c. violet (air) 10 10
1091 **172** 20c. green 15 15
1092 – 35c. orange 15 15
1093 – 90c. purple 30 20
1094 – 1cor. brown 45 35
1095 – 2cor.50 purple 1·00 1·10
DESIGNS—POSTAGE (as Type **171**): 5c. Health Ministry; 6c. Municipal Building; 10c. College; 75c. G.P.O., Managua. AIR (as Type **172**): 5c. College; 35c. Health Ministry; 90c. National Bank; 1cor. Municipal Building; 2cor.50, National Palace.

173 San Cristobal Volcano

174 Ruben Dario Monument, Managua

1947. (a) Postage.
1096 **173** 2c. orange and black 10 10
1097 – 3c. violet and black 10 10
1098 – 4c. grey and black 10 10
1099 – 5c. red and black 20 10
1100 – 6c. green and black 15 10
1101 – 8c. brown and black 15 10
1102 – 10c. red and black 25 15
1103 – 20c. blue and black 1·10 25
1104 – 30c. purple and black 70 25
1105 – 50c. red and black 1·90 70
1106 – 1cor. brown and black 60 35
DESIGNS—as Type **173**: 3c. Lion on Ruben Dario's tomb, Leon Cathedral; 4c. Race stand; 5c. Soldiers' Monument; 6c. Sugar cane; 8c. Tropical fruits; 10c. Cotton; 20c. Horses; 30c. Coffee plant; 50c. Prize bullock; 1cor. Agricultural landscape.

(b) Air.
1107 **174** 5c. red and green 10 10
1108 – 6c. orange and black 10 10
1109 – 8c. brown and red 10 10
1110 – 10c. blue and brown 15 10
1111 – 20c. orange and blue 15 10
1112 – 25c. green and red 20 15
1113 – 35c. brown and black 30 15
1114 – 50c. black and violet 20 10
1115 – 1cor. red and black 45 25
1116 – 1cor.50 green and red 50 45
1117 – 5cor. red and brown 3·75 3·75
1118 – 10cor. brown and violet 3·00 3·00
1119 – 25cor. yellow and green 6·00 6·00
DESIGNS—As Type **174**: 6c. Baird's tapir; 8c. Highway and Lake Managua; 10c. Genizaro Dam; 20c. Ruben Dario Monument, Managua; 25c. Sulphur Lagoon, Nejapa; 35c. Managua Airport; 50c. Mouth of Rio Prinzapolka; 1cor. Thermal Baths, Tipitapa; 1cor.50, Rio Tipitapa; 5cor. Embassy building; 10cor. Girl carrying basket of fruit; 2cor. Franklin D. Roosevelt Monument, Managua.

175 Softball 176 Pole-vaulting
177 Tennis 178 National Stadium, Managua

1949. 10th World Amateur Baseball Championships. (a) Postage as T **175/6**.
1120 **175** 1c. brown 10 10
1121 – 2c. blue 50 15
1122 **176** 3c. green 25 10
1123 – 4c. purple 15 15
1124 – 5c. orange 40 15
1125 – 10c. green 40 15
1126 – 15c. red 50 15
1127 – 25c. blue 50 20
1128 – 35c. green 80 20
1129 – 40c. violet 1·75 30
1130 – 60c. black 1·40 35
1131 – 1cor. red 1·50 90
1132 – 2cor. purple 2·75 1·50
DESIGNS—VERT: 2c. Scout; 5c. Cycling; 25c. Boxing; 35c. Basketball. HORIZ: 4c. Diving; 10c. Stadium; 15c. Baseball; 40c. Yachting; 60c. Table tennis; 1cor. Football; 2cor. Tennis.

(b) Air as T **177**.
1133 **177** 1c. red 10 10
1134 – 2c. black 10 10
1135 – 3c. red 10 10
1136 – 4c. black 10 10
1137 – 5c. blue 35 15
1138 – 15c. green 65 10
1139 – 25c. purple 1·25 25
1140 – 30c. brown 1·00 25
1141 – 40c. violet 50 25
1142 – 75c. mauve 2·50 1·60
1143 – 1cor. blue 3·00 80
1144 – 2cor. olive 1·25 1·00
1145 – 5cor. green 2·10 2·10
DESIGNS—SQUARE: 2c. Football; 3c. Table tennis; 4c. Stadium; 5c. Yachting; 15c. Basketball; 25c. Boxing; 30c. Baseball; 40c. Cycling; 75c. Diving; 1cor. Pole-vaulting; 2cor. Scout; 5cor. Softball.

1949. Obligatory Tax stamps. Stadium Construction Fund.
1146 **178** 5c. blue 20 10
1146a 5c. red 20 10

179 Rowland Hill 180 Heinrich von Stephan

1950. 75th Anniv of U.P.U. Frames in black.
1147 **179** 20c. red (postage) 15 10
1148 – 25c. green 15 10
1149 – 75c. blue 50 50
1150 – 80c. green 30 25
1151 – 4cor. blue 85 80

DESIGNS—VERT: 25c. Portrait as Type **180**; 75c. Monument, Berne; 80c., 4cor. Obverse and reverse of Congress Medal.

1152 – 16c. red (air) 15 10
1153 **180** 20c. orange 15 10
1154 – 25c. black 15 15
1155 – 30c. red 25 10
1156 – 85c. green 55 50
1157 – 1cor.10 brown 50 35
1158 – 2cor.14 green . . . . 1·25 1·25
DESIGNS—HORIZ: 16c. Rowland Hill; 25, 30c. U.P.U. Offices, Berne; 85c. Monument, Berne; 1cor.10 and 2cor.14,Obverse and reverse of Congress Medal.

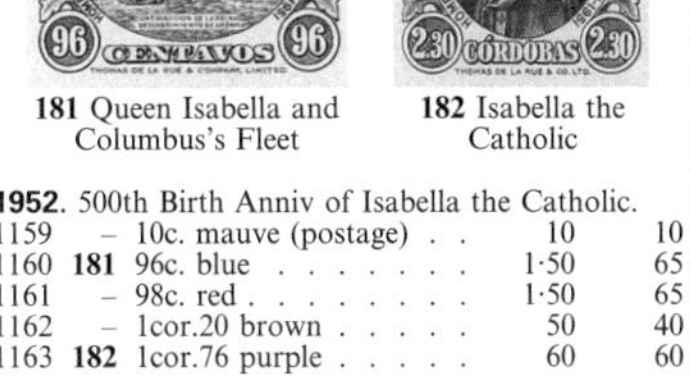

181 Queen Isabella and Columbus's Fleet
182 Isabella the Catholic

1952. 500th Birth Anniv of Isabella the Catholic.
1159 – 10c. mauve (postage) . . 10 10
1160 **181** 96c. blue . . . . . . 1·50 65
1161 – 98c. red . . . . 1·50 65
1162 – 1cor.20 brown 50 40
1163 **182** 1cor.76 purple 60 60

1164 2cor.30 red (air) . . . . 1·40 1·10
1165 – 2cor.80 orange . . . . 1·00 95
1166 – 3cor. green . . . . . 4·25 1·75
1167 **181** 3cor.30 blue . . . . . 4·25 2·00
1168 – 3cor.60 green . . . . 1·50 1·25
DESIGNS—VERT: 10c., 3cor.60, Queen facing right; 98c., 3cor. Queen and "Santa Maria"; 1cor.20, 2cor.80, Queen and Map of Americas.

183 O.D.E.C.A. Flag

1953. Foundation of Organization of Central American States.
1169 **183** 4c. blue (postage) . . . 10 10
1170 – 5c. green 10 10
1171 – 6c. brown 10 10
1172 – 15c. olive 20 15
1173 – 50c. sepia 25 15

1174 – 20c. red (air) 10 10
1175 **183** 25c. blue 15 10
1176 – 30c. brown 15 15
1177 – 60c. green 25 20
1178 – 1cor. purple 35 45
DESIGNS: 5c., 1cor. Map of C. America; 6c., 20c. Hands holding O.D.E.C.A. arms; 15c., 30c. Five presidents of C. America; 50c., 60c. Charter and flags.

184 Pres. Solorzano
185 Pres. Arguello

1953. Presidential Series. Portraits in black.
(a) Postage. As T **184**.
1179 **184** 4c. red 10 10
1180 – 6c. blue (D. M. Chamorro) 10 10
1181 – 8c. brown (Diaz) 10 10
1182 – 15c. red (Somoza) . . . 15 10
1183 – 50c. green (E. Chamorro) 20 15

(b) Air. As T **185**.
1184 **185** 4c. red 10 10
1185 – 5c. orange (Moncada) 10 10
1186 – 20c. blue (J. B. Sacasa) 10 10
1187 – 25c. blue (Zelaya) . . . 10 10
1188 – 30c. lake (Somoza) . . . 10 10
1189 – 35c. green (Martinez) . . 20 20
1190 – 40c. plum (Guzman) . . 20 20
1191 – 45c. olive (Cuadra) . . . 20 20
1192 – 50c. red (P. J. Chamorro) 35 25
1193 – 60c. blue (Zavala) . . . 40 40
1194 – 85c. brown (Cardenas) 40 40
1195 – 1cor.10 purple (Carazo) 60 55
1196 – 1cor.20 bistre (R. Sacasa) 65 55

186 Sculptor and U.N. Emblem

1954. U.N.O. Inscr "HOMENAJE A LA ONU".
1197 **186** 3c. drab (postage) . . . 10 10
1198 A 4c. green 15 10
1199 B 5c. green 20 10
1200 C 15c. green 55 20
1201 D 1cor. turquoise 45 40

1202 E 3c. red (air) 10 10
1203 F 4c. orange 10 10
1204 C 5c. red 15 10
1205 D 30c. pink 75 15
1206 B 2cor. red 80 70
1207 A 3cor. brown . . . . . . 1·50 1·00
1208 **186** 5cor. purple . . . . . . 1·75 1·40
DESIGNS: A, Detail from Nicaragua's coat of arms; B, Globe; C, Candle and Nicaragua's Charter; D, Flags of Nicaragua and U.N.; E, Torch; F, Trusting hands.

187 Capt. D. L. Ray
188 North American Sabre

1954. National Air Force. Frames in black.
(a) Postage. Frames as T **187**.
1209 **187** 1c. black 10 10
1210 – 2c. black 10 10
1211 – 3c. myrtle 10 10
1212 – 4c. orange 15 10
1213 – 5c. green 20 10
1214 – 15c. turquoise 15 10
1215 – 1cor. violet 35 25

(b) Air. Frames as T **188**.
1216 – 10c. black 10 10
1217 **188** 15c. black 15 10
1218 – 20c. mauve 15 10
1219 – 25c. red 20 10
1220 – 30c. blue 10 10
1221 – 50c. blue 75 50
1222 – 1cor. green 65 35
DESIGNS—POSTAGE: 2c. North American Sabre; 3c. Douglas Boston; 4c. Consolidated Liberator; 5c. North American Texan trainer; 15c. Pres. Somoza; 1cor. Emblem. AIR: 10c. D. L. Ray; 20c. Emblem; 25c. Hangars; 30c. Pres. Somoza; 50c. North American Texan trainers; 1cor. Lockheed Lightning airplanes.

189 Rotary Slogans
190a

1955. 50th Anniv of Rotary International.
1223 **189** 15c. orange (postage) . . 10 10
1224 A 20c. olive 15 15
1225 B 35c. violet 15 15
1226 C 40c. red 15 15
1227 D 90c. black 30 25

1228 D 1c. red (air) 10 10
1229 A 2c. blue 10 10
1230 C 3c. green 10 10
1231 **189** 4c. violet 10 10
1232 B 5c. brown 10 10
1233 25c. turquoise 15 15
1234 **189** 30c. black 15 10
1235 C 45c. mauve 30 25
1236 A 50c. green 25 20
1237 D 1cor. blue 45 30
DESIGNS—VERT: A, Clasped hands; B, Rotarian and Nicaraguan flags; D, Paul P. Harris. HORIZ: C, World map and winged emblem.

1956. National Exhibition. Surch **Conmemoracion Exposicion Nacional Febrero 4-16, 1956** and value.
1238 5c. on 6c. brown (No. 1171) (postage) 10 10
1239 5c. on 6c. black & bl (No. 1180) 10 10
1240 5c. on 8c. brn & blk (No. 1101) 10 10
1241 15c. on 35c. violet (No. 1225) 15 10
1242 15c. on 80c. grn & blk (No. 1150) 15 10
1243 15c. on 90c. black (No. 1227) 15 10
1244 30c. on 35c. black and green (No. 1189) (air) 10 15
1245 30c. on 45c. blk & ol (No. 1191) 25 15
1246 30c. on 45c. mauve (No. 1235) 25 15
1247 2cor. on 5cor. purple (No. 1208) 50 35

1956. Obligatory Tax. Social Welfare Fund.
1247a **190a** 5c. blue 10 10

191 Gen. J. Dolores Estrada
192 President Somoza

1956. Cent of War of 1856. Inscr as in T **191**.
1248 – 5c. brown (postage) . . 10 10
1249 – 10c. lake 10 10
1250 – 15c. grey 10 10
1251 – 25c. red 15 15
1252 – 50c. purple 30 20

1253 **191** 30c. red (air) 10 10
1254 – 60c. brown 20 15
1255 – 1cor.50 green 20 35
1256 – 2cor.50 blue 30 30
1257 – 10cor. orange . . . . . 1·90 1·75
DESIGNS—VERT: 5c. Gen. M. Jerez; 10c. Gen. F. Chamorro; 50c. Gen. J. D. Estrada; 1cor.50, E. Mangalo; 10cor. Commodore H. Paulding. HORIZ: 15c. Battle of San Jacinto; 25c. Granada in flames; 60c. Bas-relief; 2cor.50, Battle of Rivas.

1957. Air. National Mourning for Pres. G. A. Somoza. Various frames. Inscr as in T **192**. Centres in black.
1258 – 15c. black 10 10
1259 – 30c. blue 15 15
1260 **192** 2cor. violet 80 70
1261 – 3cor. olive . . . . . . 1·25 1·10
1262 – 5cor. sepia . . . . . . 1·90 1·90

193 Scout and Badge
194 Clasped Hands, Badge and Globe

1957. Birth Centenary of Lord Baden-Powell.
1263 **193** 10c. olive & vio (postage) 10 10
1264 – 15c. sepia and purple . . 15 15
1265 – 20c. brown and blue . . 15 15
1266 – 25c. brown and turquoise 15 15
1267 – 50c. olive and red . . . 35 35

1268 **194** 3c. olive and red (air) . . 15 15
1269 – 4c. blue and brown . . . 15 15
1270 – 5c. brown and green . . 15 15
1271 – 6c. drab and violet . . . 15 15
1272 – 8c. red and black 15 15
1273 – 30c. black and green . . 15 15
1274 – 40c. black and blue . . . 15 15
1275 – 75c. sepia and purple . . 35 35
1276 – 85c. grey and red . . . 40 40
1277 – 1cor. brown and green 40 40
DESIGNS—VERT: 4c. Scout badge; 5c., 15c. Wolf cub; 6c. Badge and flags; 8c. Badge and emblems of scouting 20c. Scout; 25., 1cor. Lord Baden-Powell; 30., 50c. Joseph A. Harrison; 75c. Rover Scout; 85c. Scout. HORIZ: 40c. Presentation to Pres. Somoza.

195 Pres. Luis Somoza
197 Archbishop of Managua

196 Managua Cathedral

1957. Election of Pres. Somoza. Portrait in brown.
(a) Postage. Oval frame.
1278 **195** 10c. red 10 10
1279 15c. blue 10 10
1280 35c. purple 10 10
1281 50c. brown 15 15
1282 75c. green 40 40

(b) Air. Rectangular frame.
1283 – 20c. blue 10 10
1284 – 25c. mauve 15 10
1285 – 30c. sepia 15 15
1286 – 40c. turquoise 15 15
1287 – 2cor. violet 95 95

1957. Churches and Priests. Centres in olive.
1288 **196** 5c. green (postage) . . . 10 10
1289 – 10c. purple 10 10
1290 **197** 15c. blue 10 10
1291 – 20c. sepia 15 10
1292 – 50c. green 20 15
1293 – 1cor. violet 30 30

1294 **197** 30c. green (air) 10 10
1295 **196** 60c. brown 15 15
1296 – 75c. blue 25 25
1297 – 90c. red 30 30
1298 – 1cor.50 turquoise 35 35
1299 – 2cor. purple 40 40
DESIGNS—HORIZ: As Type **196**: 20, 90c. Leon Cathedral; 50c., 1cor.50, La Merced, Granada Church. VERT: As Type **197**: 10, 75c. Bishop of Nicaragua; 1, 2cor. Father Mariano Dubon.

198 "Honduras" (freighter)

1957. Nicaraguan Merchant Marine Commemoration. Inscr as in T **198**.
1300 **198** 4c. black, blue and myrtle (postage) . . . 30 10
1301 – 5c. violet, blue and brown 30 10
1302 – 6c. black, blue and red 30 10
1303 – 10c. black, green and sepia 30 10
1304 – 15c. brown, blue and red 50 10
1305 – 50c. brown, blue and violet 60 20

1306 – 25c. purple, blue and ultramarine (air) . . . 60 20
1307 – 30c. grey, buff and brown 15 10
1308 – 50c. bistre, blue and violet 20 20
1309 – 60c. black, turquoise and purple 85 30
1310 – 1cor. black, blue and red 1·10 30
1311 – 2cor.50 brown, blue and black . . . . 2·25 1·25
DESIGNS: 5c. Gen. A. Somoza, founder of Mamenic (National) Shipping Line, and "Guatemala" (freighter); 6c. "Guatemala"; 10c. "Salvador" (freighter); 15c. Freighter between hemispheres; 25c. "Managua" (freighter); 30c. Ship's wheel and world map; 50c. (No. 1305), Hemispheres and ship; 50c. (No. 1308), Mamenic Shipping Line flag; 60c. "Costa Rica" (freighter); 1cor. "Nicarao" (freighter); 2cor.50, Map, freighter and flag.

199 Exhibition Emblem

1958. Air. Brussels International Exn. Inscr "EXPOSICION MUNDIAL DE BELGICA 1958".
1312 **199** 25c. black, yellow & green 10 10
1313 – 30c. multicoloured . . . 15 15
1314 – 45c. black, ochre and blue 15 15
1315 **199** 1cor. black, blue and dull purple 25 25
1316 – 2cor. multicoloured . . . 25 25
1317 – 10cor. sepia, purple and blue . . . . 1·40 1·00
DESIGNS: As Type **199**: 30c., 20cor. Arms of Nicaragua; 45c., 10cor. Nicaraguan pavilion.

200 Emblems of C. American Republics

1958. 17th Central American Lions Convention. Inscr as in T **200**. Emblems (5c., 60c.) multicoloured; Lions badge (others) in blue, red, yellow (or orange and buff).
1318 **200** 5c. blue (postage) . . . 10 10
1319 – 10c. blue and orange . . 10 10
1320 – 20c. blue and green . . . 10 10
1321 – 50c. blue and purple . . 15 15
1322 – 75c. blue and mauve . . 30 25
1323 – 1cor.50 blue, salmon and drab 45 45

1324 – 30c. blue and orange (air) 10 10
1325 **200** 60c. blue and pink . . . 20 15
1326 – 90c. blue 25 20
1327 – 1cor.25 blue and olive 35 30
1328 – 2cor. blue and green . . 60 50
1329 – 3cor. blue, red and violet 95 90
DESIGNS—HORIZ: 10c., 1cor.25, Melvin Jones; 20, 30c. Dr. T. A. Arias; 50, 90c. Edward G. Barry; 75c., 2cor. Lions emblem; 1cor.50, 3cor. Map of C. American Isthmus.

201 Arms of La Salle 202 U.N. Emblem

1958. Brothers of the Nicaraguan Christian Schools Commemoration. Inscr as in T **201**.

1330 **201** 5c. red, blue and yellow (postage) 10 10
1331 – 10c. sepia, blue and green 10 10
1332 – 15c. sepia, brown & bistre 10 10
1333 – 20c. black, red and bistre 10 10
1334 – 50c. sepia, orange & bis 15 15
1335 – 75c. sepia, turquoise & green 25 20
1336 – 1cor. black, violet & bis 40 30
1337 **201** 30c. blue, red & yellow (air) 10 10
1338 – 60c. sepia, purple & grey 25 20
1339 – 85c. black, red and blue 30 25
1340 – 90c. black, green & ochre 35 35
1341 – 1cor.25 black, red and ochre 50 45
1342 – 1cor.50 sepia, green and grey 60 55
1343 – 1cor.75 black, brn & bl 65 55
1344 – 2cor. sepia, green & grey 65 65

DESIGNS—HORIZ: 10, 60c. Managua Teachers Institute. VERT: 15, 85c. De La Salle (founder); 20, 90c. Brother Carlos; 50c., 1cor.50, Brother Antonio; 75c., 1cor.25, Brother Julio; 1cor., 1cor.75, Brother Argeo; 2cor. Brother Eugenio.

1958. Inauguration of U.N.E.S.C.O. Headquarters Building, Paris. Inscr as in T **202**.

1345 **202** 10c. blue & mauve (postage) 10 10
1346 – 15c. mauve and blue . . 10 10
1347 – 25c. brown and green . . 10 10
1348 – 40c. black and red . . . 15 15
1349 – 45c. mauve and blue . . 20 20
1350 **202** 50c. green and brown . . 25 25
1351 – 60c. blue and mauve (air) 25 15
1352 – 75c. brown and green . . 25 20
1353 – 90c. green and brown . . 30 25
1354 – 1cor. mauve and blue . . 40 30
1355 – 3cor. red and black . . . 60 60
1356 – 5cor. blue and mauve . . 1·00 85

DESIGNS—VERT: 15c. Aerial view of H.Q. 25, 45c. Facade composed of letters "UNESCO"; 40c. H.Q. and Eiffel Tower. In oval vignettes—60c. As 15c.; 75c., 5cor. As 25c.; 90c., 3cor. As 40c.; 1cor. As Type **202**.

203 204

1959. Obligatory Tax. Consular Fiscal stamps surch. Serial Nos. in red.

1357 **203** 5c. on 50c. blue 10 10
1358 **204** 5c. on 50c. blue 10 10

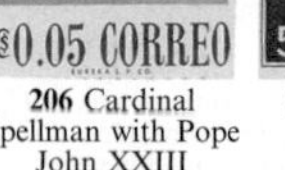

205 206 Cardinal Spellman with Pope John XXIII 207 Abraham Lincoln

1959. Obligatory Tax.

1359 **205** 5c. blue 15 10

1959. Cardinal Spellman Commemoration.

1360 **206** 5c. flesh & green (postage) 10 10
1361 A 10c. multicoloured . . . 10 10
1362 B 15c. red, black and green 10 10
1363 C 20c. yellow and blue . . 10 10
1364 D 25c. red and blue 10 10
1365 E 30c. blue, red & yell (air) 10 10
1366 **206** 35c. bronze and orange 10 10
1367 A 1cor. multicoloured . . . 30 30
1368 B 1cor.5 red and black . . 35 30
1369 C 1cor.50 yellow and blue 45 35
1370 D 2cor. blue, violet and red 55 45
1371 E 5cor. multicoloured . . . 75 55

DESIGNS—VERT: A, Cardinal's Arms; B, Cardinal; D, Cardinal wearing sash. HORIZ: C, Cardinal and Cross; E, Flags of Nicaragua, Vatican City and U.S.A.

1960. 150th Birth Anniv of Abraham Lincoln. Portrait in black.

1372 **207** 5c. red (postage) 10 10
1373 10c. green 10 10
1374 15c. orange 10 10
1375 1cor. purple 25 25
1376 2cor. blue 30 45
1377 30c. blue (air) 10 10
1378 35c. red 15 10
1379 70c. purple 20 20
1380 1cor.5 green 35 35
1381 1cor.50 violet 50 45
1382 – 5cor. ochre and black . . 55 55

DESIGN—HORIZ: 5cor. Scroll inscr "Dar al que necesite—A. Lincoln".

1960. Air. 10th Anniv of San Jose (Costa Rica) Philatelic Society. Optd **X Aniversario Club Filatelico S. J.—C. R.**

1383 2cor. red (No. 1206) 70 60
1384 2cor.50 blue (No. 1256) . . 75 75
1385 3cor. green (No. 1166) . . . 1·40 90

1960. Red Cross Fund for Chilean Earthquake Relief. Nos. 1372/82 optd **Resello** and Maltese Cross. Portrait in black.

1386 **207** 5c. red (postage) 10 10
1387 10c. green 10 10
1388 15c. orange 10 10
1389 1cor. purple 25 25
1390 2cor. blue 30 25
1391 30c. blue (air) 25 20
1392 35c. red 20 20
1393 70c. purple 25 25
1394 1cor.5 green 30 30
1395 1cor.50 violet 40 35
1396 – 5cor. ochre and black . . 1·00 1·00

210

1961. Air. World Refugee Year. Inscr "ANO MUNDIAL DEL REFUGIADO".

1397 – 2cor. multicoloured . . . 20 20
1398 **210** 5cor. ochre, blue & green 60 60

DESIGN: 2cor. Procession of refugees.

211 Pres. Roosevelt, Pres. Somoza and Officer

1961. Air. 20th Anniv of Nicaraguan Military Academy.

1399 **211** 20c. multicoloured . . . 10 10
1400 – 25c. red, blue and black 10 10
1401 – 30c. multicoloured . . . 10 10
1402 – 35c. multicoloured . . . 10 10
1403 – 40c. multicoloured . . . 10 10
1404 – 45c. black, flesh and red 15 15
1405 **211** 60c. multicoloured . . . 15 15
1406 – 70c. multicoloured . . . 20 20
1407 – 1cor.5 multicoloured . . 25 25
1408 – 1cor.50 multicoloured . . 35 35
1409 – 2cor. multicoloured . . . 50 50
1410 – 5cor. black, flesh & grey 70 60

DESIGNS—VERT: 25, 70c. Flags; 35c., 1cor.50, Standard bearers; 40c., 2cor. Pennant and emblem. HORIZ: 30c., 1cor.5 Group of officers; 45c., 5cor. Pres. Somoza and Director of Academy.

1961. Air. Consular Fiscal stamps as T **203/4** with serial Nos. in red, surch **Correo Aereo** and value.

1411 20c. on 50c. blue 15 10
1412 20c. on 1cor. olive 15 10
1413 20c. on 2cor. green 15 10
1414 20c. on 3cor. red 15 10
1415 20c. on 5cor. red 15 10
1416 20c. on 10cor. violet . . . 15 10
1417 20c. on 20cor. brown . . . 15 10
1418 20c. on 50cor. brown . . . 15 10
1419 20c. on 100cor. lake 15 10

213 I.J.C. Emblem and Global Map of the Americas

1961. Air. Junior Chamber of Commerce Congress.

1420 2c. multicoloured 10 10
1421 3c. black and yellow 10 10
1422 4c. multicoloured 10 10
1423 5c. black and red 10 10
1424 6c. multicoloured 15 10
1425 10c. multicoloured 15 10
1426 15c. black, green and blue 10 10
1427 30c. black and blue 15 10
1428 35c. multicoloured 15 10
1429 70c. black, red and yellow 20 20
1430 1cor.5 multicoloured 35 30
1431 5cor. multicoloured 70 70

DESIGNS—HORIZ: 2c., 15c. Type **213**; 4c., 35c. "J.C.I." upon Globe. VERT: 3c., 30c. I.J.C. emblem; 5c., 70c. Scroll; 6c., 1cor.5, Handclasp; 10c., 5cor. Regional map of Nicaragua.

1961. Air. 1st Central American Philatelic Convention, San Salvador. Optd **Convencion Filatelica–Centro–America–Panama–San Salvador–27 Julio 1961**.

1432 **158** 1cor.25 multicoloured . . 25 25

215 R. Cabezas

1961. Air. Birth Centenary of Cabezas.

1433 **215** 20c. blue and orange . . 10 10
1434 – 40c. purple and blue . . 15 15
1435 – 45c. sepia and green . . 15 15
1436 – 70c. green and brown . . 25 20
1437 – 2cor. blue and pink . . . 60 40
1438 – 10cor. purple and turquoise . . . . . . 1·50 1·50

DESIGNS—HORIZ: 40c. Map and view of Cartago; 45c. 1884 newspaper; 70c. Assembly outside building; 2cor. Scroll; 10cor. Map and view of Masaya.

216 Official Gazettes 219 "Cattleya skinneri"

1961. Centenary of Regulation of Postal Rates.

1439 **216** 5c. brown and turquoise 10 10
1440 – 10c. brown and green . . 10 10
1441 – 15c. brown and red . . . 10 10

DESIGNS: 10c. Envelopes and postmarks; 15c. Martinez and Somoza.

1961. Air. Dag Hammarskjold Commemoration. Nos. 1351/6 optd **Homenaje a Hammarskjold Sept. 18-1961**.

1442 60c. blue and mauve 30 30
1443 75c. brown and green . . . 35 35
1444 90c. green and brown . . . 45 45
1445 1cor. mauve and blue . . . 50 50
1446 3cor. red and black 80 80
1447 5cor. blue and mauve . . . 1·50 1·50

1962. Air. Surch **RESELLO C$ 1.00**.

1448 – 1cor. on 1cor.10 brown (No. 1157) 30 25
1449 **207** 1cor. on 1cor.5 black and green 30 25

See also Nos. 1498/1500a, 1569/70, 1608/14, 1669/76 and 1748/62.

1962. Obligatory Tax. Nicaraguan Orchids. Mult.

1450 5c. Type **219** 10 10
1451 5c. "Bletia roezlii" 10 10
1452 5c. "Sobralia pleiantha" . . 10 10
1453 5c. "Lycaste macrophylla" 10 10
1454 5c. "Schomburgkia tibicinus" 10 10
1455 5c. "Maxillaria tenuifolia" 10 10
1456 5c. "Stanhopea ecornuta" 10 10
1457 5c. "Oncidium ascendens" and "O. cebolleta" . . . 10 10
1458 5c. "Cycnoches egertonianum" 10 10
1459 5c. "Hexisia bidentata" . . 10 10

220 U.N.E.S.C.O. "Audience" 222 Arms of Nueva Segovia

1962. Air. 15th Anniv of U.N.E.S.C.O.

1460 **220** 2cor. multicoloured . . . 15 15
1461 – 5cor. multicoloured . . . 80 80

DESIGN: 5cor. U.N. and U.N.E.S.C.O. emblems.

1962. Air. Malaria Eradication. Nos. 1425, 1428/31 optd with mosquito surrounded by **LUCHA CONTRA LA MALARIA**.

1462 – 10c. 35 30
1463 – 35c. 45 30
1464 – 70c. 60 45
1465 – 1cor.5 . . . . 80 65
1466 – 5cor. . . . . 1·00 1·25

1962. Urban and Provincial Arms. Arms mult; inscr black; background colours below.

1467 **222** 2c. mauve (postage) . . 10 10
1468 – 3c. blue 10 10
1469 – 4c. lilac 10 10
1470 – 5c. yellow 10 10
1471 – 6c. brown 10 10
1472 **222** 30c. red (air) 10 10
1473 – 50c. orange 15 10
1474 – 1cor. green 25 20
1475 – 2cor. grey 45 40
1476 – 5cor. blue 75 60

ARMS: 3c., 50c. Leon; 4c., 1cor. Managua; 5c., 2cor. Granada; 6c., 5cor. Rivas.

223 Liberty Bell

1963. Air. 150th Anniv of Independence.

1477 **223** 30c. drab, blue & black 15 10

224 Blessing

1963. Air. Death Tercentenary of St. Vincent de Paul and St. Louise de Marillac.

1478 – 60c. black and orange 15 10
1479 **224** 1cor. olive and orange 25 20
1480 – 2cor. black and red . . . 50 45

DESIGNS—VERT: 60c. "Comfort" (St. Louise and woman). HORIZ: 2cor. St. Vincent and St. Louise.

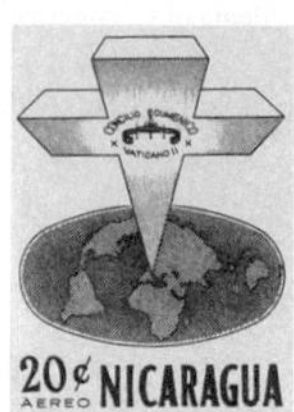

225 "Map Stamp" 226 Cross on Globe

1963. Air. Central American Philatelic Societies Federation Commemoration.

1481 **225** 1cor. blue and yellow . . 30 20

1963. Air. Ecumenical Council, Vatican City.

1482 **226** 20c. red and yellow . . . 15 10

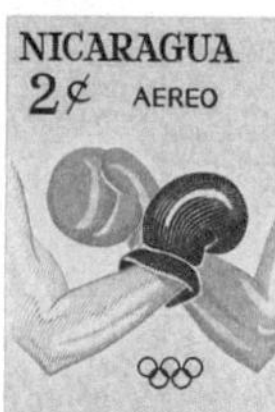

227 Ears of Wheat 228 Boxing

1963. Air. Freedom from Hunger.

1483 **227** 10c. green and light green 10 10
1484 – 25c. sepia and yellow . . 15 10

DESIGN: 25c. Barren tree and campaign emblem.

1963. Air. Sports. Multicoloured.

1485 2c. Type **228** 10 10
1486 3c. Running 10 10
1487 4c. Underwater harpooning 10 10
1488 5c. Football 10 10
1489 6c. Baseball 15 10
1490 10c. Tennis 20 10
1491 15c. Cycling 20 10
1492 20c. Motor-cycling 20 10
1493 35c. Chess 30 15
1494 60c. Angling 45 20
1495 1cor. Table-tennis 55 35

1496 2cor. Basketball	75	55
1497 5cor. Golf	1·90	1·10

1964. Air. Surch **Resello** or **RESELLO** (1500a) and value.

1498 – 5c. on 6c. (No. 1424)	35	10
1499 – 10c. on 30c. (No. 1365)	45	15
1500 **207** 15c. on 30c.	70	20
1500a **201** 20c. on 30c.	15	10

See also Nos. 1448/9, 1569/70, 1608/14 and 1669/76.

1964. Optd **CORREOS**.

1501 5c. multicoloured (No. 1451)	10	10

231 Flags

232 "Alliance Emblem"

1964. Air. "Centro America".

1502 **231** 40c. multicoloured	15	15

1964. Air. "Alliance for Progress". Multicoloured.

1503 5c. Type **232**	10	10
1504 10c. Red Cross post (horiz)	10	10
1505 15c. Highway (horiz)	10	10
1506 20c. Ploughing (horiz)	10	10
1507 25c. Housing (horiz)	15	10
1508 30c. Presidents Somoza and Kennedy and Eugene Black (World Bank) (horiz)	15	10
1509 35c. School and adults (horiz)	20	15
1510 40c. Chimneys (horiz)	25	15

233 Map of Member Countries

1964. Air. Central American "Common Market". Multicoloured.

1511 15c. Type **233**	10	10
1512 25c. Ears of wheat	10	10
1513 40c. Cogwheels	10	10
1514 50c. Heads of cattle	15	10

1964. Air. Olympic Games, Tokyo. Nos. 1485/7, 1489 and 1495/6 optd **OLIMPIADAS TOKYO - 1964**.

1515 2c. Type **108**	10	10
1516 3c. Running	10	10
1517 4c. Underwater harpooning	10	10
1518 6c. Baseball	10	10
1519 1cor. Table-tennis	1·10	1·10
1520 2cor. Basketball	2·25	2·25

235 Rescue of Wounded Soldier

1965. Air. Red Cross Centenary. Multicoloured.

1521 20c. Type **235**	10	10
1522 25c. Blood transfusion	15	10
1523 40c. Red Cross and snowbound town	15	15
1524 10cor. Red Cross and map of Nicaragua	1·50	1·50

236 Statuettes

1965. Air. Nicaraguan Antiquities. Multicoloured.

1525 5c. Type **236**	10	10
1526 10c. Totem	10	10
1527 15c. Carved dog (horiz)	10	10
1528 20c. Composition of "objets d'art"	10	10
1529 25c. Dish and vase (horiz)	10	10
1530 30c. Pestle and mortar	10	10
1531 35c. Statuettes (different) (horiz)	10	10
1532 40c. Deity	15	10
1533 50c. Wine vessel and dish	15	10
1534 60c. Bowl and dish (horiz)	20	10
1535 1cor. Urn	45	15

237 Pres. Kennedy

238 A. Bello

1965. Air. Pres. Kennedy Commemorative.

1536 **237** 35c. black and green	15	10
1537 75c. black and mauve	25	15
1538 1cor.10 black and blue	35	25
1539 2cor. black and brown	90	55

1965. Air. Death Centenary of Andres Bello (poet and writer).

1540 **238** 10c. black and brown	10	10
1541 15c. black and blue	10	10
1542 45c. black and purple	15	10
1543 80c. black and green	20	15
1544 1cor. black and yellow	25	20
1545 2cor. black and grey	45	45

1965. 9th Central American Scout Camporee. Nos. 1450/9 optd with scout badge and **CAMPOREE SCOUT 1965**.

1546 5c. multicoloured	20	20
1547 5c. multicoloured	20	20
1548 5c. multicoloured	20	20
1549 5c. multicoloured	20	20
1550 5c. multicoloured	20	20
1551 5c. multicoloured	20	20
1552 5c. multicoloured	20	20
1553 5c. multicoloured	20	20
1554 5c. multicoloured	20	20
1555 5c. multicoloured	20	20

240 Sir Winston Churchill

241 Pope John XXIII

1966. Air. Churchill Commemorative.

1556 **240** 20c. mauve and black	10	10
1557 – 35c. green and black	15	10
1558 – 60c. ochre and black	15	15
1559 – 75c. red	20	20
1560 – 1cor. purple	30	25
1561 **240** 2cor. violet, lilac & black	60	55
1562 – 3cor. blue and black	65	60

DESIGNS—HORIZ: 35c., 1cor. Churchill broadcasting. VERT: 60c., 3cor. Churchill crossing the Rhine; 75c. Churchill in Hussars' uniform.

1966. Air. Closure of Vatican Ecumenical Council. Multicoloured.

1564 20c. Type **241**	10	10
1565 35c. Pope Paul VI	15	15
1566 1cor. Archbishop Gonzalez y Robleto	30	25
1567 2cor. St. Peter's, Rome	30	25
1568 3cor. Papal arms	60	40

1967. Air. Nos. 1533/4 surch **RESELLO** and value.

1569 10c. on 50c. multicoloured	10	10
1570 15c. on 60c. multicoloured	10	10

See also Nos. 1448/9, 1498/1500a, 1608/14 and 1669/76.

243 Dario and Birthplace

1967. Air. Birth Centenary of Ruben Dario (poet). Designs showing Dario and view. Multicoloured.

1571 5c. Type **243**	10	10
1572 10c. Monument, Managua	10	10
1573 20c. Leon Cathedral (site of Dario's tomb)	10	10
1574 40c. Allegory of the centaurs	15	10
1575 75c. Allegory of the mute swans	30	20
1576 1cor. Roman triumphal march	25	20
1577 2cor. St. Francis and the wolf	45	40
1578 5cor. "Faith" opposing "Death"	65	60

244 "Megalura peleus"

1967. Air. Butterflies. Multicoloured.

1580 5c. "Heliconius petiveranua" (vert)	10	10
1581 10c. "Colaenis julia" (vert)	10	10
1582 15c. Type **244**	10	10
1583 20c. "Aneyluris jurgensii"	10	10
1584 25c. "Thecla regalis"	10	10
1585 30c. "Doriana thia" (vert)	10	10
1586 35c. "Lymnias pixae" (vert)	15	10
1587 40c. "Metamorpho dido"	25	10
1588 50c. "Papilio arcas" (vert)	25	15
1589 60c. "Ananea cleomestra"	35	15
1590 1cor. "Victorina epaphaus" (vert)	60	30
1591 2cor. "Prepona demophon"	1·10	50

245 McDivitt and White

1967. Air. Space Flight of McDivitt and White. Multicoloured.

1592 5c. Type **245**	10	10
1593 10c. Astronauts and "Gemini 5" on launching pad	10	10
1594 15c. "Gemini 5" and White in Space	10	10
1595 20c. Recovery operation at sea	15	10
1596 35c. Type **245**	10	10
1597 40c. As 10c.	15	10
1598 75c. As 15c.	20	20
1599 1cor. As 20c.	35	25

246 National Flower of Costa Rica

1967. Air. 5th Year of Central American Economic Integration. Designs showing national flowers of Central American countries. Multicoloured.

1600 40c. Type **246**	15	10
1601 40c. Guatemala	15	10
1602 40c. Honduras	15	10
1603 40c. Nicaragua	15	10
1604 40c. El Salvador	15	10

247 Presidents Diaz and Somoza

1968. Air. Visit of Pres. Diaz of Mexico.

1605 – 20c. black	10	10
1606 **247** 40c. olive	20	10
1607 – 1cor. brown	35	20

DESIGNS—VERT: 20c. Pres. Somoza greeting Pres. Diaz; 1cor. Pres. Diaz of Mexico.

1968. Surch **RESELLO** and value.

1608 – 5c. on 6c. (No. 1180) (postage)	10	10
1609 – 5c. on 6c. (No. 1471)	10	10
1610 – 5c. on 6c. (No. 1424) (air)	10	10
1611 – 5c. on 6c. (No. 1489)	10	10
1612 **156** 5c. on 8c. (No. 1035)	10	10
1614 – 1cor. on 1cor.50 (No. 1369)	25	20

See also Nos. 1448/9, 1498/1500a, 1569/70 and 1669/76.

249 Mangoes

1968. Air. Nicaraguan Fruits. Multicoloured.

1615 5c. Type **249**	10	10
1616 10c. Pineapples	10	10
1617 15c. Oranges	10	10
1618 20c. Pawpaws	10	10
1619 30c. Bananas	10	10
1620 35c. Avocado pears	15	10
1621 50c. Water-melons	15	10
1622 75c. Cashews	25	15
1623 1cor. Sapodilla plums	35	20
1624 2cor. Cocoa beans	45	20

250 "The Crucifixion" (Fra Angelico)

1968. Air. Religious Paintings. Multicoloured.

1625 10c. Type **250**	10	10
1626 15c. "The Last Judgement" (Michelangelo) (vert)	10	10
1627 35c. "The Beautiful Gardener" (Raphael) (vert)	15	15
1628 2cor. "The Spoliation of Christ" (El Greco) (vert)	45	30
1629 3cor. "The Conception" (Murillo) (vert)	60	45

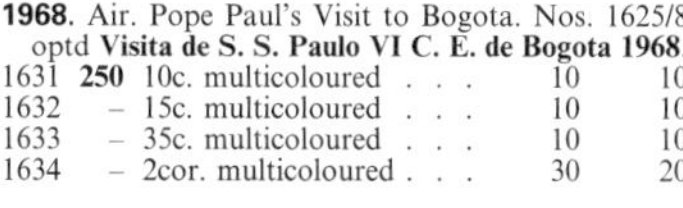

1968. Air. Pope Paul's Visit to Bogota. Nos. 1625/8 optd **Visita de S. S. Paulo VI C. E. de Bogota 1968**.

1631 **250** 10c. multicoloured	10	10
1632 – 15c. multicoloured	10	10
1633 – 35c. multicoloured	10	10
1634 – 2cor. multicoloured	30	20

252 Basketball

1969. Air. Olympic Games, Mexico. Mult.

1635 10c. Type **252**	10	10
1636 15c. Fencing (horiz)	10	10
1637 20c. High-diving	10	10
1638 35c. Running	10	10
1639 50c. Hurdling (horiz)	15	10
1640 75c. Weightlifting	20	15
1641 1cor. Boxing (horiz)	35	20
1642 2cor. Football	55	55

253 Midas Cichlid

1969. Air. Fishes. Multicoloured.

1644 10c. Type **253**	10	10
1645 15c. Moga cichlid	10	10
1646 20c. Common carp	20	10
1647 30c. Tropical gar	25	10
1648 35c. Swordfish	30	10
1649 50c. Big-mouthed sleeper	35	15
1650 75c. Atlantic tarpon	40	20
1651 1cor. Lake Nicaragua shark	60	25
1652 2cor. Sailfish	75	45
1653 3cor. Small-toothed sawfish	1·40	70

1969. Air. Various stamps surch **RESELLO** and value.

1655 10c. on 25c. (No. 1507)	10	10
1656 10c. on 25c. (No. 1512)	10	10
1657 15c. on 25c. (No. 1529)	10	10
1658 50c. on 70c. (No. 1379)	15	10

255 Scenery, Tower and Emblem

258 "Minerals"

1969. Air. "Hemisfair" (1968) Exhibition.

1659 **255** 30c. blue and red	10	10
1660 35c. purple and red	10	10
1661 75c. red and blue	15	10

1662 1cor. purple and black 30 20
1663 2cor. purple and green 55 40

1969. Various stamps surch. (a) Optd **CORREO**.
1665 5c. (No. 1450) 10 10
1666 5c. (No. 1453) 10 10
1667 5c. (No. 1454) 10 10
1668 5c. (No. 1459) 10 10

(b) Optd **RESELLO** and surch.
1670 10c. on 30c. (No. 1324) 10 10
1671 10c. on 30c. (No. 1427) 10 10
1669 10c. on 25c. (No. 1529) 10 10
1672 10c. on 30c. (No. 1530) 10 10
1673 15c. on 35c. (No. 1531) 10 10
1674 20c. on 30c. (No. 1307) 10 10
1675 20c. on 30c. (No. 1401) 10 10
1676 20c. on 35c. (No. 1509) 10 10

1969. Air. Nicaraguan Products. Multicoloured.
1677 5c. Type **258** 10 10
1678 10c. "Fish" 10 10
1679 15c. "Bananas" 10 10
1680 20c. "Timber" 10 10
1681 35c. "Coffee" 10 10
1682 40c. "Sugar-cane" 15 10
1683 60c. "Cotton" 20 10
1684 75c. "Rice and Maize" 20 15
1685 1cor. "Tobacco" 30 20
1686 2cor. "Meat" 35 25

1969. 50th Anniv of I.L.O. Obligatory tax stamps. Nos. 1450/9, optd **O.I.T. 1919-1969**.
1687 5c. multicoloured 10 10
1688 5c. multicoloured 10 10
1689 5c. multicoloured 10 10
1690 5c. multicoloured 10 10
1691 5c. multicoloured 10 10
1692 5c. multicoloured 10 10
1693 5c. multicoloured 10 10
1694 5c. multicoloured 10 10
1695 5c. multicoloured 10 10
1696 5c. multicoloured 10 10

260 Girl carrying Tinaja

261 Pele (Brazil)

1970. Air. 8th Inter-American Savings and Loans Conference, Managua.
1697 **260** 10c. multicoloured 10 10
1698 15c. multicoloured 10 10
1699 20c. multicoloured 10 10
1700 35c. multicoloured 10 10
1701 50c. multicoloured 15 10
1702 75c. multicoloured 20 15
1703 1cor. multicoloured 30 20
1704 2cor. multicoloured 60 40

1970. World Football "Hall of Fame" Poll-winners. Multicoloured.
1705 5c. Type **261** (postage) 10 10
1706 10c. Puskas (Hungary) 10 10
1707 15c. Matthews (England) 10 10
1708 40c. Di Stefano (Argentina) 10 10
1709 2cor. Facchetti (Italy) 55 45
1710 3cor. Yashin (Russia) 70 65
1711 5cor. Beckenbauer (West Germany) 70 90
1712 20c. Santos (Brazil) (air) 10 10
1713 80c. Wright (England) 20 15
1714 1cor. Flags of 16 World Cup finalists 25 20
1715 4cor. Bozsik (Hungary) 90 75
1716 5cor. Charlton (England) 1·10 90

262 Torii (Gate)

263 Module and Astronauts on Moon

1970. Air. EXPO 70, World Fair, Osaka, Japan.
1717 **262** 25c. multicoloured 10 10
1718 30c. multicoloured 10 10
1719 35c. multicoloured 10 10
1720 75c. multicoloured 25 15
1721 1cor.50 multicoloured 35 30
1722 3cor. multicoloured 45 35

1970. Air. "Apollo 11" Moon Landing (1969). Mult.
1724 35c. Type **263** 10 10
1725 40c. Module landing on Moon 10 10
1726 60c. Astronauts with U.S. flag 20 15
1727 75c. As 40c. 25 15
1728 1cor. As 60c. 35 20
1729 2cor. Type **263** 40 35

264 F. D. Roosevelt

265 "The Annunciation" (Grunewald)

1970. Air. 25th Death Anniv of Franklin D. Roosevelt.
1730 **264** 10c. black 10 10
1731 – 15c. brown and black 10 10
1732 – 20c. green and black 10 10
1733 **264** 35c. purple and black 10 10
1734 – 50c. brown 15 10
1735 **264** 75c. blue 20 15
1736 – 1cor. red 25 20
1737 – 2cor. black 30 35
PORTRAITS: 15c., 1cor. Roosevelt with stamp collection; 20c., 50c., 2cor. Roosevelt (full-face).

1970. Air. Christmas. Paintings. Multicoloured.
1738 10c. Type **265** 10 10
1739 10c. "The Nativity" (detail, El Greco) 10 10
1740 10c. "The Adoration of the Magi" (detail, Durer) 10 10
1741 10c. "Virgin and Child" (J. van Hemessen) 10 10
1742 10c. "The Holy Shepherd" (Portuguese School, 16th cent) 10 10
1743 15c. Type **265** 10 10
1744 20c. As No. 1739 10 10
1745 35c. As No. 1740 15 10
1746 75c. As No. 1741 20 15
1747 1cor. As No. 1742 30 20

1971. Surch **RESELLO** and new value.
1748 30c. on 90c. black (No. 1227) (postage) 10·00 10·00
1749 10c. on 1cor.5 red, black & red (No. 1368) (air) 10 10
1750 10c. on 1cor.5 mult (No. 1407) 10 10
1751 10c. on 1cor.5 mult (No. 1430) 10 10
1752 15c. on 1cor.50 green and red (No. 1116) 10 10
1753 15c. on 1cor.50 green (No. 1255) 10 10
1754 15c. on 1cor.50 yellow and blue (No. 1369) 10 10
1755 15c. on 1cor.50 black and violet (No. 1381) 10 10
1756 20c. on 85c. black and red (No. 1276) 15 10
1757 20c. on 85c. black, red and blue (No. 1339) 15 10
1758 25c. on 90c. black, green and ochre (No. 1440) 15 15
1759 30c. on 1cor.10 black and purple (No. 1195) 15 15
1760 40c. on 1cor.10 brown and black (No. 1157) 65 65
1761 40c. on 1cor.50 mult (No. 1408) 65 65
1762 1cor. on 1cor.10 black and blue (No. 1538) 1·60 1·60

266 Basic Mathematical Equation

1971. Scientific Formulae. "The Ten Mathematical Equations that changed the Face of the Earth". Multicoloured.
1763 10c. Type **266** (postage) 10 10
1764 15c. Newton's Law 10 10
1765 20c. Einstein's Law 10 10
1766 1cor. Tsiolkovsky's Law 25 25
1767 2cor. Maxwell's Law 90 75
1768 25c. Napier's Law (air) 10 10
1769 30c. Pythagoras' Law 10 10
1770 40c. Boltzmann's Law 15 10
1771 1cor. Broglie's Law 30 20
1772 2cor. Archimedes' Law 55 40

267 Peace Emblem

1971. "Is There a Formula for Peace?"
1773 **267** 10c. blue and black 10 10
1774 15c. blue, black and violet 10 10
1775 20c. blue, black & brown 10 10
1776 40c. blue, black and green 10 10
1777 50c. blue, black & purple 15 10

1778 80c. blue, black and red 15 15
1779 1cor. blue, black & green 30 20
1780 2cor. blue, black & violet 55 35

268 Montezuma Oropendola

269 "Moses with the Tablets of the Law" (Rembrandt)

1971. Air. Nicaraguan Birds. Multicoloured.
1781 10c. Type **268** 45 20
1782 15c. Turquoise-browed motmot 45 20
1783 20c. White-throated magpie-jay 55 20
1784 25c. Scissor-tailed flycatcher 55 20
1785 30c. Spotted-breasted oriole (horiz) 70 20
1786 35c. Rufous-naped wren 85 20
1787 40c. Great kiskadee 85 20
1788 75c. Red-legged honeycreeper (horiz) 1·50 40
1789 1cor. Great-tailed grackle (horiz) 1·75 50
1790 2cor. Belted kingfisher 5·50 1·00

1971. "The Ten Commandments". Paintings. Multicoloured.
1791 10c. Type **269** (postage) 10 10
1792 15c. "Moses and the Burning Bush" (Botticelli) (1st Commandment) 10 10
1793 20c. "Jepthah's Daughter" (Degas) (2nd Commandment) (horiz) 10 10
1794 30c. "St. Vincent Ferrer preaching in Verona" (Morone) (3rd Commandment) (horiz) 10 10
1795 35c. "Noah's Drunkenness" (Michelangelo) (4th Commandment) (horiz) 10 10
1796 40c. "Cain and Abel" (Trevisani) (5th Commandment) (horiz) 10 10
1797 50c. "Joseph accused by Potiphar's Wife" (Rembrandt) (6th Commandment) 10 10
1798 60c. "Isaac blessing Jacob" (Eeckhout) (7th Commandment) (horiz) 15 10
1799 75c. "Susannah and the Elders" (Rubens) (8th Commandment) (horiz) 25 20
1800 1cor. "Bathsheba after her Bath" (Rembrandt) (9th Commandment) (air) 25 20
1801 2cor. "Naboth's Vineyard" (Smetham) (10th Commandment) 40 35

270 U Thant and Pres. Somoza

1971. Air. 25th Anniv of U.N.O.
1802 **270** 10c. brown and red 10 10
1803 15c. green and emerald 10 10
1804 20c. blue and light blue 10 10
1805 25c. red and purple 10 10
1806 30c. brown and orange 10 10
1807 40c. green and grey 15 10
1808 1cor. green and sage 25 20
1809 2cor. brown & light brown 30 35

1972. Olympic Games, Munich. Nos. 1709, 1711, 1713 and 1716 surch **OLIMPIADAS MUNICH 1972**, emblem and value or optd only (5cor.).
1810 40c. on 2cor. multicoloured (postage) 10 10
1811 50c. on 3cor. multicoloured 15 10
1812 20c. on 80c. mult (air) 10 10
1813 60c. on 4cor. multicoloured 15 10
1814 5cor. multicoloured 65 65

272 Figurine and Apoyo Site on Map

1972. Air. Pre-Columbian Art. A. H. Heller's Pottery Discoveries. Multicoloured.
1815 10c. Type **272** 10 10
1816 15c. Cana Castilla 10 10
1817 20c. Catarina 10 10
1818 25c. Santa Helena 10 10
1819 30c. Mombacho 10 10
1820 35c. Tisma 10 10
1821 40c. El Menco 10 10
1822 50c. Los Placeres 15 10
1823 60c. Masaya 15 15
1824 80c. Granada 20 15
1825 1cor. Las Mercedes 30 20
1826 2cor. Nindiri 55 35

273 "Lord Peter Wimsey" (Dorothy Sayers)

1972. Air. 50th Anniv of International Criminal Police Organization (INTERPOL). Famous Fictional Detectives. Multicoloured.
1827 5c. Type **273** 10 10
1828 10c. "Philip Marlowe" (Raymond Chandler) 10 10
1829 15c. "Sam Spade" (D. Hammett) 6·00 20
1830 20c. "Perry Mason" (Erle Stanley Gardner) 10 10
1831 25c. "Nero Wolfe" (Rex Stout) 10 10
1832 35c. "C. Auguste Dupin" (Edgar Allan Poe) 10 10
1833 40c. "Ellery Queen" (F. Dannay and M. Lee) 10 10
1834 50c. "Father Brown" (G. K. Chesterton) 10 10
1835 60c. "Charlie Chan" (Earl D. Biggers) 15 10
1836 80c. "Inspector Maigret" (Georges Simenon) 25 15
1837 1cor. "Hercule Poirot" (Agatha Christie) 25 20
1838 2cor. "Sherlock Holmes" (A. Conan Doyle) 70 70

274 "The Shepherdess and her Brothers"

1972. Air. Christmas. Scenes from Legend of the Christmas Rose. Multicoloured.
1839 10c. Type **274** 10 10
1840 15c. Adoration of the Wise Men 10 10
1841 20c. Shepherdess crying 10 10
1842 35c. Angel appears to Shepherdess 10 10
1843 40c. Christmas Rose 10 10
1844 60c. Shepherdess thanks angel for roses 15 10
1845 80c. Shepherdess takes roses to Holy Child 15 15
1846 1cor. Holy Child receiving roses 20 15
1847 2cor. Nativity scene 45 35

275 Sir Walter Raleigh and Elizabethan Galleon

1973. Air. Causes of the American Revolution. Multicoloured.
1849 10c. Type **275** 40 10
1850 15c. Signing "Mayflower Compact" 10 10
1851 20c. Acquittal of Peter Zenger (vert) 10 10
1852 25c. Acclaiming American resistance (vert) 10 10
1853 30c. Revenue stamp (vert) 10 10
1854 35c. "Serpent" slogan—"Join or die" 10 10
1855 40c. Boston Massacre (vert) 10 10
1856 50c. Boston Tea-party 10 10
1857 60c. Patrick Henry on trial (vert) 15 10
1858 75c. Battle of Bunker Hill 20 10
1859 80c. Declaration of Independence 20 15
1860 1cor. Liberty Bell 30 20
1861 2cor. US seal (vert) 90 60

1973. Nos. 1450/54, 1456 and 1458/9 optd **CORREO**.
1862 **219** 5c. multicoloured 25 10
1863 – 5c. multicoloured 25 10
1864 – 5c. multicoloured 25 10
1865 – 5c. multicoloured 25 10
1866 – 5c. multicoloured 25 10
1867 – 5c. multicoloured 25 10

1868 – 5c. multicoloured 25 10
1869 – 5c. multicoloured 25 10

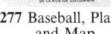

277 Baseball, Player and Map — 278 Givenchy, Paris

1973. Air. 20th International Baseball Championships, Managua (1972).
1870 **277** 15c. multicoloured . . . 10 10
1871 20c. multicoloured . . . 10 10
1872 40c. multicoloured . . . 10 10
1873 10cor. multicoloured . . 1·50 90

1973. World-famous Couturiers. Mannequins. Mult.
1875 1cor. Type **278** (postage) . . 25 20
1876 2cor. Hartnell, London . . 40 40
1877 5cor. Balmain, Paris . . . . 1·00 90
1878 10c. Lourdes, Nicaragua (air) 10 10
1879 15c. Halston, New York . . 10 10
1880 20c. Pino Lancetti, Rome 10 10
1881 35c. Madame Gres, Paris . . 10 10
1882 40c. Irene Galitzine, Rome 10 10
1883 80c. Pedro Rodriguez, Barcelona 15 15

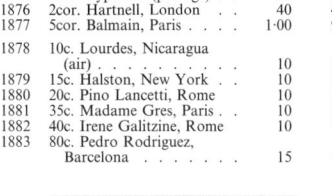

279 Diet Chart

1973. Air. Child Welfare. Multicoloured.
1885 5c.+5c. Type **279** 10 10
1886 10c.+5c. Senora Samoza with baby, and Children's Hospital 10 10
1887 15c.+5c. "Childbirth" . . . 10 10
1888 20c.+5c. "Immunization" . . 10 10
1889 30c.+5c. Water purification 10 10
1890 35c.+5c. As No. 1886 . . . 10 10
1891 50c.+10c. Alexander Fleming and "Antibiotics" 30 10
1892 60c.+15c. Malaria control 15 10
1893 70c.+10c. Laboratory analysis 15 15
1894 80c.+20c. Gastroenteritis . . 20 15
1895 1cor.+50c. As No. 1886 . . 30 25
1896 2cor. Pediatric surgery . . . 45 35

280 Virginia and Father

1973. Christmas. "Does Santa Claus exist?" (Virginia O'Hanlon's letter to American "Sun" newspaper). Multicoloured.
1897 2c. Type **280** (postage) . . . 10 10
1898 3c. Text of letter 10 10
1899 4c. Reading the reply . . . 10 10
1900 5c. Type **280** 10 10
1901 15c. As 3c. 10 10
1902 20c. As 4c. 10 10
1903 1cor. Type **280** (air) 20 15
1904 2cor. As 3c. 35 30
1905 4cor. As 4c. 75 65

281 Churchill making Speech, 1936

1974. Birth Cent of Sir Winston Churchill.
1907 **281** 2c. multicoloured (postage) 10 10
1908 – 3c. black, blue and brown 10 10
1909 – 4c. multicoloured 10 10
1910 – 5c. multicoloured 10 10
1911 – 10c. brown, green & blue 30 10
1912 – 5cor. multicoloured (air) 90 80
1913 – 6cor. black, brown & bl 1·00 90
DESIGNS: 3c. "The Four Churchills" (wartime cartoon); 4c. Candle, cigar and "Action" stickers; 5c. Churchill, Roosevelt and Stalin at Yalta; 10c. Churchill landing in Normandy, 1944; 5cor. Churchill giving "V" sign; 6cor. "Bulldog Churchill" (cartoon).

282 Presentation of World Cup to Uruguay, 1930

1974. World Cup Football Championship. Mult.
1915 1c. Type **282** (postage) . . . 10 10
1916 2c. Victorious Italian team, 1934 . . . . 10 10
1917 3c. Presentation of World Cup to Italy, 1938 . . . . 10 10
1918 4c. Uruguay's winning goal, 1950 . . . . 10 10
1919 5c. Victorious West Germany, 1954 . . . . . 10 10
1920 10c. Rejoicing Brazilian players, 1958 . . . . . . 10 10
1921 15c. Brazilian player holding World Cup, 1962 . . . . 10 10
1922 20c. Queen Elizabeth II presenting Cup to Bobby Moore, 1966 . . . . . . 10 10
1923 25c. Victorious Brazilian players, 1970 . . . . . . 10 10
1924 10cor. Football and flags of participating countries, 1974 (air) . . . . 1·75 1·75

283 "Malachra sp."

284 Nicaraguan 7½c. Stamp of 1937

1974. Wild Flowers and Cacti. Multicoloured.
1926 2c. Type **283** (postage) . . . 10 10
1927 3c. "Paguira insignis" . . . 10 10
1928 4c. "Convolvulus sp." . . . 10 10
1929 5c. "Pereschia autumnalis" . 10 10
1930 10c. "Ipomea tuberosa" . . 10 10
1931 15c. "Hibiscus elatus" . . . 10 10
1932 20c. "Plumeria acutifolia" . 10 10
1933 1cor. "Centrosema sp." (air) 20 20
1934 3cor. "Hylocereus undatus" 60 55

1974. Centenary of U.P.U.
1935 **284** 2c. red, green & blk (postage) 10 20
1936 – 3c. blue, green and black 10 10
1937 – 4c. multicoloured 10 10
1938 – 5c. brown, mauve & blk 10 10
1939 – 10c. red, brown and black 10 10
1940 – 20c. green, blue and black 10 10
1941 – 40c. multicoloured (air) 10 10
1942 – 3cor. green, black & pink 50 40
1943 – 5cor. blue, black and lilac . . . . 1·00 80
DESIGNS—VERT: 3c. 5c. stamp of 1937; 5c. 2c. stamp of 1937; 10c. 1c. stamp of 1937; 20c. ½c. stamp of 1937; 40c. 10c. stamp of 1961; 5cor. 4cor. U.P.U. stamp of 1950. HORIZ: 4c. 10c. air stamp of 1934; 3cor. 85c. U.P.U. air stamp of 1950.

1974. Air. West Germany's Victory in World Cup Football Championship. No. 1924 optd **TRIUMFADOR ALEMANIA OCCIDENTAL**.
1945 10cor. multicoloured . . . . 1·75 1·60

286 Tamandua

1974. Nicaraguan Fauna. Multicoloured.
1947 1c. Type **286** (postage) . . . 10 10
1948 2c. Puma 10 10
1949 3c. Common raccoon . . . 10 10
1950 4c. Ocelot 10 10
1951 5c. Kinkajou 10 10
1952 10c. Coypu 10 10
1953 15c. Collared peccary . . . 15 10
1954 20c. Baird's tapir 15 10
1955 3cor. Red brocket (air) . . . 1·50 1·40
1956 5cor. Jaguar . . . . 2·40 2·00

287 "Prophet Zacharias"

1975. Christmas. 500th Birth Anniv of Michelangelo. Multicoloured.
1957 1c. Type **287** (postage) . . . 10 10
1958 2c. "Christ amongst the Jews" 10 10
1959 3c. "The Creation of Man" (horiz) 10 10
1960 4c. Interior of Sistine Chapel, Rome 10 10
1961 5c. "Moses" 10 10
1962 10c. "Mouscron Madonna" 10 10
1963 15c. "David" 10 10
1964 20c. "Doni Madonna" . . . 10 10
1965 40c. "Madonna of the Steps" (air) 10 10
1966 80c. "Pitti Madonna" . . . 15 15
1967 2cor. "Christ and Virgin Mary" 35 30
1968 5cor. "Michelangelo" (self-portrait) 75 75

288 Giovanni Martinelli ("Othello")

1975. Great Opera Singers. Multicoloured.
1970 1c. Type **288** (postage) . . . 10 10
1971 2c. Tito Gobbi ("Simone Boccanegra") 10 10
1972 3c. Lotte Lehmann ("Der Rosenkavalier") 10 10
1973 4c. Lauritz Melchior ("Parsifal") 10 10
1974 5c. Nellie Melba ("La Traviata") 10 10
1975 15c. Jussi Bjoerling ("La Boheme") 10 10
1976 20c. Birgit Nilsson ("Turandot") 10 10
1977 25c. Rosa Ponselle ("Norma") (air) 10 10
1978 35c. Guiseppe de Luca ("Rigoletto") 10 10
1979 40c. Joan Sutherland ("La Figlia del Reggimiento") 10 10
1980 50c. Enzio Pinza ("Don Giovanni") 10 10
1981 60c. Kirsten Flagstad ("Tristan and Isolde") . . 15 10
1982 80c. Maria Callas ("Tosca") 15 15
1983 2cor. Fyodor Chaliapin ("Boris Godunov") . . . 60 35
1984 5cor. Enrico Caruso ("La Juive") . . . . 1·10 60

289 The First Station

290 "The Spirit of 76"

1975. Easter. The 14 Stations of the Cross.
1986 **289** 1c. multicoloured (postage) 10 10
1987 – 2c. multicoloured 10 10
1988 – 3c. multicoloured 10 10
1989 – 4c. multicoloured 10 10
1990 – 5c. multicoloured 10 10
1991 – 15c. multicoloured . . . 10 10
1992 – 20c. multicoloured . . . 10 10
1993 – 25c. multicoloured . . . 10 10
1994 – 35c. multicoloured . . . 10 10
1995 – 40c. multicoloured (air) 10 10
1996 – 50c. multicoloured . . . 10 10
1997 – 80c. multicoloured . . . 15 15
1998 – 1cor. multicoloured . . . 20 15
1999 – 5cor. multicoloured . . . 80 65
DESIGNS: 2c. to 5cor. Different Stations of the Cross.

1975. Bicentenary of American Independence (1st series). Multicoloured.
2000 1c. Type **290** (postage) . . . 10 10
2001 2c. Pitt addressing Parliament 10 10
2002 3c. Paul Revere's Ride (horiz) 10 10
2003 4c. Demolishing statue of George III (horiz) 10 10
2004 5c. Boston Massacre 10 10
2005 10c. Tax stamp and George III 3d. coin (horiz) . . . 10 10
2006 15c. Boston Tea Party (horiz) 10 10
2007 20c. Thomas Jefferson . . . 10 10
2008 25c. Benjamin Franklin . . 10 10
2009 30c. Signing of Declaration of Independence (horiz) 10 10
2010 35c. Surrender of Cornwallis at Yorktown (horiz) . . . 10 10
2011 40c. Washington's Farewell (horiz) (air) 10 10
2012 50c. Washington addressing Congress (horiz) 10 10
2013 2cor. Washington arriving for Presidential Inauguration (horiz) . . . 70 30
2014 5cor. Statue of Liberty and flags 75 45
See also Nos. 2056/71.

291 Saluting the Flag

1975. "Nordjamb 75" World Scout Jamboree, Norway. Multicoloured.
2016 1c. Type **291** (postage) . . . 10 10
2017 2c. Scout canoe 10 10
2018 3c. Scouts shaking hands . . 10 10
2019 4c. Scout preparing meal . . 10 10
2020 5c. Entrance to Nicaraguan camp 10 10
2021 20c. Scouts meeting 10 10
2022 35c. Aerial view of camp (air) 10 10
2023 40c. Scouts making music 10 10
2024 1cor. Camp-fire 20 15
2025 10cor. Lord Baden-Powell 1·25 1·10

292 President Somoza

1975. President Somoza's New Term of Office, 1974–81.
2027 **292** 20c. multicoloured (postage) 10 10
2028 40c. multicoloured . . . 10 10
2029 1cor. multicoloured (air) 20 20
2030 10cor. multicoloured . . 1·25 1·10
2031 20cor. multicoloured . . 3·25 2·75

293 "Chess Players" (L. Carracci)

1975. Chess. Multicoloured.
2032 1c. Type **293** (postage) . . . 10 10
2033 2c. "Arabs playing Chess" (Delacroix) 10 10
2034 3c. "Cardinals playing Chess" (V. Marais-Milton) 10 10
2035 4c. "Duke Albrecht V of Bavaria and Anna of Austria at Chess" (H. Muelich) (vert) . . . 10 10
2036 5c. "Chess game" (14th-century Persian manuscript) 10 10
2037 10c. "Origins of Chess" (India, 1602) 10 10
2038 15c. "Napoleon playing Chess in Schonbrunn Palace in 1809" (A. Uniechowski) (vert) 10 10
2039 20c. "The Chess Game in the House of Count Ingenheim" (J.E. Hummel) 10 10
2040 40c. "The Chess-players" (T. Eakins) (air) 10 10
2041 2cor. Fischer v Spassky match, Reykjavik, 1972 55 35
2042 5cor. "William Shakespeare and Ben Jonson playing Chess" (K. van Mander) 60 50

294 Choir of King's College, Cambridge

1975. Christmas. Famous Choirs. Multicoloured.
2044 1c. Type **294** (postage) . . . 10 10
2045 2c. Abbey Choir, Einsiedeln 10 10
2046 3c. Regensburg Cathedral choir 10 10
2047 4c. Vienna Boys' choir . . . 10 10
2048 5c. Sistine Chapel choir . . 10 10
2049 15c. Westminster Cathedral choir 10 10
2050 20c. Mormon Tabernacle choir 10 10
2051 50c. School choir, Montserrat (air) 10 10
2052 1cor. St. Florian children's choir 20 15
2053 2cor. "Little Singers of the Wooden Cross" (vert) . . 45 35
2054 5cor. Pope with choristers of Pueri Cantores 60 50

295 "The Smoke Signal" (F. Remington)

1976. Bicent of American Revolution (2nd series). "200 Years of Progress". Multicoloured.
2056 1c. Type **295** (postage) . . . 10 10
2057 1c. Houston Space Centre 10 10
2058 2c. Lighting candelabra, 1976 . . . . 10 10
2059 2c. Edison's lamp and houses 10 10
2060 3c. "Agriculture 1776" . . . 10 10
2061 3c. "Agriculture 1976" . . . 10 10
2062 4c. Harvard College, 1776 10 10
2063 4c. Harvard University, 1976 . . . . 10 10
2064 5c. Horse and carriage . . . 15 10
2065 5c. Boeing 747-100 airliner 15 10
2066 80c. Philadelphia, 1776 (air) 25 15
2067 80c. Washington, 1976 . . . 25 15
2068 2cor.75 "Bonhomme Richard" (American frigate) (John Paul Jones's flagship) and H.M.S. "Seraphis" (frigate), Battle of Flamborough Head . . 1·50 70
2069 2cor.75 U.S.S. "Glenard Phipscomp" (nuclear submarine) . . . . 1·50 70
2070 4cor. Wagon train 90 70
2071 4cor. Amtrak gas turbine train, 1973 . . . . 3·25 1·75

296 Italy, 1968

1976. Olympic Games, Victors in Rowing and Sculling. Multicoloured.
2073 1c. Denmark 1964 (postage) 10 10
2074 2c. East Germany 1972 . . 10 10
2075 3c. Type **296** 10 10
2076 4c. Great Britain 1936 . . . 10 10
2077 5c. France 1952 (vert) . . . 10 10
2078 35c. U.S.A. 1920 (vert) . . . 10 10
2079 55c. Russia 1956 (vert) (air) 20 10
2080 70c. New Zealand 1972 (vert) 20 15
2081 90c. New Zealand 1968 . . 25 20
2082 20cor. U.S.A. 1956 . . . . 2·75 2·50

1976. Air. Olympic Games, Montreal. East German Victory in Rowing Events. No. 2082 optd **REPUBLICA DEMOCRATICA ALEMANA VENCEDOR EN 1976.**
2084 20cor. multicoloured . . . . 2·75 2·50

299 Mauritius 1847 2d. "Post Office"

1976. Rare and Famous Stamps. Multicoloured.
2087 1c. Type **299** (postage) . . . 10 10
2088 2c. Western Australia 1854 "Inverted Mute Swan" . . 85 15
2089 3c. Mauritius 1847 1d. "Post Office" 10 10
2090 4c. Jamaica 1920 1s. inverted frame 10 10
2091 5c. U.S 1918 24c. inverted aircraft 10 10
2092 10c. Swiss 1845 Basel "Dove" 10 10
2093 25c. Canada 1959 Seaway inverted centre 10 10
2094 40c. Hawaiian 1851 2c. "Missionary" (air) 10 10
2095 1cor. G.B. 1840 "Penny Black" 20 20
2096 2cor. British Guiana 1850 1c. black on magenta . . 40 35
2097 5cor. Honduras 1925 airmail 25c. on 10c. . . . . . . 3·50 1·10
2098 10cor. Newfoundland 1919 "Hawker" airmail stamp 1·25 1·10

300 Olga Nunez de Saballos (Member of Parliament)

1977. Air. International Women's Year. Multicoloured.
2100 35c. Type **300** 10 10
2101 1cor. Josefa Toledo de Aguerri (educator) 20 20
2102 10cor. Hope Portocarreo de Samoza (President's wife) 1·25 1·00

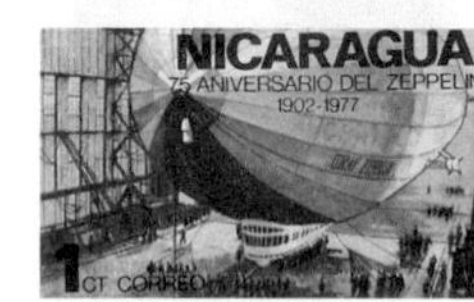

301 "Graf Zeppelin" in Hangar

1977. 75th Anniv of First Zeppelin Flight. Mult.
2104 1c. Type **301** (postage) . . . 10 10
2105 2c. "Graf Zeppelin" in flight 10 10
2106 3c. Giffard's steam-powered dirigible airship, 1852 . . 15 10
2107 4c. "Graf Zeppelin" in mooring hangar 15 10
2108 5c. "Graf Zeppelin" on ground 15 10
2109 35c. Astra airship "Ville de Paris" (air) 35 15
2110 70c. "Schwaben" 40 20
2111 3cor. "Graf Zeppelin" over Lake Constance . . . . . 1·00 65
2112 10cor. LZ-2 on Lake Constance . . . . 3·75 2·25

302 Lindbergh and Map

1977. 50th Anniv of Lindbergh's Transatlantic Flight. Multicoloured.
2114 1c. Type **302** (postage) . . . 10 10
2115 2c. Map and "Spirit of St. Louis" 10 10
2116 3c. Charles Lindbergh (vert) 10 10
2117 4c. "Spirit of St. Louis" crossing Atlantic 10 10
2118 5c. Charles Lindbergh standing by "Spirit of St. Louis" 10 10
2119 20c. Lindbergh, route and "Spirit of St. Louis" . . . 20 15
2120 55c. Lindbergh landing in Nicaragua (1928) (air) . . 20 15
2121 80c. "Spirit of St. Louis" and route map 35 15
2122 2cor. "Spirit of St. Louis" flying along Nicaraguan coast 65 35
2123 10cor. Passing Momotombo (Nicaragua) . . . . . . 1·90 1·25

303 Christmas Festival

1977. Christmas. Scenes from Tchaikovsky's "Nutcracker" Suite. Multicoloured.
2125 1c. Type **303** 10 10
2126 2c. Doll's dance 10 10
2127 3c. Clara and snowflakes . . 10 10
2128 4c. Snow fairy and prince 10 10
2129 5c. Snow fairies 10 10
2130 15c. Sugar fairy and prince 10 10
2131 40c. Waltz of the Flowers 10 10
2132 90c. Chinese dance 20 15
2133 1cor. Senora Bonbonierre 20 20
2134 10cor. Arabian dance . . . 1·40 1·25

304 "Mr. and Mrs. Andrews". (Gainsborough)

1978. Paintings. Multicoloured.
2136 1c. Type **304** (postage) . . . 10 10
2137 2c. "Giovanna Bacelli" (Gainsborough) 10 10
2138 3c. "Blue Boy" (Gainsborough) 10 10
2139 4c. "Francis I" (Titian) . . 10 10
2140 5c. "Charles V at Battle of Muhlberg" (Titian) . . . 10 10
2141 25c. "Sacred Love" (Titian) 10 10
2142 5cor. "Hippopotamus and Crocodile Hunt" (Rubens) (air) 60 50
2143 10cor. "Duke of Lerma on Horseback" (Rubens) . . 1·75 1·40

305 Gothic Portal with Rose Window, Small Basilica of St. Francis

1978. 750th Anniv of Canonisation of St. Francis of Assisi. Multicoloured.
2145 1c. Type **305** (postage) . . . 10 10
2146 2c. St. Francis preaching to birds 10 10
2147 3c. Painting of St. Francis 10 10
2148 4c. Franciscan genealogical tree 10 10
2149 5c. Portiuncola 10 10
2150 15c. Autographed blessing 10 10
2151 25c. Windows of Large Basilica 10 10
2152 80c. St. Francis and wolf (air) 15 10
2153 10cor. St. Francis . . . . . 1·60 1·50

306 Locomotive No. 6, 1921

1978. Centenary of Railway. Multicoloured.
2155 1c. Type **306** (postage) . . . 10 10
2156 2c. Lightweight cargo locomotive 10 10
2157 3c. Steam locomotive No. 10, 1909 . . . . . . 10 10
2158 4c. Baldwin steam locomotive No. 31, 1906 10 10
2159 5c. Baldwin steam locomotive No. 21, 1911 10 10
2160 15c. Presidential Pullman coach 15 10
2161 35c. Steam locomotive No. 33, 1907 (air) 20 15
2162 4cor. Baldwin steam locomotive No. 36, 1907 2·50 90
2163 10cor. Juniata steam locomotive, 1914, U.S.A. 6·25 2·25

307 Mongol Warriors ("Michael Strogoff")

1978. 150th Birth Anniv of Jules Verne. Mult.
2165 1c. Type **307** (postage) . . . 10 10
2166 2c. Sea scene ("The Mysterious Island") . . . 10 10
2167 3c. Sea monsters ("Journey to the Centre of the Earth") 10 10
2168 4c. Balloon and African elephant ("Five Weeks in a Balloon") 20 10
2169 90c. Submarine ("Twenty Thousand Leagues Under the Sea") (air) 75 20
2170 10cor. Balloon, Indian, steam locomotive and elephant ("Around the World in Eighty Days") 6·50 4·00

308 Icarus

1978. 75th Anniv of History of Aviation. First Powered Flight. Multicoloured.
2172 1c. Type **308** (postage) . . . 10 10
2173 2c. Montgolfier balloon (vert) 10 10
2174 3c. Wright Flyer I 10 10
2175 4c. Orville Wright in Wright Type A (vert) 10 10
2176 55c. Vought-Sikorsky VS-300 helicopter prototype (air) 30 10
2177 10cor. Space Shuttle . . . . 2·10 1·00

309 Ernst Ocwirk and Alfredo di Stefano

310 "St. Peter" (Goya)

1978. World Cup Football Championship, Argentina. Multicoloured.
2179 20c. Type **309** (postage) . . 10 10
2180 25c. Ralk Edstrom and Oswaldo Piazza 10 10
2181 50c. Franz Beckenbauer and Dennis Law (air) 10 10
2182 5cor. Dino Zoff and Pele . . 65 50

1978. Christmas. Multicoloured.
2184 10c. Type **310** (postage) . . 10 10
2185 15c. "St. Gregory" (Goya) 10 10
2186 3cor. "The Apostles John and Peter" (Durer) (air) 40 30
2187 10cor. "The Apostles Paul and Mark" (Durer) . . . 1·40 1·00

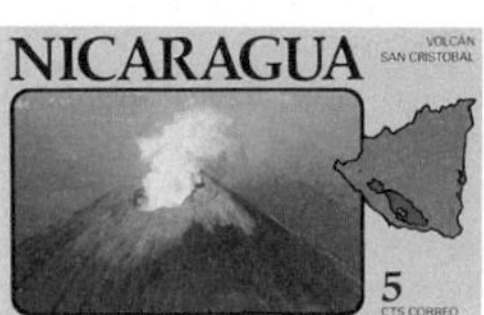

311 San Cristobal

1978. Volcanoes and Lakes. Multicoloured.
2189 5c. Type **311** (postage) . . . 10 10
2190 5c. Lake de Cosiguina . . . 10 10
2191 20c. Telica 10 10
2192 20c. Lake Jiloa 10 10
2193 35c. Cerro Negro (air) . . . 10 10
2194 35c. Lake Masaya 10 10
2195 90c. Momotombo 20 15
2196 90c. Lake Asososca 20 15
2197 1cor. Mombacho 20 15
2198 1cor. Lake Apoyo 20 15
2199 10cor. Concepcion . . . . 1·60 80
2200 10cor. Lake Tiscapa . . . . 1·60 80

312 General O'Higgins

1979. Air. Birth Bicentenary of Bernardo O'Higgins (liberation hero).
2201 **312** 20cor. multicoloured . . 3·75 1·90

313 Ginger Plant and Broad-tailed Hummingbird

1979. Air. Flowers. Multicoloured.
2202 50c. Type **313** 60 20
2203 55c. Orchids 10 10
2204 70c. Poinsettia 15 10

2205 80c. "Poro poro" 15 10
2206 2cor. "Morpho cypris" (butterfly) and Guayacan flowers 50 30
2207 4cor. Iris 45 30

314 Children with football

315 Indian Postal Runner

316 Einstein and Albert Schweitzer

317 Loggerhead Turtle

1980. Year of Liberation (1979) and Nicaragua's Participation in Olympic Games. Unissued stamps overprinted. (a) International Year of the Child. Mult.

2208 20c. Children on roundabout (postage) 15 15
2209 90c. Type **314** (air) 65 65
2210 2cor. Children with stamp albums 1·50 1·50
2211 2cor.20 Children playing with toy steam train and aircraft 14·00 14·00
2212 10cor. Baseball 7·50 7·50

(b) Death Centenary of Sir Rowland Hill. Mult.

2214 20c. Type **315** (postage) 20 20
2215 35c. Pony express 40 40
2216 1cor. Pre-stamp letter (horiz) 1·10 1·10
2217 1cor.80 Sir Rowland Hill examining sheet of Penny Black stamps (air) 1·90 1·90
2218 2cor.20 Penny Blacks (horiz) 2·40 2·40
2219 5cor. Nicaraguan Zeppelin flight cover (horiz) 5·50 5·50

(c) Birth Centenary of Albert Einstein (physicist). Multicoloured.

2221 5c. Type **316** (postage) 15 15
2222 10c. Einstein and equation 25 25
2223 15c. Einstein and 1939 World Fair pavilion 40 40
2224 20c. Einstein and Robert Oppenheimer 50 50
2225 25c. Einstein in Jerusalem 65 65
2226 1cor. Einstein and Nobel Prize medal (air) 2·50 2·50
2227 2cor.75 Einstein and space exploration 7·00 7·00
2228 10cor. Einstein and Mahatma Gandhi 15·00 15·00

(d) Endangered Turtles. Multicoloured.

2230 90c. Type **317** 1·00 80
2231 2cor. Leatherback turtle 2·25 1·75
2232 2cor.30 Ridley turtle 1·75 1·75
2233 10cor. Hawksbill turtle 7·50 7·50

318 Rigoberto Lopez Perez and Crowds pulling down Statue

1980. 1st Anniv of the Revolution. Multicoloured.

2235 40c. Type **318** 10 10
2236 75c. Street barricade 10 10
2237 1cor. "Learn to Read" emblem (vert) 15 10
2238 1cor.25 German Pomares Ordonez and jungle fighters 20 15
2239 1cor.85 Victory celebrations (vert) 25 15
2240 2cor.50 Carlos Fonesca and camp-fire 35 35
2241 5cor. Gen. Augusto Sandino and flag (vert) 70 55

1980. Literacy Year. Unissued stamps optd **1980 ANO DE LA ALFABETIZACION**. (a) International Year of the Child. As Nos. 2208/12.

2243 – 20c. Children on roundabout (postage) 1·00 1·00
2244 **314** 90c. Children with football (air) 1·00 1·00
2245 – 2cor. Children with stamp albums 1·00 1·00
2246 – 2cor.20 Children playing with toy steam train and airplane 2·00 2·00
2247 – 10cor. Baseball 4·50 4·50

(b) Death Centenary of Sir Rowland Hill. Nos. 2214/16.

2249 **315** 20c. Indian postal runner 70 70
2250 – 35c. Pony express 70 70
2251 – 1cor. Pre-stamp letter (horiz) 70 70

(c) Birth Centenary of Albert Einstein (physicist). As Nos. 2221/8.

2253 5c. Optd **"YURI GAGARIN/12/IV/1961/ LER HOMBRE EN EL ESPACIO"** (postage) 1·10 1·10
2254 10c. Optd **"LURABA 1981"** and space shuttle 1·10 1·10
2255 15c. Optd **"SPACE SHUTTLE"** and craft 1·10 1·10
2256 20c. Optd **ANO DE LA ALFABETIZACION** 1·10 1·10
2257 25c. Optd **"16/VII/1969/LER HOMBRE A LA LUNA"** and **"APOLLO XI"** 1·10 1·10
2258 1cor. Optd As No. 2256 (air) 1·10 1·10
2259 2cor.75 Optd As No. 2256 1·10 1·10
2260 10cor.75 Optd **"LUNOJOD 1"** and vehicle 1·10 1·10

(d) Air. Endangered Species. Turtles. As Nos. 2230/3. Multicoloured.

2262 **317** 90c. Loggerhead turtle 1·00 1·00
2263 – 2cor. Leatherback turtle 1·00 1·00
2264 – 2cor.20 Ridley turtle 1·00 1·00
2265 – 10cor. Hawksbill turtle 1·00 1·00

321 Footballer and El Molinon Stadium

1981. World Cup Football Championship, Spain. (1st issue). Venues. Multicoloured.

2268 5c. Type **321** 10 10
2269 20c. Sanchez Pizjuan, Seville 10 10
2270 25c. San Mames, Bilbao 10 10
2271 30c. Vincent Calderon, Madrid 10 10
2272 50c. R.C.D. Espanol, Barcelona 10 10
2273 4cor. New Stadium, Valladolid 55 35
2274 5cor. Balaidos, Vigo 55 35
2275 10cor. Santiago Bernabeu, Madrid 1·10 65

See also Nos. 2325/31.

322 Adult Education

1981. 2nd Anniv of Revolution. Multicoloured.

2277 50c. Type **322** (postage) 10 10
2278 2cor.10 Workers marching (air) 30 15
2279 3cor. Roadbuilding and container ship 65 30
2280 6cor. Medical services 50 25

323 Allegory of Revolution

1981. 20th Anniv of Sandinista National Liberation Front. Multicoloured.

2281 50c. Type **323** (postage) 10 10
2282 4cor. Sandinista guerrilla (air) 25 10

324 Postman

1981. 12th Postal Union of the Americas and Spain Congress, Managua. Multicoloured.

2283 50c. Type **324** (postage) 10 10
2284 2cor.10 Pony Express (air) 30 15
2285 3cor. Postal Headquarters, Managua 45 25
2286 6cor. Government building, globe and flags of member countries 50 25

326 "Nymphaea capensis"

1981. Water Lilies. Multicoloured.

2288 50c. Type **326** (postage) 10 10
2289 1cor. "Nymphaea daubenyana" 15 10
2290 1cor.20 "Nymphaea Marliacea Chromat" 20 10
2291 1cor.80 "Nymphaea Dir. Geo. T. Moore" 25 15
2292 2cor. "Nymphaea lotus" 30 15
2293 2cor.50 "Nymphaea B.G. Berry" 35 20
2294 10cor. "Nymphaea Gladstoniana" (air) 60 40

328 Cardinal Tetra

1981. Tropical Fishes. Multicoloured.

2296 50c. Type **328** (postage) 15 10
2297 1cor. Guppy 30 20
2298 1cor.85 Striped headstander 50 30
2299 2cor.10 Skunk corydoras 65 35
2300 2cor.50 Black-finned pearlfish 75 40
2301 3cor.50 Long-finned killie (air) 1·10 65
2302 4cor. Red swordtail 1·25 80

330 Lineated Woodpecker

331 Satellite in Orbit

1981. Birds. Multicoloured.

2304 50c. Type **330** (postage) 35 15
2305 1cor.20 Keel-billed toucan (horiz) 70 25
2306 1cor.80 Finsch's conure (horiz) 80 35
2307 2cor. Scarlet macaw 1·10 40
2308 3cor. Slaty-tailed trogon (air) 1·25 50
2309 4cor. Violet sabrewing (horiz) 1·75 60
2310 6cor. Blue-crowned motmot 3·50 1·00

1981. Satellite Communications. Multicoloured.

2311 50c. Type **331** (postage) 10 10
2312 1cor. "Intelstat IVA" 15 10
2313 1cor.50 "Intelstat V" moving into orbit 20 15
2314 2cor. Rocket releasing "Intelstat V" 30 20
2315 3cor. Satellite and Space Shuttle (air) 45 25
2316 4cor. "Intelstat V" and world maps 55 30
2317 5cor. Tracking stations 70 45

332 Steam Locomotive at Lake Granada

1981. Locomotives. Multicoloured.

2318 50c. Type **332** (postage) 20 10
2319 1cor. Vulcan Iron Works steam locomotive No. 35, 1946 40 10
2320 1cor.20 Baldwin steam locomotive No. 21, 1911 (inscribed "Philadelphia Iron Works") 45 10
2321 1cor.80 Steam crane, 1909 70 10
2322 2cor. General Electric Model "U10B" diesel locomotive, 1960s 75 10
2323 2cor.50 German diesel railbus, 1954 (dated "1956") 90 15
2324 6cor. Japanese-built diesel railbus, 1967 (air) 2·40 35

333 Heading Ball

1982. World Cup Football Championship, Spain (2nd issue). Multicoloured.

2325 5c. Type **333** (postage) 10 10
2326 20c. Running with ball 10 10
2327 25c. Running with ball (different) 10 10
2328 2cor.50 Saving goal 35 20
2329 3cor.50 Goalkeeper diving for ball (horiz) 50 30
2330 4cor. Kicking ball (air) 55 35
2331 10cor. Tackle (horiz) 60 40

334 Cocker Spaniel

1982. Pedigree Dogs. Multicoloured.

2333 5c. Type **334** (postage) 10 10
2334 20c. Alsatian 10 10
2335 25c. English setter 10 10
2336 2cor.50 Brittany spaniel 35 20
2337 3cor. Boxer (air) 45 25
2338 3cor.50 Pointer 50 30
2339 6cor. Collie 60 30

335 Satellite Communications

1982. Air. I.T.U. Congress.

2340 **335** 25cor. multicoloured 2·10 1·50

336 "Dynamine myrrhina"

1982. Butterflies. Multicoloured.

2341 50c. Type **336** (postage) 20 10
2342 1cor.20 "Eunica alcmena" 40 10
2343 1cor.50 "Callizona acesta" 40 10
2344 2cor. "Adelpha leuceria" 60 20
2345 3cor. "Parides iphidamas" (air) 1·00 30

2346 3cor.50 "Consul hippona" 1·10 35
2347 4cor. "Morpho peleides" 1·25 40

337 Dog and Russian Rocket

1982. Space Exploration. Multicoloured.
2348 5c. Type **337** (postage) 10 10
2349 15c. Satellite (vert) 10 10
2350 50c. "Apollo–Soyuz" link 10 10
2351 1cor.50 Satellite 20 15
2352 2cor.50 Docking in space 35 20
2353 5cor. Russian space station (air) 45 20
2354 6cor. Space shuttle "Columbia" (vert) 60 30

338 Mailcoach

1982. Centenary of U.P.U. Membership. Mult.
2355 50c. Type **338** (postage) 10 10
2356 1cor.20 "Victoria" (packet steamer) 1·10 35
2357 3cor.50 Steam locomotive, 1953 (air) 2·75 25
2358 10cor. Boeing 727-100 airliner 1·50 1·10

339 Cyclists

1982. 14th Central American and Caribbean Games. Multicoloured.
2359 10c. Type **339** (postage) 10 10
2360 15c. Swimming (horiz) 10 10
2361 25c. Basketball 10 10
2362 50c. Weightlifting 10 10
2363 2cor.50 Handball (air) 35 20
2364 3cor. Boxing (horiz) 45 25
2365 9cor. Football (horiz) 75 45

341 Washington passing through Trenton

1982. 250th Birth Anniv of George Washington. Multicoloured.
2368 50c. Mount Vernon, Washington's house (39 × 49 mm) (postage) 10 10
2369 1cor. Washington signing the Constitution (horiz) 15 10
2370 2cor. Type **341** 30 20
2371 2cor.50 Washington crossing the Delaware (horiz) (air) 35 20
2372 3cor.50 Washington at Valley Forge (horiz) 50 30
2373 4cor. Washington at the Battle of Trenton 55 35
2374 6cor. Washington at Princeton 60 55

342 Carlos Fonseca, Dove and Flags

1982. 3rd Anniv of Revolution. Multicoloured.
2375 50c. Type **342** (postage) 10 10
2376 2cor.50 Ribbons forming dove (vert) (air) 35 20
2377 1cor. Augusto Sandino and dove (vert) 55 30
2378 6cor. Dove 60 55

343 "Vase of Flowers" (R. Penalba)

1982. Paintings. Multicoloured.
2379 25c. Type **343** (postage) 10 10
2380 50c. "El Gueguense" (M. Garcia) (horiz) 10 10
2381 1cor. "The Couple" (R. Perez) 15 10
2382 1cor.20 "Canales Valley" (A. Mejias) (horiz) 20 10
2383 1cor.85 "Portrait of Senora Castellon" (T. Jerez) 25 15
2384 2cor. "The Vendors" (L. Cerrato) 30 20
2385 9cor. "Sitting Woman" (A. Morales) (horiz) (air) 55 35

344 Lenin and Dimitrov, Moscow, 1921

1982. Birth Centenary of Georgi Dimitrov (Bulgarian statesman). Multicoloured.
2387 50c. Type **344** (postage) 10 10
2388 2cor.50 Dimitrov & Todor Yikov, Sofia, 1946 (air) 35 20
2389 4cor. Dimitrov and flag 55 35

345 Ausberto Narvaez

1982. 26th Anniv of State of Resistance Movement. Multicoloured.
2390 50c. Type **345** (postage) 10 10
2391 2cor.50 Cornelio Silva 35 20
2392 4cor. Rigoberto Lopez Perez (air) 55 35
2393 6cor. Edwin Castro 60 55

346 Old Ruins at Leon

1982. Tourism. Multicoloured.
2394 50c. Type **346** (postage) 10 10
2395 1cor. Ruben Dario Theatre and Park, Managua 15 10
2396 1cor.20 Independence Square, Granada 20 10
2397 1cor.80 Corn Island 25 15
2398 2cor. Carter Santiago Volcano, Masaya 30 20
2399 2cor.50 El Coyotepe Fortress, Masaya (air) 35 20
2400 3cor.50 Luis A. Velazquez Park, Managua 50 30

347 Karl Marx and View of Trier

1982. Death Centenary of Karl Marx. Mult.
2401 1cor. Type **347** (postage) 15 10
2402 4cor. Marx and grave in Highgate Cemetery (air) 55 35

348 Stacking Cane and Fruit

1982. World Food Day. Multicoloured.
2403 50c. Picking Fruit (horiz) 10 10
2404 1cor. Type **348** 15 10
2405 2cor. Cutting sugar cane (horiz) 30 20
2406 10cor. F.A.O. and P.A.N. emblems (horiz) 85 65

349 "Santa Maria"

1982. 490th Anniv of Discovery of America. Multicoloured.
2407 50c. Type **349** (postage) 65 20
2408 1cor. "Nina" 1·25 30
2409 1cor.50 "Pinta" 1·75 45
2410 2cor. Columbus and fleet 2·00 70
2411 2cor.50 Fleet and map of route (air) 2·00 70
2412 4cor. Arrival in America 55 35
2413 7cor. Death of Columbus 65 60

350 "Lobelia laxiflora"

351 "Micrurus lemniscatus"

1982. Woodland Flowers. Multicoloured.
2415 50c. Type **350** (postage) 10 10
2416 1cor.20 "Bombacopsis quinata" 20 10
2417 1cor.80 "Mimosa albida" 25 15
2418 2cor. "Epidendrum alatum" 30 20
2419 2cor.50 Passion flower "Passiflora foetida" wrongly inscr "Pasiflora" (air) 35 20
2420 3cor.50 "Clitoria sp." 50 30
2421 5cor. "Russelia sarmentosa" 70 45

1982. Reptiles. Multicoloured.
2422 10c. Type **351** (postage) 10 10
2423 50c. Common iguana "Iguana iguana" (horiz) 10 10
2424 2cor. "Lachesis muta" (snake) (horiz) 30 20
2425 2cor.50 Hawksbill turtle "Eretmochelys imbricata" (horiz) (air) 35 20
2426 3cor. Boa constrictor "Constrictor constrictor" 45 25
2427 3cor.50 American crocodile "Crocodilus acutus" (horiz) 50 30
2428 5cor. Diamond-back rattlesnake "Sistrurus catenatus" (horiz) 70 45

352 Tele-cor Building, Managua

1982. Telecommunications Day. Multicoloured.
2429 1cor. Type **352** (postage) 15 10
2430 50c. Interior of radio transmission room (air) 10 10

353 Girl with Dove

1983. Air. Non-Aligned States Conference.
2431 **353** 4cor. multicoloured 55 35

354 Jose Marti and Birthplace

1983. 130th Birth Anniv of Jose Marti (Cuban revolutionary).
2432 **354** 1cor. multicoloured 15 10

355 Boxing

356 "Neomarica coerulea"

1983. Olympic Games, Los Angeles (1st issue). Multicoloured.
2433 50c. Type **355** (postage) 10 10
2434 1cor. Gymnastics 15 10
2435 1cor.50 Running 20 15
2436 2cor. Weightlifting 30 20
2437 4cor. Discus (air) 55 35
2438 5cor. Basketball 70 45
2439 6cor. Cycling 90 55
See also Nos. 2609/15.

1983. Flowers.
2441 **356** 1cor. blue 15 10
2442 – 1cor. violet 15 10
2443 – 1cor. mauve 15 10
2444 – 1cor. brown 15 10
2445 – 1cor. green 15 10
2446 – 1cor. blue 15 10
2447 – 1cor. green 15 10
2448 – 1cor. green 15 10
2449 – 1cor. mauve 15 10
2450 – 1cor. red 15 10
2451 – 1cor. grey 15 10
2452 – 1cor. yellow 15 10
2453 – 1cor. brown 15 10
2454 – 1cor. purple 15 10
2455 – 1cor. green 15 10
2456 – 1cor. black 15 10

DESIGNS: No. 2442, "Tabebula ochraceae"; 2443, "Laelia sp"; 2444, "Plumeria rubra"; 2445, "Brassavola nodosa"; 2446, "Stachytarpheta indica"; 2447, "Cochiospermum sp"; 2448, "Malvaviscus arboreus"; 2449, "Telecoma stans"; 2450, "Hibiscus rosa-sinensis"; 2451, "Cattleya lueddemanniana"; 2452, "Tagetes erecta"; 2453, "Senecio sp"; 2454, "Sobralia macrantha"; 2455, "Thumbergia alata"; 2456, "Bixa orellana".
See also Nos. 2739/54, 2838/53 and 3087/3102.

357 Momotombo Geothermal Electrical Plant

1983. Air. Energy.
2457 **357** 2cor.50 multicoloured 35 20

358 Map of Nicaragua and Girl picking Coffee

1983. Papal Visit.
2458 – 50c. red, black and blue (postage) 10 10
2459 **358** 1cor. multicoloured 15 10
2460 – 4cor. multicoloured (air) 55 35
2461 – 7cor. multicoloured 1·00 60
DESIGNS: 50c. Demonstrating crowd; 4cor. Pres. Cordova Rivas and Pope John Paul II; 7cor. Pope outside Managua Cathedral.

359 "Xilophanes chiron"

1983. Moths. Multicoloured.
2463 15c. Type **359** (postage) 10 10
2464 50c. "Protoparce ochus" 15 10
2465 65c. "Pholus lasbruscae" 25 10
2466 1cor. "Amphypterus gannascus" 30 10
2467 1cor.50 "Pholus licaon" 40 15
2468 2cor. "Agrius cingulata" 60 25
2469 10cor. "Rothschildia jurulla" (vert) (air) 3·25 95

360 La Recoleccion Church, Leon

1983. Monuments. Multicoloured.
2470 50c. Subtiava Church, Leon (horiz) (postage) 10 10
2471 1cor. La Inmaculada Castle, Rio San Juan (horiz) 15 10
2472 2cor. Type **360** 30 20
2473 4cor. Ruben Dario Monument, Managua (air) 55 35

361 Passenger Carriage

1983. Railway Wagons. Multicoloured.
2474 15c. Type **361** (postage) 10 10
2475 65c. Goods wagon No. 1034 25 10
2476 1cor. Tanker wagon No. 931 30 10
2477 1cor.50 Xolotlan hopper wagon 45 10
2478 4cor. Railcar (air) 1·25 35
2479 5cor. Tipper truck 1·50 40
2480 7cor. Railbus 2·25 60

362 Helping Earthquake Victim

1983. Red Cross. Multicoloured.
2481 50c. Aiding flood victims (horiz) (postage) 10 10
2482 1cor. Placing stretcher patient into ambulance (horiz) 15 10
2483 4cor. Type **362** (air) 55 35
2484 5cor. Doctor examining wounded soldier (horiz) 70 45

363 Raising Telephone Pole

1983. World Communications Year.
2485 **363** 1cor. multicoloured 15 10

365 Basketball

1983. 9th Pan-American Games. Multicoloured.
2487 15c. Basketball (horiz) (postage) 10 10
2488 50c. Water polo (horiz) 10 10
2489 65c. Running (horiz) 15 10
2490 1cor. Type **365** 15 10
2491 2cor. Weightlifting 30 20
2492 7cor. Fencing (horiz) (air) 65 30
2493 8cor. Gymnastics (horiz) 70 40

367 Container Ship being Unloaded

1983. 4th Anniv of Revolution. Multicoloured.
2496 1cor. Type **367** 55 15
2497 2cor. Telcor building, Leon 30 20

368 Carlos Fonseca

369 Simon Bolivar on Horseback

1983. Founders of Sandinista National Liberation Front. Multicoloured.
2498 50c. Escobar, Navarro, Ubeda, Pomares and Ruiz (postage) 10 10
2499 1cor. Santos Lopez, Borge, Buitrago and Mayorga 15 10
2500 4cor. Type **368** (air) 55 35

1983. Birth Bicentenary of Simon Bolivar. Mult.
2501 50c. Bolivar and Sandinista guerrilla 10 10
2502 1cor. Type **369** 15 10

371 Movements of a Pawn

1983. Chess. Multicoloured.
2504 15c. Type **371** (postage) 10 10
2505 65c. Knight's movements 10 10
2506 1cor. Bishop's movements 15 10
2507 2cor. Rook's movements 30 20
2508 4cor. Queen's movements (air) 55 35
2509 5cor. King's movements 70 45
2510 7cor. Game in progress 75 60

372 Speed Skating

1983. Winter Olympic Games, Sarajevo (1984) (1st issue). Multicoloured.
2511 50c. Type **372** (postage) 10 10
2512 1cor. Slalom 15 10
2513 1cor.50 Luge 20 15
2514 2cor. Ski jumping 30 20
2515 4cor. Figure skating (air) 55 35
2516 5cor. Downhill skiing 70 45
2517 6cor. Biathlon 90 55

373 Soldiers with German Shepherd Dog

374 "Madonna of the Chair"

1983. Armed Forces.
2519 **373** 4cor. multicoloured 55 35

1983. 500th Birth Anniv of Raphael. Multicoloured.
2520 50c. Type **374** (postage) 10 10
2521 1cor. "Esterhazy Madonna" 15 10
2522 1cor.50 "Sistine Madonna" 20 15
2523 2cor. "Madonna of the Linnet" 30 20
2524 4cor. "Madonna of the Meadow" (air) 55 35
2525 5cor. "Madonna of the Garden" 70 45
2526 6cor. "Adoration of the Kings" 90 55

375 Pottery Idol

1983. Archaeological Finds. Multicoloured.
2528 50c. Type **375** (postage) 10 10
2529 1cor. Pottery dish with ornamental lid 15 10
2530 2cor. Vase with snake design 30 20
2531 4cor. Pottery dish (air) 55 35

376 Metal being poured into Moulds

1983. Nationalization of Mines. Multicoloured.
2532 1cor. Type **376** (postage) 15 10
2533 4cor. Workers and mine (air) 55 35

377 Radio Operator and Sinking Liner

1983. "Fracap '83" Congress of Radio Amateurs of Central America and Panama. Multicoloured.
2534 1cor. Type **377** 70 15
2535 4cor. Congress emblem and town destroyed by earthquake 55 35

378 Tobacco

1983. Agrarian Reform.
2536 **378** 1cor. green 15 10
2537 – 2cor. orange 30 20
2538 – 4cor. brown 35 35
2539 – 5cor. blue 45 45
2540 – 6cor. lavender 55 55
2541 – 7cor. purple 60 60
2542 – 8cor. purple 70 65
2543 – 10cor. brown 90 90
DESIGNS: 2cor. Cotton; 4cor. Maize; 5cor. Sugar; 6cor. Cattle; 7cor. Rice; 8cor. Coffee; 10cor. Bananas.
See also Nos. 2755/62 and 2854/61.

379 Fire Engine with Ladder

1983. Fire Engines. Multicoloured.
2544 50c. Type **379** (postage) 10 10
2545 1cor. Water tanker 15 10
2546 6cor. Crew vehicle, 1930 90 55
2547 1cor.50 Pump with extension fire hoses (air) 20 15
2548 2cor. Pump with high-pressure tank 30 20
2548a 4cor. Water tanker 60 40
2549 5cor. Fire engine, 1910 70 45

380 Jose Marti and General Sandino

1983. Nicaragua–Cuba Solidarity. Multicoloured.
2550 1cor. Type **380** (postage) 15 10
2551 4cor. Teacher, doctor and welder (air) 55 35

381 "Adoration of the Shepherds" (Hugo van der Gaes)

382 Anniversary Emblem

1983. Christmas. Multicoloured.
2552 50c. Type **381** (postage) 10 10
2553 1cor. "Adoration of the Kings" (Domenico Ghirlandaio) 15 10
2554 2cor. "Adoration of the Shepherds" (El Greco) 30 20
2555 7cor. "Adoration of the Kings" (Konrad von Soest) (air) 65 30

1984. Air. 25th Anniv of Cuban Revolution.
2557 **382** 4cor. red, blue and black 45 20
2558 – 6cor. multicoloured 55 30
DESIGN: 6cor. Fidel Castro and Che Guevara.

383 Bobsleigh

1984. Winter Olympic Games, Sarajevo. Mult.
2559 50c. Type **383** (postage) 10 10
2560 50c. Biathlon 10 10
2561 1cor. Slalom 20 15
2562 1cor. Speed skating 20 15
2563 4cor. Skiing (air) 45 45
2564 5cor. Ice-dancing 55 55
2565 10cor. Ski-jumping 90 60

384 Chinchilla

1984. Cats. Multicoloured.
2567 50c. Type **384** (postage) 10 10
2568 50c. Longhaired white 10 10
2569 1cor. Red tabby 20 15
2570 2cor. Tortoiseshell 35 20
2571 4cor. Burmese 70 45
2572 3cor. Siamese (air) 50 35
2573 7cor. Longhaired silver 70 35

385 National Arms **386** Blanca Arauz

1984. 50th Death Anniv of Augusto Sandino. Mult.
2574 1cor. Type **385** (postage) . . 20 15
2575 4cor. Augusto Sandino (air) 35 20

1984. International Women's Day.
2576 **386** 1cor. multicoloured . . . 20 15

387 Sunflower **388** "Soyuz"

1984. Agricultural Flowers. Multicoloured.
2577 50c. Type **387** (postage) . . 10 10
2578 50c. "Poinsettia pulcherrima" 10 10
2579 1cor. "Cassia alata" 20 15
2580 1cor. "Antigonon leptopus" 20 15
2581 3cor. "Bidens pilosa" (air) 50 35
2582 4cor. "Althaea rosea" . . . 70 45
2583 5cor. "Rivea corymbosa" 85 55

1984. Space Anniversaries. Multicoloured.
2584 50c. Type **388** (15th anniv of "Soyuz 6", "7" and "8" flights) (postage) 10 10
2585 50c. "Soyuz" (different) (15th anniv of "Soyuz 6", "7" and "8" flights) . . . 10 10
2586 1cor. "Apollo 11" approaching Moon (15th anniv of 1st manned landing) 20 15
2587 2cor. "Luna I" (25th anniv of 1st Moon satellite) . . 35 20
2588 3cor. "Luna II" (25th anniv of 1st Moon landing) (air) 50 35
2589 4cor. "Luna III" (25th anniv of 1st photographs of far side of Moon) . . . 70 45
2590 9cor. Rocket (50th anniv of Korolev's book on space flight) . . . . 1·25 75

389 "Noli me Tangere" (detail) **390** Daimler, 1886

1984. 450th Death Anniv of Correggio (artist). Multicoloured.
2591 50c. Type **389** (postage) . . 10 10
2592 50c. "Madonna of St. Jerome" (detail) . . . 10 10
2593 1cor. "Allegory of Virtue" 20 15
2594 2cor. "Allegory of Pleasure" 35 20
2595 3cor. "Ganymedes" (detail) (air) 50 35
2596 5cor. "The Danae" (detail) 55 55
2597 8cor. "Leda and the Swan" (detail) . . . . 1·00 60

1984. 150th Birth Anniv of Gottlieb Daimler (automobile designer). Multicoloured.
2599 1cor. Type **390** (postage) . . 10 10
2600 1cor. Abadal, 1914 (horiz) 10 10
2601 2cor. Ford, 1903 . . . . . 1·50 45
2602 2cor. Renault, 1899 . . . . 35 20
2603 3cor. Rolls Royce, 1910 (horiz) (air) 50 35
2604 4cor. Metallurgique, 1907 (horiz) 70 45
2605 7cor. Bugatti "Mod 40" (horiz) 75 50

392 Mail Transport

1984. Air. 19th Universal Postal Union Congress Philatelic Salon, Hamburg.
2607 **392** 15cor. multicoloured . . 5·75 2·10

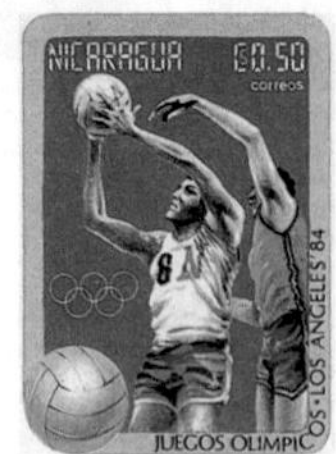

393 Basketball

1984. Olympic Games, Los Angeles (2nd issue). Multicoloured.
2609 50c. Type **393** (postage) . . 10 10
2610 50c. Volleyball 10 10
2611 1cor. Hockey 20 15
2612 2cor. Tennis (air) 35 20
2613 3cor. Football (horiz) . . . 50 35
2614 4cor. Water polo (horiz) . . 70 45
2615 9cor. Soccer (horiz) . . . . 1·10 75

395 Rural Construction Site

1984. 5th Anniv of Revolution. Multicoloured.
2618 5c. Type **395** (postage) . . . 10 10
2619 1cor. Diesel locomotive, Pacific–Atlantic line . . . 1·50 30
2620 4cor. Ploughing with oxen and tractor (Agrarian reform) (air) 40 20
2621 7cor. State Council building 75 35

396 "Children defending Nature" (Pablo Herrera Berrios)

1984. U.N.E.S.C.O. Environmental Protection Campaign. Multicoloured.
2622 50c. Type **396** (postage) . . 10 10
2623 1cor. Living and dead forests 20 15
2624 2cor. Fisherman and dried river bed 35 20
2625 10cor. Hands holding plants (vert) (air) 85 75

397 Red Cross Airplane and Ambulance

1984. 50th Anniv of Nicaraguan Red Cross. Mult.
2626 1cor. Type **397** (postage) . . 30 15
2627 7cor. Battle of Solferino (125th anniv) (air) 90 45

399 Ventura Escalante and Dominican Republic Flag

1984. Baseball. Multicoloured.
2629 50c. Type **399** (postage) . . 10 10
2630 50c. Danial Herrera and Mexican flag 10 10
2631 1cor. Adalberto Herrera and Venezuelan flag 20 15
2632 1cor. Roberto Clemente and Nicaraguan flag 20 15
2633 3cor. Carlos Colas and Cuban flag (air) 30 35
2634 4cor. Stanley Cayasso and Argentinian flag 45 45
2635 5cor. Babe Ruth and U.S.A.. flag 55 55

400 Central American Tapir

1984. Wildlife Protection. Multicoloured.
2636 25c. Type **400** (postage) . . 10 10
2637 25c. Young tapir 10 10
2638 3cor. Close-up of tapir (air) 15 10
2639 4cor. Mother and young . . 20 15

401 Football in 1314

1985. World Cup Football Championship, Mexico (1986) (1st issue). Multicoloured.
2640 50c. Type **401** (postage) . . 10 10
2641 50c. Football in 1500 . . . 10 10
2642 1cor. Football in 1872 . . . 10 10
2643 1cor. Football in 1846 . . . 10 10
2644 2cor. Football in 1883 (air) 10 10
2645 4cor. Football in 1890 . . . 20 15
2646 6cor. Football in 1953 . . . 30 20
See also Nos. 2731/7 and 2812/18.

402 "Strobilomyces retisporus"

1985. Fungi. Multicoloured.
2648 50c. Type **402** (postage) . . 10 10
2649 50c. "Boletus calopus" . . . 10 10
2650 1cor. "Boletus luridus" . . 15 10
2651 1cor. "Xerocomus illudens" (air) 15 10
2652 4cor. "Gyrodon merulioides" 55 25
2653 5cor. "Tylopilus plumbeoviolaceus" . . . 65 30
2654 8cor. "Gyroporus castaneus" . . . . 1·10 40

403 Postal Runner and Map

1985. 13th Postal Union of the Americas and Spain Congress. Multicoloured.
2655 1cor. Type **403** (postage) . . 10 10
2656 7cor. Casa Aviocar mail plane over map (air) . . . 45 20

406 Steam Locomotive, Oldenburg

1985. 150th Anniv of German Railway. Mult.
2659 1cor. Type **406** (postage) . . 20 10
2660 1cor. Electric locomotive, Prussia 20 10
2661 9cor. Steam locomotive No. 88, Prussia (air) . . . 75 15
2662 9cor. Double-deck tram . . 75 15
2663 15cor. Steam locomotive, Wurttemberg . . . . . . 1·10 25
2664 21cor. Steam locomotive, Germany . . . . 1·75 40

407 Douglas, 1928

1985. Centenary of Motor Cycle. Multicoloured.
2666 50c. Type **407** (postage) . . 10 10
2667 50c. FN, 1928 . . . . . . 10 10
2668 1cor. Puch, 1938 . . . . . 10 10
2669 2cor. Wanderer, 1939 (air) 10 10
2670 4cor. Honda, 1949 . . . . 10 10
2671 5cor. BMW, 1984 . . . . . 10 10
2672 7cor. Honda, 1984 . . . . 40 10

408 "Matelea quirosii" **409** "Capitulation of German Troops" (P. Krivonogov)

1985. Flowers. Multicoloured.
2673 50c. Type **408** (postage) . . 10 10
2674 50c. "Ipomea nil" 10 10
2675 1cor. "Lysichitum americanum" 10 10
2676 2cor. "Clusia sp." (air) . . . 10 10
2677 4cor. "Vanilla planifolia" . . 10 10
2678 7cor. "Stemmadenia obovata" 75 40

1985. 40th Anniv of End of World War II. Mult.
2679 9cor.50 Type **409** (postage) 1·00 50
2680 28cor. Woman behind barbed wire and Nuremberg trial (air) . . 3·00 1·50

410 Lenin and Red Flag **413** Common Pheasant

412 Victoria de Julio Sugar Factory

1985. 115th Birth Anniv of Lenin. Multicoloured.
2681 4cor. Type **410** 10 10
2682 21cor. Lenin addressing crowd 45 30

1985. Air. 6th Anniv of Revolution. Multicoloured.
2684 9cor. Type **412** 20 15
2685 9cor. Soldier and flag . . . 20 15

1985. Domestic Birds. Multicoloured.
2686 50c. Type **413** 25 20
2687 50c. Hen 50 10
2688 1cor. Helmeted guineafowl 35 20
2689 2cor. Swan goose 65 20
2690 6cor. Ocellated turkey . . . 2·10 35
2691 8cor. Duck . . . . 1·75 10

414 Luis A. Delgadillo **415** Zeledon

1985. International Music Year. Multicoloured.

2692 1cor. Type **414** (postage) 10 10
2693 1cor. Masked dancer with floral headdress 10 10
2694 9cor. Masked procession (air) 65 40
2695 9cor. Crowd outside church 65 40
2696 15cor. Masked dancer in brimmed hat 1·10 55
2697 21cor. Procession resting 1·50 75

1985. Air. Birth Centenary of Benjamin Zeledon.

2698 **415** 15cor. multicoloured 1·00 55

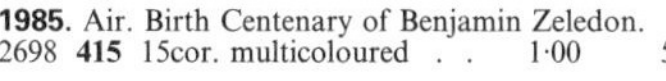

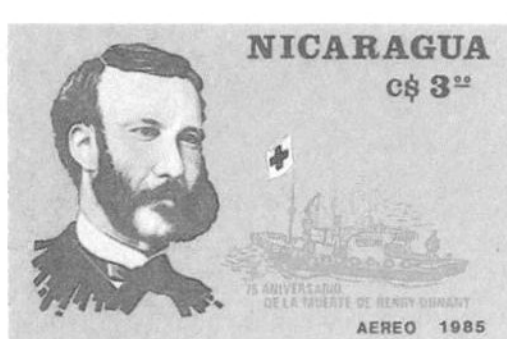

416 Dunant and Lifeboat

1985. 75th Death Anniv of Henri Dunant (founder of Red Cross). Multicoloured.

2699 3cor. Type **416** 40 10
2700 15cor. Dunant and Ilyushin Il-86 and Tupolev Tu-154 aircraft 1·25 55

417 Fire Engine

1985. 6th Anniv of SINACOI Fire Service. Mult.

2701 1cor. Type **417** (postage) 10 10
2702 1cor. Fire station 10 10
2703 1cor. Engine with water jet 10 10
2704 3cor. Foam tender (air) 10 10
2705 9cor. Airport fire engine 50 15
2706 15cor. Engine at fire 85 45
2707 21cor. Fireman in protective clothing 1·10 75

418 Halley, Masaya Volcano and Comet

1985. Appearance of Halley's Comet. Mult.

2708 1cor. Type **418** (postage) 10 10
2709 3cor. Armillary sphere and 1910 trajectory 10 10
2710 3cor. "Venus" space probe and Tycho Brahe underground observatory 10 10
2711 9cor. Habermel's astrolabe and comet's path through solar system (air) 50 15
2712 15cor. Hale Telescope, Mt. Palomar, and Herschel's telescope 85 45
2713 21cor. Galileo's telescope and sections through telescopes of Newton, Cassegrain and Ritchey 1·25 60

419 Tapir eating

1985. Protected Animals. Baird's Tapir. Mult.

2714 1cor. Type **419** (postage) 10 10
2715 3cor. Tapir in water (air) 10 10
2716 5cor. Tapir in undergrowth 10 10
2717 9cor. Mother and calf 20 15

420 "Rosa spinosissima"

1986. Wild Roses. Multicoloured.

2718 1cor. Type **420** 10 10
2719 1cor. Dog rose ("R. canina") 10 10
2720 3cor. "R. eglanteria" 10 10
2721 5cor. "R. rubrifolia" 10 10
2722 9cor. "R. foetida" 20 15
2723 100cor. "R. rugosa" 2·00 1·10

421 Crimson Topaz **422** Footballer and Statue

1986. Birds. Multicoloured.

2724 1cor. Type **421** 10 10
2725 3cor. Orange-billed nightingale thrush 10 10
2726 3cor. Troupial 10 10
2727 5cor. Painted bunting 20 15
2728 10cor. Frantzius's nightingale thrush 60 40
2729 21cor. Great horned owl 1·25 1·00
2730 75cor. Great kiskadee 5·50 3·00

1986. World Cup Football Championship, Mexico (2nd issue). Multicoloured.

2731 1cor. Type **422** (postage) 10 10
2732 1cor. Footballer and sculptured head 10 10
2733 3cor. Footballer and water holder with man as stem (air) 10 10
2734 3cor. Footballer and sculpture 10 10
2735 5cor. Footballer and sculptured head (different) 10 10
2736 9cor. Footballer and sculpture (different) 20 15
2737 100cor. Footballer and sculptured snake's head 3·00 1·50

1986. (a) Flowers. As Nos. 2441/56 but values changed.

2739 5cor. blue 10 10
2740 5cor. violet 10 10
2741 5cor. purple 10 10
2742 5cor. orange 10 10
2743 5cor. green 10 10
2744 5cor. blue 10 10
2745 5cor. green 10 10
2746 5cor. green 10 10
2747 5cor. mauve 10 10
2748 5cor. red 10 10
2749 5cor. grey 10 10
2750 5cor. orange 10 10
2751 5cor. brown 10 10
2752 5cor. brown 10 10
2753 5cor. green 10 10
2754 5cor. black 10 10

DESIGNS: No. 2739, Type **356**; 2740, "Tabebula ochraceae"; 2741, "Laella sp"; 2742, Frangipani ("Plumeria rubra"); 2743, "Brassavola nodosa"; 2744, "Strachytarpheta indica"; 2745, "Cochlospermum sp"; 2746, "Malvaviscus arboreus"; 2747, "Tecoma stans"; 2748, Chinese hibiscus ("Hibiscus rosa-sinensis"); 2749, "Cattleya lueddemanniana"; 2750, African marigold ("Tagetes erecta"); 2751, "Senecio sp"; 2752, "Sobralia macrantha"; 2753, "Thumbergia alata"; 2754, "Bixa orellana".

(b) Agrarian Reform. As T **378**.

2755 1cor. brown 10 10
2756 9cor. violet 20 15
2757 15cor. purple 30 20
2758 21cor. red 45 30
2759 33cor. orange 65 45
2760 42cor. green 90 55
2761 50cor. brown 1·00 65
2762 100cor. blue 2·00 1·50

DESIGNS: 1cor. Type **378**; 9cor. Cotton; 15cor. Maize; 21cor. Sugar; 33cor. Cattle; 42cor. Rice; 50cor. Coffee; 100cor. Bananas.

423 Alfonso Cortes

1986. National Libraries. Latin American Writers. Multicoloured.

2763 1cor. Type **423** (postage) 10 10
2764 3cor. Azarias H. Pallais 10 10
2765 3cor. Salomon de la Selva 10 10
2766 5cor. Ruben Dario 10 10
2767 9cor. Pablo Neruda 10 10
2768 15cor. Alfonso Reyes (air) 45 25
2769 100cor. Pedro Henriquez Urena 3·00 1·50

424 Great Britain Penny Black and Nicaragua 1929 25c. Stamp

1986. Air. 125th Anniv of Nicaraguan Stamps. Designs showing G.B. Penny Black and Nicaragua stamps.

2770 **424** 30cor. multicoloured 90 45
2771 – 40cor. brown, black and grey 1·25 60
2772 – 50cor. red, black and grey 1·50 75
2773 – 100cor. blue, black and grey 3·00 1·50

DESIGNS: 40c. 1903 1p. stamp; 50c. 1892 5p. stamp; 1p. 1862 2c. stamp.

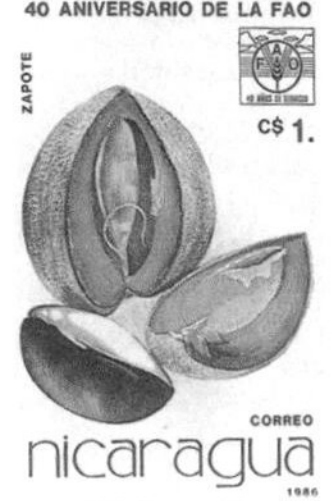

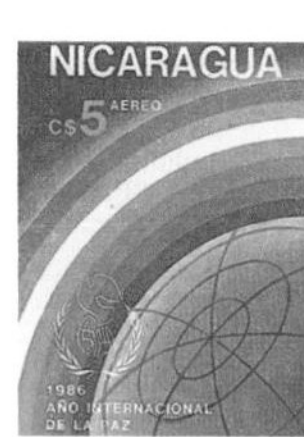

425 Sapodilla **426** Rainbow and Globe

1986. 40th Anniv of F.A.O. Multicoloured.

2774 1cor. Type **425** (postage) 10 10
2775 1cor. Maranon 10 10
2776 3cor. Tree-cactus 10 10
2777 3cor. Granadilla 10 10
2778 5cor. Custard-apple (air) 10 10
2779 21cor. Melocoton 65 35
2780 100cor. Mamey 3·00 1·50

1986. Air. International Peace Year. Multicoloured.

2781 5cor. Type **426** 10 10
2782 10cor. Dove and globe 30 10

427 Lockheed L-1011 TriStar 500

1986. "Stockholmia 86" International Stamp Exhibition. Multicoloured.

2783 1cor. Type **427** (postage) 10 10
2784 1cor. Yakovlev Yak-40 10 10
2785 3cor. B.A.C. One Eleven 10 10
2786 3cor. Boeing 747-100 10 10
2787 9cor. Airbus Industrie A300 (air) 30 10
2788 15cor. Tupolev Tu-154 45 10
2789 100cor. Concorde (vert) 3·00 1·50

428 "Pinta" and 16th-century Map

1986. 500th Anniv (1992) of Discovery of America by Columbus (1st issue). Multicoloured.

2791 1cor. Type **428** (postage) 80 30
2792 1cor. "Santa Maria" and "Nina" 80 30
2793 9cor. Juan de la Cosa (air) 30 10
2794 9cor. Christopher Columbus 30 10
2795 21cor. King and Queen of Spain 65 35
2796 100cor. Courtiers behind Columbus and Indians 3·00 1·50

The designs of the same value and Nos. 2795/6 were printed together in se-tenant pairs within their sheets, Nos. 2791/2 and 2795/6 forming composite designs.

See also Nos. 2903/8.

429 Fonseca and Flags

1986. Air. 25th Anniv of Sandinista Front and 10th Death Anniv of Carlos Fonseca (co-founder).

2798 **429** 15cor. multicoloured 10 10

430 Rhinoceros **431** "Theritas coronata"

1986. Air. Endangered Animals. Multicoloured.

2799 15cor. Type **430** 45 10
2800 15cor. Zebra 45 10
2801 25cor. Elephant 75 40
2802 25cor. Giraffe 75 40
2803 50cor. Tiger 1·50 75
2804 50cor. Mandrill 1·50 75

1986. Butterflies. Multicoloured.

2805 10cor. Type **431** (postage) 20 10
2806 15cor. "Salamis cacta" (air) 20 10
2807 15cor. "Charayes nitebis" 20 10
2808 15cor. "Papilio maacki" 20 10
2809 25cor. "Palaeochrysophonus hippothoe" 20 10
2810 25cor. "Euphaedro cyparissa" 20 10
2811 30cor. "Ritra aurea" 20 10

432 Player and French Flag **433** Ernesto Mejia Sanchez

1986. Air. World Cup Football Championship, Mexico (3rd issue). Finalists. Multicoloured. Designs showing footballers and national flags.

2812 10cor. Type **432** 10 10
2813 10cor. Argentina 10 10
2814 10cor. West Germany 10 10
2815 15cor. England 10 10
2816 15cor. Brazil 10 10
2817 25cor. Spain 10 10
2818 50cor. Belgium (horiz) 10 10

1987. Ruben Dario Cultural Order of Independence. Multicoloured.

2820 10cor. Type **433** (postage) 10 10
2821 10cor. Fernando Gordillo 10 10
2822 10cor. Francisco Perez Estrada 10 10
2823 15cor. Order medal (air) 10 10
2824 30cor. Julio Cortazar 20 20
2825 60cor. Enrique Fernandez Morales 35 25

434 Ice Hockey **435** Development

1987. Winter Olympic Games, Calgary (1988). Multicoloured.
2826 10cor. Type **434** (postage) 10 10
2827 10cor. Speed skating 10 10
2828 15cor. Downhill skiing (air) 10 10
2829 15cor. Figure skating . . . 10 10
2830 20cor. Shooting 15 10
2831 30cor. Slalom 20 10
2832 40cor. Ski jumping 25 10

1987. U.N.I.C.E.F. Child Survival Campaign. Multicoloured.
2834 10cor. Type **435** (postage) 10 10
2835 25cor. Vaccination (air) . . 75 40
2836 30cor. Oral rehydration therapy 90 45
2837 50cor. Breast-feeding . . . 1·50 75

1987. (a) Flowers. As Nos. 2441/56 and 2739/54 but values changed.
2838 10cor. blue 10 10
2839 10cor. violet 10 10
2840 10cor. purple 10 10
2841 10cor. red 10 10
2842 10cor. green 10 10
2843 10cor. blue 10 10
2844 10cor. green 10 10
2845 10cor. green 10 10
2846 10cor. mauve 10 10
2847 10cor. red 10 10
2848 10cor. green 10 10
2849 10cor. orange 10 10
2850 10cor. brown 10 10
2851 10cor. purple 10 10
2852 10cor. turquoise 10 10
2853 10cor. black 10 10
DESIGNS: No. 2838, Type **356**; 2839, "Tabebula ochraceae"; 2840, "Laelia sp"; 2841, Frangipani; 2842, "Brassavola nodosa"; 2843, "Stachytarpheta indica"; 2844, "Cochlospermum sp"; 2845, "Malvaviscus arboreus"; 2846, "Tecoma stans"; 2847, Chinese hibiscus; 2848, "Cattleya lueddermanniana"; 2849, African marigold; 2850, "Senecio sp"; 2851, "Sobralla macrantha"; 2852, "Thumbergia alata"; 2853, "Bixa orellana".

(b) Agrarian Reform. As T **378**. Dated "1987".
2854 10cor. brown 10 10
2855 10cor. violet 10 10
2856 15cor. purple 10 10
2857 25cor. red 15 10
2858 30cor. orange 20 10
2859 50cor. brown 30 20
2860 60cor. green 35 25
2861 100cor. blue 65 45
DESIGNS: No. 2854, Type **378**; 2855, Cotton; 2856, Maize; 2857, Sugar; 2858, Cattle; 2859, Coffee; 2860, Rice; 2861, Bananas.

436 Flags and Buildings **438** Tennis Player

437 "Mammuthus columbi"

1987. 77th Interparliamentary Conf, Managua.
2862 **436** 10cor. multicoloured . . 10 10

1987. Prehistoric Animals. Multicoloured.
2863 10cor. Type **437** (postage) 10 10
2864 10cor. Triceratops 10 10
2865 10cor. Dimetrodon 10 10
2866 15cor. Uintaterium (air) . . 10 10
2867 15cor. Dinichthys 10 10
2868 30cor. Pteranodon 60 35
2869 40cor. Tilosaurus 85 45

1987. "Capex 87" International Stamp Exhibition, Toronto.
2870 10cor. multicoloured (Type **438**) (postage) . . . 10 10
2871 10cor. mult 10 10
2872 15cor. mult (male player) (air) 45 10
2873 15cor. mult (female player) 45 10
2874 20cor. multicoloured 60 30
2875 30cor. multicoloured 60 45
2876 40cor. multicoloured 85 60
DESIGNS: Nos. 2871/6, Various tennis players.

439 Dobermann Pinscher **441** Levski

440 Modern Wooden Houses

1987. Dogs. Multicoloured.
2878 10cor. Type **439** (postage) 10 10
2879 10cor. Bull mastiff 10 10
2880 15cor. Japanese spaniel (air) 45 10
2881 15cor. Keeshond 45 10
2882 20cor. Chihuahua 60 30
2883 30cor. St. Bernard 90 45
2884 40cor. West Gotha spitz . . 85 60

1987. Air. International Year of Shelter for the Homeless. Multicoloured.
2885 20cor. Type **440** 15 10
2886 30cor. Modern brick-built houses 20 10

1987. Air. 150th Birth Anniv of Vasil Levski (revolutionary).
2887 **441** 30cor. multicoloured . . 20 10

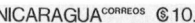

442 "Opuntia acanthocarpa major"

1987. Cacti. Multicoloured.
2888 10cor. Type **442** (postage) 10 10
2889 10cor. "Lophocereus schottii" 10 10
2890 10cor. "Echinocereus engelmanii" 10 10
2891 20cor. Saguaros (air) . . . 60 30
2892 20cor. "Lemaireocereus thurberi" 60 30
2893 30cor. "Opuntia fulgida" . . 90 45
2894 50cor. "Opuntia ficus indica" . . . . 1·50 75

443 High Jumping

1987. 10th Pan-American Games, Indiana. Mult.
2895 10cor. Type **443** (postage) 10 10
2896 10cor. Handball 10 10
2897 15cor. Running (air) 45 10
2898 15cor. Gymnastics 45 10
2899 20cor. Baseball 60 30
2900 30cor. Synchronized swimming (vert) 90 45
2901 40cor. Weightlifting (vert) 1·25 60

445 "Cosmos"

1987. Cosmonautics Day. Multicoloured.
2904 10cor. Type **445** (postage) 10 10
2905 10cor. "Sputnik" 10 10
2906 15cor. "Proton" (air) . . . 45 10
2907 25cor. "Luna" 75 40
2908 25cor. "Meteor" 75 40
2909 30cor. "Electron" 90 45
2910 50cor. "Mars-1" . . . . . 1·50 75

446 Native Huts and Terraced Hillside

1987. Air. 500th Anniv (1992) of Discovery of America by Columbus (2nd issue). Mult.
2911 15cor. Type **446** 45 20
2912 15cor. Columbus's fleet . . 90 30
2913 20cor. Spanish soldiers in native village 60 30
2914 30cor. Mounted soldiers killing natives 90 45
2915 40cor. Spanish people and houses . . . . 1·25 60
2916 50cor. Church and houses 1·50 75

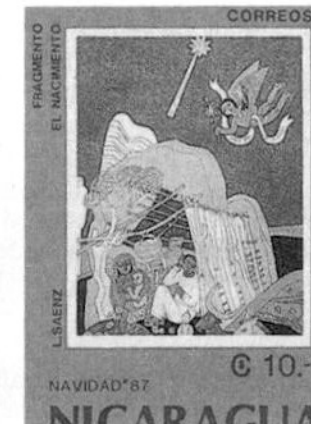

447 Tropical Gar

1987. World Food Day. Fishes. Multicoloured.
2917 10cor. Type **447** (postage) 20 10
2918 10cor. Atlantic tarpon ("Tarpon atlanticus") . . 20 10
2919 10cor. Jaguar guapote ("Cichlasoma managuense") 20 10
2920 15cor. Banded astyanax ("Astyana fasciatus") (air) 90 45
2921 15cor. Midas cichlid ("Cichlasoma citrimellum") 90 45
2922 20cor. Wolf cichlid . . . . 1·25 65
2923 50cor. Lake Nicaragua shark . . . . 3·00 1·50

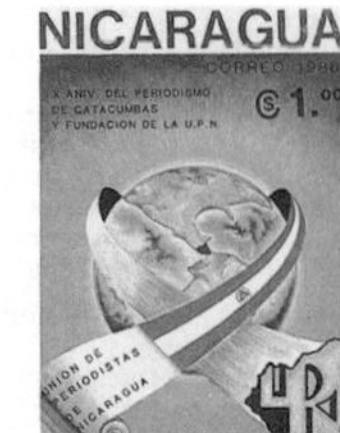

448 Lenin **449** "Nativity"

1987. 70th Anniv of Russian Revolution. Mult.
2924 10cor. Type **448** (postage) 10 10
2925 30cor. "Aurora" (cruiser) (horiz) (air) 50 15
2926 50cor. Russian arms 30 20

1987. Christmas. Details of Painting by L. Saenz. Multicoloured.
2927 10cor. Type **449** 10 10
2928 20cor. "Adoration of the Magi" 60 30
2929 25cor. "Adoration of the Magi" (close-up detail) . . 75 40
2930 50cor. "Nativity" (close-up detail) . . . . 1·50 75

1987. Surch.
2931 **435** 400cor. on 10cor. mult (postage) 30 15
2935 **440** 200cor. on 20cor. multicoloured (air) . . 15 10
2932 – 600cor. on 50cor. mult (No. 2837) 40 20
2933 – 1000cor. on 25cor. mult (No. 2835) 70 35
2936 – 3000cor. on 30cor. mult (No. 2886) . . . . . 2·10 1·00
2934 – 5000cor. on 30cor. mult (No. 2836) . . . . . 3·50 1·75

451 Cross-country Skiing **452** Flag around Globe

1988. Winter Olympic Games, Calgary. Mult.
2937 10cor. Type **451** 10 10
2938 10cor. Rifle-shooting (horiz) 10 10
2939 15cor. Ice hockey 45 10
2940 20cor. Ice skating 60 30
2941 25cor. Downhill skiing . . . 75 40
2942 30cor. Ski jumping (horiz) 90 45
2943 40cor. Slalom . . . . 1·25 60

1988. 10th Anniv of Nicaragua Journalists' Association. Multicoloured.
2945 1cor. Type **452** (postage) . . 10 10
2946 5cor. Churches of St. Francis Xavier, Sandino and Fatima, Managua, and speaker addressing journalists (42 × 27 mm) (air) . . . . 1·25 60

453 Basketball

1988. Olympic Games, Seoul. Multicoloured.
2947 10cor. Type **453** 10 10
2948 10cor. Gymnastics 10 10
2949 15cor. Volleyball 45 10
2950 20cor. Long jumping . . . 60 30
2951 25cor. Football 75 40
2952 30cor. Water polo 90 45
2953 40cor. Boxing . . . . . . 1·25 60

454 Brown Bear

1988. Mammals and their Young. Multicoloured.
2955 10c. Type **454** (postage) . . 10 10
2956 15c. Lion 10 10
2957 25c. Cocker spaniel 10 10
2958 50c. Wild boar 15 10
2959 4cor. Cheetah (air) 55 20
2960 7cor. Spotted hyena . . . . 1·00 40
2961 8cor. Red fox . . . . 1·25 50

455 Slide Tackle

1988. "Essen '88" International Stamp Fair and European Football Championship, Germany. Mult.
2963 50c. Type **455** (postage) . . 10 10
2964 1cor. Footballers 15 10
2965 2cor. Lining up shot (vert) (air) 30 10
2966 3cor. Challenging for ball (vert) 50 20
2967 4cor. Heading ball (vert) . . 65 25
2968 5cor. Tackling (vert) 80 30
2969 6cor. Opponent winning possession . . . . 1·00 40

456 Bell JetRanger III (½-size illustration)

1988. "Finlandia 88" International Stamp Exhibition, Helsinki. Helicopters. Multicoloured.
2971 4cor. Type **456** (postage) . . 15 10
2972 12cor. MBB-Kawasaki BK-117A-3 (air) 20 10
2973 16cor. Boeing-Vertol B-360 30 10
2974 20cor. Agusta A.109 MR11 40 10
2975 24cor. Sikorsky S-61N . . . 55 20
2976 28cor. Aerospatiale SA.365 Dauphin 2 . . . . 60 25
2977 56cor. Sikorsky S-76 Spirit 1·25 50

457 Flags and Map   458 Casimiro Sotelo Montenegro

1988. 9th Anniv of Revolution. Multicoloured.
2979 1cor. Type **457** (postage) 20 10
2980 5cor. Landscape and hands releasing dove (air) 80 30

1988. Revolutionaries.
2981 **458** 4cor. blue (postage) 15 10
2982 – 12cor. mauve (air) 20 10
2983 – 16cor. green 30 10
2984 – 20cor. red 45 15
2985 – 24cor. brown 55 20
2986 – 28cor. violet 65 25
2987 – 50cor. red 1·25 45
2988 – 100cor. purple 2·40 1·00
DESIGNS: 12cor. Ricardo Morales Aviles; 16cor. Silvio Mayorga Delgado; 20cor. Pedro Arauz Palacios; 24cor. Oscar A. Turcios Chavarrias; 28cor. Julio C. Buitrago Urroz; 50cor. Jose B. Escobar Perez; 100cor. Eduardo E. Contreras Escobar.

459 "Acacia baileyana"   460 West Indian Fighting Conch

1988. Flowers. Multicoloured.
2989 4cor. Type **459** (postage) 15 10
2990 12cor. "Anigozanthos manglesii" (air) 20 10
2991 16cor. "Telopia speciosissima" 30 10
2992 20cor. "Eucalyptus ficifolia" 45 15
2993 24cor. "Boronia heterophylla" 60 30
2994 28cor. "Callistemon speciosus" 70 35
2995 30cor. "Nymphaea caerulea" (horiz) 80 40
2996 50cor. "Clianthus formosus" 1·25 60

1988. Molluscs. Multicoloured.
2997 4cor. Type **460** (postage) 20 10
2998 12cor. Painted polymita (air) 30 10
2999 16cor. Giant sundial 40 10
3000 20cor. Japanese baking oyster 55 10
3001 24cor. Yoka star shell 75 20
3002 28cor. Gawdy frog shell 80 25
3003 50cor. Mantled top 1·75 50

461 Zapotecan Funeral Urn   462 "Chrysina macropus"

1988. 500th Anniv (1992) of Discovery of America by Columbus (3rd issue). Multicoloured.
3004 4cor. Type **461** (postage) 15 10
3005 12cor. Mochican ceramic seated figure (air) 20 10
3006 16cor. Mochican ceramic head 30 10
3007 20cor. Tainan ceramic vessel 45 10
3008 28cor. Nazcan vessel (horiz) 65 20
3009 100cor. Incan ritual pipe (horiz) 2·40 1·00

1988. Beetles. Multicoloured.
3011 4cor. Type **462** (postage) 15 10
3012 12cor. "Plusiotis victoriana" (air) 20 10
3013 16cor. "Ceratotrupes bolivari" 30 10
3014 20cor. "Gymnetosoma stellata" 50 15
3015 24cor. "Euphoria lineoligera" 60 20
3016 28cor. "Euphoria candezei" 70 30
3017 50cor. "Sulcophanaeus chryseicollis" 1·25 50

463 Dario

1988. Air. Centenary of Publication of "Blue" by Ruben Dario.
3018 **463** 25cor. multicoloured 60 20

464 Simon Bolivar, Jose Marti, Gen. Sandino and Fidel Castro

1989. Air. 30th Anniv of Cuban Revolution.
3019 **464** 20cor. multicoloured 50 20

465 Pochomil Tourist Centre

1989. Tourism. Multicoloured.
3020 4cor. Type **465** (postage) 15 10
3021 12cor. Granada Tourist Centre (air) 45 15
3022 20cor. Olof Palme Convention Centre 65 30
3023 24cor. Masaya Volcano National Park 55 20
3024 28cor. La Boquita Tourist Centre 70 25
3025 30cor. Xiloa Tourist Centre 75 30
3026 50cor. Managua Hotel 1·25 60

466 Footballers   467 Downhill Skiing

1989. Air. World Cup Football Championship, Italy (1990).
3028 **466** 100cor. multicoloured 10 10
3029 – 200cor. multicoloured 10 10
3030 – 600cor. multicoloured 10 10
3031 – 1000cor. multicoloured 30 10
3032 – 2000cor. multicoloured 60 10
3033 – 3000cor. multicoloured 90 40
3034 – 5000cor. multicoloured 1·50 50
DESIGNS: 200cor. to 5000cor. Different footballers.

1989. Air. Winter Olympic Games, Albertville (1992) (1st issue). Multicoloured.
3036 50cor. Type **467** 10 10
3037 300cor. Ice hockey 10 10
3038 600cor. Ski jumping 10 10
3039 1000cor. Ice skating 30 10
3040 2000cor. Biathlon 60 10
3041 3000cor. Slalom 90 40
3042 5000cor. Skiing 1·50 50
See also Nos. 3184/90.

468 Water Polo

1989. Air. Olympic Games, Barcelona (1992). Mult.
3044 100cor. Type **468** 10 10
3045 200cor. Running 10 10
3046 600cor. Diving 10 10
3047 1000cor. Gymnastics 30 10
3048 2000cor. Weightlifting 60 10
3049 3000cor. Volleyball 90 40
3050 5000cor. Wrestling 1·50 50
See also Nos. 3192/8.

469 Procession of States General at Versailles   470 American Darter

1989. "Philexfrance 89" International Stamp Exhibition, Paris, and Bicentenary of French Revolution. Multicoloured.
3052 50cor. Type **469** (postage) 15 10
3054 300cor. Oath of the Tennis Court (36 × 28 mm) (air) 10 10
3055 600cor. "The 14th of July" (29 × 40 mm) 10 10
3056 1000cor. Tree of Liberty (36 × 28 mm) 30 10
3057 2000cor. "Liberty guiding the People" (Eugene Delacroix) (29 × 40 mm) 60 10
3058 3000cor. Storming the Bastille (36 × 28 mm) 90 40
3059 5000cor. Lafayette taking oath (28 × 36 mm) 1·50 50

1989. Air. "Brasiliana 89" International Stamp Exhibition, Rio de Janeiro. Birds. Multicoloured.
3060 100cor. Type **470** 20 20
3061 200cor. Swallow-tailed kite 20 20
3062 600cor. Turquoise-browed motmot 25 20
3063 1000cor. Painted redstart 40 20
3064 2000cor. Great antshrike (horiz) 80 20
3065 3000cor. Northern royal flycatcher 1·10 90
3066 5000cor. White-flanked antwren (horiz) 2·00 1·10

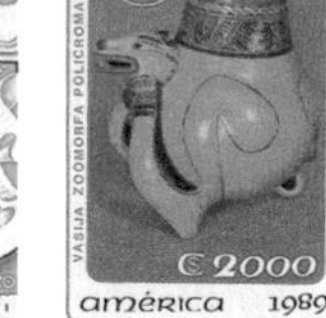

471 Anniversary Emblem   472 Animal-shaped Vessel

1989. Air. 10th Anniv of Revolution.
3068 **471** 300cor. multicoloured 10 10

1989. Air. America. Pre-Columbian Artefacts.
3070 **472** 2000cor. multicoloured 60 10

Currency Reform. 150000 (old) cordoba = 1 (new) cordoba
The following issues, denominated in the old currency, were distributed by agents but were not issued (each set consists of seven values and is dated "1990"):
"London 90" International Stamp Exn. Ships
World Cup Football Championship, Italy
Olympic Games, Barcelona (1992)
Fungi
Winter Olympic Games, Albertville (1992)

473 Little Spotted Kiwi

1991. "New Zealand 1990" International Stamp Exhibition, Auckland. Birds. Multicoloured.
3071 5c. Type **473** 15 10
3072 5c. Takahe 15 10
3073 10c. Red-fronted parakeet 20 15
3074 20c. Weka rail 45 25
3075 30c. Kagu (vert) 25 40
3076 60c. Kea 1·25 90
3077 70c. Kakapo 1·50 1·00

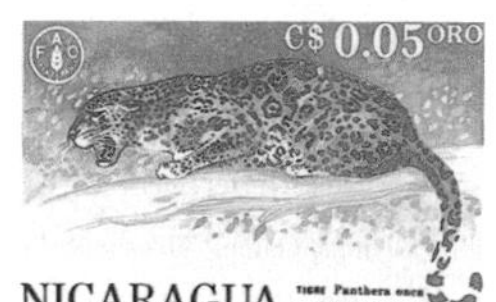

474 Jaguar

1991. 45th Anniv of Food and Agriculture Organization. Animals. Multicoloured.
3079 5c. Type **474** 10 10
3080 5c. Ocelot (vert) 10 10
3081 10c. Black-handed spider monkey (vert) 15 10
3082 20c. Baird's tapir 30 15
3083 30c. Nine-banded armadillo 45 20
3084 60c. Coyote 85 45
3085 70c. Two-toed sloth 1·00 50

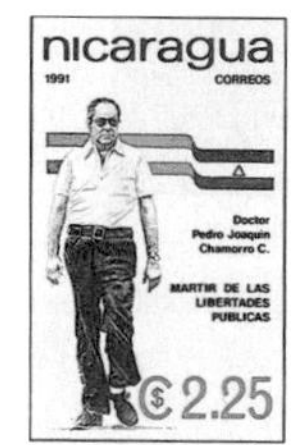

475 Dr. Chamorro   476 Steam Locomotive, 1920s, Peru

1991. Dr. Pedro Joaquin Chamorro (campaigner for an independent Press).
3086 **475** 2cor.25 multicoloured 50 20

1991. Flowers. As T **356** but with currency inscribed in "oro".
3087 – 1cor. blue 25 10
3088 – 2cor. green 45 20
3089 – 3cor. brown 70 30
3090 – 4cor. purple 95 40
3091 – 5cor. red 1·10 45
3092 – 6cor. green 1·40 55
3093 **356** 7cor. blue 1·60 65
3094 – 8cor. green 1·90 75
3095 – 9cor. green 2·10 85
3096 – 10cor. violet 2·25 90
3097 – 11cor. mauve 2·50 1·00
3098 – 12cor. yellow 2·75 1·10
3099 – 13cor. red 3·00 1·25
3100 – 14cor. green 3·25 1·25
3101 – 15cor. mauve 3·50 1·40
3102 – 16cor. black 3·75 1·50
DESIGNS: 1cor. "Stachytarpheta indica"; 2cor. "Cochlospermum sp."; 3cor. "Senecio sp."; 4cor. "Sobralia macrantha"; 5cor. Frangipani; 6cor. "Brassavola nodosa"; 8cor. "Malvaviscus arboreus"; 9cor. "Cattleya lueddemanniana"; 10cor. "Tabebula ochraceae"; 11cor. "Laelia sp."; 12cor. African marigold; 13cor. Chinese hibiscus; 14cor. "Thumbergia alata"; 15cor. "Tecoma stans"; 16cor. "Bixa orellana".

1991. Steam Locomotives of South and Central America. Multicoloured.
3103 25c. Type **476** 30 10
3104 25c. Locomotive No. 508, 1917, Bolivia 30 10
3105 50c. Class N/O locomotive, 1910s, Argentina 50 10
3106 1cor.50 Locomotive, 1952, Chile 90 20
3107 2cor. Locomotive No. 61, 1944, Colombia 1·25 25
3108 3cor. Locomotive No. 311, 1947, Brazil 2·00 35
3109 3cor.50 Locomotive No. 60, 1910, Paraguay 2·25 45

477 Match Scene (West Germany versus Netherlands)

1991. West Germany, Winners of World Cup Football Championship (1990). Multicoloured.
3111 25c. Type **477** 10 10
3112 25c. Match scene (West Germany versus Colombia) (vert) 10 10
3113 50c. West German players and referee 10 10
3114 1cor. West German players forming wall (vert) 25 10
3115 1cor.50 Diego Maradona (Argentina) (vert) 35 15
3116 3cor. Argentinian players and Italian goalkeeper (vert) 70 30
3117 3cor.50 Italian players 80 30

478 "Prepona praeneste"

1991. Butterflies. Multicoloured.
3119 25c. Type **478** 10 10
3120 25c. "Anartia fatima" 10 10
3121 50c. "Eryphanis aesacus" 10 10
3122 1cor. "Heliconius melpomene" 25 10
3123 1cor.50 "Chlosyne janais" 35 15

3124 3cor. "Marpesia iole" . . . 70 30
3125 3cor.50 Rusty-tipped page 80 30

479 Dove and Cross

1991. 700th Anniv of Swiss Confederation.
3127 **479** 2cor.25 red, black and yellow 50 20

480 Yellow-headed Amazon

1991. "Rainforest is Life". Fauna. Multicoloured.
3128 2cor.25 Type **480** 50 20
3129 2cor.25 Keel-billed toucan 50 20
3130 2cor.25 Scarlet macaw . . . 50 20
3131 2cor.25 Resplendent quetzal 50 20
3132 2cor.25 Black-handed spider monkey 50 20
3133 2cor.25 White-throated capuchin 50 20
3134 2cor.25 Three-toed sloth . . 50 20
3135 2cor.25 Chestnut-headed oropendola 50 20
3136 2cor.25 Violet sabrewing . . 50 20
3137 2cor.25 Tamandua 50 20
3138 2cor.25 Jaguarundi 50 20
3139 2cor.25 Boa constrictor . . 50 20
3140 2cor.25 Common iguana . . 50 20
3141 2cor.25 Jaguar 50 20
3142 2cor.25 White-necked jacobin 50 20
3143 2cor.25 "Doxocopa clothilda" (butterfly) . . . 50 20
3144 2cor.25 "Dismorphia deione" (butterfly) 50 20
3145 2cor.25 Golden arrow-poison frog 50 20
3146 2cor.25 "Callithomia hezia" (butterfly) 50 20
3147 2cor.25 Chameleon 50 20
Nos. 3128/47 were issued together, se-tenant, forming a composite design.

481 "Isochilus major"

1991. Orchids. Multicoloured.
3148 25c. Type **481** 10 10
3149 25c. "Cycnoches ventricosum" 10 10
3150 50c. "Vanilla odorata" . . . 10 10
3151 1cor. "Helleriella nicaraguensis" 25 10
3152 1cor.50 "Barkeria spectabilis" 35 15
3153 3cor. "Maxillaria hedwigae" 70 30
3154 3cor.50 "Cattleya aurantiaca" 80 30

482 Concepcion Volcano

1991. America (1990).
3156 **482** 2cor.25 multicoloured . . 50 20

483 Warehouse and Flags

1991. 30th Anniv of Central American Bank of Economic Integration.
3157 **483** 1cor.50 multicoloured . . 35 15

484 "The One-eyed Man"

1991. Death Centenary (1990) of Vincent van Gogh (painter). Multicoloured.
3158 25c. Type **484** 10 10
3159 25c. "Head of Countrywoman with Bonnet" 10 10
3160 50c. "Self-portrait" 10 10
3161 1cor. "Vase with Carnations and other Flowers" . . . 25 10
3162 1cor.50 "Vase with Zinnias and Geraniums" 35 15
3163 3cor. "Portrait of Tanguy Father" 70 30
3164 3cor.50 "Portrait of a Man" (horiz) 80 30

485 Painting by Rafaela Herrera (1st-prize winner)

1991. National Children's Painting Competition.
3166 **485** 2cor.25 multicoloured . . 50 20

486 Golden Pavilion

1991. "Phila Nippon '91" International Stamp Exhibition, Tokyo. Multicoloured.
3167 25c. Type **486** 10 10
3168 50c. Himaji Castle 10 10
3169 1cor. Head of Bunraku doll 25 10
3170 1cor.50 Japanese cranes . . 35 15
3171 2cor.50 Phoenix pavilion . . 60 25
3172 3cor. "The Guardian" (statue) 70 30
3173 3cor.50 Kabuki actor . . . 80 30

487 Turquoise-browed Motmot

488 Columbus's Fleet

1992. Birds. Multicoloured.
3175 50c. Type **487** 15 10
3176 75c. Collared trogon 20 10
3177 1cor. Broad-billed motmot 25 10
3178 1cor.50 Wire-tailed manakin 40 15
3179 1cor.75 Paradise tanager (horiz) 45 20
3180 2cor.25 Resplendent quetzal 60 25
3181 2cor.25 Black-spotted bare-eye 60 25

1992. America (1991). Voyages of Discovery.
3183 **488** 2cor.25 multicoloured . . 35 15

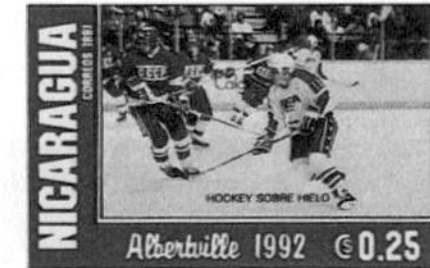

489 Ice Hockey

1992. Winter Olympic Games, Albertville (2nd issue). Multicoloured.
3184 25c. Type **489** 10 10
3185 25c. Four-man bobsleighing 10 10
3186 50c. Skiing (vert) 15 10
3187 1cor. Speed skating 25 10
3188 1cor.50 Cross-country skiing 40 15
3189 3cor. Double luge 75 30
3190 3cor.50 Ski jumping (vert) 90 35

490 Fencing

491 Ceramic Vase with Face (Lorenza Pineda Co-operative)

1992. Olympic Games, Barcelona (2nd issue) Mult.
3192 25c. Type **490** 10 10
3193 25c. Throwing the javelin (horiz) 10 10
3194 50c. Basketball 15 10
3195 1cor.50 Running 40 15
3196 2cor. Long jumping 50 20
3197 3cor. Running 75 30
3198 3cor.50 Show jumping . . . 90 35

1992. Contemporary Arts and Crafts. Mult.
3200 25c. Type **491** 10 10
3201 25c. Ceramic spouted vessel (Jose Oritz) (horiz) . . . 10 10
3202 50c. Blue-patterned ceramic vase (Elio Gutierrez) . . . 15 10
3203 1cor. "Christ" (Jose de los Santos) 25 10
3204 1cor.50 "Family" (sculpture, Erasmo Moya) 40 15
3205 3cor. "Bird-fish" (Silvio Chavarria Co-operative) (horiz) 85 30
3206 3cor.50 Filigree ceramic vessel (Maria de los Angeles Bermudez) . . . 90 35

492 "Picnic Table with Three Objects" (Alejandro Arostegui)

493 Rivoli's Hummingbird

1992. Contemporary Paintings. Multicoloured.
3208 25c. Type **492** 10 10
3209 25c. "Prophetess of the New World" (Alberto Ycaza) 10 10
3210 50c. "Flames of Unknown Origin" (Bernard Dreyfus) (horiz) 15 10
3211 1cor.50 "Owl" (Orlando Sobalvarro) (horiz) . . . 40 15
3212 2cor. "Pegasus at Liberty" (Hugo Palma) (horiz) . . 50 20
3213 3cor. "Avocados" (Omar d'Leon) (horiz) 75 30
3214 3cor.50 "Gueguense" (Carlos Montenegro) . . 90 35

1992. 2nd U.N. Conference on Environment and Development, Rio de Janeiro. Tropical Forest Wildlife. Multicoloured.
3216 1cor.50 Type **493** 40 15
3217 1cor.50 Harpy eagle ("Aguila arpia") 40 15
3218 1cor.50 Orchid 40 15
3219 1cor.50 Keel-billed toucan and morpho butterfly . . 40 15
3220 1cor.50 Resplendent quetzal 40 15
3221 1cor.50 Guardabarranco . . 40 15
3222 1cor.50 Howler monkey ("Mono aullador") . . . 40 15
3223 1cor.50 Sloth ("Perezoso") 40 15
3224 1cor.50 Squirrel monkey ("Mono ardilla") 40 15
3225 1cor.50 Blue and yellow macaw ("Guacamaya") 40 15
3226 1cor.50 Emerald boa and scarlet tanager 40 15
3227 1cor.50 Poison-arrow frog 40 15
3228 1cor.50 Jaguar 40 15
3229 1cor.50 Anteater 40 15
3230 1cor.50 Ocelot 40 15
3231 1cor.50 Coati 40 15
Nos. 3216/31 were issued together, se-tenant, forming a composite design of a forest.

494 Fabretto with Children

1992. Father Fabretto, "Benefactor of Nicaraguan Children".
3232 **494** 2cor.25 multicoloured . . 60 25

495 "Nicaraguan Identity" (Claudia Gordillo)

1992. Winning Entry in Photography Competition.
3233 **495** 2cor.25 multicoloured . . 60 25

496 "The Indians of Nicaragua" (Milton Jose Cruz)

1992. Winning Entry in Children's Painting Competition.
3234 **496** 2cor.25 multicoloured . . 60 25

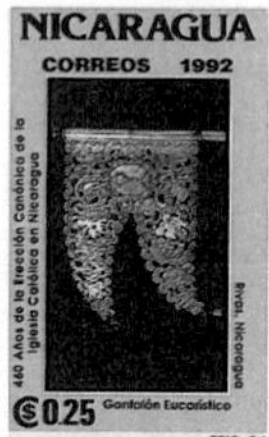

497 Eucharistical Banner

498 Rivas Cross, 1523

1993. 460th Anniv of Catholic Church in Nicaragua. Multicoloured.
3235 25c. Type **497** 10 10
3236 50c. "Shrine of the Immaculate Conception" 10 10
3237 1cor. 18th-century document 20 10
3238 1cor.50 16th-century baptismal font 30 10
3239 2cor. "The Immaculate Conception" 40 15
3240 2cor.25 Monsignor Diego Alvarez Osorio (1st Bishop of Leon) 50 20
3241 3cor. "Christ on the Cross" 65 25

1993. America (1992). 500th Anniv of Discovery of America by Columbus.
3242 **498** 2cor.25 multicoloured . . 50 20

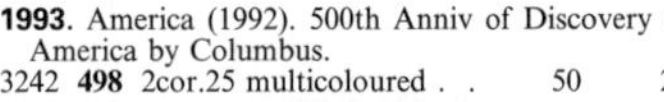

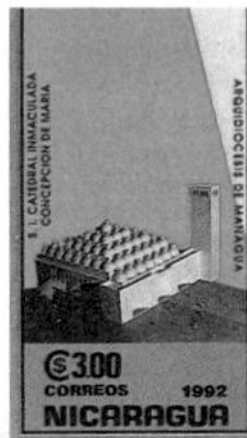

499 Cathedral

1993. Inauguration of Cathedral of the Immaculate Conception of Mary, Managua. Multicoloured.
3243 3cor. Type **499** 65 25
3244 4cor. Cross, Virgin Mary and map of Nicaragua (2nd Provincial Council) 85 35
Nos. 3243/4 were issued together, se-tenant, forming a composite design.

500 Emblem and Voters queueing outside Poll Station

1993. 23rd General Assembly of Organization of American States.
3245 **500** 3cor. multicoloured . . . 85 45

501 Anniversary Emblem

1993. 90th Anniv of Pan-American Health Organization.
3246 **501** 3cor. multicoloured . . . 85 45

502 "Sonatina" (Alma Iris Perez)

1993. Winning Entry in Children's Painting Competition.
3247 **502** 3cor. multicoloured . . . 85 45

503 Racoon Buttterflyfish

1993. Butterflyfishes. Multicoloured.
3248 1cor.50 Type **503** 50 25
3249 1cor.50 Rainford's butterflyfish ("Chaetodon rainfordi") 50 25
3250 1cor.50 Mailed butterflyfish ("Chaetodon reticulatus") 50 25
3251 1cor.50 Thread-finned butterflyfish ("Chaetodon auriga") 50 25
3252 1cor.50 Pennant coralfish ("Heniochus acuminatus") 50 25
3253 1cor.50 Dark-banded butterflyfish ("Coradion fulvocinctus") 50 25
3254 1cor.50 Mirror butterflyfish ("Chaetodon speculum") 50 25
3255 1cor.50 Lined butterflyfish ("Chaetodon lineolatus") 50 25
3256 1cor.50 Bennett's butterflyfish ("Chaetodon bennetti") 50 25
3257 1cor.50 Black-backed butterflyfish ("Chaetodon melanotus") 50 25
3258 1cor.50 Golden butterflyfish ("Chaetodon aureus") . . 50 25
3259 1cor.50 Saddle butterflyfish ("Chaetodon ephippium") 50 25
3260 1cor.50 Pyramid butterflyfish ("Hemitaurichthys polylepis") 50 25
3261 1cor.50 Dotted butterflyfish ("Chaetodon semeion") 50 25
3262 1cor.50 Klein's butterflyfish ("Chaetodon kleinii") . . 50 25
3263 1cor.50 Copper-banded butterflyfish ("Chelmon rostratus") 50 25

504 Four-man Bobsleigh

1993. Multicoloured. (a) Winter Olympic Games, Lillehammer, Norway (1994).
3264 25c. Type **504** 10 10
3265 25c. Skiing 10 10
3266 50c. Speed skating 15 10
3267 1cor.50 Ski jumping 45 20
3268 2cor. Women's figure skating 55 25
3269 3cor. Pairs' figure skating 85 45
3270 3cor.50 Shooting (biathlon) 1·00 45

(b) Olympic Games, Atlanta (1996).
3271 25c. Swimming 10 10
3272 25c. Diving 10 10
3273 50c. Long distance running 15 10
3274 1cor. Hurdling 30 15
3275 1cor.50 Gymnastics 45 20
3276 3cor. Throwing the javelin 85 45
3277 3cor.50 Sprinting . . . . . 1·00 50

505 "Bromeliaceae sp." **506** Tomas Brolin (Sweden)

1994. Tropical Forest Flora and Fauna. Mult.
3279 2cor. Type **505** 50 25
3280 2cor. Sparkling-tailed hummingbird ("Tilmatura dupontii") 50 25
3281 2cor. "Anolis biporcatus" (lizard) 50 25
3282 2cor. Lantern fly ("Fulgara laternaria") 50 25
3283 2cor. Sloth ("Bradypus sp.") 50 25
3284 2cor. Ornate hawk eagle ("Spizaetus ornatus") . . 50 25
3285 2cor. Lovely cotinga ("Cotinga amabilis") . . 50 25
3286 2cor. Schegel's lance-head snake ("Bothrops schlegelii") 50 25
3287 2cor. "Odontoglossum sp." (orchid) and bee 50 25
3288 2cor. Red-eyed tree frog ("Agalychnis callidryas") 50 25
3289 2cor. "Heliconius sapho" (butterfly) 50 25
3290 2cor. Passion flower ("Passiflora vitifolia") . . 50 25

Nos. 3279/90 were issued together, se-tenant, forming a composite design.

1994. World Cup Football Championship, U.S.A.. Players.
3292 50c. Type **506** 15 10
3293 1cor. Jan Karas (Poland) and Antonio Luiz Costa (Brazil) 30 15
3294 1cor. Maxime Bossis and Michel Platini (France) 30 15
3295 1cor.50 Harold Schumacher (Germany) 45 20
3296 2cor. Andoni Zubizarreta (Spain) 55 30
3297 2cor.50 Lothar Matthaeus (Germany) and Diego Maradona (Argentine Republic) 75 35
3298 3cor.50 Bryan Robson (England) and Carlos Santos (Portugal) . . . . 1·00 50

507 "Four in One" (Julio Lopez)

1994. Contemporary Arts. Multicoloured.
3300 50c. Rush mat (Rosalia Sevilla) (horiz) 15 10
3301 50c. Type **507** 15 10
3302 1cor. Ceramic church (Auxiliadora Bush) . . . 30 15
3303 1cor. Statuette of old woman (Indiana Robleto) 30 15
3304 2cor.50 "Santiago" (Jose de los Santos) 55 30
3305 3cor. "Gueguense" (Ines Gutierrez de Chong) . . . 85 45
3306 4cor. Ceramic hornet's nest (Elio Gutierrez) 95 45

508 "Callicore patelina"

1994. "Hong Kong '94" International Stamp Exhibition. Butterflies. Multicoloured.
3308 1cor.50 Type **508** 35 15
3309 1cor.50 "Chlosyne narva" 35 15
3310 1cor.50 Giant brimstone ("Anteos maerula") . . . 35 15
3311 1cor.50 Diadem ("Marpesia petreus") 35 15
3312 1cor.50 "Pierella helvetia" 35 15
3313 1cor.50 "Eurytides epidaus" 35 15
3314 1cor.50 Doris ("Heliconius doris") 35 15
3315 1cor.50 "Smyrna blomfildia" 35 15
3316 1cor.50 "Eueides lybia olympia" 35 15
3317 1cor.50 "Adelpha heraclea" 35 15
3318 1cor.50 "Heliconius hecale zuleika" 35 15
3319 1cor.50 "Parides montezuma" 35 15
3320 1cor.50 "Morpho polyphemus" 35 15
3321 1cor.50 "Eresia alsina" . . . 35 15
3322 1cor.50 "Prepona omphale octavia" 35 15
3323 1cor.50 "Morpho grenadensis" 35 15

509 "The Holy Family" (anonymous)

1994. Christmas (1993). Paintings. Multicoloured
3324 1cor. Type **509** 25 15
3325 4cor. "Nativity" (Lezamon) 95 45

510 Sculpture

1994. Chontal Culture Statuary. Multicoloured, colour of frame given.
3326 **510** 50c. yellow 15 10
3327 – 50c. yellow 15 10
3328 – 1cor. emerald 30 15
3329 – 1cor. green 30 15
3330 – 2cor.50 blue 55 35
3331 – 3cor. blue 85 45
3332 – 4cor. green 95 45

DESIGNS: 50c. (No. 3327) to 4cor. Different sculptures.

511 "Virgin of Nicaragua" (Celia Lacayo)

1994. Contemporary Paintings. Multicoloured.
3334 50c. Type **511** 15 10
3335 50c. "Woman embroidering" (Guillermo Rivas Navas) 15 10
3336 1cor. "Couple dancing" (June Beer) 30 15
3337 1cor. "Song of Peace" (Alejandro Canales) . . . 30 15
3338 2cor.50 "Sapodilla Plums" (Genaro Lugo) (horiz) . . 55 30
3339 3cor. "Figure and Fragments" (Leonel Vanegas) 85 45
3340 4cor. "Eruption of Agua Volcano" (Asilia Guillen) (horiz) 95 45

512 Nicolas Copernicus and Satellite

1994. Astronomers. Mutlicoloured.
3342 1cor.50 Type **512** 35 15
3343 1cor.50 Tycho Brahe and astronomers 35 15
3344 1cor.50 Galileo Galilei and "Galileo" space probe . . 35 15
3345 1cor.50 Sir Isaac Newton and telescope 35 15
3346 1cor.50 Edmond Halley, space probe and Halley's Comet 35 15
3347 1cor.50 James Bradley and Greenwich Observatory 35 15
3348 1cor.50 William Herschel and telescope 35 15
3349 1cor.50 John Goodricke and Algol (star) 35 15
3350 1cor.50 Karl Friedrich Gauss and Gottingen Observatory 35 15
3351 1cor.50 Friedrich Bessel and 1838 star telescope . . . 35 15
3352 1cor.50 William Cranch Bond (wrongly inscr "Granch") and Harvard College Observatory . . . 35 15
3353 1cor.50 Sir George Airy and stellar disk 35 15
3354 1cor.50 Percival Lowell and Flagstaff Observatory, Arizona, U.S.A. 35 15
3355 1cor.50 George Hale (wrongly inscr "Halle") and solar spectroscope . . 35 15
3356 1cor.50 Edwin Hubble and Hubble telescope 35 15
3357 1cor.50 Gerard Kuiper and Miranda (Uranus moon) 35 15

Nos. 3342/57 were issued together, se-tenant, forming a composite design.

513 1886 Benz Tricycle

1994. Automobiles. Multicoloured.
3359 1cor.50 Type **513** 35 15
3360 1cor.50 1909 Benz Blitzen 35 15
3361 1cor.50 1923 Mercedes Benz 24/100/140 . . . . 35 15
3362 1cor.50 1928 Mercedes Benz SSK 35 15
3363 1cor.50 1934 Mercedes Benz 500K Cabriolet 35 15
3364 1cor.50 1949 Mercedes Benz 170S 35 15
3365 1cor.50 1954 Mercedes Benz W196 . . . . 35 15
3366 1cor.50 1954 Mercedes Benz 300SL 35 15
3367 1cor.50 1896 Ford Quadricycle 35 15
3368 1cor.50 1920 Ford taxi cab 35 15
3369 1cor.50 1928 Ford Roadster 35 15
3370 1cor.50 1932 Ford V-8 . . . 35 15
3371 1cor.50 1937 Ford V-8 78 35 15
3372 1cor.50 1939 Ford 91 Deluxe Tudor Sedan . . . 35 15
3373 1cor.50 1946 Ford V-8 Sedan Coupe 35 15
3374 1cor.50 1958 Ford Custom 300 . . . . 35 15

514 Hugo Eckener and Count Ferdinand von Zeppelin

1994. Zeppelin Airships. Multicoloured.
3376 1cor.50 Type **514** 35 15
3377 1cor.50 "Graf Zeppelin" over New York, 1928 . . 35 15
3378 1cor.50 "Graf Zeppelin" over Tokyo, 1929 . . . . 35 15
3379 1cor.50 "Graf Zeppelin" over Randolph Hearst's villa, 1929 . . . . . . 35 15
3380 1cor.50 Charles Lindbergh, Hugo Eckener and "Graf Zeppelin" at Lakehurst, 1929 . . . . 35 15
3381 1cor.50 "Graf Zeppelin" over St. Basil's Cathedral, Moscow (wrongly inscr "Santra Sofia") 35 15
3382 1cor.50 "Graf Zeppelin" over Paris, 1930 . . . . . 35 15
3383 1cor.50 "Graf Zeppelin" over Cairo, Egypt, 1931 35 15
3384 1cor.50 "Graf Zeppelin" over Arctic Sea 35 15
3385 1cor.50 "Graf Zeppelin" over Rio de Janeiro, 1932 35 15
3386 1cor.50 "Graf Zeppelin" over St. Paul's Cathedral, London, 1935 . . . . . 35 15
3387 1cor.50 "Graf Zeppelin" over St. Peter's Cathedral, Rome 35 15
3388 1cor.50 "Graf Zeppelin" over Swiss Alps 35 15
3389 1cor.50 "Graf Zeppelin over Brandenburg Gate, Berlin 35 15
3390 1cor.50 Hugo Eckener piloting "Graf Zeppelin" 35 15
3391 1cor.50 Captain Ernest Lehman, "Graf Zeppelin" and Dornier Do-X flying boat 35 15

515 Gabriel Horvilleur

1994. Nicaraguan Philatelists. Multicoloured.
3393 1cor. Type **515** 15 10
3394 3cor. Jose Cauadra 85 45
3395 4cor. Alfredo Pertz 95 45

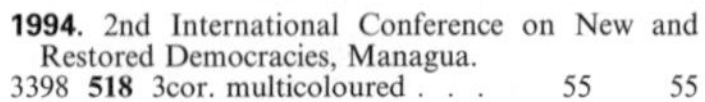

517 "Poponjoche" (Thelma Gomez)

518 Conference Emblem

1994. 1st Nicaraguan Tree Conference.
3397 **517** 4cor. multicoloured . . . 95 45

1994. 2nd International Conference on New and Restored Democracies, Managua.
3398 **518** 3cor. multicoloured . . . 55 55

519 Pulpit, Leon Cathedral

520 Mascot and Emblem

1994. Religious Art. Multicoloured.
3399 50c. Type **519** 15 10
3400 50c. "St. Anna" (porcelain figure), Chinandega Church 15 10
3401 1cor. "St. Joseph and Child" (porcelain figure), St. Peter's Church, Rivas 30 15
3402 1cor. "St. James", Jinotepe Church 30 15
3403 2cor.50 Gold chalice, Subtiava Temple, Leon 55 30
3404 3cor. Processional cross, Niquinohomo Church, Masaya 85 45
3405 4cor. "Lord of Miracles" (crucifix), Lord of Miracles Temple, Managua 95 45

1994. 32nd World Amateur Baseball Championship.
3407 **520** 4cor. multicoloured . . . 1·00 1·00

521 Mt. Sorak

1994. "Philakorea 1994" International Stamp Exhibition, Seoul. Views of South Korea. Mult.
3408 1cor.50 Type **521** 25 10
3409 1cor.50 Bronze Statue of Kim Yu-Shin 25 10
3410 1cor.50 Woedolgae (solitary rock) 25 10
3411 1cor.50 Stream, Mt. Hallasan, Cheju Island . . 25 10
3412 1cor.50 Mirukpong and Pisondae 25 10
3413 1cor.50 Ch'onbuldong Valley 25 10
3414 1cor.50 Bridge of the Seven Nymphs 25 10
3415 1cor.50 Piryong Waterfall 25 10

522 Piano on Stage

1994. 25th Anniv of Ruben Dario National Theatre, Managua.
3417 **522** 3cor. multicoloured . . . 55 20

523 Tyrannosaurus Rex

1994. Prehistoric Animals. Multicoloured.
3418 1cor.50 Type **523** 25 10
3419 1cor.50 Plateosaurus 25 10
3420 1cor.50 Pteranodon 25 10
3421 1cor.50 Camarasaurus 25 10
3422 1cor.50 Euplocephalus . . . 25 10
3423 1cor.50 Sacuanjoche 25 10
3424 1cor.50 Deinonychus . . . 25 10
3425 1cor.50 Chasmosaurus . . . 25 10
3426 1cor.50 Dimorphodon . . . 25 10
3427 1cor.50 Ametriorhynchids 25 10
3428 1cor.50 Ichthyosaurus . . . 25 10
3429 1cor.50 Pterapsis and compsognathus 25 10
3430 1cor.50 Cephalopod 25 10
3431 1cor.50 Archelon 25 10
3432 1cor.50 Griphognatus and gyroptychius 25 10
3433 1cor.50 Plesiosaur and nautiloid 25 10

Nos. 3418/33 were issued together, se-tenant, forming a composite design.

524 Hawker Typhoon 1B

1994. 50th Anniv of D-Day. Multicoloured.
3434 3cor. Type **524** 55 20
3435 3cor. Douglas C-47 Skytrain transport dropping paratroops 55 20
3436 3cor. H.M.S. "Mauritius" (cruiser) bombarding Houlgate, Normandy . . 55 20
3437 3cor. Formation of Mulberry Harbours to transport supplies to beach 55 20
3438 3cor. British AVRE Churchill tank 55 20
3439 3cor. Tank landing craft . . 55 20

525 Renate Stecher (women's 200 m, 1972)

526 Detachment of Command module "Eagle"

1994. Centenary of International Olympic Committee. Gold Medal Winners. Multicoloured.
3440 3cor.50 Type **525** 60 25
3441 3cor.50 Cassius Clay (Muhammad Ali) (boxing, 1960) 60 25

1994. 25th Anniv of First Manned Moon Landing. Multicoloured.
3443 3cor. Type **526** 55 20
3444 3cor. Launch of "Saturn V", Cape Canaveral, Florida 55 20
3445 3cor. Command module orbiting Moon 55 20
3446 3cor. Footprint on Moon 55 20
3447 3cor. Primary space capsule separating 55 20
3448 3cor. Command module . . 55 20
3449 3cor. Lunar module landing on Moon 55 20
3450 3cor. Astronaut on Moon 55 20

527 "The Death Cart" (Erick Joanello Montoya)

1994. 1st Prize in Children's Painting Competition.
3452 **527** 4cor. multicoloured . . . 70 30

528 Black-crowned Night Heron

1994. Woodland Animals. Multicoloured.
3453 2cor. Type **528** 35 15
3454 2cor. Scarlet macaw ("Ara macao") 35 15
3455 2cor. Cattle egrets ("Bubulcus ibis") (wrongly inscr "Bulbulcus") 35 15
3456 2cor. American black vultures ("Coragyps atratus") 35 15
3457 2cor. Brazilian rainbow boa ("Epicrates cenchria") . . 35 15
3458 2cor. Red-legged honeycreepers ("Cyanerpes cyaneus") . . 35 15
3459 2cor. Plain chachalaca ("Ortalis vetula") 35 15
3460 2cor. Sloth ("Bradypus griseus") 35 15
3461 2cor. Jaguar ("Felis onca") 35 15
3462 2cor. American darter ("Anhinga anhinga") . . 35 15
3463 2cor. Baird's tapir ("Tapirus bairdi") 35 15
3464 2cor. Anteater ("Myrmecophaga jubata") 35 15
3465 2cor. Iguana ("Iguana iguaana") 35 15
3466 2cor. Snapping turtle ("Chelydra serpentina") 35 15
3467 2cor. Red-billed whistling ducks ("Dendrocygna autumnalis") 35 15
3468 2cor. Ocelot ("Felis pardalis") 35 15

Nos. 3453/68 were issued together, se-tenant, forming a composite design.

529 "The Kid" (dir. Charlie Chaplin)

530 "Discovery of America"

1994. Centenary of Motion Pictures. Multicoloured.
3470 2cor. Type **529** 35 15
3471 2cor. "Citizen Kane" (dir. Orson Welles) 35 15
3472 2cor. "Lawrence of Arabia" (dir. David Lean) 35 15
3473 2cor. "Ivan the Terrible" (dir. Sergio Eisenstein) . . 35 15
3474 2cor. "Metropolis" (dir. Fritz Lang) 35 15
3475 2cor. "The Ten Commandments" (dir. Cecil B. De Mille) 35 15
3476 2cor. "Gandhi" (dir. Richard Attenborough) 35 15
3477 2cor. "Casablanca" (dir. Michael Curtiz) 35 15
3478 2cor. "Platoon" (dir. Oliver Stone) 35 15
3479 2cor. "The Godfather" (dir. Francis Ford Coppola) 35 15
3480 2cor. "2001: A Space Odyssey" (dir. Stanley Kubrick) 35 15
3481 2cor. "The Ocean Depths" (dir. Jean Renoir) 35 15

1994. 15th Death Anniv of Rodrigo Penalba (artist). Multicoloured.
3483 50c. Type **530** 10 10
3484 1cor. "Portrait of Mauricio" 20 10
3485 1cor.50 "Portrait of Franco" 25 10
3486 2cor. "Portrait of Mimi Hammer" 35 15
3487 2cor.50 "Seated Woman" 45 20
3488 3cor. "Still-life" (horiz) . . 55 20
3489 4cor. "Portrait of Maria Augusta" 70 30

531 Hen and Cock

1994. Endangered Species. The Highland Guan. Multicoloured.
3491 50c. Type **531** 10 10
3492 1cor. Cock 20 10
3493 2cor.50 Hen 45 20
3494 3cor. Cock and hen (different) 55 25

SILVER CURRENCY

The following were for use in all places on the Atlantic coast of Nicaragua where the silver currency was in use. This currency was worth about 50c. to the peso.

Earlier issues (overprints on Nicaraguan stamps) were also issued for Zelaya. These are listed in the Stanley Gibbons Part 15 (Central America) Catalogue.

G 1 Steam Locomotive

1912.
G 1 **Z 1** 1c. green . . . . 1·75 90
G 2 2c. red . . . . . 1·25 55
G 3 3c. brown . . . 1·75 85
G 4 4c. lake . . . . 1·75 70
G 5 5c. blue . . . . 1·75 70
G 6 6c. red . . . . . 9·75 5·00
G 7 10c. grey . . . . 1·75 70
G 8 15c. lilac . . . . 1·75 1·10
G 9 20c. blue . . . . 1·75 1·10
G10 25c. black and green . . . . 2·25 1·60
G11 35c. black and brown . . . . 3·25 1·90
G12 50c. green . . . 3·25 1·90
G13 1p. orange . . . 5·00 3·25
G14 2p. brown . . . 9·75 6·00
G15 5p. green . . . . 20·00 12·50

OFFICIAL STAMPS

Overprinted **FRANQUEO OFICIAL**.

1890. Stamps of 1890.
O37 **6** 1c. blue 30 60
O38 2c. blue 30 60
O39 5c. blue 30 70
O40 10c. blue 30 75
O41 20c. blue 35 90
O42 50c. blue . . . . 35 1·10
O43 1p. blue . . . . 40 1·75
O44 2p. blue . . . . 40 2·75
O45 5p. blue . . . . 45 6·00
O46 10p. blue . . . . 45 11·50

1891. Stamps of 1891.
O47 **7** 1c. green 15 40
O48 2c. green 15 40
O49 5c. green 15 40
O50 10c. green 15 40
O51 20c. green 15 70
O52 50c. green 15 75
O53 1p. green 15 90
O54 2p. green 15 90
O55 5p. green . . . . 15 2·25
O56 10p. green . . . . 15 3·50

1892. Stamps of 1892.
O57 **8** 1c. brown 15 30
O58 2c. brown 15 30
O59 5c. brown 15 30
O60 10c. brown 15 30
O61 20c. brown 15 50
O62 50c. brown 15 70
O63 1p. brown . . . . 15 1·10
O64 2p. brown . . . . 15 1·75
O65 5p. brown . . . . 15 2·75
O66 10p. brown . . . . 15 3·50

1893. Stamps of 1893.
O67 **9** 1c. black 15 30
O68 2c. black 15 30
O69 5c. black 15 30
O70 10c. black 15 30
O71 20c. black 15 50
O72 25c. black 15 65
O73 50c. black 15 70
O74 1p. black . . . . 15 1·00
O75 2p. black . . . . 15 1·25
O76 5p. black . . . . 15 2·75
O77 10p. black . . . . 15 3·50

1894. Stamps of 1894.
O78 **10** 1c. orange 15 30
O79 2c. orange 15 30
O80 5c. orange 15 30
O81 10c. orange 15 30
O82 20c. orange 15 30
O83 50c. orange 15 45
O84 1p. orange . . . . 15 1·00
O85 2p. orange . . . . 15 1·75
O86 5p. orange . . . . 15 3·50
O87 10p. orange . . . . 15 4·50

1895. Stamps of 1895.
O88 **11** 1c. green 15 30
O89 2c. green 15 30
O90 5c. green 15 30
O91 10c. green 15 30
O92 20c. green 15 50
O93 50c. green 15 80
O94 1p. green 15 80
O95 2p. green . . . . 15 1·25
O96 5p. green . . . . 15 1·90
O97 10p. green . . . . 15 2·40

1896. Stamps of 1896, dated "1896", optd **FRANQUEO OFICIAL** in oval frame.
O 99 **12** 1c. red . . . . 1·50 1·90
O100 2c. red . . . . 1·50 1·90
O101 5c. red . . . . 1·50 1·90
O102 10c. red . . . . 1·50 1·90
O103 20c. red . . . . 1·90 1·90
O104 50c. red . . . . 3·00 3·00
O105 1p. red . . . . 7·25 7·25

O106 2p. red 7·25 7·25
O107 5p. red 9·50 9·50

1896. Nos. D99/103 handstamped **Franqueo Oficial**.
O108 D **13** 1c. orange — 4·25
O109 2c. orange — 4·25
O110 5c. orange — 3·00
O111 10c. orange — 3·00
O112 20c. orange — 3·00

1897. Stamps of 1897, dated "1897", optd **FRANQUEO OFICIAL** in oval frame.
O113 **12** 1c. red 2·00 2·00
O114 2c. red 2·00 2·00
O115 5c. red 2·00 2·00
O116 10c. red 1·90 2·10
O117 20c. red 1·90 2·40
O118 50c. red 3·00 3·00
O119 1p. red 8·25 8·25
O120 2p. red 9·75 9·75
O121 5p. red 15·00 15·00

1898. Stamps of 1898 optd **FRANQUEO OFICIAL** in oval frame.
O124 **13** 1c. red 2·00 2·00
O125 2c. red 2·00 2·00
O126 4c. red 2·00 2·00
O127 5c. red 1·50 1·50
O128 10c. red 2·40 2·40
O129 15c. red 3·75 3·75
O130 20c. red 3·75 3·75
O131 50c. red 5·00 5·00
O132 1p. red 6·50 6·50
O133 2p. red 6·50 6·50
O134 5p. red 6·50 6·50

1899. Stamps of 1899 optd **FRANQUEO OFICIAL** in scroll.
O137 **14** 1c. green 15 60
O138 2c. brown 15 60
O139 4c. red 15 60
O140 5c. blue 15 40
O141 10c. orange 15 60
O142 15c. brown 15 1·25
O143 20c. green 15 2·00
O144 50c. red 15 2·00
O145 1p. orange 15 6·00
O146 2p. violet 15 6·00
O147 5p. blue 15 9·00

O 16 O 38

1900.
O148 O **16** 1c. purple 45 45
O149 2c. orange 35 35
O150 4c. olive 45 45
O151 5c. blue 90 30
O152 10c. violet 90 25
O153 20c. brown 65 25
O154 50c. lake 90 35
O155 1p. blue 2·10 1·50
O156 2p. orange 2·40 2·40
O157 5p. black 3·00 3·00

1903. Stamps of 1900 surch **OFICIAL** and value, with or without ornaments.
O197 **15** 1c. on 10c. mauve 1·25 1·50
O198 2c. on 3c. green 1·50 1·90
O199 4c. on 3c. green 5·75 5·75
O200 4c. on 10c. mauve 5·75 5·75
O201 5c. on 3c. green 70 70

1903. Surch.
O202 O **16** 10c. on 20c. brown 15 15
O203 30c. on 20c. brown 15 15
O204 50c. on 20c. brown 35 25

1905.
O219 O **38** 1c. green 20 20
O220 2c. red 20 20
O221 5c. blue 20 20
O222 10c. brown 20 20
O223 20c. orange 20 20
O224 50c. olive 20 20
O225 1p. lake 20 20
O226 2p. violet 20 20
O227 5p. black 20 20

1907. Surch **Vale 10 c.**
O239 O **38** 10c. on 1c. green 55 55
O241 10c. on 2c. red 15·00 11·50
O243 20c. on 2c. red 13·50 9·00
O245 50c. on 1c. green 1·10 1·10
O247 50c. on 2c. red 13·50 6·50

1907. Surch **Vale 20 cts** or **Vale $1.00.**
O249 O **38** 20c. on 1c. green 70 70
O250 $1 on 2c. red 1·10 1·10
O251 $2 on 2c. red 1·10 1·10
O252 $3 on 2c. red 1·10 1·10
O253 $4 on 5c. blue 1·40 1·40

1907. No. 206 surch **OFICIAL** and value.
O256 **49** 10c. on 1c. green 9·00 7·75
O257 15c. on 1c. green 9·00 7·75
O258 20c. on 1c. green 9·00 7·75
O259 50c. on 1c. green 9·00 7·75
O260 1p. on 1c. green 8·25 7·75
O261 2p. on 1c. green 8·25 7·75

1907. Fiscal stamps as T **50** surch **10 cts. CORREOS 1907 OFICIAL 10 CTS.**
O262 **50** 10c. on 2c. orange 10 10
O263 35c. on 1c. blue 10 10
O264 70c. on 1c. blue 10 10
O266 1p. on 2c. orange 10 15
O267 2p. on 2c. orange 10 15
O268 3p. on 5c. brown 10 15
O269 4p. on 5c. brown 15 15
O270 5p. on 5c. brown 15 15

1908. Stamp of 1905 surch **OFICIAL VALE** and value.
O271 **37** 10c. on 3c. violet 9·00 7·75
O272 15c. on 3c. violet 9·00 7·75
O273 20c. on 3c. violet 9·00 7·75
O274 35c. on 3c. violet 9·00 7·75
O275 50c. on 3c. violet 9·00 7·75

1908. Fiscal stamps as T **50** surch as last but dated 1908.
O276 **50** 10c. on 1c. blue 55 35
O277 10c. on 2c. orange 75 30
O278 35c. on 1c. blue 55 35
O279 35c. on 2c. orange 80 45
O280 50c. on 1c. blue 55 35
O281 50c. on 2c. orange 80 45
O282 70c. on 2c. orange 80 45
O283 1p. on 1c. blue 23·00 23·00
O284 1p. on 2c. orange 80 45
O285 2p. on 1c. blue 65 55
O286 2p. on 2c. orange 80 45

1909. Stamps of 1905 optd **OFICIAL**.
O290 **37** 10c. lake 15 15
O291 15c. black 45 35
O292 20c. olive 70 55
O293 50c. green 1·10 70
O294 1p. yellow 1·25 90
O295 2p. red 1·75 1·40

1911. Stamps of 1905 optd **OFICIAL** and surch **Vale** and value.
O296 **37** 5c. on 3c. orange 3·75 3·75
O297 10c. on 4c. violet 3·00 3·00

1911. Railway tickets, surch **Timbre Fiscal Vale 10 ctvs.** further surch for official postal use. Printed in red. (a) Surch **Correo oficial Vale** and value on front.
O334 **64** 10c. on 10c. on 1st class 5·25 4·50
O335 15c. on 10c. on 1st class 5·25 4·50
O336 20c. on 10c. on 1st class 5·25 4·50
O337 50c. on 10c. on 1st class 7·00 6·25
O338 $1 on 10c. on 1st class 8·00 11·00
O339 $2 on 10c. on 1st class 11·50 16·00

(b) Surch **CORREO OFICIAL** and new value on front.
O340 **64** 10c. on 10c. on 1st class 30·00 27·00
O341 15c. on 10c. on 1st class 30·00 27·00
O342 20c. on 10c. on 1st class 30·00 28·00
O343 50c. on 10c. on 1st class 27·00 24·00

(c) No. 322 surch on front **Correo Oficial Vale 1911** and new value and with **15 cts.** on back obliterated by heavy bar.
O344 **64** 5c. on 10c. on 1st class 10·00 9·50
O345 10c. on 10c. on 1st class 11·50 11·00
O346 15c. on 10c. on 1st class 13·00 12·00
O347 20c. on 10c. on 1st class 15·00 18·00
O348 50c. on 10c. on 1st class 17·00 16·00

(d) No. 322 surch on front **Correo Oficial 1912** and new value and with the whole surch on back obliterated.
O349 **64** 5c. on 10c. on 1st class 12·00 9·50
O350 10c. on 10c. on 1st class 12·00 9·50
O351 15c. on 10c. on 1st class 12·00 9·50
O352 20c. on 10c. on 1st class 12·00 9·50
O353 25c. on 10c. on 1st class 12·00 9·50
O354 50c. on 10c. on 1st class 12·00 9·50
O355 $1 on 10c. on 1st class 12·00 9·50

1913. Stamps of 1912 optd **OFICIAL**.
O356 **70** 1c. blue 10 10
O357 2c. blue 10 10
O358 3c. blue 10 10
O359 4c. blue 10 10
O360 5c. blue 10 10
O361 6c. blue 10 15
O362 10c. blue 10 15
O363 15c. blue 10 15
O364 20c. blue 15 20
O365 25c. blue 15 15
O366 **71** 35c. blue 20 20
O367 **70** 50c. blue 1·10 1·10
O368 1p. blue 25 25
O369 2p. blue 25 25
O370 5p. blue 35 35

1915. Optd **OFICIAL**.
O406 **79** 1c. blue 15 15
O407 **80** 2c. blue 15 15
O408 **79** 3c. blue 15 15
O409 **80** 4c. blue 15 15
O410 **79** 5c. blue 15 15
O411 **80** 6c. blue 15 15
O412 10c. blue 15 15
O413 **79** 15c. blue 15 15
O414 **80** 20c. blue 15 15
O415 **79** 25c. blue 25 25
O416 **80** 50c. blue 45 45

1925. Optd **Oficial** or **OFICIAL**.
O513 **79** ½c. green 10 10
O514 1c. violet 10 10
O515 **80** 2c. red 10 10
O516 **79** 3c. olive 10 10
O517 **80** 4c. red 10 10
O518 **79** 5c. black 10 10
O519 **80** 6c. brown 10 10
O520 10c. yellow 10 10
O521 **79** 15c. brown 10 10
O522 **80** 20c. brown 10 10
O523 **79** 25c. orange 40 40
O524 **80** 50c. blue 45 45

1929. Air. Official stamps of 1925 additionally optd **Correo Aereo**.
O618 **79** 25c. orange 35 35
O619 **80** 50c. blue 55 55

1931. Stamp of 1924 surch **OFICIAL C$ 0.05 Correos 1928**.
O651 **99** 5c. on 10c. brown 25 25

1931. No. 648 additionally surch **OFICIAL** and value.
O652 **99** 5c. on 10c. brown 25 25

1931. Stamps of 1914 optd **1931** (except 6c., 10c.), and also optd **OFICIAL**.
O670 **79** 1c. olive (No. 762) 20 20
O707 **80** 2c. red 6·50 6·50
O671 **79** 3c. blue 20 20
O672 5c. sepia 20 20
O673 **80** 6c. brown 25 25
O675 10c. brown 25 25
O674 10c. blue (No. 697) 1·10 1·10
O710 **79** 15c. orange 70 70
O711 25c. sepia 70 70
O712 25c. violet 1·75 1·75

1932. Air. Optd **Correo Aereo OFICIAL** only.
O688 **79** 15c. orange 45 45
O689 **80** 20c. orange 50 50
O690 **79** 25c. violet 50 50
O691 **80** 50c. green 60 60
O692 1cor. yellow 60 60

1932. Air. Optd **1931 Correo Aereo OFICIAL**.
O693 **79** 25c. sepia 25·00 25·00

1932. Optd **OFICIAL**.
O694 **79** 1c. olive 10 10
O695 **80** 2c. red 10 10
O696 **79** 3c. blue 15 10
O697 **80** 4c. blue 15 10
O698 **79** 5c. sepia 15 15
O699 **80** 6c. brown 20 10
O700 10c. brown 30 25
O701 **79** 15c. orange 40 25
O702 **80** 20c. orange 40 30
O703 **79** 25c. violet 1·25 50
O704 **80** 50c. green 15 15
O705 1cor. yellow 20 20

1933. 441st Anniv of Columbus's Departure from Palos. As T **133**, but inscr "CORREO OFICIAL". Roul.
O777 1c. yellow 60 60
O778 2c. yellow 60 60
O779 3c. brown 60 60
O780 4c. brown 60 60
O781 5c. brown 60 60
O782 6c. blue 75 75
O783 10c. violet 75 75
O784 15c. purple 75 75
O785 20c. green 75 75
O786 25c. green 1·75 1·75
O787 50c. red 2·25 2·25
O788 1cor. red 3·50 3·50

1933. Optd with T **134** and **OFICIAL**.
O814 **79** 1c. green 10 10
O815 **80** 2c. red 10 10
O816 **79** 3c. blue 10 10
O817 **80** 4c. blue 10 10
O818 **79** 5c. brown 10 10
O819 **80** 6c. grey 10 10
O820 10c. brown 10 10
O821 **79** 15c. red 15 15
O822 **80** 20c. orange 15 15
O823 **79** 25c. violet 15 15
O824 **80** 50c. green 25 25
O825 1cor. yellow 50 45

1933. Air. Optd with T **134** and **CORREO Aereo OFICIAL**.
O826 **79** 15c. violet 20 20
O827 **80** 20c. green 20 20
O828 **79** 25c. olive 20 20
O829 **80** 50c. green 35 35
O830 1cor. red 60 50

1935. Nos. O814/25 optd **RESELLO – 1935** in a box.
O864 **79** 1c. green 10 10
O865 **80** 2c. red 10 10
O866 **79** 3c. blue 10 10
O867 **80** 4c. blue 10 10
O868 **79** 5c. brown 10 10
O869 **80** 6c. grey 10 10
O870 10c. brown 10 10
O871 **79** 15c. red 15 15
O872 **80** 20c. orange 15 15
O873 **79** 25c. violet 15 15
O874 **80** 50c. green 20 20
O875 1cor. yellow 35 35

1935. Air. Nos. O826/30 optd **RESELLO – 1935** in a box.
O877 **79** 15c. violet 30 25
O878 **80** 20c. green 30 25
O879 **79** 25c. olive 30 30
O880 **80** 50c. green 90 90
O881 1cor. red 90 90

(O **141**) O **151** Islets in the Great Lake

1937. Nos. 913, etc, optd with Type O **141**.
O935 **79** 1c. red 25 15
O936 **80** 2c. blue 25 15
O937 **79** 3c. brown 30 25
O938 5c. red 35 30
O939 **80** 10c. green 40 35
O940 **79** 15c. green 50 40
O941 25c. orange 60 45
O942 **80** 50c. brown 85 50
O943 1cor. blue 2·25 1·00

1937. Air. Nos. 926/30 optd with Type O **141**.
O944 **112** 15c. orange 50 35
O945 20c. red 50 35
O946 25c. black 50 45
O947 50c. violet 50 45
O948 1cor. orange 50 45

1939.
O1020 O **151** 2c. red 15 15
O1021 3c. blue 15 15
O1022 6c. brown 15 15
O1023 7½c. green 15 15
O1024 10c. brown 15 15
O1025 15c. orange 15 15
O1026 25c. violet 30 30
O1027 50c. green 45 45

O **152** Pres. Somoza

1939. Air.
O1028 O **152** 10c. brown 30 30
O1029 15c. blue 30 30
O1030 20c. yellow 30 30
O1031 25c. violet 30 30
O1032 30c. red 30 30
O1033 50c. orange 40 40
O1034 1cor. olive 75 75

O **175** Managua Airport

1947. Air.
O1120 O **175** 5c. brown and black 15 10
O1121 – 10c. blue and black 15 15
O1122 – 15c. violet and black 15 15
O1123 – 20c. orange & black 20 10
O1124 – 25c. blue and black 15 15
O1125 – 50c. red and black 15 15
O1126 – 1cor. grey and black 40 35
O1127 – 2cor.50 brown and black 75 90
DESIGNS: 10c. Sulphur lagoon, Nejapa; 15c. Ruben Dario Monument, Managua; 20c. Baird's tapir; 25c. Genizaro Dam; 50c. Thermal baths, Tipitapa; 1cor. Highway and Lake Managua; 2cor.50, Franklin D. Roosevelt Monument, Managua.

O **181** U.P.U. Offices, Berne

1950. Air. 75th Anniv of U.P.U. Inscr as in Type O **181**. Frames in black.
O1159 – 5c. purple 10 10
O1160 – 10c. green 10 10
O1161 – 25c. purple 10 10
O1162 O **181** 50c. orange 15 10
O1163 – 1cor. blue 35 30
O1164 – 2cor.60 black 2·10 1·75
DESIGNS—HORIZ: 5c. Rowland Hill; 10c. Heinrich von Stephan; 25c. Standehaus, Berne; 1cor. Monument, Berne; 2cor.60, Congress Medal.

1961. Air. Consular Fiscal stamps as T **203/4** with serial Nos. in red, surch **Oficial Aereo** and value.
O1448 10c. on 1cor. olive 10 10
O1449 15c. on 20cor. brown 10 10
O1450 20c. on 100cor. lake 10 10
O1451 25c. on 50c. blue 15 10
O1452 35c. on 50cor. brown 15 15
O1453 50c. on 3cor. red 15 15
O1454 1cor. on 2cor. green 25 20
O1455 2cor. on 5cor. red 25 45
O1456 5cor. on 10cor. violet 60 60

POSTAGE DUE STAMPS

D 13

D 16

1896.

D 99 D 13 1c. orange . . . . . . 45 1·10
D100 2c. orange . . . . . . 45 1·10
D101 5c. orange . . . . . . 45 1·10
D102 10c. orange . . . . . 45 1·10
D103 20c. orange . . . . . 45 1·10
D104 30c. orange . . . . . 45 1·10
D105 50c. orange . . . . . 45 1·40

1897.

D108 D 13 1c. violet . . . . . . 45 1·10
D109 2c. violet . . . . . . 45 1·10
D110 5c. violet . . . . . . 45 1·10
D111 10c. violet . . . . . . 45 1·10
D112 20c. violet . . . . . . 75 1·25
D113 30c. violet 45 90
D114 50c. violet 45 90

1898.

D124 D 13 1c. green . . . . . . 15 1·25
D125 2c. green . . . . . . 15 1·25
D126 5c. green . . . . . . 15 1·25
D127 10c. green . . . . . . 15 1·25
D128 20c. green . . . . . . 15 1·25
D129 30c. green . . . . . . 15 1·25
D130 50c. green . . . . . . 15 1·25

1899.

D137 D 13 1c. red . . . . 15 1·25
D138 2c. red . . . . 15 1·25
D139 5c. red . . . . 15 1·25
D140 10c. red . . . . 15 1·25
D141 20c. red . . . . 15 1·25
D142 50c. red . . . . 15 1·25

1900.

D146 D 16 1c. red 70
D147 2c. orange 70
D148 5c. blue 70
D149 10c. violet 70
D150 20c. brown 70
D151 30c. green . . . . . . 1·40
D152 50c. lake . . . . . . 1·40

NIGER Pt. 6; Pt. 14

Area south of the Sahara. In 1920 was separated from Upper Senegal and Niger to form a separate colony. From 1944 to 1959 used the stamps of French West Africa.

In 1958 Niger became an autonomous republic within the French Community and on 3 August 1960 an independent republic.

100 centimes = 1 franc.

1921. Stamps of Upper Senegal and Niger optd **TERRITOIRE DU NIGER**.

1 7 1c. violet and purple . . . . 10 2·50
2 2c. purple and grey . . . . . 10 2·25
3 4c. blue and black . . . . . 15 2·50
4 5c. chocolate and brown . . 15 2·25
5 10c. green and light green . . 1·10 2·75
25 10c. pink on blue . . . . . 10 2·25
6 15c. yellow and brown . . . 50 2·00
7 20c. black and purple . . . . 40 2·25
8 25c. green and black . . . . 40 2·50
9 30c. carmine and red . . . . 1·75 3·00
26 30c. red and green . . . . . 45 2·75
10 35c. violet and red . . . . . 70 2·50
11 40c. red and grey . . . . . 80 2·50
12 45c. brown and blue . . . . 35 3·00
13 50c. blue and ultramarine . . 1·50 2·75
27 50c. blue and grey . . . . . 45 3·00
28 60c. red . . . . 35 2·75
14 75c. brown and yellow . . . 60 3·50
15 1f. purple and brown . . . . 50 3·00
16 2f. blue and green . . . . . 70 3·50
17 5f. black and violet . . . . . 90 3·75

1922. Stamps of 1921 surch.

18 7 25c. on 15c. yellow & brown 50 3·00
19 25c. on 2f. blue and green . . 1·75 2·75
20 25c. on 5f. black and violet 1·40 2·75
21 60 on 75c. violet on pink . . 15 2·25
22 65 on 45c. brown and blue 1·60 3·75
23 85c. on 75c. brown & yellow 1·10 3·75
24 1f.25 on 1f. light blue & blue 55 3·25

3 Wells

5 Zinder Fort

4 Canoe on River Niger

1926.

29 3 1c. green and purple . . . . 10 1·25
30 2c. red and grey . . . . . . 10 2·50
31 3c. brown and mauve . . . . 10 2·75
32 4c. black and brown . . . . 20 2·75
33 5c. green and red . . . . . 75 2·25
34 10c. green and blue . . . . . 10 1·25
35 15c. light green and green . . 35 2·25
36 15c. red and lilac . . . . . . 10 2·25
37 4 20c. brown and blue . . . . 15 2·50
38 25c. pink and black . . . . 85 2·25
39 30c. light green and green . . 1·90 2·75
40 30c. mauve and yellow . . . 75 2·50
41 35c. blue and red on blue . . 55 2·25
42 35c. green and deep green . . 1·40 2·75
43 40c. grey and purple . . . . 15 2·25
44 45c. mauve and yellow . . . 1·10 3·00
45 45c. green and turquoise . . 1·10 3·25
46 50c. green and red on green 15 45
47 55c. brown and red . . . . 1·60 3·25
48 60c. brown and red . . . . 35 3·00
49 65c. red and green . . . . . 1·25 2·75
50 70c. red and green . . . . . 1·90 3·25
51 75c. mauve and green on pink . . . . 1·40 3·00
52 80c. green and purple . . . . 2·25 3·50
53 90c. red and carmine . . . . 1·10 3·25
54 90c. green and red . . . . . 1·50 3·00
55 5 1f. green and red . . . . . 4·50 7·00
56 1f. orange and red . . . . . 1·60 1·25
57 1f. red and green . . . . . . 1·00 3·00
58 1f.10 green and brown . . . 4·00 4·75
59 1f.25 red and green . . . . . 1·25 2·25
60 1f.25 orange and red . . . . 2·00 3·00
61 1f.40 brown and mauve . . . 2·00 3·00
62 1f.50 light blue and blue . . 1·60 2·00
63 1f.60 green and brown . . . 2·00 3·25
64 1f.75 brown and mauve . . . 1·90 3·75
65 1f.75 ultramarine and blue 1·75 3·25
66 2f. brown and orange . . . . 1·25 2·00
67 2f.25 ultramarine and blue 2·00 3·25
68 2f.50 brown . . . . 2·00 3·25
69 3f. grey and mauve . . . . . 1·50 2·00
70 5f. black and purple on pink 90 2·50
71 10f. mauve and lilac . . . . 1·25 3·25
72 20f. orange and green . . . . 1·60 3·25

1931. "Colonial Exhibition" key types inscr "NIGER".

73 E 40c. green . . . . 2·25 2·25
74 F 50c. mauve . . . . 2·00 2·25
75 G 90c. red . . . . 2·50 2·75
76 H 1f.50 blue . . . . 2·50 2·75

1937. International Exhibition, Paris. As Nos. 71/6a of Mauritania.

77 20c. violet . . . . 45 3·00
78 30c. green . . . . 1·00 3·50
79 40c. red . . . . 75 3·00
80 50c. brown and agate . . . . 75 2·75
81 90c. red . . . . 85 3·25
82 1f.50 blue . . . . 55 2·75
MS82a 120 × 100 mm. 3f. mauve Imperf . . . . 6·25 9·75

1938. Int Anti-cancer Fund. As T **22** of Mauritania.

83 1f.75+50c. blue . . . . 6·75 21·00

1939. Caille. As T **27** of Mauritania.

84 90c. orange . . . . 40 3·00
85 2f. violet . . . . 25 2·00
86 2f.25 blue . . . . 25 3·25

1939. New York World's Fair. As T **28** of Mauritania.

87 1f.25 red . . . . 1·75 3·25
88 2f.25 blue . . . . 45 3·00

1939. 150th Anniv of French Revolution. As T **29** of Mauritania.

89 45c.+25c. green and black . . 5·00 12·50
90 70c.+30c. brown and black . . 5·00 12·50
91 90c.+35c. orange and black . . 6·00 12·50
92 1f.25+1f. red and black . . . 5·50 12·50
93 2f.25+2f. blue and black . . . 6·25 12·50

1940. Air. As T **30** of Mauritania.

94 1f.90 blue . . . . 1·60 3·00
95 2f.90 red . . . . 95 3·00
96 4f.50 green . . . . 1·75 3·25
97 4f.90 olive . . . . 95 3·25
98 6f.90 orange . . . . 1·00 3·00

1941. National Defence Fund. Surch **SECOURS NATIONAL** and additional value.

98a 4 +1f. on 50c. green and red on green . . . . 4·25 5·00
98b +2f. on 80c. green & pur . . 6·25 7·00
98c 5 +2f. on 1f.50 lt blue & bl 9·00 10·50
98d +3f. on 2f. brown & orge 8·50 10·50

5a Zinder Fort

5c "Vocation"

5b Weighing Baby

1942. Marshal Petain issue.

98e 5a 1f. green . . . . 55 2·00
98f 2f.50 blue . . . . 10 2·00

1942. Air. Colonial Child Welfare Fund.

98g – 1f.50+3f.50 green . . . . 20 3·25
98h – 2f.+6f. brown . . . . . . 20 3·25
98i 5b 3f.+9f. red . . . . 50 3·25

DESIGNS: 49 × 28 mm: 1f.50, Maternity Hospital, Dakar; 2f. Dispensary, Mopti.

1942. Air. Imperial Fortnight.

98j 5c 1f.20+1f.80 blue and red . . 15 3·25

1942. Air. As T 32 of Mauritania but inscr "NIGER" at foot.

98k 50f. red and yellow . . . . . 1·75 3·50

7 Giraffes

8 Carmine Bee Eater

1959. Wild Animals and Birds. Inscr "PROTECTION DE LA FAUNE".

99 – 50c. turquoise, green and black (postage) . . . . . 1·40 1·75
100 – 1f. multicoloured 40 90
101 – 2f. multicoloured 40 90
102 – 5f. mauve, black and brown 50 65
103 – 7f. red, black and green . . 95 95
104 – 10f. multicoloured . . . . . 1·75 1·75
105 – 15f. sepia and turquoise . . 1·75 1·75
106 – 20f. black and violet . . . . 1·75 1·40
107 7 25f. multicoloured . . . . . 2·00 1·50
108 30f. brown, bistre and green 2·00 1·75
109 – 50f. blue and brown . . . . 3·50 1·75
110 – 60f. sepia and green . . . . 4·50 2·75
111 – 85f. brown and bistre . . . 4·75 2·50
112 – 100f. bistre and green . . . 6·25 2·75

113 8 200f. multicoloured (air) . . 20·00 7·00
114 – 500f. green, brown and blue 17·00 12·50

DESIGNS—As Type **7**: HORIZ: 50c., 10f. African manatee. VERT: 1, 2f. Crowned cranes; 5, 7f. Saddle-bill stork; 15, 20f. Barbary sheep; 50, 60f. Ostriches; 85, 100f. Lion. As Type **8**: VERT: 500f. Game animals.

1960. 10th Anniv of African Technical Co-operation Commission. As T **4** of Malagasy Republic.

115 25f. brown and ochre . . . . 1·75 2·25

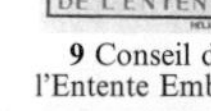

9 Conseil de l'Entente Emblem

11 Pres. Diori Hamani

1960. 1st Anniv of Conseil de l'Entente.

116 9 25f. multicoloured . . . . . 1·25 2·25

1960. Independence. No. 112 surch **200 F Independance 3-8-60**.

117 200f. on 100f. bistre and green . . . . 9·00 9·00

1960.

118 11 25f. black and bistre . . . 35 25

12 U.N. Emblem and Niger Flag

1961. Air. 1st Anniv of Admission into U.N.

119 12 25f. red, green and orange 40 25
120 100f. green, red and emerald . . . . 1·40 90

1962. Air. "Air Afrique" Airline. As T **42** of Mauritania.

121 100f. violet, black and brown 1·50 75

1962. Malaria Eradication. As T **43** of Mauritania.

122 25f.+5f. brown 45 45

13 Athletics

1962. Abidjan Games, 1961. Multicoloured.

123 15f. Boxing and cycling (vert) 25 15
124 25f. Basketball and football (vert) 35 20
125 85f. Type **13** . . . . 1·10 55

1962. 1st Anniv of Union of African and Malagasy States. As T **45** of Mauritania.

126 72 30f. mauve 40 30

14 Pres. Hamani and Map

15 Running

1962. 4th Anniv of Republic.

127 14 25f. multicoloured 35 25

1963. Freedom from Hunger. As T **51** of Mauritania.

128 25f.+5f. purple, brn & olive 55 55

1963. Dakar Games.

129 – 15f. brown and blue . . . 25 15
130 15 25f. red and brown 35 20
131 – 45f. black and green . . . 70 40

DESIGNS—HORIZ: 15f. Swimming. VERT: 45f. Volleyball.

16 Agadez Mosque

1963. Air. 2nd Anniv of Admission to U.P.U. Multicoloured.

132 50f. Type **16** 75 40
133 85f. Gaya Bridge . . . . 1·25 60
134 100f. Presidential Palace, Niamey . . . . 1·25 70

17 Wood-carving

1963. Traditional Crafts. Multicoloured.
135 5f. Type **17** (postage) 15 15
136 10f. Skin-tanning (horiz) . . 20 15
137 25f. Goldsmith 40 20
138 30f. Mat-making (horiz) . . . 60 30
139 85f. Potter . . . . 1·40 80
140 100f. Canoe building (horiz) (47 × 27 mm) (air) . . . . 2·00 1·10

1963. Air. African and Malagasy Posts and Telecommunications Union. As T **56** of Mauritania.
141 85f. multicoloured 95 55

1963. Air. Red Cross Centenary. Optd with cross and **Centenaire de la Croix-Rouge** in red.
142 **12** 25f. red, green and orange 60 40
143 100f. green, red and emerald . . . . 1·40 85

19 Costume Museum

1963. Opening of Costume Museum, Niamey. Vert costume designs. Multicoloured.
144 15f. Berber woman 20 15
145 20f. Haussa woman 35 15
146 25f. Tuareg woman 45 20
147 30f. Tuareg man 55 20
148 60f. Djerma woman . . . . 1·25 50
149 85f. Type **19** . . . . 1·50 60

20 "Europafrique"  **22** Man and Globe

21 Groundnut Cultivation

1963. Air. European–African Economic Convention.
150 **20** 50f. multicoloured . . . . 2·50 2·00

1963. Air. Groundnut Cultivation Campaign.
151 **21** 20f. blue, brown and green 35 20
152 – 45f. brown, blue and green 75 25
153 – 85f. multicoloured . . . . 1·40 65
154 – 100f. olive, brown and blue 1·50 90
DESIGNS: 45f. Camel transport; 85f. Fastening sacks; 100f. Dispatch of groundnuts by lorry.

1963. Air. 1st Anniv of "Air Afrique" and DC-8 Service Inauguration. As T **59** of Mauritania.
155 50f. multicoloured 70 45

1963. 15th Anniv of Declaration of Human Rights.
156 **22** 25f. blue, brown and green 45 25

23 "Telstar"

1964. Air. Space Telecommunications.
157 **23** 25f. olive and violet . . . 40 20
158 – 100f. green and purple . . 1·10 80
DESIGN: 100f. "Relay".

24 "Parkinsonia aculeata"  **25** Statue, Abu Simbel

1964. Flowers. Multicoloured.
159 5f. Type **24** 60 30
160 10f. "Russelia equisetiformis" 50 30
161 15f. "Lantana camara" . . . 1·00 45
162 20f. "Agryeia nervosa" . . . 1·00 45
163 25f. "Luffa cylindrica" . . . 1·00 45
164 30f. "Hibiscus rosa-sinensis" 1·40 60
165 45f. "Plumierai rubra" . . . 2·00 1·25
166 50f. "Catharanthus roseus" 2·00 1·25
167 60f. "Caesalpinia pulcherrima" . . . . . . 3·50 1·50
Nos. 164/7 have "REPUBLIQUE DU NIGER" at the top and the value at bottom right.

1964. Air. Nubian Monuments Preservation.
168 **25** 25f. green and brown . . . 65 45
169 30f. brown and blue . . . 1·00 70
170 50f. blue and purple . . . 2·00 1·25

26 Globe and "Tiros" Satellite

1964. Air. World Meteorological Day.
171 **26** 50f. brown, blue and green 1·10 65

27 Sun Emblem and Solar Flares  **28** Convoy of Lorries

1964. International Quiet Sun Years.
172 **27** 30f. red, violet and sepia 50 35

1964. O.M.N.E.S. (Nigerian Mobile Medical and Sanitary Organization) Commemoration.
173 **28** 25f. orange, olive and blue 40 20
174 – 30f. multicoloured 50 20
175 – 50f. multicoloured 80 30
176 – 60f. purple, orange & turq 90 35
DESIGNS: 30f. Tending children; 50f. Tending women; 60f. Open-air laboratory.

29 Rocket, Stars and Stamp Outline

1964. Air. "PHILATEC 1964" Int Stamp Exn, Paris.
177 **29** 50f. mauve and blue . . . 85 60

30 European, African and Symbols of Agriculture and Industry **31** Pres. Kennedy

1964. Air. 1st Anniv of European–African Economic Convention.
178 **30** 50f. multicoloured 65 40

1964. Air. Pres. Kennedy Commemoration.
179 **31** 100f. multicoloured . . . . 1·25 1·10

32 Water-polo

1964. Air. Olympic Games, Tokyo.
180 **32** 60f. brown, deep green and purple . . . . 1·00 50
181 – 85f. brown, blue and red 1·00 60
182 – 100f. blue, red and green 1·25 70
183 – 250f. blue, brown and green . . . . 2·50 1·75
DESIGNS—HORIZ: 85f. Relay-racing. VERT: 100f. Throwing the discus; 250f. Athlete holding Olympic Torch.

1964. French, African and Malagasy Co-operation. As T **68** of Mauritania.
184 50f. brown, orange and violet 65 40

33 Azawak Tuareg Encampment

1964. Native Villages. Multicoloured.
185 15f. Type **33** 20 20
186 20f. Songhai hut 25 20
187 25f. Wogo and Kourtey tents 30 20
188 30f. Djerma hut 40 25
189 60f. Sorkawa fishermen's encampment . . . . 1·00 30
190 85f. Hausa urban house . . . 1·25 50

34 Doctors and Patient and Microscope Slide  **35** Abraham Lincoln

1964. Anti-leprosy Campaign.
191 **34** 50f. multicoloured 50 45

1965. Death Centenary of Abraham Lincoln.
192 **35** 50f. multicoloured 60 50

36 Instruction by "Radio-Vision"

1965. "Human Progress". Inscr as in T **36**.
193 **36** 20f. brown, yellow and blue 30 20
194 – 25f. sepia, brown and green 35 20
195 – 30f. purple, red and green 45 25
196 – 50f. purple, blue and brown 70 35
DESIGNS: 25f. Student; 30f. Adult class; 50f. Five tribesmen ("Alphabetization").

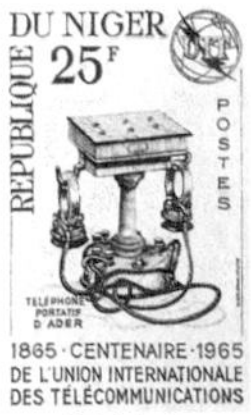

37 Ader's Telephone  **38** Pope John XXIII

1965. I.T.U. Centenary.
197 **37** 25f. black, lake and green 50 25
198 – 30f. green, purple and red 60 30
199 – 50f. green, purple and red 1·00 50
DESIGNS: 30f. Wheatstone's telegraph; 50f. "Telautographe".

1965. Air. Pope John Commemoration.
200 **38** 100f. multicoloured . . . . 1·40 75

39 Hurdling

1965. 1st African Games, Brazzaville.
201 **39** 10f. purple, green & brown 20 15
202 – 15f. red, brown and grey 30 15
203 – 20f. purple, blue and green 40 20
204 – 30f. purple, green and lake 50 25
DESIGNS—VERT: 15f. Running; 30f. Long-jumping. HORIZ: 20f. Pole-vaulting.

40 "Capture of Cancer" (the Crab)  **41** Sir Winston Churchill

1965. Air. Campaign against Cancer.
205 **40** 100f. brown, black & green 1·40 80

1965. Air. Churchill Commemoration.
206 **41** 100f. multicoloured . . . . 1·40 80

42 Interviewing

1965. Radio Club Promotion.
207 **42** 30f. brown, violet and green 30 15
208 – 45f. red, black and buff . . 45 25
209 – 50f. multicoloured 55 30
210 – 60f. purple, blue and ochre 60 40
DESIGNS—VERT: 45f. Recording; 50f. Listening to broadcast. HORIZ: 60f. Listeners' debate.

43 "Agricultural and Industrial Workers" 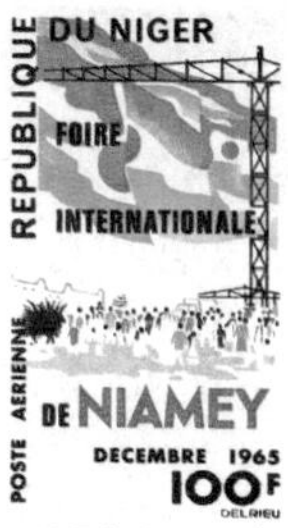 **44** Fair Scene and Flags

1965. Air. International Co-operation Year.
211 **43** 50f. brown, black and bistre 70 35

1965. Air. International Fair, Niamey.
212 **44** 100f. multicoloured . . . . 1·10 70

45 Dr. Schweitzer and Diseased Hands

1966. Air. Schweitzer Commemoration.
213 **45** 50f. multicoloured 80 45

46 "Water Distribution and Control"

1966. Int Hydrological Decade Inauguration.
214 **46** 50f. blue, orange and violet . . . 70 35

47 Weather Ship "France I"

1966. Air. 6th World Meteorological Day.
215 **47** 50f. green, purple and blue . . . 1·50 70

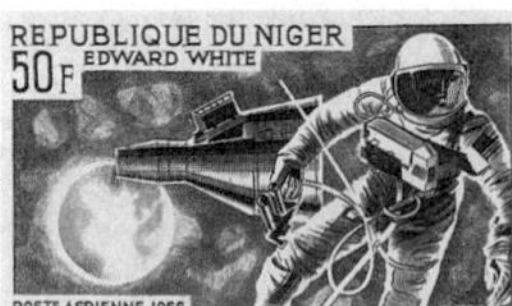

48 White and "Gemini" Capsule

1966. Air. Cosmonauts.
216 **48** 50f. black, brown and green . . . 75 40
217 – 50f. blue, violet and orange . . . 75 40
DESIGN: No. 217, Leonov and "Voskhod" capsule.

49 Head-dress and Carvings

1966. World Festival of Negro Arts, Dakar.
218 **49** 30f. black, brown and green . . . 45 25
219 – 50f. violet, brown and blue . . . 60 35
220 – 60f. lake, violet and brown . . . 70 40
221 – 100f. black, red and blue . . . 1·25 70
DESIGNS: 50f. Carved figures and mosaics; 60f. Statuettes, drums and arch; 100f. Handicrafts and church.

50 "Diamant" Rocket and Gantry
52 Cogwheel Emblem and Hemispheres

51 Goalkeeper saving Ball

1966. Air. French Space Vehicles. Multicoloured designs each showing different satellites.
222 45f. Type **50** . . . 70 40
223 60f. "A 1" (horiz) . . . 80 45
224 90f. "FR 1" (horiz) . . . 1·00 50
225 100f. "D 1" (horiz) . . . 1·50 75

1966. World Cup Football Championship.
226 – 30f. red, brown and blue . . . 55 25
227 **51** 50f. brown, blue and green . . . 75 35
228 – 60f. blue, purple and bistre . . . 85 50
DESIGNS—VERT: 30f. Player dribbling ball; 60f. Player kicking ball.

1966. Air. Europafrique.
229 **52** 50f. multicoloured . . . 70 45

53 Parachutist

1966. 5th Anniv of National Armed Forces. Mult.
230 20f. Type **53** . . . 35 15
231 30f. Soldiers with standard (vert) . . . 45 20
232 45f. Armoured patrol vehicle (horiz) . . . 70 30

1966. Air. Inauguration of DC-8F Air Services. As T **87** of Mauritania.
233 30f. olive, black and grey . . . 60 25

54 Inoculating cattle

1966. Campaign for Prevention of Cattle Plague.
234 **54** 45f. black, brown and blue . . . 1·00 50

55 "Voskhod 1"
56 U.N.E.S.C.O. "Tree"

1966. Air. Astronautics.
235 **55** 50f. blue, indigo and lake . . . 65 35
236 – 100f. violet, blue and lake . . . 1·25 75
DESIGN—HORIZ: 100f. "Gemini 6" and "7".

1966. 20th Anniv of U.N.E.S.C.O.
237 **56** 50f. multicoloured . . . 70 25

57 Japanese Gate, Atomic Symbol and Cancer ("The Crab")
58 Furnace

1966. Air. International Cancer Congress, Tokyo.
238 **57** 100f. multicoloured . . . 1·40 75

1966. Malbaza Cement Works.
239 **58** 10f. blue, orange and brown . . . 15 10
240 – 20f. blue and green . . . 30 15
241 – 30f. brown, grey and blue . . . 45 20
242 – 50f. indigo, brown and blue . . . 65 30
DESIGNS—HORIZ: 20f. Electrical power-house; 30f. Works and cement silos; 50f. Installation for handling raw materials.

59 Niamey Mosque

1967. Air.
243 **59** 100f. blue, green and grey . . . 1·10 70

60 Durer (self-portrait)

1967. Air. Paintings. Multicoloured.
244 50f. Type **60** . . . 80 60
245 100f. David (self-portrait) . . . 1·50 90
246 250f. Delacroix (self-portrait) . . . 3·00 2·00
See also Nos. 271/2 and 277/9.

61 Red-billed Hornbill
62 Bobsleigh Course, Villard-de-Lans

1967. Birds.
247 **61** 1f. bistre, red and green (postage) . . . 25 20
248 – 2f. black, brown and green . . . 25 20
249 – 30f. multicoloured . . . 1·25 35
249a – 40f. purple, orange and green . . . 1·40 60
250 – 45f. brown, green and blue . . . 1·75 35
250a – 65f. yellow, brown & pur . . . 2·00 80
251 – 70f. multicoloured . . . 2·40 1·00
251a – 250f. blue, purple and green (48 × 27 mm) (air) . . . 7·25 2·25
BIRDS: 2f. Lesser pied kingfishers; 30f. Common gonolek; 40f. Red bishop; 45f., 65f. Little masked weaver; 70f. Chestnut-bellied sandgrouse; 250f. Splendid glossy starlings.

1967. Grenoble—Winter Olympics Town (1968).
252 **62** 30f. brown, blue and green . . . 40 25
253 – 45f. brown, blue and green . . . 60 30
254 – 60f. brown, blue and green . . . 80 50
255 – 90f. brown, blue and green . . . 1·10 65
DESIGNS: 45f. Ski-jump, Autrans; 60f. Ski-jump, St. Nizier du Moucherotte; 90f. Slalom course, Chamrousse.

63 Family and Lions Emblem
64 Weather Ship

1967. 50th Anniv of Lions International.
256 **63** 50f. blue, red and green . . . 60 35

1967. Air. World Meteorological Day.
257 **64** 50f. red, black and blue . . . 1·50 70

65 View of World Fair

1967. Air. World Fair, Montreal.
258 **65** 100f. black, blue and purple . . . 2·75 75

66 I.T.Y. Emblem and Jet Airliner
67 Scouts around Campfire

1967. International Tourist Year.
259 **66** 45f. violet, green and purple . . . 45 35

1967. World Scout Jamboree, Idaho, U.S.A.
260 **67** 30f. brown, lake and blue . . . 40 20
261 – 45f. blue, brown and orange . . . 60 30
262 – 80f. lake, slate and bistre . . . 1·25 50
DESIGNS—HORIZ: 45f. Jamboree emblem and scouts. VERT: 80f. Scout cooking meal.

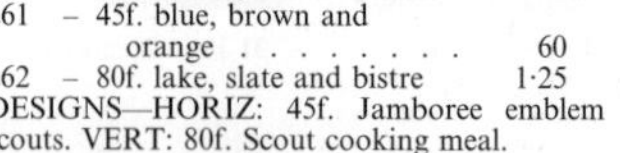

68 Audio-Visual Centre

1967. Air. National Audio-Visual Centre, Niamey.
263 **68** 100f. violet, blue and green . . . 90 50

69 Carrying Patient
70 "Europafrique"

1967. Nigerian Red Cross.
264 **69** 45f. black, red and green . . . 60 20
265 – 50f. black, red and green . . . 75 25
266 – 60f. black, red and green . . . 1·00 35
DESIGNS: 50f. Nurse with mother and child; 60f. Doctor giving injection.

1967. Europafrique.
267 **70** 50f. multicoloured . . . 60 30

71 Dr. Konrad Adenauer
72 African Women

1967. Air. Adenauer Commemoration.
268 **71** 100f. brown and blue . . . 1·40 70

1967. Air. 5th Anniv of African and Malagasy Post and Telecommunications Union (U.A.M.P.T.). As T **101** of Mauritania.
270 100f. violet, green and red . . . 1·10 60

1967. Air. Death Centenary of Jean Ingres (painter). Paintings by Ingres. As T **60**. Multicoloured.
271 100f. "Jesus among the Doctors" (horiz) . . . 1·60 1·00
272 150f. "Jesus restoring the Keys to St. Peter" (vert) . . . 2·25 1·50

1967. U.N. Women's Rights Commission.
273 **72** 50f. brown, yellow and blue . . . 60 35

1967. 5th Anniv of West African Monetary Union. As T **103** of Mauritania.
274 30f. green and purple . . . 35 20

73 Nigerian Children

1967. Air. 21st Anniv of U.N.I.C.E.F.
275 **73** 100f. brown, blue and green . . . 1·25 95

74 O.C.A.M. Emblem

1968. Air. O.C.A.M. Conference, Niamey.
276 **74** 100f. orange, green and blue . . . . 1·10 60

1968. Air. Paintings (self-portraits). As T **60**. Multicoloured.
277 50f. J.-B. Corot 70 40
278 150f. Goya . . . . 1·90 1·00
279 200f. Van Gogh . . . . . . 2·50 1·50

75 Allegory of Human Rights

1968. Human Rights Year.
280 **75** 50f. indigo, brown and blue 60 30

76 Breguet 27 Biplane over Lake

1968. Air. 35th Anniv of 1st France–Niger Airmail Service.
281 **76** 45f. blue, green and mauve 95 35
282 – 80f. slate, brown and blue 1·60 55
283 – 100f. black, green and blue 2·50 75
DESIGNS—Potez 25TOE biplane: 80f. On ground; 100f. In flight.

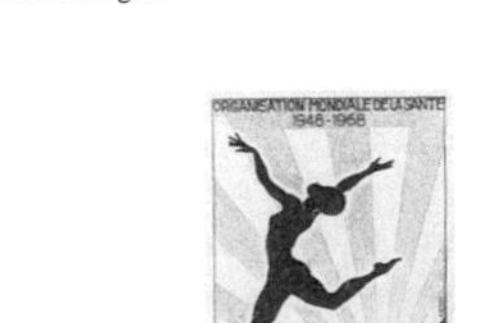

77 "Joyous Health"

1968. 20th Anniv of W.H.O.
284 **77** 50f. indigo, blue and brown 60 35

78 Cyclists of 1818 and 1968

1968. Air. 150th Anniv of Bicycle.
285 **78** 100f. green and red . . . . 1·50 70

79 Beribboned Rope

1968. Air. 5th Anniv of Europafrique.
286 **79** 50f. multicoloured 65 40

80 Fencing

1968. Air. Olympic Games, Mexico.
287 **80** 50f. purple, violet and green 50 35
288 – 100f. black, purple and blue 85 50
289 – 150f. purple and orange . . 1·25 70
290 – 200f. blue, brown and green . . . . 1·75 1·25
DESIGNS—VERT: 100f. High-diving; 150f. Weight-lifting. HORIZ: 200f. Horse-jumping.

81 Woodland Kingfisher

1969. Birds. Dated "1968". Multicoloured.
292 5f. African grey hornbill (postage) 20 10
293 10f. Type **81** 30 15
294 15f. Senegal coucal 70 25
295 20f. Rose-ringed parakeets . . 85 45
296 25f. Abyssinian roller . . . . 1·10 60
297 50f. Cattle egret . . . . . . 1·60 85
298 100f. Violet starling (27 × 49 mm) (air) . . . . 3·50 1·75
See also Nos. 372/7, 567/8 and 714/15.

82 Mahatma Gandhi

1968. Air. "Apostles of Non-Violence".
299 **82** 100f. black and yellow . . 1·75 60
300 – 100f. black and turquoise 1·00 50
301 – 100f. black and grey . . . 1·00 50
302 – 100f. black and orange . . 1·00 50
PORTRAITS: No. 300, President Kennedy; No. 301, Martin Luther King; No. 302, Robert F. Kennedy.

1968. Air. "Philexafrique" Stamp Exhibition, Abidjan (Ivory Coast, 1969) (1st issue). As T **113a** of Mauritania. Multicoloured.
304 100f. "Pare, Minister of the Interior" (J. L. La Neuville) . . . . 1·60 1·60

83 Arms of the Republic

1968. Air. 10th Anniv of Republic.
305 **83** 100f. multicoloured . . . . 1·00 50

1969. Air. Napoleon Bonaparte. Birth Bicentenary. As T **114b** of Mauritania. Multicoloured.
306 50f. "Napoleon as First Consul" (Ingres) . . . . . 1·50 90
307 100f. "Napoleon visiting the plague victims of Jaffa" (Gros) . . . . 2·50 1·25
308 150f. "Napoleon Enthroned" (Ingres) . . . . 3·50 1·75
309 200f. "The French Campaign" (Meissonier) 5·00 2·50

1969. Air. "Philexafrique" Stamp Exhibition, Abidjan, Ivory Coast (2nd issue). As T **114a** of Mauritania.
310 50f. brown, blue and orange 1·25 1·00
DESIGN: 50f. Giraffes and stamp of 1926.

84 Boeing 707 over Rain-cloud and Anemometer

1969. Air. World Meteorological Day.
311 **84** 50f. black, blue and green 90 35

85 Workers supporting Globe

1969. 50th Anniv of I.L.O.
312 **85** 30f. red and green 40 20
313 50f. green and red 50 35

86 Panhard and Levassor (1909)

1969. Air. Veteran Motor Cars.
314 **86** 25f. green 45 20
315 – 45f. violet, blue and grey 55 25
316 – 50f. brown, ochre and grey 1·10 35
317 – 70f. purple, red and grey 1·50 45
318 – 100f. green, brown and grey . . . . 1·75 65
DESIGNS: 45f. De Dion Bouton 8 (1904); 50f. Opel "Doktor-wagen" (1909); 70f. Daimler (1910); 100f. Vermorel 12/16 (1912).

87 Mother and Child

88 Mouth and Ear

1969. 50th Anniv of League of Red Cross Societies.
319 **87** 45f. red, brown and blue 60 25
320 – 50f. red, grey and green . . 70 25
321 – 70f. red, brown and ochre 1·00 40
DESIGNS—VERT: 70f. Man with Red Cross parcel. HORIZ: 50f. Symbolic Figures, Globe and Red Crosses.

1969. 1st French Language Cultural Conf, Niamey.
322 **88** 100f. multicoloured . . . . 1·25 60

89 School Building

1969. National School of Administration.
323 **89** 30f. black, green and orange 30 20

1969. Air. 1st Man on the Moon. No. 114 optd **L'HOMME SUR LA LUNE JUILLET 1969 APOLLO 11** and moon module.
324 500f. green, brown and blue 6·50 6·50

91 "Apollo 8" and Rocket

1969. Air. Moon Flight of "Apollo 8". Embossed on gold foil.
325 **91** 1000f. gold . . . . 15·00 15·00

1969. 5th Anniv of African Development Bank. As T **122a** of Mauritania.
326 30f. brown, green and violet 35 15

92 Child and Toys

1969. Air. International Toy Fair, Nuremburg.
327 **92** 100f. blue, brown and green . . . . 2·75 75

93 Linked Squares

1969. Air. "Europafrique".
328 **93** 50f. yellow, black and violet 55 30

94 Trucks crossing Sahara

1969. Air. 45th Anniv of "Croisiere Noire" Trans-Africa Expedition.
329 **94** 50f. brown, violet & mauve 75 35
330 – 100f. violet, red and blue 1·50 65
331 – 150f. multicoloured . . . . 2·00 1·25
332 – 200f. green, indigo and blue . . . . 3·00 1·50
DESIGNS: 100f. Crossing the mountains; 150f. African children and expedition at Lake Victoria; 200f. Route Map, European greeting African and Citroen truck.

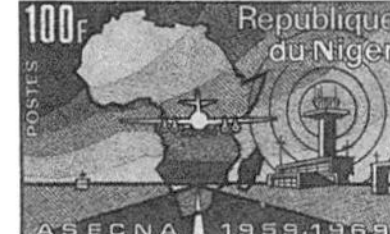

94a Aircraft, Map and Airport

1969. 10th Anniv of Aerial Navigation Security Agency for Africa and Madagascar (A.S.E.C.N.A.).
333 **94a** 100f. red . . . . 1·50 70

95 Classical Pavilion

1970. National Museum.
334 **95** 30f. blue, green and brown 30 15
335 – 45f. blue, green and brown 45 25
336 – 50f. blue, brown and green 50 25
337 – 70f. brown, blue and green 70 40
338 – 100f. brown, blue and green . . . . 1·10 60
DESIGNS: 45f. Temporary exhibition pavilion; 50f. Audio-visual pavilion; 70f. Local musical instruments gallery; 100f. Handicrafts pavilion.

96 Niger Village and Japanese Pagodas

97 Hypodermic "Gun" and Map

1970. Air. "EXPO 70" World Fair, Osaka, Japan (1st issue).
339 **96** 100f. multicoloured 90 45

1970. One Hundred Million Smallpox Vaccinations in West Africa.
340 **97** 50f. blue, purple and green 70 30

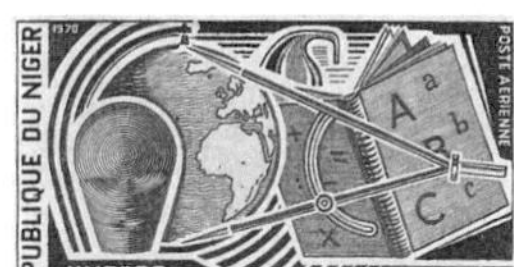

98 Education Symbols

1970. Air. International Education Year.
341 **98** 100f. slate, red and purple 1·00 45

99 Footballer

1970. World Cup Football Championship, Mexico.
342 **99** 40f. green, brown and purple 60 25
343 – 70f. purple, brown and blue . . . . 1·00 40
344 – 90f. red and black . . . . 1·25 60

DESIGNS: 70f. Football and Globe; 90f. Two footballers.

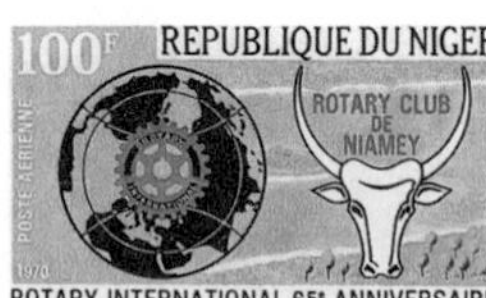

100 Rotary Emblems

1970. Air. 65th Anniv of Rotary International.
345 **100** 100f. multicoloured . . . 1·25 55

101 Bay of Naples and Niger Stamp

1970. Air. 10th "Europafrique" Stamp Exn, Naples.
346 **101** 100f. multicoloured . . . 1·00 60

102 Clement Ader's "Avion III" and Modern Airplane

1970. Air. Aviation Pioneers.
347 **102** 50f. grey, blue and red . . 70 25
348 – 100f. red, grey and blue 1·50 60
349 – 150f. lt brown, brn & grn 1·50 75
350 – 200f. red, bistre and violet 2·25 1·00
351 – 250f. violet, grey and red 3·50 1·40
DESIGNS: 100f. Joseph and Etienne Montgolfier balloon and rocket; 150f. Isaac Newton and gravity diagram; 200f. Galileo and rocket in planetary system; 250f. Leonardo da Vinci's drawing of a "flying machine" and Chanute's glider.

103 Cathode Ray Tube illuminating Books, Microscope and Globe

1970. Air. World Telecommunications Day.
352 **103** 100f. brown, green and red . . . . 1·25 50

1970. Inauguration of New U.P.U. Headquarters Building, Berne. As T **81** of New Caledonia.
353 30f. red, slate and brown . . 35 20
354 60f. violet, red and blue . . . 60 30

1970. Air. Safe Return of "Apollo 13". Nos. 348 and 350 optd **Solidarite Spatiale Apollo XIII 11-17 Avril 1970**.
355 100f. red, slate and blue . . . 1·00 50
356 200f. red, bistre and violet . . 1·75 75

105 U.N. Emblem, Man, Woman and Doves

1970. Air. 25th Anniv of U.N.O.
357 **105** 100f. multicoloured . . . 1·00 50
358 150f. multicoloured . . . 1·50 75

106 Globe and Heads

1970. Air. International French Language Conference, Niamey. Die-stamped on gold foil.
359 **106** 250f. gold and blue . . . 2·50 2·50

107 European and African Women

1970. Air. "Europafrique".
360 **107** 50f. red and green 55 30

108 Japanese Girls and "EXPO 70" Skyline

1970. Air. "EXPO 70" World Fair, Osaka, Japan. (2nd issue).
361 **108** 100f. purple, orange & grn 90 40
362 – 150f. blue, brown & green 1·25 60
DESIGN: 150f. "No" actor and "EXPO 70" by night.

109 Gymnast on Parallel Bars

111 Beethoven, Keyboard and Manuscripts

1970. Air. World Gymnastic Championships, Ljubljana.
363 **109** 50f. blue 50 30
364 – 100f. green . . . . 1·10 55
365 – 150f. purple . . . . . . 1·75 75
366 – 200f. red . . . . 2·00 95
GYMNASTS—HORIZ: 100f. Gymnast on vaulting-horse; 150f. Gymnast in mid-air. VERT: 200f. Gymnast on rings.

1970. Air. Moon Landing of "Luna 16". Nos. 349 and 351 surch **LUNA 16 – Sept. 1970 PREMIERS PRELEVEMENTS AUTOMATIQUES SUR LA LUNE** and value.
367 100f. on 150f. light brown, brown and green . . . . . 1·10 50
368 200f. on 250f. violet, grey and red . . . . 2·40 1·00

1970. Air. Birth Bicentenary of Beethoven. Mult.
369 100f. Type **111** . . . . 1·40 55
370 150f. Beethoven and allegory, "Hymn of Joy" . . . . . 2·25 85

112 John F. Kennedy Bridge, Niamey

1970. Air. 12th Anniv of Republic.
371 **112** 100f. multicoloured . . . 1·10 45

1971. Birds. Designs similar to T **81**. Variously dated between 1970 and 1972. Multicoloured.
372 5f. African grey hornbill . . 65 30
373 10f. Woodland kingfisher . . 85 30
374 15f. Senegal coucal . . . . . 1·75 1·00
375 20f. Rose-ringed parakeet . . 2·10 1·00
376 35f. Broad-tailed paradise whydah . . . . 3·00 1·50
377 50f. Cattle egret . . . . . 3·75 2·75
The Latin inscription on No. 377 is incorrect, reading "Bulbucus ibis" instead of "Bubulcus ibis".
See also Nos. 714/15.

114 Pres. Nasser

1971. Air. Death of Pres. Gamal Nasser (Egyptian statesman). Multicoloured.
378 100f. Type **114** 75 40
379 200f. Nasser waving . . . . 1·50 75

115 Pres. De Gaulle

1971. Air. De Gaulle Commemoration. Embossed on gold foil.
380 **115** 1000f. gold . . . . 38·00 38·00

116 "MUNICH" and Olympic Rings

1971. Air. Publicity for 1972 Olympic Games, Munich.
381 **116** 150f. purple, blue & green 1·25 70

117 "Apollo 14" leaving Moon

118 Symbolic Masks

1971. Air. Moon Mission of "Apollo 14".
382 **117** 250f. green, orange & blue 2·25 1·25

1971. Air. Racial Equality Year.
383 **118** 100f. red, green and blue 90 40
384 – 200f. brown, green & blue 1·75 80
DESIGN: 200f. "Peoples" and clover-leaf emblem.

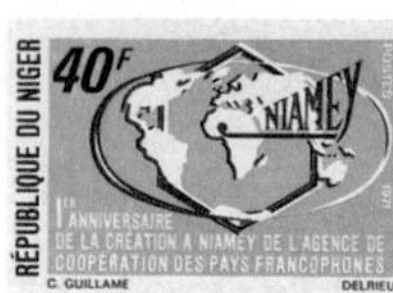

119 Niamey on World Map

1971. 1st Anniv of French-speaking Countries Co-operative Agency.
385 **119** 40f. multicoloured 50 25

120 African Telecommunications Map

1971. Air. Pan-African Telecommunications Network.
386 **120** 100f. multicoloured . . . 75 40

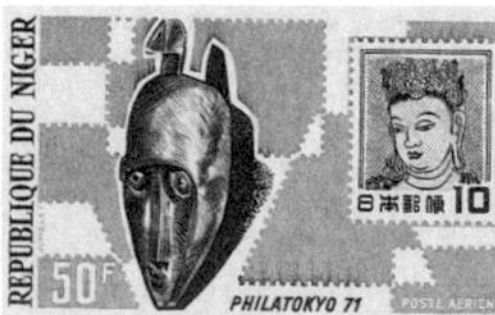

121 African Mask and Japanese Stamp

1971. Air. "PHILATOKYO 71" International Stamp Exhibition, Japan.
387 **121** 50f. olive, purple and green 65 30
388 – 100f. violet, red and green 1·10 45
DESIGN: 100f. Japanese scroll painting and Niger stamp.

122 "Longwood House, St. Helena" (C. Vernet)

1971. Air. 150th Anniv of Napoleon's Death. Paintings. Multicoloured.
389 150f. Type **122** . . . . 1·75 70
390 200f. "Napoleon's Body on his Camp-bed" (Marryat) 2·50 90

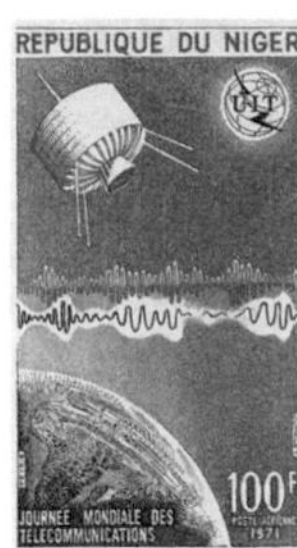

123 Satellite, Radio Waves, and Globe

1971. Air. World Telecommunications Day.
391 **123** 100f. multicoloured . . . 1·10 50

124 Pierre de Coubertin and Discus-throwers

1971. Air. 75th Anniv of Modern Olympic Games.
392 **124** 50f. red and blue 50 25
393 – 100f. multicoloured . . . 90 40
394 – 150f. blue and purple . . 1·40 65
DESIGNS—VERT: 100f. Male and female athletes holding torch. HORIZ: 150f. Start of race.

125 Scout Badges and Mount Fuji

1971. 13th World Scout Jamboree, Asagiri, Japan.
395 **125** 35f. red, purple and orange 40 20
396 – 40f. brown, plum and green 45 20
397 – 45f. green, red and blue 60 25
398 – 50f. green, violet and red 70 30
DESIGNS—VERT: 40f. Scouts and badge; 45f. Scouts converging on Japan. HORIZ: 50f. "Jamboree" in rope, and marquee.

126 "Apollo 15" on Moon

1971. Air. Moon Mission of "Apollo 15".

399 **126** 150f. blue, violet & brown 1·50 70

127 Linked Maps

1971. 2nd Anniv of Renewed "Europafrique" Convention, Niamey.

400 **127** 50f. multicoloured 60 30

128 Gouroumi (Hausa) **129** De Gaulle in Uniform

1971. Musical Instruments.

401 **128** 25f. brown, green and red 30 10
402 – 30f. brown, violet & green 35 15
403 – 35f. blue, green and purple 35 25
404 – 40f. brown, orange & grn 45 25
405 – 45f. ochre, brown and blue 55 35
406 – 50f. brown, red and black 95 45

DESIGNS: 30f. Molo (Djerma); 35f. Garaya (Hausa); 40f. Godjie (Djerma-Sonrai); 45f. Inzad (Tuareg); 50f. Kountigui (Sonrai).

1971. Air. 1st Death Anniv of Gen. Charles De Gaulle (French statesman).

407 **129** 250f. multicoloured . . . 5·00 4·00

1971. Air. 10th Anniv of African and Malagasy Posts and Telecommunications Union. As T **139a** of Mauritania. Multicoloured.

408 100f. U.A.M.P.T. H.Q. and rural scene 90 45

130 "Audience with Al Hariri" (Baghdad, 1237)

1971. Air. Moslem Miniatures. Multicoloured.

409 100f. Type **130** . . . . 1·00 45
410 150f. "Archangel Israfil" (Iraq, 14th-cent) (vert) . . 1·50 70
411 200f. "Horsemen" (Iraq, 1210) . . . . 2·25 1·25

131 Louis Armstrong **132** "Children of All Races"

1971. Air. Death of Louis Armstrong (American jazz musician). Multicoloured.

412 100f. Type **131** . . . . 1·50 55
413 150f. Armstrong playing trumpet . . . . 2·00 85

1971. 25th Anniv of U.N.I.C.E.F.

414 **132** 50f. multicoloured 60 45

133 "Adoration of the Magi" (Di Bartolo)

1971. Air. Christmas. Paintings. Multicoloured.

415 100f. Type **133** . . . . 1·00 45
416 150f. "The Nativity" (D. Ghirlandaio) (vert) . . 1·50 70
417 200f. "Adoration of the Shepherds" (Perugino) . . 2·00 1·00

134 Presidents Pompidou and Hamani

1972. Air. Visit of Pres. Pompidou of France.

418 **134** 250f. multicoloured . . . 4·75 3·50

135 Ski "Gate" and Cherry Blossom

1972. Air. Winter Olympic Games, Sapporo, Japan.

419 **135** 100f. violet, red and green 90 40
420 – 150f. red, purple and violet . . . . 1·25 70

DESIGN—HORIZ: 150f. Snow crystals and Olympic flame.

1972. Air. U.N.E.S.C.O. "Save Venice" Campaign. As T **127** of Mali.

422 50f. multicoloured (vert) . . 50 25
423 100f. multicoloured (vert) . . 1·00 45
424 150f. multicoloured (vert) . . 1·50 70
425 200f. multicoloured . . . . . 2·00 1·00

DESIGNS: Nos. 422/5 depict various details of Guardi's painting, "The Masked Ball".

136 Johannes Brahms and Music **137** Saluting Hand

1972. Air. 75th Death Anniv of Johannes Brahms (composer).

426 **136** 100f. green, myrtle and red . . . . 1·50 55

1972. Air. Int Scout Seminar, Cotonou, Dahomey.

427 **137** 150f. violet, blue & orange . . . . 1·50 60

138 Star Symbol and Open Book

1972. International Book Year.

428 **138** 35f. purple and green . . 35 20
429 – 40f. blue and lake . . . . 1·40 35

DESIGN: 40f. Boy reading, 16th-century galleon and early aircraft.

139 Heart Operation

1972. Air. World Heart Month.

430 **139** 100f. brown and red . . . 1·50 55

140 Bleriot XI crossing the Channel, 1909

1972. Air. Milestones in Aviation History.

431 **140** 50f. brown, blue and lake 1·10 50
432 – 75f. grey, brown and blue 1·75 60
433 – 100f. ultramarine, blue and purple . . . . . . 3·25 1·40

DESIGNS: 75f. Lindbergh crossing the Atlantic in "Spirit of St. Louis"; 100f. First flight of Concorde, 1969.

141 Satellite and Universe

1972. Air. World Telecommunications Day.

434 **141** 100f. brown, purple & red 1·10 45

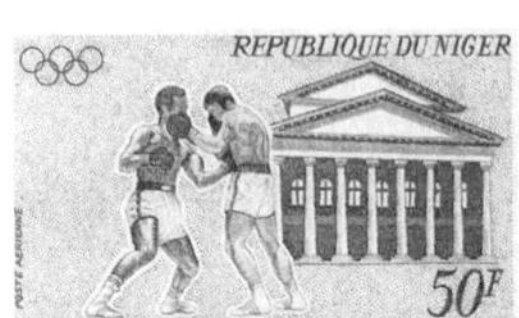

142 Boxing

1972. Air. Olympic Games, Munich. Sports and Munich Buildings.

435 **142** 50f. brown and blue . . . 50 20
436 – 100f. brown and green . . 75 40
437 – 150f. brown and red . . . 1·25 60
438 – 200f. brown and mauve 1·75 85

DESIGNS—VERT: 100f. Long-jumping; 150f. Football. HORIZ: 200f. Running.

143 A. G. Bell and Telephone

1972. Air. 50th Death Anniv of Alexander Graham Bell (inventor of telephone).

440 **143** 100f. blue, purple and red 1·10 55

144 "Europe on Africa" Map

1972. Air. "Europafrique" Co-operation.

441 **144** 50f. red, green and blue 50 25

145 Herdsman and Cattle **146** Lottery Wheel

1972. Medicinal Salt-ponds at In-Gall. Multicoloured.

442 35f. Type **145** 50 25
443 40f. Cattle in salt-pond . . . 60 25

1972. 6th Anniv of National Lottery.

444 **146** 35f. multicoloured 35 25

147 Postal Runner

1972. Air. U.P.U. Day. Postal Transport.

445 **147** 50f. brown, green and lake 60 25
446 – 100f. green, blue and lake 90 45
447 – 150f. green, violet and lake . . . . 1·75 70

DESIGNS: 100f. Rural mail van; 150f. Loading Fokker Friendship mail plane.

1972. 10th Anniv of West African Monetary Union. As T **149** of Mauritania.

448 40f. grey, violet and brown 40 25

1972. Air. Gold Medal Winners. Munich Olympic Games. Nos. 435/8 optd with events and names, etc.

449 **142** 50f. brown and blue . . . 50 20
450 – 100f. brown and green . . 85 40
451 – 150f. brown and red . . . 1·40 60
452 – 200f. brown and mauve 1·75 80

OVERPRINTS: 50f. **WELTER CORREA MEDAILLE D'OR**; 100f. **TRIPLE SAUT SANEIEV MEDAILLE D'OR**; 150f. **FOOTBALL POLOGNE MEDAILLE D'OR**; 200f. **MARATHON SHORTER MEDAILLE D'OR.**

148 "The Raven and the Fox"

1972. Air. Fables of Jean de la Fontaine.

453 **148** 25f. black, brown & green 1·10 40
454 – 50f. brown, green & purple 60 25
455 – 75f. brown, green & brown . . . . 1·00 45

DESIGNS: 50f. "The Lion and the Rat"; 75f. "The Monkey and the Leopard".

149 Astronauts on Moon

1972. Air. Moon Flight of "Apollo 17".

456 **149** 250f. multicoloured . . . 2·75 1·25

150 Dromedary Race

1972. Niger Sports.

457 **150** 35f. purple, red and blue 75 40
458 – 40f. lake, brown and green . . . . 1·00 60

DESIGN: 40f. Horse race.

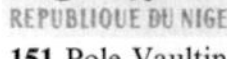

151 Pole Vaulting

153 Knight and Pawn

152 "Young Athlete"

1973. 2nd African Games, Lagos, Nigeria. Mult.
459 35f. Type **151** 30 25
460 40f. Basketball 35 25
461 45f. Boxing 45 25
462 75f. Football 70 45

1973. Air. Antique Art Treasures.
463 **152** 50f. red 50 25
464 – 100f. violet . . . . 1·00 40
DESIGN: 100f. "Head of Hermes".

1973. World Chess Championships, Reykjavik, Iceland.
465 **153** 100f. green, blue and red 2·50 1·00

154 "Abutilon pannosum"

155 Interpol Badge

1973. Rare African Flowers. Multicoloured.
466 30f. Type **154** 70 30
467 45f. "Crotalaria barkae" . . 80 30
468 60f. "Dichrostachys cinerea" 1·40 45
469 80f. "Caralluma decaisneana" 1·60 55

1973. 50th Anniv of International Criminal Police Organization (Interpol).
470 **155** 50f. multicoloured 85 30

156 Scout with Radio

1973. Air. Scouting in Niger.
471 **156** 25f. brown, green and red 25 20
472 – 50f. brown, green and red 55 25
473 – 100f. brown, green and red . . . . 1·25 50
474 – 150f. brown, green and red . . . . 2·25 90
DESIGNS: 50f. First aid; 100f. Care of animals; 150f. Care of the environment.

157 Hansen and Microscope

158 Nurse tending Child

1973. Centenary of Dr. Hansen's Discovery of Leprosy Bacillus.
475 **157** 50f. brown, green and blue 85 35

1973. 25th Anniv of W.H.O.
476 **158** 50f. brown, red and blue 65 25

159 "The Crucifixion" (Hugo van der Goes)

1973. Air. Easter. Paintings. Multicoloured.
477 50f. Type **159** 55 25
478 100f. "The Deposition" (Cima de Conegliano) (horiz) . . . . 1·10 50
479 150f. "Pieta" (Bellini) (horiz) 1·60 65

160 Douglas DC-8 and Mail Van

1973. Air. Stamp Day.
480 **160** 100f. brown, red and green . . . . 1·50 55

161 W.M.O. Emblem and "Weather Conditions"

1973. Air. Centenary of W.M.O.
481 **161** 100f. brown, red and green . . . . 1·10 45

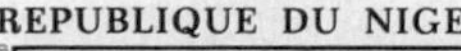

162 "Crouching Lioness" (Delacroix)

1973. Air. Paintings by Delacroix. Multicoloured.
482 150f. Type **162** . . . . . . 2·00 1·00
483 200f. "Tigress and Cub" . . 3·25 1·50

163 Crocodile

1973. Wild Animals from "Park W".
484 **163** 25f. multicoloured 45 20
485 – 35f. grey, gold and black 75 30
486 – 40f. multicoloured 75 30
487 – 80f. multicoloured . . . . 1·25 50
DESIGNS: 35f. African elephant; 40f. Hippopotamus; 80f. Warthog.

164 Eclipse over Mountain

1973. Total Eclipse of the Sun.
488 **164** 40f. violet 60 30

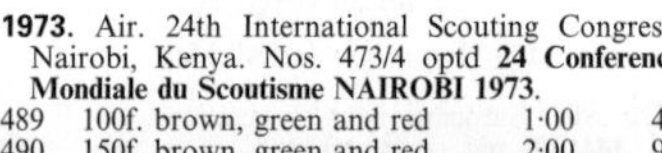

1973. Air. 24th International Scouting Congress, Nairobi, Kenya. Nos. 473/4 optd **24 Conference Mondiale du Scoutisme NAIROBI 1973**.
489 100f. brown, green and red 1·00 40
490 150f. brown, green and red 2·00 90

166 Palomino

1973. Horse-breeding. Multicoloured.
491 50f. Type **166** 90 30
492 75f. French trotter . . . . . 1·40 40
493 80f. English thoroughbred . . 1·50 55
494 100f. Arab thoroughbred . . 2·00 65

1973. Pan-African Drought Relief. African Solidarity. No. 436 surch **SECHERESSE SOLIDARITE AFRICAINE** and value.
495 **145** 100f. on 35f. multicoloured . . . . . 1·40 1·00

168 Rudolf Diesel and Oil Engine

1973. 60th Death Anniv of Rudolf Diesel (engineer).
496 **168** 25f. blue, purple and grey 80 45
497 – 50f. grey, green and blue 1·40 65
498 – 75f. blue, black and mauve . . . . 2·10 1·00
499 – 125f. blue, red and green 3·50 1·25
DESIGNS: 50f. Series "BB 100" diesel locomotive; 75f. Type "060-DB1" diesel locomotive, France; 125f. Diesel locomotive No. 72004, France.

1973. African and Malagasy Posts and Telecommunications Union. As T **155a** of Mauritania.
500 100f. red, green and brown 75 50

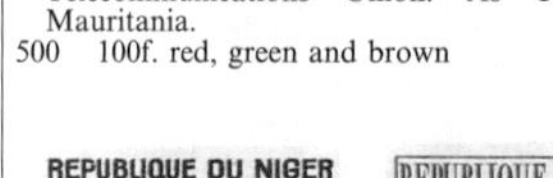

168a African Mask and Old Town Hall, Brussels

171 "Apollo"

1973. Air. African Fortnight, Brussels.
501 **168a** 100f. purple, blue and red . . . . 1·00 50

169 T.V. Set and Class

1973. Schools Television Service.
502 **169** 50f. black, red and blue 60 30

1973. 3rd International French Language and Culture Conf, Liege. No. 385 optd **3e CONFERENCE DE LA FRANCOPHONIE LIEGE OCTOBRE 1973**.
503 **110** 40f. multicoloured 50 25

1973. Classical Sculptures.
504 **171** 50f. green and brown . . 60 30
505 – 50f. black and brown 60 30
506 – 50f. brown and red . . . 60 30
507 – 50f. purple and red . . . 60 30
DESIGNS: No. 505, "Atlas"; No. 506, "Hercules"; No. 507, "Venus".

172 Bees and Honeycomb

1973. World Savings Day.
508 **172** 40f. brown, red and blue 45 25

173 "Food for the World"

1973. Air. 10th Anniv of World Food Programme.
509 **173** 50f. violet, red and blue 60 30

174 Copernicus and "Sputnik 1"

175 Pres. John Kennedy

1973. Air. 500th Birth Anniv of Copernicus (astronomer).
510 **174** 150f. brown, blue and red 1·40 70

1973. Air. 10th Death Anniv of U.S. President Kennedy.
511 **175** 100f. multicoloured . . . 1·00 50

176 Kounta Songhai Blanket

178 Lenin

177 Barges on River Niger

1973. Niger Textiles. Multicoloured.
513 35f. Type **176** 50 30
514 40f. Tcherka Snghai blanket (horiz) 70 40

1974. Air. 1st Anniv of Ascent of Niger by "Fleet of Hope".
515 **177** 50f. blue, green and red 75 35
516 – 75f. purple, blue and green . . . . 1·00 45
DESIGN: 75f. "Barban Maza" (tug) and barge.

1974. Air. 50th Death Anniv of Lenin.
517 **178** 50c. brown 50 30

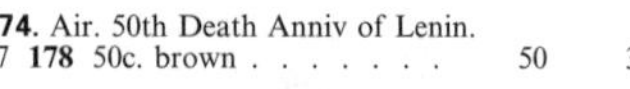

179 Slalom Skiing

1974. Air. 50th Anniv of Winter Olympic Games.
518 **179** 200f. red, brown and blue 2·50 1·00

180 Newly-born Baby

1974. World Population Year.
519 **180** 50f. multicoloured 50 25

181 Footballers and "Global" Ball

1974. Air. World Cup Football Championship, West Germany.

520 **181** 75f. violet, black & brown 65 35
521 – 150f. brown, green & turq 1·40 55
522 – 200f. blue, orange & green 1·75 1·00

DESIGNS: 150, 200f. Football scenes similar to Type **181**.

182 "The Crucifixion" (Grunewald)

1974. Air. Easter. Paintings. Multicoloured.

524 50f. Type **182** 50 25
525 75f. "Avignon Pieta" (attributed to E. Quarton) 75 35
526 125f. "The Entombment" (G. Isenmann) 1·25 65

183 Class 230K Locomotive, 1948, France and Locomotive No. 5511, 1938, U.S.A.

1974. Famous Railway Locomotives of the Steam Era.

527 **183** 50f. green, black and violet 1·25 40
528 – 75f. green, black & brown 1·90 55
529 – 100f. multicoloured 2·50 85
530 – 150f. brown, black and red 3·75 1·25

DESIGNS: 75f. Class 21 locomotive, 1893, France; 100f. Locomotive, 1866, U.S.A. and "Mallard", Great Britain; 150f. Marc Seguin locomotive, 1829, France and Stephenson's "Rocket", 1829.

184 Map of Member Countries

1974. 15th Anniv of Conseil de l'Entente.

531 **184** 40f. multicoloured 40 20

185 Knights

1974. Air. 21st Chess Olympiad, Nice.

532 **185** 50f. brown, blue & indigo 1·25 65
533 – 75f. purple, brown & green 1·75 75

DESIGN: 75f. Kings.

186 Marconi and "Elettra" (steam yacht)

1974. Birth Centenary of Guglielmo Marconi (radio pioneer).

534 **186** 50f. blue, brown & mauve 50 30

187 Astronaut on Palm of Hand

1974. Air. 5th Anniv of 1st Landing on Moon.

535 **187** 150f. brown, blue & indigo 1·25 60

188 Tree on Palm of Hand

190 Camel Saddle

189 "The Rhinoceros" (Longhi)

1974. National Tree Week.

536 **188** 35f. turquoise, grn & brn 40 30

1974. Air. Europafrique.

537 **189** 250f. multicoloured 5·00 3·00

1974. Handicrafts.

538 **190** 40f. red, blue and brown 45 20
539 – 50f. blue, red and brown 55 30

DESIGN: 50f. Statuettes of horses.

192 Frederic Chopin

1974. 125th Death Anniv of Frederic Chopin.

541 **192** 100f. black, red and blue 1·50 55

1974. Beethoven's Ninth Symphony Commemoration. As T **192**.

542 100f. lilac, blue and indigo 1·50 55

DESIGN: 100f. Beethoven.

193 European Woman and Douglas DC-8 Airliners

194 "Skylab" over Africa

1974. Air. Centenary of U.P.U.

543 **193** 50f. turquoise, grn & pur 50 25
544 – 100f. blue, mauve & ultram 2·25 75
545 – 150f. brown, blue & indigo 1·50 80
546 – 200f. brown, orange & red 1·60 1·25

DESIGNS: 100f. Japanese woman and electric locomotives; 150f. American Indian woman and liner; 200f. African woman and road vehicles.

1974. Air. "Skylab" Space Laboratory.

547 **194** 100f. violet, brown & blue 1·00 45

195 Don-don Drum

197 "Virgin and Child" (Correggio)

196 Tree and Compass Rose

1974.

548 **195** 60f. purple, green and red 90 45

1974. 1st Death Anniv of Tenere Tree (desert landmark).

549 **196** 50f. brown, blue and ochre 2·00 1·00

1974. Air. Christmas. Multicoloured.

550 100f. Type **197** 1·00 35
551 150f. "Virgin and Child, and St. Hilary" (F. Lippi) 1·50 55
552 200f. "Virgin and Child" (Murillo) 2·00 95

198 "Apollo" Spacecraft

1975. Air. "Apollo–Soyuz" Space Test Project.

553 **198** 50f. green, red and blue 50 25
554 – 100f. grey, red and blue 80 40
555 – 150f. purple, plum & blue 1·25 60

DESIGNS: 100f. "Apollo" and "Soyuz" docked; 150f. "Soyuz" spacecraft.

199 European and African Women

1975. Air. Europafrique.

556 **199** 250f. brown, purple & red 2·25 1·75

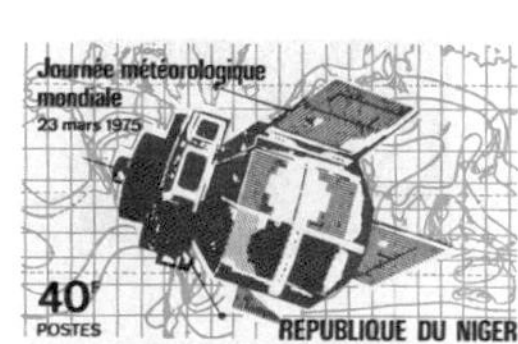

200 Communications Satellite and Weather Map

1975. World Meteorological Day.

557 **200** 40f. red, black and blue 40 20

201 "Christ in the Garden of Olives" (Delacroix)

1975. Air. Easter. Multicoloured.

558 75f. Type **201** 65 35
559 125f. "The Crucifixion" (El Greco) (vert) 1·10 50
560 150f. "The Resurrection" (Limousin) (vert) 1·25 75

202 Lt-Col. S. Kountche, Head of State

1975. Air. 1st Anniv of Military Coup.

561 **202** 100f. multicoloured 1·00 50

203 "City of Truro", 1903, Great Britain

1975. Famous Locomotives. Multicoloured.

562 50f. Type **203** 1·25 35
563 75f. Class 05 steam locomotive No. 003, 1937, Germany 1·60 50
564 100f. "General", 1855, U.S.A. (dated "1863") 2·50 75
565 125f. Series BB 15000 electric locomotive, 1971, France 3·00 90

1975. Birds. As Nos. 296 and 298, but dated "1975". Multicoloured.

567 25f. Abyssinian roller (postage) 1·25 35
568 100f. Violet starlings (air) 3·25 90

205 "Zabira" Leather Bag

1975. Niger Handicrafts. Multicoloured.

569 35f. Type **205** 30 20
570 40f. Chequered rug 45 25
571 45f. Flower pot 50 30
572 60f. Gourd 75 35

206 African Woman and Child

1975. International Women's Year.

573 **206** 50f. blue, brown and red 75 50

207 Dr. Schweitzer and Lambarene Hospital

1975. Birth Centenary of Dr. Albert Schweitzer.

574	**207** 100f. brown, green & black	1·00	55

208 Peugeot, 1892

1975. Early Motor-cars.

575	**208** 50f. blue and mauve	60	30
576	– 75f. purple and blue	1·00	40
577	– 100f. mauve and green	1·40	60
578	– 125f. green and red	1·50	70

DESIGNS: 75f. Daimler, 1895; 100f. Fiat, 1899; 125f. Cadillac, 1903.

209 Tree and Sun

1975. National Tree Week.

579	**209** 40f. green, orange and red	40	25

210 Boxing

1975. Traditional Sports.

580	**210** 35f. brown, orange & black	35	20
581	– 40f. brown, green & black	40	20
582	– 45f. brown, blue and black	50	25
583	– 50f. brown, red and black	55	30

DESIGNS—VERT: 40f. Boxing; 50f. Wrestling. HORIZ: 45f. Wrestling.

211 Leontini Tetradrachme

1975. Ancient Coins.

584	**211** 50f. grey, blue and red	60	20
585	– 75f. grey, blue and mauve	85	30
586	– 100f. grey, orange and blue	1·25	40
587	– 125f. grey, purple & green	1·50	60

COINS: 75f. Athens tetradrachme; 100f. Himer diadrachme; 125f. Gela tetradrachme.

212 Putting the Shot

1975. Air. "Pre-Olympic Year". Olympic Games, Montreal (1976).

588	**212** 150f. brown and red	1·10	55
589	– 200f. red, chestnut and brown	1·50	85

DESIGN: 200f. Gymnastics.

213 Starving Family

1975. Pan-African Drought Relief.

590	**213** 40f. blue, brown & orange	55	30
591	– 45f. brown and blue	1·10	50
592	– 60f. blue, green and orange	1·00	40

DESIGNS: 45f. Animal skeletons; 60f. Truck bringing supplies.

214 Trading Canoe crossing R. Niger

1975. Tourism. Multicoloured.

593	40f. Type **214**	50	25
594	45f. Boubon Camp entrance	55	25
595	50f. Boubon Camp view	60	35

215 U.N. Emblem and Peace Dove

1975. Air. 30th Anniv of U.N.O.

596	**215** 100f. light blue and blue	85	40

216 "Virgin of Seville" (Murillo)

1975. Air. Christmas. Multicoloured.

597	50f. Type **216**	50	35
598	75f. "Adoration of the Shepherds" (Tintoretto) (horiz)	75	45
599	125f. "Virgin with Angels" (Master of Burgo d'Osma)	1·25	75

1975. Air. "Apollo–Soyuz" Space Link. Nos. 533/5 optd **JONCTION 17 Juillet 1975**.

600	**198** 50f. green, red and blue	50	25
601	– 100f. grey, red and blue	75	45
602	– 150f. purple, plum & blue	1·25	75

218 "Ashak"

1976. Literacy Campaign. Multicoloured.

603	25f. Type **218**	15	10
604	30f. "Kaska"	20	15
605	40f. "Iccee"	25	15
606	50f. "Tuuri-nya"	30	20
607	60f. "Lekki"	35	25

219 Ice Hockey

1976. Winter Olympic Games, Innsbruck, Austria. Multicoloured.

608	40f. Type **219** (postage)	35	20
609	50f. Tobogganing	40	20
610	150f. Ski-jumping	1·25	50
611	200f. Figure-skating (air)	1·50	75
612	300f. Cross-country skiing	2·00	1·00

220 Early Telephone and Satellite

1976. Telephone Centenary.

614	**220** 100f. orange, blue & green	85	50

221 Baby and Ambulance

1976. World Health Day.

615	**221** 50f. red, brown and purple	50	25

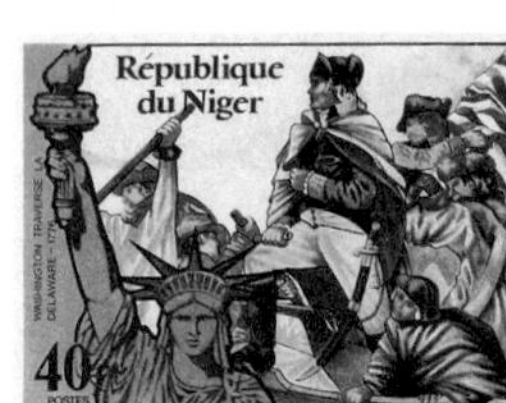

222 Washington crossing the Delaware (after Leutze)

1976. Bicentenary of American Revolution. Mult.

616	40f. Type **222** (postage)	30	15
617	50f. First soldiers of the Revolution	40	20
618	150f. Joseph Warren – martyr of Bunker Hill (air)	1·10	35
619	200f. John Paul Jones aboard the "Bonhomme Richard"	1·50	60
620	300f. Molly Pitcher – heroine of Monmouth	2·00	90

223 Distribution of Provisions

1976. 2nd Anniv of Military Coup. Multicoloured.

622	50f. Type **223**	35	25
623	100f. Soldiers with bulldozer (horiz)	1·10	45

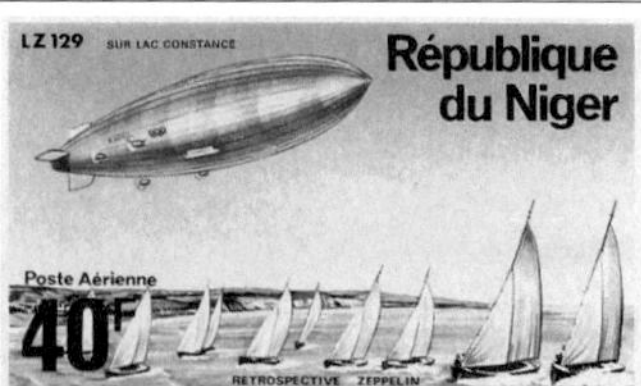

224 "Hindenburg" crossing Lake Constance

1976. Air. 75th Anniv of Zeppelin Airships. Multicoloured.

624	40f. Type **224**	40	15
625	50f. LZ-3 over Wurzberg	50	25
626	150f. L-9 over Friedrichshafen	1·40	55
627	200f. LZ-2 over Rothenburg (vert)	1·75	70
628	300f. "Graf Zeppelin II" over Essen	4·25	90

225 "Europafrique" Symbols

1976. "Europafrique".

630	**225** 100f. multicoloured	1·40	50

226 Plant Cultivation

1976. Communal Works. Multicoloured.

631	25f. Type **226**	15	10
632	30f. Harvesting rice	20	15

227 Boxing

1976. Olympic Games, Montreal. Multicoloured.

633	40f. Type **227**	25	15
634	50f. Basketball	40	20
635	60f. Football	45	25
636	80f. Cycling (horiz)	60	20
637	100f. Judo (horiz)	70	30

228 Motobecane "125"

1976. Motorcycles.

639	**228** 50f. violet, brown & turq	60	25
640	– 75f. green, red & turquoise	85	35
641	– 100f. brown, orange & pur	1·25	50
642	– 125f. slate, olive and black	1·50	75

DESIGNS: 75f. Norton "Challenge"; 100f. B.M.W. "903"; 125f. Kawasaki "1000".

229 Cultivation Map

1976. Operation "Sahel Vert". Multicoloured.
643 40f. Type **229** 30 15
644 45f. Tending plants (vert) . . 35 20
645 60f. Planting sapling (vert) . . 55 30

1976. International Literacy Day. Nos. 603/7 optd **JOURNEE INTERNATIONALE DE L'ALPHABETISATION**.
646 **218** 25f. multicoloured 15 15
647 – 30f. multicoloured 15 15
648 – 40f. multicoloured 20 15
649 – 50f. multicoloured 25 20
650 – 60f. multicoloured 30 20

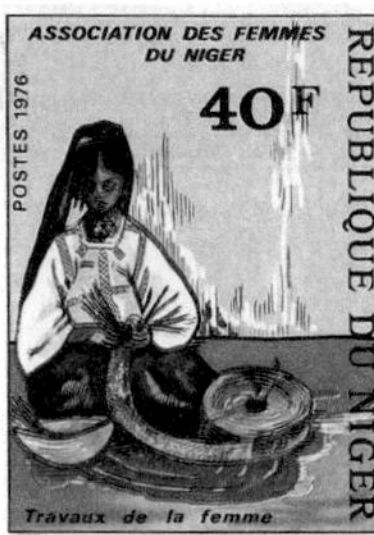

231 Basket Making

1976. Niger Women's Association. Multicoloured.
651 40f. Type **231** 35 20
652 45f. Hairdressing (horiz) . . 40 25
653 50f. Making pottery 50 35

232 Wall Paintings

1976. "Archaeology". Multicoloured.
654 40f. Type **232** 45 25
655 50f. Neolithic statuettes . . . 50 25
656 60f. Dinosaur skeleton . . . 90 35

233 "The Nativity" (Rubens)

1976. Air. Christmas. Multicoloured.
657 50f. Type **233** 50 25
658 100f. "Holy Night" (Correggio) . . . . 1·10 45
659 150f. "Adoration of the Magi" (David) (horiz) . . 1·50 90

234 Benin Ivory Mask

1977. 2nd World Festival of Negro-African Arts, Lagos.
660 **234** 40f. brown 40 20
661 – 50f. blue 60 30
DESIGNS—HORIZ: 50f. Nigerian stick dance.

235 Students in Class **236** Examining Patient

1977. Alphabetization Campaign.
662 **235** 40f. multicoloured 30 15
663 50f. multicoloured 40 20
664 60f. multicoloured 60 20

1977. Village Health. Multicoloured.
665 40f. Type **236** 50 20
666 50f. Examining baby 60 30

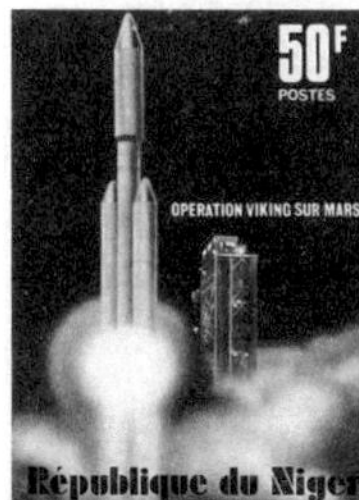

237 Rocket Launch

1977. "Viking" Space Mission. Multicoloured.
667 50f. Type **237** (postage) . . . 45 15
668 80f. "Viking" approaching Mars (horiz) 65 20
669 100f. "Viking" on Mars (horiz) (air) 65 25
670 150f. Parachute descent . . . 1·00 30
671 200f. Rocket in flight . . . . 1·40 45

238 Marabou Stork

1977. Fauna Protection.
673 **238** 80f. sepia, bistre and red 2·00 80
674 – 90f. brown and turquoise 1·25 60
DESIGN: 90f. Bushbuck.

239 Satellite and Weather Symbols

1977. World Meteorological Day.
675 **239** 100f. blue, black & turq 1·00 50

240 Gymnastic Exercise

1977. 2nd Youth Festival, Tahoua. Multicoloured.
676 40f. Type **240** 35 20
677 50f. High jumping 40 25
678 80f. Choral ensemble 70 35

241 Red Cross and Children playing

1977. World Health Day. Child Immunization Campaign.
679 **241** 80f. red, mauve and orange 75 35

242 Fly, Dagger, and W.H.O. Emblem in Eye

1977. Fight against Onchocerciasis (blindness caused by worm infestation).
680 **242** 100f. blue, grey and red 1·40 55

243 Guirka Tahoua Dance

1977. "Popular Arts and Traditions". Multicoloured.
681 40f. Type **243** 45 25
682 50f. Maifilafili Gaya 50 20
683 80f. Naguihinayan Loga . . 80 45

244 Four Cavalrymen

1977. Chiefs' Traditional Cavalry. Multicoloured.
684 40f. Type **244** 55 25
685 50f. Chieftain at head of cavalry 65 30
686 60f. Chieftain and cavalry . . 90 45

245 Planting Crops

1977. "Operation Green Sahel" (recovery of desert).
687 **245** 40f. multicoloured 50 25

246 Albert John Luthuli (Peace, 1960)

1977. Nobel Prize Winners. Multicoloured.
688 50f. Type **246** 30 15
689 80f. Maurice Maeterlinck (Literature, 1911) 55 20
690 100f. Allan L. Hodgkin (Medicine, 1963) 70 25
691 150f. Albert Camus (Literature, 1957) . . . . 1·00 35
692 200f. Paul Ehrlich (Medicine, 1908) . . . . 1·50 40

247 Mao Tse-tung

1977. 1st Death Anniv of Mao Tse-tung (Chinese leader).
694 **247** 100f. black and red . . . 80 50

248 Vittorio Pozzo (Italy)

1977. World Football Cup Elimination Rounds. Multicoloured.
695 40f. Type **248** 30 10
696 50f. Vincente Feola, Spain . . 35 15
697 80f. Aymore Moreira, Portugal 50 20
698 100f. Sir Alf Ramsey, England 75 25
699 200f. Helmut Schon, West Germany . . . . 1·40 45

249 Horse's Head and Parthenon

1977. U.N.E.S.C.O. Commemoration.
701 **249** 100f. blue, red and pale blue . . . . 1·25 60

250 Carrying Water **252** Paul Follereau and Leper

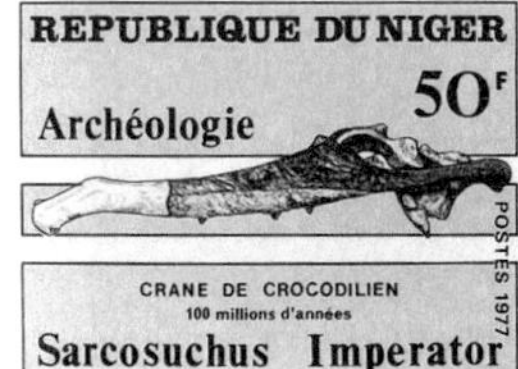

251 Crocodile Skull

1977. Women's Work. Multicoloured.
702 40f. Type **250** 35 30
703 50f. Pounding maize 40 25

1977. Archaeology. Multicoloured.
704 50f. Type **251** 60 40
705 80f. Neolithic tools 90 60

1978. 25th Anniv of World Leprosy Day.
706 **252** 40f. red, blue and orange 30 15
707 – 50f. black, red and orange 40 20
DESIGN—HORIZ: 50f. Follereau and two lepers.

253 "The Assumption"

1978. 400th Birth Anniv of Peter Paul Rubens. Paintings. Multicoloured.
708 50f. Type **253** 30 15
709 70f. "The Artist and his Friends" (horiz) 40 20
710 100f. "History of Maria de Medici" 70 25
711 150f. "Alathea Talbot" . . . 1·10 35
712 200f. "Portrait of the Marquise de Spinola" . . . 1·50 40

1978. As Nos. 376/7 but redrawn and background colour of 35f. changed to blue, 35f. undated, 50f. dated "1978".
714 35f. Broad-tailed paradise whydah . . . . 1·50 75
715 50f. Cattle egret . . . . . . 2·50 95
The 50f. is still wrongly inscribed "Balbucus".

254 Putting the Shot

1978. National Schools and University Sports Championships. Multicoloured.
716 40f. Type **254** 20 15
717 50f. Volleyball 30 20
718 60f. Long-jumping 35 20
719 100f. Throwing the javelin . . 55 35

255 Nurse assisting Patient

1978. Niger Red Cross.
720 **255** 40f. multicoloured 30 20

256 Station and Dish Aerial

1978. Goudel Earth Receiving Station.
721 **256** 100f. multicoloured . . . 65 40

257 Football and Flags of Competing Nations

1978. World Cup Football Championship, Argentina. Multicoloured.
722 40f. Type **257** 25 10
723 50f. Football in net 35 15
724 100f. Globe and goal 75 25
725 200f. Tackling (horiz) . . . . 1·40 55

258 "Fireworks"

1978. Air. 3rd African Games, Algiers. Multicoloured.
727 40f. Type **258** 25 20
728 150f. Olympic rings emblem 1·00 60

259 Niamey Post Office

1978. Niamey Post Office. Multicoloured.
729 40f. Type **259** 25 15
730 60f. Niamey Post Office (different) 35 25

260 Aerial View of Water-works

1978. Goudel Water-works.
731 **260** 100f. multicoloured . . . 55 40

261 R.T.N. Emblem

1978. Air. 20th Anniv of Niger Broadcasting.
732 **261** 150f. multicoloured . . . 90 60

262 Golden Eagle and Oldenburg 2g. Stamp of 1859

1978. Air. "Philexafrique" Stamp Exhibition, Libreville, Gabon (1st issue) and Int Stamp Fair, Essen, West Germany. Multicoloured.
733 100f. Type **262** . . . . 2·50 1·25
734 100f. Giraffes and Niger 1959 2f. stamp . . . . 2·50 1·25
See also Nos. 769/70.

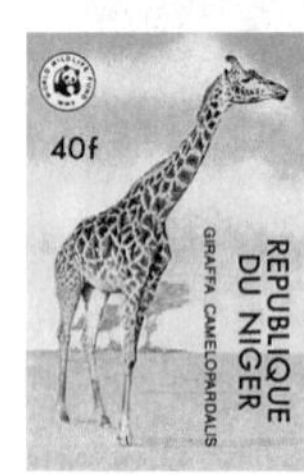

263 Giraffe

REPUBLIQUE DU NIGER
PALESTINE
40f. 5f

265 Dome of the Rock, Jerusalem

1978. Endangered Animals. Multicoloured.
735 40f. Type **263** 45 25
736 50f. Ostrich 85 25
737 70f. Cheetah 75 35
738 150f. Scimitar oryx (horiz) . . 1·50 75
739 200f. Addax (horiz) . . . . . 2·00 95
740 300f. Hartebeest (horiz) . . . 2·50 1·25

1978. World Cup Football Championship Finalists. Nos. 695/9 optd.
741 **248** 40f. multicoloured 30 20
742 – 50f. multicoloured 40 20
743 – 80f. multicoloured 55 25
744 – 100f. multicoloured . . . 65 40
745 – 200f. multicoloured . . . 1·40 75
OVERPRINTS: 40f. **EQUIPE QUATRIEME: ITALIE**; 50f. **EQUIPE TROISIEME: BRESIL**; 80f. **EQUIPE SECONDE: PAYS BAS**; 100f. **EQUIPE VAINQUEUR: ARGENTINE**. 200 f; **ARGENTINE - PAYS BAS 3 - 1**.

1978. Palestinian Welfare.
747 **265** 40f.+5f. multicoloured . . 40 30

266 Laying Foundation Stone, and View of University

1978. Air. Islamic University of Niger.
748 **266** 100f. multicoloured . . . 60 40

HONORE DAUMIER 1808-1879
REPUBLIQUE DU NIGER 50F

267 Tinguizi **268** "The Homecoming" (Daumier)

1978. Musicians. Multicoloured.
749 100f. Type **267** 75 40
750 100f. Chetima Ganga (horiz) 75 40
751 100f. Dan Gourmou 75 40

1979. Paintings. Multicoloured.
752 50f. Type **268** 50 20
753 100f. "Virgin in Prayer" (Durer) 60 20
754 150f. "Virgin and Child" (Durer) 90 30
755 200f. "Virgin and Child" (Durer) (different) . . . . 1·25 40

269 Feeder Tanks

1979. Solar Energy. Multicoloured.
757 40f. Type **269** 30 20
758 50f. Solar panels on house roofs (horiz) 40 25

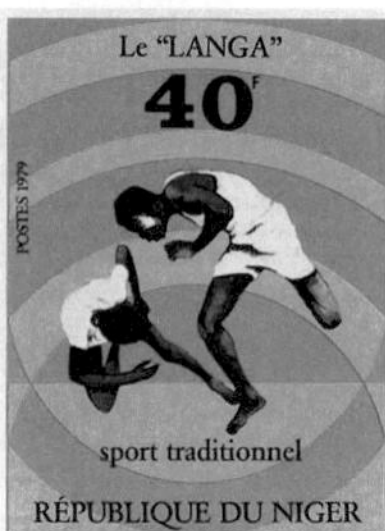

270 Langha Contestants

1979. Traditional Sports. Multicoloured.
759 40f. Type **270** 25 15
760 50f. Langha contestants clasping hands 35 20

271 Children with Building Bricks

1979. International Year of the Child. Multicoloured.
761 40f. Type **271** 25 15
762 100f. Children with book . . 60 25
763 150f. Children with model airplane . . . . 1·25 45

272 Rowland Hill, Peugeot Mail Van and French "Ceres" Stamp of 1849

1979. Death Centenary of Sir Rowland Hill. Mult.
764 40f. Type **272** 25 15
765 100f. Canoes and Austrian newspaper stamp, 1851 . . 60 25
766 150f. "DC-3" aircraft & U.S. "Lincoln" stamp, 1869 . . 1·10 35
767 200f. Advanced Passenger Train (APT), Great Britain and Canada 7½d. stamp, 1857 . . . . 2·25 40

273 Zabira Decorated Bag and Niger 45f. Stamp, 1965

1979. "Philexafrique 2" Exhibition, Gabon (2nd issue).
769 **273** 50f. multicoloured 65 40
770 – 150f. blue, red and carmine . . . . 1·60 1·10
DESIGN: 150f. Talking Heads, world map, satellite and U.P.U. emblem.

274 Alcock and Brown Statue and Vickers Vimy Aircraft

1979. 60th Anniv of First Transatlantic Flight.
771 **274** 100f. multicoloured . . . 1·00 35

275 Djermakoye Palace

1979. Historic Monuments.
772 **275** 100f. multicoloured . . . 55 40

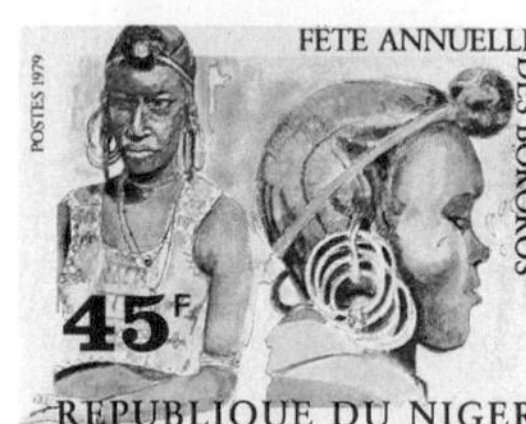

276 Bororos in Festive Headdress

1979. Annual Bororo Festival. Multicoloured.
773 45f. Type **276** 30 20
774 60f. Bororo women in traditional costume (vert) 35 25

277 Boxing

1979. Pre-Olympic Year.
775 **277** 45f. multicoloured 30 15
776 – 100f. multicoloured . . . 55 25
777 – 150f. multicoloured . . . 85 35
778 – 250f. multicoloured . . . 1·25 45
DESIGNS: 100f. to 250f. Various boxing scenes.

278 Class of Learner-drivers

1979. Driving School.
780 **278** 45f. multicoloured 30 20

279 Douglas DC-10 over Map of Niger

1979. Air. 20th Anniv of ASECNA (African Air Safety Organization).
781 **279** 150f. multicoloured . . . 1·10 60

1979. "Apollo 11" Moon Landing. Nos. 667/8, 670/1 optd **alunissage apollo XI juillet 1969** and lunar module.
782 50f. Type **237** (postage) . . . 30 20
783 80f. "Viking" approaching Mars (horiz) 50 35
784 150f. Parachute descent (air) 90 60
785 200f. Rocket in flight . . . . 1·25 80

281 Four-man Bobsleigh

1979. Winter Olympic Games, Lake Placid (1980). Multicoloured.
787 40f. Type **281** 25 15
788 60f. Downhill skiing 35 15
789 100f. Speed skating 60 25
790 150f. Two-man bobsleigh . . 90 35
791 200f. Figure skating . . . . 1·10 45

282 Le Gaweye Hotel

1980. Air.
793 **282** 100f. multicoloured . . . 60 40

283 Sultan and Court

1980. Sultan of Zinder's Court. Multicoloured.
794 45f. Type **283** 30 20
795 60f. Sultan and court (different) 40 20

284 Chain Smoker and Athlete **285** Walking

1980. World Health Day. Anti-smoking Campaign.
796 **284** 100f. multicoloured . . . 65 40

1980. Olympic Games, Moscow. Multicoloured.
797 60f. Throwing the javelin . . 35 15
798 90f. Type **285** 50 20
799 100f. High jump (horiz) . . . 55 25
800 300f. Running (horiz) . . . . 1·50 55

1980. Winter Olympic Games Medal Winners. Nos. 787/91 optd.
802 **281** 40f. **VAINQUEUR R.D.A.** 25 15
803 – 60f. **VAINQUEUR STENMARK SUEDE** 30 20
804 – 100f. **VAINQUEUR HEIDEN Etats-Unis** . . 60 30
805 – 150f. **VAINQUEURS SCHERER-BENZ Suisse** 90 45
806 – 200f. **VAINQUEUR COUSINS Grande Bretagne** . . . . 1·25 65

287 Village Scene

1980. Health Year.
808 **287** 150f. multicoloured . . . 75 50

288 Class 150 (first locomotive in Japan, 1871)

1980. Steam Locomotives. Multicoloured.
809 45f. Type **288** 80 10
810 60f. "Fred Merril", 1848, U.S.A. . . . . 1·10 10
811 90f. Series 61, 1934, Germany 1·75 20
812 100f. Type P2, 1900, Prussia 2·25 20
813 130f. "Aigle", 1846, France 3·25 30

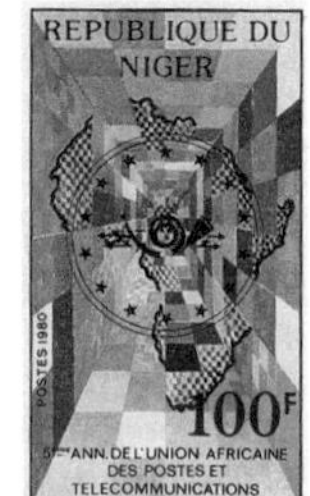

289 Steve Biko and Map of Africa **292** U.A.P.T. Emblem

291 Footballer

1980. 4th Death Anniv of Steve Biko (South African Anti-apartheid Worker).
815 **289** 150f. multicoloured . . . 80 60

1980. Olympic Medal Winners. Nos. 787/800 optd.
816 **285** 60f. **KULA (URSS)** . . . 35 15
817 – 90f. **DAMILANO (IT)** . . 55 25
818 – 100f. **WZSOLA (POL)** 60 30
819 – 300f. **YIFTER (ETH)** . . 1·60 90

1980. World Cup Football Championship, Spain (1982). Various designs showing Football.
821 **291** 45f. multicoloured 25 15
822 – 60f. multicoloured 30 15
823 – 90f. multicoloured 55 20
824 – 100f. multicoloured . . . 60 25
825 – 130f. multicoloured . . . 80 30

1980. 5th Anniv of African Posts and Telecommunications Union.
827 **292** 100f. multicoloured . . . 55 40

293 Earthenware Statuettes

1981. Kareygorou Culture Terracotta Statuettes. Multicoloured.
828 45f. Type **293** 25 20
829 60f. Head (vert) 35 20
830 90f. Head (different) (vert) . . 50 30
831 150f. Three heads 90 50

294 "Self-portrait"

1981. Paintings by Rembrandt. Multicoloured.
832 60f. Type **294** 40 15
833 90f. "Portrait of Hendrickje at the Window" 60 20
834 100f. "Portrait of an Old Man" 65 25
835 130f. "Maria Trip" 90 35
836 200f. "Self-portrait" (different) . . . . 1·25 45
837 400f. "Portrait of Saskia" . . 2·25 1·00

295 Ostrich

1981. Animals. Multicoloured.
839 10f. Type **295** 55 25
840 20f. Scimitar oryx 25 15
841 25f. Addra gazelle 20 15
842 30f. Arabian bustard 95 45
843 60f. Giraffe 50 20
844 150f. Addax . . . . 1·00 45

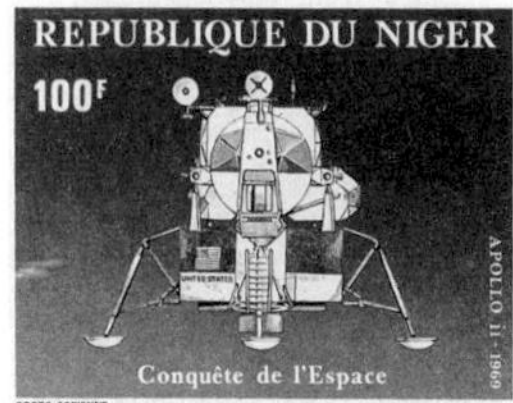

296 "Apollo 11"

1981. Air. Conquest of Space. Multicoloured.
845 100f. Type **296** 60 25
846 150f. Boeing 747 SCA carrying space shuttle . . . 1·00 40
847 200f. Rocket carrying space shuttle . . . . 1·25 40
848 300f. Space shuttle flying over planet . . . . 3·00 1·00

297 Tanks

1981. 7th Anniv of Military Coup.
849 **297** 100f. multicoloured . . . 1·00 40

298 Disabled Archer

1981. International Year of Disabled People.
850 **298** 50f. dp brown, red & brown 50 20
851 – 100f. brown, red and green 75 40
DESIGN: 100f. Disabled draughtsman.

299 Ballet Mahalba

1981. Ballet Mahalba. Multicoloured.
852 100f. Type **299** 70 35
853 100f. Ballet Mahalba (different) 70 35

300 "Portrait of Olga in an Armchair"

1981. Air. Birth Centenary of Pablo Picasso (artist). Multicoloured.
854 60f. Type **300** 40 20
855 90f. "The Family of Acrobats" 55 25
856 120f. "The Three Musicians" 70 35
857 200f. "Paul on a Donkey" . . 1·10 55
858 400f. "Young Girl drawing in an Interior" (horiz) . . . . 2·40 1·25

301 Mosque and Ka'aba

1981. 15th Centenary of Hejira.
859 **301** 100f. multicoloured . . . 60 35

302 Carriage

1981. British Royal Wedding.
860 **302** 150f. multicoloured . . . 60 35
861 – 200f. multicoloured . . . 1·00 55
862 – 300f. multicoloured . . . 1·25 1·00
DESIGNS: 200f., 300f. Similar designs showing carriages.

303 Sir Alexander Fleming

1981. Birth Centenary of Sir Alexander Fleming (discoverer of Penicillin).
864 **303** 150f. blue, brown and green . . . . 1·50 60

304 Pen-nibs, Envelope, Flower and U.P.U. Emblem

1981. International Letter Writing Week.
865 **304** 65f. on 45f. blue and red 40 20
866 – 85f. on 60f. blue, orange and black 50 30
DESIGN: 85f. Quill, hand holding pen and U.P.U. emblem.

305 Crops, Cattle and Fish

1981. World Food Day.
867 **305** 100f. multicoloured . . . 1·00 35

306 Tackling

1981. World Cup Football Championship, Spain (1982). Multicoloured.
868 40f. Type **306** 25 20
869 65f. Goalkeeper fighting for ball 40 30
870 85f. Passing ball 55 35
871 150f. Running with ball . . . 1·00 60
872 300f. Jumping for ball . . . 2·25 1·10

307 Peugeot, 1912

1981. 75th Anniv of French Grand Prix Motor Race. Multicoloured.
874 20f. Type **307** 25 15
875 40f. Bugatti, 1924 . . . . . 35 20
876 65f. Lotus-Climax, 1962 . . . 55 30
877 85f. Georges Boillot 75 35
878 150f. Phil Hill . . . . 1·10 60

308 "Madonna and Child" (Botticelli)

309 Children watering Plants

1981. Christmas. Various Madonna and Child Paintings by named artists. Multicoloured.
880 100f. Type **308** 60 40
881 200f. Botticini . . . . 1·25 75
882 300f. Botticini (different) . . 2·00 1·10

1982. School Gardens. Multicoloured.
883 65f. Type **309** 50 30
884 85f. Tending plants and examining produce 60 35

310 Arturo Toscanini (conductor, 25th death anniv)

1982. Celebrities' Anniversaries. Multicoloured.
885 120f. Type **310** . . . . 1·00 45
886 140f. "Fruits on a Table" (Manet, 150th birth anniv) (horiz) 80 55
887 200f. "L'Estaque" (Braque, birth centenary) (horiz) . . 1·25 60
888 300f. George Washington (250th birth anniv) . . . . 2·00 90
889 400f. Goethe (poet, 150th death anniv) . . . . 2·50 1·25
890 500f. Princess of Wales (21st birthday) . . . . 2·75 1·50

311 Palace of Congresses

1982. Palace of Congresses.
892 **311** 150f. multicoloured . . . 90 60

312 Martial Arts

1982. 7th Youth Festival, Agadez. Multicoloured.
893 65f. Type **312** 40 30
894 100f. Traditional wrestling . . 60 40

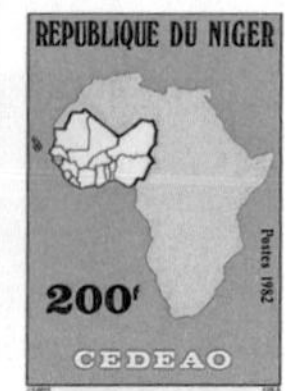

313 Planting a Tree

315 Map of Africa showing Member States

314 Scouts in Pirogue

1982. National Re-afforestation Campaign. Multicoloured.
895 150f. Type **313** . . . . 1·00 60
896 200f. Forest and desert . . . 1·25 75

1982. 75th Anniv of Boy Scout Movement. Mult.
897 65f. Type **314** 55 30
898 85f. Scouts in inflatable dinghy 65 30
899 130f. Scouts in canoe . . . . 1·25 45
900 200f. Scouts on raft . . . . 1·75 60

1982. Economic Community of West African States.
902 **315** 200f. yellow, black and blue . . . . 1·25 75

316 Casting Net

1982. Niger Fishermen. Multicoloured.
903 65f. Type **316** 85 30
904 85f. Net fishing 70 40

1982. Birth of Prince William of Wales. Nos. 860/2 optd **NAISSANCE ROYALE 1982**.
905 **302** 150f. multicoloured . . . 75 60
906 – 200f. multicoloured . . . 1·00 75
907 – 300f. multicoloured . . . 1·40 1·10

318 Hands reaching towards Mosque

1982. 13th Islamic Foreign Ministers Meeting, Niamey.
909 **318** 100f. multicoloured . . . 60 40

319 "Flautist"

1982. Norman Rockwell Paintings. Multicoloured.
910 65f. Type **319** 40 25
911 85f. "Clerk" 50 25
912 110f. "Teacher and Pupil" . . 70 35
913 150f. "Girl Shopper" 90 50

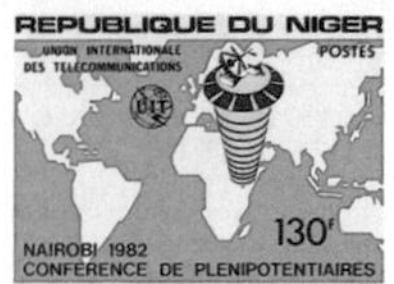

320 World Map and Satellite

1982. I.T.U. Delegates' Conference, Nairobi.
914 **320** 130f. blue, light blue and black . . . . 1·00 50

1982. World Cup Football Championship Winners. Nos. 868/72 optd.
915 40f. Type **306** 25 20
916 65f. Goalkeeper fighting for ball 40 30
917 85f. Passing ball 45 25
918 150f. Running with ball . . . 90 50
919 300f. Jumping for ball . . . 1·75 1·10

OVERPRINTS: 40f. **1966 VAINQUEUR GRANDE - BRETAGNE**; 65f. **"1970 VAINQUEUR BRESIL"**; 85f. **"1974 VAINQUEUR ALLEMAGNE (RFA)"**; 150f. **"1978 VAINQUEUR ARGENTINE"**; 300f. **"1982 VAINQUEUR ITALIE"**.

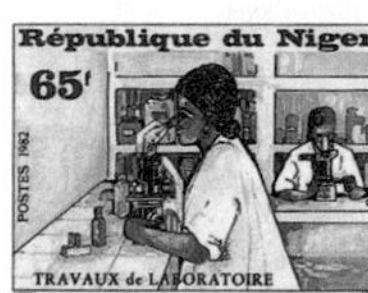

322 Laboratory Workers with Microscopes

1982. Laboratory Work. Multicoloured.
921 65f. Type **322** 60 40
922 115f. Laboratory workers . . 80 50

323 "Adoration of the Kings"

1982. Air. Christmas. Paintings by Rubens. Multicoloured.
923 200f. Type **323** . . . . 1·25 50
924 300f. "Mystic Marriage of St. Catherine" . . . . . 2·00 75
925 400f. "Virgin and Child" . . 2·50 1·00

324 Montgolfier Balloon

1983. Air. Bicent of Manned Flight. Mult.
926 65f. Type **324** 45 15
927 85f. Charles's hydrogen balloon 60 20
928 200f. Goodyear Aerospace airship (horiz) . . . . . 1·25 60
929 250f. Farman H.F.III biplane (horiz) . . . . 1·50 70
930 300f. Concorde . . . . . . 3·00 1·40
931 500f. "Apollo 11" spacecraft 3·00 1·40

No. 928 is wrongly inscribed "Zeppelin".

325 Harvesting Rice

326 E.C.A. Anniversary Emblem

1983. Self-sufficiency in Food. Multicoloured.
932 65f. Type **325** 60 30
933 85f. Planting rice 80 40

1983. 25th Anniv of Economic Commission for Africa.
934 **326** 120f. multicoloured . . . 75 40
935 200f. multicoloured . . . 1·25 70

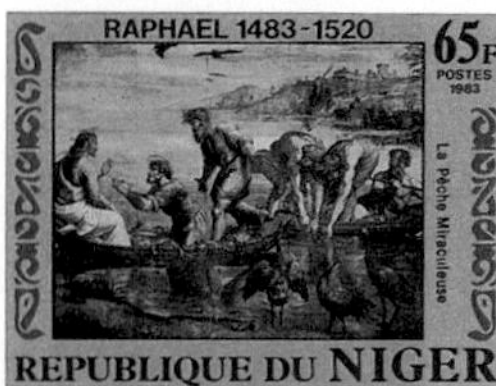

327 "The Miraculous Draught of Fishes"

1983. 500th Birth Anniv of Raphael. Multicoloured.
936 65f. Type **327** 50 20
937 85f. "Grand Ducal Madonna" (vert) 50 20
938 100f. "The Deliverance of St. Peter" 60 25
939 150f. "Sistine Madonna" (vert) . . . . 1·00 45
940 200f. "The Fall on the Way to Calvary" (vert) . . . . 1·10 60
941 300f. "The Entombment" . . 1·75 80
942 400f. "The Transfiguration" (vert) . . . . 2·25 1·10
943 500f. "St. Michael fighting the Dragon" (vert) . . . . 3·00 1·40

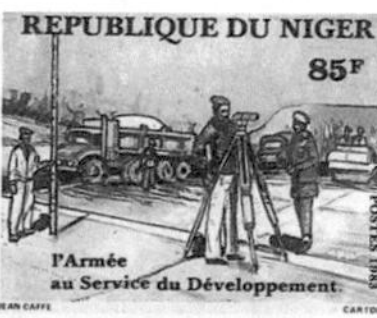

328 Surveying

1983. The Army in the Service of Development. Multicoloured.
944 85f. Type **328** 60 25
945 150f. Road building . . . . 1·00 50

329 Palace of Justice

1983. Palace of Justice, Agadez.
946 **329** 65f. multicoloured 40 20

330 Javelin

1983. Air. Olympic Games, Los Angeles. Mult.
947 85f. Type **330** 50 20
948 200f. Shotput . . . . 1·10 60
949 250f. Throwing the hammer (vert) . . . . 1·50 70
950 300f. Discus . . . . 1·75 80

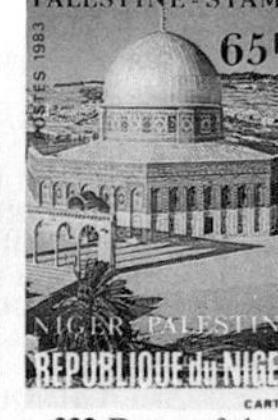

331 Rural Post Vehicle

332 Dome of the Rock

1983. Rural Post Service. Multicoloured.
952 65f. Type **331** 50 20
953 100f. Post vehicle and map 75 30

1983. Palestine.
954 **332** 65f. multicoloured 65 20

333 Class watching Television

1983. International Literacy Day. Multicoloured.
955 40f. Type **333** 25 15
956 65f. Teacher at blackboard (vert) 40 25
957 85f. Learning weights (vert) 55 30
958 100f. Outdoor class 60 35
959 150f. Woman reading magazine (vert) . . . . . 1·00 50

334 Three Dancers

1983. 7th Dosso Dance Festival. Multicoloured.
960 65f. Type **334** 50 25
961 85f. Four dancers 60 35
962 120f. Two dancers 90 50

335 Post Van

1983. World Communications Year. Multicoloured.
963 80f. Type **335** 60 40
964 120f. Sorting letters 80 40
965 150f. W.C.Y. emblem (vert) 1·00 50

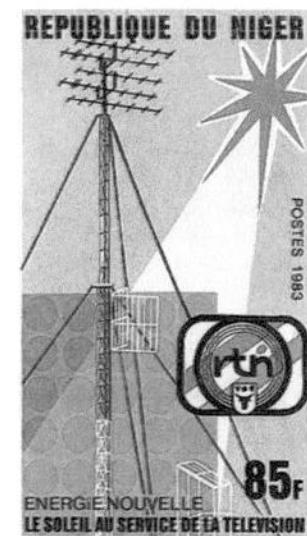

336 Television Antenna and Solar Panel

1983. Solar Energy in the Service of Television. Multicoloured.
966 85f. Type **336** 60 30
967 130f. Land-rover and solar panel 90 45

337 "Hypolimnas misippus"

1983. Butterflies. Multicoloured.
968 75f. Type **337** 70 35
969 120f. "Papilio demodocus" 1·10 50
970 250f. "Vanessa antiopa" . . 2·00 90
971 350f. "Charexes jasius" . . . 2·75 1·40
972 500f. "Danaus chrisippus" . . 4·50 1·75

338 "Virgin and Child with Angels" **339** Samariya Emblem

1983. Air. Christmas. Paintings by Botticelli. Multicoloured.
973 120f. Type **338** 75 40
974 350f. "Adoration of the Magi" (horiz) . . . . . . 2·25 1·00
975 500f. "Virgin of the Pomegranate" . . . . . . 3·00 1·25

1984. Samariya.
976 **339** 80f. black, orange & green 50 30

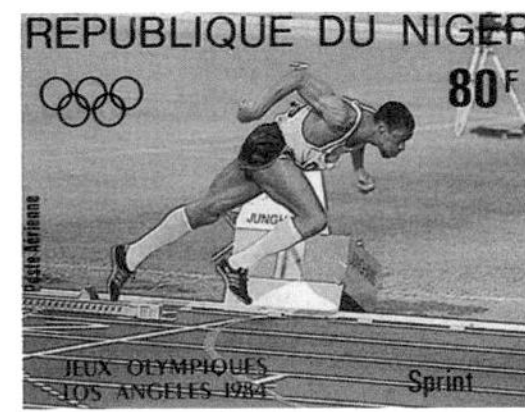

340 Running

1984. Air. Olympic Games, Los Angeles. Mult.
977 80f. Type **340** 40 20
978 120f. Pole vault 60 30
979 140f. High jump 80 30
980 200f. Triple jump (vert) . . . 1·25 45
981 350f. Long jump (vert) . . . 2·00 1·00

341 Boubon's Tetra

1984. Fish.
983 **341** 120f. multicoloured . . . 2·75 80

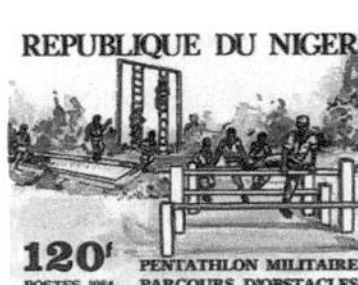

342 Obstacle Course

1984. Military Pentathlon. Multicoloured.
984 120f. Type **342** 80 40
985 140f. Shooting 95 50

343 Radio Station

1984. New Radio Station.
986 **343** 120f. multicoloured . . . 85 40

344 Flags, Agriculture and Symbols of Unity and Growth

1984. 25th Anniv of Council of Unity.
987 **344** 65f. multicoloured 40 25
988 85f. multicoloured 50 40

345 "Paris" (early steamer)

1984. Ships. Multicoloured.
989 80f. Type **345** 75 30
990 120f. "Jacques Coeur" (full-rigged ship) 85 40
991 150f. "Bosphorus" (full-rigged ship) . . . . 1·40 50
992 300f. "Comet" (full-rigged ship) . . . . 2·50 1·10

346 Daimler

1984. Motor Cars. Multicoloured.
993 100f. Type **346** 75 30
994 140f. Renault . . . . 1·10 45
995 250f. Delage "D 8" . . . . . 1·75 70
996 400f. Maybach "Zeppelin" 2·75 90

347 "Rickmer Rickmers" (full-rigged ship)

1984. Universal Postal Union Congress, Hamburg.
997 **347** 300f. blue, brown and green . . . . 2·75 1·75

348 Cattle

1984. Ayerou Market. Multicoloured.
998 80f. Type **348** 60 40
999 120f. View of market . . . . 1·00 60

349 Viper

1984.
1000 **349** 80f. multicoloured . . . 75 40

350 Carl Lewis (100 and 200 m)

1984. Air. Olympic Games Medal Winners. Multicoloured.
1001 80f. Type **350** 50 20
1002 120f. J. Cruz (800 m) . . . 70 40
1003 140f. A. Cova (10,000 m) . . 80 45
1004 300f. Al Joyner (Triple jump) . . . . 1·75 90

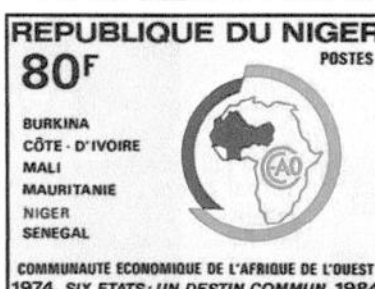

351 Emblem

1984. 10th Anniv of Economic Community of West Africa.
1006 **351** 80f. multicoloured . . . 50 30

352 Emblem and Extract from General Kountche's Speech

1984. United Nations Disarmament Decennials.
1007 **352** 400f. black and green . . 2·50 1·75
1008 500f. black and blue . . 3·00 1·75

353 Football

1984. Air. Preliminary Rounds of World Cup Football Championship, Mexico.
1009 **353** 150f. multicoloured . . . 1·00 45
1010 – 250f. multicoloured . . . 1·75 80
1011 – 450f. multicoloured . . . 2·50 1·25
1012 – 500f. multicoloured . . . 3·00 1·75
DESIGNS: 250 to 500f. Footballing scenes.

354 "The Visitation" (Ghirlandaio)

1984. Air. Christmas. Multicoloured.
1013 100f. Type **354** 60 30
1014 200f. "Virgin and Child" (Master of Saint Verdiana) . . . . 1·25 65
1015 400f. "Virgin and Child" (J. Koning) . . . . 2·50 1·25

1984. Drought Relief. Nos. 895/6 optd **Aide au Sahel 84**.
1016 150f. multicoloured . . . . 1·00 80
1017 200f. multicoloured . . . . 1·25 1·10

356 Organization Emblem

1985. 10th Anniv of World Tourism Organization.
1018 **356** 100f. black, orange and green 70 40

357 Breast-feeding Baby

360 Profile and Emblem

358 Black-necked Stilt

1985. Infant Survival Campaign. Multicoloured.
1019 85f. Type **357** 70 30
1020 110f. Feeding baby and changing nappy 90 40

1985. Air. Birth Centenary of John J. Audubon (ornithologist). Multicoloured.
1021 110f. Type **358** . . . . . . 1·10 45
1022 140f. Greater flamingo (vert) 1·50 65
1023 200f. Atlantic puffin . . . . 2·25 95
1024 350f. Arctic tern (vert) . . . 4·25 1·25

1985. 15th Anniv of Technical and Cultural Co-operation Agency.
1026 **360** 110f. brown, red & violet 65 40

361 Dancers

1985. 8th Niamey Festival. Multicoloured.
1027 85f. Type **361** 60 40
1028 110f. Four dancers (vert) . . 70 50
1029 150f. Dancers (different) . . 1·00 65

362 Wolf ("White Fang") and Jack London

1985. International Youth Year. Multicoloured.
1030 85f. Type **362** 60 25
1031 105f. Woman with lion and Joseph Kessel 75 30
1032 250f. Capt. Ahab harpooning white whale ("Moby Dick") . . . . . 1·75 90
1033 450f. Mowgli on elephant ("Jungle Book") . . . . 2·75 1·50

363 Two Children on Leaf

1985. "Philexafrique" Stamp Exhibition, Lome, Togo (1st issue). Multicoloured.
1034 200f. Type **363** . . . . . . 1·25 1·00
1035 200f. Mining . . . . 1·25 1·00
See also Nos. 1064/5.

364 "Hugo with his Son Francois" (A. de Chatillon)

1985. Death Centenary of Victor Hugo (writer).
1036 **364** 500f. multicoloured . . . 3·00 1·75

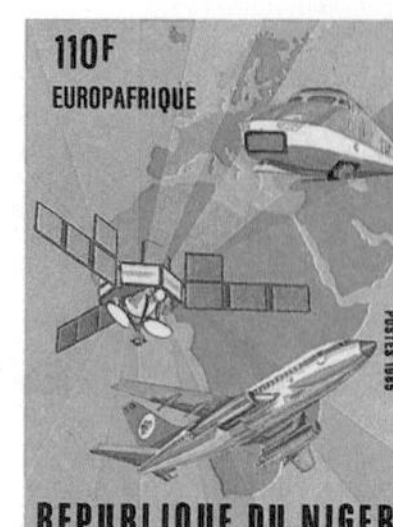

365 French Turbotrain TGV 001, Satellite and Boeing 737 on Map

1985. Europafrique.
1037 **365** 110f. multicoloured . . . 2·75 55

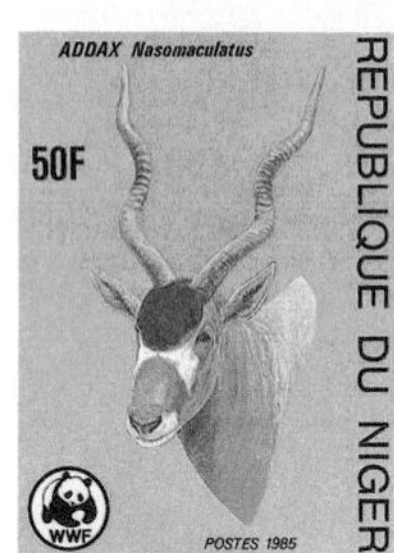

366 Addax

1985. Endangered Animals. Multicoloured.
1038 50f. Type **366** 40 15
1039 60f. Addax (different) (horiz) 45 25
1040 85f. Two scimitar oryxes (horiz) 55 25
1041 110f. Oryx 75 35

367 "Oedaleus sp" on Millet

368 Cross of Agadez

1985. Vegetation Protection. Multicoloured.
1042 85f. Type **367** 55 20
1043 110f. "Dysdercus volkeri" (beetle) 75 35
1044 150f. Fungi attacking sorghum and millet (horiz) . . . . 2·50 60
1045 210f. Sudan golden sparrows in tree . . . . 2·10 85
1046 390f. Red-billed queleas in tree . . . . 4·25 2·10

1985.
1047 **368** 85f. green 45 15
1048 – 110f. brown 55 15
DESIGN: 110f. Girl carrying water jar on head.

369 Arms, Flags and Agriculture

1985. 25th Anniv of Independence.
1049 **369** 110f. multicoloured . . . 70 40

370 Baobab

373 "Boletus"

371 Man watching Race

1985. Protected Trees. Multicoloured.
1050 110f. Type **370** 80 50
1051 210f. "Acacia albida" . . . 1·40 1·00
1052 390f. Baobab (different) . . 3·00 1·60

1985. Niamey–Bamako Powerboat Race. Mult.
1053 110f. Type **371** 70 45
1054 150f. Helicopter and powerboat . . . . 1·60 85
1055 250f. Powerboat and map . . 1·75 1·25

1985. "Trees for Niger". As Nos. 1050/2 but new values and optd **DES ARBRES POUR LE NIGER**.
1056 **370** 30f. multicoloured . . . 25 20
1057 – 85f. multicoloured . . . 55 40
1058 – 110f. multicoloured . . . 70 55

1985. Fungi. Multicoloured.
1059 85f. Type **373** . . . . 1·40 30
1060 110f. "Hypholoma fasciculare" . . . . . . 2·10 45
1061 200f. "Coprinus comatus" 3·00 1·10
1062 300f. "Agaricus arvensis" (horiz) . . . . 4·50 1·50
1063 400f. "Geastrum fimbriatum" (horiz) . . . 5·75 2·10

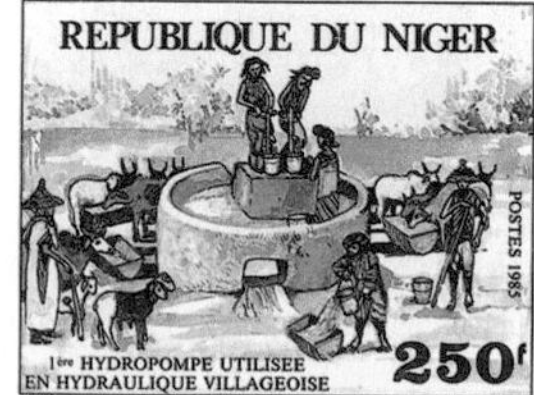

374 First Village Water Pump

1985. "Philexafrique" Stamp Exhibition, Lome, Togo (2nd issue). Multicoloured.
1064 250f. Type **374** . . . . . . 1·75 1·25
1065 250f. Handicapped youths playing dili (traditional game) . . . . 1·75 1·25

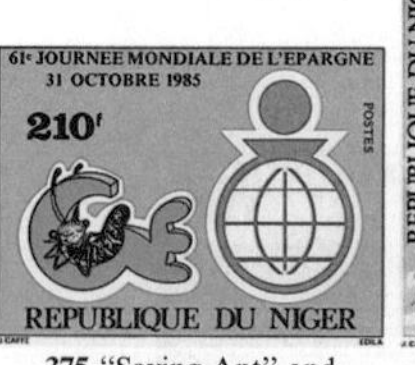

375 "Saving Ant" and Savings Bank Emblem

376 Gouroumi

1985. World Savings Day.
1066 **375** 210f. multicoloured . . . 1·40 85

1985. Musical Instruments. Multicoloured.
1067 150f. Type **376** . . . . . . 1·10 60
1068 210f. Gassou (drums) (horiz) 1·60 1·00
1069 390f. Algaita (flute) . . . . 2·75 1·50

377 "The Immaculate Conception"

379 National Identity Card

378 Comet over Paris, 1910

1985. Air. Christmas. Paintings by Murillo. Mult.
1071 110f. "Madonna of the Rosary" 65 35
1072 250f. Type **377** . . . . . . 1·75 90
1073 390f. "Virgin of Seville" . . 2·50 1·25

1985. Air. Appearance of Halley's Comet. Multicoloured.
1074 110f. Type **378** 70 35
1075 130f. Comet over New York 85 40
1076 200f. "Giotto" satellite . . . 1·50 70
1077 300f. "Vega" satellite . . . 2·25 1·00
1078 390f. "Planet A" space probe . . . . 2·50 1·25

1986. Civil Statutes Reform. Each black, green and orange.
1079 85f. Type **379** 65 30
1080 110f. Civil registration emblem 75 40

380 Road Signs

381 Oumarou Ganda (film producer)

1986. Road Safety Campaign.
1081 **380** 85f. black, yellow and red 75 30
1082 – 110f. black, red and green . . . . 1·00 40
DESIGN: 110f. Speed limit sign, road and speedometer ("Watch your speed").

1986. Honoured Artists. Multicoloured.
1083 60f. Type **381** 35 20
1084 85f. Idi na Dadaou 50 30
1085 100f. Dan Gourmou 60 40
1086 130f. Koungoui (comedian) 80 45

382 Martin Luther King

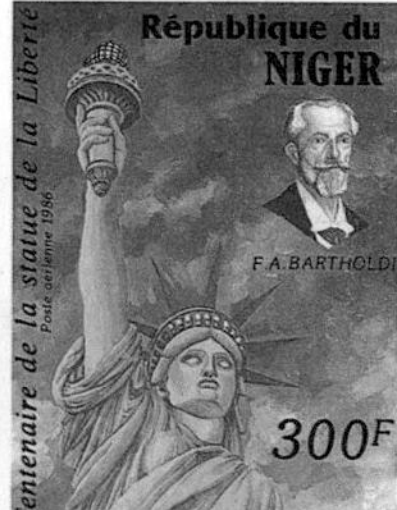

384 Statue and F. A. Bartholdi

383 Footballer and 1970 40f. Stamp

1986. Air. 18th Death Anniv of Martin Luther King (human rights activist).
1087 **382** 500f. multicoloured . . . 3·25 1·90

1986. Air. World Cup Football Championship, Mexico. Multicoloured.
1088 130f. Type **383** . . . . . . 1·00 30
1089 210f. Footballer and 1970 70f. stamp . . . . 1·25 45
1090 390f. Footballer and 1970 90f. stamp . . . . 2·75 1·00
1091 400f. Footballer and Mexican figure on "stamp" . . . . 2·75 1·00

1986. Air. Centenary of Statue of Liberty.
1093 **384** 300f. multicoloured . . . 2·25 1·10

385 Truck

1986. "Trucks of Hope". Multicoloured.
1094 85f. Type **385** 75 30
1095 110f. Mother and baby (vert) . . . . 1·00 40

386 Nelson Mandela and Walter Sisulu

387 Food Co-operatives

1986. International Solidarity with S. African and Namibian Political Prisoners Day. Multicoloured.
1096 200f. Type **386** . . . . . . 1·50 80
1097 300f. Nelson Mandela . . . 2·25 1·00

1986. 40th Anniv of F.A.O. Multicoloured.
1098 50f. Type **387** 30 20
1099 60f. Anti-desertification campaign 35 25
1100 85f. Irrigation 50 35
1101 100f. Rebuilding herds of livestock 60 40
1102 110f. Reafforestation . . . 75 45

388 Trees and Woman with Cooking Pots

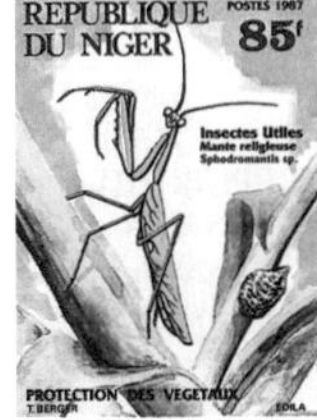
389 "Sphodromantis sp."

1987. "For a Green Niger". Multicoloured.
1103 85f. Type **388** 55 30
1104 110f. Trees, woman and cooking pots (different) 70 40

1987. Protection of Vegetation. Useful Insects. Multicoloured.
1105 85f. Type **389** 60 40
1106 110f. "Delta sp." 85 50
1107 120f. "Cicindela sp." . . . 95 65

390 Transmitter, Map and Woman using Telephone

1987. Liptako–Gourma Telecommunications Network.
1108 **390** 110f. multicoloured . . . 80 50

391 Morse Key and Operator, 19th-century

1987. 150th Anniv of Morse Telegraph. Mult.
1109 120f. Type **391** 75 40
1110 200f. Samuel Morse (inventor) (vert) . . . . . 1·25 70
1111 350f. Morse transmitter and receiver . . . . 2·25 1·25

392 Tennis Player

1987. Olympic Games, Seoul (1988). Multicoloured.
1112 85f. Type **392** 50 40
1113 110f. Pole vaulter 70 40
1114 250f. Footballer . . . . . . 1·50 90

393 Ice Hockey

1987. Winter Olympic Games, Calgary (1988) (1st issue). Multicoloured.
1116 85f. Type **393** 60 35
1117 110f. Speed skating 70 35
1118 250f. Figure skating (pairs) 1·75 90
See also Nos. 1146/9.

394 Long-distance Running

1987. African Games, Nairobi. Multicoloured.
1120 85f. Type **394** 50 35
1121 110f. High jumping 60 35
1122 200f. Hurdling . . . . . . 1·25 70
1123 400f. Javelin throwing . . . 2·50 1·40

395 Chief's Stool, Sceptre and Crown

1987. 10th Anniv of National Tourism Office. Multicoloured.
1124 85f. Type **395** 50 35
1125 110f. Nomad, caravan and sceptre handle 60 35
1126 120f. Houses 70 40
1127 200f. Bridge over River Niger . . . . 1·25 70

396 Yaama Mosque at Dawn

1987. Aga Khan Prize.
1128 **396** 85f. multicoloured . . . 50 35
1129 – 110f. multicoloured . . . 60 35
1130 – 250f. multicoloured . . . 1·50 90
DESIGNS: 110, 250f. Yaama mosque at various times of the day.

397 Court Building

398 "Holy Family of the Sheep" (Raphael)

1987. Appeal Court, Niamey. Multicoloured.
1131 85f. Type **397** 50 30
1132 110f. Front entrance 60 35
1133 140f. Side view 90 55

1987. Christmas.
1134 **398** 110f. multicoloured . . . 65 40

399 Water Drainage

1988. Health Care. Multicoloured.
1136 85f. Type **399** 70 40
1137 110f. Modern sanitation . . 80 40
1138 165f. Refuse collection . . . 1·25 65

400 Singer and Band

402 New Great Market, Niamey

1988. Award of Dan-Gourmou Music Prize.
1139 **400** 85f. multicoloured . . . 80 50

1988. Winter Olympic Games Winners. Nos. 1116/18 optd.
1140 85f. **Medaille d'or URSS** . . 50 35
1141 110f. **Medaille d'or 5.000-10.000 m-GUSTAFSON (Suede)** . . 60 40
1142 250f. **Medaille d'or E. GORDEEVA - S. GRINKOV URSS** . . . 1·50 90

1988.
1143 **402** 85f. multicoloured . . . 60 40

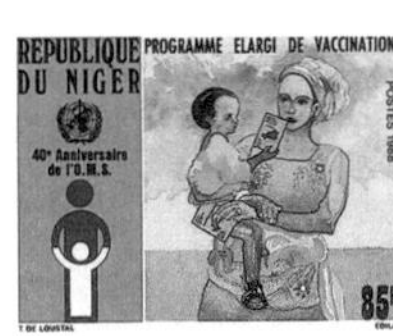
403 Mother and Child

1988. U.N.I.C.E.F. Child Vaccination Campaign and 40th Anniv of W.H.O. Multicoloured.
1144 85f. Type **403** 70 40
1145 110f. Doctor and villagers 90 50

404 Kayak

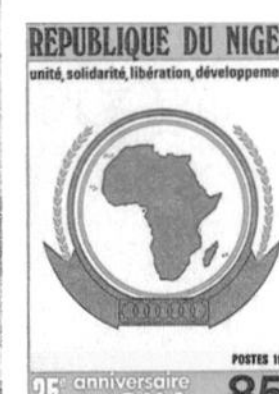
405 Emblem

1988. Air. Olympic Games, Seoul (2nd issue) and 125th Birth Anniv of Pierre de Coubertin (founder of modern Olympic Games). Multicoloured.
1146 85f. Type **404** 50 20
1147 165f. Rowing (horiz) 90 50
1148 200f. Two-man kayak (horiz) . . . . 1·25 70
1149 600f. One-man kayak . . . 3·50 2·00

1988. 25th Anniv of Organization of African Unity.
1151 **405** 85f. multicoloured . . . 50 30

406 Team working

407 Anniversary Emblem

1988. Dune Stabilization.
1152 **406** 85f. multicoloured . . . 60 40

1988. 125th Anniv of International Red Cross.
1153 **407** 85f. multicoloured . . . 60 30
1154 110f. multicoloured . . . 80 40

409 Emblem

410 Couple, Globe and Laboratory Worker

1989. Niger Press Agency.
1159 **409** 85f. black, orange & grn 45 30

1989. Campaign against AIDS.
1160 **410** 85f. multicoloured . . . 55 30
1161 110f. multicoloured . . . 85 40

411 Radar, Tanker and Signals

412 General Ali Seybou (Pres.)

1989. 30th Anniv of International Maritime Organization.
1162 **411** 100f. multicoloured . . . 1·75 75
1163 120f. multicoloured . . . 2·10 1·00

1989. 15th Anniv of Military Coup. Mult.
1164 85f. Type **412** 45 25
1165 110f. Soldiers erecting flag 65 35

413 Eiffel Tower

1989. "Philexfrance 89" International Stamp Exhibition, Paris. Multicoloured.
1166 100f. Type **413** 60 40
1167 200f. Flags on stamps . . . 1·25 65

414 "Planting a Tree of Liberty"

1989. Bicentenary of French Revolution.
1168 **414** 250f. multicoloured . . . 1·50 1·00

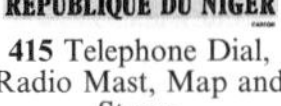

415 Telephone Dial, Radio Mast, Map and Stamp

417 Emblem

1989 – 20ème Anniversaire du Premier Homme sur la Lune
416 "Apollo 11" Launch

1989. 30th Anniv of West African Posts and Telecommunications Association.
1169 **415** 85f. multicoloured . . . 45 30

1989. Air. 20th Anniv of First Manned Landing on Moon. Multicoloured.
1170 200f. Type **416** . . . . . . 1·25 65
1171 300f. Crew . . . . 2·00 1·00
1172 350f. Astronaut and module on lunar surface . . . . 2·25 1·25
1173 400f. Astronaut and U.S. flag on lunar surface . . . 2·50 1·25

1989. 25th Anniv of African Development Bank.
1174 **417** 100f. multicoloured . . . 60 30

418 Before and After Attack, and "Schistocerca gregaria"

1989. Locusts.
1175 **418** 85f. multicoloured . . . 50 30

419 Auguste Lumiere and 1st Cine Performance, 1895

1989. 35th Death Anniv of Auguste Lumiere and 125th Birth Anniv of Louis Lumiere (photo-graphy pioneers). Multicoloured.
1176 150f. Type **419** 90 55
1177 250f. Louis Lumiere and first cine-camera, 1894 . . 1·50 85
1178 400f. Lumiere brothers and first colour cine-camera, 1920 . . . . 2·50 1·25

420 Tractor, Map and Pump

1989. 30th Anniv of Agriculture Development Council.
1179 **420** 75f. multicoloured . . . 45 30

421 Zinder Regional Museum

422 "Russelia equisetiformis"

1989. Multicoloured.
1180 85f. Type **421** 45 30
1182 165f. Temet dunes 90 60

1989. Flowers. Multicoloured.
1183 10f. Type **422** 15 10
1184 20f. "Argyreia nervosa" . . 15 10
1185 30f. "Hibiscus rosa-sinensis" 20 10
1186 50f. "Catharanthus roseus" 35 20
1187 100f. "Cymothoe sangaris" (horiz) 75 35

423 Emblem

424 Adults learning Alphabet

1990. 10th Anniv of Pan-African Postal Union.
1188 **423** 120f. multicoloured . . . 70 40

1990. International Literacy Year. Multicoloured.
1189 85f. Type **424** 45 25
1190 110f. Adults learning arithmetic 65 35

425 Emblem

427 Leland and Child

426 Footballers and Florence

1990. 20th Anniv of Islamic Conference Organization.
1191 **425** 85f. multicoloured . . . 50 30

1990. Air. World Cup Football Championship, Italy. Multicoloured.
1192 130f. Type **426** . . . . . . 1·00 40
1193 210f. Footballers and Verona . . . . 1·40 75
1194 500f. Footballers and Bari 3·25 1·75
1195 600f. Footballers and Rome 3·75 2·00

1990. Mickey Leland (American Congressman) Commemoration.
1196 **427** 300f. multicoloured . . . 1·75 1·00
1197 500f. multicoloured . . . 3·00 1·75

428 Emblem

429 Flags and Envelopes on Map

1990. 1st Anniv of National Movement for the Development Society.
1198 **428** 85f. multicoloured . . . 50 30

1990. 20th Anniv of Multinational Postal Training School, Abidjan.
1199 **429** 85f. multicoloured . . . 65 30

430 Gymnastics

1990. Olympic Games, Barcelona (1992). Mult.
1200 85f. Type **430** 40 25
1201 110f. Hurdling 60 35
1202 250f. Running . . . . . . 1·50 90
1203 400f. Show jumping . . . . 2·75 1·40
1204 500f. Long jumping . . . . 3·00 1·75

431 Arms, Map and Flag

432 Emblem

1990. 30th Anniv of Independence.
1206 **431** 85f. multicoloured . . . 45 30
1207 110f. multicoloured . . . 65 40

1990. 40th Anniv of United Nations Development Programme.
1208 **432** 100f. multicoloured . . . 50 30

433 The Blusher

434 Christopher Columbus and "Santa Maria"

1991. Butterflies and Fungi. Multicoloured.
1209 85f. Type **433** (postage) . . 1·00 30
1210 110f. "Graphium pylades" (female) 75 25
1211 200f. "Pseudacraea hostilia" 1·25 55
1212 250f. Cracked green russula 2·50 1·10
1213 400f. "Boletus impolitus" (air) . . . . 3·75 1·60
1214 500f. "Precis octavia" . . . 2·75 1·25

1991. 540th Birth of Christopher Columbus. Mult.
1216 85f. Type **434** (postage) . . 70 25
1217 110f. 15th-century Portuguese caravel . . . 1·00 30
1218 200f. 16th-century four-masted caravel . . . . . 1·60 65
1219 250f. "Estremadura" (Spanish caravel), 1511 . . 2·00 85
1220 400f. "Vija" (Portuguese caravel), 1600 (air) . . . 3·25 1·10
1221 500f. "Pinta" . . . . 3·50 1·50

435 Speed Skating

1991. Winter Olympic Games, Albertville (1992). Multicoloured.
1223 110f. Type **435** 60 25
1224 300f. Ice-hockey . . . . . 1·25 80
1225 500f. Women's downhill skiing . . . . 2·50 1·25
1226 600f. Two-man luge . . . . 2·75 1·25

436 Flag and Boy holding Stone

437 Hairstyle

1991. Palestinian "Intifada" Movement.
1227 **436** 110f. multicoloured . . . 75 30

1991. Traditional Hairstyles. Multicoloured.
1228 85f. Type **437** 20 10
1229 110f. Netted hairstyle . . . 25 15
1230 165f. Braided hairstyle . . . 40 20
1231 200f. Plaited hairstyle . . . 45 25

438 Boubon Market

1991. African Tourism Year. Multicoloured.
1232 85f. Type **438** 20 10
1233 110f. Timia waterfalls (vert) 25 15
1234 130f. Ruins at Assode . . . 30 15
1235 200f. Tourism Year emblem (vert) 45 25

439 Anatoly Karpov and Gary Kasparov

1991. Anniversaries and Events. Multicoloured.
1236 85f. Type **439** (World Chess Championship) (postage) 20 10
1237 110f. Ayrton Senna and Alain Prost (World Formula 1 motor racing championship) 25 15
1238 200f. Reading of Declaration of Human Rights and Comte de Mirabeau (bicentenary of French Revolution) . . . 45 25
1239 250f. Dwight D. Eisenhower, Winston Churchill and Field-Marshal Montgomery (50th anniv of America's entry into Second World War) . . . . 3·50 85
1240 400f. Charles de Gaulle and Konrad Adenauer (28th anniv of Franco-German Co-operation Agreement) (air) 95 55
1241 500f. Helmut Kohl and Brandenburg Gate (2nd anniv of German reunification) . . . . . . 1·10 60

440 Japanese "ERS-1" Satellite

1991. Satellites and Transport. Multicoloured.
1243 85f. Type **440** (postage) . . 20 10
1244 110f. Japanese satellite observing Aurora Borealis 25 15
1245 200f. Louis Favre and "BB 415" diesel locomotive . . 2·50 45
1246 250f. "BB-BB 301" diesel locomotive . . . . 3·00 55
1247 400f. "BB 302" diesel locomotive (air) . . . . . 4·50 70
1248 500f. Lockheed Stealth fighter-bomber and Concorde . . . . 1·10 60

441 Crowd and Emblem on Map

443 Couple adding Final Piece to Globe Jigsaw

442 Timberless House

1991. National Conference (to determine new constitution).
1250 **441** 85f. multicoloured . . . 20 10

1992.
1251 **442** 85f. multicoloured . . . 20 10

1992. World Population Day. Multicoloured.
1252 85f. Type **443** 20 10
1253 110f. Children flying globe kite (after Robert Parker) 25 15

444 Columbus and Fleet

1992. 500th Anniv of Discovery of America by Columbus.
1254 **444** 250f. multicoloured . . . 60 35

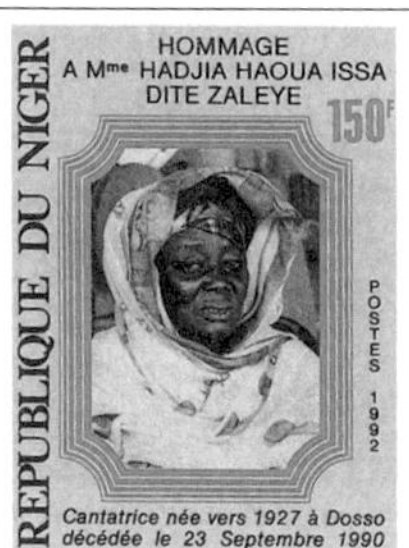

445 Zaleye

1992. 2nd Death Anniv of Hadjia Haqua Issa (Zaleye) (singer).

1255	**445**	150f. multicoloured	35	20

446 Conference Emblem **447** College Emblem

1992. International Nutrition Conference, Rome.

1256	**446**	145f. multicoloured	35	20
1257		350f. multicoloured	80	45

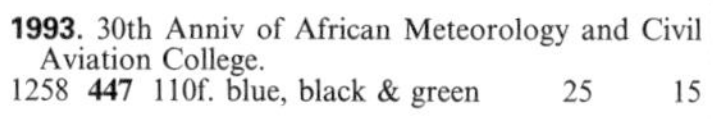

1993. 30th Anniv of African Meteorology and Civil Aviation College.

1258	**447**	110f. blue, black & green	25	15

448 Girl planting Sapling

1993. Anti-desertification Campaign.

1259	**448**	85f. multicoloured	20	10
1260		165f. multicoloured	40	20

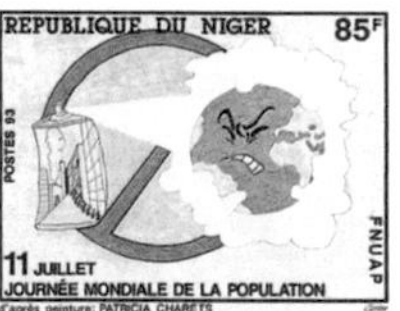

449 Aerosol spraying Globe (Patricia Charets)

1993. World Population Day. Children's Drawings. Multicoloured.

1261	85f. Type **449**	20	10
1262	110f. Tree and person with globe as head looking at high-rise tower blocks (Mathieu Chevrault)	25	15

450 Jerusalem

1993. "Jerusalem, Holy City".

1268	**450**	110f. multicoloured	30	15

451 People of Different Races

1994. Award of Nobel Peace Prize to Nelson Mandela and F. W. de Klerk (South African statesmen).

1269	**451**	270f. multicoloured	70	40

OFFICIAL STAMPS

O **13** Djerma Women

1962. Figures of value in black.

O121	O **13**	1f. violet	10	10
O122		2f. green	10	10
O123		5f. blue	15	10
O124		10f. red	15	10
O125		20f. blue	20	15
O126		25f. orange	25	20
O127		30f. blue	30	25
O128		35f. green	35	30
O129		40f. brown	35	35
O130		50f. slate	40	40
O131		60f. turquoise	50	45
O132		85f. turquoise	70	40
O133		100f. purple	85	40
O134		200f. blue	1·50	80

1988. As Type O **13**, but figures of value in same colour as remainder of design.

O1155	O **13**	5f. blue	10	10
O1156		10f. red	10	10
O1157		15f. yellow	10	10
O1158		20f. blue	20	10
O1159		45f. orange	25	20
O1160		50f. green	30	20

POSTAGE DUE STAMPS

1921. Postage Due stamps of Upper Senegal and Niger "Figure" key-type optd **TERRITOIRE DU NIGER**.

D18	M	5c. green	15	2·75
D19		10c. red	15	2·75
D20		15c. grey	20	2·75
D21		20c. brown	20	1·25
D22		30c. blue	30	3·00
D23		50c. black	60	3·00
D24		60c. orange	20	3·50
D25		1f. violet	30	2·50

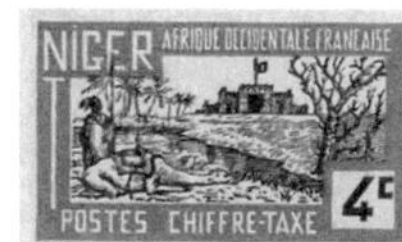

D **6** Zinder Fort

1927.

D73	D **6**	2c. red and blue	10	2·75
D74		4c. black and orange	10	2·50
D75		5c. violet and yellow	15	2·50
D76		10c. violet and red	15	2·00
D77		15c. orange and green	15	2·50
D78		20c. sepia and red	20	1·90
D79		25c. sepia and black	35	2·25
D80		30c. grey and violet	45	2·75
D81		50c. red on green	60	3·25
D82		60c. orange & lilac on bl	45	3·25
D83		1f. violet & blue on blue	55	2·75
D84		2f. mauve and red	1·90	3·25
D85		3f. blue and brown	2·00	3·75

D **13** Cross of Agadez

1962.

D123	D **13**	50c. green	10	10
D124		1f. violet	10	10
D125		2f. myrtle	10	10
D126	A	3f. mauve	10	10
D127		5f. green	15	15
D128		10f. orange	15	15
D129	B	15f. blue	15	15
D130		20f. red	20	20
D131		50f. brown	40	40

DESIGNS: A, Cross of Iferouane; B, Cross of Tahoua.

D **450** Cross of Iferouane

1993.

D1263	D **450**	5f. multicoloured	10	10
D1264		10f. orange and black	10	10
D1265	–	15f. multicoloured	10	10
D1266	–	20f. mve, yell & blk	10	10
D1267	–	50f. multicoloured	10	10

DESIGN: 15 to 50f. Cross of Tahoua.

NIGER COAST PROTECTORATE Pt. 1

A district on the west coast of Africa. In 1900 became part of Southern Nigeria.

12 pence = 1 shilling;
20 pence = 1 pound.

1892. Stamps of Gt. Britain (Queen Victoria) optd **BRITISH PROTECTORATE OIL RIVERS**.

1	**71**	½d. red	10·00	7·00
2	**57**	1d. lilac	6·00	7·50
3	**73**	2d. green and red	23·00	8·00
4	**74**	2½d. purple and blue	6·50	2·25
5	**78**	5d. purple and blue	9·00	6·50
6	**82**	1s. green	55·00	75·00

1893. Half of No. 2 surch **½d**.

7	**57**	½d. on half of 1d. lilac	£150	£140

1893. Nos. 1 to 6 surch in words (½d., 1s.) or figures (others).

20	**73**	½d. on 2d. green and red	£325	£225
21	**74**	½d. on 2½d. purple on blue	£300	£180
37	**73**	1s. on 2d. green and red	£425	£350
40		5s. on 2d. green and red	£9000	£10000
41	**78**	10s. on 5d. purple and blue	£6000	£8000
42	**82**	20s. on 1s. green	£70000	

13 **14**

1893. Various frames with "OIL RIVERS" barred out and "NIGER COAST" above.

45	**13**	½d. red	4·00	4·00
46		1d. blue	6·00	3·25
47d		2d. green	19·00	13·00
48		2½d. red	8·50	3·50
49b		5d. lilac	14·00	13·00
50		1s. black	14·00	12·00

1894. Various frames.

66	**14**	½d. green	3·50	1·50
67		1d. red	4·50	1·50
68		2d. red	1·75	1·75
69		2½d. blue	7·50	2·00
55		5d. purple	6·50	5·50
71		6d. brown	7·00	6·50
56a		1s. black	42·00	7·00
73b		2s.6d. brown	22·00	80·00
74b		10s. violet	80·00	£160

1894. Surch with large figures.

58	½ on half 1d. (No. 46)	£750	£300
59	1 on half 2d. (No. 2)	£1500	£325

1894. No. 67 bisected and surch.

64	**14**	½d. on half of 1d. red	£2000	£400

1894. Surch **ONE HALF PENNY** and bars.

65	**14**	½d. on 2½d. blue	£350	£225

NIGERIA Pt. 1

A former British colony on the west coast of Africa, comprising the territories of Northern and Southern Nigeria and Lagos. Attained full independence within the British Commonwealth in 1960 and became a Federal Republic in 1963.

The Eastern Region (known as Biafra (q.v)) seceded in 1967, remaining independent until overrun by Federal Nigerian troops during January 1970.

1914. 12 pence = 1 shilling;
20 shillings = 1 pound.
1973. 100 kobo = 1 naira.

1

1914.

15	**1**	½d. green	1·25	40
16		1d. red	3·25	30
17		1½d. orange	4·25	15
18		2d. grey	1·50	5·00
20		2d. brown	1·25	15
21		2½d. blue	1·00	6·00
5a		3d. purple on yellow	1·50	2·75
22		3d. violet	5·00	3·25
23		3d. blue	6·00	1·50
24		4d. black and red on yellow	65	55
25a		6d. purple	7·00	8·00
26		1s. black on green	1·25	2·00
9		2s.6d. black and red on blue	16·00	6·50
10		5s. green and red on yellow	13·00	50·00
11d		10s. green and red on green	35·00	£100
12		£1 purple and black on red	£170	£200

1935. Silver Jubilee. As T **14a** of Kenya, Uganda and Tanganyika.

30	1½d. blue and grey	80	1·00
31	2d. green and blue	1·50	1·00
32	3d. brown and blue	3·00	13·00
33	1s. grey and purple	3·00	29·00

3 Apapa Wharf **5** Victoria–Buea Road

1936.

34	**3**	½d. green	1·50	1·40
35	–	1d. red	50	40
36	–	1½d. brown	2·00	40
37	–	2d. black	50	80
38	–	3d. blue	2·00	1·50
39	–	4d. brown	2·00	2·00
40	–	6d. violet	50	60
41	–	1s. green	1·75	4·75
42	**5**	2s.6d. black and blue	3·75	23·00
43	–	5s. black and green	7·00	28·00
44	–	10s. black and grey	48·00	70·00
45	–	£1 black and orange	75·00	£150

DESIGNS—VERT: 1d. Cocoa; 1½d. Tin dredger; 2d. Timber industry; 3d. Fishing village; 4d. Cotton ginnery; 6d. Habe minaret; 1s. Fulani cattle. HORIZ: 5s. Oil palms; 10s. River Niger at Jebba; £1 Canoe pulling.

1937. Coronation. As T **14b** of Kenya, Uganda and Tanganyika.

46	1d. red	60	2·50
47	1½d. brown	1·60	2·75
48	3d. blue	1·60	2·75

15 King George VI

1938.

49	**15**	½d. green	10	10
50a		1d. red	75	30
50b		1d. lilac	10	20
51a		1½d. brown	10	10
52		2d. black	10	1·25
52ab		2d. red	10	50
52b		2½d. orange	10	1·00
53		3d. blue	10	10
53b		3d. black	15	75
54		4d. orange	48·00	3·00
54a		4d. blue	15	1·75
55		6d. violet	40	10
56a		1s. olive	30	10
57		1s.3d. blue	90	30
58c	–	2s.6d. black and blue	2·00	4·25
59b	–	5s. black and orange	7·00	3·00

DESIGNS: 2s.6d., 5s. As Nos. 42 and 44 but with portrait of King George VI.

1946. Victory. As T **4a** of Pitcairn Islands.

60	1½d. brown	35	10
61	4d. blue	35	2·00

1948. Royal Silver Wedding. As T **4b/c** of Pitcairn Islands.

62	1d. mauve	35	30
63	5s. orange	5·50	9·50

1949. U.P.U. As T **4d/g** of Pitcairn Islands.

64	1d. purple	15	25
65	3d. blue	1·25	3·00
66	6d. purple	30	3·00
67	1s. olive	50	2·00

1953. Coronation. As T **4h** of Pitcairn Islands.

68	1½d. black and green	40	10

18 Old Manilla Currency

26 Victoria Harbour

29 New and Old Lagos

1953.

69 **18** ½d. black and orange . . 15 30
70 – 1d. black and bronze . . 20 10
71 – 1½d. turquoise 50 40
72 – 2d. black and ochre . . . 4·00 30
72cb – 2d. slate . . . . 3·50 40
73 – 3d. black and purple . . . 55 10
74 – 4d. black and blue . . . 2·50 20
75 – 6d. brown and black . . . 30 10
76 – 1s. black and purple . . . 40 10
77 **26** 2s.6d. black and green . . 6·00 50
78 – 5s. black and red . . . . 3·50 1·40
79 – 10s. black and brown . . 13·00 2·50
80 **29** £1 black and violet . . . 23·00 7·50

DESIGNS—HORIZ (As Type **18**): 1d. Bornu horsemen; 1½d. "Groundnuts"; 2d. "Tin"; 3d. Jebba Bridge and R. Niger; 4d. "Cocoa"; 1s. "Timber". (As Type **26**): 5s. "Palm oil"; 10s. "Hides and skins". VERT (As Type **18**): 6d. Ife bronze.

1956. Royal Visit. No. 72 optd **ROYAL VISIT 1956**.
81 2d. black and ochre 40 30

31 Victoria Harbour

1958. Centenary of Victoria, S. Cameroons.
82 **31** 3d. black and purple 20 30

32 Lugard Hall

1959. Attainment of Self-government. Northern Region of Nigeria.
83 **32** 3d. black and purple 15 10
84 – 1s. black and green 55 60
DESIGN: 1s. Kano Mosque.

35 Legislative Building

1960. Independence Commemoration.
85 **35** 1d. black and red 10 10
86 – 3d. black and blue 15 10
87 – 6d. green and brown . . . 20 20
88 – 1s.3d. blue and yellow . . . 40 20
DESIGNS—As Type **35**: 3d. African paddling canoe; 6d. Federal Supreme Court. LARGER (40 × 24 mm): 1s.3d. Dove, torch and map.

39 Groundnuts **48** Central Bank

1961.

89 **39** ½d. green 10 60
90 – 1d. violet 80 10
91 – 1½d. red . . . . 80 2·00
92 – 2d. blue 30 10
93 – 3d. green 40 10
94 – 4d. blue . . . . 40 1·75
95 – 6d. yellow and black . . . 80 10
96 – 1s. green . . . . 4·50 10
97 – 1s.3d. orange . . . . . . 1·50 10
98 **48** 2s.6d. black and yellow . . 2·75 15
99 – 5s. black and green . . . . 65 1·00
100 – 10s. black and blue . . . . 3·50 4·00
101 – £1 black and red . . . . . 12·00 14·00

DESIGNS—VERT (as Type **39**): 1d. Coal mining; 1½d. Adult education; 2d, Pottery; 3d. Oyo carver; 4d. Weaving; 6d. Benin mask; 1s. Yellow casqued hornbill; 1s.3d. Camel train. HORIZ (as Type **48**: 5s. Nigeria Museum; 10s. Kano airport; £1 Lagos railway station.

52 Globe and Diesel-electric Locomotive

1961. Admission into U.P.U. Inscr as in T **52**.
102 **52** 1d. orange and blue . . . 30 10
103 – 3d. olive and black 30 10
104 – 1s.3d. blue and red 80 20
105 – 2s.6d. green and blue . . . 85 2·00
DESIGNS: 3d. Globe and mail van; 1s.3d. Globe and Bristol 175 Britannia aircraft; 2s.6d. Globe and liner.

56 Coat of Arms **61** "Health"

1961. 1st Anniv of Independence.
106 **56** 3d. multicoloured 10 10
107 – 4d. green and orange . . . 20 10
108 – 6d. green 30 10
109 – 1s.3d. grey and blue . . . 35 10
110 – 2s.6d. green and blue . . . 40 2·00
DESIGNS—HORIZ: 4d. Natural resources map; 6d. Nigerian eagle; 1s 3d. Eagles in flight; 2s.6d. Nigerians and flag.

1962. Lagos Conf of African and Malagasy States.
111 **61** 1d. bistre 10 10
112 – 3d. purple 10 10
113 – 6d. green 15 10
114 – 1s. brown 20 10
115 – 1s.3d. blue 25 20
DESIGNS: Map and emblems symbolising Culture (3d.); Commerce (6d.); Communications (1s.); Co-operation (1s.3d.).

66 Malaria Eradication Emblem and Parasites

1962. Malaria Eradication.
116 **66** 3d. green and red 15 10
117 – 6d. blue and purple 20 10
118 – 1s.3d. mauve and blue . . 20 10
119 – 2s.6d. blue and brown . . 30 90
DESIGNS (embodying emblem): 6d. Insecticide-spraying; 1s.3d. Aerial spraying, 2s.6d. Mother, child and microscope.

70 National Monument

1962. 2nd Anniv of Independence.
120 **70** 3d. green and blue 10 10
121 – 5s. red, green and violet . . 1·00 1·00
DESIGN—VERT: 5s. Benin bronze.

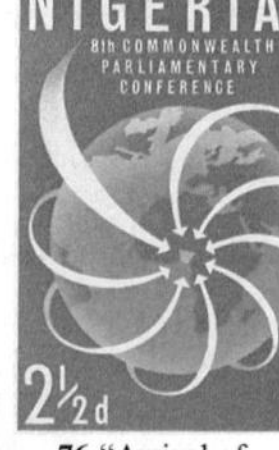

72 Fair Emblem **76** "Arrival of Delegates"

1962. International Trade Fair, Lagos.
122 **72** 1d. red and olive 10 10
123 – 6d. black and red 15 10
124 – 1s. black and brown . . . 15 10
125 – 2s.6d. yellow and blue . . 60 20
DESIGNS—HORIZ: 6d. "Cogwheels of Industry"; 1s. "Cornucopia of Industry"; 2s.6d. Oilwells and tanker.

1962. 8th Commonwealth Parliamentary Conference, Lagos.
126 **76** 2½d. blue . . . . 15 1·10
127 – 4d. blue and rose 15 30
128 – 1s.3d. sepia and yellow . . 20 20
DESIGNS—HORIZ: 4d. National Hall. VERT: 1s.3d. Mace as Palm Tree.

80 Tractor and Maize **81** Mercury Capsule and Kano Tracking Station

1963. Freedom from Hunger.
129 – 3d. olive . . . . 1·00 20
130 **80** 6d. mauve . . . . 1·50 20
DESIGN—VERT: 3d. Herdsman.

1963. "Peaceful Use of Outer Space".
131 **81** 6d. blue and green 25 10
132 – 1s.3d. black and turquoise 35 20
DESIGN: 1s.3d. Satellite and Lagos Harbour.

83 Scouts shaking Hands

1963. 11th World Scout Jamboree. Marathon.
133 **83** 3d. red and bronze 30 20
134 – 1s. black and red 95 80
MS134a 93 × 95 mm. Nos. 133/4 1·75 1·75
DESIGN: 1s. Campfire.

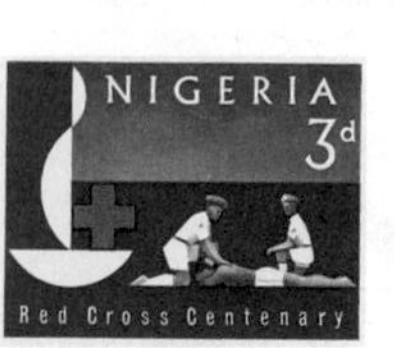

85 Emblem and First Aid Team **88** President Azikiwe and State House

1963. Centenary of Red Cross.
135 **85** 3d. red and blue 40 10
136 – 6d. red and green 60 10
137 – 1s.3d. red and sepia . . . 80 70
MS137a 102 × 102 mm. No. 137 (block of four) . . . . . . 8·50 11·00
DESIGNS: 6d. Emblem and "Hospital Services"; 1s.3d. Patient and emblem.

1963. Republic Day.
138 **88** 3d. olive and green 10 10
139 – 1s.3d. brown and sepia . . 10 10
140 – 2s.6d. turquoise and blue 15 15
The buildings on the 1s.3d. and the 2s.6d. are the Federal Supreme Court and the Parliament Building respectively.

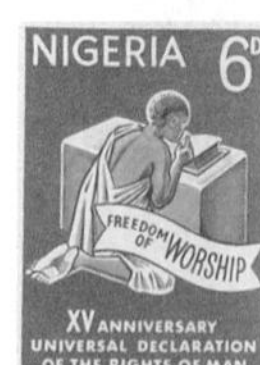

90 "Freedom of worship" **93** Queen Nefertari

1963. 15th Anniv of Declaration of Human Rights.
141 – 3d. red 10 10
142 **90** 6d. green 15 10
143 – 1s.3d. blue 30 10
144 – 2s.6d. purple 45 30
DESIGNS—HORIZ: 3d. (Inscr "1948–1963"), Charter and broken whip. VERT: 1s.3d. "Freedom from Want"; 2s.6d. "Freedom of Speech".

1964. Nubian Monuments Preservation.
145 **93** 6d. olive and green 50 10
146 – 2s.6d. brown, olive & green 1·75 2·25
DESIGN: 2s.6d. Rameses II.

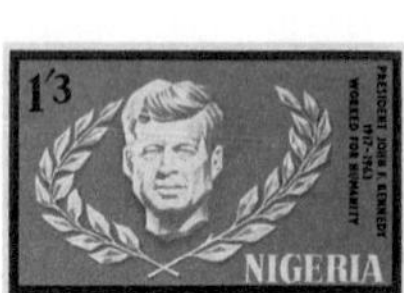

95 President Kennedy **98** President Azikiwe

1964. Pres. Kennedy Memorial Issue.
147 **95** 1s.3d. lilac and black . . . 30 15
148 – 2s.6d. multicoloured . . . 40 65
149 – 5s. multicoloured . . . . . 70 1·75
MS149a 154 × 135 mm. No. 149 (block of four). Imperf . . . . 7·00 12·00
DESIGNS: 2s.6d. Kennedy and flags; 5s. Kennedy (U.S. coin head) and flags.

1964. 1st Anniv of Republic.
150 **98** 3d. brown 10 10
151 – 1s.3d. green 35 10
152 – 2s.6d. green 70 90
DESIGNS—25 × 42 mm: 1s.3d. Herbert Macaulay; 2s.6d. King Jaja of Opobo.

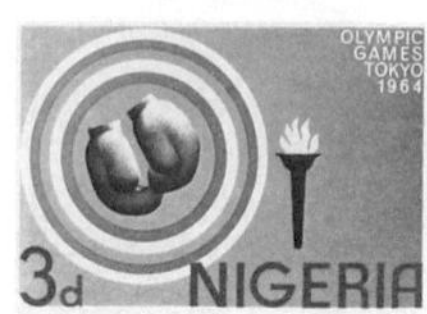

101 Boxing Gloves

1964. Olympic Games, Tokyo.
153 **101** 3d. sepia and green . . . 45 10
154 – 6d. green and blue . . . 60 10
155 – 1s.3d. sepia and olive . . 1·00 15
156 – 2s.6d. sepia and brown . . 1·75 3·75
MS156a 102 × 102 mm. No. 156 (block of four). Imperf . . . . 3·00 4·25
DESIGNS—HORIZ: 6d. High-jumping. VERT: 1s.3d. Running. TRIANGULAR (60 × 30 mm): 2s.6d. Hurdling.

105 Scouts on Hill top **109** "Telstar"

1965. 50th Anniv of Nigerian Scout Movement.
157 **105** 1d. brown 10 10
158 – 3d. red, black and green . . 15 10
159 – 6d. red, sepia and green . . 25 20
160 – 1s.3d. brown, yellow and deep green 40 85
MS160a 76 × 104 mm. No. 160 (block of four). Imperf . . . . 5·00 8·50
DESIGNS: 3d. Scout badge on shield; 6d. Scout badges; 1s.3d. Chief Scout and Nigerian scout.

1965. International Quiet Sun Years.
161 **109** 6d. violet and turquoise . . 15 15
162 – 1s.3d. green and lilac . . 15 15
DESIGN: 1s.3d. Solar satellite.

111 Native Tom-tom and Modern Telephone

1965. Centenary of I.T.U.

163	**111**	3d. black, red and brown	20	10
164	–	1s.3d. black, green & blue	2·00	1·00
165	–	5s. multicoloured	5·00	7·00

DESIGNS—VERT: 1s.3d. Microwave aerial. HORIZ: 5s. Telecommunications satellite and part of globe.

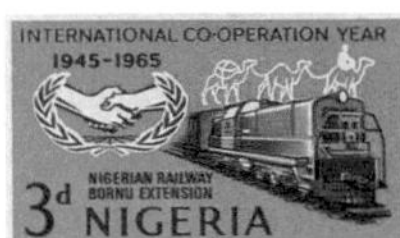

114 I.C.Y. Emblem and Diesel-hydraulic Locomotive

1965. International Co-operation Year.

166	**114**	3d. green, red and orange	3·00	20
167	–	1s. black, blue and lemon	3·00	40
168	–	2s.6d. green, blue & yellow	9·00	7·00

DESIGNS: 1s. Students and Lagos Teaching Hospital; 2s.6d. Kainji (Niger) Dam.

117 Carved Frieze

1965. 2nd Anniv of Republic.

169	**117**	3d. black, red and yellow	10	10
170	–	1s.3d. brown, green & blue	25	10
171	–	5s. brown, sepia and green	60	1·25

DESIGNS—VERT: 1s.3d. Stone Images at Ikom; 5s. Tada bronze.

121 African Elephants

1965.

172	–	½d. multicoloured	1·00	2·75
173	**121**	1d. multicoloured	50	15
174	–	1½d. multicoloured	8·00	8·50
222	–	2d. multicoloured	2·25	90
176	–	3d. multicoloured	1·25	30
177a	–	4d. multicoloured	30	10
225	–	6d. multicoloured	2·25	20
179	–	9d. blue and red	3·00	60
227	–	1s. multicoloured	2·50	20
181	–	1s.3d. multicoloured	8·50	1·50
182	**227**	2s.6d. light brown, buff and brown	75	1·75
183	–	5s. chestnut, yellow and brown	1·75	3·00
184	–	10s. multicoloured	6·50	3·25
185	–	£1 multicoloured	17·00	9·00

DESIGNS—VERT (as T **121**): ½d. Lion and cubs; 6d. Saddle-bill stork. (26½ × 46mm): 10s. Hippopotamus. HORIZ (as T **121**): 1½d. Splendid sunbird; 2d. Village weaver and red-headed malimbe; 3d. Cheetah; 4d. Leopards; 9d. Grey parrots. (46 × 26½ mm): 1s. Blue-breasted kingfishers; 1s.3d. Crowned cranes; 2s.6d. Kobs; 5s. Giraffes; £1 African buffalo.

The 1d., 3d., 4d., 1s., 1s.3d., 2s.6d., 5s. and £1 exist optd **F.G.N.** (Federal Government of Nigeria) twice in black. They were prepared in November 1968 as official stamps, but the scheme was abandoned. Some stamps held at a Head Post Office were sold in error and passed through the post. The Director of Posts then decided to put limited supplies on sale, but they had no postal validity.

1966. Commonwealth Prime Ministers' Meeting, Lagos. Optd **COMMONWEALTH P. M. MEETING 11. JAN. 1966**.

186	**48**	2s.6d. black and yellow	30	30

135 Y.W.C.A. Emblem and H.Q., Lagos

1966. Diamond Jubilee of Nigerian Y.W.C.A.

187	**135**	4d. multicoloured	15	10
188		9d. multicoloured	15	60

137 Telephone Handset and Linesman

1966. 3rd Anniv of Republic.

189	–	4d. green	10	10
190	**137**	1s.6d. black, brown & violet	30	50
191	–	2s.6d. multicoloured	1·00	2·25

DESIGNS—VERT: 4d. Dove and flag. HORIZ: 2s.6d. North Channel Bridge over River Niger, Jebba.

139 "Education, Science and Culture"

1966. 20th Anniv of U.N.E.S.C.O.

192	**139**	4d. black, lake and orange	40	10
193		1s.6d. black, lake & turq	1·75	2·50
194		2s.6d. black, lake and pink	2·75	5·00

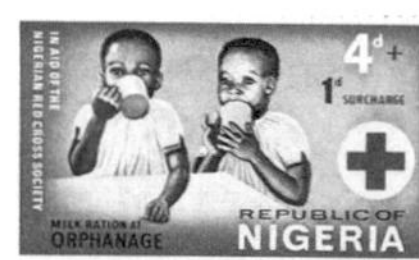

140 Children drinking

1966. Nigerian Red Cross.

195	**140**	4d.+1d. black, vio & red	30	30
196	–	1s.6d.+3d. multicoloured	55	3·75
197	–	2s.6d.+3d. multicoloured	65	4·25

DESIGNS—VERT: 1s.6d. Tending patient. HORIZ: 2s.6d. Tending casualties and badge.

143 Surveying

1967. Int Hydrological Decade. Mult.

198	4d. Type **143**	10	10
199	2s.6d. Water gauge on dam (vert)	25	1·50

145 Globe and Weather Satellite

1967. World Meteorological Day.

200	**145**	4d. mauve and blue	15	10
201	–	1s.6d. black, yellow & blue	65	90

DESIGN: 1s.6d. Passing storm and sun.

147 Eyo Masqueraders

1967. 4th Anniv of Republic. Multicoloured.

202	4d. Type **147**	15	10
203	1s.6d. Crowds watching acrobat	50	1·50
204	2s.6d. Stilt dancer (vert)	75	3·25

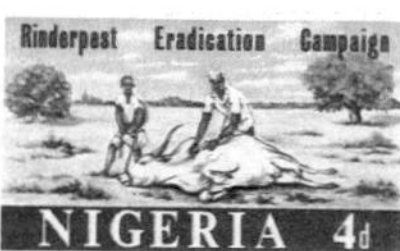

150 Tending Sick Animal

1967. Rinderpest Eradication Campaign.

205	**150**	4d. multicoloured	15	10
206		1s.6d. multicoloured	55	1·50

151 Smallpox Vaccination

1968. 20th Anniv of W.H.O.

207	**151**	4d. mauve and black	15	10
208	–	1s.6d. orange, lemon & blk	55	1·00

DESIGN: 1s.6d. African and mosquito.

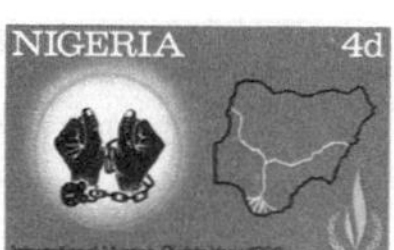

153 Chained Hands and Outline of Nigeria

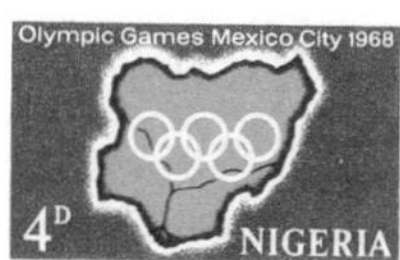

155 Hand grasping at Doves of Freedom

1968. Human Rights Year.

209	**153**	4d. blue, black and yellow	10	10
210	–	1s.6d. green, red and black	20	1·00

DESIGN—VERT: 1s.6d. Nigerian flag and Human Rights emblem.

1968. 5th Anniv of Federal Republic.

211	**155**	4d. multicoloured	10	10
212		1s.6d. multicoloured	20	1·00

156 Map of Nigeria and Olympic Rings

1968. Olympic Games, Mexico.

213	**156**	4d. black, green and red	20	10
214	–	1s.6d. multicoloured	80	30

DESIGN: 1s.6d. Nigerian athletes, flag and Olympic rings.

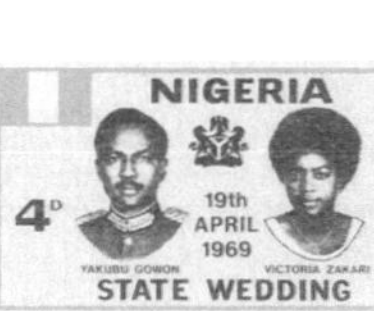

158 G.P.O., Lagos

1969. Inauguration of Philatelic Service.

215	**158**	4d. black and green	10	10
216		1s.6d. black and blue	20	50

159 Yakubu Gowon and Victoria Zakari

160 Bank Emblem and "5th Anniversary"

1969. Wedding of General Gowon.

217	**159**	4d. brown and green	15	10
218		1s.6d. black and green	90	30

1969. 5th Anniv of African Development Bank.

233	**160**	4d. orange, black and blue	10	10
234	–	1s.6d. yellow, black and purple	20	1·25

DESIGN: 1s.6d. Bank emblem and rays.

162 I.L.O. Emblem

1969. 50th Anniv of I.L.O.

235	**162**	4d. black and violet	10	10
236	–	1s.6d. green and black	75	1·50

DESIGN: 1s.6d. World map and I.L.O. emblem.

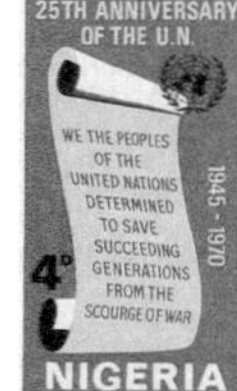

164 Olumo Rock

1969. International Year of African Tourism.

237	**164**	4d. multicoloured	15	10
238	–	1s. black and green	20	10
239	–	1s.6d. multicoloured	1·25	95

DESIGNS—VERT: 1s. Traditional musicians; 1s.6d. Assob Falls.

167 Symbolic Tree

169 Scroll

168 U.P.U. Headquarters Building

1970. "Stamp of Destiny". End of Civil War.

240	**167**	4d. gold, blue and black	10	10
241	–	1s. multicoloured	10	10
242	–	1s.6d. green and black	15	10
243	–	2s. multicoloured	20	20

DESIGNS—VERT: 1s. Symbolic wheel; 1s.6d. United Nigerians supporting map. HORIZ: 2s. Symbolic torch.

1970. New U.P.U. Headquarters Building.

244	**168**	4d. violet and yellow	10	10
245		1s.6d. blue and indigo	40	20

1970. 25th Anniv of United Nations.

246	**169**	4d. brown, buff and black	10	10
247	–	1s.6d. blue, brown & gold	30	20

DESIGN: 1s.6d. U.N. Building.

170 Oil Rig

172 Ibibio Face Mask

171 Children and Globe

1970. 10th Anniv of Independence.

248	2d. Type **170**	25	10
249	4d. University graduate	15	10
250	6d. Durbar horsemen	30	10
251	9d. Servicemen raising flag	40	10
252	1s. Footballer	40	10
253	1s.6d. Parliament building	40	40
254	2s. Kainji Dam	70	90
255	2s.6d. Agricultural produce	70	1·00

1971. Racial Equality Year. Multicoloured.

256	4d. Type **171**	10	10
257	1s. Black and white men uprooting "Racism" (vert)	10	10
258	1s.6d. "The World in Black and White" (vert)	15	75
259	2s. Black and white men united	15	1·50

1971. Antiquities of Nigeria.

260	**172**	4d. black and blue	10	10
261	–	1s.3d. brown and ochre	15	30
262	–	1s.9d. green, brown & yell	20	1·25

DESIGNS: 1s.3d. Benin bronze; 1s.9d. Ife bronze.

173 Children and Symbol

174 Mast and Dish Aerial

1971. 25th Anniv of U.N.I.C.E.F.

263	**173**	4d. multicoloured	10	10
264	–	1s.3d. orange, red & brn	15	40
265	–	1s.9d. turquoise and deep turquoise	15	1·00

DESIGNS: Each with U.N.I.C.E.F. symbol: 1s.3d. Mother and child; 1s.9d. Mother carrying child.

1971. Opening of Nigerian Earth Satellite Station.
266 **174** 4d. multicoloured 15 10
267 – 1s.3d. green, blue & black 25 50
268 – 1s.9d. brown, orange & blk . . . . 25 1·00
269 – 3s. mauve, black and purple . . . . 45 2·00
DESIGNS: Nos. 267/9 as Type **174**, but showing different views of the Satellite Station.

175 Trade Fair Emblem
177 Nok Style Terracotta Head

176 Traffic

1972. All-Africa Trade Fair.
270 **175** 4d. multicoloured 10 10
271 – 1s.3d. lilac, yellow & gold 15 35
272 – 1s.9d. yellow, orange & blk . . . . 15 1·60
DESIGNS—HORIZ: 1s.3d. Map of Africa with pointers to Nairobi. VERT: 1s.9d. Africa on globe.

1972. Change to Driving on the Right.
273 **176** 4d. orange, brown & black 50 10
274 – 1s.3d. multicoloured . . . 1·25 70
275 – 1s.9d. multicoloured . . . 1·25 1·25
276 – 3s. multicoloured . . . . 1·75 3·00
DESIGNS: 1s.3d. Roundabout; 1s.9d. Highway; 3s. Road junction.

1972. All-Nigeria Arts Festival. Multicoloured.
277 4d. Type **177** 10 10
278 1s.3d. Bronze pot from Igbo-Ukwu 25 60
279 1s.9d. Bone harpoon (horiz) 30 1·75

178 Hides and Skins

1973.
290 **178** 1k. multicoloured . . . 10 20
281 – 2k. multicoloured . . . 35 10
292 – 3k. multicoloured . . . 15 10
282a – 5k. multicoloured . . . 50 10
294 – 7k. multicoloured . . . 30 1·25
295 – 8k. multicoloured . . . 40 10
344 – 10k. multicoloured . . . 1·00 20
297 – 12k. black, green and blue . . . . 30 2·75
298 – 15k. multicoloured . . . 30 60
299 – 18k. multicoloured . . . 50 30
300 – 20k. multicoloured . . . 65 30
301 – 25k. multicoloured . . . 85 45
302 – 30k. black, yellow & blue . . . . 40 1·50
303 – 35k. multicoloured . . . 6·00 4·75
288a – 50k. multicoloured . . . 50 90
305 – 1n. multicoloured . . . 50 75
306 – 2n. multicoloured . . . 75 2·00
DESIGNS—HORIZ: 2k. Natural gas tanks; 3k. Cement works; 5k. Cattle-ranching; 7k. Timber mill; 8k. Oil refinery; 10k. Cheetahs, Yankari Game Reserve; 12k. New Civic Building; 15k. Sugar-cane harvesting; 20k. Vaccine production; 25k. Modern wharf; 35k. Textile machinery; 1n. Eko Bridge; 2n. Teaching Hospital, Lagos. VERT: 18k. Palm oil production; 30k. Argungu Fishing Festival; 50k. Pottery.

179 Athlete

1973. 2nd All-African Games, Lagos.
307 **179** 5k. lilac, blue and black 15 10
308 – 12k. multicoloured . . . 20 50
309 – 18k. multicoloured . . . 45 1·00
310 – 25k. multicoloured . . . 50 1·50
DESIGNS—HORIZ: 12k. Football; 18k. Table tennis. VERT: 25k. National stadium.

180 All-Africa House, Addis Ababa

1973. 10th Anniv of O.A.U. Multicoloured.
311 5k. Type **180** 10 10
312 18k. O.A.U. flag (vert) . . . 30 40
313 30k. O.A.U. emblem and symbolic flight of ten stairs (vert) 50 80

181 Dr. Hansen
182 W.M.O. Emblem and Weather-vane

1973. Cent of Discovery of Leprosy Bacillus.
314 **181** 5k.+2k. brown, pink and black 30 85

1973. Centenary of I.M.O./W.M.O.
315 **182** 5k. multicoloured 30 10
316 30k. multicoloured . . . 1·50 2·25

183 University Complex

1973. 25th Anniv of Ibadan University. Multicoloured.
317 5k. Type **183** 10 10
318 12k. Students' population growth (vert) 15 20
319 18k. Tower and students . . 25 35
320 30k. Teaching Hospital . . . 35 65

184 Lagos 1d. Stamp of 1874

1974. Stamp Centenary.
321 – 5k. green, orange & black 15 10
322 – 12k. multicoloured . . . 30 40
323 **184** 18k. green, mauve & black 50 70
324 – 30k. multicoloured . . . 1·50 2·00
DESIGNS: 5k. Graph of mail traffic growth; 12k. Northern Nigeria £25 stamp of 1904; 30k. Forms of mail transport.

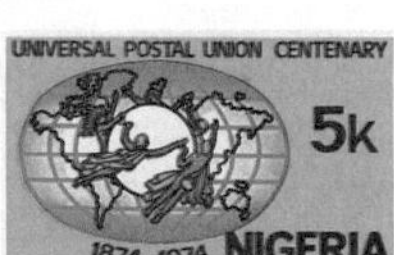

185 U.P.U. Emblem on Globe

1974. Centenary of U.P.U.
325 **185** 5k. blue, orange and black 15 10
326 – 18k. multicoloured . . . 2·00 60
327 – 30k. brown, green & black . . . . 1·75 1·75
DESIGNS: 18k. World transport map; 30k. U.P.U. emblem and letters.

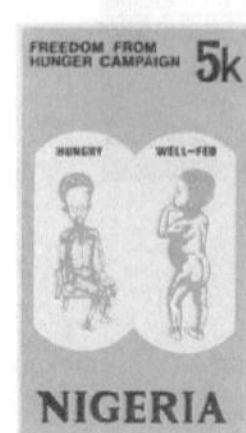

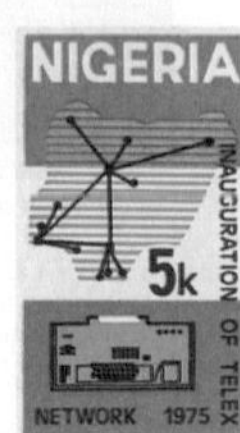

186 Starving and Well-fed Children
187 Telex Network and Teleprinter

1974. Freedom from Hunger Campaign.
328 **186** 5k. green, buff and black 10 10
329 – 12k. multicoloured . . . 30 50
330 – 30k. multicoloured . . . 80 1·75
DESIGNS—HORIZ: 12k. Poultry battery. VERT: 30k. Water-hoist.

1975. Inauguration of Telex Network.
331 **187** 5k. black, orange & green 10 10
332 – 12k. black, yellow & brn 20 20
333 – 18k. multicoloured . . . 30 30
334 – 30k. multicoloured . . . 50 50
DESIGNS: 12, 18, 30k. are as Type **187** but with the motifs arranged differently.

188 Queen Amina of Zaria
190 Alexander Graham Bell

1975. International Women's Year.
335 **188** 5k. green, yellow and blue 35 10
336 18k. purple, blue & mauve . . . . 1·00 80
337 30k. multicoloured . . . 1·25 1·60

1976. Centenary of Telephone.
355 **190** 5k. multicoloured 10 10
356 – 18k. multicoloured . . . 40 55
357 – 25k. blue, light blue and brown . . . . 70 1·00
DESIGNS—HORIZ: 18k. Gong and modern telephone system. VERT: 25k. Telephones, 1876 and 1976.

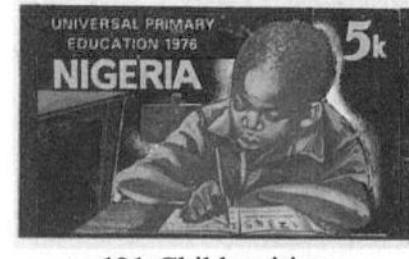

191 Child writing

1976. Launching of Universal Primary Education.
358 **191** 5k. yellow, violet & mauve 10 10
359 – 18k. multicoloured . . . 45 60
360 – 25k. multicoloured . . . 70 1·00
DESIGNS—VERT: 18k. Children entering school; 25k. Children in class.

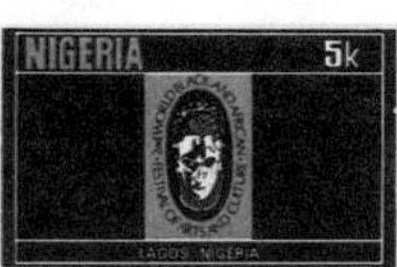

192 Festival Emblem

1976. 2nd World Black and African Festival of Arts and Culture, Nigeria.
361 **192** 5k. gold and brown . . . 35 10
362 – 10k. brown, yellow & blk 35 55
363 – 12k. multicoloured . . . 80 90
364 – 18k. yellow, brown & blk 90 90
365 – 30k. red and black . . . 1·00 1·50
DESIGNS: 10k. National Arts Theatre; 12k. African hair-styles; 18k. Musical instruments; 30k. "Nigerian arts and crafts".

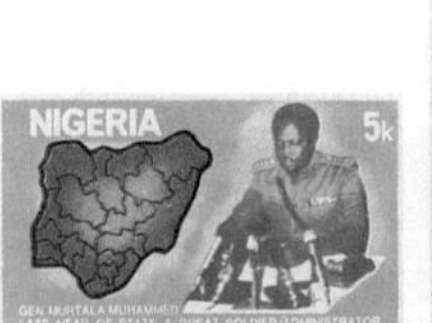

193 General Murtala Muhammed and Map of Nigeria
194 Scouts saluting

1977. 1st Death Anniv of General Muhammed (Head of State). Multicoloured.
366 5k. Type **193** 10 10
367 18k. General in dress uniform (vert) 20 35
368 30k. General in battle dress (vert) 30 70

1977. 1st All-African Scout Jamboree, Jos, Nigeria. Multicoloured.
369 5k. Type **194** 15 10
370 18k. Scouts cleaning street (horiz) 60 70
371 25k. Scouts working on farm (horiz) . . . . 70 1·25
372 30k. Jamboree emblem and map of Africa (horiz) . . . 80 2·00

195 Trade Fair Complex

1977. 1st Lagos Int Trade Fair.
373 **195** 5k. black, blue and green 10 10
374 – 18k. black, blue and purple 20 25
375 – 30k. multicoloured . . . 30 45
DESIGNS: 18k. Globe and Trade Fair emblem; 30k. Weaving and basketry.

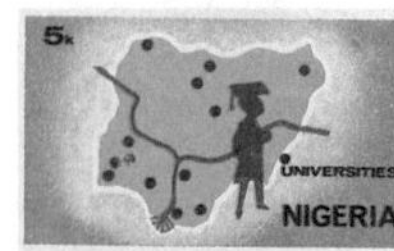

196 Map showing Nigerian Universities

1978. Global Conference on Technical Co-operation between Developing Countries, Buenos Aires.
376 **196** 5k. multicoloured 10 10
377 – 12k. multicoloured . . . 15 15
378 – 18k. multicoloured . . . 25 25
379 – 30k. yellow, violet & black 45 60
DESIGNS: 12k. Map of West African highways and telecommunications; 18k. Technologists undergoing training; 30k. World map.

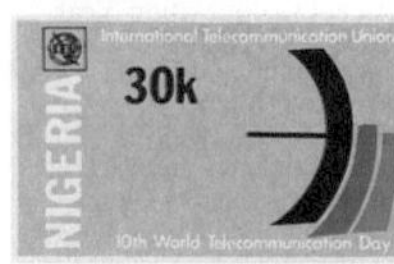

197 Microwave Antenna

1978. 10th World Telecommunications Day.
380 **197** 30k. multicoloured . . . 50 60

198 Students on "Operation Feed the Nation"

1978. "Operation Feed the Nation" Campaign. Multicoloured.
381 5k. Type **198** 10 10
382 18k. Family backyard farm 20 20
383 30k. Plantain farm (vert) . . 35 60

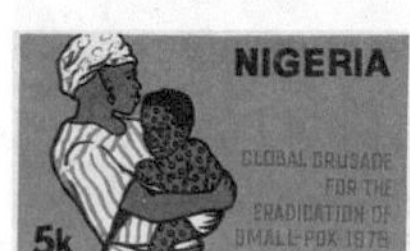

199 Mother with Infected Child

1978. Global Eradication of Smallpox.
384 **199** 5k. black, brown and lilac 15 10
385 – 12k. multicoloured . . . 25 40
386 – 18k. black, brown & yell 40 55
387 – 30k. black, silver and pink 55 1·10
DESIGNS—HORIZ: 12k. Doctor and infected child; 18k. Group of children being vaccinated. VERT: 30k. Syringe.

200 Nok Terracotta Human Figure, Bwari (900 B.C.–100 A.D.)
201 Anti-Apartheid Emblem

1978. Antiquities.
388 **200** 5k. black, blue and red 10 10
389 – 12k. multicoloured . . . 15 10
390 18k. black, blue and red 20 15
391 – 30k. multicoloured . . . 25 20
DESIGNS—HORIZ: 12k. Igbo-Ukwu bronze snail shell, Igbo Isaiah (9th-century A.D.). VERT: 18k. Ife bronze statue of a king (12th–15th century A.D.); 30k. Benin bronze equestrian figure (about 1700 A.D.).

1978. International Anti-Apartheid Year.
392 **201** 18k. black, yellow and red 15 15

202 Wright Brothers and Wright Type A

1978. 75th Anniv of Powered Flight.
393 **202** 5k. multicoloured 20 10
394 – 18k. black, blue and light blue 60 20
DESIGN: 18k. Nigerian Air Force formation.

203 Murtala Muhammed Airport

1979. Opening of Murtala Muhammed Airport.
395 **203** 5k. black, grey and blue 40 30

204 Child with Stamp Album

1979. 10th Anniv of National Philatelic Service.
396 **204** 5k. multicoloured 10 20

205 Mother and Child

1979. International Year of the Child. Multicoloured.
397 5k. Type **205** 10 10
398 18k. Children studying . . . 35 30
399 25k. Children playing (vert) 40 50

206 Trainee Teacher making Audio Visual Aid Materials
207 Necom House

1979. 50th Anniv of International Bureau of Education. Multicoloured.
400 10k. Type **206** 10 10
401 30k. Adult education class . . 25 30

1979. 50th Anniv of Consultative Committee of International Radio.
402 **207** 10k. multicoloured . . . 15 20

208 Trainees of the Regional Air Survey School, Ile-Ife

1979. 21st Anniv of Economic Commission for Africa.
403 **208** 10k. multicoloured . . . 20 20

209 Football Cup and Map of Nigeria

1980. African Cup of Nations Football Competition, Nigeria. Multicoloured.
404 10k. Type **209** 20 10
405 30k. Footballer (vert) 60 50

210 Wrestling

1980. Olympic Games, Moscow.
406 **210** 10k. multicoloured . . . 10 10
407 – 20k. black and green . . 10 10
408 – 30k. black, orange & blue 15 15
409 – 45k. multicoloured . . . 20 20
DESIGNS—VERT: 20k. Long jump; 45k. Netball. HORIZ: 30k. Swimming.

211 Figures supporting O.P.E.C. Emblem

1980. 20th Anniv of O.P.E.C. (Organization of Petroleum Exporting Countries).
410 **211** 10k. black, blue and yellow 15 10
411 – 45k. black, blue and mauve 70 60
DESIGN—VERT: 45k. O.P.E.C. emblem and globe.

212 Tank Locomotive No. 2, Wushishi Tramway

1980. 25th Anniv of Nigerian Railway Corporation. Multicoloured.
412 10k. Type **212** 75 10
413 20k. Loading goods train . . 1·00 85
414 30k. Freight train . . . . . 1·40 1·25

213 Metric Scales
215 Disabled Woman sweeping

214 "Communication" Symbols and Map of West Africa

1980. World Standards Day.
415 **213** 10k. red and black . . . 10 10
416 – 30k. multicoloured . . . 35 40
DESIGN—HORIZ: 30k. Quality control.

1980. 5th Anniv of Economic Community of West African States.
417 **214** 10k. black, orange & olive 10 10
418 – 25k. black, green and red 30 10
419 – 30k. black, yellow & brn 20 15
420 – 45k. black, turquoise & bl 25 25
DESIGNS: 25k. "Transport"; 30k. "Agriculture"; 45k. "Industry".

1981. International Year for Disabled Persons.
421 **215** 10k. multicoloured . . . 20 10
422 – 30k. black, brown and blue 65 65
DESIGN: 30k. Disabled man filming.

216 President launching "Green Revolution" (food production campaign)

1981. World Food Day.
423 **216** 10k. multicoloured . . . 10 10
424 – 25k. black, yellow & green 20 50
425 – 30k. multicoloured . . . 25 55
426 – 45k. black, brown & yell 45 85
DESIGNS—VERT: 25k. Food crops; 30k. Harvesting tomatoes. HORIZ: 45k. Pig farming.

217 Rioting in Soweto

1981. Anti-Apartheid Movement.
427 **217** 30k. multicoloured . . . 35 55
428 – 45k. black, red and green 50 1·25
DESIGN—VERT: 45k. "Police brutality".

218 "Preservation of Wildlife"

1982. 75th Anniv of Boy Scout Movement. Multicoloured.
429 30k. Type **218** 50 55
430 45k. Lord Baden-Powell taking salute 75 95

219 Early Inoculation

1982. Centenary of Robert Koch's Discovery of Tubercle Bacillus.
431 **219** 10k. multicoloured . . . 20 15
432 – 30k. black, brown and green 50 65
433 – 45k. black, brown and green . . . . 80 1·40
DESIGNS—HORIZ: 30k. Technician and microscope. VERT: 45k. Patient being X-rayed.

220 "Keep Your Environment Clean"

1982. 10th Anniv of U.N. Conference on Human Environment.
434 **220** 10k. multicoloured . . . 10 10
435 – 20k. orange, grey and black 20 40
436 – 30k. multicoloured . . . 35 60
437 – 45k. multicoloured . . . 55 85
DESIGNS: 20k. "Check air pollution"; 30k. "Preserve natural environment"; 45k. "Reafforestation concerns all".

221 "Salamis parhassus"
222 Carving of "Male and Female Twins"

1982. Nigerian Butterflies. Multicoloured.
438 10k. Type **221** 15 10
439 20k. "Iterus zalmoxis" . . . 30 30
440 30k. "Cymothoe beckeri" . . 40 40
441 45k. "Papilio hesperus" . . . 70 70

1982. 25th Anniv of National Museum. Multicoloured.
442 10k. Type **222** 10 10
443 20k. Royal bronze leopard (horiz) 20 35
444 30k. Soapstone seated figure 35 90
445 45k. Wooden helmet mask 50 1·75

223 Three Generations

1983. Family Day. Multicoloured.
446 10k. Type **223** 15 10
447 30k. Parents with three children (vert) 50 65

224 Satellite View of Globe

1983. Commonwealth Day.
448 **224** 10k. brown and black . . 10 10
449 – 25k. multicoloured . . . 20 30
450 – 30k. black, purple and grey 55 35
451 – 45k. multicoloured . . . 35 45
DESIGNS—HORIZ: 25k. National Assembly Buildings. VERT: 30k. Drilling for oil; 45k. Athletics.

225 Corps Members on Building Project
226 Postman on Bicycle

1983. 10th Anniv of National Youth Service Corps. Multicoloured.
452 10k. Type **225** 15 10
453 25k. On the assault-course (vert) 30 30
454 30k. Corps members on parade 40 40

1983. World Communications Year. Multicoloured.
455 10k. Type **226** 15 10
456 25k. Newspaper kiosk (horiz) 30 45
457 30k. Town crier blowing elephant tusk (horiz) . . . 35 80
458 45k. T.V. newsreader (horiz) 45 1·10

227 Pink Shrimp

1983. World Fishery Resources.
459 **227** 10k. red, blue and black 15 10
460 – 25k. multicoloured . . . 30 40
461 – 30k. multicoloured . . . 30 45
462 – 45k. multicoloured . . . 40 70
DESIGNS: 25k. Long-necked croaker; 30k. Barracuda; 45k. Fishing techniques.

228 On Parade
229 Crippled Child

1983. Centenary of Boys' Brigade and 75th Anniv of Founding in Nigeria. Multicoloured.
463 10k. Type **228** 40 10
464 30k. Members working on cassava plantation (horiz) 1·50 1·50
465 45k. Skill training (horiz) . . 2·25 2·75

1984. Stop Polio Campaign.
466 **229** 10k. blue, black and brown 20 15
467 – 25k. orange, black & yell 40 75
468 – 30k. red, black and brown 60 1·10
DESIGNS—HORIZ: 25k. Child receiving vaccine. VERT: 30k. Healthy child.

230 Waterbuck
232 Boxing

231 Obverse and Reverse of 1969 £1 Note

1984. Nigerian Wildlife.
469 **230** 10k. green, brown & black 15 10
470 – 25k. multicoloured . . . 30 50
471 – 30k. brown, black & green 40 90
472 – 45k. blue, orange & black 45 1·50
DESIGNS—HORIZ: 25k. Hartebeest; 30k. African buffalo. VERT: 45k. Diademed monkey.

1984. 25th Anniv of Nigerian Central Bank.
473 **231** 10k. multicoloured . . . 20 10
474 – 25k. brown, black & green 45 60
475 – 30k. red, black and green 55 75

DESIGNS: 25k. Central Bank; 30k. Obverse and reverse of 1959 £5 note.

1984. Olympic Games, Los Angeles. Mult.
476 10k. Type **232** 15 10
477 25k. Discus-throwing 35 50
478 30k. Weightlifting 40 60
479 45k. Cycling 60 90

233 Irrigation Project, Lesotho **234** Pin-tailed Whydah

1984. 20th Anniv of African Development Bank.
480 **233** 10k. multicoloured . . . 15 10
481 – 25k. multicoloured . . . 30 50
482 – 30k. black, yellow and blue 35 60
483 – 45k. black, brown and blue . . . . 1·75 90
DESIGNS—HORIZ: 25k. Bomi Hills Road, Liberia; 30k. School building project, Seychelles; 45k. Coal mining, Niger.

1984. Rare Birds. Multicoloured.
484 10k. Type **234** 75 20
485 25k. Spur-winged plover . . 1·50 70
486 30k. Red bishop . . . . . . 1·50 1·75
487 45k. Double-spurred francolin 1·75 2·50

235 Boeing 747 Airliner taking-off

1984. 40th Anniv of International Civil Aviation Organization. Multicoloured.
488 10k. Type **235** 40 10
489 45k. Boeing 707 airliner circling globe . . . . . . 1·50 2·25

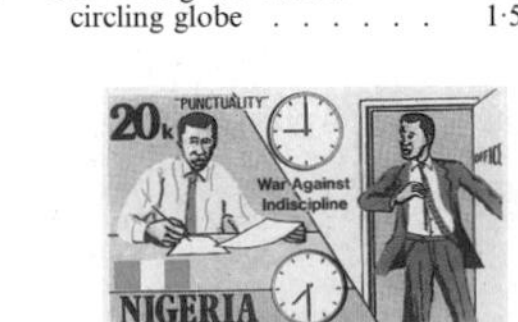

236 Office Workers and Clocks ("Punctuality")

1985. "War against Indiscipline". Mult.
490 20k. Type **236** 30 35
491 50k. Cross over hands passing banknotes ("Discourage Bribery") . . 55 75

237 Footballers receiving Flag from Major-General Buhari **239** Globe and O.P.E.C. Emblem

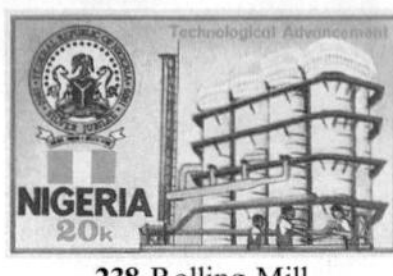

238 Rolling Mill

1985. International Youth Year. Mult.
492 20k. Type **237** 30 20
493 50k. Girls of different tribes with flag (vert) 55 70
494 55k. Members of youth organizations with flags (vert) 55 80

1985. 25th Anniv of Independence. Mult.
495 20k. Type **238** 25 10
496 50k. Map of Nigeria 40 45
497 55k. Remembrance Arcade . . 40 50
498 60k. Eleme, first Nigerian oil refinery . . . . 1·00 1·25
MS499 101 × 101 mm. Nos. 495/8 5·00 6·50

1985. 25th Anniv of Organization of Petroleum Exporting Countries.
500 **239** 20k. blue and red 75 35
501 – 50k. black and blue . . . 1·50 75
DESIGN—HORIZ: 50k. World map and O.P.E.C. emblem.

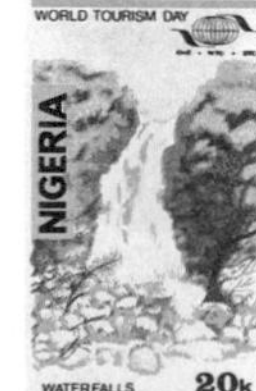

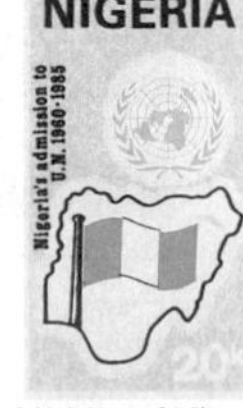

240 Waterfall **241** Map of Nigeria and National Flag

1985. World Tourism Day. Multicoloured.
502 20k. Type **240** 35 10
503 50k. Pottery, carved heads and map of Nigeria (horiz) 45 50
504 55k. Calabash carvings and Nigerian flag 45 50
505 60k. Leather work 45 55

1985. 40th Anniv of United Nations Organization and 25th Anniv of Nigerian Membership.
506 **241** 20k. black, green and blue 20 10
507 – 50k. black, blue and red 35 75
508 – 55k. black, blue and red 35 85
DESIGNS—HORIZ: 50k. United Nations Building, New York; 55k. United Nations logo.

242 Rock Python **243** Social Worker with Children

1986. African Reptiles.
509 **242** 10k. multicoloured . . . 30 10
510 – 20k. black, brown and blue 50 90
511 – 25k. multicoloured . . . 50 1·00
512 – 30k. multicoloured . . . 50 1·00
DESIGNS: 20k. Long snouted crocodile; 25k. Gopher tortoise; 30k. Chameleon.

1986. Nigerian Life. Multicoloured.
513 1k. Type **243** 10 10
514 2k. Volkswagen motor assembly line (horiz) . . 10 10
515 5k. Modern housing estate (horiz) 10 10
516 10k. Harvesting oil palm fruit 10 10
517 15k. Unloading freighter (horiz) 15 10
518 20k. "Tecoma stans" (flower) 15 10
519 25k. Hospital ward (horiz) 15 10
519a 30k. Birom dancers (horiz) 15 10
520 35k. Telephonists operating switchboard (horiz) . . . 15 10
521 40k. Nkpokiti dancers . . 15 10
522 45k. Hibiscus (horiz) . . . 15 10
523a 50k. Post Office counter (horiz) 15 10
524 1n. Stone quarry (horiz) 15 15
525a 2n. Students in laboratory (horiz) 15 15
525ba 10n. Lekki Beach (horiz) 20 15
525c 20n. Ancient wall, Kano (horiz) . . . . 4·50 1·75
525d 50n. Rock bridge (horiz) 4·00 3·50
525e 100n. Ekpe masquerader 2·50 3·25
525f 500n. National Theatre (horiz) . . . . 8·00 8·50

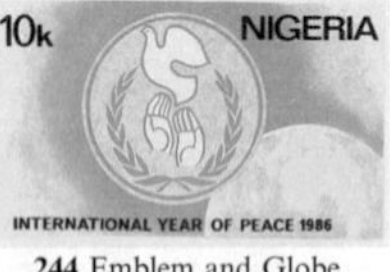

244 Emblem and Globe

1986. International Peace Year. Mult.
526 10k. Type **244** 20 10
527 20k. Hands of five races holding globe . . . . . . 60 1·50

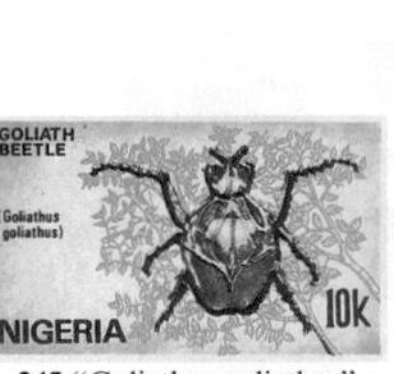

245 "Goliathus goliathus" (beetle) **246** Oral Rehydration Therapy

1986. Nigerian Insects. Multicoloured.
528 10k. Type **245** 30 10
529 20k. "Vespa vulgaris" (wasp) 40 40
530 25k. "Acheta domestica" (cricket) 45 90
531 30k. "Anthrenus verbasci" (beetle) . . . . 55 1·50
MS532 119 × 101 mm. Nos. 528/31 4·50 6·50

1986. 40th Anniv of U.N.I.C.E.F.
533 **246** 10k. multicoloured . . . 30 10
534 – 20k. black, brown & yell 40 40
535 – 25k. multicoloured . . . 45 70
536 – 30k. multicoloured . . . 55 1·00
DESIGNS: 20k. Immunization; 25k. Breast-feeding; 30k. Mother and child.

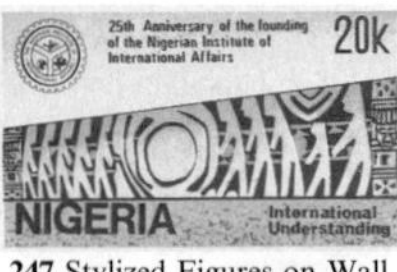

247 Stylized Figures on Wall ("International Understanding")

1986. 25th Anniv of Nigerian Institute of International Affairs.
537 **247** 20k. black, blue and green 50 50
538 – 30k. multicoloured . . . 75 1·25
DESIGN—VERT: 30k. "Knowledge" (bronze sculpture).

248 Freshwater Clam

1987. Shells.
539 **248** 10k. multicoloured . . . 65 10
540 – 20k. black, brown and pink . . . . 1·00 1·75
541 – 25k. multicoloured . . . 1·00 2·00
542 – 30k. multicoloured . . . 1·25 2·50
DESIGNS: 20k. Periwinkle; 25k. Bloody cockle (inscr "BLOODY COCKLE"); 30k. Mangrove oyster.

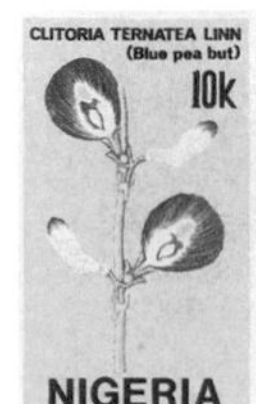

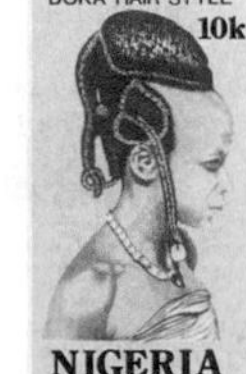

249 "Clitoria ternatea" **250** Doka Hairstyle

1987. Nigerian Flowers.
543 **249** 10k. multicoloured . . . 10 10
544 – 20k. brown, yellow and green 15 25
545 – 25k. multicoloured . . . 15 45
546 – 30k. multicoloured . . . 20 1·00
DESIGNS: 20k. "Hibiscus tiliaceus"; 25k. "Acanthus montanus"; 30k. "Combretum racemosum".

1987. Women's Hairstyles.
547 **250** 10k. black, brown and grey 10 10
548 – 20k. multicoloured . . . 15 25
549 – 25k. black, brown and red 20 55
550 – 30k. multicoloured . . . 20 1·00
DESIGNS: 20k. Eting; 25k. Agogo; 30k. Goto.

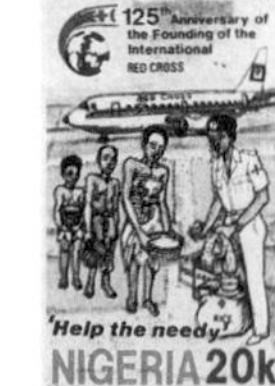

251 Family sheltering under Tree **252** Red Cross Worker distributing Food

1987. International Year of Shelter for the Homeless. Multicoloured.
551 20k. Type **251** 15 15
552 30k. Family and modern house 15 90

1988. 125th Anniv of International Red Cross. Multicoloured.
553 20k. Type **252** 65 30
554 30k. Carrying patient to ambulance . . . . 65 1·75

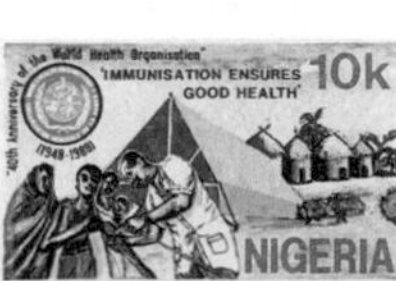

253 Doctor vaccinating Baby **254** O.A.U. Logo

1988. 40th Anniv of W.H.O. Multicoloured.
555 10k. Type **253** 25 10
556 20k. W.H.O. logo and outline map of Nigeria 60 60
557 30k. Doctor and patients at mobile clinic 60 60

1988. 25th Anniv of Organization of African Unity.
558 **254** 10k. brown, green & orge 15 15
559 – 20k. multicoloured . . . 15 15
DESIGN: 20k. Four Africans supporting map of Africa.

255 Pink Shrimp

1988. Shrimps.
560 **255** 10k. multicoloured . . . 20 10
561 – 20k. black and green . . 25 15
562 – 25k. black, red and brown 25 25
563 – 30k. orange, brown & blk 30 60
MS564 120 × 101 mm. Nos. 560/3 1·50 2·00
DESIGNS: 20k. Tiger shrimp; 25k. Deepwater roseshrimp; 30k. Estuarine prawn.

256 Weightlifting

1988. Olympic Games, Seoul. Multicoloured.
565 10k. Type **256** 25 10
566 20k. Boxing 35 35
567 30k. Athletics (vert) 50 65

257 Banknote Production Line ($\frac{1}{2}$-size illustration)

1988. 25th Anniv of Nigerian Security Printing and Minting Co. Ltd.
568 **257** 10k. multicoloured . . . 10 10
569 – 20k. black, silver and green 20 20
570 – 25k. multicoloured . . . 30 30
571 – 30k. multicoloured . . . 50 50
DESIGNS—HORIZ (As T **257**): 20k. Coin production line. VERT (37 × 44 mm): 25k. Montage of products; 30k. Anniversary logos.

258 Tambari

1989. Nigerian Musical Instruments.
572 **258** 10k. multicoloured . . . 10 10
573 – 20k. multicoloured . . . 20 20
574 – 25k. brown, green & black 30 30
575 – 30k. brown and black . . 50 50
DESIGNS: 20k. Kundung; 25k. Ibid; 30k. Dundun.

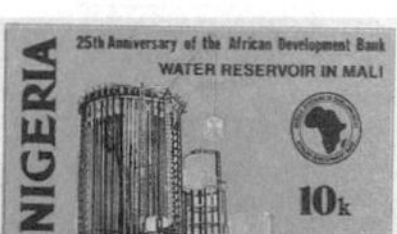

259 Construction of Water Towers, Mali

1989. 25th Anniv of African Development Bank. Multicoloured.
576 10k. Type **259** 10 10
577 20k. Paddy field, Gambia . . 15 15
578 25k. Bank Headquarters, Abidjan, Ivory Coast . . . 25 25
579 30k. Anniversary logo (vert) 35 35

260 Lighting Campfire

1989. 70th Anniv of Nigerian Girl Guides Association. Multicoloured.
580 10k. Type **260** 30 10
581 20k. Guide on rope bridge (vert) 70 60

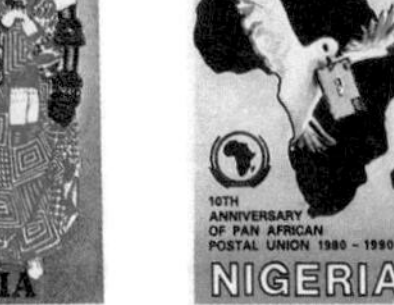

261 Etubom Costume **262** Dove with Letter and Map of Africa

1989. Traditional Costumes. Multicoloured.
582 10k. Type **261** 30 10
583 20k. Fulfulde 35 25
584 25k. Aso-Ofi 40 75
585 30k. Fuska Kura . . . . . . 50 1·50

1990. 10th Anniv of Pan African Postal Union. Multicoloured.
586 10k. Type **262** 25 10
587 20k. Parcel and map of Africa 50 50

263 Oil Lamps

1990. Nigerian Pottery.
588 **263** 10k. black, brown & violet 10 10
589 – 20k. black, brown & violet 20 20
590 – 25k. brown and violet . . 25 25
591 – 30k. multicoloured . . . 35 35
MS592 120 × 100 mm. Nos. 588/91 80 90
DESIGNS: 20k. Water pots; 25k. Musical pots; 50k. Water jugs.

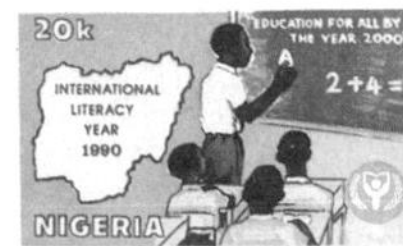

264 Teacher and Class

1990. International Literacy Year.
593 **264** 20k. multicoloured . . . 20 10
594 – 30k. brown, blue & yellow 30 30
DESIGN: 30k. Globe and book.

265 Globe and OPEC Logo

1990. 30th Anniv of the Organization of Petroleum Exporting Countries. Multicoloured.
595 10k. Type **265** 10 10
596 20k. Logo and flags of member countries (vert) . . 20 20
597 25k. World map and logo . . 25 25
598 30k. Logo within inscription "Co-operation for Global Energy Security" (vert) . . 35 35

266 Grey Parrot **267** Eradication Treatment

1990. Wildlife. Multicoloured.
599 20k. Type **266** 20 10
600 30k. Roan antelope 20 10
601 1n.50 Grey-necked bald crow ("Rockfowl") 60 80
602 2n.50 Mountain gorilla . . . 85 1·25
MS603 118 × 119 mm. Nos. 599/602 1·75 2·25

1991. National Guineaworm Eradication Day. Multicoloured.
604 10k. Type **267** 15 10
605 20k. Women collecting water from river (horiz) 25 25
606 30k. Boiling pot of water . . 25 25

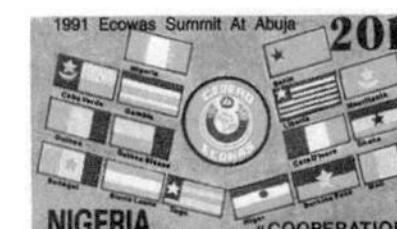

268 Hand holding Torch (Progress) **269** National Flags

1991. Organization of African Unity Heads of State and Governments Meeting, Abuja. Each showing outline map of Africa. Multicoloured.
607 20k. Type **268** 15 10
608 30k. Cogwheel (Unity) . . . 20 25
609 50k. O.A.U. flag (Freedom) 20 45

1991. Economic Community of West African States Summit Meeting, Abuja. Multicoloured.
610 20k. Type **269** 15 10
611 50k. Map showing member states 30 45

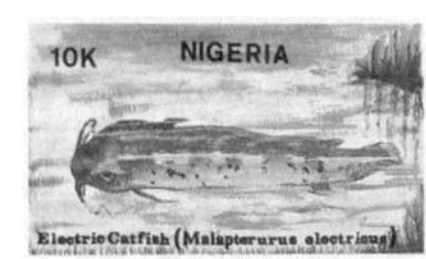

270 Electric Catfish

1991. Nigerian Fishes. Multicoloured.
612 10k. Type **270** 15 10
613 20k. Nile perch 25 25
614 30k. Nile mouthbrooder ("Talapia") 35 35
615 50k. Sharp-toothed catfish . . 50 55
MS616 121 × 104 mm. Nos. 612/15 2·00 2·50

271 Telecom '91 Emblem

1991. "Telecom '91" 6th World Telecommunication Exhibition, Geneva.
617 **271** 20k. black, green and violet 30 10
618 – 50k. multicoloured . . . 40 30
DESIGN—VERT: 50k. Emblem and patchwork.

272 Boxing

1992. Olympic Games, Barcelona (1st issue). Multicoloured.
619 50k. Type **272** 15 15
620 1n. Nigerian athlete winning race 25 25
621 1n.50 Table tennis 35 35
622 2n. Taekwondo 45 45
MS623 120 × 117 mm. Nos. 619/22 1·75 2·00
See also No. 624.

273 Football **274** Blood Pressure Gauge

1992. Olympic Games, Barcelona (2nd issue).
624 **273** 1n.50 multicoloured . . . 50 50

1992. World Health Day. Multicoloured.
625 50k. Type **274** 15 15
626 1n. World Health Day '92 emblem 20 20
627 1n.50 Heart and lungs . . . 30 30
628 2n. Interior of heart 45 45
MS629 123 × 111 mm. Nos. 625/8 1·10 1·25

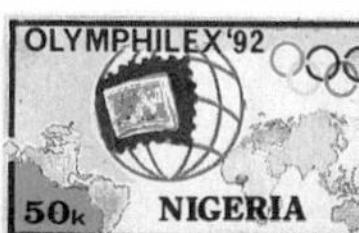

275 Map of World and Stamp on Globe

1992. "Olymphilex '92" Olympic Stamp Exhibition, Barcelona. Multicoloured.
630 50k. Type **275** 20 10
631 1n.50 Examining stamps . . 40 40
MS632 120 × 109 mm. Nos. 630/1 1·60 1·75

276 Gathering Plantain Fruit **277** Centre Emblem

1992. 25th Anniv of International Institute of Tropical Agriculture.
633 **276** 50k. multicoloured . . . 10 10
634 – 1n. multicoloured 15 15
635 – 1n.50 black, brown & grn 20 20
636 – 2n. multicoloured 25 25
MS637 121 × 118 mm. Nos. 633/6 1·25 1·50
DESIGNS—VERT: 1n.50, Harvesting cassava tubers; 2n. Stacking yams. HORIZ: 1n. Tropical foods.

1992. Commissioning of Maryam Babangida National Centre for Women's Development.
638 **277** 50k. gold, emerald and green 10 10
639 – 1n. multicoloured 15 15
640 – 1n.50 multicoloured . . . 20 20
641 – 2n. multicoloured 30 30
DESIGNS—VERT: 1n. Women working in fields; 2n. Woman at loom. HORIZ: 1n.50, Maryam Babangida National Centre.
All examples of No. 641 are without a "NIGERIA" inscription.

278 Healthy Food and Emblem **279** Sabada Dance

1992. International Conference on Nutrition, Rome. Multicoloured.
642 50k. Type **278** 10 10
643 1n. Child eating 15 15
644 1n.50 Fruit (vert) 20 20
645 2n. Vegetables 25 25
MS646 120 × 100 mm. Nos. 642/5 1·50 1·75

1992. Traditional Dances. Multicoloured.
647 50k. Type **279** 10 10
648 1n. Sato 15 15
649 1n.50 Asian Ubo Ikpa . . . 20 20
650 2n. Dundun 25 25
MS651 126 × 107 mm. Nos. 647/50 1·50 1·75

280 African Elephant

1993. Wildlife. Multicoloured.
652 1n.50 Type **280** . . . . . . 1·25 30
653 5n. Stanley crane (vert) . . . 1·50 40
654 20n. Roan antelope . . . . . 2·25 1·25
655 30n. Lion . . . . 2·50 1·50

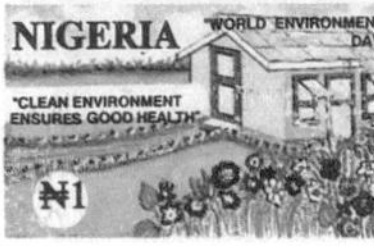

281 Suburban Garden

1993. World Environment Day. Multicoloured.
656 1n. Type **281** 10 10
657 1n.50 Water pollution 15 10
658 5n. Forest road 50 60
659 10n. Rural house . . . . . . 90 1·25

282 Oni Figure **283** "Bulbophyllum distans"

1993. 50th Anniv of National Museums and Monuments Commission. Multicoloured.
660 1n. Type **282** 10 10
661 1n.50 Bronze head of Queen Mother 10 10
662 5n. Bronze pendant (horiz) 30 50
663 10n. Nok head . . . . 70 1·00

1993. Orchids. Multicoloured.
664 1n. Type **283** 10 10
665 1n.50 "Eulophia cristata" . . 15 10
666 5n. "Eulophia horsfallii" . . . 45 55
667 10n. "Eulophia quartiniana" 1·00 1·25
MS668 103 × 121 mm. Nos. 664/7 1·75 2·00

284 Children in Classroom and Adults carrying Food

1994. International Year of the Family. Mult.
669 1n.50 Type **284** 10 10
670 10n. Market . . . . 1·00 1·50

285 Hand with Tweezers holding 1969 4d. Philatelic Service Stamp

1994. 25th Anniv of Nat Philatelic Service. Mult.
671 1n. Type **285** 10 10
672 1n.50 Philatelic Bureau . . . 15 10
673 5n. Stamps forming map of Nigeria 45 60
674 10n. Philatelic counter . . . 1·00 1·40

286 "I Love Stamps"

1994. 120th Anniv of First Postage Stamps in Nigeria. Multicoloured.
675 1n. Type **286** 10 10
676 1n.50 "I Collect Stamps" . . 15 15
677 5n. 19th-century means of communication 45 60
678 10n. Lagos stamp of 1874 . . 1·00 1·40

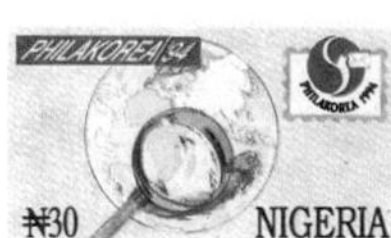

287 Magnifying Glass over Globe

1994. "Philakorea '94" International Stamp Exhibition, Seoul.
679 **287** 30n. multicoloured . . . 1·75 2·40
MS680 127 × 115 mm. **287** 30n. multicoloured . . . . 2·25 4·00

288 Geryon Crab

1994. Crabs. Multicoloured.
681 1n. Type **288** 10 10
682 1n.50 Spider crab 10 10
683 5n. Red spider crab 45 55
684 10n. Geryon maritae crab . . 90 1·25

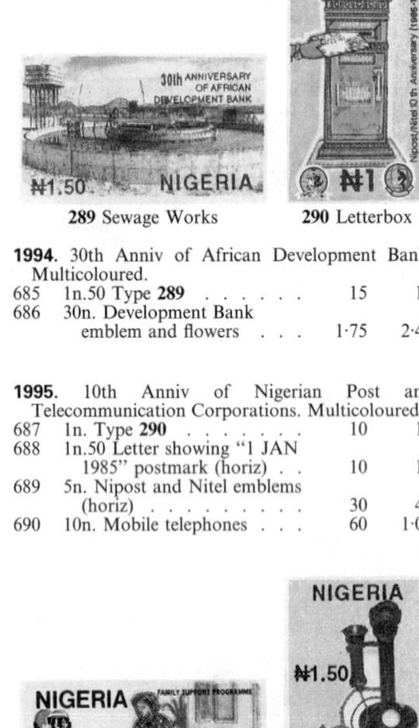

289 Sewage Works **290** Letterbox

1994. 30th Anniv of African Development Bank. Multicoloured.
685 1n.50 Type **289** 15 10
686 30n. Development Bank emblem and flowers 1·75 2·40

1995. 10th Anniv of Nigerian Post and Telecommunication Corporations. Multicoloured.
687 1n. Type **290** 10 10
688 1n.50 Letter showing "1 JAN 1985" postmark (horiz) 10 10
689 5n. Nipost and Nitel emblems (horiz) 30 45
690 10n. Mobile telephones 60 1·00

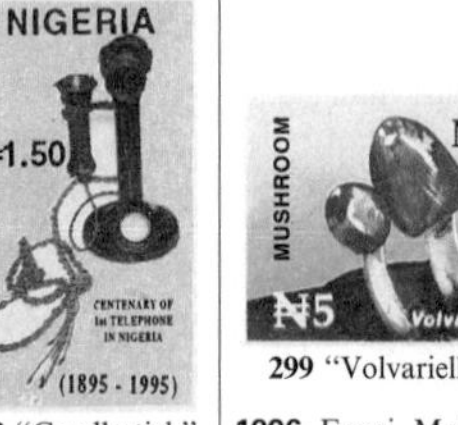

291 Woman preparing Food **292** "Candlestick" Telephone

1995. Family Support Programme. Multicoloured.
691 1n. Type **291** 10 10
692 1n.50 Mother teaching children 10 10
693 5n. Family meal 30 45
694 10n. Agricultural workers and tractor 60 90

1995. Cent of First Telephone in Nigeria. Mult.
695 1n.50 Type **292** 10 10
696 10n. Early equipment 60 1·00

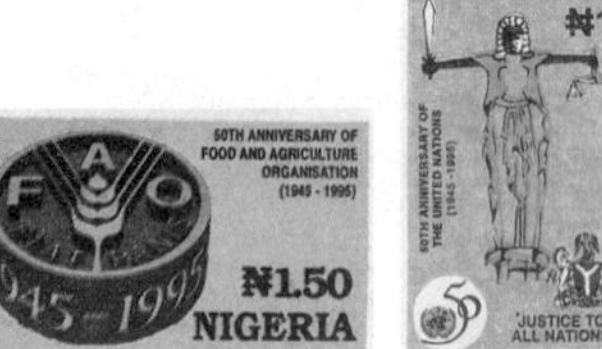

293 F.A.O. Emblem **294** "Justice" and 50th Anniversary Emblem

1995. 50th Anniv of F.A.O. Multicoloured.
697 1n.50 Type **293** 10 10
698 30n. Fishing canoes 1·90 2·25

1995. 50th Anniv of United Nations. Multicoloured.
699 1n. Type **294** 10 10
700 1n.50 Toxic waste (horiz) 10 10
701 5n. Tourist hut (horiz) 30 40
702 10n. Nigerian armoured car on U.N. duty (horiz) 1·25 1·40

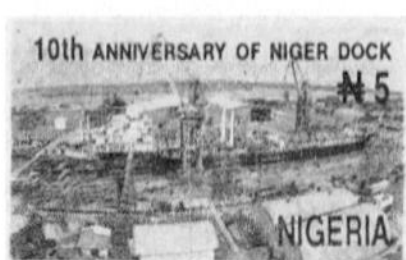

295 Container Ship in Dock

1996. 10th Anniv of Niger Dock. Multicoloured.
703 5n. Type **295** 35 30
704 10n. "Badagri" (tourist launch) on crane 65 60
705 20n. Shipping at dock 1·00 1·50
706 30n. "Odoragushin" (ferry) 1·50 2·50

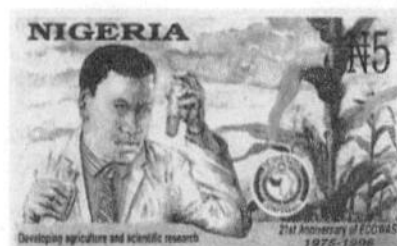

296 Scientist and Crops

1996. 21st Anniv of E.C.O.W.A.S. (Economic Community of West African States). Multicoloured.
707 5n. Type **296** 30 30
708 30n. Queue at border crossing 1·50 2·25

297 Judo **298** Nigerian Flag and Exhibition Emblem

1996. Olympic Games, Atlanta. Multicoloured.
709 5n. Type **297** 35 30
710 10n. Tennis 80 60
711 20n. Relay race 1·00 1·50
712 30n. Football 1·50 2·25

1996. "ISTANBUL '96" International Stamp Exhibition.
713 **298** 30n. mauve, green and black 1·50 2·25

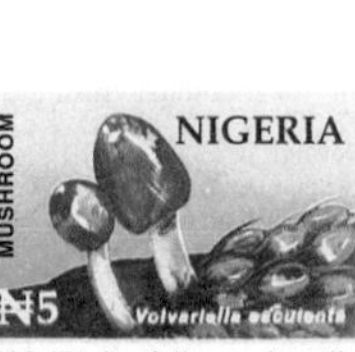

299 "Volvariella esculenta" **300** Boy with Toys

1996. Fungi. Multicoloured.
714 5n. Type **299** 45 30
715 10n. "Lentinus subnudus" 90 60
716 20n. "Tricholoma lobayensis" 1·25 1·50
717 30n. "Pleurotus tuber-regium" 1·50 2·25

1996. 50th Anniv of U.N.I.C.E.F. Multicoloured.
718 5n. Type **300** 30 30
719 30n. Girl reading book (horiz) 1·50 2·25

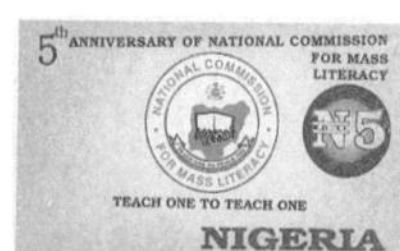

301 Literacy Logo

1996. 5th Anniv of Mass Literacy Commission.
720 **301** 5n. emerald, green and black 30 30
721 – 30n. emerald, green and black 1·50 2·25
DESIGN: 30n. Hands holding book and literacy logo.

302 Three Footballers

1998. World Cup Football Championship, France. Multicoloured.
722 5n. Type **302** 25 30
723 10n. Player with ball (vert) 55 60
724 20n. Player receiving ball (vert) 1·10 1·25
725 30n. Two opposing players 1·60 2·25

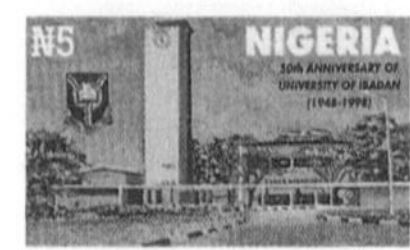

303 University Tower and Complex

1998. 50th Anniv of Ibadan University. Mult.
726 5n. Type **303** 25 30
727 30n. Anniversary logo and University crest 1·60 2·25

304 Ship and Logo

1998. 8th Anniv of Economic Community of West African States Military Arm (ECOMOG). Multicoloured.
728 5n. Type **304** 25 30
729 30n. Logo and original member states 1·25 1·75
730 50n. Current member states 2·25 3·50

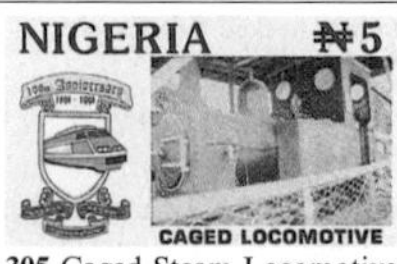

305 Caged Steam Locomotive

1999. Centenary of Nigerian Railway Corporation. Multicoloured.
731 5n. Type **305** 25 30
732 10n. Iddo Terminus 55 60
733 20n. Diesel locomotive No. 2131 1·10 1·25
734 30n. Passenger train pulling into station 1·60 2·25

306 Football and Globe

1999. 11th World Youth Football Championship, Nigeria. Multicoloured.
735 5n.+5n. Type **306** 15 30
736 10n.+5n. Player throwing ball 20 35
737 20n.+5n. Player scoring goal 35 50
738 30n.+5n. Map of Nigeria showing venues 50 70
739 40n.+5n. World Youth Football Championship logo 60 80
740 50n.+5n. Player being tackled 75 95
MS741 120 × 115 mm. Nos. 735/40 2·50 2·75

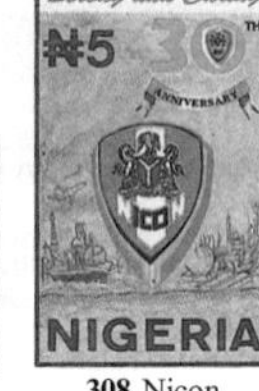

307 Sea Life and F.E.P.A. Emblem **308** Nicon Emblem

1999. 10th Anniv of Federal Environmental Protection Agency. Multicoloured.
742 5n. Type **307** 30 30
743 10n. Forest 65 60
744 20n. Monkeys 1·40 1·10
745 30n. Villagers and wildlife 2·25 2·25

1999. 30th Anniv of Nicon Insurance Corporation. Multicoloured.
746 5n. Type **308** 25 30
747 30n. Emblem and Nicon Building (horiz) 1·00 1·50

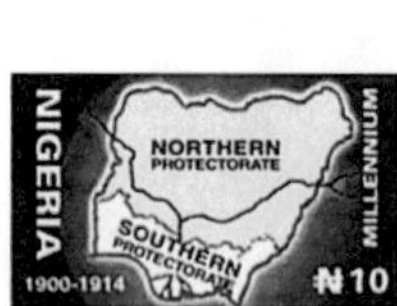

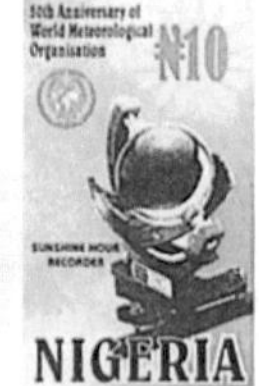

309 Map of Nigeria in 1900 **310** Sunshine Hour Recorder

2000. New Millennium (1st Issue). Multicoloured.
748 10n. Type **309** 35 15
749 20n. Map of Nigeria in 1914 55 40
750 30n. Coat of arms 60 70
751 40n. Map of Nigeria in 1996 85 1·10
See also Nos. 786/9.

2000. 50th Anniv of World Meteorological Organization.
752 **310** 10n. multicoloured 15 15
753 – 30n. brown and blue 55 75
DESIGN—HORIZ: 30n. Meteorological station.

311 "Freedom of the Press" **312** Boxing

2000. Return to Democracy. Multicoloured.
754 10n. Type **311** 10 15
755 20n. "Justice for All" (horiz) 25 30
756 30n. Parliamentary Mace 35 50
757 40n. President Olusegun Obasanjo 50 70
MS758 99 × 109 mm. Nos. 754/7 1·10 1·40

2000. Olympic Games, Sydney. Multicoloured.
759 10n. Type **312** 10 15
760 20n. Weightlifting 25 30
761 30n. Women's football 35 50
762 40n. Men's football 50 65
MS763 136 × 118 mm. Nos. 759/62 1·10 1·40

313 Obafemi Awolowo **314** Hug Plum

2000. 40th Anniv of Nigeria's Independence.
764 **313** 10n. black, emerald and green 10 15
765 – 20n. black, emerald and green 25 30
766 – 30n. black, emerald and green 35 40
767 – 40n. multicoloured 80 70
768 – 50n. multicoloured 95 1·00
DESIGNS—VERT: 20n. Abubakar Tafawa Balewa; 30n. Nnamdi Azikiwe. HORIZ: 40n. Liquified gas station; 50n. Container ships.

2001. Fruits. Multicoloured.
769 20n. Type **314** 30 30
770 30n. White star apple 40 40
771 40n. African breadfruit 60 65
772 50n. Akee apple 70 80

315 *Daily Times* Headquarters, Lagos **316** Broad-tailed Paradise Whydah

2001. 75th Anniv of *The Daily Times of Nigeria*. Multicoloured.
773 20n. Type **315** 25 30
774 30n. First issue of *Nigerian Daily Times*, 1926 35 40
775 40n. *Daily Times* printing works, Lagos 50 55
776 50n. *Daily Times* masthead, 1947 60 65

2001. Wildlife. Multicoloured.
777 10n. Type **316** 10 15
778 15n. Fire-bellied woodpecker 15 20
779 20n. Grant's zebra (horiz) 15 20
780 25n. Aardvark (horiz) 20 25
781 30n. Preuss's guenon (monkey) 25 30
782 40n. Great ground pangolin (horiz) 35 40
783 50n. Pygmy chimpanzee (*Pan paniscus*) (horiz) 40 45
784 100n. Red-eared guenon (monkey) 85 90

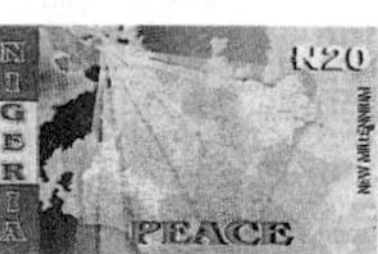

317 "Children encircling Globe" (Urska Golob) **318** Map of Nigeria and Dove

2001. U.N. Year of Dialogue among Civilisations.
785 **317** 20n. multicoloured 25 30

2002. New Millennium (2nd issue). Multicoloured.
786 20n. Type **318** 40 30
787 30n. Globe and satellite dish 55 40
788 40n. Handshake across flag in shape of Nigeria 85 80
789 50n. Two overlapping hearts 85 1·00

319 Kola Nuts

2002. Cash Crops. Multicoloured.
790 20n. Type **319** 30 25
791 30n. Oil palm 40 35
792 40n. Cassava 50 50
793 50n. Maize (vert) 60 70

320 Nigerian Player dribbling Ball

2002. World Cup Football Championship, Japan and Korea. Multicoloured.
794 20n. Type **320** 20 25
795 30n. Footballs around Globe 30 35
796 40n. Footballer's legs and World Cup Trophy (horiz) 40 45
797 50n. World Cup Trophy . . 45 50

321 Nurse caring for Patient

2003. World AIDS Day. Multicoloured.
798 20n. Type **321** 15 20
799 50n. Counselling on AIDS 40 45

322 Girl and Boy in Class **323** Athlete running

2003. Universal Basic Education. Multicoloured.
800 20n. Type **322** 15 20
801 50n. Boy writing in book (horiz) 40 45

2003. 8th All Africa Games, Abuja. Multicoloured.
802 20n. Type **323** 15 20
803 30n. High jump (horiz) . . . 25 30
804 40n. Taekwondo (horiz) . . . 35 40
805 50n. Long jump 40 45
MS806 172 × 98 mm. Nos. 802/5 1·20 1·30

POSTAGE DUE STAMPS

D **1**

1959.
D1 D **1** 1d. orange . . . . 15 1·00
D2 2d. orange . . . . 20 1·00
D3 3d. orange . . . . 25 1·50
D4 6d. orange . . . . 25 5·00
D5 1s. black . . . . 50 6·50

1961.
D 6 D **1** 1d. red 15 40
D 7 2d. blue 20 45
D 8 3d. green 25 60
D 9 6d. yellow . . . . 30 1·40
D10 1s. blue . . . . 50 2·25

1973. As Type D **1**.
D11 2k. red 10 10
D12 3k. blue 10 10
D13 5k. yellow 10 10
D14 10k. green 10 10

NIUAFO'OU Pt. 1

A remote island, part of the Kingdom of Tonga, with local autonomy.

100 seniti = 1 pa'anga.

1 Map of Niuafo'ou **2a** SPIA De Havilland D.H.C. 6 Turin Otter 300

1983.
1 **1** 1s. stone, black and red . . . 30 90
2 2s. stone, black and green . . 30 90
3 3s. stone, black and blue . . 30 90
4 3s. stone, black and brown 30 90
5 5s. stone, black and purple 40 90
6 6s. stone, black and blue . . 40 90
7 9s. stone, black and green . . 40 90
8 10s. stone, black and blue . . 40 90
9 13s. stone, black and green 65 90
10 15s. stone, black and brown 70 1·25
11 20s. stone, black and blue . . 75 1·25
12 29s. stone, black and purple 1·00 80
13 32s. stone, black and green 1·00 90
14 47s. stone, black and red . . 1·40 1·40

1983. No. 820 of Tonga optd **NIUAFO'OU KINGDOM OF TONGA** or surch also.
15 1p. on 2p. green and black . . 2·50 3·50
16 2p. green . . . . 3·50 5·00

1983. Inauguration of Niuafo'ou Airport.
17 **2a** 29s. multicoloured . . . . . 1·50 1·00
18 1p. multicoloured . . . . . 3·00 3·25

1983. As T **1**, but without value, surch.
19 3s. stone, black and blue . . . 30 50
20 5s. stone, black and blue . . . 30 50
21 32s. stone, black and blue . . 1·75 1·25
22 2p. stone, black and blue . . . 8·50 10·00

4 Eruption of Niuafo'ou

1983. 25th Anniv of Re-settlement. Mult.
23 5s. Type **4** 40 30
24 29s. Lava flow . . . . 1·00 1·00
25 32s. Islanders fleeing to safety 1·10 1·00
26 1p.50 Evacuation by canoe . . 3·50 5·00

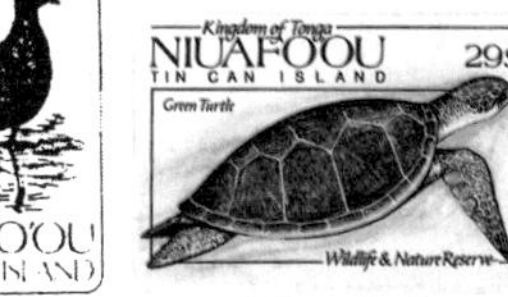

5 Purple Swamphen **6** Green Turtle

1983. Birds of Niuafo'ou.
27 **5** 1s. black and mauve . . . . 1·00 1·25
28 – 2s. black and blue . . . . . 1·00 1·25
29 – 3s. black and green . . . . 1·00 1·25
30 – 5s. black and yellow . . . . 1·25 1·25
31 – 6s. black and orange . . . . 1·50 1·60
32 – 9s. multicoloured . . . . . 1·75 1·25
33 – 10s. multicoloured . . . . . 1·75 2·00
34 – 13s. multicoloured . . . . . 2·25 1·60
35 – 15s. multicoloured . . . . . 2·25 2·50
36 – 20s. multicoloured . . . . . 2·50 2·75
37 – 29s. multicoloured . . . . . 2·75 1·50
38 – 32s. multicoloured . . . . . 2·75 1·60
39 – 47s. multicoloured . . . . . 3·25 2·25
40 – 1p. multicoloured . . . . . 6·00 8·50
41 – 2p. multicoloured . . . . . 8·00 12·00
DESIGNS—VERT (22 × 29 mm): 2s. White collared kingfisher; 3s. Red-headed parrot finch; 5s. Buff-banded rail ("Banded Rail"); 6s. Polynesian scrub hen ("Niuafo'ou megapode"); 9s. Green honeyeater; 10s. Purple swamphen (different). (22 × 36 mm): 29s. Red-headed parrot finch (different); 32s. White-collared kingfisher (different). (29 × 42 mm): 1p. As 10s. HORIZ (29 × 22 mm): 13s. Buff-banded rail ("Banded Rail") (different): 15s. Polynesian scrub hen (different). (36 × 22 mm): 20s. As 13s.; 47s. As 15s. (42 × 29 mm): 2p. As 15s.

1984. Wildlife and Nature Reserve. Mult.
42 29s. Type **6** 70 70
43 32s. Insular flying fox (vert) 70 70
44 47s. Humpback whale . . . . 3·00 1·75
45 1p.50 Polynesian scrub hen ("Niuafo'ou megapode") (vert) . . . . 5·00 7·50

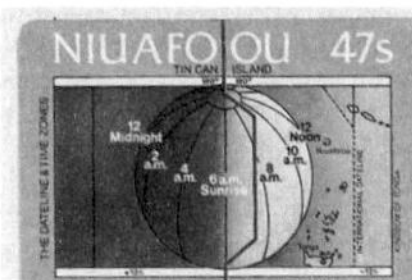

7 Diagram of Time Zones

1984. Cent of International Dateline. Mult.
46 47s. Type **7** 60 50
47 2p. Location map showing Niuafo'ou . . . . 1·90 3·25

8 Australia 1913 £2 Kangaroo Definitive **9** Dutch Brass Band entertaining Tongans

1984. "Ausipex" International Stamp Exhibition, Melbourne. Multicoloured.
48 32s. Type **8** 75 60
49 1p.50 Niuafo'ou 1983 10s. map definitive . . . . . . 2·25 3·00
MS50 90 × 100 mm. As Nos. 48/9, but without exhibition logo and with face value at foot . . . . 1·75 2·50

1985. 400th Birth Anniv of Jacob Le Maire (discoverer of Niuafo'ou).
51 **9** 13s. brown, yellow & orange 25 40
52 – 32s. brown, yellow and blue 55 60
53 – 47s. brown, yellow and green 75 80
54 – 1p.50 brown, cinnamon and yellow . . . . 2·25 3·00
MS55 90 × 90 mm. 1p.50 brown, light brown and blue. Imperf 1·50 2·00
DESIGNS: 32s. Tongans preparing kava; 47s. Tongan canoes and outriggers; 1p.50, "Eendracht" at anchor off Tafahi Island.

10 "Ysabel", 1902

1985. Mail Ships. Multicoloured.
56B 9s. Type **10** 35 55
57A 13s. "Tofua I", 1908 . . . . 70 55
58B 47s. "Mariposa", 1934 . . . 1·10 1·60
59B 1p.50 "Matua", 1936 . . . . 2·50 4·00

11 Preparing to fire Rocket

1985. Niuafo'ou Rocket Mails. Multicoloured.
60B 32s. Type **11** . . . . 1·00 80
61A 42s. Rocket in flight . . . . 1·25 1·00
62B 57s. Ship's crew watching rocket's descent . . . . . 1·60 1·40
63A 1p.50 Islanders reading mail 3·50 4·50

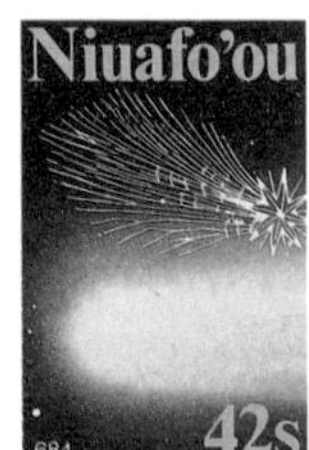

12 Halley's Comet, 684 A.D.

1986. Appearance of Halley's Comet. Multicoloured.
64 42s. Type **12** . . . . 5·00 3·00
65 42s. Halley's Comet, 1066, from Bayeux Tapestry . . . 5·00 3·00
66 42s. Edmond Halley . . . . . 5·00 3·00
67 42s. Halley's Comet, 1910 . . 5·00 3·00
68 42s. Halley's Comet, 1986 . . 5·00 3·00
69 57s. Type **12** . . . . 5·00 3·50
70 57s. As No. 65 . . . . 5·00 3·50
71 57s. As No. 66 . . . . 5·00 3·50
72 57s. As No. 67 . . . . 5·00 3·50
73 57s. As No. 68 . . . . 5·00 3·50

Nos. 64/8 and 69/73 were printed together, se-tenant, forming composite designs.

1986. Nos. 32/9 surch.
74 4s. on 9s. Green honeyeater 85 2·00
75 4s. on 10s. Purple swamphen 85 2·00
76 42s. on 13s. Buff-banded rail ("Banded Rail") . . . . . 2·75 2·00
77 42s. on 15s. Polynesian scrub hen . . . . 2·75 2·00
78 57s. on 29s. Red-headed parrot finch . . . . 3·25 2·25
79 57s. on 32s. White-collared kingfisher . . . . 3·25 2·25
80 2p.50 on 20s. Buff-banded rail ("Banded Rail") . . . . . 9·00 11·00
81 2p.50 on 47s. Polynesian scrub hen . . . . 9·00 11·00

13a Peace Corps Surveyor and Pipeline

1986. "Ameripex '86" International Stamp Exhibition, Chicago. 25th Anniv of United States Peace Corps. Multicoloured.
82 57s. Type **13a** . . . . 1·25 1·25
83 1p.50 Inspecting crops . . . . 2·25 3·00
MS84 90 × 90 mm. Nos. 82/3, magnifying glass and tweezers. Imperf . . . . 3·75 5·00

14 Swimmers with Mail

1986. Centenary of First Tonga Stamps. Designs showing Niuafo'ou mail transport. Multicoloured.
85 42s. Type **14** 90 90
86 57s. Collecting tin can mail . . 1·10 1·10
87 1p. Ship firing mail rocket . . 2·00 2·50
88 2p.50 "Collecting the Mails" (detail) (C. Mayger) . . . . 3·50 4·75
MS89 135 × 80 mm. No. 88 . . . 5·00 7·00

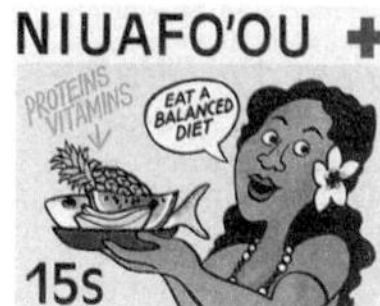

15 Woman with Nourishing Foods ("Eat a balanced diet")

1987. Red Cross. Preventive Medicine. Mult.
90 15s. Type **15** 60 60
91 42s. Nurse with baby ("Give them post-natal care") . . . 1·60 1·60
92 1p. Man with insecticide ("Insects spread disease") 2·50 3·25
93 2p.50 Boxer ("Say no to alcohol, drugs, tobacco") . . 4·00 5·50

16 Hammerhead

1987. Sharks. Multicoloured.
94 29s. Type **16** . . . . 2·00 1·75
95 32s. Tiger shark . . . . 2·00 1·75
96 47s. Grey nurse shark . . . . 2·50 2·25
97 1p. Great white shark . . . . 4·00 6·00
MS98 90 × 90 mm. 2p. Shark and fishes . . . . 11·00 12·00

17 Capt. E. C. Musick and Sikorsky S.42A Flying Boat "Samoan Clipper"

1987. Air Pioneers of the South Pacific. Multicoloured.
99 42s. Type **17** . . . . 1·75 1·40
100 57s. Capt. J. W. Burgess and Short S. 30 modified "G" Class flying boat "Aotearoa" . . . . 2·00 1·75

101 1p.50 Sir Charles Kingsford Smith and Fokker F.VIIa/3m "Southern Cross" . . . 3·00 3·75
102 2p. Amelia Earhart and Lockheed 10E Electra . . 3·50 4·50

18 Polynesian Scrub Hen and 1983 1s. Map Definitive

1988. 5th Annivs of First Niuafo'ou Postage Stamp (42, 57s.) and Niuafo'ou Airport Inauguration (1, 2p.). Multicoloured.
103 42s. Type **18** . . . . 1·00 75
104 57s. As Type **18**, but with stamp at left . . . . 1·00 95
105 1p. Concorde and 1983 Airport Inauguration 29s. stamp . . . . 4·00 3·25
106 2p. As 1p. but with stamp at left . . . . 4·50 4·00

19 Sailing Ship and Ship's Boat

20 Audubon's Shearwaters and Blowholes, Houma, Tonga

1988. Bicentenary of Australian Settlement. Sheet 115×110 mm containing T **19** and similar vert designs. Multicoloured.
MS107 42s. Type **19**; 42s. Aborigines; 42s. Early settlement; 42s. Marine and convicts; 42s. Sheep station; 42s. Mounted stockman; 42s. Kangaroos and early Trans Continental locomotive; 42s. Kangaroos and train carriages; 42s. Flying Doctor aircraft; 42s. Cricket match; 42s. Wicket and Sydney skyline; 42s. Fielders and Sydney Harbour Bridge . . . . 35·00 35·00
Each horizontal strip of 4 within No. **MS**107 shows a composite design.

1988. Islands of Polynesia. Multicoloured.
108 42s. Type **20** . . . . 1·50 95
109 57s. Brown kiwi at Akaroa Harbour, New Zealand . . 2·25 1·40
110 90s. Red-tailed tropic birds at Rainmaker Mountain, Samoa . . . . 2·50 2·50
111 2p.50 Laysan albatross at Kapoho Volcano, Hawaii 4·75 6·00

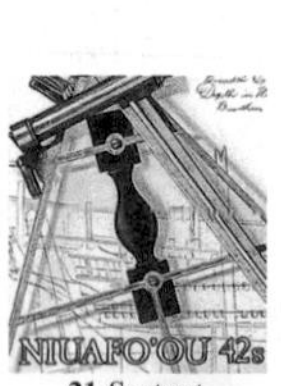

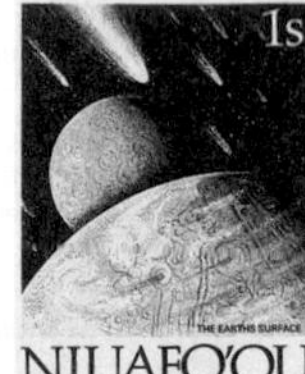

21 Sextant **23** Formation of Earth's Surface

22 Spiny Hatchetfish

1989. Bicentenary of Mutiny on the Bounty. Sheet 115×110 mm containing T **21** and similar vert designs. Multicoloured.
MS112 42s. Type **21**; 42s. Capt. Bligh; 42s. Lieutenant, 1787; 42s. Midshipman, 1787; 42s. Tahitian woman and contemporary newspaper; 42s. Breadfruit plant; 42s. Pistol and extract from "Mutiny on the Bounty"; 42s. Book illustration of Bligh cast adrift; 42s. Profile of Tahitian woman and extract from contemporary newspaper; 42s. Signatures of "Bounty officers"; 42s. Fletcher Christian; 42s. Tombstone of John Adams, Pitcairn Island . . . . 13·00 15·00

1989. Fishes of the Deep. Multicoloured.
113 32s. Type **22** . . . . 85 1·00
114 42s. Snipe eel . . . . 1·00 1·00
115 57s. Viperfish . . . . 1·25 1·50
116 1p.50 Football anglerfish . . 3·00 4·00

1989. The Evolution of the Earth. Multicoloured.
(a) Size 27×35½ mm.
117 1s. Type **23** 40 70
118 2s. Cross-section of Earth's crust 40 70
119 5s. Volcano 50 70
120 10s. Cross-section of Earth during cooling 50 70
120a 13s. Gem stones 75 50
121 15s. Sea 50 50
122 20s. Mountains 50 50
123 32s. River gorge 60 40
124 42s. Early plant life, Silurian era 80 45
124a 45s. Early marine life . . . 80 70
125 50s. Fossils and Cambrian lifeforms 90 55
126 57s. Carboniferous forest and coal seams . . . . . 1·00 55
126a 60s. Dinosaurs feeding . . . 1·25 85
126b 80s. Tyrannosaurus and triceratops fighting . . . 1·50 1·40
(b) Size 25½×40 mm.
127 1p. Dragonfly and amphibians, Carboniferous era . . . . 1·50 1·50
128 1p.50 Dinosaurs, Jurassic era . . . . 2·50 2·75
129 2p. Archaeopteryx and mammals, Jurassic era . . 3·00 3·00
130 5p. Human family and domesticated dog, Pleistocene era . . . . . 4·50 5·50
130a 10p. Mammoth and sabre-tooth tiger . . . . 7·50 9·00

24 Astronaut on Moon and Newspaper Headline

1989. "World Stamp Expo '89" International Stamp Exhibition, Washington.
131 **24** 57s. multicoloured . . . . 1·75 1·25

1989. 20th Universal Postal Union Congress, Washington. Miniature sheet, 185×150 mm, containing designs as Nos. 117/20, 121/4, 125/6 and 127/30, but wuth U.P.U. emblem at top right and some new values.
MS132 32s.×5 (as Nos. 117/20, 121); 42s.×5 (as Nos. 122/4, 125/6); 57s.×5 (as Nos. 127/30, 131) . . . . 22·00 24·00

25 Lake Vai Lahi

1990. Niuafo'ou Crater Lake. Multicoloured.
133 42s. Type **25** . . . . 70 1·00
134 42s. Islands in centre of lake 70 1·00
135 42s. South-west end of lake and islet . . . . 70 1·00
136 1p. Type **25** . . . . 1·40 1·60
137 1p. As No. 134 . . . . . . 1·40 1·60
138 1p. As No. 135 . . . . . . 1·40 1·60
Nos. 133/8 were printed together in se-tenant strips of each value, forming a composite design.

26 Penny Black and Tin Can Mail Service

1990. 150th Anniv of the Penny Black. Mult.
139 42s. Type **26** . . . . 1·25 1·00
140 57s. U.S.A. 1847 10c. stamp 1·40 1·25
141 75s. Western Australia 1854 1d. stamp . . . . 1·60 2·00
142 2p.50 Mafeking Siege 1900 1d. stamp . . . . 5·00 6·00

27 Humpback Whale surfacing

1990. Polynesian Whaling. Multicoloured.
143 15s. Type **27** . . . . 2·00 1·75
144 42s. Whale diving under canoe . . . . 2·50 1·90
145 57s. Tail of Blue whale . . . 2·75 1·90
146 2p. Old man and pair of whales . . . . 7·25 8·00
MS147 120×93 mm. 1p. Pair of whales (38×30 mm) . . . . . 10·00 11·00

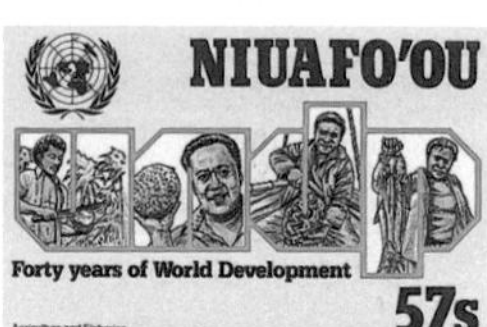

27a Agriculture and Fisheries

1990. 40th Anniv of U.N. Development Programme. Multicoloured.
148 57s. Type **27a** . . . . 90 1·40
149 57s. Education . . . . 90 1·40
150 2p.50 Healthcare . . . . . . 3·25 4·00
151 2p.50 Communications . . . 3·25 4·00

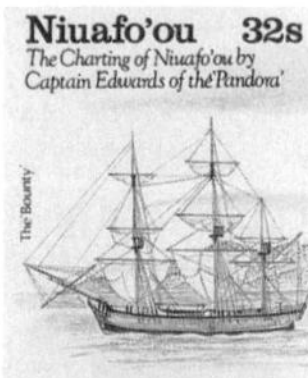

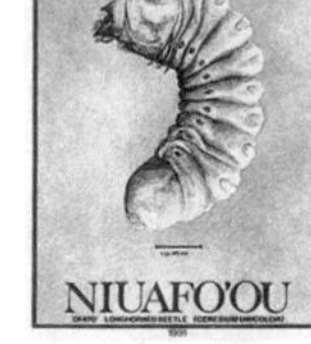

28 H.M.S. "Bounty" **30** Longhorned Beetle Grub

1991. Bicentenary of Charting of Niuafo'ou. Multicoloured.
152 32s. Type **28** . . . . 1·25 1·75
153 42s. Chart of "Pandora's" course . . . . 1·40 1·75
154 57s. H.M.S. "Pandora" (frigate) . . . . 1·75 1·75
MS155 120×93 mm. 2p. Capt. Edwards of the "Pandora"; 3p. Capt. Bligh of the "Bounty" 11·00 12·00

1991. Ornithological and Scientific Expedition to Niuafo'ou. No. **MS**147 surch **1991 ORNITHOLOGICAL AND SCIENTIFIC EXPEDITION T $1**.
MS156 120×93 mm. 1p. on 1p. multicoloured . . . . 2·75 3·50

1991. Longhorned Beetle. Multicoloured.
157 42s. Type **30** . . . . 80 1·00
158 57s. Adult beetle . . . . . . 90 1·00
159 1p.50 Grub burrowing . . . 2·75 3·25
160 2p.50 Adult on tree trunk . . 4·00 4·50

31 Heina meeting the Eel

1991. Christmas. The Legend of the Coconut Tree. Multicoloured.
161 15s. Type **31** 35 60
162 42s. Heina crying over the eel's grave . . . . 90 1·00
MS163 96×113 mm. 15s. Type **31**; 42s. No. 162; 1p.50, Heina's son collecting coconuts; 3p. Milk flowing from coconut . . . . 9·00 10·00

31a Columbus

1992. 500th Anniv of Discovery of America by Columbus. Sheet 119×109 mm. containing vert designs as T **31a**. Multicoloured.
MS164 57s. Columbus; 57s. Queen Isabella and King Ferdinand; 57s. Columbus being blessed by Abbot of Palos; 57s. 15th-century compass; 57s. Wooden traverse, windrose and the "Nina"; 57s. Bow of "Santa Maria"; 57s. Stern of "Santa Maria"; 57s. The "Pinta"; 57s. Crew erecting cross; 57s. Sailors and Indians; 57s. Columbus reporting to King and Queen; 57s. Coat of Arms . . 17·00 18·00

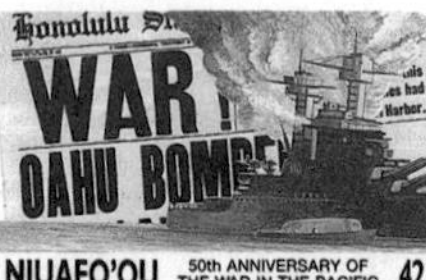

31b American Battleship Ablaze, Pearl Harbor

1992. 50th Anniv of War in the Pacific. Multicoloured.
165 42s. Type **31b** . . . . 1·10 1·25
166 42s. Destroyed American Douglas B-18 Bolo aircraft, Hawaii . . . . 1·10 1·25
167 42s. Newspaper and Japanese Mitsubishi A6M Zero-Sen fighter . . . . 1·10 1·25
168 42s. Pres. Roosevelt signing Declaration of War . . . . 1·10 1·25
169 42s. Japanese T95 light tank and Gen. MacArthur . . . 1·10 1·25
170 42s. Douglas SBD Dauntless dive bomber and Admiral Nimitz . . . . 1·10 1·25
171 42s. Bren gun and Gen. Sir Thomas Blamey . . . . . 1·10 1·25
172 42s. Australian mortar crew, Kokoda . . . . 1·10 1·25
173 42s. U.S.S. "Mississippi" in action and Maj. Gen. Julian C. Smith . . . . . 1·10 1·25
174 42s. U.S.S. "Enterprise" (aircraft carrier) . . . . . 1·10 1·25
175 42s. American marine and Maj. Gen. Curtis Lemay 1·10 1·25
176 42s. Boeing B-29 Superfortress bomber and Japanese surrender, Tokyo Bay . . . . 1·10 1·25
Nos. 165/76 were printed together, se-tenant, forming a composite design.

31c King Taufa'ahau Tupou IV and Queen Halaevalu During Coronation

1992. 25th Anniv of the Coronation of King Tupou IV.
177 **31c** 45s. multicoloured 75 75
178 – 80s. multicoloured . . . . 1·50 1·75
179 – 80s. black and brown . . 1·50 1·75
180 – 80s. multicoloured . . . . 1·50 1·75
181 – 2p. multicoloured . . . . 2·50 3·00
DESIGNS—(34×23 mm): No. 177, Type **31c**. (48×35 mm): No. 178, King Tupou IV and Tongan national anthem; 179, Extract from Investiture ceremony; 180, Tongan choir; 181, As 45s.
Nos. 177/81 show the King's first name incorrectly spelt as "Tauf'ahau".

32 Male and Female Scrub Hens searching for Food

1992. Endangered Species. Polynesian Scrub Hen. Multicoloured.
182 45s. Type **32** . . . . 1·00 1·25
183 60s. Female guarding egg . . 1·25 1·40

184 80s. Chick . . . . 1·60 1·75
185 1p.50 Head of male . . . . 2·75 3·50

33 1983 2s. Map Definitive and 1993 60s. Dinosaur Definitive

1993. 10th Anniv of First Niuafo'ou Stamp. Multicoloured.
186 60s. Type **33** . . . . 1·00 1·10
187 80s. 1983 5s. definitive and 1993 80s. dinosaurs definitive . . . . 1·25 1·40

34 De Havilland Twin Otter 200/300 of South Pacific Island Airways

34a King Tupou IV and "Pangai" (patrol boat)

1993. 10th Anniv of First Flight to Niuafo'ou. Multicoloured.
188 1p. Type **34** . . . . 1·50 2·00
189 2p.50 De Havilland Twin Otter 200/300 of Friendly Islands Airways . . . . . 3·50 4·50

1993. 75th Birthday of King Taufa'ahau Tupou IV. Multicoloured.
190 45s. Type **34a** 55 65
191 80s. King Tupou IV and musical instruments (38½ × 51 mm) . . . . . . 1·25 1·75
192 80s. King Tupou IV and sporting events (38½ × 51 mm) . . . . . . 1·25 1·75
193 80s. King Tupou IV with De Havilland Twin Otter 200/300 airplane and telecommunications . . . . 1·25 1·75
194 2p. As 45s. but larger (38½ × 51 mm) . . . . . . 2·75 3·25

35 Blue-crowned Lorikeets

35a "Crater Lake Megapode and Volcano" (Paea Puletau)

1993. Natural History of Lake Vai Lahi. Multicoloured.
195 60s. Type **35** . . . . 1·00 1·25
196 60s. White-tailed tropic bird and reef heron . . . . . . 1·00 1·25
197 60s. Black admiral (butterfly) and Niuafo'ou coconut beetle . . . . 1·00 1·25
198 60s. Niuafo'ou dragonfly, pacific black ducks and Niuafo'ou moths . . . . . 1·00 1·25
199 60s. Niuafo'ou megapode . . 1·00 1·25
Nos. 195/9 were printed together, se-tenant, forming a composite design.

1993. Children's Painting Competition Winners.
200 **35a** 10s. multicoloured . . . . 50 1·00
201 – 10s. black and grey . . . 50 1·00
202 – 1p. multicoloured . . . . 3·50 3·75
203 – 1p. multicoloured . . . . 3·50 3·75
DESIGNS: Nos. 200 and 202, Type **35a**; Nos. 201 and 203, "Ofato Beetle Grubs of Niuafo'ou" (Peni Finau).

36 "Scarabaeidea"

1994. Beetles. Multicoloured.
204 60s. Type **36** . . . . 85 1·00
205 80s. "Coccinellidea" . . . 1·10 1·40
206 1p.50 "Cerambycidea" . . . 2·00 2·50
207 2p.50 "Pentatomidae" . . . 3·75 4·25

37 Stern of H.M.S. "Bounty"

38 Blue-crowned Lory and Lava Flows

1994. Sailing Ships. Multicoloured.
208 80s. Type **37** . . . . 1·75 2·25
209 80s. Bow of H.M.S. "Bounty" . . . . 1·75 2·25
210 80s. H.M.S. "Pandora" (frigate) . . . . 1·75 2·25
211 80s. Whaling ship . . . . . 1·75 2·25
212 80s. Trading schooner . . . 1·75 2·25

1994. Volcanic Eruptions on Niuafo'ou. Multicoloured.
213 80s. Type **38** . . . . 1·25 1·75
214 80s. Pacific ducks over lava flows . . . . 1·25 1·75
215 80s. Megapodes and palm trees . . . . 1·25 1·75
216 80s. White-tailed tropic birds and inhabitants . . . . . 1·25 1·75
217 80s. Reef heron and evacuation, 1946 . . . . . 1·25 1·75
Nos. 213/17 were printed together, se-tenant, forming a composite design.

1995. Visit South Pacific Year '95. Save the Whales. Nos. 143/6 surch **SAVE THE WHALES VISIT SOUTH PACIFIC YEAR '95**, emblem and value.
218 60s. on 42s. Whale diving under canoe . . . . 2·00 1·75
219 80s. on 15s. Type **27** . . . . 2·25 2·25
220 80s. on 57s. Tail of blue whale . . . . 2·25 2·25
221 2p. on 2p. Old man and pair of whales . . . . 4·25 4·50
MS222 120 × 93 mm. 1p.50 on 1p. Pair of whales (38 × 30 mm) . . 3·25 4·00

39a American Marine

1995. 50th Anniv of End of World War II in the Pacific.
223 **39a** 60s. yellow, black and blue . . . . 1·25 1·50
224 – 60s. yellow, black and blue . . . . 1·25 1·50
225 – 60s. yellow, black and blue . . . . 1·25 1·50
226 – 60s. yellow, black and blue . . . . 1·25 1·50
227 – 60s. yellow, black and blue . . . . 1·25 1·50
228 **39a** 80s. yellow, black and red 1·25 1·50
229 – 80s. yellow, black and red 1·25 1·50
230 – 80s. yellow, black and red 1·25 1·50
231 – 80s. yellow, black and red 1·25 1·50
232 – 80s. yellow, black and red 1·25 1·50
DESIGNS: Nos. 224 and 229, Marine firing and side of tank; 225 and 230, Tank; 226 and 231, Marines leaving landing craft; 227 and 232, Beach assault and palm trees.
Nos. 223/32 were printed together, se-tenant, forming two composite designs.

39b Dinosaurs Feeding

1995. "Singapore '95" International Stamp Exhibitions. Designs showing exhibition emblem. Multicoloured.
233 45s. Type **39b** (as No. 126a) 1·00 1·50
234 60s. Tyrannosaurus fighting Triceratops (as No. 126b) 1·00 1·50
MS235 110 × 70 mm. 2p. Plesiosaurus . . . . 2·50 3·25

39c Great Wall of China (½-size illustration)

1995. Beijing International Coin and Stamp Show '95. Sheet 143 × 87 mm.
MS236 **39c** 1p.40 multicoloured 2·00 2·50

39d St. Paul's Cathedral and Searchlights

1995. 50th Anniv of United Nations and End of Second World War.
237 **39d** 60s. multicoloured . . . . 1·00 1·50
238 – 60s. black and blue . . . 1·00 1·50
239 – 60s. multicoloured . . . . 1·00 1·50
240 – 80s. multicoloured . . . . 1·25 1·50
241 – 80s. blue and black . . . 1·25 1·50
242 – 80s. multicoloured . . . . 1·25 1·50
DESIGNS—HORIZ: No. 239, Concorde; 240, Allied prisoners of war and Burma Railway; 242, Mt. Fuji and express train. VERT—25 × 35 mm: Nos. 238 and 241, U.N. anniversary emblem.

40 Charles Ramsay and Swimmers with Poles

1996. Tin Can Mail Pioneers. Multicoloured.
243 45s. Type **40** 90 90
244 60s. Charles Ramsay and encounter with shark . . . 1·25 1·25
245 1p. Walter Quensell and transferring mail from canoes to ship . . . . . . 2·00 2·00
246 3p. Walter Quensell and Tin Can Mail cancellations . . 6·00 6·50

40a Cave Painting, Lake Village and Hunter

1996. 13th Congress of International Union of Prehistoric and Protohistoric Sciences, Forli, Italy. Multicoloured.
247 1p. Type **40a** . . . . 2·25 2·25
248 1p. Egyptians with Pyramid, Greek temple, and Romans with Colosseum . . . . . 2·25 2·25

40b Dolls, Model Truck and Counting Balls

41 Island and Two Canoes

1996. 50th Anniv of U.N.I.C.E.F. Children's Toys. Multicoloured.
249 80s. Type **40b** . . . . 1·75 2·00
250 80s. Teddy bear, tricycle and model car . . . . 1·75 2·00
251 80s. Book, model helicopter, pedal car and roller skates 1·75 2·00
Nos. 249/51 were printed together, se-tenant, forming a composite design.

1996. 50th Anniv of Evacuation of Niuafo'ou. Multicoloured.
252 45s. Type **41** . . . . 85 1·10
253 45s. Erupting volcano and canoes . . . . 85 1·10
254 45s. End of island, volcanic cloud and canoe . . . . . 85 1·10
255 45s. Family and livestock in outrigger canoe . . . . . 85 1·10
256 45s. Islanders reaching "Matua" (inter-island freighter) . . . . 85 1·10
257 60s. Type **41** . . . . 95 1·10
258 60s. As No. 253 . . . . . . 95 1·10
259 60s. As No. 254 . . . . . . 95 1·10
260 60s. As No. 255 . . . . . . 95 1·10
261 60s. As No. 256 . . . . . . 95 1·10
Nos. 252/6 and 257/61 respectively were printed together, se-tenant, forming the same composite design.

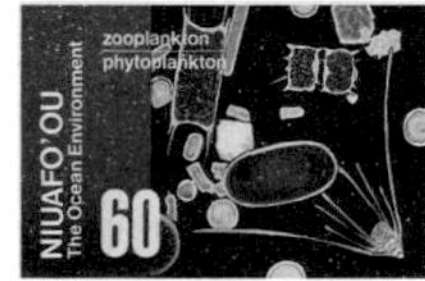

42 Plankton

1997. The Ocean Environment.
262 **42** 60s. multicoloured . . . . 1·00 1·00
263 – 80s. multicoloured . . . . 1·25 1·25
264 – 1p.50 multicoloured . . . 2·25 2·50
265 – 2p.50 multicoloured . . . 3·00 3·50
DESIGNS: 80s. to 2p.50, Different plankton.

42a Black-naped Tern

1997. "Pacific '97" International Stamp Exhibition, San Francisco. Sheet 85 × 110 mm.
MS266 **42a** 2p. multicoloured . . 2·75 3·25

42b King and Queen on Wedding Day

1997. King and Queen of Tonga's Golden Wedding and 30th Anniv of Coronation. Multicoloured.
267 80s. Type **42b** . . . . 1·75 1·75
268 80s. King Tupou in Coronation robes . . . . 1·75 1·75
MS269 82 × 70 mm. 5p. King Tupou with pages (horiz) . . . . . . 7·00 7·50

43 Blue-crowned Lory Nestlings

43a King Taufa'ahau Tupou IV

1998. Endangered Species. Blue-crowned Lory. Multicoloured.
270 10s. Type **43** . . . . 1·50 1·50
271 55s. Feeding on flowers . . . 3·00 1·25
272 80s. Perched on branch . . . 4·00 2·00
273 3p. Pair on branch . . . . . 8·00 9·00
MS274 160 × 112 mm. Nos. 270/3 × 2 24·00 24·00

1998. Diana, Princess of Wales Commemoration. Sheet, 145 × 70 mm, containing vert designs as T **91** of Kiribati. Multicoloured.
MS275 10s. Princess Diana in tartan jacket, 1987; 80s. Wearing white dress, 1992; 1p. Wearing check jacket, 1993; 2p.50, Wearing black jacket (sold at 4p.40+50s. charity premium) . . . . 5·50 6·00

1998. 80th Birthday of King Taufa'ahau Tupou IV.
276 **43a** 2p.70 multicoloured . . . 2·50 3·25

43b Tiger and Top Left Quarter of Clock Face

1998. Chinese New Year ("Year of the Tiger"). Sheet, 126 × 85 mm, containing horiz designs as T **43b**, each showing tiger and quarter segment of clock face. Multicoloured.

MS277 55s. Type **43b**; 80s. Top right quarter; 1p. Bottom left quarter; 1p. Bottom right quarter 3·75 4·50

No. **MS**277 also includes "SINGPEX '98" Stamp Exhibition, Singapore emblem on the sheet margin.

43c "Amphiprion melanopus"

1998. International Year of the Ocean. Multicoloured.

278 10s. Type **43c** 40 50
279 55s. "Amphiprion perideraion" 80 90
280 80s. "Amphiprion chrysopterus" 1·00 1·10

43d Angel playing lute (inscr in Tongan)

1998. Christmas. Multicoloured.

281 20s. Type **43d** 70 55
282 55s. Angel playing violin (inscr in English) 1·10 60
283 1p. Children and bells (inscr in Tongan) 1·60 1·75
284 1p.60 Children and candles (inscr in English) 2·25 3·00

43e Rabbit on Hind Legs

1999. Chinese New Year ("Year of the Rabbit"). Sheet 126 × 85 mm, containing horiz designs as T **43e**, showing rabbits and segments of flower (each red, yellow and grey).

MS285 10s. Type **43e**; 55s. Rabbit facing left; 80s. Rabbit facing right; 1p. Two rabbits 2·50 3·25

44 "Eendracht" (Le Maire)

1999. Early Explorers. Multicoloured.

286 80s. Type **44** 2·00 1·00
287 2p.70 Tongiaki (outrigger canoe) 3·25 4·00
MS288 120 × 72 mm. Nos. 286/7 5·50 6·50

No. **MS**288 also includes the "Australia '99" emblem on the sheet margin.

44a "Cananga odorata"

1999. Fragrant Flowers. Multicoloured.

289 55s. Type **44a** 75 60
290 80s. "Gardenia tannaensis" (vert) 1·00 80
291 1p. "Coleus amboinicus" (vert) 1·40 1·50
292 2p.50 "Hernandia moerenhoutiana" 2·75 3·75

45 Dove over Tafahi Island

2000. New Millennium. Sheet, 120 × 80 mm, containing T **45** and similar vert design. Multicoloured.

MS293 1p. Type **45**; 2p.50, Kalia (traditional canoe) passing island 2·75 3·50

45a Dragon in the Sky

2000. Chinese New Year ("Year of the Dragon"). Sheet, 126 × 85 mm, containing horiz designs as T **46a**. Multicoloured.

MS294 10s. Type **45a**; 55s. Dragon in the sky (facing left); 80s. Sea dragon (facing right); 1p. Sea dragon (facing left) 2·25 2·75

45b Queen Elizabeth the Queen Mother

46 Tongan Couple

2000. "The Stamp Show 2000" International Stamp Exhibition, London. Queen Elizabeth the Queen Mother's 100th Birthday. Sheet, 105 × 71 mm, containing designs as T **45b**.

MS295 1p.50, Type **45b**; 2p.50, Queen Salote Tupou III of Tonga 3·50 4·00

2000. "EXPO 2000" World Stamp Exhibition, Anaheim, U.S.A. Space Communications. Sheet, 120 × 90 mm, containing T **46** and similar vert designs. Multicoloured.

MS296 10s. Type **46**; 2p.50, Telecom dish aerial; 2p.70, "Intelsat" satelite 4·50 5·50

47 *Jamides bochus* (butterfly)

2000. Butterflies. Multicoloured.

297 55s. Type **47** 85 70
298 80s. *Hypolimnas bolina* 1·10 90
299 1p. *Eurema hecabe aprica* 1·40 1·40
300 2p.70 *Danaus plexippus* 2·50 3·00

48 Snake

2001. Chinese New Year ("Year of the Snake") and "Hong Kong 2001" Stamp Exhibition. Sheet, 125 × 87 mm, containing horiz designs as T **48** showing decorative snakes.

MS301 10s. multicoloured; 55s. multicoloured; 80s. multicoloured; 1p. multicoloured 2·00 2·25

49 Seale's Flying Fish

2001. Fishes. Multicoloured.

302 80s. Type **49** 1·10 80
303 1p. Swordfish 1·40 1·40
304 2p.50 Skipjack tuna 2·50 3·00
MS305 121 × 92 mm. Nos. 302/4 3·25 4·00

50 Pawpaw

2001. Tropical Fruit. Sheet, 120 × 67 mm, containing T **50** and similar vert designs. Multicoloured.

MS306 55s. Type **50**; 80s. Limes; 1p. Mango; 2p.50, Bananas 3·75 4·50

51 Barn Owl in Flight

2001. Barn Owls. Multicoloured.

307 10s. Type **51** 30 50
308 55s. Adult feeding young in nest 75 55
309 2p.50 Adult and fledglings in nest 2·25 2·75
310 2p.70 Barn owl in palm tree 2·25 2·75
MS311 170 × 75 mm. Nos. 307/10 5·00 6·00

51a Queen Elizabeth with Princess Elizabeth, Coronation, 1937

2002. Golden Jubilee. Sheet 162 × 95 mm, containing designs as T **51a**.

MS312 15s. brown, violet and gold; 90s. multicoloured; 1p.20, multicoloured; 1p.40, multicoloured; 2p.25, multicoloured 8·00 8·50

DESIGNS—HORIZ (as Type **51a**): 15s. Type **51a**; 90s. Queen Elizabeth in lilac outfit; 1p.20, Princess Elizabeth in garden; 1p.40, Queen Elizabeth in red hat and coat. VERT (38 × 51 mm): 2p.25, Queen Elizabeth after Annigoni.

51b Two Horses with Foal

2002. Chinese New Year ("Year of the Horse"). Sheet, 126 × 89 mm, containing vert designs as T **51b**. Multicoloured.

MS313 65s. Two horses with foal; 80s. Horse drinking from river; 1p. Horse standing in river; 2p.50 Horse and foal on river bank 5·00 6·00

52 Polynesian Scrub Fowl with Eggs

2002. Polynesian Scrub Fowl. Multicoloured.

314 15s. Type **52** 30 50
315 70s. Two birds on rocks 90 90
316 90s. Polynesian scrub fowl by tree (vert) 1·10 1·10
317 2p.50 Two birds in undergrowth (vert) 2·25 2·75
MS318 72 × 95 mm. Nos. 316/17 3·50 4·25

53 Octopus (*Octopus vulgaris*)

2002. Cephalopods. Multicoloured.

319 80s. Type **53** 80 75
320 1p. Squid (*Sepioteuthis lessoniana*) 95 1·10
321 2p.50 Nautilus (*Nautilus belauensis*) 2·25 2·75
MS322 120 × 83 mm. Nos. 319/21 4·00 4·50

54 CASA C-212 Aviocar

2002. Mail Planes. Sheet, 140 × 80 mm, containing T **54** and similar horiz designs. Multicoloured.

MS323 80s. Type **54**; 1p.40 Britten-Norman Islander; 2p.50 DHC 6-300 Twin Otter 4·25 4·50

54a Ram

2003. Chinese New Year ("Year of the Sheep"). Sheet 128 × 88 mm, containing horiz designs as T **54a**.

MS324 65s. Type **54a**, 80s. Three ewes; 1p. Three black-faced ewes; 2p.50 Two ewes 2·75 3·00

NIUE Pt. 1

One of the Cook Is. group in the S. Pacific. A dependency of New Zealand, the island achieved local self-government in 1974.

1902. 12 pence = 1 shilling;
20 shillings = 1 pound.
1967. 100 cents = 1 dollar.

1902. T **42** of New Zealand optd **NIUE** only.

1 **42** 1d. red £300 £300

Stamps of New Zealand surch **NIUE.** and value in native language.

1902. Pictorials of 1898 etc.

8 **23** ½d. green 1·00 1·00
9 **42** 1d. red 60 1·00
2 **26** 2½d. blue (B) 1·25 4·00
13 **28** 3d. brown 9·50 5·00
14 **31** 6d. red 12·00 11·00
16 **34** 1s. orange 35·00 35·00

1911. King Edward VII stamps.

17 **51** ½d. green 50 50
18 6d. red 2·00 7·00
19 1s. orange 6·50 45·00

1917. Dominion and King George V stamps.

21 **53** 1d. red 12·00 5·50
22 **62** 3d. brown 42·00 80·00

1917. Stamps of New Zealand (King George V, etc) optd **NIUE.** only.

23 **62** ½d. green 70 2·50
24 **53** 1d. red 10·00 8·50
25 **62** 1½d. grey 1·00 2·25
26 1½d. brown 70 4·50
28a 2½d. blue 1·25 6·00
29a 3d. brown 1·25 1·50
30a 6d. red 4·75 24·00
31a 1s. orange 5·50 25·00

1918. Stamps of New Zealand optd **NIUE.**

33 F **4** 2s. blue 16·00 32·00
34 2s.6d. brown 21·00 48·00
35 5s. green 25·00 50·00
36 10s. red £100 £140
37 £1 red £140 £190

1920. Pictorial types as Cook Islands (1920), but inscr "NIUE".

38 **9** ½d. black and green 3·75 3·75
45 – 1d. black and red 1·75 1·00
40 – 1½d. black and red 2·50 8·00

46 – 2½d. black and blue 4·25 11·00
41 – 3d. black and blue 75 14·00
47 **7** 4d. black and violet 7·00 20·00
42 – 6d. brown and green 1·75 18·00
43 – 1s. black and brown 1·75 18·00

1927. Admiral type of New Zealand optd **NIUE.**
49 **71** 2s. blue 18·00 32·00

1931. No. 40 surch **TWO PENCE.**
50 2d. on 1½d. black and red 2·25 1·00

1931. Stamps of New Zealand (Arms types) optd **NIUE.**
83 **F 6** 2s.6d. brown 3·50 11·00
84 5s. green 7·50 11·00
53 10s. red 35·00 £100
86 £1 pink 42·00 60·00

1932. Pictorial stamps as Cook Islands (1932) but inscr additionally "NIUE".
89 **20** ½d. black and green 50 2·25
90 – 1d. black and red 50 1·50
64 **22** 2d. black and brown 50 1·50
92 – 2½d. black and blue 60 1·25
66 – 4d. black and blue 1·75 4·00
67 – 6d. black and orange 70 75
61 – 1s. black and violet 2·25 5·00

1935. Silver Jubilee. As Nos. 63, 92 and 67, with colours changed, optd **SILVER JUBILEE OF KING GEORGE V. 1910-1935.**
69 1d. red 60 3·50
70 2½d. blue 3·25 7·50
71 6d. green and orange 3·25 6·00

1937. Coronation. New Zealand stamps optd **NIUE.**
72 **106** 1d. red 30 10
73 2½d. blue 40 1·00
74 6d. orange 40 20

1938. As 1938 issue of Cook Islands, but inscr "NIUE COOK ISLANDS".
95 **29** 1s. black and violet 1·50 85
96 **30** 2s. black and brown 8·50 3·00
97 – 3s. blue and green 15·00 7·00

1940. As No. 132 of Cook Islands but inscr "NIUE COOK ISLANDS".
78 **32** 3d. on 1½d. black and purple 75 20

1946. Peace. New Zealand stamps optd **NIUE** (twice on 2d.).
98 **132** 1d. green 30 10
99 – 2d. purple (No. 670) 30 10
100 – 6d. brown & red (No. 674) 30 70
101 **139** 8d. black and red 40 70

18 Map of Niue

19 H.M.S. "Resolution"

1950.
113 **18** ½d. orange and blue 10 60
114 **19** 1d. brown and green 2·25 1·75
115 – 2d. black and red 1·00 1·25
116 – 3d. blue and violet 10 15
117 – 4d. olive and purple 10 15
118 – 6d. green and orange 60 1·00
119 – 9d. orange and brown 10 1·25
120 – 1s. purple and black 10 15
121 – 2s. brown and green 1·50 4·25
122 – 3s. blue and black 4·50 4·25
DESIGNS—HORIZ: 2d. Alofi landing; 3d. Native hut; 4d. Arch at Hikutavake; 6d. Alofi bay; 1s. Cave, Makefu. VERT: 9d. Spearing fish; 2s. Bananas; 3s. Matapa Chasm.

1953. Coronation. As Types of New Zealand but inscr "NIUE".
123 **164** 3d. brown 65 40
124 **168** 6d. grey 95 40

26

27 "Pua"

1967. Decimal Currency. (a) Nos. 113/22 surch.
125 **17** ½c. on ½d. 10 10
126 **18** 1c. on 1d. 1·10 15
127 – 2c. on 2d. 10 10
128 – 2½c. on 3d. 10 10
129 – 3c. on 4d. 10 10
130 – 5c. on 6d. 10 10
131 – 8c. on 9d. 10 10
132 – 10c. on 1s. 10 10
133 – 20c. on 2s. 35 1·00
134 – 30c. on 3s. 65 1·50

(b) Arms type of New Zealand without value, surch as in T **26**.
135 **26** 25c. brown 30 55
136 50c. green 70 80
137 $1 mauve 45 1·25
138 $2 pink 50 2·00

1967. Christmas. As T **278** of New Zealand but inscr "NIUE".
139 2½c. multicoloured 10 10

1969. Christmas. As No. 905 of New Zealand but inscr "NIUE".
140 2½c. multicoloured 10 10

1969. Flowers. Multicoloured; frame colours given.
141 **27** ½c. green 10 10
142 – 1c. red 10 10
143 – 2c. olive 10 10
144 – 2½c. brown 10 10
145 – 3c. blue 10 10
146 – 5c. red 10 10
147 – 8c. violet 10 10
148 – 10c. yellow 10 10
149 – 20c. blue 35 1·25
150 – 30c. green 1·10 1·75
DESIGNS: 1c. "Golden Shower"; 2c. Flamboyant; 2½c. Frangipani; 3c. Niue crocus; 5c. Hibiscus; 8c. "Passion Fruit"; 10c. "Kampui"; 20c. Queen Elizabeth II (after Anthony Buckley); 30c. Tapeu orchid.
For 20c. design as 5c. see No. 801.

37 Kalahimu

1970. Indigenous Edible Crabs. Mult.
151 3c. Type **37** 10 10
152 5c. Kalavi 10 10
153 30c. Unga 30 25

1970. Christmas. As T **314** of New Zealand, but inscr "NIUE".
154 2½c. multicoloured 10 10

38 Outrigger Canoe, and Fokker F.27 Friendship over Jungle

1970. Opening of Niue Airport. Multicoloured.
155 3c. Type **38** 10 20
156 5c. "Tofua II" (cargo liner) and Fokker F.27 Friendship over harbour 15 20
157 8c. Fokker F.27 Friendship over airport 15 30

39 Spotted Triller

1971. Birds. Multicoloured.
158 5c. Type **39** 15 35
159 10c. Purple-capped fruit dove 40 20
160 20c. Blue-crowned lory 60 20

1971. Christmas. As T **325** of New Zealand, but inscr "Niue".
161 3c. multicoloured 10 10

40 Niuean Boy

41 Octopus Lure

1971. Niuean Portraits. Multicoloured.
162 4c. Type **40** 10 10
163 6c. Girl with garland 10 20
164 9c. Man 10 40
165 14c. Woman with garland 15 80

1972. South Pacific Arts Festival, Fiji. Multicoloured.
166 3c. Type **41** 10 10
167 5c. War weapons 15 15
168 10c. Sika throwing (horiz) 20 15
169 25c. Vivi dance (horiz) 30 25

42 Alofi Wharf

1972. 25th Anniv of South Pacific Commission. Multicoloured.
170 4c. Type **42** 10 10
171 5c. Medical services 15 10
172 6c. Schoolchildren 15 10
173 18c. Dairy cattle 25 20

1972. Christmas. As T **332** of New Zealand, but inscr "NIUE".
174 3c. multicoloured 10 10

43 Silver Sweeper

1973. Fishes. Multicoloured.
175 8c. Type **43** 25 25
176 10c. Peacock hind ("Loi") 25 30
177 15c. Yellow-edged lyretail ("Malau") 30 40
178 20c. Ruby snapper ("Palu") 30 45

44 "Large Flower Piece" (Jan Brueghel)

46 King Fataaiki

45 Capt. Cook and Bowsprit

1973. Christmas. Flower studies by the artists listed. Multicoloured.
179 4c. Type **44** 10 10
180 5c. Bollongier 10 10
181 10c. Ruysch 20 20

1974. Bicent of Capt. Cook's Visit. Mult.
182 2c. Type **45** 20 20
183 3c. Niue landing place 20 20
184 8c. Map of Niue 20 30
185 20c. Ensign of 1774 and Administration Building 30 65

1974. Self-government. Multicoloured.
186 4c. Type **46** 10 15
187 8c. Annexation Ceremony, 1900 10 15
188 10c. Legislative Assembly Chambers (horiz) 10 15
189 20c. Village meeting (horiz) 15 25

47 Decorated Bicycles

48 Children going to Church

1974. Christmas. Multicoloured.
190 3c. Type **47** 10 10
191 10c. Decorated motorcycle 10 10
192 20c. Motor transport to church 20 30

1975. Christmas. Multicoloured.
193 4c. Type **48** 10 10
194 5c. Child with balloons on bicycle 10 10
195 10c. Balloons and gifts on tree 20 20

49 Hotel Buildings

1975. Opening of Tourist Hotel. Mult.
196 8c. Type **49** 10 10
197 20c. Ground-plan and buildings 20 20

50 Preparing Ground for Taro

1976. Food Gathering. Multicoloured.
198 1c. Type **50** 10 10
199 2c. Planting taro 10 10
200 3c. Banana gathering 10 10
201 4c. Harvesting taro 10 10
202 5c. Gathering shellfish 30 10
203 10c. Reef fishing 10 10
204 20c. Luku gathering 15 15
205 50c. Canoe fishing 20 60
206 $1 Coconut husking 25 80
207 $2 Uga gathering 45 1·40
See also Nos. 249/58 and 264/73.

51 Water

1976. Utilities. Multicoloured.
208 10c. Type **51** 10 10
209 15c. Telecommunications 15 15
210 20c. Power 15 15

52 Christmas Tree, Alofi

1976. Christmas. Multicoloured.
211 9c. Type **52** 15 15
212 15c. Church service, Avatele 15 15

53 Queen Elizabeth II and Westminster Abbey

1977. Silver Jubilee. Multicoloured.
213 $1 Type **53** 60 50
214 $2 Coronation regalia 80 75
MS215 72 × 104 mm. Nos. 213/14 1·10 1·60
Stamps from the miniature sheet have a blue border.

54 Child Care

1977. Personal Services. Multicoloured.
216 10c. Type **54** 15 10
217 15c. School dental clinic 20 20
218 20c. Care of the aged 20 20

55 "The Annunciation"

58 "The Deposition of Christ" (Caravaggio)

57 "An Island View in Atooi"

1977. Christmas. Paintings by Rubens. Multicoloured.
219 10c. Type **55** 20 10
220 12c. "Adoration of the Magi" 20 15
221 20c. "Virgin in a Garland" 35 40
222 35c. "The Holy Family" . . 55 90
MS223 82 × 129 mm. Nos. 219/22 1·10 1·25

1977. Nos. 198/207, 214, 216 and 218 surch.
224 12c. on 1c. Type **50** 25 25
225 16c. on 2c. Planting taro . . 30 30
226 20c. on 3c. Banana gathering 30 40
227 35c. on 4c. Harvesting taro 30 45
228 40c. on 5c. Gathering shellfish 30 50
229 60c. on 20c. Luku gathering 30 55
230 70c. on $1 Coconut husking 30 55
231 85c. on $2 Uga gathering . . 30 60
232 $1.10 on 10c. Type **22** . . . 30 60
233 $2.60 on 20c. Care of the aged 50 70
234 $3.20 on $2 Coronation regalia 60 80

1978. Bicent of Discovery of Hawaii. Paintings by John Webber. Multicoloured.
235 12c. Type **57** 85 40
236 16c. "A View of Karakaooa, in Owhyhee" 95 50
237 20c. "An Offering before Capt. Cook in the Sandwich Islands" . . . . 1·00 60
238 30c. "Tereoboo, King of Owhyhee bringing presents to Capt. Cook" . . . . . 1·10 70
239 35c. "A Canoe in the Sandwich Islands, the rowers masked" . . . . . 1·25 80
MS240 121 × 121 mm. Nos. 235/9 4·75 2·75

1978. Easter. Paintings from the Vatican Galleries. Multicoloured.
241 10c. Type **58** 20 10
242 20c. "The Burial of Christ" (Bellini) 40 25
MS243 102 × 68 mm. Nos. 241/2 1·00 1·00

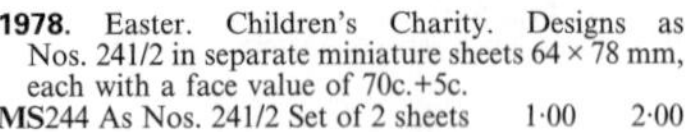

1978. Easter. Children's Charity. Designs as Nos. 241/2 in separate miniature sheets 64 × 78 mm, each with a face value of 70c.+5c.
MS244 As Nos. 241/2 Set of 2 sheets 1·00 2·00

59 Flags of Niue and U.K.

1978. 25th Anniv of Coronation. Mult.
245 $1.10 Type **59** 60 90
246 $1.10 Coronation portrait by Cecil Beaton 60 90
247 $1.10 Queen's personal flag for New Zealand 60 90
MS248 87 × 98 mm. Nos. 245/7 with white borders . . . . 2·50 1·50

1978. Designs as Nos. 198/207 but margin colours changed and silver frame.
249 12c. Type **50** 20 20
250 16c. Planting taro 20 20
251 30c. Banana gathering . . . 30 25
252 35c. Harvesting taro 30 30
253 40c. Gathering shellfish . . . 40 40
254 60c. Reef fishing 40 35
255 75c. Luku gathering 40 40
256 $1.10 Canoe fishing 50 80
257 $3.20 Coconut husking . . . 60 90
258 $4.20 Uga gathering 65 95

60 "Festival of the Rosary"

1978. Christmas. 450th Death Anniv of Durer. Multicoloured.
259 20c. Type **60** 40 20
260 30c. "The Nativity" 50 30
261 35c. "Adoration of the Magi" 60 35
MS262 143 × 82 mm. Nos. 259/61 1·50 2·00

1978. Christmas. Children's Charity. Designs as Nos. 259/61 in separate miniature sheets 74 × 66 mm., each with a face value of 60c.+5c.
MS263 As Nos. 259/61 Set of 3 sheets . . . . 1·00 2·00

1979. Air. Designs as Nos. 249/58 but gold frames and additionally inscr "AIRMAIL".
264 15c. Planting taro 20 15
265 20c. Banana gathering . . . 20 15
266 23c. Harvesting taro 25 15
267 50c. Canoe fishing 65 20
268 90c. Reef fishing 65 35
269 $1.35 Type **50** . . . . 65 1·50
270 $2.10 Gathering shellfish . . 65 1·75
271 $2.60 Luku gathering . . . . 65 1·75
272 $5.10 Coconut husking . . . 80 1·75
273 $6.35 Uga gathering . . . . 80 1·75

61 "Pieta" (Gregorio Fernandez)

1979. Easter. Paintings. Multicoloured.
274 30c. Type **61** 30 25
275 35c. "Burial of Christ" (Pedro Roldan) 35 25
MS276 82 × 82 mm. Nos. 274/5 1·00 1·00

1979. Easter. Children's Charity. Designs as Nos. 274/5 in separate miniature sheets 86 × 69 mm., each with a face value of 70c.+5c.
MS277 As Nos. 274/5 Set of 2 sheets 1·10 1·75

62 "The Nurse and Child" (Franz Hals)

63 Penny Black Stamp

1979. International Year of the Child. Details of Paintings. Multicoloured.
278 16c. Type **62** 20 15
279 20c. "Child of the Duke of Osuna" (Goya) 20 20
280 30c. "Daughter of Robert Strozzi" (Titian) 35 35
281 35c. "Children eating Fruit" (Murillo) 45 40
MS282 80 × 115 mm. Nos. 278/81 1·25 2·25

1979. International Year of the Child. Children's Charity. Designs as Nos. 278/81 in separate miniature sheets 99 × 119 mm, each with a face value of 70c.+5c.
MS283 As Nos. 278/81 Set of 4 sheets . . . . 1·00 1·50

1979. Death Cent of Sir Rowland Hill. Mult.
284 20c. Type **63** 15 15
285 20c. Sir Rowland Hill and original Bath mail coach 15 15
286 30c. Basel 1845 2½r. stamp 15 20
287 30c. Sir Rowland Hill and Alpine village coach . . . 15 20
288 35c. U.S.A. 1847 5c. stamp 20 20
289 35c. Sir Rowland Hill and "Washington" (first transatlantic U.S.A. mail vessel) 20 20
290 50c. France 1849 20c. stamp 25 20
291 50c. Sir Rowland Hill and French Post Office railway van, 1849 . . . . 25 20
292 60c. Bavaria 1849 1k. stamp 25 20
293 60c. Sir Rowland Hill and Bavarian coach with mail 25 20
MS294 143 × 149 mm. Nos. 284/93 2·50 3·00
The two versions of each value were issued se-tenant within the sheet, forming composite designs.

64 Cook's Landing at Botany Bay

1979. Death Bicentenary of Captain Cook. Multicoloured.
295 20c. Type **64** 55 30
296 30c. Cook's men during a landing on Erromanga . . 75 40
297 35c. H.M.S. "Resolution" and H.M.S. "Discovery" in Queen Charlotte's Sound 85 45
298 75c. Death of Captain Cook, Hawaii . . . . 1·50 70
MS299 104 × 80 mm. Nos. 295/8 3·75 2·50

65 Launch of "Apollo 11"

66 "Virgin of Tortosa" (P. Serra)

1979. 10th Anniv of First Manned Moon Landing. Multicoloured.
300 30c. Type **65** 35 20
301 35c. Lunar module on Moon 45 25
302 60c. Sikorsky Sea King helicopter, recovery ship and command module after splashdown 90 40
MS303 120 × 82 mm. Nos. 300/2 1·25 1·60
Stamps from No. **MS**303 have the inscription in gold on a blue panel.

1979. Christmas. Paintings. Multicoloured.
304 20c. Type **66** 10 10
305 25c. "Virgin with Milk" (R. di Mur) 15 15
306 30c. "Virgin and Child" (S. di G. Sassetta) 20 20
307 50c. "Virgin and Child" (J. Huguet) 25 25
MS308 95 × 113 mm. Nos. 304/7 75 1·25

1979. Christmas Children's Charity. Designs as Nos. 304/7 in separate miniature sheets, 49 × 84 mm, each with a face value of 85c.+5c.
MS309 As Nos. 304/7 Set of 4 sheets 1·00 2·00

1980. Hurricane Relief. Surch **HURRICANE RELIEF Plus 2c.** (a) On Nos. 284/93 **HURRICANE RELIEF** spread over each se-tenant pair.
310 **63** 20c.+2c. multicoloured . . 20 40
311 – 20c.+2c. multicoloured (No. 285) 20 40
312 – 30c.+2c. multicoloured (No. 286) 25 45
313 – 30c.+2c. multicoloured (No. 287) 25 45
314 – 35c.+2c. multicoloured (No. 288) 30 50
315 – 35c.+2c. multicoloured (No. 289) 30 50
316 – 50c.+2c. multicoloured (No. 290) 35 65
317 – 50c.+2c. multicoloured (No. 291) 35 65
318 – 60c.+2c. multicoloured (No. 292) 35 70
319 – 60c.+2c. multicoloured (No. 293) 35 70

(b) On Nos. 295/8.
320 **64** 20c.+2c. multicoloured . . 40 50
321 – 30c.+2c. multicoloured . . 40 60
322 – 35c.+2c. multicoloured . . 40 65
323 – 75c.+2c. multicoloured . . 70 1·10

(c) On Nos. 300/2.
324 **65** 30c.+2c. multicoloured . . 25 40
325 – 35c.+2c. multicoloured . . 25 45
326 – 60c.+2c. multicoloured . . 50 75

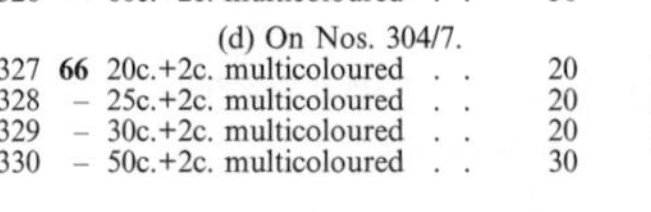

(d) On Nos. 304/7.
327 **66** 20c.+2c. multicoloured . . 20 35
328 – 25c.+2c. multicoloured . . 20 40
329 – 30c.+2c. multicoloured . . 20 45
330 – 50c.+2c. multicoloured . . 30 70

68 "Pieta" (Bellini)

1980. Easter. "Pieta". Paintings. Mult.
331 25c. Type **68** 20 15
332 30c. Botticelli 25 20
333 35c. A. van Dyck 25 20
MS334 75 × 104 mm. As Nos. 331/3, but each with additional premium of **+ 2c.** 55 90
The premiums on No. **MS**334 were used to support Hurricane Relief.

1980. Easter. Hurricane Relief. Designs as Nos. 331/3 in separate miniature sheets, 75 × 52 mm, each with a face value of 85c.+5c.
MS335 As Nos. 331/3 Set of 3 sheets 1·00 1·50

69 Ceremonial Stool, New Guinea

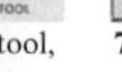

72 Queen Elizabeth the Queen Mother

1980. South Pacific Festival of Arts, New Guinea. Multicoloured.
336 20c. Type **69** 10 10
337 20c. Ku-Tagwa plaque, New Guinea 10 10
338 20c. Suspension hook, New Guinea 10 10
339 20c. Ancestral board, New Guinea 10 10
340 25c. Platform post, New Hebrides 10 10
341 25c. Canoe ornament, New Ireland 10 10
342 25c. Carved figure, Admiralty Islands 10 10
343 25c. Female with child, Admiralty Islands 10 10
344 30c. The God A'a, Rurutu (Austral Islands) 15 15
345 30c. Statue of Tangaroa, Cook Islands 15 15
346 30c. Ivory pendant, Tonga 15 15
347 30c. Tapa (Hiapo) cloth, Niue 15 15
348 35c. Feather box (Waka), New Zealand 15 15
349 35c. Hei-Tiki amulet, New Zealand 15 15
350 35c. House post, New Zealand 15 15
351 35c. Feather image of god Ku, Hawaii 15 15
MS352 Four sheets, each 86 × 124 mm. (a) Nos. 336, 340, 344, 348; (b) Nos. 337, 341, 345, 349; (c) Nos. 338, 342, 346, 350; (d) Nos. 339, 343, 347, 351. Each stamp with an additional premium of 2c. Set of 4 sheets . . . . . 1·50 2·00

1980. "Zeapex '80" International Stamp Exhibition, Auckland. Nos. 284/93 optd (A) **ZEAPEX'80 AUCKLAND** or (B) **NEW ZEALAND STAMP EXHIBITION** and emblem.
353 **63** 20c. multicoloured (A) . . 25 15
354 – 20c. multicoloured (B) . . 25 15
355 – 30c. multicoloured (A) . . 25 15
356 – 30c. multicoloured (B) . . 25 15
357 – 35c. multicoloured (A) . . 25 15
358 – 35c. multicoloured (B) . . 25 15
359 – 50c. multicoloured (A) . . 30 20
360 – 50c. multicoloured (B) . . 30 20
361 – 60c. multicoloured (A) . . 30 20
362 – 60c. multicoloured (B) . . 30 20
MS363 143 × 149 mm. Nos. 353/62, each additionally surcharged **+ 2c.** 3·50 2·75

1980. 80th Birthday of The Queen Mother.
364 **72** $1.10 multicoloured . . . 80 1·50
MS365 55 × 80 mm. **72** $3 multicoloured . . . . 1·00 1·75

73 100 m Dash

74 "The Virgin and Child"

1980. Olympic Games, Moscow.
366 **73** 20c. multicoloured 20 15
367 – 20c. multicoloured 20 15
368 – 25c. multicoloured 20 20
369 – 25c. multicoloured 20 20
370 – 30c. multicoloured 25 20
371 – 30c. multicoloured 25 20
372 – 35c. multicoloured 25 25
373 – 35c. multicoloured 25 25
MS374 119 × 128 mm. Nos. 366/73, each stamp including premium of 2c. . . . . 1·00 1·00
DESIGNS: No. 367, Allen Wells, Great Britain (winner 100 m dash); 368, 400 m freestyle 369, Ines Diers (winner, D.D.R.); 370, Soling Class; 371, Winner, Denmark; 372, Football; 373, Winner, Czechoslovakia.
Nos. 366/7, 368/9, 370/1 and 372/3 were printed se-tenant in pairs each pair forming a composite design. On the 25c. and 35c. stamps the face value is at right on the first design and at left on the second in each pair. For the 30c. No. 370 has a yacht with a green sail at left and No. 371 a yacht with a red sail.

1980. Christmas.
375 **74** 20c. multicoloured 15 15
376 – 25c. multicoloured 15 15

377 – 30c. multicoloured 20 20
378 – 35c. multicoloured 20 20
MS379 87 × 112 mm. Nos. 375/8 85 1·25
DESIGNS: 25c. to 35c. Various Virgin and Child paintings by Andrea del Sarto.

1980. Christmas. Children's Charity. Designs as Nos. 375/8 in separate miniature sheets 62 × 84 mm, each with a face value of 80c.+5c.
MS380 As Nos. 375/8 Set of 4 sheets 1·25 1·75

75 "Phalaenopsis sp."

77 Prince Charles

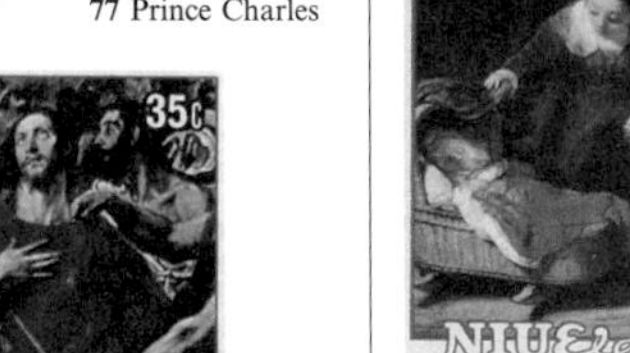

76 "Jesus Defiled" (El Greco)

1981. Flowers (1st series). Multicoloured.
381 2c. Type **75** 10 10
382 2c. Moth orchid 10 10
383 5c. "Euphorbia pulcherrima" 10 10
384 5c. Poinsettia 10 10
385 10c. "Thunbergia alata" . . 10 10
386 10c. Black-eyed Susan . . . 10 10
387 15c. "Cochlospermum hibiscoides" 15 15
388 15c. Buttercup tree 15 15
389 20c. "Begonia sp." 20 20
390 20c. Begonia 20 20
391 25c. "Plumeria sp." 25 25
392 25c. Frangipani 25 25
393 30c. "Strelitzia reginae" . . . 30 30
394 30c. Bird of Paradise 30 30
395 35c. "Hibiscus syriacus" . . . 30 30
396 35c. Rose of Sharon 30 30
397 40c. "Nymphaea sp." 35 35
398 40c. Water lily 35 35
399 50c. "Tibouchina sp." . . . 45 45
400 50c. Princess flower 45 45
401 60c. "Nelumbo sp." 55 55
402 60c. Lotus 55 55
403 80c. "Hybrid hibiscus" . . . 75 75
404 80c. Yellow hibiscus 75 75
405 $1 Golden shower tree ("cassia fistula") . . . . . 1·00 1·00
406 $2 "Orchid var" . . . . . 4·00 2·50
407 $3 "Orchid sp." . . . . . 4·50 3·50
408 $4 "Euphorbia pulcherrima poinsettia" . . . . . . 2·75 4·00
409 $6 "Hybrid hibiscus" . . . . 3·50 6·00
410 $10 Scarlet hibiscus ("hibiscus rosa-sinensis") . . . . . 6·00 9·00
Nos. 405/10 are larger, 47 × 35 mm.
See also Nos. 527/36.

1981. Easter. Details of Paintings. Mult.
425 35c. Type **76** 40 30
426 50c. "Pieta" (Fernando Gallego) 60 50
427 60c. "The Supper of Emmaus" (Jacopo de Pontormo) 65 55
MS428 69 × 111 mm. As Nos. 425/7, but each with charity premium of 2c. . . . . 1·00 1·75

1981. Easter. Children's Charity. Designs as Nos. 425/7 in separate miniature sheets 78 × 86 mm, each with a face value of 80c.+5c.
MS429 As Nos. 425/7 Set of 3 sheets 1·00 2·00

1981. Royal Wedding. Multicoloured.
430 75c. Type **77** 25 60
431 95c. Lady Diana Spencer . . 30 70
432 $1.20 Prince Charles and Lady Diana Spencer . . . 30 80
MS433 78 × 85 mm. Nos. 430/2 2·00 2·50

78 Footballer Silhouettes

1981. World Cup Football Championship, Spain (1982).
434 **78** 30c. green, gold and blue 20 20
435 – 30c. green, gold and blue 20 20
436 – 30c. green, gold and blue 20 20
437 – 35c. blue, gold and orange 20 20
438 – 35c. blue, gold and orange 20 20
439 – 35c. blue, gold and orange 20 20
440 – 40c. orange, gold and green 20 20
441 – 40c. orange, gold and green 20 20
442 – 40c. orange, gold and green 20 20
MS443 162 × 122 mm. 30c.+3c., 35c.+3c., 40c.+3c. (each × 3). As Nos. 434/42 . . . . 1·60 2·00

DESIGNS—Various footballer silhouettes: 435, gold figure 3rd from left; 436, gold figure 4th from left; 437, gold figure 3rd from left; 438, gold figure 4th from left; 439, gold figure 2nd from left; 440, gold figure 3rd from left displaying close control; 441, gold figure 2nd from left; 442, gold figure 3rd from left, heading.

1982. International Year for Disabled Persons. Nos. 430/2 surch **+5c.**
444 75c.+5c. Type **77** 50 85
445 95c.+5c. Lady Diana Spencer 60 1·00
446 $1.20+5c. Prince Charles and Lady Diana . . . . 60 1·25
MS447 78 × 85 mm. As Nos. 444/6, with each surcharged **+ 10c.** . . 1·75 4·50

80 "The Holy Family with Angels" (detail)

81 Prince of Wales

1981. Christmas. 375th Birth Anniv of Rembrandt. Multicoloured.
448 20c. Type **80** 65 45
449 35c. "Presentation in the Temple" 85 55
450 50c. "Virgin and Child in Temple" . . . . 95 1·10
451 60c. "The Holy Family" . . 1·25 1·50
MS452 79 × 112 mm. Nos. 448/51 3·25 3·75

1982. Christmas. Children's Charity. Designs as Nos. 448/51 in separate miniature sheets 66 × 80 mm, each with a face value of 80c.+5c.
MS453 As Nos. 448/51 Set of 4 sheets . . . . 2·00 2·50

1982. 21st Birthday of Princess of Wales. Multicoloured.
454 50c. Type **81** 40 55
455 $1.25 Prince and Princess of Wales 60 90
456 $2.50 Princess of Wales . . . 1·50 1·40
MS457 81 × 101 mm. Nos. 454/6 4·75 3·50
The stamps from No. **MS**457 are without white borders.

1982. Birth of Prince William of Wales (1st issue). Nos. 430/3 optd.
458 75c. Type **77** . . . . 1·50 2·00
459 75c. Type **77** . . . . 1·50 2·00
460 95c. Lady Diana Spencer . . 2·50 2·50
461 95c. Lady Diana Spencer . . 2·50 2·50
462 $1.20 Prince Charles and Lady Diana Spencer . . . 2·50 2·75
463 $1.20 Prince Charles and Lady Diana Spencer . . . 2·50 2·75
MS464 78 × 85 mm. Nos. 430/2 6·00 6·00
OVERPRINTS: Nos. 458, 460 and 462 **COMMEMORATING THE ROYAL BIRTH 21 JUNE 1982**; 459, 461 and 463 **BIRTH OF PRINCE WILLIAM OF WALES 21 JUNE 1982**; **MS**464 **PRINCE WILLIAM OF WALES 21 JUNE 1982**.

1982. Birth of Prince William of Wales (2nd issue). As Nos. 454/6, but with changed inscriptions. Multicoloured.
465 50c. Type **81** 50 65
466 $1.25 Prince and Princess of Wales . . . . 1·00 1·25
467 $2.50 Princess of Wales . . . 4·00 3·00
MS468 81 × 101 mm. As Nos. 465/7 7·00 5·50

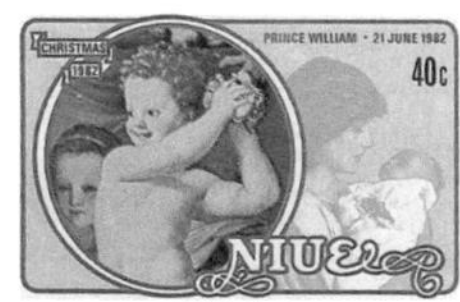

83 Infant

1982. Christmas. Paintings of Infants by Bronzion, Murillo and Boucher.
469 **83** 40c. multicoloured . . . . 1·50 80
470 – 52c. multicoloured . . . . 1·60 95
471 – 83c. multicoloured . . . . 2·50 2·50
472 – $1.05 multicoloured . . . 2·75 2·75
MS473 110 × 76 mm. Designs as Nos. 469/72 (each 31 × 27 mm), but without portrait of Princess and Prince William . . . . . 5·00 2·75

84 Prince and Princess of Wales with Prince William

86 Scouts signalling

85 Prime Minister Robert Rex

1982. Christmas. Children's Charity. Sheet 72 × 58 mm.
MS474 **84** 80c.+5c. multicoloured 1·50 1·50

1983. Commonwealth Day. Multicoloured.
475 70c. Type **85** 50 55
476 70c. H.M.S. "Resolution" and H.M.S. "Adventure" off Niue, 1774 . . . . . . 50 55
477 70c. Passion flower 50 55
478 70c. Limes 50 55

1983. 75th Anniv of Boy Scout Movement and 125th Birth Anniv of Lord Baden-Powell. Multicoloured.
479 40c. Type **86** 35 40
480 50c. Planting sapling 45 50
481 83c. Map-reading 85 90
MS482 137 × 90 mm. As Nos. 479/81, but each with premium of 3c. . . . . 1·25 1·75

1983. 15th World Scout Jamboree, Alberta, Canada. Nos. 479/81 optd **XV WORLD JAMBOREE CANADA.**
483 40c. Type **86** 35 40
484 50c. Planting sapling 45 50
485 83c. Map-reading 85 90
MS486 137 × 90 mm. As Nos. 483/5, but each with premium of 3c. 1·60 1·75

88 Black Right Whale

1983. Protect the Whales. Multicoloured.
487 12c. Type **88** 75 65
488 25c. Fin whale 95 80
489 35c. Sei whale . . . . . . 1·50 1·25
490 40c. Blue whale . . . . . . 1·75 1·50
491 58c. Bowhead whale . . . . 1·90 1·60
492 70c. Sperm whale . . . . . 2·25 1·75
493 83c. Humpback whale . . . 2·50 2·25
494 $1.05 Minke whale . . . . . 3·00 2·50
495 $2.50 Grey whale . . . . . 4·25 4·00

89 Montgolfier Balloon, 1783

1983. Bicentenary of Manned Flight. Mult.
496 25c. Type **89**(postage) 55 25
497 40c. Wright Brothers Flyer I, 1903 . . . . 1·40 45
498 58c. Airship "Graf Zeppelin", 1928 . . . . 1·50 60
499 70c. Boeing 247, 1933 . . . . 1·75 85
500 83c. "Apollo 8", 1968 . . . 1·75 1·00
501 $1.05 Space shuttle "Columbia", 1982 . . . . 2·00 1·40
MS502 118 × 130 mm. Nos. 496/501 (air) . . . . 3·00 3·25

90 "The Garvagh Madonna"

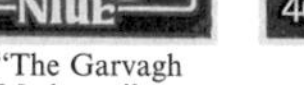

91 Morse Key Transmitter

1983. Christmas. 500th Birth Anniv of Raphael. Multicoloured.
503 30c. Type **90** 85 40
504 40c. "Madonna of the Granduca" 90 45
505 58c. "Madonna of the Goldfish" . . . . 1·25 60
506 70c. "The Holy Family of Francis I" . . . . 1·40 70
507 83c. "The Holy Family with Saints" . . . . 1·50 80
MS508 120 × 114 mm. As Nos. 503/7 but each with a premium of 3c. 3·25 2·75

1983. Various stamps surch. (a) Nos. 393/4, 399/404 and 407.
509 52c. on 30c. "Strelitzia reginae" 70 45
510 52c. on 30c. Bird of paradise 70 45
511 58c. on 50c. "Tibouchina sp." 70 55
512 58c. on 50c. Princess flower 70 55
513 70c. on 60c. "Nelumbo sp." 85 60
514 70c. on 60c. Lotus 85 60
515 83c. on 80c. "Hybrid hibiscus" . . . . 1·00 75
516 83c. on 80c. Yellow hibiscus 1·00 75
517 $3.70 on $3 "Orchid sp." . . 6·00 3·25

(b) Nos. 431/2 and 455/6.
518 $1.10 on 95c. Lady Diana Spencer . . . . 2·50 2·25
519 $1.10 on $1.25 Prince and Princess of Wales . . . . 1·50 2·00
520 $2.60 on $1.20 Prince Charles and Lady Diana . . . . . 3·00 3·50
521 $2.60 on $2.50 Princess of Wales . . . . 2·75 3·25

1983. Christmas. 500th Birth Anniv of Raphael. Children's Charity. Designs as Nos. 503/7 in separate miniature sheets, 65 × 80 mm, each with face value of 85c.+5c.
MS522 As Nos. 503/7 Set of 5 sheets 3·50 3·25

1984. World Communications Year. Multicoloured.
523 40c. Type **91** 30 35
524 52c. Wall-mounted phone . . 40 45
525 83c. Communications satellite 60 65
MS526 114 × 90 mm. Nos. 523/5 1·10 1·50

92 "Phalaenopsis sp."

93 Discus throwing

1984. Flowers (2nd series). Multicoloured.
527 12c. Type **92** 25 15
528 25c. "Euphorbia pulcherrima" 35 20
529 30c. "Cochlospermum hibiscoides" 40 25
530 35c. "Begonia sp." 40 25
531 40c. "Plumeria sp." 50 30
532 52c. "Strelitzia reginae" . . . 65 40
533 58c. "Hibiscus syriacus" . . . 70 45
534 70c. "Tibouchina sp." . . . 1·00 60
535 83c. "Nelumbo sp." . . . . 1·10 70
536 $1.05 "Hybrid hibiscus" . . . 1·25 85
537 $1.75 "Cassia fistula" . . . . 2·00 1·50
538 $2.30 "Orchid var" . . . . . 4·50 2·00
539 $3.90 "Orchid sp." . . . . . 6·00 4·00
540 $5 "Euphorbia pulcherrima poinsettia" . . . . 5·00 4·50
541 $6.60 "Hybrid hibiscus" . . . 6·00 6·00
542 $8.30 "Hibiscus rosa-sinensis" 8·00 7·00
Nos. 537/42 are larger, 39 × 31 mm.

1984. Olympic Games, Los Angeles. Multicoloured.
547 30c. Type **93** 25 30
548 35c. Sprinting (horiz) 30 35
549 40c. Horse racing (horiz) . . 35 40
550 58c. Boxing (horiz) 50 55
551 70c. Javelin-throwing 60 65

94 Koala

98 "The Nativity" (A. Vaccaro)

96 Niue National Flag and Premier Sir Robert Rex

1984. "Ausipex" International Stamp Exhibition, Melbourne. (a) Designs showing Koala Bears.
552 **94** 25c. multicoloured (postage) 70 50
553 – 35c. multicoloured 80 55
554 – 40c. multicoloured 90 60
555 – 58c. multicoloured . . . . 1·00 85
556 – 70c. multicoloured . . . . 1·25 1·00

(b) Vert designs showing Kangaroos.
557 – 83c. multicoloured (air) . . 1·50 1·25
558 – $1.05 multicoloured . . . . 1·75 1·60
559 – $2.50 multicoloured . . . . 3·00 4·00
MS560 110 × 64 mm. $1.75 Wallaby; $1.75 Koala bear . . . . . . 4·00 4·00
See also Nos. **MS**566/7.

1984. Olympic Gold Medal Winners, Los Angeles. Nos. 547/51 optd.
561 30c. Type **93** 65 30
562 35c. Sprinting 70 35
563 40c. Horse racing 75 35
564 58c. Boxing 80 50
565 70c. Javelin-throwing 85 60
OPTS: 30c. **Discus Throw Rolf Danneberg Germany**; 35c. **1,500 Metres Sebastian Coe Great Britain**; 40c. **Equestrian Mark Todd New Zealand**; 58c. **Boxing Tyrell Biggs United States**; 70c. **Javelin Throw Arto Haerkoenen Finland**.

1984. "Ausipex" International Stamp Exhibition, Melbourne (2nd issue). Designs as Nos. 552/60 in miniature sheets of six or four. Multicoloured.
MS566 109 × 105 mm. Nos. 552/6 and $1.75 Koala bear (as No. **MS**560) . . . . 6·00 4·75
MS567 80 × 105 mm. Nos. 557/9 and $1.75 Wallaby (as No. **MS**560) 6·00 4·75

1984. 10th Anniv of Self-government. Mult.
568 40c. Type **96** . . . . 1·10 50
569 58c. Map of Niue and Premier Rex . . . . 1·10 60
570 70c. Premier Rex receiving proclamation of self-government . . . . . . 1·10 70
MS571 110 × 83 mm. Nos. 568/70 2·00 2·00
MS572 100 × 74 mm. $2.50 As 70c. (50 × 30 mm) . . . . 2·00 2·00

1984. Birth of Prince Henry. Nos. 430 and 454 surch **$2 Prince Henry 15. 9. 84.**
573 $2 on 50c. Type **81** . . . . . 2·50 2·75
574 $2 on 75c. Type **77** . . . . . 2·50 2·75

1984. Christmas. Multicoloured.
575 40c. Type **98** 60 35
576 58c. "Virgin with Fly" (anon, 16th-century) 75 50
577 70c. "The Adoration of the Shepherds" (B. Murillo) . . 85 60
578 80c. "Flight into Egypt" (B. Murillo) 95 70
MS579 115 × 111 mm. As Nos. 575/8 but each stamp with a 5c. premium 2·50 2·25
MS580 Four sheets, each 66 × 98 mm. As Nos. 575/8, but each stamp 30 × 42 mm. with a face value of 95c.+10c. Set of 4 sheets . . . . 3·75 3·00

99 House Wren

1985. Birth Bicentenary of John J. Audubon (ornithologist). Multicoloured.
581 40c. Type **99** . . . . 2·75 1·00
582 70c. Veery . . . . 3·00 1·60
583 83c. Grasshopper sparrow . . 3·25 2·00
584 $1.50 Henslow's sparrow . . 3·50 2·25
585 $2.50 Vesper sparrow . . . . 5·00 4·25
MS586 Five sheets, each 54 × 60 mm. As Nos. 581/5 but each stamp 34 × 26 mm with a face value of $1.75 and without the commemorative inscription Set of 5 sheets . . . . 13·00 8·50

100 The Queen Mother in Garter Robes

1985. Life and Times of Queen Elizabeth the Queen Mother. Multicoloured.
587 70c. Type **100** . . . . 1·50 1·50
588 $1.15 In open carriage with the Queen . . . . 1·60 1·60
589 $1.50 With Prince Charles during 80th birthday celebrations . . . . 1·75 1·75
MS590 70 × 70 mm. $3 At her desk in Clarence House (38 × 35 mm) 6·50 2·75
See also No. **MS**627.

1985. South Pacific Mini Games, Rarotonga. Nos. 547/8 and 550/1 surch **MINI SOUTH PACIFIC GAMES, RAROTONGA** and emblem.
591 52c. on 70c. Javelin throwing 40 55
592 83c. on 58c. Boxing 65 80
593 95c. on 35c. Sprinting 75 90
594 $2 on 30c. Type **93** . . . . . 1·50 2·00

1985. Pacific Islands Conference, Rarotonga. Nos. 475/8 optd **PACIFIC ISLANDS CONFERENCE, RAROTONGA** and emblem.
595 70c. Type **85** 55 75
596 70c. "Resolution" and "Adventure" off Niue, 1774 . . . . 55 75
597 70c. Passion flower 55 75
598 70c. Limes 55 75
Nos. 595 also shows an overprinted amendment to the caption which now reads **Premier Sir Robert Rex K.B.E.**

103 "R. Strozzi's Daughter" (Titian)

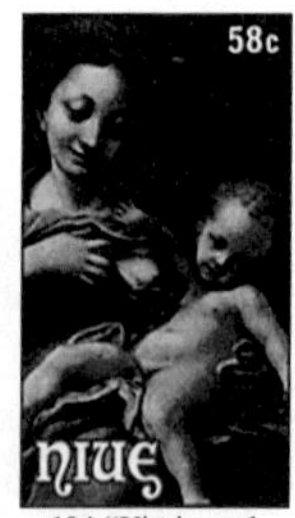

104 "Virgin and Child"

1985. International Youth Year. Mult.
599 58c. Type **103** . . . . 2·00 90
600 70c. "The Fifer" (E. Manet) 2·25 1·00
601 $1.15 "Portrait of a Young Girl" (Renoir) . . . . . . 3·00 1·90
602 $1.50 "Portrait of M. Berard" (Renoir) . . . 3·25 2·50
MS603 Four sheets, each 63 × 79 mm. As Nos. 599/602 but each with a face value of $1.75+10c. Set of 4 sheets . . . 14·00 11·00

1985. Christmas. Details of Paintings by Correggio. Multicoloured.
604 58c. Type **104** . . . . 1·50 85
605 85c. "Adoration of the Magi" 1·75 1·40
606 $1.05 "Virgin with Child and St. John" . . . . 2·25 2·50
607 $1.45 "Virgin and Child with St. Catherine" . . . . . . 2·75 3·50
MS608 83 × 123 mm. As Nos. 604/7 but each stamp with a face value of 60c.+10c. . . . . 3·00 2·75
MS609 Four sheets, each 80 × 90 mm. 65c. Type **104**; 95c. As No. 605; $1.20, As No. 606; $1.75, As No. 607 (each stamp 49 × 59 mm). Imperf Set of 4 sheets . . . . 4·00 4·00

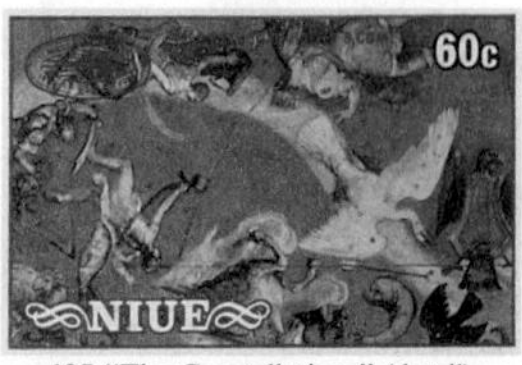

105 "The Constellations" (detail)

1986. Appearance of Halley's Comet. Designs showing details from ceiling painting "The Constellations" by Giovanni de Vecchi. Nos. 611/13 show different spacecraft at top left. Multicoloured.
610 60c. Type **105** 50 50
611 75c. "Vega" spacecraft . . . 65 65
612 $1.10 "Planet A" spacecraft 90 90
613 $1.50 "Giotto" spacecraft . . 1·25 1·25
MS614 125 × 91 mm. As Nos. 610/13 but each stamp with a face value of 95c. . . . . 4·75 4·25
Stamps from No. **MS**614 are without borders.

106 Queen Elizabeth II and Prince Philip

107 U.S.A. 1847 Franklin 5c. Stamp and Washington Sculpture, Mt. Rushmore, U.S.A.

1986. 60th Birthday of Queen Elizabeth II. Multicoloured.
615 $1.10 Type **106** . . . . . . 80 1·00
616 $1.50 Queen and Prince Philip at Balmoral . . . . 1·00 1·25
617 $2 Queen at Buckingham Palace . . . . 1·50 1·75
MS618 110 × 70 mm. As Nos. 615/17, but each stamp with a face value of 75c. . . . . . 2·75 3·25
MS619 58 × 89 mm. $3 Queen and Prince Philip at Windsor Castle 3·50 4·25

1986. "Ameripex '86" International Stamp Exhibition, Chicago. Multicoloured.
620 $1 Type **107** . . . . 3·25 3·25
621 $1 Flags of Niue and U.S.A. and Mt. Rushmore sculptures . . . . 3·25 3·25
Nos. 620/1 were printed together, se-tenant, forming a composite design.

108 "Statue under Construction, Paris, 1883" (Victor Dargaud)

1986. Centenary of Statue of Liberty. Multicoloured.
622 $1 Type **108** . . . . 2·00 2·00
623 $2.50 "Unveiling of Statue of Liberty" (Edmund Morand) . . . . 2·75 3·50
MS624 107 × 73 mm. As Nos. 622/3, but each stamp with a face value of $1.25 . . . . 2·50 3·00
See also No. **MS**648

109 Prince Andrew, Miss Sarah Ferguson and Westminster Abbey

1986. Royal Wedding.
625 **109** $2.50 multicoloured . . . 3·25 3·50
MS626 106 × 68 mm. $5 Prince Andrew and Miss sarah Ferguson (43 × 30 mm) . . . . 7·50 8·00

1986. 86th Birthday of Queen Elizabeth the Queen Mother. Nos. 587/9 in miniature sheet, 109 × 83 mm.
MS627 Nos. 587/9 . . . . 12·00 12·00

110 Great Egret

111 "Virgin and Child" (Perugino)

1986. "Stampex '86" Stamp Exhibition, Adelaide. Australian Birds. Multicoloured.
628 40c. Type **110** . . . . 2·75 1·75
629 60c. Painted finch (horiz) . . 3·00 2·00
630 75c. Australian king parrot 3·25 2·25
631 80c. Variegated wren (horiz) 3·50 2·50
632 $1 Peregrine falcon . . . . . 4·00 2·75
633 $1.65 Azure kingfisher (horiz) 5·50 4·00
634 $2.20 Budgerigars . . . . . 6·00 6·00
635 $4.25 Emu (horiz) . . . . . 7·50 7·50

1986. Christmas. Paintings from Vatican Museum. Multicoloured.
636 80c. Type **111** . . . . 2·00 1·75
637 $1.15 "Virgin of St. N. dei Frari" (Titian) . . . . . . 2·25 2·00
638 $1.80 "Virgin with Milk" (Lorenzo di Credi) . . . . 3·25 3·50
639 $2.60 "Madonna of Foligno" (Raphael) . . . . 4·00 5·00
MS640 87 × 110 mm. As Nos. 636/9, but each stamp with a face value of $1.50 . . . . 8·50 6·00
MS641 70 × 100 mm. $7.50 As No. 639, but 27 × 43 mm . . . 8·00 9·00

1986. Visit of Pope John Paul II to South Pacific. Nos. 636/9 surch **CHRISTMAS VISIT TO SOUTH PACIFIC OF POPE JOHN PAUL II NOVEMBER 21 24 1986**.
642 80c.+10c. Type **111** . . . . . 3·00 2·50
643 $1.15+10c. "Virgin of St. N. dei Frari" (Titian) . . . . 3·50 3·00
644 $1.80+10c. "Virgin with Milk" (Lorenzo di Credi) 4·75 4·00
645 $2.60+10c. "Madonna of Foligno" (Raphael) . . . . 6·00 5·00
MS646 87 × 110 mm. As Nos. 642/5, but each stamp with a face value of $1.50+10c. . . . . 15·00 12·00
MS647 70 × 100 mm. $7.50+50c. As No. 645, but 27 × 43 mm . . . 15·00 12·00

112a Sailing Ship under Brooklyn Bridge

1987. Centenary of Statue of Liberty (1986) (2nd issue). Two sheets, each 122 × 122 mm, containing T **112a** and similar multicoloured designs.
MS648 Two sheets. (a) 75c. Type **112a**; 75c. Restoring Statue's flame; 75c. Steam-cleaning Statue's torch; 75c. "Esmerelda" (children cadet barquentine) off Manhattan; 75c. Cadet barque at dusk. (b) 75c. Statue of Liberty at night (vert); 75c. Statue at night (side view) (vert); 75c. Cleaning Statue's crown (vert); 75c. Statue at night (rear view) (vert); 75c. Cleaning a finial (vert) Set of 2 sheets . . 8·00 9·00

113 Boris Becker, Olympic Rings and Commemorative Coin

1987. Olympic Games, Seoul (1988). Tennis (1st issue). Designs showing Boris Becker in play.
649 **113** 80c. multicoloured . . . . 2·75 2·00
650 – $1.15 multicoloured . . . 3·00 2·25
651 – $1.40 multicoloured . . . 3·25 2·50
652 – $1.80 multicoloured . . . 4·00 3·25

1987. Olympic Games, Seoul (1988). Tennis (2nd issue). As T **113** but showing Steffi Graf.
653 85c. multicoloured . . . . . 2·75 1·75
654 $1.05 multicoloured . . . . 3·00 2·00
655 $1.30 multicoloured . . . . 3·25 2·25
656 $1.75 multicoloured . . . . 3·50 2·75

1987. Royal Ruby Wedding. Nos. 616/17 surch **40TH WEDDING ANNIV. 4.85.**
657 $4.85 on $1.50 Queen and Prince Philip at Balmoral 4·75 4·50
658 $4.85 on $2 Queen at Buckingham Palace . . . . 4·75 4·50

115 "The Nativity"

1987. Christmas. Religious Paintings by Durer. Multicoloured.
659 80c. Type **115** . . . . 1·50 1·25
660 $1.05 "Adoration of the Magi" . . . . 1·75 1·75

661 $2.80 "Celebration of the Rosary" . . . . 3·25 3·75
MS662 100 × 140 mm. As Nos. 659/61, but each size 48 × 37 mm with a face value of $1.30 . . . . 7·50 4·50
MS663 90 × 80 mm. $7.50 As No. 661, but size 51 × 33 mm 7·50 7·00

Nos. 659/61 each include detail of an angel with lute as in T **115**.

Stamps from the miniature sheets are without this feature.

116 Franz Beckenbauer in Action

1988. West German Football Victories. Mult.

664 20c. Type **116** 70 70
665 40c. German "All Star" team in action 90 90
666 60c. Bayern Munich team with European Cup, 1974 1·10 1·10
667 80c. World Cup match, England, 1966 . . . . . . 1·40 1·40
668 $1.05 World Cup match, Mexico, 1970 . . . . . . 1·60 1·60
669 $1.30 Beckenbauer with pennant, 1974 . . . . . . 2·00 2·00
670 $1.80 Beckenbauer and European Cup, 1974 . . . 2·25 2·25

1988. Steffi Graf's Tennis Victories. Nos. 653/6 optd.

671 85c. mult (optd **Australia 24 Jan 88 French Open 4 June 88**) . . . . 2·25 1·50
672 $1.05 multicoloured (optd **Wimbledon 2 July 88 U S Open 10 Sept. 88**) . . . . 2·75 1·75
673 $1.30 multicoloured (optd **Women's Tennis Grand Slam: 10 September 88**) . . 2·75 1·90
674 $1.75 mult (optd **Seoul Olympic Games Gold Medal Winner**) . . . . . . 2·75 2·10

118 Angels

1988. Christmas. Details from "The Adoration of the Shepherds" by Rubens. Multicoloured.

675 60c. Type **118** . . . . 1·75 1·50
676 80c. Shepherds . . . . 2·00 1·75
677 $1.05 Virgin Mary . . . . . 2·75 2·50
678 $1.30 Holy Child . . . . . . 3·50 3·00
MS679 83 × 103 mm. $7.20 The Nativity (38 × 49 mm) . . . . 6·00 7·50

119 Astronaut and "Apollo 11" Emblem

1989. 20th Anniv of First Manned Landing on Moon. Multicoloured.

680 $1.50 Type **119** . . . . . . 4·50 4·50
681 $1.50 Earth and Moon . . . 4·50 4·50
682 $1.50 Astronaut and "Apollo 11" emblem . . . 4·50 4·50
MS683 160 × 64 mm. As Nos. 680/2, but each stamp with a face value of $1.15 . . . . 5·00 5·00

120 Priests

1989. Christmas. Details from "Presentation in the Temple" by Rembrandt. Multicoloured.

684 70c. Type **120** . . . . 3·00 2·75
685 80c. Virgin and Christ Child in Simeon's arms . . . . . 3·00 2·75
686 $1.05 Joseph . . . . 3·50 3·25
687 $1.30 Simeon and Christ Child . . . . 4·00 3·75
MS688 84 × 110 mm. $7.20 "Presentation in the Temple" (39 × 49 mm) . . . . 12·00 13·00

121 Fritz Walter

1990. World Cup Football Championship, Italy. German Footballers. Multicoloured.

689 80c. Type **121** . . . . 2·50 2·50
690 $1.15 Franz Beckenbauer . . 2·75 2·75
691 $1.40 Uwe Seeler . . . . . . 3·00 3·00
692 $1.80 German team emblem and signatures of former captains . . . . 4·00 4·00

122 "Merchant Maarten Looten" (Rembrandt)

123 Queen Elizabeth the Queen Mother

1990. 150th Anniv of the Penny Black. Rembrandt Paintings. Multicoloured.

693 80c. Type **122** . . . . 3·25 2·50
694 $1.05 "Rembrandt's Son Titus with Pen in Hand" 3·50 3·00
695 $1.30 "The Shipbuilder and his Wife" . . . . . . 3·75 3·25
696 $1.80 "Bathsheba with King David's Letter" . . . . . 4·00 3·50
MS697 82 × 143 mm. As Nos. 693/6, but each with a face value of $1.50 7·50 7·50

1990. 90th Birthday of Queen Elizabeth the Queen Mother.

698 **123** $1.25 multicoloured . . . 4·25 3·75
MS699 84 × 64 mm. **123** $7 multicoloured . . . . 13·00 11·00

124 "Adoration of the Magi" (Dirk Bouts)

129 "The Virgin and Child with Sts. Jerome and Dominic" (Lippi)

1990. Christmas. Religious Paintings. Mult.

700 70c. Type **124** . . . . 3·00 2·75
701 80c. "Holy Family" (Fra Bartolommeo) . . . . . . 3·25 3·00
702 $1.05 "Nativity" (Memling) 3·50 3·50
703 $1.30 "Adoration of the Kings" (Bruegel the Elder) 4·50 4·50
MS704 100 × 135 mm. $7.20 "Virgin and Child Enthroned" (detail, Cosimo Tura) . . . . 11·00 12·00

1990. "Birdpex '90" Stamp Exhibition, Christchurch, New Zealand. No. 410 optd **Birdpex '90** and logo.

705 $10 Scarlet hibiscus . . . . . 12·00 13·00

1991. 65th Birthday of Queen Elizabeth II. No. 409 optd **SIXTY FIFTH BIRTHDAY QUEEN ELIZABETH II**.

706 $6 "Hybrid hibiscus" . . . . 12·00 12·00

1991. 10th Wedding Anniv of Prince and Princess of Wales. Nos. 430/2 optd **TENTH ANNIVERSARY**.

707A 75c. Type **77** . . . . 2·25 1·75
708A 95c. Lady Diana Spencer 3·25 2·75
709A $1.20 Prince Charles and Lady Diana . . . . . . 3·25 2·75

1991. Christmas. Religious Paintings. Mult.

710 20c. Type **129** . . . . 1·25 85
711 50c. "The Isenheim Altarpiece" (M. Grunewald) . . . . . 2·25 1·75
712 $1 "The Nativity" (G. Pittoni) . . . . 3·50 3·50
713 $2 "Adoration of the Kings" (J. Brueghel the Elder) . . 4·50 5·50
MS714 79 × 104 mm. $7 "Adoration of the Sheperds" (G. Reni) . . 10·00 12·00

130 Buff-banded Rail

1992. Birds. Multicoloured.

718 20c. Type **130** . . . . 1·50 80
719 50c. Red-tailed tropic bird . . 1·75 1·10
720 70c. Purple swamphen . . . 2·25 1·25
721 $1 Pacific pigeon . . . . . . 2·75 1·75
722 $1.50 White-collared kingfisher . . . . 2·50 2·25
723 $2 Blue-crowned lory . . . . 2·50 2·50
724 $3 Purple-capped fruit dove 2·50 3·00
726 $5 Barn owl . . . . 5·50 5·50
727 $7 Longtailed koel ("Cockoo") (48½ × 35 mm) 5·50 7·50
728 $10 Reef heron (48½ × 35 mm) . . . . . . 7·50 9·50
729 $15 Spotted triller ("Polynesian Triller") (48½ × 35 mm) . . . . . . 11·00 14·00

131 Columbus before King Ferdinand and Queen Isabella

1992. 500th Anniv of Discovery of America by Columbus. Multicoloured.

731 $2 Type **131** . . . . 3·50 3·00
732 $3 Fleet of Columbus . . . . 6·00 5·50
733 $5 Claiming the New World for Spain . . . . 7·00 6·50

132 Tennis and $10 Commemorative Coin

1992. Olympic Games, Barcelona. Mult.

734 $2.50 Type **132** . . . . . . 6·00 5·00
735 $2.50 Olympic flame and national flags . . . . . . 6·00 5·00
736 $2.50 Gymnastics and different $10 coin . . . . 6·00 5·00
MS737 152 × 87 mm. $5 Water polo 11·00 12·00

1992. 6th Festival of Pacific Arts, Rarotonga. Nos. 336/51 surch **$1**.

738 $1 on 20c. Type **69** . . . . . 1·00 1·00
739 $1 on 20c. Ku-Tagwa plaque, New Guinea . . . . 1·00 1·00
740 $1 on 20c. Suspension hook, New Guinea . . . . 1·00 1·00
741 $1 on 20c. Ancestral board, New Guinea . . . . 1·00 1·00
742 $1 on 25c. Platform post, New Hebrides . . . . . . 1·00 1·00
743 $1 on 25c. Canoe ornament, New Ireland . . . . . . 1·00 1·00
744 $1 on 25c. Carved figure, Admiralty Islands . . . . 1·00 1·00
745 $1 on 25c. Female with child, Admiralty Islands . . . . 1·00 1·00
746 $1 on 30c. The God A'a, Rurutu, Austral Islands . . 1·00 1·00
747 $1 on 30c. Statue of Tangaroa, Cook Islands . . 1·00 1·00
748 $1 on 30c. Ivory pendant, Tonga . . . . 1·00 1·00
749 $1 on 30c. Tapa (Hiapo) cloth, Niue . . . . 1·00 1·00
750 $1 on 35c. Feather box (Waka), New Zealand . . 1·00 1·00
751 $1 on 35c. Hei-Tiki amulet, New Zealand . . . . . 1·00 1·00
752 $1 on 35c. House post, New Zealand . . . . 1·00 1·00
753 $1 on 35c. Feather image of god Ku, Hawaii . . . . . 1·00 1·00

134 "St. Catherine's Mystic Marriage" (detail) (Memling)

135 Queen on Official Visit

1992. Christmas.

754 **134** 20c. multicoloured . . . . 1·25 75
755 – 50c. multicoloured . . . . 2·00 1·50
756 – $1 multicoloured . . . . 3·00 3·00
757 – $2 multicoloured . . . . 4·50 5·50
MS758 87 × 101 mm. $7 multicoloured (as 50c., but larger (36 × 47 mm) . . . . 11·00 12·00

DESIGNS: 50c., $1, $2 Different details from "St. Catherine's Mystic Marriage" by Hans Memling.

1992. 40th Anniv of Queen Elizabeth II's Accession. Multicoloured.

759 70c. Type **135** . . . . 2·25 1·75
760 $1 Queen in green evening dress . . . . 2·75 2·25
761 $1.50 Queen in white embroidered evening dress 3·25 2·75
762 $2 Queen with bouquet . . . 3·75 3·25

136 Rough-toothed Dolphin

1993. Endangered Species. South Pacific Dolphins. Multicoloured.

763 20c. Type **136** . . . . 1·25 90
764 50c. Fraser's dolphin . . . . 2·00 1·60
765 75c. Pantropical spotted dolphin . . . . 2·50 2·75
766 $1 Risso's dolphin . . . . . 3·00 3·50

1993. Premier Sir Robert Rex Commemoration. Nos. 568/70 optd **1909 IN MEMORIAM 1992 SIR ROBERT R REX K.B.E.** or surch also.

767 40c. Type **96** . . . . 2·50 2·50
768 58c. Map of Niue and Premier Rex . . . . 2·50 2·50
769 70c. Premier Rex receiving proclamation of self-government . . . . 2·50 2·50
770 $1 on 40c. Type **96** . . . . . 2·75 2·75
771 $1 on 58c. Map of Niue and Premier Rex . . . . 2·75 2·75
772 $1 on 70c. Premier Rex receiving proclamation of self-government . . . . . 2·75 2·75

138 Queen Elizabeth II in Coronation Robes and St. Edward's Crown

1993. 40th Anniv of Coronation.

773 **138** $5 multicoloured . . . . 12·00 12·00

139 "Virgin of the Rosary" (detail) (Guido Reni)

1993. Christmas.

774 **139** 20c. multicoloured 85 75
775 – 70c. multicoloured . . . . 2·00 1·25
776 – $1 multicoloured . . . . 2·25 1·50
777 – $1. 50 multicoloured . . . . 3·00 3·50
778 – $3 multicoloured (32 × 47 mm) . . . . . 4·75 6·50

DESIGNS: 70c. to $3 Different details of "Virgin of the Rosary" (Reni).

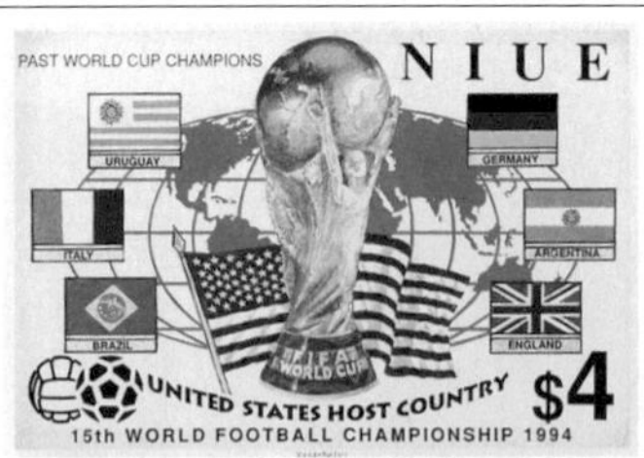

140 World Cup and Globe with Flags of U.S.A. and Previous Winners

1994. World Cup Football Championship, U.S.A.
779 **140** $4 multicoloured . . . . 6·50 7·50

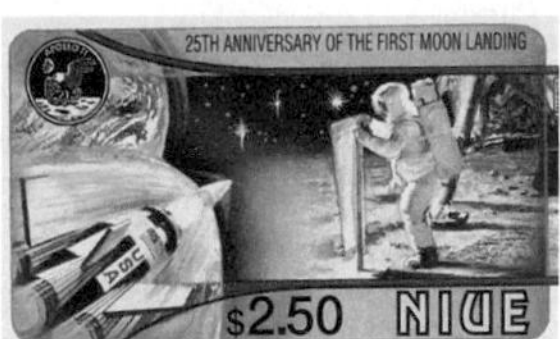

141 "Apollo 11" and Astronaut on Moon

1994. 25th Anniv of First Manned Moon Landing. Multicoloured.
780 $2.50 Type **141** . . . . . . 6·00 6·00
781 $2.50 Astronaut and flag . . 6·00 6·00
782 $2.50 Astronaut and equipment . . . . 6·00 6·00

142 "The Adoration of the Kings" (Jan Gossaert)

1994. Christmas. Religious Paintings. Multicoloured.
783 70c. Type **142** . . . . 1·00 1·25
784 70c. "Madonna and Child with Sts. John and Catherine" (Titian) . . . . 1·00 1·25
785 70c. "The Holy Family and Shepherd" (Titian) . . . . 1·00 1·25
786 70c. "The Virgin and Child with Saints" (Gerard David) . . . . 1·00 1·25
787 $1 "The Adoration of the Shepherds" (cherubs detail) (Poussin) . . . . 1·25 1·50
788 $1 "The Adoration of the Shepherds" (Holy Family detail) (Poussin) . . . . 1·25 1·50
789 $1 "Madonna and Child with Sts. Joseph and John" (Sebastiano) . . . . 1·25 1·50
790 $1 "The Adoration of the Kings" (Veronese) . . . . 1·25 1·50

143 Long John Silver and Jim Hawkins ("Treasure Island")

145 Tapeu Orchid

1994. Death Centenary of Robert Louis Stevenson (author). Multicoloured.
791 $1.75 Type **143** . . . . . . 3·50 3·00
792 $1.75 Transformation of Dr. Jekyll ("Dr. Jekyll and Mr. Hyde") . . . . 3·50 3·00
793 $1.75 Attack on David Balfour ("Kidnapped") . . 3·50 3·00
794 $1.75 Robert Louis Stevenson, tomb and inscription . . . . 3·50 3·00

1996. Nos. 720 and 722 surch.
795 50c. on 70c. Purple swamphen . . . . 7·00 4·00
796 $1 on $1.50 White-collared kingfisher . . . . 8·00 6·50

1996. Flowers. Multicoloured.
797 70c. Type **145** 80 80
798 $1 Frangipani . . . . 1·00 1·00
799 $1.20 "Golden Shower" . . . 1·40 1·75
800 $1.50 "Pua" . . . . 1·90 2·50

1996. Redrawn design as No. 146.
801 20c. red and green . . . . . 1·75 1·25

146 "Jackfish" (yacht)

1996. Sailing Ships. Multicoloured.
802 70c. Type **146** . . . . 1·10 1·10
803 $1 "Jennifer" (yacht) . . . . 1·60 1·60
804 $1.20 "Mikeva" (yacht) . . . 1·90 2·00
805 $2 "Eye of the Wind" (cadet brig) . . . . 2·50 3·00

147 "Desert Star" (ketch)

149 Ox

148 "Acropora gemmifera"

1996. "Taipei '96" International Philatelic Exhibition, Taiwan. Sheet 90 × 80 mm.
MS806 **147** $1.50 multicoloured 2·00 2·50

1996. Corals. Multicoloured.
807 20c. Type **148** 55 55
808 50c. "Acropora nobilis" . . . 80 60
809 70c. "Goniopora lobata" . . 1·00 70
810 $1 "Sylaster sp." . . . . . . 1·10 90
811 $1.20 "Alveopora catalai" . . 1·25 1·25
812 $1.50 "Fungia scutaria" . . . 1·50 1·50
813 $2 "Porites solida" . . . . . 2·00 2·00
814 $3 "Millepora sp." . . . . . 2·75 3·25
815 $4 "Pocillopora eydouxi" . . 3·50 4·25
816 $5 "Platygyra pini" . . . . . 3·75 4·50

1997. "HONG KONG '97" International Stamp Exhibition. Chinese New Year ("Year of the Ox"). Sheet 120 × 90 mm.
MS817 **149** $1.50 multicoloured 1·50 2·25

150 Steps to Lagoon

1997. Island Scenes. Multicoloured.
818 $1 Type **150** . . . . 1·25 1·50
819 $1 Islands in lagoon . . . . 1·25 1·50
820 $1 Beach with rocks in foreground . . . . 1·25 1·50
821 $1 Over-hanging rock on beach . . . . 1·25 1·50

Nos. 818/21 were printed together, se-tenant, forming a composite design.

151 Humpback Whale

1997. Whales (1st series). Multicoloured.
822 20c. Type **151** 50 45
823 $1 Humpback whale and calf (vert) . . . . 1·25 1·25
824 $1.50 Humpback whale surfacing (vert) . . . . . 1·75 2·00
MS825 120 × 90 mm. Nos. 822/4 3·00 3·50

No. **MS**825 shows the "Pacific '97" International Stamp Exhibition, San Francisco, emblem on the margin.

See also Nos. 827/9.

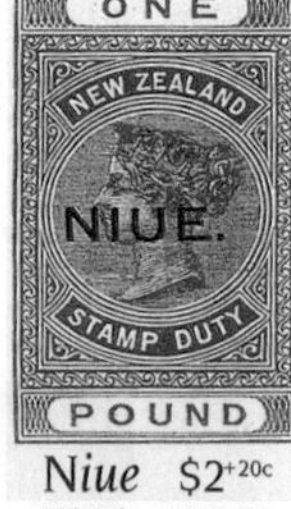

152 Niue 1902 Ovpt on New Zealand 1d.

153 Niue 1918–29 Overprint on New Zealand £1

1997. "Aupex '97" Stamp Exhibition, Auckland (1st issue). Sheet 136 × 90 mm.
MS826 **152** $2+20c. multicoloured 2·10 2·50

1997. Whales (2nd series). As T **151**. Multicoloured.
827 50c. Killer whale (vert) . . . 85 85
828 70c. Minke whale (vert) . . . 1·00 1·00
829 $1.20 Sperm whale (vert) . . 1·25 1·25

1997. "Aupex '97" Stamp Exhibition, Auckland (2nd issue). Sheet 90 × 135 mm.
MS830 **153** $2+20c. multicoloured 1·90 2·50

154 Floral Display in Woven Basket

1997. Christmas. Floral Displays. Multicoloured.
831 20c. Type **154** 45 40
832 50c. Display in white pot . . 70 60
833 70c. Display in white basket 90 90
834 $1 Display in purple vase . . 1·25 1·50

1998. Diana, Princess of Wales Commemoration. Sheet 145 × 70 mm, containing vert designs as T **91** of Kiribati. Multicoloured.
MS835 20c. Wearing white jacket, 1992; 50c. Wearing pearl-drop earrings, 1988; $1 In raincoat, 1990; $2 With Mother Theresa, 1992 (sold at $3.70+50c. charity premium) . . . . 3·00 3·50

155 Divers and Turtle

1998. Diving. Multicoloured.
836 20c. Type **155** 45 45
837 70c. Diver exploring coral reef 75 75
838 $1 Exploring underwater chasm (vert) 90 90
839 $1.20 Divers and coral fronds 1·10 1·25
840 $1.50 Divers in cave . . . . 1·40 1·75

157 Pacific Black Duck

1998. Coastal Birds (1st series). Multicoloured.
841 20c. Type **157** 70 60
842 70c. White tern ("Fairy Tern") . . . . 1·25 80
843 $1 Great frigate bird (vert) 1·25 1·10
844 $1.20 Pacific golden plover ("Lesser Golden Plover") 1·40 1·50
845 $2 Common noddy ("Brown Noddy") . . . . 2·00 2·50

See also Nos. 875/8.

158 Golden Cowrie

1998. Shells. Multicoloured.
846 20c. Type **158** 40 30
847 70c. Cowrie shell 75 65
848 $1 Spider conch . . . . . . 1·00 1·00
849 $5 Helmet shell . . . . . . 5·00 7·00

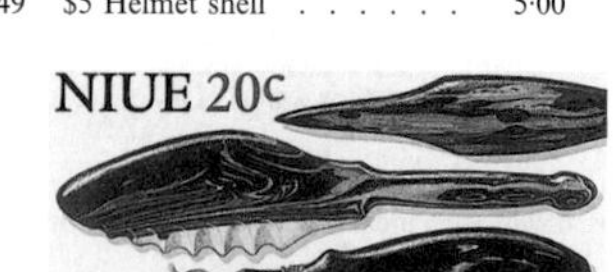

159 Clubs

1998. Ancient Weapons. Multicoloured.
850 20c. Type **159** 40 30
851 $1.20 Three spears (59 × 24 mm) . . . . . . 1·00 1·00
852 $1.50 Five spears (59 × 24 mm) . . . . . . 1·25 1·75
853 $2 Throwing stones . . . . . 1·50 2·25

160 Outrigger Canoe (first migration of Niue Fekai)

1999. "Australia '99" World Stamp Exhibition, Melbourne. Maritime History. Each blue.
854 70c. Type **160** 70 60
855 $1 H.M.S. "Resolution" (Cook) . . . . 1·25 1·00
856 $1.20 "John Williams" (missionary sailing ship) . . 1·40 1·60
857 $1.50 Captain James Cook 1·60 2·00

161 "Risbecia tryoni"

1999. Endangered Species. Nudibranchs. Mult.
858 20c. Type **161** 45 40
859 $1 "Chromodoris lochi" . . 1·10 1·00
860 $1.20 "Chromodoris elizabethina" . . . . . . 1·25 1·40
861 $1.50 "Chromodoris bullocki" . . . . 1·50 2·00
MS862 190 × 105 mm. Nos. 858/61 × 2 . . . . 6·50 8·00

162 Togo Chasm

1999. Scenic Views. Multicoloured.
863 $1 Type **162** . . . . 1·10 1·00
864 $1.20 Matapa Chasm . . . . 1·25 1·25
865 $1.50 Tufukia (horiz) . . . . 1·50 2·00
866 $2 Talava Arches (horiz) . . 1·75 2·50

163 Shallow Baskets

1999. Woven Baskets. Multicoloured.
867 20c. Type **163** 70 90
868 70c. Tray and bowl . . . . . 80 1·10
869 $1 Tall basket and deep bowls (44 × 34 mm) . . . . 1·00 1·40
870 $3 Tall basket and shallow bowls (44 × 34 mm) . . . . 2·10 2·50

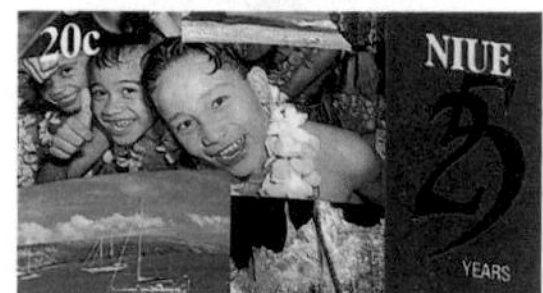

164 Children, Yachts and Forest

1999. 25th Anniv of Self-Government. Sheet, 120 × 74 mm, containing T **164** and similar horiz design. Multicoloured.
MS871 20c. Type **164**; $5 Scuba diver, young child and sunset 4·00 5·00

165 Family and Man in Canoe

1999. New Millennium. Multicoloured.
872 20c. Type **165** 90 1·10
873 70c. People pointing up 1·40 1·75
874 $4 Diver and man in traditional dress 2·50 3·00
Nos. 872/4 were printed together, se-tenant, with the backgrounds forming a composite design.

166 Purple-capped Fruit Dove
167 Queen Elizabeth the Queen Mother

2000. Coastal Birds (2nd series). Multicoloured.
875 20c. Type **166** 45 40
876 $1 Purple swamphen 1·00 90
877 $1.20 Barn owl 1·40 1·40
878 $2 Blue-crowned lory 1·75 2·25

2000. 100th Birthday of Queen Elizabeth the Queen Mother and 18th Birthday of Prince William. Multicoloured.
879 $1.50 Type **167** 1·75 1·75
880 $3 Queen Elizabeth the Queen Mother and Prince William (horiz) 2·50 3·25

168 Pole Vault

2000. Olympic Games, Sydney. Multicoloured.
881 50c. Type **168** 60 45
882 70c. Diving 75 65
883 $1 Hurdling 1·10 1·10
884 $3 Gymnastics 2·25 3·25

169 Couple in Traditional Costumes

2000. Island Dances. Multicoloured.
885 20c. Type **169** 45 70
886 70c. Woman in red costume 80 1·10
887 $1.50 Woman in white costume 1·25 1·40
888 $3 Child in costume made of leaves 1·75 1·90
Nos. 885/8 were printed together, se-tenant, with the backgrounds forming a composite design of flowers.

170 New Zealand Overprinted 1d. of 1902

2001. Centenary of First Niue Stamps. Multicoloured.
889 70c. Type **170** 75 75
890 $3 New Zealand overprinted £1 stamp of 1918–29 2·00 2·75

171 Large Green-banded Blue

2001. Butterflies. Multicoloured.
891 20c. Type **171** 40 35
892 70c. Leafwing 80 70
893 $1.50 Cairns birdwing 1·25 1·40
894 $2 Meadow argus 1·50 2·00

172 Green Turtle

2001. Turtles. Multicoloured.
895 50c. Type **172** 60 60
896 $1 Hawksbill turtle 1·00 1·00
897 $3 Green turtle on beach 2·50 3·00

173 Coconut Crab emerging from Sea

2001. Coconut Crabs. Multicoloured.
898 20c. Type **173** 40 30
899 70c. Crab on beach with coconut palms 80 70
900 $1.50 Crab climbing coconut palm 1·25 1·50
901 $3 Crab with coconut 2·50 3·00

174 Government Offices

2001. Centenary of Annexation to New Zealand. Multicoloured.
902 $1.50 Type **174** 1·25 1·40
903 $2 New Zealand Commissioner and Niue Chief 1·50 2·00

175 Three Wise Men

2001. Christmas. Multicoloured.
904 20c. Type **175** 25 20
905 70c. Dove 70 55
906 $1 Angel 90 90
907 $2 Star 1·50 2·00

OFFICIAL STAMPS

1985. Nos. 409/10 and 527/42 optd **O.H.M.S.**
O 1 12c. Type **92** 35 30
O 2 25c. "Euphorbia pulcherrima" 40 35
O 3 30c. "Cochlospermum hibiscoides" 45 35
O 4 35c. "Begonia sp." 50 40
O 5 40c. "Plumeria sp." 50 45
O 6 52c. "Strelitzia reginae" 60 50
O 7 58c. "Hibiscus syriacus" 60 55
O 8 70c. "Tibouchina sp." 75 70
O 9 83c. "Nelumbo sp." 90 80
O10 $1.05 "Hybrid hibiscus" 1·25 1·00
O11 $1.75 "Cassia fistula" 1·75 1·75
O12 $2.30 Orchid var. 5·50 2·75
O13 $3.90 Orchid sp. 6·00 4·25
O14 $4 "Euphorbia pulcherrima poinsettia" 5·50 6·00
O15 $5 "Euphorbia pulcherrima poinsettia" 5·50 6·00
O16 $6 "Hybrid hibiscus" 8·00 9·00
O17 $6.60 "Hybrid hibiscus" 8·00 9·00
O18 $8.30 "Hibiscus rosa-sinensis" 9·00 10·00
O19 $10 Scarlet hibiscus 10·00 11·00

1993. Nos. 718/29 optd **O.H.M.S.**
O20 20c. Type **130** 1·75 1·50
O21 50c. Red-tailed tropic bird 2·25 1·75
O22 70c. Purple swamphen 3·00 2·00
O23 $1 Pacific pigeon 3·25 2·00
O24 $1.50 White-collared kingfisher 4·00 3·00
O25 $2 Blue-crowned lory 4·00 3·25
O26 $3 Crimson-crowned fruit dove 2·75 3·50
O27 $5 Barn owl 9·50 6·50
O28 $7 Longtailed cuckoo (48½ × 35 mm) 6·50 8·50
O29 $10 Eastern reef heron (48½ × 35 mm) 7·50 10·00
O30 $15 Spotted triller ("Polynesian Triller") (48½ × 35 mm) 16·00 18·00

NORFOLK ISLAND Pt. 1

A small island East of New South Wales, administered by Australia until 1960 when local government was established.

1947. 12 pence = 1 shilling;
20 shillings = 1 pound.
1966. 100 cents = $1 Australian.

1 Ball Bay

1947.
1 **1** ½d. orange 85 60
2 1d. violet 50 60
3 1½d. green 50 70
4 2d. violet 55 40
5 2½d. red 80 30
6 3d. brown 70 70
6a 3d. green 14·00 7·50
7 4d. red 1·75 40
8 5½d. blue 70 30
9 6d. brown 70 30
10 9d. pink 1·25 40
11 1s. green 70 40
12 2s. brown 1·00 1·00
12a 2s. blue 20·00 8·00

12 "Hibiscus insularis"
2 Warder's Tower

4 Old Stores (Crankmill)

17 Queen Elizabeth II (after Annigoni) and Cereus

22 Red-tailed Tropic Bird

1953.
24 **12** 1d. green 15 10
25 – 2d. red and green 20 10
26 – 3d. green 70 15
13 **2** 3½d. red 1·00 90
27 – 5d. purple 55 20
14 – 6½d. green 2·25 3·25
15 **4** 7½d. blue 1·50 3·00
28 – 8d. red 80 50
16 – 8½d. brown 1·75 4·75
29 **17** 9d. blue 80 45
17 – 10d. violet 1·00 75
30 – 10d. brown and violet 1·25 1·00
31 – 1s.1d. red 80 35
32 – 2s. brown 6·00 1·00
33 – 2s.5d. violet 1·00 40
34 – 2s.8d. brown and green 2·25 55
18 – 5s. brown 32·00 8·00
35 – 5s. brown and green 3·50 75
36 **22** 10s. green 30·00 32·00
DESIGNS—VERT: 2d. "Lagunaria patersonii"; 5d. Lantana; 8d. Red hibiscus; 8½d. Barracks entrance; 10d. Salt house; 1s.1d. Fringed hibiscus; 2s. Solander's petrel; 2s.5d. Passion-flower; 2s.8d. Rose apple. HORIZ: 3d. White tern; 6½d. Airfield; 5s. Bloody Bridge.

For Nos. 25 and 28 with face values in decimal currency see Nos. 600/1.

8 Norfolk Is. Seal and Pitcairners Landing

1956. Cent of Landing of Pitcairners on Norfolk Is.
19 **8** 3d. green 75 40
20 2s. violet 1·00 75

1958. Surch.
21 **4** 7d. on 7½d. blue 75 1·00
22 – 8d. on 8½d. brown (No. 16) 75 1·00

1959. 150th Anniv of Australian P.O. No. 331 of Australia surch **NORFOLK ISLAND 5D.**
23 **143** 5d. on 4d. slate 35 30

1960. As Nos. 13 and 14/15 but colours changed and surch.
37 **2** 1s.1d. on 3½d. blue 2·75 1·50
38 2s.5d. on 6½d. turquoise 3·25 1·25
39 **4** 2s.8d. on 7½d. sepia 8·00 5·50

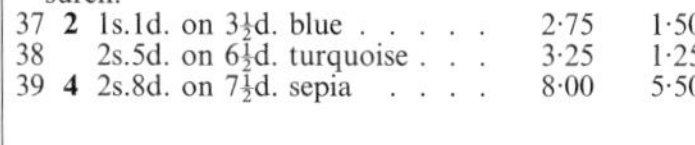

26 Queen Elizabeth II and Map

1960. Introduction of Local Government.
40 **26** 2s.8d. purple 7·00 6·50

27 Open Bible and Candle
29 Stripey

28 Open Prayer Book and Text

1960. Christmas.
41 **27** 5d. mauve 60 50

1961. Christmas.
42 **28** 5d. blue 30 70

1962. Fishes.
43 **29** 6d. sepia, yellow and green 60 25
44 – 11d. orange, brown and blue 1·00 80
45 – 1s. blue, pink and olive 60 25
46 – 1s.3d. blue, brown and green 1·00 1·75
47 – 1s.6d. sepia, violet and blue 1·50 80
48 – 2s.3d. multicoloured 3·00 80
DESIGNS: 11d. Gold-mouthed emperor; 1s. Surge wrasse ("Po'ov"); 1s.3d. Seachub ("Dreamfish"); 1s.6d. Giant grouper; 2s.3d. White trevally.

30 "Madonna and Child"
31 "Peace on Earth ..."

1962. Christmas.
49 **30** 5d. blue 45 80

1963. Christmas.
50 **31** 5d. red 40 70

32 Overlooking Kingston
33 Norfolk Pine

1964. Multicoloured.
51 5d. Type **32** 60 60
52 8d. Kingston 1·00 1·50

No.	Type	Description	Mint	Used
53		9d. The Arches (Bumboras)	1·75	30
54		10d. Slaughter Bay	1·75	30

1964. 50th Anniv of Norfolk Island as Australian Territory.

No.	Type	Description	Mint	Used
55	33	5d. black, red and orange	40	15
56		8d. black, red and green	40	1·10

34 Child looking at Nativity Scene

35 Nativity Scene

1964. Christmas.

No.	Type	Description	Mint	Used
57	34	5d. multicoloured	30	40

1965. 50th Anniv of Gallipoli Landing. As T **22** of Nauru, but slightly larger (22 × 34½ mm).

No.	Type	Description	Mint	Used
58		5d. brown, black and green	15	10

1965. Christmas.

No.	Type	Description	Mint	Used
59	35	5d. multicoloured	15	10

38 "Hibiscus insularis"

39 Headstone Bridge

1966. Decimal Currency. As earlier issue but with values in cents and dollars. Surch in black on silver tablets obliterating old value as in T **38**.

No.	Type	Description	Mint	Used
60	38	1c. on 1d.	20	10
61	–	2c. on 2d. (No. 25)	20	10
62	–	3c. on 3d. (No. 26)	75	90
63	–	4c. on 5d. (No. 27)	25	10
64	–	5c. on 8d. (No. 28)	30	10
65	–	10c. on 10d. (No. 30)	1·00	15
66	–	15c. on 1s.1d. (No. 31)	50	50
67	–	20c. on 2s. (No. 32)	2·75	2·75
68	–	25c. on 2s.5d. (No. 33)	1·00	40
69	–	30c. on 2s.8d. (No. 34)	1·00	50
70	–	50c. on 5s. (No. 35)	3·00	75
71a	22	$1 on 10s.	2·75	2·50

1966. Multicoloured.

No.	Type	Description	Mint	Used
72		7c. Type **39**	40	15
73		9c. Cemetery Road	40	15

41 St. Barnabas' Chapel (interior)

43 Star over Philip Island

1966. Centenary of Melanesian Mission. Mult.

No.	Type	Description	Mint	Used
74		4c. Type **41**	10	10
75		25c. St. Barnabas' Chapel (exterior)	20	20

1966. Christmas.

No.	Type	Description	Mint	Used
76	43	4c. multicoloured	10	10

44 H.M.S. "Resolution", 1774

1967. Multicoloured.

No.	Type	Description	Mint	Used
77		1c. Type **44**	10	10
78		2c. "La Boussole" and "L'Astrolabe", 1788	15	10
79		3c. H.M.S. "Supply" (brig), 1788	15	10
80		4c. H.M.S. "Sirius" (frigate), 1790	75	10
81		5c. "Norfolk" (sloop), 1798	20	10
82		7c. H.M.S. "Mermaid" (survey cutter), 1825	20	10
83		9c. "Lady Franklin" (full-rigged ship), 1853	20	10
84		10c. "Morayshire" (full-rigged transport), 1856	20	50
85		15c. "Southern Cross" (missionary ship), 1866	50	30
86		20c. "Pitcairn" (missionary schooner), 1891	60	40
87		25c. "Black Billy" (Norfolk Island whaleboat), 1895	1·50	75
88		30c. "Iris" (cable ship), 1907	1·50	2·00
89		50c. "Resolution" (schooner), 1926	3·25	2·75
90		$1 "Morinda" (freighter), 1931	4·00	2·75

45 Lions Badge and 50 Stars

47 Queen Elizabeth II

46 Prayer of John Adams and Candle

1967. 50th Anniv of Lions International.

No.	Type	Description	Mint	Used
91	45	4c. black, green and yellow	10	10

1967. Christmas.

No.	Type	Description	Mint	Used
92	46	5c. black, olive and red	10	10

1968.

No.	Type	Description	Mint	Used
93	47	3c. black, brown and red	10	10
94		4c. black, brown and green	10	10
95		5c. black, brown and violet	10	10
95a		6c. black, brown and lake	30	60

59 Avro Type 691 Lancastrian and Douglas DC-4 Aircraft

1968. 21st Anniv of QANTAS Air Service, Sydney–Norfolk Island.

No.	Type	Description	Mint	Used
96	59	5c. black, red and blue	15	10
97		7c. brown, red and turquoise	15	10

60 Bethlehem Star and Flowers

61 Captain Cook, Quadrant and Chart of Pacific Ocean

1968. Christmas.

No.	Type	Description	Mint	Used
98	60	5c. multicoloured	10	10

1969. Captain Cook Bicentenary (1st issue). Observation of the transit of Venus across the Sun from Tahiti.

No.	Type	Description	Mint	Used
99	61	10c. multicoloured	10	10

See also Nos. 118/19, 129, 152/5, 200/2 and 213/14.

62 Van Diemen's Land, Norfolk Island and Sailing Cutter

63 "The Nativity" (carved mother-of-pearl plaque)

1969. 125th Anniv of Annexation of Norfolk Island to Van Diemen's Land.

No.	Type	Description	Mint	Used
100	62	5c. multicoloured	10	10
101		30c. multicoloured	50	1·00

1969. Christmas.

No.	Type	Description	Mint	Used
102	63	5c. multicoloured	10	10

64 New Zealand Grey Flyeater

1970. Birds. Multicoloured.

No.	Type	Description	Mint	Used
103		1c. Scarlet robin (vert)	30	10
104		2c. Golden whistler (vert)	30	20
105		3c. Type **64**	30	10
106		4c. Long-tailed koels	60	10
107		5c. Red-fronted parakeet (vert)	1·50	60
108		7c. Long-tailed triller (vert)	45	10
109		9c. Island thrush	70	10
110		10c. Boobook owl (vert)	1·75	3·00
111		15c. Norfolk Island pigeon (vert)	1·50	65
112		20c. White-chested white-eye	8·00	3·25
113		25c. Norfolk Island parrots (vert)	2·50	40
114		30c. Collared grey fantail	8·00	1·75
115		45c. Norfolk Island starlings	2·25	80
116		50c. Crimson rosella (vert)	2·50	1·75
117		$1 Sacred kingfisher	10·00	10·00

65 Cook and Map of Australia

1970. Captain Cook Bicentenary (2nd issue). Discovery of Australia's East Coast. Mult.

No.	Type	Description	Mint	Used
118		5c. Type **65**	15	10
119		20c. H.M.S. "Endeavour" and aborigine	40	10

66 First Christmas Service, 1788

68 Rose Window, St. Barnabas Chapel, Kingston

67 Bishop Patteson, and Martyrdom of St. Stephen

1970. Christmas.

No.	Type	Description	Mint	Used
120	66	5c. multicoloured	10	10

1971. Death Cent of Bishop Patteson. Multicoloured.

No.	Type	Description	Mint	Used
121		6c. Type **67**	10	35
122		6c. Bible, Martyrdom of St. Stephen and knotted palm-frond	10	35
123		10c. Bishop Patteson and stained glass	10	35
124		10c. Cross and Bishop's Arms	10	35

1971. Christmas.

No.	Type	Description	Mint	Used
125	68	6c. multicoloured	10	10

69 Map and Flag

1972. 25th Anniv of South Pacific Commission.

No.	Type	Description	Mint	Used
126	69	7c. multicoloured	15	20

70 "St. Mark" (stained glass window) (All Saints, Norfolk Is.)

71 Cross and Pines (stained-glass window, All Saints Church)

1972. Christmas.

No.	Type	Description	Mint	Used
127	70	7c. multicoloured	10	10

1972. Cent of First Pitcairner-built Church.

No.	Type	Description	Mint	Used
128	71	12c. multicoloured	10	10

72 H.M.S. "Resolution" in the Antarctic

1973. Capt. Cook Bicentenary (3rd issue). Crossing of the Antarctic Circle.

No.	Type	Description	Mint	Used
129	72	35c. multicoloured	2·25	2·25

73 Child and Christmas Tree

1973. Christmas. Multicoloured.

No.	Type	Description	Mint	Used
130		7c. Type **73**	20	10
131		12c. Type **73**	25	10
132		35c. Fir trees and star	70	90

74 Protestant Clergyman's Quarters

1973. Historic Buildings. Multicoloured.

No.	Type	Description	Mint	Used
133		1c. Type **74**	10	10
134		2c. Royal Engineers' Office	10	10
135		3c. Double Quarters for Free Overseers	25	1·00
136		4c. Guard House	20	20
137		5c. Entrance to Pentagonal Gaol	25	15
138		7c. Pentagonal Gaol	35	35
139		8c. Prisoners' Barracks	1·25	2·25
140		10c. Officers' Quarters, New Military Barracks	50	55
141		12c. New Military Barracks	50	30
142		14c. Beach Stores	50	70
143		15c. The Magazine	1·25	50
144		20c. Entrance, Old Military Barracks	50	1·00
145		25c. Old Military Barracks	1·25	1·50
146		30c. Old Stores (Crankmill)	50	60
147		50c. Commissariat Stores	50	2·00
148		$1 Government House	1·00	4·00

75 Royal Couple and Map

1974. Royal Visit.

No.	Type	Description	Mint	Used
149	75	7c. multicoloured	40	20
150		25c. multicoloured	70	80

76 Chichester's De Havilland Gipsy Moth Seaplane "Madame Elijah"

1974. 1st Aircraft Landing on Norfolk Island.

No.	Type	Description	Mint	Used
151	76	14c. multicoloured	75	70

77 "Captain Cook" (engraving by J. Basire)

78 Nativity Scene (pearl-shell pew carving)

1974. Capt. Cook Bicentenary (4th issue). Discovery of Norfolk Is. Multicoloured.

No.	Type	Description	Mint	Used
152		7c. Type **77**	65	65
153		10c. H.M.S. "Resolution" (H. Roberts)	1·25	1·25

154 14c. Norfolk Island pine . . 1·00 1·50
155 25c. "Norfolk Island flax" (G. Raper) . . . . 1·00 2·00

1974. Christmas.
156 **78** 7c. multicoloured 15 10
157 30c. multicoloured 60 75

79 Norfolk Pine

1974. Centenary of Universal Postal Union. Multicoloured. Imperf. Self-adhesive.
158 10c. Type **79** 35 50
159 15c. Offshore islands 45 55
160 35c. Crimson rosella and sacred kingfisher 85 85
161 40c. Pacific map 85 95
MS162 106 × 101 mm. Map of Norfolk Is. cut-to-shape with reduced size replicas of Nos. 158/61 . . . . 20·00 24·00

80 H.M.S. "Mermaid" (survey cutter)

1975. 150th Anniv of Second Settlement. Multicoloured.
163 10c. Type **80** . . . . 40 1·10
164 35c. Kingston, 1835 (from painting by T. Seller) . . . 60 1·25

81 Star on Norfolk Island Pine

82 Memorial Cross

1975. Christmas.
165 **81** 10c. multicoloured 15 10
166 15c. multicoloured 20 10
167 35c. multicoloured 30 35

1975. Cent of St. Barnabas Chapel. Mult.
168 30c. Type **82** 20 15
169 60c. Laying foundation stone, and Chapel in 1975 . . . . 40 40

83 Launching of "Resolution"

1975. 50th Anniv of Launching of "Resolution" (schooner). Multicoloured.
170 25c. Type **83** 25 40
171 45c. "Resolution" at sea . . 40 70

84 Whaleship "Charles W. Morgan"

1976. Bicent of American Revolution. Mult.
172 18c. Type **84** 20 35
173 25c. Thanksgiving Service . . 20 35
174 40c. Boeing B-17 Flying Fortress over Norfolk Island 30 85
175 45c. California quail 45 85

85 Antarctic Tern and Sun

86 "Vanessa ita"

1976. Christmas.
176 **85** 18c. multicoloured 25 15
177 25c. multicoloured 40 20
178 45c. multicoloured 70 50

1977. Butterflies and Moths. Multicoloured.
179 1c. Type **86** 10 40
180 2c. "Utetheisa pulchelloides" 10 40
181 3c. "Agathia asterias" . . . 10 20
182 4c. "Cynthia kershawi" . . . 10 25
183 5c. "Leucania loreyimima" 15 1·10
184 10c. "Hypolimnas bolina" . . 30 1·10
185 15c. "Pyrrhorachis pyrrhogona" 30 30
186 16c. "Austrocarea iocephala" 30 30
187 17c. "Pseudocoremia christiani" 35 30
188 18c. "Cleora idiocrossa" . . 35 30
189 19c. "Simplicia caeneusalis" 35 30
190 20c. "Austrocidaria ralstonae" 40 30
191 30c. "Hippotion scrofa" . . . 50 60
192 40c. "Papilio amynthor (ilioneus)" 50 40
193 50c. "Tiracola plagiata" . . . 50 75
194 $1 "Precis villida" 60 75
195 $2 "Cepora perimale" . . . 75 1·40

87 Queen's View, Kingston

1977. Silver Jubilee.
196 **87** 25c. multicoloured 35 30

88 Hibiscus Flowers and Oil Lamp

89 Captain Cook (from a portrait by Nathaniel Dance)

1977. Christmas.
197 **88** 18c. multicoloured 15 10
198 25c. multicoloured 15 10
199 45c. multicoloured 30 35

1978. Capt. Cook Bicentenary (5th issue). Discovery of Hawaii. Multicoloured.
200 18c. Type **89** 30 20
201 25c. Discovery of northern Hawaiian islands 30 30
202 80c. British flag against island background 60 70

90 Guide Flag and Globe

1978. 50th Anniv of Girl Guides. Multicoloured. Imperf. Self-adhesive.
203 18c. Type **90** 25 45
204 25c. Trefoil and scarf badge 30 55
205 35c. Trefoil and Queen Elizabeth 45 75
206 45c. Trefoil and Lady Baden-Powell 55 75

91 St. Edward's Crown

1978. 25th Anniv of Coronation. Mult.
207 25c. Type **91** 15 15
208 70c. Coronation regalia . . . 40 45

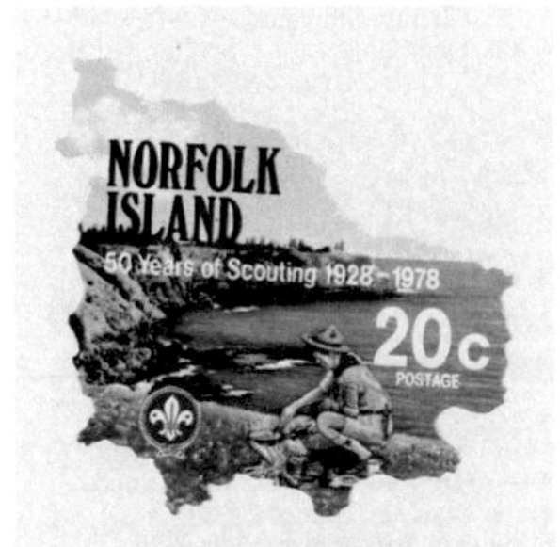

92 View of Duncombe Bay with Scout at Camp Fire

1978. 50th Anniv of Boy Scout Movement. Multicoloured. Imperf. Self-adhesive.
209 20c. Type **92** 30 45
210 25c. View from Kingston and emblem 35 55
211 35c. View of Anson Bay and Link Badge 50 90
212 45c. Sunset scene and Lord Baden-Powell 55 95

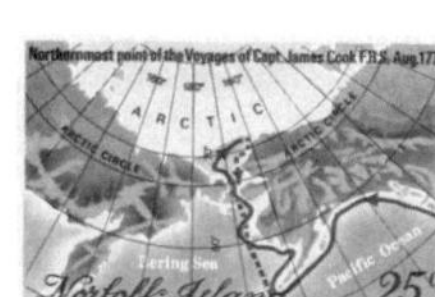

93 Chart showing Route of Arctic Voyage

1978. Captain Cook Bicentenary (6th issue). Northern-most Voyages. Multicoloured.
213 25c. Type **93** 30 30
214 90c. "H.M.S. 'Resolution' and H.M.S. 'Discovery' in Pack Ice" (Webber) . . . 80 80

94 Poinsettia and Bible

95 Cook and Village of Staithes near Marton

1978. Christmas. Multicoloured.
215 20c. Type **94** 15 10
216 30c. Native oak and bible . . 20 15
217 55c. Hibiscus and bible . . . 30 30

1978. 250th Birth Anniv of Captain Cook. Multicoloured.
218 20c. Type **95** 30 25
219 80c. Cook and Whitby Harbour . . . . 70 1·25

96 H.M.S. "Resolution"

1979. Death Bicent of Captain Cook. Mult.
220 20c. Type **96** 25 30
221 20c. Cook (statue) 25 30
222 40c. Cook's death 30 50
223 40c. Cook's death (different) 30 50
Nos. 220/1 were issued se-tenant, in horizontal pairs throughout the sheet, forming a composite design. A chart of Cook's last voyage is shown in the background. Nos. 222/3 were also issued se-tenant, the horizontal pair forming a composite design taken from an aquatint by John Clevely.

97 Assembly Building

1979. First Norfolk Island Legislative Assembly.
224 **97** $1 multicoloured 50 50

98 Tasmania 1853 1d. Stamp and Sir Rowland Hill

1979. Death Centenary of Sir Rowland Hill.
225 **98** 20c. blue and brown . . . 20 10
226 – 30c. red and grey 25 15
227 – 55c. violet and indigo . . . 40 30
MS228 142 × 91 mm. No. 227 . . 55 1·25
DESIGNS: 30c. Great Britain 1841 1d. red; 55c. 1947 "Ball Bay" 1d. stamp.

99 I.Y.C. Emblem and Map of Pacific showing Norfolk Island as Pine Tree

1979. International Year of the Child.
229 **99** 80c. multicoloured 40 45

100 Emily Bay

1979. Christmas.
230 **100** 15c. multicoloured 15 15
231 – 20c. multicoloured 15 15
232 – 30c. multicoloured 15 15
MS233 152 × 83 mm. Nos. 230/2 1·00 1·75
DESIGNS: 20, 30c. Different scenes.
Nos. 230/2 were printed together, se-tenant, forming a composite design.

101 Lions International Emblem

1980. Lions Convention.
234 **101** 50c. multicoloured 35 30

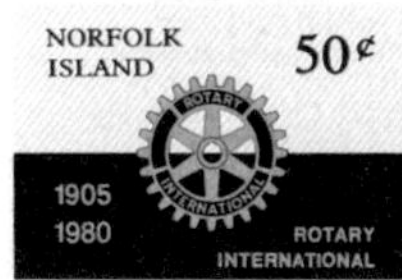

102 Rotary International Emblem

1980. 75th Anniv of Rotary International.
235 **102** 50c. multicoloured 35 30

103 De Havilland Gipsy Moth Seaplane "Madame Elijah"

1980. Airplanes. Multicoloured.

236 1c. Hawker Siddeley H.S.748 . . . 15 20

237 2c. Type **103** 15 20

238 3c. Curtis P-40E Kittyhawk I 15 20

239 4c. Chance Vought F4U-1 Corsair 15 30

240 5c. Grumman TBF Avenger 15 30

241 15c. Douglas SBD-5 Dauntless 30 30

242 20c. Cessna 172D Skyhawk 30 30

243 25c. Lockheed 414 Hudson 30 35

244 30c. Lockheed PV-1 Ventura 40 2·00

245 40c. Avro Type 685 York . . 50 55

246 50c. Douglas DC-3 . . . . . 65 65

247 60c. Avro Type 691 Lancastrian 75 75

248 80c. Douglas DC-4 . . . . . 1·00 1·00

249 $1 Beech 200 Super King Air 1·00 1·00

250 $2 Fokker F.27 Friendship 2·00 3·00

251 $5 Lockheed C-130 Hercules 3·00 2·00

104 Queen Elizabeth the Queen Mother

1980. 80th Birthday of The Queen Mother.

252 **104** 22c. multicoloured 20 20

253 60c. multicoloured 35 40

105 Red-tailed Tropic Birds

1980. Christmas. Birds. Multicoloured.

254 15c. Type **105** 30 25

255 22c. White terns 30 25

256 35c. White-capped noddys . . 30 25

257 60c. White terns (different) 40 45

106 "Morayshire" and View of Norfolk Island

1981. 125th Anniv of Pitcairn Islanders' Migration to Norfolk Island. Multicoloured.

258 5c. Type **106** 15 15

259 35c. Islanders arriving ashore 40 30

260 60c. View of new settlement 60 45

MS261 183 × 127 mm. Nos. 258/60 1·25 1·75

107 Wedding Bouquet from Norfolk Island

1981. Royal Wedding. Multicoloured.

262 35c. Type **107** 15 15

263 55c. Prince Charles at horse trials 25 25

264 60c. Prince Charles and Lady Diana Spencer 25 35

108 Uniting Church in Australia

1981. Christmas. Churches. Multicoloured.

265 18c. Type **108** 10 10

266 24c. Seventh Day Adventist Church 15 15

267 30c. Church of the Sacred Heart 15 20

268 $1 St. Barnabas Chapel . . . 35 70

109 Pair of White-chested White-Eyes

1981. White-chested White-Eye ("Silvereye"). Mult.

269 35c. Type **109** 35 40

270 35c. Bird on nest 35 40

271 35c. Bird with egg 35 40

272 35c. Parents with chicks . . . 35 40

273 35c. Fledgelings 35 40

110 Aerial view of Philip Island

1982. Philip and Nepean Islands. Mult.

274 24c. Type **110** 20 20

275 24c. Close-up view of Philip Island landscape 20 20

276 24c. Gecko ("Phyllodactylus guentheri"), Philip Island 20 20

277 24c. Sooty tern, Philip Island 20 20

278 24c. Philip Island hibiscus ("hibiscus insularis") . . . 20 20

279 35c. Aerial view of Nepean Island 25 25

280 35c. Close-up view of Nepean Island landscape 25 25

281 35c. Gecko ("phyllodactylus guentheri"), Nepean Island 25 25

282 35c. Blue-faced boobies, Nepean Island 25 25

283 35c. "Carpobrotus glaucescens" (flower), Nepean Island 25 25

111 Sperm Whale

1982. Whales.

284 **111** 24c. multicoloured 50 35

285 – 55c. multicoloured 75 95

286 – 80c. black, mauve & stone 1·00 2·00

DESIGNS: 55c. Black right whale; 80c. Humpback whale.

112 "Diocet", Wrecked 20 April 1873

1982. Shipwrecks. Multicoloured.

287 24c. H.M.S. "Sirius", wrecked 19 March 1790 . . 50 50

288 27c. Type **112** 50 50

289 35c. "Friendship", wrecked 17 May 1835 . . . . . . 90 80

290 40c. "Mary Hamilton", wrecked 6 May 1873 . . . 90 1·25

291 55c. "Fairlie", wrecked 14 February 1840 . . . . 1·25 1·25

292 65c. "Warrigal", wrecked 18 March 1918 . . . . . 1·25 1·75

113 R.N.Z.A.F. Lockheed 414 Hudson dropping Christmas Supplies, 1942

1982. Christmas. 40th Anniv of First Supply-plane Landings on Norfolk Island (Christmas Day 1942). Multicoloured.

293 27c. Type **113** 75 35

294 40c. R.N.Z.A.F. Lockheed 414 Hudson landing Christmas supplies 1942 . . 95 65

295 75c. Christmas, 1942 . . . . 1·10 1·40

114 50th (Queen's Own) Regiment

115 "Panaeolus papilionaceus"

1982. Military Uniforms. Multicoloured.

296 27c. Type **114** 25 35

297 40c. 58th (Rutlandshire) Regiment 30 75

298 55c. 80th (Staffordshire Volunteers) Battalion Company 35 95

299 65c. 11th (North Devonshire) Regiment . . . . 40 1·25

1983. Fungi. Multicoloured.

300 27c. Type **115** 30 35

301 40c. "Coprinus domesticus" 40 50

302 55c. "Marasmius niveus" . . 45 70

303 65c. "Cymatoderma elegans var lamellatum" 50 85

116 Beechcraft 18

1983. Bicentenary of Manned Flight. Mult.

304 10c. Type **116** 15 15

305 27c. Fokker F.28 Fellowship 25 35

306 45c. French military Douglas C-54 . . . . 40 60

307 75c. Sikorsky S-61N helicopter 60 95

MS308 105 × 100 mm. Nos. 304/7 1·75 2·75

117 St. Matthew

119 Popwood

118 Cable Ship "Chantik"

1983. Christmas. 150th Birth Anniv of Sir Edward Burne-Jones.

309 5c. Type **117** 10 10

310 24c. St. Mark 20 30

311 30c. Jesus Christ 25 40

312 45c. St. Luke 35 55

313 85c. St. John . . . . 55 1·10

DESIGNS: showing stained glass windows from St. Barnabas Chapel, Norfolk Island.

1983. World Communications Year. ANZCAN Cable. Multicoloured.

314 30c. Type **118** 25 40

315 45c. "Chantik" during in-shore operations 30 55

316 75c. Cable ship "Mercury" 40 95

317 85c. Diagram of cable route 40 1·10

1984. Flowers. Multicoloured.

318 1c. Type **119** 30 70

319 2c. Strand morning glory . . 40 70

320 3c. Native phreatia 45 70

321 4c. Philip Island wisteria . . 45 70

322 5c. Norfolk Island palm . . . 70 70

323 10c. Evergreen 50 70

324 15c. Bastard oak 60 70

325 20c. Devil's guts 60 70

326 25c. White oak 60 80

327 30c. Ti . . . . 60 1·00

328 35c. Philip Island hibiscus . . 60 1·00

329 40c. Native wisteria . . . . 60 1·25

330 50c. Native jasmine . . . . . 70 1·25

331 $1 Norfolk Island hibiscus . . 70 1·75

332 $3 Native oberonia . . . . . 1·10 4·00

333 $5 Norfolk Island pine . . . 1·50 4·50

120 Morwong

1984. Reef Fishes. Multicoloured.

334 30c. Type **120** 30 45

335 45c. Black-spotted goatfish 30 65

336 75c. Surgeonfish . . . . . . 40 1·10

337 85c. Three-striped butterflyfish . . . . 45 1·40

121 Owl with Eggs

123 Font, Kingston Methodist Church

122 1953 7½d. and 1974 Cook Bicent 10c. Stamps

1984. Boobook Owl. Multicoloured.

338 30c. Type **121** 75 90

339 30c. Fledgeling 75 90

340 30c. Young owl on stump . . 75 90

341 30c. Adult on branch 75 90

342 30c. Owl in flight 75 90

1984. "Ausipex" International Stamp Exhibition, Melbourne. Multicoloured.

343 30c. Type **122** 30 35

344 45c. John Buffett commemorative postal stationery envelope 50 75

345 75c. Design from Presentation Pack for 1982 Military Uniforms issue . . 90 1·75

MS346 151 × 93 mm. Nos. 343/5 4·00 4·50

1984. Christmas. Centenary of Methodist Church on Norfolk Island. Multicoloured.

347 5c. Type **123** 10 25

348 24c. Church service in Old Barracks, Kingston, late 1800s 25 40

349 30c. The Revd. & Mrs. A. H. Phelps and sailing ship . . 35 45

350 45c. The Revd. A. H. Phelps and First Congregational Church, Chester, U.S.A. 40 65

351 85c. Interior of Kingston Methodist Church . . . . 80 1·40

124 The Revd. Nobbs teaching Pitcairn Islanders

126 The Queen Mother (from photo by Norman Parkinson)

125 "Fanny Fisher"

1984. Death Centenary of Revd. George Hunn Nobbs (leader of Pitcairn community). Multicoloured.

352 30c. Type **124** 25 45

353 45c. The Revd. Nobbs with sick islander 30 65

354 75c. Baptising baby . . . . . 45 1·10

355 85c. Presented to Queen Victoria, 1852 . . . . . . 55 1·40

1985. 19th-Century Whaling Ships (1st series). Multicoloured.

356 5c. Type **125** 30 50

357 33c. "Costa Rica Packet" . . 60 55

358	50c. "Splendid"	1·00	1·50
359	90c. "Onward"	1·25	2·25

See also Nos. 360/3.

1985. 19th-Century Whaling Ships (2nd series). As T **125**. Multicoloured.

360	15c. "Waterwitch"	50	70
361	20c. "Canton"	55	80
362	60c. "Aladdin"	1·10	1·75
363	80c. "California"	1·10	2·25

1985. Life and Times of Queen Elizabeth the Queen Mother. Multicoloured.

364	5c. The Queen Mother (from photo by Dorothy Wilding)	10	10
365	33c. With Princess Anne at Trooping the Colour	25	25
366	50c. Type **126**	40	55
367	90c. With Prince Henry at his christening (from photo by Lord Snowdon)	60	1·00
MS368	91 × 73 mm. $1 With Princess Anne at Ascot Races	1·50	1·50

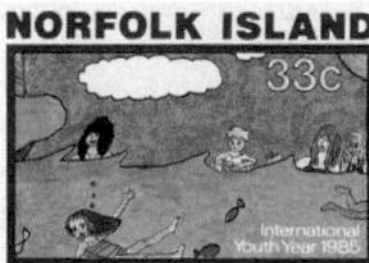

127 "Swimming"

1985. International Youth Year. Children's Paintings. Multicoloured.

369	33c. Type **127**	40	40
370	50c. "A Walk in the Country"	70	85

128 Prize-winning Cow and Owner

1985. 125th Anniv of Royal Norfolk Island Agricultural and Horticultural Show. Mult.

371	80c. Type **128**	75	80
372	90c. Show exhibits	85	90
MS373	132 × 85 mm. Nos. 371/2	1·75	2·50

129 Shepherds with Flock

131 "Giotto" Spacecraft

130 Long-spined Sea Urchin

1985. Christmas. Multicoloured.

374	27c. Type **129**	40	30
375	33c. Mary and Joseph with donkey	50	40
376	50c. The Three Wise Men	80	65
377	90c. The Nativity	1·25	1·25

1986. Marine Life. Multicoloured.

378	5c. Type **130**	10	10
379	33c. Blue starfish	30	35
380	55c. Southern eagle ray	50	85
381	75c. Snowflake moray	70	1·25
MS382	100 × 95 mm. Nos. 378/81	3·00	4·00

1986. Appearance of Halley's Comet. Mult.

383	$1 Type **131**	75	1·50
384	$1 Halley's Comet	75	1·50

Nos. 383/4 were printed together, se-tenant, forming a composite design.

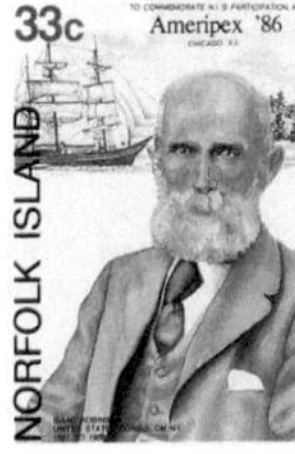

132 Isaac Robinson (U.S. Consul 1887–1908)

133 Princess Elizabeth and Dog

1986. "Ameripex '86" International Stamp Exhibition, Chicago. Multicoloured.

385	33c. Type **132**	30	35
386	50c. Ford "Model T" (first vehicle on island) (horiz)	50	50
387	80c. Statue of Liberty	55	80
MS388	125 × 100 mm. Nos. 385/7	1·50	2·25

No. 387 also commemorates the Centenary of the Statue of Liberty.

1986. 60th Birthday of Queen Elizabeth II. Multicoloured.

389	5c. Type **133**	10	10
390	33c. Queen Elizabeth II	40	35
391	80c. Opening Norfolk Island Golf Club	1·60	1·40
392	90c. With Duke of Edinburgh in carriage	1·25	1·60

134 Stylized Dove and Norfolk Island

135 British Convicts, 1787

1986. Christmas.

393	**134** 30c. multicoloured	25	30
394	40c. multicoloured	30	45
395	$1 multicoloured	70	1·50

1986. Bicentenary (1988) of Norfolk Island Settlement (1st issue). Governor Phillip's Commission. Multicoloured.

396	36c. Type **135**	80	35
397	55c. Judge passing sentence of transportation	1·50	85
398	90c. Governor Phillip meeting Home Secretary (inscr "Home Society")	2·50	3·50
399	90c. As No. 398, but correctly inscr "Home Secretary"	2·25	3·25
400	$1 Captain Arthur Phillip	2·50	2·50

See also Nos. 401/4, 421/4, 433/5, 436/7 and 438/43.

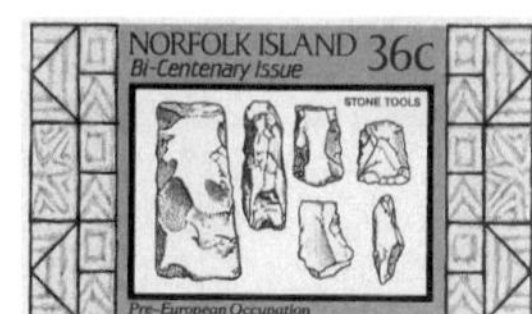

136 Stone Tools

1986. Bicentenary (1988) of Norfolk Island Settlement (2nd issue). Pre-European Occupation. Multicoloured.

401	36c. Type **136**	50	85
402	36c. Bananas and taro	50	85
403	36c. Polynesian outrigger canoe	50	85
404	36c. Maori chief	50	85

137 Philip Island from Point Ross

138 Male Red-fronted Parakeet

1987. Norfolk Island Scenes. Multicoloured.

405	1c. Cockpit Creek Bridge	50	1·50
406	2c. Cemetery Bay Beach	50	1·50
407	3c. Island guesthouse	50	1·50
408	5c. Type **137**	30	1·00
409	15c. Cattle in pasture	80	2·00
410	30c. Rock fishing	30	1·25
411	37c. Old Pitcairner-style house	1·40	2·00
412	40c. Shopping centre	35	1·25
413	50c. Emily Bay	45	1·25
414	60c. Bloody Bridge	2·00	3·00
415	80c. Pitcairner-style shop	1·75	2·75
416	90c. Government House	1·25	2·25
417	$1 Melanesian Memorial Chapel	1·00	1·75
418	$2 Convict Settlement, Kingston	1·25	3·50
419	$3 Ball Bay	2·00	5·00
420	$5 Northern cliffs	2·50	7·00

1987. Bicentenary of Norfolk Island Settlement (1988) (3rd issue). The First Fleet. As T **135**. Multicoloured.

421	5c. Loading supplies, Deptford	50	75
422	55c. Fleet leaving Spithead	1·75	2·25
423	55c. H.M.S. "Sirius" leaving Spithead	1·75	2·25
424	$1 Female convicts below decks	2·25	3·00

Nos. 422/3 were printed together, se-tenant, forming a composite design.

1987. Red-fronted Parakeet ("Green Parrot"). Multicoloured.

425	5c. Type **138**	2·00	1·75
426	15c. Adult with fledgeling and egg	2·50	2·25
427	36c. Young parakeets	3·50	3·25
428	55c. Female parakeet	4·50	3·75

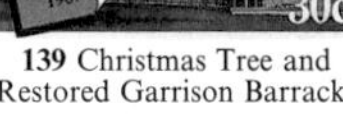

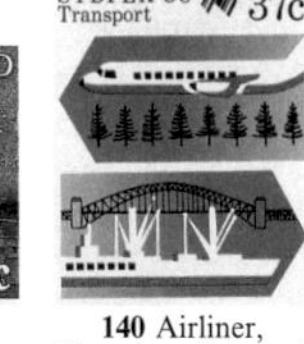

139 Christmas Tree and Restored Garrison Barracks

140 Airliner, Container Ship and Sydney Harbour Bridge

1987. Christmas. Multicoloured.

429	30c. Type **139**	30	30
430	42c. Children opening presents	45	55
431	58c. Father Christmas with children	60	1·00
432	63c. Children's party	70	1·25

1987. Bicentenary of Norfolk Island Settlement (1988) (4th issue). Visit of La Perouse (navigator). As T **135**. Multicoloured.

433	37c. La Perouse with King Louis XVI	95	55
434	90c. "L'Astrolabe" and "La Boussole" off Norfolk Island	2·75	3·00
435	$1 "L'Astrolabe" wrecked in Solomon Islands	2·75	3·00

1988. Bicentenary of Norfolk Island Settlement (5th issue). Arrival of First Fleet at Sydney. As T **135**. Multicoloured.

436	37c. Ship's cutter approaching Port Jackson	1·50	75
437	$1 Landing at Sydney Cove	3·00	3·50

1988. Bicentenary of Norfolk Island Settlement (6th issue). Foundation of First Settlement. As T **135**. Multicoloured.

438	5c. Lt. Philip Gidley King	20	50
439	37c. Raising the flag, March 1788	85	75
440	55c. King exploring	1·75	1·50
441	70c. Landing at Sydney Bay, Norfolk Island	2·00	2·50
442	90c. H.M.S. "Supply" (brig)	2·25	2·75
443	$1 Sydney Bay settlement, 1788	2·25	2·75

1988. "Sydpex '88" National Stamp Exhibition, Sydney. Multicoloured.

444	37c. Type **140**	95	1·25
445	37c. Exhibition label under magnifying glass (horiz)	95	1·25
446	37c. Telephone and dish aerial	95	1·25
MS447	118 × 84 mm. Nos. 444/6	4·50	5·00

141 Flowers and Decorations

142 Pier Store and Boat Shed

1988. Christmas. Multicoloured.

448	30c. Type **141**	50	40
449	42c. Flowers	70	70
450	58c. Fishes and beach	85	95
451	63c. Norfolk Island	95	1·25

1988. Restored Buildings from the Convict Era. Multicoloured.

452	39c. Type **142**	45	40
453	55c. Royal Engineers Building	60	60
454	90c. Old Military Barracks	1·00	1·60
455	$1 Commissariat Store and New Military Barracks	1·10	1·60

143 "Lamprima aenea"

1989. Endemic Insects. Multicoloured.

456	39c. Type **143**	65	40
457	55c. "Insulascirtus nythos"	90	75
458	90c. "Caedicia araucariae"	1·40	2·25
459	$1 "Thrincophora aridela"	1·60	2·25

144 H.M.S. "Bounty" off Tasmania

1989. Bicentenary of the Mutiny on the "Bounty". Multicoloured.

460	5c. Type **144**	60	60
461	39c. Mutineers and Polynesian women, Pitcairn Island	1·75	1·25
462	55c. Lake Windermere, Cumbria (Christian's home county)	2·25	2·25
463	$1.10 "Mutineers casting Bligh adrift" (Robert Dodd)	3·50	4·50
MS464	110 × 85 mm. 39c. No. 461; 90c. Isle of Man 1989 Mutiny 35p., No. 414; $1 Pitcairn Islands 1989 Settlement Bicent 90c., No. 345	6·00	7·00

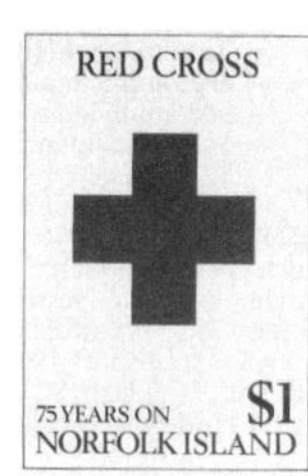

145 Norfolk Island Flag

146 Red Cross

1989. 10th Anniv of Internal Self-government. Multicoloured.

465	41c. Type **145**	90	55
466	55c. Old ballot box	95	65
467	$1 Norfolk Island Act, 1979	1·75	2·00
468	$1.10 Island crest	1·75	2·75

1989. 75th Anniv of Red Cross on Norfolk Island.

469	**146** $1 red and blue	3·00	3·25

147 "Gethsemane"

1989. Christmas. Designs showing opening lines of hymns and local scenes. Multicoloured.

470	36c. Type **147**	90	40
471	60c. "In the Sweet Bye and Bye"	1·75	2·00
472	75c. "Let the Lower Lights be Burning"	2·25	3·00
473	80c. "The Beautiful Stream"	2·25	3·00

148 John Royle (first announcer)

149 H.M.S. "Bounty" on fire, Pitcairn Island, 1790

1989. 50th Anniv of Radio Australia. Designs each showing Kingston buildings. Mult.

474	41c. Type **148**	95	65
475	65c. Radio waves linking Australia and Norfolk Island	1·75	2·50
476	$1.10 Anniversary kookaburra logo	2·75	4·25

1990. History of the Norfolk Islanders (1st series). Settlement on Pitcairn Island. Mult.

477	70c. Type **149**	2·50	3·00
478	$1.10 Arms of Norfolk Island	2·75	3·50

See also Nos. 503/4 and 516/17.

150 H.M.S. "Sirius" striking Reef

1990. Bicentenary of Wreck of H.M.S. "Sirius". Multicoloured.
479 41c. Type **150** . . . . 1·75 2·00
480 41c. H.M.S. "Sirius" failing to clear bay . . . . 1·75 2·00
481 65c. Divers at work on wreck 2·50 3·00
482 $1 Recovered artifacts and chart of site . . . . 2·75 3·25
Nos. 479/80 were printed together, se-tenant, forming a composite design.

151 Unloading Lighter, Kingston

152 "Ile de Lumiere" (freighter)

1990. Ships.
483 **151** 5c. brown 20 50
484 10c. brown 20 50
485 – 45c. multicoloured . . . . 1·00 60
486 – 50c. multicoloured . . . . 1·00 1·00
487 – 65c. multicoloured . . . . 1·00 1·25
488 **152** 70c. multicoloured . . . . 1·00 1·25
489 – 75c. multicoloured . . . . 2·00 2·00
490 – 80c. multicoloured . . . . 2·00 2·25
491 – 90c. multicoloured . . . . 2·00 2·25
492 – $1 multicoloured . . . . 2·00 2·00
493 – $2 multicoloured . . . . 2·25 3·50
494 – $5 multicoloured . . . . 5·00 7·00
DESIGNS—As T **152**: 45c. "La Dunkerquoise" (French patrol vessel); 50c. "Dmitri Mendeleev" (Russian research vessel); 65c. "Pacific Rover" (tanker); 75c. "Norfolk Trader" (freighter); 80c. "Roseville" (transport); 90c. "Kalia" (container ship); $1 "Bounty" (replica); $2 H.M.A.S. "Success" (supply ship); $5 H.M.A.S. "Whyalla" (patrol vessel).

153 Santa on House Roof

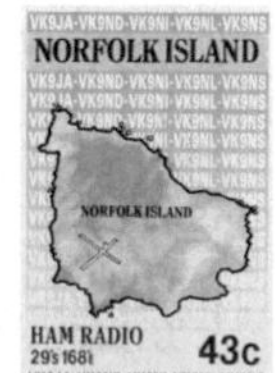

154 William Charles Wentworth

1990. Christmas. Multicoloured.
499 38c. Type **153** 75 45
500 43c. Santa at Kingston Post Office 80 50
501 65c. Santa over Sydney Bay, Kingston (horiz) . . . . . 1·75 2·25
502 85c. Santa on Officers' Quarters (horiz) . . . . . 2·00 2·75

1990. History of the Norfolk Islanders (2nd series). The First Generation.
503 **154** 70c. brown and cinnamon 1·25 1·50
504 – $1.20 brown and cinnamon . . . . . . 2·00 2·50
DESIGN: $1.20, Thursday October Christian.

155 Adult Robin and Chicks in Nest

156 Map of Norfolk Island

1990. "Birdpex '90" Stamp Exhibition, Christchurch, New Zealand. Scarlet Robin. Multicoloured.
505 65c. Type **155** . . . . 1·25 1·50
506 $1 Hen on branch . . . . . 1·75 2·00
507 $1.20 Cock on branch . . . 1·75 2·25
MS508 70 × 90 mm. $1 Hen; $1 Cock and hen . . . . 4·50 4·75
Each inscribed "Norfolk Island Robin".

1991. Ham Radio Network. Multicoloured.
509 43c. Type **156** . . . . 1·25 70
510 $1 Globe showing Norfolk Island . . . . 2·75 3·00
511 $1.20 Map of south-west Pacific . . . . 2·75 4·00

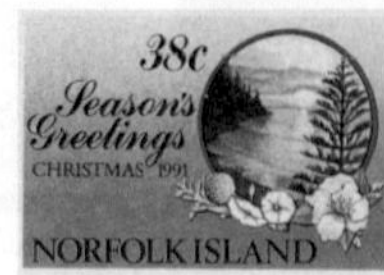

157 Display in "Sirius" Museum

158 H.M.S. "Pandora" wrecked on Great Barrier Reef (1791)

1991. Norfolk Island Museums. Mult.
512 43c. Type **157** 90 65
513 70c. 19th-century sitting room, House Museum (horiz) . . . . 1·75 2·50
514 $1 Carronade, "Sirius" Museum (horiz) . . . . . 2·50 3·25
515 $1.20 Reconstructed jug and beaker, Archaeological Museum . . . . 2·50 3·75

1991. History of the Norfolk Islanders (3rd series). Search for the "Bounty". Multicoloured.
516 $1 Type **158** . . . . 2·75 2·50
517 $1.20 H.M.S. "Pandora" leaving bay . . . . 2·75 3·00

159 Hibiscus and Island Scene

1991. Christmas.
518 **159** 38c. multicoloured 90 45
519 43c. multicoloured . . . . 1·00 55
520 65c. multicoloured . . . . 1·50 2·00
521 85c. multicoloured . . . . 1·75 2·50

160 Tank and Soldier in Jungle

161 Coat of Arms

1991. 50th Anniv of Outbreak of Pacific War. Multicoloured.
522 43c. Type **160** . . . . 1·25 65
523 70c. Boeing B-17 Flying Fortress on jungle airstrip 2·25 2·75
524 $1 Warships . . . . 2·75 3·50

1992. 500th Anniv of Discovery of America by Columbus. Multicoloured.
525 45c. Type **161** 85 55
526 $1.05 "Santa Maria" . . . . 2·00 2·75
527 $1.20 Columbus and globe 2·50 3·25

162 Deployment Map

163 Norfolk Pines above Ball Bay

1992. 50th Anniv of Battle of the Coral Sea. Multicoloured.
528 45c. Type **162** . . . . 1·25 60
529 70c. H.M.A.S. "Australia" (cruiser) . . . . 2·00 2·50
530 $1.05 U.S.S. "Yorktown" (aircraft carrier) . . . . . 2·75 3·50

1992. 50th Anniv of Battle of Midway. As T **162**. Multicoloured.
531 45c. Battle area . . . . . . 1·25 60
532 70c. Consolidated PBY-5 Catalina flying boat over task force . . . . 2·00 2·50
533 $1.05 Douglas SBD Dauntless dive bomber and "Akagi" (Japanese aircraft carrier) burning . . . . . 2·75 3·50

1992. 50th Anniv of Battle of Guadalcanal. As T **162**. Multicoloured.
534 45c. American troops landing (horiz) . . . . 1·25 60
535 70c. Machine-gun crew (horiz) . . . . 2·00 2·50
536 $1.05 Map of Pacific with Japanese and American flags (horiz) . . . . 2·75 3·50

1992. Christmas. Multicoloured.
537 40c. Type **163** 70 40
538 45c. Headstone Creek 75 45
539 75c. South side of Ball Bay 1·50 2·25
540 $1.20 Rocky Point Reserve 2·00 3·00

164 Boat Shed and Flaghouses, Kingston

1993. Tourism. Historic Kingston. Mult.
541 45c. Type **164** . . . . 80 1·00
542 45c. Old Military Barracks 80 1·00
543 45c. All Saints Church . . . 80 1·00
544 45c. Officers' Quarters . . . 80 1·00
545 45c. Quality Row . . . . . 80 1·00
Nos. 541/5 were printed together, se-tenant, forming a composite design.

165 Fire Engine

1993. Emergency Services. Multicoloured.
546 45c. Type **165** . . . . 1·00 60
547 70c. Cliff rescue squad . . . 1·10 1·75
548 75c. Ambulance . . . . . . 1·40 1·90
549 $1.20 Police car . . . . . . 2·50 3·00

166 Blue Sea Lizard ("Glaucus atlanticus")

1993. Nudibranchs. Multicoloured.
550 45c. Type **166** 80 55
551 45c. Ocellate nudibranch ("Phyllidia ocellata") . . . 80 55
552 75c. "Bornella sp." . . . . . 1·50 1·75
553 85c. "Glossodoris rubroannolata" . . . . . 1·75 2·25
554 95c. "Halgerda willeyi" . . . 2·00 2·50
555 $1.05 "Ceratosoma amoena" 2·00 3·00

167 Christmas Wreath

168 Maori Stone Clubs

1993. Christmas.
556 **167** 40c. multicoloured 60 50
557 45c. multicoloured 60 50
558 75c. multicoloured . . . . 1·00 1·50
559 $1.20 multicoloured . . . 1·90 2·75

1993. Bicentenary of Contact with New Zealand. Multicoloured.
560 70c. Type **168** . . . . 1·25 1·50
561 $1.20 First Maori map of New Zealand, 1793 . . . . 2·00 2·75

169 Alvaro de Saavedra, Route Map and "Florida"

1994. Pacific Explorers. Multicoloured.
562 5c. Vasco Nunez de Balboa, map and "Barbara" . . . 55 65
563 10c. Ferdinand Magellan, map and "Vitoria" 70 65
564 20c. Juan Sebastian del Cano, map and "Vitoria" . . . 1·00 85
565 50c. Type **169** . . . . . . 1·00 1·00
566 70c. Ruy Lopez de Villalobos, map and "San Juan" . . . . 1·25 1·25
567 75c. Miguel Lopez de Legaspi, map and "San Lesmes" . . . . 1·25 1·25
568 80c. Sir Francis Drake, map and "Golden Hind" . . . 1·25 1·25
569 85c. Alvaro de Mendana, map and "Santiago" . . . 1·25 1·25
570 90c. Pedro Fernandes de Quiros, map and "San Pedro y Pablo" . . . . . 1·25 1·25
571 $1 Luis Baez de Torres, map and "San Pedrico" . . . . 1·40 1·40
572 $2 Abel Tasman, map and "Heemskerk" . . . . . . 2·00 2·50
573 $5 William Dampier, map and "Cygnet" . . . . . . 4·25 5·50
MS574 100 × 80 mm. $1.20 "Golden Hind" (Drake) (32 × 52 mm) 2·75 2·75

170 Sooty Tern

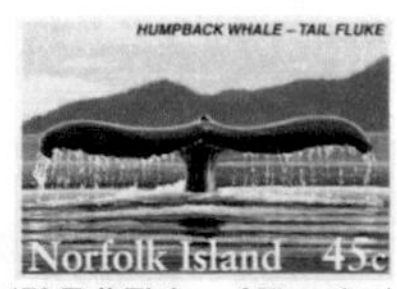

171 House and Star

1994. Sea Birds. Multicoloured.
575 45c. Type **170** . . . . 95 1·10
576 45c. Red-tailed tropic bird . . 95 1·10
577 45c. Australian gannet . . . 95 1·10
578 45c. Wedge-tailed shearwater 95 1·10
579 45c. Masked booby . . . . . 95 1·10
Nos. 575/9 were printed together, se-tenant, forming a composite design.

1994. Christmas. Multicoloured. Self-adhesive.
580 45c. Type **171** 80 55
581 75c. Figures from stained-glass windows . . . . . . 1·50 2·00
582 $1.20 Rainbow and "The Church of God" (missionary sailing ship) . . 2·50 3·00

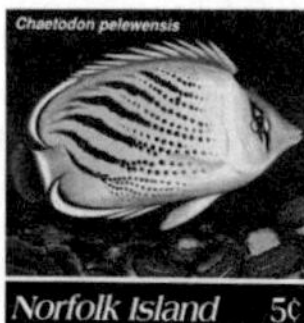

172 Chevrolet, 1926

1995. Vintage Motor Vehicles. Multicoloured.
583 45c. Type **172** 75 55
584 75c. Ford Model "A", 1928 1·25 1·75
585 $1.05 Ford Model "A A/C", 1929 . . . . 1·60 2·00
586 $1.20 Ford Model "A", 1930 1·75 2·25

173 Tail Flukes of Humpback Whale

1995. Humpback Whale Conservation. Multicoloured.
587 45c. Type **173** . . . . 1·00 55
588 75c. Mother and calf . . . . 1·50 2·00
589 $1.05 Whale breaching (vert) 1·75 2·50
MS590 107 × 84 mm. $1.20 Humpback whale (29 × 49 mm) 2·50 2·75

174 Dot-and-Dash Butterflyfish

1995. Butterflyfishes. Multicoloured.
591 5c. Type **174** 30 75
592 45c. Blue-spotted butterflyfish 85 50
593 $1.20 Three-belted butterflyfish . . . . 2·25 2·75
594 $1.50 Three-finned butterflyfish . . . . 2·50 3·25

1995. "JAKARTA '95" Stamp Exhibition, Indonesia. No. **MS**590 optd "Selamat Hari Merdeka" and emblem on sheet margin in gold.
MS595 107 × 84 mm. $1.20 Humpback whale . . . . . . 1·75 2·50

175 International 4 × 4 Refueller, 1942

1995. Second World War Vehicles. Multicoloured.
596 5c. Type **175** 30 75
597 45c. Ford Sedan, 1942 . . . 75 45
598 $1.20 Ford 3 ton tipper, 1942 2·00 2·50
599 $2 D8 caterpillar with scraper 3·00 4·00

1995. Flower designs as 1960 issues, but with face values in decimal currency.
600 5c. pink and green (as No. 25) 15 20
601 5c. red (as No. 28) 15 20

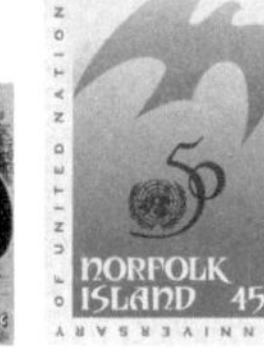

176 Servicing Fighter

177 Peace Dove and Anniversary Emblem

1995. 50th Anniv of End of Second World War in the Pacific. Multicoloured.
602 5c. Type **176** 40 50
603 45c. Sgt. Tom Derrick, VC (vert) 70 45
604 75c. Gen. Douglas MacArthur (vert) . . . . 1·25 1·50
605 $1.05 Girls celebrating victory 1·75 2·00
606 $10 Pacific War medals (50 × 30 mm) . . . . . . 16·00 19·00
The $10 also includes the "Singapore '95" International stamp exhibition logo.

1995. Christmas. 50th Anniv of United Nations. Each including U.N. anniversary emblem.
607 **177** 45c. gold and blue 60 45
608 – 75c. gold and violet . . . 1·00 1·25
609 – $1.05 gold and red . . . 1·40 2·00
610 – $1.20 gold and green . . 1·60 2·25
DESIGNS: 75c. Star of Bethlehem; $1.05, Symbolic candles on cake; $1.20, Olive branch.

178 Skink on Bank

1996. Endangered Species. Skinks and Geckos. Multicoloured.
611 5c. Type **178** 55 75
612 5c. Gecko on branch 55 75
613 45c. Skink facing right . . . 70 75
614 45c. Gecko on flower 70 75

179 Sopwith Pup Biplane and Emblem

181 "Naticarlus oncus"

1996. 75th Anniv of Royal Australian Air Force. Aircraft. Multicoloured.
615 45c. Type **179** 70 70
616 45c. Wirraway fighter 70 70
617 75c. F-111C jet fighter . . . 1·25 1·50
618 85c. F/A-18 Hornet jet fighter 1·40 1·60

180 Rat

1996. Chinese New Year ("Year of the Rat"). Sheet 100 × 75 mm.
MS619 **180** $1 black, red and brown 1·50 2·25

1996. Shells. Multicoloured.
620 45c. Type **181** 70 85
621 45c. "Janthina janthina" . . 70 85
622 45c. "Cypraea caputserpentis" 70 85
623 45c. "Argonauta nodosa" . . 70 85

182 Shopping

183 The Nativity

1996. Tourism. Multicoloured.
624 45c. Type **182** 50 50
625 75c. Celebrating Bounty Day 1·00 1·00
626 $2.50 Horse riding . . . . . 3·75 4·50
627 $3.70 Unloading lighter . . . 4·50 5·75

1996. Christmas. Multicoloured.
628 45c. Type **183** 50 50
629 45c. Star and boat sheds . . 50 50
630 75c. Star, bungalow and ox 90 1·50
631 85c. Star, fruit, flowers and ox . . . . 1·10 1·75

184 Coat of Arms

185 Calf

1997.
632 **184** 5c. blue and yellow . . . 20 30
633 – 5c. brown 20 30
DESIGN: No. 633, Great Seal of Norfolk Island.

1997. Beef Cattle. Sheet 67 × 67 mm.
MS634 **185** $1.20 multicoloured 2·00 2·50

1997. "HONG KONG '97" International Stamp Exhibition. As No. **MS**634, but with exhibition emblem on sheet margin.
MS635 67 × 67 mm. **185** $1.20 multicoloured . . . . 2·25 3·00

186 "Cepora perimale"

1997. Butterflies. Multicoloured.
636 75c. Type **186** . . . . 1·00 1·00
637 90c. "Danaus chrysippus" . . 1·25 1·60
638 $1 "Danaus hamata" . . . . 1·40 1·60
639 $1.20 "Danaus plexippus" . . 1·50 2·25

187 Dusky Dolphins

1997. Dolphins. Multicoloured.
640 45c. Type **187** 75 60
641 75c. Common dolphin and calf . . . . 1·25 1·40
MS642 106 × 80 mm. $1.05 Dolphin 1·75 2·00

1997. "Pacific '97" International Stamp Exhibition, San Francisco. As No. **MS**642, but with exhibition emblem on sheet margin.
MS643 106 × 80 mm. $1.05 Dolphin 2·50 3·00

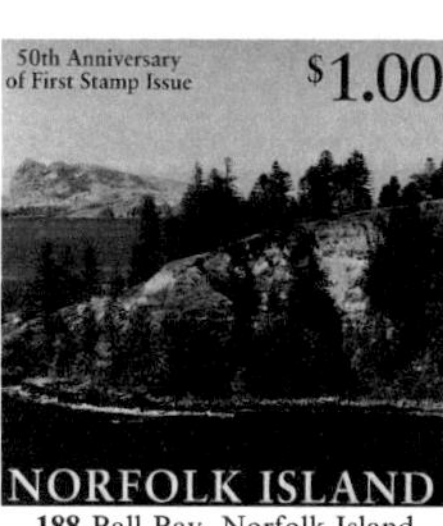

188 Ball Bay, Norfolk Island

1997. 50th Anniv of Norfolk Island Stamps. Multicoloured.
644 $1 Type **188** . . . . 1·25 1·75
645 $1.50 1947 2d. stamp . . . . 1·25 1·75
646 $8 Ball Bay and 1947 2s. bistre stamp (90 × 45 mm) 7·50 11·00

1997. Golden Wedding of Queen Elizabeth and Prince Philip. As T **87** of Kiribati. Multicoloured.
647 20c. Queen Elizabeth 50 60
648 25c. Prince Philip in carriage-driving trials 50 60
649 25c. Prince Philip 55 65
650 50c. Queen in phaeton at Trooping the Colour . . . 70 80
MS651 110 × 70 mm. $1.50 Queen Elizabeth and Prince Philip in landau (horiz) . . . . 2·25 2·75
Nos. 647/8 and 649/50 were each printed together, se-tenant, with the backgrounds forming composite designs.

189 Royal Yacht "Britannia" leaving Hong Kong

1997. Return of Hong Kong to China. Sheet 126 × 91 mm.
MS652 **189** 45c. multicoloured 1·00 1·50
No. **MS**652 is inscribed "Brittania" in error.

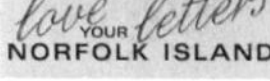

190 Christmas Tree

191 Oriental Pearl T.V. Tower, Shanghai

1997. Annual Festivals. Multicoloured.
653 45c. Type **190** 60 45
654 75c. Fireworks (New Year's Eve) . . . . 90 1·25
655 $1.20 Rose (Valentine's Day) 1·40 1·75

1997. "Shanghai '97" International Stamp and Coin Exhibition, shanghai. Sheet 103 × 138 mm.
MS656 **191** 45c. multicoloured 1·00 1·50

192 Tiger Mask

1998. Chinese New Year ("Year of the Tiger"). Sheet 75 × 95 mm.
MS657 **192** 45c. multicoloured 1·00 1·50

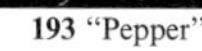

193 "Pepper"

194 Entrance to Pentagonal Gaol

1998. Cats. Multicoloured.
658 45c. Type **193** 65 65
659 45c. "Tabitha" at window . . 65 65
660 75c. "Midnight" . . . . 85 1·00
661 $1.20 "Rainbow" with flower pot . . . . 1·25 1·50

1998.
662 **194** 5c. black and blue 15 25
663 – 5c. black and green . . . 15 25
DESIGN: No. 663, Ruined First Settlement cottage.

1998. Diana, Princess of Wales Commemoration. As T **91** of Kiribati.
664 45c. Princess Diana with bouquet, 1991 . . . . . . 50 50
MS665 145 × 70 mm. 45c. Wearing blue and white dress, 1989; 45c. Wearing pearl earrings, 1990; 45c. No. 664; 45c. Wearing striped dress (sold at $1.80+45c. charity premium) . . . . 1·60 2·00

195 Tweed Trousers

196 Hammer Throwing

1998. Reef Fishes. Multicoloured.
666 10c. Type **195** 30 40
667 20c. Conspicuous angelfish 55 50
668 30c. Moon wrasse 65 50
669 45c. Wide-striped clownfish 75 50
670 50c. Racoon butterflyfish . . 80 80
671 70c. Artooti (juvenile) . . . . 1·00 1·00
672 75c. Splendid hawkfish . . . 1·00 1·00
673 85c. Scorpion fish . . . . . 1·25 1·25
674 90c. Orange fairy basslet . . 1·25 1·25
675 $1 Sweetlips . . . . 1·25 1·25
676 $3 Moorish idol . . . . . . 2·75 3·50
677 $4 Gold-ribbon soapfish . . 3·25 4·25
MS678 110 × 85 mm. $1.20 Shark (29 × 39 mm) . . . . 1·50 1·75
Nos. 672 and 675 are incorrectly inscribed "Splendid Hawkefish" and "Sweetlip".

1998. 16th Commonwealth Games, Kuala Lumpur.
679 **196** 75c. red and black . . . . 85 1·00
680 – 95c. violet and black . . . 1·00 1·25
681 – $1.05 mauve and black . . 1·10 1·40
MS682 80 × 100 mm. 85c. green and black . . . . 1·00 1·50
DESIGNS—HORIZ: 95c. Trap shooting. VERT: 85c. Flag bearer; $1.05, Lawn bowls.

197 "Norfolk" (sloop)

1998. Bicentenary of the Circumnavigation of Tasmania by George Bass and Matthew Flinders.
683 **197** 45c. multicoloured . . . . 1·25 85
MS684 101 × 69 mm. **197** $1.20 multicoloured . . . . 2·00 2·25

198 Blue whale

1998. Whales of the Southern Oceans (joint issue with Namibia and South Africa). Sheet 103 × 70 mm.
MS685 **198** $1.50 multicoloured 1·90 2·25

199 "Peace on Earth"

1998. Christmas. Multicoloured.
686 45c. Type **199** 55 50
687 75c. "Joy to the World" . . 85 80
688 $1.05 "A Season of Love" . . 1·25 1·75
689 $1.20 "Light of the World" 1·25 1·75

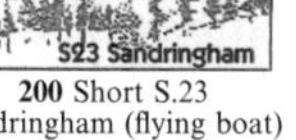

200 Short S.23 Sandringham (flying boat)

201 Soft Toy Rabbit

1999. Aircraft. Each red and green.
690 5c. Type **200** 25 40
691 5c. DC-4 "Norfolk Trader" 25 40

1999. Chinese New Year ("Year of the Rabbit"). Sheet 80 × 100 mm.
MS692 **201** 95c. multicoloured 1·00 1·50

202 Hull of "Resolution" under Construction

1999. "Australia '99" International Stamp Exhibition, Melbourne. Schooner "Resolution". Multicoloured.
693 45c. Type **202** . . . . 1·25 1·25
694 45c. After being launched . . 1·25 1·25
695 45c. In Emily Bay . . . . . 1·25 1·25
696 45c. Off Cascade . . . . . . 1·25 1·25
697 45c. Alongside at Auckland 1·25 1·25

203 Pacific Black Duck **204** Solander's Petrel in Flight

1999. "iBRA '99" International Stamp Exhibition, nuremburg. Sheet 80 × 100 mm.
MS698 **203** $2.50 multicoloured 3·25 3·75

1999. Endangered Species. Solander's Petrel ("Providence Petrel"). Multicoloured.
699 75c. Type **204** . . . . 1·50 1·00
700 $1.05 Head of Solander's petrel (horiz) . . . . . . 1·60 1·40
701 $1.20 Adult and fledgling (horiz) . . . . 1·60 1·60
MS702 130 × 90 mm. $4.50 Solander's petrel in flight (35 × 51 mm) . . . . 6·50 6·50
See also No. **MS**738.

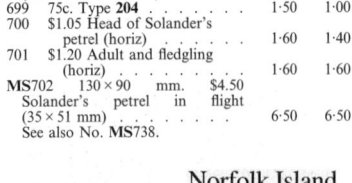

205 "Cecile Brunner" Rose **206** Pottery

1999. Roses. Multicoloured.
703 45c. Type **205** 60 40
704 75c. Green rose 85 90
705 $1.05 "David Buffett" rose 1·25 1·75
MS706 60 × 81 mm. $1.20 "A Country Woman" Rose . . . 1·40 1·75
No. **MS**706 also commemorates the 50th anniversary of the Country Women's Association on Norfolk Island.

1999. "China '99" International Stamp Exhibition, Beijing. No. **MS**692 with "China '99" logo optd on the margin in red.
MS707 80 × 100 mm. 95c. Type **201** 1·00 1·25

1999. Handicrafts of Norfolk Island. Multicoloured.
708 45c. Type **206** 50 50
709 45c. Woodcarving 50 50
710 75c. Quilting 75 90
711 $1.05 Basket-weaving . . . . 1·00 1·50

1999. "Queen Elizabeth the Queen Mother's Century". As T **267** of Lesotho. Multicoloured (except $1.20).
712 45c. Inspecting bomb damage, Buckingham Palace, 1940 . . . . 70 70
713 45c. At Abergeldy Castle sale of work, 1955 . . . . . . 70 70
714 75c. Queen Mother, Queen Elizabeth and Prince William, 1994 . . . . . . 95 95
715 $1.20 Inspecting the King's Regiment (black) . . . . . 1·50 1·75
MS716 145 × 70 mm. $3 Queen Elizabeth, 1937, and Amy Johnson's flight to Australia, 1930 3·25 3·50

207 Bishop George Augustus Selwyn

1999. Christmas. 150th Anniv of Melanesian Mission. Multicoloured (except 75c.).
717 45c. Type **207** 80 90
718 45c. Bishop John Coleridge Patteson 80 90
719 75c. "150 YEARS MELANESIAN MISSION" (black) . . . . 90 1·00
720 $1.05 Stained-glass windows 1·00 1·40
721 $1.20 "Southern Cross" (missionary ship) and religious symbols . . . . . 1·00 1·40
Nos. 717/21 were printed together, se-tenant, with the backgrounds forming a composite design.

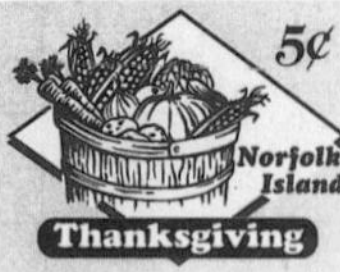

208 Basket of Food (Thanksgiving)

2000. Festivals.
722 **208** 5c. black and blue 15 25
723 – 5c. black and blue 15 25
DESIGN: No. 723, Musician playing guitar (Country Music Festival).

209 Dragon

2000. Chinese New Year ("Year of the Dragon"). Sheet 106 × 86 mm.
MS724 **209** $2 multicoloured . . 1·75 2·00

210 Domestic Goose

2000. Ducks and Geese. Multicoloured.
725 45c. Type **210** 55 50
726 75c. Pacific black duck . . . 1·00 1·00
727 $1.05 Mallard drake . . . . 1·25 1·50
728 $1.20 Aylesbury duck . . . . 1·25 1·50

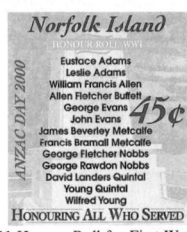

211 Honour Roll for First World War

2000. Anzac Day. Multicoloured.
729 45c. Type **211** 60 50
730 75c. Honour rolls for Second World War and Korea . . 80 1·10

212 Young Boy, Shipwright and Whaleboat

2000. "Whaler Project 2000". Two sheets, each 96 × 76 mm, containing T **212**. Multicoloured.
MS731 **212** $4 multicoloured . . 4·00 4·50
MS732 $4 mult ("THE STAMP SHOW 2000" and Crown Agents logos added in gold) Imperf . . 4·00 4·50

213 Captain William Bligh and Bounty

2000. "Bounty" Day. Multicoloured.
733 45c. Type **213** 70 55
734 75c. Fletcher Christian and Tahiti . . . . 90 1·10

214 Turtle **215** Malcolm Champion (Olympic Gold Medal Winner, Stockholm, 1912)

2000. 8th Festival of Pacific Arts, New Caledonia. Multicoloured. (a) Size 24 × 29 mm. Self-adhesive.
735 45c. Urn and swat 50 50

(b) Sheet 130 × 70 mm.
MS736 75c. Type **214**; $1.05 Traditional mosaic; $1.20 Mask and spearhead; $2 Decorated utensils . . . . 4·00 4·50

2000. "Olymphilex 2000" International Stamp Exhibition, Sydney. Sheet 120 × 70 mm.
MS737 **215** $3 multicoloured . . 2·75 3·00

2000. "Canpex 2000" National Stamp Exhibition, Christchurch, New Zealand. Sheet 120 × 90 mm.
MS738 $2.40 No. 701 × 2 . . . . 2·25 2·50

216 Sun over Pines

2000. Christmas. Multicoloured.
739 45c. Type **216** 70 45
740 75c. Candle over pines . . . 1·00 80
741 $1.05 Moon over pines . . . 1·25 1·25
742 $1.20 Star over pines . . . . 1·50 1·50

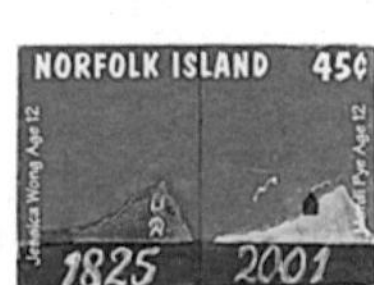

217 "Norfolk Island in 1825 and 2001" (Jessica Wong and Mardi Pye)

2000. New Millennium. Children's drawings. Mult.
743 45c. Type **217** 70 70
744 45c. "Seabirds over Norfolk Island" (Roxanne Spreag) 70 70
745 75c. "Trees and Clothes" (Tara Grube) . . . . . . 1·10 1·10
746 75c. "Underwater Scene" (Thomas Greenwood) . . . 1·10 1·10

218 Red-fronted Parakeet ("Green Parrot") **219** Purple Swamphen

2001. Green Parrot.
747 **218** 5c. red and green 10 10

2001. Chinese New Year "Year of the Snake" and International Stamp Exhibition, Hong Kong.
748 **219** 45c. multicoloured . . . . 1·00 75
MS749 110 × 70 mm. $2.30 Norfolk Island eel and purple swamphen (as Type **219**, but without country inscr and face value). Imperf 1·90 2·25

220 "Old Clothes" **222** Woman and Child in Victorian Dress

221 Satellite over China

2001. Centenary of Australian Federation. Cartoons from *The Bulletin Magazine*. Multicoloured.
750 45c. Type **220** 65 70
751 45c. "Tower of Babel" 65 70
752 45c. "The Political Garotters" 65 70
753 45c. "Promises, Promises!" 65 70
754 45c. "The Gout of Federation" 65 70
755 45c. "The Federal Spirit" . . 65 70
756 75c. "Australia Faces the Dawn" 80 90
757 $1.05 "The Federal Capital Question" . . . . 1·00 1·40
758 $1.20 "The Imperial Fowl-Yard" . . . . 1·10 1·50

2001. Invercargill "Stamp Odyssey 2001" National Stamp Exhibition, New Zealand. Sheet, 136 × 105 mm, containing T **221** and similar vert designs. Multicoloured.
MS759 75c. Type **221**; 75c. Satellite over Pacific; 75c. Satellite over Australia . . . . 2·50 2·75

2001. Bounty Day.
760 **222** 5c. black and green . . . 10 10

223 *Jasminium simplicifolium*

2001. Perfume from Norfolk Island. Multicoloured.
761 45c. Type **223** 10 10
762 75c. Girl's face in perfume bottle 55 60
763 $1.05 Girl and roses 75 90
764 $1.20 Taylor's Road, Norfolk Island . . . . 85 1·00
765 $1.50 Couple shopping for perfume . . . . 1·10 1·40
MS766 145 × 98 mm. $3 Girl and perfume bottle ("NORFOLK ISLAND" in two lines) (60 × 72 mm) . . . . 2·40 2·75
MS767 145 × 98 mm. $3 As No. **MS**766, but with "NORFOLK ISLAND" in one line across the top of the sheet and face value at bottom right . . . . 3·25 3·50
Nos. 761/5 were printed on paper impregnated with the Jasmine fragrance.
No. **MS**767 was issued imperf.

224 Whaleboat **226** Miamiti (cartoon owl) holding Island Flag

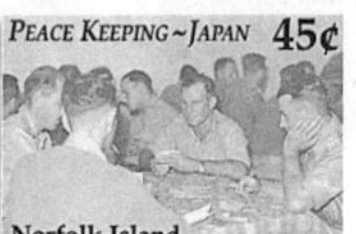

225 Australian Soldiers playing Cards

2001. Local Boats. Multicoloured.
768 45c. Type **224** 40 35
769 $1 Motor launch 80 90
770 $1 Family rowing boat (horiz) 80 90
771 $1.50 Sailing cutter (horiz) . . 1·25 1·40
No. 768 also comes self-adhesive.

2001. Centenary of Australian Army. B.C.O.F. Japan.
773 **225** 45c. brown and blue . . . 45 50
774 – 45c. brown and blue . . . 45 50
775 – $1 brown and green . . . 90 1·00
776 – $1 brown and green . . . 90 1·00
DESIGNS: No. 774, Christmas float; 775, Birthday cake; 776, Australian military policeman directing traffic.

2001. 6th South Pacific Mini Games (1st issue).
777 **226** 10c. brown and green . . 20 25
See also Nos. 794/5.

227 Strawberry Guava **228** Sacred Kingfisher

2001. Christmas. Island Plants. Each incorporating carol music. Multicoloured.
778 45c. Type **227** 45 45
779 45c. Poinsettia 45 45
780 $1 Christmas croton 80 90
781 $1 Hibiscus 80 90
782 $1.50 Indian shot . . . . . 1·25 1·50
No. 779 is inscribed "Pointsettia" in error.

2002. "Nuffka" (Sacred Kingfisher).
783 **228** 10c. deep blue and blue 20 25

229 Red-tailed Tropic Bird

2002. Cliff Ecology. Multicoloured.
784 45c. Type **229** 50 40
785 $1 White oak blossom . . . 80 90
786 $1 White oak tree 80 90
787 $1.50 Eagle ray . . . . . . 1·25 1·60

2002. Golden Jubilee. As T **211** of Pitcairn Islands.
788 45c. black, red and gold . . . 45 35
789 75c. multicoloured 70 70
790 $1 black, red and gold . . . 80 85
791 $1.50 multicoloured . . . . 1·25 1·40
MS792 162×95 mm. Nos. 788/91 and $3 multicoloured . . . . 6·00 6·50
DESIGNS:—HORIZ:45c. Elizabeth, Duchess of York with Princesses Elizabeth and Margaret, 1930; 75c. Queen Elizabeth in multicoloured hat, 1977; $1 Queen Elizabeth wearing Imperial State Crown, Coronation 1953; $1.50, Queen Elizabeth at Windsor Horse Show, 2000. VERT (38 × 51 mm)— $3 Queen Elizabeth after Annigoni.
Designs as Nos. 788/91 in No. **MS**792 omit the gold frame around each stamp and the "Golden Jubilee 1952-2002" inscription.

230 Derelict Steam Engine

2002. Restoration of Yeaman's Mill Steam Engine.
793 **230** $4.50 multicoloured . . . 3·25 3·75

231 Miamiti (cartoon owl) running **232** Lawn Bowls Player

2002. 6th South Pacific Mini Games (2nd issue). Multicoloured.
794 50c. Type **231** 35 40
795 $1.50 Miamiti playing tennis 1·10 1·25

2002. Bounty Bowls Tournament.
796 **232** 10c. black and green . . . 10 10

233 *Streblorrhiza speciosa* **234** Running

2002. Phillip Island Flowers. Multicoloured.
797 10c. Type **233** 10 10
798 20c. *Plumbago zeylanica* . . . 15 20
799 30c. *Canavalia rosea* 25 30
800 40c. *Ipomea pes-caprae* . . . 35 40
801 45c. *Hibiscus insularis* 40 45
802 50c. *Solanum laciniatum* . . . 40 45
803 95c. *Phormium tenax* 80 85
804 $1 *Lobelia anceps* 85 90
805 $1.50 *Carpobrotus glaucescens* 1·30 1·40
806 $2 *Abutilon julianae* . . . . . 1·70 1·80
807 $3 *Wollastonia biflora* . . . . 2·50 2·75
808 $5 *Oxalis corniculata* . . . . 4·25 4·50
No. 797 is inscribed "specioca" in error.

2002. 17th Commonwealth Games, Manchester. Multicoloured.
809 10c. Type **234** 10 10
810 45c. Cycling (horiz) 30 35
811 $1 Lawn bowls 70 75
812 $1.50 Shooting (horiz) . . . 1·10 1·25

235 Adult Sperm Whale and Calf

2002. Norfolk Island--New Caledonia Joint Issue. Operation Cetaces (marine mammal study). Multicoloured.
813 $1 Type **235** 70 75
814 $1 Sperm whale attacked by giant squid 70 75
A similar set was issued by New Caledonia.

236 White Tern incubating Egg

2002. Christmas. White Tern. Multicoloured.
815 45c. Type **236** 30 35
816 45c. White tern chick 30 35
817 $1 Two White terns in flight 70 75
818 $1.50 White tern landing . . 1·10 1·25

237 Horses in Riding School

2003. Horses on Norfolk Island. Multicoloured.
819 45c. Type **237** 40 45
820 45c. Mares and foals in paddock 40 45
821 45c. Showjumpers 40 45
822 75c. Racehorses 65 70
823 75c. Draught horses 65 70

238 Old Warehouse Buildings at Seashore

2003. Photographic Scenes of Norfolk Island (1st series). Multicoloured.
824 50c. Type **238** 40 45
825 95c. Beached boat (with rainbow markings) and sandy shore 80 85
826 $1.10 Grazing cattle and pine trees . . . . 95 1·10
827 $1.65 Sandy shore and headland with single pine tree . . . . 1·40 1·50

239 "Southern Prize"

2003. Day Lilies. Multicoloured.
828 50c. Type **239** 40 45
829 50c. "Becky Stone" 40 45
830 50c. "Cameroons" 40 45
831 50c. "Chinese Autumn" . . . 40 45
832 50c. "Scarlet Orbit" 40 45
833 50c. "Ocean Rain" 40 45
834 50c. "Gingerbread Man" . . 40 45
835 50c. "Pink Corduroy" . . . 40 45
836 50c. "Elizabeth Hinrichsen" 40 45
837 50c. "Simply Pretty" 40 45

240 Maeve and Gil Hitch **241** Seashore with Trees and Stream

2003. 1st Norfolk Island Writer's Festival. Black, violet and lilac (Nos. 838/9 and 844/5) or multicoloured (Nos. 840/3).
838 10c. Type **240** 10 10
839 10c. Alice Buffett 10 10
840 10c. Nan Smith 10 10
841 10c. Archie Bigg 10 10
842 50c. Colleen McCullough . . 40 45
843 50c. Peter Clarke 40 45
844 50c. Bob Tofts 40 45
845 50c. Merval Hoare 40 45

2004. Island Landscapes. Multicoloured.
846 50c. Type **241** 40 45
847 50c. Sandy shore with wooden post and small boat 40 45
848 50c. Rocky bay with pine trees on headland 40 45
849 50c. Grazing cattle, pine trees and ruined building . . . 40 45

242 Queen Elizabeth II wearing Imperial State Crown **243** Globe ("Peace on Earth")

2003. 50th Anniv of Coronation.
MS850 115×85 mm. 10c. Type **242** (black, deep violet and violet); $3 Queen wearing flowered hat and dress (multicoloured) . . . . . 2·50 2·75

2003. Christmas. Multicoloured.
851 50c. Type **243** 40 45
852 50c. Bird and rainbow ("Joy to the World") 40 45
853 $1.10 Heart-shaped Christmas present ("Give the gift of Love") . . . . 95 1·00
854 $1.65 Candle ("Trust in Faith") . . . . 1·40 1·50

244 De Havilland D.H.60G Gipsy Moth Floatplane (first aircraft at Norfolk Island, 1931)

2003. Centenary of Powered Flight. Multicoloured (except Type **244**).
855 50c. Type **244** (black, brown and violet) 40 45
856 $1.10 Boeing 737 (Norfolk Island–Australia service) 95 1·00
857 $1.65 Douglas DC-4 (passenger service 1949–977) . . . . 1·40 1·50
MS858 110×83 mm. $1.65 Wright *Flyer I*, 1903 (47×29 mm) . . 1·40 1·50

NORTH BORNEO Pt. 1

A territory in the north of the Island of Borneo in the China Sea, formerly under the administration of the British North Borneo Company. A Crown Colony since 1946. Joined Malaysia in 1963 and renamed Sabah in 1964.

100 cents = 1 dollar (Malayan).

1

1883. "POSTAGE NORTH BORNEO" at top.
8 **1** ½c. mauve . . . . 95·00 £180
9 1c. orange £180 £325
10 2c. brown . . . . 26·00 24·00
11 4c. pink . . . . 17·00 50·00
12 8c. green . . . . 19·00 50·00
13 10c. blue . . . . 29·00 50·00

1883. Surch **8 Cents.** vert.
2 **1** 8c. on 2c. brown £950 £650

1883. Surch **EIGHT CENTS**.
3 **1** 8c. on 2c. brown £450 £190

> Where there are three price columns, prices in the second column are for postally used stamps and those in the third column are for stamps cancelled with black bars.

4 **5**

1883. Inscr "NORTH BORNEO".
4 **4** 50c. violet . . . . . . £130 – 25·00
5 **5** $1 red . . . . £110 – 12·00
For these designs with "BRITISH" in place of value in words at top, see Nos. 46/7.

1886. Optd **and Revenue**.
14 **1** ½c. mauve £120 £200
15 10c. blue £170 £200

1886. Surch in words and figures.
18 **1** 3c. on 4c. pink . . . . 95·00 £110
19 5c. on 8c. green £110 £110

9 **10**

13 **19**

1886. Inscr "BRITISH NORTH BORNEO".
22 **9** ½c. red . . . . . . 3·00 13·00
24 1c. orange . . . . 2·00 8·00
25 2c. brown . . . . . 2·00 8·50
26 4c. pink . . . . . 3·00 10·00
27 8c. green . . . . . 11·00 19·00
28 10c. blue . . . . . 7·00 26·00
45 **10** 25c. blue . . . . . 60·00 80·00 75
46 – 50c. violet . . . . . 85·00 £130 75
47 – $1 red . . . . . . 27·00 £110 75
48 **13** $2 green . . . . . £130 £180 1·50
49 **19** $5 purple . . . . . £180 £190 8·50
50 – $10 brown . . . . £250 £325 12·00
DESIGNS: 50c. As Type **4**; $1, As Type **5**. $10 As Type **19** but with different frame.

14

1888. Inscr "POSTAGE & REVENUE".

36b	**14**	½c. red	1·50	4·25	60
37		1c. orange	2·25	4·25	50
38b		2c. brown	3·75	14·00	50
39		3c. violet	2·50	12·00	50
40		4c. pink	6·00	32·00	50
41		5c. grey	2·75	21·00	50
42		6c. red	8·00	21·00	50
43a		8c. green	19 00	25·00	50
44b		10c. blue	6·50	21·00	50

1890. Surch in words.

51	**10**	2c. on 25c. blue	70·00	90·00
52		8c. on 25c. blue	95·00	£110

1891. Surch in figures and words.

63	**14**	1c. on 4c. pink	23·00	14·00
64		1c. on 5c. grey	7·00	6·00
54	**9**	6c. on 8c. green	£8000	£4250
55	**14**	6c. on 8c. green	22·00	10·00
56	**9**	6c. on 10c. blue	60·00	21·00
57	**14**	6c. on 10c. blue	£150	26·00
65	**10**	8c. on 25c. blue	£140	£160

24 Dyak Chief

25 Sambar Stag ("Cervus unicolor")

26 Sago Palm

27 Great Argus Pheasant

28 Arms of the Company

29 Malay Prau

30 Estuarine Crocodile

31 Mt. Kinabalu

32 Arms of the Company with Supporters

1894.

66	**24**	1c. black and bistre	1·25	9·50	50
69	**25**	2c. black and red	5·50	4·75	50
70	**26**	3c. green and mauve	2·75	8·50	50
72	**27**	5c. black and red	14·00	11·00	60
73a	**28**	6c. black and brown	4·50	18·00	60
74	**29**	8c. black and lilac	6·50	11·00	60
75a	**30**	12c. black and blue	28·00	80·00	2·50
78	**31**	18c. black and green	27·00	50·00	2·00
79	**32**	24c. blue and red	23·00	80·00	2·00

1894. As Nos. 47, etc, but inscr "THE STATE OF NORTH BORNEO".

81	25c. blue	9·00	30·00	1·00
82	50c. violet	22·00	60·00	1·75
83	$1 red	12·00	24·00	1·25
84	$2 green	20·00	75·00	2·50
85b	$5 purple	£200	£275	8·00
86	$10 brown	£225	£325	15·00

1895. No. 83 surch in figures and words.

87	4 cents on $1 red	6·50	1·50	50
88	10 cents on $1 red	19·00	1·75	50
89	20 cents on $1 red	40·00	17·00	50
90	30 cents on $1 red	29·00	27·00	50
91	40 cents on $1 red	29·00	48·00	50

37 Orang-utan

41 Sun Bear

43 Borneo Steam Train

1897. As 1894 issue with insertion of native inscriptions.

92a	**24**	1c. black and bistre	11·00	2·75	40
94a	**25**	2c. black and red	22·00	3·00	40
95		2c. black and green	48·00	2·00	60
97	**26**	3c. green and mauve	18·00	3·00	50
98	**37**	4c. black and green	9·00	–	1·50
99		4c. black and red	35·00	8·00	50
100a	**27**	5c. black & orange	95·00	3·00	50
101a	**28**	6c. black and brown	28·00	4·00	50
102b	**29**	8c. black and lilac	40·00	2·75	60
104	**41**	10c. brown and grey	90·00	42·00	2·75
106b	**30**	12c. black and blue	90·00	35·00	1·50
107	**43**	16c. green & brown	£130	90·00	3·25
108	**31**	18c. black and green	22·00	75·00	1·50
110b		18c. black & green*	70·00	12·00	1·50
109	**32**	24c. blue and red*	20·00	90·00	1·75
111b		24c. blue and red*	45·00	55·00	2·50

*No. 110b is inscribed "POSTAGE & REVENUE" at the sides instead of "POSTAL REVENUE" as in No. 108. No. 111b has the words "POSTAGE & REVENUE" at the sides below the Arms; these words were omitted in No. 109.

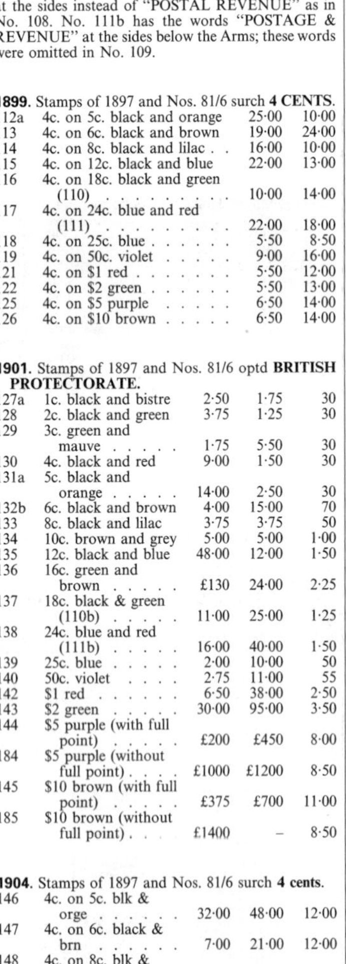

1899. Stamps of 1897 and Nos. 81/6 surch **4 CENTS**.

112a	4c. on 5c. black and orange	25·00	10·00
113	4c. on 6c. black and brown	19·00	24·00
114	4c. on 8c. black and lilac	16·00	10·00
115	4c. on 12c. black and blue	22·00	13·00
116	4c. on 18c. black and green (110)	10·00	14·00
117	4c. on 24c. blue and red (111)	22·00	18·00
118	4c. on 25c. blue	5·50	8·50
119	4c. on 50c. violet	9·00	16·00
121	4c. on $1 red	5·50	12·00
122	4c. on $2 green	5·50	13·00
125	4c. on $5 purple	6·50	14·00
126	4c. on $10 brown	6·50	14·00

1901. Stamps of 1897 and Nos. 81/6 optd **BRITISH PROTECTORATE.**

127a	1c. black and bistre	2·50	1·75	30
128	2c. black and green	3·75	1·25	30
129	3c. green and mauve	1·75	5·50	30
130	4c. black and red	9·00	1·50	30
131a	5c. black and orange	14·00	2·50	30
132b	6c. black and brown	4·00	15·00	70
133	8c. black and lilac	3·75	3·75	50
134	10c. brown and grey	5·00	5·00	1·00
135	12c. black and blue	48·00	12·00	1·50
136	16c. green and brown	£130	24·00	2·25
137	18c. black & green (110b)	11·00	25·00	1·25
138	24c. blue and red (111b)	16·00	40·00	1·50
139	25c. blue	2·00	10·00	50
140	50c. violet	2·75	11·00	55
142	$1 red	6·50	38·00	2·50
143	$2 green	30·00	95·00	3·50
144	$5 purple (with full point)	£200	£450	8·00
184	$5 purple (without full point)	£1000	£1200	8·50
145	$10 brown (with full point)	£375	£700	11·00
185	$10 brown (without full point)	£1400	–	8·50

1904. Stamps of 1897 and Nos. 81/6 surch **4 cents**.

146	4c. on 5c. blk & orge	32·00	48·00	12·00
147	4c. on 6c. black & brn	7·00	21·00	12·00
148	4c. on 8c. blk & lilac	13·00	26·00	12·00
149	4c. on 12c. black & bl	26·00	40·00	12·00
150	4c. on 18c. black and green (110b)	14·00	38·00	12·00
151a	4c. on 24c. bl & red (111b)	17·00	48·00	12·00
152	4c. on 25c. blue	4·25	25·00	12·00
153	4c. on 50c. violet	4·75	38·00	12·00
154	4c. on $1 red	6·00	48·00	12·00
155	4c. on $2 green	6·00	48·00	12·00
156	4c. on $5 purple	12·00	48·00	12·00
157	4c. on $10 brown	12·00	48·00	12·00

51 Malayan Tapir

52 Traveller's Tree

64

(68)

1909. No. 177 is surch **20 CENTS**.

277	**51**	1c. black and brown	1·00	70	–
160	**52**	2c. black and green	1·00	70	30
278		2c. black and red	85	60	–
162	–	3c. black and red	2·75	2·75	40
279	–	3c. black and green	3·00	75	–
280	–	4c. black and red	50	10	–
281	–	5c. black and brown	5·00	2·75	–
282	–	6c. black and green	6·00	90	–
283	–	8c. black and red	3·25	50	–
284	–	10c. black and blue	3·75	90	–
285	–	12c. black and blue	21·00	80	–
174	–	16c. black and brown	26·00	7·00	1·00
175	–	18c. black and green	90·00	32·00	1·00
177	–	20c. on 18c. blk & grn	7·00	1·00	30
176	–	24c. black and green	28·00	3·50	1·75
178	**64**	25c. black and green	9·50	4·50	2·00
179	–	50c. black and blue	10·00	4·50	2·25
180	–	$1 black and brown	17·00	4·00	2·75
181	–	$2 black and lilac	65·00	17·00	4·75
182	–	$5 black and red	£100	£110	30·00
183	–	$10 black and orange	£350	£400	65·00

DESIGNS—As T **51**: 3c. Jesselton railway station; 4c. Sultan of Sulu, his staff and W. C. Cowie, first Chairman of the Company; 5c. Asiatic elephant; 8c. Ploughing with buffalo; 24c. Dwarf cassowary. As T **52**: 6c. Sumatran rhinoceros; 10c. Wild boar; 12c. Palm cockatoo; 16 c Rhinoceros hornbill; 18 c Banteng. As T **64** but Arms with supporters: $5, $10.

1916. Stamps of 1909 surch.

186	2c. on 3c. black and red	24·00	15·00
187	4c. on 6c. black and olive	19·00	17·00
188	10c. on 12c. black and blue	50·00	65·00

1916. Nos. 277 etc, optd with T **68**.

189	1c. black and brown	7·50	35·00
203	2c. black and green	27·00	50·00
191	3c. black and red	27·00	48·00
192	4c. black and red	5·50	32·00
193	5c. black and brown	35·00	55·00
206	6c. black and green	48·00	65·00
207	8c. black and red	25·00	55·00
196	10c. black and blue	40·00	70·00
197	12c. black and blue	90·00	90·00
198	16c. black and brown	90·00	90·00
199	20c. on 18c. black and green	38·00	85·00
200	24c. black and mauve	£100	£100
201	25c. black and green	£325	£400

1918. Nos. 159, etc, surch **RED CROSS TWO CENTS.**

214	1c.+2c. black and brown	3·50	12·00
215	2c.+2c. black and green	1·00	8·50
216	3c.+2c. black and red	14·00	19·00
218	4c.+2c. black and red	70	5·00
219	5c.+2c. black and brown	8·00	22·00
221	6c.+2c. black and olive	5·00	24·00
222	8c.+2c. black and red	5·50	11·00
223	10c.+2c. black and blue	8·00	24·00
224	12c.+2c. black and blue	21·00	45·00
225	16c.+2c. black and brown	22·00	45·00
226	24c.+2c. black and mauve	22·00	45·00
229	25c.+2c. black and green	10·00	42·00
230	50c.+2c. black and blue	12·00	42·00
231	$1+2c. black and brown	45·00	50·00
232	$2+2c. black and lilac	75·00	95·00
233	$5+2c. black and red	£350	£500
234	$10+2c. black and orange	£375	£500

The premium of 2c. on each value was for Red Cross Funds.

1918. Nos. 159, etc, surch **FOUR CENTS** and a red cross.

235	1c.+4c. black and brown	60	5·00
236	2c.+4c. black and green	65	8·00
237	3c.+4c. black and red	1·00	3·75
238	4c.+4c. black and red	40	4·75
239	5c.+4c. black and brown	2·00	22·00
240	6c.+4c. black and olive	1·90	12·00
241	8c.+4c. black and red	1·25	9·50
242	10c.+4c. black and blue	3·75	12·00
243	12c.+4c. black and blue	14·00	14·00
244	16c.+4c. black and brown	8·00	16·00
245	24c.+4c. black and mauve	11·00	20·00
246	25c.+4c. black and green	6·00	50·00
248	50c.+4c. black and blue	15·00	45·00
249	$1+4c. black and brown	15·00	60·00
250	$2+4 c black and lilac	48·00	80·00
251	$5+4c. black and red	£275	£400
252	$10+4c. black and orange	£300	£400

The premium of 4c. on each value was for Red Cross Funds.

1922. Nos. 159, etc, optd **MALAYA-BORNEO EXHIBITION 1922.**

253	1c. black and brown	12·00	60·00
255	2c. black and green	2·00	21·00
256	3c. black and red	14·00	55·00
257	4c. black and red	2·25	38·00
258	5c. black and brown	9·00	55·00
260	6c. black and green	8·50	60·00
262	8c. black and red	6·00	48·00
263	10c. black and blue	11·00	55·00
265	12c. black and blue	7·00	21·00
267	16c. black and brown	18·00	60·00
268	20c. on 18c. black and green	18·00	75·00
270	24c. black and mauve	32·00	60·00
274	25c. black and green	6·50	50·00
275	50c. black and blue	9·50	55·00

1923. No. 280 surch **THREE CENTS** and bars.

276	–	3c. on 4c. black and red	1·25	6·00

73 Head of a Murut

76 Mount Kinabalu

1931. 50th Anniv of North Borneo Company.

295	**73**	3c. black and green	1·25	80
296	–	6c. black and orange	16·00	3·25
297	–	10c. black and red	4·25	13·00
298	**76**	12c. black and blue	4·75	8·00
299	–	25c. black and violet	38·00	35·00
300	–	$1 black and green	27·00	£100
301	–	$2 black and brown	48·00	£110
302	–	$5 black and purple	£150	£425

DESIGNS—VERT: 6c. Orang-utan; 10c. Dyak warrior; $1, $2, $5 Arms. HORIZ: 25c. Clouded leopard.

81 Buffalo Transport

82 Palm Cockatoo

1939.

303	**81**	1c. green and brown	3·25	1·75
304	**82**	2c. purple and blue	5·00	1·75
305	–	3c. blue and green	3·75	2·00
306	–	4c. green and violet	7·00	50
307	–	6c. blue and red	6·50	8·00
308	–	8c. red	10·00	1·50
309	–	10c. violet and green	38·00	6·00
310	–	12c. green and blue	27·00	6·00
311	–	15c. green and brown	23·00	8·00
312	–	20c. violet and blue	15·00	4·00
313	–	25c. green and brown	20·00	11·00
314	–	50c. brown and violet	22·00	8·50
315	–	$1 brown and red	80·00	19·00
316	–	$2 violet and olive	£120	£100
317	–	$5 blue	£300	£200

DESIGNS—VERT: 3c. Native; 4c. Proboscis monkey; 6c. Mounted Bajaus; 10c. Orang-utan; 15c. Dyak; $1, $2 Arms. HORIZ: 8c. Map of Eastern Archipelago; 12c. Murut with blow-pipe; 20c. River scene; 25c. Native boat; 50c. Mt. Kinabalu; $5 Arms with supporters.

1941. Optd **WAR TAX**.

318	**81**	1c. green and brown	1·75	3·50
319	**82**	2c. purple and blue	7·00	4·00

1945. British Military Administration. Stamps of 1939 optd **BMA**.

320	**81**	1c. green and brown	7·00	2·00
321	**82**	2c. purple and blue	14·00	2·00
322	–	3c. blue and green	1·25	1·25
323	–	4c. green and violet	16·00	16·00
324	–	6c. blue and red	1·25	1·25
325	–	8c. red	3·00	75
326	–	10c. violet and green	3·00	40
327	–	12c. green and blue	6·00	2·75
328	–	15c. green and brown	1·50	1·00
329	–	20c. violet and blue	4·25	1·25
330	–	25c. green and brown	6·50	1·50
331	–	50c. brown and violet	3·00	1·75
332	–	$1 brown and red	48·00	40·00
333	–	$2 violet and olive	48·00	32·00
334	–	$5 blue	20·00	14·00

1947. Stamps of 1939 optd with Crown over GR monogram and bars obliterating "THE STATE OF" and "BRITISH PROTECTORATE".

335	**81**	1c. green and brown	15	1·00
336	**82**	2c. purple and blue	1·75	90
337	–	3c. blue and green	15	90
338	–	4c. green and violet	70	90
339	–	6c. blue and red	25	20
340	–	8c. red	30	20
341	–	10c. violet and green	1·50	40
342	–	12c. green and blue	2·00	2·75
343	–	15c. green and brown	2·25	30
344	–	20c. violet and blue	2·50	85
345	–	25c. green and brown	2·75	50
346	–	50c. brown and violet	2·75	85
347	–	$1 brown and red	5·50	1·75

348 – $2 violet and olive . . . . 14·00 17·00
349 – $5 blue . . . . 22·00 17·00

1948. Silver Wedding. As T **4b/c** of Pitcairn Islands.
350 8c. red 30 80
351 $10 mauve . . . . 22·00 35·00

1949. U.P.U. As T **4d/g** of Pitcairn Islands.
352 8c. red 60 30
353 10c. brown . . . . 3·25 1·00
354 30c. brown . . . . 1·25 1·75
355 55c. blue . . . . 1·25 2·50

100 Mt. Kinabalu

102 Coconut Grove

1950.
356 **100** 1c. brown . . . . 15 1·25
357 – 2c. blue 15 50
358 **102** 3c. green 15 15
359 – 4c. purple 15 10
360 – 5c. violet 15 10
361 – 8c. red 75 85
362 – 10c. purple . . . . . . 1·25 15
363 – 15c. blue . . . . 2·00 65
364 – 20c. brown . . . . . . 1·25 10
365 – 30c. buff . . . . 3·50 20
366 – 50c. red ("JESSELTON") . . . 85 3·25
366a – 50c. red ("JESSELTON") . . . 8·00 2·25
367 – $1 orange . . . . 3·75 1·00
368 – $2 green . . . . 5·50 14·00
369 – $5 green . . . . 15·00 21·00
370 – $10 blue . . . . 40·00 55·00
DESIGNS—VERT: 4c. Hemp drying; 5c. Cattle at Kota Belud; 30c. Suluk river canoe; 50c. Clock tower, Jesselton; $1 Bajau horsemen. HORIZ: 2c. Musician; 8c. Map; 10c. Log pond; 15c. Malay prau, Sandakan; 20c. Bajau chief; $2 Murut with blowpipe; $5 Net fishing; $10, King George VI and arms.

1953. Coronation. As T **4h** of Pitcairn Islands.
371 10c. black and red . . . . . 1·25 60

1954. As 1950 but with portrait of Queen Elizabeth II.
372 1c. brown 10 30
373 2c. blue 60 15
374 3c. green . . . . 1·00 2·00
375 4c. purple 75 20
376 5c. violet 75 10
377 8c. red 60 30
378 10c. purple 30 10
379 15c. blue . . . . 1·00 10
380 20c. brown 30 15
381 30c. buff . . . . 2·00 20
382 50c. red (No. 366a) . . . . . 5·00 20
383 $1 orange . . . . 6·50 20
384 $2 green . . . . 12·00 1·25
385 $5 green . . . . 10·00 26·00
386 $10 blue . . . . 24·00 35·00

117 Malay Prau

1956. 75th Anniv of Foundation of British North Borneo Co. Inscr "CHARTER 1ST NOVEMBER 1881".
387 – 10c. black and red . . . . 1·00 40
388 **117** 15c. black and brown . . 30 30
389 – 35c. black and green . . . 30 1·50
390 – $1 black and slate . . . . 65 2·50
DESIGNS—HORIZ: 10c. Borneo Railway, 1902; 35c. Mt. Kinabalu. VERT: $1 Arms of Chartered Company.

120 Sambar Stag

1961.
391 **120** 1c. green and red 20 10
392 – 4c. olive and orange . . . 20 90
393 – 5c. sepia and violet . . . 30 10
394 – 6c. black and turquoise . . 50 40
395 – 10c. green and red 50 10
396 – 12c. brown and myrtle . . 30 10
397 – 20c. turquoise and blue . . 3·50 10
398 – 25c. black and red 80 90
399 – 30c. sepia and olive . . . 70 20
400 – 35c. slate and brown . . . 1·75 90
401 – 50c. green and bistre . . . 1·75 20
402 – 75c. blue and purple . . . 9·00 90
403 – $1 brown and green . . . 13·00 80
404 – $2 brown and slate . . . 30·00 3·00
405 – $5 green and purple . . . 38·00 18·00
406 – $10 red and blue . . . . 30·00 35·00
DESIGNS—HORIZ: 4c. Sun bear; 5c. Clouded leopard; 6c. Dusun woman with gong; 10c. Map of Borneo; 12c. Banteng; 20c. Butterfly orchid; 25c. Sumatran rhinoceros; 30c. Murut with blow-pipe; 35c. Mt. Kinabalu; 50c. Dusun and buffalo transport; 75c. Bajau horseman. VERT: $1 Orang-utan; $2 Rhinoceros hornbill; $5 Crested wood partridge; $10 Arms of N. Borneo.

1963. Freedom from Hunger. As T **20a** of Pitcairn Islands.
407 12c. blue . . . . 1·50 75

POSTAGE DUE STAMPS

Overprinted **POSTAGE DUE**.

1895. Issue of 1894.
D 2 **25** 2c. black and red 16·00 24·00 2·00
D 3 **26** 3c. green & mve 6·00 16·00 1·00
D 5 **27** 5c. black and red 55·00 25·00 3·00
D 6a **28** 6c. black & brn 14·00 48·00 2·50
D 7 **29** 8c. black and lilac . . . . . 48·00 50·00 2·75
D 8b **30** 12c. black & blue . . . . . 70·00 50·00 2·50
D10 **31** 18c. black & grn 70·00 60·00 4·00
D11b **32** 24c. blue and red 27·00 55·00 4·00

1897. Issue of 1897.
D12 **25** 2c. black and red 8·50 9·00 1·50
D13 2c. black & green 50·00 † 70
D14 **26** 3c. green & mve 18·00 † 50
D16a 4c. black and red 40·00 † 50
D17a **27** 5c. black & orge 20·00 45·00 1·75
D18 **28** 6c. black & brn 5·00 30·00 70
D20 **29** 8c. black & lilac 6·00 † 50
D21a **30** 12c. black & blue 95·00 † 4·00
D22 **31** 18c. black and green (No. 108) . . † † £600
D23 18c. black and green (No. 110b) . . 50·00 † 4·00
D24 **32** 24c. blue and red (No. 109) . . – † £300
D25 24c. blue and red (No. 111b) . . 23·00 † 2·25

1902. Issue of 1901.
D37 1c. black and bistre – † 28·00
D38 2c. black and green 13·00 3·75 30
D39 3c. green and mauve 4·75 3·25 30
D40 4c. black and red . . 11·00 6·50 30
D41 5c. black and orange 23·00 4·50 30
D42 6c. black and brown 16·00 11·00 40
D43 8c. black and lilac 20·00 4·25 40
D45 10c. brown and grey 80·00 18·00 1·40
D46 12c. black and blue 24·00 15·00 2·00
D47 16c. green & brown 48·00 20·00 2·00
D48 18c. black and green 9·50 19·00 1·50
D49 24c. blue and red . . 11·00 23·00 1·75

1919. Issue of 1909.
D52 2c. black and green . . . . 11·00 75·00
D66 2c. black and red . . . . . 50 1·75
D67 3c. black and green . . . . 6·50 24·00
D55 4c. black and red . . . . . 1·00 1·25
D57 5c. black and brown . . . 9·00 22·00
D70 6c. black and olive . . . . 5·00 2·75
D62 8c. black and red . . . . . 1·50 1·50
D63 10c. black and blue . . . . 13·00 19·00
D64 12c. black and blue . . . . 55·00 48·00
D65a 16c. black and brown . . . 19·00 50·00

POSTAGE DUE

D **2** Crest of the Company

1939.
D85 D **2** 2c. brown . . . . 6·50 75·00
D86 4c. red . . . . 6·50 £100
D87 6c. violet . . . . 22·00 £130
D88 8c. green . . . . 23·00 £225
D89 10c. blue . . . . 50·00 £350

For later issues see **SABAH**.

JAPANESE OCCUPATION

1942. Stamps of North Borneo optd as T **1** of Japanese Occupation of Brunei. (a) Issue of 1939.
J 1 **81** 1c. green and brown £160 £225
J 2 **82** 2c. purple and blue £160 £225
J 3 – 3c. blue and green £130 £225
J 4a – 4c. green and violet . . . . 50·00 £120
J 5 – 6c. blue and red £130 £250
J 6 – 8c. red £160 £190
J 7 – 10c. violet and green £150 £250
J 8 – 12c. green and blue £170 £400
J 9 – 15c. green and brown £160 £400
J10 – 20c. violet and blue £190 £450
J11 – 25c. green and brown £190 £450
J12 – 50c. brown and violet . . . £275 £500
J13 – $1 brown and red £275 £650
J14 – $2 violet and olive £425 £850
J15 – $5 blue £500 £900

(b) War Tax Issue of 1941.
J16 **81** 1c. green and brown £475 £275
J17 **82** 2c. purple and blue £1200 £450

2 Mt. Kinabalu

3 Borneo Scene

1943.
J18 **2** 4c. red . . . . 17·00 40·00
J19 **3** 8c. blue . . . . 15·00 40·00

本 日 大
便 郵 國 帝
オネルボ北

(**4**) ("Imperial Japanese Postal Service, North Borneo")

本 日 大
便 郵 國 帝
貳
弗

(**5**) ("Imperial Japanese Postal Service, North Borneo")

1944. Optd with T **4**. (a) On stamps of North Borneo.
J20 **81** 1c. green and brown . . . . . 5·00 12·00
J21 **82** 2c. purple and blue . . . . . 7·50 9·00
J22 – 3c. blue and green . . . . . 4·50 9·00
J23 – 4c. green and violet . . . . . 7·50 15·00
J24 – 6c. blue and red . . . . . . 5·50 6·50
J25 – 8c. red . . . . 7·50 17·00
J26 – 10c. violet and green . . . . 8·50 13·00
J27 – 12c. green and blue . . . . . 9·50 13·00
J28 – 15c. green and brown . . . . 9·00 16·00
J29 – 20c. violet and blue . . . . 22·00 45·00
J30 – 25c. green and brown . . . . 22·00 45·00
J31 – 50c. brown and violet . . . . 65·00 £120
J32 – $1 brown and red . . . . . . 90·00 £150

(b) On stamps of Japanese Occupation of North Borneo.
J21a 2c. purple and blue (J2) £425
J22a 3c. blue and green (J3) £425
J25a 8c. red (J6) £425
J26b 10c. violet and green (J7) . . . £200 £375
J27a 12c. green and blue (J8) £425
J28a 15c. green and brown (J9) . . . £425

1944. No. J1 surch with T **5**.
J33 **81** $2 on 1c. green and brown £4500 £3750

本 日 大
五
弗
便 郵 國 帝

(**6**)

1944. No. 315 of North Borneo surch with T **6**.
J34 $5 on $1 brown and red . . . £4000 £2750

1944. Stamps of Japan optd as bottom line in T **4**.
J35 **126** 1s. brown . . . . 8·00 20·00
J36 **84** 2s. red . . . . 7·00 17·00
J37 – 3s. green (No. 319) . . . . . 6·50 20·00
J38 **129** 4s. green . . . . 9·50 18·00
J39 – 5s. red (No. 396) . . . . . . 9·00 21·00
J40 – 6s. orange (No. 322) . . . . 9·50 22·00
J41 – 8s. violet (No. 324) . . . . . 6·50 22·00
J42 – 10s. red (No. 399) . . . . . 7·00 22·00
J43 – 15s. blue (No. 401) . . . . . 9·00 22·00
J44 – 20s. blue (No. 328) . . . . . 80·00 90·00
J45 – 25s. brown (No. 329) . . . . 55·00 70·00
J46 – 30s. blue (No. 330) . . . . . £170 95·00
J47 – 50s. olive and brown (No. 331) . . . . 60·00 70·00
J48 – 1y. brown (No. 332) . . . . 60·00 95·00

NORTH GERMAN CONFEDERATION Pt. 7

The North German Confederation was set up on 1 January 1868, and comprised the postal services of Bremen, Brunswick, Hamburg Lubeck, Mecklenburg (both), Oldenburg, Prussia (including Hanover, Schleswig-Holstein with Bergedorf and Thurn and Taxis) and Saxony.

The North German Confederation joined the German Reichspost on 4 May 1871, and the stamps of Germany were brought into use on 1 January 1872.

Northern District: 30 groschen = 1 thaler.
Southern District: 60 kreuzer = 1 gulden.

1

3

1868. Roul or perf. (a) Northern District.
19 **1** ¼g. mauve . . . . 17·00 11·00
22 ⅓g. green . . . . 4·75 1·20
23 ½g. orange . . . . 4·75 1·20
25 1g. red . . . . 4·25 40
27 2g. blue . . . . 7·50 85
29 5g. bistre . . . . 8·75 7·00

(b) Southern District.
30 – 1k. green . . . . 13·00 8·25
13 – 2k. orange . . . . 55·00 32·00
33 – 3k. red . . . . 7·50 1·70
36 – 7k. blue . . . . 11·00 7·50
18 – 18k. bistre . . . . 37·00 50·00
The 1k. to 18k. have the figures in an oval.

1869. Perf.
38 **3** 10g. grey . . . . £325 65·00
39 – 30g. blue £250 £130
The frame of the 30g. is rectangular.

OFFICIAL STAMPS

O **5**

1870. (a) Northern District.
O40 O **5** ¼g. black and brown . . 24·00 48·00
O41 ⅓g. black and brown . . 11·00 22·00
O42 ½g. black and brown . . 2·75 3·50
O43 1g. black and brown . . 2·75 55
O44 2g. black and brown . . 7·50 4·75

(b) Southern District.
O45 1k. black and grey . . . . . 29·00 £275
O46 2k. black and grey . . . . . 70·00 £900
O47 3k. black and grey . . . . . 26·00 48·00
O48 7k. black and grey . . . . . 39·00 £275

NORTH INGERMANLAND Pt. 10

Stamps issued during temporary independence of this Russian territory, which adjoins Finland.

100 pennia = 1 mark.

1 18th-century Arms of Ingermanland

4 Gathering Crops

1920.
1 **1** 5p. green . . . . 2·25 4·25
2 10p. red . . . . 2·25 4·25
3 25p. brown . . . . 2·25 4·25
4 50p. blue . . . . 2·25 4·25
5 1m. black and red . . . . . 26·00 45·00
6 5m. black and purple £100 £160
7 10m. black and brown £180 £250

1920. Inscr as in T **2**.
8 – 10p. blue and green . . . . 3·00 7·50
9 – 30p. green and brown . . . . 3·00 7·50
10 – 50p. brown and blue . . . . 3·00 7·50
11 – 80p. grey and red . . . . . 3·00 7·50
12 **4** 1m. grey and red . . . . . 14·00 40·00
13 – 5m. red and violet . . . . . 8·00 19·00
14 – 10m. violet and brown . . . 7·75 19·00
DESIGNS—VERT: 10p. Arms; 30p. Reaper; 50p. Ploughing; 80p. Milking. HORIZ: 5m. Burning church; 10m. Zither players.

NORTH WEST RUSSIA Pt. 10

Issues made for use by the various Anti-bolshevist Armies during the Russian Civil War, 1918–20.

100 kopeks = 1 rouble.

NORTHERN ARMY

1 "OKCA" = Osobiy Korpus Severnoy Armiy—(trans "Special Corps, Northern Army")

1919. As T **1** inscr "OKCA".
1 **1** 5k. purple 10 40
2 10k. blue 10 40
3 15k. yellow 10 40
4 20k. red 10 40
5 50k. green 10 40

NORTH-WESTERN ARMY

Сѣв. Зап.
Армія

(**2**)

1919. Arms types of Russia optd as T **2**. Imperf or perf.
6 **22** 2k. green . . . 3·00 7·50
16 3k. red . . . 3·00 7·50
7 5k. lilac . . . 3·00 7·50
8 **23** 10k. blue . . . 4·50 10·00
9 **10** 15k. blue and brown . . . 4·00 7·50
10 **14** 20k. red and blue . . . 5·00 8·50
11 **10** 20k. on 14k. red and blue £250
12 25k. violet and green . . . 8·00 12·00
13 **14** 50k. green and purple . . . 8·00 12·00
14 **15** 1r. orange & brown on brn 16·00 24·00
17 **11** 3r.50 green and red . . . 32·00 45·00
18 **22** 5r. blue on green . . . 24·00 32·00
19 **11** 7r. pink and green . . . 90·00 £160
15 **20** 10r. grey and red on yellow 60·00 85·00

1919. No. 7 surch.
20 **22** 10k. on 5k. lilac . . . 4·00 7·50

WESTERN ARMY

1919. Stamps of Latvia optd with Cross of Lorraine in circle with plain background. Imperf. (a) Postage stamps.
21 **1** 3k. lilac . . . 30·00 40·00
22 5k. red . . . 30·00 40·00
23 10k. blue . . . £110 £190
24 20k. orange . . . 30·00 40·00
25 25k. grey . . . 30·00 40·00
26 35k. brown . . . 30·00 40·00
27 50k. violet . . . 30·00 40·00
28 75k. green . . . 30·00 55·00

(b) Liberation of Riga issue.
29 **4** 5k. red . . . 25·00 45·00
30 15k. green . . . 15·00 35·00
31 35k. brown . . . 15·00 35·00

1919. Stamps of Latvia optd with Cross of Lorraine in circle with burele background and characters **3. A** (= "Z. A."). Imperf. (a) Postage stamps.
32 **1** 3k. lilac . . . 4·00 8·00
33 5k. red . . . 4·00 8·00
34 10k. blue . . . 90·00 £170
35 20k. orange . . . 8·00 16·00
36 25k. grey . . . 22·00 45·00
37 35k. brown . . . 14·00 24·00
38 50k. violet . . . 14·00 24·00
39 75k. green . . . 14·00 24·00

(b) Liberation of Riga issue.
40 **4** 5k. red . . . 2·75 6·50
41 15k. green . . . 2·75 6·50
42 35k. brown . . . 2·75 6·50

1919. Arms type of Russia surch with Cross of Lorraine in ornamental frame and **LP** with value in curved frame. Imperf or perf.
43 **22** 10k. on 2k. green . . . 4·50 6·00
54 20k. on 3k. red . . . 4·00 7·50
44 **23** 30k. on 4k. red . . . 4·50 7·00
45 **22** 40k. on 5k. lilac . . . 4·50 7·00
46 **23** 50k. on 10k. blue . . . 4·50 6·00
47 **10** 70k. on 15k. blue and brown . . . 4·50 6·00
48 **14** 90k. on 20k. red and blue 6·00 8·00
49 **10** 1r. on 25k. violet and green 4·50 6·00
50 1r.50 on 35k. green & brown . . . 35·00 55·00
51 **14** 2r. on 50k. green and purple 6·00 10·00
52 **10** 4r. on 70k. red and brown 16·00 24·00
53 **15** 6r. on 1r. orange, brown on brown . . . 16·00 25·00
56 **11** 10r. on 3r.50 green & pur 40·00 48·00

NORTHERN NIGERIA Pt. 1

A British protectorate on the west coast of Africa. In 1914 incorporated into Nigeria.

12 pence = 1 shilling;
20 shillings = 1 pound.

1 5

1900.
1 **1** ½d. mauve and green . . . 2·75 13·00
2 1d. mauve and red . . . 3·50 3·75
3 2d. mauve and yellow . . . 12·00 42·00
4 2½d. mauve and blue . . . 9·00 38·00
5 5d. mauve and brown . . . 22·00 45·00
6 6d. mauve and violet . . . 19·00 29·00
7 1s. green and black . . . 24·00 65·00
8 2s.6d. green and blue . . . 95·00 £400
9 10s. green and brown . . . £225 £550

1902. As T **1**, but portrait of King Edward VII.
10 ½d. purple and green . . . 2·00 1·00
11 1d. purple and red . . . 2·25 75
12 2d. purple and yellow . . . 2·00 3·00
13 2½d. purple and blue . . . 1·50 9·00
14 5d. purple and brown . . . 2·75 5·00
15 6d. purple and violet . . . 7·50 4·50
16 1s. green and black . . . 3·50 6·00
17 2s.6d. green and blue . . . 8·00 45·00
18 10s. green and brown . . . 48·00 55·00

1910. As last. New colours etc.
28 ½d. green . . . 2·00 1·25
29 1d. red . . . 2·00 1·25
30 2d. grey . . . 4·50 2·25
31 2½d. blue . . . 2·25 7·00
32 3d. purple on yellow . . . 3·50 75
34 5d. purple and green . . . 4·00 12·00
35a 6d. purple . . . 5·00 6·00
36 1s. black and green . . . 2·25 75
37 2s.6d. black and red on blue 10·00 29·00
38 5s. green and red on yellow 23·00 75·00
39 10s. green and red on green 42·00 48·00

1912.
40 **5** ½d. green . . . 1·50 60
41 1d. red . . . 1·50 60
42 2d. grey . . . 3·00 7·50
43 3d. purple on yellow . . . 2·25 1·25
44 4d. black and red on yellow 1·25 2·25
45 5d. purple and olive . . . 4·00 10·00
46 6d. purple and violet . . . 4·00 4·25
47 9d. purple and red . . . 2·00 12·00
48 1s. black on green . . . 4·50 2·25
49 2s.6d. black and red on blue 7·00 40·00
50 5s. green and red on yellow 20·00 80·00
51 10s. green and red on green 38·00 48·00
52 £1 purple and black on red £170 £110

NORTHERN RHODESIA Pt. 1

A British territory in central Africa, north of the Zambesi. From 1954 to 1963 part of the central African Federation and using the stamps of Rhodesia and Nyasaland (q.v.). A new constitution was introduced on 3 January 1964, with internal self-government and independence came on 24 October 1964 when the country was renamed Zambia (q.v.).

12 pence = 1 shilling;
20 shillings = 1 pound.

1

1925. The shilling values are larger and the view is in first colour.
1 **1** ½d. green . . . 1·75 80
2 1d. brown . . . 1·75 10
3 1½d. red . . . 1·75 30
4 2d. orange . . . 2·00 10
5 3d. blue . . . 2·00 1·25
6 4d. violet . . . 4·00 50
7 6d. grey . . . 4·25 40
8 8d. purple . . . 3·75 45·00
9 10d. olive . . . 4·25 40·00
10 1s. orange and black . . . 3·75 1·75
11 2s. brown and blue . . . 15·00 23·00
12 2s.6d. black and green . . . 15·00 8·00
13 3s. violet and blue . . . 23·00 19·00
14 5s. grey and violet . . . 30·00 17·00
15 7s.6d. purple and black . . . £100 £150
16 10s. green and black . . . 70·00 70·00
17 20s. red and purple . . . £150 £170

1935. Silver Jubilee. As T **10a** of Gambia.
18 1d. blue and olive . . . 80 1·50
19 2d. green and blue . . . 80 1·50
20 3d. brown and blue . . . 2·50 5·50
21 6d. grey and purple . . . 3·75 1·50

1937. Coronation. As T **10b** of Gambia.
22 1½d. red . . . 30 35
23 2d. brown . . . 40 35
24 3d. blue . . . 60 1·25

1938. As 1925, but with portrait of King George VI facing right and "POSTAGE & REVENUE" omitted.
25 ½d. green . . . 10 10
26 ½d. brown . . . 75 1·50
27 1d. brown . . . 20 20
28 1d. green . . . 75 1·25
29 1½d. red . . . 45·00 70
30 1½d. orange . . . 30 10
31 2d. brown . . . 45·00 1·75
32 2d. red . . . 30 50
33 2d. purple . . . 45 1·50
34 3d. blue . . . 40 30
35 3d. red . . . 50 2·75
36 4d. violet . . . 30 40
37 4½d. blue . . . 55 6·00
38 6d. grey . . . 30 10
39 9d. violet . . . 50 4·25
40 1s. orange and black . . . 3·25 60
41 2s.6d. black and green . . . 7·00 3·50
42 3s. violet and blue . . . 13·00 8·00
43 5s. grey and violet . . . 13·00 8·50
44 10s. green and black . . . 15·00 13·00
45 20s. red and purple . . . 40·00 48·00

1946. Victory. As T **4a** of Pitcairn Islands.
46 1½d. orange . . . 20 20
47 2d. red . . . 10 50

1948. Silver Wedding. As T **4b/c** of Pitcairn Islands.
48 1½d. orange . . . 30 10
49 20s. red . . . 45·00 48·00

1949. U.P.U. As T **4d/g** of Pitcairn Islands.
50 2d. red . . . 20 30
51 3d. blue . . . 1·50 1·75
52 6d. grey . . . 55 1·75
53 1s. orange . . . 55 1·00

5 Cecil Rhodes and Victoria Falls

1953. Birth Centenary of Cecil Rhodes.
54 **5** ½d. brown . . . 50 75
55 1d. green . . . 40 75
56 2d. mauve . . . 40 20
57 4½d. blue . . . 40 3·25
58 1s. orange and black . . . 75 4·50

6 Arms of the Rhodesias and Nyasaland

9 Arms

1953. Rhodes Centenary Exhibition.
59 **6** 6d. violet . . . 70 1·25

1953. Coronation. As T **4h** of Pitcairn Islands.
60 1½d. black and orange . . . 70 20

1953. As 1938 but with portrait of Queen Elizabeth II facing left.
61 ½d. brown . . . 65 10
62 1d. green . . . 65 10
63 1½d. orange . . . 1·25 10
64 2d. purple . . . 1·25 10
65 3d. red . . . 80 10
66 4d. violet . . . 1·25 2·00
67 4½d. blue . . . 1·50 4·25
68 6d. grey . . . 1·25 10
69 9d. violet . . . 1·25 4·25
70 1s. orange and black . . . 70 10
71 2s.6d. black and green . . . 8·00 3·75
72 5s. grey and purple . . . 8·00 12·00
73 10s. green and black . . . 6·50 25·00
74 20s. red and purple . . . 22·00 27·00

1963. Arms black, gold and blue; portrait and inscriptions black; background colours given.
75 **9** ½d. violet . . . 50 1·25
76 1d. blue . . . 80 10
77 2d. brown . . . 40 10
78 3d. yellow . . . 20 10
79 4d. green . . . 40 30
80 6d. green . . . 50 10
81 9d. bistre . . . 40 1·60
82 1s. purple . . . 40 10
83 1s.3d. purple . . . 2·00 10
84 2s. orange . . . 2·00 3·25
85 2s.6d. purple . . . 2·00 1·75
86 5s. mauve . . . 7·50 7·50
87 10s. mauve . . . 8·50 16·00
88 20s. blue . . . 9·00 18·00
Nos. 84/88 are larger (27 × 23 mm).

POSTAGE DUE STAMPS

D 1 D 2

1929.
D1 **D 1** 1d. black . . . 2·50 2·50
D2 2d. black . . . 3·00 3·00
D3 3d. black . . . 3·00 26·00
D4 4d. black . . . 9·50 30·00

1963.
D 5 **D 2** 1d. orange . . . 1·10 4·50
D 6 2d. blue . . . 1·10 4·00
D 7 3d. lake . . . 1·25 5·00
D 8 4d. blue . . . 1·25 8·50
D 9 6d. purple . . . 6·00 9·00
D10 1s. green . . . 7·00 24·00

For later issues see **ZAMBIA**.

NORWAY Pt. 11

In 1814 Denmark ceded Norway to Sweden, from 1814 to 1905 the King of Sweden was also King of Norway after which Norway was an independent Kingdom.

1855. 120 skilling = 1 speciedaler.
1877. 100 ore = 1 krone.

1 3 King Oscar I

1855. Imperf.
1 **1** 4s. blue . . . £4000 75·00

1856. Perf.
4 **3** 2s. yellow . . . £500 75·00
6 3s. lilac . . . £250 42·00
7 4s. blue . . . £225 6·50
11 8s. red . . . £950 18·00

4 5

1863.
12 **4** 2s. yellow . . . £550 £100
13 3s. lilac . . . £425 £250
16 4s. blue . . . £150 5·25
17 8s. pink . . . £600 28·00
18 24s. brown . . . 55·00 70·00

1867.
21 **5** 1s. black . . . 60·00 29·00
23 2s. buff . . . 26·00 26·00
26 3s. lilac . . . £250 55·00
27 4s. blue . . . 60·00 4·75
29 8s. red . . . £300 21·00

6 10 With background shading

A

1872. Value in "Skilling".
33 **6** 1s. green . . . 11·00 18·00
36 2s. blue . . . 12·00 34·00
39 3s. red . . . 55·00 5·75
42 4s. mauve . . . 21·00 31·00
44 6s. brown . . . £300 29·00
45 7s. brown . . . 32·00 33·00

1877. Letters without serifs as Type A. Value in "ore".
47 **10** 1ore brown . . . 4·75 3·75
83 2ore brown . . . 4·75 4·25
84c 3ore orange . . . 36·00 2·10
52 5ore blue . . . 19·00 7·25
85d 5ore green . . . 21·00 80
86a 10ore red . . . 43·00 75
55 12ore green . . . 75·00 10·50
75b 12ore brown . . . 13·00 8·00
76 20ore brown . . . 85·00 12·00
87 20ore blue . . . 45·00 1·40
88 25ore mauve . . . 43·00 6·75
61 35ore green . . . 19·00 6·25
62 50ore purple . . . 35·00 5·75
63 60ore blue . . . 30·00 9·25

9 King Oscar II

1878.
68 **9** 1k. green and light green . . . 32·00 5·50
69 1k.50 blue and ultramarine 65·00 24·00
70 2k. brown and pink . . . 46·00 15·00

1888. Surch **2 ore**.
89a **6** 2ore on 12ore brown . . . 2·00 2·20

D

1893. Letters with serifs as Type D.
133 **10** 1ore drab . . . 70 40
134 2ore brown . . . 45 30
135 3ore orange . . . 60 30
136 5ore green . . . 6·75 20
529 5ore purple . . . 20 15
138 7ore green . . . 85 25
139 10ore red . . . 6·50 15
140 10ore green . . . 10·50 40
529a 10ore grey . . . 20 15
141 12ore violet . . . 80 90
530 15ore brown . . . 35 20
143 15ore blue . . . 60 30
144 20ore blue . . . 9·50 20
530a 20ore green . . . 20 15
146 25ore mauve . . . 60·00 25
147 25ore red . . . 9·50 50
531 25ore blue . . . 15 15
148 30ore grey . . . 16·00 35
149 30ore blue . . . 7·50 3·00
119 35ore green . . . 15·00 4·50
150 35ore brown . . . 22·00 30
151 40ore green . . . 11·00 35

152 40ore blue 32·00 30
531b 50ore purple 10 10
154 60ore blue 38·00 55
531c 60ore orange 10 10
531d 70ore orange 20 20
531e 80ore brown 20 15
531f 90ore brown 25 25
See also Nos. 279 etc and 1100/3.

1905. Surch.
122 **5** 1k. on 2s. buff 55·00 27·00
123 1k.50 on 2s. buff 80·00 55·00
124 2k. on 2s. buff 95·00 47·00

1906. Surch.
162 **10** 5ore on 25ore mauve 70 50
125 **6** 15ore on 4s. mauve 5·50 3·25
126 30ore on 7s. brown 12·00 6·00

15 King Haakon VII
16 King Haakon VII

1907.
127 **15** 1k. green 48·00 25·00
128 1½k. blue 70·00 65·00
129 2k. red 95·00 90·00

1910.
155a **16** 1k. green 70 15
156 1½k. blue 2·30 40
157 2k. red 3·00 55
158 5k. violet 4·75 3·50

17 Constitutional Assembly (after O. Wergeland)
19

1914. Centenary of Independence.
159 **17** 5ore green 1·90 40
160 10ore red 4·25 55
161 20ore blue 11·00 5·00

1922.
163 **19** 10ore green 15·00 45
164 20ore purple 24·00 20
165 25ore red 30·00 60
166 45ore blue 2·75 70

20 **21** **22**

1925. Air. Amundsen's Polar Flight.
167 **20** 2ore brown 2·00 1·80
168 3ore orange 3·75 3·00
169 5ore mauve 7·00 5·75
170 10ore green 9·50 10·50
171 15ore blue 9·50 11·50
172 20ore mauve 12·50 16·00
173 25ore red 3·50 3·50

1925. Annexation of Spitzbergen.
183 **21** 10ore green 6·25 6·75
184 15ore blue 6·25 3·75
185 20ore purple 6·25 1·10
186 45ore blue 7·25 4·75

1926. Size 16 × 19½ mm.
187 **22** 10ore green 85 15
187a 14ore orange 1·00 1·70
188 15ore brown 1·00 20
189 20ore purple 38·00 14·50
189a 20ore red 1·30 15
190 25ore red 14·00 1·60
190a 25ore brown 1·70 20
190b 30ore blue 1·90 25
191 35ore brown 85·00 20
191a 35ore violet 3·25 15
192 40ore blue 7·25 95
193 40ore grey 2·50 15
194 50ore pink 2·75 20
195 60ore blue 3·00 20
For stamps as Type **22** but size 17 × 21 mm, see Nos. 284, etc.

1927. Surcharged with new value and bar.
196 **22** 20ore on 25ore red 4·75 1·00
197 **19** 30ore on 45ore blue 13·50 1·10
198 **21** 30ore on 45ore blue 5·50 3·25

24 Akershus Castle
25 Ibsen
28 Abel

1927. Air.
199a **24** 45ore blue (with frame-lines) 7·25 1·80
323 45ore blue (without frame-lines) 1·20 30

1928. Ibsen Centenary.
200 **25** 10ore green 7·75 1·40
201 15ore brown 3·25 1·80
202 20ore red 3·75 40
203 30ore blue 4·25 2·10

1929. Postage Due stamps optd **Post Frimerke** (204/6 and 211) or **POST** and thick bar (others).
204 D **12** 1ore brown 40 60
205 4ore mauve (No. D96a) 40 35
206 10ore green 1·80 1·90
207 15ore brown 3·25 2·75
208 20ore purple 1·40 45
209 40ore blue 3·75 60
210 50ore purple 7·75 6·50
211 100ore yellow 3·00 1·90
212 200ore violet 4·50 2·50

1929. Death Cent of N. H. Abel (mathematician).
213 **28** 10ore green 4·25 60
214 15ore brown 3·25 1·20
215 20ore red 1·10 25
216 30ore blue 2·25 1·30

1929. Surch **14 ORE 14**.
217 **5** 14ore on 2s. buff 1·70 3·00

30 St. Olaf (sculpture, Brunlanes Church)
31 Nidaros Trondhjem Cathedral

32 Death of St. Olaf (after P. N. Arbo)

1930. 9th Death Centenary of St. Olaf.
219 **30** 10ore green 8·50 30
220 **31** 15ore sepia and brown 1·10 45
221 **30** 20ore red 1·40 35
222 **32** 30ore blue 6·75 1·80

33 North Cape and "Bergensfjord" (liner)

1930. Norwegian Tourist Association Fund. Size 35½ × 21½ mm.
223 **33** 15ore+25ore brown 1·70 2·30
224 20ore+25ore red 21·00 22·00
225 30ore+25ore blue 55·00 50·00
For smaller stamps in this design see Nos. 349/51, 442/66 and 464/6.

34 Radium Hospital

1931. Radium Hospital Fund.
226 **34** 20ore+10ore red 9·50 3·75

35 Bjornson
36 L. Holberg

1932. Birth Cent of Bjornstjerne Bjornson (writer).
227 **35** 10ore green 9·75 45
228 15ore brown 95 90
229 20ore red 1·80 30
230 30ore blue 2·75 1·60

1934. 250th Birth Anniv of Holberg (writer).
231 **36** 10ore green 3·25 25
232 15ore brown 60 50
233 20ore red 14·50 20
234 30ore blue 2·75 1·50

37 Dr. Nansen
38 No background shading
38b King Haakon VII

1935. Nansen Refugee Fund.
235 **37** 10ore+10ore green 2·10 2·00
236 15ore+10ore brown 7·25 7·25
237 20ore+10ore red 1·20 1·00
238 30ore+10ore blue 7·50 7·00
See also Nos. 275/8.

1937.
279 **38** 1ore green 80 45
280 2ore brown 45 55
281 3ore orange 70 65
282 5ore mauve 40 15
283 7ore green 60 20
413 10ore grey 45 15
285 12ore violet 75 1·20
414 15ore green 1·20 40
415 15ore brown 30 15
416 20ore brown 2·75 1·50
417 20ore green 30 15

1937. As T **22**, but size 17 × 21 mm.
284 **22** 10ore green 45 15
286 14ore orange 1·80 2·40
287 15ore green 1·70 20
288a 20ore red 35 15
289 25ore brown 1·90 20
289a 25ore red 95 15
290 30ore blue 2·20 20
290a 30ore grey 6·25 25
291 35ore violet 2·20 20
292 40ore grey 3·50 20
292a 40ore blue 3·25 20
293 50ore purple 2·10 30
293a 55ore orange 17·00 20
294 60ore blue 2·75 20
294a 80ore brown 17·00 15

1937.
255 **38b** 1k. green 10 20
256 1k.50 blue 70 1·50
257 2k. red 60 3·75
258 5k. purple 6·00 22·00

39 Reindeer

41 Joelster in Sunnfjord

1938. Tourist Propaganda.
262 **39** 15ore brown 1·00 55
263 – 20ore red 90 25
264 **41** 30ore blue 1·00 75
DESIGN—As T **39** but VERT: 20ore, Stave Church, Borgund.

42 Queen Maud
43 Lion Rampant
44 Dr. Nansen

1939. Queen Maud Children's Fund.
267 **42** 10ore+5ore green 45 3·75
268 15ore+5ore brown 45 3·75
269 20ore+5ore red 45 3·00
270 30ore+5ore blue 45 3·75

1940.
271 **43** 1k. green 80 15
272 1½k. blue 1·70 30
273 2k. red 2·50 85
274 5k. purple 3·75 3·50
See also Nos. 318/21.

1940. National Relief Fund.
275 **44** 10ore+10ore green 1·50 2·40
276 15ore+10ore brown 1·50 3·00
277 20ore+10ore red 45 80
278 30ore+10ore blue 95 1·60

46 Femboring (fishing boat) and Iceberg
47 Colin Archer (founder) and Lifeboat "Colin Archer"

1941. Haalogaland Exhibition and Fishermen's Families Relief Fund.
295 **46** 15ore+10ore blue 1·10 2·50

1941. 50th Anniv of National Lifeboat Institution.
296 **47** 10ore+10ore green 80 1·10
297 15ore+10ore brown 1·10 1·80
298 – 20ore+10ore red 1·00 55
299 – 30ore+10ore blue 2·30 4·25
DESIGN—VERT: 20ore, 30ore, "Osloskoyta" (lifeboat).

48 Soldier and Flags
51 Oslo University

1941. Norwegian Legion Support Fund.
300 **48** 20ore+80ore red 29·00 42·00

1941. Stamps of 1937 optd **V** (= Victory).
301B **38** 1ore green 35 2·50
302B 2ore brown 35 3·75
303B 3ore orange 35 3·00
304B 5ore mauve 35 30
305A 7ore green 75 2·75
306B **22** 10ore green 35 25
307B **38** 12ore violet 70 12·00
308A **22** 14ore orange 1·30 8·75
309A 15ore green 60 1·10
310B 20ore red 25 25
311B 25ore brown 50 45
312B 30ore blue 1·20 1·80
313A 35ore violet 1·50 85
314B 40ore grey 85 50
315B 50ore purple 1·20 1·90
316A 60ore blue 1·90 1·40
317B **43** 1k. green 1·50 45
318B 1½k. blue 3·25 10·50
319B 2k. red 10·50 34·00
320B 5k. purple 18·00 75·00

1941. As No. 413, but with "V" incorporated in the design.
321 10ore green 80 8·25

1941. Centenary of Foundation of Oslo University Building.
322 **51** 1k. green 24·00 32·00

52 Queen Ragnhild's Dream
53 Stiklestad Battlefield

1941. 700th Death Anniv of Snorre Sturlason (historian).
324 **52** 10ore green 25 15
325 – 15ore brown 30 50
326 – 20ore red 25 15
327 – 30ore blue 1·40 1·80
328 – 50ore violet 1·00 1·30
329 **53** 60ore blue 1·00 1·40
DESIGNS (illustrations from "Sagas of Kings")—As T **53**: 15ore Einar Tambarskjelve at Battle of Svolder; 30ore King Olav II sails to his wedding; 50ore Svipdag's men enter Hall of the Seven Kings. As T **52**: 20ore Snorre Sturlason.

55 Vidkun Quisling

1942. (a) Without opt.
330 **55** 20ore+30ore red 4·00 13·50
(b) Optd **1-2-1942**.
331 **55** 20ore+30ore red 4·00 13·50
See also No. 336.

56 Rikard Nordraak
57 Embarkation of the Viking Fleet

1942. Birth Centenary of Rikard Nordraak (composer).
332 **56** 10ore green 1·10 1·40
333 **57** 15ore brown 1·10 1·70
334 **56** 20ore red 1·10 1·40
335 – 30ore blue 1·10 1·40
DESIGN—As Type **57**: 30ore Mountains across sea and two lines of the National Anthem.

1942. War Orphans' Relief Fund. As T **55** but inscr "RIKSTINGET 1942".
336 20ore+30ore red 45 3·25

58 J. H. Wessel
59 Reproduction of Types **55** and **1**

1942. Birth Bicentenary of Wessel (poet).
337 **58** 15ore brown 10 20
338 20ore red 10 20

1942. Inaug of European Postal Union, Vienna.
339 **59** 20ore red 15 45
340 30ore blue 15 1·00

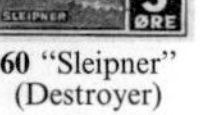
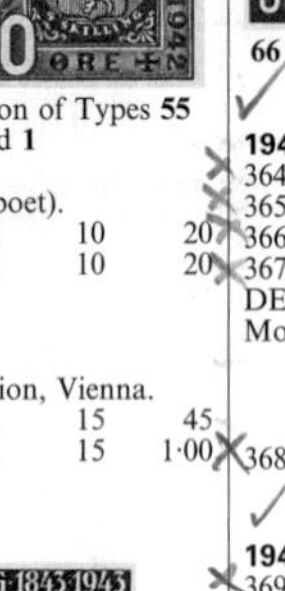

60 "Sleipner" (Destroyer)
61 Edvard Grieg

1943.
341 **60** 5ore purple 20 15
342 – 7ore green 30 30
343 **60** 10ore green 20 10
344 – 15ore green 60 65
345 – 20ore red 20 20
346 – 30ore blue 80 90
347 – 40ore green 65 80
348 – 60ore blue 70 85
DESIGNS: 7ore, 30ore Merchant ships in convoy; 15ore Airman; 20ore "Vi Vil Vinne" (We will win) written on the highway; 40ore Soldiers on skis; 60ore King Haakon VII.

For use on correspondence posted at sea on Norwegian merchant ships and (in certain circumstances) from Norwegian camps in Gt. Britain during the German Occupation of Norway. After liberation all values were put on sale in Norway.

1943. Norwegian Tourist Association Fund. As T **33**, but reduced to 27 × 21 mm.
349 **33** 15ore+25ore brown 65 80
350 20ore+25ore red 80 1·50
351 30ore+25ore blue 1·20 1·50

1943. Birth Centenary of Grieg (composer).
352 **61** 10ore green 20 25
353 20ore red 20 25
354 40ore green 20 25
355 60ore blue 20 25

62 Soldier's Emblem
63 Fishing Station

1943. Soldiers' Relief Fund.
356 **62** 20ore+30ore red 40 3·00

1943. Winter Relief Fund.
357 **63** 10ore+10ore green 75 2·20
358 – 20ore+10ore red 70 2·50
359 – 40ore+10ore grey 70 2·50
DESIGNS: 20ore Mountain scenery; 40ore Winter landscape.

64 Sinking of "Baroy" (freighter)
65 Gran's Bleriot XI "Nordsjoen"

1944. Shipwrecked Mariners' Relief Fund.
360 **64** 10ore+10ore green 65 3·25
361 – 15ore+10ore brown 65 3·25
362 – 20ore+10ore red 65 3·25
DESIGNS—HORIZ: 15ore "Sanct Svithun" (cargo liner) attacked by Bristol Type 142 Blenheim Mk IV airplane. VERT: 20ore Sinking of "Irma" (freighter).

1944. 30th Anniv of First North Sea Flight, by Tryggve Gran.
363 **65** 40ore blue 55 1·20

66 Girl Spinning
67 Arms
68 Henrik Wergeland

1944. Winter Relief Fund. Inscr as in T **66**.
364 **66** 5ore+10ore mauve 55 1·80
365 – 10ore+10ore green 55 1·80
366 – 15ore+10ore purple 55 1·80
367 – 20ore+10ore red 55 1·80
DESIGNS: 10ore Ploughing; 15ore Tree felling; 20ore Mother and children.

1945.
368 **67** 1½k. blue 1·70 45

1945. Death Centenary of Wergeland (poet).
369 **68** 10ore green 15 25
370 15ore brown 40 70
371 20ore red 10 20

69 Red Cross Sister
70 Folklore Museum Emblem

1945. Red Cross Relief Fund and Norwegian Red Cross Jubilee.
372 **69** 20ore+10ore red 35 40

1945. 50th Anniv of National Folklore Museum.
373 **70** 10ore green 35 25
374 20ore red 35 25

71 Crown Prince Olav
72 "R.N.A.F."

1946. National Relief Fund.
375 **71** 10ore+10ore green 35 35
376 15ore+10ore brown 35 35
377 20ore+10ore red 35 35
378 30ore+10ore blue 90 1·20

1946. Honouring Norwegian Air Force trained in Canada.
379 **72** 15ore red 45 75

73 King Haakon VII
74 Fridtjof Nansen, Roald Amundsen and "Fram"

1946.
380 **73** 1k. green 1·10 15
381 1½k. blue 3·00 15
382 2k. brown 20·00 15
383 5k. violet 13·50 50

1947. Tercentenary of Norwegian Post Office.
384 – 5ore mauve 30 15
385 – 10ore green 30 15
386 – 15ore brown 60 15
387 – 25ore red 50 15
388 – 30ore grey 75 15
389 – 40ore blue 1·80 25
390 – 45ore violet 1·50 55
391 – 50ore brown 2·20 35
392 **74** 55ore orange 3·25 25
393 – 60ore grey 2·75 1·10
394 – 80ore brown 3·00 40
DESIGNS: 5ore Hannibal Sehested (founder of postal service) and Akershus Castle; 10ore "Postal-peasant"; 15ore Admiral Tordenskiold and 18th-century warship; 25ore Christian M. Falsen; 30ore Cleng Peerson and "Restaurationen" (emigrant sloop), 1825; 40ore "Constitutionen" (paddle-steamer), 1827; 45ore First Norwegian locomotive "Caroline"; 50ore Svend Foyn and "Spes et Fides" (whale catcher); 60ore Coronation of King Haakon and Queen Maud in Nidaros Cathedral; 80ore King Haakon and Oslo Town Hall.

75 Petter Dass
76 King Haakon VII

1947. Birth Tercentenary of Petter Dass (poet).
395 **75** 25ore red 60 60

1947. 75th Birthday of King Haakon VII.
396 **76** 25ore orange 45 55

77 Axel Heiberg
80 A. L. Kielland

1948. 50th Anniv of Norwegian Forestry Society and Birth Centenary of Axel Heiberg (founder).
397 **77** 25ore red 55 35
398 80ore brown 1·30 30

1948. Red Cross. Surch **25+5** and bars.
399 **69** 25+5 ore on 20+10 ore red 50 65

1949. Nos. 288a and 292a surch.
400 **22** 25ore on 20ore red 30 15
401 45ore on 40ore blue 1·80 50

1949. Birth Centenary of Alexander L. Kielland (author).
402 **80** 25ore red 85 20
403 40ore blue 85 45
404 80ore brown 1·40 65

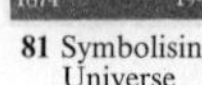

81 Symbolising Universe
82 Pigeons and Globe

1949. 75th Anniv of U.P.U.
405 **81** 10ore green and purple 45 45
406 **82** 25ore red 25 20
407 – 40ore blue 25 45
DESIGN—37 × 21 mm: 40ore Dove, globe and signpost.

84 King Harald Haardraade and Oslo Town Hall
85 Child with Flowers

1950. 900th Anniv of Founding of Oslo.
408 **84** 15ore green 45 55
409 25ore red 35 20
410 45ore blue 45 55

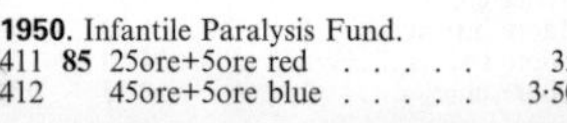

1950. Infantile Paralysis Fund.
411 **85** 25ore+5ore red 35 65
412 45ore+5ore blue 3·50 3·75

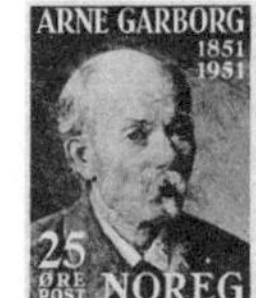

87 King Haakon VII
88 Arne Garborg (after O. Rusti)

1950.
418 **87** 25ore red 50 15
419 25ore grey 11·00 20
419a 25ore green 65 15
420 30ore grey 5·25 60
421 30ore red 50 15
422a 35ore red 3·00 15
422b 40ore purple 1·10 25
423 45ore blue 95 1·50
424 50ore brown 1·50 15
425 55ore orange 1·60 95
426 55ore blue 1·00 45
427 60ore blue 7·75 15
427a 65ore blue 70 25
427b 70ore brown 8·50 25
428 75ore purple 1·50 25
429 80ore brown 1·60 25
430 90ore orange 95 25

1951. Birth Centenary of Garborg (author).
431 **88** 25ore red 35 30
432 45ore blue 1·50 2·10
433 80ore brown 2·10 1·70
"NOREG" on the stamps was the spelling advocated by Arne Garborg.

89 Ice Skater
92 King Haakon VII

1951. 6th Winter Olympic Games. Inscr "OSLO 1952".
434 **89** 15ore+5ore green 1·80 2·50
435 – 30ore+10ore red 1·80 2·50
436 – 55ore+20ore blue 6·00 9·00
DESIGNS—As T **89**: 30ore Ski jumping. 38 × 21 mm: 55ore Winter landscape.

1951. Surch in figures.
440 **38** 20ore on 15ore green 45 20
437 **87** 30ore on 25ore red 50 15

1952. 80th Birthday of King Haakon.
438 **92** 30ore scarlet and red 25 20
439 55ore blue and grey 70 75

94 "Supplication"
95 Medieval Sculpture

1953. Anti-cancer Fund.
441 **94** 30ore+10ore red and cream 1·00 1·30

1953. Norwegian Tourist Association Fund. As T **33** but smaller 27½ × 21 mm.
442 **33** 20ore+10ore green 5·50 7·25
464 25ore+10ore green 2·50 3·50
443 30ore+15ore red 5·50 7·25
465 35ore+15ore red 3·50 4·75
444 55ore+25ore blue 10·00 11·00
466 65ore+25ore blue 2·50 3·00

1953. 8th Cent of Archbishopric of Nidaros.
445 **95** 30ore red 50 45

96 Stephenson Locomotive on Hoved Railway, 1854, and Horse-drawn Sledge
97 C. T. Nielsen (first Director)

1954. Centenary of Norwegian Railways.
446 **96** 20ore green 45 25
447 – 30ore red 45 20
448 – 55ore blue 1·10 1·00

DESIGNS: 30ore Diesel-hydraulic express train; 55ore Alfred Andersen (engine driver) in locomotive cab.

1954. Centenary of Telegraph Service.
449 **97** 20ore black and green . . 15 25
450 – 30ore red 15 20
451 – 55ore blue 80 75
DESIGNS: 30ore Radio masts at Tryvannshogda; 55ore Telegraph lineman on skis.

98 "Posthorn" Type Stamp

100 King Haakon and Queen Maud

1955. Norwegian Stamp Centenary.
452 – 20ore blue and green . . . 15 25
453 **98** 30ore deep red and red . . 15 10
454 – 55ore blue and grey . . . 35 50
DESIGNS: 20ore Norway's first stamp; 55ore "Lion" type stamp.

1955. Stamp Cent and Int Stamp Exn, Oslo. Nos. 452/4 with circular opt **OSLO NORWEX**.
455 – 20ore blue and green . . . 6·75 8·25
456 **98** 30ore deep red and red . . 6·75 8·25
457 – 55ore blue and grey . . . 6·75 8·25
Nos. 455/7 were only on sale at the Exhibition P.O. at face plus 1k. entrance fee.

1955. Golden Jubilee of King Haakon.
458 **100** 30ore red 25 20
459 55ore blue 35 45

101 Crown Princess Martha

101a Whooper Swans

1956. Crown Princess Martha Memorial Fund.
460 **101** 35ore+10ore red 50 65
461 65ore+10ore blue . . . 2·10 2·20

1956. Northern Countries' Day.
462 **101a** 35ore red 35 40
463 65ore blue 35 55

102 Jan Mayen Island (after aquarell, H. Mohn)

103 Map of Spitzbergen

1957. Int Geophysical Year. Inscr "INTERN. GEOFYSISK AR 1957–1958".
467 **102** 25ore green 60 35
468 **103** 35ore red and grey . . . 60 20
469 – 65ore green and blue . . 70 50
DESIGN—VERT: 65ore Map of Antarctica showing Queen Maud Land.

104 King Haakon VII

1957. 85th Birthday of King Haakon.
470 **104** 35ore red 15 20
471 65ore blue 50 60

105 King Olav V

106 King Olav V

1958.
472 **105** 25ore green 60 15
473 30ore violet 95 20
474 35ore red 45 25
474a 35ore green . . . . . . 2·00 15
475 40ore red 45 20
475a 40ore grey . . . . . . 2·20 1·10
476 45ore red 50 15
477 50ore brown . . . . . . 3·75 15
478 50ore red . . . . 4·00 15
479 55ore grey . . . . . . 1·10 80
480 60ore violet . . . . . . 2·75 80
481 65ore blue 95 40
482 80ore brown . . . . . . 4·50 55
483 85ore brown . . . . . . 1·00 25
484 90ore orange 50 15
485 **106** 1k. green 45 30
486 1k.50 blue . . . . . . 1·80 15
487 2k. red . . . . 1·30 40
488 5k. purple . . . . . . 23·00 15
489 10k. orange . . . . . . 3·25 15

107 Asbjorn Kloster (founder)

108 Society's Centenary Medal

1959. Cent of Norwegian Temperance Movement.
490 **107** 45ore brown 30 25

1959. 150th Anniv of Royal Norwegian Agricultural Society.
491 **108** 45ore brown and red . . 30 40
492 90ore grey and blue . . . 1·20 1·50

109 Sower

110 White Anemone

1959. Centenary of Norwegian Royal College of Agriculture.
493 **109** 45ore black and brown . . 45 40
494 – 90ore black and blue . . 85 90
DESIGN—VERT: 90ore Ears of corn.

1960. Tuberculosis Relief Funds.
495 **110** 45ore+10ore yellow, green and red . . . . 1·60 1·70
496 – 90ore+10ore mult . . . . 3·00 5·00
DESIGN: 90ore Blue anemone.

111 Society's Original Seal

112 Refugee Mother and Child

1960. Bicentenary of Royal Norwegian Society of Scientists.
497 **111** 45ore red on grey 35 35
498 90ore blue on grey . . . 1·00 1·20

1960. World Refugee Year.
499 **112** 45ore+25ore black and pink . . . . 2·40 3·50
500 90ore+25ore blk & bl . . 5·50 7·00

113 Viking Longship

1960. Norwegian Ships.
501 **113** 20ore black and grey . . 90 65
502 – 25ore black and green . . 80 65
503 – 45ore black and red . . . 80 50
504 – 55ore black and brown . 1·90 2·00
505 – 90ore black and blue . . 1·60 1·40
SHIPS: 25ore Hanse kogge; 45ore "Skomvaer" (barque); 55ore "Dalfon" (tanker); 90ore "Bergensfjord" (liner).

113a Conference Emblem

113b Douglas DC-8

1960. Europa.
506 **113a** 90ore blue 45 45

1961. 10th Anniv of Scandinavian Airlines System (SAS).
507 **113b** 90ore blue 35 55

114 Throwing the Javelin

1961. Centenary of Norwegian Sport.
508 **114** 20ore brown 40 45
509 – 25ore green 40 55
510 – 45ore red 40 20
511 – 90ore mauve . . . . . 2·30 85
DESIGNS: 25ore Ice skating; 45ore Ski jumping; 90ore Yachting.

115 Haakonshallen Barracks and Rosenkrantz Tower

1961. 700th Anniv of Haakonshallen, Bergen.
512 **115** 45ore black and red . . . 35 20
513 1k. black and green . . . 35 35

116 Oslo University

1961. 150th Anniv of Oslo University.
514 **116** 45ore red 20 20
515 1k.50 blue 30 35

117 Nansen

119 Frederic Passy and Henri Dunant (winners in 1901)

118 Amundsen, "Fram" and Dog-team

1961. Birth Centenary of Fridtjof Nansen (polar explorer).
516 **117** 45ore black and red . . . 25 20
517 90ore black and blue . . 50 50

1961. 50th Anniv of Amundsen's Arrival at South Pole.
518 **118** 45ore red and grey . . . 35 30
519 – 90ore deep blue and blue 65 85
DESIGN: 90ore Amundsen's party and tent at South Pole.

1961. Nobel Peace Prize.
520 **119** 45ore red 35 20
521 1k. green 45 35

120 Prof. V. Bjerknes

1962. Birth Centenary of Prof. Vilhelm Bjerknes (physicist).
522 **120** 45ore black and red . . . 30 20
523 1k.50 black and blue . . 55 35

121 Etrich/Rumpler Taube Monoplane "Start"

1962. 50th Anniv of Norwegian Aviation.
524 **121** 1k.50 brown and blue . . 95 45

122 Branch of Fir, and Cone

125 Reef Knot

123 Europa "Tree"

1962. Cent of State Forestry Administration.
525 **122** 45ore grey, black and red 60 45
526 1k. grey, black and green 3·00 25

1962. Europa.
527 **123** 50ore red 35 20
528 90ore blue 55 95

1962.
531g – 25ore green 70 15
532 – 30ore drab . . . . . . 2·50 2·40
532a – 30ore green 25 25
533 **125** 35ore green 20 15
533a – 40ore red 95 30
534 – 40ore green 20 15
534a – 45ore green 30 50
535 **125** 50ore red . . . . 2·10 15
535a 50ore grey 20 15
536 – 55ore brown 30 55
536a **125** 60ore green . . . . . . 4·50 15
537 60ore red 60 30
537b – 65ore violet 75 30
538 **125** 65ore red 35 15
538a 70ore brown 20 15
539 – 75ore green 20 15
539a – 80ore purple . . . . . 1·50 1·40
539b – 80ore brown 30 15
540 – 85ore brown 30 25
540a – 85ore buff 30 25
540b – 90ore blue 30 20
541 – 100ore violet 30 15
541a – 100ore red 30 15
542 – 110ore red 30 15
542a – 115ore brown 45 35
543 – 120ore blue 40 25
543a – 125ore red 30 15
544 – 140ore blue 40 25
544a – 750ore brown . . . . . 1·20 15
DESIGNS: 25, 40, 90, 100 (2), 110, 120, 125ore, Runic drawings; 30, 45, 55, 75, 85ore, Ear of wheat and Atlantic cod; 65 (537b), 80, 140ore, "Stave" (wooden) church and "Aurora Borealis"; 115ore Fragment of Urnes stave-church; 750ore Sigurd Farnesbane (the Dragon killer) and Regin (the blacksmith), portal from Hylestad stave-church.

126 Camilla Collett

127 Boatload of Wheat

1963. 150th Birth Anniv of Camilla Collett (author).
545 **126** 50ore red 20 30
546 90ore blue . . . . 55 1·70

1963. Freedom from Hunger.
547 **127** 25ore bistre 35 40
548 35ore green 45 60
549 – 50ore red 35 30
550 – 90ore blue . . . . . . 1·00 1·10
DESIGN—37½ × 21 mm: 50, 90ore Birds carrying food on cloth.

128 River Mail Boat

1963. Tercentenary of Southern-Northern Norwegian Postal Services.
551 **128** 50ore red . . . . 1·10 50
552 – 90ore blue . . . . . . 2·10 2·00
DESIGN: 90ore Femboring (Northern sailing vessel).

129 Ivar Aasen

130 "Co-operation"

1963. 150th Birth Anniv of Ivar Aasen (philologist).
553 **129** 50ore red and grey . . . 35 20
554 90ore blue and grey . . . 80 75
The note after No. 433 re "NOREG" also applies here.

1963. Europa.
555 **130** 50ore orange and purple 50 20
556 90ore green and blue . . 1·50 1·50

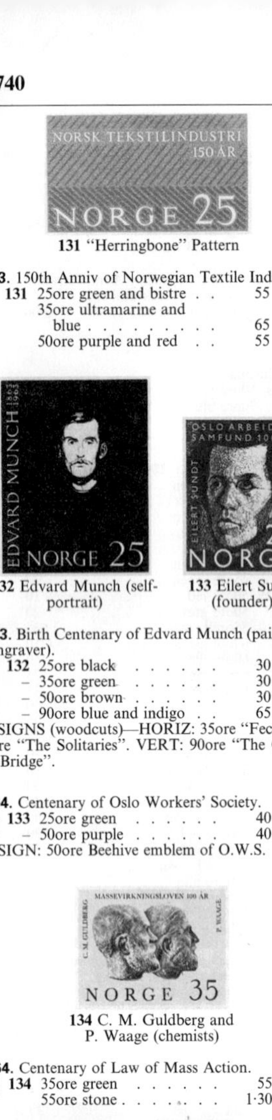

131 "Herringbone" Pattern

1963. 150th Anniv of Norwegian Textile Industry.
557 **131** 25ore green and bistre . . 55 55
558 35ore ultramarine and blue 65 75
559 50ore purple and red . . 55 45

132 Edvard Munch (self-portrait)

133 Eilert Sundt (founder)

1963. Birth Centenary of Edvard Munch (painter and engraver).
560 **132** 25ore black 30 25
561 – 35ore green 30 25
562 – 50ore brown 30 15
563 – 90ore blue and indigo . . 65 65
DESIGNS (woodcuts)—HORIZ: 35ore "Fecundity"; 50ore "The Solitaries". VERT: 90ore "The Girls on the Bridge".

1964. Centenary of Oslo Workers' Society.
564 **133** 25ore green 40 40
565 – 50ore purple 40 25
DESIGN: 50ore Beehive emblem of O.W.S.

134 C. M. Guldberg and P. Waage (chemists)

1964. Centenary of Law of Mass Action.
566 **134** 35ore green 55 45
567 55ore stone . . . . 1·30 1·20

135 Eidsvoll Manor

1964. 150th Anniv of Norwegian Constitution.
568 **135** 50ore grey and red . . . 35 30
569 – 90ore black and blue . . 80 95
DESIGN: 90ore Storting (Parliament House), Oslo.

On 1 June 1964 a stamp depicting the U.N. refugee emblem and inscr "PORTO BETALT ... LYKKEBREVET 1964" was put on sale. It had a franking value of 50ore but was sold for 2k.50, the balance being for the Refugee Fund. In addition, each stamp bore a serial number representing participation in a lottery which took place in September. The stamp was on sale until 15 July and had validity until 10 August.

136 Harbour Scene

137 Europa "Flower"

1964. Cent of Norwegian Seamen's Mission.
570 **136** 25ore green and yellow 50 50
571 90ore blue and cream . . 1·20 1·40

1964. Europa.
572 **137** 90ore deep blue and blue 1·70 1·70

138 H. Anker and O. Arvesen (founders)

139 "Radio-telephone"

1964. Cent of Norwegian Folk High Schools.
573 **138** 50ore pink 55 30
574 90ore blue . . . . 1·90 1·90

The note after No. 433 re "NOREG" also applies here.

1965. Centenary of I.T.U.
575 **139** 60ore purple 55 25
576 – 90ore grey . . . . 1·00 1·00
DESIGN: 90ore "T.V. transmission".

140 Dove of Peace and Broken Chain

1965. 20th Anniv of Liberation.
577 **140** 30ore+10ore brown, green and sepia 25 30
578 – 60ore+10ore blue and red 25 30
DESIGN: 60ore Norwegian flags.

141 Mountain Landscapes

1965. Centenary of Norwegian Red Cross.
579 **141** 60ore brown and red . . 35 25
580 – 90ore blue and red . . . 2·50 2·10
DESIGN: 90ore Coastal view.

142 Europa "Sprig"

144 Rondane Mountains (after H. Sohlberg)

143 St. Sunniva and Bergen Buildings

1965. Europa.
581 **142** 60ore red 50 30
582 90ore blue . . . . 1·10 1·10

1965. Bicentenary of Harmonien Philharmonic Society.
583 – 30ore black and green . . 45 25
584 **143** 90ore black and blue . . 90 95
DESIGN—VERT: 30ore St. Sunniva.

1965. Rondane National Park.
585 **144** 1k.50 blue . . . . 1·00 25

145 "Rodoy Skier" (rock carving)

146 "The Bible"

1966. World Skiing Championships, Oslo. Inscr "VM OSLO 1966".
586 **145** 40ore brown 45 85
587 – 55ore green . . . . . . 1·20 1·20
588 – 60ore brown 45 25
589 – 90ore blue . . . . . . 85 1·10
DESIGNS—HORIZ: 55ore Ski jumper; 60ore Cross-country skier. VERT: 90ore Holmenkollen ski jumping tower, Oslo.

1966. 150th Anniv of Norwegian Bible Society.
590 **146** 60ore red 45 25
591 90ore blue . . . . 70 1·10

147 Guilloche Pattern

148 J. Sverdrup (after C. Krohg)

1966. 150th Anniv of Bank of Norway.
592 **147** 30ore green 45 40
593 – 60ore red (Bank building) 30 15
No. 593 is size $27\frac{1}{2} \times 21$ mm.

1966. 150th Birth Anniv of Johan Sverdrup (statesman).
594 **148** 30ore green 35 25
595 60ore purple 30 25

149 Europa "Ship"

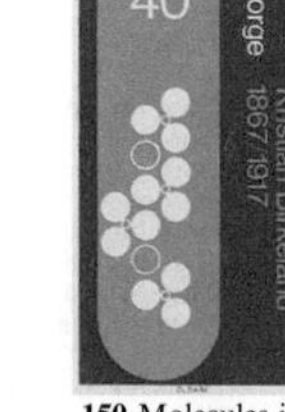

150 Molecules in Test-tube

1966. Europa.
596 **149** 60ore red 50 25
597 90ore blue . . . . 1·10 95

1966. Birth Centenaries of S. Eyde (industrialist) (1966) and K. Birkeland (scientist) (1967), founders of Norwegian Nitrogen Industry.
598 **150** 40ore blue and light blue 1·20 1·10
599 – 55ore mauve and red . . 1·60 1·40
DESIGN: 55ore Ear of wheat and conical flask.

151 E.F.T.A. Emblem

152 "Owl" and Three Swords

1967. European Free Trade Association.
600 **151** 60ore red 40 20
601 90ore blue . . . . 1·30 1·40

1967. 150th Anniv of Higher Military Training.
602 **152** 60ore brown 50 40
603 90ore green . . . . . . 1·60 1·60

153 Cogwheels

154 Johanne Dybwad

1967. Europa.
604 **153** 60ore deep plum, plum and purple 35 20
605 90ore deep violet, violet and blue . . . . 1·00 1·10

1967. Birth Centenary of J. Dybwad (actress).
606 **154** 40ore blue 40 30
607 60ore red 40 10

155 I. Skrefsrud (missionary and founder)

156 Climbers on Mountain-top

1967. Centenary of Norwegian Santal Mission.
608 **155** 60ore brown 40 20
609 – 90ore blue 90 75
DESIGN—HORIZ: 90ore Ebenezer Church, Benagaria, Santal, India.

1968. Centenary of Norwegian Mountain Touring Association.
610 **156** 40ore brown 75 75
611 – 60ore red 75 25
612 – 90ore blue . . . . . . 1·40 1·10
DESIGNS: 60ore Mountain cairn and scenery; 90ore Glitretind peak.

157 "The Blacksmiths"

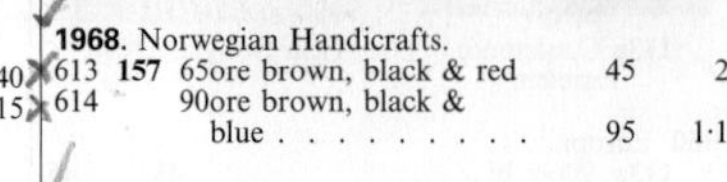

158 Vinje

1968. Norwegian Handicrafts.
613 **157** 65ore brown, black & red 45 25
614 90ore brown, black & blue . . . . 95 1·10

1968. 150th Birth Anniv of Aasmund Vinje (poet).
615 **158** 50ore brown 35 40
616 65ore red 35 15
See note below No. 433.

159 Cross and Heart

160 Cathinka Guldberg (first deaconess)

1968. Centenary of Norwegian Lutheran Home Mission Society.
617 **159** 40ore red and green . . . 2·40 2·40
618 65ore red and violet . . . 50 15

1968. Centenary of Deaconess House, Oslo.
619 **160** 50ore blue 40 30
620 65ore red 40 20

161 K. P. Arnoldson and F. Bajer

1968. Nobel Peace Prize Winners of 1908.
621 **161** 65ore brown 40 25
622 90ore blue 75 75

161a Viking Ships (from old Swedish coin)

1969. 50th Anniv of Northern Countries' Union.
623 **161a** 65ore red 45 20
624 90ore blue 75 80

162 Transport

1969. Centenary of "Rutebok for Norge" ("Communications of Norway") and Road Safety Campaign.
625 **162** 50ore green 30 50
626 – 65ore red and green . . . 20 25
DESIGN: 65ore Pedestrian-crossing.

163 Colonnade

1969. Europa.
627 **163** 65ore black and red . . . 75 20
628 90ore black and blue . . 45 95

164 J. Hjort and Atlantic Cod Eggs

1969. Birth Centenary of Professor Johan Hjort (fisheries pioneer).
629 **164** 40ore brown and blue . . 75 60
630 – 90ore blue and green . . 2·40 1·20
DESIGN: 90ore Hjort and polyp.

165 Traena Islands

1969.
631 **165** 3k.50 black 70 20

166 King Olav V 167 "Mother and Child"

1969.

632 **166** 1k. green 30 15
633 1k.50 blue 45 15
634 2k. red 45 15
635 5k. blue 95 15
636 10k. brown . . . . . . 2·75 15
637 20k. brown . . . . . . 2·50 15
637a 50k. green . . . . 9·75 40

1969. Birth Centenary of Gustav Vigeland (sculptor).
638 **167** 65ore black and red . . . 25 20
639 – 90ore black and blue . . 75 85
DESIGN: 90ore "Family" (sculpture).

168 Punched Cards 169 Queen Maud

1969. Bicentenary of 1st National Census. Mult.
640 65ore Type **168** 25 20
641 90ore "People" (diagram) . . 75 85

1969. Birth Centenary of Queen Maud.
642 **169** 65ore purple 25 10
643 90ore blue 75 75

170 Wolf ("Canis lupus") 171 "V" Symbol

1970. Nature Conservation Year.
644 **170** 40ore brown and blue . . 75 80
645 – 60ore grey and brown . . 75 1·50
646 – 70ore brown and blue . . 1·00 45
647 – 100ore brown and blue 2·30 1·00
DESIGNS—VERT: 60ore Pale pasque flower ("Pulsatilla vernalis"); 70ore Voringsfossen Falls. HORIZ: 100ore White-tailed sea eagle ("Haliaeetus albicilla").

1970. 25th Anniv of Liberation.
648 **171** 70ore red and violet . . 1·20 40
649 – 100ore blue and green . . 1·20 1·10
DESIGN—HORIZ: 100ore Merchant ships in convoy.

172 "Citizens" 173 Hands reaching for Globe

1970. 900th Anniv of Bergen.
650 **172** 40ore green 95 80
651 – 70ore purple . . . . . . 1·70 40
652 – 1k. blue . . . . 1·30 1·50
DESIGNS: 70ore "City between the Mountains"; 1k. "Ships".

1970. 25th Anniv of United Nations.
653 **173** 70ore red . . . . 1·80 45
654 100ore green . . . . . . 1·20 1·20

174 G. O. Sars 175 Ball-game

1970. Norwegian Zoologists.
655 **174** 40ore brown 75 95
656 – 50ore lilac 85 70
657 – 70ore brown . . . . . . 1·00 25
658 – 100ore blue . . . . . . 1·00 1·00
ZOOLOGISTS: 50ore Hans Strom; 70ore J. E. Gunnerus; 100ore Michael Sars.

1970. Centenary of Central School of Gymnastics, Oslo.
659 **175** 50ore brown and blue . . 50 40
660 – 70ore brown and red . . 75 10
DESIGN—HORIZ: 70ore "Leapfrog" exercise.

176 Tonsberg's Seal c. 1340

1971. 1100th Anniv of Tonsberg.
661 **176** 70ore red 50 20
662 100ore blue 75 70

177 Parliament House, Oslo

1971. Centenary of Introduction of Annual Parliamentary Sessions.
663 **177** 70ore lilac and red . . . 40 30
664 100ore green and blue . . 75 65

178 "Helping Hand"

1971. "Help for Refugees".
665 **178** 50ore green and black . . 45 60
666 70ore red and black . . . 30 25

179 "Hauge addressing Followers" (A. Tidemand)

1971. Birth Centenary of Hans Nielson Hauge (church reformer).
667 **179** 60ore black 45 35
668 70ore brown 30 25

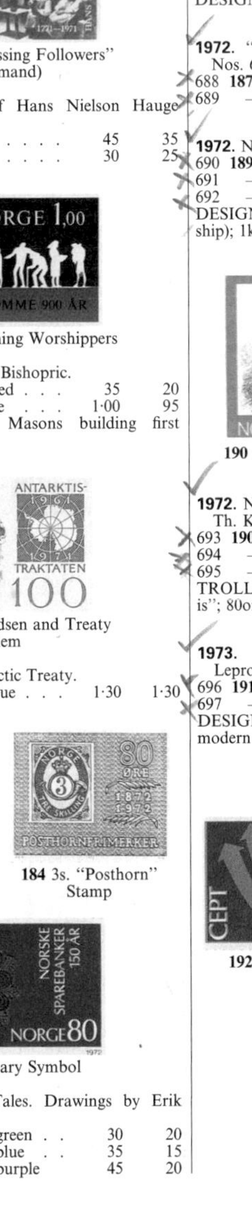

180 Bishop welcoming Worshippers

1971. 900th Anniv of Oslo Bishopric.
669 – 70ore black and red . . . 35 20
670 **180** 1k. black and blue . . . 1·00 95
DESIGN—VERT: 70ore Masons building first church.

181 Roald Amundsen and Treaty Emblem

1971. 10th Anniv of Antarctic Treaty.
671 **181** 100ore red and blue . . . 1·30 1·30

182 "The Preacher and the King" 184 3s. "Posthorn" Stamp

183 Anniversary Symbol

1971. Norwegian Folk Tales. Drawings by Erik Werenskiold.
672 – 40ore black and green . . 30 20
673 **182** 50ore black and blue . . 35 15
674 – 70ore black and purple 45 20
DESIGNS—VERT: 40ore "The Farmer and the Woman"; 70ore "The Troll and the Girl".

1972. 150th Anniv of Norwegian Savings Banks.
675 **183** 80ore gold and red . . . 45 20
676 1k.20 gold and blue . . . 45 65

1972. Centenary of Norwegian "Posthorn" Stamps.
677 **184** 80ore red and brown . . 35 9·00
678 1k. blue and violet . . . 55 45
MS679 120 × 71 mm. Nos. 677/8 (sold at 2k.50) . . . . 3·24 4·24

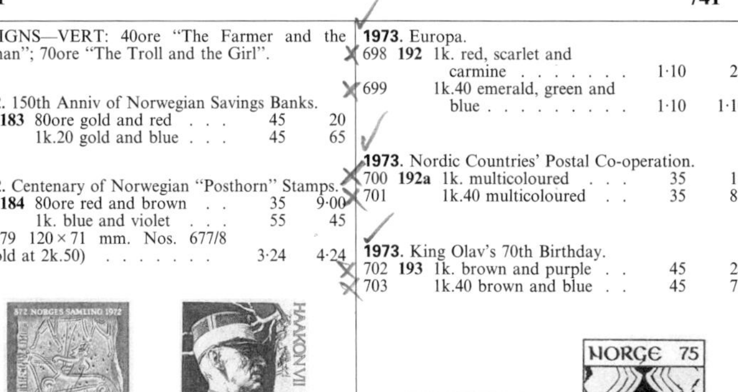

185 Alstad "Picture" Stone (detail) 186 King Haakon VII

1972. 1100th Anniv of Norway's Unification. Relics.
680 **185** 50ore green 55 60
681 – 60ore brown 80 85
682 – 80ore red . . . . 1·10 35
683 – 1k.20 blue 35 95
DESIGNS: 60ore Portal, Hemsedal Church (detail); 80ore Figurehead of Oseberg Viking ship; 1k.20, Sword-hilt (Lodingen).

1972. Birth Centenary of King Haakon VII.
684 **186** 80ore red . . . . 1·00 25
685 1k.20 blue . . . . 75 1·00

187 "Joy" (Ingrid Ekrem) 189 "Maud"

1972. "Youth and Leisure".
686 **187** 80ore mauve 45 20
687 – 1k.20 blue . . . . 75 1·20
DESIGN: 1k.20, "Solidarity" (Ole Instefjord).

1972. "Interjunex 1972" Stamp Exhibition, Oslo. Nos. 686/7 optd **INTERJUNEX 72**.
688 **187** 80ore mauve . . . . . . 1·90 2·40
689 – 1k.20 blue . . . . 1·90 2·40

1972. Norwegian Polar Ships.
690 **189** 60ore olive and green . . 1·10 75
691 – 80ore red and black . . 1·20 30
692 – 1k.20 blue and red . . . 1·20 1·10
DESIGNS: 80ore "Fram" (Amundsen and Nansen's ship); 1k.20, "Gjoa".

190 "Little Man" 191 Dr. Hansen and Bacillus Diagram

1972. Norwegian Folk Tales. Drawings of Trolls by Th. Kittelsen.
693 **190** 50ore black and green . . 30 20
694 – 60ore black and blue . . 45 35
695 – 80ore black and pink . . 30 15
TROLLS: 60ore "The troll who wonders how old he is"; 80ore "Princess riding on a bear".

1973. Centenary of Hansen's Identification of Leprosy Bacillus.
696 **191** 1k. red and blue 45 20
697 – 1k.40 blue and red . . . 65 95
DESIGN: 1k.40, As Type **191** but bacillus as seen in modern microscope.

192 Europa "Posthorn" 193 King Olav V

192a "The Nordic House", Reykjavik

1973. Europa.
698 **192** 1k. red, scarlet and carmine . . . . 1·10 25
699 1k.40 emerald, green and blue . . . . 1·10 1·10

1973. Nordic Countries' Postal Co-operation.
700 **192a** 1k. multicoloured . . . 35 15
701 1k.40 multicoloured . . 35 85

1973. King Olav's 70th Birthday.
702 **193** 1k. brown and purple . . 45 20
703 1k.40 brown and blue . . 45 75

194 J. Aall

195 Bone Carving

1973. Birth Centenary of Jacob Aall (industrialist).
704 **194** 1k. purple 30 20
705 1k.40 blue 30 65

1973. Lapp Handicrafts.
706 **195** 75ore brown and cream 25 30
707 – 1k. red and cream 35 15
708 – 1k.40 black and blue . . 40 65
DESIGNS: 1k. Detail of weaving; 1k.40, Detail of tinware.

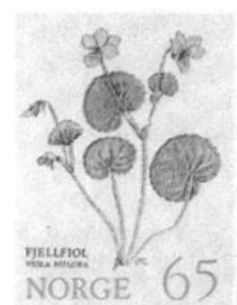

196 Yellow Wood Violet

197 Land Surveying

1973. Mountain Flowers. Multicoloured.
709 65ore Type **196** 15 20
710 70ore Rock speedwell 20 60
711 1k. Mountain heath 20 15

1973. Bicent of Norwegian Geographical Society.
712 **197** 1k. red 25 15
713 – 1k.40 blue 45 70
DESIGN: 1k.40, Old map of Hestbraepiggene (mountain range).

198 Lindesnes

199 "Bridal Procession on Hardanger Fjord" (A. Tidemand and H. Gude)

1974. Norwegian Capes.
714 **198** 1k. green 45 25
715 – 1k.40 blue . . . . 1·00 1·00
DESIGN: 1k.40, North Cape.

1974. Norwegian Paintings. Multicoloured.
716 1k. Type **199** 30 15
717 1k.40 "Stugunoset from Filefjell" (J. Dahl) 35 65

200 Gulating Law Manuscript, 1325

201 Trees and Saw Blade

1974. 700th Anniv of King Magnus Lagaboter National Legislation.
718 **200** 1k. red and brown . . . 30 15
719 – 1k.40 blue and brown . . 50 70
DESIGN: 1k.40, King Magnus Lagaboter (sculpture in Stavanger Cathedral).

1974. Industrial Accident Prevention.
720 **201** 85ore green, deep green and emerald . . . . . 1·00 1·50
721 – 1k. carmine, red and orange 75 30
DESIGN: 1k. Flower and cogwheel.

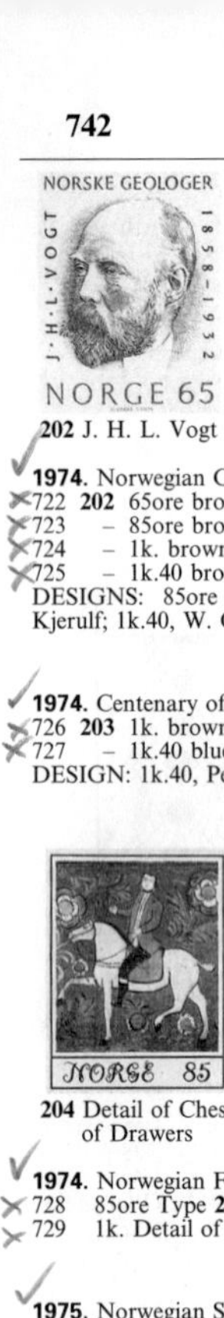

202 J. H. L. Vogt

203 Buildings of the World

1974. Norwegian Geologists.
722 **202** 65ore brown and green 25 25
723 – 85ore brown and purple 70 1·00
724 – 1k. brown and orange . . 50 20
725 – 1k.40 brown and blue . . 75 80
DESIGNS: 85ore V. M. Goldschmidt; 1k. Th. Kjerulf; 1k.40, W. C. Brogger.

1974. Centenary of Universal Postal Union.
726 **203** 1k. brown and green . . . 45 20
727 – 1k.40 blue and brown . . 50 65
DESIGN: 1k.40, People of the World.

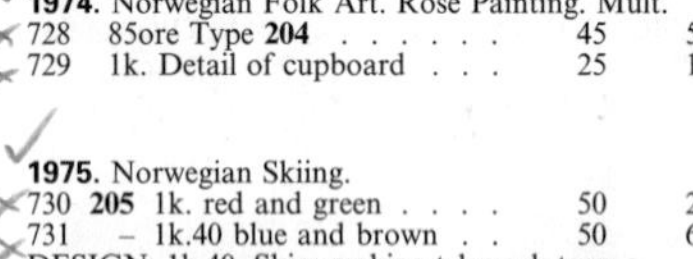

204 Detail of Chest of Drawers

205 Woman Skier, 1900

1974. Norwegian Folk Art. Rose Painting. Mult.
728 85ore Type **204** 45 50
729 1k. Detail of cupboard . . . 25 15

1975. Norwegian Skiing.
730 **205** 1k. red and green 50 25
731 – 1k.40 blue and brown . . 50 65
DESIGN: 1k.40, Skier making telemark turn.

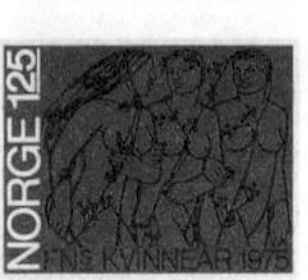

206 "Three Women with Ivies" Gate, Vigeland Park, Oslo

207 Nusfjord Fishing Harbour, Lofoten Islands

1975. International Women's Year.
732 **206** 1k.25 violet and purple 30 15
733 1k.40 ultramarine and blue 30 70

1975. European Architectural Heritage Year.
734 **207** 1k. green 30 45
735 – 1k.25 red 25 15
736 – 1k.40 blue 30 60
DESIGNS: 1k.25, Old Stavanger; 1k.40, Roros.

208 Norwegian 1k. Coin, 1875 (Monetary Convention)

1975. Cent of Monetary and Metre Conventions.
737 **208** 1k.25 red 20 20
738 – 1k.40 blue 40 55
DESIGN: 1k.40, O. J. Broch (original Director of the International Bureau of Weights and Measures) (Metre Convention).

209 Camping and Emblem

1975. World Scout Jamboree, Lillehammer. Mult.
739 1k.25 Type **209** 25 20
740 1k.40 Skiing and emblem . . 45 75

210 Colonist's Peat House

1975. 150th Anniv of First Emigrations to America.
741 **210** 1k.25 brown 45 20
742 – 1k.40 blue 45 55
DESIGNS: 1k.40, C. Peerson and extract from letter to America, 1874.

211 "Templet" (Temple Mountain), Tempelfjord, Spitzbergen

212 "Television Screen" (T. E. Johnsen)

1975. 50th Anniv of Norwegian Administration of Spitzbergen.
743 **211** 1k. grey 30 45
744 – 1k.25 purple 30 10
745 – 1k.40 blue . . . . . . 80 1·20
DESIGNS: 1k.25, Miners leaving pit; 1k.40, Polar bear.

1975. 50th Anniv of Norwegian Broadcasting System. Multicoloured.
746 1k.25 Type **212** 15 20
747 1k.40 Telecommunications antenna (N. Davidsen) (vert) 25 50

213 "The Annunciation"

1975. Paintings from "Altaket" (wooden vault) of "Al" Stave Church, Hallingdal.
748 80ore Type **213** 20 20
749 1k. "The Visitation" 20 25
750 1k.25 "The Nativity" (30 × 38 mm) 20 10
751 1k.40 "The Adoration" (30 × 38 mm) 45 55

214 "Halling" (folk dance)

215 Silver Sugar Caster, Stavanger, 1770

1976. Norwegian Folk Dances. Multicoloured.
752 80ore Type **214** 30 50
753 1k. "Springar" 30 25
754 1k.25 "Gangar" 30 10

1976. Centenary of Oslo Museum of Applied Art.
755 **215** 1k.25 brown, red and pink 20 20
756 – 1k.40 lilac, blue and azure 35 65
DESIGN: 1k.40, Goblet, Nostetangen Glass-works, 1770.

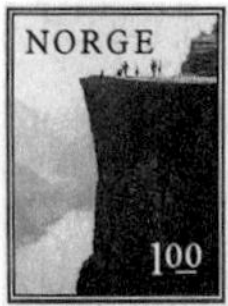

216 Bishop's "Mitre" Bowl, 1760

217 "The Pulpit", Lyse Fjord

1976. Europa. Early Products of Herrebo Potteries, Halden.
757 **216** 1k.25 red and mauve . . 30 20
758 – 1k.40 ultramarine & blue 50 65
DESIGN: 1k.40, Decorative plate, 1760.

1976. Norwegian Scenery. Multicoloured.
759 1k. Type **217** 30 45
760 1k.25 Peak of Gulleplet ("The Golden Apple"), Balestrand, Sognefjord . . 45 25

218 Social Development Graph

219 Olav Duun and Cairn, Dun Mountain, Joa Island, Namsen Fjord

1976. Cent of Norwegian Central Bureau of Statistics.
761 **218** 1k.25 red 40 15
762 – 2k. blue 45 35
DESIGN: 2k. National productivity graph.

1976. Birth Centenary of Olav Duun (novelist).
763 **219** 1k.25 multicoloured . . . 40 25
764 1k.40 multicoloured . . . 45 80

220 "Slindebirkin" (T. Fearnley)

221 Details of "April"

1976. Norwegian Paintings. Multicoloured.
765 1k.25 Type **220** 45 20
766 1k.40 "Gamle Furutraer" (L. Hertervig) 55 65

1976. Tapestry from Baldishol Stave Church. Mult.
767 80ore Type **221** 25 20
768 1k. Detail of "May" 25 25
769 1k.25 "April" and "May" section of tapestry (48 × 30 mm) 25 15

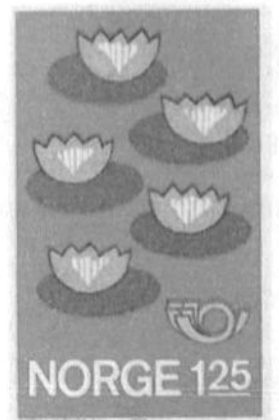

222 Five Water-lilies

223 Akershus Castle, Oslo

1977. Nordic Countries Co-operation in Nature Conservation and Environment Protection.
770 **222** 1k.25 multicoloured . . . 30 15
771 1k.40 multicoloured . . . 30 65

1977.
772 – 1k. green 25 20
773 – 1k.10 purple 25 20
774 **223** 1k.25 red 20 15
775 – 1k.30 brown 30 15
776 – 1k.40 lilac 25 20
777 – 1k.50 red 30 15
778 – 1k.70 green 40 40
779 – 1k.75 green 35 15
780 – 1k.80 blue 45 35
781 – 2k. red 45 15
782 – 2k.20 blue 45 40
783 – 2k.25 violet 45 35
784 – 2k.50 red 45 15
785 – 2k.75 red 50 60
786 – 3k. blue 50 25
787 – 3k.50 violet 60 25
DESIGNS—HORIZ: 1k. Austraat Manor; 1k.10, Trondenes Church, Harstad; 1k.30, Steinviksholm Fortress, Asen Fjord; 1k.40, Ruins of Hamar Cathedral; 2k.20, Tromsdalen Church; 2k.50, Loghouse, Breiland; 2k.75, Damsgard Palace, Laksevag, near Bergen; 3k. Ruins of Selje Monastery; 3k.50, Lindesnes lighthouse. VERT: 1k.50, Stavanger Cathedral; 1k.70, Rosenkrantz Tower, Bergen; 1k.75, Seamen's commemoration hall, Stavern; 1k.80, Torungen lighthouses, Arendal; 2k. Tofte royal estate, Dovre; 2k.25, Oscarshall (royal residence), Oslofjord.

224 Hamnoy, Lofoten Islands

225 Spruce

1977. Europa. Multicoloured.
795 1k.25 Type **224** 50 25
796 1k.80 Huldrefossen, Nordfjord (vert) 50 55

1977. Norwegian Trees.
797 **225** 1k. green 25 25
798 – 1k.25 brown 25 20
799 – 1k.80 black 35 45
DESIGNS: 1k.25, Fir; 1k.80, Birch.
See note below No. 433.

226 "Constitutionen" (paddle-steamer) at Arendal

1977. Norwegian Coastal Routes.
800 **226** 1k. brown 20 20
801 – 1k.25 red 30 25
802 – 1k.30 green 90 85
803 – 1k.80 blue 45 40
DESIGNS: 1k.25, "Vesteraalen" (coaster) off Bodo; 1k.30, "Kong Haakon" and "Dronningen" at Stavanger, 1893 (ferries); 1k.80, "Nordstjernen" and "Harald Jarl" (ferries).

227 "From the Herring Fishery" (after photo by S. A. Borretzen)

1977. Fishing Industry.
804 **227** 1k.25 brown on orange 20 20
805 – 1k.80 blue on blue . . . 30 60
DESIGN: 1k.80, Saithe and fish hooks.
See note below No. 433.

228 "Saturday Evening" (H. Egedius)

1977. Norwegian Paintings. Multicoloured.
806 1k.25 Type **228** 30 20
807 1k.80 "Forest Lake in Lower Telemark" (A. Cappelen) 40 65

229 "David with the Bells"

230 "Peer and the Buck Reindeer" (after drawing by P. Krohg for "Peer Gynt")

1977. Miniatures from the Bible of Aslak Bolt. Mult.
808 80ore Type **229** 20 15
809 1k. "Singing Friars" 20 30
810 1k.25 "The Holy Virgin with the Child" (34 × 27 mm) . . 20 25

1978. 150th Birth Anniv of Henrik Ibsen (dramatist).
811 **230** 1k.25 black and stone . . 25 25
812 – 1k.80 multicoloured . . . 35 50
DESIGN: 1k.80, Ibsen (after E. Werenskiold).

231 Heddal Stave Church, Telemark

232 Lenangstindene and Jaegervasstindene, Troms

1978. Europa.
813 **231** 1k.25 brown and orange 40 20
814 – 1k.80 green and blue . . 75 65
DESIGN: 1k.80, Borgund stave church, Sogn.

1978. Norwegian Scenery. Multicoloured.
815 1k. Type **232** 30 25
816 1k.25 Gaustatoppen, Telemark 30 25

233 King Olav in Sailing-boat

1978. 75th Birthday of King Olav V.
817 **233** 1k.25 brown 30 30
818 – 1k.80 violet 30 40
DESIGN—VERT: 1k.80, King Olav delivering royal speech at opening of Parliament.

234 Amundsen's Polar Flight Stamp of 1925

1978. "Norwex 80" International Stamp Exhibition (1st issue).
819 **234** 1k.25 green and grey . . 40 60
820 1k.25 blue and grey . . 40 60
821 – 1k.25 green and grey . . 40 60
822 – 1k.25 blue and grey . . 40 60
823 **234** 1k.25 purple and grey . . 40 60
824 1k.25 red and grey . . . 40 60

825 – 1k.25 purple and grey . . 40 60
826 – 1k.25 blue and grey . . . 40 60
DESIGNS: Nos. 821/2, 825/6, Annexation of Spitzbergen stamp of 1925.

On Nos. 819/26 each design incorporates a different value of the 1925 issues.

See also Nos. **MS**847 and **MS**862.

235 Willow Pipe Player

236 Wooden Doll, c. 1830

1978. Musical Instruments.
827 **235** 1k. green 20 20
828 – 1k.25 red 30 20
829 – 1k.80 blue 45 45
830 – 7k.50 grey . . . . 1·20 25
831 – 15k. brown . . . . 2·50 25
DESIGNS: 1k.25, Norwegian violin; 1k.80, Norwegian zither; 7k.50, Ram's horn; 15k. Jew's harp.

See note below No. 433.

1978. Christmas. Antique Toys from Norwegian Folk Museum. Multicoloured.
835 80ore Type **236** 20 20
836 1k. Toy town, 1896/7 . . . . 20 30
837 1k.25 Wooden horse from Torpo, Hallingdal 20 15

237 Ski Jumping at Huseby, 1879

238 "Portrait of Girl" (M. Stoltenberg)

1979. Centenary of Skiing Competitions at Huseby and Holmenkollen.
838 **237** 1k. green 30 25
839 – 1k.25 red 30 25
840 – 1k.80 blue 25 55
DESIGNS: 1k.25, Crown Prince Olav ski jumping at Holmenkollen, 1922; 1k.80, Cross-country skiing at Holmenkollen, 1976.

1979. International Year of the Child. Mult.
841 1k.25 Type **238** 25 20
842 1k.80 "Portrait of Boy" (H. C. F. Hosenfelder) . . 35 60

239 Road to Briksdal Glacier

240 Falkberget (after Harald Dal)

1979. Norwegian Scenery. Multicoloured.
843 1k. Type **239** 30 25
844 1k.25 Skjernoysund, near Mandal 30 15

1979. Birth Centenary of Johan Falkberget (novelist).
845 **240** 1k.25 brown 30 20
846 – 1k.80 blue 40 60
DESIGN: 1k.80, "Ann-Magritt and the Hovi Bullock" (statue by Kristofer Leirdal).

241 Dornier Do-J Wal Flying Boat N-25

1979. "Norwex 80" International Stamp Exhibition, Oslo (2nd issue). Arctic Aviation. Sheet 113 × 91 mm containing T **241** and similar horiz designs, each black, yellow and ultramarine.
MS847 1k.25 Type **241** (Amundsen and Ellsworth, 1925); 2k. Airship N.1 *Norge* (Amundsen, Ellsworth and Nobile, 1926); 2k.80, Loening OA-2 amphibian *Live Eriksson* (Thor Solberg, 1935); 4k. Douglas DC-7C *Reider Viking* (first scheduled flight over North Pole, 1957) (sold at 15k.) . . . . . 3·75 4·50

242 Steam Train on Kylling Bridge, Verma, Romsdal

243 Glacier Buttercup ("Ranunculus glacialis")

1979. Norwegian Engineering.
848 **242** 1k.25 black and brown . . 30 15
849 – 2k. black and blue . . . 30 15
850 – 10k. brown and bistre . . 1·60 40
DESIGNS: 2k. Vessingsjo Dam, Nea, Sor-Trondelag; 10k. Statfjord A offshore oil drilling and production platform.

1979. Flowers. Multicoloured.
851 80ore Type **243** 25 15
852 1k. Alpine cinquefoil ("Potentilla crantzii") . . . 20 25
853 1k.25 Purple saxifrage ("Saxifraga oppositifolia") 20 15
See also Nos. 867/8.

244 Leaf and Emblems

245 Oystercatcher Chick ("Haematopus ostralegus")

1980. Centenary of Norwegian Christian Youth Association. Multicoloured.
854 1k. Type **244** 25 25
855 1k.80 Plant and emblems . . 35 50

1980. Birds (1st series). Multicoloured.
856 1k. Type **245** 20 25
857 1k. Mallard chick ("Anas platyrhynchos") 20 25
858 1k.25 White-throated dipper ("Cinclus cinclus") 25 15
859 1k.25 Great tit ("Parus major") 25 15
See also Nos. 869/72, 894/5 and 914/15.

246 Telephone and Dish Aerial

1980. Centenary of Norwegian Telephone Service.
860 **246** 1k.25 brown, purple & bl 25 25
861 – 1k.80 multicoloured . . . 35 45
DESIGN: 1k.80, Erecting a telephone pole.

247 *Bergen* (paddle-steamer)

1980. "Norwex 80" International Stamp Exhibition, Oslo (3rd issue). Sheet 113 × 90 mm containing T **247** and similar horiz designs.
MS862 1k.25, red and black; 2k. yellow and black; 2k.80, yellow, green and black; 4k. dull blue and black (sold at 15k.) . . . . . 3·50 3·50
DESIGNS: 2k. Steam locomotive and carriages, 1900; 2k.80, Motor coach, 1940; 4k. Boeing 737 and Douglas DC-9 aircraft.

248 "Vulcan as an Armourer" (Hassel Jerverk after Bech)

1980. Nordic Countries' Postal Co-operation. Cast-iron Stove Ornaments.
863 **248** 1k.25 brown 25 10
864 – 1k.80 violet 35 55
DESIGN: 1k.80, "Hercules at a burning Altar" (Moss Jerverk after Henrich Bech).

249 "Jonsokbal" (Nikolai Astrup)

1980. Norwegian Paintings. Multicoloured.
865 1k.25 Type **249** 25 20
866 1k.80 "Seljefloyten" (Christian Skredsvig) . . . 40 50

1980. Flowers. As T **243**. Multicoloured.
867 80ore Rowan berries ("Sorbus aucparia") . . . 20 20
868 1k. Dog rose hips ("Rosa canina") 20 20

1981. Birds (2nd series). As T **245**. Multicoloured.
869 1k.30 Lesser white-fronted goose ("Anser erythropus") 25 25
870 1k.30 Peregrine falcon ("Falco peregrinus") . . . 25 25
871 1k.50 Atlantic puffin ("Fratercula arctica") . . . 30 25
872 1k.50 Black guillemot ("Cepphus grylle") 30 25

250 Cow

251 "The Mermaid" (painting by Kristen Aanstad on wooden dish from Hol)

1981. Centenary of Norwegian Milk Producers' National Association. Multicoloured.
873 1k.10 Type **250** 30 25
874 1k.50 Goat 30 15
See note below No. 433.

1981. Europa. Multicoloured.
875 1k.50 Type **251** 40 20
876 2k.20 "The Proposal" (painting by Ola Hansson on box from Nes) 60 55
See note below No. 433.

252 Weighing Anchor

1981. Sailing Ship Era.
877 **252** 1k.30 green 55 25
878 – 1k.50 red 45 25
879 – 2k.20 blue . . . . 1·00 60
DESIGNS—VERT: 1k.50, Climbing the rigging. HORIZ: 2k.20, "Christian Radich" (cadet ship).

253 "Skibladner" (paddle-steamer)

1981. Norwegian Lake Shipping.
880 **253** 1k.10 brown 45 20
881 – 1k.30 green 45 35
882 – 1k.50 red 45 20
883 – 2k.30 blue 90 45
DESIGNS: 1k.30, "Victoria" (ferry); 1k.50, "Faemund II" (ferry); 2k.30, "Storegut" (train ferry).

254 Handicapped People as Part of Community

1981. International Year of Disabled Persons.
884 **254** 1k.50 pink, red and blue 30 25
885 – 2k.20 blue, deep blue and red 45 50
DESIGN: 2k.20, Handicapped and non-handicapped people walking together.

255 "Interior in Blue" (Harriet Backer)

1981. Norwegian Paintings. Multicoloured.
886 1k.50 Type **255** 30 25
887 1k.70 "Peat Moor on Jaeren" (Kitty Lange Kielland) . . 45 50

256 Hajalmar Branting and Christian Lange

1981. Nobel Peace Prize Winners of 1921.
888 **256** 5k. black 90 25

257 "One of the Magi" (detail from Skjak tapestry, 1625)

258 Ski Sticks

1981. Tapestries. Multicoloured.
889 1k.10 Type **257** 20 15
890 1k.30 "Adoration of Christ" (detail, Skjak tapestry, 1625) 20 35
891 1k.50 "Marriage in Cana" (pillow slip from Storen, 18th century) (29 × 36 mm) 20 15

1982. World Ski Championships, Oslo.
892 **258** 2k. red and blue 45 25
893 – 3k. blue and red 50 40
DESIGN: 3k. Skis.

1982. Birds (3rd series). As T **245**. Multicoloured.
894 2k. Bluethroat ("Luscinia svecica") 35 15
895 2k. European robin ("Erithacus rubecula") . . 35 15

259 Nurse

260 King Haakon VII disembarking from "Heimdal" after Election, 1905

1982. Anti-tuberculosis Campaign. Mult.
896 2k. Type **259** 45 15
897 3k. Microscope 50 45
See note below No. 433.

1982. Europa.
898 **260** 2k. brown 95 25
899 – 3k. blue . . . . 1·10 50
DESIGN: 3k. Crown Prince Olav greeting King Haakon VII after liberation, 1945.

261 "Girls from Telemark" (Erik Werenskiold)

1982. Norwegian Paintings. Multicoloured.
900 1k.75 Type **261** 40 40
901 2k. "Tone Veli by Fence" (Henrik Sorenson) (vert) 40 25
See note below No. 433.

262 Consecration Ceremony, Nidaros Cathedral, Trondheim

1982. 25th Anniv of King Olav V's Reign.
902 **262** 3k. violet 50 55

263 "Bjornstjerne Bjornson on Balcony at Aulestad" (Erik Werenskiold)

1982. Writers' Birth Anniversaries. Multicoloured.
903 1k.75 Type **263** (150th anniv) 45 25
904 2k. "Sigrid Undset" (after A. C. Svarstad) (birth centenary) 45 25

264 Construction of Letter "A"

265 Fridtjof Nansen

1982. Centenary of Graphical Union of Norway.
905 **264** 2k. yellow, green and black 45 25
906 – 3k. multicoloured 50 45
DESIGN: 3k. Offset litho printing rollers.

1982. 1922 Nobel Peace Prize Winner.
907 **265** 3k. blue 50 40
See note below No. 433.

266 "Christmas Tradition" (Adolf Tidemand)

267 Buhund (farm dog)

1982. Christmas.
908 **266** 1k.75 multicoloured . . . 35 15

1983. Norwegian Dogs. Multicoloured.
909 2k. Type **267** 45 35
910 2k.50 Elkhound 45 15
911 3k.50 Lundehund (puffin hunter) 45 60
See note below No. 433.

268 Mountain Scenery

269 Edvard Grieg with Concerto in A minor

1983. Nordic Countries' Postal Co-operation. "Visit the North". Multicoloured.
912 2k.50 Type **268** 45 15
913 3k.50 Fjord scenery 60 55

1983. Birds (4th series). As T **245**. Mult.
914 2k.50 Barnacle goose ("Branta leucopsis") . . . 45 15
915 2k.50 Little auk ("Alle alle") 45 15

1983. Europa.
916 **269** 2k.50 red . . . . 1·00 25
917 – 3k.50 blue and green . . 1·00 75
DESIGN—VERT: 3k.50, Statue of Niels Henrik Abel (mathematician) by Gustav Vigeland.

270 Arrows forming Posthorn

1983. World Communications Year. Multicoloured.
918 2k.50 Type **270** 45 20
919 3k.50 Arrows circling globe 60 60

271 King Olav V and Royal Birch, Molde

1983. 80th Birthday of King Olav V.
920 **271** 5k. green . . . . 1·00 25

272 Lie

273 Northern Femboring

1983. 150th Birth Anniv of Jonas Lie (author).
921 **272** 2k.50 red 45 25

1983. North Norwegian Ships.
922 **273** 2k. blue and brown . . . 45 35
923 – 3k. brown and blue . . . 50 50
DESIGNS: 3k. Northern jekt.
See note below No. 433.

274 "The Sleigh Ride" (Axel Ender)

275 Post Office Counter

1983. Christmas. Multicoloured.
924 2k. Type **274** 45 25
925 2k.50 "The Guests are arriving" (Gustav Wendel) 45 15

1984. Postal Work. Multicoloured.
926 2k. Type **275** 35 25
927 2k.50 Postal sorting 45 25
928 3k.50 Postal delivery 60 50

276 Freshwater Fishing

277 Magnetic Meridians and Parallels

1984. Sport Fishing.
929 **276** 2k.50 red 30 10
930 – 3k. green 35 40
931 – 3k.50 blue 90 45
DESIGNS: 3k. Atlantic salmon fishing; 3k.50, Sea fishing.

1984. Birth Bicentenary of Christopher Hansteen (astronomer and geophysicist).
932 **277** 3k.50 blue 60 45
933 – 5k. red . . . . 1·00 40
DESIGN—VERT: 5k. Portrait of Hansteen by Johan Gorbitz.

278 Bridge

279 Vegetables, Fruit and Herbs

1984. Europa. 25th Anniv of European Post and Telecommunications Conference.
934 **278** 2k.50 multicoloured . . . 75 15
935 3k.50 multicoloured . . . 95 55

1984. Centenary of Norwegian Horticultural Society. Multicoloured.
936 2k. Type **279** 25 30
937 2k.50 Rose and garland of flowers 50 15

280 Honey Bees

281 Holberg (after J. M. Bernigeroth)

1984. Centenaries of Norwegian Beekeeping Society and Norwegian Poultry-breeding Society. Mult.
938 2k.50 Type **280** 45 15
939 2k.50 Leghorn cock 45 15
See note below No. 433.

1984. 300th Birth Anniv of Ludvig Holberg (writer).
940 **281** 2k.50 red 45 25

282 Children reading

284 Karius and Baktus (tooth decay bacteria)

283 Entering Parliamentary Chamber, 2 July 1884

1984. 150th Anniv of "Norsk Penning-Magazin" (1st weekly magazine in Norway).
941 **282** 2k.50 purple, blue and red 45 15
942 – 3k.50 orange and violet 60 45
DESIGN: 3k.50, 1st edition of "Norsk Penning-Magazin".

1984. Cent of Norwegian Parliament.
943 **283** 7k.50 brown . . . . . . 1·50 70

1984. Characters from Stories by Thorbjorn Egner. Multicoloured.
944 2k. Type **284** 60 20
945 2k. The tree shrew playing guitar 60 20
946 2k.50 Kasper, Jesper and Jonatan (Rovers) in Kardemomme Town . . . 65 15
947 2k.50 Chief Constable Bastian 65 15

285 Mount Sagbladet (Saw Blade)

1985. Antarctic Mountains. Multicoloured.
948 2k.50 Type **285** 50 10
949 3k.50 Mount Hoggestabben (Chopping Block) 65 70

286 Return of Crown Prince Olav, 1945

1985. 40th Anniv of Liberation.
950 **286** 3k.50 red and blue . . . 60 50

287 Kongsten Fort

1985. 300th Anniv of Kongsten Fort.
951 **287** 2k.50 multicoloured . . . 45 15

288 Bronze Cannon, 1596

289 "Boy and Girl" (detail)

1985. Artillery Anniversaries. Multicoloured.
952 3k. Type **288** (300th anniv of Artillery) 50 50
953 4k. Cannon on sledge carriage, 1758 (bicentenary of Artillery Officers Training School) 70 40

1985. International Youth Year. Sculptures in Vigeland Park, Oslo. Multicoloured.
954 2k. Type **289** 35 25
955 3k.50 Bronze fountain (detail) 70 55
See note below No. 433.

290 Torgeir Augundsson (fiddler)

291 Workers at Glomfjord

1985. Europa. Music Year.
956 **290** 2k.50 red 75 20
957 – 3k.50 blue 90 50
DESIGN: 3k.50, Ole Bull (composer and violinist).

1985. Centenary of Electricity in Norway.
958 **291** 2k.50 red and scarlet . . 45 15
959 – 4k. blue and green . . . 70 35
DESIGN: 4k. Men working on overhead cable.

292 Ekofisk Centre

1985. Stamp Day. Norwegian Working Life (1st series). Offshore Oil Industry. Sheet 112 × 91 mm containing T **292** and similar horiz designs. Multicoloured.
MS960 2k.+1k. Type **292**; 2k.+1k. Drilling rig *Treasure Scout* and supply ship *Odin Viking*; 2k.+1k. Towing *Stratfjord C* platform to oil field, 1984; 2k.+1k. Drilling team on rig *Neptuno Nordraug* 3·25 5·00
See also Nos. **MS**989 and **MS**1012.

293 Carl Deichman on Book Cover

294 Wreath

1985. Bicentenary of Public Libraries.
961 **293** 2k.50 sepia and brown . . 50 15
962 – 10k. green . . . . 1·90 50
DESIGN—HORIZ: 10k. Library interior.

1985. Christmas. Multicoloured.
963 2k. Type **294** 60 25
964 2k.50 Northern bullfinches 60 15

295 "Berghavn" (dredger) **296** Sun

1985. 250th Anniv of Port Authorities and Bicentenary of Hydrography in Norway.
965 **295** 2k.50 purple, orange & bl 55 5·00
966 – 5k. blue, green and brown 75 45
DESIGN: 5k. Sextant and detail of chart No. 1 of Lt. F.C. Grove showing Trondheim sealane, 1791.

1986.
967 **296** 2k.10 orange and brown 45 15
968 – 2k.30 green and blue . . 45 15
970 – 2k.70 pink and red . . . 60 20
971 – 4k. blue and green . . . 85 15
DESIGNS: 2k.30, Atlantic cod and herring; 2k.70, Flowers; 4k. Star ornaments.

297 Marksman in Prone Position

1986. World Biathlon Championships. Mult.
977 2k.50 Type **297** 70 10
978 3k.50 Marksman standing to take aim 55 55

298 Industry and Countryside **299** Stone Cutter

1986. Europa. Multicoloured.
979 2k.50 Type **298** 60 20
980 3k.50 Dead and living forest, mountains and butterflies 1·00 70

1986. Centenary of Norwegian Craftsmen's Federation.
981 **299** 2k.50 lake and red . . . 45 15
982 – 7k. blue and red . . . . 1·10 60
DESIGN: 7k. Carpenter.

300 Moss

1986. Nordic Countries' Postal Co-operation. Twinned Towns. Multicoloured.
983 2k.50 Type **300** 50 15
984 4k. Alesund 60 40
See note below No. 433.

301 Hans Polson Egede (missionary) and Map **303** "Olav Kyrre founds Diocese in Nidaros"

302 Timber being debarked and cut

1986. Birth Anniversaries.
985 **301** 2k.10 brown and red . . 45 50
986 – 2k.50 red, green and blue 50 15
987 – 3k. brown and red . . . 50 40
988 – 4k. purple and lilac . . . 70 40
DESIGNS: 2k.10, Type **301** (300th anniv); 2k.50, Herman Wildenvey (poet) and poem carved in wall at Stavern (centenary); 3k. Tore Ojasaeter (poet) and old cupboard from Skjak (centenary); 4k. Engebret Soot (engineer) and lock gates, Orje (centenary).
See note below No. 433.

1986. Stamp Day. Norwegian Working Life (2nd series). Paper Industry. Sheet 113 × 91 mm containing T **302** and similar horiz designs. Multicoloured.
MS989 2k.50+1k. Type **302**; 2k.50+1k. Boiling plant; 2k.50+1k. Paper factory; 2k.50+1k. Paper being dried and rolled into bales . . . . 4·50 5·25

1986. Christmas. Stained Glass Windows by Gabriel Kielland in Nidaros Cathedral, Trondheim. Multicoloured.
990 2k.10 Type **303** 50 20
991 2k.50 "The King and the Peasant at Sul" 50 15

304 Doves **305** Numeral

1986. International Peace Year.
992 **304** 15k. red, blue and green 3·25 60

1987.
993 **305** 3k.50 yellow, red and blue 60 50
994 4k.50 blue, yellow & green 75 40

306 Wooden Building

1987. Europa. Multicoloured.
1000 2k.70 Type **306** 75 15
1001 4k.50 Building of glass and stone . . . . 1·30 40

307 The Final Vote **309** Funnel-shaped Chanterelle ("Cantharellus tubaeformis")

308 Rehabilitation Centre, Mogadishu

1987. 150th Anniv of Laws on Local Councils (granting local autonomy).
1002 **307** 12k. green . . . . 2·40 50

1987. Norwegian Red Cross in Somalia. Sheet 113 × 91 mm.
MS1003 **308** 4k.50 multicoloured 90 1·00

1987. Fungi (1st series). Multicoloured.
1004 2k.70 Type **309** 45 15
1005 2k.70 The gypsy ("Rozites caperata") 45 15
See also Nos. 1040/1 and 1052/3.

310 Bjornstad Farm from Vaga

1987. Centenary of Sandvig Collections, Maihaugen.
1006 **310** 2k.70 sepia and brown 50 15
1007 – 3k.50 purple and blue . 60 50
DESIGN: 3k.50, "Horse and Rider" (wooden carving, Christen Erlandsen Listad).

311 Valevag Churchyard

1987. Birth Centenary of Fartein Valen (composer).
1008 **311** 2k.30 blue and green . . 45 40
1009 – 4k.50 brown 90 25
DESIGN—VERT: 4k.50, Fartein Valen.
See note below No. 433.

312 "Storm at Sea" (Christian Krohg)

1987. Paintings. Multicoloured.
1010 2k.70 Type **312** 50 15
1011 5k. "The Farm" (Gerhard Munthe) . . . . 1·00 40

313 Eggs and Alevin

1987. Stamp Day. Norwegian Working Life (3rd series). Atlantic Salmon Farming. Sheet 113 × 91 mm containing T **313** and similar horiz designs. Multicoloured.
MS1012 2k.30+50ore Type **313**; 2k.70+50ore Hatching tanks and parr; 3k.50+50ore Marine stage; 4k.50+50ore Harvested salmon 4·25 4·75

314 Cat with Children making Decorations

1987. Christmas. Multicoloured.
1013 2k.30 Type **314** 50 40
1014 2k.70 Dog with children making gingersnaps . . . 50 15

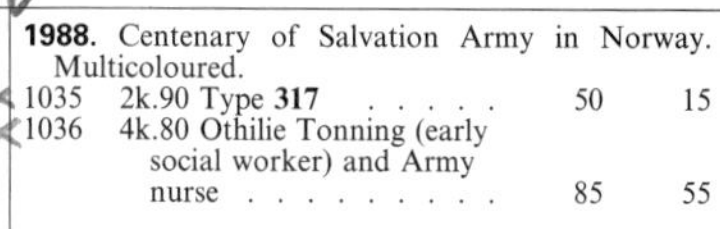

315 Dales Pony **316** Western Capercaillie

1987. Native Ponies.
1015 **315** 2k.30 deep brown, green and brown 45 50
1016 – 2k.70 buff, brown & blue 50 20
1017 – 4k.50 brown, red and blue 70 40
DESIGNS: 2k.70, Fjord pony; 4k.50, Nordland pony.
See note below No. 433.

1988. Wildlife.
1018 – 2k.60 deep brown, brown and green . . . 50 20
1019 **316** 2k.90 black, brn & grn 50 15
1020 – 3k. brown, grey and green 50 15
1021 – 3k.20 ultramarine, green and blue 50 15
1022 – 3k.80 brown, blue & blk 60 15
1023 – 4k. brown, red and green 70 15
1024 – 4k.50 brown, green & bl 75 25
1025 – 5k.50 brown, grey & grn 95 25
1026 – 6k.40 brown, blk & grn 1·10 35
DESIGNS: 2k.60, Fox; 3k. Stoat; 3k.20, Mute swan; 3k.80, Reindeer; 4k. Eurasian red squirrel; 4k.50, Beaver; 5k.50, Lynx; 6k.40, Tengmalm's owl.

317 Band

1988. Centenary of Salvation Army in Norway. Multicoloured.
1035 2k.90 Type **317** 50 15
1036 4k.80 Othilie Tonning (early social worker) and Army nurse 85 55

318 Building Fortress

1988. Military Anniversaries.
1037 **318** 2k.50 green 45 25
1038 – 2k.90 brown 50 15
1039 – 4k.60 blue 75 45
DESIGNS: 2k.50, Type **318** (300th anniv of Defence Construction Service); 2k.90, Corps members in action (centenary of Army Signals corps); 4k.60, Making pontoon bridge (centenary of Engineer Corps).

1988. Fungi (2nd series). As T **309**. Mult.
1040 2k.90 Wood blewits ("Lepista nuda") 50 15
1041 2k.90 "Lactarius deterrimus" 50 15

319 Globe **320** King Olav V

1988. European Campaign for Interdependence and Solidarity of North and South.
1042 **319** 25k. multicoloured . . . 5·25 75

1988. 85th Birthday of King Olav V. Multicoloured.
1043 2k.90 Type **320** 50 15
MS1044 121 × 91 mm. 2k.90 King Olav arriving as baby; 2k.90 Type **320**; 2k.90 King Olav at Holmenkollen . . . . 2·10 2·40

321 "Prinds Gustav" (paddle-steamer) **322** King Christian IV

1988. Europa. Transport and Communications.
1045 **321** 2k.90 black, red and blue 85 15
1046 – 3k.80 blue, red & yellow 1·30 75
DESIGN: 3k.80, Heroybrua Bridge.

1988. 400th Anniv of Christian IV's Accession to Danish and Norwegian Thrones.
1047 **322** 2k.50 black, stone & vio 60 20
1048 – 10k. multicoloured . . . 1·75 40
DESIGN: 10k. 1628 silver coin and extract from decree on mining in Norway.

323 Handball

1988. Stamp Day. Sport. Sheet 113 × 91 mm containing T **323** and similar horiz designs. Multicoloured.
MS1049 2k.90 Type **323**; 2k.90 Football; 2k.90 Basketball; 2k.90 Volleyball (sold at 15k.) . . . 3·75 4·00

NORGE 2.90 Norge 5.00

324 Ludvig with Ski Stick **325** Start and Finish of Race

1988. Christmas. Multicoloured.
1050 2k.90 Type **324** 55 15
1051 2k.90 Ludvig reading letter 55 15

1989. Fungi (3rd series). As T **309**. Multicoloured.
1052 3k. Chanterelle ("Cantharellus cibarius") 50 15
1053 3k. Butter mushroom ("Suillus luteus") 50 15

1989. World Cross-country Championship, Stavanger.
1054 **325** 5k. multicoloured . . . 90 35

326 Vardo

327 Setesdal Woman

1989. Town Bicentenaries.
1055 **326** 3k. blue, red & light blue 50 15
1056 – 4k. purple, blue & orange 60 50
DESIGN: 4k. Hammerfest.

1989. Nordic Countries' Postal Co-operation. Traditional Costumes. Multicoloured.
1057 3k. Type **327** 50 25
1058 4k. Kautokeino man 85 55

328 Children making Snowman

329 Rooster and Cover of 1804 First Reader

1989. Europa. Children's Games. Multicoloured.
1059 3k.70 Type **328** . . . . . 1·00 60
1060 5k. Cat's cradle . . . . . . 1·50 70
See note below No. 433.

1989. 250th Anniv of Primary Schools.
1061 **329** 2k.60 multicoloured . . 50 45
1062 – 3k. brown 50 15
DESIGN: 3k. Pocket calculator and child writing.

330 "Impressions of the Countryside" (detail)

1989. Stamp Day. Sheet 107 × 85 mm. containing T **330** and similar horiz designs, forming a composite design of the painting by Jakob Weidemann.
MS1063 3k. × 4 multicoloured (sold at 15k.) . . . . 3·75 5·25

331 Bjorg Eva Jensen (300m. speed skating 1980)

1989. Winter Olympic Games, Lillehammer (1994) (1st issue). Norwegian Gold Medallists. Sheet 113 × 91 mm containing T **331** and similar horiz designs. Multicoloured.
MS1064 4k. Type **331**; 4k. Eirik Kvalfoss (biathlon, 1984); 4k. Tom Sandberg (combined cross-country and ski-jumping, 1984); 4k. Women's team (10km cross-country relay, 1984) (sold at 20k.) 4·50 6·00
See also Nos. **MS**1083, **MS**1097, **MS**1143, 1150/1, **MS**1157, 1169/70 and 1175/80.

332 Arnulf Overland (poet, centenary)

333 Star Decoration

1989. Writers' Birth Anniversaries.
1065 **332** 3k. red and blue 50 15
1066 – 25k. blue, orange & green . . . . 4·50 75
DESIGN: 25k. Hanna Winsnes (pseudonym Hugo Schwartz) (bicentenary).

1989. Christmas. Tree Decorations. Mult.
1067 3k. Type **333** 50 15
1068 3k. Bauble 50 15

334 Larvik Manor

335 Emblem

1989. Manor Houses.
1069 **334** 3k. brown 50 15
1070 – 3k. green 50 15
DESIGN: No. 1070, Rosendal Barony.

1990. Winter Cities Events, Tromso.
1071 **335** 5k. multicoloured . . . 90 35

336 Common Spotted Orchid ("Dactylorhiza fuchsii")

337 Merchant Navy, Airforce, Home Guard, "Moses" (coastal gun) and Haakon VII's Monogram

1990. Orchids (1st series). Multicoloured.
1072 3k.20 Type **336** 50 15
1073 3k.20 Dark red helleborine ("Epipactis atrorubens") 50 15
See also Nos. 1141/2.

1990. 50th Anniv of Norway's Entry into Second World War. Multicoloured.
1074 3k.20 Type **337** 50 15
1075 4k. Second Battle of Narvik, 1940 . . . . 70 50

338 Penny Black

1990. 150th Anniv of the Penny Black. Sheet 113 × 91 mm containing T **338** and similar vert design.
MS1076 5k. Type **338**; 5k. First Norwegian stamp (sold at 15k.) 3·50 3·75

339 Trondheim Post Office

340 "Tordenskiold" (from print by J. W. Tegner after Balthazar Denner)

1990. Europa. Post Office Buildings. Mult.
1077 3k.20 Type **339** 85 25
1078 4k. Longyearbyen Post Office . . . . 1·30 50

1990. 300th Birth Anniv of Admiral Tordenskiold (Peter Wessel). Multicoloured.
1079 3k.20 Type **340** 50 15
1080 5k. Tordenskiold's coat-of-arms 75 40

341 Svendsen

343 "Children and Snowman" (Ragni Engstrom Nilsen)

342 Thoreleif Haug (cross-country skiing, 1924)

1990. 150th Birth Anniv of Johan Svendsen (composer and conductor).
1081 **341** 2k.70 black and red . . 50 40
1082 – 15k. brown and yellow 2·50 45
DESIGN: 15k. Svendsen Monument (Stinius Fredriksen), Oslo.

1990. Winter Olympic Games, Lillehammer (1994) (2nd issue). Norwegian Gold Medallists. Sheet 113 × 91 mm containing T **342** and similar horiz designs. Multicoloured.
MS1083 4k. Type **342**; 4k. Sonja Henie (figure skating, 1928, 1932, 1936); 4k. Ivar Ballangrud (speed skating, 1928, 1936); 4k. Hjalmar Andersen (speed skating, 1952) (sold at 20k.) . . . . 5·00 6·00

1990. Christmas. Children's Prize-winning Drawings. Multicoloured.
1084 3k.20 Type **343** 55 15
1085 3k.20 "Christmas Church" (Jorgen Ingier) 55 15

344 Nobel Medal and Soderblom

1990. 60th Anniv of Award of Nobel Peace Prize to Nathan Soderblom, Archbishop of Uppsala.
1086 **344** 30k. brown, blue and red 5·75 70

345 Plan and Elevation of Container Ship and Propeller

1991. Centenaries of Federation of Engineering Industries (1989) and Union of Iron and Metal Workers.
1087 **345** 5k. multicoloured . . . 85 60

346 Satellite transmitting to Tromso

1991. Europa. Europe in Space. Mult.
1088 3k.20 Type **346** 85 25
1089 4k. Rocket leaving Andoya rocket range . . . . . . 1·20 40
See note below No. 433.

347 Christiansholm Fortress (late 17th- century)

348 Fountain, Vigeland Park, Oslo

1991. 350th Anniv of Kristiansand. Each black, blue and red.
1090 3k.20 Type **347** 60 25
1091 5k.50 Present day view of Christiansholm Fortress 95 30

1991. Nordic Countries' Postal Co-operation. Tourism. Multicoloured.
1092 3k.20 Type **348** 60 15
1093 4k. Globe, North Cape Plateau 95 65

349 "Skomvaer III" (lifeboat)

1991. Centenary of Norwegian Society for Sea Rescue.
1094 **349** 3k.20 brown, black & grn 50 25
1095 – 27k. brown, grey & purple . . . . 5·50 85
DESIGN—VERT: 27k. "Colin Archer" (first lifeboat).

350 Engraving on Steel

1991. Stamp Day. Stamp Engraving. Sheet 113 × 91 mm containing T **350** and similar horiz designs.
MS1096 2k.70 Type **350**; 3k.20 Engraver using magnifying glass; 4k. Engraver's hands seen through magnifying glass; 5k. Positive impression of engraving and burin (sold at 20k.) . . . . 4·00 4·75

351 Birger Ruud (ski jumping, 1932, 1936; downhill, 1936)

1991. Winter Olympic Games, Lillehammer (1994) (3rd issue). Norwegian Gold Medallists. Sheet 113 × 91 mm containing T **351** and similar horiz designs. Multicoloured.
MS1097 4k. Type **351**; 4k. Johann Grottumsbraten (cross-country skiing, 1928, 1932); 4k. Knut Johannesen (speed skaing, 1960, 1964); 4k. Magnar Solberg (biathlon, 1960, 1968, 1972) (sold at 20k.) . . . . 4·75 5·75

352 Posthorn

1991.
1098 **352** 1k. black and orange . . 30 15
1099 2k. red and green . . . 45 25
1100 3k. green and blue . . . 50 15
1101 4k. red and orange . . . 70 15
1102 5k. blue and green . . . 90 25
1103 6k. red and green . . . 1·00 25
1104 7k. blue and brown . . . 1·30 25
1105 8k. green and purple . . 1·40 40
1106 9k. brown and blue . . . 1·60 35

353 Guisers with Goat Head

1991. Christmas. Guising. Multicoloured.
1120 3k.20 Type **353** 55 25
1121 3k.20 Guisers with lantern 55 25

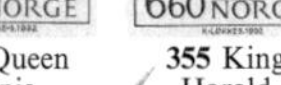

354 Queen Sonja
355 King Harald
356 King Harald

1992.

1122 354 2k.80 lake, purple & red 50 25
1123 3k. green, deep green and turquoise 50 15
1124 355 3k.30 blue, ultramarine and light blue 60 15
1125 3k.50 black and grey 60 15
1127 4k.50 deep red and red 75 50
1128 5k.50 brown, sepia & blk 95 25
1129 5k.60 orange, red and vermilion 1·00 25
1131 6k.50 emerald, green and turquoise 1·10 55
1132 6k.60 maroon, purple and brown 1·10 25
1133 7k.50 violet, lilac and purple 50 65
1134 8k.50 chestnut, deep brown and brown 60 60
1135 356 10k. green 1·75 25
1438 20k. violet 3·25 1·30
1138 30k. blue 4·75 50
1139 50k. green 9·50 1·30

1992. Orchids (2nd series). As T **336**. Mult.
1141 3k.30 Lady's slipper orchid ("Cypripedium calceolus") 60 25
1142 3k.30 Fly orchid ("Ophrys insectifera") 60 25

357 Hallgeir Brenden (cross-country skiing, 1952, 1956)

1992. Winter Olympic Games, Lillehammer (4th issue). Norwegian Gold Medallists. Sheet 113×91 mm containing T **357** and similar horiz designs. Multicoloured.
MS1143 4k. Type **357**; 4k. Arnfinn Bergmann (ski jumping, 1952); 4k. Stein Eriksen (super slalom, 1952); 4k. Simon Slattvik (combined, 1952) (sold at 20k.) 4·25 5·50

358 "Restaurationen" (emigrant sloop)

1992. Europa. 500th Anniv of Discovery of America by Columbus. Transatlantic Ships. Multicoloured.
1144 3k.30 Type **358** 95 25
1145 4k.20 "Stavangerfjord" (liner) and American skyline 1·40 45
See note below No. 433.

359 Norwegian Pavilion, Rainbow and Ship
360 Molde

1992. "Expo '92" World's Fair, Seville. Mult.
1146 3k.30 Type **359** 60 25
1147 5k.20 Mountains, rainbow, fish and oil rig 95 45

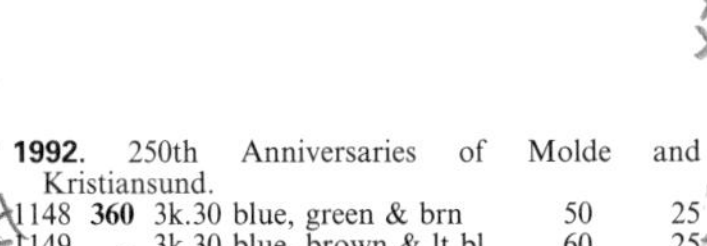

1992. 250th Anniversaries of Molde and Kristiansund.
1148 360 3k.30 blue, green & brn 50 25
1149 – 3k.30 blue, brown & lt bl 60 25
DESIGN: No. 1149, Kristiansund.

361 Banners and Lillehammer Buildings
363 Gnomes below Pillar Box

362 Flask with Etched Figures (Serre Petersen)

1992. Winter Olympic Games, Lillehammer (1994) (5th issue). Multicoloured.
1150 3k.30 Type **361** 60 25
1151 4k.20 Flags 70 50

1992. Stamp Day. Sheet 113×91 mm containing T **362** and similar horiz designs. Multicoloured.
MS1152 2k.80 Type **362**; 3k.30 Monogrammed carafe; 4k.20 Cut-glass salad bowl; 5k.20 Engraved goblet (Heinrich Gottlieb Kohler) (sold at 20k.) 5·00 4·00

1992. Christmas. Christmas card designs by Otto Moe. Multicoloured.
1153 3k.30 Type **363** 55 25
1154 3k.30 Gnome posting letter 55 25

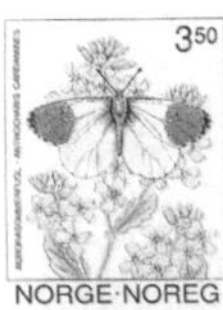

364 Orange-tip ("Anthocaris cardamines")
366 Grieg

365 Finn Chr. Jagge (slalom)

1993. Butterflies (1st series). Multicoloured.
1155 3k.50 Type **364** 60 25
1156 3k.50 Small tortoiseshell ("Aglais urticae") 60 25
See also Nos. 1173/4.

1993. Winter Olympic Games, Lillehammer (1994) (6th issue). Norwegian Gold Medallists at 1992 Games. Sheet 113×91 mm containing T **365** and similar horiz designs. Multicoloured.
MS1157 4k.50 Type **365**; 4k.50 Bjorn Daehlie (cross-country skiing); 4k.50 Geir Karlstad (speed skating); 4k.50 Vegard Ulvang (cross-country skiing) 4·25 6·00

1993. 150th Birth Anniv of Edvard Grieg (composer). Multicoloured.
1158 3k.50 Type **366** 60 25
1159 5k.50 "Spring" 95 40

367 Two-man Kayak on Lake
368 Richard With (founder) and "Vesteraalen"

1993. Nordic Countries' Postal Co-operation. Tourist Activities. Multicoloured.
1160 4k. Type **367** 70 25
1161 4k.50 White-water rafting 90 40

1993. Centenary of Express Coaster Service.
1162 368 3k.50 blue, violet and red 60 25
1163 – 4k.50 multicoloured 90 45
DESIGN: 4k.50, "Kong Harald".

369 Handball
370 Johann Castberg (politician)

1993. Sports Events. Multicoloured.
1164 3k.50 Type **369** (Women's World Championship, Norway) 60 25
1165 5k.50 Cycling (World Championships, Oslo and Hamar) 95 40

1993. Centenary of Workforce Protection Legislation.
1166 370 3k.50 brown and blue 60 25
1167 – 12k. blue and brown 2·25 55
DESIGN: 12k. Betzy Kjelsberg (first woman factory inspector).

371 Deail of Altarpiece (Jakob Klukstad), Lesja Church

1993. Stamp Day. Wood Carvings of Acanthus Leaves. Sheet 113×91 mm containing T **371** and similar horiz designs. Multicoloured.
MS1168 3k. Type **371**; 3k.50 Detail of dresser (Ola Teigeroen); 4k.50 Detail of Fliksaker chest (Jens Strammerud); 5k.50 Detail of pulpit, Our Saviour's Church, Oslo (sold at 21k.) 4·75 4·75

372 Torch Bearer on Skis
373 Store Mangen Chapel

1993. Winter Olympic Games, Lillehammer (1994) (7th issue). Morgedal–Lillehammer Torch Relay. Multicoloured.
1169 3k.50 Type **372** 60 25
1170 3k.50 Lillehammer 60 25
Nos. 1169/70 were issued together, se-tenant, forming a composite design.

1993. Christmas. Multicoloured.
1171 3k.50 Type **373** 60 25
1172 3k.50 Stamnes church, Sandnessjoen 60 25

1994. Butterflies (2nd series). As T **364**. Mult.
1173 3k.50 Northern clouded yellow ("Colias hecla") 60 25
1174 3k.50 Freya's fritillary ("Clossiana freija") 60 25

374 Flags
375 Cross-country Skiing

1994. Winter Olympic Games, Lillehammer (8th issue). Multicoloured.
1175 3k.50 Type **374** 80 30
1176 3k.50 Flags (different) 80 30
1177 3k.50 Lillehammer (church) and rings 80 30
1178 3k.50 Lillehammer (ski jump) and rings 80 30
1179 4k.50 Flags of European countries 75 50
1180 5k.50 Flags of non-European countries 95 40
Nos. 1175/8 were issued together, se-tenant, forming a composite design.

1994. Paralympic Games, Lillehammer. Mult.
1181 4k.50 Type **375** 1·10 50
1182 5k.50 Downhill skiing 1·00 45

376 King Christian VII's Signature and Seal

1994. Bicentenary of Tromso.
1183 376 3k.50 red, bistre & brn 60 25
1184 – 4k.50 blue, yellow and light blue 75 55
DESIGN: 4k.50, Tromsdalen church.

377 Mount Floy Incline Railway Cars, Bergen

1994. Tourism. Multicoloured.
1185 4k. Type **377** 70 40
1186 4k.50 "Svolvaer Goat" (rock formation), Lofoten 85 55
1187 5k.50 Beacon, World's End, Tjome 95 35

378 Osterdal Farm Buildings

1994. Cent of Norwegian Folk Museum, Bygdoy.
1188 378 3k. multicoloured 50 40
1189 – 3k.50 blue, yellow and purple 60 25
DESIGN: 3k.50, Horse-drawn sleigh, 1750 (Torsten Hoff).

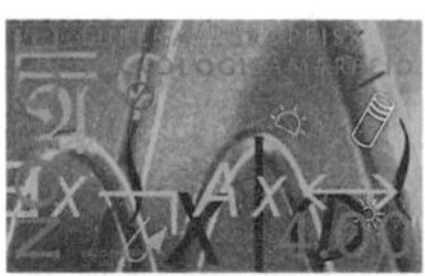

379 Technological Symbols and Formula ("Glass Flasks")

1994. EUREKA (European technology co-operation organization) Conference of Ministers, Lillehammer. Multicoloured.
1190 4k. Type **379** 60 45
1191 4k.50 Technological symbols ("Electronic Chips") 85 45

380 Electric Tram and Street Plan of Oslo, 1894
382 Sledge

381 Engraved Brooch

1994. Centenary of Electric Trams. Multicoloured.
1192 3k.50 Type **380** 60 25
1193 12k. Articulated tram and Oslo route map 3·50 85

1994. Stamp Day. Jewellery. Sheet 113×91 mm containing T **381** and similar horiz designs. Multicoloured.
MS1194 3k. Type **381**; 3k.50 Silver and gem studded brooch; 4k.50 "Rings" brooch; 5k.50 Brooch with medallions and central stone (sold at 21k.) 4·75 3·35

1994. Christmas.
1195 382 3k.50 red and black 60 25
1196 – 3k.50 ultramarine, blue and black 60 25
DESIGN: No. 1196, Kick-sledge.

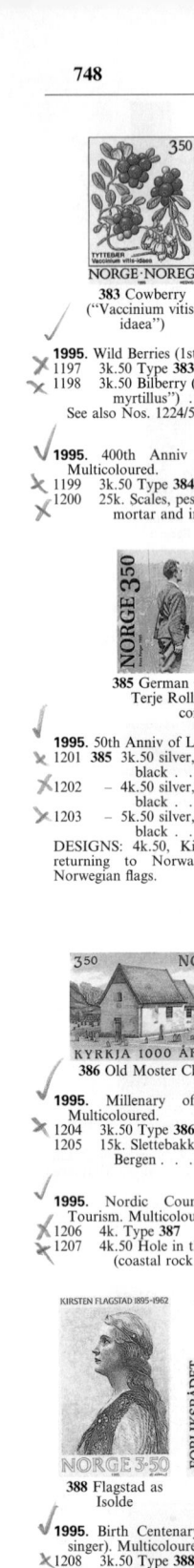

383 Cowberry ("Vaccinium vitis-idaea")

384 Swan Pharmacy, Bergen

1995. Wild Berries (1st Series). Multicoloured.

1197 3k.50 Type **383** 60 25
1198 3k.50 Bilberry ("Vaccinium myrtillus") 60 25

See also Nos. 1224/5.

1995. 400th Anniv of Norwegian Pharmacies. Multicoloured.

1199 3k.50 Type **384** 60 25
1200 25k. Scales, pestle and mortar and ingredients . . 5·25 1·90

385 German Commander saluting Terje Rollem (Home Guard commander)

1995. 50th Anniv of Liberation of Norway.

1201 **385** 3k.50 silver, green and black 60 25
1202 – 4k.50 silver, blue and black 90 70
1203 – 5k.50 silver, red and black 95 40

DESIGNS: 4k.50, King Haakon VII and family returning to Norway; 5k.50, Children waving Norwegian flags.

386 Old Moster Church

387 Skudeneshavn

1995. Millenary of Christianity in Norway. Multicoloured.

1204 3k.50 Type **386** 60 25
1205 15k. Slettebakken Church, Bergen . . . . 3·00 1·20

1995. Nordic Countries' Postal Co-operation. Tourism. Multicoloured.

1206 4k. Type **387** 70 55
1207 4k.50 Hole in the Hat (coastal rock formation) 85 55

388 Flagstad as Isolde

389 Disputants in Conflict

1995. Birth Centenary of Kirsten Flagstad (opera singer). Multicoloured.

1208 3k.50 Type **388** 60 25
1209 5k.50 Flagstad in scene from "Lohengrin" (Wagner) . . 95 40

1995. Bicentenary of Conciliation Boards. Multicoloured.

1210 7k. Type **389** . . . . . . 1·25 70
1211 12k. Disputants in conciliation with mediator 60 85

390 Letter and Vice-regent Hannibal Sehested (founder)

1995. 350th Anniv (1997) of Norwegian Postal Service (1st issue). Multicoloured.

1212 3k.50 Type **390** (letter post, 1647) 80 55
1213 3k.50 Wax seal (registered post, 1745) 80 55
1214 3k.50 Postmarks (1845) . . . 80 55
1215 3k.50 Banknotes, coins and money orders (transfer of funds, 1883) 80 55
1216 3k.50 Editions of "Norska Intelligenz-Sedler" and "Arkiv" (newspapers and magazines, 1660) 80 55
1217 3k.50 Address label, cancellations and "Constitutionen" (paddle-steamer) (parcel post, 1827) 80 55
1218 3k.50 Stamps (1855) 80 55
1219 3k.50 Savings book (Post Office Savings Bank, 1950) 80 55

The dates are those of the introduction of the various services.

See also Nos. 1237/44 and 1283/90.

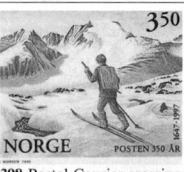

391 Trygve Lie (first Secretary-General) and Emblem

392 Woolly Hat

1995. 50th Anniv of U.N.O. Multicoloured.

1220 3k.50 Type **391** 60 25
1221 5k.50 Relief worker, water pump and emblem . . . 95 40

1995. Christmas. Multicoloured.

1222 3k.50 Type **392** 60 25
1223 3k.50 Mitten 65 25

1996. Wild Berries (2nd series). As T **383**. Multicoloured.

1224 3k.50 Wild strawberries ("Fragaria vesca") 60 25
1225 3k.50 Cloudberries ("Rubus chamaemorus") 60 25

393 Advent Bay

394 Cross-country Skier (Hakon Paulsen)

1996. Svalbard Islands. Multicoloured.

1226 10k. Type **393** . . . . . . 1·90 70
1227 20k. Polar bear . . . . . . 4·25 1·40

1996. Centenary of Modern Olympic Games. Children's Drawings. Multicoloured.

1228 3k.50 Type **394** 60 25
1229 5k.50 Athlete (Emil Tanem) 95 40

395 Besseggen

396 Steam Train, Urskog-Holand Line

1996. Tourism. U.N.E.S.C.O. World Heritage Sites. Multicoloured.

1230 4k. Type **395** 70 50
1231 4k.50 Stave church, Urnes 75 50
1232 5k.50 Rock carvings, Alta 95 40

See also Nos. 1291/3.

1996. Railway Centenaries. Multicoloured.

1233 3k. Type **396** 50 35
1234 4k.50 Steam train, Setesdal line 90 60

397 Location Map and Height Indicator

1996. Natural Gas Production at Troll, near Bergen. Multicoloured.

1235 3k.50 Type **397** 60 30
1236 25k. Planned route map of pipelines to Europe for next 200 years . . . . . 4·75 1·90

398 Postal Courier crossing Mountains

1996. 350th Anniv (1997) of Postal Service (2nd issue). Multicoloured.

1237 3k.50 Type **398** 75 65
1238 3k.50 "Framnaes" (fjord steamer) 75 65
1239 3k.50 Postal truck in Oslo 75 65
1240 3k.50 Taking mail on board "Ternen" (seaplane) on Jonsvatn Lake, Trondheim 75 65
1241 3k.50 Loading mail train at East Station, Oslo 75 65
1242 3k.50 Rural postman at Mago farm, Nittedal . . . 75 65
1243 3k.50 Serving customer, Elverum post office . . . 75 65
1244 3k.50 Computer, letters and globe 75 65

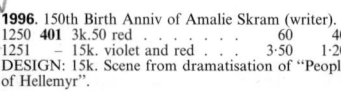

399 Leif Juster, Sean Connery, Liv Ullmann and Olsen Gang

1996. Centenary of Motion Pictures. Multicoloured.

1245 3k.50 Type **399** 60 25
1246 5k.50 Wenche Foss, Jack Fjeldstad, Marilyn Monroe, blood and gun 95 40
1247 7k. Charlie Chaplin in "Modern Times", Ottar Gladvedt, Laurel and Hardy and Marlene Dietrich . . . . 1·25 65

400 Left Detail of Embroidery

401 Skram

1996. Christmas. Embroidery Details from Telemark Folk Costume. Multicoloured.

1248 3k.50 Type **400** 60 25
1249 3k.50 Right detail 60 25

Nos. 1248/9 were issued together, se-tenant, forming a composite design.

1996. 150th Birth Anniv of Amalie Skram (writer).

1250 **401** 3k.50 red 60 40
1251 – 15k. violet and red . . . 3·50 1·20

DESIGN: 15k. Scene from dramatisation of "People of Hellemyr".

402 Posthorn

403 Coltsfoot

1997. Multicoloured, colour of oval given.

1252 **402** 10ore red 10 15
1253 20ore blue 10 15
1254 30ore orange 10 15
1255 40ore black 10 20
1256 50ore green 10 20

1997. Flowers. Multicoloured.

1259 3k.20 Red clover 50 25
1260 3k.40 Marsh marigold . . 50 20
1261 3k.60 Red campion 65 25
1262 3k.70 Type **403** 65 20
1263 3k.80 Wild pansy 70 30
1264 4k. Wood anemone . . . 70 25
1265 4k.30 Lily of the valley . . 70 35
1266 4k.50 White clover 75 25
1267 5k. Harebell 75 25
1268a 5k.40 Oeder's lousewort . . 70 25
1269 5k.50 Hepatica 95 45
1270 6k. Ox-eye daisy 70 40
1271 7k. Yellow wood violet . . 75 60
1272 7k.50 Pale pasque flower 95 35
1273a 8k. White water-lily . . . 1·50 40
1274 13k. Purple saxifrage . . . 2·20 60
1275a 14k. Globe flower . . . . 2·50 80
1276b 25k. Melancholy thistle . . 2·20 1·40

404 Bumble Bee

405 Ski Jumping

1997. Insects (1st series). Multicoloured.

1277 3k.70 Type **404** 60 25
1278 3k.70 Ladybird 60 25

See also Nos. 1306/7.

1997. World Nordic Skiing Championships, Trondheim. Multicoloured.

1279 3k.70 Type **405** 60 25
1280 5k. Speed skiing 75 35

406 King Harald (photo by Erik Johansen)

1997. 60th Birthdays of King Harald and Queen Sonja. Multicoloured.

1281 3k.70 Type **406** 60 25
1282 3k.70 Queen Sonja and King Harald (photo by Knut Falch) (horiz) . . . 60 25

407 Hammer, Plumb Line and Hook (post-war reconstruction)

1997. 350th Anniv of Postal Service (3rd issue). Post-war History. Multicoloured.

1283 3k.70 Type **407** 70 75
1284 3k.70 "Kon Tiki" (replica of balsa raft) (Thor Heyerdahl's expedition from Peru to Polynesia, 1947) 70 75
1285 3k.70 Grouse feather (official bird of Rondane National Park (first National Park, 1962)) . . 70 75
1286 3k.70 Hands of man and woman (Welfare State (introduction of National Insurance, 1967)) 70 75
1287 3k.70 Drilling platform, Ekofisk oil field (discovery of oil in Norwegian sector of North Sea, 1969) . . . 70 75
1288 3k.70 Grete Waitz (first women's world Marathon champion, 1983) 70 75
1289 3k.70 Askoy Bridge, 1992 (communications) 70 75
1290 3k.70 Crown Prince Haakon Magnus lighting Olympic flame (Winter Olympic Games, Lillehammer, 1994) 70 75

1997. Tourism. As T **395**. Multicoloured.

1291 4k.30 Roros 70 90
1292 5k. Faerder Lighthouse . . 75 60
1293 6k. Nusfjord . . . . 1·20 45

408 University, Cathedral, Statue of King Olav, City Gate and Broadcasting Tower

409 Gerhardsen and Storting (Parliament House)

1997. Millenary of Trondheim. Multicoloured.

1294 3k.70 Type **408** 60 25
1295 12k. Trees, mine, King Olav, pilgrims, burning buildings and harbour . . 2·00 1·20

1997. Birth Centenary of Einar Gerhardsen (Prime Minister 1945–51, 1955–63 and 1963–65).

1296 **409** 3k.70 black, stone and red 60 25
1297 – 25k. black, flesh and green . . . . 4·00 1·90

DESIGN: 25k. Gerhardsen, mountain, factory and electricity pylon.

410 Thematic Subjects

411 Harald Saeverud (composer)

1997. Inauguration of National Junior Stamp Club. Multicoloured.
1298 3k.70 Type **410** 60 25
1299 3k.70 Thematic subjects including fish and tiger . . 60 25

1997. Birth Centenaries.
1300 **411** 10k. blue . . . . 1·60 95
1301 – 15k. green . . . . 2·75 1·40
DESIGN: 15k. Tarjei Vesaas (writer).

412 Dass in Rowing Boat

1997. 350th Birth Anniv of Petter Dass (priest and poet). Multicoloured.
1302 **412** 3k.20 blue and brown . . 60 45
1303 – 3k.70 green, blue and brown 60 25
DESIGN: 3k.70, Dass and Alstahaug Church.

413 Golden Calendar Stick Symbols against Candle Flames

414 Roses

1997. Christmas. Multicoloured. Self-adhesive.
1304 3k.70 Type **413** 60 40
1305 3k.70 Silver calendar stick symbols against night sky 60 40

1998. Insects (2nd series). As T **404**. Multicoloured.
1306 3k.80 Dragonfly 60 25
1307 3k.80 Grasshopper 60 25

1998. St. Valentine's Day. Self-adhesive.
1308 **414** 3k.80 multicoloured . . 75 35

415 "Hornelen" (passenger and mail steamer)

416 Holmenkollen Ski Jump, Oslo

1998. Nordic Countries' Postal Co-operation. Ships.
1309 **415** 3k.80 blue and green . . 60 25
1310 – 4k.50 green and blue . . 75 65
DESIGN: No. 1310, "Kommandoren" (passenger catamaran).

1998. Tourist Sights. Multicoloured.
1311 3k.80 Type **416** 60 40
1312 4k.50 Fisherman, Alesund Harbour 75 90
1313 5k.50 Mt Hamaroyskaftet 95 95

417 Egersund Harbour

1998. Bicentenary of Egersund.
1314 **417** 3k.80 blue and pink . . 30 35
1315 – 6k. blue and mauve . . 1·00 45
DESIGN: No. 1315, Egersund ceramics.

418 Silver

1998. Minerals. Multicoloured.
1316 3k.40 Type **418** 60 40
1317 5k.20 Cobalt 95 55

419 "Water Rider" (Frans Widerberg)

1998. Contemporary Art. Multicoloured.
1318 6k. Type **419** . . . . . . 1·00 65
1319 7k.50 "Red Moon" (carpet, Synnove Anker Aurdal) 1·20 80
1320 13k. "King Haakon VII" (sculpture, Nils Aas) . . . 2·20 1·50

420 Hopscotch

1998. Children's Games (1st series). Multicoloured.
1321 3k.80 Type **420** 60 25
1322 5k.50 Throwing coins at a stick 95 80
See also Nos 1355/6.

421 Boeing 747, Douglas DC-3 and Junkers Ju 52 Airliners

1998. Inauguration of Oslo Airport, Gardermoen. Multicoloured.
1323 3k.80 Type **421** 45 25
1324 6k. Boeing 737 airliner and map of former approaches to Gardermoen Airport 1·00 60
1325 24k. Terminal building, control tower and wings drawn by Leonardo da Vinci . . . . 3·75 2·10

422 Main Entrance and Guard

1998. 150th Anniv of Royal Palace, Oslo.
1326 **422** 3k.40 purple 60 50
1327 – 3k.80 blue, pink and yellow 70 25
DESIGN: 3k.80, Main front of palace.

423 Music Score

424 Cheese Slicer (Thor Bjorklund)

1998. Christmas. Multicoloured. Self-adhesive.
1328 3k.80 Type **423** (red background) 65 25
1329 3k.80 Music score (blue background) 65 25

1999. Norwegian Inventions. Self-adhesive.
1330 **424** 3k.60 black and blue . . 60 30
1331 – 4k. black and red . . . 70 30
1332 – 4k.20 black and green 70 25
DESIGNS: 4k. Paper clip (Johan Vaaler); 4k.20 Aerosol can (Erik Rotheim).

425 Salmon and Fly

1999. Fishes and Fishing Flies. Multicoloured. Self-adhesive.
1333 4k. Type **425** 70 25
1334 4k. Cod and fly 70 30

426 Heart blowing Flowers out of Posthorn

427 "The Pioneer" (statue, Per Palle Storm)

1999. St. Valentine's Day.
1335 **426** 4k. multicoloured . . . 70 40

1999. Centenary of Norwegian Confederation of Trade Unions.
1336 **427** 4k. multicoloured . . . 70 25

428 Poland v Norway, Class B Championship, 1998

1999. World Ice Hockey Championships, Norway. Multicoloured.
1337 4k. Type **428** 70 65
1338 7k. Switzerland v Sweden, Class A Championship, 1998 . . . . 1·20 65

429 Mute Swans

1999. Tourism. Multicoloured.
1339 4k. Type **429** 70 65
1340 5k. Hamar Cathedral . . . 75 45
1341 6k. Sami man from Troms 1·00 35

430 Emigration

1999. "Norway 2000" (1st issue). Norwegian History. Multicoloured.
1342 4k. Type **430** 70 55
1343 6k. King Olav and Bible (conversion to Christianity, 11th century) 1·00 95
1344 14k. Medal of King Christian IV and quarry workers (union of Norway and Denmark) 2·30 1·90
1345 26k. Oslo at Beier Bridge, 1850s (industrialization) 4·25 90

431 Horse Ferry, Amli, East Agder, 1900

1999. "Norway 2000" (2nd issue). Photographs of Everyday Life. Multicoloured.
1346 4k. Type **431** . . . . . . 65 16·00
1347 4k. Men hewing rock during construction of Valdres railway line, 1900 . . . . 65 16·00
1348 4k. Taxi driver Aarseth Odd filling up car with petrol, Kleive, 1930 . . . . . . 65 16·00
1349 4k. Dairymaid Mathea Isaksen milking cow, Karmoy, 1930 . . . . . 65 16·00
1350 4k. Haymakers, Hemsedal, 1943 . . . . 65 16·00
1351 4k. Cross-country skier Dagfinn Knutsen, 1932 65 16·00
1352 4k. "Bolgen" (coastal fishing boat), Varanger Fjord, 1977 . . . . 65 16·00
1353 4k. Boy Jon Andre Koch holding football, 1981 . . 65 16·00
MS1354 136 × 148 mm. Nos. 1346/53 5·00 6·00

432 Skateboarding

434 Family bringing in Logs

433 Wenche Foss and Per Haugen in "An Ideal Husband" (Oscar Wilde)

1999. Children's Games (2nd series). Multicoloured.
1355 4k. Type **432** 70 75
1356 6k. Inline skating . . . . . 1·00 60

1999. Centenary of National Theatre.
1357 **433** 3k.60 purple and orange 60 60
1358 – 4k. ultramarine and blue 70 50
DESIGN: 4k. Toralv Maurstad and Tore Segelcke in "Per Gynt" (Henrik Ibsen).

1999. Christmas. Multicoloured. Self-adhesive.
1359 4k. Type **434** 70 50
1360 4k. Family sitting by window 70 30

435 "Sunset" (Sverre Simonsen)

1999. Year 2000. Winning entries in photographic competition. Multicoloured. Self-adhesive.
1361 4k. Type **435** 75 45
1362 4k. "Winter Nights" (Poul Christensen) 75 40

436 Eye within Heart

2000. St. Valentine's Day.
1363 **436** 4k. multicoloured . . . 70 30

437 "Angry Child" (statue, Gustav Vigeland)

2000. Millenary of Oslo City. Multicoloured.
1364 4k. Type **437** 70 70
1365 6k. Christian IV statue . . . 1·00 95
1366 8k. City Hall and clock face 1·50 2·20
1367 27k. Oslo Stock Exchange and Mercury (statue) . . 4·75 1·30

438 Golden Eagle

2000. Endangered Species. Multicoloured.
1368 5k. Type **438** 95 80
1369 6k. European moose . . . . 1·00 60
1370 7k. Sperm whale . . . . . 1·30 40

439 "Power and Energy"

2000. "EXPO 2000" World's Fair, Hanover, Germany. Paintings by Marianne Heske. Mult.
1371 4k.20 "The Quiet Room" 70 45
1372 6k.30 Type **439** . . . . . 1·10 60

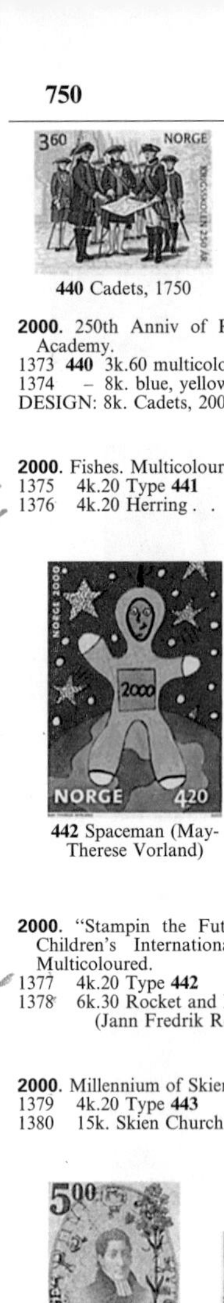

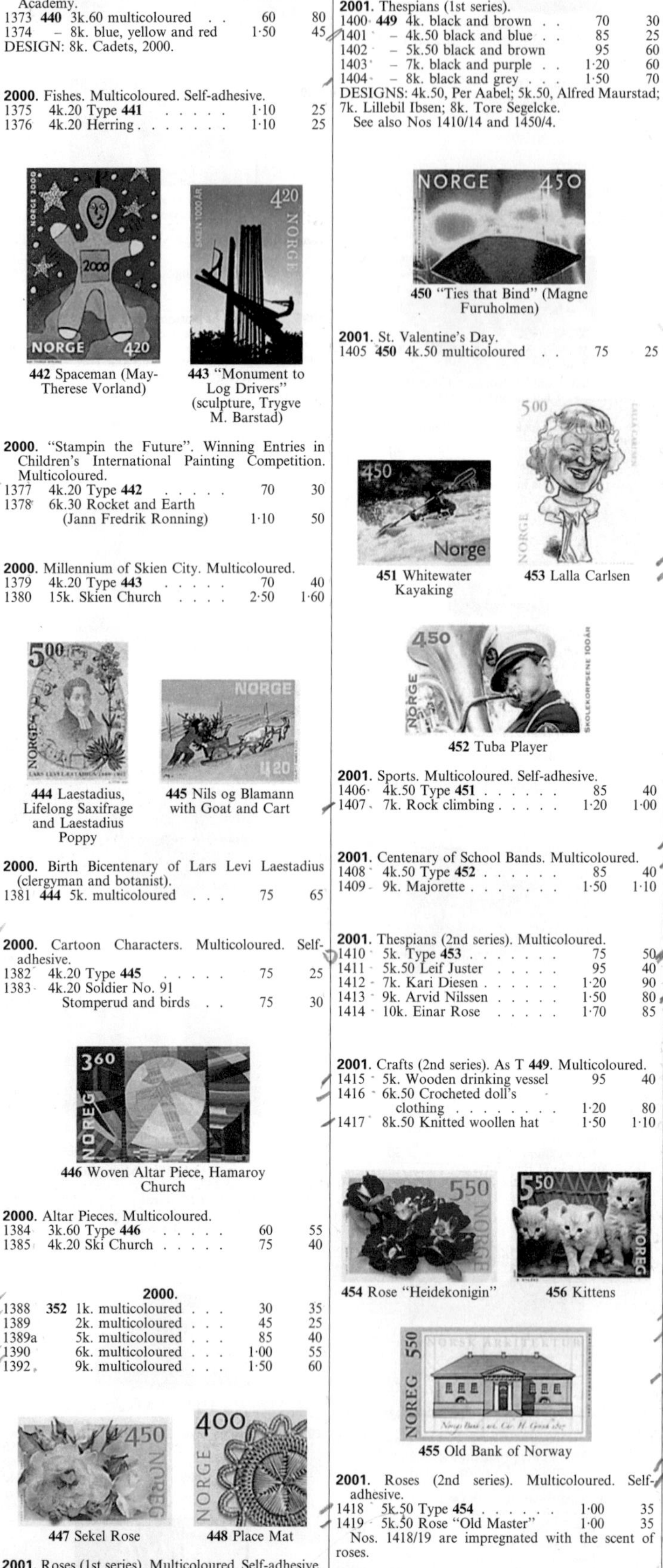

440 Cadets, 1750

441 Mackerel

2000. 250th Anniv of Royal Norwegian Military Academy.
1373 **440** 3k.60 multicoloured . . 60 80
1374 – 8k. blue, yellow and red 1·50 45
DESIGN: 8k. Cadets, 2000.

2000. Fishes. Multicoloured. Self-adhesive.
1375 4k.20 Type **441** . . . . . 1·10 25
1376 4k.20 Herring . . . . 1·10 25

442 Spaceman (May-Therese Vorland)

443 "Monument to Log Drivers" (sculpture, Trygve M. Barstad)

2000. "Stampin the Future". Winning Entries in Children's International Painting Competition. Multicoloured.
1377 4k.20 Type **442** 70 30
1378 6k.30 Rocket and Earth (Jann Fredrik Ronning) 1·10 50

2000. Millennium of Skien City. Multicoloured.
1379 4k.20 Type **443** 70 40
1380 15k. Skien Church . . . . 2·50 1·60

444 Laestadius, Lifelong Saxifrage and Laestadius Poppy

445 Nils og Blamann with Goat and Cart

2000. Birth Bicentenary of Lars Levi Laestadius (clergyman and botanist).
1381 **444** 5k. multicoloured . . . 75 65

2000. Cartoon Characters. Multicoloured. Self-adhesive.
1382 4k.20 Type **445** 75 25
1383 4k.20 Soldier No. 91 Stomperud and birds . . 75 30

446 Woven Altar Piece, Hamaroy Church

2000. Altar Pieces. Multicoloured.
1384 3k.60 Type **446** 60 55
1385 4k.20 Ski Church 75 40

2000.
1388 **352** 1k. multicoloured . . . 30 35
1389 2k. multicoloured . . . 45 25
1389a 5k. multicoloured . . . 85 40
1390 6k. multicoloured . . . 1·00 55
1392 9k. multicoloured . . . 1·50 60

447 Sekel Rose

448 Place Mat

2001. Roses (1st series). Multicoloured. Self-adhesive.
1395 4k.50 Type **447** 75 70
1396 4k.50 Namdal rose 75 55
See also Nos 1418/19 and 1491/2.

2001. Crafts (1st series). Multicoloured. Self-adhesive.
1397 4k. Type **448** 70 25
1398 4k.50 Pot with lid 85 35
1399 7k. Bunad (woven cloth) . . 1·20 55
See also Nos. 1415/17.

449 Aase Bye

2001. Thespians (1st series).
1400 **449** 4k. black and brown . . 70 30
1401 – 4k.50 black and blue . . 85 25
1402 – 5k.50 black and brown 95 60
1403 – 7k. black and purple . . 1·20 60
1404 – 8k. black and grey . . . 1·50 70
DESIGNS: 4k.50, Per Aabel; 5k.50, Alfred Maurstad; 7k. Lillebil Ibsen; 8k. Tore Segelcke.
See also Nos 1410/14 and 1450/4.

450 "Ties that Bind" (Magne Furuholmen)

2001. St. Valentine's Day.
1405 **450** 4k.50 multicoloured . . 75 25

451 Whitewater Kayaking

453 Lalla Carlsen

452 Tuba Player

2001. Sports. Multicoloured. Self-adhesive.
1406 4k.50 Type **451** 85 40
1407 7k. Rock climbing . . . . . 1·20 1·00

2001. Centenary of School Bands. Multicoloured.
1408 4k.50 Type **452** 85 40
1409 9k. Majorette . . . . 1·50 1·10

2001. Thespians (2nd series). Multicoloured.
1410 5k. Type **453** 75 50
1411 5k.50 Leif Juster 95 40
1412 7k. Kari Diesen . . . . . . 1·20 90
1413 9k. Arvid Nilssen . . . . . 1·50 80
1414 10k. Einar Rose . . . . . 1·70 85

2001. Crafts (2nd series). As T **449**. Multicoloured.
1415 5k. Wooden drinking vessel 95 40
1416 6k.50 Crocheted doll's clothing . . . . . . 1·20 80
1417 8k.50 Knitted woollen hat 1·50 1·10

454 Rose "Heidekonigin"

456 Kittens

455 Old Bank of Norway

2001. Roses (2nd series). Multicoloured. Self-adhesive.
1418 5k.50 Type **454** . . . . . 1·00 35
1419 5k.50 Rose "Old Master" 1·00 35
Nos. 1418/19 are impregnated with the scent of roses.

2001. Norwegian Architecture. Multicoloured.
1420 5k.50 Type **455** 95 35
1421 8k.50 Ivar Aasen Centre . . 1·50 75

2001. Pets. Multicoloured.
1422 5k.50 Type **456** . . . . . 1·00 45
1423 7k.50 Goat . . . . 1·40 70

457 Aung San Suu Kyi (Burmese opposition leader), 1991

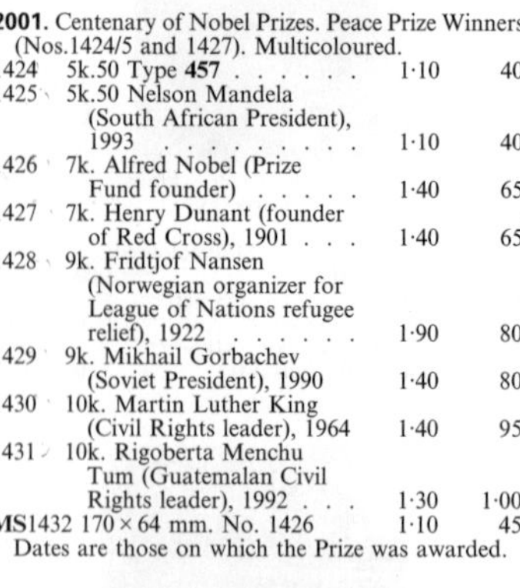

2001. Centenary of Nobel Prizes. Peace Prize Winners (Nos.1424/5 and 1427). Multicoloured.
1424 5k.50 Type **457** . . . . . 1·10 40
1425 5k.50 Nelson Mandela (South African President), 1993 . . . . 1·10 40
1426 7k. Alfred Nobel (Prize Fund founder) . . . 1·40 65
1427 7k. Henry Dunant (founder of Red Cross), 1901 . . . 1·40 65
1428 9k. Fridtjof Nansen (Norwegian organizer for League of Nations refugee relief), 1922 . . . . . 1·90 80
1429 9k. Mikhail Gorbachev (Soviet President), 1990 1·40 80
1430 10k. Martin Luther King (Civil Rights leader), 1964 1·40 95
1431 10k. Rigoberta Menchu Tum (Guatemalan Civil Rights leader), 1992 . . . 1·30 1·00
MS1432 170 × 64 mm. No. 1426 1·10 45
Dates are those on which the Prize was awarded.

458 Snow-covered Trees and Lights

2001. Northern Lights. Multicoloured.
1433 5k. Type **458** 95 45
1434 5k.50 Lights and reindeer 1·00 50

459 Gingerbread Man

460 Tordis Maurstad

2001. Christmas. Multicoloured. Self-adhesive.
1435 5k.50 Type **459** . . . . . 1·10 40
1436 5k.50 Gingerbread house . . 1·10 40

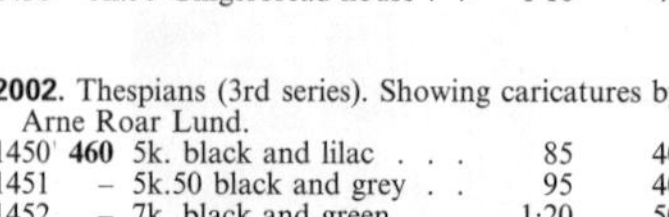

2002. Thespians (3rd series). Showing caricatures by Arne Roar Lund.
1450 **460** 5k. black and lilac . . . 85 40
1451 – 5k.50 black and grey . . 95 40
1452 – 7k. black and green . . 1·20 50
1453 – 9k. black and green . . 1·50 60
1454 – 10k. black and brown . . 1·70 70
DESIGNS: 5k.50 Rolf Just Nilsen; 7k. Lars Tvinde; 9k. Henry Gleditsch; 10k. Norma Balean.

461 Boys tackling

462 Scene from "Askeladden and the Good Helpers"

2002. Centenary of Norwegian Football Association (1st issue). Multicoloured. Self-adhesive.
1455 5k.50 Type **461** 90 40
1456 5k.50 German referee Peter Hertel and player 90 40
1457 5k.50 Girls tackling 90 40
1458 5k.50 Boy kicking ball . . . 90 40
See also Nos. 1469/**MS**1475.

2002. Fairytale Characters. Multicoloured. Self-adhesive.
1459 5k.50 Type **462** 90 40
1460 9k. Giant troll (drawing by Theodor Kittelsen) . . . 1·50 60

463 "Monument to Whaling"

2002. Nordic Countries' Postal Co-operation. Modern Art. Sculptures. Multicoloured.
1461 7k.50 Type **463** . . . . . 1·30 50
1462 8k.50 "Throw" (Kåre Groven) . . . . 1·40 55

464 Holmestrand

2002. City Charter Anniversaries. Multicoloured.
1463 5k.50 Type **464** (300th anniv) 90 40
1464 5k.50 Kongsberg (200th anniv) 90 40

465 Abel

2002. Birth Bicentenary of Niels Henrik Abel (mathematician). Multicoloured.
1465 5k.50 Type **465** 90 40
1466 22k. Mathematical rosette 3·75 2·25

466 Johan Borgen

468 Clown on Tightrope

467 Norwegian Team (Olympic Games, Berlin, 1936)

2002. Writers' Birth Centenaries. Portraits by Nils Aas.
1467 **466** 11k. yellow and green . . 1·80 75
1468 – 20k. green and blue . . 3·50 2·00
DESIGN: 20k. Nordahl Grieg.

2002. Centenary of Norwegian Football Association (2nd issue). Multicoloured.
1469 5k. Type **467** 85 35
1470 5k.50 No. 9 player and Brazil No. 4 player (World Cup, France, 1998) 90 35
1471 5k.50 Norway and U. S. A. women players (Olympic Games, Sydney, 2000)) . . 90 35
1472 7k. Player capturing ball from Sweden No. 11 player (Norway–Sweden, 1960) . . . . 1·20 45
1473 9k. Player with chevron sleeves (Norway–England, 1981) . . . . 1·50 60
1474 10k. Winning team members (Rosenborg–Milan (Champions League, 1996)) . . . . 1·70 65
MS1475 140 × 127 mm. Nos. 1469/74 7·00 7·00

2002. Europa. Circus. Multicoloured.
1476 5k.50 Type **468** 90 35
1477 8k.50 Elephant, horse and chimpanzee . . . . 1·40 55

2002. "Nordia 2002" Nordic Stamp Exhibition, Kristiansand. Nos. 1465/6 surch **NORDIC 2002**.
1478 5k.50 multicoloured 90 35
1479 22k. multicoloured . . . . 3·75 2·20

470 Landstad on Horseback and Frontispiece of "Norske Folkeviser"

2002. Birth Bicentenary of Magnus Brostrup Landstad (folk-song collector and hymn writer). Multicoloured.
1480 5k. Type **470** 85 35
1481 5k.50 Landstad and frontispiece of Kirkefalmebog 90 35

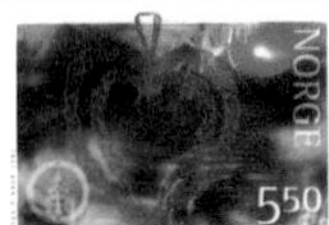

471 Straw Heart-shaped Decoration

2002. Christmas. Multicoloured. Self-adhesive.
1482 5k.50 Type **471** 90 35
1483 5k.50 Paper star-shaped decoration 90 35

472 "Nordmandens Krone" (Kare Espolin Johnson)

2003. Graphic Art (1st series). Multicoloured.
1484 5k. Type **472** 85 35
1485 8k.50 "Bla Hester" (Else Hagen) . . . . 1·40 55
1486 9k. "Dirigent og Solist" (Niclas Gulbrandsen) . . 1·50 60
1487 11k. "Olympia" (Svein Strand) . . . . 1·80 75
1488 22k. "Still Life XVII" (Rigmor Hansen) . . . . 3·75 2·20
See also Nos. 1515/16.

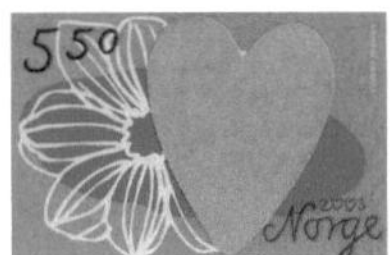

473 Heart

2002. St. Valentine.
1489 **473** 5k.50 multicoloured . . 90 35

474 Doudji Knife Handle (Havard Larsen)

475 Rose "Grand Prix"

2003. Crafts. Coil stamp. Self-adhesive.
1490 **474** 5k.50 multicoloured . . 90 35

2003. Roses (3rd series). Multicoloured. Self-adhesive.
1491 5k.50 Type **475** 90 35
1492 5k.50 Rose "Champagne" 90 35

476 Operating Theatre

477 Forest Troll

2003. 400th Anniv of Public Health Service. Multicoloured.
1493 5k.50 Type **476** 85 35
1494 7k. Doctor examining baby 1·10 45

2003. Fairytale Characters (2nd series). Showing drawings by Theodor Kittelsen. Self-adhesive. Multicoloured.
1495 5k.50 Type **477** 85 35
1496 9k. Water sprite (horiz) . . 1·40 45

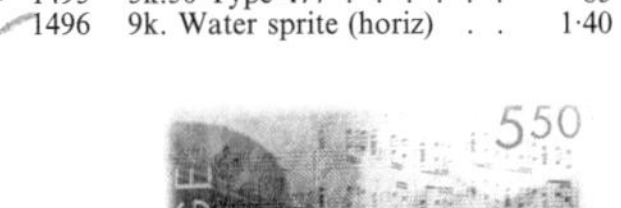

478 Hand and Violin

2003. Bergen International Festival. Multicoloured.
1497 5k.50 Type **478** 85 35
1498 10k. Children's faces . . . . 1·60 65

479 Child holding Bread

2003. World Refugee Day. Multicoloured.
1499 5k.50 Type **479** 85 35
1500 10k. Refugees . . . . 1·60 65

480 Crown Prince Olav as a Child

482 Dagbladet (Per Krohg)

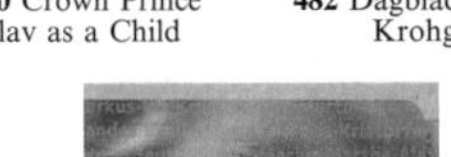

481 Baby

2003. Birth Centenary of King Olav V (1903–1991). Multicoloured.
1501 5k.50 Type **480** 85 35
1502 8k.50 Crown Prince Olav and Crown Princess Martha . . . . 1·40 60
1503 11k. King Olav V . . . . . 1·80 75
MS1504 170 × 101 mm. Nos. 1501/3 4·00 4·00

2003. Greetings Stamps. Multicoloured. Self-adhesive.
1505 5k.50 Type **481** 85 35
1506 5k.50 Hand wearing ring . . 85 35
1507 5k.50 Lily 85 35
1508 5k.50 Couple 85 35
1509 5k.50 Children and cake . . 85 35

2003. Europa. Poster Art. Multicoloured.
1510 8k.50 Type **482** . . . . . . 1·40 60
1511 9k. Winter Olympics, Oslo (Knut Yran) . . . . . . 1·50 60
1512 10k. Music festival (Willibald Storn) . . . . 1·60 65

483 Bjornstjerne Bjornson (literature, 1903)

2003. Norwegian Nobel Prize Winners. Multicoloured.
1513 11k. Type **483** . . . . . . 1·80 70
1514 22k. Lars Onsager (chemistry, 1968) . . . . 3·50 1·40

484 "Winter Landscape 1980" (Terje Grostad)

2003. Graphic Art (2nd series). Multicoloured.
1515 5k. Type **484** 80 30
1516 5k.50 "Goatherd and Goats" (Rolf Nesch) . . . 85 35

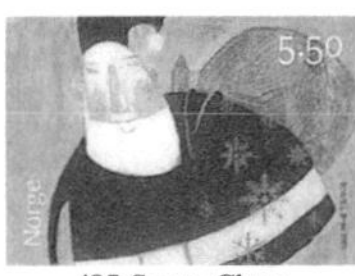

485 Santa Claus

2003. Christmas. Self-adhesive gum. Multicoloured.
1517 5k.50 Type **485** 85 35
1518 5k.50 Present 85 35

OFFICIAL STAMPS

O 22 O 36

1925.
O187 **O 22** 5ore mauve 70 65
O188 10ore green 35 20
O189 15ore blue . . . . . . 1·50 1·70
O190 20ore purple 40 20
O191 30ore grey . . . . . . 2·00 3·25
O192 40ore blue . . . . . . 1·00 1·00
O193 60ore blue . . . . . . 3·50 3·75

1929. Surch **2 2**.
O219 **O 22** 2ore on 5ore mauve 40 60

1933.
O231 **O 36** 2ore brown . . . . . 55 1·10
O243 5ore purple . . . . . 75 1·10
O233 7ore orange . . . . . 4·25 4·50
O245 10ore green 60 30
O235 15ore green 65 45
O247 20ore red 75 30
O237 25ore brown 50 50
O238 30ore blue 65 50
O248 35ore violet 60 40
O249 40ore grey 90 50
O250 60ore blue 90 80
O241 70ore brown . . . . . 1·10 1·70
O242 100ore blue . . . . . 1·25 1·50

O 39 O 58 Quisling Emblem

1937.
O267 **O 39** 5ore mauve 25 25
O268 7ore orange 40 60
O269 10ore green 25 20
O270 15ore brown 25 20
O271 20ore red 25 20
O260 25ore brown 95 65
O273 25ore red 25 20
O261 30ore blue 70 60
O275 30ore grey 80 40
O276 35ore purple 40 25
O277 40ore grey 40 25
O278 40ore blue . . . . . . 2·75 25
O279 50ore lilac 60 20
O280 60ore blue 45 20
O281 100ore blue . . . . . 1·10 35
O282 200ore orange . . . . 1·40 30

1942.
O336 **O 58** 5ore mauve . . . . . 70 1·30
O337 7ore orange . . . . . 70 1·30
O338 10ore green 20 25
O339 15ore brown . . . . . 1·40 9·25
O340 20ore red 20 25
O341 25ore brown . . . . . 2·50 13·50
O342 30ore blue . . . . . . 2·10 12·00
O343 35ore purple . . . . . 2·10 7·25
O344 40ore grey 35 30
O345 60ore blue . . . . . . 1·90 6·75
O346 1k. blue . . . . 2·10 9·50

1949. Surch **25** and bar.
O402 **O 39** 25ore on 20ore red . . 30 30

O 89

O 99

1951.
O434 **O 89** 5ore mauve 60 20
O435 10ore grey 60 10
O436 15ore brown 75 35
O437 30ore red 60 10
O438 35ore brown 90 45
O439 60ore blue 90 25
O440 100ore violet . . . . . 2·10 35

1955.
O458 **O 99** 5ore purple 20 15
O459 10ore grey 20 15
O460 15ore brown . . . . . 45 1·30
O461 20ore green 50 15
O736 25ore green 20 20
O463 30ore red . . . . . . 1·40 55
O464 30ore green . . . . . 1·25 20
O465 35ore red 45 15
O466 40ore lilac 60 15
O467 40ore green 30 75
O468 45ore red . . . . . . 1·00 15
O469 50ore brown . . . . . 1·60 25
O470 50ore red 95 25
O471 50ore blue 45 25
O738 50ore grey 20 25
O739 60ore blue . . . . . . 85 3·50
O473 60ore red 50 15
O475 65ore red 75 30
O476 70ore brown . . . . . 3·00 65
O477 70ore red 20 20
O478 75ore purple . . . . . 9·00 9·00
O479 75ore green 60 55
O481 80ore brown 55 20
O741 80ore red 30 15
O482 85ore brown . . . . . 60 1·60
O483 90ore orange 70 15
O484 1k. violet 70 15
O485 1k. red 20 15
O486 1k.10 red 60 55
O744 1k.25 red 60 15
O745 1k.30 purple . . . . . 95 1·20
O746 1k.50 red 45 15
O747 1k.75 green . . . . . 1·00 1·00
O748 2k. green 50 15
O749 2k. red 60 15
O750 3k. violet 85 45
O488 5k. violet . . . . . . 9·75 6·00
O752 5k. blue 70 25

POSTAGE DUE STAMPS

D 12

1889. Inscr "at betale" and "PORTOMAERKE".
D95 **D 12** 1ore green 70 75
D96a 4ore mauve 95 45
D97 10ore red . . . . . . 5·25 40
D98 15ore brown . . . . . 5·00 60
D99 20ore blue . . . . . 5·50 35
D94 50ore purple . . . . . 3·00 1·30

1922. Inscr "a betale" and "PORTOMERKE".
D162 **D 12** 4ore purple . . . . . 4·75 6·50
D163 10ore green . . . . . 3·50 1·10
D164 20ore purple . . . . . 5·25 3·00
D165 40ore blue . . . . . 10·50 60
D166 100ore yellow . . . . 38·00 6·75
D167 200ore violet . . . . 46·00 16·00

NOSSI-BE Pt. 6

An island north-west of Madagascar, declared a French protectorate in 1840. In 1901 it became part of Madagascar and Dependencies.

100 centimes = 1 franc.

1889. Stamp of French Colonies, "Peace and Commerce" type, surch.
8 H 25c. on 40c. red on yellow . . £1600 £550

1889. Stamps of French Colonies, "Commerce" type, surch.
4 J 5c. on 10c. black on lilac . . . £1900 £550
2 5c. on 20c. red on green . . . £2250 £750
6 15 on 20c. red on green . . . £1900 £550
7 25 on 30c. brown on drab . . £1600 £450
9 25 on 40c. red on yellow . . . £1600 £450

1890. Stamps of French Colonies, "Commerce" type, surch. (a) **N S B 0 25**.
10 J 0 25 on 20c. red on green . . £275 £200
11 0 25 on 75c. red on pink . . £275 £200
12 0 25 on 1f. green £275 £200

(b) **N S B 25 c**.
13 J 25c. on 20c. red on green . . £275 £200
14 25c. on 75c. red on pink . . £250 £200
15 25c. on 1f. green £250 £200

(c) **N S B 25** in frame.
16 J 25 on 20c. red on green . . . £650 £450
17 25 on 75c. red on pink . . . £650 £450
18 25 on 1f. green £650 £450

1893. Stamps of French Colonies, "Commerce" type, surch **NOSSI-BE** and bar over value in figures.
36 J 25 on 20c. red on green . . . 29·00 26·00
37 50 on 10c. black on lilac . . 35·00 26·00
38 75 on 15c. blue £170 £140
39 1f. on 5c. green . . . . . . 75·00 60·00

1893. Stamps of French Colonies, "Commerce" type, optd **Nossi Be**.
40a J 10c. black on lilac . . . . . 16·00 6·50
41 15c. blue . . . . 16·00 15·00
42 20c. red on green . . . . . 75·00 44·00

1894. "Tablet" key-type inscr "NOSSI-BE" in red (1, 5, 15, 25, 75c., 1f.) or blue (others).
44 D 1c. black on blue . . . . . 1·10 90
45 2c. brown on buff . . . . . 1·25 1·75
46 4c. brown on grey . . . . . 2·00 2·50
47 5c. green on green . . . . . 2·00 1·75
48 10c. black on lilac . . . . . 2·50 2·75
49 15c. blue . . . . 7·75 3·00
50 20c. red on green . . . . . 7·50 5·00
51 25c. black on pink . . . . . 8·75 6·75
52 30c. brown on drab . . . . 9·25 7·75
53 40c. red on yellow . . . . . 12·50 10·00
54 50c. red on pink . . . . . . 8·25 7·00
55 75c. brown on orange . . . 29·00 11·50
56 1f. green . . . . 12·00 18·00

POSTAGE DUE STAMPS

1891. Stamps of French Colonies, "Commerce" type, surch **NOSSI-BE chiffre-taxe A PERCEVOIR** and value.
D19 J 0.20 on 1c. black on blue £225 £160
D20 0.30 on 2c. brown on buff £225 £160
D21 0.35 on 4c. brown on grey £250 £180
D22 0.35 on 20c. red on green £275 £180
D23 0.50 on 30c. brn on drab 65·00 55·00
D24 1f. on 35c. black on orge £150 £100

1891. Stamps of French Colonies, "Commerce" type, surch **Nossi-Be A PERCEVOIR** and value.
D25 J 5c. on 20c. red on green . . £120 £120
D26 10c. on 15c. blue on blue £130 £130
D33 0.10 on 5c. green . . . . . 16·00 11·00
D27 15c. on 10c. black on lilac 90·00 90·00
D34 0.15 on 20c. red on green 18·00 20·00
D28 25c. on 5c. green on green 90·00 90·00
D35 0.25 on 75c. red on pink . . £375 £350

NOVA SCOTIA Pt. 1

An eastern province of the Dominion of Canada, whose stamps it now uses.

Currency: As Canada.

1

2 Emblem of the United Kingdom

1853. Imperf.
1 **1** 1d. brown £2000 £400
4 **2** 3d. blue £750 £140
5 6d. green £4000 £450
8 1s. purple £14000 £2750

3

4

1860. Perf.
9 **3** 1c. black 3·50 13·00
20 2c. purple 3·50 14·00
13 5c. blue £375 17·00
26 **4** 8½c. green 17·00 40·00
28 10c. red 6·00 25·00
17 12½c. black 28·00 26·00

NYASALAND PROTECTORATE Pt. 1

A British Protectorate in central Africa. Formerly known as British Central Africa. From 1954 to 1963 part of the Central African Federation using the stamps of Rhodesia and Nyasaland (q.v.). From July 1964 independent within the Commonwealth under its new name of Malawi.

12 pence = 1 shilling;
20 shillings = 1 pound.

1891. Stamps of Rhodesia optd **B.C.A.**
1 **1** 1d. black 5·00 4·75
2 2d. green and red 5·00 4·00
3 4d. brown and black 5·50 5·00
5 6d. blue 8·00 8·00
6 8d. red and blue 14·00 28·00
7 1s. brown 15·00 11·00
8 2s. red 26·00 50·00
9 2s.6d. purple 65·00 85·00
10 3s. brown and green 65·00 65·00
11 4s. black and red 60·00 85·00
12 5s. yellow 70·00 75·00
13 10s. green £140 £190
14 – £1 blue £700 £550
15 – £2 red £900
16 – £5 olive £1500
17 – £10 brown £3250 £4000

1892. Stamps of Rhodesia surch **B.C.A.** and value in words.
18 **1** 3s. on 4s. black and red £325 £325
19 4s. on 5s. yellow 70·00 85·00

1895. No. 2 surch **ONE PENNY.** and bar.
20 **1** 1d. on 2d. green and red 9·00 30·00

5 Arms of the Protectorate

7 Arms of the Protectorate

1895. The 2s.6d. and higher values are larger.
32 **5** 1d. black 3·25 4·75
33 2d. black and green 15·00 5·00
34 4d. black and orange 23·00 17·00
35 6d. black and blue 26·00 13·00
36 1s. black and red 26·00 15·00
37 2s.6d. black and mauve £140 £130
38 3s. black and yellow £100 55·00
39 5s. black and olive £150 £180
29 £1 black and orange £900 £375
40 £1 black and blue £850 £475
30 £10 black and orange £4500 £3750
31 £25 black and green £8000

1897. The 2s.6d. and higher values are larger.
43 **7** 1d. black and blue 3·25 1·25
57d 1d. purple and red 2·50 50
44 2d. black and yellow 2·00 2·00
45 4d. black and red 6·50 1·50
57e 4d. purple and olive 8·50 11·00
46 6d. black and green 45·00 4·25
58 6d. purple and brown 3·75 3·00
47 1s. black and purple 11·00 7·00
48 2s.6d. black and blue 48·00 42·00
49 3s. black and green £190 £225
50 4s. black and red 70·00 80·00
50a 10s. black and olive £140 £150
51 £1 black and purple £275 £160
52 £10 black and yellow £4500 £1700

1897. No. 49 surch **ONE PENNY.**
53 **7** 1d. on 3s. black and green 6·00 9·50

10

11

1898.
56a **10** 1d. red and blue (imperf) £2500 £160
57 1d. red and blue (perf) £2500 21·00

1903. The 2s.6d. and higher values are larger.
59 **11** 1d. grey and red 7·00 1·75
60 2d. purple 3·50 1·00
61 4d. green and black 2·50 9·00
62 6d. grey and brown 3·25 2·00
62b 1s. grey and blue 3·50 11·00
63 2s.6d. green 48·00 75·00
64 4s. purple 65·00 80·00
65 10s. green and black £120 £200
66 £1 grey and red £275 £180
67 £10 grey and blue £4500 £3250

13

14

1908.
73 **13** ½d. green 1·75 2·00
74 1d. red 4·00 1·00
75 3d. purple on yellow 1·50 4·25
76 4d. black and red on yellow 1·50 1·50
77 6d. purple 3·75 11·00
72 1s. black on green 2·75 11·00
78 **14** 2s.6d. black and red on blue 48·00 85·00
79 4s. red and black 80·00 £120
80 10s. green and red on green £120 £225
81 £1 purple and black on red £450 £550
82 £10 purple and blue £7500 £5000

1913. As 1908, but portrait of King George V.
100 ½d. green 1·50 50
101 1d. red 2·25 50
102 1½d. orange 3·25 17·00
103 2d. grey 1·00 50
89 2½d. blue 2·25 7·00
90 3d. purple on yellow 4·50 4·50
91 4d. black and red on yellow 2·00 2·50
107 6d. purple 3·00 3·25
93a 1s. black on green 5·50 1·50
109 2s. purple and blue on blue 15·00 12·00
94 2s.6d. black and red on blue 11·00 13·00
111 4s. red and black 19·00 27·00
112 5s. green and red on yellow 38·00 75·00
96 10s. green and red on green 80·00 £100
98 £1 purple and black on red £180 £140
99e £10 purple and blue £2750 £1700

17 King George V and Symbol of the Protectorate

1934.
114 **17** ½d. green 75 1·25
115 1d. brown 75 75
116 1½d. red 75 3·00
117 2d. grey 80 1·25
118 3d. blue 2·50 1·75
119 4d. mauve 2·50 3·50
120 6d. violet 2·50 50
121 9d. olive 6·00 9·00
122 1s. black and orange 8·50 14·00

1935. Silver Jubilee. As T **14a** of Kenya, Uganda and Tanganyika.
123 1d. blue and grey 1·00 2·00
124 2d. green and blue 1·00 1·25
125 3d. brown and blue 7·00 16·00
126 1s. grey and purple 17·00 42·00

1937. Coronation. As T **14b** of Kenya, Uganda and Tanganyika.
127 ½d. green 30 1·00
128 1d. brown 50 1·00
129 2d. grey 50 2·00

1938. As T **17** but with head of King George VI and "POSTAGE REVENUE" omitted.
130 ½d. green 30 1·50
130a ½d. brown 10 1·75
131 1d. brown 2·75 30
131a 1d. green 30 75
132 1½d. red 4·25 4·50
132a 1½d. grey 30 5·00
133 2d. grey 8·00 1·25
133a 2d. red 30 1·75
134 3d. blue 60 50
135 4d. mauve 2·75 1·25
136 6d. violet 2·75 1·25
137 9d. olive 2·75 2·75
138 1s. black and orange 3·50 1·50

1938. As T **14** but with head of King George VI facing right.
139 2s. purple and blue on blue 10·00 10·00
140 2s.6d. black and red on blue 12·00 12·00
141 5s. green and red on yellow 42·00 20·00
142 10s. green and red on green 50·00 42·00
143 £1 purple and black on red 35·00 28·00

20 Lake Nyasa

21 King's African Rifles

1945.
144 **20** ½d. black and brown 50 10
145 **21** 1d. black and green 20 70
160 – 1d. brown and green 50 20
146 – 1½d. black and grey 30 50
147 – 2d. black and red 1·50 85
148 – 3d. black and blue 20 30
149 – 4d. black and red 1·75 80
150 – 6d. black and violet 1·50 90
151 **20** 9d. black and olive 1·50 3·00
152 – 1s. blue and green 1·50 20
153 – 2s. green and purple 4·50 4·75
154 – 2s.6d. green and blue 7·50 4·75
155 – 5s. purple and blue 4·50 6·50
156 – 10s. red and green 14·00 14·00
157 – 20s. red and black 18·00 27·00

DESIGNS—HORIZ: 1½d., 6d. Tea estate; 2d., 1s., 10s. Map of Nyasaland; 4d., 2s.6d. Tobacco; 5s., 20s. Badge of Nyasaland. VERT: 1d. (No. 160), Leopard and sunrise; 3d., 2s. Fishing village.

1946. Victory. As T **4a** of Pitcairn Islands.
158 1d. green 10 30
159 2d. red 30 10

1948. Silver Wedding. As T **4b/c** of Pitcairn Islands.
161 1d. green 15 10
162 10s. mauve 15·00 26·00

1949. U.P.U. As T **4d/g** of Pitcairn Islands.
163 1d. green 30 20
164 3d. blue 2·00 3·00
165 6d. purple 50 50
166 1s. blue 30 50

27 Arms in 1891 and 1951

1951. Diamond Jubilee of Protectorate.
167 **27** 2d. black and red 1·25 1·50
168 3d. black and blue 1·25 1·50
169 6d. black and violet 1·25 2·00
170 5s. black and blue 3·75 7·00

1953. Rhodes Centenary Exhibition. As T **6** of Northern Rhodesia.
171 6d. violet 50 30

1953. Coronation. As T **4h** of Pitcairn Islands.
172 2d. black and orange 70 80

29 Grading Cotton

1953. As 1945 but with portrait of Queen Elizabeth II as in T **29**. Designs as for corresponding values except where stated.
173 **20** ½d. black and brown 10 1·50
174 – 1d. brn & grn (as No. 160) 65 40
175 – 1½d. black and grey 20 1·90
176a – 2d. black and orange 30 30
177 **29** 2½d. green and black 20 50
178 – 3d. black and red (as 4d.) 30 20
179 – 4½d. black and blue (as 3d.) 30 40
180 – 6d. black and violet 90 1·50
181 **20** 9d. black and olive 1·00 2·50
182 – 1s. blue and green 2·25 50
183 – 2s. green and red 2·00 3·25
184 – 2s.6d. green and blue 3·25 5·00
185 – 5s. purple and blue 7·00 5·00
186 – 10s. red and green 4·50 18·00
187 – 20s. red and black 17·00 26·00

30

32 Mother and Child

34 Tea Industry

1963. Revenue stamps optd **POSTAGE** as in T **30** or surch also.
188 **30** ½d. on 1d. blue 30 30
189 1d. green 30 10
190 2d. red 30 30
191 3d. blue 30 10
192 6d. purple 30 10
193 9d. on 1s. red 40 25
194 1s. purple 45 10
195 2s.6d. black 1·25 2·25
196 5s. brown 3·25 1·50
197 10s. olive 4·50 7·00
198 £1 violet 5·00 7·00

1964.
199 **32** ½d. violet 10 30
200 – 1d. black and green 10 10
201 – 2d. brown 10 10
202 – 3d. brown, green and bistre 10 10
203 – 4d. blue and yellow 20 30
204 **34** 6d. purple, green and blue 70 60
205 – 1s. brown, blue and yellow 15 10
206 – 1s.3d. bronze and brown 3·25 10
207 – 2s.6d. brown and blue 3·25 50
208 – 5s. blue, green, yellow & blk 1·50 1·50
209 – 10s. green, salmon and black 2·50 3·00
210 – £1 brown and yellow 7·00 9·00

DESIGNS—HORIZ (as Type **32**): 1d. Chambo (fish); 2d. Zebu bull; 3d. Groundnuts; 4d. Fishing. (As Type **34**): 1s. Timber; 1s.3d. Turkish tobacco industry; 2s.6d. Cotton industry; 5s. Monkey Bay, Lake Nyasa; 10s. Forestry, Afzelia. VERT (as Type **34**): £1 Nyala.

POSTAGE DUE STAMPS

1950. As Type D **1** of Gold Coast, but inscr "NYASALAND".
D1 1d. red 3·75 23·00
D2 2d. blue 11·00 23·00
D3 3d. green 11·00 6·00
D4 4d. purple 20·00 42·00
D5 6d. orange 27·00 £120

For later issues see **MALAWI**.

NYASSA COMPANY — Pt. 9

In 1894 Portugal granted a charter to the Nyassa Company to administer an area in the Northern part of Mozambique, including the right to issue its own stamps. The lease was terminated in 1929 and the administration was transferred to Mozambique whose stamps were used there.

1898. 1000 reis = 1 milreis.
1913. 100 centavos = 1 escudo.

1898. "Figures" and "Newspaper" key-types inscr "MOCAMBIQUE" optd **NYASSA**.

No.	Type	Description	Unused	Used
1	V	2½r. brown	2·10	1·90
2	R	5r. orange	2·10	1·90
3		10r. mauve	2·10	1·90
4		15r. brown	2·10	1·90
5		20r. lilac	2·10	1·90
6		25r. green	2·10	1·90
7		50r. blue	2·10	1·90
8		75r. pink	2·50	2·30
9		80r. green	2·50	2·30
10		100r. brown on buff	2·50	2·30
11		150r. red on pink	7·50	7·00
12		200r. blue on blue	4·50	4·25
13		300r. blue on brown	6·75	4·25

1898. "King Carlos" key-type inscr "MOCAMBIQUE" optd **NYASSA**.

No.	Type	Description	Unused	Used
14	S	2½r. grey	1·40	1·30
15		5r. red	1·40	1·30
16		10r. green	1·40	1·30
17		15r. brown	1·90	1·60
18		20r. lilac	1·90	1·60
19		25r. green	1·90	1·60
20		50r. blue	1·90	1·60
21		75r. pink	2·10	1·90
22		80r. mauve	2·50	1·40
23		100r. blue on blue	2·50	1·40
24		150r. brown on yellow	2·50	1·40
25		200r. purple on pink	2·50	1·50
26		300r. blue on pink	3·50	1·50

2 Giraffe — 3 Dromedaries

1901.

No.	Type	Description	Unused	Used
27	2	2½r. brown and black	1·30	65
28		5r. violet and black	1·30	65
29		10r. green and black	1·30	65
30		15r. brown and black	1·30	65
31		20r. red and black	1·30	80
32		25r. orange and black	1·30	80
33		50r. blue and black	1·30	80
34	3	75r. red and black	1·50	1·10
35		80r. bistre and black	1·50	1·10
36		100r. brown and black	1·50	1·10
37		150r. brown and black	1·70	1·20
38		200r. green and black	1·70	1·20
39		300r. green and black	1·70	1·20

1903. (a) Surch in figures and words.

No.	Type	Description	Unused	Used
40	3	65r. on 80r. mauve and black	1·20	90
41		115r. on 150r. brown & black	1·20	90
42		130r. on 300r. green & black	1·20	90

(b) Optd **PROVISORIO**.

No.	Type	Description	Unused	Used
43	2	15r. brown and black	1·20	90
44		25r. orange and black	1·20	90

1910. Optd **PROVISORIO** and surch in figures and words.

No.	Type	Description	Unused	Used
50	2	5r. on 2½r. brown and black	1·20	95
51	3	50r. on 100r. bistre and black	1·20	95

9 Dromedaries

12 Vasco de Gama's Flagship "Sao Gabriel"

1911. Optd **REPUBLICA**.

No.	Type	Description	Unused	Used
53	9	2½r. violet and black	1·10	70
54		5r. black	1·10	70
55		10r. green and black	1·10	70
56	–	20r. red and black	1·10	70
57	–	25r. brown and black	1·10	70
58	–	50r. blue and black	1·10	70
59	–	75r. brown and black	1·10	70
60	–	100r. brown & black on green	1·10	70
61	–	200r. green & black on orge	1·30	1·20
62	12	300r. black on blue	2·75	1·90
63		400r. brown and black	3·25	2·10
64		500r. violet and green	4·25	3·25

DESIGNS—HORIZ: 20, 25, 50r. Common zebra. VERT: 75, 100, 200r. Giraffe.

1918. Surch **REPUBLICA** and value in figures.
(a) Stamps of 1901.

No.	Type	Description	Unused	Used
65	2	¼c. on 2½c. brown and black	£150	£110
66		½c. on 5r. violet and black	£150	£110
67		1c. on 10r. green and black	£150	£110
68		1½c. on 15r. brown and black	2·40	1·30
69		2c. on 20r. red and black	4·75	3·50
70		3½c. on 25r. orange and black	1·50	1·10
71		5c. on 50r. blue and black	1·50	1·10
72	3	7½c. on 75r. red and black	1·70	1·10
73		8c. on 80r. mauve and black	1·50	1·10
74		10c. on 100r. bistre and black	1·50	1·10
75		15c. on 150r. brown & black	1·50	1·10
76		20c. on 200r. green and black	1·50	1·10
77		30c. on 300r. green and black	2·50	2·30

(b) Nos. 43/4 and 40/2.

No.	Type	Description	Unused	Used
78	2	1½c. on 15r. brown and black	2·30	2·30
79		3½c. on 25r. orange and black	3·50	2·75
80	3	40c. on 65r. on 80r.	21·00	19·00
81		50c. on 115r. on 150r.	3·00	2·30
82		1c. on 130r. on 300r.	3·00	2·30

1921. Stamps of 1911 surch in figures and words.

No.	Type	Description	Unused	Used
83	9	¼c. on 2½r. violet and black	60	60
85		½c. on 5r. black	60	60
86		1c. on 10r. green and black	60	60
87	12	1½c. on 300r. black on blue	60	60
88	–	2c. on 20r. red and black	60	60
89	–	2½c. on 25r. brown and black	60	60
90	12	3c. on 400r. brown & black	60	60
91	–	5c. on 50r. blue and black	60	60
92	–	7½c. on 75r. brown & black	60	60
93	–	10c. on 100r. brown and black on green	60	60
94	12	12c. on 500r. violet & green	60	60
95	–	20c. on 200r. green and black on orange	60	60

16 Giraffe

19 Common Zebra

1921.

No.	Type	Description	Unused	Used
96	16	¼c. purple	95	80
97		½c. blue	95	80
98		1c. black and green	95	80
99		1½c. orange and black	95	80
100	–	2c. black and red	95	80
101	–	2½c. green and black	95	80
102	–	4c. red and black	95	80
103	–	5c. black and blue	95	80
104	–	6c. violet and black	95	80
123	–	7½c. brown and black	90	65
124	–	8c. green and black	90	65
125	–	10c. brown and black	90	65
126	–	15c. red and black	90	65
127	–	20c. blue and black	90	65
110	19	30c. brown and black	95	80
111		40c. blue and black	95	80
112		50c. green and black	95	80
113		1e. brown and black	95	80
114	–	2e. black and brown	3·75	3·00
115	–	5e. brown and blue	3·50	2·50

DESIGNS—As Type **16**: 2c. to 6c. Vasco da Gama; 7½c. to 20c. Vasco da Gama's flagship "Sao Gabriel". As Type **19**: 2, 5e. Native dhow.

CHARITY TAX STAMPS

The notes under this heading in Portugal also apply here.

1925. Marquis de Pombal Commem. Nos. C327/9 of Mozambique optd **NYASSA**.

No.	Type	Description	Unused	Used
C141	C 22	15c. brown	7·25	6·00
C142	–	15c. brown	7·25	6·00
C143	C 25	15c. brown	7·25	6·00

POSTAGE DUE STAMPS

D 21 "Sao Gabriel"

1924.

No.	Type	Description	Unused	Used
D132	–	½c. green	2·50	2·10
D133	–	1c. blue	2·50	2·10
D134	–	2c. red	2·50	2·10
D135	–	3c. red	2·50	2·10
D136	D 21	5c. brown	2·50	2·10
D137		6c. brown	2·50	2·10
D138		10c. purple	2·50	2·10
D139	–	20c. red	2·50	2·10
D140	–	50c. purple	2·50	2·10

DESIGNS: ½c., 1c. Giraffe; 2c., 3c. Common zebra; 20c., 50c. Vasco da Gama.

1925. De Pombal stamps of Mozambique, Nos. D327/9, optd **NYASSA**.

No.	Type	Description	Unused	Used
D144	C 22	30c. brown	8·75	8·75
D145	–	30c. brown	8·75	8·75
D146	C 25	30c. brown	8·75	8·75

OBOCK — Pt. 6

A port and district on the Somali Coast. During 1894 the administration was moved to Djibouti, the capital of French Somali Coast, and the Obock post office was closed.

1892. Stamps of French Colonies, "Commerce" type, optd **OBOCK**.

No.	Type	Description	Unused	Used
1	J	1c. black on blue	29·00	26·00
2		2c. brown on buff	32·00	29·00
12		4c. brown on grey	17·00	17·00
13		5c. green on green	17·00	17·00
14		10c. black on lilac	19·00	18·00
15		15c. blue	19·00	18·00
16		20c. red on green	38·00	29·00
17		25c. black on pink	16·00	14·50
8		35c. black on orange	£275	£275
18		40c. red on buff	48·00	38·00
19		75c. red on pink	£225	£160
20		1f. green	55·00	50·00

1892. Nos. 14, 15, 17 and 20 surch.

No.	Type	Description	Unused	Used
39	J	1 on 25c. black on red	9·00	11·00
40		2 on 10c. black on lilac	55·00	38·00
41		2 on 15c. blue	9·00	16·00
42		4 on 15c. blue	10·00	17·00
43		4 on 25c. black on red	17·00	16·00
44		5 on 25c. black on red	27·00	20·00
45		20 on 10c. black on lilac	65·00	60·00
46		30 on 10c. black on lilac	75·00	70·00
47		35 on 25c. black on red	70·00	55·00
48		75 on 1f. olive	75·00	75·00
49		5f. on 1f. olive	£550	£475

1892. "Tablet" key-type inscr "OBOCK" in red (1, 5, 15, 25, 75c., 1f.) or blue (others).

No.	Type	Description	Unused	Used
50	D	1c. black on blue	2·75	3·75
51		2c. brown on buff	1·10	1·90
52		4c. brown on grey	1·60	1·75
53		5c. green on green	3·50	4·25
54		10c. black on lilac	6·00	5·25
55		15c. blue	12·00	7·25
56		20c. red on green	22·00	21·00
57		25c. black on pink	20·00	20·00
58		30c. brown on drab	19·00	11·00
59		40c. red on yellow	18·00	10·50
60		50c. red on pink	20·00	13·00
61		75c. brown on orange	25·00	13·00
62		1f. green	32·00	32·00

5

1893.

No.	Type	Description	Unused	Used
63	5	2f. grey	55·00	55·00
64		5f. red	£120	£110

The 5f. stamp is larger than the 2f.

6

7

1894.

No.	Type	Description	Unused	Used
65	6	1c. black and red	35	55
66		2c. red and green	1·90	1·50
67		4c. red and orange	95	1·10
68		5c. green and brown	1·60	75
69		10c. black and green	5·25	4·00
70		15c. blue and red	3·00	1·25
71		20c. orange and purple	6·00	1·40
72		25c. black and blue	8·25	3·00
73		30c. yellow and green	25·00	11·00
74		40c. orange and green	11·50	7·50
75		50c. red and blue	8·50	6·75
76		75c. lilac and orange	9·50	7·00
77		1f. olive and purple	8·25	9·00
78	7	2f. orange and lilac	£110	£110
79		5f. red and blue	90·00	80·00
80		10f. lake and red	£120	£110
81		25f. blue and brown	£600	£575
82		50f. green and lake	£650	£650

Length of sides of Type **7**: 2f. 37 mm; 5f. 42 mm; 10f. 46 mm; 25, 50f. 49 mm.

POSTAGE DUE STAMPS

1892. Postage Due stamps of French Colonies optd **OBOCK**.

No.	Type	Description	Unused	Used
D25	U	1c. black	38·00	45·00
D26		2c. black	32·00	35·00
D27		3c. black	38·00	38·00
D28		4c. black	23·00	27·00
D29		5c. black	13·00	10·50
D30		10c. black	28·00	28·00
D31		15c. black	18·00	17·00
D32		20c. black	22·00	23·00
D33		30c. black	26·00	27·00
D34		40c. black	48·00	45·00
D35		60c. black	60·00	60·00
D36		1f. brown	£150	£150
D37		2f. brown	£160	£160
D38		5f. brown	£325	£325

For later issues see **DJIBOUTI**.

OCEANIC SETTLEMENTS — Pt. 6

Scattered French islands in the E. Pacific Ocean, including Tahiti and the Marquesas.

In 1957 the Oceanic Settlements were renamed French Polynesia.

1892. "Tablet" key-type.

No.	Type	Description	Unused	Used
1	D	1c. black and red on blue	70	50
2		2c. brown and blue on buff	90	1·10
3		4c. brown and blue on grey	1·50	1·25
14		5c. green and red	1·10	55
5		10c. black and blue on lilac	21·00	8·50
15		10c. red and blue	80	55
6		15c. blue and red	15·00	7·25
16		15c. grey and red	1·75	3·25
7		20c. red and blue on green	6·75	9·00
8		25c. black and red on pink	38·00	12·50
17		25c. blue and red	8·00	3·00
9		30c. brown and blue on drab	15·00	11·50
18		35c. black and red on yellow	3·00	3·75
10		40c. red and blue on yellow	90·00	80·00
19		45c. black and red on green	2·75	4·25
11		50c. red and blue on pink	4·25	5·75
20		50c. brown and red on blue	£170	£150
12		75c. brown and red on orange	8·75	10·00
13		1f. green and red	15·00	14·00

2 Tahitian Woman

3 Kanakas

4 Valley of Fautaua

1913.

No.	Type	Description	Unused	Used
21	2	1c. brown and violet	20	45
22		2c. grey and brown	20	1·25
23		4c. blue and orange	30	1·50
24		5c. light green and green	1·25	1·90
46		5c. black and blue	65	2·25
25		10c. orange and red	2·25	2·00
47		10c. light green and green	2·00	2·50
48		10c. purple and red on blue	1·90	2·50
25a		15c. black and orange	2·00	2·25
26		20c. violet and black	65	3·00
49		20c. green	1·90	3·00
50		20c. brown and red	1·90	2·50
27	3	25c. blue and ultramarine	2·50	1·50
51		25c. red and violet	50	2·00
28		30c. brown and grey	3·50	4·25
52		30c. red and carmine	2·00	3·75
53		30c. red and black	1·60	2·75
54		30c. green and blue	2·50	3·50
29		35c. red and green	1·40	2·75
30		40c. green and black	1·90	2·75
31		45c. red and orange	1·60	2·75
32		50c. black and brown	10·50	12·00
55		50c. blue and ultramarine	1·60	3·00
56		50c. blue and grey	1·25	2·00
57		60c. black and green	1·25	3·00
58		65c. mauve and brown	3·50	3·75
33		75c. violet and purple	2·25	3·00
59		90c. mauve and red	10·50	18·00
34	4	1f. black and red	2·75	2·50
60		1f.10 brown and mauve	2·25	3·25
61		1f.40 violet and brown	4·25	4·75
62		1f.50 light blue and blue	13·00	9·75
35		2f. green and brown	7·00	12·00
36		5f. blue and violet		

1915. "Tablet" key-type optd **E F O 1915** and bar.

No.	Type	Description	Unused	Used
37	D	10c. red	95	3·00

1915. Red Cross. No. 37 surch **5c** and red cross.

No.	Type	Description	Unused	Used
38	D	10c.+5c. red	10·50	24·00

1915. Red Cross. Surch **5c** and red cross.

No.	Type	Description	Unused	Used
41	2	10c.+5c. orange and red	3·00	3·25

1916. Surch.

No.	Type	Description	Unused	Used
42	2	10c. on 15c. black and orange	35	3·00
67	4	25c. on 2f. green and brown	90	3·25
68		25c. on 5f. blue and violet	60	3·25
63	3	60 on 75c. brown and blue	20	2·50
64	4	65 on 1f. brown and blue	1·10	3·50
65		85 on 1f. brown and blue	1·50	3·50
66	3	90 on 75c. mauve and red	2·25	3·50

69 **4** 1f.25 on 1f. ultramarine & bl 50 3·00
70 1f.50 on 1f. light blue & blue 1·75 3·00
71 20f. on 5f. mauve and red 10·00 24·00

1921. Surch **1921** and new value.
43 **2** 05 on 2c. grey and brown 26·00 26·00
44 **3** 10 on 45c. red and orange 28·00 28·00
45 **2** 25 on 15c. black and orange 5·50 3·25

1924. Surch **45c. 1924.**
72 **2** 45c. on 10c. orange and red 2·75 3·75

1926. Surch in words.
73 **4** 3f. on 5f. blue and grey 75 3·50
74 10f. on 5f. black and green 4·00 5·75

13 Papetoia Bay

1929.
75 **13** 3f. sepia and green 5·00 7·00
76 5f. sepia and blue 6·00 12·50
77 10f. sepia and red 13·00 45·00
78 20f. sepia and mauve 30·00 38·00

1931. "International Colonial Exhibition", Paris, key-types.
79 E 40c. black and green 5·25 6·50
80 F 50c. black and mauve 6·25 7·50
81 G 90c. black and red 5·75 7·75
82 H 1f.50 black and blue 6·25 7·25

14 Spearing Fish

15 Tahitian Girl

16 Native Gods

1934.
83 **14** 1c. black 15 2·25
84 2c. red 15 2·50
85 3c. blue 15 3·00
86 4c. orange 15 3·00
87 5c. mauve 35 3·00
88 10c. brown 15 3·00
89 15c. green 20 3·00
90 20c. red 15 2·75
91 **15** 25c. blue 1·25 2·50
92 30c. green 95 3·25
93 30c. orange 30 3·00
94 **16** 35c. green 2·75 4·50
95 **15** 40c. mauve 50 3·00
96 45c. red 8·25 11·00
97 45c. green 1·10 3·25
98 50c. violet 65 1·60
99 55c. blue 4·75 6·75
100 60c. black 50 3·00
101 65c. brown 3·75 4·25
102 70c. pink 1·60 3·50
103 75c. olive 7·50 9·75
104 80c. purple 1·10 3·50
105 90c. red 1·00 3·00
106 **16** 1f. brown 1·50 2·75
107 1f.25 purple 9·25 10·00
108 1f.25 red 1·50 3·00
109 1f.40 orange 1·50 3·00
110 1f.50 blue 1·50 2·00
111 1f.60 violet 1·50 3·00
112 1f.75 green 7·00 5·75
113 2f. red 80 3·50
114 2f.25 blue 1·10 3·50
115 2f.50 black 1·60 3·50
116 3f. orange 85 3·50
117 5f. mauve 1·75 3·50
118 10f. green 2·00 4·75
119 20f. brown 2·25 5·00

17 Flying Boat

1934. Air.
120 **17** 5f. green 1·50 3·00

1937. International Exhibition, Paris. As Nos. 168/73 of St.-Pierre et Miquelon.
121 20c. violet 1·40 3·75
122 30c. green 80 3·75
123 40c. red 65 3·25
124 50c. brown 70 3·00
125 90c. red 65 4·25
126 1f.50 blue 1·10 6·50

17a Pierre and Marie Curie

1938. International Anti-cancer Fund.
127 **17a** 1f.75+50c. blue 6·75 22·00

17b

1939. New York World's Fair.
128 **17b** 1f.25 red 80 3·75
129 2f.25 blue 1·10 3·25

17c Storming the Bastille

1939. 150th Anniv of French Revolution.
130 **17c** 45c.+25c. green and black (postage) 9·25 22·00
131 70c.+30c. brown & black 11·50 22·00
132 90c.+35c. orange & black 10·50 22·00
133 1f.25+1f. red and black 15·00 22·00
134 2f.25+2f. blue and black 13·00 22·00
135 5f.+4f. black & orge (air) 29·00 45·00

1941. Adherence to General de Gaulle. Optd **FRANCE LIBRE**. (a) Nos. 75/8.
136 **13** 3f. brown and green 1·60 4·25
137 5f. brown and blue 1·60 8·50
138 10f. brown and red 6·00 15·00
139 20f. brown and mauve 42·00 85·00

(b) Nos. 106 and 115/19.
140 **16** 1f. brown 1·25 6·75
141 2f.50 black 1·25 8·50
142 3f. red 2·00 8·50
143 5f. mauve 3·50 8·50
144 10f. green 22·00 55·00
145 20f. brown 21·00 55·00

(c) Air stamp of 1934.
146 **17** 5f. green 2·25 3·50

19 Polynesian Travelling Canoe

19a Airplane

1942. Free French Issue. (a) Postage.
147 **19** 5c. brown 15 2·75
148 10c. blue 15 2·75
149 25c. green 60 2·75
150 30c. red 15 2·75
151 40c. green 15 2·75
152 80c. purple 15 2·75
153 1f. mauve 75 75
154 1f.50 red 1·00 2·75
155 2f. black 1·00 1·75
156 2f.50 blue 1·10 3·25
157 4f. violet 85 3·00
158 5f. yellow 80 3·25
159 10f. brown 1·75 3·50
160 20f. green 1·60 3·00

(b) Air. As T **19a**.
161 1f. orange 1·10 2·50
162 1f.50 red 1·10 2·50
163 5f. purple 1·50 3·25
164 10f. black 1·60 3·75
165 25f. blue 2·50 4·25
166 50f. green 3·00 4·25
167 100f. red 2·75 4·25

19b

1944. Mutual Aid and Red Cross Funds.
168 **19b** 5f.+20f. blue 1·10 3·50

1945. Surch in figures.
169 **19** 50c. on 5c. brown 25 2·75
170 60c. on 5c. brown 25 2·75
171 70c. on 5c. brown 50 3·00
172 1f.20 on 5c. brown 60 2·75
173 2f.40 on 25c. green 80 3·25
174 3f. on 25c. green 80 2·75
175 4f.50 on 25c. green 1·40 3·50
176 15f. on 2f.50 blue 1·10 3·75

20a Felix Eboue

1945. Eboue.
177 **20a** 2f. black 15 3·00
178 25f. green 1·60 3·75

20b "Victory"

1946. Air. Victory.
179 **20b** 8f. green 35 3·75

20c Legionaries by Lake Chad

1946. Air. From Chad to the Rhine.
180 **20c** 5f. red 1·25 4·00
181 – 10f. brown 55 4·00
182 – 15f. green 1·25 4·00
183 – 20f. red 1·60 4·00
184 – 25f. purple 1·25 5·00
185 – 50f. black 1·50 5·50

DESIGNS: 10f. Battle of Koufa; 15f. Tank Battle, Mareth; 20f. Normandy Landings; 25f. Liberation of Paris; 50f. Liberation of Strasbourg.

21 Moorea Coastline

22 Tahitian Girl

23 Wandering Albatross over Moorea

1948. (a) Postage as T **21/22**.
186 **21** 10c. brown 15 35
187 30c. green 15 40
188 40c. blue 15 2·25
189 – 50c. lake 50 2·50
190 – 60c. olive 65 3·00
191 – 80c. blue 75 3·00
192 – 1f. lake 2·25 95
193 – 1f.20 blue 2·25 3·00
194 – 1f.50 blue 90 1·60
195 **22** 2f. brown 2·75 75
196 2f.40 lake 2·75 3·25
197 3f. violet 7·75 90
198 4f. blue 2·25 85
199 – 5f. brown 2·75 55
200 – 6f. blue 3·00 65
201 – 9f. brown, black and red 3·50 5·00
202 – 10f. olive 3·75 65
203 – 15f. red 5·00 1·50
204 – 20f. blue 5·75 95
205 – 25f. brown 5·25 1·90

(b) Air. As T **23**.
206 – 13f. light blue and deep blue 3·50 2·25
207 **23** 50f. lake 25·00 14·00
208 – 100f. violet 17·00 11·00
209 – 200f. blue 48·00 18·00

DESIGNS: As T **22**: 50c. to 80c. Kanaka fisherman; 9f. Bora-Bora girl; 1f. to 1f.50, Faa village; 5 , 6 , 10f. Bora-Bora and Pandanus pine; 15f. to 25f. Polynesian girls. As T **23**: 13f. Pahia Peak and palms; 100f. Airplane over Moorea; 200f. Wandering albatross over Maupiti Island.

24a People of Five Races, Aircraft and Globe

1949. Air. 75th Anniv of U.P.U.
210 **24a** 10f. blue 5·00 20·00

24b Doctor and Patient

1950. Colonial Welfare.
211 **24b** 10f.+2f. green and blue 5·25 7·00

24c

25 "Nafea" (after Gauguin)

1952. Centenary of Military Medals.
212 **24c** 3f. violet, yellow and green 7·25 11·00

1953. Air. 50th Death Anniv of Gauguin (painter).
213 **25** 14f. sepia, red and turquoise 36·00 65·00

25a Normandy Landings, 1944

1954. Air. 10th Anniv of Liberation.
214 **25a** 3f. green and turquoise 5·75 6·00

26 Schooner in Dry Dock, Papeete

1956. Economic and Social Development Fund.
215 **26** 3f. turquoise 85 1·10

POSTAGE DUE STAMPS

1926. Postage Due stamps of France surch **Etabts Francais de l'Oceanie 2 francs a percevoir** (No. D80) or optd **Etablissements Francais de l'Oceanie** (others).
D73 **D 11** 5c. blue 25 2·75
D74 10c. brown 25 2·25
D75 20c. olive 35 3·00
D76 30c. red 50 3·00
D77 40c. red 1·10 4·25
D78 60c. green 95 4·25
D79 1f. red on yellow 80 4·25
D80 2f. on 1f. red 1·10 4·75
D81 3f. mauve 4·00 13·50

D 14 Fautaua Falls

D 24

1929.
D82 D 14 5c. brown and blue . . 20 2·50
D83 10c. green and orange 15 2·75
D84 30c. red and brown . . 40 3·00
D85 50c. brown and green 65 2·75
D86 60c. green and violet . . 2·00 5·00
D87 – 1f. mauve and blue . . 1·75 4·00
D88 – 2f. brown and red . . . 1·25 3·50
D89 – 3f. green and blue . . . 75 3·50
DESIGN: 1 to 3f. Polynesian man.

1948.
D210 D 24 10c. green . . . . . . 15 1·00
D211 30c. brown . . . . . 15 2·75
D212 50c. red . . . . 20 2·75
D213 1f. blue . . . . 35 2·75
D214 2f. green . . . . . . 75 3·25
D215 3f. red . . . . 1·25 3·50
D216 4f. violet . . . . . . 1·00 3·50
D217 5f. mauve . . . . . . 1·40 4·25
D218 10f. blue . . . . . . 2·50 5·50
D219 20f. lake . . . . . . 2·50 7·00

For later issues see **FRENCH POLYNESIA**.

OLDENBURG Pt. 7

A former Grand Duchy in North Germany. In 1867 it joined the North German Federation.

72 grote = 1 thaler.

1

2

3

1852. Imperf.
1 1 $\frac{1}{3}$sgr. black on green £1100 £1100
2 $\frac{1}{30}$th. black on blue . . . . . . £325 22·00
5 $\frac{1}{15}$th. black on red . . . . . . £700 75·00
8 $\frac{1}{10}$th. black on yellow . . . . . £700 75·00

1859. Imperf.
17 2 $\frac{1}{3}$g. yellow £275 £3250
10 $\frac{1}{3}$g. black on green £2250 £2750
19 $\frac{1}{2}$g. green £400 £750
21 $\frac{1}{2}$g. brown £375 £450
11 1g. black on blue . . . . . £650 36·00
23 1g. blue £200 £140
15 2g. black on red £800 £550
26 2g. red £400 £400
16 3g. black on yellow £800 £550
28 3g. yellow £400 £400

1862. Roul.
30 3 $\frac{1}{3}$g. green £180 £180
32 $\frac{1}{2}$g. orange . . . . £180 90·00
42 1g. red . . . . 9·00 45·00
36 2g. blue . . . . £180 45·00
39 3g. bistre . . . . £180 45·00

OMAN (SULTANATE) Pt. 19

In January 1971, the independent Sultanate of Muscat and Oman was renamed Sultanate of Oman.

NOTE. Labels inscribed "State of Oman" or "Oman Imamate State" are said to have been issued by a rebel administration under the Imam of Oman. There is no convincing evidence that these labels had any postal use within Oman and they are therefore omitted. They can be found, however, used on covers which appear to emanate from Amman and Baghdad.

1971. 1000 baizas = 1 rial saidi.
1972. 1000 baizas = 1 rial omani.

1971. Nos. 110/21 of Muscat and Oman optd **SULTANATE of OMAN** in English and Arabic.
122 12 5b. purple 10 10
142 10b. brown 20 10
124 20b. brown 40 25
125 A 25b. black and violet . . . 50 25
126 30b. black and blue . . . 70 40
127 40b. black and orange . . 95 50
128 14 50b. mauve and blue . . . 1·25 65
129 B 75b. green and brown . . . 1·60 90
130 C 100b. blue and orange . . 1·90 1·25
131 $\frac{1}{4}$r. brown and green . . . 6·25 3·75
132 E $\frac{1}{2}$r. violet and red . . . . . 12·50 6·25
133 F 1r. red and violet . . . . . 24·00 14·00

19 Sultan Qabus and Buildings ("Land Development")

1971. National Day. Multicoloured.
134 10b. Type **19** 35 25
135 40b. Sultan in military uniform and Omanis ("Freedom") 95 65
136 50b. Doctors and patients ("Health Services") . . . . 1·25 1·00
137 100b. Children at school ("Education") . . . . . . 2·50 1·90

1971. No. 94 of Muscat and Oman surch **SULTANATE of OMAN 5** in English and Arabic.
138 5b. on 3b. purple . . . . . 20·00 8·25

21 Child in Class

1971. 25th Anniv of U.N.I.C.E.F.
139 21 50b.+25b. multicoloured 2·50 2·50

22 Book Year Emblem

1972. International Book Year.
140 22 25b. multicoloured . . . . 3·25 1·25

سلطنة عمان
25 B ٢٥ ب
(24)

1972. Nos. 102 of Muscat and Oman and 127 of Oman optd with T **24**.
144 25b. on 1r. blue and orange 21·00 13·00
145 25b. on 40b. black and orange . . . . 21·00 13·00

26 Matrah, 1809

1972.
158 26 5b. multicoloured 20 10
147 10b. multicoloured 20 10
148 20b. multicoloured 30 10
149 25b. multicoloured 30 10
150 – 30b. multicoloured 45 25
151 – 40b. multicoloured 55 30
152 – 50b. multicoloured 70 45
153 – 75b. multicoloured . . . . 1·00 55
154 – 100b. multicoloured . . . 1·40 85
155 – $\frac{1}{4}$r. multicoloured . . . . . 3·50 1·40
156 – $\frac{1}{2}$r. multicoloured . . . . . 6·75 3·50
157 – 1r. multicoloured . . . . . 15·50 6·50
DESIGNS—26 × 21 mm: 30b. to 75b. Shinas, 1809. 42 × 25 mm: 100b. to 1r. Muscat, 1809.

29 Government Buildings

1973. Opening of Ministerial Complex.
170 29 25b. multicoloured 45 35
171 100b. multicoloured . . . 1·90 1·25

30 Oman Crafts (dhow building)

1973. National Day. Multicoloured.
172 15b. Type **30** 40 25
173 50b. Seeb International Airport . . . . 2·25 1·25
174 65b. Dhow and tanker . . . 2·25 1·25
175 100b. "Ship of the Desert" (camel) . . . . 3·25 1·90

31 Aerial View of Port

1974. Inauguration of Port Qabus.
176 31 100b. multicoloured . . . 2·75 2·00

32 Map on Open Book

1974. Illiteracy Eradication Campaign. Mult.
177 25b. Type **32** 60 30
178 100b. Hands reaching for open book (vert) . . . . . 2·40 1·60

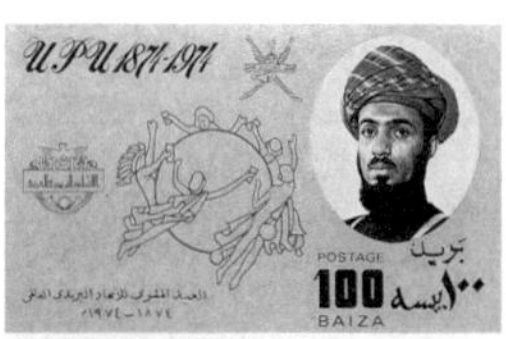

33 Sultan Qabus bin Said and Emblems

1974. Centenary of U.P.U.
179 33 100b. multicoloured . . . 1·75 1·25

34 Arab Scribe

1975. "Eradicate Illiteracy".
180 34 25b. multicoloured . . . . 3·50 95

35 New Harbour, Mina Raysoot

1975. National Day. Multicoloured.
181 30b. Type **35** 25 25
182 50b. Stadium and map . . . 65 40
183 75b. Water desalination plant 65 65
184 100b. Television station . . . 1·00 75
185 150b. Satellite Earth station and map . . . . 1·25 1·25
186 250b. Telecommunications symbols and map . . . . 2·50 2·00

36 Arab Woman and Child with Nurse

1975. International Women's Year. Mult.
187 75b. Type **36** 70 65
188 150b. Mother and children (vert) . . . . 1·25 1·25

37 Presenting Colours and Opening of Seeb–Nizwa Highway

1976. National Day. Multicoloured.
201 25b. Type **37** 25 20
202 40b. Parachutists and harvesting 90 45
203 75b. Agusta-Bell AB-212 helicopters and Victory Day procession . . . . . 1·75 90
204 150b. Road construction and Salalah T.V. Station . . . 2·00 1·50

38 Great Bath, Moenjodaro

1977. "Save Moenjodaro" Campaign.
205 38 125b. multicoloured . . . 2·25 1·90

39 A.P.U. Emblem

40 Coffee Pots

1977. 25th Anniv of Arab Postal Union.
206 39 30b. multicoloured 65 40
207 75b. multicoloured . . . . 1·90 1·10

1977. National Day. Multicoloured.
208 40b. Type **40** 60 40
209 75b. Earthenware pots . . . 1·10 50
210 100b. Khor Rori inscriptions 1·25 75
211 150b. Silver jewellery . . . . 2·25 1·25

1978. Surch in English and Arabic.
212 40b. on 150b. mult (No. 185) 12·00 12·00
213 50b. on 150b. mult (No. 188) 15·00 15·00
214 75b. on 250b. mult (No. 186) 24·00 24·00

42 Mount Arafat, Pilgrims and Kaaba

1978. Pilgrimage to Mecca.
215 42 40b. multicoloured . . . . 1·75 1·40

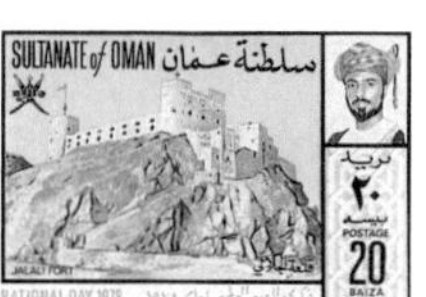

43 Jalali Fort

1978. National Day. Forts. Multicoloured.
216 20b. Type **43** 25 20
217 25b. Nizwa Fort 30 25
218 40b. Rostaq Fort 70 40
219 50b. Sohar Fort 80 50
220 75b. Bahla Fort . . . . . . 1·00 80
221 100b. Jibrin Fort . . . . . . 1·50 1·00

44 World Map, Koran and Symbols of Arab Achievements

1979. The Arabs.
222 44 40b. multicoloured 45 40
223 100b. multicoloured . . . 1·60 1·25

45 Child on Swing

1979. International Year of the Child.
224 **45** 40b. multicoloured . . . . 1·90 1·50

46 Gas Plant

1979. National Day. Multicoloured.
225 25b. Type **46** 95 45
226 75b. Dhow and modern trawler . . . . 2·25 1·50

47 Sultan Qabus on Horseback

1979. Armed Forces Day. Multicoloured.
227 40b. Type **47** . . . . 2·25 75
228 100b. Soldier . . . . 3·00 1·90

48 Mosque, Mecca

1980. 1400th Anniv of Hegira. Multicoloured.
229 50b. Type **48** 60 50
230 150b. Mosque and Kaaba . . 2·25 1·60

49 Bab Alkabir

1980. National Day. Multicoloured.
231 75b. Type **49** 55 50
232 100b. Corniche 90 80
233 250b. Polo match . . . . . 2·50 2·25
234 500b. Omani women . . . . 4·25 4·00

50 Sultan and Naval Patrol Boat

1980. Armed Forces Day. Multicoloured.
235 150b. Type **50** . . . . 1·60 1·50
236 750b. Sultan and mounted soldiers . . . . 7·00 7·00

51 Policewoman helping Children across Road

1981. National Police Day. Multicoloured.
237 50b. Type **51** 70 50
238 100b. Police bandsmen . . . 1·25 1·00
239 150b. Mounted police . . . . 1·75 1·50
240 ½r. Police headquarters . . . 5·50 4·75

1981. Nos. 231, 234 and 235/6 surch **POSTAGE** and new value in English and Arabic.
241 **50** 20b. on 150b. multicoloured 50 30
242 – 30b. on 750b. multicoloured 75 40
243 **49** 50b. on 75b. multicoloured 1·25 75
244 – 100b. on 500b. multicoloured . . . . . 2·75 1·75

53 Sultan's Crest

1981. Welfare of Blind.
245 **53** 10b. black, blue and red 40 25

54 Palm Tree, Fishes and Wheat

1981. World Food Day.
246 **54** 50b. multicoloured . . . . 2·00 1·25

55 Pilgrims at Prayer

1981. Pilgrimage to Mecca.
247 **55** 50b. multicoloured . . . . 1·60 75

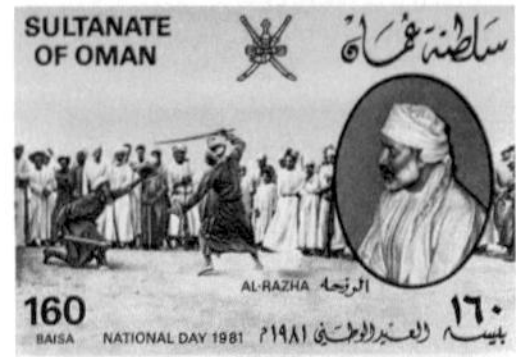

56 Al Razha

1981. National Day. Multicoloured.
248 160b. Type **56** . . . . 1·50 1·50
249 300b. Sultan Qabus bin Said 2·50 2·50

57 Muscat Port, 1981

1981. Retracing the Voyage of Sinbad. Mult.
250 50b. Type **57** 50 50
251 100b. The "Sohar" (replica of medieval dhow) . . . . . . 1·25 1·25
252 130b. Map showing route of voyage . . . . 1·60 1·60
253 200b. Muscat Harbour, 1650 2·25 2·25

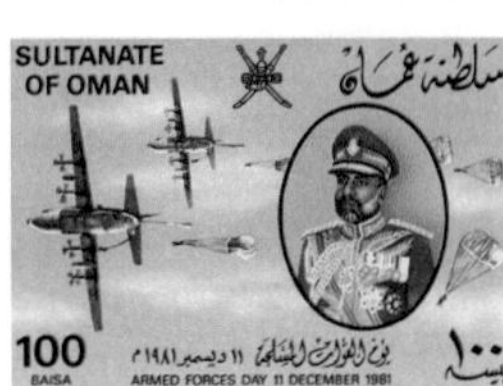

58 Parachute-drop

1981. Armed Forces Day. Multicoloured.
255 100b. Type **58** . . . . 1·40 85
256 400b. Missile-armed corvettes 4·75 4·75

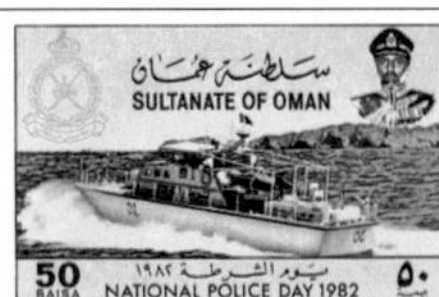

59 Police Launch

1982. National Police Day. Multicoloured.
257 50b. Type **59** . . . . 1·75 70
258 100b. Royal Oman Police Band at Cardiff . . . . . 1·60 1·10

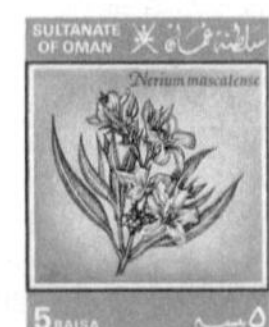

60 "Nerium mascatense"

1982. Flora and Fauna. Multicoloured.
259 5b. Type **60** 10 10
260 10b. "Dionysia mira" 10 10
261 20b. "Teucrium mascatense" 15 10
262 25b. "Geranium mascatense" 15 15
263 30b. "Cymatium boschi" (horiz) 25 20
264 40b. Eloise's acteon (horiz) 25 20
265 50b. Teulere's cowrie (horiz) 30 25
266 75b. Lovely cowrie (horiz) . . 45 40
267 100b. Arabian chukar (25 × 33 mm) . . . . . . 1·90 1·25
268 ¼r. Hoopoe (25 × 33 mm) . . 5·00 4·50
269 ½r. Arabian tahr (25 × 39 mm) . . . . . . 4·25 3·75
270 1r. Arabian oryx (25 × 39 mm) . . . . . . 8·00 7·50

Nos. 259/62 show flowers, Nos. 263/6 shells, Nos. 267/8 birds and Nos. 269/70 animals.

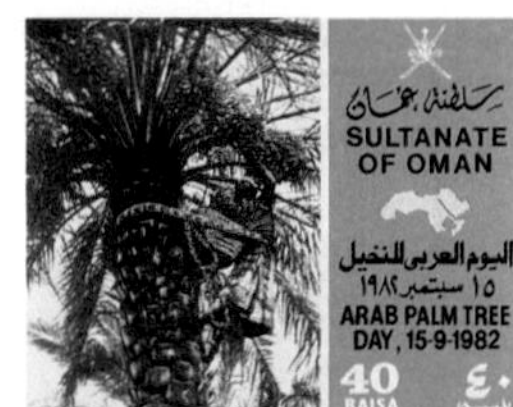

61 Palm Tree

1982. Arab Palm Tree Day. Multicoloured.
271 40b. Type **61** 90 50
272 100b. Palm tree and nuts . . 2·10 1·25

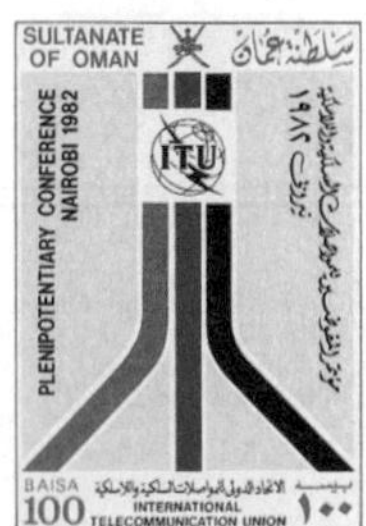

62 I.T.U. Emblem

1982. I.T.U. Delegates Conference, Nairobi.
273 **62** 100b. multicoloured . . . 2·00 1·25

63 Emblem and Cups

1982. Municipalities Week.
274 **63** 40b. multicoloured . . . . 1·50 70

64 State Consultative Council Inaugural Session

1982. National Day. Multicoloured.
275 40b. Type **64** 50 45
276 100b. Petroleum refinery . . 1·75 1·25

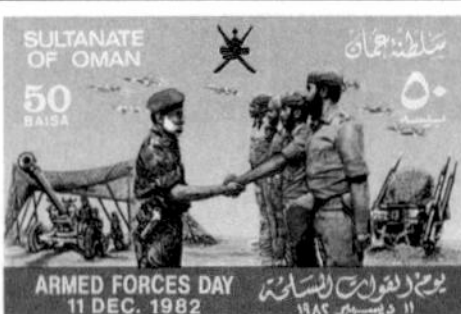

65 Sultan meeting Troops

1982. Armed Forces Day. Multicoloured.
277 50b. Type **65** 75 50
278 100b. Mounted army band 2·00 1·25

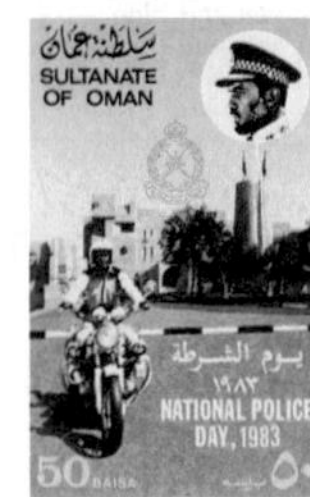

66 Police Motorcyclist and Headquarters

1983. National Police Day.
279 **66** 50b. multicoloured . . . . 1·60 1·00

67 Satellite, W.C.Y. Emblem and Dish Aerial

1983. World Communications Year.
280 **67** 50b. multicoloured . . . . 1·60 1·00

68 Bee Hives

1983. Bee-keeping. Multicoloured.
281 50b. Type **68** . . . . 1·25 1·00
282 50b. Bee collecting nectar . . 1·25 1·00

Nos. 281/2 were issued together, se-tenant, each pair forming a composite design.

69 Pilgrims at Mudhalfa

1983. Pilgrimage to Mecca.
283 **69** 40b. multicoloured . . . . 1·90 1·00

70 Emblem, Map and Sultan

1983. Omani Youth Year.
284 **70** 50b. multicoloured . . . . 1·40 70

71 Sohar Copper Mine

1983. National Day. Multicoloured.
285 50b. Type **71** 90 50
286 100b. Sultan Qabus University and foundation stone . . . . 1·50 1·00

72 Machine Gun Post

1983. Armed Forces Day.
287 **72** 100b. multicoloured . . . 2·25 1·25

73 Police Cadets Parade

1984. National Police Day.
288 **73** 100b. multicoloured . . . 1·90 1·25

74 Footballers and Cup

1984. 7th Arabian Gulf Cup Football Tournament. Multicoloured.
289 40b. Type **74** 60 40
290 50b. Emblem and pictograms of footballers . . . . . . 1·00 65

75 Stoning the Devil

1984. Pilgrimage to Mecca.
291 **75** 50b. multicoloured . . . . 1·60 90

76 New Central Post Office and Automatic Sorting Machine

1984. National Day. Multicoloured.
292 130b. Type **76** . . . . 1·25 1·10
293 160b. Map of Oman with telecommunications symbols . . . . 1·90 1·75

77 Scouts reading Map

1984. 16th Arab Scouts Conference, Muscat. Multicoloured.
294 50b. Scouts pegging tent . . 45 40
295 50b. Type **77** 45 40
296 130b. Scouts assembled round flag . . . . 1·25 1·10
297 130b. Scout, cub, guide, brownie and scout leaders 1·25 1·10

78 Sultan, Jet Fighters and "Al Munassir" (landing craft)

1984. Armed Forces Day.
298 **78** 100b. multicoloured . . . 1·50 1·25

79 Bell 214ST Helicopter lifting Man from "Al-Ward" (tanker)

1985. National Police Day.
299 **79** 100b. multicoloured . . . 3·25 1·40

80 Al-Khaif Mosque and Tent, Mina

1985. Pilgrimage to Mecca.
300 **80** 50b. multicoloured . . . . 1·00 50

81 I.Y.Y. Emblem and Youth holding Olive Branches

1985. International Youth Year. Mult.
301 50b. Type **81** 50 50
302 100b. Emblem and young people at various activities 90 90

82 Palace before and after Restoration

1985. Restoration of Jabrin Palace. Mult.
303 100b. Type **82** 75 70
304 250b. Restored ceiling . . . 2·75 2·50

83 Drummers

1985. International Omani Traditional Music Symposium.
305 **83** 50b. multicoloured . . . . 1·00 55

84 Scenes of Child Care and Emblem

1985. U.N.I.C.E.F. Child Health Campaign.
306 **84** 50b. multicoloured . . . . 1·00 55

85 Flags around Map of Gulf

1985. 6th Supreme Council Session of Gulf Co-operation Council, Muscat. Multicoloured.
307 40b. Type **85** 60 50
308 50b. Portraits of rulers of Council member countries 80 60

86 Sultan Qabus University and Students

1985. National Day. Multicoloured.
309 20b. Type **86** 20 15
310 50b. Tractor and oxen ploughing field 45 40
311 100b. Port Qabus cement factory and Oman Chamber of Commerce . . 90 80
312 200b. Road bridge, Douglas DC-10 airliner and communications centre . . 2·25 1·50
313 250b. Portrait of Sultan Qabus (vert) . . . . 1·75 1·60

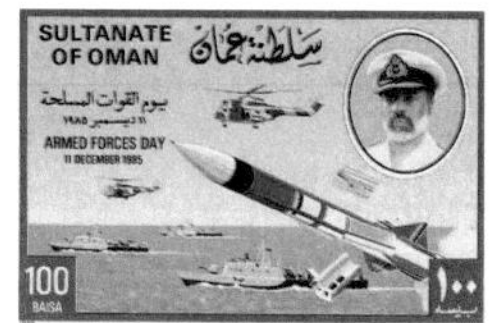

87 Military Exercise at Sea

1985. Armed Forces Day.
314 **87** 100b. multicoloured . . . 1·50 1·00

88 Red-tailed Butterflyfish

1985. Marine Life. Multicoloured.
315 20b. Type **88** 50 20
316 50b. Black-finned melon butterflyfish 90 55
317 100b. Gardiner's butterflyfish 1·60 1·10
318 150b. Narrow-barred Spanish mackerel . . . . 2·50 2·25
319 200b. Lobster (horiz) . . . . 1·60 1·50

89 Frankincense Tree

1985. Frankincense Production.
320 **89** 100b. multicoloured . . . 60 50
321 3r. multicoloured . . . . . 20·00 14·00

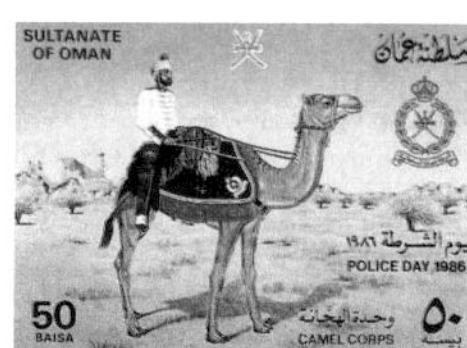

90 Camel Corps Member

1986. National Police Day.
322 **90** 50b. multicoloured 95 65

91 Cadet Barquentine "Shabab Oman", 1986

1986. Participation of "Shabab Oman" in Statue of Liberty Centenary Celebrations. Multicoloured.
323 50b. "Sultana" (full-rigged sailing ship), 1840 . . . . 70 50
324 100b. Type **91** . . . . 1·50 1·10

92 Crowd around Holy Kaaba

1986. Pilgrimage to Mecca.
326 **92** 50b. multicoloured 85 40

93 Scouts erecting Tent

1986. 17th Arab Scout Camp, Salalah. Multicoloured.
327 50b. Type **93** 55 35
328 100b. Scouts making survey 1·10 65

94 Sports Complex

1986. Inauguration of Sultan Qabus Sports Complex.
329 **94** 100b. multicoloured . . . 1·10 75

95 Mother and Baby, Emblem and Tank on Globe

1986. International Peace Year.
330 **95** 130b. multicoloured . . . 1·25 90

96 Al-Sahwa Tower

1986. National Day. Multicoloured.
331 50b. Type **96** 50 30
332 100b. Sultan Qabus University (inauguration) 1·10 65
333 130b. 1966 stamps and F.D.C. cancellation (20th anniv of first Oman stamp issue) (57 × 27 mm) . . . . 1·40 95

97 Camel Corps

1987. National Police Day.
334 **97** 50b. multicoloured 85 60

98 Family

1987. Arabian Gulf Social Work Week.
335 **98** 50b. multicoloured 85 45

99 Aqueduct

101 Examples of Work and Hand holding Cup

100 Crowd around Holy Kaaba

1987. International Environment Day. Mult.
336 50b. Greater flamingoes . . . 2·10 80
337 130b. Type **99** . . . . 1·25 80

1987. Pilgrimage to Mecca. Multicoloured.
338 50b. Type **100** 60 50
339 50b. Al-Khaif Mosque and tents, Mina 60 50
340 50b. Stoning the Devil . . . 60 50
341 50b. Pilgrims at Mudhalfa . . 60 50
342 50b. Pilgrims at prayer . . . 60 50
343 50b. Mount Arafat, pilgrims and Kaaba 60 50

1987. 3rd Municipalities Month.
344 **101** 50b. multicoloured . . . 75 50

102 Marine Science and Fisheries Centre

1987. National Day. Multicoloured.
345 50b. Type **102** 65 35
346 130b. Royal Hospital . . . . 1·10 85

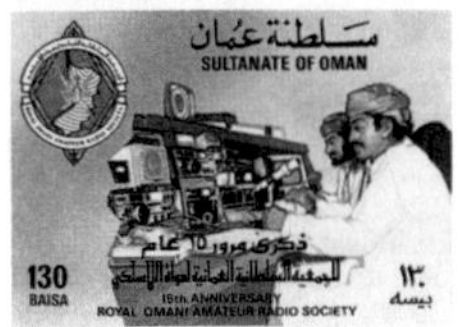
103 Radio Operators

1987. 15th Anniv of Royal Omani Amateur Radio Society.
347 **103** 130b. multicoloured . . . 95 80

104 Weaver

1988. Traditional Crafts. Multicoloured.
348 50b. Type **104** 35 30
349 100b. Potter 60 50
350 150b. Halwa maker 85 75
351 200b. Silversmith . . . . . . 1·00 85

105 Show Jumping

106 Emblem

1988. Olympic Games, Seoul. Multicoloured.
353 100b. Type **105** 55 50
354 100b. Hockey 55 50
355 100b. Football 55 50
356 100b. Running 55 50
357 100b. Swimming 55 50
358 100b. Shooting 55 50

1988. 40th Anniv of W.H.O. "Health for All".
360 **106** 100b. multicoloured . . . 75 65

107 Tending Land and Crops

1988. National Day. Agriculture Year. Mult.
361 100b. Type **107** 70 70
362 100b. Livestock 70 70

108 Dhahira Region (woman's)

1989. Costumes. Multicoloured.
363 30b. Type **108** 15 10
364 40b. Eastern region (woman's) 20 15
365 50b. Batinah region (woman's) 25 20
366 100b. Interior region (woman's) 55 45
367 130b. Southern region (woman's) 70 60
368 150b. Muscat region (woman's) 80 70
369 200b. Dhahira region (man's) 1·10 95
370 ¼r. Eastern region (man's) . . 1·40 1·25
371 ½r. Southern region (man's) 2·75 2·40
372 1r. Muscat region (man's) . . 5·25 4·50

109 Fishing

1989. National Day. Agriculture Year. Mult.
375 100b. Type **109** . . . . . . 1·00 70
376 100b. Agriculture 65 55

110 Flags and Omani State Arms

1989. 10th Supreme Council Session of Arab Co-operation Council, Muscat. Multicoloured.
377 50b. Type **110** 30 25
378 50b. Council emblem and Sultan Qabus 30 25

111 Emblem and Map

1990. 5th Anniv (1989) of Gulf Investment Corporation.
379 **111** 50b. multicoloured . . . 30 25
380 130b. multicoloured . . . 80 70

112 Emblem and Douglas DC-10 Airliner

113 Map

1990. 40th Anniv of Gulf Air.
381 **112** 80b. multicoloured . . . 50 45

1990. Omani Ophiolite Symposium, Muscat.
382 **113** 80b. multicoloured . . . 60 50
383 150b. multicoloured . . . 1·25 1·10

114 Ahmed bin Na'aman al-Ka'aby (envoy), "Sultana" and Said bin Sultan al-Busaidi

1990. 150th Anniv of First Omani Envoy's Journey to U.S.A.
384 **114** 200b. multicoloured . . . 1·25 1·10

115 Sultan Qabus Rose

1990. 20th Anniv of Sultan Qabus's Accession.
385 **115** 200b. multicoloured . . . 1·25 1·10

116 National Day Emblem

1990. National Day.
386 **116** 100b. red and green on gold foil 60 50
387 – 200b. green and red on gold foil . . . . 1·25 1·10
DESIGN: 200b. Sultan Qabus.

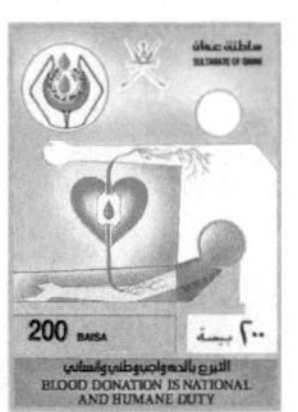
117 Donor and Recipient

1991. Blood Donation.
389 **117** 50b. multicoloured . . . 35 30
390 200b. multicoloured . . . 1·50 1·25

118 Industrial Emblems

1991. National Day and Industry Year. Mult.
391 100b. Type **118** 70 60
392 200b. Sultan Qabus . . . . . 1·25 1·10

119 Weapons, Military Transport and Sultan Qabus

1991. Armed Forces Day.
394 **119** 100b. multicoloured . . . 90 60

120 Interior of Museum and National Flags

121 Satellite Picture of Asia

1992. Inaug of Omani-French Museum, Muscat.
395 **120** 100b. multicoloured . . . 65 55

1992. World Meteorological Day.
397 **121** 220b. multicoloured . . . 1·40 1·25

122 Emblem and Hands

123 Emblem and Hands protecting Handicapped Child

1992. World Environment Day.
398 **122** 100b. multicoloured . . . 65 55

1992. Welfare of Handicapped Children.
399 **123** 70b. multicoloured . . . 50 45

124 Sultan Qabus and Books

1992. Publication of Sultan Qabus "Encyclopedia of Arab Names".
400 **124** 100b. multicoloured . . . 60 50

125 Sultan Qabus, Factories and Industry Year Emblem

1992. National Day. Multicoloured.
401 100b. Type **125** 60 50
402 200b. Sultan Qabus and Majlis As'shura (Consultative Council) emblem . . . . 1·25 1·10

126 Mounted Policemen and Sultan Qabus

1993. National Police Day.
403 **126** 80b. multicoloured . . . 50 45

127 Census Emblem

1993. Population, Housing and Establishments Census.
404 **127** 100b. multicoloured . . . 55 50

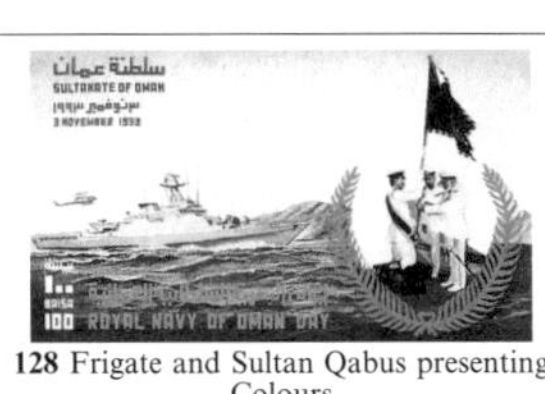

128 Frigate and Sultan Qabus presenting Colours

1993. Navy Day.
405 **128** 100b. multicoloured . . . 75 55

129 Youth Year Emblem

1993. National Day and Youth Year. Multi.
406 100b. Type **129** 55 50
407 200b. Sultan Qabus . . . . . 1·10 95

130 Scout Headquarters and Emblem

1993. 61st Anniv of Scouting in Oman (408) and 10th Anniv of Sultan Qabus as Chief Scout (409). Multicoloured.
408 100b. Type **130** 35 30
409 100b. Scout camp and Sultan Qabus 35 30
Nos. 408/9 were issued together, se-tenant, forming a composite design.

131 Sei Whale and School of Dolphins

1993. Whales and Dolphins in Omani Waters. Multicoloured.
410 100b. Type **131** 55 45
411 100b. Sperm whale and dolphins 55 45
Nos. 410/11 were issued together, se-tenant, forming a composite design.

132 Water Drops and Falaj (ancient water system)

133 Municipality Building

1994. World Water Day.
413 **132** 50b. multicoloured . . . 30 25

1994. 70th Anniv of Muscat Municipality.
414 **133** 50b. multicoloured . . . 30 25

134 Centenary Emblem and Sports Pictograms

1994. Centenary of International Olympic Committee.
415 **134** 100b. multicoloured . . . 55 50

135 Emblem

1994. National Day. Multicoloured.
416 50b. Type **135** 15 10
417 50b. Sultan Qabus 15 10

136 Airplane and Emblem

1994. 50th Anniv of I.C.A.O.
418 **136** 100b. multicoloured . . . 30 25

137 Arms

139 Emblem and National Colours

138 Meeting

1994. 250th Anniv of Al-Busaid Dynasty. Multicoloured.
419 50b. Type **137** dated "1744–1775" 15 10
420 50b. Type **137** dated "1775–1779" 15 10
421 50b. Type **137** dated "1779–1792" 15 10
422 50b. Type **137** dated "1792–1804" 15 10
423 50b. Type **137** dated "1804–1807" 15 10
424 50b. Said bin Sultan (1807–1856) 15 10
425 50b. Type **137** dated "1856–1866" 15 10
426 50b. Type **137** dated "1866–1868" 15 10
427 50b. Type **137** dated "1868–1871" 15 10
428 50b. Turki bin Said (1871–1888) 15 10
429 50b. Feisal bin Turki (1888–1913) 15 10
430 50b. Taimur bin Feisal (1913–1932) 15 10
431 50b. Arms, Sultan Qabus and family tree 15 10
432 50b. Said bin Taimur (1932–1970) 15 10
433 50b. Sultan Qabus (1970–) 15 10

1995. Open Parliament.
435 **138** 50b. multicoloured . . . 15 10

1995. 50th Anniv of Arab League.
436 **139** 100b. multicoloured . . . 30 25

140 Anniversary Emblem

1995. 50th Anniv of U.N.O.
437 **140** 100b. multicoloured . . . 30 25

141 Sultan Qabus in Robes

1995. National Day. Multicoloured.
438 50b. Type **141** 15 10
439 100b. Sultan Qabus in military uniform 30 25

142 Council Emblem

1995. 16th Supreme Council Session of Gulf Co-operation Council, Oman. Multicoloured.
441 100b. Type **142** 30 25
442 200b. Sultan Qabus, members' flags and map 65 55

143 Ash'shashah

1996. Omani Sailing Vessels. Multicoloured.
443 50b. Type **143** 20 10
444 100b. Al-Battil 35 25
445 200b. Al-Boum 70 55
446 250b. Al-Badan 85 65
447 350b. As'sanbuq . . . . . . 1·25 90
448 450b. Al-Galbout . . . . . 1·50 1·10
449 650b. Al-Baghlah . . . . . 2·40 1·75
450 1r. Al-Ghanjah . . . . . . 3·50 2·75

144 Emblem, Poppy Head, Skull-like Face smoking Cigarette and Syringe

1996. United Nations Decade against Drug Abuse.
451 **144** 100b. multicoloured . . . 30 25

145 Shooting

1996. Olympic Games, Atlanta. Multicoloured.
452 100b. Type **145** 30 25
453 100b. Swimming 30 25
454 100b. Cycling 30 25
455 100b. Running 30 25
Nos. 452/5 were issued together, se-tenant, forming a composite design.

146 Tournament Emblem and Flags of Participating Countries

1996. 13th Arabian Gulf Cup Football Championship.
456 **146** 100b. multicoloured . . . 30 25

147 Sultan Qabus and Sur (left detail)

1996. National Day. Multicoloured.
457 50b. Type **147** 15 10
458 50b. Sultan Qabus and Sur (right detail) 15 10
Nos. 457/8 were issued together, se-tenant, forming a composite design.

148 Mother with Children

1996. 50th Anniv of U.N.I.C.E.F.
459 **148** 100b. multicoloured . . . 30 25

149 Nakl Fort

1997. Tourism. Multicoloured.
460 100b. Type **149** 30 25
461 100b. Wadi Tanuf (waterfall in centre of stamp) 30 25
462 100b. Fort on Muthrah Corniche 30 25
463 100b. Wadi Dayqah Dam . . 30 25
464 100b. Bahla fort (overlooking tree-covered plain) 30 25
465 100b. Wadi Darbut waterfall (near top of stamp) 30 25

150 Sultan Qabus and Dhofar Waterfalls

1997. National Day. Multicoloured.
466 100b. Type **150** 30 25
467 100b. Sultan Qabus seated by waterfalls 30 25

151 Guide Activities

1997. 25th Anniv of Oman Girl Guides.
468 **151** 100b. multicoloured . . . 30 25

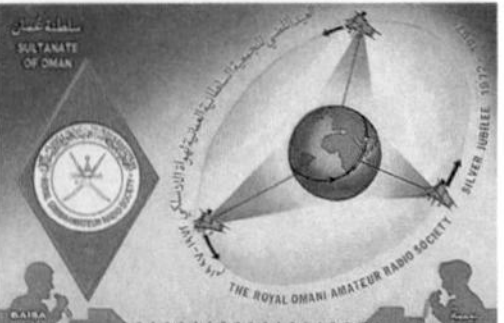

152 Society and Anniversary Emblems

1997. 25th Anniv of Royal Omani Amateur Radio Society.
469 **152** 100b. multicoloured . . . 30 25

153 Dagger and Sheath

1998. Al-Khanjar Assaidi. Multicoloured, background colours given.
470 **153** 50b. green 15 10
471 50b. red 15 10
471a 80b. yellow 20 15
472 100b. violet 30 25
473 200b. brown 65 55

154 Car, Traffic Lights, Hand and Police Motor Cycle

1998. Gulf Co-operation Council Traffic Week.
474 **154** 100b. multicoloured . . . 30 25

155 Sohar Fort

1998. Tourism. Multicoloured.
475 100b. Type **155** 30 25
476 100b. Wadi Shab 30 25
477 100b. Nizwa town 30 25
478 100b. Eid celebration (religious holiday) 30 25
479 100b. View of river 30 25
480 100b. Three young girls by an aqueduct 30 25

156 Exhibition Emblem

1998. 4th Arab Gulf Countries Stamp Exhibition, Muscat.
481 **156** 50b. multicoloured . . . 15 10

157 U.P.U. Emblem and Doves

1998. World Stamp Day.
482 **157** 100b. multicoloured . . . 30 25

158 Year Emblem

1998. National Day. Year of the Private Sector. Multicoloured.
483 100b. Sultan Qabus 30 25
484 100b. Type **158** 30 25

159 Map and Container Ship at Quayside

1998. Inauguration of Salalah Port Container Terminal.
486 **159** 50b. multicoloured . . . 15 10

160 Sultan Qabus, Dove and Olive Branch

1998. International Peace Award.
487 **160** 500b. multicoloured . . . 1·60 1·40

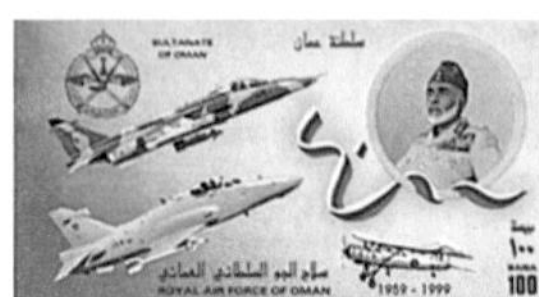

161 Military Aircraft and Sultan Qabus

1999. 40th Anniv of Royal Air Force of Oman.
488 **161** 100b. multicoloured . . . 35 30

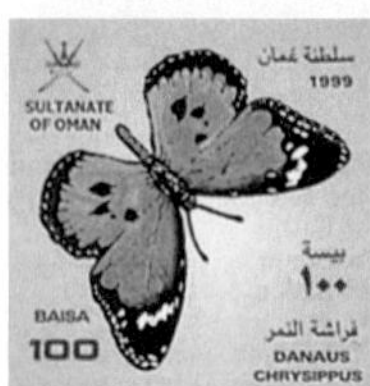

162 African Monarch

1999. Butterflies. Multicoloured.
489 100b. Type **162** 35 30
490 100b. Chequered swallowtail (*Papilio demoleus*) 35 30
491 100b. Blue pansy (*Precis orithya*) 35 30
492 100b. Yellow pansy (*Precis hierta*) 35 30

163 Longbarbel Goatfish

1999. Marine Life. Multicoloured.
494 100b. Type **163** 35 30
495 100b. Red-eyed round herring (*Etrumeus teres*) 35 30
496 100b. Brown-spotted grouper (*Epinephelus chlorostigma*) 35 30
497 100b. Blue-spotted emperor (*Lethrinus lentjan*) 35 30
498 100b. Blood snapper (*Lutjanus erythropterus*) . . 35 30
499 100b. Wahoo (*Acanthocybium solandri*) 35 30
500 100b. Long-tailed tuna (*Thunnus tonggol*) 35 30
501 100b. Crimson jobfish (*Pristipomoides filamentosus*) 35 30
502 100b. Yellow-finned tuna (*Thunnus albacares*) 35 30
503 100b. Cultured shrimp (*Penaeus indicus*) 35 30
504 100b. Pharaoh cuttlefish (*Sepia pharaonis*) 35 30
505 100b. Tropical rock lobster (*Panulirus homarus*) 35 30

164 Sand Cat

1999. Wildlife. Multicoloured.
506 100b. Type **164** 35 30
507 100b. Genet 35 30
508 100b. Leopard 35 30
509 100b. Sand fox 35 30
510 100b. Caracal lynx 35 30
511 100b. Hyena 35 30

165 Globe and Emblem

1999. 125th Anniv of Universal Postal Union.
513 **165** 200b. multicoloured . . . 70 60

166 Sultan Qabus and Musicians

1999. National Day. Multicoloured.
514 100b. Type **166** 35 30
515 100b. Sultan Qabus and horsemen 35 30
Nos. 514/15 were issued together, se-tenant, forming a composite design.

168 Water Droplet and Dried Earth

2000. World Water Week.
517 **168** 100b. multicoloured . . . 35 25

169 Emblem, Airplane and Silhouette of Bird

2000. 50th Anniv of Gulf Air.
518 **169** 100b. multicoloured . . . 35 25

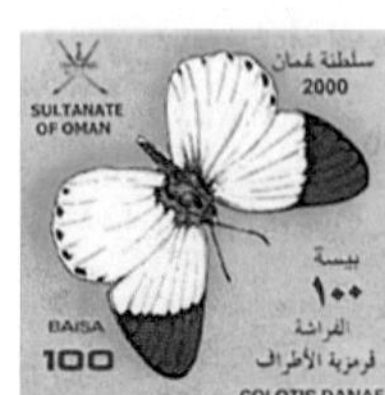

170 Crimson-tip Butterfly (*Colotis danae*)

2000. Butterflies. Multicoloured.
519 100b. Type **170** 35 25
520 100b. *Anaphaeis aurota* . . . 35 25
521 100b. *Tarucus rosaceus* . . . 35 25
522 100b. Long-tailed blue (*Lampides boeticus*) 35 25

171 Yellow Seahorse (*Hippocampus kuda*)

2000. Marine Life. Multicoloured.
524 100b. Type **171** 35 25
525 100b. Yellow boxfish (*Ostracion cubicus*) 35 25
526 100b. Japanese pineconefish (*Monocentris japonica*) . . 35 25
527 100b. Broad-barred lionfish (*Pterois antennata*) 35 25
528 100b. *Rhinecanthus assasi* . . 35 25
529 100b. Blue-spotted stingray (*Taeniura lymma*) 35 25

172 Arabian Tahr

2000. Mammals. Multicoloured.
531 100b. Type **172** 35 25
532 100b. Nubian ibex 35 25
533 100b. Arabian oryx 35 25
534 100b. Arabian gazelle 35 25

173 Emblem

2000. Olympic Games, Sydney. Multicoloured.
536 100b. Type **173** 35 25
537 100b. Running 35 25
538 100b. Swimming 35 25
539 100b. Rifle-shooting 35 25

174 Sultan Qabus

2000. National Day. Multicoloured.
541 100b. Type **174** 35 25
542 100b. Sitting 35 25
543 100b. Wearing uniform including red beret 35 25
544 100b. Wearing (white) naval uniform 35 25
545 100b. Anniversary emblem 35 25
546 100b. Wearing (beige) police uniform 35 25

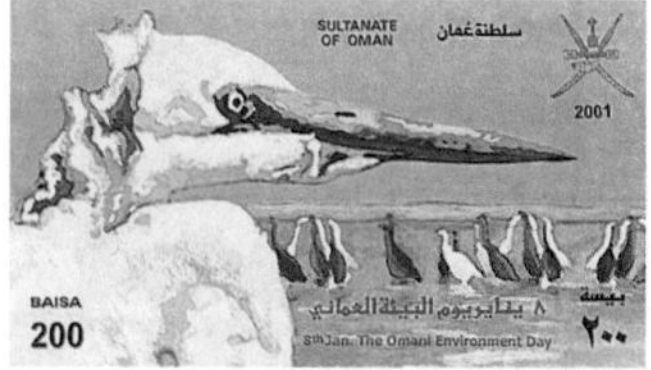

175 Egret and Sea Birds

2001. Environment Day. Sheet 83 × 46 mm.
MS548 **175** 200b. multicoloured 60 60

176 Dagger and Sheath **177** Child and Tank

2001. Al-Khanjar A'suri. Multicoloured, background colours given. (a) Size 24 × 27 mm.

549	**176**	50b. red	15	10
550		80b. yellow	25	20
		(b) Size 26 × 34 mm.		
551	**176**	100b. blue	30	25
552		200b. white	60	45
MS553		80 × 100 mm. Nos. 549/552	1·25	1·25

2001. Al Aqsa Uprising. Sheet 105 × 100 mm.

MS554	**177**	100b. multicoloured	30	30

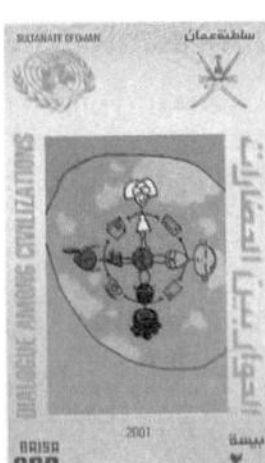
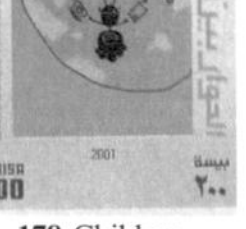
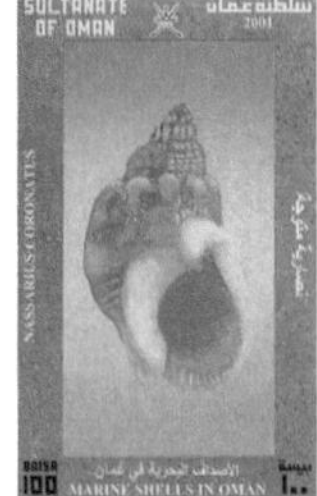

178 Children encircling Globe **180** *Cerithium caeruleum*

179 Globe, Tree, Map and Sunrise

2001. United Nations Year of Dialogue among Civilizations.

555	**178**	200b. multicoloured	60	45

2001. National Day. Year of the Environment. Multicoloured.

556	100b. Type **179**	30	25
557	100b. Sunrise and Sultan Qabas	30	25

Nos. 556/7 were issued together, se-tenant, forming a composite design.

2001. Shells. Multicoloured.

558	100b. Type **180**	30	25
559	100b. *Nassarius coronatus*	30	25
560	100b. *Cerithdea cingulata*	30	25
561	100b. *Epitoneum pallash*	30	25

181 Necklace

2001. Traditional Jewellery. Four sheets, each 71 × 71 mm containing T **181** and similar multicoloured designs.

MS562 (a) 100b. Type **181**; (b) 100b. Necklace with barred pendant (horiz) (63 × 28 mm); (c) 100b. "Mazrad" necklace (circular) (38 × 38 mm); (d) 100b. Hair decoration (triangular) (64 × 32 mm) . . . 1·10 1·10

182 Map enclosed in Circle

2001. 22nd Supreme Session of Gulf Co-operation Council, Oman. Multicoloured.

563	50b. Type **182**	10	10
564	100b. Sultan Qabas	30	25

183 Interior of Dome

2002. Inauguration of Sultan Qabus Grand Mosque, Baushar. Multicoloured.

565	50b. Type **183**	10	10
566	50b. Dome	10	10
567	50b. Entrance	10	10
568	50b. Decorated roof	10	10
MS569	120 × 90 mm. 100b. Aerial view of mosque. Imperf	30	30

184 Olive Ridley Turtle

2002. Turtles. Multicoloured.

570	100b. Type **184**	30	25
571	100b. Atlantic green turtle	30	25
572	100b. Hawksbill	30	25
573	100b. Loggerhead	30	25
MS574	130 × 98 mm. Nos. 570/3. Imperf	1·20	1·20

185 Adult and Child's Hands **187** Collared Dove (*Streptopelia decaocto*)

186 Sultan Qabus and Cheetah

2002. Early Intervention for Children with Special Needs. Ordinary or self-adhesive gum.

575	**185**	100b. multicoloured	30	25

2002. National Day. Year of the Environment. Sheet 100 × 80 mm.

MS577	**186**	100b. multicoloured	30	25

2002. Birds. Multicoloured.

578	50b. Type **187**	15	10
579	50b. Black-headed tchagra (*Tchagra senegala*)	15	10
580	50b. Ruppell's weaver (*Ploceus galbula*)	15	10
581	50b. Bonelli's eagle (*Hieraetus fasciatus*)	15	10
582	50b. White-eyed bulbul (*Pycnontus xanthopygos*)	15	10
583	50b. Northern eagle owl (*Bubo bubo*)	15	10
584	50b. Dunn's lark (*Eremalauda dunni*)	15	10
585	50b. Cape dikkop (*Burhinus capensis*)	15	10
586	50b. Graceful prinia (*Prinia gracilis*)	15	10
587	50b. Indian grey francolin (*Francolinus pondicerianus*)	15	10
588	50b. Tristram's grackle (*Onychognathus tristramii*)		
589	50b. Red-wattled plover (*Vanellus indicus* (inscr "Hoplopterus indicus"))	15	10
590	50b. House crow (*Corvus splendens*)	15	10
591	50b. Houbara bustard (*Chlamydotis undulate*)	15	10
592	50b. White-collared kingfisher (*Halcyon chloris*)	15	10
593	50b. Crowned sand grouse (*Pterocles coronatus*)	15	10

188 Muscat Gate and Festival Emblem

2003. Muskat Festival.

594	**188**	100b. multicoloured	30	25

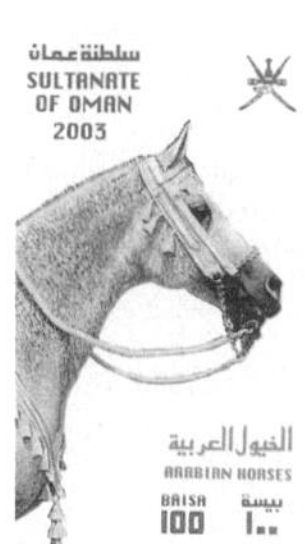

189 Horse's Head

2003. Arabian Horses. Four sheets, each 95 × 80 mm containing T **189** and similar vert designs. Multicoloured.

MS595 (a) 100b. Type **189**; (b) 100b. Chestnut; (c) 100b. Grey; (d) 100b. Wearing tasselled breast harness 1·10 1·10

190 Chinese and Omani Buildings (½-size illustration)

2003. 25th Anniv of Oman—China Diplomatic Relations.

596	**190**	70b. multicoloured	20	15

ORANGE FREE STATE (ORANGE RIVER COLONY) Pt. 1

British possession 1848–54. Independent 1854–99. Annexed by Great Britain, 1900. Later a province of the Union of South Africa.

12 pence = 1 shilling;
20 shillings = 1 pound.

1 **38** King Edward VII, Springbok and Gnu

1869.

48	**1**	½d. brown	2·00	50
84		½d. yellow	2·00	35
2		1d. brown	10·00	45
68		1d. purple	2·75	30
50		2d. mauve	12·00	30
51		3d. blue	2·50	2·00
19		4d. blue	4·00	2·50
7		6d. red	10·00	2·00
9		1s. orange	32·00	1·50
87		1s. brown	18·00	1·50
20		5s. green	9·00	11·00

1877. Surch in figures.

75	**1**	½d. on 3d. blue	5·50	3·00
36		½d. on 5s. green	14·00	3·75
54		1d. on 3d. blue	4·50	60
57		1d. on 4d. blue	25·00	4·50
22		1d. on 5s. green	50·00	19·00
53		2d. on 3d. blue	30·00	2·00
67		2½d. on 3d. blue	12·00	70
83		2½d. on 3d. blue	5·00	80
40		3d. on 4d. blue	29·00	16·00
12		4d. on 6d. red	£180	25·00

1896. Surch **Halve Penny.**

77	**1**	½d. on 3d. blue	65	50

1900. Surch **V.R.I.** and value in figures.

112	**1**	½d. on ½d. orange	30	20
113		1d. on 1d. purple	30	20
114		2d. on 2d. mauve	1·00	30
104		2½d. on 3d. blue (No. 83)	13·00	10·00
117		3d. on 3d. blue	60	30
118		4d. on 4d. blue	2·00	2·50
108		6d. on 6d. red	38·00	35·00
120		6d. on 6d. blue	70	40
121		1s. on 1s. brown	4·00	45
122		5s. on 5s. green	7·00	8·50

1900. Stamps of Cape of Good Hope optd **ORANGE RIVER COLONY.**

133	**17**	½d. green	40	10
134		1d. red	1·00	10
135	**6**	2½d. blue	1·00	35

1902. No. 120 surch **4d** and bar.

136	**1**	4d. on 6d. blue	1·50	75

1902. Surch **E. R. I. 6d**.

137	**1**	6d. on 6d. blue	3·50	9·50

1902. No. 20 surch **One Shilling** and star.

138	**1**	1s. on 5s. green	7·00	12·00

1903.

139	**38**	½d. green	8·00	1·25
140		1d. red	4·25	10
141		2d. brown	4·75	80
142		2½d. blue	1·60	50
143		3d. mauve	7·00	90
150		4d. red and green	4·50	2·25
145		6d. red and mauve	8·50	1·00
146		1s. red and brown	26·00	1·75
147		5s. blue and brown	75·00	22·00

MILITARY FRANK STAMP

M 1

1899.

M1	M **1**	(–) black on yellow	13·00	45·00

POLICE FRANK STAMPS

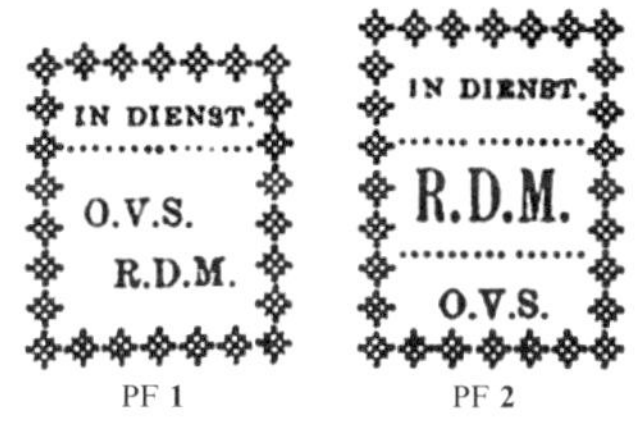

PF 1 PF 2

1896.

PF2	PF **1**	(–) black	£140	£170

1899.

PF3	PF **2**	(–) black on yellow	£130	£130

ORCHHA Pt. 1

A state of Central India. Now uses Indian stamps.

12 pies = 1 anna; 16 annas = 1 rupee.

1 2

1913. Imperf.

1	**1**	½a. green	32·00	90·00
2		1a. red	20·00	£160

1914. Imperf.

3a	**2**	¼a. blue	40	3·75
4		½a. green	55	4·75
5c		1a. red	2·50	5·00
6		2a. brown	4·50	23·00
7b		4a. yellow	8·50	29·00

3 Maharaja Vir Singh II

5 Maharaja Vir Singh II

1935.

8b	3	¼a. purple and grey	50	2·50
9		½a. grey and green	50	1·75
10		¾a. mauve and green	50	1·75
11	–	1a. green and brown	50	1·75
12	3	1¼a. grey and mauve	45	1·75
13		1½a. brown and red	45	1·75
14		2a. blue and orange	45	1·75
15		2½a. brown and orange	65	1·90
16		3a. blue and mauve	65	1·90
17		4a. purple and green	65	3·75
18		6a. black and buff	70	3·75
19		8a. brown and purple	2·00	4·75
20		12a. green and purple	1·00	4·75
21		12a. blue and purple	26·00	65·00
22		1r. brown and green	80	5·50
24		2r. brown and yellow	2·75	14·00
25		3r. black and blue	1·50	14·00
26		4r. black and brown	2·75	16·00
27		5r. blue and purple	3·00	17·00
28	–	10r. green and red	7·00	24·00
29	–	15r. black and green	12·00	55·00
30	–	25r. orange and blue	16·00	65·00

DESIGN: 1a., 10r. to 25r. As Type **3**, but inscr "POSTAGE & REVENUE". There are two different versions of the portrait for the 1r. value.

1939.

31	5	¼a. brown	3·75	65·00
32		½a. green	3·75	50·00
33		¾a. blue	4·25	85·00
34		1a. red	3·75	17·00
35		1¼a. blue	3·75	85·00
36		1½a. mauve	4·00	£100
37		2a. red	3·75	65·00
38		2½a. green	3·75	£180
39		3a. violet	5·50	90·00
40		4a. slate	7·00	25·00
41		8a. mauve	11·00	£180
42	–	1r. green	19·00	
43	–	2r. violet	40·00	£475
44	–	5r. orange	£120	
45	–	10r. green	£140	
46	–	15r. lilac	£9000	
47	–	25r. purple	£6500	

The rupee values are larger (25 × 30 mm) and have different frame.

PAHANG Pt. 1

A state of the Federation of Malaya, incorporated in Malaysia in 1963.

100 cents = 1 dollar (Straits or Malayan).

1889. Nos. 52/3 and 63 of Straits Settlements optd **PAHANG**.

4a		2c. red	4·50	8·00
2		8c. orange	£1700	£1500
3		10c. grey	£225	£250

1891. No. 68 of Straits Settlements surch **PAHANG Two CENTS**.

7		2c. on 24c. green	£150	£160

9 Tiger

10 Tiger

1891.

11	9	1c. green	4·25	3·25
12		2c. red	4·50	3·25
13		5c. blue	11·00	40·00

1895.

14	10	3c. purple and red	6·50	2·75
15		4c. purple and red	17·00	12·00
16		5c. purple and yellow	25·00	21·00

1897. No. 13 divided, and each half surch.

18	9	2c. on half of 5c. blue	£1300	£375
18d		3c. on half of 5c. blue	£1300	£375

1898. Stamps of Perak optd **Pahang**.

19	44	10c. purple and orange	18·00	25·00
20		25c. green and red	85·00	£150
21		50c. purple and black	£350	£375
22		50c. green and black	£225	£275
23	45	$1 green	£350	£425
24		$5 green and blue	£1100	£1600

1898. Stamp of Perak surch **Pahang Four cents**.

25	44	4c. on 8c. purple and blue	3·75	5·50

1899. No. 16 surch **Four cents**.

28	10	4c. on 5c. purple and yellow	16·00	55·00

15 Sultan Sir Abu Bakar

16 Sultan Sir Abu Bakar

1935.

29	15	1c. black	15	40
30		2c. green	80	50
31		3c. green	15·00	15·00
32		4c. orange	50	50
33		5c. brown	60	10
34		6c. red	13·00	1·75
35		8c. grey	60	10
36		8c. red	2·25	50·00
37		10c. purple	60	10
38		12c. blue	1·75	1·25
39		15c. blue	12·00	50·00
40		25c. purple and red	80	1·50
41		30c. purple and orange	80	1·10
42		40c. red and purple	75	2·00
43		50c. black on green	2·75	1·50
44		$1 black and red on blue	2·00	8·00
45		$2 green and red	19·00	28·00
46		$5 green and red on green	7·50	60·00

1948. Silver Wedding. As T **4b/c** of Pitcairn Islands.

47		10c. violet	15	60
48		$5 green	24·00	40·00

1949. U.P.U. As T **4d/g** of Pitcairn Islands.

49		10c. purple	30	20
50		15c. blue	1·10	1·25
51		25c. orange	35	1·25
52		50c. black	70	2·00

1950.

53	16	1c. black	10	10
54		2c. orange	20	10
55		3c. green	30	80
56		4c. brown	80	10
57a		5c. purple	50	15
58		6c. grey	30	30
59		8c. red	50	1·50
60		8c. green	85	75
61		10c. mauve	25	10
62		12c. red	85	1·25
63		15c. blue	75	10
64		20c. black and green	50	2·75
65		20c. blue	1·00	10
66		25c. purple and orange	50	10
67		30c. red and purple	1·25	35
68		35c. red and purple	60	25
69		40c. red and purple	1·50	7·50
70		50c. black and blue	1·50	10
71		$1 blue and purple	2·75	2·75
72		$2 green and red	13·00	21·00
73		$5 green and brown	55·00	70·00

1953. Coronation. As T **4h** of Pitcairn Islands.

74		10c. black and purple	1·25	10

1957. As Nos. 92/102 of Kedah but inset portrait of Sultan Sir Abu Bakar.

75		1c. black	10	10
76		2c. red	10	10
77		4c. sepia	10	10
78		5c. lake	10	10
79		8c. green	1·00	2·25
80		10c. sepia	1·25	10
81		10c. purple	3·50	30
82		20c. blue	2·25	20
83		50c. black and blue	45	75
84		$1 blue and purple	6·00	2·00
85		$2 green and red	4·00	9·00
86		$5 brown and green	11·00	15·00

17 "Vanda hookeriana"

1965. As Nos. 115/21 of Kedah but with inset portrait of Sultan Sir Abu Bakar as in T **17**.

87	17	1c. multicoloured	10	1·25
88	–	2c. multicoloured	10	1·25
89	–	5c. multicoloured	15	10
90	–	6c. multicoloured	30	1·25
91	–	10c. multicoloured	20	10
92	–	15c. multicoloured	1·00	10
93	–	20c. multicoloured	1·60	40

The higher values used in Pahang were Nos. 20/7 of Malaysia (National Issue).

18 "Precis orithya"

19 Sultan Haji Ahmad Shah

1971. Butterflies. As Nos. 124/30 of Kedah, but with portrait of Sultan Sir Abu Bakar as in T **18**.

96	–	1c. multicoloured	20	1·75
97	–	2c. multicoloured	50	2·00
98	–	5c. multicoloured	1·00	50
99	–	6c. multicoloured	1·50	2·25
100	–	10c. multicoloured	1·00	30
101	18	15c. multicoloured	1·75	10
102	–	20c. multicoloured	2·00	50

The higher values in use with this issue were Nos. 64/71 of Malaysia (National Issues).

1975. Installation of the Sultan.

103	19	10c. green, lilac and gold	50	1·25
104		15c. black, yellow and green	60	10
105		50c. black, blue and green	1·75	4·25

1977. As Nos. 97/8, 100/102 but with portrait of Sultan Haji Ahmad Shah.

106	–	2c. multicoloured	60·00	55·00
107	–	5c. multicoloured	70	1·25
108	–	10c. multicoloured	1·00	75
109	18	15c. multicoloured	1·00	30
110	–	20c. multicoloured	4·00	1·75

20 "Rhododendron scortechinii"

21 Rice

1979. Flowers. As Nos. 135/41 of Kedah but with portrait of Sultan Haji Ahmad Shah as in T **20**.

111		1c. "Rafflesia hasseltii"	10	1·00
112		2c. "Pterocarpus indicus"	10	1·00
113		5c. "Lagerstroemia speciosa"	10	30
114		10c. "Durio zibethinus"	15	10
115		15c. "Hibiscus rosa-sinensis"	15	10
116		20c. Type **20**	20	10
117		25c. "Etlingera elatior" (inscr "Phaeomeria speciosa")	40	40

1986. As Nos. 152/8 of Kedah but with portrait of Sultan Ahmad Shah as in T **21**.

125		1c. Coffee	10	10
126		2c. Coconuts	10	10
127		5c. Cocoa	10	10
128		10c. Black pepper	10	10
129		15c. Rubber	10	10
130		20c. Oil palm	10	10
131		30c. Type **21**	10	15

PAKHOI Pt. 17

An Indo-Chinese Post Office in China, closed in 1922.

1903. Stamps of Indo-China, "Tablet" key-type, surch **PACKHOI** and value in Chinese.

1	D	1c. black and red on blue	9·25	10·00
2		2c. brown and blue on buff	4·75	5·25
3		4c. brown and blue on grey	5·25	5·00
4		5c. green and red	2·75	4·00
5		10c. red and blue	1·75	4·50
6		15c. grey and red	3·50	5·50
7		20c. red and blue on green	8·50	11·00
8		25c. blue and red	5·50	8·50
9		25c. black and red on pink	6·50	9·50
10		30c. brown and blue on drab	15·00	13·00
11		40c. red and blue on yellow	55·00	55·00
12		50c. red and blue on pink	£275	£275
13		50c. brown and red on blue	80·00	65·00
14		75c. brown and red on orange	70·00	65·00
15		1f. green and red	75·00	65·00
16		5f. mauve and blue on lilac	£110	£110

1906. Stamps of Indo-China surch **PAK-HOI** and value in Chinese.

17	8	1c. green	2·50	2·75
18		2c. red on yellow	2·25	2·25
19		4c. mauve on blue	2·50	2·50
20		5c. green	3·00	1·90
21		10c. red	2·75	2·50
22		15c. brown on blue	6·25	6·50
23		20c. red on green	3·75	3·75
24		25c. blue	3·50	3·75
25		30c. brown on cream	4·50	4·00
26		35c. black on yellow	4·00	4·00
27		40c. black on grey	3·75	4·25
28		50c. olive on green	8·00	6·50
29	D	75c. brown on orange	60·00	60·00
30	8	1f. green	26·00	26·00
31		2f. brown on yellow	45·00	42·00
32	D	5f. mauve on lilac	£100	£110
33	8	10f. red on green	£110	£110

1908. Stamps of Indo-China (Native types) surch **PAKHOI** and value in Chinese.

34	10	1c. black and brown	1·50	1·00
35		2c. black and brown	1·00	1·25
36		4c. black and blue	1·00	1·50
37		5c. black and green	1·40	1·75
38		10c. black and red	1·75	3·25
39		15c. black and violet	2·50	3·25
40	11	20c. black and violet	2·50	2·75
41		25c. black and blue	2·75	3·50
42		30c. black and brown	3·25	4·25
43		35c. black and green	3·25	4·25
44		40c. black and brown	3·00	4·25
45		50c. black and red	3·75	4·25
46	12	75c. black and orange	6·25	6·25
47	–	1f. black and red	8·00	8·00
48	–	2f. black and green	17·00	18·00
49	–	5f. black and blue	80·00	£100
50	–	10f. black and violet	£110	£110

1919. As last, surch in addition in figures and words.

51	10	⅖c. on 1c. black and green	50	2·75
52		⅘c. on 2c. black and brown	1·25	3·00
53		1⅗c. on 4c. black and blue	1·50	2·75
54		2c. on 5c. black and green	2·00	3·25
55		4c. on 10c. black and red	3·75	4·00
56		6c. on 15c. black and violet	3·00	3·00
57	11	8c. on 20c. black and violet	4·25	4·25
58		10c. on 25c. black and blue	4·50	4·25
59		12c. on 30c. black & brown	3·00	3·25
60		14c. on 35c. black and green	2·50	3·00
61		16c. on 40c. black & brown	3·50	3·75
62		20c. on 50c. black and red	2·75	3·25
63	12	30c. on 75c. black & orange	3·50	4·00
64	–	40c. on 1f. black and red	12·50	12·50
65	–	80c. on 2f. black and green	5·25	5·25
66	–	2pi. on 5f. black and blue	12·00	14·00
67	–	4pi. on 10f. black and violet	24·00	29·00

PAKISTAN Pt. 1

A Dominion created in 1947 from territory with predominantly Moslem population in Eastern and Western India. Became an independent Islamic Republic within the British Commonweath in 1956. The eastern provinces declared their independence in 1971 and are now known as Bangladesh.

On 30 January 1972 Pakistan left the Commonweath but rejoined on 1 October 1989.

1947. 12 pies = 1 anna;
16 annas = 1 rupee.
1961. 100 paisa = 1 rupee.

1947. King George VI stamps of India optd **PAKISTAN**.

1	100a	3p. grey	10	10
2		½a. purple	10	10
3		9p. green	10	10
4		1a. red	10	10
5	101	1½a. violet	10	10
6		2a. red	10	20
7		3a. violet	10	20
8		3½a. blue	65	2·25
9	102	4a. brown	20	20
10		6a. green	1·00	75
11		8a. violet	30	60
12		12a. red	1·00	20
13	–	14a. purple (No. 277)	2·50	2·00
14	93	1r. grey and brown	1·75	1·25
15		2r. purple and brown	3·25	1·75
16		5r. green and blue	4·00	4·00
17		10r. purple and claret	4·00	2·75
18		15r. brown and green	48·00	80·00
19		25r. violet and purple	55·00	45·00

3 Constituent Assembly Building, Karachi

1948. Independence.
20 **3** 1½a. blue . . . . 1·00 70
21 – 2½a. green . . . . 1·00 20
22 – 3a. brown . . . . 1·00 35
23 – 1r. red . . . . 1·00 70
DESIGNS—HORIZ: 2½a. Entrance to Karachi Airport; 3a. Gateway to Lahore Fort. VERT: 1r. Crescent and Stars in foliated frame.

7 Scales of Justice **9** Lloyds Barrage

12 Salimullah Hostel, Dacca University

13 Khyber Pass

1948. Designs with crescent moon pointing to right.
24 **7** 3p. red 10 10
25 6p. violet 60 10
26 9p. green 50 10
27 – 1a. blue 10 50
28 – 1½a. green 10 10
29 – 2a. red . . . . 1·00 50
30 **9** 2½a. green . . . . 2·75 6·50
31 – 3a. green . . . . 7·50 1·00
32 **9** 3½a. blue . . . . 3·50 5·50
33 4a. brown 50 10
34 – 6a. blue 50 70
35 – 8a. black 50 70
36 – 10a. red . . . . 4·75 7·00
37 – 12a. red . . . . 7·50 1·00
38 **12** 1r. blue . . . . 5·50 10
39 2r. brown . . . . 20·00 60
40a 5r. red . . . . 12·00 20
41b **13** 10r. mauve . . . . 18·00 1·25
42 15r. green . . . . 18·00 14·00
210b 25r. violet . . . . 3·00 4·00
DESIGNS—VERT (as Type **7**): 1a., 1½a., 2a. Star and Crescent; 6a., 8a., 12a. Karachi Port Trust. HORIZ (as Type **12**): 3a., 10a. Karachi Airport.

1949. As 1948 but with crescent moon pointing to left.
44a – 1a. blue . . . . 3·75 10
45a – 1½a. green . . . . 3·00 10
46a – 2a. red . . . . 3·50 10
47 – 3a. green . . . . 12·00 1·00
48 – 6a. blue . . . . 9·00 1·25
49 – 8a. black . . . . 7·00 1·50
50 – 10a. red . . . . 17·00 2·00
51 – 12a. red . . . . 22·00 50

16

1949. 1st Death Anniv of Mohammed Ali Jinnah.
52 **16** 1½a. brown . . . . 2·00 1·25
53 3a. green . . . . 2·00 1·25
54 – 10a. black . . . . 6·00 8·00
DESIGN: 10a. inscription reads "QUAID-I-AZAM MOHAMMAD ALI JINNAH" etc.

17 Pottery

1951. 4th Anniv of Independence.
55 **17** 2½a. red . . . . 1·75 1·25
56 – 3a. purple . . . . 1·00 10
57 **17** 3½a. blue (A) . . . . . . 1·25 3·75
57a – 3½a. blue (B) . . . . . . 3·50 5·00
58 – 4a. green 75 10
59 – 6a. orange . . . . 1·00 10
60 – 8a. sepia . . . . 4·50 25
61 – 10a. violet . . . . 2·00 1·75
62 – 12a. slate . . . . 2·00 10
DESIGNS—VERT: 3, 12a. Airplane and hour-glass; 4, 6a. Saracenic leaf pattern. HORIZ: 8, 10a. Archway and lamp.
(A) has Arabic fraction on left as in Type **17**, (B) has it on right.
For similar 3½a. see No. 88.

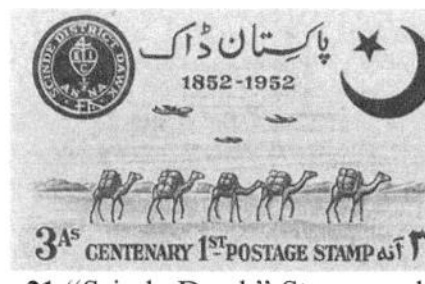

21 "Scinde Dawk" Stamp and Ancient and Modern Transport

1952. Cent of "Scinde Dawk" Issue of India.
63 **21** 3a. green on olive 75 85
64 12a. brown on salmon . . . 1·00 15

22 Kaghan Valley

24 Tea Plantation, East Pakistan

1954. 7th Anniv of Independence.
65 **22** 6p. violet 10 10
66 – 9p. blue . . . . 3·25 2·00
67 – 1a. red 10 10
68 – 1½a. red 10 10
69 **24** 14a. myrtle . . . . 1·25 10
70 – 1r. green . . . . 11·00 10
71 – 2r. orange . . . . 2·75 10
DESIGNS—HORIZ (as Type **22**): 9p. Mountains, Gilgit; 1a. Badshahi Mosque, Lahore. (As Type **24**): 1r. Cotton plants, West Pakistan; 2r. Jute fields and river, East Pakistan. VERT (as Type **22**): 1½a. Mausoleum of Emperor Jehangir, Lahore.

29 View of K2

1954. Conquest of K2 (Mount Godwin-Austen).
72 **29** 2a. violet 40 30

30 Karnaphuli Paper Mill, East Bengal **35** Map of West Pakistan

1955. 8th Anniv of Independence.
73 **30** 2½a. red (A) . . . . 50 1·40
73a – 2½a. red (B) . . . . 30 1·40
74 – 6a. blue . . . . 1·00 10
75 – 8a. violet . . . . 3·75 10
76 – 12a. red and orange . . . 4·00 10
DESIGNS: 6a. Textile mill, W. Pakistan; 8a. Jute mill, E. Pakistan; 12a. Main Sui gas plant.
(A) has Arabic fraction on left as in Type **30**, (B) has it on right.
For similar 2½a. see No. 87.

1955. 10th Anniv of U.N. Nos. 68 and 76 optd **TENTH ANNIVERSARY UNITED NATIONS 24.10.55.**
77 1½a. red . . . . 1·50 5·00
78 12a. red and orange . . . . . 50 3·50

1955. West Pakistan Unity.
79 **35** 1½a. green . . . . 40 1·25
80 2a. brown 50 10
81 12a. red . . . . 1·25 50

36 Constituent Assembly Building, Karachi

1956. Republic Day.
82 **36** 2a. green 80 10

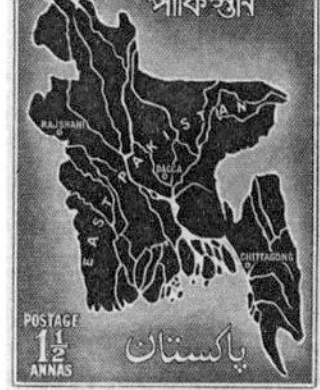

37 **38** Map of East Pakistan

1956. 9th Anniv of Independence.
83 **37** 2a. red 65 10

1956. 1st Session of National Assembly of Pakistan at Dacca.
84 **38** 1½a. green . . . . 40 1·50
85 2a. brown 40 10
86 12a. red . . . . 40 1·25

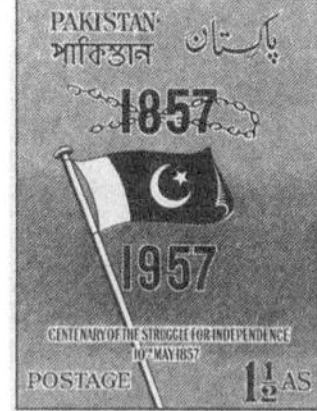

41 Orange Tree **42** Pakistani Flag

1957. 1st Anniv of Republic.
87 – 2½a. red 20 10
88 – 3½a. blue 30 10
89 **41** 10r. green and orange . . . 80 20
DESIGNS: 2½a. as Type **30** without value in Arabic at right; 3½a. as Type **17** without value in Arabic at right.

1957. Centenary of Struggle for Independence (Indian Mutiny).
90 **42** 1½a. green 50 10
91 12a. blue . . . . 1·25 10

43 Pakistani Industries

1957. 10th Anniv of Independence.
92 **43** 1½a. blue 20 30
93 4a. salmon . . . . 45 1·50
94 12a. mauve 45 50

1958. 2nd Anniv of Republic. As T **41**.
209 15r. red and purple . . . . 2·00 3·00
DESIGN: 15r. Coconut tree.

45

1958. 20th Death Anniv of Mohammed Iqbal (poet).
96 **45** 1½a. olive and black 55 40
97 2a. brown and black 55 10
98 14a. turquoise and black . . 90 10

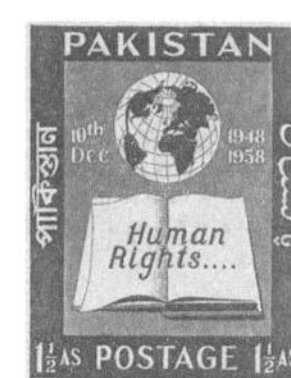

46 U.N. Charter and Globe

1958. 10th Anniv of Declaration of Human Rights.
99 **46** 1½a. turquoise 10 10
100 14a. sepia 45 10

1958. Scout Jamboree. Optd **PAKISTAN BOY SCOUT 2nd NATIONAL JAMBOREE CHITTAGONG Dec. 58-Jan. 59.**
101 **22** 6p. violet 20 10
102 – 8a. violet (No. 75) 40 10

1959. Revolution Day. No. 74 optd **REVOLUTION DAY Oct. 27, 1959.**
103 6a. blue 80 10

49 "Centenary of An Idea" **50** Armed Forces Badge

1959. Red Cross Commemoration.
104 **49** 2a. red and green 30 10
105 10a. red and blue 55 10

1960. Armed Forces Day.
106 **50** 2a. red, blue and green . . 50 10
107 14a. red and blue . . . . 1·00 10

51 Map of Pakistan

1960.
108 **51** 6p. purple 40 10
109 2a. red 60 10
110 8a. green . . . . 1·25 10
111 1r. blue . . . . 2·00 10

52 "Uprooted Tree" **55** "Land Reforms, Rehabilitation and Reconstruction"

53 Punjab Agricultural College

1960. World Refugee Year.
112 **52** 2a. red 20 10
113 10a. green 30 10

1960. Golden Jubilee of Punjab Agricultural College, Lyallpur.
114 **53** 2a. blue and red 10 10
115 – 8a. green and violet . . . 20 10
DESIGN: 8a. College arms.

1960. Revolution Day.
116 **55** 2a. green, pink and brown 10 10
117 14a. green, yellow and blue 50 75

56 Caduceus **57** "Economic Co-operation"

1960. Centenary of King Edward Medical College, Lahore.
118 **56** 2a. yellow, black and blue 50 10
119 14a. green, black and red 1·75 1·00

1960. Int Chamber of Commerce C.A.F.E.A. Meeting, Karachi.
120 **57** 14a. brown 50 10

58 Zam-Zama Gun, Lahore ("Kim's Gun" after Rudyard Kipling)

1960. 3rd Pakistan Boy Scouts' National Jamboree, Lahore.
121 **58** 2a. red, yellow and green 80 10

1961. Surch in "PAISA".
122 – 1p. on 1½a. red (No. 68) 40 10
123 **7** 2p. on 3p. red 10 10
124 **51** 3p. on 6p. purple 15 10
125 – 7p. on 1a. red (No. 67) . . 40 10
126 **51** 13p. on 2a. red 40 10
127 **37** 13p. on 2a. red 30 10
See also Nos. 262/4.

60 Khyber Pass

61 Shalimar Gardens, Lahore
62 Chota Sona Masjid (gateway)

1961.
170 **60** 1p. violet 10 10
132 2p. red . . . . 1·00 10
133 3p. purple 75 10
173 5p. blue 10 10
135 7p. green . . . . 2·00 10
175 **61** 10p. brown 10 10
176 13p. violet 10 10
176a 15p. purple 20 10
176b 20p. green 30 10
138 25p. blue . . . . 5·50 10
178 40p. purple 15 30
179 50p. green 15 10
141 75p. red 40 70
142 90p. green 70 70
204 **62** 1r. red 30 10
144 1r.25 violet 75 80
206 2r. orange 55 15
207 5r. green . . . . 5·50 65

1961. Lahore Stamp Exn. No. 110 optd **LAHORE STAMP EXHIBITION 1961** and emblem.
145 **51** 8a. green . . . . 1·00 1·75

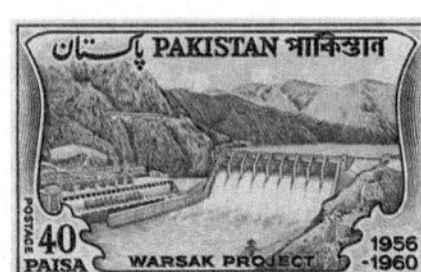

64 Warsak Dam and Power Station

1961. Completion of Warsak Hydro-electric Project.
146 **64** 40p. black and blue . . . 60 10

65 Narcissus

1961. Child Welfare Week.
147 **65** 13p. turquoise 50 10
148 90p. mauve . . . . 1·25 20

66 Ten Roses
67 Police Crest and "Traffic Control"

1961. Co-operative Day.
149 **66** 13p. red and green 40 10
150 90p. red and blue 85 90

1961. Police Centenary.
151 **67** 13p. silver, black and blue 50 10
152 40p. silver, black and red 1·00 20

68 Locomotive "Eagle", 1861

1961. Railway Centenary.
153 **68** 13p. green, black and yellow 75 80
154 – 50p. yellow, black and green . . . . 1·00 1·50
DESIGN: 50p. Diesel locomotive No. 20 and tracks forming "1961".

1962. 1st Karachi–Dacca Jet Flight. No. 87 surch with Boeing 720B airliner and **FIRST JET FLIGHT KARACHI–DACCA 13 Paisa**.
155 13p. on 2½a. red . . . . . . 1·75 1·25

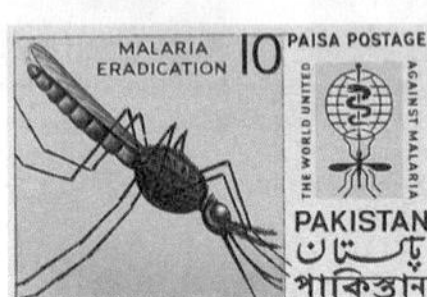

71 "Anopheles sp." (mosquito)

1962. Malaria Eradication.
156 **71** 10p. black, yellow and red 35 10
157 – 13p. black, lemon and red 35 10
DESIGN: 13p. Mosquito pierced by blade.

73 Pakistan Map and Jasmine

1962. New Constitution.
158 **73** 40p. green, turquoise & grey 70 10

74 Football

1962. Sports.
159 **74** 7p. black and blue 10 10
160 – 13p. black and green . . . 60 1·50
161 – 25p. black and purple . . . 20 10
162 – 40p. black and brown . . . 2·00 2·50
DESIGNS: 13p. Hockey; 25p. Squash; 40p. Cricket.

78 Marble Fruit Dish and Bahawalpuri Clay Flask

1962. Small Industries.
163 **78** 7p. lake 10 10
164 – 13p. green . . . . 2·50 2·50
165 – 25p. violet 10 10
166 – 40p. green 10 10
167 – 50p. red 10 10
DESIGNS: 13p. Sports equipment; 25p. Camelskin lamp and brassware; 40p. Wooden powder-bowl and basket-work; 50p. Inlaid cigarette-box and brassware.

83 "Child Welfare"

1962. 16th Anniv of U.N.I.C.E.F.
168 **83** 13p. black, blue and purple 35 10
169 40p. black, yellow and blue 35 10

1963. Pakistan U.N. Force in West Irian. Optd **U.N. FORCE W. IRIAN**.
182 **61** 13p. violet 10 75

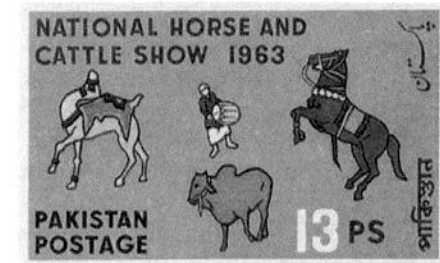

85 "Dancing" Horse, Camel and Bull

1963. National Horse and Cattle Show.
183 **85** 13p. blue, sepia and pink 10 10

86 Wheat and Tractor

1963. Freedom from Hunger.
184 **86** 13p. brown . . . . 2·00 10
185 – 50p. bistre . . . . 3·50 55
DESIGN: 50p. Lifting rice.

1963. 2nd International Stamp Exhibition, Dacca. Surch **13 PAISA INTERNATIONAL DACCA STAMP EXHIBITION 1963**.
186 **51** 13p. on 2a. red 50 50

89 Centenary Emblem

1963. Centenary of Red Cross.
187 **89** 40p. red and olive . . . . 2·00 15

90 Paharpur

1963. Archaeological Series.
188 **90** 7p. blue 55 10
189 – 13p. sepia 55 10
190 – 40p. red 90 10
191 – 50p. violet 95 10
DESIGNS—VERT: 13p. Moenjodaro. HORIZ: 40p. Taxila; 50p. Mainamati.

1963. Centenary of Pakistan Public Works Department. Surch **100 YEARS OF P.W.D. OCTOBER, 1963 13**.
192 **60** 13p. on 3p. purple 10 10

95 Ataturk's Mausoleum

1963. 25th Death Anniv of Kemal Ataturk.
193 **95** 50p. red 50 10

96 Globe and U.N.E.S.C.O. Emblem

1963. 15th Anniv of Declaration of Human Rights.
194 **96** 50p. brown, red and blue 40 10

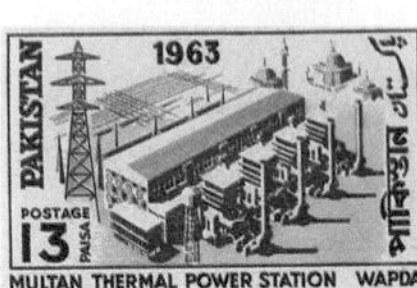

97 Thermal Power Installations

1963. Completion of Multan Thermal Power Station.
195 **97** 13p. blue 10 10

99 Temple of Thot, Queen Nefertari and Maids

1964. Nubian Monuments Preservation.
211 **99** 13p. blue and red 30 10
212 – 50p. purple and black . . . 70 10
DESIGN: 50p. Temple of Abu Simbel.

101 "Unisphere" and Pakistan Pavilion

1964. New York World's Fair.
213 **101** 13p. blue 10 10
214 – 1r.25 blue and orange . . 40 20
DESIGN—VERT: 1r.25, Pakistan Pavilion on "Unisphere".

103 Shah Abdul Latif's Mausoleum
106 Bengali and Urdu Alphabets

104 Mausoleum of Quaid-i-Azam

1964. Death Bicentenary of Shah Abdul Latif of Bhit.
215 **103** 50p. blue and red . . . . 1·00 10

1964. 16th Death Anniv of Mohammed Ali Jinnah (Quaid-i-Azam).
216 **104** 15p. green . . . . 1·00 10
217 – 50p. green . . . . 2·25 10
DESIGN: 50p. As Type **104**, but 26½ × 31½ mm.

1964. Universal Children's Day.
218 **106** 15p. brown 10 10

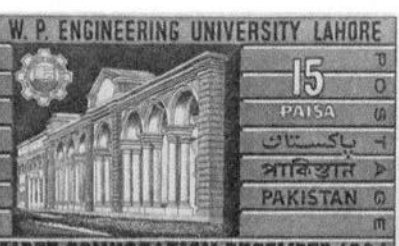

107 University Building

1964. 1st Convocation of the West Pakistan University of Engineering and Technology, Lahore.
219 **107** 15p. brown 10 10

108 "Help the Blind"

1965. Blind Welfare.
220 **108** 15p. blue and yellow . . . 20 10

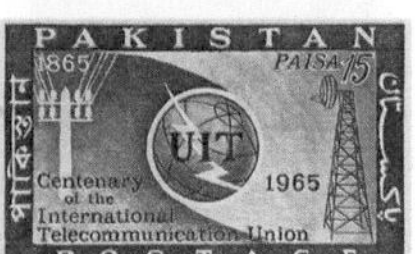

109 I.T.U. Emblem and Symbols

1965. Centenary of I.T.U.
221 **109** 15p. purple . . . . 1·50 30

110 I.C.Y. Emblem

1965. International Co-operation Year.
222 **110** 15p. black and blue . . . 50 15
223 50p. green and yellow . . 1·50 40

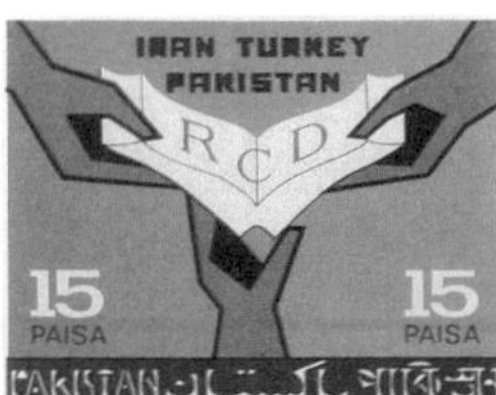

111 "Co-operation"

1965. 1st Anniv of Regional Development Co-operation Pact. Multicoloured.
224 15p. Type **111** 20 10
225 50p. Globe and flags of Turkey, Iran and Pakistan (54½ × 30¾ mm) . . . . . 1·10 10

113 Soldier and Tanks

1965. Pakistan Armed Forces. Multicoloured.
226 7p. Type **113** 75 30
227 15p. Naval Officer and "Tughril" (destroyer) . . . 1·50 10
228 50p. Pilot and Lockheed F-104C Starfighters . . . . 2·50 30

116 Army, Navy and Air Force Crests

1966. Armed Forces Day.
229 **116** 15p. blue, green and buff 1·00 10

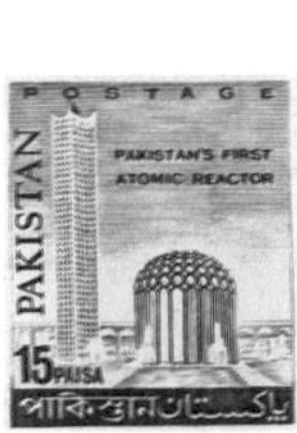

117 Atomic Reactor, Islamabad

119 Children

118 Bank Crest

1966. Inauguration of Pakistan's 1st Atomic Reactor.
230 **117** 15p. black 10 10

1966. Silver Jubilee of Habib Bank.
231 **118** 15p. green, orange & sepia 10 10

1966. Universal Children's Day.
232 **119** 15p. black, red and yellow 10 10

120 U.N.E.S.C.O. Emblem

1966. 20th Anniversary of U.N.E.S.C.O.
233 **120** 15p. multicoloured . . . 2·75 30

121 Flag, Secretariat Building and President Ayub

1966. Islamabad (new capital).
234 **121** 15p. multicoloured . . . 35 10
235 50p. multicoloured . . . 65 10

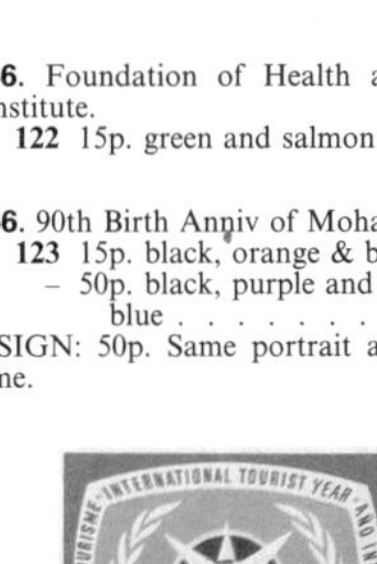

122 Avicenna

123 Mohammed Ali Jinnah

1966. Foundation of Health and Tibbi Research Institute.
236 **122** 15p. green and salmon . . 40 10

1966. 90th Birth Anniv of Mohammed Ali Jinnah.
237 **123** 15p. black, orange & blue 15 10
238 – 50p. black, purple and blue 35 10
DESIGN: 50p. Same portrait as 15p. but different frame.

124 Tourist Year Emblem

1967. International Tourist Year.
239 **124** 15p. black, blue and brown 10 10

125 Emblem of Pakistan T.B. Association

126 Scout Salute and Badge

1967. Tuberculosis Eradication Campaign.
240 **125** 15p. red, sepia and brown 10 10

1967. 4th National Scout Jamboree.
241 **126** 15p. brown and purple . . 15 10

127 "Justice"

1967. Cent of West Pakistan High Court.
242 **127** 15p. multicoloured . . . 10 10

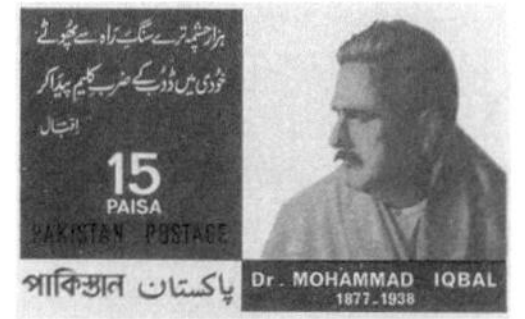

128 Dr. Mohammed Iqbal (philosopher)

1967. Iqbal Commemoration.
243 **128** 15p. sepia and red 15 10
244 1r. sepia and green . . . 35 10

129 Hilal-i-Isteqlal Flag

1967. Award of Hilal-i-Isteqlal (for Valour) to Lahore, Sialkot and Sargodha.
245 **129** 15p. multicoloured . . . 10 10

130 "20th Anniversary"

1967. 20th Anniv of Independence.
246 **130** 15p. red and green . . . 10 10

131 "Rice Exports"

1967. Pakistan Exports. Multicoloured.
247 10p. Type **131** 10 15
248 15p. Cotton plant, yarn and textiles (vert) (27 × 45 mm) 10 10
249 50p. Raw jute, bale and bags (vert) (27 × 45 mm) 20 15

134 Clay Toys

1967. Universal Children's Day.
250 **134** 15p. multicoloured . . . 10 10

135 Shah and Empress of Iran and Gulistan Palace, Teheran

1967. Coronation of Shah Mohammed Riza Pahlavi and Empress Farah of Iran.
251 **135** 50p. purple, blue and ochre . . . . 1·00 10

136 "Each For All–All for Each"

1967. Co-operative Day.
252 **136** 15p. multicoloured . . . 10 10

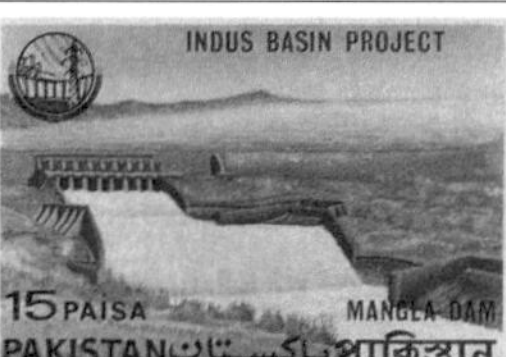

137 Mangla Dam

1967. Indus Basin Project.
253 **137** 15p. multicoloured . . . 10 10

138 Crab pierced by Sword

139 Human Rights Emblem

1967. The Fight Against Cancer.
254 **138** 15p. red and black . . . 70 10

1968. Human Rights Year.
255 **139** 15p. red and blue 10 15
256 50p. red, yellow and grey 10 15

140 Agricultural University, Mymensingh

1968. First Convocation of East Pakistan Agricultural University.
257 **140** 15p. multicoloured . . . 10 10

141 W.H.O. Emblem

1968. 20th Anniv of W.H.O.
258 **141** 15p. orange and red . . . 10 15
259 50p. orange and blue . . 10 15

142 Kazi Nazrul Islam (poet, composer and patriot)

1968. Nazrul Islam Commemoration.
260 **142** 15p. sepia and yellow . . 35 15
261 50p. sepia and red 65 15

1968. Nos. 56, 74 and 61 surch.
262 4p. on 3a. purple . . . . . . 1·00 1·75
263 4p. on 6a. blue . . . . . . 1·25 1·75
264 60p. on 10a. violet . . . . . 1·00 35

144 Children running with Hoops

1968. Universal Children's Day.
265 **144** 15p. multicoloured . . . 10 10

145 National Assembly

1968. "A Decade of Development".
266 **145** 10p. multicoloured . . . 10 10
267 – 15p. multicoloured . . . 10 10
268 – 50p. multicoloured . . . 2·00 20
269 – 60p. blue, purple and red 50 35
DESIGNS: 15p. Industry and Agriculture; 50p. Army, Navy and Air Force; 60p. Minaret and atomic reactor plant.

149 Chittagong Steel Mill

1969. Pakistan's First Steel Mill, Chittagong.
270 **149** 15p. grey, blue and olive 10 10

150 "Family"

1969. Family Planning.
271 **150** 15p. purple and blue . . . 10 10

151 Olympic Gold Medal and Hockey Player

1969. Olympic Hockey Champions.
272 **151** 15p. multicoloured . . . 75 50
273 1r. multicoloured . . . . 2·25 1·00

152 Mirza Ghalib and Lines of Verse

1969. Death Centenary of Mirza Ghalib (poet).
274 **152** 15p. multicoloured . . . 20 15
275 50p. multicoloured . . . 50 15
The lines of verse on No. 275 are different from those in Type **152**.

153 Dacca Railway Station

1969. 1st Anniv of New Dacca Railway Station.
276 **153** 15p. multicoloured . . . 30 10

154 I.L.O. Emblem and "1919–1969"

1969. 50th Anniv of I.L.O.
277 **154** 15p. buff and green . . . 10 10
278 50p. brown and red . . . 40 10

155 "Ladyon Balcony" (18th-cent Mogul)

1969. 5th Anniv of Regional Co-operation for Development. Miniatures. Multicoloured.
279 20p. Type **155** 15 10
280 50p. "Kneeling Servant" (17th-cent Persian) 15 10
281 1r. "Suleiman the Magnificent holding Audience" (16th-cent Turkish) 20 10

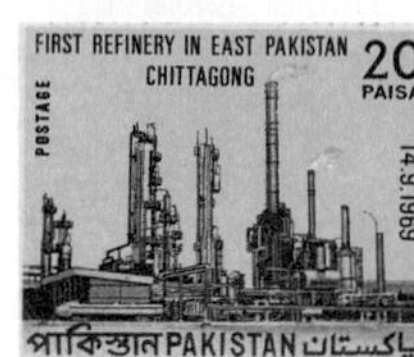

158 Eastern Refinery, Chittagong

1969. 1st East Pakistan Oil Refinery.
282 **158** 20p. multicoloured . . . 10 10

159 Children playing outside "School"

1969. Universal Children's Day.
283 **159** 20p. multicoloured . . . 10 10

160 Japanese Doll and P.I.A. Air Routes

1969. Inauguration of P.I.A. Pearl Route, Dacca–Tokyo.
284 **160** 20p. multicoloured . . . 40 10
285 50p. multicoloured . . . 60 40

161 "Reflection of Light" Diagram

1969 Millenary Commemorative of Ibn-al-Haitham (physicist).
286 **161** 20p. black, yellow and blue 10 10

162 Vickers Vimy and Karachi Airport

1969. 50th Anniv of 1st England–Australia Flight.
287 **162** 50p. multicoloured . . . 70 35

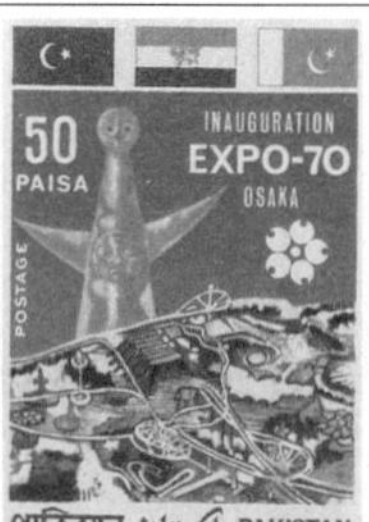

163 Flags, Sun Tower and Expo Site Plan

1970. "Expo-70" World Fair, Osaka.
288 **163** 50p. multicoloured . . . 20 30

164 New U.P.U. H.Q. Building

1970. New U.P.U. Headquarters Building.
289 **164** 20p. multicoloured . . . 15 10
290 50p. multicoloured . . . 25 25

165 U.N. H.Q. Building

1970. 25th Anniv of United Nations. Mult.
291 20p. Type **165** 10 10
292 50p. U.N. emblem 15 20

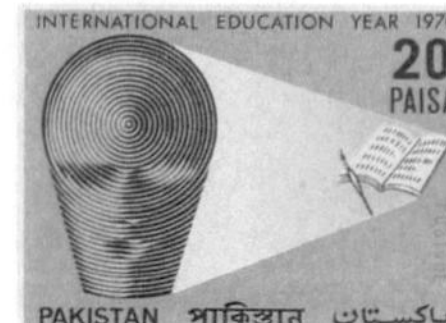

167 I.E.Y. Emblem, Book and Pen

1970. International Education Year.
293 **167** 20p. multicoloured . . . 10 10
294 50p. multicoloured . . . 20 20

168 Saiful Malook Lake (Pakistan)

1970. 6th Anniv of Regional Co-operation for Development. Multicoloured.
295 20p. Type **168** 15 10
296 50p. Seeyo-Se-Pol Bridge, Esfahan (Iran) 20 10
297 1r. View from Fethiye (Turkey) 20 15

171 Asian Productivity Symbol

1970. Asian Productivity Year.
298 **171** 50p. multicoloured . . . 20 20

172 Dr. Maria Montessori

1970. Birth Centenary of Dr. Maria Montessori (educationist).
299 **172** 20p. multicoloured . . . 15 10
300 50p. multicoloured . . . 15 30

173 Tractor and Fertilizer Factory

1970. 10th Near East F.A.O. Regional Conference, Islamabad.
301 **173** 20p. green and brown . . 15 20

174 Children and Open Book **175** Pakistan Flag and Text

1970. Universal Children's Day.
302 **174** 20p. multicoloured . . . 15 10

1970. Elections for National Assembly.
303 **175** 20p. green and violet . . 15 10

1970. Elections for Provincial Assemblies. As No. 303 but inscr "PROVINCIAL ASSEMBLIES".
304 **175** 20p. green and red . . . 15 10

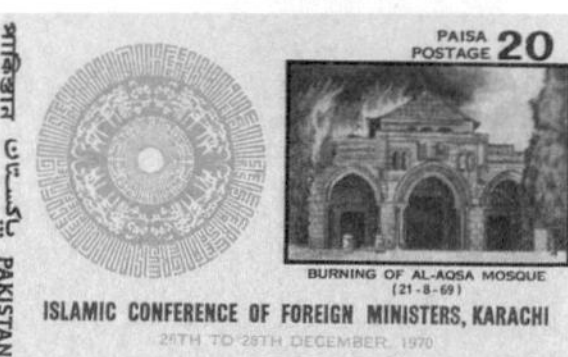

176 Conference Crest and burning Al-Aqsa Mosque

1970. Conference of Islamic Foreign Ministers, Karachi.
305 **176** 20p. multicoloured . . . 15 15

177 Coastal Embankments

1971. East Pakistan Coastal Embankments Project.
306 **177** 20p. multicoloured . . . 15 15

178 Emblem and United Peoples of the World **180** Chaharbagh School (Iran)

179 Maple Leaf Cement Factory, Daudkhel

1971. Racial Equality Year.
307 **178** 20p. multicoloured . . . 10 15
308 50p. multicoloured . . . 20 45

1971. 20th Anniv of Colombo Plan.
309 **179** 20p. brown, black & violet 10 10

1971. 7th Anniv of Regional Co-operation for Development. Multicoloured.
310 10p. Selimiye Mosque (Turkey) (horiz) 10 15
311 20p. Badshahi Mosque, Lahore (horiz) 20 25
312 50p. Type **180** 30 35

181 Electric Train and Boy with Toy Train

1971. Universal Children's Day.
313 **181** 20p. multicoloured . . . 1·75 50

182 Horseman and Symbols

1971. 2500th Anniv of Persian Monarchy.
314 **182** 10p. multicoloured . . . 20 30
315 20p. multicoloured . . . 30 40
316 50p. multicoloured . . . 40 75

183 Hockey-player and Trophy

1971. World Cup Hockey Tournament, Barcelona.
317 **183** 20p. multicoloured . . . 1·75 1·00

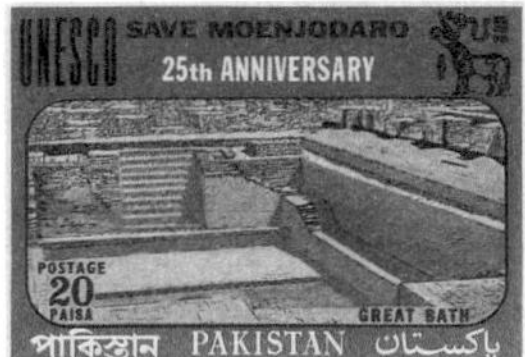

184 Great Bath, Moenjodaro

1971. 25th Anniv of U.N.E.S.C.O. and Campaign to save the Moenjodaro Excavations.
318 **184** 20p. multicoloured . . . 20 30

185 U.N.I.C.E.F. Symbol

1971. 25th Anniv of U.N.I.C.E.F.
319 **185** 50p. multicoloured . . . 30 60

186 King Hussein and Jordanian Flag

1971. 50th Anniv of Hashemite Kingdom of Jordan.
320 **186** 20p. multicoloured . . . 15 20

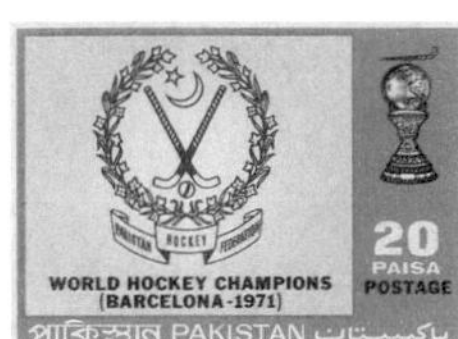

187 Badge of Hockey Federation and Trophy

1971. Hockey Championships Victory.
321 **187** 20p. multicoloured . . . 2·50 1·00

188 Reading Class

1972. International Book Year.
322 **188** 20p. multicoloured . . . 20 40

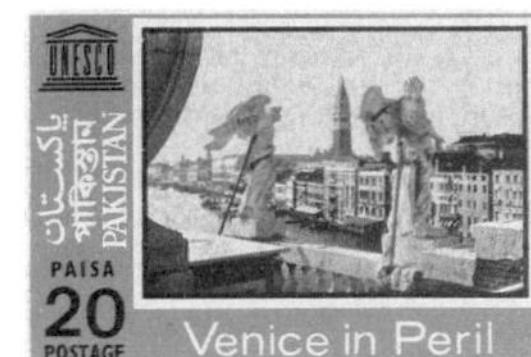

189 View of Venice

1972. U.N.E.S.C.O. Campaign to Save Venice.
323 **189** 20p. multicoloured . . . 30 40

190 E.C.A.F.E. Emblem and Discs

1972. 25th Anniv of E.C.A.F.E.
324 **190** 20p. multicoloured . . . 15 30

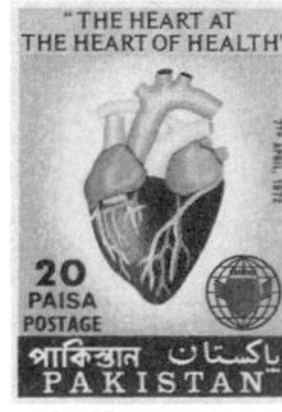

191 Human Heart **192** "Only One Earth"

1972. World Health Day.
325 **191** 20p. multicoloured . . . 20 30

1972. U.N. Conference on the Human Environment, Stockholm.
326 **192** 20p. multicoloured . . . 20 30

193 "Fisherman" (Cevat Dereli) **194** Mohammed Ali Jinnah and Tower

1972. 8th Anniv of Regional Co-operation for Development. Multicoloured.
327 10p. Type **193** 20 20
328 20p. "Iranian Woman" (Behzad) 35 25
329 50p. "Will and Power" (A. R. Chughtai) 55 70

1972. 25th Anniv of Independence. Mult.
330 10p. Type **194** 10 10
331 20p. "Land Reform" (74 × 23½) 15 30
332 20p. "Labour Reform" (74 × 23½) 15 30
333 20p. "Education Policy" (74 × 23½) 15 30
334 20p. "Health Policy" (74 × 23½) 15 30
335 60p. National Assembly Building (46 × 28 mm) . . 25 40

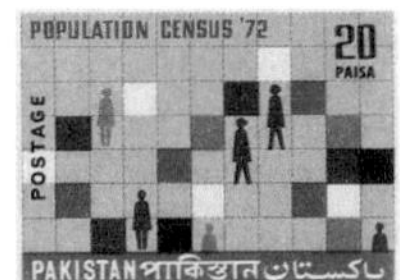

195 Donating Blood **196** People and Squares

1972. National Blood Transfusion Service.
336 **195** 20p. multicoloured . . . 20 30

1972. Centenary of Population Census.
337 **196** 20p. multicoloured . . . 20 20

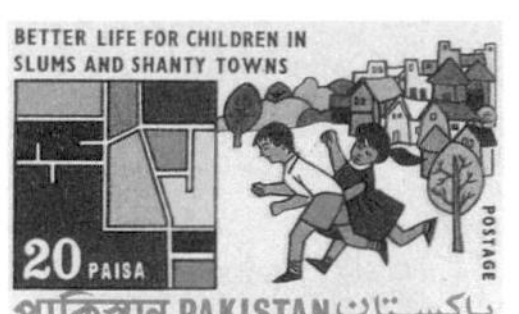

197 Children from Slums

1972. Universal Children's Day.
338 **197** 20p. multicoloured . . . 20 30

198 People and Open Book

1972. Education Week.
339 **198** 20p. multicoloured . . . 20 30

199 Nuclear Power Plant

1972. Inauguration of Karachi Nuclear Power Plant.
340 **199** 20p. multicoloured . . . 20 40

200 Copernicus in Observatory

1973. 500th Birth Anniv of Nicholas Copernicus (astronomer).
341 **200** 20p. multicoloured . . . 20 30

201 Moenjodaro Excavations

1973. 50th Anniv of Moenjodaro Excavations.
342 **201** 20p. multicoloured . . . 20 30

202 Elements of Meteorology

1973. Centenary of I.M.O./W.M.O.
343 **202** 20p. multicoloured . . . 30 40

203 Prisoners-of-war

1973. Prisoners-of-war in India.
344 **203** 1r.25 multicoloured . . . 1·75 2·50

204 National Assembly Building and Constitution Book

1973. Constitution Week.
345 **204** 20p. multicoloured . . . 70 65

205 Badge and State Bank Building

1973. 25th Anniv of Pakistan State Bank.
346 **205** 20p. multicoloured . . . 15 30
347 1r. multicoloured 30 50

206 Lut Desert Excavations (Iran) **207** Constitution Book and Flag

1973. 9th Anniv of Regional Co-operation for Development. Multicoloured.
348 20p. Type **206** 30 20
349 60p. Main Street, Moenjodaro (Pakistan) . . 55 50
350 1r.25 Mausoleum of Antiochus I (Turkey) . . . 75 1·25

1973. Independence Day and Enforcement of the Constitution.
351 **207** 20p. multicoloured . . . 15 30

208 Mohammed Ali Jinnah (Quaid-i-Azam)

1973. 25th Death Anniv of Mohammed Ali Jinnah.
352 **208** 20p. green, yellow & black 15 30

209 Wallago

1973. Fishes. Multicoloured.
353 10p. Type **209** . . . . 1·10 1·10
354 20p. Rohu . . . . 1·25 1·25
355 60p. Mozambique mouthbrooder . . . . . . 1·40 1·40
356 1r. Catla . . . . 1·40 1·40

210 Children's Education

1973. Universal Children's Day.
357 **210** 20p. multicoloured . . . 15 40

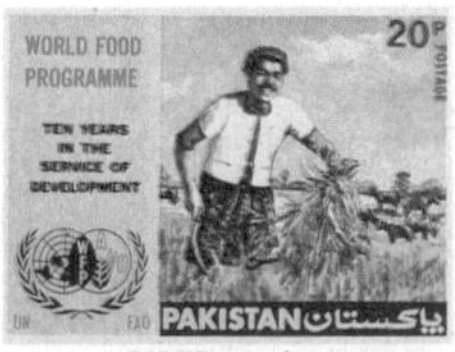

211 Harvesting

1973. 10th Anniv of World Food Programme.
358 **211** 20p. multicoloured . . . 60 40

212 Ankara and Kemal Ataturk

1973. 50th Anniv of Turkish Republic.
359 **212** 50p. multicoloured . . . 45 35

213 Boy Scout **214** "Basic Necessities"

1973. National Silver Jubilee Jamboree.
360 **213** 20p. multicoloured . . . 1·75 50

1973. 25th Anniv of Declaration of Human Rights.
361 **214** 20p. multicoloured . . . 30 40

215 Al-Biruni and Nandana Hill

1973. Al-Biruni Millennium Congress.
362 **215** 20p. multicoloured . . . 50 20
363 1r.25 multicoloured . . . 1·25 90

216 Dr. Hansen, Microscope and Bacillus **218** Conference Emblem

217 Family and Emblem

1973. Centenary of Hansen's Discovery of Leprosy Bacillus.
364 **216** 20p. multicoloured . . . 1·00 80

1974. World Population Year.
365 **217** 20p. multicoloured . . . 10 10
366 1r.25 multicoloured . . . 30 40

1974. Islamic Summit Conference, Lahore. Multicoloured.
367 20p. Type **218** 10 10
368 65p. Emblem on "Sun" (42 × 30 mm) 25 60
MS369 102 × 102 mm. Nos. 367/8. Imperf . . . . 1·50 4·75

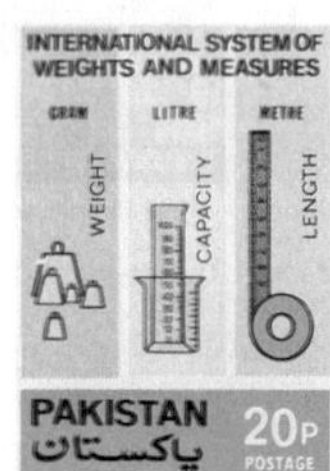

219 Units of Weight and Measurement

1974. Adoption of Int Weights and Measures System.
370 **219** 20p. multicoloured . . . 15 25

220 "Chand Chauthai" Carpet, Pakistan

1974. 10th Anniversary of Regional Co-operation for Development. Multicoloured.
371 20p. Type **220** 20 15
372 60p. Persian carpet, 16th-century 40 55
373 1r.25 Anatolian carpet, 15th-century . . . . 65 1·25

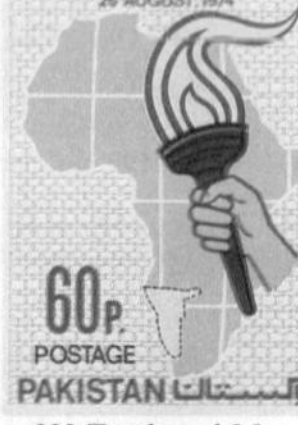

221 Hands protecting Sapling **222** Torch and Map

1974. Tree Planting Day.
374 **221** 20p. multicoloured . . . 50 60

1974. Namibia Day.
375 **222** 60p. multicoloured . . . 50 80

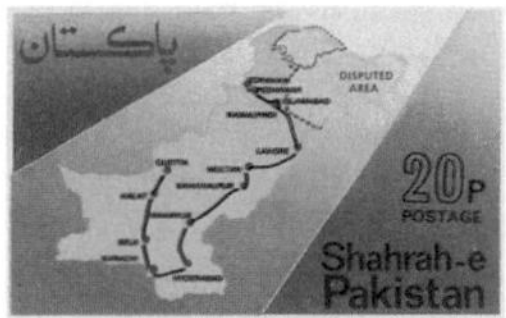

223 Highway Map

1974. Shahrah-e-Pakistan (Pakistan Highway).
376 **223** 20p. multicoloured . . . 1·25 1·00

224 Boy at Desk **225** U.P.U. Emblem

1974. Universal Children's Day.
377 **224** 20p. multicoloured . . . 30 40

1974. Centenary of U.P.U. Multicoloured.
378 20p. Type **225** 20 20
379 2r.25 U.P.U. emblem, Boeing 707 and mail-wagon (30 × 41 mm) . . . . . . 55 1·40
MS380 100 × 101 mm. Nos. 378/9. Imperf . . . . 1·25 5·00

226 Liaquat Ali Khan **227** Dr. Mohammed Iqbal (poet and philosopher)

1974. Liaquat Ali Khan (First Prime Minister of Pakistan).
381 **226** 20p. black and red . . . 30 40

1974. Birth Centenary of Dr. Iqbal (1977) (1st issue).
382 **227** 20p. multicoloured . . . 30 40
See also Nos. 399, 433 and 445/9.

228 Dr. Schweitzer and River Scene

1975. Birth Centenary of Dr. Albert Schweitzer.
383 **228** 2r.25 multicoloured . . . 4·00 3·25

229 Tourism Year Symbol

1975. South East Asia Tourism Year.
384 **229** 2r.25 multicoloured . . . 60 1·00

230 Assembly Hall, Flags and Prime Minister Bhutto

1975. 1st Anniv of Islamic Summit Conference, Lahore.
385 **230** 20p. multicoloured . . . 35 35
386 1r. multicoloured . . . . 75 1·40

231 "Scientific Research"

1975. International Women's Year. Mult.
387 20p. Type **231** 20 25
388 2r.25 Girl teaching woman ("Adult Education") . . . 1·10 2·00

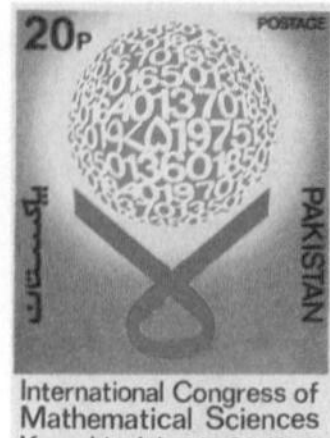

232 "Globe" and Algebraic Symbol **233** Pakistani Camel-skin Vase

1975. International Congress of Mathematical Sciences, Karachi.
389 **232** 20p. multicoloured . . . 50 60

1975. 11th Anniv of Regional Co-operation for Development. Multicoloured.
390 20p. Type **233** 25 30
391 60p. Iranian tile (horiz) . . . 50 1·00
392 1r.25 Turkish porcelain vase 75 1·50

234 Sapling and Dead Trees **235** Black Partridge

1975. Tree Planting Year.
393 **234** 20p. multicoloured . . . 35 50

1975. Wildlife Protection (1st series).
394 **235** 20p. multicoloured . . . 1·25 35
395 2r.25 multicoloured . . . 4·00 4·75
See also Nos. 400/1, 411/12, 417/18, 493/6, 560, 572/3, 581/2, 599, 600, 605, 621/2, 691, 702, 752, 780/3, 853 and 1027.

236 "Today's Girls" **238** Dr. Mohammed Iqbal

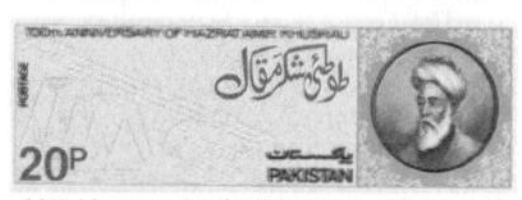

237 Hazrat Amir Khusrau, Sitar and Tabla (½-size illustration)

1975. Universal Children's Day.
396 **236** 20p. multicoloured . . . 30 50

1975. 700th Birth Anniv of Hazrat Amir Khusrau (poet and musician).
397 **237** 20p. multicoloured . . . 20 50
398 2r.25 multicoloured . . . 80 2·00

1975. Birth Cent (1977) of Dr. Iqbal (2nd issue).
399 **238** 20p. multicoloured . . . 30 50

239 Urial (wild sheep)

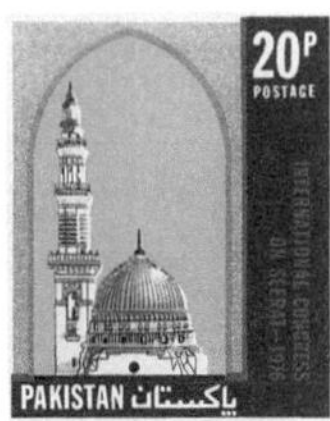

241 Dome and Minaret of the Rauza-e-Mubarak

240 Moenjodaro Remains

1975. Wildlife Protection (2nd series).
400 **239** 20p. multicoloured . . . 30 30
401 3r. multicoloured . . . . 1·75 3·25

1976. "Save Moenjodaro" (1st issue). Multicoloured.
402 10p. Type **240** 65 80
403 20p. Remains of houses . . . 75 90
404 65p. The Citadel 75 90
405 3r. Well inside a house . . . 75 90
406 4r. The "Great Bath" . . . . 85 1·00
See also Nos. 414 and 430.

1976. International Congress on Seerat.
407 **241** 20p. multicoloured . . . 15 20
408 3r. multicoloured 55 90

242 Alexander Graham Bell and Dial

1976. Telephone Centenary.
409 **242** 3r. multicoloured . . . . 1·25 2·00

243 College Arms within "Sun"

1976. Cent of National College of Arts, Lahore.
410 **243** 20p. multicoloured . . . 30 50

244 Common Peafowl

1976. Wildlife Protection (3rd series).
411 **244** 20p. multicoloured . . . 1·00 35
412 3r. multicoloured . . . . 3·50 4·50

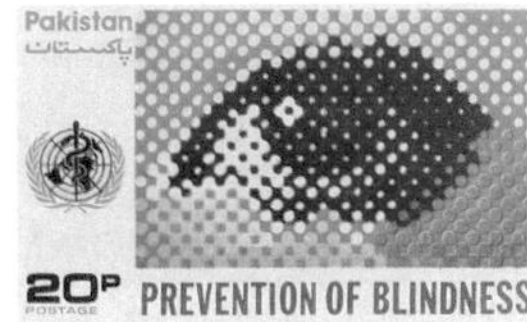

245 Human Eye

1976. Prevention of Blindness.
413 **245** 20p. multicoloured . . . 1·00 70

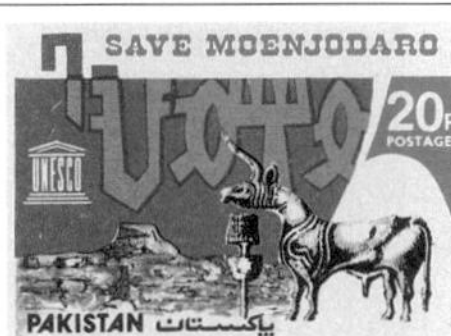

246 Unicorn and Ruins

1976. "Save Moenjodaro" (2nd series).
414 **246** 20p. multicoloured . . . 30 40

247 Jefferson Memorial

1976. Bicent of American Revolution. Mult.
415 90p. Type **247** 75 60
416 4r. "Declaration of Independence" (47 × 36 mm) . . . . . . 3·00 5·00

248 Ibex

1976. Wildlife Protection (4th series).
417 **248** 20p. multicoloured . . . 30 35
418 3r. multicoloured . . . . 1·25 2·50

249 Mohammed Ali Jinnah

1976. 12th Anniv of Regional Co-operation for Development. Multicoloured.
419 20p. Type **249** 65 90
420 65p. Reza Shah the Great (Iran) 65 90
421 90p. Kemal Ataturk (Turkey) 65 90

250 Urdu Text

251 Mohammed Ali Jinnah and Wazir Mansion

1976. Birth Cent of Mohammed Ali Jinnah (1st issue). (a) Type **250**.
422 **250** 5p. black, blue and yellow 20 25
423 10p. black, yellow & pur 20 25
424 15p. black and blue . . . 20 25
425 1r. black, yellow and blue 30 30
(b) Type **251**. Background Buildings given. Mult.
426 20p. Type **251** 20 25
427 40p. Sind Madressah 20 25
428 50p. Minar Qarardad-e-Pakistan 20 25
429 3r. Mausoleum 45 50
See also No. 436.

252 Dancing-girl, Ruins and King Priest

1976. "Save Moenjodaro" (3rd series).
430 **252** 65p. multicoloured . . . 35 80

253 U.N. Racial Discrimination Emblem

1976. U.N. Decade to Combat Racial Discrimination.
431 **253** 65p. multicoloured . . . 30 60

254 Child in Maze and Basic Services

1976. Universal Children's Day.
432 **254** 20p. multicoloured . . . 60 60

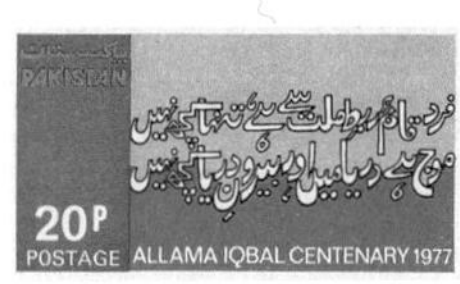

255 Verse from "Allama Iqbal"

1976. Birth Centenary (1977) of Dr. Iqbal (3rd issue).
433 **255** 20p. multicoloured . . . 15 30

256 Mohammed Ali Jinnah giving Scout Salute

257 Children Reading

1976. Quaid-i-Azam Centenary Jamboree.
434 **256** 20p. multicoloured . . . 1·00 60

1976. Children's Literature.
435 **257** 20p. multicoloured . . . 65 65

258 Mohammed Ali Jinnah

1976. Birth Centenary of Mohammed Ali Jinnah (2nd issue).
436 **258** 10r. green and gold . . . 2·75 3·50

259 Rural Family

261 Forest

260 Turkish Vase, 1800 B.C.

1977. Social Welfare and Rural Development Year.
437 **259** 20p. multicoloured . . . 40 10

1977. 13th Anniv of Regional Co-operation for Development.
438 **260** 20p. orange, blue & black 45 10
439 – 65p. multicoloured . . . 65 40
440 – 90p. multicoloured . . . 90 1·50
DESIGNS: 60p. Pakistani toy bullock cart from Moenjodaro; 90p. Pitcher with spout from Sialk Hill, Iran.

1977. National Tree Plantation Campaign.
441 **261** 20p. multicoloured . . . 20 30

262 Desert Scene

1977. U.N. Conference on Desertification, Nairobi.
442 **262** 65p. multicoloured . . . 1·00 45

263 "Water for Children of the World"

265 Iqbal and Spirit of the Poet Roomi (from painting by Behzad)

264 Aga Khan III

1977. Universal Children's Day.
443 **263** 50p. multicoloured . . . 40 30

1977. Birth Centenary of Aga Khan III.
444 **264** 2r. multicoloured . . . . 55 1·00

1977. Birth Centenary of Dr. Mohammed Iqbal (4th issue). Multicoloured.
445 20p. Type **265** 50 60
446 65p. Iqbal looking at Jamaluddin Afghani and Saeed Haleem Pasha at prayer (Behzad) 50 60
447 1r.25 Urdu verse 55 65
448 2r.25 Persian verse 60 75
449 3r. Iqbal 65 85

266 The Holy "Khana-Kaaba" (House of God, Mecca)

1977. Haj (pilgrimage to Mecca).
450 **266** 65p. multicoloured . . . 30 30

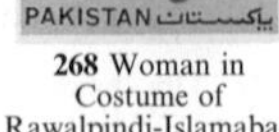

267 Rheumatic Patient and Healthy Man

268 Woman in Costume of Rawalpindi-Islamabad

1977. World Rheumatism Year.
451 **267** 65p. blue, black and yellow 30 20

1978. Indonesia–Pakistan Economic and Cultural Co-operation Organization.
452 **268** 75p. multicoloured . . . 30 20

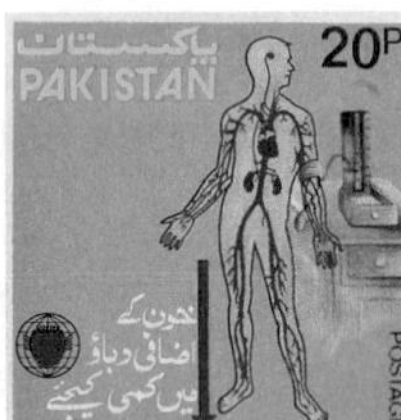

269 Human Body and Sphygmomanometer

1978. World Hypertension Month.
453 **269** 20p. multicoloured . . . 15 10
454 – 2r. multicoloured 60 90
The 2r. value is as Type **269** but has the words "Down with high blood pressure" instead of the Urdu inscription at bottom left.

270 Henri Dunant

1978. 150th Birth Anniv of Henri Dunant (founder of the Red Cross).
455 **270** 1r. multicoloured . . . . 1·00 20

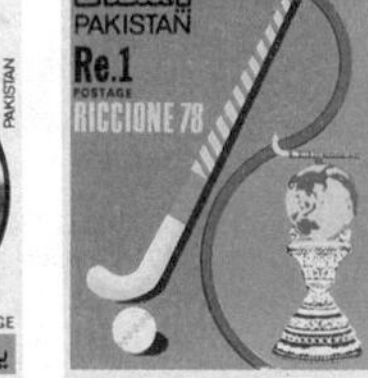

271 Red Roses (Pakistan)

272 "Pakistan, World Cup Hockey Champions"

1978. 14th Anniv of Regional Co-operation for Development. Roses. Multicoloured.
456 20p. Type **271** 35 20
457 90p. Pink roses (Iran) 50 20
458 2r. Yellow rose (Turkey) . . 75 25

1978. "Riccione '78" International Stamp Fair. Multicoloured.
459 1r. Type **272** . . . . 1·25 25
460 2r. Fountain at Piazza Turismo 50 35

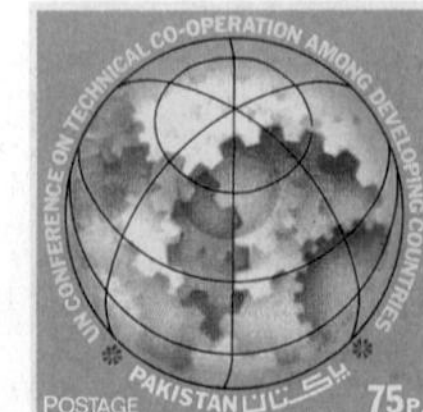

273 Cogwheels within Globe Symbol

1978. U.N. Technical Co-operation amongst Developing Countries Conference.
461 **273** 75p. multicoloured . . . 15 10

274 St. Patrick's Cathedral, Karachi

275 Minar-i-Qarardad-e-Pakistan

1978. Centenary of St. Patrick's Cathedral, Karachi. Multicoloured.
462 1r. Type **274** 10 10
463 2r. Stained glass window . . 25 25

1978.
464 **275** 2p. green 10 10
465 3p. black 10 10
466 5p. blue 10 10
467 – 10p. blue and turquoise 10 10
468 – 20p. green 60 10
469 – 25p. green and mauve 1·25 10
470 – 40p. blue and mauve . . 10 10
471 – 50p. lilac and green . . 30 10
472 – 60p. black 10 10
473b – 75p. red . . . . 1·00 10
474 – 90p. mauve and blue . . 30 10
475 – 1r. green 60 10
476 – 1r.50 orange 20 10
477 – 2r. red 20 10
478 – 3r. blue 20 10
479 – 4r. black 20 10
480 – 5r. brown 20 10
DESIGNS—HORIZ (25 × 20 mm): 10p. to 90p. Tractor. VERT (21 × 25 mm): 1r. to 5r. Mausoleum of Ibrahim Khan Makli, Thatta.

277 Emblem and "United Races" Symbol

278 Maulana Mohammad Ali Jauhar

1978. International Anti-Apartheid Year.
481 **277** 1r. multicoloured 15 15

1978. Birth Centenary of Maulana Mohammad Ali Jauhar (patriot).
482 **278** 50p. multicoloured . . . 50 20

279 Panavia MRCA Tornado, De Havilland Dragon Rapide and Wright Flyer I

1978. 75th Anniv of Powered Flight. Mult.
483 65p. Type **279** . . . . 1·00 1·75
484 1r. McDonnell Douglas Phantom II, Lockheed Tristar 500 and Wright Flyer I . . . . 1·10 1·75
485 2r. North American X-15, Tupolev Tu-104 and Wright Flyer I . . . . . . 1·25 2·00
486 2r.25 Mikoyan Gurevich MiG-15, Concorde and Wright Flyer I . . . . . . 1·25 2·25

280 "Holy Koran illuminating Globe" and Raudha-e-Mubarak (mausoleum)

1979. "12th Rabi-ul-Awwal" (Prophet Mohammed's birthday).
487 **280** 20p. multicoloured . . . 40 15

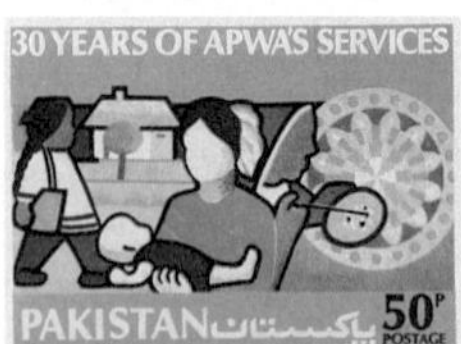

281 "Aspects of A.P.W.A."

1979. 30th Anniv of A.P.W.A. (All Pakistan Women's Association).
488 **281** 50p. multicoloured . . . 75 15

282 Tippu Sultan Shaheed of Mysore

1979. Pioneers of Freedom (1st series). Multicoloured.
490 10r. Type **282** . . . . 75 1·60
491 15r. Sir Syed Ahmad Khan 1·00 2·25
492 25r. Altaf Hussain Hali . . . 1·50 2·25
See also Nos. 757, 801/27, 838/46, 870/2, 904/6, 921/8, 961/2, 1007, 1019/20 and 1075/7.

283 Himalayan Monal Pheasant

1979. Wildlife Protection (5th series). Pheasants. Multicoloured.
493 20p. Type **283** . . . . 1·25 60
494 25p. Kalij pheasant . . . . . 1·25 80
495 40p. Koklass pheasant . . . 1·60 1·75
496 1r. Cheer pheasant . . . . . 3·00 2·00

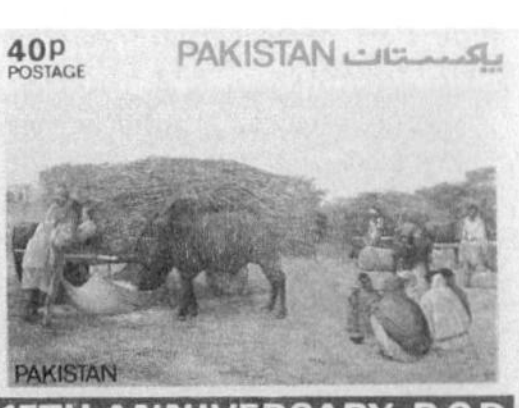

284 "Pakistan Village Scene" (Ustad Bakhsh)

1979. 15th Anniv of Regional Co-operation for Development. Multicoloured.
497 40p. Type **284** 20 25
498 75p. "Iranian Goldsmith" (Kamal al Molk) 20 25
499 1r.60 "Turkish Harvest" (Namik Ismail) 25 30

285 Guj Embroidered Shirt (detail)

1979. Handicrafts (1st series). Multicoloured.
500 40p. Type **285** 20 20
501 1r. Enamel inlaid brass plate 25 25
502 1r.50 Baskets 30 30
503 2r. Chain-stitch embroidered rug (detail) 40 40
See also Nos. 578/9, 595/6 and 625/8.

286 Children playing on Climbing-frame

1979. S.O.S. Children's Village, Lahore.
504 **286** 50p. multicoloured . . . 40 40

287 "Island" (Z. Maloof)

1979. International Year of the Child. Children's Paintings. Multicoloured.
505 40p. Type **287** 15 15
506 75p. "Playground" (R. Akbar) 25 25
507 1r. "Fairground" (M. Azam) 25 25
508 1r.50 "Hockey Match" (M. Tayyab) 30 30
MS509 79 × 64 mm. 2r. "Child looking at Faces in the Sky" (M. Mumtaz) (vert). Imperf . . 1·00 2·00

288 Warrior attacking Crab

289 Pakistan Customs Emblem

1979. "Fight Against Cancer".
510 **288** 40p. black, yellow and purple 70 70

1979. Centenary of Pakistan Customs Service.
511 **289** 1r. multicoloured 30 30

290 Boeing 747-200 and Douglas DC-3 Airliners

1980. 25th Anniv of Pakistan International Air Lines.
512 **290** 1r. multicoloured . . . . 1·75 90

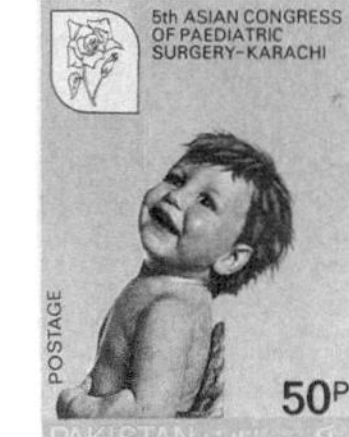

291 Islamic Pattern **292** Young Child

1980.

513 **291** 10p. green and yellow . . 10 10
514 15p. deep green and green 10 10
515 25p. violet and red . . . 10 50
516 35p. red and green . . . 10 50
517 – 40p. red and brown . . . 15 10
518 – 50p. violet and green . . 10 50
519 – 80p. green and black . . 15 50

The 40 to 80p. values also show different Islamic patterns, the 40p. being horizontal and the remainder vertical.

1980. 5th Asian Congress of Paediatric Surgery, Karachi.
530 **292** 50p. multicoloured . . . 75 1·50

293 Conference Emblem

1980. 11th Islamic Conference of Foreign Ministers, Islamabad.
531 **293** 1r. multicoloured . . . . 1·00 75

294 Karachi Port (½-size illustration)

1980. Centenary of Karachi Port Authority.
532 **294** 1r. multicoloured . . . . 1·75 1·40

1980. "Riccione 80" International Stamp Exhibition. Nos. 505/8 optd **RICCIONE 80**.
533 **287** 40p. multicoloured . . . 30 80
534 – 75p. multicoloured . . . 40 90
535 – 1r. multicoloured 45 90
536 – 1r.50 multicoloured . . . 60 1·10

296 College Emblem with Old and New Buildings

1980. 75th Anniv of Command and Staff College, Quetta.
537 **296** 1r. multicoloured 20 15

1980. World Tourism Conference, Manila. No. 496 optd **WORLD TOURISM CONFERENCE MANILA 80**.
538 1r. Cheer pheasant . . . . . 1·00 30

298 Birth Centenary Emblem

1980. Birth Cent of Hafiz Mahmood Shairani.
539 **298** 40p. multicoloured . . . 30 1·00

299 Shalimar Gardens, Lahore

1980. Aga Khan Award for Architecture.
540 **299** 2r. multicoloured . . . . 40 1·75

300 Rising Sun

1980. 1400th Anniv of Hegira (1st issue). Multicoloured.
541 40p. Type **300** 10 10
542 2r. Ka'aba and symbols of Moslem achievement (33 × 33 mm) 25 45
543 3r. Holy Koran illuminating the World (30 × 54 mm) . . 30 80
MS544 106 × 84 mm. 4r. Candles. Imperf . . . . 45 1·00

See also No. 549

301 Money Order Form **302** Postcards encircling Globe

1980. Centenary of Money Order Service.
545 **301** 40p. multicoloured . . . 20 60

1980. Centenary of Postcard Service.
546 **302** 40p. multicoloured . . . 20 60

303 Heinrich von Stephan and U.P.U. Emblem

1981. 150th Birth Anniv of Heinrich von Stephan (U.P.U. founder).
547 **303** 1r. multicoloured 30 20

304 Aircraft and Airmail Letters

1981. 50th Anniv of Airmail Service.
548 **304** 1r. multicoloured 60 20

305 Mecca

1981. 1400th Anniv of Hegira (2nd issue).
549 **305** 40p. multicoloured . . . 20 60

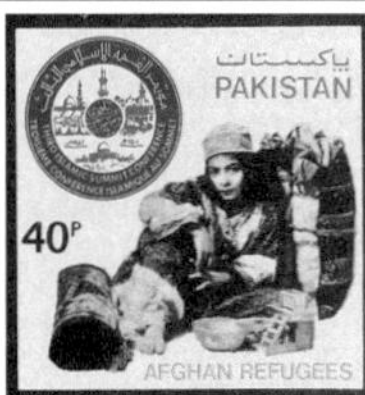

306 Conference Emblem and Afghan Refugees

1981. Islamic Summit Conference (1st issue). Multicoloured.
550 40p. Type **306** 30 10
551 40p. Conference emblem encircled by flags and Afghan refugees (28 × 58 mm) 30 10
552 1r. Type **306** 50 10
553 1r. As No. 551 . . . . 50 10
554 2r. Conference emblem and map showing Afghanistan (48 × 32 mm) 65 50

307 Conference Emblem

1981. Islamic Summit Conference (2nd issue). Multicoloured.
555 40p. Type **307** 10 15
556 40p. Conference emblem and flags (28 × 46 mm) 10 15
557 85p. Type **307** 20 40
558 85p. As No. 556 . . . . . . 20 40

308 Kemal Ataturk

1981. Birth Centenary of Kemal Ataturk (Turkish statesman).
559 **308** 1r. multicoloured 50 15

309 Green Turtle

1981. Wildlife Protection (6th series).
560 **309** 40p. multicoloured . . . 1·25 40

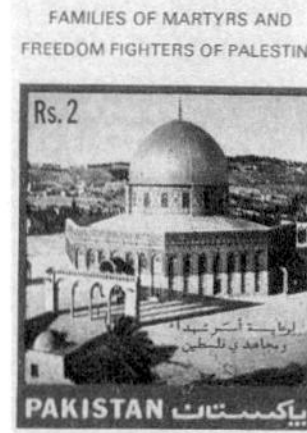

310 Dome of the Rock

1981. Palestinian Welfare.
561 **310** 2r. multicoloured 35 35

311 Malubiting West

1981. Mountain Peaks (1st series). Karakoram Range. Multicoloured.
562 40p. Type **311** 40 40
563 40p. Malubiting West (24 × 31 mm) 40 40
564 1r. Haramosh 55 75
565 1r. Haramosh (24 × 31 mm) 55 75
566 1r.50 K6 . . . . 70 1·00
567 1r.50 K6 (24 × 31 mm) . . . 70 1·00
568 2r. K2, Broad Peak, Gasherbrum 4 and Gasherbrum 2 . . . . . . 70 1·40
569 2r. K2 (24 × 31 mm) . . . . 70 1·40

See also Nos. 674/5.

312 Pakistan Steel "Furnace No. 1"

1981. 1st Firing of Pakistan Steel "Furnace No. 1", Karachi.
570 **312** 40p. multicoloured . . . 20 10
571 2r. multicoloured . . . . 60 1·75

313 Western Tragopan

1981. Wildlife Protection (7th series).
572 **313** 40p. multicoloured . . . 2·25 75
573 – 2r. multicoloured . . . . 4·25 4·25

DESIGN: 2r. As Type **313** but with background showing a winter view.

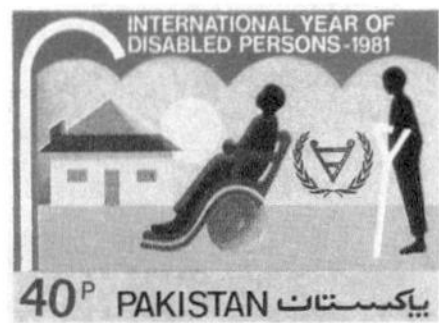

314 Disabled People and I.Y.D.P. Emblem

1981. International Year for Disabled Persons.
574 **314** 40p. multicoloured . . . 30 50
575 2r. multicoloured . . . . 1·10 1·75

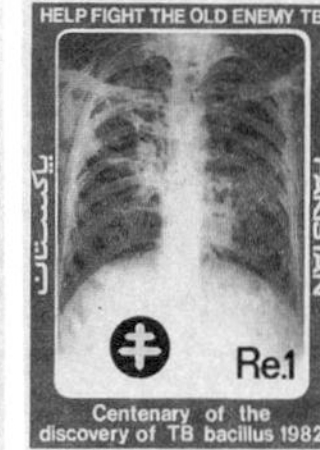

315 World Hockey Cup below Flags of participating Countries **317** Chest X-Ray of Infected Person

316 Camel Skin Lamp

1982. Pakistan—World Cup Hockey Champions. Multicoloured.
576 1r. Type **315** . . . . 2·00 1·50
577 1r. World Hockey Cup above flags of participating countries . . . . 2·00 1·50

1982. Handicrafts (2nd series). Multicoloured.
578 1r. Type **316** 70 80
579 1r. Hala pottery 70 80
See also Nos. 595/6.

1982. Centenary of Robert Koch's Discovery of Tubercle Bacillus.
580 **317** 1r. multicoloured . . . . 1·25 1·50

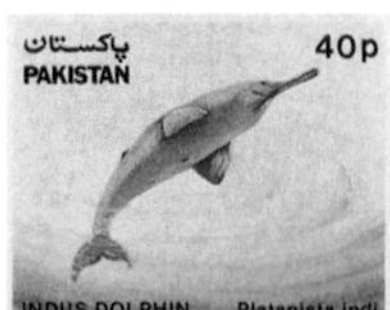

318 Indus Dolphin

1982. Wildlife Protection (8th series).
581 **318** 40p. multicoloured . . . 1·50 1·25
582 – 1r. multicoloured . . . . 3·00 2·50
DESIGN: 1r. As Type **318** but with design reversed.

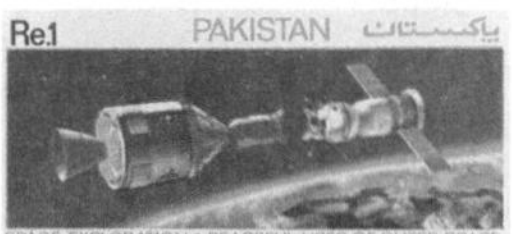

319 "Apollo–Soyuz" Link-up, 1975

1982. Peaceful Use of Outer Space.
583 **319** 1r. multicoloured . . . . 2·00 1·25

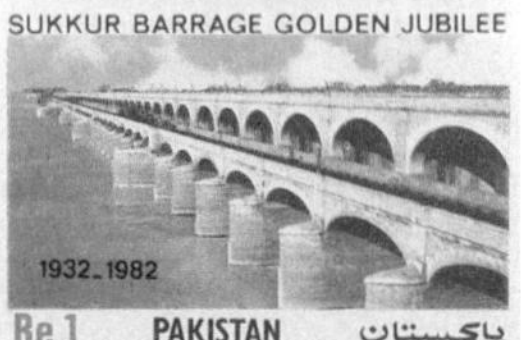

320 Sukkur Barrage

1982. 50th Anniv of Sukkur Barrage.
584 **320** 1r. multicoloured 30 30

321 Pakistan National Flag and Stylized Sun
324 Scout Emblem and Tents

323 Arabic Inscription and University Emblem (¾-size illustration)

1982. Independence Day. Multicoloured.
585 40p. Type **321** 20 30
586 85p. Map of Pakistan and stylized torch . . . . . . 45 1·25

1982. "Riccione '82" Stamp Exhibition. No. 584 optd **RICCIONE-82**.
587 **320** 1r. multicoloured 20 20

1982. Centenary of the Punjab University.
588 **323** 40p. multicoloured . . . 1·00 50

1983. 75th Anniv of Boy Scout Movement.
589 **324** 2r. multicoloured 50 50

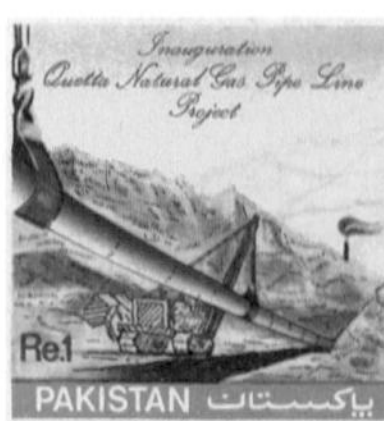

325 Laying Pipeline

1983. Inaug of Quetta Natural Gas Pipeline Project.
590 **325** 1r. multicoloured 30 30

326 "Papilio polyctor"

1983. Butterflies. Multicoloured.
591 40p. Type **326** . . . . 1·25 20
592 50p. "Atrophaneura aristolochiae" . . . . . . 1·50 20
593 60p. "Danaus chrysippus" . . 1·75 60
594 1r.50 "Papilio demoleus" . . 2·50 2·25

1983. Handicrafts (3rd series). As T **316**. Multicoloured.
595 1r. Five flower motif needlework, Sind 15 15
596 1r. Straw mats 15 15

327 School of Nursing and University Emblem

1983. Presentation of Charter to Aga Khan University, Karachi.
597 **327** 2r. multicoloured . . . . 1·25 1·75

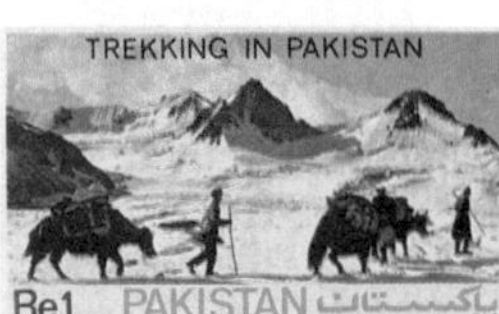

328 Yak Caravan crossing Zindiharam-Darkot Pass, Hindu Kush

1983. Trekking in Pakistan.
598 **328** 1r. multicoloured . . . . 1·50 1·50

329 Marsh Crocodile
331 Floral Design

330 Goitred Gazelle

1983. Wildlife Protection (9th series).
599 **329** 3r. multicoloured . . . . 3·50 2·00

1983. Wildlife Protection (10th series).
600 **330** 1r. multicoloured . . . . 2·50 2·00

1983. 36th Anniv of Independence. Mult.
601 60p. Type **331** 10 10
602 4r. Hand holding flaming torch 40 45

332 Traditional Weaving, Pakistan

1983. Indonesian–Pakistan Economic and Cultural Co-operation Organization, 1969–1983. Mult.
603 2r. Type **332** 20 25
604 2r. Traditional weaving, Indonesia 20 25

333 "Siberian Cranes" (Great White Cranes) (Sir Peter Scott)

1983. Wildlife Protection (11th series).
605 **333** 3r. multicoloured . . . . 3·00 3·25

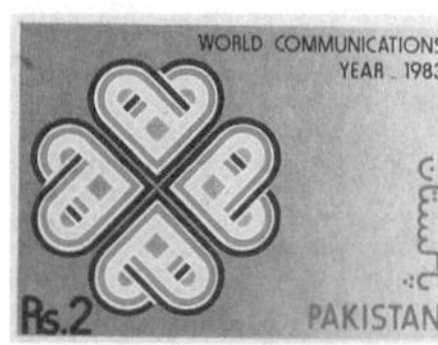

334 W.C.Y. Emblem

1983. World Communications Year. Multicoloured.
606 2r. Type **334** 20 25
607 3r. W.C.Y. emblem (different) (33 × 33 mm) 30 35

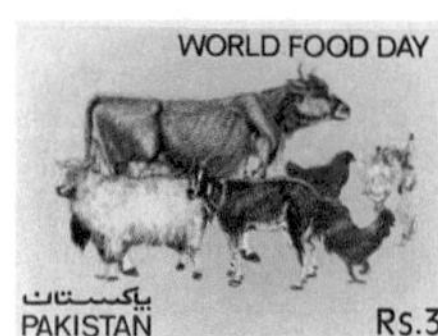

335 Farm Animals

1983. World Food Day. Multicoloured.
608 3r. Type **335** . . . . 1·50 1·75
609 3r. Fruit . . . . 1·50 1·75
610 3r. Crops . . . . 1·50 1·75
611 3r. Sea food . . . . 1·50 1·75

336 Agriculture Produce and Fertilizer Factory
337 Lahore, 1852

1983. National Fertilizer Corporation.
612 **336** 60p. multicoloured . . . 15 30

1983. National Stamp Exn, Lahore. Mult.
613 60p. Musti Durwaza Dharmsala 60 75
614 60p. Khabgha 60 75
615 60p. Type **337** 60 75
616 60p. Summan Burj Hazuri . . 60 75
617 60p. Flower Garden, Samadhi Northern Gate . . 60 75
618 60p. Budda Darya, Badshahi Masjid 60 75

338 Winner of "Enterprise" Event
340 Jahangir Khan (World Squash Champion)

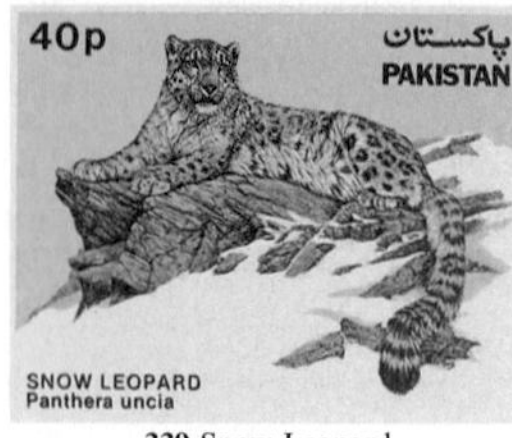

339 Snow Leopard

1983. Yachting Champions, Asian Games, Delhi. Multicoloured.
619 60p. Type **338** . . . . 1·75 1·75
620 60p. Winner of "OK" Dinghy event . . . . . . 1·75 1·75

1984. Wildlife Protection (12th series).
621 **339** 40p. multicoloured . . . 1·75 90
622 1r.60 multicoloured . . . 4·75 6·00

1984. Squash.
623 **340** 3r. multicoloured . . . . 2·25 1·75

341 P.I.A. Boeing 707 Airliner

1984. 20th Anniv of Pakistan International Airways Service to China.
624 **341** 3r. multicoloured . . . . 5·00 5·50

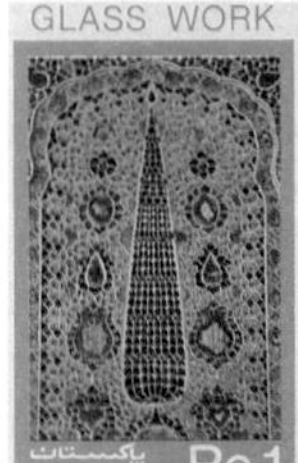

342 Glass-work
343 Attock Fort

1984. Handicrafts (4th series). Multicoloured, frame colours given.
625 **342** 1r. blue 25 15
626 – 1r. red 25 15
627 – 1r. green 25 15
628 – 1r. violet 25 15
DESIGNS: showing glass-work in Sheesh Mahal, Lahore Fort. Nos. 627/8 are horizontal designs.

1984. Forts.
629 – 5p. black and purple . . . 20 30
630 – 10p. black and red . . . 20 10
631 – 15p. violet and brown . . . 75 10
632 **343** 20p. black and violet . . 60 10
633 – 50p. brown and red . . . 1·50 10
634 – 60p. light brown & brown 1·00 10
635 – 70p. blue . . . . 1·50 10
636 – 80p. brown and red . . . 1·50 10
DESIGNS: 5p. Kot Diji Fort; 10p. Rohtas Fort; 15p. Bala Hissar Fort; 50p. Hyderabad Fort; 60p. Lahore Fort; 70p. Sibi Fort; 80p. Ranikot Fort.

344 Shah Rukn i Alam's Tomb, Multan

1984. Aga Khan Award for Architecture.
647 **344** 60p. multicoloured . . . 2·00 2·25

345 Radio Mast and Map of World

1984. 20th Anniv of Asia–Pacific Broadcasting Union.
648 **345** 3r. multicoloured . . . . 1·00 60

346 Wrestling

1984. Olympic Games, Los Angeles. Mult.
649 3r. Type **346** . . . . 1·25 1·50
650 3r. Boxing . . . . 1·25 1·50
651 3r. Athletics . . . . 1·25 1·50
652 3r. Hockey . . . . 1·25 1·50
653 3r. Yachting . . . . 1·25 1·50

347 Jasmine (National flower) and Inscription

1984. Independence Day. Multicoloured.
654 60p. Type **347** 10 10
655 4r. Symbolic torch 45 50

348 Gearwheel Emblem and Flags of Participating Nations

1984. Pakistan International Trade Fair.
656 **348** 60p. multicoloured . . . 1·00 30

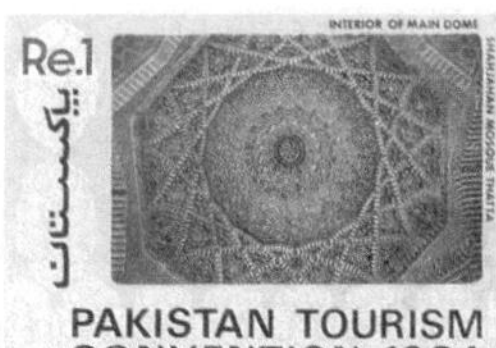

349 Interior of Main Dome

1984. Tourism Convention, Shahjahan Mosque, Thatta. Multicoloured.
657 1r. Type **349** 50 60
658 1r. Brick and glazed tile work 50 60
659 1r. Gateway 50 60
660 1r. Symmetrical archways . . 50 60
661 1r. Interior of a dome . . . 50 60

350 Bank Emblem in Floral Pattern

1984. 25th Anniv of United Bank Ltd.
662 **350** 60p. multicoloured . . . 80 80

351 Conference Emblem

1984. 20th United Nations Conference of Trade and Development.
663 **351** 60p. multicoloured . . . 80 40

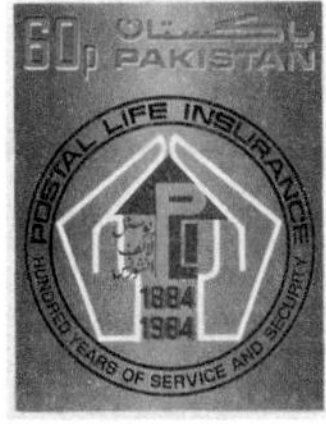

352 Postal Life Insurance Emblem within Hands

353 Bull (wall painting)

1984. Centenary of Postal Life Insurance. Multicoloured.
664 60p. Type **352** 70 15
665 1r. "100" and Postal Life Insurance emblem 90 15

1984. U.N.E.S.C.O. Save Moenjadoro Campaign. Multicoloured.
666 2r. Type **353** . . . . 1·40 1·00
667 2r. Bull (seal) . . . . 1·40 1·00

354 International Youth Year Emblem and "75"

1985. 75th Anniv of Girl Guide Movement.
668 **354** 60p. multicoloured . . . 3·25 1·50

355 Smelting Ore

1985. Inauguration of Pakistan Steel Corporation. Multicoloured.
669 60p. Type **355** 65 25
670 1r. Pouring molten steel from ladle (28 × 46 mm) . . . . 1·10 25

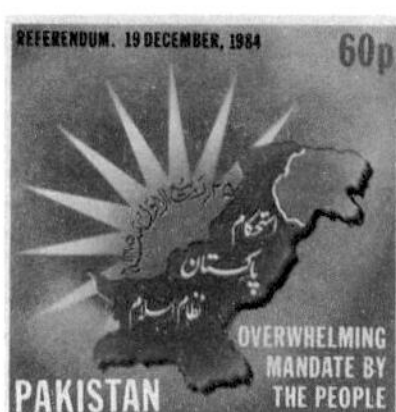

356 Map of Pakistan and Rays of Sun

1985. Presidential Referendum of 19 December 1984.
671 **356** 60p. multicoloured . . . 1·75 55

357 Ballot Box and Voting Paper

1985. March Elections. Multicoloured.
672 1r. Type **357** 65 15
673 1r. Minar-e-Qarardad-e-Pakistan Tower, and word "Democracy" (31 × 43 mm) 65 15

1985. Mountain Peaks (2nd series). As T **311**. Multicoloured.
674 40p. Rakaposhi (Karakoram Range) . . . . 1·75 75
675 2r. Nangaparbat (Western Himalayas) . . . . 3·75 5·00

358 Trophy and Medals from Olympic Games 1984, Asia Cup 1985 and World Cup 1982

1985. Pakistan Hockey Team "Grand Slam" Success.
676 **358** 1r. multicoloured . . . . 2·50 2·00

359 King Edward Medical College

1985. 125th Anniv of King Edward Medical College, Lahore.
677 **359** 3r. multicoloured . . . . 1·75 85

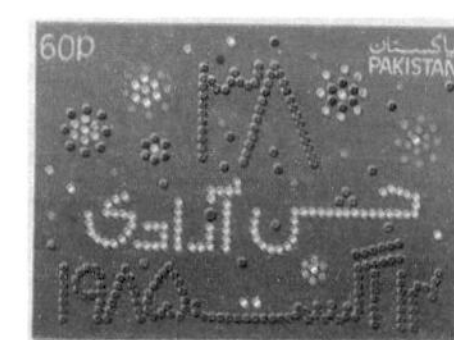

360 Illuminated Inscription in Urdu

1985. Independence Day. Multicoloured.
678 60p. Type **360** 40 50
679 60p. Illuminated "XXXVIII" (inscr in English) 40 50

361 Sind Madressah-tul-Islam, Karachi

1985. Centenary of Sind Madressah-tul-Islam (theological college), Karachi.
680 **361** 2r. multicoloured . . . . 1·75 85

362 Jamia Masjid Mosque by Day

1985. Inauguration of New Jamia Masjid Mosque, Karachi. Multicoloured.
681 1r. Type **362** 90 50
682 1r. Jamia Masjid illuminated at night 90 50

363 Lawrence College, Murree

1985. 125th Anniv of Lawrence College, Murree.
683 **363** 3r. multicoloured . . . . 2·00 85

364 United Nations Building, New York

1985. 40th Anniv of United Nations Organization. Multicoloured.
684 1r. Type **364** 30 15
685 2r. U.N. Building and emblem 40 50

365 Tents and Jamboree Emblem

1985. 10th National Scout Jamboree.
686 **365** 60p. multicoloured . . . 2·25 2·50

366 Islamabad

1985. 25th Anniv of Islamabad.
687 **366** 3r. multicoloured . . . . 2·50 1·00

367 Map of S.A.A.R.C. Countries and National Flags

1985. 1st Summit Meeting of South Asian Association for Regional Co-operation, Dhaka, Bangladesh. Multicoloured.
688 1r. Type **367** . . . . 1·50 4·00
689 2r. National flags (39 × 39 mm) . . . . . . 75 2·00

368 Globe and Peace Dove

1985. 25th Anniv of U.N. General Assembly's Declaration on Independence for Colonial Territories.
690 **368** 60p. multicoloured . . . 1·00 60

369 Peregrine Falcon

1986. Wildlife Protection (13th series). Peregrine Falcon.
691 **369** 1r.50 multicoloured . . . 4·25 4·25

370 A.D.B.P. Building, Islamabad

1986. 25th Anniv of Agricultural Development Bank of Pakistan.
692 **370** 60p. multicoloured . . . 1·75 50

371 Government S.E. College

1986. Centenary of Government Sadiq Egerton College, Bahawalpur.
693 **371** 1r. multicoloured . . . . 2·75 50

372 Emblem and Bar Graph **373** "1947 1986"

1986. 25th Anniv of Asian Productivity Organization.
694 **372** 1r. multicoloured . . . . 2·75 30

1986. 39th Anniv of Independence. Multicoloured.
695 80p. Type **373** . . . . 1·50 25
696 1r. Illuminated inscription in Urdu . . . . 1·50 25

374 Open Air Class **375** Mother and Child

1986. International Literacy Day.
697 **374** 1r. multicoloured . . . . 1·75 30

1986. U.N.I.C.E.F. Child Survival Campaign.
698 **375** 80p. multicoloured . . . 2·00 65

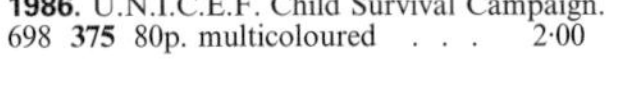

376 Aitchison College

1986. Centenary of Aitchison College, Lahore.
699 **376** 2r.50 multicoloured . . . 1·75 1·00

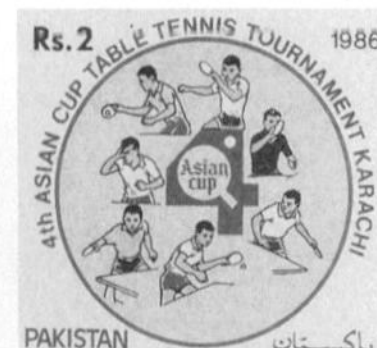

377 Two Doves carrying Olive Branches **378** Table Tennis Players

1986. International Peace Year.
700 **377** 4r. multicoloured 60 75

1986. 4th Asian Cup Table Tennis Tournament, Karachi.
701 **378** 2r. multicoloured . . . . 2·00 1·00

379 Argali

1986. Wildlife Protection (14th series). Argali.
702 **379** 2r. multicoloured . . . . 3·00 3·00

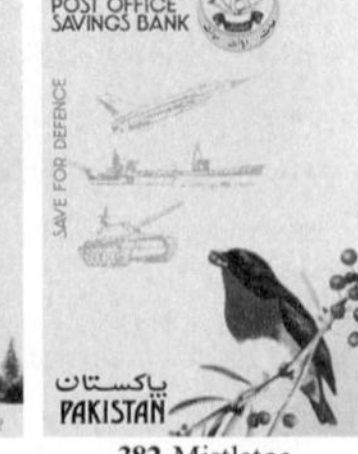

380 Selimiye Mosque, Edirne, Turkey **382** Mistletoe Flowerpecker and Defence Symbols

1986. "Ecophilex '86" International Stamp Exhibition, Islamabad. Multicoloured.
703 3r. Type **380** . . . . 1·40 1·60
704 3r. Gawhar Shad Mosque, Mashhad, Iran . . . . . . 1·40 1·60
705 3r. Grand Mosque, Bhong, Pakistan . . . . 1·40 1·60

381 St. Patrick's School

1987. 125th Anniv of St. Patrick's School, Karachi.
706 **381** 5r. multicoloured . . . . 2·50 1·50

1987. Post Office Savings Bank Week. Multicoloured.
707 5r. Type **382** . . . . 1·10 1·25
708 5r. Spotted pardalote and laboratory apparatus . . . 1·10 1·25
709 5r. Black-throated blue warbler and agriculture symbols . . . . 1·10 1·25
710 5r. Red-capped manakin and industrial skyline . . . . . 1·10 1·25

383 New Parliament House, Islamabad

1987. Inauguration of New Parliament House, Islamabad.
711 **383** 3r. multicoloured 50 60

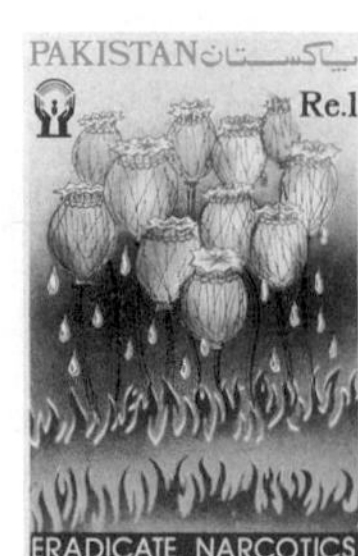

384 Opium Poppies and Flames

1987. Campaign Against Drug Abuse.
712 **384** 1r. multicoloured 65 30

385 Flag and National Anthem Score

1987. 40th Anniv of Independence. Mult.
713 80p. Type **385** . . . . 1·25 20
714 3r. Text of speech by Mohammed Ali Jinnah, Minar-e-Qardad-e-Pakistan Tower and arms . . . . . 1·50 50

386 Hawker Tempest Mk II

1987. Air Force Day. Military Aircraft. Mult.
715 3r. Type **386** . . . . 1·25 1·25
716 3r. Hawker Fury . . . . . . 1·25 1·25
717 3r. Supermarine Attacker . . 1·25 1·25
718 3r. North American F-86 Sabre . . . . 1·25 1·25
719 3r. Lockheed F-104C Starfighter . . . . 1·25 1·25
720 3r. Lockheed C-130 Hercules 1·25 1·25
721 3r. Shenyang/Tianjin F-6 . . 1·25 1·25
722 3r. Dassault Mirage III . . . 1·25 1·25
723 3r. North American A-5A Vigilante . . . . 1·25 1·25
724 3r. General Dynamics F-16 Fighting Falcon . . . . . 1·25 1·25

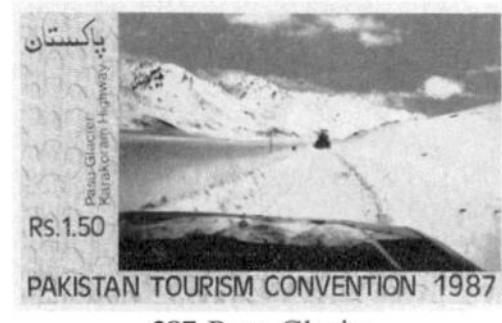

387 Pasu Glacier

1987. Pakistan Tourism Convention. Views along Karakoram Highway. Multicoloured.
725 1r.50 Type **387** 60 55
726 1r.50 Apricot trees 60 55
727 1r.50 Karakoram Highway 60 55
728 1r.50 View from Khunjerab Pass 60 55

388 Shah Abdul Latif Bhitai Mausoleum

1987. Shah Abdul Latif Bhitai (poet) Commem.
729 **388** 80p. multicoloured . . . 30 30

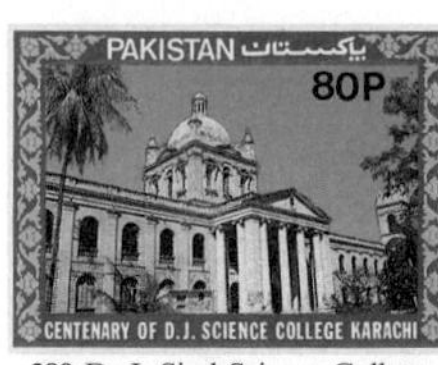

389 D. J. Sind Science College, Karachi

1987. Centenary of D. J. Sind Science College, Karachi.
730 **389** 80p. multicoloured . . . 20 20

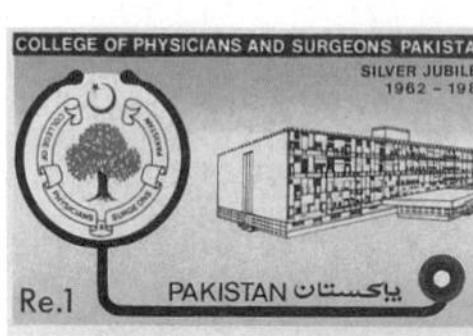

390 College Building

1987. 25th Anniv of College of Physicians and Surgeons.
731 **390** 1r. multicoloured . . . . 1·50 30

391 Homeless People, Houses and Rising Sun

1987. International Year of Shelter for the Homeless.
732 **391** 3r. multicoloured 50 50

392 Cathedral Church of the Resurrection, Lahore

1987. Centenary of Cathedral Church of the Resurrection, Lahore.
733 **392** 3r. multicoloured 50 50

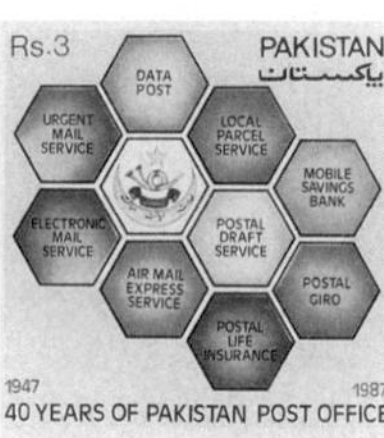

393 Honeycomb and Arms

1987. 40th Anniv of Pakistan Post Office.
734 **393** 3r. multicoloured 50 50

394 Corporation Emblem

1987. Radio Pakistan's New Programme Schedules.
735 **394** 80p. multicoloured . . . 15 15

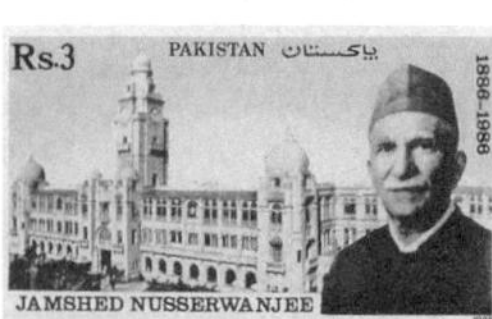

395 Jamshed Nusserwanjee Mehta and Karachi Municipal Corporation Building

1988. Birth Centenary (1986) of Jamshed Nusserwanjee Mehta (former President of Karachi Municipal Corporation).
736 **395** 3r. multicoloured 50 50

396 Leprosy Symbols within Flower **398** Globe

397 W.H.O. Building, Geneva

1988. World Leprosy Day.
737 **396** 3r. multicoloured 75 50

1988. 40th Anniv of W.H.O.
738 **397** 4r. multicoloured 60 50

1988. 125th Anniv of Int Red Cross and Crescent.
739 **398** 3r. multicoloured 50 50

399 Crescent, Leaf Pattern and Archway

1988. Independence Day.
740 **399** 80p. multicoloured . . . 10 10
741 4r. multicoloured 45 50

400 Field Events

1988. Olympic Games, Seoul. Multicoloured.
742 10r. Type **400** . . . . 1·10 1·10
743 10r. Track events . . . . . . 1·10 1·10
744 10r. Jumping and pole vaulting . . . . 1·10 1·10
745 10r. Gymnastics . . . . . . 1·10 1·10
746 10r. Table tennis, tennis, hockey and baseball . . . 1·10 1·10
747 10r. Volleyball, football, basketball and handball . . 1·10 1·10
748 10r. Wrestling, judo, boxing and weightlifting . . . . . 1·10 1·10
749 10r. Shooting, fencing and archery . . . . 1·10 1·10
750 10r. Water sports . . . . . 1·10 1·10
751 10r. Equestrian events and cycling . . . . 1·10 1·10

401 Markhor

1988. Wildlife Protection (15th series).
752 **401** 2r. multicoloured 65 50

402 Islamia College, Peshawar

1988. 75th Anniv of Islamia College, Peshawar.
753 **402** 3r. multicoloured 50 50

403 Symbols of Agriculture, Industry and Education with National Flags

1988. South Asian Association for Regional Co-operation 4th Summit Meeting, Islamabad. Multicoloured.
754 25r. Type **403** . . . . 1·50 1·50
755 50r. National flags on globe and symbols of communications (33 × 33 mm) . . . . . . 3·25 3·25
756 75r. Stamps from member countries (52 × 29 mm) . . 4·50 4·50

1989. Pioneers of Freedom (2nd series). As T **282**. Multicoloured.
757 3r. Maulana Hasrat Mohani 30 30

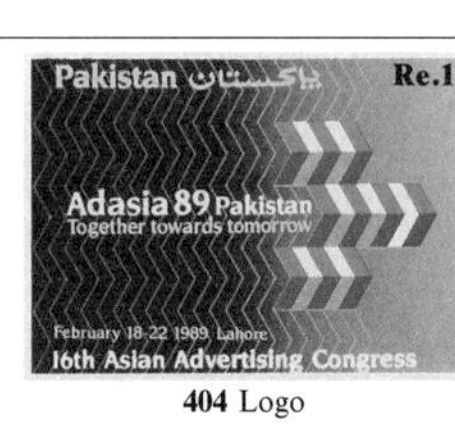

404 Logo

1989. "Adasia 89" 16th Asian Advertising Congress, Lahore.
758 **404** 1r. multicoloured ("Pakistan" in yellow) 1·10 1·40
759 1r. multicoloured ("Pakistan" in blue) . . 1·10 1·40
760 1r. multicoloured ("Pakistan" in white) 1·10 1·40

405 Zulfikar Ali Bhutto

1989. 10th Death Anniv of Zulfikar Ali Bhutto (statesman). Multicoloured.
761 1r. Type **405** 20 10
762 2r. Zulfikar Ali Bhutto (different) 30 30

406 "Daphne" Class Submarine

1989. 25 Years of Pakistan Navy Submarine Operations. Multicoloured.
763 1r. Type **406** . . . . 1·10 1·25
764 1r. "Fleet Snorkel" class submarine . . . . 1·10 1·25
765 1r. "Agosta" class submarine 1·10 1·25

407 "The Oath of the Tennis Court" (David)

1989. Bicentenary of French Revolution.
766 **407** 7r. multicoloured . . . . 1·75 1·00

408 Pitcher, c. 2200 B.C.

1989. Archaeological Artefacts. Terracotta pottery from Baluchistan Province. Mult.
767 1r. Type **408** 30 30
768 1r. Jar, c. 2300 B.C. 30 30
769 1r. Vase, c. 3600 B.C. 30 30
770 1r. Jar, c. 2600 B.C. 30 30

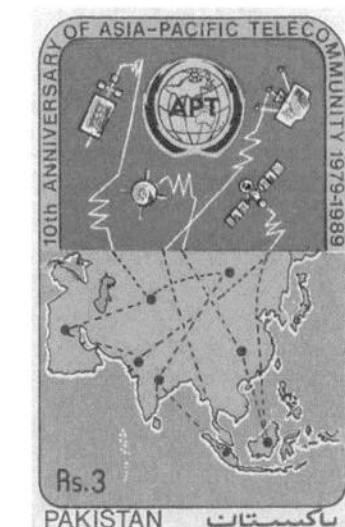

409 Satellites and Map of Asian Telecommunications Network

1989. 10th Anniv of Asia–Pacific Telecommunity.
771 **409** 3r. multicoloured 50 50

410 Container Ship at Wharf

1989. Construction of Integrated Container Terminal, Port Qasim.
772 **410** 6r. multicoloured . . . . 3·00 3·75

411 Mohammed Ali Jinnah

412 Mausoleum of Shah Abdul Latif Bhitai

1989.
773 **411** 1r. multicoloured 70 10
774 1r.50 multicoloured . . . 80 50
775 2r. multicoloured 90 30
776 3r. multicoloured . . . . 1·10 50
777 4r. multicoloured . . . . 1·40 70
778 5r. multicoloured . . . . 1·40 70

1989. 300th Birth Anniv of Shah Abdul Latif Bhitai (poet).
779 **412** 2r. multicoloured 50 50

413 Asiatic Black Bear

414 Ear of Wheat encircling Globe

1989. Wildlife Protection (16th series). Asiatic Black Bear. Multicoloured.
780 4r. Type **413** . . . . 90 1·10
781 4r. Bear among boulders . . 90 1·10
782 4r. Standing on rock . . . . 90 1·10
783 4r. Sitting by trees . . . . . 90 1·10

1989. World Food Day.
784 **414** 1r. multicoloured 35 35

415 Games Emblem and Flags of Member Countries

1989. 4th South Asian Sports Federation Games, Islamabad.
785 **415** 1r. multicoloured 35 35

416 Patchwork Kamblee (cloth) entering Gate of Heaven

1989. 800th Birth Anniv of Baba Farid (Muslim spiritual leader).
786 **416** 3r. multicoloured 40 40

417 Pakistan Television Logo

1989. 25th Anniv of Television Broadcasting in Pakistan.
787 **417** 3r. multicoloured 40 40

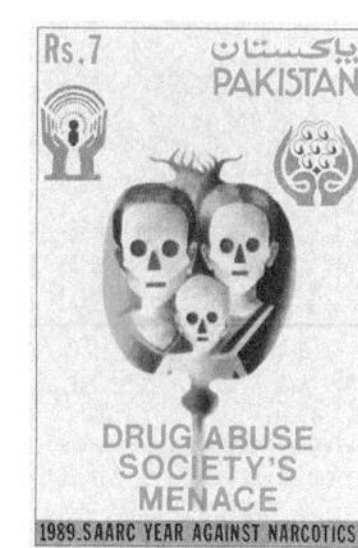

418 Family of Drug Addicts in Poppy Bud

1989. South Asian Association for Regional Co-operation Anti-Drugs Campaign.
788 **418** 7r. multicoloured . . . . 2·25 1·40

419 Murray College, Sialkot

1989. Centenary of Murray College, Sialkot.
789 **419** 6r. multicoloured . . . . 75 1·00

420 Government College, Lahore

1989. 125th Anniv of Government College, Lahore.
790 **420** 6r. multicoloured . . . . 65 1·25

421 Fields, Electricity Pylons and Rural Buildings

1989. 10th Anniv of Centre for Asia and Pacific Integrated Rural Development.
791 **421** 3r. multicoloured 55 75

422 Emblem and Islamic Patterns

1990. 20th Anniv of Organization of the Islamic Conference.
792 **422** 1r. multicoloured . . . . 1·25 20

423 Hockey Match

1990. 7th World Hockey Cup, Lahore.
793 **423** 2r. multicoloured . . . . 4·50 4·25

424 Mohammed Iqbal addressing Crowd and Liaquat Ali Khan taking Oath

1990. 50th Anniv of Passing of Pakistan Resolution. Multicoloured.
794 1r. Type **424** . . . . 80 1·00
795 1r. Maulana Mohammad Ali Jauhar and Mohammed Ali Jinnah with banner . . . . 80 1·00
796 1r. Women with Pakistan flag, and Mohammed Ali Jinnah taking Governor-General's oath, 1947 . . . 80 1·00
797 7r. Minar-i-Qarardad-e-Pakistan Monument and Resolution in Urdu and English (86 × 42 mm) . . . 2·25 2·75
Nos. 794/6 were printed together, se-tenant, forming a composite design.

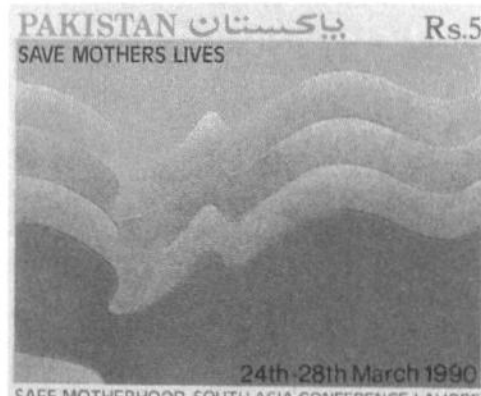

425 Pregnant Woman resting

1990. "Safe Motherhood" South Asia Conference, Lahore.
798 **425** 5r. multicoloured . . . . 75 1·00

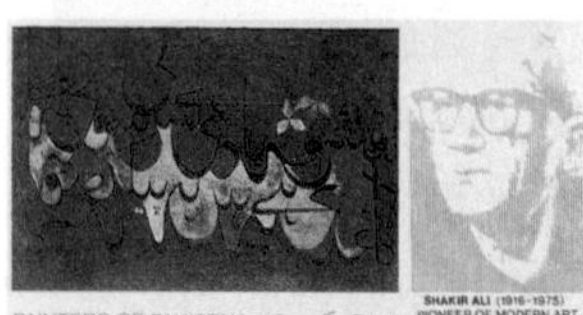

426 "Decorated Verse by Ghalib" (Shakir Ali)

1990. Painters of Pakistan (1st series). Shakir Ali.
799 **426** 1r. multicoloured . . . . 2·25 1·25
See also Nos. 856/7.

427 Satellite in Night Sky

1990. Launch of "Badr I" Satellite.
800 **427** 3r. multicoloured . . . . 3·50 3·25

428 Allama Mohammed Iqbal

1990. Pioneers of Freedom (3rd series). Each brown and green.
801 1r. Type **428** 35 40
802 1r. Mohammed Ali Jinnah 35 40
803 1r. Sir Syed Ahmad Khan . . 35 40
804 1r. Nawab Salimullah 35 40
805 1r. Mohtarma Fatima Jinnah 35 40
806 1r. Aga Khan III 35 40
807 1r. Nawab Mohammad Ismail Khan 35 40
808 1r. Hussain Shaheed Suhrawardy 35 40
809 1r. Syed Ameer Ali 35 40
810 1r. Nawab Bahadur Yar Jung 35 40
811 1r. Khawaja Nazimuddin . . 35 40
812 1r. Maulana Obaidullah Sindhi 35 40
813 1r. Sahibzada Abdul Qaiyum Khan 35 40
814 1r. Begum Jahanara Shah Nawaz 35 40
815 1r. Sir Ghulam Hussain Hidayatullah 35 40
816 1r. Qazi Mohammad Isa . . 35 40
817 1r. Sir M. Shahnawaz Khan Mamdot 35 40
818 1r. Pir Sahib of Manki Sharif 35 40
819 1r. Liaquat Ali Khan 35 40
820 1r. Maulvi A. K. Fazl-ul-Haq 35 40
821 1r. Allama Shabbir Ahmad Usmani 35 40
822 1r. Sadar Abdur Rab Nishtar 35 40
823 1r. Bi Amma 35 40
824 1r. Sir Abdullah Haroon . . 35 40
825 1r. Chaudhry Rahmat Ali . . 35 40
826 1r. Raja Sahib of Mahmudabad 35 40
827 1r. Hassanally Effendi . . . 35 40
See also Nos. 838/46, 870/2, 904/6, 921/8, 961/2, 1007, 1019/20 and 1075/7.

429 Cultural Aspects of Indonesia and Pakistan

1990. Indonesia–Pakistan Economic and Cultural Co-operation Organization.
828 **429** 7r. multicoloured . . . . 2·25 2·25

430 Globe, Open Book and Pen

1990. International Literacy Year.
829 **430** 3r. multicoloured . . . . 1·00 1·50

431 College Crests **432** Children and Globe

1990. Joint Meeting between Royal College of Physicians, Edinburgh, and College of Physicians and Surgeons, Pakistan.
830 **431** 2r. multicoloured 60 75

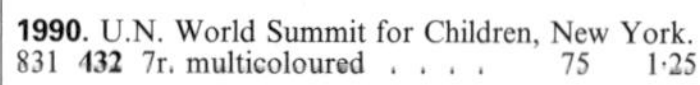

1990. U.N. World Summit for Children, New York.
831 **432** 7r. multicoloured . . . . 75 1·25

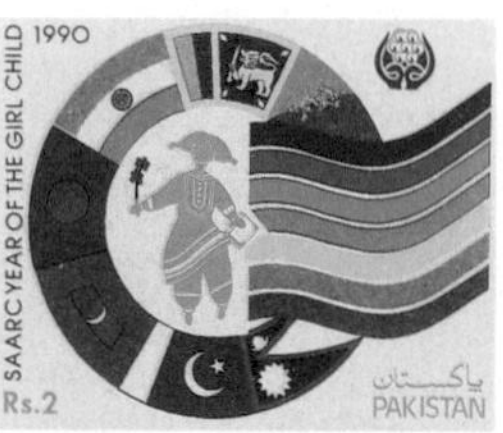

433 Girl within Members' Flags

1990. South Asian Association for Regional Co-operation Year of Girl Child.
832 **433** 2r. multicoloured 70 75

434 Paper passing over Rollers **435** Civil Defence Worker protecting Islamabad

1990. 25th Anniv of Security Papers Limited.
833 **434** 3r. multicoloured . . . . 2·50 1·50

1991. International Civil Defence Day.
834 **435** 7r. multicoloured . . . . 1·25 1·50

436 Logo and Flags of Member Countries

1991. South and West Asia Postal Union Commemoration.
835 **436** 5r. multicoloured . . . . 1·60 1·90

437 Globe and Figures

1991. World Population Day.
836 **437** 10r. multicoloured . . . . 1·90 2·50

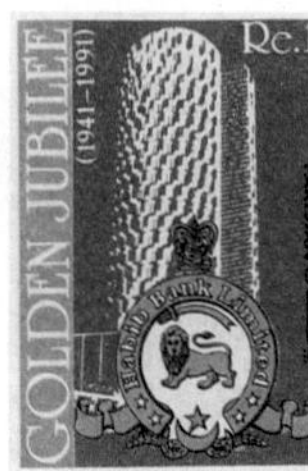

438 Mentally Handicapped Athlete **439** Habib Bank Headquarters and Emblem

1991. Pakistan Participation in Special Olympic Games.
837 **438** 7r. multicoloured . . . . 1·75 2·25

1991. Pioneers of Freedom (4th series). As T **428**. Each brown and green.
838 1r. Maulana Zafar Ali Khan 55 65
839 1r. Maulana Mohamed Ali Jauhar 55 65
840 1r. Chaudhry Khaliquzzaman 55 65
841 1r. Hameed Nizami 55 65
842 1r. Begum Ra'ana Liaquat Ali Khan 55 65
843 1r. Mirza Abol Hassan Ispahani 55 65
844 1r. Raja Ghazanfar Ali Khan 55 65
845 1r. Malik Barkat Ali 55 65
846 1r. Mir Jaffer Khan Jamali 55 65

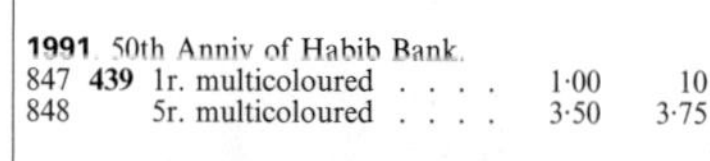

1991. 50th Anniv of Habib Bank.
847 **439** 1r. multicoloured . . . . 1·00 10
848 5r. multicoloured . . . . 3·50 3·75

440 St. Joesph's Convent School

1991. 130th Anniv (1992) of St. Joesph's Convent School, Karachi.
849 **440** 5r. multicoloured . . . . 3·50 3·75

441 Emperor Sher Shah Suri **443** Houbara Bustard

442 Jinnah Antarctic Research Station

1991. Emperor Sher Shah Suri (founder of road network) Commemoration.
850 **441** 5r. multicoloured . . . . 1·50 2·00
MS851 92 × 80 mm. 7r. Emperor on horseback and portrait as Type **441**. Imperf . . . . . . 1·40 2·25

1991. Pakistan Scientific Expedition to Antarctica.
852 **442** 7r. multicoloured . . . . 2·50 2·50

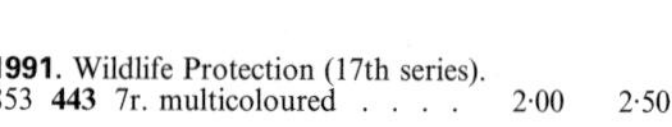

1991. Wildlife Protection (17th series).
853 **443** 7r. multicoloured . . . . 2·00 2·50

444 Mosque

1991. 300th Death Anniv of Hazrat Sultan Bahoo.
854 **444** 7r. multicoloured . . . . 1·75 2·25

445 Development Symbols and Map of Asia

1991. 25th Anniv of Asian Development Bank.
855 **445** 7r. multicoloured . . . . 2·75 2·75

1991. Painters of Pakistan (2nd series). As T **426**. Multicoloured.
856 1r. "Procession" (Haji Muhammad Sharif) . . . . 1·75 1·50
857 1r. "Women harvesting" (Ustad Allah Bux) . . . . 1·75 1·50

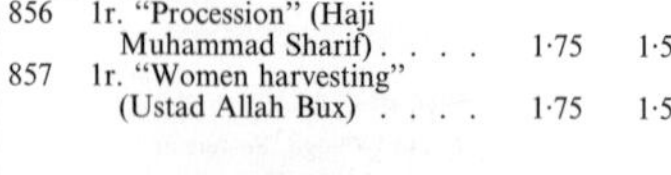

446 American Express Travellers Cheques of 1891 and 1991 (¾-size illustration)

1991. Centenary of American Express Travellers Cheques.
858 **446** 7r. multicoloured . . . . 1·75 2·50

447 Flag, Banknote and Banking Equipment

1992. 1st Anniv of Muslim Commercial Bank Privatization. Multicoloured.
859 1r. Type **447** 20 10
860 7r. Flag with industrial and commercial scenes . . . . 80 1·10

448 Imran Khan (team captain) and Trophy

1992. Pakistan's Victory in World Cricket Championship. Multicoloured.
861 2r. Type **448** 70 70
862 5r. Trophy and national flags (horiz) . . . . 1·50 1·50
863 7r. Pakistani flag, trophy and symbolic cricket ball . . . 1·75 2·00

449 "Rehber-1" Rocket and Satellite View of Earth

1992. International Space Year. Mult.
864 1r. Type **449** 25 10
865 2r. Satellite orbiting Earth and logo 35 50

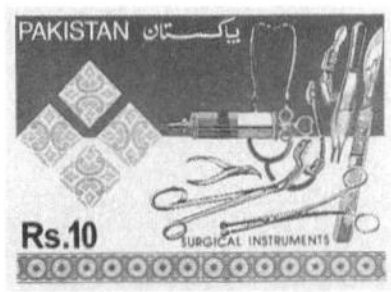

450 Surgical Instruments

1992. Industries. Multicoloured.
866 10r. Type **450** . . . . 90 1·25
867 15r. Leather goods . . . . . 1·10 1·75
868 25r. Sports equipment . . . 2·25 2·75

451 Globe and Symbolic Family

1992. Population Day.
869 **451** 6r. multicoloured . . . . 1·00 1·25

1992. Pioneers of Freedom (5th series). As T **428**. Each brown and green.
870 1r. Syed Suleman Nadvi . . 1·10 1·25
871 1r. Nawab Iftikhar Hussain Khan Mamdot . . . . . . 1·10 1·25
872 1r. Maulana Muhammad Shibli Naumani . . . . . 1·10 1·25

452 Scout Badge and Salute

1992. 6th Islamic Scout Jamboree and 4th Islamic Scouts Conference. Multicoloured.
873 6r. Type **452** 50 75
874 6r. Conference centre and scout salute 50 75

453 College Building

1992. Centenary of Islamia College, Lahore.
875 **453** 3r. multicoloured 50 70

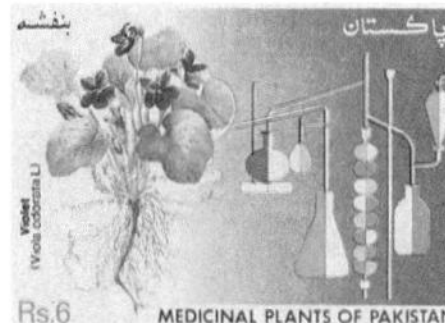

454 "Viola odorata" (flower) and Symbolic Drug Manufacture

1992. Medicinal Plants (1st series).
876 **454** 6r. multicoloured . . . . 2·25 1·75
See also Nos. 903, 946, 1010, 1026, 1037, 1099, 1123, 1142 and 1159.

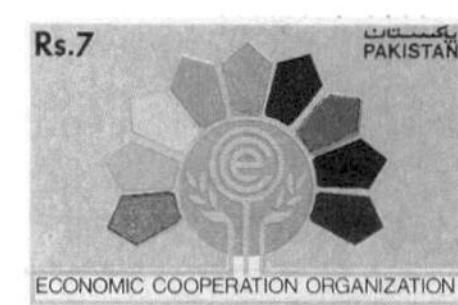

455 Emblem

1992. Extraordinary Ministerial Council Session of Economic Co-operation Organization, Islamabad.
877 **455** 7r. multicoloured . . . . 1·00 1·75

456 Emblems and Field **457** Alhambra Palace, Granada, Spain

1992. International Conference on Nutrition, Rome.
878 **456** 7r. multicoloured . . . . 70 1·25

1992. Cultural Heritage of Muslim Granada.
879 **457** 7r. multicoloured . . . . 70 1·25

458 Mallard **459** Baluchistan Costume

Four different versions of designs as T **458**:
Type A. "Rs.5" at right with rainbow 8 mm beneath "P" of "PAKISTAN"
Type B. "Rs.5" at right with rainbow 2 mm beneath "P"
Type C. "Rs.5" at left with rainbow 2 mm beneath "N" of "PAKISTAN"
Type D. "Rs.5" at left with rainbow 8 mm beneath "N"

1992. Water Birds. Multicoloured.
880 5r. Type **458** (A) 60 70
881 5r. Type **458** (B) 60 70
882 5r. Type **458** (C) 60 70
883 5r. Type **458** (D) 60 70
884 5r. Greylag goose (A) 60 70
885 5r. As No. 884 (B) 60 70
886 5r. As No. 884 (C) 60 70
887 5r. As No. 884 (D) 60 70
888 5r. Gadwall (A) 60 70
889 5r. As No. 888 (B) 60 70
890 5r. As No. 888 (C) 60 70
891 5r. As No. 888 (D) 60 70
892 5r. Common shelduck (A) . . 60 70
893 5r. As No. 892 (B) 60 70
894 5r. As No. 892 (C) 60 70
895 5r. As No. 892 (D) 60 70
Nos. 880/95 were printed together, se-tenant, each horizontal row having a composite design of a rainbow.

1993. Women's Traditional Costumes. Multicoloured.
896 6r. Type **459** . . . . 1·25 1·50
897 6r. Punjab . . . . 1·25 1·50
898 6r. Sindh . . . . 1·25 1·50
899 6r. North-west Frontier Province . . . . 1·25 1·50

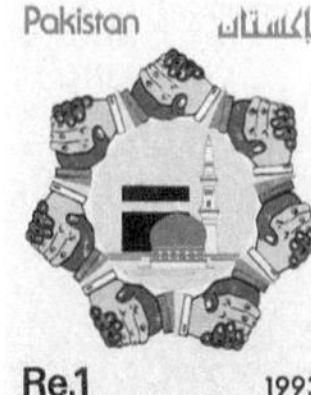

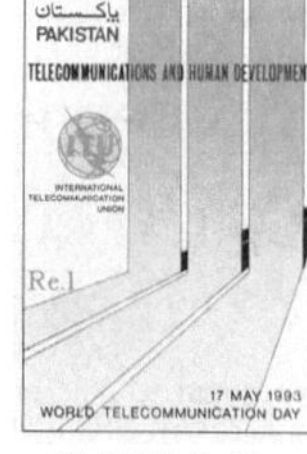

460 Clasped Hands and Islamic Symbols **461** I.T.U. Emblem

1993. 21st Conference of Islamic Foreign Ministers, Karachi.
900 **460** 1r. multicoloured 65 10
901 6r. multicoloured . . . . 1·75 2·25

1993. 25th Anniv of World Telecommunication Day.
902 **461** 1r. multicoloured . . . . 1·25 30

1993. Medicinal Plants (2nd issue). As T **454**. Multicoloured.
903 6r. Fennel and symbolic drug manufacture . . . . 2·75 2·25

1993. Pioneers of Freedom (6th series). As T **428**. Each brown and red.
904 1r. Ghulam Mohammad Bhurgri . . . . 1·00 1·00
905 1r. Ahmed Yar Khan . . . . 1·00 1·00
906 1r. Mohammad Pir Sahib Zakori Sharif . . . . . . 1·00 1·00

462 College Building and Arms

1993. Centenary of Gordon College, Rawalpindi.
907 **462** 2r. multicoloured . . . . 1·50 1·50

463 Juniper Forest

1993. Campaign to Save the Juniper Forest, Ziarat.
907a **463** 1r. multicoloured . . . . 1·25 30
908 7r. multicoloured . . . . 3·00 2·75

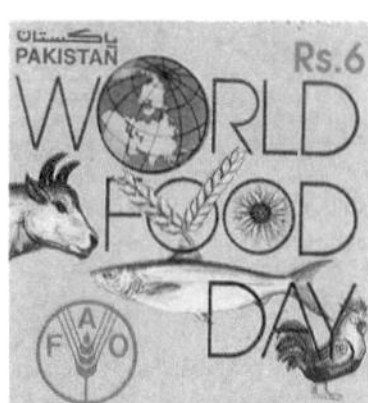

464 Globe, Produce and Emblem

1993. World Food Day.
909 **464** 6r. multicoloured . . . . 1·00 1·25

465 Burn Hall Institution, Abbottabad **466** Peace Dove carrying Letter and National Flags

1993. 50th Anniv of Burn Hall Institutions.
910 **465** 7r. multicoloured . . . . 2·25 2·50

1993. South and West Asia Postal Union Commemoration.
911 **466** 7r. multicoloured . . . . 2·25 2·50

467 Congress Emblem **468** Wazir Mansion (birthplace)

1993. Pakistan College of Physicians and Surgeons International Medical Congress.
912 **467** 1r. multicoloured . . . . 1·50 30

1993. 45th Death Anniv of Mohammed Ali Jinnah.
913 **468** 1r. multicoloured . . . . 1·25 30

469 Emblem and National Flag

1994. 75th Anniv of I.L.O.
914 **469** 7r. multicoloured . . . . 1·75 1·75

470 Ratan Jot (flower)

1994. Ratification of International Biological Diversity Convention. Multicoloured.
915 6r. Type **470** 50 65
916 6r. Wetlands habitat 50 65
917 6r. Golden mahseer ("Tor puttitora") (fish) 50 65
918 6r. Brown bear 50 65

471 Silhouette of Family and Emblem

1994. International Year of the Family.
919 **471** 7r. multicoloured 70 80

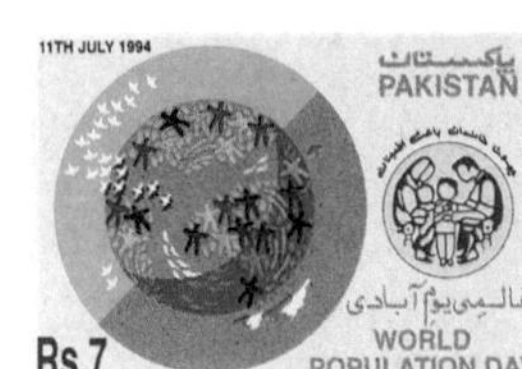

472 Symbolic Globe and Logo

1994. World Population Day.
920 **472** 7r. multicoloured 70 80

1994. Pioneers of Freedom (7th series). As T **428**. Each brown and green.
921 1r. Nawab Mohsin-Ul-Mulk 25 35
922 1r. Sir Shahnawaz Bhutto . . 25 35
923 1r. Nawab Viqar-Ul-Mulk . . 25 35
924 1r. Pir Ilahi Bux 25 35
925 1r. Sheikh Abdul Qadir . . . 25 35
926 1r. Dr. Sir Ziauddin Ahmed 25 35
927 1r. Jam Mir Ghulam Qadir Khan 25 35
928 1r. Sardar Aurangzeb Khan 25 35

473 Hala Pottery, Pakistan   **474** Boy writing and Globe

1994. Indonesia–Pakistan Economic and Cultural Co-operation Organization. Multicoloured.
929 10r. Type **473** . . . . 1·50 1·75
930 10r. Lombok pottery, Indonesia . . . . 1·50 1·75

1994. International Literacy Day.
931 **474** 7r. multicoloured 60 70

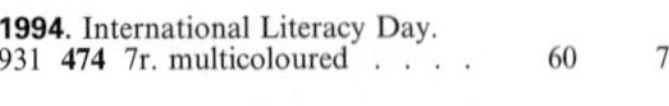

475 Mohammed Ali Jinnah and Floral Pattern

1994.
932 **475** 1r. multicoloured 20 10
933 2r. multicoloured 25 10
934 3r. multicoloured 30 10
935 4r. multicoloured 30 10
936 5r. multicoloured 30 15
937 7r. multicoloured 30 20
938 10r. multicoloured 20 25
939 12r. multicoloured 25 30
940 15r. multicoloured 30 35
941 20r. multicoloured 40 45
942 25r. multicoloured 50 55
943 30r. multicoloured 60 65

476 Gateway and Emblem   **477** Engraver

1994. 2nd South Asian Association for Regional Co-operation and 12th National Scout Jamborees, Quetta.
944 **476** 7r. multicoloured 60 75

1994. 1st Int Festival of Islamic Artisans at Work.
945 **477** 2r. multicoloured . . . . 1·00 60

478 Henbane   **479** Abu-l Kasim Firdausi (poet)

1994. Medicinal Plants (3rd issue).
946 **478** 6r. multicoloured 75 80

1994. Millenary of "Shah Namah" (poem).
947 **479** 1r. multicoloured 25 15

480 Museum Building

1994. Centenary of Lahore Museum.
948 **480** 4r. multicoloured 60 70

481 World Cup Trophies for 1971, 1978, 1982 and 1994

1994. Victory of Pakistan in World Cup Hockey Championship.
949 **481** 5r. multicoloured 75 80

482 Tourist Attractions

1995. 20th Anniv of World Tourism Organization.
950 **482** 4r. multicoloured 60 75

483 Khan Khushal of Khattak and Army

1995. Khan Khushal of Khattak (poet) Commemoration.
951 **483** 7r. multicoloured . . . . 1·50 1·50

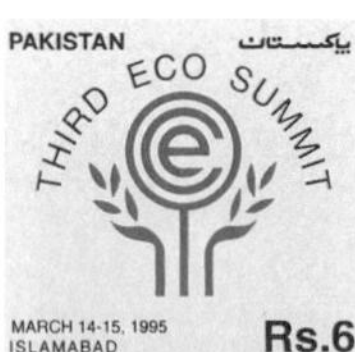

484 E.C.O. Emblem

1995. 3rd Economic Co-operation Organization Summit, Islamabad.
952 **484** 6r. multicoloured . . . . 85 1·00

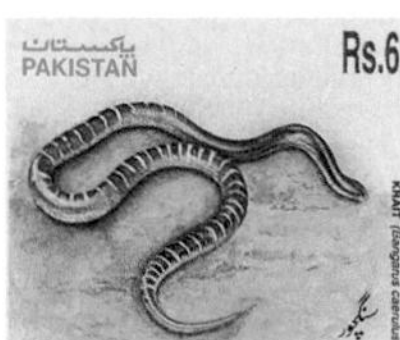

485 Common Indian Krait

1995. Snakes. Multicoloured.
953 6r. Type **485** 70 85
954 6r. Indian cobra 70 85
955 6r. Indian python 70 85
956 6r. Russell's viper 70 85

486 Globe and Environments

1995. Earth Day.
957 **486** 6r. multicoloured 70 75

487 Victoria Carriage, Karachi

1995. Traditional Transport.
958 **487** 5r. multicoloured 65 70

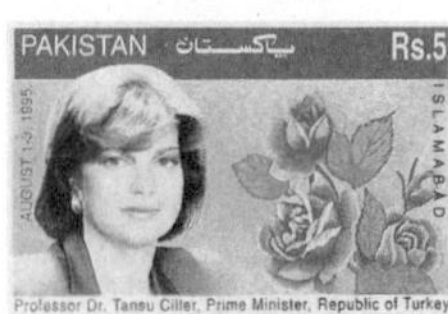

488 Prime Minister Tansu Ciller of Turkey and Rose

1995. 1st Muslim Women Parliamentarians' Conference, Islamabad. Multicoloured.
959 5r. Type **488** 80 90
960 5r. Prime Minister Benazir Bhutto and jasmine 80 90

1995. Pioneers of Freedom (8th series). As T **428**. Each brown and green.
961 1r. Maulana Shaukat Ali . . 70 50
962 1r. Chaudhry Ghulam Abbas 70 50

489 Oil Sardine

1995. Fishes. Multicoloured.
963 6r. Type **489** 70 75
964 6r. Mozambique mouthbrooder ("Tilapia") 70 75
965 6r. Brown trout 70 75
966 6r. Rohu 70 75

490 "Erasmia pulchella"

1995. Butterflies. Multicoloured.
967 6r. Type **490** 50 70
968 6r. "Callicore astarte" (inscr "Catogramme") 50 70
969 6r. "Ixias pyrene" 50 70
970 6r. "Heliconius" 50 70

491 Major Raja Aziz Bhatti Shaheed and Medal

1995. Defence Day.
971 **491** 1r.25 multicoloured . . . 1·25 80

492 Presentation Convent School, Rawalpindi

1995. Centenary of Presentation Convent School, Rawalpindi.
972 **492** 1r.25 multicoloured . . . 85 70

493 Women Soldiers, Golfer and Scientist   **494** "Louis Pasteur in Laboratory" (Edelfelt)

1995. 4th World Conference on Women, Peking. Multicoloured.
973 1r.25 Type **493** 30 40
974 1r.25 Women graduates, journalist, computer operator and technicians 30 40
975 1r.25 Sewing machinist and women at traditional crafts 30 40
976 1r.25 Army officer and women at traditional tasks 30 40

1995. Death Centenary of Louis Pasteur (chemist).
977 **494** 5r. multicoloured . . . . 1·00 1·00

495   **496** Liaquat Ali Khan

1995.
978 **495** 5p. blue, orange and brown 10 10
979 15p. orange, violet and brown 15 10
980 25p. blue, mauve and purple 25 10
981 75p. green, brown and deep brown 70 10

1995. Birth Centenary (1995) of Liaquat Ali Khan (statesman).
987 **496** 1r.25 multicoloured . . . 40 20

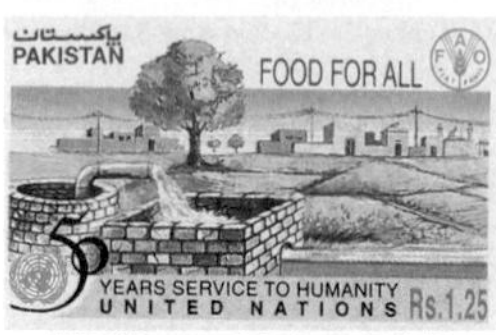

497 Village and Irrigated Fields

1995. 50th Anniv of F.A.O.
988 **497** 1r.25 multicoloured . . . 40 20

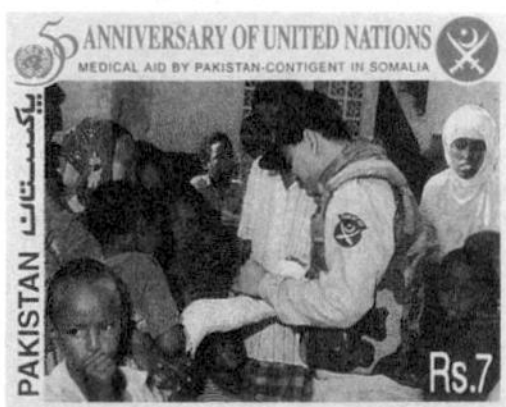

498 Pakistani Soldier treating Somali Refugees

1995. 50th Anniv of United Nations.
989 **498** 7r. multicoloured . . . . 80 1·00

499 Education Emblem   **500** Hand holding Book, Eye and Pen Nib

1995. 80th Anniv (1993) of Kinnaird College for Women, Lahore.
990 **499** 1r.25 multicoloured . . . 40 20

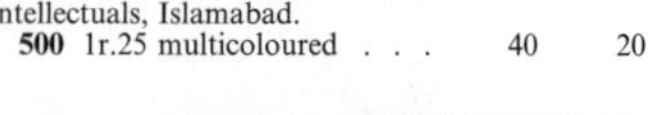

1995. International Conference of Writers and Intellectuals, Islamabad.
991 **500** 1r.25 multicoloured . . . 40 20

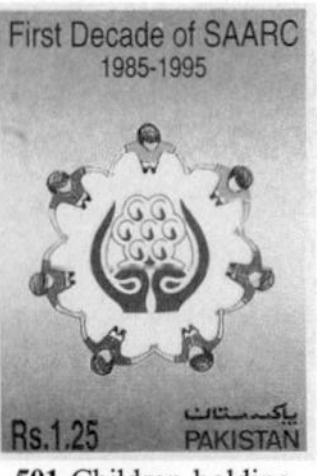

501 Children holding Hands and S.A.A.R.C. Logo   **502** Jet Skier

1995. 10th Anniv of South Asian Association for Regional Co-operation.
992 **501** 1r.25 multicoloured . . . 40 20

1995. National Water Sports Gala, Karachi. Multicoloured.
993 1r.25 Type **502** 30 40
994 1r.25 Local punts 30 40
995 1r.25 Sailboard 30 40
996 1r.25 Water skier 30 40

503 Mortar Board and Books

1995. 20th Anniv of Allama Iqbal Open University.
997 **503** 1r.25 multicoloured . . . 40 20

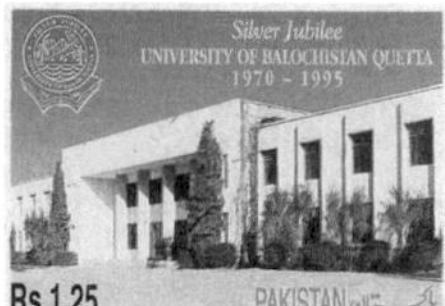

504 Balochistan Quetta University Building

1995. 25th Anniv of Balochistan Quetta University.
998 **504** 1r.25 multicoloured . . . 40 20

505 Zulfikar Ali Bhutto,Flag and Crowd

1996. 17th Death Anniv of Zulfikar Ali Bhutto (former Prime Minister). Multicoloured.
999 1r.25 Type **505** . . . . . . 1·00 20
1000 4r. Zulfikar Ali Bhutto and flag (53 × 31 mm) . . . . 2·25 1·75
MS1001 118 × 74 mm. 8r. Zulfikar Ali Bhutto and crowd. Imperf 1·75 1·75

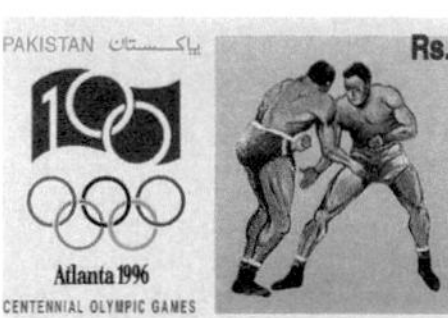

506 Wrestling

1996. Olympic Games, Atlanta. Multicoloured.
1002 5r. Type **506** 60 70
1003 5r. Boxing 60 70
1004 5r. Pierre de Coubertin . . . 60 70
1005 5r. Hockey 60 70
MS1006 112 × 100 mm. 25r. Designs as Nos. 1002/5, but without face values. Imperf . . . . 2·25 2·75

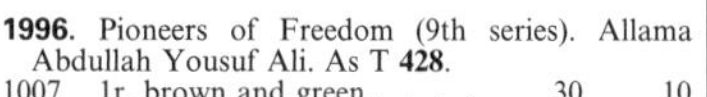

1996. Pioneers of Freedom (9th series). Allama Abdullah Yousuf Ali. As T **428**.
1007 1r. brown and green 30 10

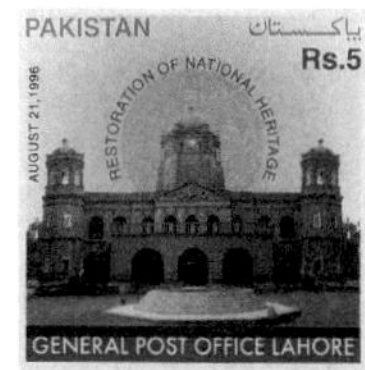

507 G.P.O. Building, Lahore

1996. Restoration of G.P.O. Building, Lahore.
1008 **507** 5r. multicoloured 45 60

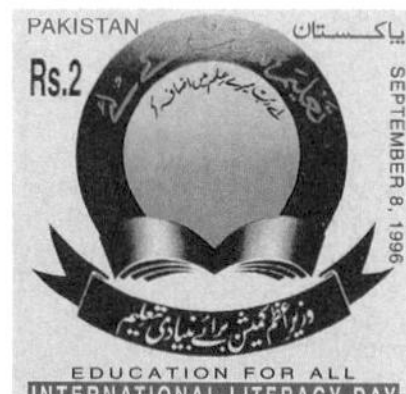

508 Symbolic Open Book and Text

1996. International Literacy Day.
1009 **508** 2r. multicoloured 40 25

509 Yarrow **510** Faiz Ahmed Faiz

1996. Medicinal Plants (4th series).
1010 **509** 3r. multicoloured 75 80

1997. 86th Birth Anniv of Faiz Ahmed Faiz (poet).
1011 **510** 3r. multicoloured 50 50

511 Golden Jubilee and O.I.C. Emblems **512** Amir Timur

1997. Special Summit Conference of Organization of Islamic Countries commemorating 50th anniv of Pakistan.
1012 **511** 2r. multicoloured 35 35

1997. 660th Birth Anniv of Timur (founder of Timurid Empire).
1013 **512** 3r. multicoloured 50 50

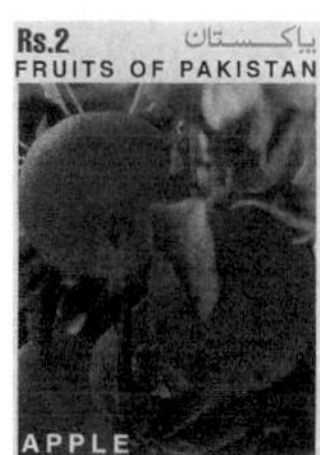

513 Jalal-al-din Moulana Rumi **514** Apple

1997. Pakistan–Iran Joint Issue.
1014 3r. Type **513** 40 50
1015 3r. Allama Mohammad Iqbal (poet) 40 50

1997. Fruit.
1016 **514** 2r. multicoloured 35 35

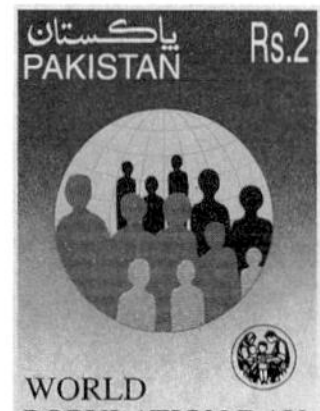

515 People on Globe

1997. World Population Day.
1017 **515** 2r. multicoloured 35 35

516 Stylized Dove of Peace

1997. 40th Anniv of Co-operation between International Atomic Energy Agency and Pakistan Atomic Energy Corporation.
1018 **516** 2r. multicoloured 35 35

1997. Pioneers of Freedom (10th series). As T **428**. Each brown and green.
1019 1r. Mohammad Ayub Khuhro 50 50
1020 1r. Begum Salma Tassaduq Hussain 50 50

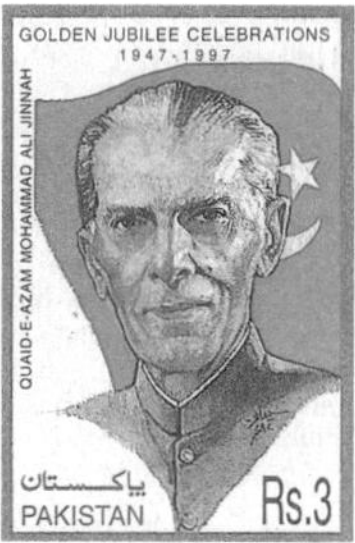

517 Mohammed Ali Jinnah

1997. 50th Anniv of Independence. Multicoloured.
1021 3r. Type **517** 10 10
1022 3r. Allama Mohammad Iqbal 10 10
1023 3r. Mohtarma Fatima Jinnah 10 10
1024 3r. Liaquat Ali Khan . . . 10 10

518 College Building

1997. 75th Anniv of Lahore College for Women.
1025 **518** 3r. multicoloured . . . . 1·00 75

519 Garlic

1997. Medicinal Plants (5th series).
1026 **519** 2r. multicoloured 60 50

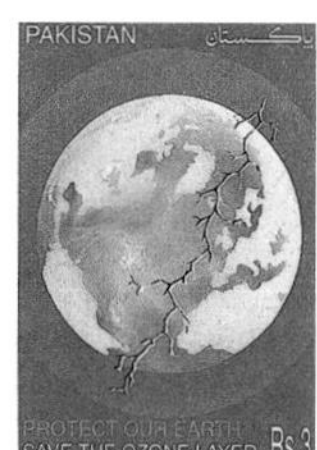

520 Himalayan Monal Pheasant **521** Globe and Cracked Ozone Layer

1997. Wildlife Protection (18th series).
1027 **520** 2r. multicoloured . . . . 1·50 75

1997. Save Ozone Layer Campaign.
1028 **521** 3r. multicoloured . . . . 1·00 75

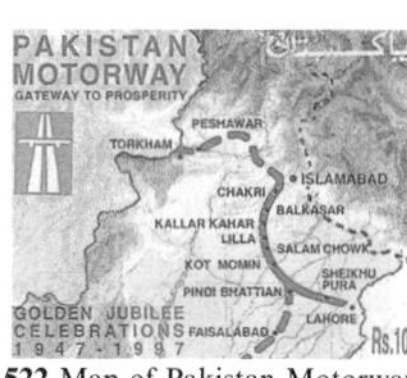

522 Map of Pakistan Motorway Project

1997. Pakistan Motorway Project.
1029 **522** 10r. multicoloured . . . 20 25
MS1030 117 × 97 mm. No. 1029 (sold at 15r.) . . . . 2·25 2·50

523 Emblem and Disabled People

1997. International Day for the Disabled.
1031 **523** 4r. multicoloured 10 10

524 Karachi Grammar School

1997. 150th Anniv of Karachi Grammar School.
1032 **524** 2r. multicoloured . . . . 1·00 60

525 Mirza Ghalib

1998. Birth Bicentenary (1997) of Mirza Ghalib (poet).
1033 **525** 2r. multicoloured 10 10
No. 1033 is inscr "DEATH ANNIVERSARY".

526 Servicemen, Pakistan Flag and "50"

1998. 50th Anniv (1997) of Armed Forces.
1034 **526** 7r. multicoloured 15 20

527 Sir Syed Ahmed Khan

1998. Death Centenary of Sir Syed Ahmed Khan (social reformer).
1035 **527** 7r. brown, green & stone 15 20

528 Olympic Torch and Sports

1998. 27th National Games, Peshawar.
1036 **528** 7r. multicoloured 15 20

529 Thornapple

1998. Medicinal Plants (6th series).
1037 **529** 2r. multicoloured 10 10

530 Silver Jubilee Emblem **531** Mohammed Ali Jinnah

1998. 25th Anniv of Senate.

1038	**530**	2r. multicoloured	10	10
1039		5r. multicoloured	10	15

1998.

1039a	**531**	1r. red and black . . .	10	10
1040		2r. blue and red	10	10
1041		3r. green and brown . .	10	10
1042		4r. purple and orange	10	10
1043		5r. brown and green . .	10	15
1044		6r. green and blue . . .	10	15
1045		7r. red and violet . . .	15	20

532 College Building

1998. Cent of Government College, Faisalabad.

1046	**532**	5r. multicoloured	10	15

533 "Mohammed Ali Jinnah" (S. Akhtar)

1998. 50th Death Anniv of Mohammed Ali Jinnah.

1047	**533**	15r. multicoloured . . .	35	40
MS1048		72 × 100 mm. **533** 15r. multicoloured (sold at 20r.) . .	1·50	1·75

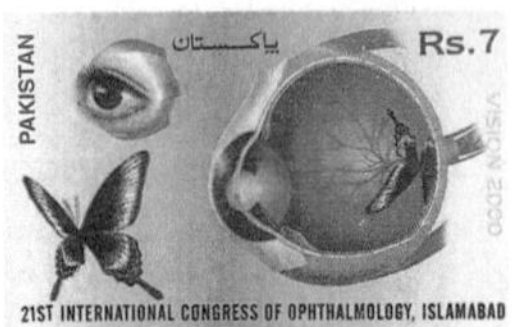

534 Cross-section of Eye

1998. 21st International Ophthalmology Congress, Islamabad.

1049	**534**	7r. multicoloured	15	20

535 United Nations Emblems and Bukhari

1998. Birth Centenary of Syed Ahmed Shah Patrus Bukhari.

1050	**535**	5r. multicoloured	10	15

536 Map, "50 years" and Stamps

538 Dr. Abdus Salam

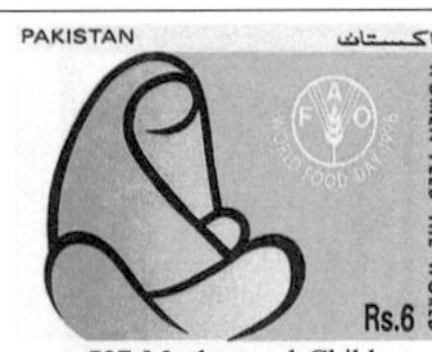

537 Mother and Child

1998. 50th Anniv of Philately in Pakistan.

1051	**536**	6r. multicoloured	15	20

1998. World Food Day.

1052	**537**	6r. multicoloured	15	20

1998. Scientists of Pakistan (1st series). Dr. Abdus Salam.

1053	**538**	2r. multicoloured	10	10

See also No. 1068.

539 Satellite Dish Aerial

1998. "Better Pakistan" Development Plan. Mult.

1054	2r. Type **539**	10	10
1055	2r. Combine harvester . . .	10	10
1056	2r. Airliner	10	10
1057	2r. Children and doctor . .	10	10

540 Globe and Human Rights Emblem

1998. 50th Anniv of Universal Declaration of Human Rights.

1058	**540**	6r. multicoloured	15	20

541 Pakistani Woman carrying Water Pot

1998. 50th Anniv of U.N.I.C.E.F. in Pakistan. Multicoloured.

1059	2r. Type **541**	10	10
1060	2r. Woman reading	10	10
1061	2r. Woman with goitre . . .	10	10
1062	2r. Young boy receiving oral vaccine	10	10

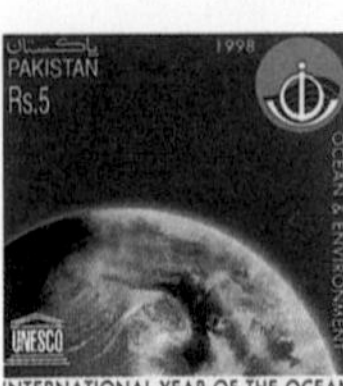

542 Earth seen from Space

1998. International Year of the Ocean.

1063	**542**	5r. multicoloured	10	15

543 Marchers and Route Map

1998. Qaumi Parcham March, Khyber to Chaghi.

1064	**543**	2r. multicoloured	10	10

544 Centenary Logo **545** Dr. Salimuz Zaman Siddiqui

1999. Centenary of Saudi Dynasty of Saudi Arabia. Multicoloured.

1065	2r. Type **544**	10	10
1066	15r. As Type **544**, but with mosaic pattern in corners	35	40
MS1067	73 × 100 mm. 15r. No. 1066 (sold at 20r.)	1·50	1·75

1999. Scientists of Pakistan (2nd series). Dr. Salimuz Zaman Siddiqui.

1068	**545**	5r. multicoloured	10	15

546 Mountains and Pakistan Flag

1999. "Atoms for Peace".

1069	**546**	5r. multicoloured	10	15

547 Plan and View of Mosque **548** Fasting Buddha Statue (drapery on left knee)

1999. Completion of Data Darbar Mosque Complex, Lahore.

1070	**547**	7r. multicoloured	15	20

1999. Archaeological Heritage. Multicoloured.

1071	7r. Type **548**	15	20
1072	7r. Fasting Buddha (drapery on right knee)	15	20
MS1073	107 × 90 mm. Nos. 1071/2 (sold at 25r.)	1·75	2·00

No. **MS**1073 includes the "China '99" International Stamp Exhibition, Beijing, logo on the margin.

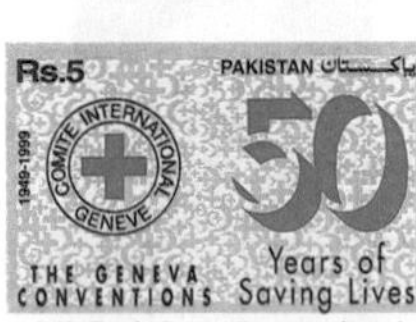

549 Red Cross International Committee Emblem and "50"

1999. 50th Anniv of Geneva Conventions.

1074	**549**	5r. red and black	10	15

1999. Pioneers of Freedom (11th series). As T **428**. Each brown and green.

1075	2r. Maulana Abdul Hamid Badayuni	10	10
1076	2r. Chaudhry Muhammad Ali	10	10
1077	2r. Sir Adamjee Haji Dawood	10	10

550 Ustad Nusrat Fateh Ali Khan

1999. Ustad Nusrat Fateh Ali Khan (musician) Commemoration.

1078	**550**	2r. multicoloured	10	10

551 Islamic Development Bank Building **552** Crowd celebrating

1999. 25th Anniv of Islamic Development Bank.

1079	**551**	5r. multicoloured	10	15

1999. 50th Anniv of People's Republic of China. Multicoloured.

1080	2r. Type **552**	10	10
1081	15r. Bust of Mao Tse-tung (Chinese leader) and emblem (horiz)	35	40

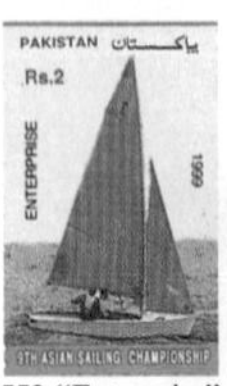

553 "Enterprise" Sailing Dinghy **554** "Optimist" Sailing Dinghies

1999. 9th Asian Sailing Championship. Sailing Craft. Multicoloured.

1082	2r. Type **553**	10	10
1083	2r. "470" dinghy	10	10
1084	2r. "Optimist" dinghy . . .	10	10
1085	2r. "Laser" dinghy	10	10
1086	2r. "Mistral" sailboard . . .	10	10

1999. 10th Asian "Optimist" Sailing Championship.

1087	**554**	2r. multicoloured	10	10

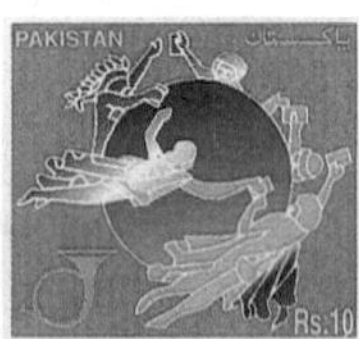

555 U.P.U. Emblem

1999. 125th Anniv of Universal Postal Union.

1088	**555**	10r. multicoloured . . .	20	25

556 Hakim Mohammed Said **557** National Bank of Pakistan Building

1999. 1st Death Anniv of Hakim Mohammed Said.

1089	**556**	5r. multicoloured	10	15

1999. 50th Anniv of National Bank of Pakistan.

1090	**557**	5r. multicoloured	10	15

558 Evolution of the "Shell" Emblem **559** Profiles of Children in "10"

1999. Centenary of Shell in Pakistan.

1091	**558**	4r. multicoloured	10	10

1999. 10th Anniv of United Nations Rights of the Child Convention.

1092	**559**	2r. emerald, green and red	10	10

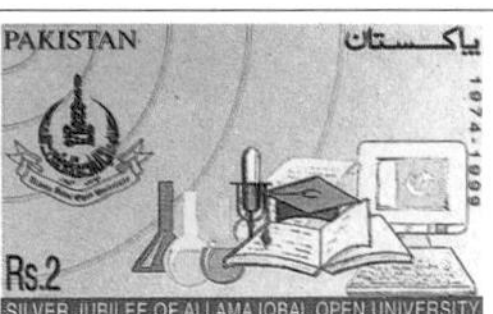
560 Science Equipment, Books and Computer

1999. 25th Anniv of Allama Iqbal Open University. Multicoloured.
1093 2r. Type **560** 10 10
1094 3r. Scholastic symbols as Type **560** 10 10
1095 5r. Map of Pakistan 10 15

561 Josh Malihabadi

1999. Birth Centenary of Josh Malihabadi (poet).
1096 **561** 5r. multicoloured 10 15

562 Dr. Afzal Qadri and Locusts

1999. 25th Death Anniv of Dr. Afzal Qadri (scientist).
1097 **562** 3r. multicoloured 10 10

563 Ghulam Bari Aleeg 564 Plantain

1999. 50th Death Anniv of Ghulam Bari Aleeg (writer).
1098 **563** 5r. multicoloured 10 15

1999. Medicinal Plants (7th series).
1099 **564** 5r. multicoloured 10 15

565 Mosque (½-size illustration)

1999. Eid-ul-Fitr Greetings.
1100 **565** 2r. multicoloured 25 10
1101 15r. multicoloured . . . 1·50 1·75

566 Woman and Young Boy

2000. 25th Anniv of S.O.S. Children's Villages in Pakistan.
1102 **566** 2r. multicoloured 10 10

567 Racing Cyclists

2000. Centenary of International Cycling Union.
1103 **567** 2r. multicoloured 10 10

568 Doves

2000. Pakistan Convention on Human Rights and Human Dignity.
1104 **568** 2r. multicoloured 10 10

569 College Building

2000. Centenary of Edwardes College, Peshawar.
1105 **569** 2r. multicoloured 10 10

570 Mahomed Ali Habib

2000. Mahomed Ali Habib (founder of Habib Bank Ltd) Commemoration.
1106 **570** 2r. multicoloured 10 10

571 Emblems and Symbols

2000. 50th Anniv of Institute of Cost and Management Accountants. Multicoloured.
1107 2r. Type **571** 10 10
1108 15r. Emblems, graph, keyboard and globe . . . 35 40

572 Ahmed Jaffer

2000. 10th Death Anniv of Ahmed Jaffer (prominent businessman).
1109 **572** 10r. multicoloured . . . 20 25

573 "Sarfaroshaane Tehreeke Pakistan" (detail)

2000. "Sarfaroshaane Tehreeke Pakistan" (painting). Showing different details. Multicoloured.
1110 5r. Type **573** 10 15
1111 5r. Bullock carts with tree in foreground 10 15
1112 5r. Bullock carts and crowd carrying Pakistan flag . . 10 15
1113 5r. Unloading bullock cart 10 15

574 Captain Muhammad Sarwar

2000. Defence Day. Showing winners of Nishan-e-Haider medal. Multicoloured.
1114 5r. Type **574** 10 15
1115 5r. Major Tufail Muhammad 10 15
See also No. 1173/4.

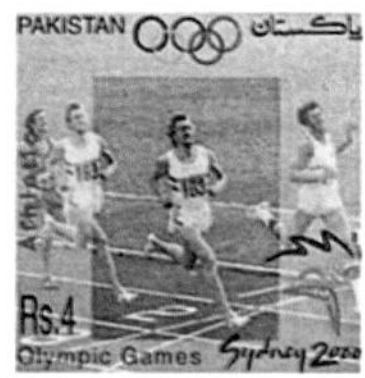
575 Athletics

2000. Olympic Games, Sydney. Multicoloured.
1116 4r. Type **575** 10 10
1117 4r. Hockey 10 10
1118 4r. Weightlifting 10 10
1119 4r. Cycling 10 10

576 Emblem and Building 577 Conference Emblem

2000. 125th Anniv of National College of Arts, Lahore.
1120 **576** 5r. multicoloured 10 15

2000. "Creating the Future" Business Conference.
1121 **577** 5r. multicoloured 10 15

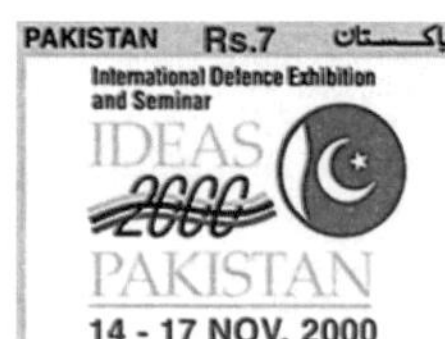
578 Exhibition Emblem

2000. "Ideas 2000" International Defence Exhibition and Seminar.
1122 **578** 7r. multicoloured 15 20

579 Liquorice

2000. Medicinal Plants (8th series).
1123 **579** 2r. multicoloured 10 10

580 Crippled Child and Rotary Emblem

2000. "A World Without Polio" Campaign.
1124 **580** 2r. multicoloured 10 10

581 Refugee Family and Emblems

2000. 50th Anniv of United Nations High Commissioner for Refugees.
1125 **581** 2r. multicoloured 10 10

582 Hafeez Jalandhri

2001. Birth Centenary of Hafeez Jalandhri (poet).
1126 **582** 2r. multicoloured 10 10

583 Habib Bank AG Zurich Head Office

2001. Habib Bank AG Zurich Commemoration.
1127 **583** 5r. multicoloured 10 15

584 Chashma Nuclear Power Station

2001. Opening of Chashma Nuclear Power Station.
1128 **584** 4r. multicoloured 10 10

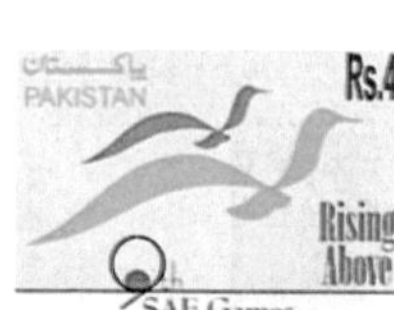
585 S.A.F. Games Emblem

2001. 9th S.A.F. Games, Islamabad.
1129 **585** 4r. multicoloured (blue background) 10 10
1130 4r. multicoloured (pink background) 10 10

586 "Ma Gu's Birthday Offering"

2001. 50th Anniv of Pakistan–China Friendship. Multicoloured.
1131 4r. Type **586** 10 10
1132 4r. "Two Pakistani Women drawing Water" 10 10
1133 4r. Girls in traditional Yugur and Hunza costumes 10 10
No. 1131 is inscribed "BIRTTHDAY" in error.

587 Mohammad Ali Jinnah 589 Khawaja Ghulam Farid

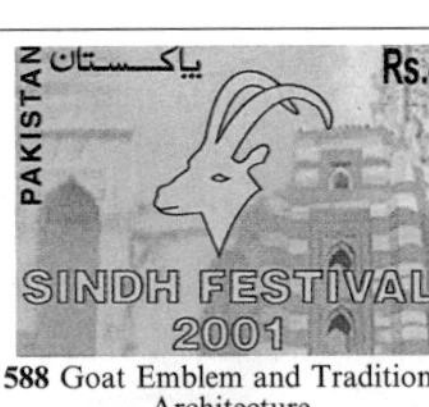

588 Goat Emblem and Traditional Architecture

2001. 125th Birth Anniv of Mohammad Ali Jinnah ("Quaid-e-Azam") (1st issue).
1134 **587** 4r. multicoloured 10 10
See also Nos. 1152/6.

2001. Defence Day. As T **574** showing winners of Nishan-e-Haider medal. Multicoloured.
1135 4r. Major Shabbir Sharif Shaheed 10 10
1136 4r. Major Mohammad Akram Shaheed 10 10

2001. Sindh Festival, Karachi.
1137 **588** 4r. yellow, black and green 10 10

2001. Death Centenary of Khawaja Ghulam Farid (poet).
1138 **589** 5r. multicoloured 10 15

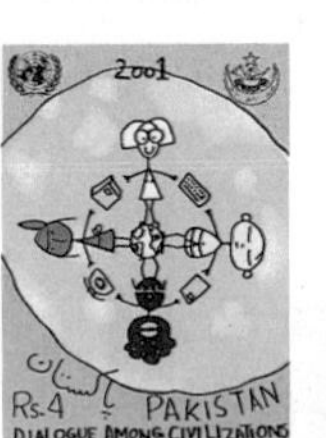

590 "Children encircling Globe" (Urska Golob)

591 Syed Imitaz Ali Taj

2001. U.N. Year of Dialogue among Civilizations.
1139 **590** 4r. multicoloured 10 10

2001. Syed Imitaz Ali Taj (writer) Commemoration.
1140 **591** 5r. multicoloured 10 15

592 Pres. Saparmurat Niyazov of Turkmenistan

593 Peppermint

2001. 10th Anniv of Turkmenistan Independence.
1141 **592** 5r. multicoloured 10 15

2001. Medicinal Plants (9th series).
1142 **593** 4r. multicoloured 10 10

594 Convent of Jesus and Mary, Lahore

2001. 125th Anniv of Convent of Jesus and Mary, Lahore.
1143 **594** 4r. multicoloured 10 10

595 Dr. Ishtiaq Husain Qureshi

596 Blue Throat

2001. 20th Death Anniv of Dr. Ishtiaq Husain Qureshi (historian).
1144 **595** 4r. multicoloured 10 10

2001. Birds. Multicoloured.
1145 4r. Type **596** 10 10
1146 4r. Hoopoe 10 10
1147 4r. Pin-tailed sandgrouse . . 10 10
1148 4r. Magpie robin 10 10

597 Handshake beneath Flags of U.A.E. and Pakistan

598 Nishtar Medical College, Multan

2001. 30th Anniv of Diplomatic Relations between Pakistan and United Arab Emirates. Multicoloured.
1149 5r. Type **597** 10 15
1150 30r. Pres. Sheikh Zayed bin Sultan Al Nahyan of U.A.E. and Mohammed Ali Jinnah (horiz) . . . . 1·50 1·75

2001. 50th Anniv of Nishtar Medical College, Multan.
1151 **598** 5r. multicoloured 10 15

599 Mohammad Ali Jinnah taking Oath as Governor General, 1947

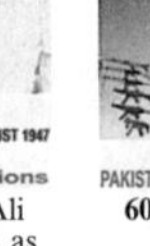

600 Troops and Ordnance

2001. 125th Birth Anniv of Mohammad Ali Jinnah ("Quaid-e-Azam") (2nd issue). Multicoloured.
1152 4r. Type **599** 10 10
1153 4r. Opening State Bank, Karachi, 1948 . . . . . 10 10
1154 4r. Taking salute, Peshawar, 1948 . . . . 10 10
1155 4r. Inspecting guard of honour, 1948 (55 × 27 mm) 10 10
1156 4r. With anti-aircraft gun crew, 1948 (55 × 27 mm) 10 10

2001. 50th Anniv of Pakistan Ordnance Factories.
1157 **600** 4r. multicoloured 10 10

601 Samandar Khan Samandar

2002. Samandar Khan Samandar (poet) Commemoration.
1158 **601** 5r. multicoloured 10 15

602 Hyssop

2002. Medicinal Plants (10th series).
1159 **602** 5r. multicoloured 10 15

603 Statues of Buddha

2002. 50th Anniv of Diplomatic Relations between Pakistan and Japan.
1160 **603** 5r. multicoloured 10 15

604 Pakistan and Kyrgyzstan Flags

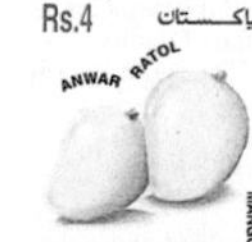

605 Anwar Ratol Mangoes

2002. 10th Anniv of Diplomatic Relations between Pakistan and Kyrgyzstan.
1161 **604** 5r. multicoloured 10 15

2002. Fruits of Pakistan. Mangoes. Multicoloured.
1162 4r. Type **605** 10 10
1163 4r. Dusehri mangoes 10 10
1164 4r. Chaunsa mangoes . . . 10 10
1165 4r. Sindhri mango 10 10

606 Begum Noor us Sabah

607 Children with Animals and Pakistan Flag

2002. 55th Independence Day Celebrations. Political Figures. Multicoloured.
1166 4r. Type **606** 10 10
1167 4r. I. Chundrigar 10 10
1168 4r. Habib Ibrahim Rahimtoola 10 10
1169 4r. Qazi Mureed Ahmed . . 10 10

2002. World Summit on Sustainable Development, Johannesburg. Multicoloured.
1170 4r. Type **607** 10 10
1171 4r. Mountain and cartoon character (37 × 37 mm) . . 10 10

608 Mohammad Aly Rangoonwala (politician/ philanthropist)

2002. Mohammad Aly Rangoonwala Commem.
1172 **608** 4r. multicoloured 10 10

2002. Defence Day. As T **574** showing winners of Nishan-e-Haider medal. Multicoloured.
1173 4r. Lance Naik Muhammad Mahfuz Shaheed 10 10
1174 4r. Sawar Muhammad Hussain Shaheed 10 10

609 Muhammad Iqbal in Academic Gown

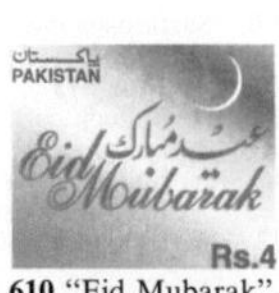

610 "Eid Mubarak"

2002. 125th Birth Anniv of Muhammad Iqbal (writer). Multicoloured.
1174 4r. Type **609** 10 10
1175 4r. Muhammad Iqbal in library 10 10

2002. Eid-ul-Fitr Festival.
1176 **610** 4r. multicoloured 10 10

611 Hakim Muhammad Hassan Qarshi and Plants

2002. Hakim Muhammad Hassan Qarshi (pioneer of Tibb homeopathic medicine) Commemoration.
1177 **611** 4r. multicoloured 10 10

612 Red-legged Partridge, Markhor and White Flowers

2003. National Philatelic Exhibition, Karachi.
1178 **612** 4r. multicoloured 10 10

613 Anniversary Emblem

614 Minaret Emblem

2003. 50th Anniv of Pakistan Academy of Sciences.
1179 **613** 4r. multicoloured 10 10

2003. Centenary Celebrations of North West Frontier Province.
1180 **614** 4r. multicoloured 10 10

615 Golden Jubilee Emblem

2003. 50th Anniv of Pakistan Council of Scientific and Industrial Research, Islamabad.
1181 **615** 4r. brown, green and yellow 10 10

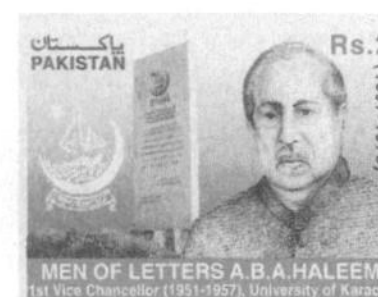

616 Prof. A. B. A. Haleem

2003. Prof. A. B. A. Haleem (1st Vice Chancellor of Karachi University) Commemoration.
1182 **616** 2r. multicoloured 10 10

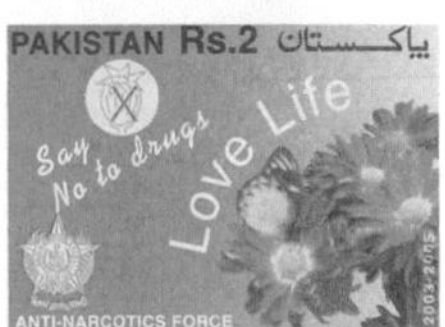

617 Flowers and Anti Narcotics Force Badge

2003. "Say No to Drugs".
1183 **617** 2r. multicoloured 10 10

618 Sir Syed Memorial, Islamabad

2003. Sir Syed Memorial, Islamabad.
1184 **618** 2r. multicoloured 10 10

619 *Rosa damascene* **620** Fatima Jinnah

2003. Medicinal Plants (11th series).
1185 **619** 2r. multicoloured 10 10

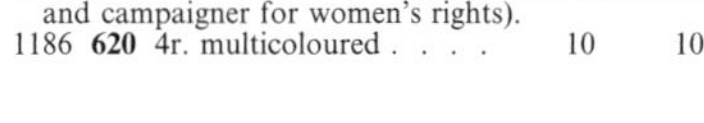

2003. 110th Birth Anniv of Fatima Jinnah (politician and campaigner for women's rights).
1186 **620** 4r. multicoloured 10 10

621 Abdul Rahman (PO employee killed in raid, 2002) **622** Moulana Abdul Sattar Khan Niazi (politician, 88th)

2003. Commemorations. Multicoloured.
1187 2r. Type **621** 10 10
1188 2r. M. A. Rahim (trade union leader and philanthropist) 10 10

2003. Birth Anniversaries. Multicoloured.
1189 2r. Type **622** 10 10
1190 2r. Muhammad Yousaf Khattak (politician, 86th) 10 10
1191 2r. Moulana Muhammad Ismail Zabeeh (politician, centenary) 10 10

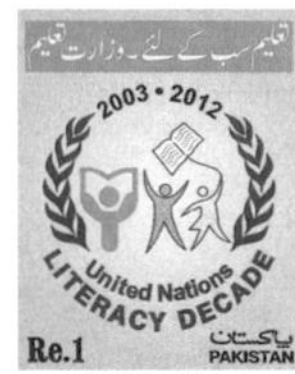

623 Emblem

2003. United Nations Literacy Decade.
1192 **623** 1r. multicoloured 10 10

624 Pilot Officer Rashid Minhas and Nishan-e-Haider Medal

2003. 32nd Death Anniv of Pilot Officer Rashid Minhas.
1193 **624** 2r. multicoloured 10 10

625 Pakistan Academy of Letters, Islamabad

2003. 25th Anniv of Pakistan Academy of Letters (2001).
1194 **625** 2r. multicoloured 10 10

626 Karakoram Highway

2003. 25th Anniv of Karakoram Highway.
1195 **626** 2r. multicoloured 10 10

627 Nanga Parbat

2003. 50th Anniv of First Ascent of Nanga Parbat Mountain.
1196 **627** 2r. multicoloured 10 10

628 PAF Public School, Sargodha

2003. 50th Anniv of PAF Public School, Sargodha.
1197 **628** 4r. multicoloured 10 10

629 Leather Coats

2003. Achievement of 10 Billion US Dollar Exports Target, 2002–3. Multicoloured.
1198 1r. Type **629** 10 10
1199 1r. Towels 10 10
1200 1r. Readymade garments . . 10 10
1201 1r. Cargo ship being loaded by crane, Port Qasim . . 10 10
1202 1r. Fisheries 10 10
1203 1r. Yarn 10 10
1204 1r. Sports equipment . . . 10 10
1205 1r. Fabrics 10 10
1206 1r. Furniture 10 10
1207 1r. Surgical instruments . . 10 10
1208 1r. Gems and jewellery . . . 10 10
1209 1r. Leather goods 10 10
1210 1r. Information technology 10 10
1211 1r. Rice 10 10
1212 1r. Auto parts 10 10
1213 1r. Carpets 10 10
1214 1r. Marble and granite . . . 10 10
1215 1r. Fruits 10 10
1216 1r. Cutlery 10 10
1217 1r. Engineering goods . . . 10 10

630 Boy in Wheelchair with Boy and Girl **631** Globe

2003. International Day for Disabled.
1218 **630** 2r. multicoloured 10 10

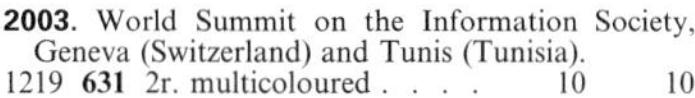

2003. World Summit on the Information Society, Geneva (Switzerland) and Tunis (Tunisia).
1219 **631** 2r. multicoloured 10 10

632 Khalid Class Submarine (Agosta 90B) **633** Pakistan Air Force Plane, Siachen, 1988–90

2003. Submarine Construction in Pakistan. Multicoloured.
1220 1r. Type **632** 10 10
1221 2r. Khalid Class submarine (Agosta 90B) and Pakistan flag (horiz) . . . 10 10

2003. Centenary of Powered Flight. Pakistan Air Force. Multicoloured.
1222 2r. Type **633** 10 10
1223 2r. Old and modern Pakistan Air Force planes 10 10

634 Emblem

2004. 12th Summit Meeting of South Asian Association for Regional Co-operation, Islamabad.
1224 **634** 4r. multicoloured 10 10

OFFICIAL STAMPS

1947. King George VI Official stamps of India optd **PAKISTAN**.
O 1 **O 20** 3p. slate . . . . 1·50 75
O 2 ½a. purple 30 10
O 3 9p. green . . . . . . 5·00 2·75
O 4 1a. red 30 10
O 5 1½a. violet 30 10
O 6 2a. orange 30 10
O 7 2½a. violet . . . . . 7·00 8·50
O 8 4a. brown . . . . . 1·25 60
O 9 8a. violet . . . . . . 1·75 1·50
O10 **93** 1r. slate and brown (No. O138) . . . . . 80 1·50
O11 2r. purple and brown (No. O139) . . . . . 4·25 3·75
O12 5r. green and blue (No. O140) . . . . 18·00 32·00
O13 10r. purple and red (No. O141) . . . . . 48·00 90·00

1948. Optd **SERVICE**. Crescent moon pointing to right.
O14 **7** 3p. red 10 10
O15 6p. violet 10 10
O37 9p. green 10 10
O17 – 1a. blue . . . . 3·75 10
O18 – 1½a. green . . . . . . 3·50 10
O19 – 2a. red . . . . 1·50 10
O20 – 3a. green . . . . 26·00 8·00
O21 **9** 4a. brown . . . . 1·00 10
O22 – 8a. black . . . . 2·25 8·50
O23 **12** 1r. blue . . . . 1·00 10
O42 2r. brown . . . . 4·25 20
O61 5r. red . . . . 7·50 15
O26 **13** 10r. mauve . . . . 15·00 45·00

1949. Optd **SERVICE**. Crescent moon pointing to left.
O38 – 1a. blue 10 10
O39 – 1½a. green 10 10
O40 – 2a. red 15 10
O30 – 3a. green . . . . 26·00 5·50
O31 – 8a. black . . . . 42·00 17·00

1951. 4th Anniv of Independence. As Nos. 56, 58 and 60 but inscr "SERVICE" instead of "PAKISTAN POSTAGE".
O32 3a. purple . . . . 7·50 9·50
O33 4a. green . . . . 2·00 10
O34 8a. sepia . . . . 8·00 3·75

1954. 7th Anniv of Independence. Nos. 65/71 optd **SERVICE**.
O53 6p. violet 10 10
O54 9p. blue 10 10
O55 1a. red 10 10
O56 1½a. red 10 10
O57 14a. myrtle . . . . 50 4·00
O58 1r. green 50 10
O51 2r. orange . . . . 1·75 15

1955. 8th Anniv of Independence. Nos. 74/5 optd **SERVICE**.
O63 6a. blue 15 10
O64 8a. violet 15 10

1959. 9th Anniv of Independence. Optd **SERVICE**.
O65 **37** 2a. red 10 10

1961. 1st Anniv of Republic. Optd **SERVICE**.
O62 **41** 10r. green and orange . . 7·00 8·50

1961. Optd **SERVICE**.
O66 **51** 8a. green 20 10
O67 1r. blue 20 10

1961. New currency. Provisional stamps. Nos. 122 etc. optd **SERVICE**.
O68 – 1p. on 1½a. red 10 10
O69 **7** 2p. on 3p. red 10 10
O70 **51** 3p. on 6p. purple 10 10
O71 – 7p. on 1a. red 10 10
O72 **51** 13p. on 2a. red 10 10
O73 **37** 13p. on 2a. red 10 10

1961. Definitive issue optd **SERVICE**.
O 74 **60** 1p. violet 10 10
O 75 2p. red 10 10
O 79 3p. purple 10 10
O 94 5p. blue 10 10
O 81 7p. green 10 10
O 82 **61** 10p. brown 10 10
O 83 13p. violet 10 10
O 98 15p. purple . . . . . . 10 1·75
O 99 20p. green 10 40
O100 25p. blue . . . . 9·00 3·00
O 85 40p. purple 10 10
O102 50p. turquoise 10 15
O 87 75p. red 20 10
O104 90p. green . . . . . . 5·50 4·50
O 88 **62** 1r. red 35 10
O 89 2r. orange . . . . 1·50 20
O 90 5r. green . . . . 4·25 7·00

1979. Optd **SERVICE**.
O109 **275** 2p. green 10 30
O110 – 3p. black 10 30
O111 – 5p. blue 10 30
O112 **275** 10p. blue and turquoise 10 30
O113 – 20p. green (No. 468) . . 10 10
O114 – 25p. green and mauve (No. 489) 10 10
O115 – 40p. blue and mauve (No. 470) 30 10
O116 – 50p. lilac and green (No. 471) 10 10
O117 – 60p. black (No. 472) . . 1·00 10
O118 – 75p. red (No. 473) . . . 1·00 10
O119 – 1r. green (No. 475) . . . 2·25 10
O120 – 1r.50 orange (No. 476) 20 30
O121 – 2r. red (No. 477) 20 10
O122 – 3r. blue (No. 478) . . . 30 30
O123 – 4r. black (No. 479) . . 2·75 50
O124 – 5r. brown (No. 480) . . 2·75 50

1980. As Nos. 513/19 but inscr "SERVICE".
O125 **291** 10p. green and yellow 1·00 10
O126 15p. deep green & green 1·00 10
O127 25p. violet and red . . . 15 70
O128 35p. red and green . . . 20 80
O129 – 40p. red and brown . . 1·00 10
O130 – 50p. red and green . . . 20 40
O131 – 80p. green and black . . 30 1·50

1984. Nos. 629/30 and 632/6 optd **SERVICE**.
O132 – 5p. black and purple . . 10 60
O133 – 10p. black and red . . . 15 40
O135 **343** 20p. black and violet . . 30 40
O136 – 50p. brown and red . . 40 40
O137 – 60p. lt brown & brown 45 50
O138 – 70p. blue 50 70
O139 – 80p. brown and red . . 55 70

1989. No. 773 optd **SERVICE**.
O140 **411** 1r. multicoloured . . . 3·50 85

O 7 State Bank of Pakistan Building, Islamabad

1990.
O141 **O 7** 1r. red and green . . . 10 10
O142 2r. red and pink 10 10
O143 3r. red and blue 10 10
O144 4r. red and brown . . . 10 10
O145 5r. red and purple . . . 10 15
O146 10r. red and brown . . 20 25

PALAU Pt. 22

Formerly part of the United States Trust Territory of the Pacific Islands, Palau became an autonomous republic on 1 January 1981. Until 1983 it continued to use United States stamps.

Palau became an independent republic on 1 October 1994.

100 cents = 1 dollar.

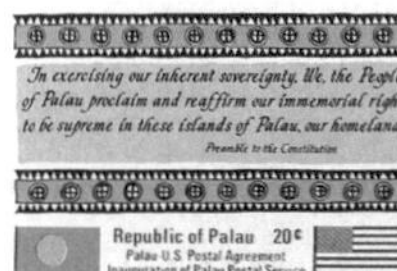

1 Preamble to Constitution

1983. Inaug of Postal Independence. Mult.
1 20c. Type **1** 60 45
2 20c. Natives hunting (design from Koror meeting house) 60 45
3 20c. Preamble to Constitution (different) 60 45
4 20c. Three fishes (design from Koror meeting house) 60 45

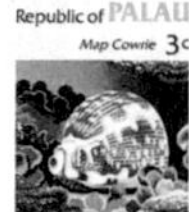

2 Palau Fruit Dove **3** Map Cowrie

1983. Birds. Multicoloured.
5 20c. Type **2** 85 85
6 20c. Morning bird 85 85
7 20c. Palau white-eye (inscr "Giant White-eye") 85 85
8 20c. Palau fantail 85 85

1983. Marine Life. Multicoloured.
9 1c. Sea fan 10 10
10 3c. Type **3** 10 10
11 5c. Jellyfish 15 10

12 10c. Hawksbill turtle 20 10
13 13c. Giant clam 25 15
14 14c. Trumpet triton 30 25
15 20c. Parrotfish 40 25
16 22c. Indo-Pacific hump-headed ("Bumphead") parrotfish 40 30
17 25c. Soft coral and damselfishes 40 30
17a 28c. Chambered nautilus . . 55 40
18 30c. Dappled sea cucumber 55 40
18a 33c. Sea anemone and anemonefishes ("Clownfish") 55 40
19 37c. Sea urchin 75 40
19a 39c. Green sea turtle 75 60
19b 44c. Sailfish 85 70
20 50c. Starfish . . . . 1·00 60
21 $1 Common squid . . . . . 1·75 1·00
22 $2 Dugong . . . . 3·25 2·25
23 $5 Pink sponge . . . . . . 7·50 5·50
24 $10 Spinner dolphin . . . . 12·50 11·00

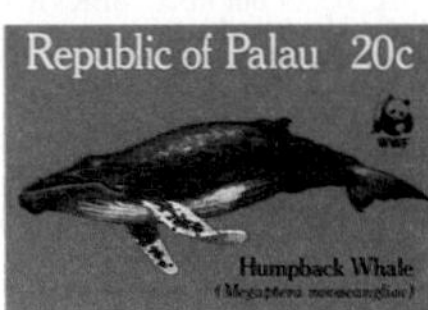

4 Humpback Whale

1983. World Wildlife Fund. Whales. Mult.
25 20c. Type **4** 70 45
26 20c. Blue whale 70 45
27 20c. Fin whale 70 45
28 20c. Sperm whale 70 45

5 "Spear fishing at New Moon" **6** King Abba Thulle

1983. Christmas. Paintings by Charlie Gibbons. Mult.
29 20c. Type **5** 55 35
30 20c. "Taro Gardening" . . . 55 35
31 20c. "First Child Ceremony" 55 35
32 20c. "Traditional Feast at the Bai" 55 35
33 20c. "Spear Fishing from Red Canoe" 55 35

1983. Bicentenary of Captain Henry Wilson's Voyage to Palau.
34 **6** 20c. brown, blue & deep blue 55 35
35 – 20c. brown, blue & deep blue 55 35
36 – 20c. brown, blue & deep blue 55 35
37 – 20c. brown, blue & deep blue 55 35
38 – 20c. brown, blue & deep blue 55 35
39 – 20c. brown, blue & deep blue 55 35
40 – 20c. brown, blue & deep blue 55 35
41 – 20c. brown, blue & deep blue 55 35
DESIGNS—VERT: No. 37, Ludec (King Abba Thulle's wife); 38, Capt. Henry Wilson; 41, Prince Lee Boo. HORIZ: (47 × 20 mm): 35, Mooring in Koror; 36, Village scene in Pelew Islands; 39, Approaching Pelew; 40, Englishman's camp on Ulong.

7 Trumpet Triton

1984. Sea Shells (1st series). Multicoloured.
42 20c. Type **7** 50 40
43 20c. Horned helmet 50 40
44 20c. Giant clam 50 40
45 20c. Laciniate conch 50 40
46 20c. Royal oak ("cloak") scallop 50 40
47 20c. Trumpet triton (different) 50 40
48 20c. Horned helmet (different) 50 40
49 20c. Giant clam (different) . . 50 40
50 20c. Laciniate conch (different) 50 40
51 20c. Royal oak ("cloak") scallop (different) 50 40
Nos. 43/6 have mauve backgrounds, Nos. 48/51 blue backgrounds.
See also Nos. 145/9, 194/8, 231/5, 256/60 and 515/19.

8 White-tailed Tropic Bird

1984. Air. Birds. Multicoloured.
52 40c. Type **8** . . . . 1·25 1·10
53 40c. White tern (inscr "Fairy Tern") . . . . 1·25 1·10
54 40c. White-capped noddy (inscr "Black Noddy") . . . 1·25 1·10
55 40c. Black-naped tern . . . . 1·25 1·10

9 "Oroolong" (Wilson's schooner)

1984. 19th Universal Postal Union Congress Philatelic Salon, Hamburg. Multicoloured.
56 40c. Type **9** . . . . 1·00 75
57 40c. Missionary ship "Duff" 1·00 75
58 40c. German expeditionary steamer "Peiho" . . . . . 1·00 75
59 40c. German gunboat "Albatros" . . . . 1·00 75

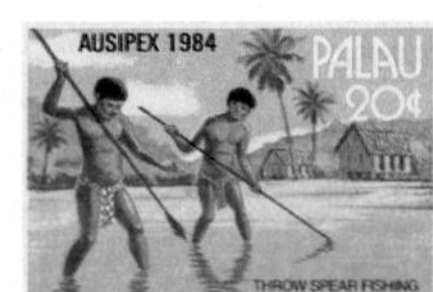

10 Spear Fishing

1984. "Ausipex 84" International Stamp Exhibition, Melbourne. Fishing. Multicoloured.
60 20c. Type **10** 55 35
61 20c. Kite fishing 55 35
62 20c. Underwater spear fishing 55 35
63 20c. Net fishing 55 35

11 Mountain Apple

1984. Christmas. Multicoloured.
64 20c. Type **11** 50 35
65 20c. Beach morning glory . . 50 35
66 20c. Turmeric 50 35
67 20c. Plumeria 50 35

12 Chick

1985. Birth Bicentenary of John J. Audubon (ornithologist). Designs showing Audubon's Shearwater. Multicoloured.
68 22c. Type **12** (postage) 80 80
69 22c. Head of shearwater . . . 80 80
70 22c. Shearwater flying 80 80
71 22c. Shearwater on lake . . . 80 80
72 44c. "Audubon's Shearwater" (Audubon) (air) . . . . . . 1·50 1·50

13 Borotong (cargo canoe)

1985. Traditional Canoes and Rafts. Multicoloured.
73 22c. Type **13** 70 45
74 22c. Kabeki (war canoe) . . . 70 45
75 22c. Olechutel (bamboo raft) 70 45
76 22c. Kaeb (racing/sailing canoe) 70 45

14 Boy with Guitar **16** Mother cuddling Child

15 Raising German Flag at Palau, 1885, and German 1880 20pf. Stamp

1985. International Youth Year. Multicoloured.
77 44c. Type **14** 75 60
78 44c. Boy with fishing rod . . . 75 60
79 44c. Boy with baseball bat . . 75 60
80 44c. Boy with spade 75 60
Nos. 77/80 were issued together se-tenant, each block forming a composite design showing a ring of children of different races.

1985. Air. Centenary of Vatican Treaty (granting German trading privileges in Caroline Islands). Multicoloured.
81 44c. Type **15** 90 75
82 44c. Early German trading post, Angaur, and Marshall Islands 1899 5pf. overprinted stamp 90 75
83 44c. Abai (village meeting house) and Caroline Islands 1901 5m. yacht stamp . . . 90 75
84 44c. "Cormoran" (German cruiser), 1914, and Caroline Islands 1901 40pf. yacht stamp 90 75

1985. Christmas. Multicoloured.
85 14c. Mother with child on lap 35 15
86 22c. Type **16** 55 30
87 33c. Mother supporting child in arms 85 50
88 44c. Mother lifting child in air 1·00 70

17 Consolidated Catalina Amphibian over Natural Bridge

1985. Air. 50th Anniv of First Trans-Pacific Airmail Flight. Multicoloured.
89 44c. Type **17** . . . . 1·00 65
90 44c. Douglas DC-6B approaching Airai–Koror Passage . . . . 1·00 65
91 44c. Grumman Albatross flying boat over Airai Village . . . . 1·00 65
92 44c. Douglas DC-4 landing at Airai . . . . 1·00 65

18 Comet and Kaeb, 1758

1985. Appearance of Halley's Comet. Multicoloured.
94 44c. Type **18** 85 60
95 44c. Comet and U.S.S. "Vincennes", 1835 . . . . . 85 60
96 44c. Comet and "Scharnhorst" (German cruiser), 1910 . . . 85 60
97 44c. Comet and tourist cabin cruiser, 1986 . . . . 85 60

19 Micronesian Flycatchers

1986. Songbirds. Multicoloured.
98 44c. Type **19** ("Mangrove Flycatchers") . . . . 1·10 1·10
99 44c. Cardinal honeyeaters . . 1·10 1·10
100 44c. Blue-faced parrot finches 1·10 1·10
101 44c. Grey-brown white-eye ("Dusky White-eye") and bridled white eye . . . . . 1·10 1·10

20 Spear Fisherman

1986. "Ameripex '86" International Stamp Exhibition, Chicago. Sea and Reef World. Multicoloured.
102 14c. Type **20** 90 55
103 14c. Olechutel (native raft) 90 55
104 14c. Kaebs (sailing canoes) 90 55
105 14c. Rock islands and sailfish 90 55
106 14c. Inter-island ferry and two-winged flyingfishes . . 90 55
107 14c. Bonefishes 90 55
108 14c. Jacks 90 55
109 14c. Japanese mackerel . . . 90 55
110 14c. Sailfishes 90 55
111 14c. Barracuda 90 55
112 14c. Undulate triggerfishes . . 90 55
113 14c. Dolphin (fish) 90 55
114 14c. Spear fisherman with grouper 90 55
115 14c. Manta ray 90 55
116 14c. Striped marlin 90 55
117 14c. Black-striped parrotfishes 90 55
118 14c. Red-breasted wrasse . . 90 55
119 14c. Malabar blood snappers 90 55
120 14c. Malabar blood snapper and clupeid ("Herring") school 90 55
121 14c. Dugongs 90 55
122 14c. Powder-blue surgeonfishes 90 55
123 14c. Spotted eagle ray . . . 90 55
124 14c. Hawksbill turtle 90 55
125 14c. Needlefishes 90 55
126 14c. Tuna 90 55
127 14c. Octopus 90 55
128 14c. Anemonefishes ("Clownfish") 90 55
129 14c. Squid 90 55
130 14c. Groupers 90 55
131 14c. Moorish idols 90 55
132 14c. Queen conch and starfish 90 55
133 14c. Diadem soldierfishes . . . 90 55
134 14c. Starfish and stingrays . . 90 55
135 14c. Lionfish 90 55
136 14c. Emperor angelfishes . . 90 55
137 14c. Saddle butterflyfishes . . 90 55
138 14c. Spiny lobster 90 55
139 14c. Mangrove crab 90 55
140 14c. Giant clam ("Tridacna gigas") 90 55
141 14c. Moray 90 55
Nos. 102/41 are each inscribed on the back (over the gum) with the name of the subject featured on the stamp.
Nos. 102/41 were printed together, se-tenant, forming a composite design.

21 Presidential Seal

1986. Air. Haruo I. Remeliik (first President) Commemoration. Multicoloured.
142 44c. Type **21** 90 60
143 44c. Kabeki (war canoe) passing under Koror–Babeldaob Bridge 90 60
144 44c. Presidents Reagan and Remeliik 90 60

1986. Sea Shells (2nd series). As T **7**. Multicoloured.
145 22c. Commercial trochus . . 55 40
146 22c. Marble cone 55 40
147 22c. Fluted giant clam . . . 55 40
148 22c. Bullmouth helmet . . . 55 40
149 22c. Golden cowrie 55 40

23 Crab inhabiting Soldier's rusting Helmet

1986. International Peace Year. Multicoloured.
150 22c. Type **23** (postage) . . . 50 40
151 22c. Marine life inhabiting airplane 50 40
152 22c. Rusting tank behind girl 50 40
153 22c. Abandoned assault landing craft, Airai 65 65

154 22c. Statue of Liberty, New York (centenary) (air) 75 70

24 Gecko

1986. Reptiles. Multicoloured.

155 22c. Type **24** 60 45
156 22c. Emerald tree skink 60 45
157 22c. Estuarine crocodile 60 45
158 22c. Leatherback turtle 60 45

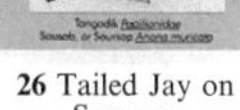

25 Girl with Guitar and Boy leading Child on Goat **26** Tailed Jay on Soursop

1986. Christmas. Multicoloured.

159 22c. Type **25** 35 25
160 22c. Boys singing and girl carrying flowers 35 25
161 22c. Mother holding baby 35 25
162 22c. Children carrying baskets of fruit 35 25
163 22c. Girl with white terns 45 45

Nos. 159/63 were issued together, se-tenant, forming a composite design.

1987. Butterflies (1st series). Multicoloured.

164 44c. Type **26** 95 75
165 44c. Common mormon on sweet orange 95 75
166 44c. Common eggfly on swamp cabbage 95 75
167 44c. Oleander butterfly on fig 95 75

See also Nos. 223/6.

27 Bat flying

1987. Air. Palau Fruit Bat. Multicoloured.

168 44c. Type **27** 90 70
169 44c. Bat hanging from branch 90 70
170 44c. Bat feeding 90 70
171 44c. Head of bat 90 70

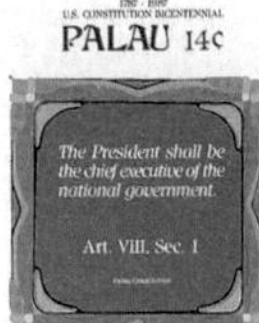

28 "Ixora casei" **31** "The President shall be the chief executive ..."

29 Babeldaob

1987. Flowers. Multicoloured.

172 1c. Type **28** 10 10
173 3c. "Lumnitzera littorea" 10 10
174 5c. "Sonneratia alba" 10 10
175 10c. Woody vine 15 10
176 14c. "Bikkia palauensis" 20 10
177 15c. "Limophila aromatica" 20 10
178 22c. "Bruguiera gymnorhiza" 30 20
179 25c. "Fragraea ksid" 30 20
180 36c. "Ophiorrhiza palauensis" 45 35
181 39c. "Cerbera manghas" 60 40
182 44c. "Samadera indica" 65 45
183 45c. "Maesa canfieldiae" 55 45
184 50c. "Dolichandrone spathacea" 80 55
185 $1 "Barringtonia racemosa" 1·50 1·10
186 $2 "Nepenthes mirabilis" 2·50 2·00
187 $5 Orchid 6·00 4·50
188 $10 Bouquet of mixed flowers 12·00 9·00

1987. "Capex '87" International Stamp Exhibition, Toronto. Multicoloured.

190 22c. Type **29** 40 30
191 22c. Floating Garden Islands 40 30
192 22c. Rock Island 40 30
193 22c. Koror 40 30

1987. Sea Shells (3rd series). As T **7**. Multicoloured.

194 22c. Black-striped triton 50 35
195 22c. Tapestry turban 50 35
196 22c. Adusta murex 50 35
197 22c. Little fox mitre 50 35
198 22c. Cardinal mitre 50 35

1987. Bicentenary of United States of America Constitution. Multicoloured.

199 14c. Type **31** 25 20
200 14c. Palau and U.S. Presidents' seals (24 × 37 mm) 25 20
201 14c. "The executive power shall be vested ..." 25 20
202 22c. "The legislative power of Palau ..." 35 25
203 22c. Palau Olbiil Era Kelulau and U.S. Senate seals (24 × 37 mm) 35 25
204 22c. "All legislative powers herein granted ..." 35 25
205 44c. "The judicial power of Palau ..." 70 60
206 44c. Palau and U.S. Supreme Court seals (24 × 37 mm) 70 60
207 44c. "The judicial power of the United States ..." 70 60

The three designs of the same value were printed together in se-tenant strips, the top stamp of each strip bearing extracts from the Palau Constitution and the bottom stamp extracts from the U.S. Constitution.

32 Japanese Mobile Post Office and 1937 Japan ½s. Stamp

1987. Links with Japan. Multicoloured.

208 14c. Type **32** 30 25
209 22c. Phosphate mine and Japan 1942 5s. stamp 50 40
210 33c. Douglas DC-2 flying over Badrulchau monuments and Japan 1937 2s.+2s. stamp 65 50
211 44c. Japanese Post Office, Koror, and Japan 1927 10s. stamp 90 65

33 Huts, White Tern and Outrigger Canoes **34** Snapping Shrimp and Watchman Goby

1987. Christmas. Multicoloured.

213 22c. Type **33** 65 65
214 22c. Flying white tern carrying twig 65 65
215 22c. Holy Family in kaeb 65 65
216 22c. Angel and kaeb 65 65
217 22c. Outrigger canoes and hut 65 65

Nos. 213/17 were issued together, se-tenant, forming a composite design; each stamp bears a verse of the carol "I Saw Three Ships".

1987. 25th Anniv of World Ecology Movement. Multicoloured.

218 22c. Type **34** 50 40
219 22c. Mauve vase sponge and sponge crab 50 40
220 22c. Lemon ("Pope's") damselfish and blue-streaked cleaner wrasse 50 40
221 22c. Clown anemonefishes and sea anemone 50 40
222 22c. Four-coloured nudibranch and banded coral shrimp 50 40

1988. Butterflies (2nd series). As T **26**.

223 44c. Orange tiger on "Tournefotia argentia" 65 55
224 44c. Swallowtail on "Citrus reticulata" 65 55
225 44c. Lemon migrant on "Crataeva speciosa" 65 55
226 44c. "Appias ada" (wrongly inscr "Colias philodice") on "Crataeva speciosa" 65 55

35 Whimbrel **39** Angel Violinist and Singing Cherubs

37 Baseball

1988. Ground-dwelling Birds. Multicoloured.

227 44c. Type **35** 1·10 1·10
228 44c. Chinese little bittern ("Yellow Bittern") 1·10 1·10
229 44c. Nankeen ("Rufous Night Heron") 1·10 1·10
230 44c. Buff-banded rail ("Banded Rail") 1·10 1·10

1988. Sea Shells (4th series). As T **7**. Mult.

231 25c. Striped engina 45 35
232 25c. Ivory cone 45 35
233 25c. Plaited mitre 45 35
234 25c. Episcopal mitre 45 35
235 25c. Isabelle cowrie 45 35

1988. Olympic Games, Seoul. Multicoloured.

237 25c.+5c. Type **37** 40 35
238 25c.+5c. Running 40 35
239 45c.+5c. Diving 70 55
240 45c.+5c. Swimming 70 55

1988. Christmas. Multicoloured.

242 25c. Type **39** 40 30
243 25c. Angels and children singing 40 30
244 25c. Children adoring child 55 55
245 25c. Angels and birds flying 55 55
246 25c. Running children and angels playing trumpets 40 30

Nos. 242/6 were issued together, se-tenant, forming a composite design.

41 Nicobar Pigeon **43** Robin-redbreast Triton

42 False Chanterelle

1989. Endangered Birds. Multicoloured.

248 45c. Type **41** 1·10 1·10
249 45c. Palau ground dove 1·10 1·10
250 45c. Marianas scrub hen 1·10 1·10
251 45c. Palau scops owl 1·10 1·10

1989. Fungi. Multicoloured.

252 45c. Type **42** (inscr "Gilled Auricularia") 90 60
253 45c. Black fellows' bread ("Rock mushroom") 90 60
254 45c. Chicken mushroom ("Polyporous") 90 60
255 45c. Veiled stinkhorn 90 60

1989. Sea Shells (5th series). Multicoloured.

256 25c. Type **43** 50 45
257 25c. Hebrew cone 50 45
258 25c. Tadpole triton 50 45
259 25c. Lettered cone 50 45
260 25c. Rugose mitre 50 45

44 Cessna 207 Stationair 7 **46** Jettison of Third Stage

1989. Air. Aircraft. Multicoloured.

261 36c. Type **44** 50 40
262 39c. Embraer Bandeirante airliner 60 50
264 45c. Boeing 727 jetliner 70 60

No. 261 is wrongly inscribed "Skywagon".

1989. 20th Anniv of First Manned Landing on Moon. Multicoloured.

267 25c. Type **46** 35 25
268 25c. Command Module adjusting position 35 25
269 25c. Lunar Excursion Module "Eagle" docking 35 25
270 25c. Space module docking 35 25
271 25c. Propulsion for entry into lunar orbit 35 25
272 25c. Third stage burn 35 25
273 25c. Command Module orbiting Moon 35 25
274 25c. Command Module and part of "Eagle" 35 25
275 25c. Upper part of "Eagle" on Moon 35 25
276 25c. Descent of "Eagle" 35 25
277 25c. Nose of rocket 35 25
278 25c. Reflection in Edwin "Buzz" Aldrin's visor 35 25
279 25c. Neil Armstrong and flag on Moon 35 25
280 25c. Footprints and astronaut's oxygen tank 35 25
281 25c. Upper part of astronaut descending ladder 35 25
282 25c. Launch tower and body of rocket 35 25
283 25c. Survival equipment on Aldrin's space suit 35 25
284 25c. Blast off from lunar surface 35 25
285 25c. View of Earth and astronaut's legs 35 25
286 25c. Leg on ladder 35 25
287 25c. Lift off 35 25
288 25c. Spectators at launch 35 25
289 25c. Capsule parachuting into Pacific 35 25
290 25c. Re-entry 35 25
291 25c. Space Module jettison 35 25
292 $2.40 "Buzz" Aldrin on Moon (photo by Neil Armstrong) (34 × 47 mm) 3·50 2·50

Nos. 267/91 were issued together, se-tenant, forming a composite design.

47 Girl as Astronaut **48** Bridled Tern

1989. Year of the Young Reader. Multicoloured.

293 25c. Type **47** 35 25
294 25c. Boy riding dolphin 40 40
295 25c. Cheshire Cat in tree 40 40
296 25c. Mother Goose 40 40
297 25c. Baseball player 35 25
298 25c. Girl reading 35 25
299 25c. Boy reading 35 25
300 25c. Mother reading to child 35 25
301 25c. Girl holding flowers listening to story 35 25
302 25c. Boy in baseball strip 35 25

1989. "World Stamp Expo '89" International Stamp Exhibition, Washington D.C. Stilt Mangrove. Multicoloured.

303 25c. Type **48** 50 50
304 25c. Lemon migrant (inscr "Sulphur Butterfly") 50 50
305 25c. Micronesian flycatcher ("Mangrove Flycatcher") 50 50
306 25c. White-collared kingfisher 50 50
307 25c. Fruit bat 50 50
308 25c. Estuarine crocodile 50 50
309 25c. Nankeen ("Rufous Night Heron") 50 50
310 25c. Stilt mangrove 50 50
311 25c. Bird's nest fern 50 50
312 25c. Beach hibiscus tree 50 50
313 25c. Common eggfly (butterfly) 50 50
314 25c. Dog-faced watersnake 45 35
315 25c. Mangrove jingle shell 45 35
316 25c. Palau bark cricket 45 35
317 25c. Periwinkle and mangrove oyster 45 35
318 25c. Jellyfish 45 35
319 25c. Flat-headed grey ("Striped") mullet 45 35
320 25c. Mussels, sea anemones and algae 45 35
321 25c. Pajama cardinalfish 45 35
322 25c. Black-tailed snappers 45 35

Nos. 303/22 are each inscribed on the back (over the gum) with the name of the subject featured on the stamp.

Nos. 303/22 were issued together, se-tenant, forming a composite design.

49 Angels, Sooty Tern and Audubon's Shearwater

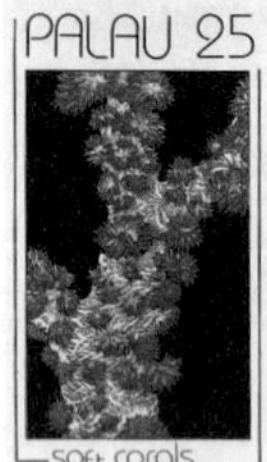

50 Pink Coral

1989. Christmas. Carol of the Birds. Mult.

323	25c. Type **49**	55	55
324	25c. Palau fruit dove and angel	55	55
325	25c. Madonna and child, cherub and birds	55	55
326	25c. Angel, blue-faced parrot finch, Micronesian flycatcher and cardinal honeyeater	55	55
327	25c. Angel, Micronesian flycatcher and black-headed gulls	55	55

Nos. 323/7 were printed together, se-tenant, forming a composite design.

1990. Soft Corals. Multicoloured.

328	25c. Type **50**	50	35
329	25c. Mauve coral	50	35
330	25c. Yellow coral	50	35
331	25c. Orange coral	50	35

See also Nos. 392/5.

51 Siberian Rubythroat

1990. Forest Birds. Multicoloured.

332	45c. Type **51**	75	75
333	45c. Palau bush warbler	75	75
334	45c. Micronesian starling	75	75
335	45c. Common cicdabird ("Cicadabird")	75	75

52 Prince Lee Boo, Capt. Henry Wilson and H.M.S. "Victory"

1990. "Stamp World London 90" International Stamp Exhibition. Prince Lee Boo's Visit to England, 1784, and 150th Anniv of the Penny Black. Multicoloured.

336	25c. Type **52**	40	25
337	25c. St. James's Palace	40	25
338	25c. Rotherhithe Docks	40	25
339	25c. Oroolong House, Devon (Capt. Wilson's home)	40	25
340	25c. Vincenzo Lunardi's balloon	40	25
341	25c. St. Paul's Cathedral	40	25
342	25c. Prince Lee Boo's grave	40	25
343	25c. St. Mary's Church, Rotherhithe	40	25
344	25c. Memorial tablet to Prince Lee Boo	40	25

53 "Corymborkis veratrifolia"

55 White Tern, Pacific Golden Plover and Sanderling

54 Plane Butterfly on Beach Sunflower

1990. "Expo 90" International Garden and Greenery Exposition, Osaka. Orchids. Multicoloured.

346	45c. Type **53**	60	40
347	45c. "Malaxis setipes"	60	40
348	45c. "Dipodium freycinetianum"	60	40
349	45c. "Bulbophyllum micronesiacum"	60	40
350	45c. "Vanda teres"	60	40

1990. Butterflies. Multicoloured.

351	45c. Type **54**	70	55
352	45c. Painted lady on coral tree	70	55
353	45c. "Euploea nemertes" on sorcerer's flower	70	55
354	45c. Meadow argus (inscr "Buckeye") on beach pea	70	55

1990. Lagoon Life. Multicoloured.

355	25c. Type **55**	50	50
356	25c. Bidekill fisherman	35	25
357	25c. Yacht and insular halfbeaks	35	25
358	25c. Palauan kaebs	35	25
359	25c. White-tailed tropic bird	50	50
360	25c. Spotted eagle ray	35	25
361	25c. Great barracudas	35	25
362	25c. Reef needlefish	35	25
363	25c. Reef needlefish and black-finned reef ("Reef Blacktip") shark	35	25
364	25c. Hawksbill turtle	35	25
365	25c. Six-feelered threadfins and octopus	35	25
366	25c. Narrow-banded batfish and six-feelered threadfins	35	25
367	25c. Lionfish and six-feelered threadfins	35	25
368	25c. Snowflake moray and six-feelered threadfins	35	25
369	25c. Inflated and uninflated porcupinefishes and six-feelered threadfins	35	25
370	25c. Regal angelfish, blue-streaked cleaner wrasse, blue sea star and corals	35	25
371	25c. Clown triggerfish and spotted garden eels	35	25
372	25c. Anthias and spotted garden eels	35	25
373	25c. Sail-finned snapper ("Bluelined sea bream"), blue-green chromis, blue ("Sapphire") damselfish and spotted garden eel	35	25
374	25c. Masked ("Orange-spine") unicornfish and ribbon-striped ("White-tipped") soldierfish	35	25
375	25c. Slatepencil sea urchin and leopard sea cucumber	35	25
376	25c. Pacific partridge tun (shell)	35	25
377	25c. Mandarin fish and spotted garden eel	35	25
378	25c. Tiger cowrie	35	25
379	25c. Feather starfish and orange-finned anemonefish	35	25

Nos. 355/79 were printed together, se-tenant, forming a composite design.

56 "Delphin", 1890, and Card

1990. Pacifica. Mail Transport. Multicoloured.

380	45c. Type **56**	65	45
381	45c. Right-hand half of card flown on 1951 inaugural U.S. civilian airmail flight and forklift unloading mail from Boeing 727	65	45

Nos. 380/1 were issued together, se-tenant, forming a composite design.

57 Girls singing and Boy with Butterfly

1990. Christmas. Multicoloured.

382	25c. Type **57**	45	45
383	25c. White terns perching on girl's songbook	45	45
384	25c. Girl singing and boys playing flute and guitar	45	45
385	25c. Couple with baby	30	20
386	25c. Three girls singing	30	20

58 Consolidated B-24S Liberator Bombers over Peleliu

1990. 46th Anniv of U.S. Action in Palau Islands during Second World War.

387	45c. Type **58**	65	50
388	45c. Landing craft firing rocket barrage	65	50
389	45c. 1st Marine division attacking Peleliu	65	50
390	45c. U.S. Infantryman and Palauan children	65	50

1991. Hard Corals. As T **50**.

392	30c. Staghorn coral	40	30
393	30c. Velvet leather coral	40	30
394	30c. Van Gogh's cypress coral	40	30
395	30c. Violet lace coral	40	30

59 Statue of Virgin Mary, Nkulangelul Point

1991. Angaur, The Phosphate Island. Mult.

396	30c. Type **59**	55	35
397	30c. Angaur Post Office opening day cancellation and kaeb (sailing canoe) (41 × 27 mm)	55	35
398	30c. Billfish and Caroline Islands 40pf. "Yacht" stamp (41 × 27 mm)	55	35
399	30c. Steam locomotive at phosphate mine	55	35
400	30c. Lighthouse Hill and German copra freighter	55	35
401	30c. Dolphins and map showing phosphate mines (41 × 27 mm)	55	35
402	30c. Estuarine crocodile (41 × 27 mm)	55	35
403	30c. Workers cycling to phosphate plant	55	35
404	30c. Freighter loading phosphate	55	35
405	30c. Hammerhead shark and German overseer (41 × 27 mm)	55	35
406	30c. Angaur cancellation and Marshall Islands 10pf. "Yacht" stamp (41 × 27 mm)	55	35
407	30c. Rear Admiral Graf von Spee and "Scharnhorst" (German cruiser)	55	35
408	30c. "Emden" (German cruiser) and Capt. Karl von Muller	55	35
409	30c. Crab-eating macaque (41 × 27 mm)	55	35
410	30c. Sperm whale (41 × 27 mm)	55	35
411	30c. H.M.A.S. "Sydney" (cruiser) shelling radio tower	55	35

Nos. 396/411 were issued together, se-tenant, with the centre block of eight stamps forming a composite design of a map of the island.

60 Moorhen

61 Pope Leo XIII and 19th-century Spanish and German Flags

1991. Birds. Multicoloured.

412	1c. Palau bush warbler	15	15
413	4c. Type **60**	15	15
414	6c. Buff-banded rail ("Banded Rail")	15	15
415	19c. Palau fantail	30	20
416	20c. Micronesian flycatcher ("Mangrove Flycatcher")	30	20
417	23c. Purple swamphen	35	30
418	29c. Palau fruit dove	45	40
419	35c. Crested tern	50	40
420	40c. Reef herons (inscr "Pacific Reef-Heron")	60	55
421	45c. Micronesian pigeon	65	60
422	50c. Great frigate bird	70	60
423	52c. Little pied cormorant	75	70
424	75c. Jungle nightjar	1·10	1·10
425	95c. Cattle egret	1·40	1·25
426	$1.34 Sulphur-crested cockatoo	2·00	1·75
427	$2 Blue-faced parrot finch	3·00	2·75
428	$5 Eclectus parrots	7·00	7·00
429	$10 Palau bush warblers feeding chicks (51 × 28 mm)	13·50	13·50

1991. Centenary of Christianity in Palau Islands. Multicoloured.

432	29c. Type **61**	40	30
433	29c. Ibedul Ilengelekei and Church of the Sacred Heart, Koror, 1920	40	30
434	29c. Marino de la Hoz, Emilio Villar and Elias Fernandez (Jesuit priests executed in Second World War)	40	30
435	29c. Centenary emblem and Fr. Edwin G. McManus (compiler of Palauan–English dictionary)	40	30
436	29c. Present Church of the Sacred Heart, Koror	40	30
437	29c. Pope John Paul II and Palau and Vatican flags	40	30

62 Pacific White-sided Dolphin

1991. Pacific Marine Life. Multicoloured.

438	29c. Type **62**	45	30
439	29c. Common dolphin	45	30
440	29c. Rough-toothed dolphin	45	30
441	29c. Bottle-nosed dolphin	45	30
442	29c. Common (inscr "Harbor") porpoise	45	30
443	29c. Head and body of killer whale	45	30
444	29c. Tail of killer whale, spinner dolphin and yellow-finned tuna	45	30
445	29c. Dall's porpoise	45	30
446	29c. Finless porpoise	45	30
447	29c. Map of Palau Islands and bottle-nosed dolphin	45	30
448	29c. Dusky dolphin	45	30
449	29c. Southern right whale dolphin	45	30
450	29c. Striped dolphin	45	30
451	29c. Fraser's dolphin	45	30
452	29c. Peale's dolphin	45	30
453	29c. Spectacled porpoise	45	30
454	29c. Spotted dolphin	45	30
455	29c. Hourglass dolphin	45	30
456	29c. Risso's dolphin	45	30
457	29c. Hector's dolphin	45	30

63 McDonnell Douglas Wild Weasel Fighters

1991. Operation Desert Storm (liberation of Kuwait). Multicoloured.

458	20c. Type **63**	35	30
459	20c. Lockheed Stealth fighter-bomber	35	30
460	20c. Hughes Apache helicopter	35	30
461	20c. "M-109 TOW" missile on "M998 HMMWV" vehicle	35	30
462	20c. President Bush of U.S.A.	35	30
463	20c. M2 "Bradley" tank	35	30
464	20c. U.S.S. "Ranger" (aircraft carrier)	35	30
465	20c. "Pegasus" (patrol boat)	35	30
466	20c. U.S.S. "Wisconsin" (battleship)	35	30
467	$2.90 Sun, dove and yellow ribbon	3·25	2·75

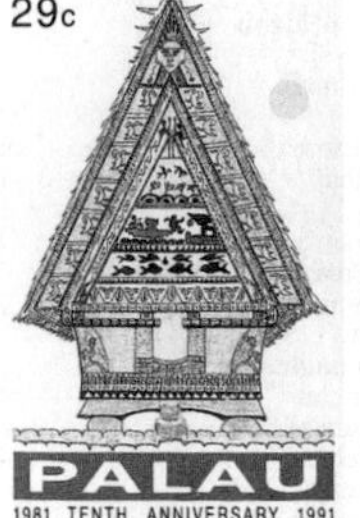

64 Bai Gable

66 "Silent Night, Holy Night!"

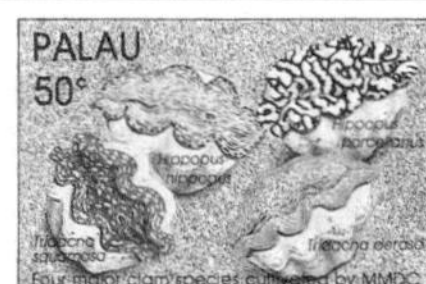

65 Bear's-paw Clam, China Clam, Fluted Giant Clam and "Tridacna derasa"

1991. 10th Anniv of Republic of Palau and Palau–Pacific Women's Conference, Koror. Bai (community building) Decorations. Mult. Imperf (self-adhesive) (50c.), perf (others).

469 29c. Type **64** (postage) . . . 40 30
470 29c. Interior of bai (left side) (32 × 48 mm) 40 30
471 29c. Interior of bai (right side) (32 × 48 mm) 40 30
472 29c. God of construction . . 40 30
473 29c. Bubuu (spider) (value at left) (30 × 23 mm) 40 30
474 29c. Delerrok, the money bird (facing right) (31 × 23 mm) 40 30
475 29c. Delerrok (facing left) (31 × 23 mm) 40 30
476 29c. Bubuu (value at right) (30 × 23 mm) 40 30
477 50c. Bai gable (as in Type **64**) (24 × 51 mm) (air) 65 45

Nos. 469/76 were issued together, se-tenant, Nos. 470/1 forming a composite design.

1991. Conservation and Cultivation of Giant Clams. Multicoloured.

478 50c. Type **65** 70 50
479 50c. Symbiotic relationship between giant clam and "Symbiodinium microadriaticum" 70 50
480 50c. Hatchery 70 50
481 50c. Diver measuring clams in sea-bed nursery 70 50
482 50c. Micronesian Mariculture Demonstration Center, Koror (108 × 16 mm) . . . 70 50

1991. Christmas. Multicoloured.

483 29c. Type **66** 40 30
484 29c. "All is calm, all is bright;" 40 30
485 29c. "Round yon virgin mother and child!" 40 30
486 29c. "Holy Infant, so tender and mild," 40 30
487 29c. "Sleep in heavenly peace." 40 30

Nos. 483/7 were issued together, se-tenant, forming a composite design.

67 Flag, Islands and Children

1991. 25th Anniv of Presence of United States Peace Corps in Palau. Children's paintings.

488 29c. Type **67** 40 30
489 29c. Volunteers arriving by airplane 40 30
490 29c. Health care 40 30
491 29c. Fishing 40 30
492 29c. Agriculture 40 30
493 29c. Education 40 30

68 "Zuiho Maru" (commercial trochus shell breeding and marine research)

1991. "Phila Nippon '91" International Stamp Exhibition, Tokyo. Japanese Heritage in Palau. Multicoloured.

494 29c. Type **68** 55 55
495 29c. Man carving story board (traditional arts) 40 30
496 29c. Tending pineapple crop (agricultural training) . . . 55 55
497 29c. Klidm (stone carving), Koror (archaeological research) 40 30
498 29c. Teaching carpentry and building design 40 30
499 29c. Kawasaki "Mavis" flying boat (air transport) 40 30

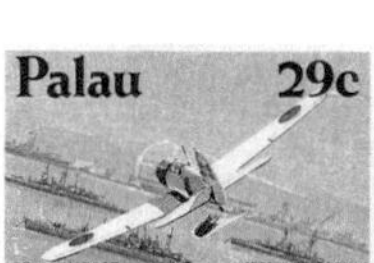

69 Mitsubishi Zero-Sen attacking Shipping at Pearl Harbor

70 "Troides criton"

1991. Pacific Theatre in Second World War (1st issue). Multicoloured.

501 29c. Type **69** 40 30
502 29c. U.S.S. "Nevada" underway from Pearl Harbor 40 30
503 29c. U.S.S. "Shaw" exploding at Pearl Harbor 40 30
504 29c. Douglas Dauntless dive bombers attacking Japanese carrier "Akagi" 40 30
505 29c. U.S.S. "Wasp" sinking off Guadalcanal 40 30
506 29c. Battle of Philippine Sea 40 30
507 29c. Landing craft storming Saipan Beach 40 30
508 29c. U.S. 1st Cavalry on Leyte 40 30
509 29c. Battle of Bloody Nose Ridge, Peleliu 40 30
510 29c. U.S. troops landing at Iwo Jima 40 30

See also Nos. 574/83, 601/10 and 681/90.

1992. Butterflies. Multicoloured.

511 50c. Type **70** 65 45
512 50c. "Alcides zodiaca" . . . 65 45
513 50c. "Papilio poboroi" . . . 65 45
514 50c. "Vindula arsinoe" . . . 65 45

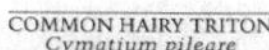

71 Common Hairy Triton

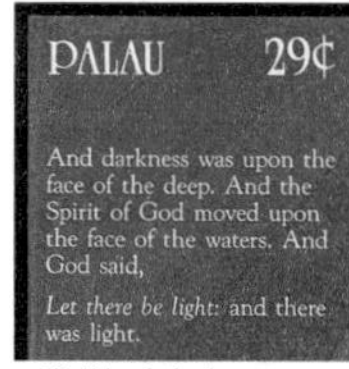

73 "And darkness was upon the face of the deep ..."

72 Christopher Columbus

1992. Sea Shells (6th series). Multicoloured.

515 29c. Type **71** 50 35
516 29c. Eglantine cowrie 50 35
517 29c. Sulcate swamp cerith . . 50 35
518 29c. Black-spined murex . . 50 35
519 29c. Black-mouth moon . . . 50 35

1992. Age of Discovery from Columbus to Drake. Multicoloured.

520 29c. Type **72** 45 30
521 29c. Ferdinand Magellan . . 45 30
522 29c. Sir Francis Drake . . . 45 30
523 29c. Cloud blowing northerly wind 45 30
524 29c. Compass rose 45 30
525 29c. Dolphin and "Golden Hind" (Drake's ship) . . . 45 30
526 29c. Corn cobs and "Santa Maria" (Columbus's ship) 45 30
527 29c. Mythical fishes 45 30
528 29c. Betel palm, cloves and black pepper 55 55
529 29c. "Vitoria" (Magellan's ship), Palau Islands, Audubon's shearwater and crested tern 55 55
530 29c. White-tailed tropic bird, bicoloured parrotfish, pineapple and potatoes . . 45 30
531 29c. Compass 45 30
532 29c. Mythical sea monster . . 45 30
533 29c. Paddles and astrolabe . 45 30
534 29c. Parallel ruler, divider and Inca gold treasure . . 45 30
535 29c. Backstaff 45 30
536 29c. Cloud blowing southerly wind 45 30
537 29c. Amerigo Vespucci . . . 45 30
538 29c. Francisco Pizarro . . . 45 30
539 29c. Vasco Nunez de Balboa 45 30

With the exception of Nos. 523 and 536 each stamp is inscribed on the back (over the gum) with the name of the subject featured on the stamp.

Nos. 520/39 were issued together, se-tenant, the backgrounds forming a composite design of the hemispheres.

1992. 2nd U.N. Conference on Environment and Development, Rio de Janeiro. The Creation of the World from the Book of Genesis, Chapter 1. Multicoloured.

540 29c. Type **73** 40 30
541 29c. Sunlight 40 30
542 29c. "Let there be a firmament in the midst of the waters, ..." 40 30
543 29c. Sky and clouds 40 30
544 29c. "Let the waters under the heaven ..." 40 30
545 29c. Tree 40 30
546 29c. Waves and sunlight (no inscr) 40 30
547 29c. Waves and sunlight ("... and it was good.") 40 30
548 29c. Waves and clouds (no inscr) 40 30
549 29c. Waves and clouds ("... and it was so.") 40 30
550 29c. Plants on river bank (no inscr) 40 30
551 29c. Plants on river bank ("... and it was good.") 40 30
552 29c. "Let there be lights in the firmament ..." 40 30
553 29c. Comet, planet and clouds 40 30
554 29c. "Let the waters bring forth abundantly the moving creature ..." . . . 50 50
555 29c. Great frigate bird and red-tailed tropic bird flying and collared lory on branch 50 50
556 29c. "Let the earth bring forth the living creature after his kind ..." 40 30
557 29c. Woman, man and rainbow 40 30
558 29c. Mountains ("... and it was good.") 40 30
559 29c. Sun and hills 40 30
560 29c. Killer whale and fishes 40 30
561 29c. Fishes ("... and it was good.") 40 30
562 29c. Elephants and squirrel 40 30
563 29c. Orchard and cat ("... and it was very good.") . . 40 30

Nos. 540/63 were issued together, se-tenant, forming six composite designs each covering four stamps.

75 Presley and Dove

1992. 15th Death Anniv of Elvis Presley (entertainer). Multicoloured.

565 29c. Type **75** 55 40
566 29c. Presley and dove's wing 55 40
567 29c. Presley in yellow cape 55 40
568 29c. Presley in white and red shirt (¾ face) 55 40
569 29c. Presley singing into microphone 55 40
570 29c. Presley crying 55 40
571 29c. Presley in red shirt (¾ face) 55 40
572 29c. Presley in purple shirt (full face) 55 40
573 29c. Presley (left profile) . . . 55 40

76 Grumman Avenger

1992. Air. Pacific Theatre in Second World War (2nd issue). Aircraft. Multicoloured.

574 50c. Type **76** 75 50
575 50c. Curtiss P-40C of the Flying Tigers fighters . . . 75 50
576 50c. Mitsubishi Zero-Sen fighter 75 50
577 50c. Hawker Hurricane Mk I fighter 75 50
578 50c. Consolidated Catalina flying boat 75 50
579 50c. Curtiss Hawk 75 fighter 75 50
580 50c. Boeing Flying Fortress bomber 75 50
581 50c. Brewster Buffalo fighter 75 50
582 50c. Vickers Supermarine Walrus flying boat 75 50
583 50c. Curtiss Kittyhawk I fighter 75 50

77 "Thus Every Beast"

1992. Christmas. "The Friendly Beasts" (carol). Multicoloured.

584 29c. Type **77** 40 30
585 29c. "By Some Good Spell" 40 30
586 29c. "In the Stable Dark was Glad to Tell" 55 55
587 29c. "Of the Gift He Gave Emanuel" (angel on donkey) 40 30
588 29c. "The Gift He Gave Emanuel" (Palau fruit doves) 55 55

78 Dugong

1993. Animals. Multicoloured.

589 50c. Type **78** 75 50
590 50c. Blue-faced booby ("Masked Booby") 95 95
591 50c. Crab-eating macaque . . 75 50
592 50c. New Guinea crocodile 75 50

79 Giant Deepwater Crab

1993. Seafood. Multicoloured.

593 29c. Type **79** 45 30
594 29c. Scarlet shrimp 45 30
595 29c. Smooth nylon shrimp . . 45 30
596 29c. Armed nylon shrimp . . 45 30

80 Oceanic White-tipped Shark

1993. Sharks. Multicoloured.

597 50c. Type **80** 75 50
598 50c. Great hammerhead . . . 75 50
599 50c. Zebra ("Leopard") shark 75 50
600 50c. Black-finned reef shark 75 50

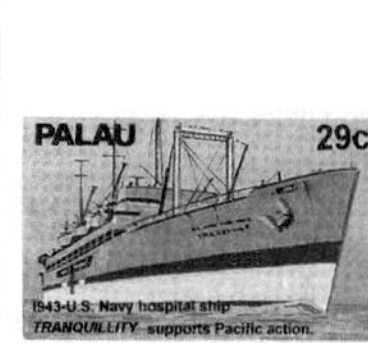

81 U.S.S. "Tranquility" (hospital ship)

82 Girl with Goat

1993. Pacific Theatre in Second World War (3rd issue). Multicoloured.

601 29c. Capture of Guadalcanal 40 30
602 29c. Type **81** 40 30
603 29c. New Guineans drilling 40 30
604 29c. Americans land in New Georgia 40 30
605 29c. U.S.S. "California" (battleship) 40 30
606 29c. Douglas Dauntless dive bombers over Wake Island 40 30
607 29c. Flame-throwers on Tarawa 40 30
608 29c. American advance on Makin 40 30
609 29c. North American B-25 Mitchells bomb Simpson Harbour, Rabaul 40 30
610 29c. Aerial bombardment of Kwajalein 40 30

1992. Christmas. Multicoloured.

611 29c. Type **82** 70 70
612 29c. Children with garlands and goats 70 70

613 29c. Father Christmas . . . 40 30
614 29c. Musicians and singer . . 70 70
615 29c. Family carrying food . . 40 30

83 Pterosaur

85 Flukes of Whale's Tail

84 "After Child-birth Ceremony" (Charlie Gibbons)

1993. Monsters of the Pacific. Multicoloured.
616 29c. Type **83** 50 40
617 29c. Outrigger canoe 50 40
618 29c. Head of plesiosaur . . . 50 40
619 29c. Pterosaur and neck of plesiosaur 50 40
620 29c. Pterosaur (flying towards left) 50 40
621 29c. Giant crab 50 40
622 29c. Tentacles of squid and two requiem sharks 50 40
623 29c. Hammerhead shark, tentacle of squid and neck of plesiosaur 50 40
624 29c. Head of lake serpent . . 50 40
625 29c. Hammerhead shark and neck of serpent 50 40
626 29c. Squid ("Kraken") . . . 50 40
627 29c. Manta ray, tentacles of squid and body of plesiosaur 50 40
628 29c. Three barracudas and body of plesiosaur 50 40
629 29c. Angelfishes and serpent's claw 50 40
630 29c. Octopus and body of serpent 50 40
631 29c. Nautilus and body of plesiosaur 50 40
632 29c. Moorish idols (two striped fishes) 50 40
633 29c. Lionfish 50 40
634 29c. Squid 50 40
635 29c. Requiem shark and body of kronosaur 50 40
636 29c. Zebra shark and sea-bed 50 40
637 29c. Squid and sea-bed . . . 50 40
638 29c. Giant nautilus and tail of serpent 50 40
639 29c. Head of kronosaur . . . 50 40
640 29c. Lionfish, body of kronosaur and sea-bed . . 50 40

Nos. 616/40 were issued together, se-tenant, forming a composite design.

1993. International Year of Indigenous Peoples. Multicoloured.
641 29c. Type **84** 75 60
642 29c. "Village in Early Palau" (Charlie Gibbons) 75 60

1993. Jonah and The Whale. Multicoloured.
644 29c. Type **85** 50 40
645 29c. Bird and part of fluke 50 40
646 29c. Two birds 50 40
647 29c. Kaeb (canoe) 50 40
648 29c. Sun, birds and dolphin 50 40
649 29c. Shark and whale's tail 50 40
650 29c. Shoal of brown fishes and part of whale 50 40
651 29c. Hammerhead shark, shark's tail and fishes . . . 50 40
652 29c. Dolphin (fish) and shark's head 50 40
653 29c. Dolphin and fishes . . . 50 40
654 29c. Scombroid and other fishes and part of whale . . 50 40
655 29c. Two turtles swimming across whale's body . . . 50 40
656 29c. Shoal of pink fishes and whale's back 50 40
657 29c. Spotted eagle ray, manta ray and top of whale's head 50 40
658 29c. Two groupers and shoal of small brown fishes . . . 50 40
659 29c. Jellyfish and wrasse (blue fish) 50 40
660 29c. Wrasse, other fishes and whale's dorsal fin 50 40
661 29c. Whale's eye and corner of mouth 50 40
662 29c. Opened mouth 50 40
663 29c. Jonah 50 40
664 29c. Convict tang (yellow and black striped fish) and brain corals on sea bed . . 50 40
665 29c. Hump-headed bannerfishes and sea anemone 50 40
666 29c. Undulate triggerfish (blue-striped) and corals on sea bed 50 40
667 29c. Brown and red striped fish, corals and part of whale's jaw 50 40
668 29c. Two groupers (spotted) on sea bed 50 40

Nos. 644/68 were issued together, se-tenant, forming a composite design.

86 Alfred's Manta

1994. "Hong Kong '94" International Stamp Exhibition. Rays. Multicoloured.
669 40c. Type **86** 55 40
670 40c. Spotted eagle ray . . . 55 40
671 40c. Coachwhip stingray . . 55 40
672 40c. Black-spotted stingray 55 40

87 Crocodile's Head

1994. The Estuarine Crocodile. Multicoloured.
673 20c. Type **87** 40 30
674 20c. Hatchling and eggs . . . 40 30
675 20c. Crocodile swimming underwater 40 30
676 20c. Crocodile half-submerged 40 30

88 Red-footed Booby

1994. Sea Birds. Multicoloured.
677 50c. Type **88** . . . . 1·25 1·25
678 50c. Great frigate bird . . . 1·25 1·25
679 50c. Brown booby . . . . . 1·25 1·25
680 50c. Little pied cormorant . . 1·25 1·25

89 U.S. Marines capture Kwajalein

1994. Pacific Theatre in Second World War (4th issue). Multicoloured.
681 29c. Type **89** 40 30
682 29c. Aerial bombardment of Japanese airbase, Truk . . 40 30
683 29c. U.S.S. 284 "Tullibee" (submarine) (Operation Desecrate) 40 30
684 29c. Landing craft storming Saipan beach 40 30
685 29c. Shooting down Japanese Mitsubishi Zero-Sen bombers, Mariana Islands (Turkey Shoot) 40 30
686 29c. Liberated civilians, Guam 40 30
687 29c. U.S. troops taking Peleliu 40 30
688 29c. Securing Angaur 40 30
689 29c. General Douglas MacArthur 40 30
690 29c. U.S. Army memorial . . 40 30

90 Allied Warships

1994. 50th Anniv of D-day (Allied Landings in Normandy). Multicoloured.
691 50c. C-47 transport aircraft dropping paratroopers . . 65 45
692 50c. Type **90** 65 45
693 50c. Troops disembarking from landing craft 65 45
694 50c. Tanks coming ashore . . 65 45
695 50c. Sherman tank crossing minefield 65 45
696 50c. Aircraft attacking German positions 65 45
697 50c. Gliders dropping paratroops behind lines . . 65 45
698 50c. Pegasus Bridge 65 45
699 50c. Allied forces pushing inland 65 45
700 50c. Beach at end of 6 June 1944 . . . . 65 45

91 Baron Pierre de Coubertin (founder of modern games)

1994. Centenary of International Olympic Committee. Multicoloured.
701 **91** 29c. multicoloured 40 30

92 Top of "Saturn V" Rocket and Command and Lunar Modules joined

93 Sail-finned Goby

1994. 25th Anniv of First Manned Moon Landing. Multicoloured.
703 29c. Type **92** 50 40
704 29c. Lunar module preparing to land (side view) 50 40
705 29c. Lunar module leaving surface (top view) 50 40
706 29c. Command module (view of circular end) 50 40
707 29c. Earth viewed from Moon 50 40
708 29c. "Saturn V" third stage 50 40
709 29c. Neil Armstrong descending ladder to lunar surface 50 40
710 29c. Footprint in lunar surface 50 40
711 29c. Alan Shepard and lunar module on Moon 50 40
712 29c. Command module separating from service module 50 40
713 29c. "Saturn V" second stage (rocket inscr "USA USA") 50 40
714 29c. Rear view of "Apollo 17" astronaut at Splitrock Valley of Taurus-Littrow 50 40
715 29c. Lunar module reflected in visor of Edwin Aldrin 50 40
716 29c. James Irwin and David Scott raising flag on "Apollo 15" mission . . . 50 40
717 29c. Command module descending with parachutes deployed 50 40
718 29c. "Saturn V" lifting off from Kennedy Space Center 50 40
719 29c. "Apollo 17" astronaut Harrison Schmitt collecting lunar surface samples with shovel 50 40
720 29c. "Apollo 16" astronaut John Young and lunar rover vehicle 50 40
721 29c. "Apollo 12" astronaut Charles Conrad collecting samples with machine . . . 50 40
722 29c. Command module after splashdown 50 40

Nos. 703/22 were issued together, se-tenant, forming a composite design.

1994. "Philakorea 1994" International Stamp Exhibition, Seoul. Philatelic Fantasies. Designs showing named animal with various postal items. Multicoloured.
723 29c. Type **93** (postage) . . . 45 35
724 29c. Black-saddled ("Sharpnose") puffers . . . 45 35
725 29c. Lightning butterflyfish 45 35
726 29c. Clown anemonefish . . 45 35
727 29c. Parrotfish 45 35
728 29c. Narrow-banded batfish 45 35
729 29c. Clown triggerfish 45 35
730 29c. Twin-spotted wrasse . . 45 35
731 40c. Palau fruit bat 55 45
732 40c. Crocodile 55 45
733 40c. Dugong 55 45
734 40c. Banded sea snake . . . 55 45
735 40c. Bottle-nosed dolphin . . 55 45
736 40c. Hawksbill turtle 55 45
737 40c. Common octopus . . . 55 45
738 40c. Manta ray 55 45
739 50c. Palau fantail and chicks (air) . . . . 1·00 1·00
740 50c. Banded crake . . . . . 1·00 1·00
741 50c. Grey-rumped ("Island") swiftlets . . . . 1·00 1·00
742 50c. Micronesian kingfisher 1·00 1·00
743 50c. Red-footed booby . . . 1·00 1·00
744 50c. Great frigate bird . . . 1·00 1·00
745 50c. Palau scops owl . . . . 1·00 1·00
746 50c. Palau fruit dove . . . . 1·00 1·00

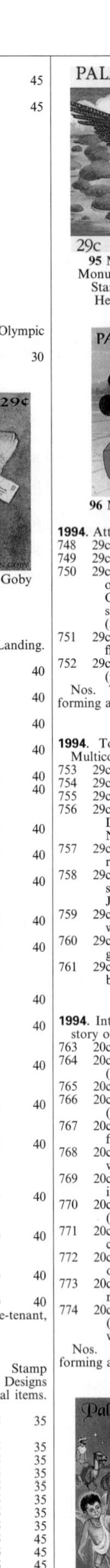

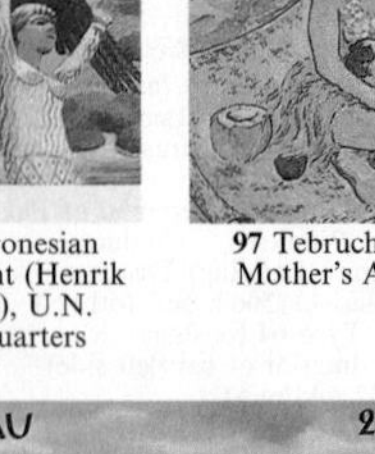

95 Micronesian Monument (Henrik Starcke), U.N. Headquarters

97 Tebruchel in Mother's Arms

96 Mickey and Minnie Mouse at Airport

1994. Attainment of Independence. Multicoloured.
748 29c. Type **95** 45 35
749 29c. Presidential seal 45 35
750 29c. Pres. Kuniwo Nakamura of Palau and Pres. William Clinton of United States shaking hands (56 × 41 mm) 45 35
751 29c. Palau and United States flags 45 35
752 29c. Score of "Belau Er Kid" (national anthem) 45 35

Nos. 748/52 were issued together, se-tenant, forming a composite design.

1994. Tourism. Walt Disney cartoon characters. Multicoloured.
753 29c. Type **96** 50 40
754 29c. Goofy on way to hotel 50 40
755 29c. Donald Duck on beach 50 40
756 29c. Minnie Mouse and Daisy Duck learning Ngloik (dance) 50 40
757 29c. Mickey and Minnie rafting to natural bridge 50 40
758 29c. Uncle Scrooge finding stone money in Babeldaob Jungle 50 40
759 29c. Goofy and napoleon wrasse after collision . . . 50 40
760 29c. Minnie visiting clam garden 50 40
761 29c. Grandma Duck weaving basket 50 40

1994. International Year of the Family. Illustrating story of Tebruchel. Multicoloured.
763 20c. Type **97** 25 15
764 20c. Tebruchel's father (kneeling on beach) 25 15
765 20c. Tebruchel as youth . . . 25 15
766 20c. Tebruchel's wife (standing on beach) . . . 25 15
767 20c. Tebruchel with catch of fish 25 15
768 20c. Tebruchel's pregnant wife sitting in house . . . 25 15
769 20c. Tebruchel's aged mother in dilapidated house . . . 25 15
770 20c. Tebruchel's aged father (standing) 25 15
771 20c. Tebruchel holding first child 25 15
772 20c. Tebruchel's wife (sitting on beach mat) 25 15
773 20c. Tebruchel with aged mother 25 15
774 20c. Tebruchel's father (sitting cross-legged) and wife holding child 25 15

Nos. 763/74 were issued together, se-tenant, forming a composite design.

98 Wise Men and Cherubs

99 Bora Milutinovic (coach)

1994. Christmas. "O Little Town of Bethlehem" (carol). Multicoloured.
775 29c. Type **98** 45 35
776 29c. Angel, shepherds with sheep and cherub 45 35
777 29c. Angels and Madonna and Child 40 40
778 29c. Angels, Bethlehem and shepherd with sheep . . . 45 35
779 29c. Cherubs and Palau fruit doves 40 40

Nos. 775/9 were issued together, se-tenant, forming a composite design.

1994. World Cup Football Championship, U.S.A. Multicoloured.

780	29c. Type **99**	45	35
781	29c. Cle Kooiman	45	35
782	29c. Ernie Stewart	45	35
783	29c. Claudio Reyna	45	35
784	29c. Thomas Dooley	45	35
785	29c. Alexi Lalas	45	35
786	29c. Dominic Kinnear	45	35
787	29c. Frank Klopas	45	35
788	29c. Paul Caligiuri	45	35
789	29c. Marcelo Balboa	45	35
790	29c. Cobi Jones	45	35
791	29c. U.S.A. flag and World Cup trophy	45	35
792	29c. Tony Meola	45	35
793	29c. John Doyle	45	35
794	29c. Eric Wynalda	45	35
795	29c. Roy Wegerle	45	35
796	29c. Fernando Clavijo	45	35
797	29c. Hugo Perez	45	35
798	29c. John Harkes	45	35
799	29c. Mike Lapper	45	35
800	29c. Mike Sorber	45	35
801	29c. Brad Friedel	45	35
802	29c. Tab Ramos	45	35
803	29c. Joe-Max Moore	45	35
804	50c. Babeto (Brazil)	70	50
805	50c. Romario (Brazil)	70	50
806	50c. Franco Baresi (Italy)	70	50
807	50c. Roberto Baggio (Italy)	70	50
808	50c. Andoni Zubizarreta (Spain)	70	50
809	50c. Oleg Salenko (Russia)	70	50
810	50c. Gheorghe Hagi (Rumania)	70	50
811	50c. Dennis Bergkamp (Netherlands)	70	50
812	50c. Hristo Stoichkov (Bulgaria)	70	50
813	50c. Tomas Brolin (Sweden)	70	50
814	50c. Lothar Matthaus (Germany)	70	50
815	50c. Arrigo Sacchi (Italy coach), Carlos Alberto Parreira (Brazil coach), flags and World Cup trophy	70	50

100 Yellow Boxfish ("Cube Trunkfish")

101 Presley

1995. Fishes. Multicoloured.

816	1c. Type **100**	10	10
817	2c. Lionfish	10	10
818	3c. Scarlet-finned ("Long-jawed") squirrelfish	10	10
819	4c. Harlequin ("Longnose") filefish	10	10
820	5c. Ornate butterflyfish	10	10
821	10c. Yellow seahorse	15	10
822	20c. Magenta dottyback (22 × 30 mm)	25	15
836	20c. Magenta dottyback (17½ × 21 mm)	25	15
823	32c. Reef lizardfish (22 × 30 mm)	40	30
837	32c. Reef lizardfish (17½ × 21 mm)	40	30
824	50c. Multibarred goatfish	65	45
825	55c. Barred blenny	70	50
826	$1 Fingerprint pufferfish	1·25	90
827	$2 Long-nosed hawkfish	2·50	1·75
828	$3 Mandarin fish	3·25	2·75
829	$5 Palette ("Blue") surgeonfish	6·50	4·75
830	$10 Coral hind (47 × 30 mm)	13·00	9·50

1995. 60th Birth Anniv of Elvis Presley (entertainer). Multicoloured.

838	32c. Type **101**	55	45
839	32c. Presley wearing white shirt and blue jacket	55	45
840	32c. Presley with microphone and flower	55	45
841	32c. Presley wearing blue shirt and jumper	55	45
842	32c. Presley with rose	55	45
843	32c. Presley with brown hair wearing white shirt	55	45
844	32c. Presley wearing blue open-necked shirt	55	45
845	32c. Presley (in green shirt) singing	55	45
846	32c. Presley as boy (with fair hair)	55	45

102 Grey-rumped ("Palau") Swiftlets

1995. Air. Birds. Multicoloured.

847	50c. Type **102**	1·25	1·25
848	50c. Barn swallows	1·25	1·25
849	50c. Jungle nightjar	1·25	1·25
850	50c. White-breasted wood swallow	1·25	1·25

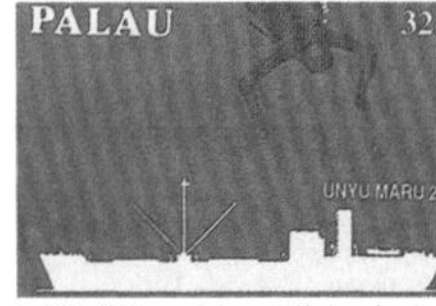

103 "Unyu Maru 2" (tanker)

1995. Japanese Fleet Sunk off Rock Islands (1944). Multicoloured.

851	32c. Type **103**	45	35
852	32c. "Wakatake" (destroyer)	45	35
853	32c. "Teshio Maru" (freighter)	45	35
854	32c. "Raizan Maru" (freighter)	45	35
855	32c. "Chuyo Maru" (freighter)	45	35
856	32c. "Shinsei Maru" (No. 18 freighter)	45	35
857	32c. "Urakami Maru" (freighter)	45	35
858	32c. "Ose Maru" (tanker)	45	35
859	32c. "Iro" (tanker)	45	35
860	32c. "Shosei Maru" (freighter)	45	35
861	32c. Patrol Boat 31	45	35
862	32c. "Kibi Maru" (freighter)	45	35
863	32c. "Amatsu Maru" (tanker)	45	35
864	32c. "Gozan Maru" (freighter)	45	35
865	32c. "Matuei Maru" (freighter)	45	35
866	32c. "Nagisan Maru" (freighter)	45	35
867	32c. "Akashi" (repair ship)	45	35
868	32c. "Kamikazi Maru" (freighter)	45	35

Nos. 851/68 were issued together, se-tenant, forming a composite design.

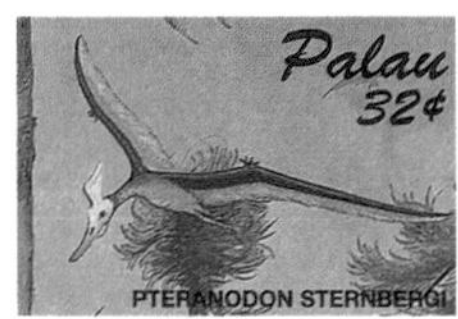

104 "Pteranodon sternbergi"

1995. 25th Anniv of Earth Day. Prehistoric Winged Animals. Multicoloured.

869	32c. Type **104**	45	35
870	32c. "Pteranodon ingens"	45	35
871	32c. Pterodactyls	45	35
872	32c. Dorygnathus	45	35
873	32c. Dimorphodon	45	35
874	32c. Nyctosaurus	45	35
875	32c. "Pterodactylus kochi"	45	35
876	32c. Ornithodesmus	45	35
877	32c. "Diatryma" sp.	65	65
878	32c. Archaeopteryx	65	65
879	32c. Campylognathoides	45	35
880	32c. Gallodactylus	45	35
881	32c. Batrachognathus	45	35
882	32c. Scaphognathus	45	35
883	32c. Peteinosaurus	45	35
884	32c. "Ichthyornis" sp.	65	65
885	32c. Ctenochasma	45	35
886	32c. Rhamphorhynchus	45	35

Nos. 869/86 were issued together, se-tenant, forming a composite design.

105 Fairey Delta 2

1995. Research and Experimental Jet-propelled Aircraft. Multicoloured.

887	50c. Type **105**	70	50
888	50c. B-70 Valkyrie	70	50
889	50c. Douglas X-3 Stiletto	70	50
890	50c. Northrop/Nasa HL-10	70	50
891	50c. Bell XS-1	70	50
892	50c. Tupolev Tu-144	70	50
893	50c. Bell X-1	70	50
894	50c. Boulton Paul P.111	70	50
895	50c. EWR VJ 101C	70	50
896	50c. Handley Page HP-115	70	50
897	50c. Rolls Royce TMR "Flying Bedstead"	70	50
898	50c. North American X-15	70	50

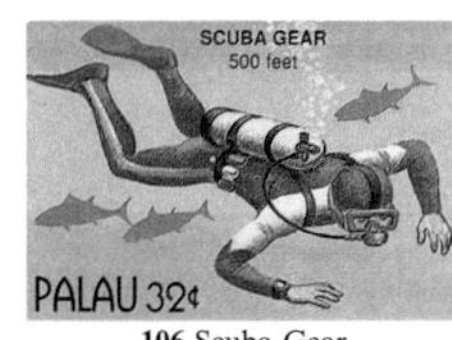

106 Scuba Gear

1995. Submersibles. Multicoloured.

900	32c. Type **106**	45	35
901	32c. Cousteau midget submarine "Denise"	45	35
902	32c. Jim suit	45	35
903	32c. Beaver IV	45	35
904	32c. "Ben Franklin"	45	35
905	32c. U.S.S. "Nautilus" (submarine)	45	35
906	32c. Deep Rover	45	35
907	32c. Beebe bathysphere	45	35
908	32c. "Deep Star IV"	45	35
909	32c. U.S. Navy Deep Submergence Rescue Vehicle	45	35
910	32c. "Aluminaut" (aluminium submarine)	45	35
911	32c. "Nautile"	45	35
912	32c. "Cyana"	45	35
913	32c. French Navy (F.N.R.S.) bathyscaphe	45	35
914	32c. Woods Hole Oceanographic Institute's "Alvin"	45	35
915	32c. "Mir I" (research submarine)	45	35
916	32c. "Archimede" (bathyscaphe)	45	35
917	32c. "Trieste" (bathyscaphe)	45	35

Nos. 900/917 were issued together, se-tenant, forming a composite design.

107 Dolphins, Diver and Pufferfish

1995. "Singapore'95" International Stamp Exhibition. Marine Life. Multicoloured.

918	32c. Type **107**	45	35
919	32c. Turtle and diver	45	35
920	32c. Grouper, anemonefish and crab on sea-bed (emblem on right)	45	35
921	32c. Parrotfish, lionfish and angelfish (emblem on left)	45	35

108 Dove in Helmet (Peace)

1995. 50th Annivs of U.N.O. and F.A.O. Mult.

922	60c. Type **108**	85	65
923	60c. Ibedul Gibbons (Palau chief) in flame (human rights)	85	65
924	60c. Palau atlas in open book (education)	85	65
925	60c. Bananas in tractor (agriculture)	85	65

Nos. 922/5 were issued together, se-tenant, the centre of each block forming a composite design of the U.N. emblem.

109 Palau Fruit Doves

1995. 1st Anniv of Independence. Each showing Palau national flag. Multicoloured.

927	20c. Type **109**	30	20
928	20c. Rock Islands	30	20
929	20c. Map of Palau islands	30	20
930	20c. Orchid and hibiscus	30	20
931	32c. Raccoon butterflyfish, soldierfish and conch shell	45	35

110 "Preparing Tin-Fish" (William Draper)

1995. 50th Anniv of the End of Second World War. Multicoloured.

932	32c. Type **110**	45	35
933	32c. "Hellcat's Take-off into Palau's Rising Sun" (Draper)	45	35
934	32c. "Dauntless Dive Bombers over Malakal Harbor" (Draper)	45	35
935	32c. "Planes Return from Palau" (Draper)	45	35
936	32c. "Communion Before Battle" (Draper)	45	35
937	32c. "The Landing" (Draper)	45	35
938	32c. "First Task Ashore" (Draper)	45	35
939	32c. "Fire Fighters save Flak-torn Pilot" (Draper)	45	35
940	32c. "Young Marine Headed for Peleliu" (Tom Lea)	45	35
941	32c. "Peleliu" (Lea)	45	35
942	32c. "Last Rites" (Lea)	45	35
943	32c. "The Thousand Yard Stare" (Lea)	45	35
944	60c. "Admiral Chester W. Nimitz" (Albert Murray) (vert)	85	65
945	60c. "Admiral William F. Halsey" (Murray) (vert)	85	65
946	60c. "Admiral Raymond A. Spruance" (Murray) (vert)	85	65
947	60c. "Vice-Admiral Marc A. Mitscher" (Murray) (vert)	85	65
948	60c. "General Holland M. Smith" (Murray) (vert)	85	65

111 Angel with Animals

1995. Christmas. "We Three Kings of Orient Are" (carol). Multicoloured.

950	32c. Type **111**	45	35
951	32c. Two wise men	45	35
952	32c. Shepherd at crib	45	35
953	32c. Wise man and shepherd	45	35
954	32c. Children with goat	45	35

Nos. 950/4 were issued together, se-tenant, forming a composite design.

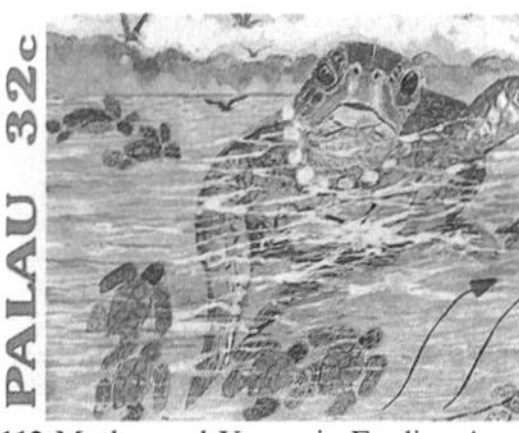

112 Mother and Young in Feeding Area

1995. Year of the Sea Turtle. Multicoloured.

955	32c. Type **112**	45	35
956	32c. Young adult females meeting males	45	35
957	32c. Sun, cockerel in tree and mating area	45	35
958	32c. Woman and hatchlings	45	35
959	32c. Couple and nesting area	45	35
960	32c. House and female swimming to lay eggs	45	35

Nos. 955/60 were issued together, se-tenant, forming a composite design of the turtle's life cycle.

113 Lennon

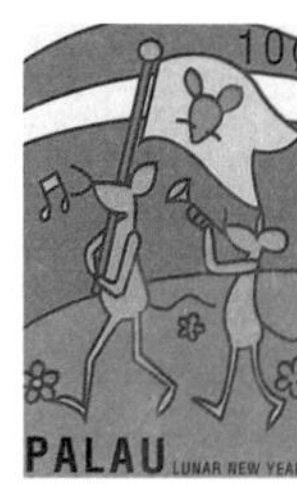

114 Rats leading Procession

1995. 15th Death Anniv of John Lennon (entertainer).

961 **113** 32c. multicoloured 45 35

1996. Chinese New Year. Year of the Rat. Multicoloured.

962 10c. Type **114** 20 10
963 10c. Three rats playing instruments 20 10
964 10c. Rats playing tuba and banging drum 20 10
965 10c. Family of rats outside house 20 10

Nos. 962/5 were issued together, se-tenant, forming a composite design of a procession.

115 Girls

1996. 50th Anniv of U.N.I.C.E.F. Each showing three children. Multicoloured.

967 32c. Type **115** 45 35
968 32c. Girl in centre wearing lei around neck 45 35
969 32c. Girl in centre wearing headscarf 45 35
970 32c. Boy in centre and girls holding bunches of grass 45 35

Nos. 967/70 were issued together, se-tenant, forming a composite design of the children around a globe and the U.N.I.C.E.F. emblem.

116 Basslet and Vermiculate Parrotfish ("P")

1996. Underwater Wonders. Illuminated letters spelling out PALAU. Multicoloured.

971 32c. Type **116** 50 40
972 32c. Yellow-striped cardinalfish ("A") 50 40
973 32c. Pair of atoll butterflyfish ("L") 50 40
974 32c. Starry moray and slate-pencil sea urchin ("A") . . 50 40
975 32c. Blue-streaked cleaner wrasse and coral hind ("Grouper") ("U") 50 40

117 Ferdinand Magellan and "Vitoria"

1996. "CAPEX'96" International Stamp Exhibition, Toronto, Canada. Circumnavigators. Multicoloured.

976 32c. Type **117** (postage) . . . 50 40
977 32c. Charles Wilkes and U.S.S. "Vincennes" (sail frigate) 50 40
978 32c. Joshua Slocum and "Spray" (yacht) 50 40
979 32c. Ben Carlin and "Half-Safe" (amphibian) 50 40
980 32c. Edward Beach and U.S.S. "Triton" (submarine) 50 40
981 32c. Naomi James and "Express Crusader" (yacht) 50 40
982 32c. Sir Ranulf Fiennes and snow vehicle 50 40
983 32c. Rick Hansen and wheelchair 50 40
984 32c. Robin Knox-Johnson and "Enza New Zealand" (catamaran) 50 40
986 60c. Lowell Smith and Douglas world cruiser seaplanes (air) 85 60
987 60c. Ernst Lehmann and "Graf Zeppelin" (dirigible airship) 85 60
988 60c. Wiley Post and Lockheed Vega "Winnie Mae" 85 60
989 60c. Yuri Gagarin and "Vostok I" (spaceship) . . 85 60
990 60c. Jerrie Mock and Cessna 180 "Spirit of Columbus" 85 60
991 60c. H. Ross Perot jnr. and Bell LongRanger III helicopter "Spirit of Texas" 85 60
992 60c. Brooke Knapp and Gulfstream III "The American Dream" 85 60
993 60c. Jeana Yeager and Dick Rutan and "Voyager" . . 85 60
994 60c. Fred Lasby and Piper Commanche 85 60

118 Simba, Nala and Timon ("The Lion King")

1996. Disney Sweethearts. Multicoloured.

995 1c. Type **118** 10 10
996 2c. Georgette, Tito and Oliver ("Oliver & Company") 10 10
997 3c. Duchess, O'Malley and Marie ("The Aristocats") 10 10
998 4c. Bianca, Jake and Polly ("The Rescuers Down Under") 10 10
999 5c. Tod, Vixey and Copper ("The Fox and the Hound") 10 10
1000 6c. Thumper, Flower and their Sweethearts ("Bambi") 10 10
1001 60c. As No. 995 . . . . . 85 60
1002 60c. Bernard, Bianca and Mr. Chairman ("The Rescuers") 85 60
1003 60c. As No. 996 . . . . . 85 60
1004 60c. As No. 997 . . . . . 85 60
1005 60c. As No. 998 . . . . . 85 60
1006 60c. As No. 999 . . . . . 85 60
1007 60c. Robin Hood, Maid Marian and Alan-a-Dale ("Robin Hood") 85 60
1008 60c. As No. 1000 . . . . . 85 60
1009 60c. Pongo, Perdita and the Puppies ("101 Dalmatians") 85 60

119 Hakeem Olajuwan (basketball)

1996. Centenary of Modern Olympic Games and Olympic Games, Atlanta. Multicoloured.

1011 32c. Type **119** 45 35
1012 32c. Pat McCormick (gymnastics) 45 35
1013 32c. Jim Thorpe (pentathlon and decathlon) 45 35
1014 32c. Jesse Owens (athletics) 45 35
1015 32c. Tatyana Gutsu (gymnastics) 45 35
1016 32c. Michael Jordan (basketball) 45 35
1017 32c. Fu Mingxia (diving) . . 45 35
1018 32c. Robert Zmelik (decathlon) 45 35
1019 32c. Ivan Pedroso (long jumping) 45 35
1020 32c. Nadia Comaneci (gymnastics) 45 35
1021 32c. Jackie Joyner-Kersee (long jumping) 45 35
1022 32c. Michael Johnson (running) 45 35
1023 32c. Kristin Otto (swimming) 45 35
1024 32c. Vitai Scherbo (gymnastics) 45 35
1025 32c. Johnny Weissmuller (swimming) 45 35
1026 32c. Babe Didrikson (track and field athlete) 45 35
1027 32c. Eddie Tolan (track athlete) 45 35
1028 32c. Krisztina Egerszegi (swimming) 45 35
1029 32c. Sawao Kato (gymnastics) 45 35
1030 32c. Aleksandr Popov (swimming) 45 35
1031 40c. Fanny Blankers-Koen (track and field athlete) (vert) 65 50
1032 40c. Bob Mathias (decathlon) (vert) 65 50
1033 60c. Torchbearer entering Wembley Stadium, 1948 65 50
1034 60c. Entrance to Olympia Stadium, Athens, and flags 65 50

Nos. 1011/30 were issued together, se-tenant, forming a composite design of the athletes and Olympic rings.

120 The Creation

1996. 3000th Anniv of Jerusalem. Illustrations by Guy Rowe from "In Our Image: Character Studies from the Old Testament". Mult.

1035 20c. Type **120** 30 20
1036 20c. Adam and Eve 30 20
1037 20c. Noah and his Wife . . 30 20
1038 20c. Abraham 30 20
1039 20c. Jacob's Blessing 30 20
1040 20c. Jacob becomes Israel 30 20
1041 20c. Joseph and his Brethren 30 20
1042 20c. Moses and Burning Bush 30 20
1043 20c. Moses and the Tablets 30 20
1044 20c. Balaam 30 20
1045 20c. Joshua 30 20
1046 20c. Gideon 30 20
1047 20c. Jephthah 30 20
1048 20c. Samson 30 20
1049 20c. Ruth and Naomi . . . 30 20
1050 20c. Saul anointed 30 20
1051 20c. Saul denounced 30 20
1052 20c. David and Jonathan . . 30 20
1053 20c. David and Nathan . . 30 20
1054 20c. David mourns 30 20
1055 20c. Solomon praying . . . 30 20
1056 20c. Solomon judging . . . 30 20
1057 20c. Elijah 30 20
1058 20c. Elisha 30 20
1059 20c. Job 30 20
1060 20c. Isaiah 30 20
1061 20c. Jeremiah 30 20
1062 20c. Ezekiel 30 20
1063 20c. Nebuchadnezzar's Dream 30 20
1064 20c. Amos 30 20

121 Nankeen Night Heron

1996. Birds over Palau Lagoon. Multicoloured.

1065 50c. Eclectus parrot (female) ("Iakkotsiang") 70 55
1066 50c. Type **121** 70 55
1067 50c. Micronesian pigeon ("Belochel") 70 55
1068 50c. Eclectus parrot (male) ("Iakkotsiang") 70 55
1069 50c. White tern ("Sechosech") 70 55
1070 50c. Common noddy ("Mechadelbedaoch") . . 70 55
1071 50c. Nicobar pigeon ("Laib") 70 55
1072 50c. Chinese little bittern ("Cheloteachel") 70 55
1073 50c. Little pied cormorant ("Deroech") 70 55
1074 50c. Black-naped tern ("Kerkirs") 70 55
1075 50c. White-tailed tropic bird ("Dudek") 70 55
1076 50c. Sulphur-crested cockatoo ("Iakkotsiang") (white bird) 70 55
1077 50c. White-capped noddy ("Bedaoch") 70 55
1078 50c. Bridled tern ("Bedebedchakl") 70 55
1079 50c. Reef heron (grey) ("Sechou") 70 55
1080 50c. Grey-tailed tattler ("Kekereielderariik") . . 70 55
1081 50c. Reef heron (white) ("Sechou") 70 55
1082 50c. Audubon's shearwater ("Ochaieu") 70 55
1083 50c. Black-headed gull ("Oltirakladial") 70 55
1084 50c. Ruddy turnstone ("Omechederiibabad") . . 70 55

Nos. 1065/84 were issued together, se-tenant, forming a composite design.

122 Lockheed U-2

1996. Spy Planes. Multicoloured.

1085 40c. Type **122** 55 40
1086 40c. General Dynamics EF-111A 55 40
1087 40c. Lockheed YF-12A . . 55 40
1088 40c. Lockheed SR-71 . . . 55 40
1089 40c. Teledyne Ryan Tier II Plus 55 40
1090 40c. Lockheed XST 55 40
1091 40c. Lockheed ER-2 . . . . 55 40
1092 40c. Lockheed F-117A Nighthawk 55 40
1093 40c. Lockheed EC-130E . . 55 40
1094 40c. Ryan Firebee 55 40
1095 40c. Lockheed Martin/ Boeing Darkstar 55 40
1096 40c. Boeing E-3A Sentry . . 55 40

123 "The Birth of a New Nation"

1996. 2nd Anniv of Independence. Illustrations from "Kirie" by Koh Sekiguchi. Multicoloured.

1098 20c. Type **123** 30 20
1099 20c. "In the Blue Shade of Trees" 30 20

124 Pandanus

1996. Christmas. "O Tannenbaum" (carol). Decorated Trees. Multicoloured.

1100 32c. Type **124** 45 35
1101 32c. Mangrove 45 35
1102 32c. Norfolk Island pine . . 45 35
1103 32c. Papaya 45 35
1104 32c. Casuarina 45 35

Nos. 1100/4 were issued together, se-tenant, forming a composite design.

125 "Viking I" in Orbit (½-size illustration)

1996. Space Missions to Mars. Multicoloured.

1105 32c. Type **125** 45 35
1106 32c. "Viking I" emblem (top half) 45 35
1107 32c. "Mars Lander" firing de-orbit engines 45 35
1108 32c. "Viking I" emblem (bottom half) 45 35
1109 32c. Phobos (Martian moon) 45 35
1110 32c. "Mars Lander" entering Martian atmosphere 45 35
1111 32c. "Mariner 9" (first mission, 1971) 45 35
1112 32c. Parachute opens for landing and heat shield jettisons 45 35
1113 32c. Projected U.S./Russian manned spacecraft, 21st century (top half) 45 35
1114 32c. "Lander" descent engines firing 45 35
1115 32c. Projected U.S./Russian spacecraft (bottom half) 45 35
1116 32c. "Viking I Lander" on Martian surface, 1976 . . 45 35

Nos. 1105/16 were issued together, se-tenant, forming several composite designs.

126 Northrop XB-35 Bomber

1996. Oddities of the Air. Aircraft Designs. Multicoloured.

1118 60c. Type **126** 85 65
1119 60c. Leduc O.21 . . . . . . 85 65
1120 60c. Convair Model 118 flying car 85 65
1121 60c. Blohm und Voss BV 141 . . . . 85 65
1122 60c. Vought V-173 . . . . 85 65
1123 60c. McDonnell XF-85 Goblin 85 65
1124 60c. North American F-82B Twin Mustang fighter . . 85 65
1125 60c. Lockheed XFV-1 vertical take-off fighter . . 85 65

1126 60c. Northrop XP-79B 85 65
1127 60c. Saunders Roe SR/A1 flying boat fighter 85 65
1128 60c. "Caspian Sea Monster" hovercraft 85 65
1129 60c. Grumman X-29 demonstrator 85 65

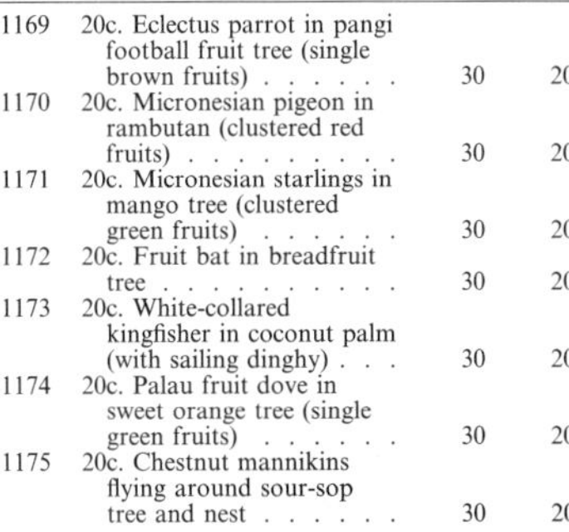

129 Pemphis

130 "Apollo 15" Command Module splashing-down

1997. "Hong Kong '97" Stamp Exhibition. Flowers. Multicoloured.

1133 1c. Type **129** 10 10
1134 2c. Sea lettuce 10 10
1135 3c. Tropical almond 10 10
1136 4c. Guettarda 10 10
1137 5c. Pacific coral bean 10 10
1138 32c. Black mangrove 45 35
1139 32c. Cordia 45 35
1140 32c. Lantern tree 45 35
1141 32c. Palau rock-island flower 45 35
1142 50c. Fish-poison tree 65 50
1143 50c. Indian mulberry 65 50
1144 50c. Pacific poison-apple 65 50
1145 50c. "Ailanthus" sp. 65 50
1146 $3 Sea hibiscus (73 × 48 mm) 3·75 2·75

1997. Bicentenary of the Parachute. Multicoloured.

1147 32c. Type **130** (postage) 45 35
1148 32c. Skydiving team in formation (40 × 23 mm) 45 35
1149 32c. Cargo drop from airplane 45 35
1150 32c. Parasailing (40 × 23 mm) 45 35
1151 32c. Parachutist falling to earth 45 35
1152 32c. Parachute demonstration team (40 × 23 mm) 45 35
1153 32c. Parachutist falling into sea 45 35
1154 32c. Drag-racing car (40 × 23mm) 45 35
1156 60c. Parachuting demonstration (air) 85 65
1157 60c. "The Blue Flame" (world land-speed record attempt) (40 × 23 mm) 85 65
1158 60c. Atmospheric Re-entry Demonstrator (capsule with three canopies) 85 65
1159 60c. Spies parachuting behind enemy lines during Second World War (40 × 23 mm) 85 65
1160 60c. Andre Jacques Garnerin's first successful parachute descent (from balloon), 1797 85 65
1161 60c. C-130E airplane demonstrating Low Altitude Parachute Extraction System (airplane and capsule with four canopies) (40 × 23 mm) 85 65
1162 60c. U.S. Army parachutist flying parafoil 85 65
1163 60c. Parachute (one canopy) slowing high performance airplane (40 × 23mm) 85 65

131 Pacific Black Duck beneath Banana Tree

1997. Palau's Avian Environment. Multicoloured.

1164 20c. Type **131** 30 20
1165 20c. Pair of red junglefowl beneath calamondin (clustered orange fruits) 30 20
1166 20c. Nicobar pigeon in parinari tree (single orange fruits) 30 20
1167 20c. Cardinal honeyeater in wax apple tree (clustered brown fruits) 30 20
1168 20c. Purple swamphen and Chinese little bittern amid taro plants 30 20
1169 20c. Eclectus parrot in pangi football fruit tree (single brown fruits) 30 20
1170 20c. Micronesian pigeon in rambutan (clustered red fruits) 30 20
1171 20c. Micronesian starlings in mango tree (clustered green fruits) 30 20
1172 20c. Fruit bat in breadfruit tree 30 20
1173 20c. White-collared kingfisher in coconut palm (with sailing dinghy) 30 20
1174 20c. Palau fruit dove in sweet orange tree (single green fruits) 30 20
1175 20c. Chestnut mannikins flying around sour-sop tree and nest 30 20

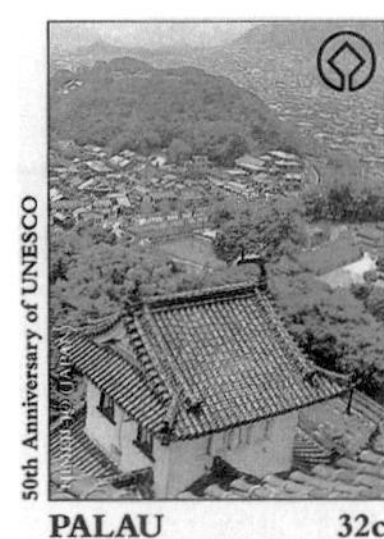

132 Himeji Temple, Japan

1997. 50th Anniv of U.N.E.S.C.O. Multicoloured.

1176 32c. Type **132** 45 35
1177 32c. Kyoto, Japan 45 35
1178 32c. Pagoda roofs, Himeji Temple (white inscr at left) 45 35
1179 32c. Garden, Himeji Temple 45 35
1180 32c. Path and doorway, Himeji Temple 45 35
1181 32c. Pagoda roofs, Himeji Temple (white inscr at right) 45 35
1182 32c. Roof ridge and decoration, Himeji Temple 45 35
1183 32c. Inscribed post and veranda, Himeji Temple 45 35
1184 60c. Ceiling, Augustusburg Castle, Germany (horiz) 85 65
1185 60c. Augustusburg Castle (horiz) 85 65
1186 60c. Falkenlust Castle, Germany (horiz) 85 65
1187 60c. Roman ruins, Trier, Germany (horiz) 85 65
1188 60c. House, Trier (horiz) 85 65

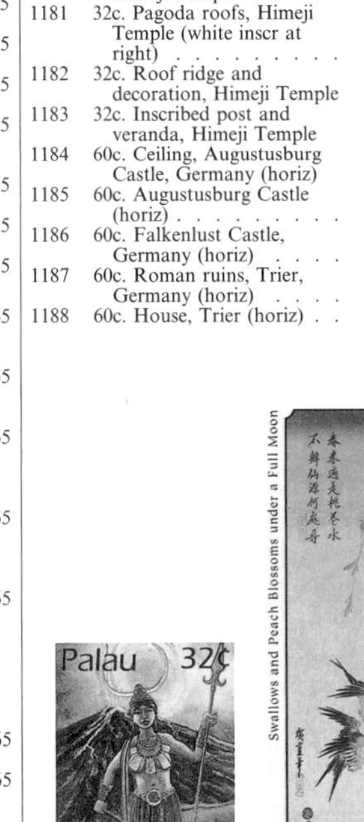

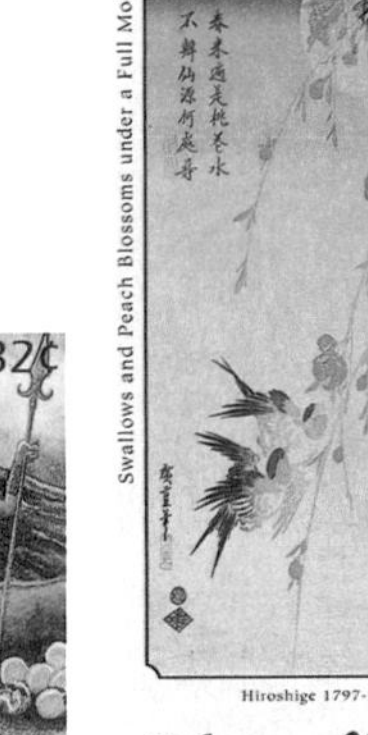

133 Darago, Philippines

134 "Swallows and Peach Blossoms under a Full Moon"

1997. "Pacific 97" International Stamp Exhibition, San Francisco. Volcano Goddesses of the Pacific. Multicoloured.

1190 32c. Type **133** 45 35
1191 32c. Fuji, Japan 45 35
1192 32c. Pele, Hawaii 45 35
1193 32c. Pare and Hutu, Polynesia 45 35
1194 32c. Dzalarhons, Haida tribe, North America 45 35
1195 32c. Chuginadak, Aleutian Islands, Alaska 45 35

1997. Birth Bicentenary of Ando Hiroshige (Japanese painter). Multicoloured.

1196 32c. Type **134** 55 45
1197 32c. "Parrot on a Flowering Branch" 55 45
1198 32c. "Crane and Rising Sun" 55 45
1199 32c. "Cock, Unbrella and Morning Glories" 55 45
1200 32c. "Titmouse hanging Head Downward on a Camellia Branch" 55 45

135 Bai (community building)

1997. 3rd Anniv of Independence.

1202 **135** 32c. multicoloured 45 35

136 "Albatross" (U.S.A.)

1997. Oceanic Research. Research Vessels. Multicoloured.

1203 32c. Type **136** 45 35
1204 32c. "Mabahiss" (Egypt) 45 35
1205 32c. "Atlantis II" (U.S.A.) 45 35
1206 32c. Hans Hass's "Xarifa" (schooner) 45 35
1207 32c. "Meteor" (Germany) 45 35
1208 32c. "Egabras III" (U.S.A.) 45 35
1209 32c. "Discoverer" (U.S.A.) 45 35
1210 32c. "Kaiyo" (Japan) 45 35
1211 32c. "Ocean Defender" (Great Britain) 45 35

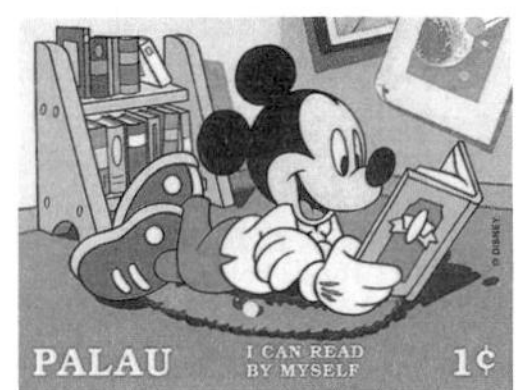

137 "I Can Read by Myself"

1997. Literacy Campaign. Walt Disney cartoon characters. Multicoloured.

1213 1c. Type **137** 10 10
1214 2c. "Start Them Young" 10 10
1215 3c. "Share your Knowledge" 10 10
1216 4c. "The insatiable Reader" 10 10
1217 5c. "Reading is the ultimate Luxury" 10 10
1218 10c. "Real Men read" 10 10
1219 32c. "Exercise your Right to Read" 45 35
1220 32c. As No. 1217 45 35
1221 32c. As No. 1215 45 35
1222 32c. As No. 1214 45 35
1223 32c. "Reading is fundamental" 45 35
1224 32c. As No. 1216 45 35
1225 32c. "Reading Time is Anytime" 45 35
1226 32c. As No. 1218 45 35
1227 32c. Type **137** 45 35

138 Boy and Girl

139 Diana, Princess of Wales

1997. Christmas. "Some Children See Him" (carol). Multicoloured.

1229 32c. Type **138** 45 35
1230 32c. Asian boy and white girl 45 35
1231 32c. Madonna and Child behind boy and girl 45 35
1232 32c. White girl and Oriental children 45 35
1233 32c. Asian boy and Palauan girl 45 35

Nos. 1229/33 were issued together, se-tenant, forming a composite design.

1997. Diana, Princess of Wales Commemoration.

1234 **139** 60c. multicoloured 85 65

141 Nucleus of Galaxy M100

1998. Hubble Space Telescope. Multicoloured.

1236 32c. Type **141** 45 35
1237 32c. Top of Hubble telescope 45 35
1238 32c. Astronaut on robot arm 45 35
1239 32c. Astronaut fixing new camera to telescope 45 35
1240 32c. Astronaut in cargo space of shuttle "Endeavour" 45 35
1241 32c. Hubble released after repair 45 35

142 Mother Teresa

1998. Mother Teresa (founder of Missionaries of Charity) Commemoration. Portraits of Mother Teresa. Multicoloured.

1243 60c. Type **142** 85 65
1244 60c. Facing right 85 65
1245 60c. Wearing cross 85 65
1246 60c. Wearing cardigan 85 65

143 Ladybird Remotely Operated Vehicle, Japan

1998. International Year of the Ocean. Deep-sea Robots. Multicoloured.

1247 32c. Type **143** 45 35
1248 32c. Slocum Glider 45 35
1249 32c. "Hornet" 45 35
1250 32c. "Scorpio" 45 35
1251 32c. "Odyssey" Autonomous Underwater Vehicle 45 35
1252 32c. Jamstec Survey System launcher, Japan 45 35
1253 32c. "Scarab II" (servicer of undersea telephone cables) 45 35
1254 32c. U.S. Navy torpedo finder 45 35
1255 32c. Jamstec Survey System vehicle, Japan 45 35
1256 32c. Cetus tether for undersea cables 45 35
1257 32c. Deep-sea remotely operated vehicle 45 35
1258 32c. Abe (autonomous benthic explorer) 45 35
1259 32c. OBSS 45 35
1260 32c. Remote controlled vehicle 225G "Swimming Eyeball" (for inspection of undersea oil rigs) 45 35
1261 32c. Japanese Underwater Remotely Operated Vehicle 45 35
1262 32c. Benthos remotely piloted vehicle 45 35
1263 32c. Curv III (cable-controlled underwater research vehicle) 45 35
1264 32c. "Smartie", Great Britain 45 35

1998. "Israel 98" International Stamp Exhibition, Tel Aviv. Nos. 1035/64 optd with emblem.

1266 20c. multicoloured 35 20
1267 20c. multicoloured 35 20
1268 20c. multicoloured 35 20
1269 20c. multicoloured 35 20
1270 20c. multicoloured 35 20
1271 20c. multicoloured 35 20
1272 20c. multicoloured 35 20
1273 20c. multicoloured 35 20
1274 20c. multicoloured 35 20
1275 20c. multicoloured 35 20
1276 20c. multicoloured 35 20
1277 20c. multicoloured 35 20
1278 20c. multicoloured 35 20
1279 20c. multicoloured 35 20
1280 20c. multicoloured 35 20
1281 20c. multicoloured 35 20

1282 20c. multicoloured 35 20
1283 20c. multicoloured 35 20
1284 20c. multicoloured 35 20
1285 20c. multicoloured 35 20
1286 20c. multicoloured 35 20
1287 20c. multicoloured 35 20
1288 20c. multicoloured 35 20
1289 20c. multicoloured 35 20
1290 20c. multicoloured 35 20
1291 20c. multicoloured 35 20
1292 20c. multicoloured 35 20
1293 20c. multicoloured 35 20
1294 20c. multicoloured 35 20
1295 20c. multicoloured 35 20

145 Hut **146** Footballer

1998. The Legend of Orachel. Multicoloured.
1296 40c. Type **145** 55 45
1297 40c. Outrigger canoes moored by hut 55 45
1298 40c. Hut and man in canoe 55 45
1299 40c. Bird in tree 55 45
1300 40c. Front half of three-man canoe 55 45
1301 40c. Rear half of canoe and head of snake 55 45
1302 40c. Crocodile, fishes and coral 55 45
1303 40c. Shark and fishes 55 45
1304 40c. Turtle, jellyfish and body of snake 55 45
1305 40c. Underwater bai (community building) 55 45
1306 40c. Orachel swimming underwater and fishes 55 45
1307 40c. Coral, fishes and seaweed 55 45

1998. World Cup Football Championship, France. Multicoloured.
1308 50c. Type **146** 70 55
1309 50c. Player in blue and white striped shirt 70 55
1310 50c. Player in green shirt and white shorts 70 55
1311 50c. Player in white shirt and blue shorts 70 55
1312 50c. Player in green shirt and black shorts 70 55
1313 50c. Player in red short-sleeved shirt 70 55
1314 50c. Player in yellow shirt and blue shorts 70 55
1315 50c. Player in red long-sleeved shirt 70 55

147 Scuba Fishing

1998. 4th Micronesian Islands Games, Palau. Multicoloured.
1317 32c. Type **147** 45 35
1318 32c. Spear throwing 45 35
1319 32c. Swimming 45 35
1320 32c. Coconut throwing 45 35
1321 32c. Games emblem 45 35
1322 32c. Coconut tree climbimg 45 35
1323 32c. Canoe racing 45 35
1324 32c. Coconut husking 45 35
1325 32c. Diving 45 35

148 Rudolph and other Reindeer

1998. Christmas. "Rudolph the Red Nosed Reindeer" (carol). Multicoloured.
1326 32c. Type **148** 45 35
1327 32c. Two reindeer and girl in yellow dress 45 35
1328 32c. Two reindeer, boy and girl 45 35
1329 32c. Two reindeer, girl in long pink dress and star 45 35
1330 32c. Father Christmas and sleigh 45 35
Nos. 1326/30 were issued together, se-tenant, forming a composite design.

149 Princess Dot (ant)

1998. "A Bug's Life" (computer animated film). Multicoloured.
1331 20c. Type **149** 30 20
1332 20c. Heimlich (caterpillar), Francis (ladybird) and Slim (stick insect) 30 20
1333 20c. Hopper (grasshopper) 30 20
1334 20c. Princess Atta (ant) 30 20
1335 32c. Princess Atta and Flick (ant) in boat 45 35
1336 32c. Princess Atta and Flick sitting on heart 45 35
1337 32c. Flick with Princess Atta sitting on leaf 45 35
1338 32c. Flick handing Princess Atta a flower 45 35
1339 50c. Butterfly, Heimlich, Francis and other bugs (horiz) 70 55
1340 50c. Slim, Francis and Heimlich (horiz) 70 55
1341 50c. Manny (praying mantis) (horiz) 70 55
1342 50c. Francis (horiz) 70 55
1343 60c. Slim and Flick juggling 85 65
1344 60c. Francis on cycle, Heimlich and Slim 85 65
1345 60c. Manny hynotizing Flick 85 65
1346 60c. Manny, Rosie (spider) and other bugs 85 65

150 Group Photograph of Astronauts, 1962

1999. John Glenn's Return to Space. Multicoloured.
1348 60c. Type **150** 75 55
1349 60c. Glenn in space helmet (looking straight ahead) 75 55
1350 60c. Group photograph of five astronauts 75 55
1351 60c. Glenn in space helmet (head turned to left) 75 55
1352 60c. Glenn in civilian suit 75 55
1353 60c. Glenn in space helmet (eyes looking right) 75 55
1354 60c. Glenn with Pres. John Kennedy 75 55
1355 60c. Glenn in space suit (bare-headed) ("John Glenn, 1962") 75 55
1356 60c. Glenn (head raised)
1357 60c. "Discovery" (space shuttle) on launch pad 75 55
1358 60c. Glenn and two fellow astronauts with three NASA employees 75 55
1359 60c. Glenn (wearing glasses and looking straight ahead) 75 55
1360 60c. "Discovery" in hangar 75 55
1361 60c. Glenn in space suit (bare-headed) ("John Glenn") 75 55
1362 60c. Glenn (wearing glasses and looking down) 75 55
1363 60c. Glenn in space suit and inner helmet 75 55

151 Rachel Carson (naturalist)

1999. Environmental Heroes of the 20th Century. Multicoloured.
1365 33c. Type **151** 40 30
1366 33c. Ding Darling (President of U.S. National Wildlife Federation, 1936) 40 30
1367 33c. David Brower 40 30
1368 33c. Jacques Cousteau (oceanologist) 40 30
1369 33c. Roger Tory Peterson (ornithologist) 40 30
1370 33c. Prince Philip, Duke of Edinburgh (President of World Wide Fund for Nature) 40 30
1371 33c. Joseph Wood Krutch 40 30
1372 33c. Aldo Leopold 40 30
1373 33c. Dian Fossey (zoologist) (wrongly inscr "Diane") 40 30

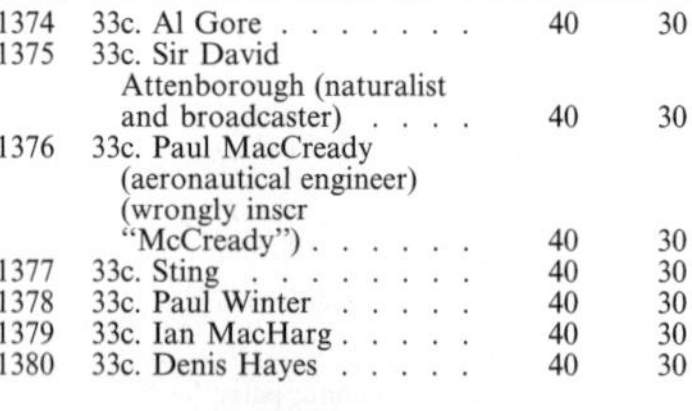
1374 33c. Al Gore 40 30
1375 33c. Sir David Attenborough (naturalist and broadcaster) 40 30
1376 33c. Paul MacCready (aeronautical engineer) (wrongly inscr "McCready") 40 30
1377 33c. Sting 40 30
1378 33c. Paul Winter 40 30
1379 33c. Ian MacHarg 40 30
1380 33c. Denis Hayes 40 30

152 "Soyuz" Spacecraft **153** Haruo Remeliik

1999. "Mir" Space Station. Multicoloured.
1381 33c. Type **152** 40 30
1382 33c. "Specktr" science module 40 30
1383 33c. Rear of space shuttle 40 30
1384 33c. "Kuant 2" scientific and air lock module 40 30
1385 33c. "Kristall" technological module 40 30
1386 33c. Front of "Atlantis" (space shuttle) and docking module 40 30

1999.
1388 **153** 1c. multicoloured 10 10
1389 – 2c. multicoloured 10 10
1390 – 20c. multicoloured 25 20
1391 – 22c. multicoloured 30 35
1392 – 33c. multicoloured 40 30
1393 – 50c. multicoloured 65 50
1394 – 55c. multicoloured 70 55
1395 – 60c. multicoloured 75 55
1395a – 70c. violet and deep violet 80 60
1396 – 77c. multicoloured 95 70
1396a – 80c. green and emerald 95 70
1400 – $3.20 multicoloured 4·00 3·00
1400a – $12.25 rose and red 15·00 13·00
DESIGNS: 2c. Lazarus Salii; 20c. Charlie Gibbons; 22c. Admiral Raymond Spuance; 33c. Pres. Kuniwo Nakamura; 50c. Admiral William Halsey; 55c. Colonel Lewis Puller; 60c. Franklin Roosevelt (US President 1933–45); 70c. General Douglas MacArthur; 77c. Harry Truman (US President 1945–53); 80c. Admiral Chester W. Nimitz; $3.20 Jimmy Carter (US President 1977–81); $12.25 President John F. Kennedy.

154 Leatherback Turtle

1999. Endangered Reptiles and Amphibians. Multicoloured.
1405 33c. Type **154** 40 30
1406 33c. Kemp's Ridley turtle 40 30
1407 33c. Green turtles 40 30
1408 33c. Marine iguana 40 30
1409 33c. Table Mountain ghost frog 40 30
1410 33c. Spiny turtle 40 30
1411 33c. Hewitt's ghost frog 40 30
1412 33c. Geometric tortoise 40 30
1413 33c. Limestone salamander 40 30
1414 33c. Desert rain frog 40 30
1415 33c. Cape plantanna 40 30
1416 33c. Long-toed tree frog 40 30

155 Caroline Islands 1901 5 and 20pf. Stamps and Golsdorf Steam Railway Locomotive

1999. "iBRA '99" International Stamp Exhibition, Nuremberg, Germany. Multicoloured.
1418 55c. Type **155** 70 55
1419 55c. Caroline Islands 1901 5m. yacht stamp and carriage of Leipzig–Dresden Railway 70 55

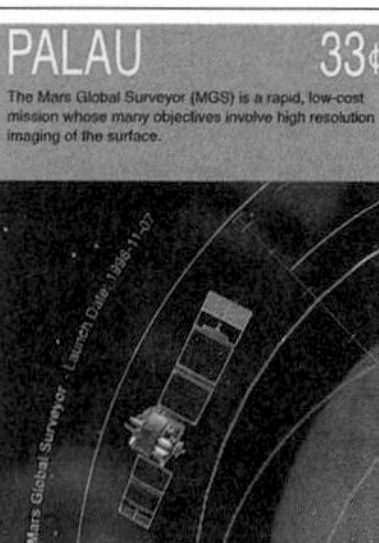

156 "Mars Global Surveyor" in Orbit

1999. Space Missions to Mars. Multicoloured.
1421 33c. Type **156** 40 30
1422 33c. "Mars Climate" Orbiter 40 30
1423 33c. "Mars Polar" Lander 40 30
1424 33c. "Deep Space 2" 40 30
1425 33c. "Mars Surveyor 2001" Orbiter 40 30
1426 33c. "Mars Surveyor 2001" Lander 40 30
Nos. 1421/6 were issued together, se-tenant, forming a composite design.

157 "Banza natida"

1999. Earth Day. Pacific Insects. Multicoloured.
1428 33c. Type **157** 40 30
1429 33c. "Drosophila heteroneura" (fruit-fly) 40 30
1430 33c. "Nesomicromus lagus" 40 30
1431 33c. "Megalagrian leptodemus" 40 30
1432 33c. "Pseudopsectra cookeorum" 40 30
1433 33c. "Ampheida neocaledonia" 40 30
1434 33c. "Pseudopsectra swezeyi" 40 30
1435 33c. "Deinacrida heteracantha" 40 30
1436 33c. Beech forest butterfly 40 30
1437 33c. Hercules moth 40 30
1438 33c. Striped sphinx moth 40 30
1439 33c. Tussock butterfly 40 30
1440 33c. Weevil 40 30
1441 33c. Bush cricket 40 30
1442 33c. Longhorn beetle 40 30
1443 33c. "Abathrus bicolor" 40 30
1444 33c. "Stylogymnusa subantartica" 40 30
1445 33c. Moth butterfly 40 30
1446 33c. "Paraconosoma naviculare" 40 30
1447 33c. Cairn's birdwing ("Ornithoptera priamus") 40 30

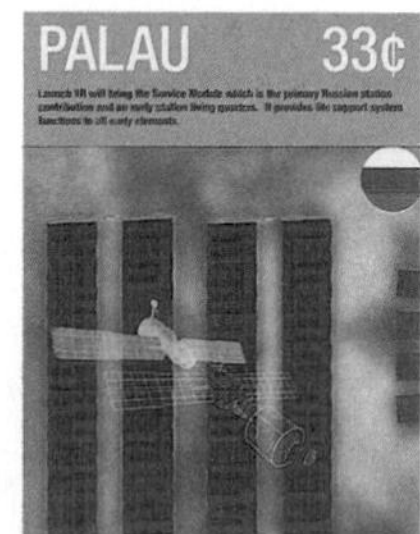

158 Launch 1R (living quarters)

1999. International Space Station, 1998–2004. Multicoloured.
1448 33c. Type **158** 40 30
1449 33c. Launch 14A (final solar arrays) 40 30
1450 33c. Launch 8A (mechanical arm) 40 30
1451 33c. Launch 1J (Japanese experiment module) 40 30
1452 33c. Launch 1E (Colombus Orbital Facility laboratory) 40 30
1453 33c. Launch 16A (habitation module) 40 30

159 William Gibson **161** Queen Mother and Attendants

160 "Women Divers"

1999. The Information Age: Visionaries in the Twentieth Century. Multicoloured.

No.	Description	Mint	Used
1455	33c. Type **159**	40	30
1456	33c. Danny Hillis	40	30
1457	33c. Steve Wozntak	40	30
1458	33c. Steve Jobs	40	30
1459	33c. Nolan Bushnell	40	30
1460	33c. John Warnock	40	30
1461	33c. Ken Thompson	40	30
1462	33c. Al Shugart	40	30
1463	33c. Rand and Robyn Miller	40	30
1464	33c. Nicolas Negroponte	40	30
1465	33c. Bill Gates	40	30
1466	33c. Arthur C. Clarke	40	30
1467	33c. Marshall McLuhan	40	30
1468	33c. Thomas Watson Jr	40	30
1469	33c. Gordon Moore	40	30
1470	33c. James Gosling	40	30
1471	33c. Sabeer Bhatia and Jack Smith	40	30
1472	33c. Esther Dyson	40	30
1473	33c. Jerry Young and David Filo	40	30
1474	33c. Jeff Bezos	40	30
1475	33c. Bob Kahn	40	30
1476	33c. Jaron Lanier	40	30
1477	33c. Andy Grove	40	30
1478	33c. Jim Clark	40	30
1479	33c. Bob Metcalfe	40	30

1999. 150th Death Anniv of Katsushika Hokusai (Japanese artist). Multicoloured.

No.	Description	Mint	Used
1480	33c. Type **160**	40	30
1481	33c. "Bull and Parasol"	40	30
1482	33c. Drawing of bare-breasted woman	40	30
1483	33c. Drawing of fully-clothed woman (sitting)	40	30
1484	33c. "Japanese Spaniel"	40	30
1485	33c. "Porter in Landscape"	40	30
1486	33c. "Bacchanalian Revelry" (musician in bottom right corner)	40	30
1487	33c. "Bacchanalian Revelry" (different)	40	30
1488	33c. Drawing of woman (crouching)	40	30
1489	33c. Drawing of woman (reclining on floor)	40	30
1490	33c. "Ox-herd" (ox)	40	30
1491	33c. "Ox-herd" (man on bridge)	40	30

1999. "Queen Elizabeth the Queen Mother's Century".

No.	Description	Mint	Used
1493	**161** 60c. black and gold	75	55
1494	– 60c. black and gold	75	55
1495	– 60c. multicoloured	75	55
1496	– 60c. multicoloured	75	55

DESIGNS: No. 1494, Queen Mother with corgi; 1495, Queen Mother in pink coat and hat; 1496, Queen Mother in yellow evening dress and tiara.

162 Launch of Rocket

1999. 30th Anniv of First Manned Moon Landing. Multicoloured.

No.	Description	Mint	Used
1498	33c. Type **162**	40	30
1499	33c. Spacecraft above Earth and Moon's surface	40	30
1500	33c. Astronaut descending ladder	40	30
1501	33c. Distant view of rocket launch	40	30
1502	33c. Astronaut planting flag on Moon	40	30
1503	33c. "Apollo 11" crew members	40	30

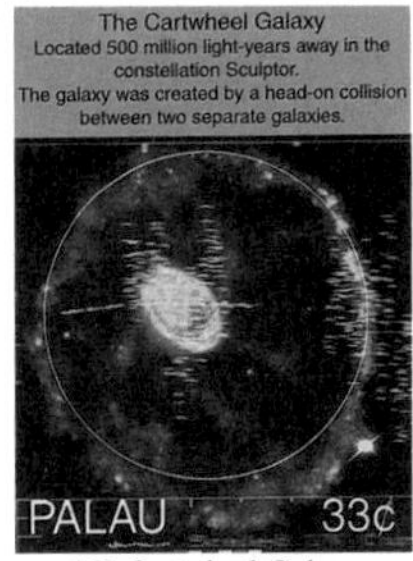

163 Cartwheel Galaxy

1999. Images from Space: Hubble Telescope. Multicoloured.

No.	Description	Mint	Used
1505	33c. Type **163**	40	30
1506	33c. Stingray Nebula	40	30
1507	33c. Planetary Nebula NGC 3918	40	30
1508	33c. Cat's Eye Nebula	40	30
1509	33c. Galaxy NGC 7742	40	30
1510	33c. Eight-burst Nebula	40	30

164 Calves and Chickens

165 "Keep Safe"

1999. Christmas. "Puer Nobis" (carol). Mult.

No.	Description	Mint	Used
1512	20c. Type **164**	25	20
1513	20c. Donkey, geese and rabbit	25	20
1514	20c. Child Jesus, cats and lambs	25	20
1515	20c. Geese, goat and sheep	25	20
1516	20c. Donkey and cockerel	25	20

Nos. 1512/16 were issued together, se-tenant, forming a composite design.

1999. "How to Love Your Dog". Multicoloured.

No.	Description	Mint	Used
1517	33c. Type **165**	40	30
1518	33c. Girl with puppies (Show affection)	40	30
1519	33c. Dog asleep (A place of one's own)	40	30
1520	33c. Girl with Scottish terrier (Communicate)	40	30
1521	33c. Dog eating (Good food)	40	30
1522	33c. Vet examining dog (Annual check-up)	40	30
1523	33c. Girl with prone dog (Teach rules)	40	30
1524	33c. Dog with disc (Exercise and play)	40	30
1525	33c. Dog with basket (Let him help)	40	30
1526	33c. Dog with heart on collar (Unconditional love)	40	30

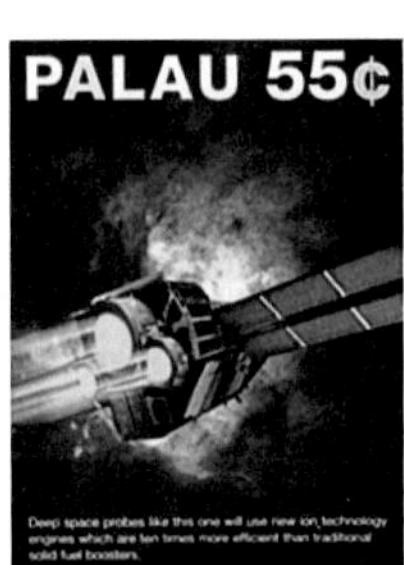

166 Deep Space Probe

2000. Projected Space Probes. Multicoloured.

No.	Description	Mint	Used
1528	55c. Type **166**	80	50
1529	55c. Piggy back probe	80	50
1530	55c. Deep space telescope probe	80	50
1531	55c. Space probe on course to rendezvous with comet	80	50
1532	55c. Yellow space probe orbiting planet	80	50
1533	55c. Deep space probe with advanced onboard artificial intelligence	80	50

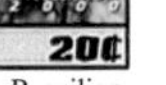

167 Native Brazilian Indians, 1800

168 Lech Walesa and Shipyard Workers

2000. New Millennium (1st series). The Nineteenth Century 1800–1850. Multicoloured.

No.	Description	Mint	Used
1535	20c. Type **167**	30	20
1536	20c. Broken manacles (Haiti slave revolt, 1800)	30	20
1537	20c. Napoleon I (assumption of title of Emperor of France, 1804)	30	20
1538	20c. Shaka (Zulu leader)	30	20
1539	20c. Monster (publication of *Frankenstein* (novel) by Mary Shelley, 1818)	30	20
1540	20c. Simon Bolivar (revolutionary)	30	20
1541	20c. Camera (development of photography)	30	20
1542	20c. Dripping tap (introduction of water purification system, 1829)	30	20
1543	20c. Steam locomotive (inauguration in Great Britain of first passenger-carrying railway, 1830)	30	20
1544	20c. Discovery of electromagnetic induction by Michael Faraday, 1831	30	20
1545	20c. First use of anaesthesia in surgery by Crawford Williamson Long, 1842	30	20
1546	20c. Morse key (transmission of first message by Samuel Morse, 1844)	30	20
1547	20c. Poster (first convention on Women's Rights, Seneca Falls, U.S.A., 1848)	30	20
1548	20c. Karl Marx (publication of the *Communist Manifesto*), 1848	30	20
1549	20c. Charles Darwin's (naturalist) voyage on *Beagle* (56 × 36 mm)	30	20
1550	20c. Revolution in Germany, 1848	30	20
1551	20c. Commencement of Taiping Rebellion, China, 1850	30	20

There are a number of errors in the stamp inscriptions and descriptions.

See also Nos. 1552/68, 1691/1702 and 1741/57.

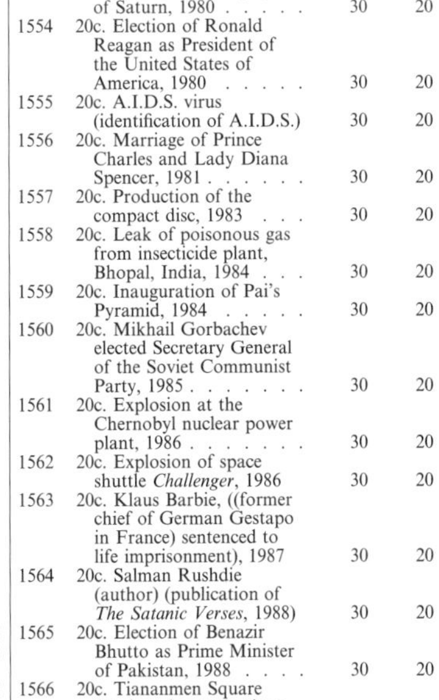

2000. New Millennium (2nd series). The Twentieth Century 1980–1989. Multicoloured.

No.	Description	Mint	Used
1552	20c. Type **168** (foundation of Solidarity (trade union), 1980)	30	20
1553	20c. First photographic image taken by *Voyager I* of Saturn, 1980	30	20
1554	20c. Election of Ronald Reagan as President of the United States of America, 1980	30	20
1555	20c. A.I.D.S. virus (identification of A.I.D.S.)	30	20
1556	20c. Marriage of Prince Charles and Lady Diana Spencer, 1981	30	20
1557	20c. Production of the compact disc, 1983	30	20
1558	20c. Leak of poisonous gas from insecticide plant, Bhopal, India, 1984	30	20
1559	20c. Inauguration of Pai's Pyramid, 1984	30	20
1560	20c. Mikhail Gorbachev elected Secretary General of the Soviet Communist Party, 1985	30	20
1561	20c. Explosion at the Chernobyl nuclear power plant, 1986	30	20
1562	20c. Explosion of space shuttle *Challenger*, 1986	30	20
1563	20c. Klaus Barbie, ((former chief of German Gestapo in France) sentenced to life imprisonment), 1987	30	20
1564	20c. Salman Rushdie (author) (publication of *The Satanic Verses*, 1988)	30	20
1565	20c. Election of Benazir Bhutto as Prime Minister of Pakistan, 1988	30	20
1566	20c. Tiananmen Square (student demonstrations, 1989)	30	20
1567	20c. Demonstrators breaching Berlin Wall, 1989 (59 × 39 mm)	30	20
1568	20c. Development of the World Wide Web	30	20

170 Bill Clinton (1992–2000)

171 Australopithecine (Southern Ape species, Africa)

2000. Former United States Presidents.

No.	Description	Mint	Used
1570	**170** $1 black and brown	1·40	85
1571	– $2 black and blue	2·75	1·60
1572	– $3 black and mauve	4·25	2·50
1574	– $5 black and brown	7·00	4·25
1575	– $11.75 black and brown (40 × 23 mm)	17·00	10·00

DESIGNS: $2 Ronald Reagan (1980–88); $3 Gerald Ford (1974–76); $5 George Bush (1988–92); $11.75 John F. Kennedy (1960–63).

2000. Pre-historic Discoveries of the 20th-Century. Multicoloured.

No.	Description	Mint	Used
1580	20c. Type **171**	25	15
1581	20c. Australopithecine skull	25	15
1582	20c. Homo habilis using hand axe	25	15
1583	20c. Hand-axe	25	15
1584	20c. Homo habilis skull	25	15
1585	20c. Australo pithecine skeleton "Lucy"	25	15
1586	20c. Archaic Homo sapien skull	25	15
1587	20c. Diapithicine skull	25	15
1588	20c. Homo erectus family	25	15
1589	20c. Wood hut	25	15
1590	20c. Australopithecine ethopis skull	25	15
1591	20c. Homo sapien	25	15
1592	20c. Homo sapien skull	25	15
1593	20c. Discovery of Taung Baby, 1924	25	15
1594	20c. Homo erectus skull	25	15
1595	20c. Louis Leaky (archaeologist)	25	15
1596	20c. Neanderthal skull	25	15
1597	20c. Neanderthal man	25	15
1598	20c. Development of the fully bipedal foot	25	15
1599	20c. Raymond Dart (discoverer of Taung Baby)	25	15

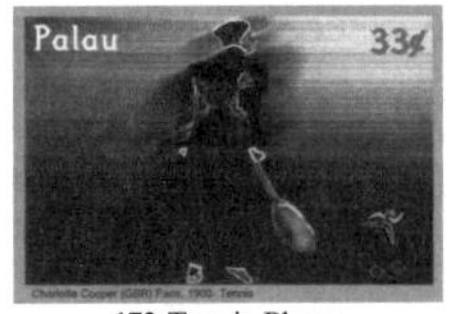

172 Tennis Player

2000. Olympic Games, Sydney. Multicoloured.

No.	Description	Mint	Used
1600	33c. Type **172**	40	25
1601	33c. Shot put	40	25
1602	33c. Greek flag and stadium	40	25
1603	33c. Ancient Olympic athletes	40	25

173 Re-usable Launch Vehicle

2000. Projected Unmanned Craft and Space Exploration. Multicoloured.

No.	Description	Mint	Used
1604	33c. Type **173**	40	25
1605	33c. Single stage vertical take-off craft	40	25
1606	33c. Robotic rocket plane	40	25
1607	33c. Single-stage craft	40	25
1608	33c. Fully-automated deep-space exploration craft	40	25
1609	33c. Magnetohydrodynamics-powered launch craft	40	25
MS1610	Four sheets, each 100 × 135 mm. (a) $2 Spacecraft taking-off (privately funded launch craft); (b) $2 Emergency crew return craft using parachutes (horiz); (c) $2 Interplanetary space craft (horiz); (d) $2 Space shuttle leaving space station	5·50	5·50

174 Banded Crake (*Rallina eurizonoides*)

2000. Birds. Multicoloured.
1611 20c. Type **174** 25 15
1612 20c. Micronesian kingfisher (*Halcyon cinnamomina*) . . 25 15
1613 20c. Little pied cormorant (*Phalacrocorax melanoleucos*) 25 15
1614 20c. Eastern reef heron (*Egretta sacra*) 25 15
1615 20c. Nicobar pigeon (*Caloenas nicobarica*) . . 25 15
1616 20c. Rufous night heron (*Nycticorax caledonicus*) 25 15
1617 33c. Palau ground dove (*Gallicolumba canifrons*) 40 25
1618 33c. Palau scops owl (*Pyrroglaux podargina*) . . 40 25
1619 33c. Mangrove flycatcher (*Cyornis rufigastra*) (wrongly inscr "Pyrrboglaux podargina") 40 25
1620 33c. Palau bushwarbler (*Cettia annae*) 40 25
1621 33c. Palau fantail (*Rhipidura lepida*) 40 25
1622 33c. Morning bird (*Cellurincincla tenebrosa*) 40 25
MS1623 Two sheets, each 76×126 mm. (a) $2 Palau whiteeye (*Megazosterops palauensis*) (horiz); (b) $2 Palau fruitdove (*Ptilinopus pelewensis*) (horiz) . . . . 4·75 4·75

No. 1611 is inscribed "Slatey-legged Crake" and No. 1614 "Pacific reef egret" both in error. There are also several errors in the Latin names.

175 Booker T. Washington (educationist)

2000. 20th-Century Personalities. Multicoloured.
1624 33c. Type **175** 40 25
1625 33c. Buckmeister Fuller (inventor and designer) . . 40 25
1626 33c. Marie Curie (physicist) 40 25
1627 33c. Walt Disney (animator and producer) 40 25
1629 33c. Franklin D. Roosevelt (32nd United States President) 40 25
1629 33c. Henry Ford (car manufacturer) 40 25
1630 33c. Betty Friedan (author and feminist leader) . . . 40 25
1631 33c. Sigmund Freud (founder of psychoanalysis) 40 25
1632 33c. Mahatma Ghandi (Indian leader) 40 25
1633 33c. Mikhail Gorbachev (Soviet President) 40 25
1633 33c. Stephan Hawkings (theoretical physicist) . . 40 25
1635 33c. Martin Luther King Jr. (civil rights leader) . . . 40 25
1636 33c. Toni Morrison (writer) 40 25
1637 33c. Georgia O'Keeffe (artist) 40 25
1638 33c. Rosa Parks (civil rights activist) 40 25
1639 33c. Carl Sagan (astronomer) 40 25
1640 33c. Jonas Salk (immunologist) 40 25
1641 33c. Sally Ride (astronaut and astrophysicist) . . . 40 25
1642 33c. Nikola Tesla (electrical engineer and physicist) . . 40 25
1643 33c. Wilbur and Orville Wright (aviation pioneer) 40 25

176 Reef Bass (*Pseudogramma gregoryi*)

2000. Marine Life of the Atlantic and Pacific Oceans. Multicoloured.
1644 20c. Type **176** 25 15
1645 20c. Great white shark (*Carcharodon carcharias*) 25 15
1646 20c. Sharptail eel (*Myrichthys breviceps*) . . 25 15
1647 20c. Sailfish (*Istiophorus platypterus*) 25 15
1648 20c. Southern stingray (*Dasyatis americana*) . . . 25 15
1649 20c. Ocean triggerfish (*Canthidermis sufflamen*) 25 15
1650 55c. Scalloped hammerhead (*Sphyrna lewini*) (vert) . . 65 40
1651 55c. White-tipped reef shark (*Triaenodon obesus*) (vert) 65 40
1652 55c. Moon jellyfish (*Aurelia aurita*) (vert) 65 40
1653 55c. Lionfish (*Pterois volitans*) (vert) 65 40
1654 55c. Seahorse (*Hippocampus abdominalis*) (vert) 65 40
1655 55c. Spotted eagle ray (*Aetobatus narinari*) (vert) 65 40
MS1656 Two sheets, each 110×85 mm. (a) $2 Short bigeye (*Pristigenys alta*) (vert); (b) $2 Gaff-topsail catfish (*Bagre marinus*) (vert) . . . . 4·75 4·75

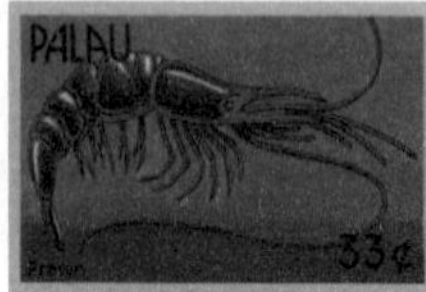

177 Prawn

2000. Marine Life. Multicoloured.
1657 33c. Type **177** 40 25
1658 33c. Deep sea angler 40 25
1659 33c. Rooster fish 40 25
1660 33c. Grenadier 40 25
1661 33c. *Platyberix opalescens* 40 25
1662 33c. Lantern fish 40 25
1663 33c. Emperor angelfish . . . 40 25
1664 33c. Nautilus 40 25
1665 33c. Moorish idol 40 25
1666 33c. Seahorse 40 25
1667 33c. Clown triggerfish . . . 40 25
1668 33c. Clown fish 40 25
MS1669 Two sheets, each 106×75 mm. (a) $2 Giant squid; (b) $2 Manta ray . . . . . . 4·75 4·75

178 James Watson (co-discoverer of structure of D.N.A.)

2000. Advances in Science and Medicine. Multicoloured.
1670 33c. Type **178** 40 25
1671 33c. Har Gobing Khorana and Robert Holley (work on genetic code) 40 25
1672 33c. Hamilton Smith and Werner Arber (discovered restriction enzymes) . . . 40 25
1673 33c. Centrifugation machine and D.N.A. double helix 40 25
1674 33c. Richard Roberts (discovered R.N.A. splicing and split genes) 40 25
1675 33c. Maurice Wilkins (co-discoverer of structure of D.N.A.) 40 25
1676 33c. D.N.A. double helix . . 40 25
1677 33c. Frederick Sanger and Walter Gilbert (developed methods for determining nucleotide sequences for D.N.A. molecules) . . . 40 25
1678 33c. Kary Mullis (discovered polymerase chain reaction) 40 25
1679 33c. D.N.A. double helix and frogs (mapping location of genes) 40 25
1680 33c. Francis Crick (co-discoverer of structure of D.N.A.) 40 25
1681 33c. Marshall Nirenberg (work on genetic code) . . 40 25
1682 33c. Daniel Nathans (discovered restriction enzymes) 40 25
1683 33c. Harold Varmus and Michael Bishop (identified several genes involved in cancer) 40 25
1684 33c. Phillip Sharp (discovered polymerase chain reaction) 40 25
1685 33c. Sheep (cloning sheep to produce Dolly, 1997) . . 40 25
1686 33c. D.N.A. being separated by electrophoresis 40 25
1687 33c. Paul Berg (first developed methods for cloning genes, 1980) . . . 40 25
1688 33c. Michael Smith and D.N.A. (discovered polymerase chain reaction) 40 25
1689 33c. D.N.A. and deer (human genome project) 40 25
MS1690 Two sheets, each 97×117 mm. (a) $2 Dolly (cloned sheep) (37×50 mm). (b) $2 D.N.A. and deer (37×50 mm) 4·75 4·75

179 Hourglass and Map of South East Asia

2000. New Millennium (3rd series). Multicoloured.
1691 20c. Type **179** 25 15
1692 20c. Hourglass and map of North America 25 15
1693 20c. Hourglass and map of Europe 25 15
1694 20c. Hourglass and map of Australia 25 15
1695 20c. Hourglass and map of South America 25 15
1696 20c. Hourglass and map of Africa 25 15
1697 55c. Clock face and clouds (vert) 35 20
1698 55c. Clock face and building faÇade (vert) 35 20
1699 55c. Clock face and coastline (vert) 35 20
1700 55c. Clock face and farm buildings (vert) 35 20
1701 55c. Clock face and forest (vert) 35 20
1702 55c. Clock face and desert (vert) 35 20

180 American Bald Eagle **181** Rhamphorhynchus

2000. Endangered Species. Multicoloured.
1703 33c. Type **180** 40 25
1704 33c. Small whorled pogonia 40 25
1705 33c. Arctic peregrine falcon 40 25
1706 33c. Golden lion tamarin . . 40 25
1707 33c. American alligator . . 40 25
1708 33c. Brown pelican 40 25
1709 33c. Aleutian Canada goose 40 25
1710 33c. Western grey kangaroo 40 25
1711 33c. Palau scops owl 40 25
1712 33c. Jocotoco antpitta . . . 40 25
1713 33c. Orchid 40 25
1714 33c. Red lechwe 40 25
MS1715 Two sheets, each 120×92 mm. (a) $2 Lahontan cutthroat trout (horiz); (b) $2 Leopard . . . . 4·75 4·75

2000. Dinosaurs. Multicoloured.
1716 33c. Type **181** 40 25
1717 33c. Ceratosaurus 40 25
1718 33c. Apatosaurus 40 25
1719 33c. Stegosaurus 40 25
1720 33c. Archaeopteryx 40 25
1721 33c. Allosaurus 40 25
1722 33c. Parasaurolophus . . . 40 25
1723 33c. Pteranodonrus 40 25
1724 33c. Tyrannosaurus 40 25
1725 33c. Triceratops 40 25
1726 33c. Ankylosaurus 40 25
1727 33c. Velociraptor 40 25
MS1728 Two sheets, each 94×71 mm. (a) $2 Jurassic landscape; (b) $2 Cretaceous landscape . . . . 4·75 4·75

Nos. 1716/21 and 1722/7 were each issued together, se-tenant, forming a composite design.

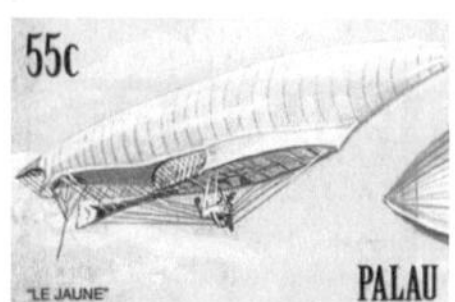

182 Lebaudy–Juillot Airship Le Jaune

2000. Centenary of First Zeppelin Flight and Airship Development. Multicoloured.
1729 55c. Type **182** 40 25
1730 55c. Forlanini airship *Leonardo DaVinci* 40 25
1731 55c. Thomas Baldwin's airship U.S. Military No. 1, 1908 . . . . . . 40 25
1732 55c. Astra-Torres 1 . . . . 40 25
1733 55c. Rear of Astra-Torres 1 and Parseval PL VII . . . 40 25
1734 55c. Rear of Parseval PL VII and Lebaudy airship *Liberte* **MS**1735 Two sheets, each 110×85 mm. (a) $2 Santos-Dumont airship Ballon No. 9 La Badaleuse; (b) $2 Santos-Dumont Ballon No. 6 circling Eiffel Tower . . . 4·75 4·75

Nos. 1729/34 were issued together, se-tenant, forming a composite design.

183 Duke and Duchess of York **184** Viking Diver attacking Danish Ship

2000. 100th Birthday of Queen Elizabeth the Queen Mother. Multicoloured.
1736 55c. Type **183** 40 25
1737 55c. As Duchess of York wearing cloche hat . . . 40 25
1738 55c. Wearing green floral hat 40 25
1739 55c. Wearing blue hat . . . 40 25
MS1740 99×84 mm. $2 Wearing yellow coat and hat . . . . . 1·25 1·25

2000. New Millennium (4th series). Development of Diving Equipment. Multicoloured.
1741 33c. Type **184** 40 25
1742 33c. Issa (12th-century Arab diver) 40 25
1743 33c.15 th-century salvage diver using breathing tube 40 25
1744 33c. 17 th-century diver wearing leather suit and carrying halberd 40 25
1745 33c. Edmund Halley's wooden diving bell, 1690 40 25
1746 33c. David Bushnell's diving bell Turtle, 1776 . . . . 40 25
1747 33c. Diver wearing suit and Siebe helmet,1819 . . . . 40 25
1748 33c. *Hunley* (Confederate submarine) 40 25
1749 33c. Argonaut (first underwater salvage vehicle), 1899 . . . . . . 40 25
1750 33c. John Williamson's underwater filming vehicle photosphere, 1914 . . . . 40 25
1751 33c. Diver wearing brass helmet, weighted boots, with air supply and safety lines (circa 1930) 40 25
1752 33c. William Beebe and Otis Barton's bathysphere, 1934 . . . . 40 25
1753 33c. Coelacanth (prehistoric fish previously thought extinct) 40 25
1754 33c. Italian divers on chariot planting explosive charges on ship hull during World War II 40 25
1755 33c. *Trieste* (bathyscaphe) (record dive by Jaques Picard and Lt. Don Walsh, 1960) 40 25
1756 33c. *Alvin* (submersible) surveying thermal vents in Galapagos Rift (1977) (60×40 mm) 40 25
1757 33c. Sylvia Earle wearing Jim Suit, 1979 . . . . . 40 25

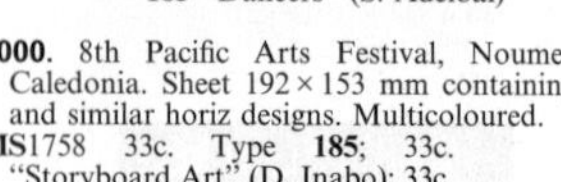

185 "Dancers" (S. Adelbai)

2000. 8th Pacific Arts Festival, Noumea, New Caledonia. Sheet 192×153 mm containing T **185** and similar horiz designs. Multicoloured.
MS1758 33c. Type **185**; 33c. "Storyboard Art" (D. Inabo); 33c. "Traditional Money" (M. Takeshi); 33c. "Clay Lamp and Bowl" (W. Watanabe); 33c. "Meeting House" (P. Tiakl); "Outrigger Canoe" (S. Adelbai); 33c. "Weaver" (M. Vitarelli); 33c. "Rock Island Scene" (W. Marcil); 33c. "Contemporary Music" (J. Imetuker) . . . . 2·75 2·75

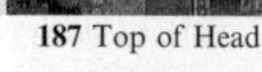

186 Turtle Shell Bracelet **187** Top of Head

2000. 45th Anniv of Belau National Museum. Multicoloured.

1759	33c. Type **186**	35	20
1760	33c. Bust (sculpture) (H. Hijikata)	35	20
1761	33c. "Turtle Shell Women's Money"	35	20
1762	33c. "Cherecheroi" (T. Suzuki)	35	20
1763	33c. Money jar (B. Sylvester)	35	20
1764	33c. "Prince Lebu" (Ichikawa)	35	20
1765	33c. "Beach at Lild" (H. Hijikata)	35	20
1766	33c. Traditional mask	35	20
1767	33c. Taro platter (T. Rebluud)	35	20
1768	33c. "Meresebang" (Ichikawa)	35	20
1769	33c. Woman and child (sculpture) (B. Sylvester)	35	20
1770	33c. "Birth Ceremony" (I. Kishigawa)	35	20

2000. 80th Birthday of Pope John Paul II. Sheet 158 × 243 mm containing T **187** and similar vert designs showing collage of miniature religious photographs. Multicoloured, country inscription and face value at left (a) or right (b).
MS1771 50c. Type **187**; 50c. Ear (a); 50c. Neck and collar (a); 50c. Shoulder (a); 50c. Forehead (b); 50c. Forehead and eye (b); 50c. Nose and cheek (b); 50c. Hands (b) 4·50 4·50

No. **MS**1771 was issued with the stamps arranged in two vertical columns separated by a gutter also containing miniature photographs. When viewed as a whole, the miniature sheet forms a portrait of Pope John Paul II.

188 Face enclosed by Snake

2000. Chinese New Year. Year of the Snake. Two sheets, each 69 × 99 mm containing T **188** and similar horiz design.
MS1772 (a) 60c. Type **188**; (b) 60c. Face with snake head-dress 1·30 1·30

189 Indian Red Admiral (*Vanessa indica*)

2000. Butterflies. Multicoloured.

1773	33c. Type **189**	35	20
1774	33c. Chequered swallowtail (*Papilio demoleus*)	35	20
1775	33c. Yamfly (*Loxura atymnus*)	35	20
1776	33c. Fiery jewel (*Hypochrysops ignite*)	35	20

MS1777 Four sheets. (a) 119 × 134 mm. 33c. Cairn's birdwing (*Ornithoptera priamus*); 33c. Meadow argus (*Junonia villida*); 33c. Orange albatross (*Appias nero*); 33c. Glasswing (*Acraea andromacha*); 33c. Beak butterfly (*Libythea geoffroyi*); 33c. Great eggfly (*Hypolimnas bolina*); (b) 119 × 134 mm. 33c. Large green-banded blue (*Danis danis*); 33c. Union jack (*Delias mysis*); 33c. Broad-bordered grass yellow (*Eurema brigitta*); 33c. Striped blue crow (*Euploea mulciber*); 33c. Red lacewing (*Cethosia bibles*); 33c. Palmfly (*Elyminias hypermnestra*) (inscr "Elyminas agondas"); (c) 107 × 77 mm. $2 Clipper (*Parthenos Sylvia*); (d) 107 × 77 mm. $2 Blue triangle (*Graphium sarpedon*) 8·50 8·50

190 Little Kingfisher

2000. Flora and Fauna. Four sheets containing T **190** and similar multicoloured designs.
MS1778 (a) 132 × 80 mm. 33c. Type **190**; 33c. Mangrove snake; 33c. Bats and breadfruit; 33c. Giant tree frog; 33c. Giant centipede; 33c. Crab-eating macaque; (b) 90 × 112 mm. 33c. Giant spiral ginger; 33c. Good luck plant; 33c. Leaves and green coconuts; 33c. Orchid and butterfly; 33c. Crocodile; 33c. Orchid; (c) 120 × 93 mm. $2 Claw and mouth of land crab (vert); (d) 119 × 93 mm. $2 Head and fin of fish 6·00 6·00

2001. As T **153** with additional imprint date at foot. Multicoloured.

1779	1c. Type **153**	10	10
1780	11c. As No. 1389	10	10
1781	60c. As No.1395	65	40

191 "Washing the Copybook" (Torii Kiyomitsu) **192** *Teracotona euprepia*

2001. Japanese Art. Six sheets containing T **191** and similar vert designs. Multicoloured.
MS1795 (a) 161 × 120 mm. 60c. × 5 Type **191**; "Woman playing Shamisen and woman reading letter" (Iwasa Matabei); "Ichikawa Danjuro (actor) as Samurai" (Katsukawa Shunsho); "Gentleman entertained by courtesans" (Torrii Kiyonaga); "Geisha at teahouse" (Torrii Kiyonaga); (b) 161 × 120 mm. 60c. × 5 "Preparing Sashimi" (Kitagawa Utamaro); "Sanogawa Ichimatsu and Onoe Kikugoro (actors) in Plum Blossoms and Young Herbs" (Ishikawa Toyonobu); "Courtesan adjusting her comb" (Kaigetsudo Dohan); "Nakamura Tomijuro (actor) as woman dancing" (Katsukawa Shunsho); "Woman with poem card and writing brush" (Yashima Gakutei); (c) 187 × 113 mm. 60c. × 6 "Kitano Shrine, Kyoto" (Anon.); (d) 91 × 104 mm. $2 "Raiko attacks demon kite" (detail, Totoya Hokkei); (e) 123 × 105 mm. $2 "Beauty writing letter" (detail, Kaigetsudo Doshin) (28 × 42 mm); (e) 150 × 102 mm. $2 "Fireworks at Ikenohata" (detail, Kobayashi Kiyochika) (28 × 42 mm) 17·00 17·00

No. **MS**1795c was made up of six stamps, each stamp forming part of the composite design of the painting.

2001. Moths. Multicoloured.

1796	20c. Type **192**	20	15
1797	21c. Basker (*Euchromia lethe*)	20	15
1798	80c. White-lined sphinx (*Hyles lineate*)	45	30
1799	$1 Isabella Tiger Moth (*Pyrrharctia Isabella*) (Inscr "Pyrrrharctia")	1·10	65

MS1800 (a) 133 × 115 mm. 34c. × 6 Cinnabar moth (*Tyria jacobeae*); Beautiful tiger moth (*Amphicallia bellatrix*); Garden tiger moth (*Arctia caja*); *Zygaena occitanica*; Jersey tiger moth (*Euplagia quadripunctaria*); *Utetheisa ornatrix*; (b) 133 × 115 mm. 70c. × 6 Milionia isodoxa (inscr "Milonia"); *Cephonodes kingi*; *Anaphe panda*; Io moth (*Automeris io*); Tau emperor (*Aglia tau*); Lime hawk moth (*Mimas tiliae*); (c) 98 × 71 mm. $2 Owl moth (*Brahmaea wallichii*); (d) 98 × 71 mm. $2 Isabel moth (*Graellsia isabellae*) (inscr "Graaellsia") 10·50 10·50

193 Ivo Andric (1961) **194** Communal Meeting House (Bai)

2001. Centenary of the First Nobel Prize for Literature. Six sheets containing T **193** and similar vert designs. Multicoloured.
MS1801 (a) 148 × 209 mm. 34c. × 6 Type **193**; Eyvind Johnson (1974); Salvatore Quasimodo (1959); Mikhael Sholokhov (1965); Pablo Neruda (1971); Saul Bellow (1976); (b) 148 × 209 mm. 70c. × 6 Boris Pasternak (1958); Francois Mauriac (1952); Frans Eemil Sillanpaa (1939); Roger Martin du Gard (1937); Pearl Buck (1938); Andre Gide (1947); (c) 148 × 209 mm. 80c. × 6 Karl Gjellerup (1917); Anatole France (1921); Sinclair Lewis (1930); Jacinto Benavente (1922); John Galsworthy (1932); Erik A. Karlfeldt (1931); (d) 108 × 128 mm. $2 Bertrand Russell (1950); (e) 108 × 128 mm. $2 Luigi Pirandello (1934); (f) 108 × 128 mm. $2 Harry Martinson (1974) 18·00 18·00

2001. Christmas. Multicoloured.

1802	20c. Type **194**	20	15
1803	34c. No. 1786	35	20

195 Foot and Football (1950) **197** Yellow-faced Mynah (*Mino dumontii*)

196 "Groom taking Horses to Pasture" (Han Kan)

2001. History of Football World Cup Championships. Poster Designs. Four sheets containing T **195** and similar vert designs. Multicoloured.
MS1804 (a) 154 × 109 mm. 34c. × 6 Type **195**; Goalkeeper and ball (1954); Ball enclosed in scarf of flags (1958); Globe and ball (1962); Championship mascot (1966); Silhouette of ball (1970); (b) 154 × 109 mm. Player with raised arms (1978); Stylized player (1982); Silhouette of player against statues (1986); Amphitheatre (1990); "94", ball and player (1994); Championship emblem (1998); (c) 88 × 75 mm. $2 Trophy (detail); (d) 88 × 75 mm. $2 "Uruguay" (1930) 11·00 11·00

2001. Sheet 200 × 136 mm containing T **196**. Multicoloured.
MS1805 60c. × 4 Type **196** 1·75 1·75

2001. Birds. Four sheets containing T **197** and similar vert designs. Multicoloured.
MS1806 (a) 120 × 120 mm. 55c. × 6 Type **197**; Red-breasted pitta (*Pitta erythogaster*); Red-bearded Bee-eater (*Nyctyornis amictus*); Superb fruit dove (*Ptilinopus superbus*); Coppersmith barbet (*Megalaima haemacephala*); Diard's trogon (*Harpactes diardii*); (b) 120 × 120 mm. 60c. × 6 Spectacled monarch (*Monarcha trivirgatus*); Blue-tailed pitta (*Pitta guajana*) (inscr "Banded pitta"); Rufous-backed kingfisher (*Ceyx rufidorsa*); Scarlet robin (*Petroica multicolour*); Golden whistler (*Pachycephala pectoralis*); Mid-mountain rail babbler (*Ptilorrhoa castanonota*) (inscr "Jewel babbler"); (c) 105 × 75 mm. $2 River kingfisher (*Alcedo atthis*); (d) 105 × 75 mm. $2 Asiatic paradise flycatcher (*Tersiphone paradise*) 12·00 12·00

PALESTINE Pt. 1

A territory at the extreme east of the Mediterranean Sea, captured from the Turks by Great Britain in 1917 and under Military Occupation until 1920. It was a British Mandate of the League of Nations from 1923 to May 1948 when the State of Israel was proclaimed.

1918. 10 milliemes = 1 piastre.
1927. 1,000 mills = £P1.

1 **(2)**

1918.

3	**1**	1p. blue	2·00	2·00

1918. Surch with T **2**.

4	**1**	5m. on 1p. blue	4·00	2·75

3 "E.E.F." = Egyptian Expeditionary Force

فلسطين
PALESTINE
פלשתינה א״י
(4)

1918.

5	**3**	1m. brown	30	40
6		2m. green	30	45
7		3m. brown	35	35
8		4m. red	35	40
9		5m. orange	1·75	30
10		1p. blue	35	30
11		2p. olive	1·00	60
12		5p. purple	1·75	2·25
13		9p. ochre	3·75	4·75
14		10p. blue	3·00	3·25
15		20p. grey	11·00	16·00

Nos. 1/15 were also valid in Transjordan, Cilicia, Lebanon and Syria.

1920. Optd with T **4**.

71	**3**	1m. brown	85	30
61		2m. green	1·50	30
72		2m. yellow	1·00	30
62		3m. brown	1·50	30
73		3m. blue	1·50	15
74		4m. red	1·50	20
75		5m. orange	1·75	30
76		6m. green	1·50	30
77		7m. brown	1·50	30
78		8m. red	1·50	30
79		1p. grey	2·00	30
65		1p. blue	2·00	35
80		13m. blue	2·00	15

No.	Type	Description	Mint	Used
66		2p. olive	2·25	40
82		5p. purple	4·75	1·25
87		9p. ochre	9·00	9·00
88		10p. blue	7·50	2·50
26		20p. grey	25·00	42·00
89		20p. violet	9·00	5·50

9 Rachel's Tomb

10 Dome of the Rock

11 Citadel, Jerusalem

12 Sea of Galilee

1927.

No.	Type	Description	Mint	Used
90	9	2m. blue	75	10
91		3m. green	75	10
92	10	4m. red	4·00	1·25
104		4m. purple	1·00	10
93	11	5m. orange	1·75	10
94a	10	6m. green	75	20
95	11	7m. red	5·50	60
105		7m. violet	60	10
96	10	8m. brown	12·00	6·00
106		8m. red	1·25	20
97	9	10m. grey	1·00	10
98	10	13m. blue	6·00	30
107		13m. brown	1·00	10
108a		15m. blue	2·25	40
99	11	20m. olive	1·75	15
100	12	50m. purple	1·50	30
101		90m. bistre	55·00	60·00
102		100m. blue	2·25	70
103b		200m. violet	7·50	3·50
109		250m. brown	4·00	1·75
110		500m. red	4·50	3·00
111		£P1 black	6·00	3·50

POSTAGE DUE STAMPS

D 1

D 2

1920.

No.	Type	Description	Mint	Used
D1	D 1	1m. brown	15·00	25·00
D2		2m. green	10·00	10·00
D3		4m. red	10·00	10·00
D4		8m. mauve	7·00	7·00
D5		13m. blue	6·00	6·00

1924.

No.	Type	Description	Mint	Used
D 6	D 2	1m. brown	90	2·00
D 7		2m. yellow	2·25	1·75
D 8		4m. green	2·00	1·25
D 9		8m. red	3·00	90
D10		13m. blue	2·75	2·50
D11		5p. violet	8·50	1·75

1928. As Type **D 2**, but inscr "MIL" instead of "MILLIEME".

No.	Type	Description	Mint	Used
D12	D 2	1m. brown	50	85
D13		2m. yellow	1·00	60
D14		4m. green	1·25	1·60
D15		6m. brown	15·00	5·00
D16		8m. red	1·75	1·00
D17		10m. grey	1·25	60
D18		13m. blue	1·75	1·75
D19		20m. olive	1·75	1·25
D20		50m. violet	2·50	1·25

PANAMA Pt. 15

Country situated on the C. American isthmus. Formerly a State or Department of Colombia, Panama was proclaimed an independent republic in 1903.

1878. 100 centavos = 1 peso.
1906. 100 centesimos = 1 balboa.

1 Coat of Arms

3 Map

1878. Imperf. The 50c. is larger.

No.	Type	Description	Mint	Used
1	1	5c. green	15·00	13·50
2		10c. blue	38·00	35·00
3		20c. red	24·00	21·00
4		50c. yellow	9·75	

1887. Perf.

No.	Type	Description	Mint	Used
5	3	1c. black on green	50	65
6		2c. black on pink	1·25	1·00
7		5c. black on blue	90	35
7a		5c. black on grey	1·50	45
8		10c. black on yellow	90	45
9		20c. black on lilac	90	45
10		50c. brown	1·50	75

5 Map of Panama

38 Map of Panama

1892.

No.	Type	Description	Mint	Used
12a	5	1c. green	15	15
12b		2c. red	20	20
12c		5c. blue	90	45
12d		10c. orange	20	20
12e		20c. violet	25	25
12f		50c. brown	30	25
12g		1p. lake	3·75	2·40

1894. Surch **HABILITADO 1894** and value.

No.	Type	Description	Mint	Used
13	5	1c. on 2c. red	35	35
15	3	5c. on 20c. black on lilac	1·50	1·00
18		10c. on 50c. brown	1·90	1·90

1903. Optd **REPUBLICA DE PANAMA**.

No.	Type	Description	Mint	Used
70	5	1c. green	1·25	75
36		2c. red	55	55
37		5c. blue	1·25	55
38		10c. orange	1·25	1·25
39		20c. violet	2·40	2·40
75	3	50c. brown	14·00	14·00
40	5	50c. brown	6·00	4·25
41		1p. lake	29·00	24·00

1903. Optd **PANAMA** twice.

No.	Type	Description	Mint	Used
53	5	1c. green	25	25
54		2c. red	25	25
55		5c. blue	30	30
56		10c. orange	30	30
64		20c. violet	90	90
65		50c. brown	1·50	1·50
66		1p. lake	3·50	2·75

1904. Optd **Republica de Panama**.

No.	Type	Description	Mint	Used
94	5	1c. green	35	35
97		2c. red	45	45
98		5c. blue	45	45
99		10c. orange	45	45
100		20c. violet	45	45
103	3	50c. brown	1·75	1·75
104	5	1p. lake	9·50	8·25

1905.

No.	Type	Description	Mint	Used
151	38	½c. orange	55	45
136		1c. green	55	40
137		2c. red	70	55

1906. Surch **PANAMA** twice and new value and thick bar.

No.	Type	Description	Mint	Used
138	5	1c. on 20c. violet	25	25
139		2c. on 50c. brown	25	25
140		5c. on 1p. lake	55	45

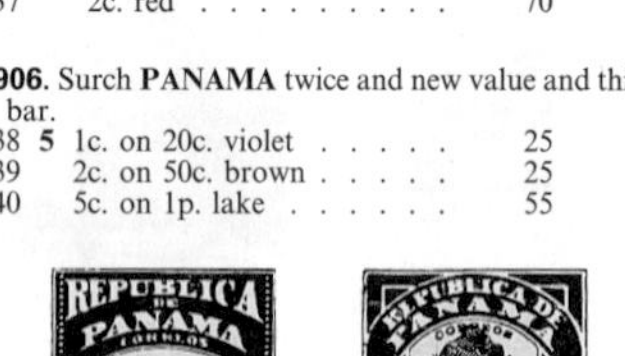

41 Panamanian Flag

42 Vasco Nunez de Balboa

43 F. de Cordoba

44 Arms of Panama

45 J. Arosemena

46 M. J. Hurtado

47 J. de Obaldia

1906.

No.	Type	Description	Mint	Used
142	41	½c. multicoloured	40	35
143	42	1c. black and green	40	35
144	43	2c. black and red	55	35
145	44	2½c. red	55	35
146	45	5c. black and blue	1·00	35
147	46	8c. black and purple	55	40
148	47	10c. black and violet	55	35
149	–	25c. black and brown	1·50	60
150	–	50c. black	3·75	2·10

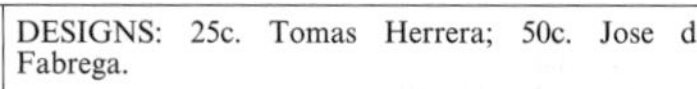

DESIGNS: 25c. Tomas Herrera; 50c. Jose de Fabrega.

48 Balboa

49 De Cordoba

50 Arms

51 Arosemena

52 Hurtado

53 Obaldia

1909.

No.	Type	Description	Mint	Used
152	48	1c. black and green	65	50
153	49	2c. black and red	65	30
154	50	2½c. red	90	30
155	51	5c. black and blue	1·10	30
156	52	8c. black and purple	4·25	2·50
157	53	10c. black and purple	2·10	1·10

56 Balboa viewing Pacific Ocean

57 Balboa reaches the Pacific

1913. 400th Anniv of Discovery of Pacific Ocean.

No.	Type	Description	Mint	Used
160	56	2½c. yellow and green	45	40

1915. Panama Exhibition and Opening of Canal.

No.	Type	Description	Mint	Used
161	–	½c. black and olive	45	35
162	–	1c. black and green	55	35
163	57	2c. black and red	65	35
164	–	2½c. black and red	65	35
165	–	3c. black and violet	1·00	35
166	–	5c. black and blue	2·50	50
167	–	10c. black and orange	1·50	50
168	–	20c. black and brown	7·25	2·40

DESIGNS: ½c. Chorrera Falls; 1c. Relief Map of Panama Canal; 2½c. Cathedral ruins, Old Panama; 3c. Palace of Arts, National Exhibition; 5c. Gatun Locks; 10c. Culebra Cut; 20c. Archway, S. Domingo Monastery.

62 Balboa Docks

1918. Views of Panama Canal.

No.	Type	Description	Mint	Used
178	–	12c. black and violet	20·00	5·50
179	–	15c. black and blue	12·00	2·75
180	–	24c. black and brown	35·00	9·00
181	62	50c. black and orange	42·00	20·00
182	–	1b. black and violet	45·00	22·00

DESIGNS: 12c. "Panama" (cargo liner) in Gaillard Cut, north; 15c. "Panama" in Gaillard Cut, south; 24c. "Cristobal" (cargo liner) in Gatun Locks; 1b. "Nereus" (U.S. Navy collier) in Pedro Miguel Locks.

1919. 400th Anniv of Founding of City of Panama. No. 164 surch **1519 1919 2 CENTESIMOS 2**.

No.	Type	Description	Mint	Used
183		2c. on 2½c. black and red	45	45

64 Arms of Panama

65 Vallarino

68 Bolivar's Speech

70 Hurtado

1921. Independence Centenary. Dated "1821 1921".

No.	Type	Description	Mint	Used
184	64	½c. orange	55	30
185	65	1c. green	55	25
186	–	2c. red ("Land Gate", Panama City)	70	30
187	65	2½c. red (Bolivar)	95	75
188	–	3c. violet (Cervantes statue)	95	75
189	68	5c. blue	90	45
190	65	8c. olive (Carlos Ycaza)	3·50	2·10
191	–	10c. violet (Government House 1821–1921)	2·40	85
192	–	15c. blue (Balboa statue)	3·00	1·25
193	–	20c. brown (Los Santos Church)	5·00	2·40
194	65	24c. sepia (Herrera)	5·00	3·00
195	–	50c. black (Fabrega)	8·75	4·50

1921. Birth Centenary of Manuel Jose Hurtado (writer).

No.	Type	Description	Mint	Used
196	70	2c. green	55	35

1923. No. 164 surch **1923 2 CENTESIMOS 2**.

No.	Type	Description	Mint	Used
197		2c. on 2½c. black and red	35	35

72

73 Simon Bolivar

74 Statue of Bolivar

75 Congress Hall, Panama

1924.

No.	Type	Description	Mint	Used
198	72	½c. orange	20	10
199		1c. green	20	10
200		2c. red	25	10
201		5c. blue	35	15
202		10c. violet	40	20
203		12c. olive	45	45
204		15c. blue	55	45
205		24c. brown	2·25	65
206		50c. orange	3·75	90
207		1b. black	5·50	2·25

1926. Bolivar Congress.

No.	Type	Description	Mint	Used
208	73	½c. orange	35	15
209		1c. green	35	15
210		2c. red	40	25
211		4c. grey	40	25
212		5c. blue	65	40
213	74	8c. purple	75	65
214		10c. violet	60	60
215		12c. olive	90	90
216		15c. blue	1·25	1·10
217		20c. brown	2·40	1·25
218	75	24c. slate	3·00	1·50
219		50c. black	7·00	3·50

78 "Spirit of St. Louis" over Map

1928. Lindbergh's Flying Tour.

No.	Type	Description	Mint	Used
222	–	2c. red on rose	55	35
223	78	5c. blue on green	75	55

DESIGN—VERT: 2c. "Spirit of St. Louis" over Old Panama with opt **HOMENAJE A LINDBERGH**.

1928. 25th Anniv of Independence. Optd **1903 NOV 3 BRE 1928**.

No.	Type	Description	Mint	Used
224	70	2c. green	30	20

1929. Air. No. E226 surch with Fokker Universal airplane and **CORREO AEREO 25 25 VEINTICINCO CENTESIMOS**.

No.	Type	Description	Mint	Used
225	E 81	25c. on 10c. orange	1·10	90

1929. Air. Nos. E226/7 optd **CORREO AEREO** or additionally surch with new value in **CENTESIMOS**.

No.	Type	Description	Mint	Used
238	E 81	5c. on 10c. orange	55	55
228		10c. orange	55	55
268		10c. on 20c. brown	90	55
229		15c. on 10c. orange	55	55
269		20c. brown	90	55
230		25c. on 20c. brown	1·25	1·10

83

87

1930. Air.

No.	Type	Description	Mint	Used
231	83	5c. blue	20	10
232		5c. orange	35	10
233		7c. red	35	10
234		8c. black	35	10

235 15c. green 45 10
236 20c. red 50 10
237 25c. blue 55 55

1930. No. 182 optd with airplane and **CORREO AEREO**.
239 1b. black and violet 20·00 16·00

1930. Air.
244 **87** 5c. blue 20 10
245 10c. orange 35 25
246 30c. violet 6·75 4·00
247 50c. red 1·25 35
248 1b. black 6·75 4·25

1930. Bolivar's Death Centenary. Surch **1830 - 1930 17 DE DICIEMBRE UN CENTESIMO**.
249 **73** 1c. on 4c. grey 25 20

89 Seaplane over Old Panama

92 Manuel Amador Guerrero

1931. Air. Opening of service between Panama City and western provinces.
250 **89** 5c. blue 1·00 90

1932. Optd **HABILITADA** or surch also.
251 **64** ½c. orange (postage) 35 20
252 **73** ½c. orange 20 20
253 1c. green 25 20
270 **68** 1c. on 5c. blue 45 35
254 **73** 2c. red 20 20
255 5c. blue 45 30
256 – 10c. violet (No. 191) 70 35
258 **74** 10c. on 12c. olive 75 40
259 10c. on 15c. blue 70 35
257 20c. brown 1·00 1·10
260 **83** 20c. on 25c. blue (air) 4·00 55

1932. Birth Centenary of Dr. Guerrero (first president of republic).
261 **92** 2c. red 45 20

95 National Institute

1934. 25th Anniv of National Institute.
262 – 1c. green 55 55
263 – 2c. red 55 55
264 – 5c. blue 75 60
265 **95** 10c. brown 2·10 1·00
266 – 12c. green 3·50 1·50
267 – 15c. blue 4·75 1·75
DESIGNS—VERT: 1c. J. D. de Obaldia; 2c. E. A. Morales; 5c. Sphinx and Quotation from Emerson. HORIZ: 12c. J. A. Facio; 15c. P. Arosemena.

(98)

100 Urraca Monument

99 Custom House Ruins, Portobelo

1936. Birth Centenary of Pablo Arosemena. (a) Postage. Surch as T **98**, but without **CORREO AEREO**.
271 **72** 2c. on 24c. brown 55 45

(b) Air. Surch with T **98**.
272 **72** 5c. on 50c. orange 60 50

1936. 4th Spanish–American Postal Congress (1st issue). Inscr "IV CONGRESO POSTAL AMERICO-ESPANOL".
273 **99** ½c. orange (postage) 40 25
274 – 1c. green 40 25
275 – 2c. red 40 25
276 – 5c. blue 45 30
277 – 10c. violet 75 45
278 – 15c. blue 75 60
279 – 20c. red 95 1·00
280 – 25c. brown 1·50 1·40
281 – 50c. orange 8·50 2·75
282 – 1b. black 9·00 7·00
DESIGNS: 1c. "Panama" (Old tree); 2c. "La Pollera" (woman in costume); 5c. Bolivar; 10c. Ruins of Old Panama Cathedral; 15c. Garcia y Santos; 20c. Madden Dam; 25c. Columbus; 50c. "Resolute" (liner) in Gaillard Cut; 1b. Panama Cathedral.

283 **100** 5c. blue (air) 70 40
284 – 10c. orange 90 65
285 – 20c. red 1·25 1·00
286 – 30c. violet 2·10 1·90
287 – 50c. red 30·00 18·00
288 – 1b. black 9·00 6·50
DESIGNS—HORIZ: 10c. "Man's Genius Uniting the Oceans"; 20c. Panama; 50c. San Pedro Miguel Locks; 1b. Courts of Justice. VERT: 30c. Balboa Monument.

1937. 4th Spanish–American Postal Congress (2nd issue). Nos. 273/88 optd **UPU**.
289 **99** ½c. orange (postage) 35 20
290 – 1c. green 45 20
291 – 2c. red 45 20
292 – 5c. blue 45 30
293 – 10c. violet 75 45
294 – 15c. blue 4·75 2·40
295 – 20c. red 1·10 1·10
296 – 25c. brown 1·75 90
297 – 50c. orange 7·00 4·25
298 – 1b. black 8·75 7·50
299 **99** 5c. blue (air) 45 45
300 – 10c. orange 70 55
301 – 20c. red 95 75
302 – 30c. violet 3·50 2·40
303 – 50c. red 25·00 20·00
304 – 1b. black 11·50 9·50

1937. Optd **1937-38**.
305 **73** ½c. orange 50 45
306 **65** 1c. green 30 25
307 **73** 1c. green 30 25
308 **70** 2c. green 35 25
309 **73** 2c. red 35 30

1937. Surch **1937-38** and value.
310 **73** 2c. on 4c. grey 45 30
311 **78** 2c. on 8c. olive 45 30
312 **74** 2c. on 8c. purple 45 30
313 2c. on 10c. violet 45 30
314 2c. on 12c. olive 45 30
315 – 2c. on 15c. blue (No. 192) 45 30
316 **65** 2c. on 24c. sepia 45 30
317 2c. on 50c. black 45 30

1937. Air. Optd **CORREO AEREO** or surch also.
318 **73** 5c. blue 45 45
319 **74** 5c. on 15c. blue 45 45
320 5c. on 20c. brown 45 45
321 **75** 5c. on 24c. slate 45 45
322 **62** 5c. on 1b. black and violet 6·75 3·75
323 – 10c. on 10c. violet (No. 191) 1·40 90
324 **75** 10c. on 50c. black 1·40 90

105 Fire-Engine

106 Firemen's Monument

107 Fire-Brigade Badge

1937. 50th Anniv of Fire Brigade.
325 – ½c. orange (postage) 45 25
326 – 1c. green 45 25
327 – 2c. red 45 30
328 **105** 5c. blue 65 30
329 **106** 10c. violet 1·10 65
330 – 12c. green 1·50 1·10
331 **107** 5c. blue (air) 55 35
332 – 10c. orange 70 45
333 – 20c. red 90 55
DESIGNS—VERT: ½c. R. Arango; 1c. J. A. Guizado; 10c. (No. 332), F. Arosemena; 12c. D. H. Brandon; 20c. J. G. Duque. HORIZ: 2c. House on fire.

108 Basketball Player

111 Old Panama Cathedral and Statue of Liberty

1938. Air. Central American and Caribbean Olympic Games.
334 **108** 1c. red 80 30
335 – 2c. green (Baseball player) (horiz) 80 15
336 – 7c. grey (Swimmer) (horiz) 1·10 35
337 – 8c. brown (Boxers) (horiz) 1·10 35
338 – 15c. blue (Footballer) 2·60 1·10

1938. Opening of Aguadulce Normal School, Santiago. Optd **NORMAL DE SANTIAGO JUNIO 5 1938** or surch also.
340 **72** 2c. red (postage) 30 25
341 **87** 7c. on 30c. violet (air) 45 45
342 **83** 8c. on 15c. green 45 45

1938. 150th Anniv of U.S. Constitution. Flags in red, white and blue.
343 **111** 1c. black and green (postage) 45 20
344 2c. black and red 55 25
345 5c. black and blue 60 45
346 12c. black and olive 1·10 65
347 15c. black and blue 1·40 75
348 7c. black and grey (air) 50 30
349 8c. black and blue 70 30
350 15c. black and brown 90 70
351 50c. black and orange 12·00 9·00
352 1b. black 12·00 9·00
Nos. 343/7 are without the Douglas DC-3 airliner.

112 Pierre and Marie Curie

1939. Obligatory Tax. Cancer Research Fund. Dated "1939".
353 **112** 1c. red 55 15
354 1c. green 55 15
355 1c. orange 55 15
356 1c. blue 55 15

113 Gatun Locks

1939. 25th Anniv of Opening of Panama Canal.
357 **113** ½c. yellow (postage) 2·10 2·10
358 – 1c. green 2·25 1·75
359 – 2c. red 55 15
360 – 5c. blue 1·75 20
361 – 10c. violet 5·50 90
362 – 12c. olive 75 55
363 – 15c. blue 75 70
364 – 50c. orange 1·75 1·25
365 – 1b. brown 3·50 2·25
DESIGNS: 1c. "Santa Elena" (liner) in Pedro Miguel Locks; 2c. Allegory of canal construction; 5c. "Rangitata" (liner) in Culebra Cut; 10c. Panama canal ferry; 12c. Aerial view; 15c. Gen. Gorgas; 50c. M. A. Guerrero; 1b. Woodrow Wilson.

366 – 1c. red (air) 35 10
367 – 2c. green 35 15
368 – 5c. blue 55 20
369 – 10c. violet 70 25
370 – 15c. blue 95 35
371 – 20c. red 2·50 95
372 – 50c. brown 3·00 90
373 – 1b. black 6·00 4·00
PORTRAITS: 1c. B. Porras; 2c. Wm. H. Taft; 5c. P. J. Sosa; 10c. L. B. Wise; 15c. A. Reclus; 20c. Gen. Goethals; 50c. F. de Lesseps; 1b. Theodore Roosevelt.

115 Flags of American Republics

120a "Liberty"

1940. Air. 50th Anniv of Pan-American Union.
374 **115** 15c. blue 45 30

1940. Air. No. 370 surch **55**.
375 5c. on 15c. blue 25 25

No. 363 surch **AEREO SIETE**.
376 7c. on 15c. blue 40 30

No. 371 surch **SIETE**.
377 7c. on 20c. red 40 30

No. 374 surch **8-8**.
378 **115** 8c. on 15c. blue 40 30

1941. Obligatory Tax. Cancer Research Fund. Optd **LUCHA CONTRA EL CANCER**.
379 **72** 1c. green 1·40 1·10

1941. Enactment of New Constitution. (a) Postage. Optd **CONSTITUCION 1941**.
380 **72** ½c. orange 35 20
381 1c. green 35 20
382 2c. red 35 25
383 5c. blue 45 20
384 10c. violet 65 45
385 15c. blue 1·00 65
386 50c. orange 5·50 2·50
387 1b. black 13·00 4·50

(b) Air. Surch **CONSTITUCION 1941 AEREO** and value in figures.
388 E **81** 7c. on 10c. orange 65 65
389 **72** 15c. on 24c. brown 2·25 1·50

(c) Air. Optd **CONSTITUCION 1941**.
390 **83** 20c. red 3·25 2·25
391 **87** 50c. red 7·50 4·25
392 1b. black 17·00 9·00

1941. Obligatory Tax. Cancer Research Fund. Dated "1940".
393 **112** 1c. red 45 10
394 1c. green 45 10
395 1c. orange 45 10
396 1c. blue 45 10

1942. Telegraph stamps as T **120a** optd or surch. (a) Optd **CORREOS 1942** and (No. 397) surch **2c**.
397 2c. on 5c. blue 70 55
398 10c. violet 90 70

(b) Air. Optd **CORREO AEREO 1942**.
399 20c. brown 1·75 1·50

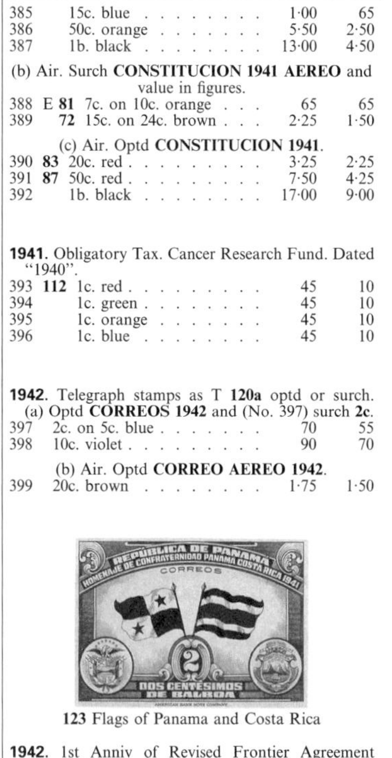
123 Flags of Panama and Costa Rica

1942. 1st Anniv of Revised Frontier Agreement between Panama and Costa Rica.
400 **123** 2c. red (postage) 30 25
401 15c. green (air) 60 15

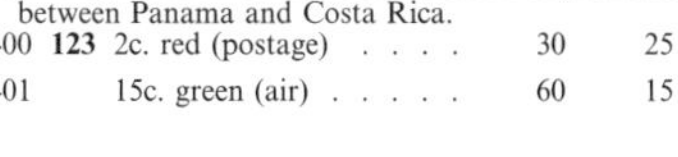

1942. Obligatory Tax. Cancer Research Fund. Dated "1942".
402 **112** 1c. violet 45 15

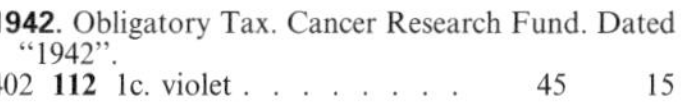

127 Balboa reaches Pacific

129 J. D. Arosemena Normal School

131 A. G. Melendez

1942. (a) Postage stamps.
403 – ½c. red, blue and violet 10 10
404 – ½c. blue, orange and red 15 10
405 – 1c. green 10 10
406 – 1c. red 10 10
407 – 2c. red ("ACARREO") 20 10
408 – 2c. red ("ACARREO") 45 10
409 – 2c. black and red 15 10
410 **127** 5c. black and blue 20 10
411 – 5c. blue 30 10
412 – 10c. orange and red 45 20
413 – 10c. orange and purple 35 20
414 – 15c. black and blue 35 55
415 – 15c. black 35 20
416 – 50c. black and red 85 60
417 – 1b. black 1·75 70
DESIGNS—VERT: ½c. National flag; 1c. Farm girl; 10c. Golden Altar, Church of St. Jose; 50c. San Blas Indian woman and child. HORIZ: 2c. Oxen drawing sugar cart; 15c. St. Thomas's Hospital; 1b. National highway.

(b) Air.
418 – 2c. red 45 10
419 – 7c. red 55 20
420 – 8c. black and blue 20 10
421 – 10c. black and blue 20 15
422 – 15c. violet 30 10
423 – 15c. grey 35 15
424 **129** 20c. brown 35 10
425 20c. green 35 20
426 – 50c. green 1·25 45
427 – 50c. red 3·50 2·60
428 – 50c. blue 60 40
429 – 1b. orange, yellow and black 1·40 65
DESIGNS—HORIZ: 2c., 7c. Black marlin; 8c., 10c. Gate of Glory, Portobelo; 15c. Taboga Is; 50c. Fire Brigade H.Q., Panama City; 1b. Idol (Golden Beast).

1943. Obligatory Tax. Cancer Research Fund. Dated "1943".
433 **112** 1c. green 45 15
434 1c. red 45 15

435 1c. orange 45 15
436 1c. blue 45 15

1943. Air.
437 **131** 3b. grey . . . . 5·50 5·50
438 – 5b. blue (T. Lefevre) . . . 8·50 7·00

1945. Obligatory Tax. Cancer Research Fund. Dated "1945".
439 **112** 1c. red 45 20
440 1c. green 45 20
441 1c. orange 45 20
442 1c. blue 45 20

1946. Obligatory Tax. Cancer Research Fund. Surch **CANCER B/. 0.01 1947**.
443 **72** 1c. on ½c. orange 55 15
444 1c. on 1c. green 55 15
445 – 1c. on ½c. red, blue and violet (No. 403) 45 10
446 **72** 1c. on 12c. olive 45 15
447 1c. on 24c. brown 45 15

1947. Air. Surch **AEREO 1947** and value.
448 – 5c. on 7c. red (No. 419) . . 20 20
449 **83** 5c. on 8c. black 20 20
450 – 5c. on 8c. black and brown (No. 420) 20 20
451 **83** 10c. on 15c. green 55 35
452 – 10c. on 15c. violet (422) . . 30 25

134 Flag of Panama **135** National Theatre

1947. 2nd Anniv of National Constitutional Assembly.
453 **134** 2c. red, deep red and blue (postage) 15 10
454 – 5c. blue 20 20
455 **135** 8c. violet (air) 45 30
DESIGN—As Type **134**: 5c. Arms of Panama.

1947. Cancer Research Fund. Dated "1947".
456 **112** 1c. red 45 10
457 1c. green 45 10
458 1c. orange 45 10
459 1c. blue 45 10

1947. Surch **HABILITADA CORREOS** and value.
460 **83** ½c. on 8c. black 10 10
461 – ½c. on 8c. black and brown (No. 420) . . . 10 10
462 – 1c. on 7c. red (No. 419) 15 15
463 **135** 2c. on 8c. violet 20 15

1947. Surch **Habilitada CORREOS B/. 0.50.**
464 **72** 50c. on 24c. brown 65 65

138 J. A. Arango

1948. Air. Honouring members of the Revolutionary Junta of 1903.
465 – 3c. black and blue 35 25
466 **138** 5c. black and brown . . . 35 25
467 – 10c. black and orange . . 35 25
468 – 15c. black and red 35 55
469 – 20c. black and red 40 40
470 – 50c. black . . . . 3·75 1·60
471 – 1b. black and green . . . 3·00 2·75
472 – 2b. black and yellow . . . 7·00 6·00
PORTRAITS—HORIZ: 3c. M. A. Guerrero; 10c. F. Boyd; 15c. R. Arias. VERT: 20c. M. Espinosa; 50c. Carlos Arosemena (engineer); 1b. N. de Obarrio; 2b. T. Arias.

140 Firemen's Monument

1948. 50th Anniv of Colon Fire Brigade.
473 **140** 5c. black and red 20 15
474 – 10c. black and orange . . 35 20
475 – 20c. black and blue . . . 70 40
476 – 25c. black and brown . . 70 55
477 – 50c. black and violet . . . 90 55
478 – 1b. black and green . . . 1·50 90

DESIGNS—HORIZ: 10c. Fire engine; 20c. Fire hose; 25c. Fire Brigade Headquarters. VERT: 50c. Commander Walker; 1b. First Fire Brigade Commander.

142 F. D. Roosevelt and J. D. Arosemena **144** Roosevelt Monument, Panama

1948. Air. Homage to F. D. Roosevelt.
479 **142** 5c. black and red 20 15
480 – 10c. orange 30 30
481 **144** 20c. green 35 35
482 – 50c. black and blue . . . 40 35
483 – 1b. black 90 75
DESIGNS—HORIZ: 10c. Woman with palm symbolizing "Four Freedoms"; 50c. Map of Panama Canal. VERT: 1b. Portrait of Roosevelt.

147 Cervantes

148 Monument to Cervantes

1948. 400th Birth Anniv of Cervantes.
484 **147** 2c. black and red (postage) 30 15
485 **148** 5c. black and blue (air) 20 10
486 – 10c. black and mauve . . 35 30
DESIGN—HORIZ: 10c. Don Quixote and Sancho Panza (inscr as Type **148**).

1949. Air. Jose Gabriel Duque (philanthropist). Birth Centenary. No. 486 optd **"CENTENARIO DE JOSE GABRIEL DUQUE" "18 de Enero de 1949"**.
487 10c. black and mauve 40 40

1949. Obligatory Tax. Cancer Research Fund. Surch **LUCHA CONTRA EL CANCER** and value.
488 **142** 1c. on 5c. black and red 35 10
489 – 1c. on 10c. orange (No. 480) 35 10

1949. Incorporation of Chiriqui Province Cent. Stamps of 1930 and 1942 optd **1849 1949 CHIRIQUI CENTENARIO**. (a) On postage stamps as No. 407. (i) Without surcharge.
491 – 2c. red 20 10

(ii) Surch **1 UN CENTESIMO 1** also.
490 – 1c. on 2c. red 20 10

(b) Air.
492 – 2c. red (No. 418) 20 20
493 **83** 5c. blue 30 30
494 – 15c. grey (No. 423) 40 40
495 – 50c. red (No. 427) . . . . 1·75 1·75

1949. 75th Anniv of U.P.U. Stamps of 1930 and 1942/3 optd **1874 1949 U.P.U.** No. 625 is also surch **B/0.25.**
496 – 1c. green (No. 405) (postage) 20 10
497 – 2c. red (No. 407) 30 15
498 **127** 5c. blue 45 25
499 – 2c. red (No. 418) (air) . . 20 20
500 **83** 5c. orange 55 35
501 – 10c. black and blue (No. 421) 20 20
502 **131** 25c. on 3b. grey 30 30
503 – 50c. red (No. 427) . . . . 1·60 1·60

1949. Cancer Research Fund. Dated "1949".
504 **112** 1c. brown 45 10

153 Father Xavier **154** St. Xavier University

1949. Bicentenary of Founding of St. Xavier University.
505 **153** 2c. black and red (postage) 25 15
506 **154** 5c. black and blue (air) 35 15

155 Dr. Carlos J. Finlay **156** "Aedes aegypti"

1950. Dr. Finlay (medical research worker).
507 **155** 2c. black and red (postage) 35 15
508 **156** 5c. black and blue (air) 85 40

1950. Death Centenary of San Martin. Optd **CENTENARIO del General** (or **Gral.) Jose de San Martin 17 de Agosto de 1950** or surch also. The 50c. is optd **AEREO** as well.
509 – 1c. green (No. 405) (postage) 15 10
510 – 2c. on ½c. blue, orange and red (No. 404) . . . 20 10
511 **127** 5c. black and blue 25 20
512 – 2c. red (No. 418) (air) . . 35 30
513 **83** 5c. orange 35 35
514 – 10c. black & blue (No. 421) 55 45
515 **83** 25c. blue 90 70
516 – 50c. black & violet (No. 477) . . . . . . 1·40 1·00

158 Badge **159** Stadium

1950. Obligatory Tax. Physical Culture Fund. Dated "1950".
517 – 1c. black and red 70 20
518 **158** 1c. black and blue 70 20
519 **159** 1c. black and green . . . 70 20
520 – 1c. black and orange . . 70 20
521 – 1c. black and violet . . . 70 20
DESIGNS—VERT: No. 520, as Type **159** but medallion changed and incorporating four "F"s; 521, Discus thrower. HORIZ: No. 517, as Type **159** but front of stadium.

1951. Birth Tercentenary of Jean-Baptiste de La Salle (educational reformer). Optd **Tercer Centenario del Natalicio de San Juan Baptista de La Salle. 1651-1951.**
522 2c. black and red (No. 409) 15 15
523 5c. blue (No. 411) 25 15

1952. Air. Surch **AEREO 1952** and value.
524 2c. on 10c. black and blue (No. 421) 20 15
525 5c. on 10c. black and blue (No. 421) 25 10
526 1b. on 5b. blue (No. 438) . . 23·00 23·00

1952. Surch **1952** and figure of value.
527 1c. on ½c. (No. 404) 15 10

Air. Optd **AEREO** also.
528 5c. on 2c. (No. 408) 15 10
529 25c. on 10c. (No. 413) . . . 70 65

164 Isabella the Catholic **167** Masthead of "La Estrella"

1952. 500th Birth Anniv of Isabella the Catholic.
530 **164** 1c. black & grn (postage) 10 10
531 2c. black and red 15 10
532 5c. black and blue 20 15
533 10c. black and violet . . . 25 20
534 4c. black and orange (air) 10 10
535 5c. black and olive . . . 15 10
536 10c. black and buff . . . 35 30
537 25c. black and slate . . . 55 35
538 50c. black and brown . . 75 45
539 1b. black . . . . 3·00 3·00

1953. Surch **B/.0.01 1953.**
540 1c. on 10c. (No. 413) 10 10
541 1c. on 15c. black (No. 415) 15 10

1953. Air. No. 421 surch **5 1953**.
542 5c. on 10c. black and blue . . 35 10

1953. Air. Centenary of "La Estrella de Panama", Newspaper.
543 **167** 5c. red 20 15
544 10c. blue 25 25

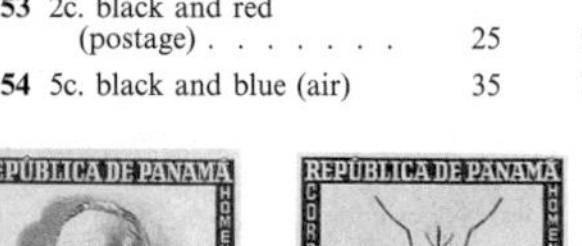

168 Pres. and Senora Amador Guerrero

1953. 50th Anniv of Panama Republic.
545 – 2c. violet (postage) . . . 15 10
546 **168** 5c. orange 20 10
547 – 12c. purple 35 15
548 – 20c. indigo . . . . 2·25 45
549 – 50c. yellow 90 65
550 – 1b. blue . . . . 2·25 1·00
DESIGNS—VERT: 2c. Blessing the flat; 50c. Old Town Hall. HORIZ: 12c. J. A. Santos and J. De La Ossa; 20c. Revolutionary council; 1b. Obverse and reverse of coin.

551 – 2c. blue (air) 10 10
552 – 5c. green 15 10
553 – 7c. grey 20 15
554 – 25c. black . . . . 1·40 70
555 – 50c. brown 65 70
556 – 1b. orange . . . . 2·25 1·00
DESIGNS—VERT: 2c. Act of Independence. HORIZ: 5c. Pres. and Senora Remon Cantera; 7c. Girl in national costume; 25c. National flower; 50c. Salazar, Huertas and Domingo; 1b. National dance.

1954. Surch in figures.
557 – 3c. on 1c. red (No. 406) (postage) 10 10
558 **167** 1c. on 5c. red (air) . . . 10 10
559 1c. on 10c. blue 10 10

170 Gen. Herrera at Conference Table

1954. Death Centenary of Gen. Herrera.
560 – 3c. violet (postage) . . . 20 10
561 **170** 6c. green (air) 15 10
562 – 1b. black and red . . . . 2·25 2·10
DESIGNS—VERT: 3c. Equestrian statue. HORIZ: 1b. Cavalry charge.

171 Rotary Emblem and Map

1955. Air. 50th Anniv of Rotary International.
563 **171** 6c. violet 15 10
564 21c. red 55 35
565 1b. black . . . . 3·50 1·90

172 Tocumen Airport **173** President Remon Cantera

1955.
566 **172** ½c. brown 10 10

1955. National Mourning for Pres. Remon Cantera.
567 **173** 3c. black & pur (postage) 15 10
568 6c. black and violet (air) 20 15

174 V. de la Guardia y Azala and M. Chiaria **175** F. de Lesseps

1955. Centenary of Cocle Province.
569 **174** 5c. violet 20 10

1955. 150th Birth Anniv of De Lesseps (engineer).
570 **175** 3c. lake on pink (postage) 30 10
571 – 25c. blue on blue . . . . 4·25 2·50
572 – 50c. violet on lilac 90 60
573 – 5c. myrtle on green (air) 20 10
574 – 1b. black and mauve . . 3·00 1·75

DESIGNS—VERT: 5c. P. J. Sosa; 50c. T. Roosevelt. HORIZ: 25c. First excavations for Panama Canal; 1b. "Ancon I" (first ship to pass through canal) and De Lesseps.

1955. Air. No. 564 surch.
575 **171** 15c. on 21c. red 45 35

177 Pres. Eisenhower (United States) **178** Bolivar Statue

1956. Air. Pan-American Congress, Panama and 30th Anniv of First Congress.
576 – 6c. black and blue 30 20
577 – 6c. black and bistre 30 20
578 – 6c. black and green 30 20
579 – 6c. sepia and green 30 20
580 – 6c. green and yellow 30 20
581 – 6c. green and violet 30 20
582 – 6c. blue and lilac 30 20
583 – 6c. green and purple 30 20
584 – 6c. blue and olive 30 20
585 – 6c. sepia and yellow 30 20
586 – 6c. blue and sepia 30 20
587 – 6c. green and mauve 30 20
588 – 6c. sepia and red 30 20
589 – 6c. green and blue 30 20
590 – 6c. sepia and blue 30 20
591 – 6c. black and orange 30 20
592 – 6c. sepia and grey 30 20
593 – 6c. black and pink 30 20
594 **177** 6c. blue and red 70 35
595 – 6c. blue and grey 30 20
596 – 6c. green and brown 30 20
597 **178** 20c. grey 40 55
598 – 50c. green 75 75
599 – 1b. sepia 1·50 95
PRESIDENTIAL PORTRAITS as Type **177**: No. 576, Argentina; 577, Bolivia; 578, Brazil; 579, Chile; 580, Colombia; 581, Costa Rica; 582, Cuba; 583, Dominican Republic; 584, Ecuador; 585, Guatemala; 586, Haiti; 587, Honduras; 588, Mexico; 589, Nicaragua; 590, Panama; 591, Paraguay; 592, Peru; 593, Salvador; 595, Uruguay; 596, Venezuela. As Type **178**—HORIZ: No. 598, Bolivar Hall. VERT: No. 599, Bolivar Medallion.

179 Arms of Panama City **180** Pres. Carlos A. Mendoza

1956. 6th Inter-American Congress of Municipalities, Panama City.
600 **179** 3c. green (postage) 15 10
601 – 25c. red (air) 55 35
602 – 50c. black 65 55
DESIGNS: 25c. Stone bridge, Old Panama; 50c. Town Hall, Panama.

1956. Birth Centenary of Pres. Carlos A. Mendoza.
604 **180** 10c. green and red 20 15

182 Dr. Belisario Porras

1956. Birth Centenary of Dr. Porras.
605 – 15c. grey (postage) 45 20
606 **182** 25c. blue and red 65 45
607 – 5c. green (air) 10 10
608 – 15c. red 30 25
DESIGNS—HORIZ: 15c. (No. 605), National Archives; 15c. (No. 608), St. Thomas's Hospital. VERT: 5c. Porras Monument.

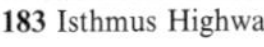

183 Isthmus Highway **185** Manuel E. Batista

1957. 7th Pan-American Highway Congress.
609 **183** 3c. green (postage) 15 10
610 – 10c. black (air) 20 15
611 – 20c. black and blue 35 35
612 – 1b. green 1·75 1·75
DESIGNS—VERT: 10c. Highway under construction; 20c. Darien Forest; 1b. Map of Pan-American Highway.

1957. Air. Surch **1957 x 10c x**.
614 **173** 10c. on 6c. black & violet 20 20

1957. Birth Centenary of Manuel Espinosa Batista (independence leader).
615 **185** 5c. blue and green 15 10

186 Portobelo Castle **189** U.N. Emblem

1957. Air. Buildings. Centres in black.
616 **186** 10c. grey 25 15
617 – 10c. purple 25 15
618 – 10c. violet 25 15
619 – 10c. grey and green 25 15
620 – 10c. blue 25 15
621 – 10c. brown 25 15
622 – 10c. orange 25 15
623 – 10c. light blue 25 15
624 – 1b. red 2·10 95
DESIGNS—HORIZ: No. 617, San Jeronimo Castle; 618, Portobelo Customs-house; 619, Panama Hotel; 620, Pres. Remon Cantera Stadium; 621, Palace of Justice; 622, Treasury; 623, San Lorenzo Castle. VERT: No. 624, Jose Remon Clinics.

1957. Surch **1957** and value.
625 **172** 1c. on ½c. brown 10 10
626 3c. on ½c. brown 10 10

1958. Air. Surch **1958** and value.
627 **170** 5c. on 6c. green 20 10

1958. Air. 10th Anniv of U.N.O.
628 **189** 10c. green 20 10
629 21c. blue 45 35
630 50c. orange 45 45
631 – 1b. red, blue and grey 1·75 1·40
DESIGN: 1b. Flags of Panama and United Nations.

1958. No. 547 surch **3c 1958**.
633 3c. on 12c. purple 10 10

191 Flags Emblem **192** Brazilian Pavilion

1958. 10th Anniv of Organization of American States. Emblem (T **191**) multicoloured within yellow and black circular band; background colours given below.
634 **191** 1c. grey (postage) 10 10
635 2c. green 10 10
636 3c. red 15 10
637 7c. blue 25 10
638 5c. blue (air) 15 10
639 10c. red 20 15
640 – 50c. black, yellow and grey 35 35
641 **191** 1b. black 1·75 1·40
DESIGN—VERT: 50c. Headquarters building.

1958. Brussels International Exhbition.
642 **192** 1c. green & yellow (postage) 10 10
643 – 3c. green and blue 15 10
644 – 5c. slate and brown 15 10
645 – 10c. brown and blue 20 20
646 – 15c. violet and grey (air) 35 35
647 – 50c. brown and slate 60 60
648 – 1b. turquoise and lilac 1·25 1·25
DESIGNS—PAVILIONS: As Type **192**: 3c. Argentina; 5c. Venezuela; 10c. Great Britain; 15c. Vatican City; 50c. United States; 1b. Belgium.

193 Pope Pius XII **194** Children on Farm

1959. Pope Pius XII Commemoration.
650 **193** 3c. brown (postage) 15 10
651 – 5c. violet (air) 15 15
652 – 30c. mauve 30 25
653 – 50c. grey 75 60
PORTRAITS (Pope Pius XII): 5c. when Cardinal; 30c. wearing Papal tiara; 50c. enthroned.

1959. Obligatory Tax. Youth Rehabilitation Institute. Size 35 × 24 mm.
655 **194** 1c. grey and red 15 10

195 U.N. Headquarters, New York **197** J. A. Facio

1959. 10th Anniv of Declaration of Human Rights.
656 **195** 3c. olive & brown (postage) 10 10
657 – 15c. green and orange 35 25
658 – 5c. blue and green (air) 15 10
659 – 10c. brown and grey 20 15
660 – 20c. slate and brown 35 35
661 – 50c. blue and green 60 60
662 **195** 1b. blue and red 1·40 1·25
DESIGNS: 5c., 15c. Family looking towards light; 10c., 20c. U.N. emblem and torch; 50c. U.N. flag.

1959. 8th Latin-American Economic Commission Congress. Nos. 656/61 optd **8A REUNION C.E.P.A.L. MAYO 1959** or surch also.
663 **195** 3c. olive and brown (postage) 10 10
664 15c. green and orange 35 20
665 – 5c. blue and green (air) 10 10
666 – 10c. brown and grey 25 15
667 – 20c. slate and brown 45 35
668 – 1b. on 50c. blue and green 1·60 1·60

1959. 50th Anniv of National Institute.
670 – 3c. red (postage) 10 10
671 – 13c. green 30 15
672 – 21c. blue 40 30
673 **197** 5c. black (air) 10 10
674 – 10c. black 20 10
DESIGNS—VERT: 3c. E. A. Morales (founder); 10c. Ernesto de la Guardia, Nr; 13c. A. Bravo. HORIZ: 21c. National Institute building.

1959. Obligatory Tax. Youth Rehabilitation Institute. As No. 655, but colours changed and inscr "1959".
675 **194** 1c. green and black 10 10
676 1c. blue and black 10 10
See also No. 690.

198 Football **200** Administration Building

1959. 3rd Pan-American Games, Chicago. Inscr "III JUEGOS DEPORTIVOS PANAMERICANOS".
677 **198** 1c. green & grey (postage) 10 10
678 – 3c. brown and blue 15 10
679 – 20c. brown and green 50 45
680 – 5c. brown and black (air) 15 10
681 – 10c. brown and grey 25 20
682 – 50c. brown and blue 45 40
DESIGNS: 3c. Swimming; 5c. Boxing; 10c. Baseball; 20c. Hurdling; 50c. Basketball.

1960. Air. World Refugee Year. Nos. 554/6 optd **NACIONES UNIDAS ANO MUNDIAL. REFUGIADOS. 1959–1960.**
683 25c. black 35 35
684 50c. brown 70 55
685 1b. orange 1·50 1·10

1960. Air. 25th Anniv of National University.
686 **200** 10c. green 15 15
687 – 21c. blue 30 20
688 – 25c. blue 50 35
689 – 30c. black 55 40
DESIGNS: 21c. Faculty of Science; 25c. Faculty of Medicine; 30c. Statue of Dr. Octavio Mendez Pereira (first rector) and Faculty of Law.

1960. Obligatory Tax. Youth Rehabilitation Institute. As No. 655 but smaller (32 × 22 mm) and inscr "1960".
690 **194** 1c. grey and red 10 10

202 Fencing **204** "Population"

1960. Olympic Games.
691 **202** 3c. purple & violet (postage) 10 10
692 – 5c. green and turquoise 20 10
693 – 5c. red and orange (air) 10 10
694 – 10c. black and bistre 20 15
695 – 25c. deep blue and blue 45 40
696 – 50c. black and brown 60 45
DESIGNS—VERT: 5c. (No. 692), Football; (No. 693), Basketball; 25c. Javelin-throwing; 50c. Runner with Olympic Flame. HORIZ: 10c. Cycling.

1960. Air. 6th National Census (5c.) and Central American Census.
698 **204** 5c. black 10 10
699 – 10c. brown 20 15
DESIGN: 10c. Two heads and map.

205 Boeing 707 Airliner

1960. Air.
700 **205** 5c. blue 15 10
701 10c. green 40 20
702 20c. brown 85 40

206 Pastoral Scene

1961. Agricultural Census (16th April).
703 **206** 3c. turquoise 10 10

207 Helen Keller School

1961. 25th Anniv of Lions Club.
705 – 3c. blue (postage) 10 10
706 **207** 5c. black (air) 10 10
707 – 10c. green 20 10
708 – 21c. blue, red and yellow 40 30
DESIGNS: 3c. Nino Hospital; 10c. Children's Colony, Verano; 21c. Lions emblem, arms and slogan.

1961. Air. Obligatory Tax. Youth Rehabilitation Fund. Surch **1 c "Rehabilitacion de Menores"**.
709 – 1c. on 10c. black and bistre (No. 694) 10 10
710 **205** 1c. on 10c. green 10 10

1961. Air. Surch **HABILITAD. en** and value.
712 **200** 1c. on 10c. green 10 10
713 – 1b. on 25c. blue and blue (No. 695) 1·25 1·25

210 Flags of Costa Rica and Panama

1961. Meeting of Presidents of Costa Rica and Panama.
715 **210** 3c. red and blue (postage) 15 10
716 – 1b. black and gold (air) 1·25 75
DESIGN: 1b. Pres. Chiari of Panama and Pres. Echandi of Costa Rica.

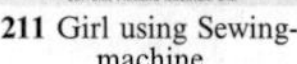

211 Girl using Sewing-machine
212 Campaign Emblem

1961. Obligatory Tax. Youth Rehabilitation Fund.
717 **211** 1c. violet 10 10
718 1c. yellow 10 10
719 1c. green 10 10
720 1c. blue 10 10
721 1c. purple 10 10
722 – 1c. mauve 10 10
723 – 1c. grey 10 10
724 – 1c. blue 10 10
725 – 1c. orange 10 10
726 – 1c. red 10 10
DESIGN: Nos. 722/6, Boy sawing wood.

1961. Air. Malaria Eradication.
727 **212** 5c.+5c. red 60 30
728 10c.+10c. blue 60 30
729 15c.+15c. green 60 30

213 Dag Hammarskjold
214 Arms of Panama

1961. Air. Death of Dag Hammarskjold.
730 **213** 10c. black and grey . . . 20 15

1962. Air. (a) Surch **Vale B/.0.15**.
731 **200** 15c. on 10c. green 30 20

(b) No. 810 surch **XX** over old value and **VALE B/.1.00**.
732 – 1b. on 25c. deep blue and blue . . . . 1·25 75

1962. 3rd Central American Inter-Municipal Co-operation Assembly.
733 **214** 3c. red, yellow and blue (postage) 10 10
734 – 5c. black and blue (air) 20 10
DESIGN—HORIZ: 5c. City Hall, Colon.

215 Mercury on Cogwheel
217 Social Security Hospital

1962. 1st Industrial Census.
735 **215** 3c. red 10 10

1962. Surch **VALE** and value with old value obliterated.
736 **212** 10c. on 5c.+5c. red . . . 90 45
737 20c. on 10c.+10c. blue . . 1·50 90

1962. Opening of Social Security Hospital, Panama City.
738 **217** 3c. black and red 10 10

218 Colon Cathedral
221 Col. Glenn and Capsule "Friendship 7"

220 Thatcher Ferry Bridge nearing Completion

1962. "Freedom of Worship". Inscr "LIBERTAD DE CULTOS". Centres in black.
739 – 1c. red and blue (postage) 10 10
740 – 2c. red and cream 10 10
741 – 3c. blue and cream . . . 10 10
742 – 5c. red and green 10 10
743 – 10c. green and cream . . 20 15
744 – 10c. mauve and blue . . . 20 15
745 – 15c. blue and green . . . 30 20
746 **218** 20c. red and pink 35 25
747 – 25c. green and pink . . . 45 35
748 – 50c. blue and pink . . . 60 55
749 – 1b. violet and cream . . . 1·75 1·40
DESIGNS—HORIZ: 1c. San Francisco de Veraguas Church; 3c. David Cathedral; 25c. Orthodox Greek Temple; 1b. Colon Protestant Church. VERT: 2c. Panama Old Cathedral; 5c. Nata Church; 10c. Don Bosco Temple; 15c. Virgin of Carmen Church; 50c. Panama Cathedral.

750 – 5c. violet and flesh (air) . . 10 10
751 – 7c. light mauve and mauve 15 10
752 – 8c. violet and blue 15 10
753 – 10c. violet and salmon . . . 20 10
754 – 10c. green and purple . . . 20 20
755 – 15c. red and orange 25 20
756 – 21c. sepia and blue 35 30
757 – 25c. blue and pink 45 35
758 – 30c. mauve and blue 50 45
759 – 50c. purple and green . . . 70 70
760 – 1b. blue and salmon . . . . 1·25 1·10
DESIGNS—HORIZ: 5c. Cristo Rey Church; 7c. San Miguel Church; 21c. Canal Zone Synagogue; 25c. Panama Synagogue; 50c. Canal Zone Protestant Church. VERT: 8c. Santuario Church; 10c. Los Santos Church; 15c. Santa Ana Church; 30c. San Francisco Church; 1b. Canal Zone Catholic Church.

1962. Air. 9th Central American and Caribbean Games, Jamaica. Nos. 693 and 695 optd **"IX JUEGOS C.A. Y DEL CARIBE KINGSTON - 1962"** or surch also.
762 5c. red and orange 15 15
764 10c. on 25c. deep blue & blue 55 50
765 15c. on 25c. deep blue & blue 40 35
766 20c. on 25c. deep blue & blue 45 45
763 25c. deep blue and blue . . . 55 50

1962. Opening of Thatcher Ferry Bridge, Canal Zone.
767 **220** 3c. black and red (postage) 10 10
768 – 10c. black and blue (air) 20 15
DESIGN: 10c. Completed bridge.

1962. Air. Col. Glenn's Space Flight.
769 **221** 5c. red 10 10
770 – 10c. yellow 20 20
771 – 31c. blue 45 40
772 – 50c. green 65 65
DESIGNS—HORIZ: "Friendship": 10c. Over Earth; 31c. In space. VERT: 50c. Col. Glenn.

222 U.P.A.E. Emblem
225 F.A.O. Emblem

223 Water Exercise

1963. Air. 50th Anniv of Postal Union of Americas and Spain.
774 **222** 10c. multicoloured 20 15

1963. 75th Anniv of Panama Fire Brigade.
775 **223** 1c. black & green (postage) 10 10
776 – 3c. black and blue 10 10
777 – 5c. black and red 10 10
778 – 10c. black and orange (air) 15 15
779 – 15c. black and purple . . 20 20
780 – 21c. blue, gold and red . . 50 45
DESIGNS: 3c. Brigade officers; 5c. Brigade president and advisory council; 10c. "China" pump in action, 1887; 15c. "Cable 14" station and fire-engine; 21c. Fire Brigade badge.

1963. Air. Red Cross Cent (1st issue). Nos. 769/71 surch with red cross **1863 1963** and premium.
781 **215** 5c.+5c. red . . . . 1·40 1·40
782 – 10c.+10c. yellow . . . . 2·75 2·75
783 – 31c.+15c. blue . . . . . 2·75 2·75
See also No. 797.

1963. Air. Freedom from Hunger.
784 **225** 10c. red and green 20 20
785 15c. red and blue 30 25

1963. Air. 22nd Central American Lions Convention. Optd **"XXII Convencion Leonistica Centroamericana Panama, 18-21 Abril 1963"**.
786 **207** 5c. black 10 10

1963. Air. Surch **HABILITADO Vale B./0.04**.
789 **200** 4c. in 10c. green 10 10

1963. Air. Nos. 743 and 769 optd **AEREO** vert.
790 10c. green and cream 20 15
791 20c. brown and green 30 25

1963. Air. Freedom of the Press. No. 693 optd **LIBERTAD DE PRENSA 20-VIII-63**.
792 5c. red and orange 10 10

1963. Air. Visit of U.S. Astronauts to Panama. Optd **"Visita Astronautas Glenn-Schirra Sheppard Cooper a Panama"** or surch also.
793 **221** 5c. red . . . . 2·50 2·50
794 10c. on 5c. red . . . . . 3·25 3·25

1963. Air. Surch **HABILITADO 10c.**
796 **221** 10c. on 5c. red . . . . . 5·50 5·50

1963. Air. Red Cross Centenary (2nd issue). No. 781 surch **"Centenario Cruz Roja Internacional 10c"** with premium obliterated.
797 **221** 10c. on 5c.+5c. red . . . 6·00 6·00

1963. Surch **VALE** and value.
798 **217** 4c. on 3c. black and red (postage) 15 10
799 – 4c. on 3c. black, blue and cream (No. 741) . . . 15 10
800 **220** 4c. on 3c. black and red 15 10
801 – 4c. on 3c. black and blue (No. 776) 15 10
802 **182** 10c. on 25c. blue and red 35 15
803 – 10c. on 25c. blue (No. 688) (air) 20 15

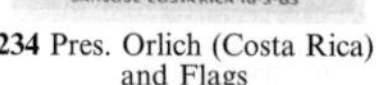

234 Pres. Orlich (Costa Rica) and Flags
236 Vasco Nunez de Balboa

235 Innsbruck

1963. Presidential Reunion, San Jose (Costa Rica). Multicoloured. Presidents and flags of their countries.
804 1c. Type **234** (postage) . . . 10 10
805 2c. Somoza (Nicaragua) . . . 15 15
806 3c. Villeda (Honduras) . . . 20 15
807 4c. Chiari (Panama) 25 20
808 5c. Rivera (El Salvador) (air) 30 30
809 10c. Ydigoras (Guatemala) 55 45
810 21c. Kennedy (U.S.A.) . . . 1·60 1·40

1963. Winter Olympic Games, Innsbruck.
811 ½c. red and blue (postage) . . 10 10
812 1c. red, brown and turquoise 10 10
813 3c. red and blue 25 15
814 4c. red, brown and green . . 35 20
815 5c. red, brown and mauve (air) 45 25
816 15c. red, brown and blue . . 1·10 90
817 21c. red, brown and myrtle 2·25 1·90
818 31c. red, brown and blue . . 3·00 2·25
DESIGNS: ½c. (expressed "B/0.005"), 3c. Type **235**; 1, 4c. Speed-skating; 5c. to 31c. Skiing (slalom).

1964. 450th Anniv of Discovery of Pacific Ocean.
820 **236** 4c. green on flesh (postage) 10 10
821 10c. violet on pink (air) 20 20

237 Boy Scout
238 St. Paul's Cathedral, London

1964. Obligatory Tax for Youth Rehabilitation Institute.
822 **237** 1c. red 10 10
823 1c. grey 10 10
824 1c. light blue 10 10
825 1c. olive 10 10
826 1c. violet 10 10
827 – 1c. brown 10 10
828 – 1c. orange 10 10
829 – 1c. turquoise 10 10
830 – 1c. violet 10 10
831 – 1c. yellow 10 10
DESIGN: Nos. 827/31, Girl guide.

1964. Air. Ecumenical Council, Vatican City (1st issue). Cathedrals. Centres in black.
832 21c. red (Type **238**) 55 35
833 21c. blue (Kassa, Hungary) 55 35
834 21c. green (Milan) 55 35
835 21c. black (St. John's, Poland) 55 35
836 21c. brown (St. Stephen's, Vienna) 55 35
837 21c. brown (Notre Dame, Paris) 55 35
838 21c. violet (Moscow) 55 35
839 21c. violet (Lima) 55 35
840 21c. red (Stockholm) 55 35
841 21c. mauve (Cologne) 55 35
842 21c. bistre (New Delhi) . . . 55 35
843 21c. deep turquoise (Basel) 55 35
844 21c. green (Toledo) 55 35
845 21c. red (Metropolitan, Athens) 55 35
846 21c. olive (St. Patrick's, New York) 55 35
847 21c. green (Lisbon) 55 35
848 21c. turquoise (Sofia) 55 35
849 21c. deep brown (New Church, Delft, Netherlands) 55 35
850 21c. deep sepia (St. George's Patriarchal Church, Istanbul) 55 35
851 21c. blue (Basilica, Guadalupe, Mexico) . . . 55 35
852 1b. blue (Panama) . . . . . 1·75 1·75
853 2b. green (St. Peter's, Rome) 3·00 3·00
See also Nos. 882, etc.

1964. As Nos. 749 and 760 but colours changed and optd **HABILITADA**.
855 1b. black, red & blue (postage) . . . . 1·75 1·60
856 1b. black, green & yellow (air) . . . . 1·75 1·25

1964. Air. No. 756 surch **VALE B/. 0.50**.
857 50c. on 21c. black, sepia and blue 65 40

241 Discus-thrower

1964. Olympic Games, Tokyo.
858 ½c. ("B/0.005") purple, red, brown and green (postage) 10 10
859 1c. multicoloured 10 10
860 5c. black, red and olive (air) 35 25
861 10c. black, red and yellow . . 70 45
862 21c. multicoloured . . . . . 1·40 90
863 50c. multicoloured . . . . . 2·75 1·75
DESIGNS: ½c. Type **241**; 1c. Runner with Olympic Flame; 5c. to 50c. Olympic Stadium, Tokyo, and Mt. Fuji.

1964. Air. Nos. 692 and 742 surch **Aereo B/.0.10**.
865 10c. on 5c. green and turquoise 20 15
866 10c. on 5c. black, red and green 20 15

243 Space Vehicles (Project "Apollo")

1964. Space Exploration. Multicoloured.

No.	Type	Description	Unused	Used
867		½c. ("B/0.005") Type **243** (postage)	10	10
868		1c. Rocket and capsule (Project "Gemini")	10	10
869		5c. W. M. Schirra (air)	20	20
870		10c. L. G. Cooper	30	30
871		21c. Schirra's capsule	75	75
872		50c. Cooper's capsule	3·25	3·00

1964. No. 687 surch **Correos B/. 0.10**.

No.	Type	Description	Unused	Used
874		10c. on 21c. blue	15	15

245 Water-skiing

1964. Aquatic Sports. Multicoloured.

No.	Type	Description	Unused	Used
875		½c. ("B/0.005") Type **245** (postage)	10	10
876		1c. Underwater swimming	10	10
877		5c. Fishing (air)	20	10
878		10c. Sailing (vert)	1·50	60
879		21c. Speedboat racing	2·75	1·50
880		31c. Water polo at Olympic Games, 1964	3·50	1·75

1964. Air. Ecumenical Council, Vatican City (2nd issue). Stamps of 1st issue optd **1964**. Centres in black.

No.	Type	Description	Unused	Used
882		21c. red (No. 832)	70	50
883		21c. green (No. 834)	70	50
884		21c. olive (No. 836)	70	50
885		21c. deep sepia (No. 850)	70	50
886		1b. blue (No. 852)	2·75	2·00
887		2b. green (No. 853)	5·50	4·50

247 General View

248 Eleanor Roosevelt

1964. Air. New York's World Fair.

No.	Type	Description	Unused	Used
889	**247**	5c. black and yellow	30	25
890	–	10c. black and red	75	60
891	–	15c. black and green	1·25	80
892	–	21c. black and blue	1·90	1·50

DESIGNS: 10c., 15c. Fair pavilions (different); 21c. Unisphere.

1964. Mrs. Eleanor Roosevelt Commemoration.

No.	Type	Description	Unused	Used
894	**248**	4c. black and red on yellow (postage)	15	10
895		20c. black and green on buff (air)	50	45

249 Dag Hammarskjold — 250 Pope John XXIII

1964. Air. U.N. Day.

No.	Type	Description	Unused	Used
897	**249**	21c. black and blue	70	50
898	–	21c. blue and black	70	50

DESIGN: No. 898, U.N. Emblem.

1964. Air. Pope John Commemoration.

No.	Type	Description	Unused	Used
900	**250**	21c. black and bistre	70	50
901	–	21c. mult (Papal Arms)	70	50

251 Slalom Skiing Medals

1964. Winter Olympic Winners' Medals. Medals in gold, silver and bronze.

No.	Type	Description	Unused	Used
903	**251**	½c. ("B/0.005") turquoise (postage)	10	10
904	–	1c. deep blue	10	10
905	–	2c. brown	20	15
906	–	3c. mauve	25	15
907	–	4c. lake	35	20
908	–	5c. violet (air)	45	25
909	–	6c. blue	55	30
910	–	7c. violet	65	35
911	–	10c. green	90	50
912	–	21c. red	1·40	95
913	–	31c. blue	2·50	1·40

DESIGNS—Medals for: 1c., 7c. Speed-skating; 2c., 21c. Bobsleighing; 3c., 10c. Figure-skating; 4c. Ski-jumping; 5c., 6c., 31c. Cross-country skiing. Values in the same design show different medal-winners and country names.

252 Red-billed Toucan

1965. Birds. Multicoloured.

No.	Type	Description	Unused	Used
915		1c. Type **252** (postage)	65	10
916		2c. Scarlet macaw	65	10
917		3c. Woodpecker sp.	1·00	15
918		4c. Blue-grey tanager (horiz)	1·00	25
919		5c. Troupial (horiz) (air)	1·25	40
920		10c. Crimson-backed tanager (horiz)	2·60	55

253 Red Snapper

1965. Marine Life. Multicoloured.

No.	Type	Description	Unused	Used
921		1c. Type **253** (postage)	10	10
922		2c. Dolphin (fish)	10	10
923		8c. Shrimp (air)	20	15
924		12c. Smooth hammerhead	60	25
925		13c. Sailfish	65	30
926		25c. Lined seahorse (vert)	80	35

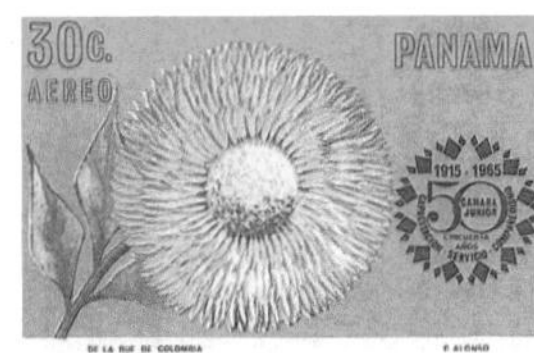

254 Double Daisy and Emblem

1966. Air. 50th Anniv of Junior Chamber of Commerce. Flowers. Multicoloured: background colour given.

No.	Type	Description	Unused	Used
927	**254**	30c. mauve	55	45
928	–	30c. flesh (Hibiscus)	55	45
929	–	30c. olive (Mauve orchid)	55	45
930	–	40c. green (Water lily)	60	55
931	–	40c. blue (Gladiolus)	60	55
932	–	40c. pink (White orchid)	60	55

Each design incorporates the Junior Chamber of Commerce Emblem.

1966. Surch. (a) Postage.

No.	Type	Description	Unused	Used
933		13c. on 25c. (No. 747)	30	20

(b) Air.

No.	Type	Description	Unused	Used
934		3c. on 5c. (No. 680)	10	10
935		13c. on 25c. (No. 695)	30	25

256 Chicken

1967. Domestic Animals. Multicoloured.

No.	Type	Description	Unused	Used
936		1c. Type **256** (postage)	10	10
937		3c. Cockerel	10	10
938		5c. Pig (horiz)	10	10
939		8c. Cow (horiz)	15	10
940		10c. Pekingese dog (air)	25	20
941		13c. Zebu (horiz)	30	20
942		30c. Cat	60	50
943		40c. Horse (horiz)	75	60

257 American Darter

1967. Wild Birds. Multicoloured.

No.	Type	Description	Unused	Used
944		½c. Type **257**	70	15
945		1c. Resplendent quetzal	70	15
946		3c. Turquoise-browed motmot	90	20
947		4c. Red-necked aracari (horiz)	1·00	30
948		5c. Chestnut-fronted macaw	1·40	30
949		13c. Belted kingfisher	5·00	1·40

258 "Deer" (F. Marc)

1967. Wild Animals. Paintings. Multicoloured.

No.	Type	Description	Unused	Used
950		1c. Type **258** (postage)	10	10
951		3c. "Cougar" (F. Marc) (vert)	10	10
952		5c. "Monkeys" (F. Marc)	10	10
953		8c. "Fox" (F. Marc)	20	10
954		10c. "St. Jerome and the Lion" (Durer) (vert) (air)	20	15
955		13c. "The Hare" (Durer) (vert)	30	20
956		20c. "Lady with the Ermine" (Da Vinci) (vert)	45	25
957		30c. "The Hunt" (Delacroix)	65	45

259 Map of Panama and People

1969. National Population Census.

No.	Type	Description	Unused	Used
958	**259**	5c. blue	10	10
959	–	10c. purple	20	15

DESIGN—VERT: 10c. People and map of the Americas.

260 Cogwheel

1969. 50th Anniv of Rotary Int in Panama.

No.	Type	Description	Unused	Used
960	**260**	13c. black, yellow and blue	20	20

261 Cornucopia and Map

1969. 1st Anniv of 11 October Revolution.

No.	Type	Description	Unused	Used
961	**261**	10c. multicoloured	20	10

262 Tower and Map

1969.

No.	Type	Description	Unused	Used
962	**262**	3c. black and orange	10	10
963	–	5c. green	10	10
964	–	8c. brown	20	15
965	–	13c. black and green	25	15
966	–	20c. brown	35	25
967	–	21c. yellow	35	25
968	–	25c. green	45	30
969	–	30c. black	50	45
970	–	34c. brown	55	45
971	–	38c. blue	60	45
972	–	40c. yellow	65	45
973	–	50c. black and purple	85	65
974	–	59c. purple	1·00	60

DESIGNS—HORIZ: 5c. Peasants; 13c. Hotel Continental; 25c. Del Rey Bridge; 34c. Panama Cathedral; 38c. Municipal Palace; 40c. French Plaza; 50c. Thatcher Ferry Bridge; 59c. National Theatre. VERT: 8c. Nata Church; 20c. Virgin of Carmen Church; 21c. Altar, San Jose Church; 30c. Dr. Arosemena statue.

263 Discus-thrower and Stadium

1970. 11th Central American and Caribbean Games, Panama (1st series).

No.	Type	Description	Unused	Used
975	**263**	1c. multicoloured (postage)	10	10
976		2c. multicoloured	10	10
977		3c. multicoloured	10	10
978		5c. multicoloured	10	10
979		10c. multicoloured	20	15
980		13c. multicoloured	25	15
981	–	13c. multicoloured	25	15
982	**263**	25c. multicoloured	45	35
983		30c. multicoloured	55	45
984	–	13c. multicoloured (air)	1·00	25
985	–	30c. multicoloured	60	45

DESIGNS—VERT: No. 981, "Flor del Espirited Santo" (flowers); 985, Indian girl. HORIZ: No. 984, Thatcher Ferry Bridge and palm.

See also Nos. 986/94.

264 J. D. Arosemena and Stadium

1970. Air. 11th Central American and Caribbean Games, Panama (2nd series). Multicoloured.

No.	Type	Description	Unused	Used
986		1c. Type **264**	10	10
987		2c. Type **264**	10	10
988		3c. Type **264**	10	10
989		5c. Type **264**	10	10
990		13c. Basketball	20	15
991		13c. New Gymnasium	20	15
992		13c. Revolution Stadium	20	15
993		13c. Panamanian couple in festive costume	20	15
994		30c. Eternal Flame and stadium	45	35

265 A. Tapia and M. Sosa (first comptrollers)

1971. 40th Anniv of Panamanian Comptroller-General's Office. Multicoloured.

No.	Type	Description	Unused	Used
996		3c. Comptroller-General's Building (1970) (vert)	10	10
997		5c. Type **265**	10	10
998		8c. Comptroller-General's emblem (vert)	15	10
999		13c. Comptroller-General's Building (1955–70)	30	15

266 "Man and Alligator"

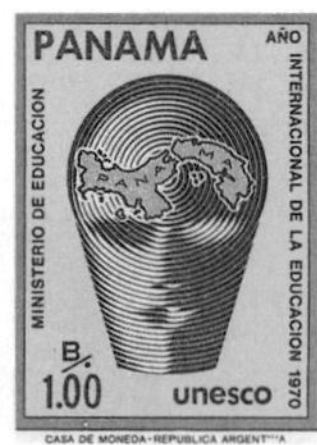

267 Map of Panama on I.E.Y. Emblem

1971. Indian Handicrafts.
1000 **266** 8c. multicoloured 20 15

1971. International Education Year.
1001 **267** 1b. multicoloured . . . 1·50 1·50

268 Astronaut on Moon

269 Panama Pavilion

1971. Air. "Apollo 11" and "Apollo 12" Moon Missions. Multicoloured.
1002 13c. Type **268** 35 25
1003 13c. "Apollo 12" astronauts 35 25

1971. Air. "EXPO 70" World Fair, Osaka, Japan.
1004 **269** 10c. multicoloured . . . 15 15

270 Conference Text and Emblem

1971. 9th Inter-American Loan and Savings Association Conference, Panama City.
1005 **270** 25c. multicoloured . . . 60 35

271 Panama Flag

1971. Air. American Tourist Year. Multicoloured.
1006 5c. Type **271** 10 10
1007 13c. Map of Panama and Western Hemisphere . . . 30 20

272 New U.P.U. H.Q. Building

1971. Inauguration of New U.P.U. Headquarters Building, Berne. Multicoloured.
1008 8c. Type **272** 20 10
1009 30c. U.P.U. Monument, Berne (vert) 60 35

273 Cow and Pig

1971. 3rd Agricultural Census.
1010 **273** 3c. multicoloured 10 10

274 Map and "4S" Emblem

1971. "4S" Programme for Rural Youth.
1011 **274** 2c. multicoloured 10 10

275 Gandhi

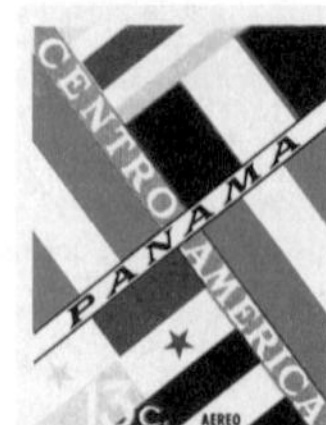

276 Central American Flags

1971. Air. Birth Centenary (1969) of Mahatma Gandhi.
1012 **275** 10c. multicoloured . . . 20 15

1971. Air. 150th Anniv of Central American States' Independence from Spain.
1013 **276** 13c. multicoloured . . . 30 20

277 Early Panama Stamp

278 Altar, Nata Church

1971. Air. 2nd National, Philatelic and Numismatic Exhibition, Panama.
1014 **277** 8c. blue, black and red 20 15

1972. Air. 450th Anniv of Nata Church.
1015 **278** 40c. multicoloured . . . 50 45

279 Telecommunications Emblem

1972. Air. World Telecommunications Day.
1016 **279** 13c. black, blue & lt blue 20 15

280 "Apollo 14" Badge

1972. Air. Moon Flight of "Apollo 14".
1017 **280** 13c. multicoloured . . . 60 25

281 Children on See-saw

1972. 25th Anniv (1971) of U.N.I.C.E.F. Mult.
1018 1c. Type **281** (postage) . . . 10 10
1019 5c. Boy sitting by kerb (vert) (air) 10 10
1020 8c. Indian mother and child (vert) 15 10
1021 50c. U.N.I.C.E.F. emblem (vert) 70 45

282 Tropical Fruits

1972. Tourist Publicity. Multicoloured.
1023 1c. Type **282** (postage) . . . 10 10
1024 2c. "Isle of Night" 10 10
1025 3c. Carnival float (vert) . . 10 10
1026 5c. San Blas textile (air) . . 10 10
1027 8c. Chaquira (beaded collar) 20 10
1028 25c. Ruined fort, Portobelo 35 30

283 Map and Flags

284 Baseball Players

1973. Obligatory Tax. Panama City Post Office Building Fund. 7th Bolivar Games.
1030 **283** 1c. black 10 10

1973. Air. 7th Bolivar Games.
1031 **284** 8c. red and yellow . . . 15 10
1032 – 10c. black and blue . . . 20 15
1033 – 13c. multicoloured . . . 30 20
1034 – 25c. black, red and green 55 30
1035 – 50c. multicoloured . . . 1·25 55
1036 – 1b. multicoloured . . . 2·50 1·10
DESIGNS—VERT: 10c. Basketball; 13c. Flaming torch. HORIZ: 25c. Boxing; 50c. Panama map and flag, Games emblem and Bolivar; 1b. Games' medals.

1973. U.N. Security Council Meeting, Panama City. Various stamps surch **O.N.U.** in laurel leaf, **CONSEJO DE SEGURIDAD 15 - 21 Marzo 1973** and value.
1037 8c. on 59c. (No. 974) (postage) 10 10
1038 10c. on 1b. (No. 1001) . . . 15 15
1039 13c. on 30c. (No. 969) . . . 20 15
1040 13c. on 40c. (No. 1015) (air) 25 15

286 Farming Co-operative

1973. Obligatory Tax. Post Office Building Fund.
1041 **286** 1c. green and red 10 10
1042 – 1c. grey and red 10 10
1043 – 1c. yellow and red . . . 10 10
1044 – 1c. orange and red . . . 10 10
1045 – 1c. blue and red 10 10
DESIGNS: No. 1042, Silver coins; 1043, V. Lorenzo; 1044, Cacique Urraca; 1045, Post Office building.
See also Nos. 1061/2.

287 J. D. Crespo (educator)

290 Women's upraised Hands

1973. Famous Panamanians. Multicoloured.
1046 3c. Type **287** (postage) . . . 10 10
1047 5c. Isabel Obaldia (educator) (air) 10 10
1048 8c. N. V. Jaen (educator) . . 20 15
1049 10c. "Forest Scene" (Roberto Lewis, painter) 20 15
1050 13c. R. Miro (poet) 35 20
1051 13c. "Portrait of a Lady" (M. E. Amador, painter) 35 20
1052 20c. "Self-Portrait" (Isaac Benitez, painter) 55 20
1053 21c. M. A. Guerrero (statesman) 55 25
1054 25c. Dr. B. Porras (statesman) 55 30
1055 30c. J. D. Arosemena (statesman) 70 35
1056 34c. Dr. O. M. Pereira (writer) 90 45
1057 38c. Dr. R. J. Alfaro (writer) . . . . 1·10 50

1973. Air. 50th Anniv of Isabel Obaldia Professional School. Nos. 1047, 1054 and 1056 optd **1923 1973 Godas de Oro Escuela Profesional Isabel Herrera Obaldia** and EP emblem.
1058 5c. multicoloured 15 10
1059 25c. multicoloured 55 30
1060 34c. multicoloured 60 55

1974. Obligatory Tax. Post Office Building Fund. As Nos. 1044/5.
1061 1c. orange 10 10
1062 2c. blue 10 10

1974. Surch **VALE** and value.
1063 5c. on 30c. black (No. 969) (postage) 10 10
1064 10c. on 34c. brown (No. 970) 15 10
1065 13c. on 21c. yellow (No. 967) 20 15
1066 1c. on 25c. multicoloured (No. 1028) (air) 10 10
1067 3c. on 20c. mult (No. 1052) 10 10
1068 8c. on 38c. mult (No. 1057) 15 10
1069 10c. on 34c. mult (No. 1056) 15 15
1070 13c. on 21c. mult (No. 1053) 20 15

1975. Air. International Women's Year.
1071 **290** 17c. multicoloured . . . 45 20

291 Bayano Dam

1975. Air. 7th Anniv of October 1968 Revolution.
1073 **291** 17c. black, brown & blue 20 15
1074 – 27c. blue and green . . . 30 25
1075 – 33c. multicoloured . . . 1·10 30
DESIGNS—VERT: 27c. Victoria sugar plant, Veraguas, and sugar cane. HORIZ: 33c. Tocumen International Airport.

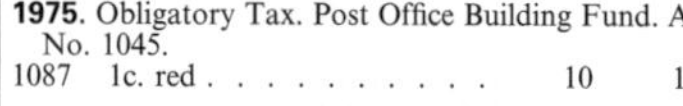
1975. Obligatory Tax. Various stamps surch **VALE PRO EDIFICIO** and value.
1076 – 1c. on 30c. black (No. 969) (postage) . . 10 10
1077 – 1c. on 40c. yellow (No. 972) 10 10
1078 – 1c. on 50c. black and purple (No. 973) . . . 10 10
1079 – 1c. on 30c. mult (No. 1009) 10 10
1080 **282** 1c. on 1c. multicoloured 10 10
1081 – 1c. on 2c. multicoloured (No. 1024) 10 10
1082 **278** 1c. on 40c. mult (air) . . 10 10
1083 – 1c. on 25c. mult (No. 1028) 10 10
1084 – 1c. on 25c. mult (No. 1052) 10 10
1085 – 1c. on 20c. mult (No. 1054) 10 10
1086 – 1c. on 30c. mult (No. 1055) 10 10

1975. Obligatory Tax. Post Office Building Fund. As No. 1045.
1087 1c. red 10 10

294 Bolivar and Thatcher Ferry Bridge

1976. 150th Anniv of Panama Congress (1st issue). Multicoloured.
1088 6c. Type **294** (postage) . . . 10 10
1089 23c. Bolivar Statue (air) . . 30 25
1090 35c. Bolivar Hall, Panama City (horiz) 50 30
1091 41c. Bolivar and flag . . . 60 40

295 "Evibacus princeps"

1976. Marine Fauna. Multicoloured.
1092 2c. Type **295** (postage) . . . 10 10
1093 3c. "Ptitosarcus sinuosus" (vert) 10 10

1094 4c. "Acanthaster planci" . . 10 10
1095 7c. "Oreaster reticulatus" . . 10 10
1096 17c. Porcupinefish (vert) (air) 60 20
1097 27c. "Pocillopora damicornis" 40 25

296 "Simon Bolivar"

1976. 150th Anniv of Panama Congress (2nd issue). Designs showing details of Bolivar Monument or flags of Latin-American countries. Multicoloured.
1099 20c. Type **296** 30 20
1100 20c. Argentina 30 20
1101 20c. Bolivia 30 20
1102 20c. Brazil 30 20
1103 20c. Chile 30 20
1104 20c. "Battle scene" 30 20
1105 20c. Colombia 30 20
1106 20c. Costa Rica 30 20
1107 20c. Cuba 30 20
1108 20c. Ecuador 30 20
1109 20c. El Salvador 30 20
1110 20c. Guatemala 30 20
1111 20c. Guyana 30 20
1112 20c. Haiti 30 20
1113 20c. "Congress assembly" . . 30 20
1114 20c. "Liberated people" . . 30 20
1115 20c. Honduras 30 20
1116 20c. Jamaica 30 20
1117 20c. Mexico 30 20
1118 20c. Nicaragua 30 20
1119 20c. Panama 30 20
1120 20c. Paraguay 30 20
1121 20c. Peru 30 20
1122 20c. Dominican Republic . . 30 20
1123 20c. "Bolivar and standard-bearer" 30 20
1124 20c. Surinam 30 20
1125 20c. Trinidad and Tobago 30 20
1126 20c. Uruguay 30 20
1127 20c. Venezuela 30 20
1128 20c. "Indian Delegation" . . 30 20

297 Nicanor Villalaz (designer of Panama Arms)
298 National Lottery Building, Panama City

1976. Villalaz Commemoration.
1130 **297** 5c. blue 10 10

1976. "Progressive Panama".
1131 **298** 6c. multicoloured 10 10

299 Cerro Colorado, Copper Mine

1976. Air.
1132 **299** 23c. multicoloured . . . 30 20

300 Contadora Island

1977. Tourism.
1133 **300** 3c. multicoloured 10 10

301 Secretary-General of Pan-American Union, A. Orfila

1978. Signing of Panama–U.S.A. Treaty. Mult.
1134 3c. Type **301** 10 10
1135 23c. Treaty signing scene (horiz) 30 25
1136 40c. President Carter . . . 55 30
1137 50c. Gen. O. Torrijos of Panama 70 50
Nos. 1134 and 1136/7 were issued together se-tenant in horizontal stamps of three showing Treaty signing as No. 1135.

302 Signing Ratification of Panama Canal Treaty

1978. Ratification of Panama Canal Treaty.
1138 **302** 3c. multicoloured 10 10
1139 – 5c. multicoloured 10 10
1140 – 35c. multicoloured . . . 50 25
1141 – 41c. multicoloured . . . 60 30
DESIGNS: 5, 35, 41c. As Type **302**, but with the design of the Ratification Ceremony spread over the three stamps, issued as a se-tenant strip in the order 5c. (29 × 39 mm), 41c. (44 × 39 mm), 35c. (29 × 39 mm).

303 Colon Harbour and Warehouses

1978. 30th Anniv of Colon Free Zone.
1142 **303** 6c. multicoloured 10 10

304 Children's Home and Melvin Jones

1978. Birth Centenary of Melvin Jones (founder of Lions International).
1143 **304** 50c. multicoloured . . . 70 55

305 Pres. Torrijos, "Flavia" (liner) and Children

1979. Return of Canal Zone. Multicoloured.
1144 3c. Type **305** . . . . 1·25 55
1145 23c. Presidents Torrijos and Carter, liner and flags of Panama and U.S.A. . . . 50 25

306 "75" and Bank Emblem

1979. 75th Anniv of National Bank.
1146 **306** 6c. black, red and blue 10 10

307 Rotary Emblem
308 Children inside Heart

1979. 75th Anniv of Rotary International.
1147 **307** 17c. blue and yellow . . 25 20

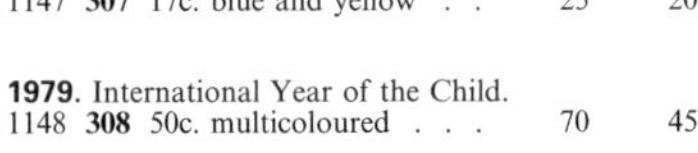

1979. International Year of the Child.
1148 **308** 50c. multicoloured . . . 70 45

309 U.P.U. Emblem and Globe
310 Colon Station

1979. 18th Universal Postal Union Congress, Rio de Janeiro.
1149 **309** 35c. multicoloured . . . 50 30

1980. Centenary of Trans-Panamanian Railway.
1150 **310** 1c. purple and lilac . . . 20 35

311 Postal Headquarters, Balboa (inauguration)
318 Boys in Children's Village

1980. Anniversaries and Events.
1151 **311** 3c. multicoloured 10 10
1152 – 6c. multicoloured 10 10
1153 – 17c. multicoloured . . . 25 20
1154 – 23c. multicoloured . . . 30 20
1155 – 35c. blue, black and red 50 30
1156 – 41c. pink and black . . 60 40
1157 – 50c. multicoloured . . . 70 45
DESIGNS—HORIZ: 17c. Map of Central America and flags (census of the Americas); 23c. Tourism and Convention Centre (opening); 35c. Bank emblem (Inter-American Development Bank, 25th anniv); 41c. F. de Lesseps (Panama Canal cent); 50c. Olympic Stadium, Moscow (Olympic Games). VERT. 6c. National flag (return of Canal Zone).

1980. Olympic Games, Lake Placid and Moscow. (a) Optd **1980 LAKE PLACID MOSCU** and venue emblems.
1158 20c. (No. 1099) 80 80
1159 20c. (1101) 80 80
1162 20c. (1103) 80 80
1164 20c. (1105) 80 80
1166 20c. (1107) 80 80
1168 20c. (1109) 80 80
1170 20c. (1111) 80 80
1172 20c. (1113) 80 80
1174 20c. (1115) 80 80
1176 20c. (1117) 80 80
1178 20c. (1119) 80 80
1180 20c. (1121) 80 80
1182 20c. (1123) 80 80
1184 20c. (1125) 80 80
1186 20c. (1127) 80 80

(b) Optd with Lake Placid Olympic emblems and medals total of country indicated.
1159 20c. "**ALEMANIA D.**" (1101) 80 80
1161 20c. "**AUSTRIA**" (1102) . . 80 80
1163 20c. "**SUECIA**" (1104) . . . 80 80
1165 20c. "**U.R.S.S.**" (1106) . . . 80 80
1167 20c. "**ALEMANIA F.**" (1108) 80 80
1169 20c. "**ITALIA**" (1110) . . . 80 80
1171 20c. "**U.S.A.**" (1112) 80 80
1173 20c. "**SUIZA**" (1114) . . . 80 80
1175 20c. "**CANADA/GRAN BRETANA**" (1116) . . . 80 80
1177 20c. "**NORUEGA**" (1118) 80 80
1179 20c. "**LICHTENSTEIN**" (1120) 80 80
1181 20c. "**HUNGRIA/ BULGARIA**" (1122) . . . 80 80
1183 20c. "**FINLANDIA**" (1124) 80 80
1185 20c. "**HOLANDA**" (1126) 80 80
1187 20c. "**CHECOS-LOVAQUIA/FRANCIA**" (1128) 80 80
Nos. 1158, etc, occur on 1st, 3rd and 5th rows and Nos. 1159, etc, occur on the others.

(c) Lake Placid and Moscow and venue with Olympic rings.
1188 20c. (No. 1099) 80 80
1190 20c. (1101) 80 80
1192 20c. (1103) 80 80
1194 20c. (1105) 80 80
1196 20c. (1107) 80 80
1198 20c. (1109) 80 80
1200 20c. (1111) 80 80
1202 20c. (1113) 80 80
1204 20c. (1115) 80 80
1206 20c. (1117) 80 80
1208 20c. (1119) 80 80
1210 20c. (1121) 80 80
1212 20c. (1123) 80 80
1214 20c. (1125) 80 80
1216 20c. (1127) 80 80

(d) Optd with country names as indicated.
1189 20c. "**RUSIA/ALEMANIA D.**" (1101) 80 80
1191 20c. "**SUECIA/ FINLANDIA**" (1102) . . 80 80
1193 20c. "**GRECIA/BELGICA/ INDIA**" (1104) 80 80
1195 20c. "**BULGARIA/CUBA**" (1106) 80 80
1197 20c. "**CHECOS-LOVAQUIA/ YUGOSLAVIA**" (1108) 80 80
1199 20c. "**ZIMBAWE/COREA DEL NORTE/ MONGOLIA**" (1110) . . 80 80
1201 20c. "**ITALIA/HUNGRIA**" (1112) 80 80
1203 20c. "**AUSTRALIA/ DINAMARCA**" (1114) . . 80 80
1205 20c. "**TANZANIA/ MEXICO/HOLANDA**" (1116) 80 80
1207 20c. "**RUMANIA/ FRANCIA**" (1118) . . . 80 80
1209 20c. "**BRASIL/ETIOPIA**" (1120) 80 80
1211 20c. "**IRLANDA/UGANDA/ VENEZUELA**" (1122) . . 80 80
1213 20c. "**GRAN BRETANA/ POLONIA**" (1124) . . . 80 80
1215 20c. "**SUIZA/ESPANA/ AUSTRIA**" (1126) . . . 80 80
1217 20c. "**JAMAICA/LIBANO/ GUYANA**" (1128) 80 80
Nos. 1188, etc, occur on 1st, 3rd and 5th rows and Nos. 1189, etc, on the others.

1980. Medal Winners at Winter Olympic Games, Lake Placid. (a) Optd with 1980, medals and venue emblems.
1219 20c. 1980 medals and venue and emblems (No. 1099) 80 80
1221 20c. As No. 1219 (1101) . . 80 80
1223 20c. As No. 1219 (1103) . . 80 80
1225 20c. As No. 1219 (1105) . . 80 80
1227 20c. As No. 1219 (1107) . . 80 80
1229 20c. As No. 1219 (1109) . . 80 80
1231 20c. As No. 1219 (1111) . . 80 80
1233 20c. As No. 1219 (1113) . . 80 80
1235 20c. As No. 1219 (1115) . . 80 80
1237 20c. As No. 1219 (1117) . . 80 80
1239 20c. As No. 1219 (1119) . . 80 80
1241 20c. As No. 1219 (1121) . . 80 80
1243 20c. As No. 1219 (1123) . . 80 80
1245 20c. As No. 1219 (1125) . . 80 80
1247 20c. As No. 1219 (1127) . . 80 80

(b) Optd with 1980 medals and venue emblems and Olympic torch and country indicated.
1220 20c. "**ALEMANIA D.**" (1100) 80 80
1222 20c. "**AUSTRIA**" (1102) . . 80 80
1224 20c. "**SUECIA**" (1104) . . . 80 80
1226 20c. "**U.R.S.S.**" (1106) . . . 80 80
1228 20c. "**ALEMANIA F.**" (1108) 80 80
1230 20c. "**ITALIA**" (1110) . . . 80 80
1232 20c. "**U.S.A.**" (1112) 80 80
1234 20c. "**SUIZA**" (1114) . . . 80 80
1236 20c. "**CANADA/GRAN BRETANA**" (1116) . . . 80 80
1238 20c. "**NORUEGA**" (1118) 80 80
1240 20c. "**LICHTENSTEIN**" (1120) 80 80
1242 20c. "**HUNGRIA/ BULGARIA**" (1122) . . . 80 80
1244 20c. "**FINLANDIA**" (1124) 80 80
1246 20c. "**HOLANDIA**" (1126) 80 80
1248 20c. "**CHECOS-LOVAQUIA/FRANCIA**" (1128) 80 80
Nos. 1219, etc, occur on 1st, 3rd and 5th rows and Nos. 1220, etc, on the others.

1980. World Cup Football Championship, Argentina (1978) and Spain (1980). Optd with: A. Football cup emblems. B. "**ESPAMER 80**" and "Argentina '78" emblems and inscriptions "**ESPANA '82/ CAMPEONATO/MUNDIAL DE FUTBOL**". C. World Cup Trophy and "**ESPANA '82.**". D. "**ESPANA 82/Football/Argentina '78/BESPAMER '80 MADRID**". E. FIFA globes emblem and "**ESPANA '82/ARGENTINAA '78/ESPANA '82**". F. With ball and inscription as for B.
1249 20c. No. 1099 (A, C, E) . . 80 80
1250 20c. No. 1100 (B, D, F) . . 80 80
1251 20c. No. 1101 (A, C, E) . . 80 80
1252 20c. No. 1102 (B, D, F) . . 80 80
1253 20c. No. 1103 (A, C, E) . . 80 80
1254 20c. No. 1104 (B, D, F) . . 80 80
1255 20c. No. 1105 (A, C, E) . . 80 80
1256 20c. No. 1106 (B, D, F) . . 80 80
1257 20c. No. 1107 (A, C, E) . . 80 80
1258 20c. No. 1108 (B, D, F) . . 80 80
1259 20c. No. 1109 (A, C, E) . . 80 80
1260 20c. No. 1110 (B, D, F) . . 80 80
1261 20c. No. 1111 (A, C, E) . . 80 80
1262 20c. No. 1112 (B, D, F) . . 80 80
1263 20c. No. 1113 (A, C, E) . . 80 80
1264 20c. No. 1114 (B, D, F) . . 80 80
1265 20c. No. 1115 (A, C, E) . . 80 80
1266 20c. No. 1116 (B, D, F) . . 80 80
1267 20c. No. 1117 (A, C, E) . . 80 80
1268 20c. No. 1118 (B, D, F) . . 80 80
1269 20c. No. 1119 (A, C, E) . . 80 80
1270 20c. No. 1120 (B, D, F) . . 80 80
1271 20c. No. 1121 (A, C, E) . . 80 80
1272 20c. No. 1122 (B, D, F) . . 80 80
1273 20c. No. 1123 (A, C, E) . . 80 80
1274 20c. No. 1124 (B, D, F) . . 80 80
1275 20c. No. 1125 (A, C, E) . . 80 80
1276 20c. No. 1126 (B, D, F) . . 80 80
1277 20c. No. 1127 (A, C, E) . . 80 80
1278 20c. No. 1128 (B, D, F) . . 80 80

1980. Obligatory Tax. Children's Village. Mult.
1280 2c. Type **318** 10 10
1281 2c. Boy with chicks 10 10
1282 2c. Working in the fields . . 10 10
1283 2c. Boys with pig 10 10

319 Jean Baptiste de la Salle and Map showing La Salle Schools **320** Louis Braille

1981. Education in Panama by the Christian Schools.
1285 **319** 17c. blue, black and red 25 20

1981. International Year of Disabled People.
1286 **320** 23c. multicoloured . . . 30 20

321 Statue of the Virgin

1981. 150th Anniv of Apparition of Miraculous Virgin to St. Catharine Laboure.
1287 **321** 35c. multicoloured . . . 50 35

322 Crimson-backed Tanager

1981. Birds. Multicoloured.
1288 3c. Type **322** 55 10
1289 6c. Chestnut-fronted macaw (vert) 70 15
1290 41c. Violet sabrewing (vert) 2·75 1·00
1291 50c. Keel-billed toucan . . . 3·75 1·25

323 "Boy feeding Donkey" (Ricardo Morales) **324** Banner

1981. Obligatory Tax. Christmas. Children's Village. Multicoloured.
1292 2c. Type **323** 10 10
1293 2c. "Nativity" (Enrique Daniel Austin) 10 10
1294 2c. "Bird in Tree" (Jorge Gonzalez) 10 10
1295 2c. "Church" (Eric Belgrane) 10 10

1981. National Reaffirmation.
1297 **324** 3c. multicoloured 10 10

325 General Herrera **326** Ricardo J. Alfaro

1982. 1st Death Anniv of General Omar Torrijos Herrera. Multicoloured.
1298 5c. Aerial view of Panama (postage) 10 10
1299 6c. Colecito army camp . . 10 10
1300 17c. Bayano river barrage 25 20
1301 50c. Felipillo engineering works 70 45
1302 23c. Type **325** (air) 35 25
1303 35c. Security Council reunion 50 30
1304 41c. Gen. Omar Torrijos airport . . . . 1·25 45

1982. Birth Cent of Ricardo J. Alfaro (statesman).
1306 **326** 3c. black, mauve and blue (postage) 10 10
1307 – 17c. black and mauve (air) 25 15
1308 – 23c. multicoloured . . . 30 20
DESIGNS: 17c. Profile of Alfaro wearing spectacles (as humanist); 23c. Portrait of Alfaro (as lawyer).

328 Pig Farming **329** Pele (Brazilian footballer)

1982. Obligatory Tax. Christmas. Children's Village. Multicoloured.
1309 2c. Type **328** 10 10
1310 2c. Gardening 10 10
1311 2c. Metalwork (horiz) . . . 10 10
1312 2c. Bee-keeping (horiz) . . . 10 10

1982. World Cup Football Championship, Spain. Multicoloured.
1314 50c. Italian team (horiz) (postage) 70 45
1315 23c. Football emblem and map of Panama (air) . . 30 20
1316 35c. Type **329** 50 30
1317 41c. World Cup Trophy . . 60 35

330 Chamber of Trade Emblem

1983. "Expo Comer" Chamber of Trade Exhibition.
1319 **330** 17c. lt blue, blue, & gold 25 15

331 Dr. Nicolas Solano **332** Pope John Paul II giving Blessing

1983. Air. Birth Centenary (1982) of Dr. Nicolas Solano (anti-tuberculosis pioneer).
1320 **331** 23c. brown 35 20

1983. Papal Visit. Multicoloured.
1321 6c. Type **332** (postage) . . . 10 10
1322 17c. Pope John Paul II . . . 25 15
1323 35c. Pope and map of Panama (air) 50 30

333 Map of Americas and Sunburst **334** Simon Bolivar

1983. 24th Assembly of Inter-American Development Bank Governors.
1324 **333** 50c. light blue, blue and gold 70 45

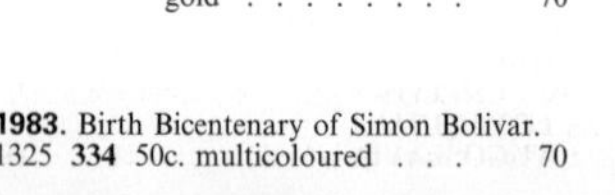

1983. Birth Bicentenary of Simon Bolivar.
1325 **334** 50c. multicoloured . . . 70 45

335 Postal Union of the Americas and Spain Emblem **336** Moslem Mosque

1983. World Communications Day. Mult.
1327 30c. Type **335** 45 25
1328 40c. W.C.Y. emblem 60 40
1329 50c. Universal Postal Union emblem 70 45
1330 60c. "Flying Dove" (Alfredo Sinclair) 85 55

1983. Freedom of Worship. Multicoloured.
1332 3c. Type **336** 10 10
1333 5c. Bahai temple 10 10
1334 6c. Church of St. Francis of the Mountains, Veraguas 10 10
1335 17c. Shevet Ahim synagogue 25 15

337 "The Annunciation" (Dagoberto Moran) **338** Ricardo Miro (writer)

1983. Obligatory Tax. Christmas. Children's Village. Multicoloured.
1336 2c. Type **337** 10 10
1337 2c. Church and houses (Leonidas Molinar) (vert) 10 10
1338 2c. Bethlehem and star (Colon Olmedo Zambrano) (vert) 10 10
1339 2c. Flight into Egypt (Hector Ulises Velasquez) (vert) 10 10

1983. Famous Panamanians. Multicoloured.
1341 1c. Type **338** 10 10
1342 3c. Richard Newman (educationalist) 10 10
1343 5c. Cristobal Rodriguez (politician) 10 10
1344 6c. Alcibiades Arosemena (politician) 10 10
1345 35c. Cirilo Martinez (educationalist) 50 30

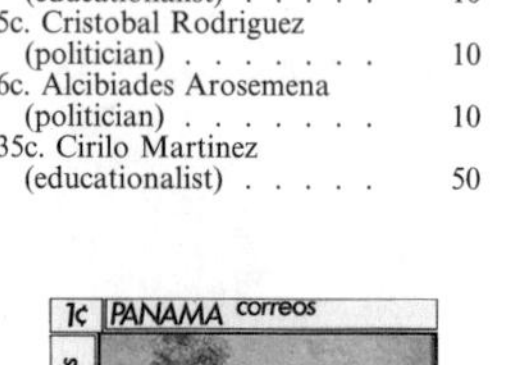

339 "Rural Architecture" (Juan Manuel Cedero)

1983. Paintings. Multicoloured.
1346 1c. Type **339** 10 10
1347 1c. "Large Nude" (Manuel Chong Neto) 10 10
1348 3c. "On another Occasion" (Spiros Vamvas) 10 10
1349 6c. "Punta Chame" (Guillermo Trujillo) . . . 10 10
1350 28c. "Neon Light" (Alfredo Sinclair) 30 20
1351 35c. "The Prophet" (Alfredo Sinclair) (vert) 50 30
1352 41c. "Highland Girls" (Al Sprague) (vert) 60 40
1353 1b. "One Morning" (Ignacio Mallol Pibernat) . . . . 1·40 75

340 Tonosi Double Jug

1984. Archaeological Finds. Multicoloured.
1354 30c. Type **340** 35 10
1355 40c. Dish on stand 60 20
1356 50c. Jug decorated with human face (vert) 70 25
1357 60c. Waisted bowl (vert) . . . 85 35

341 Boxing

1984. Olympic Games, Los Angeles. Mult.
1359 19c. Type **341** 35 25
1360 19c. Baseball 35 25
1361 19c. Basketball (vert) . . . 35 25
1362 19c. Swimming (vert) . . . 35 25

342 Roberto Duran

1984. Roberto Duran (boxer) Commem.
1363 **342** 26c. multicoloured . . . 45 30

343 Shooting

1984. Olympic Games, Los Angeles (2nd series). Multicoloured.
1364 6c. Type **343** (postage) . . . 15 10
1366 30c. Weightlifting (air) . . . 50 30
1367 37c. Wrestling 65 45
1368 1b. Long jump . . . . . . 1·25 90

344 "Pensive Woman" (Manuel Chong Neto)

1984. Paintings. Multicoloured.
1369 1c. Type **344** 10 10
1370 3c. "The Child" (Alfredo Sinclair) (horiz) 10 10
1371 6c. "A Day in the Life of Rumalda" (Brooke Alfaro) (horiz) 15 10
1372 30c. "Highlanders" (Al Sprague) 50 10
1373 37c. "Ballet Interval" (Roberto Sprague) (horiz) 65 15
1374 44c. "Wood on Chame Head" (Guillermo Trujillo) (horiz) 75 25
1375 50c. "La Plaza Azul" (Juan Manuel Cedeno) (horiz) 60 25
1376 1b. "Ira" (Spiros Vamvas) (horiz) . . . . 1·25 90

345 Map, Pres. Torrijos Herrera and Liner in Canal Lock

1984. 5th Anniv of Canal Zone Postal Sovereignty.
1377 **345** 19c. multicoloured . . . 1·10 1·10

346 Emblem as Seedling **347** Boy

1984. Air. World Food Day.
1378 **346** 30c. red, green and blue . . . 50 45

1984. Obligatory Tax. Christmas. Children's Village. Multicoloured.
1379 2c. Type **347** 10 10
1380 2c. Boy in tee-shirt 10 10
1381 2c. Boy in checked shirt . . 10 10
1382 2c. Cub scout 10 10

348 American Manatee

1984. Animals. Each in black.
1384 3c. Type **348** (postage) . . . 10 10
1385 30c. "Tayra" (air) 60 25
1386 44c. Jaguarundi 85 40
1387 50c. White-lipped peccary . . 90 40

349 Copper One Centesimo Coins, 1935

1985. Coins. Multicoloured.
1389 3c. Type **349** (postage) . . . 10 10
1390 3c. Silver ten centesimo coins, 1904 . . . . 10 10
1391 3c. Silver five centesimo coins, 1916 . . . . 10 10
1392 30c. Silver 50 centesimo coins, 1904 (air) 50 30
1393 37c. Silver half balboa coins, 1962 . . . . 65 45
1394 44c. Silver balboa coins, 1953 . . . . 75 50

350 Figures on Map reaching for Dove

352 Scouts with Statue of Christ

351 Tanker in Dock

1985. Contadora Peace Movement.
1395 **350** 10c. multicoloured . . . 15 10
1396 20c. multicoloured . . . 30 20
1397 30c. multicoloured . . . 40 25

1985. 70th Anniv of Panama Canal.
1399 **351** 19c. multicoloured . . . 2·75 90

1985. Obligatory Tax. Christmas. Children's Village. Multicoloured.
1400 2c. Type **352** 10 10
1401 2c. Children holding cards spelling "Feliz Navidad" . . 10 10
1402 2c. Children holding balloons 10 10
1403 2c. Group of cub scouts . . 10 10

353 "40" on Emblem

1986. 40th Anniv (1985) of U.N.O.
1405 **353** 23c. multicoloured . . . 30 20

354 Boys in Cab of Crane

1986. International Youth Year (1985).
1406 **354** 30c. multicoloured . . . 40 25

355 "Awaiting Her Turn" (Al Sprague)

1986. Paintings. Multicoloured.
1407 3c. Type **355** 10 10
1408 5c. "Aerobics" (Guillermo Trujillo) (horiz) 10 10
1409 19c. "House of Cardboard" (Eduardo Augustine) . . 30 20
1410 30c. "Tierra Gate" (Juan Manuel Cedeno) (horiz) 40 25
1411 36c. "Supper for Three" (Brood Alfaro) 50 30
1412 42c. "Tenderness" (Alfredo Sinclair) 60 40
1413 50c. "Lady of Character" (Manuel Chong Neto) . . 70 45
1414 60c. "Calla Lilies No. 1" (Maigualida de Diaz) (horiz) 80 55

356 Atlapa Convention Centre

1986. Miss Universe Contest. Multicoloured.
1415 23c. Type **356** 30 20
1416 60c. Emblem 80 55

357 Comet and Globe

358 Angels

1986. Appearance of Halley's Comet.
1417 **357** 23c. multicoloured . . . 25 15
1418 – 30c. blue, brown and yellow 35 25
DESIGN: 30c. Panama la Vieja Cathedral tower.

1986. Obligatory Tax. 20th Anniv of Children's Village. Children's drawings. Multicoloured.
1420 2c. Type **358** 10 10
1421 2c. Cupids 10 10
1422 2c. Indians 10 10
1423 2c. Angels (different) . . . 10 10

359 Basketball

360 Argentina Player

1986. 15th Central American and Caribbean Games, Santiago. Multicoloured.
1425 20c. Type **359** 20 10
1426 23c. Sports 25 15

1986. World Cup Football Championship, Mexico. Multicoloured.
1427 23c. Type **360** 25 15
1428 30c. West Germany player 35 25
1429 37c. West Germany and Argentina players 45 30

361 Crib

362 Dove and Globe

1986. Christmas. Multicoloured.
1431 23c. Type **361** 25 15
1432 36c. Tree and presents . . . 40 25
1433 42c. As No. 1432 . . . . . 45 30

1986. International Peace Year. Multicoloured.
1434 8c. Type **362** 10 10
1435 19c. Profiles and emblem . . 20 10

363 Mask

365 Mountain Rose

364 Headquarters Building

1987. Tropical Carnival. Multicoloured.
1436 20c. Type **363** 20 10
1437 35c. Sun with eye mask . . 40 25

1987. 50th Anniv (1985) of Panama Lions Club.
1439 **364** 37c. multicoloured . . . 45 30

1987. Flowers and Birds. Multicoloured.
1440 3c. Type **365** 10 10
1441 5c. Blue-grey tanager (horiz) 40 10
1442 8c. Golden cup 10 10
1443 15c. Tropical kingbird (horiz) 80 25
1444 19c. "Barleria micans" (flower) 20 10
1445 23c. Brown pelican (horiz) 1·10 40
1446 30c. "Cordia dentata" (flower) 35 25
1447 36c. Rufous pigeon (horiz) 1·50 65

366 Octavio Menendez Pereira (founder) and Anniversary Monument

1987. 50th Anniv (1986) of Panama University.
1448 **366** 19c. multicoloured . . . 20 10

367 Emblem in "40"

1987. 40th Anniv (1985) of F.A.O.
1449 **367** 10c. brown, yellow and black 10 10
1450 45c. brown, green and black 50 30

368 Heinrich Schutz

369 Development Projects

1987. Composers and 7th Anniv (1986) of National Theatre.
1451 **368** 19c. multicoloured . . . 20 10
1452 – 30c. green, mauve & brown 35 25
1453 – 37c. brown, blue and deep blue 45 30
1454 – 60c. green, yellow & black 70 45
DESIGNS—HORIZ: 30c. National Theatre. VERT: 37c. Johann Sebastian Bach; 60c. Georg Friedrich Handel.

1987. 25th Anniv (1986) of Inter-American Development Bank.
1455 **369** 23c. multicoloured . . . 25 15

370 Horse-drawn Fire Pump, 1887, and Modern Appliance

372 "Adoration of the Magi" (Albrecht Nentz)

371 Wrestling

1987. Centenary of Fire Service. Multicoloured.
1456 25c. Type **370** 30 20
1457 35c. Fireman carrying boy 40 25

1987. 10th Pan-American Games, Indianapolis. Mult.
1458 15c. Type **371** 20 10
1459 25c. Tennis (vert) 25 15
1460 30c. Swimming 35 25
1461 41c. Basketball (vert) . . . 45 30
1462 60c. Cycling (vert) 70 45

1987. Christmas. Multicoloured.
1464 22c. Type **372** 25 15
1465 35c. "The Virgin adored by Angels" (Matthias Grunewald) 40 25
1466 37c. "Virgin and Child" (Konrad Witz) 45 30

373 Distressed Family and Poor Housing

374 Heart falling into Crack

1987. International Year of Shelter for the Homeless. Multicoloured.
1467 45c. Type **373** 50 30
1468 50c. Happy family and stylized modern housing 50 30

1988. Anti-drugs Campaign.
1469 **374** 10c. red and orange . . 10 10
1470 17c. red and green . . . 20 10
1471 25c. red and blue 30 20

375 Hands and Sapling

376 Breastfeeding

1988. Reafforestation Campaign.
1472 **375** 35c. deep green and green 40 25
1473 40c. red and purple . . . 45 30
1474 45c. brown and bistre . . 50 30

1988. U.N.I.C.E.F. Infant Survival Campaign. Mult.
1475 20c. Type **376** 25 15
1476 31c. Vaccination 35 25
1477 45c. Children playing by lake (vert) 50 30

377 Rock Beauty and Cuban Hogfish

1988. Fishes. Multicoloured.
1478 7c. Type **377** 15 10
1479 35c. French angelfish 65 30
1480 60c. Black-barred soldierfish 1·10 55
1481 1b. Spotted drum . . . . . 2·00 1·25

378 Emblem and Clasped Hands

379 "Virgin with Donors"

1988. 75th Anniv of Girl Guide Movement.
1482 **378** 35c. multicoloured . . . 35 25

1988. Christmas. Anonymous Paintings from Museum of Colonial Religious Art. Mult.
1483 17c. Type **379** (postage) . . 20 10
1484 45c. "Virgin of the Rosary with St. Dominic" 50 30
1485 35c. "St. Joseph with the Child" (air) 35 25

380 Athletes and Silver Medal (Brazil)

1989. Seoul Olympic Games Medals. Mult.
1486 17c. Type **380** (postage) . . 20 10
1487 25c. Wrestlers and gold medal (Hungary) 30 20
1488 60c. Weightlifter and gold medal (Turkey) 70 45
1490 35c. Boxers and bronze medal (Colombia) (air) . . 35 25

381 St. John Bosco

382 Anniversary Emblem

1989. Death Centenary of St. John Bosco (founder of Salesian Brothers). Multicoloured.
1491 10c. Type **381** 15 10
1492 20c. Menor Basilica and St. John with people . . . 25 15

1989. 125th Anniv of Red Cross Movement.
1493 **382** 40c. black and red . . . 50 30
1494 – 1b. multicoloured . . . 1·50 90
DESIGN: 1b. Red Cross workers putting patient in ambulance.

383 "Ancon I" (first ship through Canal)

1989. Air. 75th Anniv of Panama Canal.
1495 **383** 35c. red, black and yellow . . . . 2·25 80
1496 – 60c. multicoloured . . . 3·25 1·25
DESIGN: 60c. Modern tanker.

384 Barriles Ceremonial Statue

1989. America. Pre-Columbian Artefacts. Mult.
1497 20c. Type **384** 25 15
1498 35c. Ceramic vase 45 30

385 "March of the Women on Versailles" (engraving)

1989. Bicent of French Revolution. Mult.
1499 25c. Type **385** (postage) . . 30 20
1500 35c. "Storming the Bastille" (air) 45 30
1501 45c. Birds 55 35

386 "Holy Family"

1989. Christmas. Multicoloured.
1502 17c. Type **386** 20 10
1503 35c. 1988 crib in Cathedral 45 30
1504 45c. "Nativity" 55 35
The 17 and 45c. show children's paintings.

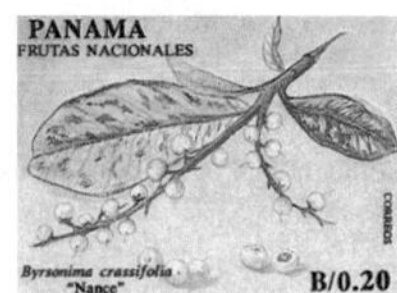

387 "Byrsonima crassifolia"

1990. Fruit. Multicoloured.
1505 20c. Type **387** 20 10
1506 35c. "Bactris gasipaes" . . . 40 25
1507 40c. "Anacardium occidentale" 40 25

388 Sinan

1990. 88th Birthday of Rogelio Sinan (writer).
1508 **388** 23c. brown and blue . . 25 15

389 Pond Turtle

1990. Reptiles. Multicoloured.
1509 35c. Type **389** 40 25
1510 45c. Olive loggerhead turtle 50 35
1511 60c. Red-footed tortoise . . 65 40

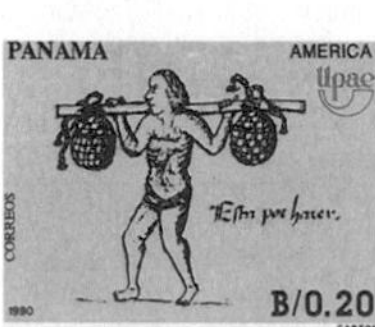

390 Carrying Goods on Yoke (after Oviedo)

1990. America.
1512 **390** 20c. brown, light brown and gold 20 10
1513 – 35c. multicoloured . . . 70 50
DESIGN—VERT: 35c. Warrior wearing gold chest ornament and armbands.

391 Dr. Guillermo Patterson, jun., "Father of Chemistry"

393 St. Ignatius

392 In Sight of Land

1990. Chemistry in Panama.
1514 **391** 25c. black and turquoise 25 15
1515 – 35c. multicoloured . . . 40 25
1516 – 45c. multicoloured . . . 50 35
DESIGNS: 35c. Evaporation experiment; 45c. Books and laboratory equipment.

1991. America. 490th Anniv of Discovery of Panama Isthmus by Rodrigo Bastidas.
1517 **392** 35c. multicoloured . . . 50 35

1991. 450th Anniv of Society of Jesus and 500th Birth Anniv of St. Ignatius de Loyola (founder).
1518 **393** 20c. multicoloured . . . 30 20

394 Declaration of Women's Right to Vote

1991. 50th Anniv of First Presidency of Dr. Arnulfo Arias Madrid.
1519 **394** 10c. brown, stone & gold 15 10
1520 – 10c. brown, stone & gold 15 10
DESIGN: No. 1520, Department of Social Security headquarters.

395 "Glory to God ..." (Luke 2: 14) and Score of "Gloria in Excelsis"

1991. Christmas. Multicoloured.
1521 35c. Type **395** 50 35
1522 35c. Nativity 50 35

396 Adoration of the Kings

1992. Epiphany.
1523 **396** 10c. multicoloured . . . 15 10

397 Family and Housing Estate

1992. "New Lives" Housing Project.
1524 **397** 5c. multicoloured 10 10

398 Costa Rican and Panamanian shaking Hands

1992. 50th Anniv (1991) of Border Agreement with Costa Rica. Multicoloured.
1525 20c. Type **398** 30 20
1526 40c. Map showing Costa Rica and Panama 55 35
1527 50c. Presidents Calderon and Arias and national flags 70 45

399 Pollutants and Hole over Antarctic

1992. "Save the Ozone Layer".
1528 **399** 40c. multicoloured . . . 55 35

400 Exhibition Emblem

1992. "Expocomer 92" 10th International Trade Exhibition, Panama City.
1529 **400** 10c. multicoloured . . . 15 10

401 Portrait

402 Maria Olimpia de Obaldia

1992. 1st Death Anniv of Dame Margot Fonteyn (ballet dancer). Portraits by Pietro Annigoni. Multicoloured.
1530 35c. Type **401** 50 35
1531 45c. On stage 60 40

1992. Birth Centenary of Maria Olimpia de Obaldia (poet).
1532 **402** 10c. multicoloured . . . 15 10

403 Athletics Events and Map of Spain

1992. Olympic Games, Barcelona.
1533 **403** 10c. multicoloured . . . 15 10

404 Paca

1992. Endangered Animals.
1534 **404** 5c. brown, stone & black 10 10
1535 – 10c. black, brn & stone 25 25
1536 – 15c. brown, blk & stone 20 15
1537 – 20c. multicoloured . . . 30 20
DESIGNS: 10c. Harpy eagle; 15c. Jaguar; 20c. Iguana.

405 Zion Baptist Church, Bocas del Toro

1992. Centenary of Baptist Church in Panama.
1538 **405** 20c. multicoloured . . . 30 20

406 Columbus's Fleet

1992. America. 500th Anniv of Discovery of America by Columbus. Multicoloured.
1539 20c. Type **406** 45 30
1540 35c. Columbus planting flag 75 50

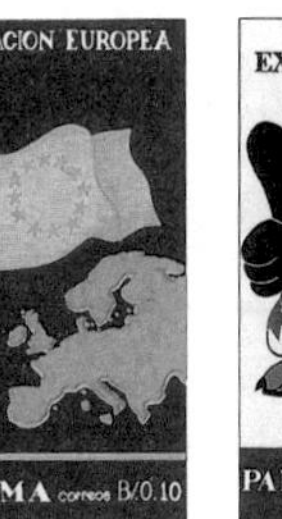

407 Flag and Map of Europe
408 Mascot

1992. European Single Market.
1541 **407** 10c. multicoloured . . . 15 10

1992. "Expo '92" World's Fair, Seville.
1542 **408** 10c. multicoloured . . . 15 10

409 Occupations

1992. American Workers' Health Year.
1543 **409** 15c. multicoloured . . . 20 15

410 Angel and Shepherds

1992. Christmas. Multicoloured.
1544 20c. Type **410** 30 20
1545 35c. Mary and Joseph arriving at Bethlehem . . 50 35

411 Jesus lighting up the Americas

1993. 500th Anniv (1992) of Evangelization of the American Continent.
1546 **411** 10c. multicoloured . . . 15 10

412 Woman on Crutches and Wheelchair-bound Man

1993. National Day of Disabled Persons.
1547 **412** 5c. multicoloured 10 10

413 Herrera (bust)

1993. 32nd Death Anniv of Dr. Jose de la Cruz Herrera (essayist).
1548 **413** 5c. multicoloured 10 10

414 Nutritious Foods and Emblems

1993. International Nutrition Conference, Rome.
1549 **414** 10c. multicoloured . . . 15 10

415 Caravel and Columbus in Portobelo Harbour

1994. 490th Anniv (1992) of Columbus's Fourth Voyage and Exploration of the Panama Isthmus.
1550 **415** 50c. multicoloured . . . 65 45

416 Panama Flag and Greek Motifs
418 Chinese Family and House

1995. 50th Anniv of Greek Community in Panama.
1551 **416** 20c. multicoloured . . . 25 15

1995. Various stamps surch.
1553 – 20c. on 23c. multicoloured (1459) 25 15
1554 **373** 25c. on 45c. multicoloured 30 20
1555 – 30c. on 45c. multicoloured (1510) 40 25
1556 **375** 35c. on 45c. brown and bistre 45 30
1557 – 35c. on 45c. multicoloured (1477) 45 30
1558 – 40c. on 41c. multicoloured (1461) 50 35
1559 – 50c. on 60c. multicoloured (1511) 65 45
1560 – 1b. on 50c. multicoloured (1480) 1·25 85

1996. Chinese Presence in Panama. 142nd Anniv of Arrival of First Chinese Immigrants.
1561 **418** 60c. multicoloured . . . 75 50

419 The King's Bridge from the North (16th century)

1996. 475th Anniv (1994) of Founding by the Spanish of Panama City. Multicoloured.
1563 15c. Type **419** 20 15
1564 20c. City arms, 1521 (vert) 25 15
1565 25c. Plan of first cathedral 30 20
1566 35c. Present-day ruins of Cathedral of the Assumption of Our Lady 45 30

420 "60", Campus and Emblem

1996. 60th Anniv of Panama University.
1567 **420** 40c. multicoloured . . . 50 35

421 Anniversary Emblem

1996. 75th Anniv of Panama Chapter of Rotary International.
1568 **421** 5b. multicoloured . . . 6·25 4·25

422 Great Tinamou

1996. America (1993). Endangered Species.
1569 **422** 20c. multicoloured . . . 25 15

423 Northern Coati

1996. Mammals. Multicoloured.
1570 25c. Type **423** 30 20
1571 25c. Collared anteater ("Tamandua mexicana") 30 20
1572 25c. Two-toed anteater ("Cyclopes didactylus") 30 20
1573 25c. Puma 30 20

424 De Lesseps
425 "50" and Emblem

1996. Death Centenary of Ferdinand, Vicomte de Lesseps (builder of Suez Canal).
1574 **424** 35c. multicoloured . . . 45 30

1996. 50th Anniv of U.N.O.
1575 **425** 45c. multicoloured . . . 55 35

426 Emblem and Motto
427 Bello

1996. 25th Anniv (1993) of Panama Chapter of Kiwanis International.
1576 **426** 40c. multicoloured . . . 50 35

1996. 25th Anniv (1995) of Andres Bello Covenant for Education, Science, Technology and Culture.
1577 **427** 35c. multicoloured . . . 45 30

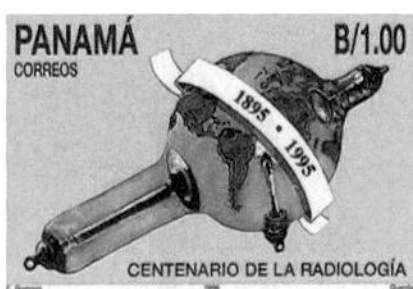

428 World Map on X-ray Equipment

1996. Centenary of Discovery of X-rays by Wilhelm Rontgen.
1578 **428** 1b. multicoloured . . . 1·25 85

429 Madonna and Child

1996. Christmas.
1579 **429** 35c. multicoloured . . . 45 30

430 Diesel Train and Panama Canal

1996. America (1994). Postal Transport.
1580 **430** 30c. multicoloured . . . 35 25

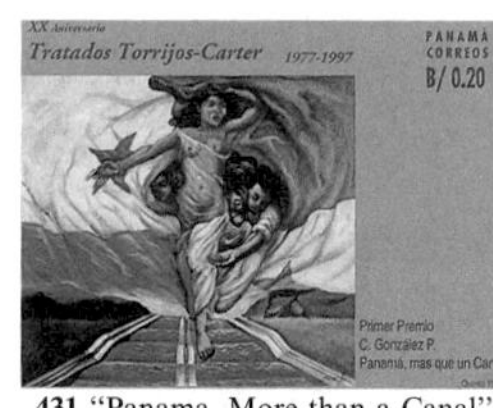

431 "Panama, More than a Canal" (C. Gonzalez)

1997. 20th Anniv of Torrijos–Carter Treaty (transferring Control of Canal Zone to Panama in Year 2000). Multicoloured.
1581 20c. Type **431** 25 15
1582 30c. "A Curtain of Our Flag" (A. Siever) (vert) 35 25
1583 45c. "Perpetual Steps" (R. Martinez) 55 35
1584 50c. Kurt Waldheim (U.N. Secretary-General), President Carter of U.S.A. and President Torrijos of Panama at signing ceremony 60 40

432 Pedro Miguel Locks

1997. World Congress on Panama Canal. Mult.
1586 45c. Type **432** 55 35
1587 45c. Miraflores Locks . . . 55 35

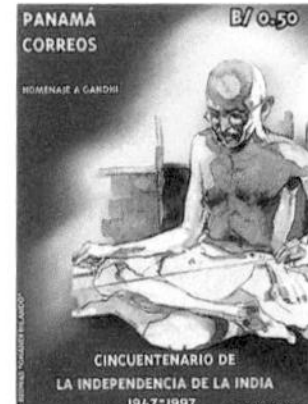

433 "Gandhi Spinning" (P. Biswas)
435 Mary and Joseph searching for Lodgings

434 Crocodile on Rock

1997. 50th Anniv of Independence of India.
1589 **433** 50c. multicoloured . . . 60 40

1997. The American Crocodile. Multicoloured.
1590 25c. Type **434** 30 20
1591 25c. Looking across water 30 20
1592 25c. Two crocodiles 30 20
1593 25c. Head with mouth open 30 20

1997. Christmas.
1594 **435** 35c. multicoloured . . . 45 30

436 Fire Engines from 1941 and 1948

1997. Centenary of Colon City Fire Brigade.
1595 **436** 20c. multicoloured . . . 25 15

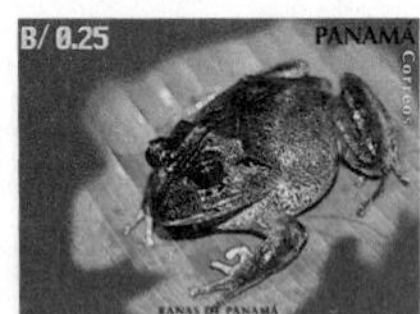

437 "Eleutherodactylus biporcatus" (robber frog)

1997. Frogs. Multicoloured.
1596 25c. Type **437** 30 20
1597 25c. "Hyla colymba" (tree frog) 30 20
1598 25c. "Hyla rufitela" (tree frog) 30 20
1599 25c. "Nelsonephryne aterrima" 30 20

438 Women wearing Polleras

1997. America (1996). Traditional Costumes.
1600 **438** 20c. multicoloured . . . 25 15

439 Arosemena **440** Emblem

1997. Death Centenary of Justo Arosemena (President, 1855–56).
1601 **439** 40c. multicoloured . . . 50 35

1997. 85th Anniv of Colon Chamber of Commerce, Agriculture and Industry.
1602 **440** 1b. multicoloured . . . 1·25 85

441 Douglas DC-3

1997. 50th Anniv of Panamanian Aviation Company. Multicoloured.
1603 35c. Type **441** 45 30
1604 35c. Martin 4-0-4 . . . . . 45 30
1605 35c. Avro HS-748 . . . . . 45 30
1606 35c. Lockheed L-168 Electra 45 30
1607 35c. Boeing 727-100 . . . . 45 30
1608 35c. Boeing 737-200 Advanced 45 30

442 Wailing Wall **444** Central Avenue, San Felipe

443 Building Facade and Emblem

1997. 3000th Anniv of Jerusalem. Multicoloured.
1609 20c. Type **442** 25 15
1610 25c. Service in the Basilica of the Holy Sepulchre . . 30 20
1611 60c. Dome of the Rock . . 75 50

1998. 50th Anniv of Organization of American States.
1613 **443** 40c. multicoloured . . . 10 10

1998. Tourism. Multicoloured.
1614 10c. Type **444** 10 10
1615 20c. Tourists in rainforest 25 15
1616 25c. Gatun Locks, Panama Canal (horiz) 30 20
1617 35c. Panama City (horiz) . . 45 30
1618 40c. San Jeronimo Fort, San Felipe de Portobelo (horiz) 50 30
1619 45c. Rubber raft, River Chagres (horiz) 55 35
1620 60c. Beach, Dog's Island, Kuna Yala (horiz) 75 50

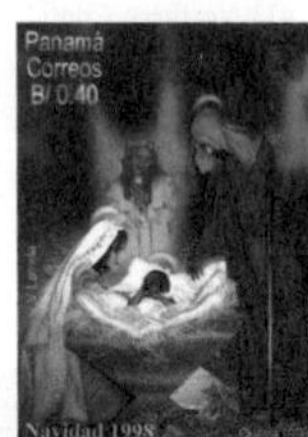

445 Nativity

2000. Christmas.
1621 **445** 40c. multicoloured . . . 45 25

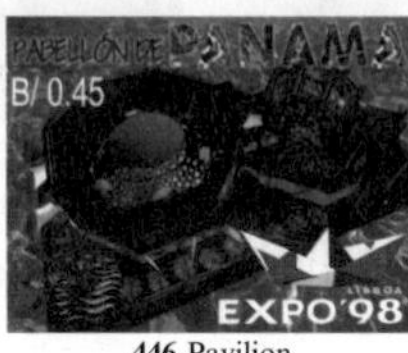

446 Pavilion

2000. "World Expo'98" World's Fair, Lisbon, Portugal.
1622 **446** 45c. multicoloured . . . 50 30

447 Harpy Eagle

2000. The Harpy Eagle. Entries in painting competition by named artist.
1623 **447** 20c. black and green . . 25 15
1624 – 20c. multicoloured . . . 25 15
1625 – 20c. multicoloured . . . 25 15
1626 – 20c. multicoloured . . . 25 15
DESIGNS: No. 1624, J. JimEnez; 1625, S. Castro; 1626, J. Ramos.

448 Emblem

2000. 40th Anniv of Business Executives' Association.
1627 **448** 50c. multicoloured . . . 60 35

449 Emblem

2000. 50th Anniv of Colon Free Trade Zone.
1628 **449** 15c. multicoloured . . . 20 15

450 Emblem

2000. 50th Anniv of Universal Declaration of Human Rights.
1629 **450** 15c. multicoloured . . . 20 15

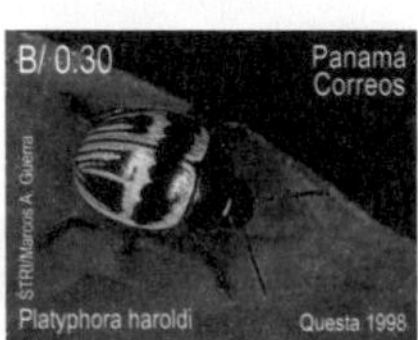

451 *Platyphora haroldi*

2000. Beetles. Multicoloured.
1630 30c. Type **451** 35 20
1631 30c. *Stilodes leoparda* . . . 35 20
1632 30c. *Stilodes fuscolineata* . . 35 20
1633 30c. *Platyphora boucardi* . . 35 20

452 Cruise Ship

2000. Return of Control of Panama Canal to Panama (1999). Multicoloured.
1634 20c. Type **452** 25 15
1635 35c. Cruise ship at lock gate 40 25
1636 40c. View down canal . . . 45 25
1637 45c. Cruise ship passing through lock 50 30

453 Constructing Canal

2000. 85th Anniv of Panama Canal. Multicoloured.
1638 40c. Type **453** 45 25
1639 40c. Construction of canal (different) 45 25
MS1640 106 × 56 mm. 1b.50 View of canal at early stage of construction 1·75 1·75

454 Crowd and Madrid wearing surgical mask

2001. Birth Centenary of Dr. Arnulfo Arias Madrid.
1641 **454** 20c. black and brown . . 25 15
1642 – 20c. black and sepia . . 25 15
1643 – 30c. multicoloured . . . 35 20
1644 – 30c. multicoloured . . . 35 20
DESIGNS: No. 1642, Crowd and Madrid holding glasses; 1643, Flag, building faÇade and Madrid; 1644, Crowd and Madrid.

Nos. 1641/25 and 1643/4 respectively were each issued together, se-tenant, forming a composite design.

455 Baby Jesus

2001. Year 2000.
1645 **455** 20c. multicoloured . . . 25 15

456 Crowned Globe, Rainbow and Birds

2001. "Dreaming of the Future". Winning Entries in Stamp Design Competition. Multicoloured.
1646 20c. Type **456** 25 15
1647 20c. Globe in flower (L. Guerra) 25 15
MS1648 105 × 54 mm. 75c. Tree, birds, globe and children (J. Aguilar) (horiz); 75c. Blue birds holding ribbons, globe and children holding hands (S. Sitton) (horiz) 90 90

457 Angel and Baby Jesus **458** Banco General Tower (Carlos Medina)

2001. Christmas.
1649 **457** 35c. multicoloured . . . 40 25

2001. Architecture of 1990s. Multicoloured.
1650 35c. Type **458** 40 25
1651 35c. Los Delfines condominium (Edwin Brown) 40 25
MS1652 104 × 54 mm. 75c. Circular building (Ricardo Moreno and Jesus Santamaria) (horiz); 75c. Building with three gables (Ricardo Moreno and Jesus Santamaria) (horiz) . . . . . 1·75 1·75

459 *Psychopsis krameriana*

2001. Orchids. Multicoloured.
1653 35c. Type **459** 40 25
1654 35c. *Cattleya dowiana* . . . 40 25
MS1655 104 × 54 mm. 75c. *Peristeria elata*; 75c. *Miltoniopsis roezlii* 1·75 1·75

460 1878 50c. Sovereign State and 1904 1c. Republic of Panama Stamps

2001. 18th U. P. A. E. P. Congress, Panama.
1656 **460** 5b. multicoloured . . . 6·00 6·00

461 Hospital Buildings and Dr Jaime de la Guardia (founder)

2001. 50th Anniv of San Fernando Clinical Hospital.
1657 **461** 20c. multicoloured . . . 25 15

ACKNOWLEDGEMENT OF RECEIPT STAMPS

1898. Handstamped **A. R. COLON COLOMBIA**.
AR24 **5** 5c. blue . . . . 4·50 3·75
AR25 10c. orange . . . . 8·00 8·00

1902. Handstamped **AR** in circle.
AR32 **5** 5c. blue . . . . 3·00 3·00
AR33 10c. orange . . . . 6·00 6·00

1903. No. AR169 of Colombia handstamped **AR** in circle.
AR34 AR **60** 5c. red . . . . . . 11·00 11·00

AR 37

1904.
AR135 AR **37** 5c. blue 90 90

1916. Optd **A.R.**
AR177 **50** 2½c. red 90 90

EXPRESS LETTER STAMPS

1926. Optd **EXPRESO**.
E220 **57** 10c. black and orange . . 4·25 2·10
E221 20c. black and brown . . 5·50 2·10

E **81** Cyclist Messenger

1929.
E226 E **81** 10c. orange 90 70
E227 20c. brown . . . . . . 1·75 1·10

INSURANCE STAMPS

1942. Surch **SEGURO POSTAL HABILITADO** and value.
IN430 5c. on 1b. black (No. 373) 45 35
IN431 10c. on 1b. brown (No. 365) 70 55
IN432 25c. on 50c. brown (No. 372) . . . . 1·25 1·25

POSTAGE DUE STAMPS

D **58** San Geronimo Castle Gate, Portobelo

1915.
D169 D **58** 1c. brown . . . . . . 1·90 30
D170 – 2c. brown . . . . . . 2·75 25
D171 – 4c. brown . . . . . . 3·75 55
D172 – 10c. brown . . . . . 2·75 1·10
DESIGNS—VERT: 2c. Statue of Columbus. HORIZ: 4c. House of Deputies. VERT: 10c. Pedro J. Sosa.
No. D169 is wrongly inscr "CASTILLO DE SAN LORENZO CHAGRES".

D **86**

1930.
D240 D **86** 1c. green 70 25
D241 2c. red 70 20
D242 4c. blue 75 30
D243 10c. violet 75 40

REGISTRATION STAMPS

R **4**

1888.
R12 R **4** 10c. black on grey . . . 6·00 4·00

1897. Handstamped **R COLON** in circle.
R22 **5** 10c. orange . . . . 4·25 4·00

R **15**

1900.
R29 R **15** 10c. black on blue . . . 2·50 2·10
R30 10c. red . . . . 18·00 15·00

1902. No. R30 surch by hand.
R31 R **15** 20c. on 10c. red . . . . 15·00 12·00

1903. Type R **85** of Colombia optd **REPUBLICA DE PANAMA**.
R42 20c. red on blue . . . . . . 27·00
R43 20c. blue on blue . . . . . 27·00

1903. Nos. R42/3 surch.
R46 10c. on 20c. red on blue . . 50·00 50·00
R47 10c. on 20c. blue on blue . . 50·00 50·00

1904. Optd **PANAMA**.
R60 **5** 10c. orange . . . . 2·10 2·10

1904. Type R **6** of Colombia surch **Panama 10** and bar.
R67 10c. on 20c. red on blue . . 38·00 35·00
R68 10c. on 20c. blue on blue . . 38·00 35·00

1904. Type R **85** of Colombia optd **Republica de Panama**.
R106 20c. red on blue . . . . . 5·00 5·00

R **35**

1904.
R133 R **35** 10c. green 70 30

1916. Stamps of Panama surch **R 5 cts**.
R175 **46** 5c. on 8c. black & purple 2·10 1·40
R176 **52** 5c. on 8c. black & purple 2·10 50

TOO LATE STAMPS

1903. Too Late stamp of Colombia optd **REPUBLICA DE PANAMA**.
L44 L **86** 5c. violet on red . . . . 7·50 5·50

L **36**

1904.
L134 L **36** 2½c. red 70 40

1910. Typewritten optd **Retardo**.
L158 **50** 2½c. red . . . . 75·00 75·00

1910. Optd **RETARDO**.
L159 **50** 2½c. red . . . . 38·00 30·00

1916. Surch **RETARDO UN CENTESIMO**.
L174 **38** 1c. on ½c. orange . . . . 15·00 12·00

APPENDIX

The following stamps have either been issued in excess of postal needs or have not been available to the public in reasonable quantities at face value. Such stamps may later be given full listing if there is evidence of regular postal use.

1964.

Satellites. Postage ½, 1c.; Air 5, 10, 21, 50c.

1965.

Tokyo Olympic Games Medal Winners. Postage ½, 1, 2, 3, 4c.; Air 5, 6, 7, 10, 21, 31c.

Space Research. Postage ½, 1, 2, 3c.; Air 5, 10, 11, 31c.

400th Birth Anniv of Galileo. Air 10, 21c.

Peaceful Uses of Atomic Energy. Postage ½, 1, 4c.; Air 6, 10, 21c.

Nobel Prize Medals. Air 10, 21c.

Pres. John Kennedy. Postage ½, 1c.; Air 10+5c., 21+10c., 31+15c.

1966.

Pope Paul's Visit to U.N. in New York. Postage ½, 1c.; Air 5, 10, 21, 31c.

Famous Men. Postage ½c.; Air 10, 31c.

Famous Paintings. Postage ½c.; Air 10, 31c.

World Cup Football Championship. Postage ½, ½c.; Air 10, 10, 21, 21c.

Italian Space Research. Postage ½, 1c.; Air 5, 10, 21c.

Centenary of I.T.U. Air 31c.

World Cup Winners. Optd on 1966 World Cup Issue. Postage ½, ½c.; Air 10, 10, 21, 21c.

Religious Paintings. Postage ½, 1, 2, 3c.; Air 21, 21c.

Churchill and Space Research. Postage ½c.; Air 10, 31c.

3rd Death Anniv of Pres. John Kennedy. Postage ½, 1c.; Air 10, 31c.

Jules Verne and Space Research. Postage ½, 1c.; Air 5, 10, 21, 31c.

1967.

Religious Paintings. Postage ½, 1c.; Air 5, 10, 21, 31c.

Mexico Olympics. Postage ½, 1c.; Air 5, 10, 21, 31c.

Famous Paintings. Postage 5c. × 3; Air 21c. × 3.

Goya's Paintings. Postage 2, 3, 4c.; Air 5, 8, 10, 13, 21c.

1968.

Religious Paintings. Postage 1, 1, 3c.; Air 4, 21, 21c.

Mexican President's Visit. Air 50c., 1b.

Winter Olympic Games, Grenoble. Postage ½, 1c.; Air 5, 10, 21, 31c.

Butterflies. Postage ½, 1, 3, 4c.; Air 5, 13c.

Ship Paintings. Postage ½, 1, 3, 4c.; Air 5, 13c.

Fishes. Postage ½, 1, 3, 4c.; Air 5, 13c.

Winter Olympic Medal Winners. Postage 1, 2, 3, 4, 5, 6, 8c.; Air 13, 30c.

Paintings of Musicians. Postage 5, 10, 15, 20, 25, 30c.

Satellite Transmissions from Panama T.V. (a) Olympic Games, Mexico. Optd on 1964 Satellites issue. Postage ½c.; Air 50c. (b) Pope Paul's Visit to Latin America. Postage ½c.; Air 21c. (c) Panama Satellite Transmissions. Inauguration. (i) optd on Space Research issue of 1965. Postage 5c.; Air 31c. (ii) optd on Churchill and Space Research issue of 1966. Postage ½c.; Air 10c.

Hunting Paintings. Postage 1, 3, 5, 10c.; Air 13, 30c.

Horses and Jockeys. Postage 5, 10, 15, 20, 25, 30c.

Mexico Olympics. Postage 1, 2, 3, 4, 5, 6, 8c.; Air 13, 30c.

1969.

1st International Philatelic and Numismatic Exhibition. Optd on 1968 Issue of Mexican President's Visit. Air 50c., 1b.

Telecommunications Satellites. Air 5, 10, 15, 20, 25, 30c.

Provisionals. Surch "Decreto No. 112 (de 6 de marzo de 1969)" and new values on No. 781 and 10c.+5c. and 21c.+10c. of 1965 Issue of 3rd Death Anniv of Pres. John Kennedy. Air 5c. on 5c.+5c., 5c. on 10c.+5c., 10c. on 21c.+10c.

Pope Paul VI Visit to Latin America. Religious Paintings. Postage 1, 2, 3, 4, 5c.; Air 6, 7, 8, 10c.

PAPAL STATES Pt. 8

Parts of Italy under Papal rule till 1870 when they became part of the Kingdom of Italy.

1852. 100 bajocchi = 1 scudo.
1866. 100 centesimi = 1 lira.

1 2

1852. Papal insignia as in T **1** and **2** in various shapes and frames. Imperf.
2 ½b. black on grey . . . . . . £425 42·00
5 ½b. black on lilac . . . . . . 35·00 £120
10 1b. black on green . . . . . 46·00 55·00
11 2b. black on green . . . . . £130 11·00
14 2b. black on white . . . . . 8·50 50·00
15 3b. black on brown . . . . . 60·00 26·00
16 3b. black on yellow . . . . . 23·00 £160
17 4b. black on brown . . . . . £4500 65·00
19 4b. black on yellow . . . . . £120 34·00
20 5b. black on pink . . . . . . £150 7·50
22 6b. black on lilac £850 £190
23 6b. black on grey . . . . . . £550 48·00
25 7b. black on blue . . . . . . £850 60·00
26 8b. black on white . . . . . £400 32·00
27 50b. blue £12000 £1500
29 1s. pink £3000 £3000

1867. Same types. Imperf.
30 2c. black on green £110 £200
32 3c. black on grey £1800 £2250
33 5c. black on blue £130 £170
34 10c. black on red . . . . . . £850 55·00
35 20c. black on red . . . . . . £120 75·00
36 40c. black on yellow £140 £170
37 80c. black on pink £140 £450

1868. Same types. Perf.
42 2c. black on green . . . . . . 8·00 60·00
43 3c. black on grey . . . . . . 35·00 £3000
45 5c. black on blue . . . . . . 9·75 38·00
46 10c. black on orange . . . . . 2·75 11·00
49 20c. black on mauve . . . . . 3·75 30·00
50 20c. black on red . . . . . . 2·20 13·00
52 40c. black on yellow . . . . . 5·50 85·00
55 80c. black on pink . . . . . 25·00 £325

PAPUA Pt. 1

(Formerly **BRITISH NEW GUINEA**)

The eastern portion of the island of New Guinea, to the North of Australia, a territory of the Commonwealth of Australia, now combined with New Guinea. Australian stamps were used after the Japanese defeat in 1945 until the combined issue appeared in 1952.

12 pence = 1 shilling;
20 shilling = 1 pound.

1 Lakatoi (native canoe) with Hanuabada Village in Background

6

1901.
9 **1** ½d. black and green . . . . 8·50 3·75
10 1d. black and red . . . . . 3·50 2·00
11 2d. black and violet . . . . 9·50 4·00
12 2½d. black and blue . . . . 13·00 12·00
13 4d. black and brown . . . . 32·00 50·00
6 6d. black and green . . . . 45·00 35·00
7 1s. black and orange . . . . 60·00 65·00
8 2s.6d. black and brown . . . £550 £500

1906. Optd **Papua**.
38 **1** ½d. black and green . . . . 9·00 10·00
39 1d. black and red . . . . . 3·50 5·00
40 2d. black and violet . . . . 4·50 2·25
24 2½d. black and blue . . . . 3·75 15·00
42 4d. black and brown . . . . 27·00 50·00
43 6d. black and green . . . . 29·00 42·00
19 1s. black and orange . . . . 20·00 38·00
37 2s.6d. black and brown . . . 32·00 50·00

1907.
66 **6** ½d. black and green . . . . 1·60 3·75
94 1d. black and red . . . . . 1·40 1·25
68 2d. black and purple . . . . 3·50 5·50
51a 2½d. black and blue . . . . 5·50 6·50
63 4d. black and brown . . . . 4·75 9·00
80 6d. black and green . . . . 7·50 7·50
81 1s. black and orange . . . . 5·50 19·00
82 2s.6d. black and brown . . 35·00 45·00

1911.
84a **6** ½d. green . . . . 50 2·25
85 1d. red 70 75
86 2d. mauve 70 75
87 2½d. blue . . . . 4·75 8·50
88 4d. olive . . . . 2·25 11·00
89 6d. brown . . . . 3·75 5·00
90 1s. yellow . . . . 9·00 15·00
91 2s.6d. red . . . . 32·00 38·00

1916.
93 **6** ½d. green and olive . . . . 80 1·00
95 1½d. blue and brown . . . . 1·50 80
96 2d. purple and red . . . . 1·75 75
97 2½d. green and blue . . . . 4·75 12·00
98 3d. black and turquoise . . 1·75 1·75
99 4d. brown and orange . . . 2·50 5·00
100 5d. grey and brown . . . . 4·25 16·00
101 6d. purple . . . . 3·25 9·50
127 9d. lilac and violet . . . . 4·50 30·00
102 1s. brown and olive . . . . 3·50 7·00
128 1s.3d. lilac and blue . . . . 7·50 32·00
103 2s.6d. red and pink . . . . 19·00 40·00
104 5s. black and green . . . . 45·00 48·00
105 10s. green and blue £140 £160

1917. Surch **ONE PENNY**.
106a **6** 1d. on ½d. green . . . . . 1·00 1·25
107 1d. on 2d. mauve . . . . 12·00 15·00
108 1d. on 2½d. blue . . . . . 1·25 3·75
109 1d. on 4d. green . . . . . 1·75 4·50
110 1d. on 6d. brown . . . . 8·00 17·00
111 1d. on 2s.6d. red . . . . . 1·50 6·00

1929. Air. Optd **AIR MAIL**.
114 **6** 3d. black and turquoise . . 1·00 7·00

AIR MAIL

(11)

1930. Air. Optd with T **11**.
118 **6** 3d. black and turquoise . . 1·00 6·00
119 6d. purple . . . . 7·00 10·00
120 1s. brown and olive . . . . 4·25 15·00

1931. Surch in words or figures and words.
122 **6** 2d. on 1½d. blue and brown 1·00 2·00
125 5d. on 1s. brown and olive 1·00 1·75
126 9d. on 2s.6d. red and pink 5·50 8·50
123 1s.3d. on 5d. black and green . . . . 4·25 9·00

15 Motuan Girl

18 Raggiana Bird of Paradise

20 Native Mother and Child

1932.

130 **15** ½d. black and orange . . . 1·50 3·25
131 – 1d. black and green . . . 1·75 60
132 – 1½d. black and red . . . . 1·50 8·00
133 **18** 2d. red . . . . 11·00 30
134 – 3d. black and blue . . . . 3·25 6·50
135 **20** 4d. olive . . . . 5·50 9·50
136 – 5d. black and green . . . 3·00 3·00
137 – 6d. brown . . . . 7·50 5·50
138 – 9d. black and violet . . . 10·00 21·00
139 – 1s. green . . . . 4·00 8·50
140 – 1s.3d. black and purple . . 15·00 26·00
141 – 2s. black and green . . . . 15·00 24·00
142 – 2s.6d. black and mauve . . 25·00 38·00
143 – 5s. black and brown . . . 55·00 55·00
144 – 10s. violet . . . . 85·00 85·00
145 – £1 black and grey £180 £150

DESIGNS—VERT (as T **15**): 1d. Chieftain's son; 1½d. Tree houses; 3d. Papuan dandy; 5d. Masked dancer; 9d. Shooting fish; 1s. Ceremonial platform; 1s.3d. Lakatoi; 2s. Papuan art; 2s.6d. Pottery-making; 5d. Native policeman; £1 Delta house. VERT (as T **18**): 6d. Papuan mother. HORIZ: (as T **20**): 10s. Lighting fire.

31 Hoisting the Union Jack

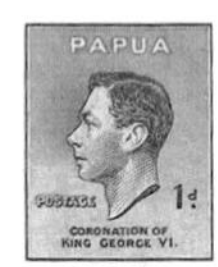
35 King George VI

1934. 50th Anniv of Declaration of British Protectorate. Inscr "1884 1834".

146 **31** 1d. green . . . . 1·00 3·50
147 – 2d. red . . . . 1·75 3·00
148 **31** 3d. blue . . . . 1·75 3·00
149 – 5d. purple . . . . 11·00 15·00

DESIGN: 2d., 5d. Scene on H.M.S. "Nelson".

1935. Silver Jubilee. Optd **HIS MAJESTY'S JUBILEE 1910 1935 (1910 – 1935** on 2d.).

150 – 1d. black & green (No. 131) . . . . 75 3·00
151 **18** 2d. red . . . . 2·00 3·00
152 – 3d. black and blue (No. 134) . . . . 1·75 3·00
153 – 5d. black & green (No. 136) . . . . 2·50 3·00

1937. Coronation.

154 **35** 1d. green 45 15
155 2d. red . . . . 45 1·00
156 3d. blue . . . . 45 1·00
157 5d. purple . . . . 45 1·60

36 Port Moresby

1938. Air. 50th Anniv of Declaration of British Possession.

158 **36** 2d. red . . . . 3·00 2·25
159 3d. blue . . . . 3·00 2·25
160 5d. green . . . . 3·00 3·25
161 8d. red . . . . 6·00 14·00
162 1s. mauve . . . . 19·00 15·00

37 Natives poling Rafts

1939. Air.

163 **37** 2d. red . . . . 3·00 4·00
164 3d. blue . . . . 3·00 8·00
165 5d. green . . . . 3·00 1·75
166 8d. red . . . . 8·00 2·75
167 1s. mauve . . . . 10·00 7·50
168 1s.6d. olive . . . . 30·00 35·00

OFFICIAL STAMPS

1931. Optd **O S**.

O55 **6** ½d. green and olive . . . 2·00 4·75
O56a 1d. black and red . . . . 4·00 8·00
O57 1½d. blue and brown . . . 1·60 12·00
O58 2d. brown and purple . . 3·75 9·50
O59 3d. black and turquoise . . 2·50 22·00
O60 4d. brown and orange . . 2·50 18·00
O61 5d. grey and brown . . . 6·00 38·00
O62 6d. purple and red . . . 4·00 8·50
O63 9d. lilac and violet . . . . 30·00 48·00
O64 1s. brown and olive . . . 9·00 30·00
O65 1s.3d. lilac and blue . . . 30·00 48·00
O66 2s.6d. red and pink . . . 40·00 85·00

PAPUA NEW GUINEA Pt. 1

Combined territory on the island of New Guinea administered by Australia under trusteeship. Self-government was established during 1973.

1952. 12 pence = 1 shilling;
20 shillings = 1 pound.
1966. 100 cents = $1 Australian.
1975. 100 toea = 1 kina.

1 Matschie's Tree Kangaroo

7 Kiriwina Chief House

1952.

1 **1** ½d. green 30 10
2 – 1d. brown 20 10
3 – 2d. blue 35 10
4 – 2½d. orange . . . . 3·50 50
5 – 3d. myrtle 50 10
6 – 3½d. red 50 10
6a – 3½d. black . . . . 6·00 90
18 – 4d. red 75 10
19 – 5d. green 75 10
7 **7** 6½d. purple . . . . 1·25 10
20 – 7d. green . . . . 4·50 10
8 – 7½d. blue . . . . 2·50 1·00
21 – 8d. blue . . . . 75 1·50
9 – 9d. brown . . . . 2·75 40
10 – 1s. green . . . . 1·75 10
11 – 1s.6d. myrtle . . . . . . 5·00 60
22 – 1s.7d. brown . . . . . . 9·50 5·50
12 – 2s. blue . . . . 3·00 10
23 – 2s.5d. red . . . . 2·50 1·75
13 – 2s.6d. purple . . . . . . 3·00 40
24 – 5s. red and olive . . . . 9·00 1·00
14 – 10s. slate . . . . 32·00 13·00
15 – £1 brown . . . . 32·00 13·00

DESIGNS—VERT (as T **1**): 1d. Buka head-dresses; 2d. Native youth; 2½d. Greater bird of paradise; 3d. Native policeman; 3½d. Papuan head-dress; 4d., 5d. Cacao plant. (As T **7**): 7½d. Kiriwina Yam house; 1s.6d. Rubber tapping; 2s. Sepik dancing masks; 5s. Coffee beans; £1 Papuan shooting fish. HORIZ (as T **7**): 7, 8d. Klinki plymill; 9d. Copra making; 1s. Lakatoi; 1s.7d., 2s.5d. Cattle; 2s.6d. Native shepherd and flock; 10s. Map of Papua and New Guinea.

1957. Nos. 4, 1 and 10 surch.

16 – 4d. on 2½d. orange . . . . . 1·50 10
25 **1** 5d. on ½d. green 75 10
17 – 7d. on 1s. green 40 10

23 Council Chamber, Port Moresby

1961. Reconstitution of Legislative Council.

26 **23** 5d. green and yellow . . . . 1·00 25
27 2s.3d. green and salmon . . 3·00 1·50

24 Female, Goroka, New Guinea

26 Female Dancer

39 Waterfront, Port Moresby

28 Traffic Policeman

1961.

28 **24** 1d. lake 70 10
29 – 3d. blue 30 10
47 **39** 8d. green 30 15
30 **26** 1s. green . . . . 1·50 15
31 – 2s. purple 45 15
48 – 2s.3d. blue 30 30
32 **28** 3s. green . . . . 1·00 1·75

DESIGNS—As Type **24**: 3d. Tribal elder, Tari, Papua. As Type **39**: 2s.3d. Piaggio P-166B Portofino aircraft landing at Tapini. As Type **26**: 2s. Male dancer.

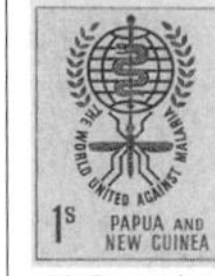
29 Campaign Emblem

30 Map of South Pacific

1962. Malaria Eradication.

33 **29** 5d. lake and blue 30 15
34 1s. red and brown 50 25
35 2s. black and green 60 70

1962. 5th South Pacific Conference, Pago Pago.

36 **30** 5d. red and green 50 15
37 1s.6d. violet and yellow . . 75 70
38 2s.6d. green and blue . . . 75 1·40

31 Throwing the Javelin

1962. 7th British Empire and Commonwealth Games, Perth.

39 **31** 5d. brown and blue 20 10
40 – 5d. brown and orange . . . 20 10
41 – 2s.3d. brown and green . . 70 75

SPORTS—As T **31**: No. 40, High jump. 32 × 23 mm: No. 41, Runners.

34 Raggiana Bird of Paradise

37 Queen Elizabeth II

36 Rabaul

1963.

42 **34** 5d. yellow, brown and sepia 1·00 10
43 – 6d. red, brown and grey . . 60 1·25
44 **36** 10s. multicoloured . . . . . 12·00 6·00
45 **37** £1 brown, gold and green 2·00 1·75

DESIGN—As Type **34**: 6d. Common phalanger.

38 Centenary Emblem

40 Games Emblem

1963. Centenary of Red Cross.

46 **38** 5d. red, grey and green . . 60 10

1963. 1st South Pacific Games, Suva.

49 **40** 5d. brown 10 10
50 1s. green 30 60

41 Watam Head

45 Casting Vote

1964. Native Artefacts. Multicoloured.

51 11d. Type **41** 25 10
52 2s.5d. Watam head (different) 30 1·75
53 2s.6d. Bosmun head 30 10
54 5s. Medina head 35 20

1964. Common Roll Elections.

55 **45** 5d. brown and drab 10 10
56 2s.3d. brown and blue . . . 20 25

46 "Health Centres"

50 Striped Gardener Bowerbird

1964. Health Services.

57 **46** 5d. violet 10 10
58 – 8d. green 10 10
59 – 1s. blue 15 10
60 – 1s.2d. red 20 35

DESIGNS: 8d. "School health"; 1s. "Infant child and maternal health"; 1s.2d. "Medical training".

1964. Multicoloured.

61 1d. Type **50** 40 10
62 3d. Adelbert bowerbird . . . 50 10
63 5d. Blue bird of paradise . . . 55 10
64 6d. Lawes's parotia 75 10
65 8d. Black-billed sicklebill . . . 1·00 20
66 1s. Emperor of Germany bird of paradise . . . . 1·00 10
67 2s. Brown sicklebill 75 30
68 2s.3d. Lesser bird of paradise 75 85
69 3s. Magnificent bird of paradise . . . . 75 1·25
70 5s. Twelve-wired bird of paradise . . . . 8·00 1·50
71 10s. Magnificent riflebird . . . 3·25 9·00

Nos. 66/71 are larger, 25½ × 36½ mm.

61 Canoe Prow

1965. Sepik Canoe Prows in Port Moresby Museum.

72 **61** 4d. multicoloured 50 10
73 – 1s.2d. multicoloured . . . . 1·00 1·75
74 – 1s.6d. multicoloured 50 10
75 – 4s. multicoloured 50 50

Each show different carved prows as Type **61**.

61a "Simpson and his Donkey"

1965. 50th Anniv of Gallipoli Landing.

76 **61a** 2s.3d. brown, black & green 20 10

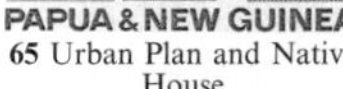

65 Urban Plan and Native House

69 "Papilio ulysses"

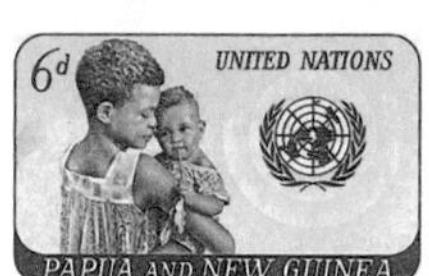

66 Mother and Child

1965. 6th South Pacific Conference, Lae.

77 **65**	6d. multicoloured	10	10
78 –	1s. multicoloured	10	10

No. 78 is similar to Type **65** but with the plan on the right and the house on the left. Also "URBANISATION" reads downwards.

1965. 20th Anniv of U.N.O.

79 **66**	6d. sepia, blue and turquoise	10	10
80 –	1s. brown, blue and violet	10	10
81 –	2s. blue, green and olive	10	10

DESIGNS—VERT: 1s. Globe and U.N. emblem; 2s. U.N. emblem and globes.

1966. Decimal Currency. Butterflies. Mult.

82	1c. Type **69**	40	1·00
83	3c. "Cyrestis acilia"	40	1·00
84	4c. "Graphium weiskei"	40	1·00
85	5c. "Terinos alurgis"	40	10
86	10c. "Ornithoptera priamus" (horiz)	50	30
86a	12c. "Euploea callithoe" (horiz)	2·50	2·25
87	15c. "Papilio euchenor" (horiz)	1·00	80
88	20c. "Parthenos sylvia" (horiz)	50	25
89	25c. "Delias aruna" (horiz)	70	1·25
90	50c. "Apaturina erminea" (horiz)	10·00	1·25
91	$1 "Doleschallia dascylus" (horiz)	3·00	1·75
92	$2 "Ornithoptera paradisea" (horiz)	6·00	8·50

80 "Molala Harai"

84 Throwing the Discus

1966. Folklore. Elema Art (1st series).

93 **80**	2c. black and red	10	10
94 –	7c. black, yellow and blue	10	30
95 –	30c. black, red and green	15	15
96 –	60c. black, red and yellow	40	50

DESIGNS: 7c. "Marai"; 30c. "Meavea Kivovia"; 60c. "Toivita Tapaivita".

1966. South Pacific Games, Noumea. Mult.

97	5c. Type **84**	10	10
98	10c. Football	15	10
99	20c. Tennis	20	40

87 "Mucuna novoguineensis"

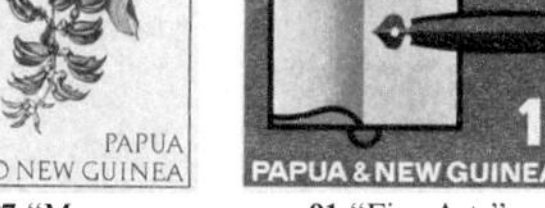

91 "Fine Arts"

1966. Flowers. Multicoloured.

100	5c. Type **87**	15	10
101	10c. "Tecomanthe dendrophila"	15	10
102	20c. "Rhododendron macgregoriae"	20	10
103	60c. "Rhododendron konori"	50	1·40

1967. Higher Education. Multicoloured.

104	1c. Type **91**	10	10
105	3c. "Surveying"	10	10
106	4c. "Civil Engineering"	10	10
107	5c. "Science"	10	10
108	20c. "Law"	10	10

96 "Sagra speciosa"

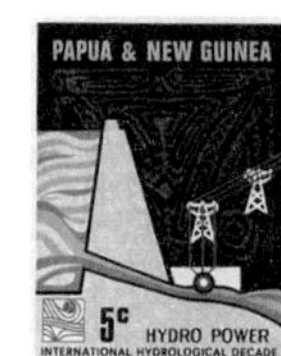

100 Laloki River

1967. Fauna Conservation (Beetles). Mult.

109	5c. Type **96**	15	10
110	10c. "Eupholus schoenherri"	15	10
111	20c. "Sphingnotus albertisi"	25	10
112	25c. "Cyphogastra albertisi"	25	10

1967. Laloki River Hydro-electric Scheme, and "New Industries". Multicoloured.

113	5c. Type **100**	10	10
114	10c. Pyrethrum	10	10
115	20c. Tea plant	15	10
116	25c. Type **100**	15	10

103 Air Attack at Milne Bay

107 Papuan Lory

1967. 25th Anniv of Pacific War. Multicoloured.

117	2c. Type **103**	10	50
118	5c. Kokoda Trail (vert)	10	10
119	20c. The Coast watchers	25	10
120	50c. Battle of the Coral Sea	80	70

1967. Christmas. Territory Parrots. Mult.

121	5c. Type **107**	20	10
122	7c. Pesquet's parrot	25	90
123	20c. Dusky lory	30	10
124	25c. Edward's fig parrot	35	10

111 Chimbu Head-dress

115 "Hyla thesaurensis"

1968. "National Heritage". Designs showing different Head-dresses. Multicoloured.

125	5c. Type **111**	10	10
126	10c. Southern Highlands (horiz)	15	10
127	20c. Western Highlands (horiz)	15	10
128	60c. Chimbu (different)	40	45

1968. Fauna Conservation (Frogs). Mult.

129	5c. Type **115**	15	50
130	10c. "Hyla iris"	15	10
131	15c. "Ceratobatrachus guentheri"	15	10
132	20c. "Nyctimystes narinosa"	20	50

119 Human Rights Emblem and Papuan Head-dress (abstract)

1968. Human Rights Year. Multicoloured.

133	5c. Type **119**	10	20
134	10c. Human Rights in the World (abstract)	10	10

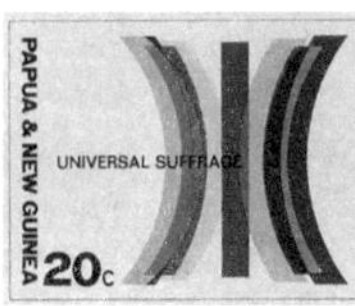

121 Leadership (abstract)

1968. Universal Suffrage. Multicoloured.

135	20c. Type **121**	15	20
136	25c. Leadership of the Community (abstract)	15	30

123 Common Egg Cowrie

1968. Sea Shells. Multicoloured.

137	1c. Type **123**	10	10
138	3c. Laciniate conch	30	1·25
139	4c. Lithograph cone	20	1·25
140	5c. Marbled cone	25	10
141	7c. Episcopal mitre	35	10
142	10c. "Cymbiola rutila ruckeri"	45	10
143	12c. Checkerboard bonnet	1·25	2·00
144	15c. Scorpion conch	60	1·00
145	20c. Fluted giant clam or scale tridacna	70	10
146	25c. Camp pitar venus	70	70
147	30c. Ramose murex	70	1·00
148	40c. Chambered or pearly nautilus	75	1·00
149	60c. Trumpet triton	70	60
150	$1 Manus green papuina	1·00	75
151	$2 Glory of the sea cone	13·00	3·25

138 Tito Myth

142 "Fireball" Class Dinghy

1969. Folklore. Elema Art (2nd series).

152 **138**	5c. black, yellow and red	10	50
153 –	5c. black, yellow and red	10	50
154 –	10c. black, grey and red	15	50
155 –	10c. black, grey and red	15	50

DESIGNS: No. 153, Iko Myth; 154, Luvuapo Myth; 155, Miro Myth.

1969. 3rd South Pacific Games, Port Moresby.

156 **142**	5c. black	10	25
157 –	10c. violet	10	10
158 –	20c. green	15	20

DESIGNS—HORIZ: 10c. Swimming pool, Boroko; 20c. Games arena, Konedobu.

145 "Dendrobium ostrinoglossum"

149 Bird of Paradise

1969. Flora Conservation (Orchids). Multicoloured.

159	5c. Type **145**	25	10
160	10c. "Dendrobium lawesii"	25	70
161	20c. "Dendrobium pseudofrigidum"	30	90
162	30c. "Dendrobium conanthum"	30	70

1969.

162a **149**	2c. blue, black and red	10	65
163	5c. green, brown & orge	10	10

150 Native Potter

151 Tareko

1969. 50th Anniv of I.L.O.

164 **150**	5c. multicoloured	10	10

1969. Musical Instruments.

165 **151**	5c. multicoloured	10	10
166 –	10c. black, green & yellow	10	10
167 –	25c. black, yellow & brown	15	15
168 –	30c. multicoloured	25	15

DESIGNS: 10c. Garamut; 25c. Iviliko; 30c. Kundu.

155 Prehistoric Ambun Stone

159 King of Saxony Bird of Paradise

1970. "National Heritage". Multicoloured.

169	5c. Type **155**	10	10
170	10c. Masawa canoe of Kula Circuit	10	10
171	25c. Torres' map, 1606	40	15
172	30c. H.M.S. "Basilisk" (paddle-sloop), 1873	65	25

1970. Fauna Conservation. Birds of Paradise. Mult.

173	5c. Type **159**	70	15
174	10c. King bird of paradise	70	60
175	15c. Raggiana bird of paradise	1·00	1·00
176	25c. Sickle-crested bird of paradise	1·25	70

163 Douglas DC-6B and Mt. Wilhelm

1970. Australian and New Guinea Air Services. Multicoloured.

177	5c. Type **163**	25	30
178	5c. Lockheed Electra and Mt. Yule	25	30
179	5c. Boeing 727-100 and Mt. Giluwe	25	30
180	5c. Fokker Friendship and Manam Island	25	30
181	25c. Douglas DC-3 and Matupi Volcano	35	40
182	30c. Boeing 707 and Hombrom's Bluff	35	60

169 N. Miklouho-Maclay (scientist) and Effigy

1970. 42nd A.N.Z.A.A.S. Congress, Port Moresby. Multicoloured.

183	5c. Type **169**	10	10
184	10c. B. Malinowski (anthropologist) and native hut	20	10
185	15c. T. Salvadori (ornithologist) and double-wattled cassowary	90	25
186	20c. F. R. R. Schlechter (botanist) and flower	60	25

A.N.Z.A.A.S. = Australian–New Zealand Association for the Advancement of Science.

170 Wogeo Island Food Bowl

171 Eastern Highlands Dwelling

1970. Native Artefacts. Multicoloured.

187	5c. Type **170**	10	10
188	10c. Lime pot	20	10
189	15c. Albom sago storage pot	20	10
190	30c. Manus island bowl (horiz)	25	30

1971. Native Dwellings. Multicoloured.

191	5c. Type **171**	10	10
192	7c. Milne Bay stilt dwelling	15	90
193	10c. Purari Delta dwelling	15	10
194	40c. Sepik dwelling	25	90

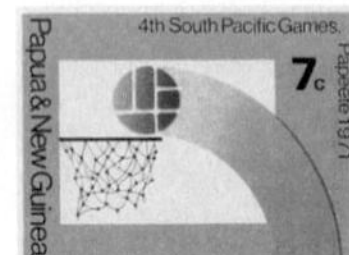

172 Spotted Phalanger 173 "Basketball"

1971. Fauna Conservation. Multicoloured.

195 5c. Type **172** 30 10
196 10c. Long-fingered possum 35 10
197 15c. Feather-tailed possum 50 80
198 25c. Long-tailed echidna . . 70 80
199 30c. Ornate tree kangaroo (horiz) 70 50

1971. 4th South Pacific Games, Papeete. Mult.

200 7c. Type **173** 10 10
201 14c. "Sailing" 15 20
202 21c. "Boxing" 15 30
203 28c. "Athletics" 15 40

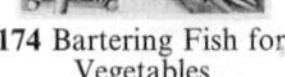

174 Bartering Fish for Vegetables 175 Sia Dancer

1971. Primary Industries. Multicoloured.

204 7c. Type **174** 10 10
205 9c. Man stacking yams . . . 15 30
206 14c. Vegetable market . . . 25 10
207 30c. Highlanders cultivating garden 45 65

1971. Native Dancers. Multicoloured.

208 7c. Type **175** 20 10
209 9c. Urasena dancer 20 20
210 20c. Siassi Tubuan dancers (horiz) 50 75
211 28c. Sia dancers (horiz) . . . 65 90

176 Papuan Flag over Australian Flag

1971. Constitutional Development.

212 **176** 7c. multicoloured 30 10
213 – 7c. multicoloured 30 10

DESIGN: No. 213, Crest of Papua New Guinea and Australian coat of arms.

177 Map of Papua New Guinea and Flag of South Pacific Commission

1972. 25th Anniv of South Pacific Commission.

214 **177** 15c. multicoloured 45 55
215 – 15c. multicoloured 45 55

DESIGN: No. 215, Man's face and flag of the Commission.

178 Turtle

1972. Fauna Conservation (Reptiles). Mult.

216 7c. Type **178** 35 10
217 14c. Rainforest dragon . . . 50 1·25
218 21c. Green python . . . . . 55 1·50
219 30c. Salvador's monitor . . . 60 1·25

179 Curtiss MF-6 Seagull and "Eureka" (schooner)

1972. 50th Anniv of Aviation. Multicoloured.

220 7c. Type **179** 40 10
221 14c. De Havilland D.H.37 and native porters . . . . 60 1·25
222 20c. Junkers G.31 and gold dredger . . . . 70 1·25
223 25c. Junkers F-13 and mission church . . . . . . 70 1·25

180 New National Flag 181 Rev. Copland King

1972. National Day. Multicoloured.

224 7c. Type **180** 20 10
225 10c. Native drum 25 25
226 30c. Trumpet triton 45 50

1972. Christmas. Missionaries. Multicoloured.

227 7c. Type **181** 25 40
228 7c. Rev. Dr. Flierl 25 40
229 7c. Bishop Verjus 25 40
230 7c. Pastor Ruatoka 25 40

182 Mt. Tomavatur Station 183 Queen Carola's Parotia

1973. Completion of Telecommunications Project, 1968–72. Multicoloured.

231 7c. Type **182** 15 20
232 7c. Mt. Kerigomma Station 15 20
233 7c. Sattelburg Station 15 20
234 7c. Wideru Station 15 20
235 9c. Teleprinter 15 20
236 30c. Network map 35 50

Nos. 235/6 are larger, 36×26 mm.

1973. Birds of Paradise. Multicoloured.

237 7c. Type **183** . . . . 1·00 35
238 14c. Goldie's bird of paradise 2·25 1·00
239 21c. Ribbon-tailed bird of paradise . . . . 2·50 1·50
240 28c. Princess Stephanie's bird of paradise . . . . 3·00 2·00

Nos. 239/40 are size 18×49 mm.

184 Wood Carver

1973. Multicoloured.

241 1c. Type **184** 10 10
242 3c. Wig-makers 30 10
243 5c. Mt. Bagana 55 10
244 6c. Pig exchange . . . . . . 80 1·50
245 7c. Coastal village 20 10
246 8c. Arawe mother 25 30
247 9c. Fire dancers 20 20
248 10c. Tifalmin hunter 40 10
249 14c. Crocodile hunters . . . 35 70
250 15c. Mt. Elimbari 50 30
251 20c. Canoe-racing, Manus . . 60 40
252 21c. Making sago . . . . . 30 1·00
253 25c. Council House 30 45
254 28c. Menyamya bowmen . . 30 1·00
255 30c. Shark-snaring 30 50
256 40c. Fishing canoes, Madang 30 40
257 60c. Tapa cloth-making . . . 40 50
258 $1 Asaro Mudmen . . . . . 45 1·10
259 $2 Enga "Sing Sing" . . . . 1·75 6·00

185 Stamps of German New Guinea, 1897

1973. 75th Anniv of Papua New Guinea Stamps.

260 **185** 1c. multicoloured 10 15
261 – 6c. indigo, blue and silver 15 30
262 – 7c. multicoloured 15 30
263 – 9c. multicoloured 15 30
264 – 25c. orange and gold . . 30 80
265 – 30c. plum and silver . . . 30 90

DESIGNS—As Type **185**: 6c. 2 mark stamp of German New Guinea, 1900; 7c. Surcharged registration label of New Guinea, 1914. 46×35 mm: 9c. Papuan 1s. stamp, 1901. 45×38 mm: 25c. ½d. stamp of New Guinea, 1925; 30c. Papuan 10s. stamp, 1932.

186 Native Carved Heads 187 Queen Elizabeth II (from photo by Karsh)

1973. Self-government.

266 **186** 7c. multicoloured 30 15
267 10c. multicoloured 50 65

1974. Royal Visit.

268 **187** 7c. multicoloured 25 15
269 30c. multicoloured . . . . 75 1·50

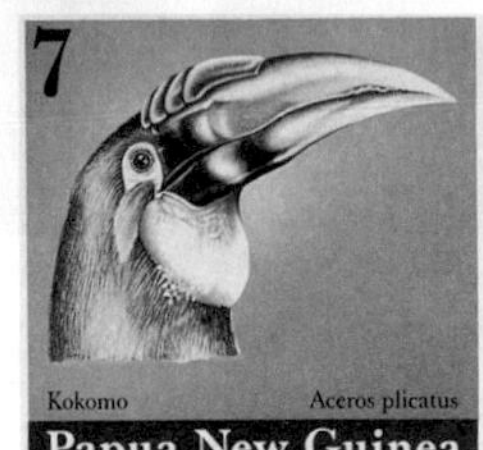

188 Blyth's Hornbill

1974. Birds' Heads. Multicoloured.

270 7c. Type **188** . . . . 1·25 70
271 10c. Double-wattled cassowary (33×49 mm) . . 2·00 3·25
272 30c. New Guinea harpy eagle 4·00 8·50

189 "Dendrobium bracteosum" 191 1-toea Coin

190 Motu Lakatoi

1974. Flora Conservation. Multicoloured.

273 7c. Type **189** 30 10
274 10c. "D. anosmum" 40 60
275 20c. "D. smillieae" . . . . . 50 1·40
276 30c. "D. insigne" . . . . . 60 1·75

1974. National Heritage. Canoes. Multicoloured.

277 7c. Type **190** 30 10
278 10c. Tami two-master morobe 30 55
279 25c. Aramia racing canoe . . 60 3·00
280 30c. Buka Island canoe . . . 60 1·00

1975. New Coinage. Multicoloured.

281 1t. Type **191** 10 30
282 7t. New 2t. and 5t. coins . . 25 10
283 10t. New 10t. coin 25 30
284 20t. New 20t. coin 40 80
285 1k. New 1k. coin . . . . . . 1·25 4·50

SIZES: 10, 20t. As Type **191**; 7t., 1k. 45×26 mm.

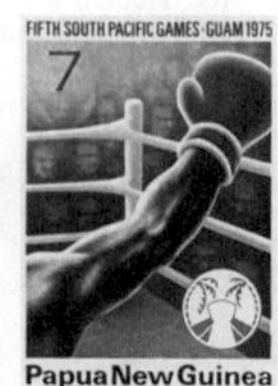

192 "Ornithoptera alexandrae" 193 Boxing

1975. Fauna Conservation (Birdwing Butterflies). Multicoloured.

286 7t. Type **192** 30 10
287 10t. "O. victoriae" 40 65
288 30t. "O. allottei" . . . . . . 70 2·00
289 40t. "O. chimaera" . . . . . 90 3·50

1975. 5th South Pacific Games, Guam. Mult.

290 7t. Type **193** 10 10
291 20t. Running 15 30
292 25t. Basketball 30 45
293 30t. Swimming 30 50

194 Map and National Flag

1975. Independence. Multicoloured.

294 7t. Type **194** 20 10
295 30t. Map and National emblem 40 65
MS296 116×58 mm. Nos. 294/5 1·10 1·75

195 M.V. "Bulolo"

1976. Ships of the 1930s. Multicoloured.

297 7t. Type **195** 20 10
298 15t. M.V. "Macdhui" 30 30
299 25t. M.V. "Malaita" 35 65
300 60t. S.S. "Montoro" . . . . 50 2·50

196 Rorovana Carvings

1976. Bougainville Art. Multicoloured.

301 7t. Type **196** 10 10
302 20t. Upe hats 20 35
303 25t. Kapkaps . . . . 25 1·00
304 30t. Canoe paddles 30 80

197 Rabaul House

1976. Native Dwellings. Multicoloured.

305 7t. Type **197** 10 10
306 15t. Aramia house 15 20
307 30t. Telefomin house 25 60
308 40t. Tapini house . . . . . 25 1·50

198 Landscouts

1976. 50th Annivs of Survey Flight and Scouting in Papua New Guinea. Multicoloured.

309 7t. Type **198** 20 10
310 10t. De Havilland D.H.50A seaplane 20 20
311 15t. Seascouts 30 40
312 60t. De Havilland D.H.50A seaplane on water . . . . 80 3·00

199 Father Ross and New Guinea Highlands

1976. William Ross Commemoration.

313 **199** 7t. multicoloured 40 15

200 Picture Wrasse

1976. Fauna Conservation (Tropical Fish). Mult.
314 5t. Type **200** 25 10
315 15t. Emperor angelfish . . . 35 45
316 30t. Six-blotched hind 55 80
317 40t. Thread-finned butterflyfish . . . . 65 1·10

201 Man from Kundiawa **202** Headdress, Wasara Tribe

1977. Headdresses. Multicoloured.
318 1t. Type **201** 10 10
319 5t. Masked dancer, Abelam area of Maprik 10 10
320 10t. Headdress from Koiari 20 15
321 15t. Woman with face paint, Hanuabada 25 20
322 20t. Orokaiva dancer 40 30
323 25t. Haus Tambaran dancer, Abelam area of Maprik . . 30 30
324 30t. Asaro Valley headdress 30 35
325 35t. Singsing costume, Garaina 30 45
326 40t. Waghi Valley headdress 30 35
327 50t. Trobriand Island dancer 40 60
328 1k. Type **202** . . . . 50 1·50
329 2k. Headdress, Meko tribe 75 3·00
SIZES: 1, 5, 20t. 25 × 31 mm; 35, 40t. 23 × 38 mm; 1k. 28 × 35 mm; 2k. 33 × 23 mm; others 26 × 26 mm.

203 National Flag and Queen Elizabeth II

1977. Silver Jubilee. Multicoloured.
330 7t. Type **203** 20 10
331 15t. The Queen and national emblem 25 35
332 35t. The Queen and map of P.N.G. 40 70

204 White-breasted Ground Pigeon

1977. Fauna Conservation (Birds). Mult.
333 5t. Type **204** 35 10
334 7t. Victoria crowned pigeon 35 10
335 15t. Pheasant pigeon 65 65
336 30t. Orange-fronted fruit dove . . . . 80 1·10
337 50t. Banded imperial pigeon 1·25 3·50

205 Guides and Gold Badge **206** Kari Marupi Myth

1977. 50th Anniv of Guiding in Papua New Guinea. Multicoloured.
338 7t. Type **205** 20 10
339 15t. Guides mapping 25 20
340 30t. Guides washing 40 50
341 35t. Guides cooking 40 60

1977. Folklore. Elema Art (3rd series).
342 **206** 7t. multicoloured 15 10
343 – 20t. multicoloured 35 35
344 – 30t. red, blue and black 40 75
345 – 35t. red, yellow and black 40 75
DESIGNS: 20t. Savoripi clan myth; 30t. Oa-Laea myth; 35t. Oa-Iriarapo myth.

207 Blue-tailed Skink

1978. Fauna Conservation (Skinks). Mult.
346 10t. Type **207** 20 10
347 15t. Green tree skink 25 25
348 35t. Crocodile skink 30 70
349 40t. New Guinea blue-tongued skink 45 85

208 "Roboastra arika"

1978. Sea Slugs. Multicoloured.
350 10t. Type **208** 20 10
351 15t. "Chromodoris fidelis" . . 25 30
352 35t. "Flabellina macassarana" 45 85
353 40t. "Chromodoris marginata" . . . . 50 1·00

209 Present Day Royal Papua New Guinea Constabulary

1978. History of Royal Papua New Guinea Constabulary. Uniformed Police and Constabulary Badges. Multicoloured.
354 10t. Type **209** 20 10
355 15t. Mandated New Guinea Constabulary, 1921–41 . . 25 15
356 20t. British New Guinea Armed Constabulary, 1890–1906 . . . . 25 40
357 25t. German New Guinea Police, 1899–1914 . . . . 30 45
358 30t. Royal Papua and New Guinea Constabulary, 1906–64 . . . . 30 60

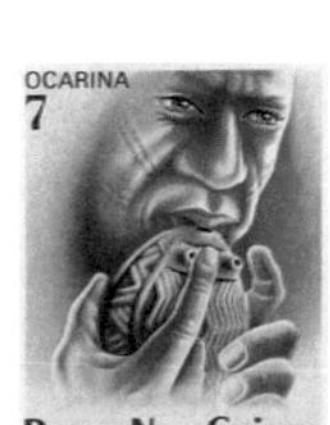

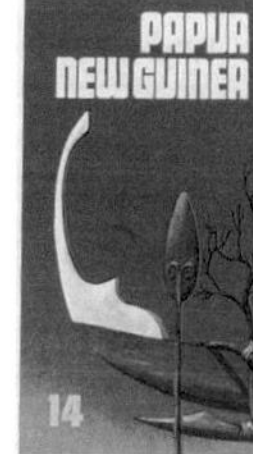

210 Ocarina **211** East New Britain Canoe Prow

1979. Musical Instruments. Mult.
359 7t. Type **210** 10 10
360 20t. Musical bow (horiz) . . 20 20
361 28t. Launut 25 30
362 35t. Nose flute (horiz) . . . 30 45

1979. Traditional Canoe Prows and Paddles. Mult.
363 14t. Type **211** 20 15
364 21t. Sepik war canoe 30 25
365 25t. Trobriand Island canoe 30 30
366 40t. Milne Bay canoe 40 60

212 Katudababila (waist belt) **213** "Aenetus cyanochlora"

1979. Traditional Currency. Multicoloured.
367 7t. Type **212** 10 10
368 15t. Doga (chest ornament) 20 30
369 25t. Mwali (armshell) 35 55
370 35t. Soulava (necklace) . . . 45 75

1979. Fauna Conservation. Moths. Multicoloured.
371 7t. Type **213** 20 10
372 15t. "Celerina vulgaris" . . . 30 35
373 20t. "Alcidis aurora" (vert) 30 75
374 25t. "Phyllodes conspicillator" . . . . . . 35 1·00
375 30t. "Lyssa patroclus" (vert) 40 1·00

214 "The Right to Affection and Love" **216** Detail from Betrothal Ceremony Mural, Minj District, Western Highlands Province

215 "Post Office Service"

1979. International Year of the Child. Mult.
376 7t. Type **214** 10 10
377 15t. "The right to adequate nutrition and medical care" 15 15
378 30t. "The right to play" . . . 20 20
379 60t. "The right to a free education" 45 60

1980. Admission to U.P.U. (1979). Multicoloured.
380 7t. Type **215** 10 10
381 25t. "Wartime mail" 25 25
382 35t. "U.P.U. emblem 35 40
383 40t. "Early postal services" 40 50

1980. South Pacific Festival of Arts.
384 **216** 20t. yellow, orange & blk 15 35
385 – 20t. mult (two figures, left-hand in black and yellow; right-hand in black, yellow and red) 15 35
386 – 20t. mult (two figures, left-hand in black and orange; right-hand in black) 15 35
387 – 20t. mult (two figures, one behind the other) . . . 15 35
388 – 20t. mult (one figure) . . 15 35
DESIGNS: Nos. 385/8, further details of Betrothal Ceremony.
Nos. 384/8 were issued together in horizontal se-tenant strips of five within the sheet, forming a composite design.

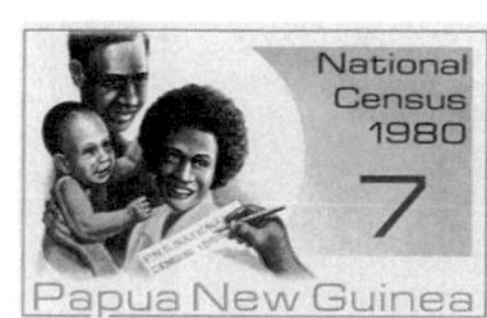

217 Family being Interviewed

1980. National Census. Multicoloured.
389 7t. Type **217** 10 10
390 15t. Population symbol . . . 15 15
391 40t. Papua New Guinea map 30 40
392 50t. Heads symbolizing population growth 35 50

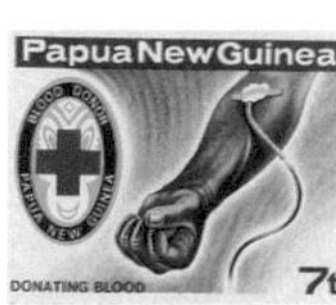

218 Donating Blood

1980. Red Cross Blood Bank. Multicoloured.
393 7t. Type **218** 15 10
394 15t. Receiving transfusion . . 20 20
395 30t. Map of Papua New Guinea showing blood transfusion centres 25 25
396 60t. Blood and its components 40 60

219 Dugong

1980. Mammals. Multicoloured.
397 7t. Type **219** 10 10
398 30t. New Guinea marsupial cat (vert) 30 45
399 35t. Tube-nosed bat (vert) . . 30 45
400 45t. Rufescent bandicoot . . 40 55

220 White-headed Kingfisher **221** Native Mask

1981. Kingfishers. Multicoloured.
401 3t. Type **220** 25 60
402 7t. Forest kingfisher 25 10
403 20t. Sacred kingfisher 30 50
404 25t. White-tailed kingfisher (26 × 46 mm) 30 85
405 60t. Blue-winged kookaburra 60 3·00

1981.
406 **221** 2t. violet and orange . . . 10 20
407 – 5t. red and green 10 20
DESIGN: 5t. Hibiscus flower.

222 Mortar Team

1981. Defence Force. Multicoloured.
408 7t. Type **222** 15 10
409 15t. Douglas DC-3 and aircrew 25 25
410 40t. "Aitape" (patrol boat) and seamen 35 65
411 50t. Medical team examining children 35 75

223 M.A.F. (Missionary Aviation Fellowship) Cessna Super Skywagon

1981. "Mission Aviation". Multicoloured.
412 10t. Type **223** 20 10
413 15t. Catholic mission British Aircraft Swallow "St. Paulus" 25 15
414 20t. S.I.L. (Summer Institute of Linguistics) Hiller 12E helicopter 25 25
415 30t. Lutheran mission Junkers F-13 . . . . . . 35 40
416 35t. S.D.A. (Seventh Day Adventist Church) Piper PA-23 Aztec 35 55

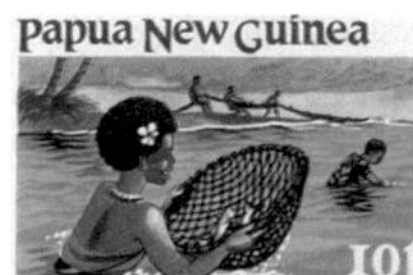

224 Scoop Net Fishing

1981. Fishing. Multicoloured.
417 10t. Type **224** 15 10
418 15t. Kite fishing 20 30
419 30t. Rod fishing 30 50
420 60t. Scissor net fishing . . . 55 85

225 Buhler's Papuina

1981. Land Snail Shells. Multicoloured.
421 5t. Type **225** 10 10
422 15t. Yellow naninia 20 25
423 20t. Adonis papuina and Hermoine papuina 20 35
424 30t. Hinde's papuina and New Pommeranian papuina 30 50
425 40t. "Papuina strabo" . . . 40 80

226 Lord Baden-Powell and Flag-raising Ceremony

1981. 75th Anniv of Boy Scout Movement. Mult.

426 15t. Type **226** 20 15
427 25t. Scout leader and camp 20 30
428 35t. Scout and hut building 20 45
429 50t. Percy Chaterton and Scouts administering first aid 30 75

227 Yangoru and Boiken Bowls, East Sepik

1981. Native Pottery. Multicoloured.

430 10t. Type **227** 10 10
431 20t. Utu cooking pot and small Gumalu pot, Madang 20 30
432 40t. Wanigela pots, Northern (37 × 23 mm) 40 55
433 50t. Ramu Valley pots, Madang (37 × 23 mm) . . 45 80

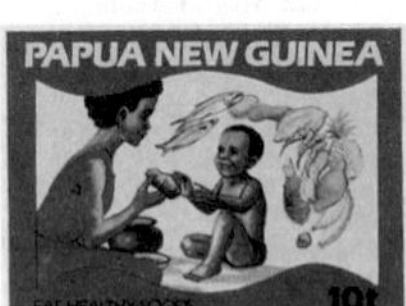

228 "Eat Healthy Foods"

1982. Food and Nutrition. Multicoloured.

434 10t. Type **228** 10 10
435 15t. Protein foods 20 30
436 30t. Protective foods 40 55
437 40t. Energy foods 45 70

229 "Stylophora sp."

1982. Multicoloured.

438 1t. Type **229** 10 20
439 3t. "Dendrophyllia sp." (vert) 60 1·25
440 5t. "Acropora humilis" . . . 15 10
441 10t. "Dendronephthya sp." (vert) 80 60
442 12t. As 10t. . . . . 3·50 6·00
443 15t. "Distichopora sp." . . . 20 20
444 20t. "Isis sp" (vert) 90 25
445 25t. "Acropora sp." (vert) . . 50 50
446 30t. "Dendronephthya sp." (different) (vert) . . . . . 1·25 90
447 35t. "Stylaster elegans" (vert) 1·25 50
448 40t. "Antipathes sp." (vert) 1·25 1·50
449 45t. "Turbinarea sp." (vert) 2·00 1·00
450 1k. "Xenia sp." . . . . . . 1·00 85
451 3k. "Distichopora sp." (vert) 2·75 3·50
452 5k. Raggiana bird of paradise (33 × 33 mm) . . . . . . 7·00 9·00

230 Missionaries landing on Beach **231** Athletics

1982. Centenary of Catholic Church in Papua New Guinea. Mural on Wall of Nordup Catholic Church, East New Britain. Multicoloured.

457 10t. Type **230** 20 65
458 10t. Missionaries talking to natives 20 65
459 10t. Natives with slings and spears ready to attack . . 20 65

Nos. 457/9 were issued together, se-tenant, forming a composite design.

1982. Commonwealth Games and "Anpex 82" Stamp Exhibition, Brisbane. Multicoloured.

460 10t. Type **231** 15 10
461 15t. Boxing 20 25
462 45t. Rifle-shooting 40 70
463 50t. Bowls 45 75

232 National Flag

1983. Commonwealth Day. Multicoloured.

464 10t. Type **232** 15 10
465 15t. Basket-weaving and cabbage-picking 20 30
466 20t. Crane hoisting roll of material 25 35
467 50t. Lorries and ships 60 75

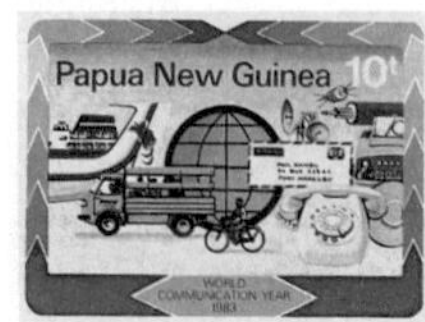

233 Transport Communications

1983. World Communications Year. Multicoloured.

468 10t. Type **233** 30 10
469 25t. "Postal service" 50 25
470 30t. "Telephone service" . . 55 30
471 60t. "Transport service" . . . 1·10 90

234 "Chelonia depressa"

1984. Turtles. Multicoloured.

472 5t. Type **234** 20 10
473 10t. "Chelonia mydas" . . . 25 10
474 15t. "Eretmochelys imbricata" 30 30
475 20t. "Lepidochelys olivacea" 40 35
476 25t. " Caretta caretta" . . . 45 50
477 40t. "Dermochelys coriacea" 60 75

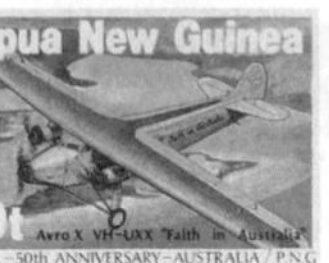

235 Avro Type 618 Ten "Faith in Australia"

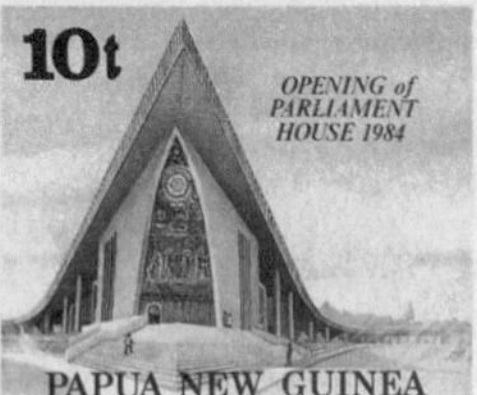

236 Parliament House

1984. 50th Anniv of First Airmail Australia–Papua New Guinea. Multicoloured.

478 20t. Type **235** 40 30
479 25t. De Havilland Dragon Express "Carmania" . . . 40 45
480 40t. Westland Widgeon . . . 50 80
481 60t. Consolidated PBY-5 Catalina flying boat . . . 70 1·25

1984. Opening of New Parliament House.

482 **236** 10t. multicoloured 30 30

237 Ceremonial Shield and Club, Central Province

1984. Ceremonial Shields. Multicoloured.

483 10t. Type **237** 20 10
484 20t. Ceremonial shield, West New Britain 30 35
485 30t. Ceremonial shield, Madang Province 45 75
486 50t. Ceremonial shield, East Sepik . . . . 75 3·00

See also Nos. 558/61.

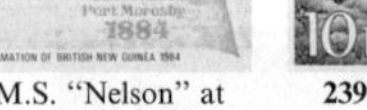

238 H.M.S. "Nelson" at Port Moresby, 1884 **239** Fergusson Island

1984. Centenary of Protectorate Proclamations for British New Guinea and German New Guinea. Multicoloured.

487 10t. Type **238** 35 55
488 10t. Papua New Guinea flag and Port Moresby, 1984 35 55
489 45t. Papua New Guinea flag and Rabaul, 1984 . . . . 50 1·90
490 45t. German warship "Elizabeth" at Rabaul, 1884 . . . . 50 1·90

Nos. 487/8 and 489/90 were issued in se-tenant pairs, each pair forming a composite picture.

1985. Tourist Scenes. Multicoloured.

491 10t. Type **239** 25 10
492 25t. Sepik River 50 60
493 40t. Chimbu Gorge (horiz) 75 1·40
494 60t. Dali Beach, Vanimo (horiz) . . . . 1·25 1·90

1985. No. 408 surch **12t**.

495 **222** 12t. on 7t. multicoloured 60 75

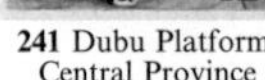

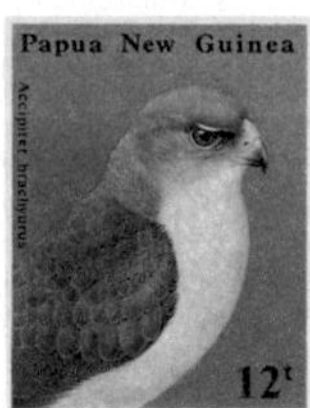

241 Dubu Platform, Central Province **242** Head of New Britain Collared Sparrow Hawk

1985. Ceremonial Structures. Multicoloured.

496 15t. Type **241** 35 15
497 20t. Tamuniai house, West New Britain 50 50
498 30t. Traditional yam tower, Trobriand Island 65 80
499 60t. Huli grave, Tari . . . . 1·00 1·75

1985. Birds of Prey. Multicoloured.

500 12t. Type **242** . . . . 70 1·50
501 12t. New Britain collared sparrow hawk in flight . . 70 1·50
502 30t. Doria's goshawk . . . . 1·00 1·75
503 30t. Doria's goshawk in flight 1·00 1·75
504 60t. Long-tailed honey buzzard . . . . 1·50 2·25
505 60t. Long-tailed honey buzzard in flight . . . . . 1·50 2·25

243 National Flag and Parliament House **244** Early Postcard, Aerogramme, Inkwell and Spectacles

1985. 10th Anniv of Independence.

506 **243** 12t. multicoloured . . . . 60 1·00

1985. Centenary of Papua New Guinea Post Office. Multicoloured.

507 12t. Type **244** 45 10
508 30t. Queensland 1897 1d. die with proof and modern press printing stamps . . . 1·10 1·00
509 40t. Newspaper of 1885 announcing shipping service and loading mail into aircraft . . . . 1·75 2·25
510 60t. Friedrich-Wilhelmshafen postmark of 1892 and Port Moresby F.D.C. postmark of 9 October 1985 . . . . 2·00 3·75

MS511 As Nos. 507/10, but designs continue on sheet margins . . 6·00 7·00

245 Figure with Eagle **246** Valentine or Prince Cowrie

1985. Nombowai Wood Carvings. Mult.

512 12t. Type **245** 50 10
513 30t. Figure with clam shell 1·25 75
514 60t. Figure with dolphin . . 2·00 3·00
515 80t. Figure of woman with cockerel . . . . 2·50 5·00

1986. Sea Shells. Multicoloured.

516 15t. Type **246** 75 15
517 35t. Bulow's olive . . . . . 1·60 1·40
518 45t. Parkinson's olive . . . . 2·00 2·25
519 70t. Golden cowrie . . . . . 2·50 5·75

246a Princess Elizabeth in A.T.S. Uniform, 1945

1986. 60th Birthday of Queen Elizabeth II. Mult.

520 15t. Type **246a** 15 15
521 35t. Silver Wedding Anniversary photograph (by Patrick Lichfield), Balmoral, 1972 . . . . . 20 40
522 50t. Queen inspecting guard of honour, Port Moresby, 1982 . . . . 40 85
523 60t. On board Royal Yacht "Britannia", Papua New Guinea, 1982 . . . . . . 65 1·00
524 70t. At Crown Agents' Head Office, London, 1983 . . . 40 1·25

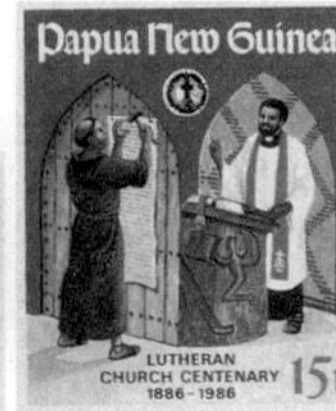

247 Rufous Fantail **248** Martin Luther nailing Theses to Cathedral Door, Wittenberg and Modern Lutheran Pastor

1986. "Ameripex '86" International Stamp Exhibition, Chicago. Small Birds (1st series). Multicoloured.

525 15t. Type **247** 90 30
526 35t. Streaked berry pecker . . 1·75 1·25
527 45t. Red-breasted pitta . . . 1·90 1·25
528 70t. Olive-yellow robin (vert) 2·50 6·50

See also Nos. 597/601.

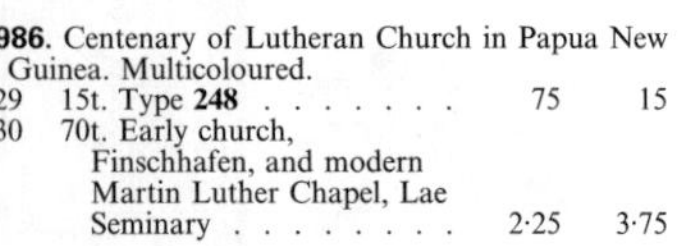

1986. Centenary of Lutheran Church in Papua New Guinea. Multicoloured.

529 15t. Type **248** 75 15
530 70t. Early church, Finschhafen, and modern Martin Luther Chapel, Lae Seminary . . . . 2·25 3·75

249 "Dendrobium vexillarius" **250** Maprik Dancer

1986. Orchids. Multicoloured.

531 15t. Type **249** 95 20
532 35t. "Dendrobium lineale" 2·00 75
533 45t. "Dendrobium johnsoniae" . . . . 2·00 1·10
534 70t. "Dendrobium cuthbertsonii" . . . . . . 2·75 6·00

1986. Papua New Guinea Dancers. Multicoloured.

535 15t. Type **250** 80 15
536 35t. Kiriwina . . . . 1·60 80

537 45t. Kundiawa 1·75 95
538 70t. Fasu 3·00 4·25

251 White-bonnet Anemonefish

1987. Anemonefish. Multicoloured.
539 17t. Type **251** 70 25
540 30t. Orange-finned anemonefish 1·40 1·10
541 35t. Fire anemonefish ("Tomato clownfish") 1·50 1·40
542 70t. Spine-cheeked anemonefish 2·50 6·00

252 "Roebuck" (Dampier), 1700

1987. Ships. Multicoloured.
543 1t. "La Boudeuse" (De Bougainville, 1768) 50 1·25
544 5t. Type **252** 1·00 1·75
545 10t. H.M.S. "Swallow" (Philip Carteret), 1767 1·25 1·75
546 15t. H.M.S. "Fly" (Blackwood), 1845 1·75 1·00
547 17t. As 15t. 1·75 75
548 20t. H.M.S. "Rattlesnake" (Owen Stanley), 1849 1·75 1·00
549 30t. "Vitiaz" (Maclay), 1871 1·75 2·50
550 35t. "San Pedrico" (Torres) and zabra, 1606 70 1·00
551 40t. "L'Astrolabe" (D'Urville), 1827 2·00 2·75
552 45t. "Neva" (D. Albertis), 1876 75 1·25
553 60t. Spanish galleon (Jorge de Meneses), 1526 2·50 3·50
554 70t. "Eendracht" (Schouten and Le Maire), 1616 1·75 2·75
555 1k. H.M.S. "Blanche" (Simpson), 1872 2·50 3·00
556 2k. "Merrie England" (steamer), 1889 3·25 3·00
557 3k. "Samoa" (German colonial steamer), 1884 4·00 6·00

For some of these designs redrawn for "Australia '99" World Stamp Exhibition see Nos. 857/60.

1987. War Shields. As T **237**. Multicoloured.
558 15t. Gulf Province 20 25
559 35t. East Sepik 45 50
560 45t. Madang Province 55 60
561 70t. Telefomin 85 90

1987. No. 442 surch **15t**.
562 15t. on 12t. "Dendronephthya sp." (vert) 65 65

254 "Protoreaster nodosus"

1987. Starfish. Multicoloured.
563 17t. Type **254** 55 25
564 35t. "Gomophia egeriae" 1·10 70
565 45t. "Choriaster granulatus" 1·25 80
566 70t. "Neoferdina ocellata" 1·75 3·50

255 Cessna Stationair 6 taking off, Rabaraba

1987. Aircraft in Papua New Guinea. Mult.
567 15t. Type **255** 1·00 25
568 35t. Britten Norman Islander over Hombrum Bluff 1·75 90
569 45t. De Havilland Twin Otter 100 over Highlands 1·75 1·00
570 70t. Fokker F.28 Fellowship over Madang 2·75 6·50

256 Pre-Independence Policeman on Traffic Duty and Present-day Motorcycle Patrol

1988. Centenary of Royal Papua New Guinea Constabulary. Multicoloured.
571 17t. Type **256** 45 25
572 35t. British New Guinea Armed Constabulary, 1890, and Governor W. MacGregor 80 50
573 45t. Police badges 90 65
574 70t. German New Guinea Police, 1888, and Dr. A Hahl (founder) 1·50 1·75

257 Lakatoi (canoe) and Sydney Opera House

1988. "Sydpex '88" Nat Stamp Exn, Sydney.
575 **257** 35t. multicoloured 80 1·25

258 Papua New Guinea Flag on Globe and Fireworks

1988. Bicent of Australian Settlement. Mult.
576 35t. Type **258** 1·00 1·50
577 35t. Australian flag on globe and fireworks 1·00 1·50
MS578 90 × 50 mm. Nos. 576/7 1·50 2·25

Nos. 576/7 were printed together, se-tenant, forming a composite design.

259 Male and Female Butterflies in Courtship

1988. Endangered Species. "Ornithoptera alexandrae" (butterfly). Multicoloured.
579 5t. Type **259** 1·00 1·75
580 17t. Female laying eggs and mature larva (vert) 2·00 40
581 25t. Male emerging from pupa (vert) 2·75 3·50
582 35t. Male feeding 3·25 3·50

260 Athletics

1988. Olympic Games, Seoul. Multicoloured.
583 17t. Type **260** 30 30
584 45t. Weightlifting 70 70

261 "Rhododendron zoelleri" **263** Writing Letter

1989. Rhododendrons. Multicoloured.
585 3t. Type **261** 10 10
586 20t. "Rhododendron cruttwellii" 50 30
587 60t. "Rhododendron superbum" 1·25 1·50
588 70t. "Rhododendron christianae" 1·50 1·75

1989. Int Letter Writing Week. Multicoloured.
589 20t. Type **263** 30 30
590 35t. Stamping letter 55 50
591 60t. Posting letter 90 1·10
592 70t. Reading letter 1·10 1·40

264 Village House, Buka Island, North Solomons

1989. Traditional Dwellings. Multicoloured.
593 20t. Type **264** 40 35
594 35t. Tree house, Koiari, Central Province 70 60
595 60t. Longhouse, Lauan, New Ireland 1·25 1·40
596 70t. Decorated house, Basilaki, Milne Bay 1·50 1·60

265 Tit Berrypecker (female) **266** Motu Motu Dancer, Gulf Province

1989. Small Birds (2nd issue). Multicoloured.
597 20t. Type **265** 1·00 1·00
598 20t. Tit berrypecker (male) 1·00 1·00
599 35t. Blue-capped babbler 1·50 80
600 45t. Black-throated robin 1·50 1·00
601 70t. Large mountain sericornis 2·25 2·50

1989. No. 539 surch **20t**.
602 20t. on 17t. Type **251** 60 70

1989. Traditional Dancers. Multicoloured.
603 20t. Type **266** 65 35
604 35t. Baining, East New Britain 1·10 90
605 60t. Vailala River, Gulf Province 2·00 2·25
606 70t. Timbunke, East Sepik Province 2·00 2·50

267 Hibiscus, People going to Church and Gope Board

1989. Christmas. Designs showing flowers and carved panels. Multicoloured.
607 20t. Type **267** 40 35
608 35t. Rhododendron, Virgin and Child and mask 60 60
609 60t. D'Albertis creeper, Christmas candle and war shield 1·25 1·60
610 70t. Pacific frangipani, peace dove and flute mask 1·40 1·90

268 Guni Falls **270** Gwa Pupi Dance Mask

269 Boys and Census Form

1990. Waterfalls. Multicoloured.
611 20t. Type **268** 60 35
612 35t. Rouna Falls 85 75
613 60t. Ambua Falls 1·40 1·50
614 70t. Wawoi Falls 1·60 1·75

1990. National Census. Multicoloured.
615 20t. Type **269** 40 30
616 70t. Family and census form 1·50 2·25

1990. Gogodala Dance Masks. Multicoloured.
617 20t. Type **270** 80 30
618 35t. Tauga paiyale 1·25 70
619 60t. A: ga 2·00 3·25
620 70t. Owala 2·00 3·75

271 Sepik and Maori Kororu Masks

1990. "New Zealand 1990" International Stamp Exhibition, Auckland.
621 **271** 35t. multicoloured 75 1·00

272 Dwarf Cassowary and Great Spotted Kiwi

1990. 150th Anniv of Treaty of Waitangi. Mult.
622 20t. Type **272** 1·25 50
623 35t. Double-wattled cassowary and brown kiwi 1·50 1·50

273 Whimbrel

1990. Migratory Birds. Multicoloured.
624 20t. Type **273** 85 40
625 35t. Sharp-tailed sandpiper 1·25 80
626 60t. Ruddy turnstone 2·25 3·25
627 70t. Terek sandpiper 2·50 3·25

274 Jew's Harp **276** Magnificent Riflebird

275 Weigman's Papuina

1990. Musical Instruments. Multicoloured.
628 20t. Type **274** 60 30
629 35t. Musical bow 90 50
630 60t. Wantoat drum 1·75 2·25
631 70t. Gogodala rattle 1·75 2·50

1991. Land Shells. Multicoloured.
632 21t. Type **275** 65 30
633 40t. "Papuina globula" and "Papuina azonata" 1·00 85

634	50t. "Planispira deaniana"	1·40	1·60
635	80t. Chance's papuina and golden-mouth papuina	2·00	2·75

1991. Birds of Paradise. Multicoloured. (a) Face values shown as "t" or "K".

636	1t. Type **276**	15	40
637	5t. Loria's bird of paradise	20	40
638	10t. Sickle-crested bird of paradise	20	40
639	20t. Wahnes' parotia	50	30
640	21t. Crinkle-collared manucode	1·50	30
641	30t. Goldie's bird of paradise	30	40
642	40t. Wattle-billed bird of paradise	50	50
643	45t. King bird of paradise	5·00	80
644	50t. Short-tailed paradigalla bird of paradise	50	55
645	60t. Queen Carola's parotia	7·50	2·75
646	90t. Emperor of Germany bird of paradise	8·00	4·00
647	1k. Magnificent bird of paradise	1·75	1·75
648	2k. Superb bird of paradise	1·90	2·00
649	5k. Trumpet bird	2·25	6·50
650	10k. Lesser bird of paradise (32×32 mm)	5·00	10·00

(b) Face values shown as "T".

650a	21t. Crinkle-collared manucode	90	40
650b	45t. King bird of paradise	2·00	1·00
650c	60t. Queen Carola's parotia	2·25	2·25
650d	90t. Emperor of Germany bird of paradise	2·75	3·50

For designs as Nos. 642, 644 and 647/8 but without "1992 BIRD OF PARADISE" at foot, see Nos. 704/7.

277 Cricket

1991. 9th South Pacific Games. Multicoloured.

651	21t. Type **277**	1·75	40
652	40t. Athletics	1·50	1·00
653	50t. Baseball	1·75	2·25
654	80t. Rugby Union	2·75	4·00

278 Cathedral of St. Peter and St. Paul, Dogura

1991. Cent of Anglican Church in Papua New Guinea. Multicoloured.

655	21t. Type **278**	70	30
656	40t. Missionaries landing, 1891, and Kaieta shrine	1·40	1·40
657	80t. First church and Modawa tree	2·25	3·50

279 Rambusto Headdress, Manus Province

281 Canoe Prow Shield, Bamu

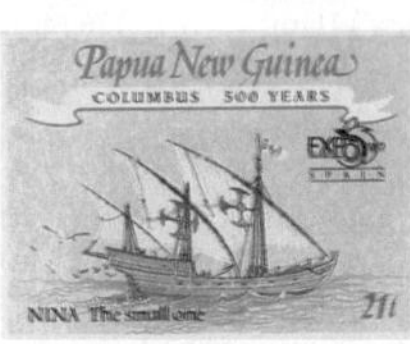

280 "Nina"

1991. Tribal Headdresses. Multicoloured.

658	21t. Type **279**	60	30
659	40t. Marawaka, Eastern Highlands	1·10	1·40
660	50t. Tufi, Oro Province	1·25	2·00
661	80t. Sina Sina, Simbu Province	2·00	4·00

1992. 500th Anniv of Discovery of America by Columbus and "EXPO '92" World's Fair, Seville. Multicoloured.

662	21t. Type **280**	60	30
663	45t. "Pinta"	1·25	1·00
664	60t. "Santa Maria"	1·75	2·00
665	90t. Christopher Columbus and ships	2·25	3·50

1992. "World Columbian Stamp Expo '92", Chicago. Sheet, 110×80 mm, containing Nos. 664/5.

MS666	60t. "Santa Maria"; 90t. Christopher Columbus and ships (sold at 1k. 70)	4·25	5·50

1992. Papuan Gulf Artifacts. Multicoloured.

667	21t. Type **281**	40	30
668	45t. Skull rack, Kerewa	85	75
669	60t. Ancestral figure, Era River	1·25	1·50
670	90t. Gope (spirit) board, Urama	1·60	2·75

282 Papuan Infantryman

283 "Hibiscus tiliaceus"

1992. 50th Anniv of Second World War Campaigns in Papua New Guinea. Multicoloured.

671	21t. Type **282**	60	30
672	45t. Australian militiaman	1·25	90
673	60t. Japanese infantryman	1·75	2·25
674	90t. American infantryman	2·50	3·75

1992. Flowering Trees. Multicoloured.

675	21t. Type **283**	65	30
676	45t. "Castanospermum australe"	1·50	1·00
677	60t. "Cordia subcordata"	2·50	2·75
678	90t. "Acacia auriculiformis"	2·75	4·00

284 Three-striped Dasyure

1993. Mammals. Multicoloured.

679	21t. Type **284**	40	30
680	45t. Striped bandicoot	90	80
681	60t. Dusky black-eared giant rat	1·25	1·50
682	90t. Painted ringtail possum	1·75	2·75

285 Rufous Wren Warbler

1993. Small Birds. Multicoloured.

683	21t. Type **285**	45	30
684	45t. Superb pitta	90	80
685	60t. Mottled whistler	1·25	1·50
686	90t. Slaty-chinned longbill	1·60	2·75

1993. "Taipei '93" Asian Int Stamp Exn, Taiwan. Nos. 683/6 optd **TAIPEI'93** and emblem.

687	21t. Type **285**	75	30
688	45t. Superb pitta	1·40	80
689	60t. Mottled whistler	1·60	2·75
690	90t. Slaty-chinned longbill	2·00	3·50

287 Thread-finned Rainbowfish

1993. Freshwater Fishes. Multicoloured.

691	21t. Type **287**	60	30
692	45t. Peacock gudgeon	1·25	80
693	60t. Northern rainbowfish	1·60	2·25
694	90t. Popondetta blue-eye	2·25	4·00

288 Blue Bird of Paradise

1993. "Bangkok '93" Asian International Stamp Exhibition, Thailand. Sheet 100×65 mm.

MS695	**288** 2k. multicoloured	6·00	7·50

289 Douglas DC-3

1993. 20th Anniv of Air Niugini. Multicoloured.

696	21t. Type **289**	75	25
697	45t. Fokker F.27 Friendship	1·75	70
698	60t. De Havilland D.H.C.7 Dash Seven	2·00	2·25
699	90t. Airbus Industrie A310	2·75	4·25

290 Girl holding Matschie's Tree Kangaroo

292 Hagen Axe, Western Highlands

1994. Matschie's (Huon Gulf) Tree Kangaroo. Mult.

700	21t. Type **290**	35	25
701	45t. Adult male	90	60
702	60t. Female with young in pouch	1·25	1·75
703	90t. Adolescent on ground	1·90	3·25

1994. "Hong Kong '94 International Stamp Exhibition. Designs as Nos. 642, 644 and 647/8, but without "1992 BIRD OF PARADISE" at foot. Multicoloured.

704	40t. Yellow-breasted bird of paradise	85	1·25
705	50t. Short-tailed paradigalla bird of paradise	1·25	1·50
706	1k. Magnificent bird of paradise	2·00	2·75
707	2k. Superb bird of paradise	3·00	4·00

1994. Nos. 541 and 551 surch.

708	21t. on 35t. Fire anemonefish	7·00	50
709	1k.20 on 40t. "L'Astrolabe" (D'Urville)	1·50	1·50

1994. Artifacts. Multicoloured.

710	1t. Type **292**	10	50
711	2t. Telefomin shield, West Sepik	10	50
712	20t. Head mask, Gulf Province	80	30
713	21t. Kanganaman stool, East Sepik	30	10
714	45t. Trobriand lime gourd, Milne Bay	50	25
715	60t. Yuat River flute stopper, East Sepik	1·00	30
716	90t. Tami Island dish, Morobe	60	40
717	1k. Kundu (drum), Ramu River estuary	3·50	2·50
723	5k. Gogodala dance mask, Western Province	1·70	1·80
724	10k. Malanggan mask, New Ireland	3·50	3·75

293 Ford Model "T", 1920

1994. Historical Cars. Multicoloured.

725	21t. Type **293**	35	25
726	45t. Chevrolet "490", 1915	90	60
727	60t. Austin "7", 1931	1·25	1·75
728	90t. Willys jeep, 1942	1·90	3·00

294 Grizzled Tree Kangaroo

298 Peter To Rot

297 "Daphnis hypothous pallescens"

1994. "Phila Korea '94" International Stamp Exhibition, Seoul. Tree Kangaroos. Sheet 106×70 mm, containing T **294** and similar vert design. Multicoloured.

MS729	90t. Type **294**; 1k.20, Doria's tree kangaroo	70	75

1994. Surch.

730	–	5t. on 35t. mult (No. 604)	1·00	75
731	–	5t. on 35t. mult (No. 629)	14·00	10·00
732	**271**	10t. on 35t. mult	22·00	5·50
733	–	10t. on 35t. mult (No. 623)	10·00	3·50
734	–	21t. on 80t. mult (No. 635)	40·00	75
735	–	50t. on 35t. mult (No. 612)	27·00	13·00
736	–	50t. on 35t. mult (No. 618)	90·00	18·00
737	–	65t. on 70t. mult (No. 542)	2·00	1·40
738	–	65t. on 70t. mult (No. 616)	2·00	1·40
739	–	1k. on 70t. mult (No. 614)	17·00	5·00
740	–	1k. on 70t. mult (No. 620)	2·00	3·00

1994. Moths. Multicoloured.

741	21t. Type **297**	35	25
742	45t. "Tanaorhinus unipuncta"	80	65
743	60t. "Neodiphthera sciron"	1·10	1·50
744	90t. "Parotis marginata"	1·60	2·50

1995. Beatification of Peter To Rot (catechist) and Visit of Pope John Paul II. Multicoloured.

745	21t. Type **298**	10	10
746	1k. on 90t. Pope John Paul II	35	40

No. 746 was not issued without surcharge.

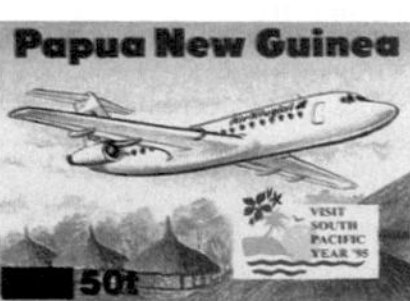

299 Airliner over Holiday Village

1995. Tourism. Multicoloured.

747	21t. "Melanesian Discoverer" (cruise ship) and launch	10	10
748	21t. Tourist taking photo of traditional mask	10	10
749	50t. on 45t. Type **299**	15	20
750	50t. on 45t. Holiday homes	15	20
751	65t. on 60t. Tourists and guide crossing river	20	25
752	65t. on 60t. White water rafting	20	25
753	1k. on 90t. Scuba diver and "Chertan" (launch)	35	40
754	1k. on 90t. Divers and wreck of aircraft	35	40

Nos. 749/54 were not issued without surcharge.

1995. Nos. 643, 646, 650b, 650d and 692/4 surch **21t**.

755	21t. on 45t. King bird of paradise (643)	1·50	1·00
757	21t. on 45t. King bird of paradise (650b)	4·75	3·00
759	21t. on 45t. Peacock gudgeon	55	40
760	21t. on 60t. Northern rainbowfish	1·50	2·00
756	21t. on 90t. Emperor of Germany bird of paradise (646)	1·50	1·00
758	21t. on 90t. Emperor of Germany bird of paradise (650d)	6·00	1·00
761	21t. on 90t. Popondetta blue-eye	55	60

302 "Lentinus umbrinus"

302a "Lentinus umbrinus"

1995. Fungi. Multicoloured.

762	25t. Type **302**	45	30
765a	25t. Type **302a**	35	35
763	50t. "Amanita hemibapha"	80	80
764	65t. "Boletellus emodensis"	95	1·25
765	1k. "Ramaria zippellii"	1·60	2·25

On Type **302a** the fungi illustration is larger, 26×32 mm instead of 27×30½ mm, face value and inscriptions are in a different type and there is no imprint date at foot.

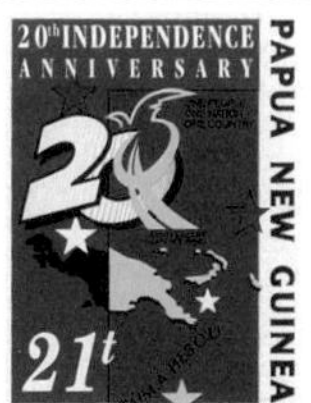

303 Anniversary Emblem and Map of Papua New Guinea

1995. 20th Anniv of Independence. Multicoloured.
766 21t. Type **303** 30 25
767 50t. Emblem and lines on graph 70 80
768 1k. As 50t. . . . . 1·40 2·25

304 "Dendrobium rigidifolium"

1995. "Singapore '95" International Stamp Exhibition. Orchids. Sheet 150 × 95 mm, containing T **304** and similar horiz designs. Multicoloured.
MS769 21t. Type **304**; 45t. "Dendrobium convolutum"; 60t. "Dendrobium spectabile"; 90t. "Dendrobium tapiniense" (sold at 3k.) 75 80

305 Pig

1995. Chinese New Year ("Year of the Pig"). Sheet 150 × 95 mm.
MS770 **305** 3k. multicoloured . . 1·00 1·10
No. **MS**770 is inscribed "BEIJING '95" on the sheet margin.

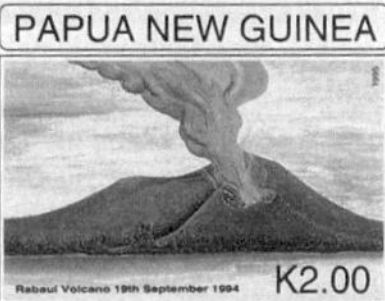

306 Volcanic Eruption, Tavarvur

1995. 1st Anniv of Volcanic Eruption, Rabaul.
771 **306** 2k. multicoloured 70 75

307 "Zosimus aeneus"

1995. Crabs. Multicoloured.
772 21t. Type **307** 40 25
773 50t. "Cardisoma carnifex" . . 75 60
774 65t. "Uca tetragonon" . . . 90 1·25
775 1k. "Eriphia sebana" . . . . 1·25 2·00

308 Pesquet's Parrot

309 "Lagriomorpha indigacea"

1996. Parrots. Multicoloured.
776 25t. Type **308** . . . . 1·00 30
777 50t. Rainbow lory . . . . . 1·60 65
778 65t. Green-winged king parrot . . . . 1·75 1·60
779 1k. Red-winged parrot . . . 2·00 2·75

1996. Beetles. Multicoloured.
780 25t. Type **309** 10 15
781 50t. "Eupholus geoffroyi" . . 15 20
782 65t. "Promechus pulcher" . . 20 25
783 1k. "Callistola pulchra" . . . 35 40

310 Guang Zhou Zhong Shang Memorial Hall

1996. "China '96" 9th Asian International Stamp Exhibition, Peking. Sheet 105 × 70 mm.
MS784 **310** 70t. multicoloured . . 25 30

311 Rifle-shooting

1996. Olympic Games, Atlanta. Multicoloured.
785 25t. Type **311** 10 15
786 50t. Athletics 15 20
787 65t. Weightlifting 20 25
788 1k. Boxing 35 40

312 Air Traffic Controller

1996. Centenary of Radio. Multicoloured.
789 25t. Type **312** 10 15
790 50t. Radio disc-jockey . . . 15 20
791 65t. Dish aerials 20 25
792 1k. Early radio transmitter 35 40

313 Dr. Sun Yat-sen

1996. "TAIPEI '96" 10th Asian International Stamp Exhibition, Taiwan. Sheet 105 × 70 mm, containing T **313** and similar vert design. Multicoloured.
MS793 65t. Type **313**; 65t. Dr. John Guise (former speaker of Papua New Guinea House of Assembly) 45 50

314 "Hibiscus rosa-sinensis"

1996. Flowers. Multicoloured.
794 1t. Type **314** 10 10
795 5t. "Bougainvillea spectabilis" 10 10
796 10t. "Thunbergia fragrans" (vert) 10 10
797 20t. "Caesalpinia pulcherrima" (vert) 10 10
798 25t. "Hoya sp." (vert) . . . 10 15
799 30t. "Heliconia spp." (vert) 10 15
800 50t. "Amomum goliathensis" (vert) 15 20
801 65t. "Plumeria rubra" . . . 20 25
802 1k. "Mucuna novoguineensis" 35 40

315 Ox and National Flag

1997. "HONG KONG '97" International Stamp Exhibition. Sheet 130 × 90 mm.
MS808 **315** 1k.50 multicoloured 50 55

316 Gogodala Canoe Prow

1997. Canoe Prows. Multicoloured.
809 25t. Type **316** 10 15
810 50t. East New Britain 15 20
811 65t. Trobriand Island 20 25
812 1k. Walomo 35 40

1997. Golden Wedding of Queen Elizabeth and Prince Philip. As T **87** of Kiribati. Multicoloured.
813 25t. Prince Philip on polo pony, 1972 . . . . 10 15
814 25t. Queen Elizabeth at Windsor Polo Club 10 15
815 50t. Prince Philip carriage-driving, 1995 . . . . . . 15 20
816 50t. Queen Elizabeth and Prince Edward on horseback 15 20
817 1k. Prince Philip waving and Peter and Zara Phillips on horseback 35 40
818 1k. Queen Elizabeth waving and Prince Harry on horseback 35 40
MS819 105 × 71 mm. 2k. Queen Elizabeth and Prince Philip in landau (horiz) 70 75
Nos. 813/14, 815/16 and 818/19 respectively were printed together, se-tenant, with the backgrounds forming composite designs.

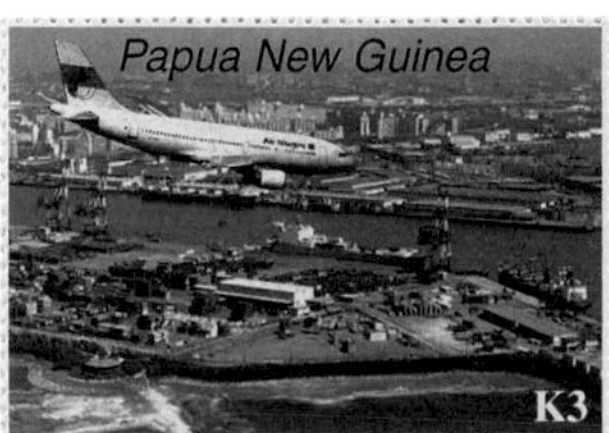

317 Air Niugini Airliner over Osaka

1997. Inaugural Air Niugini Port moresby to Osaka Flight. Sheet 110 × 80 mm.
MS820 **317** 3k. multicoloured . . 1·00 1·10

318 "Pocillopora woodjonesi"

1997. Pacific Year of the Coral Reef. Corals. Mult.
821 25t. Type **318** 10 15
822 50t. "Subergorgia mollis" . . 15 20
823 65t. "Oxypora glabra" . . . 20 25
824 1k. "Turbinaria reinformis" 35 40

319 Greater Sooty Owl

1998. Birds. Multicoloured.
825 25t. Type **319** 50 20
826 50t. Wattled brush turkey . . 70 45
827 65t. New Guinea grey-headed goshawk . . . . 80 1·00
828 1k. Forest bittern . . . . . 1·25 2·00

1998. Diana, Princess of Wales Commemoration. Sheet, 145 × 70 mm, containing vert designs as T **91** or Kiribati. Multicoloured.
MS829 1k., Wearing pink jacket, 1992; 1k. Wearing purple dress; 1988; 1k. wearing tartan jacket, 1990; 1k. Carrying bouquets, 1990 (sold at 4k.+50t. charity premium) 1·50 1·60

320 Mother Teresa and Child

1998. Mother Teresa Commemoration. Mult.
830 65t. Type **320** 20 25
831 1k. Mother Teresa 35 40

1998. No. 774 surch **25t**.
832 25t. on 65t. "Uca tetragonon" 10 15

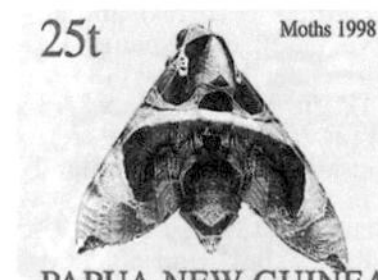

322 "Daphnis hypothous pallescens"

1998. Moths. Multicoloured.
833 25t. Type **322** 10 15
834 50t. "Theretra polistratus" 15 20
835 65t. "Psilogramma casurina" 20 25
836 1k. "Meganoton hyloicoides" 35 40

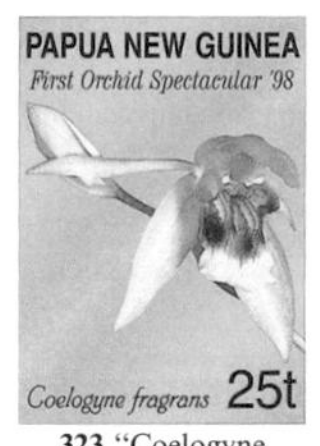

323 "Coelogyne fragrans"
324 Weightlifting

1998. Orchids. Multicoloured.
837 25t. Type **323** 10 15
838 50t. "Den cuthbertsonii" . . 15 20
839 65t. "Den vexillarius "var" retroflexum" 20 25
840 1k. "Den finisterrae" 35 40

1998. 16th Commonwealth Games, Kuala Lumpur, Malaysia. Multicoloured.
841 25t. Type **324** 10 15
842 50t. Lawn bowls 15 20
843 65t. Rugby Union 20 25
844 1k. Squash 35 40

325 Double Kayak

1998. Sea Kayaking World Cup, Manus Island. Multicoloured.
845 25t. Type **325** 10 15
846 50t. Running 15 20
847 65t. Traditional canoe and modern kayak 20 25
848 1k. Single kayak and stylized bird of paradise 35 40

326 The Holy Child

1998. Christmas. Multicoloured.
849 25t. Type **326** 10 15
850 50t. Mother breast-feeding baby 15 20
851 65t. Holy Child and tribal elders 20 25
852 1k. Map of Papua New Guinea and festive bell . . 35 40

1999. "Australia '99" World Stamp Exhibition, Melbourne. Designs as Nos. 543, 552 and 556/7, showing ships, redrawn to include exhibition emblem at top right and with some face values changed. Multicoloured.
853 25t. "La Boudeuse" (De Bougainville) (as No. 543) 10 15
854 50t. "Neva" (D'Albertis) (as No. 552) 15 20

855 65t. "Merrie England" (steamer) (as No. 556) . . 20 25
856 1k. "Samoa" (German colonial steamer) (as No. 557) 35 40
MS857 165 × 110 mm. 5t. H.M.S. "Rattlesnake" (Owen Stanley) (as No. 548); 10t. H.M.S. "Swallow" (Philip Carteret) (as No. 545); 15t. "Roebuck" (Dampier) (as No. 544); 20t. H.M.S. "Blanche" (SImpson) (as No. 55); 30t. "Vitaz" (Maclay) (as No. 549); 40t. "San Pedrico" (Torres) and zabra (as No. 550); 60t. Spanish galleon (Jorge de Meneses) (as No. 553); 1k.20, "L' Astrolabe" (D' Urville) (as No. 551) . . . 1·00 1·10

No. 855 is inscribed "Merrir England" in error. Of the designs in No. **MS**857 the 5t. is inscribed "Simpson Blanche 1872", 10t. "Carterel", 15t. "Dampien", 40t. "eabra" and 60t. "Menesis", all in error.

327 German New Guinea 1900 Yacht Type 2m. Stamp

1999. "iBRA '99" International Stamp Exhibition, Nuremberg. Multicoloured.
858 1k. Type **327** 35 40
859 1k. German New Guinea 1897 3pf. and 5pf. optd on Germany 35 40

328 Father Jules Chevalier

1999. "PhilexFrance '99" International Stamp Exhibition, Paris. Famous Frenchmen. Mult.
860 25t. Type **327** 10 15
861 50t. Bishop Alain-Marie . . . 15 20
862 65t. Joseph-Antoine d'Entrecasteaux (explorer) 20 25
863 1k. Louis de Bougainville (explorer) 35 40

329 Hiri Claypot and Traditional Dancer

1999. Hiri Moale Festival. Multicoloured (except No. **MS**686).
864 25t. Type **329** 10 15
865 50t. Three dancers 15 20
866 65t. Hiri Lagatoi (trading canoe) and dancer 20 25
867 1k. Hiri Sorcerer and dancer 35 40
MS868 140 × 64mm. 1k. Hiri Sorcerer (deep blue and blue); 1k. Hiri Claypot (deep purple and blue); 1k. Hiri Lagatoi (green and blue) . . . . 1·00 1·10

330 Lap-top Computer, Globe and Watch

1999. New Millennium. Modern Technology. Each showing Globe. Multicoloured.
869 25t. Type **330** 10 15
870 50t. Globe within concentric circles 15 20
871 65t. Compact disc, web site and man using computer 20 25
872 1k. Keyboard, dish aerial and solar eclipse 35 40

331 *Turbo petholatus*

2000. Sea Shells. Multicoloured.
873 25t. Type **331** 10 15
874 50t. *Charonia tritonis* 15 20
875 65t. *Cassis cornuta* 20 25
876 1k. *Ovula ovum* 35 40

332 Rabbit **333** Shell

2000. Chinese New Year ("Year of the Rabbit") (1999). Sheet, 145 × 70mm, containing T **332** and similar vert designs. Multicoloured.
MS877 65t. Type **332**; 65t. Light brown rabbit running; 65t. White rabbit grinning; 65t. Pink rabbit hiding behind grass knoll . . . 90 95

2000. 25th Anniv of Independence. Multicoloured.
878 25t. Type **333** 10 15
879 50t. Raggiana bird of Paradise 15 20
880 65t. Ornament 20 25
881 1k. Red bird of Paradise perched on spear and drums 35 40
MS882 145 × 75 mm. Nos. 878/81 80 1·00

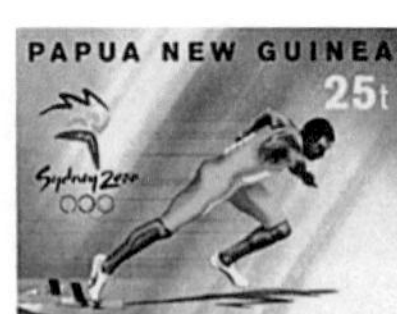

334 Athletics

2000. Olympic Games, Sydney. Multicoloured.
883 25t. Type **334** 10 15
884 50t. Swimming 15 20
885 65t. Boxing 20 25
886 1k. Weightlifting 35 40
MS887 80 × 90 mm. 3k. Runner with Olympic Torch (34 × 45 mm) (sold at 3k.50) . . . . 1·10 1·25

No. **MS**887 includes the "Olymphilex 2000" stamp exhibition logo on the sheet margin.

335 Queen Mother in Yellow Coat and Hat

2000. Queen Elizabeth the Queen Mother's 100th Birthday. Multicoloured.
888 25t. Type **335** 10 15
889 50t. Queen Mother with bouquet of roses 15 20
890 65t. Queen Mother in green coat 20 25
891 1k. Lady Elizabeth Bowes-Lyon 35 40

336 Comb-crested Jacana

2001. Water Birds. Multicoloured.
892 35t. Type **336** 10 15
893 70t. Masked lapwing 25 30
894 90t. Australian white ibis . . 30 35
895 1k.40 Black-tailed godwit . . 50 55

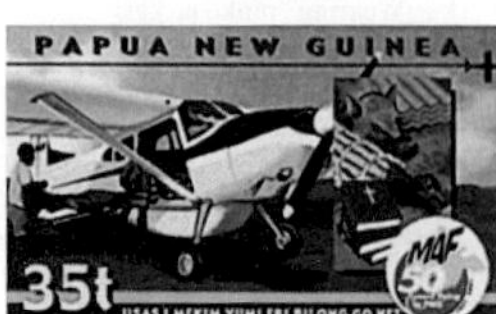

337 Cessna 170 Aircraft

2001. 50th Anniv of Mission Aviation Fellowship. Multicoloured.
896 35t. Type **337** 10 15
897 70t. Auster Autocar 25 30
898 90t. Cessna 260 . . . . . . 30 35
899 1k.40 Twin Otter 50 55

338 Flags of China and Papua New Guinea

2001. 25th Anniv of Diplomatic Relations between Papua New Guinea and China. Multicoloured.
900 10t. Type **338** 10 10
901 50t. Dragon and bird of paradise 15 20
902 2k. Tian An Men (Gate of Heavenly Peace), Beijing, and Parliament House, Port Moresby 70 75

2001. Nos. 745, 862, 866, 871 and 883 surch.
903 50t. on 21t. Type **248** 50 40
904 50t. on 25t. Type **334** 15 20
905 50t. on 65t. Compact disc, web site and man using computer 15 20
906 2k.65 on 65t. Joseph-Antoine d'Entrecasteaux 90 95
907 2k.65 on 65t. Hiri Lagatoi (trading canoe) and dancer 90 95

341 Flag of Enga Province

2001. Provincial Flags. Multicoloured.
908 10t. Type **341** 15 10
909 15t. Simbu Province 15 10
910 20t. Manus Province 15 10
911 50t. Central Province 30 20
912 2k. New Ireland Province . . 1·25 1·00
913 5k. Sandaun Province . . . . 2·25 2·50

2002. Golden Jubilee. As T **211** of St. Helena.
914 1k.25 multicoloured 40 45
915 1k.45 multicoloured 50 55
916 2k. black, brown and gold . . 70 75
917 2k.65 multicoloured 90 95
MS918 162 × 95 mm. Nos. 914/17 and 5k. multicoloured . . . . 4·00 4·25

DESIGNS–HORIZ:1k.25, Queen Elizabeth with Princesses Elizabeth and Margaret, 1941; 1k.45, Queen Elizabeth in evening dress, 1975; 2k. Princess Elizabeth, Duke of Edinburgh and children, 1951; 2k.65, Queen Elizabeth at Henley-on-Thames. VERT (38 × 51 mm)–5k. Queen Elizabeth after Annigoni.

Designs as Nos. 914/17 in No. **MS**918 omit the gold frame around each stamp and the "Golden Jubilee 1952–2002" inscription.

342 Lakotoi (trading canoe) and Hanuabada Village

2002. Centenary of First Papuan Stamps (2001).
919 **342** 5t. black and mauve . . . 10 10
920 15t. black and brown . . 10 10
921 20t. black and blue . . . 10 10
922 1k.25 black and brown . . 40 45
923 1k.45 black and green . . 50 55
924 10k. black and orange . . 3·50 3·75
MS925 127 × 99 mm. Nos. 919/24 4·50 5·00

The design of Type **342** is adapted from that of the first Papua issue of 1901.

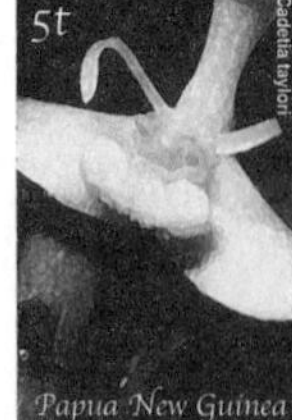

343 Queen Elizabeth with Princess Elizabeth in South Africa **344** *Cadetia taylori*

2002. Queen Elizabeth the Queen Mother Commemoration. Multicoloured (No. 929) or black and blue (others).
926 2k. Type **343** 70 75
927 2k. Queen Elizabeth with Princess Elizabeth at Balmoral, 1951 . . . . . 70 75
928 2k. Queen Mother at Sandown races, 2001 (26 × 30 mm) 70 75
929 2k. Queen Mother with Irish Guards, 1988 (41 × 30 mm) 70 75
930 2k. Queen Mother at the Derby, 1988 (26 × 30 mm) 70 75
931 2k. Queen Mother at Ascot races, 1966 . . . . 70 75
932 2k. King George VI with Queen Elizabeth at Balmoral, 1951 . . . . . 70 75
MS933 Two sheets, each 65 × 101 mm. (a) 3k. Queen Mother at Lord Linley's wedding, 1993; 3k. At Aintree racecourse, 1991 (wearing brooch). (b) 3k. Lady Elizabeth Bowes-Lyon as a young girl; 3k. Queen Mother on Remembrance Day, 1988 (each 26 × 40 mm) . . . . 4·00 4·25

2002. Orchids. Multicoloured.
934 5t. Type **344** 10 10
935 30t. *Dendrobium anosmum* . . 10 10
936 45t. *Dendrobium bigibbum* . . 15 20
937 1k.25 *Dendrobium cuthbertsonii* 40 45
938 1k.45 *Spiranthes sinensis* . . 50 55
939 2k.65 *Thelymitra carnea* . . . 75 80
MS940 135 × 135 mm. 2k. *Dendrobium bracteosum*; 2k. *Calochilus campestris*; 2k. *Anastomus oscitans*; 2k. *Thelymitra carnea*; 2k. *Dendrobium macrophyllum*; 2k. *Dendrobium johnsoniae* (all horiz) 4·00 4·25

345 *Ornithoptera chimaera*

2002. Birdwing Butterflies. Multicoloured.
941 50t. Type **345** 15 20
942 50t. *Ornithoptera goliath* . . 15 20
943 1k.25 *Ornithoptera meridionalis* 40 45
944 1k.45 *Ornithoptera paradisea* 50 55
945 2k.65 *Ornithoptera victoriae* 75 80
946 5k. *Ornithoptera alexandrae* 1·70 1·80

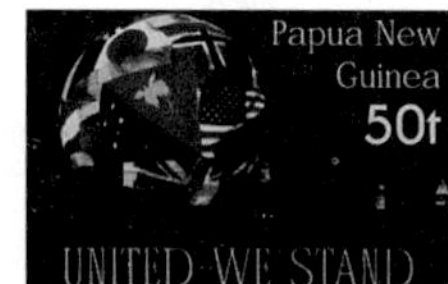

346 Globe covered in National Flags and New York Skyline

2002. "United We Stand". Support for Victims of 11 September 2001 Terrorist Attacks. Sheet 174 × 123 mm.
MS947 **346** 50t. × 4 multicoloured 60 65

347 Mt. Wilhelm, Papua New Guinea

2003. International Year of Mountains. Multicoloured.
948 50t. Type **347** 15 20
949 1k.25 Matterhorn, Switzerland 40 45
950 1k.45 Mount Fuji, Japan . . 50 55
951 2k.65 Massif des Aravis, France 75 80

348 Sago Storage Pot **349** Papuan Scout Troop

2003. Clay Pots. Multicoloured.
952 65t. Type **348** 20 25
953 1k. Smoking pot 35 40
954 1k.50 Water jar 50 55
955 2k.50 Water jar on stand . . 75 80
956 4k. Ridge pot . . . . 1·40 1·50

2003. 20th World Scout Jamboree, Thailand. Multicoloured.
957 50t. Type **349** 15 20
958 1k.25 Scouts in workshop . . 40 45
959 1k.45 Scouts on wooden platform with banner . . . 50 55
960 2k.65 Scouts 75 80

350 Princess Elizabeth

351 Prince William

2003. 50th Anniv of Coronation.

No.	Type	Description	Unused	Used
961	350	65t. brown, bistre and black	20	25
962	–	65t. deep lilac, lilac and black	20	25
963	–	1k.50 deep blue, blue and black	50	55
964	–	2k. deep purple, purple and black	70	75
965	–	2k.50 black and grey	75	80
966	–	4k. brown, cinnamon and black	1·40	1·50
MS967		146 × 116 mm. 2k. multicoloured; 2k. multicoloured; 2k. multicoloured; 2k. multicoloured; 2k. multicoloured; 2k. multicoloured		
MS968		97 × 67 mm. 8k. multicoloured	4·00	4·00

DESIGNS: No. 962, Queen Elizabeth II in Coronation robes and crown; 963, Queen wearing white evening dress, sash and tiara; 964, Queen seated, wearing tiara; 965, Queen in Coronation robes, with Imperial State Crown and sceptre; 966, Princess Elizabeth as teenager; **MS**967, Princess Elizabeth aged 21; Queen wearing diadem, 1952; Wearing hat with blue flowers, c. 1958; Wearing tiara, c. 1970; Wearing red hat with black bow, c. 1985; Wearing black robes and hat with white cockade, c. 1992; **MS**968, Wearing garter robes (from painting by Annigoni).

2003. 21st Birthday of Prince William of Wales. Multicoloured.

No.	Description	Unused	Used
969	65t. Type **351**	20	25
970	65t. Wearing red and blue t-shirt	20	25
971	1k.50 As toddler	50	55
972	2k. Wearing grey jacket and blue tie	70	75
973	2k.50 Prince William	75	80
974	4k. Playing polo	1·40	1·50
MS975	146 × 116 mm. 2k. As toddler; 2k. Wearing sunglasses; 2k. Wearing blue jacket and tie (facing forwards); 2k. Wearing blue jacket and tie (facing right); 2k. Wearing blue shirt; 2k. Wearing black and yellow t-shirt	4·00	4·25
MS976	95 × 66 mm. 8k. Prince William	2·75	3·00

352 Gabagaba Village

2003. Coastal Villages. Multicoloured.

No.	Description	Unused	Used
977	65t. Type **352**	20	25
978	65t. Wanigela (Koki)	20	25
979	1k.50 Tubuserea	50	55
980	2k. Hanuabada	70	75
981	2k.50 Barakau	75	80
982	4k. Porebada	1·40	1·50

353 Orville Wright circling Fort Myer, Virginia, 1908

2003. Centenary of Powered Flight. Multicoloured (except No. **MS**987).

No.	Description	Unused	Used
983	65t. Type **353**	20	25
984	1k.50 Orville Wright piloting "Baby Grand" biplane, Belmont New York, 1910	50	55
985	2k.50 Wilbur Wright holding anemometer, Pau, France, 1909	75	80
986	4k. Wilbur Wright piloting Wright Model A, Pau, France, 1909	1·40	1·50
MS987	176 × 96 mm. 2k.50 Wright *Flyer I* outside hangar, Kitty Hawk, North Carolina, 1903 (multicoloured); 2k.50 Wright *Flyer I* rolled out from hangar (black, grey and brown); 2k.50 Wright *Flyer I* being prepared for takeoff (black, green and brown); 2k.50 Wright *Flyer I* taking off, 1903 (multicoloured)	3·50	3·75
MS988	105 × 76 mm. 10k. Wright *Flyer I*, 1903	3·50	3·75

354 Matschie's Tree Kangaroo

2003. Endangered Species. Tree Kangaroos. Multicoloured.

No.	Description	Unused	Used
989	65t. Grizzled tree kangaroo	20	25
990	1k.50 Type **354**	50	55
991	2k.50 Doria's tree kangaroo	75	80
992	4k. Goodfellow's tree kangaroo	1·40	1·50
MS993	168 × 127 mm. As Nos. 989/92, each × 2, but without white margins	5·75	6·25

355 Indo-Pacific Hump-backed Dolphin

2003. Protected Species. Dolphins. Multicoloured.

No.	Description	Unused	Used
994	65t. Type **355**	20	25
995	65t. Two Indo-Pacific bottlenose dolphins	20	25
996	1k.50 Indo-Pacific bottlenose dolphin leaping	50	55
997	2k. Irrawaddy dolphin	70	75
998	2k.50 Indo-Pacific hump-backed dolphin leaping	75	80
999	4k. Irrawaddy dolphin with diver	1·40	1·50
MS1000	147 × 112 mm. 1k.50 Indo-Pacific hump-backed dolphin; 1k.50 Indo-Pacific bottlenose dolphin; 1k.50 Two Indo-Pacific bottlenose dolphins; 1k.50 Irrawaddy dolphin with diver; 1k.50 Irrawaddy dolphin; 1k.50 Indo-Pacific hump-backed dolphin	3·00	3·25

POSTAGE DUE STAMPS

1960. Stamps of 1952 surch **POSTAL CHARGES** and value.

No.	Description	Unused	Used
D2	1d. on 6½d. purple	3·25	5·00
D3	3d. on ½d. green	3·50	2·00
D1	6d. on 7½d. blue (A)	£800	£425
D4	6d. on 7½d. blue (B)	27·00	7·50
D5	1s.3d. on 3½d. black	4·00	2·50
D6	3s. on 2½d. orange	14·00	4·50

In (A) value and "POSTAGE" is obliterated by a solid circle and a series of "IX's" but these are omitted in (B).

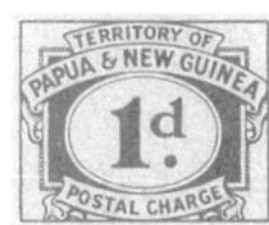

D 3

1960.

No.	Type	Description	Unused	Used
D 7	D 3	1d. orange	65	75
D 8		3d. brown	70	75
D 9		6d. blue	75	40
D10		9d. red	75	1·75
D11		1s. green	75	50
D12		1s.3d. violet	1·00	2·00
D13		1s.6d. blue	4·00	6·00
D14		3s. yellow	2·50	75

PARAGUAY Pt. 20

A republic in the centre of S. America, independent since 1811.

1870. 8 reales = 1 peso.
1878. 100 centavos = 1 peso.
1944. 100 centimos = 1 guarani.

1

7

1870. Various frames. Values in "reales". Imperf.
1 **1** 1r. red . . . . 4·00 2·25
3 2r. blue . . . . 55·00 32·00
4 3r. black . . . . 90·00 55·00

1878. Handstamped with large **5**. Imperf.
5 **1** 5c. on 1r. red . . . . 40·00 26·00
9 5c. on 2r. blue . . . . £140 75·00
13 5c. on 3r. black . . . . . . £110 70·00

1879. Prepared for use but not issued (wrong currency). Values in "reales". Perf.
14 **7** 5r. orange 40
15 10r. brown 50

1879. Values in "centavos". Perf.
16 **7** 5c. brown . . . . 1·10 70
17 10c. green . . . . 1·60 95

1881. Handstamped with large figures.
18 **7** 1 on 10c. green . . . . . . 8·00 4·75
19 2 on 10c. green . . . . . . 8·00 4·75

1881. As T **1** (various frames), but value in "centavos". Perf.
20 **1** 1c. blue 40 40
21a 2c. red 30 40
22 4c. brown 40 50

1884. No. 1 handstamped with large **1**. Imperf.
23 **1** 1c. on 1r. red . . . . 2·40 1·40

13

24

1884. Perf.
24 **13** 1c. green 30 15
25 2c. red 40 15
26 5c. blue 40 15

1887.
32 **24** 1c. green 15 15
33a 2c. red 15 15
34 5c. blue 30 20
35 7c. brown 30 25
36 10c. mauve 45 30
37 15c. orange 45 30
38 20c. pink 45 30
50 40c. blue . . . . 2·00 70
51 60c. orange 95 30
52 80c. blue 80 30
53 1p. green 85 30

25

27 C. Rivarola

1889. Imperf or perf.
40 **25** 15c. purple . . . . 1·60 95

1892.
42 **27** 1 CENTAVOS grey 15 10
54 1 CENTAVO grey 15 10
43 – 2c. green 15 10
44 – 4c. red 10 10
57 – 5c. purple 15 10
46 – 10c. violet 30 25
47 – 14c. brown 55 30
48 – 20c. red 95 30
49 – 30c. green . . . . 1·25 30
84 – 1p. blue 40 25
PORTRAITS: 2c. S. Jovellano; 4c. J. Bautista Gil; 5c. H. Uriarte; 10c. C. Barreiro; 14c. Gen. B. Caballero; 20c. Gen. P. Escobar; 30c. J. Gonzales; 1p. J. B. Egusquisa.

1892. 400th Anniv of Discovery of America. No. 46 optd **1492 12 DE OCTUBRE 1892** in oval.
41 10c. violet . . . . 5·75 1·50

1895. Surch **PROVISORIO 5**.
59 **24** 5c. on 7c. brown 30 30

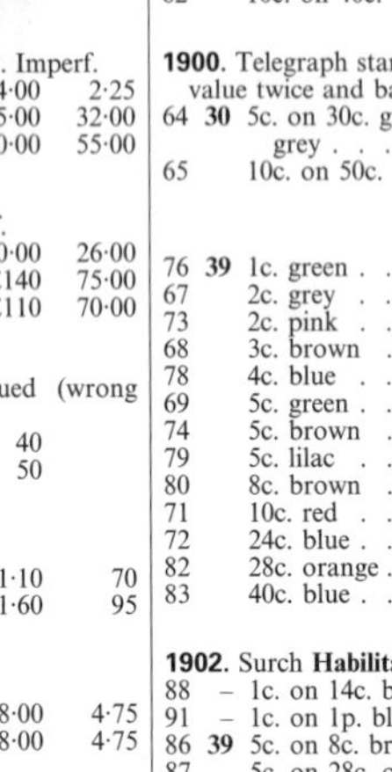
30 39

1896. Telegraph stamps as T **30** surch **CORREOS 5 CENTAVOS** in oval.
60 **30** 5c. on 2c. brown, blk & grey 45 20
61 5c. on 4c. orange, blk & grey 45 20

1898. Surch **Provisorio 10 Centavos**.
63 **24** 10c. on 15c. orange 35 35
62 10c. on 40c. blue 25 25

1900. Telegraph stamps as T **30** surch with figures of value twice and bar.
64 **30** 5c. on 30c. green, blk & grey . . . . 1·60 70
65 10c. on 50c. lilac, blk & grey 3·50 1·50

1900.
76 **39** 1c. green 10 10
67 2c. grey 10 10
73 2c. pink 20 15
68 3c. brown 10 10
78 4c. blue 15 10
69 5c. green 10 10
74 5c. brown 20 10
79 5c. lilac 25 10
80 8c. brown 20 15
71 10c. red 20 15
72 24c. blue 45 20
82 28c. orange 25 35
83 40c. blue 25 10

1902. Surch **Habilitado en** and new values.
88 – 1c. on 14c. brown (No. 47) 30 20
91 – 1c. on 1p. blue (No. 84) . . 20 15
86 **39** 5c. on 8c. brown (No. 80) 35 20
87 5c. on 28c. orange (No. 82) 20 30
89 **24** 5c. on 60c. orange (No. 51) 20 25
90 5c. on 80c. blue (No. 52) . . 30 25
85 **39** 20c. on 24c. blue (No. 72) 35 20

46

47

1903.
92 **46** 1c. grey 20 15
93 2c. green 25 20
94a 5c. blue 25 10
95 10c. brown 45 20
96 20c. red 45 25
97 30c. blue 50 25
98 60c. violet . . . . 1·25 55

1903.
99 **47** 1c. green 15 10
100 2c. orange 15 10
101 5c. blue 20 15
102 10c. violet 30 20
103 20c. green 50 25
104 30c. blue 90 30
105 60c. brown 95 35

48

50

51 National Palace, Asuncion

1904.
106 **48** 10c. blue 35 20

1904. End of successful Revolt against Govt. (begun in August). Surch **PAZ 12 Dic. 1904.30 centavos**.
107 **48** 30c. on 10c. blue 50 35

1905.
108 **50** 1c. orange 15 10
109 1c. red 15 10
110 1c. blue 15 10
112 2c. green . . . . 40·00
113 2c. red 15 10
114 5c. blue 15 10
116 5c. yellow 15 10
117 10c. brown 15 10
118 10c. green 15 10
119 10c. blue 15 10
120 20c. lilac 45 35
121 20c. brown 45 35
122 20c. green 35 20
123 30c. blue 45 20
124 30c. grey 45 20
125 30c. lilac 50 35
126 60c. brown 35 25
128 60c. pink . . . . 4·00 1·40
129 **51** 1p. black and red . . . . 1·75 80
130 1p. black and brown . . . 65 35
131 1p. black and green . . . 35 35
132 2p. black and blue 35 25
133 2p. black and red 35 25
134 2p. black and brown . . . 40 30
135 5p. black and red 90 35
136 5p. black and blue 90 35
137 5p. black and green . . . 90 35
138 10p. black and brown . . . 80 35
139 10p. black and blue . . . 80 35
141 20p. black and green . . . 2·25 1·25
142 20p. black and yellow . . . 2·25 1·25
143 20p. black and purple . . . 2·25 1·25

1907. Surch **Habilitado en** and value and bars.
159 **50** 5c. on 1c. blue 10 10
160 5c. on 2c. red 15 10
145 5c. on 2c. green 40 25
172 **39** 5c. on 28c. orange . . . . 1·60 60
173 5c. on 40c. blue 30 25
163 **50** 5c. on 60c. brown 15 10
162 5c. on 60c. pink 20 15
175 20c. on 1c. blue 20 15
180 **24** 20c. on 2c. red . . . . . . 4·00 2·10
177 **50** 20c. on 2c. red . . . . . . 6·75 3·50
178 20c. on 30c. blue . . . . . 2·00 1·10
179 20c. on 30c. lilac 30 30

1907. Official stamps surch **Habilitado en**, value and bars. Where not otherwise stated, the design is as T **50** but with "OFICIAL" below the lion.
164 – 5c. on 10c. green 30 20
149 – 5c. on 10c. brown 30 20
150 – 5c. on 10c. lilac 30 20
181 **24** 5c. on 15c. orange (No. O63) . . . . 3·00 2·40
182 5c. on 20c. pink (No. O64) · 45·00 32·00
166 – 5c. on 20c. brown 30 25
151 – 5c. on 20c. green 30 20
167 – 5c. on 20c. pink 30 25
152 – 5c. on 20c. lilac 30 20
157 **46** 5c. on 30c. blue (No. O104) 95 85
154 – 5c. on 30c. blue 50 50
169 – 5c. on 30c. yellow 10 10
168 – 5c. on 30c. grey 20 15
183 **24** 5c. on 50c. grey (No. O65) 21·00 15·00
158 **46** 5c. on 60c. violet (No. O105) 35 25
155 – 5c. on 60c. brown 20 15
171 – 5c. on 60c. blue 20 10
184 **24** 20c. on 5c. blue (No. O60) 1·90 1·50
174 **46** 20c. on 5c. blue (No. O101) . . . . 1·90 1·50

1907. Official stamps, as T **50** and **51** with "OFICIAL" added, optd **Habilitado** and one bar.
146 5c. grey 30 20
148 5c. blue 25 15
185 1p. black and orange 35 35
186 1p. black and red 30 25

1907. Official stamps, as T **51** with "OFICIAL" added, surch **Habilitado 1908 UN CENTAVO** and bar.
188 1c. on 1p. black and red . . 20 20
189 1c. on 1p. black and brown 1·00 50

1908. Optd **1908**.
190 **50** 1c. green 10 10
191 5c. yellow 10 10
192 10c. brown 10 10
193 20c. orange 10 10
194 30c. red 40 30
195 60c. mauve 30 30
196 **51** 1p. blue 15 15

1909. Optd **1909**.
197 **50** 1c. blue 10 10
198 1c. red 10 10
199 5c. green 10 10
200 5c. orange 10 10
201 10c. red 20 15
202 10c. brown 20 15
203 20c. lilac 20 20
204 20c. yellow 10 10
205 30c. brown 45 30
206 30c. blue 45 30

62

63

65

1910.
207 **62** 1c. brown 10 10
208 5c. lilac 10 10
209 5c. green 10 10
210 5c. blue 10 10
211 10c. green 10 10
212 10c. violet 10 10
213 10c. red 10 10
214 20c. red 10 10
215 50c. red 45 20
216 75c. blue 15 10

1911. No. 216 perf diagonally and each half used as 20c.
217 **62** 20c. (½ of 75c.) blue . . . 15 10

1911. Independence Centenary.
218 **63** 1c. black and olive 10 10
219 2c. black and blue 10 10
220 5c. black and red 20 10
221 10c. brown and blue . . . 30 15
222 20c. blue and olive 30 15
223 50c. blue and lilac 45 30
224 75c. purple and olive . . . 45 30

1912. Surch **Habilitada en VEINTE** and thin bar.
225 **62** 20c. on 50c. red 10 10

1913.
226 **65** 1c. black 10 10
227 2c. orange 10 10
228 5c. mauve 10 10
229 10c. green 10 10
230 20c. red 10 10
231 40c. red 10 10
232 75c. blue 10 10
233 80c. yellow 10 10
234 1p. blue 10 10
235 1p.25 blue 30 10
236 3p. green 30 10

1918. No. D242 surch **HABILITADO EN 0.05 1918** and bar.
237 5c. on 40c. brown 10 10

1918. Nos. D239/42 optd **HABILITADO 1918**.
238 5c. brown 10 10
239 10c. brown 10 10
240 20c. brown 10 10
241 40c. brown 15 10

1918. Surch **HABILITADO EN 0.30 1918** and bar.
242 **65** 30c. on 40c. red 10 10

1920. Surch **HABILITADO en**, value and **1920**.
243 **65** 50c. on 80c. yellow 15 10
244 1p.75 on 3p. green 60 50

1920. Nos. D243/4 optd **HABILITADO 1920** or surch also.
245 1p. brown 20 10
246 1p. on 1p.50 brown 35 10

72 Parliament House, Asuncion

1920. Jubilee of Constitution.
247 **72** 50c. black and red 30 20
248 1p. black and blue 50 40
249 1p.75 black and blue . . . 20 15
250 3p. black and yellow . . . 75 25

1920. Surch **50**.
251 **65** 50 on 75c. blue 45 10

1921. Surch **50** and two bars.
252 **62** 50 on 75c. blue 10 10
253 **65** 50 on 75c. blue 25 10

75

1922.
254 **75** 50c. blue and red 10 10
255 1p. brown and blue 10 10

Between 1922 and 1936 many regular postage stamps were overprinted **C** (= Campana—country), these being used at post offices outside Asuncion but not for mail sent abroad. The prices quoted are for whichever is the cheapest.

77 Starting-point of Conspirators

80 Map

1922. Independence.
256 **77** 1p. blue 20 10
258 1p. blue and red 30 10
259 1p. grey and purple 30 10
260 1p. grey and orange . . . 30 10
257 5p. purple 30 25

261 5p. brown and blue 30 25
262 5p. black and green 30 25
263 5p. blue and red 30 25

1924. Surch **Habilitado en**, value and **1924**.
265 **65** 50c. on 75c. blue 10 10
266 $1 on 1p.25 blue 10 10
267 – $1 on 1p.50 brown (No. D244) 10 10

1924.
268 **80** 1p. blue 10 10
269 2p. red 15 10
270 4p. blue 30 10

81 Gen. Jose E. Diaz

82 Columbus

1925.
271 **81** 50c. red 10 10
272 1p. blue 10 10
273 1p. green 10 10

1925.
274 **82** 1p. blue 15 10

1926. Surch **Habilitado en** and new value.
275 **62** 1c. on 5c. blue 10 10
276 $0.02 on 5c. blue 10 10
277 **65** 7c. on 40c. red 10 10
278 15c. on 75c. blue 10 10
279 **50** $0.50 on 60c. purple (No. 195) 10 10
280 – $0.50 on 75c. blue (No. O243) 10 10
281 – $1.50 on 1p.50 brown (No. D244) 15 10
282 **80** $1.50 on 4p. blue 10 10

86

87 P. J. Caballero

88 Paraguay

89 Cassel Tower, Asuncion

90 Columbus

92 Arms of De Salazarde Espinosa, founder of Asuncion

1927.
283 **86** 1c. red 10 10
284 2c. orange 10 10
285 7c. lilac 10 10
286 7c. green 10 10
287 10c. green 10 10
288 10c. red 10 10
290 10c. blue 10 10
291 20c. blue 10 10
292 20c. purple 10 10
293 20c. violet 10 10
294 20c. pink 10 10
295 50c. blue 10 10
296 50c. red 10 10
323 50c. orange 10 10
326 50c. green 10 10
299 50c. mauve 10 10
300 50c. pink 10 10
301 70c. blue 10 10
328 **87** 1p. green 10 10
329 1p. red 10 10
330 1p. purple 10 10
331 1p. blue 10 10
304 1p. orange 10 10
332 1p. violet 10 10
333 **88** 1p.50 brown 10 10
334 1p.50 lilac 10 10
307 1p.50 pink 10 10
335 1p.50 blue 10 10
308 – 2p.50 bistre 10 10
337 – 2p.50 violet 10 10
338 – 3p. grey 10 10
310 – 3p. red 10 10
311 – 3p. violet 10 10
312 **89** 5p. brown 25 20
340 5p. violet 10 10
314 5p. orange 10 10
315 **90** 10p. red 35 35
317 10p. blue 35 35
318 **88** 20p. red 1·60 85
319 20p. green 1·60 85
320 20p. purple 1·60 85
DESIGNS—As Type **87**: 2p.50, Fulgencio Yegros; 3p. V. Ignacio Yturbe.

1928. Foundation of Asuncion, 1537.
342 **92** 10p. purple 95 70

93 Pres. Hayes of U.S.A. and Villa Hayes

1928. 50th Anniv of Hayes's Decision to award Northern Chaco to Paraguay.
343 **93** 10p. brown 3·75 1·40
344 10p. grey 3·75 1·40

1929. Air. Surch **Correo Aereo Habilitado en** and value.
357 **86** $0.95 on 7c. lilac 20 20
358 $1.90 on 20c. blue 20 20
345 – $2.85 on 5c. purple (No. O239) 95 70
348 – $3.40 on 3p. grey (No. 338) 1·90 85
359 **80** $3.40 on 4p. blue 30 30
360 $4.75 on 4p. blue 55 30
346 – $5.65 on 10c. green (No. O240) 35 45
361 – $6.80 on 3p. grey (No. 338) 35 35
349 **80** $6.80 on 4p. blue 1·90 85
347 – $11.30 on 50c. red (No. O242) 60 50
350 **89** $17 on 5p. brown (A) 1·90 85
362 $17 on 5p. brown (B) 1·50 1·10
On No. 350 (A) the surcharge is in four lines, and on No. 362 (B) it is in three lines.

95

1929. Air.
352 **95** 2.85p. green 35 30
353 – 5.65p. brown 60 30
354 – 5.65p. red 40 35
355 – 11.30p. purple 70 55
356 – 11.30p. blue 35 35
DESIGNS: 5.65p. Carrier pigeon; 11.30p. Stylized airplane.

1930. Air. Optd **CORREO AEREO** or surch also in words.
363 **86** 5c. on 10c. green 10 10
364 5c. on 70c. blue 10 10
365 10c. green 10 10
366 20c. blue 20 20
367 **87** 20c. on 1p. red 30 30
368 **86** 40c. on 50c. orange 15 10
369 **87** 1p. green 35 35
370 – 3p. grey (No. 338) 35 35
371 **90** 6p. on 10p. red 60 50
372 **88** 10p. on 20p. red 5·50 3·25
373 10p. on 20p. purple 6·50 4·75

101

103

1930. Air.
374 **101** 95c. blue on blue 40 35
375 95c. red on pink 40 35
376 – 1p.90 purple on blue 40 35
377 – 1p.90 red on pink 40 35
378 **103** 6p.80 black on blue 40 35
379 6p.80 green on pink 45 40
DESIGN: 1p.90, Asuncion Cathedral.

104 Declaration of Independence

105

1930. Air. Independence Day.
380 **104** 2p.85 blue 40 35
381 3p.40 green 35 25
382 4p.75 purple 35 25

1930. Red Cross Fund.
383 **105** 1p.50+50c. blue 1·10 70
384 1p.50+50c. red 1·10 70
385 1p.50+50c. lilac 1·10 70

106 Portraits of Archbishop Bogarin

1930. Consecration of Archbishop Bogarin.
386 **106** 1p.50 blue 1·10 60
387 1p.50 red 1·10 60
388 1p.50 violet 1·10 60

1930. Surch **Habilitado en CINCO**.
389 **86** 5c. on 7c. green 10 10

108 Planned Agricultural College at Ypacarai

1931. Agricultural College Fund.
390 **108** 1p.50+50c. blue on red 30 30

109 Arms of Paraguay

1931. 60th Anniv of First Paraguay Postage Stamps.
391 **109** 10p. brown 30 25
392 10p. red on blue 35 25
393 10p. blue on red 35 25
395 10p. grey 50 20
396 10p. blue 20 20

110 Gunboat "Paraguay"

1931. Air. 60th Anniv of Constitution and Arrival of new Gunboats.
397 **110** 1p. red 25 20
398 1p. blue 25 20
399 2p. orange 30 25
400 2p. brown 30 25
401 3p. green 65 40
402 3p. blue 65 45
403 3p. red 60 40
404 6p. green 75 60
405 6p. mauve 95 65
406 6p. blue 70 50
407 10p. red 2·00 1·40
408 10p. green 2·50 1·90
409 10p. blue 1·40 1·00
410 10p. brown 2·25 1·60
411 10p. pink 2·00 1·40

1931. As T **110**.
412 – 1p.50 violet 95 35
413 – 1p.50 blue 15 10
DESIGN: Gunboat "Humaita".
No. 413 is optd with large **C**.

112 War Memorial

113 Orange Tree and Yerba Mate

114 Yerba Mate

115 Palms

116 Yellow-headed Caracara

1931. Air.
414 **112** 5c. blue 15 10
415 5c. green 15 10
416 5c. red 20 10
417 5c. purple 15 10
418 **113** 10c. violet 10 10
419 10c. red 10 10
420 10c. brown 10 10
421 10c. blue 10 10
422 **114** 20c. red 15 10
423 20c. blue 20 10
424 20c. green 20 15
425 20c. brown 15 10
426 **115** 40c. green 20 10
426a 40c. blue 15 10
426b 40c. red 20 10
427 **116** 80c. blue 35 30
428 80c. green 35 20
428a 80c. red 25 20

1931. Air. Optd with airship "Graf Zeppelin" and **Correo Aereo "Graf Zeppelin"** or surch also.
429 **80** 3p. on 4p. blue 7·75 6·25
430 4p. blue 7·75 6·25

118 Farm Colony

1931. 50th Anniv of Foundation of San Bernardino.
431 **118** 1p. green 35 20
432 1p. red 10 10

1931. New Year. Optd **FELIZ ANO NUEVO 1932**.
433 **106** 1p.50 blue 60 60
434 1p.50 red 60 60

120 "Graf Zeppelin"

1932. Air.
435 **120** 4p. blue 1·40 1·75
436 8p. red 2·40 2·00
437 12p. green 1·90 1·75
438 16p. purple 3·75 3·00
439 20p. brown 4·00 3·75

121 Red Cross H.Q.

122 (Trans: "Has been, is and will be")

1932. Red Cross Fund.
440 **121** 50c.+50c. pink 25 25

1932. Chaco Boundary Dispute.
441 **122** 1p. purple 20 10
442 1p.50 pink 10 10
443 1p.50 brown 10 10
444 1p.50 green 10 10
445 1p.50 blue 10 10
Nos. 443/5 are optd with a large **C**.

1932. New Year. Surch **CORREOS FELIZ ANO NUEVO 1933** and value.
446 **120** 50c. on 4p. blue 35 30
447 1p. on 8p. red 35 30
448 1p.50 on 12p. green 35 30
449 2p. on 16p. purple 35 30
450 5p. on 20p. brown 1·25 75

124 "Graf Zeppelin" over Paraguay

125 "Graf Zeppelin" over Atlantic

1933. Air. "Graf Zeppelin" issue.
451 **124** 4p.50 blue . . . . 1·25 75
452 9p. red . . . . 2·50 1·90
453 13p.50 green . . . . . . 2·50 1·90
454 **125** 22p.50 brown . . . . . . 6·00 4·50
455 45p. violet . . . . 8·25 6·75

126 Columbus's Fleet

1933. 441st Anniv of Departure of Columbus from Palos. Maltese Crosses in violet.
456 **126** 10c. olive and red 45 15
457 20c. blue and lake 45 15
458 50c. red and green 75 35
459 1p. brown and blue . . . 60 40
460 1p.50 green and blue . . 60 40
461 2p. green and sepia . . . 1·75 70
462 5p. lake and olive . . . . 3·75 1·40
463 10p. sepia and blue . . . 3·75 1·40

127 G.P.O., Asuncion

1934. Air.
464 **127** 33p.75 blue . . . . 1·60 95
468 33p.75 red . . . . 1·60 95
466 33p.75 green . . . . . . 1·40 85
467 33p.75 brown . . . . . . 1·40 85

1934. Air. Optd **1934**.
469 **124** 4p.50 blue . . . . 1·75 1·75
470 9p. red . . . . 2·25 2·25
471 13p.50 green . . . . . . 6·50 6·50
472 **125** 22p.50 brown . . . . . . 5·25 5·25
473 45p. violet . . . . 11·00 11·00

1935. Air. Optd **1935**.
474 **124** 4p.50 red . . . . 2·25 2·25
475 9p. green . . . . 3·25 3·25
476 13p.50 brown . . . . . . 9·25 9·25
477 **125** 22p.50 purple . . . . . . 8·75 8·75
478 45p. blue . . . . 23·00 23·00

131 Tobacco Plant

1935. Air.
479 **131** 17p. brown . . . . 3·75 3·00
480 17p. red . . . . 6·75 5·00
481 17p. blue . . . . 4·25 3·50
482 17p. green . . . . 2·10 1·75

132 Church of the Incarnation

1935. Air.
483 **132** 102p. red . . . . 5·00 3·75
485 102p. blue . . . . 2·50 1·90
486 102p. brown . . . . . . 2·50 1·90
487 102p. violet . . . . . . 1·10 80
487a 102p. orange . . . . . 1·10 85

1937. Air. Surch **Habilitado en** and value in figures.
488 **127** $24 on 33p.75 blue . . . 40 50
489 **132** $65 on 102p. grey . . . . 1·25 95
490 $84 on 102p. green . . . 1·25 95

134 Arms of Asuncion **135** Monstrance

1937. 4th Centenary of Asuncion (1st issue).
491 **134** 50c. purple and violet . . 10 10
492 1p. green and bistre . . . 10 10
493 3p. blue and red 10 10
494 10p. yellow and red . . . 15 10
495 20p. grey and blue . . . 20 20

1937. 1st National Eucharistic Congress.
496 **135** 1p. red, yellow and blue 10 10
497 3p. red, yellow and blue 10 10
498 10p. red, yellow and blue 15 10

136 Oratory of the Virgin of Asuncion **137** Asuncion

1938. 4th Centenary of Asuncion (2nd issue).
499 **136** 5p. olive 25 10
500 5p. red 35 10
501 11p. brown 25 10

1939. Air.
502 **137** 3p.40 blue 75 45
503 3p.40 green 75 45
504 3p.40 brown 75 45

138 J. E. Diaz

1939. Reburial in National Pantheon of Ashes of C. A. Lopez and J. E. Diaz.
505 **138** 2p. brown and blue . . . 25 15
506 – 2p. brown and blue . . . 25 15
DESIGN—VERT: No. 506, C. A. Lopez.

139 Pres. Caballero and Senator Decoud

1939. 50th Anniv of Asuncion University.
507 – 50c. blk & orge (postage) 10 10
508 – 1p. black and blue . . . 15 10
509 – 2p. black and red 25 10
510 **139** 5p. black and blue . . . 35 20
511 28p. black and red (air) 4·75 3·75
512 90p. black and green . . 8·00 6·50
DESIGN: Nos. 507/9, Pres. Escobar and Dr. Zubizarreta.

140 Coats of Arms

141 Pres. Baldomir and Flags of Paraguay and Uruguay

1939. Chaco Boundary Peace Conference, Buenos Aires (1st issue).
513 **140** 50c. blue (postage) . . . 15 10
514 **141** 1p. olive 15 10
515 A 2p. green 20 10
516 B 3p. brown 35 25
517 C 5p. orange 25 20
518 D 6p. violet 40 30
519 E 10p. brown 50 35
520 F 1p. brown (air) 10 10
521 **140** 3p. blue 10 10
522 E 5p. olive 10 15
523 D 10p. violet 15 15
524 C 30p. orange 25 15
525 B 50p. brown 15 25
526 A 100p. green 60 25
527 **141** 200p. green . . . . 2·75 1·75
528 – 500p. black . . . . 13·00 10·50
DESIGNS (flag on right is that of country named): A, Benavides (Peru); B, Eagle (USA); C, Alessandri (Chile); D, Vargas (Brazil); E, Ortiz (Argentina); F, Figure of "Peace" (Bolivia); 500p. (30 × 40 mm), Map of Chaco frontiers.
See also Nos. 536/43.

143 Arms of New York **144** Asuncion–New York Air Route

1939. New York World's Fair.
529 **143** 5p. red (postage) 20 15
530 10p. blue 40 30
531 11p. green 25 45
532 22p. grey 35 30
533 **144** 30p. brown (air) . . . . 3·25 2·40
534 80p. orange . . . . 4·25 3·00
535 90p. violet . . . . 7·00 5·50

145 Soldier **147** Waterfall

1940. Chaco Boundary Peace Conference, Buenos Aires (2nd issue). Inscr "PAZ DEL CHACO".
536 **145** 50c. orange 15 10
537 – 1p. purple 15 15
538 – 3p. green 25 20
539 – 5p. brown 10 25
540 – 10p. mauve 35 20
541 – 20p. blue 30 25
542 – 50p. green . . . . 1·10 35
543 **147** 100p. black . . . . 2·50 1·60
DESIGNS: As Type **145**: VERT: 1p. Water-carrier; 5p. Ploughing with oxen. HORIZ: 3p. Cattle Farming. As Type **147**: VERT: 10p. Fishing in the Paraguay River. HORIZ: 20p. Bullock-cart; 50p. Cattle-grazing.

148 Western Hemisphere **149** Reproduction of Paraguay No. 1

1940. 50th Anniv of Pan-American Union.
544 **148** 50c. orange (postage) . . 10 10
545 1p. green 10 10
546 5p. blue 25 10
547 10p. brown 30 30
548 20p. red (air) 35 25
549 70p. blue 35 30
550 100p. green 80 65
551 500p. violet . . . . . . 2·75 1·40

1940. Cent of First Adhesive Postage Stamps. Inscr "CENTENARIO DEL SELLO POSTAL 1940".
552 **149** 1p. purple and green . . . 65 35
553 – 5p. brown and green . . . 85 45
554 – 6p. blue and brown . . . 1·75 50
555 – 10p. black and red . . . 1·90 60
DESIGNS: 5p. Sir Rowland Hill; 6p., 10p. Early Paraguayan stamps.

1940. National Mourning for Pres. Estigarribia. Surch **7-IX-40/DUELO NACIONAL/5 PESOS** in black border.
556 **145** 5p. on 50c. orange . . . 25 25

152 Dr. Francia **154** Our Lady of Asuncion

1940. Death Centenary of Dr. Francia (dictator).
557 **152** 50c. red 15 10
558 – 50c. purple 15 10
559 **152** 1p. green 15 10
560 – 5p. blue 15 10
PORTRAIT: Nos. 558 and 560, Dr. Francia seated in library.

1941. Visit of President Vargas of Brazil. Optd **Visita al Paraguay Agosto de 1941**.
560a 6p. violet (No. 518) 25 25

1941. Mothers' Fund.
561 **154** 7p.+3p. brown 35 25
562 7p.+3p. violet 35 25
563 7p.+3p. red 35 25
564 7p.+3p. blue 35 25

1942. Nos. 520/2 optd **Habilitado** and bar(s).
565 – 1p. brown 15 10
566 **140** 3p. blue 20 10
567 – 5p. olive 25 10

156 Arms of Paraguay **158** Irala's Vision

1942.
568 **156** 1p. green 10 10
569 1p. orange 10 10
570 7p. blue 10 10
571 7p. brown 10 10
For other values as Type **156** see Nos. 631, etc.

1942. 4th Centenary of Asuncion.
572 – 2p. green (postage) . . . 75 40
573 **158** 5p. red 75 40
574 – 7p. blue 75 35
575 – 20p. purple (air) 95 30
576 **158** 70p. brown . . . . 2·40 1·25
577 – 500p. olive . . . . 7·25 5·25
DESIGNS—VERT: 2p., 20p. Indian hailing ships; 7p., 500p. Irala's Arms.

160 Columbus sighting America **161** Pres. Morinigo and Symbols of Progress

1943. 450th Anniv of Discovery of America by Columbus.
578 **160** 50c. violet 25 20
579 1p. brown 20 10
580 5p. green 65 20
581 7p. blue 35 10

1943. Three Year Plan.
582 **161** 7p. blue 10 10

NOTE: From No. 583 onwards, the currency having been changed, the letter "c" in the value description indicates "centimos" instead of "centavos".

1944. St. Juan Earthquake Fund. Surch **U.P.A.E. Adhesion victimas San Juan y Pueblo Argentino centimos** and bar.
583 E 10c. on 10p. brown (No. 519) 40 25

1944. No. 311 surch **Habilitado en un centimo**.
584 1c. on 3p. violet 10 10

1944. Surch **1944/5 Centimos 5**.
585 **160** 5c. on 7p. blue 15 10
586 **161** 5c. on 7p. blue 15 10

164 Primitive Indian Postmen **181** Jesuit Relics of Colonial Paraguay

1944.
587 **164** 1c. black (postage) . . . 10 10
588 – 2c. brown 15 10
589 – 5c. olive . . . . 3·25 80
590 – 7c. blue 15 20
591 – 10c. green . . . . 1·50 45
592 – 15c. blue 40 25
593 – 50c. black 35 35
594 – 1g. red 70 40

DESIGNS—HORIZ: 2c. Ruins of Humaita Church; 7c. Marshal Francisco S. Lopez; 1g. Ytororo Heroes' Monument. VERT: 5c. First Paraguayan railway locomotive; 10c. "Tacuary" (paddle-steamer); 15c. Port of Asuncion; 50c. Meeting place of Independence conspirators.

595 – 1c. blue (air) 20 15
596 – 2c. green 10 10
597 – 3c. purple 80 20
598 – 5c. green 20 10
599 – 10c. violet 20 15
600 – 20c. brown . . . . 4·00 1·60
601 – 30c. blue 25 25
602 – 40c. olive 15 15
603 – 70c. red 25 20
604 **181** 1g. orange 90 40
605 – 2g. brown . . . . 2·25 55
606 – 5g. brown . . . . 5·50 2·75
607 – 10g. blue . . . . 13·00 9·75

DESIGNS—HORIZ: 1c. Port of Asuncion; 2c. First telegraphic apparatus in S. America; 3c. Paddle-steamer "Tacuary"; 5c. Meeting place of Independence Conspirators; 10c. Antequera Monument; 20c. First Paraguayan railway locomotive; 40c. Government House. VERT: 30c. Ytororo Heroes' Monument; 70c. As Type **164** but vert: 2g. Ruins of Humaita Church; 5g. Oratory of the Virgin; 10g. Marshal Francisco S. Lopez.

See also Nos. 640/51.

1945. No. 590 surch with figure **5** over ornaments deleting old value.
608 5c. on 7c. blue 10 10

186 Clasped Hands and Flags

1945. President Morinigo's Goodwill Visits. Designs of different sizes inscr "CONFRATERNIDAD" between crossed flags of Paraguay and another American country, mentioned in brackets.

(a) Postage.
609 **186** 1c. green (Panama) . . . 10 10
610 3c. red (Venezuela) . . . 10 10
611 5c. grey (Ecuador) 10 10
612 2g. brown (Peru) . . . . 1·50 90

(b) Air.
613 20c. orange (Colombia) . . . 10 30
614 40c. olive (Bolivia) 10 25
615 70c. red (Mexico) 40 40
616 1g. blue (Chile) 50 50
617 2g. violet (Brazil) 75 75
618 5g. green (Argentina) . . . . 2·25 2·25
619 10g. brown (U.S.A.) . . . . 6·50 6·50

The 5 and 10g. are larger, 32 × 28 and 33½ × 30 mm respectively.

1945. Surch **1945 5 Centimos 5**.
620 **160** 5c. on 7p. blue 50 20
621 **161** 5c. on 7p. blue 50 20
622 – 5c. on 7p. blue (No. 590) 50 20

1945. Surch **1945** and value.
623 **154** 2c. on 7p.+3p. brown . . 10 10
624 2c. on 7p.+3p. violet . . . 10 10
625 2c. on 7p.+3p. red 10 10
626 2c. on 7p.+3p. blue . . . 10 10
627 5c. on 7p.+3p. brown . . 20 10
628 5c. on 7p.+3p. violet . . . 20 10
629 5c. on 7p.+3p. red 20 10
630 5c. on 7p.+3p. blue . . . 20 10

1946. As T **156** but inscr "U.P.U." at foot.
631 **156** 5c. grey 10 10
631a 5c. pink 10 10
631b 5c. brown 10 10
686 10c. blue 10 10
687 10c. pink 10 10
631c 30c. green 10 10
631d 30c. brown 10 10
775 45c. green 10 10
631e 50c. mauve 10 10
776 50c. purple 10 10
858 70c. brown 10 10
777 90c. blue 10 10
778 1g. violet 10 10
860 1g.50 mauve 10 10
814 2g. ochre 10 10
780 2g.20 mauve 10 10
781 3g. brown 10 10
782 4g.20 green 10 10
862 4g.50 blue 15 10
816 5g. red 10 10
689 10g. orange 20 30
784 10g. green 20 15
818 12g.45 green 20 10
819 15g. orange 25 15
786 20g. blue 40 30
820 30g. bistre 20 30
812 50g. brown 30 25
821 100g. blue 90 50

See also Nos. 1037/49.

1946. Surch **1946 5 Centimos 5**.
632 **154** 5c. on 7p.+3p. brown . . 25 35
633 5c. on 7p.+3p. violet . . . 25 35
634 5c. on 7p.+3p. red 25 35
635 5c. on 7p.+3p. blue . . . 25 35

1946. Air. Surch **1946 5 Centimos 5**.
636 5c. on 20c. brown (No. 600) 5·50 5·75
637 5c. on 30c. blue (No. 601) . . 30 30
638 5c. on 40c. olive (No. 602) 30 30
639 5c. on 70c. red (No. 603) . . 30 30

1946. As Nos. 587/607 but colours changed and some designs smaller.
640 – 1c. red (postage) 20 15
641 – 2c. violet 10 10
642 **164** 5c. blue 10 10
643 – 10c. orange 10 10
644 – 15c. olive 15 15
645 **181** 50c. green 50 30
646 – 1g. blue 95 30

DESIGNS—VERT: 1c. Paddle-steamer "Tacuary"; 1g. Meeting place of Independence Conspirators. HORIZ: 2c. First telegraphic apparatus in S. America; 10c. Antequera Monument; 15c. Ytororo Heroes' Monument.

647 – 10c. red (air) 10 10
648 – 20c. green 80 20
649 – 1g. brown 25 25
650 – 5g. purple . . . . 2·25 1·40
651 – 10g. red . . . . 7·25 4·00

DESIGNS—VERT: 10c. Ruins of Humaita Church. HORIZ: 20c. Port of Asuncion; 1g. Govt. House; 5g. Marshal Francisco S. Lopez; 10g. Oratory of the Virgin.

189 Marshal Francisco Lopez **190** Archbishop of Paraguay

1947. Various frames.
652 **189** 1c. violet (postage) . . . 10 10
653 2c. red 10 10
654 5c. green 10 10
655 15c. blue 10 10
656 50c. green 40 40

657 32c. red (air) 10 10
658 64c. brown 25 25
659 1g. blue 40 40
660 5g. purple and blue . . . 1·60 60
661 10g. green and red . . . 2·75 95

1947. 50th Anniv of Archbishopric of Paraguay.
662 **190** 2c. grey (postage) 10 10
663 – 5c. red 10 10
664 – 10c. black 10 10
665 – 15c. green 25 15

666 – 20c. black (air) 10 10
667 – 30c. grey 10 10
668 – 40c. mauve 15 10
669 **190** 70c. red 25 25
670 – 1g. lake 30 30
671 – 2g. red 95 40
672 **190** 5g. slate and red . . . . 1·60 70
673 – 10g. brown and green . . 3·75 1·75

DESIGNS: 5, 20c., 10g. Episcopal Arms; 10, 30c, 1g. Sacred Heart Monument; 15, 40c., 2g. Vision of projected monument.

194 Torchbearer **195** C. A. Lopez, J. N. Gonzalez and "Paraguari" (freighter)

1948. Honouring the "Barefeet" (political party). Badge in red and blue.
674 **194** 5c. red (postage) 10 10
675 15c. orange 15 10

676 69c. green (air) 40 40
677 5g. blue . . . . 3·25 1·50

1948. Centenary of Paraguay's Merchant Fleet. Centres in black, red and blue.
678 **195** 2c. orange 15 10
679 5c. blue 20 10
680 10c. black 25 10
681 15c. violet 40 10
682 50c. green 60 20
683 1g. red 90 25

1949. Air. National Mourning for Archbishop of Paraguay. Surch **DUELO NACIONAL 5 CENTIMOS 5**.
684 **190** 5c. on 70c. red 15 15

1949. Air. Aid to Victims of Ecuadorean Earthquake. No. 667 surch **AYUDA AL ECUADOR 5 + 5** and two crosses.
685 5c.+5c. on 30c. slate 10 10

198 "Postal Communications" **199** President Roosevelt

1950. Air. 75th Anniv of U.P.U.
691 **198** 20c. violet and green . . . 1·50 1·60
692 30c. brown and purple . . 45 50
693 50c. green and grey . . . 50 50
694 1g. brown and blue . . . 50 50
695 5g. black and red . . . . 1·50 1·60

1950. Air. Honouring F. D. Roosevelt. Flags in red and blue.
696 **199** 20c. orange 10 10
697 30c. black 10 10
698 50c. purple 15 10
699 1g. green 25 25
700 5g. blue 30 30

1951. 1st Economic Congress of Paraguay. Surch **PRIMER CONGRESO DE ENTIDADES ECONOMICAS DEL PARAGUAY 18–IV–1951** and shield over a block of four stamps.
700a **156** 5c. pink 20 10
700b 10c. blue 35 25
700c 30c. green 50 40

Prices are for single stamps. Prices for blocks of four, four times single prices.

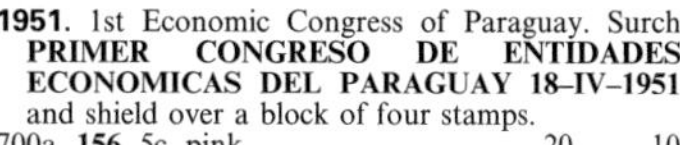

200 Columbus Lighthouse

201 Urn

1952. Columbus Memorial Lighthouse.
701 **200** 2c. brown (postage) . . . 10 10
702 5c. blue 10 10
703 10c. pink 10 10
704 15c. blue 10 10
705 20c. purple 10 10
706 50c. orange 15 10
707 1g. green 25 25

708 **201** 10c. blue (air) 10 10
709 20c. green 10 10
710 30c. purple 10 10
711 40c. pink 10 10
712 50c. bistre 10 10
713 1g. blue 15 10
714 2g. orange 25 20
715 5g. lake 25 40

202 Isabella the Catholic

1952. Air. 500th Birth Anniv of Isabella the Catholic.
716 **202** 1g. blue 10 10
717 2g. brown 20 20
718 5g. green 40 40
719 10g. purple 40 40

203 S. Pettirossi (aviator) **204** San Roque Church, Asuncion

1954. Pettirossi Commemoration.
720 **203** 5c. blue (postage) 10 10
721 20c. red 10 10
722 50c. purple 10 10
723 60c. violet 15 10

724 40c. brown (air) 10 10
725 55c. green 10 10
726 80c. blue 10 10
727 1g.30 grey 35 35

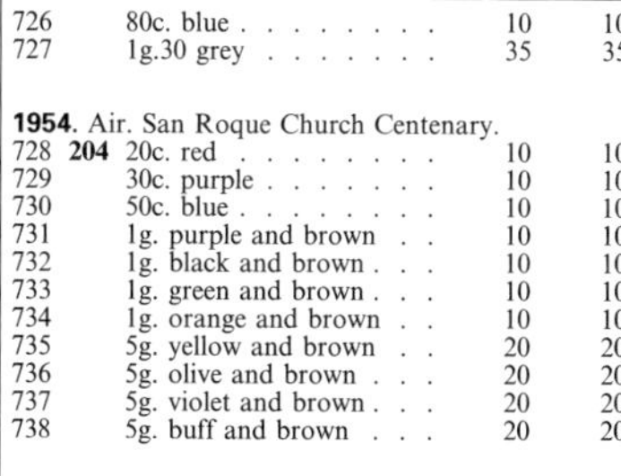

1954. Air. San Roque Church Centenary.
728 **204** 20c. red 10 10
729 30c. purple 10 10
730 50c. blue 10 10
731 1g. purple and brown . . 10 10
732 1g. black and brown . . . 10 10
733 1g. green and brown . . . 10 10
734 1g. orange and brown . . 10 10
735 5g. yellow and brown . . 20 20
736 5g. olive and brown . . . 20 20
737 5g. violet and brown . . . 20 20
738 5g. buff and brown . . . 20 20

205 Marshal Lopez, C. A. Lopez and Gen. Caballero

1954. National Heroes.
739 **205** 5c. violet (postage) . . . 10 10
740 20c. blue 10 10
741 50c. mauve 10 10
742 1g. brown 10 10
743 2g. green 15 10

744 5g. violet (air) 20 15
745 10g. olive 35 35
746 20g. grey 35 30
747 50g. pink . . . . 1·60 1·25
748 100g. blue . . . . 5·50 4·50

206 Presidents Stroessner and Peron

1955. Visit of President Peron. Flags in red and blue.
749 **206** 5c. brown & buff (postage) 10 10
750 10c. lake and buff 10 10
751 50c. grey 10 10
752 1g.30 lilac and buff . . . 10 10
753 2g.20 blue and buff . . . 20 10

754 60c. olive and buff (air) 10 10
755 2g. green 10 10
756 3g. red 20 10
757 4g.10 mauve and buff . . 30 20

207 Trinidad Campanile

1955. Sacerdotal Silver Jubilee of Mgr. Rodriguez.
758 **207** 5c. brown (postage) . . . 10 10
759 – 20c. brown 10 10
760 – 50c. brown 10 10
761 – 2g.50 green 10 10
762 – 5g. brown 15 10
763 – 15g. green 30 20
764 – 25g. green 35 35

765 **207** 2g. blue (air) 10 10
766 – 3g. green 10 10
767 – 4g. green 10 10
768 – 6g. brown 10 10
769 – 10g. red 20 10
770 – 20g. brown 30 10
771 – 30g. green 95 70
772 – 50g. blue . . . . 2·40 1·60

DESIGNS—HORIZ: 20c., 3g. Cloisters in Trinidad; 5, 10g. San Cosme Portico; 15, 20g. Church of Jesus. VERT: 50c., 4g. Cornice in Santa Maria; 2g.50, 6g. Santa Rosa Tower; 25, 30g. Niche in Trinidad; 50g. Trinidad Sacristy.

208 Angel and Marching Soldiers **209** Soldier and Flags

1957. Chaco Heroes. Inscr "HOMENAJE A LOS HEROES DEL CHACO". Flags in red, white and blue.
787 **208** 5c. green (postage) . . . 10 10
788 10c. red 10 10
789 15c. blue 10 10
790 20c. purple 10 10
791 25c. black 10 10
792 – 30c. blue 10 10
793 – 40c. black 10 10
794 – 50c. lake 10 10
795 – 1g. turquoise 10 10
796 – 1g.30 blue 10 10

797 – 1g.50 purple 10 10
798 – 2g. green 10 10
799 **209** 10c. blue (air) 10 10
800 15c. purple 10 10
801 20c. red 10 10
802 25c. blue 10 10
803 50c. turquoise 10 10
804 1g. red 10 10
805 – 1g.30 purple 10 10
806 – 1g.50 blue 10 10
807 – 2g. green 10 10
808 – 4g.10 vermilion and red 10 10
809 – 5g. black 10 10
810 – 10g. turquoise 15 15
811 – 25g. blue 40 15
DESIGNS—HORIZ: Nos. 792/8, Man, woman and flags; 805/11, "Paraguay" and kneeling soldier.

212 R. Gonzalez and St. Ignatius
213 President Stroessner

1958. 4th Centenary of St. Ignatius of Loyola.
822 **212** 50c. green 10 10
823 – 50c. brown 10 10
824 – 1g.50 violet 10 10
825 – 3g. blue 10 10
826 **212** 6g.25 red 15 10
DESIGNS—VERT: 50c. brown; 3g. Statue of St. Ignatius. HORIZ: 1g.50, Jesuit Fathers' house, Antigua.
See also Nos. 1074/81.

1958. Re-election of Pres. Stroessner. Portrait in black.
827 **213** 10c. red (postage) 10 10
828 15c. violet 10 10
829 25c. green 10 10
830 30c. lake 10 10
831 50c. mauve 10 10
832 75c. blue 10 10
833 5g. turquoise 10 10
834 10g. brown 10 15
835 12g. mauve (air) 40 35
836 18g. orange 25 40
837 23g. brown 65 40
838 36g. green 65 40
839 50g. olive 80 50
840 65g. grey 1·25 75

1959. Nos. 758/72 surch with star enclosed by palm leaves and value.
841 1g.50 on 5c. ochre (postage) 10 10
842 1g.50 on 20c. brown 10 10
843 1g.50 on 50c. purple 10 10
844 3g. on 2g.50 olive 10 10
845 6g.25 on 5g. brown 10 10
846 20g. on 15g. turquoise 35 35
847 30g. on 25g. green 50 50
848 4g. on 2g. blue (air) 10 10
849 12g.45 on 3g. olive 25 20
850 18g.15 on 6g. brown 35 30
851 23g.40 on 10g. red 25 35
852 34g.80 on 20g. bistre 40 50
853 36g. on 4g. green 40 30
854 43g.95 on 30g. green 75 60
855 100g. on 50g. blue 1·90 1·10

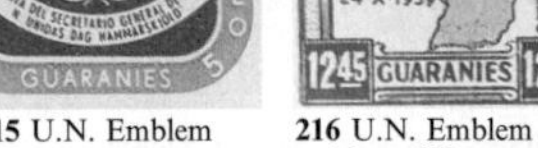

215 U.N. Emblem
216 U.N. Emblem and Map of Paraguay

1959. Air. Visit of U.N. Secretary-General.
856 **215** 5g. blue and orange 75 30

1959. Air. U.N. Day.
857 **216** 12g.45 orange and blue 25 20

217 Football
218 "Uprooted Tree"

1960. Olympic Games, Rome. Inscr "1960".
863 **217** 30c. red & green (postage) 10 10
864 50c. purple and blue 10 10
865 75c. green and orange 10 10
866 1g.50 violet and green 10 10
867 – 12g.45 blue and red (air) 25 25
868 – 18g.15 green and purple 35 35
869 – 36g. red and green 80 30
DESIGN—AIR: Basketball.

1960. World Refugee Year (1st issue).
870 **218** 25c. pink and green (postage) 10 10
871 50c. green and red 10 10
872 70c. brown and mauve 30 25
873 1g.50 blue and deep blue 30 30
874 3g. grey and brown 65 35
875 – 4g. pink and green (air) 95 70
876 – 12g.45 green and blue 1·90 1·25
877 – 18g.15 orange and red 2·75 2·00
878 – 23g.40 blue and red 3·50 2·75
DESIGN—AIR. As Type **218** but with "ANO MUNDIAL" inscr below tree.
See also Nos. 971/7.

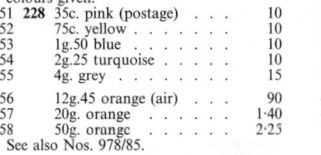

219 U.N. Emblem
220 U.N. Emblem and Flags

1960. "Human Rights". Inscr "DERECHOS HUMANOS".
879 **219** 1g. red and blue (postage) 10 10
880 – 3g. orange and blue 10 10
881 – 6g. orange and green 10 10
882 – 20g. yellow and red 15 15
883 **219** 40g. blue and red (air) 30 30
884 – 60g. red and green 75 65
885 – 100g. red and blue 1·40 95
DESIGNS: 3g., 60g. Hand holding scales; 6g. Hands breaking chain; 20g., 100g. "Freedom flame".

1960. U.N. Day. Flags and inscr in blue and red.
886 **220** 30c. blue (postage) 10 10
887 75c. yellow 10 10
888 90c. mauve 10 10
889 3g. orange (air) 10 10
890 4g. green 10 10

221 Bridge with Arms of Brazil and Paraguay
222 Timber Truck

1961. Inauguration of International Bridge between Brazil and Paraguay.
891 **221** 15c. green (postage) 10 10
892 30c. blue 10 10
893 50c. orange 10 10
894 75c. blue 10 10
895 1g. violet 10 10
896 – 3g. red (air) 15 10
897 – 12g.45 lake 30 25
898 – 18g.15 green 35 30
899 – 36g. blue 75 25
DESIGN—HORIZ: Nos. 896/9, Aerial view of bridge.

1961. Paraguayan Progress. Inscr "PARAGUAY EN MARCHA".
900 **222** 25c. red & green (postage) 10 10
901 – 90c. yellow and blue 10 10
902 – 1g. red and orange 10 10
903 – 2g. green and pink 10 10
904 – 5g. violet and green 15 10
905 **222** 12g.45 blue and buff (air) 40 25
906 – 18g.15 violet and buff 55 35
907 – 22g. blue and orange 30 40
908 – 36g. yellow, green and blue 60 50
DESIGNS: 90c., 2g., 18g.15, Motorized timber barge; 1, 5, 22g. Radio mast; 36g. Boeing 707 jetliner.

223 P. J. Caballero, J. G. R. de Francia and F. Yegros
224 "Chaco Peace"

1961. 150th Anniv of Independence. (a) 1st issue.
909 **223** 30c. green (postage) 10 10
910 50c. mauve 10 10
911 90c. violet 10 10
912 1g.50 blue 10 10
913 3g. bistre 10 10
914 4g. blue 10 10
915 5g. brown 10 10
916 – 12g.45 red (air) 20 15
917 – 18g.15 blue 30 25
918 – 23g.40 green 40 30
919 – 30g. violet 45 35
920 – 36g. red 65 50
921 – 44g. brown 70 35
DESIGN: Nos. 916/21, Declaration of Independence.

(b) 2nd issue. Inscr "PAZ DEL CHACO".
922 **224** 25c. red (postage) 10 10
923 30c. green 10 10
924 50c. brown 10 10
925 1g. violet 10 10
926 2g. blue 10 10
927 – 3g. blue (air) 20 15
928 – 4g. purple 20 20
929 – 100g. green 1·40 1·00
DESIGN: Nos. 927/9, Clasped hands.

225 Puma
226 Arms of Paraguay

(c) 3rd issue.
930 **225** 75c. violet (postage) 10 10
931 1g.50 brown 10 10
932 4g.50 green 15 10
933 10g. blue 25 20
934 – 12g.45 purple (air) 90 40
935 – 18g.15 blue 1·25 75
936 – 34g.80 brown 2·25 1·25
DESIGN: Nos. 934/6, Brazilian tapir.

(d) 4th issue.
937 **226** 15c. blue (postage) 10 10
938 25c. red 10 10
939 75c. green 10 10
940 1g. red 10 10
941 3g. brown (air) 10 10
942 12g.45 mauve 25 25
943 36g. turquoise 65 30
The air stamps have a background pattern of horiz lines.

227 Grand Hotel, Guarani

(e) 5th issue.
944 **227** 50c. grey (postage) 10 10
945 1g. green 10 10
946 4g.50 violet 10 10
947 – 3g. brown (air) 10 10
948 – 4g. blue 10 10
949 – 18g.15 orange 40 35
950 – 36g. red 30 50
The air stamps are similar to Type **227** but inscr "HOTEL GUARANI" in upper left corner. See also Nos. 978/85 and 997/1011.

228 Racquet, Net and Balls

1961. 28th South American Tennis Championships, Asuncion (1st issue). Centres multicoloured; border colours given.
951 **228** 35c. pink (postage) 10 10
952 75c. yellow 10 10
953 1g.50 blue 10 10
954 2g.25 turquoise 10 10
955 4g. grey 15 10
956 12g.45 orange (air) 90 40
957 20g. orange 1·40 40
958 50g. orange 2·25 75
See also Nos. 978/85.

229

1961. "Europa".
959 **229** 50c. red, blue and mauve 10 10
960 75c. red, blue and green 10 10
961 1g. red, blue and brown 10 10
962 1g.50 red, blue & lt blue 10 10
963 4g.50 red, blue and yellow 20 20

230 Comm. Alan Shepard and Solar System
231

1961. Commander Shepard's Space Flight.
964 – 10c. brown and blue (postage) 10 10
965 – 25c. mauve and blue 10 10
966 – 50c. orange and blue 10 10
967 – 75c. green and blue 10 10
968 **230** 18g.15 blue and green (air) 4·00 3·00
969 36g. blue and orange 4·00 3·00
970 50g. blue and mauve 5·50 3·50
DESIGN—HORIZ: Nos. 964/7, Comm. Shepard.

1961. World Refugee Year (2nd issue).
971 **231** 10c. deep blue and blue (postage) 10 10
972 25c. purple and orange 10 10
973 50c. mauve and pink 10 10
974 75c. blue and green 10 10
975 – 18g.15 red and brown (air) 55 25
976 – 36g. green and red 1·25 55
977 – 50g. orange and green 1·50 1·10
Nos. 975/7 have a different background and frame.

232 Tennis-player
233 Scout Bugler

1962. 150th Anniv of Independence (6th issue) and 28th South American Tennis Championships, Asuncion (2nd issue).
978 **232** 35c. blue (postage) 10 10
979 75c. violet 10 10
980 1g.50 brown 10 10
981 2g.25 green 10 10
982 – 4g. red (air) 10 10
983 – 12g.45 purple 60 30
984 – 20g. turquoise 80 25
985 – 50g. brown 1·60 40
Nos. 982/5 show tennis-player using backhand stroke.

1962. Boy Scouts Commemoration.
986 **233** 10c. green & pur (postage) 10 10
987 20c. green and red 10 10
988 25c. green and brown 10 10
989 30c. green and emerald 10 10
990 50c. green and blue 10 10
991 – 12g.45 mauve & blue (air) 50 40
992 – 36g. mauve and green 1·50 90
993 – 50g. mauve and yellow 1·90 90
DESIGN: Nos. 991/3, Lord Baden-Powell.

234 Pres. Stroessner and the Duke of Edinburgh
235 Map of the Americas

1962. Air. Visit of Duke of Edinburgh.
994 **234** 12g.45 blue, buff & green 20 15
995 18g.15 blue, pink and red 30 25
996 36g. blue, yellow & brown 25 20

1962. 150th Anniv of Independence (7th issue) and Day of the Americas.
997 **235** 50c. orange (postage) 10 10
998 75c. blue 10 10
999 1g. violet 10 10
1000 1g.50 green 10 10
1001 4g.50 red 10 10
1002 – 20g. mauve (air) 30 20
1003 – 50g. orange 70 50
DESIGN: 20g., 50g. Hands supporting Globe.

236 U.N. Emblem

238 Football Stadium

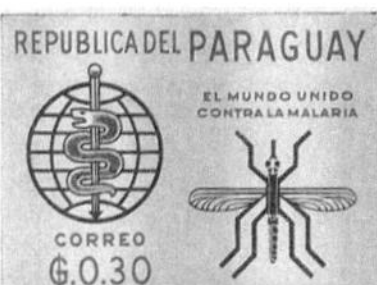

237 Mosquito and W.H.O. Emblem

1962. 150th Anniv of Independence (8th issue).
1004 **236** 50c. brown (postage) . . 10 10
1005 75c. purple 10 10
1006 1g. blue 10 10
1007 2g. brown 10 10
1008 – 12g.45 violet (air) . . . 35 35
1009 – 18g.15 green 25 25
1010 – 23g.40 red 35 35
1011 – 30g. red 80 65
DESIGN: Nos. 1008/11, U.N. Headquarters, New York.

1962. Malaria Eradication.
1012 **237** 30c. black, blue and pink (postage) 10 10
1013 50c. black, green & bistre 10 10
1014 – 75c. black, bistre and red 10 10
1015 – 1g. black, bistre and green 10 10
1016 – 1g.50 black, bistre & brown 10 10
1017 **237** 3g. black, red & blue (air) 10 10
1018 4g. black, red and green 10 10
1019 – 12g.45 black, grn & brn 25 10
1020 – 18g.15 black, red and purple 90 55
1021 – 36g. black, blue and red 1·25 85
DESIGN: Nos. 1014/16, 1019/21, Mosquito on U.N. emblem, and microscope.

1962. World Cup Football Championship, Chile.
1022 **238** 15c. brown & yell (postage) 10 10
1023 25c. brown and green . . 10 10
1024 30c. brown and violet . . 10 10
1025 40c. brown and orange 10 10
1026 50c. brown and green . . 10 10
1027 – 12g.45 black, red and violet (air) . . . . . 1·10 25
1028 – 18g.15 black, brn & vio 90 45
1029 – 36g. black, grey & brown 2·00 80
DESIGN—HORIZ: Nos. 1027/9, Footballers and Globe.

239 "Lago Ypoa" (freighter)

1962. Paraguayan Merchant Marine Commem.
1030 **239** 30c. brown (postage) . . 15 10
1031 – 90c. blue 20 10
1032 – 1g.50 purple 25 10
1033 – 2g. green 35 15
1034 – 4g.20 blue 50 20
1035 – 12g.45 red (air) 30 15
1036 – 44g. blue 30 45
DESIGNS—HORIZ: 90c. Freighter; 1g.50, "Olympo" (freighter); 2g. Freighter (diff); 4g.20, "Rio Apa" (freighter). VERT: 12g.45, 44g. Ship's wheel.

1962. As Nos. 631, etc, but with taller figures of value.
1037 **156** 50c. blue 10 10
1038 70c. lilac 10 10
1039 1g.50 violet 10 10
1040 3g. blue 10 10
1041 4g.50 brown 10 10
1042 5g. mauve 10 10
1043 10g. mauve 20 10
1044 12g.45 blue 20 10
1045 15g.45 red 25 10
1046 18g.15 purple 10 15
1047 20g. brown 10 15
1048 50g. brown 25 30
1049 100g. grey 90 30

241 Gen. A. Stroessner

242 Popes Paul VI, John XXIII and St. Peter's

1963. Re-election of Pres. Stroessner to Third Term of Office.
1050 **241** 50c. brown and drab (postage) 10 10
1051 75c. brown and pink . . 10 10
1052 1g.50 brown and mauve 10 10
1053 3g. brown and green . . 10 10
1054 12g.45 red and pink (air) 25 20
1055 18g.15 green and pink 65 30
1056 36g. violet and pink . . 85 40

1964. Popes Paul VI and John XXIII.
1057 **242** 1g.50 yellow and red (postage) 10 10
1058 3g. green and red . . . 10 10
1059 4g. brown and red . . . 10 10
1060 – 12g.45 olive & grn (air) 35 20
1061 – 18g.15 green and violet 45 30
1062 – 36g. green and blue . . . 1·25 60
DESIGNS: Nos. 1060/2, Cathedral, Asuncion.

243 Arms of Paraguay and France

245 Map of the Americas

1964. Visit of French President.
1063 **243** 1g.50 brown (postage) 10 10
1064 – 3g. blue 40 10
1065 **243** 4g. grey 10 10
1066 – 12g.45 violet (air) . . . 25 20
1067 **243** 18g.15 green 70 30
1068 – 36g. red . . . . 1·25 60
DESIGNS: 3, 12g.45, 36g. Presidents Stroessner and De Gaulle.

1965. 6th Reunion of the Board of Governors of the Inter-American Development Bank. Optd **Centenario de la Epopeya Nacional 1,864–1,870** as in T **245**.
1069 **245** 1g.50 green (postage) . . 10 10
1070 3g. pink 10 10
1071 4g. blue 10 10
1072 12g.45 brown (air) . . . 20 10
1073 36g. violet 65 45

The overprint refers to the National Epic of 1864–70, the war with Argentina, Brazil and Uruguay and this inscription occurs on many other issues from 1965 onwards.

Nos. 1069/73 without the overprint were not authorized.

246 R. Gonzalez and St. Ignatius

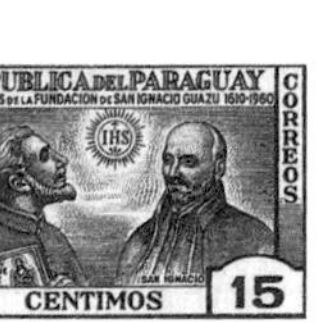

247 Ruben Dario

1966. 350th Anniv of Founding of San Ignacio Guazu Monastery.
1074 **246** 15c. blue (postage) . . . 10 10
1075 25c. blue 10 10
1076 75c. blue 10 10
1077 90c. blue 10 10
1078 – 3g. brown (air) 10 10
1079 – 12g.45 brown 10 10
1080 – 18g.15 brown 20 10
1081 – 23g.40 brown 35 25
DESIGNS: Nos. 1078/81, Jesuit Fathers' house, Antigua.

For similar stamps with different inscriptions, see Nos. 822, 824 and 826.

1966. 50th Death Anniv of Ruben Dario (poet).
1082 **247** 50c. blue 10 10
1083 70c. brown 10 10
1084 1g.50 lake 10 10
1085 3g. violet 10 10
1086 4g. turquoise 10 10
1087 5g. black 10 10
1088 – 12g.45 blue (air) 10 10
1089 – 18g.15 violet 10 10
1090 – 23g.40 brown 35 10
1091 – 36g. green 65 25
1092 – 50g. red 75 25
DESIGNS: Nos. 1088/92, Open book inscr "Paraguay de Fuego ..." by Dario.

248 Lions' Emblem on Globe

249 W.H.O. Emblem

1967. 50th Anniv of Lions International.
1093 **248** 50c. violet (postage) . . 10 10
1094 70c. blue 10 10
1095 – 1g.50 blue 10 10
1096 – 3g. brown 10 10
1097 – 4g. blue 10 10
1098 – 5g. brown 10 10
1099 – 12g.45 brown (air) . . . 10 10
1100 – 18g.15 violet 15 10
1101 – 23g.40 purple 20 10
1102 – 36g. blue 25 25
1103 – 50g. red 25 25
DESIGNS—VERT: 1g.50, 3g. M. Jones; 4, 5g. Lions headquarters, Chicago. HORIZ: 12g.45, 18g.15, Library–"Education"; 23g.40, 36g., 50g. Medical laboratory–"Health".

1968. 20th Anniv of W.H.O.
1104 **249** 3g. turquoise (postage) 10 10
1105 4g. purple 10 10
1106 5g. brown 10 10
1107 10g. violet 10 10
1108 – 36g. brown (air) 40 25
1109 – 50g. red 45 30
1110 – 100g. blue 60 35
DESIGN—VERT: Nos. 1108/10, W.H.O. emblem on scroll.

250

251

1969. World Friendship Week.
1111 **250** 50c. red 10 10
1112 70c. blue 10 10
1113 1g.50 brown 10 10
1114 3g. mauve 10 10
1115 4g. green 10 10
1116 5g. violet 10 10
1117 10g. purple 20 10

1969. Air. Campaign for Houses for Teachers.
1118 **251** 36g. blue 40 20
1119 50g. brown 75 30
1120 100g. red . . . . 1·40 50

252 Pres. Lopez

253 Paraguay 2r. Stamp of 1870

1970. Death Centenary of Pres. F. Solano Lopez.
1121 **252** 1g. brown (postage) . . 10 10
1122 2g. violet 10 10
1123 3g. pink 10 10
1124 4g. red 10 10
1125 5g. blue 10 10
1126 10g. green 10 10
1127 15g. blue (air) 10 10
1128 20g. brown 20 10
1129 30g. green 55 20
1130 40g. purple 60 25

1970. Centenary of First Paraguayan Stamps.
1131 **253** 1g. red (postage) 10 10
1132 A 2g. blue 10 10
1133 B 3g. brown 10 10
1134 **253** 5g. violet 10 10
1135 A 10g. lilac 20 10
1136 B 15g. purple (air) 65 25
1137 **253** 30g. green 80 50
1138 A 36g. red 90 30
DESIGNS: First Paraguay stamps. A, 1r.; B, 3r.

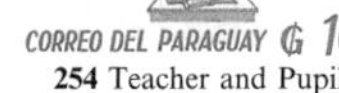

254 Teacher and Pupil

255 UNICEF Emblem

1971. International Education Year–UNESCO.
1139 **254** 3g. blue (postage) . . . 10 10
1140 5g. lilac 10 10
1141 10g. green 10 10
1142 20g. red (air) 20 10
1143 25g. mauve 25 15
1144 30g. brown 25 20
1145 50g. green 40 35

1972. 25th Anniv of UNICEF.
1146 **255** 1g. brown (postage) . . 10 10
1147 2g. blue 10 10
1148 3g. red 10 10
1149 4g. purple 10 10
1150 5g. green 10 10
1151 10g. purple 10 10
1152 20g. blue (air) 20 10
1153 25g. green 25 15
1154 30g. brown 25 20

256 Acaray Dam

1972. Tourist Year of the Americans.
1155 **256** 1g. brown (postage) . . 10 10
1156 – 2g. brown 10 10
1157 – 3g. blue 10 10
1158 – 5g. red 10 10
1159 – 10g. green 10 10
1160 – 20g. red (air) 25 10
1161 – 25g. grey 30 15
1162 – 50g. lilac . . . . 1·40 45
1163 – 100g. mauve 80 40
DESIGNS: 2g. Statue of Lopez; 3g. Friendship Bridge; 5g. Rio Tebicuary Bridge; 10g. Grand Hotel, Guarani; 20g. Motor coach; 25g. Social Service Institute Hospital; 50g. Liner "Presidente Stroessner"; 100g. Lockheed Electra airliner.

257 O.E.A. Emblem

1973. 25th Anniv of Organization of American States (O.E.A.).
1164 **257** 1g. mult (postage) . . . 10 10
1165 2g. multicoloured . . . 10 10
1166 3g. multicoloured . . . 10 10
1167 4g. multicoloured . . . 10 10
1168 5g. multicoloured . . . 10 10
1169 10g. multicoloured . . . 10 10
1170 20g. multicoloured (air) 20 10
1171 25g. multicoloured . . . 30 15
1172 50g. multicoloured . . . 25 35
1173 100g. multicoloured . . 1·00 40

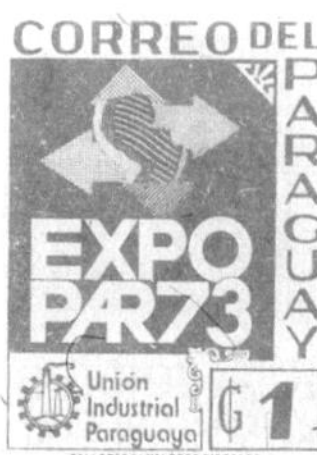

258 Exhibition Emblem

1973. International Industrial Exhibition, Paraguay.
1174 **258** 1g. brown (postage) . . 10 10
1175 2g. red 10 10
1176 3g. blue 10 10
1177 4g. green 10 10
1178 5g. lilac 10 10
1179 20g. mauve (air) 20 10
1180 25g. red 25 10

259 Carrier Pigeon with Letter

1975. Centenary of U.P.U.
1181 **259** 1g. violet & blk (postage) 10 10
1182 2g. red and black . . . 10 10
1183 3g. blue and black . . . 10 10
1184 5g. blue and black . . . 10 10
1185 10g. purple and black . . 10 10

1186 20g. brown & black (air) . . 25 15
1187 25g. green and black . . 30 20

260 Institute Buildings

1976. Inauguration (1974) of Institute of Higher Education.
1188 **260** 5g. violet, red and black (postage) 10 10
1189 10g. blue, red and black 10 10
1190 30g. brn, red & blk (air) 25 15

261 Rotary Emblem

1976. 70th Anniv of Rotary International.
1191 **261** 3g. blue, bistre and black (postage) 10 10
1192 4g. blue, bistre and mauve 10 10
1193 25g. blue, bistre and green (air) 30 15

262 Woman and I.W.Y. Emblem

1976. International Women's Year.
1194 **262** 1g. brown & blue (postage) 10 10
1195 2g. brown and red . . . 10 10
1196 20g. brown & green (air) 25 10

263 Black Palms

1977. Flowering Plants and Trees. Multicoloured.
1197 2g. Type **263** (postage) . . . 10 10
1198 3g. Mburucuya flowers . . . 10 10
1199 20g. Marsh rose (tree) (air) 35 25

264 Nanduti Lace

1977. Multicoloured.
1200 1g. Type **264** (postage) . . . 10 10
1201 5g. Nanduti weaver 10 10
1202 25g. Lady holding jar (air) 40 25

265 F. S. Lopez

1977. 150th Birth Anniv of Marshal Francisco Solano Lopez.
1203 **265** 10g. brown (postage) . . 10 10
1204 50g. blue (air) 40 50
1205 100g. green 75 60

266 General Bernardino Caballero National College

1978. Cent of National College of Asuncion.
1206 **266** 3g. red (postage) 10 10
1207 4g. blue 10 10
1208 5g. violet 10 10
1209 20g. brown (air) 20 15
1210 25g. purple 25 20
1211 30g. green 35 25

267 Marshal Jose F. Estigarribia, Trumpeter and Flag

268 Congress Emblem

1978. "Salon de Bronce" Commemoration.
1212 **267** 3g. purple, blue and red (postage) 10 10
1213 5g. violet, blue and red 10 10
1214 10g. grey, blue and red 10 10
1215 20g. green, bl & red (air) 25 15
1216 25g. violet, blue and red 30 20
1217 30g. purple, blue and red 35 25

1979. 22nd Latin American Tourism Congress, Asuncion.
1218 **268** 10g. black, blue and red (postage) 10 10
1219 50g. black, blue and red (air) 30 40

269 Spanish Colonial House, Pilar

1980. Bicentenary of Pilar City.
1220 **269** 5g. mult (postage) . . . 10 10
1221 25g. multicoloured (air) 30 20

270 Boeing 707

1980. Inauguration of Paraguayan Airlines Boeing 707 Service.
1222 **270** 20g. mult (postage) . . . 30 10
1223 100g. multicoloured (air) 1·40 70

271 Seminary, Communion Cup and Bible

1981. Air. Centenary of Metropolitan Seminary, Asuncion.
1224 **271** 5g. blue 10 10
1225 10g. brown 10 10
1226 25g. green 30 20
1227 50g. black 60 40

272 U.P.U. Monument, Berne

1981. Centenary of Admission to U.P.U.
1228 **272** 5g. red and black (postage) 10 10
1229 10g. mauve and black . . 10 10
1230 20g. green and black (air) 50 15
1231 25g. red and black . . . 60 20
1232 50g. blue and black . . . 60 40

273 St. Maria Mazzarello

275 Sun and Map of Americas

274 Stroessner and Bridge over River Itaipua

1981. Air. Death Centenary of Mother Maria Mazzarello (founder of Daughters of Mary).
1233 **273** 20g. green and black . . 50 15
1234 25g. red and black . . . 60 20
1235 50g. violet and black . . 60 40

1983. 25th Anniv of President Stroessner City.
1236 **274** 3g. green, blue & blk (postage) 10 10
1237 5g. red, blue and black 10 10
1238 10g. violet, blue and black 10 10
1239 20g. grey, blue & blk (air) 25 15
1240 25g. purple, blue & black 30 20
1241 50g. blue, grey and black 30 40

1985. Air. 25th Anniv of Inter-American Development Bank.
1242 **275** 3g. orange, yellow & pink 10 10
1243 5g. orange, yellow & mauve 10 10
1244 10g. orange, yellow & mauve 10 10
1245 50g. orange, yellow & brown 10 10
1246 65g. orange, yellow & bl 15 10
1247 95g. orange, yellow & green 20 15

276 U.N. Emblem

277 1886 1c. Stamp

1986. Air. 40th Anniv of U.N.O.
1248 **276** 5g. blue and brown . . . 10 10
1249 10g. blue and grey . . . 10 10
1250 50g. blue and black . . . 10 10

1986. Centenary of First Official Stamp.
1251 **277** 5g. deep blue, brown and blue (postage) 10 10
1252 15g. deep blue, brown and blue 10 10
1253 40g. deep blue, brown and blue 10 10
1254 – 65g. blue, green and red (air) 15 15
1255 – 100g. blue, green and red 50 25
1256 – 150g. blue, green and red 70 40
DESIGNS: 65, 100, 150g. 1886 7c. stamp.

278 Integration of the Nations Monument, Colmena

1986. Air. 50th Anniv of Japanese Immigration. Multicoloured.
1257 5g. La Colmena vineyards (horiz) 10 10
1258 10g. Flowers of cherry tree and lapacho (horiz) . . . 10 10
1259 20g. Type **278** 10 10

279 Caballero, Stroessner and Road

1987. Centenary of National Republican Association (Colorado Party).
1260 **279** 5g. multicoloured (postage) 10 10
1261 10g. multicoloured . . . 10 10
1262 25g. multicoloured . . . 10 10
1263 – 150g. multicoloured (air) 25 40
1264 – 170g. multicoloured . . 55 20
1265 – 200g. multicoloured . . 60 25
DESIGN: 150 to 200g. Gen. Bernardino Caballero (President 1881–86 and founder of party), Pres. Alfredo Stroessner and electrification of countryside.

280 Emblem of Visit

281 Silver Mate

1988. Visit of Pope John Paul II.
1266 **280** 10g. blue and black (postage) 10 10
1267 20g. blue and black . . . 10 10
1268 50g. blue and black . . . 15 10
1269 – 100g. multicoloured (air) 55 20
1270 – 120g. multicoloured . . 65 25
1271 – 150g. multicoloured . . 80 35
DESIGN—HORIZ: 100 to 150g. Pope and Caacupe Basilica.

1988. Air. Centenary of New Germany Colony. Multicoloured.
1272 90g. Type **281** 25 10
1273 105g. Mate ("Ilex paraguayensis") plantation 30 20
1274 120g. As No. 1273 . . . . 35 25

1988. Air. 75th Anniv of Paraguay Philatelic Centre. No. 1249 optd * **75o ANIVERSARIO DE FUNDACION CENTRO FILATELICO DEL PARAGUAY 15 JUNIO-1913 - 1988.**
1275 **276** 10g. blue and grey . . . 10 10

283 Pres. Stroessner and Government Palace

1988. Air. Re-election of President Stroessner.
1276 **283** 200g. multicoloured . . 55 25
1277 500g. multicoloured . . 1·40 90
1278 1000g. multicoloured . . 2·75 1·50

1989. "Parafil 89" Stamp Exhibition. Nos. 1268 and 1270 optd **PARAFIL 89**.
1279 **280** 50g. blue and black (postage) 15 10
1280 – 120g. multicoloured (air) 35 25

285 Green-winged Macaw

1989. Birds. Multicoloured.
1281 50g. Type **285** (postage) . . 20 20
1282 100g. Brazilian merganser (horiz) (air) 20 20
1283 300g. Greater rhea (horiz) 60 60
1284 500g. Toco toucan (horiz) 95 95
1285 1000g. Bare-faced curassow (horiz) . . . . 2·10 2·10
1286 2000g. Wagler's macaw and blue and yellow macaw 4·00 4·00

286 Anniversary Emblem

1990. Centenary of Organization of American States. Multicoloured.
1287 50g. Type **286** 10 10
1288 100g. Organization and anniversary emblems (vert) 10 10
1289 200g. Map of Paraguay . . 45 15

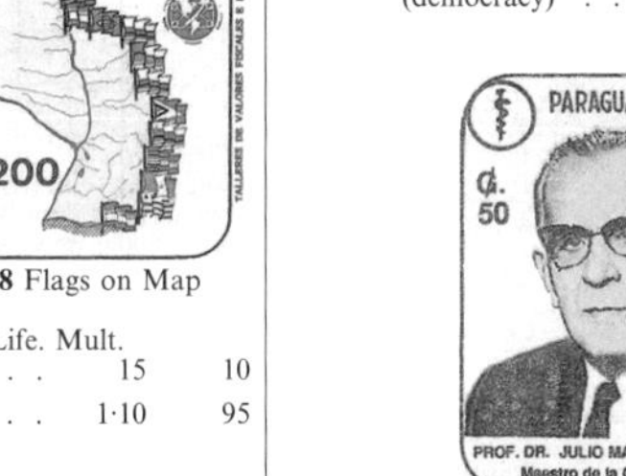

287 Basket **288** Flags on Map

1990. America. Pre-Columbian Life. Mult.
1290 150g. Type **287** (postage) . . 15 10
1291 500g. Guarani post (air) . . 1·10 95

1990. Postal Union of the Americas and Spain Colloquium. Multicoloured.
1292 200g. Type **288** 20 15
1293 250g. First Paraguay stamp 25 15
1294 350g. Paraguay 1990 America first day cover (horiz) 35 25

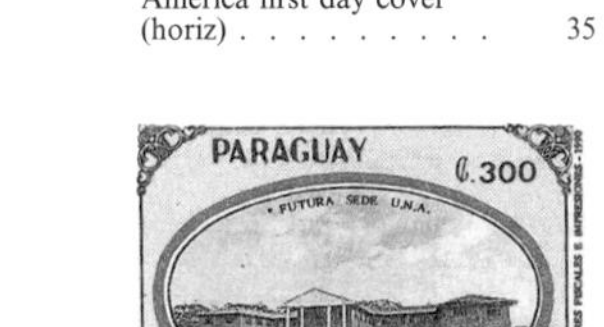

289 Planned Building

1990. Centenary of National University. Mult.
1295 300g. Type **289** 70 55
1296 400g. Present building . . . 95 75
1297 600g. Old building . . . . 1·40 1·10

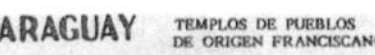

290 Guarambare Church

1990. Franciscan Churches. Multicoloured.
1298 50g. Type **290** 10 10
1299 100g. Yaguaron Church . . 25 20
1300 200g. Ita Church 45 35

1991. Visit of King and Queen of Spain. Nos. 1290/1 optd **Vista de sus Majestades Los Reyes de Espana 22-24 Octubre 1990.**
1301 **287** 150g. mult (postage) . . 15 10
1302 – 500g. multicoloured (air) 1·10 95

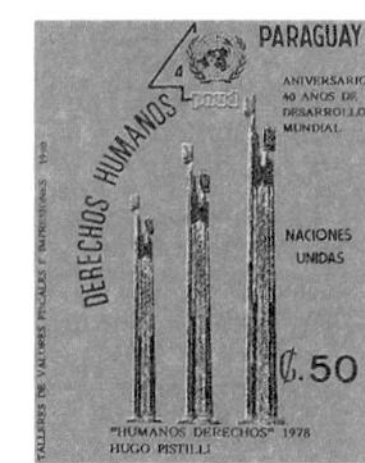

292 "Human Rights" (Hugo Pistilli)

1991. 40th Anniv of United Nations Development Programme. Multicoloured.
1303 50g. Type **292** 10 10
1304 100g. "United Nations" (sculpture, Hermann Guggiari) 10 20
1305 150f. First Miguel de Cervantes prize, awarded to Augusto Roa Bastos, 1989 . . . . 15 10

294 Hands and Ballot Box (free elections)

1991. Democracy. Multicoloured.
1308 50g. Type **294** (postage) . . 10 10
1309 100g. Sun (State and Catholic Church) (vert) 10 10
1310 200g. Arrows and male and female symbols (human rights) (vert) 55 10
1311 300g. Dove and flag (freedom of the press) (vert) (air) 50 20
1312 500g. Woman and child welcoming man (return of exiles) 70 25
1313 3000g. Crowd with banners (democracy) . . . . . . 4·75 2·75

295 Julio Manuel Morales (gynaecologist)

1991. Medical Professors.
1314 **295** 50g. mult (postage) . . . 10 10
1315 – 100g. multicoloured . . 10 10
1316 – 200g. multicoloured . . 50 10
1317 – 300g. brown, black & green 70 20
1318 – 350g. brown, black and green (air) 75 20
1319 – 500g. multicoloured . . 1·10 50
DESIGNS: 100g. Carlos Gatti (surgeon); 200g. Gustavo Gonzalez (symptomatologist); 300g. Juan Max Boettner (physician and musician); 350g. Juan Boggino (pathologist); 500g. Andres Barbero (founder of Paraguayan Red Cross).

1991. "Espamer '91" Spain–Latin America Stamp Exhibition, Buenos Aires. Nos. 1298/1300 optd **ESPAMER 91 BUENOS AIRES 5 14 Jul** and Conquistador in oval.
1323 50g. multicoloured 10 10
1324 100g. multicoloured 10 10
1325 200g. multicoloured 60 10

298 Ruy Diaz de Guzman (historian)

1991. Writers and Musicians. Multicoloured.
1326 50g. Type **298** (postage) . . 10 10
1327 100g. Maria Talavera (war chronicler) (vert) 10 10
1328 150g. Augusto Roa Bastos (writer and 1989 winner of Miguel de Cervantes Prize) (vert) 40 10
1329 200g. Jose Asuncion Flores (composer of "La Guarania") (vert) (air) . . 45 10
1330 250g. Felix Perez Cardozo (harpist and composer) . . 65 40
1331 300g. Juan Carlos Moreno Gonzalez (composer) . . 85 45

299 Battle of Tavare

1991. America. Voyages of Discovery. Mult.
1332 100g. Type **299** (postage) . . 10 10
1333 300g. Arrival of Domingo Martinez de Irala in Paraguay (air) 75 50

300 "Compass of Life" (Alfredo Moraes)

1991. Paintings. Multicoloured.
1334 50g. Type **300** (postage) . . 10 10
1335 100g. "Callejon Illuminated" (Michael Burt) 35 10
1336 150g. "Arete" (Lucy Yegros) 45 10
1337 200g. "Itinerants" (Hugo Bogado Barrios) (air) . . 50 10
1338 250g. "Travellers without a Ship" (Bernardo Ismachoviez) 65 15
1339 300g. "Guarani" (Lotte Schulz) 75 50

301 Chaco Peccary

1992. Endangered Mammals. Multicoloured.
1340 50g. Type **301** 10 10
1341 100g. Ocelot (horiz) 10 10
1342 150g. Brazilian tapir 35 10
1343 200g. Maned wolf 40 10

302 Geometric Design, Franciscan Church, Caazapa

1992. 500th Anniv of Discovery of America by Columbus (1st series). Church Roof Tiles. Mult.
1344 50g. Type **302** 10 10
1345 100g. Church, Jesuit church, Trinidad 10 10
1346 150g. Missionary ship, Jesuit church, Trinidad 50 10
1347 200g. Plant, Franciscan church, Caazapa 50 10
See also Nos. 1367/71.

1992. "Granada '92" International Thematic Stamp Exhibition. Nos. 1344/7 optd **GRANADA '92** and emblem.
1348 50g. multicoloured 10 10
1349 100g. multicoloured 10 10
1350 150g. multicoloured 40 10
1351 200g. multicoloured 50 10

304 Malcolm L. Norment (founder) and Emblem

1992. 68th Anniv of Paraguay Leprosy Foundation. Multicoloured.
1352 50g. Type **304** 10 10
1353 250g. Gerhard Hansen (discoverer of leprosy bacillus) 50 15

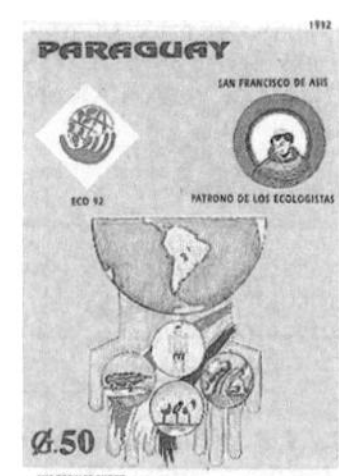

305 Southern Hemisphere and Ecology Symbols on Hands

1992. 2nd United Nations Conference on Environment and Development, Rio de Janeiro. Multicoloured.
1354 50g. Type **305** 10 10
1355 100g. Butterfly and chimneys emitting smoke 10 10
1356 250g. Tree and map of South America on globe 45 15

306 Factories and Cotton (economy)

1992. National Population and Housing Census. Multicoloured.
1357 50g. Type **306** 10 10
1358 200g. Houses (vert) 15 10
1359 250g. Numbers and stylized people (population) (vert) 20 15
1360 300g. Abacus (education) . . 50 20

307 Football

1992. Olympic Games, Barcelona. Multicoloured.
1361 50g. Type **307** 10 10
1362 100g. Tennis 10 10
1363 150g. Running 10 10
1364 200g. Swimming (horiz) . . 15 10
1365 250g. Judo 20 15
1366 350g. Fencing (horiz) . . . 50 20

308 Brother Luis Bolanos

1992. 500th Anniv of Discovery of America by Columbus (2nd series). Evangelists. Mult.
1367 50g. Type **308** (translator of Catechism into Guarani and founder of Guarani Christian settlements) . . 10 10
1368 100g. Brother Juan de San Bernardo (Franciscan and first Paraguayan martyr) 10 10
1369 150g. St. Roque Gonzalez de Santa Cruz (Jesuit missionary and first Paraguayan saint) 10 10

1370 200g. Fr. Amancio Gonzalez (founder of Melodia settlement) 15 10
1371 250g. Mgr. Juan Sinforiano Bogarin (first Archbishop of Asuncion) (vert) . . . 45 15

309 Fleet approaching Shore

1992. America. 500th Anniv of Discovery of America by Columbus. Multicoloured.
1372 150g. Type **309** (postage) . . 30 10
1373 350g. Christopher Columbus (vert) (air) 50 20

1992. 30th Anniv of United Nations Information Centre in Paraguay. Nos. 1354/6 optd **NACIONES UNIDAS 1992 - 30 AÑOS CENTRO INFORMACION OUN EN PARAGUAY**.
1374 50g. multicoloured 10 10
1375 100g. multicoloured 10 10
1376 250g. multicoloured 45 15

1992. Christmas. Nos. 1367/9 optd **Navidad 92**.
1377 50g. multicoloured 10 10
1378 100g. multicoloured 10 10
1379 150g. multicoloured 35 10

1992. "Parafil 92" Paraguay–Argentina Stamp Exhibition, Buenos Aires. Nos. 1372/3 optd **PARAFIL 92**.
1380 150g. multicoloured (postage) 35 10
1381 350g. multicoloured (air) . . 50 20

313 Planting and Hoeing

1992. 50th Anniv of Pan-American Agricultural Institute. Multicoloured.
1382 50g. Type **313** 10 10
1383 100g. Test tubes 10 10
1384 200g. Cotton plant in cupped hands 15 10
1385 250g. Cattle and maize plant 45 15

314 Yolanda Bado de Artecona

1992. Centenary of Paraguayan Writers' College. Multicoloured.
1386 50g. Type **314** 10 10
1387 100g. Jose Ramon Silva . . 10 10
1388 150g. Abelardo Brugada Valpy 10 10
1389 200g. Tomas Varela 15 10
1390 250g. Jose Livio Lezcano . . 45 15
1391 300g. Francisco I. Fernandez 50 20

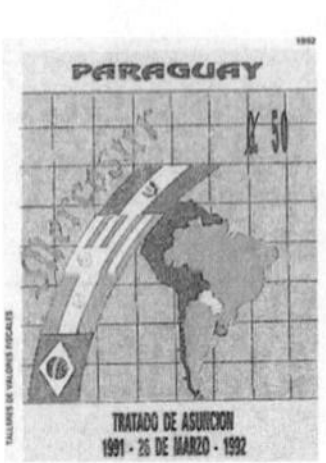

315 Members' Flags and Map of South America
316 Orange Flowers (Gilda Hellmers)

1993. 1st Anniv (1992) of Treaty of Asuncion forming Mercosur (common market of Argentina, Brazil, Paraguay and Uruguay). Multicoloured.
1392 50g. Type **315** 10 10
1393 350g. Flags encircling globe showing map of South America 65 20

1993. 50th Anniv of St. Isabel Leprosy Association. Flower paintings by artists named. Multicoloured.
1394 50g. Type **316** 10 10
1395 200g. Luis Alberto Balmelli 15 10
1396 250g. Lili del Monico . . . 20 15
1397 350g. Brunilde Guggiari . . 50 20

317 Goethe (after J. Lips) and Manuscript of Poem

1993. Centenary of Goethe College.
1398 **317** 50g. brown, black & blue 10 10
1399 – 200g. multicoloured . . 40 10
DESIGN: 200g. Goethe (after J. Tischbein).

1993. "Brasiliana 93" International Stamp Exhibition, Rio de Janeiro. Nos. 1398/9 optd **BRASILIANA 93**.
1400 50g. brown, black and blue 10 10
1401 200g. multicoloured 15 10

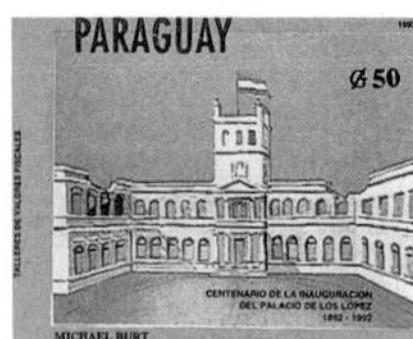

319 Palace (Michael Burt)

1993. Centenary (1992) of Los Lopez (Government) Palace, Asuncion. Paintings of palace by artists named. Multicolured.
1402 50g. Type **319** 10 10
1403 100g. Esperanza Gill 10 10
1404 200g. Emili Aparici 15 10
1405 250g. Hugo Bogado Barrios (vert) 15 10

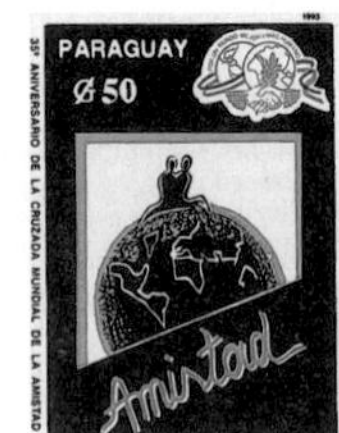

320 Couple sitting on Globe and Emblem

1993. 35th Anniv of World Friendship Crusade.
1406 **320** 50g. black, blue and mauve 10 10
1407 – 100g. multicoloured . . 10 10
1408 – 200g. multicoloured . . 15 10
1409 – 250g. multicoloured . . 15 10
DESIGNS: 100g. Dr. Ramon Artemio Bracho (founder), map of Americas and emblem; 200g. Children and sun emerging from cloud; 250g. Couple hugging and emblem.

1993. Inauguration of President Juan Carlos Wasmosy. Nos. 1402/5 optd **TRANSMISION DEL MANDO PRESIDENCIAL GRAL. ANDRES RODRIGUEZ ING. JUAN C. WASMOSY 15 DE AGOSTO 1993**.
1410 50g. multicoloured 10 10
1411 100g. multicoloured 10 10
1412 200g. multicoloured 15 10
1413 250g. multicoloured 15 10

322 "Church of the Incarnation" (Juan Guerra Gaja)

1993. Centenary of Church of the Incarnation. Paintings. Multicoloured.
1414 50g. Type **322** 10 10
1415 350g. "Church of the Incarnation" (Hector Blas Ruiz) (horiz) 25 20

323 Bush Dog

1993. America. Endangered Animals. Mult.
1416 250g. Type **323** (postage) . . 40 10
1417 50g. Great anteater (air) . . 10 10

1993. 80th Anniv of World Food Programme. Nos. 1383/4 optd **'30 ANOS DEL PROGRAMA MUNDIAL DE ALIMENTOS'** and emblem.
1418 100g. multicoloured 10 10
1419 200g. multicoloured 15 10

325 Children Carol-singing

1993. Christmas. Multicoloured.
1420 50g. Type **325** 10 10
1421 250g. Wise men following star 15 10

326 Boy and Girl Scouts

1993. 80th Anniv of Paraguay Scouts Association. Multicoloured.
1422 50g. Type **326** 10 10
1423 100g. Boy scouts in camp 10 10
1424 200g. Lord Robert Baden-Powell (founder of Scouting movement) . . . 15 10
1425 250g. Girl scout with flag 15 10

327 Cecilio Baez

1994. Centenary of First Graduation of Lawyers from National University, Asuncion.
1426 **327** 50g. red and crimson . . 10 10
1427 – 100g. yellow and orange 10 10
1428 – 250g. yellow and green 15 10
1429 – 500g. blue and deep blue 30 20
DESIGNS—VERT: 100g. Benigno Riquelme. HORIZ: 250g. Emeterio Gonzalez; 500g. J. Gaspar Villamayor.

328 Basketball
329 Penalty Kick

1994. 50th Anniv of Phoenix Sports Association. Multicoloured.
1430 50g. Type **328** 10 10
1431 200g. Football 15 10
1432 250g. Pedro Andres Garcia Arias (founder) and tennis (horiz) 15 10

1994. World Cup Football Championship, U.S.A. Multicoloured.
1433 250g. Type **329** 15 10
1434 500g. Tackle 55 20
1435 1000g. Dribbling ball past opponent . . . . 1·10 75

330 Runner

1994. Centenary of International Olympic Committee. Multicoloured.
1436 350g. Type **330** 25 20
1437 400g. Athlete lighting Olympic Flame 55 20

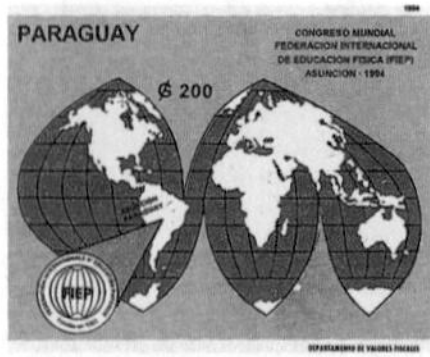

331 World Map and Emblem

1994. World Congress of International Federation for Physical Education, Asuncion. Multicoloured.
1438 200g. Type **331** 15 10
1439 1000g. Family exercising and flag (vert) . . . . . 1·25 80

1994. Brazil, Winners of World Cup Football Championship. Nos. 1433/5 optd **BRASIL Campeon Mundial de Futbol Estados Unidos '94**.
1440 250g. multicoloured 40 10
1441 500g. multicoloured 80 50
1442 1000g. multicoloured . . . 1·60 95

1994. 25th Anniv of First Manned Moon Landing. No. 1407 optd **25 Anos, Conquista de la Luna por el hombre 1969 - 1994**.
1443 100g. multicoloured 10 10

334 Barrios

1994. 50th Death Anniv of Agustin Pio Barrios Mangore (guitarist). Multicoloured.
1444 250g. Type **334** 15 10
1445 500g. Barrios wearing casual clothes and a hat 65 20

335 Police Commandant, 1913

1994. 151st Anniv of Police Force. Multicoloured.
1446 50g. Type **335** 10 10
1447 250g. Carlos Bernardino Cacabelos (first Commissioner) and Pedro Nolasco Fernandez (first Chief of Asuncion Police Dept) 15 10

336 Maguari Stork

1994. "Parafil 94" Stamp Exhibition. Birds. Mult.
1448 100g. Type **336** 35 35
1449 150g. Yellow-billed cardinal 35 35
1450 400g. Green kingfisher (vert) 2·00 75
1451 500g. Jabiru (vert) . . . . . 2·25 75

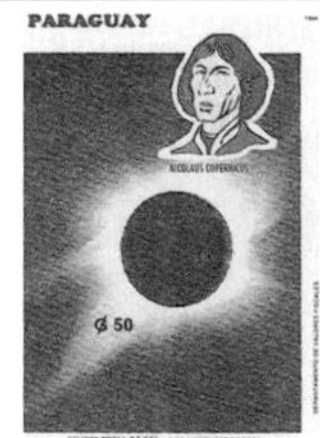

337 Nicolas Copernicus and Eclipse

1994. Total Eclipse of the Sun, November 1994. Astronomers. Multicoloured.
1452 50g. Type **337** 10 10
1453 200g. Johannes Kepler and sun dial, St. Cosmas and Damian Jesuit settlement 15 10

338 Steam Locomotive

1994. America. Postal Transport. Multicoloured.
1454 100g. Type **338** . . . . . . 1·00 60
1455 1000g. Express mail motor cycle . . . . 1·25 80

339 Mother and Child

1994. International Year of the Family. Details of paintings by Olga Blinder. Multicoloured.
1456 50g. Type **339** 10 10
1457 250g. Mother and children 15 10

340 Holy Family and Angels

1994. Christmas. Ceramic Figures. Multicoloured.
1458 150g. Type **340** 10 10
1459 700g. Holy Family (vert) . . 80 55

341 Red Cross Workers and Dr. Andres Barbero (founder)

1994. 75th Anniv of Paraguay Red Cross. Mult.
1460 150g. Scouts, anniversary emblem and Henri Dunant (founder of International Red Cross) 10 10
1461 700g. Type **341** 80 55

342 Sculpture by Herman Guggiari and Pope John Paul II

1994. 90th Anniv of San Jose College. Mult.
1462 200g. Type **342** 15 10
1463 250g. College entrance and Pope John Paul II 15 10

343 Pasteur and Hospital Facade

1995. Paraguayan Red Cross. Death Centenary of Louis Pasteur (chemist) and Centenary of Clinical Hospital.
1464 **343** 1000g. multicoloured . . 1·10 75

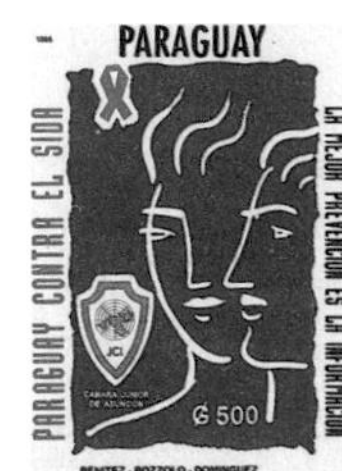

344 Couple

1995. Anti-AIDS Campaign. Multicoloured.
1465 500g. Type **344** 60 20
1466 1000g. Sad and happy blood droplets . . . . 1·00 50

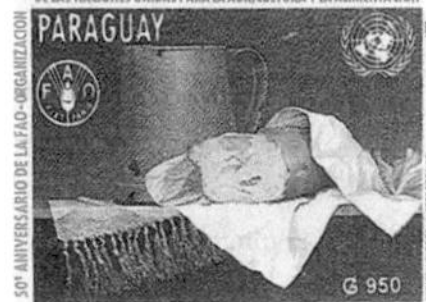

345 Jug and Loaf

1995. 50th Anniv of F.A.O. Paintings by Hernan Miranda. Multicoloured.
1467 950g. Type **345** . . . . . . 1·00 75
1468 2000g. Melon and leaf . . . 2·10 1·40

346 Olive-backed Warbler

1995. 5th Neo-tropical Ornithological Congress, Asuncion. Multicoloured.
1469 100g. Type **346** 10 10
1470 200g. Swallow-tailed manakin 15 10
1471 600g. Troupial 65 30
1472 1000g. Hooded siskin . . . 1·00 75

347 River Monday Rapids

348 "100"

1995. 5th International Town, Ecology and Tourism Symposium. Multicoloured.
1473 1150g. Type **347** . . . . . 1·25 85
1474 1300g. Aregua railway station . . . . 4·50 2·75

1995. Centenary of Volleyball.
1475 **348** 300g. multicoloured . . 20 15
1476 – 600g. blue and black . . 40 30
1477 – 1000g. multicoloured . . 1·00 75
DESIGNS: 600g. Ball hitting net; 1000g. Hands, ball and net.

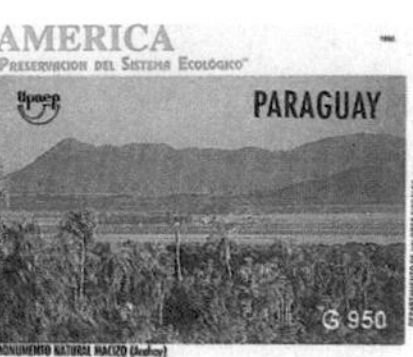

349 Macizo, Acahay

1995. America. Environmental Protection. Mult.
1478 950g. Type **349** 85 45
1479 2000g. Tinfunque Reserve, Chaco (vert) . . . . . . 1·60 1·00

350 Anniversary Emblem

1995. 50th Anniv of U.N.O. Multicoloured.
1480 200g. Type **350** 15 10
1481 3000g. Stylized figures supporting emblem . . . 3·25 2·00

351 Couple holding Star

1995. Christmas. Multicoloured.
1482 200g. Type **351** 15 10
1483 1000g. Crib 95 50

352 Marti and "Hedychium coronarium"

1995. Birth Cent of Jose Marti (revolutionary). Multicoloured.
1484 200g. Type **352** 10 10
1485 1000g. Marti, Cuban national flag and "Hedychium coronarium" (horiz) . . . . 1·10 50

353 "Railway Station" (Asuncion)

1996. 25th Latin American and Caribbean Forum of Lions International. Paintings by Esperanza Gill. Multicoloured.
1486 200g. Type **353** 10 10
1487 1000g. "Viola House" . . . 1·10 70

354 "Cattleya nobilior"

1996. Orchids. Multicoloured.
1488 100g. Type **354** 10 10
1489 200g. "Oncidium varicosum" 10 10
1490 1000g. "Oncidium jonesianum" (vert) . . . 1·00 45
1491 1150g. "Sophronitis cernua" 1·10 55

355 Emblems and Gymnast on "Stamp"

1996. Centenary of Modern Olympic Games and Olympic Games, Atlanta. Multicoloured.
1492 500g. Type **355** 30 20
1493 1000g. Emblems and runner on "stamp" 60 45

356 Bosco, Monks and Boys

1996. Centenary of Salesian Brothers in Paraguay. Multicoloured.
1494 200g. Type **356** 10 10
1495 300g. Madonna and Child, Pope John Paul II and St. John Bosco (vert) . . 15 10
1496 1000g. St. John Bosco (founder) and map . . . 40 20

357 Family Outing (Silvia Cacares Baez)

1996. 50th Anniv of UNICEF. Multicoloured.
1497 1000g. Type **357** 50 30
1498 1300g. Families (Cinthia Perez Alderete) 65 40

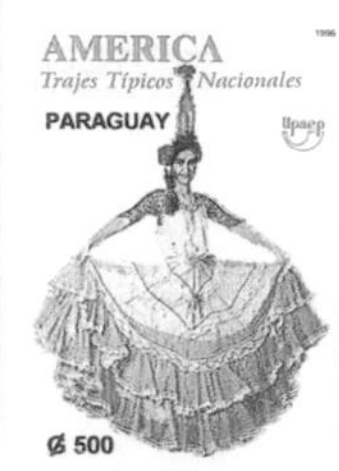

358 Pope John Paul II, Caacupe Cathedral and Virgin

359 Woman

1996. Our Lady of Caacupe. Multicoloured.
1499 200g. Type **358** 10 10
1500 1300g. Pope John Paul II, floodlit cathedral and Virgin (horiz) 65 40

1996. America. Traditional Costumes. Mult.
1501 500g. Type **359** 25 20
1502 1000g. Couple 50 30

360 Boxes and Food

1996. International Year for Eradication of Poverty. Multicoloured.
1503 1000g. Type **360** 50 30
1504 1150g. Boy with boxes and food (vert) 55 30

PARAGUAY
Mariposas del Paraguay
Eryphanis automedon
₲ 200

361 Mother and Baby

362 "Eryphanis automedon"

1996. Christmas. Multicoloured.
1505 200g. Type **361** 10 10
1506 1000g. Mother with smiling child 50 30

1997. Butterflies. Multicoloured.
1507 200g. Type **362** 10 10
1508 500g. "Dryadula phaetusa" 25 15
1509 1000g. "Vanessa myrinna" 50 30
1510 1150g. Rare tiger 55 30

363 First Government Palace (legislative building)

1997. Buildings. Multicoloured.
1511 200g. Type **363** 10 10
1512 1000g. Patri Palace (postal headquarters) 50 30

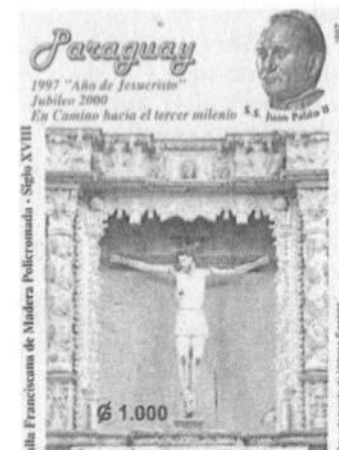

364 Crucifix, Piribebuy

1997. Year of Jesus Christ.
1513 **364** 1000g. multicoloured . . 50 30

365 Summit Emblem

1997. 11th Group of Rio Summit Meeting, Asuncion.
1514 **365** 1000g. multicoloured . . 40 20

366 Cactus

1997. "The Changing Climate—Everyone's Concern". Plants. Multicoloured.
1515 300g. Type **366** 15 10
1516 500g. "Bromelia balansae" (vert) 20 10
1517 1000g. "Monvillea kroenlaini" 40 20

367 Tiger Cat

1997. 1st Mercosur (South American Common Market), Chile and Bolivia Stamp Exhibition, Asuncion. Mammals. Multicoloured.
1518 200g. Type **367** 10 10
1519 1000g. Black howler monkey (vert) 40 20
1520 1150g. Paca 50 30

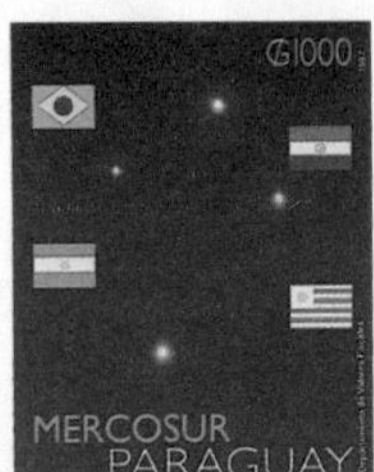

368 Members' Flags and Southern Cross

1997. 6th Anniv of Mercosur (South American Common Market).
1521 **368** 1000g. multicoloured . . 40 20

369 Postman and Letters circling Globe

370 Neri Kennedy (javelin)

1997. America. The Postman. Multicoloured.
1522 1000g. Type **369** 40 20
1523 1150g. Weather and terrain aspects of postal delivery and postman (horiz) . . . 50 30

1997. 50th Anniv of National Sports Council. Multicoloured.
1524 200g. Type **370** 10 10
1525 1000g. Ramon Milciades Gimenez Gaona (discus) 40 20

1997. "Mevifil '97" First International Exhibition of Philatelic Audio-visual and Computer Systems, Buenos Aires, Argentina. Nos. 1446/7 optd **MEVIFIL '97**.
1526 50g. multicoloured 10 10
1527 250g. multicoloured 10 10

372 Mother and Child (Olga Blinder)

373 Boy

1997. Christmas. Multicoloured.
1528 200g. Type **372** 10 10
1529 1000g. Mother and child (Hernan Miranda) 40 20

1997. "Children of the World with AIDS". Children's Paintings. Multicoloured.
1530 500g. Type **373** 20 10
1531 1000g. Girl 40 20

374 Drinking Vessel and Emblem forming "70"

375 Julio Cesar Romero (1986 World Cup team member)

1997. 70th Anniv of Asuncion Rotary Club.
1532 **374** 1150g. multicoloured . . 50 30

1998. World Cup Football Championship, France. Multicoloured.
1533 200g. Type **375** 10 10
1534 500g. Carlos Gamarra (World Cup team member) tackling opponent 20 10
1535 1000g. World Cup team (horiz) 40 20

376 Silver Tetra

1998. Fishes. Multicoloured.
1536 200g. Type **376** 10 10
1537 300g. Spotted sorubim . . . 15 10
1538 500g. Dorado 20 10
1539 1000g. Pira jagua 40 20

377 Painting by Carlos Colombino

378 Cep

1998. Paintings by artists named. Multicoloured.
1540 200g. Type **377** 10 10
1541 300g. Felix Toranzos . . . 15 10
1542 400g. Edith Gimenez . . . 15 10
1543 1000g. Ricardo Migliorisi (horiz) 40 20

1998. Fungi. Multicoloured.
1544 400g. Type **378** 15 10
1545 600g. Parasol mushroom . . 25 15
1546 1000g. Collared earthstar . . 40 20

379 Carlos Lopez's House, Botanical and Zoological Gardens, Asuncion

1998. 50th Anniv of Organization of American States. Multicoloured.
1547 500g. Type **379** 20 10
1548 1000g. Villa Palmerola, Aregua 40 20

380 Door of Sanctuary, Caazapa Church

1998. 400th Anniv of Ordination of First Paraguayan Priests by Brother Hernando de Trejo y Sanabria. Multicoloured.
1549 400g. Type **380** 15 10
1550 1700g. Statue of St. Francis of Assisi, Atyra Church (horiz) 70 40

381 "Acacia caven"

1998. Flowers. Multicoloured.
1551 100g. Type **381** 10 10
1552 600g. "Cordia trichotoma" 25 15
1553 1900g. "Glandularia" sp. . . 80 45

382 Ruins of the Mission of Jesus, Itapua

1998. Mercosur (South American Common Market) Heritage Sites.
1554 **382** 5000g. multicoloured . . 2·10 1·25

383 Serafina Davalos (first female lawyer in Paraguay) and National College

1998. America. Famous Women. Multicoloured.
1555 1600g. Type **383** 60 35
1556 1700g. Adela Speratti (first director) and Teachers' Training College 65 35

384 Abstract (Carlos Colombino)

1998. 50th Anniv of Universal Declaration of Human Rights. Multicoloured.
1557 500g. Type **384** 20 10
1558 1000g. Man on crutches (after Joel Filartiga) . . . 40 20

385 Crib

1998. Christmas. Multicoloured.
1559 300g. Type **385** 10 10
1560 1600g. Crib (different) (vert) 60 35

386 Coral Cobra

1999. Reptiles. Multicoloured.
1561 100g. Type **386** 10 10
1562 300g. Ground lizard 10 10
1563 1600g. Red-footed tortoise 65 35
1564 1700g. Paraguay caiman . . 70 40

1999. "Chaco Peace 99" Stamp Exhibition, Paraguay and Bolivia. No. 1542 optd **1era. Exposicion Filatellca Paraguayo-Boliviana PAZ DEL CHACO 99**.
1565 400g. multicoloured 15 10

388 Painting by Ignacio Nunes Soler

1999. Paintings. Showing paintings by named artists.
1566 500g. Type **388** 20 10
1567 1600g. Modesto Delgado Rodas 65 35
1568 1700g. Jaime Bestard . . . 70 40

389 Carlos Humberto Parades being tackled

1999. American Cup Football Championship, Paraguay. Multicoloured.
1569 300g. Type **389** 10 10
1570 500g. South American Football Federation Building, Luque, Paraguay (horiz) 20 10
1571 1900g. Feliciano Caceres Stadium, Luque (horiz) 75 45

390 Toucan

1999. 50th Anniv of S.O.S. Children's Villages. Multicoloured.
1572 1700g. Type **390** 70 40
1573 1900g. Toucan (different) (vert) 75 45

391 Government Palace

1999. Assassination of Dr. Luis Marua Argana (Vice-president, 1998–99). Multicoloured.
1574 100g. Type **391** 10 10
1575 500g. Dr. Argana (vert) . . 20 10
1576 1500g. Crowd before National Congress building 60 35

392 *Cochlospermum regium*

1999. Medicinal Plants. Multicoloured.
1577 600g. Type **392** 25 10
1578 700g. *Borago officinalis* . . . 30 15
1579 1700g. *Passiflora cincinnata* 70 40

393 "The Man who carries the Storm"

1999. America. A New Millennium without Arms. Showing paintings by Ricardo Migliorisi. Mult.
1580 1500g. Type **393** 60 35
1581 3000g. "The Man who dominates the Storm" (vert) . . . . 1·25 75

394 "Couple" (Olga Blinder)

1999. International Year of the Elderly. Mult.
1582 1000g. Type **394** 40 20
1583 1900g. "Old Woman" (Marma de los Reyes Omella Herrero) (vert) . . 75 45

395 "Mother and Child" (Manuel Viedma)

1999. Christmas. Multicoloured.
1584 300g. Type **395** 10 10
1585 1600g. "Nativity" (Federico Ordinana) 65 35

396 *Tabebuia impetiginosa*

1999. Centenary of Pedro Juan Caballero City. Multicoloured.
1586 1000g. Type **396** 40 20
1587 1600g. *Tabebuia pulcherrima* (vert) 65 35

397 Oratory of the Virgin Our Lady of the Assumption and National Mausoleum

1999. 40th Anniv of Inter-American Development Bank. Multicoloured.
1588 600g. Type **397** 25 15
1589 700g. Government Palace 30 15

398 Carmen Casco de Lara Castro and "Conjunction" (bronze sculpture, Domingo Rivarola)

2000. International Women's Day. Carmen Casco de Lara Castro (founder of National Commission for Human Rights). Multicoloured.
1590 400g. Type **398** 15 10
1591 2000g. Carmen Casco de Lara Castro and "Violation" (bronze sculpture, Gustavo Beckelman) 80 45

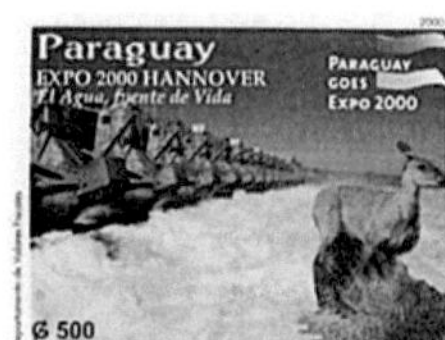

399 Hydroelectric Dam, Yacyreta, and Marsh Deer

2000. "EXPO 2000" World's Fair, Hanover, Germany. Showing bi-lateral development projects. Multicoloured.
1592 500g. Type **399** (Paraguay–Argentine Republic) . . . 20 10
1593 2500g. Hydroelectric dam, Itaipu and Brazilian tapir (Paraguay–Brazil) . . . . 1·00 60

400 Students and Pope John Paul II

2000. Centenary of the Daughters of Maria Auxiliadora College. Multicoloured.
1594 600g. Type **400** 25 15
1595 2000g. College building . . 80 45

401 Footballers chasing Ball

2000. Olympic Games, Sydney. Multicoloured.
1596 2500g. Type **401** 70 40
1597 3000g. Francisco Rojas Soto (athlete), Munich Olympics, 1972 (horiz) . . 85 50

402 Adult Hands protecting Child (Nahuel Moreno Lezcano)

2000. 10th Anniv of United Nations Convention on the Rights of the Child. Multicoloured.
1598 1500g. Type **402** 45 25
1599 1700g. Hand prints (Claudia Alessandro Irala Chavez) (horiz) 50 30

403 Firemen attending to Fire

2000. 95th Anniv of Fire Service. Multicoloured.
1600 100g. Type **403** 10 10
1601 200g. Badge and fireman wearing 1905 dress uniform 10 10
1602 1500g. Firemen attending fire (horiz) 45 25
1603 1600g. Firemen using hose (horiz) 45 25

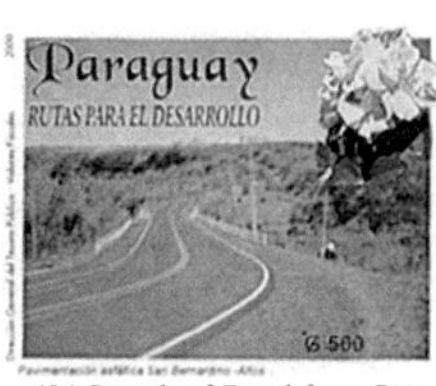

404 Stretch of Road from San Bernardino to Altos

2000. Road Development Scheme. Multicoloured.
1604 500g. Type **404** 15 10
1605 3000g. Gaspar Rodriguez de Francia motorway 85 50

405 Signpost and Emblem

2000. America. AIDS Awareness Campaign. Mult.
1606 1500g. Type **405** 45 25
1607 2500g. Ribbon emblem on noughts and crosses grid 70 40

406 "Love and Peace" (metal sculpture, Hugo Pistilli)

2000. International Year of Culture and Peace. Multicoloured.
1608 500g. Type **406** 15 10
1609 2000g. "For Peace" (metal sculpture, Herman Guggiari) 60 35

407 "Holy Family" (metal sculpture, Hugo Pistilli)

2000. Christmas. Multicoloured.
1610 100g. Type **407** 10 10
1611 500g. Poem, pen and Jose Luis Appleyard (poet and writer) 15 10
1612 2000g. Nativity (crib firgures) (horiz) 65 35

408 Country Woman (sculpture, Behage)

2000. Art. Multicoloured.
1613 200g. Type **408** 10 10
1614 1500g. Drinking vessels (Quintin Velazquez) (horiz) 45 25
1615 2000g. Silver orchid brooch (Quirino Torres) 65 35

409 Flores

2000. 30th Birth Anniv (2002) of Jose Asuncion Flores (musician). Multicoloured.
1616 100g. Type **409** 10 10
1617 1500g. Violin 45 25
1618 2500g. Trombone 70 40

OFFICIAL STAMPS

O 14 O 19

O 20 O 37

1886. Various types as O **14**, O **19** and O **20** optd **OFICIAL**. (a) Imperf.

O32		1c. orange	3·50	2·25
O33		2c. violet	3·50	2·25
O34		5c. orange	3·50	2·25
O35		7c. green	3·50	2·25
O36		10c. brown	3·50	2·25
O37		15c. blue	8·50	11·00
O38		20c. lake	3·50	2·25

(b) New colours. Perf.

O39		1c. green	80	65
O40		2c. red	80	65
O41		5c. blue	80	65
O42		7c. orange	80	65
O43		10c. lake	80	65
O44		15c. brown	15·00	9·00
O45		20c. blue	80	65

1889. Stamp of 1889 surch **OFICIAL** and value. Perf.

O47	**25**	1 on 15c. purple	1·60	75
O48		2 on 10c. purple	1·60	75

1889. Stamp of 1889 surch **OFICIAL** and value. Imperf.

O49	**25**	3 on 15c. purple	1·60	75
O50		5 on 15c. brown	1·60	75

1890. Stamps of 1887 optd **OFICIAL** or **Oficial**.

O58	**24**	1c. green	10	10
O59		2c. red	15	10
O60		5c. blue	15	10
O61		7c. brown	1·40	75
O55		10c. mauve	20	15
O63		15c. orange	20	15
O64		20c. pink	25	15
O65		50c. grey	15	15
O86		1p. green	10	10

1901.

O73	O **37**	1c. blue	30	30
O74		2c. red	10	10
O75		4c. brown	10	10
O76		5c. green	10	10
O77		8c. brown	10	10
O78		10c. red	10	10
O79		20c. blue	20	15

1903. Stamps of 1903, optd **OFICIAL**.

O 99	**46**	1c. grey	10	10
O100		2c. green	10	10
O101		5c. blue	15	10
O102		10c. brown	10	10
O103		20c. red	10	10
O104		30c. blue	10	10
O105		60c. violet	20	20

1904. As T **50**, but inscr "OFICIAL".

O106		1c. green	20	10
O107		1c. olive	30	10
O108		1c. orange	35	15
O109		1c. red	30	20
O110		2c. orange	20	10
O111		2c. green	20	10
O112		2c. red	60	40
O113		2c. grey	50	30
O114		5c. blue	25	20
O116		5c. grey	1·10	75
O117		10c. lilac	15	10
O118		20c. lilac	50	30

1913. As T **65**, but inscr "OFICIAL".

O237		1c. grey	10	10
O238		2c. orange	10	10
O239		5c. purple	10	10
O240		10c. green	10	10
O241		20c. red	10	10
O242		50c. red	10	10
O243		75c. blue	10	10
O244		1p. blue	10	10
O245		2p. yellow	20	20

1935. Optd **OFICIAL**.

O474	**86**	10c. blue	10	10
O475		50c. mauve	10	10
O476	**87**	1p. orange	10	10
O477	**122**	1p.50 green	10	10
O478	–	2p.50 violet (No. 337)	10	10

1940. 50th Anniv of Asuncion University. As T **139**, inscr "SERVICIO OFICIAL", but portraits of Pres. Escobar and Dr. Zubizarreta.

O513		50c. black and red	10	10
O514		1p. black and red	10	10
O515		2p. black and blue	10	10
O516		5p. black and blue	10	10
O517		10p. black and blue	10	10
O518		50p. black and orange	40	10

POSTAGE DUE STAMPS

D 48

1904.

D106	D **48**	2c. green	30	30
D107		4c. green	30	30
D108		10c. green	30	30
D109		20c. green	30	30

1913. As T **65**, but inscr "DEFICIENTE".

D237		1c. brown	10	10
D238		2c. brown	10	10
D239		5c. brown	10	10
D240		10c. brown	10	10
D241		20c. brown	10	10
D242		40c. brown	10	10
D243		1p. brown	10	10
D244		1p.50 brown	10	10

APPENDIX

The following stamps have either been issued in excess of postal needs or have not been available to the public in reasonable quantities at face value. Such stamps may later be given full listing if there is evidence of regular postal use.

1962.

Manned Spacecraft. Postage 15, 25, 30, 40, 50c.; Air 12g.45, 18g.15, 36g.

Previous Olympic Games (1st series). Vert designs. Postage 15, 25, 30, 40, 50c.; Air 12g.45, 18g.15, 36g.

Vatican Council. Postage 50, 70c., 1g.50, 2, 3g.; Air 5, 10g., 12g.45, 18g.15, 23g.40, 36g.

Europa. Postage 4g.; Air 36g.

Solar System. Postage 10, 20, 25, 30, 50c.; Air 12g.45, 36g., 50g.

1963.

Previous Olympic Games (2nd series). Horiz designs. Postage 15, 25, 30, 40, 50c.; Air 12g.45, 18g.15, 36g.

Satellites and Space Flights. Vert designs. Postage 10, 20, 25, 30, 50c.; Air 12g.45, 36, 50g.

Previous Winter Olympic Games. Postage 10, 20, 25, 30, 50c.; Air 12g.45, 36, 50g.

Freedom from Hunger. Postage 10, 25, 50, 75c.; Air 18g.15, 36, 50g.

"Mercury" Space Flights. Postage 15, 25, 30, 40, 50c.; Air 12g.45, 18g.15, 50g.

Winter Olympic Games. Postage 15, 25, 30, 40, 50c.; Air 12g.45, 18g.15, 50g.

1964.

Tokyo Olympic Games. Postage 15, 25, 30, 40, 50c.; Air 12g.45, 18g.15, 50g.

Red Cross Centenary. Postage 10, 25, 30, 50c.; Air 18g.15, 36, 50g.

"Gemini", "Telstar" and "Apollo" Projects. Postage 15, 25, 30, 40, 50c.; Air 12g.45, 18g.15, 50g.

Spacecraft Developments. Postage 15, 25, 30, 40, 50c.; Air 12g.45, 18g.15, 50g.

United Nations. Postage 15, 25, 30, 40, 50c.; Air 12g.45, 18g.15, 50g.

American Space Research. Postage 10, 15, 20, 30, 40c.; Air 12g.45+6g., 18g.15+9g., 20g.+20g.

Eucharistic Conference. Postage 20g.+10g., 30g.+15g., 50g.+25g., 100g.+50g.

Pope John Memorial Issue. Postage 20g.+10g., 30g.+15g., 50g.+25g., 100g.+50g.

1965.

Scouts. Postage 10, 15, 20, 30, 50c.; Air 12g.45, 18g.15, 36g.

Tokyo Olympic Games Medals. Postage 15, 25, 30, 40, 50c.; Air 12g.45, 18g.15, 50g.

Famous Scientists. Postage 10, 15, 20, 30, 40c.; Air 12g.45+6g., 18g.15+9g., 20g.+20g.

Orchids and Trees. Postage 20, 30, 90c., 1g.50, 4g.50.; Air 3, 4, 66g.

Kennedy and Churchill. Postage 15, 25, 30, 40, 50c.; Air 12g.45, 18g.15, 50g.

I.T.U. Centenary. Postage 10, 15, 20, 30, 40c.; Air 12g.45+6g., 18g.15+9g., 20g.+10g.

Pope Paul VI. Visit to United Nations. Postage 10, 15, 20, 30, 50c.; Air 12g.45, 18g.15, 36g.

1966.

"Gemini" Space Project. Postage 15, 25, 30, 40, 50c.; Air 12g.45, 18g.15, 50g.

Events of 1965. Postage 10, 15, 20, 30, 50c.; Air 12g.45, 18g.15, 36g.

Mexico Olympic Games. Postage 10, 15, 20, 30, 50c.; Air 12g.45, 18g.15, 36g.

German Space Research. Postage 10, 15, 20, 30, 50c.; Air 12g.45, 18g.15, 36g.

Famous Writers. Postage 10, 15, 20, 30, 50c.; Air 12g.45, 18g.15, 36g.

Italian Space Research. Postage 10, 15, 20, 30, 50c.; Air 12g.45, 18g.15, 36g.

Moon Missions. Postage 10, 15, 20, 30, 50c.; Air 12g.45, 18g.15, 36g.

Sports Commemorative Issue. Postage 10, 15, 20, 30, 50c.; Air 12g.45, 18g.15, 36g.

3rd Death Anniv of Pres. John Kennedy. Postage 10, 15, 20, 30, 50c.; Air 12g.45, 18g.15, 36g.

Famous Paintings. Postage 10, 15, 20, 30, 50c.; Air 12g.45, 18g.15, 36g.

1967.

Religious Paintings. Postage 10, 15, 20, 30, 50c.; Air 12g.45, 18g.15, 36g.

16th-century. Religious Paintings. Postage 10, 15, 20, 30, 50c.; Air 12g.45, 18g.15, 36g.

Impressionist Paintings. Postage 10, 15, 20, 30, 50c.; Air 12g.45, 18g.15, 36g.

European Paintings of 17th and 18th Cent. Postage 10, 15, 20, 25, 30, 50c.; Air 12g.45, 18g.15, 36g.

Birth Anniv of Pres. John Kennedy. Postage 10, 15, 20, 25, 30, 50c.; Air 12g.45, 18g.15, 36g.

Sculpture. Postage 10, 15, 20, 25, 30, 50c.; Air 12g.45, 18g.15, 50g.

Mexico Olympic Games. Archaeological Relics. Postage 10, 15, 20, 25, 30, 50c.; Air 12g.45, 18g.15, 36g.

1968.

Religious Paintings. Postage 10, 15, 20, 25, 30, 50c.; Air 12g.45, 18g.15, 36g.

Winter Olympic Games, Grenoble. Paintings. Postage 10, 15, 20, 25, 30, 50c.; Air 12g.45, 18g.15, 36g.

Paraguayan Stamps from 1870–1970. Postage 10, 15, 20, 25, 30, 50c.; Air 12g.45, 18g.15, 36g.

Mexico Olympic Games, Paintings of Children. Postage 10, 15, 20, 25, 30, 50c.; Air 12g.45, 18g.15, 36g. (Sailing ship and Olympic Rings).

Visit of Pope Paul VI to Eucharistic Congress. Religious Paintings. Postage 10, 15, 20, 25, 30, 50c.; Air 12g.45, 18g.15, 36g.

Important Events of 1968. Postage 10, 15, 20, 25, 30, 50c.; Air 12g.45, 18g.15, 50g.

1969.

Gold Medal Winners of 1968 Mexico Olympic Games. Postage 10, 15, 20, 25, 30, 50c.; Air 12g.45, 18g.15, 50g.

Int. Projects in Outer Space. Postage 10, 15, 20, 25, 30, 50c.; Air 12g.45, 18g.15, 50g.

Latin American Wildlife. Postage 10, 10, 15, 15, 20, 20, 25, 25, 30, 30, 50, 50, 75, 75 c; Air 12g.45 × 2, 18g.15 × 2.

Gold Medal Winners in Olympic Football, 1900–1968. Postage 10, 15, 20, 25, 30, 50, 75c.; Air 12g.45, 18g.15.

Paraguayan Football Champions, 1930–1966. Postage 10, 15, 20, 25, 30, 50, 75c.; Air 12g.45, 18g.15.

Paintings by Goya. Postage 10, 15, 20, 25, 30, 50, 75c.; Air 12g.45, 18g.15.

Christmas. Religious Paintings. Postage 10, 15, 20, 25, 30, 50, 75c.; Air 12g.45, 18g.15.

1970.

Moon Walk. Postage 10, 15, 20, 25, 30, 50, 75c.; Air 12g.45, 18g.15.

Easter. Paintings. Postage 10, 15, 20, 25, 30, 50, 75c.; Air 12g.45, 18g.15.

Munich Olympic Games. Postage 10, 15, 20, 25, 30, 50, 75c.; Air 12g.45, 18g.15.

Paintings from the Pinakothek Museum in Munich. Postage 10, 15, 20, 25, 30, 50, 75c.; Air 12g.45, 18g.15.

"Apollo" Space Programme. Postage 10, 15, 20, 25, 30, 50, 75c.; Air 12g.45, 18g.15.

Space Projects in the Future. Postage 10, 15, 20, 25, 30, 50, 75c.; Air 12g.45, 18g.15.

"Expo 70" World Fair, Osaka, Japan. Japanese Paintings. Postage 10, 15, 20, 25, 30, 50, 75c.; Air 12g.45, 18g.15, 50g.

Flower Paintings. Postage 10, 15, 20, 25, 30, 50, 75c.; Air 12g.45, 18g.15, 50g.

Paintings from Prado Museum, Madrid. Postage 10, 15, 20, 25, 30, 50, 75c.; Air 12g.45, 18g.15, 50g.

Paintings by Durer. Postage 10, 15, 20, 25, 30, 50, 75c.; Air 12g.45, 18g.15, 50g.

1971.

Christmas 1970/71. Religious Paintings. Postage 10, 15, 20, 25, 30, 50, 75c.; Air 12g.45, 18g.15, 50g.

Munich Olympic Games, 1972. Postage 10, 15, 20, 25, 30, 50, 75c.; Air 12g.45, 18g.15, 50g.

Paintings of Horses and Horsemen. Postage 10, 15, 20, 25, 30, 50, 75c.; Air 12g.45, 18g.15, 50g.

Famous Paintings from the Louvre, Paris. Postage 10, 15, 20, 25, 30, 50, 75c.; Air 12g.45, 18g.15, 50g.

Paintings in the National Museum, Asuncion. Postage 10, 15, 20, 25, 30, 50, 75c.; Air 12g.45, 18g.15, 50g.

Hunting Paintings. Postage 10, 15, 20, 25, 30, 50, 75c.; Air 12g.45, 18g.15, 50g.

Philatokyo '71, Stamp Exhibition, Tokyo. Japanese Paintings. Postage 10, 15, 20, 25, 30, 50, 75c.; Air 12g.45, 18g.15, 50g.

Winter Olympic Games, Sapporo, 1972. Japanese Paintings. Postage 10, 15, 20, 25, 30, 50, 75c.; Air 12g.45, 18g.15, 50g.

150th Death Anniv of Napoleon. Paintings. Postage 10, 15, 20, 25, 30, 50, 75c.; Air 12g.45, 18g.15, 50g.

Famous Paintings from the Dahlem Museum, Berlin. Postage 10, 15, 20, 25, 30, 50, 75c.; Air 12g.45, 18g.15, 50g.

1972.

Locomotives (1st series). Postage 10, 15, 20, 25, 30, 50, 75c.; Air 12g.45, 18g.15, 50g.

Winter Olympic Games, Sapporo. Postage 10, 15, 20, 25, 30, 50, 75c.; Air 12g.45, 18g.15, 50g.

Racing Cars. Postage 10, 15, 20, 25, 30, 50, 75c.; Air 12g.45, 18g.15, 50g.

Famous Sailing Ships. Postage 10, 15, 20, 25, 30, 50, 75c.; Air 12g.45, 18g.15, 50g.

Famous Paintings from the Vienna Museum. Postage 10, 15, 20, 25, 30, 50, 75c.; Air 12g.45, 18g.15, 50g.

Famous Paintings from the Asuncion Museum. Postage 10, 15, 20, 25, 30, 50, 75c.; Air 12g.45, 18g.15, 50g.

Visit of the Argentine President to Paraguay. Postage 10, 15, 20, 25, 30, 50, 75c.; Air 12g.45, 18g.15.

Visit of President of Paraguay to Japan. Postage 10, 15, 20, 25, 30, 50, 75c.; Air 12g.45, 18g.15.

Paintings of Animals and Birds. Postage 10, 15, 20, 25, 30, 50, 75c.; Air 12g.45, 18g.15.

Locomotives (2nd series). Postage 10, 15, 20, 25, 30, 50, 75c.; Air 12g.45, 18g.15.

South American Fauna. Postage 10, 15, 20, 25, 30, 50, 75c.; Air 12g.45, 18g.15.

1973.

Famous Paintings from the Florence Museum. Postage 10, 15, 20, 25, 30, 50, 75c.; Air 5, 10, 20g.

South American Butterflies. Postage 10, 15, 20, 25, 30, 50, 75c.; Air 5, 10, 20g.

Cats. Postage 10, 15, 20, 25, 30, 50, 75c.; Air 5, 10, 20g.

Portraits of Women. Postage 10, 15, 20, 25, 30, 50, 75c.; Air 5, 10, 20g.

World Cup Football Championship, West Germany (1974) (1st issue). Postage 10, 15, 20, 25, 30, 50, 75c.; Air 5, 10, 20g.

Paintings of Women. Postage 10, 15, 20, 25, 30, 50, 75c.; Air 5, 10, 20g.

Birds. Postage 10, 15, 20, 25, 30, 50, 75c.; Air 5, 10, 20g.

"Apollo" Moon Missions and Future Space Projects. Postage 10, 15, 20, 25, 30, 50, 75c.; Air 5, 10, 20g.

Visit of Pres. Stroessner to Europe and Morocco. Air 5, 10, 25, 50, 150g.

Folk Costume. Postage 25, 50, 75c., 1g., 1g.50, 1g.75, 2g.25.

Flowers. Postage 10, 20, 25, 30, 40, 50, 75c.

1974.

World Cup Football Championship, West Germany (2nd issue). Air 5, 10, 20g.

Roses. Postage 10, 15, 20, 25, 30, 50, 75c.

Famous Paintings from the Gulbenkian Museum, New York. Postage 10, 15, 20, 25, 30, 50, 75 c; Air 5, 10, 20g.

U.P.U. Centenary. Postage 10, 15, 20, 25, 30, 50, 75c.; Air 5, 10, 20g.

Famous Masterpieces. Postage 10, 15, 20, 25, 30, 50, 75c.; Air 5, 10, 20g.

Visit of Pres. Stroessner to France. Air 100g.

World Cup Football Championship, West Germany (3rd issue). Air 4, 5, 10g.

Ships. Postage 5, 10, 15, 20, 25, 35, 40, 50c.

Events of 1974. Air 4g. (U.P.U.), 5g. (President of Chile's visit), 10g. (President Stroessner's visit to South Africa).

Centenary of U.P.U. Air 4, 5, 10, 20g.

1975.

Paintings. Postage 5, 10, 15, 20, 25, 35, 40, 50c.

Christmas (1974). Postage 5, 10, 15, 20, 25, 35, 40, 50c.

"Expo '75" Okinawa, Japan. Air 4, 5, 10g.

Paintings from National Gallery, London. Postage 5, 10, 15, 20, 25, 35, 40, 50c.

Dogs. Postage 5, 10, 15, 20, 25, 35, 40, 50c.

South American Fauna. Postage 5, 10, 15, 20, 25, 35, 40, 50c.

"Espana '75". Air 4, 5, 10g.

500th Birth Anniv of Michelangelo. Postage 5, 10, 15, 20, 25, 35, 40, 50c.; Air 4, 5, 10g.

Winter Olympic Games, Innsbruck (1976). Postage 1, 2, 3, 4, 5g.; Air 10, 15, 20g.

Olympic Games, Montreal (1976). Gold borders. Postage 1, 2, 3, 4, 5g.; Air 10, 15, 20g.

Various Commemorations. Air 4g. (Zeppelin), 5g. (1978 World Cup), 10g. (Nordposta Exhibition).

Bicent (1976) of American Revolution (1st issue). Paintings of Sailing Ships. Postage 5, 10, 15, 20, 25, 35, 40, 50c.

Bicent (1976) of American Revolution (2nd issue). Paintings. Postage 5, 10, 15, 20, 25, 35, 40, 50c.

Bicent (1976) of American Revolution (3rd issue). Lunar Rover and American Cars. Air 4, 5, 10g.

Various Commemorations. Air 4g. (Concorde), 5g. (Lufthansa), 10g. ("Exfilmo" and "Espamer" Stamp Exhibitions).

Paintings by Spanish Artists. Postage 1, 2, 3, 4, 5g.; Air 10, 15, 20g.

1976.

Holy Year. Air 4, 5, 10g.

Cats. Postage 5, 10, 15, 20, 25, 35, 40, 50c.

Railway Locomotives (3rd series). Postage 1, 2, 3, 4, 5g.; Air 10, 15, 20g.

Butterflies. Postage 5, 10, 15, 20, 25, 35, 40, 50c.

Domestic Animals. Postage 1, 2, 3, 4, 5g.; Air 10, 15, 20g.

Bicent of American Revolution (4th issue) and U.S. Postal Service. Postage 1, 2, 3, 4, 5g.; Air 10, 15, 20g.

"Paintings and Planets". Postage 1, 2, 3, 4, 5g.; Air 10, 15, 20g.

Ship Paintings. Postage 1, 2, 3, 4, 5g.; Air 10, 15, 20g.

German Ship Paintings (1st issue). Postage 1, 2, 3, 4, 5g.; Air 10, 15, 20g.

Bicentenary of American Revolution (5th issue). Paintings of Cowboys and Indians. Postage 1, 2, 3, 4, 5g.; Air 10, 15, 20g.

Gold Medal Winners. Olympic Games, Montreal. Postage 1, 2, 3, 4, 5g.; Air 10, 15, 20g.

Paintings by Titian. Postage 1, 2, 3, 4, 5g.; Air 10, 15, 20g.

History of the Olympics. Postage 1, 2, 3, 4, 5g.; Air 10, 15, 20g.

1977.

Paintings by Rubens (1st issue). Postage 1, 2, 3, 4, 5g.; Air 10, 15, 20g.

Bicent of American Revolution (6th issue). Astronautics. Postage 1, 2, 3, 4, 5g.; Air 10, 15, 20g.

"Luposta 77" Stamp Exn. Zeppelin and National Costumes. Postage 1, 2, 3, 4, 5g.; Air 10, 15, 20g.

History of Aviation. Postage 1, 2, 3, 4, 5g.; Air 10, 15, 20g.

Paintings. Postage 1, 2, 3, 4, 5g.; Air 10, 15, 20g.

German Ship Paintings (2nd issue). Postage 1, 2, 3, 4, 5g.; Air 10, 15, 20g.

Nobel Prize-winners for Literature. Postage 1, 2, 3, 4, 5g.; Air 10, 15, 20g.

History of World Cup (1st issue). Postage 1, 2, 3, 4, 5g.; Air 10, 15, 20g.

History of World Cup (2nd issue). Postage 1, 2, 3, 4, 5g.; Air 10, 15, 20g.

1978.

Paintings by Rubens (2nd issue). Postage 1, 2, 3, 4, 5g.; Air 10, 15, 20g.

Chess Olympiad, Buenos Aires. Paintings of Chess Games. Postage 1, 2, 3, 4, 5g.; Air 10, 15, 20g.

Paintings by Jordaens. Postage 3, 4, 5, 6, 7, 8, 20g.; Air 10, 25g.

450th Death Anniv of Durer (1st issue). Postage 3, 4, 5, 6, 7, 8, 20g.; Air 10, 25g.

Paintings by Goya. Postage 3, 4, 5, 6, 7, 8, 20g.; Air 10, 25g.

Astronautics of the Future. Postage 3, 4, 5, 6, 7, 8, 20g.; Air 10, 25g.

Racing Cars. Postage 3, 4, 5, 6, 7, 8, 20g.; Air 10, 25g.

Paintings by Rubens (3rd issue). Postage 3, 4, 5, 6, 7, 8, 20g.; Air 10, 25g.

25th Anniv of Queen Elizabeth's Coronation (reproduction of stamps). Postage 3, 4, 5, 6, 7, 8, 20g.; Air 10, 25g.

Paintings and Stamp Exhibition Emblems. Postage 3, 4, 5, 6, 7, 8, 20g.; Air 10, 25g.

Various Commemorations. Air 75g. (Satellite Earth Station), 500g. (Coat of Arms), 1000g. (Pres. Stroessner).

International Year of the Child (1st issue). Snow White and the Seven Dwarfs. Postage 3, 4, 5, 6, 7, 8, 20g.; Air 10, 25g.

Military Uniforms. Postage 3, 4, 5, 6, 7, 8, 20g.; Air 10, 25g.

1979.

World Cup Football Championship, Argentina. Postage 3, 4, 5, 6, 7, 8, 20g.; Air 10, 25g.

Christmas (1978). Paintings of Madonnas. Postage 3, 4, 5, 6, 7, 8, 20g.; Air 10, 25g.

History of Aviation. Postage 3, 4, 5, 6, 7, 8, 20g.; Air 10, 25g.

450th Death Anniv of Durer (2nd issue). Postage 3, 4, 5, 6, 7, 8, 20g.; Air 10, 25g.

Death Centenary of Sir Rowland Hill (1st issue). Reproduction of Stamps. Postage 3, 4, 5, 6, 7, 8, 20g.; Air 10, 25g.

International Year of the Child (2nd issue). Cinderella. Postage 3, 4, 5, 6, 7, 8, 20g.; Air 10, 25g.

Winter Olympic Games, Lake Placid (1980). Postage 3, 4, 5, 6, 7, 8, 20g.; Air 10, 25g.

Sailing Ships. Postage 3, 4, 5, 6, 7, 8, 20g.; Air 10, 25g.

International Year of the Child (3rd issue). Cats. Postage 3, 4, 5, 6, 7, 8, 20g.; Air 10, 25g.

International Year of the Child (4th issue). Little Red Riding Hood. Postage 3, 4, 5, 6, 7, 8, 20g.; Air 10, 25g.

Olympic Games, Moscow (1980). Greek Athletes. Postage 3, 4, 5, 6, 7, 8, 20g.; Air 10, 25g.

Centenary of Electric Locomotives. Postage 3, 4, 5, 6, 7, 8, 20g.; Air 10, 25g.

1980.

Death Centenary of Sir Rowland Hill (2nd issue). Military Aircraft. Postage 3, 4, 5, 6, 7, 8, 20 g; Air 10, 25g.

Death Centenary of Sir Rowland Hill (3rd issue). Stamps. Postage 3, 4, 5, 6, 7, 8, 20g.; Air 10, 25g.

Winter Olympic Games Medal Winners (1st issue). Postage 3, 4, 5, 6, 7, 8, 20g.; Air 10, 25g.

Composers. Scenes from Ballets. Postage 3, 4, 5, 6, 7, 8, 20g.; Air 20, 25g.

International Year of the Child (1979) (5th issue). Christmas. Postage 3, 4, 5, 6, 7, 8, 20g.; Air 10, 25g.

Exhibitions. Paintings of Ships. Postage 3, 4, 5, 6, 7, 8, 20g.; Air 10, 25g.

World Cup Football Championship, Spain (1982) (1st issue). Postage 3, 4, 5, 6, 7, 8, 20g.; Air 10, 25g.

World Chess Championship, Merano. Postage 3, 4, 5, 6, 7, 8, 20g.; Air 10, 25g.

1981.

Winter Olympic Games Medal Winners (2nd issue). Postage 25, 50c., 1, 2, 3, 4, 5g.; Air 5, 10, 30g.

International Year of the Child (1979) (6th issue). Children and Flowers. Postage 10, 25, 50, 100, 200, 300, 400g.; Air 75, 500, 1000g.

"WIPA 1981" International Stamp Exhibition, Vienna. 1980 Composers stamp optd. Postage 4g.; Air 10g.

Wedding of Prince of Wales (1st issue). Postage 25, 50c., 1, 2, 3, 4, 5g.; Air 5, 10, 30g.

Costumes and Treaty of Itaipu. Postage 10, 25, 50, 100, 200, 300, 400g.

Paintings by Rubens. Postage 25, 50c., 1, 2, 3, 4, 5g.

Anniversaries and Events. Air 5g. (250th birth anniv of George Washington), 10g. (80th birthday of Queen Mother), 30g. ("Philatokyo '81").

Flight of Space Shuttle. Air 5, 10, 30g.

Birth Bicentenary of Ingres. Postage 25, 50c., 1, 2, 3, 4, 5g.

World Cup Football Championship, Spain (1982) (2nd issue). Air 5, 10, 30g.

Birth Centenary of Picasso. Postage 25, 50c., 1, 2, 3, 4, 5g.

"Philatelia '81" International Stamp Exhibition, Frankfurt. Picasso stamps optd. Postage 25, 50c., 1, 2, 3, 4g.

"Espamer '81" International Stamp Exhibition. Picasso stamps optd. Postage 25, 50c., 1, 2, 3, 4g.

Wedding of Prince of Wales (2nd issue). Postage 25, 50c., 1, 2, 3, 4, 5g.; Air 5, 10, 30g.

International Year of the Child (1979) (7th issue). Christmas. Postage 25, 50c., 1, 2, 3, 4, 5g.

Christmas. Paintings. Air 5, 10, 30g.

1982.

International Year of the Child (1979) (8th issue). Puss in Boots. Postage 25, 50c., 1, 2, 3, 4, 5g.

World Cup Football Championship, Spain (3rd issue). Air 5, 10, 30g.

75th Anniv of Boy Scout Movement and 125th Birth Anniv of Lord-Baden Powell (founder). Postage 25, 50c., 1, 2, 3, 4, 5g.; Air 5, 10, 30g.

"Essen 82" International Stamp Exhibition, 1981 International Year of the Child (7th issue) Christmas stamps optd. Postage 25, 50c., 1, 2, 3, 4g.

Cats. Postage 25, 50c., 1, 2, 3, 4, 5g.

Chess paintings. Air 5, 10, 30g.

"Philexfrance 82" International Stamp Exhibition. 1981 Ingres stamps optd. Postage 25, 50c., 1, 2, 3g.

World Cup Football Championship, Spain (4th issue). Postage 25, 50c., 1, 2, 3, 4, 5g.; Air 5, 10, 30g.

"Philatelia 82" International Stamp Exhibition, Hanover. 1982 Cats issue optd. Postage 25, 50c., 1, 2, 3, 4, 5g.

500th Birth Anniv of Raphael (1st issue). Postage 25, 50c., 1, 2, 3, 4, 5g.

500th Birth Anniv of Raphael (2nd issue) and Christmas (1st issue). Postage 25, 50c., 1, 2, 3, 4, 5g.

World Cup Football Championship Results. Air 5, 10, 30g.

Christmas (2nd issue). Paintings by Rubens. Air 5, 10, 30g.

Paintings by Durer. Life of Christ. Postage 25, 50c., 1, 2, 3, 4, 5g.

500th Birth Anniv of Raphael (3rd issue) and Christmas (3rd issue). Air 5, 10, 30g.

1983.

Third International Railways Congress, Malaga (1982). Postage 25, 50c., 1, 2, 3, 4, 5g.

Racing Cars. Postage 25, 50c., 1, 2, 3, 4, 5g.

Paintings by Rembrandt. Air 5, 10, 30g.

German Astronautics. Air 5, 10, 30g.

Winter Olympic Games, Sarajevo (1984). Postage 25, 50c., 1, 2, 3, 4, 5g.

Bicentenary of Manned Flight. Air 5, 10, 30g.

Pope John Paul II. Postage 25, 50c., 1, 2, 3, 4, 5g.

Olympic Games, Los Angeles (1984). Air 5, 10, 30g.

Veteran Cars. Postage 25, 50c., 1, 2, 3, 4, 5g.; Air 5, 10, 30g.

"Brasiliana '83" International Stamp Exhibition and 52nd F.I.P. Congress (1st issue). 1982 World Cup (4th issue) stamps optd. Postage 25, 50c., 1, 2, 3, 4g.

"Brasiliana '83" International Stamp Exhibition and 52nd F.I.P. Congress (2nd issue). 1982 Raphael/ Christmas stamps optd. Postage 25, 50c., 1, 2, 3, 4g.

Aircraft Carriers. Postage 25, 50c., 1, 2, 3, 4, 5g.

South American Flowers. Air 5, 10, 30g.

South American Birds. Postage 25, 50c., 1, 2, 3, 4, 5g.

25th Anniv of International Maritime Organization. Air 5, 10, 30g.

"Philatelia '83" International Stamp Exhibition, Dusseldorf. 1983 International Railway Congress stamps optd. Postage 25, 50c., 1, 2, 3, 4g.

"Exfivia - 83" International Stamp Exn, Bolivia. 1982 Durer paintings optd. Postage 25, 50c., 1, 2, 3, 4g.

Flowers, Postage 10, 25g.; Chaco soldier, Postage 50g.; Dams, Postage 75g; Air 100g.; President, Air 200g.

1984.

Bicent of Manned Flight. Postage 25, 50c., 1, 2, 3, 4, 5g.

World Communications Year. Air 5, 10, 30g.

Dogs. Postage 25, 50c., 1, 2, 3, 4, 5g.

Olympic Games, Los Angeles. Air 5, 10, 30g.

Animals. Postage 10, 25, 50, 75g.

1983 Anniversaries. Air 100g. (birth bicentenary of Bolivar), 200g. (76th anniv of boy scout movement).

Christmas (1983) and New Year. Postage 25, 50c., 1, 2, 3, 4, 5g.

Winter Olympic Games, Sarajevo. Air 5, 10, 30g.

Troubador Knights. Postage 25, 50c., 1, 2, 3, 4, 5g.

World Cup Football Championship, Spain (1982) and Mexico (1986). Air 5, 10, 30g.

International Stamp Fair, Essen. 1983 Racing Cars stamps optd. Postage 25, 50c., 1, 2, 3, 4g.

Extinct Animals. Postage 25, 50c., 1, 2, 3, 4, 5g.

60th Anniv of International Chess Federation. Air 5, 10, 30g.

19th Universal Postal Union Congress Stamp Exhibition, Hamburg (1st issue). Sailing Ships. Postage 25, 50c., 1, 2, 3, 4, 5g.

19th Universal Postal Union Congress Stamp Exhibition, Hamburg (2nd issue). Troubadour Knights stamp optd. Postage 5g.

Leaders of the World. British Railway Locomotives. Postage 25, 50c., 1, 2, 3, 4, 5g.

50th Anniv of First Lufthansa Europe–South America Direct Mail Flight. Air 5, 10, 30g.

30th Anniv of Presidency of Alfredo Stroessner. Dam stamp optd. Air 100g.

"Ausipex 84" International Stamp Exhibition, Melbourne. 1974 U.P.U. Centenary stamps optd. Postage 10, 15, 20, 25, 30, 50, 75c.

"Phila Korea 1984" International Stamp Exhibition, Seoul. Olympic Games, Los Angeles, and Extinct Animals stamps optd. Postage 5g.; Air 30g.

German National Football Championship and Sindelfingen Stamp Bourse. 1974 World Cup stamps (1st issue) optd. Postage 10, 15, 20, 25, 30, 50, 75c.

Cats. Postage 25, 50c., 1, 2, 3, 4, 5g.

Winter Olympic Games Medal Winners. Air 5, 10, 30g.

Centenary of Motor Cycle. Air 5, 10, 30g.

1985.

Olympic Games Medal Winners. Postage 25, 50c., 1, 2, 3, 4, 5g.

Christmas (1984). Costumes. Air 5, 10, 30g.

Fungi. Postage 25, 50c., 1, 2, 3, 4, 5g.

Participation of Paraguay in Preliminary Rounds of World Cup Football Championship. Air 5, 10, 30g.

"Interpex 1985" and "Stampex 1985" Stamp Exhibitions. 1981 Queen Mother's Birthday stamp optd. Postage 10g. × 2.

International Federation of Aero-Philatelic Societies Congress, Stuttgart. 1984 Lufthansa Europe–South America Mail Flight stamp optd. Air 10g.

Paraguayan Animals and Extinct Animals. Postage 25, 50c., 1, 2, 3, 4, 5g.

"Olymphilex 85" Olympic Stamps Exhibition, Lausanne. 1984 Winter Olympics Games Medal Winners stamp optd. Postage 10g.

"Israphil 85" International Stamp Exhibition, Tel Aviv. 1982 Boy Scout Movement stamp optd. Postage 5g.

Music Year. Air 5, 10, 30g.

Birth Bicentenary of John J. Audubon (ornithologist). Birds. Postage 25, 50c., 1, 2, 3, 4, 5g.

Railway Locomotives. Air 5, 10, 30g.

"Italia '85" International Stamp Exhibition, Rome (1st issue). 1983 Pope John Paul II stamp optd. Postage 5g.

50th Anniv of Chaco Peace (1st issue). 1972 Visit of Argentine President stamp optd. Postage 30c.

"Mophila 85" Stamp Exhibition, Hamburg. 1984 U.P.U. Congress Stamp Exhibition (1st issue) stamp optd. Postage 5g.

"Lupo 85" Stamp Exhibition, Lucerne. 1984 Bicentenary of Manned Flight stamp optd. Postage 5g.

"Expo 85" World's Fair, Tsukuba. 1981 "Philatokyo '81" stamp optd. Air 30g.

International Youth Year. Mark Twain. Postage 25, 50c., 1, 2, 3, 4, 5g.

75th Death Anniv of Henri Dunant (founder of Red Cross). Air 5, 10, 30g.

150th Anniv of German Railways (1st issue). Postage 25, 50c., 1, 2, 3, 4, 5g.

International Chess Federation Congress, Graz. Air 5, 10, 30g.

50th Anniv of Chaco Peace (2nd issue) and Government Achievements. Postage 10, 25, 50, 75g.; Air 100, 200g.

Paintings by Rubens. Postage 25, 50c., 1, 2, 3, 4, 5g.

Explorers and their Ships. Air 5, 10, 30g.

"Italia '85" International Stamp Exhibition, Rome (2nd issue). Paintings. Air 5, 10, 30g.

1986.

Paintings by Titian. Postage 25, 50c., 1, 2, 3, 4, 5g.

International Stamp Fair, Essen. 1985 German Railways stamps optd. Postage 25, 50c., 1, 2, 3, 4g.

Fungi. Postage 25, 50c., 1, 2, 3, 4, 5g.

"Ameripex '86" International Stamp Exhibition, Chicago. Air 5, 10, 30g.

Lawn Tennis (1st issue). Inscriptions in black or red. Air 5, 10, 30g.

Centenary of Motor Car. Postage 25, 50c., 1, 2, 3, 4, 5g.

Appearance of Halley's Comet. Air 5, 10, 30g.

Qualification of Paraguay for World Cup Football Championship Final Rounds, Mexico (1st issue). Postage 25, 50c., 1, 2, 3, 4, 5g.

Tenth Pan-American Games, Indianapolis (1987). 1985 Olympic Games Medal Winners stamp optd. Postage 5g.

Maybach Cars. Postage 25, 50c., 1, 2, 3, 4, 5g.

Freight Trains. Air 5, 10, 30g.

Qualification of Paraguay for World Cup Football Championship Final Rounds (2nd issue). Air 5, 10, 30g.

Winter Olympic Games, Calgary (1988) (1st issue). 1983 Winter Olympic Games stamp optd. Postage 5g.

Centenary of Statue of Liberty. Postage 25, 50c., 1, 2, 3, 4, 5g.

Dogs. Postage 25, 50c., 1, 2, 3, 4, 5g.

150th Anniv of German Railways (2nd issue). Air 5, 10, 30g.

Lawn Tennis (2nd issue). Postage 25, 50c., 1, 2, 3, 4, 5g.

Visit of Prince Hitachi of Japan. 1972 Visit of President of Paraguay to Japan stamps optd. Postage 10, 15, 20, 25, 30, 50, 75c.

International Peace Year. Paintings by Rubens. Air 5, 10, 30g.

Olympic Games, Seoul (1988) (1st issue). Postage 25, 50c., 1, 2, 3, 4, 5g.

27th Chess Olympiad, Dubai. 1982 Chess Paintings stamp optd. Air 10g.

1987.

World Cup Football Championship, Mexico (1986) and Italy (1990). Air 5, 10, 20, 25, 30g.

12th Spanish American Stamp and Coin Exhibition, Madrid, and 500th Anniv of Discovery of America by Columbus. 1975 South American Fauna and 1983 25th Anniv of I.M.O. stamps optd. Postage 15, 20, 25, 35, 40g.; Air 10g.

Tennis as Olympic Sport. 1986 Lawn Tennis (1st issue) stamps optd. Air 10, 30g.

Olympic Games, Barcelona (1992). 1985 Olympic Games Medal Winners stamps optd. Postage 25, 50c., 1, 2, 3, 4g.

"Olymphilex '87" Olympic Stamps Exhibition, Rome. 1985 Olympic Games Medal Winners stamp optd. Postage 5g.

Cats. Postage 1, 2, 3, 5, 60g.

Paintings by Rubens (1st issue). Postage 1, 2, 3, 5, 60g.

Saloon Cars. Air 5, 10, 20, 25, 30g.

National Topics. Postage 10g. (steel plant), 25g. (Franciscan monk), 50g. (400th anniv of Ita and Yaguaron), 75g. (450th Anniv of Asuncion); Air 100g. (airliner), 200g. (Pres. Stroessner).

"Capex 87" International Stamp Exhibition, Toronto. Cats stamps optd. Postage 1, 2, 3, 5g.

500th Anniv of Discovery of America by Columbus. Postage 1, 2, 3, 5, 60g.

Winter Olympic Games, Calgary (1988) (2nd issue). Air 5, 10, 20, 25, 30g.

Centenary of Colorado Party. National Topics and 1978 Pres. Stroessner stamps optd. Air 200, 1000g.

750th Anniv of Berlin (1st issue) and "Luposta '87" Air Stamps Exhibition, Berlin. Postage 1, 2, 3, 5, 60g.

Olympic Games, Seoul (1988) (2nd issue). Air 5, 10, 20, 25, 30g.

Rally Cars. Postage 1, 2, 3, 5, 60g.

"Exfivia 87" Stamp Exhibition, Bolivia. National Topics stamps optd. Postage 75g.; Air 100g.

"Olymphilex '88" Olympic Stamps Exhibition, Seoul. 1986 Olympic Games, Seoul (1st issue) stamps optd. Postage 2, 3, 4, 5g.

"Philatelia '87" International Stamp Exhibition, Cologne. 1986 Lawn Tennis (2nd issue) stamps optd. Postage 25, 50c., 1, 2, 3, 4g.

Italy–Argentina Match at Zurich to Launch 1990 World Cup Football Championship, Italy. 1986

Paraguay Qualification (2nd issue) stamps optd. Air 10, 30g.

"Exfilna '87" Stamp Exhibition, Gerona. 1986 Olympic Games, Seoul (1st issue) stamps optd. Postage 25, 50c.

Spanish Ships. Postage 1, 2, 3, 5, 60g.

Paintings by Rubens (2nd issue). Air 5, 10, 20, 25, 30g.

Christmas. Air 5, 10, 20, 25, 30g.

Winter Olympic Games, Calgary (1988) (3rd issue). Postage 1, 2, 3, 5, 60g.

1988.

150th Anniv of Austrian Railways. Air 5, 10, 20, 25, 30g.

"Aeropex 88" Air Stamps Exhibition, Adelaide, 1987. 750th Anniv of Berlin and "Luposta '87" stamps optd. Postage 1, 2, 3, 5g.

"Olympex" Stamp Exhibition, Calgary. 1987 Winter Olympic Games (3rd issue) stamps optd. Postage 1, 2, 3g.

Olympic Games, Seoul (3rd issue). Equestrian Events. Postage 1, 2, 3, 5, 60g.

Space Projects. Air 5, 10, 20, 25, 30g.

750th Anniv of Berlin (2nd issue). Paintings. Postage 1, 2, 3, 5, 60g.

Visit of Pope John Paul II. Postage 1, 2, 3, 5, 60g.

"Lupo Wien 88" Stamp Exhibition, Vienna. 1987 National Topics stamp optd. Air 100g.

World Wildlife Fund. Extinct Animals. Postage 1, 2, 3, 5g.

Paintings in West Berlin State Museum. Air 5, 10, 20, 25, 30g.

Bicentenary of Australian Settlement. 1981 Wedding of Prince of Wales (1st issue) optd. Postage 25, 50c., 1, 2g.

History of World Cup Football Championship (1st issue). Air 5, 10, 20, 25, 30g.

New Presidential Period, 1988–1993. 1985 Chaco Peace and Government Achievements issue optd. Postage 10, 25, 50, 75g.; Air 100, 200g.

Olympic Games, Seoul (4th issue). Lawn Tennis and Medal. Postage 1, 2, 3, 5, 60g.

Calgary Winter Olympics Gold Medal Winners. Air 5, 10, 20, 25, 30g.

History of World Cup Football Championship (2nd issue). Air 5, 10, 20, 25, 30g.

"Prenfil '88" International Philatelic Press Exhibition, Buenos Aires. "Ameripex '86" stamp optd. Air 30g.

"Philexfrance 89" International Stamp Exhibition, Paris. 1985 Explorers stamp optd. Air 30g.

PARMA Pt. 8

A former Grand Duchy of N. Italy, united with Sardinia in 1860 and now part of Italy.

100 centesimi = 1 lira.

1 Bourbon "fleur-de-lis" 2 3

1852. Imperf.

2	1	5c. black on yellow	42·00	85·00
11		5c. yellow	£5000	£600
4		10c. black	70·00	95·00
5		15c. black on pink	£1900	42·00
13		15c. red	£6000	£130
7		25c. black on purple	£9500	£140
14		25c. brown		£275
9		40c. black on blue	£1700	£225

1857. Imperf.

17	2	15c. red	£200	£325
19		25c. purple	£375	£150
20		40c. blue	46·00	£400

1859. Imperf.

28	3	5c. green	£1900	£3250
29		10c. brown	£700	£350
32		20c. blue	£1000	£160
33		40c. red	£475	£7000
35		80c. yellow	£6000	

NEWSPAPER STAMPS

1853. As T 3. Imperf.

N1	3	6c. black on pink	£1100	£250
N3		9c. black on blue	70·00	95·00

PATIALA Pt. 1

A "convention" state in the Punjab, India.

12 pies = 1 anna;
16 annas = 1 rupee.

1884. Stamps of India (Queen Victoria) with curved opt **PUTTIALLA STATE** vert.

1	23	½a. turquoise	3·75	3·75
2	–	1a. purple	48·00	55·00
3	–	2a. blue	12·00	12·00
4	–	4a. green (No. 96)	70·00	75·00
5	–	8a. mauve	£350	£380
6	–	1r. grey (No. 101)	£130	£475

1885. Stamps of India (Queen Victoria) optd **PUTTIALLA STATE** horiz.

7	23	½a. turquoise	2·25	30
11	–	1a. purple	60	30
8	–	2a. blue	4·00	1·75
9	–	4a. green (No. 96)	3·25	3·00
12	–	8a. mauve	16·00	38·00
10	–	1r. grey (No. 101)	10·00	65·00

Stamps of India optd **PATIALA STATE**.

1891. Queen Victoria.

32	40	3p. red	30	10
13	23	½a. turquoise (No. 84)	40	10
33	–	½a. green (No. 114)	90	30
14	–	9p. red	1·00	1·75
15	–	1a. purple	1·40	30
34	–	1a. red	2·50	90
17	–	1a.6p. brown	1·25	1·00
18	–	2a. blue	1·25	30
20	–	3a. orange	1·90	60
22	–	4a. green (No. 96)	2·25	60
23	–	6a. brown (No. 80)	2·50	11·00
26	–	8a. mauve	2·00	11·00
27	–	12a. purple on red	2·00	12·00
28	37	1r. green and red	4·25	42·00
29	38	2r. red and orange	£110	£650
30		3r. brown and green	£150	£700
31		5r. blue and violet	£200	£750

1903. King Edward VII.

36		3p. grey	40	10
37		½a. green (No. 122)	1·10	15
38		1a. red (No. 123)	50	10
39		2a. lilac	1·25	65
40		3a. orange	1·25	35
41		4a. olive	2·75	1·25
42		6a. bistre	3·25	7·50
43		8a. mauve	3·50	1·60
44		12a. purple on red	6·00	21·00
45		1r. green and red	3·25	3·75

1912. King Edward VII. Inscr "INDIA POSTAGE & REVENUE".

46		½a. green (No. 149)	40	25
47		1a. red (No. 150)	1·75	90

1912. King George V. Optd in two lines.

48	55	3p. grey	25	10
49	56	½a. green	70	20
50	57	1a. red	1·40	20
61		1a. brown	2·75	40
51	58	1½d. brown (A)	30	55
52	59	2a. purple	85	70
53	62	3a. orange	2·00	85
62		3a. blue	3·25	7·00
54	63	4a. olive	3·00	2·50
55	64	6a. ochre	1·25	3·25
56	65	8a. mauve	2·75	1·50
57	66	12a. red	3·50	8·00
58	67	1r. brown and green	6·00	11·00
59		2r. red and brown	13·00	£140
60		5r. blue and violet	27·00	£150

1928. King George V. Optd in one line.

63	55	3p. grey	1·75	10
64	56	½a. green	25	10
75	79	½a. green	85	30
65	80	9p. green	1·50	75
66	57	1a. brown	75	25
76	81	1a. brown	1·10	20
67	82	1a.3p. mauve	3·00	15
77	59	2a. red	40	1·40
68	70	2a. lilac	1·75	40
69	61	2a.6p. orange	4·50	1·50
70	62	3a. blue	2·75	1·50
78w		3a. red	5·50	7·00
71	71	4a. green	3·75	1·10
79	63	4a. olive	1·75	2·00
72	65	8a. mauve	5·00	2·50
73	66	1r. brown and green	7·00	7·50
74w		2r. red and orange	10·00	50·00

1937. King George VI. Optd in one line.

80	91	3p. grey	30·00	35
81		½a. brown	10·00	50
82		9p. green	4·00	1·00
83		1a. red	2·75	20
84	92	2a. red	1·50	7·50
85	–	2a.6p. violet	4·50	16·00
86	–	3a. green	4·00	7·00
87	–	3a.6p. blue	5·50	20·00
88	–	4a. brown	22·00	13·00
89	–	6a. green	21·00	45·00
90	–	8a. violet	22·00	32·00
91	–	12a. red	22·00	50·00
92	93	1r. grey and brown	22·00	38·00
93		2r. purple and brown	24·00	85·00
94		5r. green and blue	30·00	£180
95		10r. purple and red	45·00	£300
96		15r. brown and green	90·00	£475
97		25r. grey and purple	£120	£500

1943. King George VI. Optd **PATIALA** only.

(a) Issue of 1938.

98	94	3p. grey	10·00	1·75
99		½a. brown	6·50	1·25
100		9p. green	£200	5·00
101		1a. red	22·00	1·50
102	93	1r. grey and brown	12·00	80·00

(b) Issue of 1940.

103	92	3p. grey	3·00	15
104		½a. mauve	3·00	15
105		9p. green	1·00	15
106		1a. red	1·00	10
107	101	1a.3p. bistre	1·60	2·75
108		1½a. violet	12·00	2·75
109		2a. red	9·00	35
110		3a. violet	8·50	2·00
111		3½a. blue	19·00	28·00
112	102	4a. brown	8·00	2·75
113		6a. green	3·25	21·00
114		8a. violet	3·00	11·00
115		12a. purple	13·00	65·00

OFFICIAL STAMPS
Overprinted **SERVICE**.

1884. Nos. 1 to 3 (Queen Victoria).

O1	23	½a. turquoise	11·00	30
O2	–	1a. purple	90	10
O3	–	2a. blue	£4250	£120

1885. Nos. 7, 11 and 8 (Queen Victoria).

O4	23	½a. turquoise	75	20
O5	–	1a. purple	60	10
O7	–	2a. blue	60	20

1891. Nos. 13 to 28 and No. 10 (Queen Victoria).

O 8	23	½a. turquoise (No. 13)	40	10
O 9	–	1a. purple	4·50	10
O20	–	1a. red	50	10
O10a	–	2a. blue	3·25	1·75
O12	–	3a. orange	1·00	2·25
O13a	–	4a. green	1·00	30
O15	–	6a. brown	1·40	35
O16a	–	8a. mauve	2·25	1·25
O18	–	12a. purple on red	1·00	50
O19	–	1r. grey	1·40	65
O21	37	1r. green and red	5·50	9·00

1903. Nos. 36 to 45 (King Edward VII).

O22		3p. grey	30	10
O24		½a. green	40	10
O25		1a. red	60	10
O26a		2a. lilac	50	10
O28		3a. brown	3·25	2·50
O29		4a. olive	1·50	20
O30		8a. mauve	1·25	75
O32		1r. green and red	1·50	80

1907. Nos. 46/7 (King Edward VII). Inscr "INDIA POSTAGE & REVENUE".

O33		½a. green	50	20
O34		1a. red	50	10

1913. Official stamps of India (King George V). Optd **PATIALA STATE** in two lines.

O35	55	3p. grey	10	20
O36	56	½a. green	10	10
O37	57	1a. red	10	10
O38		1a. brown	7·00	1·00
O39	59	2a. mauve	60	40
O40	63	4a. olive	50	30
O41	64	6a. bistre	1·50	2·25
O42	65	8a. mauve	55	70
O43	67	1r. brown and green	1·40	1·40
O44		2r. red and brown	16·00	42·00
O45		5r. blue and violet	9·00	20·00

1927. Postage stamps of India (King George V) optd **PATIALA STATE SERVICE** in two lines.

O47	55	3p. grey	10	10
O48	56	½a. green	75	55
O58	79	½a. green	10	10
O49	57	1a. brown	15	10
O59	81	1a. brown	30	30
O50	82	1a.3p. mauve	40	10
O51	70	2a. purple	20	30
O52		2a. red	30	35
O60	59	2a. red	15	30
O53w	61	2½a. orange	60	80
O54	71	4a. green	50	30
O61	63	4a. olive	2·00	85
O55	65	8a. purple	1·00	65
O56w	66	1r. brown and green	2·75	2·75
O57		2r. red and orange	10·00	35·00

1938. Postage stamps of India (King George VI) optd **PATIALA STATE SERVICE**.

O63	91	½a. brown	75	20
O64		9p. green	13·00	55·00
O65		1a. red	75	30
O66	93	1r. grey and brown	1·00	5·50
O67		2r. purple and green	4·50	5·00
O68		5r. green and blue	15·00	50·00

1939. Surch **1A SERVICE 1A**.

O70	82	1a. on 1¼a. mauve	8·00	2·50

1940. Official stamps of India optd **PATIALA**.

O71	O 20	3p. grey	1·25	10
O72		½a. brown	4·75	10
O73		½a. purple	50	10
O74		9p. green	50	40
O75		1a. red	2·50	10
O76		1a.3p. bistre	1·00	25
O77		1½a. violet	5·00	90
O78		2a. orange	8·00	30
O79		2½a. violet	2·75	75
O80		4a. brown	1·50	2·25
O81		8a. violet	3·00	5·50

1940. Postage stamps of India (King George VI) optd **PATIALA SERVICE**.

O82	93	1r. slate and brown	5·00	9·00
O83		2r. purple and brown	12·00	55·00
O84		5r. green and blue	20·00	75·00

PENANG Pt. 1

A British Settlement which became a state of the Federation of Malaya, incorporated in Malaysia in 1963.

100 cents = 1 dollar (Straits or Malayan).

1948. Silver Wedding. As T **4b/c** of Pitcairn Islands.

1	10c. violet	30	20
2	$5 brown	30·00	28·00

1949. As Nos. 278/92 of Straits Settlement.

3	1c. black	20	20
4	2c. orange	85	20
5	3c. green	20	1·00
6	4c. brown	20	10
7	5c. purple	2·00	2·75
8	6c. grey	30	20
9	8c. red	60	3·25
10	8c. green	1·50	1·75
11	10c. mauve	20	10
12	12c. red	2·00	5·00
13	15c. blue	50	30
14	20c. black and green	50	1·00
15	20c. blue	55	1·25
16	25c. purple and orange	1·75	20
17	35c. red and purple	1·00	1·25
18	40c. red and purple	1·50	11·00
19	50c. black and blue	2·50	20
20	$1 blue and purple	17·00	2·00
21	$2 green and red	22·00	2·00
22	$3 green and brown	48·00	3·00

1949. U.P.U. As T **4d/g** of of Pitcairn Islands.

23	10c. purple	20	10
24	15c. blue	2·00	2·75
25	25c. orange	45	2·75
26	30c. black	1·50	3·50

1953. Coronation. As T **4h** of Pitcairn Islands.

27	10c. black and purple	1·50	10

1954. As T **1** of Malacca, but inscr "PENANG".

28	1c. black	10	70
29	2c. orange	50	30
30	4c. brown	70	10
31	5c. mauve	2·00	3·00
32	6c. grey	15	80
33	8c. green	20	3·50
34	10c. purple	20	10
35	12c. red	30	3·50
36	20c. blue	50	10
37	25c. purple and orange	30	10
38	30c. red and purple	30	10
39	35c. red and purple	70	60
40	50c. black and blue	50	10
41	$1 blue and purple	2·50	30
42	$2 green and red	10·00	3·75
43	$5 green and brown	45·00	3·75

1957. As Nos. 92/102 of Kedah, but inset portrait of Queen Elizabeth II.

44	1c. black	10	1·00
45	2c. red	10	1·00
46	4c. sepia	10	10
47	5c. lake	10	30
48	8c. green	1·25	2·25
49	10c. brown	30	10
50	20c. blue	60	40
51	50c. black and blue	60	70
52	$1 blue and purple	5·50	1·00
53	$2 green and red	18·00	12·00
54	$5 brown and green	21·00	12·00

1 Copra

1960. As Nos. 44/54, but with inset Arms of Penang as in T **1**.

55	1c. black	10	1·60
56	2c. red	10	1·60
57	4c. brown	10	10
58	5c. lake	10	10
59	8c. green	2·75	4·50
60	10c. purple	30	10
61	20c. blue	40	10
62	50c. black and blue	30	30
63	$1 blue and purple	4·25	1·75
64	$2 green and red	4·25	6·00
65	$5 brown and green	10·00	8·50

2 "Vanda hookeriana"

1965. As Nos. 115/21 of Kedah, but with Arms of Penang inset and inscr "PULAU PINANG" as in T **2**.

66	2	1c. multicoloured	10	1·25
67	–	2c. multicoloured	10	1·25
68	–	5c. multicoloured	20	10
69	–	6c. multicoloured	30	1·25
70	–	10c. multicoloured	20	10
71	–	15c. multicoloured	1·00	10
72	–	20c. multicoloured	1·60	30

The higher values used in Penang were Nos. 20/7 of Malaysia (National Issues).

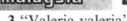

3 "Valeria valeria"

1971. Butterflies. As Nos. 124/30 of Kedah but with Arms of Penang inset and inscr "pulau pinang" as in T **3**.
75 – 1c. multicoloured . . . . . . 40 2·00
76 – 2c. multicoloured . . . . . . 70 2·00
77 – 5c. multicoloured . . . . . . 1·50 40
78 – 6c. multicoloured . . . . . . 1·50 2·00
79 – 10c. multicoloured . . . . . 1·50 15
80 – 15c. multicoloured . . . . . 1·50 10
81 **3** 20c. multicoloured . . . . . 1·75 60
The higher values in use with this issue were Nos. 64/71 of Malaysia (National Issues).

4 "Etlingera elatior" (inscr "Phaeomeria speciosa")

5 Cocoa

1979. Flowers. As Nos. 135/41 of Kedah, but with Arms of Penang and inscr "pulau pinaug" as in T **4**.
86 1c. "Rafflesia hasseltii" . . . 10 1·00
87 2c. "Pterocarpus indicus" . . 10 1·00
88 5c. "Lagerstroemia speciosa" 10 35
89 10c. "Durio zibethinus" . . . 15 10
90 15c. "Hibiscus rosa-sinensis" 15 10
91 20c. "Rhododendron scortechinii" 20 10
92 25c. Type **4** 40 30

1986. As Nos. 152/8 of Kedah but with Arms of Penang and inscr "PULAU PINANG" as in T **5**.
100 1c. Coffee 10 10
101 2c. Coconuts 10 10
102 5c. Type **5** 10 10
103 10c. Black pepper 10 10
104 15c. Rubber 10 10
105 20c. Oil palm 10 10
106 30c. Rice 10 15

PENRHYN ISLAND Pt. 1

One of the Cook Islands in the South Pacific. A dependency of New Zealand. Used Cook Islands stamps until 1973 when further issues for use in the Northern group of the Cook Islands issues appeared.

A. NEW ZEALAND DEPENDENCY

1902. Stamps of New Zealand (Pictorials) surch **PENRHYN ISLAND.** and value in native language.
4 **23** ½d. green . . . . 80 6·00
10 **42** 1d. red . . . . 1·25 4·00
1 **26** 2½d. blue (No. 249) . . . . 3·00 8·00
14 **28** 3d. brown . . . . 10·00 22·00
15 **31** 6d. red . . . . 15·00 35·00
16a **34** 1s. orange . . . . 42·00 48·00

1914. Stamps of New Zealand (King Edward VII) surch **PENRHYN ISLAND.** and value in native language.
19 **51** ½d. green . . . . 80 8·00
22 6d. red . . . . 23·00 70·00
23 1s. orange . . . . 42·00 95·00

1917. Stamps of New Zealand (King George V) optd **PENRHYN ISLAND.**
28 **62** ½d. green . . . . 1·00 2·00
29 1½d. grey . . . . 6·50 18·00
30 1½d. brown . . . . 60 18·00
24a 2½d. blue . . . . 2·00 7·00
31 3d. brown . . . . 3·50 22·00
26a 6d. red . . . . 5·00 19·00
27a 1s. orange . . . . 12·00 32·00

1920. Pictorial types as Cook Islands (1920), but inscr "PENRHYN".
32 **9** ½d. black and green . . . . 1·00 16·00
33 – 1d. black and red . . . . . 1·50 15·00
34 – 1½d. black and violet . . . 6·50 19·00
40 – 2½d. brown and black . . . 3·50 27·00
35 – 3d. black and red . . . . . 2·50 8·50
36 – 6d. brown and red . . . . . 3·25 20·00
37 – 1s. black and blue . . . . . 10·00 26·00

B. PART OF COOK ISLANDS

1973. Nos. 228/9, 231, 233/6, 239/40 and 243/5 of Cook Is. optd **PENRHYN NORTHERN** or **PENRHYN** ($1, 2).
41B 1c. multicoloured 10 10
42B 2c. multicoloured 10 10
43B 3c. multicoloured 20 10
44B 4c. multicoloured 10 10
45B 5c. multicoloured 10 10
46B 6c. multicoloured 15 30
47B 8c. multicoloured 20 40
48B 15c. multicoloured 30 50
49B 20c. multicoloured . . . . . 1·50 80
50B 50c. multicoloured . . . . . 50 1·75
51B $1 multicoloured . . . . . . 50 2·00
52B $2 multicoloured . . . . . . 50 2·25

1973. Nos. 450/2 of Cook Is. optd **PENRHYN NORTHERN**.
53 **138** 25c. multicoloured 30 20
54 – 30c. multicoloured 30 20
55 – 50c. multicoloured 30 20

10 "Ostracion sp."

1974. Fishes. Multicoloured.
56 ½c. Type **10** 50 75
57 1c. "Monodactylus argenteus" 70 75
58 2c. "Pomacanthus imperator" 80 75
59 3c. "Chelmon rostratus" . . . 80 50
60 4c. "Chaetodon ornatissimus" 80 50
61 5c. "Chaetodon melanotus" 80 50
62 8c. "Chaetodon raffessi" . . . 80 50
63 10c. "Chaetodon ephippium" 85 50
64 20c. "Pygoplites diacanthus" 1·75 50
65 25c. "Heniochus acuminatus" 1·75 50
66 60c. "Plectorhynchus chaetodonoides" . . . . . 2·50 90
67 $1 "Balistipus undulatus" . . 3·25 1·25
68 $2 Bird's-eye view of Penrhyn 3·00 12·00
69 $5 Satellite view of Australasia 3·00 5·00
Nos. 68/9 are size 63 × 25 mm.

11 Penrhyn Stamps of 1902

13 Churchill giving "V" sign

12 "Adoration of the Kings" (Memling)

1974. Cent of Universal Postal Union. Mult.
70 25c. Type **11** 20 45
71 50c. Stamps of 1920 . . . . . 35 55

1974. Christmas. Multicoloured.
72 5c. Type **12** 20 30
73 10c. "Adoration of the Shepherds" (Hugo van der Goes) 25 30
74 25c. "Adoration of the Magi" (Rubens) 40 45
75 30c. "The Holy Family" (Borgianni) 45 65

1974. Birth Cent of Sir Winston Churchill.
76 **13** 30c. brown and gold 35 85
77 – 50c. green and gold 45 90
DESIGN: 50c. Full-face portrait.

1975. "Apollo–Soyuz" Space Project. Optd **KIA ORANA ASTRONAUTS** and emblem.
78 $5 Satellite view of Australasia 1·75 2·50

15 "Virgin and Child" (Bouts)

16 "Pieta"

1975. Christmas. Paintings of the "Virgin and Child" by artists given below. Multicoloured.
79 7c. Type **15** 40 10
80 15c. Leonardo da Vinci . . . 70 20
81 35c. Raphael . . . . 1·10 35

1976. Easter. 500th Birth Anniv of Michelangelo.
82 **16** 15c. brown and gold 25 15
83 – 20c. lilac and gold 30 15
84 – 35c. green and gold 40 20
MS85 112 × 72 mm. Nos. 82/4 . . 85 1·25
DESIGNS: Nos. 83/4 show different views of the "Pieta".

17 "Washington crossing the Delaware" (E. Leutze)

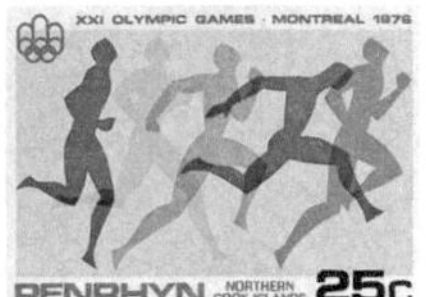
18 Running

1976. Bicentenary of American Revolution.
86 **17** 30c. multicoloured 25 15
87 – 30c. multicoloured 25 15
88 – 30c. multicoloured 25 15
89 – 50c. multicoloured 30 20
90 – 50c. multicoloured 30 20
91 – 50c. multicoloured 30 20
MS92 103 × 103 mm. Nos. 86/91 1·25 1·25
DESIGNS: Nos. 86/88, "Washington crossing the Delaware" (E. Leutze); Nos. 89/91, "The Spirit of '76" (A. M. Willard).
Nos. 86/88 and 89/91 were each printed together, se-tenant, forming a composite design of the complete painting. Type **17** shows the left-hand stamp of the 30c. design.

1976. Olympic Games, Montreal. Multicoloured.
93 25c. Type **18** 25 15
94 30c. Long jumping 30 15
95 75c. Throwing the javelin . . 55 25
MS96 86 × 128 mm. Nos. 93/5 . . 1·10 2·00

19 "The Flight into Egypt"

1976. Christmas. Durer Engravings.
97 **19** 7c. black and silver 15 10
98 – 15c. blue and silver 25 15
99 – 35c. violet and silver 35 25
DESIGNS: 15c. "Adoration of the Magi"; 35c. "The Nativity".

20 The Queen in Coronation Robes

1977. Silver Jubilee. Multicoloured.
100 50c. Type **20** 25 60
101 $1 The Queen and Prince Philip 35 65
102 $2 Queen Elizabeth II . . . 50 80
MS103 128 × 87 mm. Nos. 100/2 1·00 1·50
Stamps from the miniature sheet have silver borders.

21 "The Annunciation"

1977. Christmas. Illustrations by J. S. von Carolsfeld.
104 **21** 7c. brown, purple and gold 40 15
105 – 15c. red, purple and gold 60 15
106 – 35c. deep green, green and gold . . . . 1·00 30
DESIGNS: 15c. "The Announcement to the Shepherds"; 35c. "The Nativity".

22 Iiwi

23 "The Road to Calvary"

1978. Bicentenary of Discovery of Hawaii. Birds and Artefacts. Multicoloured.
107 20c. Type **22** 80 30
108 20c. Elgin cloak 80 30
109 30c. Apapane 90 40
110 30c. Feather image of a god 90 40
111 35c. Moorhen 90 45
112 35c. Feather cape, helmet and staff 90 45
113 75c. Hawaii O-o . . . . . . 1·50 80
114 75c. Feather image and cloak 1·50 80
MS115 Two sheets, each 78 × 119 mm. containing. (a) Nos. 107, 109, 111, 113. (b) Nos. 108, 110, 112, 114 . . . . 5·00 7·00

1978. Easter. 400th Birth Anniv of Rubens. Multicoloured.
116 10c. Type **23** 20 10
117 15c. "Christ on the Cross" 25 15
118 35c. "Christ with Straw" . . 45 25
MS119 87 × 138 mm. Nos. 116/18 1·00 1·60
Stamps from No. **MS**119 are slightly larger (28 × 36 mm).

1978. Easter. Children's Charity. Designs as Nos. 116/18 in separate miniature sheets, 49 × 68 mm, each with a face value of 60c.+5c.
MS120 As Nos. 116/18. Set of 3 sheets . . . . 90 1·50

24 Royal Coat of Arms

25 "Madonna of the Pear"

1978. 25th Anniv of Coronation.
121 **24** 90c. black, gold and mauve 30 60
122 – 90c. multicoloured 30 60
123 – 90c. black, gold and green 30 60
MS124 75 × 122 mm. Nos. 121/3 1·10 2·00
DESIGNS: No. 122, Queen Elizabeth II; No. 123, New Zealand coat of arms.

1978. Christmas. 450th Death Anniv of Albrecht Durer. Multicoloured.
125 30c. Type **25** 65 30
126 35c. "The Virgin and Child with St. Anne" (Durer) . . 65 30
MS127 101 × 60 mm. Nos. 125/6 1·00 1·25

26 Sir Rowland Hill and G.B. Penny Black Stamp

27 Max and Moritz

1979. Death Centenary of Sir Rowland Hill. Mult.
128 75c. Type **26** 40 55
129 75c. 1974 U.P.U. Centenary 25c. and 50c. commemoratives 40 55
130 90c. Sir Rowland Hill 45 70
131 90c. 1978 Coronation Anniversary 90c. commemorative 45 70
MS132 116 × 58 mm. Nos. 128/31 1·25 1·50
Stamps from No. **MS**132 have cream backgrounds.

1979. International Year of the Child. Illustrations from "Max and Moritz" stories by Wilhelm Busch. Multicoloured.
133 12c. Type **27** 15 15
134 12c. Max and Moritz looking down chimney 15 15
135 12c. Max and Moritz making off with food 15 15
136 12c. Cook about to beat dog 15 15
137 15c. Max sawing through bridge 20 15
138 15c. Pursuer approaching bridge 20 15
139 15c. Collapse of bridge . . . 20 15
140 15c. Pursuer in river 20 15
141 20c. Baker locking shop . . . 20 20
142 20c. Max and Moritz emerge from hiding 20 20
143 20c. Max and Moritz falling in dough 20 20
144 20c. Max and Moritz made into buns 20 20

28 "Christ carrying Cross" (Book of Ferdinand II)
29 "Queen Elizabeth, 1937" (Sir Gerald Kelly)

1980. Easter. Scenes from 15th-cent Prayer Books. Multicoloured.
145 12c. Type **28** 15 20
146 20c. "The Crucifixion" (William Vrelant, Book of Duke of Burgundy) 20 25
147 35c. "Descent from the Cross" (Book of Ferdinand II) 30 45
MS148 111 × 65 mm. Nos. 145/7 55 1·00
Stamps from No. **MS**148 have cream borders.

1980. Easter. Children's Charity. Designs as Nos. 145/7 in separate miniature sheets 54 × 85 mm, each with a face value of 70c.+5c.
MS149 As Nos. 145/7. Set of 3 sheets 75 1·00

1980. 80th Birthday of The Queen Mother.
150 **29** $1 multicoloured . . . . . 1·25 1·25
MS151 55 × 84 mm. **29** $2.50 multicoloured . . . . 1·60 1·60

30 Falk Hoffman, East Germany (platform diving) (gold)
31 "The Virgin of Counsellors" (Luis Dalmau)

1980. Olympic Medal Winners. Multicoloured.
152 10c. Type **30** 30 10
153 10c. Martina Jaschke, East Germany (platform diving) 30 10
154 20c. Tomi Polkolainen, Finland (archery) 35 15
155 20c. Kete Losaberidse, U.S.S.R. (archery) 35 15
156 30c. Czechoslovakia (football) 40 20
157 30c. East Germany (football) 40 20
158 50c. Barbel Wockel, East Germany (200 m) 50 30
159 50c. Pietro Mennea, Italy (200 m) 50 30
MS160 150 × 106 mm. Nos. 152/9 1·40 1·75
Stamps from No. **MS**160 have gold borders.

1980. Christmas. Mult.
161 20c. Type **31** 15 15
162 35c. "Virgin and Child" (Serra brothers) 20 20
163 50c. "The Virgin of Albocacer" (Master of the Porciuncula) 30 30
MS164 135 × 75 mm. Nos. 161/3 1·50 1·50

1980. Christmas. Children's Charity. Design as Nos. 161/3 in separate miniature sheets, 54 × 77 mm, each with a face value of 70c.+5c.
MS165 As Nos. 161/3. Set of 3 sheets 1·50 1·50

32 Amatasi
33 "Jesus at the Grove" (Veronese)

1981. Sailing Craft and Ships (1st series). Mult.
166 1c. Type **32** 20 15
167 1c. Ndrua (canoe) 20 15
168 1c. Waka (canoe) 20 15
169 1c. Tongiaki (canoe) 20 15
170 3c. Va'a Teu'ua (canoe) . . . 40 15
171 3c. "Vitoria" (Del Cano's ship) 40 15
172 3c. "Golden Hind" (Drake's ship) 40 15
173 3c. "La Boudeuse" (Bougainville's ship) . . . 40 15
174 4c. H.M.S. "Bounty" 50 15
175 4c. "L'Astrolabe" (Dumont d'Urville's ship) 50 15
176 4c. "Star of India" (full-rigged ship) 50 15
177 4c. "Great Republic" (clipper) 50 15
178 6c. "Balcutha" (clipper) . . . 50 20
179 6c. "Coonatto" (clipper) . . 50 20
180 6c. "Antiope" (clipper) . . . 50 20
181 6c. "Taeping" (clipper) . . . 50 20
182 10c. "Preussen" (full-rigged ship) 50 75
183 10c. "Pamir" (barque) . . . 50 75
184 10c. "Cap Hornier" (full-rigged ship) 50 75
185 10c. "Patriarch" (clipper) . . 50 75
186 15c. Type **32** 50 85
187 15c. As No. 167 . . . . . . 50 85
188 15c. As No. 168 . . . . . . 50 85
189 15c. As No. 169 . . . . . . 50 85
190 20c. As No. 170 . . . . . . 50 85
191 20c. As No. 171 . . . . . . 50 85
192 20c. As No. 172 . . . . . . 50 85
193 20c. As No. 173 . . . . . . 50 85
194 30c. As No. 174 . . . . . . 50 95
195 30c. As No. 175 . . . . . . 50 95
196 30c. As No. 176 . . . . . . 50 95
197 30c. As No. 177 . . . . . . 50 95
198 50c. As No. 178 . . . . . . 1·00 1·75
199 50c. As No. 179 . . . . . . 1·00 1·75
200 50c. As No. 180 . . . . . . 1·00 1·75
201 50c. As No. 181 . . . . . . 1·00 1·75
202 $1 As No. 182 . . . . 2·50 1·50
203 $1 As No. 183 . . . . 2·50 1·50
204 $1 As No. 184 . . . . 2·50 1·50
205 $1 As No. 185 . . . . 2·50 1·50
206 $2 "Cutty Sark" (clipper) . . 4·50 3·25
207 $4 "Mermerus" (clipper) . . 9·00 5·00
208 $6 H.M.S. "Resolution" and H.M.S. "Discovery" (Cook's ships) . . . . . . 15·00 12·00
Nos. 186/201 are 41 × 35 mm, Nos. 202/5 41 × 25 mm and Nos. 206/8 47 × 33 mm in size.
Nos. 181 and 201 are wrongly inscribed "TEAPING".
See also Nos. 337/55.

1981. Easter. Paintings. Multicoloured.
218 30c. Type **33** 40 20
219 40c. "Christ with Crown of Thorns" (Titian) 55 25
220 50c. "Pieta" (Van Dyck) . . 60 30
MS221 110 × 68 mm. Nos. 218/20 2·75 2·00

1981. Easter. Children's Charity. Designs as Nos. 218/20 in separate miniature sheets 70 × 86 mm, each with a face value of 70c.+5c.
MS222 As Nos. 218/20. Set of 3 sheets . . . . 1·25 1·50

34 Prince Charles as Young Child
35 Footballers

1981. Royal Wedding. Multicoloured.
223 40c. Type **34** 15 35
224 50c. Prince Charles as schoolboy 15 40
225 60c. Prince Charles as young man 20 40
226 70c. Prince Charles in ceremonial Naval uniform 20 45
227 80c. Prince Charles as Colonel-in-Chief, Royal Regiment of Wales 20 45
MS228 99 × 89 mm. Nos. 223/7 90 2·00

1981. International Year for Disabled Persons. Nos. 223/7 surch **+5c**.
229 **34** 40c.+5c. multicoloured . . 15 50
230 – 50c.+5c. multicoloured . . 15 55
231 – 60c.+5c. multicoloured . . 20 55
232 – 70c.+5c. multicoloured . . 20 60
233 – 80c.+5c. multicoloured . . 20 65
MS234 99 × 89 mm. As Nos. 229/33, but 10c. premium on each stamp 80 2·50

1981. World Cup Football Championship, Spain (1982). Multicoloured.
235 15c. Type **35** 20 15
236 15c. Footballer wearing orange jersey with black and mauve stripes 20 15
237 15c. Player in blue jersey . . 20 15
238 35c. Player in blue jersey . . 30 25
239 35c. Player in red jersey . . . 30 25
240 35c. Player in yellow jersey with green stripes 30 25
241 50c. Player in orange jersey 40 35
242 50c. Player in mauve jersey 40 35
243 50c. Player in black jersey . . 40 35
MS244 113 × 151 mm. As Nos. 235/43, but each stamp with a premium of 3c. . . . . . . 4·75 2·75

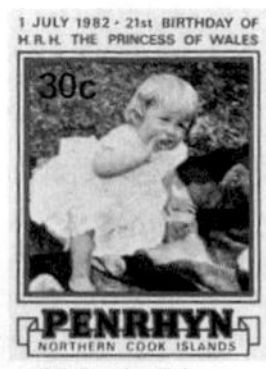

36 "The Virgin on a Crescent"
37 Lady Diana Spencer as Baby

1981. Christmas. Engravings by Durer.
245 **36** 30c. violet, purple and stone . . . . 90 1·00
246 – 40c. violet, purple and stone . . . . 1·25 1·40
247 – 50c. violet, purple and stone . . . . 1·50 1·75
MS248 134 × 75 mm. As Nos. 245/7, but each stamp with a premium of 2c. . . . . 2·00 2·25
MS249 Designs as Nos. 245/7 in separate miniature sheets, 58 × 85 mm, each with a face value of 70c.+5c. Set of 3 sheets . . 1·50 1·75
DESIGNS: 40c. "The Virgin at the Fence"; 50c. "The Holy Virgin and Child".

1982. 21st Birthday of Princess of Wales. Multicoloured.
250 30c. Type **37** 30 30
251 50c. As young child 40 45
252 70c. As schoolgirl 60 60
253 80c. As teenager 70 80
254 $1.40 As a young lady . . . 1·10 1·25
MS255 87 × 110 mm. Nos. 250/4 6·50 3·50

1982. Birth of Prince William of Wales (1st issue). Nos. 223/7 optd **BIRTH OF PRINCE WILLIAM OF WALES 21 JUNE 1982**.
256 40c. Type **34** 30 35
257 50c. Prince Charles as schoolboy 40 45
258 60c. Prince Charles as young man 45 55
259 70c. Prince Charles in ceremonial Naval uniform 50 60
260 80c. Prince Charles as Colonel-in-Chief, Royal Regiment of Wales 50 65
MS261 99 × 89 mm. Nos. 256/60 6·00 7·00

1982. Birth of Prince William of Wales (2nd issue). As Nos. 250/5 but with changed inscriptions. Multicoloured.
262 30c. As Type **37** (A) 60 55
263 30c. As Type **37** (B) 60 55
264 50c. As No. 251 (A) 70 65
265 50c. As No. 251 (B) 70 65
266 70c. As No. 252 (A) 90 80
267 70c. As No. 252 (B) 90 80
268 80c. As No. 253 (A) 95 85
269 80c. As No. 253 (B) 95 85
270 $1.40 As No. 254 (A) . . . . 1·40 1·25
271 $1.40 As No. 254 (B) . . . . 1·40 1·25
MS272 88 × 109 mm. As No. **MS**255 (C) . . . . 4·75 3·25
INSCR: A. "21 JUNE 1982. BIRTH OF PRINCE WILLIAM OF WALES"; B. "COMMEMORATING THE BIRTH OF PRINCE WILLIAM OF WALES"; C. "21 JUNE 1982. ROYAL BIRTH PRINCE WILLIAM OF WALES".

39 "Virgin and Child" (detail, Joos Van Cleve)
40 Red Coral

1982. Christmas. Details from Renaissance Paintings of "Virgin and Child". Multicoloured.
273 25c. Type **39** 30 40
274 48c. "Virgin and Child" (Filippino Lippi) 45 55
275 60c. "Virgin and Child" (Cima da Conegliano) . . . 60 70
MS276 134 × 73 mm. As Nos. 273/5 but each with 2c. charity premium 1·00 2·00

1982. Christmas. Children's Charity. Designs as Nos. 273/5, but without frames, in separate miniature sheets, 60 × 85 mm, each with a face value of 70c.+5c.
MS277 As Nos. 273/5. Set of 3 sheets 1·25 1·60

1983. Commonwealth Day. Multicoloured.
278 60c. Type **40** 40 45
279 60c. Aerial view of Penrhyn atoll 40 45
280 60c. Eleanor Roosevelt on Penrhyn during Second World War 40 45
281 60c. Map of South Pacific . . 40 45

41 Scout Emblem and Blue Tropical Flower

1983. 75th Anniv of Boy Scout Movement. Multicoloured.
282 36c. Type **41** . . . . 1·50 65
283 48c. Emblem and pink flower 1·75 75
284 60c. Emblem and orange flower . . . . 1·75 1·00
MS285 86 × 46 mm. $2 As 48c., but with elements of design reversed 1·50 3·00

1983. 15th World Scout Jamboree, Alberta, Canada. Nos. 282/4 optd **XV WORLD JAMBOREE CANADA 1983**.
286 36c. Type **41** . . . . 1·25 40
287 48c. Emblem and pink flower 1·50 55
288 60c. Emblem and orange flower . . . . 1·60 75
MS289 86 × 46 mm. $2 As 48c., but with elements of design reversed 1·50 3·50

43 School of Sperm Whales

1983. Whale Conservation. Multicoloured.
290 8c. Type **43** . . . . 1·00 70
291 15c. Harpooner preparing to strike . . . . 1·40 95
292 35c. Whale attacking boat . . 2·00 1·40
293 60c. Dead whales marked with flags . . . . 3·00 2·00
294 $1 Dead whales on slipway 3·75 3·00

44 "Mercury" (cable ship)

1983. World Communications Year. Multicoloured.
295 36c. Type **44** 80 35
296 48c. Men watching cable being laid 85 45
297 60c. "Mercury" (different) . . 1·10 60
MS298 115 × 90 mm. As Nos. 295/7 but each with charity premium of 3c. . . . . 1·25 1·60
On No. **MS**298 the values are printed in black and have been transposed with the World Communications Year logo.

1983. Various stamps surch. (a) Nos. 182/5, 190/7 and 206.
299 18c. on 10c. "Preussen" . . . 1·00 30
300 18c. on 10c. "Pamir" . . . . 1·00 30
301 18c. on 10c. "Cap Hornier" 1·00 30
302 18c. on 10c. "Patriarch" . . 1·00 30
303 36c. on 20c. Va'a Teu'ua . . 1·25 45
304 36c. on 20c. "Vitoria" . . . 1·25 45
305 36c. on 20c. "Golden Hind" 1·25 45
306 36c. on 20c. "La Boudeuse" 1·25 45
307 36c. on 30c. H.M.S. "Bounty" . . . . 1·25 45
308 36c. on 30c. "L'Astrolabe" 1·25 45
309 36c. on 30c. "Star of India" 1·25 45
310 36c. on 30c. "Great Republic" . . . . 1·25 45
311 $1.20 on $2 "Cutty Sark" . . 4·50 1·60

(b) Nos. 252/3.
312 72c. on 70c. Princess Diana as schoolgirl . . . . 4·00 1·50
313 96c. on 80c. Princess Diana as teenager . . . . 4·00 1·75

1983. Nos. 225/6, 268/9, 253 and 208 surch.
314 48c. on 60c. Prince Charles as young man . . . . 3·75 1·75
315 72c. on 70c. Prince Charles in ceremonial Naval uniform 4·25 1·90
316 96c. on 80c. As No. 253 (inscr "21 JUNE 1982 ...") 3·00 1·10
317 96c. on 80c. As No. 253 (inscr "COMMEMORATING ...") . . . . 2·00 1·10
318 $1.20 on $4.40 As young lady 3·50 1·60
319 $5.60 on $6 H.M.S. "Resolution" and "Discovery" . . . . 18·00 10·00

45 George Cayley's Airship Design, 1837

1983. Bicentenary of Manned Flight. Mult. A. Inscr "NORTHERN COOK ISLANDS".

320A	36c. Type **45**	1·00	80
321A	48c. Dupuy de Lome's man-powered airship, 1872	1·25	90
322A	60c. Santos Dumont's airship "Ballon No. 6", 1901	1·50	1·25
323A	96c. Lebaudy-Juillot's airship, No. 1 "La Jaune", 1902	2·25	1·75
324A	$1.32 Airship LZ-127 "Graf Zeppelin", 1929	3·00	2·50
MS325A	113 × 138 mm. Nos. 320A/4A	6·50	11·00

B. Corrected spelling optd in black on silver over original inscription.

320B	36c. Type **45**	35	30
321B	48c. Dupuy de Lome's man-powered airship, 1872	40	45
322B	60c. Santos Dumont's airship "Ballon No. 6", 1901	45	50
323B	96c. Lebaudy-Juillot's airship No. 1 "La Jaune", 1902	75	80
324B	$1.32 Airship LZ-127 "Graf Zeppelin", 1929	1·00	1·10
MS325B	113 × 138 mm. Nos. 320B/4B	2·25	4·25

46 "Madonna in the Meadow" 47 Waka

1983. Christmas. 500th Birth Anniv of Raphael. Multicoloured.

326	36c. Type **46**	60	40
327	42c. "Tempi Madonna"	60	40
328	48c. "The Smaller Cowper Madonna"	80	50
329	60c. "Madonna della Tenda"	95	60
MS330	87 × 115 mm. As Nos. 326/9 but each with a charity premium of 3c.	3·00	2·50

1983. Nos. 266/7, 227 and 270 surch.

331	72c. on 70c. As No. 252 (inscr "21 JUNE 1982 ...")	1·75	80
332	72c. on 70c. As No. 252 (inscr "COMMEMORATING ...")	1·00	60
333	96c. on 80c. Prince Charles as Colonel-in-Chief, Royal Regiment of Wales	1·75	65
334	$1.20 on $1.40 As No. 254 (inscr "21 JUNE 1982 ...")	2·00	70
335	$1.20 on $1.40 As No. 254 (inscr "COMMEMORATING ...")	1·50	65

1983. Christmas. 500th Birth Anniv of Raphael. Children's Charity. Designs as Nos. 326/9 in separate miniature sheets, 65 × 84 mm, each with a face value of 75c.+5c.

MS336	As Nos. 326/9. Set of 4 sheets	1·75	3·00

1984. Sailing Craft and Ships (2nd series). Multicoloured.

337	2c. Type **47**	70	70
338	4c. Amatasi	70	70
339	5c. Ndrua	70	70
340	8c. Tongiaki	70	70
341	10c. "Vitoria"	70	60
342	18c. "Golden Hind"	1·00	70
343	20c. "La Boudeuse"	70	70
344	30c. H.M.S. "Bounty"	1·00	70
345	36c. "L'Astrolabe"	70	70
346	48c. "Great Republic"	70	70
347	50c. "Star of India"	70	70
348	60c. "Coonatto"	70	70
349	72c. "Antiope"	70	70
350	80c. "Balcutha"	70	70
351	96c. "Cap Hornier"	85	85
352	$1.20 "Pamir"	2·50	1·40
353	$3 "Mermerus" (41 × 31 mm)	5·00	3·00
354	$5 "Cutty Sark" (41 × 31 mm)	5·50	5·00
355	$9.60 H.M.S. "Resolution" and H.M.S. "Discovery" (41 × 31 mm)	19·00	17·00

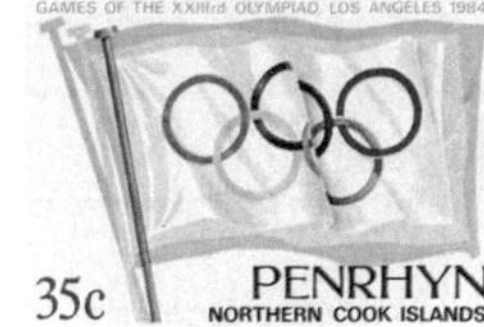

48 Olympic Flag

1984. Olympic Games, Los Angeles. Mult.

356	35c. Type **48**	30	35
357	60c. Olympic torch and flags	50	55
358	$1.80 Ancient athletes and Coliseum	1·50	1·60
MS359	103 × 86 mm. As Nos. 356/8 but each with a charity premium of 5c.	2·40	2·50

49 Penrhyn Stamps of 1978, 1979 and 1981

1984. "Ausipex" International Stamp Exhibition, Melbourne. Multicoloured.

360	60c. Type **49**	50	75
361	$1.20 Location map of Penrhyn	1·00	1·25
MS362	90 × 90 mm. As Nos. 360/1, but each with a face value of 96c.	1·75	2·00

1984. Birth of Prince Harry. Nos. 223/4 and 250/1 surch **$2 Birth of Prince Harry 15 Sept. 1984**.

363	$2 on 30c. Type **37**	1·60	1·50
364	$2 on 40c. Type **34**	1·75	1·75
365	$2 on 50c. Prince Charles as schoolboy	1·75	1·75
366	$2 on 50c. Lady Diana as young child	1·60	1·50

51 "Virgin and Child" (Giovanni Bellini) 53 Lady Elizabeth Bowes-Lyon, 1921

52 Harlequin Duck

1984. Christmas. Paintings of the Virgin and Child by different artists. Multicoloured.

367	36c. Type **51**	60	35
368	48c. Lorenzo di Credi	75	45
369	60c. Palma the Older	80	50
370	96c. Raphael	1·00	80
MS371	93 × 118 mm. As Nos. 367/70, but each with a charity premium of 5c.	2·50	3·00

1984. Christmas. Children's Charity. Designs as Nos. 367/70, but without frames, in separate miniature sheets 67 × 81 mm, each with a face value of 96c.+10c.

MS372	As Nos. 367/70. Set of 4 sheets	3·00	3·50

1985. Birth Bicentenary of John J. Audubon (ornithologist). Multicoloured.

373	20c. Type **52**	2·00	1·75
374	55c. Sage grouse	2·75	2·75
375	65c. Solitary sandpiper	3·00	3·00
376	75c. Dunlin	3·25	3·50
MS377	Four sheets, each 70 × 53 mm. As Nos. 373/6, but each with a face value of 95c.	9·00	6·50

Nos. 373/6 show original paintings.

1985. Life and Times of Queen Elizabeth the Queen Mother. Each violet, silver and yellow.

378	75c. Type **53**	40	65
379	95c. With baby Princess Elizabeth, 1926	50	80
380	$1.20 Coronation Day, 1937	65	1·00
381	$2.80 On her 70th birthday	1·25	2·00
MS382	66 × 90 mm. $5 The Queen Mother	2·40	3·25

See also No. **MS**403.

54 "The House in the Wood"

1985. International Youth Year. Birth Centenary of Jacob Grimm (folklorist). Multicoloured.

383	75c. Type **54**	2·50	2·25
384	95c. "Snow-White and Rose-Red"	2·75	2·50
385	$1.15 "The Goose Girl"	3·00	2·75

55 "The Annunciation"

1985. Christmas. Paintings by Murillo. Mult.

386	75c. Type **55**	1·25	1·25
387	$1.15 "Adoration of the Shepherds"	1·75	1·75
388	$1.80 "The Holy Family"	2·50	2·50
MS389	66 × 131 mm. As Nos. 386/8, but each with a face value of 95c.	2·75	3·00
MS390	Three sheets, each 66 × 72 mm. As Nos. 386/8, but with face values of $1.20, $1.45 and $2.75. Set of 3 sheets	4·50	4·75

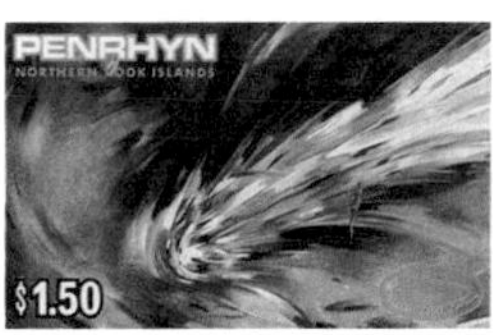

56 Halley's Comet

1986. Appearance of Halley's Comet. Design showing details of the painting "Fire and Ice" by Camille Rendal. Multicoloured.

391	$1.50 Type **56**	2·75	1·50
392	$1.50 Stylized "Giotto" spacecraft	2·75	1·50
MS393	108 × 43 mm. $3 As Nos. 391/2 (104 × 39 mm). Imperf	2·25	2·50

Nos. 391/2 were printed together, forming a composite design of the complete painting.

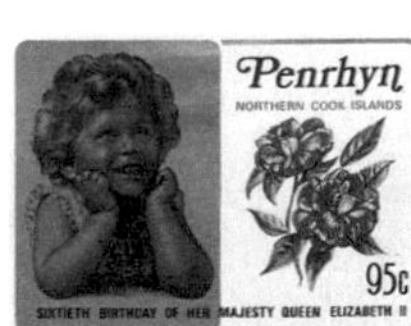

57 Princess Elizabeth aged Three, 1929, and Bouquet

1986. 60th Birthday of Queen Elizabeth II. Multicoloured.

394	95c. Type **57**	1·50	80
395	$1.45 Profile of Queen Elizabeth and St. Edward's Crown	2·00	1·25
396	$2.50 Queen Elizabeth aged three and in profile with Imperial State Crown (56 × 30 mm)	2·50	2·00

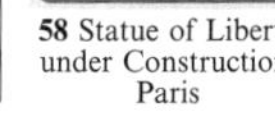

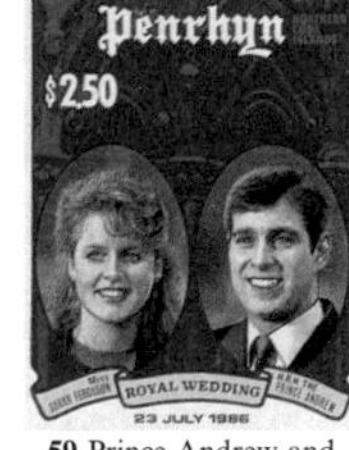

58 Statue of Liberty under Construction, Paris 59 Prince Andrew and Miss Sarah Ferguson

1986. Centenary of Statue of Liberty. Each black, gold and green.

397	95c. Type **58**	65	70
398	$1.75 Erection of Statue, New York	1·10	1·25
399	$3 Artist's impression of Statue, 1876	2·10	2·25

See also No. **MS**412.

1986. Royal Wedding. Multicoloured.

400	$2.50 Type **59**	3·50	3·50
401	$3.50 Profiles of Prince Andrew and Miss Sarah Ferguson	4·00	4·00

1986. "Stampex '86" Stamp Exhibition, Adelaide. No. **MS**362 surch **$2** in black on gold.

MS402	$2 on 96c. × 2	6·00	7·00

The "Stampex '86" exhibition emblem is overprinted on the sheet margin.

1986. 86th Birthday of Queen Elizabeth the Queen Mother. Nos. 378/81 in miniature sheet, 90 × 120 mm.

MS403	Nos. 378/81	13·00	9·50

61 "Adoration of the Shepherds" 65 "The Garvagh Madonna"

1986. Christmas. Engravings by Rembrandt. Each brown, ochre and gold.

404	65c. Type **61**	1·75	1·75
405	$1.75 "Virgin and Child"	3·00	3·00
406	$2.50 "The Holy Family"	4·25	4·25
MS407	120 × 87 mm. As Nos. 404/6, but each size 31 × 39 mm with a face value of $1.50	12·00	9·00

1986. Visit of Pope John Paul II to **South Pacific**. Nos. 404/6 surch **SOUTH PACIFIC VISIT 21 TO 24 NOVEMBER 1986 +10c**.

408	65c.+10c. Type **61**	3·00	2·00
409	$1.75+10c. "Virgin and Child"	4·50	3·50
410	$2.50+10c. "The Holy Family"	5·50	4·00
MS411	120 × 87 mm. As Nos. 408/10, but each size 31 × 39 mm with a face value of $1.50+10c.	14·00	9·00

1987. Centenary of Statue of Liberty (1986) (2nd issue). Two sheets, each 122 × 122 mm, containing multicoloured designs as **T 112a** of Niue.

MS412	Two sheets. (a) 65c. Head and torch of Statue; 65c. Torch at sunset; 65c. Restoration workers with flag; 65c. Statue and Manhattan skyline; 65c. Workers and scaffolding. (b) 65c. Workers on Statue crown (horiz); 65c. Aerial view of Ellis Island (horiz); 65c. Ellis Island Immigration Centre (horiz); 65c. View from Statue to Ellis Island and Manhattan (horiz); 65c. Restoration workers (horiz). Set of 2 sheets	7·50	11·00

1987. Royal Ruby Wedding. Nos. 68/9 optd **Fortieth Royal Wedding Anniversary 1947–87**.

413	$2 Birds-eye view of Penrhyn	2·00	2·25
414	$5 Satellite view of Australasia	3·50	4·25

1987. Christmas. Religious Paintings by Raphael. Multicoloured.

415	95c. Type **65**	1·50	1·50
416	$1.60 "The Alba Madonna"	2·00	2·00
417	$2.25 "The Madonna of the Fish"	3·00	3·00
MS418	91 × 126 mm. As Nos. 415/17, but each with a face value of $1.15	11·00	12·00
MS419	70 × 86 mm. $4.80 As No. 417, but size 36 × 39 mm.	12·00	12·00

66 Athletics

1988. Olympic Games, Seoul. Multicoloured.

420	55c. Type **66**	75	65
421	95c. Pole vaulting (vert)	1·25	1·00

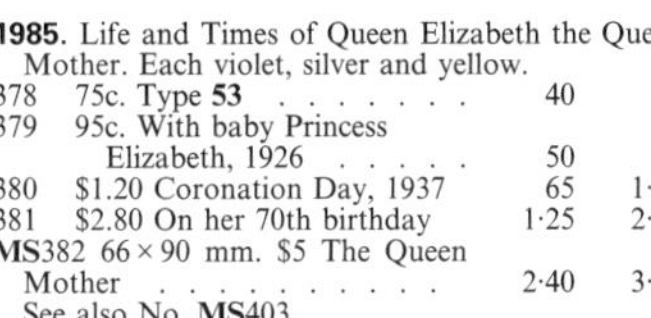

422 $1.25 Shot putting . . . . . 1·50 1·40
423 $1.50 Lawn tennis (vert) . . 2·50 1·75
MS424 110 × 70 mm. As Nos. 421 and 423, but each with a face value of $2.50 . . . . 4·00 5·00

1988. Olympic Gold Medal Winners, Seoul. Nos. 420/3 optd.
425 55c. Type **66** (optd **CARL LEWIS UNITED STATES 100 METERS**) 80 60
426 95c. Pole vaulting (optd **LOUISE RITTER UNITED STATES HIGH JUMP**) . . . . 1·25 90
427 $1.25 Shot putting (optd **ULF TIMMERMANN EAST GERMANY SHOT-PUT**) 1·50 1·25
428 $1.50 Lawn tennis (optd **STEFFI GRAF WEST GERMANY WOMEN'S TENNIS**) . . . . 4·00 1·75
MS429 110 × 70 mm. $2.50 As No. 421 (optd **JACKIE JOYNER-KERSEE United States Heptathlon**); $2.50 As No. 423 (optd **STEFFI GRAF West Germany Women's Tennis MILOSLAV MECIR Czechoslovakia Men's Tennis**) 5·00 5·50

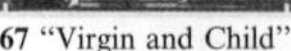
67 "Virgin and Child" **69** Virgin Mary

68 Neil Armstrong stepping onto Moon

1988. Christmas. Designs showing different "Virgin and Child" paintings by Titian.
430 **67** 70c. multicoloured 90 90
431 – 85c. multicoloured . . . . 1·00 1·00
432 – 95c. multicoloured . . . . 1·25 1·25
433 – $1.25 multicoloured . . . 1·50 1·50
MS434 100 × 80 mm. $6.40 As type **67**, but diamond-shaped (57 × 57 mm) . . . . 6·00 7·00

1989. 20th Anniv of First Manned Moon Landing. Multicoloured.
435 55c. Type **68** . . . . 1·60 70
436 75c. Astronaut on Moon carrying equipment . . . . 1·75 85
437 95c. Conducting experiment on Moon . . . . 2·25 1·10
438 $1.25 Crew of "Apollo 11" 2·50 1·40
439 $1.75 Crew inside "Apollo 11" . . . . 2·75 1·90

1989. Christmas. Details from "The Nativity" by Durer. Multicoloured.
440 55c. Type **69** 80 80
441 70c. Christ Child and cherubs 90 90
442 85c. Joseph . . . . 1·25 1·25
443 $1.25 Three women . . . . . 1·60 1·60
MS444 88 × 95 mm. $6.40 "The Nativity" (31 × 50 mm) . . . . 6·50 7·50

70 Queen Elizabeth the Queen Mother

1990. 90th Birthday of Queen Elizabeth the Queen Mother.
445 **70** $2.25 multicoloured . . . 2·50 2·50
MS446 85 × 73 mm. **70** $7.50 multicoloured . . . . 12·00 12·00

71 "Adoration of the Magi" (Veronese)

1990. Christmas. Religious Paintings. Multicoloured.
447 55c. Type **71** . . . . 1·00 1·00
448 70c. "Virgin and Child" (Quentin Metsys) . . . . . 1·40 1·40
449 85c. "Virgin and Child Jesus" (Hugo van der Goes) . . . 1·60 1·60
450 $1.50 "Adoration of the Kings" (Jan Gossaert) . . 2·50 2·50
MS451 108 × 132 mm. $6.40 "Virgin and Child with Saints, Francis, John the Baptist, Zenobius and Lucy" (Domenico Veneziano) 8·00 9·00

1990. "Birdpex '90" Stamp Exhibition, Christchurch, New Zealand. Nos. 373/6 surch **Birdpex '90** and emblem.
452 $1.50 on 20c. Type **52** . . . 1·90 2·25
453 $1.50 on 55c. Sage grouse . . 1·90 2·25
454 $1.50 on 65c. Solitary sandpiper . . . . 1·90 2·25
455 $1.50 on 75c. Dunlin . . . . 1·90 2·25

1991. 65th Birthday of Queen Elizabeth II. No. 208 optd **COMMEMORATING 65th BIRTHDAY OF H.M. QUEEN ELIZABETH II**.
456 $6 H.M.S. "Resolution" and "Discovery", 1776–80 . . . 12·00 13·00

74 "The Virgin and Child with Saints" (G. David)

1991. Christmas. Religious Paintings. Multicoloured.
457 55c. Type **74** . . . . 1·00 1·00
458 85c. "Nativity" (Tintoretto) 1·50 1·50
459 $1.15 "Mystic Nativity" (Botticelli) . . . . 1·75 1·75
460 $1.85 "Adoration of the Shepherds" (B. Murillo) . . 2·75 3·25
MS461 79 × 103 mm. $6.40 "The Madonna of the Chair" (Raphael) (vert) . . . . 11·00 11·00

74a Running

1992. Olympic Games, Barcelona. Multicoloured.
462 75c. Type **74a** . . . . 1·60 1·60
463 95c. Boxing . . . . 1·75 1·75
464 $1.15 Swimming . . . . . . 2·00 2·00
465 $1.50 Wrestling . . . . . . 2·25 2·25

75 Marquesan Canoe

1992. 6th Festival of Pacific Arts, Rarotonga. Multicoloured.
466 $1.15 Type **75** . . . . 1·60 1·60
467 $1.75 Tangaroa statue from Rarotonga . . . . 2·00 2·00
468 $1.95 Manihiki canoe . . . . 2·25 2·25

1992. Royal Visit by Prince Edward. Nos. 466/8 optd **ROYAL VISIT**.
469 $1.15 Type **75** . . . . 2·25 2·00
470 $1.75 Tangaroa statue from Rarotonga . . . . 3·00 2·75
471 $1.95 Manihiki canoe . . . . 3·75 3·50

76 "Virgin with Child and Saints" (Borgognone)

1992. Christmas. Religious Paintings by Ambrogio Borgognone. Multicoloured.
472 55c. Type **76** 75 75
473 85c. "Virgin on Throne" . . 1·10 1·10
474 $1.05 "Virgin on Carpet" . . 1·40 1·40
475 $1.85 "Virgin of the Milk" 2·25 2·25
MS476 101 × 86 mm. $6.40 As 55c., but larger (36 × 46 mm) . . . . 7·00 8·00

77 Vincente Pinzon and "Nina"

1992. 500th Anniv of Discovery of America by Columbus. Multicoloured.
477 $1.15 Type **77** . . . . 2·00 2·00
478 $1.35 Martin Pinzon and "Pinta" . . . . 2·25 2·25
479 $1.75 Christopher Columbus and "Santa Maria" . . . . 3·00 3·00

78 Queen Elizabeth II in 1953 **80** "Virgin on Throne with Child" (detail) (Tura)

79 Bull-mouth Helmet

1993. 40th Anniv of Coronation.
480 **78** $6 multicoloured . . . . . 6·50 8·50

1993. Marine Life. Multicoloured.
481 5c. Type **79** 10 10
482 10c. Daisy coral 10 10
483 15c. Hydroid coral 10 15
484 20c. Feather-star 15 20
485 25c. Sea star 20 25
486 30c. Varicose nudibranch . . 20 25
487 50c. Smooth sea star 35 40
488 70c. Black-lip pearl oyster . . 50 55
489 80c. Four-coloured nudibranch 60 65
490 85c. Prickly sea cucumber . . 60 65
491 90c. Organ pipe coral 65 70
492 $1 Blue sea lizard 75 80
493 $2 Textile cone shell . . . . 1·50 1·60
494 $3 Starfish . . . . 2·20 2·30
495 $5 As $3 . . . . 3·75 4·00
496 $8 As $3 . . . . 5·00 5·25
497 $10 As $3 . . . . 7·25 7·50
Nos. 494/7 are larger, 47 × 34 mm, and include a portrait of Queen Elizabeth II at top right.

1993. Christmas.
499 **80** 55c. multicoloured . . . . 1·00 1·00
500 – 85c. multicoloured . . . . 1·50 1·50
501 – $1.05 multicoloured . . . 1·75 1·75
502 – $1.95 multicoloured . . . 2·75 3·00
503 – $4.50 mult (32 × 47 mm) 6·00 7·00
DESIGNS: 80c. to $4.50, Different details from "Virgin on Throne with Child" (Cosme Tura).

81 Neil Armstrong stepping onto Moon

1994. 25th Anniv of First Manned Moon Landing.
504 **81** $3.25 multicoloured . . . 7·50 8·00

82 "The Virgin and Child with Sts. Paul and Jerome" (Vivarini) **84** Queen Elizabeth the Queen Mother at Remembrance Day Ceremony

83 Battleship Row burning, Pearl Harbor

1994. Christmas. Religious Paintings. Multicoloured.
505 90c. Type **82** . . . . 1·10 1·25
506 90c. "The Virgin and Child with St. John" (Luini) . . 1·10 1·25
507 90c. "The Virgin and Child with Sts. Jerome and Dominic" (Lippi) . . . . 1·10 1·25
508 90c. "Adoration of the Shepherds" (Murillo) . . . 1·10 1·25
509 $1 "Adoration of the Kings" (detail of angels) (Reni) . . 1·10 1·25
510 $1 "Madonna and Child with the Infant Baptist" (Raphael) . . . . 1·10 1·25
511 $1 "Adoration of the Kings" (detail of manger) (Reni) 1·10 1·25
512 $1 "Virgin and Child" (Borgognone) . . . . . . 1·10 1·25

1995. 50th Anniv of End of Second World War. Multicoloured.
513 $3.75 Type **83** . . . . 7·50 7·50
514 $3.75 Boeing B-25 Superfortress "Enola Gay" over Hiroshima . . . . . 7·50 7·50

1995. 95th Birthday of Queen Elizabeth the Queen Mother.
515 **84** $4.50 multicoloured . . . 9·00 9·00

85 Anniversary Emblem, United Nations Flag and Headquarters

1995. 50th Anniv of United Nations.
516 **85** $4 multicoloured . . . . . 4·00 5·50

86 Loggerhead Turtle

1995. Year of the Sea Turtle. Multicoloured.
517 $1.15 Type **86** . . . . 1·75 2·00
518 $1.15 Hawksbill turtle . . . 1·75 2·00
519 $1.65 Olive ridley turtle . . . 2·25 2·50
520 $1.65 Green turtle . . . . . 2·25 2·50

87 Queen Elizabeth II and Rose

1996. 70th Birthday of Queen Elizabeth.
521 **87** $4.25 multicoloured . . . 5·00 6·50

88 Olympic Flame, National Flags and Sports

1996. Centenary of Modern Olympic Games.
522 **88** $5 multicoloured . . . . . 6·50 8·00

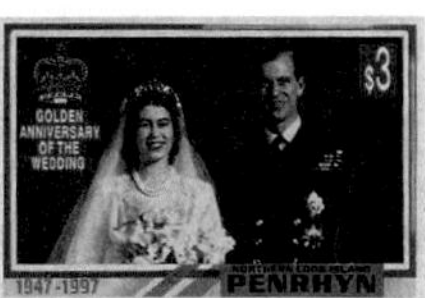

89 Royal Wedding, 1947

1997. Golden Wedding of Queen Elizabeth and Prince Philip.
523 **89** $3 multicoloured . . . . . 4·00 3·75
MS524 42 × 28 mm. **89** $4 multicoloured . . . . 4·25 5·00

90 Diana, Princess of Wales with Sons

90a King George VI and Queen Elizabeth on Wedding Day

1998. Diana, Princess of Wales Commemoration.
525 **90** $1.50 multicoloured . . . 1·50 1·75
MS526 70 × 100 mm. **90** $3.75 multicoloured . . . . 6·50 6·50

1998. Children's Charities. No. **MS**526 surch **+$1 CHILDREN'S CHARITIES**.
MS527 70 × 100 mm. **90** $3.75+$1 multicoloured . . . . 3·50 4·25

1999. New Millennium. Nos. 466/8 optd **KIA ORANA THIRD MILLENNIUM**.
528 $1.15 Type **75** . . . . 1·25 1·25
529 $1.75 Tangaroa statue from Rarotonga . . . . 1·60 1·60
530 $1.95 Manihiki canoe . . . . 1·75 1·75

2000. Queen Elizabeth the Queen Mother's 100th Birthday.
531 **90a** $2.50 purple and brown 2·25 2·40
532 – $2.50 brown . . . . . . 2·25 2·40
533 – $2.50 green and brown . . 2·25 2·40
534 – $2.50 blue and brown . . 2·25 2·40
MS535 72 × 100 mm. $10 multicoloured . . . . 7·50 8·50
DESIGNS: No. 532, Queen Elizabeth with young Princess Elizabeth; 533, Royal Family in 1930; 534, Queen Elizabeth with Princesses Elizabeth and Margaret; **MS**535, Queen Elizabeth wearing blue gown.

90b Ancient Greek Javelin-throwers

2000. Olympic Games, Sydney. Multicoloured.
536 $2.75 Type **90b** . . . . . . 2·40 2·50
537 $2.75 Modern javelin-thrower 2·40 2·50
538 $2.75 Ancient Greek discus-thrower . . . . 2·40 2·50
539 $2.75 Modern discus-thrower 2·40 2·50
MS540 90 × 99 mm. $3.50 Cook Islands Olympic Torch Relay runner in traditional costume (vert) . . . . 3·00 3·50

91 Ocean Sunfish

2003. Endangered Species. Ocean Sunfish.
541 **91** 80c. multicoloured . . . . 1·00 1·10
542 — 90c. multicoloured . . . . 1·10 1·25
543 — $1.15 multicoloured . . . 75 80
544 — $1.95 multicoloured . . . 1·25 1·40
DESIGNS: 90c. to $1.95, Ocean sunfish.

91a Statue of Liberty

2003. "United We Stand". Support for Victims of 11 September 2001 Terrorist Attacks. Multicoloured.
MS545 75 × 109 mm. **91a** $1.50 × 4 Statue of Liberty, Twin Towers and flags of USA and Cook Islands . . . . 4·50 4·75

OFFICIAL STAMPS

1978. Optd or surch **O.H.M.S.**
O 1 1c. multicoloured (No. 57) 15 10
O 2 2c. multicoloured (No. 58) 15 10
O 3 3c. multicoloured (No. 59) 25 10
O 4 4c. multicoloured (No. 60) 25 10
O 5 5c. multicoloured (No. 61) 30 10
O 6 8c. multicoloured (No. 62) 35 15
O 7 10c. multicoloured (No. 63) 40 15
O 8 15c. on 60c. mult (No. 66) 45 25
O 9 18c. on 60c. mult (No. 66) 50 25
O10 20c. multicoloured (No. 64) 50 25
O11 25c. multicoloured (No. 65) 55 30
O12 30c. on 60c. mult (No. 66) 55 35
O13 50c. multicoloured (No. 89) 1·10 55
O14 50c. multicoloured (No. 90) 1·10 55
O15 50c. multicoloured (No. 91) 1·10 55
O16 $1 multicoloured (No. 101) 1·75 45
O17 $2 multicoloured (No. 102) 3·00 50

1985. Nos. 206/8, 278/81, 337/47 and 349/55 optd **O.H.M.S.** or surch also.
O18 2c. Type **47** 70 80
O19 4c. Amatasi 70 80
O20 5c. Ndrua 70 80
O21 8c. Tongiaki 70 80
O22 10c. "Vitoria" 70 80
O23 18c. "Golden Hind" . . . . 2·00 90
O24 20c. "La Boudeuse" . . . . 1·75 90
O25 30c. H.M.S. "Bounty" . . . 2·75 1·00
O26 40c. on 36c. "L'Astrolabe" 1·75 90
O27 50c. "Star of India" . . . . 1·75 90
O28 55c. on 48c. "Great Republic" . . . . 1·75 90
O39 65c. on 60c. Type **40** . . . . 80 1·00
O40 65c. on 60c. Aerial view of Penrhyn atoll . . . . . . 80 1·00
O41 65c. on 60c. Eleanor Roosevelt on Penrhyn during Second World War 80 1·00
O42 65c. on 60c. Map of South Pacific . . . . 80 1·00
O29 75c. on 72c. "Antiope" . . . 2·50 1·60
O30 75c. on 96c. "Cap Hornier" 2·50 1·60
O31 80c. "Balcutha" . . . . . . 2·50 1·60
O32 $1.20 "Pamir" . . . . . . 2·75 1·60
O33 $2 "Cutty Sark" . . . . . . 5·50 3·25
O34 $3 "Mermerus" . . . . . . 4·25 3·50
O35 $4 "Mermerus" . . . . . . 5·50 5·00
O36 $5 "Cutty Sark" . . . . . . 8·00 6·50
O37 $6 H.M.S. "Resolution" and H.M.S. "Discovery" . . . 9·50 8·50
O38 $9.60 H.M.S. "Resolution" and H.M.S. "Discovery" 13·00 12·00

1998. Nos. 481/93 optd **O.H.M.S.**
O43 5c. Type **79** 10 10
O44 10c. Daisy coral 10 10
O45 15c. Hydroid coral 10 15
O46 20c. Feather-star 15 20
O47 25c. Sea star 20 25
O48 30c. Varicose nudibranch . . 20 25
O49 50c. Smooth sea star 35 40
O50 70c. Black-lip pearl oyster 50 55
O51 80c. Four-coloured nudibranch 60 65
O52 85c. Prickly sea cucumber . . 60 65
O53 90c. Organ pipe coral . . . 65 70
O54 $1 Blue sea lizard 75 80
O55 $2 Textile cone shell . . . . 1·50 1·60

PERAK Pt. 1

A state of the Federation of Malaya, incorporated in Malaysia in 1963.

100 cents = 1 dollar (Straits or Malayan).

Stamps of Straits Settlement optd or surch.

1878. No. 11 optd with crescent and star and **P** in oval.
1 2c. brown £1600 £1200

1880. Optd **PERAK**.
10 **9** 2c. brown . . . . 19·00 48·00
17 2c. red . . . . 3·00 2·25

1883. Surch **2 CENTS PERAK**.
16 2c. on 4c. red £550 £250

1886. No. 63a surch **ONE CENT PERAK**.
(a) Without full point.
30 1c. on 2c. red . . . . 40·00 50·00

(b) With final full point.
26 1c. on 2c. red . . . . 65·00 85·00

1886. No. 63a surch **1 CENT PERAK**.
28 1c. on 2c. red £120 £130

1886. No. 63a surch **One CENT PERAK**.
33b 1c. on 2c. red . . . . 2·25 2·25

1889. No. 17 surch **ONE CENT** (with full point).
41 1c. on 2c. red £225 £130

1891. Surch **PERAK One CENT**.
57 1c. on 2c. red . . . . 1·75 6·50
43 1c. on 6c. lilac . . . . 45·00 26·00

1891. Surch **PERAK Two CENTS**.
48 2c. on 24c. green . . . . . . 14·00 9·50

42 Tiger

44 Tiger

45 Elephants

1892.
61 **42** 1c. green . . . . 2·25 15
62 2c. red . . . . 1·75 30
63 2c. orange . . . . 50 3·25
64 5c. blue . . . . 3·25 7·50

1895. Surch **3 CENTS**.
65 **42** 3c. red . . . . 3·00 3·25

1895.
66 **44** 1c. purple and green . . . . 2·25 50
67 2c. purple and brown . . . 2·25 50
68 3c. purple and red . . . . . 2·50 40
69 4c. purple and red . . . . . 10·00 4·75
70 5c. purple and yellow . . . 3·75 55
71 8c. purple and blue . . . . 45·00 65
72 10c. purple and orange . . . 13·00 50
73 25c. green and red . . . . . £140 12·00
74 50c. purple and black . . . 48·00 29·00
75 50c. green and black £180 £160
76 **45** $1 green £170 £180
77 $2 green and red £275 £300
78 $3 green and yellow £325 £375
79 $5 green and blue £500 £500
80 $25 green and orange . . . £7000 £2500

1900. Surch in words.
81 **44** 1c. on 2c. purple and brown 50 2·25
82 1c. on 4c. purple and red . . 75 10·00
83 1c. on 5c. purple and yellow 1·75 11·00
84 3c. on 8c. purple and blue 3·75 8·50
85 3c. on 50c. green and black 2·25 5·50
86 **45** 3c. on $1 green . . . . . . 55·00 £140
87 3c. on $2 green and red . . 29·00 85·00

50 Sultan Iskandar

51 Sultan Iskandar

1935.
88 **50** 1c. black . . . . 1·00 10
89 2c. green . . . . 1·00 10
90 4c. orange . . . . 1·50 10
91 5c. brown 60 10
92 6c. red . . . . 11·00 4·25
93 8c. grey . . . . 1·00 10
94 10c. purple 70 15
95 12c. blue . . . . 2·00 1·00
96 25c. purple and red . . . . 2·00 1·00
97 30c. purple and orange . . 2·50 1·50
98 40c. red and purple . . . . 4·25 4·50
99 50c. black on green . . . . 4·50 1·25
100 $1 black and red on blue 2·50 1·25
101 $2 green and red . . . . . 20·00 8·50
102 $5 green and red on green 90·00 40·00

1938.
103 **51** 1c. black . . . . 9·00 10
104 2c. green . . . . 4·25 10
105 2c. orange . . . . 3·50 6·00
106a 3c. green . . . . 2·75 4·50
107 4c. orange . . . . 38·00 10
108 5c. brown . . . . 6·00 10
109 6c. red . . . . 27·00 10
110 8c. grey . . . . 24·00 10
111 8c. red . . . . 1·00 65·00
112 10c. purple . . . . 26·00 10
113 12c. blue . . . . 20·00 1·00
114 15c. blue . . . . 4·00 13·00
115 25c. purple and red . . . 60·00 3·25
116 30c. purple and orange . . 9·50 2·25
117 40c. red and purple . . . 50·00 2·00
118 50c. black on green . . . 32·00 75
119 $1 black and red on blue £130 16·00
120 $2 green and red . . . . £140 60·00
121 $5 green and red on green £200 £275

1948. Silver Wedding. As T **4b/c** of Pitcairn Islands.
122 10c. violet 15 10
123 $5 green . . . . 22·00 28·00

1949. U.P.U. As T **4d/g** of Pitcairn Islands.
124 10c. purple 15 10
125 15c. blue . . . . 1·50 2·00
126 25c. orange . . . . 30 1·75
127 50c. black . . . . 1·25 3·50

52 Sultan Yussuf 'Izzuddin Shah

53 Sultan Idris Shah

1950.
128 **52** 1c. black 10 10
129 2c. orange 20 10
130 3c. green . . . . 2·50 10
131 4c. brown 50 10
132 5c. purple . . . . 50 2·00
133 6c. grey 30 10
134 8c. red . . . . 65 2·25
135 8c. green . . . . 1·00 1·00
136 10c. purple 20 10
137 12c. red . . . . 1·00 3·50
138 15c. blue 75 10
139 20c. black and green . . . 75 50
140 20c. blue 75 10
141 25c. purple and orange . . 50 10
142 30c. red and purple . . . . 1·50 20
143 35c. red and purple . . . . 1·00 25
144 40c. red and purple . . . . 2·75 6·00
145 50c. black and blue . . . . 2·75 10
146 $1 blue and purple . . . . 7·00 1·00
147 $2 green and red . . . . . 13·00 7·00
148 $5 green and brown . . . 38·00 14·00

1953. Coronation. As T **4h** of Pitcairn Islands.
149 10c. black and purple . . . . 1·50 10

1957. As Nos. 92/102 of Kedah, but portrait of Sultan Yussuf Izzuddin Shah.
150 1c. black 10 20
151 2c. orange . . . . 30 1·00
152 4c. brown 20 10
153 5c. lake 20 10
154 8c. green . . . . 2·00 3·50
155 10c. sepia . . . . 1·50 10
156 10c. purple . . . . 3·50 10
157 20c. blue . . . . 2·25 10
158a 50c. black and blue 40 10
159 $1 blue and purple . . . . 6·50 40
160a $2 green and red . . . . . 3·25 2·25
161a $5 brown and green . . . . 8·00 8·00

1963. Installation of Sultan of Perak.
162 **53** 10c. multicoloured 10 10

54 "Vanda hookeriana"

1965. As Nos. 115/21 of Kedah, but with inset portrait of Sultan Idris as in T **54**.
163 **54** 1c. multicoloured 10 50
164 – 2c. multicoloured 10 70
165 – 5c. multicoloured 10 10
166 – 6c. multicoloured 15 40
167 – 10c. multicoloured 15 10
168 – 15c. multicoloured 80 10
169 – 20c. multicoloured . . . . 1·25 10
The higher values used in Perak were Nos. 20/7 of Malaysia (National Issues).

55 "Delias ninus"

1971. Butterflies. As Nos. 124/30 of Kedah, but with portrait of Sultan Idris as In T **55**.
172 **55** 1c. multicoloured 40 2·00
173 – 2c. multicoloured 1·00 2·00
174 – 5c. multicoloured 1·25 10
175 – 6c. multicoloured 1·25 2·00
176 – 10c. multicoloured 1·25 10
177 – 15c. multicoloured 1·00 10
178 – 20c. multicoloured 1·75 30

The higher values in use with this issue were Nos. 64/71 of Malaysia (National Issues).

56 "Rafflesia hasseltii" 57 Coffee

1979. Flowers. As Nos. 135/41 of Kedah but with portrait of Sultan Idris as in T **56**.
184 1c. Type **56** 10 85
185 2c. "Pterocarpus indicus" 10 85
186 5c. "Lagerstroemia speciosa" 10 20
187 10c. "Durio zibethinus" 15 10
188 15c. "Hibiscus rosa-sinensis" 15 10
189 20c. "Rhododendron scortechinii" 20 10
190 25c. "Etlingera elatior" (inscr"Phaeomeria speciosa") 40 20

1986. As Nos. 152/8 of Kedah but with portrait of Sultan Azlan Shah as in T **57**.
198 1c. Type **57** 10 10
199 2c. Coconuts 10 10
200 5c. Cocoa 10 10
201 10c. Black pepper 10 10
202 15c. Rubber 10 10
203 20c. Oil palm 10 10
204 30c. Rice 10 15

OFFICIAL STAMPS

1889. Stamps of Straits Settlements optd **P.G.S.**
O1 **30** 2c. red 3·50 4·75
O2 4c. brown 11·00 20·00
O3 6c. lilac 23·00 45·00
O4 8c. orange 29·00 65·00
O5 **38** 10c. grey 75·00 75·00
O6 **30** 12c. blue £200 £250
O7 12c. purple £250 £325
O9 24c. green £180 £200

1894. No. 64 optd **Service**.
O10 **30** 5c. blue 70·00 1·00

1895. No. 70 optd **Service**.
O11 **31** 5c. purple and yellow 2·25 50

PERLIS Pt. 1

A state of the Federation of Malaya, incorporated in Malaysia in 1963.

100 cents = 1 dollar (Straits or Malayan).

1948. Silver Wedding. As T **4b/c** of Pitcairn Islands.
1 10c. violet 30 2·75
2 $5 brown 29·00 45·00

1949. U.P.U. As T **4d/g** of Pitcairn Islands.
3 10c. purple 30 1·50
4 15c. blue 1·25 3·25
5 25c. orange 45 2·00
6 50c. black 1·00 3·75

1 Raja Syed Putra 2 "Vanda hookeriana"

1951.
7 **1** 1c. black 20 1·00
8 2c. orange 75 50
9 3c. green 1·50 2·75
10 4c. brown 1·25 30
11 5c. purple 50 3·00
12 6c. grey 1·50 1·25
13 8c. red 2·25 4·75
14 8c. green 75 3·50
15 10c. purple 50 30
16 12c. red 75 2·50
17 15c. blue 4·00 4·25
18 20c. black and green 2·25 6·50
19 20c. blue 1·00 70
20 25c. purple and orange 1·75 1·75
21 30c. red and purple 1·75 9·00
22 35c. red and purple 75 4·00
23 40c. red and purple 3·25 18·00
24 50c. black and blue 3·75 4·25
25 $1 blue and purple 7·50 20·00
26 $2 green and red 14·00 32·00
27 $5 green and brown 50·00 80·00

1953. Coronation. As T **4h** of Pitcairn Islands.
28 10c. black and purple 1·25 3·00

1957. As Nos. 92/102 of Kedah, but inset portrait of Raja Syed Putra.
29 1c. black 10 30
30 2c. red 10 30
31 4c. brown 10 30
32 5c. lake 10 10
33 8c. green 2·00 1·75
34 10c. brown 1·50 2·25
35 10c. purple 5·00 3·25
36 20c. blue 2·25 3·25
37 50c. black and blue 60 3·50
38 $1 blue and purple 7·00 11·00
39 $2 green and red 7·00 8·00
40 $5 brown and green 10·00 11·00

1965. As Nos. 115/21 of Kedah, but with inset portrait of Tunku Bendahara Abu Bakar as in T **2**.
41 **2** 1c. multicoloured 10 1·00
42 – 2c. multicoloured 10 1·50
43 – 5c. multicoloured 15 40
44 – 6c. multicoloured 65 1·50
45 – 10c. multicoloured 65 40
46 – 15c. multicoloured 1·00 40
47 – 20c. multicoloured 1·00 1·75

The higher values used in Perlis were Nos. 20/7 of Malaysia (National Issues).

3 "Danaus melanippus" 4 Raja Syed Putra

1971. Butterflies. As Nos. 124/30 of Kedah, but with portrait of Raja Syed Putra as in T **3**.
48 – 1c. multicoloured 20 1·25
49 **3** 2c. multicoloured 40 2·25
50 – 5c. multicoloured 1·25 1·25
51 – 6c. multicoloured 1·50 2·75
52 – 10c. multicolored 1·50 1·25
53 – 15c. multicoloured 1·50 50
54 – 20c. multicoloured 1·50 2·25

The higher values in use with this issue were Nos. 64/71 of Malaysia (National Issues).

1971. 25th Anniv of Installation of Raja Syed Putra.
56 **4** 10c. multicoloured 30 2·25
57 15c. multicoloured 30 75
58 50c. multicoloured 80 4·00

5 "Pterocarpus indicus" 6 Coconuts

1979. Flowers. As Nos. 135/41 of Kedah, but with portrait of Raja Syed Putra as in T **5**.
59 1c. "Rafflesia hasseltii" 10 1·00
60 2c. Type **5** 10 1·00
61 5c. "Lagerstroemia speciosa" 10 1·00
62 10c. "Durio zibethinus" 15 30
63 15c. "Hibiscus rosa-sinensis" 15 10
64 20c. "Rhododendron scortechinii" 20 10
65 25c. "Etlingera elatior" (inscr "Phaeomeria speciosa") 40 85

1986. As Nos. 152/8 of Kedah, but with portrait of Raja Syed Putra as in T **6**.
73 1c. Coffee 10 10
74 2c. Type **6** 10 10
75 5c. Cocoa 10 10
76 10c. Black pepper 10 10
77 15c. Rubber 10 10
78 20c. Oil palm 10 10
79 30c. Rice 10 15

7 Raja Syed Putra and Aspects of Perlis

1995. 50th Anniv of Raja Syed Putra's Accession. Multicoloured.
80 30c. Type **7** 60 50
81 $1 Raja Syed Putra and Palace 1·75 3·00

PERU Pt. 20

A republic on the N.W. coast of S. America independent since 1821.

1857. 8 reales = 1 peso.
1858. 100 centavos = 10 dineros = 5 pesetas = 1 peso.
1874. 100 centavos = 1 sol.
1985. 100 centimos = 1 inti.
1991. 100 centimos = 1 sol.

7 8

1858. T **7** and similar designs with flags below arms. Imperf.
8 **7** 1d. blue 75·00 5·00
13 1 peseta red 90·00 11·00
5 ½ peso yellow £1300 £225

1862. Various frames. Imperf.
14 **8** 1d. red 10·00 1·75
20 1d. green 10·00 2·10
16 1 peseta, brown 55·00 17·00
22 1 peseta, yellow 70·00 21·00

10 Vicuna 13 14

1866. Various frames. Perf.
17 **10** 5c. green 5·00 60
18 – 10c. red 5·00 1·10
19 – 20c. brown 17·00 3·50

See also No. 316.

1871. 20th Anniv of First Railway in Peru (Callao–Lima–Chorillos). Imperf.
21a **13** 5c. red £110 28·00

1873. Roul by imperf.
23 **14** 2c. blue 25·00 £200

15 Sun-god 16

20 21

1874. Various frames. Perf.
24 **15** 1c. orange 40 40
25a **16** 2c. violet 40 40
26 5c. blue 70 25
27 10c. green 15 15
28 20c. red 1·60 40
29 **20** 50c. green 7·50 2·10
30 **21** 1s. pink 1·25 1·25

For further stamps in these types, see Nos. 278, 279/84 and 314/5.

(24) (27) Arms of Chile

1880. Optd with T **24**.
36 **15** 1c. green 40 40
37 **16** 2c. red 1·10 45
39 5c. blue 1·60 70
40 **20** 50c. green 23·00 14·50
41 **21** 1s. red 80·00 38·00

1881. Optd as T **24**, but inscr "LIMA" at foot instead of "PERU".
42 **15** 1c. green 95 30
43 **16** 2c. red 15·00 7·50
44 5c. blue 1·75 45
286 10c. green 40 50
45 **20** 50c. green £375 £200
46 **21** 1s. red 85·00 45·00

1881. Optd with T **27**.
57 **15** 1c. orange 60 85
58 **16** 2c. violet 60 3·50
59 2c. red 1·90 16·00
60 5c. blue 55·00 60·00
61 10c. green 1·50 2·00
62 20c. red £100 £100

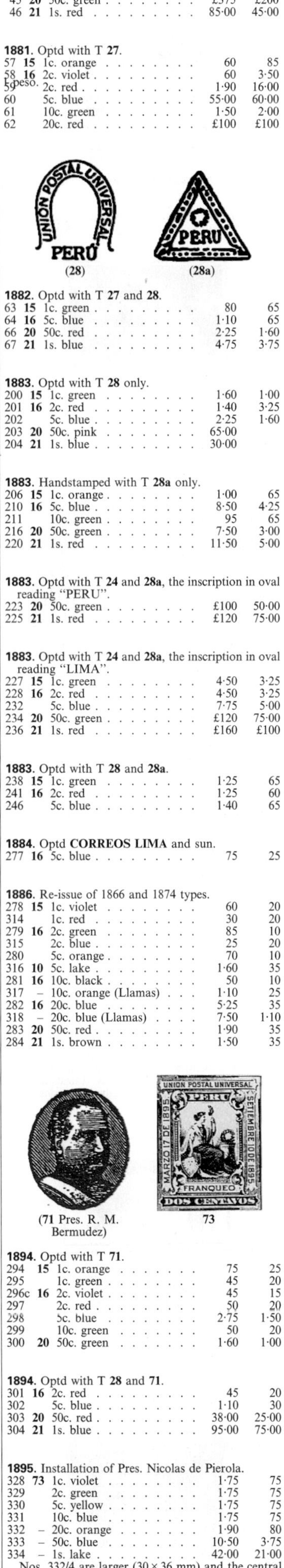

(28) (28a)

1882. Optd with T **27** and **28**.
63 **15** 1c. green 80 65
64 **16** 5c. blue 1·10 65
66 **20** 50c. red 2·25 1·60
67 **21** 1s. blue 4·75 3·75

1883. Optd with T **28** only.
200 **15** 1c. green 1·60 1·00
201 **16** 2c. red 1·40 3·25
202 5c. blue 2·25 1·60
203 **20** 50c. pink 65·00
204 **21** 1s. blue 30·00

1883. Handstamped with T **28a** only.
206 **15** 1c. orange 1·00 65
210 **16** 5c. blue 8·50 4·25
211 10c. green 95 65
216 **20** 50c. green 7·50 3·00
220 **21** 1s. red 11·50 5·00

1883. Optd with T **24** and **28a**, the inscription in oval reading "PERU".
223 **20** 50c. green £100 50·00
225 **21** 1s. red £120 75·00

1883. Optd with T **24** and **28a**, the inscription in oval reading "LIMA".
227 **15** 1c. green 4·50 3·25
228 **16** 2c. red 4·50 3·25
232 5c. blue 7·75 5·00
234 **20** 50c. green £120 75·00
236 **21** 1s. red £160 £100

1883. Optd with T **28** and **28a**.
238 **15** 1c. green 1·25 65
241 **16** 2c. red 1·25 60
246 5c. blue 1·40 65

1884. Optd **CORREOS LIMA** and sun.
277 **16** 5c. blue 75 25

1886. Re-issue of 1866 and 1874 types.
278 **15** 1c. violet 60 20
314 1c. red 30 20
279 **16** 2c. green 85 10
315 2c. blue 25 20
280 5c. orange 70 10
316 **10** 5c. lake 1·60 35
281 **16** 10c. black 50 10
317 – 10c. orange (Llamas) 1·10 25
282 **16** 20c. blue 5·25 35
318 – 20c. blue (Llamas) 7·50 1·10
283 **20** 50c. red 1·90 35
284 **21** 1s. brown 1·50 35

(71 Pres. R. M. Bermudez) 73

1894. Optd with T **71**.
294 **15** 1c. orange 75 25
295 1c. green 45 20
296c **16** 2c. violet 45 15
297 2c. red 50 20
298 5c. blue 2·75 1·50
299 10c. green 50 20
300 **20** 50c. green 1·60 1·00

1894. Optd with T **28** and **71**.
301 **16** 2c. red 45 20
302 5c. blue 1·10 30
303 **20** 50c. red 38·00 25·00
304 **21** 1s. blue 95·00 75·00

1895. Installation of Pres. Nicolas de Pierola.
328 **73** 1c. violet 1·75 75
329 2c. green 1·75 75
330 5c. yellow 1·75 75
331 10c. blue 1·75 75
332 – 20c. orange 1·90 80
333 – 50c. blue 10·50 3·75
334 – 1s. lake 42·00 21·00

Nos. 332/4 are larger (30 × 36 mm) and the central device is in a frame of laurel.

See also Nos. 352/4.

75 Atahualpa 76 Pizarro

77 General de la Mar

1896.
335 **75** 1c. blue 55 15
336 1c. green 55 10
337 2c. blue 60 15
338 2c. red 60 10
341 **76** 5c. blue 85 10
340 5c. green 85 10
342 10c. yellow . . . . 1·40 20
343 10c. black . . . . 1·40 10
344 20c. orange . . . . 2·75 25
345 **77** 50c. red . . . . 5·25 50
346 1s. red . . . . 7·00 85
347 2s. lake . . . . 3·00 65

1897. No. D31 optd **FRANQUEO**.
348 D **22** 1c. brown 50 25

82 Suspension Bridge at Paucartambo **83** Pres. D. Nicolas de Pierola

1897. Opening of New Postal Building. Dated "1897".
349 **82** 1c. blue 80 30
350 – 2c. brown 80 25
351 **83** 5c. red . . . . 1·25 30
DESIGN: 2c. G.P.O. Lima.

1899. As Nos. 328/34, but vert inscr replaced by pearl ornaments.
352 **73** 22c. green 30 15
353 – 5s. red . . . . 1·90 1·40
354 – 10s. green £425 £275

84 President Eduardo Lopez de Romana **85** Admiral Grau

1900.
357 **84** 22c. black and green . . . 10·00 70

1901. Advent of the Twentieth Century.
358 **85** 1c. black and green . . . . 1·10 25
359 – 2c. black and red . . . . 1·10 25
360 – 5c. black and lilac . . . . 1·25 25
PORTRAITS: 2c. Col. Bolognesi; 5c. Pres. Romana.

90 Municipal Board of Health Building

1905.
361 **90** 12c. black and blue . . . . 1·25 25

1907. Surch.
362 **90** 1c. on 12c. black and blue 25 20
363 2c. on 12c. black and blue 50 35

97 Bolognesi Monument **98** Admiral Grau

99 Llama **101** Exhibition Buildings

103 G.P.O., Lima **107** Columbus

1907.
364 **97** 1c. black and green . . . 25 15
365 **98** 2c. purple and red 25 15
366 **99** 4c. olive . . . . 5·00 60
367 – 5c. black and blue 40 10
368 **101** 10c. black and brown . . 1·00 25
369 – 20c. black and green . . . 19·00 90
370 **103** 50c. black . . . . 21·00 95
371 – 1s. green and violet . . . £100 2·10
372 – 2s. black and blue . . . . £100 85·00
DESIGNS—VERT: As Type **98**: 5c. Statue of Bolivar. (24 × 33 mm): 2c. Columbus Monument. HORIZ: As Type **101**: 20c. Medical School, Lima. (33 × 24 mm): 1s. Grandstand, Santa Beatrice Racecourse, Lima.

1909. Portraits.
373 – 1c. grey (Manco Capac) 15 15
374 **107** 2c. green 15 15
375 – 4c. red (Pizarro) 40 15
376 – 5c. purple (San Martin) 15 10
377 – 10c. blue (Bolivar) 55 15
378 – 12c. blue (de la Mar) . . . 85 25
379 – 20c. brown (Castilla) . . 90 40
380 – 50c. orange (Grau) . . . 5·50 30
381 – 1s. black and lake (Bolognesi) . . . . . . 9·50 30
See also Nos. 406/13, 431/5, 439/40 and 484/9.

1913. Surch **UNION POSTAL 8 Cts. Sud Americana** in oval.
382 **90** 8c. on 12c. black and blue 55 20

1915. As 1896, 1905 and 1907, surch **1915** and value.
383 **75** 1c. on 1c. green . . . . . 13·50 10·00
384 **97** 1c. on 1c. black and green 70 50
385 **98** 1c. on 2c. purple and red 1·00 85
386 **76** 1c. on 10c. black 85 60
387 **99** 1c. on 4c. green . . . . . 2·00 1·75
388 **101** 1c. on 10c. black & brown 35 20
389 2c. on 10c. black & brown 80·00 65·00
390 **90** 2c. on 12c. black and blue 65 50
391 – 2c. on 20c. black and green (No. 369) . . . . 11·50 10·00
392 **103** 2c. on 50c. black . . . . 3·00 3·00

1916. Surch **VALE**, value and **1916**.
393 1c. on 12c. blue (378) 15 15
394 1c. on 20c. brown (379) . . . 15 15
395 1c. on 50c. orange (380) . . . 15 15
396 2c. on 4c. red (375) 15 15
397 10c. on 1s. black & lake (381) 40 25

1916. Official stamps of 1909 optd **FRANQUEO 1916** or surch **VALE 2 Cts** also.
398 O **108** 1c. red 15 15
399 2c. on 50c. olive . . . 15 15
400 10c. brown 20 15

1916. Postage Due stamps of 1909 surch **FRANQUEO VALE 2 Cts. 1916**.
401 D **109** 2c. on 1c. brown . . . 40 40
402 2c. on 5c. brown . . . 15 15
403 2c. on 10c. brown . . . 15 15
404 2c. on 50c. brown . . . 15 15

1917. Surch **Un Centavo**.
405 1c. on 4c. (No. 375) 20 15

1918. Portraits as T **107**.
406 1c. black & orge (San Martin) 10 10
407 2c. black and green (Bolivar) 15 10
408 4c. black and red (Galvez) . . 25 10
409 5c. black and blue (Pardo) 15 10
410 8c. black and brown (Grau) 90 25
411 10c. black and blue (Bolognesi) 35 10
412 12c. black and lilac (Castilla) 1·10 15
413 20c. black and green (Caceres) . . . . 1·50 15

126 Columbus at Salamanca University **129** A. B. Leguia

1918.
414 **126** 50c. black and brown . . 4·25 35
415a – 1s. black and green . . . 13·00 50
416 – 2s. black and blue . . . 22·00 55

DESIGNS: 1s. Funeral of Atahualpa; 2s. Battle of Arica.

1920. New Constitution.
417 **129** 5c. black and blue 15 15
418 5c. black and brown . . . 15 15

130 San Martin **131** Oath of Independence

132 Admiral Cochrane **137** J. Olaya

1921. Centenary of Independence.
419 **130** 1c. brown (San Martin) 25 15
420 2c. green (Arenales) . . . 25 15
421 4c. red (Las Heras) . . . 85 50
422 **131** 5c. brown 35 15
423 **132** 7c. violet 70 35
424 **130** 10c. blue (Guisse) 70 35
425 12c. black (Vidal) . . . . 2·75 40
426 20c. black and red (Leguia) . . . . 2·75 70
427 50c. violet and purple (S. Martin Monument) 7·75 2·00
428 **131** 1s. green and red (San Martin and Leguia) . . 11·00 3·00

1923. Surch **CINCO Centavos 1923**.
429 5c. on 8c. black & brn (No. 410) 40 20

1924. Surch **CUATRO Centavos 1924**.
430 4c. on 5c. (No. 409) 25 15

1924. Portraits as T **107**. Size 18½ × 23 mm.
431 2c. olive (Rivadeneyra) . . . 10 10
432 4c. green (Melgar) 10 10
433 8c. black (Iturregui) . . . . 1·60 90
434 10c. red (A. B. Leguia) . . . 15 10
435 15c. blue (De la Mar) 50 15
439 1s. brown (De Saco) . . . . 7·50 85
440 2s. blue (J. Leguia) . . . . . 19·00 4·25

1924. Monuments.
436 **137** 20c. blue 95 10
437 20c. yellow . . . . 1·25 15
438 – 50c. purple (Bellido) . . . 4·25 35
See also Nos. 484/9.

139 Simon Bolivar **140**

1924. Cent of Battle of Ayacucho. Portraits of Bolivar.
441 – 2c. olive 35 10
442 **139** 4c. green 65 10
443 5c. black . . . . 1·25 10
444 **140** 10c. red 70 10
445 – 20c. blue . . . . 1·40 15
446 – 50c. lilac . . . . 4·00 50
447 – 1s. brown . . . . 10·00 2·00
448 – 2s. blue . . . . 21·00 8·25

1925. Surch **DOS Centavos 1925**.
449 **137** 2c. on 20c. blue . . . . . 1·25 50

1925. Optd**Plebiscito**.
450 10c. red (No. 434) 70 70

143 The Rock of Arica

1925. Obligatory Tax. Tacna–Arica Plebiscite.
451 **143** 2c. orange . . . . 1·50 40
452 5c. blue . . . . 2·50 50
453 5c. red . . . . 1·90 40
454 5c. green . . . . 2·25 60
455 – 10c. brown . . . . 3·00 60
456 – 50c. green . . . . 16·00 7·50
DESIGNS—HORIZ: 39 × 30 mm: 10c. Soldiers with colours. VERT: 27 × 33 mm: 50c. Bolognesi Statue.

146 The Rock of Arica

1927. Obligatory Tax. Figures of value not encircled.
457 **146** 2c. orange . . . . 2·25 50
458 2c. brown . . . . 2·75 50
459 2c. blue . . . . 2·50 50
460 2c. violet . . . . 1·75 50
461 **146** 2c. green . . . . 1·25 50
462 20c. red . . . . 6·00 1·50

1927. Air. Optd **Servicio Aereo.**
463 **9** 50c. purple (No. 438) . . . 32·00 20·00

148 Pres. A. B. Leguia **149** The Rock of Arica

1927. Air.
464 **148** 50c. green 70 35

1928. Obligatory Tax. Plebiscite Fund.
465 **149** 2c. mauve 60 20

1929. Surch **Habilitada 2 Cts. 1929.**
466 – 2c. on 8c. (No. 410) . . . 50 50
468 **137** 15c. on 20c. (No. 437) . . 70 70

1929. Surch **Habilitada 2 centavos 1929.**
467 2c. on 8c. (No. 410) 70 70

1930. Optd **Habilitada Franqueo.**
469 **149** 2c. mauve 85 85

1930. Surch **Habilitada 2 Cts. 1930.**
470 **137** 2c. on 20c. yellow 25 25

1930. Surch **Habilitada Franqueo 2 Cts. 1930.**
471 **148** 2c. on 50c. green 25 25

156 Arms of Peru **157** Lima Cathedral

1930. 6th (inscribed "seventh") Pan-American Child Congress.
472 **156** 2c. green 60 55
473 **157** 5c. red . . . . 2·00 1·00
474 – 10c. blue . . . . 1·25 85
475 – 50c. brown . . . . 17·00 10·00
DESIGNS—HORIZ: 10c. G.P.O., Lima. VERT: 50c. Madonna and Child.

1930. Fall of Leguia Govt. No. 434 optd with Arms of Peru or surch with new value in four corners also.
477 2c. on 10c. red 10 10
478 4c. on 10c. red 20 20
479 10c. red 15 10
476 15c. on 10c. red 20 15

159 Simon Bolivar **161** Pizarro

162 The Old Stone Bridge, Lima

1930. Death Centenary of Bolivar.
480 **159** 2c. brown 35 20
481 4c. red 70 30

482 10c. green 35 25
483 15c. grey 70 50

1930. As T **107** and **137** but smaller, 18 × 22 mm.
484 – 2c. olive (Rivadeneyra) . . 15 10
485 – 4c. green (Melgar) 15 10
486 – 15c. blue (De la Mar) . . 50 10
487 **137** 20c. yellow (Olaya) . . . 1·00 20
488 – 50c. purple (Bellido) . . . 1·25 25
489 – 1s. brown (De Saco) . . . 1·60 35

1931. Obligatory Tax. Unemployment Fund. Surch **Habilitada Pro Desocupados 2 Cts.**
490 **159** 2c. on 4c. red 70 35
491 2c. on 10c. green 50 35
492 2c. on 15c. grey 50 35

1931. 1st Peruvian Philatelic Exhibition.
493 **161** 2c. slate . . . . 1·90 1·10
494 4c. brown . . . . 1·90 1·10
495 **162** 10c. red . . . . 1·90 1·10
496 10c. green and mauve . . 1·90 1·10
497 **161** 15c. green . . . . 1·90 1·10
498 **162** 15c. red and grey . . . . 1·90 1·10
499 15c. blue and orange . . 1·90 1·10

163 Manco Capac

164 Oil Well

170

1931.
500 **163** 2c. olive 20 10
501 **164** 4c. green 40 30
502 – 10c. orange 85 10
503 – 15c. blue . . . . 1·50 25
504 – 20c. yellow . . . . 6·00 40
505 – 50c. lilac . . . . 5·00 40
506 – 1s. brown . . . . 11·00 85
DESIGNS—VERT: 10c. Sugar Plantation; 15c. Cotton Plantation; 50c. Copper Mines. 1s. Llamas. HORIZ: 20c. Guano Islands.

1931. Obligatory Tax. Unemployment Fund.
507 **170** 2c. green 10 10
508 2c. red 10 10

171 Arms of Piura

172 Parakas

1932. 4th Centenary of Piura.
509 **171** 10c. blue (postage) . . . 5·50 5·00
510 15c. violet . . . . 5·50 5·00
511 50c. red (air) . . . . . . 18·00 16·00

1932. 400th Anniv of Spanish Conquest of Peru. Native designs.
512 **172** 10c. purple (22 × 19½ mm) 15 10
513 – 15c. lake (25 × 19½ mm) 35 10
514 – 50c. brown (19½ × 22 mm) 75 15
DESIGNS: 15c. Chimu; 50c. Inca.

175 Arequipa and El Misti

176 Pres. Sanchez Cerro

1932. 1st Anniv of Constitutional Government.
515 **175** 2c. blue 15 10
527 2c. black 15 10
528 2c. green 15 10
516 4c. brown 15 10
529 4c. orange 15 10
517 **176** 10c. red . . . . 15·00 8·25
530 – 10c. red 50 10
518 – 15c. blue 35 10
531 – 15c. mauve 35 10
519 – 20c. lake 50 10
532 – 20c. violet 50 15
520 – 50c. green 70 15
521 – 1s. orange . . . . 5·50 35
533 – 1s. brown . . . . 6·25 40
DESIGNS—VERT: 10c. (No. 530), Statue of Liberty; 15c. to 1s. Bolivar Monument, Lima.

178 Blacksmith

179 Monument of 2nd May to Battle of Callao

1932. Obligatory Tax. Unemployment Fund.
522 **178** 2c. grey 10 10
523 2c. violet 10 10

1933. Obligatory Tax. Unemployment Fund.
524 **179** 2c. violet 15 10
525 2c. orange 15 10
526 2c. purple 15 10

181 Hawker Hart Bomber

184 F. Pizarro

185 Coronation of Huascar

186 The Inca

1934. Air.
534 **181** 2s. blue . . . . 4·50 35
535 5s. brown . . . . 9·50 70

1934. Obligatory Tax. Unemployment Fund. Optd **Pro-Desocupados**. (a) In one line.
536 **176** 2c. green 10 10
585 – 2c. purple (No. 537) . . . 10 10

(b) In two lines.
566 – 2c. purple (No. 537) 10 10

1934.
537 – 2c. purple 10 10
538 – 4c. green 15 10
539 **184** 10c. red 15 10
540 15c. blue 50 10
541 **185** 20c. blue . . . . 1·00 15
542 50c. brown . . . . 1·00 15
543 **186** 1s. violet . . . . 2·75 35
DESIGNS: 2, 4c. show the scene depicted in Type **189**.

187 Lake of the Marvellous Cure

188 Grapes

1935. Tercentenary of Founding of Ica.
544 – 4c. black 65 65
545 **187** 5c. red 65 65
546 **188** 10c. mauve . . . . 3·75 1·40
547 **187** 20c. green . . . . 1·60 1·00
548 – 35c. red . . . . 7·50 3·50
549 – 50c. brown and orange . . 5·00 3·50
550 – 1s. red and violet . . . . 14·50 8·25
DESIGNS—HORIZ: 4c. City of Ica; 50c. Don Diego Lopez and King Philip IV of Spain. VERT: 35c. Cotton blossom; 1s. Supreme God of the Nazcas.

189 Pizarro and "The Thirteen"

192 Funeral of Atahualpa

1935. 4th Centenary of Founding of Lima.
551 **189** 2c. brown (postage) . . . 35 20
552 – 4c. violet 50 35
553 – 10c. red 50 20
554 – 15c. blue 85 40
555 **189** 20c. grey . . . . 1·40 50
556 – 50c. green . . . . 1·90 1·25
557 – 1s. blue . . . . 4·00 2·40
558 – 2s. brown . . . . 11·00 6·75
DESIGNS—HORIZ: 4c. Lima Cathedral. VERT: 10c., 50c. Miss L. S. de Canevaro; 15c., 2s. Pizarro; 1s. The "Tapada" (a veiled woman).

559 **192** 5c. green (air) 35 20
560 – 35c. brown 75 35
561 – 50c. yellow . . . . 1·25 70
562 – 1s. purple . . . . 1·75 75
563 – 2s. orange . . . . 1·75 1·50
564 **192** 5s. purple . . . . 7·75 4·25
565 **189** 10s. blue . . . . 30·00 20·00
DESIGNS—HORIZ: 35c. Airplane near San Cristobal Hill; 50c., 1s. Airplane over Avenue of Barefoot Friars. VERT: 2s. Palace of Torre Tagle.

207 "San Cristobal" (caravel)

1936. Callao Centenary.
567 **207** 2c. black (postage) . . . 1·25 20
568 – 4c. green 45 15
569 – 5c. brown 45 15
570 – 10c. blue 45 20
571 – 15c. green . . . . 2·00 25
572 – 20c. brown 45 25
573 – 50c. lilac . . . . 1·25 45
574 – 1s. olive . . . . 23·00 1·60
575 – 2s. purple . . . . 15·00 5·00
576 – 5s. red . . . . 21·00 12·00
577 – 10s. brown and red . . . 45·00 30·00
578 – 35c. slate (air) . . . . . 8·00 4·00
DESIGNS—HORIZ: 4c. La Punta Naval College; 5c. Independence Square, Callao; 10c. Aerial view of Callao; 15c. "Reina del Pacifico" (liner) in Callao Docks and Custom House; 20c. Plan of Callao, 1746; 35c. "La Callao" (locomotive); 1s. Gunboat "Sacramento"; 10s. Real Felipe Fortifications. VERT: 50c. D. Jose de la Mar; 2s. Don Jose de Velasco; 5s. Fort Maipo and miniature portraits of Galvez and Nunez.

1936. Obligatory Tax. St. Rosa de Lima Cathedral Construction Fund. Optd **"Ley 8310"**.
579 **179** 2c. purple 10 10

1936. Surch **Habilitado** and value in figures and words.
580 – 2c. on 4c. green (No. 538) (postage) 10 10
581 **185** 10c. on 20c. blue 15 15
582 **186** 10c. on 1s. violet 20 20
583 **181** 5c. on 2s. blue (air) . . . 35 15
584 25c. on 5s. brown 70 25

211 Guanay Cormorants

217 Mail Steamer "Inca" on Lake Titicaca

1936.
586 **211** 2c. brown (postage) . . . 1·40 25
616 2c. green . . . . 1·75 25
587 – 4c. brown 50 25
617 – 4c. black 25 15
618 – 10c. red 10 10
619 – 15c. blue 50 25
590 – 20c. black 70 15
620 – 20c. brown 25 15
591 – 50c. yellow . . . . 2·10 50
621 – 50c. grey 70 15
592 – 1s. purple . . . . 4·25 70
622 – 1s. blue . . . . 1·40 35
593 – 2s. blue . . . . 9·00 2·00
623 – 2s. violet . . . . 3·00 35
594 – 5s. blue . . . . 9·00 3·00
595 – 10s. brown and violet . . 50·00 19·00
DESIGNS—VERT: 4c. Oil well; 10c. Inca postal runner; 1s. G.P.O., Lima; 2s. M. de Amat y Junyent; 5s. J. A. de Pando y Riva; 10s. J. D. Condemarin. HORIZ: 15c. Paseo de la Republica, Lima; 20c. Municipal Palace and Natural History Museum; 50c. University of San Marcos, Lima..

596 – 5c. green (air) 25 10
625 **217** 15c. blue 90 15
598 – 20c. grey 90 15
626 – 20c. green 85 15
627 – 25c. red 40 10
628 – 30c. brown 80 15
600 – 35c. brown . . . . 1·60 1·40
601 – 50c. yellow 75 45
629 – 50c. red . . . . 1·10 30
630 – 70c. green . . . . 1·25 50
603 – 80c. black . . . . 14·00 7·00
631 – 80c. green . . . . 4·50 1·00
604 – 1s. blue . . . . 9·00 1·50
632 – 1s. brown . . . . 6·00 60
605 – 1s. 50 brown . . . . . . 9·00 5·50
633 – 1s. 50 orange . . . . . . 5·50 40
606 – 2s. blue . . . . 15·00 6·50
634 – 2s. green . . . . 11·00 70
607 – 5s. green . . . . 20·00 3·25
608 – 10s. brown and red . . . £100 65·00

DESIGNS—HORIZ: 5c. La Mar Park; 20c. Native recorder player and llama; 30c. Chuquibambilla ram; 25, 35c. J. Chavez; 50c. Mining Area; 70c. Ford "Tin Goose" airplane over La Punta; 1s. Steam train at La Cima; 1s.50, Aerodrome at Las Palmas, Lima. 2s. Douglas DC-2 mail plane; 5s. Valley of R. Inambari. VERT: 80c. Infiernillo Canyon, Andes; 10s. St. Rosa de Lima

223 St. Rosa de Lima

1937. Obligatory Tax. St. Rosa de Lima Construction Fund.
609 **223** 2c. red 15 10

1937. Surch **Habilit.** and value in figures and words.
(a) Postage.
610 1s. on 2s. blue (593) . . . . 3·25 3·25

(b) Air.
611 15c. on 30c. brown (599) . . 45 40
612 15c. on 35c. brown (600) . . 45 25
613 15c. on 70c. green (630) . . . 3·50 2·25
614 25c. on 80c. black (603) . . . 7·50 6·00
615 1s. on 2s. blue (606) . . . . 5·50 3·00

225 Bielovucic over Lima

226 Jorge Chavez

1937. Air. Pan-American Aviation Conference.
635 **225** 10c. violet 40 10
636 **226** 15c. green 50 10
637 – 25c. brown 40 10
638 – 1s. black . . . . 1·90 1·00
DESIGNS—As T **225**: 25c. Limatambo Airport; 1s. Peruvian air routes.

229 "Protection" (by John Q. A. Ward)

230 Children's Holiday Camp

1938. Obligatory Tax. Unemployment Fund.
757c **229** 2c. brown 10 10

1938. Designs as T **230**.
693 **230** 2c. green 10 10
694 – 4c. brown 10 10
642 – 10c. red 20 10
696 – 15c. blue 10 10
727 – 15c. turquoise 10 10
644 – 20c. purple 15 10
740 – 20c. violet 10 10
698 – 50c. blue 15 10
741 – 50c. brown 15 10
699 – 1s. purple 85 10
742 – 1s. brown 25 10
700 – 2s. green . . . . 2·50 10
731 – 2s. blue 55 10
701 – 5s. brown and violet . . . 5·75 35
732 – 5s. purple and blue . . . 75 35
702 – 10s. blue and black . . . 10·00 50
733 – 10s. black and green . . . 2·50 70
DESIGNS—VERT: 4c. Chavin pottery; 10c. Automobile roads in Andes; 20c. (2) Industrial Bank of Peru; 1s. (2) Portrait of Toribio de Luzuriaga; 5s. (2) Chavin Idol. HORIZ: 15c. (2) Archaeological Museum, Lima; 50c. (2) Labourers' homes at Lima; 2s. (2) Fig Tree; 10s. (2) Mt. Huascaran.

240 Monument on Junin Plains

248 Seal of City of Lima

1938. Air. As T **240**.
650 – 5c. brown 15 10
743 – 5c. green 10 10
651 **240** 15c. brown 15 10
652 – 20c. red 40 10
653 – 25c. green 20 10
654 – 30c. orange 20 10
735 – 30c. red 15 10
655 – 50c. green 35 30
656 – 70c. grey 50 25

736 – 70c. blue 30 10
657 – 80c. green 60 10
737 – 80c. red 55 15
658 – 1s. green . . . . 5·00 2·75
705 – 1s.50 violet 45 35
738 – 1s.50 purple 45 30
660 – 2s. red and blue . . . . . 1·60 50
661 – 5s. purple . . . . 10·50 1·10
662 – 10s. blue and green . . . 55·00 27·00
DESIGNS—VERT: 20c. Rear-Admiral M. Villar; 70c. (No. 656, 736), Infiernillo Canyon; 2s. Stele from Chavin Temple. HORIZ: 5c. People's restaurant, Callao; 25c. View of Tarma; 30c. Ica River irrigation system; 50c. Port of Iquitos; 80c. Mountain roadway; 1s. Plaza San Martin, Lima; 1s.50, Nat. Radio Station, San Miguel; 5s. Ministry of Public Works; 10s. Heroe's Crypt, Lima.

1938. 8th Pan-American Congress, Lima.
663 – 10c. grey (postage) . . . 50 20
664 **248** 15c. gold, blue, red & blk 85 25
665 – 1s. brown . . . . 1·90 85
DESIGNS (39×32½ mm): 10c. Palace and Square, 1864; 1s. Palace, 1938.

666 – 25c. blue (air) 55 50
667 – 1s.50 lake . . . . 1·90 1·25
668 – 2s. black 90 45
DESIGNS—VERT: 26×37 mm: 25c. Torre Tagle Palace. HORIZ: 39×32½ mm: 1s.50, National Congress Building, Lima; 2s. Congress Presidents, Ferreyros, Paz Soldan and Arenas.

1940. No. 642 surch **Habilitada 5 cts**.
669 5c. on 10c. red 15 10

251 National Broadcasting Station

1941. Optd **FRANQUEO POSTAL**.
670 **251** 50c. yellow . . . . 1·60 15
671 1s. violet . . . . 1·60 20
672 2s. green . . . . 3·25 50
673 5s. brown . . . . 19·00 5·50
674 10s. mauve . . . . 29·00 4·75

1942. Air. No. 653 surch **Habilit 0.15**.
675 15c. on 25c. green 85 10

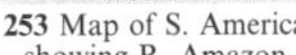

253 Map of S. America showing R. Amazon
254 Francisco de Orellana

255 Francisco Pizarro
257 Samuel Morse

1943. 400th Anniv of Discovery of R. Amazon.
676 – 2c. red 10 10
677 **254** 4c. grey 15 10
678 **255** 10c. brown 20 10
679 **253** 15c. blue 50 20
680 – 20c. olive 20 15
681 – 25c. orange . . . . 2·00 35
682 **254** 30c. red 35 20
683 **253** 50c. green 35 40
685 – 70c. violet . . . . 2·50 70
686 – 80c. blue . . . . 2·50 70
687 – 1s. brown . . . . 4·75 70
688 **255** 5s. black . . . . 9·50 4·00
DESIGNS—As Type **254**: 2, 70c. Portraits of G. Pizarro and Orellana in medallion; 20, 80c. G. Pizarro. As Type **253**: 25c., 1s. Orellana's Discovery of the R. Amazon.

1943. Surch with Arms of Peru (as Nos. 483, etc) above **10 CTVS**.
689 10c. on 10c. red (No. 642) . . 15 10

1944. Centenary of Invention of Telegraphy.
691 **257** 15c. blue 15 15
692 30c. brown 50 20

1946. Surch **Habilitada S/o 0.20**.
706 20c. on 1s. purple (No. 699) 25 10

259

261

1947. 1st National Tourist Congress, Lima. Unissued designs inscr "V Congreso Pan Americano de Carreteras 1944" optd **Habilitada I Congreso Nac. de Turismo Lima–1947**.
707 **259** 15c. black and red 25 15
708 – 1s. brown 35 20
709 – 1s.35 green 35 25
710 **261** 3s. blue 85 50
711 – 5s. green . . . . 2·10 1·25
DESIGNS—VERT: 1s. Mountain road; 1s.35, Forest road. HORIZ: 5s. Road and house.

1947. Air. 1st Peruvian Int Airways Lima–New York Flight. Optd with PIA badge and **PRIMER VUELO LIMA - NUEVA YORK**.
712 5c. brown (No. 650) . . . 10 10
713 50c. green (No. 655) 15 10

263 Basketball Players

1948. Air. Olympic Games.
714 – 1s. blue . . . . 3·75 2·25
715 **263** 2s. brown . . . . 5·75 3·00
716 – 5s. green . . . . 11·50 5·00
717 – 10s. yellow . . . . 15·00 6·50
DESIGNS: 1s. Map showing air route from Peru to Great Britain; 5s. Discus thrower; 10s. Rifleman.
No. 714 is inscr "AEREO" and Nos. 715/17 are optd **AEREO**.
The above stamps exist overprinted **MELBOURNE 1956** but were only valid for postage on one day.

1948. Air. Nos. 653, 736 and 657 surch **Habilitada S/o.** and value.
722 5c. on 25c. green 10 10
723 10c. on 25c. green 30 10
718 10c. on 70c. blue 65 20
719 15c. on 70c. blue 30 10
720 20c. on 70c. blue 30 10
724 30c. on 80c. green 90 15
721 55c. on 70c. blue 30 10

263a
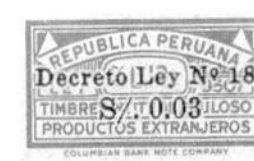

263b

1949. Anti-tuberculosis Fund. Surch **Decreto Ley No. 18** and value.
724a **263a** 3c. on 4c. blue 55 10
724b **263b** 3c. in 10c. blue 55 10

264 Statue of Admiral Grau

264a "Education"

1949.
726 **264** 10c. blue and green . . . 10 10

1950. Obligatory Tax. National Education Fund.
851 **264a** 3c. lake (16½×21 mm) 10 10
897 3c. lake (18×21½ mm) 15 10

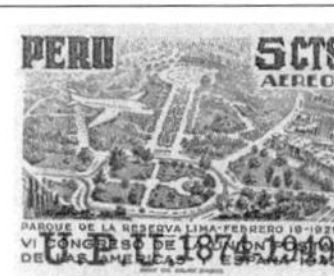

265 Park, Lima

1951. Air. 75th Anniv of U.P.U. Unissued stamps inscr "VI CONGRESO DE LA UNION POSTAL DE LAS AMREICAS Y ESPANA-1949" optd **U.P.U. 1874–1949**.
745 **265** 5c. green 10 10
746 – 30c. red and black 15 10
747 – 55c. green 15 10
748 – 95c. turquoise 20 15
749 – 1s.50 red 30 25
750 – 2s. blue 35 30
751 – 5s. red . . . . 3·00 2·10
752 – 10s. violet . . . . 4·75 3·00
753 – 20s. blue and brown . . . 8·50 5·00
DESIGNS: 30c. Peruvian flag; 55c. Huancayo Hotel; 95c. Ancash Mtns; 1s.50, Arequipa Hotel; 2s. Coaling Jetty; 5s. Town Hall, Miraflores; 10s. Congressional Palace; 20s. Pan-American flags.

1951. Air Surch **HABILITADA S/o. 0.25**.
754 25c. on 30c. red (No. 735) . . 15 10

1951. Surch **HABILITADA S/.** and figures.
755 1c. on 2c. (No. 693) 10 10
756 5c. on 15c. (No. 727) 10 10
757 10c. on 15c. (No. 727) . . . 10 10

268 Obrero Hospital, Lima

1951. 5th Pan-American Highways Congress. Unissued "VI CONGRESO DE LA UNION POSTAL" stamps, optd **V Congreso Panamericano de Carreteras 1951**.
758 – 2c. green 10 10
759 **268** 4c. red 10 10
760 – 15c. grey 15 10
761 – 20c. brown 10 10
762 – 50c. purple 15 10
763 – 1s. blue 20 10
764 – 2s. blue 30 10
765 – 5s. red . . . . 1·50 1·00
766 – 10s. brown . . . . 3·25 85
DESIGNS—HORIZ: 2c. Aguas Promenade; 50c. Archiepiscopal Palace, Lima; 1s. National Judicial Palace; 2s. Municipal Palace; 5s. Lake Llanganuco, Ancash. VERT: 15c. Inca postal runner; 20c. Old P.O., Lima; 10s. Machu-Picchu ruins.

269 Father Tomas de San Martin and Capt. J. de Aliaga

1951. Air. 4th Cent of S. Marcos University.
767 **269** 30c. black 10 10
768 – 40c. blue 15 10
769 – 50c. mauve 20 10
770 – 1s.20 green 30 15
771 – 2s. grey 35 15
772 – 5s. multicoloured . . . . 1·50 20
DESIGNS: 40c. San Marcos University; 50c. Santo Domingo Convent; 1s.20, P. de Peralto Barnuevo, Father Tomas de San Martin and Jose Baquijano; 2s. Toribio Rodriguez, Jose Hipolito Unanue and Jose Cayetano Heredia; 5s. University Arms in 1571 and 1735.

270 Engineer's School

1952. (a) Postage.
774 – 2c. purple 10 10
775 – 5c. green 30 10
776 – 10c. green 30 10
777 – 15c. grey 25 15
777a – 15c. brown . . . . 1·25 50
829 – 20c. brown 20 10
779 **270** 25c. red 15 10
779a 25c. green 30 10
780 – 30c. blue 10 10
780a – 30c. red 15 10
830 – 30c. mauve 15 10
924 – 50c. green 10 10
831 – 50c. purple 15 10
782 – 1s. brown 30 10
782a – 1s. blue 30 10
783 – 2s. turquoise 40 10
783a – 2s. grey 55 15

DESIGNS—As Type **270**: HORIZ: 2c. Hotel, Tacna; 5c. Tuna fishing boat and indigenous fish; 10c. View of Matarani; 15c. Steam train; 30c. Public Health and Social Assistance. VERT: 20c. Vicuna. Larger (35×25 mm): HORIZ: 50c. Inca maize terraces; 1s. Inca ruins, Paramonga Fort; 2s. Agriculture Monument, Lima.

(b) Air.
784 – 40c. green 65 10
785 – 75c. brown . . . . 1·10 25
834 – 80c. red 50 10
786 – 1s.25 blue 25 10
787 – 1s.50 red 20 10
788 – 2s.20 blue 65 15
789 – 3s. brown 75 25
835 – 3s. green 50 30
836 – 3s.80 orange 85 35
790 – 5s. brown 50 15
791 – 10s. brown . . . . 1·50 35
838 – 10s. red . . . . 1·00 45
DESIGNS—As Type **270**. HORIZ: 40c. Gunboat "Maranon"; 1s.50, Housing Complex. VERT: 75c., 80c. Colony of Guanay cormorants. Larger (25×25 mm.): HORIZ: 1s.25, Corpac-Limatambo Airport; 2s.20, 3s.80, Inca Observatory, Cuzco; 5s. Garcilaso (portrait). VERT: 3s. Tobacco plant, leaves and cigarettes; 10s. Manco Capac Monument (25×37 mm).
See also Nos. 867, etc.

271 Isabella the Catholic

272 "Santa Maria", "Pinta" and "Nina"
273

1953. Air. 500th Birth Anniv of Isabella the Catholic.
792 **271** 40c. red 20 10
793 **272** 1s.25 green . . . . 2·25 50
794 **271** 2s.15 purple 35 25
795 **272** 2s.20 black . . . . 4·25 75

1954. Obligatory Tax. National Marian Eucharistic Congress Fund. Roul.
796 **273** 5c. blue and red 25 10

274 Gen. M. Perez Jimenez

275 Arms of Lima and Bordeaux

1956. Visit of President of Venezuela.
797 **274** 25c. brown 10 10

1957. Air. Exhibition of French Products, Lima.
798 **275** 40c. lake, blue and green 10 10
799 – 50c. black, brown & green 15 10
800 – 1s.25 deep blue, green and blue . . . . 1·75 35
801 – 2s.20 brown and blue . . 40 30
DESIGNS—HORIZ: 50c. Eiffel Tower and Lima Cathedral; 1s.25, Admiral Dupetit-Thouars and frigate "La Victorieuse"; 2s.20, Exhibition building, Pres. Prado and Pres. Coty.

276 1857 Stamp

277 Carlos Paz Soldan (founder)

1957. Air. Centenary of First Peruvian Postage Stamp.
802 – 5c. black and grey 10 10
803 **276** 10c. turquoise and mauve 10 10
804 – 15c. brown and green . . 10 10
805 – 25c. blue and yellow . . . 10 10
806 – 30c. brown and chocolate 10 10
807 – 40c. ochre and black . . . 15 10
808 – 1s.25 brown and blue . . 35 25

809 – 2s.20 red and blue 50 30
810 – 5s. red and mauve . . . . 1·25 1·00
811 – 10s. violet and green . . . 3·25 2·00
DESIGNS: 5c. Pre-stamp Postmarks; 15c. 1857 2r. stamp; 25c. 1d. 1858; 30c. 1p. 1858 stamp; 40c. ½ peso 1858 stamp; 1s.25, J. Davila Condemarin, Director of Posts, 1857; 2s.20, Pres. Ramon Castilla; 5s. Pres. D. M. Prado; 10s. Various Peruvian stamps in shield.

1958. Air. Centenary of Lima–Callao Telegraph Service.
812 **277** 40c. brown and red . . . 10 10
813 – 1s. green 15 10
814 – 1s.25 blue and purple . . 25 15
DESIGNS—VERT: 1s. Marshal Ramon Castilla. HORIZ: 1s.25, Pres. D. M. Prado and view of Callao.
No. 814 also commemorates the political centenary of the Province of Callao.

278 Flags of France and Peru **279** Father Martin de Porras Velasquez

1958. Air. "Treasures of Peru" Exhibition, Paris.
815 **278** 50c. red, blue & deep blue 10 10
816 – 65c. multicoloured 10 10
817 – 1s.50 brown, purple & bl 25 10
818 – 2s.50 purple, turq & grn 45 20
DESIGNS—HORIZ: 65c. Lima Cathedral and girl in national costume; 1s.50, Caballero and ancient palace. VERT: 2s.50, Natural resources map of Peru.

1958. Air. Birth Centenary of D. A. Carrion Garcia (patriot).
819 **279** 60c. multicoloured 10 10
820 – 1s.20 multicoloured . . . 15 10
821 – 1s.50 multicoloured . . . 25 10
822 – 2s.20 black 30 20
DESIGNS—VERT: 1s.20, D. A. Carrion Garcia. 1s.50, J. H. Unanue Pavon. HORIZ: 2s.20, First Royal School of Medicine (now Ministry of Government Police, Posts and Telecommunications).

280 Gen. Alvarez Thomas **281** Association Emblems

1958. Air. Death Centenary of Gen. Thomas.
823 **280** 1s.10 purple, red & bistre 20 15
824 1s.20 black, red and bistre 25 15

1958. Air. 150th Anniv of Advocates' College, Lima. Emblems in bistre and blue.
825 **281** 80c. green 10 10
826 1s.10 red 15 10
827 1s.20 blue 15 10
828 1s.50 purple 20 10

282 Piura Arms and Congress Emblem **283**

1960. Obligatory Tax. 6th National Eucharistic Congress Fund.
839 **282** 10c. multicoloured . . . 20 10
839a 10c. blue and red 20 10

1960. Air. World Refugee Year.
840 **283** 80c. multicoloured 30 30
841 4s.30 multicoloured . . . 50 50

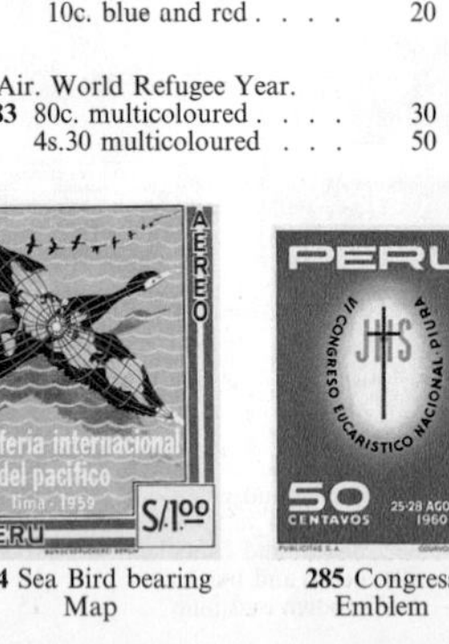

284 Sea Bird bearing Map **285** Congress Emblem

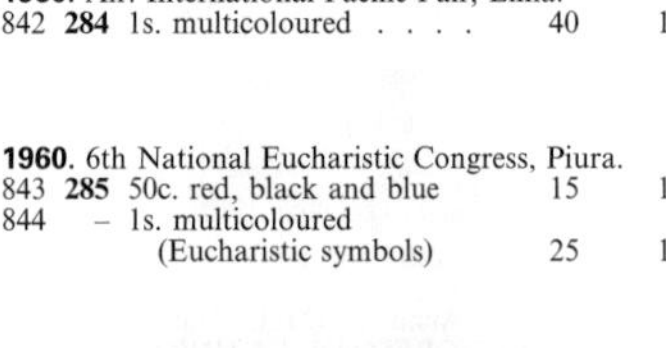

1960. Air. International Pacific Fair, Lima.
842 **284** 1s. multicoloured 40 15

1960. 6th National Eucharistic Congress, Piura.
843 **285** 50c. red, black and blue 15 10
844 – 1s. multicoloured (Eucharistic symbols) 25 10

286 1659 Coin

1961. Air. 1st National Numismatic Exhibition, Lima.
845 – 1s. grey and brown . . . 20 10
846 **286** 2s. grey and blue 25 15
DESIGNS: 1s. 1659 coin.

287 "Amazonas"

1961. Air. Centenary of World Tour of Cadet Sailing Ship "Amazonas".
847 **287** 50c. green and brown . . 35 10
848 80c. red and purple . . . 50 10
849 1s. black and green . . . 70 15

288 Globe, Moon and Stars **289** Olympic Torch

1961. Air. I.G.Y.
850 **288** 1s. multicoloured 15 15

1961. Air. Olympic Games, 1960.
852 **289** 5c. blue and black 40 35
853 10s. red and black 95 60

290 "Balloon" **291** Fair Emblem

1961. Christmas and New Year.
854 **290** 20c. blue 30 10

1961. Air. 2nd International Pacific Fair, Lima.
855 **291** 1s. multicoloured 20 15

292 Symbol of Eucharist **293** Sculptures "Cahuide" and "Cuauhtemoc"

1962. Obligatory Tax. 7th National Eucharistic Congress Fund. Roul.
857 **292** 10c. blue and yellow . . . 10 10

1962. Air. Peruvian Art Treasures Exhibition, Mexico 1960. Flags red and green.
859 **293** 1s. red 15 10
860 – 2s. turquoise 25 15
861 – 3s. brown 30 15
DESIGNS: 2s. Tupac-Amaru and Hidalgo; 3s. Presidents Prado and Lopez.

294 Frontier Maps

1962. Air. 20th Anniv of Ecuador–Peru Border Agreement.
862 **294** 1s.30 black & red on grey 25 15
863 1s.50 multicoloured . . . 25 15
864 2s.50 multicoloured . . . 30 30

295 The Cedar, Pomabamba **296** "Man"

1962. Centenary of Pomabamba and Pallasca Ancash.
865 **295** 1s. green and red (postage) 35 15
866 – 1s. black and grey (air) 10 10
DESIGN: No. 866, Agriculture, mining, etc, Pallasca Ancash (31½ × 22 mm.).

1962. As Nos. 774/91 but colours and some designs changed and new values. (a) Postage.
867 20c. purple 20 10
921 20c. red 10 10
922 30c. blue (as No. 776) . . . 10 10
923 40c. orange (as No. 784) . . 60 10
871 60c. black (as No. 774) . . . 25 10
925 1s. red 10 10

(b) Air.
873 1s.30 ochre (as No. 785) . . 60 20
874 1s.50 purple 35 10
875 1s.80 blue (as No. 777) . . . 1·25 40
876 2s. green 40 15
926 2s.60 green (as No. 783) . . 30 15
877 3s. purple 40 15
927 3s.60 purple (as No. 789) . . 45 20
878 4s.30 orange 80 30
928 4s.60 orange (as No. 788) . . 35 25
879 5s. green 80 35
880 10s. blue . . . . 1·60 40

1963. Air. Chavin Excavations Fund. Pottery.
881 – 1s.+50c. grey and pink . . 15 15
882 – 1s.50+1s. grey and blue 15 15
883 – 3s.+2s.50 grey & green . . 50 50
884 **296** 4s.30+3s. grey and green 85 65
885 – 6s.+4s. grey and olive . . 1·25 85
FIGURES—HORIZ: 1s. "Griffin"; 1s.50, "Eagle"; 3s. "Cat". VERT: 6s. "Deity".

297 Campaign and Industrial Emblems

1963. Freedom from Hunger.
886 **297** 1s. bistre and red (postage) 15 10
887 4s.30 bistre and green (air) 40 40

298 Henri Dunant and Centenary Emblem

1964. Air. Red Cross Centenary.
888 **298** 1s.30+70c. multicoloured 25 25
889 4s.30+1s.70 multicoloured 55 55

299 Chavez and Wing **300** Alliance Emblem

1964. Air. 50th Anniv of Jorge Chavez's Trans-Alpine Flight.
890 **299** 5s. blue, purple and brn 75 35

1964. "Alliance for Progress". Emblem black, green and blue.
891 **300** 40c. black & yell (postage) 10 10
892 – 1s.30 black & mauve (air) 15 10
893 **300** 3s. black and blue 30 25
DESIGN—HORIZ: 1s.30, As Type **300**, but with inscription at right.

301 Fair Poster **302** Net, Flag and Globe

1965. Air. 3rd International Pacific Fair, Lima.
894 **301** 1s. multicoloured 10 10

1965. Air. Women's World Basketball Championships, Lima.
895 **302** 1s.30 violet and red . . . 30 15
896 4s.30 bistre and red . . . 45 30

303 St. Martin de Porras (anonymous) **304** Fair Emblem

1965. Air. Canonization of St. Martin de Porras (1962). Paintings. Multicoloured.
898 1s.30 Type **303** 15 10
899 1s.80 "St. Martin and the Miracle of the Animals" (after painting by Camino Brent) 25 10
900 4s.30 "St. Martin and the Angels" (after painting by Fausto Conti) 50 25
Porras is wrongly spelt "Porres" on the stamps.

1965. 4th International Pacific Fair, Lima.
901 **304** 1s.50 multicoloured . . . 15 10
902 2s.50 multicoloured . . . 20 10
903 3s.50 multicoloured . . . 30 20

305 Father Christmas and Postmarked Envelope **312** 2nd May Monument and Battle Scene

1965. Christmas.
904 **305** 20c. black and red 15 10
905 50c. black and green . . . 20 10
906 1s. black and blue 30 10
The above stamps were valid for postage only on November 2nd. They were subsequently used as postal employees' charity labels.

1966. Obligatory Tax. Journalists' Fund. (a) Surch **HABILITADO "Fondo del Periodista Peruano" Ley 16078 S/o. 0.10.**
907 **264a** 10c. on 3c. (No. 897) . . 65 10

(b) Surch **Habilitado "Fondo del Periodista Peruano" Ley 16078 S/. 0.10.**
909 **264a** 10c. on 3c. (No. 897) . . 25 10

1966. Obligatory Tax. Journalists' Fund. No. 857 optd **Periodista Peruano LEY 16078**.
910 **292** 10c. blue and yellow . . . 10 10

1966. Nos. 757c, 851 and 897 surch **XX Habilitado S/ . 0.10.**
911 **229** 10c. on 2c. brown . . . 10 10
912 **264a** 10c. on 3c. lake (No. 897) 10 10
912b 10c. on 3c. lake (No. 851) . . . . . 2·00 70

1966. Air. Centenary of Battle of Callao. Mult.
913 1s.90 Type **312** 30 20
914 3s.60 Monument and sculpture 45 30
915 4s.60 Monument and Jose Galvez 50 40

313 Funerary Mask

1966. Gold Objects of Chimu Culture. Multicoloured.
916 1s.90+90c. Type **313** 35 35
917 2s.60+1s.30 Ceremonial knife (vert) 40 40
918 3s.60+1s.80 Ceremonial urn 90 90
919 4s.60+2s.30 Goblet (vert) . . 1·25 1·25
920 20s.+10s. Ear-ring . . . . . 4·75 4·75

314 Civil Guard Emblem

1966. Air. Civil Guard Centenary Multicoloured.
929 90c. Type **314** 10 10
930 1s.90 Emblem and activities of Civil Guard 20 10

315 Map and Mountains

1966. Opening of Huinco Hydro-electric Scheme.
931 **315** 70c. black, deep blue and blue (postage) 10 10
932 1s.90 black, blue and violet (air) 20 15

316 Globe

1967. Air. Peruvian Photographic Exhibition, Lima.
933 – 2s.60 red and black . . . 25 15
934 – 3s.60 black and blue . . . 35 25
935 **316** 4s.60 multicoloured . . . 40 30
DESIGNS: 2s.60, "Sun" carving; 3s.60, Map of Peru within spiral.

317 Symbol of Construction

1967. Six-year Construction Plan.
936 **317** 90c. black, gold and mauve (postage) . . . 10 10
937 1s.90 black, gold and ochre (air) 15 15

318 "St. Rosa" (from painting by A. Medoro)

319 Vicuna within Figure "5"

1967. Air. 350th Death Anniv of St. Rosa of Lima. Designs showing portraits of St. Rosa by artists given below. Multicoloured.
938 1s.90 Type **318** 30 15
939 2s.60 C. Maratta 40 15
940 3s.60 Anon., Cusquena School 55 25

1967. 5th International Pacific Fair, Lima.
941 **319** 1s. black, green and gold (postage) 10 10
942 1s. purple, black and gold (air) 10 10

320 Pen-nib made of Newspaper
321 Wall Reliefs (fishes)

1967. Obligatory Tax. Journalists' Fund.
943 **320** 10c. black and red 10 10

1967. Obligatory Tax. Chan-Chan Excavation Fund.
944 **321** 20c. black and blue . . . 10 10
945 – 20c. black and mauve . . 10 10
946 – 20c. black and brown . . 10 10
947 – 20c. multicoloured 10 10
948 – 20c. multicoloured 10 10
949 – 20c. black and green . . . 10 10
DESIGNS: No. 945, Ornamental pattern; No. 946, Carved "bird"; No. 947, Temple on hillside; No. 948, Corner of Temple; No. 949, Ornamental pattern (birds).

322 Lions' Emblem

323 Nazca Jug

1967. Air. 50th Anniv of Lions International.
950 **322** 1s.60 violet, blue and grey 15 10

1968. Air. Ceramic Treasures of Nazca Culture. Designs showing painted pottery jugs. Mult.
951 1s.90 Type **323** 15 15
952 2s.60 Falcon 20 15
953 3s.60 Round jug decorated with bird 25 20
954 4s.60 Two-headed snake . . 30 25
955 5s.60 Sea Bird 40 35

324 Alligator

325 "Antarqui" (Airline Symbol)

1968. Gold Sculptures of Mochica Culture. Mult.
956 1s.90 Type **324** 15 10
957 2s.60 Bird (vert) 15 10
958 3s.60 Lizard 25 15
959 4s.60 Bird (vert) 30 15
960 5s.60 Jaguar 35 20

1968. Air. 12th Anniv of APSA (Peruvian Airlines).
961 **325** 3s.60 multicoloured . . . 30 15
962 – 5s.60 brown, black & red 45 20
DESIGN: 5s.60, Alpaca and stylized Boeing 747.

326 Human Rights Emblem

327 "The Discus-thrower"

1968. Air. Human Rights Year.
963 **326** 6s.50 red, green & brown 25 20

1968. Air. Olympic Games, Mexico.
964 **327** 2s.30 brown, blue & yell 15 10
965 3s.50 blue, red and green 20 15
966 5s. black, blue and pink 25 15
967 6s.50 purple, brown & bl 35 20
968 8s. blue, mauve and lilac 40 25
969 9s. violet, green and orange 45 30

328

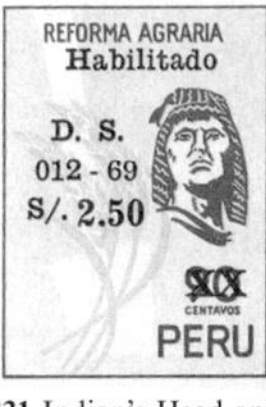

331 Indian's Head and Wheat

1968. Obligatory Tax. Unissued stamps surch as in T **328**.
970 **328** 20c. on 50c. violet, orange and black 40 40
971 20c. on 1s. blue, orange and black 40 40

1968. Obligatory Tax. Journalists' Fund. No. 897 surch **Habilitado Fondo Periodista Peruano Ley 17050 S/.** and value.
972 **264a** 20c. on 3c. lake 10 10

1968. Christmas. No. 900 surch **PRO NAVIDAD Veinte Centavos R.S. 5-11-68**.
973 20c. on 4s.30 multicoloured 25 20

1969. Unissued Agrarian Reform stamps, surch as in T **331**. Multicoloured.
974 2s.50 on 90c. Type **331** (postage) 15 10
975 3s. on 90c. Man digging . . 15 15
976 4s. on 90c. As No. 975 . . . 25 15
977 5s.50 on 1s.90 Corn-cob and hand scattering cobs (air) 30 15
978 6s 50 on 1s.90 As No. 977 . . 40 20

333 First Peruvian Coin (obverse and reverse)

1969. Air. 400th Anniv of 1st Peruvian Coinage.
979 **333** 5s. black, grey and yellow 25 15
980 5s. black, grey and green 25 15

334 Worker holding Flag and Oil Derrick

1969. Nationalization of International Petroleum Company's Oilfields and Refinery (9 October 1968).
981 **334** 2s.50 multicoloured . . . 15 10
982 3s. multicoloured 20 10
983 4s. multicoloured 25 15
984 5s.50 multicoloured . . . 30 20

335 Castilla Monument
336 Boeing 707, Globe and "Kon Tiki" (replica of balsa raft)

1969. Air. Death Centenary of President Ramon Castilla.
985 **335** 5s. blue and green 30 15
986 – 10s. brown and purple . . 70 30
DESIGN—(21 × 37 mm): 10s. President Castilla.

1969. 1st A.P.S.A. (Peruvian Airlines) Flight to Europe.
987 **336** 2s.50 mult (postage) . . . 20 10
988 3s. multicoloured (air) . . 30 10
989 4s. multicoloured 40 10
990 5s.50 multicoloured . . . 50 15
991 6s.50 multicoloured . . . 60 25

337 Dish Aerial, Satellite and Globe

1969. Air. Inauguration of Lurin Satellite Telecommunications Station, Lima.
992 **337** 20s. multicoloured . . . . 1·50 60

338 Captain Jose A. Quinones Gonzales (military aviator)

1969. Quinones Gonzales Commemoration.
994 **338** 20s. mult (postage) . . . 1·50 70
995 20s. multicoloured (air) 1·50 45

339 W.H.O. Emblem

1969. Air. 20th Anniv (1968) of W.H.O.
996 **339** 5s. multicoloured 15 15
997 6s.50 multicoloured . . . 20 15

340 Peasant breaking Chains

341 Arms of the Inca Garcilaso de la Vega (historian)

1969. Agrarian Reform Decree.
998 **340** 2s.50 deep blue, blue and red (postage) 10 10
999 3s. purple, lilac and black (air) 10 10
1000 4s. brown and light brown 15 10

1969. Air. Garcilaso de la Vega Commemoration.
1001 **341** 2s.40 black, silver & grn 10 10
1002 – 3s.50 black, buff and blue 15 10
1003 – 5s. multicoloured 20 15
DESIGNS: 3s.50, Title page, "Commentarios Reales", Lisbon, 1609; 5s. Inca Garcilaso de la Vega.

342 Admiral Grau and Ironclad Warship "Huascar"

1969. Navy Day.
1005 **342** 50s. multicoloured . . . 4·50 2·50

343 "6" and Fair Flags

1969. 6th International Pacific Fair, Lima.
1006 **343** 2s.50 mult (postage) . . 10 10
1007 3s. multicoloured (air) 15 10
1008 4s. multicoloured 15 10

344 Father Christmas and Greetings Card

345 Col. F. Bolognesi and Soldier

1969. Christmas.
1009 **344** 20c. black and red . . . 10 10
1010 20c. black and orange 10 10
1011 20c. black and brown . . 10 10

1969. Army Day.
1012 **345** 1s.20 black, gold and blue (postage) 10 10
1013 50s. black, gold and brown (air) . . . . . 3·00 1·10

346 Arms of Amazonas

1970. Air. 150th Anniv (1971) of Republic (1st issue).
1014 **346** 10s. multicoloured . . . 35 30
See also Nos. 1066/70, 1076/80 and 1081/90.

347 I.L.O. Emblem on Map

1970. Air. 50th Anniv of I.L.O.
1015 **347** 3s. deep blue and blue 15 10

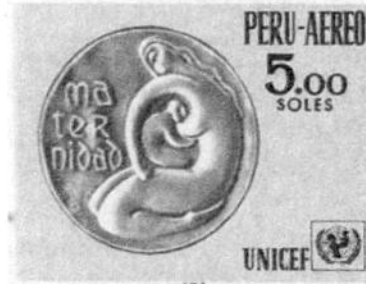

348 "Motherhood"

1970. Air. 24th Anniv of UNICEF.
1016 **348** 5s. black and yellow . . 25 15
1017 6s.50 black and pink . . 35 20

349 "Puma" Jug

350 Ministry Building

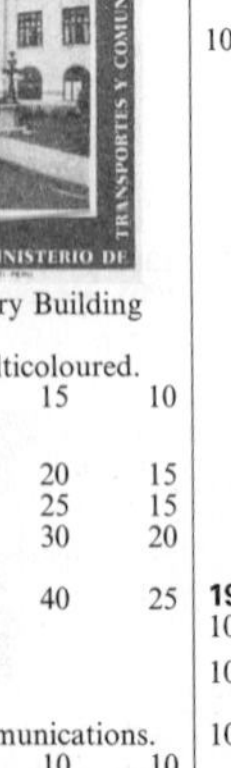

1970. Vicus Culture. Ceramic Art. Multicoloured.
1018 2s.50 Type **349** (postage) . . 15 10
1019 3s. Squatting warrior (statuette) (air) 20 15
1020 4s. Animal jug 25 15
1021 5s.50 Twin jugs 30 20
1022 6s.50 Woman with jug (statuette) 40 25

1970. Ministry of Transport and Communications.
1023 **350** 40c. black and purple . . 10 10
1024 40c. black and yellow . . 10 10
1025 40c. black and grey . . 10 10
1026 40c. black and red . . . 10 10
1027 40c. black and brown . . 10 10

351 Peruvian Anchovy

352 Telephone and Skyline

1970. Fishes. Multicoloured.
1028 2s.50 Type **351** (postage) . . 35 10
1029 2s.50 Chilean hake 35 10
1030 3s. Swordfish (air) 40 15
1031 3s. Yellow-finned tuna . . . 40 15
1032 5s.50 Atlantic wolffish . . . 1·00 25

1970. Air. Nationalization of Lima Telephone Service.
1033 **352** 5s. multicoloured . . . 30 15
1034 10s. multicoloured . . . 55 25

353 "Soldier and Farmer"

354 U.N. Headquarters and Dove

1970. Unity of Armed Forces and People.
1035 **353** 2s.50 mult (postage) . . 15 10
1036 3s. multicoloured (air) 25 10
1037 5s.50 multicoloured . . . 35 15

1970. Air. 25th Anniv of U.N.O.
1038 **354** 3s. blue and light blue 15 10

355 Rotary Emblem

1970. Air. 50th Anniv of Lima Rotary Club.
1039 **355** 10s. gold, red and black 75 25

356 Military Parade (Army Staff College, Chorrillos)

1970. Military, Naval and Air Force Academies. Multicoloured.
1040 2s.50 Type **356** 35 20
1041 2s.50 Parade, Naval Academy, La Punta . . . 35 20
1042 2s.50 Parade, Air Force Officer Training School, Las Palmas 35 20

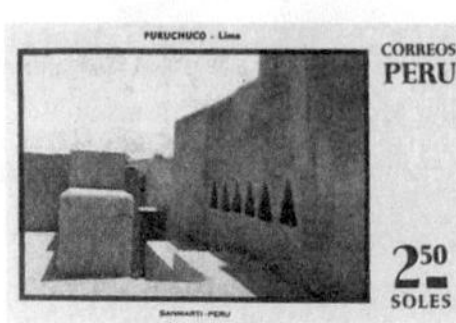

357 Puruchuco, Lima

1970. Tourism. Multicoloured.
1043 2s.50 Type **357** (postage) . . 15 10
1044 3s. Chan-Chan-Trujillo, La Libertad (air) 15 10
1045 4s. Sacsayhuaman, Cuzco (vert) 25 10
1046 5s.50 Lake Titicaca, Pomata, Puno (vert) 30 15
1047 10s. Machu-Picchu, Cuzco (vert) 60 30

358 Festival Procession

1970. Air. October Festival, Lima. Multicoloured.
1049 3s. Type **358** 15 10
1050 4s. "The Cock-fight" (T. Nunez Ureta) 25 10
1051 5s.50 Altar, Nazarenas Shrine (vert) 30 20
1052 6s.50 "The Procession" (J. Vinatea Reinoso) . . . 35 25
1053 8s. "The Procession" (Jose Sabogal) (vert) 50 20

359 "The Nativity" (Cuzco School)

1970. Christmas. Paintings by Unknown Artists. Multicoloured.
1054 1s.20 Type **359** 30 25
1055 1s.50 "The Adoration of the Magi" (Cuzquena School) 10 10
1056 1s.80 "The Adoration of the Shepherds" (Peruvian School) 10 10

360 "Close Embrace" (petroglyph)

1971. Air. "Gratitude for World Help in Earthquake of May 1970".
1057 **360** 4s. olive, black and red 25 15
1058 5s.50 blue, flesh and red 35 15
1059 6s.50 grey, blue and red 40 20

361 "St. Rosa de Lima" (F. Laso)

1971. 300th Anniv of Canonization of St. Rosa de Lima.
1060 **361** 2s.50 multicoloured . . . 15 10

362 Tiahuanaco Fabric

1971. Ancient Peruvian Textiles.
1061 **362** 1s.20 mult (postage) . . 15 10
1062 – 2s.50 multicoloured . . . 25 10
1063 – 3s. multicoloured (air) 30 10
1064 – 4s. pink, green & dp grn 40 10
1065 – 5s.50 multicoloured . . . 55 15
DESIGNS—HORIZ: 2s.50, Chancay fabric; 4s. Chancay lace. VERT: 3s. Chancay tapestry; 5s.50, Paracas fabric.

363 M. Garcia Pumacahua

364 Violet Amberjack (Nazca Culture)

1971. 150th Anniv of Independence (2nd issue). National Heroes.
1066 **363** 1s.20 blk & red (postage) 10 10
1067 – 2s.50 black and blue . . 15 10
1068 – 3s. black and mauve (air) 15 10
1069 – 4s. black and green . . . 15 10
1070 – 5s.50 black and brown 25 15
DESIGNS: 2s.50, F. Antonio de Zela; 3s. T. Rodriguez de Mendoza; 4s. J. P. Viscardo y Guzman; 5s.50, J. G. Condorcanqui, Tupac Amani.
See also Nos. 1076/80 and Nos. 1081/90.

1971. "Traditional Fisheries of Peru". Piscatorial Ceramics. Multicoloured.
1071 1s.50 Type **364** (postage) . . 25 10
1072 3s.50 Pacific bonito (Chimu Inca) (air) 55 15
1073 4s. Peruvian anchovy (Mochica) 75 20
1074 5s.50 Chilian hake (Chimu) 1·10 35
1075 8s.50 Peruvian menhaden (Nazca) . . . . 1·75 60

1971. 150th Anniv of Independence. National Heroes (3rd issue). As T **363**. Multicoloured.
1076 1s.20 M. Melgar (postage) 10 10
1077 2s.50 J. Baquijano y Carrillo 15 10
1078 3s. J. de la Riva Aguero (air) 15 10
1079 4s. H. Unanue 15 10
1080 5s.50 F. J. de Luna Pizarro 25 15

366 Liberation Expedition Monument

367 R. Palma (author and poet)

1971. 150th Anniv of Independence (4th issue). As T **366**. Multicoloured.
1081 1s.50 M. Bastidas (postage) 10 10
1082 2s. J. F. Sanchez Carrion . . 10 10
1083 2s.50 M. J. Guise 15 10
1084 3s. F. Vidal (air) 15 10
1085 3s.50 J. de San Martin . . . 15 15
1086 4s.50 Type **366** 20 15
1087 6s. "Surrender of the 'Numancia Battalion'" (horiz) (42 × 35 mm) . . . 30 15
1088 7s.50 Alvarez de Arenales Monument (horiz) (42 × 39 mm) 35 20
1089 9s. Monument to Founders of the Republic, Lima (horiz) (42 × 39 mm) . . . 40 20
1090 10s. "Proclamation of Independence" (horiz) (46 × 35 mm) 50 20

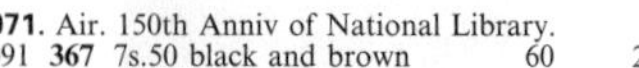

1971. Air. 150th Anniv of National Library.
1091 **367** 7s.50 black and brown 60 25

368 Weightlifting

369 "Gongora portentosa"

1971. Air. 25th World Weightlifting Championships, Huampani, Lima.
1092 **368** 7s.50 black and blue . . 60 25

1971. Peruvian Flora (1st series). Orchids. Mult.
1093 1s.50 Type **369** 25 10
1094 2s. "Odontoglossum cristatum" 30 10
1095 2s.50 "Mormolyca peruviana" 35 10

1096 3s. "Trichocentrum pulchrum" 45 15
1097 3s.50 "Oncidium sanderae" 35 20
See also Nos. 1170/4 and 1206/10.

370 Family and Flag
371 Schooner "Sacramento" of 1821

1971. Air. 3rd Anniv of October 3rd Revolution.
1098 **370** 7s.50 black, red and blue 50 30

1971. Air. 150th Anniv of Peruvian Navy and "Order of the Peruvian Sun".
1100 **371** 7s.50 blue and light blue 1·50 30
1101 – 7s.50 multicoloured . . . 50 25
DESIGN: No. 1101, Order of the Peruvian Sun.

372 "Development and Liberation" (detail)

1971. 2nd Ministerial Meeting of "The 77" Group.
1102 **372** 1s.20 multicoloured (postage) 10 10
1103 – 3s.50 multicoloured . . . 25 10
1104 – 50s. multicoloured (air) 3·00 1·50
DESIGNS—As Type **372**: 3s.50, 50s. Detail from the painting "Development and Liberation".

373 "Plaza de Armas, 1843" (J. Rugendas)

1971. "Exfilima" Stamp Exhibition, Lima.
1105 **373** 3s. black and green . . . 30 10
1106 – 3s.50 black and pink . . 40 15
DESIGN: 3s.50, "Plaza de Armas, 1971" (C. Zeiter).

374 Fair Emblem
375 Army Crest

1971. Air. 7th International Pacific Fair, Lima.
1107 **374** 4s.50 multicoloured . . . 20 15

1971. 150th Anniv of Peruvian Army.
1108 **375** 8s.50 multicoloured . . . 60 20

376 "The Flight into Egypt"

1971. Christmas. Multicoloured.
1109 1s.80 Type **376** 20 10
1110 2s.50 "The Magi" 25 10
1111 3s. "The Nativity" 35 10

377 "Fishermen" (J. Ugarte Elespuru)
378 Chimu Idol

1971. Social Reforms. Paintings. Mulicoloured
1112 3s.50 Type **377** 45 10
1113 4s. "Threshing Grain in Cajamarca" (Camilo Blas) 45 10
1114 6s. "Hand-spinning Huanca Native Women" (J. Sabogal) 60 15

1972. Peruvian Antiquities. Multicoloured.
1115 3s.90 Type **378** 35 15
1116 4s. Chimu statuette 35 15
1117 4s.50 Lambayeque idol . . . 45 15
1118 5s.40 Mochica collar 55 15
1119 6s. Lambayeque "spider" pendant 60 15

379 Peruvian Bigeye

1972. Peruvian Fishes. Multicoloured.
1120 1s.20 Type **379** (postage) . . 30 10
1121 1s.50 Common guadana . . 30 15
1122 2s.50 Jack mackerel 55 20
1123 3s. Diabolico (air) 65 20
1124 5s.50 Galapagos hogfish . . 1·25 35

380 "Peruvian Family" (T. Nunez Ureta)

1972. Air. Education Reforms.
1125 **380** 6s.50 multicoloured . . . 35 20

381 Mochica Warrior
382 White-tailed Trogon

1972. Peruvian Art (1st series). Mochica Ceramics. Multicoloured.
1126 1s.20 Type **381** 15 10
1127 1s.50 Warrior's head 15 10
1128 2s. Kneeling deer 25 10
1129 2s.50 Warrior's head (different) 35 10
1130 3s. Kneeling warrior 40 15
See also Nos. 1180/4.

1972. Air. Peruvian Birds. Multicoloured.
1131 2s. Type **382** . . . . 1·50 20
1132 2s.50 Amazonian umbrellabird . . . . . . 1·75 20
1133 3s. Andean cock of the rock 2·00 25
1134 6s.50 Red-billed toucan . . 3·75 45
1135 8s.50 Blue-crowned motmot 4·75 55

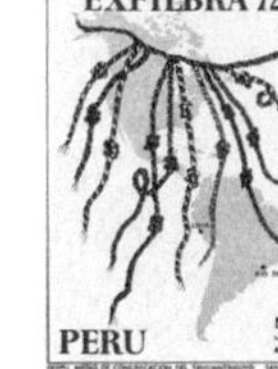

383 "The Harvest" (July)
384 "Quipu" on Map

1972. 400th Anniv of G. Poma de Ayala's "Inca Chronicles". Woodcuts.
1136 **383** 2s.50 black and red . . . 35 10
1137 – 3s. black and green . . . 60 10
1138 – 2s.50 black and pink . . 30 10
1139 – 3s. black and blue . . . 50 10
1140 – 2s.50 black and orange 50 10
1141 – 3s. black and lilac . . . 50 10
1142 – 2s.50 black and brown 35 10
1143 – 3s. black and green . . . 50 10
1144 – 2s.50 black and blue . . 35 10
1145 – 3s. black and orange . . 50 10
1146 – 2s.50 black and mauve 35 10
1147 – 3s. black and yellow . . 50 10

DESIGNS: No. 1137, "Land Purification" (August); No. 1138, "Sowing" (September); No. 1139, "Invocation of the Rains" (October); No. 1140, "Irrigation" (November); No. 1141, "Rite of the Nobility" (December); No. 1142, "Maize Cultivation Rights" (January); No. 1143, "Ripening of the Maize" (February); No. 1144, "Birds in the Maize" (March); No. 1145, "Children as camp-guards" (April); No. 1146, "Gathering the harvest" (May); No. 1147, "Removing the harvest" (June).

1972. Air. "Exfibra 72" Stamp Exn, Rio de Janeiro.
1148 **384** 5s. multicoloured 25 15

385 "The Messenger"
386 Catacaos Woman

1972. Air. Olympic Games, Munich.
1149 **385** 8s. multicoloured 55 20

1972. Air. Provincial Costumes (1st series). Mult.
1150 2s. Tupe girl 15 10
1151 3s.50 Type **386** 30 10
1152 4s. Conibo Indian 40 10
1153 4s.50 Agricultural worker playing "quena" and drum 40 15
1154 5s. "Moche" (Trujillo) girl 40 15
1155 6s.50 Ocongate (Cuzco) man and woman 55 40
1156 8s. "Chucupana" (Ayacucho) girl 60 50
1157 8s.50 "Cotuncha" (Junin) girl 70 55
1158 10s. "Pandilla" dancer . . . 60 60
See also Nos. 1248/9.

387 Ruins of Chavin (Ancash)

1972. Air. 25th Death Anniv Julio C. Tello (archaeologist). Multicoloured.
1159 1s.50 "Stone of the 12 Angles", Cuzco (vert) . . 15 10
1160 3s.50 Type **387** 30 10
1161 4s. Burial-tower, Sillustani (Puno) (vert) 30 10
1162 5s. Gateway, Chavin (Ancash) 45 15
1163 8s. "Wall of the 3 Windows", Machu Picchu (Cuzco) 55 25

388 "Territorial Waters"

1972. 4th Anniv of Armed Forces Revolution. Mult.
1164 2s. Agricultural Workers ("Agrarian Reform") (vert) 10 10
1165 2s.50 Type **388** 50 10
1166 3s. Oil rigs ("Nationalization of Petroleum Industry") (vert) 20 10

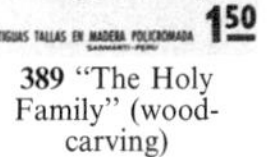
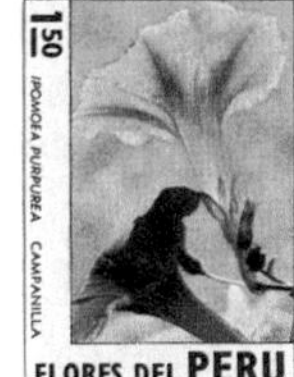

389 "The Holy Family" (wood-carving)
390 "Ipomoea purpurea"

1972. Christmas. Multicoloured.
1167 1s.50 Type **389** 15 10
1168 2s. "The Holy Family" (carved Huamanga stone) (horiz) 15 10
1169 2s.50 "The Holy Family" (carved Huamanga stone) 20 10

1972. Peruvian Flora (2nd series). Multicoloured.
1170 1s.50 Type **390** 15 10
1171 2s.50 "Amaryllis ferreyrae" 20 10
1172 3s. "Liabum excelsum" . . 30 10
1173 3s.50 "Bletia catenulata" . . 55 10
1174 5s. "Cantua buxifolia cantuta" 35 20

391 Inca Poncho
392 Mochica Cameo and Cups

1973. Air. Ancient Inca Textiles.
1175 **391** 2s. multicoloured 15 10
1176 – 3s.50 multicoloured 25 10
1177 – 4s. multicoloured 25 10
1178 – 5s. multicoloured 30 12
1179 – 8s. multicoloured 55 25
DESIGNS: Nos. 1176/9, similar to T **391**.

1973. Air. Peruvian Art (2nd series). Jewelled Antiquities. Multicoloured.
1180 1s.50 Type **392** 10 10
1181 2s.50 Gold-plated arms and hands (Lambayeque) . . 15 10
1182 4s. Bronze effigy (Mochica) 25 10
1183 5s. Gold pendants (Nazca) 30 15
1184 8s. Gold cat (Mochica) . . . 60 25

393 Andean Condor
394 "The Macebearer" (J. Sabogal)

1973. Air. Fauna Protection (1st series). Mult.
1185 2s.50 Lesser rhea . . . . . 1·00 30
1186 3s.50 Giant otter 45 10
1187 4s. Type **393** 40 20
1188 5s. Vicuna 60 15
1189 6s. Chilian flamingo . . . . 2·25 40
1190 8s. Spectacled bear 70 25
1191 8s.50 Bush dog (horiz) . . . 60 25
1192 10s. Short-tailed chinchilla (horiz) 75 30
See also Nos. 1245/6.

1973. Air. Peruvian Paintings. Multicoloured.
1193 1s.50 Type **394** 10 10
1194 8s. "Yananacu Bridge" (E. C. Brent) (horiz) . . 30 15
1195 8s.50 "Portrait of a Lady" (D. Hernandez) 35 15
1196 10s. "Peruvian Birds" (T. N. Ureta) . . . . 1·25 40
1197 20s. "The Potter" (F. Laso) 1·10 40
1198 50s. "Reed Boats" (J. V. Reinoso) (horiz) . . . . . 3·50 1·50

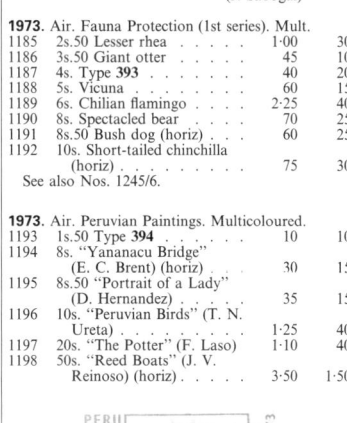

395 Basketball Net and Map

1973. Air. 1st World Basketball Festival.
1199 **395** 5s. green 35 10
1200 20s. purple . . . . . . 1·40 40

396 "Spanish Mayor on Horseback"
398 Fair Emblem (poster)

1973. 170th Birth Anniv of Pancho Fierro (painter). Multicoloured.
1201 1s.50 Type **396** 10 10
1202 2s. "Peasants" 15 10
1203 2s.50 "Father Abregu" . . . 20 10
1204 3s.50 "Dancers" 30 10
1205 4s.50 "Esteban Arredondo on horseback" 45 20

1973. Air. Peruvian Flora (3rd series). Orchids. As T **390**. Multicoloured.
1206 1s.50 "Lycaste reichenbachii" 20 10
1207 2s.50 "Masdevallia amabilis" 30 10

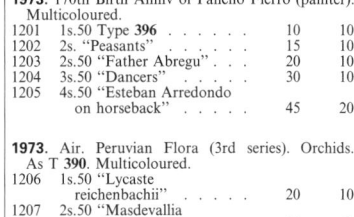

1208 3s. "Sigmatostalix peruviana" 40 10
1209 3s.50 "Porrogossum peruvianum" 40 10
1210 8s. "Oncidium incarum" . . 60 25

1973. Air. 8th International Pacific Fair, Lima.
1211 **398** 8s. red, black and grey 60 20

399 Symbol of Flight

1973. Air. 50th Anniv of Air Force Officers' School.
1212 **399** 8s.50 multicoloured . . . 60 15

400 "The Presentation of the Child"

1973. Christmas. Paintings of the Cuzco School. Multicoloured.
1213 1s.50 Type **400** 10 10
1214 2s. "The Holy Family" (vert) 15 10
1215 2s.50 "The Adoration of the Kings" 15 10

401 Freighter "Ilo"

1973. Air. National Development. Multicoloured.
1216 1s.50 Type **401** 75 20
1217 2s.50 Trawlers 85 20
1218 8s. B.A.C. One Eleven 200 airliner and seagull . . . 1·00 25

402 House of the Mulberry Tree, Arequipa

1974. Air. "Landscapes and Cities". Mult.
1219 1s.50 Type **402** 10 10
1220 2s.50 El Misti (peak), Arequipa 15 10
1221 5s. Giant puya, Cordillera Blanca, Ancash (vert) . . 30 15
1222 6s. Huascaran (peak), Cordillera Blanca, Ancash 35 15
1223 8s. Lake Querococha, Cordillera Blanca, Ancash 55 20

403 Peruvian 2c. Stamp of 1873

405 Church of San Jeronimo, Cuzco

404 Room of the Three Windows, Machu Picchu

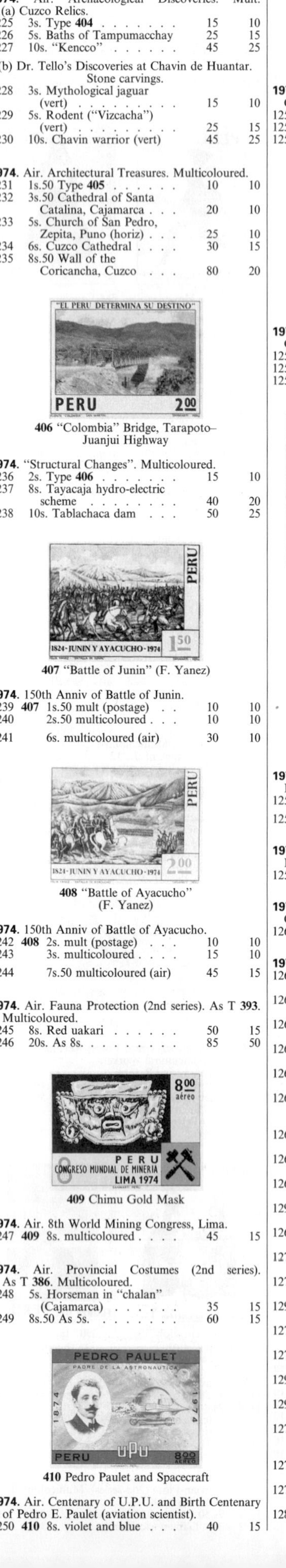

1974. Stamp Day and 25th Anniv of Peruvian Philatelic Association.
1224 **403** 6s. blue and grey 40 15

1974. Air. Archaeological Discoveries. Mult.
(a) Cuzco Relics.
1225 3s. Type **404** 15 10
1226 5s. Baths of Tampumacchay 25 15
1227 10s. "Kencco" 45 25

(b) Dr. Tello's Discoveries at Chavin de Huantar. Stone carvings.
1228 3s. Mythological jaguar (vert) 15 10
1229 5s. Rodent ("Vizcacha") (vert) 25 15
1230 10s. Chavin warrior (vert) 45 25

1974. Air. Architectural Treasures. Multicoloured.
1231 1s.50 Type **405** 10 10
1232 3s.50 Cathedral of Santa Catalina, Cajamarca . . . 20 10
1233 5s. Church of San Pedro, Zepita, Puno (horiz) . . . 25 10
1234 6s. Cuzco Cathedral 30 15
1235 8s.50 Wall of the Coricancha, Cuzco . . . 80 20

406 "Colombia" Bridge, Tarapoto–Juanjui Highway

1974. "Structural Changes". Multicoloured.
1236 2s. Type **406** 15 10
1237 8s. Tayacaja hydro-electric scheme 40 20
1238 10s. Tablachaca dam . . . 50 25

407 "Battle of Junin" (F. Yanez)

1974. 150th Anniv of Battle of Junin.
1239 **407** 1s.50 mult (postage) . . 10 10
1240 2s.50 multicoloured . . . 10 10
1241 6s. multicoloured (air) 30 10

408 "Battle of Ayacucho" (F. Yanez)

1974. 150th Anniv of Battle of Ayacucho.
1242 **408** 2s. mult (postage) . . . 10 10
1243 3s. multicoloured 15 10
1244 7s.50 multicoloured (air) 45 15

1974. Air. Fauna Protection (2nd series). As T **393**. Multicoloured.
1245 8s. Red uakari 50 15
1246 20s. As 8s. 85 50

409 Chimu Gold Mask

1974. Air. 8th World Mining Congress, Lima.
1247 **409** 8s. multicoloured 45 15

1974. Air. Provincial Costumes (2nd series). As T **386**. Multicoloured.
1248 5s. Horseman in "chalan" (Cajamarca) 35 15
1249 8s.50 As 5s. 60 15

410 Pedro Paulet and Spacecraft

1974. Air. Centenary of U.P.U. and Birth Centenary of Pedro E. Paulet (aviation scientist).
1250 **410** 8s. violet and blue . . . 40 15

411 Copper Smelter, La Oroya

1974. Expropriation of Cerro de Pasco Mining Complex.
1251 **411** 1s.50 blue and deep blue 10 10
1252 3s. red and brown . . . 15 10
1253 4s.50 green and grey . . 25 15

412 "Capitulation of Ayacucho" (D. Hernandez)

1974. Air. 150th Anniv of Spanish Forces' Capitulation at Ayacucho.
1254 **412** 3s.50 multicoloured . . . 20 10
1255 8s.50 multicoloured . . . 60 20
1256 10s. multicoloured . . . 80 25

413 "Madonna and Child"

415 Map and Civic Centre, Lima

414 "Andean Landscape" (T. Nunez Ureta)

1974. Christmas. Paintings of the Cuzco Shool. Multicoloured.
1257 1s.50 Type **413** (postage) . . 10 10
1258 6s.50 "Holy Family" (air) 30 15

1974. Air. Andean Pact Communications Ministers' Meeting, Cali, Colombia.
1259 **414** 6s.50 multicoloured . . . 35 15

1975. Air. 2nd General Conference of U.N. Organization for Industrial Development.
1260 **415** 6s. black, red and grey 25 15

1975. Air. Various stamps surch.
1261 – 1s.50 on 3s.60 purple (No. 927) 10 10
1262 – 2s. on 2s.60 green (No. 926) 15 10
1263 – 2s. on 3s.60 purple (No. 927) 15 10
1263a – 2s. on 3s.60 black and blue (No. 934) . . . 10 10
1264 – 2s. on 4s.30 orange (No. 878) 10 10
1265 – 2s. on 4s.30 multicoloured (No. 900) 15 10
1266 – 2s. on 4s.60 orange (No. 928) 10 10
1267 – 2s.50 on 4s.60 orange (No. 928) 25 10
1268 – 3s. on 2s.60 green (No. 926) 15 10
1294 – 3s.50 on 4s.60 orange (No. 928) 20 10
1269 – 4s. on 2s.60 green (No. 926) 20 10
1270 – 4s. on 3s.60 purple (No. 927) 20 10
1271 – 4s. on 4s.60 orange (No. 928) 15 10
1295 – 4s.50 on 3s.80 orange (No. 836) 20 10
1272 – 5s. on 3s.60 purple (No. 927) 20 10
1273 – 5s. on 3s.80 orange (No. 836) 35 10
1296 – 5s. on 4s.30 orange (No. 878) 30 10
1297 – 6c. on 4s.60 orange (No. 928) 40 15
1277 **316** 6s. on 4s.60 multicoloured (No. 935) 45 10
1278 – 7s. on 4s.30 orange (No. 878) 40 15
1279 – 7s.50 on 3s.60 purple (No. 927) 50 15
1280 – 8s. on 3s.60 purple (No. 927) 50 15
1281 **271** 10s. on 2s.15 purple (No. 794) 40 25
1298 – 10s. on 2s.60 green (No. 926) 60 20
1282 – 10s. on 3s.60 purple (No. 927) 60 25
1283 – 10s. on 3s.60 multicoloured (No. 940) 50 25
1284 – 10s. on 4s.30 orange (No. 878) 25 25
1285 – 10s. on 4s.60 orange (No. 928) 60 25
1286 – 20s. on 3s.60 purple (No. 927) 40 15
1287 – 24s. on 3s.60 multicoloured (No. 953) . . . . . 1·40 45
1288 – 28s. on 4s.60 multicoloured (No. 954) . . . . . 1·50 55
1289 – 32s. on 5s.60 multicoloured (No. 955) . . . . . 1·50 65
1290 – 50s. on 2s.60 green (No. 926) . . . . . 2·75 1·00
1299 – 50s. on 3s.60 purple (No. 927) . . . . . 2·25 1·50
1292 – 100s. on 3s.80 orange (No. 836) . . . . . 3·50 1·50

417 Lima on World Map

1975. Air. Conference of Non-aligned Countries' Foreign Ministers, Lima.
1311 **417** 6s.50 multicoloured . . . 40 15

418 Maria Parado de Bellido

1975. "Year of Peruvian Women" and International Women's Year. Multicoloured.
1312 1s.50 Type **418** 15 10
1313 2s. Micaela Bastidas (vert) 15 10
1314 2s.50 Juana Alarco de Dammert 20 10
1315 3s. I.W.Y. emblem (vert) . . 35 10

419 Route Map of Flight

1975. Air. 1st "Aero Peru" Flight, Rio de Janeiro–Lima–Los Angeles.
1316 **419** 8s. multicoloured 60 15

420 San Juan Macias

421 Fair Poster

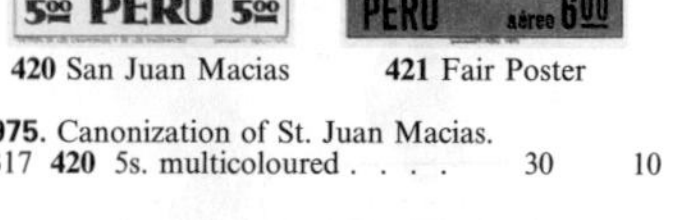

1975. Canonization of St. Juan Macias.
1317 **420** 5s. multicoloured 30 10

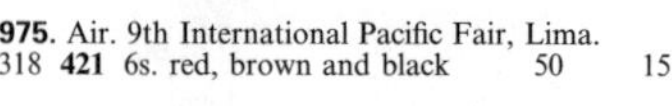

1975. Air. 9th International Pacific Fair, Lima.
1318 **421** 6s. red, brown and black 50 15

422 Col. F. Bolognesi

423 "Nativity"

1975. Air. 159th Birth Anniv of Colonel Francisco Bolognesi.
1319 **422** 20s. multicoloured . . . 1·25 35

1976. Air. Christmas (1975).
1320 **423** 6s. multicoloured 35 15

424 Louis Braille

1976. 150th Anniv of Braille System for Blind.
1321 **424** 4s.50 red, black and grey . . . 30 10

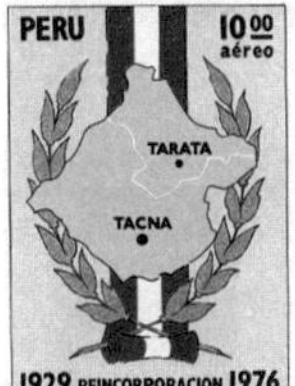

426 Inca Postal Runner **427** Map on Riband

1976. Air. 11th UPAE Congress, Lima.
1322 **426** 5s. black, brown and red . . . 50 10

1976. Air. Reincorporation of Tacna.
1323 **427** 10s. multicoloured . . . 30 15

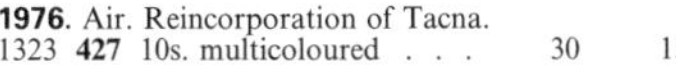

428 Peruvian Flag

1976. 1st Anniv of Second Phase of Revolution.
1324 **428** 5s. red, black and grey . . . 15 10

429 Police Badge

1976. Air. 54th Anniv of Peruvian Special Police.
1325 **429** 20s. multicoloured . . . 1·00 40

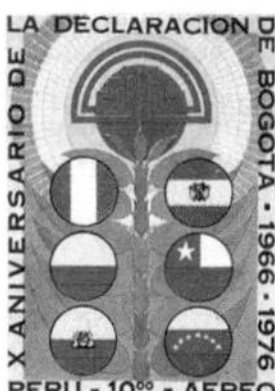

430 "Tree of Badges" **431** Chairman Pal Losonczi

1976. Air. 10th Anniv of Bogota Declaration.
1326 **430** 10s. multicoloured . . . 30 20

1976. Air. Visit of Hungarian Head of State.
1327 **431** 7s. black and blue . . . 40 15

432 "St. Francis of Assisi" (El Greco) **434** "Nativity"

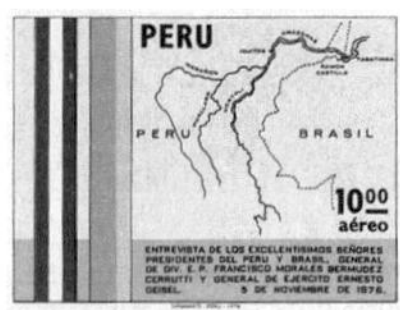

433 Map and National Colours

1976. 750th Death Anniv of St. Francis of Assisi.
1328 **432** 5s. brown and gold . . . 35 10

1976. Air. Meeting of Presidents of Peru and Brazil.
1329 **433** 10s. multicoloured . . . 30 20

1976. Christmas.
1330 **434** 4s. multicoloured 30 10

435 Military Monument and Symbols

1977. Air. Army Day.
1331 **435** 20s. black, buff and red . . . 40 40

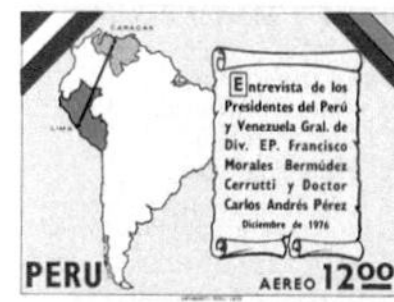

436 Map and Scroll

1977. Air. Visit of Peruvian President to Venezuela.
1332 **436** 12s. multicoloured . . . 60 25

437 Printed Circuit

1977. Air. World Telecommunications Day.
1333 **437** 20s. red, black and silver . . . 1·10 40

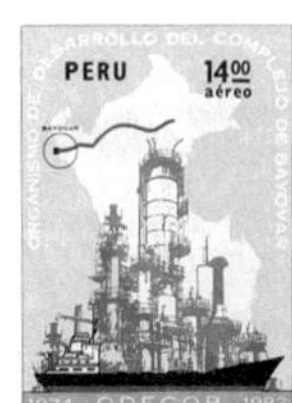

438 Inca Postal Runner **439** Petrochemical Plant, Map and Tanker

1977.
1334 **438** 6s. black and turquoise (postage) 40 15
1335 8s. black and red 40 15
1336 10s. black and blue . . . 55 25
1337 12s. black and green . . 55 35
1338 24s. black and red (air) . . 1·00 50
1339 28s. black and blue . . . 1·10 50
1340 32s. black and brown . . 1·50 70

1977. Air. Bayovar Petrochemical Complex.
1341 **439** 14s. multicoloured . . . 1·50 30

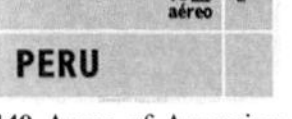

440 Arms of Arequipa **441** President Videla

1977. Air. "Gold of Peru" Exhibition, Arequipa.
1342 **440** 10s. multicoloured . . . 20 10

1977. Air. Visit of President Videla of Argentina.
1343 **441** 36s. multicoloured . . . 75 25

1977. Various stamps surch **FRANQUEO** and new value.
1344 **325** 6s. on 3s.60 multicoloured 40 15
1345 8s. on 3s.60 multicoloured 45 15
1346 – 10s. on 5s.60 brown, black and red (No. 962) 50 25
1347 **305** 10s. on 50c. black & grn . . 30 10
1348 20s. on 20c. black and red 50 20
1349 30s. on 1s. black and blue 70 35

444 Fair Emblem and Flags **445** Republican Guard Badge

1977. 10th International Pacific Fair.
1350 **444** 10s. multicoloured . . . 20 10

1977. 58th Anniv of Republican Guard.
1351 **445** 12s. multicoloured . . . 25 15

446 Admiral Miguel Grau **447** "The Holy Family"

1977. Air. Navy Day.
1352 **446** 28s. multicoloured . . . 35 25

1977. Christmas. Multicoloured.
1353 8s. Type **447** (postage) . . . 10 10
1354 20s. "The Adoration of the Shepherds" (air) 50 20

448 Open Book of Flags **449** Inca Head

1978. Air. 8th Meeting of Education Ministers.
1355 **448** 30s. multicoloured . . . 40 25

1978.
1356 **449** 6s. green (postage) . . . 10 10
1357 10s. red 15 10
1358 16s. brown 20 20
1359 24s. mauve (air) 30 25
1360 30s. pink 40 30
1361 65s. blue 90 70
1362 95s. blue . . . . 1·50 1·00

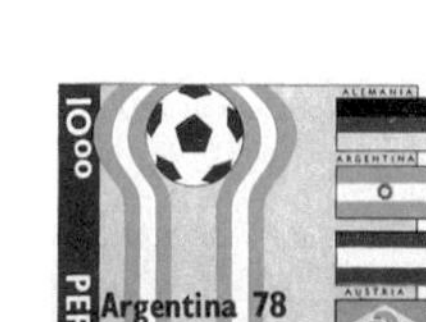

450 Emblem and Flags of West Germany, Argentina, Austria and Brazil

1978. World Cup Football Championship, Argentina (1st issue). Multicoloured.
1367 10s. Type **450** 20 10
1368 10s. Emblem and flags of Hungary, Iran, Italy and Mexico 20 10
1369 10s. Emblem and flags of Scotland, Spain, France and Netherlands 20 10
1370 10s. Emblem and flags of Peru, Poland, Sweden and Tunisia 20 10
See also Nos. 1412/15.

451 Microwave Antenna

1978. Air. 10th World Telecommunications Day.
1371 **451** 50s. grey, deep blue and blue 75 50

1978. Various stamps surch **Habilitado Dif.-Porte** and value (Nos. 1372/4), **Habilitado R.D. No. 0118** and value (Nos. 1377/8, 1381, 1384, 1390) or with value only (others).
1372 **229** 2s. on 2c. brown (postage) 10 10
1373 **229** 4s. on 2c. brown 10 10
1374 5s. on 2c. brown 10 10
1375 **313** 20s. on 1s.90+90c. multicoloured 75 60
1376 – 30s. on 2s.60+1s.30 multicoloured (No. 917) 60 60
1377 **229** 35s. on 2c. brown . . . 1·25 20
1378 50s. on 2c. brown . . . 4·00 60
1379 – 55s. on 3s.60+1s.80 multicoloured (No. 918) . . . . . . 1·10 55
1380 – 65s. on 4s.60+2s.30 multicoloured (No. 919) . . . . . . 1·75 1·10
1381 – 80s. on 5s.60 mult (No. 960) . . . . . . 1·40 40
1382 – 85s. on 20s.+10s. multicoloured (No. 920) . . . . . . 2·00 1·25
1383 – 25s. on 4s.60 mult (No. 954) (air) 20 15
1384 **316** 34s. on 4s.60 mult . . . 50 15
1385 **302** 40s. on 4s.30 bistre and red 50 20
1386 **449** 45s. on 28s. green . . . 45 25
1387 – 70s. on 2s.60 green (No. 926) . . . . . . 2·75 40
1388 **449** 75s. on 28s. green . . . 75 40
1389 – 105s. on 5s.60 mult (No. 955) . . . . . . 1·00 85
1390 – 110s. on 3s.60 purple (No. 927) . . . . . . 1·90 60
1391 – 265s. on 4s.30 mult (No. 900) . . . . . . 4·00 1·50
The 28s. value as Type **449** was not issued without a surcharge.

1978. Surch **SOBRE TASA OFICIAL** and value.
1400 **229** 3s. on 2s. brown 10 10
1401 6s. on 2c. brown 15 10

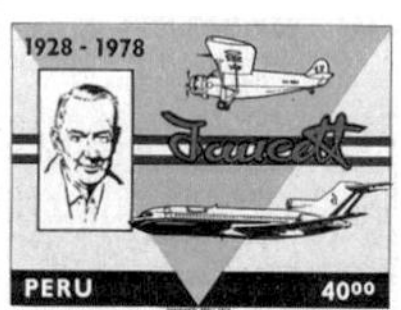

456 San Martin **457** Elmer Faucett and Stinson-Faucett F-19 and Boeing 727-200 Aircraft

1978. Air. Birth Bicentenary of General Jose de San Martin.
1410 **456** 30s. multicoloured . . . 40 30

1978. 50th Anniv of Faucett Aviation.
1411 **457** 40s. multicoloured . . . 50 30

1978. World Cup Football Championship, Argentina (2nd issue). Multicoloured.
1412 16s. As Type **450** 15 10
1413 16s. As No. 1368 . . . . . 15 10
1414 16s. As No. 1369 . . . . . 15 10
1415 16s. As No. 1370 . . . . . 15 10

458 Nazca Bowl **459** Peruvian Nativity

1978.
1416 **458** 16s. blue 15 10
1417 20s. green 15 10
1418 25s. green 20 15
1419 35s. red 35 15
1420 45s. brown 40 25
1421 50s. black 50 25
1422 55s. mauve 50 25
1423 70s. mauve 60 35
1424 75s. blue 55 40
1425 80s. brown 55 40
1426 200s. violet . . . . . . 1·90 1·50

1978. Christmas.
1436 **459** 16s. multicoloured . . . 15 10

460 Ministry of Education, Lima

461 Queen Sophia and King Juan Carlos

1979. National Education.
1437 **460** 16s. multicoloured . . . 15 10

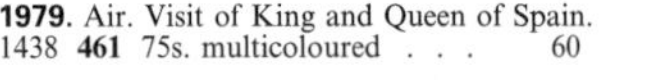

1979. Air. Visit of King and Queen of Spain.
1438 **461** 75s. multicoloured . . . 60 25

462 Red Cross Emblem

1979. Centenary of Peruvian Red Cross Society.
1439 **462** 16s. multicoloured . . . 10 10

463 "Naval Battle of Iquique" (E. Velarde)

1979. Pacific War Centenary. Multicoloured.
1440 14s. Type **463** 40 10
1441 25s. "Col. Jose Joaquin Inclan" (vert) 30 15
1442 25s. "Arica Blockade-runner, the Corvette "Union" 60 15
1443 25s. "Heroes of Angamos" 60 15
1444 25s. "Lt. Col. Pedro Ruiz Gallo" (vert) 30 15
1445 85s. "Marshal Andres H. Caceres" (vert) 45 40
1446 100s. "Battle of Angamos" (T. Castillo) . . . . 1·75 60
1447 100s. "Battle of Tarapaca" 55 45
1448 115s. "Admiral Miguel Grau" (vert) . . . . . . 1·40 50
1449 200s. "Bolognesi's Reply" (Leppiani) . . . . 1·25 90
1450 200s. "Col. Francisco Bolognesi" (vert) . . . . 1·60 1·10
1451 200s. "Col. Alfonso Ugarte" (Morizani) . . . . 1·60 1·10

A similar 200s. value, showing the Crypt of the Fallen was on sale for a very limited period only.

464 Billiard Balls and Cue

465 Arms of Cuzco

1979. 34th World Billiards Championship, Lima.
1456 **464** 34s. multicoloured . . . 30 15

1979. Inca Sun Festival, Cuzco.
1457 **465** 50s. multicoloured . . . 35 20

466 Flag and Arch

468 Exposition Emblem

1979. 50th Anniv of Reincorporation of Tacna into Peru.
1458 **466** 16s. multicoloured . . . 15 10

1979. Surch in figures only.
1459 **229** 7s. on 2c. brown 10 10
1460 9s. on 2c. brown 10 10
1461 15s. on 2c. brown . . . 15 10

1979. 3rd World Telecommunications Exhibition, Geneva.
1467 **468** 15s. orange, blue and grey 10 10

469 Caduceus

1979. Int Stomatology Congress, Lima, and 50th Anniv of Peruvian Academy of Stomatology.
1468 **469** 25s. gold, black & turq 20 15

470 Fair Emblem on World Map

1979. 11th International Pacific Fair.
1469 **470** 55s. multicoloured . . . 40 30

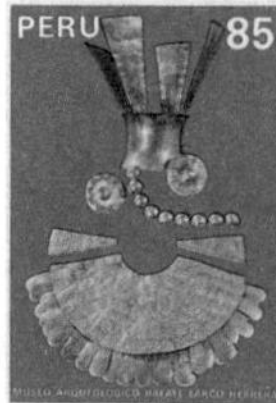

471 Regalia of Chimu Chief (Imperial period)

472 Angel with Lute

1979. Rafael Larco Herrera Museum of Archaeology.
1470 **471** 85s. multicoloured . . . 60 40

1980. Christmas.
1471 **472** 25s. multicoloured . . . 20 10

1980. Various stamps surch.
1472 **466** 20s. on 16s. multicoloured (postage) 15 10
1473 **463** 25s. on 14s. multicoloured 30 15
1474 **464** 65s. on 34s. multicoloured 45 35
1475 **458** 80s. on 70s. mauve . . . 55 40
1476 **449** 35s. on 24s. mauve (air) 25 15
1477 **438** 45s. on 32s. black and brown 30 20

474 "Respect and Comply with the Constitution"

475 Ceramic Vase (Chimu Culture)

1980. Citizens' Duties.
1478 **474** 15s. turquoise 10 10
1479 – 20s. red 15 10
1480 – 25s. blue 20 15
1481 – 30s. mauve 20 15
1482 – 35s. black 25 20
1483 – 45s. green 30 25
1484 – 50s. brown 35 25

INSCRIPTIONS: 20s. "Honour your country and protect your interests"; 25s. "Comply with the elective process"; 30s. "Comply with your military service"; 35s. "Pay your taxes"; 45s. "Work and contribute to national progress"; 50s. "Respect the rights of others".

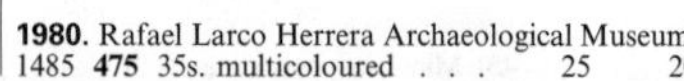

1980. Rafael Larco Herrera Archaeological Museum.
1485 **475** 35s. multicoloured . . . 25 20

476 "Liberty" and Map of Peru

478 Rebellion Memorial, Cuzco (Joaquin Ugarte)

477 Machu Picchu

1980. Return to Democracy.
1486 **476** 25s. black, buff and red 20 15
1487 – 35s. black and red . . . 25 20
DESIGN: 35s. Handshake.

1980. World Tourism Conference, Manila.
1488 **477** 25s. multicoloured . . . 20 15

1980. Bicentenary of Tupac Amaru Rebellion.
1489 **478** 25s. multicoloured . . . 20 15
See also No. 1503.

479 Nativity

1980. Christmas.
1490 **479** 15s. multicoloured . . . 10 10

480 Bolivar and Flags

482 Presidential Badge of Office, Laurel Leaves and Open Book

1981. 150th Death Anniv of Simon Bolivar.
1491 **480** 40s. multicoloured . . . 30 20

1981. Various stamps surch.
1492 – 25s. on 35s. black and red (No. 1487) 20 15
1493 **482** 40s. on 25s. multicoloured 30 20
1494 **458** 85s. on 200s. violet . . 60 45
1495 – 100s. on 115s. mult (No. 1448) 95 50
1496 **482** 130s. on 25s. mult . . . 95 40
1497 140s. on 25s. mult . . . 1·10 50

1981. Re-establishment of Constitutional Government.
1498 **482** 25s. multicoloured . . . 20 15

483 Stone Head, Pallasca

1981.
1499 **483** 30s. violet 20 15
1500 – 40s. blue 30 20
1501 – 100s. mauve 70 45
1502 – 140s. green 95 60

DESIGNS—VERT: 40s. Stone head, Huamachuco; 100s. Stone head (Chavin culture). HORIZ: 140s. Stone puma head (Chavin culture).

484 Tupac Amaru and Micaela Bastidas (sculptures by Miguel Boca Rossi)

1981. Bicentenary of Revolution of Tupac Amaru and Micaela Bastidas.
1503 **484** 60s. multicoloured . . . 40 30

485 Post Box, 1859

486 Map of Peru and I.Y.D.P. Emblem

1981. 50th Anniv of Postal and Philatelic Museum, Lima.
1504 **485** 130s. multicoloured . . . 95 60

1981. International Year of Disabled Persons.
1505 **486** 100s. violet, mauve and gold 70 45

487 Victor Raul Haya de la Torre (President of Constitutional Assembly)

490 Inca Messenger (drawing by Guaman Ponce de Ayala)

1981. Constitution.
1506 **487** 30s. violet and grey . . . 20 15

1981. No. 801 surch.
1507 30s. on 2s.20 brown & blue 20 15
1508 40s. on 2s.20 brown & blue 30 20

1981. 12th International Pacific Fair. No. 801 surch with **12 Feria Internacional del Pacifico 1981 140**.
1509 140s. on 2s.20 brown & blue 95 70

1981. Christmas.
1510 **490** 30s. black and mauve . . 20 10
1511 40s. black and red . . . 35 10
1512 130s. black and green . . 75 35
1513 140s. black and blue . . 90 40
1514 200s. black and brown 1·25 60

1982. Various stamps surch **Habilitado Franq. Postal** and value (Nos. 1520/1) or with value only (others).
1515 **229** 10s. on 2c. brown (postage) 15 10
1516 — 10s. on 10c. red (No. 642) 10 10
1517 **292** 40s. on 10c. blue and yellow 15 10
1518 **273** 70s. on 5c. blue and red 35 20
1519 **264a** 80s. on 3c. lake . . . 30 15
1520 D **109** 80s. on 10c. green . . 30 15
1521 O **108** 80s. on 10c. brown 30 15
1522 **292** 100s. on 10c. blue and yellow 40 20
1523 — 140s. on 50c. brown, yellow and red . . . 50 25
1524 — 140s. on 1s. mult . . 50 25
1525 **264a** 150s. on 3c. lake . . 40 20
1526 180s. on 3c. lake . . 55 30
1527 200s. on 3c. lake . . 70 40
1528 **273** 280s. on 5c. blue and red 85 55
1529 — 40s. on 1s.25 blue and purple (No. 814) (air) . . 30 15
1530 — 100s. on 2s.20 (No. 801) brown and blue 40 20
1531 — 240s. on 1s.25 blue and purple (No. 814) . . . . 1·25 85

Nos. 1523/4 are surcharged on labels for the Seventh Eucharistic Congress which previously had no postal validity.

493 Inca Pot **494** Jorge Basadre (after Oscar Lopez Aliaga)

1982. Indian Ceramics.
1532 **493** 40s. orange 30 15
1533 80s. lilac 50 25
1534 – 80s. red 60 25
1535 **493** 180s. green . . . . . . 1·25 70
1536 – 240s. blue . . . . 1·25 60
1537 – 280s. violet . . . . . . 1·40 70
DESIGNS: 80s., (No. 1534), 240, 280s. Nazca fish ceramic.

1982. Jorge Basadre (historian) Commemoration.
1538 **494** 100s. black and green . . 25 20

495 Julio C. Tello (bust, Victoria Macho)

1982. Birth Centenary of Julio C. Tello (archaeologist).
1539 **495** 200s. green and blue . . 45 30

496 Championship Emblem **497** Disabled Person in Wheelchair

1982. 9th World Women's Volleyball Championship, Peru.
1540 **496** 80s. red and black . . . 20 15

1982. Rights for the Disabled Year.
1541 **497** 200s. blue and red . . . 50 30

498 Andres A. Caceres Medallion

1982. Centenary of Brena Campaign.
1542 **498** 70s. brown and grey . . 20 15

499 Footballers **500** Congress Emblem

1982. World Cup Football Championship, Spain.
1543 **499** 80s. multicoloured . . . 20 15

1982. 16th Int Latin Notaries Congress, Lima.
1544 **500** 500s. black, gold and red 1·10 50

501 Bull (clay jar) **502** Pedro Vilcapaza

1982. Handicrafts Year.
1545 **501** 200s. red, brown and black 50 30

1982. Death Bicentenary of Pedro Vilcapaza (Indian leader).
1546 **502** 240s. brown and black 35 35

503 Jose Davila Condemarin (after J. Y. Pastor) **504** "Nativity" (Hilario Mendivil)

1982. Death Centenary of Jose Davila Condemarin (Director General of Posts).
1547 **503** 150s. black and blue . . 40 25

1982. Christmas.
1548 **504** 280s. multicoloured . . . 40 30

505 Centre Emblem and Hand holding Potatoes

1982. 10th Anniv of International Potato Centre.
1549 **505** 240s. brown and grey . . 35 35

506 Arms of Piura

1982. 450th Anniv of San Miguel de Piura.
1550 **506** 280s. multicoloured . . . 40 40

507 Microscope

1982. Centenary of Discovery of Tubercule Bacillus.
1551 **507** 240s. green 35 35

508 "St. Theresa of Avila" (Jose Espinoza de los Monteros)

1983. 400th Death Anniv of St. Theresa of Avila.
1552 **508** 100s. multicoloured . . . 25 15

509 Civil Defence Badge and Interlocked Hands

1983. 10th Anniv of Civil Defence System.
1553 **509** 100s. blue, orange & blk 25 15

510 Silver Shoe

1983. "Peru, Land of Silver".
1554 **510** 250s. silver, black & blue 55 35

511 Map of Signatories and 200 Mile Zone **513** "75"

512 Boeing 747-200

1983. 30th Anniv of Santiago Declaration.
1555 **511** 280s. brown, blue & black 40 40

1983. 25th Anniv of Lima–Bogota Airmail Service.
1556 **512** 150s. multicoloured . . . 60 25

1983. 75th Anniv of Lima and Callao State Lotteries.
1557 **513** 100s. blue and purple . . 20 15

514 Cruiser "Almirante Grau"

1983. Peruvian Navy. Multicoloured.
1558 150s. Type **514** 95 25
1559 350s. Submarine "Ferre" . . 1·50 55

1983. Various stamps surch.
1560 **493** 100s. on 40s. orange . . 20 15
1561 **498** 100s. on 70s. brown and grey 20 15
1562 **496** 100s. on 80s. red and black 20 15
1563 **502** 100s. on 240s. brown and black 20 15
1564 **505** 100s. on 240s. ochre, deep brown and brown 20 15
1565 **507** 100s. on 240s. green . . 20 15
1566 **506** 150s. on 280s. mult . . . 30 15
1567 **511** 150s. on 280s. brown, blue and black 30 15
1568 **504** 200s. on 280s. mult . . . 40 25
1569 **493** 300s. on 180s. green . . 55 35
1570 400s. on 180s. green . . 75 50
1571 **499** 500s. on 80s. mult . . . 95 65

516 Simon Bolivar **517** "Virgin and Child" (Cuzquena School)

1983. Birth Bicentenary of Simon Bolivar.
1572 **516** 100s. blue and black . . 20 15

1983. Christmas.
1573 **517** 100s. multicoloured . . . 20 10

518 Fair Emblem **520** Leoncio Prado

519 W.C.Y. Emblem

1983. 14th International Pacific Fair.
1574 **518** 350s. multicoloured . . . 40 15

1984. World Communications Year.
1575 **519** 700s. multicoloured . . . 75 30

1984. Death Centenary (1983) of Colonel Leoncio Prado.
1576 **520** 150s. bistre and brown 15 10

521 Container Ship "Presidente Jose Pardo" at Wharf

1984. Peruvian Industry.
1577 **521** 250s. purple 65 20
1578 – 300s. blue 90 25
DESIGN: 300s. "Presidente Jose Pardo" (container ship).

522 Ricardo Palma **523** Pistol Shooting

1984. 150th Birth Anniv (1983) of Ricardo Palma (writer).
1579 **522** 200s. violet 15 10

1984. Olympic Games, Los Angeles.
1580 **523** 500s. mauve and black 45 25
1581 – 750s. red and black . . . 60 30
DESIGN: 750s. Hurdling.

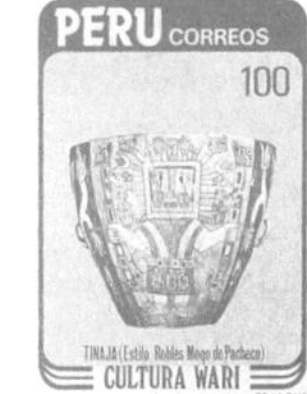

524 Arms of Callao **525** Water Jar

1984. Town Arms.
1582 **524** 350s. grey 25 15
1583 – 400s. brown 55 25
1584 – 500s. brown 65 30
DESIGNS: 400s. Cajamarca; 500s. Ayacucho.

1984. Wari Ceramics (1st series).
1585 **525** 100s. brown 10 10
1586 – 150s. brown 15 10
1587 – 200s. brown 20 10
DESIGNS: 150s. Llama; 200s. Vase.
See also Nos. 1616/18.

526 Hendee's Woolly Monkeys

1984. Fauna.
1588 **526** 1000s. multicoloured . . 75 40

527 Signing Declaration of Independence

1984. Declaration of Independence.
1589 **527** 350s. black, brown & red 25 15

528 General Post Office, Lima

529 "Canna edulis"

1984. Postal Services.
1590 **528** 50s. olive 10 10

1984. Flora.
1591 **529** 700s. multicoloured . . . 45 25

530 Grau (after Pablo Muniz)

531 Hipolito Unanue

1984. 150th Anniv of Admiral Miguel Grau. Mult.
1592 600s. Type 35 20
1593 600s. Battle of Angamos (45 × 35 mm) 85 30
1594 600s. Grau's seat, National Congress 35 20
1595 600s. "Battle of Iquique" (Guillermo Spier) (45 × 35 mm) 85 30

1984. 150th Death Anniv (1983) of Hipolito Unanue (founder of School of Medicine).
1596 **531** 50s. green 10 10

532 Destroyer "Almirante Guise"

1984. Peruvian Navy.
1597 **532** 250s. blue 35 20
1598 – 400s. turquoise and blue 75 25
DESIGN: 400s. River gunboat "America".

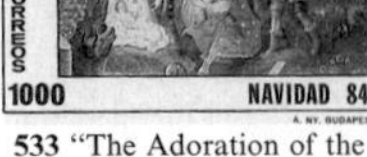

533 "The Adoration of the Shepherds"

534 Belaunde

1984. Christmas.
1599 **533** 1000s. multicoloured . . 40 15

1984. Birth Centenary (1983) of Victor Andres Belaunde (diplomat).
1600 **534** 100s. purple 15 10

535 Street in Cuzco

536 Fair Emblem

1984. 450th Anniv of Founding of Cuzco by the Spanish.
1601 **535** 1000s. multicoloured . . 40 25

1984. 15th International Pacific Fair, Lima.
1602 **536** 1000s. blue and red . . . 40 25

537 "Foundation of Lima" (Francisco Gonzalez Gamarra)

538 Pope John Paul II

1985. 450th Anniv of Lima.
1603 **537** 1500s. multicoloured . . 55 30

1985. Papal Visit.
1604 **538** 2000s. multicoloured . . 45 35

539 Dish Aerial, Huancayo

540 Jose Carlos Mariategui

1985. 15th Anniv (1984) of Entel Peru (National Telecommunications Enterprise).
1605 **539** 1100s. multicoloured . . 25 15

1985. 60th Death Anniv (1984) of Jose Carlos Mariategui (writer).
1606 **540** 800s. red 20 15

541 Emblem

1985. 25th Meeting of American Airforces Co-operation System.
1607 **541** 400s. multicoloured . . . 15 10

542 Captain Quinones

1985. 44th Death Anniv of Jose Abelardo Quinones Gonzales (airforce captain).
1608 **542** 1000s. multicoloured . . 25 15

543 Arms of Huancavelica

544 Globe and Emblem

1985.
1609 **543** 700s. orange 15 15
See also Nos. 1628/9.

1985. 14th Latin-American Air and Space Regulations Days, Lima.
1610 **544** 900s. blue 25 15

545 Francisco Garcia Calderon (head of 1881 Provisional Government)

546 Cross, Flag and Map

1985. Personalities.
1611 **545** 500s. green 20 10
1612 – 800s. green 35 15
DESIGN: 800s. Oscar Miro Quesada (philosopher and jurist).

1985. 1st Anniv of Constitucion City.
1613 **546** 300s. multicoloured . . . 15 10

547 General Post Office, Lima

548 Society Emblem, Satellite and Radio Equipment

1985. Postal Services.
1614 **547** 200s. grey 10 10

1985. 55th Anniv of Peruvian Radio Club.
1615 **548** 1300s. blue and orange 35 20

549 Robles Moqo Style Cat Vase

550 St. Francis's Monastery, Lima

1985. Wari Ceramics (2nd series).
1616 **549** 500s. brown 15 10
1617 – 500s. brown 15 10
1618 – 500s. brown 15 10
DESIGNS: No. 1617, Cat, Huaura style; No. 1618, Llama's head, Robles Moqo Style.

1985. Tourism Day.
1619 **550** 1300s. multicoloured . . 30 15

551 Title Page of "Doctrina Christiana"

552 Emblem and Curtiss "Jenny" Airplane

1985. 400th Anniv of First Book printed in South America.
1620 **551** 300s. black and stone . . 15 10

1985. 40th Anniv of I.C.A.O.
1621 **552** 1100s. black, blue and red 40 15

553 Humboldt Penguin

554 "Virgin and Child" (Cuzquena School)

1985. Fauna.
1622 **553** 1500s. multicoloured . . 2·10 20

1985. Christmas.
1623 **554** 2i.50 multicoloured . . . 20 10

555 Postman lifting Child

556 Cesar Vallejo

1985. Postal Workers' Christmas and Children's Restaurant Funds.
1624 **555** 2i.50 multicoloured . . . 30 20

1986. Poets.
1625 **556** 800s. blue 20 10
1626 – 800s. brown 20 10
DESIGN: No. 1626, Jose Santos Chocano.

557 Arms

1986. 450th Anniv of Trujillo.
1627 **557** 3i. multicoloured 30 15

1986. Town Arms. As T **543**.
1628 700s. blue 15 10
1629 900s. brown 25 15
DESIGNS: 700s. Huanuco; 900s. Puno.

558 Stone Carving of Fish

559 "Hymenocallis amancaes"

1986. Restoration of Chan-Chan.
1630 **558** 50c. multicoloured . . . 15 10

1986. Flora.
1631 **559** 1100s. multicoloured . . 25 15

560 Alpaca and Textiles

561 St. Rosa de Lima (Daniel Hernandez)

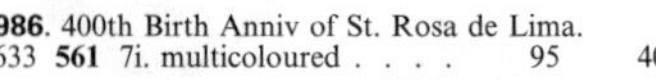

1986. Peruvian Industry.
1632 **560** 1100s. multicoloured . . 25 15

1986. 400th Birth Anniv of St. Rosa de Lima.
1633 **561** 7i. multicoloured 95 40

562 Daniel Alcides Carrion

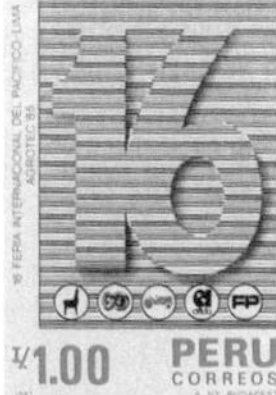

563 Emblems and "16"

1986. Death Centenary (1985) of Daniel Alcides Carrion.
1634 **562** 50c. brown 10 10

1986. 16th International Pacific Fair, Lima.
1635 **563** 1i. multicoloured 10 10

564 Woman Handspinning and Boy in Reed Canoe

1986. International Youth Year.
1636 **564** 3i.50 multicoloured . . . 65 20

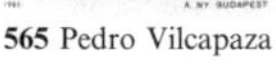
565 Pedro Vilcapaza

567 Fernando and Justo Albujar Fayaque and Manuel Guarniz

566 U.N. Building, New York

1986. 205th Anniv of Vilcapaza Rebellion.
1637 **565** 50c. brown 10 10

1986. 40th Anniv (1985) of U.N.O.
1638 **566** 3i.50 multicoloured . . . 30 20

1986. National Heroes.
1639 **567** 50c. brown 10 10

568 Nasturtium

570 Tinta Costumes, Canchis Province

569 Submarine "Casma (R-1)", 1926

1986. Flora.
1640 **568** 80c. multicoloured . . . 10 10

1986. Peruvian Navy. Each blue.
1641 1i.50 Type **569** 80 20
1642 2i.50 Submarine "Abtao", 1954 . . . . 1·40 35

1986. Costumes.
1643 **570** 3i. multicoloured 30 20

571 Sacsayhuaman Fort, Cuzco

1986. Tourism Day (1st issue).
1644 **571** 4i. multicoloured 40 30
See also No. 1654.

572 La Tomilla Water Treatment Plant

1986. 25th Anniv of Inter-American Development Bank.
1645 **572** 1i. multicoloured 10 10

573 "Datura candida"

575 Chavez, Bleriot XI and Simplon Range

574 Pope John Paul and Sister Ana

1986. Flora.
1646 **573** 80c. multicoloured . . . 10 10

1986. Beatification of Sister Ana of the Angels Monteagudo.
1647 **574** 6i. multicoloured 90 45

1986. 75th Anniv of Trans-Alpine Flight by Jorge Chavez Dartnell.
1648 **575** 5i. multicoloured . . . . 1·00 35

576 Emblem

577 "Martyrs of Uchuraccay"

1986. National Vaccination Days.
1649 **576** 50c. blue 10 10

1986. Peruvian Journalists' Fund.
1650 **577** 1i.50 black and blue . . 15 10

578 "Canis nudus"

579 Brigantine "Gamarra"

1986. Fauna.
1651 **578** 2i. multicoloured 20 15

1986. Navy Day.
1652 **579** 1i. blue and light blue 75 25
1653 – 1i. blue and red 75 25
DESIGN: No. 1653, Battleship "Manco Capac".

580 Intihuatana Cuzco

1986. Tourism Day (2nd issue).
1654 **580** 4i. multicoloured 40 30

581 Institute Building

1986. 35th Anniv (1985) of Institute of Higher Military Studies.
1655 **581** 1i. multicoloured 15 10

582 Children

583 White-winged Guan

1986. Postal Workers' Christmas and Children's Restaurant Funds.
1656 **582** 2i.50 black and brown 30 20

1986. Fauna.
1657 **583** 2i. multicoloured . . . . 2·00 40

584 Galvez

585 "St. Joseph and Child" (Cuzquena School)

1986. Birth Centenary (1985) of Jose Galvez Barrenechea (poet).
1658 **584** 50c. brown 10 10

1986. Christmas.
1659 **585** 5i. multicoloured 75 30

586 Flags, and Hands holding Cogwheel

587 Shipibo Costumes

1986. 25th Anniv of "Senati" (National Industrial Training Organization).
1660 **586** 4i. multicoloured 40 30

1987. Christmas.
1661 **587** 3i. multicoloured 30 25

588 Harvesting Mashua

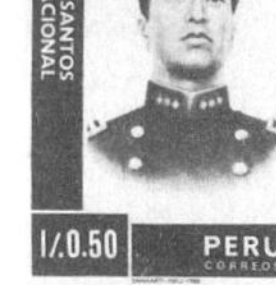
590 Santos

589 Dr. Reiche and Diagram of Nazca Lines

1987. World Food Day.
1662 **588** 50c. multicoloured . . . 10 10

1987. Dr. Maria Reiche (Nazca Lines researcher).
1663 **589** 8i. multicoloured 80 60

1987. Mariano Santos (Hero of War of the Pacific).
1664 **590** 50c. violet 10 10

591 Show Jumping

1987. 50th Anniv of Peruvian Horse Club.
1665 **591** 3i. multicoloured 30 25

592 Salaverry

593 Colca Canyon

1987. 150th Death Anniv (1986) of General Felipe Santiago Salaverry (President, 1835–36).
1666 **592** 2i. multicoloured 20 15

1987. "Arequipa 87" National Stamp Exhibition.
1667 **593** 6i. multicoloured 50 30

594 1857 1 & 2r. Stamps

595 Arguedas

1987. "Amifil 87" National Stamp Exhibition, Lima.
1668 **594** 1i. brown, blue and grey 10 10

1987. 75th Birth Anniv (1986) of Jose Maria Arguedas (writer).
1669 **595** 50c. brown 10 10

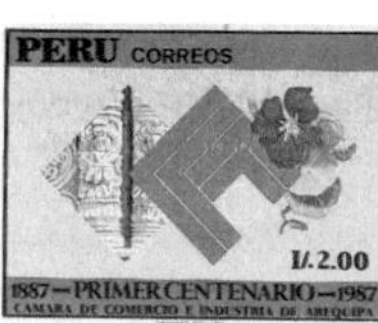
596 Carving, Emblem and Nasturtium

1987. Centenary of Arequipa Chamber of Commerce and Industry.
1670 **596** 2i. multicoloured 20 15

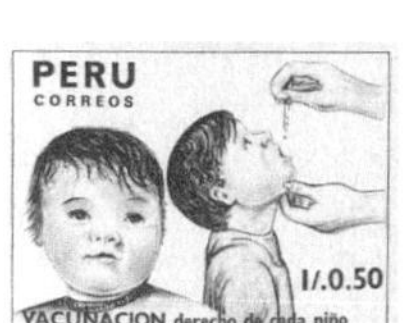
597 Vaccinating Child

598 De la Riva Aguero

1987. Child Vaccination Campaign.
1671 **597** 50c. red 10 10

1987. Birth Centenary (1985) of Jose de la Riva Aguero (historian).
1672 **598** 80c. brown 10 10

599 Porras Barrenechea

600 Footballers

1987. 90th Birth Anniv of Raul Porras Barrenechea (historian).
1673 **599** 80c. brown 10 10

1987. World Cup Football Championship, Mexico (1986).
1674 **600** 4i. multicoloured 20 15

601 Stone Carving of Man

1987. Restoration of Chan-Chan.
1675 **601** 50c. multicoloured . . . 10 10

602 Comet and "Giotto" Space Probe

1987. Appearance of Halley's Comet (1986).
1676 **602** 4i. multicoloured 45 15

603 Chavez **604** Osambela Palace

1987. Birth Centenary of Jorge Chavez Dartnell (aviator).
1677 **603** 2i. brown, ochre and gold 10 10

1987. 450th Birth Anniv of Lima.
1678 **604** 2i.50 multicoloured . . . 15 10

605 Machu Picchu

1987. 75th Anniv (1986) of Discovery of Machu Picchu.
1679 **605** 9i. multicoloured 40 30

606 St. Francis's Church

1987. Cajamarca, American Historical and Cultural Site.
1680 **606** 2i. multicoloured 10 10

607 National Team, Emblem and Olympic Rings

1988. 50th Anniv (1986) of First Peruvian Participation in Olympic Games (at Berlin).
1681 **607** 1i.50 multicoloured . . . 10 10

608 Children

1988. 150th Anniv of Ministry of Education.
1682 **608** 1i. multicoloured 10 10

609 Statue and Pope

1988. Coronation of Virgin of Evangelization, Lima.
1683 **609** 10i. multicoloured . . . 40 30

610 Emblems **611** Postman and Lima Cathedral

1988. Rotary International Anti-Polio Campaign.
1684 **610** 2i. blue, gold and red . . 10 10

1988. Postal Workers' Christmas and Children's Restaurant Funds.
1685 **611** 9i. blue 30 20

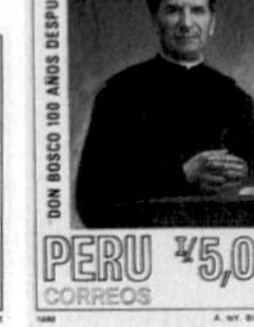

612 Flags **613** St. John Bosco

1988. 1st Meeting of Eight Latin American Presidents of Contadora and Lima Groups, Acapulco, Mexico.
1686 **612** 9i. multicoloured 30 20

1988. Death Centenary of St. John Bosco (founder of Salesian Brothers).
1687 **613** 5i. multicoloured 20 15

614 Supply Ship "Humboldt" and Globe

1988. 1st Peruvian Scientific Expedition to Antarctica.
1688 **614** 7i. multicoloured 90 20

615 Clay Wall

1988. Restoration of Chan-Chan.
1689 **615** 4i. brown and black . . 15 10

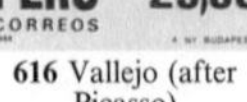

616 Vallejo (after Picasso) **617** Journalists at Work

1988. 50th Death Anniv of Cesar Vallejo (poet).
1690 **616** 25i. black, yellow & brn 50 40

1988. Peruvian Journalists' Fund.
1691 **617** 4i. blue and brown . . . 10 10

618 1908 2s. Columbus Monument Stamp **619** "17" and Guanaco

1988. "Exfilima 88" Stamp Exhibition, Lima, and 500th Anniv of Discovery of America by Christopher Columbus.
1692 **618** 20i. blue, pink and black 20 10

1988. 17th International Pacific Fair, Lima.
1693 **619** 4i. multicoloured 10 10

620 "Village Band" **621** Dogs

1988. Birth Centenary of Jose Sabogal (painter).
1694 **620** 12i. multicoloured . . . 15 10

1988. "Canino '88" International Dog Show, Lima.
1695 **621** 20i. multicoloured . . . 20 10

622 Silva and Score of "Splendour of Flowers" **623** Pope

1988. 50th Death Anniv (1987) of Alfonso de Silva (composer).
1696 **622** 20i. grey, deep brown and brown 20 10

1988. 2nd Visit of Pope John Paul II.
1697 **623** 50i. multicoloured . . . 35 25

624 Volleyball **625** Volleyball

1988. Olympic Games, Seoul.
1698 **624** 25i. multicoloured . . . 20 10

1988. Postal Workers' Christmas and Children's Restaurant Funds. Unissued stamp surch as in T **625**.
1699 **625** 95i. on 300s. black and red 60 50

626 Ceramic Vase **627** Map

1988. Chavin Culture. Unissued stamps surch as in T **626**.
1700 **626** 40i. on 100s. red 30 20
1701 80i. on 10s. black . . . 25 15

1989. Forest Boundary Road. Unissued stamp surch as in T **627**.
1702 **627** 70i. on 80s. green, black and blue 40 30

628 Arm **629** Huari Weaving

1989. Laws of the Indies. Unissued stamp surch as in T **628**.
1703 **628** 230i. on 300s. brown . . 60 15

1989. Centenary of Credit Bank of Peru.
1704 **629** 500i. multicoloured . . . 85 20

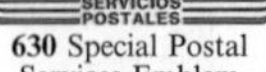

630 Special Postal Services Emblem **631** Newspaper Offices

1989. Postal Services.
1705 **630** 50i. blue and green . . . 10 10
1706 – 100i. red and pink . . . 10 10
DESIGN: 100i. National Express Post emblem.

1989. 150th Anniv of "El Comercio" (newspaper).
1707 **631** 600i. multicoloured . . . 50 10

632 Garcilaso de la Vega

1989. 450th Birth Anniv of Garcilaso de la Vega (writer).
1708 **632** 300i. multicoloured . . . 10 10

633 Emblem

1989. Express Mail Service.
1709 **633** 100i. red, blue and orange 10 10

634 Dr. Luis Loli Roca (founder of Journalists' Federation)

1989. Peruvian Journalists' Fund.
1710 **634** 100i. blue, deep blue and black 10 10

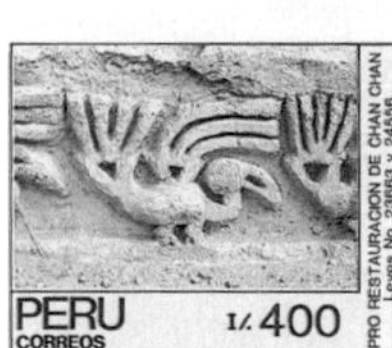

635 Relief of Birds

1989. Restoration of Chan-Chan.
1711 **635** 400i. multicoloured . . . 35 10

636 Old Map of South America

1989. Centenary of Lima Geographical Society.
1712 **636** 600i. multicoloured . . . 1·40 20

637 Painting

1989. 132nd Anniv of Society of Founders of Independence.
1713 **637** 300i. multicoloured . . . 10 10

638 Lake Huacachina

1989. 3rd Meeting of Latin American Presidents of Contadora and Lima Groups, Ica.
1714 **638** 1300i. multicoloured . . 1·10 60

639 Children buying Stamps for Commemorative Envelopes

641 Vessel with Figure of Doctor examining Patient

640 "Corryocactus huincoensis"

1989. Postal Workers' Christmas and Children's Restaurant Funds.
1715 **639** 1200i. multicoloured . . 30 20

1989. Cacti. Multicoloured.
1716 500i. Type **640** 15 10
1717 500i. "Haagocereus clavispinus" (vert) 15 10
1718 500i. "Loxanthocereus acanthurus" 15 10
1719 500i. "Matucana cereoides" (vert) 15 10
1720 500i. "Trichocereus peruvianus" (vert) 15 10

1989. America. Pre-Columbian Ceramics. Mult.
1721 5000i. Type **641** . . . . . 1·60 1·00
1722 5000i. Vessel with figure of surgeon performing cranial operation . . . . 1·60 1·00

642 Bethlehem Church

1990. Cajamarca, American Historical and Cultural Site.
1723 **642** 600i. multicoloured . . . 15 10

643 Climber in Andes

644 Pope and Virgin of Evangelization

1990. Huascaran National Park. Multicoloured.
1724 900i. Type **643** 20 15
1725 900i. Llanganuco Lake (horiz) 20 15
1726 1000i. "Puya raimondi" (plant) 25 20
1727 1000i. Snow-covered mountain peak (horiz) . . 25 20
1728 1100i. Huascaran Mountain (horiz) 30 25
1729 1100i. Andean condor over mountain slopes (horiz) 50 30

1990. 2nd Visit of Pope John Paul II.
1730 **644** 1250i. multicoloured . . 30 25

645 "Agrias beata" (female)

1990. Butterflies. Multicoloured.
1731 1000i. Type **645** 35 25
1732 1000i. "Agrias beata" (male) 35 25
1733 1000i. "Agrias amydon" (female) 35 25
1734 1000i. "Agrias sardanapalus" (female) . . 35 25
1735 1000i. "Agrias sardanapalus" (male) . . 35 25

646 Victor Raul Haya de la Torre (President of Constituent Assembly)

647 Emblem

1990. 10th Anniv of Political Constitution.
1736 **646** 2100i. multicoloured . . 45 10

1990. 40th Anniv of Peruvian Philatelic Association.
1737 **647** 300i. brown, blk & cream 60 20

648 Globe and Exhibition Emblem

1990. "Prenfil '88" International Philatelic Literature Exhibition, Buenos Aires.
1738 **648** 300i. multicoloured . . . 10 10

649 "Republic" (Antoine-Jean Gros)

1990. Bicentenary of French Revolution. Paintings. Multicoloured.
1739 2000i. Type **649** 40 10
1740 2000i. "Storming the Bastille" (Hubert Robert) 40 10
1741 2000i. "Lafayette at the Festival of the Republic" (anon) 40 10
1742 2000i. "Jean Jacques Rousseau and Symbols of the Revolution" (E. Jeaurat) 40 10

650 "Founding Arequipa" (Teodoro Nunez Ureta)

1990. 450th Anniv of Arequipa.
1743 **650** 50000i. multicoloured . . 10 10

651 Pelado Island Lighthouse

1990. Peruvian Navy. Unissued stamps, each light blue and blue, surch as in T **651**.
1744 110000i. on 200i. Type **651** 1·25 25
1745 230000i. on 400i. "Morona" (hospital ship) . . . . . 3·00 50

652 Games Mascot

653 1857 1r. Stamp and Container Ship

1990. 4th South American Games (1st issue). Multicoloured.
1746 110000i. Type **652** 25 20
1747 280000i. Shooting . . . . . . 1·10 60
1748 290000i. Athletics (horiz) . . 1·25 65
1749 300000i. Football . . . . . 1·25 65
See also Nos. 1753/6.

1990. 150th Anniv of Pacific Steam Navigation Company. Multicoloured. Self-adhesive.
1750 250000i. Type **653** . . . . 1·90 75
1751 350000i. 1857 2r. stamp and container ship . . . . . 2·75 1·00

654 Postal Van

1990. Postal Workers' Christmas and Children's Restaurant Funds.
1752 **654** 310000i. multicoloured 1·25 70

1991. 4th South American Games (2nd issue). As T **652**. Multicoloured.
1753 560000i. Swimming . . . . 1·90 1·10
1754 580000i. Show jumping (vert) . . . . 2·00 1·25
1755 600000i. Yachting (vert) . . 3·00 1·40
1756 620000i. Tennis (vert) . . . 2·10 1·40

655 Maria Jesus Castaneda de Pardo

1991. Red Cross. Unissued stamp surch.
1757 **655** 0.15i/m. on 2500i. red . . 50 25

Note. "i/m" on No. 1757 onwards indicates face value in million intis.

656 Adelie Penguins, Scientist and Station

1991. 2nd Peruvian Scientific Expedition to Antarctica. Unissued stamps surch. Multicoloured.
1758 0.40i/m. on 50000i. Type **656** . . . . 3·00 80
1759 0.45i/m. on 80000i. Station and Pomarine skua . . . 3·50 1·00
1760 0.50i/m. on 100000i. Whale, map and station . . . . 1·60 10

657 "Siphoonandra elliptica" (plant No. 1 in University herbarium)

658 "Virgin of the Milk"

1991. 300th Anniv of National University of St. Anthony Abad del Cusco. Multicoloured.
1761 10c. Type **657** 15 10
1762 20c. Bishop Manuel de Mollinedo y Angulo (first Chancellor) 50 20
1763 1s. University arms . . . . 2·50 1·00

1991. Postal Workers' Christmas and Children's Restaurant Funds. Paintings by unknown artists. Multicoloured.
1764 70c. Type **658** . . . . . 1·25 50
1765 70c. "Divine Shepherdess" 1·25 50

659 Lake

1991. America (1990). The Natural World. Mult.
1766 0.50i/m. Type **659** 90 40
1767 0.50i/m. Waterfall (vert) . . 90 40

660 Sir Rowland Hill and Penny Black

1992. 150th Anniv (1990) of the Penny Black.
1768 **660** 0.40i/m. black, grey & bl 70 35

661 Arms and College

662 Arms

1992. 150th Anniv (1990) of Our Lady of Guadalupe College.
1769 **661** 0.30i/m. multicoloured 55 10

1992. 80th Anniv (1991) of Entre Nous Society, Lima (literature society for women).
1770 **662** 10c. multicoloured . . . 10 10

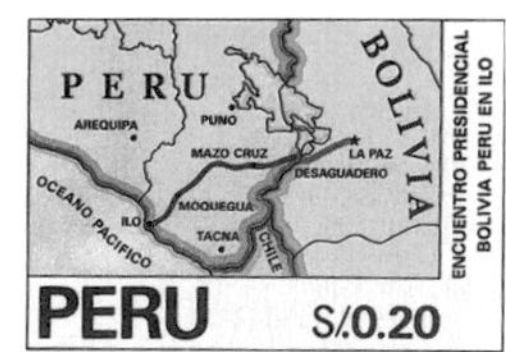

663 Map

1992. Bolivia–Peru Presidential Meeting, Ilo.
1771 **663** 20c. multicoloured . . . 15 10

664 Tacaynamo Idol

665 Raimondi

1992. Restoration of Chan-Chan.

1772	**664**	0.15i/m. multicoloured	10	10

See note below No. 1757.

1992. Death Centenary of Jose Antonio Raimondi (naturalist).

1773	**665**	0.30i/m. multicoloured	25	20

See note below No. 1757.

666 First Issue

668 1568 Eight Silver Reales Coin

667 Melgar

1992. Bicentenary (1990) of "Diario de Lima" (newspaper).

1774	**666**	35c. black and yellow . .	35	15

1992. Birth Bicentenary (1990) of Mariano Melgar (poet).

1775	**667**	60c. multicoloured . . .	50	25

1992. 1st Peruvian Coinage.

1776	**668**	70c. multicoloured . . .	1·00	35

669 Emblem

1992. 75th Anniv of Catholic University of Peru.

1777	**669**	90c. black and stone . .	1·25	35

670 Emblem

672 "Virgin of the Spindle" (painting, Santa Clara Monastery, Cuzco)

1992. 90th Anniv of Pan-American Health Organization. Self-adhesive. Imperf.

1778	**670**	3s. multicoloured	3·25	1·10

1992. Various stamps surch.

1779	–	40c. on 500i. multicoloured (1717)	30	15
1780	–	40c. on 500i. multicoloured (1718)	30	15
1781	–	40c. on 500i. multicoloured (1719)	30	15
1782	–	40c. on 500i. multicoloured (1720)	30	15
1783	**493**	50c. on 180s. green . . .	40	20
1784	**648**	50c. on 300i. mult . . .	40	20
1785	**645**	50c. on 1000i. mult . . .	40	20
1786	–	50c. on 1000i. mult (1732)	40	20
1787	–	50c. on 1000i. mult (1733)	40	20
1788	–	50c. on 1000i. mult (1734)	40	20
1789	–	50c. on 1000i. mult (1735)	40	20
1790	**647**	1s. on 300i. brown, black and cream	3·00	90
1791	**644**	1s. on 1250i. mult . . .	1·60	80
1792	**638**	1s. on 1300i. mult . . .	2·10	1·00

1993. Self-adhesive. Imperf.

1793	**672**	80c. multicoloured . . .	65	30

673 Gold Figures

1993. Sican Culture (1st series). Multicoloured. Self-adhesive. Imperf.

1794		2s. Type **673**	2·75	80
1795		5s. Gold foil figure (vert) . .	5·00	2·00

See also Nos. 1814/15.

674 Incan Gold Decoration and Crucifix on Chancay Robe

1993. 500th Anniv of Evangelization of Peru.

1796	**674**	1s. multicoloured	1·25	65

675 "The Marinera" (Monica Rojas)

676 "Madonna and Child" (statue)

1993. Paintings of Traditional Scenes. Multicoloured. Self-adhesive. Imperf.

1797		1s.50 Type **675**	1·50	60
1798		1s.50 "Fruit Sellers" (Angel Chavez)	1·50	60

1993. Centenary (1991) of Salesian Brothers in Peru. Self-adhesive. Imperf.

1799	**676**	70c. multicoloured . . .	95	25

677 Francisco Pizarro and Spanish Galleon

1993. America (1991). Voyages of Discovery. Multicoloured.

1800		90c. Type **677**	1·25	30
1801		1s. Spanish galleon and route map of Pizarros' second voyage	1·50	40

Nos. 1800/1 were issued together, se-tenant, forming a composite design.

678 Gold Mask

1993. Jewels from Funerary Chamber of "Senor of Sipan" (1st series).

1802	**678**	50c. multicoloured . . .	55	15

See also Nos. 1830/1.

679 Escriva

680 Cherry Blossom and Nazca Lines Hummingbird

1993. 1st Anniv of Beatification of Josemaria Escriva (founder of Opus Dei). Self-adhesive. Imperf.

1803	**679**	30c. multicoloured . . .	45	10

1993. 120th Anniv of Diplomatic Relations and Peace, Friendship, Commerce and Navigation Treaty with Japan. Multicoloured.

1804		1s.50 Type **680**	1·75	45
1805		1s.70 Peruvian and Japanese children and Mts. Huascaran (Peru) and Fuji (Japan)	1·90	55

681 Sea Lions

682 Delgado

1993. Stamp Exhibitions. Multicoloured.

1806		90c. Type **681** ("Amifil '93" National Stamp Exhibition, Lima)	1·10	25
1807		1s. Blue and yellow macaw ("Brasiliana '93" International Stamp Exhibition, Rio de Janeiro) (vert)	2·00	80

1993. Birth Centenary of Dr. Honorio Delgado (psychiatrist and neurologist). Self-adhesive. Imperf.

1808	**682**	50c. brown	30	15

683 Morales Macedo

684 "The Sling" (Quechua Indians)

1993. Birth Centenary of Rosalia de Lavalle de Morales Macedo (founder of Society for Protection of Children and of Christian Co-operation Bank). Self-adhesive. Imperf.

1809	**683**	80c. orange	80	25

1993. Ethnic Groups (1st series). Statuettes by Felipe Lettersten. Multicoloured. Self-adhesive. Imperf.

1810		2s. Type **684**	1·60	60
1811		3s.50 "Fire" (Orejon Indians)	3·25	1·50

See also Nos. 1850/1.

685 "20" on Stamp

686 "Virgin of Loreta"

1993. 20th International Pacific Fair.

1812	**685**	1s.50 multicoloured . . .	1·40	70

1993. Christmas.

1813	**686**	1s. multicoloured	1·00	55

687 Artefacts from Tomb, Poma

688 Ceramic Figure

1993. Sican Culture (2nd series). Multicoloured. Self-adhesive. Imperf.

1814		2s.50 Type **687**	2·25	1·10
1815		4s. Gold mask	4·00	2·00

1993. Chancay Culture. Multicoloured. Self-adhesive. Imperf.

1816		10s. Type **688**	9·25	4·50
1817		20s. Textile pattern (horiz)	19·00	9·50

689 "With AIDS There is No Tomorrow"

690 Computer Graphics

1993. International AIDS Day.

1818	**689**	1s.50 multicoloured . . .	1·40	70

1994. 25th Anniv of National Council for Science and Technology. Self-adhesive. Imperf.

1819	**690**	1s. multicoloured	1·40	25

691 "The Bridge" (woodcut from "New Chronicle and Good Government" by Poma de Ayala)

692 Engraved Mate Dish

1994. Self-adhesive. Imperf.

1820	**691**	20c. blue	35	10
1821		40c. orange	55	10
1822		50c. violet	70	15

For similar design see Nos. 1827/9.

1994. Multicoloured. Self-adhesive. Imperf.

1823		1s.50 Type **692**	2·00	40
1824		1s.50 Engraved silver and mate vessel (vert)	2·00	40
1825		3s. Figure of bull from Pucara	3·75	85
1826		3s. Glazed plate decorated with fishes	3·75	85

693 "The Bridge" (Poma de Ayala)

694 Gold Trinkets

1994.

1827	**693**	30c. brown	45	10
1828		40c. black	60	10
1829		50c. red	70	15

1994. Jewels from Funerary Chamber of Senor de Sipan (2nd series). Multicoloured.

1830		3s. Type **694**	3·75	85
1831		5s. Gold mask (vert)	6·50	1·25

695 El Brujo

1994. Archaeology. El Brujo Complex, Trujillo.

1832	**695**	70c. multicoloured . . .	75	20

696 "Baby Emmanuel" (Cuzco sculpture)

697 Brazilian Player

1995. Christmas (1994). Multicoloured.

1833		1s.80 Type **696**	1·40	50
1834		2s. "Nativity" (Huamanga ceramic)	1·50	55

1995. World Cup Football Championship, U.S.A. (1994). Multicoloured.

1835		60c. Type **697**	35	15
1836		4s.80 Mascot, pitch and flags	3·50	1·50

698 Jauja–Huancayo Road

1995. 25th Anniv (1994) of Ministry of Transport, Communications, Housing and Construction.

1837	**698**	20c. multicoloured . . .	10	10

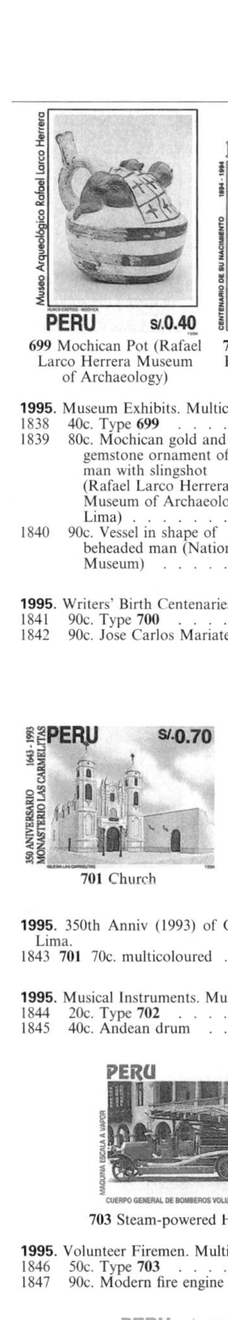

699 Mochican Pot (Rafael Larco Herrera Museum of Archaeology)

700 Juan Parra del Reigo (poet) (after David Alfaro)

1995. Museum Exhibits. Multicoloured.
1838 40c. Type **699** 20 10
1839 80c. Mochican gold and gemstone ornament of man with slingshot (Rafael Larco Herrera Museum of Archaeology, Lima) 70 20
1840 90c. Vessel in shape of beheaded man (National Museum) 80 25

1995. Writers' Birth Centenaries (1994). Mult.
1841 90c. Type **700** 75 50
1842 90c. Jose Carlos Mariategui 75 50

701 Church

702 Violoncello and Music Stand

1995. 350th Anniv (1993) of Carmelite Monastery, Lima.
1843 **701** 70c. multicoloured . . . 70 20

1995. Musical Instruments. Multicoloured.
1844 20c. Type **702** 10 10
1845 40c. Andean drum 45 10

703 Steam-powered Fire Engine

1995. Volunteer Firemen. Multicoloured.
1846 50c. Type **703** 55 10
1847 90c. Modern fire engine . . 95 25

704 Union Club and Plaza de Armas

1995. World Heritage Site. Lima. Multicoloured.
1848 90c. Type **704** 95 25
1849 1s. Cloisters of Dominican Monastery . . . . 1·10 25

705 "Bora Child"

1995. Ethnic Groups (2nd series). Statuettes by Felipe Lettersten. Multicoloured.
1850 1s. Type **705** . . . . 1·10 25
1851 1s.80 "Aguaruna Man" . . 1·90 50

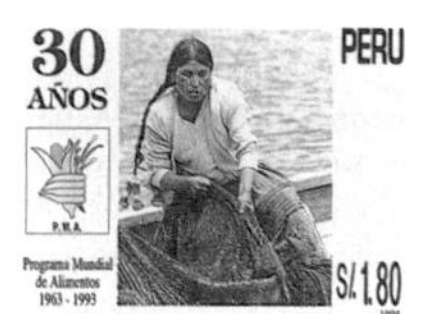

706 Woman fishing

1995. 30th Anniv (1993) of World Food Programme.
1852 **706** 1s.80 multicoloured . . . 1·90 50

707 Potato Plant

708 Reed Sailing Canoe

1995. The Potato. Multicoloured.
1853 1s.80 Type **707** . . . . . . 1·90 50
1854 2s. Mochican ceramic of potato tubers . . . . . . 2·10 55

1995. Tourism and Ecology. Lake Titicaca.
1855 **708** 2s. multicoloured . . . . 2·25 75

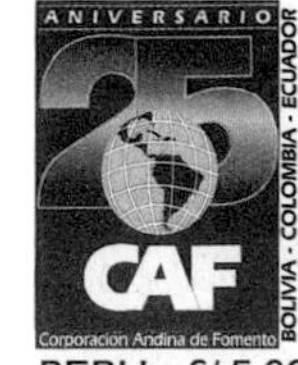

709 Great Horned Owl

710 Anniversary Emblem

1995. Endangered Animals. Multicoloured.
1856 1s. Type **709** . . . . 1·25 25
1857 1s.80 Jaguar on branch (horiz) . . . . 1·90 50

1995. 25th Anniv of Andean Development Corporation.
1858 **710** 5s. multicoloured . . . . 5·00 1·25

711 Ollantaytambo

1995. World Tourism Day.
1859 **711** 5s.40 multicoloured . . . 5·25 1·50

712 Ancient Letterbox, Head Post Office

1995. World Post Day.
1860 **712** 1s.80 multicoloured . . . 1·75 50

713 Columbus landing on Beach

1995. America (1992 and 1993). Multicoloured.
1861 1s.50 Type **713** (500th anniv of discovery of America) 1·50 40
1862 1s.70 Guanaco (vert) . . . 1·75 60

714 Cart

1995. America (1994). Postal Transport. Mult.
1863 1s.80 Type **714** . . . . . . 1·75 60
1864 2s. Post vans . . . . 2·00 55

715 Lima Cathedral (rear entrance)

1995. Doorways. Multicoloured.
1865 30c. Type **715** 40 10
1866 70c. St. Francis's Church (side entrance) 75 20

716 Peruvian Delegation, San Francisco Conference, 1945

1995. 50th Anniv of U.N.O.
1867 **716** 90c. multicoloured . . . 95 25

717 Ceramic Church (National Culture Museum)

718 Lady Olave Baden-Powell (Girl Guides)

1995. Museum Exhibits. Multicoloured.
1868 20c. Type **717** 10 10
1869 20c. "St. John the Apostle" (figurine) (Riva Aguero Institute Museum of Popular Art) 10 10
1870 40c. "Allegory of Asia" (alabaster figurine) (National Culture Museum) 45 10
1871 50c. "Archangel Moro" (figurine) (Riva Aguero Institute Museum of Popular Art) 50 10

1995. Scouting. Multicoloured.
1872 80c. Type **718** 85 20
1873 1s. Lord Robert Baden Powell (founder of Boy Scouts) 90 25

Nos. 1872/3 were issued together, se-tenant, forming a composite design.

719 "Festejo"

720 Stream in Sub-tropical Forest

1995. Folk Dances. Multicoloured.
1874 1s.80 Type **719** . . . . . . 1·75 50
1875 2s. "Marinera Limena" (horiz) . . . . 1·90 55

1995. Manu National Park, Madre de Dios. Multicoloured.
1876 50c. Type **720** 55 10
1877 90c. American chamaeleon (horiz) 95 25

721 Toma de Huinco

722 St. Toribio de Mogrovejo (Archbishop of Lima)

1995. Electricity and Development. Multicoloured.
1878 20c. Type **721** 10 10
1879 40c. Antacoto Lake 45 10

1995. Saints. Multicoloured.
1880 90c. Type **722** 90 25
1881 1s. St. Francisco Solano (missionary) 95 25

723 Cultivating Crops

1996. 50th Anniv (1995) of F.A.O.
1882 **723** 60c. multicoloured . . . 55 15

724 Crib

1996. Christmas (1995). Porcelain Figures. Multicoloured.
1883 30c. Type **724** 15 10
1884 70c. Three Wise Men (horiz) 70 15

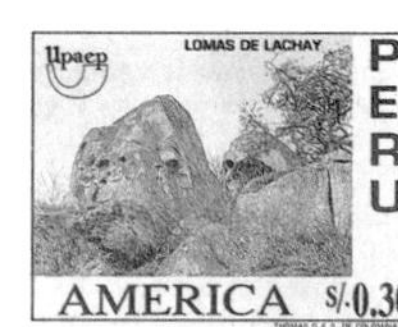

725 Lachay National Park

1996. America (1995). Environmental Protection. Multicoloured.
1885 30c. Type **725** 15 10
1886 70c. Black caiman 70 15

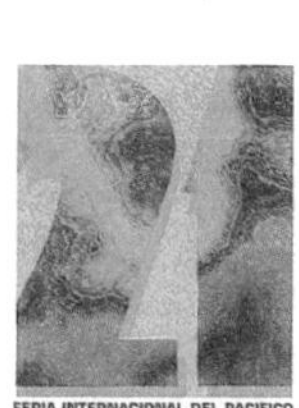

726 "21"

727 Rifle Shooting

1996. 21st International Pacific Fair, Lima.
1887 **726** 60c. multicoloured . . . 60 15

1996. Olympic Games, Barcelona (1992). Multicoloured.
1888 40c. Type **727** 45 10
1889 40c. Tennis 45 10
1890 60c. Swimming 55 15
1891 60c. Weightlifting 55 15

Nos. 1888/91 were issued together, se-tenant, forming a composite design of the sports around the games emblem.

728 Archaeological Find from Sipan

1996. "Expo'92" World's Fair, Seville.
1892 **728** 1s.50 multicoloured . . . 1·40 35

729 Vallejo (after Gaston Garreu)

1996. Birth Centenary of Cesar Vallejo (writer).
1893 **729** 50c. black 50 10

730 Avenue of the Descalzos

1996. UNESCO World Heritage Site. Lima.
1894 **730** 30c. brown and stone . . 15 10

731 "Kon Tiki" (replica of balsa raft)

1997. 50th Anniv of Thor Heyerdahl's "Kon Tiki" Expedition (voyage from Peru to Tuamoto Island, South Pacific).
1895 **731** 3s.30 multicoloured . . . 1·90 70

732 Child 733 Owl

1997. 50th Anniv (1996) of UNICEF.
1896 **732** 1s.80 multicoloured . . . 1·50 40

1997. Mochica Culture.
1897 **733** 20c. green 10 10
1898 – 30c. violet 15 10
1899 – 50c. black 45 10
1900 – 1s. orange 75 20
1901 – 1s.30 red . . . . 1·10 25
1902 – 1s.50 brown . . . . . . 1·25 30
DESIGNS—Vessels in shape of: 30c. Crayfish; 50c. Cormorant; 1s. Monkeys; 1s.30, Duck; 1s.50, Jaguar.
See also Nos. 1942/6.

734 Shooting

1997. Olympic Games, Atlanta, U.S.A. (1996). Multicoloured.
1903 2s.70 Type **734** . . . . . . 1·25 60
1904 2s.70 Volleyball . . . . . . 1·25 60
1905 2s.70 Boxing . . . . 1·25 60
1906 2s.70 Football . . . . . . 1·25 60

735 White-bellied Caique 736 Scout Badge and Tents

1997. 25th Anniv of Peru Biology College.
1907 **735** 5s. multicoloured . . . . 2·50 1·10

1997. 90th Anniv of Boy Scout Movement.
1908 **736** 6s.80 multicoloured . . . 3·25 1·50

737 Man on Reed Raft

1997. 8th International Anti-corruption Conference, Lima.
1909 **737** 2s.70 multicoloured . . . 1·50 60

738 Emblem

1997. 10th Anniv of Montreal Protocol (on reduction of use of chlorofluorocarbons).
1910 **738** 6s.80 multicoloured . . . 3·25 1·50

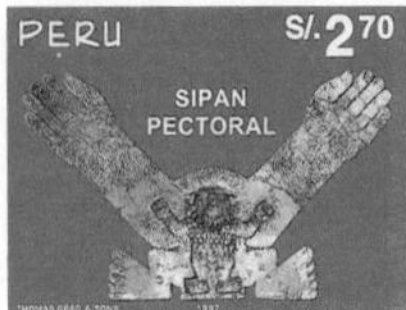

739 Pectoral

1997. Funerary Chamber of "Senor of Sipan". Multicoloured.
1911 2s.70 Type **739** . . . . . . 2·10 50
1912 3s.30 Ear-cap (vert) . . . . 2·75 60

740 Von Stephan 741 Shipibo Woman

1997. Death Centenary of Heinrich von Stephan (founder of U.P.U.).
1914 **740** 10s. multicoloured . . . 8·00 1·75

1997. America (1996). Traditional Costumes. Multicoloured.
1915 2s.70 Type **741** . . . . . . 2·25 50
1916 2s.70 Shipibo man . . . . 2·25 50

742 Inca Messenger 743 Castilla

1997. America. The Postman. Multicoloured.
1917 2s.70 Type **742** . . . . . . 2·25 50
1918 2s.70 Modern postman . . . 2·25 50

1997. Birth Bicentenary of Ramon Castilla (President, 1845–51 and 1855–62).
1919 **743** 1s.80 multicoloured . . . 1·50 30

744 Tennis 745 River Kingfisher

1997. 13th Bolivarian Games, Arequipa. Mult.
1920 2s.70 Type **744** . . . . . . 2·25 50
1921 2s.70 Football . . . . . . 2·25 50
1922 2s.70 Basketball . . . . . . 2·25 50
1923 2s.70 Volleyball . . . . . . 2·25 50
Nos. 1920/3 were issued together, se-tenant, containing a composite design of a ball in the centre.

1997. Manu National Park. Birds. Multicoloured.
1924 3s.30 Type **745** . . . . . . 2·75 60
1925 3s.30 Green woodpecker . . 2·75 60
1926 3s.30 Red crossbill . . . . 2·75 60
1927 3s.30 Eagle . . . . 2·75 60
1928 3s.30 Jabiru . . . . 2·75 60
1929 3s.30 Cuban screech owl . . 2·75 60

746 Concentric Circles over Map 747 Map and Krill

1997. 30th Anniv of Treaty of Tlatelolco (banning nuclear weapons in Latin America and the Caribbean).
1930 **746** 20s. multicoloured . . . 16·00 3·50

1997. 8th Peruvian Scientific Expedition to Antarctica.
1931 **747** 6s. multicoloured . . . . 5·00 1·00

748 Holy Family 749 Map, Emblem and Unanue

1997. Christmas.
1932 **748** 2s.70 multicoloured . . . 2·10 50

1997. 25th Anniv (1996) of Hipolito Unanue Agreement (health co-operation in Andes region).
1933 **749** 1s. multicoloured 80 15

751 Facade 753 Map and Emblem

752 School and Cadets

1997. Cent of Posts and Telegraph Headquarters.
1935 **751** 1s. multicoloured 80 15

1998. Centenary of Chorrillos Military School.
1936 **752** 2s.70 multicoloured . . . 2·10 50

1998. 50th Anniv of Organization of American States.
1937 **753** 2s.70 multicoloured . . . 2·10 50

754 Cuzco Cathedral

1998. 25th Anniv of Aeroperu. Multicoloured.
1938 1s.50 Type **754** . . . . . . 1·25 25
1939 2s.70 Airbus Industrie A320 jetliner . . . . 2·25 50

755 "Paso Horse" (Enrique Arambur Ferreyros) 756 Lima Cathedral

1998. 50th Anniv of National Association of Breeders and Owners of Paso Horses.
1940 **755** 2s.70 violet . . . . . . 2·00 50

1998. Centenary of Restoration of Lima Cathedral.
1941 **756** 2s.70 red, yellow and black . . . . 2·00 50

1998. Mochica Culture. As Nos. 1897 and 1899/1902 but values and/or colours changed.
1942 1s. blue 80 15
1943 1s.30 purple . . . . 1·00 20
1944 1s.50 blue . . . . 1·25 25
1945 2s.70 bistre . . . . 2·10 50
1946 3s.30 black . . . . 2·50 60
DESIGNS: 1s.30, Type **733**; 1s.50, Jaguar; 2s.70, Cormorant; 3s.30, Duck.

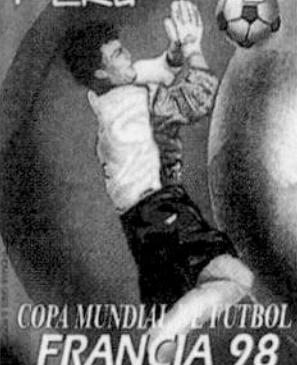

757 Ceremony, Sacsayhuaman, Cuzco 758 Goalkeeper

1998. "Inti-Raymi" Inca Festival.
1947 **757** 5s. multicoloured . . . . 3·50 85

1998. World Cup Football Championship, France. Multicoloured.
1948 2s.70 Type **758** . . . . . . 2·00 50
1949 3s.30 Two players . . . . . 2·50 60
Nos. 1948/9 were issued together, se-tenant, forming a composite design.

759 Lloque Yupanqui

1998. Inca Chiefs (1st issue). Multicoloured.
1951 2s.70 Type **759** 95 45
1952 2s.70 Sinchi Roca 95 45
1953 9s.70 Mancoc Capau . . . 3·50 1·75
See also Nos. 2008/11.

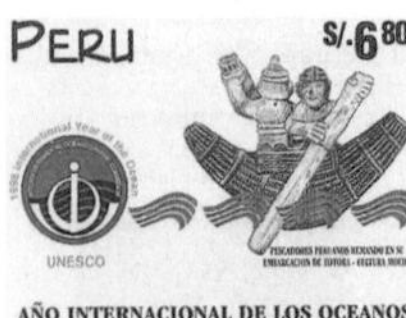

761 Fishermen (Moche sculpture) and Emblem

1998. International Year of the Ocean.
1955 **761** 6s.80 multicoloured . . . 4·50 1·25

762 Bars of Music and Conductor's Hands 763 Mother Teresa and Baby

1998. 60th Anniv of National Symphony Orchestra.
1956 **762** 2s.70 multicoloured . . . 95 45

1998. 1st Death Anniv of Mother Teresa (founder of Missionaries of Charity).
1957 **763** 2s.70 multicoloured . . . 95 45

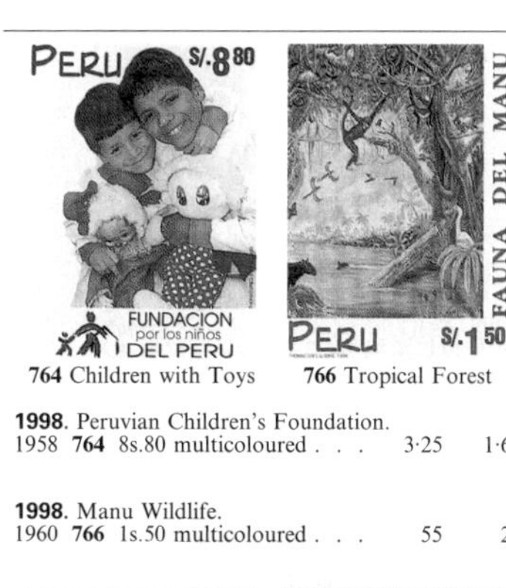

764 Children with Toys **766** Tropical Forest

1998. Peruvian Children's Foundation.
1958 **764** 8s.80 multicoloured . . . 3·25 1·60

1998. Manu Wildlife.
1960 **766** 1s.50 multicoloured . . . 55 25

767 1858 1 Dinero Stamp

768 Chabuca Granda (singer)

1998. World Stamp Day.
1961 **767** 6s.80 multicoloured . . . 2·40 1·20

1998. America. Famous Women.
1962 **768** 2s.70 multicoloured . . . 95 45

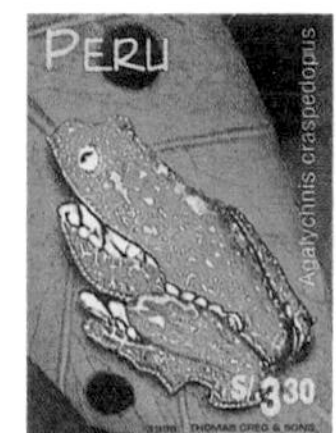

769 "Agalychnis craspedopus"

1998. Frogs. Multicoloured.
1963 3s.30 Type **769** . . . . . . 1·25 60
1964 3s.30 Amazonian horned frog ("Ceratophrys cornuta") . . . . 1·25 60
1965 3s.30 "Epipedobates macero" . . . . 1·25 60
1966 3s.30 "Phyllomedusa vaillanti" (leaf frog) . . . 1·25 60
1967 3s.30 "Dendrobates biolat" (poison arrow frog) . . . 1·25 60
1968 3s.30 "Hemiphractus proboscideus" (horned frog) . . . . 1·25 60
Nos. 1963/8 were issued together, se-tenant, forming a composite design.

770 "Chulucanas Nativity" (Lizzy Lopez)

1998. Christmas.
1969 **770** 3s.30 multicoloured . . . 1·25 60

771 Dove and Flags of Peru, Ecuador and Guarantor Countries

1998. Signing of Peru–Ecuador Peace Agreement, Brasilia.
1970 **771** 2s.70 multicoloured . . . 95 45

772 Children on Hillside

1998. 50th Anniv of Universal Declaration of Human Rights.
1971 **772** 5s. multicoloured . . . . 1·75 85

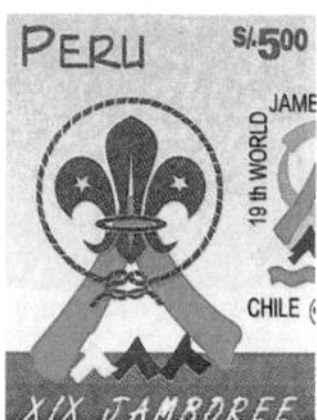

773 Scout Badge and Tents

1999. 19th World Scout Jamboree, Chile. Multicoloured.
1972 5s. Type **773** . . . . 1·75 85
1973 5s. Emblem and tents . . . 1·75 85

774 Emblem

1999. 50th Anniv of Peruvian Philatelic Association.
1974 **774** 2s.70 multicoloured . . . 95 45

775 "Evening Walk"

1999. 120th Death Anniv of Pancho Fierro (artist). Multicoloured.
1975 2s.70 Type **775** 95 45
1976 3s.30 "The Sound of the Devil" . . . . 1·25 60

776 Dancer and Detail from Costume

1999. "Puno" (traditional dance).
1977 **776** 3s.30 multicoloured . . . 1·25 60

1999. Mochica Culture. As Nos. 1943/46 but values and or colours changed.
1978 1s. red 35 15
1979 1s.50 blue 55 25
1980 1s.80 brown 65 30
1981 2s. orange 70 35
DESIGNS: Vessels in shape of—1s. Jaguar; 1s.50, Duck; 1s.80, Type **733**; 2s. Cormorant.

777 Inca blowing Conch Shell

1999. 25th Anniv of Peruvian Folklore Centre (CENDAF).
1982 **777** 1s.80 multicoloured . . . 65 30

778 Malinowski and Train crossing Bridge

1999. Death Centenary of Ernest Malinowski (designer of iron bridge between Lima and La Oroya).
1983 **778** 5s. multicoloured . . . . 1·75 85

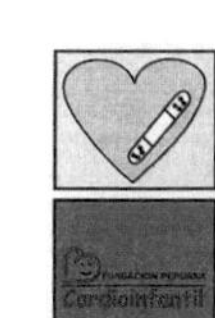

779 Sick and Healthy Hearts with Smiling Face

1999. Child Heart Care.
1984 **779** 2s.70 multicoloured . . . 95 45

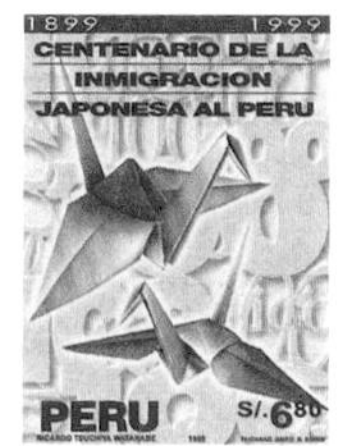

780 Origami Birds

1999. Centenary of Japanese Immigration.
1985 **780** 6s.80 multicoloured . . . 2·40 1·25

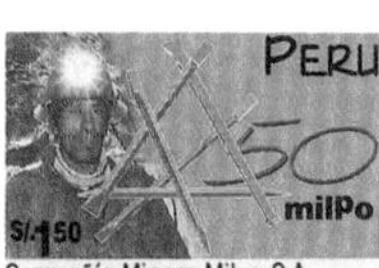

Compañía Minera Milpo S.A.
1949-1999
781 Miner and Crowbars

1999. 50th Anniv of Milpo S.A. Mining Company.
1986 **781** 1s.50 multicoloured . . . 55 25

782 Wildlife

1999. Flora and Fauna.
1987 **782** 5s. multicoloured . . . . 1·75 1·00
MS1988 79 × 98 mm. 10s. Jaguar, Manu National Park (horiz) 3·50 3·30

1999. Nos. 1888/91 surch.
1989 1s. on 40c. Rifle shooting 35 20
1990 1s. on 40c. Tennis 35 20
1991 1s. on 60c. Swimming . . . 35 20
1992 1s. on 60c. Weightlifting . . 35 20
1993 1s.50 on 40c. Rifle shooting 35 20
1994 1s.50 on 40c. Tennis 35 20
1995 1s.50 on 60c. Swimming . . 35 20
1996 1s.50 on 60c. Weightlifting 35 20
1997 2s.70 on 40c. Rifle shooting 35 20
1998 2s.70 on 40c. Tennis 35 20
1999 2s.70 on 60c. Swimming . . 35 20
2000 2s.70 on 60c. Weightlifting 35 20
2001 3s.30 on 40c. Rifle shooting 35 20
2002 3s.30 on 40c. Tennis 35 20
2003 3s.30 on 60c. Swimming . . 35 20
2004 3s.30 on 60c. Weightlifting 35 20

1999. No. 1894 surch.
2005 2s.40 on 30c. brown and ochre 80 45

785 Penguin and Antarctic Vessel

1999. 40th Anniv of Antarctic Treaty.
2006 **785** 6s.80 multicoloured . . . 2·40 1·40

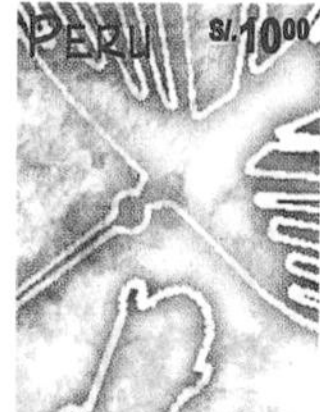

786 Bird

1999. Nazca Lines. Sheet 98 × 79 mm.
MS2007 **786** 10s. multicoloured 3·50 3 .50

1999. Inca Chiefs (2nd issue). As T **759**. Multicoloured.
2008 3s.30 Maita Capac 80 45
2009 3s.30 Inca Roca 80 45
2010 3s.30 Capac Yupanqui . . . 80 45
2011 3s.30 Yahuar Huaca 80 45

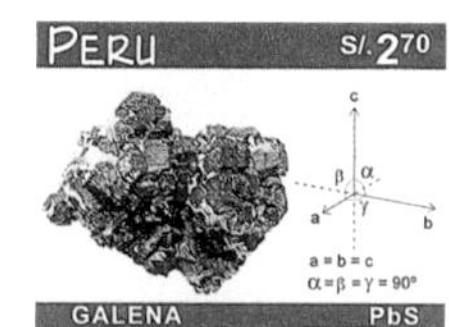

787 Galena

1999. Minerals. Multicoloured.
2012 2s.70 Type **787** 95 55
2013 3s.30 Scheelita . . . . . . 1·10 65
2014 5s. Virgotrigonia peterseni 1·75 1·00

788 Virgin of Carmen

1999.
2015 **788** 3s.30 multicoloured . . . 1·10 65

789 Building

1999. St. Catalina Monastery, Arequipa.
2016 **789** 2s.70 multicoloured . . . 95 35

790 Emblem and Dragon

1999. 150th Anniv of Chinese Immigration to Peru.
2017 **790** 1s.50 red and black . . . 55 35

791 Taking Pulse

1999. 25th Anniv of Peruvian Medical Society.
2018 **791** 1s.50 multicoloured . . . 55 35

792 Emblem

1999. 125th Anniv of Universal Postal Union.
2019 **792** 3s.30 multicoloured . . . 1·10 65

793 Sunflower growing out of Gun

1999. America. A New Millennium without Arms. Multicoloured.
2020 2s.70 Type **793** 95 55
2021 3s.30 Man emerging from Globe (horiz) . . . . . . 1·10 65

794 Woman with Fumigator

1999. Señ◊ de los Milagros Festival, Lima. Multicoloured.
2022 1s. Type **794** 35 20
2023 1s.50 Procession 55 30

795 Young Child and Emblem

1999. 40th Anniv of Inter-American Development Bank.
2024 **795** 1s.50 multicoloured . . . 55 30

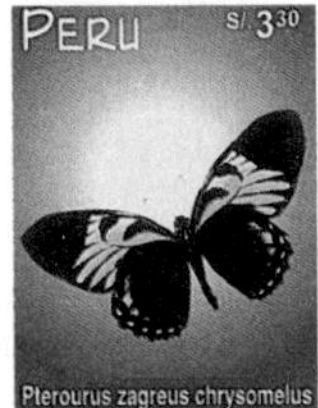

796 *Pterourus zagreus chrysomelus*

1999. Butterflies. Multicoloured.
2025 3s.30 Type **796** . . . . 1·10 65
2026 3s.30 *Asterope buckleyi* . . . 1·10 65
2027 3s.30 *Parides chabrias* . . . 1·10 65
2028 3s.30 *Mimoides pausanias* . . 1·10 65
2029 3s.30 *Nessaea obrina* . . . . 1·10 65
2030 3s.30 *Pterourus zagreus zagreus* . . . . 1·10 65

797 Map of Cunhuime Sur Sub-sector

1999. 1st Anniv of Peru–Ecuador Border Peace Agreement. Multicoloured.
2031 1s. Type **797** 35 20
2032 1s. Map of Lagartococha-Gueppi sector 35 20
2033 1s. Map of Cusumasa Bumbuiza-Yaupi Santiago sub-sector (horiz) 35 20

798 Globe

1999. 5th Anniv of Serpost S.A. (Peruvian postal services).
2034 **798** 2s.70 multicoloured . . . 95 55

799 Virgin of Belen

1999. Christmas.
2035 **799** 2s.70 multicoloured . . . 95 55

800 Mujica and Factory

1999. Birth Centenary of Ricardo Bentin Mujica (industrialist).
2036 **800** 2s.70 multicoloured . . . 95 55

801 Flags encircling Globe

2000. New Millennium. Sheet 79 × 99 mm.
MS2037 **801** 10s. multicoloured 3·50 3·50

802 Oberti and Foundry

2000. Ricardo Cilloniz Oberti (founder of Peruvian steel industry).
2038 **802** 1s.50 multicoloured . . . 55 30

803 Llamas

2000. Michell Group (Peruvian alpaca exporters). Multicoloured.
2039 1s.50 Type **803** 55 30
2040 1s.50 Llamas (different) . . 55 30
Nos. 2039/40 were issued together, se-tenant, forming a composite design.

804 Power Station

2000. 25th Anniv of Peruvian Institute of Nuclear Energy (I.P.E.N.).
2041 **804** 4s. multicoloured . . . . 1·40 80

805 Miner

2000. Mining Industry. Multicoloured.
2042 1s. Type **805** 35 20
2043 1s. View of mine 35 20
Nos. 2042/3 were issued together, se-tenant, forming a composite design.

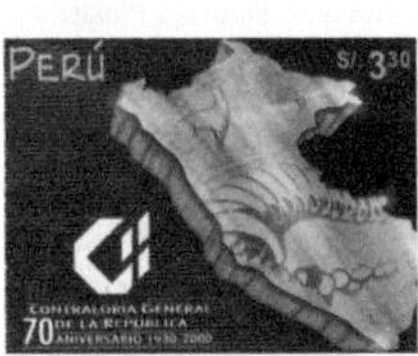

806 Stylized Outline of Peru

2000. 70th Anniv of Comptroller General of Republic.
2044 **806** 3s.30 multicoloured . . . 1·10 65

807 Field and Emilio Guimoye Hernandez

2000. Poblete Agriculture Group.
2045 **807** 1s.50 multicoloured . . . 55 30

808 Pupils carrying Flags

2000. National School Sports Games.
2046 **808** 1s.80 multicoloured . . . 60 35

809 Machu Picchu

2000. World Heritage Sites.
2047 **809** 1s.30 multicoloured . . . 45 25

810 Emblem

2000. Campaign Against Domestic Violence.
2048 **810** 3s.80 multicoloured . . . 1·25 75

811 Emblem

2000. Year
2049 **811** 3s.20 multicoloured . . . 1·10 65

812 "Cataratas de Ahuashiyacu" (Susan Hidalgo Bacalla)

2000. Winning Entries in Students' Painting Competition. Multicoloured.
2050 3s.20 Type **812** . . . . . . 1·10 65
2051 3s.20 "Laguna Yarinacocha" (Mari Trini Ramos Vargas) (horiz) . . 1·10 65
2052 3s.80 "La Campina Arequipena" (Anibal Lajo Yanez) (horiz) . . . . . 1·25 75

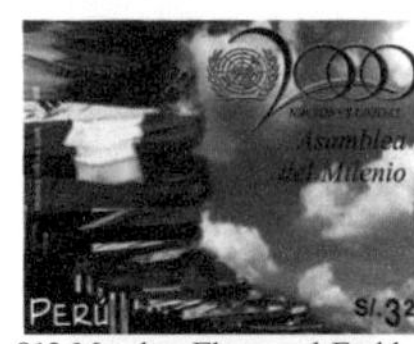

813 Member Flags and Emblem

2000. United Nations Millennium Summit, New York, U.S.A.
2053 **813** 3s.20 multicoloured . . . 1·10 65

814 San Martín

2000. 150th Death Anniv of General Jose de San Martin.
2054 **814** 3s.80 multicoloured . . . 1·25 75

815 Bus, Map of South America and Road

2000. 30th Anniv of Peru-North America Bus Route. Multicoloured.
2055 1s. Type **815** 35 20
2056 2s.70 Bus, map of North America and road 95 55
Nos. 2055/6 were issued together, se-tenant, forming a composite design.

816 Cyclist

2000. Centenary of International Cycling Union.
2057 **816** 3s.20 multicoloured . . . 1·10 65

817 Sun Dial

2000. 50th Anniv of World Meteorological Organization.
2058 **817** 1s.50 multicoloured . . . 55 30

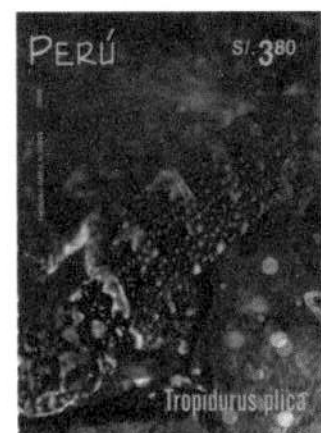

818 Western Leaf Lizard (*Tropidurus plica*)

2000. Lizards. Multicoloured.
2059 3s.80 Type **818** . . . . . . 1·25 75
2060 3s.80 Haitian ameiva (*Ameiva ameiva*) . . . . 1·25 75
2061 3s.80 Two-lined skink (*Mabouya bistriata*) . . . 1·25 75
2062 3s.80 *Neusticurus ecpleopus* 1·25 75
2063 3s.80 Blue-lipped forest anole (*Anolis fuscoauratus*) 1·25 75
2064 3s.80 Horned wood lizard (*Enyalioides palpebralis*) 1·25 75
Nos. 2059/64 were issued together, se-tenant, forming a composite design.

819 *Matucana madisoniorum*

2000. Cacti.
2065 **819** 3s.80 multicoloured . . . 1·25 75

820 Noriega and Space Shuttle

2000. Carlos Noriega (first Peruvian astronaut).
2066 **820** 3s.80 multicoloured . . . 1·25 75

821 De Mendoza and Library

2000. 250th Birth Anniv Toribio Rodríguez de Mendoza.
2067 **821** 3s.20 multicoloured . . . 1·10 65

822 Symbols of Ucayali

2000. Centenary of Ucayali Province.
2068 **822** 3s.20 multicoloured . . . 1·10 65

823 Grape Vine and Flag

2000. Wines of Peru.
2069 **823** 3s.80 multicoloured . . . 1·25 75

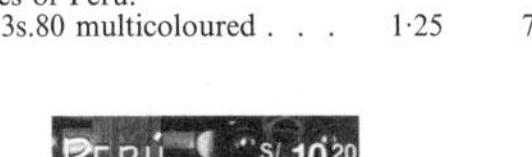

824 Flags on Watch Parts

2000. 20th Anniv of ALADI (Latin-American integration association).
2070 **824** 10s.20 multicoloured . . 3·30 3·50

825 Emblem

2000. 50th Anniv of Federation of Journalists.
2071 **825** 1s.50 multicoloured . . . 55 30

826 Petrified Forest, Santa Cruz

2000.
2072 **826** 1s.50 multicoloured . . . 45 25

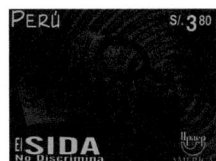

827 Male and Female Symbols

2000. America. Anti-AIDS Campaign.
2073 **827** 3s.80 multicoloured . . . 1·20 70

828 Justice Palace, Trujillo

2000. New Judicial Powers.
2074 **828** 1s.50 multicoloured . . . 45 25

829 Child at Table

2000. 90th Anniv of Peruvian Salvation Army.
2075 **829** 1s.50 multicoloured . . . 45 25

830 Ribbon and Medal

2000. 50th Anniv of League against Cancer.
2076 **830** 1s.50 multicoloured . . . 45 25

831 Steam Locomotive

2000. 150th Anniv of Peruvian Railways.
2077 **831** 1s.50 multicoloured . . . 45 25

EXPRESS LETTER STAMPS

1908. Optd **EXPRESO**.
E373 **76** 10c. black . . . . . . 17·00 12·50
E382 – 10c. blue (No. 377) . . 21·00 11·50
E383 **101** 10c. black and brown 11·50 10·00

OFFICIAL STAMPS

1890. Stamps of 1866 optd **GOBIERNO** in frame.
O287 **15** 1c. violet . . . . 1·10 1·10
O324 1c. red . . . . 7·00 7·00
O288 **16** 2c. green . . . . 1·10 1·10
O325 2c. blue . . . . 7·00 7·00
O289 5c. orange . . . . 1·60 1·60
O326 **10** 5c. lake . . . . 5·50 5·50
O290 **16** 10c. black 85 45
O291 20c. blue . . . . 2·50 1·60
O327 20c. blue (as T **10**) . . . 5·50 5·50
O292 **20** 50c. red . . . . 3·50 1·75
O293 **21** 1s. brown . . . . 4·25 3·75

1894. Stamps of 1894 (with "Head" optd) optd **GOBIERNO** in frame.
O305 **15** 1c. orange (No. 294) . . 19·00 19·00
O306 1c. green (No. 295) . . . 1·10 1·10
O307 **16** 2c. violet (No. 296) . . . 1·10 1·10
O308 2c. red (No. 297) 90 90
O309 5c. blue (No. 298) . . . 8·50 7·50
O310 10c. green (No. 299) . . 3·00 3·00
O311 **20** 50c. green (No. 300) . . 4·25 4·25

1894. Stamps of 1894 (with "Head" and "Horseshoe" optd) optd **GOBIERNO** in frame.
O312 **16** 2c. red (No. 301) . . . . 1·60 1·60
O313 5c. blue (No. 302) . . . 1·60 1·60

1896. Stamps of 1896 optd **GOBIERNO**.
O348 **75** 1c. blue 10 10
O349 **76** 10c. yellow . . . . . . 1·00 25
O350 10c. black 10 10
O351 **77** 50c. red 25 20

O 108

1909.
O382 **108** 1c. red 10 10
O572 10c. brown 40 30
O385 10c. purple 15 10
O573 50c. green 35 20

1935. Optd **Servicio Oficial**.
O567 **184** 10c. red 10 10

PARCEL POST STAMPS

P 79

1895. Different frames.
P348 **79** 1c. purple . . . . 1·90 1·60
P349 2c. brown . . . . 2·10 1·90
P350 5c. blue . . . . 8·50 5·50
P351 10c. brown . . . . 11·50 8·25
P352 20c. pink . . . . 14·50 12·00
P353 50c. green . . . . 38·00 32·00

1903. Surch in words.
P361 **79** 1c. on 20c. pink . . . . 12·50 10·00
P362 1c. on 50c. green . . . . 12·50 10·00
P363 5c. on 10c. brown . . . . 75·00 60·00

POSTAGE DUE STAMPS

D 22 **D 23** **D 109**

1874.
D31 **D 22** 1c. brown 10 10
D32 **D 23** 5c. red 30 15
D33 10c. orange 30 15
D34 20c. blue 50 30
D35 50c. brown . . . . . . 10·00 3·00

1881. Optd with T **24** ("LIMA" at foot instead of "PERU").
D47 **D 22** 1c. brown . . . . . . 3·00 2·00
D48 **D 23** 5c. red . . . . 5·50 5·00
D49 10c. orange . . . . . 5·50 5·50
D50 20c. blue . . . . . . 21·00 17·00
D51 50c. brown . . . . . 45·00 42·00

1881. Optd **LIMA CORREOS** in double-lined circle.
D52 **D 22** 1c. brown . . . . . . 4·25 4·25
D53 **D 23** 5c. red . . . . 5·50 5·00
D54 10c. orange . . . . . . 6·75 5·50
D55 20c. blue . . . . 21·00 17·00
D56 50c. brown . . . . . . 65·00 55·00

1883. Optd with T **24** (inscr "LIMA" instead of "PERU") and also with T **28a**.
D247 **D 22** 1c. brown . . . . . . 4·25 3·00
D250 **D 23** 5c. red . . . . 6·25 5·75
D253 10c. orange . . . . . 6·25 5·75
D256 20c. blue £400 £375
D258 50c. brown . . . . . 55·00 45·00

1884. Optd with T **28a** only.
D259 **D 22** 1c. brown 40 40
D262 **D 23** 5c. red 30 20
D267 10c. orange 35 25
D269 20c. blue . . . . . . 1·00 35
D271 50c. brown . . . . . 3·00 75

1894. Optd **LIMA CORREOS** in double-lined circle and with T **28a**.
D275 **D 22** 1c. brown . . . . . . 10·50 9·25

1896. Optd **DEFICIT**.
D348 **D 22** 1c. brown (D31) . . . 15 15
D349 **D 23** 5c. red (D32) 20 15
D350 10c. orange (D33) . . 55 15
D351 20c. blue (D34) . . . 70 20
D352 **20** 50c. red (283) . . . 60 20
D353 **21** 1s. brown (284) . . . 85 35

1899. As T **73**, but inscr "DEFICIT" instead of "FRANQUEO".
D355 5s. green . . . . 1·40 4·25
D356 10s. brown £800 £800

1902. Surch **DEFICIT** and value in words.
D361 1c. on 10s. (D356) 85 50
D362 5c. on 10s. (354) 50 40

1902. Surch **DEFICIT** and value in words.
D363 **23** 1c. on 20c. (D34) 60 40
D364 5c. on 20c. (D34) . . . . 1·50 1·00

1909.
D382 **109** 1c. brown 35 15
D419 1c. purple 15 15
D420 2c. purple 15 15
D570 2c. brown 15 15
D383 5c. brown 35 15
D421 5c. purple 25 20
D384 10c. brown 40 15
D422 10c. purple 40 15
D571 10c. green 40 15
D385 50c. brown 60 20
D423 50c. purple . . . . . . 1·40 50
D424 1s. purple . . . . . . 10·00 3·00
D425 2s. purple . . . . . . 19·00 6·75

1935. Optd **Deficit**.
D568 – 2c. purple (No. 537) . . 40 40
D569 **184** 10c. red 50 40

PHILIPPINES Pt. 9; Pt. 22; Pt. 21

A group of islands in the China Sea, E. of Asia, ceded by Spain to the United States after the war of 1898. Under Japanese Occupation from 1941 until 1945. An independent Republic since 1946.

1854. 20 cuartos = 1 real; 8 reales = 1 peso plata fuerte.
1864. 100 centimos = 1 peso plata fuerte.
1871. 100 centimos = 1 escudo (= ½ peso).
1872. 100 centimos = 1 peseta (= 15 peso).
1876. 1000 milesimas = 100 centavos or centimos = 1 peso.
1899. 100 cents = 1 dollar.
1906. 100 centavos = 1 peso.
1962. 100 sentimos = 1 piso.

SPANISH ADMINISTRATION

1 Queen Isabella II — **4** Queen Isabella II — **5** Queen Isabella II

1854. Imperf.
1 **1** 5c. red £1200 £180
3 10c. red £400 £120
5 1r. blue £450 £130
7a 2r. green £650 £120
On the 1r. the inscriptions are reversed.

1859. Imperf.
13 **4** 5c. red . . . . 10·00 4·00
14 10c. pink . . . . 10·00 12·00

1861. Larger lettering. Imperf.
17 **5** 5c. red . . . . 23·00 7·50

7 — **8**

1863. Imperf.
19 **7** 5c. red . . . . 9·00 3·75
20 10c. red . . . . 27·00 28·00
21 1r. mauve £500 £325
22 2r. blue £400 £275

1863. Imperf.
25 **8** 1r. green . . . . £100 38·00

1864. As T **14** of Spain, but value in "centimos de peso". Imperf.
26 $3\frac{1}{8}$c. black on buff . . . . . . 2·50 1·40
27 $6\frac{2}{8}$c. green on pink . . . . . . 2·50 70
28 $12\frac{4}{8}$c. blue on pink . . . . . . 5·00 70
29 25c. red on pink . . . . . . 10·00 4·00
30 25c. red on white . . . . . . 7·00 2·00

1868. Optd **HABILITADO POR LA NACION**. (a) On 1854 to 1863 issues of Philippines.
41 **7** 5c. red . . . . 42·00 27·00
53 **4** 10c. pink . . . . 85·00 45·00
36 **8** 1r. green . . . . 42·00 12·00
42 **7** 1r. mauve £425 £275
52 **1** 1r. blue £2000 £1000
43 **7** 2r. blue £400 £180

(b) On 1864 issues of Philippines.
31 $3\frac{1}{8}$c. black on buff . . . . . . 15·00 3·00
32 $6\frac{2}{8}$c. green on pink . . . . . . 15·00 3·00
33 $12\frac{4}{8}$c. blue on pink . . . . . . 40·00 18·00
34 25c. red . . . . 18·00 10·00

(c) On Nos. 10/11a of Cuba (as T **8** of Philippines).
44 1r. green . . . . £130 60·00
45 2r. red . . . . £170 65·00

12 — **13** King Amadeo

1871.
37 **12** 5c. blue . . . . 42·00 4·50
38 10c. green . . . . 6·00 3·75
39 20c. brown . . . . 48·00 26·00
40 40c. red . . . . 65·00 14·00

1872.
46 **13** 12c. pink . . . . 9·50 3·50
47 16c. blue . . . . 95·00 25·00
48a 25c. grey . . . . 7·50 3·50
49 62c. mauve . . . . 23·00 6·50
50a 1p.25 brown . . . . 42·00 20·00

14

1874.
54 **14** 12c. grey . . . . 11·00 3·25
55 25c. blue . . . . 3·75 1·40
56 62c. pink . . . . 32·00 3·25
57 1p.25 brown . . . . £160 48·00

15 — **16**

1875. With rosettes each side of "FILIPINAS".
58 **15** 2c. pink . . . . 1·50 50
59 2c. blue . . . . £140 65·00
60 6c. orange . . . . 7·50 1·75
61 10c. blue . . . . 2·00 45
62 12c. mauve . . . . 2·10 45
63 20c. brown . . . . 9·50 2·25
64 25c. green . . . . 7·50 45

1878. Without rosettes.
65 **16** 25m. black . . . . 1·90 30
66 25m. green . . . . 45·00 21·00
67 50m. purple . . . . 22·00 8·50
68a (62½m.) 0.0625 lilac . . . . . . 40·00 13·00
69 100m. red . . . . 75·00 32·00
70 100m. green . . . . 7·00 2·00
71 125m. blue . . . . 3·50 30
72 200m. pink . . . . 23·00 4·75
74 250m. brown . . . . 8·50 2·00

1877. Surch **HABILITADO 12 CS. PTA.** in frame.
75 **15** 12c. on 2c. pink . . . . . . 65·00 22·00
76 **16** 12c. on 25m. black . . . . . . 65·00 22·00

1879. Surch **CONVENIO UNIVERSAL DE CORREOS HABILITADO** and value in figures and words.
78 **16** 2c. on 25m. green . . . . . . 35·00 7·50
79 8c. on 100m. red . . . . . . 28·00 5·50

1880. "Alfonso XII" key-type inscr "FILIPINAS".
97 X 1c. green 30 10
82a 2c. red . . . . 60 1·25
83 2½c. brown . . . . 6·00 1·25
95 $2\frac{4}{8}$ . . . .
99 50m. bistre 30 15
85 5c. grey . . . . 60 1·25
100 6c. brown . . . . 8·00 1·25
87 $6\frac{2}{8}$c. green . . . . 4·75 7·50
88 8c. brown . . . . 27·00 14·00
89a 10c. brown . . . . 2·50 1·25
90 10c. purple . . . . 5·00 10·00
91 10c. green £300 £180
92 $12\frac{4}{8}$c. pink . . . . 1·25 1·25
93 20c. brown . . . . 2·50 1·25
94 25c. brown . . . . 3·25 1·25

1881. "Alfonso XII" key-type inscr "FILIPINAS" with various circular surcharges. (a) **HABILITADO U. POSTAL** and value.
111 X 1c. on $2\frac{4}{8}$c. blue 60 40
102 10c. on $2\frac{4}{8}$c. blue . . . . . . 6·00 1·25

(b) **HABILITADO CORREOS 2 CENTS. DE PESO.**
101 X 2c. on 2½c. brown . . . . . . 3·00 1·15

(c) **HABILITADO PA. U. POSTAL 8 CMOS.**
106 X 8c. on 2c. red . . . . . . 6·00 1·40

(d) **HABILITADO PA. CORREOS DE** and value.
107 X 10c. cuartos on 2c. red . . 3·50 1·40
112 16 cuartos on $2\frac{4}{8}$c. blue . . 8·50 2·00
103 20c. on 8c. brown . . . . . . 8·25 2·50
113 1r. on 2c. red . . . . . . 5·50 2·00
109 1r. on 5c. lilac . . . . . . 5·00 2·25
110 1r. on 8c. brown . . . . . . 9·50 3·00
105 2r. on $2\frac{4}{8}$c. blue . . . . . . 5·00 1·40

25 — **29** — **30**

31 — **34**

1881. Fiscal and telegraph stamps. (a) with circular surch **HABILITADO CORREOS, HABILITADO PARA CORREOS, HABILITADO PA. U. POSTAL** or **HABILITADO PA. CORREOS** and value in figures and words.
115 **25** 2c. on 10 cuartos bistre . . 21·00 13·50
129 **29** 2c. on 200m. green . . . . 4·75 2·25
116 **25** $2\frac{4}{8}$c. on 10 cuartos bistre . . 3·00 65
117 $2\frac{4}{8}$c. on 2r. blue . . . . . . £150 65·00
124 $6\frac{2}{8}$c. on $12\frac{4}{8}$c. lilac . . . . . . 4·75 2·75
118 8c. on 2r. blue . . . . . . 8·50 2·25
119 8c. on 10c. brown £170 £130
123 16 cmos. on 2r. blue . . . 5·75 2·40
137 **31** 20c. on 150m. blue . . . . 25·00 21·00
134 20c. on 250m. blue . . . . 95·00 80·00
127 **25** 1r. on 10 cuartos bistre . . 10·00 3·50
121 1r. on $12\frac{4}{8}$c. lilac . . . . . 7·00 3·00
130 **29** 1r. on 200m. green . . . . 55·00 35·00
131 1r. on 1 peso green . . . . 28·00 13·50
132 **30** 1r. on 10 pesetas bistre . . 40·00 21·00
133 **31** 2r. on 250m. blue . . . . 9·00 3·00

(b) With two circular surcharges as above, showing two different values.
128 **25** 8c. on 2r. on 2r. blue . . . 20·00 12·00
136 **31** 1r. on 20c. on 250m. blue 9·00 4·50

(c) Optd **HABILITADO PARA CORREOS** in straight lines.
122 **25** 10 cuartos bistre . . . . . £150 65·00
126 1r. green . . . . 85·00 65·00

1887. Various stamps with oval surch **UNION GRAL. POSTAL HABILITADO** (No. 142) or **HABILITADO PARA COMMUNICACIONES** and new value. (a) "Alfonso XII" key-type inscr "FILIPINAS".
138 X $2\frac{4}{8}$c. on 1c. green . . . . . 1·90 1·00
139 $2\frac{4}{8}$c. on 5c. lilac . . . . . . 1·25 50
140 $2\frac{4}{8}$c. on 50m. bistre . . . . 1·75 1·10
141 $2\frac{4}{8}$c. on 10c. green . . . . . 1·25 65
142 8c. on $2\frac{4}{8}$c. blue 75 40

(b) "Alfonso XII" key-type inscr "FILIPAS-IMPRESOS".
143 X $2\frac{4}{8}$c. on $\frac{1}{8}$c. green 40 15

(c) Fiscal and telegraph stamps.
144 **29** $2\frac{4}{8}$c. on 200m. green . . . 3·50 1·25
145 $2\frac{4}{8}$c. on 20c. brown . . . . 10·00 4·75
146 **34** $2\frac{4}{8}$c. on 1c. bistre 75 50

1889. Various stamps with oval surch **RECARGO DE CONSUMOS HABILITADO** and new value. (a) "Alfonso XII" key-type inscr "FILIPINAS".
147 X $2\frac{4}{8}$c. on 1c. green 15 15
148 $2\frac{4}{8}$c. on 2c. red 10 10
149 $2\frac{4}{8}$c. on $2\frac{4}{8}$c. blue 10 10
150 $2\frac{4}{8}$c. on 5c. lilac 10 10
151 $2\frac{4}{8}$c. on 50m. bistre 10 10
152 $2\frac{4}{8}$c. on $12\frac{4}{8}$c. pink 60 60

(b) "Alfonso XII" key-type inscr "FILIPAS-IMPRESOS".
160 X $2\frac{4}{8}$c. on $\frac{1}{8}$c. green 15 15

(c) Fiscal and telegraph stamps.
153 **34** $2\frac{4}{8}$c. on 1c. bistre 30 30
154 $2\frac{4}{8}$c. on 2c. red 30 30
155 $2\frac{4}{8}$c. on $2\frac{4}{8}$c. brown 10 10
156 $2\frac{4}{8}$c. on 5c. blue 10 10
157 $2\frac{4}{8}$c. on 10c. green 10 10
158 $2\frac{4}{8}$c. on 10c. mauve 60 65
159 $2\frac{4}{8}$c.on 20c. mauve 20 20
161 – $17\frac{4}{8}$c. on 5p. green . . . . 70·00
No. 161 is a fiscal stamp inscribed "DERECHO JUDICIAL" with a central motif as T **43** of Spain.

1890. "Baby" key-type inscr "FILIPINAS".
176 Y 1c. violet 40 15
188 1c. red . . . . 13·00 6·50
197 1c. green . . . . 1·75 60
162 2c. red 10 10
177 2c. violet 10 10
190 2c. brown 10 10
198 2c. blue 25 25
163 $2\frac{4}{8}$c. blue 40 10
178 $2\frac{4}{8}$c. grey 15 10
165 5c. blue 30 10
163 5c. green 40 10
199 5c. brown . . . . 7·50 3·25
181 6c. purple 20 10
192 6c. red . . . . 1·40 70
166 8c. green 20 10
182 8c. blue 40 20
193 8c. red 65 20
167 10c. green . . . . 1·40 20
172 10c. pink 50 10
202 10c. brown 20 10
173 $12\frac{4}{8}$c. green 15 10
184 $12\frac{4}{8}$c. orange 50 10
185 15c. brown 50 20
195 15c. red . . . . 1·60 70
203 15c. green . . . . 1·75 1·75
169 20c. red . . . . 55·00 29·00
186 20c. brown . . . . 1·50 25
196 20c. purple . . . . 13·00 6·50
204 20c. orange . . . . 3·75 1·75
170 25c. brown . . . . 4·25 75
175 25c. blue . . . . 1·50 15
205 40c. purple . . . . 18·00 5·00
206 80c. red . . . . 26·00 14·50

1897. Surch **HABILITADO CORREOS PARA** 1897 and value in frame. (a) "Baby" key-type inscr "FILIPINAS".
212 Y 5c. on 5c. green . . . . . 3·00 2·00
208 15c. on 15c. red . . . . . 3·00 2·00
213 15c. on 15c. brown . . . . 3·50 2·00
209 20c. on 20c. purple . . . . 15·00 8·00
214 20c. on 20c. brown . . . . 5·00 3·50
210 20c. on 25c. brown . . . . 10·00 8·00

(b) "Alfonso XII" key-type inscr "FILIPINAS".
215 X 5c. on 5c. lilac . . . . . . 4·00 2·25

1898. "Curly Head" key-type inscr "FILIPNAS 1898 y 99".
217 Z 1m. brown 15 15
218 2m. brown 15 15
219 3m. brown 15 15
220 4m. brown . . . . 6·00 1·25
221 5m. brown 15 15
222 1c. purple 15 15
223 2c. green 15 15
224 3c. brown 15 15
225 4c. orange . . . . 12·00 7·50
226 5c. red 15 15
227 6c. blue 75 45
228 8c. brown 35 15
229 10c. red . . . . 1·25 75
230 15c. grey . . . . 1·25 65
231 20c. purple . . . . 1·25 90
232 40c. lilac 75 60
233 60c. black . . . . 3·25 2·25
234 80c. brown . . . . 4·00 2·25
235 1p. green . . . . 9·50 9·25
236 2p. blue . . . . 22·00 12·00

STAMPS FOR PRINTED MATTER

1886. "Alfonso XII" key-type inscr "FILIPAS-IMPRESOS".
P138 X 1m. red 20 10
P139 $\frac{1}{8}$c. green 20 10
P140 2m. blue 20 10
P141 5m. brown 20 10

1890. "Baby" key-type inscr "FILIPAS-IMPRESOS".
P171 Y 1m. purple 10 10
P172 $\frac{1}{8}$c. purple 10 10
P173 2m. purple 10 10
P174 5m. purple 10 10

1892. "Baby" key-type inscr "FILIPAS-IMPRESOS".
P192 Y 1m. green . . . . 1·40 40
P193 $\frac{1}{8}$c. green 80 15
P194 2m. green . . . . 2·00 40
P191 5m. green . . . . £190 40·00

1894. "Baby" key-type inscr "FILIPAS-IMPRESOS".
P197 Y 1m. grey 20 20
P198 $\frac{1}{8}$c. brown 20 20
P199 2m. grey 20 20
P200 5m. grey 20 20

1896. "Baby" key-type inscr "FILIPAS-IMPRESOS".
P205 Y 1m. blue 25 15
P206 $\frac{1}{8}$c. blue 75 60
P207 2m. brown 25 15
P208 5m. blue . . . . 2·25 1·40

UNITED STATES ADMINISTRATION

1899. United States stamps of 1894 (No. 267 etc) optd **PHILIPPINES**.
252 – 1c. green . . . . 2·50 65
253 – 2c. red . . . . 1·25 50
255 – 3c. violet . . . . 4·00 1·60
256 – 4c. brown . . . . 17·00 4·75
257 – 5c. blue . . . . 4·00 1·00
258 – 6c. purple . . . . 20·00 6·00
259 – 8c. brown . . . . 22·00 6·00
260 – 10c. brown . . . . 14·00 3·00
262 – 15c. green . . . . 25·00 6·50
263 **83** 50c. orange . . . . 90·00 30·00
264 – $1 black £325 £190
266 – $2 blue £400 £200
267 – $5 green £700 £550

1903. United States stamps of 1902 optd **PHILIPPINES**.
268 **103** 1c. green . . . . 3·00 30
269 **104** 2c. red . . . . 5·00 1·25
270 **105** 3c. violet . . . . 55·00 11·00
271a **106** 4c. brown . . . . . . 60·00 16·00
272 **107** 5c. blue . . . . 8·50 70
273 **108** 6c. lake . . . . 65·00 18·00
274 **109** 8c. violet . . . . 28·00 10·00
275 **110** 10c. brown . . . . . . 16·00 1·90
276 **111** 13c. purple . . . . . . 23·00 13·00
277 **112** 15c. olive . . . . 42·00 10·00
278 **113** 50c. orange . . . . . . £100 28·00
279 **114** $1 black £350 £200
280 **115** $2 blue £600 £375
281 **116** $5 green £750 £700

1904. United States stamp of 1903 optd **PHILIPPINES**.
282a **117** 2c. red . . . . 4·25 1·60

45 Rizal — **46** Arms of Manila

1906. Various portraits as T **45** and T **46**.
337 **45** 2c. green 10 10
338 – 4c. red (McKinley) . . . 10 10
339 – 6c. violet (Magellan) . . . 30 10
340 – 8c. brown (Legaspi) . . . 25 10
341 – 10c. blue (Lawton) . . . 20 10
288 – 12c. red (Lincoln) . . . . 4·00 1·75
342 – 12c. orange (Lincoln) . . 45 15
289 – 16c. black (Sampson) . . 3·00 15
298 – 16c. green (Sampson) . . 2·00 10
344 – 16c. olive (Dewey) . . . . 1·00 15
290 – 20c. brown (Washington) 3·25 20
345 – 20c. yellow (Washington) 35 10
291 – 26c. brown (Carriedo) . . 4·50 1·75
346 – 26c. green (Carriedo) . . 65 30
292 – 30c. green (Franklin) . . 3·75 1·10
313 – 30c. blue (Franklin) . . . 2·75 35
347 – 30c. grey (Franklin) . . . 45 10
293 **46** 1p. orange . . . . 18·00 5·00
363a 1p. violet . . . . 3·50 3·50
294 2p. black . . . . 23·00 1·00
364 2p. brown . . . . 8·00 8·00
350 4p. blue . . . . 20·00 25
351 10p. green . . . . 42·00 4·50

Nos. 288, 289, 298, 290, 291, 292, 313, 293 and 294 exist perf only, the other values perf or imperf.

1926. Air. Madrid–Manila Flight. Stamps as last, optd **AIR MAIL 1926 MADRID-MANILA** and aeroplane propeller.
368 **45** 2c. green 5·50 3·25
369 4c. red 7·00 3·75
370 – 6c. violet 32·00 8·00
371 – 8c. brown 32·00 9·50
372 – 10c. blue 32·00 9·50
373 – 12c. orange 32·00 14·00
374 – 16c. green (Sampson) £1200 £1000
375 – 16c. olive (Dewey) 38·00 13·50
376 – 20c. yellow 38·00 13·50
377 – 26c. green 38·00 13·50
378 – 30c. grey 38·00 13·50
383 **46** 1p. violet £120 75·00
379 2p. brown £325 £180
380 4p. blue £475 £275
381 10p. green £750 £450

49 Legislative Palace

1926. Inauguration of Legislative Palace.
384 **49** 2c. black and green 40 25
385 4c. black and red 40 30
386 16c. black and olive 60 50
387 18c. black and brown 70 45
388 20c. black and orange 90 80
389 24c. black and grey 75 50
390 1p. black and mauve 40·00 24·00

1928. Air. London–Orient Flight by British Squadron of Seaplanes. Stamps of 1906 optd **L.O.F.** (= London Orient Flight), **1928** and Fairey IIID seaplane.
402 **45** 2c. green 35 20
403 – 4c. red 40 30
404 – 6c. violet 2·40 1·60
405 – 8c. brown 2·40 2·00
406 – 10c. blue 2·40 2·00
407 – 12c. orange 4·00 2·40
408 – 16c. olive (Dewey) 3·75 2·40
409 – 20c. yellow 4·00 2·40
410 – 26c. green 7·50 5·50
411 – 30c. grey 7·50 5·50
412 **46** 1p. violet 32·00 32·00

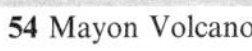

54 Mayon Volcano
57 Vernal Falls, Yosemite National Park, California, wrongly inscr "PAGSANJAN FALLS"

1932.
424 **54** 2c. green 35 15
425 – 4c. red 30 20
426 – 12c. orange 75 40
427 **57** 18c. red 16·00 7·00
428 – 20c. yellow 55 45
429 – 24c. violet 80 55
430 – 32c. brown 80 65
DESIGNS—HORIZ: 4c. Post Office, Manila; 12c. Freighters at Pier No. 7, Manila Bay; 20c. Rice plantation; 24c. Rice terraces; 32c. Baguio Zigzag.

1932. No. 350 surch in words in double circle.
431 **46** 1p. on 4p. blue 1·50 30
432 2p. on 4p. blue 2·75 55

1932. Air. Nos. 424/30 optd with Dornier Do-J flying boat "Gronland Wal" and **ROUND-THE-WORLD FLIGHT VON GRONAU 1932**.
433 2c. green 30 30
434 4c. red 30 30
435 12c. orange 40 40
436 18c. red 2·75 2·50
437 20c. yellow 1·40 1·25
438 24c. violet 1·40 1·25
439 32c. brown 1·40 1·25

1933. Air. Stamps of 1906 optd **F. REIN MADRID-MANILA FLIGHT-1933** under propeller.
440 **45** 2c. green 30 30
441 – 4c. red 35 35
442 – 6c. violet 60 60
443 – 8c. brown 1·60 1·25
444 – 10c. blue 1·40 90
445 – 12c. orange 1·25 90
446 – 16c. olive (Dewey) 1·25 90
447 – 20c. orange 1·25 90
448 – 26c. green 1·60 1·10
449 – 30c. grey 2·00 1·25

1933. Air. Nos. 337 and 425/30 optd with **AIR MAIL** on wings of airplane.
450 2c. green 40 30
451 4c. red 15 10
452 12c. orange 25 10
453 20c. yellow 25 15
454 24c. violet 35 15
455 32c. brown 40 25

66 Baseball

1934. 10th Far Eastern Championship Games.
456 **66** 2c. brown 1·25 60
457 – 6c. blue 25 15
458 – 16c. purple 50 40
DESIGNS—VERT: 6c. Tennis; 16c. Basketball.

69 Dr. J. Rizal
72 Pearl Fishing

1935. Designs as T **69/70** in various sizes (sizes in millimetres).
459 2c. red (19 × 22) 10 10
460 4c. green (34 × 22) 10 10
461 6c. brown (22½ × 28) 15 10
462 8c. violet (34 × 22) 20 15
463 10c. red (34 × 22) 30 15
464 12c. black (34 × 22) 25 20
465 16c. blue (34 × 22) 35 15
466 20c. bistre (19 × 22) 25 10
467 26c. blue (34 × 22) 40 20
468 30c. red (34 × 22) 40 30
469 1p. black and orange (37 × 27) 2·40 90
470 2p. black and brown (37 × 27) 4·25 1·25
471 4p. black and blue (37 × 27) 4·00 2·50
472 5p. black and green (27 × 37) 9·50 1·75
DESIGNS: 4c. Woman, Carabao and Rice-stalks; 6c. Filipino girl; 10c. Fort Santiago; 12c. Salt springs; 16c. Magellan's landing; 20c. "Juan de la Cruz"; 26c. Rice terraces; 30c. Blood Compact; 1p. Barasoain Church; 2p. Battle of Manila Bay; 4p. Montalban Gorge; 5p. George Washington (after painting by John Faed).

COMMONWEALTH OF THE PHILIPPINES

83 "Temples of Human Progress"

1935. Inauguration of Commonwealth of the Philippines.
483 **83** 2c. red 15 15
484 6c. violet 20 15
485 16c. blue 20 15
486 36c. green 40 25
487 50c. brown 60 50

1935. Air. "China Clipper" Trans-Pacific Air Mail Flight. Optd **P.I. U.S. INITIAL FLIGHT December-1935** and Martin M-130 flying boat.
488 10c. red (No. 463) 25 20
489 30c. red (No. 468) 40 35

85 J. Rizal y Mercado
89 Manuel L. Quezon

1936. 75th Birth Anniv of Rizal.
490 **85** 2c. yellow 10 15
491 6c. blue 15 15
492 36c. brown 45 40

1936. Air. Manila–Madrid Flight by Arnaiz and Calvo. Stamps of 1906 surch **MANILA-MADRID ARNACAL FLIGHT–1936** and value.
493 **45** 2c. on 4c. red 10 10
494 6c. on 12c. orange 15 10
495 16c. on 26c. green 20 15

1936. Stamps of 1935 (Nos. 459/72) optd **COMMON-WEALTH** (2c., 6c., 20c.) or **COMMONWEALTH** (others).
496 2c. red 10 10
497 4c. green 50 40
526 6c. brown 10 10
527 8c. violet 10 10
528 10c. red 10 10
529 12c. black 10 10
530 16c. blue 20 10
531 20c. bistre 20 10
532 26c. blue 30 20
505 30c. red 30 15
534 1p. black and orange 50 15
535 2p. black and brown 2·50 75
508 4p. black and blue 17·00 2·50
509 5p. black and green 2·40 1·25

1936. 1st Anniv of Autonomous Government.
510 **89** 2c. brown 10 10
511 6c. green 10 10
512 12c. blue 15 15

90 Philippine Is
92 Arms of Manila

1937. 33rd International Eucharistic Congress.
513 **90** 2c. green 10 10
514 6c. brown 15 10
515 12c. blue 20 10
516 20c. orange 25 10
517 36c. violet 35 30
518 50c. red 45 25

1937.
522 **92** 10p. grey 3·50 1·50
523 20p. brown 1·75 1·10

1939. Air. 1st Manila Air Mail Exhibition. Surch **FIRST AIR MAIL EXHIBITION Feb 17 to 19, 1939** and value.
548a – 8c. on 26c. green (346) 60 35
549 **92** 1p. on 10p. grey 3·00 2·40

1939. 1st National Foreign Trade Week. Surch **FIRST FOREIGN TRADE WEEK MAY 21-27, 1939** and value.
551 – 2c. on 4c. green (460) 10 10
552a **45** 6c. on 26c. green (346) 20 15
553 **92** 50c. on 20p. brown 90 85

101 Triumphal Arch
102 Malacanan Palace

103 Pres. Quezon taking Oath of Office

1939. 4th Anniv of National Independence.
554 **101** 2c. green 10 10
555 6c. red 15 10
556 12c. blue 10 10
557 **102** 2c. green 10 10
558 6c. orange 15 10
559 12c. red 20 10
560 **103** 2c. orange 10 10
561 6c. green 15 10
562 12c. violet 30 15

104 Jose Rizal
105 Filipino Vinta and Boeing 314 Flying Boat

1941.
563 **104** 2c. green 10 10
623 – 2c. brown 10 10
In No. 623 the head faces to the right.

1941. Air.
566 **105** 8c. red 90 80
567 20c. blue 1·10 50
568 60c. green 1·60 85
569 1p. sepia 80 55

For Japanese Occupation issues of 1941–45 see **JAPANESE OCCUPATION OF PHILIPPINE ISLANDS**.

1945. Victory issue. Nos. 496, 525/31, 505, 534 and 522/3 optd **VICTORY**.
610 2c. red 10 10
611 4c. green 10 10
612 6c. brown 15 10
613 8c. violet 20 15
614 10c. red 20 10
615 12c. black 25 15
616 16c. blue 40 15
617 20c. bistre 40 10
618 30c. red 70 50
619 1p. black and orange 1·40 30
620 10p. grey 40·00 14·00
621 20p. brown 35·00 16·00

INDEPENDENT REPUBLIC

111 "Independence"
113 Bonifacio Monument

1946. Proclamation of Independence.
625 **111** 2c. red 30 30
626 6c. green 60 30
627 12c. blue 90 45

1946. Optd **PHILIPPINES 50TH ANNIVERSARY MARTYRDOM OF RIZAL 1896–1946**.
628 **104** 2c. brown (No. 623) 30 20

1947.
629 – 4c. brown 15 15
630 **113** 10c. red 15 15
631 – 12c. blue 20 15
632 – 16c. grey 1·60 95
633 – 20c. brown 45 15
634 – 50c. green 1·20 10
635 – 1p. violet 2·40 60
DESIGNS—VERT: 4c. Rizal Monument; 50c., 1p. Avenue of Palm Trees. HORIZ: 12c. Jones Bridge; 16c. Santa Lucia Gate; 20c. Mayon Volcano.

115 Manuel L. Quezon
117 Presidents Quezon and Roosevelt

116 Pres. Roxas taking Oath of Office

1947.
636 **115** 1c. green 15 10

1947. 1st Anniv of Independence.
638 **116** 4c. red 20 15
639 6c. green 50 50
640 16c. purple 1·20 80

1947. Air.
641 **117** 6c. green 60 60
642 40c. orange 1·30 1·30
643 80c. blue 3·25 3·25

119 United Nations Emblem
121 General MacArthur

1947. Conference of Economic Commission for Asia and Far East, Baguio. Imperf or perf.
648 **119** 4c. red and pink 1·60 1·60
649 6c. violet and light violet 2·40 2·40
650 12c. blue and light blue 2·75 2·75

1948. 3rd Anniv of Liberation.
652 **121** 4c. violet 60 20
653 6c. red 1·10 75
654 16c. blue 1·60 75

122 Threshing Rice
125 Dr. Jose Rizal

1948. United Nations Food and Agriculture Organization Conference, Baguio.
655 **122** 2c. green & yell (postage) 90 60
656 6c. brown and stone 1·10 80
657 18c. blue and light blue 3·00 2·40
658 40c. red and pink (air) 15·00 8·00

1948.
662 **125** 2c. green 20 15

126 Pres. Manuel Roxas
127 Scout and Badge

1948. President Roxas Mourning Issue.
663 **126** 2c. black 20 15
664 4c. black 35 20

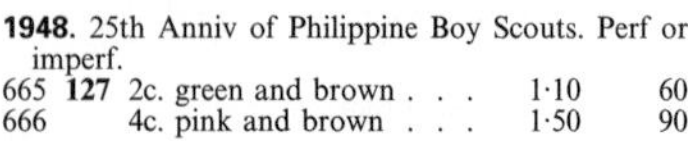

1948. 25th Anniv of Philippine Boy Scouts. Perf or imperf.
665 **127** 2c. green and brown . . . 1·10 60
666 4c. pink and brown . . . 1·50 90

128 Sampaguita, National Flower

1948. Flower Day.
667 **128** 3c. green and black . . . 35 30

130 Santos, Tavera and Kalaw

131 "Doctrina Christiana" (first book published in Philippines)

1949. Library Rebuilding Fund.
671 **130** 4c.+2c. brown . . . . . 1·10 80
672 **131** 6c.+4c. violet . . . . . . 3·25 2·20
673 – 18c.+7c. blue . . . . . . 4·50 3·75
DESIGN—VERT: 18c. Title page of Rizal's "Noli Me Tangere".

132 U.P.U. Monument, Berne

1949. 75th Anniv of U.P.U.
674 **132** 4c. green 20 10
675 6c. violet 20 15
676 18c. blue 80 30

133 General del Pilar at Tirad Pass
134 Globe

1949. 50th Death Anniv of Gen. Gregorio del Pilar.
678 **133** 2c. brown 15 15
679 4c. green 35 30

1950. 5th International Congress of Junior Chamber of Commerce.
680 **134** 2c. violet (postage) . . . 20 10
681 6c. green 30 15
682 18c. blue 65 20
683 30c. orange (air) 50 20
684 50c. red 90 20

135 Red Lauan Trees
136 Franklin D. Roosevelt

1950. 15th Anniv of Forestry Service.
685 **135** 2c. green 35 20
686 4c. violet 75 30

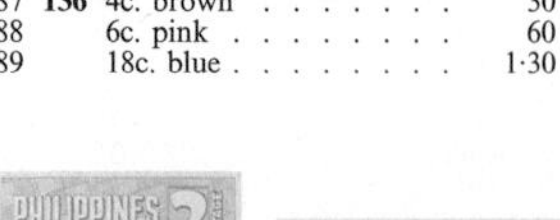

1950. 25th Anniv of Philatelic Association.
687 **136** 4c. brown 30 20
688 6c. pink 60 35
689 18c. blue . . . . 1·30 95

137 Lions Emblem
138 President Quirino taking Oath of Office

1950. "Lions" International Convention, Manila.
691 **137** 2c. orange (postage) . . . 65 65
692 4c. lilac . . . . 1·00 1·00
693 30c. green (air) . . . . . 1·00 75
694 50c. blue . . . . 1·10 1·00

1950. Pres. Quirino's Inauguration.
696 **138** 2c. red 15 10
697 4c. purple 15 15
698 6c. green 20 15

1950. Surch **ONE CENTAVO**.
699 **125** 1c. on 2c. green 15 10

140 Dove and Map
141 War Widow and Children

1950. Baguio Conference.
701 **140** 5c. green 30 20
702 6c. red 30 20
703 18c. blue 75 50

1950. Aid to War Victims.
704 **141** 2c.+2c. red 10 10
705 – 4c.+4c. violet 45 45
DESIGN: 4c. Disabled veteran.

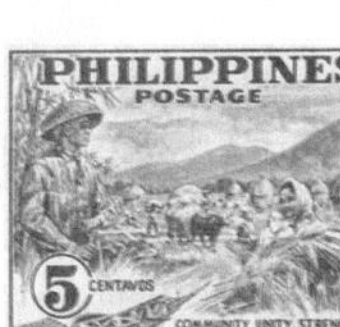

142 Arms of Manila
143 Soldier and Peasants

1950. As T **142**. Various arms and frames. (a) Arms inscr "MANILA".
706 5c. violet 60 50
707 6c. grey 50 35
708 18c. blue 60 50

(b) Arms inscr "CEBU".
709 5c. red 60 50
710 6c. brown 50 35
711 18c. violet 60 50

(c) Arms inscr "ZAMBOANGA".
712 5c. green 60 50
713 6c. brown 50 35
714 18c. blue 60 50

(d) Arms inscr "ILOILO".
715 5c. green 60 50
716 6c. violet 50 35
717 18c. blue 60 50

1951. Guarding Peaceful Labour. Perf or imperf.
718 **143** 5c. green 20 20
719 6c. purple 35 35
720 18c. blue . . . . 1·00 1·00

144 Philippines Flag and U.N. Emblem
145 Statue of Liberty

1951. U.N. Day.
721 **144** 5c. red 90 35
722 6c. green 60 35
723 18c. blue . . . . 1·60 1·10

1951. Human Rights Day.
724 **145** 5c. green 50 30
725 6c. orange 75 50
726 18c. blue . . . . 1·30 80

146 Schoolchildren
147 M. L. Quezon

1952. 50th Anniv of Philippine Educational System.
727 **146** 5c. orange 60 50

1952. Portraits.
728 **147** 1c. brown 15 15
729 – 2c. black (J. Abad Santos) 15 15
730 – 3c. red (A. Mabini) . . . 15 15
731 – 5c. red (M. H. del Pilar) 15 15
732 – 10c. blue (Father J. Burgos) 15 15
733 – 20c. red (Lapu-Lapu) . . 30 15
734 – 25c. green (Gen. A. Luna) 45 20
735 – 50c. red (C. Arellano) . . 90 30
736 – 60c. red (A. Bonifacio) . . 1·00 45
737 – 2p. violet (G. L. Jaena) 3·25 1·10

149 Aurora A. Quezon

1952. Fruit Tree Memorial Fund.
742 **149** 5c.+1c. blue 15 15
743 6c.+2c. pink 45 45
See also No. 925.

150 Milkfish and Map of Oceania

1952. Indo-Pacific Fisheries Council.
744 **150** 5c. brown . . . . 1·20 75
745 6c. blue 75 60

151 "A Letter from Rizal"

1952. Pan-Asiatic Philatelic Exhibition, Manila.
746 **151** 5c. blue (postage) 65 15
747 6c. brown 65 20
748 30c. red (air) . . . . . . 1·30 1·10

152 Wright Park, Baguio City
153 F. Baltazar (poet)

1952. 3rd Lions District Convention.
749 **152** 5c. red 95 95
750 6c. green . . . . 1·30 1·10

1953. National Language Week.
751 **153** 5c. bistre 50 35

154 "Gateway to the East"
155 Pres. Quirino and Pres. Sukarno

1953. International Fair, Manila.
752 **154** 5c. turquoise 35 15
753 6c. red 35 15

1953. Visit of President to Indonesia. Flags in yellow, blue and red.
754 **155** 5c. blue, yellow and black 20 10
755 6c. green, yellow and black 30 30

156 Doctor examining patient

1953. 50th Anniv of Philippines Medical Association.
756 **156** 5c. mauve 30 30
757 6c. blue 45 35

1954. Optd **FIRST NATIONAL BOY SCOUTS JAMBOREE APRIL 23-30, 1954** or surch also.
758 5c. red (No. 731) . . . . . . 1·30 1·10
759 18c. on 50c. green (No. 634) 2·20 1·60

158 Stamp of 1854, Magellan and Manila P.O.

1954. Stamp Centenary. Central stamp in orange.
760 **158** 5c. violet (postage) . . . 80 60
761 18c. blue . . . . 1·60 1·30
762 30c. green . . . . 3·75 2·40
763 10c. brown (air) . . . . . 1·60 1·30
764 20c. green . . . . 2·75 2·20
765 50c. red . . . . 5·50 4·75

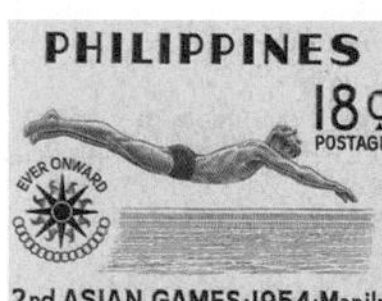

159 Diving

1954. 2nd Asian Games, Manila.
766 – 5c. blue on blue (Discus) 90 65
767 **159** 18c. green on green . . . 1·50 1·10
768 – 30c. red on pink (Boxing) 2·20 1·90

1954. Surch **MANILA CONFERENCE OF 1954** and value.
769 **113** 5c. on 10c. red 20 15
770 – 18c. on 20c. brown (No. 633) 80 75

161 "Independence" 162 "The Immaculate Conception" (Murillo)

1954. Independence Commemoration.
771 **161** 5c. red 30 20
772 18c. blue 95 60

1954. Marian Year.
773 **162** 5c. blue 60 35

163 Mayon Volcano and Filipino Vinta

1955. 50th Anniv of Rotary International.
774 **163** 5c. blue (postage) 35 15
775 18c. red . . . . 1·30 65
776 50c. green (air) . . . . . 2·50 1·10

164 "Labour" 165 Pres. Magsaysay

1955. Labour-Management Congress, Manila.
777 **164** 5c. brown . . . . 1·50 60

1955. 9th Anniv of Republic.
778 **165** 5c. blue 20 20
779 20c. red 75 75
780 30c. green . . . . 1·30 1·30

166 Lt. J. Gozar

1955. Air. Air Force Heroes.
781 **166** 20c. violet 80 15
782 – 30c. red (Lt. C. F. Basa) 1·30 30
783 **166** 50c. green . . . . 1·10 20
784 – 70c. blue (Lt. C. F. Basa) 1·90 1·30

167 Liberty Well

1956. Artesian Wells for Rural Areas.
785 **167** 5c. violet 35 35
786 20c. green 80 75

1956. 5th Conference of World Confederation of Organizations of the Teaching Profession. No. 731 optd **WCOTP CONFERENCE MANILA**.
787 5c. red 35 35

169 Nurse and War Victims 170 Monument (landing marker) in Leyte

1956. 50th Anniv of Philippines Red Cross.
788 **169** 5c. violet and red 50 50
789 20c. brown and red . . . 75 60

1956. Liberation Commem. Perf or imperf.
790 **170** 5c. red 15 15

171 St. Thomas's University 172 Statue of the Sacred Heart

1956. University of St. Thomas.
791 **171** 5c. brown and red 25 20
792 60c. brown and mauve . . 1·10 1·00

1956. 2nd National Eucharistic Congress and Centenary of the Feast of the Sacred Heart.
793 **172** 5c. green 35 30
794 20c. pink 80 80

1956. Surch **5 5**.
795 5c. on 6c. brown (No. 710) 15 15
796 5c. on 6c. brown (No. 713) 15 15
797 5c. on 6c. violet (No. 716) . . 15 15

174 Girl Guide, Badge and Camp 175 Pres. Ramon Magsaysay

1957. Girl Guides' Pacific World Camp, Quezon City, and Birth Centenary of Lord Baden-Powell. Perf or imperf.
798 **174** 5c. blue 50 50

1957. Death of Pres. Magsaysay.
799 **175** 5c. black 15 10

176 Sergio Osmena (Speaker) and First Philippine Assembly

1957. 50th Anniv of First Philippine Assembly.
800 **176** 5c. green 15 15

177 "The Spoliarium" after Juan Luna

1957. Birth Centenary of Juan Luna (painter).
801 **177** 5c. red 15 10

1957. Inauguration of President C. P. Garcia and Vice-President D. Macapagal. Nos. 732/3 surch **GARCIA-MACAPAGAL INAUGURATION DEC. 30, 1957** and value.
802 5c. on 10c. blue 20 20
803 10c. on 20c. red 30 30

179 University of the Philippines

1958. Golden Jubilee of University of the Philippines.
804 **179** 5c. red 35 15

180 Pres. Garcia

1958. 12th Anniv of Republic.
805 **180** 5c. multicoloured 15 15
806 20c. multicoloured 60 45

181 Main Hospital Building, Quezon Institute

1958. Obligatory Tax. T.B. Relief Fund.
807 **181** 5c.+5c. green and red . . 20 20
808 10c.+5c. violet and red . . 45 45

182 The Immaculate Conception and Manila Cathedral

1958. Inauguration of Manila Cathedral.
809 **182** 5c. multicoloured 20 15

1959. Surch **One Centavo**.
810 1c. on 5c. red (No. 731) . . . 15 10

1959. 14th Anniv of Liberation. Nos. 704/5 surch.
812 **141** 1c. on 2c.+2c. red 10 10
813 – 6c. on 4c.+4c. violet . . . 15 15

186 Philippines Flag 187 Bulacan Seal

1959. Adoption of Philippine Constitution.
814 **186** 6c. red, blue and yellow 15 10
815 20c. red, blue and yellow 20 20

1959. Provincial Seals. (a) Bulacan Seal and 60th Anniv of Malolos Constitution.
816 **187** 6c. green 15 10
817 20c. red 30 20

(b) Capiz Seal and 11th Death Anniv of Pres. Roxas.
818 6c. brown 10 10
819 25c. violet 30 30

The shield within the Capiz seal bears the inset portrait of Pres. Roxas.

(c) Bacolod Seal.
820 6c. green 15 10
821 10c. purple 20 15

188 Scout at Campfire

1959. 10th World Scout Jamboree, Manila.
822 **188** 6c.+4c. red on yellow (postage) 15 15
823 6c.+4c. red 35 35
824 – 25c.+5c. blue on yellow 60 60
825 – 25c.+5c. blue 75 75
826 – 30c.+10c. green (air) . . . 60 60
827 – 70c.+20c. brown . . . . 1·30 1·30
828 – 80c.+20c. violet . . . . . 1·90 1·90

DESIGNS: 25c. Scout with bow and arrow; 30c. Scout cycling; 70c. Scout with model airplane; 80c. Pres. Garcia with scout.

190 Bohol Sanatorium

1959. Obligatory Tax. T.B. Relief Fund. Nos. 807/8 surch **HELP FIGHT T B** with Cross of Lorraine and value and new design (T **190**).
830 **181** 3c.+5c. on 5c.+5c. . . . 20 20
831 6c.+5c. on 10c.+5c. . . . 20 20
832 **190** 6c.+5c. green and red . . 20 20
833 25c.+5c. blue and red . . 45 35

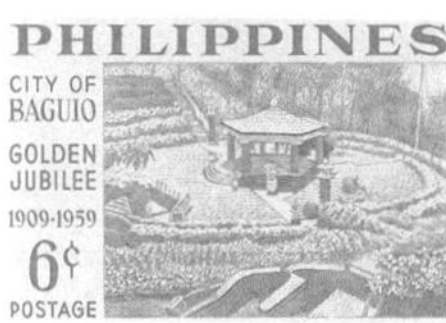
191 Pagoda and Gardens at Camp John Hay

1959. 50th Anniv of Baguio.
834 **191** 6c. green 15 10
835 25c. red 35 20

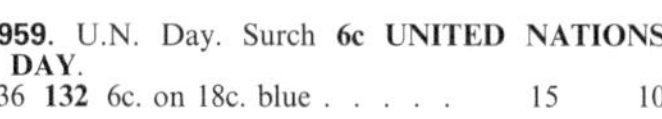
1959. U.N. Day. Surch **6c UNITED NATIONS DAY**.
836 **132** 6c. on 18c. blue 15 10

193 Maria Cristina Falls 196 Dr. Jose Rizal

195

1959. World Tourist Conference, Manila.
837 **193** 6c. green and violet . . . 15 15
838 30c. green and brown . . 60 45

1959. No. 629 surch **One** and bars.
839 1c. on 4c. brown 15 10

1959. Centenary of Manila Athenaeum (school).
840 **195** 6c. blue 10 10
841 30c. red 50 35

1959.
842 **196** 6c. blue 15 10

197 Book of the Constitution

1960. 25th Anniv of Philippines Constitution.
844 **197** 6c. brn & gold (postage) 15 15
845 30c. blue and silver (air) 45 30

198 Congress Building

1960. 5th Anniv of Manila Pact.
846 **198** 6c. green 10 10
847 25c. orange 45 35

199 Sunset, Manila Bay

1960. World Refugee Year.
848 **199** 6c. multicoloured 15 15
849 25c. multicoloured 45 30

200 North American F-86 Sabre and Boeing P-12 Fighters

1960. Air. 25th Anniv of Philippine Air Force.
850 **200** 10c. red 15 15
851 20c. blue 45 30

1960. Surch.
852 **134** 1c. on 18c. blue 20 15
853 **161** 5c. on 18c. blue 20 20
854 **163** 5c. on 18c. red 30 15
855 **158** 10c. on 18c. orange & blue 20 15
856 **140** 10c. on 18c. blue 30 20

202 Lorraine Cross 204 Pres. Quezon

1960. 50th Anniv of Philippine Tuberculosis Society. Lorraine Cross and wreath in red and gold.
857 **202** 5c. green 15 10
858 6c. blue 15 10

1960. Obligatory Tax. T.B. Relief Fund. Surch **6+5 HELP PREVENT TB**.
859 **181** 6c.+5c. on 5c.+5c. green and red 35 15

1960.
860 **204** 1c. green 15 10

205 Basketball

1960. Olympic Games.
861 **205** 6c. brown & grn (postage) 15 10
862 – 10c. brown and purple . . 20 15
863 – 30c. brown and orange (air) 60 50
864 – 70c. purple and blue . . . 1·30 1·10
DESIGNS: 10c. Running; 30c. Rifle-shooting; 70c. Swimming.

206 Presidents Eisenhower and Garcia

1960. Visit of President Eisenhower.
865 **206** 6c. multicoloured 20 15
866 20c. multicoloured 50 30

207 "Mercury" and Globe

1961. Manila Postal Conference.
867 **207** 6c. multicoloured (postage) 15 10
868 30c. multicoloured (air) 35 30

1961. Surch **20 20**.
869 20c. on 25c. green (No. 734) 30 15

1961. 2nd National Scout Jamboree, Zamboanga. Nos. 822/5 surch **2nd National Boy Scout Jamboree Pasonanca Park** and value.
870 10c. on 6c.+4c. red on yellow 15 15
871 10c. on 6c.+4c. red 50 50
872 30c. on 25c.+5c. blue on yellow 35 35
873 30c. on 25c.+5c. blue 60 60

210 La Salle College

1961. 50th Anniv of La Salle College.
874 **210** 6c. multicoloured 15 10
875 10c. multicoloured 20 15

211 Rizal when Student, School and University Buildings

1961. Birth Centenary of Dr. Jose Rizal.
876 **211** 5c. multicoloured 10 10
877 – 6c. multicoloured 10 10
878 – 10c. brown and green . . 20 20
879 – 20c. turquoise and brown 30 30
880 – 30c. multicoloured 50 35
DESIGNS: 6c. Rizal and birthplace at Calamba, Laguna; 10c. Rizal, mother and father; 20c. Rizal extolling Luna and Hidalgo at Madrid; 30c. Rizal's execution.

1961. 15th Anniv of Republic. Optd **IKA 15 KAARAWAN Republika ng Pilipinas Hulyo 4, 1961**.
881 **198** 6c. green 20 20
882 25c. orange 45 45

213 Roxas Memorial T.B. Pavilion

1961. Obligatory Tax. T.B. Relief Fund.
883 **213** 6c.+5c. brown and red . . 35 15

214 Globe, Plan Emblem and Supporting Hand

1961. 7th Anniv of Admission of Philippines to Colombo Plan.
884 **214** 5c. multicoloured 10 10
885 6c. multicoloured 15 15

1961. Philippine Amateur Athletic Federation's Golden Jubilee. Surch with P.A.A.F. monogram and **6c PAAF GOLDEN JUBILEE 1911 1961**.
886 **200** 6c. on 10c. red 20 20

216 Typist

1961. Government Employees' Association.
887 **216** 6c. violet and brown . . . 20 10
888 10c. blue and brown . . . 35 20

1961. Inauguration of Pres. Macapagal and Vice-Pres. Pelaez. Surch **MACAPAGAL-PELAEZ DEC. 30, 1961 INAUGURATION 6c**.
889 6c. on 25c. violet (No. 819) 15 10

1962. Cross obliterated by Arms and surch **6s**.
890 **181** 6c. on 5c.+5c. green and red 15 15

220 Waling-Waling 221 A. Mabini (statesman)

1962. Orchids. Multicoloured.
892 5c. Type **220** 15 15
893 6c. White Mariposa 15 15
894 10c. "Dendrobium sanderii" 20 20
895 20c. Sanggumay 35 35

1962. New Currency.
896 – 1s. brown 10 10
897 **221** 3s. red 10 10
898 – 5s. red 10 10
899 – 6s. brown 15 10
900 – 6s. blue 15 10
901 – 10s. purple 15 10
902 – 20s. blue 20 10
903 – 30s. red 50 15
904 – 50s. violet 90 15
905 – 70s. blue . . . . 1·10 50
906 – 1p. green . . . . 2·20 45
907 – 1p. orange 75 35
PORTRAITS: 1s. M. L. Quezon; 5s. M. H. del Pilar; 6s. (2) J. Rizal (different); 10s. Father J. Burgos; 20s. Lapu-Lapu; 30s. Rajah Soliman; 50s. C. Arellano; 70s. S. Osmena; 1p. (No. 906) E. Jacinto; 1p. (No. 907) J. M. Panganiban.

225 Pres. Macapagal taking Oath

1962. Independence Day.
915 **225** 6s. multicoloured 15 10
916 10s. multicoloured 20 15
917 30s. multicoloured 35 20

226 Valdes Memorial T.B. Pavilion

1962. Obligatory Tax Stamps. T.B. Relief Fund. Cross in red.
918 **226** 6s.+5s. purple 15 15
919 30s.+5s. blue 45 30
920 70s.+5s. blue . . . . . . 1·00 90

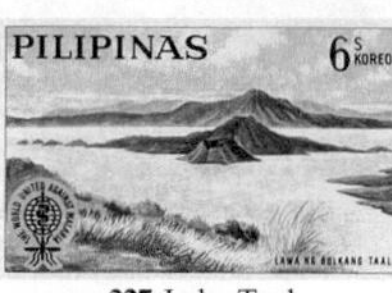
227 Lake Taal

1962. Malaria Eradication.
921 **227** 6s. multicoloured 15 15
922 10s. multicoloured 20 15
923 70s. multicoloured . . . . 1·50 1·10

1962. Bicentenary of Diego Silang Revolt. No. 734 surch **1762 1962 BICENTENNIAL Diego Silang Revolt 20**.
924 20s. on 25c. green 30 20

1962. No. 742 with premium obliterated.
925 **149** 5c. blue 20 15

230 Dr. Rizal playing Chess

1962. Rizal Foundation Fund.
926 **230** 6s.+4s. green and mauve 20 20
927 – 30s.+5s. blue and purple 50 50
DESIGN: 30s. Dr. Rizal fencing.

1963. Surch.
928 **221** 1s. on 3s. red 15 10
929 – 5s. on 6s. brown (No. 899) 15 15

1963. Diego Silang Bicentenary Art and Philatelic Exhibition, G.P.O., Manila. No. 737 surch **1763 1963 DIEGO SILANG BICENTENNIAL ARPHEX** and value.
930 6c. on 2p. violet 15 15
931 20c. on 2p. violet 30 30
932 70c. on 2p. violet 90 75

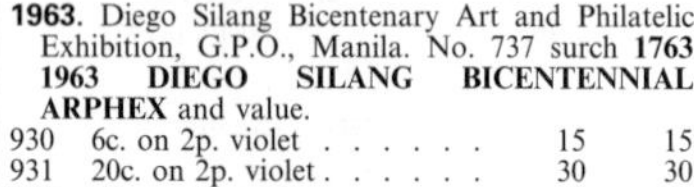
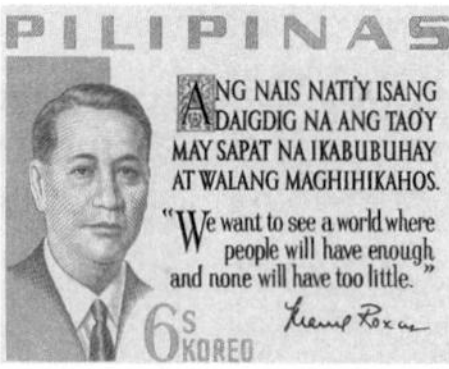
233 "We want to see ..." (Pres. Roxas)

1963. Presidential Sayings (1st issue).
933 **233** 6s. blue and black 15 10
934 30s. brown and black . . 45 15
See also Nos. 959/60, 981/2, 1015/16, 1034/5, 1055/6, 1148/9 and 1292/3.

234 Lorraine Cross on Map

1963. Obligatory Tax. T.B. Relief Fund. Cross in red.
935 **234** 6s.+5s. pink and violet . . 15 10
936 10s.+5s. pink and green 15 15
937 50s.+5s. pink & brown . . 75 50

235 Globe and Flags 236 Centenary Emblem

1963. 1st Anniv of Asian-Oceanic Postal Union.
938 **235** 6s. multicoloured 15 15
939 20s. multicoloured 20 15

1963. Red Cross Centenary. Cross in red.
940 **236** 5s. grey and violet 15 10
941 6s. grey and blue 15 15
942 20s. grey and green . . . 45 20

237 Tinikling (dance)

1963. Folk Dances. Multicoloured.
943 5s. Type **237** 15 15
944 6s. Pandanggo sa Ilaw . . . 15 15

945 10s. Itik-Itik 15 15
946 20s. Singkil 30 30

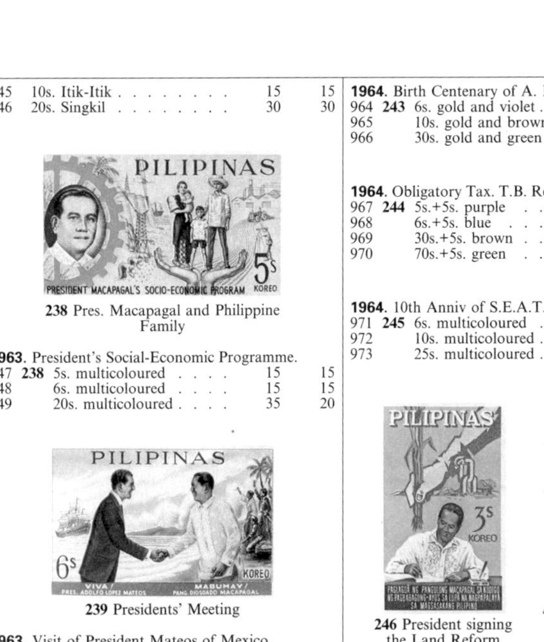

238 Pres. Macapagal and Philippine Family

1963. President's Social-Economic Programme.
947 **238** 5s. multicoloured 15 15
948 6s. multicoloured 15 15
949 20s. multicoloured 35 20

239 Presidents' Meeting

1963. Visit of President Mateos of Mexico.
950 **239** 6s. multicoloured 15 15
951 30s. multicoloured 45 15

240 Bonifacio and Flag

1963. Birth Cent of Andres Bonifacio (patriot).
952 **240** 5s. multicoloured 15 10
953 6s. multicoloured 15 15
954 25s. multicoloured 35 30

241 Harvester

242 Bamboo Organ, Catholic Church, Las Pinas

1963. Freedom from Hunger.
956 **241** 6s. multicoloured (postage) 15 10
957 30s. multicoloured (air) 60 45
958 50s. multicoloured 95 75

1963. Presidential Sayings (2nd issue). As T **233** but with portrait and saying changed.
959 6s. black and violet 15 10
960 30s. black and green 35 15
PORTRAIT AND SAYING: Pres. Magsaysay, "I believe ...".

1964. Las Pinas Organ Commemoration.
961 **242** 5s. multicoloured 15 10
962 6s. multicoloured 15 15
963 20s. multicoloured 45 20

243 A. Mabini (patriot)

245 S.E.A.T.O. Emblems and Flags

244 Negros Oriental T.B. Pavilion

1964. Birth Centenary of A. Mabini.
964 **243** 6s. gold and violet 15 10
965 10s. gold and brown . . . 15 15
966 30s. gold and green . . . 35 15

1964. Obligatory Tax. T.B. Relief Fund. Cross in red.
967 **244** 5s.+5s. purple 15 10
968 6s.+5s. blue 15 10
969 30s.+5s. brown 45 30
970 70s.+5s. green 90 80

1964. 10th Anniv of S.E.A.T.O.
971 **245** 6s. multicoloured 15 10
972 10s. multicoloured 20 15
973 25s. multicoloured 30 15

246 President signing the Land Reform Code

247 Basketball

1964. Agricultural Land Reform Code. President and inscr at foot in brown, red and sepia.
974 **246** 3s. green (postage) . . . 15 10
975 6s. blue 15 15
976 30s. brown (air) 35 20

1964. Olympic Games, Tokyo. Sport in brown. Perf or imperf.
977 **247** 6s. blue and gold 15 15
978 – 10s. pink and gold . . . 20 15
979 – 20s. yellow and gold . . . 50 20
980 – 30s. green and gold . . . 65 50
SPORTS: 10s. Relay-racing; 20s. Hurdling; 30s. Football.

1965. Presidential Sayings (3rd issue). As T **233** but with portrait and saying changed.
981 6s. black and green 15 15
982 30s. black and purple 35 15
PORTRAIT AND SAYING: Pres. Quirino, "So live ...".

248 Presidents Luebke and Macapagal

1965. Visit of President of German Federal Republic.
983 **248** 6s. multicoloured 15 10
984 10s. multicoloured 20 15
985 25s. multicoloured 35 30

249 Meteorological Emblems **250** Pres. Kennedy

1965. Cent of Philippines Meteorological Services.
986 **249** 6s. multicoloured 15 15
987 20s. multicoloured 15 15
988 50s. multicoloured 60 30

1965. John F. Kennedy (U.S. President) Commemoration.
989 **250** 6s. multicoloured 15 15
990 10s. multicoloured 20 15
991 30s. multicoloured 50 20

251 King Bhumibol and Queen Sirikit, Pres. Macapagal and Wife

1965. Visit of King and Queen of Thailand.
992 **251** 2s. multicoloured 10 10
993 6s. multicoloured 15 15
994 30s. multicoloured 50 20

252 Princess Beatrix and Mrs. Macapagal

1965. Visit of Princess Beatrix of the Netherlands.
995 **252** 2s. multicoloured 10 10
996 6s. multicoloured 15 15
997 10s. multicoloured 20 15

1965. Obligatory Tax. T.B. Relief Fund. Surch.
998 **244** 1s.+5s. on 6s.+5s. . . . 15 10
999 3s.+5s. on 6s.+5s. . . . 20 15

254 Hand holding Cross and Rosary **256** Signing Agreement

1965. 400th Anniv of Philippines Christianisation. Multicoloured.
1000 3s. Type **254** (postage) . . . 15 10
1001 6s. Legaspi-Urdaneta, monument 20 10
1002 30s. Baptism of Filipinos by Father Urdaneta, Cebu (horiz) (48 × 27 mm) (air) 50 30
1003 70s. "Way of the Cross"–ocean map of Christian voyagers' route, Spain to the Philippines (horiz) (48 × 27 mm) . . . . . . 1·30 1·20

1965. "MAPILINDO" Conference, Manila.
1005 **256** 6s. blue, red and yellow 15 15
1006 10s. multicoloured . . . 15 15
1007 25s. multicoloured . . . 45 20
The above stamps depict Pres. Sukarno of Indonesia, former Pres. Macapagal of the Philippines and Prime Minister Tunku Abdul Rahman of Malaysia.

257 Cyclists and Globe

259 Dr. A. Regidor

1965. 2nd Asian Cycling Championships, Philippines.
1008 **257** 6s. multicoloured 10 10
1009 10s. multicoloured . . . 20 15
1010 25s. multicoloured . . . 45 30

1965. Inauguration of Pres. Marcos and Vice-Pres. Lopez. Nos. 926/7 surch **MARCOS-LOPEZ INAUGURATION DEC. 30, 1965** and value.
1011 **230** 10s. on 6s.+4s. 20 20
1012 – 30s. on 30s.+5s. 50 50

1966. Regidor (patriot) Commemoration.
1013 **259** 6s. blue 15 15
1014 30s. brown 30 20

1966. Presidential Sayings (4th issue). As T **233** but with portrait and saying changed.
1015 6s. black and red 15 10
1016 30s. black and blue 35 20
PORTRAIT AND SAYING: Pres. Aguinaldo, "Have faith ...".

1966. Campaign Against Smuggling. No. 900 optd **HELP ME STOP SMUGGLING Pres. MARCOS.**
1017 6s. blue 20 15

261 Girl Scout

1966. Silver Jubilee of Philippines Girl Scouts.
1018 **261** 3s. multicoloured 15 10
1019 6s. multicoloured 15 15
1020 20s. multicoloured . . . 45 20

262 Pres. Marcos taking Oath

1966. Inauguration (1965) of Pres. Marcos.
1021 **262** 6s. multicoloured 15 15
1022 20s. multicoloured . . . 15 15
1023 30s. multicoloured . . . 30 20

263 Manila Seal and Historical Scenes

1966. Introduction of New Seal for Manila.
1024 **263** 6s. multicoloured 15 15
1025 30s. multicoloured . . . 30 15

264 Bank Facade and 1 peso Coin

1966. 50th Anniv of Philippines National Bank. Mult.
1026 6s. Type **264** 15 10
1027 10s. Old and new bank buildings 20 15

266 Bank Building

1966. 60th Anniv of Postal Savings Bank.
1029 **266** 6s. violet, yellow & green 15 10
1030 10s. red, yellow and green 20 15
1031 20s. blue, yellow & green 45 20

1966. Manila Summit Conference. Nos. 1021 and 1023 optd **MANILA SUMMIT CONFERENCE 1966 7 NATIONS** and emblem.
1032 **262** 6s. multicoloured 20 15
1033 30s. multicoloured . . . 30 30

1966. Presidential Sayings (5th issue). As T **233** but with portrait and saying changed.
1034 6s. black and brown 15 10
1035 30s. black and blue 35 15
PORTRAIT AND SAYING: Pres. Laurel; "No one can love the Filipinos better ...".

1967. 50th Anniv of Lions International. Nos. 977/80 optd with Lions emblem and **50th ANNIVERSARY LIONS INTERNATIONAL 1967**. Imperf.
1036 **247** 6c. blue and gold 15 15
1037 – 10c. pink and gold . . . 20 15
1038 – 20c. yellow and gold . . 45 20
1039 – 30c. green and gold . . . 65 65

269 "Succour" (after painting by F. Amorsolo)

1967. 25th Anniv of Battle of Bataan.
1040 **269** 5s. multicoloured 15 10
1041 20s. multicoloured . . . 20 15
1042 2p. multicoloured . . . 2·40 1·30

1967. Nos. 900 and 975 surch.
1043 – 4s. on 6s. blue 15 10
1044 **246** 5s. on 6s. blue 15 10

271 Stork-billed Kingfisher

1967. Obligatory Tax. T.B. Relief Fund. Birds. Multicoloured.

1045 1s.+5s. Type **271** 15 15
1046 5s.+5s. Rufous hornbill . . 20 20
1047 10s.+5s. Philippine eagle . . 35 20
1048 30s.+5s. Great-billed parrot 75 50

See also Nos. 1113/16.

272 Gen. MacArthur and Paratroopers landing on Corregidor

1967. 25th Anniv of Battle of Corregidor.

1049 **272** 6s. multicoloured 10 10
1050 5p. multicoloured . . . 4·50 3·75

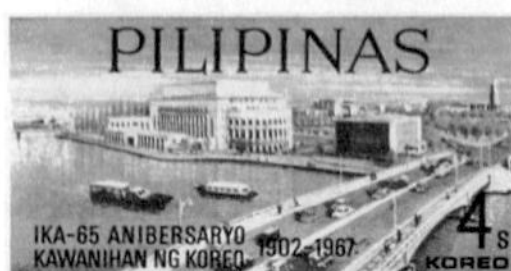

273 Bureau of Posts Building, Manila

1967. 65th Anniv of Philippines Bureau of Posts.

1051 **273** 4s. multicoloured 20 20
1052 20s. multicoloured . . . 20 15
1053 50s. multicoloured . . . 60 45

274 Escaping from Eruption

1967. Obligatory Tax. Taal Volcano Eruption (1965) (1st issue).

1054 **274** 70s. multicoloured . . . 95 80

For compulsory use on foreign air mail where the rate exceeds 70s. in aid of Taal Volcano Rehabilitation Committee.

See also No. 1071.

1967. Presidential Sayings (6th issue). As T **233** but with portrait and saying changed.

1055 10s. black and blue 15 10
1056 30s. black and violet 35 15

PORTRAIT AND SAYING: Pres. Quezon. "Social justice is far more beneficial ...".

275 "The Holy Family" (Filipino version)

1967. Christmas.

1057 **275** 10s. multicoloured . . . 20 15
1058 40s. multicoloured . . . 50 45

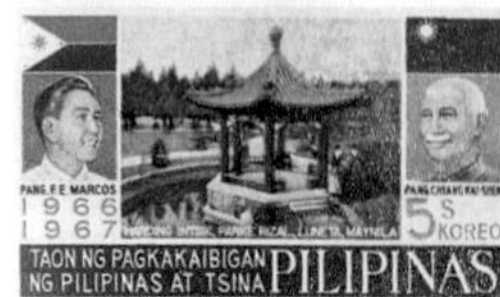

276 Pagoda, Pres. Marcos and Chiang Kai-shek

1967. China–Philippines Friendship.

1059 **276** 5s. multicoloured 10 10
1060 – 10s. multicoloured . . . 15 15
1061 – 20s. multicoloured . . . 20 15

DESIGNS (with portraits of Pres. Marcos and Chiang Kai-shek): 10s. Gateway, Chinese Garden, Rizal Park, Luneta; 20s. Chinese Garden, Rizal Park, Luneta.

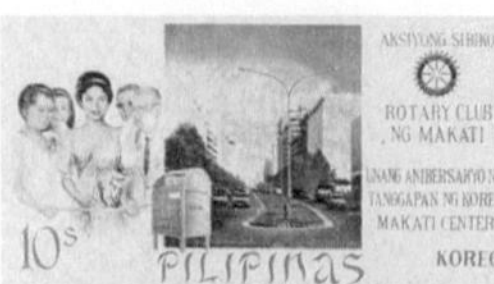

277 Ayala Avenue, Manila, Inaugural Ceremony and Rotary Badge

1968. 1st Anniv of Makati Centre Post Office, Manila.

1062 **277** 10s. multicoloured . . . 15 15
1063 20s. multicoloured . . . 20 20
1064 40s. multicoloured . . . 60 60

1968. Surch.

1065 – 5s. on 6s. (No. 981) . . 15 10
1066 – 5s. on 6s. (No. 1034) . . 15 10
1067 **244** 10s. on 6s.+5s. 15 10

280 Calderon, Barasoain Church and Constitution

1968. Birth Centenary of Felipe G. Calderon (lawyer and author of Malolos Constitution).

1068 **280** 10s. multicoloured . . . 15 10
1069 40s. multicoloured . . . 60 45
1070 75s. multicoloured . . . 1·20 1·10

281 Eruption **282** "Philcomsat", Earth Station and Globe

1968. Taal Volcano Eruption (1965) (2nd issue).

1071 **281** 70s. multicoloured . . . 95 95

Two issues were prepared by an American Agency under a contract signed with the Philippine postal authority but at the last moment this contract was cancelled by the Philippine Government. In the meanwhile the stamps had been on sale in the U.S.A. but they were never issued in the Philippines and they had no postal validity.

They comprise a set for the Mexican Olympic Games in the values 1, 2, 3 and 15s. postage and 50, 75s., 1, 2p. airmail and a set in memory of J. F. Kennedy and Robert Kennedy in the values 1, 2, 3s. postage and 5, 10p. airmail.

1968. Inauguration of "Philcomsat"–POTC Earth Station, Tanay, Rizal, Luzon.

1072 **282** 10s. multicoloured . . . 20 15
1073 40s. multicoloured . . . 60 45
1074 75s. multicoloured . . . 1·00 90

283 "Tobacco Production" (mural)

1968. Philippines Tobacco Industry.

1075 **283** 10s. multicoloured . . . 15 15
1076 40s. multicoloured . . . 60 50
1077 70s. multicoloured . . . 1·10 90

284 "Kudyapi"

1968. St. Cecilia's Day. Musical Instruments. Mult.

1078 10s. Type **284** 10 10
1079 20s. "Ludag" 10 10
1080 30s. "Kulintangan" 25 20
1081 50s. "Subing" 35 35

285 Concordia College **286** Children singing Carols

1968. Centenary of Concordia Women's College.

1082 **285** 10s. multicoloured . . . 10 10
1083 20s. multicoloured . . . 15 10
1084 70s. multicoloured . . . 50 35

1968. Christmas.

1085 **286** 10s. multicoloured . . . 15 15
1086 40s. multicoloured . . . 50 45
1087 75s. multicoloured . . . 95 80

287 Philippine Tarsier

1969. Philippines Fauna. Multicoloured.

1088 2s. Type **287** 15 15
1089 10s. Tamarau 15 15
1090 20s. Water buffalo 20 20
1091 75s. Greater Malay chevrotain . . . . 1·30 1·00

288 President Aguinaldo and Cavite Building

1969. Birth Centenary of President Amilio Aguinaldo.

1092 **288** 10s. multicoloured . . . 20 15
1093 40s. multicoloured . . . 60 35
1094 70s. multicoloured . . . 1·00 80

289 Rotary Emblem and "Bastion of San Andres"

1969. 50th Anniv of Manila Rotary Club.

1095 **289** 10s. mult (postage) . . . 15 15
1096 40s. multicoloured (air) . . 45 30
1097 75s. multicoloured . . . 95 75

290 Senator C. M. Recto **292** Jose Rizal College

1969. Recto Commemoration.

1098 **290** 10s. purple 15 10

1969. Philatelic Week. No. 1051 optd **PHILATELIC WEEK NOV. 24-30, 1968.**

1099 **273** 4s. multicoloured 20 10

1969. 50th Anniv of Jose Rizal College, Mandaluyong, Rizal.

1100 **292** 10s. multicoloured . . . 15 15
1101 40s. multicoloured . . . 60 45
1102 50s. multicoloured . . . 90 65

1969. 4th National Boy Scout Jamboree, Palayan City. No. 1019 surch **4th NATIONAL BOY SCOUT JAMBOREE PALAYAN CITY–MAY, 1969 5s.**

1103 5s. on 6s. multicoloured . . 20 15

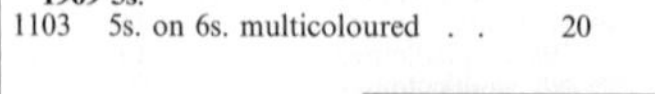

294 Red Cross Emblems and Map **295** Pres. and Mrs. Marcos harvesting Rice

1969. 50th Anniv of League of Red Cross Societies.

1104 **294** 10s. red, blue and grey 15 15
1105 40s. red, blue and cobalt 50 30
1106 75s. red, brown and buff 80 75

1969. "Rice for Progress".

1107 **295** 10s. multicoloured . . . 15 15
1108 40s. multicoloured . . . 50 35
1109 75s. multicoloured . . . 80 75

296 "The Holy Child of Leyte" (statue)

1969. 80th Anniv of Return of the "Holy Child of Leyte" to Tacloban.

1110 **296** 5s. mult (postage) . . . 15 10
1111 10s. multicoloured . . . 15 15
1112 40s. multicoloured (air) 50 35

1969. Obligatory Tax. T.B. Relief Fund. Birds as T **271**.

1113 1s.+5s. Common gold-backed woodpecker . . . 20 15
1114 5s.+5s. Philippine trogon . . 20 15
1115 10s.+5s. Johnstone's (inscr "Mt. Apo") lorikeet . . . 35 20
1116 40s.+5s. Scarlet (inscr "Johnstone's") minivet . . 50 35

297 Bank Building

1969. Inauguration of Philippines Development Bank, Makati, Rizal.

1117 **297** 10s. black, blue and green 15 10
1118 40s. black, purple and green 90 45
1119 75s. black, brown & grn 1·30 95

298 "Philippine Birdwing"

1969. Philippine Butterflies. Multicoloured.

1120 10s. Type **298** 20 15
1121 20s. Tailed jay 30 20
1122 30s. Red Helen 50 30
1123 40s. Birdwing 80 45

299 Children of the World

1969. 15th Anniv of Universal Children's Day.

1124 **299** 10s. multicoloured . . . 15 10
1125 20s. multicoloured . . . 20 15
1126 30s. multicoloured . . . 20 20

300 Memorial and Outline of Landing **303** Melchora Aquino

301 Cultural Centre

1969. 25th Anniv of U.S. Forces' Landing on Leyte.
1127 **300** 5s. multicoloured 15 10
1128 10s. multicoloured . . . 20 15
1129 40s. multicoloured . . . 50 30

1969. Cultural Centre, Manila.
1130 **301** 10s. blue 15 15
1131 30s. purple 35 20

1969. Philatelic Week. Nos. 943/6 (Folk Dances) optd **1969 PHILATELIC WEEK** or surch also.
1132 5s. multicoloured 15 15
1133 5s. on 6s. multicoloured . . 15 15
1134 10s. multicoloured 20 20
1135 10s. on 20s. multicoloured 20 20

1969. 50th Death Anniv of Melchora Aquino, "Tandang Sora" (Grand Old Woman of the Revolution).
1136 **303** 10s. multicoloured . . . 15 15
1137 20s. multicoloured . . . 20 15
1138 30s. multicoloured . . . 50 20

1969. 2nd-term Inaug of President Marcos. Surch **PASINAYA, IKA-2 PANUNUNGKULAN PANGULONG FERDINAND E. MARCOS DISYEMBRE 30, 1969.**
1139 **262** 5s. on 6s. multicoloured 20 10

305 Ladle and Steel Mills

1970. Iligan Integrated Steel Mills.
1140 **305** 10s. multicoloured . . . 15 15
1141 20s. multicoloured . . . 35 20
1142 30s. multicoloured . . . 65 30

1970. Nos. 900, 962 and 964 surch.
1143 4s. on 6s. blue 15 10
1144 **242** 5s. on 6s. multicoloured 15 10
1145 **243** 5s. on 6s. multicoloured 15 10

307 New U.P.U. Headquarters Building

1970. New U.P.U. Headquarters Building, Berne.
1146 **307** 10s. ultramarine, yellow and blue 15 15
1147 30s. blue, yellow and green 60 30

1970. Presidential Sayings (7th issue). As T **233** but with portrait and saying changed.
1148 10s. black and purple . . . 15 10
1149 40s. black and green 35 15
PORTRAIT AND SAYING: Pres. Osmena, "Ante todo el bien de nuestro pueblo" ("The well-being of our nation comes above all").

308 Dona Julia V. de Ortigas and T.B. Society Headquarters

1970. Obligatory Tax. T.B. Relief Fund.
1150 **308** 1s.+5s. multicoloured . . 15 10
1151 5s.+5s. multicoloured . . 20 20
1152 30s.+5s. multicoloured 75 50
1153 70s.+5s. multicoloured 95 65

309 I.C.S.W. Emblem

1970. 15th Int Conference on Social Welfare.
1154 **309** 10s. multicoloured . . . 15 15
1155 20s. multicoloured . . . 30 20
1156 30s. multicoloured . . . 60 20

310 "Crab" (after sculpture by A. Calder)

1970. "Fight Cancer" Campaign.
1157 **310** 10s. multicoloured . . . 20 15
1158 40s. multicoloured . . . 45 20
1159 50s. multicoloured . . . 65 35

311 Scaled Tridacna

1970. Sea Shells. Multicoloured.
1160 5s. Type **311** 15 10
1161 10s. Royal spiny oyster . . 15 10
1162 20s. Venus comb murex . . 20 15
1163 40s. Glory-of-the-sea cone 60 35

1970. Nos. 986, 1024 and 1026 surch with new values in figures and words.
1164 **249** 4s. on 6s. 15 10
1165 **263** 4s. on 6s. 15 10
1166 **264** 4s. on 6s. 15 10

313 The "Hundred Islands" and Ox-cart

1970. Tourism (1st series). Multicoloured.
1167 10s. Type **313** 15 15
1168 20s. Tree-house, Pasonanca Park, Zamboanga City . . 20 15
1169 30s. "Filipino" (statue) and sugar plantation, Negros Island 30 30
1170 2p. Calesa (horse-carriage) and Miagao Church, Iloilo . . . . 1·90 1·20
See also Nos. 1186/9, 1192/5 and 1196/9.

314 Map of the Philippines

318 Mariano Ponce

317 Pope Paul VI and Map

1970. Golden Jubilee of Philippine Pharmaceutical Association.
1171 **314** 10s. multicoloured . . . 15 10
1172 50s. multicoloured . . . 75 35

1970. U.P.U./A.O.P.U. Regional Seminar, Manila. No. 938 surch **UPU-AOPU REGIONAL SEMINAR NOV. 23 - DEC. 5, 1970 TEN 10s.**
1173 **235** 10s. on 6s. multicoloured 15 15

1970. Philatelic Week. No. 977 surch **1970 PHILATELIC WEEK 10s TEN.**
1174 **247** 10s. on 6s. brown, blue and gold 15 10

1970. Pope Paul's Visit to the Philippines.
1175 **317** 10s. mult (postage) . . . 15 15
1176 30s. multicoloured . . . 30 20
1177 40s. multicoloured (air) 45 20

1970.
1178 **318** 10s. red 15 10
1179 – 15s. brown 15 10
1180 – 40s. red 35 10
1181 – 1p. blue 95 35
DESIGNS: 15s. Josefa Llanes Escoda; 40s. Gen. Miguel Malvar; 1p. Julian Felipe.

320 "PATA" Horse and Carriage

1971. 20th PATA Conference and Workshop, Manila.
1183 **320** 5s. multicoloured 15 10
1184 10s. multicoloured . . . 15 15
1185 70s. multicoloured . . . 50 35

1971. Tourism (2nd series). Views as T **313**. Multicoloured.
1186 10s. Nayong Pilipino resort 10 10
1187 20s. Fish farm, Iloilo . . . 15 10
1188 30s. Pagsanjan Falls 20 15
1189 5p. Watch-tower, Punta Cruz . . . . 1·80 1·60

321 Emblem and Family

1971. Regional Conference of International Planned Parenthood Federation for South-East Asia and Oceania.
1190 **321** 20s. multicoloured . . . 15 10
1191 40s. multicoloured . . . 20 15

1971. Tourism (3rd series). As T **313**. Mult.
1192 10s. Aguinaldo pearl farm 15 15
1193 20s. Coral-diving, Davao . . 15 15
1194 40s. Taluksengay Mosque 20 20
1195 1p. Ifugao woman and Banaue rice-terraces . . . 1·60 65

1971. Tourism (4th series). As T **313**. Mult.
1196 10s. Cannon and Filipino vintas, Fort del Pilar . . 15 15
1197 30s. Magellan's Cross, Cebu City 15 15
1198 50s. "Big Jar", Calamba, Laguna (Rizal's birthplace) 30 20
1199 70s. Mayon Volcano and diesel train . . . . 1·60 45

1971. Surch **FIVE 5s.**
1200 **264** 5s. on 6s. multicoloured 15 10

323 G. A. Malcolm (founder) and Law Symbols

1971. 60th Anniv of Philippines College of Law.
1201 **323** 15s. mult (postage) . . . 15 15
1202 1p. multicoloured (air) 80 75

324 Commemorative Seal

1971. 400th Anniv of Manila.
1203 **324** 10s. multicoloured (postage) 15 15
1204 1p. multicoloured (air) 1·20 80

325 Arms of Faculties

1971. Centenaries of Faculties of Medicine and Surgery, and of Pharmacy, Santo Tomas University.
1205 **325** 5s. mult (postage) . . . 15 10
1206 2p. multicoloured (air) 1·60 1·50

1971. University Presidents' World Congress, Manila. Surch **MANILA MCMLXXI CONGRESS OF UNIVERSITY PRESIDENTS 5s FIVE** and emblem.
1207 **266** 5s. on 6s. violet, yellow and green 15 10

327 "Our Lady of Guia"

1971. 400th Anniv of "Our Lady of Guia", Ermita, Manila.
1208 **327** 10s. multicoloured . . . 15 15
1209 75s. multicoloured . . . 60 50

328 Bank and "Customers"

1971. 70th Anniv of First National City Bank.
1210 **328** 10s. multicoloured . . . 15 15
1211 30s. multicoloured . . . 30 20
1212 1p. multicoloured . . . 75 60

1971. Surch in figure and word.
1213 **259** 4s. on 6s. blue 15 10
1214 5s. on 6s. blue 15 10

1971. Philatelic Week. Surch **1971 - PHILATELIC WEEK 5s FIVE.**
1215 **266** 5s. on 6s. violet, yellow and green 15 10

331 Dish Aerial and Events

1972. 6th Asian Electronics Conference, Manila (1971) and Related Events.
1216 **331** 5s. multicoloured 15 10
1217 40s. multicoloured . . . 60 35

332 Fathers Burgos, Gomez and Zamora

1972. Centenary of Martyrdom of Fathers Burgos, Gomez and Zamora.
1218 **332** 5s. multicoloured 10 10
1219 60s. multicoloured . . . 45 45

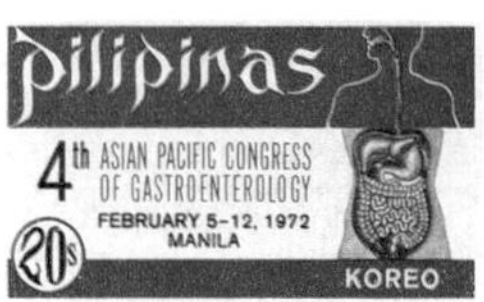

333 Human Organs

1972. 4th Asian–Pacific Gastro-enterological Congress, Manila.
1220 **333** 20s. mult (postage) . . . 20 15
1221 40s. multicoloured (air) 45 35

1972. Surch **5s FIVE.**
1222 **263** 5s. on 6s. multicoloured 15 10

1972. No. O914 with optd **G.O.** obliterated by bars.
1223 50s. violet 45 20

1972. Surch.
1224 **245** 10s. on 6s. multicoloured 15 10
1225 **251** 10s. on 6s. multicoloured 15 10
1226 – 10s. on 6s. black and red (No. 1015) 15 10

336 Memorial Gardens, Manila

1972. Tourism. "Visit Asean Lands" Campaign.
1227 **336** 5s. multicoloured 15 10
1228 50s. multicoloured . . . 90 20
1229 60s. multicoloured . . . 1·20 35

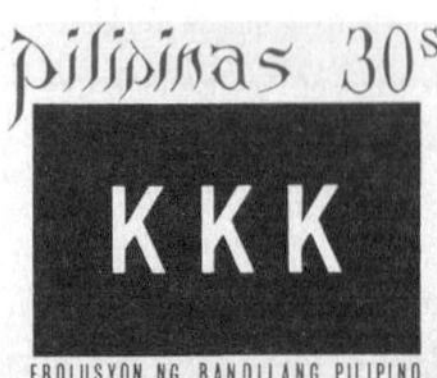

337 "KKK" Flag

1972. Evolution of Philippines' Flag.
1230 **337** 30s. red and blue 30 20
1231 – 30s. red and blue 30 20
1232 – 30s. red and blue 30 20
1233 – 30s. black and blue . . . 30 20
1234 – 30s. red and blue 30 20
1235 – 30s. red and blue 30 20
1236 – 30s. red and blue 30 20
1237 – 30s. red and blue 30 20
1238 – 30s. black, red and blue 30 20
1239 – 30s. yellow, red and blue 30 20
FLAGS: No. 1231, Three "K"s in pyramid; No. 1232, Single "K"; No. 1233, "K", skull and crossbones; No. 1234, Three "K"s and sun in triangle; No. 1235, Sun and three "K"s; No. 1236, Ancient Tagalog "K" within sun; No. 1237, Face in sun; No. 1238, Tricolor; No. 1239, Present national flag—sun and stars within triangle, two stripes.

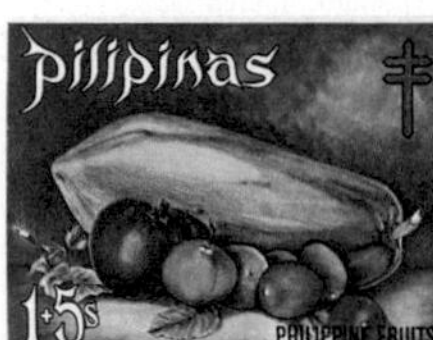

338 Mabol, Santol and Papaya

1972. Obligatory Tax. T.B. Relief Fund. Fruits. Mult.
1240 1s.+5s. Type **338** 10 10
1241 10s.+5s. Bananas, balimbang and mangosteen 15 15
1242 40s.+5s. Guava, mango, duhat and susongkalabac 30 30
1243 1p.+5s. Orange, pineapple, lanzones and sirhuelas . . 65 65

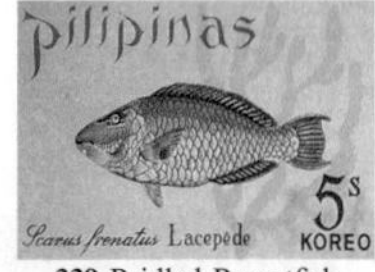

339 Bridled Parrotfish

1972. Fishes. Multicoloured.
1244 5s. Type **339** (postage) . . . 15 10
1245 10s. Klein's butterflyfish . . 15 10
1246 20s. Moorish idol 20 15
1247 50s. Two-spined angelfish (air) 75 35

340 Bank Headquarters

1972. 25th Anniv of Philippines Development Bank.
1248 **340** 10s. multicoloured . . . 15 10
1249 20s. multicoloured . . . 15 15
1250 60s. multicoloured . . . 60 35

341 Pope Paul VI

1972. 1st Anniv of Pope Paul's Visit to Philippines.
1251 **341** 10s. mult (postage) . . . 10 10
1252 50s. multicoloured . . . 45 35
1253 60s. multicoloured (air) 60 60

1972. Various stamps surch.
1254 **240** 10s. on 6s. (No. 953) . . 15 10
1255 – 10s. on 6s. (No. 959) . . 15 10
1256 **250** 10s. on 6s. (No. 989) . . 15 10

343 "La Barca de Aqueronte" (Hidalgo)

1972. 25th Anniv of Stamps and Philatelic Division, Philippines Bureau of Posts. Filipino Paintings. Multicoloured.
1257 5s. Type **343** 10 10
1258 10s. "Afternoon Meal of the Rice Workers" (Amorsolo) 15 15
1259 30s. "Espana y Filipinas" (Luna) (27 × 60 mm) . . . 20 20
1260 70s. "The Song of Maria Clara" (Amorsolo) . . . 60 60

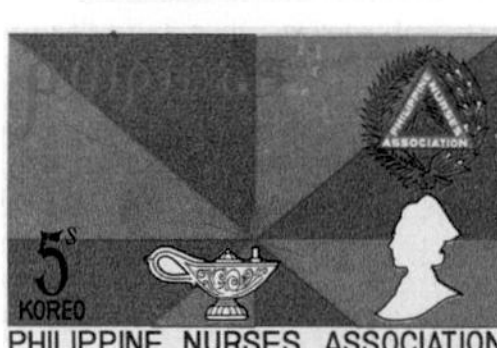

344 Lamp, Emblem and Nurse

1972. 50th Anniv of Philippine Nurses Assn.
1261 **344** 5s. multicoloured 10 10
1262 10s. multicoloured . . . 15 15
1263 70s. multicoloured . . . 45 35

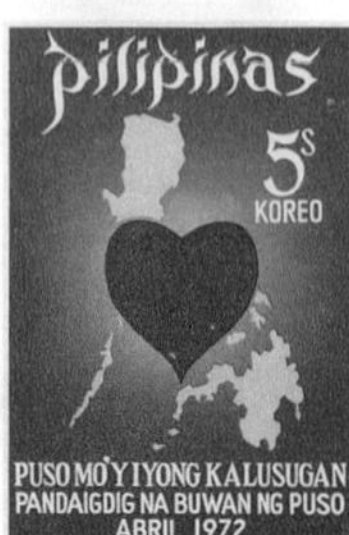

345 Heart on Map

1972. World Heart Month.
1264 **345** 5s. red, green and violet 10 10
1265 10s. red, green and blue 15 10
1266 30s. red, blue and green 20 20

346 "The First Mass" (C. V. Francisco)

1972. 450th Anniv of 1st Mass in Limasawa (1971).
1267 **346** 10s. mult (postage) . . . 15 15
1268 60s. multicoloured (air) 50 45

1972. Asia-Pacific Scout Conference, Manila. Various stamps surch **ASIA PACIFIC SCOUT CONFERENCE NOV, 1972** and value.
1269 **233** 10s. on 6s. (No. 933) . . 15 10
1270 **240** 10s. on 6s. (No. 953) . . 15 10
1271 – 10s. on 6s. (No. 981) . . 15 10

348 Olympic Emblems and Torch

1972. Olympic Games, Munich.
1272 **348** 5s. multicoloured 10 10
1273 10s. multicoloured . . . 15 15
1274 70s. multicoloured . . . 60 45

1972. Philatelic Week. Nos. 950 and 983 surch **1972 PHILATELIC WEEK TEN 10s.**
1275 **239** 10s. on 6s. multicoloured 15 10
1276 **248** 10s. on 6s. multicoloured 15 10

350 Manunggul Burial Jar

1972. Philippine Archaeological Discoveries. Multicoloured.
1277 10s. Type **350** 15 10
1278 10s. Ritual earthenware vessel 15 10
1279 10s. Metal pot 15 10
1280 10s. Earthenware vessel . . 15 10

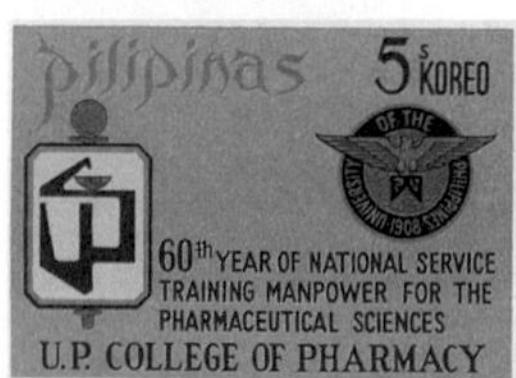

351 Emblems of Pharmacy and University of the Philippines

1972. 60th Anniv of National Training for Pharmaceutical Sciences, University of the Philippines.
1281 **351** 5s. multicoloured 10 10
1282 10s. multicoloured . . . 15 15
1283 30s. multicoloured . . . 20 15

352 "The Lantern-makers" (J. Pineda)

1972. Christmas.
1284 **352** 10s. multicoloured . . . 15 15
1285 30s. multicoloured . . . 20 15
1286 50s. multicoloured . . . 45 35

353 President Roxas and Wife

1972. 25th Anniv of Philippines Red Cross.
1287 **353** 5s. multicoloured 15 10
1288 20s. multicoloured . . . 15 15
1289 30s. multicoloured . . . 20 20

1973. Nos. 948 and 1005 surch **10s.**
1290 **238** 10s. on 6s. multicoloured 15 10
1291 **256** 10s. on 6s. blue. red and yellow 15 10

1973. Presidential Sayings (8th issue). As **T 233** but with portrait and saying changed.
1292 10s. black and bistre 15 10
1293 30s. black and mauve . . . 35 15
PORTRAIT AND SAYING: 10s., 30s. Pres. Garcia, "I would rather be right than successful".

355 University Building

1973. 60th Anniv of St. Louis University, Baguio City.
1294 **355** 5s. multicoloured 10 10
1295 10s. multicoloured . . . 10 10
1296 75s. multicoloured . . . 60 50

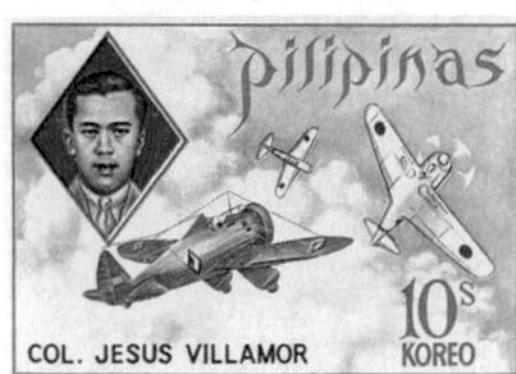

356 Col. J. Villamor and Air Battle

1973. Villamor Commemoration.
1297 **356** 10s. multicoloured . . . 15 10
1298 2p. multicoloured . . . 1·30 1·30

1973. Various stamps surch.
1299 **252** 5s. on 6s. multicoloured 15 10
1300 **266** 5s. on 6s. violet, yellow and green 15 10
1301 **318** 15s. on 10s. red (No. O1182) 15 10

359 Actor and Stage Performance

1973. 1st "Third-World" Theatre Festival, Manila.
1302 **359** 5s. multicoloured 10 10
1303 10s. multicoloured . . . 10 10
1304 50s. multicoloured . . . 35 20
1305 70s. multicoloured . . . 60 35

1973. President Marcos's Anti-smuggling Campaign. No. 1017 surch **5s.**
1306 5s. on 6s. blue 15 10

1973. 10th Death Anniv of John F. Kennedy. No. 989 surch **5s.**
1307 5s. on 6s. multicoloured . . 15 10

1973. Compulsory Tax Stamps. T.B. Relief Fund. Nos. 1241/2 surch.
1308 15s.+5s. on 10s.+5s. mult 15 15
1309 60s.+5s. on 40s.+5s. mult 45 45

363 Proclamation Scenes

1973. 75th Anniv of Philippine Independence.
1310 **363** 15s. multicoloured . . . 15 15
1311 45s. multicoloured . . . 20 20
1312 90s. multicoloured . . . 65 65

364 M. Agoncillo (maker of first national flag) **365** Imelda Marcos

1973. Perf or imperf.
1313 – 15s. violet 15 10
1314 **364** 60s. brown 35 35
1315 – 90s. blue 60 30
1316 – 1p.10 blue 75 35
1317 – 1p.50 red 95 80
1318 – 1p.50 brown 95 35
1319 – 1p.80 green . . . . . . 1·10 1·00
1320 – 5p. blue . . . . 3·00 3·00
DESIGNS: 15s. Gabriela Silang (revolutionary); 90s. Teodoro Yangco (businessman); 1p.10, Pio Valenzuela (physician); 1p.50 (No. 1317), Pedro Paterno (revolutionary); 1p.50 (No. 1318), Teodora Alonso (mother of Jose Rizal); 1p.80, E. Evangelista (revolutionary); 5p. F. M. Guerrero (writer).
For similar designs see Nos. 1455/8.

1973. Projects Inaugurated by Sra Imelda Marcos.
1321 **365** 15s. multicoloured . . . 15 15
1322 50s. multicoloured . . . 30 30
1323 60s. multicoloured . . . 35 35

366 Malakanyang Palace

1973. Presidential Palace, Manila.
1324 **366** 15s. mult (postage) . . . 15 15
1325 50s. multicoloured . . . 20 20
1326 60s. multicoloured (air) 35 35

367 Interpol Emblem **368** Scouting Activities

1973. 50th Anniv of International Criminal Police Organization (Interpol).
1327 **367** 15s. multicoloured . . . 15 10
1328 65s. multicoloured . . . 45 20

1973. Golden Jubilee of Philippine Boy Scouts. Perf or imperf.
1329 **368** 15s. bistre and green . . 15 15
1330 – 65s. blue and yellow . . 45 30
DESIGN: 65s. Scouts reading brochure.

369 Bank Emblem, Urban and Agricultural Landscapes

1974. 25th Anniv of Central Bank of the Philippines. Multicoloured.
1331 15s. Type **369** 15 10
1332 60s. Bank building, 1949 . . 35 20
1333 1p.50 Bank complex, 1974 95 60

370 "Maria Clara" Costume **373** Map of South-East Asia

1974. Centenary of U.P.U. Philippine Costumes. Multicoloured.
1334 15s. Type **370** 15 15
1335 60s. "Balintawak" 35 20
1336 80s. "Malong" 60 30

1974. Philatelic Week (1973). No. 1303 surch **1973 PHILATELIC WEEK 15s.**
1337 **359** 15s. on 10s. multicoloured 15 10

1974. 25th Anniv of Philippine "Lionism". Nos. 1297 and 1180 surch **PHILIPPINE LIONISM 1949-1974 15s** and Lions emblem.
1338 **356** 15s. on 10s. multicoloured 15 10
1339 – 45s. on 40s. red 20 20

1974. Asian Paediatrics Congress, Manila. Perf or imperf.
1340 **373** 30s. red and blue 20 15
1341 1p. red and green . . . 60 35

374 Gen. Valdes and Hospital

1974. Obligatory Tax. T.B. Relief Fund. Perf or imperf.
1342 **374** 15s.+5s. green and red 15 15
1343 1p.10+5s. blue and red 35 30

1974. Nos. 974, 1024 and 1026 surch.
1344 **246** 5s. on 3s. green 15 10
1345 **263** 5s. on 6s. multicoloured 15 10
1346 **264** 5s. on 6s. multicoloured 15 10

378 W.P.Y. Emblem

1974. World Population Year. Perf or imperf.
1347 **378** 5s. black and orange . . 15 15
1348 2p. blue and green . . . 1·10 60

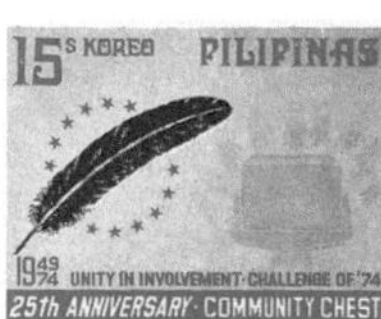
379 Red Feather Emblem

1974. 25th Anniv of Community Chest Movement in the Philippines. Perf or imperf.
1349 **379** 15s. red and blue 15 15
1350 40s. red and green . . . 20 15
1351 45s. red and brown . . . 35 15

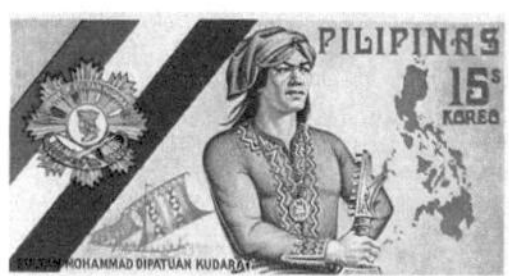
381 Sultan Mohammad Kudarat, Map, Malayan Prau and Order

1975. Sultan Kudarat of Mindanao Commem.
1352 **381** 15s. multicoloured . . . 15 10

382 Association Emblem **383** Rafael Palma

1975. 25th Anniv of Philippine Mental Health Association. Perf or imperf.
1353 **382** 45s. green and orange . . 20 15
1354 1p. green and purple . . 45 30

1975. Birth Centenary of Rafael Palma (educationalist and statesman). Perf or imperf (15s.), perf (30s.).
1355 **383** 15s. green 20 15
1436 30s. brown 15 10

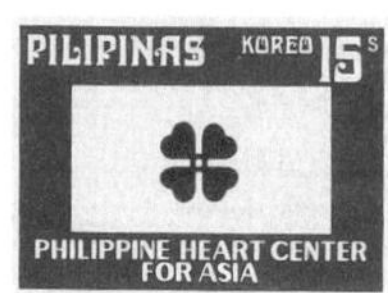
384 Heart Centre Emblem

1975. Inauguration of Philippine Heart Centre for Asia, Quezon City. Perf or imperf.
1356 **384** 15s. red and blue 15 15
1357 50s. red and green . . . 20 20

385 Cadet in Full Dress, and Academy Building

1975. 70th Anniv of Philippine Military Academy.
1358 **385** 15s. multicoloured . . . 15 15
1359 45s. multicoloured . . . 45 20

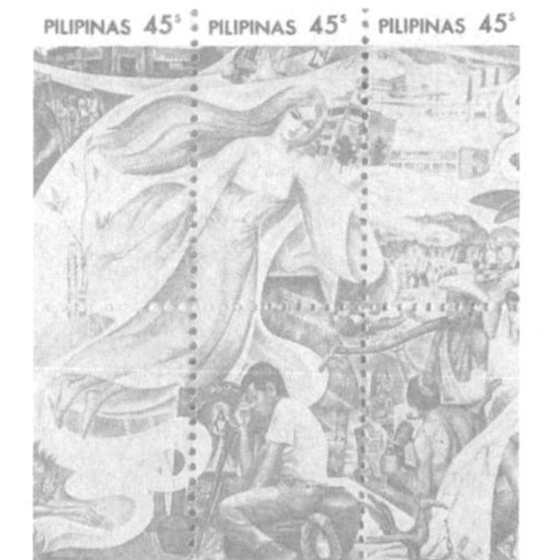
387/9, 392/4 "Helping the Disabled"

1975. 25th Anniv (1974) of Philippines Orthopaedic Association. Perf or imperf.
1360 – 45s. green (inscr at left and top) 20 15
1361 **387** 45s. green 20 15
1362 **388** 45s. green 20 15
1363 **389** 45s. green 20 15
1364 – 45s. green (inscr at top and right) 20 15
1365 – 45s. green (inscr at left and bottom) 20 15
1366 **392** 45s. green 20 15
1367 **393** 45s. green 20 15
1368 **394** 45s. green 20 15
1369 – 45s. green (inscr at bottom and right) . . 20 15
DESIGNS—23 × 30 mm: Nos. 1360, 1364/5, 1369, Details of corners of the mural.
Nos. 1360/9 were issued together, se-tenant, forming a composite design.

1975. Nos. 1153 and 1342/3 surch.
1370 **374** 5s. on 15s.+5s. green and red 10 10
1371 **308** 60s. on 70s.+5s. multicoloured 35 20
1372 **374** 1p. on 1p.10+5s. blue and red 45 30

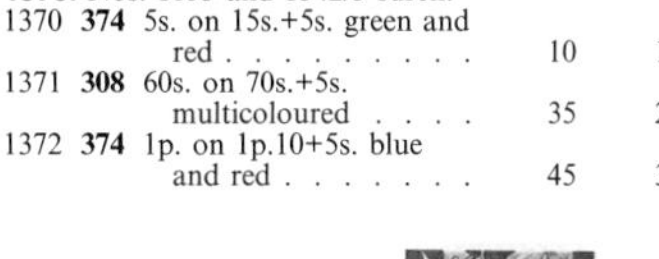

397 Planting Sapling **398** Jade Vine

1975. Forest Conservation. Multicoloured.
1373 45s. Type **397** 20 15
1374 45s. Sapling and tree-trunks 20 15

1975.
1375 **398** 15s. multicoloured . . . 15 10

399 Imelda Marcos and I.W.Y. Emblem **400** Commission Badge

1975. International Women's Year. Perf or imperf.
1376 **399** 15s. black, blue & dp blue 15 15
1377 80s. black, blue and pink 45 35

1975. 75th Anniv of Civil Service Commission. Perf or imperf.
1378 **400** 15s. multicoloured . . . 15 15
1379 50s. multicoloured . . . 30 20

401 Angat River Barrage

1975. 25th Anniv of International Irrigation and Drainage Commission. Perf or imperf.
1380 **401** 40s. blue and orange . . 20 15
1381 1p.50 blue and mauve 60 45

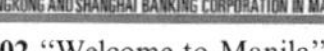

402 "Welcome to Manila" **403** N. Romualdez (legislator and writer)

1975. Centenary of Hong Kong and Shanghai Banking Corporation's Service in the Philippines.
1382 **402** 1p.50 multicoloured . . 1·30 35

1975. Birth Centenaries. Perf or imperf.
1383 **403** 60s. lilac 20 15
1384 – 90s. mauve 35 15
DESIGN: 90s. General G. del Pilar.

405 Boeing 747-100 Airliner and Martin M-130 Flying Boat

1975. 40th Anniv of First Trans-Pacific China Clipper Airmail Flight. San Francisco–Manila.
1385 **405** 60s. multicoloured . . . 45 20
1386 1p.50 multicoloured . . 1·20 60

1975. Airmail Exn. Nos. 1314 and 1318 optd **AIRMAIL EXHIBITION NOV 22-DEC 9.**
1387 **364** 60s. brown 20 20
1388 – 1p.50 brown 65 65

407 APO Emblem **408** E. Jacinto

1975. 25th Anniv of APO Philatelic Society. Perf or imperf.
1389 **407** 5s. multicoloured 15 15
1390 1p. multicoloured . . . 50 35

1975. Birth Centenary of Emilio Jacinto (military leader). Perf or imperf.
1391 **408** 65s. mauve 20 15

409 San Agustin Church

410 "Conducting" Hands

1975. Holy Year. Churches. Perf or imperf.
1392 **409** 20s. blue 15 15
1393 – 30s. black and yellow . . 15 15
1394 – 45s. red, pink and black 20 15
1395 – 60s. bistre, yellow & black 30 20
DESIGNS—HORIZ: 30s. Morong Church; 45s. Taal Basilica. VERT: 60s. San Sebastian Church.

1976. 50th Anniv of Manila Symphony Orchestra.
1396 **410** 5s. multicoloured 10 10
1397 50s. multicoloured . . . 35 30

411 Douglas DC-3 and DC-10

1976. 30th Anniv of Philippines Airlines (PAL).
1398 **411** 60s. multicoloured . . . 30 15
1399 1p.50 multicoloured . . 1·20 65

412 Felipe Agoncillo (statesman)

413 University Building

1976. Felipe Agoncillo Commemoration.
1400 **412** 1p.60 black 95 20

1976. 75th Anniv of National University.
1401 **413** 45s. multicoloured . . . 20 15
1402 60s. multicoloured . . . 35 20

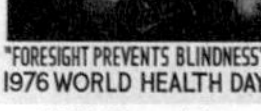

414 "Foresight Prevents Blindness"

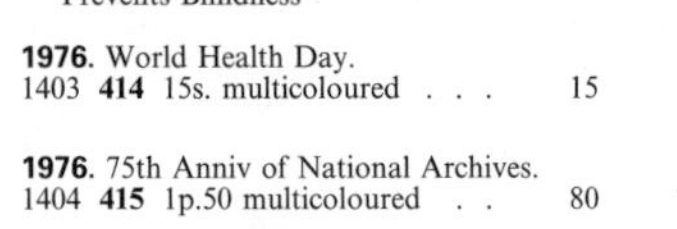

415 Emblem on Book

1976. World Health Day.
1403 **414** 15s. multicoloured . . . 15 10

1976. 75th Anniv of National Archives.
1404 **415** 1p.50 multicoloured . . 80 75

416 College Emblem and University Tower

1976. 50th Anniv of Colleges of Education and Science, Saint Thomas's University.
1405 **416** 15s. multicoloured . . . 15 10
1406 50s. multicoloured . . . 20 20

417 College Building

1976. 50th Anniv of Maryknoll College.
1407 **417** 15s. multicoloured . . . 15 10
1408 1p.50 multicoloured . . 80 60

1976. Olympic Games, Montreal. Surch **15s Montreal 1976 21st OLYMPICS, CANADA** and emblem.
1409 **348** 15s. on 10s. mult 15 10

419 Constabulary Headquarters, Manila

1976. 75th Anniv of Philippine Constabulary. Perf or imperf.
1410 **419** 15s. multicoloured . . . 15 15
1411 60s. multicoloured . . . 35 20

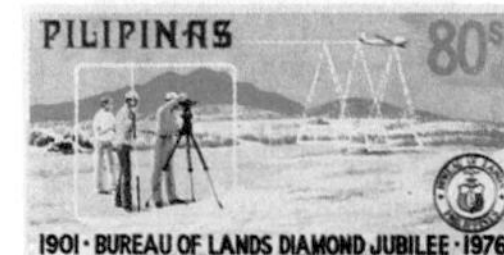

420 Land and Aerial Surveying

1976. 75th Anniv of Lands Bureau.
1412 **420** 80s. multicoloured . . . 25 25

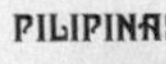

422 Badges of Banking Organizations

1976. International Monetary Fund and World Bank Joint Board of Governors Annual Meeting, Manila.
1414 **422** 60s. multicoloured . . . 20 20
1415 1p.50 multicoloured . . 80 60

423 Virgin of Antipolo

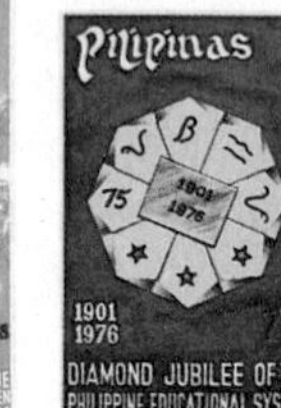

426 Facets of Education

425 "Going to Church"

1976. 350th Anniv of "Virgin of Antipolo".
1416 **423** 30s. multicoloured . . . 15 15
1417 90s. multicoloured . . . 35 35

1976. Philatelic Week. Surch **1976 PHILATELIC WEEK 30s**.
1418 **355** 30s. on 10s. mult 15 15

1976. Christmas.
1419 **425** 15s. multicoloured . . . 10 10
1420 30s. multicoloured . . . 20 15

1976. 75th Anniv of Philippine Educational System.
1421 **426** 30s. multicoloured . . . 15 15
1422 75s. multicoloured . . . 45 20

1977. Surch.
1423 1p.20 on 1p.10 blue (No. 1316) 60 35
1424 3p. on 5p. blue (No. 1320) 1·30 1·10

428 Jose Rizal

429 Flags, Map and Emblem

1977. Famous Filipinos. Multicoloured.
1425 30s. Type **428** 15 10
1426 2p.30 Dr. Galicano Apacible 95 65

1977. 15th Anniv of Asian–Oceanic Postal Union.
1427 **429** 50s. multicoloured . . . 15 10
1428 1p.50 multicoloured . . 60 45

430 Worker and Cogwheels

431 Commission Emblem

1977. 10th Anniv of Asian Development Bank.
1429 **430** 90s. multicoloured . . . 45 35
1430 2p.30 multicoloured . . 95 80

1977. National Rural Credit Commission.
1431 **431** 30s. multicoloured . . . 15 10

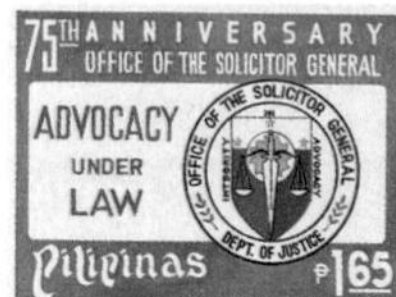

433 Solicitor-General's Emblem

1977. 75th Anniv of Office of Solicitor-General.
1433 **433** 1p.65 multicoloured . . 45 20

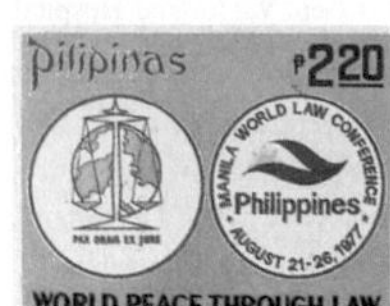

434 Conference Emblem

1977. World Law Conference, Manila.
1434 **434** 2p.20 multicoloured . . 75 30

435 A.S.E.A.N. Emblem

1977. 10th Anniv of Association of South East Asian Nationals (A.S.E.A.N.).
1435 **435** 1p.50 multicoloured . . 65 35

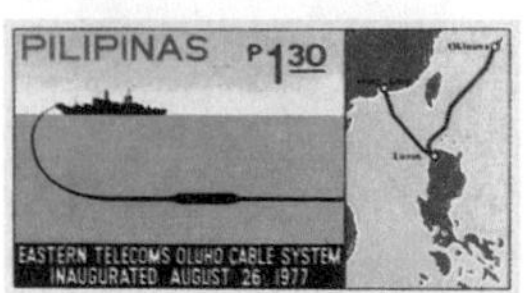

436 Cable Ship "Mercury" and Map

1977. Inauguration of OLUHO Cable (Okinawa–Luzon–Hong Kong).
1437 **436** 1p.30 multicoloured . . 60 35

437 President Marcos

1977. 60th Birthday of President Marcos.
1438 **437** 30s. multicoloured . . . 15 10
1439 2p.30 multicoloured . . 1·00 65

438 People raising Flag

439 Bishop Gregorio Aglipay (founder)

1977. 5th Anniv of "New Society".
1440 **438** 30s. multicoloured . . . 15 10
1441 2p.30 multicoloured . . 1·00 65

1977. 75th Anniv of Aglipayan Church.
1442 **439** 30s. multicoloured . . . 15 10
1443 90s. multicoloured . . . 35 20

441 Fokker F.7 Trimotor "General New" and World Map

1977. 50th Anniv of 1st Pan-Am International Air Service.
1445 **441** 2p.30 multicoloured . . 95 60

442 Eight-pointed Star and Children

445 University Badge

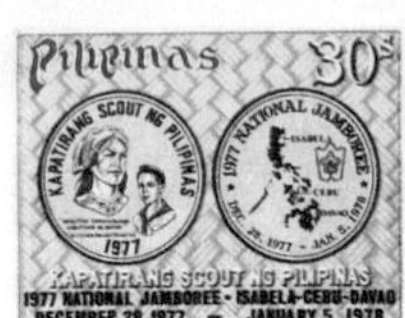

444 Scouts and Map of Philippines

1977. Christmas.
1446 **442** 30s. multicoloured . . . 15 10
1447 45s. multicoloured . . . 20 15

1977. Philatelic Week. Surch **90s 1977 PHILATELIC WEEK**.
1448 **407** 90s. on 1p. multicoloured 35 20

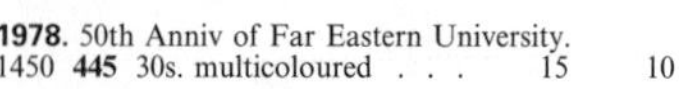

1977. National Scout Jamboree.
1449 **444** 30s. multicoloured . . . 50 15

1978. 50th Anniv of Far Eastern University.
1450 **445** 30s. multicoloured . . . 15 10

446 Sipa Player

1978. "Sipa" (Filipino ball game).
1451 **446** 5s. multicoloured 10 10
1452 – 10s. multicoloured . . . 10 10
1453 – 40s. multicoloured . . . 30 15
1454 – 75s. multicoloured . . . 45 20
DESIGNS: Nos. 1452/4, Different players.
Nos. 1451/4 were issued together, se-tenant, forming a composite design.

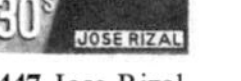

447 Jose Rizal **448** Arms of Meycauayan

1978.
1455 **447** 30s. blue 15 10
1456 – 30s. mauve 15 10
1457 – 90s. green 20 10
1458 – 1p.20 red 35 15
DESIGNS: No. 1456, Rajah Kalantiaw (Panay chief); 1457, Lope K. Santos ("Father of Filipino grammar"); 1458, Gregoria de Jesus (patriot).

1978. 400th Anniv of Meycauayan.
1459 **448** 1p.05 multicoloured . . 35 20

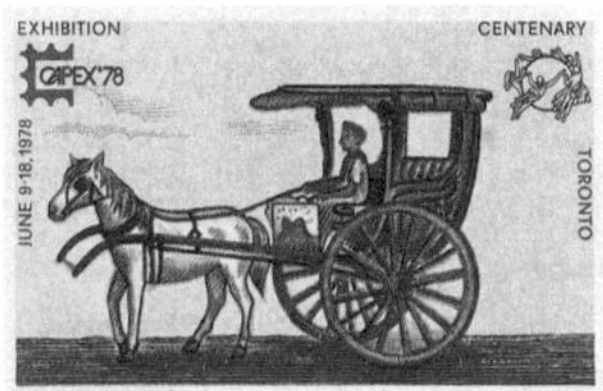

449 Horse-drawn Mail Cart

1978. "CAPEX 78" International Stamp Exhibition, Toronto. Multicoloured.
1460 2p.50 Type **449** . . . . . 1·10 75
1461 5p. Filipino vinta (sailing canoe) . . . . 3·00 1·90

450 Andres Bonifacio Monument (Guillermo Tolentino)

1978. Andres Bonifacio Monument.
1463 **450** 30s. multicoloured . . . 15 10

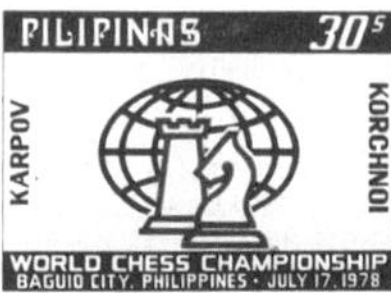

451 Knight, Rook and Globe

1978. World Chess Championship, Baguio City.
1464 **451** 30s. red and violet . . . 15 10
1465 2p. red and violet . . . 60 35

452 Miner

1978. 75th Anniv of Benguet Consolidated Mining Company.
1466 **452** 2p.30 multicoloured . . 1·20 45

453 Pres. Quezon **455** Pres. Osmena

454 Law Association and Conference Emblems

1978. Birth Centenary of Manuel L. Quezon (former President).
1467 **453** 30s. multicoloured . . . 15 10
1468 1p. multicoloured . . . 35 15

1978. 58th Int Law Association Conf, Manila.
1469 **454** 2p.30 multicoloured . . 80 60

1978. Birth Centenary of Sergio Osmena (former President).
1470 **455** 30s. multicoloured . . . 15 10
1471 1p. multicoloured . . . 35 20

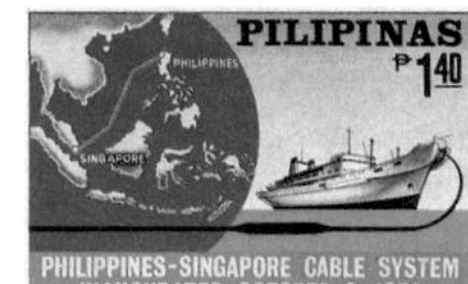

456 Map of Cable Route and Cable Ship "Mercury"

1978. Inauguration of Philippines–Singapore Submarine Cable.
1472 **456** 1p.40 multicoloured . . 60 20

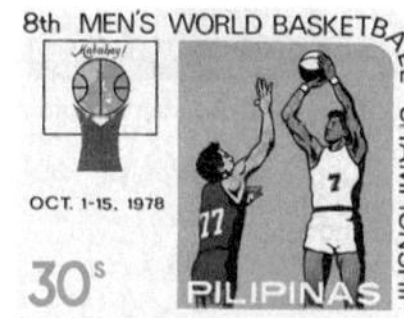

457 Basketball

1978. 8th Men's World Basketball Championship, Manila.
1473 **457** 30s. multicoloured . . . 15 10
1474 2p.30 multicoloured . . 80 60

458 Dr. Catalino Gavino and Hospital

1978. 400th Anniv of San Lazaro Hospital.
1475 **458** 50s. multicoloured . . . 20 10
1476 90s. multicoloured . . . 35 20

459 Nurse vaccinating Child **461** Man on Telephone, Map and Satellite

1978. Global Eradication of Smallpox.
1477 **459** 30s. multicoloured . . . 10 10
1478 1p.50 multicoloured . . 65 35

1978. Philatelic Week. No. 1391 surch **1978 PHILATELIC WEEK 60s.**
1479 **408** 60s. on 65s. mauve . . . 20 10

1978. 50th Anniv of Philippine Long Distance Telephone Company. Multicoloured.
1480 30s. Type **461** 10 10
1481 2p. Woman on telephone and globe 75 50
Nos. 1480/1 were issued together, se-tenant, forming a composite design.

462 Family travelling in Ox-drawn Cart

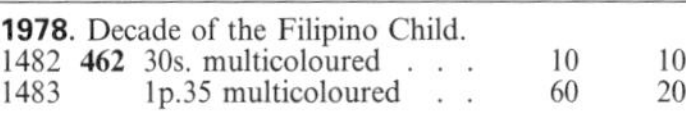

1978. Decade of the Filipino Child.
1482 **462** 30s. multicoloured . . . 10 10
1483 1p.35 multicoloured . . 60 20

463 Spanish Colonial Church and Arms

1978. 400th Anniv of Agoo Town.
1484 **463** 30s. multicoloured . . . 10 15
1485 45s. multicoloured . . . 15 20

464 Church and Arms

1978. 400th Anniv of Balayan Town.
1486 **464** 30s. multicoloured . . . 15 10
1487 90s. multicoloured . . . 35 15

465 Dr. Sison **466** Family and Houses

1978. Dr. Honoria Acosta Sison (first Filipino woman physician) Commemoration.
1488 **465** 30s. multicoloured . . . 15 10

1978. 30th Anniv of Declaration of Human Rights.
1489 **466** 30s. multicoloured . . . 10 10
1490 3p. multicoloured . . . 1·30 75

467 Melon butterflyfish

1978. Fishes. Multicoloured.
1491 30s. Type **467** 15 10
1492 1p.20 Black triggerfish . . . 45 15
1493 2p.20 Picasso triggerfish . . 80 35
1494 2p.30 Copper-banded butterflyfish 80 45
1495 5p. Atoll butterflyfish ("Chaetodon mertensi") 1·80 1·00
1496 5p. Yellow-faced butterflyfish ("Euxiphipops xanthometapon") . . . . 1·80 1·00

468 Carlos P. Romulo

1979. 80th Anniv of Carlos P. Romulo (1st Asian President of U.N. General Assembly).
1497 **468** 30s. multicoloured . . . 10 10
1498 2p. multicoloured . . . 95 45

469 Cogwheel (Rotary Emblem) **470** Rosa Sevilla de Alvero

1979. 60th Anniv of Manila Rotary Club.
1499 **469** 30s. multicoloured . . . 10 10
1500 2p.30 multicoloured . . 70 25

1979. Birth Centenary of Rosa Sevilla de Alvero (writer and educator).
1501 **470** 30s. mauve 10 10

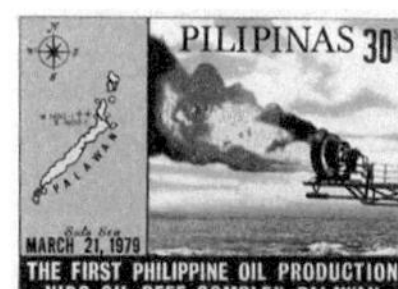

471 Burning-off Gas and Map

1979. 1st Oil Production. Nido Complex, Palawan.
1502 **471** 30s. multicoloured . . . 15 10
1503 45s. multicoloured . . . 20 10

472 Merrill's Fruit Dove

1979. Birds. Multicoloured.
1504 30s. Type **472** 30 15
1505 1p.20 Brown tit-babbler . . 50 45
1506 2p.20 Mindoro zone-tailed (inscr "Imperial") pigeon 95 45
1507 2p.30 Steere's pitta . . . . 1·00 50
1508 5p. Koch's pitta and red-breasted pitta . . . . . . 2·20 1·20
1509 5p. Great eared nightjar . . 2·20 1·20

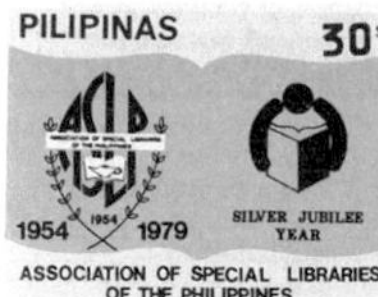

473 Association Emblem

1979. 25th Anniv of Association of Special Libraries of the Philippines.
1510 **473** 30s. green, black & yell 15 10
1511 75s. green, black & yell 30 10
1512 1p. green, black & orange 35 20

474 Conference Emblem

1979. 5th U.N. Conference on Trade and Development, Manila.
1513 **474** 1p.20 multicoloured . . 35 15
1514 2p.30 multicoloured . . 95 35

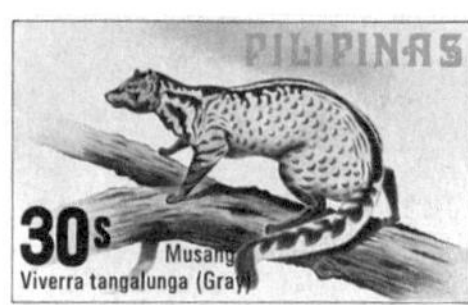

475 Malay Civet

1979. Animals. Multicoloured.
1515 30s. Type **475** 15 10
1516 1p.20 Crab-eating macaque 45 15
1517 2p.20 Javan pig 80 35
1518 2p.30 Leopard cat 80 45
1519 5p. Oriental small-clawed otter . . . . 1·80 1·00
1520 5p. Malayan pangolin . . . 1·80 1·00

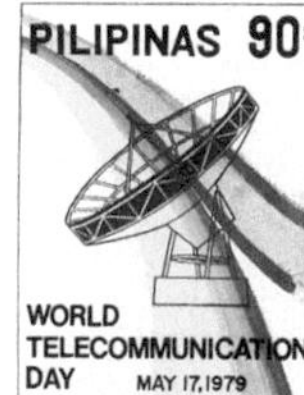

476 Dish Aerial

1979. World Telecommunications Day. Mult.
1521 90s. Type **476** 30 10
1522 1p.30 Hemispheres 45 20

477 Mussaenda "Dona Evangelina"

1979. Cultivated Mussaendas. Multicoloured.
1523 30s. Type **477** 15 10
1524 1p.20 "Dona Esperanza" 45 15
1525 2p.20 "Dona Hilaria" 80 35
1526 2p.30 "Dona Aurora" 80 45
1527 5p. "Gining Imelda" 1·80 1·00
1528 5p. "Dona Trining" 1·80 1·00

478 Manila Cathedral

1979. 400th Anniv of Archdiocese of Manila.
1529 **478** 30s. multicoloured 15 10
1530 75s. multicoloured 20 10
1531 90s. multicoloured 35 20

479 "Bagong Lakas" (patrol boat)

1979. Philippine Navy Foundation Day.
1532 **479** 30s. multicoloured 20 10
1533 45s. multicoloured 30 15

1979. Air. 1st Scout Philatelic Exhibition and 25th Anniv of 1st National Jamboree. Surch **1ST SCOUT PHILATELIC EXHIBITION JULY 4.14, 1979 QUEZON CITY AIRMAIL 90s**.
1534 **188** 90s. on 6c.+4c. red on yellow 30 30

481 Drug Addict breaking Manacles

1979. "Fight Drug Abuse" Campaign.
1536 **481** 30s. multicoloured 15 10
1537 90s. multicoloured 35 15
1538 1p.05 multicoloured 45 20

482 Afghan Hound

1979. Cats and Dogs. Multicoloured.
1539 30s. Type **482** 10 10
1540 90s. Tabby cats 35 15
1541 1p.20 Dobermann pinscher 45 20
1542 2p.20 Siamese cats 80 20
1543 2p.30 German shepherd dog 95 80
1544 5p. Chinchilla cats 1·80 95

483 Children flying Kites

1979. International Year of the Child. Paintings by Rod Dayao. Multicoloured.
1545 15s. Type **483** 10 10
1546 20s. Boys fighting with catapults 15 10
1547 25s. Girls dressing-up 15 15
1548 1p.20 Boy playing policeman 35 20

484 Hands holding Emblems

1979. 80th Anniv of Methodism in the Philippines.
1549 **484** 30s. multicoloured 15 10
1550 1p.35 multicoloured 45 15

485 Anniversary Medal and 1868 Coin

1979. 50th Anniv of Philippine Numismatic and Antiquarian Society.
1551 **485** 30s. multicoloured 15 10

486 Concorde over Manila and Paris

1979. 25th Anniv of Air France Service to the Philippines. Multicoloured.
1552 1p.05 Type **486** 50 20
1553 2p.20 Concorde over monument 1·30 60

1979. Philatelic Week. Surch **1979 PHILATELIC WEEK 90s**.
1554 **412** 90s. on 1p.60 black 35 15

488 "35" and I.A.T.A. Emblem

1979. 35th Annual General Meeting of International Air Transport Association, Manila.
1555 **488** 75s. multicoloured 30 15
1556 2p.30 multicoloured 95 65

489 Bureau of Local Government Emblem

490 Christmas Greetings

1979. Local Government Year.
1557 **489** 30s. multicoloured 15 15
1558 45s. multicoloured 20 65

1979. Christmas. Multicoloured.
1559 30s. Type **490** 15 10
1560 90s. Stars 45 30

491 Rheumatism Victim

1980. 4th Congress of Southeast Asia and Pacific Area League Against Rheumatism, Manila.
1561 **491** 30s. multicoloured 15 10
1562 90s. multicoloured 50 20

492 Birthplace and MacArthur Memorial Foundation

1980. Birth Centenary of General Douglas MacArthur (U.S. Army Chief of Staff). Mult.
1563 30s. Type **492** 15 10
1564 75s. General MacArthur 35 15
1565 2p.30 Hat, pipe and glasses 1·30 75

493 Columbus and Emblem

495 Tirona, Benitez and University

494 Soldiers and Academy Emblem

1980. 75th Anniv of Knights of Columbus Organization in Philippines.
1567 **493** 30s. multicoloured 15 10
1568 1p.35 multicoloured 80 45

1980. 75th Anniv of Philippine Military Academy.
1569 **494** 30s. multicoloured 15 10
1570 1p.20 multicoloured 75 30

1980. 60th Anniv of Philippine Women's University.
1571 **495** 30s. multicoloured 15 10
1572 1p.05 multicoloured 65 30

496 Boats and Burning City

1980. 75th Anniv of Rotary International. Details of painting by Carlos Francisco. Multicoloured.
1573 30s. Type **496** 15 10
1574 30s. Priest with cross, swordsmen and soldier 15 10
1575 30s. "K K K" flag and group around table 15 10
1576 30s. Man in midst of spearmen and civilian scenes 15 10
1577 30s. Reading the Constitution, soliders and U.S. and Philippine flags 15 10
1578 2p.30 Type **496** 1·30 60
1579 2p.30 As No. 1574 1·30 60
1580 2p.30 As No. 1575 1·30 60
1581 2p.30 As No. 1576 1·30 60
1582 2p.30 As No. 1577 1·30 60

Nos. 1573/7 and 1578/82 were issued together in se-tenant strips of five, each strip forming a composite design.

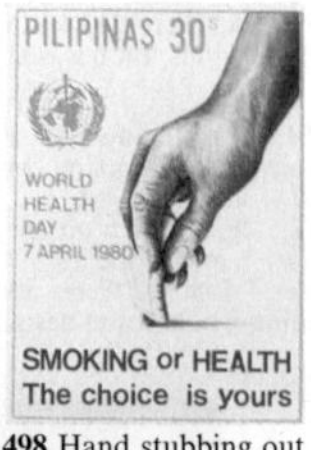

497 Mosque and Koran

498 Hand stubbing out Cigarette

1980. 600th Anniv of Islam in the Philippines.
1583 **497** 30s. multicoloured 15 10
1584 1p.30 multicoloured 75 30

1980. World Health Day. Anti-smoking Campaign.
1585 **498** 30s. multicoloured 15 10
1586 75s. multicoloured 45 20

499 Scouting Activities and Badge

1980. 40th Anniv of Girl Scouting in the Philippines.
1587 **499** 30s. multicoloured 15 10
1588 2p. multicoloured 65 30

500 Jeepney

502 Association Emblem

1980. Philippine Jeepneys (decorated jeeps). Multicoloured.
1589 30s. Type **500** 15 10
1590 1p.20 Side view of Jeepney 65 30

1980. 82nd Anniv of Independence. Surch **PHILIPPINE INDEPENDENCE 82ND ANNIVERSARY 1898 1980**.
1591 **412** 1p.35 on 1p.60 black 80 45
1592 1p.50 on 1p.80 green (No. 1319) 1·00 50

1980. 7th General Conference of International Association of Universities, Manila.
1593 **502** 30s. multicoloured 15 10
1594 2p.30 multicoloured 1·30 1·30

503 Map and Emblems

504 Filipinos and Emblem

1980. 46th Congress of International Federation of Library Associations and Institutions, Manila.
1595 **503** 30s. green and black 20 10
1596 75s. blue and black 45 20
1597 2p.30 red and black 1·50 80

1980. 5th Anniv of Kabataang Barangay (national council charged with building the "New Society").
1598 **504** 30s. multicoloured 20 10
1599 40s. multicoloured 20 15
1600 1p. multicoloured 65 30

1980. Nos. 1433, 1501, 1536, 1557 and 1559 surch.
1601 **470** 40s. on 30s. mauve 20 10
1602 **481** 40s. on 30s. multicoloured 20 10
1603 **489** 40s. on 30s. multicoloured 20 10
1604 **490** 40s. on 30s. multicoloured 20 10
1605 **433** 2p. on 1p.65 mult 1·30 65

506 Sunset, Filipino Vinta and Conference Emblem

1980. World Tourism Conference, Manila.
1606 **506** 30s. multicoloured 20 15
1607 2p.30 multicoloured 1·40 80

507 Magnifying Glass and Stamps

508 U.N. Headquarters and Philippines Flag

1980. Postage Stamp Day.
1608 **507** 40s. multicoloured . . . 20 15
1609 1p. multicoloured . . . 65 30
1610 2p. multicoloured . . . 1·30 65

1980. 35th Anniv of U.N.O.
1611 40s. Type **508** 30 15
1612 3p.20 U.N. Headquarters and U.N. and Philippines flags . . . . 1·90 1·30

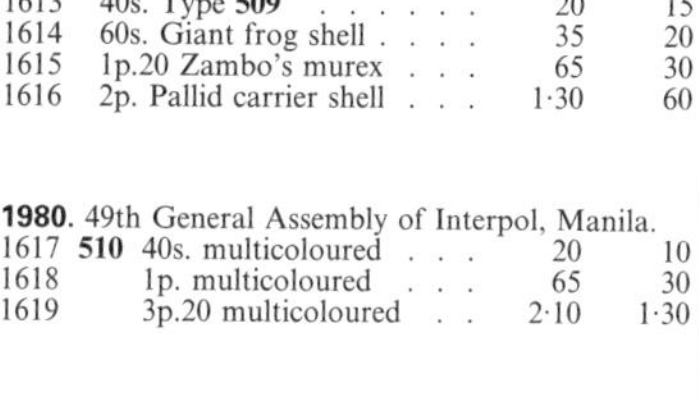

509 Alabaster Murex **510** Interpol Emblem on Globe

1980. Shells. Multicoloured.
1613 40s. Type **509** 20 15
1614 60s. Giant frog shell 35 20
1615 1p.20 Zambo's murex 65 30
1616 2p. Pallid carrier shell . . . 1·30 60

1980. 49th General Assembly of Interpol, Manila.
1617 **510** 40s. multicoloured . . . 20 10
1618 1p. multicoloured . . . 65 30
1619 3p.20 multicoloured . . 2·10 1·30

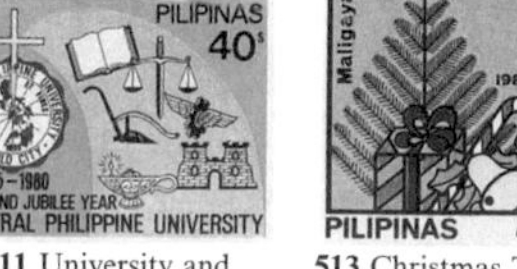

511 University and Faculty Emblems **513** Christmas Tree and Presents

1980. 75th Anniv of Central Philippine University. Multicoloured, background colour given.
1620 **511** 40s. blue 30 10
1621 3p.20 green . . . . . . 1·20 1·30

1980. Philatelic Week. No. 1377 surch **1980 PHILATELIC WEEK P1.20.**
1622 **399** 1p.20 on 80s. black, blue and pink 60 30

1980. Christmas.
1623 **513** 40s. multicoloured . . . 20 10

1981. Various stamps surch.
1624 **244** 10s. on 6s.+5s. blue . . 15 10
1625 **462** 10s. on 30s. mult 10 10
1626 **408** 40s. on 65s. mauve . . . 20 10
1627 **458** 40s. on 90s. mult 20 10
1628 **481** 40s. on 90s. mult 20 10
1629 – 40s. on 90s. mult (No. 1560) 20 10
1630 **448** 40s. on 1p.05 mult . . . 20 10
1631 **462** 40s. on 1p.35 mult . . . 20 15
1632 **399** 85s. on 80s. black, blue and pink 50 30
1633 **408** 1p. on 65s. mauve . . . 75 30
1634 **401** 1p. on 1p.50 blue and mauve 75 30
1635 **422** 1p. on 1p.50 mult . . . 60 20
1636 – 1p.20 on 1p.50 brown (No. 1318) 75 35
1637 **433** 1p.20 on 1p.65 mult . . 75 35
1638 – 1p.20 on 1p.80 green (No. 1319) 75 35
1639 **401** 2p. on 1p.50 blue and mauve . . . . 1·30 60
1640 **434** 3p.20 on 2p.20 mult . . 1·90 1·00

1981. 30th Anniv of APO Philatelic Society. Surch **NOV. 30, 1980 APO PHILATELIC SOCIETY PEARL JUBILEE 40s.**
1641 **455** 40s. on 30s. mult 20 10

516 Von Stephan and U.P.U. Emblem

1981. 150th Birth Anniv of Heinrich von Stephan (founder of U.P.U.).
1642 **516** 3p.20 multicoloured . . 1·90 95

1981. Girl Scouts Camp. No. 1589 surch **GSP RJASIA-PACIFIC REGIONAL CAMP PHILIPPINES DECEMBER 23, 1980 40s.**
1643 **500** 40s. on 30s. mult 20 10

518 Pope John Paul II **519** Parliamentary Debate

1981. Papal Visit. Multicoloured.
1644 90s. Type **518** 50 20
1645 1p.20 Pope and cardinals . . 65 30
1646 2p.30 Pope blessing crowd (horiz) . . . . 1·30 65
1647 3p. Pope and Manila Cathedral (horiz) . . . . 1·60 80

1981. Interparliamentary Union Meeting, Manila.
1649 **519** 2p. multicoloured . . . 1·40 60
1650 3p.20 multicoloured . . 1·90 1·00

520 Monument **521** President Aguinaldo's Car

1981. Jose Rizal Monument, Luneta Park.
1651 **520** 40s. black, yellow & brn 20 10

1981. 50th Anniv of Philippine Motor Association. Multicoloured.
1652 40s. Type **521** 20 10
1653 40s. 1930 model car 20 10
1654 40s. 1937 model car 20 10
1655 40s. 1937 model car (different) 20 10

522 Bubble Coral

1981. Corals. Multicoloured.
1656 40s. Type **522** 20 10
1657 40s. Branching corals . . . 20 10
1658 40s. Brain coral 20 10
1659 40s. Table coral 20 10

523 President Marcos and Flag

1981. Inauguration of President Marcos. Perf or imperf.
1660 **523** 40s. multicoloured . . . 20 10

524 St. Ignatius de Loyola (founder)

1981. 400th Anniv of Jesuits in the Philippines. Mult.
1662 40s. Type **524** 20 10
1663 40s. Dr. Jose P. Rizal and Intramuros Ateneo . . . 20 10
1664 40s. Father Frederico Faura (director) and Manila Observatory 20 10
1665 40s. Father Saturnino Urios (missionary) and map of Mindanao 20 10

525 F. R. Castro **526** Pres. Ramon Magsaysay

1981. Chief Justice Fred Ruiz Castro.
1667 **525** 40s. multicoloured . . . 20 10

1981.
1668 – 1p. brown and black . . 65 30
1669 **526** 1p.20 brown and black 75 35
1670 – 2p. purple and black . . 1·40 60

DESIGNS: 1p. General Gregorio del Pilar; 2p. Ambrosio R. Bautista.

See also Nos. 1699/1704, 1807 etc and 2031/3.

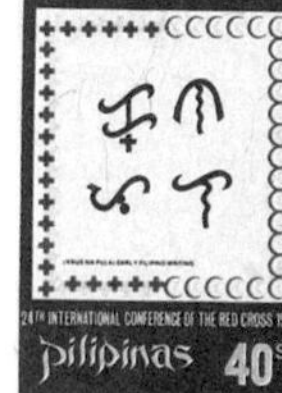

527 Man in Wheelchair **528** Early Filipino Writing

1981. International Year of Disabled Persons.
1671 **527** 40s. multicoloured . . . 30 15
1672 3p.20 multicoloured . . 1·90 1·00

1981. 24th International Red Cross Conference.
1673 **528** 40s. black, red and bistre 15 10
1674 2p. black and red . . . 1·30 50
1675 3p.20 black, red and mauve . . . . 1·90 90

529 Isabel II Gate, Manila

1981.
1676 **529** 40s. black 20 10

530 Concert in Park

1981. Opening of Concert at Park 200.
1677 **530** 40s. multicoloured . . . 20 10

1981. Philatelic Week. No. 1435 surch **P120 1981 PHILATELIC WEEK.**
1678 **435** 1p.20 on 1p.50 mult . . 75 35

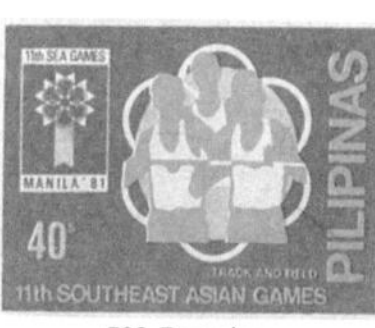

532 Running

1981. 11th South-east Asian Games, Manila.
1679 **532** 40s. yellow, green & brn 20 10
1680 – 1p. multicoloured . . . 75 30
1681 – 2p. multicoloured . . . 1·50 60
1682 – 2p.30 multicoloured . . 1·50 65
1683 – 2p.80 multicoloured . . 1·80 80
1684 – 3p.20 violet and blue . . 1·90 1·00

DESIGNS: 1p. Cycling; 2p. President Marcos and Juan Antonio Samaranch (president of International Olympic Committee); 2p.30, Football; 2p.80, Shooting; 3p.20, Bowling.

533 Manila Film Centre

1982. Manila International Film Festival. Mult.
1685 40s. Type **533** 30 10
1686 2p. Front view of trophy . . 1·50 60
1687 3p.20 Side view of trophy 1·90 1·00

534 Carriedo Fountain

1982. Centenary of Manila Metropolitan Waterworks and Sewerage System.
1688 **534** 40s. blue 20 10
1689 1p.20 brown 75 35

535 Lord Baden-Powell (founder) **537** President Marcos presenting Sword of Honour

536 Embroidered Banner

1982. 75th Anniv of Boy Scout Movement. Mult.
1690 40s. Type **535** 20 10
1691 2p. Scout . . . . 1·50 60

1982. 25th Anniv of Children's Museum and Library Inc. Multicoloured.
1692 40s. Type **536** 20 10
1693 1p.20 Children playing . . . 75 35

1982. Military Academy.
1694 **537** 40s. multicoloured . . . 20 15
1695 1p. multicoloured . . . 75 30

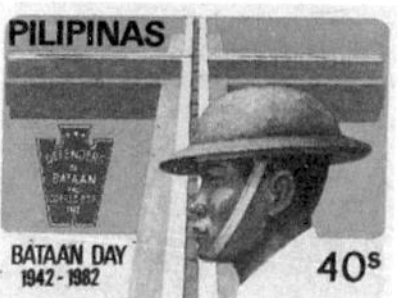

538 Soldier and Memorial

1982. Bataan Day. Multicoloured.
1696 40s. Type **538** 20 10
1697 2p. Doves and rifle . . . . 1·50 60

1982. Portraits. As T **526**.
1699 40s. blue 20 10
1700 1p. red 75 30
1701 1p.20 brown 75 35
1702 2p. mauve . . . . 1·30 60
1703 2p.30 purple . . . . 1·50 60
1704 3p.20 blue . . . . 1·90 1·00

DESIGNS: 40s. Isabelo de los Reyes (founder of first workers' union); 1p. Aurora Aragon Quezon (social worker and former First Lady); 1p.20, Francisco Dagohoy; 2p. Juan Sumulong (politician); 2p.30, Professor Nicanor Abelardo (composer); 3p.20, General Vicente Lim.

For these designs in other values, see Nos. 1811/15.

539 Worker with Tower Award

1982. Tower Awards (for best "Blue Collar" Workers). Multicoloured.
1705 40s. Type **539** (inscr "MANGGAGAWA") 20 10
1705d 40s. Type **539** (inscr "MANGGAGAWA") . . 60 10
1706 1p.20 Cogwheel and tower award (inscr "MANGGAGAWA") 75 35
1706b 1p.20 As No. 1706 but inscr "Mangagawa" . . 1·25 20

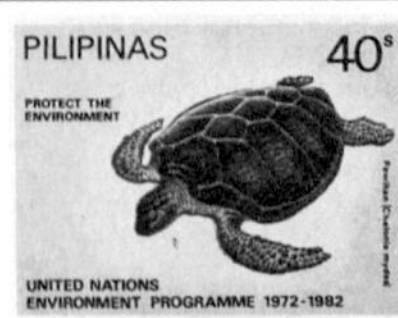

541 Green Turtle

1982. 10th Anniv of United Nations Environment Programme. Multicoloured.
1707 40s. Type **541** 30 15
1708 3p.20 Philippine eagle . . . 2·75 1·00

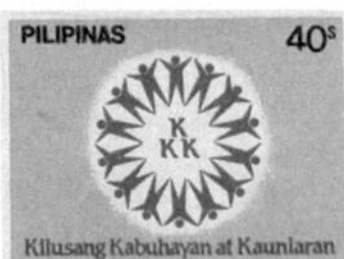

542 K.K.K. Emblem

1982. Inauguration of Kilusang Kabuhayan at Kaunlaran (national livelihood movement).
1709 **542** 40s. green, light green and black 20 10
1816 60s. green, light green and black 15 15
1817 60s. green, red and black 15 15

543 Chemistry Apparatus and Emblem

1982. 50th Anniv of Adamson University.
1710 **543** 40s. multicoloured . . . 20 10
1711 1p.20 multicoloured . . 75 35

544 Dr. Fernando G. Calderon and Emblems

1982. 75th Anniv of College of Medicine, University of the Philippines.
1712 **544** 40s. multicoloured . . . 30 15
1713 3p.20 multicoloured . . 1·90 1·00

545 President Marcos **546** Hands supporting Family

1982. 65th Birthday of President Ferdinand Marcos.
1714 **545** 40s. multicoloured . . . 20 10
1715 3p.20 multicoloured . . 1·90 1·00

1982. 25th Anniv of Social Security System.
1717 **546** 40s. black, orange & blue 20 10
1718 1p.20 black, orange and green 75 35

547 Emblem and Flags forming Ear of Wheat

1982. 15th Anniv of Association of South East Asian Nations.
1719 **547** 40s. multicoloured . . . 20 10

548 St. Theresa of Avila

1982. 400th Death Anniv of St. Theresa of Avila. Multicoloured.
1720 40s. Type **548** 20 10
1721 1p.20 St. Theresa and map of Europe, Africa and Asia 75 35
1722 2p. As 1p.20 . . . . 1·50 60

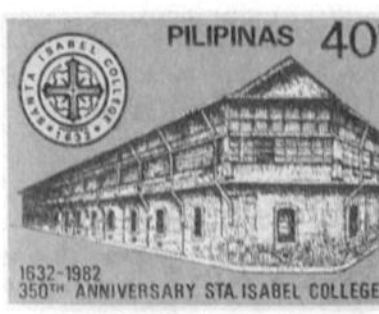

549 St. Isabel College

1982. 350th Anniv of St. Isabel College.
1723 **549** 40s. multicoloured . . . 20 15
1724 1p. multicoloured . . . 75 30

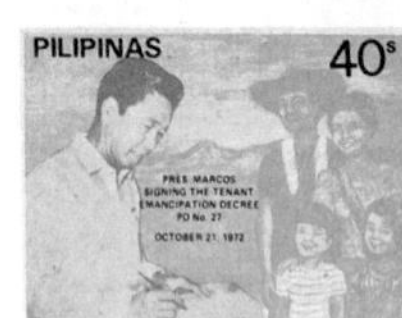

550 President Marcos signing Decree and Tenant Family

1982. 10th Anniv of Tenant Emancipation Decree.
1725a **550** 40s. green, brown and black (37 × 27 mm) 20 10
1726 40s. green, brown and black (32 × 22½ mm) 20 10

551 "Reading Tree"

1982. Literacy Campaign.
1727 **551** 40s. multicoloured . . . 20 10
1728 2p.30 multicoloured . . 1·50 60

552 Helmeted Heads

1982. 43rd World Congress of Skal Clubs, Manila.
1729 40s. Type **552** 20 10
1730 2p. Head in feathered head-dress . . . . 1·50 60

553 Dancers with Parasols

1982. 25th Anniv of Bayanihan Folk Arts Centre. Multicoloured.
1731 40s. Type **553** 20 10
1732 2p.80 Dancers (different) . . 1·80 80

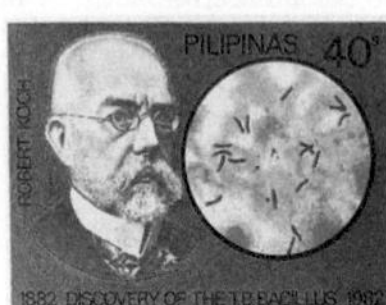

554 Dr. Robert Koch and Bacillus

1982. Cent of Discovery of Tubercule Bacillus.
1733 **554** 40s. red, blue and black 20 10
1734 2p.80 multicoloured . . 1·80 80

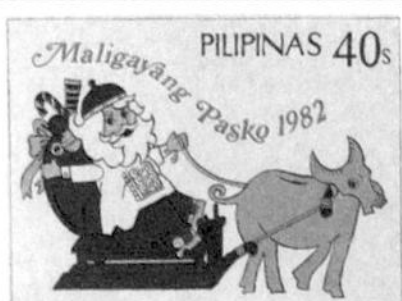

555 Father Christmas in Sleigh

1982. Christmas.
1735 **555** 40s. multicoloured . . . 20 15
1736 1p. multicoloured . . . 75 30

556 Presidential Couples and Flags

1982. State Visit of Pres. Marcos to United States.
1737 **556** 40s. multicoloured . . . 15 15
1738 3p.20 multicoloured . . 1·30 90

557 Woman with Sewing Machine **559** Eulogio Rodriguez

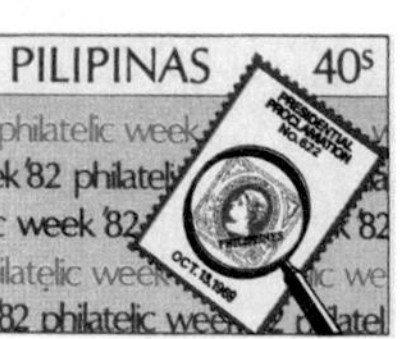

558 Stamp and Magnifying Glass

1982. U.N. World Assembly on Ageing.
1740a **557** 1p.20 green and orange 75 35
1741a – 2p. pink and blue . . . 1·50 60
DESIGN: 2p. Man with carpentry tools.

1983. Philatelic Week.
1742 **558** 40s. multicoloured . . . 20 10
1743 1p. multicoloured . . . 45 30

1983. Birth Centenary of Eulogio Rodriguez (former President of Senate).
1744a **559** 40s. multicoloured . . . 20 10
1745 1p.20 multicoloured . . 75 35

560 Symbolic Figure and Film Frame

1983. Manila International Film Festival.
1746a **560** 40s. multicoloured . . . 20 10
1747a 3p.20 multicoloured . . 1·50 95

561 Monument

1983. 2nd Anniv of Beatification of Lorenzo Ruiz.
1748 **561** 40s. yellow, red and black 20 10
1749 1p.20 multicoloured . . 75 35

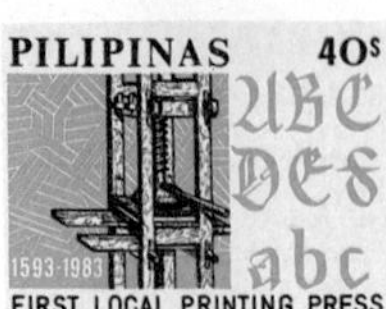

562 Early Printing Press

1983. 390th Anniv of First Local Printing Press.
1750 **562** 40s. green and black . . 20 10

563 Emblem and Ship

1983. 25th Anniv of International Maritime Organization.
1751 **563** 40s. red, black and blue 20 10

1983. 7th National Scout Jamboree. No. 1709 optd **7TH BSP NATIONAL JAMBOREE 1983**.
1752 **542** 40s. green, light green and black 20 10

1983. Nos. 1360/9 surch **40s**.
1753 – 40s. on 45c. green . . . 20 10
1754 **387** 40s. on 45c. green . . . 20 10
1755 **388** 40s. on 45c. green . . . 20 10
1756 **389** 40s. on 45c. green . . . 20 10
1757 – 40s. on 45c. green . . . 20 10
1758 – 40s. on 45c. green . . . 20 10
1759 **392** 40s. on 45c. green . . . 20 10
1760 **393** 40s. on 45c. green . . . 20 10
1761 **394** 40s. on 45c. green . . . 20 10
1762 – 40s. on 45c. green . . . 20 10

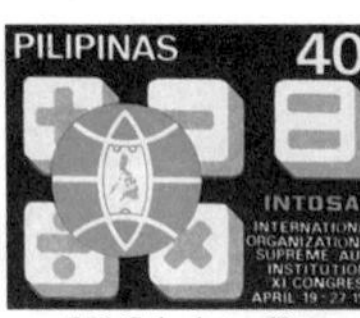

566 Calculator Keys

1983. 11th International Organization of Supreme Audit Institutions Congress.
1763 **566** 40s. blue, light blue and silver 20 10
1764 – 2p.80 multicoloured . . 1·80 80
DESIGN: 2p.80, Congress emblem.

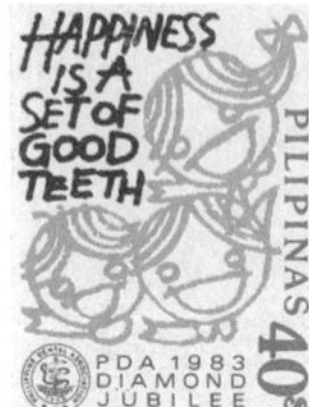

567 Smiling Children **568** Detail of Statue

1983. 75th Anniv of Philippine Dental Association.
1766 **567** 40s. green, mauve & brn 20 15

1983. 75th Anniv of University of the Philippines.
1767 **568** 40s. brown and green . . 20 15
1768 – 1p.20 multicoloured . . 65 30
DESIGN: 1p.20, Statue and diamond.

569 Yasuhiro Nakasone and Pres. Marcos

1983. Visit of Japanese Prime Minister.
1769 **569** 40s. multicoloured . . . 20 15

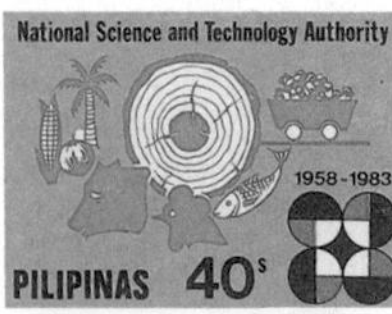

570 Agriculture and Natural Resources

1983. 25th Anniv of National Science and Technology Authority. Multicoloured.
1770 40s. Type **570** 30 15
1771 40s. Heart, medical products and food (Health and nutrition) 30 15
1772 40s. Industrial complex and air (Industry and energy) 30 15
1773 40s. House, scientific equipment and book (Sciences and social science) 30 15

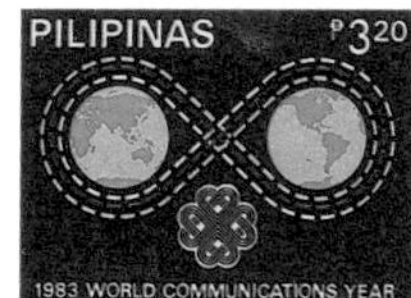

571 Globes and W.C.Y. Emblem

1983. World Communication Year.
1774 **571** 3p.20 multicoloured . . 1·90 90

572 Postman

1983. Bicent of Philippine Postal System.
1775 **572** 40s. multicoloured . . . 20 15

573 Woman with Tambourine
575 Woman casting Vote

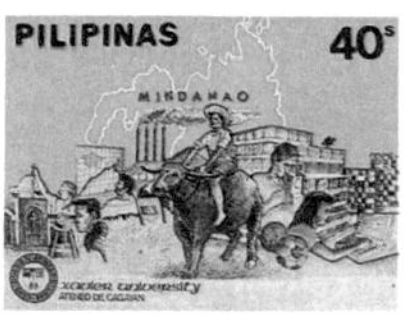

574 University Activities

1983. Christmas. Multicoloured.
1776 40s. Type **573** 20 15
1777 40s. Man turning spit (left side) 20 15
1778 40s. Pig on spit 20 15
1779 40s. Man turning spit (right side) 20 15
1780 40s. Man with guitar . . . 20 15
Nos. 1776/80 were issued together, se-tenant, forming a composite design.

1983. 50th Anniv of Xavier University.
1782 **574** 40s. multicoloured . . . 20 15
1783 60s. multicoloured . . . 35 15

1983. 50th Anniv of Female Suffrage.
1784 **575** 40s. multicoloured . . . 20 15
1785 60s. multicoloured . . . 35 15

576 Workers
578 Red-vented Cockatoo

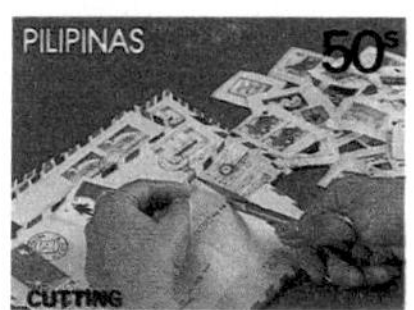

577 Cutting Stamp from Envelope

1983. 50th Anniv of Ministry of Labour and Employment.
1786 **576** 40s. multicoloured . . . 20 15
1787 60s. multicoloured . . . 35 15

1983. Philatelic Week. Multicoloured.
1788 50s. Type **577** 45 15
1789 50s. Sorting stamps 45 15
1790 50s. Soaking stamps 45 15
1791 50s. Hinging stamp 45 15
1792 50s. Mounting stamp in album 45 15

1984. Parrots. Multicoloured.
1793 40s. Type **578** 60 30
1794 2p.30 Guaiabero 80 30
1795 2p.80 Mountain racket-tailed parrot 95 35
1796 3p.20 Great-billed parrot . . 1·20 35

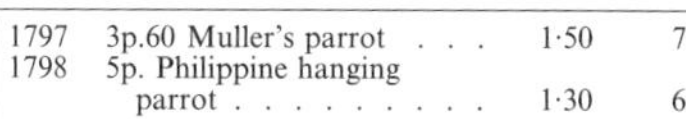
1797 3p.60 Muller's parrot . . . 1·50 75
1798 5p. Philippine hanging parrot . . . . 1·30 65

579 Princess Tarhata Kiram
580 Nun and Congregation

1984. 5th Death Anniv of Princess Tarhata Kiram.
1799 **579** 3p. deep green, green and red 75 30

1984. 300th Anniv of Religious Congregation of the Virgin Mary.
1800 **580** 40s. multicoloured . . . 15 15
1801 60s. multicoloured . . . 15 15

581 Dona Concha Felix de Calderon
583 Manila

1984. Birth Centenary of Dona Concha Felix de Calderon.
1802 **581** 60s. green and black . . 10 10
1803 3p.60 green and red . . 50 15

1984. Various stamps surch.
1804 **545** 60s. on 40s. multicoloured 15 15
1805 **558** 60s. on 40s. multicoloured 15 15
1806 – 3p.60 on 3p.20 blue (No. 1704) 95 30

1984. As Nos. 1700/4 but values changed, and new designs as T **526**.
1807 60s. brown and black . . . 15 10
1808 60s. violet and black 15 10
1809 60s. black 15 10
1913 60s. blue 20 10
1889 60s. brown 20 10
1914 60s. red 20 15
1811 1p.80 blue 20 15
1812 2p.40 purple 35 15
1813 3p. brown 35 15
1814 3p.60 red 50 15
1815 4p.20 purple 60 20
DESIGNS: No. 1807, General Artemio Ricarte; 1808, Teodoro M. Kalaw (politician); 1809, Carlos P. Garcia (4th President); 1913, Quintin Paredes (senator); 1889, Dr. Deogracias V. Villadolid; 1914, Santiago Fonacier (former Senator and army chaplain); 1811, General Vicente Lim; 1812, Professor Nicanor Abelardo; 1813, Francisco Dagohoy; 1814, Aurora Aragon Quezon; 1815, Juan Sumulong.

1984. 150th Anniv of Ayala Corporation.
1818 **583** 70s. multicoloured . . . 15 10
1819 3p.60 multicoloured . . 35 15

584 "Lady of the Most Holy Rosary with St. Dominic" (C. Francisco)

1984. "Espana 84" International Stamp Exhibition, Madrid. Multicoloured.
1820 2p.50 Type **584** 35 15
1821 5p. "Spoliarum" (Juan Luna) 80 35

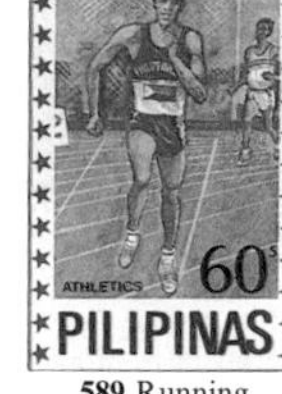

585 Maria Paz Mendoza Guazon
589 Running

586 "Adolias amlana"

1984. Birth Centenary of Dr. Maria Paz Mendoza Guazon.
1823 **585** 60s. red and blue 15 10
1824 65s. red, black and blue 15 10

1984. Butterflies. Multicoloured.
1825 60s. Type **586** 15 10
1826 2p.40 "Papilio daedalus" . . 50 20
1827 3p. "Prothoe franckii semperi" 65 30
1828 3p.60 Philippine birdwing 80 30
1829 4p.20 Lurcher 95 45
1830 5p. "Chilasa idaeoides" . . 1·30 50

1984. National Children's Book Day. Stamp from miniature sheet ("The Monkey and the Turtle") surch **7-17-84 NATIONAL CHILDREN'S BOOK DAY 20**. Perf or imperf.
1831 7p.20 on 7p.50 multicoloured . . . . . . 15·00 8·75

1984. 420th Anniv of Philippine–Mexican Friendship. Stamp from miniature sheet (Virgin of Manila) surch **420TH PHIL-MEXICAN FRIENDSHIP 8-3-84 20**. Perf or imperf.
1832 7p.20 on 7p.50 multicoloured . . . . . . 15·00 8·75

1984. Olympic Games, Los Angeles. Multicoloured.
1833 60s. Type **589** 10 10
1834 2p.40 Boxing 45 20
1835 6p. Swimming . . . . . . 1·20 60
1836 7p.20 Windsurfing . . . . . 1·50 80
1837 8p.40 Cycling . . . . 1·80 90
1838 20p. Running (woman athlete) . . . . 4·00 2·20

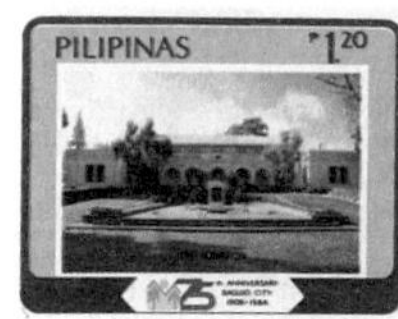

590 The Mansion

1984. 75th Anniv of Baguio City.
1840 **590** 1p.20 multicoloured . . 20 15

1984. 300th Anniv of Our Lady of Holy Rosary Parish. Stamp from miniature sheet ("Lady of the Most Holy Rosary") surch **9-1-84 300TH YR O.L. HOLY ROSARY PARISH 20**. Perf or imperf.
1841 7p.20 on 7p.50 multicoloured . . . . . . 30·00 26·00

592 Electric Train on Viaduct

1984. Light Railway Transit.
1842 **592** 1p.20 multicoloured . . 45 15

593 Australian and Philippine Stamps and Koalas

1984. "Ausipex 84" International Stamp Exhibition, Melbourne.
1843 **593** 3p. multicoloured . . . 60 30
1844 3p.60 multicoloured . . 75 30

1984. National Museum Week. Stamp from miniature sheet (as No. 1821) surch **NATIONAL MUSEUM WEEK 10-5-84 20**. Perf or imperf.
1846 7p.20 on 7p.50 multicoloured . . . . . . 15·00 8·75

1984. Asia Regional Conference of Rotary International. No. 1728 surch **14-17 NOV. 84 R.I. ASIA REGIONAL CONFERENCE P1.20.**
1847 **551** 1p.20 on 2p.30 mult . . 20 15

596 Gold Award

1984. Philatelic Week. Gold Award at "Ausipex 84" to Mario Que. Multicoloured.
1848 1p.20 Type **596** 20 15
1849 3p. Page of Que's exhibit . . 45 15

597 Caracao

1984. Water Transport. Multicoloured.
1850 60s. Type **597** 20 15
1851 1p.20 Chinese junk 20 15
1852 6p. Spanish galleon . . . . 1·30 60
1853 7p.20 Casco (Filipino cargo prau) . . . . 1·50 75
1854 8p.40 Early paddle-steamer 1·60 90
1855 20p. Modern liner . . . . . 4·00 1·90

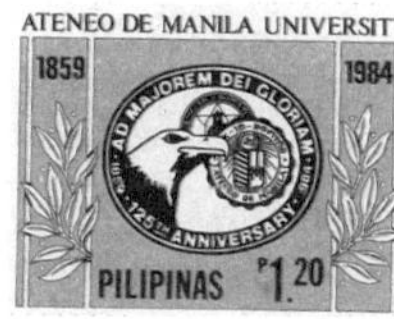

599 Anniversary Emblem

1984. 125th Anniv of Ateneo de Manila University.
1857 **599** 60s. blue and gold . . . 20 15
1858 1p.20 blue and silver . . 35 20

PILIPINAS 60s
Philippine Jaycees Commitment to Youth Development
600 Virgin and Child
602 Abstract

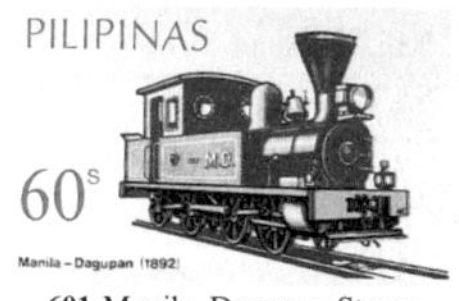

601 Manila–Dagupan Steam Locomotive, 1892

1984. Christmas. Multicoloured.
1859 60s. Type **600** 15 10
1860 1p.20 Holy Family 35 20

1984. Rail Transport. Multicoloured.
1861 60s. Type **601** 20 15
1862 1p.20 Light Rail Transit eletric train, 1984 . . . . 20 15
1863 6p. Bicol express, 1955 . . 1·30 60
1864 7p.20 Electric tram, 1905 . . 1·50 75
1865 8p.40 Diesel commuter railcar, 1972 . . . . . . 1·60 90
1866 20p. Horse tram, 1898 . . . 4·00 1·90

1984. 10th Anniv of Philippine Jaycees' Ten Outstanding Young Men Awards. Abstracts by Raul Isidro. Multicoloured.
1867 60s. brown background in circle 15 10
1868 60s. Type **602** 15 10
1869 60s. red background 15 10
1870 60s. blue and purple background 15 10
1871 60s. orange and brown background 15 10
1872 3p. As No. 1867 . . . . . 45 30
1873 3p. Type **602** 45 30
1874 3p. As No. 1869 . . . . . 45 30
1875 3p. As No. 1870 . . . . . 45 30
1876 3p. As No. 1871 . . . . . 45 30

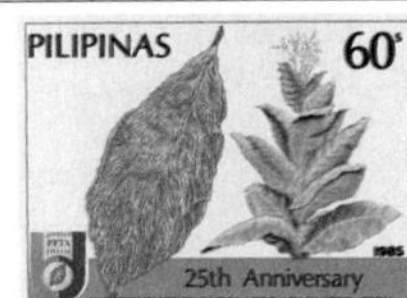

603 Tobacco Plant and Dried Leaf

1985. 25th Anniv of Philippine Virginia Tobacco Administration.
1877 **603** 60s. multicoloured . . . 15 10
1878 3p. multicoloured . . . 60 30

1985. Philatelic Week, 1984. Nos. 1848/9 optd **Philatelic Week 1984.**
1879 **596** 1p.20 multicoloured . . 20 15
1880 – 3p. multicoloured . . . 50 35

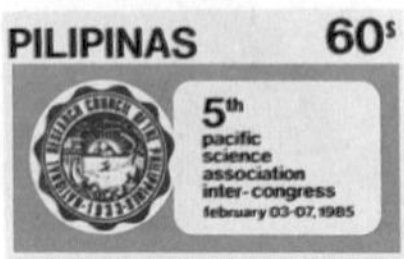

605 National Research Council Emblem

1985. 5th Pacific Science Association Congress.
1881 **605** 60s. black, blue and light blue 15 10
1882 1p.20 black, blue and orange 45 20

606 "Carmona retusa"

1985. Medicinal Plants. Multicoloured.
1883a 60s. Type **606** 20 10
1884 1p.20 "Orthosiphon aristatus" 20 15
1885 2p.40 "Vitex negundo" . . 45 30
1886 3p. "Aloe barbadensis" . . 60 35
1887 3p.60 "Quisqualis indica" 1·30 45
1888 4p.20 "Blumea balsamifera" 90 50

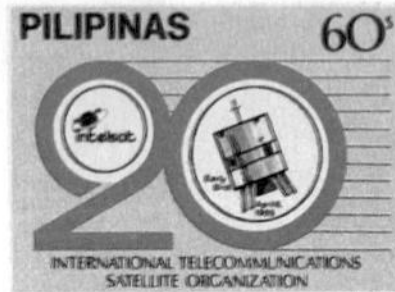

607 "Early Bird" Satellite

1985. 20th Anniv of International Telecommunications Satellite Organization.
1896 **607** 60s. multicoloured . . . 15 10
1897 3p. multicoloured . . . 60 30

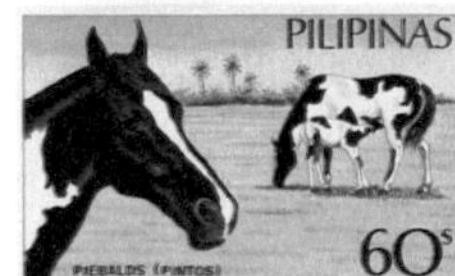

608 Piebalds

1985. Horses. Multicoloured.
1898 60s. Type **608** 20 15
1899 1p.20 Palominos 20 15
1900 6p. Bays . . . . 1·30 60
1901 7p.20 Browns . . . . 1·50 75
1902 8p.40 Greys . . . . 1·60 90
1903 20p. Chestnuts . . . . . . 4·00 1·90

609 Emblem

1985. 25th Anniv of National Tax Research Centre.
1905 **609** 60s. multicoloured . . . 15 10

610 Transplanting Rice

1985. 25th Anniv of International Rice Research Institute, Los Banos. Multicoloured.
1906 60s. Type **610** 15 10
1907 3p. Paddy fields 35 20

611 Image of Holy Child of Cebu

1985. 420th Anniv of Filipino–Spanish Treaty. Mult.
1908 1p.20 Type **611** 20 15
1909 3p.60 Rajah Tupas and Miguel Lopez de Lagazpi signing treaty 45 15

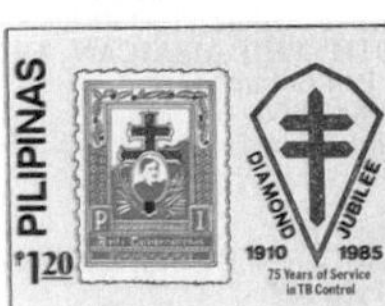

613 Early Anti-TB Label

1985. 75th Anniv of Philippine Tuberculosis Society. Multicoloured.
1911 60s. Screening for TB, laboratory work, health education and inoculation 15 10
1912 1p.20 Type **613** 30 20

1985. 45th Anniv of Girl Scout Charter. No. 1409 surch **45th ANNIVERSARY GIRL SCOUT CHARTER**, emblem and new value.
1917 **348** 2p.40 on 15s. on 10s. multicoloured 30 20
1918 4p.20 on 15s. on 10s. multicoloured 60 30
1919 7p.20 on 15s. on 10s. multicoloured 95 45

616 "Our Lady of Fatima"

617 Family planting Tree

1985. Marian Year. 2000th Birth Anniversary of Virgin Mary. Multicoloured.
1920 1p.20 Type **616** 20 15
1921 2p.40 "Our Lady of Beaterio" (Juan Bueno Silva) 30 15
1922 3p. "Our Lady of Penafrancia" 35 20
1923 3p.60 "Our Lady of Guadalupe" 60 30

1985. Tree Week. International Year of the Forest.
1924 **617** 1p.20 multicoloured . . 20 15

618 Battle of Bessang Pass

619 Vicente Orestes Romualdez

1985. 40th Anniv of Bessang Pass Campaign.
1925 **618** 1p.20 multicoloured . . 20 15

1985. Birth Centenary of Vicente Orestes Romualdez (lawyer).
1926a **619** 60s. blue 90 15
1927a 2p. mauve . . . . . . 1·20 35

620 Fishing

1985. International Youth Year. Children's Paintings. Multicoloured.
1928 2p.40 Type **620** 30 15
1929 3p.60 Picnic 50 15

621 Banawe Rice Terraces

1985. World Tourism Organization Congress, Sofia, Bulgaria.
1930 **621** 2p.40 multicoloured . . 30 20

622 Export Graph and Crane lifting Crate

624 Emblem and Dove with Olive Branch

1985. Export Promotion Year.
1931 **622** 1p.20 multicoloured . . 20 15

1985. No. 1815 surch **P360.**
1932 3p.60 on 4p.20 purple . . . 75 35

1985. 40th Anniv of U.N.O.
1933 **624** 3p.60 multicoloured . . 45 20

625 Martin M-130 Flying Boat "China Clipper"

1985. 50th Anniv of First Trans-Pacific Commercial Flight (San Francisco–Manila). Multicoloured.
1934 3p. Type **625** 35 20
1935 3p.60 Route map, "China Clipper" and anniversary emblem 50 20

1985. Philatelic Week. Nos. 1863/4 surch **PHILATELIC WEEK 1985**, No. 1937 further optd **AIRMAIL.**
1936 60s. on 6p. mult (postage) 15 10
1937 3p. on 7p.20 mult (air) . . . 60 30

627 Bible and Churches

1985. National Bible Week.
1938 **627** 60s. multicoloured . . . 15 10
1939 3p. multicoloured . . . 60 30

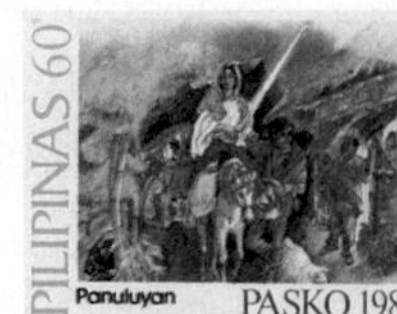

628 Panuluyan (enactment of search for an inn)

1985. Christmas. Multicoloured.
1940 60s. Type **628** 15 10
1941 3p. Pagdalaw (nativity) . . 60 30

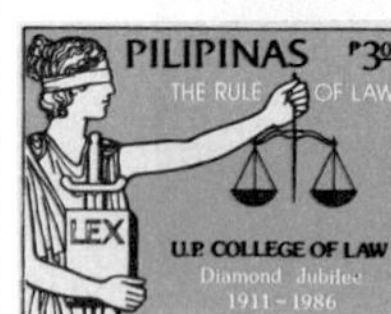

629 Justice holding Scales

630 Rizal and "Noli Me Tangere"

1986. 75th Anniv of College of Law.
1942 **629** 60s. mauve and black . . 15 10
1943 3p. green, purple & black 60 30
See also No. 2009.

1986. Centenary of Publication of "Noli Me Tangere" (Jose Rizal's first book).
1944 **630** 60s. violet 10 10
1945 – 1p.20 green 30 20
1946 – 3p.60 brown 65 30
DESIGNS: 1p.20, 3p.60, Rizal, "To the Flowers of Heidelberg" (poem) and Heidelberg University.

631 Douglas DC-3, 1946

632 Oil Refinery, Manila Bay

1986. 45th Anniv of Philippine Airlines. Each red, black and blue.
1947 60s. Type **631** 15 15
1948 60s. Douglas DC-4 Skymaster, 1946 . . . . 15 15
1949 60s. Douglas DC-6, 1948 . . 15 15
1950 60s. Vickers Viscount 784, 1957 . . . . 15 15
1951 2p.40 Fokker F.27 Friendship, 1960 . . . . 50 20
1952 2p.40 Douglas DC-8-50, 1962 . . . . 80 35
1953 2p.40 B.A.C. One Eleven 500, 1964 . . . . 50 20
1954 2p.40 Douglas DC-10-30, 1974 . . . . 50 20
1955 3p.60 Beech 18, 1941 . . . 75 35
1956 3p.60 Boeing 747-200, 1980 75 35
See also No. 2013.

1986. 25th Anniv of Bataan Refinery Corporation.
1957 **632** 60s. silver and green . . 15 10
1958 – 3p. silver and blue . . . 50 20
DESIGN—HORIZ: 3p. Refinery (different).

633 Emblem

1986. "Expo 86" World's Fair, Vancouver.
1959 **633** 60s. multicoloured . . . 15 10
1960 3p. multicoloured . . . 60 30

634 Emblem and Industrial and Agricultural Symbols

1986. 25th Anniv of Asian Productivity Organization.
1961 **634** 60s. black, green & orge 15 10
1962 3p. black, green & orange 60 30
1963 3p. brown (30 × 22 mm) 65 30

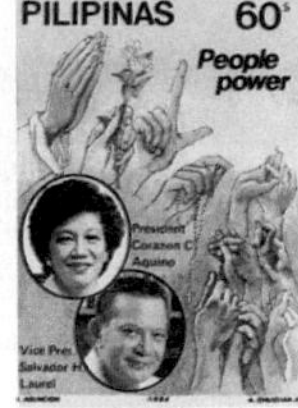

635 1906 2c. Stamp

637 Corazon Aquino, Salvador Laurel and Hands

1986. "Ameripex 86" Int Stamp Exhibition, Chicago.
1964 **635** 60s. green, black & yellow 15 10
1965 – 3p. bistre, black and green 60 30
DESIGN: 3p. 1935 20c. stamp.
See also No. 2006.

1986. "People Power". Multicoloured.
1966 60s. Type **637** 15 10
1967 1p.20 Radio antennae, helicopter and people . . 20 15
1968 2p.40 Religious procession 45 20
1969 3p. Crowds around soldiers in tanks 50 20

638 Monument and Paco and Taft Schools

1986. 75th Anniv of First La Salle School in Philippines.
1971 **638** 60s. black, lilac and green 15 15
1972 – 2p.40 black, blue & grn 45 20
1973 – 3p. black, yellow & green 50 20
DESIGNS: 2p.40, St. Miguel Febres Cordero and Paco School; 3p. St. Benilde and Taft school; 7p.20, Founding brothers of Paco school.

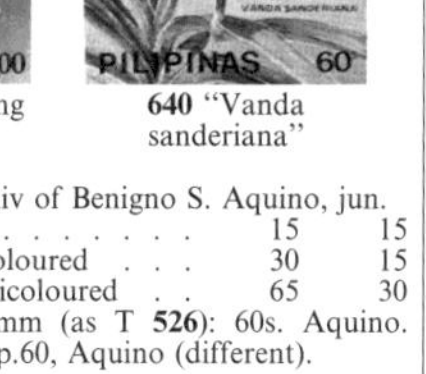

639 Aquino praying **640** "Vanda sanderiana"

1986. 3rd Death Anniv of Benigno S. Aquino, jun.
1975 – 60s. green 15 15
1976 **639** 2p. multicoloured . . . 30 15
1977 – 3p.60 multicoloured . . 65 30
DESIGNS—27 × 36 mm (as T **526**): 60s. Aquino. HORIZ (as T **639**): 3p.60, Aquino (different).
See also No. 2007.

1986. Orchids. Multicoloured.
1979 60s. Type **640** 15 10
1980 1p.20 "Epigeneium lyonii" 50 15
1981 2p.40 "Paphiopedilum philippinense" 90 20
1982 3p. "Amesiella philippinense" . . . . . 1·10 20

641 "Christ carrying the Cross" **642** Hospital

1986. 400th Anniv of Quiapo District.
1983 **641** 60s. red, black and mauve 15 10
1984 – 3p.60 blue, black & grn 60 30
DESIGN—HORIZ: 3p.60, Quiapo Church.

1986. 75th Anniv of Philippine General Hospital.
1985 **642** 60s. multicoloured . . . 15 15
1986 3p. multicoloured . . . 50 20
2012 5p. brown . . . . 1·10 15

643 Comet and Earth

1986. Appearance of Halley's Comet. Multicoloured.
1987 60s. Type **643** 10 10
1988 2p.40 Comet, Moon and Earth 45 30

644 Handshake **645** Emblem

1986. 74th International Dental Federation Congress, Manila. Multicoloured.
1989 60s. Type **644** 15 10
1990 3p. Jeepney, Manila 75 35
See also Nos. 2008 and 2011.

1986. 75th Anniv of Manila Young Men's Christian Association.
1991 **645** 2p. blue 45 15
1992 3p.60 red 65 35
2058 4p. blue 70 45

646 Old and New Buildings

1986. 85th Anniv of Philippine Normal College.
1993 – 60s. multicoloured . . . 15 10
1994 **646** 3p.60 yellow, brown & bl 90 45
DESIGN: 60s. Old and new buildings (different).

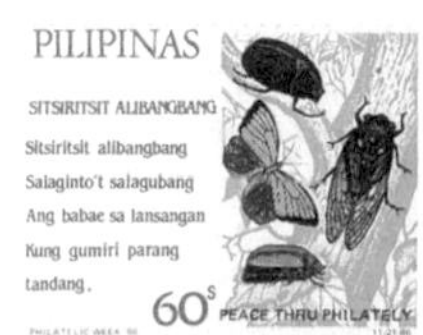

647 Butterfly and Beetles

1986. Philatelic Week and International Peace Year.
1995 **647** 60s. multicoloured . . . 15 10
1996 – 1p. blue and black . . . 20 15
1997 – 3p. multicoloured . . . 75 35
DESIGNS—VERT: 1p. Peace Year emblem. HORIZ: 3p. Dragonflies.

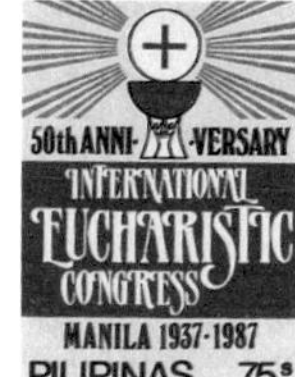

648 Mother and Child **651** Emblem

650 Manila Hotel, 1912

1986. Christmas. Multicoloured.
1998 60s. Type **648** 15 10
1999 60s. Couple with child and cow 15 10
2000 60s. Mother and child with doves 15 10
2001 1p. Mother and child receiving gifts (horiz) . . 30 15
2002 1p. Mother and child beneath arch (horiz) . . . 30 15
2003 1p. Madonna and shepherd adoring child (horiz) . . . 30 15
2004 1p. Shepherds and animals around child in manger (horiz) 30 15

1987. No. 1944 surch **P100**.
2005 **630** 1p. on 60s. violet 15 10

1987. As previous issues but smaller, 22 × 30 mm, 30 × 22 mm or 32 × 22 mm (5p.50), and values and colours changed.
2006 – 75s. green (As No. 1965) 15 10
2007 – 1p. blue (As No. 1975) 20 15
2008 **644** 3p.25 green 75 15
2009 **629** 3p.50 brown 80 15
2011 – 4p.75 green (As No. 1990) . . . . . . 1·10 15
2013 – 5p.50 blue (As No. 1956) 1·10 20

1987. 75th Anniv of Manila Hotel.
2014 **650** 1p. bistre and black . . 20 15
2015 – 4p. multicoloured . . . 75 35
2016 – 4p.75 multicoloured . . 90 45
2017 – 5p.50 multicoloured . . 1·10 50

DESIGNS: 4p. Hotel; 4p.75, Lobby; 5p.50, Staff in ante-lobby.

1987. 50th Anniv of International Eucharistic Congress, Manila. Multicoloured.
2018 75s. Type **651** 15 10
2019 1p. Emblem (different) (horiz) 30 15

652 Pres. Cory Aquino taking Oath

1987. Ratification of New Constitution.
2020 **652** 1p. multicoloured . . . 20 15
2021 – 5p.50 blue and brown . . 1·20 60
2060 – 5p.50 green and brown (22 × 31 mm) 80 15
DESIGN: 5p.50, Constitution on open book and dove.

653 Dr. Jose P. Laurel (founder) and Tower

1987. 35th Anniv of Lyceum.
2022 **653** 1p. multicoloured . . . 20 10
2023 2p. multicoloured . . . 60 15

654 City Seal, Man with Philippine Eagle and Woman with Fruit

1987. 50th Anniv of Davao City.
2024 **654** 1p. multicoloured . . . 15 10

655 Salary and Policy Loans **656** Emblem and People in Hand

1987. 50th Anniv of Government Service Insurance System. Multicoloured.
2025 1p. Type **655** 20 15
2026 1p.25 Disability and medicare 20 15
2027 2p. Retirement benefits . . . 35 20
2028 3p.50 Survivorship benefits 65 35

1987. 50th Anniv of Salvation Army in Philippines.
2029 **656** 1p. multicoloured . . . 30 10

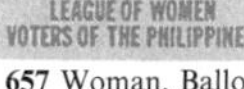

657 Woman, Ballot Box and Map **659** Man with Outstretched Arm

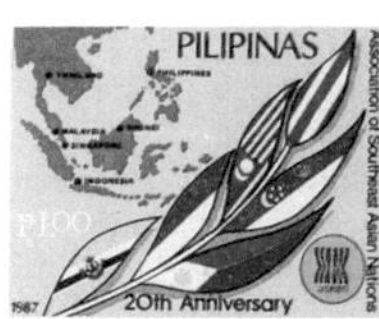

658 Map and Flags as Leaves

1987. 50th Anniv of League of Women Voters.
2030 **657** 1p. blue and mauve . . 15 10

1987. As T **526**.
2031 1p. green 15 10
2032 1p. blue 15 10
2033 1p. red 15 10
2034 1p. purple and red 15 10

DESIGNS: No. 2031, Gen. Vicente Lukban; 2032, Wenceslao Q. Vinzons; 2033, Brigadier-General Mateo M. Capinpin; 2034, Jesus Balmori.

1987. 20th Anniv of Association of South-East Asian Nations.
2035 **658** 1p. multicoloured . . . 30 10

1987. Exports.
2036 **659** 1p. multicoloured . . . 15 10
2037 – 2p. green, yellow & brn 30 15
2059 – 4p.75 blue and black . . 65 15
DESIGN: 2p., 4p.75, Man, cogwheel and factory.

660 Nuns, People and Crucifix within Flaming Heart **661** Statue and Stained Glass Window

1967. 125th Anniv of Daughters of Charity in the Philippines.
2038 **660** 1p. blue, red and black 20 10

1987. Canonization of Blessed Lorenzo Ruiz de Manila (first Filipino saint). Multicoloured.
2039 1p. Type **661** 20 15
2040 5p.50 Lorenzo Ruiz praying before execution . . . . 1·30 35

1987. No. 2012 surch **P4.75**.
2042 **642** 4p.75 on 5p. brown . . 95 15

663 Nun and Emblem

1987. 75th Anniv of Good Shepherd Sisters in Philippines.
2043 **663** 1p. multicoloured . . . 20 10

664 Founders

1987. 50th Anniv of Philippines Boy Scouts.
2044 **664** 1p. multicoloured . . . 20 10

665 Family with Stamp Album

1987. 50th Anniv of Philippine Philatelic Club.
2045 **665** 1p. multicoloured . . . 20 10

666 Monks, Church and Wrecked Galleon **668** Dove with Letter

667 Flags

1987. 400th Anniv of Dominican Order in Philippines.
2046 **666** 1p. black, blue and orange 15 15
2047 – 4p.75 multicoloured . . 80 30
2048 – 5p.50 multicoloured . . 1·30 45
DESIGNS: 4p.75, J. A. Jeronimo Guerrero, Diego de Sta. Maria and Letran Dominican college; 5p.50, Pope and monks.

1987. 3rd Association of South-east Asian Nations Summit Meeting.
2049 **667** 4p. multicoloured . . . 95 10

1987. Christmas. Multicoloured.
2050 1p. Type **668** 15 15
2051 1p. People and star decoration 15 15
2052 4p. Crowd going to church 80 20
2053 4p.75 Mother and children exchanging gifts 80 30
2054 5p.50 Children and bamboo cannons . . . . 1·20 30
2055 8p. Children at table bearing festive fare . . . . 1·50 50
2056 9p.50 Woman at table . . . 1·60 65
2057 11p. Woman having Christmas meal . . . . . 1·90 65

669 Emblem, Headquarters and Dr. Rizal

1987. 75th Anniv of Grand Lodge of Philippine Masons.
2061 **669** 1p. multicoloured . . . 30 10

670 Foodstuffs in Split Globe

1987. 40th Anniv of U.N.O. Multicoloured.
2062 1p. Type **670** (International Fund for Agricultural Development) 20 15
2063 1p. Means of transport and communications (Asian and Pacific Transport and Communications Decade) 20 15
2064 1p. People and hands holding houses (International Year of Shelter for the Homeless) 20 15
2065 1p. Happy children playing musical instruments (World Health Day: UNICEF child vaccination campaign) . . 20 15

671 Official Seals and Gavel

1988. Opening Session of 1987 Congress. Mult.
2066 1p. Type **671** 20 10
2067 5p.50 Congress in session and gavel (horiz) . . . . 1·40 45

672 Children and Bosco

1988. Death Centenary of St. John Bosco (founder of Salesian Brothers).
2068 **672** 1p. multicoloured . . . 15 10
2069 5p.50 multicoloured . . 1·20 45

673 Emblem

675 Envelope with Coded Addresses

1988. Buy Philippine-Made Movement Month.
2070 **673** 1p. multicoloured . . . 15 15

1988. Various stamps surch **P 3.00**.
2071 – 3p. on 3p.60 brown (No. 1946) 50 20
2072 **645** 3p. on 3p.60 red 60 20
2073 – 3p. on 3p.60 mult (No. 1977) 75 30
2074 – 3p. on 3p.60 blue, black and green (No. 1984) 50 20
2075 **646** 3p. on 3p.60 yellow, brown and blue . . . 75 30

1988. Postal Codes.
2076 **675** 60s. multicoloured . . . 15 10
2077 1p. multicoloured . . . 20 15

676 "Vesbius purpureus" (soldier bug)

677 Solar Eclipse

1988. Insect Predators. Multicoloured.
2078 1p. Type **676** 15 10
2079 5p.50 "Campsomeris aurulenta" (dagger wasp) 1·10 45

1988.
2080 **677** 1p. multicoloured . . . 15 10
2081 5p.50 multicoloured . . 1·20 45

678 Teodoro

679 Emblem

1988. 101st Birth Anniv of Toribio Teodoro (industrialist).
2082 **678** 1p. cinnamon, brn & red 15 10
2083 1p.20 blue, brown & red 20 15

1988. 75th Anniv of College of Holy Spirit.
2084 **679** 1p. brown, gold & black 15 10
2085 – 4p. brown, green & black 80 30
DESIGN: 4p. Arnold Janssen (founder) and Sister Edelwina (director, 1920–47).

680 Emblem

681 Luna and Hidalgo

1988. Newly Restored Democracies International Conference.
2086 **680** 4p. blue, ultram & blk 95 30

1988. National Juan Luna and Felix Resurreccion Hidalgo Memorial Exhibition.
2087 **681** 1p. black, yellow & brn 15 10
2088 5p.50 black, cinnamon and brown . . . . . 1·00 35

682 Magat Dam, Ramon, Isabela

1988. 25th Anniv of National Irrigation Administration.
2089 **682** 1p. multicoloured . . . 1·10 1·10
2090 5p.50 multicoloured . . 1·20 50

683 Scuba Diving, Siquijor

1988. Olympic Games, Seoul (1st issue). Multicoloured. Perf or imperf.
2091 1p. Type **683** 15 15
2092 1p.20 Big game fishing, Aparri, Cagayan 20 15
2093 4p. Yachting, Manila Central 75 45
2094 5p.50 Mountain climbing, Mt. Apo, Davao . . . . 1·10 65
2095 8p. Golfing, Cebu City . . . 1·50 95
2096 11p. Cycling (Tour of Mindanao), Marawi City 2·20 1·30
See also Nos. 2113/18.

684 Headquarters, Plaza Santa Cruz, Manila

686 Balagtas

1988. Banking Anniversaries. Multicoloured.
2097 1p. Type **684** (50th anniv of Philippine International Commercial Bank) . . . 15 15
2098 1p. Family looking at factory and countryside (25th anniv of Land Bank) 15 15
2099 5p.50 Type **684** 95 50
2100 5p.50 As No. 2098 . . . . 95 50

1988. Various stamps surch.
2101 1p.90 on 2p.40 mult (No. 1968) 45 15
2102 1p.90 on 2p.40 black, blue and green (No. 1972) . . 45 15
2103 1p.90 on 2p.40 mult (No. 1981) 45 15
2104 1p.90 on 2p.40 mult (No. 1988) 45 15

1988. Birth Bicentenary of Francisco Balagtas Baltasco (writer). Each green, brown and yellow.
2105 1p. Type **686** 15 10
2106 1p. As Type **686** but details reversed 15 10

687 Hospital

688 Brown Mushroom

1988. 50th Anniv of Quezon Institute (tuberculosis hospital).
2107 **687** 1p. multicoloured . . . 15 15
2108 5p.50 multicoloured . . 1·00 60

1988. Fungi. Multicoloured.
2109 60s. Type **688** 15 10
2110 1p. Rat's ear fungus 20 15
2111 2p. Abalone mushroom . . 35 20
2112 4p. Straw mushroom . . . 90 45

689 Archery

691 Red Cross Work

690 Department of Justice

1988. Olympic Games, Seoul (2nd issue). Multicoloured. Perf or imperf.
2113 1p. Type **689** 20 15
2114 1p.20 Tennis 20 15
2115 4p. Boxing 60 30
2116 5p.50 Athletics 90 45
2117 8p. Swimming . . . . . . 1·30 60
2118 11p. Cycling . . . . 1·80 95

1988. Law and Justice Week.
2120 **690** 1p. multicoloured . . . 15 10

1988. 125th Anniv of Red Cross.
2121 **691** 1p. multicoloured . . . 15 15
2122 5p.50 multicoloured . . 1·00 50

692 Girl and Boy

693 Map and Shrimps

1988. 50th Anniv of Christian Children's Fund.
2123 **692** 1p. multicoloured . . . 15 10

1988. 50th Anniv of Bacolod City Charter.
2124 **693** 1p. multicoloured . . . 15 10

694 Breastfeeding

695 A. Aragon Quezon

1988. Child Survival Campaign. Multicoloured.
2125 1p. Type **694** 15 10
2126 1p. Growth monitoring . . 15 10
2127 1p. Immunization 15 10
2128 1p. Oral rehydration 15 10
2129 1p. Access for the disabled (U.N. Decade of Disabled Persons) 15 10

1988. Birth Centenary of Aurora Aragon Quezon.
2130 **695** 1p. multicoloured . . . 15 10
2131 5p.50 multicoloured . . 90 60

696 Post Office

697 Sampaloc Branch Transmitter

1988. Philatelic Week. Multicoloured.
2132 1p. Type **696** (inscr "1938") 20 15
2132b 1p. Type **696** (inscr "1988") 35 15
2133 1p. Stamp counter 20 15
2134 1p. Fern and stamp displays 20 15
2135 1p. People looking at stamp displays 20 15

1988. 10 Years of Technological Improvements by Philippine Long Distance Telephone Company.
2136 **697** 1p. multicoloured . . . 15 10

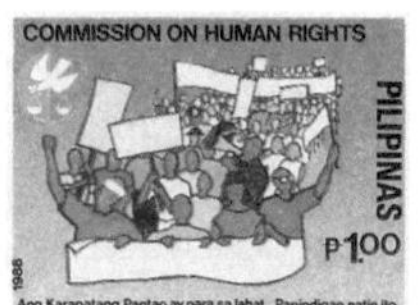

698 Clasped Hands and Dove   699 Crowd with Banners

1988. Christmas. Multicoloured.
2137 75s. Type **698** 15 15
2138 1p. Children making decorations (horiz) . . . 15 15
2139 2p. Man carrying decorations on yoke (horiz) 30 20
2140 3p.50 Christmas tree 60 30
2141 4p.75 Candle and stars . . . 80 35
2142 5p.50 Reflection of star forming heart (horiz) . . 95 45

1988. Commission on Human Rights (2143) and 40th Anniv of Universal Declaration of Human Rights (2144). Multicoloured.
2143 1p. Type **699** 15 10
2144 1p. Doves escaping from cage 15 10

700 Church, 1776   701 Statue and School

1988. 400th Anniv of Malate. Multicoloured.
2145 1p. Type **700** 15 10
2146 1p. Our Lady of Remedies Church anniversary emblem and statue of Virgin (Eduardo Castrillo) 15 10
2147 1p. Church, 1880 . . . . . 15 10
2148 1p. Church, 1988 . . . . . 15 10

1988. 50th Anniv of University of Santo Tomas Graduate School.
2149 **701** 1p. multicoloured . . . 15 10

702 Order's Activities   703 Miguel Ver (first leader)

1989. 50th Anniv of Oblates of Mary Immaculate.
2150 **702** 1p. multicoloured . . . 15 10

1989. 47th Anniv of Recognition of Hunters ROTC Guerrilla Unit (formed by Military Academy and University students). Mult.
2151 1p. Type **703** 15 10
2152 1p. Eleuterio Adevoso (leader after Ver's death) 15 10

704 Foodstuffs and Paulino Santos   705 Sinulog

1989. 50th Anniv of General Santos City.
2153 **704** 1p. multicoloured . . . 15 10

1989. "Fiesta Islands '89" (1st series). Mult.
2154 4p.75 Type **705** 95 35
2155 5p.50 Cenaculo (Lenten festival) 95 45
2156 6p.25 Iloilo Paraw Regatta 95 65
See also Nos. 2169/71, 2177/9, 2194/6 and 2210.

706 Tomas Mapua   707 Adventure Pool

1989. Birth Centenaries. Multicoloured.
2157 1p. Type **706** 15 10
2158 1p. Camilo Osias 15 10
2159 1p. Dr. Olivia Salamanca 15 10
2160 1p. Dr. Francisco Santiago 15 10
2161 1p. Leandro Fernandez . . 15 10

1989. 26th International Federation of Landscape Architects World Congress, Manila. Mult.
2162 1p. Type **707** 15 10
2163 1p. Paco Park 15 10
2164 1p. Street improvements in Malacanang area 15 10
2165 1p. Erosion control on upland farm 15 10

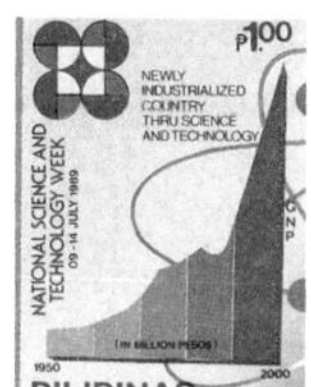

708 Palawan Peacock- Pheasant   709 Entrance and Statue of Justice

1989. Environment Month. Multicoloured.
2166 1p. Type **708** 15 10
2167 1p. Palawan bear cat . . . 15 10

1989. Supreme Court.
2168 **709** 1p. multicoloured . . . 30 15

1989. "Fiesta Islands '89" (2nd series). As T **705**. Multicoloured.
2169 60s. Turumba 15 10
2170 75s. Pahiyas 15 15
2171 3p.50 Independence Day . . 50 30

710 Birds, Quill, "Noli Me Tangere" and Flags

1989. Bicentenary of French Revolution and Decade of Philippine Nationalism.
2172 **710** 1p. multicoloured . . . 15 15
2173 5p.50 multicoloured . . 90 60

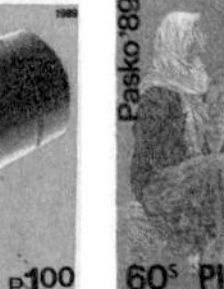

711 Graph   713 Monument, Flag, Civilian and Soldier

1989. National Science and Technology Week. Multicoloured.
2174 1p. Type **711** 15 10
2175 1p. "Man" (Leonardo da Vinci) and emblem of Philippine Science High School) 15 10

1989. New Constitution stamp of 1987 surch **P4 75**.
2176 4p.75 on 5p.50 green and brown (2060) 75 50

1989. "Fiesta Island 89" (3rd series). As T **705**.
2177 1p. Pagoda Sa Wawa (carnival float) 15 15
2178 4p.75 Cagayan de Oro Fiesta 80 35
2179 5p.50 Penafrancia Festival 95 45

1989. 50th Anniv of National Defence Department.
2180 **713** 1p. multicoloured . . . 20 10

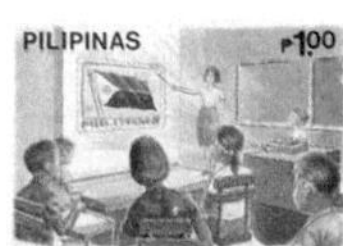

714 Map and Satellite   715 Annunciation

1989. 10th Anniv of Asia–Pacific Telecommunity.
2181 **714** 1p. multicoloured . . . 30 15

1989. Christmas. Multicoloured.
2182 60s. Type **715** 10 10
2183 75s. Mary and Elizabeth . . 15 10
2184 1p. Mary and Joseph travelling to Bethlehem 15 10
2185 2p. Search for an inn . . . 30 20
2186 4p. Magi and star 65 45
2187 4p.75 Adoration of shepherds 75 50

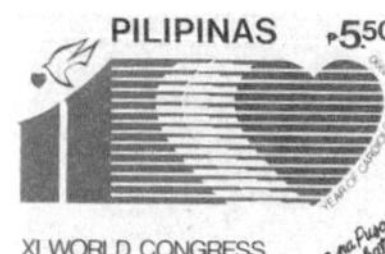

716 Lighthouse, Liner and Lifebelt

1989. International Maritime Organization.
2188 **716** 1p. multicoloured . . . 20 10

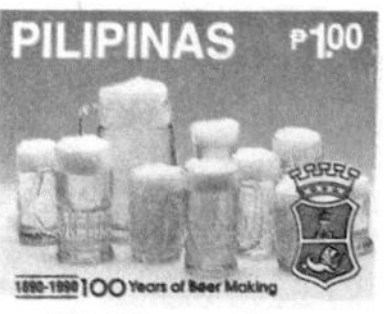

717 Spanish Philippines 1854 5c. and Revolutionary Govt 1898 2c. Stamps

1989. "World Stamp Expo '89" International Stamp Exhibition, Washington D.C. Multicoloured.
2189 1p. Type **717** 15 10
2190 4p. U.S. Administration 1899 50c. and Commonwealth 1935 6c. stamps 75 50
2191 5p.50 Japanese Occupation 1942 2c. and Republic 1946 6c. stamps 90 60

718 Teacher using Stamp as Teaching Aid

1989. Philatelic Week. Philately in the Classroom. Multicoloured.
2192 1p. Type **718** 15 10
2193 1p. Children working with stamps 15 10

1989. "Fiesta Islands '89" (4th series). As T **705**.
2194 1p. Masked festival, Negros 15 15
2195 4p.75 Grand Canao, Baguio 80 35
2196 5p.50 Fireworks 95 45

719 Heart

1990. 11th World Cardiology Congress, Manila.
2197 **719** 5p.50 red, blue and black 95 45

720 Glasses of Beer

1990. Centenary of San Miguel Brewery.
2198 **720** 1p. multicoloured . . . 15 15
2199 5p.50 multicoloured . . 95 45

721 Houses and Family

1990. Population and Housing Census. Multicoloured, colours of houses given.
2200 **721** 1p. blue 15 10
2201 1p. pink 15 10

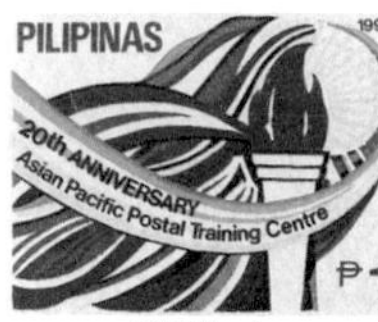

722 Scouts   723 Claro Recto (politician)

1990. 50th Anniv of Philippine Girl Scouts.
2202 **722** 1p. multicoloured . . . 35 10
2203 1p.20 multicoloured . . 35 15

1990. Birth Centenaries. Multicoloured.
2204 1p. Type **723** 15 10
2205 1p. Manuel Bernabe (poet) 15 10
2206 1p. Guillermo Tolentino (sculptor) 15 10
2207 1p. Elpidio Quirino (President 1948–53) . . . 15 10
2208 1p. Dr. Bienvenido Gonzalez (University President, 1937–51) . . . 15 10

724 Badge and Globe

1990. 50th Anniv of Legion of Mary.
2209 **724** 1p. multicoloured . . . 15 10

1990. "Fiesta Islands '89" (5th series). As No. 2179 but new value.
2210 4p. multicoloured 95 35

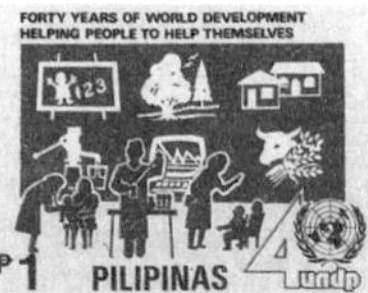

725 Torch

1990. 20th Anniv of Asian–Pacific Postal Training Centre.
2211 **725** 1p. multicoloured . . . 15 15
2212 4p. multicoloured . . . 65 35

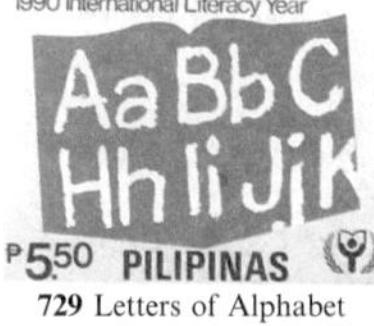

726 Catechism Class   727 Waling Waling Flowers

1990. National Catechetical Year.
2213 **726** 1p. multicoloured . . . 15 10
2214 3p.50 multicoloured . . 60 35

1990. 29th Orient and South-East Asian Lions Forum, Manila. Multicoloured.
2215 1p. Type **727** 20 15
2216 4p. Sampaguita flowers . . 65 30

728 Areas for Improvement

1990. 40th Anniv of United Nations Development Programme.
2217 **728** 1p. multicoloured . . . 15 10
2218 5p.50 multicoloured . . 90 60

729 Letters of Alphabet

1990. International Literacy Year.
2219 **729** 1p. green, orange & black 15 10
2220 5p.50 green, yellow & blk 90 60

730 "Laughter" (A. Magsaysay-Ho)

1990. Philatelic Week. Multicoloured.
2221 1p. "Family" (F. Amorsolo) (horiz) 20 15
2222 4p.75 "The Builders" (V. Edades) . . . . . . 1·20 60
2223 5p.50 Type **730** . . . . . 1·40 75

731 Star

1990. Christmas. Multicoloured.
2224 1p. Type **731** 15 10
2225 1p. Stars within stars (blue background) 15 10
2226 1p. Red and white star . . . 15 10
2227 1p. Gold and red star (green background) 15 10
2228 5p.50 Geometric star (Paskuhan Village, San Fernando) 15 10

732 Figures

1990. International White Cane Safety Day.
2229 **732** 1p. black, yellow and blue 20 15

733 La Solidaridad in 1990 and 1890 and Statue of Rizal

1990. Centenary of Publication of "Filipinas Dentro de Cien Anos" by Jose Rizal.
2230 **733** 1p. multicoloured . . . 20 15

734 Crowd before Figure of Christ

735 Tailplane and Stewardess

1991. 2nd Plenary Council of the Philippines.
2231 **734** 1p. multicoloured . . . 20 15

1991. 50th Anniv of Philippine Airlines.
2232 **735** 1p. mult (postage) . . . 15 15
2233 5p.50 multicoloured (air) 95 60

736 Gardenia

737 Sheepshank

1991. Flowers. Multicoloured.
2234 60s. Type **736** 10 10
2235 75s. Yellow bell 10 10
2475 1p. Yellow bell 10 10
2236 1p. Yellow plumeria 15 15
2237 1p. Red plumeria 15 15
2238 1p. Pink plumeria 15 15
2239 1p. White plumeria 15 15
2240 1p.20 Nerium 15 10
2241 3p.25 Ylang-ylang 60 35
2242 4p. Pink ixora 60 35
2243 4p. White ixora 60 35
2244 4p. Yellow ixora 60 35
2245 4p. Red ixora 60 35
2246 4p.75 Orange bougainvillea 65 45
2247 4p.75 Purple bougainvillea 65 45
2248 4p.75 White bougainvillea 65 45
2249 4p.75 Red bougainvillea . . 65 45
2250 5p. Canna 75 45
2251 5p.50 Red hibiscus 95 65
2252 5p.50 Yellow hibiscus . . . 95 65
2253 5p.50 White hibiscus 95 65
2254 5p.50 Pink hibiscus 95 65
See also Nos. 2322/41.

1991. 12th Asia–Pacific and 9th National Boy Scouts Jamboree. Multicoloured.
2255 1p. Reef knot 20 15
2256 4p. Type **737** 60 30
2257 4p.75 Granny knot 65 30

738 Jorge Vargas

739 "Antipolo" (Carlos Francisco) and Score

1991. Birth Centenaries. Multicoloured.
2259 1p. Type **738** 15 10
2260 1p. Ricardo Paras 15 10
2261 1p. Jose Laurel 15 10
2262 1p. Vicente Fabella 15 10
2263 1p. Maximo Kalaw 15 10

1991. 400th Anniv of Antipolo.
2264 **739** 1p. multicoloured . . . 20 15

740 Philippine Eagle

1991. Endangered Species. The Philippine Eagle. Multicoloured.
2265 1p. Type **740** 45 30
2266 4p.75 Eagle on branch . . . 1·90 1·30
2267 5p.50 Eagle in flight . . . . 2·20 1·50
2268 8p. Eagle feeding chick . . 3·25 2·20

741 Emblem

1991. Centenary of Founding of Society of Lawyers (from 1904 Philippine Bar Association).
2269 **741** 1p. multicoloured . . . 20 15

742 Flags and Induction Ceremony

743 First Regular Division Emblem

1991. 50th Anniv of Induction of Philippine Reservists into United States Army Forces in the Far East. Background colours given where necessary in brackets.
2270 **742** 1p. multicoloured . . . 20 15
2272 **743** 2p. red, black and yellow 20 15
2273 – 2p. multicoloured (yellow) (2nd Regular) 20 15
2274 – 2p. multicoloured (yellow) (11th) 20 15
2275 – 2p. blue, yellow and black (yellow) (21st) 20 15
2276 **743** 2p. red and black . . . 20 15
2277 – 2p. black, blue and red (2nd Regular) 20 15
2278 – 2p. multicoloured (white) (11th) 20 15
2279 – 2p. blue, yellow and black (white) (21st) . . 20 15
2280 – 2p. multicoloured (yellow) (31st) 20 15
2281 – 2p. multicoloured (yellow) (41st) 20 15
2282 – 2p. multicoloured (yellow) (51st) 20 15
2283 – 2p. multicoloured (yellow) (61st) 20 15
2284 – 2p. red, blue and black (31st) 20 15
2285 – 2p. multicoloured (white) (41st) 20 15
2286 – 2p. blue, black and red (51st) 20 15
2287 – 2p. multicoloured (white) (61st) 20 15
2288 – 2p. multicoloured (yellow) (71st) 20 15
2289 – 2p. multicoloured (yellow) (81st) 20 15
2290 – 2p. multicoloured (yellow) (91st) 20 15
2291 – 2p. multicoloured (yellow) (101st) . . . 20 15
2292 – 2p. multicoloured (white) (71st) 20 15
2293 – 2p. multicoloured (white) (81st) 20 15
2294 – 2p. multicoloured (white) (91st) 20 15
2295 – 2p. multicoloured (white) (101st) 20 15
2296 – 2p. blue, black and yellow (Bataan Force) 20 15
2297 – 2p. yellow, red and black (yellow) (Philippine) 20 15
2298 – 2p. multicoloured (yellow) (Air Corps) 20 15
2299 – 2p. black, blue and yellow (Offshore Patrol) 20 15
2300 – 2p. blue and black (Bataan Force) . . . 20 15
2301 – 2p. yellow, red and black (white) (Philippine) . . 20 15
2302 – 2p. multicoloured (white) (Air Corps) 20 15
2303 – 2p. black and blue (Offshore Patrol) . . . 20 15
Nos. 2272/2303 (all as T **743**) show divisional emblems.

744 Basilio

745 St. John of the Cross

1991. Centenary of Publication of "El Filibusterismo" by Jose Rizal. Characters from the novel. Each red, blue and black.
2304 1p. Type **744** 15 15
2305 1p. Simoun 15 15
2306 1p. Father Florentino . . . 15 15
2307 1p. Juli 15 15

1991. 400th Death Anniv of St. John of the Cross.
2308 **745** 1p. multicoloured . . . 20 15

746 Faces (Children's Fund)

1991. United Nations Agencies.
2310 **746** 1p. multicoloured . . . 15 15
2311 – 4p. multicoloured . . . 60 20
2312 – 5p.50 black, red and blue 80 35
DESIGNS: 4p. Hands supporting boatload of people (High Commissioner for Refugees); 5p.50, 1951 15c. and 1954 3c. U.N. stamps (40th anniv of Postal Administration).

747 "Bayanihan" (Carlos "Botong" Francisco)

1991. Philatelic Week. Multicoloured.
2313 2p. Type **747** 30 15
2314 7p. "Sari-Sari Vendor" (Mauro Malang Santos) 1·00 50
2315 8p. "Give Us This Day" (Vicente Manansala) . . . 1·20 60

748 Gymnastics

1991. 16th South-East Asian Games, Manila. Multicoloured.
2316 2p. Type **748** 30 15
2317 2p. Gymnastics (emblem at bottom) 30 15
2318 6p. Arnis (martial arts) (emblem at left) (vert) . . 65 15
2319 6p. Arnis (emblem at right) (vert) 65 15
Designs of the same value were issued together, se-tenant, each pair forming a composite design.

1991. Flowers. As T **736**. Multicoloured.
2322 1p.50 Type **736** 15 15
2323 2p. Yellow plumeria 20 20
2324 2p. Red plumeria 20 20
2325 2p. Pink plumeria 20 20
2326 2p. White plumeria 20 20
2327 3p. Nerium 30 30
2328 5p. Ylang-ylang 50 50
2329 6p. Pink ixora 60 60
2330 6p. White ixora 60 60
2331 6p. Yellow ixora 60 60
2332 6p. Red ixora 75 75
2333 7p. Orange bougainvillea . . 75 75
2334 7p. Purple bougainvillea . . 75 75
2335 7p. White bougainvillea . . 75 75
2336 7p. Red bougainvillea . . . 80 80
2337 8p. Red hibiscus 80 80
2338 8p. Yellow hibiscus 80 80
2339 8p. White hibiscus 80 75
2340 8p. Pink hibiscus 80 80
2341 10p. Canna . . . . 1·00 1·00

750 Church

751 Player

1991. Christmas. Children's Paintings. Mult.
2342 2p. Type **750** 20 15
2343 6p. Christmas present . . . 65 45
2344 7p. Santa Claus and tree . . 75 50
2345 8p. Christmas tree and star 90 60

1991. Centenary of Basketball. Multicoloured.
2346 2p. Type **751** 35 15
2347 6p. Basketball player and map (issue of first basketball stamp, 1934) (horiz) 90 30
2348 7p. Girls playing basketball (introduction of basketball in Philippines, 1904) (horiz) . . . . 1·00 35
2349 8p. Players . . . . 1·30 50

752 Monkey firing Cannon

1991. New Year. Year of the Monkey.
2351 **752** 2p. multicoloured . . 45 15
2352 6p. multicoloured . . . 1·30 30

753 Pres. Aquino and Mailing Centre Emblem

1992. Kabisig Community Projects Organization. Multicoloured.
2353 2p. Type **753** 20 20
2354 6p. Housing 65 30
2355 7p. Livestock 80 35
2356 8p. Handicrafts 95 45

754 "Curcuma longa"

1992. Asian Medicinal Plants Symposium, Los Banos, Laguna. Multicoloured.
2357 2p. Type **754** 35 20
2358 6p. "Centella asiatica" . . . 75 30
2359 7p. "Cassia alata" 90 35
2360 8p. "Ervatamia pandacaqui" 1·00 45

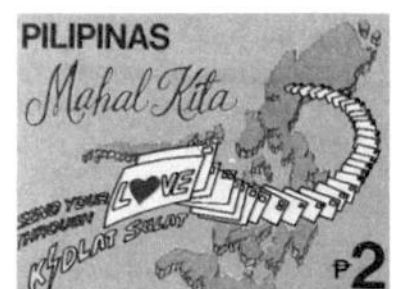

755 "Mahal Kita", Envelopes and Map

1992. Greetings Stamps. Multicoloured.
2361 2p. Type **755** 20 15
2362 2p. As No. 2361 but inscr "I Love You" 20 15
2363 6p. Heart and doves ("Mahal Kita") 75 35
2364 6p. As No. 2363 but inscr "I Love You" 75 35
2365 7p. Basket of flowers ("Mahal Kita") 80 35
2366 7p. As No. 2365 but inscr "I Love You" 80 35
2367 8p. Cupid ("Mahal Kita") 1·60 45
2368 8p. As No. 2367 but inscr "I Love You" . . . . 1·60 45

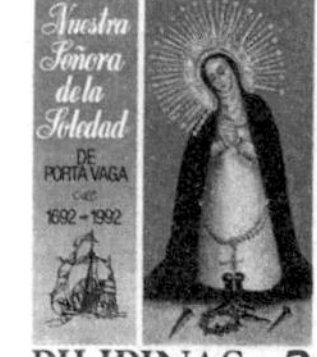

756 Philippine Pavilion and Couple Dancing
757 "Our Lady of the Sun" (icon)

1992. "Expo '92" World's Fair, Seville. Mult.
2369 2p. Type **756** 20 15
2370 8p. Pavilion, preacher and conquistador holding globe 95 45

1992. 300th Anniv of Apparition of Our Lady of the Sun at Gate, Vaga Cavite.
2372 **757** 2p. multicoloured . . . 20 15
2373 8p. multicoloured . . . 95 45

758 Fish Farming

1992. 75th Anniv of Department of Agriculture. Multicoloured.
2374 2p. Type **758** 20 15
2375 2p. Pig farming 20 15
2376 2p. Sowing seeds 20 15

759 Race Horses and Emblem
760 Manuel Roxas (President, 1946–48)

1992. 125th Anniv of Manila Jockey Club.
2377 **759** 2p. multicoloured . . . 20 15

1992. Birth Centenaries. Multicoloured.
2379 2p. Type **760** 20 15
2380 2p. Natividad Almeda-Lopez (judge) 20 15
2381 2p. Roman Ozaeta (judge) 20 15
2382 2p. Engracia Cruz-Reyes (women's rights campaigner and environmentalist) 20 15
2383 2p. Fernando Amorsolo (artist) 20 15

761 Queen, Bishop and 1978 30s. Stamp

1992. 30th Chess Olympiad, Manila. Mult.
2384 2p. Type **761** 20 15
2385 6p. King, queen and 1962 6s.+4s. stamp 65 45

762 Bataan Cross

1992. 50th Anniv of Pacific Theatre in Second World War. Multicoloured.
2387 2p. Type **762** 20 15
2388 6p. Map inside "W" 65 45
2389 8p. Corregidor eternal flame 95 65

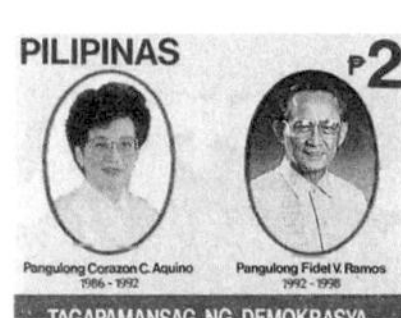

763 President Aquino and President-elect Ramos

1992. Election of Fidel Ramos to Presidency.
2391 **763** 2p. multicoloured . . . 30 15

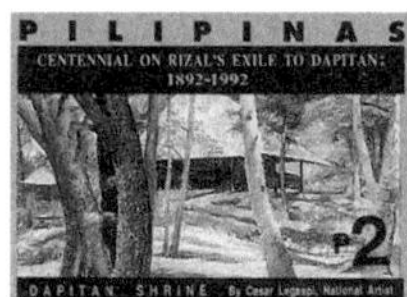

764 "Dapitan Shrine" (Cesar Legaspi)

1992. Centenary of Dr. Jose Rizal's Exile to Dapitan. Multicoloured.
2392 2p. Type **764** 20 15
2393 2p. Portrait (after Juan Luna) (vert) 20 15

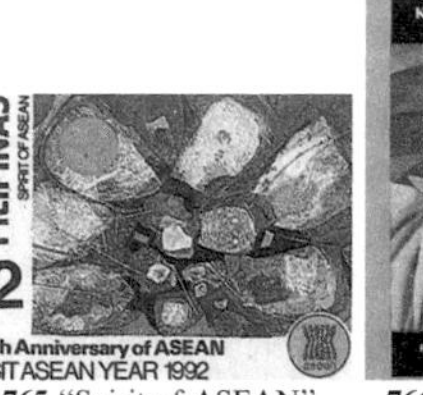

765 "Spirit of ASEAN" (Visit Asean Year)
766 Member of the Katipunan

1992. 25th Anniv of Association of South-East Asian Nations. Multicoloured.
2394 2p. Type **765** 20 15
2395 2p. "ASEAN Sea" (25th Ministerial Meeting and Postal Ministers' Conf) 20 15
2396 6p. Type **765** 65 45
2397 6p. As No. 2395 . . . . . 65 45

1992. Centenary of Katipunan ("KKK") (revolutionary organization). Multicoloured.
2398 2p. Type **766** 20 15
2399 2p. Revolutionaries 20 15
2400 2p. Plotting (horiz) 20 15
2401 2p. Attacking (horiz) . . . 20 15

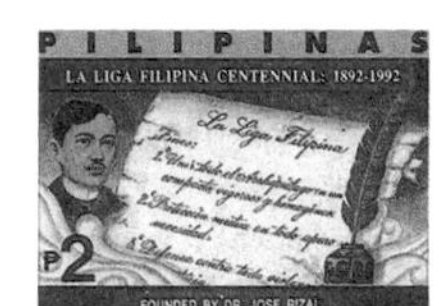

767 Dr. Jose Rizal, Text and Quill

1992. Centenary of La Liga Filipina.
2402 **767** 2p. multicoloured . . . 20 15

768 Swimming

1992. Olympic Games, Barcelona. Multicoloured.
2403 2p. Type **768** 20 15
2404 7p. Boxing 75 50
2405 8p. Hurdling 90 60

769 School, Emblem and Students

1992. Centenaries. Multicoloured.
2407 2p. Type **769** (Sisters of the Assumption in the Philippines) 20 15
2408 2p. San Sebastian's Basilica, Manila (centenary (1991) of blessing of fifth construction) (vert) . . . 20 15

770 Masonic Symbols

1992. Centenary of Nilad Lodge (first Filipino Masonic Lodge).
2409 **770** 2p. black and green . . 20 15
2410 – 6p. multicoloured . . . 65 45
2411 – 8p. multicoloured . . . 90 60
DESIGNS: 6p. Antonio Luna and symbols; 8p. Marcelo del Pilar ("Father of Philippine Masonry") and symbols.

771 Ramos taking Oath

1992. Swearing in of President Fidel Ramos. Mult.
2412 2p. Type **771** 20 15
2413 8p. President taking oath in front of flag 95 45

772 Flamingo Guppy

1992. Freshwater Aquarium Fishes (1st series). Multicoloured.
2414 1p.50 Type **772** 15 10
2415 1p.50 Neon tuxedo guppy 15 10
2416 1p.50 King cobra guppy . . 15 10
2417 1p.50 Red-tailed guppy . . 15 10
2418 1p.50 Tiger lace-tailed guppy 15 10
2419 2p. Pearl-scaled goldfish . . 30 15
2420 2p. Red-capped goldfish . . 30 15
2421 2p. Lion-headed goldfish . . 30 15
2422 2p. Black moor goldfish . . 30 15
2423 2p. Bubble-eyed goldfish . . 30 15
2424 4p. Delta topsail platy ("Variatus") 60 60
2425 4p. Orange-spotted hi-fin platy 60 60
2426 4p. Red lyre-tailed swordtail 60 60
2427 4p. Bleeding heart hi-fin platy 60 60
See also Nos. 2543/56.

774 Couple

1992. Greetings Stamps. "Happy Birthday". Multicoloured.
2430 2p. Type **774** 20 15
2431 6p. Type **774** 65 45
2432 7p. Balloons and candles on birthday cake 75 50
2433 8p. As No. 2432 . . . . . 95 60

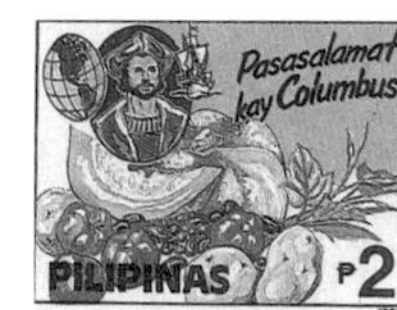

775 Melon, Beans, Tomatoes and Potatoes

1992. 500th Anniv of Discovery of America by Columbus. Multicoloured.
2434 2p. Type **775** 20 15
2435 6p. Maize and sweet potatoes 65 45
2436 8p. Pineapple, cashews, avocado and water melon 90 60

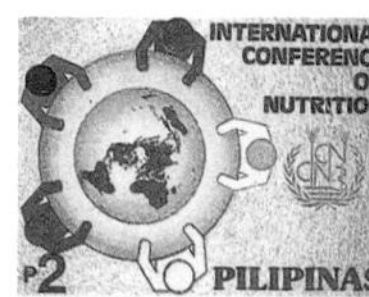

777 Figures around World Map

1992. International Nutrition Conference, Rome.
2438 **777** 2p. multicoloured . . . 20 15

778 Mother and Child
780 Family and Canoe

1992. Christmas.
2439 **778** 2p. multicoloured . . . 20 15
2440 – 6p. multicoloured . . . 65 45
2441 – 7p. multicoloured . . . 75 50
2442 – 8p. multicoloured . . . 95 60
DESIGNS: 6p. to 8p. Various designs showing mothers and children.

1992. Anti-drugs Campaign. Multicoloured.
2444 2p. Type **780** 20 15
2445 8p. Man carrying paddle, children and canoe . . . 90 60

781 Damaged Trees
782 Red Junglefowl

1992. Mt. Pinatubo Fund (for victims of volcanic eruption). Multicoloured.
2446 25s. Type **781** 10 10
2447 1p. Mt. Pinatubo erupting 10 10
2448 1p. Cattle in ash-covered field 10 10
2449 1p. Refugee settlement . . . 10 10
2450 1p. People shovelling ash . . 10 10

1992. New Year. Year of the Cock. Mult.
2451 2p. Type **782** 20 15
2452 6p. Maranao Sarimanok (mythical bird) 65 45

784 Badges of 61st and 71st Divisions, Cebu Area Command
785 "Family" (Cesar Legaspi) (family ties)

1992. Philippine Guerrilla Units of Second World War (1st series). Multicoloured.
2455 2p. Type **784** 20 15
2456 2p. Vinzon's Guerrillas and badges of 48th Chinese Guerrilla Squadron and 101st Division 20 15

2457 2p. Anderson's Command, Luzon Guerrilla Army Forces and badge of Bulacan Military Area . . 20 15
2458 2p. President Quezon's Own Guerrillas and badges of Marking's Fil-American Troops and Hunters ROTC Guerrillas 20 15
See also Nos. 2594/7, 2712/15 and 2809/12.

1992. Philatelic Week. Multicoloured.
2459 2p. Type **785** 20 15
2460 6p. "Pounding Rice" (Nena Saguil) (hard work and industry) 65 45
2461 7p. "Fish Vendors" (Romeo Tabuena) (flexibility and adaptability) 75 50

786 Black Shama

1992. Endangered Birds. Multicoloured. (a) As T **786**.
2462 2p. Type **786** 20 15
2463 2p. Blue-headed fantail . . . 20 15
2464 2p. Mindoro zone-tailed (inscr "Imperial") pigeon 20 15
2465 2p. Sulu hornbill 20 15
2466 2p. Red-vented (inscr "Philippine") cockatoo . . 20 15

(b) Size 29 × 39 mm.
2467 2p. Philippine trogon . . . 20 20
2468 2p. Rufous hornbill 20 20
2469 2p. White-bellied black woodpecker 20 20
2470 2p. Spotted wood kingfisher 20 20

(c) Size 36 × 26½ mm.
2471 2p. Brahminy kite 20 20
2472 2p. Philippine falconet . . . 20 20
2473 2p. Reef heron 20 20
2474 2p. Philippine duck (inscr "Mallard") 20 20

787 Flower (Jasmine) **788** Flower (Jasmine)

1993. National Symbols. Multicoloured. (a) As T **787**. "Pilipinas" in brown at top.
2476 1p. Type **787** 15 10
2571 2p. Flag 20 15
2478 6p. Leaf (palm) 65 45
2479 7p. Costume 75 50
2480 8p. Fruit (mango) 90 60

(b) As T **788**. "Pilipinas" in red at foot.
2481 60s. Tree 15 10
2512 1p. Flag 10 10
2513 1p. House 10 10
2514 1p. Costume 10 10
2515 1p. As No. 2481 . . . . . 10 10
2516 1p. Type **788** 10 10
2517 1p. Fruit 10 10
2518 1p. Leaf 10 10
2519 1p. Fish (milkfish) 10 10
2520 1p. Animal (water buffalo) 10 10
2521 1p. Bird (Philippine trogons) 10 10
2482 1p.50 As No. 2519 . . . . 15 10
2565 2p. Hero (Dr. Jose Rizal) 20 15
2566 2p. As No. 2513 . . . . . 20 15
2567 2p. As No. 2514 . . . . . 20 15
2568 2p. Dance ("Tinikling") . . 20 15
2569 2p. Sport (Sipa) 20 15
2570 2p. As No. 2521 . . . . . 20 15
2572 2p. As No. 2520 . . . . . 20 15
2573 2p. Type **788** 20 15
2574 2p. As No. 2481 . . . . . 20 15
2575 2p. As No. 2517 . . . . . 20 15
2576 2p. As No. 2518 . . . . . 20 15
2577 2p. As No. 2519 . . . . . 20 15
2578 2p. As No. 2512 . . . . . 20 15
2644 3p. As No. 2520 . . . . . 15 15
2645 5p. As No. 2521 . . . . . 30 20
2646 6p. As No. 2518 . . . . . 35 15
2647 7p. As No. 2514 . . . . . 40 25
2486 8p. As No. 2517 . . . . . 1·00 60
2649 10p. As No. 2513 . . . . . 55 30
See also Nos. 2781/94, 2822/44, 2980/5 and 2991.

789 "Euploea mulciber dufresne"

1993. Butterflies. Multicoloured. (a) As T **789**.
2488 2p. Type **789** 20 15
2489 2p. "Cheritra orpheus" . . 20 15
2490 2p. "Delias henningia" . . . 20 15
2491 2p. "Mycalesis ita" 20 15
2492 2p. "Delias diaphana" . . . 20 15

(b) Size 28 × 35 mm.
2493 2p. "Papilio rumanzobia" 20 20
2494 2p. "Papilio palinurus" . . 20 20
2495 2p. "Trogonoptera trojana" 20 20
2496 2p. Tailed jay ("Graphium agamemnon") 20 20
Nos. 2488/92 were issued together, se-tenant, forming a composite design.

791 Nicanor Abelardo **792** Boxing and Judo

1993. Birth Centenaries. Multicoloured.
2499 2p. Type **791** 20 15
2500 2p. Pilar Hidalgo-Lim . . . 20 15
2501 2p. Manuel Viola Gallego 20 15
2502 2p. Maria Ylagan-Orosa . . 20 15
2503 2p. Eulogio B. Rodriguez 20 15

1993. 17th South-East Asian Games, Singapore. Multicoloured.
2504 2p. Weightlifting, archery, fencing and shooting (79 × 29 mm) 20 15
2505 2p. Type **792** 20 15
2506 2p. Athletics, cycling, gymnastics and golf (79 × 29 mm) 20 15
2507 6p. Table tennis, football, volleyball and badminton (79 × 29 mm) 65 45
2508 6p. Billiards and bowling . . 65 45
2509 6p. Swimming, water polo, yachting and diving (79 × 29 mm) 65 45

794 "Spathoglottis chrysantha"

1993. Orchids. Multicoloured.
2522 2p. Type **794** 20 15
2523 2p. "Arachnis longicaulis" 20 15
2524 2p. "Phalaenopsis mariae" 20 15
2525 2p. "Coelogyne marmorata" 20 15
2526 2p. "Dendrobium sanderae" 20 15
2527 3p. "Dendrobium serratilabium" 30 20
2528 3p. "Phalaenopsis equestris" 30 20
2529 3p. "Vanda merrillii" . . . 30 20
2530 3p. "Vanda luzonica" . . . 30 20
2531 3p. "Grammatophyllum martae" 30 20

796 Dog in Window ("Thinking of You")

1993. Greetings Stamps. Multicoloured.
2534 2p. Type **796** 20 15
2535 2p. As No. 2534 but inscr "Naaalala Kita" 20 15
2536 6p. Dog looking at clock ("Thinking of You") . . 65 45
2537 6p. As No. 2536 but inscr "Naaalala Kita" 65 45
2538 7p. Dog looking at calendar ("Thinking of You") . . 75 50
2539 7p. As No. 2538 but inscr "Naaalala Kita" 75 50
2540 8p. Dog with pair of slippers ("Thinking of You") 90 60
2541 8p. As No. 2540 but inscr "Naaalala Kita" 90 60

797 Palms and Coconuts **799** Map and Emblem

798 Albino Ryukin Goldfish

1993. "Tree of Life".
2542 **797** 2p. multicoloured . . . 20 15

1993. Freshwater Aquarium Fishes (2nd series). Multicoloured. (a) As T **798**.
2543 2p. Type **798** 20 15
2544 2p. Black oranda goldfish 20 15
2545 2p. Lion-headed goldfish . . 20 15
2546 2p. Celestial goldfish 20 15
2547 2p. Pompon goldfish 20 15
2548 2p. Paradise fish 20 15
2549 2p. Pearl gourami 20 15
2550 2p. Red-tailed black shark (carp) 20 15
2551 2p. Tiger barb 20 15
2552 2p. Cardinal tetra 20 15

(b) Size 29 × 39 mm.
2553 2p. Pearl-scaled freshwater angelfish 20 15
2554 2p. Zebra freshwater angelfish 20 20
2555 2p. Marble freshwater angelfish 20 20
2556 2p. Black freshwater angelfish 20 20

1993. Basic Petroleum and Minerals Inc. "Towards Self-sufficiency in Energy".
2558 **799** 2p. multicoloured . . . 20 15

801 Globe, Scales, Book and Gavel

1993. 16th Int Law Conference, Manila. Mult.
2560 2p. Type **801** 20 15
2561 6p. Globe, scales, gavel and conference emblem on flag of Philippines (vert) . . . 65 45
2562 7p. Woman holding scales, conference building and globe 80 50
2563 8p. Fisherman pulling in nets and emblem (vert) . . 95 65

802 Our Lady of La Naval (statue) and Galleon

1993. 400th Anniv of Our Lady of La Naval.
2564 **802** 2p. multicoloured . . . 20 15

803 Woman and Terraced Hillside

1993. International Year of Indigenous Peoples. Women in traditional costumes. Multicoloured.
2579 2p. Type **803** 20 15
2580 6p. Woman, plantation and mountain 65 45
2581 7p. Woman and mosque . . 80 50
2582 8p. Woman and Filipino vintas (sail canoes) . . . 95 65

804 Trees

1993. Philatelic Week. "Save the Earth". Mult.
2583 2p. Type **804** 20 15
2584 6p. Marine flora and fauna 65 45
2585 7p. Dove and irrigation system 80 50
2586 8p. Effects of industrial pollution 95 65

805 1949 6c.+4c. Stamp and Symbols **806** Moon-buggy and Society Emblem

1993. 400th Anniv of Publication of "Doctrina Christiana" (first book published in Philippines).
2587 **805** 2p. multicoloured . . . 20 15

1993. 50th Anniv of Filipino Inventors Society. Multicoloured.
2588 2p. Type **806** 20 15
2589 2p. Rice-harvesting machine 20 15
Nos. 2588/9 were issued together, se-tenant, forming a composite design.

807 Holy Family **808** Northern Luzon

1993. Christmas. Multicoloured.
2590 2p. Type **807** 20 15
2591 6p. Church goers 65 45
2592 7p. Cattle and baskets of food 80 50
2593 8p. Carol-singers 95 65

1993. Philippine Guerrilla Units of Second World War (2nd series). Multicoloured.
2594 2p. Type **808** 20 15
2595 2p. Bohol Area Command 20 15
2596 2p. Leyte Area Command 20 15
2597 2p. Palawan Special Battalion and Sulu Area Command 20 15

809 Dove over City (peace and order)

1993. "Philippines 2000" (development plan). Multicoloured.
2598 2p. Type **809** 20 15
2599 6p. Means of transport and communications 65 45
2600 7p. Offices, roads and factories (infrastructure and industry) 80 50
2601 8p. People from different walks of life (people empowerment) 95 65

810 Shih Tzu

1993. New Year. Year of the Dog. Multicoloured.
2603 2p. Type **810** 20 15
2604 6p. Chow 65 45

811 Jamboree Emblem and Flags

1993. 1st Association of South-East Asian Nations Scout Jamboree, Makiling. Multicoloured.
2606 2p. Type **811** 20 15
2607 6p. Scout at camp-site, flags and emblem 65 45

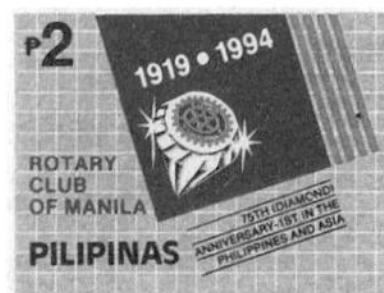

812 Club Emblem on Diamond

1994. 75th Anniv of Manila Rotary Club.
2609 **812** 2p. multicoloured . . . 20 15

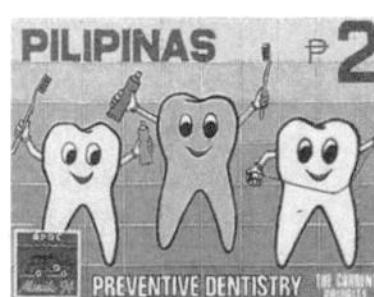

813 Teeth and Dental Hygiene Products

1994. 17th Asian–Pacific Dental Congress, Manila. Multicoloured.
2610 2p. Type **813** 20 15
2611 6p. Teeth, flags of participating countries and teeth over globe with Philippines circled (vert) 65 45

814 "Acropora micropthalma"

1994. Corals. Multicoloured.
2612 2p. Type **814** 20 15
2613 2p. "Seriatopora hystrix" . . 20 15
2614 2p. "Acropora latistella" . . 20 15
2615 2p. "Millepora tenella" . . 20 15
2616 2p. "Millepora tenella" (different) 20 15
2617 2p. "Pachyseris valenciennesi" 20 15
2618 2p. "Pavona decussata" . . 20 15
2619 2p. "Galaxea fascicularis" 20 15
2620 2p. "Acropora formosa" . . 20 15
2621 2p. "Acropora humilis" . . 20 15
2622 2p. "Isis sp." (vert) 20 20
2623 2p. "Plexaura sp." (vert) . . 20 20
2624 2p. "Dendronepthya sp." (vert) 20 20
2625 2p. "Heteroxenia sp." (vert) 20 20

815 New Year Stamps of 1991 and 1992 bearing Exhibition Emblem

1994. "Hong Kong '94" Stamp Exhibition. Multicoloured.
2627 2p. Type **815** 20 15
2628 6p. 1993 New Year stamps 65 45

816 Class of 1944 Emblem

817 Airplane over Harbour, Man and Cogwheel and Emblem

1994. 50th Anniv of Philippine Military Academy Class of 1944
2630 **816** 2p. multicoloured . . . 20 15

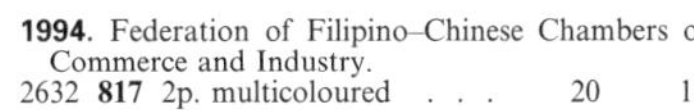

1994. Federation of Filipino–Chinese Chambers of Commerce and Industry.
2632 **817** 2p. multicoloured . . . 20 15

818 Stork carrying Baby ("Binabati Kita")

819 Gloria Diaz (Miss Universe 1969)

1994. Greetings Stamps. Multicoloured.
2633 2p. Type **818** 20 15
2634 2p. As No. 2633 but inscr "Congratulations" 20 15
2635 2p. Bouquet ("Binabati Kita") 20 15
2636 2p. As No. 2635 but inscr "Congratulations" 20 15
2637 2p. Mortar board, scroll and books ("Binabati Kita") 20 15
2638 2p. As No. 2637 but inscr "Congratulations" 20 15
2639 2p. Bouquet, doves and heads inside heart ("Binabati Kita") 20 15
2640 2p. As No. 2639 but inscr "Congratulations" 20 15

1994. Miss Universe Beauty Contest. Multicoloured.
2653 2p. Type **819** 20 15
2654 2p. Margie Moran (Miss Universe 1973) 20 15
2655 6p. Crown 65 45
2656 7p. Contestant 80 60

820 Antonio Molina (composer)

821 Map, Forest and Emblem (Baguio City)

1994. Birth Centenaries. Multicoloured.
2658 2p. Type **820** 20 15
2659 2p. Jose Yulo (Secretary of Justice) 20 15
2660 2p. Josefa Jara-Martinez (social worker) 20 15
2661 2p. Nicanor Reyes (accountant) 20 15
2662 2p. Sabino Padilla (judge) 20 15

1994. Export Processing Zones. Multicoloured.
2664 2p. Type **821** 20 15
2665 2p. Cross on hilltop (Bataan) 20 15
2666 2p. Octagonal building (Mactan) 20 15
2667 2p. Aguinaldo Shrine (Cavite) 20 15
2668 7p. Map and products . . . 80 50
2669 8p. Globe and products . . . 95 65
Nos. 2264/7 and 2668/9 repectively were issued together, se-tenant, forming composite designs.

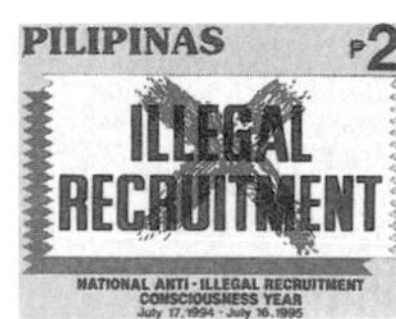

822 Cross through "ILLEGAL RECRUITMENT"

1994. Anti-illegal Recruitment Campaign.
2670 **822** 2p. multicoloured . . . 20 15

823 Palawan Bearcat

1994. Mammals. Multicoloured.
2671 6p. Type **823** 75 45
2672 6p. Philippine tarsier 75 45
2673 6p. Malayan pangolin (inscr "Scaly Anteater") 75 45
2674 6p. Indonesian ("Palawan") porcupine 75 45

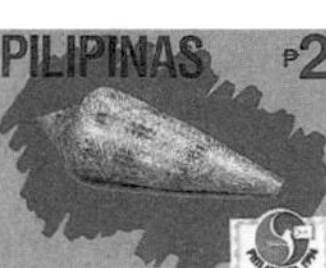

824 Glory of the Sea Cone ("Conus gloriamaris")

1994. "Philakorea 1994" International Stamp Exhibition, Seoul. Shells. Multicoloured.
2676 2p. Type **824** 20 15
2677 2p. Striate cone ("Conus striatus") 20 15
2678 2p. Geography cone ("Conus geographus") . . 20 15
2679 2p. Textile cone ("Conus textile") 20 15

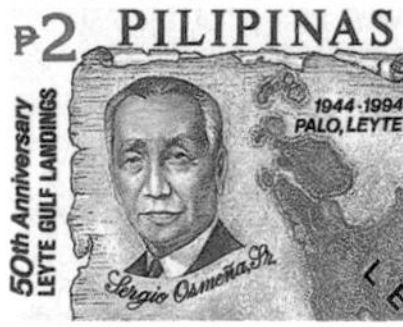

825 Sergio Osmena, Snr.

1994. 50th Anniv of Leyte Gulf Landings. Multicoloured.
2682 2p. Type **825** 20 15
2683 2p. Soldiers landing at Palo 20 15
2684 2p. "Peace – A Better World" emblem 20 15
2685 2p. Carlos Romulo 20 15
Nos. 2682/5 were issued together, se-tenant, forming a composite design.

826 Family (International Year of the Family)

1994. Anniversaries and Event. Multicoloured.
2686 2p. Type **826** 20 15
2687 6p. Workers (75th anniv of I.L.O.) 75 45
2688 7p. Aircraft and symbols of flight (50th anniv of I.C.A.O.) 90 60

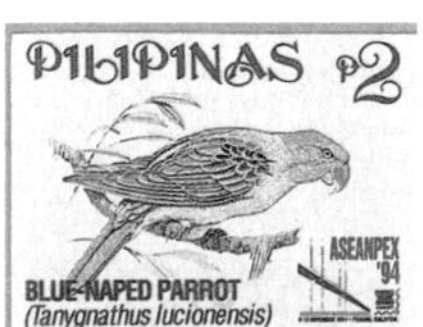

827 Blue-naped Parrot

1994. "Aseanpex '94" Stamp Exhibition, Penang, Malaysia. Birds. Muilticoloured.
2689 2p. Type **827** 20 15
2690 2p. Luzon bleeding heart ("Bleeding Heart Pigeon") 20 15
2691 2p. Palawan peacock-pheasant 20 15
2692 2p. Koch's pitta 20 15

828 Presidents Fidel Ramos and W. Clinton

1994. Visit of United States President William Clinton to Philippines.
2694 **828** 2p. multicoloured . . . 20 15
2695 8p. multicoloured . . . 1·00 65

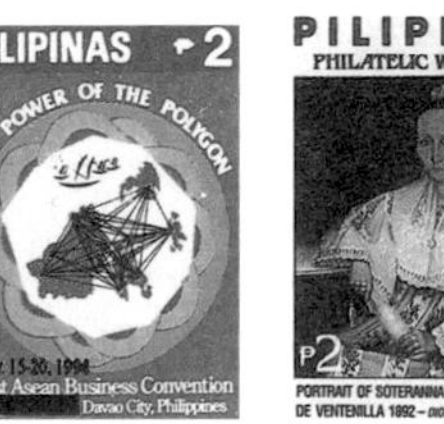

829 Convention Emblem

830 "Soteranna Puson y Quintos de Ventenilla" (Dionisio de Castro)

1994. Association of South-East Asian Nations Eastern Business Convention, Davao City.
2696 **829** 2p. multicoloured . . . 30 15
2697 6p. multicoloured . . . 75 50

1994. Philatelic Week. Portraits. Multicoloured.
2698 2p. Type **830** . . . . . . 30 1·70
2699 6p. "Quintina Castor de Sadie" (Simon Flores y de la Rosa) 75 50
2700 7p. "Portrait of the Artist's Mother" (Felix Hidalgo y Padilla) 90 60
2701 8p. "Una Bulaquena" (Juan Luna y Novicio) . . . . 1·00 65

831 Wreath

1994. Christmas. Multicoloured.
2703 2p. Type **831** 30 15
2704 6p. Angels 75 50
2705 7p. Bells 90 60
2706 8p. Christmas basket . . . 1·00 65

832 Piggy Bank

1994. New Year. Year of the Pig. Multicoloured.
2707 2p. Type **832** 30 15
2708 6p. Pig couple 75 50

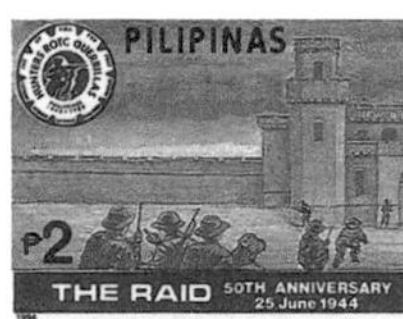

833 Raid on Prison

1994. 50th Anniversaries of Raid by Hunters ROTC Guerrillas on Psew Bilibi Prison and of Mass Escape by Inmates. Multicoloured.
2710 2p. Type **833** 20 15
2711 2p. Inmates fleeing 20 15
Nos. 2710/11 were issued together, se-tenant, forming a composite design.

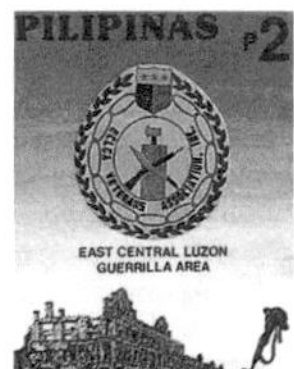

834 East Central Luzon Guerrilla Area

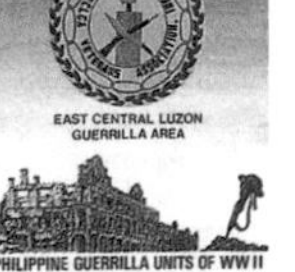

835 Ribbon on Globe

1994. Philippine Guerrilla Units of Second World War (3rd series). Multicoloured.
2712 2p. Type **834** 20 15
2713 2p. Mindoro Provincial Battalion and Marinduque Guerrilla Force 20 15
2714 2p. Zambales Military District and Masbate Guerrilla Regiment . . . 20 15
2715 2p. Samar Area Command 20 15

1994. National AIDS Awareness Campaign.
2716 **835** 2p. multicoloured . . . 20 15

836 Flag

1994. Centenary of Declaration of Philippine Independence. Multicoloured.
2717 2p. Type **836** 20 15
2718 2p. Present state flag 20 15
2719 2p. Anniversary emblem . . 20 15
Nos. 2717/19 were issued together, se-tenant, forming a composite design.

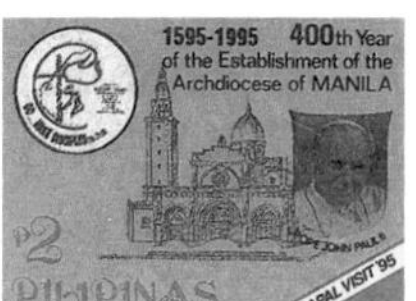

837 Pope John Paul II and Manila Cathedral

1995. Papal Visit. Multicoloured.
2720 2p. Type **837** (400th anniv of Manila Archdiocese) . . . 20 15
2721 2p. Pope and Cebu Cathedral (400th anniv of Diocese) 20 15
2722 2p. Pope and Caceres Cathedral (400th anniv of Diocese) 20 15
2723 2p. Pope and Nueva Segovia Cathedral (400th anniv of Diocese) 20 15
2724 2p. Pope, globe and Pope's arms 30 20
2725 6p. Pope and Federation of Asian Bishops emblem (6th Conference, Manila) 75 50
2726 8p. Pope, youths and emblem (10th World Youth Day) . . . . . . 1·00 65

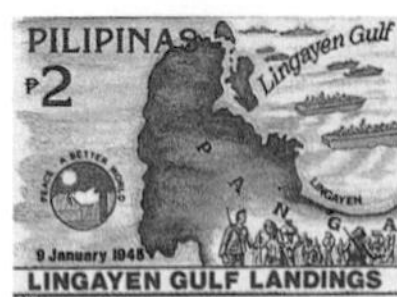

839 Landing Craft and Map

1995. 50th Anniv of Lingayen Gulf Landings. Multicoloured.
2729 2p. Type **839** 20 15
2730 2p. Map and emblems of 6th, 37th, 40th and 43rd army divisions 20 15
Nos. 2729/30 were issued together, se-tenant, forming a composite design.

840 Monument (Peter de Guzman) and Ruins of Intramuros (½-size illustration)

1995. 50th Anniv of Battle for the Liberation of Manila. Multicoloured.
2731 2p. Type **840** 10 10
2732 8p. Monument and ruins of Legislative Building and Department of Agriculture 40 20

841 Diokno

1995. 8th Death Anniv of Jose Diokno (politician).
2733 **841** 2p. multicoloured . . . 20 15

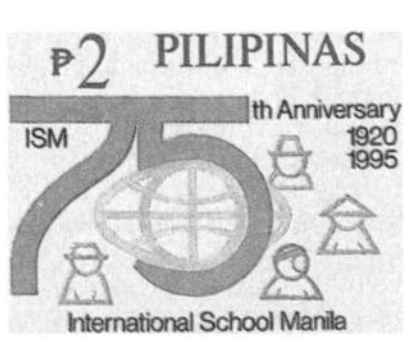

842 Anniversary Emblem and Ethnic Groups

1995. 75th Anniv of International School, Manila. Multicoloured.
2734 2p. Type **842** 20 15
2735 8p. Globe and cut-outs of children . . . . 1·00 65

843 Greater Malay Mouse Deer

1995. Mammals. Multicoloured.
2736 2p. Type **843** 20 15
2737 2p. Tamarau 20 15
2738 2p. Visayan warty pig . . . 20 15
2739 2p. Palm civet 20 15

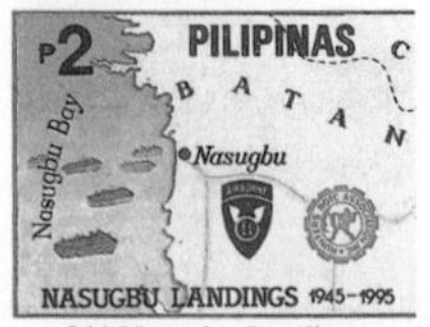

844 Nasugbu Landings

1995. 50th Anniversaries. Multicoloured.
2741 2p. Type **844** 20 15
2742 2p. Tagaytay Landings . . . 20 15
2743 2p. Battle of Nichols Airbase and Fort McKinley 20 15
Nos. 2741/2 were issued together, se-tenant, forming a composite design.

845 Memorial

1995. 50th Anniv of Liberation of Baguio.
2744 **845** 2p. multicoloured . . . 20 15

846 Cabanatuan Camp

847 Victorio Edades (artist)

1995. 50th Anniv of Liberation of Internment and Prisoner of War Camps. Multicoloured.
2745 2p. Type **846** 20 15
2746 2p. Entrance to U.S.T. camp 20 15
2747 2p. Los Banos camp 20 15
Nos. 2746/7 are wrongly inscribed "Interment".

1995. Birth Centenaries. Multicoloured.
2748 2p. Type **847** 20 15
2749 2p. Jovita Fuentes (opera singer) 20 15
2750 2p. Candido Africa (medical researcher) 20 15
2751 2p. Asuncion Arriola-Perez (politician) 20 15
2752 2p. Eduardo Quisumbing (botanist) 20 15

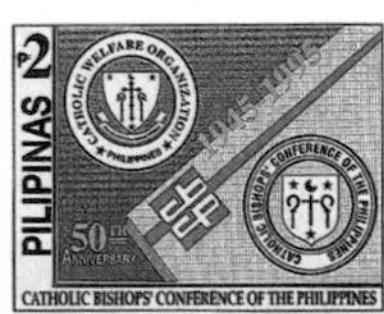

848 Emblems and Bible

1995. 50th Anniv of Philippine Catholic Bishops' Conference, Manila.
2754 **848** 2p. multicoloured . . . 20 15

849 Ferrer

850 Neolithic Burial Jar, Manunggul

1995. 8th Death Anniv of Jaime Ferrer (administrator).
2755 **849** 2p. multicoloured . . . 20 15

1995. Archaeology. Multicoloured.
2756 2p. Type **850** 20 15
2757 2p. Iron age secondary burial jar, Ayub Cave, Mindanao 20 15
2758 2p. Iron age secondary burial jar (different), Ayub Cave 20 15
2759 2p. Neolithic ritual drinking vessel, Leta-Leta Cave, Palawan 20 15

852 Right Hand supporting Wildlife

1995. Association of South-East Asian Nations Environment Year. Multicoloured.
2762 2p. Type **852** 20 15
2763 2p. Left hand supporting wildlife 20 15
Nos. 2762/3 were issued together, se-tenant, forming a composite design.

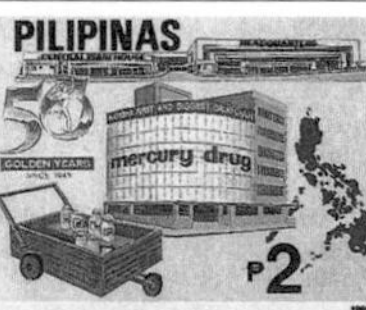

853 Anniversary Emblem, Buildings and Trolley

1995. 50th Anniv of Mercury Drug Corporation.
2765 **853** 2p. multicoloured . . . 20 15

854 Parish Church

1995. 400th Anniv of Parish of Saint Louis Bishop, Lucban.
2766 **854** 2p. multicoloured . . . 20 15

855 Instructor and Pupils

1995. 25th Anniv of Asian-Pacific Postal Training Centre, Bangkok.
2768 **855** 6p. multicoloured . . . 80 50

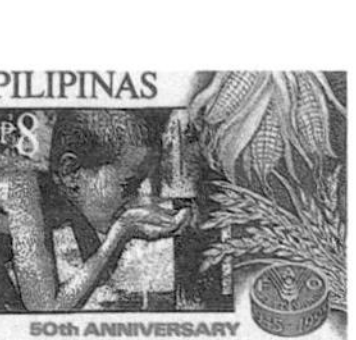

856 Crops and Child drinking from Well

857 Carlos Romulo

1995. 50th Anniv of F.A.O.
2769 **856** 8p. multicoloured . . . 1·10 75

1995. 50th Anniv of U.N.O. Multicoloured.
2770 2p. Jose Bengzon (inscr "Cesar Bengzon") 55 55
2771 2p. Rafael Salas (Assistant Secretary General) 55 55
2772 2p. Salvador Lopez (Secretary) 55 55
2773 2p. Jose Ingles (Under-secretary) 55 55
2775 2p. Type **857** 20 15
No. 2770 depicts Jose Bengzon in error for his brother Cesar.

858 Anniversary Emblem

859 Eclipse

1995. 50th Anniv of Manila Overseas Press Club.
2779 **858** 2p. multicoloured . . . 20 15

1995. Total Solar Eclipse.
2780 **859** 2p. multicoloured . . . 20 15

860 Flag

861 "Two Igorot Women" (Victorio Edades)

1995. National Symbols. With blue barcode at top. "Pilipinas" in red. Variously dated. Multicoloured.
2781 2p. Flag ("Pillipinas" at top) 20 15
2782 2p. Hero (Jose Rizal) . . . 20 15
2783 2p. House 20 15
2784 2p. Costume 20 15
2785 2p. Dance 20 15
2786 2p. Sport 20 15
2787 2p. Bird (Philippine eagle) 20 15
2788 2p. Type **860** 20 15
2789 2p. Animal (water buffalo) 20 15
2790 2p. Flower (jasmine) 20 15
2791 2p. Tree 20 15
2792 2p. Fruit (mango) 20 15
2793 2p. Leaf (palm) 20 15
2794 2p. Fish (milkfish) 20 15
For designs with barcode but "Pilipinas" in blue, see Nos. 2822/44.

1995. National Stamp Collecting Month (1st issue). Paintings by Filipino artists. Multicoloured.
2795 2p. Type **861** 30 15
2796 6p. "Serenade" (Carlos Francisco) 90 50
2797 7p. "Tuba Drinkers" (Vicente Manansala) . . . 95 65
2798 8p. "Genesis" (Hernando Ocampo) . . . . 1·00 80

862 Tambourine

863 Abacus and Anniversary Emblem

1995. Christmas. Musical instruments and Lines from Carols. Multicoloured.
2800 2p. Type **862** 20 15
2801 6p. Maracas 75 50
2802 7p. Guitar 95 65
2803 8p. Drum . . . . 1·20 80

1995. 50th Anniv of Sycip Gorres Velayo & Co. (accountants).
2804 **863** 2p. multicoloured . . . 20 15

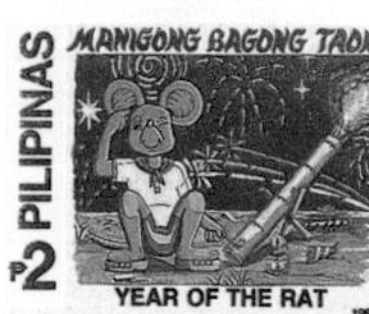

865 Rat and Fireworks

1995. New Year. Year of the Rat. Multicoloured.
2806 2p. Type **865** 30 20
2807 6p. Model of rat 80 50

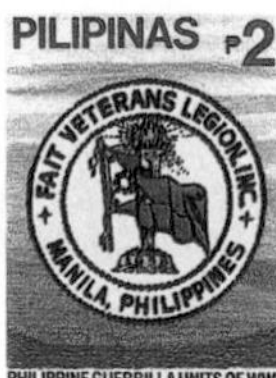

866 Badge of Fil-American Irregular Troops Veterans Legion

1995. Philippine Guerrilla Units of Second World War (4th series). Multicoloured.
2809 2p. Type **866** 20 15
2810 2p. Badge of Bicol Brigade Veterans 20 15
2811 2p. Map of Fil-American Guerrilla forces (Cavite) and Hukbalahap unit (Pampanga) 20 15
2812 2p. Map of South Tarlac military district and Northwest Pampanga . . 20 15

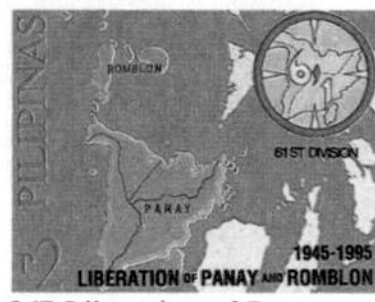

867 Liberation of Panay and Romblon

1995. 50th Anniversaries. Multicoloured.
2813 2p. Type **867** 20 15
2814 2p. Liberation of Cebu . . . 20 15
2815 2p. Battle of Ipo Dam . . . 20 15
2816 2p. Battle of Bessang Pass 20 15
2817 2p. Surrender of General Yamashita 20 15

868 Jose Rizal

870 "Treating Patient" (Manuel Baldemor)

1995. Centenary of Declaration of Philippine Independence Revolutionaries. Multicoloured.

2818 2p. Type **868** 20 15
2819 2p. Andres Bonifacio 20 15
2820 2p. Apolinario Mabini 20 15

1996. National Symbols. As T **860**, with blue barcode at top. "Pilipinas" in blue. Variously dated. Multicoloured.

2822 1p. Flower (jasmine) 15 10
2823 1p.50 Fish (milkfish) 20 15
2823a 2p. Flower (jasmine) 30 30
2824 3p. Animal (water buffalo) 35 30
2825 4p. Flag ("Pilipinas" at top) 50 35
2826 4p. Hero (Jose Rizal) 50 35
2827 4p. House 50 35
2828 4p. Costume 50 35
2829 4p. Dance 50 35
2830 4p. Sport 50 35
2831 4p. Bird (Philippine eagle) 50 35
2832 4p. Type **860** 50 35
2833 4p. Animal (head of water buffalo) (dated "1995") 50 35
2834 4p. Flower (jasmine) 50 35
2835 4p. Tree 50 35
2836 4p. Fruit (mango) 50 35
2837 4p. Leaf (palm) 50 35
2838 4p. Fish (milkfish) 50 35
2839 4p. Animal (water buffalo) (dated "1996") 50 35
2840 5p. Bird (Philippine eagle) 75 1·20
2841 6p. Leaf (palm) 80 50
2842 7p. Costume 90 60
2843 8p. Fruit (mango) 1·10 75
2844 10p. House 1·40 90

1996. 23rd International Congress of Internal Medicine, Manila.

2856 **870** 2p. multicoloured 20 15

871 Walled City of Intramuros

1996. Centenary of Sun Life of Canada (insurance company). Multicoloured.

2857 2p. Type **871** 20 15
2858 8p. Manila Bay sunset 1·10 75

872 Pair of Eastern Rosella (birds) on Branch ("I Love You")

873 University Building and Map of Islands on Grid

1996. Greetings Stamps. Multicoloured.

2859 2p. Type **872** 20 15
2860 2p. Eastern rosella (birds) ("Happy Valentine") 20 15
2861 6p. Cupid holding banner ("I Love You") 75 50
2862 6p. Cupid holding banner ("Happy Valentine") 75 50
2863 7p. Box of chocolates ("I Love You") 95 65
2864 7p. Box of chocolates ("Happy Valentine") 95 65
2865 8p. Butterfly and roses ("I Love You") 1·20 80
2866 8p. Butterfly and roses ("Happy Valentine") 1·20 80

Nos. 2861/2 were issued together, se-tenant, forming a composite design.

1996. 50th Anniv of Gregorio Araneta University Foundation.

2867 **873** 2p. multicoloured 20 15

874 Hospital

1996. 50th Anniv of Santo Tomas University Hospital.

2868 **874** 2p. multicoloured 20 15

875 Racoon Butterflyfish

1996. Fishes (1st series). Multicoloured.

2869 4p. Type **875** 50 35
2870 4p. Clown triggerfish 50 35
2871 4p. Regal angelfish 50 35
2872 4p. Mandarin fish 50 35
2873 4p. Emperor angelfish 50 35
2874 4p. Japan surgeonfish ("Powder Brown Tang") 50 35
2875 4p. Blue-girdled ("Majestic") angelfish 50 35
2876 4p. Palette surgeonfish ("Blue tang") 50 35
2877 4p. Moorish idol 50 35
2878 4p. Yellow-tailed ("Two-banded") anemonefish 50 35

See also Nos. 2885/94.

877 Francisco Ortigas

1996.

2882 **877** 4p. multicoloured 50 35

878 Mother Francisca and Convent

1996. 300th Anniv of Dominican Sisters of St. Catherine of Siena.

2883 **878** 4p. multicoloured 50 35

879 Nuclear Reactor

(880)

1996. Centenary of Discovery of Radioactivity by Antoine Henri Becquerel.

2884 **879** 4p. multicoloured 50 35

1996. Fishes (2nd series). As T **875**. Multicoloured.

2885 4p. Spotted boxfish 50 35
2886 4p. Saddle ("Saddleback") butterflyfish 50 35
2887 4p. Sail-finned tang 50 35
2888 4p. Harlequin tuskfish 50 35
2889 4p. Clown wrasse 50 35
2890 4p. Yellow-faced ("Blue-faced") angelfish 50 35
2891 4p. Long-horned cowfish 50 35
2892 4p. Queen angelfish 50 35
2893 4p. Forceps ("Long-nosed") butterflyfish 50 35
2894 4p. Yellow tang 50 35

1996. 10th Anniv of Young Philatelists' Society. Nos. 2471/4 optd with T **880**.

2897 2p. multicoloured 20 20
2898 2p. multicoloured 20 20
2899 2p. multicoloured 20 20
2900 2p. multicoloured 20 20

881 Carlos Garcia (President, 1957–61)

882 Satellite, Dish Aerial, Cock and Map

1996. Birth Centenaries. Multicoloured.

2901 4p. Type **881** 50 35
2902 4p. Casimiro del Rosario (physicist) 50 35
2903 4p. Geronima Pecson (first woman senator) 50 35
2904 4p. Cesar Bengson (member of International Court of Justice) 50 35
2905 4p. Jose Corazon de Jesus (writer) 50 35

1996. 50th Anniv of ABS–CBN Broadcasting Services in Philippines. Multicoloured.

2907 4p. Type **882** 50 35
2908 8p. Cock, satellite and hemispheres 1·10 75

883 "M" and Heart

1996. "Convention City Manila".

2909 **883** 4p. multicoloured 50 35

884 Cojuangco

1996. Birth Centenary of Jose Cojuangco (entrepreneur and Corazon Aquino's father).

2910 **884** 4p. multicoloured 50 35

885 Brass Helmet and Top Hat

1996. 50th Anniv of Republic Day. Philippine–American Friendship Day. Multicoloured.

2911 4p. Type **885** 50 35
2912 8p. Philippine eagle and American bald eagle 1·10 75

886 Boxing

1996. Centenary of Modern Olympic Games. Mult.

2914 4p. Type **886** 50 35
2915 6p. Athletics 80 50
2916 7p. Swimming 95 65
2917 8p. Equestrian 1·10 75

887 "Alma Mater" (statue, Guillermo Tolentino) and Manila Campus (after Florentino Concepcion)

1996. 50th Anniv of University of the East, Manila and Kalookan City.

2919 **887** 4p. multicoloured 50 35

888 "Dendrobium anosmum"

1996. Orchids. Multicoloured.

2920 4p. Type **888** 50 35
2921 4p. "Phalaenopsis equestris-alba" 50 35
2922 4p. "Aerides lawrenceae" 50 35
2923 4p. "Vanda javierii" 50 35
2924 4p. "Renanthera philippinensis" 50 35
2925 4p. "Dendrobium schuetzei" 50 35
2926 4p. "Dendrobium taurinum" 50 35
2927 4p. "Vanda lamellata" 50 35

889 Emblem and Globe

1996. 6th Asia–Pacific International Trade Fair, Manila.

2929 **889** 4p. multicoloured 50 35

890 Children's Activities

891 Fran's Fantasy "Aiea"

1996. 50th Anniv of UNICEF. Multicoloured.

2930 4p. Type **890** 50 35
2931 4p. Windmills, factories, generator, boy with radio and children laughing 50 35
2932 4p. Mother holding "sun" baby and children gardening 50 35
2933 4p. Wind blowing toy windmills, boy with electrical fan and children playing 50 35

1996. "Taipeh 96" Asian Stamp Exhibition. Orchids. Multicoloured.

2935 4p. Type **891** 50 35
2936 4p. Malvarosa Green Goddess "Nani" 50 35
2937 4p. Ports of Paradise "Emerald Isle" 50 35
2938 4p. Mem. Conrada Perez "Nani" 50 35
2939 4p. Pokai Tangerine "Lea" 50 35
2940 4p. Mem. Roselyn Reisman "Diana" 50 35
2941 4p. C. Moscombe x Toshie Aoki 50 35
2942 4p. Mem. Benigno Aquino "Flying Aces" 50 35

892 Communications

893 Philippine Nativity (Gilbert Miraflor)

1996. 4th Asia–Pacific Economic Co-operation Summit Conference, Subic. Multicoloured.

2944 4p. Type **892** 50 35
2945 6p. Open hands reaching towards sun (horiz) 80 50
2946 7p. Grass and buildings (horiz) 95 65
2947 8p. Members' flags lining path leading to emblem, city and sun 1·10 75

1996. Christmas. Stamp design competition winning entries. Multicoloured.

2948 4p. Type **893** 50 35
2949 6p. Church (Stephanie Miljares) (horiz) 80 50
2950 7p. Carol singer with guitars (Mark Sales) (horiz) 95 65
2951 8p. Carol singers and statue of buffalo (Lecester Glaraga) 1·10 75

894 Perez

1996. Birth Centenary of Eugenio Perez (politician).

2952 **894** 4p. multicoloured 50 35

895 Carabao

1996. New Year. Year of the Ox. Multicoloured.

2953 4p. Type **895** 50 35
2954 6p. Tamaraw 80 50

896 Rizal aged 14 **897** Father Mariano Gomez

1996. "Aseanpex '96" Association of South-East Asian Nations Stamp Exhibition, Manila. Death Centenary of Dr. Jose Rizal (1st issue). Mult.

2956 4p. Type **896** 50 35
2957 4p. Rizal aged 18 . . . . . 50 35
2958 4p. Rizal aged 25 . . . . . 50 35
2959 4p. Rizal aged 31 . . . . . 50 35
2960 4p. Title page of "Noli Me Tangere" (first novel) . . 50 35
2961 4p. Gomburza and associates 50 35
2962 4p. "Oyang Dapitana" (sculpture by Rizal) . . . 50 35
2963 4p. Bust by Rizal of Ricardo Carnicero (commandant of Dapitan) 50 35
2964 4p. Rizal's house at Calamba (horiz) 50 35
2965 4p. University of Santo Tomas, Manila (horiz) . . 50 35
2966 4p. Hotel de Oriente, Manila (horiz) 50 35
2967 4p. Dapitan during Rizal's exile (horiz) 50 35
2968 4p. Central University, Madrid (horiz) 50 35
2969 4p. British Museum, London (horiz) 50 35
2970 4p. Botanical Garden, Madrid (horiz) 50 35
2971 4p. Heidelberg, Germany (horiz) 50 35

See also No. 2976.

1996. Centenary of Declaration of Philippine Independence. Execution of Secularist Priests, 1872. Multicoloured.

2973 4p. Type **897** 50 35
2974 4p. Father Jose Burgos . . 50 35
2975 4p. Father Jacinto Zamora 50 35

898 Rizal (poster)

1996. Death Centenary of Dr. Jose Rizal (2nd issue).
2976 **898** 4p. multicoloured . . . 50 35

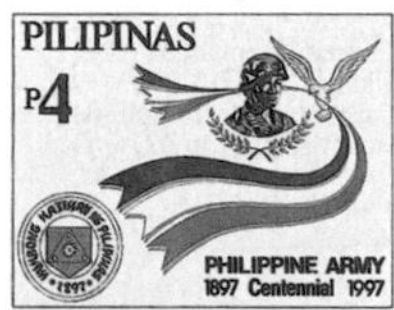

899 Soldier, Dove and National Colours

1997. Centenary of Philippine Army.
2978 **899** 4p. multicoloured . . . 50 45

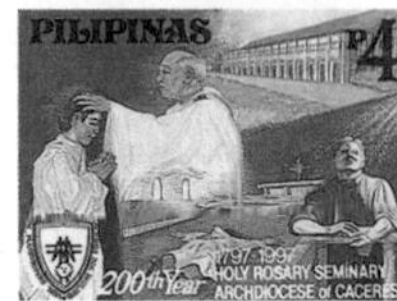

900 Ordination, Seminary, Priest prostrate before Altar and Priest at Devotions

1997. Bicentenary of Holy Rosary Seminary, Naga City.
2979 **900** 4p. multicoloured . . . 50 45

1997. National Symbols. As T **788** (no bar code). "Pilipinas" in blue. Multicoloured.

2980 1p. Flower (jasmine) 30 15
2981 5p. Bird (Philippine eagle) 1·30 45
2982 6p. Leaf (palm) . . . . . . 1·50 60
2983 7p. Costume . . . . 1·80 65
2984 8p. Fruit (mango) . . . . . 2·10 80
2985 10p. House . . . . 2·50 1·00

901 Volunteers attending Patient

1997. 50th Anniv of Philippine National Red Cross.
2986 **901** 4p. multicoloured . . . 50 45

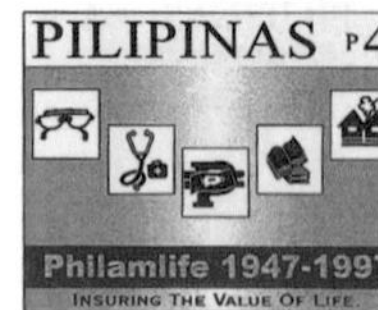

902 Insurance Services

1997. 50th Anniv of Philippine American Life Insurance Company.
2987 **902** 4p. multicoloured . . . 50 45

903 Columns

1997. Centenary of Department of Finance.
2988 **903** 4p. multicoloured . . . 50 45

904 Signatures and Globe

1997. 50th Anniv of J. Walter Thompson (Philippines) Inc. (advertising agency).
2989 **904** 4p. multicoloured . . . 50 45

1997. National Symbol. As T **860** (with bar code). "Pilipinas" in black at foot. Multicoloured.
2991 4p. Gem (South Sea pearls) 50 45

906 Visayan Warty Pig

1997. Endangered Animals. Multicoloured.

2992 4p. Type **906** 60 50
2993 4p. Sow and young Visayan warty pig 60 50
2994 4p. Visayan spotted deer buck 60 50
2995 4p. Roe and young Visayan spotted deer 60 50

907 Founding Signatories

1997. 30th Anniv of Association of South-East Asian Nations. Multicoloured.

2996 4p. Type **907** 60 50
2997 4p. Flags of founding member nations 60 50
2998 6p. Members' flags as figures forming circle around ASEAN emblem 90 75
2999 6p. Members' flags encircling globe 90 75

908 Symbols of Education and Law, University Building and Graduate

1997. 50th Anniv of Manuel L. Quezon University.
3000 **908** 4p. multicoloured . . . 50 45

909 Assembly Emblem **910** Isabelo Abaya

1997. 2nd World Scout Parliamentary Union General Assembly, Manila.
3001 **909** 4p. multicoloured . . . 50 45

1997. Battle of Candon. Multicoloured.

3002 4p. Type **910** 50 45
3003 6p. Abaya rallying revolutionaries (horiz) . . 75 65

911 Roberto Regala (diplomat and lawyer)

912 St. Theresa

1997. Birth Centenaries. Multicoloured.

3004 4p. Type **911** 50 45
3005 4p. Doroteo Espiritu (dentist) 50 45
3006 4p. Elisa Ochoa (nurse, first Congresswoman and 1930s' national tennis champion) 50 45
3007 4p. Mariano Marcos (politician) 50 45
3008 4p. Jose Romero (politician) 50 45

1997. Death Centenary of St. Theresa of Lisieux.
3009 **912** 6p. multicoloured . . . 75 65

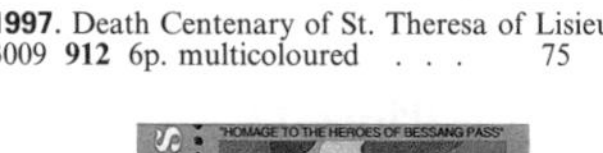

913 "Homage to the Heroes of Bessang Pass" (Hernando Ruiz Ocampo)

1997. 50th Anniv of Stamp and Philatelic Division. Modern Art. Multicoloured.

3011 4p. Type **913** 45 45
3012 6p. "Jardin III" (Fernando Zobel) 75 65
3013 7p. "Abstraction" (Nena Saguil) (vert) 80 75
3014 8p. "House of Life" (Jose Joya) (vert) 95 90

914 Man Painting with Feet

1997. Asian and Pacific Decade of Disabled Persons.
3016 **914** 6p. multicoloured . . . 75 75

915 Bonifacio writing

1997. Centenary of Declaration of Philippine Independence. Statues of Andres Bonifacio. Multicoloured.

3017 4p. Type **915** 45 45
3018 4p. Bonifacio holding flag 45 45
3019 4p. Bonifacio holding sword 45 45

916 Von Stephan

1997. Death Centenary of Heinrich von Stephan (founder of U.P.U.).
3020 **916** 4p. multicoloured . . . 50 50

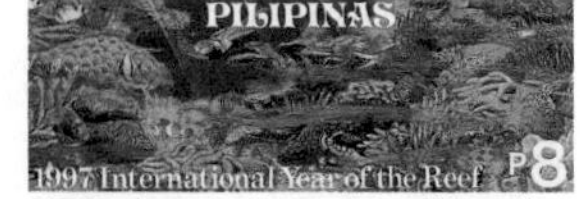

917 Underwater Scene (½-size illustration)

1997. International Year of the Reef.
3021 **917** 8p. multicoloured . . . 1·00 1·00

918 "Adoration of the Magi"

920 "Dalagang Bukid" (Fernando Amorsolo)

919 Tiger

1997. Christmas. Stained Glass Windows. Mult.

3023 4p. Type **918** 45 45
3024 6p. Mary, Jesus and Wise Men 75 75
3025 7p. Mary on donkey and Nativity 80 80
3026 8p. "Nativity" 95 95

1997. New Year. Year of the Tiger. Multicoloured.

3027 4p. Type **919** 45 45
3028 6p. Head of tiger and tiger climbing rockface 65 65

1997. Stamp Collecting Month. Paintings. Multicoloured.

3030 4p. Type **920** 45 45
3031 6p. "Bagong Taon" (Arturo Luz) 75 75
3032 7p. "Jeepneys" (Vicente Manansala) (horiz) . . . 80 80
3033 8p. "Encounter of the 'Nuestra Senora de Cavadonga' and the 'Centurion' " (Alfredo Carmelo) (horiz) 95 95

921 Hatch Grey

1997. Gamecocks. Multicoloured.

3035 4p. Type **921** 30 30
3036 4p. Spangled roundhead . . 30 30
3037 4p. Racey mug 30 30
3038 4p. Silver grey 30 30
3039 4p. Grey (vert) 30 30
3040 4p. Kelso (vert) 30 30
3041 4p. Bruner roundhead (vert) 30 30
3042 4p. Democrat (vert) 30 30

922 Philippine Eagle

1997. National Symbols. Multicoloured.

3044 20p. Type **922** . . . . . . 1·50 1·50
3045 30p. Philippine eagle (different) . . . . 2·20 2·20
3046 50p. Philippine eagle (different) . . . . 3·75 3·75

923 Flag and Stars

1998. 50th Anniv of Art Association of the Philippines. Multicoloured.
3047 4p. Type **923** 45 45
3048 4p. Hand clasping paintbrushes 50 50

924 Mother Philippines, Club Building and Emblem

925 Marie Eugenie

1998. Centenary of Club Filipino (social club).
3049 **924** 4p. multicoloured . . . 45 45

1998. Death Centenary of Blessed Marie Eugenie (founder of the Sisters of the Assumption).
3050 **925** 4p. multicoloured . . . 45 45

926 Philippine and United States Flags

927 Emilio Jacinto

1998. 50th Anniv of Fulbright (student exchange) Program.
3051 **926** 4p. multicoloured . . . 45 45

1998. Heroes of the Revolution. Multicoloured. White backgrounds. Blue barcode at foot.
3052 2p. Type **927** 20 15
3054 4p. Melchora Aquino . . . 45 35
3055 4p. Jose Rizal 35 30
3056 5p. Antonio Luna 45 35
3057 8p. Marcelo del Pilar . . . 60 50
3058 10p. Gregorio del Pilar . . . 75 65
3059 11p. Andres Bonifacio . . . 80 75
3060 13p. Apolinario Mabini . . . 95 90
3061 15p. Emilio Aguinaldo . . . 1·10 1·00
3062 18p. Juan Luna . . . . . . 1·30 1·20
See also Nos. 3179/88 and 3189/98.

928 Mt. Apo, Bagobo Woman, Orchids and Fruit

929 School and Emblem

1998. 50th Anniv of Apo View Hotel, Davao City.
3070 **928** 4p. multicoloured . . . 45 45

1998. 75th Anniv of Philippine Cultural High School.
3071 **929** 4p. multicoloured . . . 35 35

930 Old and Present School Buildings

1998. 75th Anniv of Victorino Mapa High School, San Rafael.
3072 **930** 4p. multicoloured . . . 35 35

931 Lighthouse, Warship and Past and Present Uniforms

1998. Centenary of Philippine Navy.
3073 **931** 4p. multicoloured . . . 35 35

932 University and Igorot Dancer

1998. 50th Anniv of University of Baguio.
3074 **932** 4p. multicoloured . . . 35 35

933 Training Ship and Emblem

1998. 50th Anniv of Philippine Maritime Institute.
3075 **933** 4p. multicoloured . . . 35 35

934 Forest, Palawan

1998. "EXPO '98" World's Fair, Lisbon. Mult.
3076 4p. Type **934** 35 35
3077 15p. Filipino vinta (sail canoe), Zamboanga (horiz) . . . . 1·10 1·10

935 Climbing Ilang-ilang

1998. "Florikultura'98" International Garden Festival, San Fernando, Pampanga. Illustrations from "Flowers of the Philippines" by Manuel Blanco. Multicoloured.
3079 4p. Type **935** 30 30
3080 4p. "Hibiscus rosa-sinensis" 30 30
3081 4p. "Nerium oleander" . . . 30 30
3082 4p. Arabian jasmine ("Jasminum sambac") . . 30 30
3083 4p. "Gardenia jasminoides" (vert) 30 30
3084 4p. Flame-of-the-forest ("Ixora coccinea") (vert) 30 30
3085 4p. Indian coral bean ("Erythrina indica") (vert) 30 30
3086 4p. "Abelmoschus moschatus" (vert) 30 30

936 City and Clark International Airport (½-size illustration)

1998. Clark Special Economic Zone.
3088 **936** 15p. multicoloured . . . 1·10 1·10

937 Manila Galleon

1998. Centenary of Declaration of Philippine Independence. Philippines–Mexico–Spain Friendship. Multicoloured.
3089 15p. Type **937** 65 50
3090 15p. Philippine woman with flag, Legaspi-Urdaneta Monument and galleon 1·10 1·10
3091 15p. Spanish and Philippine flags, Cebu Basilica (after M. Miguel) and "Holy Child" (statuette) . . . . 1·10 1·10

938 "Spoliarium" (Juan Luna)

939 Andres Soriano (accountant)

1998. Centenary of Declaration of Philippine Independence. Multicoloured.
3093 4p. Type **938** 20 20
3094 8p. General Emilio Aguinaldo introducing Philippine national flag at Cavite 35 35
3095 16p. Execution of Jose Rizal, 1896 . . . . 2·75 2·75
3096 16p. Andres Bonifacio and Katipunan monument . . 2·75 2·75
3097 20p. Barasoain Church (venue of first Philippine Congress, 1898) . . . . . 3·25 3·25

1998. Birth Centenaries. Multicoloured.
3098 4p. Type **939** 35 35
3099 4p. Tomas Fonacier (Univeristy dean and historian) 35 35
3100 4p. Josefa Escoda (founder of Filipino Girl Scouts and social reformer) . . . 35 35
3101 4p. Lorenzo Tanada (politician) 35 35
3102 4p. Lazaro Francisco (writer) 35 35

940 Melchora Aquino

1998. Centenary of Declaration of Philippine Independence Women Revolutionaries. Mult.
3103 4p. Type **940** 20 20
3104 4p. Nazaria Lagos 20 20
3105 4p. Agueda Kahabagan . . 20 20

1998. Centenary of Declaration of Philippine Independence. Nos. 2644 (1993), 2825/32 and 2834/9 optd **1898 1998 KALAYAAN** and emblem.
3107 3p. Animal (head of water buffalo) 30 30
3108 4p. Flag ("Pilipinas" at top) 30 30
3109 4p. Hero (Jose Rizal) . . . 30 30
3110 4p. House 30 30
3111 4p. Costume 30 30
3112 4p. Dance 30 30
3113 4p. Sport 30 30
3114 4p. Bird (Philippine eagle) 30 30
3115 4p. Type **860** 30 30
3116 4p. Flower (jasmine) 30 30
3117 4p. Tree 30 30
3118 4p. Fruit (mango) 30 30
3119 4p. Leaf (palm) 30 30
3120 4p. Fish 30 30
3121 4p. Animal (water buffalo) 30 30

942 River Pasig

1998. River Pasig Environmental Campaign.
3122 **942** 4p. multicoloured . . . 35 35

943 Bottle-nosed ("Bottlenose") Dolphin

1998. Marine Mammals. Multicoloured.
3123 4p. Type **943** 30 30
3124 4p. Humpback whale . . . 30 30
3125 4p. Fraser's dolphin 30 30
3126 4p. Melon-headed whale . . 30 30
3127 4p. Minke whale 30 30
3128 4p. Striped dolphin 30 30
3129 4p. Sperm whale 30 30
3130 4p. Pygmy killer whale . . . 30 30
3131 4p. Cuvier's beaked whale 30 30
3132 4p. Killer whale 30 30
3133 4p. Bottle-nosed ("Bottlenose") dolphin (different) 30 30
3134 4p. Spinner dolphin ("Long-snouted spinner dolphin") 30 30
3135 4p. Risso's dolphin 30 30
3136 4p. Finless porpoise 30 30
3137 4p. Pygmy sperm whale . . 30 30
3138 4p. Pantropical spotted dolphin 30 30
3139 4p. False killer whale . . . 30 30
3140 4p. Blainville's beaked whale 30 30
3141 4p. Rough-toothed dolphin 30 30
3142 4p. Bryde's whale 30 30

944 Coconuts and Products

1998. Centenary of Philippine Coconut Industry.
3144 **944** 4p. multicoloured . . . 30 30

945 Grapes, Emblem and Nun

1998. 75th Anniv of Holy Spirit Adoration Sisters in the Philippines.
3145 **945** 4p. multicoloured . . . 30 30

946 Child posting Letter

947 Holly Wreath

1998. Centenary of Postal Service. Multicoloured.
3146 6p. Type **946** 45 45
3147 6p. Globe and handshake 45 45
3148 6p. Philippine stamps, globe, airplane, galleon and building 45 45
3149 6p. Flags, dove and letters floating down to girl . . . 45 45

1998. Christmas. Multicoloured.
3151 6p. Type **947** 45 45
3152 11p. Star wreath 75 75
3153 13p. Flower wreath 90 90
3154 15p. Bell wreath . . . . . 1·00 1·00

949 Person gagged with Barbed Wire

1998. 50th Anniv of Universal Declaration of Human Rights.
3156 **949** 4p. multicoloured . . . 10 10

950 Papal Mitre

1998. Shells. Multicoloured.
3157 4p. Type **950** 30 30
3158 4p. "Vexillum citrinum" . . 30 30
3159 4p. "Rugose mitre" ("Vexillum rugosum") . . 30 30
3160 4p. "Volema carinifera" . . 30 30
3161 4p. "Teramachia dalli" . . . 30 30
3162 4p. "Nassarius vitiensis" . . 30 30
3163 4p. "Cymbiola imperialis" 30 30
3164 4p. "Cymbiola aulica" . . . 30 30

951 Sea Creatures (½-size illustration)

1998. International Year of the Ocean.
3166 **951** 15p. multicoloured . . . 45 35

952 Taking Oath

1998. Inauguration of President Joseph Ejercito Estrada. Multicoloured.
3168 6p. Type **952** 45 45
3169 15p. Inaugural speech . . . 1·00 1·00

953 Rabbit

1998. New Year. Year of the Rabbit. Multicoloured.
3170 4p. Type **953** 30 30
3171 11p. Two rabbits 75 75

954 "Dyesebel"

1998. National Stamp Collecting Month. Film Posters.
3173 **954** 6p. blue and black . . . 45 45
3174 – 11p. brown and black . . 75 75
3175 – 13p. mauve and black 90 90
3176 – 15p. green and black . . 1·00 1·00
DESIGNS: 11p. "Ang Sawa sa Lumang Simboryo"; 13p. "Prinsipe Amante"; 15p. "Anak Da Lita".

1998. Heroes of the Revolution. As Nos. 3052/62. Multicoloured. Blue barcode at foot. (a) Yellow backgrounds.
3179 6p. Type **927** 50 50
3180 6p. Melchora Aquino . . . 50 50
3181 6p. Jose Rizal 50 50
3182 6p. Antonio Luna 50 50
3183 6p. Marcelo del Pilar . . . 50 50
3184 6p. Gregorio del Pilar . . . 50 50
3185 6p. Andres Bonifacio . . . 50 50
3186 6p. Apolinario Mabini . . . 50 50
3187 6p. Emilio Aguinaldo . . . 50 50
3188 6p. Juan Luna 50 50

(b) Green backgrounds.
3189 15p. Type **927** . . . . . . 1·10 1·10
3190 15p. Melchora Aquino . . . 1·10 1·10
3191 15p. Jose Rizal . . . . . . 1·10 1·10
3192 15p. Antonio Luna . . . . 1·10 1·10
3193 15p. Marcelo del Pilar . . . 1·10 1·10
3194 15p. Gregorio del Pilar . . 1·10 1·10
3195 15p. Andres Bonifacio . . 1·10 1·10
3196 15p. Apolinario Mabini . . 1·10 1·10
3197 15p. Emilio Aguinaldo . . . 1·10 1·10
3198 15p. Juan Luna . . . . . . 1·10 1·10

(c) Pink background.
3229 5p. Jose Rizal 35 35

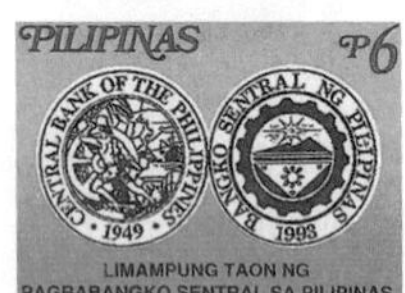

956 Old and New Bank Emblems

1999. 50th Anniv of Central Bank of the Philippines.
3199 **956** 6p. multicoloured . . . 35 35

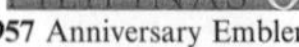

957 Anniversary Emblem

958 Scouts and Guides

1999. Centenary of Declaration of Philippine Independence. Multicoloured.
3200 6p. Type **957** 35 35
3201 6p. General Emilio Aguinaldo's house (site of declaration, June 1898) . . 35 35
3202 6p. Malolos Congress, Barasoain Church, Bulacan (ratification by regions of declaration, September 1898) 35 35
3203 6p. House in Western Negros (uprising of 5 November 1898) 35 35
3204 6p. Cry of Santa Barbara, Iloilo (inauguration of government, 17 November 1898) 35 35
3205 6p. Cebu City (Victory over Colonial Forces of Spain, December 1898) 35 35
3206 6p. Philippine flag and emblem (declaration in Butaan City of sovereignty over Mindanao, 17 January 1899) 35 35
3207 6p. Facade of Church (Ratification of Constitution, 22 January 1899) 35 35
3208 6p. Carnival procession, Malolos (Inauguration of Republic, 23 January 1899) 35 35
3209 6p. Barosoain Church and anniversary emblem . . . 35 35

1999.
3210 5p. Type **958** . . . . . . 1·10 1·10
3211 5p. Children gardening . . . 1·10 1·10
Nos. 3210/11 were originally issued as Savings Bank stamps in 1995, but were authorized for postal use from 16 January 1999.

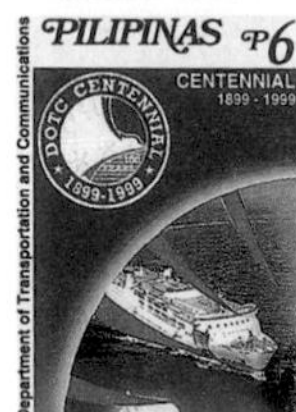

959 Cruise Liner

1999. Centenary of Department of Transportation and Communication. Multicoloured.
3212 6p. Type **959** 35 35
3213 6p. Airplane 35 35
3214 6p. Air traffic control tower 35 35
3215 6p. Satellite dish aerial and bus 35 35
Nos. 3212/15 were issued together, se-tenant, forming a composite design.

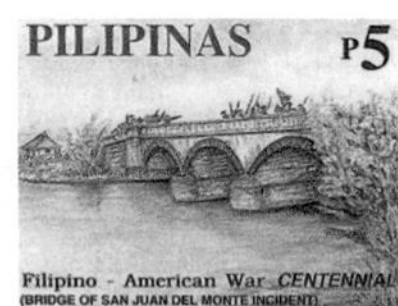

960 San Juan del Monte Bridge

1999. Centenary of American–Filipino War.
3217 **960** 5p. multicoloured . . . 35 35

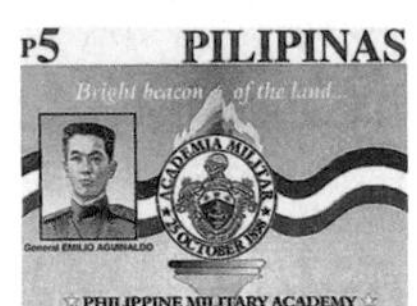

961 General Emilio Aguinaldo and Academy Arms

1999. Centenary (1998) of Philippine Military Academy.
3218 **961** 5p. multicoloured . . . 35 35

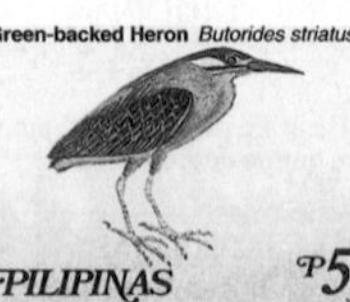

962 Green-backed Heron

1999. Birds. Multicoloured.
3219 5p. Type **962** 35 35
3220 5p. Common tern 35 35
3221 5p. Greater crested tern . . 35 35
3222 5p. Ruddy Turnstone . . . 35 35
3223 5p. Black-winged stilt . . . 35 35
3224 5p. Asiatic Dowitcher . . . 35 35
3225 5p. Whimbrel 35 35
3226 5p. Reef heron 35 35

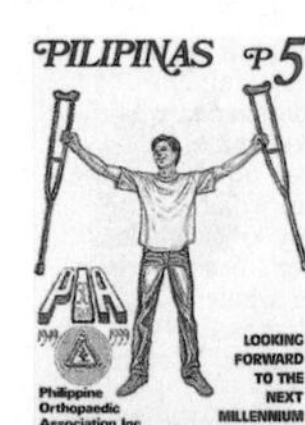

963 Man holding Crutches

1999. 50th Anniv of Philippine Orthopaedic Association.
3230 **963** 5p. multicoloured . . . 35 35

964 Francisco Ortigas and Emblem

1999. 50th Anniv of Manila Lions Club
3231 **964** 5p. multicoloured . . . 35 35

965 Entrance to Garden

1999. La Union Botanical Garden, San Fernando.
3232 5p. Type **965** 35 35
3233 5p. Kiosk 35 35
Nos. 3232/3 were issued together, se-tenant, forming a composite design.

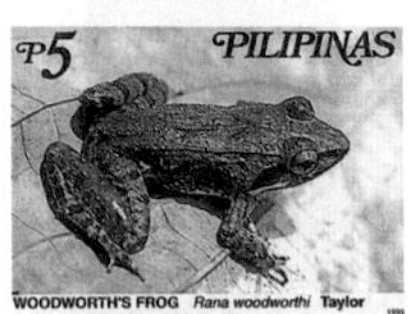

966 Gliding Tree Frog

1999. Frogs. Multicoloured.
3234 5p. Type **966** 15 10
3235 5p. Common forest frog . . 35 35
3236 5p. Woodworth's frog . . . 35 35
3237 5p. Giant Philippine frog . . 35 35

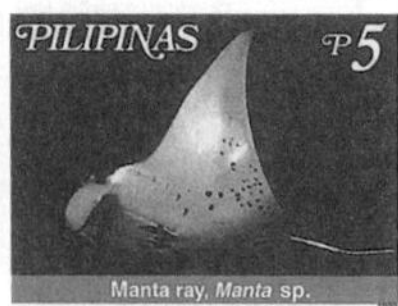

967 Manta Ray

1999. Marine Life. Multicoloured.
3239 5p. Type **967** 35 35
3240 5p. Painted rock lobster . . 35 35
3241 5p. Sea squirt 35 35
3242 5p. Banded sea snake . . . 35 35

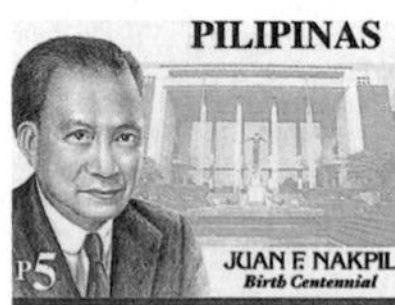

968 Nakpil

1999. Birth Centenary of Juan Nakpil (architect).
3244 **968** 5p. multicoloured . . . 35 35

969 Child writing Letter and Globe

1999. 125th Anniv of Universal Postal Union. Multicoloured.
3245 5p. Type **969** 35 35
3246 15p. Girl with stamp album 1·10 1·10

970 Waling-Waling and Cattleya "Queen Sirikit"

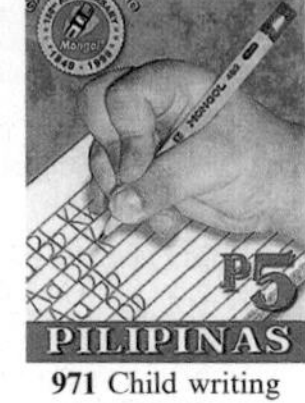

971 Child writing

1999. 50 Years of Philippines–Thailand Diplomatic Relations. Multicoloured.
3247 5p. Type **970** 35 35
3248 11p. As Type **970** but with flowers transposed 80 80

1999. 150th Anniv of Mongol Pencils.
3249 **971** 5p. multicoloured . . . 35 35

972 Emblem and Handicapped Children

1999. 75th Anniv of Masonic Charities for Handicapped Children.
3250 **972** 5p. multicoloured . . . 35 35

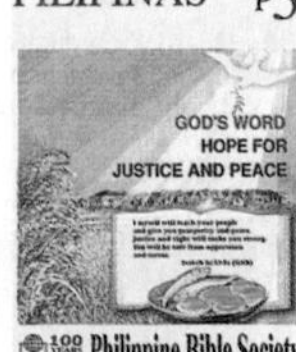

973 Sampaguita and Rose of Sharon

975 Dove, Fishes, Bread and Quotation from Isaiah

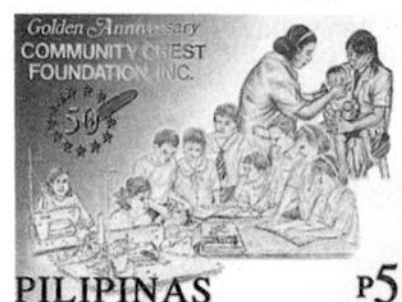

974 Teachers, Nurses and Machinists

1999. 50 Years of Philippines–South Korea Diplomatic Relations. Multicoloured.
3251 5p. Type **973** 35 35
3252 11p. As Type **973** but with flowers transposed 80 80

1999. 50th Anniv of Community Chest Foundation.
3253 **974** 5p. multicoloured . . . 35 35

1999. Centenary of Philippine Bible Society.
3254 **975** 5p. multicoloured . . . 35 35

976 Score, Jose Palma (lyricist) and Julian Felipe (composer)

1999. Centenary of National Anthem.
3255 **976** 5p. multicoloured . . . 35 35

977 St. Francis of Assisi and Parish Church

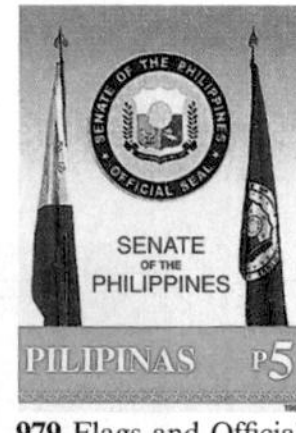

979 Flags and Official Seal

1999. 400th Anniv of St. Francis of Assisi Parish, Sariaya, Quezon.
3256 **977** 5p. multicoloured . . . 35 35

1999. The Senate.
3258 **979** 5p. multicoloured . . . 35 35

980 New Business, Arts and Sciences Faculty Building

1999. 60th Anniv of Chiang Kai Shek College, Manila.
3259 **980** 5p. multicoloured . . . 45 45

981 School Building

1999. 50th Anniv of Tanza National High School.
3260 **981** 5p. multicoloured . . . 45 45

982 St. Agustin Church, Paoay (World Heritage Day)

1999. United Nations Day. Multicoloured.
3261 5p. Type **982** 45 45
3262 11p. Elderly couple (International Year of the Older Person) 90 90
3263 15p. "Rizal Learns the Alphabet and Prayers from his Mother" (Miguel Galvez) (World Teachers' Day) . . . . 1·20 1·20

983 Angel

984 Tamaraw and Polar Bear

1999. Christmas. Multicoloured.
3264 5p. Type **983** 45 45
3265 11p. Angel holding star . . 90 90
3266 13p. Angel holding ribbon 1·10 1·10
3267 15p. Angel holding flowers 1·30 1·30

1999. 50 Years of Philippines–Canada Diplomatic Relations. Multicoloured.
3269 5p. Type **984** 45 45
3270 15p. As Type **984** but with animals transposed . . . 1·30 1·30

985 Coliseum

1999. Renovation of Araneta Coliseum.
3271 **985** 5p. multicoloured . . . 45 45

986 Sunrise

987 "Kristo" (Arturo Luz)

1999. 3rd Informal Summit of Association of South-east Asian Nations, Manila.
3272 **986** 5p. multicoloured . . . 45 45
3273 11p. multicoloured . . . 95 95

1999. National Stamp Collecting Month. Modern Sculptures. Multicoloured.
3274 5p. Type **987** 45 45
3275 11p. "Homage to Dodgie Laurel" (J. Elizalde Navarro) 90 90
3276 13p. "Hilojan" (Napoleon Abueva) . . . . 1·10 1·10
3277 15p. "Mother and Child" (Napoleon Abueva) . . . 1·30 1·30

988 Dragon

1999. New Year. Year of the Dragon. Multicoloured.
3279 5p. Type **988** 45 45
3280 15p. Dragon amongst clouds 90 90

989 Gen. Gregorio H. del Pilar

1999. Centenary of the Battle of Tirad Pass.
3282 **989** 5p. multicoloured . . . 45 45

990 *Paphiopedilum urbanianum*

1999. Orchids. Multicoloured.
3283 5p. Type **990** 45 45
3284 5p. *Phalaenopsis schilleriana* 45 45
3285 5p. *Dendrobium amethystoglossum* 45 45
3286 5p. *Paphiopedilum barbatum* 45 45

991 General Licerio Geronimo

1999. Centenary of Battle of San Mateo.
3288 **991** 5p. multicoloured . . . 45 45

992 Crowds around Soldiers in Tanks

1999. New Millennium (1st series). "People Power". Multicoloured.
3289 5p. Type **992** 45 45
3290 5p. Radio antennae, helicopters and people . . 45 45
3291 5p. Religious procession . . 45 45
Nos. 3289/91 were issued together, se-tenant, forming a composite design.
See also Nos. 3311/13, 3357/9 and 3394/6.

993 Woman holding Gender Signs

2000. 25th Anniv of National Commission on Role of Filipino Women.
3292 **993** 5p. multicoloured . . . 45 45

994 Newspaper Headline and Headquarters

995 Manuel Roxas (1946–48)

2000. Centenary of the Manila Bulletin (newspaper).
3293 **994** 5p. multicoloured . . . 45 45

2000. Presidential Office. Multicoloured.
3294 5p. Type **995** 45 45
3295 5p. Elpidio Quirino (1948–53) 45 45

996 Golfer, Sailing Boat and Swimmers

997 Joseph Ejercito Estrada (1998–2000)

2000. 150th Anniv of La Union Province. Mult.
3296 5p. Type **996** 45 45
3297 5p. Tractor, building and worker 45 45
3298 5p. Government building . . 45 45
3299 5p. Airplane, bus, satellite dish, workers and bus . . 45 45

2000. Presidential Office. Multicoloured.
3300 5p. Presidential seal (face value at top left) 35 35
3301 5p. Type **997** 35 35
3302 5p. Fidel V. Ramos (1992–98) 35 35
3303 5p. Corazon C. Aquino (1986–92) 35 35
3304 5p. Ferdinand E. Marcos (1965–86) 35 35
3305 5p. Diosdado Macapagal (1961–65) 35 35
3306 5p. Carlos P. Garcia (1957–61) 35 35
3307 5p. Ramon Magsaysay (1953–57) 35 35
3308 5p. Elpidio Quirino (1948–53) 35 35
3309 5p. Manuel Roxas (1946–48) 35 35

998 Workers and Emblem

2000. Centenary of the Civil Service Commission.
3310 **998** 5p. multicoloured . . . 45 45

999 Golden Garuda, Palawan

2000. New Millennium (2nd series). Artefacts. Mult.
3311 5p. Type **999** 75 75
3312 5p. Sunrise at Pusan Point, Davao Oriental 75 75
3313 5p. Golden Tara, Agusan 75 75

1000 Outrigger Canoe, Boracay Island

2000. Tourist Sites. Multicoloured.
3314 5p. Type **1000** 35 35
3315 5p. Chocolate Hills, Bohol 35 35
3316 5p. El Nido Forest, Palawan 35 35
3317 5p. Vigan House, Ilocos Sur 35 35

1001 Great Wall of China and Chinese Phoenix

2000. 25th Anniv of Diplomatic Relations with Republic of China. Multicoloured.
3319 5p. Type **1001** 35 35
3320 11p. Banaue rice terraces and Philippine Sarimanok 80 80

1002 Television and Emblem

2000. 50th Anniv of GMA Television and Radio Network.
3322 **1002** 5p. multicoloured . . . 45 45

1003 Church Building

1004 Carlos P. Garcia

2000. 400th Anniv of St. Thomas de Aquinas Parish, Mangaldan.
3323 **1003** 5p. multicoloured . . . 45 45

2000. Presidential Office. Multicoloured.
3324 10p. Type **1004** 90 90
3325 10p. Ramon Magsaysay . . 90 90
3326 11p. Ferdinand E. Marcos 95 95
3327 11p. Diosdado Macapagal 95 95
3328 13p. Corazon C. Aquino . . 1·00 1·00
3329 13p. Fidel V. Ramos . . . 1·00 1·00
3330 15p. Joseph Ejercito Estrada 1·20 1·20
3331 15p. Presidential seal (face value at top right) . . . . 1·20 1·20
See also Nos. 3489/98.

1005 Memorial and Map

1006 Joseph Ejercito Estrada

2000. Battle Centenaries. Multicoloured.
3332 5p. Type **1005** (Battle of Pulang Lupa) 45 45
3333 5p. Memorial and soldiers (Battle of Mabitac) . . . 45 45
3334 5p. Sun and soldiers (Battles of Cagayan, Agusan Hill and Makahambus Hill) (vert) 45 45
3335 5p. Map, memorial and bamboo signalling device (Battle of Paye) (vert) . . 45 45

2000. Presidential Office. Multicoloured.
3336 5p. Presidential seal 45 45
3337 5p. Type **1006** 45 45
3338 5p. Fidel V. Ramos 45 45
3339 5p. Corazon C. Aquino . . 45 45
3340 5p. Ferdinand E. Marcos . . 45 45
3341 5p. Diosdado Macapagal . . 45 45
3342 5p. Carlos P. Garcia 45 45
3343 5p. Ramon Magsaysay . . . 45 45
3344 5p. Elpidio Quirino 45 45
3345 5p. Manuel Roxas 45 45

1007 Ornate Chequered Beetle

2000. Insects. Multicoloured.
3346 5p. Type **1007** 35 35
3347 5p. Sharpshooter bug . . . 35 35
3348 5p. Milkweed bug 35 35
3349 5p. Spotted cucumber beetle 35 35
3350 5p. Green June beetle . . . 35 35
3351 5p. Convergent ladybird beetle 35 35
3352 5p. Eastern hercules beetle 35 35
3353 5p. Harlequin cabbage bug 35 35

1008 St. Ferdinand Cathedral, Map and Emblem

2000. 50th Anniv of Lucena Diocese.
3355 **1008** 5p. multicoloured . . . 50 50

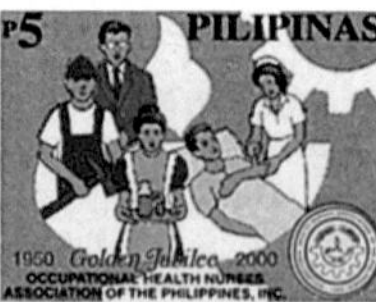

1009 Nurses and Patients

2000. 50th Anniv of Occupational Health Nurses' Association.

3356 **1009** 5p. multicoloured . . . 50 50

1010 Balanghai

2000. New Millennium (3rd series). Traditional Sea Craft. Multicoloured.

3357 5p. Type **1010** 45 45
3358 5p. Vinta 45 45
3359 5p. Caracoa 45 45

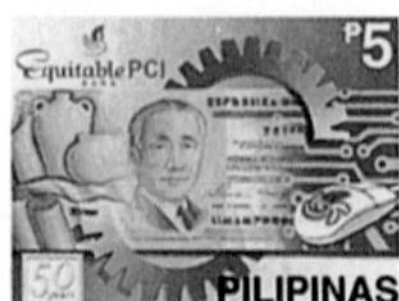

1011 Jars, Bank Note, Circuit Board, Computer Mouse and Emblem

2000. 50th Anniv of Equitable PCI Bank.

3360 **1011** 5p. multicoloured . . . 50 50

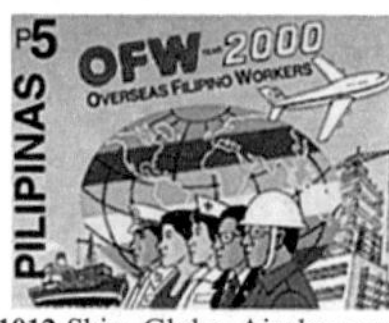

1012 Ship, Globe, Airplane and Workers

2000. Year of Overseas Filipino Workers.

3361 **1012** 5p. multicoloured . . . 50 50

1013 Pedro Poveda (founder), Buildings and Emblem

2000. 50th Anniv of the Teresian Association (international lay preacher association) in the Philippines.

3362 **1013** 5p. multicoloured . . . 50 50

1014 Congress in Session
1016 Running

1015 Soldiers, Tank and Emblem

2000. House of Representatives.

3363 **1014** 5p. multicoloured . . . 45 45

2000. 50th Anniv of Philippine Marine Corps.

3364 **1015** 5p. multicoloured . . . 45 45

2000. Olympic Games, Sydney. Multicoloured.

3365 5p. Type **1016** 45 45
3366 5p. Archery 45 45
3367 5p. Rifle shooting 45 45
3368 5p. Diving 45 45

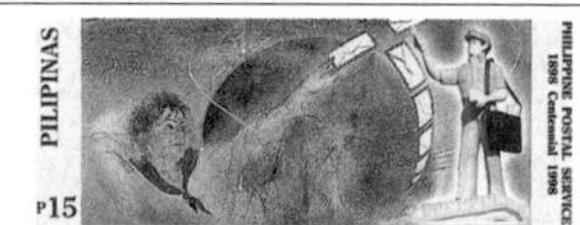

1017 Boy, Envelopes and Statue of Postman (½-size illustration)

2000. Postal Service. Sheet 100 × 60 mm.

MS3370 **1017** 15p. multicoloured 1·20 1·20

1018 B'laan Woman's Blouse, Davao del Sur

2000. "Sheer Realities: Clothing and Power in 19th-century Philippines" Exhibition, Manila. Multicoloured.

3371 5p. Type **1018** 45 45
3372 5p. T'boli T'nalak abaca cloth, South Cotabato . . 45 45
3373 5p. Kalinga/Gaddang cotton loincloth, Cordilleras (vert) 45 45
3374 5p. Portrait of Leticia Jimenez (anon) (vert) . . 45 45
MS3375 101 × 70 mm. 5p. Portrait of Teodora Devera Ygnacio (Justiniano Asuncion); 15p. Tawsug silk sash, Sulu Archipelago . . . . 2·50 2·50

= P5.00

1019 Angel cradling Sunflowers
1020 1955 5c. Labour Management Congress Stamp

2000. Christmas. Multicoloured.

3376 5p. Type **1019** 45 45
3377 5p. As No. 3376 but inscribed "CHRISTMAS JUBILEUM" 45 45
3378 11p. Angel with basket of fruit and swag of leaves 90 90
3379 13p. Angel with basket of fruit on shoulder . . . . 1·00 1·00
3380 15p. Angel with garland of flowers . . . . 1·30 1·30

2000. 50th Anniv of Amateur Philatelists Organization Philatelic Society. Multicoloured.

3381 5p. Type **1020** 35 35
3382 5p. 1957 5c. Juan Luna birth centenary stamp (horiz) 35 35
3383 5p. 1962 5c. orchid stamp 35 35
3384 5p. 1962 6 + 4c. Rizal Foundation Fund stamp (horiz) 35 35

2000. No. 1977 surch **P5.00.**

3385 5p on 3p.60 multicoloured 35 35

1022 "Portrait of an Unknown Lady" (Juan Novicio Luna)

2000. Modern Art. Multicoloured.

3386 5p. Type **1022** 35 35
3387 11p. "Nude" (Jose Joya) (horiz) 80 80
3388 13p. "Lotus Odalisque" (Rodolfo Paras-Perez) (horiz) 90 90
3389 15p. "Untitled (Nude)" (Fernando Amorsolo) (horiz) . . . . 1·00 1·00
MS3390 100 x 80 mm. 15p. "The Memorial" (Cesar Legaspi) (79 × 29 mm) . . . . 2·50 2·50

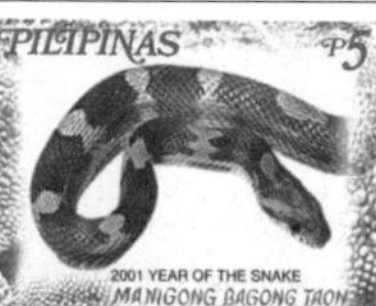

1023 Snake

2001. New Year. Year of the Snake. Multicoloured.

3391 5p. Type **1023** 35 35
3392 11p. Snake 80 80
MS3393 98 × 88 mm. Nos. 3391/2 Perf or imperf . . . . 2·20 2·20

1024 Ships in Port (Trade and Industry)

2000. New Millennium (4th series). Multicoloured.

3394 5p. Type **1024** 35 35
3395 5p. Pupils and teacher (Education and Knowledge) 35 35
3396 5p. Globe, satellite, family using computer and woman using telephone (Communications and Technology) 35 35

1025 Pesos Fuertes (1st Philippines Banknote)

2001. 150th Anniv of Philippines Bank.

3397 **1025** 5p. multicoloured . . . 35 35

1026 Eagle

2001. "Hong Kong 2001" International Stamp Exhibition. Flora and Fauna. Multicoloured.

3398 5p. Type **1026** 35 35
3399 5p. Philippine tarsier 35 35
3400 5p. "Talisman Cove" (flower) 35 35
3401 5p. Turtle 35 35
3402 5p. Tamaraw 35 35
MS3403 Five sheets, each 80 × 71 mm. (a) 11p. As Type **1026**. (b) 11p As No. 3399. (c) 11p. As No. 3400. (d) 11p. As No. 3401. (e) 11p. As No. 3402 7·50 7·50

1027 Rizal

2001. 150th Birth Anniv of General Paciano Rizal.

3404 **1027** 5p. multicoloured . . . 35 35

1028 Facade

2001. Centenary of San Beda College.

3405 **1028** 5p. multicoloured . . . 35 35

1029 High Altar, St. Peter's Basilica, Rome
1030 Presidential Seal

2001. 50th Anniv of Diplomatic Relations with Vatican City. Multicoloured.

3406 5p. Type **1029** 35 35
3407 15p. High altar, San Agustin Church, Manila . . . . . 1·10 1·10
MS3408 90 × 71 mm. 15p. Adam; 15p. God . . . . 2·20 2·20

The two stamps in No. **MS**3408 form the composite design of "Creation of Adam" (Michaelangelo).

2001. Multicoloured, background colour given.

3409 **1030** 5p. yellow 35 35
3410 10p. green 80 80
3411 11p. red 90 90
3412 13p. black . . . . . . 1·10 1·10
3413 15p. blue . . . . 1·30 1·30

1031 Our Lady of Manaoag
1032 Pres. Macapagal-Arroyo taking Presidential Oath

2001. 75th Anniv of Canonical Coronation of Our Lady of the Rosary of Manaoag.

3414 **1031** 5p. multicoloured . . . 35 35

2001. President Gloria Macapagal-Arroyo. Multicoloured.

3415 5p. Type **1032** 35 35
3416 5p. Pres. Macapagal-Arroyo waving 35 35

1033 Sydney Opera House and Philippines Cultural Centre

2001. Philippine-Australia Diplomatic Relations. Multicoloured.

3417 5p. Type **1033** 35 35
3418 13p. As Type **1033** but with subjects transposed . . . 1·10 1·10
MS3419 96 × 60 mm. 13p. Philippines Cultural Centre and Sydney Opera House (79 × 29 mm) 1·10 1·10

1034 Philippine Normal University

2001. University Centenaries. Multicoloured.

3420 5p. Type **1034** 35 35
3421 5p. Facade of Silliman University 35 35

1035 Scales of Justice and Court Building

2001. Centenary of Supreme Court.

3422 **1035** 5p. multicoloured . . . 35 35

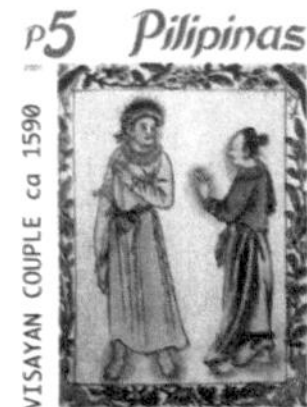

1036 Joaquin J. Ortega **1037** Visayan Couple

2001. Anniversaries. Multicoloured.
3423 5p. Type **1036** (centenary of appointment as first Civil Governor of the Province of La Union) 35 35
3424 5p. Eugenio H. Lopez (businessman, birth centenary) 35 35

2001. "PHILANIPPON '01" International Stamp Exhibition, Japan. Boxer Codex (manuscript depicting Philippine lifestyle during first century of Spanish contact). Multicoloured.
3425 5p. Type **1037** 45 45
3426 5p. Tagalog couple 45 45
3427 5p. Moros of Luzon (man wearing red tunic) 45 45
3428 5p. Moros of Luzon (woman wearing blue dress) 45 45
MS3429 82 × 107 mm. 5p. Tattooed Pintados; 5p. Pintados wearing costumes; 5p. Cagayan woman; 5p. Zambal . . . . 1·80 1·80

1038 Teachers and Thomas (transport)

2001. Centenary of Arrival of American Teachers. Multicoloured.
3430 5p. Type **1038** 45 45
3431 15p. Pupils and school building . . . . 1·30 1·30

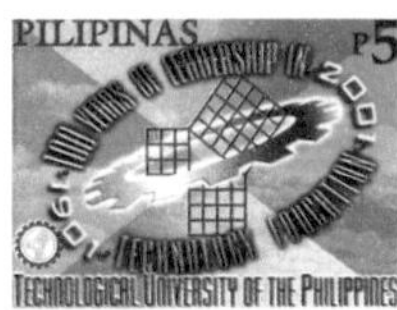

1039 Emblem

2001. Centenary of Technology University, Manila.
3432 **1039** 5p. multicoloured . . . 45 45

1040 Museum Artefacts

2001. Centenary of National Museum.
3433 **1040** 5p. multicoloured . . . 45 45

1041 1901 Lands Management Charter, Modern Surveyors and Emblems

2001. Centenary of Lands Management Bureau.
3434 **1041** 5p. multicoloured . . . 45 45

1042 Statue of St. Joseph and Seminary Building

2001. 400th Anniv of San Jose Seminary.
3435 **1042** 5p. multicoloured . . . 45 45

1043 Makati City Financial District

2001.
3436 **1043** 5p. multicoloured . . . 45 45

1044 Trumpet

2001. Musical Instruments. Multicoloured.
3437 5p. Type **1044** 45 45
3438 5p. Tuba 45 45
3439 5p. French horn 45 45
3440 5p. Trombone 45 45
MS3441 81 × 106 mm. VERT:—5p. × 4 Bass drum; Clarinet and oboe; Xylophone; Sousaphone . . . 1·80 1·80

1045 Off Shore Production Platform

2001. Malampaya Deep Water Gas to Power Project. Multicoloured.
3442 5p. Type **1045** 45 45
3443 15p. As No. 3442 but with gold border . . . . . . 1·30 1·30

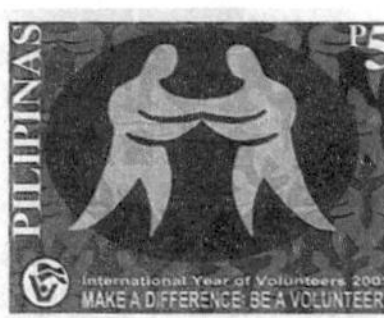

1046 Two Stylized Figures

2001. International Year of Volunteers.
3444 **1046** 5p. multicoloured . . . 45 45

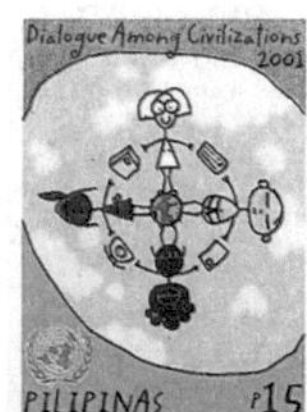

1047 Children surrounding globe

2001. United Nations Year of Dialogue among Civilizations.
3445 **1047** 15p. multicoloured . . 1·30 1·30

1048 Girls and Singers ("Herald Angels")

2001. Christmas.
3446 5p. Type **1048** 45 45
3447 11p. Boy and Christmas baubles ("Kumukutikutitap") . . 90 90
3448 13p. Children and lanterns ("Pasko ni Bitoy") . . . 1·00 1·00
3449 15p. Children blowing trumpets ("Pasko na naman") . . . . 1·30 1·30

1049 William Tell Monument **1050** St. George and Dragon

2001. 150th Anniv of Philippines–Switzerland Diplomatic Relations. Multicoloured.
3450 5p. Type **1049** 45 45
3451 15p. Jose P. Rizal Monument . . . . 1·30 1·30
MS3452 98 × 62 mm. 15p. Mayon volcano and Matterhorn (horiz) (80 × 30 mm) . . . . 1·30 1·30

2001. Centenary of Solicitor General's Office.
3453 **1050** 5p. multicoloured . . . 45 45

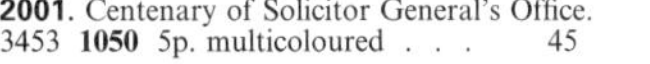

1051 "Puj" (Antonio Austria)

2001. National Stamp Collecting Month. Art. Multicoloured.
3454 5p. Type **1051** 45 45
3455 17p. "Hesus Nazereno" (Angelito Antonio) . . . 1·40 1·40
3456 21p. "Three Women with Basket" (Anita Magsaysay-Ho) (vert) . . 1·60 1·60
3457 22p. "Church with Yellow background" (Mauro Santos) . . . . 1·80 1·80
MS3458 102 × 74 mm. 22p. "Komedya ng Pakil" (Danilo Dalena) (80 × 30 mm) . . . . 1·80 1·80

1052 Couple (woman wearing brown apron)

2001. Inhabitants of Manila drawn by Jean Mallet. Multicoloured.
3462 5p. Couple in riding dress 45 45
3468 17p. Type **1052** . . . . . 1·40 1·40
3469 21p. Couple (woman wearing blue apron) . . . 1·60 1·60
3470 22p. Couple using pestles and mortar . . . . 1·80 1·80

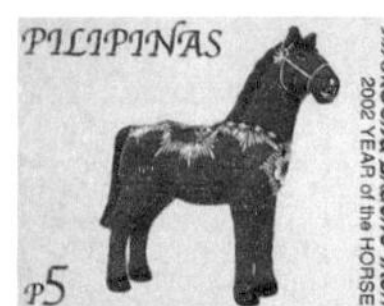

1053 Red Horse

2001. New Year. Year of the Horse. Multicoloured.
3471 5p. Type **1053** 45 45
3472 17p. White horse . . . . . 1·40 1·40
MS3473 100 × 89 mm. As Nos. 3471/2 plus 2 labels . . . 1·80 1·80
No. **MS**3473 also exists imperforate.

1054 "Sanctification in Ordinary Life" (Godofredo F. Zapanta)

2002. Birth Centenary of Josemaria Escriva de Balaguer (founder of Opus Dei religious order).
3474 **1054** 5p. multicoloured . . . 45 45

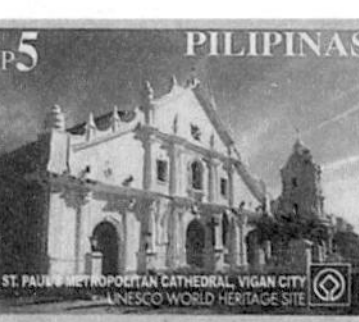

1055 St. Paul's Metropolitan Cathedral

2002. UNESCO World Heritage Sites, Vigan City, Ilocos Sur Province. Multicoloured.
3475 5p. Type **1055** 45 45
3476 22p. Calee Crisologo . . . 1·90 1·90

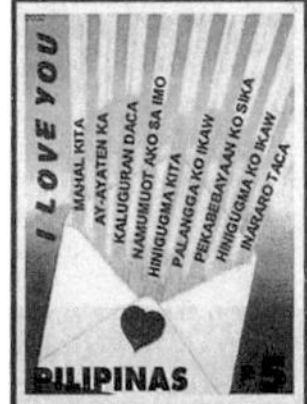

1056 Salvador Araneta **1058** Envelope and "I Love You"

1057 "Manila Customs" (painting, Auguste Nicolas Vaillant)

2002. Birth Centenary of Salvador Araneta (nationalist politician and philanthropist).
3477 **1056** 5p. multicoloured . . . 45 45

2002. Centenary of Customs Bureau.
3478 **1057** 5p. multicoloured . . . 45 45

2002. St. Valentine's Day. Multicoloured
3479 5p. Type **1058** 45 45
3480 5p. Couple enclosed in heart 45 45
3481 5p. Cat and dog 45 45
3482 5p. Air balloon 45 45

1059 "Image of the Resurrection" (detail, Fernando Amorsolo) and Hospital FaÇade

2002. Centenary of Baguio General Hospital and Medical Centre.
3483 **1059** 5p. multicoloured . . . 45 45

1060 Pedro Calungsod **1061** Virgin and Child (painting) and School FaÇade

2002. 330th Death Anniv of Pedro Calungsod. Multicoloured.
3484 5p. Type **1060** 45 45
MS3485 102 × 72 mm. 22p. Pedro Calungsod holding crucifix. Imperf . . . . 1·80 1·80

2002. Centenary of Negros Occidental High School.
3486 **1061** 5p. multicoloured . . . 45 45

1062 College Facade

2002. Centenary of La Consolacion College, Manila.
3487 **1062** 5p. multicoloured . . . 45 45

1063 Stupa, Buddha and Lotus Blossom **1064** Gloria Macapagal-Arroyo (2001–)

2002. Vesak Day.
3488 **1063** 5p. multicoloured . . . 45 45

2002. Presidential Office (2nd series). With blue barcode at foot. Multicoloured.
3489 5p. Type **1064** 45 45
3490 5p. Joseph Ejercito Estrada (1998–2000) 45 45
3491 5p. Fidel V. Ramos (1992–98) 45 45
3492 5p. Corazon C. Aquino (1986–92) 45 45
3493 5p. Ferdinand E. Marcos (1965–86) 45 45
3494 5p. Diosdado Macapagal (1961–65) 45 45
3495 5p. Carlos P. Garcia (1957–61) 45 45
3496 5p. Ramon Magsaysay (1953–57) 45 45
3497 5p. Elpidio Quirino (1948–1953) 45 45
3498 5p. Manuel Roxas (1946–1948) 45 45

1065 National Flag and School FaÇade

2002. Centenary of Cavite National High School.
3499 **1065** 5p. multicoloured . . . 45 45

1066 Emblem and Cathedral FaÇade

2002. Centenary Iglesia Filipina Independiente (religious movement).
3500 **1066** 5p. multicoloured . . . 45 45

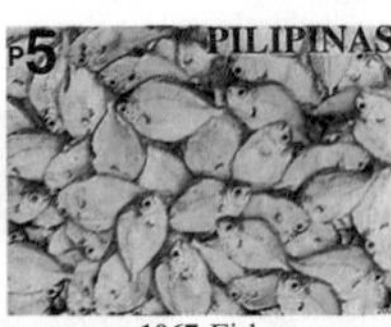

1067 Fish

2002. Marine Conservation. Multicoloured.
3501 5p. Type **1067** 45 45
3502 5p. Fish laid head to head 45 45
3503 5p. Edge of mangrove swamp 45 45
3504 5p. Hands holding minnows 45 45
MS3505 90 × 77 mm. 5p. × 4, Man using binoculars from catamaran (no fishing); Mangrove swamp (reforestation of mangroves); Divers (reef monitoring); Rows of seaweed (seaweed farming) . . 1·80 1·80
No. **MS**3505 has a brief description of each stamp in the lower margin.

1068 Edge of Mangrove Swamp

1070 Participating Countries' Flags surrounding Communication Mast

2002. Philakorea 2002 International Stamp Exhibition, Seoul. Two sheets, each 97 × 86 mm containing T **1068** and similar vert design. Multicoloured.
MS3506 (a) 5p. Type **1068**; 17p. As No. 3488 (b) As No. **MS**3506a but with gold horizontal band . . 1·60 1·60

2002. No. 2476 optd **3p**.
3507 3p. on 60s. multicoloured 35 35

2002. TELMIN, TELSOM and ATRC Telecommunications Meetings held in Manila.
3508 **1070** 5p. multicoloured . . . 45 45

1071 Kapitan Moy Building and Giant Shoe

2002. Shoe Manufacture in Marikina City.
3509 **1071** 5p. multicoloured . . . 45 45

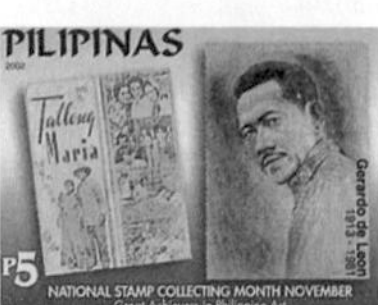

1072 Gerardo de Leon

2002. National Stamp Collecting Month. Multicoloured.
3510 5p. Type **1072** (filmmaker) 45 45
3511 17p. Francisca Reyes Aquino (folk dance researcher) . . . . 1·40 1·40
3512 21p. Pablo Antonio (architect) . . . . 1·60 1·60
3513 22p. Jose Garcia Villa (writer) . . . . 1·80 1·80
MS3514 100 × 74 mm. 22p. Honorata de la Rama (singer and actress) Imperf . . . . 1·80 1·80

1073 Kutsinta (rice cakes)

1074 Dove, Family and Crucifix

2002. Christmas. Multicoloured.
3515 5p. Type **1073** 45 45
3516 17p. Sapin-sapin (multilayered cake) . . . 1·40 1·40
3517 21p. Bibingka (rice and coconut cake) . . . . . . 1·60 1·60
3518 22p. Puto bumbong (cylindrical rice cakes) . . 1·80 1·80

2002. 4th World Meeting of Families (papal initiative), Manila (1st issue).
3519 **1074** 11p. multicoloured . . 90 90
See also No. 3528.

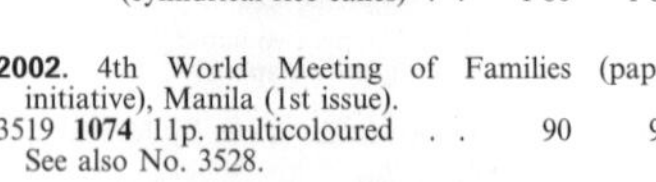
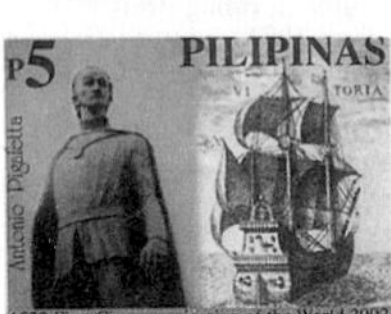

1075 Antonio Pigafetta

2002. 480th Anniv of First Circumnavigation of the Globe (1st issue). Multicoloured.
3520 5p. Type **1075** 45 45
3521 5p. Ferdinand Magellan . . 45 45
3522 5p. Charles I coin and *Vitoria* 45 45
3523 5p. Sebastian *Eleano* and *Vitoria* 45 45
See also No. **MS**3530.

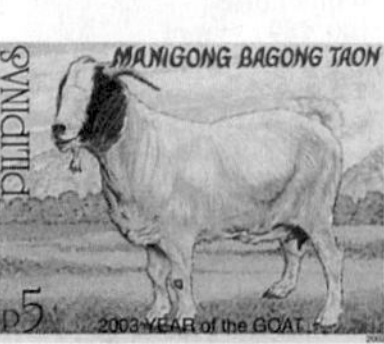

1076 Female Goat

2002. Year of the Goat. Multicoloured.
3524 5p. Type **1076** 45 45
3525 17p. Male goat . . . . . . 1·40 1·40
MS3526 99 × 88 mm. Nos. 3524/5. Perf or imperf . . . . 1·80 1·80

1077 Lyceum Building and Bust of Jose Laurel (founder)

1078 Holy Family

2002. 50th Anniv of Philippines Lyceum.
3527 **1077** 5p. multicoloured . . . 45 45

2002. 4th World Meeting of Families, Manila (2nd issue).
3528 **1078** 5p. multicoloured . . . 45 45

1079 Mt. Guiting (½-size illustration)

2002. International Year of Mountains. Sheet 96 × 70 mm.
MS3529 **1079** 22p. multicoloured 1·80 1·80

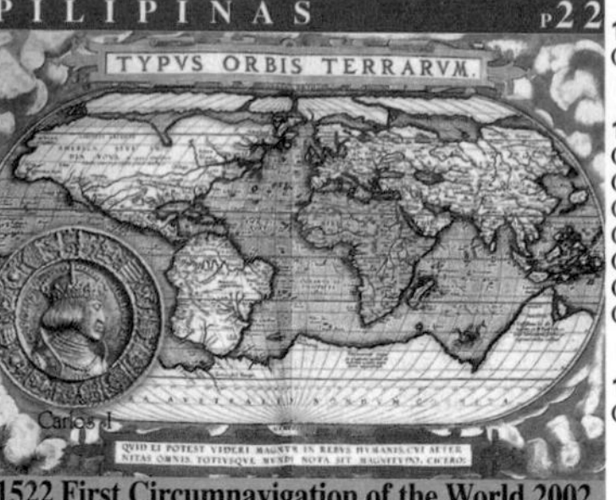

1080 Charles I Coin and 16th-century Map (⅓-size illustration)

2002. 480th Anniv of First Circumnavigation of the Globe (2nd issue). Sheet 104 × 85 mm. Imperf.
MS3530 **1080** 22p. multicoloured 1·80 1·80

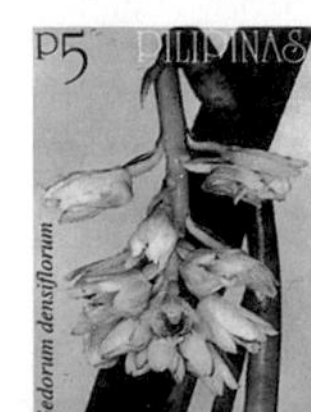

1081 *Geodorum densiflorum*

2002. Orchids. Multicoloured.
3531 5p. Type **1081** 45 45
3532 5p. *Nervilia plicata* 45 45
3533 5p. *Luisia teretifolia* 45 45
3534 5p. *Dendrobium Victoria-reginae* 45 45
MS3535 101 × 87 mm. 22p. *Grammatophylum scriptum*. Imperf 1·80 1·80

OFFICIAL STAMPS

1926. Commemorative issue of 1926 optd **OFFICIAL**.
O391 **49** 2c. black and green . . . 1·50 80
O392 4c. black and red . . . . 1·50 80
O393 18c. black and brown . . 5·50 3·25
O394 20c. black and orange . . 4·50 1·50

1931. Stamps of 1906 optd **O.B.**
O413 2c. green (No. 337) 10 10
O414 4c. red (No. 338) 10 10
O415 6c. violet (No. 339) 10 10
O416 8c. brown (No. 340) . . . 10 10
O417 10c. blue (No. 341) 55 10
O418 12c. orange (No. 342) . . . 30 15
O419 16c. olive (No. 344) 30 10
O420 20c. orange (No. 345) . . . 40 10
O421 26c. green (No. 346) . . . 50 40
O422 30c. grey (No. 347) 40 30

1935. Nos. 459/68 optd **O.B.**
O473 2c. red 10 10
O474 4c. green 10 10
O475 6c. brown 10 10
O476 8c. violet 15 15
O477 10c. red 15 10
O478 12c. black 20 15
O479 16c. blue 40 15
O480 20c. bistre 20 15
O481 26c. blue 40 35
O482 30c. red 45 40

1936. Stamps of 1935 Nos. 459/68 optd **O. B. COMMON-WEALTH** (2, 6, 20c.) or **O. B. COMMONWEALTH** (others).
O538 2c. red 10 10
O539 4c. green 10 10
O540 6c. brown 15 10
O541 8c. violet 15 10
O542 10c. red 15 10
O543 12c. black 15 15
O544 16c. blue 40 10
O545 20c. bistre 40 40
O546 26c. blue 45 45
O547 30c. red 45 45

1941. Nos. 563 and 623 optd **O. B.**
O565 **104** 2c. green 10 10
O624 – 2c. brown 10 10

1948. Various stamps optd **O.B.**
O738 **147** 1c. brown 15 10
O668 **125** 2c. green 50 10
O659 – 4c. brown (No. 629) . . 15 10
O739 – 5c. red (No. 731) . . . 15 10
O843 – 6c. blue (No. 842) . . . 15 10
O660 **113** 10c. red 20 10
O740 – 10c. blue (No. 732) . . 20 15
O661 – 16c. grey (No. 632) . . 2·20 80
O669 – 20c. brown (No. 633) 15 15
O741 – 20c. red (No. 733) . . . 50 15
O670 – 50c. green (No. 634) . . 75 45

1950. Surch **ONE CENTAVO.**
O700 **125** 1c. on 2c. green (No. O668) 10 10

1959. No. 810 optd **O B.**
O811 1c. on 5c. red 15 10

1962. Nos. 898/904 optd **G. O.**
O908 5s. red 10 10
O909 6s. brown 15 10
O910 6s. blue 15 10
O911 10s. purple 20 15
O912 20s. blue 30 15
O913 30s. red 35 30
O914 50s. violet 45 35

1970. Optd **G.O.**
O1182 **318** 10s. red 15 10

OFFICIAL SPECIAL DELIVERY STAMP

1931. No. E353b optd **O.B.**
EO423 E **47** 20c. violet 50 35

POSTAGE DUE STAMPS

1899. Postage Due stamps of United States of 1894 optd **PHILIPPINES.**
D268 D **87** 1c. red . . . . 3·75 1·00
D269 2c. red . . . . 4·00 90
D270 3c. red . . . . 13·00 4·50
D271 5c. red . . . . 10·50 1·75
D272 10c. red . . . . 14·00 4·00
D273 30c. red . . . . £180 75·00
D274 50c. red . . . . £140 70·00

D **51** Post Office Clerk

D **118**

1928.
D395 D **51** 4c. red 15 15
D396 6c. red 25 25
D397 8c. red 25 25
D398 10c. red 25 25
D399 12c. red 25 25
D400 16c. red 30 30
D401 20c. red 25 25

1937. Surch **3 CVOS. 3.**
D521 D **51** 3c. on 4c. red 20 15

1947.
D644 D **118** 3c. red 15 15
D645 4c. blue 35 30
D646 6c. green 50 45
D647 10c. orange 80 60

SPECIAL DELIVERY STAMPS

1901. Special Delivery stamp of United States of 1888 optd **PHILIPPINES.**
E268 **46** 10c. blue (No. E283) . . 85·00 80·00

1907. Special Delivery stamp of United States optd **PHILIPPINES.**
E298 E **117** 10c. blue £1500

E **47** Messenger running

1919. Perf (E353), perf or imperf (E353b).
E353 E **47** 20c. blue 45 20
E353b 20c. violet 45 15

1939. Optd **COMMONWEALTH**. Perf.
E550 E **47** 20c. violet 30 20

1945. Optd **VICTORY**.
E622 E **47** 20c. violet (No. E550) 50 50

E **120** Cyclist Messenger and Post Office

1947.

No.	Type	Description	Mint	Used
E651	E **120**	20c. purple	60	45

E **219** G.P.O., Manila

No.	Type	Description	Mint	Used
E891	E **219**	20c. mauve	35	30

PITCAIRN ISLANDS Pt. 1

An island group in the Pacific Ocean, nearly midway between Australia and America.

1940. 12 pence = 1 shilling;
20 shillings = 1 pound.
1967. 100 cents = 1 New Zealand dollar.

4 Lt. Bligh and the "Bounty"

1940.

No.	Type	Description	Mint	Used
1	–	½d. orange and green	40	60
2	–	1d. mauve and magenta	55	70
3	–	1½d. grey and red	55	50
4	**4**	2d. green and brown	1·75	1·40
5	–	3d. green and blue	1·25	1·40
5b	–	4d. black and green	15·00	11·00
6	–	6d. brown and blue	5·00	1·50
6a	–	8d. green and mauve	16·00	7·00
7	–	1s. violet and grey	3·00	2·00
8	–	2s.6d. green and brown	8·00	3·75

DESIGNS—HORIZ: ½d. Oranges; 1d. Fletcher Christian, crew and Pitcairn Is.; 1½d. John Adams and house; 3d. Map of Pitcairn Is. and Pacific; 4d. Bounty Bible; 6d. H.M.S. "Bounty"; 8d. School, 1949; 1s. Christian and Pitcairn Is.; 2s.6d. Christian, crew and Pitcairn coast.

4a Houses of Parliament, London

1946. Victory.

No.	Type	Description	Mint	Used
9	**4a**	2d. brown	60	15
10		3d. blue	60	15

4b King George VI and Queen Elizabeth

4c King George VI and Queen Elizabeth

1949. Silver Wedding.

No.	Type	Description	Mint	Used
11	**4b**	1½d. red	2·00	1·00
12	**4c**	10s. mauve	35·00	50·00

4d Hermes, Globe and Forms of Transport

4e Hemispheres, Jet-powered Vickers Viking Airliner and Steamer

4f Hermes and Globe

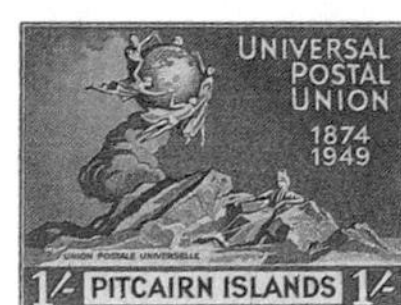

4g U.P.U. Monument

1949. U.P.U.

No.	Type	Description	Mint	Used
13	**4d**	2½d. brown	1·00	4·25
14	**4e**	3d. blue	8·00	4·25
15	**4f**	6d. green	4·00	4·25
16	**4g**	1s. purple	4·00	4·00

4h Queen Elizabeth II

1953. Coronation.

No.	Type	Description	Mint	Used
17	**4h**	4d. black and green	2·00	3·50

12 Handicrafts: Bird Model

1957.

No.	Type	Description	Mint	Used
33	–	½d. green and mauve	65	60
19	–	1d. black and green	3·50	1·75
20	–	2d. brown and blue	1·25	60
21	**12**	2½d. brown and pink	50	40
22	–	3d. green and blue	80	40
23	–	4d. red and blue (I)	90	40
23a	–	4d. red and blue (II)	5·00	1·50
24	**12**	6d. buff and blue	1·50	55
25	–	8d. green and red	60	40
26	–	1s. black and brown	2·25	40
27	–	2s. green and orange	14·00	10·00
28	–	2s.6d. blue and red	23·00	9·00

DESIGNS—HORIZ: ½d. "Cordyline terminalis"; 3d. Bounty Bay; 4d. Pitcairn School; 6d. Map of Pacific; 8d. Inland scene; 1s. Model of the "Bounty"; 2s.6d. Launching new whaleboat. VERT: 1d. Map of Pitcairn; 2d. John Adams and "Bounty" Bible; 2s. Island wheelbarrow.

The 4d. Type I is inscr "PITCAIRN SCHOOL"; Type II is inscr "SCHOOL TEACHER'S HOUSE".

20 Pitcairn Island and Simon Young

1961. Cent of Return of Pitcairn Islanders.

No.	Type	Description	Mint	Used
29	**20**	3d. black and yellow	50	45
30	–	6d. brown and blue	1·00	75
31	–	1s. orange and green	1·00	75

DESIGNS: 6d. Maps of Norfolk and Pitcairn Islands; 1s. Migrant brigantine "Mary Ann".

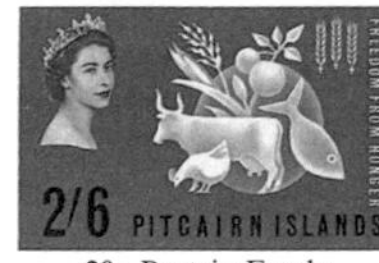

20a Protein Foods

1963. Freedom from Hunger.

No.	Type	Description	Mint	Used
32	**20a**	2s.6d. blue	7·50	3·00

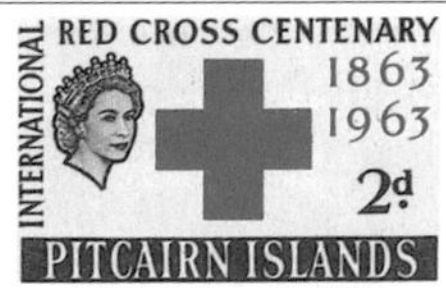

20b Red Cross Emblem

1963. Cent of Red Cross.

No.	Type	Description	Mint	Used
34	**20b**	2d. red and black	1·25	1·00
35		2s.6d. red and blue	2·75	4·00

23 Pitcairn Is. Longboat

24 Queen Elizabeth II (after Anthony Buckley)

1964. Multicoloured.

No.	Type	Description	Mint	Used
36		½d. Type **23**	10	30
37		1d. H.M.S. "Bounty"	30	30
38		2d. "Out from Bounty Bay"	30	30
39		3d. Great frigate bird	75	30
40		4d. White tern	75	30
41		6d. Pitcairn warbler	75	30
42		8d. Red-footed booby	75	30
43		10d. Red-tailed tropic birds	60	30
44		1s. Henderson Island crake	60	30
45		1s.6d. Stephen's lory	4·50	1·25
46		2s.6d. Murphy's petrel	4·00	1·50
47		4s. Henderson Island fruit dove	6·00	1·75
48		8s. Type **24**	2·75	1·75

24a I.T.U. Emblem

1965. Centenary of I.T.U.

No.	Type	Description	Mint	Used
49	**24a**	1d. mauve and brown	1·00	40
50		2s.6d. turquoise and blue	5·00	3·50

24b I.C.Y. Emblem

1965. International Co-operation Year.

No.	Type	Description	Mint	Used
51	**24b**	1d. purple and turquoise	1·00	40
52		2s.6d. green and lavender	4·00	3·00

24c Sir Winston Churchill and St. Paul's Cathedral in Wartime

1966. Churchill Commemoration.

No.	Type	Description	Mint	Used
53	**24c**	2d. blue	1·25	85
54		3d. green	3·75	1·00
55		6d. brown	4·00	1·75
56		1s. violet	5·50	2·50

25 Footballer's Legs, Ball and Jules Rimet Cup

1966. World Cup Football Championship.

No.	Type	Description	Mint	Used
57	**25**	4d. multicoloured	1·25	1·00
58		2s.6d. multicoloured	2·50	1·75

25a W.H.O. Building.

1966. Inauguration of W.H.O. Headquarters, Geneva.

No.	Type	Description	Mint	Used
59	**25a**	8d. black, green and blue	4·00	3·25
60		1s.6d. black, purple and ochre	5·50	3·75

25b "Education"

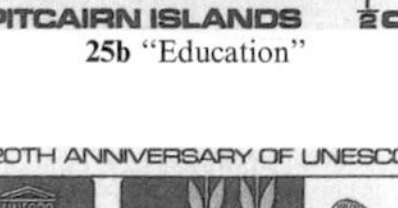

25c "Science"

25d "Culture"

1966. 20th Anniv of UNESCO.

No.	Type	Description	Mint	Used
61	**25b**	½d. multicoloured	20	1·00
62	**25c**	10d. yellow, violet and olive	3·25	2·75
63	**25d**	2s. black, purple and orange	6·00	4·25

36 Mangarevan Canoe, c. 1325

1967. Bicentenary of Discovery of Pitcairn Islands'. Multicoloured.

No.	Type	Description	Mint	Used
64		½d. Type **36**	10	20
65		1d. P. F. de Quiros and "San Pedro y San Pablo", 1606	20	20
66		8d. "San Pedro y San Pablo" and "Los Tres Reyes", 1606	25	20
67		1s. Carteret and H.M.S. "Swallow", 1767	25	25
68		1s.6d. "Hercules", 1819	25	25

1967. Decimal Currency. Nos. 36/48 surch with "Bounty" anchor and value.

No.	Type	Description	Mint	Used
69	**23**	½c. on ½d. multicoloured	10	10
70	–	1c. on 1d. multicoloured	30	1·25
71	–	2c. on 2d. multicoloured	25	1·25
72	–	2½c. on 3d. multicoloured	25	1·25
73	–	3c. on 4d. multicoloured	25	20
74	–	5c. on 6d. multicoloured	30	1·25
75	–	10c. on 8d. multicoloured	30	30
76	–	15c. on 10d. multicoloured	1·25	40
77	–	20c. on 1s. multicoloured	1·25	55
78	–	25c. on 1s.6d. multicoloured	1·75	1·25
79	–	30c. on 2s.6d. multicoloured	2·25	1·25
80	–	40c. on 4s. multicoloured	2·50	1·25
81	**24**	45c. on 8s. multicoloured	2·00	1·50

42 Bligh and "Bounty's" Launch

1967. 150th Death Anniv of Admiral Bligh.

No.	Type	Description	Mint	Used
82	**42**	1c. black, ultramarine & blue	10	10
83	–	8c. black, yellow and mauve	25	65
84	–	20c. black, brown and buff	25	70

DESIGNS: 8c. Bligh and followers cast adrift; 20c. Bligh's tomb.

45 Human Rights Emblem

1968. International Human Rights Year.
85 **45** 1c. multicoloured 10 10
86 2c. multicoloured 10 10
87 25c. multicoloured 35 35

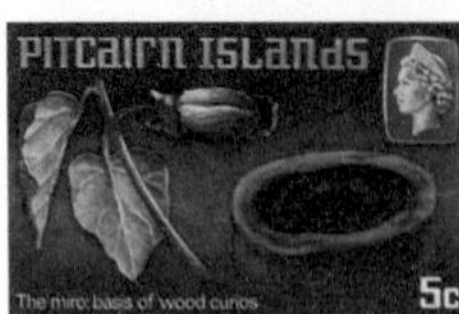

46 Moro Wood and Flower

1968. Handicrafts (1st series).
88 **46** 5c. multicoloured 20 30
89 – 10c. green, brown and orange 20 40
90 – 15c. violet, brown & salmon 25 40
91 – 20c. multicoloured 25 45
DESIGNS—HORIZ: 10c. flying fish model. VERT: 15c. "Hand" vases; 20c. Woven baskets.
See also Nos. 207/10.

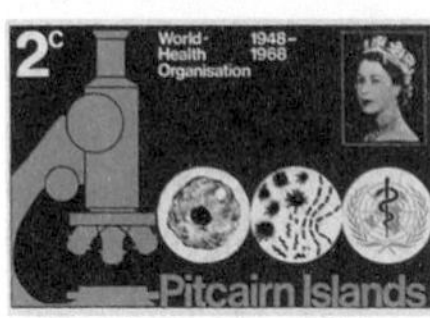

50 Microscope and Slides

1968. 20th Anniv of World Health Organization.
92 **50** 2c. black, turquoise and blue 10 20
93 – 20c. black, orange and purple 40 50
DESIGN: 20c. Hypodermic syringe and jars of tablets.

52 Pitcairn Island

64b Queen Elizabeth II

65 Lantana

1969. Multicoloured.
94 1c. Type **52** . . . . 1·50 1·00
95 2c. Captain Bligh and "Bounty" chronometer 25 15
96 3c. "Bounty" anchor (vert) 25 15
97 4c. Plans and drawing of "Bounty" . . . . 1·50 15
98 5c. Breadfruit containers and plant 60 15
99 6c. Bounty Bay 30 20
100 8c. Pitcairn longboat . . . 1·50 20
101 10c. Ship landing point . . 2·50 85
102 15c. Fletcher Christian's Cave . . . . 1·50 50
103 20c. Thursday October Christian's house 60 40
104 25c. "Flying fox" cable system (vert) 70 40
105 30c. Radio Station, Taro Ground 55 45
106 40c. "Bounty" Bible 75 60
106a 50c. Pitcairn Coat-of-Arms 2·00 11·00
106b $1 Type **64b** . . . . 7·00 17·00

1970. Flowers. Multicoloured.
107 1c. Type **65** 15 50
108 2c. "Indian Shot" 20 65
109 5c. Pulau 25 75
110 25c. Wild gladiolus . . . . . 60 2·00

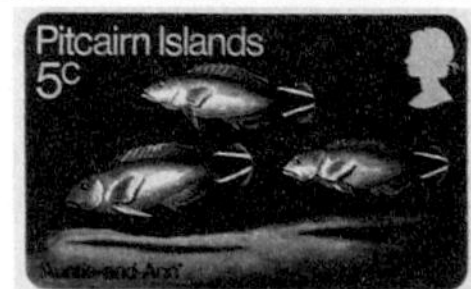

69 Band-tailed Hind

1970. Fishes. Multicoloured.
111 5c. Type **69** . . . . 2·75 70
112 10c. High-finned rudderfish 2·75 85
113 15c. Elwyn's wrasse . . . . 3·25 1·00
114 20c. Yellow wrasse ("Whistling daughter") . . 3·50 1·25

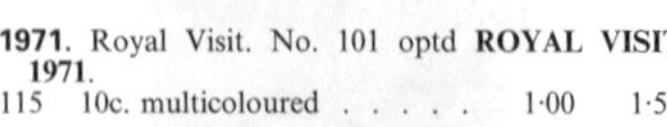

1971. Royal Visit. No. 101 optd **ROYAL VISIT 1971**.
115 10c. multicoloured . . . . . 1·00 1·50

71 Polynesian Rock Carvings

1971. Polynesian Pitcairn. Multicoloured.
116 5c. Type **71** . . . . 1·00 75
117 10c. Polynesian artefacts (horiz) . . . . 1·25 1·00
118 15c. Polynesian stone fish-hook (horiz) . . . . 1·25 1·00
119 20c. Polynesian stone deity 1·50 1·25

72 Commission Flag

74 Rose-apple

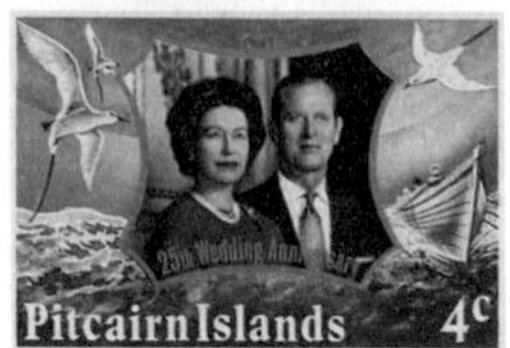

73 Red-tailed Tropic Birds and Longboat

1972. 25th Anniv of South Pacific Commission. Multicoloured.
120 4c. Type **72** 40 70
121 8c. Young and elderly (Health) 40 70
122 18c. Junior school (Education) 50 90
123 20c. Goods store (Economy) 60 1·60

1972. Royal Silver Wedding. Multicoloured, background colour given.
124 **73** 4c. green 30 60
125 20c. blue 45 90

1973. Flowers. Multicoloured.
126 4c. Type **74** 75 55
127 8c. Mountain-apple . . . . . 1·00 75
128 15c. "Lata" . . . . 1·25 1·00
129 20c. "Dorcas-flower" . . . . 1·25 1·25
130 35c. Guava . . . . 1·25 1·75

74a Princess Anne and Captain Mark Phillips

1973. Royal Wedding. Multicoloured, background colours given.
131 **74a** 10c. mauve 20 15
132 25c. green 25 30

75 Obelisk Vertagus and Episcopal Mitre Shells

1974. Shells. Multicoloured.
147 4c. Type **75** 65 80
148 10c. Turtle dove-shell . . . . 75 1·00
149 18c. Indo-Pacific limpet, fringed false limpet and "Siphonaria normalis" . . 80 1·40
150 50c. "Ctena divergen" . . . 1·25 2·00
MS151 130 × 121 mm. Nos. 147/50 3·50 14·00

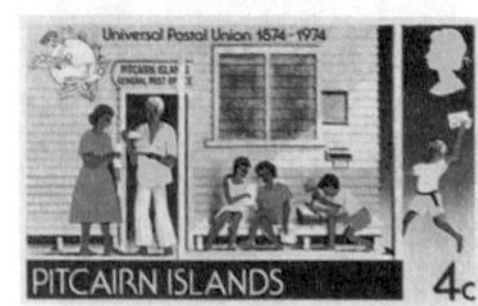

76 Island Post Office

1974. Centenary of U.P.U.
152 **76** 4c. multicoloured 20 35
153 – 20c. purple, brown & black 25 60
154 – 35c. multicoloured 35 70
DESIGNS: 20c. Pre-stamp letter, 1922; 35c. Mailship and Pitcairn longboat.

77 Churchill and Text "Lift up your Hearts ..."

1974. Birth Cent of Sir Winston Churchill.
155 **77** 20c. olive, green and grey 30 65
156 – 35c. brown, green and grey 40 75
DESIGN: 35c. Text "Give us the tools ...".

78 H.M.S. "Seringapatam" (frigate), 1830

1975. Mailboats. Multicoloured.
157 4c. Type **78** 25 50
158 10c. "Pitcairn" (missionary schooner), 1890 . . . . . 30 75
159 18c. "Athenic" (liner), 1904 35 1·10
160 50c. "Gothic" (liner), 1948 60 1·75
MS161 145 × 110mm. Nos. 157/60 11·00 16·00

79 "Polistes jadwigae" (wasp)

1975. Pitcairn Insects. Multicoloured.
162 4c. Type **79** 25 45
163 6c. "Euconocephalus sp." (grasshopper) 25 55
164 10c. "Anomis flavia" and "Chasmina tibialis" (moth) 30 70
165 15c. "Pantala flavescens" (skimmer) . . . . 40 1·00
166 20c. "Gnathothlibus erotus" (banana moth) . . . . . . 50 1·25

80 Fletcher Christian

81 Chair of Homage

1976. Bicent of American Revolution. Mult.
167 5c. Type **80** 20 65
168 10c. H.M.S. "Bounty" . . . 25 80
169 30c. George Washington . . 25 95
170 50c. "Mayflower", 1620 . . . 35 1·50

1977. Silver Jubilee. Multicoloured.
171 8c. Prince Philip's visit, 1971 10 15
172 20c. Type **81** 20 25
173 50c. Enthronement 40 50

82 The Island's Bell

84 Coronation Ceremony

83 Building a "Bounty" Model

1977. Multicoloured.
174 1c. Type **82** 10 50
175 2c. Building a longboat (horiz) 10 50
176 5c. Landing cargo (horiz) 10 50
177 6c. Sorting supplies (horiz) 10 50
178 9c. Cleaning wahoo (fish) 10 50
179 10c. Cultivation (horiz) . . 10 50
179a 15c. Sugar Mill (horiz) . . . 50 1·00
180 20c. Grating coconut and bananas (horiz) 15 50
181 35c. The Island church (horiz) 15 70
182 50c. Fetching miro logs, Henderson Is. (horiz) . . 20 80
182b 70c. Burning obsolete stamp issues . . . . 50 1·25
183 $1 Prince Philip, Bounty Bay and Royal Yacht "Britannia" (horiz) . . . 40 1·10
184 $2 Queen Elizabeth II (photograph by Reginald Davis) . . . . 50 1·75

1978. "Bounty" Day. Multicoloured.
185 6c. Type **83** 20 20
186 20c. The model at sea . . . 25 25
187 35c. Burning the model . . . 35 35
MS188 166 × 122 mm. Nos. 185/7 5·00 9·50

1978. 25th Anniv of Coronation. Sheet 94 × 78 mm.
MS189 **84** $1.20 multicoloured 80 1·75

85 Harbour before Development

1978. "Operation Pallium" (Harbour Development Project). Multicoloured.
190 15c. Type **85** 30 50
191 20c. Unloading R.F.A. "Sir Geraint" 40 60
192 30c. Work on the jetty . . . 45 70
193 35c. Harbour after development 50 80

86 John Adams and Diary Extract

1979. 150th Death Anniv of John Adams ("Bounty" mutineer). Multicoloured.
194 35c. Type **86** 30 70
195 70c. John Adams' grave and diary extract 45 90

87 Pitcairn's Island sketched from H.M.S. "Amphitrite"

1979. 19th-century Engravings.
196 **87** 6c. black, brown and stone 15 20
197 – 9c. black, violet & lt violet 15 25

198 – 20c. black, green and yellow 15 40
199 – 70c. black, scarlet and red 30 1·00
DESIGNS: 9c. Bounty Bay and Village of Pitcairn; 20c. Lookout Ridge; 70c. Church and School House.

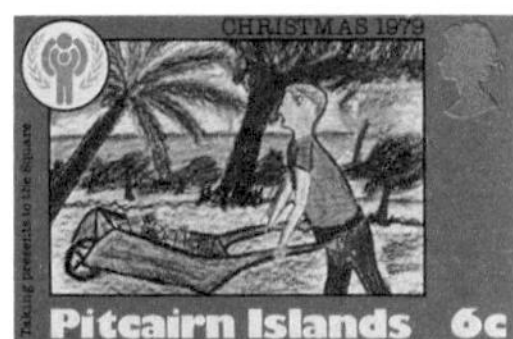

88 Taking Presents to the Square

1979. Christmas. Int Year of the Child. Mult.
200 6c. Type **88** 10 20
201 9c. Decorating trees with presents 10 25
202 20c. Chosen men distributing gifts 15 40
203 35c. Carrying presents home 20 50
MS204 198 × 73 mm. Nos. 200/3 75 1·40

89 Loading Mail from Supply Ship to Longboats

1980. "London 1980" International Stamp Exhibition. Sheet 120 × 135 mm containing T **89** and similar horiz designs. Multicoloured.
MS205 35c. Type **89**; 35c. Mail being conveyed by "Flying Fox" (hoisting mechanism) to the Edge; 35c. Tractor transporting mail from the Edge to Adamstown; 35c. Mail being off-loaded at Post Office . . . . 75 1·50

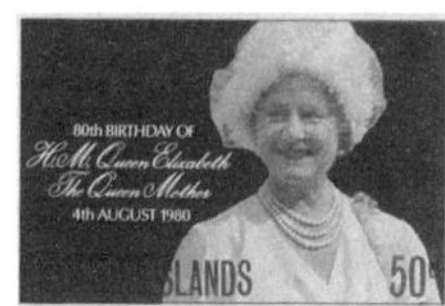

90 Queen Elizabeth the Queen Mother at Henley Regatta

1980. 80th Birthday of The Queen Mother.
206 **90** 50c. multicoloured 40 70

1980. Handicrafts (2nd series). As T **46**. Multicoloured.
207 9c. Turtles (wood carvings) 10 10
208 20c. Pitcairn wheelbarrow (wood carving) 10 15
209 35c. Gamet (wood carving) (vert) 15 25
210 40c. Woven bonnet and fan (vert) 15 25

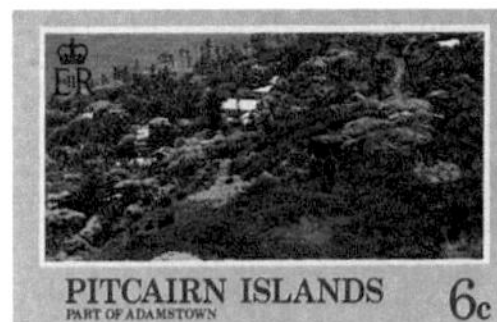

91 Part of Adamstown

1981. Landscapes. Multicoloured.
211 6c. Type **91** 10 10
212 9c. Big George 10 15
213 20c. Christian's Cave, Gannets Ridge 15 20
214 35c. Radio Station from Pawala Valley Ridge . . . 20 30
215 70c. Tatrimoa 30 45

92 Islanders preparing for Departure

1981. 125th Anniv of Pitcairn Islanders' Migration to Norfolk Island. Multicoloured.
216 9c. Type **92** 20 30
217 35c. View of Pitcairn Island from "Morayshire" 35 50
218 70c. "Morayshire" 55 90

93 Prince Charles as Colonel-in-Chief, Cheshire Regiment

95 Pitcairn Islands Coat of Arms

94 Lemon

1981. Royal Wedding. Multicoloured.
219 20c. Wedding bouquet from Pitcairn Islands 20 20
220 35c. Type **93** 25 20
221 $1.20 Prince Charles and Lady Diana Spencer . . . 75 60

1982. Fruit. Multicoloured.
222 9c. Type **94** 10 10
223 20c. Pomegranate 15 20
224 35c. Avocado 20 30
225 70c. Pawpaw 40 65

1982. 21st Birthday of Princess of Wales. Multicoloured.
226 6c. Type **95** 10 20
227 9c. Princess at Royal Opera House, Covent Garden, December 1981 . . . . . 45 20
228 70c. Balcony Kiss 70 60
229 $1.20 Formal portrait . . . . 1·50 80

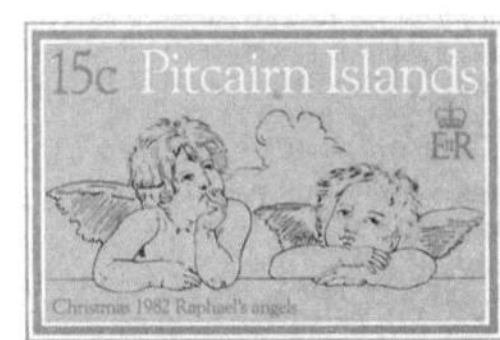

96 Raphael's Angels

1982. Christmas. Raphael's Angels.
230 **96** 15c. black, silver and pink 20 20
231 – 20c. black, silver and yellow 20 20
232 – 50c. brown, silver and stone 30 30
233 – $1 black, silver and blue 40 40
DESIGNS: 20c. to $1 Different details, the 50c. and $1 being vertical.

97 Radio Operator

1983. Commonwealth Day. Multicoloured.
234 6c. Type **97** 10 10
235 9c. Postal clerk 10 10
236 70c. Fisherman 35 65
237 $1.20 Artist . . . . 60 1·10

98 "Topaz" sights Smoke on Pitcairn

1983. 175th Anniv of Folger's Discovery of the Settlers. Multicoloured.
238 6c. Type **98** 30 20
239 20c. Three islanders approach the "Topaz" 35 30
240 70c. Capt. Mayhew Folger welcomed by John Adams 60 75
241 $1.20 Folger presented with "Bounty" chronometer . . 75 1·10

99 Hattie-Tree

1983. Trees of Pitcairn Islands (1st series). Multicoloured.
242 35c. Type **99** 25 55
243 35c. Leaves from Hattie-Tree 25 55
244 70c. Pandanus 40 90
245 70c. Pandanus and basket weaving 40 90
See also Nos. 304/7.

100 Atava wrasse

1984. Fishes. Multicoloured.
246 1c. Type **100** 20 30
247 4c. Black-eared wrasse . . . 30 35
248 6c. Long-finned parrotfish . . 30 35
249 9c. Yellow-edged lyretail . . 30 35
250 10c. Black-eared angelfish . . 30 40
251 15c. Emery's damselfish . . . 30 40
252 20c. Smith's butterflyfish . . 40 50
253 35c. Crosshatched triggerfish 50 60
254 50c. Yellow damselfish . . . 50 75
255 70c. Pitcairn angelfish 70 95
312 90c. As 9c. . . . . 3·75 4·50
256 $1 Easter Island soldierfish 70 1·25
257 $1.20 Long-finned anthias . . 75 2·00
258 $2 White trevally . . . . . . 1·25 2·50
313 $3 Wakanoura moray . . . . 5·00 7·00

101 "Southern Cross"

1984. Night Sky.
259 **101** 15c. blue, lilac and gold 20 20
260 – 20c. blue, green and gold 30 30
261 – 70c. blue, brown and gold 75 75
262 – $1 blue, light blue and gold . . . . 1·00 1·00
DESIGNS: 20c. "Southern Fish"; 70c. "Lesser Dog"; $1 "The Virgin".

102 Aluminium Longboat

1984. "Ausipex" International Stamp Exhibition, Melbourne. Sheet 134 × 86 mm containing T **102** and similar horiz design. Multicoloured.
MS263 50c. Type **102**; $2 Traditional-style wooden longboat 1·50 2·00

103 "H.M.S. "Portland" standing off Bounty Bay" (J. Linton Palmer)

104 The Queen Mother with the Queen and Princess Margaret, 1980

1985. 19th-century Paintings (1st series). Mult.
264 6c. Type **103** 30 30
265 9c. "Christian's Look Out" (J. Linton Palmer) 30 30
266 35c. "The Golden Age" (J. Linton Palmer) 65 55
267 $2 "A View of the Village, 1825" (William Smyth) (48 × 31 mm) . . . . . . 1·75 2·00
See also Nos. 308/11.

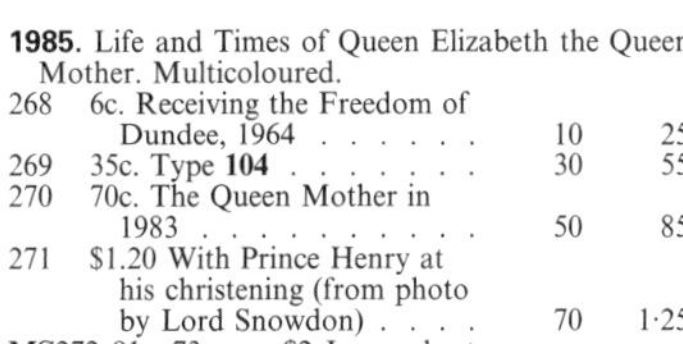

1985. Life and Times of Queen Elizabeth the Queen Mother. Multicoloured.
268 6c. Receiving the Freedom of Dundee, 1964 . . . . . . 10 25
269 35c. Type **104** 30 55
270 70c. The Queen Mother in 1983 . . . . 50 85
271 $1.20 With Prince Henry at his christening (from photo by Lord Snowdon) . . . . 70 1·25
MS272 91 × 73 mm. $2 In coach at Ascot Races . . . . 2·75 2·00

105 "Act 6" (container ship)

1985. Ships (1st issue). Multicoloured.
273 50c. Type **105** . . . . 95 1·75
274 50c. "Columbus Louisiana" (container ship) . . . . . 95 1·75
275 50c. "Essi Gina" (tanker) (48 × 35 mm) . . . . . . 95 1·75
276 50c. "Stolt Spirit" tanker (48 × 35 mm) . . . . . . 95 1·75
See also Nos. 296/9.

106 "Madonna and Child" (Raphael)

107a Prince Andrew and Miss Sarah Ferguson

107 Green Turtle

1985. Christmas. Designs showing "Madonna and Child" paintings. Multicoloured.
277 6c. Type **106** 60 50
278 9c. Krause (after Raphael) . . 60 50
279 35c. Andreas Mayer . . . . 1·00 70
280 $2 Unknown Austrian master 2·75 3·50

1986. Turtles. Multicoloured.
281 9c. Type **107** . . . . 1·00 90
282 20c. Green turtle and Pitcairn Island . . . . 1·60 1·25
283 70c. Hawksbill turtle . . . . 3·00 3·75
284 $1.20 Hawksbill turtle and Pitcairn Island . . . . . . 3·50 4·25

1986. 60th Birthday of Queen Elizabeth II. As T **246b** of Papua New Guinea.
285 6c. Princess Elizabeth at Royal Lodge, Windsor, 1946 . . . . 15 20
286 9c. Wedding of Princess Anne, 1973 . . . . 15 20
287 20c. At Order of St. Michael and St. George service, St. Paul's Cathedral, 1961 25 30
288 $1.20 At Electrical Engineering Concert, Royal Festival Hall, 1971 . . . . 60 1·25
289 $2 At Crown Agents Head Office, London 1983 . . . 75 2·00

1986. Royal Wedding. Multicoloured.
290 20c. Type **107a** 50 50
291 $1.20 Prince Andrew aboard "Bluenose II" off Halifax, Canada, 1985 . . . . . . 1·90 2·50

108 John I. Tay (pioneer missionary) and First Church

110 *Bounty* (replica)

109 Pitcairn Island Home

1986. Centenary of Seventh-Day Adventist Church on Pitcairn. Multicoloured.

No.	Description	Mint	Used
292	6c. Type **108**	50	50
293	20c. "Pitcairn" (missionary schooner) and second church (1907)	1·25	1·00
294	35c. Baptism at Down Isaac and third church (1945)	1·75	1·50
295	$2 Islanders singing farewell hymn and present church (1954)	3·75	4·25

1987. Ships (2nd series). As T **105**. Multicoloured.

No.	Description	Mint	Used
296	50c. "Samoan Reefer" (freighter)	1·00	2·25
297	50c. "Brussel" (container ship)	1·00	2·25
298	50c. "Australian Exporter" (container ship) (48 × 35 mm)	1·00	2·25
299	50c. "Taupo" (cargo liner) (48 × 35 mm)	1·00	2·25

1987. Pitcairn Island Homes.

No.	Description	Mint	Used
300 **109**	70c. black, dp violet & vio	50	60
301 –	70c. black, yellow & brn	50	60
302 –	70c. black, blue & dp blue	50	60
303 –	70c. black, green and deep green	50	60

DESIGNS: Nos. 301/3, different houses.

1987. Trees of Pitcairn Islands (2nd series). As T **99**. Multicoloured.

No.	Description	Mint	Used
304	40c. Leaves and flowers from "Erythrina variegata"	1·10	1·50
305	40c. "Erythrina variegata" tree	1·10	1·50
306	$1.80 Leaves from "Aleurites moluccana" and nut torch	1·90	2·75
307	$1.80 "Aleurites moluccana" tree	1·90	2·75

1987. 19th-century Paintings (2nd series). Paintings by Lt. Conway Shipley in 1848. As T **103**. Multicoloured.

No.	Description	Mint	Used
308	20c. "House and Tomb of John Adams"	55	60
309	40c. "Bounty Bay"	80	85
310	90c. "School House and Chapel"	1·40	2·00
311	$1.80 "Pitcairn Island" (48 × 31 mm)	2·25	3·75

1988. Bicentenary of Australian Settlement. Sheet 112 × 76 mm.

No.	Description	Mint	Used
MS314 **110**	$3 multicoloured	4·25	2·75

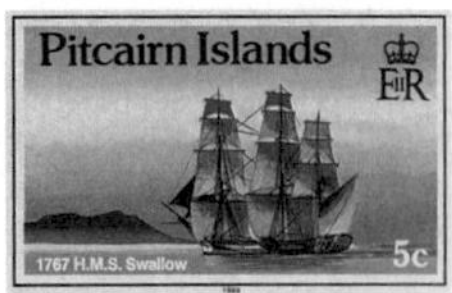

111 H.M.S. "Swallow" (survey ship), 1767

1988. Ships. Multicoloured.

No.	Description	Mint	Used
315	5c. Type **111**	50	80
316	10c. H.M.S. "Pandora" (frigate), 1791	50	80
317	15c. H.M.S. "Briton" and H.M.S. "Tagus" (frigates), 1814	55	90
318	20c. H.M.S. "Blossom" (survey ship), 1825	60	85
319	30c. "Lucy Anne" (barque), 1831	70	90
320	35c. "Charles Doggett" (whaling brig), 1831	70	90
321	40c. H.M.S. "Fly" (sloop), 1838	75	95
322	60c. "Camden" (missionary brig.), 1840	1·00	1·40
323	90c. H.M.S. "Virago" (paddle-sloop), 1853	1·25	1·75
324	$1.20 "Rakaia" (screw-steamer), 1867	1·50	2·00
325	$1.80 H.M.S. "Sappho" (screw-sloop), 1882	1·75	2·50
326	$5 H.M.S. "Champion" (corvette), 1893	4·50	5·50

112 Raising the Union Jack, 1838 **113** Angel

1988. 150th Anniv of Pitcairn Island Constitution. Each showing different extract from original Constitution. Multicoloured.

No.	Description	Mint	Used
327	20c. Type **112**	15	20
328	40c. Signing Constitution on board H.M.S. "Fly", 1838	30	35
329	$1.05 Voters at modern polling station	75	80
330	$1.80 Modern classroom	1·25	1·40

1988. Christmas. Multicoloured.

No.	Description	Mint	Used
331	90c. Type **113**	65	70
332	90c. Holy Family	65	70
333	90c. Two Polynesian Wise Men	65	70
334	90c. Polynesian Wise Man and shepherd	65	70

114 Loading Stores, Deptford

1989. Bicentenary of Pitcairn Island Settlement (1st issue). Multicoloured.

No.	Description	Mint	Used
335	20c. Type **114**	1·25	1·25
336	20c. H.M.S. "Bounty" leaving Spithead	1·25	1·25
337	20c. H.M.S. "Bounty" at Cape Horn	1·25	1·25
338	20c. Anchored in Adventure Bay, Tasmania	1·25	1·25
339	20c. Crew collecting breadfruit	1·25	1·25
340	20c. Breadfruit in cabin	1·25	1·25

See also Nos. 341/7, 356/61 and 389/94.

1989. Bicentenary of Pitcairn Island Settlement (2nd issue). As T **114**. Multicoloured.

No.	Description	Mint	Used
341	90c. H.M.S. "Bounty' leaving Tahiti	2·75	2·75
342	90c. Bligh awoken by mutineers	2·75	2·75
343	90c. Bligh before Fletcher Christian	2·75	2·75
344	90c. Provisioning "Bounty's" launch	2·75	2·75
345	90c. "Mutineers casting Bligh adrift" (Robert Dodd)	2·75	2·75
346	90c. Mutineers discarding breadfruit plants	2·75	2·75
MS347	110 × 85 mm. 90c. No. 345; 90c. Isle of Man 1989 35p. Mutiny stamp; 90c. Norfolk Island 39c. Mutiny stamp	3·75	4·00

115 R.N.Z.A.F. Lockheed Orion making Mail Drop, 1985

1989. Aircraft. Multicoloured.

No.	Description	Mint	Used
348	20c. Type **115**	1·25	60
349	80c. Beech 80 Queen Air on photo-mission, 1983	2·50	1·25
350	$1.05 Boeing-Vertol Chinook helicopter landing diesel fuel from U.S.S. "Breton", 1969	2·75	1·50
351	$1.30 R.N.Z.A.F. Lockheed Hercules dropping bulldozer, 1983	2·75	1·75

116 Ducie Island

1989. Islands of Pitcairn Group. Mult.

No.	Description	Mint	Used
352	15c. Type **116**	50	50
353	90c. Henderson Island	1·60	1·25
354	$1.05 Oeno Island	1·75	1·75
355	$1.30 Pitcairn Island	1·75	1·75

1990. Bicentenary of Pitcairn Island Settlement (3rd issue). As T **114**. Multicoloured.

No.	Description	Mint	Used
356	40c. Mutineers sighting Pitcairn Island	1·00	85
357	40c. Ship's boat approaching landing	1·00	85
358	40c. Exploring island	1·00	85
359	40c. Ferrying goods ashore	1·00	85
360	40c. Burning of H.M.S. "Bounty"	1·00	85
361	40c. Pitcairn Island village	1·00	85

117 Ennerdale, Cumbria, and Peter Heywood

1990. "Stamp World London '90" International Stamp Exhibition, London. Designs showing English landmarks and "Bounty" crew members. Multicoloured.

No.	Description	Mint	Used
362	80c. Type **117**	75	80
363	90c. St. Augustine's Tower, Hackney, and John Adams	85	90
364	$1.05 Citadel Gateway, Plymouth, and William Bligh	1·00	1·25
365	$1.30 Moorland Close, Cockermouth, and Fletcher Christian	1·25	1·40

117a Queen Elizabeth, 1937 **119** Stephen's Lory ("Redbreast")

118 "Bounty" Chronometer and 1940 1d. Definitive

1990. 90th Birthday of Queen Elizabeth the Queen Mother.

No.	Description	Mint	Used
378 **117a**	40c. multicoloured	75	85
379 –	$3 black and red	3·00	3·75

DESIGN—29 × 37 mm: $3 King George VI and Queen Elizabeth on way to Silver Wedding Service, 1948.

1990. 50th Anniv of Pitcairn Islands Stamps. Multicoloured.

No.	Description	Mint	Used
380	20c. Type **118**	80	80
381	80c. "Bounty" Bible and 1958 4d. definitive	1·60	1·75
382	90c. "Bounty" Bell and 1969 30c. definitive	1·75	1·90
383	$1.05 Mutiny on the "Bounty" and 1977 $1 definitive	2·00	2·50
384	$1.30 Penny Black and 1988 15c. definitive	2·25	2·75

1990. "Birdpex '90" International Stamp Exhibition, Christchurch, New Zealand. Multicoloured.

No.	Description	Mint	Used
385	20c. Type **119**	75	75
386	90c. Henderson Island fruit dove ("Wood Pigeon")	1·50	1·60
387	$1.30 Pitcairn warbler ("Sparrow")	1·75	2·75
388	$1.80 Henderson Island crake ("Chicken Bird")	2·00	3·00

1991. Bicent of Pitcairn Island Settlement (4th issue). Celebrations. As T **114**. Multicoloured.

No.	Description	Mint	Used
389	80c. Re-enacting landing of mutineers	2·00	2·50
390	80c. Commemorative plaque	2·00	2·50
391	80c. Memorial church service	2·00	2·50
392	80c. Cricket match	2·00	2·50
393	80c. Burning model of "Bounty"	2·00	2·50
394	80c. Firework display	2·00	2·50

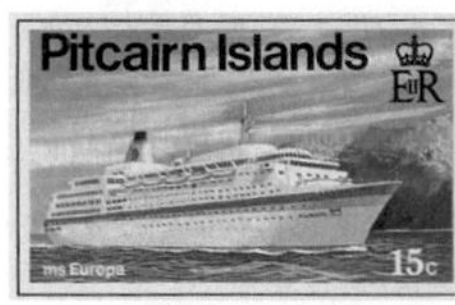

120 "Europa"

1991. Cruise Liners. Multicoloured.

No.	Description	Mint	Used
395	15c. Type **120**	1·00	60
396	80c. "Royal Viking Star"	2·00	1·75
397	$1.30 "World Discoverer"	2·50	2·75
398	$1.80 "Sagafjord"	3·00	3·50

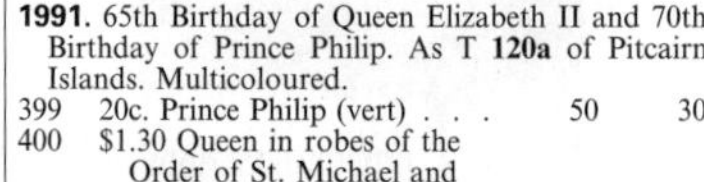

1991. 65th Birthday of Queen Elizabeth II and 70th Birthday of Prince Philip. As T **120a** of Pitcairn Islands. Multicoloured.

No.	Description	Mint	Used
399	20c. Prince Philip (vert)	50	30
400	$1.30 Queen in robes of the Order of St. Michael and St. George (vert)	1·75	1·25

121 Bulldozer

1991. Island Transport. Multicoloured.

No.	Description	Mint	Used
401	20c. Type **121**	40	30
402	80c. Two-wheeled motorcycle	1·25	1·00
403	$1.30 Tractor	1·25	1·40
404	$1.80 Three-wheeled motorcycle	2·00	2·25

122 The Annunciation

1991. Christmas. Multicoloured.

No.	Description	Mint	Used
405	20c. Type **122**	30	30
406	80c. Shepherds and lamb	90	90
407	$1.30 Holy Family	1·25	1·25
408	$1.80 Three Wise Men	1·75	1·75

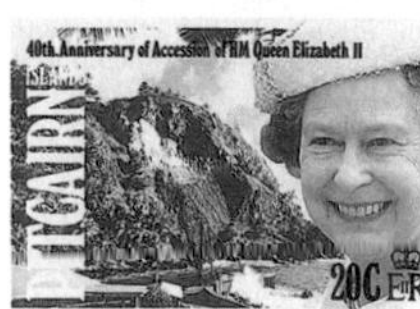

122c Bounty Bay

1992. 40th Anniv of Queen Elizabeth II's Accession. Multicoloured.

No.	Description	Mint	Used
409	20c. Type **122c**	25	25
410	60c. Sunset over Pitcairn	70	70
411	90c. Pitcairn coastline	90	90
412	$1 Three portraits of Queen Elizabeth	95	95
413	$1.80 Queen Elizabeth II	1·60	1·60

123 Insular Shark

1992. Sharks. Multicoloured.

No.	Description	Mint	Used
414	20c. Type **123**	80	50
415	$1 Sand tiger	2·00	1·50
416	$1.50 Black-finned reef shark	2·25	2·00
417	$1.80 Grey reef shark	2·50	2·00

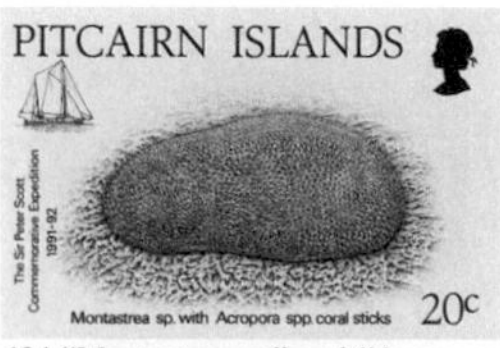

124 "Montastrea sp." and "Acropora spp." (corals)

1992. The Sir Peter Scott Memorial Expedition to Henderson Island. Multicoloured.

No.	Description	Mint	Used
418	20c. Type **124**	80	60
419	$1 Henderson sandalwood	1·75	1·50
420	$1.50 Murphy's petrel	3·00	2·75
421	$1.80 Henderson hawkmoth	3·00	3·00

125 Bligh's Birthplace at St. Tudy, Cornwall

1992. 175th Death Anniv of William Bligh. Multicoloured.

No.	Description	Mint	Used
422	20c. Type **125**	50	60
423	$1 Bligh on "Bounty"	1·50	1·50
424	$1.50 Voyage in "Bounty's" launch	2·00	2·75
425	$1.80 "William Bligh" (R. Combe) and epitaph	2·25	3·00

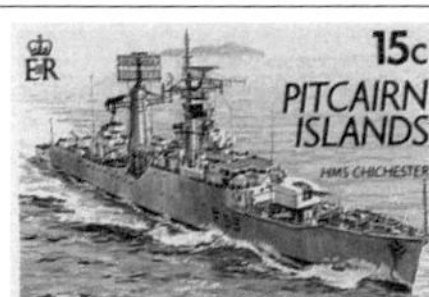

126 H.M.S. "Chichester" (frigate)

1993. Modern Royal Navy Vessels. Mult.
426 15c. Type **126** 75 50
427 20c. H.M.S. "Jaguar" (frigate) 75 50
428 $1.80 H.M.S. "Andrew" (submarine) . . . . 3·25 3·25
429 $3 H.M.S. "Warrior" (aircraft carrier) and Westland Dragonfly helicopter . . . . 5·75 5·50

127 Queen Elizabeth II in Coronation Robes

1993. 40th Anniv of Coronation.
430 **127** $5 multicoloured . . . . 6·00 7·00

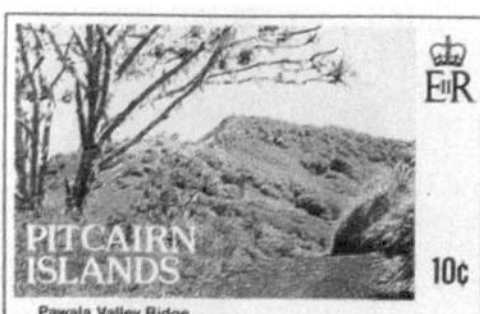

128 Pawala Valley Ridge

1993. Island Views. Multicoloured.
431 10c. Type **128** 20 20
432 90c. St. Pauls 90 90
433 $1.20 Matt's Rocks from Water Valley . . . . . . 1·25 1·50
434 $1.50 Ridge Rope to St. Paul's Pool . . . . . . 1·50 1·75
435 $1.80 Ship Landing Point . . 1·75 2·25

129 Indo-Pacific Tree Gecko

1993. Lizards. Multicoloured.
436 20c. Type **129** 80 50
437 45c. Stump-toed gecko . . . 1·00 1·25
438 45c. Mourning gecko . . . . 1·00 1·25
439 $1 Moth skink . . . . 2·00 1·50
440 $1.50 Snake-eyed skink . . . 2·50 2·75
441 $1.50 White-bellied skink . . 2·50 2·75

1994. "Hong Kong '94" International Stamp Exhibition. Nos. 437/8 and 440/1 optd **HONG KONG '94** and emblem.
442 45c. Stump-toed gecko . . . 80 90
443 45c. Mourning gecko 80 90
444 $1.50 Snake-eyed skink . . . 2·25 2·75
445 $1.50 White-bellied skink . . 2·25 2·75

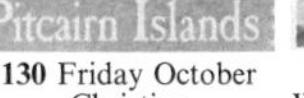

130 Friday October Christian

131 Landing Stores from Wreck of "Wildwave", Oeno Island, 1858

1994. Early Pitcairners. Multicoloured.
446 5c. Type **130** 20 30
447 20c. Moses Young 50 40
448 $1.80 James Russell McCoy 2·25 2·75
449 $3 Rosalind Amelia Young 3·75 5·00

1994. Shipwrecks. Multicoloured.
450 20c. Type **131** 65 60
451 90c. Longboat trying to reach "Cornwallis", Pitcairn Island, 1875 . . . . 1·75 1·75
452 $1.80 "Acadia" aground, Ducie Island, 1881 . . . . 3·00 3·50
453 $3 Rescuing survivors from "Oregon", Oeno Island, 1883 . . . . 4·25 4·50

132 Fire Coral

133 Angel and "Ipomoea acuminata"

1994. Corals. Multicoloured.
454 20c. Type **132** 80 70
455 90c. Cauliflower coral and arc-eyed hawkfish (horiz) 2·00 2·00
456 $1 Lobe coral and high-finned rudderfish . . . . . 2·00 2·00
MS457 100 × 70 mm. $3 Coral garden and mailed butterflyfish 4·00 5·00

1994. Christmas. Flowers. Multicoloured.
458 20c. Type **133** 35 25
459 90c. Shepherds and "Hibiscus rosa-sinensis" (vert) . . . 1·25 1·40
460 $1 Star and "Plumeria rubra" 1·25 1·40
461 $3 Holy Family and "Alpinia speciosa" (vert) . . . . . 3·00 3·25

134 White ("Fairy") Tern on Egg

1995. Birds. Multicoloured.
462 5c. Type **134** 30 60
463 10c. Red-tailed tropic bird chick (vert) 30 60
464 15c. Henderson Island crake with chick 40 70
465 20c. Red-footed booby feeding chick (vert) 40 70
466 45c. Blue-grey noddy 60 80
467 50c. Pitcairn ("Henderson Reed") warbler in nest . . 65 90
468 90c. Common noddy . . . . 1·00 1·00
469 $1 Blue-faced ("Masked") booby and chick (vert) . . 1·10 1·10
470 $1.80 Henderson Island fruit dove . . . . 1·50 1·75
471 $2 Murphy's petrel . . . . . 1·75 2·25
472 $3 Christmas Island shearwater . . . . 2·25 3·00
473 $5 Red-tailed tropic bird juvenile . . . . 3·50 4·50

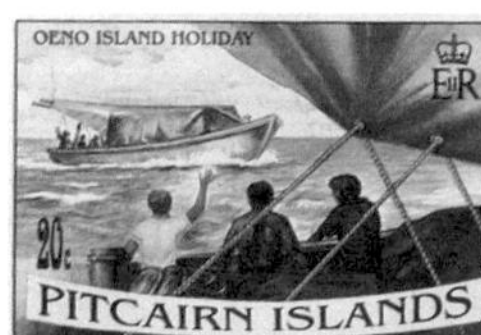

135 Islanders in Longboats

1995. Oeno Island Holiday. Multicoloured.
474 20c. Type **135** 40 60
475 90c. Playing volleyball on beach . . . . 1·25 1·25
476 $1.80 Preparing picnic . . . 2·25 3·25
477 $3 Singsong . . . . 3·50 5·00

136 Queen Elizabeth the Queen Mother

1995. 95th Birthday of Queen Elizabeth the Queen Mother. Sheet 75 × 90 mm.
MS478 **136** $5 multicoloured . . 5·50 5·00

137 Guglielmo Marconi and Early Wireless, 1901

1995. Centenary of First Radio Transmission. Multicoloured.
479 20c. Type **137** 40 60
480 $1 Pitcairn radio transmitter, c. 1938 . . . . 1·10 1·25
481 $1.50 Satellite Earth Station equipment, 1994 . . . . . 1·75 2·75
482 $3 Communications satellite in orbit, 1992 . . . . . . 3·25 5·00

137a United Nations Float, Lord Mayor's Show

1995. 50th Anniv of United Nations. Multicoloured.
483 20c. Type **137a** 30 30
484 $1 R.F.A. "Brambleleaf" (tanker) . . . . 1·40 1·25
485 $1.50 U.N. Ambulance . . . 2·00 2·25
486 $3 R.A.F. Lockheed L-1011 TriStar . . . . 3·50 3·75

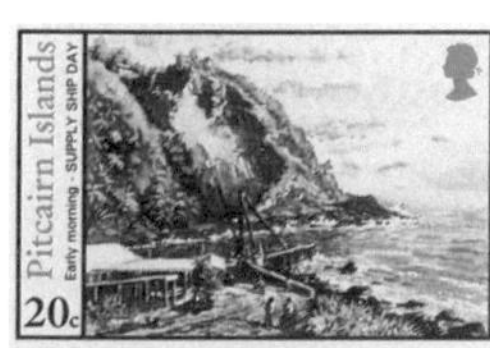

138 Early Morning at the Jetty

1996. Supply Ship Day. Multicoloured.
487 20c. Type **138** 25 30
488 40c. Longboat meeting "America Star" (freighter) 45 55
489 90c. Loading supplies into longboats . . . . 1·00 1·10
490 $1 Landing supplies on jetty 1·10 1·25
491 $1.50 Sorting supplies at the Co-op . . . . 1·75 2·25
492 $1.80 Tractor towing supplies 1·90 2·25

1996. 70th Birthday of Queen Elizabeth II. As T **55** of Tokelau, each incorporating a different photograph of the Queen. Multicoloured.
493 20c. Bounty Bay 45 45
494 90c. Jetty and landing point, Bounty Bay . . . . 1·40 1·40
495 $1.80 Matt's Rocks . . . . . 2·25 2·50
496 $3 St. Pauls . . . . 4·00 4·50

139 Chinese junk

1996. "CHINA '96" 9th Asian International Stamp Exhibition, Peking. Multicoloured.
497 $1.80 Type **139** . . . . . . 2·25 2·50
498 $1.80 H.M.S. "Bounty" . . . 2·25 2·50
MS499 80 × 79 mm. 90c. China 1984 8f. Year of the Rat stamp; 90c. Polynesian rat eating banana 2·00 2·00

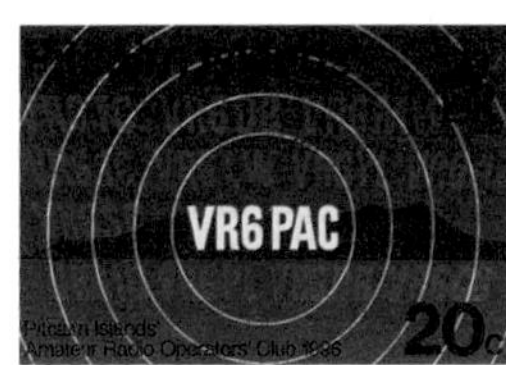

140 Island Profile and Radio Call Signs

1996. Amateur Radio Operations from Pitcairn Islands. Multicoloured.
500 20c. Type **140** 45 45
501 $1.50 Radio operator calling for medical assistance . . . 2·00 2·25
502 $1.50 Doctors giving medical advice by radio . . . . . 2·00 2·25
503 $2.50 Andrew Young (first radio operator), 1938 . . . 2·75 3·00

141 Pitcairn Warbler ("Henderson Island Reed Warbler")

142 Coat of Arms

1996. Endangered Species. Local Birds. Mult.
504 5c. Type **141** 30 30
505 10c. Stephen's lory ("Stephen's Lorikeet") . . 30 30
506 20c. Henderson Island crake ("Henderson Island Rail") 50 50
507 90c. Henderson Island fruit dove . . . . 1·25 1·25
508 $2 White tern (horiz) . . . . 2·00 2·25
509 $2 Blue-faced booby ("Masked Booby") (horiz) 2·00 2·25

1997. "HONG KONG '97" International Stamp Exhibition. Chinese New Year ("Year of the Ox"). Sheet 82 × 87 mm.
MS510 **142** $5 multicoloured . . 5·00 5·50

143 "David Barker" (supply ship)

1997. 50th Anniv of South Pacific Commission. Sheet 115 × 56 mm, containing T **143** and similar horiz design. Multicoloured.
MS511 $2.50 Type **143**; $2.50 "McLachlan" (fishing boat) . . 8·00 8·00

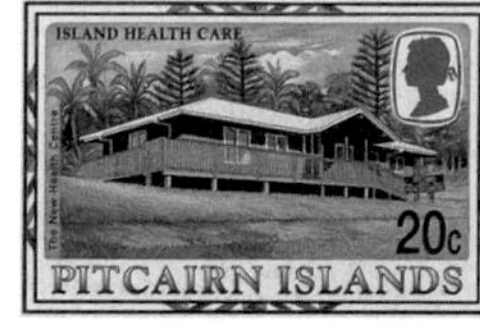

144 Health Centre

1997. Island Health Care. Multicoloured.
512 20c. Type **144** 30 25
513 $1 Nurse treating patient . . 1·00 1·00
514 $1.70 Dentist treating woman 1·75 1·90
515 $3 Evacuating patient by longboat . . . . 3·00 3·25

1997. Golden Wedding of Queen Elizabeth and Prince Philip. As T **316a** of Papua New Guinea. Multicoloured.
516 20c. Prince Philip driving carriage 30 40
517 20c. Queen Elizabeth 30 40
518 $1 Prince Philip at Royal Windsor Horse Show, 1996 1·00 1·25
519 $1 Queen Elizabeth with horse . . . . 1·00 1·25
520 $1.70 Queen Elizabeth and Prince Philip at the Derby, 1991 . . . . 1·50 1·75
521 $1.70 Prince Charles hunting, 1995 . . . . 1·50 1·75

Nos. 516/17, 518/19 and 520/21 respectively were printed together, se-tenant, with the backgrounds forming composite designs.

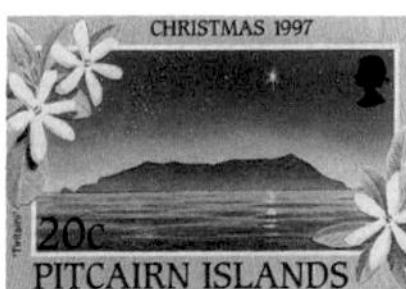

145 Island and Star

1997. Christmas. Multicoloured.
522 20c. Type **145** 35 25
523 80c. Hand ringing bell . . . 1·00 80
524 $1.20 Presents in baskets . . 1·40 1·50
525 $3 Families outside church 2·75 3·00

146 Christian's Cave

1997. Christian's Cave. Multicoloured.
526 5c. Type **146** 15 20
527 20c. View from the beach . . 35 35
528 35c. Cave entrance (vert) . . 50 50
529 $5 Pathway through forest (vert) . . . . 3·75 5·00

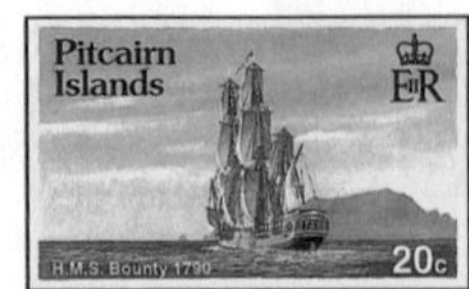

147 H.M.S. "Bounty" (Bligh), 1790

1998. Millennium Commemoration (1st issue). Sailing Ships. Multicoloured.
530 20c. Type **147** 40 40
531 90c. H.M.S. "Swallow" (Carteret), 1767 . . . . . 1·00 1·00
532 $1.80 H.M.S. "Briton" and H.M.S. "Tagus" (frigates), 1814 . . . . 1·50 1·60
533 $3 H.M.S. "Fly" (sloop), 1838 . . . . 2·50 2·75
See also Nos. 549/52 and 577/80.

1998. Diana, Princess of Wales Commemoration. Sheet, 145 × 70 mm, containing vert designs as T **91** of Kiribati. Multicoloured.
MS534 90c. Wearing pearl choker and red evening dress; 90c. Wearing white hat and pearl necklace; 90c. Carrying bouquet; 90c. Wearing white dress and hat (*sold at $3.60+40c. charity premium*) . . . . 3·50 3·75

148 "Bidens mathewsii"

1998. Flowers. Multicoloured.
535 20c. Type **148** 75 55
536 90c. "Hibiscus" sp. . . . . . 1·60 1·10
537 $1.80 "Osteomeles anthyllidifolia" . . . . . . 2·50 2·00
538 $3 "Ipomoea littoralis" . . . 3·50 4·00

149 Fishing

1998. International Year of the Ocean. Multicoloured.
539 20c. Type **149** 75 50
540 90c. Diver at wreck of "Cornwallis" (vert) . . . . 1·50 1·00
541 $1.80 Reef fish . . . . 2·25 1·75
542 $3 Murphy's petrel and great frigate bird (vert) . . . . . 3·75 2·25
MS543 86 × 86 mm. Nos. 539/42 8·00 8·50

150 George Nobbs and Class, 1838

1999. Development of Local Education. Mult.
544 20c. Type **150** 75 60
545 90c. Children outside thatched school, 1893 . . . 1·60 1·40
546 $1.80 Boy in wheelbarrow outside wooden school, 1932 . . . . 2·50 2·75
547 $3 Modern classroom with computer . . . . 3·50 4·25

151 H.M.S. "Bounty" and Anchor

1999. "Australia '99" World Stamp Exhibition, Melbourne. Pitcairn Archaeology Project. Sheet, 190 × 80 mm, containing T **151** and similar diamond-shaped designs. Multicoloured.
MS548 50c. Type **151**; $1 "Bounty" approaching Pitcairn and cannon; $1.50, "Bounty" on fire and chronometer; $2 "Bounty" sinking and metal bucket . . . . . . 5·50 5·50

152 John Adams (survivor of "Bounty" crew) and Bounty Bay

1999. Millennium Commemoration (2nd issue). Multicoloured.
549 20c. Type **152** 60 60
550 90c. "Topaz" (sealer), 1808 1·40 1·10
551 $1.80 George Hunn Nobbs and Norfolk Island . . . . 2·00 2·75
552 $3 H.M.S "Champion" (corvette), 1893 . . . . . 3·50 4·25

153 Prince Edward and Miss Sophie Rhys-Jones

1999. Royal Wedding. Multicoloured.
553 $2.50 Type **153** . . . . . . 1·90 2·50
554 $2.50 Engagement photograph . . . . 1·90 2·50

154 Bee-keepers at Work

1999. Bee-keeping. Multicoloured. Self-adhesive.
555 20c. Type **154** 75 65
556 $1 Bee on passion flower . . 1·60 1·40
557 $1.80 Bees in honeycomb . . 2·50 2·75
558 $3 Bee on flower and jar of "Mutineer's Dream" honey 3·50 4·25
MS559 74 × 100 mm. No. 556 . . 2·00 2·50
No. **MS**559 includes the "China '99" International Stamp Exhibition emblem on the sheet margin.

155 Arrival of "Yankee" (schooner), 1937

2000. Protection of "Mr. Turpen" (Galapagos Tortoise on Pitcairn). Multicoloured.
560 5c. Type **155** . . . . 80 1·10
561 20c. Off-loading Mr. Turpen at Bounty Bay . . . . . . 1·00 1·25
562 35c. Mr. Turpen . . . . . . 1·10 1·40
563 $5 Head of Mr. Turpen . . . 4·25 4·50
Nos. 560/3 were printed together, se-tenant, with the background forming a composite design.

156 *Guettarda speciosa* (flower)

2000. Flowers of Pitcairn Islands. Multicoloured.
564 10c. Type **156** 10 10
565 15c. *Hibiscus tiliaceus* 10 15
566 20c. *Selenicereus grandiflorus* 15 20
567 30c. *Metrosideros collina* . . 20 25
568 50c. *Alpinia zerumbet* 35 40
569 $1 *Syzygium jambos* 75 80
570 $1.50 *Commelina diffusa* . . . 1·10 1·20
571 $1.80 *Canna indica* . . . . . 1·20 1·30
572 $2 *Allamanda cathartica* . . . 1·50 1·60
573 $3 *Calophyllum inophyllum* 2·20 2·30
574 $5 *Ipomea indica* . . . . . . 3·75 4·00
575 $10 *Bauhinia monandra* (40 × 40 mm) . . . . . . 7·25 7·50

2000. "The Stamp Show 2000" International Stamp Exhibition, London. Sheet, 120 × 80 mm, containing Nos. 570 and 572.
MS576 $1.50 Commelina diffusa; $2 Allamanda cathartica . . . . 4·00 4·50

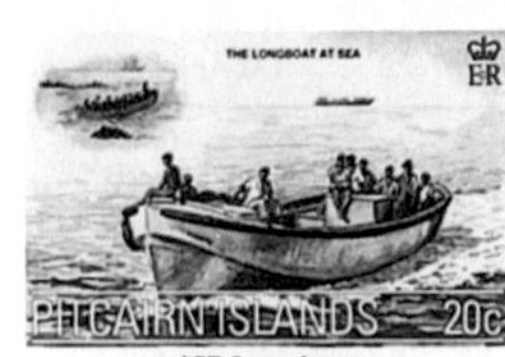

157 Longboat

2000. Millennium Commemoration (3rd issue). Communications. Multicoloured.
577 20c. Type **157** 60 60
578 90c. Landing and Longboat House . . . . 1·40 1·10
579 $1.80 Honda quad with trailer of watermelons . . . 2·25 2·50
580 $3 Woman with printer at Satellite Station . . . . . 3·00 3·50

158 Surveyor and Helicopter

2000. "EXPO 2000" World Stamp Exhibition, Anaheim, U.S.A. Anglo-American Joint Satellite Recovery Survey Mission, Henderson Island, 1966. Sheet, 120 × 180 mm, containing T **158** and similar vert design. Multicoloured.
MS581 $2.50 Type **158**; $2.50 Survey team and U.S.S. *Sunnyvale* (satellite recovery vessel) . . . 5·50 6·00
No. **MS**581 was issued folded in half horizontally with the issue title, "CLASSIFIED INFORMATION" and seal printed on the gum of the top panel. Details of the survey appear on the other side of this section.

159 Queen Elizabeth the Queen Mother

2000. Queen Elizabeth the Queen Mother's 100th Birthday. Sheet, 127 × 95 mm (oval-shaped), containing T **159** and similar vert design. Multicoloured.
MS582 $2 Type **159**; $3 Queen Mother wearing plum outfit . . 4·00 4·50

160 Wrapping Presents

2000. Christmas. Multicoloured.
583 20c. Type **160** 55 40
584 80c. Ringing island bell . . . 1·25 90
585 $1.50 Making decorations . . 2·00 2·00
586 $3 Opening presents . . . . 3·00 3·50

161 *Europa* (liner)

2001. Cruise Ships. Multicoloured.
587 $1.50 Type **161** . . . . . . 1·75 1·90
588 $1.50 *Rotterdam VI* . . . . 1·75 1·90
589 $1.50 *Saga Rose* . . . . . . 1·75 1·90
590 $1.50 *Bremen* . . . . 1·75 1·90

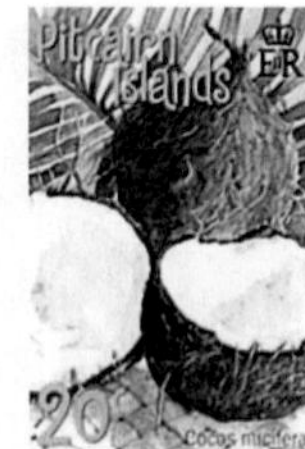

162 Coconut

2001. Tropical Fruits. Multicoloured.
591 20c. Type **162** 30 30
592 80c. Pomegranate 75 75
593 $1 Passion fruit 90 90
594 $3 Pineapple . . . . 2·25 3·00
MS595 103 × 70mm. Nos. 592 and 594 . . . . 3·00 3·50

163 Keyboard

2001. Introduction of Pitcairn Islands Internet Domain Name. Multicoloured. Self-adhesive.
596 20c. Type **163** 50 45
597 50c. Circuit board 85 70
598 $1 Microchip . . . . 1·25 1·00
599 $5 Mouse . . . . 4·75 6·00

164 Ornate Butterflyfish (*Chaetodon ornatissimus*)
165 Man carrying Driftwood

2001. Reef Fish. Multicoloured.
600 20c. Type **164** 55 45
601 80c. Mailed butterflyfish (*Chaetodon reticulatus*) . . 90 70
602 $1.50 Racoon butterflyfish (*Chaetodon lunula*) . . . . 1·60 1·75
603 $2 *Henochus chrysostomus* . . 1·90 2·00
MS604 87 × 120 mm. Nos. 600 and 603 . . . . 2·00 2·50
No. **MS**604 has the paper around the outlines of fish along the upper edge of the sheet cut away.

2001. Woodcarving. Multicoloured.
605 20c. Type **165** 55 75
606 50c. Carver at work . . . . 1·00 1·25
607 $1.50 Working on wood lathe 1·75 1·75
608 $3 Taking carvings to *World Discoverer* (cruise liner) for sale . . . . 2·50 2·75
Nos. 605/8 were printed together, se-tenant, with the backgrounds forming a composite design.

166 *Cypraea argus* Shell

2001. Cowrie Shells. Multicoloured.
609 20c. Type **166** 55 45
610 80c. *Cypraea isabella* 90 70

611 $1 *Cypraea mappa* . . . . . 1·00 1·00
612 $3 *Cypraea mauritiana* . . . 2·75 3·25

2002. Golden Jubilee. Sheet, 162 × 95 mm, containing designs as T **153** of Nauru.
MS613 50c. black, violet and gold; $1 multicoloured; $1.20 black, violet and gold; $1.50 multicoloured; $2 multicoloured 6·00 6·50
DESIGNS—HORIZ: 50c. Queen Elizabeth with Princesses Elizabeth and Margaret; $1 Queen Elizabeth in evening dress; $1.20 Princess Elizabeth in evening dress; $1.50 Queen Elizabeth in blue hat and coat. VERT (38 × 51 mm)—$2 Queen Elizabeth after Annigoni.

167 James McCoy (President of Island Council)

2002. Pitcairn Islands Celebrities. Multicoloured.
614 $1.50 Type **167** . . . . . . 1·50 1·60
615 $1.50 Admiral Sir Fairfax Moresby . . . . 1·50 1·60
616 $1.50 Gerald DeLeo Bliss (postmaster, Cristobal, Panama Canal Zone) . . . 1·50 1·60
617 $1.50 Captain Arthur Jones of Shaw Savill Line . . . . 1·50 1·60

168 "Simba Christian" (cat)

2002. Pitcairn Cats. Multicoloured.
618 20c. Type **168** 45 35
619 $1 "Miti Christian" . . . . 1·00 80
620 $1.50 "Nala Brown" . . . . 1·50 1·50
621 $3 "Alicat Palau" . . . . . 2·75 3·25
MS622 92 × 86 mm. Nos. 618 and 621 . . . . 3·00 3·50

2002. Queen Elizabeth the Queen Mother Commemoration. As T **156** of Nauru.
623 40c. black, gold and purple 45 35
624 $1 brown, gold and purple 1·00 80
625 $1.50 multicoloured . . . . 1·50 1·50
626 $2 multicoloured . . . . . 1·90 2·25
MS627 145 × 70 mm. Nos. 624 and 626 . . . . 2·75 3·00
DESIGNS: 40c. Lady Elizabeth Bowes-Lyon, 1910; $1 Lady Elizabeth Bowes-Lyon, 1923; $1.50, Queen Mother at Leatherhead, 1970; $2 Queen Mother at Scrabster. Designs as Nos. 624 and 626 in No. **MS**627 omit the "1900-2002" inscription and the coloured frame.

169 Woman cutting Palm Fronds and Fan

2002. Weaving. Multicoloured.
628 40c. Type **169** . . . . 75 1·00
629 80c. Woman preparing leaves and woven bag . . . . . 1·00 1·25
630 $1.50 Millie Christian weaving basket . . . . . 1·40 1·75
631 $2.50 Thelma Brown at basket stall in the Square 2·00 2·50
Nos. 628/31 were printed together, se-tenant, with the backgrounds forming a composite design.

170 Dudwi Nut Tree (*Aleurites moluccana*)

2002. Trees. Multicoloured.
632 40c. Type **170** 60 50
633 $1 Toa (*Cordia subcordata*) 1·00 80
634 $1.50 Miro (*Thespesia populnea*) . . . . 1·50 1·50
635 $3 Hulianda (*Cerbera manghas*) . . . . 2·75 3·25

171 *America Star* (container ship) and Island Longboat

2003. 21 Years of Blue Star Line Service to Pitcairn Islands. Sheet 158 × 75 mm.
MS636 **171** $5 multicoloured . . 4·75 5·50

172 *Conus geographus* Shell

2003. Conus Shells. Multicoloured.
637 40c. Type **172** 60 45
638 80c. *Conus textile* 85 60
639 $1 *Conus striatus* . . . . . 1·00 80
640 $1.20 *Conus marmoreus* . . . 1·25 1·25
641 $3 *Conus litoglyphus* . . . . 2·75 3·25

2003. 50th Anniv of Coronation. As T **114** of Kiribati. Multicoloured.
642 40c. Queen Elizabeth II wearing tiara 30 35
643 80c. Coronation Coach drawn by eight horses . . 60 65
644 $1.50 Queen wearing tiara and white gown . . . . . 1·10 1·20
645 $3 Queen with bishops and Maids of Honour . . . . 2·20 2·30
MS646 95 × 115 mm. 40c. As No. 642; $3 As No. 645 . . . 2·50 2·75

173 Women Storing Leaves in Earthenware Jars and *Bauhinia monandra*

174 Diadem Squirrel Fish

2003. Art of Pitcairn (3rd series). Painted Leaves. Multicoloured.
647 40c. Type **173** 30 35
648 80c. Woman washing soaked leaves and *Bauhinia monandra* 60 65
649 $1.50 Bernice Christian with dried leaf and paints and *Sapindrus saponaria* plant 1·10 1·20
650 $3 Charlotte Christian painting leaf, Bauhinia leaf and *Bounty* . . . . . . 2·20 2·30
Nos. 647/50 were printed together, se-tenant with the backgrounds forming a composite design.

2003. Squirrel Fish. Multicoloured.
651 40c. Type **174** 30 35
652 80c. Scarlet-finned squirrel fish 60 65
653 $1.50 Silver-spotted squirrel fish . . . . 1·10 1·20
654 $3 Bloodspot squirrel fish . . 2·20 2·30
MS655 100 × 80 mm. No. 654 . . 2·20 2·30

175 "Holy Virgin in a Wreath of Flowers" (detail) (Rubens and Jan Brueghel)

2003. Christmas. Multicoloured.
656 40c. Type **175** 30 35
657 $1 "Madonna della Rosa" (detail) (Raphael) 75 80
658 $1.50 "Stuppacher Madonna" (detail) (Matthias Grunewald) . . . . 1·10 1·20
659 $3 "Madonna with Cherries" (detail) (Titian) . . . . . 2·20 2·30

POLAND Pt. 5

A country lying between Russia and Germany, originally independent, but divided between Prussia, Austria and Russia in 1772/95. An independent republic since 1918. Occupied by Germany from 1939 to 1945.

1860. 100 kopeks = 1 rouble.
1918. 100 pfennig = 1 mark.
1918. 100 halerzy = 1 korona.
100 fenigow = 1 marka.
1924. 100 groszy = 1 zloty.

1 Russian Arms

2 Sigismund III Vasa Column, Warsaw

1860.
1b **1** 10k. blue and red . . . . . £675 80·00

1918. Surch **POCZTA POLSKA** and value in fen. as in T **2**.
2 **2** 5f. on 2g. brown 45 70
3 – 10f. on 6g. green 45 65
4 – 25f. on 10g. red . . . . . . 1·60 1·40
5 – 50f. on 20g. blue . . . . . 3·50 4·00
DESIGNS: 6g. Arms of Warsaw; 10g. Polish eagle; 20g. Jan III Sobieski Monument, Warsaw.

1918. Stamps of German Occupation of Poland optd **Poczta Polska** or surch also.
9 **10** 3pf. brown . . . . 10·00 7·00
10 5pf. green 50 35
6 **24** 5 on 2½pf. grey 30 20
7 **10** 5 on 3pf. brown . . . . . 1·75 1·25
11 10pf. red 20 20
12 **24** 15pf. violet 25 25
13 **10** 20pf. blue 25 25
8 **24** 25 on 7½pf. orange 30 20
14 **10** 30pf. black & orange on buff 20 20
15 40pf. black and red . . . . 1·00 50
16 60pf. mauve 40 40

1918. Stamps of Austro-Hungarian Military Post (Nos. 69/71) optd **POLSKA POCZTA** and Polish eagle.
17 10h. green . . . . 4·75 6·25
18 20h. red . . . . 4·75 6·25
19 45h. blue . . . . 4·75 6·25

1918. As stamps of Austro-Hungarian Military Post of 1917 optd **POLSKA POCZTA** and Polish eagle or surch also.
20b 3h. on 3h. olive . . . . . . 19·00 13·00
21 3h. on 15h. red . . . . . . 3·50 2·25
22 10h. on 30h. green . . . . . 3·75 2·75
23 25h. on 40h. olive . . . . . 5·00 2·75
24 45h. on 60h. red . . . . . . 3·50 3·50
25 45h. on 80h. blue . . . . . 6·00 5·00
28 50h. green . . . . 28·00 21·00
26 50h. on 60h. red . . . . . 3·50 4·00
29 90h. violet . . . . 4·75 3·50

1919. Stamps of Austria optd **POCZTA POLSKA**, No. 49 also surch **25**.
30 **49** 3h. violet £200 £190
31 5h. green £200 £190
32 6h. orange . . . . 15·00 16·00
33 10h. purple £200 £190
34 12h. blue . . . . 18·00 21·00
35 **60** 15h. red . . . . 10·00 6·75
36 20h. green . . . . 80·00 70·00
37 25h. blue £650 £600
49 **51** 25 on 80h. brown . . . . 2·25 3·00
38 **60** 30h. violet £140 £110
39 **51** 40h. green . . . . 13·50 10·00
40 50h. green . . . . 4·50 5·25
41 60h. blue . . . . 2·75 5·75
42 80h. brown . . . . 3·75 5·00
43 90h. purple £550 £600
44 1k. red on yellow . . . . 6·75 10·50
45 **52** 2k. blue . . . . 4·25 4·75
46 3k. red . . . . 45·00 60·00
47 4k. green . . . . 75·00 85·00
48a 10k. violet £3500 £3750

11

15

16

17 Agriculture

18 Ploughing in peace

19 Polish Uhlan

1919. Imperf.
50 **11** 2h. grey 35 60
51 3h. violet 35 60
52 5h. green 15 35
53 6h. orange . . . . 12·50 22·00
54 10h. red 15 35
55 15h. brown 15 15
56 20h. olive 35 55
57 25h. red 15 15
58 50h. blue 25 35
59 70h. blue 35 60
60 1k. red and grey 60 85

1919. For Southern Poland. Value in halerzy or korony. Imperf or perf.
68 **15** 3h. brown 10 10
69 5h. green 10 10
70 10h. orange 10 10
71 15h. red 10 10
72 **16** 20h. brown 10 10
85 25h. blue 10 10
86 50h. brown 10 10
75 **17** 1k. green 20 10
88 1k.50 brown 70 10
89 2k. blue 90 10
90 **18** 2k.50 purple 90 35
91 **19** 5k. blue . . . . 1·40 45

1919. For Northern Poland. Value in fenigow or marki. Imperf or perf.
104 **15** 3f. brown 10 10
105 5f. green 10 10
179 5f. blue 30 60
106 10f. purple 10 10
129 10f. brown 10 10
107 15f. red 10 10
108 **16** 20f. blue 10 10
181 20f. red 30 60
109 25f. green 10 10
110 50f. green 10 10
183 50f. orange 30 60
137 **17** 1m. violet 20 10
112 1m.50 green 50 25
138 2m. brown 20 10
114 **18** 2m.50 brown 90 55
139 3m. brown 30 10
140 **19** 5m. purple 10 10
141 6m. red 10 10
142 10m. red 25 15
143 20m. green 60 35

1919. 1st Polish Philatelic Exhibition and Polish White Cross Fund. Surch **I POLSKA WYSTAWA MAREK**, cross and new value. Imperf or perf.
116 **15** 5+5f. green 20 20
117 10+5f. purple 50 20
118 15+5f. red 20 20
119 **16** 25+5f. olive 30 20
120 50+5f. green 75 55

20

21 Prime Minster Paderewski

22 A. Trampezynski

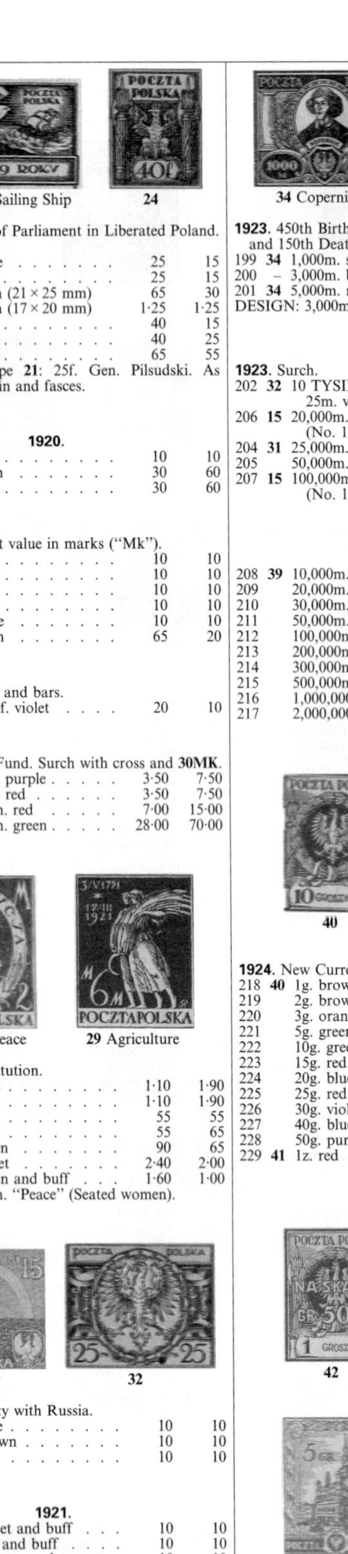

23 Eagle and Sailing Ship 24

1919. 1st Session of Parliament in Liberated Poland. Dated "1919".
121 **20** 10f. mauve 25 15
122 **21** 15f. red 25 15
123 **22** 20f. brown (21 × 25 mm) 65 30
124 20f. brown (17 × 20 mm) 1·25 1·25
125 – 25f. green 40 15
126 **23** 50f. blue 40 25
127 – 1m. violet 65 55
DESIGN—As Type **21**: 25f. Gen. Pilsudski. As Type **23**: 1m. Griffin and fasces.

1920.
146 **24** 40f. violet 10 10
182 40f. brown 30 60
184 75f. green 30 60

1920. As T **15**, but value in marks ("Mk").
147 **15** 1m. red 10 10
148 2m. green 10 10
149 3m. blue 10 10
150 4m. red 10 10
151 5m. purple 10 10
152 8m. brown 65 20

1921. Surch **3 Mk** and bars.
153 **24** 3m. on 40f. violet 20 10

1921. Red Cross Fund. Surch with cross and **30MK**.
154 **19** 5m.+30m. purple . . . . . 3·50 7·50
155 6m.+30m. red . . . . . . 3·50 7·50
156 10m.+30m. red . . . . . 7·00 15·00
157 20m.+30m. green . . . . . 28·00 70·00

28 Sun of Peace 29 Agriculture

1921. New Constitution.
158 **28** 2m. green . . . . 1·10 1·90
159 3m. blue . . . . 1·10 1·90
160 4m. red 55 55
161 **29** 6m. red 55 65
162 10m. green 90 65
163 – 25m. violet . . . . 2·40 2·00
164 – 50m. green and buff . . . 1·60 1·00
DESIGN: 25, 50m. "Peace" (Seated women).

31 Sower 32

1921. Peace Treaty with Russia.
165 **31** 10m. blue 10 10
166 15m. brown 10 10
167 20m. red 10 10

1921.
170 **32** 25m. violet and buff . . . 10 10
171 50m. red and buff 10 10
172 100m. brown and orange 10 10
173 200m. pink and black . . . 10 10
174 300m. green 10 10
175 400m. brown 10 10
176 500m. purple 10 10
177 1000m. orange 10 10
178 2000m. violet 10 10

33 Silesian Miner

1922.
185 **33** 1m. black 30 60
186 1m.25 green 30 60
187 2m. red 30 60
188 3m. green 30 60
189 4m. blue 30 60
190 5m. brown 30 60
191 6m. orange . . . . 30 1·50
192 10m. brown 30 60
193 20m. purple 30 60
194 50m. olive . . . . 30 3·75
195 80m. red . . . . 95 4·50
196 100m. violet . . . . 95 4·50
197 200m. orange . . . . . . 1·90 7·50
198 300m. blue . . . . 5·00 15·00

34 Copernicus 39

1923. 450th Birth Anniv of Copernicus (astronomer) and 150th Death Anniv of Konarski (educationist).
199 **34** 1,000m. slate 55 45
200 – 3,000m. brown 25 45
201 **34** 5,000m. red 55 55
DESIGN: 3,000m. Konarski.

1923. Surch.
202 **32** 10 TYSIECY (= 10000) on 25m. violet and buff . . 10 10
206 **15** 20,000m. on 2m. green (No. 148) 35 40
204 **31** 25,000m. on 20m. red . . . 10 10
205 50,000m. on 10m. blue . . 20 20
207 **15** 100,000m. on 5m. purple (No. 151) 10 10

1924.
208 **39** 10,000m. purple 30 30
209 20,000m. green 10 25
210 30,000m. red 70 35
211 50,000m. green 70 35
212 100,000m. brown 55 30
213 200,000m. blue 55 25
214 300,000m. mauve 55 45
215 500,000m. brown . . . . . 55 1·90
216 1,000,000m. pink . . . . . 55 5·25
217 2,000,000m. green . . . . 90 23·00

40 41 President Wojciechowski

1924. New Currency.
218 **40** 1g. brown 45 40
219 2g. brown 45 10
220 3g. orange 55 10
221 5g. green 70 10
222 10g. green 70 10
223 15g. red 70 10
224 20g. blue . . . . 2·75 10
225 25g. red . . . . 3·50 15
226 30g. violet . . . . 17·50 20
227 40g. blue . . . . 4·00 30
228 50g. purple . . . . 2·75 25
229 **41** 1z. red . . . . 22·00 2·40

42 43 Holy Gate, Vilna

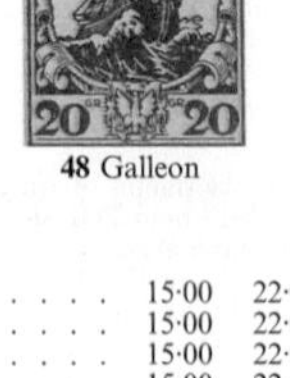

44 Town Hall, Pozan 48 Galleon

1925. National Fund.
230 **42** 1g.+50g. brown . . . . . 15·00 22·00
231 2g.+50g. brown . . . . . 15·00 22·00
232 3g.+50g. orange . . . . . 15·00 22·00
233 5g.+50g. green . . . . . 15·00 22·00
234 10g.+50g. green . . . . . 15·00 22·00
235 15g.+50g. red . . . . . . 15·00 22·00
236 20g.+50g. blue . . . . . 15·00 22·00
237 25g.+50g. red . . . . . . 15·00 22·00
238 30g.+50g. violet . . . . . 15·00 22·00
239 40g.+50g. blue . . . . . 15·00 22·00
240 50g.+50g. purple . . . . . 15·00 22·00

1925.
241 **43** 1g. brown 30 10
242 – 2g. olive 45 35
243a – 3g. blue . . . . 1·40 10
244a **44** 5g. green . . . . 1·10 10
245a – 10g. violet . . . . 1·10 10
246 – 15g. red . . . . 1·10 10
247 **48** 20g. red . . . . 6·50 10
248 **43** 24g. blue . . . . 7·00 70
249 – 30g. blue . . . . 3·75 10
250 – 40g. blue . . . . 3·00 10
251 **48** 45g. mauve . . . . 13·00 1·10
DESIGNS—As Type **43**: VERT: 2, 30g. Jan III Sobieski Statue, Lwow. As Type **44**: 3, 10g. King Sigismund Vasa Column, Warsaw. HORIZ: 15, 40g. Wawel Castle, Cracow.

49 LVG Schneider Biplane 50 Chopin

1925. Air.
252 **49** 1g. blue . . . . 45 4·75
253 2g. orange . . . . 45 4·75
254 3g. brown . . . . 45 4·75
255 5g. brown 45 55
256 10g. green . . . . 1·40 65
257 15g. mauve . . . . 1·60 75
258 20g. olive . . . . 12·50 4·75
259 30g. red . . . . 6·50 1·75
260 45g. lilac . . . . 8·50 3·50

1927.
261 **50** 40g. blue . . . . 12·00 2·40

51 Marshal Pilsudski 52 Pres. Moscicki

1927.
262 **51** 20g. red . . . . 2·00 25
262a 25g. brown . . . . 2·00 25

1927.
263 **52** 20g. red . . . . 6·00 70

53 54 Dr. Karl Kaczkowki

1927. Educational Funds.
264 **53** 10g.+5g. purple on green 7·50 10·00
265 20g.+5g. blue on yellow . . 7·50 10·00

1927. 4th Int Military Medical Congress, Warsaw.
266 **54** 10g. green . . . . 2·75 2·10
267 25g. red . . . . 5·25 4·00
268 40g. blue . . . . 7·00 3·00

55 J. Slowacki (poet) 56 Marshal Pilsudski

57 Pres. Moscicki 58 Gen. Joseph Bem

1927. Transfer of Slowacki's remains to Cracow.
269 **55** 20g. red . . . . 4·50 75

1928. Warsaw Philatelic Exhibition. Sheet 117 × 88 mm. T **56/7** in deep sepia.
MS270 50g. and 1z. (+1z.50) . . £325 £250
See also Nos. 272/3, 328 and **MS**332a/c.

1928.
272 **56** 50g. grey . . . . 2·75 20
272a 50g. green . . . . 6·50 25
273 **57** 1z. black on cream . . . 8·50 20

1928.
271 **58** 25g. red . . . . 2·25 25

59 H. Sienkiewicz 60 Slav God, "Swiatowit"

1928. Henryk Sienkiewicz (author).
274 **59** 15g. blue . . . . 1·75 25

1929. National Exhibition, Poznan.
275 **60** 25g. brown . . . . 1·75 25

61 62 King Jan III Sobieski 63

1929.
276 **61** 5g. violet 20 20
277 10g. green 55 20
278 25g. brown 35 25

1930. Birth Tercentenary of Jan III Sobieski.
279 **62** 75g. purple . . . . 5·00 25

1930. Centenary of "November Rising" (29 November 1830).
280 **63** 5g. purple 55 20
281 15g. blue . . . . 2·40 35
282 25g. lake . . . . 1·50 20
283 30g. red . . . . 8·00 3·50

64 Kosciusko, Washington and Pulaski 65

1932. Birth Bicentenary of George Washington.
284 **64** 30g. brown on cream . . . 2·25 35

1932.
284a **65** 5g. violet 20 20
285 10g. green 20 20
285a 15g. red 20 20
286 20g. grey 45 20
287 25g. bistre 45 20
288 30g. red . . . . 1·90 20
289 60g. blue . . . . 20·00 20

67 Town Hall, Torun 68 Franciszek Zwirko (airman) and Stanislaw Wigura (aircraft designer)

1933. 700th Anniv of Torun.
290 **67** 60g. blue on cream . . . . 28·00 1·10

1933. Victory in Flight round Europe Air Race, 1932.
292 **68** 30g. green . . . . 16·00 1·75

1933. Torun Philatelic Exhibition.
293 **67** 60g. red on cream . . . . 18·00 15·00

69 Altar-piece, St. Mary's Church, Cracow

1933. 4th Death Centenary of Veit Stoss (sculptor).
294 **69** 80g. brown on cream . . . 14·00 2·00

70 "Liberation of Vienna" by J. Matejko

1933. 250th Anniv of Relief of Vienna.
295 **70** 1z.20 blue on cream . . . 35·00 12·50

71 Cross of Independence

73 Marshal Pilsudski and Legion of Fusiliers Badge

1933. 15th Anniv of Proclamation of Republic.
296 **71** 30g. red . . . . 8·00 40

1934. Katowice Philatelic Exhibition. Optd **Wyst. Filat. 1934 Katowice.**
297 **65** 20g. grey . . . . 35·00 29·00
298 30g. red . . . . 35·00 29·00

1934. 20th Anniv of Formation of Polish Legion.
299 **73** 25g. blue 70 35
300 30g. brown . . . . 2·00 40

1934. Int Air Tournament. Optd **Challenge 1934.**
301 **49** 20g. olive . . . . 12·00 10·00
302 **68** 30g. green . . . . 7·50 2·50

1934. Surch in figures.
303 **69** 25g. on 80g. brown on cream . . . . 5·00 60
304 **65** 55g. on 60g. blue . . . . . 4·50 35
305 **70** 1z. on 1z.20 blue on cream 18·00 4·75

77 Marshal Pilsudski

1935. Mourning Issue.
306 **77** 5g. black 75 25
307 15g. black 75 30
308 25g. black . . . . 1·25 25
309 45g. black . . . . 4·00 2·00
310 1z. black . . . . 7·00 4·25

1935. Optd **Kopiec Marszalka Pilsudskiego.**
311 **65** 15g. red 80 65
312 **73** 25g. blue . . . . 2·75 2·00

79 Pieskowa Skala (Dog's Rock)

80 Pres. Moscicki

1935.
313 **79** 5g. blue 50 10
317 – 5g. violet 25 10
314 – 10g. green 50 10
318 – 10g. green 65 10
315 – 15g. blue . . . . 2·75 10
319 – 15g. lake 35 10
316 – 20g. black . . . . 1·00 10
320 – 20g. orange 55 10
321a – 25g. green 80 10
322 – 30g. red . . . . 1·75 10
323a – 45g. mauve . . . . 1·60 10
324a – 50g. black . . . . 2·50 10
325 – 55g. blue . . . . 6·25 40
326 – 1z. brown . . . . 3·50 70
327 **80** 3z. brown . . . . 2·50 3·50

DESIGNS: 5g. (No. 317) Monastery of Jasna Gora, Czestochowa; 10g. (314) Lake Morskie Oko; 10g. (318) "Batory" (liner) at sea passenger terminal, Gdynia; 15g. (315) "Pilsudski" (liner); 15g. (319) University, Lwow; 20g. (316) Pieniny-Czorsztyn; 20g. (320) Administrative Buildings, Katowice; 25g. Belvedere Palace, Warsaw; 30g. Castle at Mir; 45g. Castle at Podhorce; 50g. Cloth Hall, Cracow; 55g. Raczynski Library, Poznan; 1z. Vilna Cathedral.

1936. 10th Anniv of Moscicki Presidency. As T **57** but inscr "1926. 3. VI. 1936" below design.
328 **57** 1z. blue . . . . 5·00 6·00

1936. Gordon-Bennett Balloon Race. Optd **GORDON-BENNETT 30. VIII. 1936.**
329 30g. red (No. 322) . . . . . 11·00 5·75
330 55g. blue (No. 325) . . . . . 11·00 5·75

82 Marshal Smigly-Rydz

83 Pres. Moscicki

1937.
331 **82** 25g. blue 35 10
332 55g. blue 50 10

1937. Visit of King of Rumania. Three sheets each 102 × 125 mm each containing a block of four of earlier types in new colours.
MS332a **82** 25g. sepia . . . . . 21·00 32·00
MS332b **56** 50g. blue . . . . . 21·00 32·00
MS332c **57** 1z. black . . . . . . 21·00 32·00

1938. President's 70th Birthday.
333 **83** 15g. grey 40 10
334 30g. purple 60 10

84 Kosciuszko, Paine and Washington

1938. 150th Anniv of U.S. Constitution.
335 **84** 1z. blue . . . . 1·10 1·40

84a Postal Coach

1938. 5th Philatelic Exhibition, Warsaw. Sheet 130 × 103 mm.
MS335a **84a** 45g. (× 2) green; 55g. (× 2) blue . . . . £110 85·00

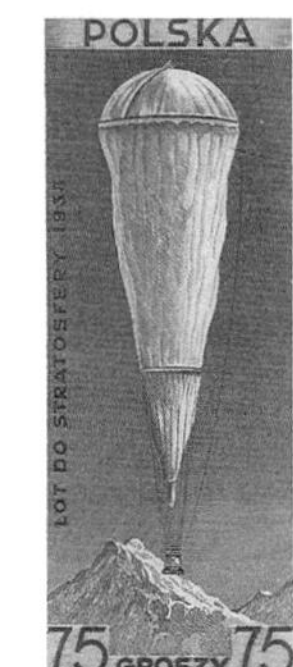

84b Stratosphere Balloon

1938. Proposed Polish Stratosphere Flight. Sheet 75 × 125 mm.
MS335b **84b** 75g. (+1z.25) violet 90·00 70·00

85a

86 Marshal Pilsudski

1938. 20th Anniv of Independence. (a) As T **85a** and **86**.
336 – 5g. orange 10 10
337 – 10g. green 10 10
338 **85a** 15g. brown (A) 15 15
357 15g. brown (B) 35 25
339 – 20g. blue 40 10
340 – 25g. purple 10 10
341 – 30g. red 50 10
342 – 45g. black 90 65
343 – 50g. mauve . . . . 1·75 10
344 – 55g. blue 50 10
345 – 75g. green . . . . 2·25 1·90
346 – 1z. orange . . . . 2·25 1·90
347 – 2z. red . . . . 8·50 11·00
348 **86** 3z. blue . . . . 8·50 14·00

(b) 102 × 105 mm, containing four portraits as T **83** but with value and inscr transposed, all in purple.
MS348a 25g. Marshal Pilsudski; 25g. Pres. Narutowicz; 25g. Pres. Moscicki; 25g. Marshal Smigly-Rydz . . . . 12·00 20·00

DESIGNS—VERT: 5g. Boleslaw the Brave; 10g. Casimir the Great; 20g. Casimir Jagiellon; 25g. Sigismund August; 30g. Stefan Batory; 45g. Chodkiewicz and Zolkiewski; 50g. Jan III Sobieski; 55g. Symbol of Constitution of May 3rd, 1791; 75g. Kosciuszko, Poniatowski and Dabrowski; 1z. November Uprising 1830–31; 2z. Romuald Traugutt.

(A) Type **85a**. (B) as Type **85a** but crossed swords omitted.

87 Teschen comes to Poland

88 "Warmth"

1938. Acquisition of Teschen.
349 **87** 25g. purple . . . . 1·50 35

1938. Winter Relief Fund.
350 **88** 5g.+5g. orange . . . . . . 40 1·40
351 25g.+10g. purple . . . . . 85 3·25
352 55g.+15g. blue . . . . . . 1·40 3·50

89 Tatra Mountaineer

1939. International Ski Championship, Zakopane.
353 **89** 15g. brown . . . . 1·10 80
354 25g. purple . . . . 1·40 1·10
355 30g. red . . . . 1·90 1·50
356 55g. blue . . . . 7·50 5·00

90 Pilsudski and Polish Legionaries

1939. 25th Anniv of 1st Battles of Polish Legions.
358 **90** 25g. purple . . . . 1·10 45
MS358a 103 × 125 mm. 25g. T **90**; 25g. T **77**; 25g. T **82** . . . . . 24·00 32·00

1939–1945. GERMAN OCCUPATION.

1939. T **94** of Germany surch **Deutsche Post OSTEN** and value.
359 **94** 6g. on 3pf. brown 20 40
360 8g. on 4pf. blue 20 40
361 12g. on 6pf. green 20 40
362 16g. on 8pf. red 65 75
363 20g. on 10pf. brown . . . 20 40
364 24g. on 12pf. red 20 40
365 30g. on 15pf. purple . . . 65 65
366 40g. on 20pf. blue 65 40
367 50g. on 25pf. blue 65 65
368 60g. on 30pf. green 80 40
369 80g. on 40pf. mauve . . . 80 65
370 1z. on 50pf. black & green 1·90 1·00
371 2z. on 100pf. black & yell 3·50 2·50

1940. Surch **General-Gouvernement**, Nazi emblem and value.
372 – 2g. on 5g. orge (No. 336) 30 35
373 – 4g. on 5g. orge (No. 336) 30 35
374 – 6g. on 10g. grn (No. 337) 30 35
375 – 8g. on 10g. grn (No. 337) 30 35
376 – 10g. on 10g. green (No. 337) 30 35
377 **107** 12g. on 15g. brown (No. 338) 30 35
378 16g. on 15g. brown (No. 338) 30 35
379 **104** 24g. on 25g. blue . . . 2·50 2·50
380 – 24g. on 25g. purple (No. 340) 30 35
381 – 30g. on 30g. red (No. 341) 45 30
382 **110** 30g. on 5g.+5g. orange 45 30
383 **105** 40g. on 30g. purple . . 65 1·00
384 **110** 40g. on 25g.+10g. pur 65 50
385 – 50g. on 50g. mauve (No. 343) 65 50
386 **104** 50g. on 55g. blue . . . 30 50
386a **D 88** 50g. on 20g. green . . 1·90 1·90
386b 50g. on 25g. green . . 12·50 11·50
386c 50g. on 30g. green . . 25·00 28·00
386d 50g. on 50g. green . . 1·90 1·60
386e 50g. on 1z. green . . . 1·90 1·60
387 – 60g. on 55g. blue (No. 344) . . . . . 9·50 6·25
388 – 80g. on 75g. green (No. 345) . . . . . 9·50 7·25
388a **110** 1z. on 55g.+15g. blue 7·50 8·25
389 – 1z. on 1z. orge (No. 346) . . . . . 9·50 6·25
390 – 2z. on 2z. red (No. 347) . . . . . 6·25 3·75
391 **108** 3z. on 3z. blue . . . . 6·25 3·75

Nos. 386a/e are postage stamps.

93 Copernicus Memorial, Cracow

95

1940.
392 – 6g. brown 25 55
393 – 8g. brown 25 55
394 – 8g. black 25 30
395 – 10g. green 25 20
396 **93** 12g. green . . . . 2·50 25
397 12g. violet 25 25
398 – 20g. brown 20 10
399 – 24g. red 20 10
400 – 30g. violet 20 10
401 – 30g. purple 20 30
402 – 40g. black 20 15
403 – 48g. brown . . . . 65 1·10
404 – 50g. blue 20 15
405 – 60g. green 20 20
406 – 80g. violet 45 25
407 – 1z. purple . . . . 1·90 80
408 – 1z. green 65 65

DESIGNS: 6g. Florian gate, Cracow; 8g. Castle Keep, Cracow; 10g. Cracow Gate, Lublin; 20g. Church of the Dominicans, Cracow; 24g. Wawel Castle, Cracow; 30g. Old Church in Lublin; 40g. Arcade, Cloth Hall, Cracow; 48g. Town Hall, Sandomir; 50g. Town Hall, Cracow; 60g. Court-yard of Wawel Castle, Cracow; 80g. St. Mary's Church, Cracow; 1z. Bruhl Palace, Warsaw.

1940. Red Cross Fund. As last, new colours, surch with Cross and premium in figures.
409 12g.+8g. green . . . . 2·40 3·25
410 24g.+16g. green . . . . . . 2·40 3·25
411 50g.+50g. green . . . . . . 3·50 4·50
412 80g.+80g. green . . . . . . 3·50 4·50

1940. 1st Anniv of German Occupation.
413 **95** 12g.+38g. green on yellow 2·00 2·50
414 – 24g.+26g. red on yellow . . 2·00 2·50
415 – 30g.+20g. violet on yellow 3·00 3·50

DESIGNS: 24g. Woman with scarf; 30g. Fur-capped peasant as Type **96**.

96

1940. Winter Relief Fund.
416 **96** 12g.+8g. green . . . . . . 1·00 75
417 24g.+16g. red . . . . . . 1·40 1·25
418 30g.+30g. brown . . . . . 1·40 1·90
419 50g.+50g. blue . . . . . . 2·40 2·50

97 Cracow

1941.
420 **97** 10z. grey and red . . . . 1·25 1·90

98 The Barbican, Cracow

99 Adolf Hitler

1941.
421 **98** 2z. blue 25 60
422 – 4z. green 50 95

DESIGN: 4z. Tyniec Monastery.

See also Nos. 465/8.

1941.
423 **99** 2g. grey 20 25
424 6g. brown 20 25
425 8g. blue 20 25
426 10g. green 20 10
427 12g. violet 20 25
428 16g. orange 25 15
429 20g. brown 20 20
430 24g. red 20 20
431 30g. purple 20 10
432 32g. green 20 35
433 40g. blue 20 20
434 48g. brown 35 40
435 50g. blue 15 55
436 60g. green 15 55
437 80g. purple 15 55
441 1z. green 45 50

442 1z.20 brown 45 75
443 1z.60 blue 40 90

1942. Hitler's 53rd Birthday. As T **99**, but premium inserted in design.
444 30g.+1z. purple on yellow . . 25 50
445 50g.+1z. blue on yellow . . . 25 50
446 1z.20+1z. brown on yellow 25 50

100 Modern Lublin

1942. 600th Anniv of Lublin.
447 – 12g.+8g. purple 10 25
448 **100** 24g.+6g. brown 10 25
449 – 50g.+50g. blue 15 35
450 **100** 1z.+1z. green 30 65
DESIGN: 12, 50g. Lublin, after an ancient engraving.

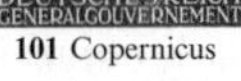
101 Copernicus

102 Adolf Hitler

1942. 3rd Anniv of German Occupation.
451 – 12g.+18g. violet 10 30
452 – 24g.+26g. red 10 30
453 – 30g.+30g. purple 10 30
454 – 50g.+50g. blue 10 30
455 **101** 1z.+1z. green 40 70
DESIGNS: 12g. Veit Stoss (Vit Stvosz); 24g. Hans Durer; 30g. J. Schuch; 50g. J. Elsner.

1943. Hitler's 54th Birthday.
456 **102** 12g.+1z. violet 20 50
457 24g.+1z. red 20 50
458 84g.+1z. green 20 50

1943. 400th Death Anniv of Nicolas Copernicus (astronomer). As No. 455, colour changed, optd **24. MAI 1543 24. MAI 1943.**
459 **101** 1z.+1z. purple 60 75

103 Cracow Gate, Lublin

103a Lwow

1943. 3rd Anniv of Nazi Party in German-occupied Poland.
460 **103** 12g.+38g. green 15 10
461 – 24g.+76g. red 15 10
462 – 30g.+70g. purple 15 10
463 – 50g.+1z. blue 15 10
464 – 1z.+2z. grey 60 25
DESIGNS: 24g. Cloth Hall, Cracow; 30g. Administrative Building, Radom; 50g. Bruhl Palace, Warsaw; 1z. Town Hall, Lwow.

1943.
465 – 2z. green 20 10
466 – 4z. violet 25 35
467 **103a** 6z. brown 35 40
468 – 10z. grey and brown . . 50 40
DESIGNS: 2z. The Barbican, Cracow; 4z. Tyniec Monastery; 10z. Cracow.

104 Adolf Hitler

105 Konrad Celtis

1944. Hitler's 55th Birthday.
469 **104** 12z.+1z. green 10 15
470 24z.+1z. brown 10 15
471 84z.+1z. violet 20 15

1944. Culture Funds.
472 **105** 12g.+18g. green 10 10
473 – 24g.+26g. red 10 10
474 – 30g.+30g. purple 10 10
475 – 50g.+50g. blue 25 25
476 – 1z.+1z. brown 25 25
PORTRAITS: 24g. Andreas Schluter; 30g. Hans Boner; 50g. Augustus the Strong; 1z. Gottlieb Pusch.

105a Cracow Castle

1944. 5th Anniv of German Occupation.
477a **105a** 10z.+10z. black and red 6·00 10·00

1941–45. ISSUES OF EXILED GOVERNMENT IN LONDON.

For correspondence on Polish sea-going vessels and, on certain days, from Polish Military camps in Great Britain.

106 Ruins of Ministry of Finance, Warsaw

107 Vickers-Armstrong Wellington and Hawker Hurricanes used by Poles in Great Britain

1941.
478 – 5g. violet . . . . 1·00 1·40
479 **106** 10g. green . . . . 1·50 1·50
480 – 25g. grey . . . . 1·75 2·00
481 – 55g. blue . . . . 2·25 2·00
482 – 75g. olive . . . . 5·75 6·50
483 – 80g. red . . . . 5·75 6·50
484 **107** 1z. blue . . . . 5·75 6·50
485 – 1z.50 brown . . . . . . 5·75 6·50
DESIGNS—VERT: 5g. Ruins of U.S. Embassy, Warsaw; 25g. Destruction of Mickiewicz Monument, Cracow; 1z.50, Polish submarine "Orzel". HORIZ: 55g. Ruins of Warsaw; 75g. Polish machine-gunners in Great Britain; 80g. Polish tank in Great Britain.

108 Vickers-Armstrong Wellington and U-boat

109 Merchant Navy

1943.
486 **108** 5g. red . . . . 85 1·10
487 **109** 10g. green . . . . 1·10 1·40
488 – 25g. violet . . . . 1·10 1·40
489 – 55g. blue . . . . 1·50 1·90
490 – 75g. brown . . . . 3·00 3·25
491 – 80g. red . . . . 3·00 3·25
492 – 1z. olive . . . . 3·00 3·25
493 – 1z.50 black . . . . 3·75 6·75
DESIGNS—VERT: 25g. Anti-tank gun in France; 55g. Poles at Narvik; 1z. Saboteurs damaging railway line. HORIZ: 75g. The Tobruk road; 80g. Gen. Sikorski visiting Polish troops in Middle East; 1z.50, Underground newspaper office.

1944. Capture of Monte Casino. Nos. 482/5 surch **MONTE CASSINO 18 V 1944** and value and bars.
494 – 45g. on 75g. olive . . . . 13·00 16·00
495 – 55g. on 80g. red . . . . . 13·00 16·00
496 **107** 80g. on 1z. blue . . . . . 13·00 16·00
497 – 1z.20 on 1z.50 brown . . 13·00 16·00

111 Polish Partisans

112 Romuald Traugutt

1945. Relief Fund for Survivors of Warsaw Rising.
498 **111** 1z.+2z. green . . . . . . 7·00 9·25

1944. INDEPENDENT REPUBLIC.

1944. National Heroes.
499 **112** 25g. red . . . . 48·00 65·00
500 – 50g. green . . . . 48·00 65·00
501 – 1z. blue . . . . 48·00 80·00
PORTRAITS: 50g. Kosciuszko; 1z. H. Dabrowski.

113 White Eagle

114 Grunwald Memorial, Cracow

1944.
502 **113** 25g. red . . . . 1·40 1·10
503 **114** 50g. green . . . . 1·40 75

1944. No. 502 surch with value **31.XII., 1943** or **1944** and **K.R.N., P.K.W.N.** or **R.T.R.P.**
504 **113** 1z. on 25g. red . . . . . 2·50 3·50
505 2z. on 25g. red . . . . . 2·50 3·50
506 3z. on 25g. red . . . . . 2·50 3·50

1945. 82nd Anniv of 1863 Revolt against Russia. Surch with value and **22.I.1863.**
507 **112** 5z. on 25g. brown . . . . 42·00 65·00

1945. Liberation. No. 502 surch **3zl**, with town names and dates as indicated.
508 3z. on 25g. Bydgoszcz 23.1.1945 . . . . 5·75 9·75
509 3z. on 25g. Czestochowa 17.1.1945 . . . . 5·75 9·75
510 3z. on 25g. Gniezno 22.1.1945 . . . . 5·75 9·75
511 3z. on 25g. Kalisz 24.1.1945 5·75 9·75
512 3z. on 25g. Kielce 15.1.1945 5·75 9·75
513 3z. on 25g. Krakow 19.1.1945 5·75 9·75
514 3z. on 25g. Lodz 19.1.1945 5·75 9·75
515 3z. on 25g. Radom 16.1.1945 5·75 9·75
516 3z. on 25g. Warszawa 17.1.1945 . . . . 14·50 20·00
517 3z. on 25g. Zakopane 29.1.1945 . . . . 8·00 13·50

120 Flag-bearer and War Victim

121 Lodz Factories

1945. Liberation of Warsaw.
518 **120** 5z. red . . . . 2·25 2·25

1945. Liberation of Lodz.
519 **121** 1z. blue 80 40

1945. 151st Anniv of Kosciuszko's Oath of Allegiance. No. 500 surch **5zl. 24.III.1794.**
520 5z. on 50g. green . . . . . . 11·50 17·00

123 Grunwald Memorial, Cracow

125 H.M.S. "Dragon" (cruiser)

1945. Cracow Monuments. Inscr "19.1.1945".
521 **123** 50g. purple 25 15
522 – 1z. brown 30 15
523 – 2z. blue . . . . 1·10 15
524 – 3z. violet 95 40
525 – 5z. green . . . . 6·00 6·75
DESIGNS—VERT: 1z. Kosciuszko Statue; 3z. Copernicus Memorial. HORIZ: 2z. Cloth Hall; 5z. Wawel Castle.

1945. 25th Anniv of Polish Maritime League.
526 **125** 50g.+2z. orange . . . . . 7·00 10·50
527 – 1z.+3z. blue . . . . . . 4·00 7·50
528 – 2z.+4z. red . . . . 2·75 7·00
529 – 3z.+5z. olive . . . . . . 2·75 7·00
DESIGNS—VERT: 1z. "Dar Pomorza" (full-rigged cadet ship); 2z. Naval ensigns. HORIZ: 3z. Crane and tower, Gdansk.

126 Town Hall, Poznan

1945. Postal Employees Congress.
530 **126** 1z.+5z. green . . . . . . 19·00 32·00

127 Kosciuszko Memorial, Lodz

128 Grunwald, 1410

1945.
531 **127** 3z. purple 70 25

1945. 535th Anniv of Battle of Grunwald.
532 **128** 5z. blue . . . . 6·75 6·25

129 Eagle and Manifesto

133 Crane Tower, Gdansk

130 Westerplatte

1945. 1st Anniv of Liberation.
533 **129** 3z. red . . . . 10·00 16·00

1945. 6th Anniv of Defence of Westerplatte.
534 **130** 1z.+9z. slate . . . . . . 21·00 27·00

1945. Surch with new value and heavy bars.
535 **114** 1z. on 50g. green 55 30
536a **113** 1z.50 on 25g. red 55 30

1945. Liberation of Gdansk (Danzig). Perf or imperf.
537 **133** 1z. olive 20 20
538 – 2z. blue 30 20
539 – 3z. purple 90 20
DESIGNS—VERT: 2z. Stock Exchange, Gdansk. HORIZ: 3z. High Gate, Gdansk.

135 St. John's Cathedral

1945. "Warsaw, 1939–1945". Warsaw before and after destruction. Imperf.
540 – 1z.50 red 20 10
541 **135** 3z. blue 20 10
542 – 3z.50 green . . . . 1·25 45
543 – 6z. grey 25 20
544 – 8z. brown . . . . 2·75 55
545 – 10z. purple 55 55
DESIGNS: 1z.50, Royal Castle; 3z.50, City Hall; 6z. G.P.O.; 8z. War Ministry; 10z. Church of the Holy Cross.

136 United Workers

1945. Trades' Union Congress.
546 **136** 1z.50+8z.50 grey . . . . 6·75 8·75

137 Soldiers of 1830 and Jan III Sobieski Statue

1945. 115th Anniv of 1830 Revolt against Russia.
547 **137** 10z. grey . . . . 8·50 12·50

1946. 1st Anniv of Warsaw Liberation. Nos. 540/5 optd **WARSZAWA WOLNA 17 Styczen 1945–1946**. Imperf.
548 1z.50 red . . . . 1·90 4·25
549 3z. blue . . . . 1·90 4·25
550 3z.50 green . . . . 1·90 4·25
551 6z. grey . . . . 1·90 4·25
552 8z. brown . . . . 1·90 4·25
553 10z. purple . . . . 1·90 4·25

139 Insurgent

140 Lisunov Li-2 over Ruins of Warsaw

1946. 83rd Anniv of 1863 Revolt.
554 **139** 6z. blue . . . . 7·50 10·50

1946. Air.
555 **140** 5z. grey 35 10
556 10z. purple 45 25
557 15z. blue . . . . 2·75 25
558 20z. purple . . . . 1·10 25
559 25z. green . . . . 2·10 35
560 30z. red . . . . 3·50 50

141 Fighting in Spain

1946. Polish Legion in the Spanish Civil War.
561 **141** 3z.+5z. red . . . . 6·00 8·75

142 Bydgoszcz

143 "Death" over Majdanek Concentration Camp

1946. 600th Anniv of City of Bydgoszcz.
562 **142** 3z.+2z. grey . . . . . . 7·25 13·00

1946. Majdanek Concentration Camp.
563 **143** 3z.+5z. green . . . . . . 2·75 4·00

144 Shield and Soldiers

145 Infantry

1946. Uprisings in Upper Silesia (1919–23) and Silesian Campaign against the Germans (1939–45).
564 **144** 3z.+7z. brown . . . . . 95 1·10

1946. 1st Anniv of Peace.
565 **145** 3z. brown 45 35

146 Polish Coastline

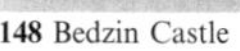

148 Bedzin Castle

147 Pres. Bierut, Premier O. Morawski and Marshal Zymierski

1946. Maritime Festival.
566 **146** 3z.+7z. blue . . . . . . 2·50 3·75

1946. 2nd Anniv of Polish Committee of National Liberation Manifesto.
567 **147** 3z. violet . . . . 3·50 6·00

1946. Imperf (5z., 10z.) or perf (6z.).
568 **148** 5z. olive 25 15
568a 5z. brown 45 15
569 – 6z. black 35 10
570 – 10z. blue 80 25
DESIGNS—VERT: 6z. Tombstone of Henry IV. HORIZ: 10z. Castle at Lanckorona.

149 Crane, Monument and Crane Tower, Gdansk

1946. The Fallen in Gdansk.
571 **149** 3z.+12z. grey . . . . . . 2·25 3·00

150 Schoolchildren at Desk

1946. Polish Work for Education and Fund for International Bureau of Education.
571a **150** 3z.+22z. red . . . . . 30·00 55·00
571b – 6z.+24z. blue . . . . . 30·00 55·00
571c – 11z.+19z. green . . . . 30·00 55·00
MS571d 128 × 80 mm. Nos. 571a/c colours slightly changed (sold at 25+75z.) £450 £900
DESIGNS: 6z. Court of Jagiellonian University, Cracow; 11z. Gregory Piramowicz (1735–1801), founder of the Education Commission.

152 Stojalowski, Bojko, Stapinski and Witos

1946. 50th Anniv of Peasant Movement and Relief Fund.
572 **152** 5z.+10z. green . . . . . 2·25 3·00
573 5z.+10z. blue . . . . . 2·25 3·00
574 5z.+10z. olive . . . . . 2·25 3·00

1947. Opening of Polish Parliament. Surch **+7 SEJM USTAWODAWCZY 19.1.1947.**
575 **147** 3z.+7z. violet . . . . . . 7·50 12·00

1947. 22nd National Ski Championships, Zakopane. Surch **5+15 zl XXII MISTRZOSTWA NARCIARSKIE POLSKI 1947.**
576 **113** 5+15z. on 25g. red . . . 3·25 5·00

1947. No. 569 surch **5 ZL** in outlined figure and capital letters between stars.
577 5z. on 6z. black 65 25

156 Home of Emil Zegadlowicz

157 Frederic Chopin (musician)

158 Boguslawski, Modrzejewska and Jaracz (actors)

159 Wounded Soldier, Nurse and Child

1947. Emil Zegadlowicz Commemoration.
578 **156** 5z.+15z. green . . . . . 2·25 3·25

1947. Polish Culture. Imperf or perf.
579 – 1z. blue 20 25
580 – 1z. grey 20 10
581 – 2z. brown 25 10
582 – 2z. orange 15 10
583 **157** 3z. green 60 25
584 3z. olive . . . . 1·90 25
585 **158** 5z. black 60 10
586 5z. brown 20 10
587 – 6z. grey . . . . 1·00 10
588 – 6z. red 35 10
589 – 10z. grey . . . . 1·25 10
590 – 10z. blue . . . . 1·50 30
591 – 15z. violet . . . . . . 1·60 30
592 – 15z. brown 35 70
593 – 20z. black . . . . . . 2·50 50
594 – 20z. purple . . . . . . 1·10 50
MS594a 210 × 128 mm. in shades similar to second issue of colours listed above (sold at 62+438z.) £1290 £250
PORTRAITS—HORIZ: 1z. Matejko, Malczewski and Chelmonski (painters); 6z. Swietochowski, Zeromski and Prus (writers); 15z. Wyspianski, Slowacki and Kasprowicz (poets). VERT: 2z. Brother Albert of Cracow; 10z. Marie Curie (scientist); 20z. Mickiewicz (poet).

1947. Red Cross Fund.
595 **159** 5z.+5z. grey and red . . . 3·00 5·00

161 Steelworker

163 Brother Albert of Cracow

1947. Occupations.
596 **161** 5z. lake . . . . 1·40 35
597 – 10z. green 45 20
598 – 15z. blue 90 30
599 – 20z. black . . . . 1·40 30
DESIGNS: 10z. Harvester; 15z. Fisherman; 20z. Miner.

1947. Air. Surch **LOTNICZA**, bars and value.
600 **114** 40z. on 50g. green . . . . 2·10 65
602 **113** 50z. on 25g. red . . . . . 3·25 1·60

1947. Winter Relief Fund.
603 **163** 2z.+18z. violet . . . . . 1·25 4·50

164 Sagittarius

165 Chainbreaker

1948. Air.
604 **164** 15z. violet . . . . 1·60 25
605 25z. blue . . . . 1·10 20
606 30z. brown . . . . 1·10 45
607 50z. green . . . . 2·25 45
608 75z. black . . . . 2·25 55
609 100z. orange . . . . . . 2·25 55

1948. Revolution Centenaries.
610 **165** 15z. brown 45 10
611 – 30z. brown . . . . 1·50 25
612 – 35z. green . . . . 3·25 55
613 – 60z. red . . . . 1·75 65
PORTRAITS—HORIZ: 30z. Generals H. Dembinski and J. Bem; 35z. S. Worcell, P. Sciegienny and E. Dembowski; 60z. F. Engels and K. Marx.

167 Insurgents

168 Wheel and Streamers

1948. 5th Anniv of Warsaw Ghetto Revolt.
614 **167** 15z. black . . . . 2·00 3·50

1948. Warsaw–Prague Cycle Race.
615 **168** 15z. red and blue . . . . 3·25 45

169 Cycle Race

170 "Oliwa" under Construction

1948. 7th Circuit of Poland Cycle Race.
616 **169** 3z. black . . . . 1·75 4·00
617 6z. brown . . . . 1·75 4·25
618 15z. green . . . . 2·50 5·50

1948. Merchant Marine.
619 **170** 6z. violet . . . . 1·40 2·00
620 – 15z. red . . . . 1·75 3·00
621 – 35z. grey . . . . 2·00 5·00
DESIGNS—HORIZ: 15z. Freighter at wharf; 35z. "General M. Zaruski" (cadet ketch).

173 Firework Display

174 "Youth"

1948. Wroclaw Exhibition.
622 **173** 6z. blue 55 30
623 15z. red 90 25
624 18z. red . . . . 1·40 45
625 35z. brown . . . . 1·40 45

1948. International Youth Conf, Warsaw.
626 **174** 15z. blue 65 25

175 Roadway, St. Anne's Church and Palace

176 Torun Ramparts and Mail Coach

1948. Warsaw Reconstruction Fund.
627 **175** 15z.+5z. green 25 25

1948. Philatelic Congress, Torun.
628 **176** 15z. brown . . . . 1·00 25

177 Streamlined Steam Locomotive No. Pm36-1 (1936), Clock and Winged Wheel

178 President Bierut

1948. European Railway Conference.
629 **177** 18z. blue . . . . 6·00 18·00

1948.
629a **178** 2z. orange 15 10
629b 3z. green 15 10
630 5z. brown 15 10
631 6z. black 95 10
631a 10z. violet 25 10
632 15z. red 80 10
633 18z. green . . . . 1·10 10
634 30z. blue . . . . 1·90 25
635 35z. purple . . . . . . 3·00 50

179 Workers and Flag

1948. Workers' Class Unity Congress. (a) Dated "8 XII 1948".
636 **179** 5z. red 85 65
637 – 15z. violet 85 65
638 – 25z. brown 85 65

(b) Dated "XII 1948".
639 **179** 5z. plum . . . . 2·00 1·60
640 – 15z. blue . . . . 2·00 1·60
641 – 25z. green . . . . 2·75 2·25

DESIGNS: 15z. Flags and portraits of Engels, Marx, Lenin and Stalin; 25z. Workers marching and portrait of L. Warynski.

180 Baby **180a** Pres. Franklin D. Roosevelt

1948. Anti-tuberculosis Fund. Portraits of babies as T **180**.
642 **180** 3z.+2z. green . . . . . . 4·00 4·75
643 – 5z.+5z. brown . . . . . 4·00 4·75
644 – 6z.+4z. purple . . . . . 2·25 4·75
645 – 15z.+10z. red . . . . . . 2·00 3·00

1948. Air. Honouring Presidents Roosevelt, Pulaski and Kosciuszko.
645a **180a** 80z. violet . . . . . . 21·00 21·00
645b – 100z. purple (Pulaski) 21·00 21·00
645c – 120z. blue (Kosciuszko) 21·00 21·00
MS645d 160×95 mm. Nos. 645a/c 300+200z. colours changed . . £250 £375

181 Workers

1949. Trades' Union Congress, Warsaw.
646 **181** 3z. red . . . . 1·10 1·25
647 – 5z. blue . . . . 1·10 1·25
648 – 15z. green . . . . 1·50 1·50
DESIGNS: 5z. inscr "PRACA" (Labour), Labourer and tractor; 15z. inscr "POKOJ" (Peace), Three labourers.

182 Banks of R. Vistula **183** Pres. Bierut

1949. 5th Anniv of National Liberation Committee.
649 **182** 10z. black . . . . 2·10 2·00
650 **183** 15z. mauve . . . . 2·10 2·00
651 – 35z. blue . . . . 2·10 2·00
DESIGN—VERT: 35z. Radio station, Rasyn.

184 Mail Coach and Map **185** Worker and Tractor

1949. 75th Anniv of U.P.U.
652 **184** 6z. violet . . . . 1·25 2·00
653 – 30z. blue (liner) . . . . . 2·25 2·00
654 – 80z. green (airplane) . . . 4·25 4·75

1949. Congress of Peasant Movement.
655 **185** 5z. red 95 25
656 10z. red 25 10
657 15z. green 25 10
658 35z. brown . . . . 1·25 1·25

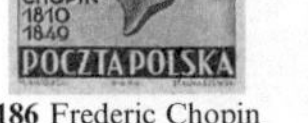

186 Frederic Chopin **187** Mickiewicz and Pushkin

1949. National Celebrities.
659 – 10z. purple . . . . 2·40 2·10
660 **186** 15z. red . . . . 3·25 2·40
661 – 35z. blue . . . . 2·40 2·40
PORTRAITS: 10z. Adam Mickiewicz; 35z. Julius Slowacki.

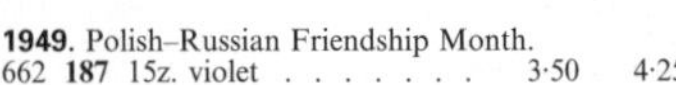

1949. Polish–Russian Friendship Month.
662 **187** 15z. violet . . . . 3·50 4·25

188 Postman **189** Mechanic, Hangar and Aeroplane

1950. 3rd Congress of Postal Workers.
663 **188** 15z. purple . . . . 2·10 2·75

1950. Air.
664 **189** 500z. lake . . . . 4·50 6·50

190 **195a**

1950. (a) With frame.
665 **190** 15z. red 60 10
(b) Without frame. Values in "zloty".
673 **195a** 5z. green 15 10
674 10z. red 15 10
675 15z. blue 95 50
676 20z. violet 45 35
677 25z. brown 45 35
678 30z. red 65 40
679 40z. brown 80 50
680 50z. olive . . . . 1·60 1·00
For values in "groszy" see Nos. 687/94.

191 J. Marchlewski **192** Workers

1950. 25th Death Anniv of Julian Marchlewski (patriot).
666 **191** 15z. black 70 35

1950. Reconstruction of Warsaw.
667 **192** 5z. brown 15 15
See also No. 695.

193 Worker and Flag **194** Statue

1950. 60th Anniv of May Day Manifesto.
668 **193** 10z. mauve . . . . 1·75 40
669 – 15z. olive . . . . 1·75 25
DESIGN—VERT: 15z. Three workers and flag.

1950. 23rd International Fair, Poznan.
670 **194** 15z. brown 35 10

195 Dove and Globe **196** Industrial and Agricultural Workers

1950. International Peace Conference.
671 **195** 10z. green 85 25
672 15z. brown 35 15

1950. Six Year Reconstruction Plan.
681 **196** 15z. blue 25 10
See also Nos. 696/e.

197 Hibner, Kniewski and Rutkowski **198** Worker and Dove

1950. 25th Anniv of Revolutionaries' Execution.
682 **197** 15z. grey . . . . 2·50 65

1950. 1st Polish Peace Congress.
683 **198** 15z. green 50 25

REVALUATION SURCHARGES. Following a revaluation of the Polish currency, a large number of definitive and commemorative stamps were locally overprinted "Groszy" or "gr". There are 37 known types of overprint and various colours of overprint. We do not list them as they had only local use, but the following is a list of the stamps which were duly authorised for overprinting: Nos. 579/94, 596/615 and 619/58. Overprints on other stamps are not authorized.

Currency Revalued: 100 old zlotys = 1 new zloty.

199 Dove (after Picasso)

1950. 2nd World Peace Congress, Warsaw.
684 **199** 40g. blue . . . . 1·75 35
685 45g. red 35 15

200 General Bem and Battle of Piski

1950. Death Centenary of General Bem.
686 **200** 45g. blue . . . . 2·50 2·00

1950. As T **195a**. Values in "groszy".
687 **195a** 5g. violet 10 10
688 10g. green 10 10
689 15g. olive 10 10
690 25g. red 10 10
691 30g. red 15 10
692 40g. orange 15 10
693 45g. blue . . . . 1·25 10
694 75g. brown 70 10

1950. As No. 667 but value in "groszy".
695 **192** 15g. green 10 10

1950. As No. 681 but values in "groszy" or "zlotys".
696 **196** 45g. blue 15 10
696b 75g. brown 30 10
696d 1z.15 green 95 10
696e 1z.20 red 70 10

201 Woman and Doves **202** Battle Scene and J. Dabrowski

1951. Women's League Congress.
697 **201** 45g. red 45 35

1951. 80th Anniv of Paris Commune.
698 **202** 45g. green 30 10

1951. Surch **45 gr.**
699 **199** 45g. on 15z. red 55 15

204 Worker with Flag **205** Smelting Works

1951. Labour Day.
700 **204** 45g. red 45 15

1951.
701 **205** 40g. blue 25 10
702 45g. black 25 10
702a 60g. brown 25 10
702c 90g. lake 85 10

206 Pioneer and Badge **207** St. Staszic

1951. Int Children's Day. Inscr "I-VI-51".
703 **206** 30g. olive . . . . 1·10 65
704 – 45g. blue (Boy, girl and map) . . . . 6·25 65

1951. 1st Polish Scientific Congress. Inscr "KONGRES NAUKI POLSKIEJ".
705 **207** 25g. red . . . . 3·75 2·75
706 – 40g. blue 60 20
707 – 45g. violet . . . . 8·00 1·60
708 – 60g. green 60 20
709 – 1z.15 purple . . . . . . 1·00 55
710 – 1z.20 grey . . . . 1·75 20
DESIGNS—As Type **207**: 40g. Marie Curie; 60g. M. Nencki; 1z.15, Copernicus; 1z.20, Dove and book. HORIZ—36×21 mm: 45g. Z. Wroblewski and Olszewski.

209 F. Dzerzhinsky **211** Young People and Globe

210 Pres. Bierut, Industry and Agriculture

1951. 25th Death Anniv of Dzerzhinsky (Russian politician).
711 **209** 45g. brown 30 25

1951. 7th Anniv of People's Republic.
712 **210** 45g. red . . . . 1·10 15
713 60g. green . . . . 16·00 5·25
714 90g. blue . . . . 3·50 65

1951. 3rd World Youth Festival, Berlin.
715 **211** 40g. blue . . . . 1·10 25

1951. Surch **45 gr.**
716 **195a** 45g. on 35z. orange . . 30 25

213 Sports Badge **214** Stalin

1951. Spartacist Games.
717 **213** 45g. green . . . . 1·25 1·10

1951. Polish–Soviet Friendship.
718 **214** 45g. red 15 10
719 90g. black . . . . 1·10 60

215 Chopin and Moniuszko **216** Mining Machinery

1951. Polish Musical Festival.
720 **215** 45g. black 40 20
721 90g. red . . . . 1·50 55

1951. Warsaw Stamp Day. Sheet 90×120 mm comprising Nos. 696a/e printed in brown.
MS721a **196** Sold at 5z. . . . . 13·50 13·50

1951. Six Year Plan (Mining).
722 **216** 90g. brown 30 15
723 1z.20 blue 30 15
724 1z.20+15g. orange 45 20

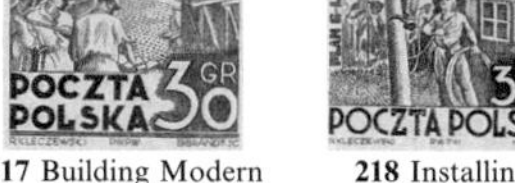

217 Building Modern Flats **218** Installing Electric Cables

1951. Six Year Plan (Reconstruction).
725 **217** 30g. green 10 10
726 30g.+15g. red 25 10
727 1z.15 purple 25 10

1951. Six Year Plan (Electrification).
728 **218** 30g. black 10 10
729 45g. red 20 10
730 45g.+15g. brown 55 10

219 M. Nowotko **220** Women and Banner

1952. 10th Anniv of Polish Workers' Coalition.
731 **219** 45g.+15g. lake 20 10
732 – 90g. brown 45 30
733 – 1z.15 orange 45 65
PORTRAITS: 90g. P. Finder; 1z.15, M. Fornalska.

1952. International Women's Day.
734 **220** 45g.+15g. brown 45 10
735 1z.20 red 50 35

221 Gen. Swierczewski **222** Ilyushin Il-12 over Farm

1952. 5th Death Anniv of Gen. Swierczewski.
736 **221** 45g.+15g. brown 45 10
737 90g. blue 50 30

1952. Air. Aeroplanes and views.
738 – 55g. blue (Tug and freighters) 35 30
739 **222** 90g. green 35 30
740 – 1z.40 purple (Warsaw) . . 45 45
741 – 5z. black (Steelworks) . . 1·40 55

223 President Bierut **224** Cyclists and City Arms

1952. Pres. Bierut's 60th Birthday.
742 **223** 45g.+15g. red 45 35
743 90g. green 80 80
744 1z.20+15g. blue . . . . . 1·00 35

1952. 5th Warsaw–Berlin–Prague Peace Cycle Race.
745 **224** 40g. blue . . . . 1·50 90

225 Workers and Banner **226** Kraszewski

1952. Labour Day.
746 **225** 45g.+15g. red 20 15
747 75g. green 55 35

1952. 140th Birth Anniv of Jozef Ignacy Kraszewski (writer).
748 **226** 25g. purple 50 25

227 Maria Konopnicka **228** H. Kollataj

1952. 110th Birth Anniv of Maria Konopnicka (poet).
749 **227** 30g.+15g. green 50 15
750 1z.15 brown 80 55

1952. 140th Death Anniv of Hugo Kollataj (educationist and politician).
751 **228** 45g.+15g. brown 35 15
752 1z. green 50 35

229 Leonardo da Vinci **231** N. V. Gogol

230 President Bierut and Children

1952. 500th Birth Anniv of Leonardo da Vinci (artist).
753 **229** 30g.+15g. blue 70 50

1952. International Children's Day.
754 **230** 45g.+15g. blue . . . . . 2·50 70

1952. Death Centenary of Nikolai Gogol (Russian writer).
755 **231** 25g. green 85 60

232 Cement Works **233** Swimmers

1952. Construction of Concrete Works, Wierzbica.
756 **232** 3z. black . . . . 2·10 35
757 10z. red . . . . 2·50 35

1952. Sports Day.
758 **233** 30g.+15g. blue . . . . . 4·25 1·10
759 – 45g.+15g. violet . . . . . 1·50 20
760 – 1z.15 green . . . . 1·40 1·50
761 – 1z.20 red 80 80
DESIGNS: 45g. Footballers; 1z.15, Runners; 1z.20, High jumper.

234 Yachts **235** Young Workers

1952. Shipbuilders' Day.
762 **234** 30g.+15g. green . . . . . 3·25 70
763 – 45g.+15g. blue 70 25
764 – 90g. plum . . . . 70 1·25
DESIGNS—VERT: 45g. Full-rigged cadet ship "Dar Pomorza"; 90g. "Brygada Makowskiego" (freighter) under construction.

1952. Youth Festival, Warsaw.
765 **235** 30g.+15g. green 40 25
766 – 45g.+15g. red 70 15
767 – 90g. brown 40 35
DESIGNS—HORIZ: 45g. Girl and boy students; 90g. Boy bugler.

236 "New Constitution" **237** L. Warynski

1952. Adoption of New Constitution.
768 **236** 45g.+15g. green & brown 1·10 15
769 3z. violet and brown . . . 40 35

1952. 70th Anniv of Party "Proletariat".
770 **237** 30g.+15g. red 55 15
771 45g.+15g. brown 55 15

238 Jaworzno Power Station **239** Frydman

1952. Electricity Power Station, Jaworzno.
772 **238** 45g.+15g. red 70 10
773 1z. black 65 50
774 1z.50 green 65 20

1952. Pleniny Mountain Resorts.
775 **239** 45g.+15g. purple 55 10
776 – 60g. green (Grywald) . . 35 45
777 – 1z. red (Niedzica) . . . . 1·00 15

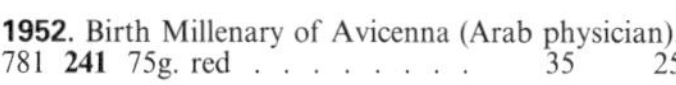

240 Pilot and Glider **241** Avicenna

1952. Aviation Day.
778 **240** 3g.+15g. green . . . . . 1·25 10
779 – 45g.+15g. red . . . . . . 2·00 70
780 – 90g. blue 35 35
DESIGNS: 45g. Pilot and Yakovlev Yak-18U; 90g. Parachutists descending.

1952. Birth Millenary of Avicenna (Arab physician).
781 **241** 75g. red 35 25

242 Victor Hugo **243** Shipbuilding

1952. 150th Birth Anniv of Victor Hugo (French author).
782 **242** 90g. brown 35 25

1952. Gdansk Shipyards.
783 **243** 5g. green 15 10
784 15g. red 15 10

244 H. Sienkiewicz (author) **245** Assault on Winter Palace, Petrograd

1952.
785 **244** 45g.+15g. brown 35 15

1952. 35th Anniv of Russian Revolution. Perf or Imperf.
786 **245** 45g.+15g. red 90 20
787 60g. brown 35 30

246 Lenin **247** Miner

1952. Polish–Soviet Friendship Month.
788 **246** 30g.+15g. purple 35 15
789 45g.+15g. brown 70 30

1952. Miners' Day.
790 **247** 45g.+15g. black 20 10
791 1z.20+15g. brown 70 35

248 H. Wieniawski (violinist) **249** Car Factory, Zeran

1952. 2nd Wieniawski Int Violin Competition.
792 **248** 30g.+15g. green . . . . . 1·00 60
793 45g.+15g. violet . . . . . 2·75 55

1952.
800 – 30g.+15g. blue 30 10
794 **249** 45g.+15g. green 20 10
801 – 60g.+20g. purple 30 10
795 **249** 1z.15 brown 70 35
DESIGN: 30, 60g. Lorry factory, Lublin.

250 Dove of Peace **251** Soldier and Flag

1952. Peace Congress, Vienna.
796 **250** 30g. green 75 30
797 60g. blue . . . . 1·40 45

1952. 10th Anniv of Battle of Stalingrad.
798 **251** 60g. red and green . . . 5·00 1·60
799 80g. red and grey 65 50

253 Karl Marx **254** Globe and Flag

1953. 70th Death Anniv of Marx.
802 **253** 60g. blue . . . . 20·00 11·50
803 80g. brown . . . . 1·10 45

1953. Labour Day.
804 **254** 60g. red . . . . 5·75 3·75
805 80g. red 45 15

255 Cyclists and Arms of Warsaw **256** Boxer

1953. 6th International Peace Cycle Race.
806 – 80g. green 85 40
807 **255** 80g. brown 85 40
808 – 80g. red . . . . 13·50 9·25
DESIGNS: As Type **255**, but Arms of Berlin (No. 806) or Prague (No. 808).

1953. European Boxing Championship, Warsaw. Inscr "17-24. V. 1953".
809 **256** 40g. lake . . . . 1·00 45
810 80g. orange . . . . . . 10·00 4·75
811 – 95g. purple 85 60
DESIGN: 95g. Boxers in ring.

257 Copernicus (after Matejko)

1953. 480th Birth Anniv of Copernicus (astronomer).
812 **257** 20g. brown . . . . 1·75 40
813 – 80g. blue . . . . 13·50 13·50
DESIGN—VERT: 80g. Copernicus and diagram.

258 "Dalmor" (trawler)

259 Warsaw Market-place

1953. Merchant Navy Day.

814	**258**	80g. green	1·60	10
815	–	1z.35 blue	1·60	3·25

DESIGN: 1z.35, "Czech" (freighter).

1953. Polish National Day.

816	**259**	20g. lake	25	20
817		2z.35 blue	4·25	3·25

260 Students' Badge

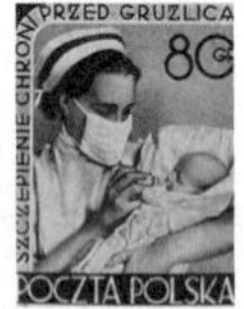

261 Nurse Feeding Baby

1953. 3rd World Students' Congress, Warsaw. Inscr "III SWIATOWY KONGRESS STUDENTOW".

(a) Postage. Perf.

818	–	40g. brown	15	15
819	**260**	1z.35 green	70	15
820	–	1z.50 blue	2·50	2·75

(b) Air. Imperf.

821	**260**	55g. plum	1·75	60
822		75g. red	90	1·60

DESIGNS—HORIZ: 40g. Students and globe. VERT: 1z.50, Woman and dove.

1953. Social Health Service.

823	**261**	80g. red	8·75	5·25
824	–	1z.75 green	40	40

DESIGN: 1z.75, Nurse, mother and baby.

262 M. Kalinowski

263 Jan Kochanowski (poet)

1953. 10th Anniv of Polish People's Army.

825	**262**	45g. brown	3·75	3·00
826	–	80g. red	80	10
827	–	1g.75 olive	80	10

DESIGNS—HORIZ: 80g. Russian and Polish soldiers. VERT: 1z.75, R. Pazinski.

1953. "Renaissance" Commemoration. Inscr "ROK ODRODZENIA".

828	**263**	20g. brown	15	10
829	–	80g. purple	60	10
830	–	1z.35 blue	2·75	1·75

DESIGNS—HORIZ: 80g. Wawel Castle. VERT: 1z.35, Mikolaj Rej (writer).

264 Palace of Science and Culture

265 Dunajec Canyon, Pieniny Mountains

1953. Reconstruction of Warsaw. Inscr "WARSZAWA".

831	**264**	80g. red	9·75	1·50
832	–	1z.75 blue	1·90	45
833	–	2z. purple	5·00	3·50

DESIGNS: 1z.75, Constitution Square; 2z. Old City Market, Warsaw.

1953. Tourist Series.

834	–	20g. lake and blue	10	10
835	–	80g. lilac and green	3·25	1·25
836	**265**	1z.75 green and brown	70	10
837	–	2z. black and red	1·10	10

DESIGNS—HORIZ: 20g. Krynica Spa; 2z. Ciechocinek Spa. VERT: 80g. Morskie Oko Lake, Tatra Mountains.

266 Skiing

267 Infants playing

1953. Winter Sports.

838	–	80g. blue	1·50	40
839	**266**	95g. green	1·25	40
840	–	2z.85 red	4·00	2·10

DESIGNS—VERT: 80g. Ice-skating; 2z.85, Ice-hockey.

1953. Children's Education.

841	**267**	10g. violet	60	15
842	–	80g. red	90	30
843	–	1z.50 green	6·00	2·25

DESIGNS: 80g. Girls and school; 1z.50, Two Schoolgirls writing.

268 Class EP 02 Electric Locomotive

269 Mill Girl

1954. Electrification of Railways.

844	–	60g. blue	8·00	4·75
845	**268**	80g. brown	90	25

DESIGN: 60g. Class EW54 electric commuter train.

1954. International Women's Day.

846	**269**	20g. green	2·45	1·50
847	–	40g. blue	60	10
848	–	80g. brown	60	10

DESIGNS: 40g. Postwoman; 80g. Woman driving tractor.

270 Flags and Mayflowers

271 "Warsaw–Berlin–Prague"

1954. Labour Day.

849	**270**	40g. brown	70	40
850		60g. blue	70	25
851		80g. red	70	25

1954. 7th International Peace Cycle Race. Inscr "2-17 MAJ 1954".

852	**271**	80g. brown	80	25
853	–	80g. blue (Dove and cycle wheel)	80	25

272 Symbols of Labour

1954. 3rd Trades' Union Congress, Warsaw.

854	**272**	25g. blue	1·25	1·10
855		80g. lake	40	25

272a Postal Coach and Plane

1954. Air. 3rd Polish Philatelic Society Congress. Sheet 57 × 76 mm.

MS855a	**272a**	5z.+(2z.50) green	26·00	21·00

273 Glider and Flags

1954. International Gliding Competition.

856	–	45g. green	65	15
857	**273**	60g. violet	1·90	70
858		60g. brown	1·25	15
859a	–	1z.35 blue	2·40	25

DESIGNS: 45g. Glider and clouds in frame; 1z.35, Glider and sky.

274 Paczkow

275 Fencing

1954. Air. Inscr "POCZTA LOTNICZA".

860	**274**	60g. green	25	10
861	–	80g. red	35	10
862	–	1z.15 black	1·75	1·60
863	–	1z.50 red	80	10
864	–	1z.55 blue	80	10
865	–	1z.95 brown	1·00	10

DESIGNS—Ilyushin Il-12 airplane over: 80g. Market-place, Kazimierz Dolny; 1z.15, Wawel Castle, Cracow; 1z.50, Town Hall, Wroclaw; 1z.55, Lazienki Palace, Warsaw; 1z.95, Cracow Tower, Lublin.

1954. 2nd Spartacist Games (1st issue). Inscr "II OGOLNOPOLSKA SPARTAKIADA".

866	**275**	25g. purple	1·25	50
867	–	60g. turquoise	1·25	35
868	–	1z. blue	2·40	70

DESIGNS—VERT: 60g. Gymnastics. HORIZ: 1z. Running.

276 Spartacist Games Badge

277 Battlefield

1954. 2nd Spartacist Games (2nd issue).

869	**276**	60g. brown	1·10	35
870		1z.55 grey	1·10	60

1954. 10th Anniv of Liberation and Battle of Studzianki.

871	**277**	60g. green	1·60	40
872	–	1z. blue	5·50	3·00

DESIGN—HORIZ: 1z. Soldier, airman and tank.

278 Steel Works

1954. 10th Anniv of Second Republic.

873	–	10g. sepia and brown	65	10
874	–	20g. green and red	35	10
876	**278**	25g. black and buff	1·00	45
877	–	40g. brown and yellow	45	15
878	–	45g. purple and mauve	45	15
880	–	60g. purple and green	40	25
881	–	1z.15 black and turquoise	6·00	15
882	–	1z.40 brown and orange	12·50	2·50
883	–	1z.55 blue and indigo	2·50	65
884	–	2z.10 blue and cobalt	3·50	1·25

DESIGNS: 10g. Coal mine; 20g. Soldier and flag; 40g. Worker on holiday; 45g. House-builders; 60g. Tractor and binder; 1z.15, Lublin Castle; 1z.40, Customers in bookshop; 1z.55, "Soldek" (freighter) alongside wharf; 2z.10, Battle of Lenino.

279 Steam Train and Signal

280 Picking Apples

1954. Railway Workers' Day.

885	**279**	40g. blue	3·00	60
886	–	60g. black	2·50	75

DESIGN: 60g. Steam night express.

1954. Polish–Russian Friendship.

887	**280**	40g. violet	1·60	1·10
888		60g. black	70	25

281 Elblag

282 Chopin and Grand Piano

1954. 500th Anniv of Return of Pomerania to Poland.

889	**281**	20g. red on blue	1·40	70
890	–	45g. brown on yellow	15	10
891	–	60g. green on yellow	20	10
892	–	1z.40 blue on pink	50	10
893	–	1z.55 brown on cream	70	10

VIEWS: 45g. Gdansk; 60g. Torun; 1z.40, Malbork; 1z.55, Olsztyn.

1954. 5th International Chopin Piano Competition, Warsaw (1st issue).

894	**282**	45g. brown	25	10
895		60g. green	60	10
896		1z. blue	1·75	80

See also Nos. 906/7.

283 Battle Scene

1954. 160th Anniv of Kosciuszko's Insurrection.

897	**283**	40g. olive	45	10
898	–	60g. brown	60	10
899	–	1z.40 black	1·50	95

DESIGNS: 60g. Kosciuszko on horseback, with insurgents; 1z.40, Street battle.

284 European Bison

285 "The Liberator"

1954. Protected Animals.

900	**284**	45g. brown and green	35	10
901	–	60g. brown and green	35	10
902	–	1z.90 brown and blue	70	10
903	–	3z. brown and turquoise	1·10	55

ANIMALS: 60g. Elk; 1z.90, Chamois; 3z. Eurasian beaver.

1955. 10th Anniv of Liberation of Warsaw.

904	**285**	40g. brown	1·60	70
905	–	60g. blue	1·60	45

DESIGN: 60g. "Spirit of Poland".

286 Bust of Chopin (after L. Isler)

287 Mickiewicz Monument

1955. 5th International Chopin Piano Competition (2nd issue).

906	**286**	40g. brown	55	25
907		60g. blue	1·60	80

1955. Warsaw Monuments.

908	–	5g. green on yellow	20	10
909	–	10g. purple on yellow	20	10
910	–	15g. black on green	20	10
911	–	20g. blue on pink	20	10
912	–	40g. violet on lilac	60	10
913	–	45g. brown on orange	1·25	25
914	**287**	60g. blue on grey	20	10
915	–	1z.55 green on grey	1·90	25

MONUMENTS: 5g. "Siren"; 10g. Dzerzhinski Statue; 15g. King Sigismund III Statue, 20g. "Brotherhood in Arms"; 40g. Copernicus; 45g. Marie Curie Statue; 1z.55, Kilinski Statue.

288 Flags and Tower

289

1955. 10th Anniv of Russo-Polish Treaty of Friendship.

916	**288**	40g. red	35	10
917		40g. brown	85	55

918 – 60g. brown 35 10
919 – 60g. turquoise 35 10
DESIGN: 60g. Statue of "Friendship".

1955. 8th International Peace Cycle Race.
920 **289** 40g. brown 45 25
921 – 60g. blue 25 10
DESIGN: 60g. "VIII" and doves.

290 Town Hall, Poznan

291 Festival Emblem

1955. 24th International Fair, Poznan.
922 **290** 40g. blue 25 25
923 60g. red 10 10

1955. Cracow Festival.
924 **291** 20g. multicoloured . . . 35 10
925 – 40g. multicoloured . . . 10 10
926 **291** 60g. multicoloured . . . 70 25
No. 925 is as T **291** but horiz and inscr "FESTIWAL SZTUKI", etc.

1955. 6th Polish Philatelic Exhibition, Poznan. Two sheets 50 × 70 mm as T **290**.
MS926a 2z.+(1z.) black and green 4·25 2·40
MS926b 3z.+(1z.50) black and red 21·00 12·50

292 "Peace" **293** Motor Cyclists

1955. 5th International Youth Festival, Warsaw.
927 – 25g. brown, pink & yellow 25 10
928 – 40g. grey and blue . . . 25 10
929 – 45g. red, mauve and yellow 45 10
930 **292** 60g. ultramarine and blue 35 10
931 – 60g. black and orange . . 35 10
932 **292** 1z. purple and blue . . . 80 80
DESIGNS: 25, 45g. Pansies and dove; 40, 60g. (No. 931) Dove and tower.

1955. 13th International Tatra Mountains Motor Cycle Race.
933 **293** 40g. brown 25 25
934 60g. green 10 10

294 Stalin Palace of Culture and Science, Warsaw

295 Athletes

1955. Polish National Day.
935 **294** 60g. blue 10 10
936 60g. grey 10 10
937 75g. green 55 25
938 75g. brown 55 25

1955. 2nd International Games. Imperf or perf.
939 **295** 20g. brown 10 10
940 – 40g. purple 15 10
941 – 60g. blue 25 10
942 – 1z. red 45 10
943 – 1z.35 lilac 55 10
944 – 1z.55 green . . . . 1·10 80
DESIGNS—VERT: 40g. Throwing the hammer; 1z. Netball; 1z.35, Sculling; 1z.55, Swimming. HORIZ: 60g. Stadium.

1955. International Philatelic Exhibition, Warsaw. Two sheets 61 × 84 mm. Imperf.
MS944a 1z.+(1z.) As No. 929 . . 4·50 3·25
MS944b 2z.+(1z.) As No. 932 . . 23·00 20·00

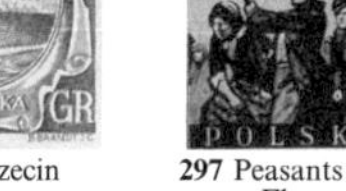

296 Szczecin **297** Peasants and Flag

1955. 10th Anniv of Return of Western Territories.
945 **296** 25g. green 10 10
946 – 40g. red (Wroclaw) . . . 25 10
947 – 60g. blue (Zielona Gora) 55 10
948 – 95g. black (Opole) . . . . 1·50 60

1955. 50th Anniv of 1905 Revolution.
949 **297** 40g. brown 55 45
950 60g. red 25 25

298 Mickiewicz **299** Statue

1955. Death Cent of Adam Mickiewicz (poet).
951 **298** 20g. brown 20 10
952 **299** 40g. brown and orange 20 10
953 – 60g. brown and green . . 25 10
954 – 95g. black and red . . . 1·40 45
DESIGNS—As Type **299**: 60g. Sculptured head; 95g. Statue.

300 Teacher and Pupil **301** Rook and Hands

1955. 50th Anniv of Polish Teachers' Union.
955 **300** 40g. brown . . . . 1·60 35
956 – 60g. blue . . . . 2·75 80
DESIGN: 60g. Open book and lamp.

1956. 1st World Chess Championship for the Deaf and Dumb, Zakopane.
957 **301** 40g. red . . . . 2·25 80
958 – 60g. blue . . . . 1·40 10
DESIGN: 60g. Knight and hands.

302 Ice Skates **304** Racing Cyclist

303 Officer and "Kilinski" (freighter)

1956. 11th World Students' Winter Sports Championship.
959 **302** 20g. black and blue . . . 3·25 1·60
960 – 40g. blue and green . . . 80 10
961 – 60g. red and mauve . . . 80 10
DESIGNS: 40g. Ice-hockey sticks and puck; 60g. Skis and ski sticks.

1956. Merchant Navy.
962 **303** 5g. green 15 10
963 – 10g. red 20 10
964 – 20g. blue 25 10
965 – 45g. brown 90 55
966 – 60g. blue 20 55
DESIGNS: 10g. Tug and barges; 20g. "Pokoj" (freighter) in dock; 45g. Building "Marceii Nowatka" (freighter); 60g. "Fryderyk Chopin" (freighter) and "Radunia" (trawler).

1956. 9th International Peace Cycle Race.
967 **304** 40g. blue . . . . 1·10 70
968 60g. green 20 10

305 Lodge, Tatra Mountains **307** Ghetto Heroes' Monument

1956. Tourist Propaganda.
969 **305** 30g. green 10 10
970 – 40g. brown 10 10
971 – 60g. blue . . . . 1·60 60
972 – 1z.15 purple 55 10
DESIGNS: 40g. Compass, rucksack and map; 60g. Canoe and map; 1z.15, Skis and mountains.

1956. No. 829 surch.
973 10g. on 80g. purple 70 35
974 40g. on 80g. purple 45 10
975 60g. on 80g. purple 45 10
976 1z.35 on 80g. purple . . . . 2·25 1·00

1956. Warsaw Monuments.
977 **307** 30g. black 10 10
978 – 40g. brown on green . . . 70 35
979 – 1z.55 purple on pink . . . 55 10
STATUES: 40g. Statue of King Jan III Sobieski; 1z.55, Statue of Prince Joseph Poniatowski.

308 "Economic Co-operation" **309** Ludwika Wawrzynska (teacher)

1956. Russo-Polish Friendship Month.
980 – 40g. brown and pink . . 45 35
981 **308** 60g. red and bistre . . . 25 10
DESIGN: 40g. Polish and Russian dancers.

1956. Ludwika Wawrzynska Commemoration.
982 **309** 40g. brown . . . . 95 1·50
983 60g. blue 35 10

310 "Lady with a Weasel" (Leonardo da Vinci) **311** Honey Bee and Hive

310a Music Quotation and Profiles of Chopin and Liszt

1956. International Campaign for Museums.
984 – 40g. green . . . . 2·25 1·40
985 – 60g. violet 95 10
986 **310** 1z.55 brown . . . . . . 1·90 25
DESIGNS: 40g. Niobe (bust); 60g. Madonna (Vit Stvosz).

1956. Stamp Day. Sheet 55 × 75 mm.
MS986a **310a** 4z. (+2z.) green . . 18·00 18·00

1956. 50th Death Anniv of Jan Dzierzon (apiarist).
987 **311** 40g. brown on yellow . . 1·10 25
988 – 60g. brown on yellow . . 25 10
DESIGN: 60g. Dr. J. Dzierzon.

312 Fencing **313** 15th-century Postman

1956. Olympic Games. Inscr "MELBOURNE 1956".
989 **312** 10g. brown and grey . . . 20 10
990 – 20g. lilac and brown . . . 25 10
991 – 25g. black and blue . . . 70 25
992 – 40g. brown and green . . 35 10
993 – 60g. brown and red . . . 60 10
994 – 1z.55 brown and violet . . 2·75 1·10
995 – 1z.55 brown and orange 1·25 35
DESIGNS: No. 990, Boxing; 991, Rowing; 992, Steeplechase; 993, Javelin throwing; 994, Gymnastics; 995, Long jumping (Elizabeth Dunska-krzesinska's gold medal).

1956. Re-opening of Postal Museum, Wroclaw.
996 **313** 60g. black on blue . . . . 3·00 2·75

314 Snow Crystals and Skier of 1907 **315** Apple Tree and Globe

1957. 50 Years of Skiing in Poland.
997 **314** 40g. blue 20 10
998 – 60g. green 20 10
999 – 1z. purple 45 35
DESIGNS (with snow crystals)—VERT: 60g. Skier jumping. HORIZ: 1z. Skier standing.

1957. U.N.O. Commemoration.
1000 **315** 5g. red and turquoise . . 25 10
1001 – 15g. blue and grey . . . 45 10
1002 – 40g. green and grey . . 80 60
MS1002a 55 × 70 mm. 1z.50 blue and green . . . . 15·00 15·00
DESIGNS—VERT: 15g. U.N.O. emblem; 40g. 1z.50, U.N.O. Headquarters, New York.

316 Skier **317** Winged Letter

1957. 12th Death Annivs of Bronislaw Czech and Hanna Marusarzowna (skiers).
1003 **316** 60g. brown 90 35
1004 60g. blue 45 10

1957. Air. 7th Polish National Philatelic Exhibition, Warsaw.
1005 **317** 4z.+2z. blue . . . . . . 3·00 3·00
MS1005a 55 × 70 mm. 4z.+2z. blue (T **317**) . . . . 7·00 6·25

318 Foil, Sword and Sabre on Map **319** Dr. S. Petrycy (philosopher)

1957. World Youth Fencing Championships, Warsaw.
1006 **318** 40g. purple 45 10
1007 – 60g. red 20 10
1008 – 60g. blue 20 10
DESIGNS: Nos. 1007/8 are arranged in se-tenant pairs in the sheet and together show two fencers duelling.

1957. Polish Doctors.
1009 **319** 10g. brown and blue . . 10 10
1010 – 20g. lake and green . . . 10 10
1011 – 40g. black and red . . . 10 10
1012 – 60g. purple and blue . . 45 25
1013 – 1z. blue and yellow . . . 20 10
1014 – 1z.35 brown and green 15 10
1015 – 2z.50 violet and red . . 35 10
1016 – 3z. brown and violet . . 45 10
PORTRAITS: 20g. Dr. W. Oczko; 40g. Dr. J. Sniadecki; 60g. Dr. T. Chalubinski; 1z. Dr. W. Bieganski; 1z.35, Dr. J. Dietl; 2z.50, Dr. B. Dybowski; 3z. Dr. H. Jordan.

320 Cycle Wheel and Flower **321** Fair Emblem

1957. 10th International Peace Cycle Race.
1017 **320** 60g. blue 25 10
1018 – 1z.50 red (Cyclist) . . . 45 25

1957. 26th International Fair, Poznan.
1019 **321** 60g. blue 25 25
1020 2z.50 green 25 25

322 Carline Thistle **323** Fireman

1957. Wild Flowers.
1021 **322** 60g. yellow, green & grey 35 10
1022 – 60g. green and blue . . . 35 10
1023 – 60g. olive and grey . . . 35 10
1024 – 60g. purple and green . . 60 35
1025 – 60g. purple and green . . 35 10

FLOWERS—VERT: No. 1022, Sea holly; 1023, Edelweiss; 1024, Lady's slipper orchid; 1025, Turk's cap lily.

1957. International Fire Brigades Conference, Warsaw. Inscr "KONGRES C.T.I.F. WARSZAWA 1957".
1026 **323** 40g. black and red . . . 10 10
1027 – 60g. green and red . . . 10 10
1028 – 2z.50 violet and red . . 25 10
DESIGNS: 60g. Flames enveloping child; 2z.50, Ear of corn in flames.

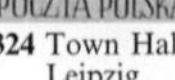

324 Town Hall, Leipzig
325 "The Letter" (after Fragonard)

1957. 4th Int Trade Union Congress, Leipzig.
1029 **324** 60g. violet 25 10

1957. Stamp Day.
1030 **325** 2z.50 green 60 10

326 Red Banner
327 Karol Libelt (founder)

1957. 40th Anniv of Russian Revolution.
1031 **326** 60g. red and blue . . . 10 10
1032 – 2z.50 brown and black 25 10
DESIGN: 2z.50, Lenin Monument, Poronin.

1957. Centenary of Poznan Scientific Society.
1033 **327** 60g. red 25 10

328 H. Wieniawski (violinist)
329 Ilyushin Il-14P over Steel Works

1957. 3rd Wieniawski Int Violin Competition.
1034 **328** 2z.50 blue 35 15

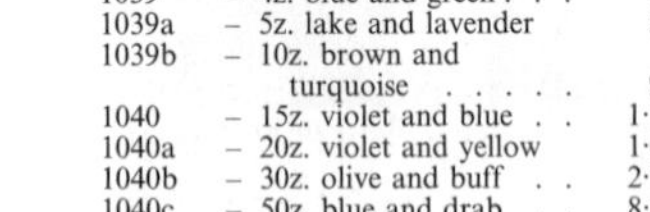

1957. Air.
1035 **329** 90g. black and pink . . 15 10
1036 – 1z.50 brown and salmon 15 10
1037 – 3z.40 sepia and buff . . 45 10
1038 – 3z.90 brown and yellow 90 60
1039 – 4z. blue and green . . . 45 10
1039a – 5z. lake and lavender 55 10
1039b – 10z. brown and turquoise 90 35
1040 – 15z. violet and blue . . 1·50 45
1040a – 20z. violet and yellow 1·60 80
1040b – 30z. olive and buff . . 2·75 1·10
1040c – 50z. blue and drab . . 8·25 1·10
DESIGNS—Ilyushin Il-14P over: 1z.50, Castle Square, Warsaw; 3z.40, Market, Cracow; 3z.90, Szczecin; 4z. Karkonosze Mountains; 5z. Old Market, Gdansk; 10z. Liw Castle; 15z. Lublin; 20z. Cable railway, Kasprowy Wierch; 30z. Porabka Dam; 50z. "Batory" (liner).
For stamp as No. 1039b, but printed in purple only, see No.1095.

330a J. A. Komensky (Comenius)
331 A. Strug

1957. 300th Anniv of Publication of Komensky's "Opera Didactica Omnia".
1041 **330a** 2z.50 red 35 10

1957. 20th Death Anniv of Andrzej Strug (writer).
1042 **331** 2z.50 brown 25 10

332 Joseph Conrad and Full-rigged Sailing Ship "Torrens"

1957. Birth Centenary of Joseph Conrad (Korzeniowski) (author).
1043 **332** 60g. brown on green . . 10 10
1044 2z.50 blue on pink . . . 50 10

333 Postman of 1558
334 Town Hall, Biecz

1958. 400th Anniv of Polish Postal Service (1st issue).
1045 **333** 2z.50 purple and blue . . 35 10
For similar stamps see Nos. 1063/7.

1958. Ancient Polish Town Halls.
1046 **334** 20g. green 10 10
1047 – 40g. brown (Wroclaw) 10 10
1048 – 60g. blue (Tarnow) (horiz) 10 10
1049 – 2z.10 lake (Gdansk) . . 15 10
1050 – 2z.50 violet (Zamosc) . . 55 35

335 Zander
336 Warsaw University

1958. Fishes.
1051 **335** 40g. yellow, black & blue 15 10
1052 – 60g. blue, indigo & green 25 10
1053 – 2z.10 multicoloured . . . 45 10
1054 – 2z.50 green, black & violet . . . . 1·50 45
1055 – 6z.40 multicoloured . . . 45 45
DESIGNS—VERT: 60g. Atlantic salmon; 2z.10, Northern pike; 2z.50, Brown trout. HORIZ 6z.40, European grayling.

1958. 140th Anniv of Warsaw University.
1056 **336** 2z.50 blue 35 10

337 Fair Emblem
338

1958. 27th International Fair, Poznan.
1057 **337** 2z.50 red and black . . . 35 10

1958. 7th International Gliding Championships.
1058 **338** 60g. black and blue . . . 10 10
1059 – 2z.50 black and grey . . 25 10
DESIGN: 2z.50, As Type **338** but design in reverse.

339 Armed Postman
340 Polar Bear on Iceberg

1958. 19th Anniv of Defence of Gdansk Post Office.
1060 **339** 60g. blue 10 10

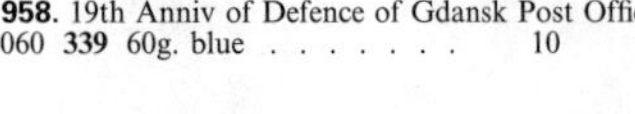
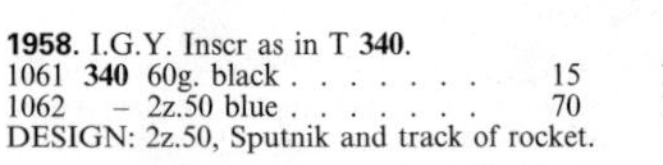

1958. I.G.Y. Inscr as in T **340**.
1061 **340** 60g. black 15 10
1062 – 2z.50 blue 70 10
DESIGN: 2z.50, Sputnik and track of rocket.

341 Tomb of Prosper Prowano (First Polish Postmaster)
342 Envelope, Quill and Postmark

1958. 400th Anniv of Polish Postal Service (2nd issue).
1063 **341** 40g. purple and blue . . 55 10
1064 – 60g. black and lilac . . . 15 10
1065 – 95g. violet and yellow . . 15 10
1066 – 2z.10 blue and grey . . . 80 45
1067 – 3z.40 brown & turquoise 55 35
DESIGNS: 60g. Mail coach and Church of Our Lady, Cracow; 95g. Mail coach (rear view); 2z.10, 16th-century postman; 3z.40, Kogge.
Nos. 1064/7 show various forms of modern transport in clear silhouette in the background.

1958. Stamp Day.
1068 **342** 60g. green, red and black 55 55

343 Partisans' Cross
345 Galleon

344 "Mail Coach in the Kielce District" (after painting by A. Kedzierskiego)

1958. 15th Anniv of Polish People's Army. Polish decorations.
1069 **343** 40g. buff, black and green 15 10
1070 – 60g. multicoloured . . . 15 10
1071 – 2z.50 multicoloured . . . 55 25
DESIGNS: 60g. Virtuti Military Cross; 2z.50, Grunwald Cross.

1958. Polish Postal Service 400th Anniv Exhibition.
1072 **344** 2z.50 black on buff . . . 90 1·10

1958. 350th Anniv of Polish Emigration to America.
1073 **345** 60g. green 25 10
1074 – 2z.50 red (Polish emigrants) 45 55

346 UNESCO Headquarters, Paris
347 S. Wyspianski (dramatist and painter)

1958. Inauguration of UNESCO Headquarters Building, Paris.
1075 **346** 2z.50 black and green . . 70 55

1958. Famous Poles.
1076 **347** 60g. violet 10 10
1077 – 2z.50 green 25 35
PORTRAIT: 2z.50, S. Moniuszko (composer).

348 "Human Rights"
349 Party Flag

348a Coach and Horses (after A. Kedzierski)

1958. 10th Anniv of Declaration of Human Rights.
1078 **348** 2z.50 lake and brown . . 60 10

1958. 400th Anniv of Polish Postal Service. Sheet 86 × 76 mm.
MS1078a **348a** 50z. blue . . . . 18·00 20·00

1958. 40th Anniv of Polish Communist Party.
1079 **349** 60g. red and purple . . . 10 10

350 Yacht
351 The "Guiding Hand"

1959. Sports.
1080 **350** 40g. ultramarine and blue 35 10
1081 – 60g. purple and salmon 35 10
1082 – 95g. purple and green . . 70 25
1083 – 2z. blue and green . . . 35 10
DESIGNS: 60g. Archer; 95g. Footballers; 2z. Horseman.

1959. 3rd Polish United Workers' Party Congress.
1084 **351** 40g. black, brown and red 10 10
1085 – 60g. multicoloured . . . 10 10
1086 – 1z.55 multicoloured . . . 45 25
DESIGNS—HORIZ: 60g. Hammer and ears of corn. VERT: 1z.55, Nowa Huta foundry.

352 Death Cap

1959. Mushrooms.
1087 **352** 20g. yellow, brown & green . . . . 2·25 10
1088 – 30g. multicoloured . . . 25 10
1089 – 40g. multicoloured . . . 55 10
1090 – 60g. multicoloured . . . 55 10
1091 – 1z. multicoloured 80 10
1092 – 2z.50 brown, green & bl 1·10 25
1093 – 3z.40 multicoloured . . . 1·25 35
1094 – 5z.60 brown, grn & yell 3·50 1·10
MUSHROOMS: 30g. Butter mushroom; 40g. Cep; 60g. Saffron milk cap; 1z. Chanterelle; 2z.50, Field mushroom; 3z.40, Fly agaric; 5z.60, Brown beech bolete.

1959. Air. 65 Years of Philately in Poland and 6th Polish Philatelic Assn Congress, Warsaw. As No. 1039b but in one colour only.
1095 10z. purple . . . . 3·25 3·75

353 "Storks" (after Chelmonski)
354 Miner

1959. Polish Paintings.
1096 **353** 40g. green 15 10
1097 – 60g. purple 35 10
1098 – 1z. black 35 10
1099 – 1z.50 brown 70 25
1100 – 6z.40 blue . . . . . . 3·25 1·10
PAINTINGS—VERT: 60g. "Motherhood" (Wyspianski); 1z. "Madame de Romanet" (Rodakowski); 1z.50, "Death" (Maiczewski). HORIZ: 6z.40, "The Sandmen" (Gierymski).

1959. 3rd Int Miners' Congress, Katowice.
1101 **354** 2z.50 multicoloured . . . 60 25

355 Sheaf of Wheat ("Agriculture") **356** Dr. L. Zamenhof

1959. 15th Anniv of People's Republic.
1102 **355** 40g. green and black . . 10 10
1103 – 60g. red and black . . . 10 10
1104 – 1z.50 blue and black . . 20 10
DESIGNS: 60g. Crane ("Building"); 1z.50, Corinthian column, and book ("Culture and Science").

1959. International Esperanto Congress, Warsaw and Birth Centenary of Dr. Ludwig Zamenhof (inventor of Esperanto).
1105 **356** 60g. black & green on green 15 10
1106 – 1z.50 green, red and violet on grey 80 35
DESIGN: 1z.50, Esperanto Star and globe.

357 "Flowering Pink" (Map of Austria) **358**

1959. 7th World Youth Festival, Vienna.
1107 **357** 60g. multicoloured . . . 10 10
1108 2z.50 multicoloured . . . 45 45

1959. 30th Anniv of Polish Airlines "LOT".
1109 **358** 60g. blue, violet and black 15 10

359 Parliament House, Warsaw

1959. 48th Inter-Parliamentary Union Conf, Warsaw.
1110 **359** 60g. green, red and black 10 10
1111 2z.50 purple, red & black 55 35

1959. Baltic States' International Philatelic Exhibition, Gdansk. No. 890 optd **BALPEX I - GDANSK 1959**.
1112 45g. brown on lemon . . . 70 70

361 Dove and Globe **362** Nurse with Bag

1959. 10th Anniv of World Peace Movement.
1113 **361** 60g. grey and blue . . . 20 10

1959. 40th Anniv of Polish Red Cross. Cross in red.
1114 **362** 40g. black and green . . 20 10
1115 – 60g. brown 20 10
1116 – 2z.50 black and red . . . 90 45
DESIGNS—VERT: 60g. Nurse with bottle and bandages. SQUARE—23 × 23 mm: 2z.50, J. H. Dunant.

363 Emblem of Polish–Chinese Friendship Society **364**

1959. Polish–Chinese Friendship.
1117 **363** 60g. multicoloured . . . 45 10
1118 2z.50 multicoloured . . . 25 10

1959. Stamp Day.
1119 **364** 60g. red, green & turq 15 10
1120 2z.50 blue, green and red 25 10

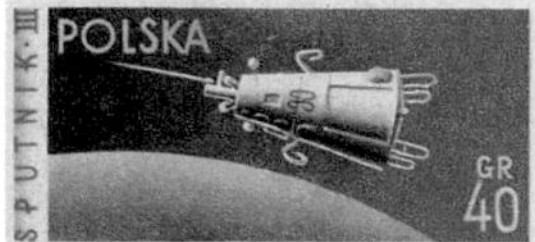

365 Sputnik "3"

1959. Cosmic Flights.
1121 **365** 40g. black and blue . . . 15 10
1122 – 60g. black and lake . . . 25 10
1123 – 2z.50 blue and green . . 1·10 60
DESIGNS: 60g. Rocket "Mieczta" encircling Sun; 2z.50, Moon rocket "Lunik 2".

366 Schoolgirl **367** Darwin

1959. "1000 Schools for Polish Millennium". Inscr as in T **366**.
1124 **366** 40g. brown and green . . 15 10
1125 – 60g. red, black and blue 15 10
DESIGN: 60g. Children going to school.

1959. Famous Scientists.
1126 **367** 20g. blue 10 10
1127 – 40g. olive (Mendeleev) 10 10
1128 – 60g. purple (Einstein) . . 15 10
1129 – 1z.50 brown (Pasteur) . . 25 10
1130 – 1z.55 green (Newton) . . 55 10
1131 – 2z.50 violet (Copernicus) 90 70

368 Costumes of Rzeszow **369** Costumes of Rzeszow

1959. Provincial Costumes (1st series).
1132 **368** 20g. black and green . . 10 10
1133 **369** 20g. black and green . . 10 10
1134 – 60g. brown and pink . . 15 10
1135 – 60g. brown and pink . . 15 10
1136 – 1z. red and blue 15 10
1137 – 1z. red and blue 15 10
1138 – 2z.50 green and grey . . 35 10
1139 – 2z.50 green and grey . . 35 10
1140 – 5z.60 blue and yellow . . 1·40 55
1141 – 5z.60 blue and yellow . . 1·40 55
DESIGNS—Male and female costumes of: Nos. 1134/5, Kurpic; 1136/7, Silesia; 1138/9, Mountain regions; 1140/1, Szamotuly.
See also Nos. 1150/9.

370 Piano **371** Polish 10k. Stamp of 1860 and Postmark

1960. 150th Birth Anniv of Chopin and Chopin Music Competition, Warsaw.
1142 **370** 60g. black and violet . . 45 10
1143 – 1z.50 black, red and blue 70 10
1144 – 2z.50 brown . . . . . . 2·25 1·50
DESIGNS—As Type **370**: 1z.50, Portion of Chopin's music. 25 × 39½ mm: 2z.50, Portrait of Chopin.

1960. Stamp Centenary.
1145 **371** 40g. red, blue and black 15 10
1146 – 60g. blue, black and violet 25 10
1147 – 1z.35 blue, red and grey 70 45
1148 – 1z.55 red, black & green 80 35
1149 – 2z.50 green, black & ol 1·40 70
DESIGNS: 1z.35, Emblem inscr "1860 1960". Reproductions of Polish stamps: 60g. No. 356; 1z.55, No. 533; 2z.50, No. 1030. With appropriate postmarks.

1960. Provincial Costumes (2nd series). As T **368/69**.
1150 40g. red and blue 10 10
1151 40g. red and blue 10 10
1152 2z. blue and yellow . . . 15 10
1153 2z. blue and yellow . . . 15 10
1154 3z.10 turquoise and green 25 10
1155 3z.10 turquoise and green 25 10
1156 3z.40 brown and turquoise 35 25
1157 3z.40 brown and turquoise 35 25
1158 6z.50 violet and green . . . 1·10 45
1159 6z.50 violet and green . . . 1·10 45
DESIGNS—Male and female costumes of: Nos. 1150/1, Cracow; 1152/3, Lowicz; 1154/5, Kujawy; 1156/7, Lublin; 1158/9, Lubusz.

372 Throwing the Discus **373** King Wladislaw Jagiello's Tomb, Wawel Castle

1960. Olympic Games, Rome. Rings and inscr in black.
1160 60g. blue (T **372**) 15 10
1161 60g. mauve (Running) . . . 15 10
1162 60g. violet (Cycling) 15 10
1163 60g. turq (Show jumping) 15 10
1164 2z.50 blue (Trumpeters) . . 70 35
1165 2z.50 brown (Boxing) . . . 70 35
1166 2z.50 red (Olympic flame) 70 35
1167 2z.50 green (Long jump) . . 70 35
Stamps of the same value were issued together, se-tenant, forming composite designs illustrating a complete circuit of the stadium track.

1960. 550th Anniv of Battle of Grunwald.
1168 **373** 60g. brown 25 10
1169 – 90g. green 60 35
1170 – 2z.50 black . . . . . . 2·75 1·50
DESIGNS—As Type **373**: 90g. Proposed Grunwald Monument. HORIZ: 78 × 35½ mm: 2z.50, "Battle of Grunwald" (after Jan Matejko).

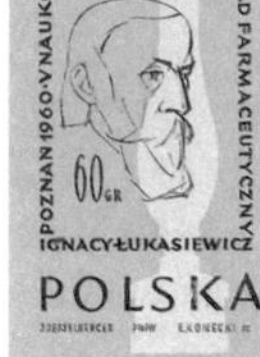

374 1860 Stamp and Postmark **375** Lukasiewicz (inventor of petrol lamp)

1960. International Philatelic Exn, Warsaw.
1171 **374** 10z.+10z. red, black and blue . . . . 6·25 8·00

1960. Lukasiewicz Commemoration and 5th Pharmaceutical Congress. Poznan.
1172 **375** 60g. black and yellow . . 15 10

376 "The Annunciation" **377** Paderewski

1960. Altar Wood Carvings of St. Mary's Church, Cracow, by Veit Stoss.
1173 **376** 20g. blue 25 10
1174 – 30g. brown 15 10
1175 – 40g. violet 25 10
1176 – 60g. green 25 10
1177 – 2z.50 red . . . . 1·10 25
1178 – 5z.60 brown . . . . . . 4·25 4·75
MS1178a 86 × 107 mm. 10z. black 8·00 6·50
DESIGNS: 30g. "The Nativity"; 40g. "Homage of the Three Kings"; 60g. "The Resurrection"; 2z.50, "The Ascension"; 5z.60, "The Descent of the Holy Ghost". VERT: (72 × 95 mm). 10z. The Assumption of the Virgin.

1960. Birth Centenary of Paderewski.
1179 **377** 2z.50 black 35 35

1960. Stamp Day. Optd **DZIEN ZNACZKA 1960**.
1180 **371** 40g. red, blue and black 1·25 70

379 Gniezno **380** Great Bustard

1960. Old Polish Towns as T **379**.
1181 5g. brown 10 10
1182 10g. green 10 10
1183 20g. brown 10 10
1184 40g. red 10 10
1185 50g. violet 10 10
1186 60g. lilac 10 10
1187 60g. blue 10 10
1188 80g. blue 15 10
1189 90g. brown 15 10
1190 95g. green 35 10
1191 1z. red and lilac 15 10
1192 1z.15 green and orange . . 35 10
1193 1z.35 mauve and green . . . 15 10
1194 1z.50 brown and blue . . . 35 10
1195 1z.55 lilac and yellow . . . 35 10
1196 2z. blue and lilac 20 10
1197 2z.10 brown and yellow . . 20 10
1198 2z.50 violet and green . . . 25 10
1199 3z.10 red and grey 35 35
1200 5z.60 grey and green 60 35
TOWNS: 10g. Cracow; 20g. Warsaw; 40g. Poznan; 50g. Plock; 60g. mauve, Kalisz; 60g. blue, Tczew; 80g. Frombork; 90g. Torum; 95g. Puck; 1z. Slupsk; 1z.15, Gdansk; 1z.35, Wroclaw; 1z.50, Szczecin; 1z.55, Opole; 2z. Kolobrzeg; 2z.10, Legnica; 2z.50, Katowice; 3z.10, Lodz; 5z.60, Walbrzych.

1960. Birds. Multicoloured.
1201 10g. Type **380** 10 10
1202 20g. Common Raven . . . 10 10
1203 30g. Great cormorant . . . 10 10
1204 40g. Black stork 25 10
1205 50g. Eagle owl 55 10
1206 60g. White-tailed sea eagle 55 10
1207 75g. Golden eagle 55 10
1208 90g. Short-toed eagle . . . 60 35
1209 2z.50 Rock thrush . . . . 3·25 1·75
1210 4z. River kingfisher . . . . 2·75 1·25
1211 5z.60 Wallcreeper . . . . . 4·50 1·40
1212 6z.50 European roller . . . 6·50 3·25

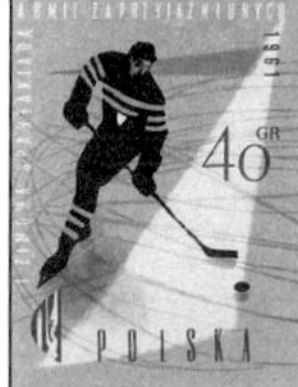

381 Front page of Newspaper "Proletaryat" (1883) **382** Ice Hockey

1961. 300th Anniv of Polish Newspaper Press.
1213 – 40g. green, blue and black 55 25
1214 **381** 60g. yellow, red and black 55 25
1215 – 2z.50 blue, violet & black . . . . 3·25 2·75
DESIGNS—Newspaper front page: 40g. "Mercuriusz" (first issue, 1661); 2z.50, "Rzeczpospolita" (1944).

1961. 1st Winter Military Spartakiad.
1216 **382** 40g. black, yellow & lilac 35 10
1217 – 60g. multicoloured . . . 95 15
1218 – 1z. multicoloured . . . . 5·25 2·75
1219 – 1z.50 black, yell & turq 90 35
DESIGNS: 60g. Ski jumping; 1z. Rifle-shooting; 1z.50, Slalom.

383 Congress Emblem **384** Yuri Gagarin

1961. 4th Polish Engineers' Conference.
1220 **383** 60g. black and red . . . 15 10

1961. World's 1st Manned Space Flight.
1221 **384** 40g. black, red and brown 60 10
1222 – 60g. red, black and blue 60 35
DESIGN: 60g. Globe and star.

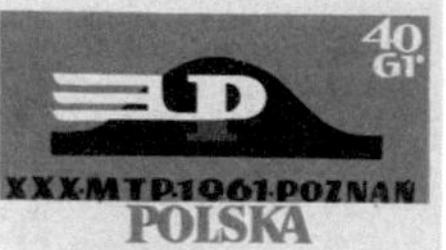

385 Fair Emblem

1961. 30th International Fair, Poznan.
1223 **385** 40g. black, red and blue 10 10
1224 1z.50 black, blue and red 25 10
See also No. **MS**1245a.

386 King Mieszko I

1961. Famous Poles (1st issue).
1225 **386** 60g. black and blue . . . 10 10
1226 – 60g. black and red . . . 10 10
1227 – 60g. black and green . . 10 10
1228 – 60g. black and violet . . 80 25
1229 – 60g. black and brown . . 10 10
1230 – 60g. black and olive . . 10 10
PORTRAITS: No. 1226, King Casimire the Great; 1227, King Casmir Jagiellon; 1228, Copernicus; 1229, A. F. Modrzewski; 1230, Kosciuszko.
See also Nos. 1301/6 and 1398/1401.

387 "Leskov" (trawler support ship)

1961. Shipbuilding Industry. Multicoloured.
1231 60g. Type **387** 25 10
1232 1z.55 "Severodvinsk" (depot ship) 35 10
1233 2z.50 "Rambutan" (coaster) 60 35
1234 3z.40 "Krynica" (freighter) 90 45
1235 4z. "B 54" freighter . . . . 1·25 70
1236 5z.60 "Bavsk" (tanker) . . . 4·25 1·90
SIZES: 2z.50, As Type **387**; 5z.60, 108 × 21 mm; Rest, 81 × 21 mm.

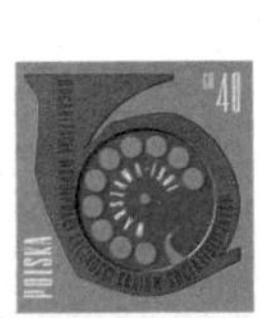
388 Posthorn and Telephone Dial

389 Opole Seal

1961. Communications Ministers' Conference, Warsaw.
1237 **388** 40g. red, green and blue 10 10
1238 – 60g. violet, yellow & purple 15 10
1239 – 2z.50 ultram, blue & bis 55 10
MS1239a 108 × 66 mm. Nos. 1237/9 (sold at 5z.) . . . . 5·25 3·25
DESIGNS: 60g. Posthorn and radar screen; 2z.50, Posthorn and conference emblem.

1961. Polish Western Provinces.
1240 40g. brown on buff 15 10
1241 40g. brown on buff 15 10
1242 60g. violet on pink 15 10
1243 60g. violet on pink 15 10
1243a 95g. green on blue 25 25
1243b 95g. green on blue 25 25
1244 2z.50 sage on green . . . 45 25
1245 2z.50 sage on green . . . 45 25
DESIGNS—VERT: No. 1240, Type **389**; 1242, Henry IV's tomb; 1243a, Seal of Conrad II; 1244, Prince Barnim's seal. HORIZ: No. 1241, Opole cement works; 1243, Wroclaw apartment-house; 1243b, Factory interior, Zielona Gora; 1245, Szczecin harbour.
See also Nos. 1308/13.

1961. "Intermess II" Stamp Exhibition. Sheet 121 × 51 mm containing pair of No. 1224 but imperf.
MS1245a 1z.50 (× 2) (sold at 4z.50+2z.50) . . . . 5·50 3·50

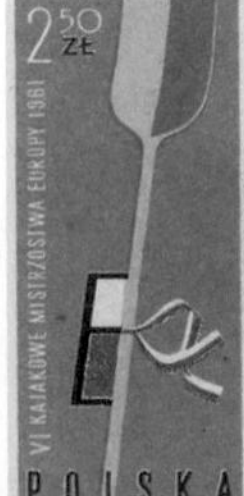

390 Beribboned Paddle

391 Titov and Orbit within Star

1961. 6th European Canoeing Championships. Multicoloured.
1246 40g. Two canoes within letter "E" (horiz) 15 10
1247 60g. Two four-seater canoes at finishing post (horiz) 15 10
1248 2z.50 Type **390** . . . . . . 1·25 60

1961. 2nd Russian Manned Space Flight.
1249 **391** 40g. black, red and pink 45 10
1250 – 60g. blue and black . . . 45 10
DESIGN: 60g. Dove and spaceman's orbit around globe.

392 Monument

393 P.K.O. Emblem and Ant

1961. 40th Anniv of 3rd Silesian Uprising.
1251 **392** 60g. grey and green . . 10 10
1252 – 1z.55 grey and blue . . . 25 10
DESIGN: 1z.55, Cross of Silesian uprisers.

1961. Savings Month.
1253 – 40g. red, yellow and black 15 10
1254 **393** 60g. brown, yellow & black 15 10
1255 – 60g. blue, violet and pink 15 10
1256 – 60g. green, red and black 15 10
1257 – 2z.50 mauve, grey & black . . . . 2·25 1·25
DESIGNS: No. 1253, Savings Bank motif; 1255, Bee; 1256, Squirrel; 1257, Savings Bank book.

394 "Mail Cart" (after J. Chelmonski)

1961. Stamp Day and 40th Anniv of Postal Museum.
1258 **394** 60g. brown 25 10
1259 60g. green 25 10

395 Congress Emblem

396 Emblem of Kopasyni Mining Family, 1284

1961. 5th W.F.T.U. Congress, Moscow.
1260 **395** 60g. black 15 10

1961. Millenary of Polish Mining Industry.
1261 **396** 40g. purple and orange 15 10
1262 – 60g. grey and blue . . . 15 10
1263 – 2z.50 green and black . . 55 25
DESIGNS: 60g. 14th-century seal of Bytom; 2z.50, Emblem of Int Mine Constructors' Congress, Warsaw, 1958.

397 Child and Syringe

398 Cogwheel and Wheat

1961. 15th Anniv of UNICEF.
1264 **397** 40g. black and blue . . . 10 10
1265 – 60g. black and orange 10 10
1266 – 2z.50 black and turquoise 60 25
DESIGNS—HORIZ: 60g. Children of three races. VERT: 2z.50, Mother and child, and feeding bottle.

1961. 15th Economic Co-operative Council Meeting, Warsaw.
1267 **398** 40g. red, yellow and blue 15 10
1268 – 60g. red, blue & ultram 15 10
DESIGN: 60g. Oil pipeline map, E. Europe.

399 Caterpillar-hunter

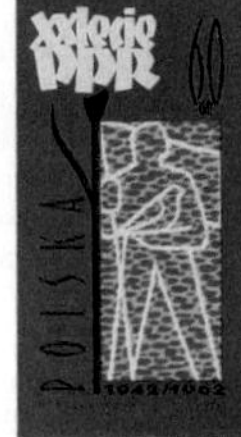

400 Worker with Flag and Dove

1961. Insects. Multicoloured.
1269 20g. Type **399** 15 10
1270 30g. Violet ground beetle . . 15 10
1271 40g. Alpine longhorn beetle 15 10
1272 50g. "Cerambyx cerdo" (longhorn beetle) 15 10
1273 60g. "Carabus auronitens" (ground beetle) 15 10
1274 80g. Stag beetle 25 10
1275 1z.15 Clouded apollo (butterfly) 55 10
1276 1z.35 Death's-head hawk moth 35 10
1277 1z.50 Scarce swallowtail (butterfly) 60 10
1278 1z.55 Apollo (butterfly) . . 60 10
1279 2z.50 Red wood ant . . . . 1·10 45
1280 5z.60 White-tailed bumble bee . . . . 5·75 3·50
Nos. 1275/80 are square, 36½ × 36½ mm.

1962. 20th Anniv of Polish Workers' Coalition.
1281 **400** 60g. brown, black and red 10 10
1282 – 60g. bistre, black and red 10 10
1283 – 60g. blue, black and red 10 10
1284 – 60g. grey, black and red 10 10
1285 – 60g. blue, black and red 10 10
DESIGNS: No. 1282, Steersman; 1283, Worker with hammer; 1284, Soldier with weapon; 1285, Worker with trowel and rifle.

401 Two Skiers Racing

1962. F.I.S. Int Ski Championships, Zakopane.
1286 **401** 40g. blue, grey and red 10 10
1287 40g. blue, brown and red 90 25
1288 – 60g. blue, grey and red 20 10
1289 – 60g. blue, brown and red 1·10 60
1290 – 1z.50 blue, grey and red 35 10
1291 – 1z.50 violet, grey and red 1·75 60
MS1291a 67 × 80 mm. 10z. (+5z.) blue, grey and red . . . . . . 4·25 4·00
DESIGNS—HORIZ: 60g. Skier racing. VERT: 1z.50, Ski jumper; 10z. F.I.S. emblem.

402 Majdanek Monument

1962. Concentration Camp Monuments.
1292 – 40g. blue 10 10
1293 **402** 60g. black 25 10
1294 – 1z.50 violet 35 15
DESIGNS—VERT: (20 × 31 mm): 40g. Broken carnations and portion of prison clothing (Auschwitz camp); 1z.50, Treblinka monument.

403 Racing Cyclist

1962. 15th International Peace Cycle Race.
1295 **403** 60g. black and blue . . . 25 10
1296 – 2z.50 black and yellow 55 10
1297 – 3z.40 black and violet . . 90 45
DESIGNS—74½ × 22 mm: 2z.50, Cyclists & "XV". As Type **403**: 3z.40, Arms of Berlin, Prague and Warsaw, and cycle wheel.

405 Lenin Walking

406 Gen. K. Swierczewski-Walter (monument)

1962. 50th Anniv of Lenin's Sojourn in Poland.
1298 **405** 40g. green and light green 45 10
1299 – 60g. lake and pink . . . 15 10
1300 – 2z.50 brown and yellow 45 10
DESIGNS: 60g. Lenin; 2z.50, Lenin wearing cap, and St. Mary's Church, Cracow.

1962. Famous Poles (2nd issue). As T **386**.
1301 60g. black and green 10 10
1302 60g. black and brown . . . 10 10
1303 60g. black and blue 40 10
1304 60g. black and bistre . . . 10 10
1305 60g. black and purple . . . 10 10
1306 60g. black and turquoise . . 10 10
PORTRAITS: No. 1301, A. Mickiewicz (poet); 1302, J. Slowacki (poet); 1303, F. Chopin (composer); 1304, R. Traugutt (patriot); 1305, J. Dabrowski (revolutionary); 1306, Maria Konopnicka (poet).

1962. 15th Death Anniv of Gen. K. Swierczewski-Walter (patriot).
1307 **406** 60g. black 15 10

1962. Polish Northern Provinces. As T **389**.
1308 60g. blue and grey 10 10
1309 60g. blue and grey 10 10
1310 1z.55 brown and yellow . . 20 10
1311 1z.55 brown and yellow . . 20 10
1312 2z.50 slate and grey 55 33
1313 2z.50 slate and grey 55 35
DESIGNS—VERT: No. 1308, Princess Elizabeth's seal; 1310, Gdansk Governor's seal; 1312, Frombork Cathedral. HORIZ: No. 1309, Insulators factory, Szczecinek; 1311, Gdansk shipyard; 1313, Laboratory of Agricultural College, Kortowo.

407 "Crocus scepusiensis" (Borb)

408 "The Poison Well", after J. Malczewski

1962. Polish Protected Plants. Plants in natural colours.
1314 **407** 60g. yellow 15 10
1315 A 60g. brown 70 35
1316 B 60g. pink 15 10
1317 C 90g. green 25 10
1318 D 90g. olive 25 10
1319 E 90g. green 25 10
1320 F 1z.50 blue 35 10
1321 G 1z.50 green 45 10
1322 H 1z.50 turquoise 35 10
1323 I 2z.50 green 80 55
1324 J 2z.50 turquoise 80 55
1325 K 2z.50 blue . . . . 1·10 55
PLANTS: A, "Platanthera bifolia" (Rich); B, "Aconitum callibotryon" (Rchb.); C, "Gentiana clusii" (Perr. et Song); D, "Dictamnus albus" (L.); E, "Nymphaca alba" (L.); F, "Daphne mezereum" (L.); G, "Pulsatilla vulgaris" (Mill.); H, "Anemone silvestris" (L.); I, "Trollius europaeus" (L.); J, "Galanthus nivalis" (L.); K, "Adonis vernalis" (L.).

1962. F.I.P. Day ("Federation Internationale de Philatelie").
1326 **408** 60g. black on cream . . 25 25

409 Pole Vault

1962. 7th European Athletic Championships, Belgrade. Multicoloured.
1327 40g. Type **409** 10 10
1328 60g. 400 m relay 10 10
1329 90g. Throwing the javelin 10 10
1330 1z. Hurdling 10 10
1331 1z.50 High-jumping 10 10
1332 1z.55 Throwing the discus 10 10
1333 2z.50 100 m final 45 15
1334 3z.40 Throwing the hammer 95 35

410 "Anopheles sp."

411 Cosmonauts "in flight"

1962. Malaria Eradication.
1335 **410** 60g. brown and turquoise 10 10
1336 – 1z.50 multicoloured . . . 15 10
1337 – 2z.50 multicoloured . . . 60 25
MS1337a 60 × 81 mm. 3z. multicoloured . . . . 1·25 45
DESIGNS: 1z.50, Malaria parasites in blood; 2z.50, Cinchona plant; 3z. Anopheles mosquito.

1962. 1st "Team" Manned Space Flight.
1338 **411** 60g. green, black & violet 15 10
1339 – 2z.50 red, black and turquoise 45 25
MS1339a 70 × 94 mm. 10z. red, black and blue . . . . 2·75 2·00
DESIGN: 2z.50, Two stars (representing space-ships) in orbit.

412 "A Moment of Determination" (after painting by A. Kamienski)

413 Mazovian Princes' Mansion, Warsaw

1962. Stamp Day.
1340 **412** 60g. black 10 10
1341 2z.50 brown 45 20

1962. 25th Anniv of Polish Democratic Party.
1342 **413** 60g. black on red . . . 15 10

414 Cruiser "Aurora"

1962. 45th Anniv of Russian Revolution.
1343 **414** 60g. blue and red . . . 15 10

415 J. Korczak (bust after Dunikowski)

1962. 20th Death Anniv of Janusz Korczak (child educator).
1344 **415** 40g. sepia, bistre & brn 15 10
1345 – 60g. multicoloured . . . 35 10
1346 – 90g. multicoloured . . . 35 10
1347 – 1z. multicoloured 35 10
1348 – 2z.50 multicoloured . . . 70 10
1349 – 5z.60 multicoloured . . . 2·40 40
DESIGNS: 60g. to 5z.60, Illustrations from Korczak's children's books.

416 Old Town, Warsaw

1962. 5th T.U. Congress, Warsaw.
1350 **416** 3z.40 multicoloured . . . 70 25

417 Master Buncombe

419 Tractor and Wheat

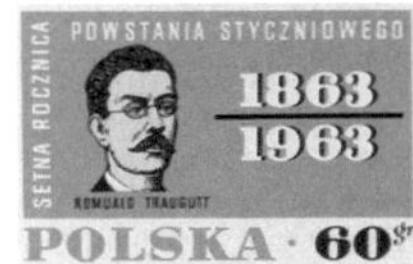

418 R. Traugutt (insurgent leader)

1962. Maria Konopnicka's Fairy Tale "The Dwarfs and Orphan Mary". Multicoloured.
1351 40g. Type **417** 45 10
1352 60g. Lardie the Fox and Master Buncombe . . . . 1·40 1·00
1353 1z.50 Bluey the Frog making music 55 10
1354 1z.55 Peter's kitchen 55 25
1355 2z.50 Saraband's concert in Nightingale Valley 70 70
1356 3z.40 Orphan Mary and Subearthy . . . . 2·25 1·60

1963. Centenary of January (1863) Rising.
1357 **418** 60g. black, pink & turq 15 10

1963. Freedom from Hunger. Multicoloured.
1358 40g. Type **419** 15 10
1359 60g. Millet and hoeing . . . 80 25
1360 2z.50 Rice and mechanical harvester 70 35

420 Cocker Spaniel

1963. Dogs.
1361 **420** 20g. red, black and lilac 10 10
1362 – 30g. black and red . . . 10 10
1363 – 40g. ochre, black and lilac 25 10
1364 – 50g. ochre, black and blue 25 10
1365 – 60g. black and blue . . . 25 10
1366 – 1z. black and green . . . 70 25
1367 – 2z.50 brown, yell & blk 1·10 45
1368 – 3z.40 black and red . . . 3·00 1·40
1369 – 6z.50 black and yellow 6·00 3·75
DOGS—HORIZ: 30g. Sheep-dog; 40g. Boxer; 2z.50, Gun-dog "Ogar"; 6z.50, Great Dane. VERT: 50g. Airedale terrier; 60g. French bulldog; 1z. French poodle; 3z.40, Podhale sheep-dog.

421 Egyptian Galley (15th century B.C.)

422 Insurgent

1963. Sailing Ships (1st series).
1370 **421** 5g. brown on bistre . . . 10 10
1371 – 10g. turquoise on green 15 10
1372 – 20g. blue on grey . . . 15 10
1373 – 30g. black on olive . . . 20 10
1374 – 40g. blue on blue 20 10
1375 – 60g. purple on brown . . 35 10
1376 – 1z. black on blue 40 10
1377 – 1z.15 green on pink . . 65 10
SHIPS: 10g. Phoenician merchantman (15th cent B.C.); 20g. Greek trireme (5th cent B.C.); 30g. Roman merchantman (3rd cent A.D.); 40g. "Mora" (Norman ship, 1066); 60g. Hanse kogge (14th cent); 1z. Hulk (16th cent); 1z.15, Carrack (15th cent).
See also Nos. 1451/66.

1963. 20th Anniv of Warsaw Ghetto Uprising.
1378 **422** 2z.50 brown and blue . . 30 10

423 Centenary Emblem

424 Lizard

1963. Red Cross Centenary.
1379 **423** 2z.50 red, blue and yellow 65 20

1963. Protected Reptiles and Amphibians. Reptiles in natural colours: inscr in black: background colours given.
1380 **424** 30g. green 10 10
1381 – 40g. olive 10 10
1382 – 50g. brown 10 10
1383 – 60g. grey 10 10
1384 – 90g. green 10 10
1385 – 1z.15 grey 10 10
1386 – 1z.35 blue 10 10
1387 – 1z.50 turquoise 30 15
1388 – 1z.55 pale blue 30 10
1389 – 2z.50 lavender 30 20
1390 – 3z. green 75 20
1391 – 3z.40 purple . . . . . . 1·90 1·90
DESIGNS: 40g. Copperhead (snake); 50g. Marsh tortoise; 60g. Grass snake; 90g. Blindworm; 1z.15, Tree toad; 1z.35, Mountain newt; 1z.50, Crested newt; 1z.55, Green toad; 2z.50, "Bombina" toad; 3z. Salamander; 3z.40, "Natterjack" (toad).

425 Epee, Foil, Sabre and Knight's Helmet

1963. World Fencing Championships, Gdansk.
1392 **425** 20g. yellow and brown 10 10
1393 – 40g. light blue and blue 10 10
1394 – 60g. vermilion and red 10 10
1395 – 1z.15 light green & green 10 10
1396 – 1z.55 red and violet . . 35 10
1397 – 6z.50 yellow, pur & bis 1·25 60
MS1397a 110 × 93 mm. Nos. 1393/6 30·00 30·00
DESIGNS—HORIZ: Fencers with background of: 40g. Knights jousting; 60g. Dragoons in sword-fight; 1z.15, 18th-century duellists; 1z.55, Old Gdansk. VERT: 6z.50, Inscription and Arms of Gdansk.

1963. Famous Poles (3rd issue). As T **386**.
1398 60g. black and brown . . . 10 10
1399 60g. black and brown . . . 10 10
1400 60g. black and turquoise . . 10 10
1401 60g. black and green 10 10
PORTRAITS: No. 1398, L. Warynski (patriot); 1399, L. Krzywicki (economist); 1400, M. Sklodowska-Curie (scientist); 1401, K. Swierczewski (patriot).

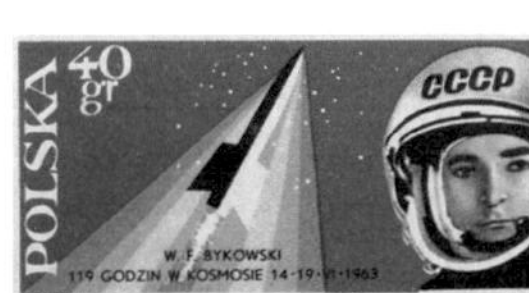

426 Bykovsky and "Vostok 5"

1963. 2nd "Team" Manned Space Flights.
1402 **426** 40g. black, green and blue 10 10
1403 – 60g. black, blue and green 10 10
1404 – 6z.50 multicoloured . . . 90 30
DESIGNS: 60g. Tereshkova and "Vostok 6"; 6z.50, "Vostoks 5 and 6" in orbit.

427 Basketball

1963. 13th European (Men's) Basketball Championships, Wroclaw.
1405 **427** 40g. multicoloured . . . 10 10
1406 – 50g. green, black and pink 10 10
1407 – 60g. black, green and red 10 10
1408 – 90g. multicoloured . . . 10 10
1409 – 2z.50 multicoloured . . . 20 10
1410 – 5z.60 multicoloured . . . 1·50 40
MS1410a 76 × 86 mm. 10z. (+5z.) multicoloured . . . . 2·25 1·10
DESIGNS: 50g. to 2z.50, As Type **427** but with ball, players and hands in various positions; 5z.60, Hands placing ball in net; 10z. Town Hall, People's Hall and Arms of Wroclaw.

428 Missile

1963. 20th Anniv of Polish People's Army. Multicoloured.
1411 20g. Type **428** 10 10
1412 40g. "Blyskawica" (destroyer) 10 10
1413 60g. PZL-106 Kruk (airplane) 10 10
1414 1z.15 Radar scanner 10 10
1415 1z.35 Tank 10 10
1416 1z.55 Missile carrier 10 10
1417 2z.50 Amphibious troop carrier 10 10
1418 3z. Ancient warrior, modern soldier and two swords 30 20

429 "A Love Letter" (after Czachorski)

1963. Stamp Day.
1419 **429** 60g. brown 20 10

1963. Visit of Soviet Cosmonauts to Poland. Nos. 1402/4 optd **23-28. X. 1963** and **w Polsce** together with Cosmonauts' names.
1420 **426** 40g. black, green and blue 20 10
1421 – 60g. black, blue and green 30 10
1422 – 6z.50 multicoloured . . . 1·40 75

431 Tsiolkovsky's Rocket and Formula

432 Mazurian Horses

1963. "The Conquest of Space". Inscr in black.
1423 **431** 30g. turquoise 10 10
1424 – 40g. olive 10 10
1425 – 50g. violet 10 10
1426 – 60g. brown 10 10
1427 – 1z. turquoise 10 10
1428 – 1z.50 red 10 10
1429 – 1z.55 blue 10 10
1430 – 2z.50 purple 10 10
1431 – 5z.60 green 65 30
1432 – 6z.50 turquoise . . . . 1·10 30
MS1432a 78 × 106 mm. Nos. 1431/2 (two of each) . . . . 30·00 30·00
DESIGNS: 40g. "Sputnik 1"; 50g. "Explorer 1"; 60g. Banner carried by "Lunik 2"; 1z. "Lunik 3"; 1z.50, "Vostok 1"; 1z.55, "Friendship 7"; 2z.50, "Vostoks 3 and 4"; 5z.60, "Mariner 2"; 6z.50, "Mars 1".

1963. Polish Horse-breeding. Multicoloured.
1433 20g. Arab stallion "Comet" 15 10
1434 30g. Wild horses 15 10
1435 40g. Sokolski horse 20 10
1436 50g. Arab mares and foals 20 10
1437 60g. Type **432** 20 10
1438 90g. Steeplechasers 45 10
1439 1z.55 Arab stallion "Witez II" 80 10
1440 2z.50 Head of Arab horse (facing right) . . . . . . 1·50 10
1441 4z. Mixed breeds . . . . . 3·75 60
1442 6z.50 Head of Arab horse (facing left) . . . . . . 5·25 2·40
SIZES—TRIANGULAR (55 × 27½ mm): 20, 30, 40g. HORIZ: (75 × 26 mm): 50, 90g., 4z. VERT: as Type **432**: 1z.55, 2z.50, 6z.50.

433 Ice Hockey

1964. Winter Olympic Games, Innsbruck. Mult.
1443 20g. Type **433** 10 10
1444 30g. Slalom 10 10

1445 40g. Downhill skiing 10 10
1446 60g. Speed skating 10 10
1447 1z. Ski-jumping 10 10
1448 2z.50 Tobogganing 10 10
1449 5z.60 Cross-country skiing 75 60
1450 6z.50 Pairs, figure skating 1·50 80
MS1450a 110 × 94 mm. Nos. 1448 and 1450 (two of each) . . . . 23·00 23·00

1964. Sailing Ships (2nd series). As T **421** but without coloured backgrounds. Some new designs.
1451 **421** 5g. brown 10 10
1452 – 10g. green 10 10
1453 – 20g. blue 10 10
1454 – 30g. bronze 10 10
1455 – 40g. blue 10 10
1456 – 60g. purple 10 10
1457 – 1z. brown 15 10
1458 – 1z.15 brown 15 10
1459 – 1z.35 blue 15 10
1460 – 1z.50 purple 15 10
1461 – 1z.55 black 15 10
1462 – 2z. violet 15 10
1463 – 2z.10 green 15 10
1464 – 2z.50 mauve 20 10
1465 – 3z. olive 30 10
1466 – 3z.40 brown 30 10
SHIPS—HORIZ: 10g. to 1z.15, As Nos. 1370/7; 1z.50, "Ark Royal" (English galleon, 1587); 2z.10, Ship of the line (18th cent); 2z.50, Sail frigate (19th cent); 3z. "Flying Cloud" (clipper, 19th cent). VERT: 1z.35, Columbus's "Santa Maria"; 1z.55, "Wodnik" (Polish warship, 17th cent); 2z. Dutch fleute (17th cent); 3z.40, "Dar Pomorza" (cadet ship).

434 "Flourishing Tree"

1964. 20th Anniv of People's Republic (1st issue).
1467 **434** 60g. multicoloured . . . 10 10
1468 – 60g. black, yellow and red 10 10
DESIGN: No. 1468, Emblem composed of symbols of agriculture and industry.
See also Nos. 1497/1506.

435 European Cat

436 Casimir the Great (founder)

1964. Domestic Cats. As T **435**.
1469 30g. black and yellow . . . 15 10
1470 40g. multicoloured 15 10
1471 50g. black, turquoise & yellow 15 10
1472 60g. multicoloured 35 10
1473 90g. multicoloured 30 10
1474 1z.35 multicoloured 30 10
1475 1z.55 multicoloured 50 10
1476 2z.50 yellow, black and violet 80 45
1477 3z.40 multicoloured . . . . 1·90 80
1478 6z.50 multicoloured . . . . 3·75 1·90
CATS—European: 30, 40, 60g., 1z.55, 2z.50, 6z.50. Siamese: 50g. Persian: 90g., 1z.35, 3z.40.
Nos. 1472/5 are horiz.

1964. 600th Anniv of Jagiellonian University, Cracow.
1479 **436** 40g. purple 10 10
1480 – 40g. green 10 10
1481 – 60g. violet 10 10
1482 – 60g. blue 10 10
1483 – 2z.50 sepia 65 10
PORTRAITS: No. 1480, Hugo Kollataj (educationist and politician); 1481, Jan Dlugosz (geographer and historian); 1482, Copernicus (astronomer); 1483 (36 × 37 mm), King Wladislaw Jagiello and Queen Jadwiga.

437 Northern Lapwing

1964. Birds. Multicoloured.
1484 30g. Type **437** 15 10
1485 40g. Bluethroat 15 10
1486 50g. Black-tailed godwit . . 15 10
1487 60g. Osprey (vert) 20 10
1488 90g. Grey heron (vert) . . . 30 10
1489 1z.35 Little gull (vert) . . . 45 10
1490 1z.55 Common shoveler . . 45 10
1491 5z.60 Black-throated diver 1·00 30
1492 6z.50 Great crested grebe . . 1·40 65

438 Red Flag on Brick Wall

1964. 4th Polish United Workers' Party Congress, Warsaw. Inscr "PZPR". Multicoloured.
1493 60g. Type **438** 10 10
1494 60g. Beribboned hammer . . 10 10
1495 60g. Hands reaching for Red Flag 10 10
1496 60g. Hammer and corn emblems 10 10

439 Factory and Cogwheel

441 Battle Scene

440 Gdansk Shipyard

1964. 20th Anniv of People's Republic (2nd issue).
1497 **439** 60g. black and blue . . . 10 10
1498 – 60g. black and green . . 10 10
1499 – 60g. red and orange . . 10 10
1500 – 60g. blue and grey . . . 10 10
1501 **440** 60g. blue and green . . . 10 10
1502 – 60g. violet and mauve 10 10
1503 – 60g. brown and violet . . 10 10
1504 – 60g. bronze and green 10 10
1505 – 60g. purple and red . . . 10 10
1506 – 60g. brown and yellow 10 10
DESIGNS—As Type **439**: No. 1498, Tractor and ear of wheat; 1499, Mask and symbols of the arts; 1500, Atomic symbol and book. As Type **440**: No. 1502, Lenin Foundry, Nowa Huta; 1503, Cement Works, Chelm; 1504, Turoszow power station; 1505, Petro-chemical plant, Plock; 1506, Tarnobrzeg sulphur mine.

1964. 20th Anniv of Warsaw Insurrection.
1507 **441** 60g. multicoloured . . . 10 10

442 Relay-racing

443 Congress Emblem

1964. Olympic Games, Tokyo. Multicoloured.
1508 20g. Triple-jumping 10 10
1509 40g. Rowing 10 10
1510 60g. Weightlifting 10 10
1511 90g. Type **442** 10 10
1512 1z. Boxing 10 10
1513 2z.50 Football 30 10
1514 5z.60 High jumping (women) 90 30
1515 6z.50 High-diving . . . . . 1·40 45
MS1515a 83 × 111 mm. Nos. 1514/15 (two of each) . . . . 30·00 23·00
SIZES: DIAMOND—20g. to 60g. SQUARE—90g. to 2z.50. VERT: (23½ × 36 mm)—5z.60, 6z.50.

MS1515b 79 × 106 mm. 2z.50 Rifle-shooting, 2z.50 Canoeing, 5z. Fencing, 5z. Basketball . . . . 3·50 1·50

1964. 15th Int Astronautical Congress, Warsaw.
1516 **443** 2z.50 black and violet . . 35 10

444 Hand holding Hammer

445 S. Zeromski

1964. 3rd Congress of Fighters for Freedom and Democracy Association, Warsaw.
1517 **444** 60g. red, black and green 10 10

1964. Birth Cent of Stefan Zeromski (writer).
1518 **445** 60g. brown 10 10

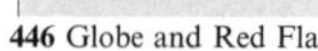

446 Globe and Red Flag

448 Eleanor Roosevelt

447 18th-century Stage Coach (after Brodowski)

1964. Centenary of "First International".
1519 **446** 60g. black and red . . . 10 10

1964. Stamp Day.
1520 **447** 60g. green 20 10
1521 60g. brown 20 10

1964. 80th Birth Anniv of Eleanor Roosevelt.
1522 **448** 2z.50 brown 20 10

449 Battle of Studzianki (after S. Zoltowski)

1964. "Poland's Struggle" (World War II) (1st issue).
1523 – 40g. black 10 10
1524 – 40g. violet 10 10
1525 – 60g. blue 10 10
1526 – 60g. green 10 10
1527 **449** 60g. bronze 10 10
DESIGNS—VERT: No. 1523, Virtuti Militari Cross; 1524, Westerplatte Memorial, Gdansk; 1525, Bydgoszcz Memorial. HORIZ: No. 1526, Soldiers crossing the Oder (after S. Zoltowski).
See also Nos. 1610/12.

449a W. Komarov

1964. Russian Three-manned Space Flight. Sheet 114 × 63 mm depicting crew.
MS1527a 60g. black and red (T **449a**); 60g. black and green (Feoktistov); 60g. black and blue (Yegorov) 95 50

450 Cyclamen

451 Spacecraft of the Future

1964. Garden Flowers. Multicoloured.
1528 20g. Type **450** 10 10
1529 30g. Freesia 10 10
1530 40g. Rose 10 10
1531 50g. Peony 10 10
1532 60g. Lily 10 10
1533 90g. Poppy 10 10
1534 1z.35 Tulip 10 10
1535 1z.50 Narcissus 65 30
1536 1z.55 Begonia 20 10
1537 2z.50 Carnation 45 10
1538 3z.40 Iris 75 30
1539 5z.60 Japanese camelia . . . 1·25 60
Nos. 1534/9 are smaller, 26½ × 37 mm.

1964. Space Research. Multicoloured.
1540 20g. Type **451** 10 10
1541 30g. Launching rocket . . . 10 10
1542 40g. Dog "Laika" and rocket 10 10
1543 60g. "Lunik 3" and Moon 10 10
1544 1z.55 Satelite 10 10
1545 2z.50 "Elektron 2" 35 10
1546 5z.60 "Mars 1" 50 10
1547 6z.50+2z. Gagarin seated in capsule . . . . 3·50 30

452 "Siren of Warsaw"

1965. 20th Anniv of Liberation of Warsaw.
1548 **452** 60g. green 10 10

453 Edaphosaurus

1965. Prehistoric Animals (1st series). Mult.
1549 20g. Type **453** 10 10
1550 30g. Cryptocleidus (vert) . . 10 10
1551 40g. Brontosaurus 10 10
1552 60g. Mesosaurus (vert) . . . 10 10
1553 90g. Stegosaurus 10 10
1554 1z.15 Brachiosaurus (vert) 10 10
1555 1z.35 Styracosaurus 20 10
1556 3z.40 Corythosaurus (vert) 50 10
1557 5z.60 Rhamphorhynchus (vert) . . . . 1·40 45
1558 6z.50 Tyrannosaurus . . . . 1·90 1·10
See also Nos. 1639/47.

454 Petro-chemical Works, Plock, and Polish and Soviet Flags

1965. 20th Anniv of Polish–Soviet Friendship Treaty. Multicoloured.
1559 60g. Seal (vert, 27 × 38½ mm) 10 10
1560 60g. Type **454** 10 10

455 Polish Eagle and Civic Arms

1965. 20th Anniv of Return of Western and Northern Territories to Poland.
1561 **455** 60g. red 10 10

456 Dove of Peace **457** I.T.U. Emblem

1965. 20th Anniv of Victory.
1562 **456** 60g. red and black . . . 10 10

1965. Centenary of I.T.U.
1563 **457** 2z.50 black, violet & blue 45 10

458 Clover-leaf Emblem and "The Friend of the People" (journal) **459** "Dragon" Dinghies

1965. 70th Anniv of Peasant Movement. Mult.
1564 40g. Type **458** 10 10
1565 60g. Ears of corn and industrial plant (horiz) . . 10 10

1965. World Finn Sailing Championships, Gdynia. Multicoloured.
1566 30g. Type **459** 10 10
1567 40g. "5.5 m." dinghies . . . 10 10
1568 50g. "Finn" dinghies (horiz) 10 10
1569 60g. "V" dinghies 10 10
1570 1z.35 "Cadet" dinghies (horiz) 20 10
1571 4z. "Star" yachts (horiz) . . 65 35
1572 5z.60 "Flying Dutchman" dinghies . . . . 1·25 60
1573 6z.50 "Amethyst" dinghies (horiz) . . . . 1·90 1·90
MS1573a 79×59 mm. 15z. Finn dinghies . . . . 1·75 1·10

460 Marx and Lenin **461** 17th-cent Arms of Warsaw

1965. Postal Ministers' Congress, Peking.
1574 **460** 60g. black on red . . . 10 10

1965. 700th Anniv of Warsaw.
1575 **461** 5g. red 10 10
1576 – 10g. green 10 10
1577 – 20g. blue 10 10
1578 – 40g. brown 10 10
1579 – 60g. orange 10 10
1580 – 1z.50 black 10 10
1581 – 1z.55 blue 10 10
1582 – 2z.50 purple 10 10
MS1583 51×62 mm. 3z.40 black and bistre 75 50
DESIGNS—VERT: 10g. 13th-cent antiquities. HORIZ: 20g. Tombstone of last Masovian dukes; 40g. Old Town Hall; 60g. Barbican; 1z.50, Arsenal; 1z.55, National Theatre; 2z.50, Staszic Palace; 3z.40, T **462**.

463 I.Q.S.Y. Emblem

1965. International Quiet Sun Year. Multicoloured. Background colours given.
1584 **463** 60g. blue 10 10
1585 60g. violet 10 10
1586 – 2z.50 red 30 10
1587 – 2z.50 brown 30 10
1588 – 3z.40 orange 45 10
1589 – 3z.40 olive 45 10
DESIGNS: 2z.50, Solar scanner; 3z.40, Solar System.

464 "Odontoglossum grande" **465** Weightlifting

1965. Orchids. Multicoloured.
1590 20g. Type **464** 10 10
1591 30g. "Cypripedium hibridum" 10 10
1592 40g. "Lycaste skinneri" . . 10 10
1593 50g. "Cattleya warzewicza" 10 10
1594 60g. "Vanda sanderiana" . . 10 10
1595 1z.35 "Cypripedium hibridum" (different) . . 30 10
1596 4z. "Sobralia" 45 30
1597 5z.60 "Disa grandiflora" . . 1·25 45
1598 6z.50 "Cattleya labiata" . . 1·90 50

1965. Olympic Games, Tokyo. Polish Medal Winners. Multicoloured.
1599 30g. Type **465** 10 10
1600 40g. Boxing 10 10
1601 50g. Relay-racing 10 10
1602 60g. Fencing 10 10
1603 90g. Hurdling (women's 80 m) 10 10
1604 3z.40 Relay-racing (women's) 45 10
1605 6z.50 "Hop, step and jump" 90 60
1606 7z.10 Volleyball (women's) 1·25 45

466 "The Post Coach" (after P. Michalowski)

1965. Stamp Day.
1607 **466** 60g. brown 20 10
1608 – 2z.50 green 30 10
DESIGN: 2z.50, "Coach about to leave" (after P. Michalowski).

467 U.N. Emblem **468** Memorial, Holy Cross Mountains

1965. 20th Anniv of U.N.O.
1609 **467** 2z.50 blue 30 10

1965. "Poland's Struggle" (World War II) (2nd issue).
1610 **468** 60g. brown 10 10
1611 – 60g. green 10 10
1612 – 60g. brown 10 10
DESIGNS—VERT: No. 1611, Memorial Plaszow. HORIZ: No. 1612, Memorial, Chelm-on-Ner.

469 Wolf

1965. Forest Animals. Multicoloured.
1613 20g. Type **469** 10 10
1614 30g. Lynx 10 10
1615 40g. Red fox 10 10
1616 50g. Eurasian badger . . . 10 10
1617 60g. Brown bear 10 10
1618 1z.50 Wild boar 35 10
1619 2z.50 Red deer 35 10
1620 5z.60 European bison . . . 90 30
1621 7z.10 Elk . . . . 1·50 50

470 Gig

1965. Horse-drawn Carriages in Lancut Museum. Multicoloured.
1622 20g. Type **470** 10 10
1623 40g. Coupe 10 10
1624 50g. Ladies' "basket" (trap) 10 10
1625 60g. "Vis-a-vis" 10 10
1626 90g. Cab 10 10
1627 1z.15 Berlinka 15 10
1628 2z.50 Hunting brake 45 10
1629 6z.50 Barouche . . . . . . 1·25 30
1630 7z.10 English brake . . . . 1·75 50
Nos. 1627/9 are 77×22 mm and No. 1630 is 104×22 mm.

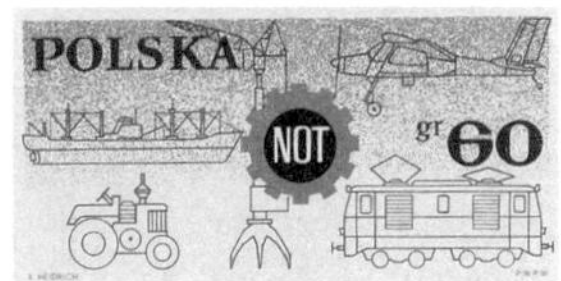

471 Congress Emblem and Industrial Products

1966. 5th Polish Technicians' Congress, Katowice.
1631 **471** 60g. multicoloured . . . 10 10

1966. 20th Anniv of Industrial Nationalization. Designs similar to T **471**. Multicoloured.
1632 60g. Pithead gear (vert) . . 10 10
1633 60g. "Henryk Jedza" (freighter) 10 10
1634 60g. Petro-chemical works, Plock 10 10
1635 60g. Combine-harvester . . 10 10
1636 60g. Class EN 57 electric train 10 10
1637 60g. Exhibition Hall, 35th Poznan Fair 10 10
1638 60g. Crane (vert) 10 10

1966. Prehistoric Animals (2nd series). As T **453**. Multicoloured.
1639 20g. Terror fish 10 10
1640 30g. Lobefin 10 10
1641 40g. Ichthyostega 10 10
1642 50g. Mastodonsaurus . . . 10 10
1643 60g. Cynognathus 10 10
1644 2z.50 Archaeopteryx (vert) 10 10
1645 3z.40 Brontotherium 60 10
1646 6z.50 Machairodus 90 45
1647 7z.10 Mammuthus . . . . 2·10 50

472 H. Sienkiewicz (novelist) **473** Footballers (Montevideo, 1930)

1966. 50th Death Anniv of Henryk Sienkiewicz.
1648 **472** 60g. black on buff . . . 10 10

1966. World Cup Football Championship.
(a) Football scenes representing World Cup finals.
1649 20g. Type **473** 10 10
1650 40g. Rome, 1934 . . . . . 10 10
1651 60g. Paris, 1938 . . . . . . 10 10
1652 90g. Rio de Janeiro, 1950 . 10 10
1653 1z.50 Berne, 1954 . . . . 60 10
1654 3z.40 Stockholm, 1958 . . . 60 10
1655 6z.50 Santiago, 1962 . . . . 1·25 10
1656 7z.10 "London", 1966 (elimination match, Glasgow, 1965) . . . . . 1·75 35

(b) 61×81 mm.
MS1657 **474** 13z.50+1z.50 . . . 2·40 1·40

475 Soldier with Flag, and Dove of Peace **476** Women's Relay-racing

477

1966. 21st Anniv of Victory Day.
1658 **475** 60g. red and black on silver 10 10

1966. 8th European Athletic Championships, Budapest. Multicoloured.
1659 20g. Runner starting race (vert) 10 10
1660 40g. Type **476** 10 10
1661 60g. Throwing the javelin (vert) 10 10
1662 90g. Women's hurdles . . . 10 10
1663 1z.35 Throwing the discus (vert) 10 10
1664 3z.40 Finish of race 45 10
1665 6z.50 Throwing the hammer (vert) 75 35
1666 7z.10 High-jumping . . . . 1·10 60
MS1667 **477** 110×66 mm. 5z. Imperf . . . . 2·40 1·25

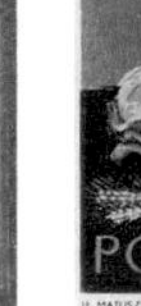

478 White Eagle **479** Flowers and Produce

1966. Polish Millenary (1st issue). Each red and black on gold.
1668 60g. Type **478** 10 10
1669 60g. Polish flag 10 10
1670 2z.50 Type **478** 10 10
1671 2z.50 Polish flag 10 10
See also Nos. 1717/18.

1966. Harvest Festival. Multicoloured.
1672 40g. Type **479** 20 10
1673 60g. Woman and loaf . . . 20 10
1674 3z.40 Festival bouquet . . . 50 35
The 3z.40 is 49×48 mm.

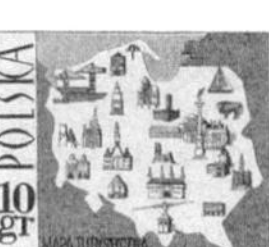

480 Chrysanthemum **481** Tourist Map

1966. Flowers. Multicoloured.
1675 10g. Type **480** 10 10
1676 20g. Poinsettia 10 10
1677 30g. Centaury 10 10
1678 40g. Rose 10 10
1679 60g. Zinnia 10 10
1680 90g. Nasturtium 10 10
1681 5z.60 Dahlia 90 30
1682 6z.50 Sunflower 80 45
1683 7z.10 Magnolia . . . . . . 1·90 50

1966. Tourism.
1684 **481** 10g. red 10 10
1685 – 20g. olive 10 10
1686 – 40g. blue 10 10
1687 – 60g. brown 10 10
1688 – 60g. black 10 10
1689 – 1z.15 green 15 10
1690 – 1z.35 red 10 10
1691 – 1z.55 violet 10 10
1692 – 2z. green 40 10
DESIGNS: 20g. Hela Lighthouse; 40g. Yacht; 60g. (No. 1687), Poniatowski Bridge, Warsaw; 60g. (No. 1688), Mining Academy, Kielee; 1z.15, Dunajee Gorge; 1z.35, Old oaks, Rogalin; 1z.55, Silesian Planetarium; 2z. "Batory" (liner).

482 Roman Capital

1966. Polish Culture Congress.
1693 **482** 60g. red and brown . . 10 10

483 Stable-man with Percherons

1966. Stamp Day.
1694 **483** 60g. brown 10 10
1695 – 2z.50 green 10 10
DESIGN: 2z.50, Stablemen with horses and dogs.

484 Soldier in Action

1966. 30th Anniv of Jaroslav Dabrowski Brigade.
1696 **484** 60g. black, green and red 10 10

485 Woodland Birds

1966. Woodland Birds. Multicoloured.
1697 10g. Type **485** 15 10
1698 20g. Green woodpecker . . 15 10
1699 30g. Jay 20 10
1700 40g. Golden oriole 20 10
1701 60g. Hoopoe 20 10
1702 2z.50 Common redstart . . 45 35
1703 4z. Spruce siskin . . . . . 1·50 35
1704 6z.50 Chaffinch . . . . . . 1·50 60
1705 7z.10 Great tit . . . . . . 1·50 60

486 Ram (ritual statuette) **487** "Vostok 1"

1966. Polish Archaeological Research.
1706 **486** 60g. blue 10 10
1707 – 60g. green 10 10
1708 – 60g. brown 10 10
DESIGNS—VERT: No. 1707, Plan of Biskupin settlement. HORIZ: No. 1708, Brass implements and ornaments.

1966. Space Research. Multicoloured.
1709 20g. Type **487** 10 10
1710 40g. "Gemini" 10 10
1711 60g. "Ariel 2" 10 10
1712 1z.35 "Proton 1" 10 10
1713 1z.50 "FR 1" 20 10
1714 3z.40 "Alouette" 35 10
1715 6z.50 "San Marco 1" . . . 1·25 10
1716 7z.10 "Luna 9" . . . . . . 1·50 30

488 Polish Eagle and Hammer

1966. Polish Millenary (2nd issue).
1717 **488** 40g. purple, lilac and red 10 10
1718 – 60g. purple, green and red 10 10
DESIGN: 60g. Polish eagle and agricultural and industrial symbols.

489 Dressage

1967. 150th Anniv of Racehorse Breeding in Poland. Multicoloured.
1719 10g. Type **489** 15 10
1720 20g. Cross-country racing 15 10
1721 40g. Horse-jumping 15 10
1722 60g. Jumping fence in open country 30 10
1723 90g. Horse-trotting 30 10
1724 5z.90 Playing polo 90 10
1725 6z.60 Stallion "Ofir" . . . . 1·40 45
1726 7z. Stallion "Skowrenek" . . 2·10 45

490 Black-wedged Butterflyfish

1967. Exotic Fishes. Multicoloured.
1727 5g. Type **490** 10 10
1728 10g. Emperor angelfish . . . 10 10
1729 40g. Racoon butterflyfish . . 10 10
1730 60g. Clown triggerfish . . . 10 10
1731 90g. Undulate triggerfish . . 10 10
1732 1z.50 Picasso triggerfish . . 20 10
1733 4z.50 Black-finned melon butterflyfish 75 10
1734 6z.60 Semicircle angelfish . . 95 45
1735 7z. Saddle butterflyfish . . . 1·25 75

491 Auschwitz Memorial

1967. Polish Martyrdom and Resistance, 1939–45.
1736 **491** 40g. brown 10 10
1737 – 40g. black 10 10
1738 – 40g. violet 10 10
DESIGNS—VERT: No. 1737, Auschwitz-Monowitz Memorial; 1738, Memorial guide's emblem.
See also Nos. 1770/2, 1798/9 and 1865/9.

492 Cyclists

1967. 20th International Peace Cycle Race.
1739 **492** 60g. multicoloured . . . 10 10

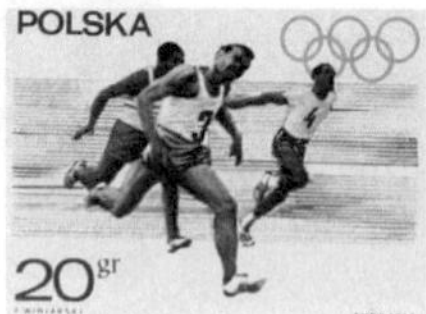

493 Running

1967. Olympic Games (1968). Multicoloured.
1740 20g. Type **493** 10 10
1741 40g. Horse-jumping 10 10
1742 60g. Relay-running 10 10
1743 90g. Weight-lifting 10 10
1744 1z.35 Hurdling 10 10
1745 3z.40 Gymnastics 45 15
1746 6z.60 High-jumping 60 35
1747 7z. Boxing . . . . 1·10 65
MS1748 65 × 86 mm. 10z.+5z. multicoloured . . . . 1·90 1·25
DESIGN: (30 × 30 mm.)—10z. Kusocinski winning 10,000 meters race at Olympic Games, Los Angeles, 1932.

494 Socialist Symbols

1967. Polish Trade Unions Congress, Warsaw.
1749 **494** 60g. multicoloured . . . 10 10

495 "Arnica montana"

1967. Protected Plants. Multicoloured.
1750 40g. Type **495** 10 10
1751 60g. "Aquilegia vulgaris" . . 10 10
1752 3z.40 "Gentiana punctata" . 35 10
1753 4z.50 "Lycopodium clavatum" 35 10
1754 5z. "Iris sibirica" 60 10
1755 10z. "Azalea pontica" . . . 1·10 30

496 Katowice Memorial **497** Marie Curie

1967. Inauguration of Katowice Memorial.
1756 **496** 60g. multicoloured . . . 10 10

1967. Birth Centenary of Marie Curie.
1757 **497** 60g. lake 10 10
1758 – 60g. brown 10 10
1759 – 60g. violet 10 10
DESIGNS: No. 1758, Marie Curie's Nobel Prize diploma; 1759, Statue of Marie Curie, Warsaw.

498 "Fifth Congress of the Deaf" (sign language)

1967. 5th World Federation of the Deaf Congress, Warsaw.
1760 **498** 60g. black and blue . . . 10 10

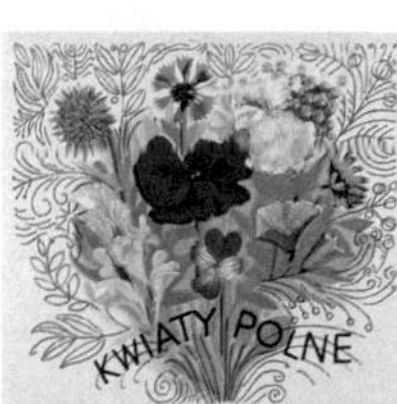

499 Bouquet

1967. "Flowers of the Meadow". Multicoloured.
1761 20g. Type **499** 10 10
1762 40g. Red poppy 10 10
1763 60g. Field bindweed 10 10
1764 90g. Wild pansy 10 10
1765 1z.15 Tansy 10 10
1766 2z.50 Corn cockle 20 10
1767 3z.40 Field scabious 45 30
1768 4z.50 Scarlet pimpernel . . 1·40 35
1769 7z.90 Chicory . . . . 1·50 30

1967. Polish Martyrdom and Resistance, 1939–45 (2nd series). As T **491**.
1770 40g. blue 10 10
1771 40g. green 10 10
1772 40g. black 10 10
DESIGNS—HORIZ: No. 1770, Stutthof Memorial. VERT: No. 1771, Walez Memorial; 1772, Lodz-Radogoszez Memorial.

500 "Wilanow Palace" (from painting by W. Kasprzycki)

1967. Stamp Day.
1773 **500** 60g. brown and blue . . 10 10

501 Cruiser "Aurora"

1967. 50th Anniv of October Revolution. Each black, grey and red.
1774 60g. Type **501** 10 10
1775 60g. Lenin 10 10
1776 60g. "Luna 10" 10 10

502 Peacock **503** Kosciuszko

1967. Butterflies. Multicoloured.
1777 10g. Type **502** 10 10
1778 20g. Swallowtail 10 10
1779 40g. Small tortoiseshell . . . 10 10
1780 60g. Camberwell beauty . . 15 10
1781 2z. Purple emperor 30 10
1782 2z.50 Red admiral 35 10
1783 3z.40 Pale clouded yellow 35 10
1784 4z.50 Marbled white . . . . 1·75 80
1785 7z.90 Large blue . . . . . 1·90 80

1967. 150th Death Anniv of Tadeusz Kosciuszko (national hero).
1786 **503** 60g. chocolate and brown 10 10
1787 2z.50 green and red . . . 20 10

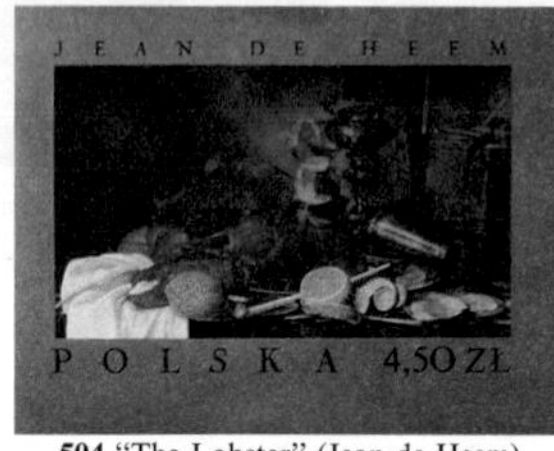

504 "The Lobster" (Jean de Heem)

1967. Famous Paintings.
1788 – 20g. multicoloured . . . 20 10
1789 – 40g. multicoloured . . . 10 10
1790 – 60g. multicoloured . . . 10 10
1791 – 2z. multicoloured 30 20
1792 – 2z.50 multicolured . . . 30 20
1793 – 3z.40 multicoloured . . . 60 20
1794 **504** 4z.50 multicoloured . . . 1·10 60
1795 – 6z.60 multicoloured . . . 1·40 75
DESIGNS (Paintings from the National Museums, Warsaw and Cracow). VERT: 20g. "Lady with a Weasel" (Leonardo da Vinci); 40g. "The Polish Lady" (Watteau); 60g. "Dog fighting Heron" (A. Hondius); 2z. "Fowler tuning Guitar" (J. B. Greuze); 2z.50, "The Tax Collectors" (M. van Reymerswaele); 3z.40, "Daria Fiodorowna" (F. S. Rokotov). HORIZ: 6z.60, "Parable of the Good Samaritan" (landscape, Rembrandt).

505 W. S. Reymont

1967. Birth Centenary of W. S. Reymont (novelist).
1796 **505** 60g. brown, red and ochre 10 10

506 J. M. Ossolinski (medallion), Book and Flag

1967. 150th Anniv of Ossolineum Foundation.
1797 **506** 60g. brown, red and blue 10 10

1967. Polish Martyrdom and Resistance, 1939–45 (3rd series). As T **491**.
1798 40g. red 10 10
1799 40g. brown 10 10
DESIGNS—VERT: No. 1798, Zagan Memorial. HORIZ: No. 1799, Lambinowice Memorial.

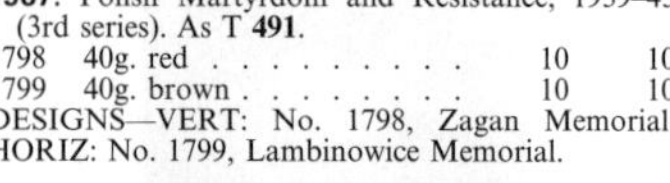

507 Ice Hockey

1968. Winter Olympic Games, Grenoble. Mult.
1800 40g. Type **507** 10 10
1801 60g. Downhill 10 10
1802 90g. Slalom 10 10

1803 1z.35 Speed-skating 10 10
1804 1z.55 Ski-walking 10 10
1805 2z. Tobogganing 20 20
1806 7z. Rifle-shooting on skis . . 50 45
1807 7z.90 Ski-jumping (different) 95 60

508 "Puss in Boots" 510 "Peace" (poster by H. Tomaszewski)

509 "Passiflora quadrangularis"

1968. Fairy Tales. Multicoloured.
1808 20g. Type **508** 10 10
1809 40g. "The Raven and the Fox" 10 10
1810 60g. "Mr. Twardowski" . . 10 10
1811 2z. "The Fisherman and the Fish" 20 10
1812 2z.50 "Little Red Riding Hood" 30 10
1813 3z.40 "Cinderella" 45 10
1814 5z.50 "The Waif" . . . . . 1·25 45
1815 7z. "Snow White" . . . . . 1·50 60

1968. Flowers. Multicoloured.
1816 10g. "Clianthus dampieri" 10 10
1817 20g. Type **509** 10 10
1818 30g. "Strelitzia reginae" . . 10 10
1819 40g. "Coryphanta vivipara" 10 10
1820 60g. "Odontonia" 10 10
1821 90g. "Protea cyneroides" . . 10 10
1822 4z.+2z. "Abutilon" 20 10
1823 8z.+4z. "Rosa polyantha" 1·90 30

1968. 2nd Int Poster Biennale, Warsaw. Mult.
1824 60g. Type **510** 10 10
1825 2z.50 Gounod's "Faust" (poster by Jan Lenica) . . 10 10

511 Zephyr Glider

1968. 11th World Gliding Championships, Leszno. Gliders. Multicoloured.
1826 60g. Type **511** 10 10
1827 90g. Stork 10 10
1828 1z.50 Swallow 15 10
1829 3z.40 Fly 35 20
1830 4z. Seal 80 30
1831 5z.50 Pirate 95 30

512 Child with "Stamp" 513 Part of Monument

1968. "75 years of Polish Philately". Multicoloured.
1832 60g. Type **512** 10 10
1833 60g. Balloon over Poznan 10 10

1968. Silesian Insurrection Monument, Sosnowiec.
1834 **513** 60g. black and purple . . 10 10

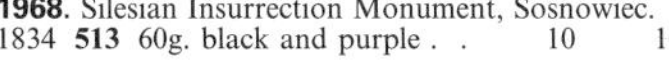

514 Relay-racing

1968. Olympic Games, Mexico. Multicoloured.
1835 30g. Type **514** 10 10
1836 40g. Boxing 10 10
1837 60g. Basketball 10 10
1838 90g. Long-jumping 10 10
1839 2z.50 Throwing the javelin 15 10
1840 3z.40 Gymnastics 30 10
1841 4z. Cycling 35 10
1842 7z.90 Fencing 65 10
1843 10z.+5z. Torch runner and Aztec bas-relief (56×45 mm) . . . . . . 1·75 30

515 "Knight on a Bay Horse" (P. Michalowski)

1968. Polish Paintings. Multicoloured.
1844 40g. Type **515** 10 10
1845 60g. "Fisherman" (L. Wyczolkowski) . . . 10 10
1846 1z.15 "Jewish Woman with Lemons" (A. Gierymski) 10 10
1847 1z.35 "Eliza Parenska" (S. Wyspianski) 15 10
1848 1z.50 "Manifesto" (W. Weiss) 20 10
1849 4z.50 "Stanczyk" (Jan Matejko) (horiz) 50 10
1850 5z. "Children's Band" (T. Makowski) (horiz) . . 80 10
1851 7z. "Feast II" (Z. Waliszewski) (horiz) 90 35

516 "September, 1939" (Bylina)

1968. 25th Anniv of Polish People's Army. Designs show paintings.
1852 40g. violet and olive on yellow 10 10
1853 40g. blue and violet on lilac 10 10
1854 40g. green and blue on grey 10 10
1855 40g. black and brown on orange 10 10
1856 40g. purple & green on green 10 10
1857 60g. brown & ultram on bl 10 10
1858 60g. purple & green on green 10 10
1859 60g. olive and red on pink 10 10
1860 60g. green and brown on red 20 10
1861 60g. blue & turquoise on blue 30 10
PAINTINGS AND PAINTERS: No. 1852, Type **516**; 1853, "Partisans" (Maciag); 1854, "Lenino" (Bylina); 1855, "Monte Cassino" (Boratynski); 1856, "Tanks before Warsaw" (Garwatowski); 1857, "Neisse River" (Bylina); 1858, "On the Oder" (Mackiewicz); 1859, "In Berlin" (Bylina); 1860, "Blyskawica" (destroyer) (Mokwa); 1861, "Pursuit" (Mikoyan Gurevich MiG-17 aircraft) (Kulisiewicz).

517 "Party Members" (F. Kowarski)

1968. 5th Polish United Workers' Party Congress, Warsaw. Multicoloured designs showing paintings.
1862 60g. Type **517** 10 10
1863 60g. "Strike" (S. Lentz) (vert) 10 10
1864 60g. "Manifesto" (W. Weiss) (vert) 10 10

1968. Polish Martyrdom and Resistance, 1939–45 (4th series). As T **491**.
1865 40g. grey 10 10
1866 40g. brown 10 10
1867 40g. brown 10 10
1868 40g. blue 10 10
1869 40g. brown 10 10
DESIGNS—HORIZ: No. 1865, Tomb of Unknown Soldier, Warsaw; 1866, Guerillas' Monument, Kartuzy. VERT: No. 1867, Insurgents' Monument, Poznan; 1868, People's Guard Insurgents' Monument, Polichno; 1869, Rotunda, Zamosc.

518 "Start of Hunt" (W. Kossak)

1968. Paintings. Hunting Scenes. Multicoloured.
1870 20g. Type **518** 10 10
1871 40g. "Hunting with Falcon" (J. Kossak) 10 10
1872 60g. "Wolves' Raid" (A. Wierusz-Kowalski) . . 10 10
1873 1z.50 "Home-coming with a Bear" (J. Falat) 30 10
1874 2z.50 "The Fox-hunt" (T. Sutherland) 20 10
1875 3z.40 "The Boar-hunt" (F. Snyders) 30 10
1876 4z.50 "Hunters' Rest" (W. G. Pierow) . . . . . 1·25 45
1877 8z.50 "Hunting a Lion in Morocco" (Delacroix) . . 1·25 90

519 Maltese Terrier 520 House Sign

1969. Pedigree Dogs. Multicoloured.
1878 20g. Type **519** 10 10
1879 40g. Wire-haired fox-terrier (vert) 20 10
1880 60g. Afghan hound 20 20
1881 1z.50 Rough-haired terrier 20 10
1882 2z.50 English setter 45 10
1883 3z.40 Pekinese 50 20
1884 4z.50 Alsatian (vert) . . . . 1·10 30
1885 8z.50 Pointer (vert) . . . . 2·25 65

1969. 9th Polish Democratic Party Congress.
1886 **520** 60g. red, black and grey 10 10

521 "Dove" and Wheat-ears 522 Running

1969. 5th Congress of United Peasant's Party.
1887 **521** 60g. multicoloured . . . 10 10

1969. 75th Anniv of International Olympic Committee and 50th Anniv of Polish Olympic Committee. Multicoloured.
1888 10g. Type **522** 10 10
1889 20g. Gynmastics 10 10
1890 40g. Weightlifting 10 10
1891 60g. Throwing the javelin 10 10
1892 2z.50+50g. Throwing the discus 10 10
1893 3z.40+1z. Running 20 10
1894 4z.+1z.50 Wrestling 60 30
1895 7z.+2z. Fencing . . . . . . 1·10 35

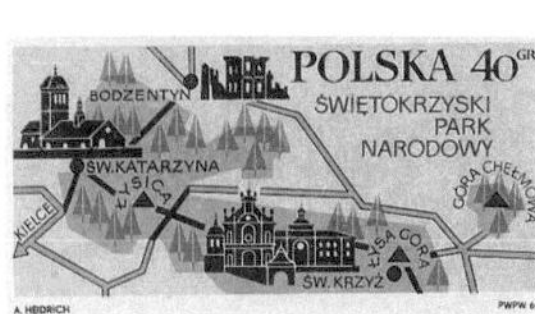

523 Pictorial Map of Swietokrzyski National Park

1969. Tourism (1st series). Multicoloured.
1896 40g. Type **523** 10 10
1897 60g. Niedzica Castle (vert) 10 10
1898 1z.35 Kolobrzeg Lighthouse and yacht 20 10
1899 1z.50 Szczecin Castle and Harbour 20 10
1900 2z.50 Torun and Vistula River 15 10
1901 3z.40 Klodzko, Silesia (vert) 20 20
1902 4z. Sulejow 35 30
1903 4z.50 Kazimierz Dolny market-place (vert) . . . 35 30
See also Nos. 1981/5.

524 Route Map and "Opty"

1969. Leonid Teliga's World Voyage in Yacht "Opty".
1904 **524** 60g. multicoloured . . . 10 10

525 Copernicus (after woodcut by T. Stimer) and Inscription 526 "Memory" Flame and Badge

1969. 500th Birth Anniv (1973) of Copernicus (1st issue).
1905 **525** 40g. brown, red & yellow 10 10
1906 – 60g. blue, red and green 10 10
1907 – 2z.50 olive, red & purple 35 30
DESIGNS: 60g. Copernicus (after J. Falck) and 15th-century globe; 2z.50, Copernicus (after painting by J. Matejko) and diagram of heliocentric system.
See also Nos. 1995/7, 2069/72, 2167/70, 2213/14 and 2217/21.

1969. 5th National Alert of Polish Boy Scout Association.
1908 **526** 60g. black, red and blue 10 10
1909 – 60g. red, black and green 10 10
1910 – 60g. black, green and red 10 10
DESIGN: No. 1909, "Defence" eagle and badge; 1910, "Labour" map and badge.

528 Coal-miner

1969. 25th Anniv of Polish People's Republic. Multicoloured.
1911 60g. Frontier guard and arms 10 10
1912 60g. Plock petro-chemical plant 10 10
1913 60g. Combine-harvester . . 10 10
1914 60g. Grand Theatre, Warsaw 10 10
1915 60g. Curie statue and University, Lublin 10 10
1916 60g. Type **528** 10 10
1917 60g. Sulphur-worker 10 10
1918 60g. Steel-worker 10 10
1919 60g. Shipbuilder 10 10
Nos. 1911/5 are vert and have white arms embossed in the top portion of the stamps.

529 Astronauts and Module on Moon

1969. 1st Man on the Moon.
1920 **529** 2z.50 multicoloured . . . 60 45

530 "Motherhood" (S. Wyspianski)

1969. Polish Paintings. Multicoloured.
1921 20g. Type **530** 10 10
1922 40g. "Hamlet" (J. Malczewski) 10 10
1923 60g. "Indian Summer" (J. Chelmonski) 10 10
1924 2z. "Two Girls" (Olga Bonznanska) (vert) . . . 20 10
1925 2z.50 "The Sun of May" (J. Mehoffer) (vert) . . . 10 10
1926 3z.40 "Woman combing her Hair" (W. Slewinski) . . 30 30
1927 5z.50 "Still Life" (J. Pankiewicz) 60 30
1928 7z. "Abduction of the King's Daughter" (W. Wojtkiewicz) . . . . 1·25 45

531 "Nike" statue **533** Krzczonow (Lublin) Costumes

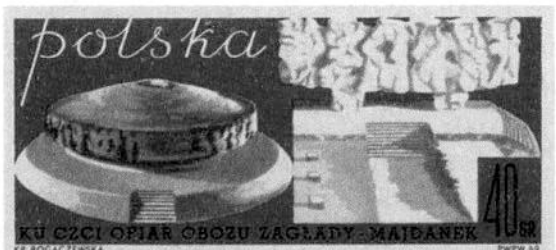

532 Majdanek Memorial

1969. 4th Congress of Fighters for Freedom and Democracy Association.
1929 **531** 60g. red, black and brown 10 10

1969. Inauguration of Majdanek Memorial.
1930 **532** 40g. black and mauve . . 10 10

1969. Provincial Costumes. Multicoloured.
1931 40g. Type **533** 10 10
1932 60g. Lowicz (Lodz) 10 10
1933 1z.15 Rozbasrk (Katowice) 10 10
1934 1z.35 Lower Silesia (Wroclaw) 10 10
1935 1z.50 Opoczno (Lodz) . . . 30 10
1936 4z.50 Sacz (Cracow) 60 15
1937 5z. Highlanders, Cracow . . 45 30
1938 7z. Kurple (Warsaw) 65 35

534 "Pedestrians Keep Left" **535** "Welding" and I.L.O. Emblem

1969. Road Safety. Multicoloured.
1939 40g. Type **534** 10 10
1940 60g. "Drive Carefully" (horses on road) 10 10
1941 2z.50 "Do Not Dazzle" (cars on road at night) . . 15 10

1969. 50th Anniv of I.L.O.
1942 **535** 2z.50 blue and gold . . . 20 10

536 "The Bell-founder" **537** "Angel" (19th-century)

1969. Miniatures from Behem's Code of 1505. Multicoloured.
1943 40g. Type **536** 10 10
1944 60g. "The Painter" 10 10
1945 1z.35 "The Woodcarver" . . 10 10
1946 1z.55 "The Shoemaker" . . 20 10
1947 2z.50 "The Cooper" 20 10
1948 3z.40 "The Baker" 20 20
1949 4z.50 "The Tailor" 60 30
1950 7z. "The Bowyer" . . . . . 1·00 60

1969. Polish Folk Sculpture. Multicoloured.
1951 20g. Type **537** 10 10
1952 40g. "Sorrowful Christ" (19th-century) 10 10
1953 60g. "Sorrowful Christ" (19th-cent) (different) . . 10 10
1954 2z. "Weeping Woman" (19th-century) 20 10
1955 2z.50 "Adam and Eve" (F. Czajkowski) 20 10
1956 3z.40 "Girl with Birds" (L. Kudla) 30 10
1957 5z.50+1z.50 "Choir" (A. Zegadlo) 75 35
1958 7z.+1z. "Organ-grinder" (Z. Skretowicz) 80 50
Nos. 1957/8 are larger, size 25 × 35 mm.

538 Leopold Staff

1969. Modern Polish Writers.
1959 **538** 40g. black, olive & green 10 10
1960 – 60g. black, red and pink 10 10
1961 – 1z.35 black, deep blue and blue 10 10
1962 – 1z.50 black, violet & lilac 10 10
1963 – 1z.55 black, deep green and green 10 10
1964 – 2z.50 black, deep blue and blue 20 10
1965 – 3z.40 black, brn & flesh 30 25
DESIGNS: 60g. Wladyslaw Broniewski; 1z.35, Leon Kruczkowski; 1z.50, Julian Tuwim; 1z.55, Konstanty Ildefons Galczynski; 2z.50, Maria Dabrowska; 3z.40, Zofia Nalkowska.

539 Nike Monument

1970. 25th Anniv of Liberation of Warsaw.
1966 **539** 60g. multicoloured . . . 20 10

540 Early Printing Works and Colour Dots

1970. Centenary of Printers' Trade Union.
1967 **540** 60g. multicoloured . . . 10 10

541 Mallard

1970. Game Birds. Multicoloured.
1968 40g. Type **541** 10 10
1969 60g. Common pheasant . . 30 10
1970 1z.15 Eurasian woodcock 20 10
1971 1z.35 Ruff 30 10
1972 1z.50 Wood pigeon 30 10
1973 3z.40 Black grouse 35 10
1974 7z. Grey partridge . . . . . 1·90 45
1975 8z.50 Western capercaillie 2·75 50

542 Lenin at Desk

1970. Birth Centenary of Lenin.
1976 **542** 40g. grey and red . . . 10 10
1977 – 60g. brown and red . . . 10 10
1978 – 2z.50 black and red . . . 10 10
MS1979 134 × 81 mm. No. 1977 × 4 2·10 45
DESIGNS: 60g. Lenin addressing meeting; 2z.50, Lenin at Party conference.

543 Polish and Russian Soldiers in Berlin

1970. 25th Anniv of Liberation.
1980 **543** 60g. multicoloured . . . 10 10

1970. Tourism (2nd series). As T **523**, but with imprint "PWPW 70". Multicoloured.
1981 60g. Town Hall, Wroclaw (vert) 10 10
1982 60g. View of Opol 10 10
1983 60g. Legnica Castle 10 10
1984 60g. Bolkow Castle 10 10
1985 60g. Town Hall, Brzeg . . . 10 10

544 Polish "Flower"

1970. 25th Anniv of Return of Western Territories.
1986 **544** 60g. red, silver and green 10 10

545 Movement Flag **546** U.P.U. Emblem and New Headquarters

1970. 75th Anniv of Peasant Movement.
1987 **545** 60g. multicoloured . . . 10 10

1970. New U.P.U. Headquarters Building, Berne.
1988 **546** 2z.50 blue and turquoise 20 10

547 Footballers **548** Hand with "Lamp of Learning"

1970. Gornik Zabrze v. Manchester City, Final of European Cup-winners Cup Championship.
1989 **547** 60g. multicoloured . . . 20 10

1970. 150th Anniv of Plock Scientific Society.
1990 **548** 60g. olive, red and black 10 10

549 "Olympic Runners" (from Greek amphora)

1970. 10th Session of Int Olympic Academy.
1991 **549** 60g. red, yellow and black 10 10
1992 – 60g. violet, blue and black 10 10
1993 – 60g. multicoloured . . . 10 10
MS1994 71 × 101 mm. 10z.+5z. multicoloured . . . . 1·90 1·00
DESIGNS: No. 1992, "The Archer"; 1993, Modern runners; **MS**1994, "Horse of Fame" emblem of Polish Olympic Committee.

550 Copernicus (after miniature by Bacciarelli) and Bologna

1970. 500th Birth Anniv (1973) of Copernicus (2nd issue).
1995 **550** 40g. green, orange & lilac 10 10
1996 – 60g. lilac, green & yellow 10 10
1997 – 2z.50 brown, blue & green 35 10
DESIGNS: 60g. Copernicus (after miniature by Lesseur) and Padua; 2z.50, Copernicus (by N. Zinck, after lost Goluchowska portrait) and Ferrara.

551 "Aleksander Orlowski" (self-portrait)

1970. Polish Miniatures. Multicoloured.
1998 20g. Type **551** 10 10
1999 40g. "Jan Matejko" (self-portrait) 10 10
2000 60g. "Stefan Batory" (unknown artist) 10 10
2001 2z. "Maria Leszczynska" (unknown artist) 10 10
2002 2z.50 "Maria Walewska" (Marie-Victorie Jacquetot) 20 10
2003 3z.40 "Tadeusz Kosciuszko" (Jan Rustem) 20 10
2004 5z.50 "Samuel Linde" (G. Landolfi) 65 40
2005 7z. "Michal Oginski" (Nanette Windisch) . . . 1·40 20

552 U.N. Emblem within "Eye"

1970. 25th Anniv of United Nations.
2006 **552** 2z.50 multicoloured . . . 20 10

553 Piano Keyboard and Chopin's Signature

554 Population Pictograph

1970. 8th International Chopin Piano Competition.
2007 **553** 2z.50 black and violet . . 20 10

1970. National Census. Multicoloured.
2008 40g. Type **554** 10 10
2009 60g. Family in "house" . . 10 10

555 Destroyer "Piorun" (½-size illustration)

1970. Polish Warships, World War II.
2010 **555** 40g. brown 10 10
2011 – 60g. black 10 10
2012 – 2z.50 brown 35 10
DESIGNS: 60g. "Orzel" (submarine); 2z.50, H.M.S. "Garland" (destroyer loaned to Polish Navy).

556 "Expressions" (Maria Jarema)

1970. Stamp Day. Contemporary Polish Paintings. Multicoloured.
2013 20g. "The Violin-cellist" (J. Nowosielski) (vert) . . 10 10
2014 40g. "View of Lodz" (B. Liberski) (vert) . . . 10 10
2015 60g. "Studio Concert" (W. Taranczewski) (vert) 10 10
2016 1z.50 "Still Life" (Z. Pronaszko) (vert) . . 10 10
2017 2z. "Hanging-up Washing" (A. Wroblewski) (vert) . . 10 10
2018 3z.40 Type **556** 20 10
2019 4z. "Canal in the Forest" (P. Potworowski) 45 10
2020 8z.50 "The Sun" (W. Strzeminski) 95 10

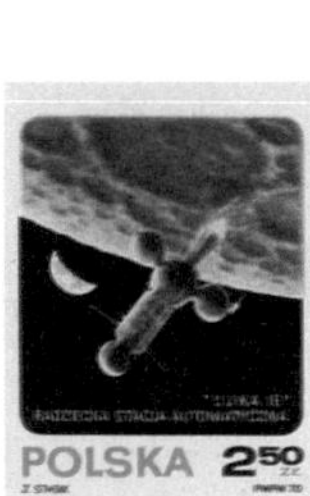

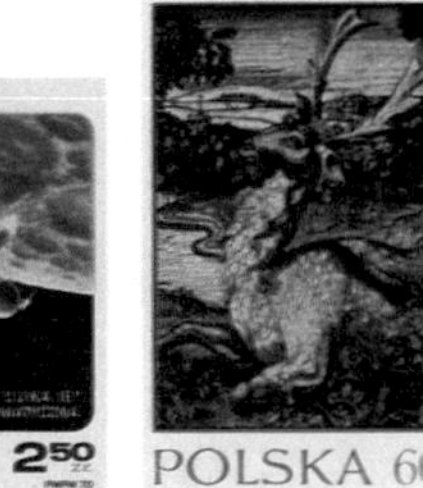

557 "Luna 16" landing on Moon

558 "Stag" (detail from "Daniel" tapestry)

1970. Moon Landing of "Luna 16".
2021 **557** 2z.50 multicoloured . . . 30 10

1970. Tapestries in Wawel Castle. Multicoloured.
2022 60g. Type **558** 10 10
2023 1z.15 "White Stork" (detail) 30 10
2024 1z.35 "Panther fighting Dragon" 10 10
2025 2z. "Man's Head" (detail, "Deluge" tapestry) . . . 20 10
2026 2z.50 "Child with Bird" (detail, "Adam Tilling the Soil" tapestry) 25 10
2027 4z. "God, Adam and Eve" (detail, "Happiness in Paradise" tapestry) . . . 45 30
2028 4z.50 Royal Monogram tapestry 75 30
MS2029 Two sheets, each 62 × 89 mm. (a) 5z.50 Polish coat-of-arms; (b) 7z.+3z. Monogram and satyrs. Imperf. Set of 2 sheets 2·10 1·25

559 Cadet ship "Dar Pomorza"

1971. Polish Ships. Multicoloured.
2030 40g. Type **559** 10 10
2031 60g. Liner "Stefan Batory" 10 10
2032 1z.15 Ice-breaker "Perkun" 15 10
2033 1z.35 Lifeboat "R-1" . . . 20 10
2034 1z.50 Bulk carrier "Ziemia Szczecinska" 30 10
2035 2z.50 Tanker "Beskidy" . . 30 10
2036 5z. Freighter "Hel" 65 20
2037 8z.50 Ferry "Gryf" . . . . 1·40 50

560 Checiny Castle

1971. Polish Castles. Multicoloured.
2038 20g. Type **560** 10 10
2039 40g. Wisnicz 10 10
2040 60g. Bedzin 10 10
2041 2z. Ogrodzieniec 15 10
2042 2z.50 Niedzica 15 10
2043 3z.40 Kwidzyn 35 10
2044 4z. Pieskowa Skala 35 10
2045 8z.50 Lidzbark Warminski 90 30

561 Battle of Pouilly, J. Dabrowski and W. Wroblewski

1971. Centenary of Paris Commune.
2046 **561** 60g. brown, blue and red 10 10

562 Plantation

563 "Bishop Marianos"

1971. Forestry Management. Multicoloured.
2047 40g. Type **562** 10 10
2048 60g. Forest (27 × 47 mm) . . 10 10
2049 1z.50 Tree-felling 20 10

1971. Fresco. Discoveries made by Polish Expedition at Faras, Nubia. Multicoloured.
2050 40g. Type **563** 10 10
2051 60g. "St. Anne" 10 10
2052 1z.15 "Archangel Michael" 10 10
2053 1z.35 "The Hermit, Anamon" 10 10
2054 1z.50 "Head of Archangel Michael" 10 10
2055 4z.50 "Evangelists' Cross" 35 10
2056 5z. "Christ protecting a nobleman" 60 20
2057 7z. "Archangel Michael" (half-length) 75 45

564 Revolutionaries

1971. 50th Anniv of Silesian Insurrection.
2058 **564** 60g. brown and gold . . 10 10
MS2059 108 × 106 mm. No. 2058 × 3 . . . . 2·10 95

565 "Soldiers"

1971. 25th Anniv of UNICEF Children's Drawings. Multicoloured.
2060 20g. "Peacock" (vert) . . . 10 10
2061 40g. Type **565** 10 10
2062 60g. "Lady Spring" (vert) 10 10
2063 2z. "Cat and Ball" 10 10
2064 2z.50 "Flowers in Jug" (vert) 20 10
2065 3z.40 "Friendship" 30 10
2066 5z.50 "Clown" (vert) . . . 70 30
2067 7z. "Strange Planet" 80 35

566 Fair Emblem

567 Copernicus's House, Torun

1971. 40th International Fair, Poznan.
2068 **566** 60g. multicoloured . . . 10 10

1971. 500th Birth Anniv (1973) of Copernicus (3rd issue). Multicoloured.
2069 40g. Type **567** 10 10
2070 60g. Collegium Naius, Jagiellonian University, Cracow (horiz) 10 10
2071 2z.50 Olsztyn Castle (horiz) 20 10
2072 4z. Frombork Cathedral . . 70 20

568 Folk Art Pattern

569 "Head of Worker" (X. Dunikowski)

1971. Folk Art. "Paper Cut-outs" showing various patterns.
2073 **568** 20g. black, green and blue 10 10
2074 – 40g. blue, green & cream 10 10
2075 – 60g. brown, blue and grey 10 10
2076 – 1z.15 purple, brn & buff 10 10
2077 – 1z.35 green, red & yellow 10 10

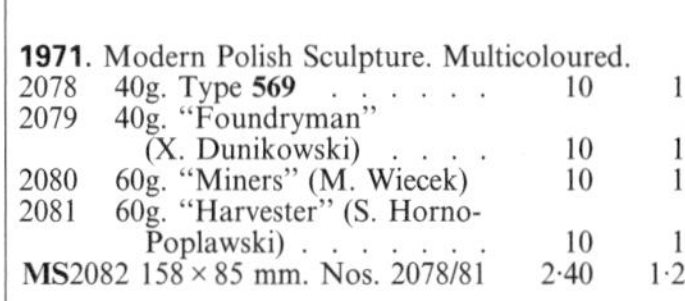

1971. Modern Polish Sculpture. Multicoloured.
2078 40g. Type **569** 10 10
2079 40g. "Foundryman" (X. Dunikowski) 10 10
2080 60g. "Miners" (M. Wiecek) 10 10
2081 60g. "Harvester" (S. Horno-Poplawski) 10 10
MS2082 158 × 85 mm. Nos. 2078/81 2·40 1·25

570 Congress Emblem and Computer Tapes

1971. 6th Polish Technical Congress, Warsaw.
2083 **570** 60g. violet and red . . . 10 10

571 "Angel" (J. Mehoffer)

573 PZL P-11C Fighters

572 "Mrs. Fedorowicz" (W. Pruszkowski)

1971. Stained Glass Windows. Multicoloured.
2084 20g. Type **571** 10 10
2085 40g. "Lillies" (S. Wyspianski) 10 10
2086 60g. "Iris" (S. Wyspianski) 10 10
2087 1z.35 "Apollo" (S. Wyspianski) 10 10
2088 1z.55 "Two Wise Men" (14th-century) 10 10
2089 3z.40 "The Flight into Egypt" (14th-century) . . 30 10
2090 5z.50 "Jacob" (14th-century) 50 10
2091 8z.50+4z. "Madonna" (15th-century) 80 10

1971. Contemporary Art from National Museum, Cracow. Multicoloured.
2092 40g. Type **572** 10 10
2093 50g. "Woman with Book" (T. Czyzeski) 10 10
2094 60g. "Girl with Chrysanthemums" (O. Boznanska) 10 10
2095 2z.50 "Girl in Red Dress" (J. Pankiewicz) (horiz) . . 10 10
2096 3z.40 "Reclining Nude" (L. Chwistek) (horiz) . . 20 10
2097 4z.50 "Strange Garden" (J. Mehoffer) 35 10
2098 5z. "Wife in White Hat" (Z. Pronaszko) 45 10
2099 7z.+1z. "Seated Nude" (W. Weiss) 65 45

1971. Polish Aircraft of World War II. Mult.
2100 90g. Type **573** 10 10
2101 1z.50 PZL 23A Karas fighters 20 10
2102 3z.40 PZL P-37 Los bomber 30 20

574 Royal Castle, Warsaw (pre-1939)

1971. Reconstruction of Royal Castle, Warsaw.
2103 **574** 60g. black, red and gold 10 10

575 Astronauts in Moon Rover

576 "Lunokhod 1"

1971. Moon Flight of "Apollo 15".
2104 **575** 2z.50 multicoloured . . . 45 10
MS2105 122 × 157 mm. No. 2104 × 6 plus 2 stamp-size se-tenant labels, showing Space scenes 3·75 2·75

1971. Moon Flight of "Lunik 17" and "Lunokhod 1".
2106 **576** 2z.50 multicoloured . . . 45 10
MS2107 158 × 118 mm. No. 2106 × 6 plus 2 stamp-size se-tenant labels, showing Space scenes 3·75 1·90

577 Worker at Wheel **578** Ship-building

1971. 6th Polish United Workers' Party Congress. (a) Party Posters.
2108 **577** 60g. red, blue and grey 10 10
2109 60g. red and grey (Worker's head) 10 10
(b) Industrial Development. Each in gold and red.
2110 60g. Type **578** 10 10
2111 60g. Building construction 10 10
2112 60g. Combine-harvester 10 10
2113 60g. Motor-car production 10 10
2114 60g. Pit-head 10 10
2115 60g. Petro-chemical plant 10 10
MS2116 102 × 115 mm. Nos. 2110/15 1·10 80

579 "Prunus cerasus"

1971. Flowers of Trees and Shrubs. Multicoloured.
2117 10g. Type **579** 10 10
2118 20g. "Malusniedzwetzskyana" 10 10
2119 40g. "Pyrus L." 10 10
2120 60g. "Prunus persica" 10 10
2121 1z.15 "Magnolia kobus" 10 10
2122 1z.35 "Crategus oxyacantha" 10 10
2123 2z.50 "Malus M." 10 10
2124 3z.40 "Aesculus carnea" 20 10
2125 5z. "Robinia pseudacacia" 75 20
2126 8z.50 "Prunus avium" 1·40 50

580 "Worker" (sculpture, J. Januszkiewicz)

1972. 30th Anniv of Polish Workers' Coalition.
2127 **580** 60g. black and red 10 10

581 Luge

1972. Winter Olympic Games, Sapporo, Japan. Multicoloured.
2128 40g. Type **581** 10 10
2129 60g. Slalom (vert) 10 10
2130 1z.65 Biathlon (vert) 20 10
2131 2z.50 Ski jumping 35 25
MS2132 85 × 68 mm. 10z.+5z. Downhill skiing 2·10 1·25

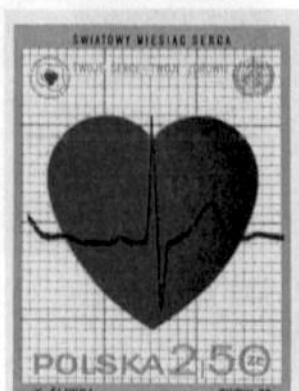

582 "Heart" and Cardiogram Trace **583** Running

1972. World Heart Month.
2133 **582** 2z.50 multicoloured 20 10

1972. Olympic Games, Munich. Multicoloured.
2134 20g. Type **583** 10 10
2135 30g. Archery 10 10
2136 40g. Boxing 10 10
2137 60g. Fencing 10 10
2138 2z.50 Wrestling 10 10
2139 3z.40 Weightlifting 10 10
2140 5z. Cycling 60 10
2141 8z.50 Shooting 95 20
MS2142 70 × 80 mm. 10z.+5z. As 30g. 1·40 75

584 Cyclists **585** Polish War Memorial, Berlin

1972. 25th International Peace Cycle Race.
2143 **584** 60g. multicoloured 10 10

1972. "Victory Day, 1945".
2144 **585** 60g. green 10 10

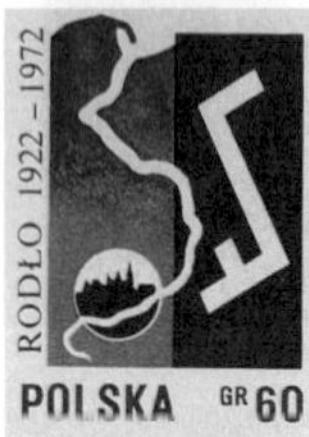

586 "Rodlo" Emblem **587** Polish Knight of 972 A.D.

1972. 50th Anniv of Polish Posts in Germany.
2145 **586** 60g. ochre, red and green 10 10

1972. Millenary of Battle of Cedynia.
2146 **587** 60g. multicoloured 10 10

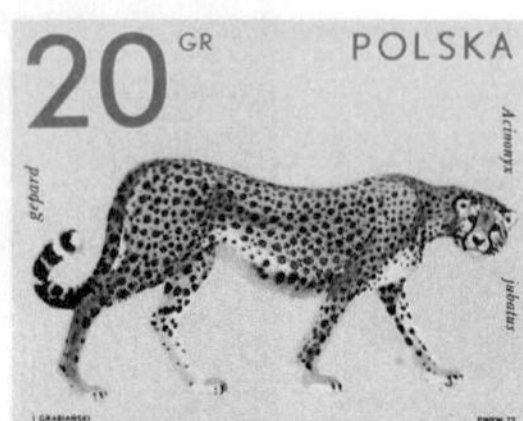

588 Cheetah

1972. Zoo Animals. Multicoloured.
2147 20g. Type **588** 10 10
2148 40g. Giraffe (vert) 20 10
2149 60g. Toco toucan 30 10
2150 1z.35 Chimpanzee 20 10
2151 1z.65 Common gibbon 30 10
2152 3z.40 Crocodile 35 10
2153 4z. Red kangaroo 65 10
2154 4z.50 Tiger (vert) 2·75 60
2155 7z. Mountain zebra 3·00 1·25

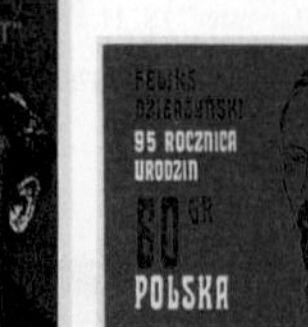

589 L. Warynski. (founder) **590** F. Dzerzhinsky

1972. 90th Anniv of Proletarian Party.
2156 **589** 60g. multicoloured 10 10

1972. 95th Birth Anniv of Feliks Dzerzhinsky (Russian politician).
2157 **590** 60g. black and red 10 10

591 Global Emblem **592** Scene from "In Barracks" (ballet)

1972. 25th Int Co-operative Federation Congress.
2158 **591** 60g. multicoloured 10 10

1972. Death Centenary of Stanislaus Moniuszko (composer). Scenes from Works.
2159 **592** 10g. violet and gold 10 10
2160 – 20g. black and gold 10 10
2161 – 40g. green and gold 10 10
2162 – 60g. blue and gold 10 10
2163 – 1z.15 blue and gold 10 10
2164 – 1z.35 blue and gold 10 10
2165 – 1z.55 green and gold 20 10
2166 – 2z.50 brown and gold 20 10
DESIGNS: 20g. "The Countess" (opera); 40g. "The Haunted Manor" (opera); 60g. "Halka" (opera); 1z.15, "New Don Quixote" (ballet); 1z.35, "Verbum Nobile"; 1z.55, "Ideal" (operetta); 2z.50, "Pariah" (opera).

593 "Copernicus the Astronomer"

1972. 500th Birth Anniv (1973) of Nicolas Copernicus. (4th issue).
2167 **593** 40g. black and blue 10 10
2168 – 60g. black and orange 10 10
2169 – 2z.50 black and red 10 10
2170 – 3z.40 black and green 15 10
MS2171 62 × 102 mm. 10z.+5z. multicoloured 2·75 1·40
DESIGNS: 60g. Copernicus and Polish eagle; 2z.50, Copernicus and Medal; 3z.40, Copernicus and page of book; VERT: (29 × 48 mm)—10z.+5z. Copernicus charting the planets.

594 "The Amazon" (P. Michalowski)

1972. Stamp Day. Polish Paintings. Multicoloured.
2172 30g. Type **594** 10 10
2173 40g. "Ostafi Laskiewicz" (J. Metejko) 10 10
2174 60g. "Summer Idyll" (W. Gerson) 10 10
2175 2z. "The Neapolitan Woman" (A. Kotsis) 10 10
2176 2z.50 "Girl Bathing" (P. Szyndler) 10 10
2177 3z.40 "The Princess of Thum" (A. Grottger) 10 10
2178 4z. "Rhapsody" (S. Wyspianski) 15 30
2179 8z.50+4z. "Young Woman" (J. Malczewski) (horiz) 35 35

1972. Nos. 1578/9 surch.
2180 50g. on 40g. brown 10 10
2181 90g. on 40g. brown 10 10
2182 1z. on 40g. brown 10 10
2183 1z.50 on 60g. orange 10 10
2184 2z.70 on 40g. brown 15 10
2185 4z. on 60g. orange 30 10
2186 4z.50 on 60g. orange 30 10
2187 4z.90 on 60g. orange 45 10

596 "The Little Soldier" (E. Piwowarski)

1972. Children's Health Centre.
2188 **596** 60g. black and pink 10 10

597 "Royal Castle, Warsaw". (E. J. Dahlberg, 1656) **598** Chalet, Chocholowska Valley

1972. Restoration of Royal Castle, Warsaw.
2189 **597** 60g. black, violet and blue 10 10

1972. Tourism. Mountain Chalets. Multicoloured.
2190 40g. Type **598** 10 10
2191 60g. Hala Ornak (horiz) 10 10
2192 1z.55 Hala Gasienicowa 10 10
2193 1z.65 Valley of Five Lakes (horiz) 15 10
2194 2z.50 Morskie Oko 30 10

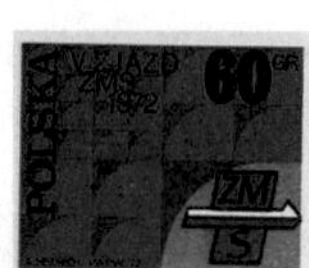

599 Trade Union Banners **600** Congress Emblem

1972. 7th Polish Trade Union Congresses.
2195 **599** 60g. multicoloured 10 10

1972. 5th Socialist Youth Union Congress.
2196 **600** 60g. multicoloured 10 10

601 Japanese Azalea

1972. Flowering Shrubs. Multicoloured.
2197 40g. Type **601** 10 10
2198 50g. Alpine rose 10 10
2199 60g. Pomeranian honeysuckle 10 10
2200 1z.65 Chinese quince 10 10
2201 2z.50 Korean cranberry 25 10
2202 3z.40 Pontic azalea 35 10
2203 4z. Delavay's white syringa 75 20
2204 8z.50 Common lilac ("Massena") 1·60 65

602 Piast Knight (10th-century) **603** Copernicus

1972. Polish Cavalry Through the Ages. Mult.
2205 20g. Type **602** 10 10
2206 40g. 13th-century knight 10 10
2207 60g. Knight of Wladyslaw Jagiello's Army (15th-century) (horiz) 10 10
2208 1z.35 17th-century hussar 10 10
2209 4z. Lancer of National Guard (18th-century) 50 10
2210 4z.50 "Congress Kingdom" cavalry officer 50 10
2211 5z. Trooper of Light Cavalry (1939) (horiz) 1·10 10
2212 7z. Trooper of People's Army (1945) 1·10 60

1972. 500th Birth Anniv (1973) of Copernicus (5th issue).
2213 **603** 1z. brown 15 10
2214 1z.50 ochre 20 10

604 Couple with Hammer and Sickle — **605** "Copernicus as Young Man" (Bacciarelli)

1972. 50th Anniv of U.S.S.R. Multicoloured.
2215 40g. Type **604** 10 10
2216 60g. Red star and globe . . 10 10

1973. 500th Birth Anniv of Copernicus (6th issue). Multicoloured.
2217 1z. Type **605** 10 10
2218 1z.50 "Copernicus" (anon) 10 10
2219 2z.70 "Copernicus" (Zinck Nor) 20 10
2220 4z. "Copernicus" (from Strasbourg clock) 45 30
2221 4z.90 "Copernicus" (Jan Matejko) (horiz) 60 30

606 Coronation Sword — **607** Statue of Lenin

1973. Polish Art. Multicoloured.
2222 50g. Type **606** 10 10
2223 1z. Kruzlowa Madonna (detail) 10 10
2224 1z. Armour of hussar . . . 10 10
2225 1z.50 Carved head from Wavel Castle 10 10
2226 1z.50 Silver cockerel 10 10
2227 2z.70 Armorial eagle 30 10
2228 4z.90 Skarbimierz Madonna 60 35
2229 8z.50 "Portrait of Tenczynski" (anon) . . . 95 60

1973. Unveiling of Lenin's Statue, Nowa Huta.
2230 **607** 1z. multicoloured 10 10

608 Coded Letter

1973. Introduction of Postal Codes.
2231 **608** 1z. multicoloured 10 10

609 Wolf

1973. International Hunting Council Congress and 50th Anniv of Polish Hunting Association. Game Animals. Multicoloured.
2232 50g. Type **609** 10 10
2233 1z. Mouflon 10 10
2234 1z.50 Elk 10 10
2235 2z.70 Western capercaillie 10 10
2236 3z. Roe deer 10 10
2237 4z.50 Lynx 55 10
2238 4z.90 Red deer . . . . . . 1·10 35
2239 5z. Wild boar . . . . 1·25 45

610 "Salyut" — **611** Open Book and Flame

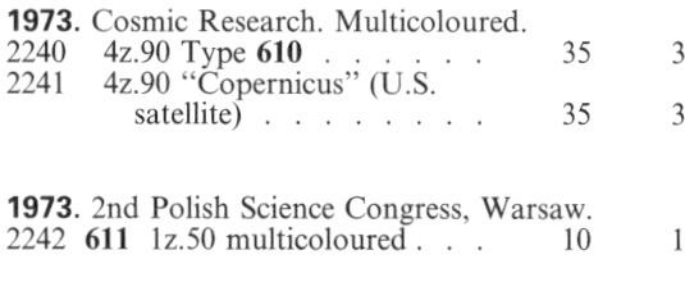

1973. Cosmic Research. Multicoloured.
2240 4z.90 Type **610** 35 30
2241 4z.90 "Copernicus" (U.S. satellite) 35 30

1973. 2nd Polish Science Congress, Warsaw.
2242 **611** 1z.50 multicoloured . . . 10 10

612 Ancient Seal of Poznan — **613** M. Nowotko

1973. "Polska 73" Philatelic Exhibition, Poznan. Multicoloured.
2243 1z. Type **612** 10 10
2244 1z.50 Tombstone of N. Tomicki 10 10
2245 2z.70 Kalisz paten 20 10
2246 4z. Bronze gates, Gniezno Cathedral (horiz) 30 10
MS2247 91 × 66 mm. 10z.+5z. purple and olive . . . . 1·50 95
MS2248 91 × 66 mm. 10z.+5z. purple and lilac . . . . 6·00 1·10

1973. 80th Birth Anniv of Marceli Nowotko (party leader).
2249 **613** 1z.50 black and red . . . 10 10

614 Cherry Blossom

1973. Protection of the Environment. Mult.
2250 50g. Type **614** 10 10
2251 90g. Cattle in meadow . . . 10 10
2252 1z. White stork on nest . . 30 10
2253 1z.50 Pond life 10 10
2254 2z.70 Meadow flora 15 10
2255 4z.90 Ocean fauna 35 10
2256 5z. Forest life . . . . 1·90 30
2257 6z.50 Agricultural produce 1·25 50

615 Motor-cyclist

1973. World Speedway Race Championships, Chorzow.
2258 **615** 1z.50 multicoloured . . . 10 10

616 "Copernicus" (M. Bacciarelli)

1973. Stamp Day.
2259 **616** 4z.+2z. multicoloured . . 45 30

617 Tank

1973. 30th Anniv of Polish People's Army. Mult.
2260 1z. Type **617** 10 10
2261 1z. Mikoyan Gurevich MiG-21D airplane 10 10
2262 1z.50 Guided missile 10 10
2263 1z.50 "Puck" (missile boat) 15 10

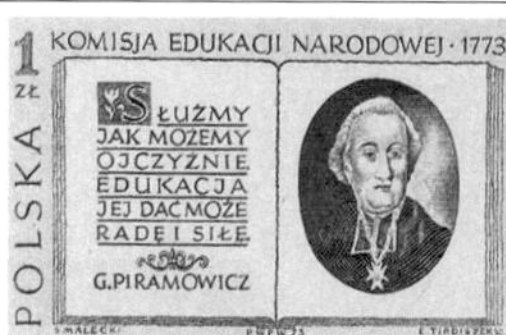

618 G. Piramowicz and Title Page

1973. Bicent of Nat Educational Commission.
2264 **618** 1z. brown and yellow . . 10 10
2265 – 1z.50 green, & light green 10 10
DESIGN: 1z.50, J. Sniadecki, H. Kollataj and J. U. Niemcewicz.

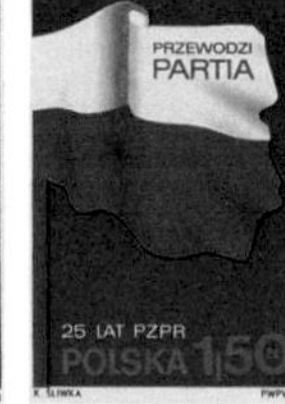

619 Pawel Strzelecki (explorer) and Red Kangaroo — **620** Polish Flag

1973. Polish Scientists. Multicoloured.
2266 1z. Type **619** 10 10
2267 1z. Henryk Arctowski (Polar explorer) and Adelie penguins 20 10
2268 1z.50 Stefan Rogozinkski (explorer) and "Lucy-Margaret" (schooner) . . 15 10
2269 1z.50 Benedykt Dybowski (zoologist) and sable, Lake Baikal 10 10
2270 2z. Bronislaw Malinowski (anthropologist) and New Guinea dancers 10 10
2271 2z.70 Stefan Drzewiecki (oceanographer) and submarine 20 10
2272 3z. Edward Strasburger (botanist) and classified plants 20 10
2273 8z. Ignacy Domeyko (geologist) and Chilean desert landscape 80 30

1973. 25th Anniv of Polish United Workers' Party.
2274 **620** 1z.40 red, blue and gold 10 10

621 Jelcz-Berliet Coach

1973. Polish Motor Vehicles. Multicoloured.
2275 50g. Type **621** 10 10
2276 90g. Jelcz "316" truck . . . 10 10
2277 1z. Polski-Fiat "126p" saloon 10 10
2278 1z.50 Polski-Fiat "125p" saloon and mileage records 10 10
2279 4z. Nysa "M-521" utility van 30 25
2280 4z.50 Star "660" truck . . . 60 30

622 Iris — **623** Cottage, Kurpie

1974. Flowers. Drawings by S. Wyspianski.
2281 **622** 50g. purple 10 10
2282 – 1z. green 10 10
2283 – 1z.50 red 10 10
2284 – 3z. violet 30 10
2285 – 4z. blue 30 10
2286 – 4z.50 green 45 10
FLOWERS: 1z. Dandelion; 1z.50, Rose; 3z. Thistle; 4z. Cornflower; 4z.50, Clover.

1974. Wooden Architecture. Multicoloured.
2287 1z. Type **623** 10 10
2288 1z.50 Church, Sekowa . . . 10 10
2289 4z. Town Hall, Sulmierzycc 20 10
2290 4z.50 Church, Lachowice . . 30 10
2291 4z.90 Windmill, Sobienie Jeziory 45 20
2292 5z. Orthodox Church, Ulucz 50 20

624 19th-century Mail Coach — **625** Cracow Motif

1974. Centenary of Universal Postal Union.
2293 **624** 1z.50 multicoloured . . . 10 10

1974. "SOCPHILEX IV" Int Stamp Exn, Katowice. Regional Floral Embroideries. Multicoloured.
2294 50g. Type **625** 10 10
2295 1z.50 Lowicz motif 10 10
2296 4z. Silesian motif 20 10
MS2297 69 × 71 mm. No. 2296 × 3 1·10 30

626 Association Emblem — **627** Soldier and Dove

1974. 5th Congress of Fighters for Freedom and Democracy Association, Warsaw.
2298 **626** 1z.50 red 10 10

1974. 29th Anniv of Victory over Fascism in Second World War.
2299 **627** 1z.50 multicoloured . . . 10 10

628 "Comecon" Headquarters, Moscow

1974. 25th Anniv of Council for Mutual Economic Aid.
2300 **628** 1z.50 brown, red & blue 10 10

629 World Cup Emblem

1974. World Cup Football Championship, West Germany. Multicoloured.
2301 4z.90 Type **629** 25 15
2302 4z.90 Players and Olympic Gold Medal of 1972 . . . 25 15
MS2303 116 × 83 mm. Nos. 2301/2 10·50 9·00
See also No. **MS**2315.

630 Model of 16th-century Galleon — **631** Title page of "Chess" by J. Kochanowski

1974. Sailing Ships. Multicoloured.
2304 1z. Type **630** 10 10
2305 1z.50 Sloop "Dal" (1934) 10 10
2306 2z.70 Yacht "Opty" (Teliga's circumnavigation, 1969) 10 10
2307 4z. Cadet ship "Dar Pomorza", 1972 . . . . . 40 10
2308 4z.90 Yacht "Polonez" (Baranowski's circumnavigation, 1973) 55 25

1974. 10th Inter-Chess Festival, Lublin. Mult.
2309 1z. Type **631** 10 15
2310 1z.50 "Education" (18th-century engraving, D. Chodowiecki) 20 15

632 Lazienkowska Road Junction

1974. Opening of Lazienkowska Flyover.
2311 **632** 1z.50 multicoloured . . . 15 15

633 Face and Map of Poland　**634** Strawberries

1974. 30th Anniv of Polish People's Republic.
2312 **633** 1z.50 black, gold and red 15 10
2313 – 1z.50 multicoloured (silver background) . . 15 10
2314 – 1z.50 multicoloured (red background) 15 10
DESIGN—31 × 43 mm: Nos. 2313/14, Polish "Eagle".

1974. Poland–Third Place in World Cup Football Championship. Sheet 107 × 121 mm containing four stamps as No. 2301, but with inscr in silver instead of black, and two labels.
MS2315 **629** 4z.90 × 4 multicoloured 3·00 1·90

1974. 19th International Horticultural Congress, Warsaw. Fruits, Vegetables and Flowers. Mult.
2316 50g. Type **634** 10 10
2317 90g. Blackcurrants 10 10
2318 1z. Apples 10 10
2319 1z.50 Cucumbers 20 10
2320 2z.70 Tomatoes 30 10
2321 4z.50 Green peas 75 10
2322 4z.90 Pansies . . . . 1·10 20
2323 5z. Nasturtiums . . . . . . 1·50 30

635 Civic Militia and Security Service Emblem　**636** "Child in Polish Costume" (L. Orlowski)

1974. 30th Anniv of Polish Civic Militia and Security Service.
2324 **635** 1z.50 multicoloured . . . 10 10

1974. Stamp Day. "The Child in Polish Costume" Painting. Multicoloured.
2325 50g. Type **636** 10 10
2326 90g. "Girl with Pigeon" (anon) 10 10
2327 1z. "Portrait of a Girl" (S. Wyspianski) 10 10
2328 1z.50 "The Orphan from Poronin" (W. Slewinski) 10 10
2329 3z. "Peasant Boy" (K. Sichulski) 20 10
2330 4z.50 "Florence Page" (A. Gierymski) 35 10
2331 4z.90 "Tadeusz and Dog" (P. Michalowski) 45 30
2332 6z.50 "Boy with Doe" (A. Kotsis) 60 35

637 "The Crib", Cracow

1974. Polish Art. Multicoloured.
2333 1z. Type **637** 10 10
2334 1z.50 "The Flight to Egypt" (15th-century polyptych) 10 10
2335 2z. "King Sigismund III Vasa" (16th-century miniature) 20 10
2336 4z. "King Jan Olbracht" (16th-century title-page) 75 30

638 Angler and Fish　**639** "Pablo Neruda" (O. Guayasamin)

1974. Polish Folklore. 16th-century Woodcuts (1st series).
2337 **638** 1z. black 10 10
2338 – 1z.50 blue 10 10
DESIGN: 1z.50, Hunter and wild animals.
See also Nos. 2525/6.

1974. 70th Birth Anniv of Pablo Neruda (Chilean poet).
2339 **639** 1z.50 multicoloured . . . 10 10

640 "Nike" Memorial and National Opera House

1975. 30th Anniv of Warsaw Liberation.
2340 **640** 1z.50 multicoloured . . . 10 10

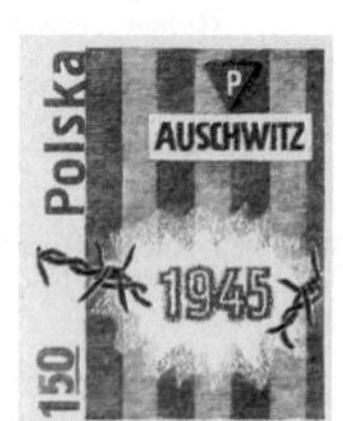

641 Male Lesser Kestrel　**642** Broken Barbed Wire

1975. Birds of Prey. Multicoloured.
2341 1z. Type **641** 25 10
2342 1z. Lesser kestrel (female) 25 10
2343 1z.50 Western red-footed falcon (male) 25 10
2344 1z.50 Western red-footed falcon (female) 25 10
2345 2z. Northern hobby 30 10
2346 3z. Common kestrel 55 10
2347 4z. Merlin . . . . 1·40 75
2348 8z. Peregrine falcon . . . . 2·10 1·50

1975. 30th Anniv of Auschwitz Concentration Camp Liberation.
2349 **642** 1z.50 black and red . . . 10 10

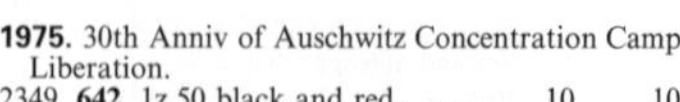

643 Hurdling

1975. 6th European Indoor Athletic Championships, Katowice. Multicoloured.
2350 1z. Type **643** 10 10
2351 1z.50 Pole vault 10 10
2352 4z. Triple jump 30 10
2353 4z.90 Running 30 10
MS2354 72 × 63 mm. 10z.+5z. green and silver (Montreal Olympics emblem) (26 × 31 mm) . . . . 1·90 90

644 "St. Anne" (Veit Stoss)

1975. "Arphila 1975" International Stamp Exhibition, Paris.
2355 **644** 1z.50 multicoloured . . . 10 10

645 Globe and "Radio Waves"

1975. International Amateur Radio Union Conference, Warsaw.
2356 **645** 1z.50 multicoloured . . . 10 10

646 Stone, Pine and Tatra Mountains　**647** Hands holding Tulips and Rifle

1975. Centenary of Mountain Guides' Association. Multicoloured.
2357 1z. Type **646** 10 10
2358 1z. Gentians and Tatra Mountains 10 10
2359 1z.50 Sudety Mountains (horiz) 10 10
2360 1z.50 Branch of yew (horiz) 10 10
2361 4z. Beskidy Mountains . . . 30 15
2362 4z. Arnica blossoms 30 10

1975. 30th Anniv of Victory over Fascism.
2363 **647** 1z.50 multicoloured . . . 15 10

648 Flags of Member Countries

1975. 20th Anniv of Warsaw Treaty Organization.
2364 **648** 1z.50 multicoloured . . . 10 10

649 Hens

1975. 26th European Zoo-technical Federation Congress, Warsaw. Multicoloured.
2365 50g. Type **649** 10 10
2366 1z. Geese 10 10
2367 1z.50 Cattle 10 10
2368 2z. Cow 10 10
2369 3z. Wielkopolska horse . . 30 20
2370 4z. Pure-bred Arab horses 30 20
2371 4z.50 Pigs . . . . 1·10 80
2372 5z. Sheep . . . . 1·75 1·10

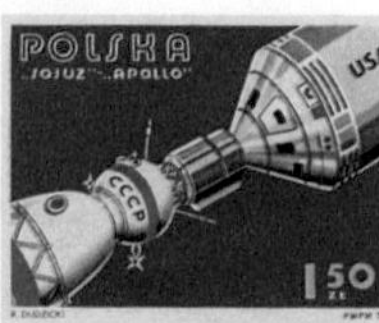

650 "Apollo" and "Soyuz" Spacecraft linked

1975. "Apollo–Soyuz" Space Project. Mult.
2373 1z.50 Type **650** 10 10
2374 4z.90 "Apollo" spacecraft 45 10
2375 4z.90 "Soyuz" spacecraft . . 45 25
MS2376 119 × 156 mm. Nos. 2373 × 2, 2374 × 2 and 2375 × 2 . . 5·25 3·25

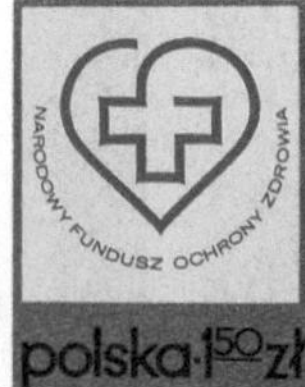

651 Organization Emblem

1975. National Health Protection Fund.
2377 **651** 1z.50 blue, black & silver 10 10

652 U.N. Emblem

1975. 30th Anniv of U.N.O.
2378 **652** 4z. multicoloured 30 10

653 Polish Flag within "E" for Europe

1975. European Security and Co-operation Conference, Helsinki.
2379 **653** 4z. red, blue and black 30 25

654 "Bolek and Lolek"

1975. Children's Television Characters. Mult.
2380 50g. Type **654** 10 15
2381 1z. "Jacek" and "Agatka" 10 15
2382 1z.50 "Reksio" (dog) . . . 10 15
2383 4z. "Telesfor" (dragon) . . 45 15

655 Institute Emblem　**656** Women's Faces

1975. 40th Session of International Statistics Institute.
2384 **655** 1z.50 multicoloured . . . 10 10

1975. International Women's Year.
2385 **656** 1z.50 multicoloured . . . 10 10

657 Albatros Biplane

1975. 50th Anniv of First Polish Airmail Stamps. Multicoloured.
2386 2z.40 Type **657** 15 15
2387 4z.90 Ilyushin Il-62 airplane 40 15

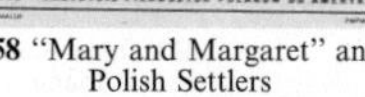

658 "Mary and Margaret" and Polish Settlers　**659** Frederic Chopin

1975. Bicentenary of American Revolution. Poles in American Life. Multicoloured.
2388 1z. Type **658** 15 10
2389 1z.50 Polish glass-works, Jamestown 10 10
2390 2z.70 Helena Modrzejewska (actress) 10 10
2391 4z. K. Pulaski (soldier) . . . 25 10
2392 6z.40 T. Kosciuzko (soldier) 60 30
MS2393 117 × 102 mm. 4z.90 Washington; 4z.90 Kosciuszko; 4z.90 Pulaski . . . . 1·10 70

1975. 9th International Chopin Piano Competition.
2394 **659** 1z.50 black, lilac & gold 10 20

660 "Self-portrait"
661 Market Place, Kazimierz Dolny

1975. Stamp Day. Birth Centenary of Xawery Dunikowski (sculptor). Multicoloured.
2395 50g. Type **660** 10 10
2396 1z. "Breath" 10 10
2397 1z.50 "Maternity" 15 10
2398 8z.+4z. "Silesian Insurrectionists" 90 35

1975. European Architectural Heritage Year.
2399 **661** 1z. green 10 10
2400 – 1z.50 brown 10 10
DESIGN—VERT: 1z.50, Town Hall, Zamosc.

662 "Lodz" (W. Strzeminski)
664 Symbolized Figure "7"

663 Henry IV's Eagle Gravestone Head (14th-century)

1975. "Lodz 75" National Stamp Exhibition.
2401 **662** 4z.50 multicoloured . . . 30 20
MS2402 80 × 101 mm. No. 2401 95 65

1975. Piast Dynasty of Silesia.
2403 **663** 1z. green 10 10
2404 – 1z.50 brown 10 10
2405 – 4z. violet 25 10
DESIGNS: 1z.50, Seal of Prince Boleslaw of Legnica; 4z. Coin of last Prince, Jerzy Wilhelm.

1975. 7th Congress of Polish United Workers Party.
2406 **664** 1z. multicoloured 10 10
2407 – 1z.50 red, blue and silver 10 10
DESIGN: 1z.50, Party initials "PZPR".

665 Ski Jumping

1976. Winter Olympic Games, Innsbruck. Mult.
2408 50g. Type **665** 10 10
2409 1z. Ice hockey 10 10
2410 1z.50 Skiing 10 10
2411 2z. Skating 10 10
2412 4z. Tobogganing 30 10
2413 6z.40 Biathlon 40 30

666 Richard Trevithick and his Locomotive, 1803

1976. History of the Railway Locomotive. Mult.
2414 50g. Type **666** 10 10
2415 1z. Murray and Blenkinsop's steam locomotive and carriage, 1810 . . . . . 10 10
2416 1z.50 George Stephenson and his locomotive "Rocket", 1829 . . . . . 10 10
2417 1z.50 Polish "Universal" electric locomotive No. ET22-001, 1969 . . . . . 10 10
2418 2z.70 Robert Stephenson and his locomotive "North Star", 1837 . . . 10 10
2419 3z. Joseph Harrison and his locomotive, 1840 . . . . 15 10
2420 4z.50 Locomotive "Thomas Rogers", 1855, U.S.A. . . 75 45
2421 4z.90 A. Xiezopolski and Series Ok22 steam locomotive, 1922 . . . . 75 45

667 Flags of Member Countries

1976. 20th Anniv of Institute for Nuclear Research (C.M.E.A.).
2422 **667** 1z.50 multicoloured . . . 15 10

668 Early Telephone, Satellite and Radar

1976. Telephone Centenary.
2423 **668** 1z.50 multicoloured . . . 10 10

669 Jantar Glider
670 Player

1976. Air. Contemporary Aviation.
2424 **669** 5z. blue 35 10
2425 – 10z. brown 75 10
2425a – 20z. olive . . . . . . 1·50 10
2425b – 50z. lake . . . . . . 3·50 60
DESIGN: 10z. Mil Mi-6 helicopter; 20z. PZL-106A agricultural airplane; 50z. PZL-Mielec TS-11 Iskra jet trainer over Warsaw Castle.

1976. World Ice Hockey Championships, Katowice. Multicoloured.
2426 1z. Type **670** 10 10
2427 1z.50 Player (different) . . . 10 10

671 Polish U.N. Soldier

1976. Polish Troops in U.N. Sinai Force.
2428 **671** 1z.50 multicoloured . . . 10 10

672 "Glory to the Sappers" (S. Kulon)
673 "Interphil 76"

1976. War Memorials. Multicoloured.
2429 1z. Type **672** 10 10
2430 1z. 1st Polish Army Monument, Sandau, Laba (B. Koniuszy) 10 10

1976. "Interphil '76" Int Stamp Exn, Philadelphia.
2431 **673** 8z.40 multicoloured . . . 55 30

674 Wielkopolski Park and Tawny Owl

1976. National Parks. Multicoloured.
2432 90g. Type **674** 30 10
2433 1z. Wolinski Park and white-tailed sea eagle . . 30 10
2434 1z.50 Slowinski Park and seagull 35 10
2435 4z.50 Bieszezadzki Park and lynx 30 10
2436 5z. Ojcowski Park and bat 30 20
2437 6z. Kampinoski Park and elk 35 30

675 Peace Dove within Globe

1976. 25th Anniv of U.N. Postal Administration.
2438 **675** 8z.40 multicoloured . . . 60 25

676 Fencing
677 National Theatre

1976. Olympic Games, Montreal. Multicoloured.
2439 50g. Type **676** 10 10
2440 1z. Cycling 10 10
2441 1z.50 Football 10 10
2442 4z.20 Boxing 30 10
2443 6z.90 Weightlifting 55 15
2444 8z.40 Athletics 60 25
MS2445 78 × 94 mm. 10z.+5z. black and red (Volleyball) (23 × 29 mm) 1·50 85

1976. Cent of National Theatre, Poznan.
2446 **677** 1z.50 green and orange 15 10

678 Aleksander Czekanowski and Baikal Landscape
679 "Sphinx"

1976. Death Centenary of Aleksander Czekanowski (geologist).
2447 **678** 1z.50 multicoloured . . . 15 15

1976. Stamp Day. Corinthian Vase Paintings (7th century B.C.). Multicoloured.
2448 1z. Type **679** 10 10
2449 1z.50 "Siren" (horiz) 10 10
2450 2z. "Lion" (horiz) 15 10
2451 4z.20 "Bull" (horiz) 30 10
2452 4z.50 "Goat" (horiz) 30 25
2453 8z.+4z. "Sphinx" (different) 1·00 45

680 Warszawa "M 20"

1976. 25th Anniv of Zeran Motor-car Factory, Warsaw. Multicoloured.
2454 1z. Type **680** 10 10
2455 1z.50 Warszawa "223" . . . 10 10
2456 2z. Syrena "104" 15 10
2457 4z.90 Polski - Fiat "125P" 40 15
MS2458 137 × 109 mm. Nos. 2454/7 1·90 1·10

681 Molten Steel Ladle

1976. Huta Katowice Steel Works.
2459 **681** 1z.50 multicoloured . . . 15 15

682 Congress Emblem
683 "Wirzbieto Epitaph" (painting on wood, 1425)

1976. 8th Polish Trade Unions Congress.
2460 **682** 1z.50 orange, bistre and brown 15 15

1976. Polish Art. Multicoloured.
2461 1z. Type **683** 10 15
2462 6z. "Madonna and Child" (painted carving, c.1410) 40 15

684 Tanker "Zawrat" at Oil Terminal, Gdansk

1976. Polish Ports. Multicoloured.
2463 1z. Type **684** 10 10
2464 1z. Ferry "Gryf" at Gdansk 10 10
2465 1z.50 Loading container ship "General Bem", Gdynia 20 10
2466 1z.50 Liner "Stefan Batory" leaving Gdynia 20 10
2467 2z. Bulk carrier "Ziemia Szczecinska" loading at Szczecin 25 10
2468 4z.20 Loading coal, Swinoujscie 30 10
2469 6z.90 Pleasure craft, Kolobrzeg 40 30
2470 8z.40 Coastal map 60 30

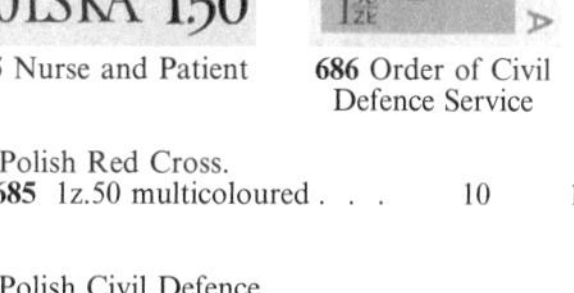

685 Nurse and Patient
686 Order of Civil Defence Service

1977. Polish Red Cross.
2471 **685** 1z.50 multicoloured . . . 10 10

1977. Polish Civil Defence.
2472 **686** 1z.50 multicoloured . . . 10 10

687 Ball in Road

1977. Child Road Safety Campaign.
2473 **687** 1z.50 multicoloured . . . 10 10

688 Dewberries 689 Computer Tape

1977. Wild Fruits. Multicoloured.
2474 50g. Type **688** 10 10
2475 90g. Cowberries 10 10
2476 1z. Wild strawberries . . . 10 10
2477 1z.50 Bilberries 15 10
2478 2z. Raspberries 15 10
2479 4z.50 Sloes 30 10
2480 6z. Rose hips 40 10
2481 6z.90 Hazelnuts 45 30

1977. 30th Anniv of Russian–Polish Technical Co-operation.
2482 **689** 1z.50 multicoloured . . . 10 10

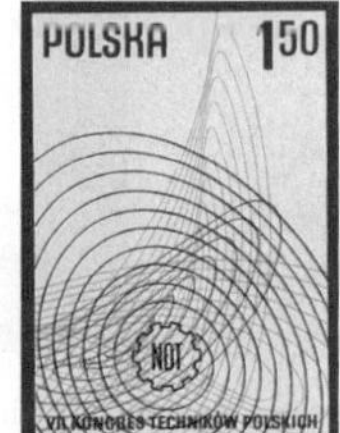

690 Pendulum Traces and Emblem

1977. 7th Polish Congress of Technology.
2483 **690** 1z.50 multicoloured . . . 10 10

691 "Toilet of Venus"

1977. 400th Birth Anniv of Peter Paul Rubens. Multicoloured.
2484 1z. Type **691** 10 10
2485 1z.50 "Bathsheba at the Fountain" 10 10
2486 5z. "Helena Fourment with Fur Coat" 30 10
2487 6z. "Self-portrait" 45 30
MS2488 76 × 62 mm. 8z.+4z. sepia ("The Stoning of St. Stephan") (21 × 26 mm) . . . . 1·40 85

692 Dove 694 Wolf

693 Cyclist

1977. World Council of Peace Congress.
2489 **692** 1z.50 blue, yellow & black 10 10

1977. 30th International Peace Cycle Race.
2490 **693** 1z.50 multicoloured . . . 10 10

1977. Endangered Animals. Multicoloured.
2491 1z. Type **694** 10 10
2492 1z.50 Great bustard 30 15
2493 1z.50 Common kestrel . . . 30 15
2494 6z. European otter 40 25

695 "The Violinist" (J. Toorenvliet) 697 H. Wieniawski and Music Clef

696 Midsummer's Day Bonfire

1977. "Amphilex 77" Stamp Exhibition, Amsterdam.
2495 **695** 6z. multicoloured 40 30

1977. Folk Customs. 19th-century Wood Engravings. Multicoloured.
2496 90g. Type **696** 10 10
2497 1z. Easter cock (vert) . . . 10 10
2498 1z.50 "Smigus" (dousing of women on Easter Monday, Miechow district) (vert) 10 10
2499 3z. Harvest Festival, Sandomierz district (vert) 25 10
2500 6z. Children with Christmas crib (vert) 40 10
2501 8z.40 Mountain wedding dance 55 25

1977. Wieniawski International Music Competitions, Poznan.
2502 **697** 1z.50 black, red and gold 25 10

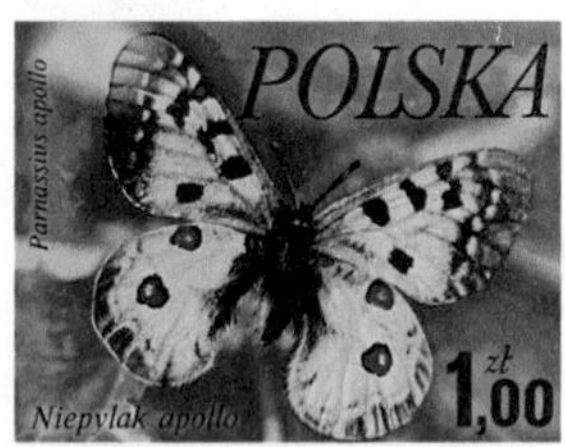

698 Apollo ("Parnassius apollo")

1977. Butterflies. Multicoloured.
2503 1z. Type **698** 30 10
2504 1z. Large tortoiseshell ("Nymphalis polychloros") 30 10
2505 1z.50 Camberwell beauty ("Nymphalis antiopa") . . 40 10
2506 1z.50 Swallowtail ("Papilio machaon") 40 10
2507 5z. High brown fritillary . . 1·10 10
2508 6z.90 Silver-washed fritillary 1·90 45

699 Keyboard and Arms of Slupsk 700 Feliks Dzerzhinsky

1977. Piano Festival, Slupsk.
2509 **699** 1z.50 mauve, blk & grn 15 10

1977. Birth Centenary of Feliks Dzerzhinsky (Russian politician).
2510 **700** 1z.50 brown and ochre 15 15

701 "Sputnik" circling Earth 702 Silver Dinar (11th century)

1977. 60th Anniv of Russian Revolution and 20th Anniv of 1st Artificial Satellite (1st issue).
2511 **701** 1z.50 red and blue . . . 15 15
MS2512 99 × 125 mm. No. 2511 × 3 plus three labels 75 75
See also No. 2527.

1977. Stamp Day. Polish Coins. Multicoloured.
2513 50g. Type **702** 10 10
2514 1z. Cracow grosz, 14th-century 10 10
2515 1z.50 Legnica thaler, 17th-century 10 10
2516 4z.20 Gdansk guilder, 18th-century 30 10
2517 4z.50 Silver 5z. coin, 1936 30 10
2518 6z. Millenary 100z. coin, 1966 . . . . 55 25

703 Wolin Gate, Kamien Pomorski 704 "Sputnik 1" and "Mercury" Capsule

1977. Architectural Monuments. Multicoloured.
2519 1z. Type **703** 10 10
2520 1z. Larch church, Debno . . 10 10
2521 1z.50 Monastery, Przasnysz (horiz) 10 10
2522 1z.50 Plock cathedral (horiz) 10 10
2523 6z. Kornik castle (horiz) . . 45 10
2524 6z.90 Palace and garden, Wilanow (horiz) 55 30

1977. Polish Folklore. 16th-century woodcuts (2nd series). As T **638**.
2525 4z. sepia 25 30
2526 4z.50 brown 30 10
DESIGNS: 4z. Bird snaring; 4z.50, Bee-keeper and hives.

1977. 20th Anniv of 1st Space Satellite (2nd issue).
2527 **704** 6z.90 multicoloured . . . 45 40

705 DN Category Iceboats

1978. 6th World Ice Sailing Championships.
2528 **705** 1z.50 black, grey & blue 15 10
2529 – 1z.50 black, grey & blue 25 10
DESIGN: No. 2529, Close-up of DN iceboat.

706 Electric Locomotive and Katowice Station

1978. Railway Engines. Multicoloured.
2530 50g. Type **706** 10 10
2531 1z. Steam locomotive No. Py27 and tender No. 721, Znin-Gasawa railway . . 10 10
2532 1z. Streamlined steam locomotive No. Pm36-1 (1936) and Cegielski's factory, Poznan 10 10
2533 1z.50 Electric locomotive and Otwock station . . . 10 10
2534 1z.50 Steam locomotive No. 17 KDM and Warsaw Stalowa station 10 10
2535 4z.50 Steam locomotive No. Ty51 and Gdynia station 30 10
2536 5z. Steam locomotive No. Tr21 and locomotive works, Chrzanow 40 10
2537 6z. Cockerill steam locomotive and Vienna station 55 30

707 Czeslaw Tanski and Glider

1978. Aviation History and 50th Anniv of Polish Aero Club. Multicoloured.
2538 50g. Type **707** 10 10
2539 1z. Franciszek Zwirko and Stanislaw Wigura with RWD-6 aircraft (vert) . . 10 10
2540 1z.50 Stanislaw Skarzynski and RWD-5 bis monoplane (vert) 10 10
2541 4z.20 Mil Mi-2 helicopter (vert) 25 10
2542 6z.90 PZL-104 Wilga 35 monoplane 75 25
2543 8z.40 SZD-45 Ogar powered glider 60 25

708 Tackle

1978. World Cup Football Championship, Argentina. Multicoloured.
2544 1z.50 Type **708** 10 10
2545 6z.90 Ball on field (horiz) 45 30

709 Biennale Emblem 710 Kazimierz Stanislaw Gzowski (bridge engineer)

1978. 7th International Poster Biennale, Warsaw.
2546 **709** 1z.50 mauve, yell & vio 15 15

1978. "Capex 78" International Stamp Exhibition, Toronto. Sheet 68 × 79 mm.
MS2547 **710** 8z.40+4z. multicoloured . . . . 1·10 70

711 Polonez Saloon Car

1978. Car Production.
2548 **711** 1z.50 multicoloured . . . 10 10

712 Fair Emblem 713 Miroslaw Hermaszewski

1978. 50th International Fair, Poznan.
2549 **712** 1z.50 multicoloured . . . 10 10

1978. 1st Pole in Space. Multicoloured. With or without date.
2550 1z.50 Type **713** 10 10
2551 6z.90 M. Hermaszewski and globe 55 25

714 Globe containing Face

1978. 11th World Youth and Students Festival, Havana.
2552 **714** 1z.50 multicoloured . . . 10 10

715 Flowers

1978. 30th Anniv Polish Youth Union. Sheet 69 × 79 mm.
MS2553 **715** 1z.50 multicoloured 40 40

716 Mosquito and Malaria Organisms

717 Pedunculate Oak

1978. 4th International Congress of Parasitologists, Warsaw and Cracow. Multicoloured.
2554 1z.50 Type **716** 10 10
2555 6z. Tsetse fly and sleeping sickness organism 40 40

1978. Environment Protection. Trees. Mult.
2556 50g. Norway Maple 10 10
2557 1z. Type **717** 10 10
2558 1z.50 White Poplar 10 10
2559 4z.20 Scots Pine 25 10
2560 4z.50 White Willow 25 10
2561 6z. Birch 40 15

718

1978. "PRAGA 1978" International Stamp Exhibition. Sheet 69 × 79 mm.
MS2562 **718** 6z. multicoloured 1·10 60

719 Communications

1978. 20th Anniv of Socialist Countries Communications Organization.
2563 **719** 1z.50 red, lt blue & blue 10 10

720 "Peace" (Andre Le Brun)

1978.
2564 **720** 1z. violet 10 10
2565 1z.50 turquoise 10 10
2565a 2z. brown 10 10
2565b 2z.50 blue 25 10

721 Polish Unit of U.N. Middle East Force

1978. 35th Anniv of Polish People's Army. Mult.
2566 1z.50 Colour party of Tadeusz Kosciuszko 1st Warsaw Infantry Division 10 10
2567 1z.50 Mechanized Unit colour party 10 10
2568 1z.50 Type **721** 10 10

722 "Portrait of a Young Man" (Raphael)

1978. Stamp Day.
2569 **722** 6z. multicoloured 40 30

723 Janusz Korczak with Children

1978. Birth Centenary of Janusz Korczak (pioneer of children's education).
2570 **723** 1z.50 multicoloured . . . 25 10

724 Wojciech Boguslawski

1978. Polish Dramatists. Multicoloured.
2571 50g. Type **724** 10 10
2572 1z. Aleksander Fredro . . . 10 10
2573 1z.50 Juliusz Slowacki . . . 10 10
2574 2z. Adam Mickiewicz . . . 10 10
2575 4z.50 Stanislaw Wyspianski 30 10
2576 6z. Gabriela Zapolska . . . 45 25

725 Polish Combatants' Monument and Eiffel Tower

1978. Monument to Polish Combatants in France, Paris.
2577 **725** 1z.50 brown, blue & red 20 10

726 Przewalski Horses

1978. 50th Anniv of Warsaw Zoo. Multicoloured.
2578 50g. Type **726** 10 10
2579 1z. Polar bears 10 10
2580 1z.50 Indian elephants . . . 25 10
2581 2z. Jaguars 30 10
2582 4z.20 Grey seals 30 10
2583 4z.50 Hartebeests 30 10
2584 6z. Mandrills 45 30

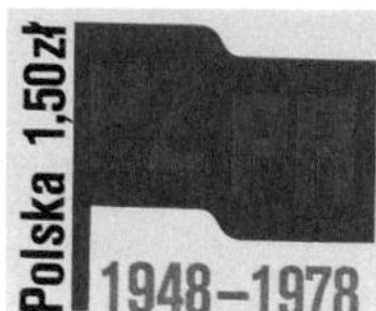

727 Party Flag

1978. 30th Anniv of Polish Workers' United Party.
2585 **727** 1z.50 red, gold and black 10 10

728 Stanislaw Dubois

1978. Leaders of Polish Workers' Movement.
2586 **728** 1z.50 blue and red . . . 10 10
2587 – 1z.50 lilac and red . . . 10 10
2588 – 1z.50 olive and red . . . 10 10
2589 – 1z.50 brown and red . . 10 10
DESIGNS: No. 2587, Aleksander Zawadzki; 2588, Julian Lenski; 2589, Aldolf Warski.

729 Ilyushin Il-62M and Fokker F.VIIb/3m

1979. 50th Anniv of LOT Polish Airlines.
2590 **729** 6z.90 multicoloured . . . 55 25

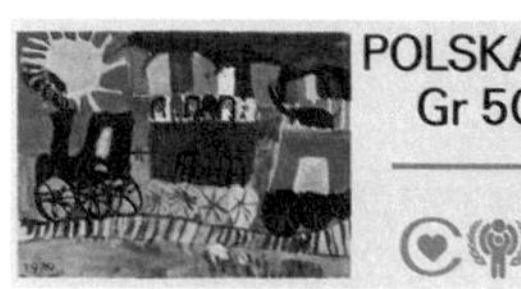

730 Steam Train

1979. International Year of the Child. Children's Paintings. Multicoloured.
2591 50g. Type **730** 10 10
2592 1z. "Mother with Children" 10 10
2593 1z.50 Children playing . . . 10 10
2594 6z. Family Group 40 25

731 "Portrait of Artist's Wife with Foxgloves" (Karol Mondrala)

1979. Contemporary Graphics.
2595 – 50g. lilac 10 10
2596 **731** 1z. green 10 10
2597 – 1z.50 blue 10 10
2598 – 4z.50 brown 30 10
DESIGNS—HORIZ: 50g. "Lightning" (Edmund Bartlomiejezyk). VERT: 1z.50, "The Musicians" (Tadeusz Kulisiewicz); 4z.50, "Head of a Young Man" (Wladyslaw Skoczylas).

732 A. Frycz Modrzewski (political writer), King Stefan Batory and Jan Zamoyski (chancellor)

1979. 400th Anniv (1978) of Royal Tribunal in Piotrkow Trybunalski.
2599 **732** 1z.50 brown and deep brown 10 10

733 Pole Vaulting

1979. 60th Anniv of Polish Olympic Committee.
2600 **733** 1z. Lilac, brown and red 10 10
2601 – 1z.50 lilac, brown and red 10 10
2602 – 6z. lilac, brown and red 40 10
2603 – 8z.40 lilac, brown and red 60 25
MS2604 102 × 61 mm. 10z.+5z. brown 90 75
DESIGNS: 1z.50, High jump; 6z. Skiing; 8z.40, Horse riding; 10z. Olympic rings.

734 European Flounder

1979. Centenary of Polish Angling. Multicoloured.
2605 50g. Type **734** 10 10
2606 90g. Eurasian perch 10 10
2607 1z. European grayling . . . 10 10
2608 1z.50 Atlantic salmon . . . 10 10
2609 2z. Brown trout 15 10
2610 4z.50 Northern pike 30 10
2611 5z. Common carp 45 10
2612 6z. Wels 45 20

735 "30 Years of RWPG"

1979. 30th Anniv of Council of Mutual Economic Aid.
2613 **735** 1z.50 red, ultram & blue 10 10

736 Soldier, Civilian and Congress Emblem

738 Pope and Auschwitz Concentration Camp Memorial

737 St. George's Church, Sofia

1979. 6th Congress of Association of Fighters for Liberty and Democracy.
2614 **736** 1z.50 red and black . . . 10 10

1979. "Philaserdica 79" International Stamp Exhibition, Sofia, Bulgaria.
2615 **737** 1z.50 orange, brn & red 10 10

1979. Visit of Pope John Paul II. Multicoloured.
2616 1z.50 Pope and St. Mary's Church, Cracow 25 10
2617 8z.40 Type **738** 70 30
MS2618 68 × 79 mm. 50z. Framed portrait of Pope (26 × 35 mm) 7·00 5·25

739 River Paddle-steamer "Ksiaze Ksawery" and Old Warsaw

1979. 150th Anniv of Vistula River Navigation. Multicoloured.
2619 1z. Type **739** 10 10
2620 1z.50 River paddle-steamer "General Swierczewski" and Gdansk 10 10
2621 4z.50 River tug "Zubr" and Plock 25 10
2622 6z. Passenger launch "Syrena" and modern Warsaw 45 25

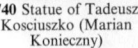

740 Statue of Tadeusz Kosciuszko (Marian Konieczny) **741** Mining Machinery

1979. Monument to Tadeusz Kosciuszko in Philadelphia.
2623 **740** 8z.40 multicoloured . . . 40 25

1979. Wieliczka Salt Mine.
2624 **741** 1z. brown and black . . 10 10
2625 – 1z.50 turquoise and black 10 10
DESIGN: 1z.50, Salt crystals.

742 Heraldic Eagle **743** Rowland Hill and 1860 Stamp

1979. 35th Anniv of Polish People's Republic.
2626 – 1z.50 red, silver and black 15 10
2627 **742** 1z.50 red, silver and blue 15 10
MS2628 120 × 84 mm. Nos. 2626/7 plus label 40 45
DESIGN: No. 2626, Girl and stylized flag.

1979. Death Centenary of Sir Rowland Hill.
2629 **743** 6z. blue, black and orange 40 10

744 "The Rape of Europa" (Bernardo Stozzi)

1979. International Stamp Exhibition. Sheet 86 × 63 mm.
MS2630 **744** 10z. multicoloured 75 60

745 Wojciech Jastrzebowski

1979. 7th Congress of International Ergonomic Association, Warsaw.
2631 **745** 1z.50 multicoloured . . . 15 10

746 Monument (Wincenty Kucma)

1979. Unveiling of Monument to Defenders of Polish Post, Gdansk, and 40th Anniv of German Occupation.
2632 **746** 1z.50 grey, sepia and red 15 10
MS2633 79 × 69 mm. **746** 10z.+5z. grey, sepia and red. Imperf . . 1·00 85

747 Radio Mast and Telecommunications Emblem

1979. 50th Anniv of International Radio Communication Advisory Committee.
2634 **747** 1z.50 multicoloured . . . 15 10

748 Violin

1979. Wieniawski Young Violinists' Competition, Lublin.
2635 **748** 1z.50 blue, orange & green 15 10

749 Statue of Kazimierz Pulaski, Buffalo (K. Danilewicz) **750** Franciszek Jozwiak (first Commander)

1979. Death Bicentenary of Kazimierz Pulaski (American Revolution Hero).
2636 **749** 8z.40 multicoloured . . . 60 30

1979. 35th Anniv of Civic Militia and Security Force.
2637 **750** 1z.50 blue and gold . . . 15 10

751 Post Office in Rural Area

1979. Stamp Day. Multicoloured.
2638 1z. Type **751** 10 10
2639 1z.50 Parcel sorting machinery 10 10
2640 4z.50 Loading containers on train 45 10
2641 6z. Mobile post office . . . 60 25

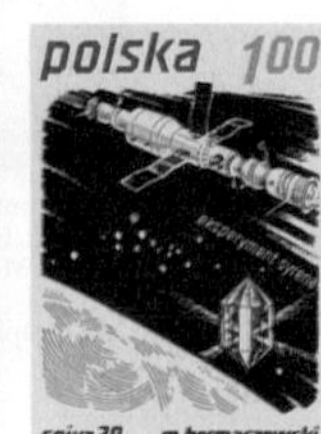

752 "The Holy Family" (Ewelina Peksowa) **753** "Soyuz 30-Salyut 6" Complex and Crystal

1979. Polish Folk Art. Glass Paintings. Mult.
2642 2z. Type **752** 10 10
2643 6z.90 "The Nativity" (Zdzislaw Walczak) . . . 45 25

1979. Space Achievements. Multicoloured.
2644 1z. Type **753** (1st anniv of 1st Pole in space) 10 10
2645 1z.50 "Kopernik" and "Copernicus" satellites . . 10 10
2646 2z. "Lunik 2" and "Ranger 7" spacecraft (20th anniv of 1st unmanned Moon landing) 10 10
2647 4z.50 Yuri Gagarin and "Vostok 1" 10 10
2648 6z.90 Neil Armstrong, lunar module and "Apollo 11" (10th anniv of first man on Moon) 25 30
MS2649 120 × 103 mm. Nos. 2644/8 plus label (sold at 20z.90) . . . 1·25 1·25

754 Coach and Four **755** Slogan on Map of Poland

1980. 150th Anniv of Sierakow Stud Farm. Mult.
2650 1z. Type **754** 10 10
2651 2z. Horse and groom . . . 10 10
2652 2z.50 Sulky racing 10 10
2653 3z. Hunting 25 10
2654 4z. Horse-drawn sledge . . 30 10
2655 6z. Haywain 45 10
2656 6z.50 Grooms exercising horses 55 25
2657 6z.90 Show jumping 60 30

1980. 8th Polish United Workers' Party Congress. Multicoloured.
2658 2z.50 Type **755** 25 10
2659 2z.50 Janusz Stann (26 × 46 mm) 25 10

756 Horse Jumping

1980. Olympic Games, Moscow, and Winter Olympic Games, Lake Placid. Multicoloured.
2660 2z. Type **756** 10 10
2661 2z.50 Archery 25 10
2662 6z.50 Skiing 45 10
2663 8z.40 Volleyball 60 30

757 Town Plan and Old Town Hall

1980. 400th Anniv of Zamosc.
2665 **757** 2z.50 buff, green & brn 15 10

758 Satellite orbiting Earth

1980. "Intercosmos" Space Programme. Sheet 63 × 79 mm.
MS2666 **758** 6z.90+3z. multicoloured 60 70

759 Seals of Poland and Russia

1980. 35th Anniv of Soviet–Polish Friendship Treaty.
2667 **759** 2z.50 multicoloured . . . 25 10

760 "Lenin in Cracow" (Zbigniew Pronaszko)

1980. 110th Birth Anniv of Lenin.
2668 **760** 2z.50 multicoloured . . . 25 10

761 Workers with Red Flag

1980. 75th Anniv of Revolution of 1905.
2669 **761** 2z.50 red, black & yellow 25 10

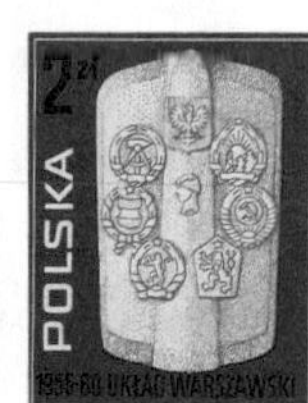

762 Dove **763** Shield with Crests of Member Nations

1980. 35th Anniv of Liberation.
2670 **762** 2z.50 multicoloured . . . 25 10

1980. 25th Anniv of Warsaw Pact.
2671 **763** 2z. grey and red 25 10

764 Speleological Expedition, Cuba

1980. Polish Scientific Expeditions. Multicoloured.
2672 2z. Type **764** 10 10
2673 2z. Antarctic 30 10
2674 2z.50 Archaeology, Syria . . 25 10
2675 2z.50 Ethnology, Mongolia 25 10
2676 6z.50 Mountaineering, Nepal 40 10
2677 8z.40 Paleontology, Mongolia 55 25

765 School and Arms **766** "Clathrus ruber"

1980. 800th Anniv of Malachowski School, Plock.
2678 **765** 2z. green and black . . . 15 10

1980. Fungi. Multicoloured.
2679 2z. Type **766** 20 10
2680 2z. "Xerocomus parasiticus" 20 10
2681 2z.50 Old man of the woods ("Strobilomyces floccopus") 25 10
2682 2z.50 "Phallus hadriani" . . 25 10
2683 8z. Cauliflower fungus . . . 40 20
2684 10z.50 Giant puff-ball . . . 40 45

767 T. Ziolowski and "Lwow"

1980. Polish Merchant Navy School. Cadet Ships and their Captains.

No.	Type	Description	Unused	Used
2685	**767**	2z. black, mauve and violet	20	10
2686	–	2z.50 black, light blue and blue	25	10
2687	–	6z. black, pale green and green	30	10
2688	–	6z.50 black, yellow and grey	40	10
2689	–	6z.90 black, grey and green	45	25
2690	–	8z.40 black, blue and green	55	25

DESIGNS: 2z.50, A. Garnuszewski and "Antoni Garnuszewski"; 6z. A. Ledochowski and "Zenit"; 6z.50, K. Porebski and "Jan Turleski"; 6z.90, G. Kanski and "Horyzont"; 8z.40, Maciejewicz and "Dar Pomorza".

768 Town Hall

769 "Atropa belladonna"

1980. Millenary of Sandomir.

No.	Type	Description	Unused	Used
2691	**768**	2z.50 brown and black	15	10

1980. Medicinal Plants. Multicoloured.

No.	Description	Unused	Used
2692	2z. Type **769**	15	10
2693	2z.50 "Datura innoxia"	20	10
2694	3z.40 "Valeriana officinalis"	25	10
2695	5z. "Menta piperita"	30	10
2696	6z.50 "Calendula officinalis"	40	25
2697	8z. "Salvia officinalis"	55	30

770 Jan Kochanowski

771 U.N. General Assembly

1980. 450th Birth Anniv of Jan Kochanowski (poet).

No.	Type	Description	Unused	Used
2698	**770**	2z.50 multicoloured	25	15

1980. 35th Anniv of U.N.O.

No.	Type	Description	Unused	Used
2703	**771**	8z.40 brown, blue & red	60	30

772 Chopin and Trees

1980. 10th International Chopin Piano Competition, Warsaw.

No.	Type	Description	Unused	Used
2704	**772**	6z.90 multicoloured	45	30

773 Postman emptying Post Box

1980. Stamp Day. Multicoloured.

No.	Description	Unused	Used
2705	2z. Type **773**	20	10
2706	2z.50 Mail sorting	20	10
2707	6z. Loading mail onto aircraft	45	10
2708	6z.50 Letter boxes	55	25
MS2709	12 × 94 mm. Nos. 2705/8	3·50	1·75

774 Child embracing Dove

1980. United Nations Declaration on the Preparation of Societies for Life in Peace.

No.	Type	Description	Unused	Used
2710	**774**	8z.40 multicoloured	60	30

775 "Battle of Olszynka Grochowska" (Wojciech Kossak)

1980. 150th Anniv of Battle of Olszynka Grochowska.

No.	Type	Description	Unused	Used
2711	**775**	2z.50 multicoloured	25	15

776 Fire Engine

1980. Warsaw Horse-drawn Vehicles. Mult.

No.	Description	Unused	Used
2712	2z. Type **776**	15	10
2713	2z.50 Omnibus	20	10
2714	3z. Brewery dray	25	10
2715	5z. Sledge-cab	30	10
2716	6z. Horse tram	40	30
2717	6z.50 Droshky cab	50	45

777 "Honour to the Silesian Rebels" (statue by Jan Borowczak)

778 Picasso

1981. 60th Anniv of Silesian Rising.

No.	Type	Description	Unused	Used
2718	**777**	2z.50 green	15	10

1981. Birth Centenary of Pablo Picasso (artist).

No.	Type	Description	Unused	Used
2719	**778**	8z.40 multicoloured	60	30
MS2720		95 × 130 mm. No. 2719 × 2 plus labels (sold at 20z.80)	2·50	1·40

779 Balloon of Pilatre de Rozier and Romain, 1785

780 "Iphigenia" (Anton Maulbertsch)

1981. Balloons. Multicoloured.

No.	Description	Unused	Used
2721	2z. Type **779**	20	10
2722	2z. Balloon of J. Blanchard and J. Jeffries, 1785	20	10
2723	2z.50 Eugene Godard's quintuple "acrobatic" balloon, 1850	25	10
2724	3z. F. Hynek and Z. Burzynski's "Kosciuszko", 1933	25	10
2725	6z. Z. Burzynski and N. Wyescki's "Polonia II", 1935	45	25
2726	6z.50 Ben Abruzzo, Max Anderson and Larry Newman's "Double Eagle II", 1978	45	25
MS2727	59 × 98 mm. 10z.50 Balloon SP-BCU *L.O.P.P.* and Gordon Bennett statuette	80	95

1981. "WIPA 1981" International Stamp Exhibition, Vienna.

No.	Type	Description	Unused	Used
2728	**780**	10z.50 multicoloured	85	30

781 Wroclaw, 1493

782 Sikorski

1981. Towns.

No.	Type	Description	Unused	Used
2729	–	4z. violet	30	15
2730	–	5z. green	55	15
2731	–	6z. orange	60	15
2732	**781**	6z.50 brown	55	25
2733	–	8z. blue	70	30

DESIGNS—VERT: 4z. Gdansk, 1652; 5z. Cracow, 1493. HORIZ: 6z. Legnica, 1744; 8z. Warsaw, 1618.

1981. Birth Centenary of General Wladyslaw Sikorski (statesman).

No.	Type	Description	Unused	Used
2744	**782**	6z.50 multicoloured	55	25

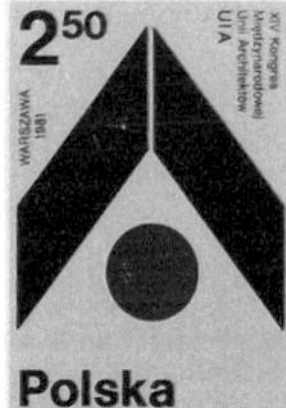

783 Faience Vase

784 Congress Emblem

1981. Pottery. Multicoloured.

No.	Description	Unused	Used
2745	1z. Type **783**	15	10
2746	2z. Porcelain cup and saucer in "Baranowka" design	25	10
2747	2z.50 Porcelain jug, Korzec manufacture	25	10
2748	5z. Faience plate with portrait of King Jan III Sobieski by Thiele	45	25
2749	6z.50 Faience "Secession" vase	60	25
2750	8z.40 Porcelain dish, Cmielow manufacture	75	30

1981. 14th International Architects' Union Congress, Warsaw.

No.	Type	Description	Unused	Used
2751	**784**	2z. yellow, black and red	25	10

785 Wild Boar, Rifle and Oak Leaves

786 European Bison

1981. Game Shooting. Multicoloured.

No.	Description	Unused	Used
2752	2z. Type **785**	15	10
2753	2z. Elk, rifle and fir twigs	15	10
2754	2z.50 Red fox, shotgun, cartridges and fir branches	25	10
2755	2z.50 Roe deer, feeding rack, rifle and fir branches	25	10
2756	6z.50 Mallard, shotgun, basket and reeds	70	55
2757	6z.50 Barnacle goose, shotgun and reeds (horiz)	70	55

1981. Protection of European Bison. Mult.

No.	Description	Unused	Used
2758	6z.50 Type **786**	70	30
2759	6z.50 Two bison, one grazing	70	30
2760	6z.50 Bison with calf	70	30
2761	6z.50 Calf Feeding	70	30
2762	6z.50 Two bison, both looking towards right	70	30

787 Tennis Player

1981. 60th Anniv of Polish Tennis Federation.

No.	Type	Description	Unused	Used
2763	**787**	6z.50 multicoloured	55	30

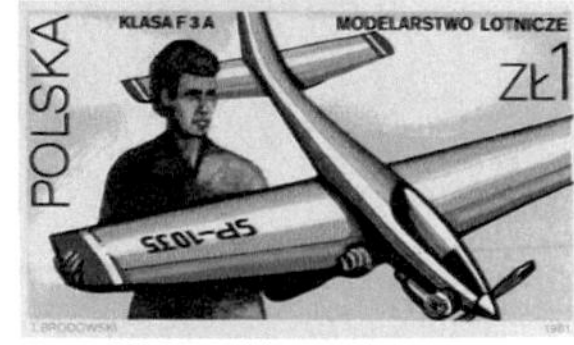

788 Boy with Model Airplane

1981. Model Making. Multicoloured.

No.	Description	Unused	Used
2764	1z. Type **788**	15	10
2765	2z. Model of "Atlas 2" tug	30	10
2766	2z.50 Cars	30	10
2767	4z.20 Man with gliders	30	10
2768	6z.50 Racing cars	60	20
2769	8z. Boy with yacht	70	20

789 Disabled Pictogram

791 H. Wieniawski and Violin Head

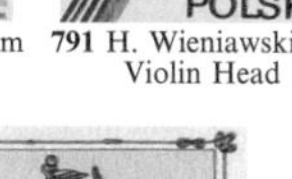

790 17th-cent Flint-lock Pistol

1981. International Year of Disabled Persons.

No.	Type	Description	Unused	Used
2770	**789**	8z.40 green, light green and black	70	30

1981. Stamp Day. Antique Weapons. Mult.

No.	Description	Unused	Used
2771	2z.50 Type **790**	25	10
2772	8z.40 17th-century gala sabre	70	25

1981. Wieniawski Young Violinists' Competition.

No.	Type	Description	Unused	Used
2773	**791**	2z.50 multicoloured	25	15

792 Bronislaw Wesolowski

793 F.A.O. Emblem and Globe

1981. Activists of Polish Workers' Movement.

No.	Type	Description	Unused	Used
2774	**792**	50g. green and black	10	10
2775	–	2z. blue and black	15	10
2776	–	2z.50 brown and black	20	10
2777	–	6z.50 mauve and black	70	25

DESIGNS: 2z. Malgorzata Fornalska; 2z.50, Maria Koszutska; 6z.50, Marcin Kasprzak.

1981. World Food Day.

No.	Type	Description	Unused	Used
2778	**793**	6z.90 brown, orange & yellow	55	25

794 Helena Modrzejewska (actress)

1981. Bicentenary of Cracow Old Theatre.

No.	Type	Description	Unused	Used
2779	**794**	2z. purple, grey and violet	15	10
2780	–	2z.50 blue, stone & brn	25	10
2781	–	6z.50 violet, blue & grn	55	25
2782	–	8z. brown, green and red	85	25

DESIGNS: 2z.50, Stanislaw Kozmian (politician, writer and theatre director); 6z.50, Konrad Swinarski (stage manager and scenographer); 8z. Old Theatre building.

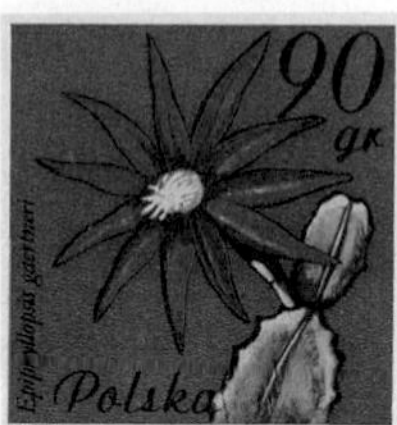

795 Cracow and Vistula River

796 Gdansk Memorial

1981. Vistula River Project. Sheet 62 × 51 mm.
MS2783 **795** 10z.50 multicoloured . . . 1·25 1·10

1981. Memorials to the Victims of the 1970 Uprisings.
2784 **796** 2z.50+1z. grey, black and red 30 10
2785 – 6z.50+1z. grey, black and blue 75 30
DESIGN: 6z.50, Gdynia Memorial.

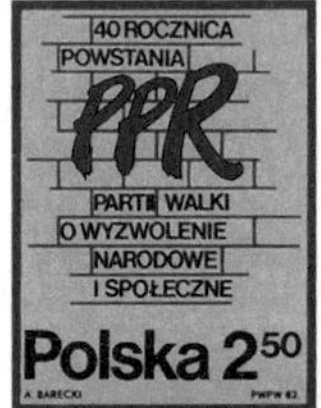

797 "Epiphyllopsis gaertneri"

1981. Succulent Plants. Multicoloured.
2786 90g. Type **797** 15 10
2787 1z. "Cereus tonduzii" . . . 15 10
2788 2z. "Cylindropuntia leptocaulis" 15 10
2789 2z.50 "Cylindropuntia fulgida" 25 10
2790 2z.50 "Coralluma lugardi" 25 10
2791 6z.50 "Nopalea cochenillifera" . . . . . 1·60 30
2792 6z.50 "Lithops helmutii" . . 60 30
2793 10z.50 "Cylindropuntia spinosior" . . . . 1·00 40

798 Writing on Wall

799 Faience Plate

1982. 40th Anniv of Polish Workers' Coalition.
2794 **798** 2z.50 pink, red and black 25 15

1982. Polish Ceramics. Multicoloured.
2795 1z. Type **799** 15 15
2796 2z. Porcelain cup and saucer, Korzec 25 15
2797 2z.50 Porcelain tureen and sauce-boat, Barnowka . . 25 15
2798 6z. Porcelain inkpot, Horodnica 55 30
2799 8z. Faience "Hunter's Tumbler", Lubartow . . 65 30
2800 10z.50 Faience figurine of nobleman, Biala Podlaska 1·10 45

800 Ignacy Lukasiewicz and Lamp

801 Karol Szymanowski

1982. Death Centenary of Ignacy Lukasiewicz (inventor of petroleum lamp).
2801 **800** 1z. multicoloured 15 10
2802 – 2z. multicoloured 25 10
2803 – 2z.50 multicoloured . . . 30 10
2804 – 3z.50 multicoloured . . . 30 10
2805 – 9z. multicoloured 85 30
2806 – 10z. multicoloured . . . 90 35

DESIGNS: 2z. to 10z. Different designs showing lamps.

1982. Birth Centenary of Karol Szymanowski (composer).
2807 **801** 2z.50 brown and gold . . 25 25

802 RWD 6, 1932

1982. 50th Anniv of Polish Victory in Tourist Aircraft Challenge Competition. Multicoloured.
2808 27z. Type **802** 75 25
2809 31z. RWD 9 (winner of 1934 Challenge) . . . . . 1·00 30
MS2810 89 × 101 mm. Nos. 2808/9 2·25 1·60

803 Henryk Sienkiewicz (literature, 1905)

804 Football as Globe

1982. Polish Nobel Prize Winners.
2811 **803** 3z. green and black . . . 10 10
2812 – 15z. brown and black . . 40 15
2813 – 25z. blue 90 25
2814 – 31z. grey and black . . . 75 45
DESIGNS: 15z. Wladyslaw Reymont (literature, 1924); 25z. Marie Curie (physics, 1903, and chemistry, 1911); 31z. Czeslaw Milosz (literature, 1980).

1982. World Cup Football Championship, Spain. Multicoloured.
2815 25z. Type **804** 75 30
2816 27z. Bull and football (35 × 28 mm) 85 55

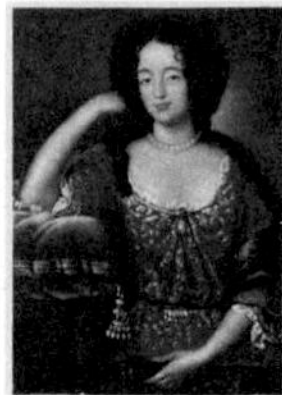

805 "Maria kazimiera Sobieska"

1982. "Philexfrance 82" International Stamp Exhibition, Paris. Sheet 69 × 86 mm.
MS2817 **805** 65z. multicoloured 2·40 2·40

806 Stanislaw Sierakowski and Boleslaw Domanski (former Association presidents)

807 Text around Globe

1982. 60th Anniv of Association of Poles in Germany.
2818 **806** 4z.50 red and green . . . 40 15

1982. 2nd U.N. Conference on the Exploration and Peaceful Uses of Outer Space, Vienna.
2819 **807** 31z. multicoloured . . . 75 40

1982. No. 2732 surch **10** ".
2820 10z. on 6z.50 brown 30 10

809 Father Augustyn Kordecki (prior)

810 Marchers with Banner

1982. 600th Anniv of "Black Madonna" (icon) of Jasna Gora. Multicoloured.
2821 2z.50 Type **809** 10 10
2822 25z. "Siege of Jasna Gora by Swedes, 1655" (detail) (horiz) 40 10
2823 65z. "Black Madonna" . . 1·10 45
MS2824 122 × 108 mm. No. 2823 × 2 (sold at 140z.) . . . . . . 10·50 12·50
The premium on No. **MS**2824 was for the benefit of the Polish Philatelic Federation.

1982. Centenary of Proletarian Party.
2825 **810** 6z. multicoloured 30 15

811 Norbert Barlicki

812 Dr. Robert Koch

1982. Activists of Polish Workers' Movement.
2826 **811** 5z. light blue, blue and black 10 15
2827 – 6z. deep green, green and black 10 15
2828 – 15z. pink, red and black 25 15
2829 – 20z. mauve, violet and black 40 15
2830 – 29z. light brown, brown and black 45 15
DESIGNS: 6z. Pawel Finder; 15z. Marian Buczek; 20z. Cezaryna Wojnarowska; 29z. Ignacy Daszynski.

1982. Centenary of Discovery of Tubercle Bacillus. Multicoloured.
2831 10z. Type **812** 25 15
2832 25z. Dr. Odo Bujwid . . . 85 30

813 Carved Head of Woman

813a Head of Ruler

1982. Carved Heads from Wawel Castle.
2835 **813a** 3z.50 brown 15 10
2836 – 5z. green 15 10
2837 – 5z. red 10 10
2838 – 10z. blue 15 10
2839 – 15z. brown 15 10
2840 – 20z. grey 45 10
2841 **813a** 20z. blue 15 10
2842 – 40z. brown 75 10
2833 **813** 60z. orange and brown 1·25 25
2843 – 60z. green 15 10
2834 – 100z. ochre and brown 2·75 40
2843a – 200z. black . . . . . 2·25 30
DESIGNS—As T **813**: 100z. Man. As T **813a**: 5z. (2836), Warrior; 5z. (2837), 15z. Woman wearing chaplet; 10z. Man in cap; 20z. (2840), Thinker; 40z. Man in beret; 60z. Young man; 200z. Man.

814 Maximilian Kolbe (after M. Koscielniak)

1982. Sanctification of Maximilian Kolbe (Franciscan concentration camp victim).
2844 **814** 27z. multicoloured . . . 1·00 40

815 Polar Research Station

1982. 50th Anniv of Polish Polar Research.
2845 **815** 27z. multicoloured . . . 1·10 40

816 "Log Floats on Vistula River" (drawing by J. Telakowski)

817 Stanislaw Zaremba

1982. Views of the Vistula River.
2846 **816** 12z. blue 25 10
2847 – 17z. blue 30 10
2848 – 25z. blue 40 25
DESIGNS: 17z. "Kazimierz Dolny" (engraving by Andriollo); 25z. "Danzig" (18th-cent engraving).

1982. Mathematicians.
2849 **817** 5z. lilac, blue and black 25 15
2850 – 6z. orange, violet and black 25 15
2851 – 12z. blue, brown and black 40 15
2852 – 15z. yellow, brown and black 60 25
DESIGNS: 6z. Waclaw Sierpinski; 12z. Zygmunt Janiszewski; 15z. Stefan Banach.

818 Military Council Medal

1982. 1st Anniv of Military Council.
2853 **818** 2z.50 multicoloured . . . 25 15

819 Deanery Gate

1982. Renovation of Cracow Monuments (1st series).
2854 **819** 15z. black, olive & green 45 15
2855 – 25z. black, purple & mauve 55 25
MS2856 75 × 93 mm. 65z. green, purple and sepia (22 × 27 mm) 1·25 90
DESIGNS: 25z. Gateway of Collegium Iuridicum; 65z. Street plan of Old Cracow.
See also Nos. 2904/5, 2968/9; 3029/3, 3116 and 3153.

820 Bernard Wapowski Map, 1526

1982. Polish Maps.
2857 **820** 5z. multicoloured 10 10
2858 – 6z. brown, black and red 15 10
2859 – 8z. multicoloured 20 10
2860 – 25z. multicoloured . . . 55 30
DESIGNS: 6z. Map of Prague, 1839; 8z. Map of Poland from Eugen Romer's Atlas, 1908; 25z. Plan of Cracow by A. Buchowiecki, 1703, and Astrolabe.

821 "The Last of the Resistance" (Artur Grottger)

1983. 120th Anniv of January Uprising.
2861 **821** 6z. brown 15 10

822 "Grand Theatre, Warsaw, 1838" (Maciej Zaleski)

1983. 150th Anniv of Grand Theatre, Warsaw.
2862 **822** 6z. multicoloured 15 10

823 Wild Flowers

1983. Environmental Protection. Multicoloured.
2863 5z. Type **823** 15 10
2864 6z. Mute swan and river fishes 30 15
2865 17z. Hoopoe and trees . . . 90 35
2866 30z. Sea fishes 90 45
2867 31z. European bison and roe deer 90 45
2868 38z. Fruit 90 60

824 Karol Kurpinski (composer)

1983. Celebrities.
2869 **824** 5z. light brown and brown 25 10
2870 – 6z. purple and violet . . 25 10
2871 – 17z. light green and green 60 30
2872 – 25z. light brown and brown 65 30
2873 – 27z. light blue and blue 75 30
2874 – 31z. lilac and violet . . . 85 30
DESIGNS: 6z. Maria Jasnorzewska Pawlikowska (poetess); 17z. Stanislaw Szober (linguist); 25z. Tadeusz Banachiewicz (astronomer and mathematician); 27z. Jaroslaw Iwaskiewicz (writer); 31z. Wladyslaw Tatarkiewicz (philosopher and historian).

825 3000 Metres Steeplechase

1983. Sports Achievements.
2875 **825** 5z. pink and violet . . . 25 15
2876 – 6z. pink, brown and black 25 15
2877 – 15z. yellow and green . . 45 15
2878 – 27z.+5z. light blue, blue and black . . . . . . 1·00 30
DESIGNS: 6z. Show jumping; 1z. Football; 27z.+5z. Pole vault.

826 Ghetto Heroes Monument (Natan Rappaport)

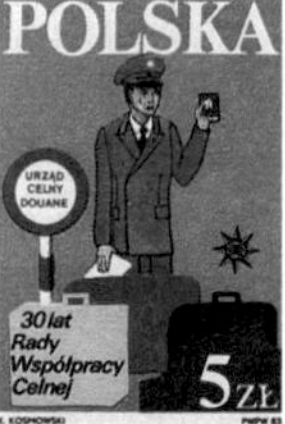
827 Customs Officer and Suitcases

1983. 40th Anniv of Warsaw Ghetto Uprising.
2879 **826** 6z. light brown & brown 25 15

1983. 30th Anniv of Customs Co-operation Council.
2880 **827** 5z. multicoloured 15 15

828 John Paul II and Jasna Gora Sanctuary

829 Dragoons

1983. Papal Visit. Multicoloured.
2881 31z. Type **828** 85 40
2882 65z. Niepokalanow Church and John Paul holding crucifix . . . . 1·90 75
MS2883 107 × 81 mm. No. 2882 1·90 1·90

1983. 300th Anniv of Polish Relief of Vienna (1st issue). Troops of King Jan III Sobieski. Mult.
2884 5z. Type **829** 15 10
2885 5z. Armoured cavalryman 15 10
2886 6z. Infantry non-commissioned officer and musketeer 25 10
2887 15z. Light cavalry lieutenant 30 30
2888 27z. "Winged" hussar and trooper with carbine . . . 90 45
See also Nos. 2893/6.

830 Arrow piercing "E"

1983. 50th Anniv of Deciphering "Enigma" Machine Codes.
2889 **830** 5z. red, grey and black 15 15

831 Torun

1983. 750th Anniv of Torun.
2890 **831** 6z. multicoloured 25 15

832 Child's Painting

1983. "Order of the Smile" (Politeness Publicity Campaign).
2892 **832** 6z. multicoloured 25 15
MS2891 142 × 116 mm. No. 2890 × 4 . . . . 2·75 2·75

833 King Jan III Sobieski

1983. 300th Anniv of Relief of Vienna (2nd issue). Multicoloured.
2893 5z. Type **833** 25 15
2894 6z. King Jan III Sobieski (different) 25 15
2895 6z. "King Jan III Sobieski on Horseback" (Francesco Trevisani) . . 25 15
2896 25z. "King Jan III Sobieski" (Jerzy Eleuter) 90 30
MS2897 97 × 75 mm. 65z. +10z. "King Jan III Sobieski at Vienna" (Jan Matejko). Imperf . . . . 1·90 1·90

834 Wanda Wasilewska

835 Profiles and W.C.Y. Emblem

1983. 40th Anniv of Polish People's Army. Multicoloured.
2898 **834** 5z. multicoloured 10 10
2899 – 5z. deep green, green and black 10 10
2900 – 6z. multicoloured 25 10
2901 – 6z. multicoloured 25 10
DESIGNS—VERT: No. 2899, General Zygmunt Berling; 2900, "The Frontier Post" (S. Poznanski). HORIZ: No. 2901, "Taking the Oath" (S. Poznanski).

1983. World Communications Year.
2902 **835** 15z. multicoloured . . . 45 25

836 Boxing

1983. 60th Anniv of Polish Boxing Federation.
2903 **836** 6z. multicoloured 25 15

1983. Renovation of Cracow Monuments (2nd series). As T **819**.
2904 5z. brown, purple and black 15 10
2905 6z. black, green and blue . . 15 15
DESIGNS—HORIZ: 5z. Cloth Hall. VERT: 6z. Town Hall tower.

837 Biskupiec Costume

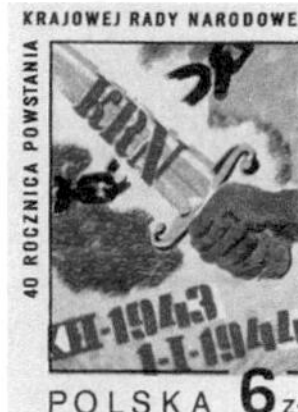
838 Hand with Sword (poster by Zakrzewski and Krolikowski, 1945)

1983. Women's Folk Costumes. Multicoloured.
2906 5z. Type **837** 15 10
2907 5z. Rozbark 15 10
2908 6z. Warmia & Mazuria . . 25 10
2909 6z. Cieszyn 25 10
2910 25z. Kurpie 90 30
2911 38z. Lubusk . . . . 1·25 55

1983. 40th Anniv of National People's Council.
2912 **838** 6z. multicoloured 25 10

839 Badge of "General Bem" Brigade

840 Dulcimer

1983. 40th Anniv of People's Army.
2913 **839** 5z. multicoloured 25 10

1984. Musical Instruments (1st series). Mult.
2914 5z. Type **840** 15 10
2915 6z. Kettle drum and tambourine 25 15
2916 10z. Accordion 40 30
2917 15z. Double bass 45 40
2918 17z. Bagpipe 55 45
2919 29z. Country band (wood carvings by Tadeusz Zak) 90 65

841 Wincenty Witos

842 "Clematis lanuginosa"

1984. 110th Birth Anniv of Wincenty Witos (leader of Peasants' Movement).
2920 **841** 6z. brown and green . . 25 10

1984. Clematis. Multicoloured.
2921 5z. Type **842** 20 10
2922 6z. "C. tangutica" 25 10
2923 10z. "C. texensis" 30 10
2924 17z. "C. alpina" 45 15
2925 25z. "C. vitalba" 90 30
2926 27z. "C. montana" . . . . 1·00 45

843 "The Ecstasy of St. Francis" (El Greco)

1984. "Espana 84" International Stamp Exhibition, Madrid.
2927 **843** 27z. multicoloured . . . 90 40

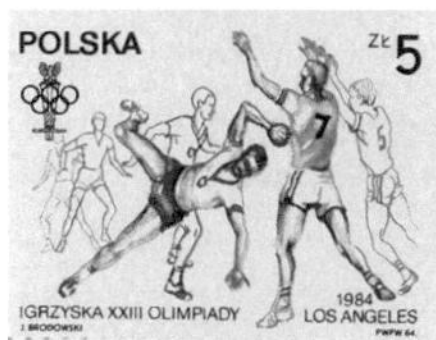
844 Handball

1984. Olympic Games, Los Angeles, and Winter Olympics, Sarajevo. Multicoloured.
2928 5z. Type **844** 10 10
2929 6z. Fencing 15 10
2930 15z. Cycling 45 25
2931 16z. Janusz Kusocinski winning 10,000 m race, 1932 Olympics, Los Angeles 60 30
2932 17z. Stanislawa Walasiewiczowna winning 100 m race, 1932 Olympics, Los Angeles . . 60 30
2933 31z. Women's slalom (Winter Olympics) . . . . 1·00 45
MS2934 129 × 78 mm. Nos. 2931/2 1·25 1·10
The 10z. premium on **MS**2934 was for the benefit of the Polish Olympic Committee.

845 Monte Cassino Memorial Cross and Monastery

846 "German Princess" (Lucas Cranach)

1984. 40th Anniv of Battle of Monte Cassino.
2935 **845** 15z. olive and red . . . 55 25

1984. 19th U.P.U. Congress, Hamburg.
2936 **846** 27z.+10z. multicoloured 55 1·90

847 "Warsaw from the Praga Bank" (Canaletto)

1984. Paintings of Vistula River. Multicoloured.
2937 5z. Type **847** 25 25
2938 6z. "Trumpet Festivity" (A. Gierymski) 25 25
2939 25z. "The Vistula near Bielany District" (J. Rapacki) 90 65
2940 27z. "Steamship Harbour in the Powisle District" (F. Kostrzewski) . . . . 1·00 75

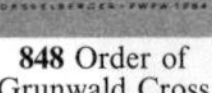

848 Order of Grunwald Cross

849 Group of Insurgents

1984. 40th Anniv of Polish People's Republic. Multicoloured.
2941 5z. Type **848** 25 10
2942 6z. Order of Revival of Poland 25 10
2943 10z. Order of Banner of Labour, First Class . . . 30 10
2944 16z. Order of Builders of People's Poland 60 30
MS2945 156 × 101 mm. Nos. 2941/4 4·25 6·00

1984. 40th Anniv of Warsaw Uprising. Mult.
2946 4z. Type **849** 25 10
2947 5z. Insurgent on postal duty 25 10
2948 6z. Insurgents fighting . . . 25 10
2949 25z. Tending wounded . . . 95 30

850 Defence of Oksywie Holm and Col. Stanislaw Dabek

1984. 45th Anniv of German Invasion. Mult.
2950 5z. Type **850** 25 10
2951 6z. Battle of Bzura River and Gen. Tadeusz Kutrzeba 25 10

See also Nos. 3004/5, 3062, 3126/8, 3172/4 and 3240/3.

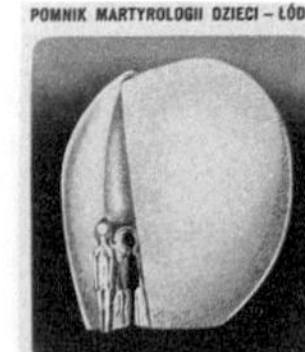

851 "Broken Heart" (monument, Lodz Concentration Camp)

1984. Child Martyrs.
2952 **851** 16z. brown, blue and deep brown 45 25

852 Militiaman and Ruins

1984. 40th Anniv of Security Force and Civil Militia. Multicoloured.
2953 5z. Type **852** 15 10
2954 6z. Militiaman in control centre 25 10

853 First Balloon Flight, 1784 (after Chostovski)

1984. Polish Aviation.
2955 **853** 5z. black, green & mauve 25 10
2956 – 5z. multicoloured 25 10
2957 – 6z. multicoloured 25 10
2958 – 10z. multicoloured . . . 30 10
2959 – 16z. multicoloured . . . 40 15
2960 – 27z. multicoloured . . . 90 30
2961 – 31z. multicoloured . . . 1·10 50

DESIGNS: No. 2956, Michal Scipio del Campo and biplane (1st flight over Warsaw, 1911); 2957, Balloon "Polonez" (winner, Gordon Bennett Cup, 1983); 2958, PWS 101 and Jantar gliders (Lilienthal Medal winners); 2959, PZL-104 Wilga airplane (world precise flight champion, 1983); 2960, Jan Nagorski and Farman M.F.7 floatplane (Arctic zone flights, 1914); 2961, PZL P-37 Los and PZL P-7 aircraft.

854 Weasel

1984. Fur-bearing Animals. Multicoloured.
2962 4z. Type **854** 15 10
2963 5z. Stoat 15 10
2964 5z. Beech marten 25 10
2965 10z. Eurasian beaver 25 10
2966 10z. Eurasian otter 25 10
2967 65z. Alpine marmot . . . . 1·90 60

1984. Renovation of Cracow Monuments (3rd series). As T **819**.
2968 5z. brown, black and green 15 10
2969 15z. blue, brown and black 30 15

DESIGNS—VERT: 5z. Wawel cathedral. HORIZ: 15z. Wawel castle (royal residence).

855 Protestant Church, Warsaw

1984. Religious Architecture. Multicoloured.
2970 5z. Type **855** 10 10
2971 10z. Saint Andrew's Roman Catholic church, Krakow 25 10
2972 15z. Greek Catholic church, Rychwald 40 10
2973 20z. St. Maria Magdalena Orthodox church, Warsaw 55 10
2974 25z. Tykocin synagogue, Kaczorow (horiz) 60 30
2975 31z. Tatar mosque, Kruszyiany (horiz) . . . 75 30

856 Steam Fire Hose (late 19th century)

1985. Fire Engines. Multicoloured.
2976 4z. Type **856** 10 10
2977 10z. "Polski Fiat", 1930s . . 25 10
2978 12z. "Jelcz 315" fire engine 30 10
2979 15z. Manual fire hose, 1899 40 10
2980 20z. "Magirus" fire ladder on "Jelcz" chassis 55 30
2981 30z. Manual fire hose (early 18th century) 84 40

857 "Battle of Raclawice" (Jan Styka and Wojciech Kossak)

1985.
2982 **857** 27z. multicoloured . . . 60 30

858 Wincenty Rzymowski

859 Badge on Denim

1985. 35th Death Anniv of Wincenty Rzymowski (founder of Polish Democratic Party).
2983 **858** 10z. violet and red . . . 30 15

1985. International Youth Year.
2984 **859** 15z. multicoloured . . . 40 15

860 Boleslaw III, the Wry-mouthed, and Map

1985. 40th Anniv of Return of Western and Northern Territories to Poland. Multicoloured.
2985 5z. Type **860** 10 10
2986 10z. Wladyslaw Gomulka (vice-president of first postwar government) and map 30 15
2987 20z. Piotr Zaremba (Governor of Szczecin) and map 60 25

861 "Victory, Berlin 1945" (Joesf Mlynarski)

1985. 40th Anniv of Victory over Fascism.
2988 **861** 5z. multicoloured 15 15

862 Warsaw Arms and Flags of Member Countries

864 Cadet Ship "Iskra"

863 Wolves in Winter

1985. 30th Anniv of Warsaw Pact.
2989 **862** 5z. multicoloured 15 15

1985. Protected Animals. The Wolf. Mult.
2990 5z. Type **863** 15 10
2991 10z. She-wolf with cubs . . 30 25
2992 10z. Close-up of wolf . . . 30 25
2993 20z. Wolves in summer . . 60 45

1985. Musical Instruments (2nd series). As T **840**. Multicoloured.
2994 5z. Rattle and tarapata . . 15 10
2995 10z. Stick rattle and berlo 30 10
2996 12z. Clay whistles 40 10
2997 20z. Stringed instruments 60 25
2998 25z. Cow bells 85 25
2999 31z. Wind instruments . . . 1·00 30

1985. 40th Anniv of Polish Navy.
3000 **864** 5z. blue and yellow . . . 15 10

865 Tomasz Nocznicki

1985. Leaders of Peasants' Movement.
3001 **865** 10z. green 25 10
3002 – 20z. brown 45 25

DESIGN: 20z. Maciej Rataj.

866 Hockey Players

1985. 60th Anniv (1986) of Polish Field Hockey Association.
3003 **866** 5z. multicoloured 15 10

1985. 46th Anniv of German Invasion. As T **850**. Multicoloured.
3004 5z. Defence of Wizna and Capt. Wladyslaw Raginis 15 10
3005 10z. Battle of Mlawa and Col. Wilhelm Liszka-Lawicz 30 10

867 Type 20k Goods Wagon

1985. PAFAWAG Railway Rolling Stock. Mult.
3006 5z. Type **867** 15 10
3007 10z. Electric locomotive No. ET22-001, 1969 . . . . . 25 10
3008 17z. Type OMMK wagon 40 25
3009 20z. Type 111A passenger carriage 55 30

868 "Madonna with Child St. John and Angel" (Sandro Botticelli)

1985. "Italia '85" International Stamp Exhibition, Rome. Sheet 81 × 108 mm.

MS3010 **868** 65z.+15z. multicoloured . . . . 1·90 1·90

869 Green-winged Teal

1985. Wild Ducks. Multicoloured.

3011	5z. Type **869**	15	10
3012	5z. Garganey	15	10
3013	10z. Tufted duck	30	10
3014	15z. Common goldeneye . .	40	10
3015	25z. Eider	65	30
3016	29z. Red-crested pochard . .	1·00	30

870 U.N. Emblem and "Flags"

1985. 40th Anniv of U.N.O.

3017 **870** 27z. multicoloured . . . 60 30

871 Ballerina **872** "Marysia and Burek in Ceylon"

1985. Bicentenary of Polish Ballet.

3018	**871** 5z. green, orange and red	15	10
3019	– 15z. brown, violet & orange	45	10

DESIGN: 15z. Male dancer.

1985. Birth Centenary of Stanislaw Ignacy Witkiewicz (artist). Multicoloured.

3020	5z. Type **872**	15	10
3021	10z. "Woman with Fox" (horiz)	30	10
3022	10z. "Self-portrait"	30	10
3023	20z. "Compositions (1917–20)"	55	30
3024	25z. "Nena Stachurska" . .	65	30

873 Oliwa Church Organ and Bach **874** Human Profile

1985. 300th Birth Anniv of Johann Sebastian Bach (composer). Sheet 67 × 79 mm.

MS3025 **873** 65z. multicoloured 1·50 1·25

1986. Congress of Intellectuals for Defence of Peaceful Future of the World, Warsaw.

3026 **874** 10z. ultramarine, violet and blue 30 10

875 Michal Kamienski and Planetary and Comet's Orbits

1985. Appearance of Halley's Comet.

3027	**875** 25z. blue and brown . .	60	30
3028	– 25z. deep blue, blue and brown	60	30

DESIGN: No. 3028, "Vega", "Planet A", "Giotto" and "Ice" space probes and comet.

1986. Renovation of Cracow Monuments (4th series). As T **819**.

3029	5z. dp brown, brown & black	10	10
3030	10z. green, brown and black	25	10

DESIGNS: 5z. Collegium Maius (Jagiellonian University Museum); 10z. Kazimierz Town Hall.

876 Sun **877** Grey Partridge

1986. International Peace Year.

3031 **876** 25z. yellow, light blue and blue 45 25

1986. Game. Multicoloured.

3032	5z. Type **877**	30	30
3033	5z. Common rabbit	10	10
3034	10z. Common pheasants (horiz)	55	55
3035	10z. Fallow deer (horiz) . .	15	10
3036	20z. Hare	30	30
3037	40z. Argali	65	65

878 Kulczynski **880** Paderewski (composer)

879 "Warsaw Fire Brigade, 1871" (detail, Jozef Brodowski)

1986. 10th Death Anniv (1985) of Stanislaw Kulczynski (politician).

3038 **878** 10z. light brown and brown 25 10

1986. 150th Anniv of Warsaw Fire Brigade.

3039 **879** 10z. dp brown & brown 25 10

1986. "Ameripex '86" International Stamp Exhibition, Chicago.

3040 **880** 65z. blue, black and grey 1·40 45

881 Footballers

1986. World Cup Football Championship, Mexico.

3041 **881** 25z. multicoloured . . . 45 30

882 "Wilanow"

1986. Passenger Ferries. Multicoloured.

3042	10z. Type **882**	25	15
3043	10z. "Wawel"	25	15
3044	15z. "Pomerania"	30	15
3045	25z. "Rogalin"	55	25
MS3046	Two sheets, each 116 × 98 mm. (a) Nos. 3042/3 (sold at 30z.); (b) Nos. 3044/5 (sold at 55z.)	6·00	2·40

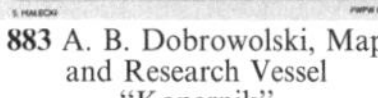

883 A. B. Dobrowolski, Map and Research Vessel "Kopernik" **885** "The Paulinite Church on Skalka in Cracow" (detail), 1627

884 Workers and Emblem

1986. 25th Anniv of Antarctic Agreement.

3047	**883** 5z. green, black and red	10	15
3048	– 40z. lavender, violet and orange	1·90	30

DESIGN: 40z. H. Arctowski, map and research vessel "Profesor Siedlecki".

1986. 10th Polish United Workers' Party Congress, Warsaw.

3049 **884** 10z. blue and red 25 10

1986. Treasures of Jasna Gora Monastery. Mult.

3050	5z. Type **885**	15	10
3051	5z. "Tree of Jesse", 17th-century	15	10
3052	20z. Chalice, 18th-century	40	25
3053	40z. "Virgin Mary" (detail, chasuble column), 15th-century	1·10	30

886 Precision Flying (Waclaw Nycz)

1986. 1985 Polish World Championship Successes. Multicoloured.

3054	5z. Type **886**	15	10
3055	10z. Windsurfing (Malgorzata Palasz-Piasecka)	40	10
3056	10z. Glider areobatics (Jerzy Makula)	30	10
3057	15z. Wrestling (Bogdan Daras)	30	10
3058	20z. Individual road cycling (Lech Piasecki)	45	25
3059	30z. Women's modern pentathlon (Barbara Kotowska)	75	30

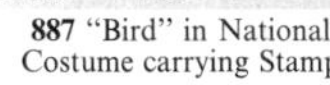

887 "Bird" in National Costume carrying Stamp **888** Schweitzer

1986. "Stockholmia '86" International Stamp Exhibition.

3060	**887** 65z. multicoloured . . .	1·40	45
MS3061	94 × 80 mm. No. 3060	1·60	1·60

1986. 47th Anniv of German Invasion. As T **850**. Multicoloured.

3062 10z. Battle of Jordanow and Col. Stanislaw Maczek . . 25 10

1986. 10th Death Anniv (1985) of Albert Schweitzer (medical missionary).

3063 **888** 5z. brown, lt brown & blue 15 10

889 Airliner and Postal Messenger **890** Basilisk

1986. World Post Day.

3064	**889** 40z. brown, blue and red	75	30
MS3065	81 × 81 mm. No. 3064 × 2 (sold at 120z.)	10·50	9·00

1986. Folk Tales. Multicoloured.

3066	5z. Type **890**	15	15
3067	5z. Duke Popiel (vert) . . .	15	15
3068	10z. Golden Duck	25	15
3069	10z. Boruta the Devil (vert)	25	15
3070	20z. Janosik the Robber (vert)	40	15
3071	50z. Lajkonik (vert)	1·10	40

891 Kotarbinski **892** 20th-century Windmill, Zygmuntow

1986. Birth Centenary of Tadeusz Kotarbinski (philosopher).

3072 **891** 10z. deep brown and brown 25 30

1986. Wooden Architecture. Multicoloured.

3073	5z. Type **892**	15	10
3074	5z. 17th-century church, Baczal Dolny	15	10
3075	10z. 19th-century Oravian cottage, Zubrzyca Gorna	25	10
3076	15z. 18th-century Kashubian arcade cottage, Wdzydze	25	15
3077	25z. 19th-century barn, Grzawa	55	25
3078	30z. 19th-century watermill, Siolkowice Stare	75	30

893 Mieszko (Mieczyslaw) I

1986. Polish Rulers (1st series). Drawings by Jan Matejko.

3079	**893** 10z. brown and green . .	30	30
3080	– 25z. black and purple . .	75	45

DESIGN: 25z. Queen Dobrawa (wife of Mieszko I).

See also Nos. 3144/5, 3193/4, 3251/2, 3341/2, 3351/2, 3387/8, 3461/4, 3511/12, 3548/51, 3641/4, 3705/8, 3732/5, 3819/22 and 3887/91.

894 Star

1986. New Year.

3081 **894** 25z. multicoloured . . . 45 30

895 Trip to Bielany, 1887

1986. Centenary of Warsaw Cyclists' Society.

3082 **895** 5z. multicoloured 10 15
3083 – 5z. brown, light brown and black 10 15
3084 – 10z. multicoloured . . . 25 15
3085 – 10z. multicoloured . . . 25 15
3086 – 30z. multicoloured . . . 60 30
3087 – 50z. multicoloured . . . 1·10 45

DESIGNS: No. 3083, Jan Stanislaw Skrodaki (1895 touring record holder); 3084, Dynasy (Society's headquarters, 1892–1937); 3085, Mieczyslaw Baranski (1896 Kingdom of Poland road cycling champion); 3086, Karolina Kociecka; 3087, Henryk Weiss (Race champion).

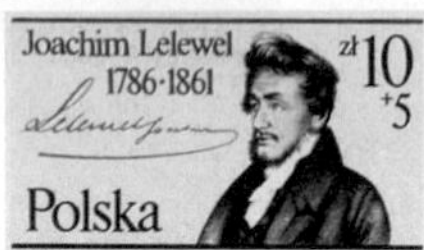

896 Lelewel

1986. Birth Bicentenary of Joachim Lelewel (historian).

3088 **896** 10z.+5z. multicoloured 30 15

897 Krill and "Antoni Garnuszewski" (cadet freighter)

1987. 10th Anniv of Henryk Arctowski Antarctic Station, King George Island, South Shetlands. Multicoloured.

3089 5z. Type **897** 10 10
3090 5z. Antarctic toothfish, marbled rockfish and "Zulawy" (supply ship) 10 10
3091 10z. Southern fulmar and "Pogoria" (cadet brigantine) 30 10
3092 10z. Adelie penguin and "Gedania" (yacht) 30 10
3093 30z. Fur seal and "Dziunia" (research vessel) 40 10
3094 40z. Leopard seals and "Kapitan Ledochowski" (research vessel) 45 30

898 "Portrait of a Woman"

1987. 50th Death Anniv (1986) of Leon Wyczolkowski (artist). Multicoloured.

3095 5z. "Cineraria Flowers" (horiz) 10 10
3096 10z. Type **898** 15 10
3097 10z. "Wooden Church" (horiz) 15 10
3098 25z. "Beetroot Lifting" . . 40 10
3099 30z. "Wading Fishermen" (horiz) 45 15
3100 40z. "Self-portrait" (horiz) 60 40

899 "Ravage" (from "War Cycle") and Artur Grottger

1987. 150th Birth Anniv of Artur Grottger (artist).

3101 **899** 15z. brown and stone . . 25 10

900 Swierczewski **901** Strzelecki

1987. 90th Birth Anniv of General Karol Swierczewski.

3102 **900** 15z. green and olive . . 25 10

1987. 190th Birth Anniv of Pawel Edmund Strzelecki (scientist and explorer of Tasmania).

3103 **901** 65z. green 60 30

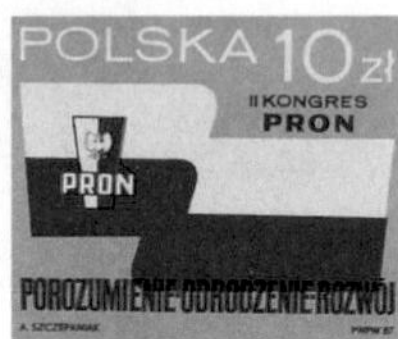

902 Emblem and Banner

1987. 2nd Patriotic Movement for National Revival Congress.

3104 **902** 10z. red, blue and brown 15 10

903 CWS "T-1" Motor Car, 1928

1987. Polish Motor Vehicles. Multicoloured.

3105 10z. Type **903** 10 10
3106 10z. Saurer-Zawrat bus, 1936 . . . . 10 10
3107 15z. Ursus-A lorry, 1928 . . 25 10
3108 15z. Lux-Sport motor car, 1936 . . . . 25 10
3109 25z. Podkowa "100" motor cycle, 1939 . . . . 30 10
3110 45z. Sokol "600 RT" motor cycle, 1935 . . . . 55 55

904 Royal Palace, Warsaw

1987.

3111 **904** 50z. multicoloured . . . 60 30

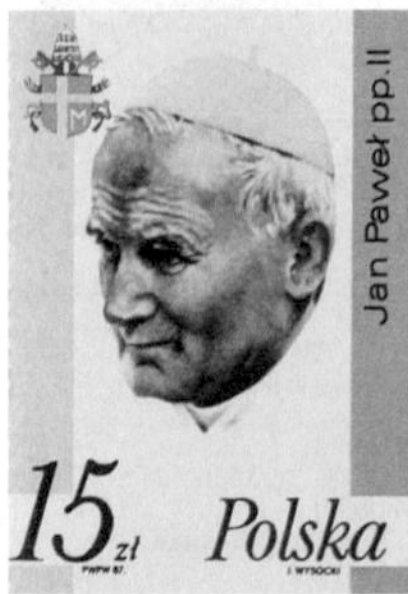

905 Pope John Paul II

1987. 3rd Papal Visit. Multicoloured.

3112 15z. Type **905** 25 15
3113 45z. Pope and signature . . 45 30
MS3114 77 × 66 mm. 50z. Profile of Pope (21 × 27 mm) 60 60

906 Polish Settler at Kasubia, Ontario

1987. "Capex '87" International Stamp Exhibition, Toronto.

3115 **906** 50z.+20z. multicoloured 75 40

1987. Renovation of Cracow Monuments (5th series). As T **819**.

3116 10z. lilac, black and green 15 10

DESIGN: 10z. Barbican.

907 Ludwig Zamenhof (inventor) and Star

1987. Cent of Esperanto (invented language).

3117 **907** 5z. brown, green & black 60 25

908 "Poznan Town Hall" (Stanislaw Wyspianski) **909** Queen Bee

1987. "Poznan 87" National Stamp Exhibition.

3118 **908** 15z. brown and orange 25 15

1987. "Apimondia 87" International Bee Keeping Congress, Warsaw. Multicoloured.

3119 10z. Type **909** 15 10
3120 10z. Worker bee 15 10
3121 15z. Drone 25 10
3122 15z. Hive in orchard 25 10
3123 40z. Worker bee on clover flower 60 25
3124 50z. Forest bee keeper collecting honey 75 30

910 1984 Olympic Stamp and Laurel Wreath

1987. "Olymphilex '87" Olympic Stamps Exhibition, Rome. Sheet 83 × 57 mm.

MS3125 **910** 45z.+10z. multicoloured 75 85

The premium was for the benefit of the Polish Olympic Committee's fund.

1987. 48th Anniv of German Invasion. As T **850**. Multicoloured.

3126 10z. Battle of Mokra and Col. Julian Filipowicz . . 15 10
3127 10z. Fighting at Oleszyce and Brig.-Gen. Jozef Rudolf Kustron 15 10
3128 15z. PZL P-7 aircraft over Warsaw and Col. Stefan Pawlikowski 30 10

911 Hevelius and Sextant **912** High Jump (World Acrobatics Championships, France)

1987. 300th Death Anniv of Jan Hevelius (astronomer). Multicoloured.

3129 15z. Type **911** 25 10
3130 40z. Hevelius and map of constellations (horiz) . . . 55 25

1987. 1986 Polish World Championship Successes. Multicoloured.

3131 10z. Type **912** 15 10
3132 15z. Two-man canoe (World Canoeing Championships, Canada) 25 10
3133 20z. Marksman (Free pistol event, World Marksmanship Championships, East Germany) 30 15
3134 25z. Wrestlers (World Wrestling Championships, Hungary) 45 15

913 "Stacionar 4" Telecommunications Satellite

1987. 30th Anniv of launch of "Sputnik 1" (first artificial satellite). Sheet 67 × 82 mm.

MS3135 **913** 40z. multicoloured 55 60

914 Warsaw Post Office and Ignacy Franciszek Przebendowski (Postmaster General)

1987. World Post Day.

3136 **914** 15z. green and red . . . 25 10

915 "The Little Mermaid" **916** Col. Stanislaw Wieckowski (founder)

1987. "Hafnia 87" International Stamp Exhibition, Copenhagen. Hans Christain Andersen's Fairy Tales. Multicoloured.

3137 10z. Type **915** 15 10
3138 10z. "The Nightingale" . . 15 10
3139 20z. "The Wild Swans" . . 25 15
3140 20z. "The Little Match Girl" 25 15
3141 30z. "The Snow Queen" . . 40 30
3142 40z. "The Tin Soldier" . . . 55 15

1987. 50th Anniv of Democratic Clubs.

3143 **916** 15z. black and blue . . . 25 10

1987. Polish Rulers (2nd series). As T **893**. Drawings by Jan Matejko.

3144 10z. green and blue 15 15
3145 15z. blue and ultramarine 40 30

DESIGNS: 10z. Boleslaw I, the Brave; 15z. Mieszko (Mieczyslaw) II.

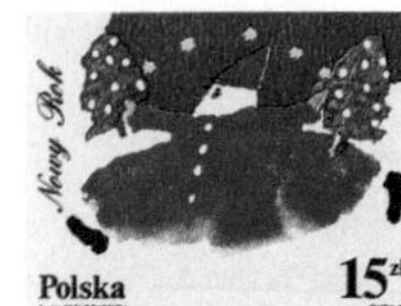

917 Santa Claus with Christmas Trees

1987. New Year.

3146 **917** 15z. multicoloured . . . 15 15

918 Emperor Dragonfly

1988. Dragonflies. Multicoloured.

3147 10z. Type **918** 15 10
3148 15z. Four-spotted libellula ("Libellula quadrimaculata") (vert) 30 10
3149 15z. Banded agrion ("Calopteryx splendens") 30 10
3150 20z. "Condulegaster annulatus" (vert) 30 10

3151 30z. "Sympetrum pedemontanum" 40 25
3152 50z. "Aeschna viridis" (vert) 65 30

1988. Renovation of Cracow Monuments (6th series). As T **819**.
3153 15z. yellow, brown and black 15 10
DESIGN: 15z. Florianska Gate.

919 Composition

1988. International Year of Graphic Design.
3154 **919** 40z. multicoloured . . . 40 40

920 17th-century Friesian Wall Clock with Bracket Case

1988. Clocks and Watches. Multicoloured.
3155 10z. Type **920** 15 10
3156 10z. 20th-century annual clock (horiz) 15 10
3157 15z. 18th-century carriage clock 15 10
3158 15z. 18th-century French rococo bracket clock . . 15 10
3159 20z. 19th-century pocket watch (horiz) 25 10
3160 40z. 17th-cent tile-case clock from Gdansk by Benjamin Zoll (horiz) . . 40 15

921 Atlantic Salmon and Reindeer

1988. "Finlandia 88" International Stamp Exhibition, Helsinki.
3161 **921** 45z.+30z. multicoloured 60 30

922 Triple Jump **924** Wheat as Graph on VDU

923 Kukuczka

1988. Olympic Games, Seoul. Multicoloured.
3162 15z. Type **922** 25 10
3163 20z. Wrestling 25 10
3164 20z. Canoeing 25 10
3165 25z. Judo 25 10
3166 40z. Shooting 40 15
3167 55z. Swimming 55 30

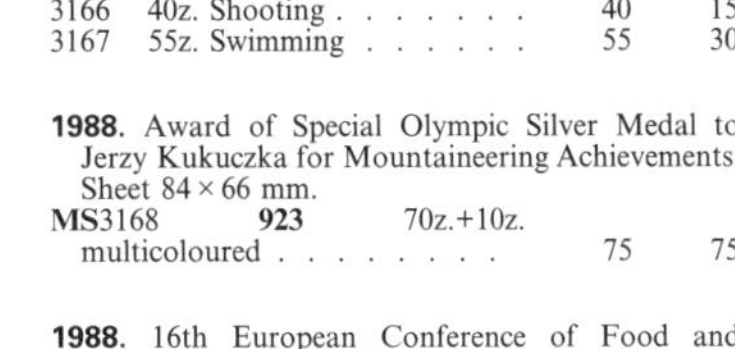

1988. Award of Special Olympic Silver Medal to Jerzy Kukuczka for Mountaineering Achievements. Sheet 84 × 66 mm.
MS3168 **923** 70z.+10z. multicoloured 75 75

1988. 16th European Conference of Food and Agriculture Organization, Cracow. Multicoloured.
3169 15z. Type **924** 15 10
3170 40z. Factory in forest . . . 30 10

925 PZL P-37 Los Bomber

1988. 70th Anniv of Polish Republic (1st issue). 60th Anniv of Polish State Aircraft Works.
3171 **925** 45z. multicoloured . . . 30 10
See also Nos. 3175, 3177, 3181/88 and 3190/2.

1988. 49th Anniv of German Invasion. As T **850**. Multicoloured.
3172 15z. Battle of Modlin and Brig.-Gen. Wiktor Thommee 25 10
3173 20z. Battle of Warsaw and Brig.-Gen. Walerian Czuma 25 10
3174 20z. Battle of Tomaszow Lubelski and Brig.-Gen. Antoni Szylling 25 10

1988. 70th Anniv of Polish Republic (2nd issue). 50th Anniv of Stalowa Wola Ironworks. As T **925**. Multicoloured.
3175 15z. View of plant 15 10

926 Postal Emblem and Tomasz Arciszewski (Postal Minister, 1918–19)

1988. World Post Day.
3176 **926** 20z. multicoloured . . . 15 10

1988. 70th Anniv of Polish Republic (3rd issue). 60th Anniv of Military Institute for Aviation Medicine. As T **925**. Multicoloured.
3177 20z. Hanriot XIV hospital aircraft (38 × 28 mm) . . 15 10

927 On the Field of Glory Medal

1988. Polish People's Army Battle Medals (1st series). Multicoloured.
3178 20z. Type **927** 15 10
3179 20z. Battle of Lenino Cross 15 10
See also Nos. 3249/50.

928 "Stanislaw Malachowski" and "Kazimierz Nestor Sapieha"

1988. Bicentenary of Four Years Diet (political and social reforms). Paintings of Diet Presidents by Jozef Peszko.
3180 **928** 20z. multicoloured . . . 15 10

929 Ignacy Daszynski (politician)

1988. 70th Anniv of Polish Republic (4th issue). Personalities.
3181 **929** 15z. green, red and black 10 10
3182 – 15z. green, red and black 10 10
3183 – 20z. brown, red and black 15 10
3184 – 20z. brown, red and black 15 10
3185 – 20z. brown, red and black 15 10
3186 – 200z. purple, red & black 1·40 55
3187 – 200z. purple, red & black 1·40 55
3188 – 200z. purple, red & black 1·40 55
MS3189 102 × 60 mm. Nos. 3186/8 13·50 13·50
DESIGNS: No. 3182, Wincenty Witos (politician); 3183, Julian Marchlewski (trade unionist and economist); 3184, Stanislaw Wojciechowski (politician); 3185, Wojciech Korfanty (politician); 3186, Ignacy Paderewski (musician and politician); 3187; Marshal Jozef Pilsudski; 3188, Gabriel Narutowicz (President, 1922).

1988. 70th Anniv of Polish Republic (5th issue). As T **925**. Multicoloured.
3190 15z. Coal wharf, Gdynia Port (65th anniv) (38 × 28 mm) 10 10
3191 20z. Hipolit Cegielski (founder) and steam locomotive (142nd anniv of H. Cegielski Metal Works, Poznan) (38 × 28 mm) 15 10
3192 40z. Upper Silesia Tower (main entrance) (60th anniv of International Poznan Fair) 30 10

1988. Polish Rulers (3rd series). Drawings by Jan Matejko. As T **893**.
3193 10z. deep brown and brown 30 10
3194 15z. deep brown and brown 45 10
DESIGNS: 10z. Queen Rycheza; 15z. Kazimierz (Karol Odnowiciel) I.

930 Snowman

1988. New Year.
3195 **930** 20z. multicoloured . . . 15 10

931 Flag **932** "Blysk"

1988. 40th Anniv of Polish United Workers' Party.
3196 **931** 20z. red and black . . . 15 10

1988. Fire Boats. Multicoloured.
3197 10z. Type **932** 10 10
3198 15z. "Plomien" 10 10
3199 15z. "Zar" 10 10
3200 20z. "Strazak II" 25 10
3201 20z. "Strazak 4" 25 10
3202 45z. "Strazak 25" 40 30

933 Ardennes

1989. Horses. Multicoloured.
3203 15z. Lippizaner (horiz) . . . 10 10
3204 15z. Type **933** 10 10
3205 20z. English thoroughbred (horiz) 25 10
3206 20z. Arab 25 10
3207 30z. Great Poland race-horse (horiz) 40 10
3208 70z. Polish horse 75 30

934 Wire-haired Dachshund

1989. Hunting Dogs. Multicoloured.
3209 15z. Type **934** 10 10
3210 15z. Cocker spaniel 10 10
3211 20z. Czech fousek pointer 10 10
3212 20z. Welsh terrier 10 10
3213 25z. English setter 15 10
3214 45z. Pointer 30 30

935 Gen. Wladyslaw Anders and Plan of Battle **936** Marianne

1989. 45th Anniv of Battle of Monte Cassino.
3215 **935** 80z. multicoloured . . . 40 30
See also Nos. 3227, 3247, 3287 and 3327.

1989. Bicentenary of French Revolution.
3216 **936** 100z. black, red and blue 40 25
MS3217 93 × 118 mm. No. 3216 × 2 plus two labels (sold at 270z.) 90 1·10

937 Polonia House

1989. Opening of Polonia House (cultural centre), Pultusk.
3218 **937** 100z. multicoloured . . . 45 25

938 Monument (Bohdan Chmielewski)

1989. 45th Anniv of Civic Militia and Security Force.
3219 **938** 35z. blue and brown . . 25 15

939 Xaweri Dunikowski (artist) **941** Firemen

940 Astronaut

1989. Recipients of Order of Builders of the Republic of Poland. Multicoloured.
3220 35z. Type **939** 15 10
3221 35z. Stanislaw Mazur (farmer) 15 10
3222 35z. Natalia Gasiorowska (historian) 15 10
3223 35z. Wincenti Pstrowski (initiator of worker performance contests) . . 15 10

1989. 20th Anniv of First Manned Landing on Moon.
3224 **940** 100z. multicoloured . . . 45 25
MS3225 85 × 85 mm. No. 3224 2·10 1·40

1989. World Fire Fighting Congress, Warsaw.
3226 **941** 80z. multicoloured . . . 30 10

1989. 45th Anniv of Battle of Falaise. As T **935**. Multicoloured.
3227 165z. Plan of battle and Gen. Stanislaw Maczek (horiz) 60 30

942 Daisy

943 Museum Emblem

1989. Plants. (a) Perf.

3229	**942**	40z. green	15	10
3230	–	60z. violet	15	10
3231	**942**	150z. red	30	10
3232	–	500z. mauve	30	10
3233	–	700z. green	15	10
3234	–	1000z. blue	90	30

(b) Self-adhesive. Imperf.

3297	–	2000z. green	40	25
3298	–	5000z. violet	85	40

DESIGNS: 60z. Juniper; 500z. Wild rose; 700z. Lily of the valley; 1000z. Blue cornflower; 2000z. Water lily; 5000z. Iris.

1989. 50th Anniv of German Invasion. As T **850**.

3240	25z. grey, orange and black	25	10
3241	25z. multicoloured	25	10
3242	35z. multicoloured	40	30
3243	35z. multicoloured	40	30

DESIGNS: No. 3240, Defence of Westerplatte and Captain Franciszek Dabrowski; 3241, Defence of Hel and Captain B. Przybyszewski; 3242, Battle of Kock and Brig.-Gen. Franciszek Kleeberg; 3243, Defence of Lwow and Brig.-Gen. Wladyslaw Langner.

1989. Caricature Museum.
3244 **943** 40z. multicoloured . . . 15 10

944 Rafal Czerwiakowski (founder of first university Surgery Department)

945 Emil Kalinski (Postal Minister, 1933–39)

1989. Polish Surgeons' Society Centenary Congress, Cracow.

3245	**944**	40z. blue and black	25	10
3246	–	60z. green and black	25	10

DESIGN: 60z. Ludwik Rydygier (founder of Polish Surgeons' Society).

1989. 45th Anniv of Landing at Arnhem. As T **935**. Multicoloured.
3247 210z. Gen. Stanislaw Sosabowski and plan of battle . . . 75 45

1989. World Post Day.
3248 **945** 60z. multicoloured . . . 25 25

1989. Polish People's Army Battle Medals (2nd series). As T **927**. Multicoloured.

3249	60z. "For Participation in the Struggle for the Rule of the People"	25	15
3250	60z. Warsaw 1939–45 Medal	25	15

1989. Polish Rulers (4th series). As T **893**. Drawings by Jan Matejko.

3251	20z. black and grey	30	10
3252	30z. sepia and brown	30	30

DESIGNS: 20z. Boleslaw II, the Bold; 30z. Wladyslaw I Herman.

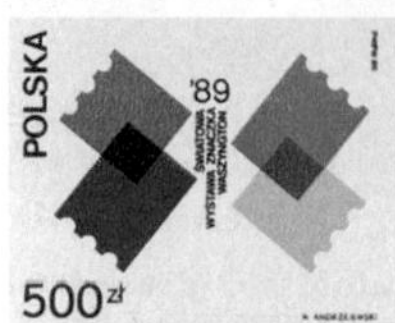
946 Stamps

1989. "World Stamp Expo '89" International Stamp Exhibition, Washington D.C.
3253 **946** 500z. multicoloured . . . 1·10 65

947 Cross and Twig

949 Photographer and Medal depicting Maksymilian Strasz

948 Ignacy Paderewski and Roman Dmowski (Polish signatories)

1989. 70th Anniv of Polish Red Cross.
3254 **947** 200z. red, green and black . . . 45 25

1989. 70th Anniv of Treaty of Versailles.
3255 **948** 350z. multicoloured . . . 60 60

1989. 150th Anniv of Photography. Multicoloured.

3256	40z. Type **949**	15	10
3257	60z. Lens shutter as pupil of eye (horiz)	15	10

1989. No. 2729 surch **500**.
3258 500z. on 4z. violet . . . 90 45

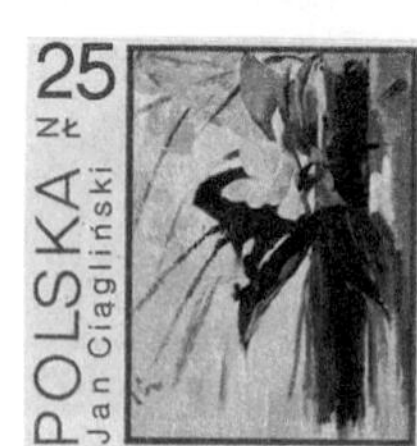
951 Painting by Jan Ciaglinski

1989. Flower Paintings by Artists Named. Mult.

3259	25z. Type **951**	10	10
3260	30z. Wojciech Weiss	10	10
3261	35z. Antoni Kolasinski	15	10
3262	50z. Stefan Nacht-Samborski	15	10
3263	60z. Jozef Pankiewicz	15	10
3264	85z. Henryka Beyer	25	25
3265	110z. Wladyslaw Slewinski	30	30
3266	190z. Czeslaw Wdowiszewski	40	40

952 Christ

1989. Icons (1st series). Multicoloured.

3267	50z. Type **952**	15	10
3268	60z. Two saints with books	15	10
3269	90z. Three saints with books	25	15
3270	150z. Displaying scriptures (vert)	40	40
3271	200z. Madonna and child (vert)	45	45
3272	350z. Christ with saints and angels (vert)	45	45

See also Nos. 3345/50.

1990. No. 2839 surch **350 zl**.
3273 350z. on 15z. brown . . . 60 30

954 Krystyna Jamroz

955 High Jumping

1990. Singers. Multicoloured.

3274	100z. Type **954**	25	25
3275	150z. Wanda Werminska	25	25
3276	350z. Ada Sari	40	40
3277	500z. Jan Kiepura	45	45

1990. Sports. Multicoloured.

3278	100z. Yachting	15	25
3279	200z. Rugby	15	30
3280	400z. Type **955**	15	30
3281	500z. Ice skating	15	40
3282	500z. Diving	15	45
3283	1000z. Gymnastics	25	30

956 Kozlowski

1990. Birth Centenary (1989) of Roman Kozlowski (palaeontologist).
3284 **956** 500z. brown and red . . 15 25

957 John Paul II

1990. 70th Birthday of Pope John Paul II.
3285 **957** 1000z. multicoloured . . 30 30

958 1860 10k. Stamp and Anniversary Stamp

1990. 130th Anniv of First Polish Postage Stamp. Sheet 65 × 68 mm.
MS3286 **958** 1000z. orange and blue 60 30

1990. 50th Anniv of Battle of Narvik. As T **935**. Multicoloured.
3287 1500z. Gen. Zygmunt Bohusz-Szyszko and plan of battle . . . 30 25

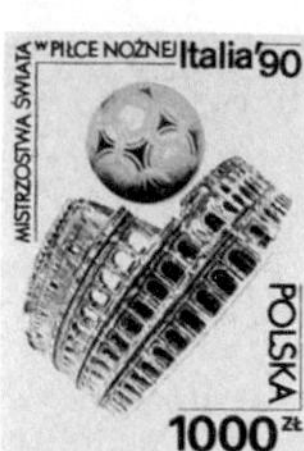
959 Ball and Colosseum

1990. World Cup Football Championship, Italy.
3288 **959** 1000z. multicoloured . . 15 25

1990. No. 3230 surch **700 zl**.
3289 700z. on 60z. violet . . . 15 15

961 Memorial

963 Stagnant Pond Snail

962 People and "ZUS"

1990. 34th Anniv of 1956 Poznan Uprising.
3290 **961** 1500z. multicoloured . . 25 15

1990. 70th Anniv of Social Insurance.
3291 **962** 1500z. blue, mauve & yellow . . . 30 25

1990. Shells. No value expressed.

3292	–	B (500z.) lilac	25	10
3293	**963**	A (700z.) green	45	10

DESIGN: B, River snail.

964 Cross

1990. 50th Anniv of Katyn Massacre.
3294 **964** 1500z. black and red . . 25 10

965 Weather Balloon

1990. Polish Hydrology and Meteorology Service. Multicoloured.

3295	500z. Type **965**	10	10
3296	700z. Water-height gauge	25	10

966 Women's Kayak Pairs

1990. 23rd World Canoeing Championships. Mult.

3305	700z. Type **966**	25	10
3306	1000z. Men's kayak singles	30	30

967 Victory Sign

968 Jacob's Ladder

1990. 10th Anniv of Solidarity Trade Union.
3307 **967** 1500z. grey, black and red . . . 25 30

1990. Flowers. Multicoloured.

3308	200z. Type **968**	10	10
3309	700z. Floating heart water fringe ("Nymphoides peltata")	15	10
3310	700z. Dragonhead ("Dracocephalum ruyschiana")	15	10
3311	1000z. "Helleborus purpurascens"	25	10
3312	1500z. Daphne cneorum	45	40
3313	1700z. Campion	65	45

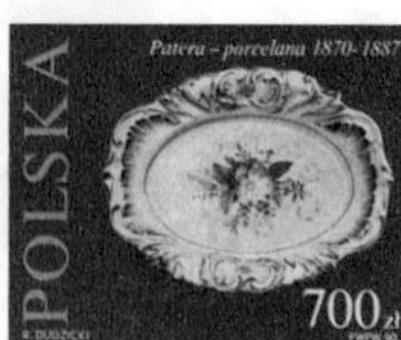
969 Serving Dish, 1870–87

1990. Bicentenary of Cmieow Porcelain Works. Multicoloured.

3314	700z. Type **969**	15	10
3315	800z. Plate, 1887–90 (vert)	25	10
3316	1000z. Cup and saucer, 1887	30	10
3317	1000z. Figurine of dancer, 1941–44 (vert)	30	10
3318	1500z. Chocolate box, 1930–90	55	25
3319	2000z. Vase, 1979 (vert)	60	40

970 Little Owl

972 Collegiate Church, Tum (12th century)

971 Walesa

1990. Owls. Multicoloured.
3320 200z. Type **970** 15 10
3321 500z. Tawny owl (value at left) 35 10
3322 500z. Tawny owl (value at right) 35 10
3323 1000z. Short-eared owl . . . 50 25
3324 1500z. Long-eared owl . . . 80 30
3325 2000z. Barn owl . . . . . 1·10 40

1990. Lech Walesa, 1984 Nobel Peace Prize Winner and new President.
3326 **971** 1700z. multicoloured . . 40 25

1990. 50th Anniv of Battle of Britain. As T **935**. Multicoloured.
3327 1500z. Emblem of 303 Squadron, Polish Fighter Wing R.A.F. and Hawker Hurricane 45 45

1990. Historic Architecture. Multicoloured.
3328 700z. Type **972** 25 20
3329 800z. Reszel Castle (11th century) 25 25
3330 1500z. Chelmno Town Hall (16th century) 60 60
3331 1700z. Church of the Nuns of the Visitation, Warsaw (18th century) 60 60

973 "King Zygmunt II August" (anon)

974 Silver Fir

1991. Paintings. Multicoloured.
3332 500z. Type **973** 15 10
3333 700z. "Adoration of the Magi" (Pultusk Codex) 25 10
3334 1000z. "St Matthew" (Pultusk Codex) 30 10
3335 1500z. "Expelling of Merchants from Temple" (Nikolai Haberschrack) 45 30
3336 1700z. "The Annunciation" (miniature) 55 30
3337 2000z. "Three Marys" (Nikolai Haberschrack) 60 40

1991. Cones. Multicoloured.
3338 700z. Type **974** 15 10
3339 1500z. Weymouth pine . . . 25 25
See also Nos. 3483/4.

975 Radziwill Palace

977 Chmielowski

1991. Admission of Poland into European Postal and Telecommunications Conference.
3340 **975** 1500z. multicoloured . . 30 25

1991. Polish Rulers (5th series). Drawings by Jan Matejko. As T **893** but surch.
3341 1000z. on 40z. black & green 40 25
3342 1500z. on 50z. black and red 55 30
DESIGNS: 1000z. Boleslaw III, the Wry Mouthed; 1500z. Wladyslaw II, the Exile.
Nos. 3341/2 were not issued unsurcharged.

1991. 75th Death Anniv of Adam Chmielowski ("Brother Albert") (founder of Albertine Sisters).
3343 **977** 2000z. multicoloured . . 40 25

978 Battle (detail of miniature, Schlackenwerth Codex, 1350)

1991. 750th Anniv of Battle of Legnica.
3344 **978** 1500z. multicoloured . . 30 25

1991. Icons (2nd series). As T **952**. Mult.
3345 500z. "Madonna of Nazareth" 10 10
3346 700z. "Christ the Acheirophyte" 15 10
3347 1000z. "Madonna of Vladimir" 25 10
3348 1500z. "Madonna of Kazan" 40 15
3349 2000z. "St. John the Baptist" 55 25
3350 2200z. "Christ the Pentocrator" 85 30

1991. Polish Rulers (6th series). Drawings by Jan Matejko. As T **893**.
3351 1000z. black and red 30 25
3352 1500z. black and blue . . . 45 25
DESIGNS: 1000z. Boleslaw IV, the Curly; 1500z. Mieszko (Mieczyslaw) III, the Old.

979 Title Page of Constitution

980 Satellite in Earth Orbit

1991. Bicentenary of 3rd May Constitution.
3353 **979** 2000z. brown, buff & red 40 30
3354 – 2500z. brown, stone & red 55 40
MS3355 85 × 85 mm. 3000z. multicoloured 75 75
DESIGNS: 2500z. "Administration of Oath by Gustav Taubert" (detail, Johann Friedrich Bolt); 3000z. "Constitution, 3 May 1791" (Jan Matejko).

1991. Europa. Europe in Space.
3356 **980** 1000z. multicoloured . . 25 25

981 Map and Battle Scene

1991. 50th Anniv of Participation of "Piorun" (destroyer) in Operation against "Bismarck" (German battleship).
3357 **981** 2000z. multicoloured . . 45 30

982 Arms of Cracow

983 Pope John Paul II

1991. European Security and Co-operation Conference Cultural Heritage Symposium, Cracow.
3358 **982** 2000z. purple and blue 40 30

1991. Papal Visit. Multicoloured.
3359 1000z. Type **983** 25 10
3360 2000z. Pope in white robes 40 30

984 Bearded Penguin

985 Making Paper

1991. 30th Anniv of Antarctic Treaty.
3361 **984** 2000z. multicoloured . . 40 30

1991. 500th Anniv of Paper Making in Poland.
3362 **985** 2500z. blue and red . . . 40 30

986 Prisoner

1991. Commemoration of Victims of Stalin's Purges.
3363 **986** 2500z. red and black . . 40 30

987 Pope John Paul II

1991. 6th World Youth Day, Czestochowa. Sheet 70 × 87 mm.
MS3364 **987** 3500z. multicoloured 75 85

988 Ball and Basket

1991. Centenary of Basketball.
3365 **988** 2500z. multicoloured . . 55 30

989 "Self-portrait" (Leon Wyczolkowski)

1991. "Bydgoszcz '91" National Stamp Exn.
3366 **989** 3000z. green and brown 55 40
MS3367 155 × 92 mm. No. 3366 × 4 2·25 2·40

990 Twardowski

1991. 125th Birth Anniv of Kazimierz Twardowski (philosopher).
3368 **990** 2500z. black and grey . . 60 40

991 Swallowtail

1991. Butterflies and Moths. Multicoloured.
3369 1000z. Type **991** 25 25
3370 1000z. Dark crimson underwing ("Mormonia sponsa") 25 25
3371 1500z. Painted lady ("Vanessa cardui") . . . 30 25
3372 1500z. Scarce swallowtail ("Iphiclides podalirius") 30 25
3373 2500z. Scarlet tiger moth ("Panaxia dominula") . . 55 40
3374 2500z. Peacock ("Nymphalis io") 55 40
MS3375 127 × 63 mm. 15000z. Black-veined white (*Aporia crataegi*) (46 × 33 mm) plus label for "Phila Nippon '91" International Stamp Exhibition 1·90 2·25

992 "The Shepherd's Bow" (Francesco Solimena)

1991. Christmas.
3376 **992** 1000z. multicoloured . . 30 25

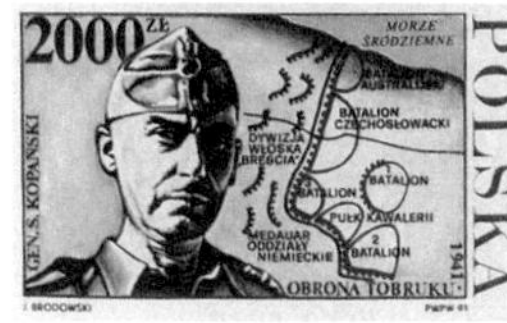

993 Gen. Stanislaw Kopanski and Battle Map

1991. 50th Anniv of Participation of Polish Troops in Battle of Tobruk.
3377 **993** 2000z. multicoloured . . 40 45

994 Brig.-Gen. Michal Tokarzewski-Karaszewicz

995 Lord Baden-Powell (founder)

1991. World War II Polish Underground Army Commanders.
3378 **994** 2000z. black and red . . 40 25
3379 – 2500z. red and violet . . 45 30
3380 – 3000z. violet and mauve 55 40
3381 – 5000z. brown and green 90 60
3382 – 6500z. dp brown & brn 1·10 75
DESIGNS: 2500z. Gen. Broni Kazimierz Sosnkowski; 3000z. Lt.-Gen. Stefan Rowecki; 5000z. Lt.-Gen. Tadeusz Komorowski; 6500z. Brig.-Gen. Leopold Okulicki.

1991. 80th Anniv of Scout Movement in Poland.
3383 **995** 1500z. yellow and green 30 10
3384 – 2000z. blue and yellow 45 30
3385 – 2500z. violet and yellow 55 30
3386 – 3500z. brown and yellow 65 45
DESIGNS: 2000z. Andrzej Malkowski (Polish founder); 2500z. "Watch on the Vistula" (Wojciech Kossak); 3500z. Polish scout in Warsaw Uprising, 1944.

1992. Polish Rulers (7th series). As T **893**.
3387 1500z. brown and green . . 40 25
3388 2000z. black and blue . . . 55 40
DESIGNS: 1500z. Kazimierz II, the Just; 2000z. Leszek I, the White.

996 Sebastien Bourdon

1992. Self-portraits. Multicoloured.
3389 700z. Type **996** 15 10
3390 1000z. Sir Joshua Reynolds 25 10
3391 1500z. Sir Godfrey Kneller 25 10
3392 2000z. Bartolome Esteban Murillo 40 25
3393 2200z. Peter Paul Rubens 45 25
3394 3000z. Diego de Silva y Velazquez 60 45

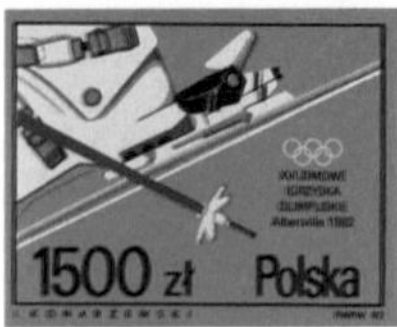

997 Skiing

1992. Winter Olympic Games, Albertville. Mult.

3395 1500z. Type **997** 25 25
3396 2500z. Ice hockey 45 30

998 Manteuffel

1992. 90th Birth Anniv of Tadeusz Manteuffel (historian).

3397 **998** 2500z. brown 45 30

999 Nicolas Copernicus (astronomer)

1992. Famous Poles. Multicoloured.

3398 1500z. Type **999** 25 10
3399 2000z. Frederic Chopin (composer) 40 25
3400 2500z. Henryk Sienkiewicz (writer) 45 25
3401 3500z. Marie Curie (physicist) 60 30
MS3402 80 × 81 mm. 5000z. Kazimierz Funk (biochemist) 75 75

1000 Columbus and Left-hand Detail of Map

1992. Europa. 500th Anniv of Discovery of America by Columbus. Multicoloured.

3403 1500z. Type **1000** 25 25
3404 3000z. "Santa Maria" and right-hand detail of Juan de la Costa map, 1500 . . 55 45

Nos. 3403/4 were issued together, se-tenant, forming a composite design.

1001 River Czarna Wiselka **1003** Family and Heart

1002 Prince Jozef Poniatowski

1992. Environmental Protection. River Cascades. Multicoloured.

3405 2000z. Type **1001** 45 15
3406 2500z. River Swider 60 40
3407 3000z. River Tanew 60 30
3408 3500z. Mickiewicz waterfall 60 40

1992. Bicentenary of Order of Military Virtue. Multicoloured.

3409 1500z. Type **1002** 25 25
3410 3000z. Marshal Jozef Pilsudski 40 30
MS3411 108 × 93 mm. 20000z. "Virgin Mary of Czestochowa" (icon) (36 × 57 mm) . . . . . 3·00 3·50

1992. Children's Drawings. Multicoloured.

3412 1500z. Type **1003** 25 10
3413 3000z. Butterfly, sun, bird and dog 60 30

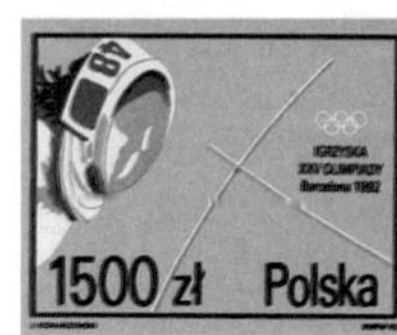

1004 Fencing

1992. Olympic Games, Barcelona. Multicoloured.

3414 1500z. Type **1004** 25 10
3415 2000z. Boxing 40 30
3416 2500z. Running 45 30
3417 3000z. Cycling 55 40

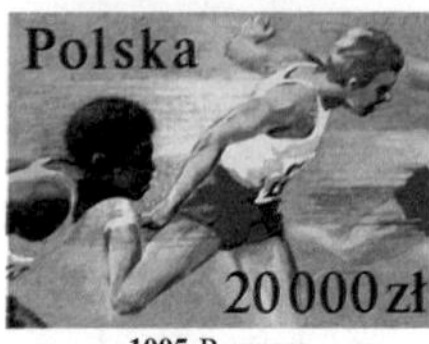

1005 Runners

1992. "Olymphilex '92" Olympic Stamps Exhibition, Barcelona. Sheet 86 × 81 mm.

MS3418 **1005** 20000z. multicoloured 3·50 3·25

1006 Statue of Korczak

1992. 50th Death Anniv of Janusz Korczak (educationist).

3419 **1006** 1500z. black, brown & yellow 30 30

1007 Flag and "V" **1008** Wyszinski

1992. 5th Polish Veterans World Meeting.

3420 **1007** 3000z. multicoloured . . 55 54

1992. 11th Death Anniv of Stefan Wyszinski (Primate of Poland) (3421) and 1st Anniv of World Youth Day (3422). Multicoloured.

3421 1500z. Type **1008** 30 15
3422 3000z. Pope John Paul II embracing youth 60 45

1009 National Colours encircling World Map

1992. World Meeting of Expatriate Poles, Cracow.

3423 **1009** 3000z. multicoloured . . 60 45

1010 Polish Museum, Adampol

1992. 150th Anniv of Polish Settlement at Adampol, Turkey.

3424 **1010** 3500z. multicoloured . . 60 45

1011 18th-century Post Office Sign, Slonim

1992. World Post Day.

3425 **1011** 3500z. multicoloured . . 60 45

1012 "Dedication" (self-portrait)

1992. Birth Centenary of Bruno Schulz (writer and artist).

3426 **1012** 3000z. multicoloured . . 55 45

1013 "Seated Girl" (Henryk Wicinski)

1992. Polish Sculptures. Multicoloured.

3427 2000z. Type **1013** 40 15
3428 2500z. "Portrait of Tytus Czyzewski" (Zbigniew Pronaszko) 45 30
3429 3000z. "Polish Nike" (Edward Wittig) 60 45
3430 3500z. "The Nude" (August Zamoyski) 60 45
MS3431 107 × 90 mm. Nos. 3427/30 1·60 1·60

1014 "10th Theatrical Summer in Zamosc" (Jan Mlodozeniec)

1992. Poster Art (1st series). Multicoloured.

3432 1500z. Type **1014** 25 10
3433 2000z. "Red Art" (Franciszek Starowieyski) 45 30

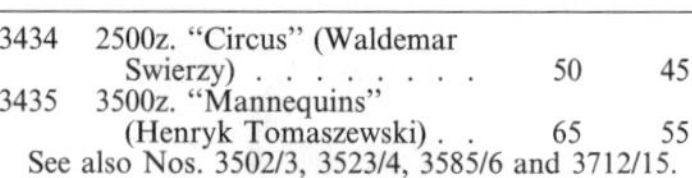

3434 2500z. "Circus" (Waldemar Swierzy) 50 45
3435 3500z. "Mannequins" (Henryk Tomaszewski) . . 65 55

See also Nos. 3502/3, 3523/4, 3585/6 and 3712/15.

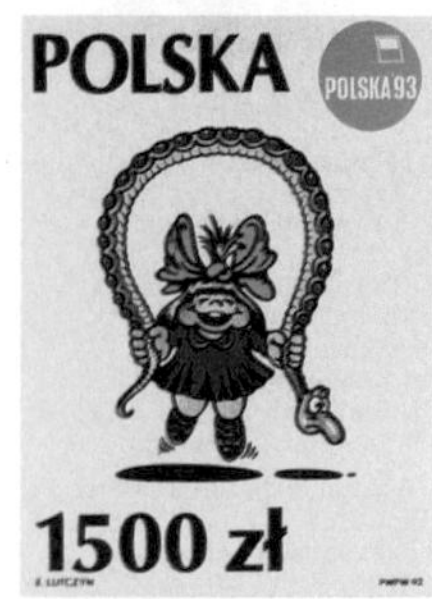

1015 Girl skipping with Snake

1992. "Polska '93" International Stamp Exn, Poznan (1st issue). Multicoloured.

3436 1500z. Type **1015** 25 10
3437 2000z. Boy on rocking horse with upside-down runners 45 25
3438 2500z. Boy firing bird from bow 45 30
3439 3500z. Girl placing ladder against clockwork giraffe 65 55

See also Nos. 3452, 3453/6 and 3466/9.

1016 Medal and Soldiers

1992. 50th Anniv of Formation of Polish Underground Army. Multicoloured.

3440 1500z. Type **1016** 25 25
3441 3500z. Soldiers 60 55
MS3442 75 × 95 mm. 20000z.+500z. "WP AK" (26 × 32 mm) . . . 3·00 3·00

1017 Church and Star **1018** Wheat

1992. Christmas.

3443 **1017** 1000z. multicoloured . . 15 10

1992. International Nutrition Conference, Rome. Multicoloured.

3444 1500z. Type **1018** 25 10
3445 3500z. Glass, bread, vegetables and jug on table 55 45

1019 Arms of Sovereign Military Order **1020** Arms, 1295

1992. Postal Agreement with Sovereign Military Order of Malta.

3446 **1019** 3000z. multicoloured . . 55 45

1992. History of the White Eagle (Poland's arms). Each black, red and yellow.

3447 2000z. Type **1020** 40 10
3448 2500z. 15th-century arms . . 45 30
3449 3000z. 18th-century arms . . 60 30
3450 3500z. Arms, 1919 . . . . 65 40
3451 5000z. Arms, 1990 . . . . 90 55

1021 Exhibition Emblem and Stylized Stamp

1992. Centenary of Polish Philately and "Polska '93" International Stamp Exhibition, Poznan (2nd issue).
3452 **1021** 1500z. multicoloured . . 25 10

1022 Amber

1993. "Polska '93" International Stamp Exhibition, Poznan (3rd issue). Amber. Multicoloured.
3453 1500z. Type **1022** 25 10
3454 2000z. Pinkish amber . . . 40 25
3455 2500z. Amber in stone . . . 45 45
3456 3000z. Amber containing wasp 60 55
MS3457 82 × 88 mm. 20000z. Detail of map with necklace representing amber route (44 × 29 mm) . . 2·40 2·75

1023 Downhill Skier **1024** Flower-filled Heart

1993. Winter University Games, Zakopane.
3458 **1023** 3000z. multicoloured . . 45 45

1993. St. Valentine's Day. Multicoloured.
3459 1500z. Type **1024** 25 25
3460 3000z. Heart in envelope . . 55 45

1993. Polish Rulers (8th series). As T **983** showing drawings by Jan Matejko.
3461 1500z. brown and green . . 30 25
3462 2000z. black and mauve . . 55 30
3463 2500z. black and green . . . 65 40
3464 3000z. deep brown and brown 85 55
DESIGNS: 1500z. Wladyslaw Laskonogi; 2000z. Henryk I; 2500z. Konrad I of Masovia; 3000z. Boleslaw V, the Chaste.

1025 Arsenal

1993. 50th Anniv of Attack by Szare Szeregi (formation of Polish Scouts in the resistance forces) on Warsaw Arsenal.
3465 **1025** 1500z. multicoloured . . 30 30

1026 Jousters with Lances

1993. "Polska '93" International Stamp Exhibition, Poznan (4th issue). Jousting at Golub Dobrzyn. Designs showing a modern and a medieval jouster. Multicoloured.
3466 1500z. Type **1026** 25 10
3467 2000z. Jousters 30 30
3468 2500z. Jousters with swords 75 40
3469 3500z. Officials 65 40

1027 Szczecin **1028** Jew and Ruins

1993. 750th Anniv of Granting of Town Charter to Szczecin.
3470 **1027** 1500z. multicoloured . . 30 30

1993. 50th Anniv of Warsaw Ghetto Uprising.
3471 **1028** 4000z. black, yellow & blue 90 60

1029 Works by A. Szapocznikow and J. Lebenstein

1993. Europa. Contemporary Art. Multicoloured.
3472 1500z. Type **1029** 25 25
3473 4000z. "CXCIX" (S. Gierawski) and "Red Head" (B. Linke) 65 55

1030 "King Alexander Jagiellonczyk in the Sejm" (Jan Laski, 1505)

1993. 500th Anniv of Parliament.
3474 **1030** 2000z. multicoloured . . 30 30

1031 Nullo

1993. 130th Death Anniv of Francesco Nullo (Italian volunteer in January 1863 Rising).
3475 **1031** 2500z. multicoloured . . 45 45

1032 Lech's Encounter with the White Eagle after Battle of Gniezno

1993. "Polska'93" International Stamp Exhibition, Poznan (5th issue). Sheet 103 × 86 mm.
MS3476 **1032** 50000z. brown . . 6·75 6·75

1033 Cap **1034** Copernicus and Solar System

1993. 3rd World Congress of Cadets of the Second Republic.
3477 **1033** 2000z. multicoloured . . 30 30

1993. 450th Death Anniv of Nicolas Copernicus (astronomer).
3478 **1034** 2000z. multicoloured . . 40 40

1035 Fiki Miki and Lion

1993. 40th Death Anniv of Kornel Makuszynski (writer of children's books). Multicoloured.
3479 1500z. Type **1035** 30 25
3480 2000z. Billy goat 45 30
3481 3000z. Fiki Miki 60 45
3482 5000z. Billy goat riding ostrich . . . . 1·00 60

1993. Cones. As T **974**. Multicoloured.
3483 10000z. Arolla pine . . . . 1·40 85
3484 20000z. Scots pine . . . . . 3·00 1·50

1036 Eurasian Tree Sparrow

1993. Birds. Multicoloured.
3485 1500z. Type **1036** 30 15
3486 2000z. Pied wagtail 40 25
3487 3000z. Syrian woodpecker 60 45
3488 4000z. Eurasian goldfinch 85 65
3489 5000z. Common starling . . 90 85
3490 6000z. Northern bullfinch 1·25 90

1037 Soldiers Marching

1993. Bicentenary of Dabrowski's "Mazurka" (national anthem) (1st issue).
3491 **1037** 1500z. multicoloured . . 30 30
See also Nos. 3526, 3575, 3639 and 3700.

1038 "Madonna and Child" (St. Mary's Basilica, Lesna Podlaska)

1993. Sanctuaries to St. Mary. Multicoloured.
3492 1500z. Type **1038** 25 25
3493 2000z. "Madonna and Child" (St. Mary's Church, Swieta Lipka) . . 40 30

1039 Handley Page Halifax and Parachutes

1993. The Polish Rangers (Second World War air troop).
3494 **1039** 1500z. multicoloured . . 30 30

1040 Trumpet Player

1993. "Jazz Jamboree '93" International Jazz Festival, Warsaw.
3495 **1040** 2000z. multicoloured . . 40 30

1041 Postman **1042** St. Jadwiga (miniature, Schlackenwerther Codex)

1993. World Post Day.
3496 **1041** 2500z. brown, grey and blue 40 40

1993. 750th Death Anniv of St. Jadwiga of Silesia.
3497 **1042** 2500z. multicoloured . . 45 45

1043 Pope John Paul II

1993. 15th Anniv of Pope John Paul II. Sheet 70 × 92 mm.
MS3498 **1043** 20000z. multicoloured 3·00 3·00

1044 Golden Eagle and Crown **1045** St. Nicholas

1993. 75th Anniv of Republic. Multicoloured.
3499 4000z. Type **1044** 65 55
MS3500 66 × 89 mm. 20000z. Silhouette and shadow of flying eagle (31 × 38 mm) . . . . . . 3·75 3·75

1993. Christmas.
3501 **1045** 1500z. multicoloured . . 30 30

1993. Poster Art (2nd series). As T **1014**. Mult.
3502 2000z. "Come and see Polish Mountains" (M. Urbaniec) 30 30
3503 5000z. Production of Alban Berg's "Wozzeck" (J. Lenica) 75 60

1046 Daisy shedding Petals **1047** Cross-country Skiing

1994. Greetings Stamp.
3504 **1046** 1500z. multicoloured . . 40 40

1994. Winter Olympic Games, Lillehammer, Norway. Multicoloured.
3505 2500z. Type **1047** 45 45
3506 5000z. Ski jumping 85 75
MS3507 81 × 80 mm. 10000z. Downhill skiing . . . . 1·00 60

1048 Bem and Cannon

1994. Birth Bicentenary of General Jozef Bem.
3508 **1048** 5000z. multicoloured . . 75 75

1049 Jan Zamojski (founder) **1050** Cracow Battalion Flag and Scythes

1994. 400th Anniv of Zamojski Academy, Zamosc.
3509 **1049** 5000z. grey, black and brown 75 60

1994. Bicentenary of Tadeusz Kosciuszko's Insurrection.
3510 **1050** 2000z. multicoloured . . 40 40

1994. Polish Rulers (9th series). Drawings by Jan Matejko. As T **893**.
3511 2500z. black and blue . . . 45 25
3512 5000z. black, deep violet and violet 85 90
DESIGN: 2500z. Leszek II, the Black; 5000a. Przemysl II.

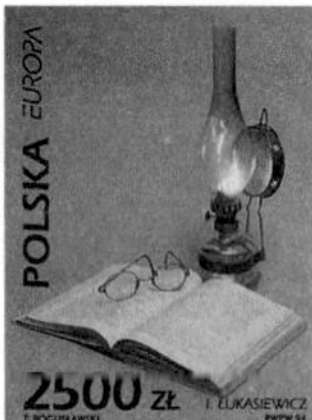

1051 Oil Lamp, Open Book and Spectacles **1052** "Madonna and Child"

1994. Europa. Inventions and Discoveries. Mult.
3513 2500z. Type **1051** (invention of modern oil lamp by Ignacy Lukasiewicz) . . . 45 40
3514 6000z. Illuminated filament forming "man in the moon" (astronomy) . . . 1·10 85

1994. St. Mary's Sanctuary, Kalwaria Zebrzydowska.
3515 **1052** 4000z. multicoloured . . 60 45

1053 Abbey Ruins and Poppies

1994. 50th Anniv of Battle of Monte Cassino.
3516 **1053** 6000z. multicoloured . . 75 60

1054 Mazurka

1994. Traditional Dances. Multicoloured.
3517 3000z. Type **1054** 30 30
3518 4000z. Coralski 40 40
3519 9000z. Krakowiak 85 75

1055 Cogwheels

1994. 75th Anniv of International Labour Organization.
3520 **1055** 6000z. deep blue, blue and black 60 55

1056 Optic Fibre Cable

1994. 75th Anniv of Polish Electricians Association.
3521 **1056** 4000z. multicoloured . . 55 40

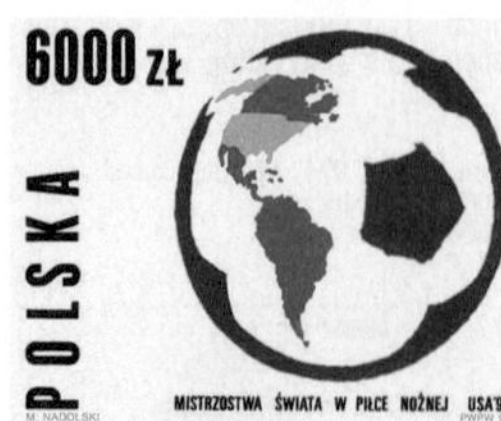

1057 Map of Americas on Football

1994. World Cup Football Championship, U.S.A.
3522 **1057** 6000z. multicoloured . . 75 75

1994. Poster Art (3rd series). As T **1014**. Mult.
3523 4000z. "Monsieur Fabre" (Wiktor Gorka) 45 55
3524 6000z. "8th OISTAT Congress" (Hurbert Hilscher) (horiz) 75 75

1058 Znaniecki **1059** Polish Eagle and Ribbon

1994. 36th Death Anniv of Professor Florian Znaniecki.
3525 **1058** 9000z. green, bistre & yellow . . . . 1·25 85

1994. Bicentenary of Dabrowski's Mazurka (2nd issue). As T **1037**. Multicoloured.
3526 2500z. Troops preparing to charge 45 40

1994. 50th Anniv of Warsaw Uprising.
3527 **1059** 2500z. multicoloured . . 45 35

1060 "Stamp" protruding from Pocket **1061** Basilica of St. Brigida, Gdansk

1994. "Philakorea 1994" International Stamp Exhibition, Seoul.
3528 **1060** 4000z. multicoloured . . 60 45

1994. Sanctuaries.
3529 **1061** 4000z. multicoloured . . 60 40

1062 "Nike" (goddess of Victory)

1994. Centenary of International Olympic Committee.
3530 **1062** 4000z. multicoloured . . 60 40

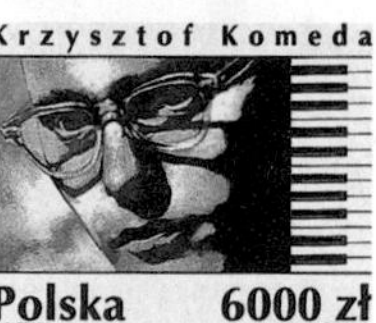

1063 Komeda and Piano Keys

1994. 25th Death Anniv of Krzysztof Komeda (jazz musician).
3531 **1063** 6000z. multicoloured . . 60 50

1064 Long-finned Bristle-mouthed Catfish **1065** Arms of Polish Post, 1858

1994. Fishes. Multicoloured.
3532 4000z. Type **1064** 60 45
3533 4000z. Freshwater angelfish ("Pterophyllum scalare") 60 45
3534 4000z. Red swordtail ("Xiphophorus helleri"), neon tetra ("Paracheirodon innesi") and Berlin platy 60 45
3535 4000z. Neon tetra ("Poecilia reticulata") and guppies 60 45
Nos. 3532/5 were issued together, se-tenant, forming a composite design.

1994. World Post Day.
3536 **1065** 4000z. multicoloured . . 45 40

1066 Kolbe

1994. Maximilian Kolbe (concentration camp victim) Year.
3537 **1066** 2500z. multicoloured . . 45 40

1067 Pigeon

1994. Pigeons. Multicoloured.
3538 4000z. Type **1067** 25 30
3539 4000z. Friar pigeon 25 30
3540 6000z. Silver magpie pigeon 40 50
3541 6000z. Danzig pigeon (black) 40 50
MS3542 79 × 94 mm. 10000z. Short-tail pigeon . . . . 1·25 1·40

1068 Musicians playing Carols

1994. Christmas.
3543 **1068** 2500z. multicoloured . . 35 30

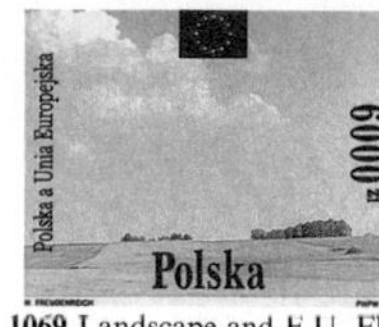

1069 Landscape and E.U. Flag

1994. Application by Poland for Membership of European Union.
3544 **1069** 6000z. multicoloured . . 90 70

Currency reform. 10000 (old) zlotys = 1 (new) zloty

1070 "I Love You" on Pierced Heart

1995. Greetings Stamp.
3545 **1070** 35g. red and blue . . . 25 30

1071 Rain, Sun and Water

1995. 75th Anniv of Hydrological-Meteorological Service.
3546 **1071** 60g. multicoloured . . 50 40

1072 Flag and Sea **1073** St. John

1995. 75th Anniv of Poland's "Marriage to the Sea" (symbolic ceremony commemorating renewal of access to sea).
3547 **1072** 45g. multicoloured . . 40 30

1995. Polish Rulers (10th series). As T **893** showing drawings by Jan Matejko.
3548 35g. deep brown, brown and light brown 25 25
3549 45g. olive, deep green and green 35 30
3550 60g. brown and ochre . . . 45 40
3551 80g. black and blue 60 60
DESIGNS: 35g. Waclaw II; 45g. Wladyslaw I; 60g. Kazimierz III, the Great; 80g. Ludwik Wegierski.

1995. 500th Birth Anniv of St. John of God (founder of Order of Hospitallers).
3552 **1073** 60g. multicoloured . . 45 30

1074 Eggs

1995. Easter. Decorated Easter eggs. Mult. background colours given.
3553 **1074** 35g. red 25 25
3554 – 35g. lilac 25 25
3555 – 45g. blue 35 40
3556 – 45g. green 35 40

1995. Cones. As T **974**. Multicoloured.
3557 45g. European larch 30 35
3558 80g. Mountain pine 60 60

1075 Polish Officer's Button and Leaf

1995. Katyn Commemoration Year.
3559 **1075** 80g. multicoloured . . 60 50

1076 Rose and Barbed Wire

1995. Europa. Peace and Freedom. Multicoloured.
3560 35g. Type **1076** (liberation of concentration camps) 30 35
3561 80g. Flowers in helmet . . . 60 55

1077 Commom Cranes

1995. 50th Anniv of Return of Western Territories.
3562 **1077** 45g. multicoloured . . 60 40

1078 Pope and Wadowice Church Font

1995. 75th Birthday of Pope John Paul II.
3563 **1078** 80g. multicoloured . . 40 45

1079 Puppets under Spotlight ("Miromagia")

1995. 50th Anniv of Groteska Fairy Tale Theatre. Multicoloured.
3564 35g. Type **1079** 30 25
3565 35g. Puppets in scene from play 30 25
3566 45g. Puppet leaning on barrel ("Thomas Fingerchen") (vert) . . . 40 30
3567 45g. Clown ("Bumstara Circus") 40 30

1080 Cockerill Steam Locomotive and Train, 1845, Warsaw–Vienna

1995. 150th Anniv of Polish Railways. Mult.
3568 35g. Type **1080** 30 20
3569 60g. "Lux-Torpedo" diesel railcar, 1927 . . . . . . 50 35
3570 80g. Electric freight train . . 70 45
3571 1z. Eurocity "Sobieski" express, 1992, Warsaw–Vienna 85 55

1081 Symbols of Nations

1995. 50th Anniv of U.N.O.
3572 **1081** 80g. multicoloured . . 60 50

1082 Bank

1995. 125th Anniv of Warsaw Commercial Bank.
3573 **1082** 45g. multicoloured . . 40 40

1083 Loaf and Four-leaved Clover

1995. Centenary of Peasant Movement.
3574 **1083** 45g. multicoloured . . 40 40

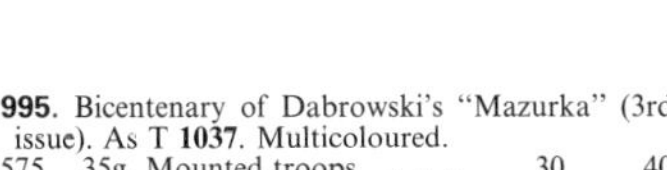

1995. Bicentenary of Dabrowski's "Mazurka" (3rd issue). As T **1037**. Multicoloured.
3575 35g. Mounted troops . . . 30 40

1084 Rowan Berries

1085 Madonna and Child

1995. Fruits of Trees. No value expressed. Mult.
3576 A (35g.) Type **1084** 30 25
3577 B (45g.) Acorns and sessile oak leaves 30 35

1995. Basilica of the Holy Trinity, Lezajsk.
3578 **1085** 45g. multicoloured . . 40 35

1086 Marshal Josef Pilsudski

1995. 75th Anniv of Defence of Warsaw and of Riga Peace Conference.
3579 **1086** 45g. multicoloured . . 40 40

1087 Dressage

1995. World Carriage Driving Championships, Poznan. Multicoloured.
3580 60g. Type **1087** 40 40
3581 80g. Cross-country event . . 55 55

1088 Warsaw Technical University

1089 Russian Space Station and U.S. Spacecraft

1995. "Warsaw '95" National Stamp Exhibition. Multicoloured.
3582 35g. Type **1088** 30 40
MS3583 94 × 71 mm. 1z. Castle Place, Warsaw (horiz) 75 85

1995. 11th World Cosmonauts Congress, Warsaw.
3584 **1089** 80g. multicoloured . . 60 50

1995. Poster Art (4th series). As T **1014**. Mult.
3585 35g. "The Crazy Locomotive" (Jan Sawka) 25 25
3586 45g. "The Wedding" (Eugeniusz Get Stankiewicz) 40 40

1090 Bar from Polonaise (Frederic Chopin)

1091 Postman

1995. 13th International Chopin Piano Competition.
3587 **1090** 80g. multicoloured . . 60 50

1995. Post Day. Multicoloured.
3588 45g. Type **1091** 40 25
3589 80g. Feather fixed to envelope by seal 60 55

1092 Acrobatic Pyramid

1094 Crib

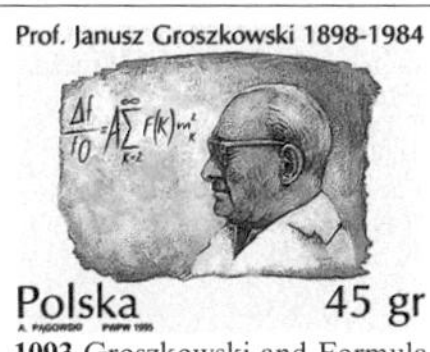

1093 Groszkowski and Formula

1995. World Acrobatic Sports Championships, Wroclaw.
3590 **1092** 45g. multicoloured . . 40 40

1995. 11th Death Anniv of Professor Janusz Groszkowski (radio-electronic scientist).
3591 **1093** 45g. multicoloured . . 40 40

1995. Christmas. Multicoloured.
3592 35g. Type **1094** 40 25
3593 45g. Wise men, Christmas tree and star of Bethlehem 40 25
Nos. 3592/3 were issued together, se-tenant, forming a composite design.

1095 Blue Tit

1995. Song Birds. Multicoloured.
3594 35g. Type **1095** 25 20
3595 45g. Long-tailed tit 35 25
3596 60g. Great grey shrike . . . 45 35
3597 80g. Hawfinch 60 45

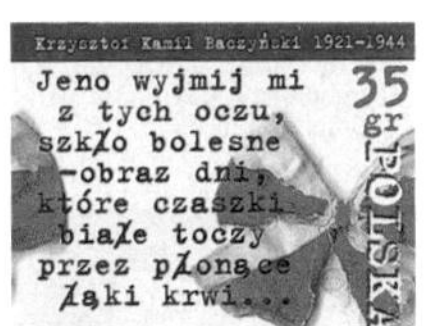

1096 Extract from Poem and Bow

1996. 75th Birth Anniv of Krzysztof Kamil Baczynski (poet).
3598 **1096** 35g. multicoloured . . 30 40

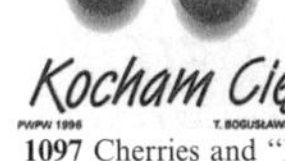

1097 Cherries and "I love you"

1098 Romanesque-style Inowlodz Church

1996. Greetings Stamp.
3599 **1097** 40g. multicoloured . . 40 30

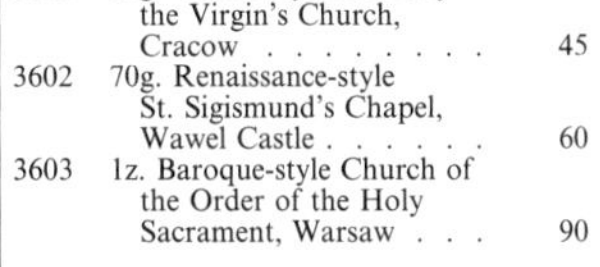

1996. Architectural Styles. Multicoloured.
3600 40g. Type **1098** 40 30
3601 55g. Gothic-style St. Mary the Virgin's Church, Cracow 45 35
3602 70g. Renaissance-style St. Sigismund's Chapel, Wawel Castle 60 50
3603 1z. Baroque-style Church of the Order of the Holy Sacrament, Warsaw . . . 90 75

1099 "Oceania"

1996. Sailing Ships. Multicoloured.
3604 40g. Type **1099** 30 30
3605 55g. "Zawisza Czarny" (cadet schooner) 45 40
3606 70g. "General Zaruski" (cadet ketch) 55 55
3607 75g. "Fryderyk Chopin" (cadet brig) 60 55

1100 16th-century Warsaw

1101 Bull (Taurus)

1996. 400th Anniv of Warsaw.
3608 **1100** 55g. multicoloured . . 45 35

1996. Signs of the Zodiac. Multicoloured.
3609 5g. Workman in water (Aquarius) 15 15
3610 10g. "Fish-person" holding fish (Pisces) 15 15
3611 20g. Type **1101** 10 10
3612 25g. Twins looking through keyhole (Gemini) 15 15
3613 30g. Crab smoking pipe (Cancer) 15 15
3614 40g. Maid and cogwheels (Virgo) 25 25
3615 50g. Lion in military uniform (Leo) 30 25
3616 55g. Couple with head and shoulders as scales (Libra) 30 30
3617 70g. Ram with ram-head (Aries) 45 25
3618 1z. Woman with scorpion's tail hat (Scorpio) 70 35
3619 2z. Archer on motor cycle (Sagittarius) . . . . . . 1·40 75
3620 5z. Office worker shielding face with paper mask (Capricorn) . . . . 3·25 1·60

1102 Hanka Ordonowna (singer)

1996. Europa. Famous Women. Multicoloured.
3621 40g. Type **1102** 30 25
3622 1z. Pola Negri (actress) . . 70 65

1103 Flag of Osiek and Old Photographs forming "1921"

1996. 75th Anniv of Silesian Uprising.
3623 **1103** 55g. red, green and black 40 40

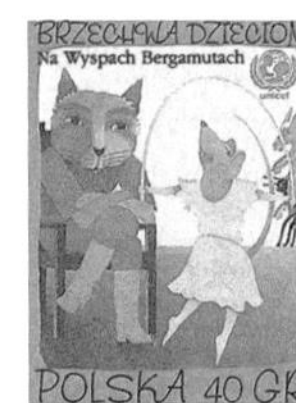

1104 "On Bergamuty Islands"

1996. 50th Anniv of UNICEF. Scenes from Fairy Tales by Jan Brzechwa. Multicoloured.
3624 40g. Type **1104** 35 30
3625 40g. Waiters carrying trays of apples (nursery rhyme) 35 30
3626 55g. Vegetable characters ("At the Market Stall") 55 40
3627 55g. Chef holding duck ("Wacky Duck") 55 40
3628 70g. Woman and birdchild ("The Fibber") 60 60
3629 70g. Red fox ("The Impishness of Witalis Fox") 60 60

1105 "City Walls and Building"

1996. Paintings by Stanislaw Noakowski. Mult.
3630 40g. Type **1105** 30 25
3631 55g. "Renaissance Bedroom" 40 35
3632 70g. "Rural Gothic Church" 50 50
3633 1z. "Renaissance Library" 70 65

1106 Discus on Ribbon

1108 St. Mary of Przeczycka

1107 Tweezers holding Stamp showing Emblem

1996. Olympic Games, Atlanta, and Centenary of Modern Olympic Games. Multicoloured.
3634 40g. Type **1106** (gold medal, Halina Konopacka, 1928) 25 25
3635 55g. Tennis ball (horiz) . . 40 35
3636 70g. Polish Olympic Committee emblem (horiz) 50 45
3637 1z. Bicycle wheel 70 50

1996. "Olymphilex '96" International Sports Stamp Exhibition, Atlanta.
3638 **1107** 1z. multicoloured . . . 70 65

1996. Bicentenary of Dabrowski's Mazurka (4th issue). As T **1037**. Multicoloured.
3639 40g. Charge of Polish cavalry at Somosierra . . 45 30

1996. St. Mary's Church, Przeczycka.
3640 **1108** 40g. multicoloured . . 45 35

1996. Polish Rulers (11th series). As T **893**.
3641 40g. brown and bistre . . . 30 25
3642 55g. lilac and mauve 45 35
3643 70g. deep grey and grey . . 55 50
3644 1z. deep green, green and yellow 80 65
DESIGNS: 40g. Queen Jadwiga (wife of Wladyslaw II); 55g. Wladyslaw II Jagiello; 70g. Wladyslaw III Warnenczyk; 1z. Kazimierz IV Jagiellonczyk.

1109 Mt. Giewont and Edelweiss

1996. The Tatra Mountains. Multicoloured.
3645 40g. Type **1109** 30 20
3646 40g. Mt. Krzesanica and spring gentian 30 20
3647 55g. Mt. Koscielec and leopard's bane 45 25
3648 55g. Mt. Swinica and clusius gentian 45 25
3649 70g. Mt. Rysy and ragwort 55 30
3650 70g. Mieguszowieckie peaks and pine trees 55 30

1110 Seifert

1996. 50th Birth Anniv of Zbigniew Seifert (jazz musician).
3651 **1110** 70g. multicoloured . . 75 45

1111 "Changing of Horses at Post Station" (detail, Mieczyslaw Watorski)

1996. World Post Day. 75th Anniv of Post and Telecommunications Museum, Wroclaw. Paintings. Multicoloured.
3652 40g. Type **1111** 30 25
MS3653 102 × 81 mm. 1z.+20g. "Mail Coach at Jagniatkowo with View over Karkonosze" (Professor Tager) (42 × 30 mm) 90 85

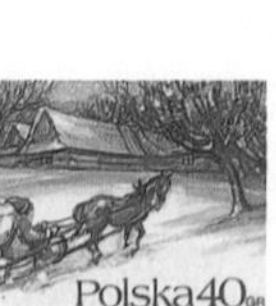

1112 Father Christmas on Horse-drawn Sleigh

1113 Head of Male

1996. Christmas. Multicoloured.
3654 40g. Type **1112** 25 10
3655 55g. Carol singers with star lantern 35 25

1996. The European Bison. Multicoloured.
3656 55g. Type **1113** 40 40
3657 55g. Head of female 40 40
3658 55g. Pair of bison 40 40
3659 55g. Male 40 40

1114 Wislawa Szymborska

1996. Award of Nobel Prize for Literature to Wislawa Szymborska (poet).
3660 **1114** 1z. multicoloured . . . 75 65

1115 "I Love You" on King of Hearts Playing Card

1997. Greetings Stamps. Multicoloured.
3661 B (40g.) Type **1115** 30 25
3662 A (55g.) Queen of hearts playing card . . . . . . 45 1·00
Nos. 3661/2 were issued together, se-tenant, forming a composite design.
No. 3661 was sold at the rate for postcards and No. 3662 for letters up to 20 grams.

1116 Blessing the Palms

1997. Easter. Traditional Customs. Multicoloured.
3663 50g. Type **1116** 30 25
3664 60g. Woman and child painting Easter eggs . . . 40 35
3665 80g. Priest blessing the food 55 45
3666 1z.10 Man throwing water over woman's skirts on Easter Monday 65 45

1117 Long Market and Town Hall (after Mateusz Deisch)

1997. Millenary of Gdansk. Each brown, cinnamon and red.
3667 50g. Type **1117** 60 40
MS3668 94 × 71 mm. 1z.10 St. Mary's Church and Hall of the Main Town (after Mateusz Merian) (horiz) 75 85

1118 St. Adalbert and Monks addressing Pagans

1997. Death Millenary of St. Adalbert (Bishop of Prague).
3669 **1118** 50g. brown 30 25
3670 – 60g. green 40 35
3671 – 1z.10 lilac 70 40
DESIGNS—VERT: 60g. St. Adalbert and anniversary emblem; 1z.10, St. Adalbert.

1119 Mansion House, Lopuszna

1120 The Crock of Gold

1997. Polish Manor Houses. Multicoloured.
3671a 10g Lipkowie, Warsaw . . 10 10
3672 50g. Type **1119** 20 10
3673 55g. Henryk Sienkewicz Museum, Oblegorek . . 35 20
3674 60g. Zyrzyn 50 20
3675 65g. Stanislaw Wyspianski Museum, Bronowice, near Cracow 60 20
3675a 70g. Modlnica 65 35
3675b 80g. Grabonog, Gostyn . . 75 35
3676 90g. Obory, near Warsaw 90 60
3676a 1z. Krzelawice 95 45
3677 1z.10 Ozarow . . . . . . 1·00 35
3678 1z.20 Jozef Krasnewski Museum, Biala 65 35
3678a 1z.40 Winna Gora 75 80
3678b 1z.50 Sulejowku, Warsaw 45 15
3678c 1z.55 Zelazowa Wola . . . 80 80
3678d 1z.60 Potok Zloty 80 95
3678e 1z.65 Sucha, Wegrow . . . 90 95
3679 1z.70 Tulowice . . . . . . 95 1·00
3679a 1z.85 Kasna Dolna 90 80
3679b 1z.90 Petrykozach Mszczonowa 60 20
3680 2z.20 Kuznocin . . . . . 1·10 95
3681 2z.65 Liwia, Wegrow . . . 1·50 1·10
3682 3z. Janowcu, Pulaw . . . 90 30
3683 10z. Koszuty . . . . . . 5·50 4·00
See also Nos. 3727/8.

1997. Europa. Tales and Legends. Multicoloured.
3685 50g. Type **1120** 30 35
3686 1z.10 Wars, Sawa and mermaid-siren 70 80

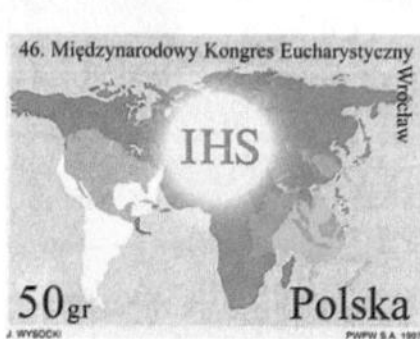

1121 World Map and Emblem

1997. 46th International Eucharistic Congress, Wroclaw.
3687 **1121** 50g. multicoloured . . 30 35

1122 San Francisco–Oakland Bay Bridge

1997. "Pacific 97" International Stamp Exhibition, San Francisco.
3688 **1122** 1z.30 multicoloured . . 75 75

1123 Pope John Paul II

1997. 5th Papal Visit. Sheet 76 × 90 mm.
MS3689 **1123** 1z.10 multicoloured 75 85

1124 European Long-eared Bat

1997. Bats. Multicoloured.
3690 50g. Type **1124** 30 20
3691 60g. Common noctule . . . 40 25
3692 80g. Brown bat 50 35
3693 1z.30 Red bat 85 55

1125 "Founding of the Main School" (Jan Matejko)

1997. 600th Anniv of Faculty of Theology, Jagiellonian University, Cracow.
3694 **1125** 80g. multicoloured . . 60 55

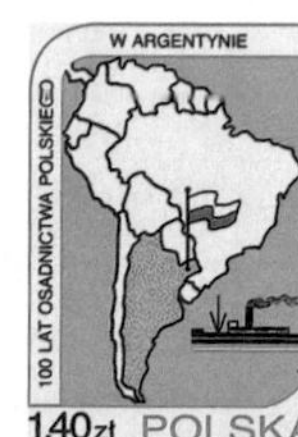

1126 Map highlighting Settled Area

1997. Centenary of Polish Migration to Argentina.
3695 **1126** 1z.40 multicoloured . . 80 75

1127 "Return from War to the Village"

1997. Paintings by Juliusz Kossak. Multicoloured.
3696 50g. Type **1127** 30 25
3697 60g. "Cracowian Wedding" 35 35
3698 80g. "In the Stable" 50 45
3699 1z.10 "Stablehand with Pair of Horses" 65 60

1997. Bicentenary of Dabrowski's "Mazurka" (5th issue). As T **1037**.
3700 50g. Dabrowski and Wybicki's arrival in Poznan, 1806 . . . . . . 35 35
MS3701 85 × 77 mm. 1z.10 Manuscript of lyrics and Jozef Wybicki (composer) 75 65

1128 Strzelecki and Route Map around Australia

1997. Birth Bicentenary of Pawel Strzelecki (explorer).
3702 **1128** 1z.50 multicoloured . . 90 90

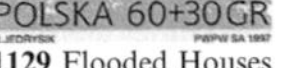

1129 Flooded Houses **1130** "Holy Mother of Consolation" (icon)

1997. Flood Relief Fund.
3703 **1129** 60g.+30g. multicoloured 75 65

1997. Church of the Holy Mother of Consolation and St. Michael the Archangel, Gorka Duchowa.
3704 **1130** 50g. multicoloured . . 30 40

1997. Polish Rulers (12th series). As T **893**.
3705 50g. agate, brown and bistre 35 30
3706 60g. purple and blue 45 40
3707 80g. green, deep green and olive 60 50
3708 1z.10 purple and lilac . . . 80 65
DESIGNS: 50g. Jan I Olbracht; 60g. Aleksander Jagiellonczyk; 80g. Zygmunt I, the Old; 1z.10, Zygmunt II August.

1131 Kosz **1132** Globe and posthorn

1997. 24th Death Anniv of Mieczyslaw Kosz (jazz musician).
3709 **1131** 80g. multicoloured . . 60 50

1997. World Post Day.
3710 **1132** 50g. multicoloured . . 35 35

1133 St. Basil's Cathedral, Moscow

1997. "Moskva 97" International Stamp Exhibition, Moscow.
3711 **1133** 80g. multicoloured . . 60 70

1997. Poster Art (5th series). As T **1014**.
3712 50g. multicoloured 35 25
3713 50g. black 35 25
3714 60g. multicoloured 40 45
3715 60g. multicoloured 40 45
POSTERS—HORIZ: No. 3712, Advertisement for Radion washing powder (Tadeusz Gronowski). VERT: No. 3713, Production of Cieslawiz Witkiewicz's play "Shoemakers" (Roman Cieslewicz); 3714, Production of Aleksander Fredro's play "A Husband and a Wife" (Andrzej Pagowski); 3715, Production of ballet "Goya" (Wiktor Sadowski).

1134 Nativity

1997. Christmas. Multicoloured.
3716 50g. Type **1134** 25 20
3717 60g. Christmas Eve feast (horiz) 35 25
3718 80g. Family going to church for Midnight Mass (horiz) 45 30
3719 1z.10 Waits (carol singers representing animals) . . 60 40

1135 Common Shelducks

1997. Praecocial Chicks. Multicoloured.
3720 50g. Type **1135** 35 35
3721 50g. Goosanders ("Mergus merganser") 35 35
3722 50g. Common snipes ("Gallinago gallinago") 35 35
3723 50g. Moorhens ("Gallinula chloropus") 35 35

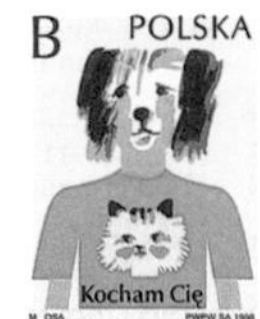

1136 Ski Jumping **1137** Dog wearing Cat T-shirt inscr "I Love You"

1998. Winter Olympic Games, Nagano, Japan.
3724 **1136** 1z.40 multicoloured . . 80 75

1998. Greetings Stamps. No value expressed. Multicoloured.
3725 B (55g.) Type **1137** 35 25
3726 A (65g.) Cat wearing dog T-shirt 35 35

1998. Polish Manor Houses. No value expressed. As T **1119**. Multicoloured.
3727 B (55g.) Gluchy 35 25
3728 A (65g.) Jan Kochanwoski Museum, Czarnolas . . . 35 35

1138 Paschal Lamb **1140** Grey Seal

1139 Polish National Guard and Civilians at Lvov Barricades

1998. Easter. Multicoloured.
3729 55g. Type **1138** 35 20
3730 65g. The Resurrected Christ 35 20

1998. 150th Anniv of 1848 Revolutions.
3731 **1139** 55g. brown 45 25

1998. Polish Rulers (13th series). As T **893**.
3732 55g. brown and light brown 35 20
3733 65g. purple, deep purple and mauve 40 35
3734 80g. deep green and green 50 45
3735 90g. lilac, purple and mauve 60 45
DESIGNS: 55g. Henryk Walezy; 65g. Queen Anna Jagiellonka (wife of Stefan I); 80g. Stefan I Batory; 90g. Zygmunt III Wasa.

1998. Protection of Baltic Sea. Marine Life. Mult.
3736 65g. Type **1140** 45 35
3737 65g. "Patoschistus microps" (fish), jellyfish and shells 45 35
3738 65g. Twaite shad ("Alosa fallax") and pipefish ("Syngnathus typhle") . . 45 35
3739 65g. Common sturgeon ("Acipenser sturio") . . . 45 35
3740 65g. Atlantic salmon ("Salmo salar") 45 35
3741 65g. Common porpoise . . 45 35
MS3742 76 × 70 mm. 1z.20 Grey seal 1·60 1·40
Nos. 3736/41 were issued together, se-tenant, forming a composite design.

1141 Exhibition Emblem and 1948 Israeli 500 m. Stamp

1998. "Israel '98" International Stamp Exhibition, Tel Aviv.
3743 **1141** 90g. multicoloured . . 75 80

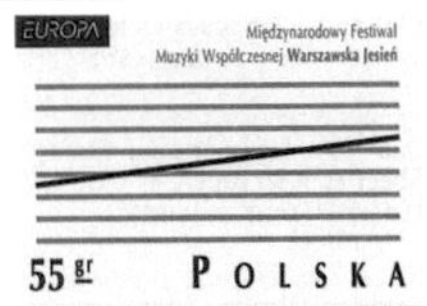

1142 Festival Emblem

1998. Europa. National Festivals.
3744 **1142** 55g. multicoloured . . 55 50
3745 – 1z.20 black, red and blue 90 95
DESIGNS: 55g. Type **1142** ("Warsaw Autumn" International Festival of Music); 1z.20, State flag and opening bars of "Welcome the May Dawn" (3rd of May Constitution Day).

1144 "Longing Holy Mother" **1145** "Triple Self-portrait"

1998. Coronation of "Longing Holy Mother" (icon in Powsin Church).
3752 **1144** 55g. multicoloured . . 45 75

1998. 30th Death Anniv of Nikifor (Epifan Drowniak) (artist). Multicoloured.
3753 55g. Type **1145** 35 40
3754 65g. "Cracow Office" . . . 40 50
3755 1z.20 "Orthodox Church" 75 80
3756 2z.35 "Ucrybow Station" . . 1·50 1·60

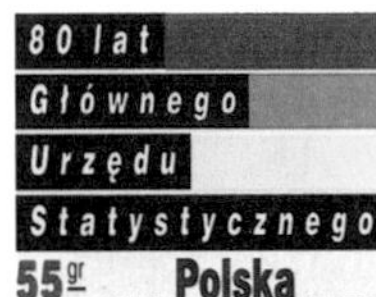

1146 Anniversary Inscription

1998. 80th Anniv of Main Board of Statistics.
3757 **1146** 55g. multicoloured . . 45 40

1147 "Madonna and Child"

1998. Basilica of the Visitation of St. Mary the Virgin, Sejny.
3758 **1147** 55g. multicoloured . . 45 40

1148 Jesus (stained glass window)

1998. Bicentenary of Diocese of Warsaw.
3759 **1148** 65g. multicoloured . . 45 50

1998. 17th Congress of Polish Union of Stamp Collectors. Sheet 114 × 77 mm containing T **1141** and similar horiz design. Each blue and cream.
MS3760 65g. × 2 Composite design showing 17th-century engraving of Szczecin from Descriptio Urbis Stettinensis by Paul Feideborn 85 95

1150 Pierre and Marie Curie (physicists)

1998. Centenary of Discovery of Polonium and Radium.
3761 **1150** 1z.20 multicoloured . . 70 80

1151 Mazowsze Dancers

1998. 50th Anniv of Mazowsze Song and Dance Group. Multicoloured.
3762 65g. Type **1151** 40 50
3763 65g. Dancers (different) . . 40 50
Nos. 3762/3 were issued together, se-tenant, forming a composite design.

1152 Mniszchow Palace

1998. Belgium Embassy, Warsaw.
3764 **1152** 1z.20 multicoloured . . 70 75

1153 "King Sigismund" (Studio of Rubens) **1154** Coloured Envelopes

1998. 400th Anniv of Battle of Stangebro.
3765 **1153** 1z.20 brown . . . . . 70 1·00

1998. World Post Day.
3766 **1154** 65g. multicoloured . . 45 50

1155 Pope John Paul II and People of Different Races **1157** "Nativity"

1156 State Flags and 1919 Seal

1998. 20th Anniv of Selection of Karol Wojtyla to Papacy.
3767 **1155** 65g. multicoloured . . 45 50

1998. 80th Anniv of Independence.
3768 **1156** 65g. black, red and gold 45 50

1998. Christmas. Polyptych, Grudziadz. Mult.
3769 55g. Type **1157** 40 40
3770 65g. "Adoration of the Wise Men" 40 50

1158 Anniversary Emblem

1998. 50th Anniv of Universal Declaration of Human Rights.
3771 **1158** 1z.20 blue and ultramarine 75 80

1159 Maryla Wereszczakowna and Moonlit Night

1998. Birth Bicentenary of Adam Mickiewicz (poet). Multicoloured.

3772 55g. Type **1159** 30 35
3773 65g. Cranes flying over tomb of Maria Potocka 40 45
3774 90g. Burning candles and cross 45 60
3775 1z.20 House, field of flowers and uhlan's shako 60 75
MS3776 61 × 76 mm. 2z.45 Mickiewicz (bust by Jean David d'Angers) (30 × 38 mm) . . . . 1·60 2·00

1160 "Piorun" (destroyer), 1942–46

1999. 80th Anniv (1998) of Polish Navy. Mult.

3777 55g. Type **1160** 40 35
3778 55g. "Piorun" (missile corvette), 1994 . . . . . 40 35

1161 Dominoes

1999. Greetings stamps. Value expressed by letter. Multicoloured.

3779 B (60g.) Type **1161** 40 35
3780 A (65g.) Dominoes (different) 40 45

1162 Ernest Malinowski and Railway Bridge over Varrugas Canyon

1999. Polish Engineers. Multicoloured.

3781 1z. Type **1162** (death cent) 55 60
3782 1z.60 Rudolf Modrzejewski and Benjamin Franklin Bridge over Delaware River, Philadelphia . . . 85 95

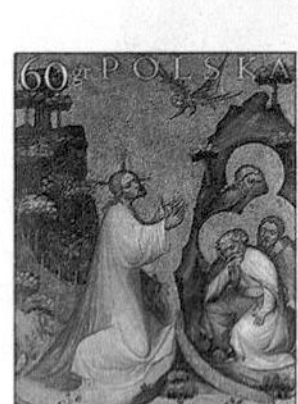

1163 "Prayer in Ogrojec"

1165 "Victorious St. Mary of Kozielsk" (sculpture)

1164 Chinese Ideograms

1999. Easter. Multicoloured.

3783 60g. Type **1163** 30 35
3784 65g. "Carrying the Cross" 30 35
3785 1z. "Pieta" 50 55
3786 1z.40 "Resurrection" . . . 75 70

Nos. 3783/4 and 3786 show details of the Grudzic polyptych.

1999. "China '99" International Stamp Exhibition, Peking. Sheet 80 × 96 mm.

MS3787 **1164** 1z.70 multicoloured 90 1·10

1999. Images of Virgin Mary made by Polish Prisoners of War. Multicoloured.

3788 60g. Type **1165** 30 35
3789 70g. "St. Mary of Katyn" (bas-relief, Stanislaw Balos) 40 35

1166 Jan Skrzetuski passing Zbara Fortress ("With Fire and Sword")

1999. "Heroes of the Trilogy" (novels) by Henryk Sienkiewicz. Multicoloured.

3790 70g. Type **1166** 35 35
3791 70g. Onufry Zagloba and 17th-century map of Poland (all three parts) 35 35
3792 70g. Longinus Podbipieta defending Zbara and three Tartars ("With Fire and Sword") 35 35
3793 70g. Bohun with Helena Kuncewiczowna on way to Czarci Jar ("With Fire and Sword") 35 35
3794 70g. Andrzej Kmicic and cannon at Jasna Gora Monastery ("The Deluge") 35 35
3795 70g. Michal Jerzy Wolodyjowski and Basia Jeziorkowska fencing ("Pan Michael") 35 35

1167 Polish Flag and N.A.T.O. Emblem

1999. 50th Anniv of North Atlantic Treaty Organization and Accession of Poland.

3796 **1167** 70g. multicoloured . . 45 35

1168 Anniversary Emblem and Headquarters, Strasbourg

1999. 50th Anniv of Council of Europe.

3797 **1168** 1z. multicoloured . . . 55 60

1169 Three-toed Woodpecker

1999. Europa. Parks and Gardens. Bialowieski National Park.

3798 **1169** 1z.40 multicoloured . . 75 90

1170 Mountain Biking

1999. Youth Sports. Multicoloured.

3799 60g. Type **1170** 40 35
3800 70g. Snowboarding 40 50
3801 1z. Skateboarding 60 60
3802 1z.40 Rollerblading . . . . 85 1·00

1171 St. Mary's Church, Cracow, Pope John Paul II and Crowd

1999. 6th Papal Visit to Poland. Multicoloured.

3803 60g. Type **1171** 35 30
3804 70g. Pope and crowd with crosses 40 40
3805 1z. Pope and cheering teenagers 60 50
3806 1z.40 Eiffel Tower (Paris), "Christ the Saviour" (statue, Rio de Janeiro), Pope and church at Fatima, Portugal 80 65

1172 Ignacy Paderewski and Roman Dmowski (signatories)

1999. 80th Anniv of Treaty of Versailles.

3807 **1172** 1z.40 multicoloured . . 85 1·00

1173 "St. Mary Carefully Listening" (icon)

1174 Great Diving Beetle ("Dytiscus marginalis")

1999. St. Mary's Sanctuaries. Multicoloured.

3808 60g. Type **1173** (church of St. Mary Queen of Poland, Rokitno) 40 40
3809 70g. "Mary" (statue, Ms. Jazlowiecka), Convent of Order of the Immaculate Conception, Szymanow 40 50

1999. Insects. Multicoloured.

3810 60g. Type **1174** 30 35
3811 60g. "Corixa punctata" . . 30 35
3812 70g. "Limnophilus" 40 45
3813 70g. "Perla marginata" . . 40 45
3814 1z.40 Emperor dragonfly ("Anax imperator") . . . 80 95
3815 1z.40 "Ephemera vulgata" 80 95

1175 Ksiaz Castle

1999. "Walbrzych '99" 18th National Stamp Exhibition. Sheet 74 × 105 mm.

MS3816 **1175** 1z. blue 75 85

1176 Red Deer

1999. Eastern Carpathian Mountains International Biosphere Reserve (covering Polish, Ukrainian and Slovakian National Parks). Multicoloured.

3817 1z.40 Type **1176** 70 90
3818 1z.40 Wild cat 70 90

1999. Polish Rulers (14th series). As T **893**.

3819 60g. black and green 35 20
3820 70g. brown and light brown 40 35
3821 1z. black and blue 60 40
3822 1z.40 deep purple and purple 80 45

DESIGNS: 60g. Wladyslaw IV Waza; 70g. Jan II Kazimierz; 1z. Michal Korybut Wisniowiecki; 1z.40, Jan III Sobieski.

1177 U.P.U. Emblem

1999. 125th Anniv of Universal Postal Union.

3823 **1177** 1z.40 multicoloured . . 70 85

1178 Chopin and Academy of Fine Arts, Warsaw

1999. 150th Death Anniv of Frederic Chopin (composer).

3824 **1178** 1z.40 green 70 85

1179 Popieluszko

1999. 15th Death Anniv of Father Jerzy Popieluszko.

3825 **1179** 70g. multicoloured . . 40 50

1180 Barbed Wire

1999. Homage to 20th-century Heroes of Poland. Sheet 93 × 70 mm.

MS3826 **1180** 1z. multicoloured 60 70

1181 Angel ("Silent Night")

1999. Christmas. Inscr in Polish with the opening lines of carols. Multicoloured.

3827 60g. Type **1181** 35 25
3828 70g. Angel ("Sleep, Jesus Baby") 40 25
3829 1z. Angel ("Let's Go Everybody to the Stable") 55 40
3830 1z.40 Angel ("The God is Born") 80 60

1182 Polish Museum, Rapperswil Castle, Switzerland

1999. Polish Overseas Cultural Buildings. Mult.

3831 1z. Type **1182** 60 40
3832 1z.40 Marian Priests' Museum, Fawley Court, England 80 60
3833 1z.60 Polish Library, Paris, France 95 65
3834 1z.80 Polish Institute and Gen. Sikorski Museum, London, England . . . . 1·10 75

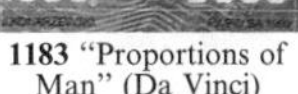

1183 "Proportions of Man" (Da Vinci)
1185 Otto III granting Crown to Boleslaw I

1184 Bronislaw Malinowski (sociologist)

2000. New Year 2000.
3835 **1183** A (70g.) multicoloured 55 50

2000. Polish Personalities. Multicoloured.
3836 1z.55 Type **1184** 75 75
3837 1z.95 Jozef Zwierzycki (geologist) . . . . 1·10 1·00

2000. 1000th Anniv of the Gniezno Summit and the Catholic Church in Poland. Multicoloured.
3838 70g. Type **1185** 45 45
3839 80g. Archbishop of Gnesna, and Bishops of Cracovina, Wratislavia and Colberga 45 45
MS3840 77 × 65 mm. 1z.55 Provincial representatives presenting gifts to Otto III as Roman Emperor (horiz) . . . 90 80

1186 Jesus in Tomb

2000. Easter. Multicoloured.
3841 70g. Type **1186** 45 45
3842 80g. Resurrected Christ . . 45 45

1187 Saurolophus

2000. Prehistoric Animals. Multicoloured.
3843 70g. Type **1187** 40 45
3844 70g. Gallimimus 40 45
3845 80g. Saichania 45 50
3846 80g. Protoceratops 45 50
3847 1z.55 Prenocephale . . . . 85 1·00
3848 1z.55 Velociraptor . . . . . 85 1·00

1188 Wajda

2000. Presentation of American Film Academy Award to Andrzej Wajda (film director).
3849 **1188** 1z.10 black 60 95

1189 Pope John Paul kneeling, St. Peter's Basilica, Rome

2000. Holy Year 2000 Opening of Holy Door, St. Peter's Basilica, Rome.
3850 **1189** 80g. multicoloured . . 45 45

1190 Artist and Model, Poster for *Wesele* (play), and Building

2000. Crakow, European City of Culture.
3851 **1190** 70g. multicoloured . . 40 45
3852 – 1z.55 multicoloured . . 95 90
MS3853 110 × 77 mm. 1z.75 blue (39 × 30 mm) 95 90
DESIGNS: No. 3852, Jagiellonian University, Pope John Paul II, Queen Jadwiga and Krzysztof Penderecki (composer). 38 × 30 mm—**MS**3853, View of Crakow (wood carving), 1489.

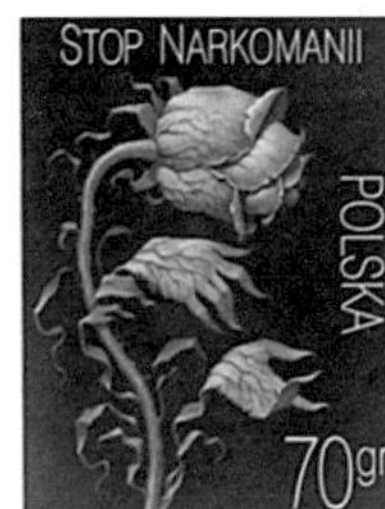

1191 Dying Rose

2000. "Stop Drug Addiction" Campaign.
3854 **1191** 70g. multicoloured . . 40 45

JAN PAWEŁ II
80. ROCZNICA URODZIN
POLSKA GR 80

1192 "Building Europe"
1193 Pope John Paul II

2000. Europa.
3855 **1192** 1z.55 multicoloured . . 90 75

2000. 80th Birthday of Pope John Paul II.
3856 **1193** 80g. violet 45 45
3857 – 1z.10 multicoloured . . 60 60
3858 – 1z.55 green 75 90
DESIGNS: No. 3857, Holy Mother, Czestochowa; 3858, Pastoral Staff.

1194 Woman's Face and Fan

2000. "Espana 2000" International Stamp Exhibition, Madrid.
3859 **1194** 1z.55 multicoloured . . 90 85

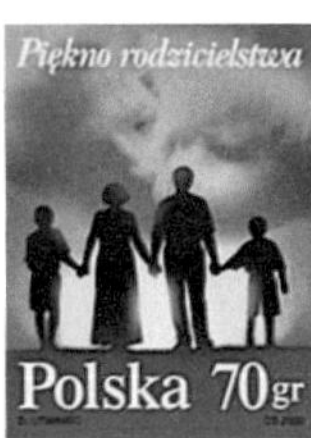

1195 Family

2000. Parenthood.
3860 **1195** 70g. multicoloured . . 40 45

1196 Cathedral, FaÇade

2000. Millenary of Wroclaw. Sheet 70 × 90 mm.
MS3861 **1196** 1z.55 multicoloured 85 55

1197 Karol Marcinkowski

2000. Personalities. Multicoloured.
3862 70g. Type **1197** (founder of Scientific Assistance Association) 35 20
3863 80g. Josemaria Escriva de Balaguer (founder of Priests' Association of St. Cross, 1943) 35 30

1198 Gerwazy and the Count

2000. *Pan Tadeusz* (poem by Adam Mickiewicz). Illustrations by Michal Elwiro Andriolli from the 1882 edition.
3864 **1198** 70g. brown 40 15
3865 – 70g. brown 40 15
3866 – 80g. green 45 20
3867 – 80g. green 45 20
3868 – 1z.10 purple 60 30
3869 – 1z.10 purple 60 30
DESIGNS: No. 3865, Telimenta reclining and the Judge; 3866, Father Robak, Judge and Gerwazy; 3867, Gathering in forest; 3868, Jankiel playing musical instrument; 3869, Zosia and Tadeusz.

PIOTR MICHAŁOWSKI
70gr POLSKA

1199 Pope John Paul II and St. Peter's Basilica, Rome
1200 "Self-portrait"

2000. National Pilgrimage to Rome. Multicoloured.
3870 80g. Type **1199** 45 30
3871 1z.55 Cross and Colosseum 85 60

2000. Birth Bicentenary of Piotr Michalowski (artist). Multicoloured.
3872 70g. Type **1200** 70 25
3873 80g. "Portrait of a Boy in a Hat" 80 30
3874 1z.10 "Stable-boy Bridling Percherons" (horiz) . . . 1·10 40
3875 1z.55 "Horses with Cart" (horiz) . . . . 1·50 55

1201 Mary and Jesus (painting), Rozanystok

2000. St. Mary's Sanctuaries. Multicoloured.
3876 70g. Type **1201** 25 10
3877 1z.55 Mary with crown supported by angels, Lichen 55 20

1202 John Bosco (founder of movement)

2000. Salesian Society (religious educational institution) in Poland.
3878 **1202** 80g. multicoloured . . 45 30

1203 Victory Sign

2000. 20th Anniv of Solidarity Trade Union. Sheet 60 × 78 mm.
MS3879 **1203** 1z.65 multicoloured 95 60

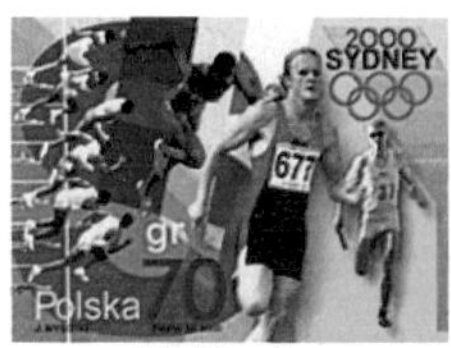

1204 Running

2000. Olympic Games, Sydney. Multicoloured.
3880 70g. Type **1204** 35 25
3881 80g. Diving, wind-surfing, sailing and kayaking . . . 40 30
3882 1z.10 Weight lifting, high jumping and fencing . . . 55 40
3883 1z.55 Athletics, basketball and judo 80 55

1205 Postman (Tomasz Wistuba)
1207 Priest and Cross

1206 Man with Postage Stamp Wings

2000. World Post Day. Winning Entries in Children's Painting Competition. Multicoloured.
3884 70g. Type **1205** 40 30
3885 80g. Customers and flying stork in Post Office (Katarzyna Chrzanowska) (horiz) 45 30
3886 1z.10 Post Office on "stamp" (Joanna Zbik) (horiz) 60 40
3887 1z.55 Woman at Post Office counter (Katarzyna Lonak) (horiz) 85 55

2000. 50th Anniv of Polish Philatelic Union. Sheet 75 × 60 mm.
MS3888 **1206** 1z.55 multicoloured 90 50

2000. Polish Rulers (15th series). As T **893**.
3889 70g. black, green and olive 40 30
3890 80g. black and purple . . . 45 30
3891 1z.10 black, blue and cobalt 60 40
3892 1z.55 black and brown . . . 85 55

DESIGNS; 70g. August II; 80g. Stanislaw Leszczynski; 1z.10, August III; 1z.55, Stanislaw August Poniatowski.

2000. 60th Anniv of Katyn Massacre. Mult.
3893 70g. Type **1207** 35 20
3894 80g. Pope John Paul II kneeling at monument, Muranow 40 30

1208 Nativity

2000. Christmas. Multicoloured.
3895 70g. Type **1208** 35 30
3896 80g. Wedding at Cana . . . 40 35
3897 1z.10 The Last Supper . . . 55 45
3898 1z.55 The Ascension 80 85

1209 Building Facade

1210 Privately Issued Stamp

2000. Centenary of Warsaw Art Gallery.
3899 **1209** 70g. multicoloured 45 40

2000. Underground Post during Martial Law, 1982–89.
3900 **1210** 80g. multicoloured . . 45 35

1211 Pope John Paul II, Emblem and Crowd

2001. End of Holy Year 2000. Value expressed by letter.
3901 **1211** A (1z.10) mult 40 15

1212 Mountains reflected in Ski Goggles

2001. 20th University Games, Zakopane.
3902 **1212** 1z. multicoloured . . . 35 10

1213 Computer Mouse

2001. The Internet.
3903 **1213** 1z. multicoloured . . . 35 10

1214 Adam Malysz (ski jumper)

2001. World Classic Seniors Championships. Multicoloured.
3904 1z. Type **1214** 35 10
3905 1z. As Type **1214** but additionally inscribed "Adam Malysz" 35 10
3906 1z. As No. 3905 but additionally inscribed "Mistrzem Swiata" . . . 35 10

1215 Tomb of the Resurrected Christ

2001. Easter. Multicoloured.
3907 1z. Type **1215** 35 10
3908 1z.90 Resurrected Christ and Apostles 35 10

1216 Emblem and Basketball Players

2001. 12th Salesian Youth World Championships, Warsaw.
3909 **1216** 1z. multicoloured . . . 35 10

1217 Water Droplet

2001. Europa. Water Resources.
3910 **1217** 1z.90 multicoloured . . 65 20

1218 Man and Mermaid on Beach ("Holiday Greetings")

2001. Greetings Stamps. Multicoloured.
3911 1z. Type **1218** 35 10
3912 1z. Man presenting bouquet to woman ("Best Wishes") 35 10

1219 "Christ Blessing Children of Wrzesnia" (Marian Turwid) (stained-glass window), Parish Church, Wrzesnia

2001. Centenary of Support of Wrzesnia Schoolchildren for the Language.
3913 **1219** 1z. multicoloured . . . 35 10

1220 Polish Scientific Institute and Wanda Stachiewicz Library,Montreal, Canada

2001. Polish Institutions Abroad. Multicoloured.
3914 1z. Type **1220** 35 10
3915 1z.90 Bust of Josef Pilsudski, Josef Pilsudski Institute, New York . . . 65 20
3916 2z.10 Polonia Museum, Archives and Library, Orchard Lake, Michigan 75 25
3917 2z.20 Polish Museum, Chicago 75 25

1221 Snowdrop (*Galanthus nivalis*) and European Lynx (*Lynx lynx*)

2001. Convention on International Trade of Wild Animals and Plants Threatened with Extinction (C.I.T.E.S.). Multicoloured.
3918 1z. Type **1221** 35 10
3919 1z. Apollo butterfly (*Parnassius apollo*) and orchid (*Orchis sambucina*) 35 10
3920 1z. Northern eagle owl (*Bubo bubo*) and *Adonis vernalis* (plant) 35 10
3921 1z.90 Lady's slipper orchid (*Cypripedium calceolus*) and brown bear (*Ursus arctos*) 65 20
3922 1z.90 Peregrine falcon (*Falco peregrinus*) and *Orchis pallens* 65 20
3923 1z.90 Wide leaf orchid (*Orchis latifolia*) and European otter (*Lutra lutra*) 65 20
MS3924 90 × 70 mm. 2z. World map and emblem (35 × 28 mm) . . . 1·25 80

1222 Cardinal Wyszynski and Text

2001. Birth Centenary of Cardinal Stefan Wyszynski (Primate of Poland, 1948–81).
3925 **1222** 1z. multicoloured . . . 35 10

1223 Father Kolbe and Handwriting

2001. 60th Death Anniv of Maksymilian Maria Kolbe (founder of Knighthood of the Immaculate, and concentration camp victim).
3926 **1223** 1z. multicoloured . . . 35 10

1224 "St. Mary of the Beautiful Love" (icon)

1225 Model of Sanctuary

2001. St. Mary's Sanctuaries. Multicoloured.
3927 1z. Type **1224** (Cathedral of St. Martin and St. Nicolas, Bydgoszcz) 35 10
3928 1z. St. Mary of Ludzmierz, Basilica of the Assumption of St. Mary, Ludzmierz 35 10
3929 1z.90 St. Mary the Winner, Church of St. Mary in Piasek, Wroclaw 65 20

2001. Completion of Section of God's Mercy Sanctuary at Cracow-Lagiewniki.
3930 **1225** 1z. multicoloured . . . 35 10

1226 Ligia, Vinius and Petrinius

2001. *Quo Vadis* (film directed by Jerzy Kawalerowicz). Depicting scenes from the film. Multicoloured.
3931 1z. Type **1226** 35 10
3932 1z. Nero singing at feast . . 35 10
3933 1z. St. Peter in the catacombs and the baptism of Chilon Chilonides 35 10
3934 1z. Chilon Chilonides and crowd fleeing 35 10
3935 1z. Liga tied to the back of a bull and in the arms of Ursus 35 10
3936 1z. St. Peter blessing Vincius and Liga 35 10

1227 Copper Furnace

2001. "Euro Cuprum 2001" European Stamp Exhibition, Lubin. Multicoloured.
3937 1z. Type **1227** 35 10
3938 1z.90 Engraver at work and men dressing copper sheets 65 20
3939 2z. Inking plates and engraving press 70 20
MS3940 88 × 76 mm. 3z. 18th-century engraving of Lubin and burin (50 × 39 mm) 90 30

1228 "Battle of Chocim" (detail, Stanislaw Batowski-Kaczor) and Breast-plate of Stanislaw Skorkowski's Armour

2001. "One Century Passes it Over to Another Century" Exhibition, Polish Military Museum, Warsaw.
3941 **1228** 1z. multicoloured . . . 35 10

1229 Steam and Electric Locomotives

2001. 75th Anniv of Polish State Railways.
3942 **1229** 1z. multicoloured . . . 35 10

1230 Street Scene (Marcin Kuron)

2001. Winners of "Poland in 21st Century" (children's painting competition). Multicoloured.
3943 1z. Type **1230** 35 10
3944 1z.90 Rockets behind girl and boy (Agata Grzyb) 65 20
3945 2z. Futuristic car and house on wheels (Joanna Sadrakula) 70 25

1231 Football and Players

1232 Children encircling Globe

2001. Qualification of Poland for World Cup Football Championship, Japan and South Korea.
3946 **1231** 1z. multicoloured . . . 35 10

2001. World Post Day. United Nations Year of Dialogue among Civilizations.
3947 **1232** 1z.90 multicoloured . . 65 20

1233 "100 Years Ago" (detail, Wlodzimierz Kugler)

2001. 80th Anniv of Post and Telecommunication Museum, Wroclaw. Sheet 87 × 70 mm.

MS3948 **1233** 3z.+75g. multicoloured . . . . 1·10 35

1234 Violin Peg Box and Scroll

2001. 12th Henryk Wieniawski International Violin Competition, Poznan.

3949 **1234** 1z. multicoloured . . . 35 10

1235 Pope John Paul II

2001. Papal Day.

3950 **1235** 1z. multicoloured . . . 35 10

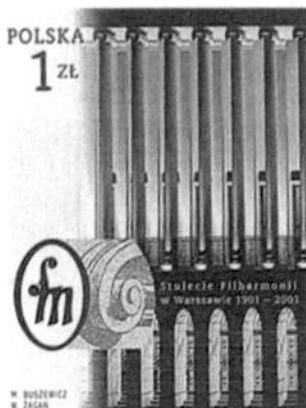

1236 Building Facade

2001. Centenary of National Philharmonic Orchestra.

3951 **1236** 1z. multicoloured . . . 35 10

1237 Pope John Paul II

2001. New Millennium. Multicoloured.

3952 1z. Type **1237** 35 10

3953 1z. President Lech Walesa and cover of 1791 constitution 35 10

3954 1z. Covers of *Glos Wolny Wolnosc Ubespieczaiacy, Kultura, Zniewolony umysl* and *O skutecznym rad sposobie* (magazines) . . . 35 10

3955 1z. Wojciech Boguslawski (actor and dramatist) and Jerzy Grotowski (director) 35 10

3956 1z. General Jozef Pilsudski (soldier and President 1918–22) and posters (1989) 35 10

3957 1z. N.A.T.O. emblem and General Kazimierz Pulaski (soldier) 35 10

3958 1z. Nicolaus Copernicus and Aleksander Wolszczan (astronomers) 35 10

3959 1z. Jan of Glogow (wood engraving) (mathematician and astronomer) and Tadeusz Kotarbinski (physicist) 35 10

3960 1z. "Do Broni" (poster, 1920) and "Bitwa pod Grunwaldem" (detail) (painting, Jan Matejko) 35 10

3961 1z. Leaders of November Uprising, 1830 . . . . . 35 10

3962 1z. Head of John the Apostle (detail) (wooden altarpiece, Wit Stwosz) and sculpture by Magdalena Abakanowicz 35 10

3963 1z. Frederik Chopin, Krzysztof Penderecki (composers) and score of *Mazurka No. 10* by Karol Szymanowski 35 10

3964 1z. Royal Castle, Warsaw and view of Cracow (wood engraving) 35 10

3965 1z. Jan III Sobieski (painting) and emblem of European Union 35 10

3966 1z. Wislawa Szymborska (Nobel Prizewinner for Literature) and Mikolaj Rej (poet) 35 10

3967 1z. Janusz Kusocinski and Robert Korzeniowski (athletes) 35 10

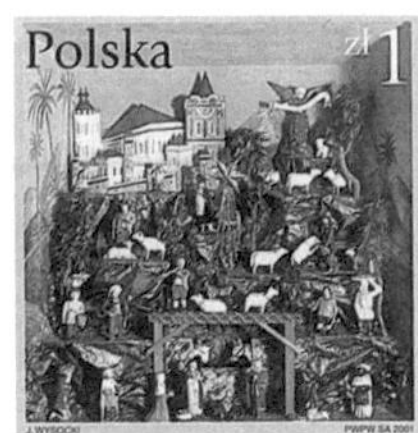

1238 Lower Silesian Crib

2001. Christmas. Multicoloured.

3968 1z. Type **1238** 35 10

3969 1z.90 Lower Silesian Crib (different) 35 10

1239 Radio Station Building and Virgin Mary (statue)

2001. 10th Anniv of "Radio Maryia" (religious broadcasting station). Multicoloured.

3970 1z. Type **MS**1239 . . . . . 30 10

MS3971 176 × 78 mm. 1z. Virgin Mary (statue) and crowd; 1z. Type **1239**; 1z. Crowd and crowned Virgin Mary (statue) 90 30

1240 Pear and Apple

2002. Valentine's Day.

3972 **1240** 1z.10 multicoloured . . 25 10

1241 Downhill, Biathlon, Ice-skating, and Ski Jumping

2002. Winter Olympic Games, Salt Lake City, U.S.A.

3973 **1241** 1z.10 multicoloured . . 25 10

1242 Jan Czerski

2002. Explorers. Multicoloured.

3974 2z. Type **1242** 50 15

3975 2z. Bronislaw Pilsudski . . . 50 15

1243 Gniezno **1244** Flowers

2002. Polish Cities. Multicoloured.

3975a 1z.20 Torun 25 10

3975ba 1z.80 Kalisz 40 10

3976 2z. Type **1243** 50 15

3977 2z.10 Krakow 50 15

3977a 2z.60 Pfock (horiz) . . . 60 20

3978 3z.20 Warsaw 75 25

3978a 3z.40 Kazimiera Dolny 80 30

2002. Easter. Multicoloured.

3979 1z.10 Type **1244** 25 10

3980 2z. Chicks 50 15

1245 Labrador Retriever and Puppies

2002. Domestic and Wild Animals. Multicoloured.

3981 1z.10 Type **1245** 25 10

3982 1z.10 Cat and kittens . . . 25 10

3983 1z.10 Wolf and cubs 25 10

3984 1z.10 Lynx and kittens . . . 25 10

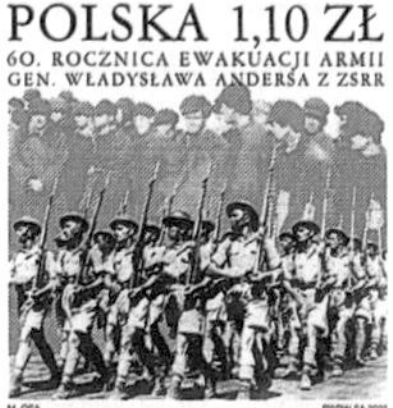

1246 Soldiers marching

2002. 60th Anniv of Evacuation of General Wladislaw Ander's Army from U.S.S.R.

3985 **1246** 1z.10 multicoloured . . 25 10

1247 Trees (Amanda Zejmis)

1249 Radio Microphone

1248 Stylized Figures

2002. Paintings. Multicoloured.

3986 1z.10 Type **1257** 25 10

3987 1z.10 Vase and ornaments (Henryk Paraszczuk) . . . 25 10

3988 2z. Landscape (Lucjan Matula) (horiz) 50 15

3989 3z.20 Basket of flowers (Jozefa Laciak) (horiz) . . 75 25

2002. National Census.

3990 **1248** 1z.10 multicoloured . . 25 10

2002. 50th Anniv of "Radio Free Europe".

3991 **1249** 2z. multicoloured . . . 50 15

1250 Fireman

2002. 10th Anniv of State Fire Brigade.

3992 **1250** 1z.10 multicoloured . . 25 10

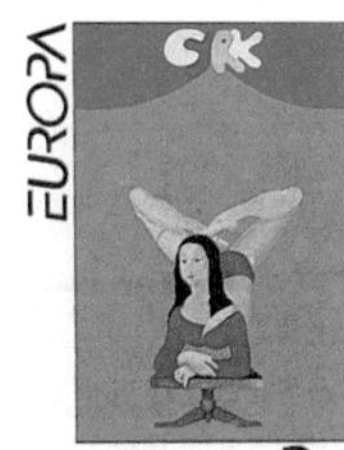

1251 Circus Artist

2002. Europa. Circus.

3993 **1251** 2z. multicoloured . . . 50 15

1252 "Madonna with the Child, St. John the Baptist and the Angel" (Sandro Botticelli)

2002. 140th Anniv of the National Gallery, Warsaw.

3994 **1252** 1z.10 multicoloured . . 25 10

1253 Maria Konopnicka **1254** Scooter

2002. 160th Birth Anniv of Maria Konopnicka (poet and writer).

3995 **1253** 1z.10 brown, ochre and green 25 10

2002. Children's Games. Multicoloured.

3996 1z.10 Type **1254** 25 10

3997 1z.10 Flying kite 25 10

3998 1z.10 Badminton 25 10

1255 Football and Globe

2002. World Cup Football Championship, Japan and South Korea. Multicoloured.

3999 1z.10 Type **1255** 25 10

4000 2z. Player chasing ball . . . 50 15

1256 Domeyko and Santiago University, Chile

2002. Birth Bicentenary of Ignacego Domeyki (scientist).

4015 **1256** 2z.60 multicoloured . . 60 20

1257 Hibiscus and Tulips

2002. "Philakorea 2002" International Philatelic Exhibition, Seoul and "Amphilex 2002" International Philatelic Exhibition, Amsterdam.
4016 **1257** 2z. multicoloured . . . 50 15

1258 Pope John Paul II and Basilica of Virgin Mary of the Angel, Kalwaria Zebrzydowska

2002. 7th Papal Visit To Poland (1st issue). Multicoloured.
4017 1z.10 Type **1258** 25 10
4018 1z.80 Pope John Paul II and Sanctuary of God's Mercy, Sisters of Virgin Mary's Convent, Lagiewniki 40 10
See also No. **MS**4022.

1259 "Holy Lady of Assistance"

2002. St. Mary's Sanctuaries. Multicoloured.
4019 1z.10 Type **1259** (Church of the Holy Lady of Assistance, Jaworzno) . . 25 10
4020 1z.10 "Holy Virgin of Opole" (Cathedral of Holy Cross, Opole) . . . 25 10
4021 2z. "Holy Virgin of Trabki" (Church of the Assumption of the Holy Lady, Trabki Wielkie) . . 50 15

1260 Pope John Paul II and Wawel Castle, Cracow

2002. 7th Papal Visit To Poland (2nd issue). Sheet 73 × 57 mm.
MS4022 1260 3z.20 black 75 75

1261 Spa Building, Ciechocinku

2002. 18th Polish Philatelic Association Convention, Ciechocinku. Sheet 74 × 105 mm.
MS4023 1261 3z.20 brown . . . 75 75

1262 Czesnik Raptusiewicz and Dyndalski

2002. "Zemsta" (Revenge) (film directed by Andrzej Wajda). Sheet 177 × 137 mm containing T **1262**, Showing scenes from the film. Multicoloured.
MS4024 1z.10 Type **1262**; 1z.10 Klara and Waclaw; 1z.10 Papkin; 1z.10 Regent Milczek and Papkin; 1z.10 Regent Milczek and Czesnik Raptusiewicz; 1z.10 Podstolina and Klara . . . . 1·60 1·60

1263 Schwarzkopf Okl-359

2002. Steam Locomotives. Showing locomotives from Wolsztyn Railway Museum. Multicoloured.
4025 1z.10 Type **1263** 25 10
4026 1z.10 Fablok 0149-7 . . . . 25 10
4027 2z. Krolewiec Tki3-87 . . . 50 15
4028 2z. Express locomotive Pm 36-2 . . . . 50 15

1264 Hands holding Pens

2002. World Post Day.
4029 **1264** 2z. multicoloured . . . 50 15

1265 Emblem

2002. Anti-Cancer Campaign.
4030 **1265** 1z.10 multicoloured . . 25 10

1266 Emblem

2002. 50th Anniv of Polish Television. Sheet 185 × 115 mm containing T **1266** Showing emblems of television programmes. Multicoloured.
MS4031 1z.10 Type **1266** (TV News); 1z.10 TV Theatre; 1z.10 "Pegaz" (cultural programme); 1z.10 "Teleranek" (children's programme) . . . . 1·00 1·00

1267 St. Stanislaw

2002. Saints. Sheet 136 × 165 mm containing T **1267** and similar vert designs. Multicoloured.
MS4032 1z.10 Type **1267**; 1z.10 St. Kazimierz; 1z.10 St. Faustyna Kowalska; 1z.10 St. Benedict; 1z.10 St. Cyril and St. Methody; 1z.10 St. Catherine of Siena . . 1·60 1·60

1268 Christmas Tree Baubles

2002. Christmas. Multicoloured.
4033 1z.10 Type **1268** 25 10
4034 2z. Small purple and large yellow baubles 50 15

1269 "POLSKA" superimposed on "EUROPA"

2003. Poland's Accession to European Union (1st issue). Negotiations.
4035 **1269** 1z.20 multicoloured . . 35 10
See also No. 4067 and 4069.

1270 Pope John Paul II

1271 Pope John Paul II on Balcony of St. Peter's Basilica, 1978

2003. 25th Anniv of the Pontificate of Pope John Paul II (1st issue). Multicoloured.
4036 1z.20 Type **1270** 35 10
4037 1z.20 Celebrating mass, Victory Square, Warsaw, 1979 . . . . 35 10
4038 1z.20 Addressing young people, Parc des Princes Stadium, Paris, 1980 . . . 35 10
4039 1z.20 Assassination attempt, St. Peter Square, 1981 . . 35 10
4040 1z.20 Giving homily surrounded by flowers, Portugal, 1982 . . . . . 35 10
4041 1z.20 Kneeling in front of Holy Doors, start of Holy Year of Redemption, 1983 35 10
4042 1z.20 Meeting Sandro Pertini, Pres. of Italy, 1984 . . . . 35 10
4043 1z.20 International Youth Day, Rome, 1985 . . . . 35 10
4044 1z.20 First visit of Pope to Synagogue, 1986 . . . . 35 10
4045 1z.20 Inaugurating Year of Mary, 1987 . . . . 35 10
4046 1z.20 Visiting European Parliament, Strasbourg, 1988 . . . . 35 10
4047 1z.20 Meeting Mikhail Gorbachev, Pres. Soviet Union, 1989 . . . . . . 35 10
4048 1z.20 Visiting lepers in Guinea-Bissau, 1990 . . . 35 10
4049 1z20 Addressing Bishop's Synod, 1991 . . . . . . 35 10
4050 1z.20 Pronouncing the Catechism, 1992 . . . . 35 10
4051 1z.20 Enthroned, Assissi, 1993 . . . . 35 10
4052 1z.20 Celebrating Mass in the Sistine Chapel, 1994 35 10
4053 1z.20 Addressing the United Nations, 1995 . . . . . 35 10
4054 1z.20 Walking through the Brandenburg Gate with Chancellor Helmut Kohl, 1996 . . . . 35 10
4055 1z.20 Celebrating Mass in Sarajevo, 1997 . . . . . 35 10
4056 1z.20 With Fidel Castro, Cuba, 1998 . . . . 35 10
4057 1z.20 Opening door, Christmas, 1999 . . . . . 35 10
4058 1z.20 With young people, World Youth Day, Rome, 2000 . . . . 35 10
4059 1z.20 Closing door of St. Peter's Basilica, 2001 35 10
4060 1z.20 Visiting the Italian Parliament, 2002 . . . . 35 10

2003. 25th Anniv of the Pontificate of Pope John Paul II (2nd issue).
4061 **1271** 10z. silver . . . . . . 3·00 90

1272 "Christ Anxious"

1273 Andrzej Modrzewski

2003. 500th Birth Anniv of Andrzej Frycz Modrzewski (writer).
4062 **1272** 1z.20 black 35 10

2003. Easter. Folk Sculpture. Multicoloured.
4063 1z.20 Type **1273** 35 10
4064 2z.10 "Christ Vanquisher" 60 15

1274 Poznan Ancient and Modern

2003. 750th Anniv of Poznan.
4065 **1274** 1z.20 multicoloured . . 35 10
MS4066 95 × 72 mm 3z.40 cinnamon and black (40 × 31 mm) . . . . 1·00 1·00
DESIGN: 3z.40 Ancient view of city and city arms.

1275 Portico and Clouds

2003. Poland's Accession to European Union (2nd issue).
4067 **1275** 1z.20 multicoloured . . 35 10

1276 Poster for "Vanitas" Exhibition (Wieslaw Walkuski)

2003. Europa. Poster Art.
4068 **1276** 2z.10 multicoloured . . 60 15

1277 "POLSKA" superimposed on "EUROPA"

2003. Poland's Accession to European Union (3rd issue). Referendum.
4069 **1277** 1z.20 multicoloured . . 35 10

1278 Island Palace (south view)

2003. Royal Baths, Lazienki Park, Warsaw. Multicoloured.
4070 1z.20 Type **1278** 35 10
4071 1z.80 Island Palace (north view) 55 15
4072 2z.10 Myslewicki Palace . . 60 15
4073 2z.60 Amphitheatre 75 20

1279 Pyramids and Camel (Anna Golebiewska)

2003. Children's Paintings. Stamp Design Competition Winners. Designs on theme "My Dream Vacation". Multicoloured.
4074 1z.20 Type **1279** 35 10
4075 1z.80 Girl windsurfing (Marlena Krejpcio) (vert) 55 15
4076 2z.10 Wind-surfer and fish (Michal Korze) 60 15
4077 2z.60 Girl and hens (Ewa Zadjdler) 75 20

1280 "Krak" (anonymous)

2003. Fairy Tales. Multicoloured.
4078 1z.20 Type **1280** 35 10
4079 1z.80 "Stupid Mateo" (Josef Kraszewski) 55 15
4080 2z.10 "Frog Princess" (Antoni Glinski) 60 15
4081 2z.60 "Crock of Gold" (Josef Kraszewski) 75 20

1281 Katowice Cathedral

2003. Katowice 2003 National Stamp Exhibition. Sheet 94 × 71 mm.
MS4082 **1281** 3z.40 black, brown and ochre . . . . 1·00 1·00
No. **MS**4082 also exists imperforate.

MILITARY POST

I. Polish Corps in Russia, 1918.

1918. Stamps of Russia optd **POCZTA Pol. Korp.** and eagle. Perf or imperf. (70k.).
M 1 **22** 3k. red . . . . 55·00 55·00
M 2 **23** 4k. red . . . . 55·00 55·00
M 3 **22** 5k. red . . . . 17·00 13·50
M 4 **23** 10k. blue . . . . 17·00 13·50
M 5 **22** 10k. on 7k. blue (No.151) £425 £500
M 6 **10** 15k. blue and purple . . . 3·75 3·75
M 7 **14** 20k. red and blue . . . . 6·75 5·50
M 8 **10** 25k. mauve and green . . 85·00 70·00
M 9 35k. green and purple . . 3·75 3·75
M10 **14** 40k. green and purple . . 13·50 9·75
M11 **10** 70k. orge & brn (No. 166) £275 £225

1918. Stamps of Russia surch **Pol. Korp.**, eagle and value. (a) Perf on Nos. 92/4.
M12A **22** 10k. on 3k. red . . . . 3·50 3·50
M13A 35k. on 1k. orange . . . 50·00 50·00
M14A 50k. on 2k. green . . . 3·50 3·50
M15A 1r. on 3k. red . . . . . 70·00 65·00

(b) Imperf on Nos. 155/7.
M12B **22** 10k. on 3k. red . . . . 1·40 1·40
M13B 35k. on 1k. orange . . . 55 55
M14B 50k. on 2k. green . . . 1·40 1·40
M15B 1r. on 3k. red . . . . . 3·25 2·40

II. Polish Army in Russia, 1942.

M 3 "We Shall Return"

1942.
M16 M **3** 50k. brown £170 £425

NEWSPAPER STAMPS

1919. Newspaper stamps of Austria optd **POCZTA POLSKA**. Imperf.
N50 N **53** 2h. brown . . . . . . 8·75 10·50
N51 4h. green . . . . . . 1·75 2·25
N52 6h. blue . . . . . . 1·75 2·25
N53 10h. orange . . . . . 35·00 42·00
N54 30h. red . . . . . . 3·75 5·50

OFFICIAL STAMPS

O 24

O 70

1920.
O128 O **24** 3f. red 10 25
O129 5f. red 10 10
O130 10f. red 10 10
O131 15f. red 10 10
O132 25f. red 10 10
O133 50f. red 10 10
O134 100f. red 25 25
O135 150f. red 30 30
O136 200f. red 30 35
O137 300f. red 30 35
O138 600f. red 40 50

1933. (a) Inscr "ZWYCZAJNA".
O295 O **70** (No value) mauve . . 15 15
O306 (No value) blue . . . 20 20

(b) Inscr "POLECONA".
O307 O **70** (No value) red 20 20

O 93

1940. (a) Size 31 × 23 mm.
O392 O **93** 6g. brown . . . . . . 1·25 1·60
O393 8g. grey . . . . 1·25 1·60
O394 10g. green . . . . . . 1·25 1·60
O395 12g. green . . . . . . 1·25 1·60
O396 20g. brown . . . . . 1·25 2·25
O397 24g. red . . . . 9·50 45
O398 30g. red . . . . 1·60 2·25
O399 40g. violet . . . . . . 1·60 3·75
O400 48g. green . . . . . . 5·00 3·75
O401 50g. blue . . . . . . 1·25 2·25
O402 60g. green . . . . . . 1·25 1·75
O403 80g. purple . . . . . 1·25 1·75

(b) Size 35 × 26 mm.
O404 O **93** 1z. purple and grey . . 3·75 4·50
O405 3z. brown and grey . . 3·75 4·50
O406 5z. orange and grey . . 5·00 5·75

(c) Size 21 × 16 mm.
O407 O **93** 6g. brown . . . . . . 65 1·00
O408 8g. grey . . . . 1·25 1·75
O409 10g. green . . . . . . 1·90 1·90
O410 12g. green . . . . . . 1·90 1·60
O411 20g. brown . . . . . 95 1·00
O412 24g. red 95 85
O413 30g. red . . . . 1·25 2·25
O414 40g. violet . . . . . . 1·90 2·00
O415 50g. blue . . . . . . 1·90 2·00

O 102

O 128

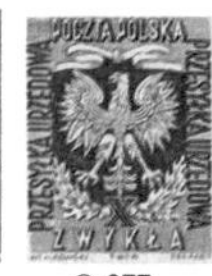

O 277

1943.
O456 O **102** 6g. brown 30 60
O457 8g. blue 30 60
O458 10g. green 30 60
O459 12g. violet 30 60
O460 16g. orange 30 60
O461 20g. green 30 60
O462 24g. red 30 60
O463 30g. purple 30 60
O464 40g. blue 30 60
O465 60g. green 30 60
O466 80g. purple 30 60
O467 100g. grey 30 95

1945. No value. (a) With control number below design. Perf or imperf.
O534 O **128** (5z.) blue 45 25
O535 (10z.) red 45 25

(b) Without control number below design. Perf.
O748 O **128** (60g.) pale blue . . . 35 25
O805 (60g.) indigo 55 25
O806 (1.55z.) red 55 25

The blue and indigo stamps are inscr "ZWYKLA" (Ordinary) and the red stamps "POLECONA" (Registered).

1954. No value.
O871 O **277** (60g.) blue 20 15
O872 (1.55z.) red ("POLECONA") 40 15

POSTAGE DUE STAMPS

1919. Postage Due Stamps of Austria optd **POCZTA POLSKA**.
D50 D **55** 5h. red . . . . 5·50 5·00
D51 10h. red £1750 £2750
D52 15h. red . . . . 3·25 2·50
D53 20h. red £550 £550
D54 25h. red . . . . 19·00 17·00
D55 30h. red £950 £950
D56 40h. red £220 £220
D57 D **56** 1k. blue £2000 £2500
D58 5k. blue £2000 £2500
D59 10k. blue £9750 £9000

1919. Postage Due Provisionals of Austria optd **POCZTA POLSKA**.
D60 **50** 15 on 36h. (No. D287) . . £300 £325
D61 50 on 42h. (No. D289) . . 30·00 25·00

D 20 D 28 D 63

1919. Sold in halerzy or fenigow.
D 92 D **20** 2h. blue 10 10
D 93 4h. blue 10 10
D 94 5h. blue 10 10
D 95 10h. blue 10 10
D 96 20h. blue 10 10
D 97 30h. blue 10 10
D 98 50h. blue 10 10
D145 100h. blue 20 10
D146 200f. blue 75 10
D147 500h. blue 75 10
The 20, 100 and 500 values were sold in both currencies.

1919. Sold in fenigow.
D128 D **20** 2f. red 10 25
D129 4f. red 10 10
D130 5f. red 10 10
D131 10f. red 10 10
D132 20f. red 10 10
D133 30f. red 10 10
D134 50f. red 25 25
D135 100f. red 30 30
D136 200f. red 30 35

1921. Stamps of 1919 surch with new value and **doplata**. Imperf.
D154 **11** 6m. on 15h. brown . . . 70 90
D155 6m. on 25h. red 50 55
D156 20m. on 10h. red . . . . 1·90 2·10
D157 20m. on 50h. blue . . . 1·00 1·75
D158 35m. on 70h. blue . . . 8·75 12·50

1921. Value in marks. (a) Size 17 × 22 mm.
D159 D **28** 1m. blue 20 10
D160 2m. blue 20 10
D161 4m. blue 20 10
D162 6m. blue 20 10
D163 8m. blue 20 10
D164 20m. blue 20 10
D165 50m. blue 20 10
D166 100m. blue 20 10

(b) Size 19 × 24 mm.
D199 D **28** 50m. blue 10 10
D200 100m. blue 10 10
D201 200m. blue 10 10
D202 500m. blue 10 10
D203 1000m. blue 10 10
D204 2000m. blue 10 10
D205 10,000m. blue 10 10
D206 20,000m. blue 10 10
D207 30,000m. blue 10 10
D208 50,000m. blue 10 10
D209 100,000m. blue 10 10
D210 200,000m. blue 10 10
D211 300,000m. blue 30 20
D212 500,000m. blue 40 40
D213 1,000,000m. blue . . . 75 55
D214 2,000,000m. blue . . . 1·10 90
D215 3,000,000m. blue . . . 1·40 1·10

1923. Surch.
D216 D **28** 10,000 on 8m. blue . . 10 15
D217 20,000 on 20m. blue 10 35
D218 50,000 on 2m. blue . . 1·25 60

1924. As Type D **28** but value in "groszy" or "zloty". (a) Size 20 × 25½ mm.
D229 D **28** 1g. brown 10 10
D230 2g. brown 20 10
D231 4g. brown 20 10
D232 6g. brown 20 10
D233 10g. brown . . . . . 3·25 10
D234 15g. brown . . . . . 3·25 10
D235 20g. brown . . . . . 6·75 10
D236 25g. brown . . . . . 4·75 10
D237 30g. brown 95 10
D238 40g. brown . . . . . 1·40 10
D239 50g. brown . . . . . 1·40 10
D240 1z. brown 90 10
D241 2z. brown 90 25
D242 3z. brown . . . . . . 1·40 45
D243 5z. brown . . . . . . 1·40 30

(b) Size 19 × 24 mm.
D290 D **28** 1g. brown 20 10
D291 2g. brown 20 10
D292 10g. brown 90 10
D293 15g. brown . . . . . 1·40 10
D294 20g. brown . . . . . 3·25 10
D295 25g. brown . . . . . 30·00 10

1930.
D280 D **63** 5g. brown 35 20

1934. Nos. D79/84 surch.
D301 D **28** 10g. on 2z. brown . . 20 15
D302 15g. on 2z. brown . . 20 15
D303 20g. on 1z. brown . . 20 15
D304 20g. on 5z. brown . . 1·75 35
D305 25g. on 40g. brown . . 60 35
D306 30g. on 40g. brown . . 65 45
D307 50g. on 40g. brown . . 65 45
D308 50g. on 3z. brown . . 2·10 60

1934. No. 273 surch **DOPLATA** and value.
D309 10g. on 1z. black on cream 70 20
D310 20g. on 1z. black on cream 1·50 55
D311 25g. on 1z. black on cream 70 20

D 88

D 97

1938.
D350 D **88** 5g. green 15 10
D351 10g. green 15 10
D352 15g. green 15 10
D353 20g. green 40 10
D354 25g. green 10 10
D355 30g. green 10 10
D356 50g. green 45 50
D357 1z. green . . . . . . 2·25 1·75

1940. German Occupation.
D420 D **97** 10g. orange 25 75
D421 20g. orange . . . . . 25 1·00
D422 30g. orange . . . . . 25 1·00
D423 50g. orange . . . . . 70 2·00

D 126

D 190

1945. Size 26 × 19½ mm. Perf.
D530 D **126** 1z. brown 10 10
D531 2z. brown 20 10
D532 3z. brown 25 20
D533 5z. brown 40 25

1946. Size 29 × 21½ mm. Perf or imperf.
D646 D **126** 1z. brown 10 10
D647 2z. brown 10 10
D572 3z. brown 10 10
D573 5z. brown 10 10
D574 6z. brown 10 10
D575 10z. brown 10 10
D649 15z. brown 10 10
D577 25z. brown 50 20
D651 100z. brown 55 35
D652 150z. brown 80 45

1950.
D665 D **190** 5z. red 15 15
D666 10z. red 15 15
D667 15z. red 15 15
D668 20z. red 15 15
D669 25z. red 30 15
D670 50z. red 45 15
D671 100z. red 55 30

1951. Value in "groszy" or "zloty".
D701 D **190** 5g. red 10 10
D702 10g. red 10 10
D703 15g. red 10 10
D704 20g. red 10 10
D705 25g. red 10 10
D706 30g. red 10 10
D707 50g. red 10 10
D708 60g. red 10 10
D709 90g. red 25 10
D710 1z. red 25 10
D711 2z. red 45 25
D712 5z. purple 95 30

1953. As last but with larger figures of value and no imprint below design.
D804 D **190** 5g. brown 10 10
D805 10g. brown 10 10
D806 15g. brown 10 10
D807 20g. brown 10 10
D808 25g. brown 10 10
D809 30g. brown 10 10
D810 50g. brown 10 10
D811 60g. brown 10 10
D812 90g. brown 25 10
D813 1z. brown 25 10
D814 2z. brown 45 10

1980. As Type D **190** but redrawn without imprint.
D2699 1z. red 10 10
D2700 2z. drab 10 10
D2701 3z. violet 30 10
D2702 5z. brown 50 30

D 1143

1998.
D3746 D **1143** 5g. blue, vio & yell 10 10
D3747 10g. blue, turq & yell 10 10
D3748 20g. bl, grn & yell 10 10
D3749 50g. black & yell 15 10
D3750 80g. bl, orge & yell 25 10
D3751 1z. blue, red & yell 35 15

POLISH POST IN DANZIG Pt. 5

For Polish post in Danzig, the port through which Poland had access to the sea between the two Great Wars.

100 groszy = 1 zloty.

Stamps of Poland optd **PORT GDANSK**.

1925. Issue of 1924.
R 1 **40** 1g. brown . . . . 30 1·50
R 2 2g. brown . . . . 30 3·50
R 3 3g. orange . . . . 30 1·50
R 4 5g. green . . . . 9·50 6·50
R 5 10g. green . . . . 3·50 3·25
R 6 15g. red . . . . 19·00 5·00
R 7 20g. blue . . . . 1·50 1·50
R 8 25g. red . . . . 1·00 1·50
R 9 30g. violet . . . . 1·00 1·50
R10 40g. blue . . . . 1·00 1·50
R11 50g. purple . . . . 2·75 1·75

1926. Issues of 1925–28.
R14 **44** 5g. green . . . . 70 3·00
R15 – 10g. violet (No. 245a) . . 70 3·00
R16 – 15g. red (No. 246) . . . . 2·10 3·50
R17 **48** 20g. red . . . . 1·75 1·75
R18 **51** 25g. brown . . . . 2·75 1·75
R19 **57** 1z. black and cream . . . 19·00 23·00

1929. Issues of 1928/9.
R21 **61** 5g. violet . . . . 1·00 1·50
R22 10g. green . . . . 1·00 1·50
R23 **59** 15g. blue . . . . 2·45 4·50
R24 **61** 25g. brown . . . . 2·10 1·50

1933. Stamp of 1928 with vert opt.
R25 **57** 1z. black on cream . . . . 60·00 90·00

1934. Issue of 1932.
R26 **65** 5g. violet . . . . 2·40 3·50
R27 10g. green . . . . 23·00 90·00
R28 15g. red . . . . 2·40 3·50

1936. Issue of 1935.
R29 **79** 5g. blue (No. 313) . . . . 2·10 3·50
R31 – 5g. violet (No. 317) . . . 70 1·75
R30 – 15g. blue (No. 315) . . . 2·10 5·00
R32 – 15g. lake (No. 319) . . . 70 1·75
R33 – 25g. green (No. 321a) . . 2·10 3·50

R **6** Port of Danzig

1938. 20th Anniv of Polish Independence.
R34 R **6** 5g. orange . . . . 40 1·50
R35 15g. brown . . . . 40 1·50
R36 25g. purple . . . . 40 1·50
R37 55g. blue . . . . 70 2·75

POLISH POST OFFICE IN TURKEY Pt. 5

Stamps used for a short period for franking correspondence handed in at the Polish Consulate, Constantinople.

100 fenigow = 1 marka.

1919. Stamps of Poland of 1919 optd **LEVANT**. Perf.
1 **15** 3f. brown . . . . 35·00
2 5f. green . . . . 35·00
3 10f. purple . . . . 35·00
4 15f. red . . . . 35·00
5 20f. blue . . . . 35·00
6 25f. olive . . . . 35·00
7 50f. green . . . . 35·00
8 **17** 1m. violet . . . . 40·00
9 1m.50 green . . . . 40·00
10 2m. brown . . . . 40·00
11 **18** 2m.50 brown . . . . 40·00
12 **19** 5m. purple . . . . 40·00

PONTA DELGADA Pt. 9

A district of the Azores, whose stamps were used from 1868, and again after 1905.

1000 reis = 1 milreis.

1892. As T **26** of Portugal but inscr "PONTA DELGADA".
6 5r. yellow . . . . 2·50 1·80
7 10r. mauve . . . . 2·50 1·70
8 15r. brown . . . . 3·50 2·50
9 20r. lilac . . . . 3·50 2·50
3 25r. green . . . . 7·25 1·50
12 50r. blue . . . . 7·50 3·75
25 75r. pink . . . . 7·25 6·00
14 80r. green . . . . 12·00 9·00
15 100r. brown on yellow . . . . 12·00 7·25
28 150r. red on pink . . . . . . 55·00 34·00
16 200r. blue on blue . . . . . . 55·00 50·00
17 300r. blue on brown . . . . . 55·00 50·00

1897. "King Carlos" key-types inscr "PONTA DELGADA".
29 S 2½r. grey 50 35
30 5r. orange 50 35
31 10r. green 50 35
32 15r. brown . . . . 3·25 3·00
45 15r. green . . . . 1·70 1·20
33 20r. lilac . . . . 1·70 1·30
34 25r. green . . . . 2·50 1·30
46 25r. red . . . . 1·50 45
35 50r. blue . . . . 2·50 1·30
48 65r. blue . . . . 1·20 50
36 75r. pink . . . . 5·50 1·30
49 75r. brown on yellow . . . . 11·50 7·00
37 80r. mauve . . . . 1·50 1·30
38 100r. blue on blue . . . . . 3·50 1·30
50 115r. brown on pink . . . . 2·75 1·40
51 130r. brown on cream . . . . 1·90 1·40
39 150r. brown on yellow . . . 1·90 1·50
52 180r. grey on pink . . . . . 1·90 1·40
40 200r. purple on pink . . . . 6·50 5·75
41 300r. blue on pink . . . . . 6·50 5·75
42 500r. black on blue . . . . . 14·00 11·00

POONCH Pt. 1

A state in Kashmir, India. Now uses Indian stamps.

12 pies = 1 anna;
16 annas = 1 rupee.

1 4

1876. Imperf.
1 **1** 6p. red £10000 £130
2 ½a. red . . . . — £4000

1880. Imperf.
32 **1** 1p. red . . . . 2·50 3·00
12 **4** ½a. red . . . . 2·50 3·25
50 1a. red . . . . 2·00 3·25
52 2a. red (22×22 mm) . . . . 3·25 3·25
31 4a. red (28×27 mm) . . . . 4·00 4·25

These stamps were printed on various coloured papers.

OFFICIAL STAMPS

1888. Imperf.
O1 **1** 1p. black . . . . 2·25 2·50
O2 **4** ½a. black . . . . 2·75 3·50
O3 1a. black . . . . 2·50 2·75
O4 2a. black . . . . 3·75 3·75
O5 4a. black . . . . 6·00 9·50

PORT LAGOS Pt. 6

French Post Office in the Turkish Empire. Closed in 1898.

25 centimes = 1 piastre.

1893. Stamps of France optd **Port-Lagos** and the three higher values surch also in figures and words.
75 **10** 5c. green . . . . 19·00 17·00
76 10c. black on lilac . . . . . 32·00 29·00
77 15c. blue . . . . 35·00 55·00
78 1p. on 25c. black on pink . . 65·00 65·00
79 2p. on 50c. red . . . . . . £100 80·00
80 4p. on 1f. green . . . . . . 60·00 60·00

PORT SAID Pt. 6

French Post Office in Egypt. Closed 1931.

1902. 100 centimes = 1 franc.
1921. 10 milliemes = 1 piastre.

1899. Stamps of France optd **PORT SAID**.
101 **10** 1c. black on blue . . . . . 30 1·00
102 2c. brown on buff . . . . 50 1·60
103 3c. grey . . . . 50 2·75
104 4c. brown on grey . . . . 35 2·75
105 5c. green . . . . 65 2·75
107 10c. black on lilac . . . . 4·00 4·75
109 15c. blue . . . . 3·25 7·75
110 20c. red on green . . . . 4·25 10·00
111 25c. black on pink . . . . 1·75 30
112 30c. brown . . . . 7·00 10·00
113 40c. red on yellow . . . . 8·25 7·50
115 50c. red . . . . 14·00 12·50
116 1f. green . . . . 20·00 17·00
117 2f. brown on blue . . . . 38·00 55·00
118 5f. mauve on lilac . . . . 60·00 80·00

1899. No. 107 surch. (a) **25c VINGT-CINQ**.
119 **10** 25c. on 10c. black on lilac £325 £130

(b) **VINGT-CINQ** only.
121 **10** 25c. on 10c. black on lilac 95·00 23·00

1902. "Blanc", "Mouchon" and "Merson" key-types inscr "PORT SAID".
122 A 1c. grey 10 85
123 2c. purple . . . . 40 1·40
124 3c. red . . . . 15 1·75
125 4c. brown . . . . 25 1·40
126a 5c. green . . . . 1·40 1·50
127 B 10c. red . . . . 1·10 30
128 15c. red . . . . 1·60 2·50
128a 15c. orange . . . . 3·75 3·75
129 20c. brown . . . . 90 2·50
130 25c. blue 70 15
131 30c. mauve . . . . 3·00 2·75
132 C 40c. red and blue . . . . 2·00 3·50
133 50c. brown and lilac . . . 1·75 2·25
134 1f. red and green . . . . 7·25 8·25
135 2f. lilac and buff . . . . 5·50 14·50
136 5f. blue and buff . . . . 20·00 35·00

1915. Red Cross. Surch **5c** and red cross.
137 B 10c.+5c. red . . . . . . 50 3·00

1921. Surch with value in figures and words (without bars).
151a A 1m. on 1c. grey . . . . . 2·25 2·75
152 2m. on 5c. green . . . . . 1·50 2·75
153 B 4m. on 10c. red . . . . . 85 3·25
166a A 5m. on 1c. grey . . . . . 7·00 11·00
167 5m. on 2c. purple . . . . 13·00 13·00
154 5m. on 3c. red . . . . . 6·25 10·00
141 5m. on 4c. brown . . . . 8·50 11·00
155 B 6m. on 15c. orange . . . 1·25 3·50
156 6m. on 15c. red . . . . . 11·50 14·00
157 8m. on 20c. brown . . . . 1·50 3·50
168 A 10m. on 2c. purple . . . . 11·00 12·50
142 10m. on 4c. brown . . . . 20·00 24·00
158 B 10m. on 25c. blue . . . . 2·25 2·00
159 10m. on 30c. mauve . . . 3·75 7·50
144 12m. on 30c. mauve . . . 30·00 42·00
145 A 15m. on 4c. brown . . . . 8·00 9·25
169 B 15m. on 15c. red . . . . 60·00 60·00
170 15m. on 20c. brown . . . 55·00 55·00
146 C 15m. on 40c. red and blue 55·00 65·00
160 15m. on 50c. brown and lilac . . . . 3·25 5·50
161 B 15m. on 50c. blue . . . . 4·25 3·75
162 30m. on 1f. red and green 2·75 7·75
171 C 30m. on 50c. brown & lilac £225 £225
172 60m. on 50c. brown and lilac £225 £225
149 60m. on 2f. lilac and buff 70·00 70·00
164 60m. on 2f. red and green 6·00 11·00
173 150m. on 50c. brown and lilac £250 £250
165 150m. on 5f. blue and buff 6·25 10·50

1925. Surch with value in figures and words and bars over old value.
174 A 1m. on 1c. grey . . . . . 25 3·00
175 2m. on 5c. green . . . . . 1·60 3·00
176 B 4m. on 10c. red . . . . . 1·10 3·00
177 A 5m. on 3c. red . . . . . 65 2·25
178 B 6m. on 15c. orange . . . . 1·25 3·25
179 8m. on 20c. brown . . . . 1·40 3·25
180 10m. on 25c. blue . . . . 1·40 3·25
181 15m. on 50c. blue . . . . 1·75 2·25
182 C 30m. on 1f. red and green 1·75 2·75
183 60m. on 2f. red and green 1·25 3·50
184 150m. on 5f. blue and buff 3·00 4·25

1927. Altered key types. Inscr "Mm" below value.
185 A 3m. orange . . . . 2·25 3·25
186 B 15m. blue . . . . 1·10 2·50
187 20m. mauve . . . . 2·25 3·75
188 C 50m. red and green . . . . 3·25 4·75
189 100m. blue and yellow . . 2·00 6·00
190 250m. green and red . . . 7·00 10·00

1927. "French Sinking Fund" issue. As No. 186 (colour changed) surch **+5 Mm Caisse d'Amortissement**.
191 B 15m.+5m. orange . . . . . 1·75 4·50
192 15m.+5m. mauve . . . . . 2·25 4·50
193 15m.+5m. brown . . . . . 2·25 4·50
194 15m.+5m. lilac . . . . . 3·25 6·75

POSTAGE DUE STAMPS

1921. Postage Due stamps of France surch in figures and words.
D174 D **11** 2m. on 5c. blue . . . 38·00 48·00
D175 4m. on 10c. brown . . 42·00 48·00
D176 10m. on 30c. red . . . 42·00 48·00
D166 12m. on 10c. brown . . 38·00 45·00
D167 15m. on 5c. blue . . . 40·00 55·00
D177 15m. on 50c. purple . . 55·00 60·00
D168 30m. on 20c. olive . . 48·00 60·00
D169 30m. on 50c. purple . . £1800 £2000

For 1928 issues, see Alexandria.

PORTUGAL Pt. 9

A country on the S.W. coast of Europe, a kingdom until 1910, when it became a republic.

1853. 1000 reis = 1 milreis.
1912. 100 centavos = 1 escudo.
2002. 100 cents = 1 euro.

1 Queen Maria II 5 King Pedro V 9 King Luis

1853. Various frames. Imperf.
1 **1** 5r. brown £3000 £900
4 25r. blue . . . . £1000 20·00
6 50r. green £3500 £950
8 100r. lilac £33000 £2000

1855. Various frames. Imperf.
18a **5** 5r. brown . . . . £400 75·00
21 25r. blue . . . . £400 14·00
22 25r. pink . . . . £300 7·00
13 50r. green . . . . £500 75·00
15 100r. lilac . . . . £800 95·00

1862. Various frames. Imperf.
24 **9** 5r. brown . . . . £130 28·00
28 10r. yellow . . . . £150 49·00
30 25r. pink . . . . £110 5·00
32 50r. green . . . . £750 80·00
34 100r. lilac . . . . £850 95·00

14 King Luis 15

1866. With curved value labels. Imperf.
35 **14** 5r. black . . . . £110 10·50
36 10r. yellow £250 £150
38 20r. bistre . . . . £200 70·00
39 25r. pink . . . . £250 8·50
41 50r. green . . . . £250 70·00
43 80r. orange . . . . £250 70·00
45 100r. purple £325 £120
46 120r. blue . . . . £325 75·00

1867. With curved value labels. Perf.
52 **14** 5r. black . . . . £120 46·00
54 10r. yellow £250 £110
56 20r. bistre £300 £110
57 25r. pink . . . . 65·00 7·00
60 50r. green £250 £110
61 80r. orange £350 £110
62 100r. lilac £250 £110
64 120r. blue . . . . £300 70·00
67 240r. lilac £1000 £500

1870. With straight value labels. Perf.
69 **15** 5r. black . . . . 55·00 5·50
70 10r. yellow . . . . 75·00 28·00
158 10r. green . . . . 95·00 39·00
74 15r. brown . . . . £110 30·00
76 20r. bistre . . . . 75·00 26·00
143 20r. red . . . . £350 55·00
80 25r. red . . . . 44·00 3·75
115 50r. green . . . . £150 44·00
117 50r. blue . . . . £325 55·00
148 80r. orange . . . . £120 19·00
153 100r. mauve . . . . 70·00 14·00
93 120r. blue . . . . £275 75·00
95 150r. blue £350 £120
155 150r. yellow . . . . £130 14·00
99 240r. lilac £1500 £1100
156 300r. mauve . . . . £120 32·00
128 1000r. black . . . . £275 85·00

16 King Luis 17

1880. Various frames for T **16**.
185 **16** 5r. black . . . . 28·00 4·25
188 25r. grey . . . . 30·00 3·75
190 25r. brown . . . . 30·00 3·75
180 **17** 25r. grey . . . . £325 30·00
184 **16** 50r. blue . . . . £325 16·00

19 King Luis

26 King Carlos

1882. Various frames.
229 **19** 5r. black 14·50 1·40
231 10r. green 37·00 4·25
232 20r. red 44·00 18·00
212 25r. brown 30·00 2·50
234 25r. mauve 29·00 3·25
236 50r. blue 46·00 3·25
216 500r. black £500 £325
217 500r. mauve £275 55·00

1892.
271 **26** 5r. orange 12·50 2·10
239 10r. mauve 29·00 5·50
256 15r. brown 35·00 9·00
242 20r. lilac 55·00 12·50
275 25r. green 40·00 2·75
244 50r. blue 35·00 9·75
245 75r. red 65·00 8·50
262 80r. green 90·00 55·00
248 100r. brown on buff 65·00 6·75
265 150r. red on pink £160 55·00
252 200r. blue on blue £160 46·00
267 300r. blue on brown £180 70·00

1892. Optd **PROVISORIO**.
284 **19** 5r. black 17·00 9·00
283 10r. green 17·00 9·00
297 **15** 15r. brown 17·00 14·50
290 **19** 20r. red 41·00 23·00
291 25r. mauve 14·50 5·50
292 50r. blue 75·00 65·00
293 **15** 80r. orange £110 95·00

1893. Optd **1893 PROVISORIO** or surch also.
302 **19** 5r. black 14·50 7·25
303 10r. green 17·00 9·75
304 20r. red 41·00 23·00
309 20r. on 25r. mauve 55·00 50·00
305 25r. mauve £110 £100
306 50r. blue £110 £110
310 **15** 50r. on 80r. orange £130 £110
312 75r. on 80r. orange 75·00 75·00
308 80r. orange £110 £110

32 Prince Henry in his Caravel and Family Motto

1894. 500th Birth Anniv of Prince Henry the Navigator.
314 **32** 5r. orange 3·75 70
315 10r. red 3·75 70
316 15r. brown 11·50 3·50
317 20r. lilac 11·50 4·25
318 – 25r. green 10·00 1·40
319 – 50r. blue 29·00 6·25
320 – 75r. red 55·00 12·00
321 – 80r. green 55·00 14·50
322 – 100r. brown on buff 42·00 10·50
323 – 150r. red £140 34·00
324 – 300r. blue on buff £150 39·00
325 – 500r. purple £325 80·00
326 – 1000r. black on buff £600 £120
DESIGNS: 25r. to 100r. Prince Henry directing movements of his fleet; 150r. to 1000r. Prince Henry's studies.

35 St. Anthony's Vision

37 St. Anthony ascending into Heaven

1895. 700th Birth Anniv of St. Anthony (Patron Saint). With a prayer in Latin printed on back.
327 **35** 2½r. black 4·25 1·10
328 – 5r. orange 4·25 1·10
329 – 10r. mauve 14·00 8·50
330 – 15r. brown 15·00 8·50
331 – 20r. lilac 15·00 9·00
332 – 25r. purple and green 13·50 1·10
333 **37** 50r. brown and blue 33·00 23·00
334 75r. brown and red 50·00 41·00
335 80r. brown and green 65·00 65·00
336 100r. black and brown 60·00 31·00
337 – 150r. red and bistre £170 £110
338 – 200r. blue and bistre £160 £120
339 – 300r. grey and bistre £225 £140
340 – 500r. brown and green £400 £325
341 – 1000r. lilac and green £650 £400
DESIGNS—HORIZ: 5r. to 25r. St. Anthony preaching to fishes. VERT: 150r. to 1000r. St. Anthony from picture in Academy of Fine Arts, Paris.

39 King Carlos

1895. Numerals of value in red (Nos. 354 and 363) or black (others).
342 **39** 2½r. grey 25 15
343 5r. orange 25 15
344 10r. green 55 25
345 15r. green 49·00 2·50
346 15r. brown 95·00 3·75
347 20r. lilac 90 35
348 25r. green 65·00 25
349 25r. red 40 15
351 50r. blue 55 25
352 65r. blue 55 25
353 75r. red £120 4·50
354 75r. brown on yellow 1·80 75
355 80r. mauve 2·30 1·10
356 100r. blue on blue 1·10 40
357 115r. brown on pink 5·00 2·75
358 130r. brown on cream 4·00 1·40
359 150r. brown on yellow £150 24·00
360 180r. grey on pink 16·00 9·50
361 200r. puple on pink 17·00 2·30
362 300r. blue on pink 3·75 2·10
363 500r. black on blue 10·00 4·75

40 Departure of Fleet

43 Muse of History

44 Da Gama and Camoens and "Sao Gabriel" (flagship)

1898. 4th Centenary of Discovery of Route to India by Vasco da Gama.
378 **40** 2½r. green 1·40 35
379 – 5r. red 1·40 35
380 – 10r. purple 9·00 1·60
381 **43** 25r. green 5·25 55
382 **44** 50r. blue 11·00 3·25
383 – 75r. brown 46·00 11·00
384 – 100r. brown 32·00 11·00
385 – 150r. brown 70·00 29·00
DESIGNS—HORIZ: 5r. Arrival at Calicut; 10r. Embarkation at Rastello; 100r. Flagship "Sao Gabriel"; 150r. Vasco da Gama. VERT: 75r. Archangel Gabriel, Patron Saint of the Expedition.

48 King Manoel II

49

1910.
390 **48** 2½r. lilac 20 15
391 5r. black 20 15
392 10r. green 30 20
393 15r. brown 2·75 1·40
394 20r. red 85 70
395 25r. brown 65 20
396 50r. blue 1·50 70
397 75r. brown 9·75 5·25
398 80r. grey 2·75 2·30
399 100r. brown on green 10·50 3·25
400 200r. green on orange 6·25 4·50
401 300r. black on blue 7·00 5·25
402 **49** 500r. brown and green 14·00 12·50
403 1000r. black and blue 32·00 25·00

1910. Optd **REPUBLICA**.
404 **48** 2½r. lilac 30 10
405 5r. black 30 10
406 10r. green 3·75 1·20
407 15r. brown 1·20 90
408 20r. red 4·50 1·60
409 25r. brown 85 25
410 50r. blue 6·25 2·10
411 75r. brown 9·50 4·00
412 80r. grey 3·50 2·50
413 100r. brown on green 2·10 75
414 200r. green on orange 2·50 1·80
415 300r. black on blue 4·00 3·00
416 **49** 500r. brown and green 10·00 8·75
417 1000r. black and blue 25·00 21·00

1911. Optd **REPUBLICA** or surch also.
441 **40** 2½r. green 45 10
442a D **48** 5r. black 90 35
443a 10r. mauve 1·50 70
444 – 15r. on 5r. red (No. 379) 85 35
445a D **48** 20r. orange 6·00 3·25
446 **43** 25r. green 45 20
447 **44** 50r. blue 3·50 1·60
448 – 75r. brown (No. 383) 46·00 33·00
449 – 80r. on 150r. (No. 385) 7·00 5·00
450 – 100r. brown (No. 384) 7·00 3·25
451 D **48** 200r. brown on buff £130 70·00
452 300r. on 50r. grey 95·00 44·00
453 500r. on 100r. red on pink 49·00 25·00
454 – 1000r. on 10r. (No. 380) 65·00 39·00

1911. Vasco da Gama stamps of Madeira optd **REPUBLICA** or surch also.
455 2½r. green 12·50 8·75
456 15r. on 5r. red 2·75 2·10
457 25r. green 6·25 5·00
458 50r. blue 11·50 8·75
459 75r. brown 11·50 5·75
460 80r. on 150r. brown 13·50 11·50
461 100r. brown 39·00 8·75
462 1000r. on 10r. purple 39·00 26·00

56 Ceres

60 Presidents of Portugal and Brazil and Airmen Gago Coutinho and Sacadura Cabral

1912.
484 **56** ¼c. brown 60 30
485 ½c. black 1·80 90
486 1c. green 1·30 40
515 1c. brown 25 20
488 1½c. brown 7·25 3·00
516 1½c. green 30 20
490 2c. red 7·25 1·80
517 2c. yellow 25 20
702 2c. brown 15 15
492 2½c. lilac 50 20
521 3c. red 30 20
703 3c. blue 15 15
495 3½c. green 35 20
523 4c. green 1·80 25
704 4c. orange 15 15
497 5c. blue 7·25 70
705 5c. brown 15 15
527 6c. purple 35 20
706 6c. brown 15 15
815 6c. red 35 20
500 7½c. brown 9·00 2·10
529 7½c. blue 35 20
530 8c. grey 50 35
531 8c. green 70 55
532 8c. orange 60 45
503 10c. brown 17·00 1·10
707 10c. red 15 15
504 12c. blue 1·10 55
534 12c. green 60 40
535 13½c. blue 1·50 1·10
481 14c. blue on yellow 2·50 1·60
536 14c. purple 70 55
505 15c. brown 1·10 55
708 15c. black 25 15
709 16c. blue 25 15
474 20c. brown on green 18·00 1·80
475 20c. brown on buff 18·00 5·00
539 20c. brown 70 40
540 20c. green 55 45
541 20c. grey 55 45
542 24c. blue 70 40
543 25c. pink 60 30
710 25c. grey 25 15
819 25c. green 55 30
476 30c. brown on pink £130 11·50
477 30c. brown on yellow 12·00 2·30
545 30c. brown 60 35
820 32c. green 55 30
548 36c. red 2·00 45
549 40c. blue 1·20 85
550 40c. brown 70 40
712 40c. green 35 15
713 48c. pink 1·20 90
478 50c. orange on orange 16·00 1·40
553 50c. yellow 1·40 70
824 50c. red 1·80 90
554 60c. blue 1·80 70
715 64c. blue 2·10 1·80
826 75c. red 1·90 95
510 80c. pink 1·80 1·10
558 80c. lilac 1·20 60
827 80c. green 1·90 95
559 90c. blue 2·10 75
717 96c. red 2·30 1·20
480 1e. green on blue 21·00 1·40
561 1e. lilac 4·50 2·30
565 1e. blue 6·00 2·50
566 1e. purple 2·10 90
829 1e. red 4·25 1·00
562 1e.10 brown 4·50 2·00
563 1e.20 green 2·75 1·40
830 1e.20 brown 3·25 1·10
831 1e.25 blue 2·75 1·10
568 1e.50 lilac 18·00 4·25
720 1e.60 blue 2·50 60
721 2e. green 15·00 1·10
833 2e. mauve 20·00 6·75
572 2e.40 green £225 £160
573 3e. pink £225 £140
722 3e.20 green 5·75 1·10
723 4e.50 yellow 5·75 1·10
575 5e. green 46·00 10·50
724 5e. brown 80·00 3·75
725 10e. red 9·00 2·10
577 20e. blue £350 £200

1923. Portugal–Brazil Trans-Atlantic Flight.
578 **60** 1c. brown 15 70
579 2c. orange 15 70
580 3c. blue 15 70
581 4c. green 15 70
582 5c. brown 15 70
583 10c. brown 15 70
584 15c. black 15 70
585 20c. green 15 70
586 25c. red 15 70
587 30c. brown 65 2·00
588 40c. brown 15 70
589 50c. yellow 35 90
590 75c. purple 35 1·10
591 1e. blue 35 2·10
592 1e.50 grey 70 2·40
593 2e. green 70 6·25

62 Camoens at Ceuta

63 Saving the "Lusiad"

1924. 400th Birth Anniv of Camoens (poet). Value in black.
600 **62** 2c. blue 15 15
601 3c. orange 15 15
602 4c. grey 15 15
603 5c. green 15 15
604 6c. red 15 15
605 **63** 8c. brown 15 15
606 10c. violet 15 15
607 15c. green 15 15
608 16c. purple 20 20
609 20c. orange 35 20
610 – 25c. violet 35 20
611 – 30c. brown 35 20
612 – 32c. green 85 1·10
613 – 40c. blue 30 25
614 – 48c. red 1·30 1·30
615 – 50c. red 1·40 95
616 – 64c. green 1·40 95
617 – 75c. lilac 1·50 95
618 – 80c. brown 1·10 95
619 – 96c. red 1·10 95
620 – 1e. turquoise 1·10 85
621 – 1e.20 brown 5·50 5·00
622 – 1e.50 red 1·30 90
623 – 1e.60 blue 1·30 90
624 – 2e. green 5·50 5·00
625 – 2e.40 green on green 3·75 2·75
626 – 3e. blue on blue 1·60 1·10
627 – 3e.20 black on turquoise 1·60 1·00
628 – 4e.50 black on yellow 4·25 3·00
629 – 10e. brown on pink 9·50 8·50
630 – 20e. violet on mauve 9·50 7·25
DESIGNS—VERT: 25c. to 48c. Luis de Camoens; 50c. to 96c. 1st Edition of "Lusiad"; 20e. Monument to Camoens. HORIZ: 1e. to 2e. Death of Camoens; 2e.40 to 10e. Tomb of Camoens.

65 Branco's House at S. Miguel de Seide

67 Camilo Castelo Branco

1925. Birth Centenary of Camilo Castelo Branco (novelist). Value in black.
631 **65** 2c. orange 20 15
632 3c. green 20 15
633 4c. blue 20 15
634 5c. red 20 15
635 6c. purple 20 15
636 8c. brown 20 15
637 A 10c. blue 20 15
638 **67** 15c. green 20 15
639 A 16c. orange 30 30
640 20c. violet 30 30
641 **67** 25c. red 30 30
642 A 30c. bistre 30 30
643 32c. green 1·10 1·10
644 **67** 40c. black and green 70 70
645 A 48c. red 3·25 3·25
646 B 50c. green 70 70
647 64c. brown 3·25 3·25
648 75c. grey 65 65
649 **67** 80c. brown 65 65
650 B 96c. red 1·50 1·50
651 1e. lilac 1·50 1·50
652 1e.20 green 1·50 1·50
653 C 1e.50 blue on blue 27·00 14·00
654 **67** 1e.60 blue 5·25 4·00
655 C 2e. green on green 6·50 4·50
656 2e.40 red on orange 55·00 33·00
657 3e. red on blue 70·00 43·00
658 3e.20 black on green 33·00 33·00
659 **67** 4e.50 black and red 13·00 4·00
660 C 10e. brown on buff 13·50 4·50
661 D 20e. black on orange 14·50 4·50
DESIGNS—HORIZ: A, Branco's study. VERT: B, Teresa de Albuquerque; C, Mariana and Joao da Cruz; D, Simao de Botelho. Types B/D shows characters from Branco's "Amor de Peredicao".

76 Afonso I, first King of Portugal, 1140

80 Goncalo Mendes da Maia

77 Battle of Aljubarrota

1926. 1st Independence issue. Dated 1926. Centres in black.
671 **76** 2c. orange 20 20
672 – 3c. blue 20 20
673 **76** 4c. green 20 20
674 – 5c. brown 20 20
675 **76** 6c. orange 20 20
676 – 15c. green 20 20
677 **76** 16c. blue 70 70
678 **77** 20c. violet 70 70
679 – 25c. red 75 75
680 **77** 32c. green 95 95
681 – 40c. brown 55 55
682 – 46c. red . . . . 3·50 3·50
683 – 50c. bistre . . . . 3·50 3·50
684 – 64c. green . . . . 4·75 4·75
685 – 75c. brown . . . . 4·75 4·75
686 – 96c. red . . . . 7·25 7·25
687 – 1e. violet . . . . 7·25 7·25
688 **77** 1e.60 blue . . . . 9·75 9·75
689 – 3e. purple . . . . 29·00 29·00
690 – 4e.50 green . . . . 36·00 36·00
691 **77** 10e. red . . . . 60·00 60·00
DESIGNS—VERT: 25, 40, 50, 75c. Philippa de Vilhena arms her sons; 64c., 1e. Don Joao IV, 1640; 96c., 3e., 4e.50, Independence Monument, Lisbon. HORIZ: 3, 5, 15, 46c. Monastery of D. Joao I.

1926. 1st Independence issue surch. Centres in black.
692 2c. on 5c. brown . . . . . . 1·20 1·20
693 2c. on 46c. red . . . . 1·20 1·20
694 2c. on 64c. green . . . . . . 1·60 1·60
695 3c. on 75c. brown . . . . . 1·60 1·60
696 3c. on 96c. red . . . . 2·10 2·10
697 3c. on 1e. violet . . . . . . 1·80 1·80
698 4c. on 1e.60 blue . . . . . . 12·00 12·00
699 4c. on 3e. purple . . . . . . 4·25 4·25
700 6c. on 4e.50 green . . . . . 4·25 4·25
701 6c. on 10e. red . . . . 4·25 4·25

1927. 2nd Independence issue. Dated 1927. Centres in black.
726 **80** 2c. brown 20 15
727 – 3c. blue 20 15
728 **80** 4c. orange 20 15
729 – 5c. brown 20 15
730 – 6c. brown 20 15
731 – 15c. brown 50 40
732 – 16c. blue . . . . 1·10 40
733 **80** 25c. grey . . . . 1·30 1·20
734 – 32c. green . . . . 2·75 1·70
735 – 40c. green 70 55
736 **80** 48c. red . . . . 12·00 10·50
737 – 80c. violet . . . . 8·50 7·25
738 – 96c. red . . . . 15·00 14·00
739 – 1e.60 blue . . . . 16·00 15·00
740 – 4e.50 brown . . . . 24·00 23·00
DESIGNS—HORIZ: 3, 15, 80c. Gulmaraes Castle; 6, 32c. Battle of Montijo. VERT: 5, 16c., 1e.50, Joao das Regras; 40, 96c. Brites de Aimelda; 4e.50, J. P. Ribeiro.

1928. Surch.
742 **56** 4c. on 8c. orange 45 35
743 4c. on 30c. brown 45 35
744 10c. on ¼c. brown 45 20
745 10c. on ½c. black 60 45
746 10c. on 1c. brown 60 45
747 10c. on 4c. green 45 40
748 10c. on 4c. orange 45 40
749 10c. on 5c. brown 45 40
751 15c. on 16c. blue . . . . . 1·10 85
752 15c. on 20c. brown . . . . . 35·00 35·00
753 15c. on 20c. grey 45 35
754 15c. on 24c. blue . . . . . 2·30 1·70
755 15c. on 25c. pink 45 35
756 15c. on 25c. grey 45 35
757 16c. on 32c. green 95 85
758 40c. on 2c. yellow 45 35
760 40c. on 2c. brown 40 35
761 40c. on 3c. blue 45 40
762 40c. on 50c. yellow 40 30
763 40c. on 60c. blue 95 70
764 40c. on 64c. blue 95 85
765 40c. on 75c. pink 95 95
766 40c. on 80c. lilac 70 55
767 40c. on 90c. blue . . . . . 4·50 3·50
768 40c. on 1e. grey 90 90
769 40c. on 1e.10 brown 95 85
770 80c. on 6c. purple 90 75
771 80c. on 6c. brown 90 75
772 80c. on 48c. pink . . . . . 1·30 1·10
773 80c. on 1e.50 lilac . . . . . 2·00 1·30
774 96c. on 1e.20 green . . . . 3·75 2·50
775 96c. on 1e.20 buff . . . . . 3·75 3·00
777 1e.60 on 2e. green . . . . . 38·00 29·00
778 1e.60 on 3e.20 green . . . . 10·50 7·75
779 1e.60 on 20e. blue . . . . . 14·50 10·50

84 Storming of Santarem

1928. 3rd Independence issue. Dated 1928. Centres in black.
780 – 2c. blue 15 15
781 **84** 3c. green 15 15
782 – 4c. red 15 15
783 – 5c. green 15 15
784 – 6c. brown 15 15
785 **84** 15c. grey 75 75
786 – 16c. purple 75 75
787 – 25c. blue 75 75
788 – 32c. green . . . . 4·00 4·00
789 – 40c. brown 80 75
790 – 50c. red . . . . 9·75 6·00
791 **84** 80c. grey . . . . 10·50 7·50
792 – 96c. red . . . . 18·00 16·00
793 – 1e. mauve . . . . 29·00 29·00
794 – 1e.60 blue . . . . 13·50 12·00
795 – 4e.50 yellow . . . . 14·50 14·00
DESIGNS—VERT: 2, 25c., 1e.60, G. Paes; 6, 32, 96c. Joana de Gouveia; 4e.50, Matias de Albuquerque. HORIZ: 4, 16, 50c. Battle of Rolica; 5, 40c., 1e. Battle of Atoleiros.

1929. Optd **Revalidado**.
805 **56** 10c. red 45 35
806 15c. black 40 35
807 40c. brown 70 55
808 40c. green 60 45
810 96c. red . . . . 6·00 4·75
811 1e.60 blue . . . . 23·00 18·00

1929. Telegraph stamp surch **CORREIO 1$60** and bars.
812 – 1e.60 on 5c. brown . . . . 15·00 11·00

88 Camoens' Poem "Lusiad"
89 St. Anthony's Birthplace

1931.
835 **88** 4c. brown 25 15
836 5c. brown 25 15
837 6c. grey 25 15
838 10c. mauve 25 20
839 15c. black 25 20
840 16c. blue . . . . 1·30 70
841 25c. green . . . . 3·25 40
841a 25c. blue . . . . 3·75 40
841b 30c. green . . . . 2·00 40
842 40c. red . . . . 6·75 15
843 48c. brown . . . . 1·30 1·00
844 50c. brown 30 15
845 75c. red . . . . 5·25 1·20
846 80c. green 40 20
846a 95c. red . . . . 17·00 7·00
847 1e. purple . . . . 32·00 15
848 1e.20 green . . . . 2·30 1·00
849 1e.25 blue . . . . 2·00 20
849a 1e.60 blue . . . . 33·00 4·50
849b 1e.75 blue 70 30
850 2e. mauve 55 30
851 4e.50 orange . . . . . . 1·60 25
852 5e. green . . . . 1·60 25

1931. 700th Death Anniv of St. Anthony.
853 **89** 15c. purple 70 30
854 – 25c. myrtle and green . . . 1·10 30
855 – 40c. brown and buff . . . 40 30
856 – 75c. pink . . . . 23·00 14·50
857 – 1e.25 grey and blue . . . . 55·00 32·00
858 – 4e.50 purple and mauve . . 27·00 3·75
DESIGNS—VERT: 25c. Saint's baptismal font; 40c. Lisbon Cathedral; 75c. St. Anthony; 1e.25, Santa Cruz Cathedral, Coimbra. HORIZ: 4e.50, Saint's tomb, Padua.

90 Don Nuno Alvares Pereira

94 President Carmona

1931. 5th Death Centenary of Pereira.
859 **90** 15c. black . . . . 1·10 1·10
860 25c. green and black . . . 11·00 1·20
861 40c. orange . . . . 2·75 55
862 75c. red . . . . 22·00 22·00
863 1e.25 light blue and blue . . 27·00 22·00
864 4e.50 green and brown . . £130 55·00

1933. Pereira issue of 1931 surch.
865 **90** 15c. on 40c. orange 70 35
866 40c. on 15c. black . . . . 3·75 2·50
867 40c. on 25c. green & black . 1·10 90
868 40c. on 75c. red . . . . . 8·50 4·25
869 40c. on 1e.25 light blue and blue . . . . 8·50 4·25
870 40c. on 4e.50 green and brown . . . . 8·50 4·25

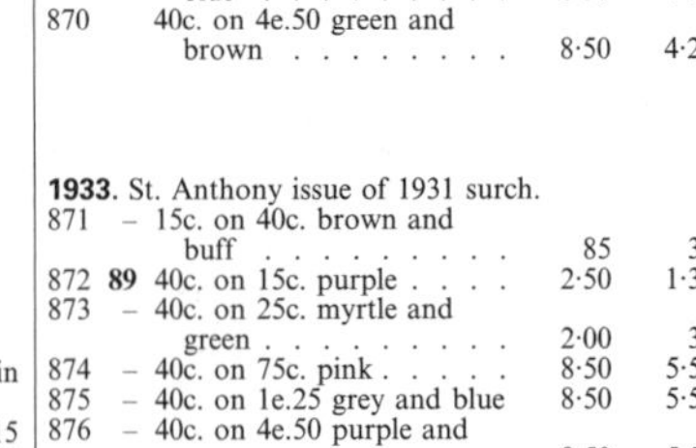

1933. St. Anthony issue of 1931 surch.
871 – 15c. on 40c. brown and buff 85 35
872 **89** 40c. on 15c. purple . . . . 2·50 1·30
873 – 40c. on 25c. myrtle and green . . . . 2·00 35
874 – 40c. on 75c. pink . . . . . 8·50 5·50
875 – 40c. on 1e.25 grey and blue 8·50 5·50
876 – 40c. on 4e.50 purple and mauve . . . . 8·50 5·50

1934.
877 **94** 40c. violet . . . . 19·00 35

95

96 Queen Maria

1934. Colonial Exhibition.
878 **95** 25c. brown . . . . 3·25 1·70
879 40c. red . . . . 20·00 40
880 1e.60 blue . . . . 31·00 13·50

1935. 1st Portuguese Philatelic Exhibition.
881 **96** 40c. red . . . . 1·50 30

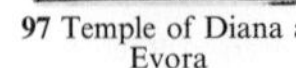
97 Temple of Diana at Evora

98 Prince Henry the Navigator

99 "All for the Nation"

100 Coimbra Cathedral

1935.
882 **97** 4c. black 45 20
883 5c. blue 55 20
884 6c. brown 80 35
885 **98** 10c. green . . . . 7·75 20
886 15c. red 35 20
887 **99** 25c. blue . . . . 6·25 45
888 40c. brown . . . . 2·10 10
889 1e. red . . . . 9·75 50
890 **100** 1e.75 blue . . . . 80·00 1·30
890a **99** 10e. grey . . . . 23·00 2·50
890b 20e. blue . . . . 31·00 2·20

102 Shield and Propeller

103 Symbol of Medicine

1937. Air.
891 **102** 1e.50 blue 45 30
892 1e.75 red 75 35
893 2e.50 red 90 35
893a 3e. blue . . . . 14·50 12·50
893b 4e. green . . . . 19·00 19·00
894 5e. red . . . . 1·80 1·30
895 10e. purple . . . . 3·25 1·40
895a 15e. orange . . . . . . 12·50 7·50
896 20e. brown . . . . 8·75 2·75
896a 50e. purple . . . . . . £170 80·00

1937. Centenary of Medical and Surgical Colleges at Lisbon and Oporto.
897 **103** 25c. blue . . . . 11·00 95

104 Gil Vicente

106 Grapes

107 Cross of Avis

1937. 400th Death Anniv of Gil Vicente (poet).
898 **104** 40c. brown . . . . 20·00 20
899 1e. red . . . . 2·75 20

1938. Wine and Raisin Congress.
900 **106** 15c. violet . . . . 1·40 55
901 25c. brown . . . . 3·25 1·80
902 40c. mauve . . . . 10·50 35
903 1e.75 blue . . . . 31·00 27·00

1940. Portuguese Legion.
904 **107** 5c. buff 35 10
905 10c. violet 35 10
906 15c. blue 35 10
907 25c. brown . . . . 23·00 1·20
908 40c. green . . . . 40·00 40
909 80c. green . . . . 2·50 55
910 1e. red . . . . 60·00 3·75
911 1e.75 blue . . . . 8·50 2·75
MS911a 155 × 170 mm. Nos. 904/11 (sold at 5e.50) £550 £850

109 Portuguese World Exhibition

113 Sir Rowland Hill

1940. Portuguese Centenaries.
912 **109** 10c. purple 25 20
913 – 15c. blue 25 25
914 – 25c. green . . . . 1·40 25
915 – 35c. green . . . . 1·20 35
916 – 40c. brown . . . . 2·75 20
917 **109** 80c. purple . . . . 5·50 35
918 – 1e. red . . . . 12·50 1·60
919 – 1e.75 blue . . . . 7·25 2·75
MS919a 160 × 229 mm. Nos. 912/9 (sold at 10e.) £275 £350
DESIGNS—VERT: 15, 35c. Statue of King Joao IV; 25c., 1e. Monument of Discoveries, Belem; 40c., 1e.75, King Afonso Henriques.

1940. Centenary of First Adhesive Postage Stamps.
920 **113** 15c. purple 30 10
921 25c. red 30 10
922 35c. green 35 15
923 40c. purple 50 15
924 50c. green . . . . 19·00 4·50
925 80c. blue . . . . 2·30 1·20
926 1e. red . . . . 22·00 3·75
927 1e.75 blue . . . . 7·00 3·75
MS928 160 × 152 mm. Nos. 920/7 (sold at 10e.) £110 £200

114 Fish-woman of Nazare

115 Caravel

1941. Costumes.
932 **114** 4c. green 20 20
933 – 5c. brown 20 20
934 – 10c. purple . . . . 3·75 1·30
935 – 15c. green 20 20
936 – 25c. purple . . . . 2·50 75
937 – 40c. green 20 20
938 – 80c. blue . . . . 3·75 2·40
939 – 1e. red . . . . 10·50 1·80
940 – 1e.75 blue . . . . 11·50 5·00
941 – 2e. orange . . . . 44·00 25·00
MS941a 163 × 146 mm. Nos. 932/41 (sold at 10e.) £200 £180
DESIGNS: 5c. Woman from Coimbra; 10c. Vinegrower of Saloio; 15c. Fish-woman of Lisbon; 25c. Woman of Olhao; 40c. Woman of Aveiro; 80c. Shepherdess of Madeira; 1e. Spinner of Viana do Castelo; 1e.75, Horsebreeder of Ribatejo; 2e. Reaper of Alentejo.

1943.
942 **115** 5c. black 10 10
943 10c. brown 10 10
944 15c. grey 10 10
945 20c. violet 10 10
946 30c. purple 10 10
947 35c. green 20 10
948 50c. purple 20 10
948a 80c. green . . . . 3·25 45
949 1e. red . . . . 7·75 10
949a 1e. lilac . . . . 2·30 20
949b 1e.20 red . . . . 3·25 25
949c 1e.50 green . . . . . . 37·00 40

950 1e.75 blue 24·00 10
950a 1e.80 orange 34·00 3·25
951 2e. brown 1·80 10
951a 2e. blue 4·75 50
952 2e.50 red 2·75 10
953 3e.50 blue 11·50 50
953a 4e. orange 50·00 2·75
954 5e. red 1·40 25
954a 6e. green 95·00 4·00
954b 7e.50 green 29·00 3·75
955 10e. grey 3·25 30
956 15e. green 29·00 1·10
957 20e. green 90·00 65
958 50e. red £250 1·10

116 Labourer

117 Mounted Postal Courier

1943. 1st Agricultural Science Congress.
959 **116** 10c. blue 85 30
960 50c. red 1·30 35

1944. 3rd National Philatelic Exhibition, Lisbon.
961 **117** 10c. brown 30 10
962 50c. violet 30 10
963 1e. red 3·75 70
964 1e.75 blue 3·75 2·30
MS964a 82 × 121 mm. Nos. 961/4 (sold at 7e.50) 49·00 £250

118 Felix Avellar Brotero

120 Vasco da Gama

1944. Birth Bicentenary of Avellar Brotero (botanist).
965 **118** 10c. brown 25 15
966 – 50c. green 1·40 15
967 – 1e. red 8·00 1·70
968 **118** 1e.75 blue 7·00 2·75
MS968a 144 × 195 mm. Nos. 965/8 (sold at 7e.50) 55·00 £110
DESIGN: 50c., 1e. Brotero's statue, Coimbra.

1945. Portuguese Navigators.
969 – 10c. brown 20 10
970 – 30c. orange 20 10
971 – 35c. green 35 20
972 **120** 50c. green 1·30 25
973 – 1e. red 3·25 70
974 – 1e.75 blue 4·00 2·20
975 – 2e. black 5·00 2·50
976 – 3e.50 red 9·00 4·50
MS976a 167 × 173 mm. Nos. 969/76 (sold at 15e.) 39·00 £140
PORTRAITS: 10c. Gil Eanes; 30c. Joao Goncalves Zarco; 35c. Bartolomeu Dias; 1e. Pedro Alvares Cabral; 1e.75, Fernao de Magalhaes (Magellan); 2e. Frey Goncalo Velho; 3e.50, Diogo Cao.

121 President Carmona

122

1945.
977 **121** 10c. violet 25 20
978 30c. brown 25 20
979 35c. green 30 20
980 50c. green 40 20
981 1e. red 10·50 1·40
982 1e.75 blue 8·50 4·25
983 2e. purple 47·00 5·50
984 3e.50 grey 34·00 8·00
MS984a 136 × 98 mm. Nos. 977/84 (sold at 15e.) £200 £250

1945. Naval School Centenary.
985 **122** 10c. brown 15 10
986 50c. green 20 15
987 1e. red 3·25 80
988 1e.75 blue 3·50 2·75
MS988a 115 × 134 mm. Nos. 985/8 (sold at 7e.50) 42·00 £140

123 Almourol Castle

1946. Portuguese Castles.
989 – 10c. purple 10 10
990 – 30c. brown 10 10
991 – 35c. green 15 10
992 – 50c. grey 35 10
993 **123** 1e. red 23·00 1·10
994 – 1e.75 blue 13·00 2·50
995 – 2e. green 42·00 4·75
996 – 3e.50 brown 19·00 6·00
MS996a 135 × 102 mm. 1e.75 grey-blue on buff (block of 4) (sold at 12e.50) £170 £325
DESIGNS: Castles at Silves (10c.); Leiria (30c.); Feira (35c.); Guimaraes (50c.); Lisbon (1e.75); Braganza (2e.) and Ourem (3e.50).

124 "Decree Founding National Bank"

125 Madonna and Child

1946. Centenary of Bank of Portugal.
997 **124** 50c. blue 55 30
MS997a 156 × 144 mm. No. 997 (block of four) (sold at 7e.50) £130 £200

1946. Tercentenary of Proclamation of St. Mary of Castile as Patron Saint of Portugal.
998 **125** 30c. grey 20 15
999 50c. green 20 15
1000 1e. red 2·30 1·10
1001 1e.75 blue 4·50 2·40
MS1001a 108 × 158 mm. Nos. 998/1001 on grey paper (sold at 7e.50) 65·00 £140

126 Caramulo Shepherdess

127 Surrender of the Keys of Lisbon

1947. Regional Costumes.
1002 **126** 10c. mauve 20 15
1003 – 30c. red 20 15
1004 – 35c. green 20 15
1005 – 50c. brown 35 15
1006 – 1e. red 13·00 55
1007 – 1e.75 blue 13·50 4·25
1008 – 2e. blue 45·00 5·00
1009 – 3e.50 green 33·00 7·75
MS1009a 135 × 98 mm. Nos. 1002/9 (sold at 15e.) £250 £275
COSTUMES. 30c. Malpique timbrel player; 35c. Monsanto flautist; 50c. Woman of Avintes; 1e. Maia field labourer; 1e.75, Woman of Algarve; 2e. Miranda do Douro bastonet player; 3e.50, Woman of the Azores.

1947. 800th Anniv of Recapture of Lisbon from the Moors.
1010 **127** 5c. green 15 10
1011 20c. red 15 10
1012 50c. violet 15 15
1013 1e.75 blue 5·00 5·25
1014 2e.50 brown 8·00 6·75
1015 3e.50 black 14·00 11·00

128 St. Joao de Brito

1948. Birth Tercentenary of St. Joao de Brito.
1016 **128** 30c. green 15 10
1017 – 50c. brown 15 10
1018 **128** 1e. red 7·75 1·80
1019 – 1e.75 blue 9·00 3·00
DESIGN: 50c., 1e.75, St. Joao de Brito (different).

130 "Architecture and Engineering"

131 King Joao I

1948. Exhibition of Public Works and National Congress of Engineering and Architecture.
1020 **130** 50c. purple 55 30

1949. Portraits.
1021 **131** 10c. violet and buff 20 10
1022 – 30c. green and buff 20 10
1023 – 35c. green and olive 40 10
1024 – 50c. blue and light blue 1·00 10
1025 – 1e. lake and red 1·00 10
1026 – 1e.75 black and grey 20·00 16·00
1027 – 2e. blue and light blue 11·00 2·20
1028 – 3e.50 chocolate & brown 40·00 19·00
MS1028a 136 × 98 mm. Nos.1021/8 (sold for 15e.) 70·00 85·00
PORTRAITS: 30c. Queen Philippa; 35c. Prince Fernando; 50c. Prince Henry the Navigator; 1e. Nun Alvares; 1e.75, Joao da Regras; 2e. Fernao Lopes; 3e.50, Afonso Domingues.

132 Statue of Angel

133 Hands and Letter

1949. 16th Congress of the History of Art.
1029 **132** 1e. red 8·75 15
1030 5e. brown 1·90 30

1949. 75th Anniv of U.P.U.
1031 **133** 1e. lilac 30 10
1032 2e. blue 75 25
1033 2e.50 green 4·25 1·30
1034 4e. brown 11·50 3·75

134 Our Lady of Fatima

135 Saint and Invalid

1950. Holy Year.
1035 **134** 50c. green 40 20
1036 1e. brown 2·30 25
1037 2e. blue 5·00 1·60
1038 5e. lilac 70·00 30·00

1950. 400th Death Anniv of San Juan de Dios.
1039 **135** 20c. violet 20 10
1040 50c. red 30 25
1041 1e. green 3·50 45
1042 1e.50 orange 11·50 3·25
1043 2e. blue 9·75 2·40
1044 4e. brown 40·00 9·00

136 G. Junqueiro

137 Fisherman with Meagre

1951. Birth Centenary of Junqueiro (poet).
1045 **136** 50c. brown 3·75 40
1046 1e. blue 1·10 30

1951. Fisheries Congress.
1047 **137** 50c. green on buff 3·00 50
1048 1e. purple on buff 80 15

138 Dove and Olive Branch

139 15th century Colonists

1951. Termination of Holy Year.
1049 **138** 20c. brown and buff 20 20
1050 90c. green and yellow 6·25 1·80
1051 – 1e. purple and pink 6·25 25
1052 – 2e.30 green and blue 9·00 2·30
PORTRAIT: 1e., 2e.30, Pope Pius XII.

1951. 500th Anniv of Colonization of Terceira, Azores.
1053 **139** 50c. blue on flesh 1·80 45
1054 1e. brown on buff 1·10 40

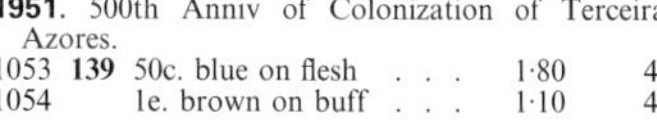

140 Revolutionaries

1951. 25th Anniv of National Revolution.
1055 **140** 1e. brown 6·50 20
1056 2e.30 blue 4·50 1·50

141 Coach of King Joao VI

1952. National Coach Museum.
1057 – 10c. purple 10 10
1058 **141** 20c. green 10 10
1059 – 50c. green 45 10
1060 – 90c. green 2·20 1·60
1061 – 1e. orange 90 10
1062 – 1e.40 pink 5·25 4·50
1063 **141** 1e.50 brown 5·00 2·50
1064 – 2e.30 blue 2·75 2·10
DESIGNS (coaches of): 10, 90c. King Felippe II; 50c., 1e.40, Papal Nuncio to Joao V; 1e., 2e.30, King Jose.

142 "N.A.T.O."

143 Hockey Players

1952. 3rd Anniv of N.A.T.O.
1065 **142** 1e. green and deep green 7·75 20
1066 3e.50 grey and blue £200 23·00

1952. 8th World Roller-skating Hockey Championship.
1067 **143** 1e. black and blue 2·75 10
1068 3e.50 black and brown 4·50 2·50

144 Teixeira

145 Marshal Carmona Bridge

1952. Birth Centenary of Prof. Gomes Teixeira (mathematician).
1069 **144** 1e. mauve and pink 70 10
1070 2e.30 deep blue and blue 6·00 4·50

1952. Centenary of Ministry of Public Works.
1071 **145** 1e. brown on stone 40 20
1072 – 1e.40 lilac on stone 9·75 5·50
1073 – 2e. green on stone 5·00 2·50
1074 – 3e.50 blue on stone 9·50 4·25
DESIGNS: 1e.40, 28th May Stadium, Braga; 2e. Coimbra University; 3e.50, Salazar Barrage.

146 St. Francis Xavier

147 Medieval Knight

1952. 4th Death Centenary of St. Francis Xavier.
1075 **146** 1e. blue 40 20
1076 2e. purple 1·50 40
1077 3e.50 blue 18·00 12·00
1078 5e. lilac 33·00 4·25

1953.
1079 **147** 5c. green on yellow 15 10
1080 10c. grey on pink 15 10
1081 20c. orange on yellow 15 10
1081a 30c. purple on buff 20 10
1082 50c. black 15 10
1083 90c. green on yellow 13·50 65
1084 1e. brown on pink 30 10
1085 1e.40 red 12·50 1·30
1086 1e.50 red on yellow 40 10
1087 2e. black 40 10
1088 2e.30 blue 15·00 90
1089 2e.50 black on pink 90 15
1089a 2e.50 green on yellow 90 15
1090 5e. purple on yellow 90 15
1091 10e. blue on yellow 4·00 25

1092 20e. brown on yellow 14·00 30
1093 50e. lilac 4·00 50

148 St. Martin of Dume
149 G. Gomes Fernandes

1953. 14th Centenary of Landing of St. Martin of Dume on Iberian Peninsula.
1094 **148** 1e. black and grey 95 10
1095 3e.50 brown and yellow 10·50 5·75

1953. Birth Centenary of Fernandes (fire-brigade chief).
1096 **149** 1e. purple and cream 55 15
1097 2e.30 blue and cream 9·00 6·00

150 Club Emblems, 1903 and 1953
151 Princess St. Joan

1953. 50th Anniv of Portuguese Automobile Club.
1098 **150** 1e. deep green and green 55 20
1099 3e.50 brown and buff 11·00 5·75

1953. 5th Centenary of Birth of Princess St. Joan
1100 **151** 1e. black and green 2·10 15
1101 3e.50 deep blue and blue 10·50 6·75

152 Queen Maria II

1953. Centenary of First Portuguese Stamps. Bottom panel in gold.
1102 **152** 50c. red 15 10
1103 1e. brown 15 10
1104 1e.40 purple 1·40 70
1105 2e.30 blue 3·50 2·10
1106 3e.50 blue 3·50 2·20
1107 4e.50 green 2·20 1·60
1108 5e. green 5·50 1·60
1109 20e. violet 49·00 8·75

153
154

1954. 150th Anniv of Trade Secretariat.
1110 **153** 1e. blue and light blue 50 15
1111 1e.50 brown and buff 2·50 75

1954. People's Education Plan.
1112 **154** 50c. blue and light blue 20 10
1113 1e. red and pink 20 10
1114 2e. deep green and green 23·00 1·40
1115 2e.50 brown and light brown 20·00 1·30

155 Cadet and College Banner
156 Father Manuel da Nobrega

1954. 150th Anniv of Military College.
1116 **155** 1e. brown and green 1·20 15
1117 3e.50 blue and green 5·25 3·00

1954. 400th Anniv of Sao Paulo.
1118 **156** 1e. brown 40 20
1119 2e.30 blue 42·00 25·00
1120 3e.50 green 11·50 3·25
1121 5e. green 33·00 5·00

157 King Sancho I, 1154–1211
158 Telegraph Poles

1955. Portuguese Kings.
1122 – 10c. purple 20 15
1123 **157** 20c. green 20 15
1124 – 50c. blue 30 15
1125 – 90c. green 2·50 1·40
1126 – 1e. brown 1·10 20
1127 – 1e.40 red 6·50 3·75
1128 – 1e.50 green 3·00 1·20
1129 – 2e. red 8·00 3·25
1130 – 2e.30 blue 7·25 2·75
KINGS: 10c. Afonso I; 50c. Afonso II; 90c. Sancho II; 1e. Afonso III; 1e.40, Diniz; 1e.50, Afonso IV; 2e. Pedro I; 2e.30, Fernando.

1955. Centenary of Electric Telegraph System in Portugal.
1131 **158** 1e. red and brown 40 15
1132 2e.30 blue and green 18·00 4·00
1133 3e.50 green and yellow 17·00 3·50

159 A. J. Ferreira da Silva
160 Steam Locomotive, 1856

1956. Birth Centenary of Ferreira da Silva (teacher).
1134 **159** 1e. deep blue, blue and azure 25 15
1135 2e.30 deep green, emerald and green 11·00 5·25

1956. Centenary of Portuguese Railways.
1136 **160** 1e. olive and green 40 10
1137 – 1e.50 blue and green 2·75 40
1138 – 2e. brown and bistre 24·00 1·40
1139 **160** 2e.50 brown and deep brown 33·00 2·40
DESIGN: 1e.50, 2e. Class 2500 electric locomotive, 1956.

161 Madonna and Child
162 Almeida Garrett (after Barata Feyo)

1956. Mothers' Day.
1140 **161** 1e. sage and green 25 10
1141 1e.50 lt brown and brown 85 30

1957. Almeida Garrett (writer) Commem.
1142 **162** 1e. brown 40 15
1143 2e.30 lilac 32·00 12·00
1144 3e.50 green 7·25 1·30
1145 5e. red 55·00 11·00

163 Cesario Verde
164 Exhibition Emblem

1957. Cesario Verde (poet) Commem.
1146 **163** 1e. brown, buff and green 40 10
1147 3e.30 black, olive and green 1·50 1·20

1958. Brussels International Exhibition
1148 **164** 1e. multicoloured 40 10
1149 3e.30 multicoloured 1·80 1·40

165 St. Elizabeth
166 Institute of Tropical Medicine, Lisbon

1958. St. Elizabeth and St. Teotonio Commem.
1150 **165** 1e. red and cream 25 10
1151 – 2e. green and cream 70 40
1152 **165** 2e.50 violet and cream 5·75 90
1153 – 5e. brown and cream 7·25 1·10
PORTRAIT: 2, 5e. St. Teotonio.

1958. 6th Int Congress of Tropical Medicine.
1154 **166** 1e. green and grey 2·75 20
1155 2e.50 blue and grey 8·25 1·50

167 Liner
168 Queen Leonora

1958. 2nd National Merchant Navy Congress.
1156 **167** 1e. brown, ochre & sepia 7·00 20
1157 4e.50 violet, lilac and blue 5·25 2·40

1958. 500th Birth Anniv of Queen Leonora. Frames and ornaments in bistre, inscriptions and value tablet in black.
1158 **168** 1e. blue and brown 20 10
1159 1e.50 turquoise and blue 4·25 75
1160 2e.30 blue and green 4·00 1·30
1161 4e.10 blue and grey 4·00 1·70

169 Arms of Aveiro
170

1959. Millenary of Aveiro.
1162 **169** 1e. multicoloured 1·90 20
1163 5e. multicoloured 14·50 2·00

1960. 10th Anniv of N.A.T.O.
1164 **170** 1e. black and lilac 35 15
1165 3e.50 green and grey 3·50 1·80

171 "Doorway to Peace"
172 Glider

1960. World Refugee Year. Symbol in black.
1166 **171** 20c. yellow, lemon & brn 15 10
1167 1e. yellow, green and blue 55 10
1168 1e.80 yellow and green 1·20 1·00

1960. 50th Anniv of Portuguese Aero Club. Multicoloured.
1169 1e. Type **172** 20 10
1170 1e.50 Light monoplane 70 25
1171 2e. Airplane and parachutes 1·40 65
1172 2e.50 Model glider 2·75 1·30

173 Padre Cruz (after M. Barata)
174 University Seal

1960. Death Centenary of Padre Cruz.
1173 **173** 1e. brown 25 15
1174 4e.30 blue 9·25 6·75

1960. 400th Anniv of Evora University.
1175 **174** 50c. blue 20 10
1176 1e. brown and yellow 40 10
1177 1e.40 purple 3·00 1·60

175 Prince Henry's Arms
175a Conference Emblem

1960. 5th Death Centenary of Prince Henry the Navigator. Multicoloured.
1178 1e. Type **175** 35 10
1179 2e.50 Caravel 3·75 30
1180 3e.50 Prince Henry the Navigator 5·25 1·50
1181 5e. Motto 8·75 85
1182 8e. Barketta 2·10 75
1183 10e. Map showing Sagres 15·00 2·00

1960. Europa.
1184 **175a** 1e. light blue and blue 20 15
1185 3e.50 red and lake 3·75 2·00

176 Emblems of Prince Henry and Lisbon

1960. 5th National Philatelic Exhibition, Lisbon.
1186 **176** 1e. blue, black and green 40 15
1187 3e.30 blue, black and light blue 5·75 3·75

177 Portuguese Flag
178 King Pedro V

1960. 50th Anniv of Republic.
1188 **177** 1e. multicoloured 30 10

1961. Cent of Lisbon University Faculty of Letters.
1189 **178** 1e. green and brown 30 10
1190 6e.50 brown and blue 3·75 95

179 Arms of Setubal
180

1961. Centenary of Setubal City.
1191 **179** 1e. multicoloured 35 10
1192 4e.30 multicoloured 20·00 6·00

1961. Europa.
1193 **180** 1e. light blue, blue and deep blue 10 10
1194 1e.50 light green, green and deep green 1·50 1·40
1195 3e.50 pink, red and lake 1·70 1·70

181 Tomar Gateway
182 National Guardsman

1961. 800th Anniv of Tomar.
1196 – 1e. multicoloured 15 10
1197 **181** 3e.50 multicoloured 1·50 1·20
DESIGN: 1e. As Type **181** but without ornamental background.

1962. 50th Anniv of National Republican Guard.
1198 **182** 1e. multicoloured 15 10
1199 2e. multicoloured 2·20 85
1200 2e.50 multicoloured 2·20 65

183 St. Gabriel (Patron Saint of Telecommunications)

184 Scout Badge and Tents

1962. St. Gabriel Commemoration.

1201	183	1e. brown, green and olive	75	10
1202		3e.50 green, brown & ol	55	45

1962. 18th International Scout Conference (1961).

1203	184	20c. multicoloured	10	10
1204		50c. multicoloured	20	10
1205		1e. multicoloured	70	10
1206		2e.50 multicoloured	4·50	55
1207		3e.50 mulitcoloured	1·00	55
1208		6e.50 multicoloured	1·30	90

185 Children with Ball

186 Europa "Honeycomb"

1962. 10th International Paediatrics Congress, Lisbon. Centres in black.

1209	–	50c. yellow and green	15	10
1210	–	1e. yellow and grey	1·00	15
1211	185	2e.80 yellow and brown	2·50	1·20
1212	–	3e.50 yellow and purple	5·50	2·00

DESIGNS: 50c. Children with book; 1e. Inoculating child; 3e.50, Weighing baby.

1962. Europa. "EUROPA" in gold.

1213	186	1e. ultramarine, light blue and blue	20	10
1214		1e.50 deep green, light green and green	1·40	75
1215		3e.50 purple, pink and claret	1·80	1·60

187 St. Zenon (the Courier)

188 Benfica Emblem and European Cup

1962. Stamp Day. Saint in yellow and pink.

1216	187	1e. black and purple	15	10
1217		2e. black and green	1·10	75
1218		2e.80 black and bistre	2·00	1·90

1963. Benfica Club's Double Victory in European Football Cup Championship (1961–62).

1219	188	1e. multicoloured	85	10
1220		4e.30 multicoloured	1·30	1·40

189 Campaign Emblem

1963. Freedom from Hunger.

1221	189	1e. multicoloured	10	10
1222		3e.30 multicoloured	1·50	1·10
1223		3e.50 multicoloured	1·40	1·10

190 Mail Coach

191 St. Vincent de Paul

1963. Centenary of Paris Postal Conference.

1224	190	1e. blue, light blue and grey	10	10
1225		1e.50 multicoloured	2·20	55
1226		5e. brown, lilac & lt brown	70	40

1963. 300th Death Anniv of St. Vincent de Paul. Inscr in gold.

1227	191	20c. ultramarine and blue	10	10
1228		1e. blue and grey	40	10
1229		2e.80 black and green	4·75	1·90
1230		5e. grey and mauve	3·75	1·40

192 Medieval Knight

1963. 800th Anniv of Military Order of Avis.

1231	192	1e. multicoloured	15	10
1232		1e.50 multicoloured	60	25
1233		2e.50 mulitcoloured	1·50	1·00

193 Europa "Dove"

1963. Europa.

1234	193	1e. grey, blue and black	30	10
1235		2e.50 grey, green & black	2·75	1·30
1236		3e.50 grey, red and black	4·75	2·40

194 Supersonic Flight

195 Pharmacist's Jar

1963. 10th Anniv of T.A.P. Airline.

1237	194	1e. blue and deep blue	15	10
1238		2e.50 light green & green	1·30	65
1239		3e.50 orange and red	1·80	1·20

1964. 400th Anniv of Publication of "Coloquios dos Simples" (Dissertation on Indian herbs and drugs) by Dr. G. d'Orta.

1240	195	50c. brown, black & bis	35	10
1241		1e. purple, black and red	35	15
1242		4e.30 blue, black & grey	4·75	4·00

196 Bank Emblem

197 Sameiro Shrine (Braga)

1964. Centenary of National Overseas Bank.

1243	196	1e. yellow, green and blue	10	10
1244		2e.50 yellow, olive & grn	2·75	1·10
1245		3e.50 yellow, green & brn	2·10	1·20

1964. Centenary of Sameiro Shrine.

1246	197	1e. yellow, brown and red	15	10
1247		2e. yellow, light brown and brown	1·90	85
1248		5e. yellow, green and blue	2·40	1·10

198 Europa "Flower"

199 Sun and Globe

1964. Europa.

1249	198	1e. deep blue, light blue and blue	45	10
1250		3e.50 brown, light brown and purple	4·00	1·20
1251		4e.30 deep green, light green and green	5·25	3·50

1964. International Quiet Sun Years.

1252	199	1e. mulitcoloured	25	10
1253		8e. multicoloured	1·50	1·20

200 Olympic "Rings"

201 E. Coelho (founder)

1964. Olympic Games, Tokyo.

1254	200	20c. multicoloured	15	10
1255		1e. multicoloured	20	20
1256		1e.50 multicoloured	1·80	1·10
1257		6e.50 multicoloured	3·00	2·00

1964. Centenary of "Diario de Noticias" (newspaper).

1258	201	1e. multicoloured	55	15
1259		5e. mutlicoloured	7·50	1·10

202 Traffic Signals

203 Dom Fernando (second Duke of Braganza)

1965. 1st National Traffic Congress Lisbon.

1260	202	1e. yellow, red and green	20	10
1261		3e.30 green, red & yellow	6·50	3·75
1262		3e.50 red, yellow & green	4·00	1·50

1965. 500th Anniv of Braganza.

1263	203	1e. red and black	20	15
1264		10e. green and black	2·75	90

204 Angel and Gateway

205 I.T.U. Emblem

1965. 900th Anniv of Capture of Coimbra from the Moors.

1265	204	1e. multicoloured	10	10
1266		2e.50 multicoloured	2·20	1·50
1267		5e. multicoloured	2·30	2·00

1965. Centenary of I.T.U.

1268	205	1e. green and brown	15	10
1269		3e.50 purple and green	1·80	1·40
1270		6e.50 blue and green	1·50	1·20

206 C. Gulbenkian

207 Red Cross Emblem

1965. 10th Death Anniv of Calouste Gulbenkian (oil industry pioneer and philanthropist).

1271	206	1e. multicoloured	65	10
1272		8e. multicoloured	60	55

1965. Centenary of Portuguese Red Cross.

1273	207	1e. red, green and black	20	10
1274		4e. red, green and black	2·75	1·30
1275		4e.30 red, light red & black	13·50	8·50

208 Europa "Sprig"

209 North American F-86 Sabre Jet Fighter

1965. Europa.

1276	208	1e. lt blue, black and blue	25	10
1277		3e.50 flesh, brown & red	6·25	1·50
1278		4e.30 light green, black and green	16·00	7·50

1965. 50th Anniv of Portuguese Air Force.

1279	209	1e. red, green and olive	20	10
1280		2e. red, green and brown	1·50	75
1281		5e. red, green and blue	2·75	1·70

210

211 Monogram of Christ

1965. 500th Birth Anniv of Gil Vicente (poet and dramatist). Designs depicting characters from Vicente's poems.

1282	210	20c. multicoloured	15	10
1283	–	1e. multicoloured	40	15
1284	–	2e.50 multicoloured	3·25	60
1285	–	6e.50 multicoloured	1·20	75

1966. International Committee for the Defence of Christian Civilisation Congress, Lisbon.

1286	211	1e. violet, gold and bistre	30	10
1287		3e.30 black, gold & pur	6·75	4·00
1288		5e. black, gold and red	4·25	1·30

212 Emblems of Agriculture, Construction and Industry

213 Giraldo the "Fearless"

1966. 40th Anniv of National Revolution.

1289	212	1e. black, blue and grey	20	10
1290		3e.50 brown, light brown and bistre	3·00	1·60
1291		4e. purple, red and pink	3·00	1·10

1966. 800th Anniv of Reconquest of Evora.

1292	213	1e. multicoloured	35	10
1293		8e. multicoloured	1·20	75

214 Salazar Bridge

215 Europa "Ship"

1966. Inauguration of Salazar Bridge, Lisbon.

1294	214	1e. red and gold	20	10
1295		2e.50 blue and gold	1·40	75
1296	–	2e.80 blue and silver	2·20	1·60
1297	–	4e.30 green and silver	2·50	1·80

DESIGN—VERT: 2e.80, 4e.30, Salazar Bridge (different view).

1966. Europa.

1298	215	1e. multicoloured	30	10
1299		3e.50 multicoloured	11·00	2·00
1300		4e.50 multicoloured	11·50	3·25

216 C. Pestana (bacteriologist)

217 Bocage

1966. Portuguese Scientists. Portraits in brown and bistre; background colours given.

1301	216	20c. green	10	10
1302	–	50c. orange	10	10
1303	–	1e. yellow	20	10
1304	–	1e.50 brown	40	10
1305	–	2e. brown	1·90	20
1306	–	2e.50 green	2·10	55
1307	–	2e.80 orange	2·40	1·80
1308	–	4e.30 blue	4·00	3·00

SCIENTISTS: 50c. E. Moniz (neurologist); 1e. E. A. P. Coutinho (botanist); 1e.50, J. C. da Serra (botanist); 2e. R. Jorge (hygienist and anthropologist); 2e.50, J. L. de Vasconcelos (ethnologist); 2e.80, M. Lemos (medical historian); 4e.30, J. A. Serrano (anatomist).

1966. Birth Bicentenary (1965) of Manuel M. B. du Bocage (poet).

1309	217	1e. black, green and bistre	10	10
1310		2e. black, green & brown	95	45
1311		6e. black, green and grey	1·50	90

218 Cogwheels **219** Adoration of the Virgin

1967. Europa.
1312 **218** 1e. blue, black & lt blue . . . 30 10
1313 3e.50 brown, black and orange . . . . 7·75 1·30
1314 4e.30 green, black and light green . . . . . 12·50 2·50

1967. 50th Anniv of Fatima Apparitions. Mult.
1315 1e. Type **219** 10 10
1316 2e.80 Fatima Church . . . 60 55
1317 3e.50 Virgin of Fatima . . . 40 30
1318 4e. Chapel of the Apparitions 55 35

220 Roman Senators **221** Lisnave Shipyard

1967. New Civil Law Code.
1319 **220** 1e. red and gold 10 10
1320 2e.50 blue and gold . . 2·20 1·20
1321 4e.30 green and gold . . 1·60 1·20

1967. Inauguration of Lisnave Shipyard, Lisbon.
1322 **221** 1e. multicoloured 15 10
1323 – 2e.80 multicoloured . . . 2·75 1·30
1324 **221** 3e.50 multicoloured . . . 1·70 1·20
1325 – 4e.30 multicoloured . . . 2·50 1·30
DESIGN: 2e.80, 4e.30, Section of ship's hull and location map.

222 Serpent Symbol **223** Flags of EFTA Countries

1967. 6th European Rheumatological Congress, Lisbon.
1326 **222** 1e. multicoloured 15 10
1327 2e. multicoloured . . . . 1·30 65
1328 5e. multicoloured . . . . 1·80 1·30

1967. European Free Trade Association.
1329 **223** 1e. multicoloured 10 10
1330 3e.50 multicoloured . . . 1·30 1·20
1331 4e.30 multicoloured . . . 3·25 3·25

224 Tombstones **225** Bento de Goes

1967. Centenary of Abolition of Death Penalty in Portugal.
1332 **224** 1e. green 10 10
1333 2e. brown . . . . 1·40 90
1334 5e. green . . . . 2·40 1·90

1968. Bento de Goes Commemoration.
1335 **225** 1e. blue, brown and green 75 10
1336 8e. purple, green & brown . . . . . . 1·50 75

226 Europa "Key" **227** "Maternal Love"

1968. Europa.
1337 **226** 1e. multicoloured 35 10
1338 3e.50 multicoloured . . . 8·75 1·80
1339 4e.30 multicoloured . . . 16·00 3·50

1968. 30th Anniv of Organization of Mothers for National Education (O.M.E.N.).
1340 **227** 1e. black, orange and grey 10 10
1341 2e. black, orange and pink . . . . 1·80 75
1342 5e. black, orange and blue . . . . 2·00 1·70

228 "Victory over Disease"

1968. 20th Anniv of W.H.O.
1343 **228** 1e. multicoloured 15 10
1344 3e.50 multicoloured . . . 1·50 65
1345 4e.30 multicoloured . . . 7·75 5·75

229 Vineyard, Girao

1968. "Lubrapex 1968" Stamp Exhibition. Madeira—"Pearl of the Atlantic". Multicoloured.
1346 50c. Type **229** 15 10
1347 1e. Firework display 20 10
1348 1e.50 Landscape 40 15
1349 2e.80 J. Fernandes Vieira (liberator of Pernambuco) (vert) . . . . 2·50 1·80
1350 3e.50 Embroidery (vert) . . 1·60 1·20
1351 4e.30 J. Goncalves Zarco (navigator) (vert) . . . 8·75 7·25
1352 20e. "Muschia aurea" (vert) 4·25 1·30

230 Pedro Alvares Cabral (from medallion)

1969. 500th Birth Anniv of Pedro Alvares Cabral (explorer).
1353 **230** 1e. blue 20 10
1354 – 3e.50 purple . . . . . . 4·50 2·40
1355 – 6e.50 multicoloured . . . 2·75 2·20
DESIGNS—VERT: 3e.50, Cabral's arms. HORIZ: 6e.50, Cabral's fleet (from contemporary docu-ments).

231 Colonnade **232** King Joseph I

1969. Europa.
1356 **231** 1e. multicoloured 40 10
1357 3e.50 multicoloured . . . 9·25 2·00
1358 4e.30 multicoloured . . . 18·00 4·25

1969. Centenary of National Press.
1359 **232** 1e. multicoloured 15 10
1360 2e. multicoloured . . . . 1·20 65
1361 8e. multicoloured . . . . 1·10 90

233 I.L.O. Emblem **234** J. R. Cabrilho (navigator and colonizer)

1969. 50th Anniv of I.L.O.
1362 **233** 1e. multicoloured 10 10
1363 3e.50 multicoloured . . . 1·70 80
1364 4e.30 multicoloured . . . 2·75 2·00

1969. Bicentenary of San Diego, California.
1365 **234** 1e. dp green, yellow & grn 10 10
1366 2e.50 brown, light brown and blue . . . . . . 1·80 65
1367 6e.50 deep brown, green and brown . . . . . 2·00 1·30

235 Vianna da Motta (from painting by C. B. Pinheiro)

1969. Birth Centenary (1968) of Jose Vianna da Motta (concert pianist).
1368 **235** 1e. multicoloured . . . . 1·00 10
1369 9e. multicoloured . . . . 1·00 90

236 Coutinho and Fairey IIID Seaplane

1969. Birth Centenary of Gago Coutinho (aviator). Multicoloured.
1370 1e. Type **236** 15 10
1371 2e.80 Coutinho and sextant 2·75 1·40
1372 3e.30 Type **236** . . . . . 2·50 1·90
1373 4e.30 As No. 1371 . . . . 2·50 2·00

237 Vasco da Gama

1969. 500th Birth Anniv of Vasco da Gama. Multicoloured.
1374 1e. Type **237** 25 15
1375 2e.50 Arms of Vasco da Gama . . . . 3·25 2·50
1376 3e.50 Route map (horiz) . . 2·40 1·10
1377 4e. Vasca da Gama's fleet (horiz) . . . . 2·20 90

238 "Flaming Sun" **239** Distillation Plant and Pipelines

1970. Europa.
1378 **238** 1e. cream and blue . . . 35 10
1379 3e.50 cream and brown 7·75 1·40
1380 4e.30 cream and green 13·50 4·25

1970. Inauguration of Porto Oil Refinery.
1381 **239** 1e. blue and light blue 10 10
1382 – 2e.80 black and green . . 2·75 2·00
1383 **239** 3e.30 green and olive . . 1·80 1·40
1384 – 6e. brown and light brown . . . . 1·50 1·20
DESIGN: 2e.80, 6e. Catalytic cracking plant and pipelines.

240 Marshal Carmona (from sculpture by L. de Almeida)

1970. Birth Centenary of Marshal Carmona.
1385 **240** 1e. green and black . . . 20 10
1386 2e.50 blue, red and black 2·00 80
1387 7e. blue and black . . . 1·80 1·30

241 Station Badge

1970. 25th Anniv of Plant-breeding Station.
1388 **241** 1e. multicoloured 10 10
1389 2e.50 multicoloured . . . 1·40 55
1390 5e. multicoloured . . . . 1·90 75

242 Emblem within Cultural Symbol

1970. Expo 70. Multicoloured.
1391 1e. Compass (postage) . . . 20 10
1392 5e. Christian symbol . . . . 1·60 1·30
1393 6e.50 Symbolic initials . . . 4·00 3·25
1394 3e.50 Type **242** (air) 75 40

243 Wheel and Star

1970. Centenaries of Covilha (Nos. 1395/6) and Santarem (Nos. 1397/8). Multicoloured.
1395 1e. Type **243** 15 10
1397 1e. Castle . . . . 3·00 1·70
1396 2e.80 Ram and weaving frame 15 10
1398 4e. Two knights . . . . . . 1·80 1·00

244 "Great Eastern" laying Cable

1970. Centenary of Portugal–England Submarine Telegraph Cable.
1399 **244** 1e. black, blue and green 10 10
1400 2e.50 black, green & buff 1·90 55
1401 – 2e.80 multicoloured . . . 3·75 2·75
1402 – 4e. multicoloured . . . . 1·80 90
DESIGN: 2e.80, 4e. Cable cross-section.

245 Harvesting Grapes **246** Mountain Windmill, Bussaco Hills

1970. Port Wine Industry. Multicoloured.
1403 50c. Type **245** 10 10
1404 1e. Harvester and jug . . . 20 10
1405 3e.50 Wine-glass and wine barge . . . . 1·10 20
1406 7e. Wine-bottle and casks 1·10 75

1971. Portuguese Windmills.
1407 **246** 20c. brown, black & sepia 10 10
1408 – 50c. brown, black & blue 10 10
1409 – 1e. purple, black and grey 25 10
1410 – 2e. red, black and mauve 90 20
1411 – 3e.30 chocolate, black and brown . . . . . 2·75 2·30
1412 – 5e. brown, black & green 2·50 75
WINDMILLS: 50c. Beira Litoral Province; 1e. "Saloio" type Estremadura Province; 2e. St. Miguel Azores; 3e.30, Porto Santo, Madeira; 5e. Pico, Azores.

247 Europa Chain

1971. Europa.
1413 **247** 1e. green, blue and black 30 15
1414 3e.50 yellow, brn & blk 6·00 65
1415 7e.50 brown, green & blk 11·00 2·10

248 F. Franco **249** Pres. Salazar

1971. Portuguese Sculptors.
1416 **248** 20c. black 10 10
1417 – 1e. red 30 10
1418 – 1e.50 brown 65 55
1419a – 2e.50 blue 1·10 40
1420 – 3e.50 mauve 1·50 65
1421 – 4e. green 2·75 2·10
DESIGNS: 1e. A. Lopes; 1e.50, A. de Costa Mota; 2e.50, R. Gameiro; 3e.50, J. Simoes de Almeida (the Younger); 4e. F. dos Santos.

1971. Pres. Antonio Salazar Commemoration
1422 **249** 1e. brown, green & orge 20 10
1423 5e. brown, purple & orge 1·80 50
1424 10e. brown, blue & orge 3·00 1·30

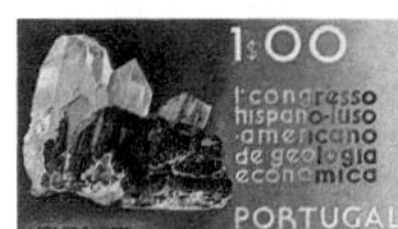

250 Wolframite

1971. 1st Spanish–Portuguese–American Congress of Economic Geology. Multicoloured.
1425 1e. Type **250** 10 10
1426 2e.50 Arsenopyrite 2·10 55
1427 3e.50 Beryllium 70 40
1428 6e.50 Chalcopyrite 1·30 60

251 Town Gate **252** Weather Equipment

1971. Bicentenary of Castelo Branco. Mult.
1429 1e. Type **251** 10 10
1430 3e. Town square and monument 1·50 70
1431 12e.50 Arms of Castelo Branco (horiz) 1·30 70

1971. 25th Anniv of Portuguese Meteorological Service. Multicoloured.
1432 1e. Type **252** 10 10
1433 4e. Weather balloon 2·40 1·20
1434 6e.50 Weather satellite 1·60 65

253 Drowning Missionaries **254** Man and his Habitat

1971. 400th Anniv of Martyrdom of Brazil Missionaries.
1435 **253** 1e. black, blue and grey 10 10
1436 3e.30 black, purple & brn 2·10 1·50
1437 4e.80 black, grn & olive 2·20 1·50

1971. Nature Conservation. Multicoloured.
1438 1e. Type **254** 10 10
1439 3e.30 Horses and trees ("Earth") 65 40
1440 3e.50 Birds ("The Atmosphere") 75 35
1441 4e.50 Fishes ("Water") 2·75 1·80

255 Clerigos Tower, Oporto

1972. Buildings and Views.
1442 – 5c. grey, black and green 15 10
1443 – 10c. black, green & blue 15 10
1444 – 30c. sepia, brown & yell 15 10
1445 – 50c. blue, orange & blk 20 10
1446p **255** 1e. black, brown & grn 55 10
1447 – 1e.50 brown, blue & blk 50 10
1448p – 2e. black, brown & pur 2·10 10
1449p – 2e.50 brown, light brown and grey 90 10
1450 – 3e. yellow, black & brn 60 10
1451p – 3e.50 green, orge & brn 1·50 10
1452 – 4e. black, yellow & blue 60 10
1453 – 4e.50 black, brn & grn 90 10
1454 – 5e. green, brown & black 6·00 10
1455 – 6e. bistre, green & black 2·20 20
1456 – 7e.50 black, orge & grn 1·20 10
1457 – 8e. bistre, black & green 1·50 10
1458 – 10e. multicoloured 60 10
1459 – 20e. multicoloured 5·25 15
1460 – 50e. multicoloured 5·00 25
1461 – 100e. multicoloured 90 65
DESIGNS—As T **255**: 5c. Aguas Livres aqueduct, Lisbon; 10c. Lima Bridge; 30c. Monastery interior, Alcobaca; 50c. Coimbra University; 1e.50, Belem Tower, Lisbon; 2e. Domus Municipalis, Braganza; 2e.50, Castle, Vila de Feira; 3e. Misericord House, Viana do Castelo; 3e.50, Window, Tomar Convent; 4e. Gateway, Braga; 4e.50, Dolmen of Carrazeda; 5e. Roman Temple, Evora; 6e. Monastery, Leca do Balio; 7e.50, Almourol Castle; 8e. Ducal Palace, Guimaraes. 31 × 22 mm: 10e. Cape Girao, Madeira; 20e. Episcopal Garden, Castelo Branco; 50e. Town Hall, Sintra; 100e. Seven Cities' Lake, Sao Miguel, Azores.

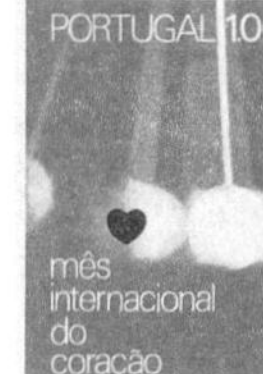

256 Arms of Pinhel **257** Heart and Pendulum

1972. Bicentenary of Pinhel's Status as a City. Multicoloured.
1464 1e. Type **256** 15 10
1465 2e.50 Balustrade (vert) 1·80 40
1466 7e.50 Lantern on pedestal (vert) 1·50 70

1972. World Heart Month.
1467 **257** 1e. red and lilac 15 10
1468 – 4e. red and green 3·25 1·30
1469 – 9e. red and brown 1·70 80
DESIGNS: 4e. Heart in spiral; 9e. Heart and cardiogram trace.

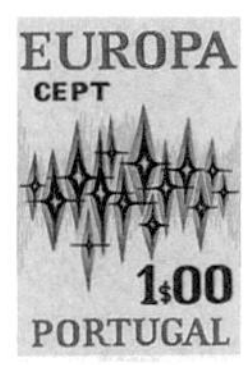

258 "Communications" **259** Container Truck

1972. Europa.
1470 **258** 1e. multicoloured 35 10
1471 3e.50 multicoloured 3·75 40
1472 6e. multicoloured 10·00 1·80

1972. 13th International Road Transport Union Congress, Estoril. Multicoloured.
1473 1e. Type **259** 15 10
1474 4e.50 Roof of taxi-cab 2·20 1·30
1475 8e. Motor-coach 1·80 1·00

260 Football

1972. Olympic Games, Munich. Multicoloured.
1476 50c. Type **260** 10 10
1477 1e. Running 15 10
1478 1e.50 Show jumping 50 20
1479 3e.50 Swimming 1·20 40
1480 4e.50 Yachting 1·60 1·20
1481 5e. Gymnastics 3·00 1·10

261 Marquis de Pombal **262** Tome de Sousa

1972. Pombaline University Reforms. Multicoloured.
1482 1e. Type **261** 15 10
1483 2e.50 "The Sciences" (emblems) 1·70 85
1484 8e. Arms of Coimbra University 1·80 1·30

1972. 150th Anniv of Brazilian Independence. Mult.
1485 1e. Type **262** 15 10
1486 2e.50 Jose Bonifacio 80 30
1487 3e.50 Dom Pedro IV 80 30
1488 6e. Dove and globe 1·80 90

263 Sacadura, Cabral, Gago, Coutinho and Fairey III D Seaplane

1972. 50th Anniv of 1st Lisbon–Rio de Janeiro Flight. Multicoloured.
1489 1e. Type **263** 10 10
1490 2e.50 Route map 85 40
1491 2e.80 Type **263** 1·10 90
1492 3e.80 As 2e.50 1·80 1·40

264 Camoens

1972. 400th Anniv of Camoens' "Lusiads" (epic poem).
1493 **264** 1e. yellow, brown & black 15 10
1494 – 3e. blue, green and black 1·40 75
1495 – 10e. brown, purple & blk 1·80 90
DESIGNS: 3e. "Saved from the Sea"; 10e. "Encounter with Adamastor".

265 Graph and Computer Tapes

1973. Portuguese Productivity Conference, Lisbon. Multicoloured.
1496 1e. Type **265** 10 10
1497 4e. Computer scale 1·40 75
1498 9e. Graphs 1·30 65

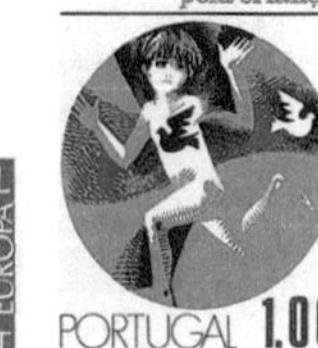

266 Europa "Posthorn" **268** Child Running

267 Pres. Medici and Arms

1973. Europa.
1499 **266** 1e. multicoloured 40 10
1500 4e. multicoloured 11·00 1·10
1501 6e. multicoloured 12·50 2·10

1973. Visit of Pres. Medici of Brazil. Mult.
1502 1e. Type **267** 15 10
1503 2e.80 Pres. Medici and globe 80 70
1504 3e.50 Type **267** 90 65
1505 4e.80 As No. 1503 95 70

1973. "For the Child".
1506 **268** 1e. dp blue, blue & brown 15 10
1507 – 4e. purple, mauve & brn 1·60 70
1508 – 7e.50 orange, ochre and brown 1·70 1·10
DESIGNS: 4e. Child running (to right); 7e.50, Child jumping.

269 Transport and Weather Map

1973. 25th Anniv of Ministry of Communications. Multicoloured.
1509 1e. Type **269** 10 10
1510 3e.80 "Telecommunications" 50 40
1511 6e. "Postal Services" 1·20 70

270 Child and Written Text

1973. Bicentenary of Primary State School Education. Multicoloured.
1512 1e. Type **270** 15 10
1513 4e.50 Page of children's primer 1·80 55
1514 5e.30 "Schooldays" (child's drawing) (horiz) 1·40 75
1515 8e. "Teacher and children" (horiz) 3·75 1·50

271 Electric Tramcar **272** League Badge

1973. Centenary of Oporto's Public Transport System. Multicoloured.
1516 1e. Horse tram 15 10
1517 3e.50 Modern bus 2·30 1·50
1518 7e.50 Type **271** 2·50 1·30
Nos. 1516/17 are 31½ × 31½ mm.

1973. 50th Anniv of Servicemen's League. Multicoloured.
1519 1e. Type **272** 10 10
1520 2e.50 Servicemen 2·30 75
1521 11e. Awards and medals 1·90 65

273 Death of Nuno Goncalves **274** Damiao de Gois (after Durer)

1973. 600th Anniv of Defence of Faria Castle by the Alcaide, Nuno Goncalves.
1522 **273** 1e. green and yellow 30 10
1523 10e. purple and yellow 2·30 1·20

1974. 400th Death Anniv of Damiao de Gois (scholar and diplomat). Multicoloured.
1524 1e. Type **274** 10 10
1525 4e.50 Title-page of "Chronicles of Prince Dom Joao" 2·50 65
1526 7e.50 Lute and "Dodecahordon" score 1·40 60

275 "The Exile" (A. Soares dos Reis)

276 Light Emission

1974. Europa
1527 **275** 1e. green, blue and olive 55 15
1528 4e. green, red and yellow 13·50 75
1529 6e. dp green, green & blue 17·00 1·40

1974. Inauguration of Satellite Communications Station Network.
1530 **276** 1e.50 green 15 10
1531 – 4e.50 blue 1·30 70
1532 – 5e.30 purple 2·20 1·10
DESIGNS: 4e.50, Spiral Waves; 5e.30, Satellite and Earth.

277 "Diffusion of Hertzian Radio Waves"

1974. Birth Centenary of Guglielmo Marconi (radio pioneer). Multicoloured.
1533 1e.50 Type **277** 15 10
1534 3e.30 "Radio waves across Space" 2·20 90
1535 10e. "Radio waves for Navigation" 1·40 60

278 Early Post-boy and Modern Mail Van

1974. Centenary of U.P.U. Multicoloured.
1536 1e.50 Type **278** 10 10
1537 2e. Hand with letters 80 10
1538 3e.30 Sailing packet and modern liner 40 20
1539 4e.50 Dove and airliner 1·40 60
1540 5e.30 Hand with letter 55 40
1541 20e. Steam and electric locomotives 2·75 1·30
MS1542 106 × 147 mm. Nos. 1536/41 (sold at 50e.) 6·25 6·25

279 Luisa Todi

280 Arms of Beja

1974. Portuguese Musicians.
1543 **279** 1e.50 purple 10 10
1544 – 2e. red 1·30 30
1545 – 2e.50 brown 80 20
1546 – 3e. blue 1·30 40
1547 – 5e.30 green 80 55
1548 – 11e. red 1·00 65
PORTRAITS: 2e. Joao Domingos Bomtempo; 2e.50, Carlos Seixas; 3e. Duarte Lobo; 5e.30, Joaode Sousa Carvalho; 11e. Marcos Portugal.

1974. Bimillenary of Beja. Multicoloured.
1549 1e.50 Type **280** 15 10
1550 3e.50 Beja's inhabitants through the ages 2·50 1·10
1551 7e. Moorish arches 2·75 1·30

281 "The Annunciation"

282 Rainbow and Dove

1974. Christmas. Multicoloured.
1552 1e.50 Type **281** 10 10
1553 4e.50 "The Nativity" 3·25 65
1554 10e. "The Flight into Egypt" 2·50 90

1974. Portuguese Armed Forces Movement of 25 April.
1555 **282** 1e.50 multicoloured 10 10
1556 3e.50 multicoloured 3·50 1·60
1557 5e. multicoloured 2·00 75

283 Egas Moniz

284 Farmer and Soldier

1974. Birth Centenary of Professor Egas Moniz (brain surgeon).
1558 **283** 1e.50 brown and orange 30 10
1559 – 3e.30 orange and brown 1·50 55
1560 – 10e. grey and blue 5·50 85
DESIGNS: 3e.30, Nobel Medicine and Physiology Prize medal, 1949; 10e. Cerebral angiograph, 1927.

1975. Portuguese Cultural Progress and Citizens' Guidance Campaign.
1561 **284** 1e.50 multicoloured 10 10
1562 3e. multicoloured 2·00 70
1563 4e.50 multicoloured 2·75 1·10

285 Hands and Dove of Peace

286 "The Hand of God"

1975. 1st Anniv of Portuguese Revolution. Multicoloured.
1564 1e.50 Type **285** 15 10
1565 4e.50 Hands and peace dove 2·75 75
1566 10e. Peace dove and emblem 3·50 1·10

1975. Holy Year. Multicoloured.
1567 1e.50 Type **286** 15 10
1568 4e.50 Hand with cross 3·50 1·10
1569 10e. Peace dove 4·50 1·20

287 "The Horseman of the Apocalypse" (detail of 12th-cent manuscript)

1975. Europa. Multicoloured.
1570 1e.50 Type **287** 80 10
1571 10e. "Fernando Pessoa" (poet) (A. Negreiros) 28·00 1·10

288 Assembly Building

1975. Opening of Portuguese Constituent Assembly.
1572 **288** 2e. black, red and yellow 30 10
1573 20e. black, green & yellow 6·00 1·50

289 Hiking

1975. 36th International Camping and Caravanning Federation Rally. Multicoloured.
1574 2e. Type **289** 1·00 10
1575 4e.50 Boating and swimming 3·00 1·10
1576 5e.30 Caravanning 1·60 1·10

290 Planting Tree

1975. 30th Anniv of U.N.O. Multicoloured.
1577 2e. Type **290** 50 10
1578 4e.50 Releasing peace dove 1·70 55
1579 20e. Harvesting corn 3·75 1·40

291 Lilienthal Glider and Modern Space Rocket

1975. 26th International Astronautical Federation Congress, Lisbon, Multicoloured.
1580 2e. Type **291** 45 10
1581 4e.50 "Apollo"–"Soyuz" space link 2·10 85
1582 5e.30 R. H. Goddard, R. E. Pelterie, H. Oberth and K. E. Tsiolkovsky (space pioneers) 1·00 85
1583 10e. Astronaut and spaceships (70 × 32 mm) 4·50 1·40

292 Surveying the Land

1975. Centenary of National Geographical Society, Lisbon. Multicoloured.
1584 2e. Type **292** 20 10
1585 8e. Surveying the sea 1·50 75
1586 10e. Globe and people 3·25 1·20

293 Symbolic Arch

294 Nurse in Hospital Ward

1975. European Architectural Heritage Year.
1587 **293** 2e. grey, blue & deep blue 30 10
1588 – 8e. grey and red 3·50 75
1589 – 10e. multicoloured 3·50 1·00
DESIGNS: 8e. Stylized building plan; 10e. Historical building being protected from development.

1975. International Women's Year. Multicoloured
1590 50c. Type **294** 10 10
1591 2e. Woman farm worker 1·10 35
1592 3e.50 Woman office worker 1·10 65
1593 8e. Woman factory worker 1·80 1·30
MS1594 104 × 115 mm. Nos. 1590/3 (sold at 25e.) 3·75 3·75

295 Pen-nib as Plough Blade

1976. 50th Anniv of National Writers Society.
1595 **295** 3e. blue and red 45 10
1596 20e. red and blue 4·25 1·30

296 First Telephone Set

1976. Telephone Centenary.
1597 **296** 3e. black, green & dp grn 95 10
1598 – 10e.50 black, red and pink 3·25 90
DESIGNS: 10e.50, Alexander Graham Bell.

297 "Industrial Progress"

298 Carved Olive-wood Spoons

1976. National Production Campaign.
1599 **297** 50c. red 20 10
1600 – 1e. green 50 15
DESIGN: 1e. Consumer goods

1976. Europa. Multicoloured.
1601 3e. Type **298** 3·25 10
1602 20e. Gold ornaments 47·00 6·25

299 Stamp Designing

1976. "Interphil 76" International Stamp Exhibition, Philadelphia. Multicoloured.
1603 3e. Type **299** 20 10
1604 7e.50 Stamp being hand-cancelled 1·20 65
1605 10e. Stamp printing 1·70 75

300 King Fernando promulgating Law

1976. 600th Anniv of Law of "Sesmarias" (uncultivated land). Multicoloured.
1606 3e. Type **300** 15 10
1607 5e. Plough and farmers repelling hunters 1·80 45
1608 10e. Corn harvesting 2·00 85
MS1609 230 × 150 mm. Nos. 1606/8 (sold at 30e.) 4·25 85·00

301 Athlete with Olympic Torch

1976. Olympic Games, Montreal. Multicoloured.
1610 3e. Type **301** 20 10
1611 7e. Women's relay 1·60 1·30
1612 10e.50 Olympic flame 2·20 1·20

302 "Speaking in the Country"

1976. Literacy Campaign. Multicoloured.
1613A 3e. Type **302** 60 10
1614A 3e. "Speaking at Sea" 60 10
1615A 3e. "Speaking in Town" 60 10
1616B 3e. "Speaking at Work" 85 10
MS1617 145 × 104 mm. Nos. 1613/16 (sold at 25e.) 12·00 12·00

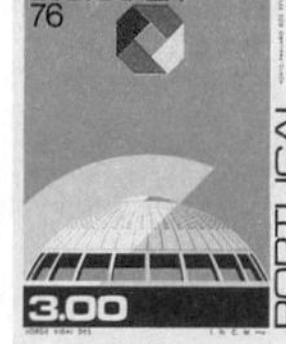

303 Azure-winged Magpie

304 "Lubrapex" Emblem and Exhibition Hall

1976. "Portucale 77" Thematic Stamp Exhibition, Oporto (1st issue). Flora and Fauna. Mult.
1618 3e. Type **303** 20 10
1619 5e. Lynx 1·20 25

1620 7e. Portuguese laurel cherry and blue tit 1·30 90
1621 10e.50 Little wild carnation and lizard 1·40 1·20
See also Nos 1673/8.

1976. "Lubrapex 1976" Luso–Brazilian Stamp Exhibition. Multicoloured.
1622 3e. Type **304** 35 10
1623 20e. "Lubrapex" emblem and "stamp" 2·50 1·50
MS1624 180 × 142 mm. Nos. 1622/3 (sold at 30e.) 3·50 4·25

305 Bank Emblem

1976. Centenary of National Trust Fund Bank.
1625 **305** 3e. multicoloured 10 10
1626 7e. multicoloured 2·20 90
1627 15e. multicoloured 3·50 1·20

306 Sheep Grazing

307 "Liberty"

1976. Water Conservation. Protection of Humid Zones. Multicoloured.
1628 1e. Type **306** 20 10
1629 3e. Marshland 1·00 20
1630 5e. Sea trout 2·10 35
1631 10e. Mallards 4·00 1·10

1976. Consolidation of Democratic Institutions.
1632 **307** 3e. grey, green and red 70 15

308 Examining Child's Eyes

1976. World Health Day. Detection and Prevention of Blindness. Multicoloured.
1633 3e. Type **308** 20 10
1634 5e. Welder wearing protective goggles 2·20 30
1635 10e.50 Blind person reading Braille 1·80 1·10

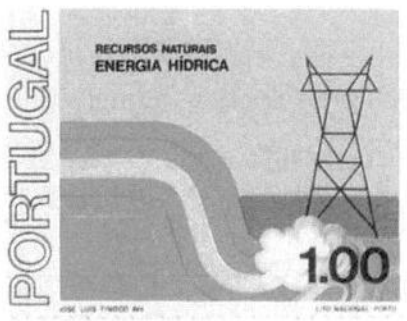

309 Hydro-electric Power

1976. Uses of Natural Energy. Multicoloured.
1636 1e. Type **309** 10 10
1637 4e. Fossil fuel (oil) 60 15
1638 5e. Geo-thermic sources 80 25
1639 10e. Wind power 1·60 80
1640 15e. Solar energy 2·75 1·50

310 Map of Member Countries

1977. Admission of Portugal to the Council of Europe.
1641 **310** 8e.50 multicoloured 1·30 1·30
1642 10e. multicoloured 1·30 1·20

311 Bottle inside Human Body

1977. 10th Anniv of Portuguese Anti-Alcoholic Society. Multicoloured.
1643 3e. Type **311** 15 10
1644 5e. Broken body and bottle 1·00 40
1645 15e. Sun behind prison bars and bottle 2·40 1·40

312 Forest

1977. Natural Resources. Forests. Multicoloured.
1646 1e. Type **312** 10 10
1647 4e. Cork oaks 75 25
1648 7e. Logs and trees 1·60 1·30
1649 15e. Trees by the sea 1·60 1·30

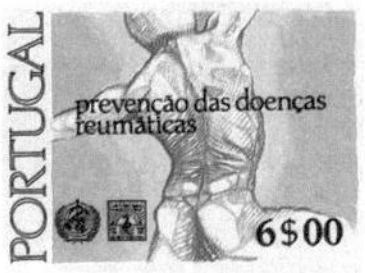

313 Exercising

315 John XXI Enthroned

314 Southern Plains

1977. International Rheumatism Year.
1650 – 4e. orange, brown & blk 20 10
1651 **313** 6e. ultramarine, blue and black 1·20 1·00
1652 – 10e. red, mauve and black 1·10 70
DESIGNS: 4e. Rheumatism victim; 10e. Group exercising.

1977. Europa. Multicoloured.
1653 4e. Type **314** 30 10
1654 8e.50 Northern terraced mountains 1·80 75
MS1655 148 × 95 mm. Nos. 1653/4 each × 3 75·00 25·00

1977. 7th Death Centenary of Pope John XXI. Multicoloured.
1656 4e. Type **315** 20 10
1657 15e. Pope as doctor 70 45

316 Compass

1977. Camoes Day.
1658 **316** 4e. multicoloured 20 10
1659 8e.50 multicoloured 1·20 1·10

317 Child and Computer

1977. Permanent Education. Multicoloured.
1660 4e. Type **317** 40 15
1661 4e. Flautist and dancers 40 15
1662 4e. Farmer and tractor 40 15
1663 4e. Students and atomic construction 40 15
MS1664 148 × 96 mm. Nos. 1660/3 (sold at 20e.) 4·25 5·50

318 Pyrite

1977. Natural Resources. The Subsoil. Mult.
1665 4e. Type **318** 20 10
1666 5e. Marble 1·00 30
1667 10e. Iron ore 1·10 55
1668 20e. Uranium 2·50 1·30

319 Alexandre Herculano

1977. Death Centenary of Alexandre Herculano (writer and politician).
1669 **319** 4e. multicoloured 25 10
1670 15e. multicoloured 1·80 55

320 Early Steam Locomotive and Peasant Cart (ceramic panel, J. Colaco)

1977. Centenary of Railway Bridge over River Douro. Multicoloured.
1671 4e. Type **320** 30 10
1672 10e. Maria Pia bridge (Eiffel) 2·30 1·80

321 Poviero (Northern coast)

1977. "Portucale 77" Thematic Stamp Exhibition, Oporto (2nd issue). Coastal Fishing Boats. Multicoloured.
1673 2e. Type **321** 45 10
1674 3e. Sea-going rowing boat, Furadouro 30 10
1675 4e. Rowing boat from Nazare 30 10
1676 7e. Caicque from Algarve 55 25
1677 10e. Tunny fishing boat, Algarve 85 60
1678 15e. Boat from Buarcos 1·30 95
MS1679 148 × 104 mm. Nos. 1673/8 (sold at 60e.) 4·25 4·25

322 "The Adoration" (Maria do Sameiro A. Santos)

1977. Christmas. Children's Paintings. Mult.
1680 4e. Type **322** 25 10
1681 7e. "Star over Bethlehem" (Paula Maria L. David) 1·20 45
1682 10e. "The Holy Family" (Carla Maria M. Cruz) (vert) 1·30 65
1683 20e. "Children following the Star" (Rosa Maria M. Cardoso) (vert) 2·75 1·10

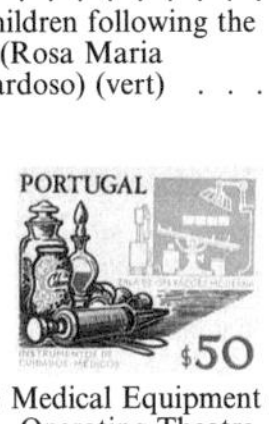

323 Medical Equipment and Operating Theatre

1978. (a) Size 22 × 17 mm.
1684 **323** 50c. green, black and red 10 10
1685 – 1e. blue, orange and black 10 10
1686 – 2e. blue, green & brown 10 10
1687 – 3e. brown, green and black 15 10
1688 – 4e. green, blue & brown 15 10
1689 – 5e. blue, green & brown 15 10
1690 – 5e.50 brown, buff and green 20 10
1691 – 6e. brown, yellow & grn 20 10
1692 – 6e.50 blue, deep blue and green 20 10
1693 – 7e. black, grey and blue 20 10
1694 – 8e. ochre, brown and grey 20 10
1694a – 8e.50 brn, blk & lt brn 30 10
1695 – 9e. yellow, brown & blk 30 10
1696 – 10e. brown, black & grn 30 10
1697 – 12e.50 blue, red and black 30 10
1698 – 16e. brown, black and violet 30 10

(b) Size 30 × 21 mm.
1699 – 20e. multicoloured 55 10
1700a – 30e. multicoloured 65 20
1701 – 40e. multicoloured 65 30
1702 – 50e. multicoloured 1·10 20
1703 – 100e. multicoloured 1·80 40
1703a – 250e. multicoloured 4·50 75
DESIGNS: 1e. Old and modern kitchen equipment; 2e. Telegraph key and masts, microwaves and dish aerial; 3e. Dressmaking and ready-to-wear clothes; 4e. Writing desk and computer; 5e. Tunny fishing boats and modern trawler; 5e.50, Manual and mechanical weaver's looms; 6e. Plough and tractor; 6e.50, Monoplane and B.A.C. One Eleven airliner; 7e. Hand press and modern printing press; 8e. Carpenter's hand tools and mechanical tool; 8e.50, Potter's wheel and modern ceramic machinery; 9e. Old cameras and modern cine and photo cameras; 10e. Axe, saw and mechanical saw; 12e.50, Navigation and radar instruments; 16e. Manual and automatic mail sorting; 20e. Hand tools and building site; 30e. Hammer, anvil, bellows and industrial complex; 40e. Peasant cart and lorry; 50e. Alembic, retorts and modern chemical plant; 100e. Carpenter's shipyard, modern shipyard and tanker; 250e. Survey instruments.

324 Mediterranean Soil

1978. Natural Resources. The Soil. Mult.
1704 4e. Type **324** 30 10
1705 5e. Rock formation 55 15
1706 10e. Alluvial soil 1·10 65
1707 20e. Black soil 2·75 90

325 Pedestrian on Zebra Crossing

1978. Road Safety.
1708 **325** 1e. blue, black and orange 15 10
1709 – 2e. blue, black and green 30 10
1710 – 2e.50 blue, black & lt bl 75 10
1711 – 5e. blue, black and red 1·40 20
1712 – 9e. blue, black & ultram 2·50 75
1713 – 12e.50 blue and black 3·75 1·90
DESIGNS: 2e. Motor cyclist; 2e.50, Children in back of car; 5e. Driver in car; 9e. View of road from driver's seat; 12e.50, Road victim ("Don't drink and drive").

326 Roman Tower of Centum Cellas, Belmonte

327 Roman Bridge, Chaves

1978. Europa. Multicoloured.
1714 10e. Type **326** 1·30 20
1715 40e. Belem Monastery, Lisbon 3·50 1·30
MS1716 111 × 96 mm. Nos. 1714/15 each × 2 (sold at 120e.) 55·00 14·00

1978. 19th Century of Chaves (Aquae Flaviae). Multicoloured.
1717 5e. Type **327** 45 15
1718 20e. Inscribed tablet from bridge 2·50 1·10

328 Running

1978. Sport for All. Multicoloured.
1719 5e. Type **328** 20 10
1720 10e. Cycling 40 30
1721 12e.50 Swimming 95 75
1722 15e. Football 95 95

329 Pedro Nunes

1978. 400th Death Anniv of Pedro Nunes (cosmographer). Multicoloured.
1723 5e. Type **329** 15 10
1724 20e. Nonio (navigation instrument) and diagram 1·50 45

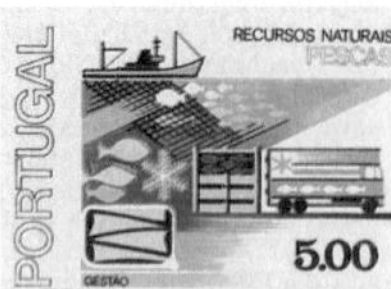

330 Trawler, Crates of Fish and Lorry

1978. Natural Resources. Fishes. Multicoloured.
1725 5e. Type **330** 20 10
1726 9e. Trawler and dockside cranes 70 20
1727 12e.50 Trawler, radar and lecture . . . . 1·30 1·00
1728 15e. Trawler with echo-sounding equipment and laboratory . . . . 2·00 1·30

331 Post Rider

1978. Introduction of Post Code. Multicoloured.
1729 5e. Type **331** 35 20
1730 5e. Pigeon with letter . . . 35 20
1731 5e. Sorting letters 35 20
1732 5e. Pen nib and post codes 35 20

332 Symbolic Figure

1978. 30th Anniv of Declaration of Human Rights. Multicoloured.
1733 14e. Type **332** 70 40
1734 40e. Similar symbolic figure, but facing right . . . . . 1·90 1·10
MS1735 120 × 100 mm. Nos. 1733/4 each × 2 . . . . 4·50 4·50

333 Sebastiao Magalhaes Lima

1978. 50th Death Anniv of Magalhaes Lima (journalist and pacifist).
1736 **333** 5e. multicoloured 30 10

334 Portable Post Boxes and Letter Balance

1978. Centenary of Post Museum. Multicoloured.
1737 4e. Type **334** 30 10
1738 5e. Morse equipment . . . 30 10
1739 10e. Printing press and Portuguese stamps of 1853 (125th anniv) . . . 1·20 25
1740 14e. Books, bookcase and entrance to Postal Library (centenary) . . . . 2·75 1·80
MS1741 120 × 99 mm. Nos. 1737/40 (sold at 40e.) . . . . 5·00 5·00

335 Emigrant at Railway Station

1979. Portuguese Emigrants. Multicoloured.
1742 5e. Type **335** 20 10
1743 14e. Emigrants at airport . . 75 55
1744 17e. Man greeting child at railway station . . . . . 1·10 1·10

336 Traffic

1979. Fight Against Noise. Multicoloured.
1745 4e. Type **336** 20 10
1746 5e. Pneumatic drill 75 15
1747 14e. Loud hailer . . . . . 1·70 70

337 N.A.T.O. Emblem

1979. 30th Anniv of N.A.T.O.
1748 **337** 5e. blue, red and brown 30 10
1749 50e. blue, yellow and red 3·00 2·40
MS1750 120 × 100 mm. Nos. 1748/9 each × 2 . . . . 4·50 4·50

338 Door-to-door Delivery

1979. Europa. Multicoloured.
1751 14e. Postal messenger delivering letter in cleft stick 60 35
1752 40e. Type **338** . . . . . . 1·40 1·00
MS1753 119 × 103 mm. Nos. 1751/2 each × 2 . . . . 28·00 5·50

339 Children playing Ball

1979. International Year of the Child. Multicoloured.
1754 5e.50 Type **339** 20 10
1755 6e.50 Mother, baby and dove 30 10
1756 10e. Child eating 50 35
1757 14e. Children of different races . . . . 1·10 95
MS1758 110 × 104 mm. Nos. 1754/7 (sold at 40e.) . . . . 3·50 3·50

340 Saluting the Flag

1979. Camoes Day.
1759 **340** 6e.50 multicoloured . . . 40 10
MS1760 148 × 125 mm. No. 1759 × 9 . . . . 4·25 3·75

341 Pregnant Woman

1979. The Mentally Handicapped. Multicoloured.
1761 6e.50 Type **341** 35 10
1762 17e. Boy sitting in cage . . 90 55
1763 20e. Face, and hands holding hammer and chisel . . . . 1·20 85

342 Children reading Book

1979. 50th Anniv of International Bureau of Education. Multicoloured.
1764 6e.50 Type **342** 40 10
1765 17e. Teaching a deaf child 1·90 1·00

343 Water Cart, Caldas de Monchique

1979. "Brasiliana 79" International Stamp Exhibition. Portuguese Country Carts. Mult.
1766 2e.50 Type **343** 15 15
1767 5e.50 Wine sledge, Madeira 20 15
1768 6e.50 Wine cart, Upper Douro 40 10
1769 16e. Covered cart, Alentejo 90 80
1770 19e. Cart, Mogadouro . . . 1·30 1·10
1771 20e. Sand cart, Murtosa . . 1·30 40

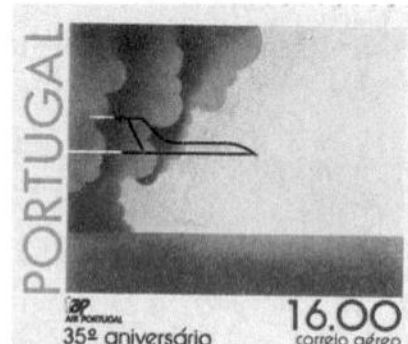

344 Aircraft flying through Storm Cloud

1979. 35th Anniv of TAP National Airline. Multicoloured.
1772 16e. Type **344** . . . . . . 1·20 60
1773 19e. Aircraft and sunset . . 1·30 85

345 Antonio Jose de Almeida

346 Family Group

1979. Republican Personalities (1st series).
1774 **345** 5e.50 mauve, grey and red 35 10
1775 – 6e.50 red, grey and carmine 35 10
1776 – 10e. brown, grey and red 60 10
1777 – 16e. blue, grey and red 1·00 65
1778 – 19e.50 green, grey and red . . . . 1·70 1·10
1779 – 20e. purple, grey and red 1·40 45
DESIGNS: 6e. Afonso Costa; 10e. Teofilo Braga; 16e. Bernardino Machado; 19e.50, Joao Chagas; 20e. Elias Garcia.
See also Nos. 1787/92.

1979. Towards a National Health Service. Mult.
1780 6e.50 Type **346** 35 10
1781 20e. Doctor examining patient . . . . 1·50 55

347 "The Holy Family"

1979. Christmas. Tile Pictures. Multicoloured.
1782 5e.50 Type **347** 40 25
1783 6e.50 "Adoration of the Shepherds" 40 20
1784 16e. "Flight into Egypt" . . 1·20 1·00

348 Rotary Emblem and Globe

1980. 75th Anniv of Rotary International. Mult.
1785 16e. Type **348** . . . . . . 1·10 65
1786 50e. Rotary emblem and torch . . . . 3·00 1·80

349 Jaime Cortesao

1980. Republican Personalities (2nd series).
1787 – 3e.50 orange and brown 20 10
1788 – 5e.50 green, olive and deep olive 30 15
1789 – 6e.50 lilac and violet . . 30 15
1790 **349** 11e. multicoloured . . . 1·60 1·10
1791 – 16e. ochre and brown . . 1·10 70
1792 – 20e. green, blue & lt blue 1·10 40
DESIGNS: 3e.50, Alvaro de Castro; 5e.50, Antonio Sergio; 6e.50, Norton de Matos; 16e. Teixeira Gomes; 20e. Jose Domingues dos Santos.

350 Serpa Pinto **352** Luis Vaz de Camoes

351 Barn Owl

1980. Europa, Multicoloured.
1793 16e. Type **350** 75 40
1794 60e. Vasco da Gama . . . . 2·30 1·10
MS1795 107 × 110 mm. Nos. 1793/4 each × 2 . . . . 15·00 2·75

1980. Protection of Species. Animals in Lisbon Zoo. Multicoloured.
1796 6e.50 Type **351** 30 10
1797 16e. Red fox 85 40
1798 19e.50 Wolf . . . . 1·20 55
1799 20e. Golden eagle . . . . . 1·20 45
MS1800 109 × 107 mm. Nos. 1796/9 3·50 3·50

1980. 400th Death Anniv of Luis Vaz de Camoes (poet).
1801 **352** 6e.50 multicoloured . . . 55 10
1802 20e. multicoloured . . . 1·30 65

353 Pinto in Japan

1980. 400th Anniv of Fernao Mendes Pinto's "A Peregrinacao" (The Pilgrimage). Multicoloured.
1803 6e.50 Type **353** 35 10
1804 10e. Sea battle . . . . . . 1·10 55

354 Lisbon and Statue of St. Vincent (Jeronimos Monastery)

1980. World Tourism Conference, Manila, Philippines. Multicoloured.
1805 6e.50 Type **354** 35 10
1806 8e. Lantern Tower, Evora Cathedral 40 25
1807 11e. Mountain village and "Jesus with Top-hat" (Mirando do Douro Cathedral) 85 50
1808 16e. Canicada dam and "Lady of the Milk" (Braga Cathedral) 1·50 80
1809 19e.50 Aveiro River and pulpit from Santa Cruz Monastery, Coimbra 1·90 90
1810 20e. Rocha beach and ornamental chimney, Algarve 1·80 55

355 Caravel

1980. "Lubrapex 80" Portuguese–Brazilian Stamp Exhibition, Lisbon. Multicoloured.
1811 6e.50 Type **355** 35 10
1812 8e. Nau 75 40
1813 16e. Galleon 1·40 60
1814 19e.50 Early paddle-steamer with sails 2·00 70
MS1815 132 × 88 mm. Nos. 1811/14 (sold at 60e.) 6·25 6·25

356 Lightbulbs

1980. Energy Conservation. Multicoloured.
1816 6e.50 Type **356** 30 10
1817 16e. Speeding car 2·10 75

357 Duke of Braganza and Open Book

1980. Bicentenary of Academy of Sciences, Lisbon. Multicoloured.
1818 6e.50 Type **357** 30 10
1819 19e.50 Uniformed academician, Academy and sextant 1·50 75

358 Cigarette contaminating Lungs

1980. Anti-Smoking Campaign. Multicoloured.
1820 6e.50 Type **358** 30 10
1821 19e.50 Healthy figure pushing away hand with cigarette 2·00 1·10

359 Head and Computer Punch-card

1981. National Census. Multicoloured.
1822 6e.50 Type **359** 30 10
1823 16e. Houses and punch-card 1·50 1·00

360 Fragata, River Tejo

1981. River Boats. Multicoloured.
1824 8e. Type **360** 30 20
1825 8e.50 Rabelo, River Douro 30 20
1826 10e. Moliceiro, Aveiro River 55 20
1827 16e. Barco, River Lima 75 50
1828 19e.50 Carocho, River Minho 90 50
1829 20e. Varino, River Tejo 90 40

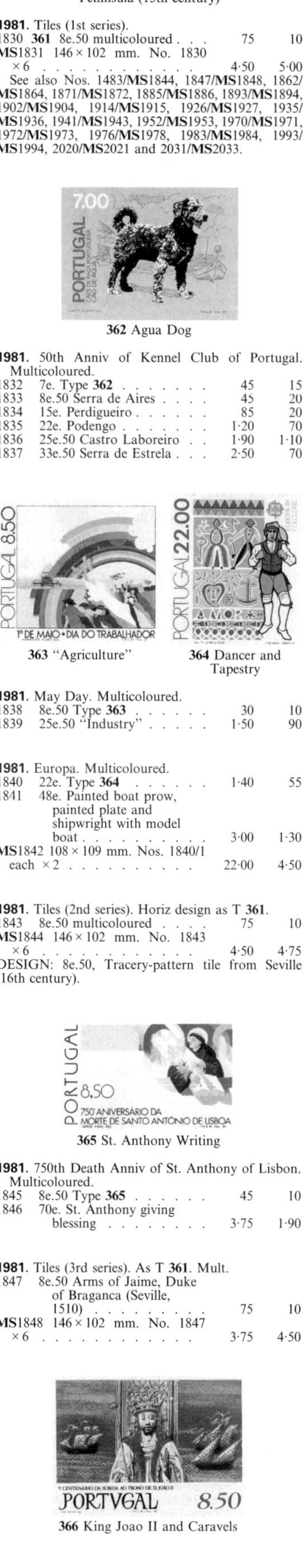

361 "Rajola" Tile from Setubal Peninsula (15th century)

1981. Tiles (1st series).
1830 **361** 8e.50 multicoloured 75 10
MS1831 146 × 102 mm. No. 1830 × 6 4·50 5·00

See also Nos. 1483/**MS**1844, 1847/**MS**1848, 1862/**MS**1864, 1871/**MS**1872, 1885/**MS**1886, 1893/**MS**1894, 1902/**MS**1904, 1914/**MS**1915, 1926/**MS**1927, 1935/**MS**1936, 1941/**MS**1943, 1952/**MS**1953, 1970/**MS**1971, 1972/**MS**1973, 1976/**MS**1978, 1983/**MS**1984, 1993/**MS**1994, 2020/**MS**2021 and 2031/**MS**2033.

362 Agua Dog

1981. 50th Anniv of Kennel Club of Portugal. Multicoloured.
1832 7e. Type **362** 45 15
1833 8e.50 Serra de Aires 45 20
1834 15e. Perdigueiro 85 20
1835 22e. Podengo 1·20 70
1836 25e.50 Castro Laboreiro 1·90 1·10
1837 33e.50 Serra de Estrela 2·50 70

363 "Agriculture" 364 Dancer and Tapestry

1981. May Day. Multicoloured.
1838 8e.50 Type **363** 30 10
1839 25e.50 "Industry" 1·50 90

1981. Europa. Multicoloured.
1840 22e. Type **364** 1·40 55
1841 48e. Painted boat prow, painted plate and shipwright with model boat 3·00 1·30
MS1842 108 × 109 mm. Nos. 1840/1 each × 2 22·00 4·50

1981. Tiles (2nd series). Horiz design as T **361**.
1843 8e.50 multicoloured 75 10
MS1844 146 × 102 mm. No. 1843 × 6 4·50 4·75

DESIGN: 8e.50, Tracery-pattern tile from Seville (16th century).

365 St. Anthony Writing

1981. 750th Death Anniv of St. Anthony of Lisbon. Multicoloured.
1845 8e.50 Type **365** 45 10
1846 70e. St. Anthony giving blessing 3·75 1·90

1981. Tiles (3rd series). As T **361**. Mult.
1847 8e.50 Arms of Jaime, Duke of Braganca (Seville, 1510) 75 10
MS1848 146 × 102 mm. No. 1847 × 6 3·75 4·50

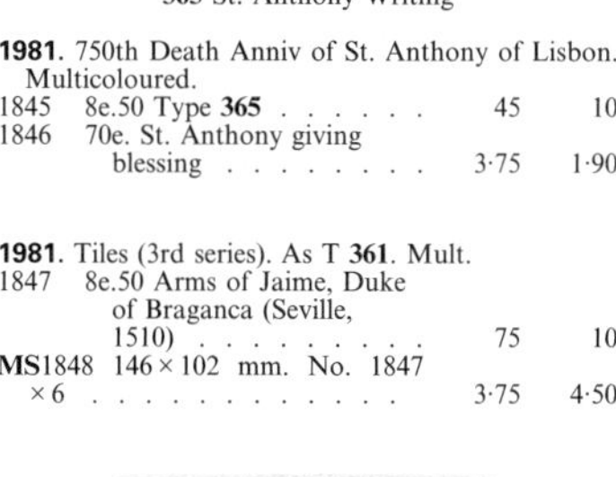

366 King Joao II and Caravels

1981. 500th Anniv of King Joao II's Accession. Multicoloured.
1849 8e.50 Type **366** 50 10
1850 27e. King Joao II on horseback 2·50 90

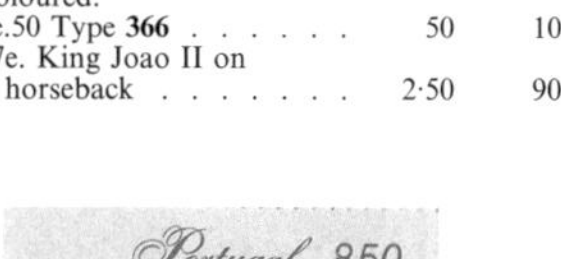

367 "Dom Luiz", 1862

1981. 125th Anniv of Portuguese Railways. Multicoloured.
1851 8e.50 Type **367** 70 10
1852 19e. Pacific steam locomotive, 1925 2·10 1·00
1853 27e. Alco 1500 diesel locomotive, 1948 2·20 1·10
1854 33e.50 Alsthom BB 2600 electric locomotive, 1974 3·00 90

368 "Perrier" Pump, 1856

1981. Portuguese Fire Engines. Multicoloured.
1855 7e. Type **368** 45 15
1856 8e.50 Ford fire engine, 1927 65 15
1857 27e. Renault fire pump, 1914 2·50 1·00
1858 33e.50 Ford "Snorkel" combined hoist and pump, 1978 3·00 95

369 "Virgin and Child"

1981. Christmas. Crib Figures. Multicoloured.
1859 7e. Type **369** 55 35
1860 8e.50 "Nativity" 75 20
1861 27e. "Flight into Egypt" 2·50 1·50

1981. Tiles (4th series). As T **361**. Multicoloured.
1862 8e.50 "Pisana" tile, Lisbon (16th century) 75 15
MS1863 146 × 102 mm. No. 1862 × 6 5·00 5·00
MS1864 120 × 102 mm. Nos. 1830, 1843, 1847 and 1862 5·00 5·00

370 St. Francis with Animals 371 Flags of E.E.C. Members

1982. 800th Birth Anniv of St. Francis of Assisi. Multicoloured.
1865 8e.50 Type **370** 40 10
1866 27e. St. Francis helping to build church 2·10 1·50

1982. 25th Anniv of European Economic Community.
1867 **371** 27e. multicoloured 1·30 70
MS1868 155 × 88 mm. No. 1867 × 4 5·00 5·00

372 Fort St. Catherina, Lighthouse and Memorial Column

1982. Centenary of Figueira da Foz City. Mult.
1869 10e. Type **372** 55 10
1870 19e. Tagus Bridge, shipbuilding yard and trawler 1·80 90

1982. Tiles (5th series). As T **361**. Multicoloured.
1871 10e. Italo-Flemish pattern tile (17th century) 75 15
MS1872 146 × 102 mm. No. 1871 × 6 3·75 4·50

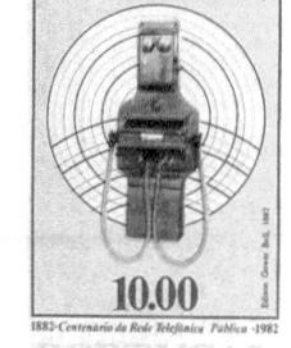

373 "Sagres I" (cadet barque) 374 Edison Gower Bell Telephone, 1883

1982. Sporting Events. Multicoloured.
1873 27e. Type **373** (Lisbon sailing races) 1·60 90
1874 33e.50 Roller hockey (25th World Championship) 2·10 1·20
1875 50e. "470" dinghies (World Championships) 3·25 1·40
1876 75e. Football (World Cup Football Championship, Spain) 4·50 1·60

1982. Centenary of Public Telephone Service. Multicoloured.
1877 10e. Type **374** 45 10
1878 27e. Consolidated telephone, 1887 1·40 1·10

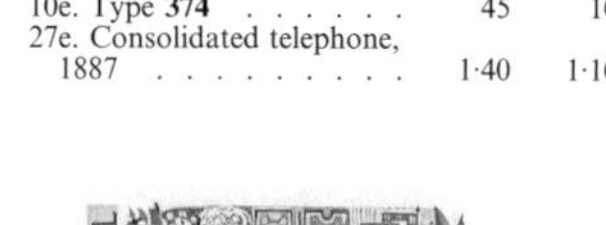

375 Embassy of King Manuel to Pope Leo X

1982. Europa.
1879 **375** 33e.50 multicoloured 2·30 75
MS1880 140 × 114 mm. No. 1879 × 4 22·00 4·25

376 Pope John Paul II and Shrine of Fatima 377 Dunlin

1982. Papal Visit. Multicoloured.
1881 10e. Type **376** 45 70
1882 27e. Pope and Sameiro Sanctuary 2·10 1·20
1883 33e.50 Pope and Lisbon Cathedral 2·30 1·10
MS1884 138 × 78 mm. Nos. 1881/3 each × 2 7·75 5·00

1982. Tiles (6th series). As T **361**. Multicoloured.
1885 10e. Altar front panel depicting oriental tapestry (17th century) 75 15
MS1886 146 × 102 mm. No. 1885 × 6 3·75 6·75

1982. "Philexfrance 82" International Stamp Exhibition, Paris. Birds. Multicoloured.
1887 10e. Type **377** 55 10
1888 19e. Red-crested pochard 1·70 60
1889 27e. Greater flamingo 2·10 90
1890 33e.50 Black-winged stilt 2·30 1·00

378 Dr. Robert Koch

1982. Centenary of Discovery of Tubercle Bacillus. Multicoloured.
1891 27e. Type **378** . . . . . . 1·60 1·10
1892 33e.50 Lungs . . . . 1·70 1·20

1982. Tiles (7th series). As T **361**. Multicoloured.
1893 10e. Polychromatic quadrilobate pattern, 1630–40 . . . . 75 10
MS1894 146×102 mm. No. 1893 ×6 . . . . 4·50 5·00

379 Wine Glass and Stop Sign

1982. "Don't Drink and Drive".
1895 **379** 10e. multicoloured . . . 55 10

380 Fairey IIID Seaplane "Lusitania"

1982. "Lubrapex 82" Brazilian–Portuguese Stamp Exhibition, Curitiba. Multicoloured.
1896 10e. Type **380** 35 10
1897 19e. Dornier Do-J Wal flying boat "Argus" . . . 1·40 75
1898 33e.50 Douglas DC-7C "Seven Seas" airliner . . 2·00 75
1899 50e. Boeing 747-282B jetliner . . . . 2·50 1·10
MS1900 155×98 mm. Nos. 1896/9 5·50 5·50

381 Marquis de Pombal

1982. Death Bicentenary of Marquis de Pombal (statesman and reformer).
1901 **381** 10e. multicoloured . . . 55 10

1982. Tiles (8th series). As T **361**. Multicoloured.
1902 10e. Monochrome quadrilobate pattern, 1670–90 . . . . 75 10
MS1903 146×102 mm. No. 1902 ×6 . . . . 4·25 4·25
MS1904 101×121 mm. Nos. 1871, 1885, 1893 and 1902 . . . . . 3·25 3·25

382 Gallic Cock and Tricolour

1983. Centenary of French Alliance (French language teaching association).
1905 **382** 27e. multicoloured . . . 1·60 75

383 Lisnave Shipyard

1983. 75th Anniv of Port of Lisbon Administration.
1906 **383** 10e. multicoloured . . . 55 10

384 Export Campaign Emblem

1983. Export Promotion
1907 **384** 10e. multicoloured . . . 55 10

385 Midshipman, 1782, and Frigate "Vasco da Gama"

386 W.C.Y. Emblem

1983. Naval Uniforms. Multicoloured.
1908 12e.50 Type **385** 55 10
1909 25e. Seaman and steam corvette "Estefania", 1845 1·50 40
1910 30e. Marine sergeant and cruiser "Adamastor", 1900 . . . . 1·80 55
1911 37e.50 Midshipman and frigate "Joao Belo", 1982 2·20 75

1983. World Cummunications Year. Mult.
1912 10e. Type **386** 55 20
1913 33e.50 W.C.Y. emblem (diff) 1·80 1·10

1983. Tiles (9th series). As T **361**. Multicoloured.
1914 12e.50 Hunter killing white bull (tile from Saldanha Palace, Lisbon, 17/18th century) 90 15
MS1915 146×102 mm. No. 1914 ×6 . . . . 4·00 4·50

387 Portuguese Helmet (16th century)

1983. "Expo XVII" Council of Europe Exhibition. Multicoloured.
1916 11e. Type **387** 55 20
1917 12e.50 Astrolabe (16th century) 75 20
1918 25e. Portuguese caravels (from 16th-century Flemish tapestry) . . . . 1·60 55
1919 30e. Carved capital (12th century) . . . . 2·10 60
1920 37e.50 Hour glass (16th century) . . . . 2·30 90
1921 40e. Detail from Chinese panel painting (16th–17th century) . . . . 2·40 85
MS1922 115×120 mm. Nos. 1916/21 8·50 8·50

388 Egas Moniz (Nobel Prize winner and brain surgeon)

1983. Europa.
1923 **388** 37e.50 multicoloured . . 2·40 70
MS1924 140×114 mm. No. 1923 ×4 . . . . 22·00 3·50

389 Passenger in Train

1983. European Ministers of Transport Conference.
1925 **389** 30e. blue, deep blue and silver . . . . 2·50 70

1983. Tiles (10th series). As T **361**. Multicoloured.
1926 12e.50 Tiles depicting birds (18th century) 90 15
MS1927 146×102 mm. No. 1926 ×6 . . . . 4·00 4·50

390 Mediterranean Monk Seal

1983. "Brasiliana 83" International Stamp Exhibition, Rio de Janeiro. Marine Mammals. Multicoloured.
1928 12e.50 Type **390** 90 15
1929 30e. Common dolphin . . . 2·20 50
1930 37e.50 Killer whale . . . . 3·00 1·20
1931 80e. Humpback whale . . . 5·00 1·10
MS1932 133×81 mm. Nos. 1928/31 9·75 2·75

391 Assassination of Spanish Administrator by Prince John

393 "Adoration of the Magi"

392 Bartolomeu de Gusmao and Model Balloon, 1709

1983. 600th Anniv of Independence. Mult.
1933 12e.50 Type **391** 80 15
1934 30e. Prince John proclaimed King of Portugal . . . . 2·75 1·20

1983. Tiles (11th series). As T **361**. Multicoloured.
1935 12e.50 Flower pot by Gabriel del Barco (18th century) 90 15
MS1936 146×102 mm. No. 1935 ×6 . . . . 4·50 5·00

1983. Bicentenary of Manned Flight. Mult.
1937 16e. Type **392** 75 10
1938 51e. Montgolfier balloon, 1783 . . . . 2·00 90

1983. Christmas. Stained Glass Windows from Monastery of Our Lady of Victory, Batalha. Multicoloured.
1939 12e.50 Type **393** 70 15
1940 30e. "The Flight into Egypt" . . . . 2·30 90

1983. Tiles (12th series). As T **361**. Multicoloured.
1941 12e.50 Turkish horseman (18th century) 90 15
MS1942 146×102 mm. No. 1941 ×6 . . . . 4·50 5·25
MS1943 120×102 mm. Nos. 1914, 1926, 1935 and 1941 . . . . . 4·25 4·25

394 Siberian Tiger

1983. Centenary of Lisbon Zoo. Multicoloured.
1944 16e. Type **394** . . . . . . 1·70 20
1945 16e. Cheetah . . . . 1·70 20
1946 16e. Blesbok . . . . 1·70 20
1947 16e. White rhino . . . . . 1·70 20

395 Fighter Pilot and Hawker Hurricane Mk II, 1954

1983. Air Force Uniforms. Multicoloured.
1948 16e. Type **395** 55 10
1949 35e. Pilot in summer uniform and Republic F-84G Thunderjet, 1960 2·10 55
1950 40e. Paratrooper in walking-out uniform and Nord 250ID Noratlas military transport plane, 1966 . . 2·00 65
1951 51e. Pilot in normal uniform and Vought A-70 Corsair II bomber, 1966 . . . . 2·50 90

1984. Tiles (13th series). As T **361**. Multicoloured.
1952 16e. Coat of arms of King Jose I (late 18th century) 90 15
MS1953 146×102 mm. No. 1952 ×6 . . . . 4·50 4·50

396 "25" on Crate (25th Lisbon International Fair)

1984. Events.
1954 35e. Type **396** . . . . . . 1·80 55
1955 40e. Wheat rainbow and globe (World Food Day) 1·90 65
1956 51e. Hand holding stylized flower (15th World Congress of International Rehabilitation) (vert) . . 2·40 90

397 National Flag

1984. 10th Anniv of Revolution.
1957 **397** 16e. multicoloured . . . 1·20 10

398 Bridge

1984. Europa
1958 **398** 51e. multicoloured . . . 2·50 1·10
MS1959 140×114 mm. No. 1958 ×4 . . . . 9·00 9·00

399 "Panel of St. Vincent"

1984. "Lubrapex 84" Portuguese–Brazilian Stamp Exhibition. Multicoloured.
1960 16e. Type **399** 70 10
1961 40e. "St. James" (altar panel) . . . . 2·30 60
1962 51e. "View of Lisbon" (painting) . . . . 3·50 95
1963 66e. "Head of Youth" (Domingos Sequeira) . . 3·50 1·20
MS1964 110×111 mm. Nos. 1960/3 8·50 8·50

400 Fencing

1984. Olympic Games, Los Angeles, and 75th Anniv of Portuguese Olympic Committee. Multicoloured.
1965 35e. Type **400** . . . . . . 1·60 30
1966 40e. Gymnastics . . . . . 2·10 60
1967 51e. Running . . . . 3·00 1·00
1968 80e. Pole vaulting . . . . . 3·25 1·10
MS1969 90×92 mm. 100e. Hurdling 7·00 7·00

1984. Tiles (14th series). As T **361**. Multicoloured.
1970 16e. Pictorial tile from Pombal Palace, Lisbon (late 18th century) 90 15
MS1971 146×102 mm. No. 1970 ×6 . . . . 4·25 4·50

1984. Tiles (15th series). As T **361**. Multicoloured.
1972 16e. Four art nouveau tiles (late 19th century) 90 15
MS1973 146×102 mm. No. 1972 ×6 . . . . 4·00 4·00

401 Gil Eanes

1984. Anniversaries. Multicoloured.

1974 16e. Type **401** (550th anniv of rounding of Cape Bojador) 50 10

1975 51e. King Pedro IV of Portugal and I of Brazil (150th death anniv) . . . 2·50 1·00

1984. Tiles (16th series). As T **361**. Multicoloured.

1976 16e. Grasshoppers and wheat (R. Bordalo Pinheiro, 19th century) . . 90 15

MS1977 146 × 102 mm. No. 1976 × 6 . . . . 3·00 3·00

MS1978 120 × 102 mm. Nos. 1952, 1970, 1972 and 1976 . . . . . 4·25 4·25

402 Infantry Grenadier, 1740, and Regiment in Formation

1985. Army Uniforms. Multicoloured.

1979 20e. Type **402** 55 10

1980 46e. Officer, Fifth Cavalry, 1810, and cavalry charge 2·50 55

1981 60e. Artillery corporal, 1891, and Krupp 9 mm gun and crew . . . . 2·75 75

1982 100e. Engineer in chemical protection suit, 1985, and bridge-laying armoured car . . . . 3·25 1·20

1985. Tiles (17th series). As T **361**. Multicoloured.

1983 20e. Detail of panel by Jorge Barrados in Lisbon Faculty of Letters (20th century) 85 15

MS1984 146 × 102 mm. No. 1983 × 6 . . . . 4·25 5·00

403 Calcada R. dos Santos Kiosk

1985. Lisbon Kiosks. Multicoloured.

1985 20e. Type **403** . . . . . . 1·20 15

1986 20e. Tivoli kiosk, Avenida da Liberdade . . . . . . 1·20 15

1987 20e. Porto de Lisboa kiosk 1·20 15

1988 20e. Rua de Artilharia Um kiosk . . . . 1·20 15

404 Flags of Member Countries

1985. 25th Anniv of European Free Trade Assn.

1989 **404** 46e. multicoloured . . . 1·50 60

405 Profiles

1985. International Youth Year.

1990 **405** 60e. multicoloured . . . 1·90 85

406 Woman holding Adufe (tambourine)

1985. Europa.

1991 **406** 60e. multicoloured . . . 3·50 1·10

MS1992 140 × 114 mm. No. 1991 × 4 . . . . 27·00 5·00

1985. Tiles (18th series). As T **361**. Multicoloured.

1993 20e. Detail of panel by Maria Keil on Avenida Infante Santo (20th century) 90 15

MS1994 146 × 102 mm. No. 1993 × 6 . . . . 4·25 5·00

407 Knight on Horseback

1985. Anniversaries. Multicoloured.

1995 20e. Type **407** (600th anniv of Battle of Aljubarrota) 70 10

1996 46e. Queen Leonor and hospital (500th anniv of Caldas da Rainha thermal hospital) . . . . 2·20 75

1997 60e. Pedro Reinel (500th anniversary of first Portuguese sea-chart) . . 2·40 1·00

408 Farmhouse, Minho

409 Aquilino Ribeiro (writer)

1985. Architecture.

1998 – 50c. black, bistre and blue 10 10

1999 – 1e. black, yellow & green 10 10

2000 – 1e.50 black, green and emerald 10 10

2001 – 2e.50 brown, orange & bl 10 10

2002 – 10e. black, purple & pink 20 10

2003 **408** 20e. brn, yell & dp yell 30 10

2004 – 22e.50 brown, blue and ochre 30 10

2005 – 25e. brown, yellow & grn 40 10

2006 – 27e. black, grn & yell . . 50 10

2007 – 29e. black, yellow & orge 50 10

2008 – 30e. black, blue & brown 50 10

2009 – 40e. black, yellow & grn 65 15

2010 – 50e. black, blue & brown 80 15

2011 – 55e. black, yellow & grn 80 15

2012 – 60e. black, orange & blue . . . . 1·10 25

2013 – 70e. black, yellow & orge 1·10 25

2014 – 80e. brown, green and red . . . . 1·10 35

2015 – 90e. brown, yellow & grn 1·30 35

2016 – 100e. brown, yellow & bl 1·60 40

2017 – 500e. black, grey and blue . . . . 6·50 75

DESIGNS: 50e. Saloia house, Estremadura; 1e. Beira inland house; 1e.50, Ribatejo house; 2e.50, Tras-os-montes houses; 10e. Minho and Douro coast house; 22e.50, Alentejo houses; 25e. Sitio house, Algarve; 27e. Beira inland house (different); 29e. Tras-os-montes house; 30e. Algarve house; 40e. Beira inland house (different); 50e. Beira coasthouse; 55e. Tras-os-montes house (different); 60e. Beira coast house (different); 70e. South Estramadura and Alentejo house; 80e. Estremadura house; 90e. Minho house; 100e. Monte house, Alentejo; 500e. Terraced houses, East Algarve.

1985. Tiles (19th series). As T **361**. Multicoloured.

2020 20e. Head of woman by Querubim Lapa (20th century) 90 15

MS2021 147 × 101 mm. No. 2020 × 6 . . . . 4·25 5·00

1985. Anniversaries. Multicoloured.

2022 20e. Type **409** (birth centenary) 65 10

2023 46e. Fernando Pessoa (poet 50th death anniv) . . . . 1·80 65

410 Berlenga National Reserve

1985. National Parks and Reserves. Multicoloured.

2024 20e. Type **410** 50 10

2025 40e. Estrela Mountains National Park . . . . . 1·70 60

2026 46e. Boquilobo Marsh National Reserve . . . . 2·50 90

2027 80e. Formosa Lagoon National Reserve . . . . 2·75 90

MS2028 100 × 68 mm. 100e. Jacinto Dunes National Reserve . . . 5·50 5·50

411 "Nativity"

412 Post Rider

1985. Christmas. Illustrations from "Book of Hours of King Manoel I". Multicoloured.

2029 20e. Type **411** 55 10

2030 46e. "Adoration of the Three Wise Men" . . . . 1·90 70

1985. Tiles (20th series). As T **361**. Multicoloured.

2031 20e. Detail of panel by Manuel Cargaleiro (20th century) 90 15

MS2032 146 × 102 mm. No. 2031 × 6 . . . . 5·00 5·00

MS2033 120 × 102 mm. Nos. 1983, 1993, 2020 and 2031 . . . . . 5·00 5·00

1985. No value expressed.

2034 **412** (–) green and deep green 85 15

413 Map and Flags of Member Countries

1985. Admission of Portugal and Spain to European Economic Community. Multicoloured.

2035 20e. Flags of Portugal and Spain uniting with flags of other members 65 10

2036 57e.50 Type **413** . . . . . 2·40 90

See also No. **MS**2056.

414 Feira Castle

1986. Castles (1st series). Multicoloured.

2037 22e.50 Type **414** 90 15

2038 22e.50 Beja Castle 90 15

See also Nos. 2040/1, 2054/5, 2065/6, 2073/4, 2086/7 2093/4, 2102/3 and 2108/9.

415 Globe and Dove

1986. International Peace Year.

2039 **415** 75e. multicoloured . . . 2·75 1·10

1986. Castles (2nd series). As T **414**. Multicoloured.

2040 22e.50 Braganca Castle . . 90 15

2041 22e.50 Guimaraes Castle . . 90 15

416 Benz Motor Tricycle, 1886

1986. Centenary of Motor Car. Multicoloured.

2042 22e.50 Type **416** . . . . . 1·30 10

2043 22e.50 Daimler motor car, 1886 . . . . 1·30 10

417 Allis Shad

1986. Europa.

2044 **417** 68e.50 multicoloured . . 2·75 95

MS2045 140 × 114 mm. No. 2044 × 4 . . . . 25·00 5·00

418 Alter

1986. "Ameripex 86" International Stamp Exn, Chicago. Thoroughbred Horses. Multicoloured.

2046 22e.50 Type **418** 55 10

2047 47e.50 Lusitano . . . . . . 1·90 75

2048 52e.50 Garrano . . . . . . 2·40 95

2049 68e.50 Sorraia . . . . . . 2·75 1·00

419 Comet

1986. Appearance of Halley's Comet. Sheet 100 × 68 mm.

MS2050 **419** 100e. multicoloured 10·50 10·50

420 Diogo Cao (navigator) and Monument

1986. Anniversaries. Multicoloured.

2051 22e.50 Type **420** (500th anniv of 2nd expedition to Africa) 55 10

2052 52e.50 Passos Manuel (Director) and capital (150th anniv of National Academy of Fine Arts, Lisbon) . . . . 1·80 75

2053 52e.50 Joao Baptista Ribeiro (painter and Oporto Academy Director) and drawing (150th anniv of Portuguese Academy of Fine Arts, Oporto) . . . 1·80 75

1986. Castles (3rd series). As T **414**. Multicoloured.

2054 22e.50 Belmonte Castle . . 55 15

2055 22e.50 Montemor-o-Velho Castle . . . . 1·60 75

1986. "Europex 86" Stamp Exhibition, Lisbon. Sheet 127 × 91 mm.

MS2056 Nos. 2035/6 each × 2 . . 5·50 5·50

421 Hand writing on Postcard

1986. Anniversaries. Multicoloured.

2057 22e.50 Type **421** (centenary of first Portuguese postcards) 90 15

2058 47e.50 Guardsman and houses (75th anniv of National Republican Guard) . . . . 1·60 70

2059 52e.50 Calipers, globe and banner (50th anniv of Order of Engineers) . . . 1·70 75

422 Seasonal Mill, Douro

1986. "Luprapex 86" Portuguese–Brazilian Stamp Exhibition, Rio de Janeiro. Multicoloured.
2060 22e.50 Type **422** 55 10
2061 47e.50 Seasonal mill, Coimbra . . . . 1·40 90
2062 52e.50 Overshot bucket mill, Gerez . . . . 1·80 1·00
2063 90e. Permanent stream mill, Braga . . . . 2·75 85
MS2064 140 × 114 mm. Nos. 2060/3 8·50 7·00

1987. Castles (4th series). As T **414**. Mult.
2065 25e. Silves Castle 90 15
2066 25e. Evora-Monte Castle . . 90 15

423 Houses on Stilts, Tocha

1987. 75th Anniv (1986) of Organized Tourism. Multicoloured.
2067 25e. Type **423** 55 10
2068 57e. Fishing boats, Espinho 2·30 1·00
2069 98e. Fountain, Arraiolos . . 3·00 90

424 Hand, Sun and Trees

1987. European Environment Year. Multicoloured.
2070 25e. Type **424** 55 10
2071 57e. Hands and flower on map of Europe . . . . . 1·60 80
2072 74e.50 Hand, sea, purple dye murex shell, moon and rainbow . . . . . . 2·75 90

1987. Castles (5th series). As T **414**. Multicoloured.
2073 25e. Leiria Castle 90 15
2074 25e. Trancoso Castle . . . 90 15

425 Bank Borges and Irmao Agency, Vila do Conde (Alvaro Siza)

1987. Europa. Architecture.
2075 **425** 74e.50 multicoloured . . 2·50 1·00
MS2076 140 × 114 mm. No. 2075 × 4 . . . . 24·00 5·50

426 Cape Mondego **427** Souza-Cardoso (self-portrait)

1987. "Capex '87" International Stamp Exhibition Toronto. Portuguese Lighthouses. Multicoloured.
2077 25e. Type **426** 90 15
2078 25e. Berlenga 90 15
2079 25e. Aveiro 90 15
2080 25e. Cape St. Vincent . . . 90 15

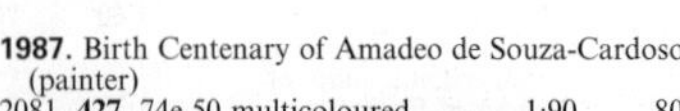
1987. Birth Centenary of Amadeo de Souza-Cardoso (painter)
2081 **427** 74e.50 multicoloured . . 1·90 80

428 Clipped 400 Reis Silver Coin

1987. 300th Anniv of Portuguese Paper Currency.
2082 **428** 100e. multicoloured . . . 2·50 75

429 Dias's Fleet leaving Lisbon

1987. 500th Anniv of Bartolomeu Dias's Voyages (1st issue). Multicoloured.
2083 25e. Type **429** 95 15
2084 25e. Ships off coast of Africa 95 15
Nos. 2083/4 were printed together, se-tenant, each pair forming a composite design.
See also Nos. 2099/2100.

430 Library

1987. 150th Anniv of Portuguese Royal Library, Rio de Janeiro.
2085 **430** 125e. multicoloured . . . 3·25 1·20

1987. Castles (6th series). As T **414**. Multicoloured.
2086 25e. Marvao Castle 95 15
2087 25e. St. George's Castle, Lisbon 95 15

431 Records and Compact Disc Player

1987. Centenary of Gramophone Record. Sheet 140 × 114 mm containing T **431** and similar horiz design. Multicoloured.
MS2088 75e. Type **431**; 125e. Early gramophone . . . . 8·50 8·50

432 Angels around Baby Jesus, Tree and Kings (Jose Manuel Coutinho)

1987. Christmas. Children's Paintings. Mult.
2089 25e. Type **432** 65 10
2090 57e. Children dancing around sunburst (Rosa J. Leitao) . . . . 1·80 75
2091 74e.50 Santa Claus flying on dove (Sonya Alexandra Hilario) . . . . 2·10 1·10
MS2092 140 × 114 mm. Nos. 2089/91 4·50 4·50

1988. Castles (7th series). As T **414**. Multicoloured.
2093 27e. Fernandine Walls, Oporto 90 15
2094 27e. Almourol Castle . . . 90 15

433 Lynx

1988. Iberian Lynx. Multicoloured.
2095 27e. Type **433** . . . . . . 1·00 15
2096 27e. Lynx carrying rabbit 1·00 15
2097 27e. Pair of lynxes . . . . . 1·00 15
2098 27e. Mother with young . . 1·00 15

434 King Joao II sending Pero da Covilha on Expedition

1988. 500th Anniv of Voyages of Bartolomeu Dias (2nd issue) (2099/2100) and Pero da Covilha (2101). Multicoloured.
2099 27e. Dias's ships in storm off Cape of Good Hope 2·50 1·00
2100 27e. Contemporary map . . 2·20 80
2101 105e. Type **434** . . . . . . 2·50 1·00
Nos. 2099/2100 are as T **429**.

1988. Castles (8th series). As T **414**. Multicoloured.
2102 27e. Palmela Castle 90 15
2103 27e. Vila Nova da Cerveira Castle 90 15

435 19th-century Mail Coach

1988. Europa. Transport and Communications.
2104 **435** 80e. multicoloured . . . 2·20 80
MS2105 139 × 112 mm. As No. 2104 × 4 but with cream background 24·00 5·25

436 Map of Europe and Monnet

1988. Birth Centenary of Jean Monnet (statesman). "Europex 88" Stamp Exhibition.
2106 **436** 60e. multicoloured . . . 1·50 60

437 Window reflecting Cordovil House and Fountain

1988. UNESCO World Heritage Site, Evora. "Lubrapex 88" Stamp Exhibition. Sheet 112 × 139 mm.
MS2107 **437** 150e. multicoloured 7·75 7·75

1988. Castles (9th series). As T **414**. Multicoloured.
2108 27e. Chaves Castle 90 15
2109 27e. Penedono Castle . . . 90 15

438 "Part of a Viola" (Amadeo de Souza-Cardoso)

1988. 20th-century Portuguese Paintings (1st series). Multicoloured.
2110 27e. Type **438** 55 10
2111 60e. "Acrobats" (Almada Negreiros) . . . . 1·60 75
2112 80e. "Still Life with Viola" (Eduardo Viana) . . . . 1·90 90
MS2113 138 × 112 mm. Nos. 2110/12 5·25 5·25
See also Nos. 2121/**MS**2125, 2131/**MS**2134, 2148/**MS**2152, 2166/**MS**2169 and 2206/**MS**2210.

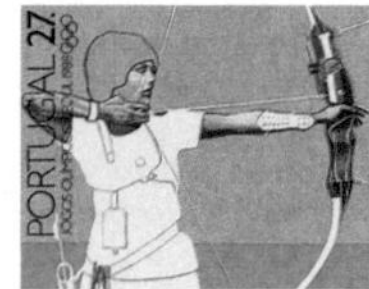

439 Archery

1988. Olympic Games, Seoul. Multicoloured.
2114 27e. Type **439** 50 10
2115 55e. Weightlifting . . . . . 1·50 80
2116 60e. Judo . . . . 1·60 85
2117 80e. Tennis . . . . 2·40 90
MS2118 114 × 67 mm. 200e. Yachting (39 × 30 mm) . . . . 9·00 9·00

440 "Winter" (House of the Fountains, Coimbra)

1988. Roman Mosaics of 3rd Century. Mult.
2119 27e. Type **440** 60 10
2120 80e. "Fish" (Baths, Faro) 1·90 75

1988. 20th Century Portuguese Paintings (2nd series). As T **438**. Multicoloured.
2121 27e. "Internment" (Mario Eloy) 10 10
2122 60e. "Lisbon Houses" (Carlos Botelho) . . . . 1·30 65
2123 80e. "Avejao Lirico" (Antonio Pedro) . . . . 1·90 75
MS2124 140 × 114 mm. Nos. 2121/3 5·25 5·25
MS2125 139 × 144 mm. Nos. 2110/12 and 2121/3 . . . . 9·00 9·00

441 Braga Cathedral

1989. Anniversaries. Multicoloured.
2126 30e. Type **441** (900th anniv) 75 30
2127 55e. Caravel, Fischer's lovebird and S. Jorge da Mina Castle (505th anniv) 1·40 65
2128 60e. Sailor using astrolabe (500th anniv of South Atlantic voyages) . . . . 1·90 85
Nos. 2127/8 also have the "India 89" Stamp Exhibition, New Delhi, emblem.

442 "Greetings" **443** Flags in Ballot Box

1989. Greetings Stamps. Multicoloured.
2129 29e. Type **442** 55 10
2130 60e. Airplane distributing envelopes inscribed "with Love" . . . . 1·10 55

1989. 20th-Century Portuguese Paintings (3rd series). As T **438**. Multicoloured.
2131 29e. "Antithesis of Calm" (Antonio Dacosta) . . . 50 10
2132 60e. "Unskilled Mason's Lunch" (Julio Pomar) . . 1·50 65
2133 87e. "Simumis" (Vespeira) 1·90 1·00
MS2134 139 × 111 mm. Nos. 2131/3 5·25 5·25

1989. 3rd Direct Elections to European Parliament.
2135 **443** 60e. multicoloured . . . 1·40 65

444 Boy with Spinning Top

1989. Europa. Children's Games and Toys. Multicoloured.
2136 80e. Type **444** . . . . . . 1·90 85
MS2137 138 × 112 mm. 80e. × 2 Type **444**; 80e. × 2 Spinning tops 32·00 9·75

445 Cable Railway

1989. Lisbon Transport. Multicoloured.
2138 29e. Type **445** 55 15
2139 65e. Electric tramcar . . . . 1·70 80
2140 87e. Santa Justa lift . . . . 1·90 1·10
2141 100e. Bus . . . . 2·30 80
MS2142 100 × 50 mm. 250e. River ferry (39 × 29 mm) . . . . . . 7·75 7·75

446 Gyratory Mill, Ansiao

1989. Windmills. Multicoloured.
2143 29e. Type **446** 55 20
2144 60e. Stone mill, Santiago do Cacem . . . . 1·70 80
2145 87e. Post mill, Afife . . . . 1·90 1·00
2146 100e. Wooden mill, Caldas da Rainha . . . . 2·30 90

447 Drummer Boy

1989. Bicentenary of French Revolution and "Philexfrance 89" International Stamp Exhibition, Paris. Sheet 111 × 139 mm.
MS2147 **447** 250e. multicoloured 7·75 7·75

1989. 20th-Century Portuguese Paintings (4th series). As T **438**.
2148 29e. blue, green and black 45 10
2149 60e. multicoloured . . . . . 1·50 60
2150 87e. multicoloured . . . . . 2·00 95
MS2151 139 × 111 mm. Nos. 2148/50 5·25 5·25
MS2152 138 × 144 mm. Nos. 231/3 and 2148/50 . . . . 9·00 9·00
DESIGNS: 29e. "046-72" (Fernando Lanhas); 60e. "Spirals" (Nadir Afonso); 87e. "Sim" (Carlos Calvet).

448 Luis I (death centenary) and Ajuda Palace, Lisbon

1989. National Palaces (1st series). Multicoloured.
2153 29e. Type **448** 40 15
2154 60e. Queluz Palace . . . . 1·40 85
See also Nos. 2211/14.

449 "Armeria pseudarmeria"

1989. Wild Flowers. Multicoloured.
2155 29e. Type **449** 40 10
2156 60e. "Santolina impressa" 1·20 65
2157 87e. "Linaria lamarckii" . . 1·70 90
2158 100e. "Limonium multiflorum" . . . . . . 2·30 1·20

450 Blue and White Plate

1990. Portuguese Faience (1st series). Mult.
2159 33e. Type **450** 55 20
2160 33e. Blue and white plate with man in centre . . . 55 20
2161 35e. Vase decorated with flowers 75 20
2162 60e. Fish-shaped jug . . . . 1·30 75
2163 60e. Blue and white plate with arms in centre . . . 1·30 75
2164 60e. Blue and white dish with lid . . . . 1·30 75
MS2165 112 × 140 mm. 250e. Plate with crown in centre . . . . . 5·50 5·50
See also Nos. 2221/**MS**2227 and 2262/**MS**2268.

1990. 20th-Century Portuguese Paintings (5th series). As T **438**. Multicoloured.
2166 32e. "Aluenda-Tordesillas" (Joaquim Rodrigo) . . . 45 10
2167 60e. "Painting" (Luis Noronha da Costa) . . . 1·20 55
2168 95e. "Painting" (Vasco Costa) . . . . 2·00 90
MS2169 138 × 111 mm. Nos. 2166/8 5·25 5·25

451 Joao Goncalves Zarco

1990. Portuguese Navigators.
2170 **451** 2e. red, pink and black 10 10
2171 – 3e. green, blue and black 10 10
2172 – 4e. purple, red and black 10 10
2173 – 5e. brown, grey & black 10 10
2174 – 6e. deep green, green and black 10 10
2175 – 10e. dp red, red & black 10 10
2176 – 32e. green, brown & blk 50 10
2177 – 35e. red, pink and black 40 10
2178 – 38e. blue, lt blue & black 40 15
2179 – 42e. green, grey & black 50 10
2180 – 45e. green, yellow & blk 45 20
2181 – 60e. yellow, purple & blk 1·00 30
2182 – 65e. brown, green & blk 95 20
2183 – 70e. violet, mauve & blk 95 20
2184 – 75e. olive, green & black 90 45
2185 – 80e. orange, brn & blk 1·30 55
2186 – 100e. red, orange & blk 1·90 65
2187 – 200e. green, yellow & blk 2·75 65
2188 – 250e. blue, green & black 4·25 1·40
2189 – 350e. red, pink and black 5·00 1·60
DESIGNS: 3e. Pedro Lopes de Sousa; 4e. Duarto Pacheco Pereira; 5e. Tristao Vaz Teixeira; 6e. Pedro Alvares Cabral; 10e. Joao de Castro; 32e. Bartolomeu Perestrelo; 35e. Gil Eanes: 38e. Vasco da Gama; 42e. Joao de Lisboa; 45e. Joao Rodrigues Cabrilho; 60e. Nuno Tristao; 65e. Joaoda Nova; 70e. Fernao de Magalhaes (Magellan); 75e. Pedro Fernandes de Queiros; 80e. Diogo Gomes; 100e. Diogo de Silves; 200e. Estevao Gomes; 250e. Diogo Cao; 350e. Bartolomeu Dias.

452 Score and Singers

1990. Anniversaries. Multicoloured.
2191 32e. Type **452** (centenary of "A Portuguesa" (national anthem)) 50 15
2192 70e. Students and teacher (700th anniv of granting of charter to Lisbon University) (vert) . . . . 1·70 75

453 Santo Tirso Post Office

1990. Europa. Post Office Buildings. Multicoloured.
2193 80e. Type **453** . . . . . . 1·40 75
MS2194 139 × 111 mm. 80e. × 2 Type **453**; 80e. × 2 19th-century Mail Coach Office . . . . . . 22·00 5·50

454 Stamping Letter

1990. "Stamp World London 90" International Stamp Exhibition and 150th Anniv of the Penny Black. Sheet 111 × 140 mm.
MS2195 **454** 250e. multicoloured 7·75 7·75

455 Street with Chairs under Trees

1990. Greetings Stamps. Multicoloured.
2196 60e. Type **455** . . . . . . 1·10 50
2197 60e. Hand holding bouquet out of car window . . . . 1·10 50
2198 60e. Man with bouquet crossing street . . . . . 1·10 50
2199 60e. Women with bouquet behind pillar box . . . . 1·10 50

456 Camilo Castelo Branco (writer)

1990. Death Anniversaries. Multicoloured.
2200 65e. Type **456** (centenary) 1·20 65
2201 70e. Brother Bartolomeu dos Martires (Bishop of Braga, 400th anniv) . . . 1·40 75

457 Barketta

1990. 15th-Century Explorers' Ships. Mult.
2202 32e. Type **457** 45 10
2203 60e. Carvel-built fishing boat 1·20 55
2204 70e. Nau . . . . 1·40 80
2205 95e. Caravel . . . . 1·90 1·10

1990. 20th-Century Portuguese Paintings (6th series). As T **438**. Multicoloured.
2206 32e. "Dom Sebastiao" (Costa Pinheiro) 45 10
2207 60e. "Domestic Scene with Green Dog" (Paula Rego) 1·10 60
2208 95e. "Homage to Magritte" (Jose de Guimaraes) . . . 2·00 95
MS2209 138 × 112 mm. Nos. 2206/8 5·25 5·25
MS2210 138 × 145 mm. Nos. 2166/8 and 2206/8 . . . . 9·00 9·00

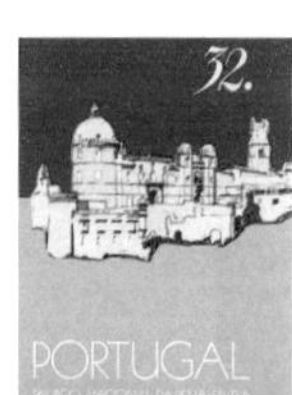

458 Pena Palace

1990. National Palaces (2nd series). Mult.
2211 32e. Type **458** 45 10
2212 60e. Vila Palace . . . . . . 1·20 55
2213 70e. Mafra Palace . . . . . 1·40 75
2214 120e. Guimaraes Palace . . 1·90 1·10

459 Carneiro

1990. 10th Death Anniv of Francisco Sa Carneiro (founder of Popular Democratic Party and Prime Minister, 1980).
2215 **459** 32e. black and brown . . 55 20

460 Steam Locomotive No. 02, 1887

1990. Centenary of Rossio Railway Station, Lisbon. Multicoloured.
2216 32e. Type **460** 45 10
2217 60e. Steam locomotive No. 010, 1891 . . . . . 1·20 55
2218 70e. Steam locomotive No. 071, 1916 . . . . . 1·40 75
2219 95e. Electric train, 1956 . . 1·90 1·00
MS2220 112 × 80 mm. 200e. Station clock (39 × 29 mm) . . . . . . 5·25 5·25

1991. Portuguese Faience (2nd series). As T **450**. Multicoloured.
2221 35e. Barrel of fish and plate (Rato factory Lisbon) . . 55 20
2222 35e. Floral vase (Bica do Sapato factory) 55 20
2223 35e. Gargoyle (Costa Briozo factory, Coimbra) 55 20
2224 60e. Dish with leaf pattern (Juncal factory) . . . . . 1·10 55
2225 60e. Coffee pot (Cavaquinho factory, Oporto) . . . . 1·10 55
2226 60e. Mug (Massarelos factory, Oporto) . . . . 1·10 55
MS2227 114 × 140 mm. 250e. Plate with portrait in centre (Miragaia factory, Oporto) . . . . 5·00 5·00

461 Greater Flamingoes

1991. European Tourism Year. Multicoloured.
2228 60e. Type **461** . . . . . . 1·10 55
2229 110e. European chameleon 1·80 75
MS2230 112 × 104 mm. 250e. Red deer (39 × 31 mm) . . . . . . 4·50 4·50

462 "Eutelsat II" Satellite

1991. Europa. Europe in Space. Multicoloured.
2231 80e. Type **462** . . . . . 1·40 80
MS2232 140 × 112 mm. 80e. × 2, Type **462**; 80e. × 2, "Olympus I" satellite . . . . 22·00 6·25

463 Caravel

1991. 16th Century Explorers' Ships. Mult.
2233 35e. Type **463** 45 10
2234 75e. Port view of nau . . . 1·30 55
2235 80e. Stern view of nau . . . 1·40 70
2236 110e. Galleon . . . . 1·80 75

464 "Isabella of Portugal and Philip the Good" (anon)

1991. "Europhalia 91 Portugal" Festival, Belgium. Sheet 140 × 112 mm.
MS2237 **464** 300e. multicoloured 7·75 7·75

465 Emerald and Diamond Bow

1991. "Royal Treasures" Exhibition, Ajuda Palace (1st issue). Multicoloured.
2238 35e. Type **465** 45 15
2239 60e. Royal sceptre . . . . . 1·10 55
2240 70e. Sash of the Grand Cross . . . . 1·40 65
2241 80e. Hilt of sabre . . . . . 2·20 90
2242 140e. Crown . . . . 1·30 60
See also Nos. 2270/4.

466 Antero de Quental (writer)

1991. Anniversaries. Multicoloured.
2243 35e. Type **466** (death centenary) 45 15
2244 110e. Arrival of expedition and baptism of Sonyo prince (500th anniv of first Portuguese missionary expedition to the Congo) . . . . 1·90 85

467 Faculty of Architecture, Oporto University (Siza Vieira)

1991. Architecture. Multicoloured.
2245 35e. Type **467** 45 10
2246 60e. Torre do Tombo (Arsenio Cordeiro Associates) 90 40
2247 80e. Maria Pia bridge over River Douro (Edgar Cardoso) and Donna Maria bridge . . . . . . 1·40 65
2248 110e. Setubal–Braga highway . . . . 1·80 75

468 King Manoel I creating Public Post, 1520

1991. History of Communications in Portugal. Mult.
2249 35e. Type **468** 45 10
2250 60e. Woman posting letter and telegraph operator (merging of posts and telegraph operations, 1881) 90 45
2251 80e. Postman, mail van and switchboard operator (creation of Posts and Telecommunications administration, 1911) . . 1·30 65
MS2252 140 × 111 mm. 110e. Modern means of communications (introduction of priority mail service, 1991) . . . . 1·80 1·80

469 Show Jumping

1991. Olympic Games, Barcelona (1992) (1st issue). Multicoloured.
2253 35e. Type **469** 45 10
2254 60e. Fencing 90 40
2255 80e. Shooting . . . . 1·40 65
2256 110e. Yachting . . . . . . 1·80 75
See also Nos. 2295/8.

470 Peugeot "19", 1899

1991. Caramulo Automobile Museum. Mult.
2257 35e. Type **470** 45 10
2258 60e. Rolls Royce "Silver Ghost", 1911 . . . . . . 90 40
2259 80e. Bugatti "35B", 1930 . . 1·40 70
2260 110e. Ferrari "1965 Inter", 1950 . . . . 1·60 75
MS2261 140 × 111 mm. 70e. × 2 Mercedes Benz 380K (1934); 70e × 2 Hispano-Suiza H6b (1924) 3·75 3·75
See also Nos. 2275/**MS**2279.

1992. Portuguese Faience (3rd series). As T **450**. Multicoloured.
2262 40e. Jug (Viana do Castelo factory) 55 30
2263 40e. Plate with flower design ("Ratinho" faience, Coimbra) 55 30
2264 40e. Dish with lid (Estremoz factory) 55 30
2265 65e. Decorated violin by Wescislau Cifka (Constancia factory, Lisbon) . . . . 1·00 45
2266 65e. Figure of man seated on barrel (Calvaquinho factory, Oporto) . . . . 1·00 45
2267 65e. Figure of woman (Fervenca factory, Oporto) . . . . 1·00 45
MS2268 112 × 140 mm. 260e. Political figures by Rafael Bordalo Pinheiro (Caldas da Rainha factory) (44 × 38 mm) . . . . 3·50 3·50

471 Astrolabe (Presidency emblem)

1992. Portuguese Presidency of European Community.
2269 **471** 65e. multicoloured . . . 95 45

1992. "Royal Treasures" Exhibition, Ajuda Palace (2nd issue). As T **465**. Multicoloured.
2270 38e. Coral diadem 45 15
2271 65e. Faberge clock 90 45
2272 70e. Gold tobacco box studded with diamonds and emeralds by Jacqumin 1·20 65
2273 85e. Royal sceptre with dragon supporting crown 1·50 80
2274 125e. Necklace of diamond stars by Estevao de Sousa 1·10 55

1992. Oeiras Automobile Museum. As T **470**. Multicoloured.
2275 38e. Citroen "Torpedo", 1922 . . . . 45 10
2276 65e. Robert Schneider, 1914 1·10 45
2277 85e. Austin "Seven", 1933 1·30 65
2278 120e. Mercedes Benz armoured "770", 1938 . . 1·60 75
MS2279 140 × 111 mm. 70e. × 2 Renault 10/14 (1911); 70e. × 2 Ford Model T (1927) . . . . 3·75 3·75

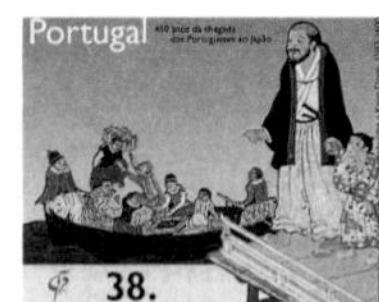

472 Portuguese Traders

1992. 450th Anniv of First Portuguese Contacts with Japan (1st issue). Details of painting attributed to Kano Domi. Multicoloured.
2280 38e. Type **472** 45 10
2281 120e. Portuguese visitors with gifts . . . . 1·60 75
See also Nos. 2342/4.

473 Portuguese Pavilion **474** Cross-staff

1992. "Expo '92" World's Fair, Seville.
2282 **473** 65e. multicoloured . . . 85 40

1992. Nautical Instruments (1st series). Mult.
2283 60e. Type **474** 75 30
2284 70e. Quadrant 95 55
2285 100e. Astrolabe 95 55
2286 120e. Compass . . . . . . 1·60 75
MS2287 140 × 112 mm. Nos. 2283/6 4·25 4·25
See also Nos. 2318/21.

475 Royal All Saints Hospital, Lisbon

1992. Anniversaries. Multicoloured.
2288 38e. Type **475** (500th anniv of foundation) 55 25
2289 70e. Lucia, Francisco and Jacinta (75th anniv of apparition of Our Lady at Fatima) 90 40
2290 120e. Crane and docks (centenary of Port of Leixoes) . . . . 1·60 70

476 Columbus with King Joao II

1992. Europa. 500th Anniv of Discovery of America. Multicoloured.
2291 85e. Type **476** . . . . . . 1·30 60
MS2292 Six sheets (a) 260e. brown and black (Type **479**);(b) 260e. blue and black (Columbus sighting land); (c) 260e. purple and black (Landing of Columbus); (d) 260e. lilac and black (Columbus welcomed at Barcelona); (e) 260e. black (Columbus presenting natives); (f) 260e. black ("America", Columbus and "Liberty") . . . . 49·00 25·00

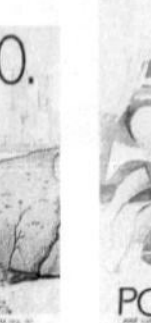

478 Black-headed Gull flying over contaminated River **479** Running

1992. 2nd United Nations Conference on Environment and Development, Rio de Janeiro. Multicoloured.
2293 70e. Type **478** 95 40
2294 120e. River kingfisher and butterfly beside clean river 1·50 80
Nos. 2293/4 were issued together, se-tenant, forming a composite design.

1992. Olympic Games, Barcelona (2nd issue). Mult.
2295 38e. Type **479** 45 15
2296 70e. Football . . . . 1·00 50
2297 85e. Hurdling . . . . 1·20 60
2298 120e. Roller hockey . . . . 1·50 65
MS2299 140 × 112 mm. 250e. Basketball . . . . 3·25 3·25

480 Bullfighter on Horse

1992. Centenary of Campo Pequeno Bull Ring, Lisbon. Multicoloured.
2300 38e. Type **480** 45 15
2301 65e. Bull charging at horse 90 40
2302 70e. Bullfighter attacking bull . . . . 1·10 60
2303 155e. Bullfighter flourishing hat . . . . 1·80 90
MS2304 140 × 113 mm. 250e. Entrance to ring (35 × 50 mm) 3·25 3·25

482 Star

1992. European Single Market.
2313 **482** 65e. multicoloured . . . 85 40

483 Industrial Safety Equipment

1992. European Year of Health, Hygiene and Safety in the Workplace.
2314 **483** 120e. multicoloured . . . 1·60 70

484 Post Office Emblem

1993. No value expressed.
2315 **484** (–) red and black 55 25

No. 2315 was sold at the current first class inland letter rate. This was 42e. at time of issue.

485 Graphic Poem

1993. Birth Centenary of Jose de Almada Negreiros (artist and poet). Multicoloured.
2316 40e. Type **485** 45 20
2317 65e. Trawlers (painting) . . 90 45

486 Sand Clock

1993. Nautical Instruments (2nd series). Mult.
2318 42e. Type **486** 45 20
2319 70e. Nocturlabio . . . . . 1·00 45
2320 90e. Kamal . . . . 1·20 65
2321 130e. Back-staff . . . . . . 1·70 75

487 View from Window

1993. Europa. Contemporary Art. Untitled paintings by Jose Escada. Multicoloured.
2322 90e. Type **487** . . . . . . 1·30 60
MS2323 140 × 112 mm. 90e. × 2 Type **487**; 90e. × 2 Body parts 5·50 5·50

488 Rossini and "The Barber of Seville"

1993. Bicentenary of San Carlos National Theatre, Lisbon. Multicoloured.
2324 42e. Type **488** 45 20
2325 70e. Verdi and "Rigoletto" 1·00 45
2326 90e. Wagner and "Tristan and Isolde" . . . . . . 1·20 65
2327 130e. Mozart and "The Magic Flute" . . . . . . 1·70 70
MS2328 140 × 112 mm. 300e. Exterior of theatre (39 × 29 mm) 3·50 3·50

489 Fireman's Helmet

1993. 125th Anniv of Association of Volunteer Firemen of Lisbon.
2329 **489** 70e. multicoloured . . . 90 40

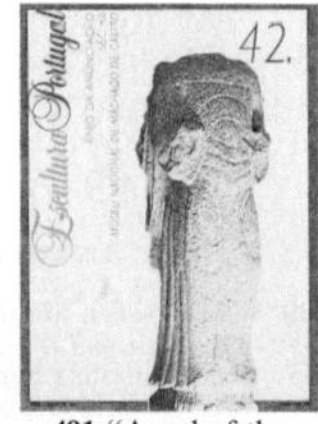

490 Santos-o-Velho, Lisbon **491** "Angel of the Annunciation" (from Oporto Cathedral)

1993. Union of Portuguese-speaking Capital Cities.
2330 **490** 130e. multicoloured . . . 1·70 75
MS2331 140 × 112 mm. No. 2330 × 4 . . . . 5·25 5·25

1993. Sculptures (1st series). Multicoloured.
2332 42e. Type **491** 45 15
2333 70e. "St Mark" (Cornelius de Holanda) (horiz) . . . 95 45
2334 75e. "Madonna and Child" 1·10 45

2335 90e. "Archangel St. Michael" . . . . . . 1·20 55
2336 130e. "Count of Ferreira" (Soares dos Reis) . . . . 1·70 80
2337 170e. "Construction" (Heldar Batista) . . . . . 2·10 95
MS2338 112 × 140 mm. 75e. Marble bust of Agrippina the Elder; 75e. "Virgin of the Annunciation" (Master of the Royal Tombs); 75e. "The Widow" (Teixeira Lopes); 75e. "Love Ode" (Canto da Maya) 3·50 3·50

See also Nos. 2380/**MS**2386 and 2466/**MS**2472.

492 Road Tanker and Electric Tanker Train

1993. Int Railways Congress, Lisbon. Mult.
2339 90e. Type **492** . . . . . . 1·00 45
2340 130e. Electric train and traffic jam . . . . 1·60 75
MS2341 140 × 112 mm. 300e. Train 3·25 3·25

493 Japanese Man with Musket

1993. 450th Anniv of First Portuguese Visit to Japan (2nd issue). Multicoloured.
2342 42e. Type **493** 45 20
2343 130e. Portuguese missionaries . . . . . . 1·70 75
2344 350e. Traders carrying goods . . . . 4·00 1·80

494 Peniche Trawler

1993. Trawlers (1st series). Multicoloured.
2345 42e. Type **494** 45 20
2346 70e. Peniche type trawler . . 85 40
2347 90e. "Germano 3" (steam trawler) . . . . 1·10 55
2348 130e. "Estrela 1" (steam trawler) . . . . 1·50 65

See also Nos. 2392/5.

495 Rural Post Bag, 1800

1993. Post Boxes. Multicoloured.
2349 42e. Type **495** 45 20
2350 70e. 19th-century wall-mounted box for railway travelling post office . . . 85 40
2351 90e. 19th-century pillar box 1·10 55
2352 130e. Modern multi-function post box . . . . 1·50 65
MS2353 140 × 112 mm. 300e. 19th-century box for animal-drawn post wagons . . . . . 3·25 3·25

496 Imperial Eagle

1993. Endangered Birds of Prey. Multicoloured.
2354 42e. Type **496** 45 20
2355 70e. Eagle owl . . . . . . 1·10 45
2356 130e. Peregrine falcon . . . 1·60 80
2357 350e. Hen harrier . . . . . 3·75 1·70

497 Knot

1993. 40th Anniv of Brazil–Portugal Consultation and Friendship Treaty.
2358 **497** 130e. multicoloured . . . 1·50 70

498 Arms

1993. 850th Anniv of Zamora Conference (recognizing Afonso I as King of Portugal). Sheet 106 × 114 mm.
MS2359 **498** 150e. multicoloured 1·80 1·80

499 Stylized Map of Member Nations

1994. 40th Anniv of Western European Union.
2360 **499** 85e. multicoloured . . . 90 45

500 Olympic Rings as Torch Flame

1994. Centenary of Int Olympic Committee. Mult.
2361 100e. Type **500** . . . . . . 1·10 55
2362 100e. "100" and rings . . . 1·10 55

501 Oliveira Martins (historian)

1994. Centenaries. Multicoloured.
2363 45e. Type **501** (death) . . . 45 20
2364 100e. Florbela Espanca (poet, birth) . . . . . . 1·10 60

502 Map and Prince Henry (½-size illustration)

1994. 600th Birth Anniv of Prince Henry the Navigator.
2365 **502** 140e. multicoloured . . . 1·50 75

503 Dove

1994. 20th Anniv of Revolution.
2366 **503** 75e. multicoloured . . . 85 40

504 Mounted Knight and Explorer with Model Caravel

1994. Europa. Discoveries. Multicoloured.
2367 100e. Type **MS**504 . . . . 1·10 55
MS2368 140 × 112 mm. 100e. × 2 Type **504**; 100e. × 2 Millet and explorer with model caravel . . 3·75 3·75

505 Emblem

1994. International Year of the Family.
2369 **505** 45e. red, black and lake 45 20
2370 140e. red, black and green . . . . 1·60 80

506 Footballer kicking Ball and World Map

1994. World Cup Football Championship, U.S.A. Multicoloured.
2371 100e. Type **506** . . . . . . 1·10 55
2372 140e. Ball and footballers' legs . . . . 1·50 75

507 King Joao II of Portugal and King Fernando of Spain (½-size illustration)

1994. 500th Anniv of Treaty of Tordesillas (defining Portuguese and Spanish spheres of influence).
2373 **507** 140e. multicoloured . . . 1·50 75

508 Music

1994. Lisbon, European Capital of Culture. Multicoloured.
2374 45e. Type **508** 40 20
2375 75e. Photography and cinema 80 30
2376 100e. Theatre and dance . . 95 55
2377 140e. Art . . . . 1·40 75
MS2378 140 × 112 mm. Nos. 2374/7 4·25 4·25

509 Emblem

1994. Portuguese Road Safety Year.
2379 **509** 45e. red, green and black 45 15

1994. Sculptures (2nd series). As T **491**. Mult.
2380 45e. Carved stonework from Citania de Briteiros (1st century) (horiz) 40 20
2381 75e. Visigothic pilaster (7th century) 55 30
2382 80e. Capital from Amorim Church (horiz) 85 45
2383 100e. Laying Christ's body in tomb (attr Joao de Ruao) (Monastery Church of Santa Cruz de Coimbra) (horiz) . . . . 1·00 50
2384 140e. Carved wood reliquary (Santa Maria Monastery, Alcobaca) (horiz) . . . . 1·40 75
2385 180e. Relief of Writers (Leopoldo de Almeida) (Lisbon National Library) (horiz) . . . . 2·00 90
MS2386 112 × 140 mm. 75e. Queen Urraca's tomb (Santa Maria Monastery, Alcobaca); 75e. Count of Ourem tomb (Colegiada de Ourem Church); 75e. Joao de Noronha and Isabel de Sousa's tomb (Santa Maria Church, Obidos); 75e. Mausoleum of Admiral Machado dos Santos (Alto de Sao Joao Cemetery, Lisbon) . . . . 2·75 2·75

510 Falconer, Peregrine Falcon and Dog

1994. Falconry. Designs showing a peregrine falcon in various hunting scenes. Multicoloured.
2387 45e. Type **510** 40 20
2388 75e. Falcon chasing duck . . 80 35
2389 100e. Falconer approaching falcon with dead duck . . 1·00 55
2390 140e. Falcons . . . . 1·40 75
MS2391 97 × 121 mm. 250e. Hooded falcon on falconer's arm 2·50 2·50

511 "Maria Arminda"

1994. Trawlers (2nd series). Multicoloured.
2392 45e. Type **511** 40 20
2393 75e. "Bom Pastor" 80 35
2394 100e. Aladores trawler with triplex haulers . . . . . 1·00 55
2395 140e. "Sueste" . . . . . . 1·40 75

512 19th-century Horse-drawn Wagon

1994. Postal Transport. Multicoloured.
2396 45e. Type **512** 40 20
2397 75e. Travelling Post Office sorting carriage No. C7, 1910 . . . . 80 40
2398 100e. Mercedes mail van, 1910 . . . . 1·00 45
2399 140e. Volkswagen mail van, 1950 . . . . 1·40 75
MS2400 140 × 112 mm. 250e. Daf truck, 1983A . . . . 2·75 2·75

513 Multiple Unit Set, Sintra Suburban Railway (½-size illustration)

1994. Modern Electric Locomotives (1st series). Multicoloured.
2401 45e. Type **513** 40 20
2402 75e. Locomotive No. 5611-7 (national network) 75 40
2403 140e. Lisbon Underground train . . . . 1·40 70

See also No. 2465.

514 Medal

1994. 150th Anniv of Montepio Geral Savings Bank (45e.) and World Savings Day (100e.). Mult.
2404 45e. Type **514** 45 20
2405 100e. Coins and bee . . . . 1·00 50

515 St. Philip's Fort, Setubal

1994. Pousadas (hotels) in Historic Buildings. Multicoloured.
2406 45e. Type **515** 40 20
2407 75e. Obidos Castle 80 40
2408 100e. Convent of Loios, Evora . . . . 1·00 45
2409 140e. Santa Marinha Monastery, Guimaraes . . 1·40 75

516 Businessman and Tourist

1994. American Society of Travel Agents World Congress, Lisbon.
2410 **516** 140e. multicoloured . . . 90 70

517 Statuette of Missionary, Mozambique

1994. Evangelization by Portuguese Missionaries. Multicoloured.
2411 45e. Type **517** 40 20
2412 75e. "Child Jesus the Good Shepherd" (carving), India 80 40
2413 100e. Chalice, Macao . . . 1·00 45
2414 140e. Carving of man in frame, Angola (horiz) . . 1·40 75

518 Africans greeting Portuguese

1994. 550th Anniv of First Portuguese Landing in Senegal.
2415 **518** 140e. multicoloured . . . 90 70

519 Battle Scene (detail of the panel, Hall of Battles, Fronteira Palace, Lisbon)

1994. 350th Anniv of Battle of Montijo. Sheet 63 × 83 mm.
MS2416 **519** 150e. multicoloured 1·40 1·40

520 Adoration of the Wise Men

1994. Christmas. Sheet 140 × 111 mm.
MS2417 **520** 150e. multicoloured 1·40 1·40

521 Great Bustard

1995. European Nature Conservation Year. Multicoloured.
2418 42e. Type **521** 40 20
2419 90e. Osprey 90 50
2420 130e. Schreiber's green lizard . . . . 1·30 60
MS2421 140 × 112 mm. Nos. 2418/20 3·25 3·25

522 St. John and Sick Man

1995. 500th Birth Anniv of St. John of God (founder of Order of Hospitallers).
2422 **522** 45e. multicoloured . . . 40 20

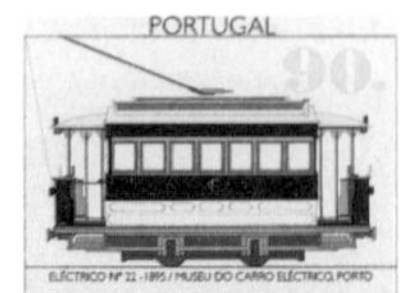

523 Electric Tramcar No. 22, 1895

1995. Centenaries of Trams and Motor Cars in Portugal. Multicoloured.
2423 90e. Type **523** 85 40
2424 130e. Panhard and Levassor motor car . . . . 1·20 65

524 Bread Seller

1995. 19th-century Itinerant Trades. Multicoloured.
2425 1e. Type **524** 10 10
2425a 2e. Laundryman 10 10
2426 3e. Broker 10 10
2427 5e. Broom seller 10 10
2428 10e. Fish seller 10 10
2431 20e. Spinning-wheel and spoon seller 20 10
2432 30e. Olive oil and vinegar seller 25 10
2434 40e. Seller of indulgences 30 15
2435 45e. General street trader 40 20
2436 47e. Hot chestnut seller . . 40 20
2436b 49e. Clothes mender . . . 40 20
2437 50e. Fruit seller 50 25
2437a 50e. Pottery seller 50 25
2438 51e. Knife grinder 35 20
2439 75e. Whitewasher 80 40
2440 78e. Cloth seller 70 35
2440b 80e. Carrier/messenger boy 80 40
2440c 85e. Goose seller 75 40
2440d 86e. Bread seller 65 30
2440e 95e. Coachman 75 40
2441 100e. Mussels seller 90 50
2441a 100e. Milk seller 80 40
2442 210e. Basket seller . . . . 1·80 90
2443 250e. Water seller . . . . 2·20 1·10
2447 250e. Pastry seller . . . . 2·20 1·10

526 Emblem

1995. 50th Anniv of U.N.O. Multicoloured.
2449 75e. Type **526** 65 35
2450 135e. Clouds and emblem 1·30 65
MS2451 140 × 111 mm. No. 2449/50 each × 2 . . . . 4·25 4·25

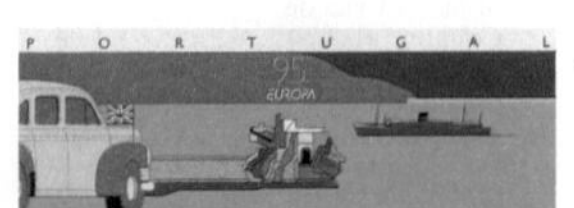

527 Evacuees from Gibraltar arriving at Madeira (½-size illustration)

1995. Europa. Peace and Freedom. Portuguese Neutrality during Second World War. Mult.
2452 95e. Type **527** 90 45
2453 95e. Refugees waiting at Lisbon for transatlantic liner and Aristides de Sousa Mendes (Portuguese Consul in Bordeaux) 90 45

528 "St. Antony holding Child Jesus"(painting)

1995. 800th Birth Anniv of St. Antony of Padua (Franciscan preacher). Multicoloured.
2454 45e. Type **528** 40 20
2455 75e. St. Antony with flowers (vert) 75 35
2456 135e. "St. Antony holding Child Jesus" (statue) . . . 1·30 65
MS2457 96 × 110 mm. 250e. "St. Anthony holding Baby Jesus" (18th-century Madeiran statue) 5·00 5·00

529 Carpenters with Axes and Women with Water, 1395

1995. 600th Anniv of Fire Service in Portugal. Multicoloured.
2458 45e. Type **529** 40 20
2459 80e. Fire cart and men carrying barrels of water, 1834 . . . . 80 35
2460 95e. Merryweather steam-powered fire engine, 1867 90 55
2461 135e. Zoost fire engine No. 1, 1908 . . . . . . 1·20 65
MS2462 Two sheets, each 120 × 100 mm. (a) 4 × 45e. Dutch fire engine, 1701; (b) 4 × 75e. Picota fire engine, 1780 and Portuguese fire cart, 1782 . . . 4·00 4·00

530 Coronation

1995. 500th Anniv of Accession of King Manoel I.
2463 **530** 45e. brown, yellow and red 40 20
MS2464 112 × 140 mm. No. 2463 × 4 . . . . 2·10 2·10

1995. Modern Electric Locomotives (2nd series). As T **513**.
2465 80e. multicoloured 70 35
DESIGN: 80e. Articulated trams.

1995. Sculptures (3rd series). As T **491**. Multicoloured.
2466 45e. "Warrior" (castle statue) 40 20
2467 75e. Double-headed fountain 75 35
2468 80e. "Truth" (monument to Eca de Queiros by Antonio Teixeira Lopes) 75 40
2469 95e. First World War memorial, Abrantes (Ruy Gameiro) 85 50
2470 135e. "Fernao Lopes" (Martins Correia) . . . . 1·20 65
2471 190e. "Fernando Pessoa" (Lagoa Henriques) . . . 1·80 85
MS2472 112 × 140 mm. 75e. "Knight" (from Chapel of the Ferreiros); 75e. "King Jose I" (J. Machado de Castro), Commerce Square, Lisbon; 75e. "King Joao IV" (Francisco Franco), Vila Vicosa; 75e. "Vimara Peres" (Barata Feyo), Oporto Cathedral Square . . . 2·50 2·50

531 "Portugal's Guardian Angel" (sculpture, Diogo Pires)

533 Archangel Gabriel

532 Queiroz

1995. Art of the Period of Discoveries (15th–16th centuries). Multicoloured.
2473 45e. Type **531** 40 20
2474 75e. Reliquary of Queen Leonor (Master Joao) . . 75 35
2475 80e. "Don Manuel" (sculpture, Nicolas Chanterenne) 75 40
2476 95e. "St. Anthony" (painting, Nuno Goncalves) 85 50
2477 135e. "Adoration of the Three Wise Men" (painting, Grao Vasco) . . 1·20 65
2478 190e. "Christ on the Way to Calvary" (painting, Jorge Afonso) . . . . 1·80 85
MS2479 140 × 112 mm. 200e. "St. Vincent" (polyptych, Nuno Goncalves) . . . . 2·10 2·10

1995. 150th Birth Anniv of Eca de Queiroz (writer).
2480 **532** 135e. multicoloured . . . 1·20 65

1995. Christmas. Multicoloured. (a) With country name at foot.
2481 80e. Type **533** . . . . . . 1·10 90
MS2482 112 × 140 mm. No. 2481 × 4 4·25 4·25

(b) With country name omitted.
2483 80e. Type **533** 75 70
MS2484 112 × 140 mm. No. 2483 × 4 . . . . 5·25 5·25

534 Airbus Industrie A340/300

1995. 50th Anniv of TAP Air Portugal.
2485 **534** 135e. multicoloured . . . 1·20 65

535 King Carlos I of Portugal (½-size illustration)

1996. Centenary of Oceanographic Expeditions. Multicoloured.
2486 95e. Type **535** 85 50
2487 135e. Prince Albert I of Monaco . . . . 1·30 60

536 Books

1996. Anniversaries. Multicoloured.
2488 80e. Type **536** (bicentenary of National Library) . . . 75 35
2489 200e. Hand writing with quill pen (700th anniv of adoption of Portuguese as official language) . . . . 1·80 90

537 Joao de Deus (poet and author of reading primer)

1996. Writers' Anniversaries. Multicoloured.
2490 78e. Type **537** (death centenary) 75 35
2491 140e. Joao de Barros (historian, philosopher and grammarian, 500th birth) . . . . 1·30 65

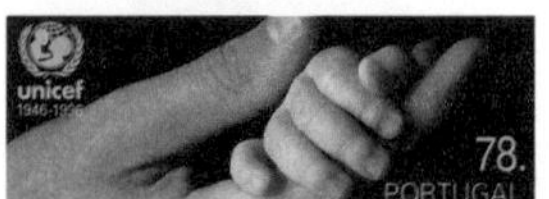

538 Holding Child's Hand (½-size illustration)

1996. 50th Anniv of UNICEF. Multicoloured.
2492 78e. Type **538** 75 40
2493 140e. Children of different races . . . . 1·20 60

539 Helena Vieira da Silva (artist, self-portrait)

1996. Europa. Famous Women.
2494 **539** 98e. multicoloured . . . 90 45
MS2495 140 × 112 mm. No. 2494 × 3 . . . . 2·75 2·75

540 Match Scene

1996. European Football Championship, England. Multicoloured.
2496 78e. Type **540** 70 40
2497 140e. Match scene (different) 1·30 60
MS2498 140 × 112 mm. Nos. 2496/7 2·10 2·10

541 Caravel and Arms (½-size illustration)

1996. 500th Death Anniv of Joao Vaz Corte-Real (explorer). Multicoloured.
2499 140e. Type **541** . . . . . . 1·30 70
MS2500 90 × 127 mm. 315e. Close-up of caravel in Type **541** (39 × 30 mm) . . . . 2·75 2·75

542 Wrestling

1996. Olympic Games, Atlanta. Multicoloured.
2501 47e. Type **542** 40 20
2502 78e. Show jumping 75 35
2503 98e. Boxing 90 50
2504 140e. Running . . . . . . 1·20 70
MS2505 96 × 110 mm. 300e. Athletes at starting blocks . . . . . . 2·50 2·50

543 Hilario and Guitar

1996. Death Centenary of Augusto Hilario (fado singer).
2506 **543** 80e. multicoloured . . . 75 35

544 Antonio Silva (actor)

1996. Centenary of Motion Pictures. Multicoloured.
2507 47e. Type **544** 40 20
2508 78e. Vasco Santana (actor) 65 35
2509 80e. Laura Alves (actress) 65 35
2510 98e. Auelio Pais dos Reis (director) 85 40
2511 100e. Leitao de Barros (director) 90 50
2512 140e. Antonio Lopes Ribeiro (director) . . . . 1·30 65
MS2513 Two sheets, each 112 × 140 mm. (a) Nos. 2507/9; (b) Nos. 2510/12 . . . . 4·75 4·75
MS2514 141 × 111 mm. Nos. 2507/12 5·00 5·00

545 King Afonso V

1996. 550th Anniv of Alphonsine Collection of Statutes.
2515 **545** 350e. multicoloured . . . 3·00 1·50

546 Perdigao

1996. Birth Centenary of Jose de Azeredo Perdigao (lawyer and Council of State member).
2516 **546** 47e. multicoloured . . . 45 20

547 Aveiro

1996. District Arms (1st series). Multicoloured.
2517 47e. Type **547** 40 20
2518 78e. Beja 65 35
2519 80e. Braga 70 35
2520 98e. Braganca 85 40
2521 100e. Castelo Branco . . . 90 50
2522 140e. Coimbra . . . . . . 1·30 65
MS2523 Two sheets, each 140 × 112 mm. (a) Nos. 2517/19; (b) Nos. 2520/2 . . . . 4·50 4·50
See also Nos. 2579/**MS**85 and 2648/**MS**54.

548 Henry of Burgundy (governor of Portucale) and his Wife Theresa

1996. 900th Anniv of Foundation of County of Portucale by King Afonso VI of Leon and Castille.
2524 **548** 47e. multicoloured . . . 45 20

549 Rojoes (Pork dish)

1996. Traditional Portuguese Dishes (1st series). Multicoloured.
2525 47e. Type **549** 40 20
2526 78e. Boticas trout 65 30
2527 80e. Oporto tripe 70 30
2528 98e. Baked cod with jacket potatoes 85 40
2529 100e. Aveiro eel 90 55
2530 140e. Peniche lobster . . . 1·30 65
See also Nos. 2569/74.

550 Lisbon Postman, 1821

1996. 175th Anniv of Home Delivery Postal Service. Multicoloured.
2531 47e. Type **550** 40 20
2532 78e. Postman, 1854 . . . . 65 35
2533 98e. Rural postman, 1893 85 40
2534 100e. Postman, 1939 . . . . 90 50
2535 140e. Modern postman, 1992 . . . . 1·30 65

551 King Manoel I in Shipyard

1996. 500th Anniv (1997) of Discovery of Sea-route to India by Vasco da Gama (1st issue). Multicoloured.
2536 47e. Type **551** 40 20
2537 78e. Departure from Lisbon 65 30
2538 98e. Fleet in Atlantic Ocean 90 50
2539 140e. Sailing around Cape of Good Hope . . . . . 1·20 65
MS2540 141 × 113 mm. 315e. "Dream of King Manuel I" (illustration from Poem IV of *The Lusiads* by Luis de Camoes) . . 2·50 2·50
See also Nos. 2592/**MS**96 and 2665/**MS**80.

552 "Banknote"

1996. 150th Anniv of Bank of Portugal.
2541 **552** 78e. multicoloured . . . 70 35

553 East Timorese Couple

1996. Rights of People of East Timor. Award of 1996 Nobel Peace Prize to Don Carlos Ximenes Belo and Jose Ramos Horton.
2542 **553** 140e. multicoloured . . . 1·20 65

554 Clouds forming Map of Europe

1996. Organization for Security and Co-operation in Europe Summit Meeting, Lisbon. Sheet 95 × 110 mm.
MS2543 **554** 200e. multicoloured 1·80 1·80

555 Portuguese Galleon

1997. Sailing Ships of the India Shipping Line. Multicoloured.
2544 49e. Type **555** 40 20
2545 80e. "Principe da Beira" (nau) 75 30
2546 100e. Bow view of "Don Fernando II e Gloria" (sail frigate) 85 50
2547 140e. Stern view of "Don Fernando II e Gloria" . . 1·30 65

556 Youth with Flower

1997. "No to Drugs – Yes to Life" (anti-drugs campaign).
2548 **556** 80e. multicoloured . . . 70 35

557 Arms

1997. Bicent of Managing Institute of Public Credit.
2549 **557** 49e. multicoloured . . . 45 20

558 Desman eating Worm **559** Moorish Girl guarding Hidden Treasure

1997. The Pyrenean Desman. Multicoloured.
2550 49e. Type **558** 45 25
2551 49e. Diving 45 25
2552 49e. With wet fur 45 25
2553 49e. Cleaning snout 45 25

1997. Europa. Tales and Legends.
2554 **559** 100e. multicoloured . . . 95 45
MS2555 140 × 107 mm. No. 2554 × 3 . . . . 2·75 2·75

560 Surfing

1997. Adventure Sports. Multicoloured.
2556 49e. Type **560** 40 20
2557 80e. Skateboarding 75 30
2558 100e. In-line skating 85 50
2559 140e. Paragliding . . . . . 1·30 65
MS2560 134 × 113 mm. 150e. B.M.X. cycling; 150e. Hang-gliding . . . . 2·50 2·50

561 Night Attack on Santarem Fortress **563** Indian Children and Jose de Anchieta

562 Frois with Japanese Man

1997. 850th Anniv of Capture from the Moors of Santarem and Lisbon. Multicoloured.
2561 80e. Type **561** 70 35
2562 80e. Victorious King Afonso riding past Lisbon city walls 70 35
MS2563 140 × 113 mm. Nos. 2561/2 each × 2 . . . . 3·00 3·00

1997. 400th Death Anniv of Father Luis Frois (author of "The History of Japan"). Multicoloured.
2564 80e. Type **562** 65 30
2565 140e. Father Frois and church (vert) . . . . . . 1·30 65
2566 140e. Father Frois and flowers (vert) . . . . . . 1·30 65

1997. Death Anniversaries of Missionaries to Brazil. Multicoloured.
2567 140e. Type **563** (400th) . . . 1·20 65
2568 350e. Antonio Vieira in pulpit (300th) . . . . . . 3·00 1·50

1997. Traditional Portuguese Dishes (2nd series). As T **549**. Multicoloured.
2569 10e. Scalded kid, Beira Baixa 10 10
2570 49e. Fried shad with bread-pap, Ribatejo 40 20
2571 80e. Lamb stew, Alentejo . . 65 35
2572 100e. Rich fish chowder, Algarve 85 40

2573 140e. Black scabbardfish fillets with maize, Madeira 1·20 65
2574 200e. Stewed octopus, Azores 1·70 90

564 Centre of Oporto

1997. "Lubrapex 97" Portuguese–Brazilian Stamp Exhibition, Oporto. UNESCO World Heritage Site. Sheet 121 × 85 mm.
MS2575 **564** 350e. multicoloured 3·25 3·25

565 Couple before Clerk **566** Laboratory, Lisbon

1997. 700th Anniv of Mutual Assurance in Portugal.
2576 **565** 100e. multicoloured 85 40

1997. 50th Anniv of National Laboratory of Civil Engineering.
2577 **566** 80e. multicoloured 65 35

567 King Dinis and Arms of Portugal and King Fernando IV and Arms of Castile and Leon

1997. 700th Anniv of Treaty of Alcanices (defining national frontiers).
2578 **567** 80e. multicoloured 65 35

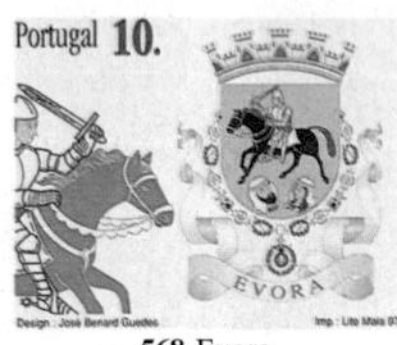

568 Evora

1997. District Arms (2nd series). Multicoloured.
2579 10e. Type **568** 10 10
2580 49e. Faro 40 20
2581 80e. Guarda 65 35
2582 100e. Leiria 85 40
2583 140e. Lisbon 1·20 65
2584 200e. Portalegre 1·70 90
MS2585 Two sheets, each 140 × 112 mm. (a) Nos. 2579, 2581 and 2583; (b) Nos. 2480, 2582 and 2584 4·50 4·50

569 Chart by Lopo Homem-Reineis, 1519

1997. Portuguese Charts. Multicoloured.
2586 49e. Type **569** 40 20
2587 80e. Chart by Joao Freire, 1546 65 30
2588 100e. Planisphere by Diogo Ribeiro, 1529 90 40
2589 140e. Chart showing Tropic of Capricorn (anon), 1630 1·20 65
MS2590 139 × 112 mm. Nos. 2586/9

570 Queen Maria I and Mail Coach

1997. Bicentenary of State Postal Service.
2591 **570** 80e. multicoloured 65 35

571 Erecting Landmark Monument, Quelimane

1997. 500th Anniv of Discovery of Portugal–India Sea Route (2nd issue). Multicoloured.
2592 49e. Type **571** 40 20
2593 80e. Arrival of fleet at Mozambique 65 30
2594 100e. Arrival of fleet in Mombasa 90 40
2595 140e. King of Melinde greeting Vasco da Gama 1·20 65
MS2596 140 × 113 mm. 315e. Vasco da Gama on beach at Natal 2·50 2·50

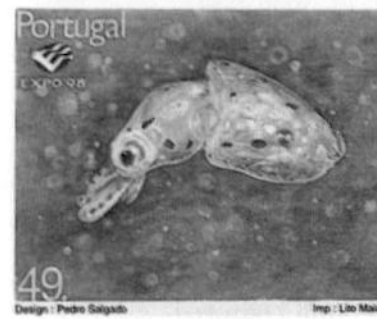

572 Squid

1997. "Expo'98" World Fair, Lisbon. Ocean Life (1st issue). Multicoloured.
2597 49e. Type **572** 40 20
2598 80e. Rock lobster larva 65 30
2599 100e. Adult "Pontellina plumata" (crustacean) 90 40
2600 140e. Senegal sole (pastlarva) 1·20 65
MS2601 110 × 150 mm. 100e. *Calcidiscus leptoporus*; 100e. *Tabellaria sp.* colonies 1·40 1·40
See also Nos. 2611/**MS**2615, 2621/**MS**2629 and 2630/41.

573 Sintra

1997. UNESCO World Heritage Site, Sintra. "Indepex 97" International Stamp Exhibition, New Delhi. Sheet 112 × 140 mm.
MS2602 **573** 350e. multicoloured 2·75 2·75

574 Officer and Plan of Almeida Fortress, 1848

1998. 350th Anniv of Portuguese Military Engineering. Multicoloured.
2603 50e. Type **574** 40 20
2604 80e. Officer and plan of Miranda do Oduro Fortress, 1834 65 30
2605 100e. Officer and plan of Moncao Fortress, 1797 90 40
2606 140e. Officer and plan of Elvas Fortress, 1806 1·20 65

575 Ivens and African Scene **576** Adoration of the Madonna (carving)

1998. Death Centenary of Roberto Ivens (explorer).
2607 **575** 140e. multicoloured 1·20 60

1998. 500th Anniv of Holy Houses Misericordia (religious social relief order).
2608 80e. Type **576** 65 30
2609 100e. Attending patient (tile mural) 85 45

577 Aqueduct ocer Alcantra

1998. 250th Anniv of Aqueduct of the Free Waters (from Sintra to Lisbon). Sheet 155 × 110 mm.
MS2610 **577** 350e. multicoloured 2·75 2·75

1998. "Expo '98" World's Fair, Lisbon (2nd issue). Ocean Life. As T **572**. Multicoloured.
2611 50e. Crab ("Pilumnus" sp.) larva 40 20
2612 85e. Monkfish ("Lophius piscatonis") larva 70 40
2613 100e. Gilthead sea bream ("Sparus aurata") larva 90 45
2614 140e. Medusa ("Cladonema radiatum") 1·20 65
MS2615 112 × 140 mm. 110e. Bioluminescent protozoan (*Noctiluca miliaris*); 110e. Dinoflagellate (*Dinophysis acuta*) 1·40 1·40

578 Vasco da Gama Bridge

1998. Opening of Vasco da Gama Bridge (from Sacavem to Montijo).
2616 **578** 200e. multicoloured 1·70 85
MS2617 125 × 85 mm. As No. 2616 but with background extended to edges 1·40 1·40

579 Coloured Balls

1998. 150th Anniv of Oporto Industrial Association.
2618 **579** 80e. multicoloured 70 35

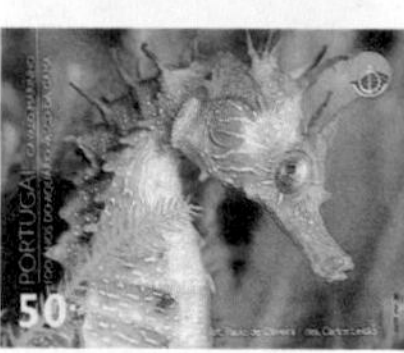
580 Seahorse

1998. International Year of the Ocean. Centenary of Vasco da Gama Aquarium. Multicoloured.
2619 50e. Type **580** 40 20
2620 80e. Angelfish and shoal 70 40

581 Diver and Astrolabe

1998. "Expo '98" World's Fair, Lisbon (3rd issue).
(a) The Ocean. Multicoloured.
2621 50e. Type **581** 40 20
2622 50e. Caravel 40 20
2623 85e. Fishes and coral reef (inscr "oceanario") 70 35
2624 85e. Underwater exploration equipment observing fishes 70 35
2625 140e. Mermaid and sea anemones 1·20 65
2626 140e. Children with hands on globe 1·20 65

(b) Miniature Sheets. Designs as T **581**.
MS2627 154 × 116 mm. 50e. Portuguese Pavilion; 85e. Pavilion of the Future; 85e. Oceanarium; 140e. Knowledge of the Seas Pavilion; 140e. Pavilion of Utopia 2·10 2·10
MS2628 Two sheets, each 147 × 90 mm. (a) Nos. 2621/6; (b) 80e. Postal mascot; stamps as in No. **MS**2627 2·10 2·10
MS2629 148 × 151 mm. Nos. 2597/**MS**2601 and 2611/**MS**2615 2·10 2·10

(c) As Nos. 2611/14 (but with Latin names removed) and 2621/6. Size 29 × 23 mm. Self-adhesive.
2630 50e. As No. 2612 40 20
2631 50e. Bioluminescent protozoan 40 20
2632 50e. As No. 2611 40 20
2633 50e. As No. 2613 40 20
2634 50e. Dinoflagellate 40 20
2635 50e. As No. 2614 40 20
2636 85e. Type **581** 75 35
2637 85e. As No. 2624 75 35
2638 85e. As No. 2626 75 35
2639 85e. As No. 2622 75 35
2640 85e. As No. 2623 but inscr "Portugal e os Oceanos" 75 35
2641 85e. As No. 2625 75 35
The designers' names and printer's imprints have been removed from Nos. 2630/41.

582 Revellers before Statues of St. Antony of Padua, St. John and St. Peter

1998. Europa. National Festivals.
2642 **582** 100e. multicoloured 85 40
MS2643 140 × 108 mm. No. 2642 × 3 2·10 2·10

583 Marie Curie

1998. Centenary of Discovery of Radium.
2644 **583** 140e. multicoloured 1·20 55

584 Ferreira de Castro and Illustration to "The Jungle"

1998. Birth Centenary of Jose Ferreira de Castro (writer).
2645 **584** 50e. multicoloured 40 20

585 Untitled Painting

1998. Death Centenary of Bernardo Marques (artist).
2646 **585** 85e. multicoloured 70 35

586 Adam (Michelangelo) (detail from Sistine Chapel ceiling)

1998. "Juvalex '98" Stamp Exhibition. 50th Anniv of Universal Declaration of Human Rights. Sheet 90 × 55 mm.
MS2647 **586** 315e. multicoloured 2·50 2·50

1998. District Arms (3rd series). As T **568**. Multicoloured.
2648 50e. Vila Real 40 20
2649 85e. Setubal 70 35
2650 85e. Viana do Castelo (150th anniv of elevation to city) 70 35
2651 100e. Santarem 85 40
2652 100e. Viseu 85 40
2653 200e. Oporto . . . . 1·60 80
MS2654 Two sheets, each 140 × 113 mm. (a) Nos. 2648, 2650 and 2653; (b) Nos. 2649 and 2651/2 . . . . 4·50 4·50

587 Glass Production

1998. 250th Anniv of Glass Production in Marinha Grande. Multicoloured.
2655 50e. Type **587** 40 20
2656 80e. Heating glass and finished product 75 30
2657 100e. Bottles and factory . . 90 40
2658 140e. Blue bottles and glass-maker . . . . 1·50 60

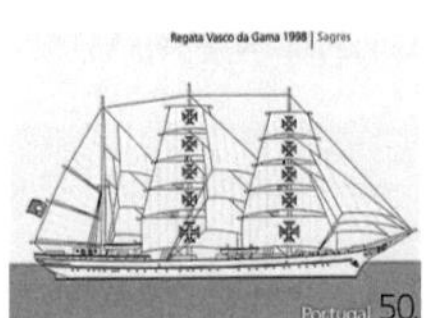
588 "Sagres II" (cadet barque), Portugal

1998. Vasco da Gama Regatta. Multicoloured.
2659 50e. Type **588** 40 20
2660 85e. "Asgard II" (Irish cadet brigantine) 75 30
2661 85e. "Rose" (American replica) 75 30
2662 100e. "Amerigo Vespucci" (Italian cadet ship) . . . 85 40
2663 100e. "Kruzenshtern" (Russian cadet barque) . . 85 40
2664 140e. "Creoula" (Portuguese cadet schooner) . . . . . 1·10 65

589 Da Gama with Pilot Ibn Madjid

1998. 500th Anniv (1997) of Discovery of Sea-route to India by Vasco da Gama (3rd issue). Mult.
2665 50e. Type **551** 40 20
2666 50e. As No. 2537 . . . . . 40 20
2667 50e. As No. 2538 . . . . . 40 20
2668 50e. As No. 2539 . . . . . 40 20
2669 50e. Type **571** 40 20
2670 50e. As No. 2593 . . . . . 40 20
2671 50e. As No. 2594 . . . . . 40 20
2672 50e. As No. 2595 . . . . . 40 20
2673 50e. Type **589** 40 20
2674 50e. "Sao Gabriel" (flagship) in storm 40 20
2675 50e. Fleet arriving at Calicut 40 20
2676 50e. Audience with the Samorin of Calicut . . . 40 20
2677 80e. As No. 2674 . . . . . 65 30
2678 100e. As No. 2675 . . . . 85 40
2679 140e. As No. 2676 . . . . 1·20 60
MS2680 140 × 112 mm. 315e. King of Melinde listening to Vasco da Gama . . . . 2·50 2·50

590 Modern Mail Van

1998. Bicentenaries of Inauguration of Lisbon–Coimbra Mail Coach Service and of Re-organization of Maritime Mail Service to Brazil. Mult.
2681 50e. Type **590** 40 20
2682 140e. Mail coach and "Postilhao da America" (brigantine) . . . . . . 1·10 60

591 Globe and Flags of participating Countries

1998. 8th Iberian-American Summit of State Leaders and Govenors, Oporto. Sheet 90 × 55 mm.
MS2683 **591** 140e. multicoloured 1·10 1·10

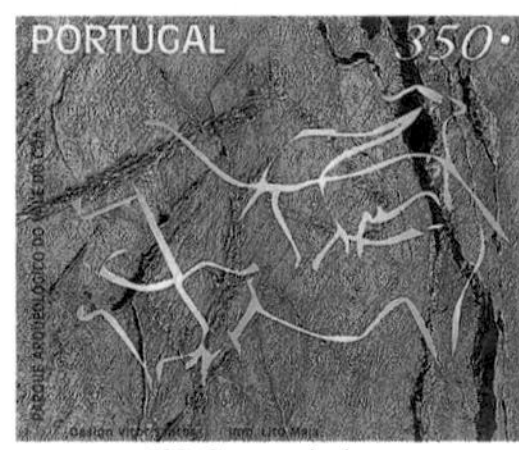
592 Cave paintings

1998. Archeological Park, Coa Valley. Sheet 140 × 113 mm.
MS2684 **592** 350e. multicoloured 2·50 2·50

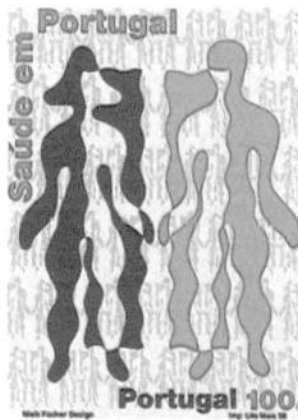

593 Male and Female Figures

595 Knife Grinder

594 Saramago

1998. Health Awareness.
2685 **593** 100e. multicoloured . . . 85 40

1998. Jose Saramago (winner of Nobel prize for Literature, 1998). Sheet 140 × 114 mm.
MS2686 **594** 200e. multicoloured 1·40 1·40

DENOMINATION. From No. 2687 Portugal stamps are denominated both in escudos and in euros. As no cash for this latter is in circulation, the catalogue continues to use the escudo value.

1999. 19th-Century Itinerant Trades. Multicoloured. Self-adhesive.
2687 51e. Type **595** 75 40
2688 95e. Coachman . . . . . . 1·20 55

596 Flags of European Union Members and Euro Emblem

1999. Introduction of the Euro (European currency).
2696 **596** 95e. multicoloured . . . 1·20 55

597 Galleon and Aborigines

1999. "Australia 99" International Stamp Exhibition, Melbourne. The Portuguese in Australia. Multicoloured.
2697 140e. Kangaroos and galleon . . . . 1·20 55
2698 140e. Type **597** . . . . . . 1·20 55
MS2699 137 × 104 mm. 350e. Motifs of Nos. 2697/8 (79 × 30 mm) 2·50 2·50
Nos. 2697/8 were issued together, se-tenant, forming a composite design.

598 Norton de Matos

1999. 50th Anniv of Candidature of General Jose Norton de Matos to Presidency of the Republic.
2700 **598** 80e. multicoloured . . . 65 35

599 Almeida Garrett

1999. Birth Bicentenary of Joao Bapista Almeida Garrett (writer).
2701 **599** 95e. multicoloured . . . 75 40
MS2702 130 × 105 mm. **599** 210e. multicoloured . . . . 1·40 1·40

600 Breguet 16 Bn2 Patria

1999. 25th Anniv of Sarmento de Beires and Brito Pais's Portugal–Macao Flight. Multicoloured.
2703 140e. Type **600** . . . . . . 1·20 55
2704 140e. De Havilland D.H.9 biplane . . . . 1·20 55
MS2705 137 × 104 mm. Nos. 2703/4 2·10 2·10

601 Carnation

1999. 25th Anniv of Revolution. Multicoloured.
2706 51e. Type **601** 40 20
2707 80e. National Assembly building (78 × 29 mm) . . 65 40
MS2708 140 × 108 mm. Nos. 2706/7 85 85

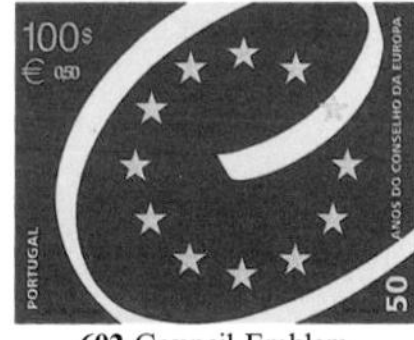
602 Council Emblem

1999. 50th Anniv of Council of Europe.
2709 **602** 100e. multicoloured . . . 80 40

603 Wolf and Iris (Peneda-Geres National Park)

1999. Europa. Parks and Gardens.
2710 **603** 100e. multicoloured . . . 80 40
MS2711 154 × 109 mm. No. 2710 × 3 70 70

604 Marquis de Pombal

1993. 300th Birth Anniv of Marquis de Pombal (statesman and reformer). Multicoloured.
2712 80e. Type **604** 65 35
MS2713 170 × 135 mm. 80e. Head of Marquis and part of statue; 210e. Hand holding quill . . . . . 2·10 2·10

605 Harbour

1999. "Meeting of Cultures". Return of Macao to China. Multicoloured.
2714 51e. Type **605** 40 20
2715 80e. Dancers 65 30
2716 95e. Procession of the Madonna 75 40
2717 100e. Ruins of St. Paul's Basilica 85 40
2718 140e. Garden with bust of Luis Camoes (horiz) . . . 1·10 60

606 De Havilland D.H.82A Tiger Moth

1999. 75th Anniv of Military Aeronautics. Multicoloured.
2719 51e. Type **606** 40 20
2720 51e. Supermarine Spitfire V6 fighter 40 20
2721 85e. Breguet Bre XIV A2 . . 70 35
2722 85e. SPAD VII-C1 . . . . 70 35
2723 95e. Caudron G-3 . . . . . 85 45
2724 95e. Junkers Ju 52/3m . . . 85 45

607 Portion by Antonio Pedro

1999. 50th Anniv of Surrealism (modern art movement) in Portugal. Designs showing details by artist named of collective painting "Cadavre Exquis". Multicoloured.
2726 51e. Type **607** 40 20
2727 80e. Vespeira 65 30
2728 95e. Moniz Pereira 75 40
2729 100e. Fernando de Azevedo 85 40
2730 140e. Antonio Domingues 1·20 60
MS2731 175 × 153 mm. Nos. 2726/30 forming a composite design of complete picture . . . . 3·25 3·25

608 Passenger Train on Bridge

1999. Inauguration of Railway Section of the 25th of April Bridge over River Tagus, Lisbon. Mult.
2732 51e. Type **608** 40 20
2733 95e. Passenger train on bridge (different) 75 45
MS2734 Two sheets, each 140 × 110 mm. (a) 350e. Close-up of part of Type **608** (79 × 30 mm); (b) 350e. Close-up of part of No. 2733 (79 × 30 mm) . . . . 5·00 5·00

609 Heinrich von Stephan (founder)

1999. 125th Anniv of Universal Postal Union. Multicoloured.
2735 95e. Type **609** 75 40
2736 140e. Globe, letter and keyboard . . . . 1·10 55
MS2737 140 × 98 mm. 315e. Combination of motifs in Nos. 2735/6 (79 × 29 mm) . . . 2·50 2·50

610 Egg Packs

1999. Convent Sweets (1st series). Multicoloured.

2738 51e. Type **610** 40 20
2739 80e. Egg pudding 65 30
2740 95e. Angel's purses 75 40
2741 100e. Abrantes straw . . . 80 40
2742 140e. Viseu chestnuts . . . 1·10 55
2743 210e. Honey cake . . . . . 1·60 90

See also Nos. 2785/90.

611 Portuguese Troops and Moslem Ships

1999. 750th Anniv of King Afonso III's Conquest of the Algarve.

2744 **611** 100e. multicoloured . . . 80 40

612 Camara Pestana (bacteriologist)

1999. Medical Anniversaries. Multicoloured.

2745 51e. Type **612** (death centenary) 40 20
2746 51e. Ricardo Jorge (founder of National Health Institute, 60th death anniv) 40 20
2747 80e. Francisco Gentil (oncologist, 35th death anniv) 65 30
2748 80e. Egas Moniz (neurosurgeon, 125th birth anniv) 65 30
2749 95e. Joao Cid dos Santos (surgeon, 23rd death anniv) 75 40
2750 95e. Reynaldo dos Santos (arteriography researcher, 30th death anniv (2000)) 75 40

613 Jose Diogo de Mascarenhas Neto (first General Mail Lieutenant)

1999. Bicentenary of the Provisional Mail Rules (re-organization of postal system).

2751 **613** 80e. multicoloured . . . 65 30

614 Barata, Stamps and Mural

1999. Birth Centenary of Jaime Martins Barata (artist and stamp designer).

2752 **614** 80e. multicoloured . . . 65 30

615 Wise Men following Star (Maria Goncalves)

1999. Christmas. National Association of Art and Creativity for and by Handicapped Persons. Designs with artists name in brackets. Multicoloured.

2753 51e. Type **615** 40 20
2754 95e. Father Christmas delivering presents (Marta Silva) 75 40
2755 140e. Father Christmas (Luis Farinha) . . . . . 1·10 60
2756 210e. The Nativity (Maria Goncalves) . . . . 1·60 80

616 Macanese Architcture

1999. Portuguese–Chinese Cultural Mix in Macao. Sheet 138 × 90 mm.

MS2757 **616** 140e. black and red 2·50 2·50

618 "Madonna and Child" (Alvaro Pires of Evora) Maia, Oporto)

620 Golden Eagle

619 Astronaut and Space Craft

2000. 2000th Birth Anniv of Jesus Christ.

2759 **618** 52e. multicoloured . . . 40 20

2000. The Twentieth Century. Conquest of Space.

2760 **619** 86e. multicoloured . . . 65 35

2000. Birds. (1st series). Multicoloured. (a) Ordinary gum. Size 30 × 27 mm.

2761 52e. Type **620** 40 20
2762 85e. Great crested grebe . . 65 30
2763 90e. Greater flamingo . . . 70 40
2764 100e. Northern gannet . . . 80 40
2765 215e. Green-winged teal . . 1·60 90

(b) Self-adhesive gum. Size 28 × 25 mm.

2766 52e. As No. 2761 . . . . . 40 20
2767 100e. As No. 2764 . . . . 65 35

See also Nos. 2832/9.

621 Crowd and Suffragetts

2000. The Twentieth Century (2nd issue). Three sheets, each 190 × 220 mm, containing T **621** and similar multicoloured designs.

MS2768 (a) 52e. Type **621** (human Rights); 52e. Fashion through the century (59 × 29 mm); 52e. Windmills, electricity pylon and birds (ecology) (59 × 39 mm); 52e. Early airplanes, car, steam locomotive and ship (transport); 52e. As No. 2760; 52e. Space shuttle on launch pad (conquest of Space). (b) 52e. Marcel Proust and Thomas Marin (novelists), James Joyce (writer), Franz Kafka (novelist), Fernando Pessoa (poet), Jorge Luis Borges and Samuel Beckett (writers) (literature) (49 × 29 mm); 52e. Achille-Claude Debussy, Igor Stravinsky, Arnold Schoenberg, Bela Bartok, George Gershwin (composers), Charlie Parker (saxophonist) and William (Bill) Evans (pianist) (music) (49 × 29 mm); 52e. Performers (theatre); 52e. Auditorium and performers (theatre) (59 × 29 mm); 52e. Sculptures and paintings (art) (49 × 29 mm); 52e. Abstract art (29 × 29 mm); 52e. Charlie Chaplin on left (cinema) (49 × 29 mm); 52e. Woody Allen on left (cinema and television) (29 × 29 mm); 52e. Old and modern buildings (architecture); 52e. Modern buildings (architecture); 52e. Front and aerial views of modern buildings (architecture). (c) 52e. Edmund Husser, Ludwig Wittgenstein and Martin Heidegger (philosophy); 52e. Jules Poincare, Kurt Godel and Andrei Kolmogorov (mathematics); 52e. Max Planck, Albert Einsteinand Niels Bohr (physics) (49 × 29 mm); 52e. Franz Boas (anthropologist),Levi Strauss (clothing manufacturer) and Margaret Mead (anthropologist) (social science and medicine); 52e. Sigmund Freud (neurologist) and Alexander Fleming (bacteriologist) (social science and medicine) (29 × 29 mm); 52e. Christiaan Barnard performing operation (organ transplant surgeon) (medicine); 52e. Office workers, Joseph Schumpeter and John Keynes (economics); 52e. Circuit boards (technology); 52e. Fibre optics (technology) (29 × 29 mm); 52e. Binary code, Alan Tuning (mathematician) and John von Neuman (mathematician) (information technology and telecommunications); 52e. Guglielmo Marconi (physicist) and satellite aerials (information technology and telecommunications); 52e. Binary code and satellite (information technology and telecommunications) (29 × 29 mm) 10·50 10·50

622 Members' Flags forming Stars

2000. Portuguese Presidency of European Union Council.

2769 **622** 100e. multicoloured . . . 80 40

623 Native Indians

2000. 500th Anniv of Discovery of Brazil. Multicoloured.

2770 52e. Type **623** 40 20
2771 85e. Native Indians watching Pedro Alvares Cabral's fleet 65 30
2772 100e. Ship's crew and sails 80 40
2773 140e. Native Indians and Portuguese sailors meeting 1·10 60
MS2774 140 × 140 mm. Nos. 2770/3 2·50 2·50

624 "Building Europe"

2000. Europa.

2775 **624** 100e. multicoloured . . . 80 40
MS2776 154 × 109 mm. No. 2775 × 3 . . . . 2·10 2·10

625 Pope John Paul II and Children

2000. Papal Visit to Portugal. Beatification of Jacinta and Francisco Marto (Children of Fatima).

2777 **625** 52e. multicoloured . . . 40 20

626 Draisienne Bicycle, 1817

2000. "The Stamp Show 2000" International Stamp Exhibition, London. Centenary of International Cycling Union. Bicycles. Mult.

2778 52e. Type **626** 40 20
2779 85e. Michaux, 1868 . . . . 65 30
2780 100e. Ariel, 1871 . . . . . 85 40
2781 140e. Rover, 1888 . . . . . 1·10 55
2782 215e. BTX, 2000 . . . . . 1·70 85
2783 350e. GT, 2000 . . . . . . 2·75 1·40
MS2784 140 × 112 mm. Nos. 2778/83

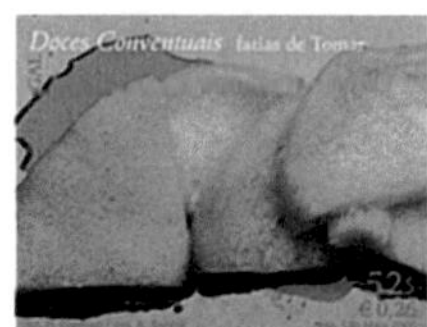

627 Slices of Tomar

2000. Convent Sweets (2nd series). Multicoloured.

2785 52e. Type **627** 40 20
2786 85e. Rodrigo's present . . . 70 30
2787 100e. Sericaia 95 40
2788 140e. Lo bread . . . . . . 1·10 55
2789 215e. Grated bread . . . . 1·30 85
2790 350e. Royal paraiso cake . . 3·00 1·40

628 Fishing Boat and Fishes

2000. Fishermen's Day.

2791 **628** 52e. multicoloured . . . 40 20

629 Portuguese Landscapes (½-size illustration)

2000. "EXPO 2000" World's Fair, Hanover, Germany. Humanity–Nature–Technology. Mult.

2792 100e. Type **629** 75 40
MS2793 140 × 113 mm. 350e. Portuguese Pavilion, Hanover (39 × 30 mm) . . . . 2·50 2·50

630 Statue and Assembly Hall

2000. 25th Anniv of Constituent Assembly.

2794 **630** 85e. multicoloured . . . 65 30

631 Fishermen and Boat

2000. Cod Fishing. Multicoloured.
2795 52e. Type **631** 40 20
2796 85e. Fishing barquentine and fisherman at ship's wheel 65 30
2797 100e. Three fishermen and boat 75 40
2798 100e. Fisherman and dories on fishing schooner . . . 75 40
2799 140e. Fisherman rowing and fishing barquentine . . . 1·10 55
2800 215e. Fisherman and fishing schooner . . . . 1·60 85
MS2801 140 × 112 mm. Nos. 2795/2800 . . . . 4·50 4·50

632 De Queiroz

2000. Death Centenary of Eca de Queiroz (author).
2802 **632** 85e. multicoloured . . . 65 30

633 Running

2000. Olympic Games, Sydney. Multicoloured.
2803 52e. Type **633** 40 20
2804 85e. Show jumping 65 30
2805 100e. Dinghy racing 75 40
2806 140e. Diving . . . . 1·10 55
MS2807 140 × 112 mm. 85e. Fencing; 215e. Beach volleyball 2·10 2·10
Nos. 2803/6 are wrongly inscribed "Sidney".

634 Airplane and Runway

2000. Inauguration of Madeira Airport Second Runway Extension.
2808 **634** 140e. multicoloured . . . 1·10 55
MS2809 110 × 80 mm. 140e. multicoloured . . . . 2·50 2·50

635 Writing Letter on Computer

2000. 50th Anniv of Snoopy (cartoon character created by Charles Schulz). Postal Service. Mult.
2810 52e. Type **635** 40 20
2811 52e. Posting letter 40 20
2812 85e. Driving post van . . . 65 30
2813 100e. Sorting post 75 40
2814 140e. Delivering post . . . 1·10 55
2815 215e. Reading letter . . . . 1·60 85
MS2816 140 × 112 mm. Nos. 2810/15 4·25 4·25

636 Drawing, Telescope and Sextant

2000. 125th Anniv of Lisbon Geographic Society. Multicoloured.
2817 85e. Type **636** 65 30
2818 100e. Sextant and drawing 75 40
Nos. 2817/18 were issued together, se-tenant, forming a composite design.

637 Carolina Michaelis de Vasconcellos (teacher)

2001. The Twentieth Century. History and Culture. Multicoloured.
2819 85e. Type **637** 70 35
2820 85e. Miguel Bombarda (doctor and politician) . . 70 35
2821 85e. Bernardino Machado (politician) 70 35
2822 85e. Tomas Alcaide (lyricist) 70 35
2823 85e. Jose Regio (writer) . . 70 35
2824 85e. Jose Rodrigues Migueis (writer) 70 35
2825 85e. Vitorino Nemesio (scholar) 70 35
2826 85e. Bento de Jesus Caraca (scholar) 70 35

638 Athletics

2001. World Indoor Athletics Championship, Lisbon. Multicoloured.
2827 85e. Type **638** 65 30
2828 90e. Pole vault 70 35
2829 105e. Shot put 80 40
2830 250e. High jump . . . . . 1·90 90
MS2831 122 × 100 mm. 350e. hurdles . . . . 2·50 2·50

2001. Birds (2nd series). As T **620**. Multicoloured.
(a) Ordinary gum. Size 27 × 25 mm.
2832 53e. Little bustard 40 20
2833 85e. Purple swamphen . . . 65 30
2834 105e. Collared Pratincole . . 80 40
2835 140e. Black-shouldered kite 1·10 55
2836 225e. Egyptian vulture . . . 1·70 90

(b) Self-adhesive gum. (i) Size 25 × 21 mm.
2837 53e. As No. 2832 . . . . . 40 20
2838 105e. As No. 2834 . . . . 80 40

(ii) Size 48 × 22 mm.
2839 85e. Purple swamphen . . . 65 30
No. 2839 is inscribed "CorreioAzul".

639 Decorated Dish

2001. Arab Artefacts. Multicoloured.
2840 53e. Type **639** 40 20
2841 90e. Painted tile 70 30
2842 105e. Carved stone tablet and fortress 80 40
2843 140e. Coin . . . . 1·10 55
2844 225e. Carved container . . . 1·70 85
2845 350e. Jug . . . . 2·75 1·40

640 Coastal Environment (Angela M. Lopes)

2001. "Stampin' the Future". Winning Entries in Children's International Painting Competition. Multicoloured.
2846 85e. Type **640** 65 30
2847 90e. Earth, Sun and watering can (Maria G. Silva) (vert) 70 35
2848 105e. Marine life (Joao A. Ferreira) 80 40

641 Statue, Building Facade and Stained Glass Window

2001. Centenary of National Fine Arts Society. Multicoloured.
2849 85e. Type **641** 65 30
2850 105e. Painting and woman holding palette and brush 80 40
MS2851 105 × 80 mm. 350e. "Hen with Chicks" (detail) (Girao) 2·50 2·50

642 Congress in Session

2001. 25th Anniv of Portuguese Republic Constitution.
2852 **642** 85e. multicoloured . . . 65 35

643 Fishes

2001. Europa. Water Resources.
2853 **643** 105e. multicoloured . . . 80 40
MS2854 140 × 110 mm. No. 2853 × 3 . . . . 2·20 2·20

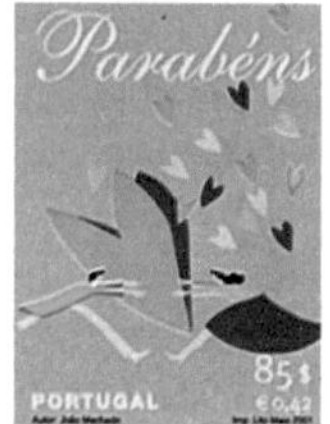

644 Couple and Heart

2001. Greetings Stamps. Multicoloured.
2855 85e. Type **644** 65 35
2856 85e. Birthday cake 65 35
2857 85e. Glasses 65 35
2858 85e. Bunch of flowers . . . 65 35
MS2859 91 × 110 mm. Nos. 2855/8 2·40 2·40

645 Open Book

2001. Porto, European City of Culture. Multicoloured.
2860 53e. Type **645** 40 20
2861 85e. Bridge and Globe . . . 65 30
2862 105e. Grand piano 80 40
2863 140e. Stage curtain . . . . 1·10 55
2864 225e. Picture frame . . . . 1·70 85
2865 350e. Firework display . . . 2·75 1·40
MS2866 140 × 110 mm. Nos. 2861/6 6·75 6·75

646 Campaign Cannon, 1773

2001. 150th Anniv of Military Museum, Lisbon. Multicoloured.
2867 85e. Type **646** 65 30
2868 105e. 16th-century armour 80 45
MS2869 140 × 112 mm. 53e. Pistol of King Jose I, 1757; 53e. Cannon on carriage, 1797; 140e. Cannon "Tigre", 1533; 140e.15th-century helmet . . . . 2·75 2·75

647 Brown Bear

2001. Lisbon Zoo. Multicoloured.
2870 53e. Type **647** 40 20
2871 85e. Emperor tamarin . . . 65 30
2872 90e. Green iguana 70 40
2873 105e. Humboldt penguin . . 85 40
2874 225e. Toco toucan . . . . . 1·70 85
2875 350e. Giraffe . . . . 2·75 1·30
MS2876 140 × 112 mm. 85e. Indian elephant (29 × 38 mm); 85e. Grevy's zebra (29 × 39 mm); Lion (29 × 38 mm); White rhinoceros (29 × 38 mm) . . . . 4·50 4·50

648 Emblem

2001. 47th Lion's European Forum, Oporto.
2877 **648** 85e. multicoloured . . . 65 30

649 Azinhoso Pillory

2001. Pillories. Multicoloured.
2878 53e. Type **649** 40 20
2879 53e. Soajo 40 20
2880 53e. Braganca 40 20
2881 53e. Linhares 40 20
2882 53e. Arcos de Valdevez . . 40 20
2883 53e. Vila de Rua 40 20
2884 53e. Sernancelhe 40 20
2885 53e. Frechas 40 20

650 Faces

2001. United Nations Year of Dialogue among Civilizations.
2886 **650** 140e. multicoloured . . . 1·00 55

651 Disney

2001. Birth Centenary of Walt Disney (artist and film producer).
2887 53e. Type **651** 40 20
MS2888 160 × 132 mm. 53e. Huey, Dewey and Louie, and 15th-century Mudejares tiles; 53e. Mickey Mouse and 16th-century tiles forming coat of arms; 53e. Minnie Mouse and 17th-century religious allegory tiles; 53e.Goofy and 18th-century tiles of birds; 53e. Type **651**; 53e. Pluto and 19th-century tile design by Rafael Bordalo Pinheiro; 53e. Donald Duck and 19th-century tiles; 53e. Scrooge McDuck and 20th-century "Querubim Lapa" tiles; 53e. Daisy Duck and 20th-century tile designs by Manuel Cargaleiro . . . . . . 3·75 3·75

652 Royal Police Guard, 1801

2001. Bicentenary of National Guard. Multicoloured.
2889 53e. Type **652** 40 20
2890 85e. Lisbon Municipal Guard bandsman, 1834 65 30
2891 90e. Infantry helmet, 1911 and modern guardsman 65 35
2892 105e. Mounted division helmet of 1911 and modern guardsmen . . . 75 40
2893 140e. Guardsmen with motorcycle and car . . . 1·10 50
2894 350e. Customs and Excise officer and boat . . . . 2·50 1·30
MS2895 117 × 90 mm. 225e. Mounted division helmet and guardsman of 1911 . . . . . 1·60 1·60

653 Chinese Junk

2001. Ships. Multicoloured.
2896 53e. Type **653** 40 20
2897 53e. Portuguese caravel . . 40 20

654 1c. Coin

2002. New Currency. Multicoloured.
2898 1c. Type **654** 10 10
2899 2c. 2c. coin 10 10
2900 5c. 5c. coin 10 10
2901 10c. 10c. coin 15 10
2902 20c. 20c. coin 30 20
2903 50c. 50c. coin 75 40
2904 €1 €1 coin . . . . 1·50 75
2905 €2 €2 coin . . . . 3·00 1·50

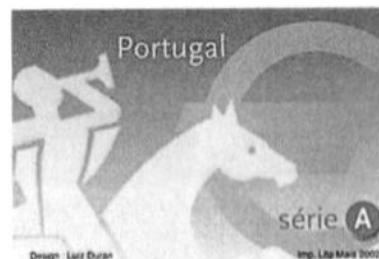
655 Horse-rider

2002. No value expressed.
2906 **655** A (28c.) multicoloured 40 20
No. 2906 was sold at the current first class inland letter rate.

657 European Bee-eater

2002. Birds (1st series). Multicoloured. (i) Ordinary gum. Size 30 × 26 mm.
2914 2c. Type **657** 10 20
2915 28c. Little tern 40 30
2916 43c. Eagle owl 65 40
2917 54c. Pin-tailed sandgrouse 80 45
2918 60c. Red-necked nightjar . . 90 55
2919 70c. Greater spotted cuckoo 1·10 30

(ii) Self-adhesive gum. Size 49 × 23 mm.
2920 43c. Little tern (different) . . 65 30

(iii) Self-adhesive gum. Size 29 × 24 mm.
2921 28c. As No. 2919 . . . . . 40 20
2922 54c. As No. 2916 . . . . . 80 40

(iiii) Self-adhesive gum. Size 27 × 23 mm.
2923 28c. As No. 2919 . . . . . 40 20
2924 54c. As No. 2916 . . . . . 80 40
See also Nos. 2988/92.

658 De Gois

2002. 500th Birth Anniv of Damiao de Gois (writer).
2925 **658** 45c. multicoloured . . . 65 30

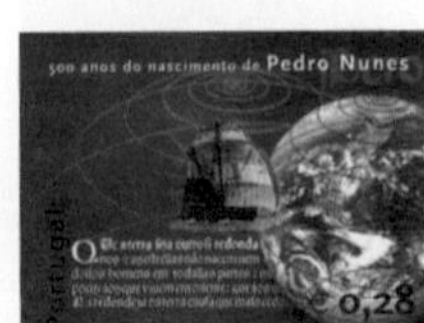
659 Loxodromic Curve, Ship and Globe

2002. 500th Birth Anniv of Pedro Nunes (mathematician). Multicoloured.
2926 28c. Type **659** 40 20
2927 28c. Nonius (navigational instrument) 40 20
2928 €1.15 Portrait of Nunes . . 1·70 85
MS2929 140 × 105 mm Nos. 2926/8 2·50 2·50

660 Children and Flower

2002. America. Youth, Education and Literacy. Multicoloured.
2930 70c. Type **660** . . . . . . 1·10 55
2931 70c. Children, book and letters . . . . 1·10 55
2932 70c. Children and pencil . . 1·10 55

661 Refracting Telescope and Polytechnic School Observatory, Lisbon

2002. Astronomy. Multicoloured.
2933 28c. Type **661** 40 20
2934 28c. 16th-century astrolabe and Colegio dos Nobres, Lisbon 40 20
2935 43c. Quadrant and Solar Observatory, Coimbra . . 65 30
2936 45c. Terrestrial telescope and King Pedro V 45 30
2937 45c. Cassegrain telescope and King Luis 45 30
2938 54c. Earth, refracting telescope and Observatory, Ajuda . . . 80 40
2939 €1.15 Cassegrain telescope and Saturn . . . . 1·70 85
2940 €1.75 Zeiss projector and planets . . . . 2·50 1·30
MS2941 140 × 111 mm. 70c. 18th-century armillary sphere; 70c. 19th-century theodolite . . . . 2·00 2·00

662 Square and Compass

2002. Bicentenary of Grande Oriente Lusitano (Masonic Grand Lodge).
2942 **662** 43c. multicoloured . . . 65 30

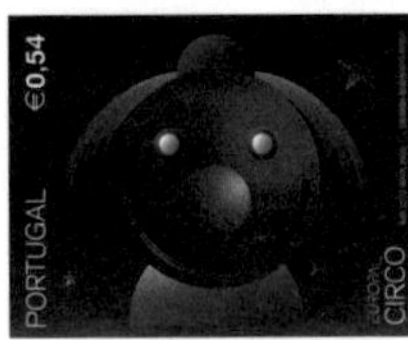
663 Clown

2002. Europa. Circus.
2943 **663** 54c. multicoloured . . . 80 40
MS2944 140 × 110 mm No. 2943 × 3 2·40 2·40

664 *Scabiosa nitens*

2002. Flowers of Azores. Multicoloured.
2945 28c. Type **664** 40 20
2946 45c. *Viburnum tinus subcordatum* 65 30
2947 54c. *Euphorbia azorica* . . . 80 40
2948 70c. *Lysimachia nemorum azorica* . . . . 1·00 55
2949 €1.15 *Bellis azorica* . . . . 1·70 85
2950 €1.75 *Spergularia azorica* 2·50 1·30
MS2951 120 × 121 mm €1.15 *Azorina vidalli*; €1.75 *Senecio malvifolius* . . . . 4·50 4·50

665 General Dynamics F-16 Fighting Falcon

2002. 50th Anniv of Portuguese Air Force. Multicoloured.
2952 28c. Type **665** 40 20
2953 43c. Sud Aviation SA 300 Puma helicopter 65 30
2954 54c. Dassault Dornier Alpha Jet A 80 40
2955 70c. Lockheed C-130 Hercules transport aircraft 1·00 55
2956 €1.25 Lockheed P-3P Orion reconnaissance aircraft . . 1·80 90
2957 €1.75 Fiat G-91 fighter aircraft . . . . 2·50 1·30
MS2958 140 × 112 mm €1.15 Four airplanes; €1.75 Aerospatiale Epsilon TB 30 . . . . 4·25 4·25

666 Gymnastics

2002. Sports and Sports Anniversaries. Multicoloured.
2959 28c. Type **666** (50th anniv of Portuguese Gymnastic Federation) 40 20
2960 28c. Walking race 40 20
2961 45c. Basketball 65 30
2962 45c. Handball 65 30
2963 54c. Roller hockey (sixth Women's World Roller Hockey Championship, Pacos de Ferriera) 75 40
2964 54c. Fencing (World Fencing Championship, Lisbon) 75 40
2965 €1.75 Footballers (World Cup Football Championship, Japan and South Korea) . . . . . . 2·50 1·20
2966 €1.75 Golf . . . . 2·50 1·20
MS2967 140 × 110 mm. €1 Footballer and part of football; €2 Torsos and legs of two players 4·25 4·25
Nos. **MS**2967 was inscribed for "PHILAKOREA 2002" International Stamp Exhibition, Seoul, in the margin.

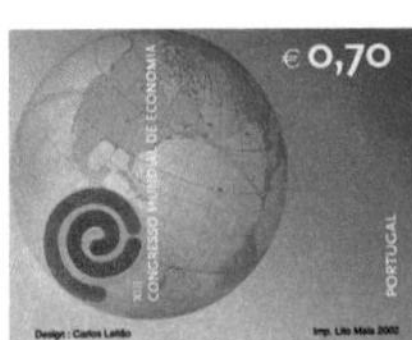
667 Globe and Emblem

2002. 13th World International Economic Association Congress.
2968 **667** 70c. multicoloured . . . 1·00 50

668 Anniversary Emblem

2002. 150th Anniv of Ministry of Public Works, Transport and Housing. Multicoloured.
2969 43c. Type **668** 60 30
MS2970 144 × 123 mm. 43c. × 6, Ship and oil terminal; Locomotive; Aeroplane; Bridge and city skyline; Factories; Houses . . . 3·75 3·75

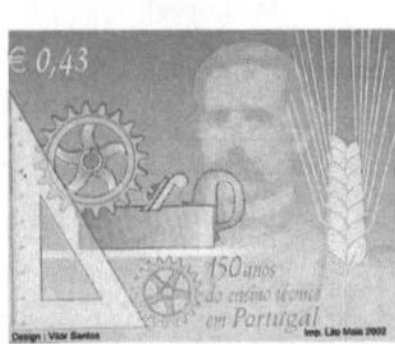
669 Portrait and Symbols of Industry and Agriculture

2002. 150th Anniv of Technical Education.
2971 **669** 43c. multicoloured . . . 60 30

670 Virgin and Child (statue) and Window, Alcobaca Monastery

671 1870 Dress Uniform

2002. UNESCO World Heritage Sites. Multicoloured.
2972 28c. Type **670** 40 20
2973 28c. Lion (statue) and embossed ceiling, Jeronimos Monastery . . 40 20
2974 43c. Column capitals, Guimaraes 60 30
2975 43c. Cherub (statue) and vineyards, Alto Douro . . 60 30
2976 54c. Corbel, lake and vineyards, Alto Douro (horiz) (80 × 30 mm) . . . 75 40
2977 54c. Houses and statues, Guimaraes (horiz) (80 × 30 mm) 75 40
2978 70c. Carved arch and statue, Jeronimos Monastery (horiz) (80 × 30 mm) . . . 1·00 50
2979 70c. Nave and tomb, Alcobaca Monastery (horiz) (80 × 30 mm) . . . 1·00 50
MS2980 Four sheets, each 141 × 114 mm. (a) €1.25 Door and statue, Alcobaca Monastery; (b) €1.25 Double doors, Jeronimos Monastery; (c) €1.25 Arches, Guimaraes; (d) €1.25 Grapes, Alto Douro . . . . . 7·00 7·00

2003. Bicentenary of Military College, Luz. Multicoloured.
2981 20c. Type **671** 30 15
2982 30c. 1806 uniform 40 20
2983 43c. 1837 parade uniform 60 30
2984 55c. 1861 uniform (rear view) 75 40
2985 70c. 1866 dress uniform . . 1·00 50
2986 €2 1912 cavalry cadet uniform . . . . 2·75 1·40
MS2987 141 × 114 mm. €1 1802 uniform; €1 1948 Porta Guiao dress uniform . . . . 2·75 2·75

2003. Birds (2nd series). As T **657**. Multicoloured. (a) Ordinary gum.
2988 1c. Green woodpecker . . . 10 10
2989 30c. Rock dove 40 20
2990 43c. Blue thrush 60 30
2991 55c. Sub-alpine warbler . . 75 40
2992 70c. Black-eared wheatear 1·00 50

(b) Self-adhesive gum. Size 27 × 23 mm.
2989a 30c. No. 2989 . . . . . .
2990a 43c. No. 2990 (50 × 23 mm)
2991a 55c. No. 2991 . . . . . .
No. 2990a is inscribed "CorreioAzul".

672 People forming Mobility Symbol

2003. European Year of the Disabled. Multicoloured.
2993 30c. Type **672** 40 20
2994 55c. People forming head shape 75 40
2995 70c. As No. 2994 but with eyes, ears and mouth pink 1·00 50

673 1853 5r. Stamp and Queen Donna Maria II

2003. 150th Anniv of First Postage Stamp (1st issue). Designs showing 1853 stamps. Multicoloured.
2996 30c. Type **673** 40 20
2997 43c. 25r. stamp and coin . . 60 30
2998 55c. 50r. stamp and portrait 75 40
2999 70c. 100r. stamp and arms 1·00 50
See also Nos. 3011 and **MS**3047.

674 *Orchis italica*

2003. Orchids. Multicoloured.

3000 46c. *Aceras anthropophorum* 65 30
3001 46c. *Dactylorhiza maculate* 65 30
MS3002 Two sheets, each 113 × 140 mm. (a) 30c. Type **674**; 30c. *Ophrys tenthredinifera*; 30c. *Ophrys fusca fusca*; 30c. *Orchis papilionacea*; 30c. *Barlia robertiana*; 30c. *Ophrys lutea*; 30c. *Ophrys fusca*; 30c. *Ophrys apifera*; 30c. *Dactylorhiza ericetorum*. (b) 30c. *Orchis champagneuxii*; 30c. *Orchis morio*; 30c. *Serapias cordigera*; 30c. *Orchis coriophora*; 30c. *Ophrys bombyliflora*; 30c. *Ophrys vernixia*; 30c. *Ophrys speculum*; 30c. *Ophrys scoplopax*; 30c. *Anacamptis pyramidalis* 7·50 7·50

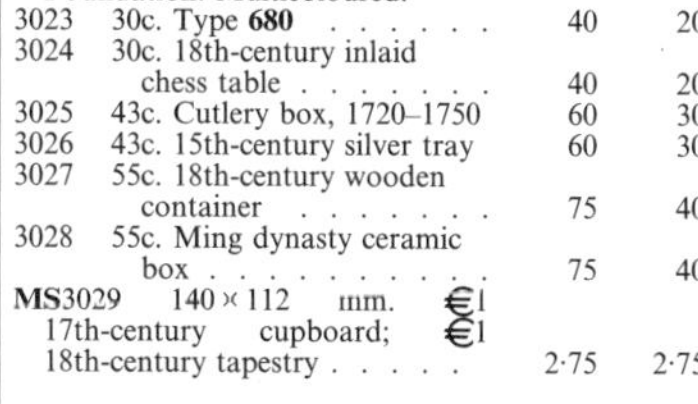

675 Jazz Festival (Joao Machado)

2003. Europa. Poster Art. Multicoloured.

3003 55c. Type **675** 75 40
3004 55c. Woman wearing swimsuit ("Espimho") (Fred Kradolfer) 75 40
MS3005 140 × 113 mm. Nos. 3004/5 1·50 1·50

676 Lawyer and Union Seal

2003. International Lawyer's Congress, Lisbon. Multicoloured.

3006 30c. Type **676** 40 20
3007 43c. Lawyers, arms and Court building 60 30
3008 55c. Medieval lawyer, Bishop and legal document 75 40
3009 70c. Lawyer's union presidential medal and female lawyer 1·00 50
MS3010 140 × 113 mm. €1 Lawyer wearing red robe and seal; €2 Seal, painted plaque and bishop 4·25 4·25

677 "150" and Stamp (Viseu)

2003. 150th Anniv of Portuguese First Stamp (2nd issue). Itinerant Exhibition.

3011 **677** 30c. multicoloured 40 20
3012 30c. multicoloured 40 20
3013 30c. multicoloured 40 20

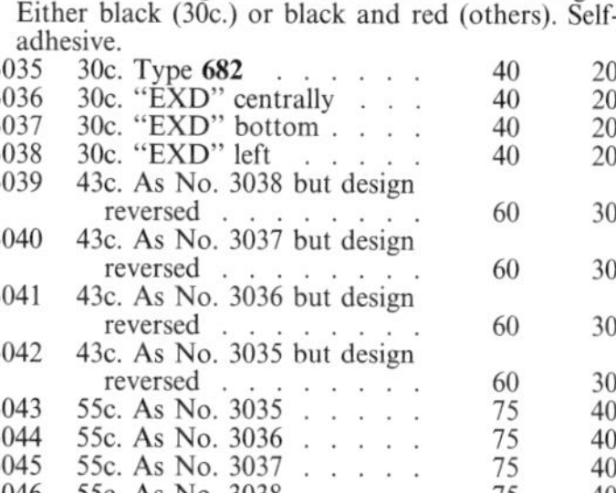

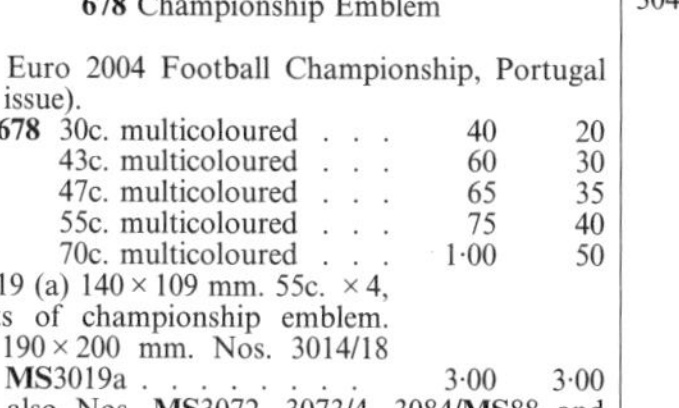

678 Championship Emblem

2003. Euro 2004 Football Championship, Portugal (1st issue).

3014 **678** 30c. multicoloured 40 20
3015 43c. multicoloured 60 30
3016 47c. multicoloured 65 35
3017 55c. multicoloured 75 40
3018 70c. multicoloured 1·00 50
MS3019 (a) 140 × 109 mm. 55c. × 4, Parts of championship emblem. (b) 190 × 200 mm. Nos. 3014/18 and **MS**3019a 3·00 3·00

See also Nos. **MS**3072, 3073/4, 3084/**MS**88 and 3110/17.

679 Open-topped Car

2003. Centenary of Portuguese Automobile Club. Multicoloured.

3020 30c. Type **679** 40 20
3021 43c. Club engineer riding motorcycle 60 30
3022 €2 Racing cars 2·75 1·40

680 Ricardo do Espirito Santo Silva

2003. 50th Anniv of Ricardo do Espirito Santo Silva Foundation. Multicoloured.

3023 30c. Type **680** 40 20
3024 30c. 18th-century inlaid chess table 40 20
3025 43c. Cutlery box, 1720–1750 60 30
3026 43c. 15th-century silver tray 60 30
3027 55c. 18th-century wooden container 75 40
3028 55c. Ming dynasty ceramic box 75 40
MS3029 140 × 112 mm. €1 17th-century cupboard; €1 18th-century tapestry 2·75 2·75

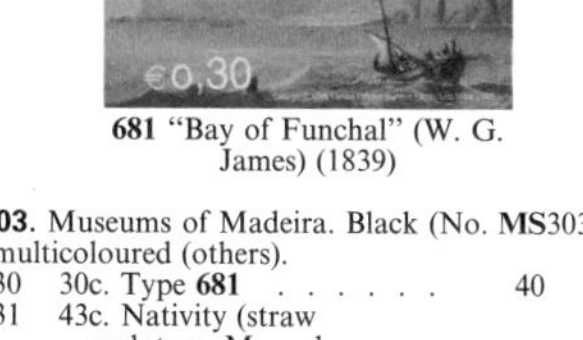

681 "Bay of Funchal" (W. G. James) (1839)

2003. Museums of Madeira. Black (No. **MS**3034) or multicoloured (others).

3030 30c. Type **681** 40 20
3031 43c. Nativity (straw sculpture, Manuel Orlando Noronha Gois) 60 30
3032 55c. "O Largo da Fonte" (Andrew Picken) (1840) 75 40
3033 70c. "Le Depart" (Martha Teles) (1983) 1·00 50
MS3034 140 × 112 mm. €1 Vicente Gomes da Silva (photograph); €2 Jorge Bettencourt (photograph) 4·25 4·25

682 Curved Shape containing "EXD"

2003. ExperimentaDesign2003 (design exhibition). Sheet containing T **682** and similar curved designs. Either black (30c.) or black and red (others). Self-adhesive.

3035 30c. Type **682** 40 20
3036 30c. "EXD" centrally 40 20
3037 30c. "EXD" bottom 40 20
3038 30c. "EXD" left 40 20
3039 43c. As No. 3038 but design reversed 60 30
3040 43c. As No. 3037 but design reversed 60 30
3041 43c. As No. 3036 but design reversed 60 30
3042 43c. As No. 3035 but design reversed 60 30
3043 55c. As No. 3035 75 40
3044 55c. As No. 3036 75 40
3045 55c. As No. 3037 75 40
3046 55c. As No. 3038 75 40

683 Queen Maria II

2003. 150th Anniv of First Portuguese Stamp (3rd issue). Four sheets, each 140 × 112 mm containing T **683** and similar multicoloured designs.

MS3047 (a) 30c. Type **683**; 30c. × 4 No. 2996 × 4 (25.9); (b) €1 Queen Maria II and euro coins (90 × 40 mm) (12.12); (c) €2.50 Seal and postal marks (80 × 30 mm) (23.9); (d) €3 King Pedro V, 1853 25r. stamp and Queen Maria II (80 × 30 mm) 11·00 11·00

684 St. John's Well, Vila Real

2003. America. Fountains. Multicoloured.

3048 30c. Type **684** 40 20
3049 43c. Fountain of Virtues, Porto 60 30
3050 55c. Fountain, Giraldo Square, Evora 75 40
3051 70c. Senora da Saude fountain, St. Marcos de Tavira 1·00 50
3052 €1 Town fountain, Castelo de Vide 1·40 70
3053 €2 St. Andreas fountain, Guarda 2·75 1·40

685 Jose I engraved Glass Tumbler (18th-century)

2003. Glass Production. Multicoloured.

3054 30c. Type **685** 40 20
3055 55c. Maria II engraved tumbler (19th-century) 75 40
3056 70c. Blue glass vase (Carmo Valente) (20th-century) 1·00 50
3057 €2 Bulbous vase (Helena Matos) (20th-century) 2·75 1·40
MS3058 140 × 112 mm. €1.50 Stained glass window (detail) (Fernando Santos) (19th-century) 2·10 2·10

686 Persian Medicine Jar and Roman Dropper

2003. Medicine and Pharmacy. Multicoloured.

3059 30c. Type **686** 40 20
3060 43c. Ceramic bottle and jar 60 30
3061 55c. Pestle and mortar 75 40
3062 70c. Still and glass bottle 1·00 50

687 Drawing Board and Chair (Jose Epinho)

2003. Contemporary Design. Multicoloured.

3063 43c. Type **687** 60 30
3064 43c. Telephone point (Pedro Silva Dias) (vert) 60 30
3065 43c. Tea trolley (Cruz de Carvlho) 60 30
3066 43c. Tap (Carlos Aguiar) 60 30
3067 43c. Desk (Daciano da Costa) 60 30
3068 43c. Knives (Eduardo Afonso Dias) 60 30
3069 43c. Stacking chairs (Leonor and Antonio Sena da Silva) 60 30
3070 43c. Flask (Carlos Rocha) (vert) 60 30
3071 43c. Chair (Antonio Garcia) (vert) 60 30

688 Championship Emblem

2003. Euro 2004 Football Championship, Portugal (2nd issue). Sheet 150 × 165 mm containing T **688** and similar horiz designs. Multicoloured.

MS3072 30c. × 10 Type **688**; Municipal stadium, Aveiro; Dr. Magalhaes Pessoa stadium, Leiria; Luz stadium, Lisbon; D. Afonso Henriques stadium, Guimaraes; Municipal stadium, Coimbra; Bessa stadium, Porto; Dragao stadium, Porto; Algarve stadium, Faro-Loule; Jose Alvalade stadium, Lisbon 4·25 4·25

689 Kinas

2004. European Football Championship 2004, Portugal (3rd series). Mascot. Multicoloured. Self adhesive.

3073 45c. Type **689** (postage) 60 30
3074 €1.75 Kinas and football (air) 2·40 1·20

No. 3073 was inscribed "CorreioAzul". No. 3074 was inscribed "Airmail Priority".

690 King Joao IV and Vila Vicosa

2004. 400th Birth Anniv of King Joao IV. Multicoloured.

3075 45c. Type **690** 60 30
3076 €1 King Joao standing 1·40 70

Nos. 3075/6 were issued together, se-tenant, forming a composite design.

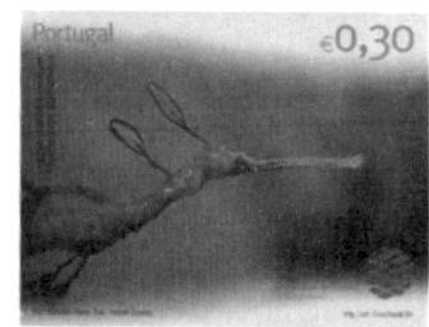

691 Seadragon (*Phyllopteryx taeniolatus*)

2004. Lisbon Oceanarium. Multicoloured.

3077 30c. Type **691** 40 20
3078 45c. Magellanic penguin (*Spheniscus magellanicus*) 60 30
3079 56c. *Hypsypops rubicundus* 75 40
3080 72c. Sea otter (*Enhydra lutris*) 1·00 50
3081 €1 Grey nurse shark (*Carcharias Taurus*) 1·40 70
3082 €2 Atlantic puffin (*Fratercula artica*) 2·75 1·40
MS3083 140 × 112 mm. €1.50 Macaroni penguin (*Eudyptes Chrysolophus*) (80 × 30 mm) 2·10 2·10

692 Foot kicking Ball

2004. European Football Championship 2004, Portugal (4th series). Official Match Ball. Multicoloured. Self-adhesive.

3084 10c. Type **692** 10 10
3085 20c. Ball right 30 15
3086 30c. Ball and line 40 20
3087 50c. Ball and goal post 75 40

693 Portugal

2004. European Football Championship 2004, Portugal (5th series). Participating Teams. Designs showing Kinas (mascot) and country flags. Multicoloured.
3089 30c. Type **693** 40 20
3090 30c. France 40 20
3091 30c. Sweden 40 20
3092 30c. Czech Republic 40 20
3093 30c. Greece 40 20
3094 30c. UK 40 20
3095 30c. Bulgaria 40 20
3096 30c. Latvia 40 20
3097 30c. Spain 40 20
3098 30c. Switzerland 40 20
3099 30c. Denmark 40 20
3100 30c. Germany 40 20
3101 30c. Russia 40 20
3102 30c. Croatia 40 20
3103 30c. Italy 40 20
3104 30c. Netherlands 40 20

2004. Birds (3rd series). As T **657**. Multicoloured.
3105 30c. Red crossbill 40 20
3106 45c. Red-rumped swallow 60 30
3107 56c. Golden oriole 75 40
3108 58c. Crested lark 75 40
3109 72c. Crested tit 1·00 50

694 "Moliceiros" Boat (Aveiro)

2004. European Football Championship 2004, Portugal (6th series). Host Cities. Multicoloured.
3110 30c. Type **694** 40 20
3111 30c. University tower (Coimbra) 40 20
3112 30c. Don Afonso Henriques (statue) (Guimaraes) 40 20
3113 30c. Castle (Leiria) 40 20
3114 30c. Tower (Faro/Loule) 40 20
3115 30c. Bom Jesus (Braga) 40 20
3116 30c. Torre di Belem (Lisbon) 40 20
3117 30c. D. Luís I Bridge (Porto) 40 20

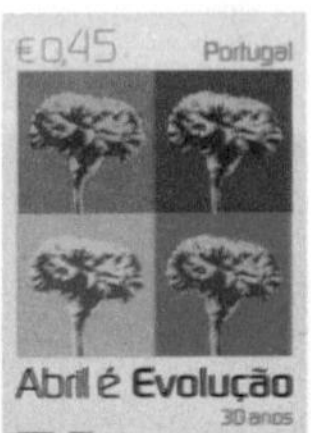
695 Carnations

2004. 30th Anniv of 25 April (Carnation revolution).
3118 **695** 45c. multicoloured 60 30

CHARITY TAX STAMPS

Used on certain days of the year as an additional postal tax on internal letters. Other values in some of the types were for use on telegrams only. The proceeds were devoted to public charities. If one was not affixed in addition to the ordinary postage, postage due stamps were used to collect the deficiency and the fine.

1911. Optd **ASSISTENCIA**.
C455 **48** 10r. green (No. 406) 9·00 2·40
C484 **56** 1c. green (No. 486) 6·25 1·90

C **57** "Lisbon" C **58** "Charity"

1913. Lisbon Festival.
C485 C **57** 1c. green 1·00 75

1915. For the Poor.
C486 C **58** 1c. red 35 30
C669 15c. red 55 55

1924. Surch **15 ctvs**.
C594 C **58** 15c. on 1c. red 1·30 75

C **71** Muse of History C **81** Hurdler

C **73** Monument to De Pombal C **75** Marquis de Pombal

1925. Portuguese Army in Flanders, 1484 and 1918.
C662 C **71** 10c. red 1·20 1·20
C663 10c. green 1·20 1·20
C664 10c. blue 1·20 1·20
C665 10c. brown 1·20 1·20

1925. Marquis de Pombal Commemoration.
C666 C **73** 15c. blue and black 1·10 80
C667 – 15c. blue and black 55 40
C668 C **75** 15c. blue and black 1·10 80
DESIGN: No. C677, Planning reconstruction of Lisbon.

1928. Olympic Games.
C741 C **81** 15c. black and red 4·00 2·75

NEWSPAPER STAMPS

N **16** N **17**

1876.
N180 N **16** 2r. black 22·00 14·50
N178 N **17** 2½r. green 14·50 1·40
N187 2½r. brown 14·50 1·40

OFFICIAL STAMPS

1938. Optd **OFICIAL**.
O900 **99** 40c. brown 55 15

O **144**

1952. No value.
O1069 O **144** (1e.) black and stone 55 10
O1070 (1e.) black and stone 70 15
On No. O1069 "CORREIO DE PORTUGAL" is in stone on a black background, on No. O1070 it is in black on the stone background.

PARCEL POST STAMPS

P **59**

1920.
P578 P **59** 1c. brown 30 30
P579 2c. orange 30 30
P580 5c. brown 30 30
P581 10c. brown 30 30
P582 20c. blue 35 30
P583 40c. red 40 30
P584 50c. black 70 60
P585 60c. blue 60 55
P586 70c. brown 3·75 2·40
P587 80c. blue 4·25 4·00
P588 90c. violet 4·25 2·75
P589 1e. green 4·50 4·00
P591 2e. lilac 13·00 4·25
P592 3e. green 25·00 5·00
P593 4e. blue 50·00 8·50
P594 5e. lilac 70·00 6·00
P595 10e. brown £100 11·00

P **101**

1936.
P891 P **101** 50c. grey 80 65
P892 1e. brown 80 65
P893 1e.50 violet 80 65
P894 2e. purple 3·25 70
P895 2e.50 green 3·25 70
P896 4e.50 purple 7·00 75
P897 5e. violet 11·00 90
P898 10e. orange 15·00 2·20

POSTAGE DUE STAMPS

D **48** Da Gama received by the Zamorin of Calicut D **49**

1898.
D386 D **48** 5r. black 4·75 4·00
D387 10r. mauve 4·75 4·00
D388 20r. orange 8·00 4·00
D389 50r. grey 65·00 12·00
D390 100r. red on pink 90·00 48·00
D391 200r. brown on buff 90·00 65·00

1904.
D392 D **49** 5r. brown 50 45
D393 10r. orange 3·25 1·10
D394 20r. mauve 9·75 4·75
D395 30r. green 6·25 3·25
D396 40r. lilac 8·25 3·25
D397 50r. red 60·00 5·50
D398 100r. blue 9·75 7·75

1911. Optd **REPUBLICA**.
D418 D **49** 5r. brown 45 30
D419 10r. orange 45 30
D420 20r. mauve 1·60 1·20
D421 30r. green 1·50 30
D422 40r. lilac 1·60 30
D423 50r. red 6·75 5·50
D424 100r. blue 7·30 6·25

1915. As Type D **49** but value in centavos.
D491 D **49** ½c. brown 80 75
D498 1c. orange 80 75
D493 2c. purple 80 75
D499 3c. green 80 75
D500 4c. lilac 80 75
D501 5c. red 80 75
D497 10c. blue 80 75

1921.
D578 D **49** ½c. green 45 45
D579 4c. green 45 45
D580 8c. green 45 45
D581 10c. green 45 45
D582 12c. green 60 60
D583 16c. green 60 60
D584 20c. green 60 60
D585 24c. green 60 60
D586 32c. green 60 60
D587 36c. green 1·60 1·60
D588 40c. green 1·60 1·60
D589 48c. green 80 80
D590 50c. green 80 80
D591 60c. green 80 80
D592 72c. green 80 80
D593 80c. green 8·75 8·75
D594 1e.20 green 3·75 3·75

D **72** D **82**

1925. Portuguese Army in Flanders, 1484 and 1918.
D662 D **72** 20c. brown 80 55

1925. De Pombal types optd **MULTA**.
D663 C **73** 30c. blue 1·60 1·20
D664 – 30c. blue 1·60 1·20
D665 C **75** 30c. blue 1·60 1·20

1928. Olympic Games.
D741 D **82** 30e. black and red 2·50 2·00

D **91** D **108** D **218**

1932.
D865 D **91** 5e. buff 60 55
D866 10e. blue 60 55
D867 20e. pink 1·50 1·20
D868 30e. blue 1·80 1·20
D869 40e. green 1·80 1·20
D870 50e. grey 2·00 1·20
D871 60e. pink 5·00 2·20
D872 80e. purple 9·50 4·75
D873 1e.20 green 16·00 15·00

1940.
D912 D **108** 5c. brown 65 50
D923 10c. lilac 35 20
D924 20c. red 35 20
D925 30c. violet 35 20
D926 40c. mauve 35 20
D927 50c. blue 35 20
D928 60c. green 35 20
D929 80c. red 35 20
D930 1e. brown 35 20
D931 2e. mauve 70 50
D922 5e. orange 13·50 11·00

1967.
D1312 D **218** 10c. brown, yellow and orange 10 10
D1313 20e. purple, yellow and brown 10 10
D1314 30e. brown, light yellow and yellow 10 10
D1315 40e. purple, yellow and bistre 10 10
D1316 50e. indigo, blue and light blue 15 10
D1317 60e. olive, blue and turquoise 15 10
D1318 80e. indigo, blue and light blue 15 10
D1319 1e. indigo, bl & ultram 15 10
D1320 2e. olive, light green and green 15 10
D1321 3e. deep green, light green and green 20 10
D1322 4e. deep green, green and turquoise 20 15
D1323 5e. brown, mauve and purple 20 15
D1324 9e. deep lilac, lilac and violet 20 15
D1325 10e. deep purple, grey and purple 20 15
D1326 20e. maroon, grey and purple 65 15
D1327 40e. lilac, grey and mauve 1·40 65
D1328 50e. maroon, grey and purple 1·60 95

D **481**

1992. Inscr "CORREIOS DE PORTUGAL".
D2305 D **481** 1e. blue, deep blue and black 10 10
D2306 2e. light green, green and black 10 10
D2307 5e. yellow, brown and black 10 10
D2308 10e. red, orange and black 15 10
D2309 20e. green, violet and black 30 10
D2310 50e. yellow, green and black 70 30
D2311 100e. orange, red and black 1·20 65
D2312 200e. mauve, violet and black 2·40 1·40

1995. Inscr "CTT CORREIOS".
D2445 D **481** 3e. multicoloured 10 10
D2446 4e. multicoloured 10 10
D2446a 5e. multicoloured 10 10
D2447 9e. multicoloured 10 10
D2447a 10e. red, orange and black 10 10
D2447b 20e. multicoloured 20 10
D2448 40e. multicoloured 40 20
D2449 50e. multicoloured 70 30
D2450 100e. orange, red and black 1·00 50

D **656** "0.01"

2002. Multicoloured.
D2907 1c. Type D **656** 10 10
D2908 2c. "0.02" 10 10
D2909 5c. "0.05" 10 10
D2910 10c. "0.10" 20 10
D2911 25c. "0.25" 45 20
D2912 50c. "0.50" 85 45
D2913 €1 "1" 1·70 85

PORTUGUESE COLONIES Pt. 9

General issues for the Portuguese possessions in Africa: Angola, Cape Verde Islands, Guinea, Lourenco Marques, Mozambique, Congo, St. Thomas and Prince Islands, and Zambezia.

1898. 1000 reis = 1 milreis.
1919. 100 centavos = 1 escudo.

1898. 400th Anniv of Vasco da Gama's Discovery of Route to India. As Nos. 378/85 of Portugal but inscr "AFRICA".

1		2½r. green	60	50
2		5r. red	60	50
3		10r. purple	60	50
4		25r. green	60	50
5		50r. blue	60	50
6		75r. brown	5·00	4·25
7		100r. brown	5·00	3·50
8		150r. brown	7·25	3·50

CHARITY TAX STAMPS

C 1

1919. Fiscal stamps optd **TAXA DE GUERRA**.

C1	C 1	1c. black and green	65	65
C2		5c. black and green	65	65

POSTAGE DUE STAMPS

D 1

1945. Value in black.

D1	D 1	10c. purple	25	25
D2		20c. purple	25	25
D3		30c. blue	25	25
D4		40c. brown	25	25
D5		50c. lilac	25	25
D6		1e. brown	1·20	1·20
D7		2e. green	2·00	2·00
D8		3e. red	3·25	3·25
D9		5e. yellow	5·00	5·00

PORTUGUESE CONGO Pt. 9

The area known as Portuguese Congo, now called Cabinda, was the part of Angola north of the River Congo. It issued its own stamps from 1894 until 1920.

1894. 1000 reis = 1 milreis.
1913. 100 centavos = 1 escudo.

1894. "Figures" key-type inscr " CONGO".

8	R	5r. orange	95	85
9		10r. mauve	1·40	90
10		15r. brown	2·40	1·90
12		20r. lilac	2·40	1·90
13		25r. green	1·50	55
22		50r. blue	2·75	1·70
5		75r. pink	5·00	3·00
6		80r. green	6·25	4·50
7		100r. brown on yellow	5·50	3·75
17		150r. red on pink	10·50	8·75
18		200r. blue on blue	10·50	8·75
19		300r. blue on brown	13·50	11·00

1898. "King Carlos" key-type inscr "CONGO".

24	S	2½r. grey	35	30
25		5r. red	35	30
26		10r. green	60	30
27		15r. brown	1·20	1·20
66		15r. green	95	15
28		20r. lilac	95	70
29		25r. green	1·20	70
67		25r. red	95	15
30		50r. blue	1·70	1·20
68		50r. brown	2·20	1·40
69		65r. blue	6·75	5·50
31		75r. pink	3·00	1·30
70		75r. purple	2·75	2·30
32		80r. mauve	3·00	2·00
33		100r. blue on blue	2·40	1·80
71		115r. brown on pink	6·75	4·75
72		130r. brown on yellow	8·00	6·75
34		150r. brown on yellow	3·25	2·50
35		200r. purple on pink	4·75	3·00
36		300r. blue on pink	4·00	2·75
73		400r. blue on cream	7·75	6·50
37		500r. black on blue	14·00	8·00
38		700r. mauve on yellow	26·00	16·00

1902. Surch.

74	S	50r. on 65r. blue	4·00	2·50
40	R	65r. on 15r. brown	3·75	2·50
41		65r. on 20r. lilac	1·80	1·40
44		65r. on 25r. green	3·75	2·50
46		65r. on 300r. blue on brn	4·75	4·50
50	V	115r. on 2½r. brown	3·75	2·50
47	R	115r. on 10r. mauve	3·75	2·50
48		115r. on 50r. blue	3·50	2·50
53		130r. on 5r. orange	3·75	2·75
54		130r. on 75r. pink	3·75	2·50
57		130r. on 100r. brn on yell	3·75	2·75
58		400r. on 80r. green	1·60	1·20
60		400r. on 150r. red on pink	2·30	1·90
61		400r. on 200r. blue on blue	2·30	1·90

1902. "King Carlos" key-type of Portuguese Congo optd **PROVISORIO**.

62	S	15r. brown	1·70	1·20
63		25r. green	1·70	1·20
64		50r. blue	1·70	1·20
65		75r. pink	4·00	4·00

1911. "King Carlos" key-type of Angola, optd **REPUBLICA** and **CONGO** with bar (200r. also surch).

75	S	2½r. grey	1·20	80
76		5r. red	1·70	1·20
77		10r. green	1·70	1·20
78		15r. green	1·70	1·20
79		25r. on 200r. purple on pink	2·50	1·70

1911. "King Carlos" key-type of Portuguese Congo optd **REPUBLICA**.

80	S	2½r. grey	20	20
81		5r. orange	30	30
82		10r. green	30	30
83		15r. green	30	30
84		20r. lilac	30	30
85		25r. red	30	30
86		50r. brown	40	30
87		75r. purple	65	55
88		100r. blue on blue	80	55
89		115r. brown on pink	1·20	95
90		130r. brown on yellow	1·20	95
143		200r. purple on pink	2·10	1·50
92		400r. blue on cream	4·75	3·00
93		500r. black on blue	4·75	3·00
94		700r. mauve on yellow	5·75	3·50

1913. Surch **REPUBLICA CONGO** and value on "Vasco da Gama" stamps of (a) Portuguese Colonies.

95		¼c. on 2½r. green	90	75
96		½c. on 5r. red	90	75
97		1c. on 10r. purple	90	75
98		2½c. on 25r. green	90	75
99		5c. on 50r. blue	1·10	1·00
100		7½c. on 75r. brown	1·90	1·70
101		10c. on 100r. brown	1·40	1·00
102		15c. on 150r. brown	1·00	1·00

(b) Macao.

103		¼c. on ½a. green	1·20	1·10
104		½c. on 1a. red	1·20	1·10
105		1c. on 2a. purple	1·20	1·10
106		2½c. on 4a. green	1·20	1·10
107		5c. on 8a. blue	1·20	1·10
108		7½c. on 12a. brown	2·40	1·60
109		10c. on 16a. brown	1·50	1·10
110		15c. on 24a. brown	1·50	1·10

(c) Portuguese Timor.

111		¼c. on ½a. green	1·20	1·10
112		½c. on 1a. red	1·20	1·10
113		1c. on 2a. purple	1·20	1·10
114		2½c. on 4a. green	1·20	1·10
115		5c. on 8a. blue	1·20	1·10
116		7½c. on 12a. brown	2·40	1·60
117		10c. on 16a. brown	1·50	1·10
118		15c. on 24a. brown	1·50	1·10

1914. "Ceres" key-type inscr "CONGO".

135	U	¼c. green	45	35
120		½c. black	55	35
121		1c. green	1·90	1·20
122		1½c. brown	1·20	75
136		2c. red	45	35
124		2½c. violet	40	35
125		5c. blue	55	55
126		7½c. brown	90	75
127		8c. grey	1·10	90
128		10c. red	1·10	90
129		15c. purple	1·20	90
130		20c. green	1·20	90
131		30c. brown on green	2·50	1·50
132		40c. brown on pink	2·50	1·70
133		50c. orange on orange	3·00	1·70
134		1c. green on blue	3·75	2·75

1914. "King Carlos" key-type of Portuguese Congo optd **PROVISORIO** and **REPUBLICA**.

146	S	15r. brown (No. 62)	85	55
147		50r. blue (No. 64)	85	55
140		75r. pink (No. 65)	1·30	1·10

1914. Provisional stamps of 1902 optd **REPUBLICA**.

148	S	50r. on 65r. blue	85	55
150	V	115r. on 2½r. brown	55	30
151	R	115r. on 10r. mauve	50	35
154		115r. on 50r. blue	1·30	75
156		130r. on 5r. orange	1·30	75
157		130r. on 75r. pink	85	55
160		130r. on 100r. brown on yellow	60	35

NEWSPAPER STAMP

1894. "Newspaper" key-type inscr "CONGO".

N24	V	2½r. brown	95	80

PORTUGUESE GUINEA Pt. 9

A former Portuguese territory, on the west coast of Africa, with adjacent islands. Used stamps of Cape Verde Islands from 1877 until 1881. In September 1974 the territory became independent and was renamed Guinea-Bissau.

1881. 1000 reis = 1 milreis.
1913. 100 centavos = 1 escudo.

1881. "Crown" key-type inscr "CABO VERDE" and optd **GUINE**.

19	P	5r. black	4·00	3·00
20		10r. yellow	£160	£160
31		10r. green	6·75	4·75
21		20r. bistre	3·25	2·20
32		20r. red	6·75	5·00
13		25r. pink	2·40	1·70
28		25r. lilac	3·00	1·90
23		40r. blue	£180	£110
29		40r. yellow	1·90	1·50
24		50r. green	£180	£110
30		50r. blue	5·75	2·50
16		100r. lilac	8·00	6·25
17		200r. orange	11·50	8·00
18		300r. brown	14·00	11·00

3

24 Ceres

1886.

35	3	5r. black	6·00	5·50
36		10r. green	7·25	4·00
37		20r. red	10·50	4·00
38		25r. purple	10·50	6·25
46		40r. brown	8·75	6·25
40		50r. blue	17·00	6·25
47		80r. grey	16·00	11·00
48		100r. brown	16·00	11·00
43		200r. lilac	38·00	22·00
44		300r. orange	48·00	36·00

1893. "Figures" key-type inscr "GUINE".

50	R	5r. yellow	1·90	1·10
51		10r. mauve	1·90	1·10
52		15r. brown	2·40	1·50
53		20r. lilac	2·40	1·50
54		25r. green	2·40	1·50
55		50r. blue	4·25	2·20
57		75r. pink	11·50	7·00
58		80r. green	11·50	7·00
59		100r. brown on buff	11·50	7·00
60		150r. red on pink	11·50	7·00
61		200r. blue on blue	19·00	15·00
62		300r. blue on brown	18·00	15·00

1898. "King Carlos" key-type inscr "GUINE".

65	S	2½r. grey	35	30
66		5r. red	35	30
67		10r. green	35	30
68		15r. brown	3·00	2·20
114		15r. green	1·80	95
69		20r. lilac	1·40	95
70		25r. green	1·70	1·10
115		25r. red	95	55
71		50r. blue	2·20	1·20
116		50r. brown	2·40	1·80
117		65r. blue	7·50	6·00
72		75r. pink	12·50	8·25
118		75r. purple	3·25	3·00
73		80r. mauve	3·00	1·90
74		100r. blue on blue	2·75	1·90
119		115r. brown on pink	8·50	6·25
120		130r. brown on yellow	8·75	6·25
75		150r. brown on yellow	9·00	3·75
76		200r. purple on pink	9·00	3·75
77		300r. blue on pink	8·00	4·75
121		400r. blue on yellow	9·50	7·00
78		500r. black on blue	12·50	7·25
79		700r. mauve on yellow	17·00	12·00

1902. Surch.

122	S	50r. on 65r. blue	4·75	3·00
81	3	65r. on 10r. green	6·75	3·75
84	R	65r. on 10r. mauve	5·75	3·00
85		65r. on 15r. brown	5·75	3·00
82	3	65r. on 20r. red	6·75	3·75
86	R	65r. on 20r. lilac	5·75	3·00
83	3	65r. on 25r. purple	6·75	3·75
88	R	65r. on 50r. blue	2·75	2·50
97	V	115r. on 2½r. brown	4·00	2·75
93	R	115r. on 5r. yellow	5·25	2·75
95		115r. on 25r. green	6·00	3·00
89	3	115r. on 40r. brown	5·75	3·50
91		115r. on 50r. blue	5·75	3·50
92		115r. on 300r. orange	7·25	4·75
98		130r. on 80r. grey	7·25	5·25
100		130r. on 100r. brown	7·75	5·25
102	R	130r. on 150r. red on pink	6·00	3·00
103		130r. on 200r. blue on blue	6·75	3·50
104		130r. on 300r. blue on brn	6·75	4·00
105	3	400r. on 5r. black	33·00	31·00
107	R	400r. on 75r. pink	4·25	4·00
108		400r. on 80r. green	2·75	1·70
109		400r. on 100r. brn on buff	3·75	1·70
106	3	400r. on 200r. lilac	12·50	7·00

1902. "King Carlos" key-type of Portuguese Guinea optd **PROVISORIO**.

110	S	15r. brown	2·40	1·50
111		25r. green	2·40	1·50
112		50r. blue	2·75	1·70
113		75r. pink	5·75	4·75

1911. "King Carlos" key-type of Portuguese Guinea optd **REPUBLICA**.

123	S	2½r. grey	45	35
124		5r. red	55	35
125		10r. green	65	35
126		15r. green	65	50
127		20r. lilac	65	50
128		25r. red	65	50
129		50r. brown	5·50	3·00
130		75r. purple	65	50
131		100r. blue on blue	65	50
132		115r. brown on pink	1·50	60
133		130r. brown on yellow	1·50	70
134		200r. purple on pink	1·50	70
135		400r. blue on yellow	7·00	2·75
136		500r. black on blue	2·30	1·70
137		700r. mauve on yellow	2·30	1·70

1913. Surch **REPUBLICA GUINE** and value on "Vasco da Gama" stamps. (a) Portuguese Colonies.

138		¼c. on 2½r. green	3·50	4·00
139		½c. on 5r. red	1·50	1·30
140		1c. on 10r. purple	1·50	1·30
141		2½c. on 25r. green	1·50	1·30
142		5c. on 50r. blue	1·50	1·30
143		7½c. on 75r. brown	3·50	2·75
144		10c. on 100r. brown	1·50	1·00
145		15c. on 150r. brown	4·25	3·50

(b) Macao.

146		¼c. on ½a. green	1·70	1·30
147		½c. on 1a. red	1·70	1·30
148		1c. on 2a. purple	1·70	1·30
149		2½c. on 4a. green	1·70	1·30
150		5c. on 8a. blue	1·70	1·30
151		7½c. on 12a. brown	3·00	2·10
152		10c. on 16a. brown	2·50	2·10
153		15c. on 24a. brown	3·25	2·20

(c) Portuguese Timor.

154		¼c. on ½a. green	1·70	1·30
155		½c. on 1a. red	1·70	1·30
156		1c. on 2a. purple	1·70	1·30
157		2½c. on 4a. green	1·70	1·30
158		5c. on 8a. blue	1·70	1·30
159		7½c. on 12a. brown	3·00	2·10
160		10c. on 16a. brown	2·50	2·10
161		15c. on 24a. brown	3·25	2·20

1913. "King Carlos" key-type of Portuguese Guinea optd **PROVISORIO** and **REPUBLICA**.

184	S	15r. brown	13·50	9·25
185		50r. blue	1·10	90
164		75r. pink	13·50	9·25

1914. "Ceres" key-type inscr "GUINE". Name and value in black.

204	U	¼c. green	75	50
209		½c. black	50	35
210		1c. green	1·10	55
211		1½c. brown	70	45
212		2c. red	75	40
213		2c. grey	30	25
214		2½c. violet	30	25
215		3c. orange	30	25
216		4c. red	30	25
217		4½c. grey	30	25
218		5c. blue	30	25
219		6c. mauve	30	30
220		7c. blue	45	25
221		7½c. brown	30	25
222		8c. grey	30	25
223		10c. red	30	25
224		12c. green	75	45
225		15c. red	30	25
226		20c. green	30	30
227		24c. blue	1·90	1·30
228		25c. brown	1·90	1·30
180		30c. brown on green	5·25	3·50
229		30c. green	90	45
181		40c. brown on pink	3·50	70
230		40c. turquoise	90	50
182		50c. orange on orange	3·50	70

231 50c. mauve 1·90 85
232 60c. blue 1·50 1·30
233 60c. red 2·10 90
234 80c. red 1·50 85
183 1e. green on blue 4·75 2·30
235 1e. blue 3·25 1·90
236 1e. pink 3·00 1·40
237 2e. purple 5·75 4·00
238 5e. bistre 14·50 7·50
239 10e. pink 27·00 10·00
240 20e. green 55·00 30·00

1915. Provisional stamps of 1902 optd **REPUBLICA**.
186 S 50r. on 65r. blue 1·10 90
187 V 115r. on 2½r. brown 1·70 1·00
190 R 115r. on 5r. yellow 1·20 75
191 115r. on 25r. green 1·10 90
192 3 115r. on 40r. brown 6·00 3·75
194 115r. on 50r. blue 1·00 90
196 130r. on 80r. grey 3·25 2·00
197 130r. on 100r. brown 2·75 2·20
199 R 130r. on 150r. red on pink 1·10 90
200 130r. on 200r. blue on blue 1·10 90
201 130r. on 300r. blue on brn 1·10 90

1920. Surch.
241 U 4c. on ½c. green 4·00 2·75
242 6c. on ½c. black 4·00 2·75
243 S 12c. on 115r. brown on pink (No. 132) 10·00 6·25

1925. Stamps of 1902 (Nos. 107/9) surch **Republica** and new value.
244 R 40c. on 400r. on 75r. pink 1·10 85
245 40c. on 400r. on 80r. green 1·10 85
246 40c. on 400r. on 100r. brown on buff 1·10 85

1931. "Ceres" key-type of Portuguese Guinea surch.
247 U 50c. on 60c. red 2·30 1·70
248 70c. on 80c. red 2·40 2·20
249 1e.40 on 2e. purple 5·75 4·00

1933.
251 **24** 1c. brown 20 15
252 5c. brown 20 15
253 10c. mauve 20 15
254 15c. black 35 30
255 20c. grey 35 30
256 30c. green 35 30
257 40c. red 85 35
258 45c. turquoise 85 35
259 50c. brown 85 55
260 60c. green 90 55
261 70c. brown 90 55
262 80c. green 1·60 60
263 85c. red 2·75 1·30
264 1e. purple 1·30 85
265 1e.40 blue 4·75 2·75
266 2e. mauve 2·50 1·40
267 5e. green 8·50 5·25
268 10e. brown 15·00 7·00
269 20e. orange 48·00 23·00

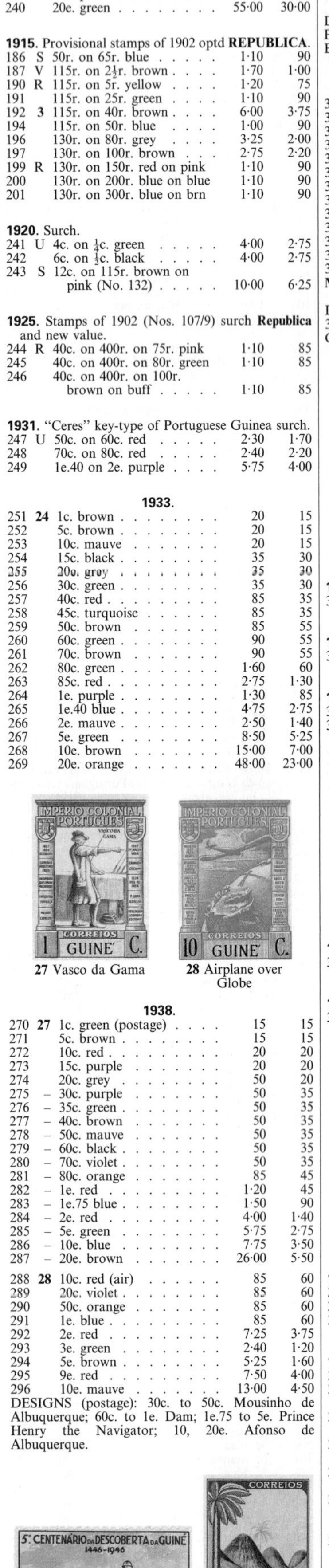

27 Vasco da Gama
28 Airplane over Globe

1938.
270 **27** 1c. green (postage) 15 15
271 5c. brown 15 15
272 10c. red 20 20
273 15c. purple 20 20
274 20c. grey 50 20
275 – 30c. purple 50 35
276 – 35c. green 50 35
277 – 40c. brown 50 35
278 – 50c. mauve 50 35
279 – 60c. black 50 35
280 – 70c. violet 50 35
281 – 80c. orange 85 45
282 – 1e. red 1·20 45
283 – 1e.75 blue 1·50 90
284 – 2e. red 4·00 1·40
285 – 5e. green 5·75 2·75
286 – 10e. blue 7·75 3·50
287 – 20e. brown 26·00 5·50
288 **28** 10c. red (air) 85 60
289 20c. violet 85 60
290 50c. orange 85 60
291 1e. blue 85 60
292 2e. red 7·25 3·75
293 3e. green 2·40 1·20
294 5e. brown 5·25 1·60
295 9e. red 7·50 4·00
296 10e. mauve 13·00 4·50
DESIGNS (postage): 30c. to 50c. Mousinho de Albuquerque; 60c. to 1e. Dam; 1e.75 to 5e. Prince Henry the Navigator; 10, 20e. Afonso de Albuquerque.

31 Cacheu Castle
32 Native Huts

1946. 500th Anniv of Discovery of Portuguese Guinea.
297 **31** 30c. black and grey 85 60
298 – 50c. green and light green 45 45
299 – 50c. purple and claret 45 45
300 – 1e.75 blue and light blue 2·75 1·10
301 – 3e.50 red and pink 4·75 1·70
302 – 5e. brown and chocolate 13·50 5·50
303 – 20e. violet and mauve 23·00 9·25
MS303a 175 × 221 mm. Nos. 297/303 (sold at 40e.) 75·00
DESIGNS—VERT: 50c. Nuno Tristao; 1e.75, President Grant; 3e.50, Teixeiro Pinto; 5e. Honorio Barreto. HORIZ: 20e. Church at Bissau.

1948.
304 **32** 5c. brown 15 10
305 – 10c. purple 2·75 1·50
306 – 20c. mauve 65 45
307 – 35c. green 85 45
308 – 50c. red 45 15
309 – 70c. blue 65 45
310 – 80c. green 1·00 45
311 – 1e. red 1·00 45
312 – 1e.75 blue 12·00 5·25
313 – 2e. blue 13·50 1·50
314 – 3e.50 brown 2·75 1·40
315 – 5e. grey 4·75 2·75
316 – 20e. violet 22·00 7·00
MS316a 176 × 158 mm. Nos. 304/16 (sold at 40e.) 90·00
DESIGNS: 10c. Crowned crane; 20c., 3e.50, Youth; 35c., 5e. Woman; 50c. Musician; 70c. Man; 80c., 20e. Girl; 1, 2e. Drummer; 1e.75, Bushbuck.

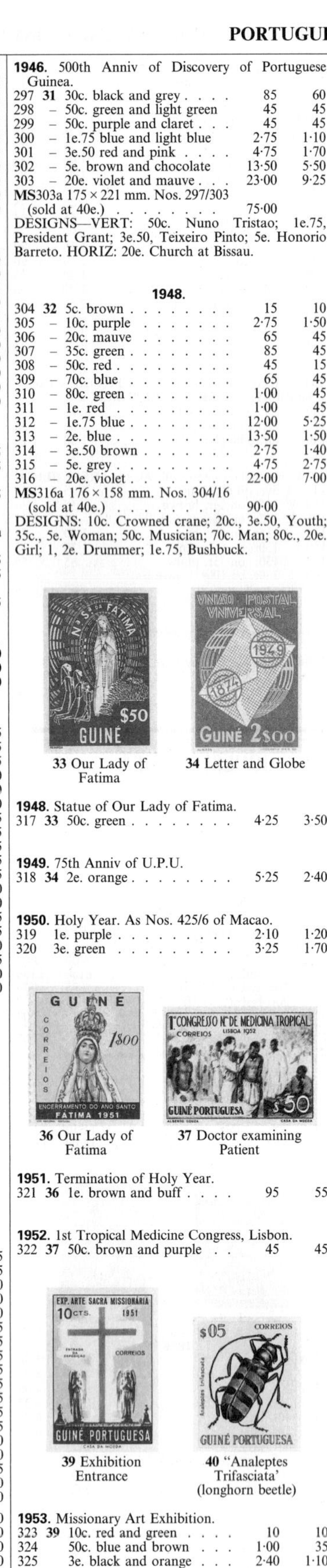

33 Our Lady of Fatima
34 Letter and Globe

1948. Statue of Our Lady of Fatima.
317 **33** 50c. green 4·25 3·50

1949. 75th Anniv of U.P.U.
318 **34** 2e. orange 5·25 2·40

1950. Holy Year. As Nos. 425/6 of Macao.
319 1e. purple 2·10 1·20
320 3e. green 3·25 1·70

36 Our Lady of Fatima
37 Doctor examining Patient

1951. Termination of Holy Year.
321 **36** 1e. brown and buff 95 55

1952. 1st Tropical Medicine Congress, Lisbon.
322 **37** 50c. brown and purple 45 45

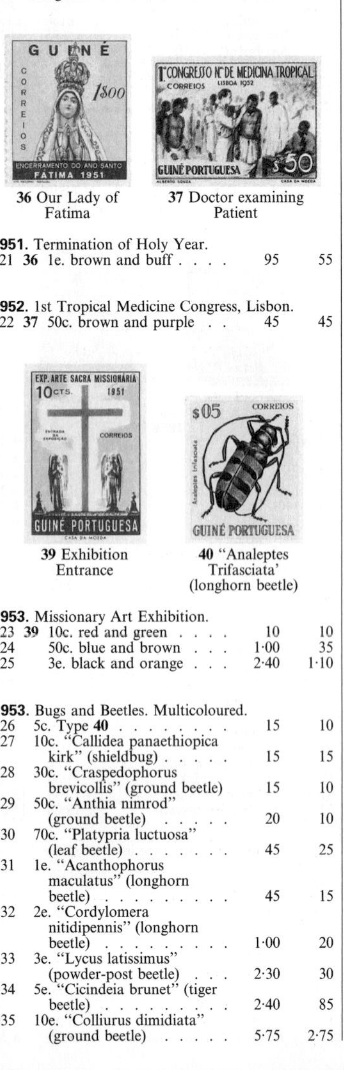

39 Exhibition Entrance
40 "Analeptes Trifasciata" (longhorn beetle)

1953. Missionary Art Exhibition.
323 **39** 10c. red and green 10 10
324 50c. blue and brown 1·00 35
325 3e. black and orange 2·40 1·10

1953. Bugs and Beetles. Multicoloured.
326 5c. Type **40** 15 10
327 10c. "Callidea panaethiopica kirk" (shieldbug) 15 15
328 30c. "Craspedophorus brevicollis" (ground beetle) 15 10
329 50c. "Anthia nimrod" (ground beetle) 20 10
330 70c. "Platypria luctuosa" (leaf beetle) 45 25
331 1e. "Acanthophorus maculatus" (longhorn beetle) 45 15
332 2e. "Cordylomera nitidipennis" (longhorn beetle) 1·00 20
333 3e. "Lycus latissimus" (powder-post beetle) 2·30 30
334 5e. "Cicindeia brunet" (tiger beetle) 2·40 85
335 10e. "Colliurus dimidiata" (ground beetle) 5·75 2·75

41 Portuguese Stamp of 1853 and Arms of Portuguese Overseas Provinces
43 Arms of Cape Verde Islands and Portuguese Guinea

42 Father M. de Nobrega and View of Sao Paulo

1953. Portuguese Stamp Centenary.
336 **41** 50c. multicoloured 1·00 85

1954. 4th Centenary of Sao Paulo.
337 **42** 1e. multicoloured 30 20

1955. Presidential Visit.
338 **43** 1e. multicoloured 30 20
339 2e.50 mulitcoloured 60 40

44 Exhibition Emblem Globe and Arms
46 Statue of Barreto at Bissau

45 "Matenus stenegalenis"

1958. Brussels International Exhibition.
340 **44** 2e.50 green 65 45

1958. 6th Int Congress of Tropical Medicine.
341 **45** 5e. multicoloured 3·00 1·30

1959. Death Centenary of Honorio Barreto (statesman).
342 **46** 2e.50 multicoloured 30 25

47 Astrolabe
48 "Medical Service"

1960. 500th Death Anniv of Prince Henry the Navigator.
343 **47** 2e.50 multicoloured 35 30

1960. 10th Anniv of African Technical Co-operation Commission.
344 **48** 1e.50 multicoloured 30 25

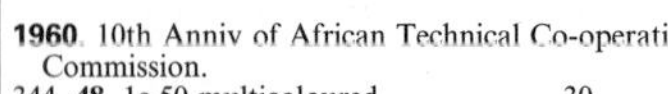

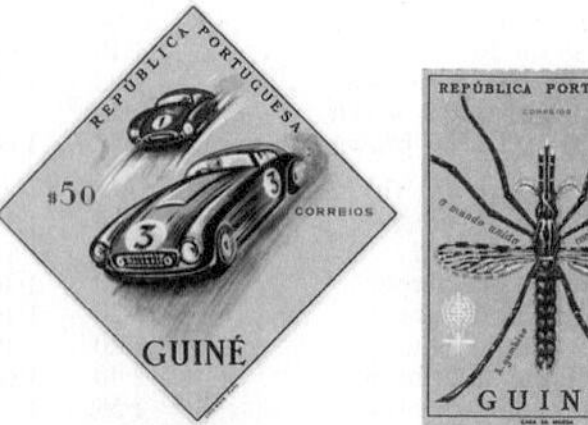

49 Motor Racing
50 "Anopheles gambiae"

1962. Sports. Multicoloured.
345 50c. Type **49** 40 10
346 1e. Tennis 65 25
347 1e.50 Putting the shot 45 25
348 2e.50 Wrestling 55 30
349 3e.50 Shooting 60 30
350 15e. Volleyball 1·60 85

1962. Malaria Eradication.
351 **50** 2e.50 multicoloured 60 40

51 Common Spitting Cobra
52 Map of Africa, Boeing 707 and Lockheed L.1049G Super Constellation

1963. Snakes. Multicoloured.
352 20c. Type **51** 15 10
353 35c. African rock python 15 10
354 70c. Boomslang 55 30
355 80c. West African mamba 55 25
356 1e.50 Symthe's watersnake 55 15
357 2e. Common night adder 25 10
358 2e.50 Green swampsnake 2·10 30
359 3e.50 Brown house snake 35 20
360 4e. Spotted wolfsnake 50 20
361 5e. Common puff adder 60 30
362 15e. Striped beauty snake 1·40 1·00
363 20e. African egg-eating snake 1·90 1·50
The 2e. and 20e. are horiz.

1963. 10th Anniv of Transportes Aereos Portugueses (airline).
364 **52** 2e.50 multicoloured 60 25

53 J. de A. Corvo
54 I.T.U. Emblem and St. Gabriel

1964. Centenary of National Overseas Bank.
365 **53** 2e.50 multicoloured 65 40

1965. Centenary of I.T.U.
366 **54** 2e.50 multicoloured 1·70 70

55 Soldier, 1548

1966. Portuguese Military Uniforms. Multicoloured.
367 25c. Type **55** 15 10
368 40c. Arquebusier, 1578 25 10
369 60c. Arquebusier, 1640 35 10
370 1e. Grenadier, 1721 40 10
371 2e.50 Captain of Fusiliers, 1740 70 10
372 4e.50 Infantryman, 1740 1·70 30
373 7e.50 Sergeant-major, 1762 3·25 1·40
374 10e. Engineers' officer, 1806 3·25 1·40

56 B. C. Lopes School and Bissau Hospital

1966. 40th Anniv of Portuguese National Revolution.
375 **56** 2e.50 multicoloured 60 40

57 O. Muzanty and Cruiser "Republica"

1967. Centenary of Military Naval Assn. Mult.
376 50c. Type **57** 25 15
377 1e. A. de Cerqueira and destroyer "Guadiana" . . 90 40

58 Chapel of the Apparitions and Monument of the Holy Spirit
63 Pres. Tomas

1967. 50th Anniv of Fatima Apparitions.
378 **58** 50c. multicoloured 20 10

1968. Visit of President Tomas of Portugal.
396 **63** 1e. multicoloured 25 15

64 Cabral's Arms
66 Admiral Coutinho's Astrolabe

1968. 500th Birth Anniv of Pedro Cabral (explorer).
397 **64** 2e.50 multicoloured 55 20

1969. Birth Centenary of Admiral Gago Coutinho.
409 **66** 1e. multicoloured 25 15

67 Arms of Vasco da Gama
68 L. A. Rebello da Silva

1969. 500th Birth Anniv of Vasco da Gama (explorer).
410 **67** 2e.50 multicoloured 30 10

1969. Centenary of Overseas Administrative Reforms.
411 **68** 50c. multicoloured 25 10

69 Arms of King Manoel I
70 Ulysses Grant and Square, Bolama

1969. 500th Birth Anniv of Manoel I.
412 **69** 2e. multicoloured 30 10

1970. Centenary of Arbitral Judgment on Sovereignty of Bolama.
413 **70** 2e.50 multicoloured 35 20

71 Marshal Carmona
73 Camoens

1970. Birth Centenary of Marshal Carmona.
414 **71** 1e.50 multicoloured 30 15

1972. 400th Anniv of Camoens' "The Lusiads" (epic poem).
422 **73** 50c. multicoloured 25 20

74 Weightlifting and Hammer-throwing

1972. Olympic Games, Munich.
423 **74** 2e.50 multicoloured 30 10

75 Fairey IIID Seaplane "Lusitania" taking-off from Lisbon

1972. 50th Anniv of 1st Lisbon–Rio de Janeiro Flight.
424 **75** 1e. multicoloured 20 10

76 W.M.O. Emblem

1973. Centenary of I.M.O./W.M.O.
425 **76** 2e. multicoloured 25 15

CHARITY TAX STAMPS

The notes under this heading in Portugal also apply here.

C **16**
C **29a** Arms
C **26**

1919. Fiscal stamp optd **REPUBLICA TAXA DE GUERRA.**
C241 C **16** 10r. brown, buff & blk 50·00 37·00

1925. Marquis de Pombal Commem stamps of Portugal but inscr "GUINE".
C247 C **73** 15c. black and red . . 65 55
C248 – 15c. black and red . . 65 55
C249 C **75** 15c. black and red . . 65 55

1934.
C270 C **26** 50c. purple and green 10·00 5·50

1938.
C297 C **29a** 50c. yellow . . . . . 9·25 4·75
C298 50c. brown and green 9·25 4·75

1942. As Type **C 29a** but smaller, 20½ × 25 mm.
C299 C **29a** 50c. black and brown 20 20
C300 50c. black and yellow 2·30 1·30
C301 50c. brown and yellow . . . . . 2·20 90
C302 2e.50 black and blue 30 35
C303 5e. black and green 35 20
C304 10e. black and blue 1·00 45
Nos. C302/4 were used at several small post offices as ordinary postage stamps during a temporary shortage.

C **59**
C **60**

1967. National Defence. No gum.
C379 C **59** 50c. red, pink and black . . . . 1·30 60
C380 1e. red, green and black 75 55
C381 5e. red, grey and black 1·70 1·80
C382 10e. red, blue and black . . . . 3·75 3·75
A 50e. in the same design was for fiscal use only.

1967. National Defence. No gum.
C383 C **60** 50c. red, pink and black 30 30
C384 1e. red, green and black 30 30
C385 5e. red, grey and black 70 60
C386 10e. red, blue and black . . . . 1·40 80

C **61** Carved Statuette of Woman
C **65** Hands grasping Sword

1967. Guinean Artifacts from Bissau Museum. Multicoloured.
C387 50c. Type C **61** 25 20
C388 1e. "Tree of life"(carving) (horiz) 25 20
C389 2e. Cow-headed statuette 30 20
C390 2e.50 "The Magistrate" (statuette) 45 50
C391 5e. "Kneeling Servant" (statuette) 60 50
C392 10e. Stylized pelican (carving) . . . . 1·10 1·10
MSC393 149 × 199 mm. Nos. C387/92. Imperf. No gold (sold at 25e.) . . . . 5·25 5·25

1968. No. C389 but inscr "TOCADOR DE BOMBOLON" surch.
C394 50c. on 2e. multicoloured 35 35
C395 1e. on 2e. multicoloured . . 35 35

1969. National Defence.
C398 C **65** 50c. multicoloured . . 35 35
C399 1e. multicoloured . . . 35 35
C400 2e. multicoloured . . . 35 35
C401 2e.50 multicoloured . . 35 35
C402 3e. multicoloured . . . 35 35
C403 4e. multicoloured . . . 40 35
C404 5e. multicoloured . . . 55 50
C405 8e. multicoloured . . . 90 90
C406 9e. multicoloured . . . 1·20 1·20
C407 10e. multicoloured . . 1·00 1·00
C408 15e. multicoloured . . 1·50 1·50
NOTE—30, 50 and 100e. stamps in the same design were for fiscal use only.

C **72** Mother and Children

1971.
C415 C **72** 50c. multicoloured . . 20 20
C416 1e. multicoloured . . . 20 20
C417 2e. multicoloured . . . 20 20
C418 3e. multicoloured . . . 20 20
C419 4e. multicoloured . . . 20 20
C420 5e. multicoloured . . . 30 20
C421 10e. multicoloured . . 60 35
Higher values were intended for fiscal use.

NEWSPAPER STAMP

1983. "Newspaper" key-type inscr "GUINE".
N50 V 2½r. brown . . . . 1·30 80

POSTAGE DUE STAMPS

1904. "Due" key-type inscr "GUINE". Name and value in black.
D122 W 5r. green 85 45
D123 10r. grey 85 45
D124 20r. brown 85 45
D125 30r. orange . . . . . . 1·40 1·10
D126 50r. brown . . . . . . 1·40 1·10
D127 60r. brown . . . . . . 3·75 2·75
D128 100r. mauve . . . . . . 3·75 2·75
D129 130r. blue . . . . . . 3·75 2·75
D130 200r. red . . . . 5·75 5·25
D131 500r. lilac . . . . 13·50 5·25

1911. "Due" key-type of Portuguese Guinea optd **REPUBLICA.**
D138 W 5r. green 20 15
D139 10r. grey 25 20
D140 20r. brown 35 25
D141 30r. orange 35 25
D142 50r. brown 45 25
D143 60r. brown . . . . . . 1·10 85
D208 100r. mauve . . . . . . 2·00 1·70
D145 130r. blue . . . . 2·20 1·70
D146 200r. red . . . . 2·20 1·70
D147 500r. lilac . . . . 1·70 1·40

1921. "Due" key-type of Portuguese Guinea. Currency changed.
D244 W ½c. green 30 25
D245 1c. grey 30 25
D246 2c. brown 30 20
D247 3c. orange 30 25
D248 5c. brown 30 25
D249 6c. brown 75 70
D250 10c. mauve 75 70
D251 13c. blue 75 70
D252 20c. red 75 70
D253 50c. grey 75 70

1925. Marquis de Pombal stamps, as Nos. C247/9 optd **MULTA.**
D254 C **73** 30c. black and red . . 65 60
D255 – 30c. black and red . . 65 60
D256 C **75** 30c. black and red . . 65 60

1952. As Type D **70** of Macao, but inscr "GUINE PORTUGUESA". Numerals in red, name in black (except 2e. in blue).
D323 10c. green and pink 15 15
D324 30c. violet and grey . . . 15 15
D325 50c. green and lemon . . . 15 15
D326 1e. blue and grey 15 15
D327 2e. black and olive 25 25
D328 5e. brown and orange . . . 55 50

PORTUGUESE INDIA Pt. 9

Portuguese territories on the west coast of India, consisting of Goa, Damao and Diu. Became part of India in December 1961.

1871. 1000 reis = 1 milreis.
1882. 12 reis = 1 tanga; 16 tangas = 1 rupia
1959. 100 centavos = 1 escudo.

1
9

1871. Perf.
35 **1** 10r. black . . . . 5·25 4·50
33a 15r. pink . . . . 12·00 8·75
26 20r. red . . . . 18·00 12·00
21 40r. blue . . . . 75·00 60·00
22 100r. green . . . . 65·00 47·00
23 200r. yellow £180 £160
27 300r. purple . . . . 85·00 90·00
28 600r. purple £150 £100
29 900r. purple £150 £100

1877. Star above value. Imperf (241/3) or perf (others).
241 **9** 1½r. black . . . . 1·60 1·20
242 4½r. green . . . . 16·00 13·00
243 6r. green . . . . 13·00 9·50
48 10r. black . . . . 29·00 25·00
49 15r. pink . . . . 32·00 28·00
50 20r. red . . . . 8·75 8·25
51 40r. blue . . . . 18·00 16·00
52 100r. green . . . . 75·00 60·00
53 200r. yellow . . . . 75·00 75·00
54 300r. purple . . . . £110 90·00
55 600r. purple . . . . £110 90·00
56 900r. purple . . . . £110 90·00

1877. "Crown" key-type inscr "INDIA PORTUGUEZA". Perf.
65 P 5r. black . . . . 5·25 3·50
58 10r. buff . . . . 8·75 7·25
78 10r. green . . . . 10·50 8·75
67 20r. bistre . . . . 7·25 5·50
68 25r. pink . . . . 8·75 7·25
79 25r. grey . . . . 38·00 29·00
80 25r. purple . . . . 28·00 21·00
69 40r. blue . . . . 14·50 8·75
81 40r. yellow . . . . 34·00 27·00
70b 50r. green . . . . 27·00 18·00
82 50r. blue . . . . 18·00 16·00
71 100r. lilac . . . . 12·00 10·50
64 200r. orange . . . . 24·00 18·00
73 300r. brown . . . . 25·00 24·00
See also Nos. 204/10.

1881. Surch in figures.
213 **1** 1½ on 10r. black . . . . . — £275
215 **9** 1½ on 10r. black . . . . . — £300
90 **1** 1½ on 20r. red . . . . . . 70·00 65·00
91 **9** 1½ on 20r. red £160 £120
217 **1** 4½ on 40r. blue . . . . . 31·00 31·00
223 4½ on 100r. green . . . . 23·00 19·00
96 5 on 10r. black . . . . . . 7·25 6·00
98 **9** 5 on 10r. black . . . . . . 65·00 27·00
101 **1** 5 on 15r. pink . . . . . . 2·40 2·40
106 5 on 20r. red . . . . 2·40 2·40
108 **9** 5 on 20r. red . . . . 2·40 2·40
224 **1** 6 on 20r. red . . . .
228 6 on 100r. green £200 £150
231 6 on 200r. yellow . . . . . — £130
233 **9** 6 on 200r. yellow £375 £300

1881. "Crown" key-type of Portuguese India surch in figures.
199 P 1½ on 4½ on 5r. black . . . 50·00 42·00
109 1½ on 5r. black . . . . . 1·70 80
200 1½ on 6 on 10r. green . . . 70·00 65·00
110 1½ on 10r. green . . . . . 1·50 1·30
111 1½ on 20r. bistre . . . . . 16·00 12·50
157 1½ on 25r. grey . . . . . . 38·00 31·00
158 1½ on 100r. lilac . . . . . 60·00 55·00

200a 1½ on 1t. on 20r. bistre — £130
201 2 on 4t. on 50r. green £300 £250
114 4½ on 5r. black 7·75 7·75
115 4½ on 10r. green £160 £160
116 4½ on 20r. bistre 3·50 3·25
162 4½ on 25r. purple 15·00 13·00
118 4½ on 100r. lilac £110 £110
119a 6 on 10r. buff 60·00 55·00
120 6 on 10r. green 12·50 9·75
121 6 on 20r. bistre 18·00 13·00
167 6 on 25r. grey 38·00 23·00
168 6 on 25r. purple 3·00 2·20
169 6 on 40r. blue 75·00 55·00
170 6 on 40r. yellow 55·00 48·00
171 6 on 50r. green 55·00 48·00
127 6 on 50r. blue 65·00 55·00
202 6 on 1t. on 10r. green £140
128 1t. on 10r. green £130 £120
129 1t. on 20r. bistre 55·00 41·00
175 1t. on 25r. grey 35·00 29·00
176 1t. on 25r. purple 15·00 11·50
132 1t. on 40r. blue 19·00 15·00
178 1t. on 50r. green 60·00 55·00
134 1t. on 50r. blue 29·00 19·00
136 1t. on 100r. lilac 23·00 14·50
137 1t. on 200r. orange 41·00 35·00
139 2t. on 25r. purple 15·00 10·00
182 2t. on 25r. grey 38·00 31·00
184 2t. on 40r. blue 35·00 31·00
141 2t. on 40r. yellow 35·00 29·00
142a 2t. on 50r. green 27·00 37·00
143 2t. on 50r. blue 90·00 75·00
144 2t. on 100r. lilac 13·00 10·00
188 2t. on 200r. orange 41·00 31·00
189 2t. on 300r. brown 38·00 35·00
190 4t. on 10r. green 11·50 9·50
191 4t. on 50r. green 11·50 9·50
148 4t. on 200r. orange 50·00 35·00
193 8t. on 20r. bistre 48·00 35·00
194 8t. on 25r. pink £225 £200
151 8t. on 40r. blue 48·00 38·00
196 8t. on 100r. lilac 41·00 35·00
197 8t. on 200r. orange 35·00 31·00
198 8t. on 300r. brown 41·00 35·00

1882. "Crown" key-type of Portuguese India.
204 P 1½r. black 70 65
205 4½r. green 1·20 60
206 6r. green 95 75
207 1t. pink 95 60
208 2t. blue 95 55
209 4t. purple 3·50 2·30
210 8t. orange 3·50 3·00

1886. "Embossed" key-type inscr "INDIA PORTUGUEZA".
244 Q 1½r. black 2·50 1·30
245 4½r. olive 3·00 1·40
246 6r. green 3·25 1·80
247 1t. red 5·00 2·75
248 2t. blue 9·25 4·50
249 4t. lilac 9·25 4·50
257 8t. orange 8·25 4·50

1895. "Figures" key-type inscr "INDIA".
271 R 1½r. black 1·20 65
259 4½r. orange 1·20 75
273 6r. green 1·20 65
274 9r. lilac 5·00 3·50
260 1t. blue 1·70 1·20
261 2t. red 1·70 75
262 4t. blue 2·10 1·20
270 8t. lilac 3·75 2·30

1898. As Vasco da Gama stamps of Portugal T **40** etc, but inscr "INDIA".
275 1½r. green 1·00 45
276 4½r. red 1·00 45
277 6r. purple 1·00 65
278 9r. green 1·50 65
279 1t. blue 2·10 1·50
280 2t. brown 2·50 1·50
281 4t. brown 2·50 2·00
282 8t. brown 5·25 3·00
DESIGNS—HORIZ: 1½r. Departure of fleet; 4½r. Arrival at Calicut; 6r. Embarkation at Rastello; 4t. Flagship "Sao Gabriel"; 8t. Vasco da Gama. VERT: 9r. Muse of History; 1t. Flagship "Sao Gabriel" and portraits of Da Gama and Camoens; 2t. Archangel Gabriel, patron saint of the expedition.

1898. "King Carlos" key-type inscr "INDIA". Value in red (No. 292) or black (others).
323 S 1r. grey 35 30
283 1½r. orange 35 25
324 1½r. grey 45 25
325 2r. orange 35 25
326 2½r. brown 45 25
327 3r. blue 45 25
284 4½r. green 1·00 65
285 6r. brown 1·00 65
328 6r. green 45 25
286 9r. lilac 1·00 65
287 1t. green 1·00 45
329 1t. red 55 25
288 2t. blue 1·20 45
330 2t. brown 2·10 1·00
331 2½t. blue 7·50 3·75
289 4t. blue on blue 2·50 1·10
332 5t. brown on yellow 2·50 1·40
290 8t. purple on pink 5·00 2·30
291 12t. blue on pink 3·75 2·30
334 12t. green on pink 5·00 2·30
292 1rp. black on blue 7·50 3·25
335 1rp. blue on yellow 10·50 9·75
293 2rp. mauve on yellow 10·50 6·25
336 2rp. black on yellow 20·00 20·00

1900. No. 288 surch **1½ Reis**.
295 S 1½r. on 2t. blue 2·10 1·20

1902. Surch.
299 R 1r. on 6r. green 60 40
298 Q 1r. on 2t. blue 70 45
300 2r. on 4½r. olive 50 40
301 R 2r. on 8t. lilac 60 40
302 Q 2½r. on 6r. green 60 40
303 R 2½r. on 9r. lilac 60 40
305 3r. on 4½r. orange 1·40 95
304 Q 3r. on 1t. red 50 40
306 R 3r. on 1t. blue 1·20 1·20
337 S 2t. on 2½t. blue and black 2·20 1·90
307 Q 2½t. on 1½r. black 1·70 1·30
310 R 2½t. on 1½r. black 1·70 1·20
309 Q 2½t. on 4t. lilac 1·70 1·20
315 R 5t. on 2t. red 1·70 1·20
317 5t. on 4t. blue 1·70 1·20
314 Q 5t. on 8t. orange 1·00 65

1902. 1898 "King Carlos" stamps optd **PROVISORIO**.
319 S 6r. brown and black 1·70 1·20
320 1t. green and black 1·70 1·20
321 2t. blue and black 1·70 1·20

1911. 1898 "King Carlos" stamps optd **REPUBLICA**. Value in black.
338 S 1r. grey 25 20
339 1½r. grey 25 20
340 2r. orange 25 20
341 2½r. brown 45 20
342 3r. blue 45 20
343 4½r. green 45 20
344 6r. green 35 20
345 9r. lilac 45 20
346 1t. red 65 20
347 2t. brown 75 20
348 4t. blue on blue 1·30 1·10
349 5t. brown on yellow 1·60 1·10
350 8t. purple on pink 4·75 2·75
402 12t. green on pink 3·00 2·30
352 1rp. blue on yellow 7·50 6·50
405 2rp. black on yellow 10·50 7·00
404 2rp. mauve on yellow 10·50 7·00

Both unused and used prices for the following issue (Nos. 371 etc.) are for entire stamps showing both halves.

1911. Various stamps bisected by vertical perforation, and each half surch. (a) On 1898 "King Carlos" key-type.
371 S 1r. on 2r. orange and black 40 40
372 1r. on 1t. red and black 40 40
378 1r. on 5t. brown and black on yellow 60 45
374 1½r. on 2½r. brown and black 70 60
354 1½r. on 4½r. green and black 15·00 7·00
355 1½r. on 9r. lilac and black 60 45
356 1½r. on 4t. blue and black on blue 60 45
375 2r. on 2½r. brown and black 60 45
357 2r. on 4t. blue and black on blue 1·00 60
376 3r. on 2½r. brown and black 60 45
377 3r. on 2t. brown and black 70 60
358 6r. on 4½r. green and black 80 65
359d 6r. on 9r. lilac and black 80 65
379 6r. on 8t. purple and black on pink 2·75 2·20

(b) On 1902 Provisional issue.
360 R 1r. on 5t. on 2t. red 7·50 6·00
361 1r. on 5t. on 4t. blue 6·25 4·50
363 Q 1r. on 5t. on 8t. orange 2·75 1·90
364 2r. on 2½r. on 6r. green 2·50 2·30
365 R 2r. on 2½r. on 9r. lilac 17·00 13·50
366 3r. on 5t. on 2t. red 7·50 4·50
367 3r. on 5t. on 4t. blue 7·50 4·50
370 Q 3r. on 5t. on 8t. orange 2·10 1·40

(c) On 1911 issue (optd **REPUBLICA**).
380 S 1r. on 1r. grey and black 40 35
381 1r. on 2r. orange and black 40 35
382 1r. on 1t. red and black 40 35
383 1r. on 5t. brown and black on yellow 40 35
384 1½r. on 4½r. green and black 60 35
419 3r. on 2t. brown and black 3·00 2·00
420 6r. on 4½r. green and black 1·40 65
386 6r. on 9r. lilac and black 60 35
422 6r. on 8t. purple and black on pink 1·50 1·20

1913. Nos. 275/82 optd **REPUBLICA**.
389 1½r. green 40 25
390 4½r. red 40 25
391 6r. purple 45 35
392 9r. green 55 35
393 1t. blue 95 35
394 2t. brown 1·30 1·40
395 4t. brown 1·10 35
396 8t. brown 1·90 1·10

1914. Stamps of 1902 optd **REPUBLICA**.
406 R 2r. on 8t. lilac 6·25 4·00
407 Q 2½r. on 6r. green 1·00 75
415 S 1t. green and black (No. 320) 7·50 4·50
458 2t. blue and black (No. 321) 1·20 1·10
459 2t. on 2½t. blue and black 1·40 1·10
408 R 5t. on 2t. red 3·00 2·20
410 5t. on 4t. blue 3·00 2·30
460 Q 5t. on 8t. orange 1·70 1·30

1914. "King Carlos" key-type of Portuguese India optd **REPUBLICA** and surch.
423 S 1½r. on 4½r. green and black 50 45
424 1½r. on 9r. lilac and black 50 45
425 1½r. on 12t. green and black on pink 80 75
426 3r. on 1t. red and black 55 45
427 3r. on 2t. brown and black 95 75
428 3r. on 8t. purple and black on pink 2·10 1·60
429 3r. on 1rp. blue and black on yellow 75 50
430 3r. on 2rp. black on yellow 95 65

1914. Nos. 390 and 392/6 surch.
433 1½ on 4½r. red 50 40
434 1½r. on 9r. green 50 40
435 3r. on 1t. blue 50 40
436 3r. on 2t. brown 80 50
437 3r. on 4t. brown 50 40
438 3r. on 8t. brown 2·20 1·20

1914. "Ceres" key-type inscr "INDIA". Name and value in black.
439 U 1r. green 50 40
440 1½r. green 50 40
441 2r. black 65 40
442 2½r. green 65 40
443 3r. lilac 75 40
474 4r. blue 1·40 1·00
444 4½r. red 75 40
445 5r. green 75 40
446 6r. brown 75 40
447 9r. blue 80 45
448 10r. red 1·00 60
449 1t. violet 1·70 60
481 1½t. green 1·40 1·00
450 2t. blue 1·70 75
483 2½t. turquoise 1·40 1·00
451 3t. brown 2·50 95
484 3t. 4 brown 5·00 2·30
452 4t. grey 1·70 1·20
453 8t. purple 6·25 4·50
454 12t. brown on green 4·50 3·50
455 1rp. brown on pink 21·00 11·50
487 1rp. brown 18·00 14·00
456 2rp. orange on orange 12·50 9·50
488 2rp. yellow 19·00 14·00
457 3rp. green on blue 14·50 9·75
489 3rp. green 29·00 23·00
490 5rp. red 33·00 26·00

1922. "Ceres" key-type of Portuguese India surch with new value.
496 U 1½r. on 8t. purple and black 1·40 95
492 1½r. on 2r. black 70 50
497 2½t. on 3t. 4 brown and black 43·00 32·00

34 Vasco da Gama and Flagship "Sao Gabriel"

1925. 400th Death Anniv of Vasco da Gama. No gum.
493 **34** 6r. brown 4·50 2·75
494 1t. purple 6·25 3·00

36 The Signature of Francis

40 "Portugal" and Galeasse

1931. St. Francis Xavier Exhibition.
498 – 1r. green 75 70
499 **36** 2r. brown 85 70
500 – 6r. purple 1·60 75
501 – 1½t. brown 5·75 3·75
502 – 2t. blue 9·50 5·50
503 – 2½t. red 13·50 5·50
DESIGNS—VERT: 1r. Monument to St. Francis; 6r. St. Francis in surplice and cassock; 1½t. St. Francis and Cross; 2½t. St. Francis's Tomb. HORIZ: 2t. Bom Jesus Church, Goa.

1933.
504 **40** 1r. brown 20 15
505 2r. brown 20 15
506 4r. mauve 20 15
507 6r. green 20 15
508 8r. black 45 35
509 1t. grey 45 35
510 1½t. red 45 35
511 2t. brown 45 35
512 2½t. blue 1·40 55
513 3t. turquoise 1·60 55
514 5t. red 2·30 55
515 1rp. green 5·75 2·20
516 2rp. purple 11·50 5·75
517 3rp. orange 15·00 8·75
518 5rp. green 32·00 21·00

1938. As T **27** and **28** of Portuguese Guinea, but inscr "ESTADO DA INDIA".
519 **27** 1r. green (postage) 20 15
520 2r. brown 20 15
521 3r. violet 20 15
522 6r. green 20 15
523 – 10r. red 45 30
524 – 1t. mauve 45 30
525 – 1½t. red 45 30
526 – 2t. orange 45 30
527 – 2½t. blue 45 30
528 – 3t. grey 1·00 35
529 – 5t. purple 1·60 45
530 – 1rp. red 4·50 90
531 – 2rp. green 6·75 2·50
532 – 3rp. blue 13·00 6·00
533 – 5rp. brown 28·00 7·25
DESIGNS: 10r. to 1½t. Mousinho de Albuquerque; 2t. to 3t. Prince Henry the Navigator; 5t. to 2rp. Dam; 3, 5rp. Afonso de Albuquerque.

534 **28** 1t. red (air) 1·40 65
535 2½t. violet 1·40 65
536 3½t. orange 1·40 65
537 4½t. blue 1·40 65
538 7t. red 1·60 65
539 7½t. green 1·80 65
540 9t. brown 6·25 1·90
541 11t. mauve 6·75 1·90

1942. Surch.
549 **40** 1r. on 8r. black 85 70
546 1r. on 5t. red 85 70
550 2r. on 8r. black 85 70
547 3r. on 1½t. red 90 75
551 3r. on 2t. brown 90 75
552 3r. on 3rp. orange 2·10 1·60
553 6r. on 2½t. blue 2·10 1·60
554 6r. on 3t. turquoise 2·10 1·60
542 1t. on 1½t. red 2·50 1·90
548 1t. on 2t. brown 2·10 1·60
543 1t. on 1rp. green 2·50 1·90
544 1t. on 2rp. purple 2·50 1·90
545 1t. on 5rp. green 2·50 1·90

48 St. Francis Xavier

50 D. Joao de Castro

1946. Portraits and View.
555 **48** 1r. black and grey 65 30
556 – 2r. purple and pink 65 30
557 – 6r. bistre and buff 65 30
558 – 7r. violet and mauve 2·75 90
559 – 9r. brown and buff 2·75 90
560 – 1t. green and light green 2·20 90
561 – 3½t. blue and light blue 2·30 1·20
562 – 1rp. purple and bistre 6·00 1·50
MS563 169×280 mm. Nos. 555/62 (sold at 1½rp.) 38·00 33·00
DESIGNS: 2r. Luis de Camoens; 6r. Garcia de Orta; 7r. Beato Joao Brito; 9r. Vice-regal Archway; 1t. Afonso de Albuquerque; 3½t. Vasco da Gama; 1rp. D. Francisco de Almeida.

1948. Portraits.
564 **50** 3r. blue and light blue 1·60 60
565 – 1t. green and light green 1·60 70
566 – 1½t. purple and mauve 2·75 1·40
567 – 2½t. red and orange 3·50 1·60
568 – 7½t. purple and brown 5·00 2·20
MS569 108×149 mm. Nos. 564/8 (sold at 1rp.) 38·00 36·00
PORTRAITS: 1t. St. Francis Xavier; 1½t. P. Jose Vaz; 2½t. D. Luis de Ataide; 7½t. Duarte Pacheco Pereira.

1948. Statue of Our Lady of Fatima. As T **33** of Portuguese Guinea.
570 1t. green 5·25 3·00

53 Our Lady of Fatima

59 Father Jose Vaz

1949. Statue of Our Lady of Fatima.
571 **53** 1r. light blue and blue 1·30 65
572 3r. yellow, orange and lemon 1·30 65
573 9r. red and mauve 1·90 80
574 2t. green and light green 6·75 1·30
575 9t. red and vermilion 6·00 2·10
576 2rp. brown and purple 11·50 2·50
577 5rp. black and green 21·00 6·25
578 8rp. blue and violet 46·00 11·50

1949. 75th Anniv of U.P.U. As T **34** of Portuguese Guinea.
579 2½t. red 3·50 1·70

1950. Holy Year. As Nos. 425/6 of Macao.
580 **65** 1r. bistre 90 35
588 1r. red 30 25
589 2r. green 30 25
590 – 3r. brown 30 25
591 **65** 6r. grey 30 65
592 – 9r. mauve 90 65
593 **65** 1t. blue 90 65
581 – 2t. green 95 55
594 – 2t. yellow 90 65
595 **65** 4t. brown 75 65

1950. Nos. 523 and 527 surch.
582 1real on 10r. red 35 30
583 1real on 2½t. blue 35 30
584 2reis on 10r. red 35 30
585 3reis on 2½t. blue 35 30

586 6reis on 2½t. blue 35 30
587 1tanga on 2½t. blue 35 30

1951. Termination of Holy Year. As T **36** of Portuguese Guinea.
596 1rp. blue and grey . . . . . 1·50 1·00

1951. 300th Birth Anniv of Jose Vaz.
597 **59** 1r. grey and slate 15 10
598 – 2r. orange and brown . . . 15 10
599 **59** 3r. grey and black 45 25
600 – 1t. blue and indigo 20 20
601 **59** 2t. purple and maroon . . 20 20
602 – 3t. green and black 40 25
603 **59** 9t. violet and blue 40 25
604 – 10t. violet and mauve . . . 95 55
605 – 12t. brown and black . . . 3·25 75
DESIGNS: 2r., 1, 3, 10t. Sancoale Church Ruins; 12t. Veneravel Altar.

60 Goa Medical School

1952. 1st Tropical Medicine Congress, Lisbon.
606 **60** 4½t. turquoise and black 4·75 1·80

1952. 4th Death Cent of St. Francis Xavier. As Nos. 452/4 of Macao but without lined background.
607 6r. multicoloured 30 20
608 2t. multicoloured . . . . . . 2·10 50
609 5t. green, silver and mauve 4·25 1·00
MS610 76 × 65 mm. 4t. green, silver and ochre (as No. 609 but smaller); 8t. slate (T **62**) . . . 16·00 16·00
MS611 90 × 100 mm. 9t. sepia and brown (T **62**) . . . . 16·00 16·00

62 St. Francis Xavier

63 Stamp of 1871

64 The Virgin

1952. Philatelic Exhibition, Goa.
612 **63** 3t. black . . . . 13·00 9·75
613 **62** 5t. black and lilac . . . . 13·00 9·75

1953. Missionary Art Exhibition.
614 **64** 6r. black and blue 25 15
615 1t. brown and buff 90 65
616 3t. lilac and yellow . . . . 2·75 1·30

1953. Portuguese Postage Stamp Centenary. As T **41** of Portuguese Guinea.
617 1t. multicoloured 95 75

66 Dr. Gama Pinto

67 Academy Buildings

1954. Birth Centenary of Dr. Gama Pinto.
618 **66** 3r. green and grey 20 15
619 2t. black and blue 35 30

1954. 4th Centenary of Sao Paulo. As T **42** of Portuguese Guinea.
620 2t. multicoloured 40 35

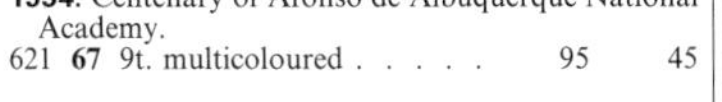

1954. Centenary of Afonso de Albuquerque National Academy.
621 **67** 9t. multicoloured 95 45

68 Mgr. Dalgado

71 M. A. de Sousa

72 F. de Almeida

73 Map of Bacaim

1955. Birth Centenary of Mgr. Dalgado.
622 **68** 1r. multicoloured 10 10
623 1t. multicoloured 30 20

1956. 450th Anniv of Portuguese Settlements in India. Multicoloured. (a) Famous Men. As T **71**.
624 6r. Type **71** 15 15
625 1½t. F. N. Xavier 20 15
626 4t. A. V. Lourenco 20 15
627 8t. Father Jose Vaz 45 25
628 9t. M. G. de Heredia 45 25
629 2rp. A. C. Pacheco . . . . . 1·70 1·10

(b) Viceroys. As T **72**.
630 3r. Type **72** 15 15
631 9r. A. de Albuquerque . . . 15 15
632 1t. Vasco da Gama 25 20
633 3t. N. da Cunha 35 20
634 10t. J. de Castro 50 20
635 3rp. C. de Braganca . . . . 2·40 1·30

(c) Settlements. As T **73**.
636 2t. Type **73** . . . . 2·75 1·80
637 2½t. Mombaim . . . . 1·30 1·00
638 3½t. Damao . . . . 1·30 1·00
639 5t. Diu 65 50
640 12t. Cochim . . . . 1·00 90
641 1rp. Goa . . . . 2·20 1·60

74 Map of Damao. Dadra and Nagar Aveli Districts

75 Arms of Vasco da Gama

1957. Centres multicoloured.
642 **74** 3r. grey 10 10
643 6r. green 10 10
644 3t. pink 20 15
645 6t. blue 20 15
646 11t. bistre 65 20
647 2rp. lilac . . . . 1·20 75
648 3rp. yellow . . . . 1·70 1·60
649 5rp. red . . . . 3·00 2·00

1958. Heraldic Arms of Famous Men. Multicoloured.
650 2r. Type **75** 10 10
651 6r. Lopo Soares de Albergaria 10 10
652 9r. D. Francisco de Almeida 10 10
653 1t. Garcia de Noronha . . . 15 15
654 4t. D. Afonso de Albuquerque 20 15
655 5t. D. Joao de Castro 35 15
656 11t. D. Luis de Ataide . . . 55 50
657 1rp. Nuno da Cunha 85 55

1958. 6th International Congress of Tropical Medicine. As T **45** of Portuguese Guinea.
658 5t. multicoloured 80 60
DESIGN: 5t. "Holarrhena antidysenterica" (plant).

1958. Brussels Int Exn. As T **44** of Portuguese Guinea.
659 1rp. multicoloured 55 50

1959. Surch in new currency.
660 – 5c. on 2r. (No. 650) . . . 15 15
661 **74** 10c. on 3r. grey 15 15
662 – 15c. on 6r. (No. 651) . . . 15 15
663 – 20c. on 9r. (No. 652) . . . 15 15
664 – 30c. on 1t. (No. 653) . . . 15 15
681 – 40c. on 1½t. (No. 566) . . 15 15
682 – 40c. on 1½t. (No. 625) . . 15 15
683 – 40c. on 2t. (No. 620) . . . 15 15
665 **73** 40c. on 2t.30 . . . . . . 15 15
666 – 40c. on 2½t. (No. 637) . . 15 35
667 – 40c. on 3½t. (No. 638) . . 15 15
668 **74** 50c. on 3t. pink 15 15
684 **64** 80c. on 3t. lilac and yellow 15 15
669 – 80c. on 3t. (No. 633) . . . 15 15
685 – 80c. on 3½t. (No. 561) . . 15 15
686 – 80c. on 5t. (No. 658) . . . 65 25
670 – 80c. on 10t. (No. 634) . . 40 35
687 – 80c. on 1rp. (No. 659) . . 1·30 85
671 – 80c. on 3rp. (No. 635) . . 65 35
672 – 1e. on 4t. (No. 654) . . . 15 15
673 – 1e.50 on 5t. (No. 655) . . 25 15
674 **74** 2e. on 6t. blue 15 15
675 2e.50 on 11t. bistre 40 15
676 – 4e. on 11t. (No. 656) . . . 50 35
677 – 4e.50 on 1rp. (No. 657) . . 65 50
678 **74** 5e. on 2rp. lilac 65 35
679 10e. on 3rp. yellow . . . . 1·00 85
680 30e. on 5rp. red . . . . . 3·00 85

78 Coin of Manoel I

79 Prince Henry's Arms

1959. Portuguese Indian Coins. Designs showing both sides of coins of various rulers. Multicoloured.
688 5c. Type **78** 10 10
689 10c. Joao III 10 10
690 15c. Sebastiao 10 10
691 30c. Filipe I 25 20
692 40c. Filipe II 25 20
693 50c. Filipe III 30 10
694 60c. Joao IV 30 10
695 80c. Afonso VI 30 10
696 1e. Pedro II 30 10
697 1e.50 Joao V 30 10
698 2e. Jose I 45 30
699 2e.50 Maria I 50 25
700 3e. Prince Regent Joao . . . 50 30
701 4e. Pedro IV 50 35
702 4e.40 Miguel 65 50
703 5e. Maria II 65 50
704 10e. Pedro V . . . . 1·00 1·00
705 20e. Luis . . . . 2·20 2·00
706 30e. Carlos . . . . 3·25 2·50
707 50e. Portuguese Republic . . 5·25 3·25

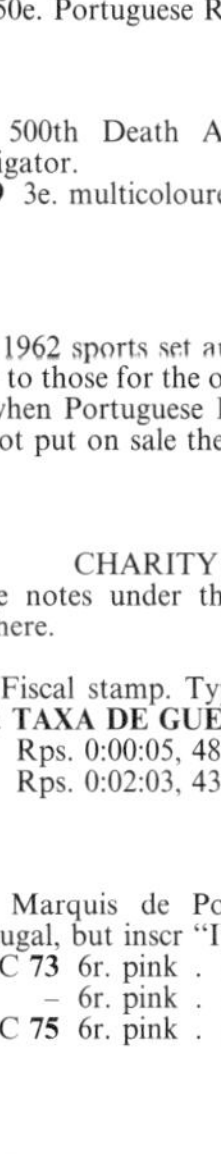

1960. 500th Death Anniv of Prince Henry the Navigator.
708 **79** 3e. multicoloured . . . . . 1·30 60

The 1962 sports set and malaria eradication stamp similar to those for the other territories were ready for issue when Portuguese India was occupied, but they were not put on sale there.

CHARITY TAX STAMPS.

The notes under this heading in Portugal also apply here.

1919. Fiscal stamp. Type C **1** of Portuguese Africa optd **TAXA DE GUERRA**.
C491 Rps. 0:00:05, 48 green . . . 2·20 1·70
C492 Rps. 0:02:03, 43 green . . . 4·75 3·00

1925. Marquis de Pombal Commem stamps of Portugal, but inscr "INDIA".
C495 C **73** 6r. pink 50 45
C496 – 6r. pink 50 45
C497 C **75** 6r. pink 50 45

C 52 Mother and Child

C 69 Mother and Child

1948. (a) Inscr "ASSISTENCIA PUBLICA".
C571 C **52** 6r. green . . . . . . 3·50 2·10
C572 6r. yellow . . . . . . 2·50 1·60
C573 1t. red . . . . 3·50 2·10
C574 1t. orange . . . . . . 2·50 1·60
C575 1t. green . . . . . . 3·75 2·30

(b) Inscr "PROVEDORIA DE ASSISTENCIA PUBLICA".
C607 C **52** 1t. grey . . . . 3·25 2·00

1951. Surch **1 tanga**.
C606 C **52** 1t. on 6r. red . . . . 2·50 1·60

1953. Optd **"Revalidado" P. A. P.** and dotted line.
C617 C **52** 1t. red . . . . 7·75 4·50

1953. Surch as in Type C **69**.
C624 C **69** 1t. on 4t. blue . . . . 9·50 6·75

C 70 Mother and Child

C 80 Arms and People

1956.
C625 C **70** 1t. black, green and red 65 40
C626 1t. blue, orange & grn 55 40

1957. Surch **6 reis**.
C650 C **70** 6r. on 1t. black, green and red 90 55

1959. Surch.
C688 C **70** 20c. on 1t. blue, orange and green 45 45
C689 40c. on 1t. blue, orange and green 45 45

1960.
C709 C **80** 20e. brown and red . . 45 45

POSTAGE DUE STAMPS

1904. "Due" key-type inscr "INDIA".
D337 W 2r. green 35 35
D338 3r. green 35 30
D339 4r. orange 35 30
D340 5r. grey 35 30
D341 6r. grey 35 30
D342 9r. brown 55 50
D343 1t. red 55 50
D344 2t. brown . . . . 1·00 60
D345 5t. blue . . . . 2·50 2·10
D346 10t. red . . . . 2·75 2·50
D347 1rp. lilac . . . . 11·50 5·50

1911. Nos. D337/47 optd **REPUBLICA**.
D354 W 2r. green 25 15
D355 3r. green 25 15
D356 4r. orange 25 15
D357 5r. grey 25 15
D358 6r. grey 30 15
D359 9r. brown 40 15
D360 1t. red 40 15
D361 2t. brown 65 35
D362 5t. blue . . . . 1·40 1·20
D363 10t. red . . . . 4·25 2·50
D364 1rp. lilac . . . . 4·25 2·50

1925. Marquis de Pombal stamps, as Nos. C495/7 optd **MULTA**.
D495 C **73** 1t. pink 35 35
D496 – 1t. pink 35 35
D497 C **75** 1t. pink 35 35

1943. Stamps of 1933 surch **Porteado** and new value.
D549 **40** 3r. on 2½t. blue 45 40
D550 6r. on 3t. turquoise . . . 1·00 60
D551 1t. on 5t. red . . . . . 1·80 1·50

1945. As Type D **1** of Portuguese Colonies, but optd **ESTADO DA INDIA**.
D555 2r. black and red 75 70
D556 3r. black and blue 75 70
D557 4r. black and yellow . . . 75 70
D558 6r. black and green 75 70
D559 1t. black and brown . . . 1·00 85
D560 2t. black and brown . . . 1·00 85

1951. Surch **Porteado** and new value and bar.
D588 2rs. on 7r. (No. 558) . . . 45 40
D589 3rs. on 7r. (No. 558) . . . 45 40
D590 1t. on 1rp. (No. 562) . . . 45 40
D591 2t. on 1rp. (No. 562) . . . 45 40

1952. As Type D **70** of Macao, but inscr "INDIA PORTUGUESA". Numerals in red, name in black.
D606 2r. olive and brown 15 15
D607 3r. black and green 15 15
D608 6r. blue and turquoise . . . 20 15
D609 1t. red and grey 25 20
D610 2t. orange, green and grey 60 50
D611 10t. blue, green and yellow 2·20 2·10

1959. Nos. D606/8 and D610/11 surch in new currency.
D688 5c. on 2r. multicoloured . . 20 15
D689 10c. on 3r. multicoloured 20 15
D690 15c. on 6r. multicoloured 30 30
D691 60c. on 2t. multicoloured 95 90
D692 60c. on 10t. multicoloured 2·75 2·40

PORTUGUESE TIMOR Pt. 9

The eastern part of Timor in the Indonesian Archipelago. Administered as part of Macao until 1896, then as a separate Portuguese Overseas Province until 1975.

Following a civil war and the intervention of Indonesian forces the territory was incorporated into Indonesia on 17 July 1976.

1885. 1000 reis = 1 milreis.
1894. 100 avos = 1 pataca.
1960. 100 centavos = 1 escudo.

1885. "Crown" key-type inscr "MACAU" optd **TIMOR**.
1 P 5r. black 95 80
12 10r. green . . . . 2·40 2·10
3 20r. red . . . . 4·50 2·50
4 25r. lilac 80 60
5 40r. yellow . . . . 2·10 1·80
6 50r. blue 95 75
7 80r. grey . . . . 2·50 1·80
8 100r. purple 95 80
19 200r. orange . . . . 2·10 1·80
20 300r. brown . . . . 2·10 1·80

1887. "Embossed" key-type inscr "CORREIO DE TIMOR".
21 Q 5r. black . . . . 1·50 95
22 10r. green . . . . 1·60 1·30

23 20r. red 2·40 1·30
24 25r. mauve 3·00 1·50
25 40r. brown 5·25 2·20
26 50r. blue 5·25 2·40
27 80r. grey 6·25 2·50
28 100r. brown 6·75 3·25
29 200r. lilac 13·50 6·75
30 300r. orange 15·00 8·00

1892. "Embossed" key-type inscr "PROVINCIA DE MACAU" surch **TIMOR 30 30**. No gum.
32 Q 30 on 300r. orange 3·00 1·80

1894. "Figures" key-type inscr "TIMOR".
33 R 5r. orange 90 50
34 10r. mauve 90 60
35 15r. brown 1·30 60
36 20r. lilac 1·30 60
37 25r. green 1·50 90
38 50r. blue 2·20 1·60
39 75r. pink 3·00 2·20
40 80r. green 3·00 2·20
41 100r. brown on buff 2·20 1·90
42 150r. red on pink 9·50 4·75
43 200r. blue on blue 9·50 5·25
44 300r. blue on brown 12·00 6·00

1894. Nos. 21/30 surch **PROVISORIO** and value in European and Chinese. No gum.
46 Q 1a. on 5r. black 90 55
47 2a. on 10r. green 90 50
48 3a. on 20r. red 1·10 90
49 4a. on 25r. purple 1·50 90
50 6a. on 40r. brown 1·50 90
51 8a. on 50r. blue 2·20 1·20
52 13a. on 80r. grey 3·00 1·80
53 16a. on 100r. brown 5·25 5·25
54 31a. on 200r. lilac 5·25 5·25
55 47a. on 300r. orange 15·00 12·00

1895. No. 32 further surch **5 avos PROVISORIO** and Chinese characters with bars over the original surch.
56 Q 5a. on 30 on 300r. orange 16·00 12·50

1898. 400th Anniv of Vasco da Gama's Discovery of Route to India. As Nos. 1/8 of Portuguese Colonies, but inscr "TIMOR" and value in local currency.
58 ½a. green 1·20 80
59 1a. red 1·20 80
60 2a. purple 1·20 80
61 4a. green 1·20 80
62 8a. blue 1·60 1·20
63 12a. brown 2·20 1·50
64 16a. brown 2·20 1·80
65 24a. brown 3·50 2·40

1898. "King Carlos" key-type inscr "TIMOR". Name and value in red (78a.) or black (others). With or without gum.
68 S ½a. grey 1·60 1·50
69 1a. red 1·60 1·50
70 2a. green 30 30
71 2½a. brown 80 65
72 3a. lilac 80 65
112 3a. green 1·40 80
73 4a. green 80 65
113 5a. red 1·20 80
114 6a. brown 1·20 80
74 8a. blue 80 65
115 9a. brown 1·20 80
75 10a. blue 80 65
116 10a. brown 1·20 80
76 12a. pink 2·40 2·20
117 12a. blue 6·00 5·25
118 13a. mauve 1·50 95
119 15a. lilac 2·50 1·80
78 16a. blue on blue 2·40 2·20
79 20a. brown on yellow 2·40 2·20
120 22a. brown on pink 2·50 2·20
80 24a. brown on buff 2·40 2·20
81 31a. purple on pink 2·40 2·20
121 31a. brown on cream 2·50 2·20
82 47a. blue on pink 4·50 3·50
122 47a. purple on pink 2·75 2·20
83 78a. black on blue 6·00 4·50
123 78a. blue on yellow 6·25 4·50

1899. Nos. 78 and 81 surch **PROVISORIO** and value in figures and bars.
84 S 10 on 16a. blue on blue 1·60 1·50
85 20 on 31a. purple on pink 1·60 1·50

1902. Surch.
88 R 5a. on 5r. orange 80 65
86 Q 5a. on 25r. mauve 1·50 80
89 R 5a. on 25r. green 80 65
90 5a. on 50r. blue 95 80
87 Q 5a. on 200r. lilac 2·20 1·50
95 V 6a. on 2½r. brown 60 50
92 Q 6a. on 10r. green 95·00 75·00
94 R 6a. on 20r. lilac 95 80
93 Q 6a. on 300r. orange 2·20 2·20
100 R 9a. on 15r. brown 95 80
98 Q 9a. on 40r. brown 2·50 2·20
101 R 9a. on 75r. pink 95 80
99 Q 9a. on 100r. brown 2·50 2·20
124 S 10a. on 12a. blue 1·60 1·50
104 R 15a. on 10r. mauve 1·50 1·30
102 Q 15a. on 20r. red 2·50 2·20
103 15a. on 50r. blue 75·00 65·00
105 R 15a. on 100r. brn on buff 1·50 1·30
106 15a. on 300r. blue on brn 1·50 1·30
107 Q 22a. on 80r. grey 5·25 4·50
108 R 22a. on 80r. green 2·50 2·40
109 22a. on 200r. blue on blue 2·50 2·40

1902. Nos. 72 and 76 optd **PROVISORIO**.
110 S 3a. lilac 1·20 80
111 12a. pink 3·00 2·20

1911. Nos. 68, etc, optd **REPUBLICA**.
125 S ½a. grey 30 30
126 1a. red 30 30
127 2a. green 30 30
128 3a. green 30 30
129 5a. red 60 30
130 6a. brown 60 30
131 9a. brown 60 30
132 10a. brown 80 75
133 13a. purple 80 75
134 15a. lilac 80 75
135 22a. brown on pink 80 75
136 31a. brown on cream 80 75
163 31a. purple on pink 1·50 1·20
137 47a. purple on pink 1·80 1·50
165 47a. blue on pink 2·40 1·90
167 78a. blue on yelow 3·00 2·20
168 78a. black on blue 3·00 3·00

1911. No. 112 and provisional stamps of 1902 optd **Republica**.
139 S 3a. green 1·00 90
140 R 5a. on 5r. orange 75 75
141 5a. on 25r. green 75 75
142 5a. on 50r. blue 1·80 1·50
144 V 6a. on 2½r. brown 1·50 95
146 R 6a. on 20r. lilac 90 75
147 9a. on 15r. brown 90 75
148 S 10a. on 12a. blue 90 75
149 R 15a. on 100r. brown on buff 1·00 1·00
150 22a. on 80r. green 1·90 1·50
151 22a. on 200r. blue on blue 1·90 1·50

1913. Provisional stamps of 1902 optd **REPUBLICA**.
192 S 3a. lilac (No. 110) 45 35
194 R 5a. on 5r. orange 45 30
195 5a. on 25r. green 45 30
196 5a. on 50r. blue 45 65
200 V 6a. on 2½r. brown 45 30
201 R 6a. on 20r. lilac 45 30
202 9a. on 15r. brown 45 30
203 9a. on 75r. pink 50 30
193 S 10a. on 10a. blue 45 35
204 R 15a. on 10r. mauve 50 30
205 15a. on 100r. brown on buff 60 30
206 15a. on 300r. blue on brn 60 30
207 22a. on 80r. green 1·50 95
208 22a. on 200r. blue on blue 2·20 1·60

1913. Vasco da Gama stamps of Timor optd **REPUBLICA** or surch also.
169 ½a. green 45 35
170 1a. red 45 35
171 2a. purple 45 35
172 4a. green 45 35
173 8a. blue 80 60
174 10a. on 12a. brown 1·50 1·20
175 16a. brown 1·20 80
176 24a. brown 1·50 1·30

1914. "Ceres" key-type inscr "TIMOR". Name and value in black.
211 U ¼a. green 60 60
212 1a. black 60 60
213 1½a. green 60 60
214 2a. green 60 60
180 3a. brown 60 45
181 4a. red 60 45
182 6a. violet 65 45
216 7a. green 95 90
217 7½a. blue 95 90
218 9a. blue 1·10 90
183 10a. blue 65 45
219 11a. grey 1·50 1·20
184 12a. brown 95 75
221 15a. mauve 4·50 2·75
185 16a. grey 95 75
222 18a. blue 4·50 2·75
223 19a. green 4·50 2·75
186 20a. red 9·50 3·00
224 36a. turquoise 4·50 2·75
187 40a. purple 5·25 3·00
225 54a. brown 4·50 2·75
188 58a. brown on green 5·25 2·50
226 72a. red 8·75 5·50
189 76a. brown on pink 5·25 4·50
190 1p. orange on orange 8·00 6·75
191 3p. green on blue 22·00 13·50
227 5p. red 37·00 16·00

1920. No. 196 surch ¼ **Avo P. P. n.° 68 19-3-1920** and bars.
229 R ¼a. on 5a. on 50r. blue 8·00 7·50 1·75

1932. Nos. 226 and 221 surch with new value and bars.
230 U 6a. on 72a. red 90 75
231 12a. on 15a. mauve 90 75

25a "Portugal" and Galeasse

1935.
232 25a ½a. brown 20 15
233 1a. brown 20 15
234 2a. green 20 15
235 3a. mauve 35 15
236 4a. black 35 20
237 5a. grey 35 30
238 6a. brown 35 30
239 7a. red 35 30
240 8a. turquoise 60 30
241 10a. red 60 30
242 12a. blue 60 30
243 14a. green 60 30
244 15a. purple 60 30
245 20a. orange 75 30
246 30a. green 75 45
247 40a. violet 2·40 1·20
248 50a. brown 2·40 1·20
249 1p. blue 5·50 3·50
250 2p. brown 14·00 5·50
251 3p. green 19·00 7·50
252 5p. mauve 31·00 15·00

26a Vasco da Gama

26b Airplane over globe

1938.
253 26a 1a. green (postage) 20 20
254 2a. brown 20 20
255 3a. violet 20 20
256 4a. green 20 20
257 – 5a. red 20 20
258 – 6a. grey 20 20
259 – 8a. purple 20 20
260 – 10a. mauve 20 20
261 – 12a. red 30 30
262 – 15a. orange 60 45
263 – 20a. blue 60 45
264 – 40a. black 90 60
265 – 50a. brown 1·30 90
266 – 1p. red 4·50 2·75
267 – 2p. olive 12·00 3·00
268 – 3p. blue 13·50 6·75
269 – 5p. brown 30·00 13·50

270 26b 1a. red (air) 45 45
271 2a. violet 50 45
272 3a. orange 50 45
273 5a. blue 60 60
274 10a. red 75 75
275 20a. green 1·60 95
276 50a. brown 3·25 2·75
277 70a. red 4·00 3·50
278 1p. mauve 8·75 4·00
DESIGNS—POSTAGE: 5a. to 8a. Mousinho de Albuquerque; 10a. to 15a. Prince Henry the Navigator; 20a. to 50a. Dam; 1p. to 5p. Afonso de Albuquerque.

1946. Stamps as above but inscr "MOCAMBIQUE" surch **TIMOR** and new value.
279 26a 1a. on 15c. purple (post) 3·25 2·75
280 – 4a. on 35c. green 3·25 2·75
281 – 8a. on 50c. mauve 3·25 2·75
282 – 10a. on 70c. violet 3·25 2·75
283 – 12a. on 1e. red 3·25 2·75
284 – 20a. on 1e.75 blue 3·25 2·75

285 26b 8a. on 50c. orange (air) 3·25 2·75
286 12a. on 1e. blue 3·25 2·75
287 40a. on 3e. green 3·25 2·75
288 50a. on 5e. brown 3·25 2·75
289 1p. on 10e. mauve 3·75 2·75

1947. Nos. 253/64 and 270/78 optd **LIBERTACAO**.
290 26a 1a. green (postage) 9·50 6·25
291 2a. brown 22·00 12·00
292 3a. violet 8·75 3·75
293 4a. green 8·75 3·75
294 – 5a. red 3·75 1·50
295 – 8a. purple 95 45
296 – 10a. mauve 3·75 1·60
297 – 12a. red 3·75 1·60
298 – 15a. orange 3·75 1·60
299 – 20a. blue 48·00 27·00
300 – 40a. black 9·50 7·50

301 26b 1a. red (air) 15·00 4·00
302 2a. violet 15·00 4·00
303 3a. orange 15·00 4·00
304 5a. blue 15·00 4·00
305 10a. red 3·75 1·30
306 20a. green 3·75 1·30
307 50a. brown 3·75 1·30
308 70a. red 15·00 3·75
309 1p. mauve 6·25 1·50

30 Girl with Gong

31 Pottery-making

1948.
310 – 1a. brown and turquoise 60 30
311 30 3a. brown and grey 1·30 65
312 – 4a. green and mauve 1·60 1·30
313 – 8a. grey and red 95 35
314 – 10a. green and brown 95 35
315 – 20a. ultramarine and blue 95 60
316 – 1p. blue and orange 19·00 4·50
317 – 3p. brown and violet 19·00 8·00
DESIGNS: 1a. Native woman; 4a. Girl with baskets; 8a. Chief of Aleixo de Ainaro; 10a. Timor chief; 20a. Warrior and horse; 1, 3p. Tribal chieftains.

1948. Honouring the Statue of Our Lady of Fatima. As T **33** of Portuguese Guinea.
318 8a. grey 5·50 5·50

1949. 75th Anniv of U.P.U. As T **34** of Portuguese Guinea
319 16a. brown 13·50 8·00

1950.
320 31 20a. blue 60 60
321 – 50a. brown (Young girl) 1·80 80

1950. Holy Year. As Nos. 425/6 of Macao.
322 40a. green 1·30 90
323 70a. brown 1·90 1·30

32 "Belamcanda chinensis"

34 Statue of The Virgin

1950.
324 32 1a. red, green and grey 45 30
325 – 3a. yellow, green and brown 1·90 1·50
326 – 10a. pink, green and blue 2·20 1·60
327 – 16a. multicoloured 4·50 2·20
328 – 20a. yellow, green and turquoise 1·90 1·60
329 – 30a. yellow, green and blue 2·20 1·60
330 – 70a. multicoloured 3·00 1·80
331 – 1p. red, yellow and green 5·25 3·75
332 – 2p. green, yellow and red 7·50 6·00
333 – 5p. pink, green and black 12·50 9·50
FLOWERS: 3a. "Caesalpinia pulcherrima"; 10a. "Calotropis gigantea"; 16a. "Delonix regia"; 20a. "Plumeria rubra"; 30a. "Allamanda cathartica"; 70a. "Haemanthus multiflorus"; 1p. "Bauhinia"; 2p. "Eurycles amboiniensis"; 5p. "Crinum longiflorum".

1951. Termination of Holy Year. As T **36** of Portuguese Guinea .
334 86a. blue and turquoise 1·50 1·30

1952. 1st Tropical Medicine Congress, Lisbon. As T **37** of Portuguese Guinea
335 10a. brown and green 80 65
DESIGN: Nurse weighing baby.

1952. 400th Death Anniv of St. Francis Xavier. Designs as No. 452/4 of Macao.
336 1a. black and grey 15 15
337 16a. brown and buff 65 50
338 1p. red and grey 3·00 1·60

1953. Missionary Art Exhibition.
339 34 3a. brown and light brown 15 10
340 16a. brown and stone 45 35
341 50a. blue and brown 1·30 1·20

1954. Portuguese Stamp Centenary. As T **41** of Portuguese Guinea.
342 10a. multicoloured 90 80

1954. 400th Anniv of Sao Paulo. As T **42** of Portuguese Guinea.
343 16a. multicoloured 75 45

35 Map of Timor

38 Elephant Jar

1956.
344 35 1a. multicoloured 10 10
345 3a. multicoloured 10 10
346 8a. multicoloured 30 20
347 24a. multicoloured 35 20
348 32a. multicoloured 45 20
349 40a. multicoloured 65 35
350 1p. multicoloured 1·90 45
351 3p. multicoloured 5·50 2·75

1958. 6th International Congress of Tropical Medicine. As T **45** of Portuguese Guinea.
352 32a. multicoloured 2·75 1·90
DESIGN: 32a. "Calophyllum inophyllum" (plant).

1958. Brussels International Exhibition. As T **44** of Portuguese Guinea.
353 40a. multicoloured 45 35

1960. New currency. Nos. 344/51 surch thus: **$05** and bars.
354 35 5c. on 1a. multicoloured 15 10
355 10c. on 3a. multicoloured 15 10
356 20c. on 8a. multicoloured 15 10
357 30c. on 24a. multicoloured 15 10

358 50c. on 32s. multicoloured 15 10
359 1e. on 40a. multicoloured 15 15
360 2e. on 40a. multicoloured 30 20
361 5e. on 1p. multicoloured 65 45
362 10e. on 3p. multicoloured 2·20 1·10
363 15e. on 3p. multicoloured 2·20 1·30

1960. 500th Death Anniv of Prince Henry the Navigator. As T **47** of Portuguese Guinea. Multicoloured.
364 4e.50 Prince Henry's motto (horiz) 45 20

1962. Timor Art. Multicoloured.
365 5c. Type **38** 10 10
366 10c. House on stilts 10 10
367 20c. Idol 20 20
368 30c. Rosary 20 20
369 50c. Model of outrigger canoe (horiz) 45 35
370 1e. Casket 35 35
371 2e.50 Archer 60 35
372 4e. Elephant 75 35
373 5e. Native climbing palm tree 95 35
374 10e. Statuette of woman 3·00 95
375 20e. Model of cockfight (horiz) 7·50 2·40
376 50e. House, bird and cat 7·25 2·40

1962. Sports. As T **49** of Portuguese Guinea. Multicoloured.
377 50c. Game shooting 10 10
378 1e. Horse-riding 65 20
379 1e.50 Swimming 50 30
380 2e. Athletes 35 35
381 2e.50 Football 65 50
382 15e. Big-game hunting 1·90 1·30

1962. Malaria Eradication. Mosquito design as T **50** of Portuguese Guinea. Multicoloured.
383 2e.50 "Anopheles sundaicus" 50 45

1964. Centenary of National Overseas Bank. As T **53** of Portuguese Guinea, but portrait of M. P. Chagas.
384 2e.50 multicoloured 60 45

1965. I.T.U. Centenary. As T **54** of Portuguese Guinea.
385 1e.50 multicoloured 90 60

1966. 40th Anniv of National Revolution. As T **56** of Portuguese Guinea, but showing different buildings. Multicoloured.
386 4e.50 Dr V. Machado's College and Health Centre, Dili 80 50

1967. Centenary of Military Naval Assn. As T **57** of Portuguese Guinea. Multicoloured.
387 10c. Gago Coutinho and gunboat "Patria" 20 20
388 4e.50 Sacadura Cabral and Fairey IIID seaplane "Lusitania" 1·50 80

39 Sepoy Officer, 1792

40 Pictorial Map of 1834, and Arms

1967. Portuguese Military Uniforms. Mult.
389 35c. Type **39** 15 15
390 1e. Infantry officer, 1815 1·30 30
391 1e.50 Infantryman 1879 20 15
392 2e. Infantryman, 1890 20 15
393 2e.50 Infantry officer, 1903 30 15
394 3e. Sapper, 1918 50 30
395 4e.50 Commando, 1964 90 30
396 10e. Parachutist, 1964 1·30 65

1967. 50th Anniv of Fatima Apparitions. As T **58** of Portuguese Guinea.
397 3e. Virgin of the Pilgrims 35 15

1968. 500th Birth Anniv of Pedro Cabral (explorer). As T **64** of Portuguese Guinea. Mult.
398 4e.50 Lopo Homen-Reineis' map, 1519 (horiz) 80 35

1969. Birth Centenary of Admiral Gago Coutinho. As T **66** of Portuguese Guinea. Mult.
399 4e.50 Frigate "Almirante Gago Coutinho" (horiz) 95 65

1969. Bicentenary of Dili (capital of Timor).
400 **40** 1e. multicoloured 35 20

1969. 500th Anniv of Vasco da Gama (explorer). As T **67** of Portuguese Guinea. Mult.
401 5e. Convert Medallion 35 20

1969. Centenary of Overseas Administrative Reforms. As T **68** of Portuguese Guinea.
402 5e. multicoloured 35 15

1969. 500th Birth Anniv of King Manoel I. As T **69** of Portuguese Guinea. Multicoloured.
403 4e. Emblem of Manoel I in Jeronimos Monastery 35 15

41 Map, Sir Ross Smith, and Arms of Britain, Timor and Australia

1969. 50th Anniv of 1st England–Australia Flight.
404 **41** 2e. multicoloured 45 30

1970. Birth Centenary of Marshal Carmona. As T **71** of Portuguese Guinea. Multicoloured.
414 1e. Portrait in civilian dress 15 15

1972. 400th Anniv of Camoens' "The Lusíads" (epic poem). As T **73** of Portuguese Guinea. Multicoloured.
415 1e. Missionaries, natives and galleon 20 15

1972. Olympic Games, Munich. As T **74** of Portuguese Guinea. Multicoloured.
416 4e.50 Football 45 20

1972. 50th Anniv of 1st Flight from Lisbon to Rio de Janeiro. As T **75** of Portuguese Guinea. Multicoloured.
417 1e. Aviators Gago Coutinho and Sacadura Cabral in Fairey IIID seaplane 35 30

1973. W.M.O. Centenary. As T **76** of Portuguese Guinea.
418 20e. multicoloured 1·50 1·10

CHARITY TAX STAMPS

The notes under this heading in Portugal also apply here.

1919. No. 211 surch **2 AVOS TAXA DA GUERRA**. With or without gum.
C228 U 2a. on ½a. green 5·25 4·50

1919. No. 196 surch **2 TAXA DE GUERRA** and bars.
C230 R 2 on 5a. on 50r. blue 30·00 18·00

1925. Marquis de Pombal Commem. As Nos. 666/8 of Portugal, but inscr "TIMOR".
C231 C **73** 2a. red 30 20
C232 – 2a. red 30 20
C233 C **75** 2a. red 30 20

1934. Educational Tax. Fiscal stamps as Type C **1** of Portuguese Colonies, with values in black, optd **Instrucao D. L. n.° 7 de 3-2-1934** or surch also. With or without gum.
C234 2a. green 1·90 1·50
C235 5a. green 3·00 1·60
C236 7a. on ½a. pink 3·50 2·20

1936. Fiscal stamps as Type C **1** of Portuguese Colonies, with value in black, optd **Assistencia D. L. n.°72**. With or without gum.
C253 10a. pink 2·20 1·60
C254 10a. green 1·60 1·50

C **29**

C **42** Woman and Star

1948. No gum.
C310 C **29** 10a. blue 1·60 1·30
C311 20a. green 2·20 1·50
The 20a. has a different emblem.

1960. Similar design. New currency. No gum.
C364 70c. blue 65 65
C400 1e.30 green 1·20 1·20

1969.
C405 C **42** 30c. blue and light blue 20 20
C406 50c. purple and orange 20 20
C407 1e. brown and yellow 20 20

1970. Nos. C364 and C400 surch **D. L. n.° 776** and value.
C408 30c. on 70c. blue 7·00 7·00
C409 30c. on 1e.30 green 7·00 7·00
C410 50c. on 70c. blue 12·00 12·00
C411 50c. on 1e.30 green 7·00 7·00
C412 1e. on 70c. blue 7·00 7·00
C413 1e. on 1e.30 green 7·00 7·00

NEWSPAPER STAMPS

1892. "Embossed" key-type inscr "PROVINCIA DE MACAU" surch **JORNAES TIMOR 2½ 2½**. No gum.
N31 Q 2½ on 20r. red 3·75 1·90
N32 2½ on 40r. brown 1·10 75
N33 2½ on 80r. grey 1·10 75

1893. "Newspaper" key-type inscr "TIMOR".
N36 V 2½r. brown 50 45

1894. No. N36 surch ½ **avo PROVISORIO** and Chinese characters.
N58 V ½a. on 2½r. brown 1·20 1·20

POSTAGE DUE STAMPS

1904. "Due" key-type inscr "TIMOR". Name and value in black. With or without gum (1, 2a.), no gum (others).
D124 W 1a. green 35 35
D125 2a. grey 35 35
D126 5a. brown 95 80
D127 6a. orange 95 80
D128 10a. brown 95 80
D129 15a. brown 1·60 1·30
D130 24a. blue 4·00 2·75
D131 40a. red 4·00 2·75
D132 50a. orange 5·50 3·25
D133 1p. lilac 12·00 7·00

1911. "Due" key-type of Timor optd **REPUBLICA**.
D139 W 1a. green 30 35
D140 2a. grey 30 35
D141 5a. brown 30 80
D142 6a. orange 35 80
D143 10a. brown 1·80 1·50
D144 15a. brown 90 1·30
D145 24a. blue 1·50 95
D146 40a. red 1·60 2·75
D147 50a. orange 2·20 3·25
D178 1p. lilac 35 35

1925. Marquis de Pombal tax stamps. As Nos. C231/3 of Timor, optd **MULTA**.
D231 C **73** 4a. red 30 20
D232 – 4a. red 30 20
D233 C **75** 4a. red 30 20

1952. As Type D **70** of Macao, but inscr "TIMOR PORTUGUES". Numerals in red; name in black.
D336 1a. sepia and brown 15 15
D337 3a. brown and orange 15 15
D338 5a. green and turquoise 15 15
D339 10a. green and light green 15 15
D340 30a. violet and light violet 20 15
D341 1p. red and orange 60 35

For subsequent issues see **EAST TIMOR**.

PRINCE EDWARD ISLAND Pt. 1

An island off the East coast of Canada, now a province of that Dominion, whose stamps it uses.

1861. 12 pence = 1 shilling.
1872. 100 cents = 1 dollar.

1

7

1861. Queen's portrait in various frames. Values in pence.
9 **1** 1d. orange 29·00 42·00
28 2d. red 6·50 9·50
30 3d. blue 10·00 13·00
31 4d. black 4·75 27·00
18 6d. green 90·00 95·00
20 9d. mauve 75·00 75·00

1870.
32 **7** 4½d. (3d. stg.) brown 45·00 60·00

8

1872. Queen's portrait in various frames. Values in cents.
35 **8** 1c. orange 4·75 15·00
38 2c. blue 16·00 38·00
37 3c. red 16·00 25·00
40 4c. green 6·00 18·00
41 6c. black 4·50 19·00
42 12c. mauve 4·25 32·00

PRUSSIA Pt. 7

Formerly a kingdom in the N. of Germany. In 1867 it became part of the North German Confederation.

1850. 12 pfennig = 1 silbergroschen; 30 silbergroschen = 1 thaler.
1867. 60 kreuzer = 1 gulden.

1 Friedrich Wilhelm IV

3

4

1850. Imperf.
14 **1** 4pf. green 65·00 26·00
4 6pf. red 70·00 35·00
22 ½sgr. (=6pf.) red £170 £160
5 1sgr. black on pink 70·00 7·00
16 1sgr. pink 27·00 2·30
6 2sgr. black on blue £100 14·00
18 2sgr. blue £100 13·00
8 3sgr. black on yellow 95·00 9·50
21 3sgr. yellow 85·00 11·50

1861. Roul.
24 **3** 3pf. lilac 22·00 31·00
26 4pf. green 8·25 7·00
28 6pf. orange 8·75 10·50
31 **4** 1sgr. pink 3·50 90
35 2sgr. blue 8·25 1·80
36 3sgr. yellow 7·25 2·20

5

7

1866. Printed in reverse on back of specially treated transparent paper. Roul.
38 **5** 10sgr. pink 65·00 55·00
39 – 30sgr. blue 80·00 £130
The 30 sgr. has the value in a square.

1867. Roul.
40 **7** 1k. green 22·00 33·00
42 2k. orange 36·00 90·00
43 3k. pink 19·00 23·00
45 6k. blue 19·00 33·00
46 9k. bistre 24·00 35·00

PUERTO RICO Pt. 9; Pt. 22

A West Indian island ceded by Spain to the United States after the war of 1898. Until 1873 stamps of Cuba were used. Now uses stamps of the U.S.A.

1873. 100 centimos = 1 peseta.
1881. 1000 milesimas = 100 centavos = 1 peso.
1898. 100 cents = 1 dollar.

A. SPANISH OCCUPATION

(**2**)

1873. Nos. 53/5 of Cuba optd with T **2**.
1 25c. de p. lilac 36·00 95
3 50c. de p. brown 95·00 4·75
4 1p. brown £225 19·00

1874. No. 57 of Cuba with opt similar to T **2** (two separate characters).
5 25c. de p. blue 31·00 2·20

1875. Nos. 61/3 of Cuba with opt similar to T **2** (two separate characters).
6 25c. de p. blue 22·00 2·20
7 50c. de p. green 31·00 2·50
8 1p. brown £120 13·50

1876. Nos. 65a and 67 of Cuba with opt similar to T **2** (two separate characters).
9 25c. de p. lilac 3·50 1·80
10 50c. de p. blue 8·25 3·00
11 1p. black 38·00 10·50

1876. Nos. 65a and 67 of Cuba with opt as last, but characters joined.
12 25c. de p. lilac 30·00 85
13 1p. black 65·00 10·00

1877. As T **9** of Philippines, but inscr "PTO-RICO 1877".
14 5c. brown 6·25 2·20
15 10c. red 19·00 2·50
16 15c. green 29·00 11·00

17 25c. blue 11·00 1·80
18 50c. bistre 19·00 4·25

1878. As T **9** of Philippines, but inscr "PTO-RICO 1878".

19 5c. grey 14·00 14·00
20 10c. brown £225 80·00
21 25c. green 1·80 1·10
22 50c. blue 6·00 2·40
23a 1p. bistre 11·00 5·25

1879. As T **9** of Philippines, but inscr "PTO-RICO 1879".

24 5c. red 12·00 5·25
25 10c. brown 12·00 5·25
26 15c. grey 12·00 5·25
27 25c. blue 4·25 1·80
28 50c. green 12·00 5·25
29 1p. lilac 55·00 23·00

1880. "Alfonso XII" key-type inscr "PUERTO-RICO 1880".

30 X ½c. green 24·00 18·00
31 ½c. red 6·50 2·40
32 1c. purple 11·00 9·50
33 2c. grey 6·50 4·25
34 3c. buff 6·50 4·25
35 4c. black 6·50 4·25
36 5c. green 3·25 1·80
37 10c. red 3·50 2·20
38 15c. brown 6·50 3·25
39 25c. lilac 3·25 1·60
40 40c. grey 12·00 1·60
41 50c. brown 25·00 16·00
42 1p. bistre 90·00 19·00

1881. "Alfonso XIII" key-type inscr "PUERTO-RICO 1881".

43 X ½m. red 25 15
45 1m. violet 25 15
46 2m. red 45 30
47 4m. green 85 25
48 6m. purple 85 50
49 8m. blue 1·90 1·20
50 1c. green 3·25 1·20
51 2c. red 4·00 3·25
52 3c. brown 9·00 5·25
53 5c. lilac 3·00 30
54 8c. brown 3·00 1·40
55 10c. grey 26·00 8·25
56 20c. bistre 34·00 16·00

1882. "Alfonso XII" key-type inscr "PUERTO-RICO".

57 X ½m. red 20 15
74 1m. red 20 15
75 1m. orange 20 20
59 2m. mauve 20 15
60 4m. purple 20 15
61 6m. brown 40 15
62 8m. green 40 15
63 1c. green 20 15
64 2c. red 1·20 15
65 3c. yellow 4·00 2·40
76 3c. brown 2·75 50
77 5c. lilac 16·00 1·20
67 8c. brown 3·50 15
68 10c. green 3·50 30
69 20c. grey 5·75 30
70 40c. blue 40·00 16·00
71 80c. bistre 60·00 22·00

1890. "Baby" key-type inscr "PUERTO-RICO".

80 Y ½m. black 20 15
95 ½m. grey 15 15
111 ½m. brown 15 15
124 ½m. purple 20 15
81 1m. green 30 15
96 1m. purple 15 15
112 1m. blue 15 15
125 1m. brown 20 15
82 2m. red 20 15
97 2m. purple 15 15
126 2m. green 20 15
83 4m. black 11·50 6·25
98 4m. blue 15 15
114 4m. brown 15 15
127 4m. green 1·00 30
84 6m. brown 40·00 16·00
99 6m. red 15 15
85 8m. bistre 29·00 23·00
100 8m. green 15 15
86 1c. brown 20 15
101 1c. green 60 15
115 1c. purple 6·00 50
128 1c. red 70 15
87 2c. purple 1·00 95
102 2c. pink 95 15
116 2c. lilac 2·40 50
129 2c. brown 70 15
88 3c. blue 6·00 50
103 3c. orange 95 15
117 3c. grey 6·00 50
131 3c. brown 25 15
118 4c. blue 1·50 50
132 4c. brown 80 15
89 5c. purple 12·50 45
104 5c. green 95 15
133 5c. blue 25 15
120 6c. orange 50 15
134 6c. lilac 25 15
90 8c. blue 16·00 1·90
105 8c. brown 15 15
121 8c. purple 13·00 5·25
135 8c. red 3·00 1·50
106 10c. red 1·40 35
122 20c. red 1·60 50
107 20c. lilac 2·30 50
136 20c. grey 7·25 1·50
93 40c. orange £120 50·00
108 40c. blue 5·75 3·75
137 40c. red 7·25 1·50
94 80c. green £475 £170
109 80c. red 14·50 11·50
138 80c. black 29·00 23·00

13 Landing of Columbus

1893. 400th Anniv of Discovery of America by Columbus.

110 **13** 3c. green £190 47·00

1898. "Curly Head" key-type inscr "PTO RICO 1898 y 99".

139 Z 1m. brown 15 15
140 2m. brown 15 15
141 3m. brown 15 15
142 4m. brown 1·50 60
143 5m. brown 15 15
144 1c. purple 15 15
145 2c. green 15 15
146 3c. brown 15 15
147 4c. orange 1·50 1·10
148 5c. pink 15 15
149 6c. blue 15 15
150 8c. brown 15 15
151 10c. red 15 15
152 15c. grey 15 15
153 20c. purple 1·80 60
154 40c. lilac 1·30 1·40
155 60c. black 1·30 1·40
156 80c. brown 4·75 5·25
157 1p. green 10·50 10·50
158 2p. blue 25·00 14·00

1898. "Baby" key-type inscr "PUERTO RICO" and optd **Habilitado PARA 1898 y '99**.

159 Y ½m. purple 10·50 6·00
160 1m. brown 45 25
161 2m. green 25 25
162 4m. green 25 25
163 1c. purple 1·20 1·20
164 2c. brown 25 25
165 3c. blue 21·00 9·50
166 3c. brown 1·80 1·80
167 4c. brown 45 45
168 4c. blue 12·50 8·25
169 5c. blue 45 45
170 5c. green 6·00 4·50
172 6c. lilac 45 30
173a 8c. red 70 30
174 20c. grey 70 70
175 40c. red 1·00 70
176 80c. black 21·00 14·00

WAR TAX STAMPS

1898. 1890 and 1898 stamps optd **IMPUESTO DE GUERRA** or surch also.

W177 Y 1m. blue 2·75 1·90
W178 1m. brown 7·25 5·25
W179 2m. red 14·00 9·00
W180 2m. green 7·25 5·25
W181 4m. green 8·00 8·00
W182a 1c. brown 7·25 4·50
W183 1c. purple 12·00 11·50
W184 2c. purple 95 95
W185 2c. pink 45 30
W186 2c. lilac 45 30
W187 2c. brown 40 35
W192 2c. on 2m. red 45 30
W193c 2c. on 5c. green 2·75 1·80
W188 3c. orange 14·00 11·50
W194 3c. on 10c. red 2·40 1·80
W195 4c. on 20c. red 14·00 10·50
W189 5c. green 1·90 1·90
W196a 5c. on ½m. brown 3·00 3·00
W197 5c. on 1m. purple 30 30
W198 5c. on 1m. blue 7·25 5·25
W199 Z 5c. on 1m. brown 7·25 5·25
W200 Y 5c. on 5c. green 7·25 4·75
W191 8c. purple 21·00 18·00

B. UNITED STATES OCCUPATION

1899. 1894 stamps of United States (No. 267 etc) optd **PORTO RICO**.

202 1c. green 4·00 1·25
203 2c. red 3·75 1·00
204 5c. blue 7·00 2·10
205 8c. brown 22·00 14·50
206 10c. brown 14·00 4·50

1900. 1894 stamps of United States (No. 267 etc) optd **PUERTO RICO**.

210 1c. green 4·75 1·10
212 2c. red 4·00 90

POSTAGE DUE STAMPS

1899. Postage Due stamps of United States of 1894 optd **PORTO RICO**.

D207 D **87** 1c. red 18·00 6·00
D208 2c. red 9·00 4·50
D209 10c. red £130 42·00

QATAR Pt. 1, Pt. 19

An independent Arab Shaikhdom with British postal administration until 23 May 1963. The stamps of Muscat were formerly used at Doha and Urm Said. Later issues by the Qatar Post Department.

1966. 100 dirhams = 1 riyal.
1967. 100 naye paise = 1 rupee.

Stamps of Great Britain surcharged **QATAR** and value in Indian currency.

1957. Queen Elizabeth II and pictorials.
1 **157** 1n.p. on 5d. brown 10 10
2 **154** 3n.p. on ½d. orange 15 15
3 6n.p. on 1d. blue 15 15
4 9n.p. on 1½d. green 15 10
5 12n.p. on 2d. brown . . . 20 2·00
6 **155** 15n.p. on 2½d. red 15 10
7 20n.p. on 3d. lilac 15 10
8 25n.p. on 4d. blue . . . . 40 1·50
9 **157** 40n.p. on 6d. purple . . . 15 10
10 **158** 50n.p. on 9d. olive 40 30
11 **159** 75n.p. on 1s.3d. green . . 50 2·50
12 1r. on 1s.6d. blue . . . . 9·00 10
13 **166** 2r. on 2s.6d. brown . . . 3·50 4·00
14 – 5r. on 5s. red . . . . . . 5·00 4·00
15 – 10r. on 10s. blue . . . . . 5·50 15·00

1957. World Scout Jubilee Jamboree.
16 **170** 15n.p. on 2½d. red 35 35
17 **171** 25n.p. on 4d. blue 35 35
18 – 75n.p. on 1s.3d. green . . 40 40

8 Shaikh Ahmad bin All al Thani

9 Peregrine Falcon

11 Oil Derrick

1961.
27 **8** 5n.p. red 10 10
28 15n.p. black 10 10
29 20n.p. purple 10 10
30 30n.p. green 10 10
31 **9** 40n.p. red . . . . 1·00 10
32 50n.p. brown . . . . 1·40 10
33 – 75n.p. blue . . . . 60 2·50
34 **11** 1r. red . . . . 1·00 10
35 2r. blue . . . . 2·00 1·25
36 – 5r. green . . . . 17·00 3·75
37 – 10r. black . . . . 40·00 6·50
DESIGNS—As Type **9**: 75n.p. Dhow. As Type **11**: 5r., 10r. Mosque.

1964. Olympic Games, Tokyo. Optd **1964**, Olympic rings and Arabic inscr or surch also.
38 **9** 50n.p. brown . . . . 2·25 1·60
39 – 75n.p. blue (No. 33) . . . . 2·50 1·75
40 – 1r. on 10r. black (No. 37) 1·10 1·00
41 **11** 2r. blue . . . . 2·50 2·00
42 5r. green (No. 36) . . . . . 7·00 6·00

1964. Pres. Kennedy Commem. Optd **John F Kennedy 1917–1963** in English and Arabic or surch also.
43 **9** 50n.p. brown . . . . 7·25 2·10
44 – 75n.p. blue (No. 33) . . . . 2·50 1·75
45 – 1r. on 10r. black (No. 37) 1·10 1·00
46 **11** 2r. blue . . . . 2·50 2·00
47 – 5r. green (No. 36) . . . . . 7·00 5·00

15 Colonnade, Temple of Isis

16 Scouts on Parade

1965. Nubian Monuments Preservation. Mult.
48 1n.p. Type **15** 10 15
49 2n.p. Temple of Isis, Philac . . 10 15
50 3n.p. Trajan's Kiosk, Philac 10 15
51 1r. As 3n.p. . . . . 1·25 30
52 1r.50 As 2n.p. . . . . 2·10 50
53 2r. Type **15** . . . . 2·50 50

1965. Qatar Scouts.
54 – 1n.p. brown and green . . . 20 15
55 – 2n.p. blue and brown . . . 20 15
56 – 3n.p. blue and green 20 15
57 – 4n.p. brown and blue . . . 20 15
58 – 5n.p. blue and turquoise . . 20 15
59 **16** 30n.p. multicoloured 50 40
60 40n.p. multicoloured 65 50
61 1r. multicoloured . . . . . 1·60 1·10
DESIGNS—TRIANGULAR (60 × 30 mm): 1, 4n.p. Qatar Scout badge; 2, 3, 5n.p. Ruler, badge, palms and camp.

17 "Telstar" and Eiffel Tower

1965. I.T.U. Centenary.
62 **17** 1n.p. brown and blue . . . 20 15
63 – 2n.p. brown and blue . . . 20 15
64 – 3n.p. violet and green . . . 20 15
65 – 4n.p. blue and brown . . . 20 15
66 **17** 5n.p. brown and violet . . . 20 15
67 – 40n.p. black and red 50 30
68 – 50n.p. brown and green . . 60 40
69 – 1r. red and green . . . . . 1·25 80
DESIGNS: 2n.p., 1r. "Syncom 3" and pagoda; 3, 40n.p. "Relay" and radar scanner; 4, 50n.p. Post Office Tower (London), globe and satellites.

18 Jigsaw Triggerfish

1965. Fish of the Arabian Gulf. Multicoloured.
70 1n.p. Type **18** 10 10
71 2n.p. Harlequin sweetlips . . . 10 10
72 3n.p. Saddle butterflyfish . . . 10 10
73 4n.p. Thread-finned butterflyfish 10 10
74 5n.p. Masked unicornfish . . . 10 10
75 15n.p. Paradise fish 35 15
76 20n.p. White-spotted surgeonfish 40 15
77 30n.p. Rio Grande cichlid . . 50 15
78 40n.p. Convict cichlid 65 20
79 50n.p. As 2n.p. . . . . 1·00 35
80 75n.p. Type **18** . . . . . . 1·60 40
81 1r. As 30n.p. . . . . 2·50 40
82 2r. As 20n.p. . . . . 5·00 1·00
83 3r. As 15n.p. . . . . 7·00 2·00
84 4r. As 5n.p. . . . . 8·50 2·60
85 5r. As 4n.p. . . . . 9·25 3·50
86 10r. As 3n.p. . . . . 16·00 7·50

19 Basketball

1966. Pan-Arab Games, Cairo (1965).
87 **19** 1r. black, grey and red . . . 90 60
88 – 1r. brown and green 90 60
89 – 1r. red and blue 90 60
90 – 1r. green and blue 90 60
91 – 1r. blue and brown 90 60
SPORTS: No. 88, Horse-jumping; No. 89, Running; No. 90, Football; No. 91, Weightlifting.

1966. Space Rendezvous. Nos. 62/9 optd with two space capsules and **SPACE RENDEZVOUS 15th. DECEMBER 1965** in English and Arabic.
92 **17** 1n.p. brown and blue . . . 15 10
93 – 2n.p. brown and blue . . . 15 10
94 – 3n.p. violet and green . . . 15 10
95 – 4n.p. blue and brown . . . 15 10
96 **17** 5n.p. brown and violet . . . 15 10
97 – 40n.p. black and red 90 25
98 – 50n.p. brown and green . . 90 30
99 – 1r. red and green . . . . . 1·90 55

21 Shaikh Ahmed

1966. Gold and Silver Coinage. Circular designs embossed on gold (G) or silver (S) foil, backed with "Walsall Security Paper" inscr in English and Arabic. Imperf. (a) Diameter 42 mm.
101 **21** 1n.p. bistre and purple (S) 15 15
102 – 3n.p. black and orange (S) 15 15
103 **21** 4n.p. violet and red (G) . . 15 15
104 – 5n.p. green and mauve (G) 15 15

(b) Diameter 55 mm.
105 **21** 10n.p. brown and violet (S) 25 15
106 – 40n.p. red and blue (S) . . 50 25
107 **21** 70n.p. blue & ultram (G) 85 45
108 – 80n.p. mauve and green (G) 85 45

(c) Diameter 64 mm.
109 **21** 1r. mauve and black (S) . . 1·50 60
110 – 2r. green and purple (S) . . 3·00 1·40
111 **21** 5r. purple and orange (G) 7·00 3·00
112 – 10r. blue and red (G) . . . 14·00 6·00
The 1, 4, 10, 70n.p. and 1 and 5r. each show the obverse side of the coins as Type **21**. The remainder show the reverse side of the coins (Shaikh's seal).

22 I.C.Y. and U.N. Emblem

1966. International Co-operation Year
113 **22** 40n.p. brown, violet & bl 1·10 65
114 A 40n.p. violet, brn & turq 1·10 65
115 B 40n.p. blue, brown & vio 1·10 65
116 C 40n.p. turquoise, vio & bl 1·10 65
DESIGNS: A, Pres. Kennedy, I.C.Y. emblem and U.N. Headquarters; B, Dag Hammarskjold and U.N. General Assembly; C, Nehru and dove.
Nos. 113/16 were issued together in blocks of four, each sheet containing four blocks separated by gutter margins. Subsequently the sheets were reissued perf and imperf with the opt **U.N. 20TH ANNIVERSARY** on the stamps. The gutter margins were also printed in various designs, face values and overprints.

23 Pres. Kennedy and New York Skyline

1966. Pres. Kennedy Commemoration. Multicoloured.
118 10n.p. Type **23** 20 15
119 30n.p. Pres. Kennedy and Cape Kennedy 40 20
120 60n.p. Pres. Kennedy and Statue of Liberty 65 40
121 70n.p. Type **23** 70 55
122 80n.p. As 30n.p. 80 55
123 1r. As 60n.p. . . . . 1·50 95

24 Horse-jumping

1966. Olympic Games Preparation (Mexico). Multicoloured.
125 1n.p. Type **24** 15 15
126 4n.p. Running 15 15
127 5n.p. Throwing the javelin . . 15 15
128 70n.p. Type **24** 85 45
129 80n.p. Running 85 50
130 90n.p. Throwing the javelin 90 70

25 J. A. Lovell and Capsule

1966. American Astronauts. Each design showing spacecraft and astronaut. Multicoloured.
132 5n.p. Type **25** 15 15
133 10n.p. T. P. Stafford 15 15
134 15n.p. A. B. Shepard 15 15
135 20n.p. J. H. Glenn 15 15
136 30n.p. M. Scott Carpenter . . 30 20
137 40n.p. W. M. Schirra 30 20
138 50n.p. V. I. Grissom 45 35
139 60n.p. L. G. Cooper 65 45
Nos. 132/4 are diamond-shaped as Type **25**, the remainder are horiz designs (56 × 25 mm).

1966. Various stamps with currency names changed to dirhams and riyals by overprinting in English and Arabic. (i) Nos. 27/37 (Definitives).
141 **8** 5d. on 5n.p. red 25 10
142 15d. on 15n.p. black . . . 35 10
143 20d. on 20n.p. purple . . . 35 15
144 30d. on 30n.p. green . . . 65 25
145 **9** 40d. on 40n.p. red . . . . 2·10 50
146 50d. on 50n.p. brown . . . 2·50 65
147 – 75d. on 75n.p. blue . . . . 2·25 55
148 **11** 1r. on 1r. red . . . . . . 2·50 50
149 2r. on 2r. blue . . . . . . 5·50 2·25
150 – 5r. on 5r. green . . . . . 12·50 7·00
151 – 10r. on 10r. black . . . . 21·00 10·00

(ii) Nos. 70/86 (Fish). Multicoloured.
152 1d. on 1n.p. 10 10
153 2d. on 2n.p. 10 10
154 3d. on 3n.p. 10 10
155 4d. on 4n.p. 10 10
156 5d. on 5n.p. 10 10
157 15d. on 15n.p. 35 10
158 20d. on 20n.p. 45 10
159 30d. on 30n.p. 60 15
160 40d. on 40n.p. 85 20
161 50d. on 50n.p. . . . . . . 1·10 30
162 75d. on 75n.p. . . . . . . 2·00 55
163 1r. on 1r. . . . . 2·25 70
164 2r. on 2r. . . . . 4·50 2·00
165 3r. on 3r. . . . . 7·50 3·50
166 4r. on 4r. . . . . 10·00 5·00
167 5r. on 5r. . . . . 12·50 6·00
168 10r. on 10r. . . . . 24·00 12·00

27 National Library, Doha

1966. Education Day. Multicoloured.
169 2n.p. Type **27** 10 10
170 3n.p. School and playing field 15 10
171 5n.p. School and gardens . . 15 10
172 1r. Type **27** . . . . 2·75 90
173 2r. As 3n.p . . . . 4·25 2·00
174 3r. As 5n.p . . . . 6·00 2·75

28 Palace, Doha

1966. Currency expressed in naye paise and rupees. Multicoloured.
175 2n.p. Type **28** 10 10
176 3n.p. Gulf Street, Shahra Al-Khalij 10 10
177 10n.p. Doha airport 30 10
178 15n.p. Garden, Rayan . . . 20 10
179 20n.p. Head Post Office, Doha 25 10
180 30n.p. Mosque Doha (vert) 40 15
181 40n.p. Shaikh Ahmad 80 20
182 50n.p. Type **28** 90 35
183 60n.p. As 3n.p. . . . . . . 1·40 50
184 70n.p. As 10n.p. . . . . . . 2·00 75
185 80n.p. As 15n.p. . . . . . . 1·90 85
186 90n.p. As 20n.p. . . . . . . 2·25 1·40
187 1r. As 30n.p. (vert) . . . . 2·40 1·50
188 2r. As 40n.p. . . . . 5·00 3·75

29 Hands holding Jules Rimet Trophy

1966. World Cup Football Championship, England.
189 **29** 60n.p. mult (postage) . . . 85 65
190 – 70n.p. multicoloured . . . 1·00 80
191 – 80n.p. multicoloured . . . 1·40 1·00
192 – 90n.p. multicoloured . . . 1·50 1·10
193 – 1n.p. blue (air) 15 15
194 – 2n.p. blue 15 15
195 – 3n.p. blue 25 25
196 – 4n.p. blue 30 30
DESIGNS: No. 190, Jules Rimet Trophy and "football" globe; No. 191, Footballers and globe; No. 192, Wembley stadium; Nos. 193/6, Jules Rimet Trophy.

30 A.P.U. Emblem

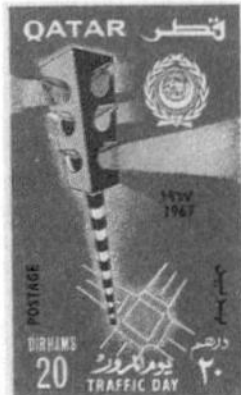

32 Traffic Lights

31 Astronauts on Moon

1967. Admission of Qatar to Arab Postal Union.

198	**30**	70d. brown and violet	1·10	60
199		80d. brown and blue	1·40	85

1967. U.S. "Apollo" Space Missions. Mult.

200	5d. Type **31**	10	10
201	10d. "Apollo" spacecraft	10	10
202	20d. Landing module on Moon	15	10
203	30d. Blast-off from Moon	25	15
204	40d. "Saturn 5" rocket	35	20
205	70d. Type **31**	75	45
206	80d. As 10d.	85	60
207	1r. As 20d.	90	80
208	1r.20 As 30d.	1·50	1·25
209	2r. As 40d.	2·10	1·75

1967. Traffic Day.

211	**32**	20d. multicoloured	35	15
212		30d. multicoloured	70	30
213		50d. multicoloured	1·10	50
214		1r. multicoloured	3·00	1·75

33 Brownsea Island and Jamboree Camp, Idaho

1967. Diamond Jubilee of Scout Movement and World Scout Jamboree, Idaho. Multicoloured.

215	1d. Type **33**	15	10
216	2d. Lord Baden-Powell	15	10
217	3d. Pony-trekking	15	10
218	5d. Canoeing	20	10
219	15d. Swimming	60	25
220	75d. Rock-climbing	1·50	85
221	2r. World Jamboree emblem	4·75	2·40

34 Norman Ship (from Bayeux Tapestry)

1967. Famous Navigators' Ships. Multicoloured.

222	1d. Type **34**	20	10
223	2d. "Santa Maria" (Columbus)	25	10
224	3d. "Sao Gabriel" (Vasco da Gama)	30	10
225	75d. "Vitoria" (Magellan)	1·75	1·25
226	1r. "Golden Hind" (Drake)	2·75	1·25
227	2r. "Gipsy Moth IV" (Chichester)	5·75	2·10

35 Arab Scribe

1968. 10th Anniv of Qatar Postage Stamps. Multicoloured.

228	1d. Type **35**	15	10
229	2d. Pigeon post (vert)	15	10
230	3d. Mounted postman	15	10
231	60d. Rowing boat postman (vert)	1·25	85
232	1r.25 Camel postman	2·25	1·50
233	2r. Letter-writing and Qatar 1n.p. stamp of 1957	3·75	2·75

36 Human Rights Emblem and Barbed Wire

1968. Human Rights Year. Multicoloured designs embodying Human Rights emblem.

234	1d. Type **36**	15	10
235	2d. Arab refugees	15	10
236	3d. Scales of justice	15	10
237	60d. Opening doors	85	50
238	1r.25 Family (vert)	1·40	1·25
239	2r. Human figures	2·40	1·75

37 Shaikh Ahmad

39 Shaikh Ahmad

38 Dhow

1968.

240	**37**	5d. green and blue	15	10
241		10d. brown and blue	15	10
242		20d. red and black	30	10
243		25d. green and purple	50	15
244	**38**	35d. green, blue and pink	1·25	20
245	–	40d. purple, blue & orange	1·00	20
246	–	60d. brown, blue and violet	2·50	45
247	–	70d. black, blue and green	1·60	55
248	–	1r. blue, yellow and green	1·90	60
249	–	1r.25 blue, pink and light blue	3·50	75
250	–	1r.50 green, blue & purple	6·50	1·40
251	**39**	2r. blue, brown and cinnamon	5·25	1·25
252		5r. purple, green and light green	11·00	4·50
253		10r. brown, ultram & blue	22·00	7·50

DESIGNS—As Type **38**: 40d. Water purification plant; 60d. Oil jetty; 70d. Qatar mosque; 1r. Palace Doha; 1r.25, Doha fort; 1r.50, Peregrine falcon.

41 Maternity Ward

1968. 20th Anniv of W.H.O. Multicoloured.

258	1d. Type **41**	15	10
259	2d. Operating theatre	15	10
260	3d. Dental surgery	15	10
261	60d. X-ray examination table	90	50
262	1r.25 Laboratory	2·50	1·50
263	2r. State Hospital Qatar	3·25	4·00

42 Throwing the Discus

1968. Olympic Games, Mexico. Multicoloured.

264	1d. Type **42**	15	10
265	2d. Olympic Flame and runner	15	10
266	3d. "68", rings and gymnast	15	10
267	60d. Weightlifting and Flame	1·25	65
268	1r.25 "Flame" in mosaic pattern (vert)	2·40	1·00
269	2r. "Cock" emblem	3·50	1·60

43 U.N. Emblem and Flags

1968. United Nations Day. Multicoloured.

270	1d. Type **43**	15	10
271	4d. Dove of Peace and world map	15	10
272	5d. U.N. Headquarters and flags	15	10
273	60d. Teacher and class	1·25	65
274	1r.50 Agricultural workers	2·40	1·00
275	2r. U. Thant and U.N. Assembly	3·50	1·60

44 Trawler "Ross Rayyan"

1969. Progress in Qatar. Multicoloured.

276	1d. Type **44**	10	10
277	4d. Primary school	10	10
278	5d. Doha International Airport	10	10
279	60d. Cement factory and road-making	1·40	50
280	1r.50 Power station and pylon	2·75	1·25
281	2r. Housing estate	3·75	1·90

45 Armoured Cars

1969. Qatar Security Forces. Multicoloured.

282	1d. Type **45**	10	10
283	2d. Traffic control	10	10
284	3d. Military helicopter	10	10
285	60d. Section of military band	1·50	70
286	1r.25 Field gun	2·75	1·50
287	2r. Mounted police	4·25	2·10

46 Tanker "Sivella" at Mooring

1969. Qatar's Oil Industry. Multicoloured.

288	1d. Type **46**	10	10
289	2d. Training school	10	10
290	3d. "Sea Shell" (oil rig) and "Shell Dolphin" (supply vessel)	10	10
291	60d. Storage tanks, Halul	1·50	85
292	1r.50 Topping plant	3·50	1·90
293	2r. Various tankers, 1890–1968	6·50	2·50

47 "Guest-house" and Dhow-building

1969. 10th Scout Jamboree, Qatar. Multicoloured.

294	1d. Type **47**	10	10
295	2d. Scouts at work	10	10
296	3d. Review and March Past	10	10
297	60d. Interior gateway	1·50	70
298	1r.25 Camp entrance	2·75	1·50
299	2r. Hoisting flag, and Shaikh Ahmad	4·00	2·10

48 Neil Armstrong

1969. 1st Man on the Moon. Multicoloured.

301	1d. Type **48**	10	10
302	2d. Edward Aldrin	10	10
303	3d. Michael Collins	10	10
304	60d. Astronaut on Moon	90	45
305	1r.25 Take-off from Moon	1·75	1·00
306	2r. Splashdown (horiz)	4·00	2·00

49 Douglas DC-8 and Mail Van

1970. Admission to U.P.U. Multicoloured.

307	1d. Type **49**	10	10
308	2d. Liner "Oriental Empress"	10	10
309	3d. Loading mail-van	10	10
310	60d. G.P.O., Doha	1·00	65
311	1r.25 U.P.U. Building, Berne	2·40	1·50
312	2r. U.P.U. Monument, Berne	3·00	1·60

50 League Emblem, Flag and Map

1970. Silver Jubilee of Arab League.

313	**50**	35d. multicoloured	45	25
314		60d. multicoloured	70	45
315		1r.25 multicoloured	1·75	85
316		1r.50 multicoloured	2·25	1·40

51 Vickers VC-10 on Runway

1970. 1st Gulf Aviation Vickers VC-10 Flight, Doha–London. Multicoloured.

317	1d. Type **51**	10	10
318	2d. Peregrine falcon and VC-10	1·10	10
319	3d. Tail view of VC-10	15	10
320	60d. Gulf Aviation emblem on map	1·00	85
321	1r.25 VC-10 over Doha	3·50	1·60
322	2r. Tail assembly of VC-10	4·50	2·25

52 "Space Achievements"

1970. International Education Year.

323	**52**	35d. multicoloured	65	25
324		60d. multicoloured	1·40	50

53 Freesias

55 Globe, "25" and U.N. Emblem

54 Toyahama Fishermen with Giant "Fish"

1970. Qatar Flowers. Multicoloured.
325 1d. Type **53** 10 10
326 2d. Azalieas 10 10
327 3d. Ixias 10 10
328 60d. Amaryllises . . . . . . 1·00 50
329 1r.25 Cinerarias . . . . . . 2·25 1·10
330 2r. Roses . . . . 3·00 1·50

1970. "EXPO 70" World Fair, Osaka. Multicoloured.
331 1d. Type **54** 10 10
332 2d. Expo emblem and map of Japan 10 10
333 3d. Fisherman on Shikoku beach 15 10
334 60d. Expo emblem and Mt. Fuji . . . . 1·40 60
335 1r.50 Gateway to Shinto Shrine . . . . 2·00 1·00
336 2r. Expo Tower and Mt. Fuji 4·25 2·75
Nos. 333, 334 and 336 are vert.

1970. 25th Anniv of U.N.O. Multicoloured.
337 1d. Type **55** 10 10
338 2d. Flowers in gun-barrel . . 10 10
339 3d. Anniversary cake 10 10
340 35d. "The U.N. Agencies" . . 1·25 45
341 1r.50 "Trumpet fanfare" . . 2·25 1·00
342 2r. "World friendship" . . . 3·50 2·00

56 Al Jahiz (philosopher) and Ancient Globe

1971. Famous Men of Islam. Multicoloured.
343 1d. Type **56** 10 10
344 2d. Saladin (soldier), palace and weapons 10 10
345 3d. Al Farabi (philosopher and musician), felucca and instruments 10 10
346 35d. Ibn Al Haithum (scientist), palace and emblems 75 40
347 1r.50 Al Motanabbi (poet), symbols and desert . . . . 3·25 2·00
348 2r. Ibn Sina (Avicenna) (physician and philosopher), medical instruments and ancient globe . . . . 4·50 2·40

57 Great Cormorant and Water Plants

1971. Qatar Fauna and Flora. Multicoloured.
349 1d. Type **57** 85 20
350 2d. Lizard and prickly pear 20 10
351 3d. Greater flamingos and palms 85 20
352 60d. Arabian oryx and yucca 1·40 80
353 1r.25 Mountain gazelle and desert dandelion . . . . . 3·50 1·75
354 2r. Dromedary, palm and bronzed chenopod . . . . 4·75 2·50

58 Satellite Earth Station, Goonhilly

1971. World Telecommunications Day. Mult.
355 1d. Type **58** 10 10
356 2d. Cable ship "Ariel" . . . 10 10
357 3d. Post Office Tower and T.V. control-room 10 10
358 4d. Modern telephones . . . 10 10
359 5d. Video-phone equipment 10 10
360 35d. As 3d. 65 35
361 75d. As 5d. . . . . 1·00 85
362 3r. Telex machine . . . . . 5·75 3·25

59 Arab Child reading Book **60** A.P.U. Emblem

1971. 10th Anniv of Education Day.
363 **59** 35d. multicoloured 40 20
364 55d. multicoloured 80 40
365 75d. multicoloured . . . . 1·25 65

1971. 25th Anniv of Arab Postal Union.
366 **60** 35d. multicoloured 50 20
367 55d. multicoloured 75 45
368 75d. multicoloured . . . . 1·10 65
369 1r.25 multicoloured . . . . 1·75 1·40

61 "Hammering Racism"

1971. Racial Equality Year. Multicoloured.
370 1d. Type **61** 10 10
371 2d. "Pushing back racism" 10 10
372 3d. War-wounded 10 10
373 4d. Working together (vert) 10 10
374 5d. Playing together (vert) . . 10 10
375 35d. Racial "tidal-wave" . . 60 30
376 75d. Type **61** . . . . 1·60 95
377 3r. As 2d. . . . . 4·50 3·25

62 Nurse and Child

1971. 25th Anniv of UNICEF. Multicoloured.
378 1d. Mother and child (vert) 10 10
379 2d. Child's face 10 10
380 3d. Child with book (vert) . . 10 10
381 4d. Type **62** 10 10
382 5d. Mother and baby 10 10
383 35d. Child with daffodil (vert) 60 30
384 75d. As 3d. . . . . 1·60 95
385 3r. As 1d. . . . . 4·50 3·25

63 Shaikh Ahmad, and Flags of Arab League and Qatar

1971. Independence.
386 **63** 35d. multicoloured 40 15
387 – 75d. multicoloured 95 55
388 – 1r.25 black, pink & brown 1·50 90
389 – 3r. multicoloured . . . . . 4·25 2·75
DESIGNS—HORIZ: 75d. As Type **63**, but with U.N. flag in place of Arab League flag. VERT: 1r.25, Shaikh Ahmad; 3r. Handclasp.

64 European Roller **66** Shaikh Khalifa bin Hamad al-Thani

1972. Birds. Multicoloured.
391 1d. Type **64** 25 25
392 2d. River kingfisher 25 25
393 3d. Rock thrush 25 25
394 4d. Caspian tern 40 25
395 5d. Hoopoe 40 25
396 35d. European bee eater . . 2·50 90
397 75d. Golden oriole . . . . . 7·25 3·25
398 3r. Peregrine falcon . . . . . 24·00 12·50

1972. Nos. 328/30 surch with value in English and Arabic.
399 10d. on 60d. multicoloured 1·00 15
400 1r. on 1r.25 multicoloured . . 4·25 85
401 5r. on 2r. multicoloured . . . 8·50 4·00

1972.
402 **66** 5d. blue and violet 15 10
403 10d. red and brown . . . 15 10
404 35d. green and orange . . 55 15
405 55d. mauve and green . . 95 35
406 75d. mauve and blue . . . 1·50 50
407 – 1r. black and brown . . . 1·75 50
408 – 1r.25 black and green . . . 2·75 70
409 – 5r. black and blue . . . . 10·00 3·50
410 – 10r. black and red . . . . 17·00 6·00
The rupee values are larger, 27 × 32 mm.
For similar design but with Shaikh's head turned slightly to right, see Nos. 444a/b.

67 Book Year Emblem

1972. International Book Year.
411 **67** 35d. black and blue . . . 50 30
412 55d. black and brown . . 75 45
413 75d. black and green . . . 1·10 75
414 1r.25 black and lilac . . . 2·00 1·25

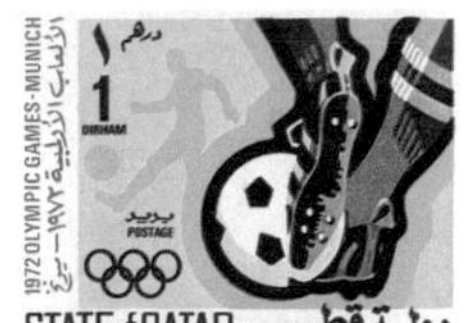

68 Football

1972. Olympic Games, Munich. Designs depicting sportsmen's hands or feet. Multicoloured.
415 1d. Type **68** 10 10
416 2d. Running (foot on starting block) 10 10
417 3d. Cycling (hand) 10 10
418 4d. Gymnastics (hand) . . . 10 10
419 5d. Basketball (hand) 15 10
420 35d. Discus (hand) 55 30
421 75d. Type **68** . . . . 1·40 90
422 3r. As 2d. . . . . 4·50 3·25

69 Underwater Pipeline Construction

1972. "Oil from the Sea". Multicoloured.
424 1d. Drilling (vert) 10 10
425 4d. Type **69** 10 10
426 5d. Offshore rig "Sea Shell" 10 10
427 35d. Underwater "prospecting" for oil . . . 80 35
428 75d. As 1d. . . . . 1·75 85
429 3r. As 5d. . . . . 8·00 3·75

70 Administrative Building

1972. Independence Day. Multicoloured.
430 10d. Type **70** 25 10
431 35d. Handclasp and Arab League flag 65 30
432 75d. Handclasp and U.N. flag . . . . 1·10 70
433 1r.25 Shaikh Khalifa . . . . 2·00 1·25

71 Dish Aerial, Satellite and Telephone (I.T.U.)

1972. United Nations Day. Multicoloured.
435 1d. Type **71** 10 10
436 2d. Archaeological team (UNESCO) 10 10
437 3d. Tractor, produce and helicopter (F.A.O.) 10 10
438 4d. Children with books (UNICEF) 10 10
439 5d. Weather satellite (W.M.O.) 10 10
440 25d. Construction workers (I.L.O.) 70 30
441 55d. Child care (W.H.O.) . . 1·75 65
442 1r. Airliner and van (U.P.U.) 3·25 1·10

72 Emblem and Flags **72a** Shaikh Khalifa

1972. 10th Session of Arab States Civil Aviation Council, Qatar.
443 **72** 25d. multicoloured 70 35
444 30d. multicoloured 95 50

1972.
444a **72a** 10d. red and brown . . 25·00 25·00
444b 25d. green and purple 25·00 25·00

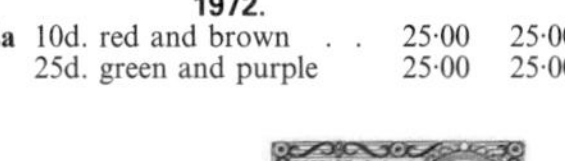

73 Shaikh Khalifa **74** Clock Tower, Doha

1973.
445 **73** 5d. multicoloured 15 10
446 10d. multicoloured 15 10
447 20d. multicoloured 35 10
448 25d. multicoloured 35 10
449 35d. multicoloured 60 15
450 55d. multicoloured . . . . 1·00 35
451 **74** 75d. purple, green and blue 2·25 65
452 **73** 1r. multicoloured . . . . . 2·25 55
453 5r. multicoloured . . . . . 8·25 2·40
454 10r. multicoloured . . . . 16·00 5·75
Nos. 452/4 are larger, 27 × 32 mm.

75 Housing Development

1973. 1st Anniv of Shaikh Khalifa's Accession. Multicoloured.
455 2d. Road construction . . . 10 10
456 3d. Type **75** 10 10
457 4d. Hospital operating theatre 10 10
458 5d. Telephone exchange . . . 10 10
459 15d. School classroom . . . 25 10
460 20d. Television studio 30 10
461 35d. Shaikh Khalifa 50 15
462 55d. Gulf Hotel, Doha . . . 95 45
463 1r. Industrial plant . . . . . 1·75 80
464 1r.35 Flour mills . . . . . . 2·25 1·40

76 Aerial Crop-spraying

1973. 25th Anniv of W.H.O. Multicoloured.

465 2d. Type **76** 10 10
466 3d. Drugs and syringe . . . 10 10
467 4d. Woman in wheelchair (Prevention of polio) . . . 10 10
468 5d. Mosquito (Malaria control) 10 10
469 55d. Mental patient (Mental Health Research) . . . . . 1·60 80
470 1r. Dead trees (Anti-pollution) . . . . 3·00 1·60

77 Weather Ship

1973. Centenary of World Meteorological Organization. Multicoloured.

471 2d. Type **77** 10 10
472 3d. Launching radio-sonde balloon 10 10
473 4d. Hawker Siddeley H.S.125 weather plane 10 10
474 5d. Meteorological station . . 10 10
475 10d. Met airplane taking-off 20 10
476 1r. "Nimbus 1" . . . . . . 2·00 95
477 1r.55 Rocket on launch-pad 3·50 1·75

78 Handclasp

1973. Independence Day. Multicoloured.

478 15d. Type **78** 10 10
479 35d. Agriculture 20 10
480 55d. Government building . . 60 30
481 1r.35 View of Doha . . . . 1·50 70
482 1r.55 Illuminated fountain . . 1·75 1·10

79 Child planting Sapling (UNESCO)

1973. United Nations Day. Multicoloured.

483 2d. Type **79** 10 10
484 4d. U.N. Headquarters, New York, and flags 10 10
485 5d. Building construction (I.L.O.) 10 10
486 35d. Nurses in dispensary (W.H.O.) 35 10
487 1r.35 Radar control (I.T.U.) 1·75 95
488 3r. Inspection of wheat and cattle (F.A.O.) . . . . . . 4·00 2·50

80 "Open Gates"

1973. 25th Anniv of Declaration of Human Rights. Multicoloured.

489 2d. Type **80** 10 10
490 4d. Freedom marchers . . . 10 10
491 5d. "Equality of Man" . . . 10 10
492 35d. Primary education . . . 35 15
493 1r.35 General Assembly, U.N. . . . . 1·75 70
494 3r. Flame emblem (vert) . . . 4·00 2·25

81 New Flyover, Doha

1974. 2nd Anniv of Shaikh Khalifa's Accession. Mult.

495 2d. Type **81** 10 10
496 3d. Education symbol 10 10
497 5d. Gas plant 10 10
498 35d. Gulf Hotel, Doha . . . 40 20
499 1r.55 Space communications station . . . . 2·00 95
500 2r.25 Shaikh Khalifa . . . . 3·00 1·75

82 Camel Caravan and Articulated Mail Van

1974. Centenary of U.P.U. Multicoloured.

501 2d. Type **82** 10 10
502 3d. Early mail wagon and Japanese "Hikari" express train 20 20
503 10d. "Hindoostan" (paddle-steamer) and "Iberia" (liner) 60 20
504 35d. Early (Handley Page H.P.42) and modern (Vickers VC-10) mail planes 55 35
505 75d. Manual and mechanized mail-sorting . . . . 1·10 70
506 1r.25 Early and modern P.O. sales counters . . . . . . 1·75 1·25

83 Doha Hospital

1974. World Population Year. Multicoloured.

507 5d. Type **83** 10 10
508 10d. W.P.Y. emblem 15 10
509 15d. Emblem within wreath 15 10
510 35d. World population map 40 20
511 1r.75 New-born infants and clock ("a birth every minute") . . . . 2·00 90
512 2r.25 "Ideal Family" group 2·50 1·50

84 Television Station

1974. Independence Day. Multicoloured.

513 5d. Type **84** 10 10
514 10d. Doha palace 15 10
515 15d. Teachers' College . . . 20 10
516 75d. Clock tower and mosque 85 40
517 1r.55 Roundabout and surroundings . . . . . . 1·75 1·00
518 2r.25 Shaikh Khalifa . . . . 2·50 1·50

85 Operating Theatre (W.H.O.)

1974. United Nations Day.

519 **85** 5d. orange, purple & black 10 10
520 – 10d. orange, red and black 15 10
521 – 20d. blue, green and black 25 10
522 – 25d. blue, brown and black 35 15
523 – 1r.75 blue, mauve & black 1·90 1·25
524 – 2r. blue, orange and black 2·75 1·60

DESIGNS. 10d. Satellite earth station (I.T.U.); 20d. Tractor (F.A.O.); 25d. Classroom (UNESCO); 1r.75, African open-air court (Human Rights); 2r. U.P.U. and U.N. emblems (U.P.U.).

86 Vickers VC-10 Airliner

1974. Arab Civil Aviation Day.

525 **86** 20d. multicoloured 60 20
526 – 25d. blue, green and yellow 70 30
527 – 30d. multicoloured . . . . 1·10 40
528 – 50d. red, green and purple 2·50 90

DESIGNS: 25d. Doha airport; 30, 50d. Flags of Qatar and the Arab League.

87 Clock Tower, Doha

1974. Tourism. Multicoloured.

529 5d. Type **87** 20 10
530 10d. White-cheeked terns, hoopoes and Shara'o Island (horiz) . . . . . . 2·25 30
531 15d. Fort Zubara (horiz) . . 30 10
532 35d. Dinghies and Gulf Hotel (horiz) 50 20
533 55d. Qatar by night (horiz) 85 35
534 75d. Arabian oryx (horiz) . . 1·60 50
535 1r.25 Khor-al-Udeid (horiz) 1·90 95
536 1r.75 Ruins Wakrah (horiz) 2·10 1·50

88 Traffic Roundabout, Doha

1975. 3rd Anniv of Shaikh Khalifa's Accession. Multicoloured.

537 10d. Type **88** 20 10
538 35d. Oil pipelines 60 20
539 55d. Laying offshore pipelines 90 35
540 1r. Oil refinery . . . . 1·60 65
541 1r.35 Shaikh Khalifa (vert) 2·40 1·10
542 1r.55 As 1r.35 . . . . 3·00 1·60

89 Flintlock Pistol

1975. Opening of National Museum. Multicoloured.

543 2d. Type **89** 10 10
544 3d. Arabesque-pattern mosaic 10 10
545 35d. Museum buildings . . . 65 35
546 75d. Museum archway (vert) 1·50 80
547 1r.25 Flint tools . . . . . . 2·25 1·40
548 3r. Gold necklace and pendant (vert) . . . . . . 4·50 3·50

90 Policeman and Road Signs

1975. Traffic Week. Multicoloured.

549 5d. Type **90** 35 15
550 15d. Traffic arrows and signal lights 90 30
551 35d. Type **90** . . . . 2·00 50
552 55d. As 15d. . . . . 3·50 1·40

91 Flag and Emblem

1975. 10th Anniv of Arab Labour Charter.

553 **91** 10d. multicoloured 25 15
554 35d. multicoloured . . . . 1·00 40
555 1r. multicoloured . . . . . 2·75 2·00

92 Government Building, Doha

1975. 4th Anniv of Independence. Multicoloured.

556 5d. Type **92** 10 10
557 15d. Museum and clock tower, Doha 30 10
558 35d. Constitution – Arabic text (vert) 55 15
559 55d. Ruler and flag (vert) . . 80 40
560 75d. Constitution – English text (vert) . . . . 1·10 70
561 1r.25 As 55d. . . . . 2·25 1·25

93 Telecommunications Satellite (I.T.U.)

1975. 30th Anniv of U.N.O. Multicoloured.

562 5d. Type **93** 10 10
563 15d. U.N. Headquarters, New York 15 10
564 35d. U.P.U. emblem and map 40 15
565 1r. Doctors tending child (U.N.I.C.E.F.) . . . . . . 1·00 55
566 1r.25 Bulldozer (I.L.O.) . . . 1·60 90
567 2r. Students in class (U.N.E.S.C.O.) . . . . . 2·75 1·50

94 Fertilizer Plant

1975. Qatar Industry. Multicoloured.

568 5d. Type **94** 15 10
569 10d. Flour mills (vert) . . . 25 10
570 35d. Natural gas plant . . . 50 15
571 75d. Oil refinery . . . . . . 1·40 70
572 1r.25 Cement works . . . . 2·00 1·25
573 1r.55 Steel mills . . . . . . 2·50 1·50

95 Modern Building, Doha

1976. 4th Anniv of Shaikh Khalifa's Accession.

574 **95** 5d. multicoloured 10 10
575 – 10d. multicoloured 10 10
576 – 35d. multicoloured 40 10
577 – 55d. multicoloured 70 30
578 – 75d. multicoloured 90 50
579 – 1r.55 multicoloured . . . . 2·75 1·90

DESIGNS: Nos. 575/6 and 579 show public buildings; Nos. 577/8 show Shaikh Khalifa with flag.

96 Tracking Aerial

97 Early and Modern Telephones

1976. Opening of Satellite Earth Station. Mult.

580 35d. Type **96** 65 15
581 55d. "Intelsat" satellite . . . 90 35
582 75d. Type **96** . . . . 1·50 70
583 1r. As 55d. . . . . 1·90 90

1976. Telephone Centenary.

584 **97** 1r. multicoloured . . . . . 1·40 80
585 1r.35 multicoloured . . . . 1·90 1·00

98 Tournament Emblem

100 Football

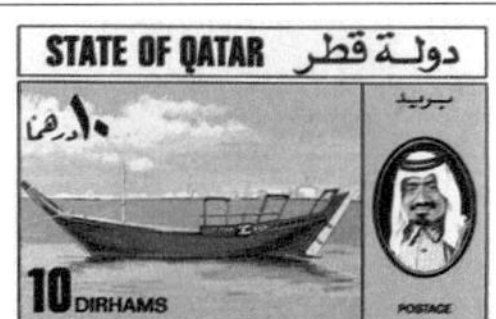

99 Qatar Dhow

1976. 4th Arabian Gulf Football Cup Tournament. Multicoloured.

586	5d. Type **98**	10	10
587	10d. Qatar Stadium	15	10
588	35d. Type **98**	75	15
589	55d. Two players with ball	1·25	35
590	75d. Player with ball	1·75	60
591	1r.25 As 10d.	3·25	1·40

1976. Dhows.

592	**99**	10d. multicoloured	25	10
593	–	35d. multicoloured	70	15
594	–	80d. multicoloured	1·60	40
595	–	1r.25 multicoloured	2·50	1·40
596	–	1r.50 multicoloured	3·25	1·75
597	–	2r. multicoloured	4·75	2·25

DESIGNS: 35d. to 2r. Various craft.

1976. Olympic Games, Montreal, Multicoloured.

598	5d. Type **100**	10	10
599	10d. Yachting	25	10
600	35d. Show jumping	55	15
601	80d. Boxing	1·40	50
602	1r.25 Weightlifting	2·25	1·25
603	1r.50 Basketball	2·50	2·10

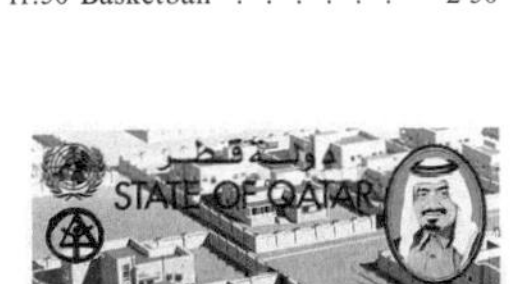

101 Urban Housing Development

1976. United Nations Conference on Human Settlements. Multicoloured.

604	10d. Type **101**	10	10
605	35d. U.N. and conference emblems	40	15
606	80d. Communal housing development	1·10	50
607	1r.25 Shaikh Khalifa	2·25	1·25

102 Kentish Plover

1976. Birds. Multicoloured.

608	5d. Type **102**	70	25
609	10d. Great cormorant	70	25
610	35d. Osprey	3·50	65
611	80d. Greater flamingo (vert)	6·50	1·50
612	1r.25 Rock thrush (vert)	9·75	3·25
613	2r. Saker falcon (vert)	14·00	4·50

103 Shaikh Khalifa and Flag

105 Shaikh Khalifa

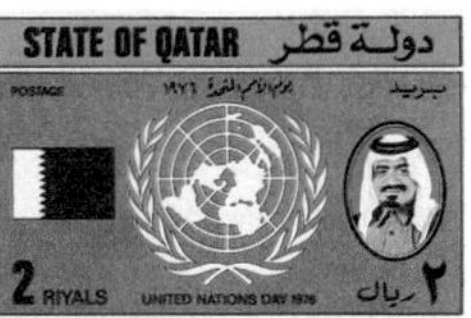

104 U.N. Emblem

1976. 5th Anniv of Independence. Multicoloured.

614	5d. Type **103**	10	10
615	10d. Type **103**	20	10
616	40d. Doha buildings (horiz)	35	15
617	80d. As 40d.	70	30
618	1r.25 "Dana" (oil rig) (horiz)	2·00	1·10
619	1r.50 United Nations and Qatar emblems (horiz)	2·10	1·50

1976. United Nations Day.

620	**104**	2r. multicoloured	3·00	1·75
621		3r. multicoloured	3·75	2·25

1977. 5th Anniv of Amir's Accession.

622	**105**	20d. multicoloured	25	10
623		1r.80 multicoloured	2·75	2·10

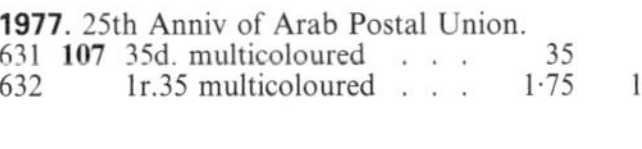

106 Shaikh Khalifa

107 Envelope and A.P.U. Emblem

1977.

624	**106**	5d. multicoloured	15	10
625		10d. multicoloured	20	10
626		35d. multicoloured	60	15
627		80d. multicoloured	1·10	35
628		1r. multicoloured	1·40	50
629		5r. multicoloured	6·75	3·25
630		10r. multicoloured	12·00	5·50

Nos. 628/30 are larger, size 25 × 31 mm.

1977. 25th Anniv of Arab Postal Union.

631	**107**	35d. multicoloured	35	15
632		1r.35 multicoloured	1·75	1·25

108 Shaikh Khalifa and Sound Waves

1977. International Telecommunications Day.

633	**108**	35d. multicoloured	35	15
634		1r.80 multicoloured	2·25	1·90

108a Shaikh Khalifa

109 Parliament Building, Doha

1977.

634a	**108a**	5d. multicoloured	15	15
634c		10d. multicoloured	25	25
634d		35d. multicoloured	60	60
634e		80d. multicoloured	1·90	1·90

1977. 6th Anniv of Independence. Multicoloured.

635	80d. Type **109**	1·10	75
636	80d. Main business district, Doha	1·10	75
637	80d. Motorway, Doha	1·10	75

110 U.N. Emblem

1977. United Nations Day.

638	**110**	20d. multicoloured	25	10
639		1r. multicoloured	1·75	1·25

111 Steel Mill

1978. 6th Anniv of Amir's Accession. Mult.

640	20d. Type **111**	20	10
641	80d. Operating theatre	80	30
642	1r. Children's classroom	1·00	50
643	5r. Shaikh Khalifa	3·75	2·75

112 Oil Refinery

1978. 7th Anniv of Independence. Multicoloured.

644	35d. Type **112**	30	15
645	80d. Apartment buildings	70	30
646	1r.35 Town centre, Doha	1·50	1·00
647	1r.80 Shaikh Khalifa	2·00	1·40

113 Man reading Alphabet

1978. International Literacy Day.

648	**113**	35d. multicoloured	30	15
649		80d. multicoloured	85	60

114 U.N. Emblem and Qatar Flag

1978. United Nations Day.

650	**114**	35d. multicoloured	30	15
651		80d. multicoloured	85	60

115 "Human Rights Flame"

116 I.Y.C. Emblem

1978. 30th Anniv of Declaration of Human Rights. Multicoloured.

652	35d. Type **115**	30	15
653	80d. Type **115**	50	40
654	1r.25 Flame and scales of justice	85	70
655	1r.80 As 1r.25	1·25	90

1979. International Year of the Child.

656	**116**	35d. mauve, blue and black	30	15
657		1r.80 green, blue & black	1·25	90

117 Shaikh Khalifa

118 Shaikh Khalifa and Laurel Wreath

1979.

658	**117**	5d. multicoloured	10	10
659		10d. multicoloured	10	10
660		20d. multicoloured	25	10
661		25d. multicoloured	25	10
662		35d. multicoloured	45	15
663		60d. multicoloured	80	15
664		80d. multicoloured	1·00	20
665		1r. multicoloured	1·10	20
666		1r.25 multicoloured	1·40	30
667		1r.35 multicoloured	1·60	40
668		1r.80 multicoloured	2·00	55
669		5r. multicoloured	5·00	1·90
670		10r. multicoloured	8·50	2·75

Nos. 665/70 are larger, size 27 × 32½ mm.

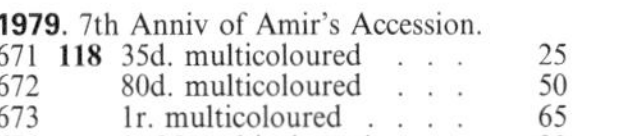

1979. 7th Anniv of Amir's Accession.

671	**118**	35d. multicoloured	25	10
672		80d. multicoloured	50	25
673		1r. multicoloured	65	35
674		1r.25 multicoloured	90	75

119 Wave Pattern and Television Screen

1979. World Telecommunications Day.

675	**119**	2r. multicoloured	1·25	90
676		2r.80 multicoloured	1·50	1·25

120 Two Children supporting Globe

1979. 50th Anniv of Int Bureau of Education.

677	**120**	35d. multicoloured	35	15
678		80d. multicoloured	75	35

121 Rolling Mill

122 U.N. Emblem and Flag of Qatar

1979. 8th Anniv of Independence. Multicoloured.

679	5d. Type **121**	10	10
680	10d. Aerial view of Doha	10	10
681	1r.25 Qatar flag	85	60
682	2r. Shaikh Khalifa	1·40	1·10

1979. United Nations Day.

683	**122**	1r.25 multicoloured	1·25	65
684		2r. multicoloured	2·25	1·60

123 Mosque Minaret and Crescent Moon

1979. 3rd World Conference on the Prophet's Seera and Sunna.

685	**123**	35d. multicoloured	40	15
686		1r.80 multicoloured	2·10	1·60

124 Shaikh Khalifa

1980. 8th Anniv of Amir's Accession.

687	**124**	20d. multicoloured	20	10
688		60d. multicoloured	60	25
689		1r.25 multicoloured	1·40	95
690		2r. multicoloured	2·25	1·75

125 Emblem

1980. 6th Congress of Arab Towns Organization, Doha.

691	**125**	2r.35 multicoloured	2·50	1·75
692		2r.80 multicoloured	3·00	2·25

126 Oil Refinery

1980. 9th Anniv of Independence. Multicoloured.
693 10d. Type **126** 15 10
694 35d. Doha 40 15
695 2r. Oil Rig . . . . 2·25 1·60
696 2r.35 Hospital . . . . 2·50 1·75

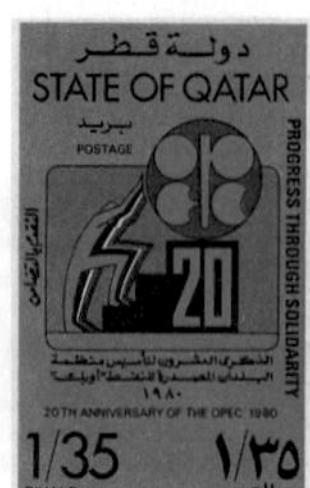
127 Figures supporting O.P.E.C. Emblem

1980. 20th Anniv of Organization of Petroleum Exporting Countries.
697 **127** 1r.35 multicoloured . . . 90 60
698 2r. multicoloured . . . . 1·60 90

128 U.N.Emblem

129 Mosque and Kaaba, Mecca

1980. United Nations Day.
699 **128** 1r.35 blue, light blue and purple 90 60
700 1r.80 turquoise, green and black . . . . 1·90 1·40

1980. 1400th Anniv of Hegira.
701 **129** 10d. multicoloured . . . 10 10
702 35d. multicoloured . . . 40 20
703 1r.25 multicoloured . . . 90 65
704 2r.80 multicoloured . . . 2·40 1·75

130 I.Y.D.P. Emblem

1981. International Year of Disabled Persons.
705 **130** 2r. multicoloured . . . . 1·90 1·25
706 3r. multicoloured . . . . 3·00 1·75

131 Student

132 Shaikh Khalifa

1981. 20th Anniv of Education Day.
707 **131** 2r. multicoloured . . . . 1·90 1·10
708 3r. multicoloured . . . . 2·75 1·60

1981. 9th Anniv of Amir's Accession.
709 **132** 10d. multicoloured . . . 10 10
710 35d. multicoloured . . . 45 25
711 80d. multicoloured . . . 75 45
712 5r. multicoloured . . . . 3·75 2·40

133 I.T.U. and W.H.O. Emblems and Ribbons forming Caduceus

134 Torch

1981. World Telecommunications Day.
713 **133** 2r. multicoloured . . . . 2·00 95
714 2r.80 multicoloured . . . 2·75 1·25

1981. 30th International Military Football Championship.
715 **134** 1r.25 multicoloured . . . 1·75 85
716 2r.80 multicoloured . . . 3·50 2·25

135 Qatar Flag

1981. 10th Anniv of Independence.
717 **135** 5d. multicoloured 10 10
718 60d. multicoloured . . . 70 30
719 80d. multicoloured . . . 1·00 50
720 5r. multicoloured . . . . 5·25 3·50

136 Tractor gathering Crops

1981. World Food Day.
721 **136** 2r. multicoloured . . . . 2·10 1·40
722 2r.80 multicoloured . . . 3·25 1·90

137 Red Crescent

1982. Qatar Red Crescent.
723 **137** 20d. multicoloured . . . 40 10
724 2r.80 multicoloured . . . 4·25 2·75

138 Shaikh Khalifa

1982. 10th Anniv of Amir's Accession.
725 **138** 10d. multicoloured . . . 10 10
726 20d. multicoloured . . . 25 10
727 1r.25 multicoloured . . . 1·40 80
728 2r.80 multicoloured . . . 3·25 2·00

139 Hamad General Hospital

1982. Hamad General Hospital.
729 **139** 10d. multicoloured . . . 10 10
730 2r.35 multicoloured . . . 2·50 1·90

140 Shaikh Khalifa

1982.
731 **140** 5d. multicoloured 10 10
732 10d. multicoloured . . . 10 10
733 15d. multicoloured . . . 40 10
734 20d. multicoloured . . . 15 10
735 25d. multicoloured . . . 20 15
736 35d. multicoloured . . . 30 15
737 60d. multicoloured . . . 50 15
738 80d. multicoloured . . . 60 15
739 – 1r. multicoloured . . . . 1·00 20
740 – 1r.25 multicoloured . . . 1·00 25
741 – 2r. multicoloured . . . . 1·40 65
742 – 5r. multicoloured . . . . 4·00 1·60
743 – 10r. multicoloured . . . . 8·00 3·50
744 – 15r. multicoloured . . . . 9·75 4·75
DESIGNS—25 × 32 mm: 1r. to 2r. Oil refinery; 5r. to 15r. Doha clock tower.

142 "Bar'zan" Container Ship

1982. 6th Anniv of United Arab Shipping Company.
745 **142** 20d. multicoloured . . . 45 15
746 2r.35 multicoloured . . . 3·50 2·25

143 A.P.U. Emblem

144 National Flag

1982. 30th Anniv of Arab Postal Union.
747 **143** 35d. multicoloured . . . 50 15
748 2r.80 multicoloured . . . 3·25 2·25

1982. 11th Anniv of Independence.
749 **144** 10d. multicoloured . . . 10 10
750 80d. multicoloured . . . 80 30
751 1r.25 multicoloured . . . 1·25 75
752 2r.80 multicoloured . . . 3·00 1·90

145 W.C.Y. Emblem

147 Arabic Script

146 Conference Emblem

1983. World Communications Year.
753 **145** 35d. multicoloured . . . 50 15
754 2r.80 multicoloured . . . 3·00 2·10

1983. 2nd Gulf Postal Organization Conference.
755 **146** 1r. multicoloured . . . . 1·25 50
756 1r.35 multicoloured . . . 1·90 75

1983. 12th Anniv of Independence.
757 **147** 10d. multicoloured . . . 10 10
758 35d. multicoloured . . . 35 20
759 80d. multicoloured . . . 75 40
760 2r.80 multicoloured . . . 2·75 2·10

148 Council Emblem

1983. 4th Session of Gulf Co-operation Council Supreme Council.
761 **148** 35d. multicoloured . . . 40 15
762 2r.80 multicoloured . . . 2·25 1·90

149 Globe and Human Rights Emblem

1983. 35th Anniv of Declaration of Human Rights. Multicoloured.
763 1r.25 Type **149** . . . . . . 1·75 70
764 2r.80 Globe and emblem in balance . . . . 3·75 1·90

150 Harbour

151 Shaikh Khalifa

1984.
765 **150** 15d. multicoloured . . . 10 10
765a **151** 25d. mult (22 × 27 mm) 20 15
766 **150** 40d. multicoloured . . . 30 20
767 50d. multicoloured . . . 40 25
767a **151** 75d. mult (22 × 27 mm) 45 35
768 1r. multicoloured 75 35
769 1r.50 multicoloured . . . 1·25 55
769a 2r. multicoloured . . . . 1·25 90
770 2r.50 multicoloured . . . 1·90 85
771 3r. multicoloured . . . . 2·50 1·25
772 5r. multicoloured . . . . 4·00 2·00
773 10r. multicoloured . . . 7·75 5·25

152 Flag and Shaikh Khalifa

1984. 13th Anniv of Independence.
774 **152** 15d. multicoloured . . . 15 10
775 1r. multicoloured 85 35
776 2r.50 multicoloured . . . 2·10 1·10
777 3r.50 multicoloured . . . 3·00 1·60

153 Teacher and Blackboard

154 I.C.A.O. Emblem

1984. International Literacy Day. Multicoloured, background colour behind board given.
778 **153** 1r. mauve 90 40
779 1r. orange 90 40

1984. 40th Anniv of I.C.A.O.
780 **154** 20d. multicoloured . . . 25 10
781 3r.50 multicoloured . . . 3·25 1·90

155 I.Y.Y. Emblem **156** Crossing the Road

1985. International Youth Year.
782 **155** 50d. multicoloured . . . 65 30
783 1r. multicoloured . . . . 1·40 45

1985. Traffic Week. Multicoloured, frame colour given.
784 **156** 1r. red . . . . 1·25 40
785 1r. blue . . . . 1·25 40

157 Emblem

1985. 40th Anniv of League of Arab States.
786 **157** 50d. multicoloured . . . 50 20
787 4r. multicoloured . . . . 3·50 2·25

158 Doha

1985. 14th Anniv of Independence. Multicoloured.
788 40d. Type **158** 30 25
789 50d. Dish aerials and microwave tower 45 30
790 1r.50 Oil refinery . . . . . . 1·25 1·00
791 4r. Cement works . . . . . 3·25 2·75

159 O.P.E.C. Emblem in "25"

1985. 25th Anniv of Organization of Petroleum Exporting Countries. Multicoloured, background colours given.
792 **159** 1r. red . . . . 1·25 70
793 1r. green . . . . 1·25 70

160 U.N. Emblem

1985. 40th Anniv of U.N.O.
794 **160** 1r. multicoloured 80 70
795 3r. multicoloured . . . . 2·00 1·90

161 Emblem

1986. Population and Housing Census.
796 **161** 1r. multicoloured 70 60
797 3r. multicoloured . . . . 2·00 1·75

162 "Qatari ibn al-Fuja'a" (container ship)

1986. 10th Anniv of United Arab Shipping Company. Multicoloured.
798 1r.50 Type **162** 90 80
799 4r. "Al Wajda" (container ship) . . . . 2·40 2·25

163 Flag and Shaikh Khalifa

1986. 15th Anniv of Independence.
800 **163** 40d. multicoloured . . . 25 20
801 50d. multicoloured . . . 35 25
802 1r. multicoloured 65 55
803 4r. multicoloured . . . . 2·40 2·25

164 Shaikh Khalifa **165** Palace

1987.
804 **164** 15r. multicoloured . . . . 7·25 6·50
805 20r. multicoloured . . . . 9·75 8·50
806 30r. multicoloured . . . . 14·00 12·50

1987. 15th Anniv of Amir's Accession.
807 **165** 50d. multicoloured . . . 35 25
808 1r. multicoloured 60 30
809 1r.50 multicoloured . . . 80 70
810 4r. multicoloured . . . . 2·25 1·90

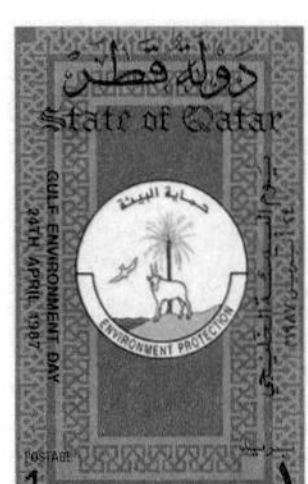

166 Emblem **167** Emblem

1987. 35th Anniv of Arab Postal Union.
811 **166** 1r. yellow, green and black 50 45
812 1r.50 multicoloured . . . 1·00 70

1987. Gulf Environment Day.
813 **167** 1r. multicoloured 60 50
814 4r. multicoloured . . . . 2·40 1·90

168 Modern Complex

1987. 16th Anniv of Independence.
815 25d. Type **168** 20 10
816 75d. Aerial view of city . . . 50 35
817 2r. Modern building . . . . 1·25 90
818 4r. Oil refinery . . . . 2·40 2·00

169 Pens in Fist **170** Anniversary Emblem

1987. International Literacy Day.
819 **169** 1r.50 multicoloured . . . 90 80
820 4r. multicoloured . . . . 2·40 1·90

1988. 40th Anniv of W.H.O.
821 **170** 1r.50 yellow, black and blue 90 80
822 2r. yellow, black and pink 1·40 95

171 State Arms, Shaikh Khalifa and Flag

1988. 17th Anniv of Independence.
823 **171** 50d. multicoloured . . . 30 25
824 75d. multicoloured . . . 45 35
825 1r.50 multicoloured . . . 85 70
826 2r. multicoloured . . . . 1·10 90

172 Post Office

1988. Opening of New Doha General Post Office.
827 **172** 1r.50 multicoloured . . . 75 65
828 4r. multicoloured . . . . 1·90 1·75

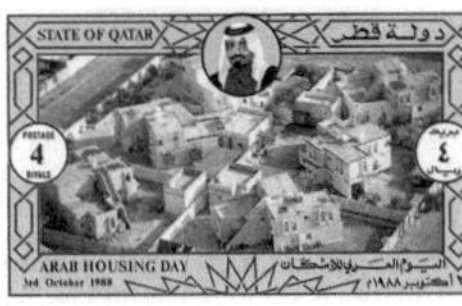

173 Housing Development

1988. Arab Housing Day.
829 **173** 1r.50 multicoloured . . . 75 70
830 4r. multicoloured . . . . 2·00 1·75

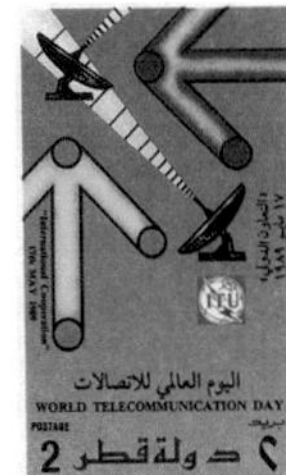

174 Hands shielding Flame **175** Dish Aerials and Arrows

1988. 40th Anniv of Declaration of Human Rights.
831 **174** 1r.50 multicoloured . . . 75 65
832 2r. multicoloured . . . . 1·00 90

1989. World Telecommunications Day.
833 **175** 2r. multicoloured 95 85
834 4r. multicoloured . . . . 1·75 1·60

176 Headquarters

1989. 10th Anniv of Qatar Red Crescent Society.
835 **176** 4r. multicoloured . . . . 1·90 1·60

177 Palace

1989. 18th Anniv of Independence.
836 **177** 75d. multicoloured . . . 35 25
837 1r. multicoloured 60 55
838 1r.50 multicoloured . . . 75 65
839 2r. multicoloured 90 85

178 Anniversary Emblem

1990. 40th Anniv of Gulf Air.
840 **178** 50d. multicoloured . . . 35 30
841 75d. multicoloured . . . 50 45
842 4r. multicoloured . . . . 2·50 2·25

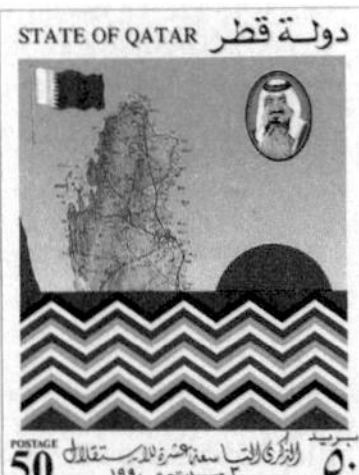

179 Map and Rising Sun

1990. 19th Anniv of Independence. Multicoloured.
843 50d. Type **179** 35 30
844 75d. Map and sunburst . . . 50 45
845 1r.50 Musicians and sword dancer . . . . 1·00 90
846 2r. As No. 845 . . . . 2·00 1·75

180 Anniversary Emblem **181** Emblem and Dhow

1990. 30th Anniv of Organization of Petroleum Exporting Countries. Multicoloured.
847 50d. Type **180** 35 30
848 1r.50 Flags of member nations . . . . 1·00 90

1990. 11th Session of Supreme Council of Gulf Co-operation Council. Multicoloured.
849 50d. Type **181** 45 30
850 1r. Council heads of state and emblem 65 55
851 1r.50 State flag and Council emblem . . . . 1·00 90
852 2r. State and Council emblems . . . . 1·25 1·10

182 "Glossonema edule" **183** Emblem

1991. Plants. Multicoloured.
853 10d. Type **182** 10 10
854 25d. "Lycium shawii" 15 10
855 50d. "Acacia tortilis" 35 30
856 75d. "Acacia ehrenbergiana" 50 45
857 1r. "Capparis spinosa" . . . 65 55
858 4r. "Cymbopogon parkeri" 2·50 2·25
No. 858 is wrongly inscribed "Cymhopogon".

1991. 20th Anniv of Independence. Multicoloured.
859 25d. Type **183** 15 10
860 75d. As Type **183** but different Arabic inscription 50 45
861 1r. View of Doha (35 × 32 mm) 65 55
862 1r.50 Palace (35 × 32 mm) . . 1·00 90

184 Seabream

1991. Fishes. Multicoloured.
863 10d. Type **184** 10 10
864 15d. Pennant coralfish . . . 10 10
865 25d. Scarlet-finned squirrelfish 15 10
866 50d. Smooth houndshark . . 45 35
867 75d. Seabream 65 55
868 1r. Golden trevally 80 65
869 1r.50 Rabbitfish . . . . . . 1·25 1·10
870 2r. Yellow-banded angelfish 1·75 1·50

185 Shaikh Khalifa

1992. Multicoloured. (a) Size 22 × 28 or 28 × 22 mm.
871 10d. Type **185** 10 10
872 25d. North Field gas project 15 10
873 50d. Map of Qatar 25 20
874 75d. Petrochemical factory (horiz) 30 25
875 1r. Oil refinery (horiz) . . . 40 35

(b) Size 25 × 32 or 32 × 25 mm.
876 1r.50 As No. 872 . . . . . . 65 60
877 2r. As No. 873 . . . . 85 75
878 3r. As No. 874 . . . . 1·40 1·25
879 4r. As No. 875 . . . . 1·75 1·50
880 5r. As No. 873 . . . . 2·10 1·75
881 10r. As No. 875 . . . . . . 4·25 3·75
882 15r. Shaikh Khalifa (different frame) . . . . 6·75 6·00
883 20r. As No. 882 . . . . . . 8·75 7·75
884 30r. As No. 882 . . . . . . 13·50 12·00

186 Shaikh Khalifa and Gateway **187** Heart in Centre of Flower

1992. 20th Anniv of Amir's Accession. Mult.
885 25d. Type **186** 15 10
886 50d. Type **186** 25 20
887 75d. Archway and "20" . . . 40 35
888 1r.50 As No 887 . . . . . . 75 65

1992. World Health Day. "Heartbeat, the Rhythm of Health". Multicoloured.
889 50d. Type **187** 25 20
890 1r.50 Heart on clockface and cardiograph (horiz) 75 65

188 Women dancing

1992. Children's Paintings. Multicoloured.
891 25d. Type **188** 15 10
892 50d. Children's playground 25 20
893 75d. Boat race 40 35
894 1r.50 Fishing fleet 90 65

189 Runner and Emblems

1992. Olympic Games, Barcelona. Multicoloured.
896 50d. Type **189** 25 20
897 1r.50 Footballer and emblems 75 65

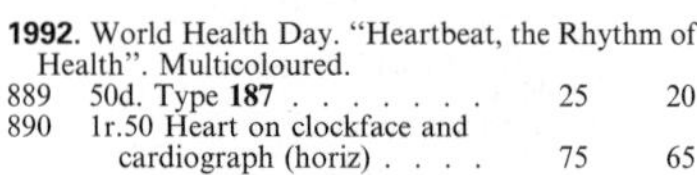
190 Shaikh Khalifa and Script

1992. 21st Anniv of Independence. Multicoloured.
898 50d. Type **190** 25 20
899 50d. Shaikh Kalifa and "21" in English and Arabic . . 25 20
900 1r. Oil well, pen and dhow (42 × 42 mm) 50 45
901 1r. Dhow in harbour (42 × 42 mm) 50 45

191 Ball, Flag and Emblem

1992. 11th Arabian Gulf Football Championship. Multicoloured.
902 50d. Type **191** 25 20
903 1r. Ball bursting goal net (vert) 50 45

192 Emblems and Globe

1992. International Nutrition Conference, Rome. Multicoloured.
904 50d. Type **192** 25 20
905 1r. Cornucopia (horiz) . . . 50 45

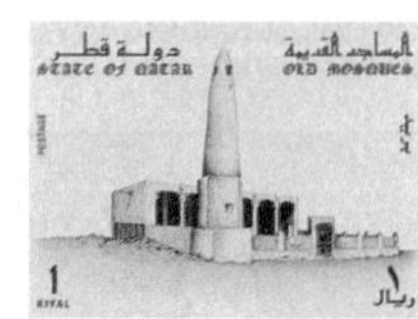

193 Mosque

1993. Old Mosques. Each sepia, yellow and brown.
906 1r. Type **193** 55 45
907 1r. Mosque (minaret without balcony) 55 45
908 1r. Mosque (minaret with wide balcony) 55 45
909 1r. Mosque (minaret with narrow balcony) 55 45

194 Presenter and Dish Aerial

1993. 25th Anniv of Qatar Broadcasting. Mult.
910 25d. Type **194** 15 10
911 50d. Rocket and satellite . . . 30 25
912 75d. Broadcasting House . . 40 35
913 1r. Journalists 55 45

195 Oil Refinery and Sea **196** Scroll, Quill and Paper

1993. 22nd Anniv of Independence. Multicoloured.
915 25d. Type **195** 15 10
916 50d. Flag and clock tower, Doha 30 25
917 75d. "22" in English and Arabic 40 35
918 1r.50 Flag and fort 80 70

1993. International Literacy Day. Multicoloured.
919 25d. Type **196** 15 10
920 50d. Fountain pen and flags spelling "Qatar" 30 25
921 75d. Fountain pen and Arabic characters 40 35
922 1r.50 Arabic text on scroll and fountain pen 80 70

197 Girls playing

1993. Children's Games. Multicoloured.
923 25d. Type **197** 15 10
924 50d. Boys playing with propeller (vert) 30 25
925 75d. Wheel and stick race (vert) 40 35
926 1r.50 Skipping 80 70

198 Lanner Falcon **199** Headquarters

1993. Falcons. Multicoloured.
928 25d. Type **198** 20 15
929 50d. Saker falcon 40 40
930 75d. Barbary falcon 55 50
931 1r.50 Peregrine falcon . . . . 1·25 1·00

1994. 30th Anniv of Qatar Insurance Company. Multicoloured.
933 50d. Type **199** 25 20
934 1r.50 Company emblem and international landmarks . . 70 60

200 Hands catching Drops from Tap **201** Gavel, Scales and National Flag

1994. World Water Day. Mulicoloured.
935 25d. Type **200** 10 10
936 1r. Hands catching raindrop, water tower, crops and United Nations emblem . . 50 45

1994. Qatar International Law Conference. Multicoloured.
937 75d. Type **201** 35 30
938 2r. Gavel and scales suspended from flag . . . 1·00 90

202 Society Emblem **203** Anniversary Emblem

1994. Qatar Society for Welfare and Rehabilitation of the Handicapped. Multicoloured.
939 25d. Type **202** 10 10
940 75d. Handicapped symbol and hands 35 30

1994. 75th Anniv of I.L.O. Multicoloured.
941 25d. Type **203** 10 10
942 2r. Anniversary emblem and cogwheel . . . . 1·00 90

204 Family and Emblem **205** Scroll

1994. International Year of the Family.
943 **204** 25d. blue and black . . . 10 10
944 – 1r. multicoloured 50 45
DESIGN: 1r. I.Y.F. emblem and stylized family standing on U.N. emblem.

1994. 23rd Anniv of Independence. Multicoloured.
945 25d. Type **205** 10 10
946 75d. Oasis 35 30
947 1r. Industry 50 45
948 2r. Scroll (different) . . . . 1·00 90

206 Map, Airplane and Emblem

1994. 50th Anniv of I.C.A.O. Multicoloured.
949 25d. Type **206** 10 10
950 75d. Anniversary emblem . . 35 30

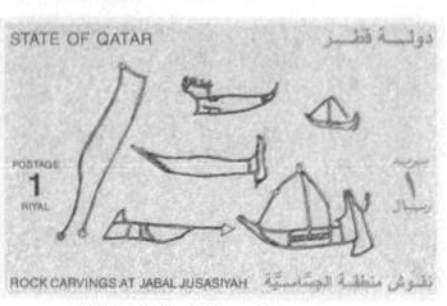

207 Ship-like Carvings

1995. Rock Carvings, Jabal Jusasiyah. Multicoloured.
951 1r. Type **207** 40 35
952 1r. Circular and geometric patterns 40 35
953 1r. Six irregular-shaped carvings 40 35
954 1r. Carvings including three multi-limbed creatures . . 40 35
955 1r. Nine multi-limbed creatures 40 35
956 1r. Fishes 70 40

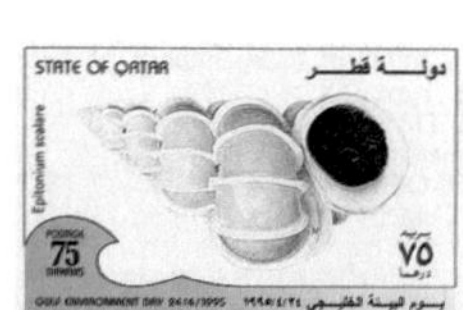

208 Precious Wentletrap ("Epitonium scalare")

1995. Gulf Environment Day. Sea Shells. Multicoloured.
957 75d. Type **208** 35 30
958 75d. Feathered cone ("Conus pennaceus") 35 30
959 75d. "Cerithidea cingulata" 35 30
960 75d. "Hexaplex kuesterianus" 35 30
961 1r. Giant spider conch ("Lambis truncata sebae") 40 35
962 1r. Woodcock murex ("Murex scolopax") . . . 40 35
963 1r. "Thais mutabilis" 40 35
964 1r. Spindle shell ("Fusinus arabicus") 40 35

209 Nursing Patient **211** Anniversary Emblem

210 Schoolchildren

1995. International Nursing Day. Multicoloured.
965 1r. Type **209** 40 35
966 1r.50 Vaccinating child . . . 60 55

1995. 24th Anniv of Independence. Multicoloured.
967 1r. Type **210** 35 30
968 1r. Palm trees 35 30
969 1r.50 Port 55 45
970 1r.50 Doha 55 45

Nos. 967/70 were issued together, se-tenant, forming a composite design.

1995. 50th Anniv of U.N.O.
971 **211** 1r.50 multicoloured . . . 55 45

212 Addra Gazelle

1996. Mammals. Multicoloured.
972 25d. Type **212** 10 10
973 50d. Beira antelope 15 10
974 75d. "Gazella dorcas pelzelni" 25 20
975 1r. Dorcas gazelle 35 30
976 1r.50 Speke's gazelle 50 40
977 2r. Soemmerring's gazelle . . . 70 55

213 Syringes through Skull

214 Map of Qatar and Games Emblem

1996. International Day against Drug Abuse. Multicoloured.
979 50d. Type **213** 15 10
980 1r. "No entry" sign over syringes in hand 35 30

1996. Olympic Games, Atlanta. Multicoloured.
981 10d. Type **214** 10 10
982 15d. Rifle shooting 10 10
983 25d. Bowling 10 10
984 50d. Table tennis 15 10
985 1r. Running 35 30
986 1r.50 Yachting 50 40

Nos. 981/6 were issued together, se-tenant, forming a composite design.

215 Map, National Flag and Shaikh Hamad

1996. 25th Anniv of Independence.
987 **215** 1r.50 multicoloured . . . 50 40
988 2r. multicoloured 70 55

216 Shaikh Hamad

217 Shaikh Hamad

1996.
990 **216** 25d. multicoloured . . . 10 10
991 50d. multicoloured . . . 15 10
992 75d. multicoloured . . . 25 20
993 1r. multicoloured 35 30
994 **217** 1r.50 multicoloured . . . 50 40
995 2r. multicoloured 70 55
997 4r. multicoloured . . . . 1·40 1·10
998 5r. multicoloured . . . . 1·75 1·40
999 10r. multicoloured . . . 3·50 2·75
1001 20r. multicoloured . . . 6·75 5·50
1002 30r. multicoloured . . . 10·00 8·00

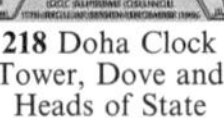

218 Doha Clock Tower, Dove and Heads of State

219 Children and UNICEF Emblem

1996. 17th Session of Gulf Co-operation Council Supreme Council, Doha. Multicoloured.
1004 1r. Type **218** 35 30
1005 1r.50 Council emblem, dove and national flag 50 40

1996. 50th Anniv of UNICEF. Multicoloured.
1006 75d. Type **219** 25 20
1007 75d. Children and emblem 25 20

220 Al-Wajbah

1997. Forts. Multicoloured.
1008 25d. Type **220** 10 10
1009 75d. Al-Zubarah (horiz) . . 25 20
1010 1r. Al-Kout Fort, Doha (horiz) 35 30
1011 3r. Umm Salal Mohammed (horiz) . . . . 1·00 80

221 World Map and Liquid Gas Containers (½-size illustration)

1997. Inauguration of Ras Laffan Port.
1012 **221** 3r. multicoloured . . . . 1·00 80

222 Palomino

1997. Arab Horses. Multicoloured.
1013 25d. Type **222** 10 10
1014 75d. Black horse 25 20
1015 1r. Grey 35 30
1016 1r.50 Bay 50 40

223 Arabic Script within Wreath, Flag and Shaikh Hamad

1997. 26th Anniv of Independence. Multicoloured.
1018 1r. Type **223** 35 30
1019 1r.50 Amir, oil refinery and Government Palace . . . 50 40

224 Graph

1997. Middle East and Northern Africa Economic Conference, Doha.
1020 **224** 2r. multicoloured 65 50

225 Nubian Flower Bee

1998. Insects. Multicoloured.
1021 2r. Type **225** 65 50
1022 2r. Domino beetle 65 50
1023 2r. Seven-spotted ladybird 65 50
1024 2r. Desert giant ant 65 50
1025 2r. Eastern death's-head hawk moth 65 50
1026 2r. Arabian darkling beetle 65 50
1027 2r. Yellow digger 65 50
1028 2r. Mole cricket 65 50
1029 2r. Migratory locust 65 50
1030 2r. Elegant rhinoceros beetle 65 50
1031 2r. Oleander hawk moth . . 65 50
1032 2r. American cockroach . . 65 50
1033 2r. Girdled skimmer 65 50
1034 2r. Sabre-toothed beetle . . 65 50
1035 2r. Arabian cicada 65 50
1036 2r. Pin-striped ground weevil 65 50
1037 2r. Praying mantis 65 50
1038 2r. Rufous bombardier beetle 65 50
1039 2r. Diadem 65 50
1040 2r. Shore earwig (inscr "Earwing") 65 50

226 Opening Oysters

1998. Early Pearl-diving Equipment. Multicoloured.
1042 25d. Type **226** 10 10
1043 75d. Opened oyster with pearl 25 20
1044 1r. Scales for weighing pearls 35 30
1045 1r.50 Basket for keeping oysters (vert) 50 40

227 Shaikh Hamad

228 Anniversary Emblem

1998. 27th Anniv of Independence. Multicoloured.
1047 1r. Type **227** 35 30
1048 1r.50 Shaikh Hamad (horiz) 50 40

1998. 25th Anniv of University of Qatar.
1049 **228** 1r. multicoloured 35 30
1050 1r.50 multicoloured . . . 50 40

229 Dromedaries

1999. Dromedaries. Multicoloured.
1051 25d. Type **229** 10 10
1052 75d. One dromedary 25 20
1053 1r. Three dromedaries . . . 35 30
1054 1r.50 Four young dromedaries with herd . . 50 40

230 Emblem

1999. General Assembly of International Equestrian Federation, Doha.
1056 **230** 1r.50 multicoloured . . . 50 40

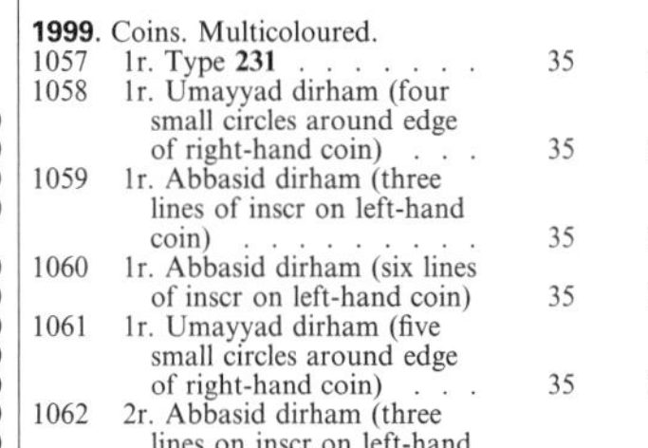

231 Umayyad Dirham

1999. Coins. Multicoloured.
1057 1r. Type **231** 35 30
1058 1r. Umayyad dirham (four small circles around edge of right-hand coin) . . . 35 30
1059 1r. Abbasid dirham (three lines of inscr on left-hand coin) 35 30
1060 1r. Abbasid dirham (six lines of inscr on left-hand coin) 35 30
1061 1r. Umayyad dirham (five small circles around edge of right-hand coin) . . . 35 30
1062 2r. Abbasid dirham (three lines on inscr on left-hand coin) 70 55
1063 2r. Umayyad dinar 70 55
1064 2r. Abbasid dinar (five lines of inscr on left-hand coin) 70 55
1065 2r. Murabitid dinar 70 55
1066 2r. Fatimid dinar 70 55

232 Shaikh Hamad

1999. 28th Anniv of Independence.
1068 **232** 1r. multicoloured 35 30
1069 1r.50 multicoloured . . . 50 45

233 Tree of Letters

234 Postal Emblems on "Stamps"

1999. 125th Anniv of Universal Postal Union. Multicoloured.
1070 1r. Type **233** 35 30
1071 1r.50 General Post Office, Doha (horiz) 50 45

1999. 5th Arab Gulf Countries Stamp Exhibition, Doha. Multicoloured.
1072 1r. Type **234** 35 30
1073 1r.50 Exhibition emblem (horiz) 50 45

235 Flower and Emblem

1999. National Committee for Children with Special Needs.
1074 **235** 1r.50 multicoloured . . . 60 50

236 Clock Tower

2000. New Millennium.
1075 **236** 1r.50 gold and red . . . 60 50
1076 2r. gold and blue 75 60

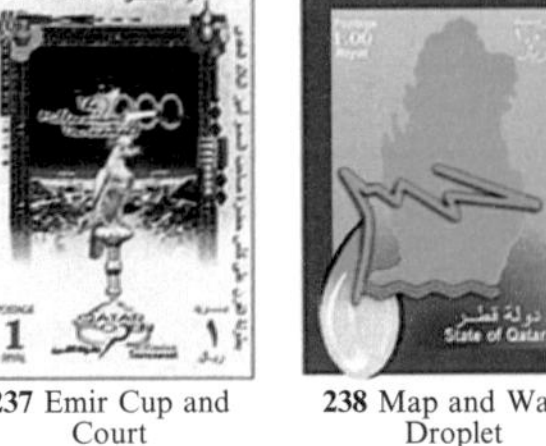

237 Emir Cup and Court

238 Map and Water Droplet

2000. New Millennium Open Tennis Championships, Qatar. Multicoloured.
1077 1r. Type **237** 40 30
1078 1r.50 Emir Cup and racquet 60 50

2000. Gulf Co-operation Council Water Week. Mult.
1079 1r. Type **238** 40 30
1080 1r.50 Dried earth and water droplet 60 50

239 Bat and Ball

2000. 15th Asian Table Tennis Championship, Doha.
1081 **239** 1r.50 multicoloured . . . 60 50

240 Shaikh Hamad, Fort and Emblem

2000. 29th Anniv of Independence. Multicoloured.
1082 1r. Type **240** 40 30
1083 1r.50 Shaikh Hamad, city and oil drilling platform 60 50

241 Emblem and Dove carrying Letter

2000. 50th Anniv of Qatar Post Office. Multicoloured.
1084 1r.50 Type **241** 60 50
1085 2r. Emblem, magnifying glass and building facade 75 60

242 Emblem

2000. 9th Islamic Summit Conference, Doha. Multicoloured.
1086 1r. Type **242** 40 30
1087 1r.50 Emblem and olive branch (47 × 30 mm) . . . 60 50

243 Gas Terminal

2001. "Clean Environment". Multicoloured.
1088 1r. Type **243** 35 30
1089 1r.50 Oryx and gas installation 50 40
1090 2r. Flamingoes and Ras Laffan city skyline . . . 70 55
1091 3r. Earth viewed from space 1·00 80

244 Castle, Koran and Ship

2001. 30th Anniv of Independence.
1092 **244** 1r. multicoloured 35 30
1093 1r.50 multicoloured . . . 50 40

245 Children encircling Globe

2001. United Nations Year of Dialogue among Civilizations. Multicoloured.
1094 1r.50 Type **245** 50 40
1095 2r. Leaves 70 55

246 Building and Emblem

2001. 4th World Trade Organization Ministerial Conference, Doho, Qatar.
1096 **246** 1r. multicoloured 35 30
1097 1r.50 multicoloured . . . 50 40

247 Door

2001. Traditional Wooden Doors. Multicoloured.
1098 25d. Type **247** 10 10
1099 75d. Small door in left-hand panel and large bolt at right 25 20
2000 1r.50 Plain doors 50 40
2001 2r. Knocker at left and smaller door in right-hand panel 70 55
MS2002 100 × 70 mm. 3r. As No. 2001 . . . . 1·00 80

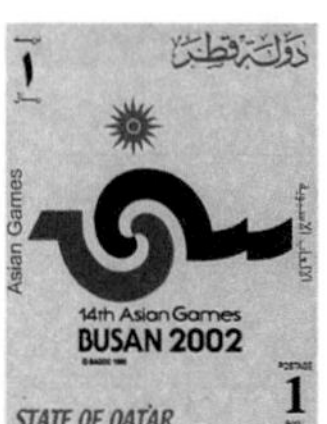

248 Uruguay, 1930 **249** Championship Emblem

2002. World Cup Football Championship, Japan and South Korea. Multicoloured.
1103 2r. Type **248** 60 50
1104 2r. Italy, 1934 . . . . . . 60 50
1105 2r. France, 1938 . . . . . 60 50
1106 2r. Brasil, 1950 . . . . . 60 50
1107 2r. Switzerland, 1954 . . . 60 50
1108 2r. Sweden, 1958 . . . . 60 50
1109 2r. Chile, 1962 . . . . . 60 50
1110 2r. England, 1966 . . . . 60 50
1111 2r. Mexico, 1970 . . . . 60 50
1112 2r. West Germany, 1974 . . 60 50
1113 2r. Argentina, 1978 . . . . 60 50
1114 2r. Spain, 1982 . . . . . 60 50
1115 2r. Mexico, 1986 . . . . 60 50
1116 2r. Italy, 1990 . . . . . 60 50
1117 2r. USA, 1994 . . . . . 60 50
1118 2r. France, 1998 . . . . 60 50
1119 2r. 2002 Championship emblem 60 50
1120 2r. World Cup trophy . . . 60 50
MS1121 133 × 78 mm. Nos. 2019/20 3·00 3·00

2002. 14th Asian Games, Busan. Sheet 133 × 73 mm containing T **249** and similar vert design. Multicoloured.
MS1122 1r. Type **249**; 1r. 15th (2006) Asian Games championship emblem 60 60

250 Emblem

2002. 1st Anniv of Global Post Code. Multicoloured.
1123 **250** 1r. multicoloured 30 25
1124 3r. multicoloured 90 70

251 Runner, Heart and No-Smoking Sign

2003. World No-Smoking Day.
1125 **251** 1r.50 multicoloured . . . 45 35
No. 1125 was printed using thermochromatic (heat sensitive) ink. When the image is pressed parts of the design disappear leaving only the runner visible.

252 Boy and Crescent

2003. 25th Anniv of Qatar Red Crescent (humanitarian organization). Multicoloured.
1126 75d. Type **252** 25 15
1127 75d. Building facade 25 15

POSTAGE DUE STAMPS

D 40

1968.
D254 **D 40** 5d. blue . . . . 13·50 13·50
D255 10d. red . . . . . . 16·00 16·00
D256 20d. green . . . . . . 20·00 20·00
D257 30d. lilac . . . . . . 21·00 21·00

QU'AITI STATE IN HADHRAMAUT
Pt. 1

The stamps of Aden were used in Qu'aiti State in Hadhramaut from 22 April 1937 until 1942.

1937. 16 annas = 1 rupee.
1951. 100 cents = 1 shilling.
1966. 1000 fils = 1 dinar.

(I) Issues inscribed "SHIHR and MUKALLA"

1 Sultan of Shihr and Mukalla **2** Mukalla Harbour

1942.
1 **1** ½a. green 80 50
2 ¾a. brown . . . . 1·50 30
3 1a. blue . . . . 1·00 1·00
4 **2** 1½a. red . . . . 1·50 50
5 – 2a. brown . . . . 1·50 1·75
6 – 2½a. blue 50 30
7 – 3a. brown and red . . . . . 1·00 75
8 – 8a. red 50 40
9 – 1r. green . . . . 4·00 3·00
10 – 2r. blue and purple . . . . . 12·00 8·00
11 – 5r. brown and green . . . . 15·00 11·00
DESIGNS—VERT: 2a. Gateway of Shihr; 3a. Outpost of Mukalla; 1r. Du'an. HORIZ: 2½a. Shibam; 8a. 'Einat; 2r. Mosque in Hureidha; 5r. Meshhed.

1946. Victory. Optd **VICTORY ISSUE 8TH JUNE 1946**.
12 **2** 1½a. red . . . . 15 1·00
13 – 2½a. blue 15 15

1949. Royal Silver Wedding. As T **4b/c** of Pitcairn Islands.
14 1½a. red . . . . 50 3·25
15 5r. green . . . . 16·00 9·00

1949. U.P.U. As T **4d/g** of Pitcairn Islands surch.
16 2½a. on 20c. blue 15 20
17 3a. on 30c. red . . . . 1·10 50
18 8a. on 50c. orange 25 60
19 1r. on 1s. blue 30 50

1951. Stamps of 1942 surch in cents or shillings.
20 5c. on 1a. blue 15 15
21 10c. on 2a. sepia 15 15
22 15c. on 2½a. blue 15 15
23 20c. on 3a. sepia and red . . . 30 50
24 50c. on 8a. red . . . . 50 1·50
25 1s. on 1r. green . . . . 2·00 30
26 2s. on 2r. blue and purple . . 7·50 14·00
27 5s. on 5r. brown and green . . 12·00 21·00

1953. Coronation. As T **4h** of Pitcairn Islands.
28 15c. black and blue . . . . . 1·00 55

(II) Issues inscribed "HADHRAMAUT"

11 Metal Work **22** Metal Work

1955. Occupations. Portrait as in T **11**.
29 **11** 5c. blue 30 10
30 – 10c. black (Mat-making) . . 75 10
31 – 15c. green (Weaving) . . . 50 10
32 – 25c. red (Pottery) 40 10
33 – 35c. blue (Building) 70 10
34 – 50c. orange (Date cultivation) 40 10
35 – 90c. brown (Agriculture) . . 50 15
36 – 1s. black and orange (Fisheries) (horiz) 50 10
37 – 1s.25 black and orange (Lime-burning) (horiz) . . 55 55
38 – 2s. black and blue (Dhow building) (horiz) . . . . . 4·00 60
39 – 5s. black and green (Agriculture) (horiz) . . . 5·00 1·75
40 – 10s. black and red (as No. 37) (horiz) . . . . . 5·50 7·50

1963. Occupations. As Nos. 29/40 but with inset portrait of Sultan Awadh bin Saleh el Qu'aiti, as in T **22**.
41 **22** 5c. blue . . . . 10 1·50
42 – 10c. black . . . . 10 1·25
43 – 15c. green . . . . 10 1·50
44 – 25c. red 10 50
45 – 35c. blue . . . . 10 1·75
46 – 50c. orange . . . . 10 1·00
47 – 70c. brown (As No. 35) . . 15 75
48 – 1s. black and lilac 20 30
49 – 1s.25 black and orange . . . 45 4·00
50 – 2s. black and blue . . . . . 3·25 1·75
51 – 5s. black and green . . . . 13·00 26·00
52 – 10s. black and red . . . . . 17·00 26·00

1966. Nos. 41/52 surch **SOUTH ARABIA** in English and Arabic, with value and bar.
53 **5** 5f. on 5c. 10 60
54 – 5f. on 10c. 10 60
55 – 10f. on 15c. 10 30
56 – 15f. on 25c. 10 60
57 – 20f. on 35c. . . . . 10 1·50
58 – 25f. on 50c. 10 60
59 – 35f. on 70c. 10 60
60 – 50f. on 1s. 10 30
61 – 65f. on 1s.25 . . . . 1·00 30
62 – 100f. on 2s. . . . . 1·50 75
63 – 250f. on 5s. . . . . 1·50 1·50
64 – 500f. on 10s. . . . . 19·00 3·00

1966. Churchill Commemoration. Nos. 54/6 optd **1874–1965 WINSTON CHURCHILL**.
65 5f. on 10c. . . . . 5·50 10·00
66 10f. on 15c. . . . . 6·50 11·00
67 15f. on 25c. . . . . 8·50 12·00

1966. President Kennedy Commemoration. Nos. 57/9 optd **1917–63 JOHN F. KENNEDY**.
68 20f. on 35c. . . . . 1·50 6·00
69 25f. on 50c. . . . . 1·75 6·50
70 35f. on 70c. . . . . 2·25 7·50

25 World Cup Emblem

1966. World Cup Football Championship.
71 **25** 5f. purple and orange . . . 1·75 25
72 – 10f. violet and green . . . . 2·00 25
73 – 15f. purple and orange . . . 2·25 30
74 – 20f. violet and green . . . . 2·50 30
75 **25** 25f. green and red . . . . . 2·75 30
76 – 35f. blue and yellow . . . . 3·25 35
77 – 50f. green and red . . . . . 3·75 40
78 **25** 65f. blue and yellow . . . . 4·50 40
MS78a 110 × 110 mm. Nos. 77/8 16·00 7·50
DESIGNS: 10, 35f. Wembley Stadium; 15, 50f. Footballers; 20f. Jules Rimet Cup and football.

29 Mexican Hat and Basket

1966. Pre-Olympic Games, Mexico (1968).

79	**29**	75f. sepia and green	1·25	75

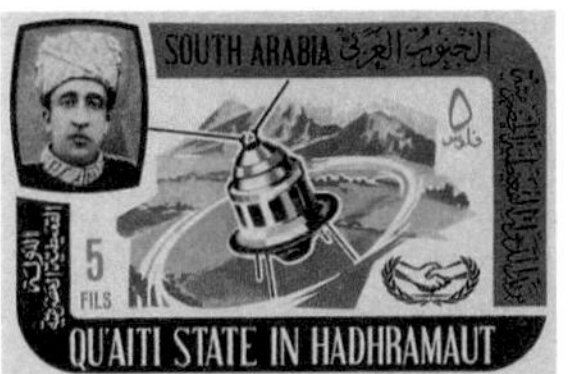

30 Telecommunications Satellite

1966. International Co-operation Year.

80	**30**	5f. mauve, purple and green	2·25	35
81	–	10f. multicoloured	2·50	35
82	–	15f. purple, blue and red	2·75	40
83	**30**	20f. blue, purple and red	3·00	45
84	–	25f. multicoloured	3·00	50
85	**30**	35f. purple, red and blue	3·50	60
86	–	50f. purple, green and red	4·50	75
87	**30**	65f. brown, violet and red	5·00	80

DESIGNS: 10f. Olympic runner (inscr "ROME 1960"); 15f. Fishes; 25f. Olympic runner (inscr "TOKIO 1964"); 50f. Tobacco plant.

APPENDIX

The following stamps have either been issued in excess to postal needs or have not been made available to the public in reasonable quantities at face value.

1967.

Stampex, London. Postage 5, 10, 15, 20, 25f.; Air 50, 65f.

Amphilex International Stamp Exhibition, Amsterdam. Air 75f.

Olympic Games, Mexico (1968). 75f.

Paintings. Postage 5, 10, 15, 20, 25f.; Air 50, 65f.

Scout Jamboree, Idaho. Air 35f.

Space Research. Postage 10, 25, 35, 50, 75f.; Air 100, 250f.

The National Liberation Front is said to have taken control of Qu'aiti State in Hadhramaut on 17 September 1967.

QUEENSLAND Pt. 1

The north eastern state of the Commonwealth of Australia whose stamps it now uses.

12 pence = 1 shilling;
20 shillings = 1 pound.

1

7

1860. Imperf.

1	**1**	1d. red	£2750	£800
2		2d. blue	£6000	£1600
3		6d. green	£4000	£800

1860. Perf.

94	**1**	1d. red	38·00	5·00
99		2d. blue	32·00	1·00
101		3d. brown	65·00	9·00
65		3d. green	85·00	6·00
53		4d. grey	£180	20·00
55		4d. lilac	£150	18·00
103		4d. yellow	£650	24·00
27		6d. green	£100	12·00
108		1s. purple	48·00	9·00
29		1s. grey	£170	22·00
119		2s. blue	95·00	27·00
121		2s.6d. red	£150	55·00
58		5s. red	£325	75·00
123		5s. yellow	£200	85·00
125		10s. brown	£425	£150
127		20s. red	£1000	£170

1879.

134	**7**	1d. brown	42·00	6·00
135		1d. orange	24·00	4·00
136		1d. red	20·00	2·25
138		2d. blue	35·00	1·25
141		4d. yellow	£150	10·00
142		6d. green	80·00	4·50
145		1s. mauve	65·00	6·00

1880. Nos. 136 surch **Half-penny**.

151	**7**	½d. on 1d. brown	£225	£140

9 13

12

14

1882.

152	**9**	2s. blue	£100	28·00
158		2s.6d. orange	42·00	22·00
159		5s. red	40·00	30·00
155		10s. brown	£140	40·00
161		£1 green	£200	60·00

1882. Shaded background around head.

185	**13**	½d. green	4·00	1·50
206	**12**	1d. orange	2·50	40
204		2d. blue	4·00	30
191	**14**	2½d. red	12·00	1·50
192	**12**	3d. brown	9·00	2·75
193		4d. yellow	13·00	2·50
170		6d. green	11·00	1·50
173		1s. mauve	11·00	2·50
182		2s. brown	60·00	30·00

15

16

17

1895. Head on white background.

208	**15**	½d. green	1·40	75
211	**16**	1d. red	4·00	20
212		2d. blue	10·00	45
213	**17**	2½d. red	14·00	3·75
215		5d. brown	16·00	3·75

19

21

1896.

229	**19**	1d. red	11·00	50

1897. Same designs, but figures in all four corners, as T **21**.

286	½d. green	1·75	2·50
232	1d. red	2·25	15
234	2d. blue	3·00	15
236	2½d. red	17·00	20·00
238	2½d. purple on blue	9·50	2·00
241	3d. brown	8·00	2·00
244	4d. yellow	9·00	2·00
294	4d. black	15·00	3·75
246	5d. brown	8·50	2·00
250	6d. green	7·00	1·75
298	1s. mauve	12·00	2·75
300	2s. green	35·00	20·00

26

27

1899.

262a	**26**	½d. green	2·50	1·25

1900. S. African War Charity. Inscr "PATRIOTIC FUND 1900".

264a	**27**	1d. (1s.) mauve	£120	£110
264b	–	2d. (2s.) violet (horiz)	£300	£275

28

1903.

265	**28**	9d. brown and blue	20·00	3·25

REGISTRATION STAMP

1861. Inscr "REGISTERED".

20	**1**	(No value) yellow	65·00	38·00

QUELIMANE Pt. 9

A district of Portuguese E. Africa, now part of Mozambique, whose stamps it now uses.

100 centavos = 1 escudo.

1913. Surch **REPUBLICA QUELIMANE** and new value on "Vasco da Gama" stamps of

(a) Portuguese Colonies.

1	¼c. on 2½r. green	1·50	1·10
2	½c. on 5r. red	1·50	1·10
3	1c. on 10r. purple	1·50	1·10
4	2½c. on 25r. green	1·50	1·10
5	5c. on 50r. blue	1·50	1·10
6	7½c. on 75r. brown	2·75	1·50
7	10c. on 100r. brown	1·70	85
8	15c. on 150r. brown	1·70	85

(b) Macao.

9	¼c. on ½a. green	1·50	1·10
10	½c. on 1a. red	1·50	1·10
11	1c. on 2a. purple	1·50	1·10
12	2½c. on 4a. green	1·50	1·10
13	5c. on 8a. blue	1·50	1·10
14	7½c. on 12a. brown	2·75	1·50
15	10c. on 16a. brown	1·70	85
16	15c. on 24a. brown	1·70	85

(c) Portuguese Timor.

17	¼c. on ½a. green	1·50	1·10
18	½c. on 1a. red	1·50	1·10
19	1c. on 2a. purple	1·50	1·10
20	2½c. on 2a. green	1·50	1·10
21	5c. on 8a. blue	1·50	1·10
22	7½c. on 12a. brown	2·75	1·50
23	10c. on 16a. brown	1·70	85
24	15c. on 24a. brown	1·70	85

1914. "Ceres" key-type inscr "QUELIMANE".

25	U	½c. green	65	60
26		½c. black	1·30	85
42		1c. green	1·30	85
28		1½c. brown	1·60	1·10
29		2c. red	1·30	1·30
30		2¼c. violet	65	50
31		5c. blue	1·20	90
43		7½c. brown	1·40	1·10
33		8c. grey	1·40	1·10
44		10c. red	1·40	1·10
35		15c. purple	1·90	1·60
45		20c. green	1·40	1·40
37		30c. brown on green	3·00	2·10
38		40c. brown on pink	3·25	2·10
39		50c. orange on orange	3·25	2·10
40		1e. green on blue	3·50	2·50

RAJASTHAN Pt. 1

Formed in 1948 from states in Rajputana, India, which included Bundi, Jaipur and Kishangarh whose separate posts functioned until 1 April 1950. Now uses Indian stamps.

12 pies = 1 anna;
16 annas = 1 rupee.

BUNDI

(1)

1949. Nos. 86/92 of Bundi or optd with T **1**.

1	**21**	¼a. green	5·50	
2		½a. violet	4·00	
3		1a. green	4·75	
11	–	2a. red	6·00	70·00
12	–	4a. orange	3·00	70·00
6	–	8a. blue	5·50	
14	–	1r. brown	7·50	

Nos. 1, 2, 3 and 6 used are worth about six times the unused prices.

JAIPUR

राजस्थान

RAJASTHAN
(2)

1949. Stamps of Jaipur optd with T **2**.

15	**7**	¼a. black and purple	5·50	17·00
16		½a. black and violet	4·00	18·00
17		¾a. black and orange	8·00	21·00
18		1a. black and blue	4·50	38·00
19		2a. black and orange	8·00	48·00
20		2½a. black and red	8·50	24·00
21		3a. black and green	9·50	55·00
22		4a. black and green	9·00	65·00
23		6a. black and blue	9·50	90·00
24		8a. black and brown	15·00	£130
25		1r. black and bistre	18·00	£180

KISHANGARH

1949. Stamps of Kishangarh handstamped with T **1**.

(a) On stamps of 1899.

26a	**2**	¼a. pink	—	£180
27		½a. blue	£350	
29		1a. lilac	14·00	38·00
30		4a. brown	70·00	90·00
31		1r. green	£225	£250
31a		2r. red	£300	
32		5r. mauve	£275	£275

(b) On stamps of 1904.

33	**13**	½a. brown	—	£130
33a		1a. blue	—	£170
34		4a. brown	13·00	
35	**2**	8a. grey	90·00	£140
36	**13**	8a. violet	11·00	
37		1r. green	12·00	
38		2r. yellow	19·00	
39		5r. brown	26·00	

(c) On stamps of 1912.

40	**14**	½a. green	—	£180
41		1a. red	—	£180
43		2a. purple	3·00	7·50
44		4a. blue	—	£425
45		8a. brown	5·00	
46		1r. mauve	10·00	
47		2r. green	10·00	
48		5r. brown	£325	

(d) On stamps of 1928.

56	**16**	¼a. blue	42·00	42·00
57		½a. green	28·00	30·00
58	–	1a. red	38·00	40·00
59	–	2a. purple	£140	£140
61	**16**	4a. brown	2·50	7·50
51		8a. violet	6·00	50·00
63		1r. green	6·50	
53		2r. yellow	16·00	
54		5r. red	16·00	

RAJPIPLA Pt. 1

A state of Bombay, India. Now uses Indian stamps.

12 pies = 1 anna;
12 annas = 1 rupee.

1 (1 pice)

2 (2a.)

1880.

1 **1** 1p. blue . . . . 3·00 30·00
2 **2** 2a. green . . . . 25·00 85·00
3 4a. red . . . . 13·00 55·00

RAS AL KHAIMA Pt. 19

Arab Shaikhdom in the Arabian Gulf. Ras al Khaima joined the United Arab Emirates in February 1972 and U.A.E. stamps were used in the shaikhdom from 1 January 1973.

1964. 100 naye paise = 1 rupee.
1966. 100 dirhams = 1 riyal.

1 Shaikh Saqr bin Mohamed al-Qasimi

3 Dhow

1964.

1 **1** 5n.p. brown and black 15 15
2 15n.p. blue and black 15 15
3 – 30n.p. brown and black . . . 15 15
4 – 40n.p. blue and black 25 20
5 – 75n.p. red and black 60 50
6 **3** 1r. brown and green . . . . . 1·75 90
7 2r. brown and violet . . . . . 3·00 1·90
8 5r. brown and blue . . . . . 6·00 5·00
DESIGNS—As Type **1**: 30n.p. to 75n.p. Seven palms.

3a Pres. Kennedy inspecting "Friendship 7"

1965. Pres. Kennedy Commemoration.
9 **3a** 2r. blue and brown . . . . 1·00 95
10 – 3r. blue and brown . . . . 1·25 1·25
11 – 4r. blue and brown . . . . 1·75 1·75
DESIGNS—HORIZ: 3r. Kennedy and wife. VERT: 4r. Kennedy and flame of remembrance.

4 Sir Winston Churchill and Houses of Parliament

1965. Churchill Commemoration.
12 **4** 2r. blue and brown 90 90
13 – 3r. blue and brown . . . . . 1·25 1·25
14 – 4r. blue and brown . . . . . 1·90 1·75
DESIGNS—HORIZ: 3r. Churchill and Pres. Roosevelt; 4r. Churchill, and Heads of State at his funeral.

1965. Olympic Games, Tokyo (1964). Optd **OLYMPIC TOKYO 1964** in English and Arabic and Olympic "rings".
15 **3** 1r. brown and green 40 40
16 2r. brown and violet 90 90
17 5r. brown and blue . . . . . 2·50 2·50

1965. Death Centenary of Abraham Lincoln. Optd **ABRAHAM LINCOLN 1809-1865** in English and Arabic.
18 **3** 1r. brown and green 40 40
19 2r. brown and violet 90 90
20 5r. brown and blue . . . . . 2·50 2·50

1965. 20th Death Anniv of Pres. Roosevelt. Optd **FRANKLIN D. ROOSEVELT 1882-1945** in English and Arabic.
21 **3** 1r. brown and green 40 40
22 2r. brown and violet 90 90
23 5r. brown and blue . . . . . 2·50 2·50

8 Satellite and Tracking Station

1966. I.T.U. Centenary. Multicoloured.
24 15n.p. Type **8** 15 10
25 50n.p. Post Office Tower, London, "Telstar" and tracking gantry 30 15
26 85n.p. Rocket on launching-pad and "Relay" 60 20
27 1r. Type **8** 70 30
28 2r. As 50n.p. . . . . 1·25 35
29 3r. As 85n.p. . . . . 1·50 65

9 Swimming

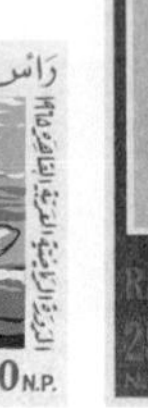

10 Carpenter

1966. Pan-Arab Games, Cairo (1965).
31 A 1n.p. brown, pink and green 10 10
32 B 2n.p. black, grey and green 10 10
33 C 3n.p. brown, pink and green 10 10
34 D 4n.p. brown, pink and purple 10 10
35 A 5n.p. black, grey and orange 10 10
36 **9** 10n.p. brown, pink and blue 15 10
37 B 25n.p. brown, pink and cinnamon 15 10
38 C 50n.p. black, grey and violet 35 15
39 D 75n.p. black, grey and blue 55 15
40 **9** 1r. black, grey and green . . 70 30
DESIGNS: A, Running; B, Boxing; C, Football; D, Fencing.

1966. American Astronauts.
42 **10** 25n.p. black, gold and purple 15 10
43 – 50n.p. black, silver & brown 25 15
44 – 75n.p. black, silver and blue 35 20
45 – 1r. black, silver and bistre 55 35
46 – 2r. black, silver and mauve 90 70
47 – 3r. black, gold and green . . 1·50 1·10
48 – 4r. black, gold and red . . . 1·75 1·25
49 – 5r. black, gold and blue . . 2·10 1·60
ASTRONAUTS: 50n.p. Glenn; 75n.p. Shepard; 1r. Cooper; 2r. Grissom; 3r. Schirra; 4r. Stafford; 5r. Lovell.

11 Shaikh Sabah of Kuwait and Shaikh Saqr of Ras al Khaima

1966. International Co-operation Year.
51 **11** 1r. black and red 50 20
52 A 1r. black and lilac 50 20
53 B 1r. black and pink 50 20
54 C 1r. black and green 50 20
55 D 1r. black and green 50 20
56 E 1r. black and yellow 50 20
57 F 1r. black and orange 50 20
58 G 1r. black and blue 50 20
SHAIKH SAQR AND WORLD LEADERS: A, Shaikh Ahmad of Qatar; B, Pres. Nasser; C, King Hussein; D, Pres. Johnson; E, Pres. De Gaulle; F, Pope Paul VI; G, Prime Minister Harold Wilson.

NEW CURRENCY SURCHARGES. During the latter half of 1966 various issues appeared surcharged in dirhams and riyals. The 1964 definitives with this surcharge are listed below as there is considerable evidence of their postal use. Nos. 24/58 also exist with these surcharges.

In August 1966 Nos. 1/14, 24/9 and 51/8 appeared surcharged in fils and rupees. As Ras Al Khaima did not adopt this currency their status is uncertain.

1966. Nos. 1/8 with currency names changed to dirhams and riyals by overprinting in English and Arabic
60 **1** 5d. on 5n.p. brown and black 20 15
60a – 5d. on 75n.p. red and black 20 15
64b **3** 5d. on 5r. brown and blue 20 15
61 **1** 15d. on 15n.p. blue & black 30 15
62 – 30d. on 30n.p. brown and black 55 20
63 – 40d. on 40n.p. blue & black 70 30
64 – 75d. on 75n.p. red and black 80 35
65 **3** 1r. on 1r. brown and green 90 45
66 2r. on 2r. brown and violet 2·00 1·75
67 5r. on 5r. brown and blue 4·50 3·00

15 W.H.O. Building and Flowers

1966. Inauguration of W.H.O. Headquarters, Geneva.
68 **15** 15d. multicoloured (postage) 20 10
69 – 35d. multicoloured 40 15
70 **15** 50d. multicoloured (air) . . 50 25
71 – 3r. multicoloured . . . . . 1·75 65
DESIGN: 35d., 3r. As Type **15** but with red instead of yellow flowers at left.

16 Queen Elizabeth II presenting Jules Rimet Cup to Bobby Moore, Captain of England Team

1966. Air. England's Victory in World Cup Football Championship. Multicoloured.
73 1r. Wembley Stadium 50 15
74 2r. Goalkeeper saving ball . . 1·00 30
75 3r. Footballers with ball . . . 1·50 50
76 4r. Type **16** . . . . 1·75 1·00

17 Shaikh Saqr

18 Oil Rig

1971.
78 **17** 5d. multicoloured . . . . .
79 **18** 20d. multicoloured . . . .
80 **17** 30d. multicoloured . . . .

For later issues see **UNITED ARAB EMIRATES**.

APPENDIX

The following stamps have either been issued in excess of postal needs or have not been available to the public in reasonable quantities at face value. Such stamps may later be given full listing if there is evidence of regular postal use.

1967.

"The Arabian Nights". Paintings. Air 30, 70d., 1, 2, 3r.

Cats. Postage 1, 2, 3, 4, 5d.: Air 3r.

Arab Paintings. 1, 2, 3, 4, 10, 20, 30d.

European Paintings. Air 60, 70d., 1, 2, 3, 5, 10r.

50th Birth Anniv of Pres. John F. Kennedy. Optd on 1965 Pres. Kennedy Commem. 2, 3, 4r.

World Scout Jamboree, Idaho. Postage 1, 2, 3, 4d.; Air 35, 75d., 1r.

U.S. "Apollo" Disaster. Optd on 1966 American Astronauts issue. 25d. on 25n.p., 50d. on 50n.p., 75d. on 75n.p., 1, 2, 3, 4, 5r.

Summer Olympics Preparation, Mexico 1968. Postage 10, 20, 30, 40d.; Air 1, 2r.

Winter Olympics Preparation, Grenoble 1968. Postage 1, 2, 3, 4, 5d.; Air 85d., 2, 3r.

1968.

Mothers' Day. Paintings. Postage 20, 30, 40, 50d.; Air 1, 2, 3, 4r.

International Human Rights Year. 2r. × 3.

International Museum Campaign. Paintings. 15, 15, 20, 25, 35, 40, 45, 60, 70, 80, 90d.; 1, 1r.25, 1r.50, 2r.50, 2r.75.

Winter Olympic Medal Winners, Grenoble. 50d., 1, 1r.50, 2, 2r.50, 3r.

Olympic Games, Mexico. Air 1, 2, 2, 3, 3, 4r. 5th Death Anniv of Pres. John F. Kennedy. Air. 2, 3r.

Christmas. Religious Paintings. Postage 20, 30, 40, 50, 60d., 1r.; Air 2, 3, 4r.

1969.

Famous Composers (1st series). Paintings. 25, 50, 75d., 1r.50, 2r.50.

Famous Operas. 20, 40, 60, 80d., 1, 2r.

Famous Men. Postage 20, 30, 50d.; Air 1r.50, 2, 3, 4, 5r.

International Philatelic Exhibition, Mexico 1968 (EFIMEX). Postage 10, 10, 25, 35, 40, 50, 60, 70d.; Air 1, 2, 3, 5, 5r.

Int Co-operation in Olympics. 1, 2, 3, 4r.

International Co-operation in Space. Air 1r.50, 2r.50, 3r.50, 4r.50.

Birth Bicentenary of Napoleon. Paintings. Postage 1r.75, 2r.75, 3r.75; Air 75d.

"Apollo" Moon Missions. Air 2, 2r.50, 3, 3r.50, 4, 4r.50, 5, 5r.50.

"Apollo 11" Astronauts. Air 2r.25, 3r.25, 4r.25, 5r.25.

"Apollo 12" Astronauts. Air 60d., 2r.60, 3r.60, 4r.60, 5r.60.

1970.

Christmas 1969. Religious Paintings. Postage 50d.; Air 3, 3r.50.

World Cup, Mexico. Air 1, 2, 3, 4, 5, 6r.

Easter. Religious Paintings. Postage 50d.; Air 3, 3r.50.

Paintings by Titian and Tiepolo. Postage 50, 50d.; Air 3, 3, 3r.50, 3r.50.

Winter Olympics, Sapporo 1972. Air 1, 2, 3, 4, 5, 6r.

Olympic Games, Munich 1972. Air 1, 2, 3, 4, 5, 6r.

Paul Gauguin's Paintings. Postage 50d.; Air 3, 3r.50.

Christmas. Religious Paintings. Postage 50d.; Air 3, 3r.50.

"World Cup Champions, Brazil". Optd on Mexico World Cup issue. Air 1, 2, 3, 4, 5, 6r.

"EXPO 70" World Fair, Osaka, Japan (1st issue). Postage 40, 45, 50, 55, 60, 65, 70, 75d.; Air 80, 85, 90, 95d., 1r.60, 1r.65, 1r.85, 2r.

"EXPO 70" World Fair, Osaka, Japan (2nd issue). Postage 55, 65, 75d.; Air 25, 85, 95d., 1r.50, 1r.75.

Space Programmes. Air 1r. × 6, 2r. × 6, 4r. × 6.

Famous Frenchmen. Air 1r. × 4, 2r. × 4, 2r.50 × 2, 3r. × 2, 4r. × 4, 5r.50 × 2.

Int Philatelic Exn (Philympia '70). Air 1r. × 4, 1r.50 × 4, 2r.50 × 4, 3r. × 4, 4r. × 4.

Events in the Life of Christ. Religious Paintings. 5, 10, 25, 50d., 1, 2, 5r.

"Stages of the Cross". Religious Paintings. 10, 20, 30, 40, 50, 60, 70, 80d., 1, 1r.50, 2, 2r.50, 3, 3r.50.

The Life of Mary. Religious Paintings. 10, 15, 30, 60, 75d., 3, 4r.

1971.

Easter. "Stages of the Cross" (1970) but with additional inscr "EASTER". 10, 20, 30, 40, 50, 60, 70, 80d., 1, 1r.50, 2, 2r.50, 3, 3r.50.

Charles de Gaulle Memorial. Postage 50d.; Air 1, 1r.50, 2, 3, 4r.

Safe Return of "Apollo 14". Postage 50d.; Air 1, 1r.50, 2, 3, 4r.

U.S.A.–Japan Baseball Friendship. Postage 10, 25, 30, 80d.; Air 50, 70d., 1, 1r.50.

Munich Olympics, 1972. Postage 50d.; Air 1, 1r.50, 2, 3, 4r.

Cats. 35, 60, 65, 110, 120, 160d.

13th World Jamboree, Japan. Postage 30, 50, 60, 75d.; Air 1, 1r.50, 3, 4r.

Sapporo Olympic Gold Medal Winners. Optd on 1970 Winter Olympics, Sapporo 1972, issue. Air 1, 2, 3, 4, 5, 6r.

Munich Olympic Medal Winners, Optd on 1970 Summer Olympics, Munich 1972, issue. Air 1, 2, 3, 4, 5, 6r.

Japanese Locomotives. Postage 30, 35, 75d.; Air 90d., 1, 1r.75.

"Soyuz 11" Russian Cosmonauts Memorial. Air 1, 2, 3, 4r.

"Apollo 15". Postage 50d.; Air 1, 1r.50, 2, 3, 4r.

Dogs. 5, 20, 75, 85, 185, 200d.

Durer's Paintings. Postage 50d.; Air 1, 1r.50 2, 3, 4r.

Famous Composers (2nd series). Postage 50d.; Air 1, 1r.50, 2, 3, 4r.

"Soyuz 11" and "Salyut" Space Projects. Postage 50 d,; Air 1, 1r.50, 2, 3, 4r.

Butterflies. Postage 15, 20, 70d.; Air 1r.25, 1r.50, 1r.70.

Wild Animals. 10, 40, 80 d.; 1r.15, 1r.30, 1r.65.

Fishes. 30, 50, 60, 90d., 1r.45, 1r.55.

Ludwig van Beethoven. Portraits. Postage 50d.; Air 1, 1r.50, 2, 3, 4r.

1972.

Birds. 50, 55, 80, 100, 105, 190d.

Winter Olympics, Sapporo (1st issue). Postage 20, 30, 50d., Air 70, 90d., 2r.50

Winter Olympics, Sapporo (2nd issue). Postage 5, 60, 80, 90d.; Air 1r.10, 1r.75

Mozart. Portraits. Postage 50d.; Air 1, 1r.50, 2, 3, 4r.

Olympic Games, Munich. Postage 50d.; Air 1, 1r.50, 2, 3, 4r.

"In Memory of Charles de Gaulle". Optd on 1971 Charles de Gaulle memorial issue. Postage 50d.; Air 1, 1r.50, 2, 3, 4r.

Winter Olympics, Sapporo (3rd issue). Postage 15, 45d.; Air 65, 75d., 1r.20, 1r.25.

Horses. Postage 10, 25, 30d.; Air 1r.40, 1r.80, 1r.95.

Parrots. 40, 45, 70, 95d., 1r.35, 1r.75.

"Apollo 16". Postage 50d.; Air 1, 1r.50, 2, 3, 4r.

European Footballers. Postage 50d.; Air 1, 1r.50, 2, 3, 4r.

A number of issues on gold or silver foil also exist, but it is understood that these were mainly for presentation purposes, although valid for postage.

In common with the other states of the United Arab Emirates the Ras al Khaima stamp contract was terminated on 1st August 1972, and any further new issues released after that date were unauthorized.

REDONDA Pt. 1

A dependency of Antigua.

The following stamps were issued in anticipation of commercial and tourist development, philatelic mail being handled by a bureau in Antigua. Since at the present time the island is uninhabited, we do not list or stock these items. It is understood that the stamps are valid for the prepayment of postage in Antigua. Miniature sheets, imperforate stamps etc, are excluded from this section.

1979.

Antigua 1976 definitive issue optd **REDONDA**. 3, 5, 10, 25, 35, 50, 75c., $1, $2.50, $5, $10.

Antigua Coronation Anniversary issue optd **REDONDA**. 10, 30, 50, 90c., $2.50.

Antigua World Cup Football Championship issue optd **REDONDA**. 10, 15c., $3.

Death Centenary of Sir Rowland Hill. 50, 90c., $2.50, $3.

International Year of the Child 25, 50c., $1, $2.

Christmas. Paintings. 8, 50, 90c., $3.

1980.

Marine Life. 8, 25, 50c., $4.

75th Anniv of Rotary International. 25, 50c., $1, $2.

Birds of Redonda. 8, 10, 15, 25, 30, 50c., $1, $2, $5.

Olympic Medal Winners, Lake Placid and Moscow. 8, 25, 50c., $3.

80th Birthday of Queen Elizabeth the Queen Mother. 10c., $2.50.

Christmas Paintings. 8, 25, 50c., $4.

1981.

Royal Wedding. 25, 55c., $4.

Christmas. Walt Disney Cartoon Characters. ½, 1, 2, 3, 4, 5, 10c., $2.50, $3.

World Cup Football Championship, Spain (1982). 30c. × 2, 50c. × 2, $1 × 2, $2 × 2.

1982.

Boy Scout Annivs. 8, 25, 50c., $3, $5.

Butterflies. 8, 30, 50c., $2.

21st Birthday of Princess of Wales. $2, $4.

Birth of Prince William of Wales. Optd on Princess of Wales 21st Birthday issue. $2, $4.

Christmas. Walt Disney's "One Hundred and One Dalmatians". ½, 1, 2, 3, 4, 5, 10c., $2.50, $3.

1983.

Easter. 500th Birth Anniv of Raphael. 10, 50, 90c., $5.

Bicent of Manned Flight. 10, 50, 90c., $2.50.

Christmas. Walt Disney Cartoon Characters. "Deck the Halls". ½, 1, 2, 3, 4, 5, 10c., $2.50, $3.

1984.

Easter. Walt Disney Cartoon Characters. ½, 1, 2, 3, 4, 5, 10c., $2, $4.

Olympic Games, Los Angeles. 10, 50, 90c., $2.50.

Christmas. 50th Birthday of Donald Duck. 45, 60, 90c., $2, $4.

1985.

Birth Bicentenary of John J. Audubon (ornithologist) (1st issue). 60, 90c., $1, $3.

Life and Times of Queen Elizabeth the Queen Mother. $1, $1.50, $2.50.

Royal Visit. 45c., $1, $4.

150th Birth Anniv of Mark Twain (author). 25, 50c., $1.50, $3.

Birth Bicentenaries of Grimm Brothers (folklorists). Walt Disney cartoon characters. 30, 60, 70c., $4.

1986.

Birth Bicentenary of John J. Audubon (ornith-ologist) (2nd issue). 90c., $1, $1.50, $3.

Appearance of Halley's Comet. 5, 15, 55c., $4.

Centenary of Statue of Liberty (1st issue). 20, 25, 30c., $4.

60th Birthday of Queen Elizabeth II. 50, 60c., $4.

Royal Wedding. 60c., $1, $4.

Christmas (1st issue). Disney characters in Hans Andersen Stories. 30, 60, 70c., $4.

Christmas (2nd issue). "Wind in the Willows" (by Kenneth Grahame). 25, 50c., $1.50, $3.

1987.

"Capex '87" International Stamp Exhibition, Toronto. Disney characters illustrating Art of Animation. 25, 30, 50, 60, 70c., $1.50, $3, $4.

Birth Centenary of Marc Chagall (artist). 10, 30, 40, 60, 90c., $1, $3, $4.

Centenary of Statue of Liberty (2nd issue). 10, 15, 25, 30, 40, 60, 70, 90c., $1, $2, $3, $4.

250th Death Anniv of Sir Isaac Newton (scientist). 20c., $2.50.

750th Anniv of Berlin. $1, $4.

Bicentenary of U.S. Constitution. 30c., $3.

16th World Scout Jamboree, Australia. 10c., $4.

1988.

500th Anniv (1992) of Discovery of America by Columbus. 15, 30, 45, 60, 90c., $1, $2, $3.

"Finlandia '88" International Stamp Exhibition, Helsinki. Disney characters in Finnish scenes. 1, 2, 3, 4, 5, 6c., $5, $6.

Olympic Games, Seoul. 25, 60c., $1.25, $3.

500th Birth Anniv of Titian. 10, 25, 40, 70, 90c., $2, $3, $4.

1989.

20th Anniv of First Manned Landing on Moon. Disney characters on Moon. ½, 1, 2, 3, 4, 5c., $5, $6.

500th Anniv (1992) of Discovery of America by Columbus (2nd issue). Pre-Columbian Societies. 15, 45, 45, 50c., $2, $2, $3, $3.

Christmas. Disney Characters and Cars of 1950s. 25, 35, 45, 60c., $1, $2, $3, $4.

1990.

Christmas. Disney Characters and Hollywood cars. 25, 35, 40, 60c., $2, $3, $4, $5.

1991.

Nobel Prize Winners. 5, 15, 25, 40, 50c., $1, $2, $4.

REUNION Pt. 6

An island in the Indian Ocean, E. of Madagascar, now an overseas department of France.

100 centimes = 1 franc.

1

1852. Imperf. No gum.

1	**1**	15c. black on blue	£25000	£16000
2		30c. black on blue	£25000	£16000

1885. Stamps of French Colonies surch **R** and value in figures. Imperf.

5	D	5c. on 30c. brown	50·00	42·00
7	H	5c. on 30c. brown	3·00	5·50
3	A	5c. on 40c. orange	£250	£225
6	F	5c. on 40c. orange	35·00	35·00
8	H	5c. on 40c. red on yellow	70·00	85·00
9		10c. on 40c. red on yellow	3·25	4·50
10		20c. on 30c. brown	48·00	45·00
4	A	25c. on 40c. orange	50·00	38·00

1891. Stamps of French Colonies optd **REUNION**. Imperf (Types F and H) or perf (Type J).

17	J	1c. black on blue	70	2·50
18		2c. brown on buff	1·10	7·50
19		4c. brown on grey	2·75	4·25
20		5c. green on green	5·00	1·60
21		10c. black on lilac	18·00	2·25
22		15c. blue on blue	42·00	1·50
23		20c. red on green	11·50	11·50
24		25c. black on pink	35·00	1·75
13	H	30c. brown	32·00	38·00
25	J	35c. black on yellow	27·00	23·00
11	F	40c. orange	£375	£350
14	H	40c. red on yellow	30·00	14·50
26	J	40c. red on buff	70·00	60·00
15	H	75c. red	£275	£275
27	J	75c. red on pink	£500	£400
12	F	80c. pink	55·00	45·00
16	H	1f. green	50·00	42·00
28	J	1f. green	£375	£375

1891. Stamps of French Colonies surch **REUNION** and new value.

29	J	02c. on 20c. red on green	3·75	6·25
30		15c. on 20c. red on green	5·75	5·50
31		2 on 20c. red on green	2·25	2·50

1892. "Tablet" key-type inscr "REUNION".

34	D	1c. black and red on blue	50	50
35		2c. brown and blue on buff	50	45
36		4c. brown and blue on grey	1·50	60
50		5c. green and red	85	40
38		10c. black and blue on lilac	3·50	1·40
51		10c. red and blue	1·40	40
39		15c. blue and red	28·00	75
52		15c. grey and red	4·75	40
40		20c. red and blue on green	9·25	9·50
41		25c. black and red on pink	10·50	1·50
53		25c. blue and red	16·00	22·00
42		30c. brown and blue on drab	13·00	7·50
43		40c. red and blue on yellow	32·00	13·00
44		50c. red and blue on pink	70·00	21·00
54		50c. brown and red on blue	35·00	38·00
55		50c. brown and blue on blue	42·00	48·00
45		75c. brown and red on orange	49·00	35·00
46		1f. green and red	30·00	28·00

1893. Stamp of French Colonies, "Commerce" type, surch **2 c.**

47	J	2c. on 20c. red on green	2·00	1·75

1901. "Tablet" key-type surch in figures.

56	D	5c. on 40c. red and blue on yellow	1·60	6·00
57		5c. on 50c. red and blue on pink	3·25	6·50
58		15c. on 75c. brown and red on orange	12·50	17·00
59		15c. on 1f. green and red	8·75	9·25

16 Map of Reunion

17 View of Saint-Denis and Arms of the Colony

18 View of St. Pierre and Crater Dolomieu

1907.

60	**16**	1c. red and lilac	30	25
61		2c. blue and brown	40	25
62		4c. red and green	45	50
63		5c. red and green	1·10	20
92		5c. violet and yellow	35	50
64		10c. green and red	3·25	20
93		10c. turquoise and green	50	25
94		10c. red and lake on blue	90	25
65		15c. blue and black	1·50	20
95		15c. turquoise and green	50	70
96		15c. red and blue	1·25	1·10
66	**17**	20c. green and olive	1·75	75
67		25c. brown and blue	3·50	45
97		25c. blue and brown	55	10
68		30c. green and brown	1·00	1·10
98		30c. pink and red	2·50	2·75
99		30c. red and grey	2·00	1·25
100		30c. light green and green	2·50	3·00
69		35c. blue and brown	1·90	1·00
101		40c. brown and green	2·25	15
70		45c. pink and violet	1·60	3·00
102		45c. red and purple	2·50	2·75
103		45c. red and mauve	2·50	4·00
71		50c. blue and brown	2·25	2·25
104		50c. ultramarine and blue	1·75	1·60
105		50c. violet and yellow	1·40	15
106		60c. brown and blue	1·60	2·75
107		65c. blue and violet	2·25	3·25
72		75c. pink and red	2·25	65
108		75c. purple and brown	3·25	4·00
109		90c. pink and red	7·50	8·25
73	**18**	1f. blue and brown	2·25	1·90
110		1f. blue	2·25	3·50
111		1f. lilac and brown	2·50	2·00
112		1f.10 mauve and brown	2·50	3·25
113		1f.50 lt blue & blue on bl	12·00	11·00
74		2f. green and red	4·00	1·10
114		3f. mauve on pink	11·00	9·50
75		5f. brown and pink	6·75	6·25

1912. "Tablet" key-type surch.

76	D	05 on 2c. brown and red on buff	25	25
77		05 on 15c. grey and red	25	40
78		05 on 20c. red and blue on green	2·25	3·00
79		05 on 25c. black and red on pink	70	2·50
80		05 on 30c. brown and blue on drab	35	1·75
81		10 on 40c. red and blue on yellow	30	2·50
82		10 on 50c. brown and blue on blue	1·75	3·00
83		10 on 75c. brown and red on orange	2·25	12·50

1915. Red Cross Surch **5c** and red cross.

90	**16**	10c.+5c. green and red	1·10	3·25

1917. Surch **0,01**.

91	**16**	0,01 on 4c. chestnut and brown	2·75	2·75

1922. Surch in figures only.

115	**17**	40 on 20c. yellow and green	55	1·60
116		50 on 45c. red and purple	2·50	1·90
117		50 on 45c. red and mauve	£200	£200
118		50 on 65c. blue and violet	2·25	3·00
119		60 on 75c. carmine and red	30	50
120	**16**	65 on 15c. blue and black	2·25	3·25
121		85 on 15c. blue and black	1·60	3·25
122	**17**	85 on 75c. pink and red	2·00	3·50
123		90 on 75c. pink and red	2·50	3·25

1924. Surch in cents and francs.

124	**18**	25c. on 5f. brown and pink	1·60	3·00
125		1f.25 on 1f. blue	1·40	2·75
126		1f.50 on 1f. light blue and blue on blue	1·75	40
127		3f. on 5f. blue and red	3·50	3·50
128		10f. on 5f. red and green	13·50	18·00
129		20f. on 5f. pink and brown	18·00	22·00

1931. "Colonial Exhibition" key-types inscr "REUNION".

130	E	40c. green and black	4·00	4·50
131	F	50c. mauve and black	4·50	4·50
132	G	90c. red and black	4·00	4·75
133	H	1f.50 blue and black	4·75	5·00

30 Cascade, Salazie

31 Anchain Peak, Salazie

32 Leon Dierx Museum

34 Caudron C-600 "Aiglon"

1933.

134	**30**	1c. purple	20	1·50
135		2c. brown	10	1·60
136		3c. mauve	25	2·00
137		4c. olive	10	2·00
138		5c. orange	10	20
139		10c. blue	10	35
140		15c. black	10	15
141		20c. blue	15	1·25
142		25c. brown	20	35
143		30c. green	75	50
144	**31**	35c. green	85	2·75
145		40c. blue	1·90	1·10
146		40c. brown	30	2·75
147		45c. mauve	95	3·00
148		45c. green	70	2·75
149		50c. red	65	15
150		55c. orange	2·00	3·00
151		60c. blue	25	2·75
152		65c. olive	3·00	2·25
153		70c. olive	2·25	2·75
154		75c. brown	5·25	5·75
155		80c. black	1·10	3·00
156		90c. red	3·50	3·75
157		90c. purple	1·25	2·00
158		1f. green	3·50	65
159		1f. red	95	3·00
160		1f. black	55	2·75
161	**32**	1f.25 brown	60	2·75
162		1f.25 red	2·00	3·00
163	**30**	1f.40 blue	1·60	3·00
164	**32**	1f.50 blue	30	15
165	**30**	1f.60 red	2·25	3·00
166	**32**	1f.75 olive	1·25	1·25
167	**30**	1f.75 blue	1·25	3·00
168	**32**	2f. red	25	2·00
169	**30**	2f.25 blue	3·00	3·50
170		2f.50 brown	2·00	3·00
171	**32**	3f. violet	1·60	1·10
172		5f. mauve	1·75	2·75

173 10f. blue . . . . 2·25 2·75
174 20f. brown . . . . 2·75 3·25

1937. Air. Pioneer Flight from Reunion to France by Laurent, Lenier and Touge. Optd **REUNION – FRANCE par avion "ROLAND GARROS"**.
174a **31** 50c. red £225 £200

1937. International Exhibition, Paris. As Nos. 168/73 of St.-Pierre et Miquelon.
175 20c. violet . . . . 1·25 3·00
176 30c. green . . . . 1·75 3·00
177 40c. red . . . . 75 2·50
178 50c. brown and agate . . . . 1·00 2·50
179 90c. red . . . . 1·40 3·00
180 1f.50 blue . . . . 1·50 3·00

1938. Air.
181 **34** 3f.65 blue and red . . . . 80 1·60
182 6f.65 brown and red . . . 1·25 3·00
183 9f.65 red and blue . . . . 55 3·25
184 12f.65 brown and green . . 1·25 3·50

1938. International Anti-cancer Fund. As T **17a** of Oceanic Settlements.
185 1f.75+50c. blue . . . . . . 4·50 17·00

1939. New York World's Fair. As T **17b** of Oceanic Settlements.
186 1f.25 red . . . . 1·75 3·25
187 2f.25 blue . . . . 1·90 3·25

1939. 150th Anniv of French Revolution. As T **17c** of Oceanic Settlements.
188 45c.+25c. green and black (postage) . . . . 7·75 11·00
189 70c.+30c. brown and black 6·50 11·00
190 90c.+35c. orange and black 5·75 12·00
191 1f.25+1f. red and black . . . 5·50 12·00
192 2f.25+2f. blue and black . . 6·00 12·00
193 3f.65+4f. blk & orge (air) . . 10·00 20·00

1943. Surch **1f.**
194 **31** 1f. on 65c. green . . . . . 85 1·25

1943. Optd **France Libre**.
198 **30** 1c. purple (postage) . . . 30 3·00
199 2c. brown . . . . 30 3·00
200 3c. purple . . . . 30 3·00
195 **16** 4c. red and green . . . . 1·10 4·50
201 **30** 4c. green . . . . 25 3·00
202 5c. red . . . . 60 3·00
203 10c. blue . . . . 25 3·00
204 15c. black . . . . 25 3·00
205 20c. blue . . . . 75 3·00
206 25c. brown . . . . 85 3·00
207 30c. green . . . . 50 3·00
208 **31** 35c. green . . . . 40 3·00
209 40c. blue . . . . 50 3·00
210 40c. brown . . . . 50 3·00
211 45c. mauve . . . . 40 2·75
212 45c. green . . . . 55 3·00
213 50c. red . . . . 75 3·00
214 55c. orange . . . . 35 3·00
215 60c. blue . . . . 2·25 3·25
216 65c. green . . . . 85 3·00
217 70c. green . . . . 1·75 3·75
196 **17** 75c. pink and red . . . . 45 3·25
218 **31** 75c. brown . . . . 2·00 4·50
219 80c. black . . . . 25 3·00
220 90c. purple . . . . 25 3·00
221 1f. green . . . . 95 3·00
222 1f. red . . . . 35 2·50
223 1f. black . . . . 1·75 3·75
240 1f. on 65c. green (No. 194) 65 2·50
224 **32** 1f.25 brown . . . . 75 3·25
225 1f.25 red . . . . 1·40 3·25
238 – 1f.25 red (No. 186) . . . . 75 4·25
226 **30** 1f.40 blue . . . . 95 3·25
227 **32** 1f.50 blue . . . . 90 3·00
228 **30** 1f.60 red . . . . 70 3·25
229 **32** 1f.75 green . . . . 60 3·00
230 **30** 1f.75 blue . . . . 2·25 5·00
231 **32** 2f. red . . . . 85 2·25
239 – 2f.25 blue (No. 187) . . . 1·50 3·75
232 **30** 2f.25 blue . . . . 50 3·75
233 2f.50 brown . . . . 1·90 7·50
234 **32** 3f. violet . . . . 55 2·50
197 **18** 5f. brown and pink . . . . 42·00 42·00
235 **32** 5f. mauve . . . . 1·10 2·00
236 10f. blue . . . . 2·25 7·50
237 20f. brown . . . . 5·25 12·50
241 **34** 3f.65 blue and red (air) . . 3·00 5·00
242 6f.65 brown and red . . . 2·75 5·00
243 9f.65 red and blue . . . . 2·25 5·00
244 12f.65 brown and green . . 3·00 5·00

37 Chief Products

1943. Free French Issue.
245 **37** 5c. brown . . . . 10 2·00
246a 10c. blue . . . . 90 1·10
247 25c. green . . . . 15 2·50
248 30c. red . . . . 55 2·50
249 40c. green . . . . 10 2·25
250 80c. mauve . . . . 25 2·25
251 1f. purple 30 30
252 1f.50 red 35 90
253 2f. black . . . . 30 1·75
254 2f.50 blue . . . . 55 2·00
255 4f. violet 45 40
256 5f. yellow 50 25
257 10f. brown 65 70
258 20f. green . . . . 95 1·40

1944. Air. Free French Administration. As T **19a** of Oceanic Settlements.
259 1f. orange 35 55
260 1f.50 red 50 35
261 5f. purple 60 50
262 10f. black . . . . 1·25 2·50
263 25f. blue . . . . 1·90 2·25
264 50f. green . . . . 1·50 1·25
265 100f. red . . . . 1·75 2·75

1944. Mutual Air and Red Cross Funds. As T **19b** of Oceanic Settlements.
266 5f.+20f. black . . . . 1·60 3·50

1945. Eboue. As T **20a** of Oceanic Settlements.
267 2f. black 40 80
268 25f. green . . . . 1·60 2·25

1945. Surch.
269 **37** 50c. on 5c. brown . . . . 95 2·75
270 60c. on 5c. brown . . . . 1·00 2·75
271 70c. on 5c. brown . . . . 45 2·75
272 1f.20 on 5c. brown . . . . 75 2·75
273 2f.40 on 25c. green . . . . 1·25 2·25
274 3f. on 25c. green 75 70
275 4f.50 on 25c. green . . . . 80 2·50
276 15f. on 2f.50 blue . . . . 45 1·25

1946. Air. Victory. As T **20b** of Oceanic Settlements.
277 8f. grey . . . . 25 1·10

1946. Air. From Chad to the Rhine. As T **20c** of Oceanic Settlements.
278 5f. red . . . . 1·75 3·25
279 10f. violet . . . . 1·00 3·00
280 15f. black . . . . 1·60 3·00
281 20f. red . . . . 1·60 2·75
282 25f. blue . . . . 1·50 3·25
283 50f. green . . . . 2·00 3·50

39 Cliffs

40 Banana Tree and Cliff

41 Mountain Landscape

42 Shadow of Airplane over Coast

1947.
284 **39** 10c. orange & grn (postage) . . . . . . 10 2·50
285 30c. orange and blue . . . 10 2·25
286 40c. orange and brown . . 10 2·75
287 – 50c. brown and green . . . 15 2·50
288 – 60c. brown and blue . . . 15 2·75
289 – 80c. green and brown . . . 15 2·75
290 – 1f. purple and blue . . . 20 50
291 – 1f.20 grey and green . . . 45 3·00
292 – 1f.50 purple and orange . . 60 3·00
293 **40** 2f. blue and green 25 30
294 3f. purple and green . . . 65 2·25
295 3f.60 pink and red . . . . 85 3·25
296 4f. blue and brown . . . . 1·00 2·25
297 **41** 5f. mauve and brown . . . 1·25 1·50
298 6f. blue and brown . . . . 1·25 2·00
299 10f. orange and blue . . . 1·60 3·00
300 – 15f. purple and blue . . . 1·50 5·25
301 – 20f. blue and orange . . . 2·25 6·00
302 – 25f. brown and mauve . . . 1·75 5·75
303 **42** 50f. green and grey (air) . . 5·75 9·00
304 – 100f. orange and brown . . 8·25 14·00
305 – 200f. blue and orange . . . 7·25 18·00

DESIGNS—20 × 37 mm: 50c. to 80c. Cutting sugar cane; 1f. to 1f.50, Cascade. 28 × 50 mm: 100f. Douglas DC-4 airplane over Reunion. 37 × 20 mm: 15f. to 25f. "Ville de Strasbourg" (liner) approaching Reunion. 50 × 28 mm: 200f. Reunion from the air.

1949. Stamps of France surch **CFA** and value. (a) Postage. (i) Ceres.
306 **218** 50c. on 1f. red . . . . . 20 1·40
307 60c. on 2f. green . . . . 1·75 4·00

(ii) Nos. 972/3 (Arms).
308 10c. on 30c. black, red and yellow (Alsace) . . . . . 20 2·75
309 30c. on 50c. brown, yellow and red (Lorraine) . . . . 35 3·00

(iii) Nos. 981, 979 and 982/a (Views).
310 5f. on 20f. blue (Finistere) . . 2·50 45
311 7f. on 12f. red (Luxembourg Palace) . . . . 2·00 2·10
312 8f. on 25f. blue (Nancy) . . . 4·25 2·10
313 10f. on 25f. brown (Nancy) 1·00 55

(iv) Marianne.
314 **219** 1f. on 3f. mauve 30 25
315 2f. on 4f. green 50 40
316 2f. on 5f. green . . . . . 3·50 6·00
317 2f. on 5f. violet 50 40
318 2f.50 on 5f. blue . . . . 5·50 16·00
319 3f. on 6f. red 75 30
320 3f. on 6f. green . . . . . 1·25 1·40
321 4f. on 10f. violet 65 25
322 6f. on 12f. blue . . . . . 1·75 80
323 6f. on 12f. orange . . . . 2·10 2·00
324 9f. on 18f. red . . . . . 2·25 7·50

(v) Conques Abbey.
325 **263** 11f. on 18f. blue . . . . 1·40 2·50

(b) Air. (i) Nos. 967/70 (Mythology).
326 – 20f. on 40f. green . . . . 1·60 90
327 **236** 25f. on 50f. pink . . . . 2·25 50
328 **237** 50f. on 100f. blue . . . . 4·50 1·90
329 – 100f. on 200f. red . . . . 20·00 11·00

(ii) Nos. 1056 and 1058/9 (Cities).
330 100f. on 200f. green (Bordeaux) . . . . 55·00 45·00
331 200f. on 500f. red (Marseilles) 40·00 30·00
332 500f. on 1000f. purple and black on blue (Paris) . . . £150 £160

1950. Stamps of France surch **CFA** and value. (a) Nos. 1050 and 1052 (Arms).
342 10c. on 50c. yellow, red and blue (Guyenne) . . . . . 15 1·60
343 1f. on 2f. red, yellow and green (Auvergne) . . . . 2·50 5·25

(b) On Nos. 1067/8 and 1068b (Views).
344 – 5f. on 20f. red (Comminges) . . . . . 2·00 55
345 **284** 8f. on 25f. blue (Wandrille) . . . . . . 1·25 50
346 – 15f. on 30f. blue (Arbois) 55 70

1951. Nos. 1123/4 of France (Arms) surch **CFA** and value.
347 50c. on 1f. red, yellow and blue (Bearn) . . . . 30 1·25
348 1f. on 2f. yellow, blue and red (Touraine) 25 30

1952. Nos. 1138 and 1144 of France surch **CFA** and value.
349 **323** 5f. on 20f. violet (Chambord) 60 30
350 **317** 8f. on 40f. violet (Bigorre) 1·90 25

1953. Stamps of France surch **CFA** and value. (a) Nos. 1162, 1168 and 1170 (Literary Figures and National Industries).
351 3f. on 6f. lake and red (Gargantua) 95 80
352 8f. on 40f. brown and chocolate (Porcelain) . . . 90 20
353 20f. on 75f. red and carmine (Flowers) 90 60

(b) Nos. 1181/2 (Arms).
354 50c. on 1f. yellow, red and black (Poitou) . . . . . . 55 1·25
355 1f. on 2f. yellow, blue and brown (Champagne) . . . 65 3·00

1954. Stamps of France surch **CFA** and value. (a) Postage. (i) Nos. 1188 and 1190 (Sports).
356 8f. on 40f. blue and brown (Canoeing) . . . . 7·50 5·00
357 20f. on 75f. red and orange (Horse jumping) . . . . . 23·00 35·00

(ii) Nos. 1205/8 and 1210/11 (Views).
358 2f. on 6f. indigo, blue and green (Lourdes) . . . . . 55 1·25
359 3f. on 8f. green and blue (Andelys) . . . . 1·10 3·00
360 4f. on 10f. brown and blue (Royan) . . . . 60 1·40
361 6f. on 12f. lilac and violet (Quimper) . . . . 90 1·50
362 9f. on 18f. indigo, blue and green (Cheverny) . . . . . 1·90 5·00
363 10f. on 20f. brown, chestnut and blue (Ajaccio) . . . 3·00 2·75

(iii) No. 1229 (Arms).
364 1f. on 2f. yellow, red and black (Angoumois) 25 25

(b) Air. Nos. 1194/7 (Aircraft).
365 50f. on 100f. brown and blue (Mystere IV) . . . . . 2·50 95
366 100f. on 200f. purple and blue (Noratlas) . . . . . 2·10 2·25
367 200f. on 500f. red and orange (Magister) . . . . 19·00 18·00
368 500f. on 1000f. indigo, purple and blue (Provence) . . . 11·00 20·00

1955. Stamps of France surch **CFA** and value. (a) Nos. 1262/5, 1266, 1268 and 1268b (Views).
369 2f. on 6f. red (Bordeaux) . . 75 1·25
370 3f. on 8f. blue (Marseilles) . . 1·25 1·00
371 4f. on 10f. blue (Nice) . . . 1·10 1·00
372 5f. on 12f. brown and grey (Cahors) 50 35
373 6f. on 18f. blue and green (Uzerche) 60 40
374 10f. on 25f. brown and chestnut (Brouage) 65 35
375 17f. on 70f. black and green (Cahors) . . . . 2·75 5·00

(b) No. 1273 (Arms).
376 50c. on 1f. yellow, red and blue (Comtat Venaissin) . . 20 25

1956. Nos. 1297/1300 of France (Sports) surch **CFA** and value.
377 8f. on 30f. black and grey (Basketball) . . . . 1·10 30
378 9f. on 40f. purple and brown (Pelota) . . . . 1·40 2·00
379 15f. on 50f. violet and purple (Rugby) . . . . 2·75 2·25
380 20f. on 75f. green, black and blue (Climbing) . . . . . 1·60 2·25

1957. Stamps of France surch **CFA** and value. (a) Postage. (i) Harvester.
381 **344** 2f. on 6f. brown 55 15
382 4f. on 12f. purple . . . . 1·40 1·10
383 5f. on 10f. green . . . . 1·25 65

(ii) France.
384 **362** 10f. on 20f. blue 45 15
385 12f. on 25f. red . . . . . 1·40 30

(iii) No. 1335 (Le Quesnoy).
386 7f. on 15f. black and green 95 30

(iv) Nos. 1351, 1352/3, 1354/5 and 1356a (Tourist Publicity).
387 3f. on 10f. chocolate and brown (Elysee) 70 60
388 6f. on 18f. brown and blue (Beynac) . . . . 1·00 1·75
389 9f. on 25f. brown and grey (Valencay) . . . . 80 2·25
390 17f. on 35f. mauve and red (Rouen) . . . . 1·40 2·25
391 20f. on 50f. brown and green (St. Remy) 75 30
392 25f. on 85f. purple (Evian-les-Bains) . . . . 2·00 65

(b) Air. Nos. 1319/20 (Aircraft).
393 200f. on 500f. black and blue (Caravelle) . . . . 8·50 10·00
394 500f. on 1000f. black, violet and brown (Alouette II) . . 15·00 21·00

1960. Nos. 1461, 1464 and 1467 of France (Tourist Publicity) surch **CFA** and value.
395 7f. on 15c. indigo and blue (Laon) . . . . 1·60 80
396 20f. on 50c. purple and green (Tlemcen) . . . . 11·00 3·25
397 50f. on 1f. violet, green and blue (Cilaos) . . . . 1·40 70

1961. Harvester and Sower stamps of France (in new currency) surch **CFA** and value.
398 **344** 5f. on 10c. green 95 75
400 **453** 10f. on 20c. red and turquoise 50 45

1961. "Marianne" stamp of France surch **12f. CFA.**
401 **463** 12f. on 25c. grey & purple 15 55

1961. Nos. 1457, 1457b and 1459/60 of France (Aircraft) surch **CFA** and value.
402 100f. on 2f. purple and blue (Noratlas) . . . . 4·25 1·40
403 100f. on 2f. indigo and blue (Mystere Falcon 20) . . . 1·75 1·50
404 200f. on 5f. black and blue (Caravelle) . . . . 5·00 3·75
405 500f. on 10f. black, violet and brown (Alouette II) . . . . 14·50 3·75

1962. Red Cross stamps of France (Nos. 1593/4) surch **CFA** and value.
409 10f.+5f. on 20c.+10c. . . . 1·75 2·25
410 12f.+5f. on 25c.+10c. . . . 1·75 2·25

1962. Satellite Link stamps of France surch **CFA** and value.
411 12f. on 25c. (No. 1587) . . . 45 2·00
412 25f. on 50c. (No. 1588) . . . 50 1·90

1963. Nos. 1541 and 1545 of France (Tourist Publicity) surch **CFA** and value.
413 7f. on 15c. grey, purple and blue (Saint-Paul) . . . . . 1·60 1·75
414 20f. on 45c. brown, green and blue (Sully) . . . . 1·10 40

1963. Nos. 1498b/9b and 1499e/f of France (Arms) surch **CFA** and value.
415 1f. on 2c. yellow, green and blue (Gueret) 10 50
416 2f. on 5c. mult (Oran) . . . 20 55
417 2f. on 5c. red, yellow and blue (Armiens) 30 50
418 5f. on 10c. blue, yellow and red (Troyes) 30 55

419 6f. on 18c. multicoloured (St. Denis) 15 50
420 15f. on 30c. red and blue (Paris) 40 55

1963. Red Cross stamps of France Nos. 1627/8 surch **CFA** and value.
421 10f.+5f. on 20c.+10c. . . . 2·75 4·00
422 12f.+5f. on 25c.+10c. . . . 2·75 4·00

1964. 'PHILATEC 1964' International Stamp Exhibition stamp of France surch **CFA** and value.
423 12f. on 25c. (No. 1629) . . . 1·00 75

1964. Nos. 1654/5 of France (Tourist Publicity) surch **CFA** and value.
431 20f. on 40c. chocolate, green and brown (Ronchamp) . . 1·40 2·00
432 35f. on 70c. purple, green and blue (Provins) . . . . . . 95 1·75

1964. Red Cross stamps of France Nos. 1665/6 surch **CFA** and value.
433 10f.+5f. on 20c.+10c. . . . 1·90 2·75
434 12f.+5f. on 25c.+10c. . . . 1·90 2·75

1965. No. 1621 of France (Saint Flour) surch **3F CFA**.
435 30f. on 60c. red, green & blue 1·10 1·75

1965. Nos 1684/5 and 1688 of France (Tourist Publicity) surch **CFA** and value.
436 25f. on 50c. blue, green and bistre (St. Marie) . . . . . 90 1·40
437 30f. on 60c. brown and blue (Aix les Bains) . . . . . . 75 1·75
438 50f. on 1f. grey, green and brown (Carnac) . . . . . 2·25 2·25

1965. Tercent of Colonization of Reunion. As No. 1692 of France, but additionally inscr 'CFA'.
439 15f. blue and red 85 65

1965. Red Cross stamps of France Nos. 1698/9 surch **CFA** and value.
440 12f.+5f. on 25c.+10c. . . . 2·50 2·75
441 15f.+5f. on 30c.+ 10c. . . . 2·50 2·75

1966. "Marianne" stamp of France surch **10f CFA**.
442 **476** 10f. on 20c. red and blue 2·50 2·25

1966. Launching of 1st French Satellite. Nos. 1696/7 (plus se-tenant label) of France surch **CFA** and value.
443 15f. on 30c. blue, turquoise and light blue . . . . . . 2·25 2·25
444 30f. on 60c. blue, turquoise and light blue . . . . . . 2·50 2·25

1966. Red Cross stamps of France Nos. 1733/4 surch **CFA** and value.
445 12f.+5f. on 25c.+10c. . . . 2·25 2·25
446 15f.+5f. on 30c.+10c. . . . 2·25 2·25

1967. World Fair Montreal. No. 1747 of France surch **CFA** and value.
447 30f. on 60c. . . . . 1·25 2·25

1967. No. 1700 of France (Arms of Auch) surch **2fCFA**.
448 2f. on 5c. red and blue . . . 45 1·75

1967. 50th Anniv of Lions Int. No. 1766 of France surch **CFA** and value.
449 20f. on 40c. . . . . 1·60 2·50

1967. Red Cross. Nos. 1772/3 of France surch **CFA** and value.
450 12f.+5f. on 25c.+10c. . . . 2·75 4·50
451 15f.+5f. on 30c .+ 10c. . . . 2·75 4·50

1968. French Polar Exploration. No. 1806 of France surch **CFA** and value.
452 20f. on 40c. . . . . 2·25 2·00

1968. Red Cross stamps of France Nos. 1812/13 surch **CFA** and value.
453 12f.+5f. on 25c.+10c. . . . 2·75 2·75
454 15f.+5f. on 30c.+10c. . . . 2·75 2·75

1969. Stamp Day. No. 1824 of France surch **CFA** and value.
455 15f.+5f. on 30c.+10c. . . . 2·25 2·50

1969. "Republique" stamps of France surch **CFA** and value.
456 **604** 15f. on 30c. green . . . . 1·50 2·00
457 20f. on 40c. mauve . . . 1·10 90

1969. No. 1735 of France (Arms of Saint-Lo) surch **10F CFA**.
458 10f. on 20c. multicoloured . . 1·50 1·60

1969. Birth Bicent of Napoleon Bonaparte. No. 1845 of France surch **CFA** and value.
459 35f. on 70c. green, violet & bl 2·50 2·50

1969. Red Cross stamps of France Nos. 1853/4 surch **CFA** and value.
460 20f.+7f. on 40c.+15c. . . . 2·50 2·75
461 20f.+7f. on 40c.+15c. . . . 2·50 2·75

1970. Stamp Day. No. 1866 of France surch **CFA** and value.
462 20f.+5f. on 40c +.10c. . . . 2·25 2·25

1970. Red Cross. Nos. 1902/3 of France surch **CFA** and value.
463 20f.+7f. on 40c.+15c. . . . 3·50 3·50
464 20f.+7f. on 40c.+15c. . . . 3·50 3·50

1971. "Marianne" stamp of France surch **25f CFA**.
465 **668** 25f. on 50c. mauve . . . 75 70

1971. Stamp Day. No. 1919 of France surch **CFA** and value.
466 25f.+5f. on 50c.+10c. . . . 1·75 2·00

1971. "Antoinette". No. 1920 of France surch **CFA** and value.
467 40f. on 80c. . . . . 2·50 2·50

1971. No. 1928 of France (Rural Aid) surch **CFA** and value.
468 **678** 15f. on 40c. . . . . . . 1·90 2·00

1971. Nos. 1931/2 of France (Tourist Publicity) surch **CFA** and value.
469 45f. on 90c. brown, green and ochre (Riquewihr) . . . . 1·40 2·00
470 50f. on 1f.10 brown, blue and green (Sedan) . . . . . . 1·50 1·90

1971. 40th Anniv of 1st Meeting of Crafts Guilds Association. No. 1935 of France surch **CFA** and value.
471 **680** 45c. on 90c. purple & red 2·25 2·00

63 Reunion Chameleon

64 De Gaulle in Uniform (June 1940)

1971. Nature Protection.
472 **63** 25f. green, brown & yellow 2·25 1·90

1971. De Gaulle Commemoration.
473 **64** 25f. black . . . . 2·75 2·75
474 – 25f. blue . . . . 2·75 2·75
475 – 25f. red . . . . 2·75 2·75
476 – 25f. black . . . . 2·75 2·75
DESIGNS: No. 473, De Gaulle in uniform (June, 1940); No. 474, De Gaulle at Brazzaville, 1944; No. 475, De Gaulle in Paris, 1944; No. 476, De Gaulle as President of the French Republic, 1970 (T **64**).

1971. Nos. 1942/3 of France (Red Cross Fund) surch **CFA** and value.
477 15f.+5f. on 30c.+10c. . . . 2·25 2·50
478 25f.+5f. on 50c.+10c. . . . 2·50 2·50

65 King Penguin, Map and Exploration Ships

1972. Bicentenary of Discovery of Crozet Islands and Kerguelen (French Southern and Antarctic Territories).
479 **65** 45f. black, blue and brown 4·00 4·25

1972. No. 1956 of France surch **CFA** and value.
480 **688** 25f.+5f. on 50c+10c. blue, drab and yellow . . . . 2·25 2·25

1972. No. 1966 of France (Blood Donors) surch **CFA** and value.
481 **692** 15f. on 40c. red . . . . . 1·90 2·00

1972. Air. No 1890 of France (Daurat and Vanier) surch **CFA** and value.
482 **662** 200f. on 5f. brn, grn & bl 4·75 3·25

1972. Postal Codes. Nos. 1969/70 of France surch **CFA** and value.
483 **695** 15f. on 30c. red, black and green . . . . . . 1·90 1·90
484 25f. on 50c. yell, blk & red . . . . 1·75 1·60

1972. Red Cross Fund. Nos. 1979/80 of France surch **CFA** and value.
485 **701** 15f.+5f. on 30c.+10c. . . 2·25 2·50
486 25f.+5f. on 50c.+10c. . . 2·50 2·50

1973. Stamp Day. No. 1996 of France surch **CFA** and value.
487 **707** 25f.+5f. on 50c.+10c. . . 2·75 2·50

1973. No. 2011 of France surch **CFA** and value.
488 **714** 45f. on 90c. green, violet and blue . . . . 2·75 2·75

1973. No. 2008 of France surch **CFA** and value.
489 50f. on 1f. green, brown & bl 1·60 2·25

1973. No. 1960 of France surch **CFA** and value.
490 100f. on 2f. purple and green 2·50 2·50

1973. No. 2021/2 of France surch **CFA** and value.
491 **721** 15f.+5f. on 30c.+10c. green and red . . . . . 2·25 2·75
492 25f.+5f. on 50c .+ 10c. red and black . . . . . 2·50 2·75

1973. No. 2026 of France surch **CFA** and value.
494 **725** 25f. on 50c. brown, blue and purple . . . . . . 2·00 2·00

1974. Stamp Day. No. 2031 surch **FCFA** and value.
495 **727** 25f.+5f. on 50c .+ 10c. 2·00 2·25

1974. French Art. No. 2033/6 surch **FCFA** and value.
496 100f. on 2f. multicoloured . . 2·50 3·25
497 100f. on 2f. multicoloured . . 2·25 3·25
498 100f. on 2f. brown and blue 2·75 3·25
499 100f. on 2f. multicoloured . . 2·50 3·25

1974. French Lifeboat Service. No. 2040 surch **FCFA** and value.
500 **731** 45f. on 90c. blue, red and brown . . . . 2·50 2·50

1974. Centenary of Universal Postal Union. No. 2057 surch **FCFA** and value.
501 **741** 60f. on 1f.20 green, red and blue . . . . 1·40 2·75

1974. "Marianne" stamps of France surch **FCFA** and value.
502 **668** 30f. on 60c. green . . . . 2·50 3·00
503 40f. on 80c. red . . . . . 2·50 3·00

1974. Red Cross Fund. "The Seasons". Nos. 2059/60 surch **FCFA** and value.
504 **743** 30f.+7f. on 60c.+15c. . . 2·50 2·75
505 – 40f.+7f . on 80c.+15c. . . 2·50 2·75

From 1 January 1975 the CFA franc was replaced by the French Metropolitan franc, and Reunion subsequently used unsurcharged stamps of France.

PARCEL POST STAMPS

P 5 P 20

1890.
P11 **P 5** 10c. black on yellow (black frame) £250 £150
P13 10c. black on yellow (blue frame) . . . . 24·00 18·00

1907. Receipt stamps surch as in Type **P 20**.
P76 **P 20** 10c. brown and black . . 22·00 13·00
P77 10c. brown and red . . 19·00 20·00

POSTAGE DUE STAMPS

D 4

D 19

1889. Imperf.
D11 **D 4** 5c. black . . . . 17·00 4·50
D12 10c. black . . . . 9·50 4·00
D13 15c. black . . . . 38·00 18·00
D14 20c. black . . . . 50·00 5·25
D15 30c. black . . . . 45·00 5·25

1907.
D76 **D 19** 5c. red on yellow . . . 10 15
D77 10c. blue on blue . . . 15 25
D78 15c. black on grey . . . 15 1·75
D79 20c. pink 70 35
D80 30c. green on green . . 65 2·50
D81 50c. red on green . . . 25 1·75
D82 60c. pink on blue . . . 1·40 2·25
D83 1f. lilac . . . . 95 2·75

1927. Surch.
D130 **D 19** 2f. on 1f. red . . . . 3·50 3·50
D131 3f. on 1f. brown . . . 13·50 18·00

D 33 Arms of Reunion

D 43

1933.
D175 **D 33** 5c. purple . . . . . . 10 1·75
D176 10c. green . . . . . . 10 2·25
D177 15c. brown . . . . . . 10 1·75
D178 20c. orange . . . . . 15 2·00
D179 30c. olive . . . . . . 15 2·50
D180 50c. blue . . . . . . 20 3·00
D181 60c. brown . . . . . 25 3·00
D182 1f. violet . . . . . . 35 3·00
D183 2f. blue . . . . 35 3·00
D184 3f. red . . . . 35 3·00

1947.
D306 **D 43** 10c. mauve . . . . . 10 2·50
D307 30c. brown . . . . . 10 2·25
D308 50c. green . . . . . 10 2·50
D309 1f. brown . . . . . . 1·10 3·00
D310 2f. red . . . . 2·00 2·75
D311 3f. brown . . . . . . 1·60 3·00
D312 4f. blue . . . . 1·40 3·25
D313 5f. red . . . . 1·50 3·25
D314 10f. green . . . . . . 1·60 3·00
D315 20f. blue . . . . . . 2·75 3·25

1949. As Type **D 250** of France, but inscr "TIMBRE TAXE" surch **CFA** and value.
D333 10c. on 1f. blue . . . . . 10 2·75
D334 50c. on 2f. blue . . . . . 10 2·75
D335 1f. on 3f. red . . . . . . 40 3·00
D336 2f. on 4f. violet . . . . . 85 3·50
D337 3f. on 5f. pink . . . . . . 2·00 8·50
D338 5f. on 10f. red . . . . . 1·10 3·75
D339 10f. on 20f. brown . . . . 1·60 4·25
D340 20f. on 50f. green . . . . 3·75 6·75
D341 50f. on 100f. green . . . . 12·00 23·00

1962. Wheat Sheaves Type of France surch **CFA** and value.
D406 **D 457** 1f. on 5c. mauve . . 1·10 25
D407 10f. on 20c. brown 3·00 3·00
D408 20f. on 50c. green . . 18·00 17·00

1964. Nos. D1650/4 and D1656/7 of France surch **CFA** and value.
D424 – 1f. on 5c. . . . . . 20 1·50
D425 – 5f. on 10c. . . . . . 30 1·50
D426 **D 539** 7f. on 15c. . . . . . 15 1·60
D427 – 10f. on 20c. . . . . 2·50 2·00
D428 – 15f. on 30c. . . . . 40 1·75
D429 – 20f. on 50c. . . . . 55 1·75
D430 – 50f. on 1f. . . . . . 1·00 2·25

RHODESIA Pt. 1

A British territory in central Africa, formerly administered by the British South Africa Co. In 1924 divided into the territories of Northern and Southern Rhodesia which issued their own stamps (q.v.). In 1964 Southern Rhodesia was renamed Rhodesia; on becoming independent in 1980 it was renamed Zimbabwe.

1890. 12 pence = 1 shilling;
20 shillings = 1 pound.
1970. 100 cents = 1 dollar.

1 Arms of the Company

1890. The pound values are larger.
18 1 ½d. blue and red . . . . . . 2·50 3·00
1 1d. black . . . . 10·00 2·75
20 2d. green and red . . . . . 19·00 2·50
21 3d. black and green . . . . 11·00 3·75
22 4d. brown and black . . . . 22·00 2·50
3 6d. blue . . . . 27·00 3·75
23 8d. red and blue . . . . . . 11·00 11·00
4 1s. brown . . . . 38·00 8·00
5 2s. red . . . . 42·00 25·00
6 2s.6d. purple . . . . 30·00 38·00
25 3s. brown and green . . . . £140 75·00
26 4s. black and red . . . . . . 32·00 50·00
8 5s. yellow . . . . 65·00 50·00
9 10s. green . . . . 80·00 £100
10 – £1 blue £180 £130
11 – £2 red £400 £150
12 – £5 green £1600 £450
13 – £10 brown £2750 £700

1891. Surch in figures.
14 1 ½d. on 6d. blue £100 £300
15 2d. on 6d. blue £110 £425
16 4d. on 6d. blue £140 £500
17 8d. on 1s. brown £140 £550

5 9

1896. The ends of ribbons containing motto cross the animals' legs.
41 5 ½d. grey and mauve . . . . 2·50 3·25
42 1d. red and green . . . . . 3·50 3·75
43 2d. brown and mauve . . . 8·50 4·50
31 3d. brown and blue . . . . 3·75 1·75
44a 4d. blue and mauve . . . . 9·00 50
46 6d. mauve and red . . . . 7·00 75
34 8d. green and mauve on buff . . . . 5·00 60
35 1s. green and blue . . . . . 15·00 2·75
47 2s. blue and green on buff 23·00 8·50
48 2s.6d. brown & pur on yell 70·00 50·00
36 3s. green and mauve on blue 65·00 32·00
37 4s. red and blue on green 48·00 2·75
49 5s. brown and green . . . . 42·00 9·00
50 10s. grey and red on rose 90·00 60·00

1896. Surch in words.
51 1 1d. on 3d. black and green £475 £500
52 1d. on 4s. black and red . . £250 £275
53 3d. on 5s. yellow £170 £225

1896. Cape of Good Hope stamps optd **BRITISH SOUTH AFRICA COMPANY**.
58 6 ½d. black (No. 48) . . . . . 11·00 17·00
59 17 1d. red (No. 58a) . . . . . 13·00 18·00
60 6 2d. brown (No. 60) . . . . 16·00 9·50
61 3d. red (No. 40) . . . . . 50·00 70·00
62 4d. blue (No. 51) . . . . . 18·00 18·00
63 4 6d. violet (No. 52a) . . . . 50·00 65·00
64 6 1s. yellow (No. 65) £140 £140

1897. The ends of motto ribbons do not cross the animals' legs.
66 9 ½d. grey and mauve . . . . 2·50 4·75
67 1d. red and green . . . . . 3·00 4·50
68 2d. brown and mauve . . . . 7·00 1·75
69 3d. brown and blue . . . . 2·50 40
70 4d. blue and mauve . . . . 10·00 1·75
71 6d. mauve and red . . . . . 6·50 3·50
72 8d. green and mauve on buff 11·00 40
73 £1 black and brown on green £350 £225

10 11

1898. Nos. 90/93a are larger (24 × 28½ mm).
75a 10 ½d. green . . . . 2·25 1·00
77 1d. red . . . . 3·50 50
79 2d. brown . . . . 2·75 60
80 2½d. bluc . . . . 4·50 80
81 3d. red . . . . 4·00 80
82 4d. olive . . . . 4·25 30
83 6d. purple . . . . 10·00 1·75
84 11 1s. brown . . . . 15·00 2·25
85 2s.6d. grey . . . . 45·00 75
86 3s. violet . . . . 14·00 1·75
87 5s. orange . . . . 38·00 10·00
88 7s.6d. black . . . . 65·00 18·00
89 10s. green . . . . 24·00 1·00
90 – £1 purple . . . . £225 85·00
91 – £2 brown . . . . 75·00 6·50
92 – £5 blue £3000 £2250
93 – £10 lilac £3250 £2250
93a – £20 brown £14000

13 Victoria Falls

1905. Visit of British Assn. and Opening of Victoria Falls Bridge across Zambesi.
94 13 1d. red . . . . 3·50 4·50
95 2½d. blue . . . . 8·00 6·00
96 5d. red . . . . 22·00 48·00
97 1s. green . . . . 24·00 38·00
98 2s.6d. black £100 £150
99 5s. violet . . . . 85·00 40·00

1909. Optd **RHODESIA.** or surch also.
100 10 ½d. green . . . . 1·75 1·25
101 1d. red . . . . 2·75 75
102 2d. brown . . . . 1·60 3·50
103 2½d. blue . . . . 1·25 70
104 3d. red . . . . 1·60 60
105 4d. olive . . . . 3·25 1·25
114 5d. on 6d. purple . . . . 6·50 12·00
106 6d. purple . . . . 5·00 4·00
116 11 7½d. on 2s.6d. grey . . . 3·50 3·75
117a 10d. on 2s. violet . . . . 4·00 3·75
107c 1s. brown . . . . 8·50 3·25
118 2s. on 5s. orange . . . . 12·00 7·50
108 2s.6d. grey . . . . 18·00 9·00
109 3s. violet . . . . 15·00 8·50
110 5s. orange . . . . 25·00 32·00
111 7s.6d. black . . . . . . 90·00 19·00
112 10s. green . . . . 32·00 12·00
113 – £1 purple . . . . £140 75·00
113d – £2 brown £3250 £275
113e – £5 blue £6500 £3000

17 18

1910.
119 17 ½d. green . . . . 10·00 1·75
123 1d. red . . . . 18·00 2·00
128 2d. black and grey . . . 50·00 6·00
131a 2½d. blue . . . . 20·00 6·00
135 3d. purple and yellow . . 35·00 12·00
140 4d. black and orange . . 35·00 12·00
141 5d. purple and olive . . . 25·00 42·00
145 6d. purple and mauve . . 30·00 14·00
148 8d. black and purple . . £130 90·00
149 10d. red and purple . . . 32·00 48·00
151 1s. black and green . . . 38·00 18·00
153 2s. black and blue . . . . 75·00 50·00
157 2s.6d. black and red . . . £275 £300
158 3s. green and violet . . . £150 £150
160a 5s. red and green £225 £180
160b 7s.6d. red and blue . . . £600 £425
164 10s. green and orange . . £375 £325
166 £1 red and black £1100 £350

1913.
187 18 ½d. green . . . . 4·50 1·50
192 1d. red . . . . 3·50 1·50
198 1½d. brown . . . . 3·50 1·50
291 2d. black and grey . . . 6·00 3·75
200 2½d. blue . . . . 4·25 25·00
259 3d. black and yellow . . . 8·50 2·00
262 4d. black and orange . . 10·00 6·00
212 5d. black and green . . . 4·00 17·00
266 6d. black and mauve . . . 6·00 5·50
230 8d. violet and green . . . 11·00 48·00
247 10d. blue and red . . . . 7·50 27·00
272 1s. black and blue . . . . 7·00 6·00
273 2s. black and brown . . . 12·00 15·00
236 2s.6d. blue and brown . . 45·00 29·00
304 3s. brown and blue . . . . 80·00 95·00
239 5s. blue and green . . . . 50·00 55·00
252 7s.6d. mauve and grey . . £120 £170
309 10s. red and green £170 £200
242 £1 black and purple . . . £375 £500

1917. Surch **Half Penny** (without hyphen or full stop).
280 18 ½d. on 1s. red . . . . . . 2·50 7·00

1917. Surch **Half-Penny.** (with hyphen and full stop).
281 18 ½d. on 1d. red . . . . . . 1·75 7·00

RHODESIA

The following stamps are for the former Southern Rhodesia, renamed Rhodesia.

59 "Telecommunications" 60 Bangala Dam

1965. Centenary of I.T.U.
351 59 6d. violet and olive . . . . 1·25 40
352 1s.3d. violet and lilac . . 1·25 40
353 2s.6d. violet and brown . . 2·00 4·50

1965. Water Conservation. Multicoloured.
354 3d. Type **60** 30 10
355 4d. Irrigation canal . . . . . 1·00 1·00
356 2s.6d. Cutting sugar cane . . 2·25 3·50

63 Sir Winston Churchill, Quill, Sword and Houses of Parliament

1965. Churchill Commemoration.
357 63 1s.3d. black and blue . . . 70 35

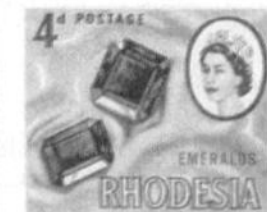

64 Coat of Arms 67 Emeralds

1965. "Independence".
358 64 2s.6d. multicoloured . . . 15 15

1966. Optd **INDEPENDENCE 11th November 1965**.

(a) On Nos. 92/105 of Southern Rhodesia.
359 45 ½d. yellow, green and blue 10 10
360 – 1d. violet and ochre . . . 10 10
361 – 2d. yellow and violet . . . 10 10
362 – 3d. brown and blue 10 10
363 – 4d. orange and green . . . 15 10
364 50 6d. red, yellow and green 15 10
365 – 9d. brown, yellow and green 30 10
366 – 1s. green and ochre 40 10
367 – 1s.3d. red, violet and green 50 20
368 – 2s. blue and ochre . . . . 60 3·25
369 – 2s.6d. blue and red . . . . 60 1·00
370 56 5s. multicoloured . . . . . 1·50 5·50
371 – 10s. multicoloured . . . . 3·00 2·25
372 – £1 multicoloured . . . . . 1·25 2·25

(b) Surch on No. 357.
373 63 5s. on 1s.3d. black and blue . . . . 3·50 9·00

1966. As Nos. 92/105 of Southern Rhodesia, but inscr "RHODESIA" as in T **67**. Some designs and colours changed.
374 – 1d. violet and ochre . . . 10 10
375 – 2d. orange & grn (As No. 96) 10 10
376 – 3d. brown and blue 10 10
377 67 4d. green and brown . . . 1·00 10
378 50 6d. red, yellow and green 15 10
379 – 9d. yellow & vio (As No. 94) 15 20
380 45 1s. yellow, green and blue 15 10
381 – 1s.3d. bl & ochre (As No. 101) 25 15
382 – 1s.6d. brn, yell & grn (As No. 98) . . . . 2·25 25
383 – 2s. red, vio & grn (As No. 100) 40 80
384 – 2s.6d. blue, red & turquoise 1·50 20
385 56 5s. multicoloured 40 90
386 – 10s. multicoloured . . . . 2·75 4·00
387 – £1 multicoloured . . . . . 5·00 8·00

Nos. 379/80 are in larger format as Type **50** of Southern Rhodesia.

Stamps in these designs were later printed locally. These vary only slightly from the above in details and shade.

For Nos. 376, 380 and 382/4 in dual currency see Nos. 408/12.

68 Zeederberg Coach, c. 1895

1966. 28th Congress of Southern Africa Philatelic Federation ("Rhopex").
388 68 3d. multicoloured 15 10
389 – 9d. multicoloured 15 20
390 – 1s.6d. blue and black . . . 25 30
391 – 2s.6d. pink, green and black 30 55
MS392 126 × 84 mm. Nos. 388/91 5·00 11·00
DESIGNS: 9d. Sir Rowland Hill; 1s.6d. The Penny Black; 2s.6d. Rhodesian stamp of 1892 (No. 12).

69 De Havilland Dragon Rapide (1946) 70 Kudu

1966. 20th Anniv of Central African Airways.
393 69 6d. multicoloured 75 35
394 – 1s.3d. multicoloured . . . 1·00 40
395 – 2s.6d. multicoloured . . . 1·75 2·00
396 – 5s. black and blue . . . . 3·00 5·00

AIRCRAFT: 1s.3d. Douglas DC-3 (1953); 2s.6d. Vickers Viscount 748 "Matopos" (1956); 5s. B.A.C. One Eleven.

1967. Dual Currency Issue. As Nos. 376, 380 and 382/4. but value in dual currency as T **70**.
408 70 3d./2½c. brown and blue . . 50 15
409 – 1s./10c. yellow, green and blue (No. 380) 50 25
410 – 1s.6d./15c. brown, yellow and green (No. 382) . . 3·50 70
411 – 2s./20c. red, violet and green (No. 383) . . . . 1·50 3·00
412 – 2s.6d./25c. ultramarine, red and blue (No. 384) . . . 16·00 25·00

71 Dr. Jameson (administrator)

1967. Famous Rhodesians (1st series) and 50th Death Anniv of Dr. Jameson.
413 71 1s.6d. multicoloured . . . 20 35

See also Nos. 426, 430, 457, 458, 469, 480, 488 and 513.

72 Soapstone Sculpture (Joram Mariga)

1967. 10th Anniv of Opening of Rhodes National Gallery.
414 72 3d. brown, green and black 10 10
415 – 9d. blue, brown and black 20 20
416 – 1s.3d. multicoloured . . . 20 25
417 – 2s.6d. multicoloured . . . 25 35
DESIGNS: 9d. "The Burgher of Calais" (detail, Rodin); 1s.3d. "The Knight" (stamp design wrongly inscr) (Roberto Crippa); 2s.6d. "John the Baptist" (Mossini).

73 Baobab Tree

1967. Nature Conservation.
418 73 4d. brown and black . . . 10 20
419 – 4d. green and black . . . 25 20
420 – 4d. grey and black 25 20
421 – 4d. orange and black . . . 10 20
DESIGNS—HORIZ: No. 419, White rhinoceros; No. 420, African elephants. VERT: No. 421, Wild gladiolus.

74 Wooden Hand Plough

1968. 15th World Ploughing Contest, Norton, Rhodesia.
422 74 3d. orange, red and brown 10 10
423 – 9d. multicoloured 15 20
424 – 1s.6d. multicoloured . . . 20 55
425 – 2s.6d. multicoloured . . . 20 75
DESIGNS: 9d. Early wheel plough; 1s.6d. Steam powered tractor, and ploughs; 2s.6d. Modern tractor, and plough.

75 Alfred Beit (national benefactor)

1968. Famous Rhodesians (2nd issue).
426 75 1s.6d. orange, black & brn 20 30

76 Raising the Flag, Bulawayo, 1893

1968. 75th Anniv of Matabeleland.
427 **76** 3d. orange, red and black . . . 15 10
428 – 9d. multicoloured 15 20
429 – 1s.6d. green, emerald & blk . . 20 60
DESIGNS: 9d. View and coat of arms of Bulawayo; 1s.6d. Allan Wilson (combatant in the Matabele War).

77 Sir William Henry Milton (administrator)

1969. Famous Rhodesians (3rd issue).
430 **77** 1s.6d. multicoloured . . . 20 55

78 2ft. Gauge Locomotive No. 15, 1897

1969. 70th Anniv of Opening of Beira–Salisbury Railway. Multicoloured.
431 3d. Type **78** 50 10
432 9d. 7th Class steam locomotive No. 43, 1903 . . 70 40
433 1s.6d. Beyer, Peacock 15th Class steam locomotive No. 413, 1951 . . . . . . 1·50 1·75
434 2s.6d. Class DE2 diesel-electric locomotive No. 1203, 1955 . . . . . 2·50 4·25

79 Low Level Bridge

1969. Bridges of Rhodesia. Multicoloured.
435 3d. Type **79** 40 10
436 9d. Mpudzi bridge 60 25
437 1s.6d. Umniati bridge . . . . 1·40 75
438 2s.6d. Birchenough bridge . . 1·75 1·50

80 Harvesting Wheat **81** Devil's Cataract, Victoria Falls

1970. Decimal Currency.
439 **80** 1c. multicoloured 10 10
440 – 2c. multicoloured 10 10
441 – 2½c. multicoloured . . . 10 10
441c – 3c. multicoloured . . . . 1·25 10
442 – 3½c. multicoloured . . . 10 10
442b – 4c. multicoloured . . . . 1·75 40
443 – 5c. multicoloured 15 10
443b – 6c. multicoloured . . . . 4·00 3·75
443c **81** 7½c. multicoloured . . . 7·00 60
444 8c. multicoloured 75 20
445 – 10c. multicoloured 60 10
446 – 12½c. multicoloured . . . 1·00 10
446a – 14c. multicoloured . . . 12·00 70
447 – 15c. multicoloured . . . 1·25 15
448 – 20c. multicoloured . . . 1·00 15
449 – 25c. multicoloured . . . 4·00 60
450 – 50c. turquoise and blue . . 1·25 55
451 – $1 multicoloured . . . . 2·25 85
452 – $2 multicoloured . . . . 5·50 15·00
DESIGNS—As Type **80**: 2c. Pouring molten metal; 2½c. Zimbabwe Ruins; 3c. Articulated lorry; 3½c., 4c. Statue of Cecil Rhodes; 5c. Mine headgear; 6c. Hydrofoil "Seaflight". As Type **81**: 10c. Yachting on Lake McIlwaine; 12½c. Hippopotamus in river; 14c., 15c. Kariba Dam; 20c. Irrigation canal. 31 × 26 mm: 25c. Bateleurs; 50c. Radar antenna and Vickers Viscount 810; $1 "Air Rescue"; $2 Rhodesian flag.

82 Despatch Rider, c. 1890

1970. Inauguration of Posts and Telecommunications Corporation. Multicoloured.
453 2½c. Type **82** 30 10
454 3½c. Loading mail at Salisbury airport 40 50
455 15c. Constructing telegraph line, c. 1890 . . . . 45 1·25
456 25c. Telephone and modern telecommunications equipment . . . . 50 2·00

83 Mother Patrick (Dominican nurse and teacher)

1971. Famous Rhodesians (4th issue).
457 **83** 15c. multicoloured 60 50

84 Fredrick Courteney Selous (big-game hunter, explorer and pioneer)

1971. Famous Rhodesians (5th issue).
458 **84** 15c. multicoloured 40 70

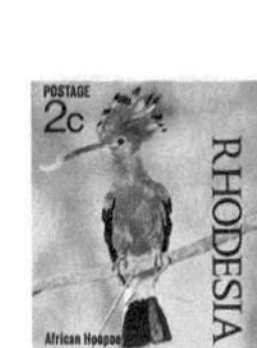

85 Hoopoe **86** Porphyritic Granite

1971. Birds of Rhodesia (1st series). Multicoloured.
459 2c. Type **85** 60 20
460 2½c. Half-collared kingfisher (horiz) 60 10
461 5c. Golden-breasted bunting 1·00 30
462 7½c. Carmine bee eater . . . 1·25 30
463 8c. Red-eyed bulbul . . . . 1·25 40
464 25c. Senegal wattled plover (horiz) . . . . 2·50 2·00
See also Nos. 537/42.

1971. "Granite 71" Geological Symposium. Multicoloured.
465 2½c. Type **86** 35 10
466 7½c. Muscovite mica seen through microscope . . . 50 30
467 15c. Granite seen through microscope . . . . 90 1·00
468 25c. Geological map of Rhodesia . . . . 90 2·25

87 Dr. Robert Moffat (missionary)

1972. Famous Rhodesians (6th issue).
469 **87** 13c. multicoloured 50 75

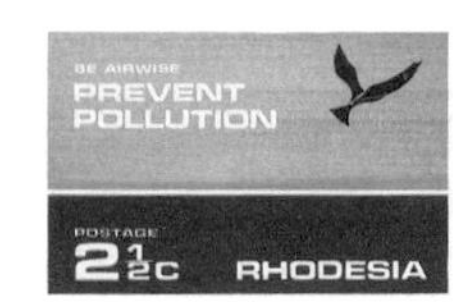

88 Bird ("Be Airwise")

1972. "Prevent Pollution". Multicoloured.
470 2½c. Type **88** 15 10
471 3½c. Antelope ("Be Countrywise") 15 20
472 7c. Fish ("Be Waterwise") . . 15 30
473 13c. City ("Be Citywise") . . 20 55

1972. "Rhophil '72". Nos. 439, 441 and 442 with commemorative inscr in margins.
MS474 1c. multicoloured . . . . 1·10 2·00
MS475 2½c. multicoloured . . . 1·10 2·00
MS476 3½c. multicoloured . . . 1·10 2·00
MS474/6 Set of 3 sheets . . . . 3·00 5·50

89 "The Three Kings" **91** W.M.O. Emblem

90 Dr. David Livingstone

1972. Christmas.
477 **89** 2c. multicoloured 10 10
478 5c. multicoloured 15 20
479 13c. multicoloured 30 55

1973. Famous Rhodesians (7th issue).
480 **90** 14c. multicoloured 50 75

1973. Centenary of I.M.O./W.M.O.
481 **91** 3c. multicoloured 10 10
482 14c. multicoloured 30 15
483 25c. multicoloured 40 75

92 Arms of Rhodesia

1973. 50th Anniv of Responsible Government.
484 **92** 2½c. multicoloured 10 10
485 4c. multicoloured 15 15
486 7½c. multicoloured 20 25
487 14c. multicoloured . . . . 35 1·25

93 George Pauling (construction engineer)

1974. Famous Rhodesians (8th issue).
488 **93** 14c. multicoloured . . . . 50 1·25

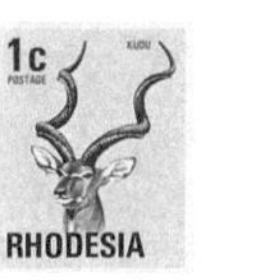

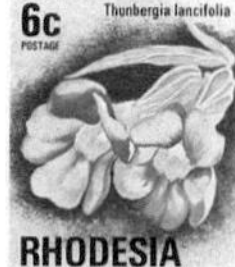

94 Greater Kudu **95** Thunbergia

96 "Charaxes varanes"

1974. Multicoloured. (a) Antelopes.
489 1c. Type **94** 10 10
490 2½c. Eland 75 10
491 3c. Roan antelope 10 10
492 4c. Reedbuck 20 10
493 5c. Bushbuck 20 60

(b) Wild Flowers.
494 6c. Type **95** 20 10
495 7½c. Flame lily 50 20
496 8c. As 7½c. 20 10
497 10c. Devil thorn 20 10
498 12c. Hibiscus . . . . 40 2·00
499 12½c. Pink sabi star . . . . 1·00 35
500 14c. Wild pimpernel . . . . 1·00 35
501 15c. As 12½c. 40 75
502 16c. As 14c. 40 30

(c) Butterflies.
503 20c. Type **96** . . . . 1·00 35
504 24c. "Precis hierta" 40 40
505 25c. As 24c. . . . . 1·50 1·75
506 50c. "Colotis regina" 40 60
507 $1 "Graphium antheus" . . . 40 60
508 $2 "Hamanumida daedalus" 40 75

97 Collecting Mail

1974. Centenary of U.P.U. Multicoloured.
509 3c. Type **97** 15 10
510 4c. Sorting mail 15 10
511 7½c. Mail delivery 20 20
512 14c. Weighing parcel 30 90

98 Thomas Baines (artist)

1975. Famous Rhodesians (9th issue).
513 **98** 14c. multicoloured 50 60

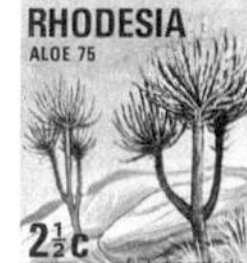

99 "Euphorbia confinalis" **100** Prevention of Head Injuries

1975. Int Succulent Congress, Salisbury ("Aloe '75"). Multicoloured.
514 2½c. Type **99** 10 10
515 3c. "Aloe excelsa" 10 10
516 4c. "Hoodia lugardii" 10 10
517 7½c. "Aloe ortholopha" . . . 15 10
518 14c. "Aloe musapana" . . . 30 10
519 25c. "Aloe saponaria" . . . 50 2·00

1975. Occupational Safety. Multicoloured.
520 2½c. Type **100** 10 10
521 4c. Bandaged hand and gloved hand 15 10
522 7½c. Broken glass and eye . . 15 15
523 14c. Blind man and welder with protective mask . . . 20 55

101 Telephones, 1876 and 1976 **103** Roan Antelope

1976. Telephone Centenary.
524 **101** 3c. grey and blue 10 10
525 – 14c. black and brown . . 20 55
DESIGN: 14c. Alexander Graham Bell.

1976. Nos. 495, 500 and 505 surch.
526 8c. on 7½c. multicoloured . . 15 15
527 16c. on 14c. multicoloured . . 15 15
528 24c. on 25c. multicoloured . . 20 60

1976. Vulnerable Wildlife. Multicoloured.
529 4c. Type **103** 10 10
530 6c. Brown hyena 15 60
531 8c. Hunting dog 15 10
532 16c. Cheetah 20 35

104 Msasa **105** Garden Bulbul ("Blackeyed-Bulbul")

1976. Trees of Rhodesia. Multicoloured.
533 4c. Type **104** 10 10
534 6c. Red mahogany 10 10

535 8c. Mukwa 15 10
536 16c. Rhodesian teak 20 55

1977. Birds of Rhodesia (2nd series). Mult.
537 3c. Type **105** 15 10
538 4c. Yellow-mantled whydah ("Yellow-mantled Wydah") 15 10
539 6c. Cape longclaw ("Orange throated longclaw") . . . 20 60
540 8c. Magpie shrike ("Eastern Long-tailed Shrike") . . . 20 35
541 16c. Lesser blue-eared glossy starling ("Lesser Blue-eared Starling") 25 60
542 24c. Green wood hoopoe ("Red-billed Wood hoopee") . . . . 30 1·10

106 "Lake Kyle" (Joan Evans)

107 Virgin and Child

1977. Landscape Paintings. Multicoloured.
543 3c. Type **106** 10 10
544 4c. "Chimanimani Mountains" (Joan Evans) 10 10
545 6c. "Rocks near Bonsor Reef" (Alice Balfour) . . . 10 30
546 8c. "A Dwala near Devil's Pass" (Alice Balfour) . . . 10 10
547 16c. "Zimbabwe" (Alice Balfour) 15 30
548 24c. "Victoria Falls" (Thomas Baines) 25 60

1977. Christmas.
549 **107** 3c. multicoloured 10 10
550 6c. multicoloured 10 20
551 8c. multicoloured 10 10
552 16c. multicoloured 15 30

108 Fair Spire

109 Morganite

1978. Trade Fair Rhodesia, Bulawayo. Multicoloured.
553 4c. Type **108** 10 10
554 8c. Fair Spire (different) . . . 15 25

1978. Gemstones, Wild Animals and Waterfalls. Multicoloured.
555 1c. Type **109** 10 10
556 3c. Amethyst 10 10
557 4c. Garnet 10 10
558 5c. Citrine 10 10
559 7c. Blue topaz 10 10
560 9c. White rhinoceros 15 10
561 11c. Lion 10 20
562 13c. Warthog . . . . 10 1·00
563 15c. Giraffe 15 20
564 17c. Common zebra 15 10
565 21c. Odzani Falls 15 40
566 25c. Goba Falls 15 15
567 30c. Inyangombi Falls . . . 15 15
568 $1 Bridal Veil Falls 20 35
569 $2 Victoria Falls 30 60

Nos. 560/4 are 26 × 23 mm, and Nos. 565/9 32 × 27 mm.

112 Wright Flyer I

1978. 75th Anniv of Powered Flight. Mult.
570 4c. Type **112** 10 10
571 5c. Bleriot XI 10 10
572 7c. Vickers Vimy "Silver Queen II" 10 10
573 9c. Armstrong Whitworth A.W.15 Atalanta 10 10
574 17c. Vickers Viking 1B "Zambezi" 10 10
575 25c. Boeing 720B 15 50

POSTAGE DUE STAMPS

D 2

D 3 Zimbabwe Bird (soapstone sculpture)

1965. Roul.
D 8 **D 2** 1d. red . . . . 50 12·00
D 9 2d. blue . . . . 40 8·00
D10 4d. green . . . . 50 8·00
D11 6d. plum . . . . 50 6·00

1966.
D12 **D 3** 1d. red . . . . 60 3·00
D13 2d. blue . . . . 75 1·50
D14 4d. green . . . . 75 3·75
D15 6d. violet . . . . 75 1·50
D16 1s. brown . . . . 75 1·50
D17 2s. black . . . . 1·00 4·50

1970. Decimal Currency. As Type D 3 but larger (26 × 22½ mm).
D18 **D 3** 1c. green . . . . 75 1·75
D19 2c. blue 75 60
D20 5c. violet . . . . 1·75 2·75
D21 6c. yellow . . . . 3·50 4·00
D22 10c. red . . . . 1·75 4·00

RHODESIA AND NYASALAND
Pt. 1

Stamps for the Central African Federation of Northern and Southern Rhodesia and Nyasaland Protectorate. The stamps of the Federation were withdrawn on 19 February 1964 when all three constituent territories had resumed issuing their own stamps.

12 pence = 1 shilling;
20 shillings = 1 pound.

1 Queen Elizabeth II

2 Queen Elizabeth II

1954.
1 **1** ½d. red 15 10
2 1d. blue 15 10
3 2d. green 15 10
3a 2½d. ochre . . . . 4·00 10
4 3d. red 20 10
5 4d. brown 60 15
6 4½d. green 30 60
7 6d. purple . . . . 2·25 10
8 9d. violet . . . . 2·00 70
9 1s. grey . . . . 2·00 10
10 **2** 1s.3d. red and blue . . . . 3·00 20
11 2s. blue and brown . . . . 7·50 2·25
12 2s.6d. black and red . . . . 6·00 1·50
13 5s. violet and olive . . . . 17·00 5·00
14 – 10s. turquoise and orange . . . 19·00 7·00
15 – £1 olive and lake . . . . . 30·00 25·00

The 10s. and £1 are as Type **2** but larger (31 × 17 mm) and have the name at top and foliage on either side of portrait.

4 De Havilland Comet 1 over Victoria Falls

5 Livingstone and Victoria Falls

1955. Cent of Discovery of Victoria Falls.
16 **4** 3d. blue and turquoise . . . 55 30
17 **5** 1s. purple and blue 55 70

6 Tea Picking

11 Lake Bangweulu

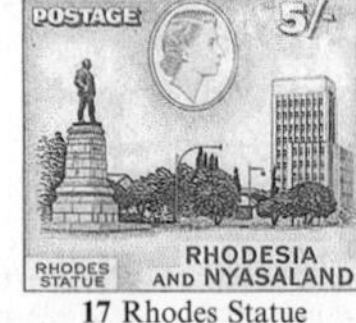

17 Rhodes Statue

1959.
18 **6** ½d. black and green . . . 60 60
19 – 1d. red and black 15 10
20 – 2d. violet and brown . . . 1·75 50
21 – 2½d. purple and blue . . . 1·25 50
22 – 3d. black and blue 30 10
23 **11** 4d. purple and green . . . 1·25 10
24 – 6d. blue and green . . . . 1·25 10
24a – 9d. brown and violet . . . 8·00 2·50
25 – 1s. green and blue . . . . 1·00 10
26 – 1s.3d. green and brown . . 3·00 10
27 – 2s. green and red . . . . . 3·25 60
28 – 2s.6d. blue and brown . . 4·25 30
29 **17** 5s. brown and green . . . 9·00 2·25
30 – 10s. brown and red . . . . 25·00 16·00
31 – £1 black and violet . . . . 45·00 48·00

DESIGNS—VERT (as Type **6**): 1d. V.H.F. mast; 2d. Copper mining; 2½d. Fairbridge Memorial. (As Type **11**): 6d. Eastern Cataract, Victoria Falls. HORIZ (as Type **6**): 3d. Rhodes's grave. (As Type **11**): 9d. Rhodesian railway trains; 1s. Tobacco; 1s.3d. Lake Nyasa; 2s. Chirundu Bridge; 2s.6d. Salisbury Airport. (As Type **17**): 10s. Mlanje; £1 Federal Coat of Arms.

20 Kariba Gorge, 1955

1960. Opening of Kariba Hydro-electric Scheme.
32 **20** 3d. green and orange . . . 70 10
33 – 6d. brown and bistre . . . 70 20
34 – 1s. blue and green . . . . . 2·50 3·75
35 – 1s.3d. blue and brown . . . 2·50 2·50
36 – 2s.6d. purple and red . . . 3·50 7·50
37 – 5s. violet and turquoise . . 8·00 11·00

DESIGNS: 6d. 330 k.V. power lines; 1s. Barrage wall; 1s.3d. Barrage and lake; 2s.6d. Interior of power station; 5s. Queen Mother and barrage wall (inscr "ROYAL OPENING").

26 Miner drilling

1961. 7th Commonwealth Mining and Metallurgical Congress.
38 **26** 6d. green and brown 50 20
39 – 1s.3d. black and blue . . . 50 80

DESIGN: 1s.3d. Surface installations, Nchanga Mine.

28 De Havilland Hercules "City of Basra" on Rhodesian Airstrip

1962. 30th Anniv of 1st London–Rhodesian Airmail Service.
40 **28** 6d. green and red 35 25
41 – 1s.3d. blue, black and yellow 1·50 50
42 – 2s.6d. red and violet . . . . 4·00 4·75

DESIGNS: 1s.3d. Short S.23 flying boat "Canopus" taking off from Zambesi; 2s.6d. Hawker Siddeley Comet 4 at Salisbury Airport.

31 Tobacco Plant

1963. World Tobacco Congress, Salisbury.
43 **31** 3d. green and olive 30 10
44 – 6d. green, brown and blue . . 40 35
45 – 1s.3d. brown and blue . . . 60 45
46 – 2s.6d. yellow and brown . . 1·00 2·75

DESIGNS: 6d. Tobacco field; 1s.3d. Auction floor; 2s.6d. Cured tobacco.

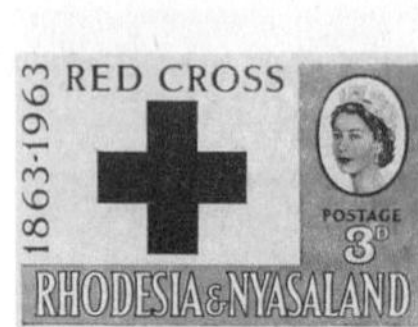

35

1963. Centenary of Red Cross.
47 **35** 3d. red 85 10

36 African "Round Table" Emblem

1963. World Council of Young Men's Service Clubs, Salisbury.
48 **36** 6d. black, gold and green 50 1·50
49 1s.3d. multicoloured . . . . 50 1·00

POSTAGE DUE STAMPS

D 1

1961.
D1 **D 1** 1d. red . . . . 3·50 5·50
D2 2d. blue . . . . 2·75 3·00
D3 4d. green . . . . 2·75 9·50
D4 6d. purple . . . . 4·50 7·50

RIAU-LINGGA ARCHIPELAGO
Pt. 21

A group of islands E of Sumatra and S of Singapore. Part of Indonesia.

100 cents or sen = 1 rupiah.

1954. Optd **RIAU**. (a) On stamps of Indonesia.
1 **96** 5s. red . . . . 70·00 34·00
2 7½s. green . . . . 1·40 1·60
3 10s. blue . . . . 75·00 75·00
4 15s. violet . . . . 3·50 2·75
5 20s. red . . . . 3·50 2·75
6 25s. green . . . . £110 44·00
7 **97** 30s. red . . . . 6·75 5·25
8 35s. violet . . . . 1·40 1·60
9 40s. green . . . . 1·40 1·60
10 45s. purple . . . . 1·40 1·60
11 50s. brown . . . . £550 60·00
12 **98** 60s. brown . . . . 1·40 2·40
13 **98** 70s. grey . . . . 3·50 2·40
14 75s. blue . . . . 12·00 3·50
15 80s. purple . . . . 2·40 3·75
16 90s. green . . . . 2·40 3·50

(b) On Netherlands Indies Nos. 566/71.
17 – 1r. violet . . . . 15·00 5·25
18 – 2r. green . . . . 3·50 6·00
19 – 3r. purple . . . . 5·25 6·00
20 – 5r. brown . . . . 5·25 6·00
21 – 10r. black . . . . 6·75 10·50
22 – 25r. brown . . . . 6·75 10·50

1958. Stamps of Indonesia optd **RIAU**.
26 **115** 5s. blue 95 95
27 10s. brown (No. 714) . . . 95 95
28 15s. purple (No. 715) . . . 95 95
29 – 20s. green (No. 716) . . . 95 95
30 – 25s. brown (No. 717) . . . 95 95
31 – 30s. orange (No. 718) . . . 95 95
32 – 50s. brown (No. 722) . . . 95 95

1960. Stamps of Indonesia optd **RIAU**.
33 **99** 1r.25 orange . . . . 4·50 6·75
34 1r.50 brown . . . . 4·50 6·75
35 2r.50 brown . . . . 6·75 10·50
36 4r. green . . . . 1·20 6·00
37 6r. mauve . . . . 1·20 6·00
38 15r. stone . . . . 1·20 6·00
39 20r. purple . . . . 1·20 13·50
40 40r. green . . . . 1·20 8·75
41 50r. violet . . . . 2·40 9·25

RIO DE ORO Pt. 9

A Spanish territory on the West Coast of North Africa, renamed Spanish Sahara in 1924.

100 centimos = 1 peseta.

1905. "Curly Head" key-type inscr "COLONIA DE RIO DE ORO".

1 Z 1c. green 3·75 3·00
2 2c. red 3·75 3·00
3 3c. black 3·75 3·00
4 4c. brown 3·75 3·00
5 5c. red 3·75 3·00
6 10c. brown 3·75 3·00
7 15c. brown 3·75 3·00
8 25c. blue 70·00 31·00
9 50c. green 36·00 13·00
10 75c. violet 36·00 18·00
11 1p. brown 85·00 7·75
12 2p. orange £110 48·00
13 3p. lilac 50·00 18·00
14 4p. green 50·00 18·00
15 5p. blue 70·00 37·00
16 10p. red £180 £120

1906. "Curly Head" key-type surch **HABILITADO PARA 15 CENTS** in circle.

17 Z 15c. on 25c. blue £200 70·00

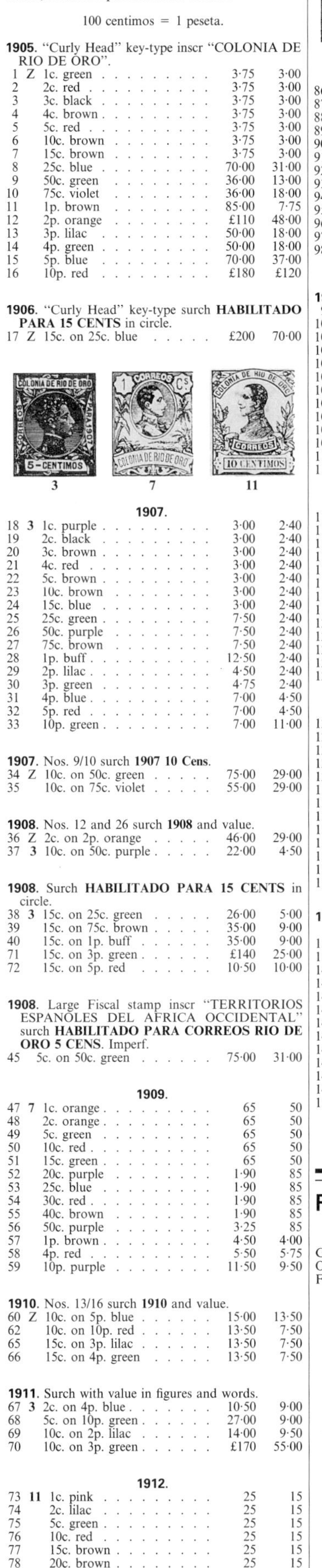

3 7 11

1907.

18 3 1c. purple 3·00 2·40
19 2c. black 3·00 2·40
20 3c. brown 3·00 2·40
21 4c. red 3·00 2·40
22 5c. brown 3·00 2·40
23 10c. brown 3·00 2·40
24 15c. blue 3·00 2·40
25 25c. green 7·50 2·40
26 50c. purple 7·50 2·40
27 75c. brown 7·50 2·40
28 1p. buff 12·50 2·40
29 2p. lilac 4·50 2·40
30 3p. green 4·75 2·40
31 4p. blue 7·00 4·50
32 5p. red 7·00 4·50
33 10p. green 7·00 11·00

1907. Nos. 9/10 surch **1907 10 Cens.**

34 Z 10c. on 50c. green 75·00 29·00
35 10c. on 75c. violet 55·00 29·00

1908. Nos. 12 and 26 surch **1908** and value.

36 Z 2c. on 2p. orange 46·00 29·00
37 3 10c. on 50c. purple 22·00 4·50

1908. Surch **HABILITADO PARA 15 CENTS** in circle.

38 3 15c. on 25c. green 26·00 5·00
39 15c. on 75c. brown 35·00 9·00
40 15c. on 1p. buff 35·00 9·00
71 15c. on 3p. green £140 25·00
72 15c. on 5p. red 10·50 10·00

1908. Large Fiscal stamp inscr "TERRITORIOS ESPAÑOLES DEL AFRICA OCCIDENTAL" surch **HABILITADO PARA CORREOS RIO DE ORO 5 CENS.** Imperf.

45 5c. on 50c. green 75·00 31·00

1909.

47 7 1c. orange 65 50
48 2c. orange 65 50
49 5c. green 65 50
50 10c. red 65 50
51 15c. green 65 50
52 20c. purple 1·90 85
53 25c. blue 1·90 85
54 30c. red 1·90 85
55 40c. brown 1·90 85
56 50c. purple 3·25 85
57 1p. brown 4·50 4·00
58 4p. red 5·50 5·75
59 10p. purple 11·50 9·50

1910. Nos. 13/16 surch **1910** and value.

60 Z 10c. on 5p. blue 15·00 13·50
62 10c. on 10p. red 13·50 7·50
65 15c. on 3p. lilac 13·50 7·50
66 15c. on 4p. green 13·50 7·50

1911. Surch with value in figures and words.

67 3 2c. on 4p. blue 10·50 9·00
68 5c. on 10p. green 27·00 9·00
69 10c. on 2p. lilac 14·00 9·50
70 10c. on 3p. green £170 55·00

1912.

73 11 1c. pink 25 15
74 2c. lilac 25 15
75 5c. green 25 15
76 10c. red 25 15
77 15c. brown 25 15
78 20c. brown 25 15
79 25c. blue 25 15
80 30c. lilac 25 15
81 40c. green 25 15
82 50c. purple 25 15
83 1p. red 2·50 65
84 4p. red 5·50 3·25
85 10p. brown 8·50 5·50

12 14 15

1914.

86 12 1c. brown 30 15
87 2c. purple 30 15
88 5c. green 30 15
89 10c. red 30 15
90 15c. red 30 15
91 20c. red 30 15
92 25c. blue 30 15
93 30c. green 30 15
94 40c. orange 30 15
95 50c. brown 30 15
96 1p. lilac 2·50 3·00
97 4p. red 7·00 3·00
98 10p. violet 8·75 8·75

1917. Nos. 73/85 optd **1917.**

99 11 1c. pink 11·00 1·30
100 2c. lilac 11·00 1·30
101 5c. green 2·50 1·30
102 10c. red 2·50 1·30
103 15c. brown 2·50 1·30
104 20c. brown 2·50 1·30
105 25c. blue 2·50 1·30
106 30c. lilac 2·50 1·30
107 40c. green 2·50 1·30
108 50c. purple 2·50 1·30
109 1p. red 14·00 6·25
110 4p. red 19·00 8·00
111 10p. brown 33·00 14·00

1919.

112 14 1c. brown 80 45
113 2c. purple 80 45
114 5c. green 80 45
115 10c. red 80 45
116 15c. red 80 45
117 20c. orange 80 45
118 25c. blue 80 45
119 30c. green 80 45
120 40c. orange 80 45
121 50c. brown 80 45
122 1p. lilac 5·50 3·75
123 4p. red 9·50 7·00
124 10p. violet 14·00 10·50

1920.

125 15 1c. purple 70 45
126 2c. pink 70 45
127 5c. red 70 45
128 10c. purple 70 45
129 15c. brown 70 45
130 20c. green 70 45
131 25c. orange 70 45
132 30c. blue 4·50 4·50
133 40c. orange 2·50 1·70
134 50c. purple 2·50 1·70
135 1p. green 2·50 1·70
136 4p. red 4·75 4·00
137 10p. brown 11·50 10·50

1921. As Nos. 14/26 of La Aguera but inscr "RIO DE ORO".

138 1c. yellow 70 45
139 2c. brown 70 45
140 5c. green 70 45
141 10c. red 70 45
142 15c. green 70 45
143 20c. blue 70 45
144 25c. blue 70 45
145 30c. pink 1·30 1·30
146 40c. violet 1·30 1·30
147 50c. orange 1·30 1·30
148 1p. mauve 4·50 2·20
149 4p. purple 7·00 5·00
150 10p. brown 12·00 11·50

For later issues see **SPANISH SAHARA**.

RIO MUNI Pt. 9

A coastal settlement between Cameroun and Gabon, formerly using the stamps of Spanish Guinea. On 12 October 1968 it became independent and joined Fernando Poo to become Equatorial Guinea.

100 centimos = 1 peseta.

1 Native Boy reading Book

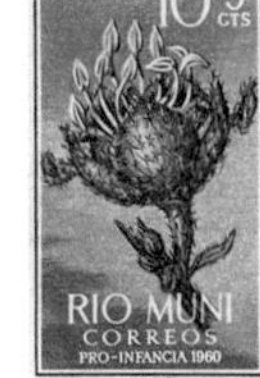

2 Cactus

1960.

1 1 25c. grey 15 15
2 50c. brown 15 15
3 75c. purple 15 15
4 1p. red 15 15
5 1p.50 green 15 15
6 2p. purple 15 15
7 3p. blue 30 15
8 5p. brown 80 20
9 10p. green 1·20 30

1960. Child Welfare Fund.

10 2 10c.+5c. purple 20 20
11 – 15c.+5c. brown 20 20
12 – 35c. green 20 20
13 2 80c. green 20 20

DESIGNS: 15c. Sprig with berries; 35c. Star-shaped flowers.

3 Bishop Juan de Ribera

4 Mandrill with Banana

1960. Stamp Day.

14 3 10c.+5c. red 20 20
15 – 20c.+5c. green 20 20
16 – 30c.+10c. brown 20 20
17 3 50c.+20c. brown 20 20

DESIGNS: 20c. Portrait of man (after Velazquez); 30c. Statue.

1961. Child Welfare. Inscr "PRO-INFANCIA 1961".

18 4 10c.+5c. red 20 20
19 – 25c.+10c. violet 20 20
20 4 80c.+20c. green 20 20

DESIGN—VERT: 25c. African elephant.

5

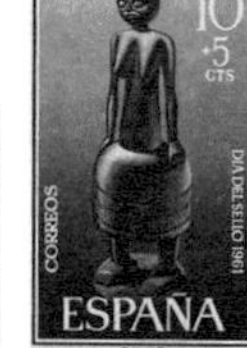

6 Statuette

1961. 25th Anniv of Gen. Franco as Head of State.

21 – 25c. grey 20 20
22 5 50c. brown 20 20
23 – 70c. green 20 20
24 5 1p. red 20 20

DESIGNS: 25c. Map; 70c. Government building.

1961. Stamp Day. Inscr "DIA DEL SELLO 1961".

25 6 10c.+5c. red 20 20
26 – 25c.+10c. purple 20 20
27 6 30c.+10c. brown 20 20
28 – 1p.+10c. orange 20 20

DESIGN: 25c., 1p. Figure holding offering.

7 Girl wearing Headdress

8 African Buffalo

1962. Child Welfare. Inscr "PRO-INFANCIA 1962".

29 7 25c. violet 20 20
30 – 50c. green 20 20
31 7 1p. brown 20 20

DESIGN: 50c. Native mask.

1962. Stamp Day. Inscr "DIA DEL SELLO 1962".

32 8 15c. green 20 20
33 – 35c. purple 20 20
34 8 1p. red 20 20

DESIGN—VERT: 35c. Gorilla.

9 Statuette

10 "Blessing"

1963. Seville Flood Relief.

35 9 50c. green 20 20
36 1p. brown 20 20

1963. Child Welfare. Inscr "PRO-INFANCIA 1963".

37 – 25c. violet 20 20
38 10 50c. green 20 20
39 – 1p. red 20 20

DESIGN: 25c., 1p. Priest.

11 Child at Prayer

12 Copal Flower

1963. "For Barcelona".

40 11 50c. green 20 20
41 1p. brown 20 20

1964. Stamp Day. Inscr "DIA DEL SELLO 1963".

42 12 25c. violet 20 20
43 – 50c. turquoise 20 20
44 12 1p. red 20 20

FLOWER—HORIZ: 50c. Cinchona blossom.

13 Giant Ground Pangolin

1964. Child Welfare. Inscr "PRO-INFANCIA 1964".

45 13 25c. violet 20 20
46 – 50c. green (Chameleon) 20 20
47 13 1p. brown 20 20

1964. Wild Life. As T 13 but without "PRO INFANCIA" inscription.

48 15c. brown 15 15
49 25c. violet 15 15
50 50c. green 15 15
51 70c. green 15 15
52 1p. brown 55 15
53 1p.50 green 55 15
54 3p. blue 1·20 20
55 5p. brown 3·00 35
56 10p. green 5·50 90

ANIMALS: 15, 70c., 3p. Crocodile; 25c., 1, 5p. Leopard; 50c., 1p.50, 10p. Black rhinoceros.

14 "Goliath" Frog

15 Woman

1964. Stamp Day.

57 14 50c. green 20 20
58 – 1p. red 20 20
59 14 1p.50 green 20 20

DESIGN—VERT: 1p. Helmeted guineafowl.

1965. 25th Anniv of End of Spanish Civil War.

60 15 50c. green 20 20
61 – 1p. red 20 20
62 – 1p.50 turquoise 20 20

DESIGNS: 1p. Nurse; 1p.50, Logging.

16 Goliath Beetle

1965. Child Welfare. Insects.

63 16 50c. green 20 20
64 – 1p. brown 20 20
65 16 1p.50 black 20 20

DESIGN: 1p. "Acridoxena hewaniana".

17 Leopard and Arms of Rio Muni

1965. Stamp Day.

66 – 50c. grey 20 20
67 17 1p. brown 25 25
68 – 2p.50 violet 1·70 1·00

DESIGN—VERT: 50c., 2p.50, Common pheasant.

18 African Elephant and Grey Parrot

1966. Child Welfare.
69 **18** 50c. brown 20 20
70 1p. lilac 20 20
71 – 1p.50 blue 20 20
DESIGN: 1p.50, African and lion.

19 Water Chevrotain

20 Floss Flowers

1966. Stamp Day.
72 **19** 10c. brown and ochre . . . 20 20
73 – 40c. brown and yellow . . . 20 20
74 **19** 1p.50 violet and red 20 20
75 – 4p. blue and green 20 20
DESIGN—VERT: 40c., 4p. Giant ground pangolin.

1967. Child Welfare.
76 **20** 10c. yellow, olive and green 20 20
77 – 40c. green, black and mauve 20 20
78 **20** 1p.50 red and blue 20 20
79 – 4p. black and green 20 20
DESIGNS: 40c., 4p. Ylang-ylang (flower).

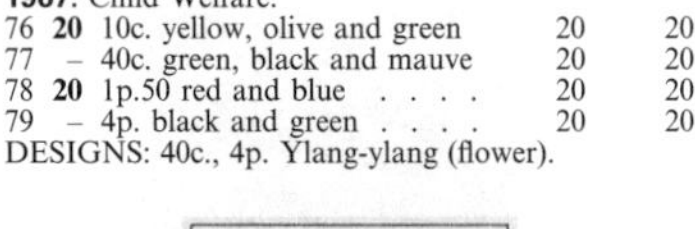

21 Bush Pig

1967. Stamp Day.
80 **21** 1p. chestnut and brown . . 20 20
81 – 1p.50 brown and green . . . 20 20
82 – 3p.50 brown and green . . . 35 35
DESIGNS—VERT: 1p.50, Potto. HORIZ: 3p.50, African golden cat.

1968. Child Welfare. Signs of the Zodiac. As T **56a** of Spanish Sahara.
83 1p. mauve on yellow 20 20
84 1p.50 brown on pink 20 20
85 2p.50 violet on yellow 35 35
DESIGNS: 1p. Cancer (crab); 1p.50, Taurus (bull); 2p.50, Gemini (twins).

ROMAGNA Pt. 8

One of the Papal states, now part of Italy. Stamps issued prior to union with Sardinia in 1860.

100 bajocchi = 1 scudo.

1

1859. Imperf.
2 **1** ½b. black on buff . . . . . 18·00 £225
3 1b. black on grey . . . . . 18·00 £110
4 2b. black on buff . . . . . 32·00 £120
5 3b. black on green . . . . . 37·00 £250
6 4b. black on brown £500 £120
7 5b. black on lilac . . . . . 46·00 £300
8 6b. black on green £250 £6000
9 8b. black on pink £180 £1400
10 20b. black on green £180 £2000

ROMANIA Pt. 3

A republic in S.E. Europe bordering on the Black Sea, originally a kingdom formed by the union of Moldavia and Wallachia.

1858. 40 parale = 1 piastre.
1867. 100 bani = 1 leu.

MOLDAVIA

1

2

1858. Imperf.
1 **1** 27p. black on red £19000 £6000
2 54p. blue on green £8500 £2500
3 81p. blue on blue £19000 £21000
4 108p. blue on pink £11000 £6000

1858. Imperf.
12 **2** 5p. black £140
13 40p. blue £140 £150
14 80p. red £425 £225

ROMANIA

4

1862. Imperf.
29 **4** 3p. yellow . . . . 45·00 £140
30 6p. red . . . . 32·00 £110
31 30p. blue . . . . 37·00 40·00

5 Prince Alexander Cuza

6 Prince Carol

7 Prince Carol

1865. Imperf.
49a **5** 2p. orange . . . . 25·00 £160
46 5p. blue . . . . 25·00 £150
48 20p. red . . . . 19·00 24·00

1866. Imperf.
60 **6** 2p. black on yellow . . . . 15·00 50·00
61 5p. black on blue . . . . . 30·00 £300
62 20p. black on red . . . . . 12·50 11·00

1868. Imperf.
71 **7** 2b. orange . . . . 24·00 17·00
72 3b. mauve . . . . 30·00 20·00
66c 4b. blue . . . . 35·00 24·00
67 18b. red . . . . £140 16·00

8

9

10

1869. Without beard. Imperf.
74 **8** 5b. orange . . . . 55·00 23·00
75 10b. blue . . . . 27·00 19·00
76 15b. red . . . . 27·00 17·00
77c 25b. blue and orange . . . 27·00 17·00
78 50b. red and blue . . . . . £120 25·00

1871. With beard. Imperf.
83 **9** 5b. red . . . . 27·00 18·00
84 10b. orange . . . . 37·00 20·00
99 10b. blue . . . . 35·00 25·00
86 15b. red . . . . £110 95·00
87 25b. brown . . . . 33·00 27·00
100 50b. red and blue £140 £160

1872. Perf.
93 **9** 5b. red . . . . 55·00 25·00
94 10b. blue . . . . 55·00 20·00
95 25b. brown . . . . 26·00 25·00

1872. Perf.
112 **10** 1½b. green . . . . 5·25 1·70
124 1½b. black . . . . 4·00 90
105 3b. green . . . . 21·00 2·20
125 3b. olive . . . . 9·50 5·00
106 5b. bistre . . . . 11·50 2·10
126 5b. green . . . . 3·25 1·00
107 10b. blue . . . . 10·00 2·40
127c 10b. red . . . . 8·50 1·00
115 15b. brown . . . . 45·00 5·00
128a 15b. red . . . . 30·00 7·00
110 25b. orange . . . . 70·00 9·00
130 25b. blue . . . . 95·00 8·75
116 30b. red . . . . £130 32·00
111 50b. red . . . . 65·00 24·00
131 50b. bistre . . . . 75·00 9·25

11 King Carol

12 King Carol

14 King Carol

1880.
146a **11** 15b. brown . . . . 9·50 95
147 25b. blue . . . . 12·50 1·20

1885. On white or coloured papers.
161 **12** 1½b. black . . . . 2·10 90
163 3b. green . . . . 3·00 90
165a 3b. violet . . . . 3·00 90
166 5b. green . . . . 3·00 90
168 10b. red . . . . 3·00 1·10
169 15b. brown . . . . 10·50 1·30
171 25b. blue . . . . 10·50 2·10
186 50b. brown . . . . 42·00 11·00

1890.
271 **14** 1½b. lake . . . . 1·10 45
272a 3b. mauve . . . . 1·20 80
273 5b. green . . . . 1·50 60
274 10b. red . . . . 7·25 65
255 15b. brown . . . . 11·50 1·90
306 25b. blue . . . . 7·50 3·50
307 50b. orange . . . . 19·00 9·25

15

17

19

1891. 25th Anniv of Reign.
300 **15** 1½b. lake . . . . 2·50 3·25
293 3b. mauve . . . . 2·50 3·25
294 5b. green . . . . 4·25 4·75
295 10b. red . . . . 4·25 4·75
303 15b. brown . . . . 4·25 4·00

1893. Various frames as T **17** and **19**.
316 1 BANI brown 80 60
426 1 BAN brown . . . . 1·10 55
317 1½b. black . . . . 1·10 40
533 3b. brown 85 30
319 5b. blue . . . . 1·10 60
534 5b. green . . . . 1·50 30
320 10b. green . . . . 1·50 60
535 10b. red . . . . 1·70 45
332 15b. pink . . . . 2·50 35
400 15b. black . . . . 1·60 50
430 15b. brown . . . . 1·60 45
545 15b. violet . . . . 2·10 50
322 25b. mauve . . . . 4·00 70
701 25b. blue 50 30
421 40b. green . . . . 9·00 85
324 50b. orange . . . . 10·50 90
325 1l. pink and brown . . . . 19·00 1·20
326 2l. brown and orange . . . . 19·00 2·00
See also Nos. 532 etc.

25 Four-in-hand Postal Coach

26 New Post Office, Bucharest

1903. Opening of New Post Office in 1901.
464 **25** 1b. brown . . . . 1·30 60
465 3b. red . . . . 2·10 95
466 5b. green . . . . 3·50 1·20
467 10b. red . . . . 3·75 1·60
468 15b. black . . . . 3·75 1·30
472 **26** 15b. black . . . . 2·40 2·00
469 **25** 25b. blue . . . . 11·00 7·00
473 **26** 25b. blue . . . . 6·25 3·50
470 **25** 40b. green . . . . 16·00 7·25
474 **26** 40b. green . . . . 8·75 5·00
471 **25** 50b. orange . . . . 21·00 9·25
475 **26** 50b. orange . . . . 8·75 5·00
476 1l. brown . . . . 8·75 5·00
477 2l. red . . . . 70·00 45·00
478 5l. lilac . . . . 90·00 50·00
See also No. 1275.

1905. Various frames as T **17** and **19**.
532 1 ban black 25 25
625b 1½b. yellow . . . . 1·40 1·10
703 40b. brown 90 55
705 50b. pink . . . . 1·00 60
432 1l. black and green . . . . 21·00 1·70
706 1l. green . . . . 1·50 40
433 2l. black and brown . . . . 16·00 2·10
707 2l. orange . . . . 2·30 60

27 Queen of Romania spinning

28 Queen of Romania weaving

1906. Welfare Fund. Motto: "God guide our Hand".
481 **27** 3b.(+7) brown . . . . . . 2·50 2·50
482 5b.(+10) green . . . . . . 2·50 2·50
483 10b.(+10) red . . . . . . 9·50 7·75
484 15b.(+10) purple . . . . . 9·00 4·50

1906. Welfare Fund. Motto: "Woman weaves the Future of the Country".
485 **28** 3b.(+7) brown . . . . . . 2·20 2·30
486 5b.(+10) green . . . . . . 2·20 2·30
487 10b.(+10) red . . . . . . 12·00 8·25
488 15b.(+10) lilac . . . . . . 7·75 4·25

29 Queen of Romania nursing wounded Soldier

30

1906. Welfare Fund. Motto: "The Wounds dressed and the Tears wiped away".
489 **29** 3b.(+7) brown . . . . . . 2·20 2·30
490 5b.(+10) green . . . . . . 2·20 2·30
491 10b.(+10) red . . . . . . 12·00 9·00
492 15b.(+10) purple . . . . . 7·75 5·75

1906. 25th Anniv of Kingdom.
493 **30** 1b. black and bistre . . . 30 30
494 3b. black and brown . . . 1·10 40
495 5b. black and green . . . 70 35
496 10b. black and red 70 35
497 15b. black and violet . . . 75 35
498 25b. black and blue . . . 9·00 4·75
499 40b. black and brown . . . 2·10 95
500 50b. black and brown . . . 2·10 95
501 1l. black and red . . . . . 2·10 95
502 2l. black and orange . . . 2·10 95

31 Prince Carol at Battle of Calafat

32

1906. 40 Years' Rule of Prince and King. Dated "1906".
503 – 1b. black and bistre . . . 15 25
504 – 3b. black and brown . . . 30 25
505 **31** 5b. black and green . . . 65 25
506 – 10b. black and red . . . 30 45
507 – 15b. black and violet . . 30 45
508 – 25b. black and blue . . . 3·50 2·50
508a – 25b. black and green . . 4·50 5·50
509 – 40b. black and brown . . 50 65
510 – 50b. black and brown . . 60 65
511 – 1l. black and red 90 90
512 – 2l. black and orange . . . 1·20 1·30
DESIGNS—HORIZ: 1b. Prince Carol taking oath of allegiance in 1866; 3b. Prince in carriage; 10b. Meeting of Prince and Osman Pasha, 1878; 15b. Carol when Prince in 1866 and King in 1906; 25b. Romanian Army crossing Danube, 1877; 40b. Triumphal entry into Bucharest, 1878; 50b. Prince at head of Army in 1877; 1l. King Carol at Cathedral in 1896; 2l. King at shrine of S. Nicholas, 1904.

1906. Welfare Fund. Motto: "But Glory, Honour and Peace to All that do Good".
513 **32** 3b.(+7) brown, bistre and blue . . . . 1·40 1·30
514 5b.(+10) green, red and bistre . . . . 1·40 1·30
515 10b.(+10) red, bistre and blue . . . . 2·75 2·50
516 15b.(+10) violet, bistre and blue . . . . 8·50 4·00

33 Peasant ploughing and Angel

1906. Jubilee Exhibition, Bucharest.
517 **33** 5b. black and green . . . 2·75 85
518 10b. black and red . . . . 2·75 85
519 – 15b. black and violet . . . 4·00 1·40
520 – 25b. black and blue . . . 4·00 1·40
521 – 30b. brown and red . . . 4·75 1·40
522 40b. brown and green . . . 6·25 1·70
523 – 50b. black and orange . . 5·50 2·00
524 – 75b. sepia and brown . . . 5·50 2·00
525 – 1l.50 brown and mauve . . 50·00 25·00
526 – 2l.50 brown and yellow . . 21·00 14·50
527 – 3l. brown and orange . . . 16·00 14·00
DESIGNS—HORIZ: 15, 25b. Exhibition Building. VERT: 30, 40b. Farmhouse; 50, 75b. (different), Royal Family pavilion; 1l.50, 2l.50, King Carol on horseback; 3l. Queen Elizabeth (Carmen Sylva).

34 Princess Maria and her Children receiving Poor Family conducted by an Angel

1907. Welfare Fund.
528 **34** 3b.(+7) brown . . . . . . 4·75 2·75
529 5b.(+10) brown and green 2·75 1·40

530		10b.(+10) brown and red	2·30	1·40
531		15b.(+10) brown and blue	1·70	1·50

35 37

1908.

575	35	5b. green	1·40	30
562		10b. red	35	10
577		15b. violet	7·75	2·10
564		25b. blue	90	15
579		40b. green	55	15
702		40b. brown	3·50	1·60
566		50b. orange	55	15
705		50b. red	75	45
581		1l. brown	1·60	30
582		2l. red	7·75	2·40

1908.

583	37	1b. black	25	10
590		3b. brown	70	15
585		5b. green	25	15
592		10b. red	45	15
599		15b. violet	11·50	8·50
594		15b. olive	60	15
692		15b. brown	65	40

38 39 Troops crossing Danube

1913. Acquisition of Southern Dobruja.

626	–	1b. black	50	30
627	38	3b. brown and grey	1·50	60
628	39	5b. black and green	1·20	20
629	–	10b. black and orange	85	20
630	–	15b. violet and brown	1·10	55
631	–	25b. brown and blue	1·50	85
632	39	40b. red and brown	3·00	1·30
633	38	50b. blue and yellow	3·75	3·00
634		1l. brown and blue	9·00	7·75
635		2l. red and red	12·00	10·50

DESIGNS—VERT (As Type **38**): 1b. "Dobruja" holding flag. HORIZ (As Type **39**): 10b. Town of Constanza; 25b. Church and School in Dobruja. (24 × 16 mm): 15b. Mircea the Great and King Carol.

1918. Surch **25. BANI**.

657	37	25b. on 1b. black	80	80

1918. Optd **1918**.

662	37	5b. green	50	30
663		10b. red	50	35

TRANSYLVANIA

The Eastern portion of Hungary. Union with Romania proclaimed in December 1918 and the final frontiers settled by the Treaty of Trianon on 4 June 1920.

The following issues for Transylvania (Nos. 747/858) were valid throughout Romania.

BANI (42) Bani (43)

(The "F" stands for King Ferdinand and "P.T.T." for Posts Telegraphs and Telephones).

The values "BANI", "LEU" or "LEI" appear above or below the monogram.

A. Issues for Cluj (Kolozsvar or Klausenburg).

1919. Various stamps of Hungary optd as T **42**.

(a) Flood Relief Charity stamps of 1913.

747	7	1l. on 1f. grey	20·00	18·00
748		1l. on 2f. yellow	£100	80·00
749		1l. on 3f. orange	48·00	42·00
750		1l. on 5f. green	2·10	1·60
751		1l. on 10f. red	2·10	1·60
752		1l. on 12f. lilac on yellow	7·75	5·75
753		1l. on 16f. green	4·25	3·00
754		1l. on 25f. blue	48·00	42·00
755		1l. on 35f. purple	4·25	3·00
756	8	1l. on 1k. red	55·00	50·00

(b) War Charity stamps of 1916.

757	20	10(+2) b. red	30	20
758	–	15(+2) b. violet	30	20
759	22	40(+2) b. lake	40	30

(c) Harvesters and Parliament Types.

760	18	2b. brown	15	20
761		3b. red	30	20
762		5b. green	30	20
763		6b. blue	30	20
764		10b. red	£140	£100
765		15b. violet (No. 244)	5·00	3·75
766		15b. violet	15	10
767		25b. blue	15	10
768		35b. brown	15	10
769		40b. olive	15	10
770	19	50b. purple	30	20
771		75b. blue	40	30
772		80b. green	40	30
773		1l. lake	40	30
774		2l. brown	55	40
775		3l. grey and violet	3·50	2·50
776		5l. brown	2·75	2·10
777		10l. lilac and brown	3·50	2·50

(d) Charles and Zita stamps.

778	27	10b. red	28·00	21·00
779		15b. violet	10·50	7·75
780		20b. brown	15	10
781		25b. blue	70	50
782	28	40b. green	30	20

B. Issues for Oradea (Nagyvarad or Grosswardein).

1919. Various stamps of Hungary optd as T **43**. (a) "Turul" Type.

794	7	2b. yellow	5·50	4·25
795		3b. orange	9·75	7·25
796		6b. drab	70	50
797		16b. green	17·00	12·50
798		50b. lake on blue	95	75
799		70b. brown and green	18·00	16·00

(b) Flood Relief Charity stamps of 1913.

800	7	1l. on 1f. grey	95	75
801		1l. on 2f. yellow	4·25	3·00
802		1l. on 3f. orange	1·40	1·00
803		1l. on 5f. green	30	20
804		1l. on 6f. drab	95	75
805		1l. on 10f. red	30	20
806		1l. on 12f. lilac on yellow	49·00	45·00
807		1l. on 16f. green	1·40	1·00
808		1l. on 20f. brown	6·25	4·75
809		1l. on 25f. blue	4·25	3·00
810		1l. on 35f. purple	4·25	3·00

(c) War Charity stamp of 1915.

811	7	5+2b. green (No. 173)	7·50	7·75

(d) War Charity stamps of 1916.

812	20	10(+2) b. red	30	20
813	–	15(+2) b. violet	15	10
814	22	40(+2) b. lake	40	30

(e) Harvesters and Parliament Types.

815	18	2b. brown	15	10
816		3b. red	15	10
817		5b. green	30	20
818		6b. blue	85	60
819		10b. red	1·40	1·00
820		15b. violet (No. 244)	£120	£100
821		15b. violet	15	10
822		20b. brown	12·50	9·25
823		25b. blue	30	20
824		35b. brown	30	20
825		40b. olive	30	20
826	19	50b. purple	30	20
827		75b. blue	40	30
828		80b. green	40	30
829		1l. lake	40	30
830		2l. brown	55	40
831		3l. grey and violet	3·50	2·50
832		5l. brown	2·75	2·10
833		10l. lilac and brown	3·50	2·50

(f) Charles and Zita stamps.

834	27	10b. red	2·75	2·10
835		20b. brown	15	10
836		25b. blue	40	30
837		40b. green	70	50

The following (Nos. 838/58) are also optd **KOZTARSASAG**.

(g) Harvesters and Parliament Types.

838	18	2b. brown	1·70	1·20
839		3b. red	40	30
840		4b. grey	30	20
841		5b. green	40	30
842		6b. blue	2·10	1·60
843		10b. red	15·00	12·50
844		20b. brown	1·70	1·20
845		40b. olive	40	30
846	19	1l. lake	30	20
847		3l. grey and violet	1·10	85
848		5l. brown	4·75	3·75

(h) Charles and Zita stamps.

849	27	10b. red	£120	£130
850		20b. brown	2·75	2·10
851		25b. blue	55	40
852	28	50b. purple	30	20

(k) Harvesters and Parliament Types inscr "MAGYAR POSTA".

853	18	5b. green	15	10
854		20b. red	15	10
855		20b. brown	15	10
856		25b. blue	70	50
857		40b. olive	95	75
858	19	5l. brown	8·25	6·25

(44) King Ferdinand's Monogram

45 King Ferdinand

46 King Ferdinand

1919. Optd with T **44**.

873	37	1b. black	05	25
874		5b. green	35	50
878a		10b. red	10	15

1920.

891	45	1b. black	10	15
892		5b. green	10	15
893		10b. red	10	15
882		15b. brown	45	25

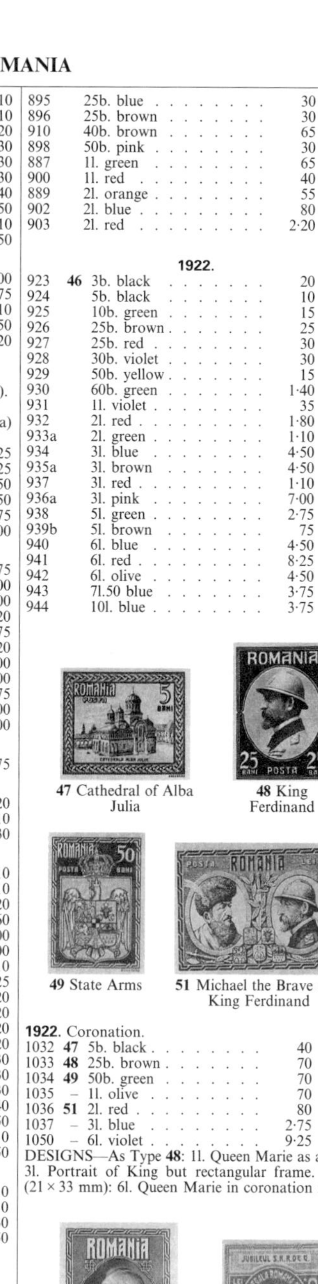

895		25b. blue	30	30
896		25b. brown	30	30
910		40b. brown	65	20
898		50b. pink	30	15
887		1l. green	65	20
900		1l. red	40	30
889		2l. orange	55	30
902		2l. blue	80	25
903		2l. red	2·20	1·30

1922.

923	46	3b. black	20	10
924		5b. black	10	10
925		10b. green	15	10
926		25b. brown	25	10
927		25b. red	30	10
928		30b. violet	30	10
929		50b. yellow	15	10
930		60b. green	1·40	50
931		1l. violet	35	10
932		2l. red	1·80	20
933a		2l. green	1·10	10
934		3l. blue	4·50	65
935a		3l. brown	4·50	60
937		3l. red	1·10	10
936a		3l. pink	7·00	1·30
938		5l. green	2·75	65
939b		5l. brown	75	10
940		6l. blue	4·50	85
941		6l. red	8·25	2·50
942		6l. olive	4·50	60
943		7l.50 blue	3·75	35
944		10l. blue	3·75	30

47 Cathedral of Alba Julia

48 King Ferdinand

49 State Arms

51 Michael the Brave and King Ferdinand

1922. Coronation.

1032	47	5b. black	40	25
1033	48	25b. brown	70	30
1034	49	50b. green	70	65
1035	–	1l. olive	70	45
1036	51	2l. red	80	50
1037	–	3l. blue	2·75	1·10
1050	–	6l. violet	9·25	5·75

DESIGNS—As Type **48**: 1l. Queen Marie as a nurse; 3l. Portrait of King but rectangular frame. Larger (21 × 33 mm): 6l. Queen Marie in coronation robes.

54 King Ferdinand

55 Map of Romania

1926. King's 60th Birthday. Imperf or perf.

1051	54	10b. green	40	30
1052		25b. orange	40	30
1053		50b. brown	40	30
1054		1l. violet	40	30
1055		2l. green	40	30
1056		3l. red	40	30
1057		5l. brown	40	30
1058		6l. olive	40	30
1059		9l. grey	40	30
1060		10l. blue	40	30

1927. 50th Anniv of Romanian Geographical Society.

1061	55	1+9l. violet	2·75	1·10
1062	–	2+8l. green	2·75	1·10
1063	–	3+7l. red	2·75	1·10
1064	–	5+5l. blue	2·75	1·20
1065	–	6+4l. olive	6·00	1·90

DESIGNS: 2l. Stephen the Great; 3l. Michael the Brave; 5l. Carol and Ferdinand; 6l. Adam Clisi Monument.

60 King Carol and King Ferdinand

1927. 50th Anniv of Independence.

1066	60	25b. red	40	10
1067	–	30b. black	30	20
1068	–	50b. green	40	20
1069	60	1l. blue	30	20
1070	–	2l. green	30	20
1071	–	3l. purple	30	25
1072	–	4l. brown	70	30
1073	–	4l.50 brown	2·00	1·20
1074	–	5l. brown	50	25
1075	–	6l. red	1·30	65

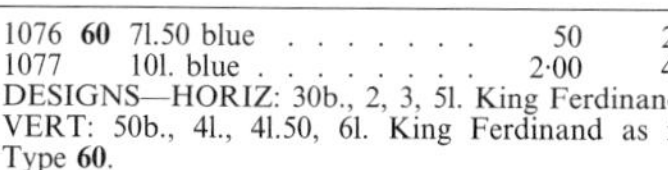

1076	60	7l.50 blue	50	25
1077		10l. blue	2·00	45

DESIGNS—HORIZ: 30b., 2, 3, 5l. King Ferdinand. VERT: 50b., 4l., 4l.50, 6l. King Ferdinand as in Type **60**.

63 King Michael

64 King Michael

1928.

1080	63	25b. black	35	15
1081		30b. pink	65	15
1082		50b. olive	35	15

1928. (a) Size 18½ × 24½ mm.

1083	64	1l. purple	45	15
1084		2l. green	1·00	15
1085		3l. red	1·00	15
1086		5l. brown	1·60	15
1087		7l.50 blue	6·75	65
1088		10l. blue	6·00	25

(b) Size 18 × 23 mm.

1129	64	1l. purple	85	15
1130		2l. green	1·00	20
1131		3l. red	2·10	15
1132		7l.50 blue	4·25	1·20
1133		10l. blue	16·00	6·25

65 Bessarabian Parliament House

1928. 10th Anniv of Annexation of Bessarabia.

1092	65	1l. green	1·40	45
1093	–	2l. brown	1·40	45
1094	–	3l. sepia	1·40	45
1095	–	5l. lake	1·70	55
1096	–	7l.50 blue	2·10	70
1097	–	10l. blue	3·25	1·50
1098	–	20l. violet	5·25	2·50

DESIGNS: 3, 5, 20l. Hotin Fortress; 7l.50, 10l. Fortress Cetatea Alba.

66 Bleriot SPAD 33 Biplane

1928. Air.

1099	66	1l. brown	6·25	4·00
1100		2l. blue	6·25	4·00
1101		5l. red	6·25	4·00

67 King Carol and King Michael

1928. 50th Anniv of Acquisition of Northern Dobruja.

1102	67	1l. green	55	40
1103	–	2l. brown	75	40
1104	67	3l. grey	85	40
1105	–	5l. mauve	85	40
1106	–	7l.50 blue	1·00	45
1107	–	10l. blue	4·25	1·10
1108	–	20l. red	5·25	1·30

DESIGNS: 2l. Constanza Harbour and Carol Lighthouse; 5l., 7l.50, Adam Clisi Monument; 10, 20l. Saligny Bridge over River Danube, Cernavoda.

68

69 The Union

1929. 10th Anniv of Union of Romania and Transylvania.
1109 **68** 1l. purple 1·40 95
1110 **69** 2l. green 1·40 95
1111 – 3l. brown 1·50 95
1112 – 4l. red 1·40 1·00
1113 – 5l. orange 1·80 1·10
1114 – 10l. blue 3·75 2·00
DESIGNS—HORIZ: 1l. Ferdinand I, Stephen the Great, Michael the Brave, Hunyadi and Brancoveanu; 10l. Ferdinand I. VERT: 2l. Union; 3l. Avram Jancu; 4l. King Michael the Brave; 5l. Bran Castle.

1930. Stamps of King Michael optd **8 IUNIE 1930** (Accession of Carol II).
1134 **63** 25b. black (postage) 35 15
1135 30b. pink 55 15
1136 50b. olive 55 15
1142 **64** 1l. purple (No. 1129) 45 15
1143 2l. green (No. 1130) 45 15
1144 3l. red (No. 1131) 55 15
1137 5l. brown 80 15
1140 7l.50 blue (No. 1087) 3·25 90
1145 7l.50 blue (No. 1132) 2·20 40
1138 10l. blue (No. 1088) 4·50 1·00
1146 10l. blue (No. 1133) 1·40 55
1147 **66** 1l. brown (air) 12·00 6·00
1148 2l. blue 12·00 6·00
1149 5l. red 12·00 6·00

72 King Carol II **73** King Carol II **76** King Carol II

1930.
1172 **72** 25b. black 30 10
1173 50b. brown 70 30
1174 1l. violet 35 10
1175 2l. green 55 10
1176 **73** 3l. red 1·30 10
1177 4l. orange 1·40 10
1178 6l. red 1·60 10
1179 7l.50 blue 1·80 15
1180 – 10l. blue 3·50 10
1181 – 16l. green 8·50 15
1182 – 20l. yellow 9·25 45
DESIGN: 10l. to 20l. Portrait as Type **72**, but in plain circle, with "ROMANIA" at top.

1930. Air.
1183 **76** 1l. violet on blue 2·30 1·30
1184 2l. green on blue 2·75 1·50
1185 5l. brown on blue 5·25 2·30
1186 10l. blue on blue 9·25 4·75

77 Map of Romania **78** Woman with Census Paper **79** King Carol II

1930. National Census.
1187 **77** 1l. violet 1·00 35
1188 **78** 2l. green 1·40 40
1189 4l. orange 2·00 20
1190 6l. red 5·00 40

1931.
1191 **79** 30l. blue and olive 1·10 55
1192 50l. blue and red 1·50 1·00
1193 100l. blue and green 3·50 1·80

80 King Carol II

81 King Carol I **82** Kings Carol II, Ferdinand I and Carol I

1931. 50th Anniv of Romanian Monarchy.
1200 **80** 1l. violet 3·00 1·40
1201 **81** 2l. green 3·50 1·60
1202 – 6l. red 7·00 2·20
1203 **82** 10l. blue 11·50 4·00
1204 – 20l. orange 14·00 5·25
DESIGNS—As Type **80**: 6l. King Carol II, facing right. As Type **81**: 20l. King Ferdinand I.

83 Naval Cadet Ship "Mircea"

1931. 50th Anniv of Romanian Navy.
1205 **83** 6l. red 4·75 2·75
1206 – 10l. blue 6·75 3·25
1207 – 12l. green 21·00 3·50
1208 – 20l. orange 10·50 6·75
DESIGNS: 10l. Monitors "Lascar Catargiu" and "Mihail Kogalniceaunu"; 16l. Monitor "Ardeal"; 20l. Destroyer "Regele Ferdinand".

84 Bayonet Attack

87 King Carol I

88 Infantry Attack **89** King Ferdinand I

1931. Centenary of Romanian Army.
1209 **84** 25b. black 1·50 80
1210 – 50b. brown 2·20 1·10
1211 – 1l. violet 2·40 1·30
1212 **87** 2l. green 3·75 1·60
1213 **88** 3l. red 9·50 5·25
1214 **89** 7l.50 blue 10·00 11·00
1215 – 16l. green 12·00 4·50
DESIGNS: 50b. Infantryman, 1870, 20 × 33 mm: 1l. Infantry and drummer, 1830, 23 × 36 mm: 16l. King Carol II in uniform with plumed helmet, 21 × 34 mm.

91 Scouts' Encampment

92a Farman F.121 Jaribu

1931. Romanian Boy Scouts' Exhibition Fund.
1221 **91** 1l.+1l. red 3·00 2·50
1222 – 2l.+2l. green 3·50 3·50
1223 – 3l.+3l. blue 4·75 4·25
1224 – 4l.+4l. brown 6·75 5·25
1225 – 6l.+6l. brown 10·50 6·75
DESIGNS—VERT: As Type **91**: 3l. Recruiting, 22 × 37½ mm; 2l. Rescue work, 22 × 41½ mm; 4l. Prince Nicholas; 6l. King Carol II in scoutmaster's uniform.

1931. Air.
1226 **92a** 2l. green 1·30 65
1227 – 3l. red 1·60 1·00
1228 – 5l. brown 1·20 1·30
1229 – 10l. blue 4·25 2·75
1230 – 20l. violet 15·00 4·25
DESIGNS—As T **92a**: 3l. Farman F.300 and biplane; 5l. Farman F.60 Goliath; 10l. Fokker F.XII. 34 × 20 mm: 20l. Three aircraft flying in formation.

95 Kings Carol II, Ferdinand I and Carol I

96 Alexander the Good

1931.
1231 **95** 16l. green 10·50 55

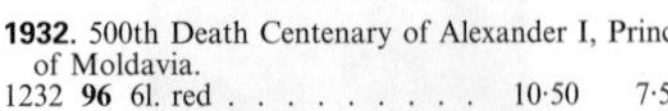

1932. 500th Death Centenary of Alexander I, Prince of Moldavia.
1232 **96** 6l. red 10·50 7·50

97 King Carol II

98 Semaphore Signaller

1932.
1248 **97** 10l. blue 11·00 35

1932. Boy Scouts' Jamboree Fund.
1256 – 25b.+25b. green 3·25 1·90
1257 **98** 50b.+50b. blue 3·25 2·75
1258 – 1l.+1l. green 4·00 3·50
1259 – 2l.+2l. red 7·25 5·25
1260 – 3l.+3l. blue 18·00 10·50
1261 – 6l.+6l. brown 19·00 15·00
DESIGNS—VERT: As Type **98**: 25b. Scouts in camp; 1l. On the trail; 3l. King Carol II; 6l. King Carol and King Michael when a Prince. HORIZ: 20 × 15 mm: 2l. Camp fire.

99 Cantacuzino and Gregory Chika

1932. 9th International Medical Congress.
1262 **99** 1l. red 4·75 5·25
1263 – 6l. orange 17·00 7·25
1264 – 10l. blue 30·00 12·50
DESIGNS: 6l. Congress in session; 10l. Hygeia and Aesculapius.

100 Tuberculosis Sanatorium

1932. Postal Employees' Fund.
1265 **100** 4l.+1l. green 3·75 2·40
1266 – 6l.+1l. brown 5·25 2·75
1267 – 10l.+1l. blue 8·50 4·50
DESIGNS—VERT: 6l. War Memorial tablet. HORIZ: 10l. Convalescent home.

102 "Bull's head"

103 Dolphins

104 Arms

1932. 75th Anniv of First Moldavian Stamps. Imperf.
1268 **102** 25b. black 65 20
1269 – 1l. purple 80 40
1270 **103** 2l. green 95 50
1271 – 3l. red 1·20 65
1272 **104** 6l. red 1·30 85
1273 – 7l.50 blue 2·75 1·20
1274 – 10l. blue 5·75 2·00
DESIGNS—As Type **103**: 1l.. Lion rampant and bridge; 3l. Eagle and castles; 7l.50, Eagle; 10l. Bull's head.

1932. 30th Anniv of Opening of G.P.O., Bucharest. As T **25** but smaller.
1275 16l. green 9·25 5·00

105 Ruins of Trajan's Bridge, Arms of Turnu-Severin and Towers of Severus

1933. Centenary of Founding of Turnu-Severin.
1279 **105** 25b. green 50 35
1280 – 50b. blue 80 45
1281 – 1l. brown 1·20 65
1282 – 2l. green 1·60 1·20
DESIGNS: 50b. Trajan at the completion of bridge over the Danube; 1l. Arrival of Prince Carol at Turnu-Severin; 2l. Trajan's Bridge.

107 Carmen Sylva and Carol I

1933. 50th Anniv of Construction of Pelesch Castle, Sinaia.
1283 **107** 1l. violet 1·60 1·20
1284 – 3l. brown 1·60 1·50
1285 – 6l. red 2·00 1·70
DESIGNS: 3l. Eagle and medallion portraits of Kings Carol I, Ferdinand I and Carol II; 6l. Pelesch Castle.

108 Wayside Shrine

110 King Carol II

1934. Romanian Women's Exhibition. Inscr "L.N.F.R. MUNCA NOASTRA ROMANEASCA".
1286 **108** 1l.+1l. brown 1·60 1·30
1287 – 2l.+1l. blue 2·20 1·70
1288 – 3l.+1l. green 2·50 2·20
DESIGNS—HORIZ: 2l. Weaver. VERT: 3l. Spinner.

1934. Mamaia Jamboree Fund. Nos. 1256/61 optd **MAMAIA 1934** and Arms of Constanza.
1289 – 26b.+25b. green 3·50 3·00
1290 **98** 50b.+50b. blue 4·00 3·25
1291 – 1l.+1l. green 5·25 4·75
1292 – 2l.+2l. red 7·50 6·50
1293 – 3l.+3l. blue 15·00 11·00
1294 – 6l.+6l. brown 17·00 14·00

1934.
1295 – 50b. brown 80 40
1296 **110** 2l. green 85 40
1297 4l. orange 2·10 45
1298 – 6l. lake 5·75 40
DESIGNS: 50b. Profile portrait of King Carol II in civilian clothes; 6l. King Carol in plumed helmet.

112 "Grapes for Health"

113 Crisan, Horia and Closca

1934. Bucharest Fruit Exhibition.
1299 **112** 1l. green 3·00 2·10
1300 – 2l. brown 3·00 2·10
DESIGN: 2l. Woman with fruit.

1935. 150th Anniv of Death of Three Romanian Martyrs. Portraits inscr "MARTIR AL NEAMULUI 1785".
1301 **113** 1l. violet 55 35
1302 – 2l. green (Crisan) 60 50
1303 – 6l. brown (Closca) 1·60 1·00
1304 – 10l. blue (Horia) 2·40 2·10

114 Boy Scouts

1935. 5th Anniv of Accession of Carol II.
1305 – 25b. black 3·00 2·00
1306 – 1l. violet 4·50 3·50
1307 **114** 2l. green 5·75 5·25
1308 – 6l.+1l. brown 7·00 7·25
1309 – 10l.+2l. blue 14·50 17·00
DESIGNS—VERT: 25b. Scout saluting; 1l. Bugler; 6l. King Carol II. HORIZ: 10l. Colour party.

1935. Portraits as T **110** but additionally inscr "POSTA".
1310 – 25b. black 15 10
1311 – 50b. brown 15 10
1312 – 1l. violet 15 10
1313 **110** 2l. green 45 10
1315 – 3l. red 75 10
1316 – 3l. blue 1·10 20
1317 **110** 4l. orange 1·20 25
1318 – 5l. red 1·10 70
1319 – 6l. lake 1·50 25
1320 – 7l.50 blue 1·80 40
1321 – 8l. purple 2·10 50
1322 **110** 9l. blue 2·50 65
1323 – 10l. blue 1·10 20
1324 – 12l. blue 1·70 85
1325 – 15l. brown 1·70 60
1326 – 16l. green 2·30 35
1327 – 20l. orange 1·40 40
1328 – 24l. red 2·50 60
PORTRAITS—IN PROFILE: 25b., 15l. In naval uniform; 50b., 3, 8, 10l. In civilian clothes. THREE-QUARTER FACE: 1, 5, 7l.50, In civilian clothes. FULL FACE: 6, 12, 16, 20, 24l. In plumed helmet.

118 King Carol II
119 Oltenia Peasant Girl

1936. Bucharest Exhibition and 70th Anniv of Hohenzollern–Sigmaringen Dynasty.
1329 **118** 6l.+1l. red . . . . 1·00 65

1936. 6th Anniv of Accession of Carol II Inscr "O.E.T.R. 8 IUNIE 1936".
1330 **119** 50b.+50b. brown . . . . 1·10 55
1331 – 1l.+1l. violet 85 60
1332 – 2l.+1l. green 85 65
1333 – 3l.+1l. red . . . . 1·20 85
1334 – 4l.+2l. red . . . . 1·40 85
1335 – 6l.+3l. grey . . . . . . 1·70 1·00
1336 – 10l.+5l. blue . . . . . . 2·75 2·50
DESIGNS (costumes of following districts)—VERT: 1l. Banat; 4l. Gori; 6l. Neamz. HORIZ: 2l. Saliste; 3l. Hateg; 10l. Suceava (Bukovina).

120 Brasov Jamboree Badge
121 Liner "Transylvania"

1936. National Scout Jamboree, Brasov.
1337 – 1l.+1l. blue . . . . . . 3·00 3·25
1338 – 3l.+3l. grey . . . . . . 4·75 4·00
1339 **120** 6l.+6l. red . . . . 6·75 4·75
DESIGNS: 1l. National Scout Badge; 3l. Tenderfoot Badge.

1936. 1st Marine Exhibition, Bucharest.
1343 – 1l.+1l. violet . . . . . . 3·00 3·75
1344 – 3l.+2l. blue . . . . . . 4·50 3·00
1345 **121** 6l.+3l. red . . . . 5·50 4·25
DESIGNS: 1l. Submarine "Delfinul"; 3l. Naval cadet ship "Mircea".

1936. 18th Anniv of Annexation of Transylvania and 16th Anniv of Foundation of "Little Entente" Nos. 1320 and 1323 optd **CEHOSLOVACIA YUGOSLAVIA 1920-1936**.
1346 7l.50 blue . . . . 2·75 3·00
1347 10l. blue . . . . 2·30 3·00

123 Creanga's Birthplace

1937. Birth Centenary of Ion Creanga (poet).
1348 **123** 2l. green 80 55
1349 – 3l. red . . . . 1·10 65
1350 **123** 4l. violet . . . . 1·60 85
1351 – 6l. brown . . . . 2·75 1·70
DESIGN: 3, 6l. Portrait of Creanga, 37 × 22 mm.

124 Footballers

1937. 7th Anniv of Accession of Carol II.
1352 **124** 25b.+25b. olive 65 25
1353 – 50b.+50b. brown 65 30
1354 – 1l.+50b. violet . . . . . 1·00 45
1355 – 2l.+1l. green . . . . . . 1·00 55
1356 – 3l.+1l. red . . . . 1·50 60
1357 – 4l.+1l. red . . . . 2·50 70
1358 – 6l.+2l. brown . . . . . 3·25 1·10
1359 – 10l.+4l. blue . . . . . . 4·00 1·60
DESIGNS—HORIZ: 50b. Swimmer; 3 l. King Carol II hunting; 10l. U.F.S.R. Inaugural Meeting. VERT: 1l. Javelin thrower; 2l. Skier; 4l. Rowing; 6l. Steeplechaser.
Premium in aid of the Federation of Romanian Sports Clubs (U.F.S.R.).

127 Curtea de Arges Cathedral
128 Hurdling

1937. "Little Entente".
1360 **127** 7l.50 blue . . . . 1·20 75
1361 10l. blue . . . . 1·80 50

1937. 8th Balkan Games, Bucharest. Inscr as in T **115**.
1362 – 1l.+1l. violet 90 70
1363 – 2l.+1l. green . . . . . . 1·00 95
1364 **128** 4l.+1l. red . . . . . . 1·00 1·30
1365 – 6l.+1l. brown . . . . . 1·40 1·30
1366 – 10l.+1l. blue . . . . . . 4·25 2·40
DESIGNS: 1l. Sprinting; 2l. Throwing the javelin; 6l. Breasting the tape; 10l. High jumping.

129 Arms of Romania, Greece, Turkey and Yugoslavia
130 King Carol II

1938. Balkan Entente.
1368 **129** 7l.50 blue . . . . 1·00 70
1369 10l. blue . . . . 1·60 50

1938. New Constitution. Profile portraits of King inscr "27 FEBRUARIE 1938". 6l. shows Arms also.
1370 **130** 3l. red 55 45
1371 – 6l. brown 95 45
1372 – 10l. blue . . . . 1·30 85

131 King Carol II and Provincial Arms
132 Dimitrie Cantemir

1938. Fund for Bucharest Exhibition celebrating 20th Anniv of Union of Provinces.
1373 **131** 6l.+1l. mauve 70 45

1938. Boy Scouts' Fund. 8th Anniv of Accession of Carol II. Inscr "STRAJA TARII 8 IUNIE 1938".
1374 **132** 25b.+25b. olive 40 40
1375 – 50b.+50b. brown 45 40
1376 – 1l.+1l. violet 60 40
1377 – 2l.+2l. green 70 40
1378 – 3l.+2l. mauve 70 40
1379 – 4l.+2l. red 75 45
1380 – 6l.+2l. brown . . . . . 1·10 50
1381 – 7l.50 blue . . . . 1·00 50
1382 – 10l. blue 95 60
1383 – 16l. green . . . . 1·60 1·60
1384 – 20l. red . . . . 2·40 1·60
PORTRAITS: 50b. Maria Doamna; 1l. Mircea the Great; 2l. Constantin Brancoveanu; 3l. Stephen the Great; 4l. Prince Cuza; 6l. Michael the Brave; 7l.50, Queen Elisabeth; 10l. King Carol II; 16l. King Ferdinand I; 20l. King Carol I.

134 "The Spring"
135 Prince Carol in Royal Carriage

1938. Birth Centenary of Nicholas Grigorescu (painter).
1385 **134** 1l.+1l. blue 75 50
1386 – 2l.+1l. green . . . . . . 1·10 80
1387 – 4l.+1l. red . . . . 1·10 85
1388 – 6l.+1l. red . . . . 1·20 1·10
1389 – 10l.+1l. blue . . . . . . 2·00 1·80
DESIGNS—HORIZ: 2l. "Escorting Prisoners" (Russo-Turkish War 1877–78); 4l. "Returning from Market". VERT: 6l. "Rodica, the Water Carrier"; 10l. Self-portrait.

1939. Birth Centenary of King Carol I.
1390 **135** 25b. black 10 10
1391 – 50b. brown 10 10
1392 – 1l. violet 20 10
1393 – 1l.50 green 10 10
1394 – 2l. blue 10 10
1395 – 3l. red 10 10
1396 – 4l. red 10 10
1397 – 5l. black 10 10
1398 – 7l. black 10 10
1399 – 8l. blue 25 15
1400 – 10l. mauve 25 15
1401 – 12l. blue 30 20
1402 – 15l. blue 35 15
1403 – 16l. green 75 45
DESIGNS—HORIZ 50b. Prince Carol at Battle of Calafat; 1l.50, Sigmaringen and Pelesch Castles; 5 l. Carol I, Queen Elizabeth and Arms of Romania. VERT: 1l. Examining plans for restoring Curtea de Arges Monastery; 2l. Carol I and Queen Elizabeth; 3l. Carol I at age of 8; 4l. In 1866; 5l. In 1877; 7l. Equestrian statue; 8l. Leading troops in 1878; 10l. In General's uniform; 12l. Bust; 16l. Restored Monastery of Curtea de Arges.

136 Romanian Pavilion N.Y. World's Fair
137 Michael Eminescu, after painting by Joano Basarab

1939. New York World's Fair.
1407 **136** 6l. lake 45 45
1408 – 12l. blue 45 45
DESIGN: 12l. Another view of Pavilion.

1939. 50th Death Anniv of Michael Eminescu (poet).
1409 **137** 5l. black 45 40
1410 – 7l. red 45 40
DESIGN: 7l. Eminescu in later years.

138 St. George and Dragon
139 Diesel Railcar, Class 142 Steam Locomotive (1936) and Locomotive "Calugareni" (1869)

1939. 9th Anniv of Accession of Carol II and Boy Scouts' Fund.
1411 **138** 25b.+25b. grey 45 45
1412 50b.+50b. brown 45 45
1413 1l.+1l. blue 45 45
1414 2l.+2l. green 60 45
1415 3l.+2l. purple 65 45
1416 4l.+2l. orange . . . . . 1·10 65
1417 6l.+2l. red . . . . 1·10 65
1418 8l. grey . . . . 1·10 70
1419 10l. blue . . . . 1·20 75
1420 12l. blue . . . . 1·40 1·00
1421 16l. green . . . . 2·75 1·80

1939. 70th Anniv of Romanian Railways.
1422 **139** 1l. violet . . . . 1·10 60
1423 – 4l. red . . . . 1·20 65
1424 – 5l. grey . . . . 1·20 1·00
1425 – 7l. mauve . . . . 1·60 1·00
1426 – 12l. blue . . . . 2·30 1·40
1427 – 15l. green . . . . 3·50 2·00
DESIGNS—HORIZ: 4l. Class 142 steam train crossing bridge, 1936; 15l. Railway Headquarters, Budapest. VERT: 5, 7l. Locomotive "Calugareni" (1869) leaving station; 12l. Diesel-mechanical twin set (1937) crossing bridge.

1940. Balkan Entente. As T **103** of Yugoslavia, but with Arms rearranged.
1428 12l. blue 65 55
1429 16l. blue 65 55

141 King Carol II
142 King Carol II

1940. Aviation Fund.
1430 **141** 1l.+50b. green 30 25
1431 2l.50+50b. green 35 30
1432 3l.+1l. red 55 40
1433 3l.50+50b. brown . . . 55 45
1434 4l.+1l. orange 70 50
1435 6l.+1l. blue . . . . . . 1·00 30
1436 9l.+1l. blue . . . . . . 1·30 95
1437 14l.+1l. green . . . . . 1·60 1·20

1940. 10th Anniv of Accession and Aviation Fund. Portraits of King Carol II.
1438 **142** 1l.+50b. purple 75 30
1439 4l.+1l. brown 75 45
1440 – 6l.+1l. blue 75 60
1441 – 8l. red . . . . 1·00 85
1442 – 16l. blue . . . . 1·40 1·10
1443 – 32l. brown . . . . . . 2·10 1·90
PORTRAITS: 6, 16l. In steel helmet; 8l. In military uniform; 32l. In flying helmet.

144 The Iron Gates of the Danube

1940. Charity. 10th Anniv of Accession of Carol II and Boy Scouts' Fund. Inscr "STRAJA TARII 8 IUNIE 1940".
1444 **144** 1l.+1l. violet 50 50
1445 – 2l.+1l. brown 55 55
1446 – 3l.+1l. green 55 60
1447 – 4l.+1l. black 65 70
1448 – 5l.+1l. orange 80 80
1449 – 8l.+1l. red 80 85
1450 – 12l.+2l. blue 90 95
1451 – 16l.+2l. grey . . . . . . 3·50 1·90
DESIGNS—HORIZ: 3l. Hotin Fortress; 4l. Hurez Monastery. VERT: 2l. Greco-Roman ruins; 5l. Church in Suceava; 8l. Alba Julia Cathedral; 12l. Village Church, Transylvania; 16l. Triumphal Arch, Bucharest.

145 King Michael
146 King Michael

1940.
1455 **145** 25b. green 10 10
1456 50b. olive 10 10
1457 1l. violet 10 10
1458 2l. orange 10 10
1608 3l. brown 10 10
1609 3l.50 brown 10 10
1459 4l. grey 10 10
1611 4l.50 brown 10 10
1460 5l. pink 10 10
1613 6l.50 violet 10 10
1461 7l. blue 10 10
1615 10l. mauve 10 10
1616 11l. blue 10 10
1463 12l. blue 10 10
1464 13l. purple 10 10
1618 15l. blue 10 10
1619 16l. blue 10 10
1620 20l. brown 10 10
1621 29l. blue 55 70
1467 30l. green 10 10
1468 50l. brown 10 10
1469 100l. brown 10 10

1940. Aviation Fund.
1470 **146** 1l.+50b. green 10 15
1471 2l.+50b. green 10 15
1472 2l.50+50b. green 10 15
1473 3l.+1l. violet 10 15
1474 3l.50+50b. pink 20 30
1475 4l.+50b. red 10 20
1476 4l.+1l. brown 10 20
1477 5l.+1l. red 55 45
1478 6l.+1l. blue 10 20
1479 7l.+1l. green 20 20
1480 8l.+1l. violet 20 20
1481 12l.+1l. brown 20 20
1482 14l.+1l. blue 20 20
1483 19l.+1l. mauve 95 30

147 Codreanu (founder)
148 Codreanu (founder)

1940. "Iron Guard" Fund.
1484 **147** 7l.+30l. grn (postage) . . 3·75 3·50
1485 **148** 20l.+5l. green (air) . . . 1·90 1·70

149 Ion Mota
150 Library

1941. Marin and Mota (legionaries killed in Spain).
1486 – 7l.+7l. red . . . . 1·50 2·75
1487 **149** 15l.+15l. blue . . . . . 5·25 5·50
PORTRAIT: 7l. Vasile Marin.

1941. Carol I Endowment Fund. Inscr "1891 1941".
1488 – 1l.50+43l.50 violet . . . 1·30 1·40
1489 **150** 2l.+43l. red . . . . . . 1·30 1·40
1490 – 7l.+38l. red . . . . . . 1·30 1·40
1491 – 10l.+35l. green . . . . . 2·20 2·00
1492 – 16l.+29l. brown . . . . . 3·00 2·30

DESIGNS: 1l.50, Ex-libris; 7l. Foundation building and equestrian statue; 10l. Foundation stone; 16l. King Michael and Carol I.

1941. Occupation of Cernauti. Nos. 1488/92 optd **CERNAUTI 5 Iulie 1941**.
1493 – 1l.50+43l.50 violet . . . 2·75 3·00
1494 **150** 2l.+43l. red . . . . . . 2·75 3·00
1495 – 7l.+38l. red . . . . . . 2·75 3·00
1496 – 10l.+35l. green . . . . . 2·75 3·00
1497 – 16l.+29l. brown . . . . 3·25 3·25

1941. Occupation of Chisinau. Nos. 1488/92 optd **CHISINAU 16 Iulie 1941**.
1498 – 1l.50+43l.50 violet . . . 2·75 3·25
1499 **150** 2l.+43l. red . . . . . . 2·75 3·25
1500 – 7l.+38l. red . . . . . . 2·75 3·25
1501 – 10l.+35l. green . . . . . 2·75 3·25
1502 – 16l.+29l. brown . . . . 3·25 3·25

153 "Charity" **154** Prince Voda

1941. Red Cross Fund. Cross in red.
1503 **153** 1l.50+38l.50 violet . . . 95 90
1504 2l.+38l. red 95 90
1505 5l.+35l. olive 95 90
1506 7l.+33l. brown 95 90
1507 10l.+30l. blue . . . . . 2·00 1·70

1941. Conquest of Transdniestria.
1572 **154** 3l. orange 15 45
1509 6l. brown 35 40
1510 12l. violet 35 55
1511 24l. blue 75 90

155 King Michael and Stephen the Great

1941. Anti-Bolshevik Crusade. Inscr "RAZBOIUL SFANT CONTRA BOLSEVISMULUI".
1512 **155** 10l.+30l. blue . . . . . 75 1·90
1513 – 12l.+28l. red . . . . . . 75 1·90
1514 – 16l.+24l. brown . . . . 1·10 2·40
1515 – 20l.+20l. violet . . . . . 1·10 2·40
DESIGNS: 12l. Hotin and Akkerman Fortresses; 16l. Arms and helmeted soldiers; 20l. Bayonet charge and Arms of Romania.

1941. Fall of Odessa. Nos. 1512/15 optd **ODESA 16 Oct. 1941**.
1517 **155** 10l.+30l. blue 75 90
1518 – 12l.+28l. red 75 90
1519 – 16l.+24l. brown . . . . 1·10 2·50
1520 – 20l.+20l. violet . . . . . 1·10 2·50

157 Hotin

1941. Restoration of Bessarabia and Bukovina (Suceava). Inscr "BASARABIA" or "BUCOVINA".
1522 – 25b. red 10 10
1523 **157** 50b. brown 10 10
1524 – 1l. violet 10 10
1525 – 1l.50 green 10 10
1526 – 2l. brown 10 10
1527 – 3l. olive 15 10
1528 – 5l. olive 25 10
1529 – 5l.50 brown 25 15
1530 – 6l.50 mauve 75 50
1531 **157** 9l.50 grey 75 60
1532 – 10l. purple 50 15
1533 – 13l. blue 75 20
1534 – 17l. brown 90 20
1535 – 26l. green . . . . 1·00 40
1536 – 39l. blue . . . . 1·40 55
1537 – 130l. yellow . . . . . . 4·00 3·00
VIEWS—VERT: 25b., 5l. Paraclis Hotin; 3l. Dragomirna; 13l. Milisauti. HORIZ: 1, 17l. Sucevita; 1l.50, Soroca; 2, 5l.50, Tighina; 6l.50, Cetatea Alba; 10, 130l. Putna; 26l. St. Nicolae, Suceava; 39l. Monastery, Rughi.

1941. Winter Relief Fund. Inscr "BASARABIA" or "BUCOVINA".
1538 – 3l.+50b. red 25 30
1539 – 5l.50+50b. orange . . . 45 50
1540 – 5l.50+1l. black 45 50
1541 – 6l.50+1l. brown 55 65
1542 – 8l.+1l. blue 55 35
1543 – 9l.50+1l. blue 80 75
1544 – 10l.50+1l. blue 80 35
1545 – 16l.+1l. mauve 95 90
1546 **157** 25l.+1l. grey . . . . . . 1·20 95

VIEWS—HORIZ: 3l. Sucevita; 5l.50, (1539), Monastery, Rughi; 5l.50, (1540), Tighina; 6l.50, Soroca; 8l. St. Nicolae, Suceava; 10l.50, Putna; 16l. Cetatea Alba. VERT: 8l.50, Milisauti.

158 Titu Maiorescu **159** Coat-of-Arms of Bukovina

1942. Prisoners of War Relief Fund through International Education Office, Geneva.
1549 **158** 9l.+11l. violet . . . . . 70 1·10
1550 20l.+20l. brown . . . . 90 1·90
1551 20l.+30l. blue . . . . . 90 2·00

1942. 1st Anniv of Liberation of Bukovina.
1553 **159** 9l.+41l. red . . . . 1·50 2·50
1554 – 18l.+32l. blue . . . . . 1·50 2·50
1555 – 20l.+30l. red . . . . . . 1·50 2·50
ARMORIAL DESIGNS: 18l. Castle; 20l. Mounds and crosses.

160 Map of Bessarabia, King Michael, Antonescu, Hitler and Mussolini **161** Statue of Miron Costin

1942. 1st Anniv of Liberation of Bessarabia.
1556 **160** 9l.+41l. brown . . . . . 1·50 2·30
1557 – 18l.+32l. olive . . . . . 1·50 2·30
1558 – 20l.+30l. blue . . . . . 1·50 2·30
DESIGNS—VERT: 18l. King Michael and Marshal Antonescu below miniature of King Stephen. HORIZ: 20l. Marching soldiers and miniature of Marshal Antonescu.

1942. 1st Anniv of Incorporation of Transdniestria.
1559 **161** 6l.+44l. brown . . . . . 1·00 1·70
1560 12l.+38l. violet . . . . 1·00 1·70
1561 24l.+26l. blue . . . . . 1·00 1·70

162 Andrei Muresanu **163** Statue of Avram Iancu

1942. 80th Death Anniv of A. Muresanu (novelist).
1562 **162** 5l.+5l. violet 80 95

1943. Fund for Statue of Iancu (national hero).
1563 **163** 16l.+4l. brown . . . . . 85 1·10

164 Nurse and wounded Soldier **165** Sword and Shield

1943. Red Cross Charity. Cross in red.
1564 **164** 12l.+88l. red 65 60
1565 16l.+84l. blue 65 60
1566 20l.+80l. olive 65 60

1943. Charity. 2nd Year of War. Inscr "22 JUNIE 1941 22 JUNIE 1943".
1568 **165** 36l.+164l. brown . . . . 1·10 2·00
1569 – 62l.+138l. blue . . . . . 1·10 2·00
1570 – 76l.+124l. red . . . . . 1·10 2·00
DESIGNS: 62l. Sword severing chain; 76l. Angel protecting soldier and family.

167 P. Maior

1943. Transylvanian Refugees' Fund (1st issue).
1576 **167** 16l.+134l. red 40 55
1577 – 32l.+118l. blue 40 55
1578 – 36l.+114l. purple 40 55
1579 – 62l.+138l. red 40 55
1580 – 91l.+109l. brown 40 55
PORTRAITS—VERT: 32l. G. Sincai; 36l. T. Cipariu; 91l. G. Cosbuc. HORIZ: 62l. Horia, Closca and Crisan.
See also Nos. 1584/8.

169 King Michael and Marshal Antonescu

1943. 3rd Anniv of King Michael's Reign.
1581 **169** 16l.+24l. blue . . . . . 1·30 1·60

170 Sports Shield **171** Calafat, 1877

1943. Charity. Sports Week.
1582 **170** 16l.+24l. blue 55 45
1583 16l.+24l. brown 55 45

1943. Transylvanian Refugees' Fund (2nd issue) Portraits as T **167**.
1584 16l.+134l. mauve 45 45
1585 51l.+99l. orange 45 45
1586 56l.+144l. red 45 45
1587 76l.+124l. blue 45 45
1588 77l.+123l. brown 45 45
PORTRAITS—VERT: 16l. S. Micu; 51l. G. Lazar; 56l. O. Goga; 76l. S. Barnutiu; 77l. A. Saguna.

1943. Centenary of National Artillery.
1596 **171** 1l.+1l. brown 20 30
1597 – 2l.+2l. violet 20 30
1598 – 3l.50+3l.50 blue 20 30
1599 – 4l.+4l. mauve 20 30
1600 – 5l.+5l. orange 35 45
1601 – 6l.50+6l.50 blue 35 45
1602 – 7l.+7l. purple 50 65
1603 – 20l.+20l. red . . . . . . 90 1·10
DESIGNS—HORIZ: (1l. to 7l. inscr battle scenes): 2l. "1916–1918"; 3l.50, Stalingrad; 4l. Crossing R. Tisza; 5l. Odessa; 6l.50, Caucasus; 7l. Sevastopol; 20l. Bibescu and King Michael.

172 Association Insignia

1943. 25th Anniv of National Engineers' Assn.
1624 **172** 21l.+29l. brown 85 65

173 Motor-cycle and Delivery Van

1944. Postal Employees' Relief Fund and Bicentenary of National Postal Service. (a) Without opt.
1625 **173** 1l.+49l. red . . . . . . 90 1·40
1626 – 2l.+48l. mauve . . . . . 90 1·40
1627 – 4l.+46l. blue . . . . . . 90 1·40
1628 – 10l.+40l. purple . . . . 90 1·40

(b) Optd **1744 1944**.
1631 **173** 1l+49l. red . . . . . . 2·40 3·00
1632 – 2l.+48l. mauve . . . . . 2·40 3·00
1633 – 4l.+46l. blue . . . . . . 2·40 3·00
1634 – 10l.+40l. purple . . . 2·40 3·00
DESIGNS—HORIZ: 2l. Mail van and eight horses; 4l. Chariot. VERT: 10l. Horseman and Globe.

174 Dr. Cretzulescu **175** Rugby Player

1944. Cent of Medical Teaching in Romania.
1637 **174** 35l.+65l. blue 80 70

1944. 30th Anniv of Foundation of National Rugby Football Association.
1638 **175** 16l.+184l. red . . . . . 2·40 3·00

176 Stefan Tomsa Church, Radaseni **177** Fruit Pickers

1944. Cultural Fund. Town of Radaseni. Inscr "RADASENI".
1639 **176** 5l.+145l. blue 55 55
1640 – 12l.+138l. red 55 55
1641 **177** 15l.+135l. orange 55 55
1642 – 32l.+118l. brown 55 55
DESIGNS—HORIZ: 12l. Agricultural Institution; 32l. School.

178 Queen Helen **179** King Michael and Carol I Foundation, Bucharest

1945. Red Cross Relief Fund. Portrait in black on yellow and Cross in red.
1643 **178** 4l.50+5l.50 violet 25 20
1644 10l.+40l. brown 45 25
1645 15l.+75l. blue 70 45
1646 20l.+80l. red 85 70

1945. King Carol I Foundation Fund.
1647 **179** 20l.+180l. orange 35 35
1648 25l.+175l. slate 35 35
1649 35l.+165l. brown 35 35
1650 76l.+125l. violet 35 35

180 A. Saguna **181** A. Muresanu

1945. Liberation of Northern Transylvania. Inscr "1944".
1652 **180** 25b. red 45 40
1653 **181** 50b. orange 20 20
1654 – 4l.50 brown 25 20
1655 – 11l. blue 25 20
1656 – 15l. green 25 20
1657 – 31l. violet 25 20
1658 – 35l. grey 25 20
1659 – 41l. olive 25 75
1660 – 55l. brown 25 20
1661 – 61l. mauve 25 20
1662 – 75l.+75l. brown 30 25
DESIGNS—HORIZ: 4l.50, Samuel Micu; 31l. George Lazar; 55l. Horia, Closca and Crisan; 61l. Petru Maior; 75l. King Ferdinand and King Michael. VERT: 11l. George Sincai; 15l. Michael the Brave; 35l. Avram Iancu; 41l. Simeon Barnutiu.

182 King Michael **183** King Michael

184 King Michael 185 King Michael

1945.

1663 **182** 50b. grey 10 10
1664 **183** 1l. brown 10 10
1665 2l. violet 10 10
1666 **182** 2l. brown 10 15
1667 **183** 4l. green 10 10
1668 **184** 5l. mauve 10 10
1669 **182** 10l. blue 10 10
1670 10l. brown 10 10
1671 **183** 10l. brown 10 10
1672 **182** 15l. mauve 10 10
1673 20l. blue 10 10
1674 20l. lilac 10 10
1675 **184** 20l. purple 10 10
1676 25l. red 10 10
1677 35l. brown 10 10
1678 40l. red 10 10
1679 **183** 50l. blue 10 15
1680 55l. red 15 15
1681 **184** 75l. green 20 10
1682 **185** 80l. orange 10 10
1683 80l. blue 10 10
1684 **182** 80l. blue 10 10
1685 **185** 100l. brown 10 10
1686 **182** 137l. green 20 10
1687 **185** 160l. green 10 10
1688 160l. violet 10 10
1689 200l. green 30 15
1690 200l. red 10 10
1691 **183** 200l. red 10 10
1692 **185** 300l. blue 10 10
1693 360l. brown 20 10
1694 400l. violet 10 10
1695 **183** 400l. red 10 10
1696 **185** 480l. brown 20 10
1697 **182** 500l. mauve 20 10
1698 **185** 600l. green 10 10
1699 **184** 860l. brown 10 15
1700 **185** 1000l. green 20 10
1701 **182** 1500l. green 20 10
1702 **185** 2400l. lilac 40 10
1703 **183** 2500l. blue 20 10
1704 **185** 3700l. blue 40 10
1705 **182** 5000l. grey 10 10
1706 8000l. green 35 15
1707 **185** 10000l. brown 55 35

186 N. Jorga

1945. War Victims' Relief Fund.
1708 – 12l.+188l. blue 25 40
1709 – 16l.+184l. brown 25 40
1710 **186** 20l.+180l. brown 25 40
1711 – 32l.+168l. red 25 40
1712 – 35l.+165l. blue 25 40
1713 – 36l.+164l. violet . . . . 1·80 1·10
PORTRAITS: 12l. Ian Gheorghe Duca (Prime Minister, 1933); 16l. Virgil Madgearu (politician); 32l. Ilie Pintilie (communist); 35l. Bernath Andrei (communist); 36l. Filimon Sarbu (saboteur)..

187 Books and Torch 188 Karl Marx

1945. Charity. 1st Romanian–Soviet Congress Fund. Inscr "ARLUS".
1715 **187** 20l.+80l. olive 25 35
1716 – 35l.+165l. red 25 35
1717 – 75l.+225l. blue 25 35
1718 80l.+420l. brown 25 35
DESIGNS: 35l. Soviet and Romanian flags; 75l. Drawn curtain revealing Kremlin; 80l. T. Vladimirescu and A. Nevsky.

189 Postman

1945. Trade Union Congress, Bucharest. Perf or imperf.
1720 **188** 75l.+425l. red . . . . . 1·40 2·00
1723 75l.+425l. blue . . . . . 3·25 5·75
1721 – 120l.+380l. blue . . . . 1·40 2·00
1724 – 120l.+380l. brown . . . 4·00 5·75
1722 – 155l.+445l. brown . . . 1·60 2·00
1725 – 155l.+445l. red . . . . . 4·00 5·75
PORTRAITS: 120l. Engels; 155l. Lenin.

1945. Postal Employees. Inscr "MUNCA P.T.T.".
1726 **189** 100l. brown 60 45
1727 100l. olive 60 45
1728 – 150l. brown 90 70
1729 – 150l. red 90 70
1730 – 250l. olive . . . . 1·10 1·10
1731 – 250l. blue . . . . 1·10 1·10
1732 – 500l. mauve . . . . . . 6·25 9·25
DESIGNS: 150l. Telegraphist; 250l. Lineman; 500l. Post Office, Bucharest.

190 Throwing the Discus 192 Agricultural and Industrial Workers

1945. Charity. With shield inscr "O.S.P.". Perf or imperf.
1733 **190** 12l.+188l. olive (post) . . 1·60 1·80
1738 – 12l.+188l. orange . . . . 1·60 1·40
1734 – 16l.+184l. blue . . . . . 1·60 1·80
1739 – 16l.+184l. purple . . . . 1·60 1·40
1735 – 20l.+180l. green . . . . 1·60 1·80
1740 – 20l.+180l. violet . . . . 1·60 1·40
1736 – 32l.+168l. mauve . . . . 1·60 1·80
1741 – 32l.+168l. green . . . . 1·60 1·40
1737 – 35l.+165l. blue . . . . . 1·60 1·80
1742 – 35l.+165l. olive . . . . 1·60 1·40

1743 – 200l.+1000l. bl (air) . . 12·00 14·00
DESIGNS—As T **190**: 16l. Diving; 20l. Skiing; 32l. Volleyball; 35l. "Sport and work". 36 × 50 mm: 200l. Airplane and bird.

1945. 1st Anniv of Romanian Armistice with Russia.
1744 **192** 100l.+400l. red 40 50
1745 – 200l.+800l. blue 40 50
DESIGN: 200l. King Michael, "Agriculture" and "Industry".

193 T. Vladimirescu 194 Destitute Children

1945. Charity. Patriotic Defence Fund. Inscr "APARAREA PATRIOTICA".
1746 – 20l.+580l. brown . . . . 4·75 6·75
1747 – 20l.+580l. mauve . . . . 4·75 6·75
1748 – 40l.+560l. blue . . . . . 4·75 6·75
1749 – 40l.+560l. green . . . . 4·75 6·75
1750 – 55l.+545l. red . . . . . 4·75 6·75
1751 – 55l.+545l. brown . . . . 4·75 6·75
1752 **193** 60l.+540l. blue . . . . . 4·75 6·75
1753 60l.+540l. brown . . . . 4·75 6·75
1754 – 80l.+520l. red . . . . . 4·75 6·75
1755 – 80l.+520l. mauve . . . . 4·75 6·75
1756 – 100l.+500l. green . . . . 4·75 6·75
1757 – 100l.+500l. brown . . . . 4·75 6·75
DESIGNS—HORIZ: 20l. "Political Amnesty"; 40l. "Military Amnesty"; 55l. "Agrarian Amnesty"; 100l. King Michael and "Recontruction". VERT: 80l. Nicholas Horia.

1945. Child Welfare Fund.
1758 **194** 40l. blue 30 25

195 I. Ionescu, G. Titeica, A. G. Idachimescu and V. Cristescu

1945. 50th Anniv of Founding of Journal of Mathematics.
1759 **195** 2l. brown 10 10
1760 – 80l. blue 60 65
DESIGN: 80l. Allegory of Learning.

196 Saligny Bridge

1945. 50th Anniv of Saligny Bridge over River Danube, Cernavoda.
1761 **196** 80l. black 30 30

197 Class E.18 Electric Locomotive, 1935, Germany

198

1945. Charity. 16th Congress of Romanian Engineers. Perf or imperf. (a) Postage.
1762 **197** 10l.+490l. olive . . . . 2·10 1·90
1767 10l.+490l. blue . . . . . 2·10 1·90
1763 – 20l.+480l. brown 30 45
1768 – 20l.+480l. violet 30 45
1764 – 25l.+475l. purple 30 45
1769 – 25l.+475l. green 30 45
1765 – 55l.+445l. blue 30 45
1770 – 55l.+445l. grey 30 45
1766 – 100l.+400l. brown 30 45
1771 – 100l.+400l. mauve . . . 30 45

(b) Air. Symbolical design as T **198**. Imperf.
1772 **198** 80l.+420l. grey . . . . . 1·10 1·10
1773 – 200l.+800l. blue . . . . 1·20 1·10
DESIGNS—As Type **197**: 20l. Coats of Arms; 25l. Arterial road; 55l. Oil wells; 100l. "Agriculture". As T **198**: 200l. Icarus and Lockheed 14 Super Electra airplane.

199 Globe and Clasped Hands

1945. Charity. World Trade Union Congress, Paris. Symbolical designs inscr "CONFERINTA MONDIAL LA SINDICALA DIN PARIS 25 SEPTEMVRE 1945".
1776 **199** 80l.+920l. mauve . . . . 9·00 9·75
1777 – 160l.+1840l. brown . . . 9·00 9·75
1778 – 320l.+1680l. violet . . . 9·00 9·75
1779 – 440l.+2560l. green . . . 9·00 9·75
DESIGNS: 160l. Globe and Dove of Peace; 320l. Hand and hammer; 440l. Scaffolding and flags.

1946. Nos 1444/5 surch in figures.
1780 10l.+90l. on 100l.+400l. . . 90 1·70
1781 10l.+90l. on 200l.+800l. . . 90 1·70
1782 20l.+80l. on 100l.+400l. . . 90 1·70
1783 20l.+80l. on 200l.+800l. . . 90 1·70
1784 80l.+120l. on 100l.+400l. . 90 1·70
1785 80l.+120l. on 200l.+800l. . 90 1·70
1786 100l.+150l. on 100l.+400l. . 90 1·70
1787 100l.+150l. on 200l.+800l. . 90 1·70

200 Sower

201 Distribution of Title Deeds

1946. Agrarian Reform. Inscr "REFORMA AGRARA".
1788 – 80l. blue 30 30
1789 **200** 50l.+450l. red 30 30
1790 **201** 100l.+900l. purple . . . 30 30
1791 – 200l.+800l. orange . . . 30 30
1792 – 400l.+1600l. green . . . 30 30
DESIGNS—VERT: 80l. Blacksmith and ploughman. HORIZ: 200l. Ox-drawn farm wagon; 400l. Plough and tractor.

202

1946. 25th Anniv of Bucharest Philharmonic Orchestra.
1794 **202** 10l. blue 10 10
1795 – 20l. brown 10 10
1796 – 55l. green 10 10
1797 – 80l. violet 20 20
1798 – 160l. orange 10 10
1799 **202** 200l.+800l. red 80 85
1800 – 350l.+1650l. blue . . . . 1·00 1·10
DESIGNS: 20l., 55l., 160l. "XXV" and musical score; 80l., 350l. G. Enescu.

203 Building Worker 205 Sower

1946. Labour Day. Designs of workers inscr "ZIUA MUNCII".
1803 **203** 10l. red 10 50
1804 10l. green 50 45
1805 20l. blue 50 45
1806 20l. brown 10 50
1807 200l. red 20 20

1946. Youth Issue.
1809 **205** 10l.+100l. red & brn . . 10 10
1810 – 10l.+200l. pur & blue . . 1·20 1·10
1811 – 80l.+200l. brn & pur . . 10 10
1812 – 80l.+300l. mve & brn . . 10 10
1813 – 200l.+400l. red & grn . . 10 10
DESIGNS: No. 1810, Hurdling; 1811, Student; 1812, Worker and factory; 1813, Marching with flag.

206 Aviator and Aircraft 207 Football

1946. Air. Youth Issue.
1814 – 200l. blue and green . . 2·75 3·00
1815 **206** 500l. blue and orange . . 2·75 3·00
DESIGN: 200l. Airplane on ground.

1946. Sports, designs inscr "O.S.P." Perf or imperf.
1816 **207** 10l. blue (postage) . . . 30 35
1817 – 20l. red 30 35
1818 – 50l. violet 30 35
1819 – 80l. brown 30 35
1820 – 160l.+1340l. green . . . 30 35

1821 – 300l. red (air) . . . . . 1·00 1·30
1822 – 300l.+1200l. blue . . . . 1·00 1·30
DESIGNS: 20l. Diving; 50l. Running; 80l. Mountaineering; 160l. Ski jumping; 300l., 300l.+1200l. Flying.

208 "Traditional Ties" 209 Banat Girl holding Distaff

1946. Romanian–Soviet Friendship Pact.
1824 **208** 80l. brown 10 20
1825 – 100l. blue 10 20
1826 – 300l. grey 10 20
1827 – 300l.+1200l. red 80 55
DESIGNS: 100l. "Cultural ties"; 300l. "Economic ties"; 300l.+1200l. Dove.
No. 1827 also exists imperf.

1946. Charity. Women's Democratic Federation.
1829 – 80l. olive 55 10
1830 **209** 80l.+320l. red 10 10
1831 – 140l.+360l. orange . . . 10 10
1832 – 300l.+450l. green . . . 20 20
1833 – 600l.+900l. blue 30 25
DESIGNS: 80l. Girl and handloom; 140l. Wallachian girl and wheatsheaf; 300l. Transylvanian horsewoman; 600l. Moldavian girl carrying water.

211 King Michael and Food Transport

1947. Social Relief Fund.
1845 – 300l. olive 10 20
1846 **211** 600l. mauve 30 25
1847 – 1500l.+3500l. orange . . 30 25
1848 – 3700l.+5300l. violet . . . 30 25
DESIGNS—VERT: 300l. Loaf of bread and hungry child; 1500l. Angel bringing food and clothing to destitute people; 3700l. Loaf of bread and starving family.

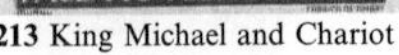

213 King Michael and Chariot

214 Symbols of Labour and Clasped Hands

1947. Peace.
1850 **213** 300l. purple 20 25
1851 – 600l. brown 20 25
1852 – 3000l. blue 20 25
1853 – 7200l. green 20 25
DESIGNS—VERT: 600l. Winged figure of Peace; 300l. Flags of four Allied Nations; 7200l. Dove of Peace.

1947. Trades Union Congress.
1854 **214** 200l. blue (postage) . . . 35 30
1855 300l. orange 35 30
1856 600l. red 35 30
1857 – 1100l. blue (air) 60 85
DESIGN—22 × 37 mm: 1100l. As Type **214** with Lockheed Super Electra airplane at top.

216 Worker and Torch

218 Symbolical of "Learning"

1947. Air. Trades Union Congress. Imperf.
1858 **216** 3000l.+7000l. brown . . 85 85

1947. Charity. People's Culture.
1859 – 200l.+200l. blue 15 20
1860 – 300l.+300l. brown . . . 15 20
1861 – 600l.+600l. green . . . 15 20
1862 – 1200l.+1200l. blue . . . 15 20
1863 **218** 1500l.+1500l. red . . . 15 20
DESIGNS—HORIZ: 200l. Boys' reading class; 300l. Girls' school; 600l. Engineering classroom; 1200l. School building.

219 King Michael

1947.
1865 **219** 1000l. blue 10 15
1869 3000l. blue 10 15
1866 5500l. green 15 15
1870 7200l. mauve 10 15
1871 15000l. blue 15 15
1867 20000l. brown 25 25
1872 21000l. mauve 15 25
1873 36000l. violet 35 30
1868 50000l. orange 40 30
Nos. 1865/8 are size 18 × 21½ mm and Nos. 1869/73 are 25 × 30 mm.

220 N. Grigorescu

221 Lisunov Li-2 Airliner

1947. Charity. Institute of Romanian–Soviet Studies.
1874 – 1500l.+1500l. purple (postage) 25 20
1875 – 1500l.+1500l. orange . . 25 20
1876 – 1500l.+1500l. green . . . 25 20
1877 **220** 1500l.+1500l. blue . . . 25 20
1878 – 1500l.+1500l. blue . . . 25 20
1879 – 1500l.+1500l. lake . . . 25 20
1880 – 1500l.+1500l. red 25 20
1881 – 1500l.+1500l. brown . . . 25 20
1882 **221** 15000l.+15000l. green (air) 75 65
PORTRAITS: No. 1874, Petru Movila; 1875, V. Babes; 1876, M. Eminescu; 1878, P. Tchaikovsky; 1879, M. Lomonosov; 1880, A. Pushkin; 1881, I. Y. Repin.
No. 1882 is imperf.

222 Miner

224 Douglas DC-4 Airliner over Black Sea

1947. Charity. Labour Day.
1883 **222** 1000l.+1000l. olive . . . 20 25
1884 – 1500l.+1500l. brown . . 15 20
1885 – 2000l.+2000l. blue . . . 15 20
1886 – 2500l.+2500l. mauve . . 15 20
1887 – 3000l.+3000l. red 20 25
DESIGNS: 1500l. Peasant; 2000l. Peasant woman; 2500l. Intellectual; 3000l. Factory worker.

1947. Air. Labour Day.
1888 – 3000l. red 25 25
1889 – 3000l. green 25 25
1890 – 3000l. brown 25 35
1891 **224** 3000l.+12,000l. blue . . 50 40
DESIGNS—24½ × 30 mm: No. 1888, Four parachutes; 1889, Air Force Monument; 1890, Douglas DC-4 over landscape.

(New currency 1 (new) leu = 100 (old) lei.)

225 King Michael and Timber Barges

227

1947. Designs with medallion portrait of King Michael.
1892 – 50b. orange 12 10
1893 **225** 1l. brown 10 10
1894 – 2l. blue 10 10
1895 – 3l. red 10 10
1896 – 5l. blue 10 10
1897 – 10l. blue 25 15
1898 – 12l. violet 60 30
1899 – 15l. blue . . . . 1·75 30
1900 – 20l. brown . . . . . . 1·00 20
1901 – 32l. brown . . . . . . 4·75 1·90
1902 – 36l. lake . . . . 6·25 1·50
DESIGNS: 50b. Harvesting; 2l. River Danube; 3l. Reshitza Industries; 5l. Curtea de Arges Cathedral; 10l. Royal Palace, Bucharest; 12, 36l. Saligny Bridge, Cernavoda; 15, 32l. Liner "Transylvania" in Port of Constantza; 20l. Oil Wells, Prahova.

1947. Balkan Games. Surch **2+3 LEI C.B.A. 1947** and bar.
1903 **219** 2+3l. on 36,000l. violet 55 70

1947. 17th Congress of General Assn of Romanian Engineers. With monogram as in T **227**.
1904 **227** 1l.+1l. red (postage) . . 10 10
1905 – 2l.+2l. brown 10 10
1906 – 3l.+3l. violet 25 25
1907 – 4l.+4l. olive 10 20
1908 – 5l.+5l. blue (air) 45 55
DESIGNS: 2l. Sawmill; 3l. Refinery; 4l. Steel mill; 5l. Gliders over mountains.

1947. Charity. Soviet–Romanian Amity. As No. 1896 surch **ARLUS 1-7-XI. 1947 +5**. Imperf.
1909 5l.+5l. blue 50 45

229 Beehive

230 Food Convoy

1947. Savings Day.
1910 **229** 12l. red 15 25

1947. Patriotic Defence.
1911 **230** 1l.+1l. blue 10 20
1912 – 2l.+2l. brown 10 20
1913 – 3l.+3l. red 10 20
1914 – 4l.+4l. blue 15 20
1915 – 5l.+5l. red 25 35
SYMBOLIC DESIGNS—HORIZ: 2l. Soldiers' parcels ("Everything for the front"); 3l. Modern hospital ("Heal the wounded"); 4l. Hungry children ("Help famine-stricken regions"). VERT: 5l. Manacled wrist and flag.

231 Allegory of work

1947. Charity. Trades Union Congress, Bucharest. Inscr "C.G.M. 1947".
1916 – 2l.+10l. red (postage) . . 15 20
1917 **231** 7l.+10l. black 20 25
1918 – 11l. red and blue (air) . . 35 45
DESIGNS—As T **231**: 2l. Industrial and agricultural workers. 23 × 18 mm: 11l. Lisunov Li-2 airliner over demonstration.

233 Map of Romania

1948. Census of 1948.
1925 **233** 12l. blue 30 20

234 Printing Works and Press

1948. 75th Anniv of Romanian State Stamp Printing Works.
1926 **234** 6l. red 95 70
1927 7l.50 green 45 10

235 Discus Thrower

237 Industrial Worker

1948. Balkan Games, 1947. Inscr as in T **235**. Imperf or perf.
1928 **235** 1l.+1l. brown (postage) 30 35
1929 – 2l.+2l. red 45 45
1930 – 5l.+5l. blue 70 70
1931 – 7l.+7l. violet (air) . . . 85 65
1932 – 10l.+10l. green . . . . . 1·30 95
DESIGNS: 2l. Runner; 5l. Heads of two young athletes; 7, 10l. Airplane over running track.

1948. Nos. 1892/1902 optd **R.P.R.** (Republica Populara Romana).
1933 50b. orange 10 20
1934 1l. brown 10 15
1935 2l. blue 45 15
1936 3l. red 55 15
1937 5l. blue 90 15
1938 10l. blue . . . . 1·10 25
1939 12l. violet . . . . 2·10 30
1940 15l. blue . . . . 2·10 35
1941 20l. brown . . . . 1·30 35
1942 32l. brown . . . . 8·50 4·00
1943 36l. lake . . . . 6·50 2·40

1948. Young Workers' Union. Imperf or perf.
1954 **237** 2l.+2l. blue (postage) . . 25 30
1955 – 3l.+3l. green 25 25
1956 – 5l.+5l. brown 25 35
1957 – 8l.+8l. red 30 35
1958 – 12l.+12l. blue (air) . . . 1·10 1·00
DESIGNS—As Type **237**: 3l. Peasant girl and wheatsheaf; 5l. Student and book. TRIANGULAR: 8l. Youths bearing Filimon Sarbu banner. 36 × 23 mm: 12l. Airplane and barn swallows.

240 "Friendship"

241 "New Constitution"

1948. Romanian–Bulgarian Amity.
1959 **240** 32l. brown 70 45

1948. New Constitution.
1960 **241** 1l. red 15 20
1961 2l. orange 35 35
1962 12l. blue . . . . 1·60 60

242 Globe and Banner

243 Aviator and Heinkel He 116A

244 Barbed Wire Entanglement

1948. Labour Day.
1963 **242** 8l.+8l. red (postage) . . 1·10 2·00
1964 – 10l.+10l. green . . . . . 1·90 2·50
1965 – 12l.+12l. brown . . . . 2·25 3·25
1966 **243** 20l.+20l. blue (air) . . . 4·25 5·00
DESIGNS—HORIZ: 10l. Peasants and mountains. VERT: 12l. Worker and factory.

1948. Army Day.
1967 – 1l.50+1l.50 red (postage) 20 30
1968 **244** 2l.+2l. purple 20 30
1969 – 4l.+4l. brown 50 55
1970 – 7l.50+7l.50 black . . . . 90 1·00
1971 – 8l.+8l. violet . . . . . . 1·00 1·10
1972 – 3l.+3l. blue (air) . . . . 3·75 4·50
1973 – 5l.+5l. blue . . . . . . 6·75 6·75
DESIGNS—VERT: 1l.50, Infantry; 3l. Ilyushin Stormovik fighter planes; 5l. Petlyakov Pe-2 dive bomber Il-2M3. HORIZ: 4l. Artillery; 7l.50, Tank; 8l. Destroyer.

245 Five Portraits

246 Proclamation of Islaz

1948. Cent of 1848 Revolution. Dated "1848 1948".
1974 – 2l.+2l. purple 20 30
1975 **245** 5l.+5l. violet 25 35
1976 **246** 11l. red 40 40
1977 – 10l.+10l. green 40 30
1978 – 36l.+18l. blue . . . . . 1·50 1·20
DESIGNS—22 × 38 mm. HORIZ: 10l. Balcescu, Petofi, Iancu, Barnutiu Baritiu and Murcu. VERT: 2l. Nicolas Balcescu; 36l. Balcescu, Kogalniceanu, Alecsandri and Cuza.

247 Emblem of Republic

1948.
2023 **247** 50b. red 70 30
1980 0.50l. red 15 10
1981 1l. brown 15 10
1982 2l. green 15 10
1983 3l. grey 25 10
1984 4l. brown 25 10
1985 5l. blue 25 10
2028 5l. violet . . . . 1·10 10
1986 10l. blue 65 10
No. 2023 is inscribed "BANI 0.50" (= ½ bani) and in No. 1980 this was corrected to "LEI 0.50".

248 Monimoa Gliders

249 Yachts

1948. Air Force and Navy Day. (a) Air Force (vert).
1987 **248** 2l.+2l. blue 75 95
1988 – 5l.+5l. violet 75 95
1989 – 8l.+8l. red . . . . 1·10 1·50
1990 – 10l.+10l. brown . . . . 1·90 1·90

(b) Navy (horiz).
1991 **249** 2l.+2l. green 75 95
1992 – 5l.+5l. grey 75 95
1993 – 8l.+8l. blue . . . . . . 1·10 1·50
1994 – 10l.+10l. red . . . . . . 1·90 2·00

DESIGNS—AIR FORCE: 5l. Aurel Vlaicu's No. 1 "Crazy Fly" airplane; 8l. Lisunov Li-2 airliner and tractor; 10l. Lisunov Li-2 airliner. NAVY: 5l. "Mircea" (cadet ship), 1882; 8l. "Romana Mare" (Danube river steamer); 10l. "Transylvania" (liner).

1948. Surch.

1995	**240**	3ll. on 32l. brown	55	30

251 Newspapers and Torch

252 Soviet Soldiers' Monument

1948. Press Week. Imperf or perf.

1996	**251**	5l.+5l. red	10	10
1997		10l. brown	30	45
1998	–	10l.+10l. violet	65	60
1999	–	15l.+15l. blue	90	1·00

DESIGNS—HORIZ: 10l. (No. 1998), Flag, torch and ink-well. VERT: 15l. Alex Sahia (journalist).

1948. Romanian–Russian Amity.

2000	**252**	10l. red (postage)	35	45
2001	–	10l.+10l. green	2·10	2·10
2002	–	15l.+15l. blue	2·40	2·75
2003	–	20l.+20l. blue (air)	7·25	7·50

DESIGNS—VERT: 10l. (No. 2001), Badge of Arlus; 15l. Kremlin. HORIZ: 20l. Lisunov Li-2 airplane.

255 Emblem of Republic

1948. Air. Designs showing aircraft.

2004	**255**	30l. red	20	10
2005	–	50l. green	30	30
2006	–	100l. blue	3·75	2·10

DESIGNS: 50l. Workers in a field; 100l. Steam train, airplane and liner.

256 Lorry

1948. Work on Communications.

2007	–	1l.+1l. black and green	30	45
2008	**256**	3l.+3l. black & brown	30	50
2009	–	11l.+11l. black & blue	1·90	1·75
2010	–	15l.+15l. black and red	4·75	3·50

DESIGNS: 1l. Dockers loading freighter; 11l. Lisunov Li-2 airliner on ground and in air; 15l. Steam train.

257 Nicolas Balcescu

1948.

2012	**257**	20l. red	40	25

258 Hands Breaking Chain

1948. 1st Anniv of People's Republic.

2013	**258**	5l. red	30	25

259 Runners

260 Lenin

1948. National Sports Organization. Imperf or perf.

2014	**259**	5l.+5l. green (postage)	2·30	2·30
2017		5l.+5l. brown	2·30	2·30
2015	–	10l.+10l. violet	4·00	4·00
2018	–	10l.+10l. red	4·00	4·00
2016	–	20l.+20l. blue (air)	16·50	15·00
2019	–	20l.+20l. green	16·50	15·00

DESIGNS—HORIZ: 10l. Parade of athletes with flags. VERT: 20l. Boy flying model airplane.

1949. 25th Death Anniv of Lenin. Perf or imperf.

2020	**260**	20l. black	20	25

261 Dancers

263 Pushkin

262 I. C. Frimu and Revolutionaries

1949. 90th Anniv of Union of Romanian Principalities.

2021	**261**	10l. blue	30	25

1949. 30th Death Anniv of Ion Frimu (union leader and journalist). Perf or imperf.

2022	**262**	20l. red	30	25

1949. 150th Birth Anniv of A. S. Pushkin (Russian poet).

2030	**263**	11l. red	55	45
2031		30l. green	65	55

264 Globe and Posthorn

265 Forms of Transport

1949. 75th Anniv of U.P.U.

2032	**264**	20l. brown	1·20	1·00
2033	**265**	30l. blue	2·75	3·00

266 Russians entering Bucharest

1949. 5th Anniv of Russian Army's Entry into Bucharest. Perf or imperf.

2034	**266**	50l. brown on green	55	55

267 "Romanian–Soviet Amity"

1949. Romanian–Soviet Friendship Week. Perf or imperf.

2035	**267**	20l. red	40	40

268 Forms of Transport

269 Stalin

1949. International Congress of Transport Unions. Perf or imperf.

2036	**268**	11l. blue	65	65
2037		20l. red	1·10	90

1949. Stalin's 70th Birthday. Perf or imperf.

2038	**269**	31l. green	30	25

270 "The Third Letter"

271 Michael Eminescu

1950. Birth Centenary of Eminescu (poet).

2040	**270**	11l. green	75	50
2041	–	11l. brown	1·10	45
2042	–	11l. mauve	75	35
2043	–	11l. violet	75	35
2044	**271**	11l. blue	70	35

DESIGNS (Scenes representing poems): No. 2041, "Angel and Demon"; 2042, "Ruler and Proletariat"; 2043, "Life".

272 "Dragaica Fair"

1950. Birth Centenary of Ion Andreescu (painter).

(a) Perf.

2045	**272**	5l. olive	70	50
2047	–	20l. brown	1·50	1·00

(b) Perf or imperf.

2046	–	11l. blue	1·10	60

DESIGNS—VERT: 11l. Andreescu. HORIZ: 20l. "The Village Well".

273 Factory and Graph

274 Worker and Flag

1950. State Plan, 1950 Inscr "PLANUL DU STAT 1950".

2048	**273**	11l. red	25	20
2049	–	31l. violet	85	35

DESIGN: 31l. Tractor and factories.

No. 2048 exists imperf.

1950. Labour Day. Perf or imperf.

2050	**274**	31l. orange	30	10

275 Emblem of Republic

276 Trumpeter and Drummer

1950.

2051	**275**	50b. black	25	20
2052		1l. red	20	10
2053		2l. grey	20	10
2054		3l. purple	25	10
2055		4l. mauve	20	10
2056		5l. brown	25	10
2057		6l. green	25	10
2058		7l. brown	25	10
2059		7l.50 blue	35	10
2060		10l. brown	45	10
2061		11l. red	45	10
2062		15l. blue	45	10
2063		20l. green	45	10
2064		31l. green	60	10
2065		36l. brown	1·00	45

For stamps as Type **275** but with inscriptions in white, see Nos. 2240, etc, and Nos. 2277/8.

1950. 1st Anniv of Romanian Pioneers Organization.

2074	**276**	8l. blue	85	45
2075	–	11l. purple	1·30	75
2076	–	31l. red	2·40	1·50

DESIGNS: 11l. Children reading; 31l. Youth parade.

277 Engineer

278 Aurel Vlaicu and his Airplane No. 1 "Crazy Fly"

1950. Industrial Nationalization.

2077	**277**	11l. red	25	25
2078		11l. blue	45	25
2079		11l. brown	45	25
2080		11l. olive	15	15

1950. 40th Anniv of 1st Flight by A. Vlaicu.

2081	**278**	3l. green	30	20
2082		6l. blue	30	25
2083		8l. blue	40	35

279 Mother and Child

1950. Peace Congress, Bucharest.

2084	**279**	11l. red	20	20
2085	–	20l. brown	30	20

DESIGN: 20l. Lathe operator and graph.

280 Statue and Flags

282 Young People and Badge

1950. Romanian–Soviet Amity.

2086	**280**	30l. brown	40	25

1950. Romanian–Hungarian Amity. Optd **TRAIASCA PRIETENIA ROMANO-MAGHIARA.**

2087	**275**	15l. blue	55	25

1950. GMA Complex Sports Facilities. Designs incorporating badge.

2088	–	3l. red	1·10	1·00
2089	**282**	5l. brown	75	70
2090		5l. blue	75	70
2091	–	11l. green	75	70
2092	–	31l. olive	1·60	1·60

DESIGNS: 3l. Agriculture and Industry; 11l. Runners; 31l. Gymnasts.

283

284 Ski-jumper

1950. 3rd Congress of "ARLUS".

2093	**283**	11l. orange on orange	30	25
2094		11l. blue on blue	30	25

1951. Winter Sports.

2095	**284**	4l. brown	45	65
2096	–	5l. red	55	55
2097	–	11l. blue	1·10	55
2098	–	20l. brown	1·10	90
2099	–	31l. green	2·75	1·60

DESIGNS: 5l. Skater; 11l. Skier; 20l. Ice hockey; 31l. Tobogganing.

286 Peasant and Tractor

1951. Agricultural and Industrial Exhibition.
2100 – 11l. brown 10 15
2101 **286** 31l. blue 45 25
DESIGN—VERT: 11l. Worker and machine.

287 Star of the Republic, Class I-II **288** Youth Camp

1951. Orders and Medals. Perf or imperf.
2102 – 2l. green 15 20
2103 – 4l. blue 20 25
2104 – 11l. red 30 35
2105 **287** 35l. brown 40 55
DESIGNS: 2l. Medal of Work; 4l. Star of the Republic, Class III–V; 11l. Order of Work.

1951. 2nd Anniv of Romanian Pioneers Organization.
2106 **288** 1l. green 65 45
2107 – 11l. blue 65 45
2108 – 35l. red 85 65
DESIGNS—VERT: 11l. Children meeting Stalin. HORIZ: 35l. Decorating boy on parade.

289 Woman and Flags **290** Ion Negulici

1951. International Women's Day. Perf or imperf.
2109 **289** 11l. brown 40 25

1951. Death Centenary of Negulici (painter).
2110 **290** 35l. red 2·25 1·75

291 Cyclists

1951. Romanian Cycle Race.
2111 **291** 11l. brown 1·10 70

292 F. Sarbu **294** Students

293 "Revolutionary Romania"

1951. 10th Death Anniv of Sarbu (patriot).
2112 **292** 11l. brown 40 25

1951. Death Centenary of C. D. Rosenthal (painter).
2113 **293** 11l. green 95 55
2114 11l. orange 95 55
2115 – 11l. brown 95 55
2116 – 11l. violet 95 55
DESIGN—VERT: Nos. 2115/16, "Rumania calls to the Masses".

1951. 3rd World Youth Festival, Berlin.
2117 **294** 1l. red 30 35
2118 – 5l. blue 60 35
2119 – 11l. purple 1·00 75
DESIGNS: 5l. Girl, boy and flag; 11l. Young people around globe.

295 "Scanteia" Building **296** Soldier and Pithead

1951. 20th Anniv of "Scanteia" (Communist newspaper).
2120 **295** 11l. blue 40 25

1951. Miners' Day.
2121 **296** 5l. blue 30 25
2122 – 11l. mauve 45 25
DESIGN: 11l. Miner and pithead.

297 Order of Defence **298** Oil Refinery

1951. Liberation Day.
2123 **297** 10l. red 30 25

1951. Five-Year Plan. Dated "1951 1955".
2124 **298** 1l. olive (postage) 25 20
2125 – 2l. red 90 20
2126 – 3l. red 50 40
2127 – 4l. brown 35 20
2128 – 5l. green 35 15
2129 – 6l. blue 1·30 90
2130 – 7l. green 85 45
2131 – 8l. brown 55 30
2132 – 11l. blue 1·10 40
2133 – 35l. violet 75 50

2134 – 30l. green (air) 3·00 2·00
2135 – 50l. brown 6·00 4·25
DESIGNS: 2l. Miner and pithead; 3l. Soldier and pylons; 4l. Steel furnace; 5l. Combine-harvester; 6l. Canal construction; 7l. Threshing machine; 8l. Sanatorium; 11l. Dam and pylons; 30l. Potato planting; 35l. Factory; 50l. Liner, steam locomotive and Lisunov Li-2 airliner.

299 Orchestra and Dancers **300** Soldier and Arms

1951. Music Festival.
2136 **299** 11l. brown 30 35
2137 – 11l. blue (Mixed choir) 40 25
2138 – 11l. mauve (Lyre and dove) (vert) 30 25

1951. Army Day.
2139 **300** 11l. blue 30 25

301 Arms of U.S.S.R. and Romania

1951. Romanian–Soviet Friendship.
2140 **301** 4l. brown on buff 20 20
2141 35l. orange 60 50

302 P. Tcancenco **304** I. L. Caragiale

303 Open Book "1907"

1951. 25th Death Anniv of Tcancenco (revolutionary).
2142 **302** 10l. olive 30 45

1952. Birth Centenary of Ion Caragiale (dramatist).
(a) Unissued values surch.
2143 **303** 20b. on 11l. red 55 40
2144 – 55b. on 11l. green 80 45
2145 **304** 75b. on 11l. blue 1·10 55

(b) Without surch.
2146 **303** 55b. red 1·00 25
2147 – 55b. green 1·00 25
2148 **304** 55b. blue 1·00 25
2149 – 1l. brown 2·50 1·20
DESIGNS—HORIZ: Nos. 2144, 2147, Profile of Caragiale; 1l. Caragiale addressing assembly.

1952. Currency revalued. Surch.
2174 **275** 3b. on 1l. red 1·30 4·50
2175 3b. on 2l. grey 1·50 90
2176 3b. on 4l. mauve 1·30 85
2177 3b. on 5l. red 1·50 90
2178 3b. on 7l.50 blue 4·25 1·30
2179 3b. on 10l. brown 1·50 90
2157a **255** 3b. on 30l. red 6·25 4·75
2158 – 3b. on 50l. (No. 2005) 1·80 1·40
2159 – 3b. on 100l. (No. 2006) 6·25 3·00
2191 **278** 10b. on 3l. green 1·50 70
2218 **301** 10b. on 4l. brown on buff 80 70
2192 **278** 10b. on 6l. blue 1·60 70
2193 10b. on 8l. blue 1·60 70
2220 **302** 10b. on 10l. olive 1·75 70
2160 **263** 10b. on 11l. red 2·40 1·80
2164 **270** 10b. on 11l. green 2·40 1·80
2165 – 10b. on 11l. (No. 2041) 2·20 1·80
2166 – 10b. on 11l. (No. 2042) 2·20 1·80
2167 – 10b. on 11l. (No. 2043) 2·20 1·80
2168 **271** 10b. on 11l. blue 2·20 1·80
2161 **263** 10b. on 30l. green 2·50 1·80
2219 **301** 10b. on 35l. orange 2·00 1·20
2199 – 20b. on 2l. (No. 2102) 2·75 1·60
2200 – 20b. on 4l. (No. 2103) 2·75 1·60
2171 **273** 20b. on 11l. red 1·70 1·10
2201 – 20b. on 11l. (No. 2104) 2·75 1·60
2194 – 20b. on 20l. (No. 2085) 1·70 80
2172 – 20b. on 31l. (No. 2049) 1·70 1·10
2202 **287** 20b. on 35l. brown 2·75 1·60
2206 **298** 35b. on 1l. olive 2·75 95
2207 – 35b. on 2l. (No. 2125) 4·50 1·40
2208 – 35b. on 3l. (No. 2126) 3·25 1·40
2209 – 35b. on 4l. (No. 2127) 2·75 1·50
2210 – 35b. on 5l. (No. 2128) 2·75 2·30
2151 **241** 50b. on 12l. blue 2·75 65
2180 **275** 55b. on 50b. black 4·50 1·20
2181 55b. on 3l. purple 4·50 1·20
2195 – 55b. on 3l. (No. 2088) 19·00 12·00
2169 **272** 55b. on 5l. olive 7·00 3·75
2204 **295** 55b. on 5l. blue 5·75 2·75
2182 **275** 55b. on 6l. green 4·50 1·20
2183 55b. on 7l. brown 4·50 1·20
2188 **276** 55b. on 8l. blue 5·25 4·00
2205 **297** 55b. on 10l. red 3·00 2·40
2170 – 55b. on 11l. (No. 2046) 7·25 3·25
2189 – 55b. on 11l. (No. 2075) 4·00 3·00
2150 **233** 55b. on 12l. blue 1·70 1·80
2184 **275** 55b. on 15l. blue 4·00 1·20
2185 55b. on 20l. green 4·25 1·80
2196 – 55b. on 20l. (No. 2098) 18·00 12·00
2186 **275** 55b. on 31l. green 4·75 1·20
2173 **274** 55b. on 31l. orange 2·75 2·50
2190 – 55b. on 31l. (No. 2076) 4·00 4·00
2197 – 55b. on 31l. (No. 2099) 17·00 12·00
2198 **286** 55b. on 31l. blue 3·00 2·75
2203 – 55b. on 35l. (No. 2108) 4·00 5·25
2187 **275** 55b. on 36l. brown 4·25 1·70
2211 – 1l. on 6l. (No. 2129) 6·00 3·75
2212 – 1l. on 7l. (No. 2130) 6·00 2·20
2213 – 1l. on 8l. (No. 2131) 4·50 2·75
2214 – 1l. on 11l. (No. 2132) 6·00 2·30
2216 – 1l. on 30l. (No. 2134) 6·75 2·10
2215 – 1l. on 35l. (No. 2133) 6·00 2·10
2217 – 1l. on 50l. (No. 2135) 13·50 4·25
2152 – 1l.75 on 2l.+2l. purple (No. 1974) 7·00 3·00
2153 **245** 1l.75 on 5l.+5l. violet 7·00 3·00
2154 **246** 1l.75 on 11l. red 7·00 3·00
2155 – 1l.75 on 10l.+10l. (No. 1977) 7·00 3·00
2156 – 1l.75 on 36l.+18l. (No. 1978) 7·00 3·00

1952. Air. Surch with airplane, **AERIANA** and value.
2162 **264** 3l. on 20l. brown 30·00 21·00
2163 **265** 5l. on 30l. blue 45·00 24·00

307 Railwayman **308** Gogol and character from "Taras Bulba"

1952. Railway Day.
2229 **307** 55b. brown 1·75 25

1952. Death Centenary of Nikolai Gogol (Russian writer).
2230 **308** 55b. blue 85 25
2231 – 1l.75 green 2·75 45
DESIGN—VERT: 1l.75, Gogol and open book.

309 Maternity Medal **310** I. P. Pavlov

1952. International Women's Day.
2232 **309** 20b. blue and purple 50 15
2233 – 55b. brown and chestnut 1·00 30
2234 – 1l.75 brown and red 2·50 45
MEDALS: 55b. "Glory of Maternity" medal; 1l.75, "Mother Heroine" medal.

1952. Romanian–Soviet Medical Congress.
2235 **310** 11l. red 1·90 25

311 Hammer and Sickle Medal **312** Boy and Girl Pioneers

1952. Labour Day.
2236 **311** 55b. brown 1·20 20

1952. 3rd Anniv of Romanian Pioneers Organization.
2237 **312** 20b. brown 80 15
2238 – 55b. green 1·80 25
2239 – 1l.75 blue 3·75 35
DESIGNS—VERT: 55b. Pioneer nature-study group. HORIZ: 1l.75, Worker and pioneers.

1952. As T **275** but with figures and inscriptions in white. Bani values size 20½ × 24¼ mm, lei values size 24½ × 29½ mm.
2240 **275** 3b. orange 25 20
2241 5b. red 35 15
2242 7b. green 40 25
2243 10b. brown 50 15
2244 20b. blue 1·75 15
2245 35b. brown 1·20 15
2246 50b. green 1·60 15
2247 55b. violet 3·50 15
2248 1l.10 brown 3·25 20
2249 1l.75 violet 15·50 35
2250 2l. olive 3·25 40
2251 2l.35 brown 3·50 35
2252 2l.55 orange 4·50 35
2253 3l. green 4·75 35
2254 5l. red 6·25 60
For similar stamps with star added at top of emblem, see Nos. 2277/8.

314 "Smirdan" (after Grigorescu) **315** Leonardo da Vinci

1952. 75th Anniv of Independence.
2255 **314** 50b. lake 55 10
2256 – 1l.10 blue 90 30
DESIGN—HORIZ: 1l.10, Romanian and Russian soldiers.

1952. 500th Anniv of Birth of Leonardo da Vinci.
2257 **315** 55b. violet 2·30 35

316 Miner

317 Students' Union Badge

1952. Miners' Day.
2258 **316** 20b. red 1·10 30
2259 55b. violet 1·00 25

1952. Int Students' Union Council, Bucharest.
2260 **317** 10b. blue 20 10
2261 – 20b. orange 1·50 25

2262 – 55b. green . . . . 1·50 30
2263 – 1l.75 red . . . . 2·75 75
DESIGNS—HORIZ: 20b. Student in laboratory (35½ × 22 mm); 1l.75, Six students dancing (30 × 24 mm). VERT: 55b. Students playing football (24 × 30 mm).

318 Soldier, Sailor and Airman

1952. Army Day.
2264 **318** 55b. blue 85 25

319 Statue and Flags **320** Workers and Views of Russia and Romania (after N. Parlius)

1952. Romanian–Soviet Friendship.
2265 **319** 55b. red 55 10
2266 **320** 1l.75 brown . . . . . . 1·50 30

321 Rowing **322** N. Balcescu (after C. Tattarescu)

1952. Physical Culture.
2267 **321** 20b. blue . . . . 1·90 20
2268 – 1l.75 red (Athletes) . . . 4·75 60

1952. Death Centenary of Balcescu (revolutionary).
2269 **322** 55b. grey . . . . 2·40 10
2270 1l.75 olive . . . . 6·00 75

323 Emblem and Flags **324**

1952. New Constitution.
2271 **323** 55b. green 95 25

1952. 5th Anniv of People's Republic.
2272 **324** 55b. multicoloured . . . 1·70 40

325 Millo, Caragiale and Mme. Romanescu **326** Foundry Worker

1953. Centenary of Caragiale National Theatre.
2273 **325** 55b. blue . . . . 1·70 25

1953. 3rd Industrial and Agricultural Congress.
2274 **326** 55b. green 60 10
2275 – 55b. orange 50 30
2276 – 55b. brown 65 10
DESIGNS—HORIZ: No. 2275, Farm workers and tractor; 2276, Workman, refinery and oil wells.

1953. As Nos. 2240, etc, but with star added at top of emblem.
2277 **275** 5b. red 35 15
2278 55b. purple . . . . . . 1·00 25

327 "The Strikers of Grivitsa" (after Nazarev)

1953. 20th Anniv of Grivitsa Strike.
2279 **327** 55b. brown . . . . . . 1·40 25

328

1953. 5th Anniv of Treaty of Friendship with Russia.
2280 **328** 55b. brown on blue . . . 1·40 25

329 Table Tennis Badge **330** Oltenian Carpet

1953. 20th World Table Tennis Championship, Bucharest.
2281 **329** 55b. green . . . . 5·00 1·00
2282 55b. brown . . . . . . 4·25 75

1953. Romanian Art.
2283 – 10b. green 35 10
2284 – 20b. brown 80 10
2285 – 35b. violet . . . . . . 1·40 10
2286 – 55b. blue . . . . 2·40 10
2287 **330** 1l. purple . . . . 4·25 20
DESIGNS—VERT: 10b. Pottery; 20b. Campulung peasant girl; 55b. Apuseni Mountains peasant girl. HORIZ: 35b. National dance.

331 Karl Marx **332** Pioneers planting Tree

1953. 70th Death Anniv of Karl Marx.
2288 **331** 1l.55 brown . . . . . . 1·70 35

1953. 4th Anniv of Romanian Pioneers Organization.
2289 **332** 35b. green 80 20
2290 – 55b. blue . . . . 1·30 20
2291 – 1l.75 brown . . . . . . 2·10 40
DESIGNS—VERT: 55b. Boy and girl flying model gliders. HORIZ: 1l.75, Pioneers and instructor.

333 Women and Flags **334**

1953. 3rd World Congress of Women.
2292 **333** 55b. brown . . . . . . 1·20 25

1953. 4th World Youth Festival.
2293 **334** 20b. orange 55 25
2294 – 55b. blue 70 40
2295 – 65b. red 95 65
2296 – 1l.75 purple . . . . . . 3·75 1·30
DESIGNS—VERT: 55b. Students releasing dove over globe. HORIZ: 65b. Girl presenting bouquet; 1l.75, Folk dancers.

335 Cornfield and Forest **336** V. V. Mayakovsky

1953. Forestry Month.
2297 – 20b. blue 65 55
2298 **335** 38b. green 00 80
2299 – 55b. brown . . . . . . 2·30 60
DESIGNS—VERT: 20b. Waterfall and trees; 55b. Forestry worker.

1953. 60th Birth Anniv of Vladimir Mayakovsky (Russian poet).
2300 **336** 55b. brown . . . . . . 1·20 35

337 Miner

1953. Miners' Day.
2301 **337** 1l.55 black . . . . . . 2·00 25

338 Telephonist, G.P.O. and P.O. Worker

1953. 50th Anniv of Construction of G.P.O.
2302 **338** 20b. brown 35 10
2303 – 55b. olive 60 10
2304 – 1l. blue . . . . 1·30 20
2305 – 1l.55 lake . . . . 2·00 45
DESIGNS: 55b. Postwoman and G.P.O.; 1l. G.P.O. radio transmitter and map; 1l.55, Telegraphist, G.P.O. and teletypist.

339 **340** Soldier and Flag

1953. 9th Anniv of Liberation.
2306 **339** 55b. brown 85 25

1953. Army Day.
2307 **340** 55b. olive 95 25

341 Girl and Model Glider

1953. Aerial Sports.
2308 **341** 10b. green and orange 1·90 35
2309 – 20b. olive and brown . . 2·75 20
2310 – 55b. purple and red . . 10·00 45
2311 – 1l.75 brown and purple 12·00 70
DESIGNS: 20b. Parachutists; 55b. Glider and pilot; 1l.75, Zlin Z-22 monoplane.

342 Workman, Girl and Flags

1953. Romanian–Soviet Friendship.
2312 **342** 55b. brown 60 10
2313 – 1l.55 lake . . . . 1·50 35
DESIGN: 1l.55, Spassky Tower (Moscow Kremlin) and Volga–Don canal.

343 "Unity"

1953. 3rd World Trades' Union Congress.
2314 **343** 55b. olive 50 20
2315 – 1l.25 red . . . . 1·30 45
DESIGN—VERT: 1l.25, Workers, flags and globe.

344 C. Porumbescu **345** Agricultural Machinery

1953. Birth Centenary of Porumbescu (composer).
2316 **344** 55b. lilac . . . . 5·25 25

1953. Agricultural designs.
2317 **345** 10b. olive 15 10
2318 – 35b. green 40 10
2319 – 2l.55 brown . . . . . . 2·75 65
DESIGNS: 35b. Tractor drawing disc harrows; 2l.55, Cows grazing.

346 Vlaicu and his Airplane No. 1 "Crazy Fly" **347** Lenin

1953. 40th Death Anniv of Vlaicu (pioneer aviator).
2320 **346** 50b. blue 85 25

1954. 30th Death Anniv of Lenin.
2321 **347** 55b. brown . . . . . . 1·10 25

348 Red Deer Stag **350** O. Bancila

349 Calimanesti

1954. Forestry Month.
2322 **348** 20b. brown on yellow . . 4·50 35
2323 – 55b. violet on yellow . . 2·30 35
2324 – 1l.75 blue on yellow . . 4·25 75
DESIGNS: 55b. Pioneers planting tree; 1l.75, Forest.

1954. Workers' Rest Homes.
2325 **349** 5b. black on yellow . . . 60 10
2326 – 1l.55 black on blue . . . 2·00 20
2327 – 2l. green on pink . . . . 4·50 25
2328 – 2l.35 brown on green . . 3·75 90
2329 – 2l.55 brown on green . . 4·25 1·10
DESIGNS: 1l.55, Sinaia; 2l. Predeal; 2l.35, Tusnad; 2l.55, Govora.

1954. 10th Death Anniv of Bancila (painter).
2330 **350** 55b. green and brown . . 2·10 1·30

351 Child and Dove of Peace **353** Stephen the Great

352 Girl Pioneer feeding Calf

1954. International Children's Day.
2331 **351** 55b. brown 85 25

1954. 5th Anniv of Romanian Pioneer Organization.
2332 **352** 20b. black 40 15
2333 – 55b. blue 70 25
2334 – 1l.75 red . . . . 3·75 55
DESIGNS: 55b. Girl Pioneers harvesting; 1l.75, Young Pioneers examining globe.

1954. 450th Death Anniv of Stephen the Great.
2335 **353** 55b. brown . . . . . . 1·40 30

354 Miner operating Coal-cutter **355** Dr. V. Babes

1954. Miners' Day.
2336 **354** 1l.75 black . . . . . . 1·40 45

1954. Birth Centenary of Babes (pathologist).
2337 **355** 55b. red . . . . 1·20 25

356 Sailor, Flag and Destroyer "Regele Ferdinand" **357** Dedication Tablet

1954. Navy Day.
2338 **356** 55b. blue 95 25

1954. 5th Anniv of Mutual Aid Organization.
2339 – 20b. violet 55 10
2340 **357** 55b. brown 95 20
DESIGN: 20b. Man receiving money from counter clerk.

358 Liberation Monument **359** Recreation Centre

1954. 10th Anniv of Liberation.
2341 **358** 55b. violet and red . . . 1·10 25

1954. Liberation Anniv Celebrations.
2342 **359** 20b. blue 25 10
2343 – 38b. violet 85 25
2344 – 55b. purple 95 20
2345 – 1l.55 brown . . . . . . 2·50 40
DESIGNS—38 × 22 mm: 55b. "Scanteia" offices. $24\frac{1}{2}$ × $29\frac{1}{2}$ mm: 38b. Opera House, Bucharest; 1l.55, Radio Station.

360 Pilot and Mikoyan Gurevich MiG-15 Jet Fighters **361** Chemical Plant and Oil Derricks

1954. Aviation Day.
2346 **360** 55b. blue . . . . 2·50 25

1954. International Chemical and Petroleum Workers Conference, Bucharest.
2347 **361** 55b. black . . . . 2·50 35

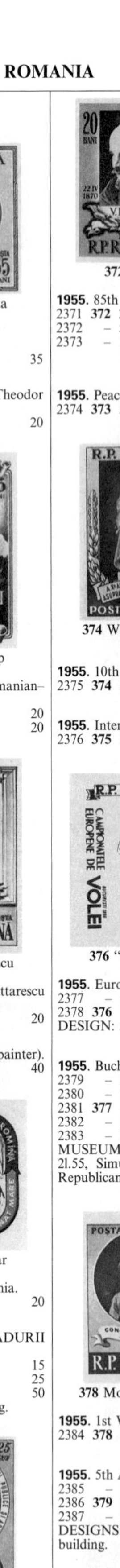

362 Dragon Pillar, Peking **363** T. Neculuta

1954. Chinese Culture Week.
2348 **362** 55b. black on yellow . . 2·40 35

1954. 50th Death Anniv of Dumitru Theodor Neculuta (poet).
2349 **363** 55b. violet . . . . . . 1·50 20

364 ARLUS Badge **365** Friendship

1954. 10th Anniv of "ARLUS" and Romanian–Russian Friendship.
2350 **364** 55b. red 50 20
2351 **365** 65b. purple 80 20

366 G. Tattarescu **367** B. Iscovescu

1954. 60th Death Anniv of Gheorghe Tattarescu (painter).
2352 **366** 55b. red . . . . 1·60 20

1954. Death Centenary of Barbu Iscovescu (painter).
2353 **367** 1l.75 brown . . . . . . 2·75 40

368 Teleprinter **369** Wild Boar

1954. Cent of Telecommunications in Romania.
2354 **368** 50b. lilac . . . . 1·00 20

1955. Forestry Month. Inscr "LUNA PADURII 1955".
2355 **369** 35b. brown . . . . . . 1·30 15
2356 – 65b. blue . . . . 1·40 25
2357 – 1l.20 red . . . . 4·25 50
DESIGNS: 65b. Tree planting; 1l.20, Logging.

370 Airman **371** Clasped Hands

1955. Occupations.
2358 – 3b. blue 15 10
2359 – 5b. violet 05 10
2360 **370** 10b. brown 15 10
2361 – 20b. mauve 05 10
2362 – 30b. blue . . . . 1·10 10
2363 – 35b. turquoise 30 10
2364 – 40b. blue . . . . 1·10 15
2365 – 55b. olive 75 10
2366 – 1l. violet . . . . 1·30 10
2367 – 1l.55 lake . . . . 2·10 10
2368 – 2l.35 buff . . . . 3·50 35
2369 – 2l.55 green . . . . . . 4·00 30
DESIGNS: 3b. Scientist; 5b. Foundryman; 20b. Miner; 30b. Tractor driver; 35b. Schoolboy; 40b. Girl student; 55b. Bricklayer; 1l. Sailor; 1l.55, Mill girl; 2l.35, Soldier; 2l.55, Telegraph linesman.

1955. International Conference of Postal Municipal Workers, Vienna.
2370 **371** 25b. red 40 25

372 Lenin **373** Dove and Globe

1955. 85th Birth Anniv of Lenin. Portraits of Lenin.
2371 **372** 20b. brown and bistre 45 20
2372 – 55b. brown (full face) . . 1·10 20
2373 – 1l. lake and red (half length) . . . . 1·50 30

1955. Peace Congress, Helsinki.
2374 **373** 55b. blue 85 25

374 War Memorial, Berlin **375** Children and Dove

1955. 10th Anniv of Victory over Germany.
2375 **374** 55b. blue 85 25

1955. International Children's Day.
2376 **375** 55b. brown 85 25

376 "Service" **377** People's Art Museum

1955. European Volleyball Championships.
2377 – 55b. mauve and pink . . 4·25 1·40
2378 **376** 1l.75 mauve and yellow 9·50 1·60
DESIGN: 55b. Volleyball players.

1955. Bucharest Museums.
2379 – 20b. mauve 30 15
2380 – 55b. brown 55 15
2381 **377** 1l.20 black . . . . . . 1·30 50
2382 – 1l.75 green . . . . . . 1·40 50
2383 – 2l.55 purple . . . . . . 4·25 65
MUSEUMS—30 × $24\frac{1}{2}$ mm: 20b. Theodor Aman; 2l.55, Simu. 34 × 23 mm: 55b. Lenin-Stalin; 1l.75, Republican Art.

378 Mother and Child **379** "Nature Study"

1955. 1st World Mothers' Congress, Lausanne.
2384 **378** 55b. blue 95 25

1955. 5th Anniv of Pioneer Headquarters, Bucharest.
2385 – 10b. blue . . . . 1·20 10
2386 **379** 20b. green . . . . 1·10 10
2387 – 55b. purple . . . . . . 2·75 10
DESIGNS: 10b. Model railway; 55b. Headquarters building.

380 Coxed Four **381** Anton Pann (folklorist)

1955. Women's European Rowing Championships, Snagov.
2388 **380** 55b. green . . . . 5·75 65
2389 – 1l. blue (Woman sculler) 10·00 1·10

1955. Romanian Writers.
2390 – 55b. blue 95 30
2391 – 55b. grey 95 30
2392 **381** 55b. olive 95 30
2393 – 55b. violet 95 30
2394 – 55b. purple 95 30

PORTRAITS—No. 2390, Dimitrie Cantemir (historian); 2391, Metropolitan Dosoftei (religious writer); 2393, Constantin Cantacuzino (historian); 2394, Ienachita Vacarescu (poet, grammarian and historian).

382 Marksman **383** Fire Engine

1955. European Sharpshooting Championships, Bucharest.
2395 **382** 1l. brown and light brown . . . . 3·25 45

1955. Firemen's Day.
2396 **383** 55b. red . . . . 1·40 40

384 **385** Spraying Fruit Trees

1955. 10th Anniv of W.F.T.U.
2397 **384** 55b. olive 45 10
2398 – 1l. blue 80 20
DESIGN: 1l. Workers and flag.

1955. Fruit and Vegetable Cultivation.
2399 **385** 10b. green 40 15
2400 – 20b. red 70 30
2401 – 55b. blue . . . . 1·40 30
2402 – 1l. lake . . . . 4·25 90
DESIGNS: 20b. Fruit picking; 55b. Harvesting grapes; 1l. Gathering vegetables.

386 **387** Michurin

1955. 4th ARLUS Congress.
2403 **386** 20b. blue and buff . . . 55 15

1955. Birth Cent of Ivan Michurin (Russian botanist).
2404 **387** 55b. blue 95 15

388 Cotton **389** Sheep and Shepherd blowing Bucium

1955.
2405 – 10b. purple (Sugar beet) 45 20
2406 **388** 20b. grey 70 20
2407 – 55b. blue (Linseed) . . . 2·10 45
2408 – 1l.55 brown (Sunflower) 4·25 85

1955.
2409 **389** 5b. brown and green . . 1·10 15
2410 – 10b. violet and bistre . . 1·30 25
2411 – 35b. brown and salmon 2·75 55
2412 – 55b. brown and bistre 5·00 70
DESIGNS: 10b. Pigs and farm girl; 35b. Cows and dairy maid; 55b. Horses and groom.

390 Johann von Schiller (novelist) **391** Bank and Book

1955. Literary Anniversaries.
2413 – 20b. blue 40 10
2414 – 55b. blue . . . . 1·20 20
2415 **390** 1l. grey . . . . 1·80 20
2416 – 1l.55 brown . . . . . . 4·25 90
2417 – 1l.75 violet . . . . . . 4·50 90
2418 – 2l. lake . . . . 5·25 1·40

DESIGNS: 20b. Hans Christian Andersen (children's writer, 150th birth anniv); 55b. Adam Mickiewicz (poet, death centenary); 1l. Type **390** (150th death anniv); 1l.55, Baron de Montesquieu (philosopher, death bicentenary); 1l.75, Walt Whitman (centenary of publication of "Leaves of Grass"); 2l. Miguel de Cervantes (350th anniv of publication of "Don Quixote").

1955. Savings Bank.
2419 **391** 55b. blue . . . . 2·10 20
2420 55b. violet . . . . . . 5·50 3·50

392 Family

393 Brown Hare

1956. National Census.
2421 – 55b. orange 30 10
2422 **392** 1l.75 brown and green 1·50 55
DESIGNS: 55b. "21 FEBRUARIE 1956" in circle.

1956. Wild Life
2423 **393** 20b. black and green . . 2·40 1·90
2424 – 20b. black and olive . . 3·00 1·90
2425 – 35b. black and blue . . 2·40 1·90
2426 – 50b. brown and blue . . 2·40 1·90
2427 – 55b. green and bistre . . 3·00 1·90
2428 – 55b. brown and turquoise . . . . . . 3·00 1·90
2429 – 1l. lake and green . . . 5·50 4·25
2430 – 1l.55 lake and blue . . . 5·75 4·25
2431 – 1l.75 brown and green 8·00 6·50
2432 – 2l. brown and blue . . . 28·00 20·00
2433 – 3l.25 black and green . . 28·00 20·00
2434 – 4l.25 brown and salmon 28·00 20·00
DESIGNS—VERT: No. 2424, Great bustard; 35b. Brown trout; 1l.55, Eurasian red squirrel; 1l.75, Western capercaillie; 4l.25, Red deer. HORIZ: 50b. Wild boar; No. 2427, Common pheasant; No. 2428, Brown bear; 1l. Lynx; 2l. Chamois; 3l.25, Pintail.
See also Nos. 2474/85.

394 Insurgents

395 Boy and Globe

1956. 85th Anniv of Paris Commune.
2435 **394** 55b. red 95 40

1956. International Children's Day.
2436 **395** 55b. violet . . . . . . 1·20 35

396 Red Cross Nurse

397 Tree

1956. 2nd Romanian Red Cross Congress.
2437 **396** 55b. olive and red . . . 1·70 35

1956. Forestry Month.
2438 **397** 20b. grey on green . . . 65 20
2439 – 55b. black on green . . 5·00 30
DESIGN: 55b. Lumber train.

398 Woman Speaking

399 Academy Buildings

1956. International Women's Congress, Bucharest.
2440 **398** 55b. green 95 35

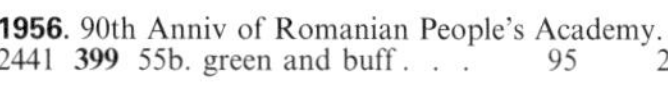
1956. 90th Anniv of Romanian People's Academy.
2441 **399** 55b. green and buff . . . 95 25

400 Vuia, Biplane, Vuia No. 1 and Yakovlev Yak-25 Fighters

1956. 50th Anniv of 1st Flight by Traian Vuia (pioneer airman).
2442 **400** 55b. brown and olive . . 1·10 35

401 Georgescu and Statues

402 Farm Girl

1956. Birth Centenary of Ion Georgescu (sculptor).
2443 **401** 55b. brown and green . . 1·40 25

1956. Collective Farming. (a) Inscr "1951–1956".
2444 **402** 55b. plum . . . . 6·00 5·50

(b) Inscr "1949–56".
2445 **402** 55b. plum 85 25

403 Black-veined White

404 Striker

1956. Insect Pests.
2446 **403** 10b. cream, black and violet . . . . 6·50 40
2447 – 55b. orange and brown 8·00 65
2448 – 1l.75 lake and olive . . . 12·00 7·50
2449 – 1l.75 brown and olive . . 15·00 1·30
PESTS: 55b. Colorado potato beetle; 1l.75 (2), May beetle.

1956. 50th Anniv of Dockers' Strike at Galatz.
2450 **404** 55b. brown on pink . . 95 25

405

406 Gorky

1956. 25th Anniv of "Scanteia" (Communist newspaper).
2451 **405** 55b. blue 85 25

1956. 20th Death Anniv of Maksim Gorky.
2452 **406** 55b. brown . . . . . . 1·40 35

407 T. Aman

408 Snowdrops and Polyanthus

1956. 125th Birth Anniv of Aman (painter).
2453 **407** 55b. grey . . . . 1·40 45

1956. Flowers. Designs multicoloured. Colours of backgrounds given.
2454 **408** 5b. blue 60 20
2455 – 55b. black . . . . 1·70 40
2456 – 1l.75 blue . . . . 4·50 55
2457 – 3l. green . . . . 8·75 95
FLOWERS: 55b. Daffodil and violets; 1l.75, Antirrhinums and campanulas; 3l. Poppies and lilies of the valley.

409 Janos Hunyadi

410 Olympic Flame

1956. 500th Death Anniv of Hunyadi.
2458 **409** 55b. violet 95 40

1956. Olympic Games.
2459 **410** 20b. red 70 20
2460 – 55b. blue . . . . 1·20 25
2461 – 1l. mauve . . . . 1·40 30
2462 – 1l.55 turquoise . . . . . 2·20 35
2463 – 1l.75 violet . . . . . . 2·75 45
DESIGNS: 55b. Water-polo; 1l. Ice-skating; 1l.55, Canoeing; 1l.75, High-jumping.

411 George Bernard Shaw (dramatist)

412 Ilyushin Il-18 Airliner over City

1956. Cultural Anniversaries.
2464 – 20b. blue 45 10
2465 – 35b. red 55 15
2466 **411** 40b. brown 55 20
2467 – 50b. brown 70 50
2468 – 55b. olive . . . . 1·20 50
2469 – 1l. turquoise . . . . . . 1·30 20
2470 – 1l.55 violet . . . . . . 2·50 20
2471 – 1l.75 blue . . . . 3·25 20
2472 – 2l.55 purple . . . . . . 4·00 35
2473 – 3l.25 blue . . . . 4·50 70
DESIGNS: 20b. Benjamin Franklin (U.S. statesman and journalist, 250th birth anniv); 35b. Toyo Oda (painter, 450th death anniv); 40b. Type **411** (birth centenary); 50b. Ivan Franco (writer, birth centenary); 55b. Pierre Curie (physicist, 50th death anniv); 1l. Henrik Ibsen (dramatist, 50th death anniv); 1l.55, Fyodor Dostoevsky (novelist, 75th death anniv); 1l.75, Heinrich Heine (poet, death centenary); 2l.55, Wolfgang Amadeus Mozart (composer, birth bicentenary); 3l.25, Rembrandt (artist, 350th birth anniv).

1956. Wild Life. As Nos. 2423/34 but colours changed. Imperf.
2474 20b. brown and green . . . 2·30 2·20
2475 20b. black and blue . . . . 3·75 3·50
2476 35b. black and blue . . . . 2·30 2·40
2477 50b. black and brown . . . 2·30 2·40
2478 55b. black and violet . . . 3·50 3·75
2479 55b. brown and green . . . 2·30 2·40
2480 1l. brown and blue . . . . 2·30 2·40
2481 1l.55 brown and bistre . . . 2·30 2·40
2482 1l.75 purple and green . . . 3·25 3·50
2483 2l. black and blue . . . . . 2·30 2·20
2484 3l.25 brown and green . . . 6·50 7·25
2485 4l.25 brown and violet . . . 3·50 3·25

1956. Air. Multicoloured.
2486 20b. Type **412** 50 40
2487 55b. Ilyushin Il-18 over mountains 75 40
2488 1l.75 Ilyushin Il-18 over cornfield . . . . 3·50 60
2489 2l.55 Ilyushin Il-18 over seashore . . . . 4·00 1·20

413 Georgi Enescu

414 "Rebels" (after Octav Bancila)

1956. 75th Birth Anniv of Enescu (musician).
2490 – 55b. blue . . . . 1·10 25
2491 **413** 1l.75 purple . . . . . . 1·70 35
DESIGN: 55b. Enescu when a child, holding violin.

1957. 50th Anniv of Peasant Revolt.
2492 **414** 55b. grey 85 25

415 Stephen the Great

416 Gheorghe Marinescu (neurologist) and Institute of Medicine

1957. 500th Anniv of Accession of Stephen the Great.
2493 **415** 55b. brown 50 35
2494 55b. olive 50 50

1957. National Congress of Medical Sciences, Bucharest, and Centenary of Medical and Pharmaceutical Teaching in Bucharest (1l.75).
2495 **416** 20b. green 25 20
2496 – 35b. brown 35 20
2497 – 55b. purple . . . . . . 1·00 30
2498 – 1l.75 red and blue . . . 3·75 1·20
DESIGNS: As T **416**: 35b. Ioan Cantacuzino (bacteriologist) and Cantacuzino Institute; 55b. Victor Babes (pathologist and bacteriologist) and Babes Institute. 66 × 23 mm: 1l.75, Nicolae Kretzulescu and Carol Dairla (physicians) and Faculty of Medicine, Bucharest.

417 Gymnast and Spectator

418 Emblems of Atomic Energy

1957. 1st European Women's Gymnastic Championships, Bucharest.
2499 **417** 20b. green 35 10
2500 – 35b. red 65 20
2501 – 55b. blue . . . . 1·20 30
2502 – 1l.75 purple . . . . . . 3·50 65
DESIGNS—HORIZ: 35b. On asymmetric bars; 55b. Vaulting over horse. VERT: 1l.75, On beam.

1957. 2nd A.S.I.T. Congress.
2503 **418** 55b. brown . . . . . . 1·10 25
2504 55b. blue . . . . 1·30 25

419 Dove and Handlebars

420 Rhododendron

1957. 10th International Cycle Race.
2505 **419** 20b. blue 25 15
2506 – 55b. brown . . . . . . 1·00 25
DESIGN: 55b. Racing cyclist.

1957. Flowers of the Carpathian Mountains.
2513 **420** 5b. red and grey 25 10
2514 – 10b. green and grey . . 35 10
2515 – 20b. orange and grey . . 40 10
2516 – 35b. olive and grey . . . 65 20
2517 – 55b. blue and grey . . . 80 20
2518 – 1l. red and grey . . . . 1·90 50
2519 – 1l.55 yellow and grey . . 2·40 35
2520 – 1l.75 violet and grey . . 4·00 45
FLOWERS: 10b. Daphne; 20b. Lily; 35b. Edelweiss; 55b. Gentian; 1l. Dianthus; 1l.55, Primula; 1l.75, Anemone.

421 N. Grigorescu

1957. 50th Death Anniv of Nicolae Grigorescu (painter).
2521 – 20b. green 50 15
2522 **421** 55b. brown . . . . . . 1·00 25
2523 – 1l.75 blue . . . . 4·50 65
DESIGNS—HORIZ: 20b. "Ox-cart"; 1l.75, "Attack on Smirdan".

422 Festival Visitors **423** Festival Emblem

1957. 6th World Youth Festival, Moscow.
2524 **422** 20b. purple 25 10
2525 – 55b. green 75 10
2526 **423** 1l. orange . . . . . . 1·40 45
2527 – 1l.75 blue . . . . 1·80 25
DESIGNS: 55b. Girl with flags (22 × 38 mm); 1l.75, Dancers (49 × 20 mm).

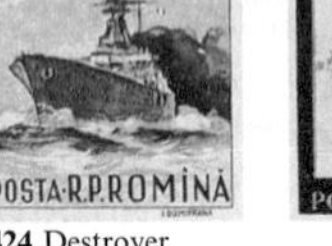

424 Destroyer "Stalingrad" **425** "The Trumpeter" (after N. Grigorescu)

1957. Navy Day.
2528 **424** 1l.75 blue . . . . 1·80 25

1957. 80th Anniv of War of Independence.
2529 **425** 20b. violet 85 25

426 Soldiers Advancing **427** Child with Dove

1957. 40th Anniv of Battle of Marasesti.
2530 **426** 1l.75 brown . . . . . . 1·20 25

1957. Red Cross.
2531 **427** 55b. green and red . . . 85 25

428 Sprinter and Bird **429** Ovid

1957. Int Athletic Championships, Bucharest.
2532 **428** 20b. black and blue . . 60 10
2533 – 55b. black and yellow . . 1·50 20
2534 – 1l.75 black and red . . . 4·00 45
DESIGNS: 55b. Javelin-thrower and bull; 1l.75, Runner and stag.

1957. Birth Bimillenary of Ovid (Latin poet).
2535 **429** 1l.75 blue . . . . 1·75 45

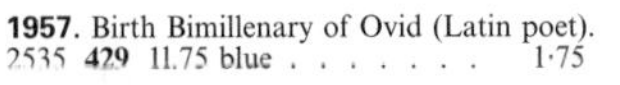

430 Congress Emblem **431** Oil Refinery, 1957

1957. 4th W.F.T.U. Congress, Leipzig.
2536 **430** 55b. blue 55 10

1957. Centenary of Romanian Petroleum Industry.
2537 **431** 20b. brown 50 10
2538 20b. blue 50 10
2539 – 55b. purple 75 35
DESIGN: 55b. Oil production, 1857 (horse-operated borer).

432 Lenin, Youth and Girl **433** Artificial Satellite encircling Globe

1957. 40th Anniv of Russian Revolution.
2540 **432** 10b. red 10 15
2541 – 35b. purple 40 15
2542 – 55b. brown 60 30
DESIGNS—HORIZ: 35b. Lenin and flags; 55b. Statue of Lenin.

1957. Air. Launching of Artificial Satellite by Russia.
2543 **433** 25b. blue 50 50
2545 25b. blue 50 35
2544 – 3l.75 green . . . . . . 4·50 95
2546 – 3l.75 blue . . . . 4·50 95
DESIGN: 3l.75 (2), Satellite's orbit around Globe.
See also Nos. 2593/6.

434 Peasant Soldiers **435** Endre Ady

1957. 520th Anniv of Bobilna Revolution.
2547 **434** 50b. purple 25 15
2548 – 55b. grey 35 20
DESIGN—VERT: 55b. Bobilna Memorial.

1957. 80th Birth Anniv of Endre Ady (Hungarian poet).
2549 **435** 55b. olive 70 25

436 Laika and "Sputnik 2" **437** Black-winged Stilt

1957. Space Flight of Laika (dog).
2550 **436** 1l.20 blue and brown . . 2·25 50
2551 1l.20 blue and brown . . 2·25 50

1957. Fauna of the Danube Delta.
2552 **437** 5b. grey & brown (postage) 30 10
2553 – 10b. orange and green 40 10
2554 – 20b. orange and red . . 45 10
2555 – 50b. orange and green 15 10
2556 – 55b. blue and purple . . 40 10
2557 – 1l.30 orange and violet 2·00 20
2558 – 3l.30 grey and blue (air) 3·00 75
2559 – 5l. orange and red . . . 5·00 1·10
DESIGNS—VERT: 10b. Great egret; 20b. White spoonbill; 50b. Stellate sturgeon. HORIZ: 55b. Stoat; 1l.30, Eastern white pelican; 3l.30, Black-headed gull; 5l. White-tailed sea eagle.

438 Emblem of Republic and Flags

1957. 10th Anniv of People's Republic.
2560 **438** 25b. buff, red and blue 15 10
2561 – 55b. yellow 65 20
2562 – 1l.20 red 75 35
DESIGNS: 55b. Emblem, Industry and Agriculture; 1l.20, Emblem, the Arts and Sports.

439 Republican Flag

1958. 25th Anniv of Strike at Grivitsa.
2563 **439** 1l. red and brown on buff 50 25
2564 1l. red and blue on buff 50 25

440 "Telecommunications"

1958. Socialist Countries' Postal Ministers Conference, Moscow.
2565 **440** 55b. violet 50 25
2566 – 1l.75 purple 85 25
DESIGN: 1l.75, Telegraph pole and pylons carrying lines.

441 Nicolae Balcescu (historian) **442** Fencer

1958. Romanian Writers.
2567 **441** 5b. blue 25 15
2568 – 10b. black 30 20
2569 – 35b. blue 45 20
2570 – 55b. brown 55 20
2571 – 1l.75 black . . . . . . 1·10 35
2572 – 2l. green . . . . 1·30 35
DESIGNS: 10b. Ion Creanga (folklorist); 35b. Alexandru Vlahuta (poet); 55b. Mihail Eminescu (poet); 1l.75, Vasile Alecsandri (poet and dramatist); 2l. Barbu Delavrancea (short-story writer and dramatist).

1958. World Youth Fencing Championships, Bucharest.
2573 **442** 1l.75 mauve 95 25

443 Symbols of Medicine and Sport **444**

1958. 25th Anniv of Sports Doctors' Service.
2574 **443** 1l.20 red and green . . . 95 25

1958. 4th Int Congress of Democratic Women.
2575 **444** 55b. blue 55 25

445 Linnaeus (botanist) **446** Parasol Mushroom

1958. Cultural Anniversaries (1957).
2576 **445** 10b. blue 20 15
2577 – 20b. brown 30 15
2578 – 40b. mauve 40 20
2579 – 55b. blue 90 15
2580 – 1l. mauve 90 20
2581 – 1l.75 blue . . . . 1·50 30
2582 – 2l. brown . . . . 2·50 35
DESIGNS: 10b. Type **445** (250th birth anniv); 20b. Auguste Comte (philosopher, death centenary); 40b. William Blake (poet and artist, birth bicentenary); 55b. Mikhail Glinka (composer, death centenary); 1l. Henry Longfellow (poet, 150th birth anniv); 1l.75, Carlo Goldoni (dramatist, 250th birth anniv); 2l. John Komensky, Comenius (educationist, 300th death anniv).

1958. Mushrooms. As T **446**.
2583 **446** 5b. brown, lt brn & blue 20 15
2584 – 10b. brown, buff and bronze 20 15
2585 – 20b. red, yellow and grey 20 15
2586 – 30b. brown, orge & green 20 20
2587 – 35b. brown, lt brn & bl 30 15
2588 – 55b. brown, red and green 50 15
2589 – 1l. brown, buff and green . . . . 1·10 20
2590 – 1l.55 pink, drab and grey 1·90 25
2591 – 1l.75 brown, buff and green . . . . 2·25 35
2592 – 2l. yellow, brown and green . . . . 4·25 35
MUSHROOMS: 10b. "Clavaria aurea"; 20b. Caesar's mushroom; 30b. Saffron milk cap; 35b. Honey fungus; 55b. Shaggy ink cap; 1l. "Morchella conica"; 1l.55, Field mushroom; 1l.75, Cep; 2l. Chanterelle.

1958. Brussels International Exhibition. Nos. 2543/4 and 2545/6 optd **EXPOZITIA UNIVERSALA BRUXELLES 1958** and star or with star only.
2593 **433** 25b. green . . . . 2·50 1·80
2595 25b. blue . . . . 18·00 13·00
2594 – 3l.75 green . . . . . . 2·50 1·40
2596 – 3l.75 blue . . . . 17·00 13·00

448 Racovita and "Belgica" (Gerlache expedition, 1897)

1958. 10th Death Anniv (1957) of Emil Racovita (naturalist and explorer).
2597 **448** 55b. indigo and blue . . 2·25 25
2598 – 1l.20 violet and olive . . 1·40 20
DESIGN: 1l.20, Racovita and grotto.

449 Sputnik encircling Globe

1958. Air. Launching of Third Artificial Satellite by Russia.
2599 **449** 3l.25 buff and blue . . . 3·25 1·00

450 Servicemen's Statue

1958. Army Day.
2600 **450** 55b. brown (postage) . . 20 15
2601 – 75b. purple 30 15
2602 – 1l.75 blue 50 20
2603 – 3l.30 violet (air) . . . . 1·30 45
DESIGNS: 75b. Soldier guarding industrial plant; 1l.75, Sailor hoisting flag, and "Royal Ferdinand" destroyer; 3l.30, Pilot and Mikoyan Gurevich MiG-17 jet fighters.

451 Costume of Oltenia **452** Costume of Oltenia

1958. Provincial Costumes.
2604 **451** 35b. red, black and yellow (female) 20 25
2605 **452** 35b. red, black and yellow (male) 20 40
2606 – 40b. red, brown and light brown (female) 20 30
2607 – 40b. red, brown and light brown (male) . . 20 30
2608 – 50b. brown, red and lilac (female) 25 25
2609 – 50b. brown, red and lilac (male) 25 25
2610 – 55b. red, brown and drab (female) 35 25
2611 – 55b. red, brown and drab (male) 35 25
2612 – 1l. carmine, brown and red (female) 90 30
2613 – 1l. carmine, brown and red (male) 90 30
2614 – 1l.75 red, brown and blue (female) . . . . 1·20 50
2615 – 1l.75 red, brown and blue (male) . . . . . 1·20 50
PROVINCES: Nos. 2606/7, Tara Oasului; 2608/9, Transylvania; 2610/11, Muntenia; 2612/3, Banat; 2614/5, Moldova.

453 Stamp Printer **454** Runner

1958. Romanian Stamp Centenary. Inscr "1858 1958".
2617 **453** 35b. blue 20 15
2618 – 55b. brown 30 15
2619 – 1l.20 blue 60 30
2620 – 1l.30 plum 65 35
2621 – 1l.55 brown 90 20
2622 – 1l.75 red . . . . 1·25 25
2623 – 2l. violet . . . . 1·50 45
2624 – 3l.30 brown . . . . . . 2·10 55
DESIGNS: 55b. Scissors and Moldavian stamps of 1858; 1l.20, Driver with whip and mail coach; 1l.30, Postman with horn and mounted courier; 1l.55 to 3l.30, Moldavian stamps of 1858 (Nos. 1/4).

1958. 3rd Youth Spartacist Games.
2627 **454** 1l. brown 65 25

455 Revolutionary Emblem **456** Boy Bugler

1958. 40th Anniv of Workers' Revolution.
2628 **455** 55b. red 40 25

1958. 10th Anniv of Education Reform.
2629 **456** 55b. red 40 25

457 Alexandru Cuza

1959. Centenary of Union of Romanian Provinces.
2630 **457** 1l.75 blue 85 20

458 First Cosmic Rocket

1959. Air. Launching of 1st Cosmic Rocket.
2631 **458** 3l.25 blue on salmon . . 8·00 1·20

459 Charles Darwin (naturalist) **460** Maize

1959. Cultural Anniversaries.
2633 **459** 55b. black (postage) . . 30 15
2634 – 55b. blue 30 15
2635 – 55b. red 30 15
2636 – 55b. purple 30 15
2637 – 55b. brown . . . . . . 30 5·75
2638 – 3l.25 blue (air) . . . . . 3·00 50
DESIGNS—No. 2633, Type **459** (150th birth anniv); 2634, Robert Burns (poet, birth bicentenary); 2635, Aleksandr Popov (radio pioneer, birth centenary); 2636, Sholem Aleichem (writer, birth centenary); 2637, Frederick Handel (composer, death bicentenary); 2638, Frederic Joliot-Curie (nuclear physicist, 10th anniv of World Peace Council).

1959. 10th Anniv of Collective Farming in Romania.
2639 **460** 55b. green 30 20
2640 – 55b. orange 30 20
2641 – 55b. purple 30 20
2642 – 55b. olive 30 20
2643 – 55b. brown 30 20
2644 – 55b. bistre 30 20
2645 – 55b. blue 30 20
2646 – 55b. bistre 30 20
2647 – 5l. red . . . . 3·00 75
DESIGNS—VERT: No. 2640, Sunflower with bee; 2641, Sugar beet. HORIZ: No. 2642, Sheep; 2643, Cattle; 2644, Rooster and hens; 2645, Farm tractor; 2646, Farm wagon and horses; 2647 (38 × 26½ mm), Farmer and wife, and wheatfield within figure "10".

461 Rock Thrush **462** Young Couple

1959. Air. Birds in natural colours. Inscriptions in grey. Colours of value tablets and backgrounds given.
2648 **461** 10b. grey on buff . . . 15 10
2649 – 20b. grey on grey . . . 15 10
2650 – 35b. grey on deep grey 15 10
2651 – 40b. red on pink 20 15
2652 – 55b. grey on green . . . 30 10
2653 – 55b. grey on cream . . . 30 10
2654 – 55b. green on azure . . 30 10
2655 – 1l. red on yellow 60 20
2656 – 1l.55 red on pink . . . . 1·10 20
2657 – 5l. grey on green . . . . 6·25 1·20
BIRDS—HORIZ: No. 2649, Golden oriole; 2656, Long-tailed tit; 2657, Wallcreeper. VERT: No. 2650, Northern lapwing; 2651, Barn swallow; 2652, Great spotted woodpecker; 2653, Eurasian goldfinch; 2654, Great tit; 2655, Northern bullfinch.

1959. 7th World Youth Festival, Vienna. Inscr "26 VII-4 VIII 1959".
2658 **462** 1l. blue 50 20
2659 – 1l.60 red 50 20
DESIGN: 1l.60, Folk-dancer in national costume.

463 Workers and Banners (**466**)

1959. 15th Anniv of Liberation.
2660 **463** 55b. multicoloured . . . 40 25

1959. Air. Landing of Russian Rocket on the Moon. Surch **h. 00.02'.24" 14-IX-1959 PRIMA RACHETA COSMICA IN LUNA 5 LEI** and bars.
2662 **458** 5l. on 3l.25 blue on salmon . . . . 14·00 2·50

1959. 8th Balkan Games. Optd with T **466** in silver.
2663 **454** 1l. brown . . . . 14·00 12·50

467 Prince Vlad Tepes and Charter

1959. 500th Anniv of Bucharest.
2664 **467** 20b. black and blue . . 35 25
2665 – 40b. black and brown . . 1·20 25
2666 – 55b. black and bistre . . 90 30
2667 – 55b. black and purple . . 95 30
2668 – 1l.55 black and lilac . . 3·75 85
2669 – 1l.75 black and turquoise 3·25 1·10
DESIGNS—HORIZ: 40b. Peace Buildings, Bucharest; 55b. (No. 2666), Atheneum; 55b. (No 2667), "Scanteia" Printing House; 1l.55, Opera House; 1l.75, "23 August" Stadium.

468 Football **469** "Lenin"

1959. International Sport. Multicoloured.
2671 20b. Type **468** (postage) . . 15 10
2672 35b. Motor-cycle racing (horiz) 20 10
2673 40b. Ice-hockey (horiz) . . . 30 20
2674 55b. Handball 30 10
2675 1l. Horse-jumping 45 10
2676 1l.50 Boxing 90 20
2677 1l.55 Rugby football (horiz) 1·00 10
2678 1l.60 Tennis (horiz) . . . . 1·20 25
2679 2l.80 Hydroplaning (horiz) (air) . . . . 1·75 75

1959. Launching of Atomic Ice-breaker "Lenin".
2680 **469** 1l.75 violet . . . . . . 1·50 35

STAMP DAY ISSUES. The annual issues for Stamp Day in November together with the stamp issued on 30 March 1963 for the Romanian Philatelists' Conference are now the only stamps which carry a premium which is expressed on se-tenant labels. This was for the Association of Romanian Philatelists. These labels were at first seperated by a vertical perforation but in the issues from 1963 to 1971 the label is an integral part of the stamp.

470 Stamp Album and Magnifier

1959. Stamp Day.
2681 **470** 1l.60(+40b.) blue 70 60

471 Foxglove **472** Cuza University

1959. Medicinal Flowers. Multicoloured.
2682 20b. Type **471** 15 10
2683 40b. Peppermint 20 20
2684 55b. False camomile 25 10
2685 55b. Cornflower 30 10
2686 1l. Meadow saffron 40 20
2687 1l.20 Monkshood 85 20
2688 1l.55 Common poppy . . . 95 20
2689 1l.60 Silver lime . . . . . . 1·10 30
2690 1l.75 Dog rose . . . . . . 2·10 30
2691 3l.20 Yellow pheasant's-eye 1·50 45

1959. Centenary of Cuza University, Jassy.
2692 **472** 55b. brown 40 25

473 Rocket, Dog and Rabbit **474** G. Cosbuc

1959. Air. Cosmic Rocket Flight.
2693 **473** 1l.55 blue . . . . 1·90 30
2694 – 1l.60 blue on cream . . 2·40 40
2695 – 1l.75 blue . . . . 2·40 40
DESIGNS—HORIZ: (52 × 29½ mm): 1l.60, Picture of "invisible" side of the Moon, with lists of place-names in Romanian and Russian. VERT—(As Type **473**): 1l.75, Lunik 3's trajectory around the Moon.

1960. Romanian Authors.
2696 **474** 20b. blue 20 20
2697 – 40b. purple 55 20
2698 – 50b. brown 65 20
2699 – 55b. purple 65 20
2700 – 1l. violet . . . . 1·30 20
2701 – 1l.55 blue . . . . . . 2·20 35
PORTRAITS: 40b. I. L. Caragiale; 50b. G. Alexandrescu; 55b. A. Donici; 1l. C. Negruzzi; 1l.55, D. Bolintineanu.

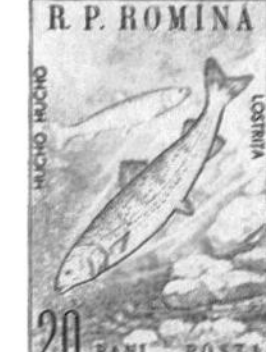

475 Huchen **476** Woman and Dove

1960. Romanian Fauna.
2702 **475** 20b. blue (postage) . . . 10 10
2703 – 55b. brown (Tortoise) . . 20 10
2704 – 1l.20 lilac (Common shelduck) . . . . . . 1·60 45
2705 – 1l.30 blue (Golden eagle) (air) . . . . 2·20 45
2706 – 1l.75 green (Black grouse) . . . . 2·20 45
2707 – 2l. red (Lammergeier) . . 2·30 65

1960. 50th Anniv of International Women's Day.
2708 **476** 55b. blue 60 30

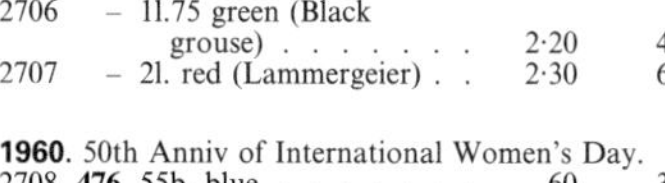

477 Lenin (after painting by M. A. Gerasimov) **478** "Victory"

1960. 90th Birth Anniv of Lenin.
2709 **477** 40b. purple 35 15
2710 – 55b. blue (Statue of Lenin by Boris Carogea) 40 15

1960. 15th Anniv of Victory.
2712 **478** 40b. blue 50 10
2714 40b. purple . . . . . . 2·30 2·50
2713 – 55b. blue 50 10
2715 – 55b. purple . . . . . . 2·30 2·50
DESIGN: 55b. Statue of soldier with flag.

479 Rocket Flight

1960. Air. Launching of Soviet Rocket.
2716 **479** 55b. blue . . . . 1·80 30

480 Diving **481** Gymnastics

1960. Olympic Games, Rome (1st issue). Mult.
2717 40b. Type **480** 70 95
2718 55b. Gymnastics . . . . . 90 1·00
2719 1l.20 High jumping . . . . 1·30 1·20
2720 1l.60 Boxing . . . . 2·00 1·30
2721 2l.45 Canoeing . . . . . . 2·10 1·40
2722 3l.70 Canoeing . . . . . . 4·50 3·25
Nos. 2717/9 and 2720/1 are arranged together in "brickwork" fashion, se-tenant, in sheets forming complete overall patterns of the Olympic rings.
No. 2722 is imperf.

1960. Olympic Games, Rome (2nd issue).
2723 – 20b. blue 15 10
2724 **481** 40b. purple 30 15
2725 – 55b. blue 55 10
2726 – 1l. red 70 10
2727 – 1l.60 purple . . . . . . 2·00 35
2728 – 2l. lilac . . . . 4·50 75
DESIGNS: 20b. Diving; 55b. High-jumping; 1l. Boxing; 1l.60, Canoeing; 2l. Football.

482 Industrial Scholars **483** Vlaicu and his Airplane No. 1 "Crazy Fly"

484 I.A.R. 817 Flying Ambulance **485** Pilot and Mikoyan Gurevich MiG-17 Jet Fighters

1960.
2731 **482** 3b. mauve (postage) . . 10 10
2732 – 5b. brown 30 10
2733 – 10b. purple 10 10
2734 – 20b. blue 10 10

2735 – 30b. red 15 10
2736 – 35b. red 15 10
2737 – 40b. bistre 25 10
2738 – 50b. violet 25 10
2739 – 55b. blue 30 10
2740 – 60b. green 30 10
2741 – 75b. olive 60 10
2742 – 1l. red 75 10
2743 – 1l.20 black 60 10
2744 – 1l.50 purple 1·10 10
2745 – 1l.55 turquoise 1·00 10
2746 – 1l.60 blue 90 10
2747 – 1l.75 brown 1·10 10
2748 – 2l. brown 1·30 15
2749 – 2l.40 violet 1·50 10
2750 – 3l. blue 2·00 15

2751 – 3l.20 blue (air) 4·50 10

DESIGNS—VERT: 5b. Diesel train; 10b. Dam; 20b. Miner; 30b. Doctor; 35b. Textile worker; 50b. Children at play; 55b. Timber tractor; 1l. Atomic reactor; 1l.20, Petroleum refinery; 1l.50, Iron-works; 1l.75, Mason; 2l. Road-roller; 2l.40, Chemist; 3l. Radio communications and television. HORIZ: 40b. Grand piano and books; 60b. Combine harvester; 75b. Cattle-shed; 1l.55, Dock scene; 1l.60, Runner; 3l.20, Baneasa Airport, Bucharest.

1960. 50th Anniv of 1st Flight by A. Vlaicu and Aviation Day.
2752 **483** 10b. brown and yellow 15 10
2753 – 20b. brown and orange 20 10
2754 **484** 35b. red 30 10
2755 – 40b. violet 35 10
2756 **485** 55b. blue 50 10
2757 – 1l.60 multicoloured 1·30 20
2758 – 1l.75 multicoloured 1·70 35

DESIGNS—As T **483**: 20b. Vlaicu in flying helmet and his No. 2 airplane; 40b. Antonov An-2 biplane spraying crops. 59 × 22 mm: 1l.60, Ilyushin Il-18 airliner and Baneasa airport control tower; 1l.75, Parachute descents.

486 Worker and Emblem

1960. 3rd Workers' Party Congress.
2759 **486** 55b. orange and red 55 25

487 Leo Tolstoy (writer)

488 Tomis (Constantza)

1960. Cultural Anniversaries.
2760 **487** 10b. purple 10 10
2761 – 20b. brown 10 10
2762 – 35b. blue 15 10
2763 – 40b. green 20 10
2764 – 55b. brown 35 10
2765 – 1l. green 65 25
2766 – 1l.20 purple 75 10
2767 – 1l.55 grey 1·20 15
2768 – 1l.75 brown 1·90 30

DESIGNS: 10b. Type **487** (50th death anniv); 20b. Mark Twain (writer, 50th death anniv); 35b. Katsushika Hokusai (painter, birth bicentenary); 40b. Alfred de Musset (poet, 150th birth anniv); 55b. Daniel Defoe (writer, 300th birth anniv); 1l. Janos Bolyai (mathematician, death centenary); 1l,20, Anton Chekhov (writer, birth centenary); 1l.55, Robert Koch (bacteriologist, 50th death anniv); 1l.75, Frederic Chopin (composer, 150th birth anniv).

1960. Black Sea Resorts. Multicoloured.
2769 20b. Type **488** (postage) 15 10
2770 35b. Constantza 30 10
2771 40b. Vasile Roaita 30 10
2772 55b. Mangalia 60 10
2773 1l. Eforie 1·00 25
2774 1l.60 Eforie (different) 1·10 20

2775 2l. Mamaia (air) 2·10 50

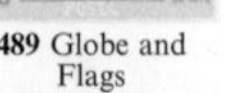

489 Globe and Flags

490 Viennese Emperor Moth

1960. International Puppet Theatre Festival, Bucharest. Designs (24 × 28½ mm, except 20b.) show puppets. Multicoloured.
2776 20b. Type **489** 20 10
2777 40b. Petrushka 25 10
2778 55b. Punch 30 10
2779 1l. Kaspar 45 10
2780 1l.20 Tindarica 55 10
2781 1l.75 Vasilache 1·00 20

1960. Air. Butterflies and Moths. Multicoloured.
2782 10b. Type **490** 25 10
2783 20b. Poplar admiral 25 10
2784 40b. Scarce copper 30 10
2785 55b. Swallowtail 55 15
2786 1l.60 Death's-head hawk moth 1·70 25
2787 1l.75 Purple emperor 2·10 35

SIZES: TRIANGULAR—36½ × 21½ mm: 20, 40b. VERT—23½ × 34 mm: 55b., 1l.60. HORIZ—34 × 23½ mm: 1l.75.

491 Children tobogganing

1960. Village Children's Games. Multicoloured.
2788 20b. Type **491** 10 10
2789 35b. "Oina" (ball-game) (horiz) 15 10
2790 55b. Ice-skating (horiz) 25 10
2791 1l. Running 50 10
2792 1l.75 Swimming (horiz) 1·40 15

492 Striker and Flag

1960. 40th Anniv of General Strike.
2793 **492** 55b. red and lake 45 20

493 Compass Points and Ilyushin Il-18 Airliner

1960. Air. Stamp Day.
2794 **493** 55b.(+45b.) blue 60 35

494 "XV", Globe and "Peace" Banner

496 Woman tending Vine (Cotnari)

495 Black Sea Herrings

1960. 15th Anniv of World Democratic Youth Federation.
2795 **494** 55b. yellow and blue 45 15

1960. Fishes.
2796 – 10b. brown, yell & grn 15 10
2797 – 20b. multicoloured 25 10
2798 – 40b. brn, lt brn & yell 40 10
2799 **495** 55b. grey, blue & orge 55 10
2800 – 1l. multicoloured 1·10 15
2801 – 1l.20 multicoloured 1·40 20
2802 – 1l.60 multicoloured 2·10 25

FISHES: 10b. Common carp; 20b. Zander; 40b. Black Sea turbot; 1l. Wels; 1l.20, Sterlet; 1l.60, Beluga.

1960. Romanian Vineyards. Multicoloured.
2803 20b. Dragasani 10 10
2804 30b. Dealul Mare (horiz) 25 10
2805 40b. Odobesti (horiz) 35 10
2806 55b. Type **496** 55 10
2807 75b. Tirnave 75 20
2808 1l. Minis 1·30 25
2809 1l.20 Murfatlar 1·90 40

497 "Furnaceman" (after I. Irimescu)

498 Slalom Racer

1961. Romanian Sculptures.
2811 **497** 5b. red 10 10
2812 – 10b. violet 10 10
2813 – 20b. black 20 10
2814 – 40b. bistre 25 10
2815 – 50b. brown 35 10
2816 – 55b. red 50 10
2817 – 1l. purple 85 15
2818 – 1l.55 blue 1·30 25
2819 – 1l.75 green 1·70 25

SCULPTURES—VERT: 10b. "Gh. Doja" (I. Vlad); 20b. "Reunion" (B. Caragea); 40b. "Enescu" (G. Anghel); 50b. "Eminescu" (C. Baraschi); 1l. "Peace" (I. Jalea); 1l.55, "Constructive Socialism" (C. Medrea); 1l.75, "Birth of an Idea" (A. Szobotka). HORIZ: 55b. "Peasant Uprising, 1907" (M. Constantinescu).

1961. Air. 50th Anniv of Romanian Winter Sports. (a) Perf.
2820 – 10b. olive and grey 20 15
2821 **498** 20b. red and grey 20 15
2822 – 25b. turquoise and grey 35 15
2823 – 40b. violet and grey 40 15
2824 – 55b. blue and grey 50 15
2825 – 1l. red and grey 70 20
2826 – 1l.55 brown and grey 1·70 30

(b) Imperf.
2827 – 10b. blue and grey 10 10
2828 **498** 20b. brown and grey 20 10
2829 – 25b. olive and grey 25 10
2830 – 40b. red and grey 50 10
2831 – 55b. turquoise and grey 65 55
2832 – 1l. violet and grey 1·00 90
2833 – 1l.55 red and grey 1·70 1·80

DESIGNS—HORIZ: Skier: racing (10b.), jumping (55b.), walking (1l.55). VERT: 25b. Skiers climbing slope; 40b. Toboggan; 1l. Rock-climber.

499 Petru Poni (chemist)

500 Yuri Gagarin in Capsule

1961. Romanian Scientists. Inscr "1961". Portraits in sepia.
2834 **499** 10b. brown and pink 10 10
2835 – 20b. purple and yellow 25 10
2836 – 55b. red and blue 40 15
2837 – 1l.55 violet and orange 1·20 35

PORTRAITS: 20b. Anghel Saligny (engineer) and Saligny Bridge, Cernavoda; 55b. Constantin Budeanu (electrical engineer); 1l.55, Gheorghe Titeica (mathematician).

1961. Air. World's First Manned Space Flight. Inscr "12 IV 1961". (a) Perf.
2838 – 1l.35 blue 55 20
2839 **500** 3l.20 blue 1·10 55

(b) Imperf.
2840 **500** 3l.20 red 5·50 2·10

DESIGN—VERT: 1l.35, Yuri Gagarin.

501 Freighter "Galati"

1961. Merchant Navy. Multicoloured.
2841 20b. Type **501** 35 10
2842 40b. "Oltenita" (Danube passenger vessel) 35 10
2843 55b. "Tomis" (hydrofoil) 55 10
2844 1l. "Arad" (freighter) 80 10
2845 1l.55 "N. Cristea" (tug) 1·30 25
2846 1l.75 "Dobrogea" (freighter) 1·50 30

502 Red Flag with Marx, Engels and Lenin

1961. 40th Anniv of Romanian Communist Party.
2847 **502** 35b. multicoloured 50 10
2848 – 55b. multicoloured 85 10

DESIGN: 55b. Two bill-posters.

503 Eclipse over Scanteia Building and Observatory

504 Roe Deer

1961. Air. Solar Eclipse.
2850 – 1l.60 blue 1·10 15
2851 **503** 1l.75 blue 1·30 15

DESIGN: 1l.60, Eclipse over Palace Square, Bucharest.

1961. Forest Animals. Inscr "1961". Multicoloured.
2852 10b. Type **504** 10 15
2853 20b. Lynx (horiz) 15 15
2854 35b. Wild boar (horiz) 25 20
2855 40b. Brown bear (horiz) 45 20
2856 55b. Red deer 60 20
2857 75b. Red fox (horiz) 70 20
2858 1l. Chamois 95 20
2859 1l.55 Brown hare 1·40 35
2860 1l.75 Eurasian badger 1·70 30
2861 2l. Roe deer 2·40 55

505 George Enescu

1961. 2nd International George Enescu Festival.
2862 **505** 3l. lavender and brown 1·40 30

506 Yuri Gagarin and German Titov

507 Iris

1961. Air. 2nd Soviet Space Flight.
2863 – 55b. blue 35 10
2864 – 1l.35 violet 70 20
2865 **506** 1l.75 red 1·30 25

DESIGNS—VERT: 55b. "Vostok 2" in flight; 1l.35, G. S. Titov.

1961. Centenary of Bucharest Botanical Gardens. Flowers in natural colours. Background and inscription colours given. Perf or imperf.
2866 – 10b. yellow and brown 10 10
2867 – 20b. green and red 10 10
2868 – 25b. blue, green and red 15 10
2869 – 35b. lilac and grey 25 10
2870 **507** 40b. yellow and violet 30 10
2871 – 55b. blue and ultramarine 45 10
2872 – 1l. orange and blue 75 15
2873 – 1l.20 blue and brown 95 15
2874 – 1l.55 brown and lake 1·10 15

FLOWERS—HORIZ: 10b. Primula; 35b. Opuntia; 1l. Hepatica. VERT: 20b. Dianthus; 25b. Peony; 55b. Ranunculus; 1l.20, Poppy; 1l.55, Gentian.

508 Cobza Player

509 Heraclitus (Greek philosopher)

1961. Musicians. Multicoloured.
2876 10b. Pan piper 10 10
2877 20b. Alpenhorn player (horiz) 15 10
2878 40b. Flautist 30 10
2879 55b. Type **508** 50 10
2880 60b. Bagpiper 65 15
2881 1l. Cembalo player 85 25

1961. Cultural Anniversaries.
2882 **509** 10b. purple 30 20
2883 – 20b. brown 30 20
2884 – 40b. green 35 20
2885 – 55b. mauve 50 20
2886 – 1l.35 blue 85 25
2887 – 1l.75 violet 1·10 30

DESIGNS: 20b. Sir Francis Bacon (philosopher and statesman, 400th birth anniv); 40b. Rabindrathr Tagore (poet and philosopher, birth centenary); 55b. Domingo Sarmiento (writer, 150th birth anniv; 1l.35, Heinrich von Kleist (dramatist, 150th death anniv); 1l.75, Mikhail Lomonosov (writer, 250th birth anniv).

510 Olympic Flame

512 Tower Building, Republic Palace Square, Bucharest

511 "Stamps Round the World"

1961. Olympic Games 1960. Gold Medal Awards. Inscr "MELBOURNE 1956" or "ROMA 1960". Perf or imperf.

2888 – 10b. turquoise and ochre 15 15
2889 **510** 20b. red 20 15
2890 – 20b. grey 20 15
2891 – 35b. brown and ochre 30 15
2892 – 40b. purple and ochre 30 15
2893 – 55b. blue 40 15
2894 – 55b. blue 40 15
2895 – 55b. red and ochre 40 15
2896 – 1l.35 blue and ochre 1·10 25
2897 – 1l.75 red and ochre 1·80 35

DESIGNS (Medals)—DIAMOND: 10b. Boxing; 35b. Pistol-shooting; 40b. Rifle-shooting; 55b. (No. 2895), Wrestling; 1l.35, High-jumping. VERT: as Type **510**: 20b. (No. 2890), Diving; 55b. (No. 2893), Water-polo; 55b. (No. 2894), Women's high-jumping. HORIZ—45 × 33 mm: 1l.75, Canoeing.

1961. Air. Stamp Day.

2899 **511** 55b.(+45b.) blue, brown and red 95 40

1961. Air. Modern Romanian Architecture. Mult.

2900 20b. Type **512** 25 10
2901 40b. Constantza Railway Station (horiz) 90 15
2902 55b. Congress Hall, Republic Palace, Bucharest (horiz) 40 10
2903 75b. Rolling mill, Hunedoara (horiz) 45 10
2904 1l. Apartment blocks, Bucharest (horiz) 60 15
2905 1l.20 Circus Building, Bucharest (horiz) 65 35
2906 1l.75 Workers' Club, Mangalia (horiz) 60 20

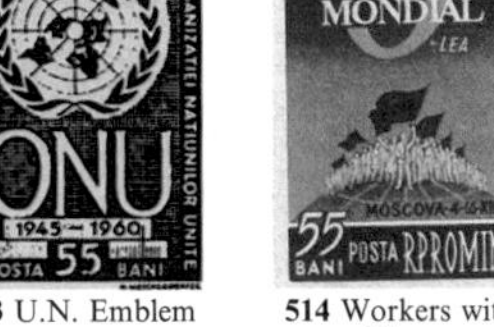

513 U.N. Emblem

514 Workers with Flags

1961. 15th Anniv of U.N.O. Perf or imperf.

2907 – 20b. multicoloured 15 10
2908 – 40b. multicoloured 45 10
2909 **513** 55b. multicoloured 65 15

DESIGNS (bearing U.N. emblem): 20b. Peace dove over Eastern Europe; 40b. Peace dove and youths of three races.

1961. 5th W.F.T.U. Congress, Moscow.

2910 **514** 55b. red 60 20

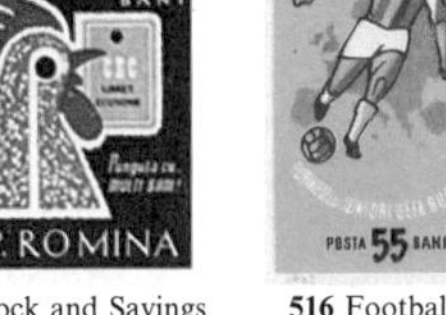

515 Cock and Savings Book

516 Footballer

1962. Savings Day. Inscr "1962". Multicoloured.

2911 40b. Type **515** 20 10
2912 55b. Savings Bank book, bee and "honeycombs" of agriculture, housing and industry 45 10

1962. European Junior Football Competition, Bucharest.

2913 **516** 55b. brown and green 95 25

517 Ear of Corn, Map and Tractor

518 Handball Player

1962. Completion of Agricultural Collectivisation Project. Inscr "1962".

2914 **517** 40b. red and orange 15 10
2915 – 55b. lake and yellow 20 10
2916 – 1l.55 yellow, red and blue 45 15

DESIGNS: 55b. Commemorative medal; 1l.55, Wheatsheaf, and hammer and sickle emblem.

1962. Women's World Handball Championships, Bucharest.

2917 **518** 55b. violet and yellow 95 20

519 Canoe Race

520 Jean Jacques Rousseau

1962. Boating and Sailing. Inscr "1962". (a) Perf.

2918 **519** 10b. blue and mauve 15 10
2919 – 20b. blue and brown 20 10
2920 – 40b. blue and brown 25 10
2921 – 55b. blue and ultramarine 35 15
2922 – 1l. blue and red 70 15
2923 – 1l.20 blue and purple 90 15
2924 – 1l.55 blue and red 1·10 15
2925 – 3l. blue and violet 1·70 35

(b) Imperf. Colours changed.

2926 **519** 10b. blue and ultramarine 20 20
2927 – 20b. blue and mauve 30 20
2928 – 40b. blue and red 45 30
2929 – 55b. blue and brown 50 40
2930 – 1l. blue and brown 90 40
2931 – 1l.20 blue and violet 1·00 50
2932 – 1l.55 blue and red 1·00 55
2933 – 3l. blue and purple 2·50 95

DESIGNS: 20b. Kayak; 40b. Racing "eight"; 55b. Sculling; 1l. "Star" yachts; 1l.20, Power boats; 1l.55, "Flying Dutchman" dinghy; 3l. Canoe slalom.

1962. Cultural Anniversaries (writers).

2934 **520** 40b. green 20 10
2935 – 55b. purple 25 15
2936 – 1l.75 blue 65 10

DESIGNS—As T **520**: 40b. Type **520** (250th birth anniv); 55b. Ion Caragiale (dramatist, 50th death anniv); 1l.75, Aleksandr Herzen (150th birth anniv).

521 Flags and Globes

1962. World Youth Festival, Helsinki.

2938 **521** 55b. multicoloured 65 20

522 Traian Vuia (aviator)

523 Anglers by Pond

1962. Romanian Celebrities.

2939 **522** 15b. brown 15 10
2940 – 20b. red 20 10
2941 – 35b. purple 20 10
2942 – 40b. blue 30 15
2943 – 55b. blue 35 10
2944 – 1l. blue 55 10
2945 – 1l.20 red 70 25
2946 – 1l.35 turquoise 95 25
2947 – 1l.55 violet 1·10 15

PORTRAITS: 20b. Alexandru Davila (writer); 35b. Vasile Pirvan (archaeologist); 40b. Ion Negulici (painter); 55b. Grigore Cobilcescu (geologist); 1l. Dr. Gheorghe Marinescu (neurologist); 1l.20, Dr. Ion Cantacuzino (bacteriologist); 1l.35, Dr. Victor Babes (bacteriologist and pathologist; 1l.55, Dr. Constantin Levaditi (medical researcher).

1962. Fishing Sport. Multicoloured.

2948 10b. Rod-fishing in fishing punts 10 10
2949 25b. Line-fishing in mountain pool 15 10
2950 40b. Type **523** 25 10
2951 55b. Anglers on beach 30 10
2952 75b. Line-fishing in mountain stream 45 10
2953 1l. Shore-fishing 50 20
2954 1l.75 Freshwater-fishing 85 20
2955 3l.25 Fishing in Danube delta 1·50 25

524 Dove and "Space" Stamps of 1957/58

527 "Vostok 3" and "4" in Orbit

1962. Air. Cosmic Flights.

2956 **524** 35b. brown 15 10
2957 – 55b. green 25 10
2958 – 1l.35 blue 60 15
2959 – 1l.75 red 1·00 35

DESIGNS—Dove and: 55b. "Space" stamps of 1959; 1l.35, "Space" stamps of 1957 ("Laika"), 1959 and 1960; 1l.75, "Spacemen" stamps of 1961.

1962. Romanian Victory in European Junior Football Competition, Bucharest. Surch **1962. Campioana Europeana 2 lei**.

2961 **516** 2l. on 55b. brown & grn 1·90 1·80

1962. Romanian Victory in Women's World Handball Championships, Bucharest. Surch **Campioana Mondiala 5 lei**.

2962 **518** 5l. on 55b. vio& yell 4·00 2·40

1962. Air. 1st "Team" Manned Space Flight.

2963 – 55b. violet 35 10
2964 **527** 1l.60 blue 85 20
2965 – 1l.75 purple 1·20 25

DESIGNS: 55b. Andrian Nikolaev (cosmonaut); 1l.75, Pavel Popovich (cosmonaut).

528 Child and Butterfly

529 Pottery

1962. Children.

2966 **528** 20b. blue, brown and red 15 10
2967 – 30b. yellow, blue and red 20 10
2968 – 40b. blue, red & turquoise 25 10
2969 – 55b. olive, blue and red 50 10
2970 – 1l.20 red, brown & blue 1·00 20
2971 – 1l.55 ochre, blue and red 1·30 25

DESIGNS—VERT: 30b. Girl feeding dove; 40b. Boy with model yacht; 1l.20, Boy violinist and girl pianist. HORIZ: 55b. Girl teaching boy to write; 1l.55, Pioneers around camp-fire.

1962. 4th Sample Fair, Bucharest. Inscr "AL IV-LEA PAVILION DE MOSTRE BUCURESTI 1962". Multicoloured.

2972 5b. Type **529** (postage) 30 15
2973 10b. Preserved foodstuffs 30 15
2974 20b. Chemical products 30 15
2975 40b. Ceramics 40 10
2976 55b. Leather goods 50 10
2977 75b. Textiles 70 2·50
2978 1l. Furniture and fabrics 85 10
2979 1l.20 Office equipment 1·20 10
2980 1l.55 Needlework 1·40 10
2981 1l.60 Fair pavilion (horiz) (air) 2·00 20

530 Lenin and Red Flag

1962. 45th Anniv of Russian Revolution.

2982 **530** 55b. brown, red and blue 65 20

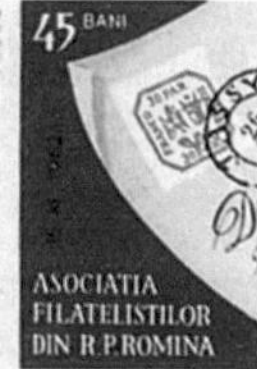

531 "The Coachmen" (after Szatmay)

1962. Air. Stamp Day and Centenary of 1st Romanian Stamps.

2983 **531** 55b.(+45b.) black and blue 1·00 30

532 Lamb

1962. Prime Farm Stock.

2984 **532** 20b. black and blue 15 10
2985 – 40b. brown, yellow & blue 15 10
2986 – 55b. green, buff and orange 25 10
2987 – 1l. brown, buff and grey 35 10
2988 – 1l.35 brown, black & green 50 15
2989 – 1l.55 brown, black & red 60 20
2990 – 1l.75 brown, cream & blue 1·00 35

DESIGNS—HORIZ: 40b. Ram; 1l.55, Heifer; 1l.75, Sows. VERT: 55b. Bull; 1l. Pig; 1l.35, Cow.

533 Arms, Industry and Agriculture

1962. 15th Anniv of People's Republic.

2991 **533** 1l.55 multicoloured 95 25

534 Strikers

1963. 30th Anniv of Grivitsa Strike.

2992 **534** 1l.75 multicoloured 1·30 25

535 Tractor-driver

1963. Freedom from Hunger.

2993 **535** 40b. blue 20 10
2994 – 55b. brown 30 10
2995 – 1l.55 red 65 10
2996 – 1l.75 green 75 20

DESIGNS (each with F.A.O. emblem): 55b. Girl harvester; 1l.55, Child with beaker of milk; 1l.75, Girl vintager.

1963. Air. Romanian Philatelists' Conference, Bucharest. No. 2983 optd **A.F.R.** surrounded by **CONFERINTA PE TARA BUCURESTI 30-III-1963** in diamond shape.

2997 **531** 55b.(+45b.) blk & bl 2·75 2·50

The opt is applied in the middle of the se-tenant pair—stamp and 45b. label.

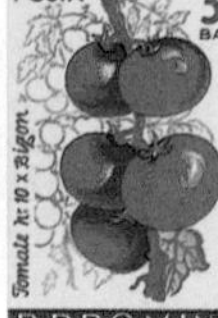

537 Sighisoara Glass Factory **538** Tomatoes

1963. Air. "Socialist Achievements".
2998 **537** 30b. blue and red . . . 25 10
2999 – 40b. green and violet . . 25 15
3000 – 55b. red and blue . . . 40 10
3001 – 1l. violet and brown . . 60 15
3002 – 1l.55 red and blue . . . 85 20
3003 – 1l.75 blue and purple . . 85 25
DESIGNS: 40b. Govora soda works; 55b. Tirgul-Jiu wood factory; 1l. Savinesti chemical works; 1l.55, Hunedoara metal works; 1l.75, Brazi thermic power station.

1963. Vegetable Culture. Multicoloured.
3004 35b. Type **538** 15 10
3005 40b. Hot peppers 25 10
3006 55b. Radishes 25 10
3007 75b. Aubergines 45 15
3008 1l.20 Mild peppers 65 20
3009 3l.25 Cucumbers (horiz) . . 1·30 30

539 Moon Rocket "Luna 4" **540** Chick

1963. Air. Launching of Soviet Moon Rocket "Luna 4". The 1l.75 is imperf.
3010 **539** 55b. red and blue . . . 20 15
3011 1l.75 red and violet . . . 95 15

1963. Domestic Poultry.
3012 **540** 20b. yellow and blue . . 20 10
3013 – 30b. red, blue and brown 25 10
3014 – 40b. blue, orange & brn 30 10
3015 – 55b. multicoloured . . . 35 10
3016 – 70b. blue, red and purple 40 10
3017 – 1l. red, grey and blue . . 45 15
3018 – 1l.35 red, blue and ochre 60 15
3019 – 3l.20 multicoloured . . . 1·20 35
POULTRY: 30b. Cockerel; 40b. Duck; 55b. White Leghorn; 70b. Goose; 1l. Rooster; 1l.35, Turkey (cock); 3l.20, Turkey (hen).

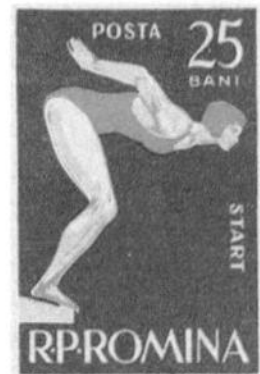

541 Diving **542** Congress Emblem

1963. Swimming. Bodies in drab.
3020 **541** 25b. green and brown . . 15 10
3021 – 30b. yellow and olive . . 20 10
3022 – 55b. red and turquoise 25 10
3023 – 1l. red and green 45 15
3024 – 1l.35 mauve and blue . . 50 15
3025 – 1l.55 orange and violet 90 20
3026 – 2l. yellow and mauve . . 90 50
DESIGNS—HORIZ: 30b. Crawl; 55b. Butterfly; 1l. Back stroke; 1l.35, Breast stroke. VERT: 1l.55, Swallow diving; 2l. Water polo.

1963. International Women's Congress, Moscow.
3027 **542** 55b. blue 45 20

543 Valery Bykovsky and Globe

1963. Air. 2nd "Team" Manned Space Flights.
3028 **543** 55b. blue 25 10
3029 – 1l.75 red . . . . 1·00 25
DESIGN: 1l.75, Valentina Tereshkova and globe.

544 Class 142 Steam Locomotive, 1936

1963. Air. Transport. Multicoloured.
3031 40b. Type **544** 50 15
3032 55b. Class 060-DA diesel-electric locomotive, 1959 50 15
3033 75b. Trolley bus 50 25
3034 1l.35 "Oltenita" (Danube passenger vessel) . . . . 1·30 30
3035 1l.75 Ilyushin Il-18 airplane 1·40 20

545 William Thackeray (novelist)

1963. Cultural Anniversaries. Inscr "MARILE ANNIVERSARI CULTURALE 1963".
3036 **545** 40b. black and lilac . . . 20 15
3037 – 50b. black and brown . . 30 15
3038 – 55b. black and olive . . 40 15
3039 – 1l.55 black and red . . . 80 15
3040 – 1l.75 black and blue . . 85 20
PORTRAITS: 40b. Type **545** (death centenary); 50b. Eugene Delacroix (painter, death centenary); 55b. Gheorghe Marinescu (neurologist, birth centenary); 1l.55, Giuseppe Verdi (composer, 150th birth anniv); 1l.75, Konstantin Stanislavsky (actor and stage director, birth centenary).

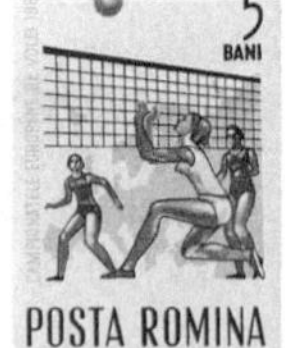

546 Walnuts **548** Volleyball

1963. Fruits and Nuts. Multicoloured.
3041 10b. Type **546** 25 10
3042 20b. Plums 25 10
3043 40b. Peaches 45 10
3044 55b. Strawberries 55 10
3045 1l. Grapes 60 10
3046 1l.55 Apples 80 15
3047 1l.60 Cherries . . . . 1·10 25
3048 1l.75 Pears . . . . 1·20 25

1963. Air. 50th Death Anniv of Aurel Vlaicu (aviation pioneer). No. 2752 surch **1913–1963 50 ani de la moarte 1,75 lei**.
3049 **483** 1l.75 on 10b. brn & yell 2·20 90

1963. European Volleyball Championships.
3050 **548** 5b. mauve and grey . . 20 10
3051 – 40b. blue and grey . . . 25 10
3052 – 55b. turquoise and grey 35 15
3053 – 1l.75 brown and grey . . 95 20
3054 – 3l.20 violet and grey . . 1·40 20
DESIGNS: 40b. to 1l.75, Various scenes of play at net; 3l.20, European Cup.

549 Romanian 1l.55 "Centenary" Stamp of 1958

1963. Air. Stamp Day and 15th U.P.U. Congress. Inscr "AL XV-LEA CONGRESS", etc.
3055 **549** 20b. brown and blue . . 15 10
3056 – 40b. blue and mauve . . 15 10
3057 – 55b. mauve and blue . . 20 10
3058 – 1l.20 violet and buff . . 40 15
3059 – 1l.55 green and red . . . 1·10 20
3060 – 1l.60+50b. mult . . . . 1·00 30
DESIGNS (Romanian stamps): 40b. (1l.20) "Laika", 1957 (blue); 55b. (3l.20) "Gagarin", 1961; 1l.20, (55b.) "Nikolaev" and (1l.75) "Popovich", 1962; 1l.55, (55b.) "Postwoman", 1953; 1l.60, U.P.U. Monument, Berne, globe, map of Romania and aircraft (76 × 27 mm).

551 Ski Jumping

1963. Winter Olympic Games, Innsbruck, 1964. (a) Perf.
3061 **551** 10b. blue and red . . . 25 15
3062 – 20b. brown and blue . . 35 15
3063 – 40b. brown and green . . 40 10
3064 – 55b. brown and violet 50 15
3065 – 60b. blue and brown . . 75 20
3066 – 75b. blue and mauve . . 90 20
3067 – 1l. blue and ochre . . . 1·10 25
3068 – 1l.20 blue and turquoise 1·40 30

(b) Imperf. Colours changed.
3069 **551** 10b. brown and green . . 60 55
3070 – 20b. brown and violet 60 55
3071 – 40b. blue and red . . . 60 55
3072 – 55b. brown and blue . . 60 55
3073 – 60b. blue and turquoise 60 55
3074 – 75b. blue and ochre . . 60 55
3075 – 1l. blue and mauve . . . 60 55
3076 – 1l.20 blue and brown . . 60 55
DESIGNS: 20b. Speed skating; 40b. Ice hockey; 55b. Figure skating; 60b. Slalom; 75b. Biathlon; 1l. Bobsleighing; 1l.20, Cross-country skiing.

552 Cone, Fern and Conifer **553** Silkworm Moth

1963. 18th Anniv of Reafforestation Campaign.
3078 **552** 55b. green 20 10
3079 – 1l.75 blue 40 15
DESIGN: 1l.75, Chestnut trees.

1963. Bee-keeping and Silkworm-breeding. Mult.
3080 10b. Type **553** 25 10
3081 20b. Moth emerging from chrysalis 35 10
3082 40b. Silkworm 45 10
3083 55b. Honey bee (horiz) . . . 55 10
3084 60b. Honey bee on flower 70 20
3085 1l.20 Honey bee approaching orange flowers (horiz) 90 25
3086 1l.35 Honey bee approaching pink flowers (horiz) . . . . 1·20 35
3087 1l.60 Honey bee and sunflowers (horiz) . . . . 1·40 35

554 Carved Pillar **556** George Stephanescu (composer)

555 Yuri Gagarin

1963. Village Museum, Bucharest.
3088 **554** 20b. purple 20 10
3089 – 40b. blue (horiz) 25 10
3090 – 55b. violet (horiz) . . . 30 10
3091 – 75b. green 40 10
3092 – 1l. red and brown . . . 60 10
3093 – 1l.20 green 70 15
3094 – 1l.75 blue and brown . . 1·20 15
DESIGNS: Various Romanian peasant houses.

1964. Air. "Space Navigation". Soviet flag, red and yellow; U.S. flag, red and blue; backgrounds, light blue; portrait and inscription colours below. (a) Perf.
3095 **555** 5b. blue 20 10
3096 – 10b. violet 25 10
3097 – 20b. bronze 30 10
3098 – 35b. grey 35 10
3099 – 40b. violet 40 15
3100 – 55b. violet 50 20
3101 – 60b. brown 50 20
3102 – 75b. blue 55 20
3103 – 1l. purple 75 25
3104 – 1l.40 purple . . . . . . 1·20 45

(b) Imperf. Colours changed.
3105 **555** 5b. violet 10 10
3106 – 10b. blue 10 10
3107 – 20b. grey 20 10
3108 – 35b. bronze 45 25
3109 – 40b. purple 60 30
3110 – 55b. purple 80 35
3111 – 60b. blue 80 50
3112 – 75b. brown . . . . . . 1·10 70
3113 – 1l. violet . . . . 1·30 85
3114 – 1l.40 violet . . . . . . 1·70 1·30
PORTRAITS (with flags of their countries)—As Type **555**: 10b. German Titov; 20b. John Glenn; 35b. Scott Carpenter; 60b. Walter Schirra; 75b. Gordon Cooper. $35\frac{1}{2} \times 33\frac{1}{2}$ mm: 40b. Andrian Nikolaev; 55b. Pavel Popovich; 1l. Valery Bykovsky; 1l.40, Valentina Tereshkova.

1964. Romanian Opera Singers and their stage roles. Portraits in brown.
3116 **556** 10b. olive 25 10
3117 – 20b. blue 35 10
3118 – 35b. green 35 10
3119 – 40b. light blue 40 10
3120 – 55b. mauve 50 10
3121 – 75b. violet 50 10
3122 – 1l. blue 60 15
3123 – 1l.35 violet 65 15
3124 – 1l.55 red . . . . 1·10 25
DESIGNS: 20b. Elena Teodorini in "Carmen"; 35b. Ion Bajenaru in "Petru Rares"; 40b. Dimitrie Popovici-Bayreuth as Alberich in "Ring of the Nibelung"; 55b. Haricled Dardee in "Tosca"; 75b. George Folescu in "Boris Godunov"; 1l. Jean Athanasiu in "Rigoletto"; 1l.35, Traian Grosarescu as Duke in "Rigoletto"; 1l.55, Nicolae Leonard as Hoffmann in "Tales of Hoffmann".

557 Prof. G. M. Murgoci **558** "Ascalaphus macaronius" (owl-fly)

1964. 8th International Soil Congress, Bucharest.
3125 **557** 1l.60 indigo, ochre and blue 60 20

1964. Insects. Multicoloured.
3126 5b. Type **558** 15 10
3127 10b. "Ammophila sabulosa" (digger wasp) 20 10
3128 35b. "Scolia maculata" (dagger wasp) 20 10
3129 40b. Swamp tiger moth . . 35 10
3130 55b. Gypsy moth 40 10
3131 1l.20 Great banded grayling 60 20
3132 1l.55 "Carabus fabricii malachiticus" (ground beetle) 70 20
3133 1l.75 "Procerus gigas" (ground beetle) . . . . . 1·30 25

559 "Nicotiana alata" **560** Cross Country

1964. Romanian Flowers. Multicoloured.
3134 10b. Type **559** 15 15
3135 20b. "Pelargonium" 20 15
3136 40b. "Fuchsia gracilis" . . . 30 15
3137 55b. "Chrysanthemum indicum" 35 15
3138 75b. "Dahlia hybrida" . . . 40 15
3139 1l. "Lilium croceum" . . . 60 15
3140 1l.25 "Hosta ovata" 75 25
3141 1l.55 "Tagetes erectus" . . . 80 25

1964. Horsemanship.
3142 – 40b. multicoloured . . . 25 10
3143 **560** 55b. brown, red and lilac 30 10
3144 – 1l.35 brown, red & green 80 20
3145 – 1l.55 mauve, blue & bis 1·10 20
DESIGNS—HORIZ: 40b. Dressage; 1l.55, Horse race. VERT: 1l.35, Show jumping.

561 Brown Scorpionfish **562** M. Eminescu (poet)

1964. Constantza Aquarium. Fish designs. Mult.
3146 5b. Type **561** 10 10
3147 10b. Peacock blenny 10 10
3148 20b. Black Sea horse-mackerel 10 10
3149 40b. Russian sturgeon . . . 20 10
3150 50b. Short-snouted seahorse 30 15
3151 55b. Tub gurnard 35 15

3152 1l. Beluga 50 15
3153 3l.20 Common stingray 2·10 30

1964. Cultural Anniversaries. Portraits in brown.
3154 **562** 5b. green 15 10
3155 – 20b. red 15 10
3156 – 35b. red 20 10
3157 – 55b. bistre 65 10
3158 – 1l.20 blue 1·00 15
3159 – 1l.75 violet 2·00 40
DESIGNS: Type **562** (75th death anniv); 20b. Ion Creanga (folklorist, 75th death anniv); 35b. Emil Girleanu (writer, 50th death anniv); 55b. Michelangelo (artist, 400th death anniv); 1l.20, Galileo Galilei (astronomer, 400th birth anniv); 1l.75, William Shakespeare (dramatist, 400th birth anniv).

563 Cheile Bicazului (gorge)

564 High Jumping

1964. Mountain Resorts.
3160 **563** 40b. lake 20 10
3161 – 55b. blue 35 10
3162 – 1l. purple 45 10
3163 – 1l.35 brown 50 10
3164 – 1l.75 green 85 15
DESIGNS—VERT: 55b. Cabin on Lake Bilea; 1l. Poiana Brasov ski-lift; 1l.75, Alpine Hotel. HORIZ: 1l.35, Lake Bicaz.

1964. Balkan Games. Multicoloured.
3165 30b. Type **564** 15 10
3166 40b. Throwing the javelin 15 10
3167 55b. Running 25 10
3168 1l. Throwing the discus 50 10
3169 1l.20 Hurdling 50 15
3170 1l.55 Flags of competing countries (24 × 44 mm) 55 20

565 Arms and Flag

1964. 20th Anniv of Liberation. Multicoloured.
3171 55b. Type **565** 20 10
3172 60b. Industrial plant (horiz) 20 10
3173 75b. Harvest scene (horiz) 30 10
3174 1l.20 Apartment houses (horiz) 55 20

566 High Jumping

1964. Olympic Games, Tokyo. Multicoloured. (a) Perf.
3176 20b. Type **566** 25 10
3177 30b. Wrestling 35 10
3178 35b. Volleyball 35 10
3179 40b. Canoeing 40 15
3180 55b. Fencing 50 15
3181 1l.20 Gymnastics 85 25
3182 1l.35 Football 1·00 25
3183 1l.55 Rifle-shooting 1·20 30

(b) Imperf. Colours changed and new values.
3184 20b. Type **566** 20 10
3185 30b. Wrestling 25 10
3186 35b. Volleyball 45 10
3187 40b. Canoeing 45 15
3188 55b. Fencing 90 30
3189 1l.60 Gymnastics 1·80 80
3190 2l. Football 1·90 1·00
3191 2l.40 Rifle-shooting 2·40 1·50

567 George Enescu

568 Python

1964. 3rd International George Enescu Festival.
3193 **567** 10b. green 20 10
3194 – 55b. purple 30 10
3195 – 1l.60 purple 75 30
3196 – 1l.75 blue 95 20
DESIGNS (Portraits of Enescu): 55b. At piano; 1l.60, Medallion; 1l.75, When an old man.

1964. Bucharest Zoo. Multicoloured.
3197 5b. Type **568** 10 10
3198 10b. Black swans 45 10
3199 35b. Ostriches 75 10
3200 40b. Crowned cranes 75 15
3201 55b. Tigers 35 10
3202 1l. Lions 55 10
3203 1l.55 Grevy's zebras 80 15
3204 2l. Bactrian camels 1·20 25

569 Brincoveanu, Cantacuzino, Lazar and Academy

570 Soldier

1964. Anniversaries. Multicoloured.
3205 20b. Type **569** 10 10
3206 40b. Cuza and seal 10 10
3207 55b. Emblems and the Arts (vert) 20 10
3208 75b. Laboratory workers and class 25 15
3209 1l. Savings Bank building 40 20
EVENTS, etc—HORIZ: 20b. 270th Anniv of Domneasca Academy; 40b., 75b. Bucharest University centenary; 1l. Savings Bank centenary. VERT: 55b. "Fine Arts" centenary (emblems are masks, curtain, piano keyboard, harp, palette and brushes).

1964. Centenary of Army Day.
3210 **570** 55b. blue and light blue 35 20

571 Post Office of 19th and 20th Centuries

1964. Air. Stamp Day.
3211 **571** 1l.60+40b. blue, red and yellow 95 25
No. 3211 is a two-part design, the two parts being arranged vert, imperf between.

572 Canoeing Medal (1956)

573 Strawberries

1964. Olympic Games—Romanian Gold Medal Awards. Medals in brown and bistre (Nos. 3218/19 and 3226/7 in sepia and gold). (a) Perf.
3212 **572** 20b. red and blue 20 10
3213 – 30b. green and blue 35 15
3214 – 35b. turquoise and blue 45 15
3215 – 40b. lilac and blue 55 25
3216 – 55b. orange and blue 60 20
3217 – 1l.20 green and blue 70 25
3218 – 1l.35 brown and blue 1·10 30
3219 – 1l.55 mauve and blue 2·40 30

(b) Imperf. Colours changed and new values.
3220 **572** 20b. orange and blue 10 15
3221 – 30b. turquoise and blue 30 20
3222 – 35b. green and blue 30 20
3223 – 40b. green and blue 35 30
3224 – 55b. red and blue 40 30
3225 – 1l.60 lilac and blue 1·30 1·00
3226 – 2l. mauve and blue 2·00 1·30
3227 – 2l.40 brown and blue 2·50 1·70
MEDALS: 30b. Boxing (1956); 35b. Pistol-shooting (1956); 40b. High-jumping (1960); 55b. Wrestling (1960); 1l.20, 1l.60, Rifle-shooting (1960); 1l.35, 2l. High-jumping (1964); 1l.55, 2l.40, Throwing the javelin (1964).

1964. Forest Fruits. Multicoloured.
3229 5b. Type **573** 15 10
3230 35b. Blackberries 20 10
3231 40b. Raspberries 25 10
3232 55b. Rosehips 30 10
3233 1l.20 Blueberries 60 15
3234 1l.35 Cornelian cherries 70 15
3235 1l.55 Hazel nuts 80 10
3236 2l.55 Cherries 1·20 25

574 "Syncom 3"

575 U.N. Headquarters, New York

1965. Space Navigation. Multicoloured.
3237 30b. Type **574** 15 10
3238 40b. "Syncom 3" (different) 20 10
3239 55b. "Ranger 7" (horiz) 35 10
3240 1l. "Ranger 7" (different) (horiz) 40 15
3241 1l.20 "Voskhod 1" (horiz) 70 10
3242 5l. Konstantin Feoktistov, Vladimir Komarov and Boris Yegorov (cosmonauts) and "Voskhod 1" (52 × 29 mm) 1·70 60

1965. 20th Anniv of U.N.O.
3243 **575** 55b. gold, blue and red 15 10
3244 – 1l.60 multicoloured 55 25
DESIGN: 1l.60, Arms and U.N. emblem on Romanian flag.

576 Spur-thighed Tortoise

1965. Reptiles. Multicoloured.
3245 5b. Type **576** 10 10
3246 10b. Crimean lizard 15 10
3247 20b. Three-lined lizard 15 10
3248 40b. Snake-eyed skink 20 10
3249 55b. Slow worm 25 10
3250 60b. Sand viper 40 10
3251 1l. Arguta 45 15
3252 1l.20 Orsini's viper 55 15
3253 1l.35 European whip snake 70 15
3254 3l.25 Four-lined rat snake 2·30 35

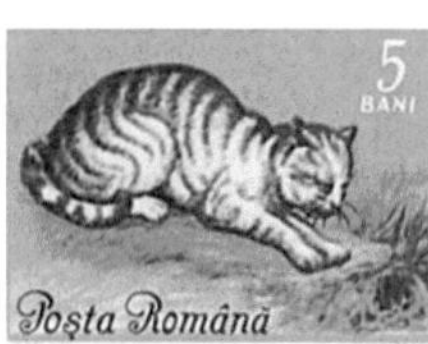

577 Tabby Cat

1965. Domestic Cats. Multicoloured.
3255 5b. Type **577** 10 10
3256 10b. Ginger tomcat 10 10
3257 40b. White Persians (vert) 20 15
3258 55b. Kittens with shoe (vert) 30 10
3259 60b. Kitten with ball of wool (vert) 45 10
3260 75b. Cat and two kittens (vert) 60 10
3261 1l.35 Siamese (vert) 1·10 20
3262 3l.25 Heads of three cats (62 × 29 mm) 2·00 50

1965. Space Flight of "Ranger 9" (24.3.65). No. 3240 surch **RANGER 9 24-3-1965 5 Lei** and floral emblem over old value.
3263 5l. on 1l. multicoloured 17·00 17·00

579 Ion Bianu (philologist)

1965. Cultural Anniversaries. Portraits in sepia.
3264 **579** 40l. blue 15 10
3265 – 55b. ochre 15 10
3266 – 60b. purple 20 10
3267 – 1l. red 50 10
3268 – 1l.35 olive 45 15
3269 – 1l.75 red 70 25
PORTRAITS, etc: 40b. Type **579** (30th death anniv); 55b. Anton Bacalbasa (writer, birth cent); 60b. Vasile Conta (philosopher, 120th birth anniv); 1l. Jean Sibelius (composer, birth cent); 1l.35, Horace (Roman poet, birth bimillenary); 1l.75, Dante Alighieri (poet, 700th birth anniv).

580 I.T.U. Emblem and Symbols

1965. Centenary of I.T.U.
3270 **580** 1l.75 blue 70 20

581 Derdap Gorge (The Iron Gate)

1965. Inaug of Derdap Hydro-electric Project.
3271 **581** 30b. (25d.) green and grey 15 10
3272 – 55b. (50d.) red and grey 25 10
DESIGN: 55b. Derdap Dam.
Nos. 3271/72 were issued simultaneously in Yugoslavia.

582 Rifleman

583 "Fat-Frumos and the Beast"

1965. European Shooting Championships, Bucharest. Multicoloured. (a) Perf.
3274 20b. Type **582** 10 10
3275 40b. Prone rifleman 20 15
3276 55b. Pistol shooting 25 10
3277 1l. "Free" pistol shooting 45 15
3278 1l.60 Standing rifleman 65 15
3279 2l. Various marksmen 85 30

(b) Imperf. Colours changed and new values.
3280 40b. Prone rifleman 15 10
3281 55b. Pistol shooting 20 10
3282 1l. "Free" pistol shooting 35 15
3283 1l.60 Standing rifleman 50 15
3284 3l.25 Type **582** 1·00 35
3285 5l. Various marksmen 1·50 60
Apart from Type **582** the designs are horiz, the 2l. and 5l. being larger, $51\frac{1}{2} \times 28\frac{1}{2}$ mm.

1965. Romanian Fairy Tales. Multicoloured.
3286 20b. Type **583** 20 10
3287 40b. "Fat-Frumos and Ileana Cosinzeana" 20 10
3288 55b. "Harap Alb" (horseman and bear) 25 10
3289 1l. "The Moralist Wolf" 45 10
3290 1l.35 "The Ox and the Calf" 70 20
3291 2l. "The Bear and the Wolf" (drawing a sledge) 95 25

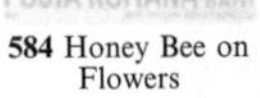

584 Honey Bee on Flowers

585 Pavel Belyaev, Aleksei Leonov, "Voskhod 2" and Leonov in Space

1965. 20th International Bee-keeping Association Federation ("Apimondia") Congress, Bucharest.

3292 **584** 55b. black, red and yellow 30 10
3293 – 1l.60 multicoloured . . . 95 15

DESIGN—HORIZ: 1l.60, Congress Hall.

1965. Space Achievements. Multicoloured.

3294 5b. "Proton 1" 10 10
3295 10b. "Sonda 3" (horiz) . . . 15 20
3296 15b. "Molnia 1" 20 20
3297 1l.75 Type **585** 60 10
3298 2l.40 "Early Bird" satellite 1·00 20
3299 3l.20 "Gemini 3" and astronauts in capsule . . 1·90 30
3300 3l.25 "Mariner 4" . . . . . 2·00 30
3301 5l. "Gemini 5" (horiz) . . . 3·00 75

586 Marx and Lenin

588 V. Alecsandri

587 Common Quail

1965. Socialist Countries' Postal Ministers' Congress, Peking.

3302 **586** 55b. multicoloured . . . 35 20

1965. Migratory Birds. Multicoloured.

3303 5b. Type **587** 15 10
3304 10b. Eurasian woodcock . . 25 10
3305 20b. Common snipe 30 10
3306 40b. Turtle dove 30 10
3307 55b. Mallard 40 10
3308 60b. White fronted goose . . 50 10
3309 1l. Common crane 60 15
3310 1l.20 Glossy ibis 75 15
3311 1l.35 Mute swan . . . . . 1·30 20
3312 3l.25 Eastern white pelican (32 × 73 mm) . . . . . . 3·75 55

1965. 75th Death Anniv of Vasile Alecsandri (poet).

3313 **588** 55b. multicoloured . . . 35 20

589 Zanzibar Water-lily

1965. Cluj Botanical Gardens. Multicoloured.

3314 5b. Bird-of-paradise flower (vert) 10 10
3315 10b. "Stanhopea tigrina" (orchid) (vert) 15 10
3316 20b. "Paphiopedilum insigne" (orchid) (vert) . . 15 10
3317 30b. Type **589** 25 10
3318 40b. "Ferocactus glaucescens" (cactus) . . 30 10
3319 55b. Tree-cotton 30 10
3320 1l. "Hibiscus rosa sinensis" 40 15
3321 1l.35 "Gloxinia hibrida" (vert) 60 15
3322 1l.75 Amazon water-lily . . 1·20 20
3323 2l.30 Hibiscus, water-lily, bird-of-paradise flower and botanical building (52 × 30 mm) . . . . . . 1·40 30

590 Running

592 Pigeon on TV Aerial

591 Pigeon and Horseman

1965. Spartacist Games. Multicoloured.

3324 55b. Type **590** 20 15
3325 1l.55 Football 55 20
3326 1l.75 Diving 60 20
3327 2l. Mountaineering (inscr "TURISM") 70 30
3328 5l. Canoeing (inscr "CAMPIONATELLE EUROPENE 1965") (horiz) . . . . 1·60 40

1965. Stamp Day.

3329 **591** 55b.+45b. blue & mve 35 10
3330 **592** 1l. brown and green . . 35 20
3331 – 1l.75 brown and green 80 20

DESIGN: As Type **592**: 1l.75, Pigeon in flight.

593 Chamois

1965. "Hunting Trophies".

3332 **593** 55b. brown, yell & mve 35 10
3333 – 1l. brown, green and red 60 10
3334 – 1l.60 brown, blue & orange . . . . 1·20 25
3335 – 1l.75 brown, red & green 1·60 25
3336 – 3l.20 multicoloured . . . 2·00 50

DESIGNS—37 × 23 mm: 1l. Brown bear; 1l.60, Red deer stag; 1l.75, Wild boar. 49 × 37½ mm: 3l.20, Trophy and antlers of red deer.

594 Dachshund

1965. Hunting Dogs. Multicoloured.

3337 5b. Type **594** 10 20
3338 10b. Spaniel 10 20
3339 40b. Retriever with eurasian woodcock 55 20
3340 55b. Fox terrier 25 20
3341 60b. Red setter 35 20
3342 75b. White setter 60 20
3343 1l.55 Pointers . . . . 1·30 45
3344 3l.25 Duck-shooting with retriever . . . . 2·30 1·20

SIZES: DIAMOND—47½ × 47½ mm: 10b. to 75b. HORIZ—43½ × 29 mm: 1l.55, 3l.25.

595 Pawn and Globe

596 Tractor, Corn and Sun

1966. World Chess Championships, Cuba. Mult.

3345 20b. Type **595** 25 10
3346 40b. Jester and bishop . . . 30 10
3347 55b. Knight and rook . . . 50 10
3348 1l. As No. 3347 . . . . . . 65 10
3349 1l.60 Type **595** . . . . . 1·40 20
3350 3l.25 As No. 3346 . . . . . 2·75 1·00

1966. Co-operative Farming Union Congress.

3351 **596** 55b. green and yellow . . 25 20

597 G. Gheorghiu-Dej

598 Congress Emblem

1966. 1st Death Anniv of Gheorghe Gheorghiu-Dej (President 1961–65).

3352 **597** 55b. black and gold . . 25 20

1966. Communist Youth Union Congress.

3354 **598** 55b. red and yellow . . 25 20

599 Dance of Moldova

1966. Romanian Folk-dancing.

3355 **599** 30b. black and purple . . 20 10
3356 – 40b. black and red . . . 35 25
3357 – 55b. black and turquoise 45 10
3358 – 1l. black and lake . . . 55 10
3359 – 1l.60 black and blue . . 90 15
3360 – 2l. black and green . . . 1·80 70

DANCES OF: 40b. Oltenia; 55b. Maramures; 1l. Muntenia; 1l.60, Banat; 2l. Transylvania.

600 Footballers

601 "Agriculture and Industry"

1966. World Cup Football Championship, England.

3361 **600** 5b. multicoloured . . . 10 15
3362 – 10b. multicoloured . . . 20 15
3363 – 15b. multicoloured . . . 25 15
3364 – 55b. multicoloured . . . 50 15
3365 – 1l.75 multicoloured . . . 1·30 40
3366 – 4l. multicoloured . . . . 2·75 2·75

DESIGNS: 10b. to 1l.75, Various footballing scenes; 4l. Jules Rimet Cup.

1966. Trade Union Congress, Bucharest.

3368 **601** 55b. multicoloured . . . 25 20

602 Red-breasted Flycatcher

603 "Venus 3"

1966. Song Birds. Multicoloured.

3369 5b. Type **602** 20 15
3370 10b. Red crossbill 35 15
3371 15b. Great reed warbler . . 55 15
3372 20b. Common redstart . . . 60 15
3373 55b. European robin 90 15
3374 1l.20 Bluethroat . . . . . . 1·20 15
3375 1l.55 Yellow wagtail . . . . 1·70 30
3376 3l.20 Penduline tit . . . . . 2·75 1·60

1966. Space Achievements. Multicoloured.

3377 10b. Type **603** 20 15
3378 20b. "FR 1" satellite . . . 25 15
3379 1l.60 "Luna 9" . . . . . . 1·10 30
3380 5l. "Gemini 6" and "7" . . 2·50 1·00

604 Urechia Nestor (historian)

606 "Hottonia palustris"

605 "House" (after Petrascu)

1966. Cultural Anniversaries.

3381 – 5b. blue, black and green 10 10
3382 – 10b. green, black and red 10 10
3383 **604** 20b. purple, black & green 10 10
3384 – 40b. brown, black & blue 10 10
3385 – 55b. green, black & brn 15 10
3386 – 1l. violet, black and bistre 50 10
3387 – 1l.35 olive, black & blue 75 15
3388 – 1l.60 purple, blk & green 1·20 30
3389 – 1l.75 purple, blk & orge 80 15
3390 – 3l.25 lake, black and blue . . . . 1·50 30

PORTRAITS: 5b. George Cosbuc (poet, birth cent); 10b. Gheorghe Sincai (historian, 150th death anniv); 20b. Type **604** (birth cent); 40b. Aron Pumnul (linguist, death cent); 55b. Stefan Luchian (painter, 50th death anniv); 1l. Sun Yat-sen (Chinese statesman, birth cent); 1l.35, Gottfried Leibnitz (philosopher, 250th death anniv); 1l.60, Romain Rolland (writer, birth cent); 1l.75, Ion Ghica (revolutionary and diplomat, 150th birth anniv); 3l.25, Constantin Cantacuzino (historian, 250th death anniv).

1966. Paintings in National Gallery, Bucharest. Multicoloured.

3391 5b. Type **605** 15 15
3392 10b. "Peasant Girl" (Grigorescu) (vert) 20 15
3393 20b. "Midday Rest" (Rescu) 30 15
3394 55b. "Portrait of a Man" (Van Eyck) (vert) 75 20
3395 1l.55 "The 2nd Class Compartment" (Daumier) 3·75 55
3396 3l.25 "The Blessing" (El Greco) (vert) . . . . . . 4·25 3·75

1966. Aquatic Flora. Multicoloured.

3397 5b. Type **606** 10 10
3398 10b. "Ceratophyllum submersum" 10 10
3399 20b. "Aldrovanda vesiculosa" 10 10
3400 40b. "Callitriche verna" . . 30 10
3401 55b. "Vallisneria spiralis" 20 10
3402 1l. "Elodea canadensis" . . 30 10
3403 1l.55 "Hippuris vulgaris" . . 50 20
3404 3l.25 "Myriophyllum spicatum" (28 × 49½ mm) 2·75 1·10

607 Diagram showing one metre in relation to quadrant of Earth

608 Putna Monastery

1966. Centenary of Metric System in Romania.

3405 **607** 55b. blue and brown . . 15 10
3406 – 1l. violet and green . . . 30 20

DESIGN: 1l. Metric abbreviations and globe.

1966. 500th Anniv of Putna Monastery.

3407 **608** 2l. multicoloured 75 30

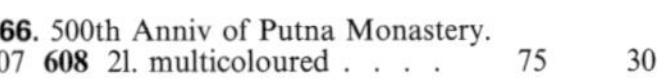

609 "Medicine"

1966. Centenary of Romanian Academy.

3408 **609** 40b. multicoloured . . . 15 10
3409 – 55b. multicoloured . . . 20 10
3410 – 1l. brown, gold and blue 30 10
3411 – 3l. brown, gold & yellow 1·10 70

DESIGNS—As Type **609**: 55b. "Science" (formula). $22\frac{1}{2} \times 33\frac{1}{2}$ mm: 1l. Gold medal. 67 × 27 mm: 3l. Ion Radulescu (writer), Mihail Kogalniceanu (historian) and Traian Savulescu (biologist).

610 Crayfish

1966. Crustaceans and Molluscs. Mult.
3412 5b. Type **610** 10 10
3413 10b. Netted nassa (vert) 15 10
3414 20b. Marbled rock crab 15 10
3415 40b. "Campylaea trizona" (snail) 25 10
3416 55b. Lucorum helix 40 10
3417 1l.35 Mediterranean blue mussel 95 20
3418 1l.75 Stagnant pond snail 1·20 20
3419 3l.25 Swan mussel 2·75 1·10

611 Bucharest and Mail Coach

1966. Stamp Day.
3420 **611** 55b.+45b. mult 65 30
No. 3420 is a two-part design arranged horiz, imperf between.

612 "Ursus spelaeus"

1966. Prehistoric Animals.
3421 **612** 5b. blue, brown and green 10 10
3422 – 10b. violet, bistre & green 10 10
3423 – 15b. brown, purple & green 10 10
3424 – 55b. violet, bistre & green 25 10
3425 – 1l.55 blue, brown & grn 1·40 20
3426 – 4l. mauve, bistre & green 2·75 50
ANIMALS: 10b. "Mamuthus trogontherii"; 15b. "Bison priscus"; 55b. "Archidiscodon"; 1l.55, "Megaceros eurycerus". (43 × 27 mm): 4l. "Deinotherium gigantissimum".

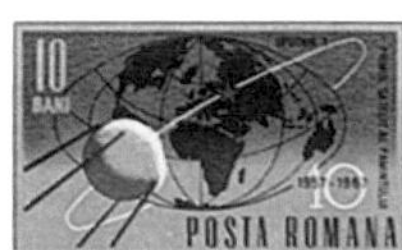

613 "Sputnik 1" orbiting Globe

1967. 10 Years of Space Achievements. Mult.
3427 10b. Type **613** (postage) 15 10
3428 20b. Yuri Gagarin and "Vostok 1" 15 10
3429 25b. Valentina Tereshkova ("Vostok 6") 20 10
3430 40b. Andrian Nikolaev and Pavel Popovich ("Vostok 3" and "4") 25 10
3431 55b. Aleksei Leonov in space ("Voskhod 2") 35 10
3432 1l.20 "Early Bird" (air) 75 20
3433 1l.55 Photo transmission ("Mariner 4") 1·00 20
3434 3l.25 Space rendezvous ("Gemini 6" and "7") 1·40 40
3435 5l. Space link up ("Gemini 8") 1·90 1·40

614 Barn Owl

1967. Birds of Prey. Multicoloured.
3442 10b. Type **614** 35 10
3443 20b. Eagle owl 55 10
3444 40b. Saker falcon 55 10
3445 55b. Egyptian vulture 65 10
3446 75b. Osprey 75 10
3447 1l. Griffon vulture 1·20 10
3448 1l.20 Lammergeier 2·20 20
3449 1l.75 Cinereous 2·50 95

615 "Washerwoman" (after I. Steriadi)

1967. Paintings.
3450 – 10b. blue, gold and red 15 10
3451 **615** 20b. green, gold & ochre 20 10
3452 – 40b. red, gold and blue 30 20
3453 – 1l.55 purple, gold & blue 50 25
3454 – 3l.20 brown, gold & brn 1·80 40
3455 – 5l. brown, gold & orange 2·20 1·50
PAINTINGS—VERT: 10b. "Model in Fancy Dress" (I. Andreescu); 40b. "Peasants Weaving" (S. Dimitrescu); 1l.55, "Venus and Cupid" (L. Cranach); 5l. "Haman beseeching Esther" (Rembrandt). HORIZ: 3l.20, "Hercules and the Lion" (Rubens).

616 Woman's Head

618 "Infantryman" (Nicolae Grigorescu)

617 Copper and Silver Coins of 1867

1967. 10th Anniv of C. Brancusi (sculptor). Sculptures.
3456 **616** 5b. brown, yellow and red 10 10
3457 – 10b. black, green & violet 15 10
3458 – 20b. black, green and red 15 10
3459 – 40b. black, red & green 15 20
3460 – 55b. black, olive and blue 30 20
3461 – 1l.20 brown, violet and orange 65 25
3462 – 3l.25 black, green and mauve 3·25 95
DESIGNS—HORIZ: 10b. Sleeping muse; 40b. "The Kiss"; 3l.25, Gate of Kisses, Targujiu. VERT: 20b. "The Endless Column"; 55b. Seated woman; 1l.20, "Miss Pogany".

1967. Centenary of Romanian Monetary System.
3463 **617** 55b. multicoloured 20 20
3464 – 1l.20 multicoloured 40 50
DESIGN: 1l.20, Obverse and reverse of modern silver coin (1966).

1967. 90th Anniv of Independence.
3465 **618** 55b. multicoloured 70 75

619 Peasants attacking (after Octav Bancila)

620 "Centaurca pinnatifida"

1967. 60th Anniv of Peasant Rising.
3466 **619** 40b. multicoloured 30 50
3467 – 1l.55 multicoloured 85 1·10
DESIGN—HORIZ: 1l.55, Peasants marching (after S. Luchian).

1967. Carpathian Flora. Multicoloured.
3468 20b. Type **620** 10 15
3469 40b. "Erysimum transsilvanicum" 15 15
3470 55b. "Aquilegia transsilvanica" 20 15
3471 1l.20 Alpine violet 55 20
3472 1l.75 Bellflower 95 25
3473 4l. Mountain avens (horiz) 2·20 1·30

621 Towers, Sibiu

1967. Historic Monuments and International Tourist Year. Multicoloured.
3474 20b. Type **621** 20 15
3475 40b. Castle at Cris 20 15
3476 55b. Wooden church, Plopis 40 15
3477 1l.60 Ruins, Neamtului 65 25
3478 1l.75 Mogosoaia Palace, Bucharest 90 25
3479 2l.25 Church, Voronet 1·30 1·30
No. 3479 is horiz, $48\frac{1}{2} \times 36$ mm.

623 "Battle of Marasesti" (E. Stoica)

1967. 50th Anniv of Battles of Marasesti, Marasti and Oituz.
3481 **623** 55b. brown, blue and grey 40 25

624 Dinu Lipatti (composer and pianist)

625 Wrestling

1967. Cultural Anniversaries.
3482 **624** 10b. violet, blue and black 10 10
3483 – 20b. blue, brown & black 10 10
3484 – 40b. brown, turq & blk 10 10
3485 – 55b. brown, red and black 15 10
3486 – 1l.20 brown, olive & black 25 15
3487 – 1l.75 green, blue & black 75 55
DESIGNS: 10b. Type **624** (50th birth anniv); 20b. Alexandru Orascu (architect, 150th birth anniv); 40b. Grigore Antipa (biologist, birth cent); 55b. Mihail Kogalniceanu (politician and historian, 150th birth anniv); 1l.20, Jonathan Swift (satirist, 300th birth anniv); 1l.75, Marie Curie (physicist, birth cent).

1967. World Wrestling Championships, Bucharest. Designs showing wrestlers and globes.
3488 **625** 10b. multicoloured 10 10
3489 – 20b. mult (horiz) 15 10
3490 – 55b. multicoloured 20 10
3491 – 1l.20 multicoloured 50 15
3492 – 2l. multicoloured (horiz) 90 60

626 Inscription on Globe

1967. International Linguists' Congress, Bucharest.
3493 **626** 1l.60 ultramarine, red and blue 60 20

627 Academy

1967. Centenary of Book Academy, Bucharest.
3494 **627** 55b. grey, brown and blue 40 20

628 Dancing on Ice

629 Curtea de Arges Monastery

1967. Winter Olympic Games, Grenoble. Mult.
3495 20b. Type **628** 10 10
3496 40b. Skiing 20 10
3497 55b. Bobsleighing 30 10
3498 1l. Downhill skiing 50 20
3499 1l.55 Ice hockey 80 20
3500 2l. Games emblem 1·10 40
3501 2l.30 Ski jumping 1·50 1·10

1967. 450th Anniv of Curtea de Arges Monastery.
3503 **629** 55b. multicoloured 35 25

630 Karl Marx and Title Page

631 Lenin

1967. Centenary of Karl Marx's "Das Kapital".
3504 **630** 40b. black, yellow and red 25 20

1967. 50th Anniv of October Revolution.
3505 **631** 1l.20 black, gold and red 40 15

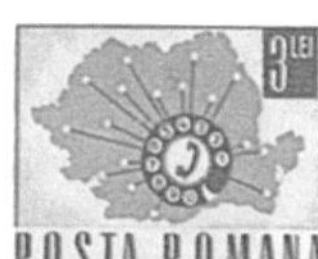

632 Arms of Romania

633 Telephone Dial and Map

1967. (a) T**632**.
3506 **632** 40b. blue 20 10
3507 55b. yellow 50 20
3508 1l.60 red 50 10

(b) T **633** and similar designs.
3509 – 5b. green 10 15
3510 – 10b. red 10 15
3511 – 20b. grey 35 15
3512 – 35b. blue 20 15
3513 – 40b. blue 10 15
3514 – 50b. orange 15 15
3515 – 55b. red 20 15
3516 – 60b. brown 35 15
3517 – 1l. green 35 15
3518 – 1l.20 violet 20 15
3519 – 1l.35 blue 70 15
3520 – 1l.50 red 35 15
3521 – 1l.55 brown 35 15
3522 – 1l.75 green 35 15
3523 – 2l. yellow 40 15
3524 – 2l.40 blue 40 15
3525 **633** 3l. turquoise 50 15
3526 – 3l.20 ochre 1·40 15
3527 – 3l.25 blue 1·60 15
3528 – 4l. mauve 2·00 15
3529 – 5l. violet 1·60 15
DESIGNS—23 × 17 mm: 5b. "Carpati" lorry; 20b. Railway Travelling Post Office coach; 35b. Zlin Z-226A Akrobat plane; 60b. Electric parcels truck. As Type **633**: 1l.20, Motorcoach; 1l.35, Mil Mi-4 helicopter; 1l.75, Lakeside highway; 2l. Postal van; 3l.20, Ilyushin Il-18 airliner; 4l. Electric train; 5l. Telex instrument and world map. 17 × 23 mm: 10b. Posthorn and telephone emblem; 40b. Power pylons; 50b. Telephone handset; 55b. Dam. As T **633** but vert: 1l. Diesel-electric train; 1l.50, Trolley-bus; 1l.55, Radio station; 2l.40, T.V. relay station; 3l.25, Liner "Transylvania".
No. 3525 also commemorates the 40th anniv of the automatic telephone service.
For Nos. 3517/29 in smaller format see Nos. 3842/57.

634 "Crossing the River Buzau" (lithograph by Raffet) ($\frac{1}{4}$-size illustration)

1967. Stamp Day.
3530 **634** 55b.+45b. blue and ochre 55 30

635 Monorail Train and Globe
636 Arms and Industrial Scene

1967. World Fair, Montreal. Multicoloured.
3531 55b. Type **635** 20 10
3532 1l. Expo emblem within atomic symbol 25 10
3533 1l.60 Gold cup and world map 35 10
3534 2l. Expo emblem 55 45

1967. 20th Anniv of Republic. Multicoloured.
3535 40b. Type **636** 15 10
3536 55b. Arms of Romania . . 15 10
3537 1l.60 Romanian flag (34×48 mm) 40 20
3538 1l.75 Arms and cultural emblems 65 60

637 I.A.R. 817 Flying Ambulance

1968. Air. Romanian Aviation.
3539 – 40b. multicoloured . . . 10 10
3540 **637** 55b. multicoloured . . . 25 10
3541 – 1l. multicoloured 30 10
3542 – 2l.40 multicoloured . . . 80 40
DESIGNS—VERT: 40b. Antonov An-2 biplane spraying crops; 1l. "Aviasan" emblem and airliner; 2l.40, Mircea Zorileanu (pioneer aviator) and biplane.

638 "Angelica and Medor" (S. Ricci)

1968. Paintings in Romanian Galleries. Mult.
3543 40b. "Young Woman" (Misu Pop) (vert) 30 20
3544 55b. "Little Girl in Red Scarf" (N. Grigorescu) (vert) 40 20
3545 1l. "Old Nicholas, the Cobza-player" (S. Luchian) (vert) 65 25
3546 1l.60 "Man with Skull" (Dierick Bouts) (vert) . . 90 25
3547 2l.40 Type **638** . . . . . . 1·10 45
3548 3l.20 "Ecce Homo" (Titian) (vert) . . . . 2·50 2·75
See also Nos. 3583/8, 3631/6, 3658/63, 3756/61 and 3779/84.

640 Human Rights Emblem
641 W.H.O. Emblem

1968. Human Rights Year.
3551 **640** 1l. multicoloured 55 20

1968. 20th Anniv of W.H.O.
3552 **641** 1l.60 multicoloured . . . 70 20

642 "The Hunter" (after N. Grigorescu)

1968. Hunting Congress, Mamaia.
3553 **642** 1l.60 multicoloured . . . 60 20

643 Pioneers and Liberation Monument

1968. Young Pioneers. Multicoloured.
3554 5b. Type **643** 10 10
3555 40b. Receiving scarves . . . 15 10
3556 55b. With models 20 10
3557 1l. Operating radio sets . . 30 10
3558 1l.60 Folk-dancing 55 20
3559 2l.40 In camp 60 45

644 Prince Mircea
645 Ion Ionescu de la Brad (scholar)

1968. 550th Death Anniv of Prince Mircea (the Old).
3560 **644** 1l.60 multicoloured . . . 70 20

1968. Cultural Anniversaries.
3561 **645** 40b. multicoloured . . . 15 10
3562 – 55b. multicoloured . . . 30 10
PORTRAITS AND ANNIVS: 40b. Type **645** (150th birth anniv); 55b. Emil Racovita (scientist, birth cent).

646 "Pelargonium zonale"
648 Throwing the Javelin

647 "Nicolae Balcescu" (Gheorghe Tattarescu)

1968. Garden Geraniums. Multicoloured.
3563 10b. Type **646** 10 10
3564 20b. "Pelargonium zonale" (orange) 10 10
3565 40b. "Pelargonium zonale" (red) 15 10
3566 55b. "Pelargonium zonale" (pink) 15 10
3567 60b. "Pelargonium grandiflorum" (red) 30 10
3568 1l.20 "Pelargonium peltatum" (red) 30 15
3569 1l.35 "Pelargonium peltatum" (pink) 40 15
3570 1l.60 "Pelargonium grandiflorum" (pink) . . 55 40

1968. 120th Anniv of 1848 Revolution. Paintings. Multicoloured.
3571 55b. Type **647** 20 10
3572 1l.20 "Avram Iancu" (B. Iscovescu) 40 10
3573 1l.60 "Vasile Alecsandri" (N. Livaditti) 80 50

1968. Olympic Games, Mexico. Multicoloured.
3574 10b. Type **648** 10 10
3575 20b. Diving 10 10
3576 40b. Volleyball 15 10
3577 55b. Boxing 20 10
3578 60b. Wrestling 20 10
3579 1l.20 Fencing 35 10
3580 1l.35 Punting 45 20
3581 1l.60 Football 85 35

1968. Paintings in the Fine Arts Museum, Bucarest. Multicoloured.
3583 10b. "The Awakening of Romania" (G. Tattarescu) (28×49 mm) 10 10
3584 20b. "Composition" (Teodorescu Sionion) . . 10 10
3585 35b. "The Judgement of Paris" (H. van Balen) . . 20 10
3586 60b. "The Mystical Betrothal of St. Catherine" (L. Sustris) 35 10
3587 1l.75 "Mary with the Child Jesus" (J. van Bylert) . . 95 20
3588 3l. "The Summer" (J. Jordaens) . . . . . . 1·40 1·10

649 F.I.A.P. Emblem within "Lens"
650 Academy and Harp

1968. 20th Anniv of International Federation of Photographic Art (F.I.A.P.).
3589 **649** 1l.60 multicoloured . . . 60 20

1968. Centenary of Georgi Enescu Philharmonic Academy.
3590 **650** 55b. multicoloured . . . 40 15

651 Triumph of Trajan (Roman metope)

1968. Historic Monuments.
3591 **651** 10b. green, blue and red 10 10
3592 – 40b. blue, brown and red 15 10
3593 – 55b. violet, brown & green 20 10
3594 – 1l.20 purple, grey and ochre 35 20
3595 – 1l.55 blue, green & pur 50 20
3596 – 1l.75 brown, bistre and orange 60 40
DESIGNS—HORIZ: 40b. Monastery Church, Moldovita; 55b. Monastery. Church, Cozia; 1l.20, Tower and Church, Tirgoviste; 1l.55, Palace of Culture, Jassy; 1l.75, Corvinus Castle, Hunedoara.

652 Old Bucharest (18th-cent painting) (Illustration reduced. Actual size 76×28 mm)

1968. Stamp Day.
3597 **652** 55b.+45b. multicoloured 70 55

653 Mute Swan

655 Neamtz Costume (female)

654 "Entry of Michael the Brave into Alba Julia" (E. Stoica)

1968. Fauna of Nature Reservations. Multicoloured.
3598 10b. Type **653** 30 10
3599 20b. Black-winged stilt . . . 35 10
3600 40b. Common shelduck . . 45 10
3601 55b. Great egret 50 10
3602 60b. Golden eagle 65 10
3603 1l.20 Great bustard . . . . 1·30 20
3604 1l.35 Chamois 55 20
3605 1l.60 European bison . . . 70 30

1968. 50th Anniv of Union of Transylvania with Romania. Multicoloured.
3606 55b. Type **654** 15 15
3607 1l. "Union Dance" (T. Aman) 25 15
3608 1l.75 "Alba Julia Assembly" 55 35

1968. Provincial Costumes (1st series). Mult.
3610 5b. Type **655** 10 10
3611 40b. Neamtz (male) 10 10
3612 55b. Hunedoara (female) . . 20 10
3613 1l. Hunedoara (male) . . . 35 10
3614 1l.60 Brasov (female) . . . 55 20
3615 2l.40 Brasov (male) 80 65
See also Nos. 3617/22.

656 Earth, Moon and Orbital Track of "Apollo 8"

1969. Air. Flight of "Apollo 8" around the Moon.
3616 **656** 3l.30 black, silver & blue 1·20 1·10

1969. Provincial Costumes (2nd series). As T **655**. Multicoloured.
3617 5b. Doli (female) 10 10
3618 40b. Doli (male) 10 10
3619 55b. Arges (female) 20 10
3620 1l. Arges (male) 35 10
3621 1l.60 Timisoara (female) . . 60 20
3622 2l.40 Timisoara (male) . . . 90 65

657 Fencing

1969. Sports.
3623 **657** 10b. grey, black & brown 10 10
3624 – 20b. grey, black and violet 10 10
3625 – 40b. grey, black and blue 10 10
3626 – 55b. grey, black and red 20 10
3627 – 1l. grey, black and green 20 10
3628 1l.20 grey, black and blue 25 15
3629 – 1l.60 grey, black and red 35 20
3630 – 2l.40 grey, black & green 70 50
DESIGNS: 20b. Throwing the javelin; 40b. Canoeing; 55b. Boxing; 1l. Volleyball; 1l.20, Swimming; 1l.60, Wrestling; 2l.40, Football.

1969. Nude Paintings in the National Gallery. As T **638**. Multicoloured.
3631 10b. "Nude" (C. Tattarescu) 10 10
3632 20b. "Nude" (T. Pallady) 10 10
3633 35b. "Nude" (N. Tonitza) 10 10
3634 60b. "Venus and Cupid" (Flemish School) 30 15
3635 1l.75 "Diana and Endymion" (M. Liberi) 75 45
3636 3l. "The Three Graces" (J. H. von Achen) . . . . 1·70 1·10
SIZES—36×49 mm: 10b., 35b., 60b., 11.75. 27×49 mm: 3l. 49×36 mm: 20b.

1969. Air. Space Link-up of "Soyuz 4" and "Soyuz 5".
3638 **658** 3l.30 multicoloured . . . 1·70 1·50

658 "Soyuz 4" and "Soyuz 5"   **659** I.L.O. Emblem

1969. 50th Anniv of International Labour Office.
3639 **659** 55b. multicoloured . . . 35 15

1969. Inter-European Cultural Economic Co-operation.
3640 **660** 55b. multicoloured . . . 30 40
3641 1l.50 multicoloured . . . 75 80

1969. Postal Ministers' Conference, Bucharest.
3642 **661** 55b. deep blue and blue 25 15

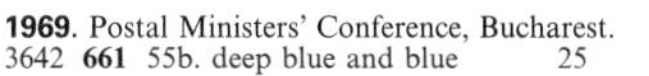

660 Stylized Head   **662** Referee introducing Boxers

661 Posthorn

1969. European Boxing Championships, Bucharest. Multicoloured.
3643 35b. Type **662** 10 10
3644 40b. Sparring 15 10
3645 55b. Leading with punch . . 20 10
3646 1l.75 Declaring the winner 70 40

663 "Apollo 9" and Module over Earth

1969. Air. "Apollo" Moon Flights. Multicoloured.
3647 60b. Type **663** 15 10
3648 2l.40 "Apollo 10" and module approaching Moon (vert) 70 20

664 Lesser Purple Emperor   **665** Astronaut and Module on Moon

1969. Butterflies and Moths. Multicoloured.
3649 5b. Type **664** 10 10
3650 10b. Willow-herb hawk moth 10 10
3651 20b. Eastern pale clouded yellow 10 10
3652 40b. Large tiger moth . . . 15 10
3653 55b. Pallas's fritillary . . 20 10
3654 1l. Jersey tiger moth . . . 40 10
3655 1l.20 Orange-tip 55 20
3656 2l.40 Meleager's blue . . . 1·10 75

1969. Air. First Man on the Moon.
3657 **665** 3l.30 multicoloured . . . 1·20 1·20

1969. Paintings in the National Gallery, Bucharest. Multicoloured. As T **638**.
3658 10b. "Venetian Senator" (School of Tintoretto) . . 10 10
3659 20b. "Sofia Kretzulescu" (G. Tattarescu) 10 10
3660 35b. "Philip IV" (Velasquez) 15 10
3661 35b. "Man Reading" (Memling) 30 10
3662 1l.75 "Lady D'Aguesseau" (Vigee-Lebrun) 55 20
3663 3l. "Portrait of a Woman" (Rembrandt) . . . . . . 1·40 80

666 Communist Flag   **667** Symbols of Learning

1969. 10th Romanian Communist Party Congress.
3665 **666** 55b. multicoloured . . . 30 15

1969. National "Economic Achievements" Exhibition, Bucharest. Multicoloured.
3666 35b. Type **667** 10 10
3667 40b. Symbols of Agriculture and Science 10 10
3668 1l.75 Symbols of Industry 60 15

668 Liberation Emblem   **669** Juggling on Trick-cycle

1969. 25th Anniv of Liberation. Multicoloured.
3669 10b. Type **668** 10 10
3670 55b. Crane and trowel . . . 10 10
3671 60b. Flags on scaffolding . . 15 10

1969. Romanian State Circus. Multicoloured.
3672 10b. Type **669** 10 10
3673 20b. Clown 10 10
3674 35b. Trapeze artists 15 10
3675 60b. Equestrian act 20 10
3676 1l.75 High-wire act 45 15
3677 3l. Performing tiger . . . . 1·10 50

670 Forces' Memorial

1969. Army Day and 25th Anniv of People's Army.
3678 **670** 55b. black, gold and red 25 15

671 Electric Train (1965) and Steam Locomotive "Calugareni" (1869)

1969. Centenary of Romanian Railways.
3679 **671** 55b. multicoloured . . . 40 20

672 "Courtyard" (M. Bouquet) ($\frac{1}{3}$-size illustration)

1969. Stamp Day.
3680 **672** 55b.+45b. multicoloured 55 60

673 Branesti Mask   **674** "Apollo 12" above Moon

1969. Folklore Masks. Multicoloured.
3681 40b. Type **673** 15 10
3682 55b. Tudora mask 15 10
3683 1l.55 Birsesti mask 40 20
3684 1l.75 Rudaria mask 55 30

1969. Moon Landing of "Apollo 12".
3685 **674** 1l.50 multicoloured . . . 40 60

675 "Three Kings" (Voronet Monastery)

1969. Frescoes from Northern Moldavian Monasteries (1st series). Multicoloured.
3686 10b. Type **675** 10 10
3687 20b. "Three Kings" (Sucevita) 10 10
3688 35b. "Holy Child in Manger" (Voronet) . . . 15 10
3689 60b. "Ship" (Sucevita) (vert) 25 10
3690 1l.75 "Walled City" (Moldovita) 55 25
3691 3l. "Pastoral Scene" (Voronet) (vert) . . . . . 1·20 70
See also Nos. 3736/42 and 3872/8.

676 "Old Mother Goose", Capra   **678** Small Pasque Flower

677 Players and Emblem

1969. New Year. Children's Celebrations. Mult.
3692 40b. Type **676** 15 10
3693 55b. Decorated tree, Sorcova 55 10
3694 1l.50 Drummers, Buhaiul . . 40 10
3695 2l.40 Singer and bellringer, Plugusorul 65 40

1970. World Ice Hockey Championships (Groups B and C), Bucharest. Multicoloured.
3696 20b. Type **677** 10 10
3697 55b. Goalkeeper 15 10
3698 1l.20 Two players 25 10
3699 2l.40 Goalmouth melee . . 60 35

1970. Flowers. Multicoloured.
3700 5b. Type **678** 10 10
3701 10b. Yellow pheasant's-eye 10 10
3702 20b. Musk thistle 10 10
3703 40b. Dwarf almond 10 10
3704 55b. Dwarf bearded iris . . 10 10
3705 1l. Flax 20 10
3706 1l.20 Sage 30 15
3707 2l.40 Peony . . . . 1·40 65

679 Japanese Woodcut   **681** Lenin

680 B.A.C. One Eleven Series 475 Jetliner and Silhouettes of Aircraft

1970. World Fair, Osaka, Japan. Expo 70. Mult.
3714 20b. Type **679** 15 15
3715 1l. Japanese pagoda (29 × 92 mm) 45 35

1970. 50th Anniv of Romanian Civil Aviation. Multicoloured.
3717 60b. Type **680** 25 10
3718 2l. Tail of B.A.C. One Eleven Series 475 and control tower at Otopeni Airport, Bucharest . . . 55 25

1970. Birth Centenary of Lenin.
3719 **681** 40b. multicoloured . . . 20 15

682 "Camille" (Monet) and Maximum Card   **683** "Prince Alexander Cuza" (Szathmary)

1970. Maximafila Franco–Romanian Philatelic Exn, Bucharest.
3720 **682** 1l.50 multicoloured . . . 65 25

1970. 150th Birth Anniv of Prince Alexandru Cuza.
3721 **683** 55b. multicoloured . . . 35 20

684 "Co-operation" Map   **685** Victory Monument, Bucharest

1970. Inter-European Cultural and Economic Co-operation.
3722 **684** 40b. green, brown & black 35 40
3723 1l.50 blue, brown & blk 75 80

1970. 25th Anniv of Liberation.
3724 **685** 55b. multicoloured . . . 30 20

686 Greek Silver Drachma, 5th cent B.C.

1970. Ancient Coins.
3725 **686** 10b. black and blue . . 10 10
3726 – 20b. black and red . . . 10 10
3727 – 35b. bronze and green 10 10
3728 – 60b. black and brown . . 15 10
3729 – 1l.75 black and blue . . 60 10
3730 – 3l. black and red . . . . 1·00 40
DESIGNS—HORIZ: 20b. Getic-Dacian silver didrachm, 2nd—1st-cent B.C.; 35b. Copper sestertius of Trajan, 106 A.D.; 60b. Mircea ducat, 1400; 1l.75, Silver groschen of Stephen the Great, 1460. VERT: 3l. Brasov klippe-thaler, 1601.

687 Footballers and Ball

1970. World Cup Football Championship, Mexico.
3731 **687** 40b. multicoloured . . . 10 10
3732 – 55b. multicoloured . . . 15 10
3733 – 1l.75 multicoloured . . . 40 20
3734 – 3l.30 multicoloured . . . 80 50

DESIGNS: Nos. 3732/4, various football scenes as Type **687**.

1970. Frescoes from Northern Moldavian Monasteries (2nd series). As T **675**. Mult.

3736 10b. "Prince Petru Rares and Family" (Moldovita) 10 10
3737 20b. "Metropolitan Grigore Rosca" (Voronet) (28 × 48 mm) 10 10
3738 40b. "Alexander the Good and Family" (Sucevita) 15 10
3739 55b. "The Last Judgement" (Voronet) (vert) 25 10
3740 1l.75 "The Last Judgement" (Voronet) (different) 65 25
3741 3l. "St. Anthony" (Voronet) 1·40 70

688 "Apollo 13" Spashdown

689 Engels

1970. Air. Space Flight of "Apollo 13".

3743 **688** 1l.50 multicoloured 1·50 95

1970. 150th Birth Anniv of Friedrich Engels.

3744 **689** 1l.50 multicoloured 50 15

690 Exhibition Hall

1970. National Events. Multicoloured.

3745 35b. "Iron Gates" Dam 10 10
3746 55b. Freighter and flag 30 10
3747 1l.50 Type **690** 30 10

EVENTS: 35b. Danube navigation projects; 55b. 75th anniv of Romanian Merchant Marine; 1l.50, 1st International Fair, Bucharest.

691 New Headquarters Building

1970. New U.P.U. Headquarters Building, Berne.

3748 **691** 1l.50 blue and ultramarine 55 15

692 Education Year Emblem

693 "Iceberg"

1970. International Education Year.

3749 **692** 55b. plum, black and red 30 20

1970. Roses. Multicoloured.

3750 20b. Type **693** 10 10
3751 35b. "Wiener Charme" 10 10
3752 55b. "Pink Lustre" 15 10
3753 1l. "Piccadilly" 45 10
3754 1l.50 "Orange Delbard" 55 10
3755 2l.40 "Sibelius" 90 75

694 "Spaniel and Pheasant" (J. B. Oudry)

695 Refugee Woman and Child

1970. Paintings in Romanian Galleries. Mult.

3756 10b. "The Hunt" (D. Brandi) (38 × 50 mm) 10 10
3757 20b. Type **694** 10 10
3758 35b. "The Hunt" (Jan Fyt) (38 × 50 mm) 10 10
3759 60b. "After the Chase" (Jordaens) (As T **694**) 25 10
3760 1l.75 "The Game Dealer" (F. Snyders) (50 × 38 mm) 60 20
3761 3l. "The Hunt" (A. de Gryeff) (As T **694**) 1·20 70

1970. Danube Flood Victims (1st issue).

3763 **695** 55b. black, blue and green (postage) 15 10
3764 – 1l.50 multicoloured 35 20
3765 – 1l.75 multicoloured 75 70
3766 – 60b. black, drab and blue (air) 35 10

DESIGNS: 60b. Helicopter rescue; 1l.50, Red Cross post; 1l.75, Building reconstruction.

See also No. 3777.

696 U.N. Emblem

698 Beethoven

697 Arab Horse

1970. 25th Anniv of United Nations.

3767 **696** 1l.50 multicoloured 35 20

1970. Horses. Multicoloured.

3768 20b. Type **697** 10 10
3769 35b. American trotter 10 10
3770 55b. Ghidran 10 10
3771 1l. Hutul 30 10
3772 1l.50 Thoroughbred 45 20
3773 2l.40 Lippizaner 1·60 80

1970. Birth Bicentenary of Ludwig van Beethoven (composer).

3774 **698** 55b. multicoloured 60 20

699 "Mail-cart in the Snow" (E. Volkers) (½-size illustration)

1970. Stamp Day.

3775 **699** 55b.+45b. mult 55 60

700 Henri Coanda's Model Airplane

1970. Air. 60th Anniv of First Experimental Turbine-powered Airplane.

3776 **700** 60b. multicoloured 55 20

701 "The Flood" (abstract, Joan Miro)

1970. Danube Flood Victims (2nd issue).

3777 **701** 3l. multicoloured 1·60 1·60

702 "Sight" (G. Coques)

1970. Paintings from the Bruckenthal Museum, Sibiu. Multicoloured.

3779 10b. Type **702** 10 10
3780 20b. "Hearing" 10 10
3781 35b. "Smell" 10 10
3782 60b. "Taste" 20 10
3783 1l.75 "Touch" 40 15
3784 3l. Bruckenthal Museum 1·00 65

Nos. 3779/84 show a series of pictures by Coques entitled "The Five Senses".

703 Vladimirescu (after Theodor Aman)

705 Alsatian

704 "Three Races"

1971. 150th Death Anniv of Tudor Vladimirescu (Wallachian revolutionary).

3786 **703** 1l.50 multicoloured 50 20

1971. Racial Equality Year.

3787 **704** 1l.50 multicoloured 55 20

1971. Dogs. Multicoloured.

3788 20b. Type **705** 10 10
3789 35b. Bulldog 10 10
3790 55b. Fox terrier 15 10
3791 1l. Setter 40 10
3792 1l.50 Cocker spaniel 60 20
3793 2l.40 Poodle 1·90 1·20

706 "Luna 16" leaving Moon

707 Proclamation of the Commune

1971. Air. Moon Missions of "Luna 16" and "Luna 17". Multicoloured.

3794 3l.30 Type **706** 1·70 95
3795 3l.30 "Lunokhod 1" on Moon 1·70 95

1971. Centenary of Paris Commune.

3796 **707** 40b. multicoloured 30 15

708 Astronaut and Moon Trolley

1971. Air. Moon Mission of "Apollo 14".

3797 **708** 3l.30 multicoloured 1·10 1·00

709 "Three Fists" Emblem and Flags

710 "Toadstool" Rocks, Babele

1971. Trade Union Congress, Bucharest.

3798 **709** 55b. multicoloured 30 15

1971. Tourism. Multicoloured.

3799 10b. Gorge, Cheile Bicazului (vert) 10 10
3800 40b. Type **710** 10 10
3801 55b. Winter resort, Poiana Brasov 15 10
3802 1l. Fishing punt and tourist launch, Danube delta 40 10
3803 1l.50 Hotel, Baile Sovata 55 10
3804 2l.40 Venus, Jupiter and Neptune Hotels, Black Sea (77 × 29 mm) 85 55

711 "Arrows"

712 Museum Building

1971. Inter-European Cultural Economic Co-operation. Multicoloured.

3805 55b. Type **711** 85 90
3806 1l.75 Stylized map of Europe 1·30 1·30

1971. Historical Museum, Bucharest.

3807 **712** 55b. multicoloured 20 15

713 "The Secret Printing-press" (S. Szonyi)

714 "Motra Tone" (Kole Idromeno)

1971. 50th Anniv of Romanian Communist Party. Multicoloured.

3808 35b. Type **713** 10 10
3809 40b. Emblem and red flags (horiz) 10 10
3810 55b. "The Builders" (A. Anastasiu) 15 10

1971. "Balkanfila III". International Stamp Exhibition, Bucharest. Multicoloured.

3811 1l.20+60b. Type **714** 60 65
3812 1l.20+60b. "Maid" (Vladimir Dimitrov-Maistora) 60 65
3813 1l.20+60b. "Rosa Botzaris" (Joseph Stieler) 60 65
3814 1l.20+60b. "Portrait of a Lady" (Katarina Ivanovic) 60 65
3815 1l.20+60b. "Agreseanca" (C. Popp de Szathmary) 60 65
3816 1l.20+60b. "Woman in Modern Dress" (Calli Ibrahim) 60 65

Each stamp has a premium-carrying "tab" as shown in Type **714**.

715 Pomegranate

1971. Flowers. Multicoloured.
3818 20b. Type **715** 10 10
3819 35b. "Calceolus speciosum" 10 10
3820 55b. "Life jagra" 10 10
3821 1l. Blood-drop emlets 30 10
3822 1l.50 Dwarf morning glory 45 20
3823 2l.40 "Phyllocactus phyllanthoides" (horiz) 1·00 30

716 "Nude" (J. Iser)

1971. Paintings of Nudes. Multicoloured.
3824 10b. Type **716** 10 10
3825 20b. "Nude" (C. Ressu) (29 × 50 mm) 10 10
3826 35b. "Nude" (N. Grigorescu) 10 10
3827 60b. "Odalisque" (Delacroix) (horiz) 10 10
3828 1l.75 "Nude in a Landscape" (Renoir) 60 25
3829 3l. "Venus and Cupid" (Il Vecchio) (horiz) 1·20 65

718 Astronauts and Lunar Rover on Moon

1971. Air. Moon Flight of "Apollo 15".
3833 **718** 1l.50 multicoloured (blue background) 1·20 1·30
No. 3833 also exists imperforate, with background colour changed to green, from a restricted printing.

719 "Fishing Boats" (M. W. Arnold)

1971. Marine Paintings. Multicoloured.
3835 10b. "Coastal Storm" (B. Peters) 10 10
3836 20b. "Seascape" (I. Backhuysen) 10 10
3837 35b. "Boat in Stormy Seas" (A. van de Eertvelt) 10 10
3838 60b. Type **719** 20 10
3839 1l.75 "Seascape" (I. K. Aivazovsky) 50 20
3840 3l. "Fishing boats, Braila" (J. A. Steriadi) 1·20 50

1971. As Nos. 3517/29 and three new designs but in smaller format, 17 × 23 or 23 × 17 mm.
3842 1l. green 45 15
3843 1l.20 violet 25 15
3844 1l.35 blue 75 15
3845 1l.50 red 35 15
3846 1l.55 brown 35 15
3847 1l.75 green 35 15
3848 2l. yellow 40 15
3849 2l.40 blue 50 15
3850 3l. blue 60 15
3851 3l.20 brown 50 15
3852 3l.25 blue 75 15
3853 3l.60 blue 80 15
3854 4l. mauve 1·80 15
3855 4l.80 blue 1·00 15
3856 5l. violet 1·30 15
3857 6l. mauve 1·50 15

NEW DESIGNS—VERT: 3l.60, Clearing letter box; 4l.80, Postman on round; 6l. Postal Ministry, Bucharest.

720 "Neagoe Basarab" (fresco, Curtea de Arges) **721** "T. Pallady" (self-portrait)

1971. 450th Death Anniv of Prince Neagoe Basarab, Regent of Wallachia.
3858 **720** 60b. multicoloured 25 15

1971. Artists' Anniversaries.
3859 **721** 40b. multicoloured 10 10
3860 – 55b. black, stone and gold 10 10
3861 – 1l.50 black, stone & gold 25 10
3862 – 2l.40 multicoloured 55 30
DESIGNS (self-portraits: 40b. Type **721** (birth centenary); 55b. Benevenuto Cellini (400th death anniv); 1l.50, Jean Watteau (250th death anniv); 2l.40, Albrecht Durer (500th birth anniv).

722 Persian Text and Seal **723** Figure Skating

1971. 2500th Anniv of Persian Empire.
3863 **722** 55b. multicoloured 35 15

1971. Winter Olympic Games, Sapporo, Japan (1972). Multicoloured.
3864 10b. Type **723** 10 15
3865 20b. Ice-hockey 10 15
3866 40b. Biathlon 10 15
3867 55b. Bobsleighing 10 15
3868 1l.75 Downhill skiing 50 25
3869 3l. Games emblem 1·00 60

724 "Lady with Letter" (Sava Hentia)

1971. Stamp Day.
3871 **724** 1l.10+90b. mult 70 70

1971. Frescoes from Northern Moldavian Monasteries (3rd series). As T **675**. Multicoloured.
3872 10b. "St. George and The Dragon" (Moldovita) (vert) 10 10
3873 20b. "Three Kings and Angel" (Moldovita) (vert) 10 10
3874 40b. "The Crucifixion" (Moldovita) (vert) 10 10
3875 55b. "Trial" (Voronet) (vert) 10 10
3876 1l.75 "Death of a Martyr" (Voronet) (vert) 60 20
3877 3l. "King and Court" (Arborea) 1·20 85

725 Matei Millo (dramatist, 75th death anniv) **726** Magellan and Ships (450th death anniv)

1971. Famous Romanians. Multicoloured.
3879 55b. Type **725** 15 10
3880 1l. Nicolae Iorga (historian, birth cent) 20 10

1971. Scientific Anniversaries.
3881 **726** 40b. mauve, blue & green 35 10
3882 – 55b. blue, green and lilac 10 10
3883 – 1l. multicoloured 25 10
3884 – 1l.50 green, blue & brn 30 15
DESIGNS AND ANNIVERSARIES: 55b. Kepler and observatory (400th birth anniv); 1l. Gagarin, rocket and Globe (10th anniv of first manned space flight); 1l.50, Lord Rutherford and atomic symbol (birth cent).

727 Lynx Cubs

1972. Young Wild Animals. Multicoloured.
3885 20b. Type **727** 10 30
3886 35b. Red fox cubs 10 30
3887 55b. Roe deer fawns 20 30
3888 1l. Wild piglets 45 15
3889 1l.50 Wolf cubs 80 15
3890 2l.40 Brown bear cubs 2·50 95

728 U.T.C. Emblem **730** Stylized Map of Europe

729 Wrestling

1972. 50th Anniv of Communist Youth Union (U.T.C.).
3891 **728** 55b. multicoloured 25 15

1972. Olympic Games, Munich (1st issue). Mult.
3892 10b. Type **729** 10 10
3893 20b. Canoeing 10 10
3894 55b. Football 10 10
3895 1l.55 High-jumping 35 10
3896 2l.90 Boxing 60 10
3897 6l.70 Volleyball 1·60 85
See also Nos. 3914/19 and 3926.

1972. Inter-European Cultural and Economic Co-operation.
3899 **730** 1l.75 gold, black & mve 1·10 85
3900 – 2l.90 gold, black & green 1·30 1·10
DESIGN: 2l.90, "Crossed arrows" symbol.

731 Astronauts in Lunar Rover **732** Modern Trains and Symbols

1972. Air. Moon Flight of "Apollo 16".
3901 **731** 3l. blue, green and pink 1·40 1·20

1972. 50th Anniv of International Railway Union.
3902 **732** 55b. multicoloured 45 20

734 "Paeonia romanica"

1972. Scarce Romanian Flowers.
3904 **734** 20b. multicoloured 10 10
3905 – 40b. purple, green & brown 10 10
3906 – 55b. brown and blue 20 10
3907 – 60b. red, green and light green 20 10
3908 – 1l.35 multicoloured 45 10
3909 – 2l.90 multicoloured 95 35
DESIGNS: 40b. "Dianthus callizonus"; 55b. Edelweiss; 60b. Vanilla orchid; 1l.35, "Narcissus stellaris"; 2l.90, Lady's slipper.

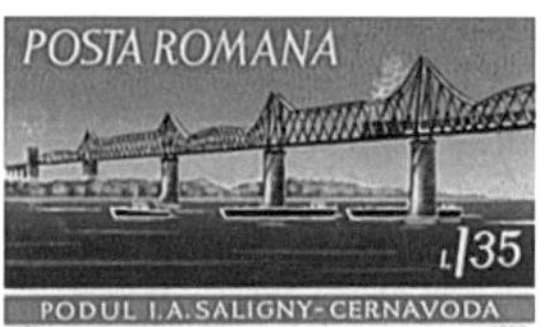

735 Saligny Bridge, Cernavoda

1972. Danube Bridges. Multicoloured.
3910 1l.35 Type **735** 50 10
3911 1l.75 Giurgeni Bridge, Vadul Oii 30 15
3912 2l.75 Friendship Bridge, Giurgiu–Ruse (Bulgaria) 2·50 25

736 North Railway Station, Bucharest, 1872

1972. Cent of North Railway Station, Bucharest.
3913 **736** 55b. multicoloured 45 20

737 Water-polo

1972. Olympic Games, Munich (2nd issue). Mult.
3914 10b. Type **737** 10 10
3915 20b. Pistol-shooting 15 10
3916 55b. Throwing the discus 15 10
3917 1l.55 Gymnastics 35 10
3918 2l.75 Canoeing 85 20
3919 6l.40 Fencing 1·60 90

738 Rotary Stamp-printing Press **740** Runner with Torch

739 "E. Stoenescu" (Stefan Popescu)

1972. Centenary of State Stamp-printing Works.
3921 **738** 55b. multicoloured . . . 30 15

1972. Romanian Art. Portraits. Multicoloured.
3922 55b. Type **739** 10 10
3923 1l.75 Self-portrait (Octav Bancila) 20 10
3924 2l.90 Self-portrait (Gheorghe Petrascu) 40 10
3925 6l.50 Self-portrait (Ion Andreescu) 85 35

1972. Olympic Games, Munich (3rd issue). Olympic Flame.
3926 **740** 55b. purple & blue on silver 45 20

741 Aurel Vlaicu, his Airplane No. 1 "Crazy Fly" and Silhouette of Boeing 707 Jetliner

1972. Air. Romanian Aviation Pioneers. Mult.
3927 60b. Type **741** 15 10
3928 3l. Traian Vuia, Vuia No. 1 and silhouette of Boeing 707 jetliner 80 40

742 Cluj Cathedral

743 Satu Mare

1972.
3929 **742** 1l.85 violet (postage) . . 25 10
3930 – 2l.75 grey 35 15
3931 – 3l.35 red 45 10
3932 – 3l.45 green 50 10
3933 – 5l.15 blue 70 10
3934 – 5l.60 blue 75 10
3935 – 6l.20 mauve 80 10
3936 – 6l.40 brown . . . . . . 1·00 10
3937 – 6l.80 red . . . . . . 1·00 10
3938 – 7l.05 black . . . . . . 1·10 10
3939 – 8l.45 red . . . . . . 1·10 10
3940 – 9l.05 green . . . . . . 1·30 10
3941 – 9l.10 blue . . . . . . 1·30 10
3942 – 9l.85 green . . . . . . 1·30 10
3943 – 10l. brown . . . . . . 1·50 10
3944 – 11l.90 blue . . . . . . 1·50 15
3945 – 12l.75 violet . . . . . . 1·80 15
3946 – 13l.30 red . . . . . . 2·00 15
3947 – 16l.20 green . . . . . . 2·50 15

3948 – 14l.60 blue (air) . . . . 3·00 30
DESIGNS—HORIZ: (As Type **742**): 2l.75, Sphinx Rock, Mt. Bucegi; 3l.45, Sinaia Castle; 5l.15, Hydro-electric power station, Arges; 6l.40, Hunidoara Castle; 6l.80, Bucharest Polytechnic complex; 9l.05, Coliseum, Sarmisegtetuza; 9l.10, Hydro-electric power station, Iron Gates. (29 × 21 mm): 11l.90, Palace of the Republic, Bucharest; 13l.30, City Gate, Alba Julia; 14l.60, Otopeni Airport, Bucharest. VERT: (As Type **742**): 3l.35, Heroes' Monument, Bucharest; 5l.60, Iasi-Biserica; 6l.20, Bran Castle; 7l.05, Black Church, Brasova; 8l.45, Atheneum, Bucharest; 9l.85, Decebal's statue, Cetatea Deva. (20 × 30 mm): 10l. City Hall Tower, Sibiu; 12l.75, T.V. Building, Bucharest; 16l.20, Clock Tower, Sighisoara.

1972. Millenium of Satu Mare.
3949 **743** 55b. multicoloured . . . 30 15

744 Davis Cup on Racquet

1972. Final of Davis Cup Men's Team Tennis Championship, Bucharest.
3950 **744** 2l.75 multicoloured . . . 85 35

745 "Venice" (Gheorghe Petrascu)

1972. U.N.E.S.C.O. "Save Venice" Campaign. Paintings of Venice. Multicoloured.
3951 10b. Type **745** 10 15
3952 20b. Gondolas (N. Darascu) 10 15
3953 55b. Palace (Petrascu) . . . 15 15
3954 1l.55 Bridge (Marius Bunescu) 40 15
3955 2l.75 Palace (Darascu) (vert) 95 70
3956 6l.40 Canal (Bunesca) . . . 2·40 1·00

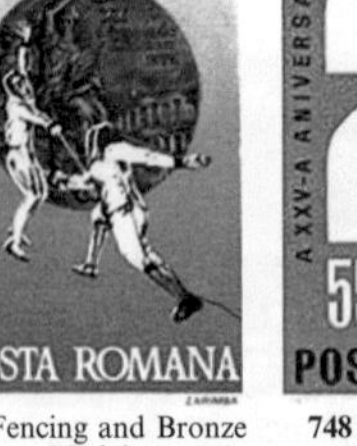
746 Fencing and Bronze Medal

748 Flags and "25"

747 "Travelling Romanies" (E. Volkers) (⅔-size illustration)

1972. Munich Olympic Games Medals. Mult.
3958 10b. Type **746** 10 15
3959 20b. Handball and Bronze Medal 10 10
3960 35b. Boxing and Silver Medal 15 10
3961 1l.45 Hurdling and Silver Medal 35 10
3962 2l.75 Shooting, Silver and Bronze Medals 70 25
3963 6l.20 Wrestling and two Gold Medals . . . . . . 1·80 80

1972. Stamp Day.
3965 **747** 1l.10+90b. mult 80 60

1972. 25th Anniv of Proclamation of Republic. Multicoloured.
3966 55b. Type **748** 15 10
3967 1l.20 Arms and "25" . . . 20 15
3968 1l.75 Industrial scene and "25" 35 15

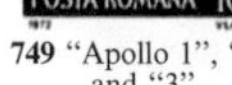
749 "Apollo 1", "2" and "3"

750 European Bee Eater

1972. "Apollo" Moon Flights. Multicoloured.
3969 10b. Type **749** 20 10
3970 35b. Grissom, Chaffee and White 20 10
3971 40b. "Apollo 4, 5, 6" . . . 30 10
3972 55b. "Apollo 7, 8" 40 10
3973 1l. "Apollo 9, 10" 55 10
3974 1l.20 "Apollo 11, 12" . . . 75 10
3975 1l.85 "Apollo 13, 14" . . . 95 15
3976 2l.75 "Apollo 15, 16" . . . 1·70 15
3977 3l.60 "Apollo 17" . . . . . 2·40 55

1973. Protection of Nature. Multicoloured. (a) Birds.
3979 1l.40 Type **750** 70 15
3980 1l.85 Red-breasted goose . . 85 20
3981 2l.75 Peduline tit . . . . . 1·20 40

(b) Flowers.
3982 1l.40 Globe flower 25 10
3983 1l.85 Martagon lily 30 30
3984 2l.75 Gentian 40 30

751 Copernicus

752 Suceava Costume (female)

1973. 500th Birth Anniv of Copernicus (astronomer).
3985 **751** 2l.75 multicoloured . . . 80 35

1973. Regional Costumes. Multicoloured.
3986 10b. Type **752** 10 15
3987 40b. Suceava (male) 10 15
3988 55b. Harghila (female) . . . 10 15
3989 1l.75 Harghila (male) . . . 30 15
3990 2l.75 Gorj (female) 50 20
3991 6l.40 Gorj (male) . . . . . 1·00 70

753 Dimitrie Paciurea (sculptor)

754 Map of Europe

1973. Anniversaries. Multicoloured.
3992 10b. Type **753** (birth centenary) 10 10
3993 40b. Ioan Slavici (writer, 125th birth anniv) 10 10
3994 55b. Gheorghe Lazar (educationist, death cent) 10 10
3995 6l.40 Alexandru Flechtenmacher (composer, birth cent) . . 1·50 60

1973. Inter-European Cultural and Economic Co-operation.
3996 **754** 3l.35 gold, blue & purple 90 85
3997 – 3l.60 gold and purple . . 1·10 1·20
DESIGN: 3l.60, Emblem.

756 Hand with Hammer and Sickle

757 W.M.O. Emblem and Weather Satellite

1973. Anniversaries. Multicoloured.
3999 40b. Type **756** 15 20
4000 55b. Flags and bayonets . . 25 20
4001 1l.75 Prince Cuza 55 20
EVENTS: 40b. 25th anniv of Romanian Workers and Peasant Party; 55b. 40th anniv of National Anti-Fascist Committee; 1l.75, Death cent of Prince Alexandru Cuza.

1973. Centenary of W.M.O.
4002 **757** 2l. multicoloured 60 20

758 "Dimitri Ralet" (anon)

759 Prince Dimitri Cantemir

1973. "Socfilex III" Stamp Exhibition, Bucharest. Portrait Paintings. Multicoloured.
4003 40b. Type **758** 10 10
4004 60b. "Enacheta Vacarescu" (A. Chladek) 10 10
4005 1l.55 "Dimitri Aman" (C. Lecca) 20 10
4006 4l.+2l. "Barbat at his Desk" (B. Iscovescu) . . . . . . 1·20 60

1973. 300th Birth Anniv of Dimitri Cantemir, Prince of Moldavia (writer). Multicoloured.
4008 **759** 1l.75 multicoloured . . . 50 25

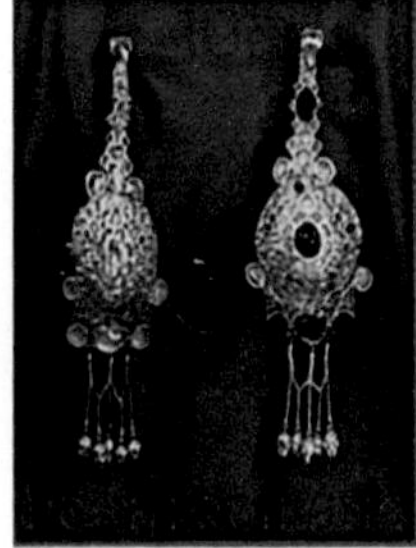
760 Fibular Brooches

1973. Treasures of Pietroasa. Multicoloured.
4010 10b. Type **760** 10 15
4011 20b. Golden figurine and bowl (horiz) 10 15
4012 55b. Gold oil flask 10 15
4013 1l.55 Brooch and bracelets (horiz) 45 15
4014 2l.75 Gold platter 65 20
4015 6l.80 Filgree cup holder (horiz) . . . . 1·40 70

762 Oboga Jar

763 "Postilion" (A. Verona)

1973. Romanian Ceramics. Multicoloured.
4018 10b. Type **762** 10 10
4019 20b. Vama dish and jug . . 10 10
4020 55b. Maginea bowl 10 10
4021 1l.55 Sibiu Saschiz jug and dish 35 10
4022 2l.75 Pisc pot and dish . . . 55 20
4023 6l.80 Oboga "bird" vessel 1·60 45

1973. Stamp Day.
4024 **763** 1l.10+90b. mult 60 65

764 "Textile Workers" (G. Saru)

765 Town Hall, Craiova

1973. Paintings showing Workers. Multicoloured.
4025 10b. Type **764** 10 10
4026 20b. "Construction Site" (M. Bunescu) (horiz) . . . 10 10
4027 55b. "Shipyard Workers" (H. Catargi) (horiz) . . . 10 10
4028 1l.55 "Working Man" (H. Catargi) 20 10
4029 2l.75 "Miners" (A. Phoebus) 40 15
4030 6l.80 "The Spinner" (N. Grigorescu) . . . . . 1·00 55

1974. (a) Buidings.
4032 **765** 5b. red 10 10
4033 – 10b. blue 10 10
4034 – 20b. orange 10 10
4035 – 35b. green 10 10
4036 – 40b. violet 10 10
4037 – 50b. blue 10 10
4038 – 55b. brown 10 10
4039 – 60b. red 10 10
4040 – 1l. blue 10 10
4041 – 1l.20 green 10 10

(b) Ships.
4042 – 1l.35 black 25 10
4043 – 1l.45 blue 25 10
4044 – 1l.50 red 25 10
4045 – 1l.55 blue 35 10
4046 – 1l.75 green 40 10
4047 – 2l.20 blue 45 10
4048 – 3l.65 lilac 75 10
4049 – 4l.70 purple . . . . . . 1·20 15

DESIGNS—VERT: 10b. "Column of Infinity", Tirgu Jiu; 40b. Romanesque church, Densus; 50b. Reformed Church, Dej; 1l. Curtea de Arges Monastery. HORIZ: 20b. Heroes' Monument, Marasesti; 35b. Citadel, Risnov; 55b. Castle, Maldarasti; 60b. National Theatre, Jassy; 1l.20, Fortress and church, Tirgu Mures; 1l.35, Danube Tug "Impingator"; 1l.45, Freighter "Dimbovita"; 1l.50, Danube passenger vessel "Muntenia"; 1l.55, Cadet barque "Mircea"; 1l.75, Liner "Transylvania"; 2l.20, Bulk carrier "Oltul"; 3l.65, Trawler "Mures"; 4l.70, Tanker "Arges".

767 "Boats at Honfleur" (Monet)

1974. Impressionist Paintings. Multicoloured.

No.	Description	Unused	Used
4056	20b. Type **767**	10	10
4057	40b. "Moret Church" (Sisley) (vert)	10	10
4058	55b. "Orchard in Blossom" (Pissarro)	10	10
4059	1l.75 "Jeanne" (Pissarro) (vert)	25	10
4060	2l.75 "Landscape" (Renoir)	45	20
4061	3l.60 "Portrait of a Girl" (Cezanne) (vert)	1·10	35

768 Trotting with Sulky

769 Nicolas Titulescu (Romanian League of Nations Delegate)

1974. Cent of Horse-racing in Romania. Mult.

No.	Description	Unused	Used
4063	40b. Type **768**	10	10
4064	55b. Three horses racing	10	10
4065	60b. Horse galloping	10	10
4066	1l.55 Two trotters racing	30	10
4067	2l.75 Three trotters racing	55	20
4068	3l.45 Two horses racing	85	30

1974. Interparliamentary Congress Session, Bucharest.

No.	Description	Unused	Used
4069 **769**	1l.75 multicoloured	35	20

771 "Anniversary Parade" (Pepene Cornelia)

1974. 25th Anniv of Romanian Pioneers Organization.

No.	Description	Unused	Used
4071 **771**	55b. multicoloured	40	15

772 "Europe"

1974. Inter-European Cultural and Economic Co-operation. Multicoloured.

No.	Description	Unused	Used
4072	2l.20 Type **772**	1·10	85
4073	3l.45 Satellite over Europe	1·30	1·10

1974. Romania's Victory in World Handball Championships. No. 3959 surch **ROMANIA CAMPIOANA MONDIALA 1974 175L.**

No.	Description	Unused	Used
4074	1l.75 on 20b. multicoloured	2·00	1·80

POSTA ROMANA 20b

774 Postal Motor Boat

1974. U.P.U. Centenary. Multicoloured.

No.	Description	Unused	Used
4075	20b. Type **774**	10	15
4076	40b. Loading mail train	40	15
4077	55b. Loading Ilyushin Il-62M mail plane	10	15
4078	1l.75 Rural postman delivering letter	30	15
4079	2l.75 Town postman delivering letter	35	25
4080	3l.60 Young stamp collectors	60	25

775 Footballers

1974. World Cup Football Championship, West Germany.

No.	Description	Unused	Used
4082 **775**	20b. multicoloured	10	10
4083	– 40b. multicoloured	10	10
4084	– 55b. multicoloured	10	10
4085	– 1l.75 multicoloured	20	10
4086	– 2l.75 multicoloured	50	15
4087	– 3l.60 multicoloured	65	25

DESIGNS: Nos. 4083/7, Football scenes similar to Type **775**.

776 Anniversary Emblem

777 U.N. and World Population Emblems

1974. 25th Anniv of Council for Mutual Economic Aid.

No.	Description	Unused	Used
4089 **776**	55b. multicoloured	25	20

1974. World Population Year Conference, Bucharest.

No.	Description	Unused	Used
4090 **777**	2l. multicoloured	35	20

778 Emblem on Map of Europe

1974. "Euromax 1974" International Stamp Exhibition, Bucharest.

No.	Description	Unused	Used
4091 **778**	4l.+3l. yellow, bl & red	1·10	35

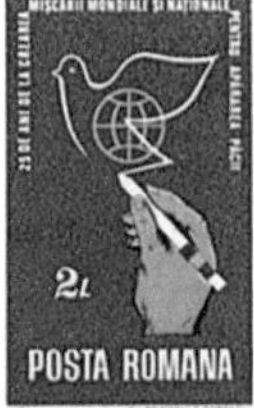

779 Hand drawing Peace Dove

780 Prince John of Wallachia (400th birth anniv)

1974. 25th Anniv of World Peace Movement.

No.	Description	Unused	Used
4092 **779**	2l. multicoloured	35	20

1974. Anniversaries.

No.	Description	Unused	Used
4093 **780**	20b. blue	10	10
4094	– 55b. red	10	10
4095	– 1l. blue	10	10
4096	– 1l.10 brown	20	10
4097	– 1l.30 purple	30	10
4098	– 1l.40 violet	35	20

DESIGNS AND ANNIVERSARIES—VERT: 1l. Iron and Steel Works, Hunedoara (220th anniv); 1l.10, Avram Iancu (revolutionary, 150th anniv); 1l.30, Dr. C. I. Parhon (birth cent); 1l.40, Dosoftel (metropolitan) (350th birth anniv). HORIZ: 55b. Soldier guarding industrial installations (Romanian People's Army, 30th anniv).

781 Romanian and Soviet Flags as "XXX"

783 "Centaurea nervosa"

1974. 30th Anniv of Liberation. Multicoloured.

No.	Description	Unused	Used
4099	40b. Type **781**	10	10
4100	55b. Citizens and flags (horiz)	10	20

1974. Nature Conservation. Wild Flowers. Mult.

No.	Description	Unused	Used
4102	20b. Type **783**	10	10
4103	40b. "Fritillaria montana"	10	10
4104	55b. Yew	60	10
4105	1l.75 "Rhododendron kotschyi"	30	15
4106	2l.75 Alpine forget-me-not	40	20
4107	3l.60 Pink	65	30

784 Bust of Isis

1974. Romanian Archaeological Finds. Sculpture. Multicoloured.

No.	Description	Unused	Used
4108	20b. Type **784**	10	10
4109	40b. Glykon serpent	10	10
4110	55b. Head of Emperor Decius	10	10
4111	1l.75 Romanian Woman	25	10
4112	2l.75 Mithras	40	25
4113	3l.60 Roman senator	65	30

785 Sibiu Market Place

1974. Stamp Day.

No.	Description	Unused	Used
4114 **785**	2l.10+1l.90 mult	90	40

1974. "Nationala 74" Stamp Exhibition. No. 4114 optd **EXPOZITIA FILATELICA "NATIONALA '74" 15–24 noiembrie Bucuresti.**

No.	Description	Unused	Used
4115 **786**	2l.10+1l.90 mult	1·50	1·50

787 Party Emblem

1974. 11th Romanian Communist Party Congress, Bucharest.

No.	Description	Unused	Used
4116 **787**	55b. multicoloured	15	10
4117	– 1l. multicoloured	20	20

DESIGN: 1l. Similar to Type **787**, showing party emblem and curtain.

788 "The Discus-thrower" (Myron)

1974. 60th Anniv of Romanian Olympic Committee.

No.	Description	Unused	Used
4118 **788**	2l. multicoloured	50	30

789 "Skylab"

790 Dr. Albert Schweitzer

1974. "Skylab" Space Laboratory Project.

No.	Description	Unused	Used
4119 **789**	2l.50 multicoloured	2·20	80

1974. Birth Centenary of Dr. Albert Schweitzer (Nobel Peace Prize-winner).

No.	Description	Unused	Used
4120 **790**	40b. brown	15	20

791 Handball

793 Torch and Inscription

792 "Rocks and Birches"

1975. World Universities Handball Championships, Romania.

No.	Description	Unused	Used
4121 **791**	55b. multicoloured	10	10
4122	– 1l.75 multicoloured (vert)	20	10
4123	– 2l.20 multicoloured	40	30

DESIGNS: 1l.75, 2l.20, similar designs to Type **791**.

1975. Paintings by Ion Andreescu. Multicoloured.

No.	Description	Unused	Used
4124	20b. Type **792**	10	10
4125	40b. "Peasant Woman with Green Kerchief"	10	10
4126	55b. "Winter in the Forest"	10	10
4127	1l.75 "Winter in Barbizon" (horiz)	25	15
4128	2l.75 Self-portrait	45	25
4129	3l.50 "Main Road" (horiz)	90	40

1975. 10th Anniv of Romanian Socialist Republic.

No.	Description	Unused	Used
4130 **793**	40b. multicoloured	20	15

794 "Battle of the High Bridge" (O. Obedeanu)

1975. 500th Anniv of Victory over the Ottomans at High Bridge.

No.	Description	Unused	Used
4131 **794**	55b. multicoloured	20	15

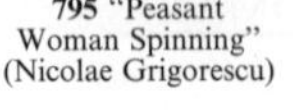

795 "Peasant Woman Spinning" (Nicolae Grigorescu)

796 "Self-portrait"

1975. International Women's Year.
4132 **795** 55b. multicoloured . . . 20 15

1975. 500th Birth Anniv of Michelangelo.
4133 **796** 5l. multicoloured 85 50

798 Mitsui Children's Science Pavilion, Okinawa

1975. International Exposition, Okinawa.
4135 **798** 4l. multicoloured 70 30

799 "Peonies" (Nicolae Tonitza)

1975. Inter-European Cultural and Economic Co-operation. Multicoloured.
4136 2l.20 Type **799** 80 80
4137 3l.45 "Chrysanthemums" (Stefan Luchian) . . . . 95 1·00

800 Dove with Coded Letter

1975. Introduction of Postal Coding.
4138 **800** 55b. multicoloured . . . 15 15

801 Convention Emblem on "Globe"

1975. Centenary of International Metre Convention.
4139 **801** 1l.85 multicoloured . . . 40 20

802 Mihail Eminescu and Museum

1975. 125th Birth Anniv of Mihail Eminescu (poet).
4140 **802** 55b. multicoloured . . . 15 15

803 Roman Coins and Stone Inscription

805 Ana Ipatescu

1975. Bimillenary of Alba Julia.
4141 **803** 55b. multicoloured . . . 15 20

1975. Death Cent of Ana Ipatescu (revolutionary).
4143 **805** 55b. mauve 20 20

806 Turnu-Severin

1975. European Architectural Heritage Year. Roman Antiquities.
4144 – 55b. black and brown . . 10 10
4145 – 1l.20 black, lt bl & bl . . 15 15
4146 – 1l.55 black and green . . 40 15
4147 – 1l.75 black and red . . . 45 20
4148 **806** 2l. black and ochre . . . 55 20
4149 – 2l.25 black and blue . . 70 50
DESIGNS—VERT: 55b. Emperor Trajan; 1l.20, Trajan's Column, Rome; 1l.55, Decebalus (sculpture); 10l. Roman remains, Gradiste. HORIZ: 1l.75, Imperial monument, Adam Clissi; 2l.25, Trajan's Bridge.

807 "Apollo" and "Soyuz" Spacecraft

1975. Air. "Apollo"–"Soyuz" Space Link. Mult.
4151 1l.75 Type **807** . . . . . . 1·10 65
4152 3l.25 "Apollo" and "Soyuz" linked together . . . . . 1·50 85

808 "Michael the Brave" (Aegidius Sadeler)

1975. 375th Anniv of First Political Union of Romanian States. Multicoloured.
4153 55b. Type **808** 10 10
4154 1l.20 "Ottoman Envoys bringing gifts to Michael the Brave" (T. Aman) (horiz) 15 10
4155 2l.75 "Michael the Brave at Calugareni" (T. Aman) 45 15

810 Larkspur

812 Policeman using Walkie-talkie

1975. Flowers. Multicoloured.
4157 20b. Type **810** 10 10
4158 40b. Long-headed poppy . . 10 10
4159 55b. Common immortelle 10 10
4160 1l.75 Common rock-rose . . 25 15
4161 2l.75 Meadow clary 45 20
4162 3l.60 Chicory 60 30

1975. International Philatelic Fair, Riccione (Italy). Optd **Tîrg international de mârci postale Riccione – Italia 23-25 august 1975**.
4163 **796** 5l. multicoloured . . . . 2·40 2·20

1975. Road Safety.
4164 **812** 55b. blue 25 20

813 Text on Map of Pelendava

1975. 1750th Anniv of First Documentary Attestations of Daco-Getian Settlements of Pelendava and 500th Anniv of Craiova. Multicoloured.
4165 20b. Type **813** 15 15
4166 55b. Map of Pelendava showing location of Craiova (82 × 33 mm) . . 15 15
4167 1l. Text on map of Pelendava 20 15
Nos. 4165/7 were issued together, se-tenant, forming a composite design.

814 Muntenia Carpet

1975. Romanian Traditional Carpets. Mult.
4168 20b. Type **814** 10 10
4169 40b. Banat 10 10
4170 55b. Oltenia 10 10
4171 1l.75 Moldova 30 10
4172 2l.75 Oltenia (different) . . 45 25
4173 3l.60 Maramures 55 30

815 T.V. "12M" Minibus

1975. Romanian Motor Vehicles. Multicoloured.
4174 20b. Type **815** 10 10
4175 40b. L.K.W. "19 A.L.P." Oil tanker 10 10
4176 55b. A.R.O. "240" Field car 10 10
4177 1l.75 L.K.W. "R 8135 F" Truck 35 10
4178 2l.75 P.K.W. "Dacia 1300" Saloon car 50 25
4179 3l.60 L.K.W. "R 19215 D.F.K." Tipper truck . . 65 30

816 Postal Transit Centre, Bucharest

1975. Stamp Day. Multicoloured.
4180 1l.50+1l.50 Type **816** . . . 70 40
4181 2l.10+1l.90 Aerial view of P.T.C. . . . . 1·30 65

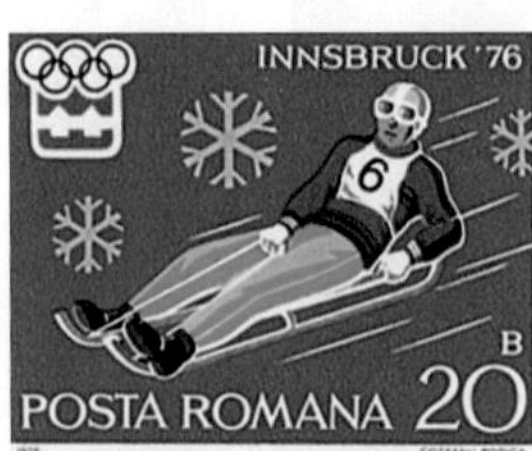

818 Tobogganing

1976. Winter Olympics Games, Innsbruck. Mult.
4183 20b. Type **818** 10 15
4184 40b. Rifle-shooting (biathlon) (vert) 10 15
4185 55b. Downhill skiing (slalom) 20 15
4186 1l.75 Ski jumping 35 20
4187 2l.75 Figure skating (women's) 50 30
4188 3l.60 Ice hockey 70 45

819 "Washington at Valley Forge" (W. Trego)

1976. Bicent of American Revolution. Mult.
4190 20b. Type **819** 10 10
4191 40b. "Washington at Trenton" (Trumbull) (vert) 10 10
4192 55b. "Washington crossing the Delaware" (Leutze) 15 10
4193 1l.75 "Capture of the Hessians" (Trumbull) . . 25 20
4194 2l.75 "Jefferson" (Sully) (vert) 45 25
4195 3l.60 "Surrender of Cornwallis at Yorktown" (Trumbull) 60 40

820 "Prayer"

1976. Birth Centenary of Constantin Brancusi (sculptor). Multicoloured.
4197 55b. Type **820** 10 15
4198 1l.75 Architectural Assembly, Tg. Jiu 25 20
4199 3l.60 C. Brancusi 65 20

821 Anton Davidoglu (mathematician) (birth cent)

823 Dr. Carol Davila

822 Inscribed Tablets, Tibiscum (Banat)

1976. Anniversaries. Multicoloured.
4200 40b. Type **821** 10 10
4201 55b. Prince Vlad Tepes (500th death anniv) . . . 10 10
4202 1l.20 Costache Negri (patriot—death centenary) 20 10
4203 1l.75 Gallery, Archives Museum (50th anniv) . . 25 10

1976. Daco-Roman Archaeological Finds. Mult.
4204 **822** 20b. multicoloured . . . 10 10
4205 – 40b. black, grey and red 10 10
4206 – 55b. multicoloured . . . 10 10
4207 – 1l.75 multicoloured . . . 40 10
4208 – 2l.75 black, grey and red 50 20
4209 – 3l.60 black, grey & green 70 35
DESIGNS: 40b. Sculptures (Banat); 55b. Inscribed tablet, coins and cup (Crisana); 1l.75, Pottery (Crisana); 2l.75, Altar and spears, Maramures (Banat); 3l.60, Vase and spears, Maramures.

1976. Centenary of Romanian Red Cross. Mult.
4211 55b. Type **823** (postage) . . 10 10
4212 1l.75 Nurse and patient . . 10 10
4213 2l.20 First aid 15 10
4214 3l.35 Blood donors (air) . . 55 20

824 King Decebalus Vase **825** Romanian Arms

1976. Inter-European Cultural and Economic Co-operation. Vases from Cluj-Napoca porcelain factory. Multicoloured.

4215 2l.20 Type **824** 50 40
4216 3l.45 Vase with portrait of King Michael the Brave 1·10 1·00

1976.

4217 **825** 1l.75 multicoloured . . . 45 20

826 De Havilland D.H.9C

1976. Air. 50th Anniv of Romanian Airline. Mult.

4218 20b. Type **826** 10 10
4219 40b. I.C.A.R. Comercial . . 15 10
4220 60b. Douglas DC-3 . . . . 25 10
4221 1l.75 Antonov An-24 . . . 40 10
4222 2l.75 Ilyushin Il-62 jetliner 60 20
4223 3l.60 Boeing 707 jetliner . . 90 20

827 Gymnastics **828** Spiru Haret

1976. Olympic Games, Montreal. Multicoloured.

4224 20b. Type **827** 10 10
4225 40b. Boxing 10 10
4226 55b. Handball 20 10
4227 1l.75 Rowing (horiz) 35 15
4228 2l.75 Gymnastics (different) (horiz) 50 20
4229 3l.60 Canoeing (horiz) . . . 65 20

1976. 125th Birth Anniv of Spiru Haret (mathematician).

4231 **828** 20b. multicoloured . . . 20 20

829 Daco-Getian Sculpture on Map of Buzau

1976. 1600th Anniv of Buzau State.

4232 **829** 55b. multicoloured . . . 20 20

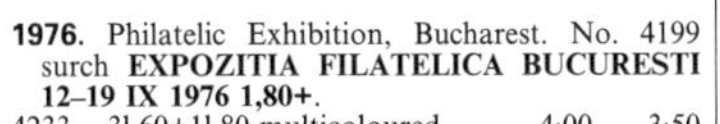
1976. Philatelic Exhibition, Bucharest. No. 4199 surch **EXPOZITIA FILATELICA BUCURESTI 12–19 IX 1976 1,80+**.

4233 3l.60+1l.80 multicoloured 4·00 3·50

831 Red Deer

1976. Endangered Animals. Multicoloured.

4234 20b. Type **831** 10 10
4235 40b. Brown bear 10 10
4236 55b. Chamois 15 10
4237 1l.75 Wild boar 25 10
4238 2l.75 Red fox 50 25
4239 3l.60 Lynx 65 35

832 Cathedral, Milan

1976. "Italia '76" International Philatelic Exhibition, Milan.

4240 **832** 4l.75 multicoloured . . . 80 20

833 D. Grecu (gymnast) and Bronze Medal

1976. Olympic Games, Montreal. Romanian Medal Winners. Multicoloured.

4241 20b. Type **833** 10 10
4242 40b. Fencing (Bronze Medal) 10 10
4243 55b. Javelin (Bronze Medal) 15 10
4244 1l.75 Handball (Silver Medal) 25 10
4245 2l.75 Boxing (Silver and Bronze Medals) (horiz) . . 40 15
4246 3l.60 Wrestling (Silver and Bronze Medals) (horiz) . . 60 35
4247 5l.70 Nadia Comaneci (gymnastics – 3 Gold, 1 Silver and 1 Bronze Medals) (27 × 42 mm) . . 1·90 95

834 "Carnations and Oranges"

1976. Floral Paintings by Stefan Luchian. Mult.

4249 20b. Type **834** 10 10
4250 40b. "Flower Arrangement" 10 10
4251 55b. "Immortelles" 10 10
4252 1l.75 "Roses in Vase" . . . 20 10
4253 2l.75 "Cornflowers" 25 20
4254 3l.60 "Carnations in Vase" 60 25

835 "Elena Cuza" (T. Aman) **836** Arms of Alba

1976. Stamp Day.

4255 **835** 2l.10+1l.90 mult 85 80

1976. Romanian Districts' Coats of Arms (1st series). Multicoloured.

4256 55b. Type **836** 20 15
4257 55b. Arad 20 15
4258 55b. Arges 20 15
4259 55b. Bacau 20 15
4260 55b. Bihor 20 15
4261 55b. Bistrita Nasaud 20 15
4262 55b. Botosani 20 15
4263 55b. Brasov 20 15
4264 55b. Braila 20 15
4265 55b. Buzau 20 15
4266 55b. Caras-Severin 20 15
4267 55b. Cluj 20 15
4268 55b. Constanta 20 15
4269 55b. Covasna 20 15
4270 55b. Dimbovita 20 15

See also Nos. 4307/31, 4496/520 and 4542/63.

837 "Ox Cart"

1977. Paintings by Nicolae Grigorescu. Mult.

4271 55b. Type **837** 15 10
4272 1l. "Self-portrait" (vert) . . 15 10
4273 1l.50 "Shepherdess" 20 10
4274 2l.15 "Girl with Distaff" . . 30 10
4275 3l.40 "Shepherd" (vert) . . 35 20
4276 4l.80 "Halt at the Well" . . 55 25

838 Telecommunications Station, Cheia

1977.

4277 **838** 55b. multicoloured . . . 15 15

839 I.C.A.R.1

1977. Air. Romanian Gliders. Multicoloured.

4278 20b. Type **839** 10 10
4279 40b. IS-3d 10 10
4280 55b. RG-5 . . . . 10 10
4281 1l.50 IS-11 . . . . 25 10
4282 3l. IS-29D 50 20
4283 3l.40 IS-28B 90 35

840 Red Deer

1977. Protected Animals. Multicoloured.

4284 55b. Type **840** 10 10
4285 1l. Mute swan 30 10
4286 1l.50 Egyptian vulture . . . 45 10
4287 2l.15 European bison . . . 35 10
4288 3l.40 White-headed duck . . 85 20
4289 4l.80 River kingfisher . . . 1·00 45

841 "The Infantryman" (Oscar Obedeanu)

1977. Cent of Independence. Paintings. Mult.

4290 55b. Type **841** 10 10
4291 1l. "Artillery Battery at Calafat" (S. Hentia) (horiz) 10 10
4292 1l.50 "Soldiers Attacking" (Stefan Luchian) 15 10
4293 2l.15 "Battle of Plevna" (horiz) 30 10
4294 3l.40 "The Artillerymen" (Nicolae Grigorescu) (horiz) 40 20
4295 4l.80+2l. "Battle of Rahova" (horiz) 90 45

842 Sinaia, Carpathians **843** Petru Rares, Prince of Moldavia

1977. Inter-European Cultural and Economic Co-operation. Views. Multicoloured.

4297 2l. Type **842** 55 30
4298 2l.40 Auroa, Black Sea . . . 75 40

1977. Anniversaries. Multicoloured.

4299 40b. Type **843** (450th anniv of accession) 15 20
4300 55b. Ion Caragiale (dramatist, 125th birth anniv) 15 20

844 Nurse with Children and Emblems

1977. 23rd Int Red Cross Conference, Bucharest.

4301 **844** 1l.50 multicoloured . . . 30 20

845 Triumphal Arch, Bucharest

1977. 60th Anniv of Battles of Marasti, Marasesti and Oituz.

4302 **845** 2l.15 multicoloured . . . 50 20

847 Postwoman and Letters

1977. Air.

4304 20l. Type **847** . . . . . . 3·00 1·00
4305 30l. Douglas DC-10 jetliner and mail . . . . 4·50 1·70

848 Mount Titano Castle, San Marino

1977. Centenary of San Marino Postage Stamps.

4306 **848** 4l. multicoloured 85 15

1977. Romanian District Coats of Arms (2nd series). As T **836**. Multicoloured.

4307 55b. Dolj 15 10
4308 55b. Galati 15 10
4309 55b. Gorj 15 10
4310 55b. Harghita 15 10
4311 55b. Hunedoara 15 10
4312 55b. Ialomita 15 10
4313 55b. Iasi 15 10
4314 55b. Ilfov 15 10
4315 55b. Maramures 15 10
4316 55b. Mehedinti 15 10
4317 55b. Mures 15 10
4318 55b. Neamt 15 10
4319 55b. Olt 15 10
4320 55b. Prahova 15 10
4321 55b. Salaj 15 10
4322 55b. Satu Mare 15 10
4323 55b. Sibiu 15 10
4324 55b. Suceava 15 10
4325 55b. Teleorman 15 10
4326 55b. Timis 15 10
4327 55b. Tulcea 15 10
4328 55b. Vaslui 15 10

4329 55b. Vilcea 15 10
4330 55b. Vrancea 15 10
4331 55b. Romanian postal emblem 15 10

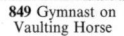

849 Gymnast on Vaulting Horse **850** Dispatch Rider and Army Officer

1977. Gymnastics. Multicoloured.
4332 20b. Type **849** 10 10
4333 40b. Floor exercise 10 10
4334 55b. Gymnast on parallel bars 10 10
4335 1l. Somersault on bar . . . 15 15
4336 2l.15 Gymnast on rings . . 30 25
4337 4l.80 Gymnastic exercise . . 1·10 65

1977. Stamp Day.
4338 **850** 2l.10+1l.90 mult 90 85

851 Two Dancers with Sticks

1977. Calusarii Folk Dance. Multicoloured.
4339 20b. Type **851** 10 10
4340 40b. Leaping dancer with stick 10 10
4341 55b. Two dancers 10 10
4342 1l. Dancer with stick . . . 15 10
4343 2l.15 Leaping dancers . . . 25 20
4344 4l.80 Leaping dancer . . . 95 50

852 "Carpati" at Cazane

1977. European Navigation on the Danube. Mult.
4346 55b. Type **852** 20 10
4347 1l. "Mircesti" near Orsova 25 10
4348 1l.50 "Oltenita" near Calafat 35 10
4349 2l.15 Hydrofoil at Giurgiu port 40 20
4350 3l. "Herculani" at Tulcea 50 25
4351 3l.40 "Muntenia" at Sulina 60 30
4352 4l.80 Map of Danube delta 1·40 80

853 Arms and Flag of Romania

1977. 30th Anniv of Romanian Republic. Mult.
4354 55b. Type **853** 10 15
4355 1l.20 Romanian-built computers 20 20
4356 1l.75 National Theatre, Craiova 35 20

854 Firiza Dam

1978. Romanian Dams and Hydro-electric Installations. Multicoloured.
4357 20b. Type **854** 10 10
4358 40b. Negovanu dam 10 10
4359 55b. Piatra Neamt power station 15 10
4360 1l. Izvorul Montelui Bicaz dam 20 10
4361 2l.15 Vidraru dam 30 20
4362 4l.80 Danube barrage and navigation system, Iron Gates 65 40

855 LZ-1 over Lake Constance

1978. Air. Airships. Multicoloured.
4363 60b. Type **855** 10 10
4364 1l. Santos Dumont's "Ballon No. 6" over Paris 20 10
4365 1l.50 Beardmore R-34 over Manhattan Island 25 10
4366 2l.15 N.4 "Italia" at North Pole 35 10
4367 3l.40 "Graf Zeppelin" over Brasov 50 20
4368 4l.80 "Graf Zeppelin" over Sibiu 95 30

856 Footballers and Emblem

1978. World Cup Football Championship, Argentina.
4370 **856** 55b. blue 10 10
4371 – 1l. orange 10 10
4372 – 1l.50 yellow 20 10
4373 – 2l.15 red 30 10
4374 – 3l.40 green 50 20
4375 – 4l.80 mauve 75 30
DESIGNS: Nos. 4371/5, Footballers and emblem, similar to Type **856**.

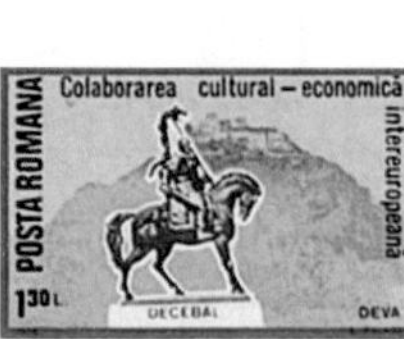

857 King Decebalus of Dacia **858** Worker and Factory

1978. Inter-European Cultural and Economic Co-operation. Multicoloured.
4377 1l.30 Type **857** 55 50
4378 3l.40 Prince Mircea the Elder . . . . 1·50 1·50

1978. 30th Anniv of Nationalization of Industry.
4379 **858** 55b. multicoloured . . . 15 15

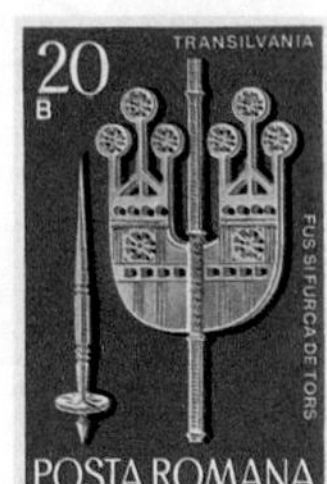

859 Spindle and Fork Handle, Transylvania

1978. Wood-carving. Multicoloured.
4380 20b. Type **859** 10 10
4381 40b. Cheese mould, Muntenia 10 10
4382 55b. Spoons, Oltenia . . . 10 10
4383 1l. Barrel, Moldavia 15 10
4384 2l.15 Ladle and mug, Transylvania 25 20
4385 4l.80 Water bucket, Oltenia 60 35

860 Danube Delta

1978. Tourism. Multicoloured.
4386 55b. Type **860** 65 30
4387 1l. Bran Castle (vert) . . . 10 10
4388 1l.50 Moldavian village . . 15 10
4389 2l.15 Muierii caves 20 10
4390 3l.40 Cable car at Boiana Brasov 40 10
4391 4l.80 Mangalia (Black Sea resort) 60 25

861 MC-6 Electron Microscope **862** Polovraci Cave

1978. Romanian Industry. Multicoloured.
4393 20b. Type **861** 10 10
4394 40b. Hydraulic excavator . . 10 10
4395 55b. Power station control room 10 10
4396 1l.50 Oil drillheads 15 10
4397 3l. C-12 combine harvester (horiz) 35 15
4398 3l.40 Petro-chemical combine, Pitesti 40 15

1978. Caves and Caverns. Multicoloured.
4399 55b. Type **862** 10 10
4400 1l. Topolnita 15 10
4401 1l.50 Ponoare 15 10
4402 2l.15 Ratei 25 10
4403 3l.40 Closani 45 15
4404 4l.80 Epuran 65 25

863 Gymnastics **865** Symbols of Equality

864 Zoomorphic Gold Plate

1978. "Daciada" Romanian Games. Multicoloured.
4405 55b. Type **863** 10 10
4406 1l. Running 15 10
4407 1l.50 Skiing 20 10
4408 2l.15 Horse jumping 25 10
4409 3l.40 Football 40 15
4410 4l.80 Handball 65 25

1978. Daco-Roman Archaeology. Multicoloured.
4411 20b. Type **864** 10 10
4412 40b. Gold torque 10 10
4413 55b. Gold cameo ring . . . 10 10
4414 1l. Silver bowl 20 10
4415 2l.15 Bronze eagle (vert) . . 35 10
4416 4l.80 Silver armband 40 25

1978. International Anti-Apartheid Year.
4418 **865** 3l.40 black, yellow & red 70 40

867 Ptolemaic Map of Dacia (2000th anniv of first record of Ziridava)

1978. Anniversaries in the History of Arad. Mult.
4420 40b. Type **867** 10 10
4421 55b. Meeting place of National Council (60th anniv of unified Romania) 10 10
4422 1l.75 Ceramic pots (950th anniv of first documentary evidence of Arad) 20 15

868 Dacian Warrior

1978. Stamp Day.
4423 **868** 6l.+3l. multicoloured . . 95 80
No. 4423 was issued se-tenant with a premium-carrying tab as shown in Type **868**.

869 Assembly at Alba Iulia **871** Dacian Warrior

870 Wright Brothers and Wright Type A

1979. 60th Anniv of National Unity. Mult.
4424 55b. Type **869** 10 10
4425 1l. Open book, flag and sculpture 15 10

1979. Air. Pioneers of Aviation. Multicoloured.
4426 55b. Type **870** 10 10
4427 1l. Louis Bleriot and Bleriot XI monoplane 15 10
4428 1l.50 Anthony Fokker and Fokker F.VIIa/3m "Josephine Ford" 20 10
4429 2l.15 Andrei Tupolev and Tupolev ANT-25 . . . . 30 10
4430 3l. Otto Lilienthal and Lilienthal monoplane glider 35 15
4431 3l.40 Traian Vuia and Vuia No. 1 . . . . 40 20
4432 4l.80 Aurel Vlaicu and No. 1 "Crazy Fly" . . . 50 30

1979. 2050th Anniv of Independent Centralized Dacic State. Details from Trajan's Column. Multicoloured.
4434 5b. Type **871** 10 10
4435 1l.50 Dacian warrior on horseback 25 10

872 "The Heroes from Vaslui" **873** Championship Emblem

1979. International Year of the Child (1st issue). Children's Paintings. Multicoloured.
4436 55b. Type **872** 10 10
4437 1l. "Tica's Folk Music Band" 10 10
4438 1l.50 "Buildingsite" 10 10
4439 2l.15 "Industrial Landscape" (horiz) 20 10

4440	3l.40 "Winter Holiday" (horiz)	35	15
4441	4l.80 "Pioneers' Celebration" (horiz)	55	20

See also Nos. 4453/6.

1979. European Junior Ice Hockey Championship, Miercurea-Ciuc, and World Championship, Galati. Multicoloured.

4442	1l.30 Type **873**	20	20
4443	3l.40 Championship emblem (different)	35	20

874 Dog's tooth Violet

876 Oil Derrick

875 Street with Mail Coach and Post-rider

1979. Protected Flowers. Multicoloured.

4444	55b. Type **874**	10	10
4445	1l. Alpine violet	10	10
4446	1l.50 "Linum borzaeanum"	15	10
4447	2l.15 "Convolvulus persicus"	20	10
4448	3l.40 Auricula	35	15
4449	4l.80 "Aquilegia transsylvanica"	45	25

1979. Inter-European Cultural and Economic Co-operation.

4450	1l.30 Type **875** (postage)	55	30
4451	3l.40 Boeing 707 and motorcycle postman (air)	65	35

1979. International Petroleum Congress, Bucharest.

4452	**876** 3l.40 multicoloured	35	15

877 Children with Flowers

878 Young Pioneer

1979. International Year of the Child (2nd issue). Multicoloured.

4453	40b. Type **877**	10	20
4454	1l. Children at creative play	15	20
4455	2l. Children with hare	30	20
4456	4l.60 Young pioneers	65	50

1979. 30th Anniv of Romanian Young Pioneers.

4457	**878** 55b. multicoloured	20	15

879 "Woman in Garden"

881 Stefan Gheorghiu

880 Brasov University

1979. Paintings by Gh. Tattarescu. Multicoloured.

4458	20b. Type **879**	10	10
4459	40b. "Muntenian Woman"	10	10
4460	55b. "Muntenian Man"	10	10
4461	1l. "General G. Magheru"	20	10
4462	2l.15 "The Artist's Daughter"	40	20
4463	4l.80 "Self-portrait"	75	25

1979. Contemporary Architecture. Multicoloured.

4464	20b. State Theatre, Tirgu Mures	10	10
4465	40b. Type **880**	10	10
4466	55b. Administration Centre, Baia Mare	10	10
4467	1l. Stefan Gheorghiu Academy, Bucharest	15	10
4468	2l.15 Adminstration Centre, Botosani	30	20
4469	4l.80 House of Culture, Tirgoviste	65	25

1979. Anniversaries. Multicoloured.

4470	40b. Type **881** (birth cent)	10	10
4471	55b. Statue of Gheorghe Lazar (poet) (birth bicent)	10	10
4472	2l.15 Fallen Workers monument (Strike at Lupeni, 50th anniv)	20	15

882 Moldavian and Wallachian Women and Monuments to Union

883 Party and National Flags

1979. 120th Anniv of Union of Moldavia and Wallachia.

4473	**882** 4l.60 multicoloured	60	20

1979. 25th Anniv of Liberation. Multicoloured.

4474	55b. Type **883**	15	10
4475	1l. "Workers' Militia" (L. Suhar) (horiz)	20	10

884 Freighter "Galati"

885 "Snapdragons"

1979. Ships. Multicoloured.

4476	55b. Type **884**	15	10
4477	1l. Freighter "Bucuresti"	20	10
4478	1l.50 Bulk carrier "Resita"	25	10
4479	2l.15 Bulk carrier "Tomis"	35	30
4480	3l.40 Tanker "Dacia"	50	15
4481	4l.80 Tanker "Independenta"	65	20

1979. "Socfilex 79" Stamp Exhibition, Bucharest. Flower Paintings by Stefan Luchian. Mult.

4482	40b. Type **885**	10	10
4483	60b. "Carnations"	15	10
4484	1l.55 "Flowers on a Stairway"	25	10
4485	4l.+2l. "Flowers of the Field"	75	70

888 Olympic Stadium, Melbourne (1956 Games)

1979. Olympic Games, Moscow (1980). Olympic Stadia. Multicoloured.

4489	55b. Type **888**	10	10
4490	1l. Rome (1960)	15	10
4491	1l.50 Tokyo (1964)	25	10
4492	2l.15 Mexico City (1968)	30	15
4493	3l.40 Munich (1972)	45	20
4494	4l.80 Montreal (1978)	70	20

1979. Municipal Coats of Arms. As T **836**. Mult.

4496	1l.20 Alba Julia	15	10
4497	1l.20 Arad	15	10
4498	1l.20 Bacau	15	10
4499	1l.20 Baia Mare	15	10
4500	1l.20 Birlad	15	10
4501	1l.20 Botosani	15	10
4502	1l.20 Brasov	15	10
4503	1l.20 Braila	15	10
4504	1l.20 Buzau	15	10
4505	1l.20 Calarasi	15	10
4506	1l.20 Cluj	15	10
4507	1l.20 Constanta	15	10
4508	1l.20 Craiova	15	10
4509	1l.20 Dej	15	10
4510	1l.20 Deva	15	10
4511	1l.20 Drobeta Turnu Severin	15	10
4512	1l.20 Focsani	15	10
4513	1l.20 Galati	15	10
4514	1l.20 Gheorghe Gheorghiu Dej	15	10
4515	1l.20 Giurgiu	15	10
4516	1l.20 Hunedoara	15	10
4517	1l.20 Iasi	15	10
4518	1l.20 Lugoj	15	10
4519	1l.20 Medias	15	10
4520	1l.20 Odorheiu Secuiesc	15	10

889 Costumes of Maramures (female)

891 Figure Skating

890 Post Coding Desks

1979. Costumes. Multicoloured.

4521	20b. Type **889**	10	10
4522	40b. Maramures (male)	10	10
4523	55b. Vrancea (female)	10	10
4524	1l.50 Vrancea (male)	20	10
4525	3l. Padureni (female)	40	20
4526	3l.40 Padureni (male)	45	30

1979. Stamp Day.

4527	**890** 2l.10+1l.90 mult	45	20

1979. Winter Olympic Games, Lake Placid (1980). Multicoloured.

4528	55b. Type **891**	10	10
4529	1l. Downhill skiing	10	10
4530	1l.50 Biathlon	20	10
4531	2l.15 Bobsleighing	25	10
4532	3l.40 Speed skating	45	20
4533	4l.80 Ice hockey	65	25

892 Locomotive "Calugareni", 1869

893 Dacian Warrior

1979. International Transport Exhibition, Hamburg. Multicoloured.

4535	55b. Type **892**	10	10
4536	1l. Steam locomotive "Orleans"	20	10
4537	1l.50 Steam locomotive No. 1059	20	10
4538	2l.15 Steam locomotive No. 150211	30	10
4539	3l.40 Steam locomotive No. 231085	45	20
4550	4l.80 Class 060-EA electric locomotive	20	10

1980. Arms (4th series). As T **836**. Multicoloured.

4542	1l.20 Oradea	20	10
4543	1l.20 Petrosani	20	10
4544	1l.20 Piatra Neamt	20	10
4545	1l.20 Pitesti	20	10
4546	1l.20 Ploiesti	20	10
4547	1l.20 Resita	20	10
4548	1l.20 Rimnicu Vilcea	20	10
4549	1l.20 Roman	20	10
4550	1l.20 Satu Mare	15	10
4551	1l.20 Sibiu	20	10
4552	1l.20 Sighetu Marmatiei	20	10
4553	1l.20 Sighisoara	20	10
4554	1l.20 Suceava	20	10
4555	1l.20 Tecuci	20	10
4556	1l.20 Timisoara	20	10
4557	1l.20 Tirgoviste	20	10
4558	1l.20 Tirgu Jiu	20	05
4559	1l.20 Tirgu-Mures	20	10
4560	1l.20 Tulcea	20	10
4561	1l.20 Turda	20	10
4562	1l.20 Turnu Magurele	20	10
4563	1l.20 Bucharest	20	10

1980. 2050th Anniv of Independent Centralized Dacian State under Burebista.

4564	55b. Type **893**	10	10
4565	1l.50 Dacian fighters with flag	20	10

894 River Kingfisher

1980. European Nature Protection Year. Mult.

4566	55b. Type **894**	25	10
4567	1l. Great egret (vert)	40	10
4568	1l.50 Red-breasted goose	45	10
4569	2l.15 Red deer (vert)	35	10
4570	3l.40 Roe deer fawn	35	20
4571	4l.80 European bison (vert)	55	30

895 Scarborough Lily

896 Tudor Vladimirescu

1980. Exotic Flowers from Bucharest Botanical Gardens. Multicoloured.

4573	55b. Type **895**	10	10
4574	1l. Floating water hyacinth	15	10
4575	1l.50 Jacobean lily	20	10
4576	2l.15 Rose of Sharon	30	10
4577	3l.40 Camellia	35	20
4578	4l.80 Lotus	60	25

1980. Anniversaries. Multicoloured.

4579	40b. Type **896** (revolutionary leader) (birth bicent)	10	10
4580	55b. Mihail Sadoveanu (writer) (birth cent)	10	10
4581	1l.50 Battle of Posada (650th anniv)	20	10
4582	2l.15 Tudor Arghezi (poet) (birth cent)	25	15
4583	3l. Horea (leader, Transylvanian uprising) (250th birth anniv)	40	20

898 Dacian Fruit Dish

899 Throwing the Javelin

1980. Bimillenary of Dacian Fortress, Petrodava (now Piatra Neamt).

4585	**898** 1l. multicoloured	15	15

1980. Olympic Games, Moscow. Multicoloured.

4586	55b. Type **899**	10	10
4587	1l. Fencing	15	10
4588	1l.50 Pistol shooting	20	10
4589	2l.15 Single kayak	30	10
4590	3l.40 Wrestling	40	20
4591	4l.80 Single skiff	60	30

901 Congress Emblem

902 Fireman carrying Child

1980. 15th International Congress of Historical Sciences.

4594	**901** 55b. deep blue and blue	15	15

1980. Firemen's Day.

4595	**902** 55b. multicoloured	15	15

903 Chinese and Romanian Stamp Collectors

906 Dacian Warrior

905 Rooks and Chessboard

1980. Romanian–Chinese Stamp Exhibition, Bucharest.

4596 **903** 1l. multicoloured 15 15

1980. 24th Chess Olympiad, Malta. Multicoloured.

4598 55b. Knights and chessboard 15 10
4599 1l. Type **905** 20 10
4600 2l.15 Male head and chessboard 40 10
4601 4l.80 Female head and chessboard 75 25

1980. Military Uniforms. Multicoloured.

4602 20b. Type **906** 10 10
4603 40b. Moldavian soldier (15th century) 10 10
4604 55b. Wallachian horseman (17th century) 10 10
4605 1l. Standard bearer (19th century) 10 10
4606 1l.50 Infantryman (19th century) 15 10
4607 2l.15 Lancer (19th century) 25 15
4608 4l.80 Hussar (19th century) 65 30

907 Burebista (sculpture, P. Mercea)

908 George Oprescu

1980. Stamp Day and 2050th Anniv of Independent Centralized Dacic State.

4609 **907** 2l. multicoloured 25 15

1981. Celebrities' Birth Anniversaries. Mult.

4610 1l.50 Type **908** (historian and art critic, centenary) 20 10
4611 2l.15 Marius Bunescu (painter, centenary) . . . 25 10
4612 3l.40 Ion Georgescu (sculptor, 125th anniv) . . 35 20

909 St. Bernard

1981. Dogs. Multicoloured.

4613 40b. Mountain sheepdog (horiz) 10 15
4614 55b. Type **909** 10 15
4615 1l. Fox terrier (horiz) . . . 15 15
4616 1l.50 Alsatian (horiz) . . . 25 15
4617 2l.15 Boxer (horiz) 35 15
4618 3l.40 Dalmatian (horiz) . . 55 20
4619 4l.80 Poodle 70 30

910 Paddle-steamer "Stefan cel Mare"

1981. 125th Anniv of European Danube Commission. Multicoloured.

4620 55b. Type **910** 15 10
4621 1l. "Prince Ferdinand de Roumanie" steam launch 20 20
4622 1l.50 Paddle-steamer "Tudor Vladimirescu" 30 20
4623 2l.15 Dredger "Sulina" . . . 35 25
4624 3l.40 Paddle-steamer "Republica Populara Romana" 45 30
4625 4l.80 Freighter in Sulina Channel 80 65

911 Bare-neck Pigeon

912 Party Flag and Oak Leaves

1981. Pigeons. Multicoloured.

4627 40b. Type **911** 10 10
4628 55b. Orbetan pigeon 10 10
4629 1l. Craiova chestnut pigeon 15 10
4630 1l.50 Timisoara pigeon . . . 35 10
4631 2l.15 Homing pigeon . . . 55 20
4632 3l.40 Salonta giant pigeon 80 20

1981. 60th Anniv of Romanian Communist Party.

4633 **912** 1l. multicoloured 20 15

914 "Soyuz 40"

1981. Air. Soviet–Romanian Space Flight. Mult.

4635 55b. Type **914** 15 10
4636 3l.40 "Soyuz"–"Salyut" link-up 40 10

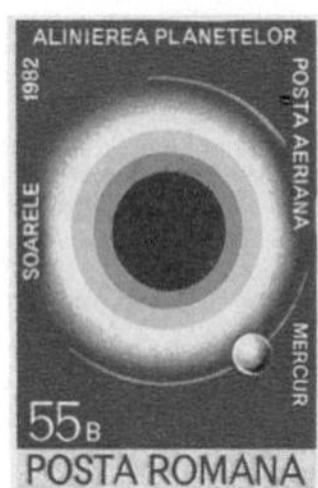

915 Sun and Mercury

916 Industrial Symbols

1981. Air. The Planets. Multicoloured.

4638 55b. Type **915** 10 10
4639 1l. Venus, Earth and Mars 20 20
4640 1l.50 Jupiter 25 25
4641 2l.15 Saturn 35 30
4642 3l.40 Uranus 50 40
4643 4l.80 Neptune and Pluto . . 80 45

1981. "Singing Romania" National Festival. Mult.

4645 55b. Type **916** 10 10
4646 1l.50 Technological symbols 25 10
4647 2l.15 Agricultural symbols 35 15
4648 3l.40 Cultural symbols . . . 70 30

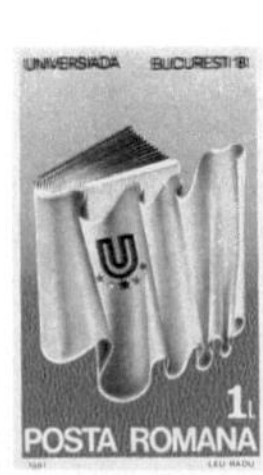

917 Book and Flag

918 "Woman in an Interior"

1981. "Universiada" Games, Bucharest. Mult.

4649 1l. Type **917** 10 10
4650 2l.15 Games emblem 25 20
4651 4l.80 Stadium (horiz) . . . 55 65

1981. 150th Birth Anniv of Theodor Aman (painter). Multicoloured.

4652 40b. "Self-portrait" 10 10
4653 55b. "Battle of Giurgiu" (horiz) 10 10
4654 1l. "Family Picnic" (horiz) 15 10
4655 1l.50 "The Painter's Studio" (horiz) 20 10
4656 2l.15 Type **918** 30 10
4657 3l.10 Aman Museum, Bucharest (horiz) 50 10

919 "The Thinker of Cernavoda" (polished stone sculpture)

920 Blood Donation

1981. 16th International Congress of Historical Sciences.

4658 **919** 3l.40 multicoloured . . . 45 35

1981. Blood Donor Campaign.

4659 **920** 55b. multicoloured . . . 15 15

921 Central Military Hospital

1981. 150th Anniv of Central Military Hospital, Bucharest.

4660 **921** 55b. multicoloured . . . 15 15

922 Paul Constantinescu

923 Children at Stamp Exhibition

1981. Romanian Musicians and Composers. Mult.

4661 40b. George Enescu 10 10
4662 55b. Type **922** 10 10
4663 1l. Dinu Lipatti 15 10
4664 1l.50 Ionel Perlea 20 10
4665 2l.15 Ciprian Porumbescu 30 15
4666 3l.40 Mihail Jora 45 20

1981. Stamp Day.

4667 **923** 2l. multicoloured 25 20

924 Hopscotch

925 Football Players

1981. Children's Games and Activities. Mult.

4668 40b. Type **924** (postage) . . 10 10
4669 55b. Football 10 10
4670 1l. Children with balloons and hobby horse 15 15
4671 1l.50 Fishing 20 15
4672 2l.15 Dog looking through school window at child 30 25
4673 3l. Child on stilts 40 35
4674 4l. Child tending sick dog 55 45
4675 4l.80 Children with model gliders (air) 70 75

Nos. 4671/15 are from illustrations by Norman Rockwell.

1981. World Cup Football Championship, Spain (1982). Multicoloured.

4676 55b. Type **925** 10 10
4677 1l. Goalkeeper saving ball 15 10
4678 1l.50 Player heading ball . . 20 15
4679 2l.15 Player kicking ball over head 30 30
4680 3l.40 Goalkeeper catching ball 50 40
4681 4l.80 Player kicking ball . . 70 45

926 Alexander the Good, Prince of Moldavia

927 Entrance to Union Square Station

1982. Anniversaries. Multicoloured.

4683 1l. Type **926** (550th death anniv) 10 15
4684 1l.50 Bogdan P. Hasdeu (historian, 75th death anniv) 15 10
4685 2l.15 Nicolae Titulescu (diplomat and politician, birth centenary) 35 10

1982. Inauguration of Bucharest Underground Railway. Multicoloured.

4686 60b. Type **927** 10 10
4687 2l.40 Platforms and train at Heroes' Square station . . 35 15

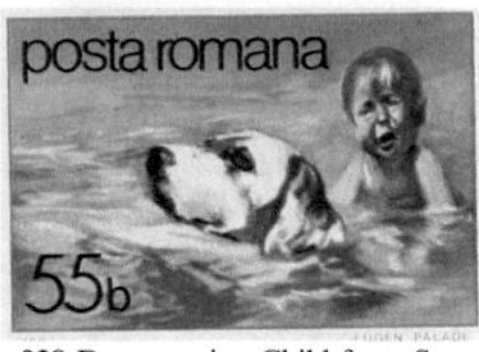

928 Dog rescuing Child from Sea

1982. Dog, Friend of Mankind. Multicoloured.

4688 55b. Type **928** 10 20
4689 1l. Shepherd and sheepdog (vert) 10 15
4690 3l. Gundog (vert) 30 15
4691 3l.40 Huskies 40 15
4692 4l. Dog carrying woman's basket (vert) 45 30
4693 4l.80 Dog guiding blind person (vert) 55 30
4694 5l. Dalmatian and child with doll 60 40
4695 6l. St. Bernard 75 35

929 Dove, Banner and Crowd

1982. 60th Anniv of Communist Youth Union. Mult.

4696 1l. Type **929** 15 15
4697 1l.20 Construction worker 15 15
4698 1l.50 Farm workers 20 15
4699 2l. Laboratory worker and students 25 20
4700 2l.50 Labourers 40 20
4701 3l. Choir, musicians and dancers 45 15

932 Harvesting Wheat

1982. 20th Anniv of Agricultural Co-operatives. Multicoloured.

4704 50b. Type **932** (postage) . . 10 10
4705 1l. Cows and milking equipment 15 10
4706 1l.50 Watering apple trees 20 10
4707 2l.50 Cultivator in vineyard 35 20
4708 3l. Watering vegetables . . . 40 25
4709 4l. Helicopter spraying cereal crop (air) 65 35

933 Vladimir Nicolae's Standard 1 Hang-glider

1982. Air. Hang-gliders. Multicoloured.
4711 50b. Type **933** 10 10
4712 1l. Excelsior D 20 10
4713 1l.50 Dedal-1 . . . . . . 25 10
4714 2l.50 Entuziast 40 15
4715 4l. AK-22 . . . . 60 30
4716 5l. Grifrom 85 35

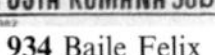

934 Baile Felix

936 Vlaicu Monument, Banesti-Prahova

935 "Legend"

1982. Spas and Health Resorts. Multicoloured.
4717 50b. Type **934** 10 10
4718 1l. Predeal (horiz) 10 10
4719 1l.50 Baile Herculane . . . 20 10
4720 2l.50 Eforie Nord (horiz) . . 40 10
4721 3l. Olimp (horiz) 50 10
4722 5l. Neptun (horiz) 70 20

1982. Paintings by Sabin Balasa. Multicoloured.
4723 1l. Type **935** 10 15
4724 1l.50 "Contrasts" 20 15
4725 2l.50 "Peace Relay" 50 25
4726 4l. "Genesis of the Romanian People" (vert) 55 35

1982. Air. Birth Centenary of Aurel Vlaicu (aviation pioneer). Multicoloured.
4727 50b. Vlaicu's glider, 1909 (horiz) 10 10
4728 1l. Type **936** 20 10
4729 2l.50 Air Heroes' Monument 45 20
4730 3l. Vlaicu's No. 1 airplane "Crazy Fly", 1910 (horiz) 50 15

938 Central Exhibition Pavilion

1982. "Tib '82" International Fair, Bucharest.
4732 **938** 2l. multicoloured 25 10

939 Young Pioneer with Savings Book and Books
940 Postwoman delivering Letters

1982. Savings Week. Multicoloured.
4733 1l. Type **939** 15 10
4734 2l. Savings Bank advertisement (Calin Popovici) 20 10

1982. Stamp Day. Multicoloured.
4735 1l. Type **940** 15 10
4736 2l. Postman 20 10

941 "Brave Young Man and the Golden Apples" (Petre Ispirescu)
942 Symbols of Industry, Party Emblem and Programme

1982. Fairy Tales. Multicoloured.
4737 50b. Type **941** 10 10
4738 1l. "Bear tricked by the Fox" (Ion Creanga) . . . 20 10
4739 1l.50 Warrior fighting bird ("Prince of Tears" (Mihai Eminescu)) 25 10
4740 2l.50 Hen with bag ("Bag with Two Coins" (Ion Creanga)) 35 10
4741 3l. Rider fighting three-headed dragon ("Ileana Simziana" (Petre Ispirescu)) 45 20
4742 5l. Man riding devil ("Danila Prepeleac" (Ion Creanga)) 75 30

1982. Romanian Communist Party National Conference, Bucharest. Multicoloured.
4743 1l. Type **942** 15 15
4744 2l. Wheat symbols of industry and Party emblem and open programme 25 15

943 Wooden Canteen from Suceava
944 Wheat, Cogwheel, Flask and Electricity Emblem

1982. Household Utensils.
4745 **943** 50b. red 10 10
4746 – 1l. blue 15 15
4747 – 1l.50 orange 20 10
4748 – 2l. blue 40 15
4749 – 3l. green 50 15
4750 – 3l.50 green 55 10
4751 – 4l. brown 70 15
4752 – 5l. blue 80 10
4753 – 6l. blue . . . . 1·00 15
4754 – 7l. purple . . . . 1·10 15
4755 – 7l.50 mauve . . . . . . 1·20 15
4756 – 8l. green . . . . 1·20 15
4757 – 10l. red . . . . 1·20 15
4758 – 20l. violet . . . . 2·50 15
4759 – 30l. blue . . . . 3·50 15
4760 – 50l. brown . . . . . . 7·25 25

DESIGNS: As T **943**—VERT: 1l. Ceramic plates from Radauti; 2l. Jug and plate from Vama-Maramures; 3l. Wooden churn and pail from North Moldavia; 4l. Wooden spoons and ceramic plate from Cluj; 5l. Ceramic bowl and pot from Marginea-Suceava. HORIZ: 1l.50, Wooden dipper from Valea Mare; 3l.50, Ceramic plates from Leheceni-Crisana. 29 × 23 mm: 10l. Wooden tubs from Hunedoara and Suceava; 30l. Wooden spoons from Alba. 23 × 29 mm: 6l. Ceramic pot and jug from Bihor; 7l. Distaff and spindle from Transylvania; 7l.50, Double wooden pail from Suceava; 8l. Pitcher and ceramic plate from Oboga and Horezu; 20l. Wooden canteen and six glasses from Horezu; 50l. Ceramic plates from Horezu.

1982. 35th Anniv of People's Republic. Mult.
4767 1l. Type **944** 15 10
4768 2l. National flag and oak leaves 20 10

945 H. Coanda and Diagram of Jet Engine

1983. Air. 25 Years of Space Exploration. Mult.
4769 50b. Type **945** 10 10
4770 1l. H. Oberth and diagram of rocket 10 10
4771 1l.50 "Sputnik 1", 1957 (first artificial satellite) . . 20 10
4772 2l.50 "Vostok 1", (first manned flight) 45 15
4773 4l. "Apollo 11, 1969 (first Moon landing) 65 20
4774 5l. Space shuttle "Columbia" 85 25

946 Rombac One Eleven 500 Jetliner
947 Matei Millo in "The Discontented" by Vasile Alecsandri

1983. Air. First Romanian-built Jetliner.
4776 **946** 11l. blue . . . . 2·00 50

1983. Romanian Actors.
4777 **947** 50b. red and black . . . 10 15
4778 – 1l. green and black . . . 10 10
4779 – 1l.50 violet and black . . 20 15
4780 – 2l. brown and black . . 30 15
4781 – 2l.50 green and black . . 40 10
4782 – 3l. blue and black . . . 45 15
4783 – 4l. green and black . . . 55 25
4784 – 5l. lilac and black . . . 75 40

DESIGNS: 1l. Mihail Pascaly in "Director Millo" by Vasile Alecsandri; 1l.50, Aristizza Romanescu in "The Dogs" by H. Lecca; 2l. C. I. Nottara in "Blizzard" by B. S. Delavrancea; 2l.50, Grigore Manolescu in "Hamlet" by William Shakespeare; 3l. Agatha Birsescu in "Medea" by Lebouvet; 4l. Ion Brezeanu in "The Lost Letter" by I. L. Caragiale; 5l. Aristide Demetriad in "The Despotic Prince" by Vasile Alecsandri.

948 Hugo Grotius
949 Aro "10"

1983. 400th Birth Anniv of Hugo Grotius (Dutch jurist).
4785 **948** 2l. brown 30 10

1983. Romanian-built Vehicles. Multicoloured.
4786 50b. Type **949** 10 10
4787 1l. Dacia "1300" Break . . 20 10
4788 1l.50 Aro "242" 25 10
4789 2l.50 Aro "244" 45 10
4790 4l. Dacia "1310" 70 15
4791 5l. Oltcit "Club" 95 25

951 National and Communist Party Flags
953 Bluethroat

952 Loading Mail into Boeing 707

1983. 50th Anniv of 1933 Workers' Revolution.
4793 **951** 2l. multicoloured 30 10

1983. Air. World Communications Year.
4794 **952** 2l. multicoloured 50 10

1983. Birds of the Danube Delta. Multicoloured.
4795 50b. Type **953** 15 10
4796 1l. Rose-coloured starling 45 10
4797 1l.50 European roller . . . 55 10
4798 2l.50 European bee eater . . 90 25
4799 4l. Reed bunting . . . . . 1·60 30
4800 5l. Lesser grey shrike . . . 2·00 40

954 Kayak

1983. Water Sports. Multicoloured.
4801 50b. Type **954** 10 15
4802 1l. Water polo 15 15
4803 1l.50 Canoeing 20 15
4804 2l.50 Diving 45 20
4805 4l. Rowing 70 25
4806 5l. Swimming (start of race) 95 40

955 Postman on Bicycle

1983. Stamp Day. Multicoloured.
4807 1l. Type **955** 15 10
4808 3l.50(+3l.) National flag as stamp 95 50

No. 4808 was issued se-tenant with a premium-carrying tab showing the Philatelic Association emblem.

956 "Geum reptans"

1983. European Flora and Fauna. Multicoloured.
4810 1l. Type **956** 20 30
4811 1l. Long-headed poppy . . 20 15
4812 1l. Stemless carline thistle 20 30
4813 1l. "Paeonia peregrina" . . 20 30
4814 1l. "Gentiana excisa" . . . 20 15
4815 1l. Eurasian red squirrel . . 20 30
4816 1l. "Grammia quenselii" (butterfly) 50 20
4817 1l. Middle-spotted woodpecker 50 45
4818 1l. Lynx 50 30
4819 1l. Wallcreeper 70 45

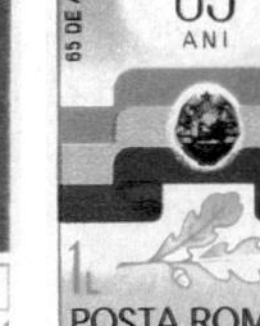

957 "Girl with Feather"
958 Flag and Oak Leaves

1983. Paintings by Corneliu Baba. Multicoloured.
4820 1l. Type **957** 20 15
4821 2l. "Congregation" 35 15
4822 3l. "Farm Workers" 65 20
4823 4l. "Rest in the Fields" (horiz) 85 30

1983. 65th Anniv of Union of Transylvania and Romania. Multicoloured.
4824 1l. Type **958** 15 15
4825 2l. National and Communist Party Flags and Parliament building, Bucharest 30 15

959 Postman and Post Office
961 Cross-country Skiing

1983. "Balkanfila IX '83" Stamp Exhibition, Bucharest. Multicoloured.
4826 1l. Type **959** 15 15
4827 2l. Postwoman and Athenaeum Concert Hall 30 15

1984. Winter Olympic Games, Sarajevo. Mult.
4830 50b. Type **961** 10 10
4831 1l. Biathlon 10 20
4832 1l.50 Ice skating 15 20
4833 2l. Speed skating 20 30

4834 3l. Ice hockey 30 35
4835 3l.50 Bobsleighing 40 15
4836 4l. Luge 45 55
4837 5l. Downhill skiing 55 65

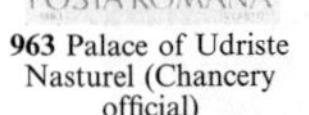

963 Palace of Udriste Nasturel (Chancery official)
967 Flowering Rush

966 Sunflower

1984. Anniversaries.
4839 50b. green, pink and silver 10 10
4840 1l. violet, green and silver 20 10
4841 1l.50 multicoloured 30 15
4842 2l. brown, blue and silver 45 10
4843 3l.50 multicoloured 80 20
4844 4l. multicoloured . . . . . 1·00 20
DESIGNS: 50b. Type **963** (325th death anniv); 1l. Miron Costin (poet, 350th birth anniv); 1l.50, Crisan (Giurgiu Marcu) (leader of peasant revolt, 250th birth anniv); 2l. Simion Barnutiu (scientist, 175th birth anniv); 3l.50, Diuliu Zamfirescu (writer, 125th birth anniv); 4l. Nicolae Milescu at Great Wall of China (explorer, 275th death anniv).

1984. Protection of Environment. Multicoloured.
4847 1l. Type **966** 15 10
4848 2l. Red deer 25 15
4849 3l. Carp 35 20
4850 4l. Jay . . . . 1·70 40

1984. Flowers of the Danube. Multicoloured.
4851 50b. Arrowhead 10 10
4852 1l. Yellow iris 10 10
4853 1l.50 Type **967** 20 10
4854 3l. White water lily 45 20
4855 4l. Fringed water lily (horiz) 65 20
4856 5l. Yellow water lily (horiz) 80 30

968 Crowd with Banners
970 Congress Emblem

969 High Jumping

1984. 45th Anniv of Anti-Fascist Demonstration.
4857 **968** 2l. multicoloured 35 30

1984. Olympic Games, Los Angeles (1st issue). Multicoloured.
4858 50b. Type **969** 10 10
4859 1l. Swimming 15 10
4860 1l.50 Running 20 15
4861 3l. Handball 50 35
4862 4l. Rowing 75 55
4863 5l. Canoeing 95 70
See also Nos. 4866/73.

1984. 25th Ear, Nose and Throat Association Congress, Bucharest.
4864 **970** 2l. multicoloured 30 15

1984. Olympic Games, Los Angeles (2nd issue). As T **969**. Multicoloured.
4866 50b. Boxing 10 10
4867 1l. Rowing 10 10
4868 1l. Handball 15 10
4869 2l. Judo 20 10
4870 3l. Wrestling 35 15
4871 3l.50 Fencing 45 20
4872 4l. Kayak 55 25
4873 5l. Swimming 65 35

972 Mihai Ciuca (bacteriologist, cent)
974 Flags, Flame and Power Station

973 Lockhead 14 Super Electra

1984. Birth Anniversaries. Dated "1983".
4874 **972** 1l. purple, blue and silver 15 15
4875 – 2l. brown and silver . . 30 15
4876 – 3l. green, brown and silver 45 25
4877 – 4l. violet, green and silver 65 40
DESIGNS: 2l. Petre S. Aurelian (agronomist, 150th anniv); 3l. Alexandru Vlahuta (writer, 125th anniv); 4l. Dimitrie Leonida (engineer, centenary).

1984. Air. 40th Anniv of International Civil Aviation Organization. Multicoloured.
4878 50b. Type **973** 15 10
4879 1l.50 Britten Norman Islander 30 10
4880 3l. Rombac One Eleven 500 jetliner 60 20
4881 6l. Boeing 707 jetliner . . . 1·10 30

1984. 40th Anniv of Liberation.
4882 **974** 2l. multicoloured 50 30

975 Lippizaner

1984. Horses. Multicoloured.
4883 50b. Type **975** 10 10
4884 1l. Hutul 15 10
4885 1l.50 Bukovina 20 10
4886 2l.50 Nonius 40 10
4887 4l. Arab 65 20
4888 5l. Romanian halfbreed . . 80 25

977 Memorial, Alba Julia
978 "Portrait of a Child" (Th. Aman)

1984. Bicentenary of Horea, Closa and Crisan Uprisings.
4890 **977** 2l. multicoloured 30 15

1984. Paintings of Children. Multicoloured.
4891 50b. Type **978** 10 15
4892 1l. "The Little Shepherd" (N. Grigorescu) 10 10
4893 2l. "Lica with an Orange" (St. Luchian) 30 10
4894 3l. "Portrait of a Child" (N. Tonitza) 45 20
4895 4l. "Portrait of a Boy" (S. Popp) 65 25
4896 5l. "Portrait of Young Girl" (I. Tuculescu) 90 30

979 Stage Coach and Romanian Philatelic Association Emblem

1984. Stamp Day.
4897 **979** 2l.(+1l.) multicoloured 45 50
No. 4897 was issued with premium-carrying label as shown in T **979**.

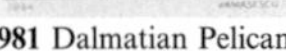

981 Dalmatian Pelicans
982 Dr. Petru Groza (former President)

1984. Protected Animals. Dalmatian Pelicans. Mult.
4899 50b. Type **981** 20 15
4900 1l. Pelican on nest 50 35
4901 1l. Pelicans on lake 50 35
4902 2l. Pelicans roosting . . . . 1·00 80

1984. Anniversaries. Multicoloured.
4903 50b. Type **982** (birth centenary) 25 15
4904 1l. Alexandru Odobescu (writer) (150th birth anniv) 55 10
4905 2l. Dr. Carol Davila (physician) (death centenary) 35 10
4906 3l. Dr. Nicolae Gh. Lupu (physician) (birth centenary) 55 15
4907 4l. Dr. Daniel Danielopolu (physician) (birth centenary) 65 25
4908 5l. Panait Istrati (writer) (birth centenary) 85 35

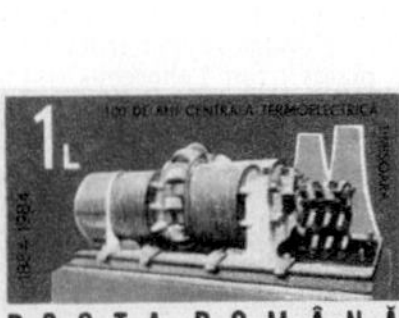

983 Generator
985 August Treboniu Laurian (linguist and historian)

1984. Centenary of Power Station and Electric Street Lighting in Timisoara. Multicoloured.
4909 1l. Type **983** 15 15
4910 2l. Street lamp 35 10

1985. Anniversaries. Multicoloured.
4912 50b. Type **985** (175th birth anniv) 10 15
4913 1l. Grigore Alexandrescu (writer) (death centenary) 20 15
4914 1l.50 Gheorghe Pop de Basesti (politician) (150th birth anniv) 30 15
4915 2l. Mateiu Caragiale (writer) (birth centenary) 35 10
4916 3l. Gheorghe Ionescu-Sisesti (scientist) (birth centenary) 55 20
4917 4l. Liviu Rebreanu (writer) (birth centenary) 85 25

986 Students in Science Laboratory
987 Racoon Dog

1985. International Youth Year. Multicoloured.
4918 1l. Type **986** 10 10
4919 2l. Students on construction site 35 10

1985. Protected Animals. Multicoloured.
4921 50b. Type **987** 10 10
4922 1l. Grey partridge 40 10
4923 1l.50 Snowy owl . . . . . 1·00 15
4924 2l. Pine marten 20 10
4925 3l. Eurasian badger 30 10
4926 3l.50 Eurasian otter 30 20
4927 4l. Western Capercaillie . . 1·60 25
4928 5l. Great bustard . . . . . 2·20 35

988 Flags and Victory Monument, Bucharest
989 Union Emblem

1985. 40th Anniv of Victory in Europe Day.
4929 **988** 2l. multicoloured 50 25

1985. Communist Youth Union Congress.
4930 **989** 2l. multicoloured 40 15

990 Route Map and Canal

1985. Danube–Black Sea Canal. Multicoloured.
4931 1l. Type **990** 25 10
4932 2l. Canal and bridge, Cernavoda . . . . 1·10 25
4933 3l. Road over Canal, Medgidia 95 15
4934 4l. Canal control tower, Agigea . . . . 1·10 25

991 Brown Pelican
992 "Fire"

1985. Birth Bicentenary of John J. Audubon (ornithologist). Multicoloured.
4936 50b. American robin (horiz) 15 10
4937 1l. Type **991** 30 10
4938 1l.50 Yellow-crowned night heron 45 15
4939 2l. Northern oriole 65 15
4940 3l. Red-necked grebe . . . 95 30
4941 4l. Mallard (horiz) . . . . 1·10 40

1985. Paintings by Ion Tuculescu. Multicoloured.
4942 1l. Type **992** 10 15
4943 2l. "Circulation" 35 15
4944 3l. "Interior of Peasant's Home" (horiz) 50 20
4945 4l. "Sunset" (horiz) 70 25

993 Peacock

1985. Butterflies and Moths. Multicoloured.

4946	50b. Type **993**	10	10
4947	1l. Swallowtail	25	10
4948	2l. Red admiral	40	15
4949	3l. Emperor moth	55	20
4950	4l. Hebe tiger moth	80	30
4951	5l. Eyed hawk moth	95	45

994 Transfagarasan Mountain Road

1985. 20th Anniv of Election of General Secretary Nicolae Ceausescu and 9th Communist Party Congress. Multicoloured.

4952	1l. Type **994**	20	15
4953	2l. Danube–Black Sea Canal	60	25
4954	3l. Bucharest underground railway	90	40
4955	4l. Irrigating fields	90	45

995 Romanian Crest, Symbols of Agriculture and "XX"

997 "Senecio glaberrimus"

1985. 20th Anniv of Romanian Socialist Republic. Multicoloured.

4956	1l. Type **995**	25	25
4957	2l. Crest, symbols of industry and "XX"	55	35

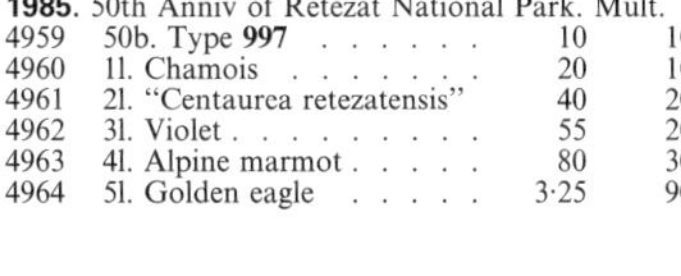

1985. 50th Anniv of Retezat National Park. Mult.

4959	50b. Type **997**	10	10
4960	1l. Chamois	20	10
4961	2l. "Centaurea retezatensis"	40	20
4962	3l. Violet	55	20
4963	4l. Alpine marmot	80	30
4964	5l. Golden eagle	3·25	90

998 Universal "530 DTC"

1985. Romanian Tractors. Multicoloured.

4966	50b. Type **998**	10	10
4967	1l. Universal "550 M HC"	25	10
4968	1l.50 Universal "650 Super"	35	10
4969	2l. Universal "850"	45	20
4970	3l. Universal "S 1801 IF" tracked front loader	65	20
4971	4l. Universal "A 3602 IF" front loader	95	30

999 Costume of Muscel (female)

1985. Costumes (1st series). Multicoloured.

4972	50b. Type **999**	10	10
4973	50b. Muscel (male)	10	10
4974	1l.50 Bistrita-Nasaud (female)	25	20
4975	1l.50 Bistrita-Nasaud (male)	25	20
4976	2l. Vrancea (female)	35	10
4977	2l. Vrancea (male)	35	10
4978	3l. Vilcea (female)	55	25
4979	3l. Vilcea (male)	55	25

See also Nos. 5143/5150.

1000 Footballer attacking Goal

1985. World Cup Football Championship, Mexico (1986) (1st issue). Multicoloured.

4980	50b. Type **1000**	10	15
4981	1l. Player capturing ball	20	15
4982	1l.50 Player heading ball	25	25
4983	2l. Player about to tackle	40	25
4984	3l. Player heading ball and goalkeeper	65	35
4985	4l. Player kicking ball overhead	1·00	45

See also Nos. 5038/43.

1001 U.N. Emblem and "40"

1002 Copper

1985. 40th Anniv of U.N.O. (4986) and 30th Anniv of Romanian Membership (4987).

4986	2l. Type **1001**	30	20
4987	2l. U.N. building, New York, U.N. emblem and Romanian crest	30	20

1985. Minerals. Multicoloured.

4988	50b. Quartz and calcite	10	15
4989	1l. Type **1002**	10	15
4990	2l. Gypsum	25	15
4991	3l. Quartz	40	20
4992	4l. Stibium	60	30
4993	5l. Tetrahedrite	90	40

1003 Posthorn

1985. Stamp Day.

4994	**1003** 2l.(+1l.) multicoloured	50	40

1004 Goofy as Hank waking to find himself at Camelot

1985. 150th Birth of Mark Twain (writer). Scenes from "A Connecticut Yankee in King Arthur's Court" (film). Multicoloured.

4995	50b. Type **1004**	2·40	1·60
4996	50b. Hank at the stake and Merlin (Mickey Mouse)	2·40	1·60
4997	50b. Hank being hoisted onto horseback in full armour	2·40	1·60
4998	50b. Pete as Sir Sagramoor on horseback	2·40	1·60

1985. Birth Bicentenaries of Grimm Brothers (folklorists). Scenes from "The Three Brothers". As T **1004**. Multicoloured.

5000	1l. Father (Donald Duck) bidding farewell to the brothers (Huey, Louie and Dewey)	3·00	2·75
5001	1l. Louie as fencing master brother	3·00	2·75
5002	1l. Louie keeping rain off his father with sword	3·00	2·75
5003	1l. Huey as blacksmith brother shoeing galloping horse	3·00	2·75
5004	1l. Dewey as barber brother shaving Brer Rabbit on the run	3·00	2·75

1005 Wright Brothers (aviation pioneers) and Wright Flyer 1

1985. Explorers and Pioneers. Multicoloured.

5006	1l. Type **1005**	15	10
5007	1l.50 Jacques Yves Cousteau (undersea explorer) and "Calypso"	45	10
5008	2l. Amelia Earhart (first woman trans-Atlantic flyer) and Fokker F.VIIb/3m seaplane "Friendship"	35	10
5009	3l. Charles Lindbergh (first solo trans-Atlantic flyer) and Ryan NYP Special "Spirit of St. Louis"	45	20
5010	3l.50 Sir Edmund Hillary (first man to reach summit of Everest)	45	25
5011	4l. Robert Peary and Emil Racovita (polar explorers)	50	25
5012	5l. Richard Byrd (polar explorer and aviator) and polar supply ship	1·20	40
5013	6l. Neil Armstrong (first man on Moon) and Moon	65	45

1006 Edmond Halley and Comet

1986. Air. Appearance of Halley's Comet.

5014	2l. Type **1006**	30	20
5015	4l. Comet, orbit and space probes	60	30

No. 5014 is wrongly inscr "Edmund".

1007 "Nina in Green"

1010 Hotel Diana, Baile Herculane

1009 Goofy playing Clarinet

1986. Paintings by Nicolae Tonitza. Multicoloured.

5016	1l. Type **1007**	10	15
5017	2l. "Irina"	30	20
5018	3l. "Forester's Daughter"	45	30
5019	4l. "Woman on Veranda"	70	30

1986. 50th Anniv of Colour Animation. Scenes from "Band Concert" (cartoon film). Mult.

5021	50b. Type **1009**	2·40	1·70
5022	50b. Clarabelle playing flute	2·40	1·70
5023	50b. Mickey Mouse conducting	2·40	1·70
5024	50b. Paddy and Peter Pig playing euphonium and trumpet	2·40	1·70
5025	1l. Conductor Mickey and flautist Donald Duck	2·75	2·75
5026	1l. Donald caught in trombone slide	2·75	2·75
5027	1l. Horace playing drums	2·75	2·75
5028	1l. Donald selling ice cream	2·75	2·75
5029	1l. Mickey and euphonium caught in tornado	2·75	2·75

1986. Spa Hotels. Multicoloured.

5031	50b. Type **1010**	10	10
5032	1l. Hotel Termal, Baile Felix	15	10
5033	2l. Hotels Delfin, Meduza and Steaua de Mare, North Eforie	35	10
5034	3l. Hotel Caciulata, Calimanesti-Caciulata	50	20
5035	4l. Villa Palas, Slanic Moldova	75	30
5036	5l. Hotel Bradet, Sovata	85	35

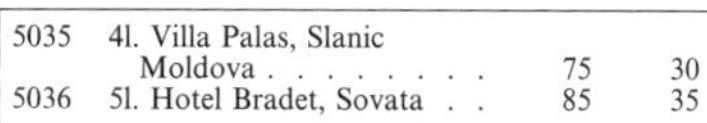

1011 Ceausescu and Red Flag

1986. 65th Anniv of Romanian Communist Party

5037	**1011** 2l. multicoloured	80	35

1012 Italy v. Bulgaria

1986. World Cup Football Championship, Mexico (2nd issue). Multicoloured.

5038	50b. Type **1012**	10	15
5039	1l. Mexico v. Belgium	10	15
5040	2l. Canada v. France	30	20
5041	3l. Brazil v. Spain	40	20
5042	4l. Uruguay v. W. Germany	60	35
5043	5l. Morocco v. Poland	70	40

1014 "Tulipa gesneriana"

1986. Garden Flowers. Multicoloured.

5045	50b. Type **1014**	10	15
5046	1l. "Iris hispanica"	10	15
5047	2l. "Rosa hybrida"	35	15
5048	3l. "Anemone coronaria"	50	20
5049	4l. "Freesia refracta"	70	30
5050	5l. "Chrysanthemum indicum"	80	40

1015 Mircea the Great and Horsemen

1986. 600th Anniv of Mircea the Great's Accession.

5051	**1015** 2l. multicoloured	30	25

1016 Thatched House with Veranda, Alba

1986. 50th Anniv of Museum of Historic Dwellings, Bucharest. Multicoloured.

5052	50b. Type **1016**	10	35
5053	1l. Stone-built house, Arges	10	35
5054	2l. House with veranda, Constanta	35	40
5055	3l. House with tiled roof and steps, Timis	50	40
5056	4l. House with ramp to veranda, Neamt	70	20
5057	5l. Two storey house with first floor veranda, Gorj	80	30

1017 Julius Popper (Tierra del Fuego, 1886–93)

1986. Polar Research. Multicoloured.

5058 50b. Type **1017** 15 10

5059 1l. Bazil Gh. Assan (Spitzbergen, 1896) . . . 35 10

5060 2l. Emil Racovita and "Belgica" (barque) (Antarctic, 1897–99) . . . 80 10

5061 3l. Constantin Dumbrava (Greenland, 1927–28) . . 60 20

5062 4l. Romanian participation in 17th Soviet Antarctic Expedition, 1971–72 . . . 1·60 25

5063 5l. 1977 "Sinoe" and 1979–80 "Tirnava" krill fishing expeditions . . . . 1·20 30

1019 The Blusher

1020 Group of Cyclists

1986. Fungi. Multicoloured.

5065 50b. Type **1019** 15 10

5066 1l. Oak mushroom 20 10

5067 2l. Peppery milk cap 45 15

5068 3l. Shield fungus 70 35

5069 4l. The charcoal burner . . 1·00 40

5070 5l. "Tremiscus helvelloides" 1·10 55

1986. Cycle Tour of Romania. Multicoloured.

5071 1l. Type **1020** 10 15

5072 2l. Motor cycle following cyclist 30 15

5073 3l. Jeep following cyclists . . 40 25

5074 4l. Winner 65 25

1021 Emblem

1022 Petru Maior (historian) (225th birth anniv)

1986. 40th Anniv of U.N.E.S.C.O. and 30th Anniv of Romanian Membership.

5076 **1021** 4l. multicoloured . . . 60 45

1986. Birth Anniversaries.

5077 **1022** 50b. purple, gold and green 10 10

5078 – 1b. green, gold and mauve 10 10

5079 – 2l. red, gold and blue 30 10

5080 – 3l. blue, gold and brown 55 20

DESIGNS: 1l. George Topirceanu (writer, centenary); 2l. Henri Coanda (engineer, centenary); 3l. Constantin Budeanu (engineer, centenary).

1023 Coach and Horses (½-size illustration)

1986. Stamp Day.

5081 **1023** 2l.(+1l.) multicoloured 50 40

No. 5081 includes the se-tenant premium-carrying tab shown in Type **1023**.

1024 F 300 Oil Drilling Rigs

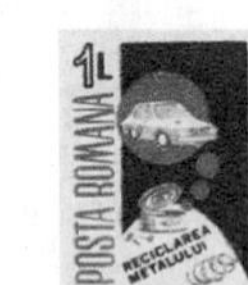

1026 Tin Can and Motor Car ("Recycle metals")

1025 "Goat"

1986. Industry. Multicoloured.

5082 50b. Type **1024** 10 10

5083 1l. "Promex" excavator (horiz) 10 10

5084 2l. Petrochemical refinery, Pitesti 35 10

5085 3l. Tipper "110 t" (horiz) . . 50 20

5086 4l. "Coral" computer . . . 70 25

5087 5l. 350 m.w. turbine (horiz) 80 35

1986. New Year Folk Customs. Multicoloured.

5088 50b. Type **1025** 10 10

5089 1l. Sorcova 10 10

5090 2l. Plugusorul 35 10

5091 3l. Buhaiul 50 15

5092 4l. Caiutii 70 25

5093 5l. Uratorii 80 35

1986. "Save Waste Materials".

5094 **1026** 1l. red and orange . . . 15 10

5095 – 2l. light green and green 40 20

DESIGN: 2l. Trees and hand with newspaper ("Recycle waste paper").

1027 Flags and Young People

1028 Anniversary Emblem

1987. 65th Anniv of Communist Youth Union. Multicoloured.

5096 1l. Type **1027** 15 40

5097 2l. Anniversary emblem . . 45 55

5098 3l. Flags and young people (different) 65 70

1987. 25th Anniv of Agricultural Co-operatives.

5099 **1028** 2l. multicoloured . . . 30 30

1030 "Birch Trees by Lake" (Ion Andreescu)

1987. Paintings. Multicoloured.

5101 50b. Type **1030** 10 15

5102 1l. "Young Peasant Girls spinning" (N. Grigorescu) 15 15

5103 2l. "Washerwoman" (St. Luchian) 30 15

5104 3l. "Interior" (St. Dimitrescu) 55 20

5105 4l. "Winter Landscape" (Al. Ciucurencu) 65 25

5106 5l. "Winter in Bucharest" (N. Tonitza) (vert) . . . 85 35

1031 "1907" and Peasants

1987. 80th Anniv of Peasant Uprising.

5107 **1031** 2l. multicoloured . . . 30 30

1032 Players

1033 1 Leu Coin

1987. 10th Students World Men's Handball Championship.

5108 **1032** 50b. multicoloured . . 10 15

5109 – 1l. multicoloured (horiz) 45 15

5110 – 2l. multicoloured . . . 30 15

5111 – 3l. multicoloured (horiz) 55 25

5112 – 4l. multicoloured . . . 70 30

5113 – 5l. multicoloured (horiz) 85 40

DESIGNS: 1l. to 5l. Various match scenes.

1987. Currency.

5114 **1033** 1l. multicoloured . . . 20 15

1034 Eastern White Pelicans in the Danube Delta

1987. Tourism. Multicoloured.

5116 50b. Type **1034** 25 10

5117 1l. Cable car above Transfagarasan mountain road 25 10

5118 2l. Cheile Bicazului 45 10

5119 3l. Ceahlau mountains . . . 75 20

5120 4l. Lake Capra, Fagaras mountains 90 25

5121 5l. Borsa orchards . . . . . 1·10 35

1035 Henri August's Glider, 1909

1987. Air. Aircraft. Multicoloured.

5122 50b. Type **1035** 10 10

5123 1l. Sky diver jumping from IS-28 B2 glider 15 10

5124 2l. IS-29 D2 glider 25 15

5125 3l. IS-32 glider 50 15

5126 4l. I.A.R.35 light airplane 65 25

5127 5l. IS-28 M2 aircraft 90 30

1036 Youth on Winged Horse

1987. Fairy Tales by Petre Ispirescu. Multicoloured.

5128 50b. Type **1036** 10 15

5129 1l. King and princesses ("Salt in the Food") . . . 15 15

5130 2l. Girl on horse fighting lion ("Ileana Simziana") 25 15

5131 3l. Youth with bow and arrow aiming at bird ("The Youth and the Golden Apples") 50 20

5132 4l. George and dead dragon ("George the Brave") . . 65 15

5133 5l. Girl looking at sleeping youth ("The Enchanted Pig") 90 20

1037 Class L 45H Diesel Shunter

1987. Railway Locomotives. Multicoloured.

5135 50b. Type **1037** 10 10

5136 1l. Class LDE 125 diesel goods locomotive 20 10

5137 2l. Class LDH 70 diesel goods locomotive 30 10

5138 3l. Class LDE 2100 diesel locomotive 50 20

5139 4l. Class LDE 3000 diesel locomotive 60 15

5140 5l. Class LE 5100 electric locomotive 80 20

1987. Costumes (2nd series). As T **999**. Mult.

5143 1l. Tirnave (female) 20 15

5144 1l. Tirnave (male) 20 15

5145 2l. Buzau (female) 35 15

5146 2l. Buzau (male) 35 15

5147 3l. Dobrogea (female) . . . 50 25

5148 3l. Dobrogea (male) 50 25

5149 4l. Ilfov (female) 65 25

5150 4l. Ilfov (male) 65 25

1040 Postal Services (½-size illustration)

1987. Stamp Day.

5151 **1040** 2l.(+1l.) multicoloured 50 30

No. 5151 includes the se-tenant premium-carrying tab shown in Type **1040**, the stamp and tab forming a composite design.

1041 Honey Bee on Flower

1987. Bee-keeping. Multicoloured.

5152 1l. Type **1041** 15 15

5153 2l. Honey bee, sunflowers and hives 45 15

5154 3l. Hives in Danube delta 50 25

5155 4l. Apiculture Complex, Bucharest 65 30

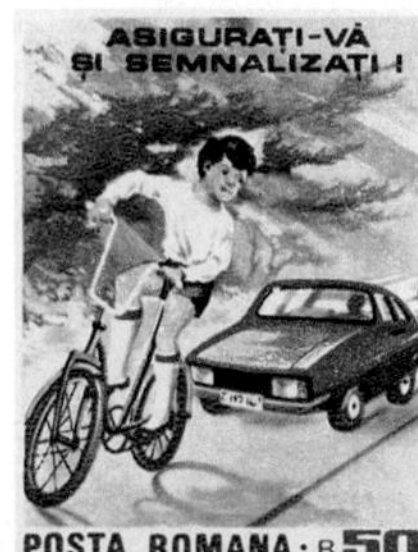

1042 Car behind Boy on Bicycle

1987. Road Safety. Multicoloured.

5156 50b. Type **1042** 10 15

5157 1l. Children using school crossing 10 15

5158 2l. Driver carelessly opening car door 15 15

5159 3l. Hand holding crossing sign and children using zebra crossing 55 25

5160 4l. Speedometer and crashed car 80 30

5161 5l. Child's face and speeding car . . . . 1·10 50

1043 Red Flag and Lenin

1987. 70th Anniv of Russian Revolution.
5162 **1043** 2l. multicoloured . . . 50 25

1044 Biathlon
1045 Crest and National Colours

1987. Winter Olympic Games, Calgary (1988). Multicoloured.
5163 50b. Type **1044** 10 15
5164 1l. Slalom 70 15
5165 1l.50 Ice hockey 15 15
5166 2l. Luge 15 15
5167 3l. Speed skating 30 15
5168 3l.50 Figure skating 55 25
5169 4l. Downhill skiing 60 30
5170 5l. Two-man bobsleigh . . . 75 40

1987. 40th Anniv of People's Republic.
5171 **1045** 2l. multicoloured . . . 40 35

1046 Pres. Ceausescu and Flags

1988. 70th Birthday and 55 Years of Revolutionary Activity of Pres. Ceausescu.
5172 **1046** 2l. multicoloured . . . 75 60

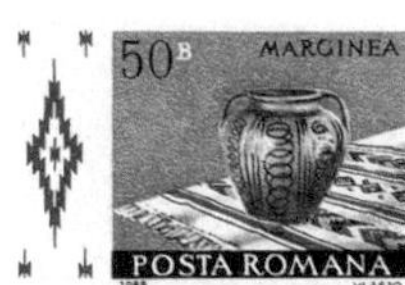

1047 Wide-necked Pot, Marginea

1988. Pottery. Multicoloured.
5173 50b. Type **1047** 10 10
5174 1l. Flask, Oboga 10 10
5175 2l. Jug and saucer, Horezu 20 10
5176 3l. Narrow-necked pot, Curtea de Arges 50 25
5177 4l. Jug, Birsa 70 25
5178 5l. Jug and plate, Vama . . 80 35

1049 Ceramic Clock
1051 Constantin Brincoveanu

1988. Clocks in Ploiesti Museum. Multicoloured.
5180 50b. Type **1049** 10 15
5181 1l.50 Gilt clock with sun at base 10 15
5182 2l. Clock with pastoral figure 20 15
5183 3l. Gilt clock surmounted by figure 50 15
5184 4l. Vase-shaped clock . . . 70 25
5185 5l. Clock surmounted by porcelain figures 80 40

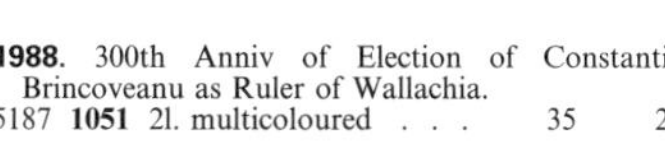

1988. 300th Anniv of Election of Constantin Brincoveanu as Ruler of Wallachia.
5187 **1051** 2l. multicoloured . . . 35 25

1052 Gymnastics

1988. Olympic Games, Seoul (1st issue). Mult.
5188 50b. Type **1052** 10 15
5189 1l.50 Boxing 15 15
5190 2l. Lawn tennis 20 20
5191 3l. Judo 50 25
5192 4l. Running 70 35
5193 5l. Rowing 80 45
See also Nos. 5197/5204.

1053 Postal Emblems and Roses

1988. Romanian–Chinese Stamp Exhibition, Bucharest.
5194 **1053** 2l. multicoloured . . . 30 25

1056 Running

1988. Olympic Games, Seoul (2nd issue). Mult.
5197 50b. Type **1056** 10 15
5198 1l. Canoeing 10 15
5199 1l.50 Gymnastics 10 15
5200 2l. Double kayak 15 15
5201 3l. Weightlifting 40 25
5202 3l.50 Swimming 45 25
5203 4l. Fencing 55 35
5204 5l. Double sculls 65 40

1058 Past and Present Postal Services (½-size illustration)

1988. Stamp Day.
5206 **1058** 2l.(+1l.) multicoloured 50 40
No. 5206 includes the se-tenant premium-carrying tab shown in T **1058**.

1060 State Arms

1988. 70th Anniv of Union of Transylvania and Romania.
5208 **1060** 2l. multicoloured . . . 50 45

1061 Athenaeum Concert Hall, Bucharest (centenary)

1988. Romanian History. Multicoloured.
5209 50b. Type **1061** 10 15
5210 1l.50 Roman coin showing Drobeta Bridge 15 15
5211 2l. Ruins (600th anniv of Suceava as capital of Moldavian feudal state) 20 15
5212 3l. Scroll, arms and town (600th anniv of first documentary reference to Pitesti) 50 25
5213 4l. Dacian warriors from Trajan's Column 70 25
5214 5l. Thracian gold helmet from Cotofenesti-Prahova 80 35

1062 Zapodeni, 17th century

1989. Traditional House Architecture. Mult.
5215 50b. Type **1062** 10 15
5216 1l.50 Berbesti, 18th century 15 15
5217 2l. Voitinel, 18th century . . 20 15
5218 3l. Chiojdu Mic, 18th century 50 25
5219 4l. Cimpanii de Sus, 19th century 70 25
5220 5l. Naruja, 19th century . . 80 35

1063 Red Cross Worker

1989. Life-saving Services. Multicoloured.
5221 50b. Type **1063** 10 15
5222 1l. Red Cross orderlies giving first aid to girl (horiz) 10 15
5223 1l.50 Fireman carrying child 15 15
5224 2l. Rescuing child from earthquake damaged building 20 15
5225 3l. Mountain rescue team transporting casualty on sledge (horiz) 45 25
5226 3l.50 Rescuing climber from cliff face 55 25
5227 4l. Rescuing child from river 65 25
5228 5l. Lifeguard in rowing boat and children playing in sea (horiz) 75 35

1064 Tasca Bicaz Cement Factory

1989. Industrial Achievements. Multicoloured.
5229 50b. Type **1064** 15 10
5230 1l.50 New railway bridge, Cernavoda 35 10
5231 2l. Synchronous motor, Resita 35 15
5232 3l. Bucharest underground 40 20
5233 4l. Mangalia–Constanta train ferry . . . . 1·10 25
5234 5l. "Gloria" (oil drilling platform) . . . . 1·10 30

1065 Flags and Symbols of Industry and Agriculture

1989. 50th Anniv of Anti-Fascist Demonstration.
5235 **1065** 2l. multicoloured . . . 60 40

1068 Ion Creanga (writer, death centenary)

1989. Anniversaries. Multicoloured.
5239 1l. Type **1068** 15 10
5240 2l. Mihai Eminescu (poet, death centenary) 25 10
5241 3l. Nicolae Teclu (scientist, 150th birth anniv) 60 10

1069 State and Communist Party Flags and Symbols of Industry and Agriculture

1989. 45th Anniv of Liberation.
5242 **1069** 2l. multicoloured . . . 50 30

1070 "Pin-Pin"

1989. Romanian Cartoon Films. Multicoloured.
5243 50b. Type **1070** 10 15
5244 1l. "Maria" 10 15
5245 1l.50 "Gore and Grigore" 15 15
5246 2l. "Pisoiul, Balanel, Manole, Monk" 20 10
5247 3l. "Gruia lui Novac" . . . 50 15
5248 3l.50 "Mihaela" 60 20
5249 4l. "Harap Alb" 65 25
5250 5l. "Homo Sapiens" 85 25

1071 Globe, Letter and Houses (½-size illustration)

1989. Stamp Day.
5251 **1071** 2l.(+1l.) multicoloured 45 20
No. 5251 includes the se-tenant premium-carrying tab as illustrated in T **1071**.

1072 Storming of the Bastille

1989. Bicentenary of French Revolution. Mult.

5252	50b. Type **1072**	10	10
5253	1l.50 Street boy and Marianne	15	10
5254	2l. Maximilien de Robespierre	20	10
5255	3l. Rouget de Lisle singing the "Marseillaise"	50	15
5256	4l. Denis Diderot (encyclopaedist)	70	20
5257	5l. Crowd with banner	85	25

1073 Conrad Haas and Diagram

1989. Air. Space Pioneers. Multicoloured.

5259	50b. Type **1073**	10	10
5260	1l.50 Konstantin Tsiolkovski and diagram	20	10
5261	2l. Hermann Oberth and equation	30	10
5262	3l. Robert Goddard and diagram	45	10
5263	4l. Sergei Pavlovich Korolev, Earth and satellite	70	20
5264	5l. Wernher von Braun and landing module	85	25

1075 State and Party Flags and Emblem

1989. 14th Communist Party Congress, Bucharest.

5266	**1075** 2l. multicoloured	60	40

1076 Date, Flag, Victory Sign and Candles

1990. Popular Uprising (1st issue).

5268	**1076** 2l. multicoloured	35	10

See also Nos. 5294/5301.

1077 Flags and Footballers

1990. World Cup Football Championship, Italy (1st issue).

5269	**1077** 50b. multicoloured	10	15
5270	– 1l.50 multicoloured	20	15
5271	– 2l. multicoloured	35	15
5272	– 3l. multicoloured	50	25
5273	– 4l. multicoloured	80	30
5274	– 5l. multicoloured	1·00	40

DESIGNS: 1l.50 to 5l. Showing flags and footballers.
See also Nos. 5276/83.

1079 Footballers

1990. World Cup Football Championship, Italy (2nd issue).

5276	**1079** 50b. multicoloured	10	15
5277	– 1l. multicoloured	15	15
5278	– 1l.50 multicoloured	20	15
5279	– 2l. multicoloured	30	15
5280	– 3l. multicoloured	45	25
5281	– 3l.50 multicoloured	20	10
5282	– 4l. multicoloured	30	10
5283	– 5l. multicoloured	20	10

DESIGNS: 1l. to 5l. Different football scenes.

1080 German Shepherds

1990. International Dog Show, Brno. Mult.

5284	50b. Type **1080**	10	15
5285	1l. English setter	20	15
5286	1l.50 Boxers	25	15
5287	2l. Beagles	30	15
5288	3l. Dobermann pinschers	50	20
5289	3l.50 Great Danes	55	30
5290	4l. Afghan hounds	60	30
5291	5l. Yorkshire terriers	75	30

1081 Fountain, Brunnen

1990. "Riccione 90" International Stamp Fair.

5292	**1081** 2l. multicoloured	30	15

1082 Athenaeum Concert Hall, Bucharest, and Chinese Temple

1990. Romanian–Chinese Stamp Exhibition, Bucharest.

5293	**1082** 2l. multicoloured	30	15

1083 Soldiers and Crowd at Television Headquarters, Bucharest

1990. Popular Uprising (2nd issue). Multicoloured.

5294	50b.+50b. Republic Palace ablaze, Bucharest (horiz)	10	15
5295	1l.+1l. Crowd in Opera Square, Timisoara	15	15
5296	1l.50+1l. Soldiers joining crowd in Town Hall Square, Tirgu Mures (horiz)	20	15
5297	2l.+1l. Type **1083**	25	15
5298	3l.+1l. Mourners at funeral, Timisoara (horiz)	30	20
5299	3l.50+1l. Crowd celebrating, Brasov	40	20
5300	4l.+1l. Crowd with banners, Sibiu (horiz)	40	30
5301	5l.+2l. Cemetery, Bucharest (horiz)	60	35

1084 "Nicolae Cobzarul" (Stefan Luchian)

1990. Paintings damaged during the Uprising. Mult.

5303	50b. Type **1084**	25	10
5304	1l.50 "Woman in White" (Ion Andreescu)	20	10
5305	2l. "Florist" (Luchian)	25	10
5306	3l. "Vase of Flowers" (Jan Brueghel, the elder)	40	20
5307	4l. "Spring" (Pieter Brueghel, the elder) (horiz)	55	25
5308	5l. "Madonna and Child" (G. B. Paggi)	65	30

1085 Flag Stamps encircling Globe (⅔-size illustration)

1990. Stamp Day.

5309	**1085** 2l.(+1l.) multicoloured	40	20

No. 5309 includes the se-tenant premium-carrying tab as shown in Type **1085**.

1086 Constantin Cantacuzino (historian, 350th birth anniv)

1087 Column of Infinity

1990. Anniversaries.

5310	**1086** 50b. brown and blue	10	10
5311	– 1l.50 green and mauve	20	10
5312	– 2l. red and blue	25	10
5313	– 3l. blue and brown	40	15
5314	– 4l. brown and blue	55	20
5315	– 5l. violet and green	70	25

DESIGNS: 1l.50, Ienachita Vacarescu (writer, 250th birth anniv); 2l. Titu Maiorescu (politician, 150th birth anniv); 3l. Nicolae Iorga (historian, 50th death anniv); 4l. Martha Bibescu (writer, birth centenary); 5l. Stefan Procupiu (scientist, birth centenary).

1990. National Day.

5316	**1087** 2l. multicoloured	30	10

1990. 1st Anniv of Popular Uprising. No. 5268 surch **L4 UN AN DE LA VICTORIA REVOLUTIEI**.

5317	**1076** 4l. on 2l. multicoloured	60	20

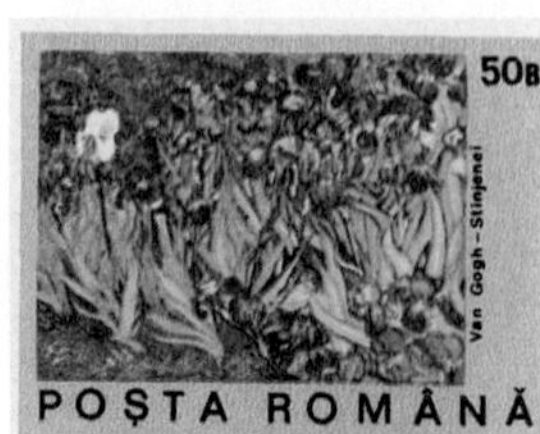

1089 "Irises"

1991. Death Centenary of Vincent van Gogh (painter). Multicoloured.

5318	50b. Type **1089**	10	10
5319	2l. "The Artist's Room"	10	10
5320	3l. "Illuminated Coffee Terrace" (vert)	20	10
5321	3l.50 "Orchard in Blossom"	30	10
5322	5l. "Sunflowers" (vert)	40	10

1090 Greater Black-backed Gull

1091 Crucifixion

1991. Water Birds.

5323	**1090** 50b. blue	10	10
5324	– 1l. green	10	10
5325	– 1l.50 bistre	10	10
5326	– 2l. blue	15	10
5327	– 3l. green	25	10
5328	– 3l.50 green	30	10
5329	– 4l. violet	35	10
5330	– 5l. brown	35	10
5331	– 6l. brown	50	10
5332	– 7l. blue	60	15

DESIGNS: 1l. Common tern; 1l.50, Pied avocet; 2l. Pomarine skua; 3l. Northern lapwings; 3l.50, Red-breasted merganser; 4l. Little egret; 5l. Dunlin; 6l. Black- tailed godwit; 7l. Whiskered tern.

1991. Easter.

5333	**1091** 4l. multicoloured	20	10

1092 "Eutelsat 1" Communications Satellite

1991. Europa. Europe in Space.

5334	**1092** 4l.50 multicoloured	35	20

1093 Posthorn

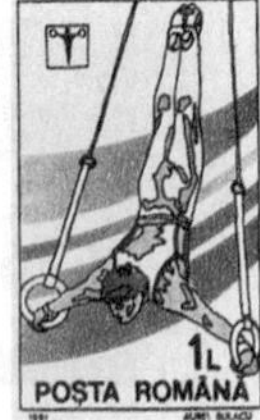

1094 Rings Exercise

1991.

5335	**1093** 4l.50 blue	25	10

1991. Gymnastics. Multicoloured.

5336	1l. Type **1094**	10	15
5337	1l. Parallel bars	10	15
5338	4l.50 Vaulting	30	15
5339	4l.50 Asymmetric bars	30	15
5340	8l. Floor exercises	45	25
5341	9l. Beam	55	30

For similar design to No. 5341, surcharged 90l. on 5l., see No. 5431.

1095 Curtea de Arges Monastery

1096 Hotel Continental, Timisoara

1991. Monasteries. Multicoloured.

5342	1l. Type **1095**	10	10
5343	1l. Putna	10	10
5344	4l.50 Varatec	30	10
5345	4l.50 Agapia (horiz)	30	10
5346	8l. Golia (horiz)	45	10
5347	9l. Sucevita (horiz)	55	10

1991. Hotels.

5349	**1096** 1l. blue	05	10
5350	– 2l. green	10	10
5351	– 4l. red	15	10
5352	– 5l. violet	30	10
5353	– 6l. brown	20	10
5354	– 8l. brown	15	10
5355	– 9l. red	50	10
5356	– 10l. green	55	10
5357	– 18l. red	65	10
5358	– 20l. orange	65	10
5359	– 25l. blue	90	10
5360	– 30l. purple	1·50	10

5361 – 45l. blue . . . . . . 1·00 10
5362 – 60l. brown . . . . . 1·20 10
5363 – 80l. violet . . . . . . 1·50 10
5364b – 120l. blue and grey . . 1·80 50
5365 – 160l. red and pink . . 2·30 40
5366 – 250l. blue and grey . . 2·75 50
5367 – 400l. brown and ochre 5·00 95
5368 – 500l. deep green & green . . . . 6·50 1·10
5369 – 800l. mauve and pink 9·00 1·80

DESIGNS—As T **1096**: HORIZ: 2l. Valea Caprei Chalet, Mt. Fagaras; 5l. Hotel Lebada, Crisan; 6l. Muntele Rosu Chalet, Mt. Ciucas; 8l. Trans-silvania Hotel, Cluj-Napoca; 9l. Hotel Orizont, Predeal; 20l. Alpin Hotel, Poiana Brasov; 25l. Constanta Casino; 30l. Miorita Chalet, Mt. Bucegi; 45l. Sura Dacilor Chalet, Poiana Brasov; 60l. Valea Draganului Tourist Complex; 80l. Hotel Florica, Venus. VERT: 4l. Intercontinental Hotel, Bucharest; 10l. Hotel Roman, Baile Herculcane; 18l. Rarau Chalet, Mt. Rarau. 26 × 40 mm: 120l. International Complex, Baile Felix; 160l. Hotel Egreta, Tulcea. 40 × 26 mm: 250l. Valea de Pesti Motel, Jiului Valley; 400l. Baisoara Tourist Complex; 500l. Bradul Hotel, Covasna; 800l. Gorj Hotel, Jiu.

Nos. 5362/9 have no frame.

1097 Gull and Sea Shore

1991. "Riccione 91" Stamp Exhibition, Riccione, Italy.
5381 **1097** 4l. multicoloured . . . 20 10

1098 Vase decorated with Scarlet and Military Macaws

1099 Academy Emblem

1991. Romanian–Chinese Stamp Exhibition. Mult.
5382 5l. Type **1098** 40 10
5383 5l. Vase with peony decoration 40 10

1991. 125th Anniv of Romanian Academy.
5384 **1099** 1l. blue 15 10

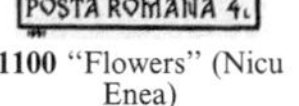

1100 "Flowers" (Nicu Enea)

1102 Map with House and People

1991. "Balcanfila '91" Stamp Exhibition, Bacau. Multicoloured.
5385 4l. Type **1100** 20 10
5386 5l.(+2l.) "Peasant Girl of Vlasca" (Georghe Tattarescu) 35 10

1991. Population and Housing Census.
5389 **1102** 5l. multicoloured . . . 25 10

1103 Bridge

1991. "Phila Nippon '91" International Stamp Exhibition, Tokyo.
5390 **1103** 10l. ochre, brown & red 45 15
5391 – 10l. multicoloured . . . 45 15
DESIGN: No. 5391, Junk.

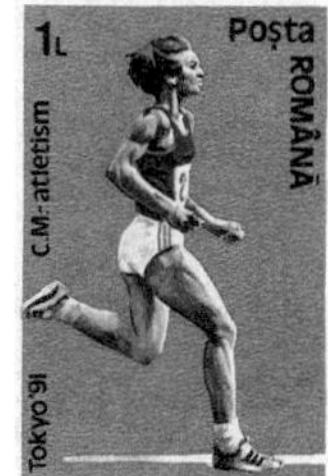

1105 Running

1991. World Athletics Championships, Tokyo. Multicoloured.
5393 1l. Type **1105** 10 10
5394 4l. Long jumping 20 10
5395 5l. High jumping 25 10
5396 5l. Athlete in starting blocks 25 10
5397 9l. Hurdling 45 20
5398 10l. Throwing the javelin . . 55 20

1106 Mihail Kogalniceanu (policitian and historian, death cent)

1991. Anniversaries.
5399 **1106** 1l. brown, blue & dp blue 10 10
5400 – 4l. green, lilac and violet 20 10
5401 – 5l. brown, blue & ultramarine 25 10
5402 – 5l. blue, brown and red 35 10
5403 – 9l. red, blue & deep blue 60 20
5404 – 10l. black, lt brn & brn 70 20

DESIGNS: No. 5400, Nicolae Titulescu (politician and diplomat, 50th death anniv); 5401, Andrei Mureseanu (poet, 175th birth anniv); 5402, Aron Pumnul (writer, 125th death anniv); 5403, George Bacovia (writer, 110th birth anniv); 5404, Perpessicius (literature critic, birth centenary).

1107 Library Building

1991. Centenary of Central University Library.
5405 **1107** 8l. brown 50 20

1108 Coach and Horses (⅔-size illustration)

1991. Stamp Day.
5406 **1108** 8l.(+2l.) multicoloured 45 30

No. 5406 includes the se-tenant premium-carrying label shown in Type **1108**.

1109 "Nativity" (17th-century icon)

1110 Biathlon

1991. Christmas.
5407 **1109** 8l. multicoloured . . . 45 20

1992. Winter Olympic Games, Albertville. Mult.
5408 4l. Type **1110** 10 10
5409 5l. Downhill skiing 10 10
5410 8l. Cross-country skiing . . 15 10
5411 10l. Two-man luge 20 10
5412 20l. Speed skating 45 10
5413 25l. Ski-jumping 60 20
5414 30l. Ice hockey 75 20
5415 45l. Men's figure skating . . 1·10 30

1112 Jug, Plate, Tray and Bowl

1992. Romanian Porcelain from Cluj Napoca. Multicoloured.
5419 4l. Type **1112** 10 15
5420 5l. Tea set 10 15
5421 8l. Jug and goblet (vert) . . 10 15
5422 30l. Tea set (different) . . . 50 20
5423 45l. Vase (vert) 70 35

1113 Atlantic Mackerels

1992. Fishes. Multicoloured.
5424 4l. Type **1113** 10 15
5425 5l. Tench 10 15
5426 8l. Brook charr 10 15
5427 10l. Romanian bullhead perch 10 15
5428 30l. Nase 45 25
5429 45l. Black Sea red mullet . . 90 40

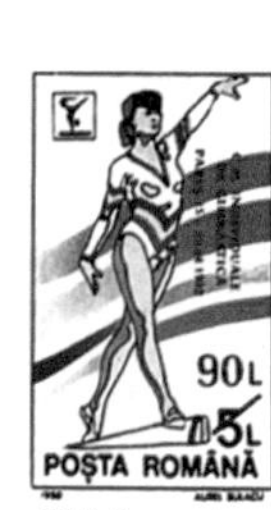

1114 Vase decorated with Scarlet and Military Macaws

1115 Gymnast on Beam

1992. Apollo Art Gallery. Unissued stamp surch.
5430 **1114** 90l. on 5l. multicoloured . . . . 1·60 40

1992. Individual Gymnastic Championships, Paris. Unissued stamp surch.
5431 **1115** 90l. on 5l. multicoloured . . . . 1·20 40

For similar 9l. value, see No. 5341.

1116 Dressage

1118 "Descent into Hell" (icon)

1992. Horses. Multicoloured.
5432 6l. Type **1116** 10 10
5433 7l. Racing (horiz) 10 10
5434 10l. Rearing 15 10
5435 25l. Jumping gate 35 10
5436 30l. Stamping foot (horiz) . . 40 20
5437 50l. Winged horse 75 25

1992. Easter.
5439 **1118** 10l. multicoloured . . . 15 10

1120 Tower and Hand Pump

1992. Centenary of Bucharest Fire Tower.
5441 **1120** 10l. multicoloured . . . 20 10

1121 Filipino Vinta and Rook

1992. 30th Chess Olympiad, Manila, Philippines. Multicoloured.
5442 10l. Type **1121** 15 10
5443 10l. Exterior of venue and chessmen 15 10

1122 Post Rider approaching Town

1992. Stamp Day.
5445 **1122** 10l.+4l. pink, violet and blue 15 10

1123 Pistol shooting

1124 Ion Bratianu

1992. Olympic Games, Barcelona. Multicoloured.
5446 6l. Type **1123** 10 10
5447 7l. Weightlifting 10 10
5448 9l. Two-man kayak (horiz) . 10 10
5449 10l. Handball 10 10
5450 25l. Wrestling (horiz) . . . 20 15
5451 30l. Fencing (horiz) 25 20
5452 50l. Running 45 30
5453 55l. Boxing (horiz) 50 30

1992. 130th Anniv of Foreign Ministry. Designs showing former Ministers.
5455 **1124** 10l. violet, green and deep green 10 05
5456 – 25l. purple, blue & dp blue 20 10
5457 – 30l. blue, purple & brn 25 10
DESIGNS: 25l. Ion Duca; 30l. Grigore Gafencu.

1125 "The Thinker of Cernavoda" (sculpture)

1992. "Expo 92" World's Fair, Seville. "Era of Discovery". Multicoloured.
5458 6l. Type **1125** 10 10
5459 7l. Trajan's bridge, Turnu-Severin 10 10
5460 10l. House on stilts 10 10
5461 25l. Saligny Bridge, Cernavoda 35 10
5462 30l. Traian Vuia's No. 1 airplane 35 10
5463 55l. Hermann Oberth's rocket 25 15

1126 Doves posting Letters in Globe

1992. World Post Day.
5465 **1126** 10l. multicoloured . . . 15 10

1127 "Santa Maria" and Bust of Columbus

1992. 500th Anniv of Discovery of America by Columbus. Multicoloured.
5466 6l. Type **1127** 15 10
5467 10l. "Nina" 15 10
5468 25l. "Pinta" 25 10
5469 55l. Columbus claiming New World 35 20

1128 Post Office Emblem

1992. 1st Anniv of Establishment of R.A. Posta Romana (postal organization).
5471 **1128** 10l. multicoloured . . . 15 10

1129 Jacob Negruzzi (writer, 150th birth anniv)
1130 American Bald Eagle

1992. Anniversaries.
5472 **1129** 6l. green and violet . . 10 10
5473 – 7l. mauve, purple and green 10 10
5474 – 9l. blue and mauve . . 10 10
5475 – 10l. light brown, brown and blue 10 10
5476 – 25l. blue and brown . . 20 15
5477 – 30l. green and blue . . 20 15
DESIGNS: 7l. Grigore Antipa (biologist, 125th birth anniv); 9l. Alexe Mateevici (poet, 75th death anniv); 10l. Cezar Petrescu (writer, birth centenary); 25l. Octav Onicescu (mathematician, birth centenary); 30l. Ecaterina Teodoroiu (First World War fighter, 75th death anniv).

1992. Animals. Multicoloured.
5478 6l. Type **1130** 10 15
5479 7l. Spotted owl 10 15
5480 9l. Brown bear 15 15
5481 10l. American black oystercatcher (horiz) . . . 15 15
5482 25l. Wolf (horiz) 25 15
5483 30l. White-tailed deer (horiz) 25 15
5484 55l. Elk (horiz) 50 30

1131 Arms

1133 Nativity

1132 Buildings and Street, Mogosoaiei

1992. New State Arms.
5486 **1131** 15l. multicoloured . . . 15 10

1992. Anniversaries. Multicoloured.
5487 7l. Type **1132** (300th anniv) 10 10
5488 9l. College building and statue, Roman (600th anniv) 10 10
5489 10l. Prince Basaral, monastery and Princess Despina (475th anniv of Curtea de Arges Monastery) 10 10
5490 25l. Bucharest School of Architecture (80th anniv) 20 10

1992. Christmas.
5491 **1133** 15l. multicoloured . . . 15 10

1134 Globe and Key-pad on Telephone

1992. New Telephone Number System.
5492 **1134** 15l. black, red and blue 15 10

1136 Mihai Voda Monastery

1993. Destroyed Bucharest Buildings. Mult.
5494 10l. Type **1136** 10 10
5495 15l. Vacaresti Monastery . . 10 10
5496 25l. Unirii Hall 20 10
5497 30l. Mina Minovici Medico-legal Institute 30 10

1137 Parseval Sigsfeld Kite-type Observation Balloon "Draken"

1993. Air. Balloons. Multicoloured.
5498 30l. Type **1137** 15 15
5499 90l. Caquot observation balloon, 1917 . . . . . . 50 15

1138 Crucifixion

1139 Hawthorn

1993. Easter.
5500 **1138** 15l. multicoloured . . . 15 10

1993. Medicinal Plants. Multicoloured.
5501 10l. Type **1139** 10 10
5502 15l. Gentian 10 10
5503 25l. Sea buckthorn 10 10
5504 30l. Billberry 15 10
5505 50l. Arnica 25 20
5506 90l. Dog rose 45 30

1140 Stanescu

1141 Mounted Courier

1993. 60th Birth Anniv of Nichita Stanescu (poet).
5507 **1140** 15l. multicoloured . . . 15 10

1993. Stamp Day.
5508 **1141** 15l.+10l. multicoloured 15 10

1143 Black-billed Magpie

1993. Birds.
5510 **1143** 5l. black and green . . 15 10
5511 – 10l. black and red . . . 15 10
5512 – 15l. black and red . . . 15 10
5513 – 20l. black and brown 20 10
5514 – 25l. black and red . . . 20 10
5515 – 50l. black and yellow 40 10
5516 – 65l. black and red . . . 55 10
5517 – 90l. black and red . . . 75 10
5518 – 160l. black and blue . . 1·30 15
5519 – 250l. black and mauve 2·10 25
DESIGNS—HORIZ: 10l. Golden eagle. VERT: 15l. Northern bullfinch; 20l. Hoopoe; 25l. Great spotted woodpecker; 50l. Golden oriole; 65l. White winged crossbill; 90l. Barn swallows; 160l. Azure tit; 250l. Rose-coloured starling.

1144 Long-hair
1147 Pine Marten

1146 Adder

1993. Cats. Multicoloured.
5520 10l. Type **1144** 10 20
5521 15l. Tabby-point long-hair 10 20
5522 30l. Red long-hair 15 20
5523 90l. Blue Persian 35 30
5524 135l. Tabby 55 25
5525 160l. Long-haired white Persian 65 30

1993. Protected Animals. Multicoloured.
5527 10l. Type **1146** 10 15
5528 15l. Lynx (vert) 10 15
5529 25l. Common shelduck . . . 15 15
5530 75l. Huchen 25 15
5531 105l. Poplar admiral 35 20
5532 280l. Alpine longhorn beetle 95 70

1993. Mammals.
5533 **1147** 10l. black and yellow 20 10
5534 – 15l. black and brown 20 10
5535 – 20l. red and black . . 20 10
5536 – 25l. black and brown 25 10
5537 – 30l. black and red . . . 25 10
5538 – 40l. black and red . . . 25 10
5539 – 75l. black and yellow 55 10
5540 – 105l. black and brown 75 10
5541 – 150l. black and orange 1·10 10
5542 – 280l. black and yellow 1·80 25
DESIGNS—HORIZ: 15l. Common rabbit; 30l. Red fox; 150l. Stoat; 280l. Egyptian mongoose. VERT: 20l. Eurasian red squirrel; 25l. Chamois; 40l. Argali; 75l. Small spotted genet; 105l. Garden dormouse.

1148 Brontosaurus

1993. Prehistoric Animals. Multicoloured.
5543 29l. Type **1148** 10 15
5544 46l. Plesiosaurus 15 15
5545 85l. Triceratops 30 15
5546 171l. Stegosaurus 60 25
5547 216l. Tyannosaurus 80 30
5548 319l. Archaeopteryx . . . . 1·10 55

1150 St. Stefan the Great, Prince of Moldavia

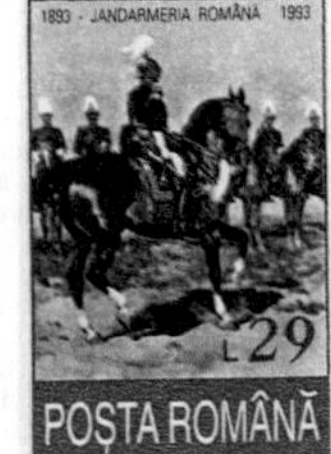
1151 Mounted Officers

1993. Icons. Multicoloured.
5550 75l. Type **1150** 15 20
5551 171l. Prince Costantin Brancoveanu of Wallachia with his sons Constantin, Stefan, Radu and Matei and Adviser Ianache Vacarescu 15 20
5552 216l. St. Antim Ivireanul, Metropolitan of Wallachia 80 20

1993. Centenary of Rural Gendarmeric Law.
5553 **1151** 29l. multicoloured . . . 15 10

1993. "Riccione 93" International Stamp Fair. No. 5292 surch **Riccione '93 3-5 septembrie 171L.**
5554 **1081** 171l. on 2l. multicoloured 60 40

1154 George Baritiu

1993. Anniversaries.
5556 **1154** 29l. flesh, black and lilac 10 15
5557 – 46l. flesh, black and blue 10 15
5558 – 85l. flesh, black & green 15 15
5559 – 171l. flesh, black & purple 25 25
5560 – 216l. flesh, black & blue 40 30
5561 – 319l. flesh, black and grey 75 40
DESIGNS: 29l. Type **1154** (politician and journalist, death centenary); 46l. Horia Creanga (architect, 50th death anniv); 85l. Armand Calinescu (leader of Peasant National Party, birth centenary); 171l. Dr. Dumitru Bagdasar (neuro-surgeon, birth centenary); 216l. Constantin Brailoiu (musician, birth centenary); 319l. Iuliu Maniu (Prime Minister, 1927–30 and 1932–33, 40th death anniv).

1993. 35th Annivs of Romanian Philatelic Association and Romanian Philatelic Federation. No. 5445 surch **35 ANI DE ACTIVITATE AFR-FFR 1958–1993 70L+45L.**
5562 **1122** 70l.+45l. on 10l.+4l. pink, violet and blue 50 40

1157 Iancu Flondor (Bukovinan politician)

1993. 75th Anniv of Union of Bessarabia, Bukovina and Transylvania with Romania.
5564 **1157** 115l. brown, blue and black 15 10
5565 – 245l. violet, yellow and green 25 20
5566 – 255l. multicoloured . . 45 20
5567 – 325l. brown, pink and deep brown 80 25
DESIGNS: 245l. Ionel Bratianu (Prime Minister, 1918–19, 1922–26 and 1927); 255l. Iuliu Maniu (Prime Minister, 1927–30 and 1932–33); 325l. Panteleimon Halippa (Bessarabian politician).

1158 Emblem

1159 "Nativity" (17th-century icon)

1993. Anniversaries. Multicoloured.
5569 115l. Type **1158** (75th anniv of General Association of Romanian Engineers) 15 20
5570 245l. Statue of Johannes Honterus (450th anniv of Romanian Humanist School) 25 25
5571 255l. Bridge, arms on book spine and seal (625th anniv of first documentary reference to Slatina) 40 25
5572 325l. Map and town arms (625th anniv of first documentary reference to Braila) 75 35

1993. Christmas.
5573 **1159** 45l. multicoloured 15 10

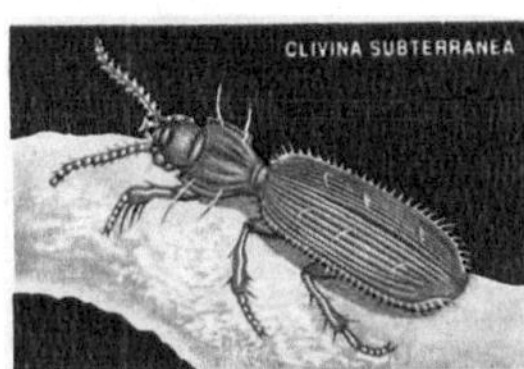

1160 "Clivina subterranea"

1993. Movile Cave Animals. Multicoloured.
5574 29l. Type **1160** 10 10
5575 46l. "Nepa anophthalma" 15 10
5576 85l. "Haemopis caeca" 20 15
5577 171l. "Lascona cristiani" 30 20
5578 216l. "Semisalsa dobrogica" 45 25
5579 319l. "Armadilidium tabacarui" 75 35

1161 Prince Alexandru Ioan Cuza and Seal

1994. 130th Anniv of Court of Accounts.
5581 **1161** 45l. multicoloured 15 10

1162 Opera House

1994. Destroyed Buildings of Bucharest. Mult.
5582 115l. Type **1162** 10 15
5583 245l. Church of Vacaresti Monastery (vert) 30 25
5584 255l. St. Vineri's Church 35 25
5585 325l. Cloisters of Vacaresti Monastery 50 30

1164 Speed Skating **1165** Sarichioi Windmill, Tulcea

1994. Winter Olympic Games, Lillehammer, Norway. Multicoloured.
5588 70l. Type **1164** 10 10
5589 115l. Skiing 15 10
5590 125l. Bobsleighing 15 10
5591 245l. Cross-country skiing 40 15
5592 255l. Ski jumping 45 15
5593 325l. Figure skating 60 20

1994. Mills. Multicoloured.
5595 70l. Type **1165** 10 15
5596 115l. Nucarilor Valley windmill, Tulcea 10 15
5597 125l. Caraorman windmill, Tulcea 20 15
5598 245l. Romanii de Jos watermill, Valcea 40 25
5599 255l. Enisala windmill, Tulcea (horiz) 50 30
5600 325l. Nistoresti watermill, Vrancea 60 40

1166 Calin the Backward **1167** "Resurrection of Christ" (17th-century icon)

1994. Fairy Tales. Multicoloured.
5601 70l. Type **1166** 10 15
5602 115l. Ileana Cosanzeana flying 15 15
5603 125l. Ileana Cosanzeana seated 20 15
5604 245l. Ileana Cosanzeana and castle 40 25
5605 255l. Agheran the Brave 50 30
5606 325l. The Enchanted Wolf carrying Ileana Cosanzeana 60 35

1994. Easter.
5607 **1167** 60l. multicoloured 15 10

1168 "Struthiosaurus transylvanicus"

1994. Prehistoric Animals. Multicoloured.
5608 90l. Type **1168** 10 15
5609 130l. Megalosaurus 15 15
5610 150l. Parasaurolophus 30 15
5611 280l. Stenonychosaurus 30 20
5612 500l. Camarasaurus 55 40
5613 635l. Gallimimus 70 45

1170 Silver Fir **1171** Players and Flags of U.S.A., Switzerland, Colombia and Romania

1994. Trees. Each green and black.
5615 15l. Type **1170** 10 10
5616 35l. Scots pine 10 10
5617 45l. White poplar 10 10
5618 60l. Pedunculate oak 15 10
5619 70l. European larch 15 10
5620 125l. Beech 20 10
5621 350l. Sycamore 35 10
5622 940l. Ash 1·10 45
5623 1440l. Norway spruce 1·50 70
5624 3095l. Large-leaved lime 2·75 1·50

1994. World Cup Football Championship, U.S.A. Designs showing various footballing scenes and flags of participating countries. Multicoloured.
5625 90l. Type **1171** 10 10
5626 130l. Brazil, Russia, Cameroun and Sweden (Group B) 10 10
5627 150l. Germany, Bolivia, Spain and South Korea (Group C) 15 10
5628 280l. Argentina, Greece, Nigeria and Bulgaria (Group D) 25 10

5629 500l. Italy, Ireland, Norway and Mexico (Group E) 55 30
5630 635l. Belgium, Morocco, Netherlands and Saudi Arabia (Group F) 70 35

1172 Torch-bearer and Centenary Emblem

1994. Centenary of International Olympic Committee. Ancient Greek Athletes. Mult.
5632 150l. Type **1172** 15 10
5633 280l. Discus-thrower and International Sports Year emblem 30 10
5634 500l. Wrestlers and Olympic Peace emblem 60 15
5635 635l. Arbitrator and "Paris 1994" centenary congress emblem 75 20

1173 National History Museum (former Postal Headquarters, Bucharest) **1176** Turning Fork

1175 Traian Vuia's Airplane No. 1, 1906

1994. Stamp Day.
5637 **1173** 90l.+60l. multicoloured 25 15

1994. Air. 50th Anniv of I.C.A.O.
5639 **1175** 110l. brown, black & blue 15 30
5640 – 350l. multicoloured 45 30
5641 – 500l. multicoloured 70 30
5642 – 635l. black, ultramarine and blue 85 30
DESIGNS: 350l. Rombac One Eleven; 500l. Boeing 737-300; 635l. Airbus Industrie A310.

1994. "Philakorea 1994" International Stamp Exhibition, Seoul.
5643 **1176** 60l. black, orange and mauve 15 10

1177 Beluga

1994. Environmental Protection of Danube Delta. Multicoloured.
5645 150l. Type **1177** 20 10
5646 280l. Orsini's viper 35 15
5647 500l. White-tailed sea eagle 60 35
5648 635l. European mink 80 45

1994. Victory of Romanian Team in European Gymnastics Championships, Stockholm. Nos. 5338/9 surch **Echipa Romaniei Compioana Europeana Stockholm 1994** and value.
5650 150l. on 4l.50 multicoloured 20 25
5651 525l. on 4l.50 multicoloured 75 40

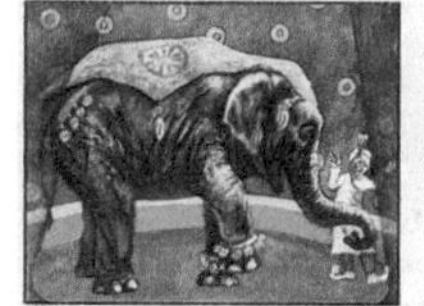

1179 Elephant

1994. The Circus. Multicoloured.
5652 90l. Type **1179** 10 15
5653 130l. Balancing bear (vert) 10 15
5654 150l. Cycling monkeys 15 15
5655 280l. Tiger jumping through hoop 30 25
5656 500l. Clown on tightrope balancing dogs 60 35
5657 635l. Clown on horseback 80 45

1994. World Post Day. No. 5465 surch **150LEI 1994 Posta - cea mai buna alegere**.
5658 **1126** 150l. on 10l. mult 25 20

1181 Emblem **1183** Snake

1182 Sterlet

1994. 20th International Fair, Bucharest.
5659 **1181** 525l. multicoloured 55 20

1994. Sturgeons.
5660 150l. Type **1182** 20 25
5661 280l. Russian sturgeon 40 25
5662 500l. Stellate sturgeon 65 45
5663 635l. Common sturgeon 85 55

1994. Romanian–Chinese Stamp Exhibition, Timisoara and Cluj-Napoca. Multicoloured.
5664 150l. Type **1183** 20 10
5665 1135l. Dragon 1·40 45

1184 Early Steam Train, Bucharest–Giurgii Line

1994. 125th Anniv of Romanian Railway Administration.
5666 **1184** 90l. multicoloured 15 10

1185 Alexandru Orascu (architect and mathematician)

1994. Anniversaries. Multicoloured.
5667 30l. Type **1185** (death centenary) 10 15
5668 60l. Gheorghe Polizu (physician, 175th birth anniv) 10 15
5669 150l. Iulia Hasdeu (writer, 125th birth anniv) 20 15
5670 280l. S. Mehedinti (scientist, 125th birth anniv) 25 15
5671 350l. Camil Petrescu (writer, birth centenary) 35 25
5672 500l. N. Paulescu (physician, 125th birth anniv) 45 35
5673 940l. L. Grigorescu (painter, birth centenary) 95 50
See also No. 5684.

1186 Nativity

1994. Christmas.
5674 **1186** 60l. multicoloured . . . 15 10

1187 St. Mary's Church, Cleveland, U.S.A.

1994.
5675 **1187** 610l. multicoloured . . 65 15

1188 Anniversary Emblem

1994. 20th Anniv of World Tourism Organization.
5676 **1188** 525l. blue, orange & black 55 20

1190 Kittens

1191 Emblem

1994. Young Domestic Animals. Multicoloured.
5678 90l. Type **1190** 10 20
5679 130l. Puppies 15 20
5680 150l. Kid 25 20
5681 280l. Foal 50 20
5682 500l. Rabbit kittens 85 30
5683 635l. Lambs . . . . 1·10 50

1994. Death Centenary of Gheorghe Tattarescu (painter). As T **1185**. Multicoloured.
5684 90l. Tattarescu 15 10

1995. Save the Children Fund.
5685 **1191** 60l. blue 15 10

1192 Tanar

1995. Brasov Youth. Neighbourhood Group Leaders. Multicoloured.
5686 40l. Type **1192** 10 20
5687 60l. Batran 10 20
5688 150l. Curcan 15 20
5689 280l. Dorobant 25 20
5690 350l. Brasovechean 40 20
5691 500l. Rosior 50 30
5692 635l. Albior 75 50

1193 Hand and Barbed Wire

1995. 50th Anniv of Liberation of Concentration Camps.
5693 **1193** 960l. black and red . . 60 30

1194 Emblems of French and Romanian State Airlines

1995. Air. 75th Anniv of Founding of Franco-Romanian Air Company.
5694 **1194** 60l. blue and red . . . 55 10
5695 – 960l. blue and black . . 60 20
DESIGN: 960l. Potez IX biplane and Paris–Bucharest route map.

1195 Ear of Wheat

1995. 50th Anniversaries. Multicoloured.
5696 675l. Type **1195** (F.A.O.) . . 40 30
5697 960l. Anniversary emblem (U.N.O.) 60 35
5698 1615l. Hand holding pen showing members' flags (signing of U.N. Charter) 1·10 55

1196 "Resurrection" (icon)

1995. Easter.
5699 **1196** 60l. multicoloured . . . 15 10

1197 "Youth without Age and Life without Death"

1995. Fairy Tales. Multicoloured.
5700 90l. Type **1197** 10 20
5701 130l. "The Old Man's Servant and the Old Woman's Servant" (vert) 10 20
5702 150l. "The Prince with the Golden Hair" 10 20
5703 280l. "Son of the Red King" 15 20
5704 500l. "Praslea the Brave and the Golden Apples" (vert) 35 20
5705 635l. "King Dafin" (drawn by golden horses) 40 25

1199 Dove with Section of Rainbow

1200 Blaga

1198 Enescu

1995. 40th Death Anniv of George Enescu (composer).
5706 **1198** 960l. orange and black 60 15

1995. Europa. Peace and Freedom. Multicoloured.
5707 150l. Type **1199** 10 15
5708 4370l. Dove wings forming "EUROPA" around rainbow . . . . 3·25 2·30

1995. Birth Centenary of Lucian Blaga (poet).
5709 **1200** 150l. multicoloured . . 15 10
See also Nos. 5745/9.

1201 Bucharest Underground Railway, 1979

1995. Transport.
5712 **1201** 470l. yellow and black (postage) 45 10
5713 – 630l. red and blue . . . 35 10
5714 – 675l. red and black . . 40 10
5715 755l. blue and black . . 50 10
5716 – 1615l. green and black 1·00 15
5717 – 2300l. green and black 1·10 20
5718 – 2550l. black and red . . 1·60 25
5719 – 285l. green and black (air) 15 10
5720 – 715l. red and blue . . . 45 10
5721 – 965l. black and blue . . 55 10
5722 – 1575l. green and black 95 15
5723 – 3410l. blue and black 1·90 1·60
DESIGNS—HORIZ: 285l. I.A.R. 80 aircraft (70th anniv of Romanian aeronautical industry); 630l. "Masagerul" (post boat); 715l. I.A.R. 316 Red Cross helicopter; 755l. "Razboieni" (container ship); 965l. Sud Aviation SA 330 Puma helicopter; 1575l. I.A.R. 818H seaplane; 2300l. Trolleybus, 1904; 2550l. Steam train, 1869; 3410l. Boeing 737-300 (75th anniv of Romanian air transport). VERT: 675l. Cable-car, Brasov; 1615l. Electric tram, 1894.

1202 "Dacia" (liner)

1203 Fallow Deer

1995. Centenary of Romanian Maritime Service. Multicoloured.
5735 90l. Type **1202** 10 20
5736 130l. "Imparatul Traian" (Danube river steamer) (horiz) 10 20
5737 150l. "Romania" (Danube river steamer) (horiz) . . 10 20
5738 280l. "Costinesti" (tanker) (horiz) 20 20
5739 960l. "Caransebes" (container ship) (horiz) . . 60 30
5740 3410l. "Tutova" (car ferry) (horiz) . . . . 2·30 1·20

1995. European Nature Conservation Year. Mult.
5741 150l. Type **1203** 10 15
5742 280l. Great bustard 25 15
5743 960l. Lady's slipper 65 20
5744 1615l. Stalagmites . . . . . 1·00 45

1995. Anniversaries. As T **1200**. Multicoloured.
5745 90l. D. Rosca (birth centenary) 10 25
5746 130l. Vasile Conta (150th birth anniv) 10 25
5747 280l. Ion Barbu (birth centenary) 20 25
5748 960l. Iuliu Hatieganu (110th birth anniv) 60 35
5749 1650l. Dimitrie Brandza (botanist) (death centenary) 95 60

1204 Youths and Torch-bearer

1995. European Youth Olympic Days.
5750 **1204** 1650l. multicoloured . . 15 15

1205 Post Wagon (½-size illustration)

1995. Stamp Day. Centenary of Upper Rhine Local Post.
5751 **1205** 960l.(+715l.) mult . . . 75 60
No. 5751 includes the se-tenant premium-carrying tab shown in Type **1205**.

1206 Saligny Bridge

1995. Centenary of Saligny Bridge, Cernavoda.
5752 **1206** 675l. multicoloured . . 50 20

1207 Mallard

1208 General Dr. Victor Anastasiu

1995. Domestic Birds. Multicoloured.
5753 90l. Type **1207** 10 15
5754 130l. Red junglefowl (hen) 10 15
5755 150l. Helmeted guineafowl 10 15
5756 280l. Common turkey . . . 20 15
5757 960l. Greylag goose 60 25
5758 1650l. Red junglefowl (cock) 1·10 40

1995. 75th Anniv of Institute of Aeronautics Medicine.
5759 **1208** 960l. ultramarine, blue and red 50 10

1209 Battle Scene

1995. 400th Anniv of Battle of Calugareni.
5760 **1209** 100l. multicoloured . . 25 10

1210 Giurgiu Castle

1995. Anniversaries. Multicoloured.
5761 250l. Type **1210** (600th anniv) 15 15
5762 500l. Neamtului Castle (600th anniv) (vert) . . . 30 15
5763 960l. Sebes-Alba Mill (700th anniv) 50 25
5764 1615l. Dorohoi Church (500th anniv) (vert) . . . 85 40
5765 1650l. Military observatory, Bucharest (centenary) (vert) 85 40

1211 Moldovita Monastery
1212 Racket

1995. U.N.E.S.C.O. World Heritage Sites. Mult.
5766 675l. Type **1211** 35 20
5767 960l. Hurez Monastery . . . 50 25
5768 1615l. Biertan Castle (horiz) 80 45

1995. 5th Open Tennis Championships, Bucharest.
5769 **1212** 1020l. multicoloured . . 50 15

1213 Ion Ionescu (editor)

1995. Centenary of Mathematics Gazette.
5770 **1213** 100l. pink and brown 15 10

1214 "Albizzia julibrissin"

1995. Plants from Bucharest Botanical Garden. Multicoloured.
5771 50l. Type **1214** 10 10
5772 100l. Yew 10 10
5773 150l. "Paulownia tomentosa" 10 10
5774 500l. Bird of Paradise flower 30 10
5775 960l. Amazon water-lily . . 55 15
5776 2300l. Azalea . . . . 1·50 45

1215 St. John's Church
1216 George Apostu (sculptor, 10th death (1996))

1995. 600th Anniv of First Documentary Reference to Piatra-Neamt.
5777 **1215** 250l. multicoloured . . 30 15

1995. Anniversaries.
5778 **1216** 150l. green and black 10 20
5779 – 250l. blue and black . . 15 20
5780 – 500l. light brown, brown and black . . 35 20
5781 – 960l. rose, purple and black 65 25
5782 – 1650l. brown and black 1·10 50
DESIGNS: 250l. Emil Cioran (philosopher, death in 1995); 500l. Eugen Ionescu (writer, 1st death anniv); 960l. Elena Vacarescu (poetess, 130th birth (1996)); 1650l. Mircea Eliade (philosopher, 10th death (1996)).

1217 Running

1995. Olympic Games, Atlanta (1996) (1st issue). Multicoloured.
5783 50l. Type **1217** 10 15
5784 100l. Gymnastics 10 15
5785 150l. Canoeing 10 15
5786 500l. Fencing 30 15
5787 960l. Rowing 60 25
5788 2300l. Boxing . . . . 1·40 60
See also Nos. 5829/33.

1218 Nativity

1995. Christmas.
5790 **1218** 100l. multicoloured . . 15 10

1219 Masked Person

1996. Folk Masks of Maramures (250l.) and Moldavia (others).
5791 **1219** 250l. multicoloured . . 10 20
5792 – 500l. multicoloured . . 15 20
5793 – 960l. mult (vert) . . . 25 20
5794 – 1650l. mult (vert) . . . 45 35
DESIGNS: 500l. to 1650l. Different masks.

1220 Tristan Tzara
1221 "Resurrection" (icon)

1996. Writers' Birth Anniversaries. Multicoloured.
5795 150l. Type **1220** (centenary) 10 20
5796 1500l. Anton Pann (bicentenary) 90 30

1996. Easter.
5797 **1221** 150l. multicoloured . . 15 10

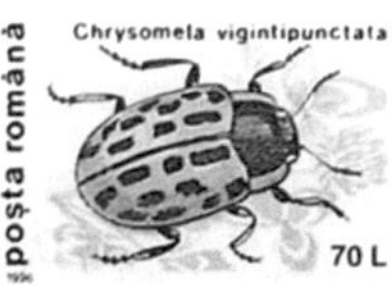

1223 "Chrysomela vigintipunctata" (leaf beetle)

1996. Beetles.
5799 **1223** 70l. yellow and black 10 10
5800 – 220l. red and black . . 10 10
5801 – 370l. brown and black 25 10
5802 – 650l. black, red & grey 35 10
5803 – 700l. red, black and green 40 10
5804 – 740l. black and yellow 30 10
5805 – 960l. black and red . . 40 10
5806 – 1000l. yellow and black 45 10
5807 – 1500l. black and brown 70 20
5808 – 2500l. red, black & green . . . . 1·00 25
DESIGNS: 220l. "Cerambyx cerdo" (longhorn beetle); 370l. "Entomoscelis adonidis"; 650l. Ladybird; 700l. Caterpillar-hunter; 740l. "Hedobia imperialis"; 960l. European rhinoceros beetle; 1000l. Bee chafer; 1500l. "Purpuricenus kaehleri" (longhorn beetle); 2500l. "Anthaxia salicis".

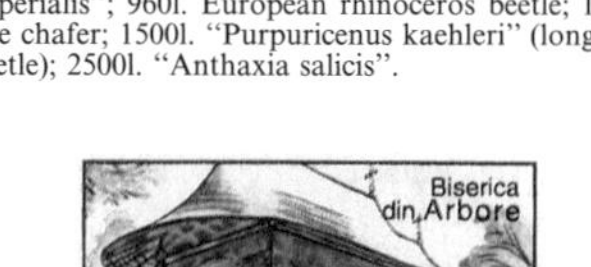

1225 Arbore Church

1996. U.N.E.S.C.O. World Heritage Sites. Mult.
5810 150l. Type **1225** 10 25
5811 1500l. Voronet Monastery 70 35
5812 2550l. Humor Monastery . . 1·00 60

1226 Ana Aslan (doctor)

1996. Europa. Famous Women. Multicoloured.
5813 370l. Type **1226** 25 25
5814 4140l. Lucia Bulandra (actress) . . . . 2·30 1·70

1227 "Mother and Children" (Oana Negoita)

1996. 50th Anniv of U.N.I.C.E.F. Prize-winning Children's Paintings. Multicoloured.
5815 370l. Type **1227** 15 25
5816 740l. "Winter Scene" (Badea Cosmin) 35 25
5817 1500l. "Children and Sun over House" (Nicoleta Georgescu) 75 40
5818 2550l. "House on Stilts" (Biborka Bartha) (vert) 1·20 70

1228 Goalkeeper with Ball

1996. European Football Championship, England. Multicoloured.
5819 220l. Type **1228** 10 10
5820 370l. Player with ball . . . 15 10
5821 740l. Two players with ball 35 10
5822 1500l. Three players with ball 70 15
5823 2550l. Player dribbling ball 1·10 25
Nos. 5819/23 were issued together, se-tenant, forming a composite design of the pitch and stadium.

1229 Metropolitan Toronto Convention Centre (venue)
1232 Boxing

1230 Factory

1996. "Capex'96" International Stamp Exhibition, Toronto, Canada.
5825 **1229** 150l. multicoloured . . 15 10

1996. 225th Anniv of Resita Works.
5827 **1230** 150l. brown 15 10

1996. 5th Anniv of Establishment of R.A. Posta Romana (postal organization). No. 5471 surch **1996 - 5 ANI DE LA INFIINTARE L150**.
5828 **1128** 150l. on 10l. multicoloured 50 60

1996. Centenary of Modern Olympic Games and Olympic Games, Atlanta (2nd issue). Mult.
5829 220l. Type **1232** 10 10
5830 370l. Running 15 10
5831 740l. Rowing 30 10
5832 1500l. Judo 75 15
5833 2550l. Gymnastics (asymmetrical bars) . . . 1·10 25

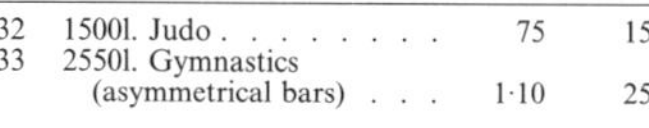

1233 Postman, Keyboard and Stamp under Magnifying Glass (⅔-size illustration)

1996. Stamp Day.
5835 **1233** 1500l.(+650l.) mult . . 95 50
No. 5835 includes the se-tenant premium-carrying tab shown in Type **1233**.

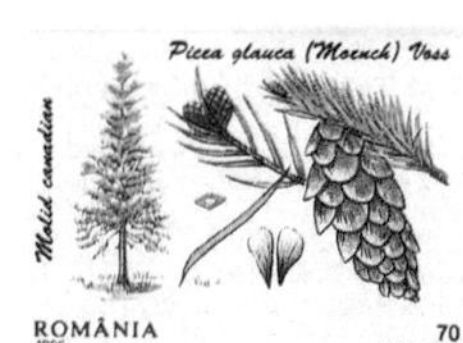

1234 White Spruce

1996. Coniferous Trees. Multicoloured.
5836 70l. Type **1234** 15 10
5837 150l. Serbian spruce 15 10
5838 220l. Blue Colorado spruce 15 10
5839 740l. Sitka spruce 40 10
5840 1500l. Scots pine 95 20
5841 3500l. Maritime pine . . . 2·10 45

1235 Grass Snake
1236 Madonna and Child

1996. Animals. Multicoloured.
5842 70l. Type **1235** 15 10
5843 150l. Hermann's tortoise . . 15 10
5844 220l. Eurasian sky lark (horiz) 15 10
5845 740l. Red fox (horiz) . . . 40 10
5846 1500l. Common porpoise . . 95 20
5847 3500l. Golden eagle (horiz) 2·10 45

1996. Christmas.
5848 **1236** 150l. multicoloured . . 15 10

1237 Stan Golestan (composer, 40th)
1241 Bow

1240 Stoat

1996. Death Anniversaries.
5849 **1237** 100l. pink and black . . 30 30
5850 – 150l. purple and black 30 30
5851 – 370l. orange and black 65 30
5852 – 1500l. red and black . . 2·50 60
DESIGNS: 150l. Corneliu Coposu (politician, 1st); 370l. Horia Vintila (writer, 4th); 1500l. Alexandru Papana (test pilot, 50th).

1997. Fur-bearing Mammals. Multicoloured.
5855 70l. Type **1240** 20 40
5856 150l. Arctic fox 20 40
5857 220l. Racoon-dog 20 40
5858 740l. European otter 30 40

5859 1500l. Muskrat 65 40
5860 3500l. Pine marten 1·50 80

1997. 26th Anniv of Greenpeace (environmental organization). The "Rainbow Warrior" (campaign ship). Multicoloured.
5861 150l. Type **1241** 20 25
5862 370l. Ship and ice 20 25
5863 1940l. Ship cruising past beach 90 25
5864 2500l. Rainbow and ship 1·10 25

1242 Thomas Edison (inventor)

1997. Birth Anniversaries. Multicoloured.
5866 200l. Type **1242** (150th anniv) 15 30
5867 400l. Franz Schubert (composer, bicentenary) 15 30
5868 3600l. Miguel de Cervantes Saavedra (writer, 450th anniv) 1·40 60

1243 Emblem

1244 Surdesti

1997. Inauguration of Mobile Telephone Network in Romania.
5869 **1243** 400l. multicoloured 20 10

1997. Churches. Each brown, agate and green.
5870 200l. Type **1244** 15 15
5871 400l. Plopis 15 15
5872 450l. Bogdan Voda 15 15
5873 850l. Rogoz 30 15
5874 3600l. Calinesti 1·30 30
5875 6000l. Birsana 2·30 50

1245 Al. Demetrescu Dan in "Hamlet", 1916

1246 Vlad Tepes Dracula (Voivode of Wallachia)

1997. 2nd Shakespeare Festival, Craiova. Mult.
5876 200l. Type **1245** 15 45
5877 400l. Constantin Serghie in "Othello", 1855 15 45
5878 2400l. Gheorghe Cozorici in "Hamlet", 1957 90 45
5879 3600l. Ion Manolescu in "Hamlet", 1924 1·30 90

1997. Europa. Tales and Legends. Dracula. Mult.
5880 400l. Type **1246** 25 45
5881 4250l. Dracula the myth 2·75 90

1247 "Dolichothele uberiformis"

1997. Cacti. Multicoloured.
5882 100l. Type **1247** 15 30
5883 250l. "Rebutia" 15 30
5884 450l. "Echinofossulocactus lamellosus" 15 30
5885 500l. "Ferocactus glaucescens" 15 30
5886 650l. "Thelocactus" 25 30
5887 6150l. "Echinofossulocactus albatus" 2·40 90

1248 National Theatre, Cathedral and Statue of Mihai Viteazul

1997. "Balcanmax'97" Maximum Cards Exhibition, Cluj-Napoca.
5888 **1248** 450l. multicoloured 15 10

1249 19th-century Postal Transport (½-size illustration)

1997. Stamp Day.
5889 **1249** 3600l.(+1500l.) multicoloured 1·90 1·20
No. 5889 includes the se-tenant premium-carrying tab shown in Type **1249**.

1997. Nos. 5349/55 and 5357 surch.
5890 250l. on 1l. blue 20 20
5891 250l. on 2l. green 20 20
5892 250l. on 4l. red 20 20
5893 450l. on 5l. violet 20 20
5894 450l. on 6l. brown 20 20
5895 450l. on 18l. red 20 20
5896 950l. on 9l. red 40 20
5897 3600l. on 8l. brown 1·60 40

1251 Archway of Vlad Tepes Dracula's House

1252 Tourism Monument

1997. Sighisoara. Multicoloured.
5898 250l. Type **1251** 20 30
5899 650l. Town Hall clocktower 30 30
5900 3700l. Steps leading to fortress and clocktower 1·60 60

1997. Rusca Montana, Banat.
5901 **1252** 950l. multicoloured 35 20

1253 Printing Works

1254 Emil Racovita (biologist) and "Belgica" (polar barque)

1997. 125th Anniv of Stamp Printing Works.
5902 **1253** 450l. red, brown and blue 20 10

1997. Centenary of Belgian Antarctic Expedition.
5903 **1254** 450l. blue, grey and black 15 30
5904 – 650l. red, yellow and black 25 30
5905 – 1600l. green, pink and black 60 30
5906 – 3700l. brown, yellow and black 1·40 55
DESIGNS: 650l. Frederick Cook (anthropologist and photographer) and "Belgica" at sea; 1600l. Roald Amundsen and "Belgica" in port; 3700l. Adrien de Gerlache (expedition commander) and "Belgica" ice-bound.

1997. "Aeromfila '97" Stamp Exhibition, Brasov. No. 5334 surch **1050 L. AEROMFILA'97 Brasov** and airplane.
5907 **1292** 1050l. on 41.50 mult 45 30

1256 Campsite

1258 Ion Mihalache (politician)

1997. Romanian Scout Association. Multicoloured.
5908 300l. Type **1256** 20 30
5909 700l. Romanian Scout Association emblem 25 30
5910 1050l. Joined hands 40 30
5911 1750l. Carvings 65 30
5912 3700l. Scouts around campfire 1·50 60
Nos. 5908/12 were issued together, se-tenant, forming a composite design.

1997. 9th Romanian–Chinese Stamp Exhibition, Bucharest. No. 5293 surch **A IX-a editie a expozitiei filatelice romano-chineza 1997 500 L.**
5913 **1082** 500l. on 2l. mult 30 20

1997. Anniversaries. Multicoloured.
5914 500l. Type **1258** (34th death anniv) 20 25
5915 1050l. King Carol I (131st anniv of accession) (black inscriptions and face value) 75 25
5916 1050l. As No. 5915 but mauve inscriptions and face value 1·00 25
5917 1050l. As No. 5915 but blue inscriptions and face value 1·00 25
5918 1050l. As No. 5915 but brown inscriptions and face value 1·00 25

1259 Rugby

1997. Sports. Multicoloured.
5919 500l. Type **1259** 20 35
5920 700l. American football (vert) 30 35
5921 1750l. Oina (Romanian bat and ball game) 65 35
5922 3700l. Mountaineering (vert) 1·60 75

1260 New Building

1998. 130th Anniv of Bucharest Chamber of Commerce and Industry.
5923 **1260** 700l. multicoloured 30 10

1261 Biathlon

1263 Four-leaved Clover (Good luck and Success)

1998. Winter Olympic Games, Nagano, Japan. Mult.
5924 900l. Type **1261** 30 20
5925 3900l. Figure skating 1·40 40

1998. Europa. National Festivals.
5927 **1263** 900l. green and red 2·40 2·30
5928 – 3900l. red, orange and green 10·00 4·50
DESIGN: 3900l. Butterfly (youth and suaveness).

1264 Alfred Nobel

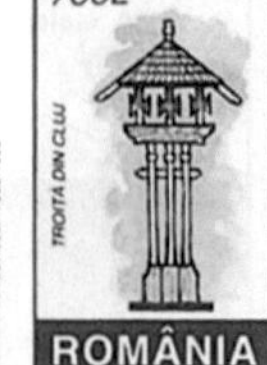

1265 Shrine, Cluj

1998. The 20th-century (1st series). Multicoloured.
5929 700l. Type **1264** (establishment of Nobel Foundation, 1901) 25 30
5930 900l. Guglielmo Marconi (first radio-telegraphic trans-Atlantic link, 1901) 35 30
5931 1500l. Albert Einstein (elaboration of Theory of Relativity, 1905) 55 30
5932 3900l. Traian Vuia (his first flight, 1906) 1·50 60
See also Nos. 5991/5, 6056/9, 6060/3, 6128/31, 6133/6, 6205/8 and 6230/3.

1998. Roadside Shrines. Multicoloured.
5933 700l. Type **1265** 30 10
5934 900l. Crucifixion, Prahovac 35 10
5935 1500l. Shrine, Arges 55 10

1267 Dr. Thoma Ionescu (founder) and Coltea Hospital, Bucharest

1998. Centenary of Romanian Surgery Society.
5937 **1267** 1050l. grey, brown and red 45 15

1998. Nos. 5350/1, 5353/4 and 5357 surch, the old value cancelled by a clover leaf.
5938 50l. on 2l. green 25 10
5939 100l. on 8l. brown 25 10
5940 200l. on 4l. red 25 10
5941 400l. on 6l. brown 25 10
5942 500l. on 18l. red 25 10

1998. Nos. 5615/17 and 5620 surch, the old value cancelled by a hare.
5944 – 700l. on 125l. green and black 40 45
5945 – 800l. on 35l. green and black 40 45
5946 – 1050l. on 45l. green and black 40 45
5947 **1170** 4150l. on 15l. green and black 1·60 70

1998. Nos. 5352 and 5355 surch, the old value cancelled by a heart.
5948 1000l. on 9l. red 45 60
5949 1500l. on 5l. violet 70 60

1272 Brown Kiwi

1998. Nocturnal Birds. Multicoloured.
5950 700l. Type **1272** 25 25
5951 1500l. Barn owl 50 25
5952 1850l. Water rail 65 25
5953 2450l. European nightjar 80 25

1998. No. 5361 surch, the old value cancelled by a sign of the zodiac.
5954 250l. on 45l. blue (Aries) 20 25
5955 350l. on 45l. blue (Taurus) 20 25
5956 400l. on 45l. blue (Gemini) 20 25
5957 450l. on 45l. blue (Cancer) 20 25
5958 850l. on 45l. blue (Leo) 30 25
5959 900l. on 45l. blue (Aquarius) 40 25
5960 1000l. on 45l. blue (Libra) 40 25
5961 1600l. on 45l. blue (Scorpio) 60 25
5962 2500l. on 45l. blue (Sagittarius) 95 25

1274 81p. Stamp and Waslui Cancellation

1998. 140th Anniv of Bull's Head Issue of Moldavia. Multicoloured.

5963 700l. Type **1274** 30 25
5964 1050l. 27p. stamp and Jassy cancellation 40 25

1275 Soldiers and Revolutionaries fighting

1998. 150th Anniv of the 1848 Revolutions.

5966 **1275** 1050l. black, yellow and red 40 30

1276 Nikolaus Lenau (poet)

1277 Diver and Marine Life

1998. German Personalities of Banat.

5967 **1276** 800l. orange, black and pink 50 30
5968 – 1850l. orange, black and green . . . . . 1·20 30
5969 – 4150l. orange, black and blue . . . . . . 2·75 45

DESIGNS: 1850l. Stefan Jager (artist); 4150l. Adam Muller-Guttenbrunn (writer).

1998. International Year of the Ocean.

5970 **1277** 1100l. multicoloured . . 40 30

1998. Nos. 5336/7 surch, the old value cancelled by a sporting emblem.

5971 **1094** 50l. on 1l. multicoloured (Figure skater) 40 45
5972 – 50l. on 1l. multicoloured (Trophy) 40 45

1279 "Tulipa gesneriana"

1281 "Proportions of Man" (Leonardo da Vinci)

1998. Flowers. Multicoloured.

5973 350l. Type **1279** 25 25
5974 850l. "Dahlia variabilis" "Rubin" 35 25
5975 1100l. Martagon lily 45 25
5976 4450l. "Rosa centifolia" . . 1·90 50

No. 5975 commemorates the 50th anniv of the Horticulture Institute, Bucharest.

1998. Various stamps surch. (a) Nos. 5399/5404, the old value cancelled by a transport emblem.

5977 **1106** 50l. on 1l. brown, blue and deep blue (Car) 15 15
5978 – 50l. on 4l. green, lilac and violet (Steam locomotive) 15 15
5979 – 50l. on 5l. brown, blue and ultramarine (Lorry) 15 15
5980 – 50l. on 5l. blue, brown and red (Helicopter) 15 15
5981 – 50l. on 9l. red, blue and deep blue (Airplane) 15 15
5982 – 50l. on 10l. black, light brown and brown (Ship) 15 15

(b) Nos. 5472/5 and 5477, the old value cancelled by a bird.

5983 **1129** 50l. on 6l. green and violet (Cockerel) . . 15 15
5984 – 50l. on 7l. mauve, purple and green (Duck) 15 15
5985 – 50l. on 9l. blue and mauve (Swan) . . . 15 15
5986 – 50l. on 10l. light brown, brown and blue (Dove) 15 15
5987 – 50l. on 30l. green and blue (Swallow) . . . 15 15

1998. 50th Anniv of Universal Declaration of Human Rights.

5988 **1281** 50l. multicoloured . . . 25 15

1282 Paciurea

1998. 125th Birth Anniv of Dimitrie Paciurea (sculptor).

5989 **1282** 850l. multicoloured . . 30 15

1283 Eclipse

1998. Total Eclipse of the Sun (1999) (1st issue).

5990 **1283** 1100l. multicoloured . . 70 20

See also No. 6050.

1284 Sinking of "Titanic" (liner), 1912

1998. The 20th century (2nd series).

5991 **1284** 350l. black, bl & red . . 30 30
5992 – 1100l. multicoloured . . 50 30
5993 – 1600l. multicoloured . . 65 30
5994 – 2000l. multicoloured . . 65 30
5995 – 2600l. blk, grey & red 95 30

DESIGNS: 1100l. Henri Coanda and his turbine-powered model airplane, 1910; 1600l. Louis Bleriot and his "Bleriot XI" airplane (first powered flight across English Channel, 1909); 2000l. Freighter in locks and map of American sea routes (opening of Panama Canal, 1914); 2600l. Prisoners in courtyard (Russian October revolution, 1917).

1998. Christmas. Nos. 5491 and 5674 surch with the old value cancelled by a Christmas emblem.

5996 **1133** 2000l. on 15l. multicoloured (Christmas tree) . . . 55 40
5997 **1186** 2600l. on 60l. multicoloured (Father Christmas) 85 40

1286 Gonovez Lighthouse

1998. Lighthouses. Multicoloured.

5998 900l. Type **1286** 20 30
5999 1000l. Constanta 20 30
6000 1100l. Sfantu Gheorghe . . 30 30
6001 2600l. Sulina 65 30

1287 Arnota Monastery

1999. Monasteries. Multicoloured.

6002 500l. Type **1287** 25 25
6003 700l. Bistrita 25 25
6004 1100l. Dintr'un Lemn . . . 35 25
6005 2100l. Govora 60 25
6006 4850l. Tismana . . . . . . 1·10 25

1999. No. 5492 surch with the old value cancelled by various fungi.

6007 **1134** 50l. on 15l. black, red and blue 20 25
6009 400l. on 15l. black, red and blue 20 25
6010 2300l. on 15l. black, red and blue 55 25
6011 3200l. on 15l. black, red and blue 75 25

1999. No. 5384 surch with the old value cancelled by a musical instrument.

6012 **1099** 100l. on 1l. blue (guitar) 20 25
6013 250l. on 1l. blue (saxophone) 20 25

1290 "Magnolia soulangiana"

1999. Shrubs. Multicoloured.

6014 350l. Type **1290** 30 25
6015 1000l. "Stewartia malacodendron" 30 25
6016 1100l. "Hibiscus rosa-sinensis" 45 25
6017 5350l. "Clematis patens" . . 1·80 25

1292 Easter Eggs

1999. Easter.

6023 **1292** 1100l. multicoloured . . 30 15

1999. No. 5799 surch with the old value cancelled by a dinosaur emblem.

6024 **1223** 100l. on 70l. yellow and black (Brontosaurus) 20 20
6025 200l. on 70l. yellow and black (Iguanodon) . . 20 20
6026 200l. on 70l. yellow and black (Allosaurus) . . 20 20
6027 1500l. on 70l. yellow and black (Diplodocus) 25 20
6028 1600l. on 70l. yellow and black (Tyrannosaurus) . . 35 20
6029 3200l. on 70l. yellow and black (Stegosaurus) 65 20
6030 6000l. on 70l. yellow and black (Plateosaurus) . . . 1·20 35

1294 Girdle of Keys (Padureni)

1295 Scarlet Macaw

1999. Jewellery. Multicoloured.

6031 1200l. Type **1294** 20 30
6032 2100l. Pendant of keys (Ilia, Hunedoara) 35 30
6033 2600l. Jewelled bib (Maramures) 40 30
6034 3200l. Necklace (Banat) (horiz) 50 30

1999. Birds. Multicoloured.

6035 1100l. Type **1295** 20 35
6036 2700l. White peafowl . . . 50 35
6037 3700l. Common peafowl . . 70 35
6038 5700l. Sulphur-crested cockatoo . . . . 1·10 55

1296 Council Flag and Headquarters, Strasbourg

1999. 50th Anniv of Council of Europe.

6039 **1296** 2300l. multicoloured . . 50 15

1297 St. Peter's Cathedral, Rome

1298 Northern Shoveler

1999. Papal Visit.

6040 **1297** 1300l. mauve and black 40 30
6041 – 1600l. mauve and black 50 30
6042 – 2300l. multicoloured . . 65 30
6043 – 6300l. multicoloured . . 1·70 50

DESIGNS: 1600l. Patriarchal Cathedral, Bucharest; 2300l. Father Teoctist (patriarch of Romanian Orthodox church); 6300l. Pope John Paul II (after Dina Bellotti).

1999. Europa. Parks and Gardens: the Danube Delta Nature Reserve. Multicoloured.

6044 1100l. Type **1298** 35 40
6045 5700l. Black stork . . . . . 1·40 60

1299 Gheorghe Cartan (historian, 150th birth anniv)

1999. Anniversaries.

6046 **1299** 600l. green, black & red 20 20
6047 – 1100l. purple, blk & red 25 20
6048 – 2600l. blue, black & red 50 20
6049 – 7300l. brown, blk & red 80 40

DESIGNS: 1100l. George Calinescu (critic and novelist, birth centenary); 2600l. Johann Wolfgang von Goethe (dramatist, 250th birth anniv); 7300l. Honore de Balzac (novelist, birth bicentenary).

1300 Moon eclipsing Sun

1999. Total Eclipse of the Sun (2nd issue).

6050 **1300** 1100l. multicoloured . . 35 20

1301 Cigarette and Man with Arms Crossed

1999. Public Health Awareness Campaign. Mult.

6051 400l. Type **1301** (anti-smoking) 15 15
6052 800l. Bottles and man cradling glass and bottle (alcohol abuse) 15 15
6053 1300l. Cannabis leaf, pills and man injecting arm (drugs) 25 15
6054 2500l. Profiles and man on intravenous drip (HIV) . . 45 15

1302 Eclipse and Pavarotti (opera singer)

1999. Luciano Pavarotti's Concert on Day of Eclipse, Bucharest.

6055 **1302** 8100l. multicoloured . . 1·70 1·00

1303 Alexander Fleming (bacteriologist)

1999. The 20th century (3rd series). Multicoloured.

6056 800l. Type **1303** (discovery of penicillin, 1928) 20 30
6057 3000l. "Swords into Ploughshares" (sculpture) and map of Europe, Africa and Asia (foundation of League of Nations, 1920) 65 30
6058 7300l. Harold Clayton Urey (chemist) (discovery of heavy water, 1932) . . . 1·50 55
6059 17000l. Deep sea drilling (first oil platform, Beaumont, Texas, 1934) 2·75 1·10

1304 Karl Landsteiner (pathologist)

1999. The 20th-century (4th series).
6060 **1304** 1500l. orange, black and yellow 15 25
6061 – 3000l. ochre, black and brown 45 25
6062 – 7300l. multicoloured . . 55 55
6063 – 17000l. multicoloured 2·75 1·20
DESIGNS: 1500l. Type **1304** (discovery of blood groups, 1900–02); 3000l. Nicolae Paulescu (biochemist) (discovery of insulin, 1921); 7300l. Otto Hahn (radiochemist) (discovery of nuclear fission, 1938); 17000l. Ernst Ruska (electrical engineer) (designer of first electron microscope, 1931).

1305 Posthorn in Envelope and Berne
1306 Grigore Vasiliu Birlic

1999. 125th Anniv of Universal Postal Union.
6064 **1305** 3100l. multicoloured . . 60 30

1999. Comic Actors. Each purple, black and red.
6065 900l. Type **1306** 15 25
6066 1500l. Toma Caragiu . . . 25 25
6067 3100l. Constantin Tanase . . 50 25
6068 7950l. Charlie Chaplin . . . 1·30 45
6069 8850l. Stan Laurel and Oliver Hardy (horiz) . . . 1·40 75

1307 Monastery

1999. 275th Anniv of Stavropoleos Church.
6070 **1307** 2100l. brown, stone and black 35 20

1308 Snowboarding
1309 Christmas Tree and Bell

1999. New Olympic Sports. Multicoloured.
6071 1600l. Type **1308** 35 35
6072 1700l. Softball 35 35
6073 7950l. Taekwondo . . . . . 1·40 70

1999. Christmas. Multicoloured.
6074 1500l. Type **1309** 25 25
6075 3100l. Father Christmas with presents 55 25

1310 Child as Flower (Antonela Vieriu)

1999. 10th Anniv of U.N. Convention on the Rights of the Child. Multicoloured.
6076 900l. Type **1310** 70 95
6077 3400l. Girl writing numbers (Ana-Maria Bulete) (vert) 55 35
6078 8850l. Group of people (Maria-Luiza Rogojeanu) 1·50 70

1311 Diana, Princess of Wales

1999. Diana, Princess of Wales Commemoration.
6079 **1311** 6000l. multicoloured . . 1·20 45

1312 Ferrari 365 GTB/4, 1968

1999. Birth Centenary (1998) of Enzo Ferrari (car designer). Multicoloured.
6080 1500l. Type **1312** 25 25
6081 1600l. Dino 246 GT, 1970 25 25
6082 1700l. 365 GT/4BB, 1973 . . 30 25
6083 7950l. Mondial 3.2, 1985 . . 1·40 50
6084 8850l. F 355, 1994 . . . . 1·50 75
6085 14500l. 456 MGT, 1998 . . 2·75 95

1313 Child with Romanian Flag

1999. 10th Anniv of Popular Uprising.
6086 **1313** 2100l. multicoloured . . 35 20

1314 European Union Flag
1316 Cupid

2000. European Union Membership Negotiations.
6087 **1314** 6100l. multicoloured . . 95 70

2000. St. Valentine's Day. Multicoloured.
6089 1500l. Type **1316** 25 50
6090 7950l. Couple . . . . 1·50 50

1317 Easter Eggs

2000. Easter.
6091 **1317** 1700l. blue, green and orange 35 20

2000. Nos. 5855 and 5842 surch, the old value cancelled by a different emblem.
6092 1700l. on 70l. multicoloured (crown) 30 20
6093 1700l. on 70l. multicoloured (snake) 30 20

1319 Greater Bird of Paradise

2000. Birds of Paradise. Multicoloured.
6094 1700l. Type **1319** 25 45
6095 2400l. Magnificent bird of paradise 35 45
6096 9050l. Superb bird of paradise . . . . 1·30 75
6097 10050l. King bird of paradise . . . . 1·50 1·00

2000. Nos. 5342/3 surch.
6098 1900l. on 1l. multicoloured 35 20
6099 2000l. on 1l. multicoloured 35 20

2000. Nos. 5310/14 surch, the old value cancelled by various book and quill emblems.
6100 1700l. on 50b. brown and black 30 20
6101 1700l. on 11.50 green and mauve 30 20
6102 1700l. on 2l. red and blue 30 20
6103 1700l. on 3l. blue and brown 30 20
6104 1700l. on 4l. brown and blue 30 20

1322 Cineraria
1324 "Building Europe"

2000. Flowers. Multicoloured.
6105 1700l. Type **1322** 30 40
6106 3100l. Indoor lily 55 40
6107 5800l. Plumeria 95 40
6108 10050l. Fuchsia . . . . . . 1·60 85

2000. Nos. 5303/7 surch, the old value cancelled by an easel with palette emblem.
6109 1700l. on 50b. multicoloured 30 20
6110 1700l. on 11.50 multicoloured 30 20
6111 1700l. on 2l. multicoloured 30 20
6112 1700l. on 3l. multicoloured 30 20
6113 1700l. on 4l. multicoloured 30 20

2000. Europa.
6114 **1324** 10150l. multicoloured 1·70 1·00

2000. Death Centenary of Vincent van Gogh (artist). Nos. 5318 and 5321 surch, the old value cancelled by paint palette emblem.
6115 1700l. on 50b. multicoloured 30 20
6116 1700l. on 31.50 multicoloured 30 20

2000. No. 5642 surch, the old value cancelled by an airship.
6117 1700l. on 635l. black, ultramarine and blue . . 25 40
6118 2000l. on 635l. black, ultramarine and blue . . 25 40
6119 3900l. on 635l. black, ultramarine and blue . . 60 40
6120 9050l. on 635l. black, ultramarine and blue . . 1·30 60

1327 Mihai the Brave and Soldiers

2000. Anniversaries. Multicoloured.
6121 3800l. Type **1327** (400th anniv of first union of the Romanian provinces (Wallachia, Transylvania and Moldavia)) 55 45
6122 9050l. Printing press (550th anniv of the 42 line Bible (first Bible printed in Latin)) (36 × 23 mm) . . . 1·20 70

2000. No. 5801 surch, the old value cancelled by a flower.
6123 10000l. on 370l. brown and black . . . . 1·40 45
6124 19000l. on 370l. brown and black . . . . 2·50 95
6125 34000l. on 370l. brown and black . . . . 4·50 1·50

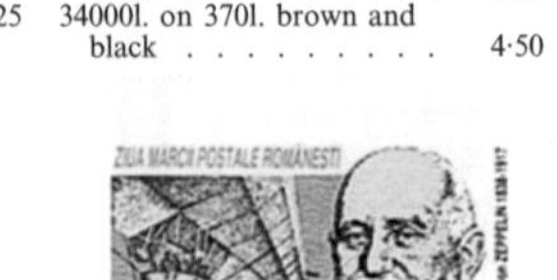

1330 Ferdinand von Zeppelin and Airship

2000. Centenary of First Zeppelin Flight.
6127 **1330** 2100l. multicoloured . . 35 20

1331 Enrico Fermi (physicist) and Mathematical Equation

2000. The 20th Century (5th series).
6128 **1331** 2100l. black, grey and red 30 25
6129 – 2200l. black and grey 30 25
6130 – 2400l. red and black . . 35 25
6131 – 6000l. multicoloured . . 90 25

DESIGNS: 2100l. Type **1331** (construction of first nuclear reactor, 1942); 2200l. United Nations Charter (signing of charter, 1945); 2400l. Edith Piaf (singer) (release of *La Vie en Rose* (song), 1947); 6000l. Sir Edmund Percival Hillary (mountaineer) (conquest of Mt. Everest, 1953).

2000. No. 5365 surch, the old value cancelled by a bird.
6132 1700l. on 160l. red and pink 25 15

1333 Globe and "Sputnik 1" Satellite

2000. The Twentieth Century (6th series).
6133 **1333** 1700l. multicoloured . . 25 30
6134 – 3900l. multicoloured . . 50 30
6135 – 6400l. black and red . . 90 30
6136 – 11300l. multicoloured 1·50 50
DESIGNS: 1700l. Type **1333** (launch of first man-made satellite, 1957); 3900l. Yuri Gagarin (first manned space flight, 1961); 6400l. Surgeons operating (first heart transplant operation, 1967); 11300l. Edwin E. Aldrin and Moon (first manned landing on Moon, 1969).

1334 Boxing

2000. Olympic Games, Sydney. Multicoloured.
6137 1700l. Type **1334** 35 45
6138 2200l. High jump 35 45
6139 3900l. Weight lifting 65 45
6140 6200l. Gymnastics . . . . . 1·20 45

1336 Palace of Agriculture Ministry
1340 Ilie Ilascu (political prisoner)

2000. Bucharest Palaces.
6143 **1336** 1700l. black and grey 25 20
6144 – 2200l. black and stone (horiz) 25 20
6145 – 2400l. black and green (horiz) 25 20
6146 – 3900l. black and brown (horiz) 55 20
DESIGNS: 2200l. Cantacuzino Palace (now George Enescu Museum); 2400l. Grigore Ghica Palace; 3900l. Stirbei Palace (now Museum of Ceramics and Glass).

2000. No. 5836 surch, the old value cancelled by a house.
6147 300l. on 70l. multicoloured 15 10

2000. No. 5349 surch.
6148 300l. on 1l. blue 15 10

2000. Air. No. 5695 surch.
6149 2000l. on 960l. blue & black 25 50
6150 4200l. on 960l. blue & black 60 50
6151 4600l. on 960l. blue & black 65 50
6152 6500l. on 960l. blue & black 95 50

2000. 50th Anniv of United Nations Convention on Human Rights.
6153 **1340** 11300l. multicoloured 1·60 85

2000. No. 5700 surch, the old value cancelled by an inkwell and quill emblem.
6154 2000l. on 90l. multicoloured 25 15

2000. No. 5556 surch.
6155 2000l. on 29l. flesh, blk & lil 25 15

1343 Leopard

2000. Big Cats
6156 **1343** 1200l. multicoloured . . 15 20
6157 – 2000l. blue and black 25 20
6158 – 2200l. multicoloured . . 25 20
6159 – 2300l. multicoloured . . 25 20
6160 – 4200l. brown, bl & blk 55 20
6161 – 6500l. multicoloured . . 90 20

DESIGNS: 2000l. Snow leopard; 2200l. Lion; 2300l. Bobcat; 4200l. Mountain lion; 6500l. Tiger.

1344 Camil Ressu **1345** Christmas Tree

2000. Self-portraits. Multicoloured.

6163	2000l. Type **1344**	25	30
6164	2400l. Jean Al Steriadi	35	30
6165	4400l. Nicolae Tonitza	55	30
6166	15000l. Nicolae Grigorescu	2·00	85

2000. Christmas.

6167	**1345** 4400l. multicoloured	65	35

1346 Jesus Christ and Angel **1349** Globe and Fireworks

2000. Birth Bimillenary of Jesus Christ. Mult.

6168	2000l. Type **1346**	25	25
6169	7000l. Jesus Christ and dove (22 × 38 mm)	95	40

2000. No. 5624 surch, the previous value cancelled by different animals.

6170	7000l. on 3095l. Large-leaved lime (Pig)	85	45
6171	10000l. on 3095l. Large-leaved lime (Bear)	1·20	60
6172	11500l. on 3095l. Large-leaved lime (Cow)	1·70	90

2001. New Millennium.

6176	**1349** 11500l. multicoloured	1·40	85

1350 Sculpture **1352** Ribbons forming Heart

2001. 125th Birth Anniv of Constantin Brancusi (sculptor). Multicoloured.

6177	4600l. Type **1350**	45	40
6178	7200l. Display of sculptures	65	40

Nos. 6177/8 were issued together, se-tenant, forming a composite design.

2001. No. 5542 surch, the previous value cancelled by different snakes.

6179	7400l. on 280l. black & yell	70	55
6180	13000l. on 280l. black & yell	1·30	90

2001. St. Valentine's Day. Each red and grey.

6181	2200l. Type **1352**	40	80
6182	11500l. Pierced heart	1·80	80

2001. Nos. 5595/6 and 5598 surch, the previous value cancelled by an ear of corn.

6183	1300l. on 245l. mult	30	40
6184	2200l. on 115l. mult	30	40
6185	5000l. on 115l. mult	55	40
6186	16500l. on 70l. mult	2·00	60

1354 Hortensia Papadat-Bengescu

2001. Birth Anniversaries. Multicoloured.

6187	1300l. Type **1354**	30	05
6188	2200l. Eugen Lovinescu (writer, 120th anniv)	30	05
6189	2400l. Ion Minulescu (poet, 120th anniv)	30	05
6190	4600l. Andre Malraux (writer, centenary)	45	05
6191	7200l. George H. Gallup (opinion pollster and journalist, centenary)	75	05
6192	35000l. Walt Disney (artist and film producer, centenary)	4·00	20

1355 Chick inside Egg **1356** Sloe (*Prunus spinosa*)

2001. Easter.

6193	**1355** 2200l. multicoloured	25	15

2001. Berries. Multicoloured.

6194	2200l. Type **1356**	10	10
6195	4600l. Red currant (*Ribes rubrum L.*)	20	10
6196	7400l. Gooseberry (*Ribes uva-crispa*)	30	10
6197	11500l. Mountain cranberry (*Vaccinium vitis-idaea L.*)	45	10

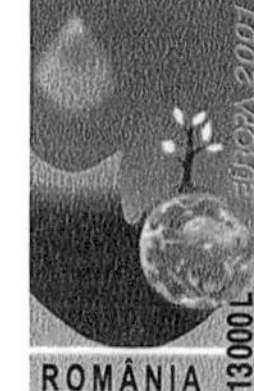

1357 Hagi **1358** Water Droplet and Globe surmounted by Tree

2001. Retirement of George Hagi (footballer).

6198	**1357** 2200l. multicoloured	10	10

2001. Europa. Water Resources.

6199	**1358** 13000l. multicoloured	50	15

1359 Collie

2001. Dogs. Multicoloured.

6200	1300l. Type **1359**	10	10
6201	5000l. Basset hound	20	10
6202	8000l. Siberian husky	30	10
6203	13500l. Ciobanesc mioritic	50	15

1360 Goddess Europa **1362** George Palade (Nobel Prize winner for medicine, 1974)

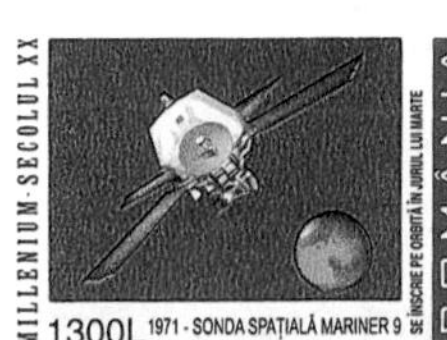

1361 Mariner 9 (spacecraft) and Mars

2001. Romanian Presidency of Organization for Security and Co-operation in Europe.

6204	**1360** 11500l. multicoloured	40	10

2001. The 20th Century (7th series). Multicoloured.

6205	1300l. Type **1361** (first orbit of Mars, 1979)	10	10
6206	2400l. Bull (discovery of Paleolithic cave paintings, Ardeche, 1994)	10	10
6207	5000l. Nadia Comaneci (gymnast) (first "10" for gymnastics, Olympic Games, Montreal, 1976)	20	10
6208	8000l. Wall (fall of the Berlin wall, 1989)	30	10

2001. 50th Anniv of United Nations High Commissioner for Refugees.

6209	**1362** 13500l. multicoloured	50	15

2001. Various stamps surch the previous values cancelled by various emblems as stated.

6210	**1100** 300l. on 4l. multicoloured (candlestick)	10	10
6211	**1110** 300l. on 4l. multicoloured (bobsled)	10	10
6212	**1132** 300l. on 7l. multicoloured (harp)	10	10
6213	– 300l. on 9l. multicoloured (No. 5488) (lyre)	10	10
6214	**1168** 300l. on 90l. multicoloured (lizard)	10	10
6215	**1190** 300l. on 90l. multicoloured (computer mouse)	10	10
6216	**1202** 300l. on 90l. multicoloured (fish)	10	10
6217	– 300l. on 90l. multicoloured (No. 5745) (chess knight)	10	10
6218	**1207** 300l. on 90l. multicoloured (fungi)	10	10
6219	**1157** 300l. on 115l. brown, blue and black (scroll)	10	10
6220	**1158** 300l. on 115l. multicoloured (train)	10	10
6221	**1162** 300l. on 115l. multicoloured (rectangle)	10	10
6222	– 300l. on 115l. multicoloured (No. 5602) (kite)	10	10

2001. Nos. 5715/16 and 5720 surch, the previous values cancelled by a sign of the zodiac.

6223	2500l. on 755l. blue and black (Pisces) (postage)	10	10
6224	2500l. on 1615l. green and black (Capricorn)	10	10
6225	2500l. on 715l. red and blue (Aquarius) (air)	10	10

1365 Trap Racing

2001. Equestrian Competitive Events. Mult.

6226	1500l. Type **1365**	10	10
6227	2500l. Dressage	10	10
6228	5300l. Show jumping	20	10
6229	8300l. Flat racing	30	10

1366 Augustin Maior and Drawing

2001. The 20th Century (8th series). Multicoloured.

6230	1500l. Type **1366** (invention of multiple telephony, 1906)	10	10
6231	5300l. Pioneer 10 (satellite) (launched, 1972)	20	10
6232	13500l. Microchip (introduction of first microprocessor, 1971)	50	15
6233	15500l. Hubble space telescope (launched, 1990)	60	15

1367 Finger Coral (*Porites porites*)

2001. Corals and Sea Anemones (1st series). Multicoloured.

6234	2500l. Type **1367**	10	10
6235	8300l. Giant sea anemone (*Condylactis gigantia*)	30	10
6236	13500l. Northern red anemone (*Anemonia telia*)	50	15
6237	37500l. Common sea fan (*Gorgonia ventalina*)	1·40	35

See also No. **MS**6260.

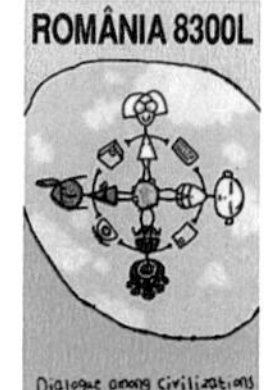

1368 Children encircling Globe

2001. United Nations Year of Dialogue among Civilizations.

6238	**1368** 8300l. multicoloured	30	10

1369 King, Bear and Cat

2001. Comics. Multicoloured.

6239	13500l. Type **1369**	50	15
6240	13500l. Fox beating drum and kicking cat	50	15
6241	13500l. King sleeping and fox beating drum	50	15
6242	13500l. Cat giving fox drum	50	15
6243	13500l. Drum exploding	50	15

1370 Top of Wreath with Baubles

2001. Christmas. Multicoloured.

6244	2500l. Type **1370**	10	10
6245	2500l. Bottom of wreath with stars	25	10

Nos. 6244/5 were issued together, se-tenant, forming a composite design of a wreath.

1371 Scorpio

2001. Signs of the Zodiac (1st series). Multicoloured.

6246	1500l. Type **1371**	10	10
6247	2500l. Libra	10	10
6248	5500l. Capricorn	20	10
6249	9000l. Pisces	35	10
6250	13500l. Aquarius	50	15
6251	16500l. Sagittarius	65	15

See also Nos. 6254/9.

1372 Building

2001. Centenary of Central Post Headquarters, Bucharest. Multicoloured.

6252	5500l. Type **1372**	20	10
6253	5500l. Obverse of medal showing building, 1901 (vert)	20	10

2002. Signs of the Zodiac (2nd series). As T **1371**. Multicoloured.

6254	1500l. Aries	10	10
6255	2500l. Taurus	10	10
6256	5500l. Gemini	20	10
6257	8700l. Cancer	30	10
6258	9000l. Leo	30	10
6259	23500l. Virgo	75	20

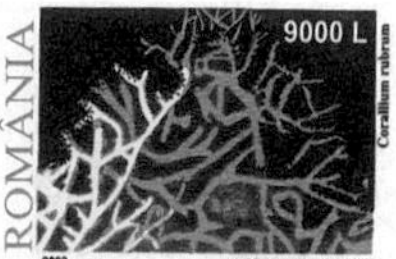

1373 Red Coral (*Corallum rubrum*)

2002. Corals and Sea Anemones (2nd series). Sheet 106 × 77 mm containing T **1373** and similar horiz designs. Multicoloured.

MS6260 9000l. Type **1373**; 9000l. Elkhorn coral (*Acropora palmate*); 16500l. Beadlet anemone (*Actinia equine*); 16500l. Pulmose anemone (*Metridium senile*) 1·70 1·70

1374 Emanuil Gojdu

2002. Birth Bicentenary of Emanuil Gojdu (nationalist).
6261 **1374** 2500l. black, blue and deep blue 10 10

1375 Mice

2002. St. Valentine's Day. Multicoloured.
6262 5500l. Type **1375** 20 10
6263 43500l. Elephants . . . . . 1·40 35

1376 Ion Mincu

2002. Birth Anniversaries.
6267 **1376** 1500l. green and black 10 10
6268 – 2500l. multicoloured . . 10 10
6269 – 5500l. multicoloured . . 20 10
6270 – 9000l. multicoloured . . 50 10
6271 – 16500l. multicoloured 55 10
6272 – 34000l. multicoloured 1·10 25
DESIGNS: Type **1376** (architect) (150th); 2500l. Costin Nenitescu (chemist) (centenary); 5500l. Alexander Dumas (writer) (bicentenary); 9000l. Serban Cioculescu (literary historian) (centenary); 16500l. Leonardo da Vinci (artist) (550th); 34000l. Victor Hugo (writer) (bicentenary).

1377 Flag and Statue of Liberty

2002. "United We Stand". Multicoloured.
6273 25500l. Type **1377** 80 20
6274 25500l. Flags and monument 80 20
Nos. 6273/4 were issued together, se-tenant, forming a composite design.

1378 Fortified Church and Tower, Saschiz **1379** Crucifixion

2002. Germanic Fortresses and Churches in Translyvania. Multicoloured.
6275 1500l. Type **1378** 10 10
6276 2500l. Church staircase, Darjiu 10 10
6277 6500l. Fortress, Viscri (horiz) 25 10
6278 10500l. Fortified church, Vorumloc (horiz) 35 10
6279 13500l. Tower gate, Calnic 45 10
6280 17500l. Fortified church, Prejmer 55 10

2002. Easter. Showing miniatures by Picu Patrut. Multicoloured.
6281 2500l. Type **1379** 10 10
6282 10500l. Resurrection 35 10

1380 Clown **1381** "Dorobantul" (Nicolae Grigorescu)

2002. Europa. Circus. Multicoloured.
6283 17500l. Type **1380** 55 10
6284 25500l. Clown (different) . . 80 20

2002. 125th Anniv of Independence. Sheet 77 × 91 mm.
MS6285 **1381** 25500l. multicoloured 80 80

1382 Post Mark

2002. 50th Anniv of International Federation Stamp Dealers' Association (IFSDA). Sheet 105 × 75 mm containing T **1382** and similar horiz designs. Multicoloured.
MS6286 10000l. Type **1382**; 10000l. IFSDA emblem; 27500l. World Trade Centre, Bucharest; 27500l. Philatelic shop, Bucharest . . . 2·40 2·40

1383 Mountains

2002. Year of Mountains (2000l.) and Year of Eco-tourism (3000l.). Multicoloured.
6287 2000l. Type **1383** 10 10
6288 3000l. Landscape and recycling symbol (32 × 24 mm) 10 10

1384 Cricket

2002. Sport. Multicoloured.
6289 7000l. Type **1384** 20 10
6290 11000l. Polo 35 10
6291 15500l. Golf 50 10
6292 19500l. Baseball 65 20

1385 Ion Luca Caragiale

2002. Anniversaries. Multicoloured.
6293 10000l. Type **1385** (playwright) (150th birth anniv) 30 10
6294 10000l. National Theatre, Bucharest (150th anniv) 30 10
Nos. 6293/4 were issued together, se-tenant, forming a composite design within the sheet.

1386 Financial Postal Service Emblem

2002. Postal Services.
6295 **1386** 2000l. multicoloured . . 10 10
6296 – 3000l. red, yellow and blue 10 10
6297 – 8000l. multicoloured . . 25 10
6298 – 10000l. purple and brown 30 10
6299 – 13000l. red, grey and black 40 10
6300 – 15500l. multicoloured 50 10
6301 – 20500l. mauve, blue and black 65 20
6302 – 27500l. multicoloured 90 20
DESIGNS: 2000l. Type **1386**; 3000l. Romania Post emblem; 8000l. Direct mailing centre emblem; 10000l. Post building (130th anniv); 13000l. Direct marketing emblem; 15500l. Rapid post emblem; 20500l. Priority post emblem; 27500l. Globe and stamp album (Romafilatelia).

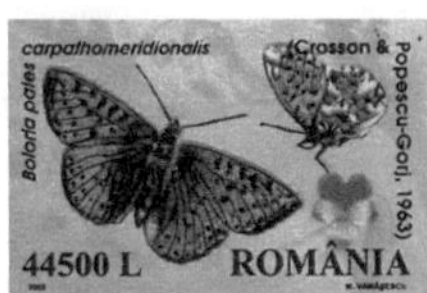

1387 *Boloria pales carpathomeridionalis*

2002. Butterflies. Sheet 101 × 71 mm containing T **1387** and similar horiz designs. Multicoloured.
MS6310 44500l. Type **1387**; 44500l. *Erebia pharte romaniae*; 44500l. *Peridea korbl herculana*; 44500l. *Tomares nogelii dobrogensis* . . 2·75 2·75

1388 Locomotive 50115 (1930)

2002. Steam Locomotives. 130th Anniv of First Locomotive made at Machine Factory, Reşiţa (**MS**6317). Multicoloured.
6311 4500l. Type **1388** 10 10
6312 6500l. 50025 (1921) 10 10
6313 7000l. 230128 (1933) 20 10
6314 11000l. 764493 (1956) . . . 35 10
6315 19500l. 142072 (1939) . . . 65 20
6316 44500l. 704209 (1909) . . . 1·40 35
MS6317 75 × 90 mm. 72500l. Steam locomotive (1872) (42 × 54 mm) 2·40 2·40

1389 Knight and Bishop **1390** Quince (*Cydonia oblonga*)

2002. 35th Chess Olympiad, Bled, Slovenia. Sheet 102 × 62 mm containing T **1389** and similar vert designs. Multicoloured.
MS6318 20500l. Type **1389**; 20500l. King and knight; 20500l. Queen and rook . . . . 1·00 1·00

2002. Fruit. Multicoloured.
6319 15500l. Type **1390** 50 10
6320 20500l. Apricot (*Armeniaca vulgaris*) 65 20
6321 44500l. Cherries (*Cerasus vulgaris*) . . . . 1·40 35
6322 73500l. Mulberry (*Morus nigra*) . . . . 2·40 60

1391 Father Christmas carrying Parcels

2002. Christmas. Multicoloured.
6323 3000l. Type **1391** 10 10
6324 15500l. Father Christmas and computer 50 10

1392 Eagle (Romanian emblem), Flags and NATO Emblem

2002. Romania Invitation to join North Atlantic Treaty Organization (NATO). Sheet 168 × 106 mm containing T **1392**.
MS6324 131000l. × 2, Type **1392** × 2 4·25 4·25
No. **MS**6324 contains a central label showing NATO emblem.

EXPRESS LETTER STAMPS

1919. Transylvania. Cluj Issue. No. E245 of Hungary optd as T **42**.
E784 E **18** 2b. olive and red . . . 30 45

1919. Transylvania. Oradea Issue. No. E245 of Hungary optd as T **42**.
E860 E **18** 2b. olive and red . . . 40 70

FRANK STAMPS

F **38**

1913. Silistra Commemoration Committee.
F626 F **38** (–) brown . . . . . . 4·25 5·25

F **108** Mail Coach and Biplane

1933. For free postage on book "75th Anniv of Introduction of Rumanian Postage Stamp".
F1286 F **108** (–) green . . . . . . 1·50 2·10

1946. For Internees' Mail via Red Cross. Nos. T1589/95 optd **SCUTIT DE TAXA POSTALA SERVICIUL PRIZONIERILOR DE RAZBOI** and cross.
F1809 T **171** (–) on 50t. orange . . 25
F1810 (–) on 1l. lilac . . . 25
F1811 (–) on 2l. brown . . . 25
F1812 (–) on 4l. blue . . . 25
F1813 (–) on 5l. violet . . . 25
F1814 (–) on 8l. green . . . 25
F1815 (–) on 10l. brown . . 25

F **209** Queen Helen

1946. For Internees' Mail via Red Cross. Perf or imperf.
F1829 F **209** (–) green and red . . 50
F1830 (–) purple and red 50
F1831 (–) red and carmine 50

F **227** King Michael F **228** Torch and Book

1947. King Michael's Fund. Perf or imperf.
(a) Postage.
F1904 F **227** (–) purple . . . . . 1·50 1·90
F1905 F **228** (–) blue . . . . . . 1·50 1·90
F1906 – (–) brown . . . . . 1·50 1·90

(b) Air. No. F1904 overprinted "**PRIN AVION**".
F1907 F **227** (–) purple . . . . . 1·80 3·25
DESIGN: As Type **227** but horiz—No. F1906, Man writing and couple reading.

NEWSPAPER STAMPS

1919. Transylvania. Cluj Issue. No. N136 of Hungary optd as T **42**.
N783 N **9** 2b. orange 35 50

1919. Transylvania. Oradea Issue. No. 136 of Hungary optd as T **43**.
N859 N **9** 2b. orange 50 70

OFFICIAL STAMPS

O 71 Rumanian Eagle and National Flag

O 80

1929.

O1115 **O 71** 25b. orange 20 15
O1116 50b. brown 20 15
O1117 1l. violet 15 10
O1118 2l. green 15 10
O1119 3l. red 30 10
O1120 4l. olive 25 15
O1221 6l. blue 1·20 20
O1222 10l. blue 35 25
O1223 25l. red 1·00 60
O1224 50l. violet 3·00 1·70

1930. Optd **8 IUNIE 1930**.
O1150 **O 71** 25b. orange 15 15
O1151 50b. brown 15 15
O1152 1l. violet 15 15
O1153 2l. green 15 15
O1159 3l. red 25 10
O1154 4l. olive 35 15
O1155 6l. blue 40 30
O1161 10l. blue 50 10
O1166 25l. red 25 10
O1157 50l. violet 3·00 1·90

1931.

O1243 **O 80** 25b. black 10 10
O1195 1l. purple 20 10
O1196 2l. green 35 20
O1197 3l. red 30 25
O1247 6l. red 85 40

PARCEL POST STAMPS

1895. As Type D **12** but inscr at top "TAXA DE FACTAGIU".
P353 25b. brown 4·50 50
P479 25b. red 4·50 80

1928. Surch **FACTAJ 5 LEI**.
P1078 **46** 5l. on 10b. green 85 25

POSTAGE DUE STAMPS
A. Ordinary Postage Due Stamps

D 12 D 38

1881.

D152 **D 12** 2b. brown 2·75 1·30
D153 5b. brown 15·00 2·20
D200 10b. brown 7·00 50
D201 30b. brown 7·00 50
D156 50b. brown 12·00 3·00
D157 60b. brown 14·00 4·25

1887.

D448 **D 12** 2b. green 45 15
D449 5b. green 30 15
D450 10b. green 30 15
D451 30b. green 30 15
D371 50b. green 1·30 1·00
D458 60b. green 3·00 80

1911.

D617 **D 38** 2b. blue on yellow 15 15
D618 5b. blue on yellow 15 15
D619 10b. blue on yellow 15 15
D604 15b. blue on yellow 15 15
D621 20b. blue on yellow 15 15
D622 30b. blue on yellow 40 15
D623 50b. blue on yellow 55 15
D624 60b. blue on yellow 60 15
D609 2l. blue on yellow 80 40

1918. Optd **TAXA DE PLATA**.
D675 **37** 5b. green 80 35
D676 10b. red 80 35

1918. Re-issue of Type D **38**. On greenish or white paper.
D1001 **D 38** 5b. black 10 10
D 722 10b. black 10 10
D 995 20b. black 10 10
D 735 30b. black 15 15
D 736 50b. black 20 30
D 998 60b. black 15 10
D1007 1l. black 25 15
D1010 2l. black 35 10
D 991 3l. black 10 10
D 992 6l. black 25 10
D1547 50l. black 35 10
D1548 100l. black 35 15

1919. Transylvania. Cluj Issue. No. D190 etc of Hungary optd as T **42**.
D786 **D 9** 1b. red and green £225 £225
D787 2b. red and green 45 45
D788 5b. red and green 42 50·00
D789 10b. red and green 20 20
D790 15b. red and green 8·00 8·00
D791 20b. red and green 20 20
D792 30b. red and green 13·50 13·50
D793 50b. red and green 5·50 6·25

1919. Transylvania. Oradea Issue. No. D190, etc of Hungary optd as T **43**.
D861 **D 9** 1b. red and green 23·00 23·00
D862 2b. red and green 20 20
D863 5b. red and green 3·50 3·50
D864 6b. red and green 2·30 2·30
D865 10b. red and green 25 25
D866 12b. red and green 35 35
D867 15b. red and green 35 35
D868 20b. red and green 20 20
D869 30b. red and green 50 60

1930. Optd **8 IUNIE 1930**.
D1168 **D 38** 1l. black 40 15
D1169 2l. black 40 15
D1170 3l. black 50 25
D1171 6l. black 90 35

D 98

D 233

1932.

D1249 **D 98** 1l. black 10 10
D1250 2l. black 10 10
D1251 3l. black 20 10
D1252 6l. black 20 10
D1835 20l. black 20 10
D1839 50l. black 25 25
D1840 80l. black 60 45
D1841 100l. black 55 30
D1842 200l. black 90 55
D1843 500l. black 1·40 90
D1844 5000l. black 1·70 1·10

1947. Type D **233** (without opts) perforated down centre.
D1919 2l. red 35
D1920 4l. blue 55
D1921 5l. black 90
D1922 10l. brown 1·80

The left half of Nos. D1919/22, showing Crown, served as a receipt and was stuck in the postman's book and so does not come postally used.

Prices for Nos. D1919/22 are for unused horizontal pairs.

1948. Nos. D1919/22, optd as in Type D **233**.
D1944 2l. red 35 20
D1945 4l. blue 55 25
D1946 5l. black 90 55
D1947 10l. brown 1·40 60

Prices for Nos. D1944 to D4055 are for unused and used horizontal pairs.

D **276** Badge and Postwoman

1950.

D2066 **D 276** 2l. red 90 90
D2067 4l. blue 90 90
D2068 5l. green 1·40 1·40
D2069 10l. brown 1·80 1·80

1952. Currency revalued. Nos. D2066/9 surch **4 Bani** on each half.
D2221 **D 276** 4b. on 2l. red 65 65
D2222 10b. on 4l. blue 65 65
D2223 20b. on 5l. green 1·40 1·40
D2224 50b. on 10l. brown 1·40 1·40

D **420** G.P.O., Bucharest and Posthorn

1957.

D2507 **D 420** 3b. black 20 10
D2508 5b. orange 20 10
D2509 10b. purple 20 10
D2510 20b. red 20 10
D2511 40b. green 65 25
D2512 1l. blue 1·80 45

D **614**

1967.

D3436 **D 614** 3b. green 10 10
D3437 5b. blue 10 10
D3438 10b. mauve 10 10
D3439 20b. red 10 10
D3440 40b. brown 20 10
D3441 1l. violet 55 20

D **766** Postal Emblems and Postman

1974.

D4050 **D 766** 5b. blue 10 10
D4051 10b. green 10 10
D4052 – 20b. red 10 10
D4053 – 40b. violet 20 10
D4054 – 50b. brown 35 10
D4055 – 1l. orange 55 10

DESIGNS: 20b., 40b. Dove with letter and Hermes with posthorn; 50b., 1l. G.P.O., Bucharest and emblem with mail van.

Prices for Nos. D4050/55 are for unused horizontal pairs.

1982. As Type **D 766**.
D4761 – 25b. violet 10 10
D4762 **D 766** 50b. yellow 10 10
D4763 – 1l. red 25 10
D4764 – 2l. green 55 10
D4765 **D 766** 3l. brown 80 10
D4766 – 4l. blue 1·20 20

DESIGNS: 25b., 1l. Dove with letter and Hermes with posthorn; 2, 4l. G.P.O., Bucharest and emblem with mail van.

D **1111**

1992.

D5417 **D 1111** 4l. red 20 10
D5418 8l. blue 45 20

D **1163**

1994.

D5586 **D 1163** 10l. brown 10 10
D5587 45l. orange 10 10

1999. Nos. D4762/4 and D4766 surch.
D6018 50l. on 50b. yellow 10 10
D6019 50l. on 1l. red 10 10
D6020 100l. on 2l. green 10 10
D6021 700l. on 1l. red 10 10
D6022 1100l. on 4l. blue 20 20

2001. Nos. D5417 and D5587 surch on both stamps in the pair.
D6173 500l. on 4l. red 10 10
D6174 1000l. on 4l. red 10 10
D6175 2000l. on 45l. orange 10 10

B. Postal Tax Due Stamps

1915. Optd **TIMBRU DE AJUTOR**.
TD643 **D 38** 5b. blue on yellow 45 20
TD644 10b. blue on yellow 65 25

TD **42**

TD **106**

1917. Green or white paper.
TD655 **TD 42** 5b. brown 25 25
TD738 5b. red 45 25
TD654 10b. red 25 25
TD741 10b. brown 45 25

1918. Optd **TAXA DE PLATA**.
TD680 **T 40** 5b. black 70 45
TD681 10b. brown 70 35

1922. As Type TD **42** but inscr "ASSISTENTA SOCIALA". On green or white paper.
TD1028 10b. brown 10 10
TD1029 20b. brown 10 10
TD1030 25b. brown 15 15
TD1031 50b. brown 10 10

1931. Aviation Fund. Optd **TIMBRUL AVIATIEI**.
TD1219 **D 38** 1l. black 20 10
TD1220 2l. black 10 10

1932.

TD1278 **TD 106** 3l. black 1·00 90

POSTAL TAX STAMPS

The following stamps were for compulsory use at certain times on inland mail to raise money for various funds. In some instances where the stamps were not applied the appropriate Postal Tax Postage Due stamps were applied.

Other denominations exist but these were purely for revenue purposes and were not applied to postal matter.

Soldiers' Families Fund

1915. Optd **TIMBRU DE AJUTOR**.
T638 **37** 5b. green 25 10
T639 10b. red 55 20

T **41** The Queen Weaving

T **47** "Charity"

1916.

T649 **T 41** 5b. black 25 20
T710 5b. green 90 20
T650 10b. brown 55 25
T711 10b. black 90 20

The 50b. and 1, 2, 5 and 50l. in similar designs were only used fiscally.

1918. Optd **1918**.
T671 **37** 5b. green (No. T638) 38·00 38·00
T667 **T 41** 5b. black 90 65
T672 **37** 10b. red (No. T639) 38·00 38·00
T668 **T 41** 10b. brown 1·40 55

1921. Social Welfare.
T978 **T 47** 10b. green 20 10
T979 25b. black 20 10

Aviation Fund

T **91**

T **98**

1931.

T1216 **T 91** 50b. green 65 10
T1217 1l. brown 1·10 10
T1218 2l. blue 1·10 25

1932.

T1253 **T 98** 50b. green 40 10
T1254 1l. brown 65 10
T1255 2l. blue 75 10

Stamps as Type **98** but inscr "FONDUL AVIATIEI" were only for fiscal use. Nos. T1252/4 could only be used fiscally after 1937.

T **105**

T **121** "Aviation"

1932. Cultural Fund.
T1276 **T 105** 2l. blue 85 65
T1277 2l. brown 75 55

These were for compulsory use on postcards.

1936.

T1340 **T 121** 50b. green 25 10
T1341 1l. brown 45 10
T1342 2l. blue 45 20

Other stamps inscr "FONDUL AVIATIEI" were only for fiscal use.

T **171** King Michael

1943.

T1589 **T 171** 50b. orange 20 20
T1590 1l. lilac 20 20
T1591 2l. brown 20 20
T1592 4l. blue 20 20
T1593 5l. violet 20 20
T1594 8l. green 20 20
T1595 10l. brown 20 20

1947. Fiscal stamps (22 × 18¾ mm), perf vert through centre surch **IOVR** and value.
T1923 1l. on 2l. red 20 20
T1924 5l. on 1l. green 80 80

1948. Vert designs (approx 18½ × 22 mm). Inscr "I.O.V.R.".
T1948 1l. red 25 45
T1949 1l. violet 65 45
T1950 2l. blue 90 65
T1951 5l. yellow 3·25 2·40

SAVINGS BANK STAMPS

1919. Transylvania. Cluj Issue. No. B199 of Hungary optd as T **42**.
B785 **B 17** 10b. purple 50 70

1919. Transylvania. Oradea Issue. No. B199 of Hungary optd as T **43**.
B861 **B 17** 10b. purple 50 70

ROMANIAN OCCUPATION OF HUNGARY Pt. 2

A. BANAT BACSKA

The following stamps were issued by the Temesvar postal authorities between the period of the Serbian evacuation and the Romanian occupation. This area was later divided, the Western part going to Yugoslavia and the Eastern part going to Romania.

100 filler = 1 korona.

1919. Stamps of Hungary optd **Banat Bacska 1919**. (a) "Turul" Type.
1 **7** 50f. red on blue 11·50 11·50

(b) War Charity stamps of 1916.
2 **20** 10f.(+2f.) red 40 40
3 – 15f.(+2f.) violet 40 40
4 **22** 40f.(+2f.) red 40 40

(c) Harvesters and Parliament Types.
5 **18** 2f. brown 55 55
6 3f. purple 55 55
7 5f. green 55 55
8 6f. blue 55 55
9 15f. purple 55 55
10 35f. brown 11·50 11·50
11 **19** 50f. purple 11·50 11·50
12 75f. blue 55 55
13 80f. green 55 55
14 1k. red 55 55
15 2k. brown 55 55
16 2k. grey and violet 19·00 19·00
17 5k. light brown and brown 1·10 1·10
18 10k. mauve and brown 2·30 2·30

(d) Charles and Zita stamps.
19 **27** 10f. pink 40 40
20 20f. brown 40 40
21 25f. blue 40 40
22 **28** 40f. green 40 40
23 50f. violet 40 40

(e) Harvesters Type inscr "MAGYAR POSTA".
24 **18** 10f. red 11·50 11·50
25 20f. brown 11·50 11·50
26 25f. blue 13·00 13·00

(f) Various Types optd **KOZTARSASAG**. (i) Harvesters and Parliament Types.
27 **18** 4f. grey 55 55
28 5f. green 55 55
29 6f. blue 55 55
30 10f. red 13·00 13·00
31 20f. brown 11·50 11·50
32 40f. green 25 25
33 **19** 1k. red 55 55
34 2k. brown 11·50 11·50
35 3k. grey and violet 11·50 11·50
36 5k. light brown and brown 11·50 11·50
37 10k. mauve and brown 11·50 11·50

(iii) Charles portrait stamps.
38 **27** 15f. purple 11·50 11·50
39 25f. blue 2·30 2·30

(g) Serbian Occupation of Temesvar stamps.
40 **18** 10f. on 2f. brown 55 55
41 **20** 45f. on 10f.(+2f.) red 75 75
42 **18** 1k.50 on 15f. purple 2·30 2·30

EXPRESS LETTER STAMP

1919. No. E245 of Hungary optd **Banat Bacska 30 FILLER 1919**.
E44 **E 18** 30f. on 2f. green and red 1·50 1·50

NEWSPAPER STAMP

1919. No. N136 of Hungary optd **Banat Bacska 1919**.
N43 **N 9** (2f.) orange 55 55

POSTAGE DUE STAMPS

1919. Nos. D191 etc optd as above.
D46 **D 9** 2f. red and green 55 55
D47 10f. red and green 55 55
D48 15f. red and green 11·50 11·50
D49 20f. red and green 55 55
D50 30f. red and green 9·25 9·25
D51 50f. black and green 13·00 13·00

SAVINGS BANK STAMP

1919. No. B199 of Hungary surch **Banat Bacska 50 FILLER 1919**.
B45 **B 17** 50f. on 10f. purple 1·50 1·50

B. DEBRECEN

This area was later returned to Hungary.

100 filler = 1 korona.

(1)

1919. Stamps of Hungary optd with **T1** or surch in addition. (a) "Turul" Type.
1 **7** 2f. yellow 22·00 14·00
2 3f. orange 28·00 28·00
3 6f. brown 4·50 4·50

(b) War Charity stamps of 1915.
4 **7** 2f.+2f. yellow (No. 171) 27·00 27·00
5 3f.+2f. orange (No. 172) 27·00 27·00

(c) War Charity stamps of 1916.
6 **20** 10f.(+2f.) red 40 40
7 – 15f.(+2f.) lilac 1·90 1·90
8 **22** 40f.(+2f.) red 90 90

(d) Harvesters and Parliament Types.
9 **18** 2f. brown 15 15
10 3f. purple 10 10
11 5f. green 40 40
12 6f. blue 15 15
13 10f. red (No. 243) 18·00 18·00
14 15f. violet (No. 244) 25·00 25·00
15 15f. purple 10 10
16 20f. brown 14·00 14·00
17 25f. blue 75 75
18 35f. brown 5·00 5·00
19 35f. on 3f. purple 25 25
20 40f. green 60 60
21 45f. on 2f. brown 25 25
22 **19** 50f. purple 60 60
23 75f. blue 15 15
24 80f. green 40 40
25 1k. red 40 40
26 2k. brown 15 15
27 3k. grey and violet 3·75 3·75
28 3k. on 75f. blue 2·10 2·10
29 5k. light brown and brown 3·75 3·75
30 5k. on 75f. blue 75 75
31 10k. mauve and brown 45·00 15·00
32 10k. on 80f. green 1·40 1·40

(e) Charles and Zita stamps.
33 **27** 10f. pink 4·50 4·25
34 15f. purple 16·00 16·00
35 20f. brown 75 75
36 25f. blue 50 50
37 **28** 40f. green 35 35
38 50f. purple 3·75 3·75

(f) Harvesters and Parliament Types inscr "MAGAR POSTA".
39 **18** 5f. green 10 10
40 6f. blue 2·50 2·50
41 10f. red 10 10
42 20f. brown 10 10
43 25f. blue 10 10
44 45f. orange 2·50 2·50
45 **19** 5k. brown 00

(g) Various Types optd **KOZTARSASAG**. (i) Harvesters and Parliament Types.
46 **18** 2f. brown 25 25
47 3f. purple 4·75 4·75
48 4f. grey 15 15
49 5f. green 10 10
50 10f. red 4·00 4·00
51 20f. brown 40 40
52 40f. green 25 25
53 **19** 1k. red 25 25
54 2k. brown 6·75 6·75
55 3k. grey and violet 1·40 1·40
56 5k. light brown and brown 60·00 60·00

(ii) War Charity stamps of 1916.
57 **20** 10f.(+2f.) red 4·75 4·75
58 – 15f.(+2f.) lilac 19·00 19·00
59 **22** 40f.(+2f.) red 1·40 1·40

(iii) Charles and Zita stamps.
60 **27** 10f. pink 4·25 4·25
61 15f. purple 7·50 7·50
62 20f. brown 1·10 1·10
63 25f. blue 50 50
64 **28** 50f. purple 70 70

2 4

1920. Types **2** and **4** and similar design, optd with inscr as T **1** but in circle.
65 **2** 2f. brown 15 15
66 3f. brown 15 15
67 4f. violet 15 15
68 5f. green 10 10
69 6f. grey 15 15
70 10f. red 10 10
71 15f. violet 25 25
72 20f. brown 10 10
73 – 25f. blue 80 80
74 – 30f. brown 80 80
75 – 35f. purple 80 80
76 – 40f. green 80 80
77 – 45f. red 80 80
78 – 50f. mauve 80 80
79 – 60f. green 80 80
80 – 75f. blue 80 80
81 **4** 80f. green 15 15
82 1k. red 25 25
83 1k.20 orange 4·25 4·25
84 2k. brown 75 75
85 3k. brown 75 75
86 5k. brown 75 75
87 10k. purple 75 75
DESIGN: Nos. 73/80, Horseman using lasso.

5

1920. War Charity. Type **5** with circular opt, and "Segely belyeg" at top.
88 **5** 20f. green 75 75
89 20f. green on blue 25 25
90 50f. brown 1·00 1·00
91 50f. brown on mauve 15 15
92 1k. green 80 80
93 1k. green on green 80 80
94 2k. green 1·10 1·10

EXPRESS LETTER STAMP

1919. No. E245 of Hungary optd with T **1**.
E66 **E 18** 2f. green and red 25 25

NEWSPAPER STAMP

1919. No. N136 of Hungary optd with T **1**.
N65 **N 9** 2f. orange 20 20

POSTAGE DUE STAMPS

1919. (a) Nos. D190 etc of Hungary optd with T **1**.
D68 **D 9** 1f. red and green 5·75 5·75
D69 2f. red and green 15 15
D70 5f. red and green 65·00 65·00
D71 6f. red and green 26·00 26·00
D72 10f. red and green 15 15
D73 12f. red and green 26·00 26·00
D74 15f. red and green 1·30 1·30
D75 20f. red and green 1·30 1·30
D76 30f. red and green 1·30 1·30

(b) With **KOZTARSASAG** opt.
D77 **D 9** 2f. red and green 3·25 3·25
D78 3f. red and green 3·25 3·25
D79 10f. red and green 3·25 3·25
D80 20f. red and green 3·25 3·25
D81 40f. red and green 3·25 3·25
D82 50f. red and green 3·25 3·25

D 6

1920.
D95 **D 6** 5f. green 35 30
D96 10f. green 35 30
D97 20f. green 35 30
D98 30f. green 35 30
D99 40f. green 35 30

SAVINGS BANK STAMP

1919. No. B199 of Hungary optd with T **1**.
B67 **B 17** 10f. purple 5·25 5·25

C. TEMESVAR

After being occupied by Serbia this area was then occupied by Romania. It later became part of Romania and was renamed Timisoara.

100 filler = 1 korona.

1919. Stamps of Hungary surch. (a) Harvesters Type.
6 **18** 30 on 2f. brown 15 15
7 1k. on 4f. grey (optd **KOZTARSASAG**) 15 15
8 150 on 3f. purple 10 10
9 150 on 5f. green 15 15

(b) Express Letter Stamp.
10 **E 18** 3 KORONA on 2f. green and red 25 25

POSTAGE DUE STAMPS

1919. Charity stamp of Hungary surch **PORTO 40**.
D11 40 on 15+(2f.) lilac (No. 265) 30 30

(D 8)

1919. Postage Due stamps of Hungary surch with Type **D 8**.
D12 **D 9** 60 on 2f. red and green 2·25 2·25
D13 60 on 10f. red and green 60 60

ROMANIAN POST OFFICES IN THE TURKISH EMPIRE Pt. 16

Romanian P.O.s in the Turkish Empire including Constantinople. Now closed.

I. GENERAL ISSUES

40 paras = 1 piastre.

1896. Stamps of Romania of 1893 surch in "PARAS".
9 10pa. on 5b. blue (No. 319) 11·00 11·00
10 20pa. on 10b. green (No. 320) 11·00 11·00
11 1pi. on 25b. mauve (No. 322) 11·00 11·00

II. CONSTANTINOPLE

100 bani = 1 leu.

(1)

1919. Stamps of Romania of 1893–1908 optd with T **1**.
18 **37** 5b. green 50 50
19 10b. red 60 60
20 15b. brown 75 75
30 – 25b. blue (No. 701) 80 80
31 – 40b. brown (No. 703) 2·50 2·50

1919. 1916 Postal Tax stamp of Romania optd with T **1**.
33 **T 41** 5b. green 1·60 1·80

ROSS DEPENDENCY Pt. 1

A dependency of New Zealand in the Antarctic on the Ross Sea.

The post office closed on 30 September 1987, but re-opened in November 1994.

1957. 12 pence = 1 shilling;
20 shillings = 1 pound.
1967. 100 cents = 1 dollar.

3 Map of Ross Dependency and New Zealand

4 Queen Elizabeth II

1957.
1 – 3d. blue 1·00 60
2 – 4d. red 1·00 60
3 **3** 8d. red and blue 1·00 60
4 **4** 1s.6d. purple 1·00 60
DESIGNS—HORIZ (As Type **3**): 3d. H.M.S. "Erebus"; 4d. Shackleton and Scott.

5 H.M.S. "Erebus"

1967. Nos. 1/4 with values inscr in decimal currency as T **5**.
5 **5** 2c. blue 7·00 5·50
6 – 3c. red 2·75 4·75
7 **3** 7c. red and blue 2·75 6·00
8 **4** 15c. purple 2·75 9·00

6 South Polar Skua

8 Adelie Penguins and South Polar Skua

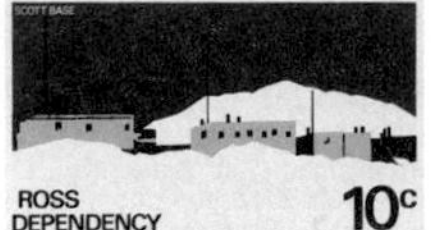

7 Scott Base

1972.
9a **6** 3c. black, grey and blue 70 1·60
10a – 4c. black, blue and violet 15 1·60

11a – 5c. black, grey and lilac . . 15 1·60
12a – 8c. black, grey and brown 15 1·60
13a 7 10c. black, green and grey 15 1·60
14a – 18c. black, violet and light violet . . . . 15 1·60

DESIGNS—As Type **6**: 4c. Lockheed Hercules airplane at Williams Field; 5c. Shackleton's Hut; 8c. Supply ship H.M.N.Z.S. "Endeavour". As Type **7**: 18c. Tabular ice flow.

1982. Multicoloured.
15 5c. Type **8** . . . . 1·25 1·40
16 10c. Tracked vehicles . . . . 20 1·00
17 20c. Scott Base 20 65
18 30c. Field party 20 40
19 40c. Vanda Station 20 40
20 50c. Scott's hut, Cape Evans 20 40

9 South Polar Skua

1994. Wildlife. Multicoloured.
21 5c. Type **9** 10 10
22 10c. Snow petrel chick 10 10
23 20c. Black-browed albatross 15 20
24 40c. Emperor penguins 30 35
25 45c. As 40c. 35 40
26 50c. Bearded penguins ("Chinstrap Penguins") . . 35 40
27 70c. Adelie penguin 50 55
28 80c. Elephant seals 60 65
29 $1 Leopard seal 75 80
30 $2 Weddell seal . . . . 1·50 1·60
31 $3 Crabeater seal pup . . . . 2·20 2·30

10 Capt. James Cook with H.M.S. "Resolution" and H.M.S. "Adventure"

1995. Antarctic Explorers. Multicoloured.
32 40c. Type **10** 75 75
33 80c. James Clark Ross with H.M.S. "Erebus" and H.M.S. "Terror" . . . . . 1·25 1·25
34 $1 Roald Amundsen and "Fram" . . . . 1·40 1·40
35 $1.20 Robert Scott with "Terra Nova" . . . . . 1·75 1·75
36 $1.50 Ernest Shackleton with "Endurance" . . . . 2·00 2·00
37 $1.80 Richard Byrd with Ford 4-AT-B Trimotor "Floyd Bennett" (airplane) . . . . 2·00 2·00

11 Inside Ice Cave **12** Snow Petrel

1996. Antarctic Landscapes. Multicoloured.
38 40c. Type **11** 40 35
39 80c. Base of glacier 70 65
40 $1 Glacier ice fall 85 80
41 $1.20 Climbers on crater rim (horiz) . . . . 1·00 95
42 $1.50 Pressure ridges (horiz) 1·25 1·25
43 $1.80 Fumarole ice tower (horiz) . . . . 1·40 1·40

1997. Antarctic Seabirds. Multicoloured. (a) With "WWF" panda emblem.
44 40c. Type **12** 80 60
45 80c. Pintado petrel ("Cape Petrel") . . . . 1·25 90
46 $1.20 Antarctic fulmar . . . . 1·60 1·25
47 $1.50 Antarctic petrel . . . . 1·60 1·25

(b) Without "WWF" panda emblem.
48 40c. Type **12** . . . . 1·10 80
49 80c. Pintado petrel ("Cape Petrel") . . . . 1·40 1·10
50 $1 Dove prion ("Antarctic Prion") . . . . 1·50 1·25
51 $1.20 Antarctic fulmar . . . . 1·50 1·40
52 $1.50 Antarctic petrel . . . . 1·50 1·40
53 $1.80 Antarctic tern . . . . . 1·60 1·50

Nos. 48/53 were printed together, se-tenant, with the backgrounds forming a composite design.

13 Sculptured Sea Ice

1997. Ice Formation. Multicoloured.
54 40c. Type **13** 50 35
55 80c. Glacial tongue 70 60
56 $1 Stranded tabular iceberg . . 90 80
57 $1.20 Autumn at Cape Evans 1·00 90
58 $1.50 Sea ice in summer thaw 1·25 1·10
59 $1.80 Sunset at tubular icebergs . . . . 1·40 1·40

14 Sea Smoke, McMurdo Sound

1999. Night Skies. Multicoloured.
60 40c. Type **14** 70 55
61 80c. Alpenglow, Mount Erebus 1·10 80
62 $1.10 Sunset, Black Island . . 1·25 1·10
63 $1.20 Pressure ridges, Ross Sea 1·50 1·25
64 $1.50 Evening light, Ross Island . . . . 1·75 1·50
65 $1.80 Mother of pearl clouds, Ross Island . . . . 2·00 1·60

15 R.N.Z.A.F. C130 Hercules

2000. Antarctic Transport. Multicoloured.
66 40c. Type **15** 60 50
67 80c. Hagglunds BV206 All Terrain carrier 90 75
68 $1.10 Tracked 4 × 4 motorbike 1·25 1·00
69 $1.20 ASV track truck . . . . 1·25 1·00
70 $1.50 Squirrel helicopter . . . 1·50 1·25
71 $1.80 Elan skidoo . . . . . . 1·50 1·25

2001. Penguins. As T **604** of New Zealand. Multicoloured.
72 40c. Two emperor penguins 65 60
73 80c. Two adelie penguins . . . 1·00 70
74 90c. Emperor penguin leaving water . . . . 1·10 80
75 $1.30 Adelie penguin in water 1·50 1·25
76 $1.50 Group of emperor penguins . . . . 1·75 1·40
77 $2 Group of adelie penguins 1·90 1·75

16 British Explorers by Sledge

2002. Antarctic Discovery Expedition, 1901–1904. Each black, grey and stone.
78 40c. Type **16** 60 50
79 80c. H.M.S. *Discovery*, at anchor 90 70
80 90c. H.M.S. *Discovery*, trapped in ice . . . . 1·00 80
81 $1.30 Sledges and tents on the ice . . . . 1·40 1·25
82 $1.50 Crew of H.M.S. *Discovery* . . . . 1·60 1·40
83 $2 Scott's base at Hut Point 1·75 1·60

17 *Odontaster validus* (red seastar)

2003. Marine Life. Multicoloured.
84 40c. Type **17** 30 35
85 90c. *Beroe cucumis* (comb jelly) 65 70
86 $1.30 *Macroptychaster accrescens* (giant seastar) . . 95 1·00
87 $1.50 *Sterechinus neumayeri* (sea urchin) . . . . 1·10 1·20
88 $2 *Perkinsiana littoralis* (fan worm) . . . . 1·50 1·60

ROUAD ISLAND (ARWAD) Pt. 6

An island in the E. Mediterranean off the coast of Syria. A French P.O. was established there during 1916.

25 centimes = 1 piastre.

1916. "Blanc" and "Mouchon" key-types inscr "LEVANT" and optd **ILE ROUAD** (vert).
1 A 5c. green £350 £180
2 B 10c. red £375 £200
3 1pi. on 25c. blue £375 £225

1916. "Blanc" "Mouchon" and "Merson" key-types inscr "LEVANT" and optd **ILE ROUAD** horiz.
4 A 1c. grey . . . . 55 3·50
5 2c. purple . . . . 40 3·25
6 3c. red . . . . 85 3·25
7 5c. green . . . . 1·90 3·25
8 B 10c. red . . . . 2·25 3·50
9 15c. red . . . . 2·00 4·00
10 20c. brown . . . . 3·00 4·50
11 1p. on 25c. blue . . . . . 2·75 4·50
12 30c. lilac . . . . 3·25 4·50
13 C 40c. red and blue . . . . . 4·00 7·00
14 2p. on 50c. brown & lav . . 6·75 10·50
15 4p. on 1f. red and yellow . . 11·00 15·00
16 30p. on 5f. blue and yellow 32·00 45·00

RUANDA-URUNDI Pt. 4

Part of German E. Africa, including Ruanda and Urundi, occupied by Belgian forces during the war of 1914–18 and a Trust Territory administered by Belgium until 1 July 1962. The territory then became two separate independent states, named Rwanda and Burundi.

100 centimes = 1 franc.

1916. Nos. 70/77 of Belgian Congo optd. (a) **RUANDA**.
1 **32** 5c. black and green . . . . 42·00
2 **33** 10c. black and red . . . . 42·00
3 **13** 15c. black and green . . . . 65·00
4 **34** 25c. black and blue . . . . 42·00
5 **14** 40c. black and red . . . . 42·00
6 – 50c. black and red . . . . 42·00
7 – 1f. black and brown £160
7a – 5f. black and orange £2000

(b) **URUNDI**.
8 **32** 5c. black and green . . . . 42·00
9 **33** 10c. black and red . . . . 42·00
10 **13** 15c. black and green . . . 65·00
11 **34** 25c. black and blue . . . . 42·00
12 **14** 40c. black and red . . . . 42·00
13 – 50c. black and red . . . . 48·00
14 – 1f. black and brown . . . £160
14a – 5f. black and orange . . . £2000

1916. Stamps of Belgian Congo of 1915 optd **EST AFRICAIN ALLEMAND OCCUPATION BELGE. DUITSCH OOST AFRIKA BELGISCHE BEZETTING.**
15 **32** 5c. black and green 60 65
16 **33** 10c. black and red 70 70
17 **13** 15c. black and green 50 60
18 **34** 25c. black and blue . . . . 3·00 1·50
19 **14** 40c. black and lake . . . . 7·75 5·00
20 – 50c. black and lake . . . . 9·25 4·75
21 – 1f. black and olive . . . . 1·40 85
22 – 5f. black and orange . . . . 2·00 1·75

1918. Belgian Congo Red Cross stamps of 1918 optd **A. O.**
23 **32** 5c.+10c. blue and green . . 15 1·10
24 **33** 10c.+15c. blue and red . . . 35 1·10
25 **13** 15c.+20c. blue and green . . 40 1·10
26 **34** 25c.+25c. blue . . . . . . 60 1·10
27 **14** 40c.+40c. blue and lake . . 60 1·40
28 – 50c.+50c. blue and lake . . 1·00 1·40
29 – 1f.+1f. blue and olive . . . 1·75 3·00
30 – 5f.+5f. blue and orange . . 8·25 8·25
31 – 10f.+10f. blue and green . . 60·00 70·00

1922. Stamps of 1916 surch.
32 – 5c. on 50c. black and lake 1·10 3·25
33 **32** 10c. on 5c. black and green 45 85
34a **14** 25c. on 40c. black and lake 2·75 1·60
35 **33** 30c. on 10c. black and red 35 1·10
36 **34** 50c. on 25c. black and blue 80 1·00

1924. Belgian Congo stamps of 1923 optd **RUANDA URUNDI**.
37 A 5c. yellow 30 65
38 B 10c. green 20 65
39 C 15c. brown 15 40
40 D 20c. green 25 60
41 E 20c. green 15 55
42 F 25c. brown 25 20
43 **46** 30c. pink 20 55
44 30c. green 15 60
66 35c. green 35 65
45 D 40c. purple 30 70
46 G 50c. blue 20 30
47 50c. orange 25 70
48 E 75c. orange 25 30
49 75c. blue 30 25
67 **46** 75c. pink 45 80
50 H 1f. brown 35 60
51 1f. blue 60 35
68 1f. pink 85 60
69 D 1f.50 blue . . . . 1·10 1·40
71 1f.75 blue . . . . 1·25 90
52 I 3f. brown . . . . 2·50 3·50
53 J 5f. grey . . . . 4·50 5·75
54 K 10f. black . . . . 16·00 16·00

1925. Stamp of Belgian Congo optd **RUANDA-URUNDI**. Inscriptions in French or in Flemish.
61 **55** 25c.+25c. black and red . . 40 1·10

1925. Native cattle type of Belgian Congo optd **RUANDA-URUNDI**.
62 **56** 45c. purple 30 95
63 60c. red 35 60

1927. Belgian Congo stamps of 1923 optd **RUANDA URUNDI** in two lines, wide apart.
64 B 10c. green . . . . 25 1·00
65 C 15c. brown . . . . 1·25 2·25
66 **46** 35c. green 20 15
67 75c. red 30 25
68 H 1f. red 45 30
69 D 1f.25 blue 50 40
70 1f.50 blue 60 80
71 1f.75 blue 95 60

1927. No. 144 of Belgian Congo optd **RUANDA URUNDI**.
72 1f.75 on 1f.50 blue . . . . . 40 1·00

1930. Native Fund stamps of Belgian Congo (Nos. 160/8), optd **RUANDA URUNDI**.
73 10c.+5c. red . . . . 40 1·10
74 20c.+10c. brown . . . . . . 90 1·50
75 35c.+15c. green . . . . . . 1·25 2·10
76 60c.+30c. purple . . . . . . 1·50 2·25
77 1f.+50c. red . . . . 2·10 3·25
78 1f.75+75c. blue . . . . . . 2·75 3·25
79 3f.50+1f.50 lake . . . . . . 5·50 7·25
80 5f.+2f.50 brown . . . . . . 4·00 5·75
81 10f.+5f. black . . . . 4·50 6·50

1931. Nos. 68 and 71 surch.
82 H 1f.25 on 1f. red . . . . . . 3·25 1·10
83 D 2f. on 1f.75 blue . . . . . . 4·00 2·25

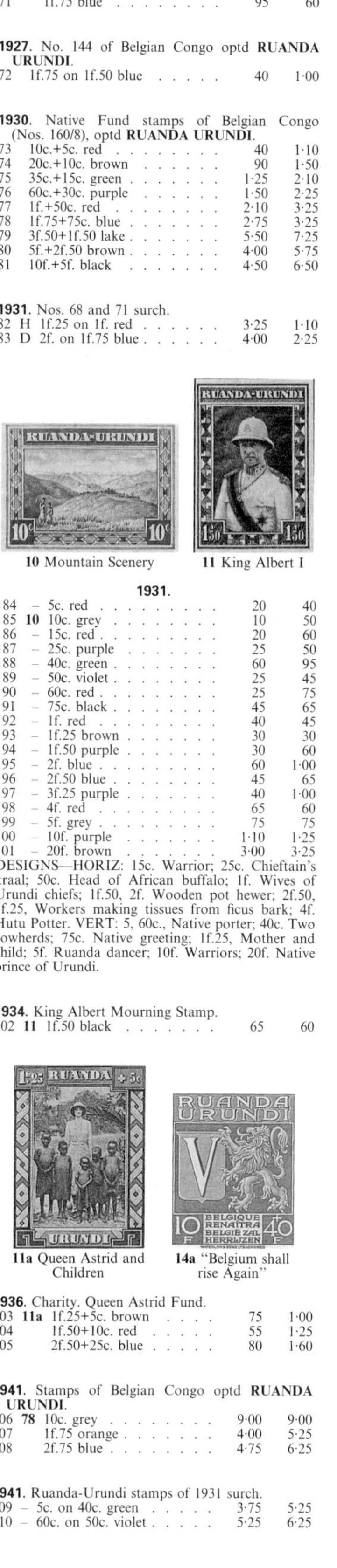

10 Mountain Scenery **11** King Albert I

1931.
84 – 5c. red 20 40
85 **10** 10c. grey 10 50
86 – 15c. red 20 60
87 – 25c. purple 25 50
88 – 40c. green 60 95
89 – 50c. violet 25 45
90 – 60c. red 25 75
91 – 75c. black 45 65
92 – 1f. red 40 45
93 – 1f.25 brown 30 30
94 – 1f.50 purple 30 60
95 – 2f. blue . . . . 60 1·00
96 – 2f.50 blue 45 65
97 – 3f.25 purple . . . . 40 1·00
98 – 4f. red 65 60
99 – 5f. grey 75 75
100 – 10f. purple . . . . 1·10 1·25
101 – 20f. brown . . . . 3·00 3·25

DESIGNS—HORIZ: 15c. Warrior; 25c. Chieftain's kraal; 50c. Head of African buffalo; 1f. Wives of Urundi chiefs; 1f.50, 2f. Wooden pot hewer; 2f.50, 3f.25, Workers making tissues from ficus bark; 4f. Hutu Potter. VERT: 5, 60c., Native porter; 40c. Two cowherds; 75c. Native greeting; 1f.25, Mother and child; 5f. Ruanda dancer; 10f. Warriors; 20f. Native prince of Urundi.

1934. King Albert Mourning Stamp.
102 **11** 1f.50 black 65 60

11a Queen Astrid and Children **14a** "Belgium shall rise Again"

1936. Charity. Queen Astrid Fund.
103 **11a** 1f.25+5c. brown . . . . 75 1·00
104 1f.50+10c. red . . . . . 55 1·25
105 2f.50+25c. blue . . . . . 80 1·60

1941. Stamps of Belgian Congo optd **RUANDA URUNDI**.
106 **78** 10c. grey . . . . 9·00 9·00
107 1f.75 orange . . . . 4·00 5·25
108 2f.75 blue . . . . 4·75 6·25

1941. Ruanda-Urundi stamps of 1931 surch.
109 – 5c. on 40c. green . . . . . 3·75 5·25
110 – 60c. on 50c. violet . . . . . 5·25 6·25

111 – 2f.50 on 1f.50 purple 2·75 3·25
112 – 3f.25 on 2f. blue 11·00 11·00

1941. Stamps of Belgian Congo optd **RUANDA URUNDI** and surch also.
113 – 5c. on 1f.50 black and brown (No. 222) 20 65
114 – 75c. on 90c. brown and red (No. 221) 1·50 1·90
115 **78** 2f.50 on 10f. red 1·90 1·90

1942. War Relief.
116 **14a** 10f.+40f. red 2·40 3·50
117 10f.+40f. blue 2·40 3·50
On No. 116 the French slogan is above the Flemish, on No. 117 vice versa.

1942. Nos. 107/8 of Ruanda-Urundi surch.
118 **78** 75c. on 1f.75 orange 3·75 3·75
119 2f.50 on 2f.75 blue 6·00 6·25

15a Head of Warrior **17** Seated Figure

1942.
120 A 5c. red 10 45
121 10c. green 10 35
122 15c. brown 10 55
123 20c. blue 10 45
124 25c. purple 10 30
125 30c. blue 10 40
126 50c. green 20 20
127 60c. brown 10 35
128 **15a** 75c. black and lilac 30 25
129 1f. black and brown 35 30
130 1f.25 black and red 40 50
131 B 1f.75 brown 1·10 1·10
132 2f. orange 1·10 75
133 2f.50 red 80 15
134 C 3f.50 green 50 20
135 5f. orange 55 35
136 6f. blue 55 35
137 7f. black 50 45
138 10f. brown 90 65
139 – 20f. black and brown 1·75 1·10
140 – 50f. black and red 3·00 2·25
141 – 100f. black and green 5·25 6·00
DESIGNS—As Type **15a** (various frames): A, Oil palms; C, Askari sentry; 20f. Head of zebra. 35 × 24 mm: B, Leopard. 29 × 34 mm: 50f. Askari sentry; 100f. Head of warrior.

1944. Red Cross Fund. Nos. 126, 130, 131 and 134 surch **Au profit de la Croix Rouge Ten voordeele van het Roode Kruis** (50c., 1f.75) or with Flemish and French reversed (others) and premium.
147 50c.+50f. green 1·40 2·50
148 1f.25+100f. black and red 1·90 3·50
149 1f.75+100f. brown 1·75 2·50
150 3f.50+100f. green 1·75 3·50

1948. Native Carvings.
151 **17** 10c. orange 15 65
152 A 15c. blue 15 95
153 B 20c. blue 30 55
154 C 25c. red 50 25
155 D 40c. purple 30 60
156 **17** 50c. brown 30 10
157 A 70c. green 40 50
158 B 75c. purple 75 40
159 C 1f. purple and orange 75 10
160 D 1f.25 red and blue 95 40
161 E 1f.50 red and green 1·75 85
162 **17** 2f. red and vermilion 65 10
163 A 2f.50 green and brown 1·10 10
164 B 3f.50 green and blue 1·25 50
165 C 5f. red and bistre 1·60 15
166 D 6f. green and orange 1·75 15
167 E 10f. brown and violet 2·25 70
168 F 20f. brown and red 3·00 90
169 E 50f. black and brown 5·25 1·50
170 F 100f. black and red 9·00 3·25
DESIGNS: A, Seated figure (different); B, Kneeling figure; C, Double mask; D, Mask; E, Mask with tassels; F, Mask with horns.

1949. Surch.
171 3f. on 2f.50 (No. 163) 65 25
172 4f. on 6f. (No. 166) 1·00 20
173 6f.50 on 6f. (No. 166) 1·25 30

18a St. Francis Xavier **19** "Dissotis"

1953. 400th Death Anniv of St. Francis Xavier.
174 **18a** 1f.50 black and blue 60 70

1953. Flowers Multicoloured.
175 10c. Type **19** 20 40
176 15c. "Protea" 20 45
177 20c. "Vellozia" 20 10
178 25c. "Littonia" 20 40
179 40c. "Ipomoea" 20 45
180 50c. "Angraecum" 35 10
181 60c. "Euphorbia" 65 60
182 75c. "Ochna" 90 40
183 1f. "Hibiscus" 90 10
184 1f.25 "Protea" 1·75 1·25
185 1f.50 "Schizoglossum" 45 10
186 2f. "Ansellia" 3·50 45
187 3f. "Costus" 1·25 10
188 4f. "Nymphaea" 1·75 40
189 5f. "Thunbergia" 1·25 20
190 7f. "Gerbera" 1·75 45
191 8f. "Gloriosa" 2·25 55
192 10f. "Silene" 4·00 50
193 20f. "Aristolochia" 7·25 85

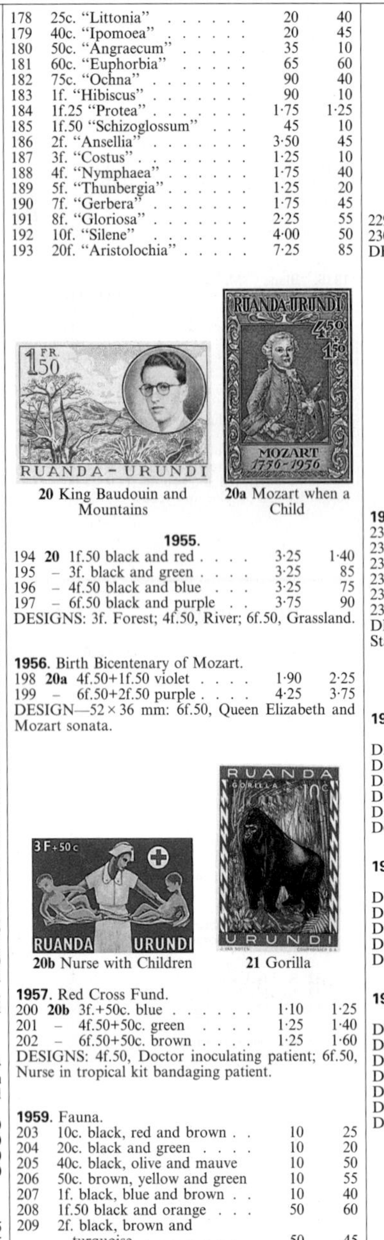

20 King Baudouin and Mountains **20a** Mozart when a Child

1955.
194 **20** 1f.50 black and red 3·25 1·40
195 – 3f. black and green 3·25 85
196 – 4f.50 black and blue 3·25 75
197 – 6f.50 black and purple 3·75 90
DESIGNS: 3f. Forest; 4f.50, River; 6f.50, Grassland.

1956. Birth Bicentenary of Mozart.
198 **20a** 4f.50+1f.50 violet 1·90 2·25
199 – 6f.50+2f.50 purple 4·25 3·75
DESIGN—52 × 36 mm: 6f.50, Queen Elizabeth and Mozart sonata.

20b Nurse with Children **21** Gorilla

1957. Red Cross Fund.
200 **20b** 3f.+50c. blue 1·10 1·25
201 – 4f.50+50c. green 1·25 1·40
202 – 6f.50+50c. brown 1·25 1·60
DESIGNS: 4f.50, Doctor inoculating patient; 6f.50, Nurse in tropical kit bandaging patient.

1959. Fauna.
203 10c. black, red and brown 10 25
204 20c. black and green 10 20
205 40c. black, olive and mauve 10 50
206 50c. brown, yellow and green 10 55
207 1f. black, blue and brown 10 40
208 1f.50 black and orange 50 60
209 2f. black, brown and turquoise 50 45
210 3f. black, red and brown 60 40
211 5f. multicoloured 45 65
212 6f.50 brown, yellow and red 25 35
213 8f. black, mauve and blue 80 80
214 10f. multicoloured 80 75
DESIGNS—VERT: 10c., 1f. Type **21**: 40c., 2f. Eastern black and white colobus. HORIZ: 20c.1f.50, African buffaloes; 50c., 6f.50, Impala; 3, 8f. African elephants; 5, 10f. Eland and common zebras.

22 African Resources

1960. 10th Anniv of African Technical Co-operation Commission. Inscr in French or Flemish.
222 **22** 3f. salmon and blue 20 60

23 High Jumping

1960. Child Welfare Fund. Olympic Games, Rome.
223 50c.+25c. blue and red 20 85
224 1f.50+50c. lake and black 40 90
225 2f.+2f. black and red 50 95
226 3f.+1f.25 red and green 1·25 1·90
227 6f.50+3f.50 green and red 1·40 1·90
DESIGNS: 50c. Type **23**: 1f.50, Hurdling; 2f. Football; 3f. Throwing the javelin; 6f.50, Throwing the discus.

1960. No. 210 surch.
228 3f.50 on 3f. black, red and brown 45 60

25 Leopard

1961.
229 **25** 20f. multicoloured 60 1·00
230 – 50f. multicoloured 1·25 1·70
DESIGN: 50f. Lion and lioness.

26 Usumbura Cathedral

1961. Usumbura Cathedral Fund.
231 **26** 50c.+25c. brown and buff 35 75
232 – 1f.+50c. dp green & grn 30 65
233 – 1f.50+75c. multicoloured 20 75
234 **26** 3f.50+1f.50 blue & lt bl 35 65
235 – 5f.+2f. red and orange 20 95
236 – 6f.50+3f. multicoloured 30 1·00
DESIGNS: 1, 5f. Side view of Cathedral; 1f.50, 6f.50, Stained glass windows.

POSTAGE DUE STAMPS

1924. Postage Due stamps of Belgian Congo optd **RUANDA URUNDI.**
D55 D **54** 5c. brown 10 35
D56a 10c. red 10 50
D57 15c. violet 15 35
D58 30c. green 30 60
D59a 50c. blue 40 65
D60 1f. grey 60 95

1943. Postage Due stamps of Belgian Congo optd **RUANDA URUNDI.**
D142 D **86** 10c. olive 10 1·00
D143 20c. blue 15 80
D144 50c. green 30 1·00
D145 1f. brown 45 1·00
D146 2f. orange 45 1·25

1959. Postage Due stamps of Belgian Congo optd **RUANDA URUNDI.**
D215 D **99** 10c. brown 40 55
D216 20c. purple 30 70
D217 50c. green 75 80
D218 1f. blue 90 80
D219 2f. red 1·00 1·10
D220 4f. violet 1·25 1·50
D221 6f. blue 1·25 1·75

For later issues see **BURUNDI** and **RWANDA**.

RUSSIA Pt. 10

A country in the E. of Europe and N. Asia. An empire until 1917 when the Russian Socialist Federal Soviet Republic was formed. In 1923 this became the Union of Soviet Socialist Republics (U.S.S.R.), eventually comprising 15 constituent republics.

In 1991 the U.S.S.R. was dissolved and subsequent issues were used in the Russian Federation only.

100 kopeks = 1 rouble.

1

5

8

9 10

11

1858. Imperf.

No.	Type	Description	Mint	Used
1	1	10k. blue and brown	£4000	£400

1858. Perf.

No.	Type	Description	Mint	Used
21	1	10k. blue and brown	32·00	25
22		20k. orange and blue	55·00	7·50
23		30k. green and red	75·00	25·00

1863.

No.	Type	Description	Mint	Used
8	5	5k. black and blue	20·00	£140

No. 8 was first issued as a local but was later authorised for general use.

1864.

No.	Type	Description	Mint	Used
18	9	1k. black and yellow	3·00	35
30		2k. black and red	6·50	60
19b		3k. black and green	4·00	45
20		5k. black and lilac	7·50	25

1875.

No.	Type	Description	Mint	Used
31	8	7k. red and grey	6·00	25
32		8k. red and grey	9·00	40
33		10k. blue and brown	25·00	3·00
34		20k. orange and blue	30·00	2·50

12 No thunderbolts

1883. Posthorns in design without thunderbolts, as T 12.

No.	Type	Description	Mint	Used
38	9	1k. orange	3·00	45
39		2k. green	4·00	45
41		3k. red	4·25	30
42b		5k. purple	3·50	15
43b		7k. blue	3·75	15
44	10	14k. red and blue	9·00	35
45		35k. green and purple	20·00	4·00
46		70k. orange and brown	40·00	4·00
47	11	3r.50 grey and black	£425	£275
48		7r. yellow and black	£450	£375

14

15

13 With thunderbolts

1889. Posthorns in design with thunderbolts as T 13. Perf.

No.	Type	Description	Mint	Used
50	9	1k. orange	25	10
51		2k. green	25	10
52		3k. red	30	10
53	14	4k. red	40	10
54	9	5k. purple	70	10
55		7k. blue	35	10
56	14	10k. blue	70	10
114A	10	14k. red and blue	10	10
100		15k. blue and purple	10	10
116A	14	20k. red and blue	10	10
102	10	25k. violet and green	10	10
103		35k. green and purple	10	10
119A	14	50k. green and purple	10	10
120A	10	70k. orange and brown	10	10
121A	15	1r. orange and brown	10	10
79	11	3r.50 grey and black	9·00	3·00
122A		3r.50 green and red	20	30
80		7r. yellow and black	8·50	5·00
124bA		7r. pink and green	20	50

For imperf stamps, see Nos. 107B/125aB.

16 Monument to Admiral Kornilov at Sevastopol

1905. War Orphans Fund (Russo-Japanese War).

No.	Type	Description	Mint	Used
88	16	3 (6) k. brown, red and green	2·75	2·00
82	–	5 (8) k. purple and yellow	2·75	2·50
83	–	7 (10) k. blue, lt blue & pink	3·50	3·00
87	–	10 (13) k. blue, lt bl & yell	5·00	3·75

DESIGNS: 5(8) k. Monument to Minin and Pozharsky, Moscow; 7(10) k. Statue of Peter the Great, St. Petersburg; 10(13) k. Moscow Kremlin.

22

23

20

1906.

No.	Type	Description	Mint	Used
107A	22	1k. orange	10	10
93		2k. green	10	10
94		3k. red	10	10
95	23	4k. red	10	10
96	22	5k. red	10	10
97		7k. blue	10	10
98a	23	10k. blue	10	10
123Aa	20	5r. blue and green	30	30
125Aa		10r. grey, red and yellow	60	65

For imperf stamps, see Nos. 107B/125aB.

25 Nicholas II

26 Elizabeth

27 The Kremlin

1913. Tercentenary of Romanov Dynasty. Views as T 27 and portraits as T 25/26.

No.	Type	Description	Mint	Used
126		1k. orange (Peter I)	30	15
127		2k. green (Alexander II)	40	15
128		3k. red (Alexander III)	40	15
129		4k. red (Peter I)	40	15
130		7k. brown (Type 25)	40	15
131		10k. blue (Nicholas II)	50	15
132		14k. green (Katherine II)	50	20
133		15k. brown (Nicholas I)	75	30
134		20k. olive (Alexander I)	1·10	30
135		25k. red (Alexis)	1·75	50
136		35k. green and violet (Paul I)	1·75	60
137		50k. grey and brown (T 26)	3·50	60
138		70k. brown and green (Michael I, the first Russian tsar)	3·50	1·25
139		1r. green (Type 27)	8·50	2·25
140		2r. brown	10·00	3·75
141		3r. violet	24·00	8·00
142		5r. brown	32·00	18·00

DESIGNS—As T 27: 2r. The Winter Palace; 3r. Romanov House, Moscow (birthplace of first Romanov tsar). 23 × 29 mm: 5r. Nicholas II.

31 Russian hero, Ilya Muromets

1914. War Charity.

No.	Type	Description	Mint	Used
151	31	1 (2) k. green & red on yell	60	1·50
144	–	3 (4) k. green and red on red	50	1·25
145	–	7 (8) k. green and brown on buff	50	2·75
161	–	10 (11) k. brown and blue on blue	1·00	2·00

DESIGNS: 3k. Cossack shaking girl's hand; 7k. Symbolical of Russia surrounded by her children; 10k. St. George and Dragon.

1915. As last. Colours changed.

No.	Type	Description	Mint	Used
155	31	1 (2) k. grey and brown	1·00	2·00
156	–	3 (4) k. black and red	1·00	2·50
158	–	10 (11) k. brown and blue	1·00	2·00

35

39

41

45 Cutting the Fetters

1915. Nos. 131, 133 and 134 printed on card with inscriptions on back as T 35. No gum.

No.	Type	Description	Mint	Used
165		10k. blue	1·50	5·00
166		15k. brown	1·50	5·00
167		20k. olive	1·50	5·00

1916. Various types surch.

No.	Type	Description	Mint	Used
168	–	10k. on 7k. brown (No. 130)	40	25
170	22	10k. on 7k. blue	40	15
169	–	20k. on 14k. green (No. 132)	40	20
171	10	20k. on 14k. red and blue	40	15

1917. Various earlier types, but imperf.

No.	Type	Description	Mint	Used
107B	22	1k. orange	10	10
108B		2k. green	10	10
109B		3k. red	10	10
110B	23	4k. red	15	25
111B	22	5k. lilac	10	10
113B	23	10k. blue	10·00	27·00
115B	10	15k. blue & pur (No. 100)	10	10
116B	14	20k. red and blue	15	30
117Bd	10	25k. vio & grn (No. 102)	50	1·00
118B		35k. grn & pur (No. 103)	15	25
119B	14	50k. green and purple	15	25
120B	10	70k. orange and brown (No. 120)	10	30
121B	15	1r. orange and brown	10	10
122B	11	3r.50 green and red	20	30
123Ba	20	5r. blue and green	30	60
124B	11	7r. pink and green	50	1·40
125B	20	10r. grey, red and yellow	22·00	30·00

1916. Types of 1913 printed on card with surch on back as T 39 or 41, or optd with figure "1" or "2" in addition on front. No gum.

No.	Type	Description	Mint	Used
172	39	1k. orange (No. 126)	20·00	35·00
175		1 on 1k. orange (No. 126)	1·00	5·00
177	41	1 on 1k. orange (No. 126)	75	4·50
173	39	2k. green (No. 127)	40·00	45·00
176		2 on 2k. green (No. 127)	1·00	5·00
178	41	2 on 2k. green (No. 127)	75	4·75
174	39	3k. red (No. 128)	1·00	4·00
179	41	3k. red (No. 128)	75	4·50

1918.

No.	Type	Description	Mint	Used
187	45	35k. blue	1·50	4·00
188		70k. brown	1·50	5·00

46 Agriculture and Industry

47 Triumph of Revolution

48 Agriculture

49 Industry

55 Science and Arts

56

64 Industry

1921. Imperf.

No.	Type	Description	Mint	Used
195	48	1r. orange	1·25	7·50
196		2r. brown	1·25	7·50
197	49	5r. blue	1·50	7·50
198	46	20r. blue	2·50	4·00
199	47	40r. blue	2·50	4·00
214	48	100r. yellow	10	10
215		200r. brown	10	25
216	55	250r. purple	10	10
217	48	300r. green	20	40
218	49	500r. blue	25	45
219		1000r. red	10	10
256	64	5000r. violet	50	85
257	46	7500r. blue	30	30
259		7500r. blue on buff	50	35
258	64	10000r. blue	5·00	10·00
260		22500r. purple on buff	50	50

1921. 4th Anniv of October Revolution. Imperf.

No.	Type	Description	Mint	Used
227	56	100r. orange	50	2·00
228		250r. violet	50	2·00
229		1000r. purple	50	2·00

57 Famine Relief Work

58

Р. С. Ф. С. Р.
ГОЛОДАЮЩИМ
250 р.+250 р.
(62)

1921. Charity. Volga Famine. Imperf.

No.	Type	Description	Mint	Used
230	57	2250r. green	5·00	7·50
231		2250r. red	3·75	8·00
232		2250r. brown	7·50	11·00
233	58	2250r. blue	10·00	15·00

1922. Surch. Imperf.

No.	Type	Description	Mint	Used
239	48	5000r. on 1r. orange	1·00	2·00
240		5000r. on 2r. brown	1·00	2·00
236	49	5000r. on 5r. blue	1·00	2·50
242	46	5000r. on 20r. blue	2·00	2·75
243	47	10000r. on 40r. blue	1·50	3·00

1922. Famine Relief. Surch as T 62. Perf.

No.	Type	Description	Mint	Used
245	45	100r.+100r. on 70k. brown	80	1·50
247		250r.+250r. on 25k. blue	80	1·75

(63)

1922. Surch as T 63. Imperf.

No.	Type	Description	Mint	Used
250	55	7500r. on 250r. purple	20	15
251		100000r. on 250r. purple	15	30

65

1922. Obligatory Tax. Rostov-on-Don issue. Famine Relief. Various sizes. Without gum. Imperf.

No.	Type	Description	Unused	Used
261	65	2T. (2000r.) green	32·00	£200
262	–	2T. (2000r.) red	25·00	£200
263	–	4T. (4000r.) red	50·00	£200
264	–	6T. (6000r.) green	40·00	£200

DESIGNS: 2T. red, Worker and family (35 × 42 mm); 4T. Clasped hands (triangular, 57 mm each side); 6T. Sower (29 × 59 mm).

РСФСР
Филателия
– детям
19 - 8 - 22

(**70** "Philately for the children")

1922. Optd with T **70**. Perf or imperf.

No.	Type	Description	Unused	Used
273	22	1k. orange	£200	£300
274		2k. green	18·00	20·00
275		3k. red	10·00	12·00
276		5k. red	8·00	12·00
277	23	10k. blue	8·00	15·00

71

73

1922. 5th Anniv of October Revolution. Imperf.

No.	Type	Description	Unused	Used
279	71	5r. black and yellow	60	45
280		10r. black and brown	60	45
281		25r. black and purple	2·50	1·25
282		27r. black and red	6·00	5·50
283		45r. black and blue	4·00	5·00

1922. Air. Optd with airplane. Imperf.

No.	Type	Description	Unused	Used
284	71	45r. black and green	22·00	45·00

1922. Famine Relief. Imperf.

No.	Type	Description	Unused	Used
285	73	20r.+5r. lilac	60	2·00
286	–	20r.+5r. violet	60	2·00
287	–	20r.+5r. blue	1·00	2·50
288	–	20r.+5r. blue	3·50	15·00

DESIGNS—HORIZ: No. 286, Freighter; No. 287, Steam train. VERT: No. 288, Airplane.

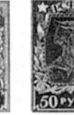

(77)

78 Worker

79 Soldier

1922. Surch as T **77**. Imperf or perf.

No.	Type	Description	Unused	Used
289	14	5r. on 20k. red and blue	3·50	20·00
290	10	20r. on 15k. blue & purple	3·75	20·00
291		20r. on 70k. orange and brown	15	30
292a	14	30r. on 50k. green & pur	35	35
293	10	40r. on 15k. blue & pur	15	15
294		100r. on 15k. blue & pur	15	20
295		200r. on 15k. blue & pur	15	20

1922. Imperf or perf.

No.	Type	Description	Unused	Used
303	78	10r. blue	10	15
304	79	50r. brown	10	15
305		70r. purple	10	15
310		100r. red	15	15

1 мая
1923 г. Филателия —
Трудящимся,
1 р.+1 р.

(80)

1923. Charity. Surch as T **80**. Imperf.

No.	Type	Description	Unused	Used
315	71	1r.+1r. on 10r. black and brown	30·00	40·00
317	55	2r.+2r. on 250r. purple	30·00	40·00
318	64	4r.+4r. on 5000r. violet	45·00	55·00

83 Worker

84 Peasant

85 Soldier

1923. Perf.

No.	Type	Description	Unused	Used
320	85	3r. red	10	10
321	83	4r. brown	10	10
322	84	5r. blue	10	10
323	85	10r. grey	15	15
324		20r. purple	25	25

86 Reaper

88 Tractor

1923. Agricultural Exn, Moscow. Imperf or perf.

No.	Type	Description	Unused	Used
325	86	1r. brown and orange	2·00	6·00
326	–	2r. green and light green	2·00	6·00
327	88	5r. blue and light blue	2·00	6·00
328	–	7r. rose and pink	2·00	6·00

DESIGNS: As Type **86**: 2r. Sower; 7r. Exhibition buildings.

90 Worker

91 Peasant

92 Soldier

93

94

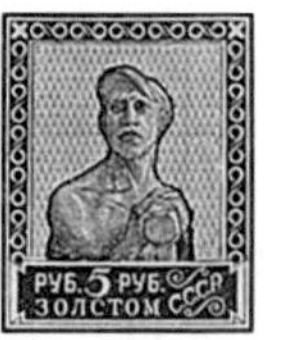
95

1923. Perf (some values also imperf).

No.	Type	Description	Unused	Used
335	90	1k. yellow	40	25
359	91	2k. green	30	15
360	92	3k. brown	35	15
361	90	4k. red	35	15
434		5k. purple	55	15
363	91	6k. blue	60	15
364	92	7k. brown	60	15
437	90	8k. olive	90	15
366	91	9k. red	90	40
341	92	10k. blue	55	15
385	90	14k. grey	1·00	20
386	91	15k. yellow	1·25	90
442	92	18k. violet	1·75	55
443	90	20k. green	2·00	30
444	91	30k. violet	2·75	40
445	92	40k. grey	4·00	60
343	91	50k. brown	4·50	60
447	92	1r. red and brown	4·75	80
375	93	2r. green and red	6·50	3·00
449	94	3r. green and brown	14·00	4·00
450	95	5r. brown and blue	17·00	5·00

96 Lenin

97 Fokker F.III Airplane

1924. Lenin Mourning. Imperf or perf.

No.	Type	Description	Unused	Used
413	96	3k. black and red	2·00	1·75
414		6k. black and red	2·00	1·75
411		12k. black and red	5·00	75
412		20k. black and red	2·75	85

1924. Air. Surch. Imperf.

No.	Type	Description	Unused	Used
417	97	5k. on 3r. blue	3·50	1·75
418		10k. on 5r. green	3·50	1·50
419		15k. on 1r. brown	2·00	1·50
420		20k. on 10r. red	2·50	1·25

С.С.С.Р.
пострадавшему
от наводнения
Ленинграду.
3 к.+10 к.

(**99** Trans "For the victims of the flood in Leningrad")

102 Lenin Mausoleum, Moscow

1924. Leningrad Flood Relief. Surch as T **99**. Imperf.

No.	Type	Description	Unused	Used
421	48	3+10k. on 100r. yellow	1·50	1·75
422		7+20k. on 200r. brown	1·50	1·75
423		14+30k. on 300r. green	2·75	2·50
424	49	12+40k. on 500r. blue	2·75	3·00
425		20+50k. on 1000r. red	2·75	2·75

1925. 1st Death Anniv of Lenin. Imperf or perf.

No.	Type	Description	Unused	Used
426	102	7k. blue	3·50	2·75
427		14k. olive	4·50	4·00
428		20k. red	5·00	4·00
429		40k. brown	7·50	4·00

104 Lenin

106 Prof. Lomonosov and Academy of Sciences, Leningrad

1925.

No.	Type	Description	Unused	Used
451	104	1r. brown	8·00	3·00
452		2r. brown	7·50	2·50
850		3r. green	2·25	75
851		5r. brown	3·50	1·50
852		10r. blue	7·50	5·00

1925. Bicentenary of Academy of Sciences.

No.	Type	Description	Unused	Used
456b	106	3k. brown	4·00	2·00
457		15k. olive	6·00	4·00

107 A. S. Popov

110 Moscow Barricade

1925. 30th Anniv of Popov's Radio Discoveries.

No.	Type	Description	Unused	Used
458	107	7k. blue	2·50	1·40
459		14k. green	4·00	2·25

1925. 20th Anniv of 1905 Rebellion. Imperf or perf.

No.	Type	Description	Unused	Used
463b	–	3k. green	3·00	1·75
464c	–	7k. brown	4·00	2·50
465a	110	14k. red	3·50	2·25

DESIGNS—VERT: 3k. Postal rioters; 7k. Orator and crowd.

111 "Decembrists in Exiles" (detail, A. Moravov)

112 Senate Square, St. Petersburg, 1825

1925. Centenary of Decembrist Rebellion. Imperf or perf.

No.	Type	Description	Unused	Used
466b	111	3k. green	2·50	2·25
467	112	7k. brown	4·00	3·25
468	–	14k. red	5·00	3·50

DESIGN—VERT: 14k. Medallion with heads of Pestel, Ryleev, Bestuzhev-Ryumin, Muravev-Apostol and Kakhovsky.

114

1926. 6th International Proletarian Esperanto Congress.

No.	Type	Description	Unused	Used
471	114	7k. red and green	5·00	3·00
472		14k. violet and green	5·00	1·75

115 Waifs

116 Lenin when a Child

1926. Child Welfare.

No.	Type	Description	Unused	Used
473	115	10k. brown	90	45
474	116	20k. blue	2·50	95

1927. Same type with new inscriptions.

No.	Type	Description	Unused	Used
475	115	8k.+2k. green	80	35
476	116	18k.+2k. red	1·75	65

ПОЧТОВАЯ
МАРКА
КОП. 8 КОП.

(117)

1927. Postage Due stamps surch with T **117**.

No.	Type	Description	Unused	Used
491	D 104	8k. on 1k. red	1·50	2·75
492		8k. on 2k. violet	1·50	2·75
493		8k. on 3k. blue	1·50	2·75
494		8k. on 7k. yellow	1·50	2·75
494c		8k. on 8k. green	1·00	2·25
494d		8k. on 10k. blue	1·50	2·75
494f		8k. on 14k. brown	1·50	2·75

1927. Various types of 7k. surch (some values imperf or perf).

No.	Type	Description	Unused	Used
495	92	8k. on 7k. brown	6·00	6·00
523	107	8k. on 7k. blue	3·00	3·25
524	–	8k. on 7k. brn (No. 464c)	6·00	5·00
527	112	8k. on 7k. brown	6·00	6·50
526	114	8k. on 7k. red and green	12·00	14·00

119 Dr. Zamenhof

1927. 40th Anniv of Publication of Zamenhof's "Langue Internationale" (Esperanto).

No.	Type	Description	Unused	Used
498	119	14k. green and brown	3·00	2·00

120 Tupolev ANT-3 Biplane and Map

1927. 1st Int Air Post Congress, The Hague.

No.	Type	Description	Unused	Used
499	120	10k. blue and brown	14·00	5·00
500		15k. red and olive	16·00	10·00

121 Worker, Soldier and Peasant

124 Sailor and Worker

122 Allegory of Revolution

1927. 10th Anniv of October Revolution.

No.	Type	Description	Unused	Used
501	121	3k. red	2·50	75
502	122	5k. brown	6·00	2·00
503	–	7k. green	8·00	2·50
504	124	8k. black and brown	4·25	85
505	–	14k. red and blue	6·00	1·25
506	–	18k. blue	4·00	1·00
507	–	28k. brown	13·00	8·00

DESIGNS—HORIZ: (As Type **122**): HORIZ: 7k. Smolny Institute; 14k. Map of Russia inscr "С.С.С.Р."; 18k. Various Russian races; 28k. Worker, soldier and peasant.

128 Worker

129 Peasant

130 Lenin

1927.

No.	Type	Description	Unused	Used
508	128	1k. orange	90	50
509	129	2k. green	90	20
510	128	4k. blue	90	20
511	129	5k. brown	90	20
512		7k. red	4·50	1·00
513	128	8k. green	2·50	20
514		10k. brown	2·00	20
515	130	14k. green	2·25	45
516		18k. olive	3·00	40
517		18k. blue	5·00	70
518	129	20k. olive	2·75	35
519	128	40k. red	6·00	60
520	129	50k. blue	8·00	1·00
521	128	70k. olive	13·00	1·40
522	129	80k. orange	24·00	5·00

131 Infantryman, Lenin Mausoleum and Kremlin

1928. 10th Anniv of Red Army.

No.	Type	Description	Mint	Used
529	**131**	8k. brown	1·60	45
530	–	14k. blue	3·00	50
531	–	18k. red	3·00	1·75
532	–	28k. green	4·00	4·00

DESIGNS: 14k. Sailor and cruiser "Aurora"; 18k. Cavalryman; 28k. Airman.

135 Young Factory Workers

137 Trumpeter sounding the Assembly

1929. Child Welfare.

No.	Type	Description	Mint	Used
536	**135**	10k.+2k. brown & sepia	1·75	1·10
537	–	20k.+2k. blue & brown	2·75	2·75

DESIGN: 20k. Children in harvest field.

See also Nos. 567/8.

1929. 1st All-Union Gathering of Pioneers.

No.	Type	Description	Mint	Used
538	**137**	10k. brown	12·00	8·00
539		14k. blue	6·00	4·00

138 Worker (after I. Shadr)

139 Factory Girl

140 Peasant

141 Farm Girl

142 Guardsman

143 Worker, Soldier and Peasant (after I. Smirnov)

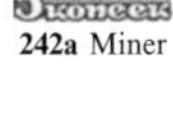

144 Lenin

242a Miner

242b Steel foundryman

242c Infantryman

242d Airman

242e Arms of U.S.S.R.

149 Central Telegraph Office, Moscow

150 Lenin Hydro-electric Power Station

743a Farm Girl

743b Architect

744 Furnaceman

1929. Perf, but some values exist imperf.

No.	Type	Description	Mint	Used
541	**138**	1k. yellow	50	15
542	**139**	2k. green	50	10
543	**140**	3k. blue	60	10
544	**141**	4k. mauve	90	15
545	**142**	5k. brown	90	10
847a	**242a**	5k. red	25	10
546	**143**	7k. red	2·00	60
547	**138**	10k. grey	1·40	10
727f	**139**	10k. blue	75	15
1214b		10k. black	65	15
554	**144**	14k. blue	1·50	60
548	**143**	15k. blue	2·00	10
847b	**242b**	15k. blue	1·75	30
847c	**242c**	15k. green	50	15
549	**140**	20k. green and blue	2·75	20
727h	**141**	20k. green	70	25
2252a	**743a**	20k. olive	80	30
2252b	**743b**	25k. brown	1·00	45
550	**139**	30k. violet and lilac	4·00	50
847d	**242d**	30k. blue	1·00	20
727l	**144**	40k. blue	1·50	40
727m	**141**	50k. brown and buff	1·25	40
847f	**242e**	60k. red	1·50	30
2253	**744**	60k. red	1·00	20
2253a		60k. blue	3·00	1·00
552	**142**	70k. red and pink	7·00	1·40
553	**140**	80k. brown and yellow	7·00	1·25
561	**149**	1r. blue	2·50	40
562	**150**	3r. brown and green	18·00	6·00

Nos. 727f, 1214b and 550 show the factory girl without factory in background. Nos. 549, 727m, 552, 553 have designs like those shown but with unshaded background.

151 Industry

153 "More metal more machines"

1929. Industrial Loan Propaganda.

No.	Type	Description	Mint	Used
563	**151**	5k. brown	2·00	1·25
564	–	10k. olive	2·50	2·00
565	**153**	20k. green	9·00	3·25
566	–	28k. violet	5·00	3·25

DESIGNS—HORIZ: 10k. Tractors. VERT: 28k. Blast furnace and graph of pig-iron output.

1930. Child Welfare.

No.	Type	Description	Mint	Used
567	**135**	10k.+2k. olive	1·50	1·75
568	–	20k.+2k. grn (as No. 537)	2·50	3·50

155 Cavalrymen (after M. Grekov)

1930. 10th Anniv of 1st Red Cavalry.

No.	Type	Description	Mint	Used
569	**155**	2k. green	2·50	1·40
570	–	5k. brown	2·50	1·40
571	–	10k. olive	5·00	3·00
572	–	14k. blue and red	2·50	2·50

DESIGNS: 5k. Cavalry attack (after Yu. Merkulov); 10k. Cavalry facing left (after M. Grekov); 14k. Cavalry charge (after Yu. Merkulov).

159 Group of Soviet Pupils

1930. Educational Exhibition, Leningrad.

No.	Type	Description	Mint	Used
573	**159**	10k. green	2·00	1·00

160

1930. Air. "Graf-Zeppelin" (airship) Flight to Moscow.

No.	Type	Description	Mint	Used
574	**160**	40k. blue	30·00	18·00
575		80k. red	35·00	13·00

162 Battleship "Potemkin"

1930. 25th Anniv of 1905 Rebellion. Imperf or perf.

No.	Type	Description	Mint	Used
576	**162**	3k. red	1·75	50
577	–	5k. blue	1·50	60
578	–	10k. red and green	2·75	1·10

DESIGNS—HORIZ: 5k. Barricade and rebels. VERT: 10k. Red flag at Presnya barricade.

165 From the Tundra (reindeer) to the Steppes (camel)

166 Above Dnieprostroi Dam

1931. Airship Construction Fund. Imperf or perf.

No.	Type	Description	Mint	Used
579c	**165**	10k. violet	4·00	2·50
580b	**166**	15k. blue	22·00	12·00
581c	–	20k. red	3·50	3·00
582b	–	50k. brown	3·50	3·00
583c	–	1r. green	5·50	5·00

DESIGNS—As Type **165**. VERT: 20k. Above Lenin's Mausoleum. HORIZ: 1r. Airship construction. As Type **166**: 50k. Above the North Pole.

See also No. E592.

170 "Graf Zeppelin" over Ice breaker "Malygin"

1931. Air. "Graf Zeppelin" (airship) North Pole Flight. Imperf or perf.

No.	Type	Description	Mint	Used
584	**170**	30k. purple	25·00	15·00
585b		35k. green	25·00	13·00
586		1r. black	25·00	15·00
587		2r. blue	25·00	15·00

172 Maksim Gorky

173 Storming the Winter Palace

1932. 40th Anniv of Publication of "Makar Chadra".

No.	Type	Description	Mint	Used
590	**172**	15k. brown	5·00	3·50
591		35k. blue	18·00	10·00

1932. Airship Construction Fund. Imperf or perf.

No.	Type	Description	Mint	Used
592	**166**	15k. black	3·50	1·50

1932. 15th Anniv of October Revolution.

No.	Type	Description	Mint	Used
593	–	3k. violet	1·25	50
594	**173**	5k. brown	1·25	50
595	–	10k. blue	3·25	1·25
596	–	15k. green	1·75	1·25
597	–	20k. red	7·25	1·75
598	–	30k. grey	9·00	1·90
599	–	35k. brown	60·00	45·00

DESIGNS—HORIZ: 10k. Dnieper Dam; 15k. Harvesting with combines; 20k. Industrial works, Magnitogorsk; 30k. Siberians listening to Moscow broadcast. VERT: 3k. Lenin's arrival in Petrograd; 35k. People of the World hailing Lenin.

175 "Liberation"

1932. 10th Anniv of International Revolutionaries' Relief Organization.

No.	Type	Description	Mint	Used
600	**175**	50k. red	14·00	6·00

176 Museum of Fine Arts

1932. 1st All-Union Philatelic Exn, Moscow.

No.	Type	Description	Mint	Used
601	**176**	15k. brown	24·00	13·00
602		35k. blue	40·00	20·00

177 Trier, Marx's Birthplace

1933. 50th Death Anniv of Marx.

No.	Type	Description	Mint	Used
603	**177**	3k. green	4·00	90
604	–	10k. brown	7·00	1·40
605	–	35k. purple	10·00	12·50

DESIGNS—VERT: 10k. Marx's grave, Highgate Cemetery; 35k. Marx.

1933. Leningrad Philatelic Exhibition. Surch **LENINGRAD 1933** in Russian characters and premium.

No.	Type	Description	Mint	Used
606	**176**	15k.+30k. black & brn	80·00	40·00
607		35k.+70k. blue	95·00	50·00

182

183

1933. Ethnographical Issue. Racial types.

No.	Type	Description	Mint	Used
608	–	1k. brown (Kazakhs)	1·75	40
609	**183**	2k. blue (Lesgins)	1·75	40
610	–	3k. green (Crimean Tatars)	1·75	40
611	–	4k. brown (Jews of Birobidzhan)	1·25	60
612	–	5k. red (Tungusians)	1·25	40
613	–	6k. blue (Buryats)	1·25	40
614	–	7k. brown (Chechens)	1·25	40
615	–	8k. red (Abkhazians)	1·75	55
616	–	9k. blue (Georgians)	3·00	60
617	–	10k. brown (Samoyedes)	4·00	1·50
618	–	14k. green (Yakuts)	3·50	40
619	–	15k. purple (Ukrainians)	4·00	1·25
620	–	15k. black (Uzbeks)	4·00	80
621	–	15k. blue (Tadzhiks)	4·00	75
622	–	15k. brown (Transcaucasians)	4·00	75
623	–	15k. green (Byelorussians)	3·50	60
624	–	15k. orange (Great Russians)	3·50	80
625	–	15k. red (Turkmens)	4·50	1·00
626	–	20k. blue (Koryaks)	9·00	1·60
627	–	30k. red (Bashkirs)	10·00	1·75
628	**182**	35k. brown (Chuvashes)	16·00	2·25

SIZES: Nos. 608, 610/11, 614/17, 626/7, As T **182**: Nos. 612/13, 618. As T **183**: Nos. 619/24, 48 × 22 mm. No. 625, 22 × 48 mm.

186 V. V. Vorovsky

1933. Communist Party Activists. Dated "1933", "1934" or "1935".

No.	Type	Description	Mint	Used
629	**186**	1k. green	65	50
718b	–	2k. violet	4·50	25
630	–	3k. blue	1·40	60
719	–	4k. purple	5·00	4·00
631	–	5k. brown	3·00	1·90
632	–	10k. blue	16·00	6·00
633	–	15k. red	40·00	20·00
720	–	40k. brown	9·00	5·00

DESIGNS: 2k. M. Frunze; 3k. V. M. Volodarsky; 4k. N. E. Bauman; 5k. M. S. Uritsky; 10k. Iacov M. Sverdlov; 15k. Viktor P. Nogin; 40k. S. M. Kirov.

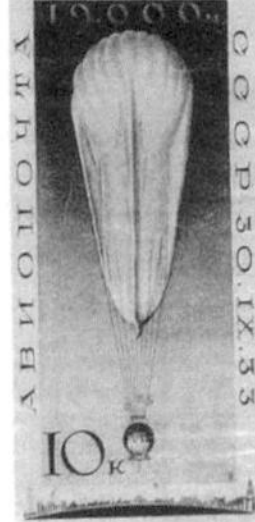

187 Stratosphere Balloon "U.S.S.R.-1" over Moscow

188 Massed Standard Bearers

1933. Air. Stratosphere record (19000 m).
634 **187** 5k. blue . . . . 80·00 19·00
635 10k. red . . . . 55·00 9·00
636 20k. violet . . . . 28·00 6·75

1933. 15th Anniv of Order of Red Banner.
637 **188** 20k. red, yellow and black 2·50 1·50

189 Commissar Shaumyan

190 Tupolev ANT-9 PS9 over Oilfield

1934. 15th Death Anniv of 26 Baku Commissars.
638 **189** 4k. brown . . . . 5·00 1·50
639 – 5k. black . . . . 5·00 1·50
640 – 20k. violet . . . . 3·00 85
641 – 35k. blue . . . . 18·00 4·00
642 – 40k. red . . . . 14·00 4·00
DESIGNS: 5k. Commissar Dzhaparidze. HORIZ: 20k. The 26 condemned commissars; 35k. Monument in Baku; 40k. Workman, peasant and soldier dipping flags in salute.

1934. Air. 10th Anniv of Soviet Civil Aviation and U.S.S.R. Airmail Service.
643 – 5k. blue . . . . 10·00 4·00
644 **190** 10k. green . . . . 10·00 4·00
645 – 20k. red . . . . 20·00 5·50
646 – 50k. blue . . . . 30·00 9·00
647 – 80k. violet . . . . 16·00 7·00
DESIGNS: Tupolev ANT-9 PS9 airplane over: 5k. Furnaces at Kuznetsk; 20k. Harvesters; 50k. Volga–Moscow Canal; 80k. Ice breaker "OB" in the Arctic.

191 New Lenin Mausoleum

1934. 10th Death Anniv of Lenin.
648 **191** 5k. brown . . . . 2·00 75
649 10k. blue . . . . 6·50 2·50
650 15k. red . . . . 6·00 2·00
651 20k. green . . . . 1·75 80
652 35k. brown . . . . 6·00 2·75

192 Fyodorov Monument, Moscow, and Hand and Rotary Presses

1934. 350th Death Anniv of Ivan Fyodorov (first Russian printer).
653 **192** 20k. red . . . . 8·00 3·75
654 40k. blue . . . . 8·00 3·00

194 Dmitri Mendeleev

1934. Birth Centenary of Dmitri Mendeleev (chemist).
655 – 5k. green . . . . 5·00 1·50
656 **194** 10k. brown . . . . 15·00 5·00
657 15k. red . . . . 13·00 4·50
658 – 20k. blue . . . . 7·50 2·50
DESIGN—VERT: 5k., 20k. Mendeleev seated.

195 A. V. Vasenko and "Osoaviakhim"

1934. Air. Stratosphere Balloon "Osoaviakhim" Disaster Victims.
659 – 5k. purple . . . . 22·00 5·00
660 **195** 10k. brown . . . . . . 55·00 6·00
661 – 20k. violet . . . . 60·00 8·00
1042 – 1r. green . . . . 8·50 3·00
1043 **195** 1r. green . . . . 8·50 3·00
1044 – 1r. blue . . . . 8·50 3·00
DESIGNS: 5k., 1r. (No. 1042). I. D. Usyskin; 20k., 1r. (No. 1044), P. F. Fedoseenko.
The 1r. values, issued in 1944, commemorated the 10th anniv of the disaster.

196 Airship "Pravda"

1934. Air. Airship Travel Propaganda.
662 **196** 5k. red . . . . 12·00 3·00
663 – 10k. lake . . . . 12·00 3·00
664 – 15k. brown . . . . 30·00 12·00
665 – 20k. black . . . . 16·00 7·50
666 – 30k. blue . . . . 55·00 26·00
DESIGNS—HORIZ: 10k. Airship landing; 15k. Airship "Voroshilov"; 30k. Airship "Lenin" and route map. VERT: 20k. Airship's gondolas and mooring mast.

199 Stalin and Marchers inspired by Lenin

1934. "Ten Years without Lenin". Portraits inscr "1924–1934".
667 – 1k. black and blue . . . 1·50 75
668 – 3k. black and blue . . . 1·50 80
669 – 5k. black and blue . . . 3·50 1·40
670 – 10k. black and blue . . . 4·25 2·50
671 – 20k. blue and orange . . 6·00 3·25
672 **199** 30k. red and orange . . 24·00 6·00
DESIGN—VERT: 1k. Lenin aged 3; 3k. Lenin as student; 5k. Lenin as man; 10k. Lenin as orator. HORIZ: 20k. Red demonstration, Lenin's Mausoleum.

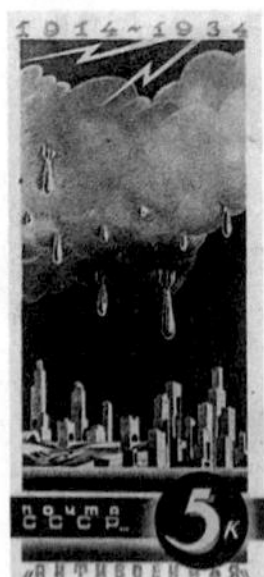

200 "War Clouds"

1935. Anti-War. Inscr "1914–1934".
673 **200** 5k. black . . . . 4·50 90
674 – 10k. blue . . . . 7·50 3·75
675 – 15k. green . . . . 13·00 5·00
676 – 20k. brown . . . . 10·00 2·75
677 – 35k. red . . . . 22·00 13·00
DESIGNS: 10k. "Flight from a burning village"; 15k. "Before war and afterwards"; 20k. "Ploughing with the sword"; 35k. "Fraternization".

202 Capt. Voronin and Ice-breaker "Chelyuskin"

1935. Air. Rescue of "Chelyuskin" Expedition.
678 **202** 1k. orange . . . . 4·00 1·00
679 – 3k. red . . . . 4·75 1·40
680 – 5k. green . . . . 5·00 1·40
681 – 10k. brown . . . . 7·25 1·75
682 – 15k. black . . . . 9·25 2·50
683 – 20k. purple . . . . 14·50 2·50
684 – 25k. blue . . . . 42·00 11·00
685 – 30k. green . . . . 45·00 13·00
686 – 40k. violet . . . . 32·00 3·75
687 **202** 50k. blue . . . . 35·00 9·00
DESIGNS—HORIZ: 3k. Prof. Schmidt and Schmidt Camp; 50k. Schmidt Camp deserted. VERT: 5k. A. V. Lyapidevsky; 10k. S. A. Levanevsky; 15k. M. G. Slepnev; 20k. I. V. Doronin; 25k. M. V. Vodopyanov; 30k. V. S. Molokov; 40k. N. P. Kamanin.

205 Underground Station

1935. Opening of Moscow Underground.
688 – 5k. orange . . . . 8·50 3·25
689 – 10k. blue . . . . 10·00 3·25
690 **205** 15k. red . . . . 80·00 24·00
691 – 20k. green . . . . 17·00 9·00
DESIGNS—As Type **205**: 5k. Excavating tunnel; 10k. Section of tunnel, escalator and station. 48½ × 23 mm: 20k. Train in station.

207 Rowing

1935. Spartacist Games.
692 – 1k. blue and orange . . . 2·75 80
693 – 2k. blue and black . . . 2·75 80
694 **207** 3k. brown and green . . . 5·50 1·50
695 – 4k. blue and red . . . . 3·00 90
696 – 5k. brown and violet . . 3·00 1·00
697 – 10k. purple and red . . . 14·00 3·00
698 – 15k. brown and black . . 30·00 8·00
699 – 20k. blue and brown . . . 22·00 3·25
700 – 35k. brown and blue . . . 30·00 13·00
701 – 40k. red and brown . . . 24·00 6·00
DESIGNS: 1k. Running; 2k. Diving; 4k. Football; 5k. Skiing; 10k. Cycling; 15k. Lawn tennis; 20k. Skating; 35k. Hurdling; 40k. Parade of athletes.

208 Friedrich Engels

Перелет
Москва—
Сан-Франциско
через Сев. полюс
1935
1 Р.

(209)

1935. 40th Death Anniv of F. Engels.
702 **208** 5k. red . . . . 6·00 60
703 10k. green . . . . 3·00 2·00
704 15k. blue . . . . 7·50 2·75
705 20k. black . . . . 5·00 3·00

1935. Air. Moscow–San Francisco via North Pole Flight. Surch with T **209**.
706 1r. on 10k. brown (No. 681) £300 £400

210 A "Lion Hunt" from a Sassanian Silver Plate

211 M. I. Kalinin

1935. 3rd International Congress of Persian Art and Archaeology, Leningrad.
707 **210** 5k. orange . . . . 7·00 1·00
708 10k. green . . . . 7·00 1·75
709 15k. purple . . . . 8·00 3·00
710 35k. brown . . . . 14·00 5·50

1935. Pres. Kalinin's 60th Birthday. Autographed portraits inscr "1875–1935".
711 – 3k. purple 75 20
712 – 5k. green . . . . 1·25 25
713 – 10k. blue . . . . 1·25 60
714 **211** 20k. brown . . . . . . 1·60 70
DESIGNS: 3k. Kalinin as machine worker; 5k. Harvester; 10k. Orator.
See also No. 1189.

212 Tolstoi

213 Pioneers securing Letter-box

1935. 25th Death Anniv of Tolstoi (writer).
715b – 3k. violet and black . . 75 25
716b **212** 10k. brown and blue . . 1·50 45
717b – 20k. brown and green 3·50 1·75
DESIGNS: 3k. Tolstoi in 1860; 20k. Monument in Moscow.

1936. Pioneer Movement.
721b **213** 1k. green . . . . 1·10 30
722 2k. red . . . . 1·00 70
723b – 3k. blue . . . . 1·25 1·60
724b – 5k. red . . . . 1·25 55
725b – 10k. blue . . . . 2·00 2·50
726 – 15k. brown . . . . . . 6·50 3·00
DESIGNS: 3, 5k. Pioneer preventing another from throwing stones; 10k. Pioneers disentangling kite line from telegraph wires; 15k. Girl pioneer saluting.

214 N. A. Dobrolyubov

215 Pushkin (after T. Paita)

1936. Birth Centenary of N. Dobrolyubov (author and critic).
727b **214** 10k. purple . . . . . . 5·00 1·00

1937. Death Centenary of A. S. Pushkin (poet).
728 **215** 10k. brown 55 30
729 20k. green 60 30
730 40k. red . . . . 1·25 50
731 – 50k. blue . . . . 2·75 75
732a – 80k. red . . . . 2·25 1·00
733a – 1r. green . . . . 4·50 1·00
DESIGN: 50k. to 1r. Pushkin's Monument, Moscow (A. Opekushin).

217 Meyerhold Theatre

218 F. E. Dzerzhinsky

1937. 1st Soviet Architectural Congress.
734 **217** 3k. red . . . . 1·25 20
735 – 5k. lake . . . . 1·25 20
736 **217** 10k. brown . . . . 1·75 25
737 – 15k. black . . . . 2·00 25
738 – 20k. olive . . . . 1·10 40
739 – 30k. black . . . . 1·75 70
740 – 40k. violet . . . . 2·25 1·25
741 – 50k. brown . . . . 3·75 1·50
DESIGNS—As T **217**: 5, 15k. G.P.O.; 20, 50k. Red Army Theatre. 45 × 27 mm: 30k. Hotel Moscow; 40k. Palace of Soviets.

1937. 10th Death Anniv of Feliks Dzerzhinsky.
742 **218** 10k. brown 40 20
743 20k. green 60 35
744 40k. red . . . . 1·75 55
745 80k. red . . . . 2·50 70

219 Yakovlev Ya-7 Air 7

1937. Air. Air Force Exhibition.
746 **219** 10k. black and brown . . 1·75 30
747 – 20k. black and green . . 1·75 30
748 – 30k. black and brown . . 2·75 40
749 – 40k. black and purple . . 5·00 90
750 – 50k. black and violet . . 6·50 1·50
751 – 80k. brown and blue . . . 7·50 2·00
752 – 1r. black, orange & brown 11·00 4·00
DESIGNS—As T **219**: 20k. Tupolev ANT-9; 30k. Tupolev ANT-6 bomber; 40k. O.S.G.A. 101 flying boat; 50k. Tupolev ANT-4 TB-1 bomber. 60 × 26 mm: 80k. Tupolev ANT-20 "Maksim Gorki"; 1r. Tupolev ANT-14 "Pravda".

220 Arms of Ukraine

221 Arms of U.S.S.R.

1937. New U.S.S.R. Constitution. Arms of Constituent Republics.

753	–	20k. blue (Armenia)	1·50	50
754	–	20k. purple (Azerbaijan)	1·50	50
755	–	20k. brown (Byelorussia)	1·50	50
756	–	20k. red (Georgia)	1·50	50
757	–	20k. green (Kazakhstan)	1·50	50
758	–	20k. red (Kirghizia)	1·50	50
759	–	20k. red (Tadzhikistan)	1·50	50
760	–	20k. red (Turkmenistan)	1·50	50
761	**220**	20k. red (Ukraine)	1·50	50
762	–	20k. orange (Uzbekistan)	1·50	50
763	–	20k. blue (R.S.F.S.R.)	1·50	50
764	**221**	40k. red (U.S.S.R.)	5·00	1·50

222 "Worker and Collective Farmer" (sculpture, Vera Mukhina)

223 Russian Pavilion, Paris Exhibition

1938. Paris International Exhibition.

765	**222**	5k. red	1·00	40
766	**223**	20k. red	1·40	40
767	**222**	50k. blue	3·50	1·00

224 Shota Rustaveli

1938. 750th Anniv of Poem "Knight in Tiger Skin".

768	**224**	20k. green	1·50	40

225 Route of North Pole Flight

227 Infantryman

1938. North Pole Flight.

769	**225**	10k. black and brown	2·40	30
770		20k. black and grey	3·75	40
771	–	40k. red and green	8·50	1·40
772	–	80k. red and deep red	2·75	1·10

DESIGN: 40k., 80k. Soviet Flag at North Pole.

1938. 20th Anniv of Red Army.

773	**227**	10k. black and red	50	20
774	–	20k. black and red	85	25
775	–	30k. black, red and blue	1·25	25
776	–	40k. black, red and blue	1·75	75
777	–	50k. black and red	2·25	75
778a	–	80k. black and red	4·75	75
779	–	1r. black and red	2·75	75

DESIGNS—VERT: 20k. Tank driver; 30k. Sailor; 40k. Airman; 50k. Artilleryman. HORIZ: 80k. Stalin reviewing cavalry; 1r. Machine gunners.

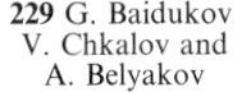

229 G. Baidukov, V. Chkalov and A. Belyakov

230 M. Gromov, A. Yumashov and S. Danilin

1938. 1st Flight over North Pole.

780	**229**	10k. red and black	2·00	50
781		20k. red and black	2·25	70
782		40k. red and brown	4·00	1·40
783		50k. red and purple	7·25	1·75

1938. 2nd Flight over North Pole.

784	**230**	10k. purple	4·00	45
785		20k. black	4·00	90
786		50k. purple	7·75	1·25

231 Ice-breaker "Murman" approaching Survivors

1938. Rescue of Papanin's North Pole Meteorological Party.

787	**231**	10k. purple	4·00	60
788		20k. blue	4·00	70
789	–	30k. brown	7·00	1·25
790	–	50k. blue	8·00	2·50

DESIGNS—VERT: 30, 50k. Papanin survivors.

233 Nurse weighing Baby

234 Children visiting Statue of Lenin

1938. Soviet Union Children.

791	**233**	10k. blue	1·25	30
792	**234**	15k. blue	1·25	35
793	–	20k. purple	1·50	35
794	–	30k. red	1·90	45
795	–	40k. brown	2·40	55
796	–	50k. blue	6·00	1·50
797	–	80k. green	7·00	2·00

DESIGNS—HORIZ: 20, 40k. Biology class; 30k. Health camp; 50, 80k. Young inventors at play.

235 Crimean landscape

1938. Views of Crimea and Caucasus.

798	**235**	5k. black	1·10	40
799	A	5k. brown	1·10	40
800	B	10k. green	2·25	45
801	C	10k. brown	2·25	50
802	D	15k. black	3·75	60
803	A	15k. black	3·75	60
804	E	20k. brown	4·00	70
805	C	30k. black	4·00	75
806	F	40k. brown	4·75	90
807	G	50k. green	4·75	1·75
808	H	80k. brown	6·50	2·25
809	I	1r. green	9·00	6·00

DESIGNS—HORIZ: A, Yalta (two views); B, Georgian military road; E, Crimean resthouse; F, Alupka; H, Crimea; I, Swallows' Nest Castle. VERT: C, Crimea (two views); D, Swallows' Nest Castle; G, Gurzuf Park.

236 Schoolchildren and Model Tupolev ANT-6 Bomber

1938. Aviation.

810	**236**	5k. purple	1·75	75
811	–	10k. brown	1·75	75
812	–	15k. red	2·25	75
813	–	20k. blue	2·25	75
814	–	30k. red	4·00	1·25
815	–	40k. blue	7·00	1·25
816	–	50k. green	12·00	1·75
817	–	80k. brown	8·00	3·25
818	–	1r. green	14·00	3·25

DESIGNS—HORIZ: 10k. Glider in flight; 40k. Yakovlev VT-2 seaplane; 1r. Tupolev ANT-6 bomber. VERT: 15k. Captive observation balloon; 20k. Airship "Osoaviakhim" over Kremlin; 30k. Parachutists; 30k. Balloon in flight; 80k. Stratosphere balloon.

237 Underground Railway

1938. Moscow Underground Railway Extension.

819	–	10k. violet	2·40	85
820	–	15k. brown	3·00	85
821	–	20k. black	3·75	85
822	–	30k. violet	4·00	1·25
823	**237**	40k. black	6·00	1·40
824	–	50k. brown	5·50	2·25

DESIGNS—VERT: 10k. Mayakovskaya station; 15k. Sokol station; 20k. Kievsskaya station. HORIZ: 30k. Dynamo station; 50k. Revolutskaya station.

238 Miner and Pneumatic Drill

239 Diving

1938. 20th Anniv of Federation of Young Lenin Communists.

825	–	20k. blue	90	30
826	**238**	30k. purple	1·75	30
827	–	40k. purple	1·50	30
828	–	50k. red	1·90	90
829	–	80k. blue	6·00	1·25

DESIGNS—VERT: 20k. Girl parachutist; 50k. Students and university. HORIZ: 40k. Harvesting; 80k. Airman, sailor and battleship "Marat".

1938. Soviet Sports.

830	**239**	5k. red	2·00	30
831	–	10k. black	2·75	50
832	–	15k. brown	4·50	85
833	–	20k. green	4·50	80
834	–	30k. purple	9·00	1·25
835	–	40k. green	10·00	80
836	–	50k. blue	9·00	2·25
837	–	80k. blue	9·00	3·50

DESIGNS: 10k. Discus throwing; 15k. Tennis; 20k. Motor cycling; 30k. Skiing; 40k. Sprinting; 50k. Football; 80k. Athletic parade.

241 Council of People's Commissars Headquarters and Hotel Moscow

1939. New Moscow. Architectural designs as T **241**.

838	–	10k. brown	1·10	70
839	**241**	20k. green	1·40	70
840	–	30k. purple	1·90	1·00
841	–	40k. blue	2·75	1·00
842	–	50k. red	5·00	2·00
843	–	80k. olive	5·00	2·00
844	–	1r. blue	9·50	2·75

DESIGNS—HORIZ: 10k. Gorky Avenue; 30k. Lenin Library; 40k. Crimea suspension and 50k. Arched bridges over River Moskva; 80k. Khimki river station. VERT: 1r. Dynamo underground station.

242 Paulina Osipenko

243 Russian Pavilion, N.Y. World's Fair

1939. Women's Moscow–Far East Flight.

845	**242**	15k. green	2·25	80
846	–	30k. purple	2·25	1·00
847	–	60k. red	4·50	1·50

PORTRAITS: 30k. Marina Raskova; 60k. Valentina Grisodubova.

1939. New York World's Fair.

848	–	30k. red and black	2·00	50
849	**243**	50k. brown and blue	4·00	85

DESIGN—VERT: (26×41½ mm): 30k. Statue over Russian pavilion.

244 T. G. Shevchenko in early Manhood

245 Milkmaid

1939. 125th Birth Anniv of Shevchenko (Ukrainian poet and painter).

853	**244**	15k. black and brown	1·75	50
854	–	30k. black and red	2·75	70
855	–	60k. brown and green	5·00	2·00

DESIGNS: 30k. Last portrait of Shevchenko; 60k. Monument to Shevchenko, Kharkov.

1939. All Union Agricultural Fair.

856	**245**	10k. red	75	25
857	–	15k. red	75	15
858a	–	20k. grey	1·00	15
859	–	30k. orange	90	25
860	–	30k. violet	90	25
861	–	45k. green	1·75	35
862	–	50k. brown	2·50	40
863a	–	60k. violet	3·00	60
864	–	80k. violet	3·00	60
865	–	1r. blue	5·00	1·25

DESIGNS—HORIZ: 15k. Harvesting; 20k. Sheep farming; 30k. (No. 860) Agricultural Fair Pavilion. VERT: 30k. (No. 859) Agricultural Fair Emblem; 45k. Gathering cotton; 50k. Thoroughbred horses; 60k. "Agricultural Wealth"; 80k. Girl with sugar beet; 1r. Trapper.

18 АВГУСТА
ДЕНЬ АВИАЦИИ СССР

(247)

1939. Aviation Day. As Nos. 811, 814/16 and 818 (colours changed) optd with T **247**.

866		10k. red	2·25	55
867		30k. blue	2·25	55
868		40k. green	3·50	55
869		50k. violet	4·50	1·25
870		1r. brown	8·00	4·00

1939. Surch.

871	**141**	30k. on 4k. mauve	15·00	10·00

249 Saltykov-Shchedrin

250 Kislovodsk Sanatorium

1939. 50th Death Anniv of M. E. Saltykov-Shchedrin (writer and satirist).

872	**249**	15k. red	60	15
873	–	30k. green	80	20
874	**249**	45k. brown	1·00	35
875	–	60k. blue	1·50	70

DESIGN: 30, 60k. Saltykov-Shchedrin in later years.

1939. Caucasian Health Resorts.

876	**250**	5k. brown	30	15
877	–	10k. red	50	20
878	–	15k. green	55	30
879	–	20k. green	1·00	30
880	–	30k. blue	1·10	30
881	–	50k. black	2·00	35
882	–	60k. purple	2·50	90
883	–	80k. red	3·25	1·10

DESIGNS: 10, 15, 30, 50, 80k. Sochi Convalescent Homes; 20k. Abkhazia Sanatorium, Novyi Afon; 60k. Sukumi Rest Home.

251 M. I. Lermontov

252 N. G. Chernyshevsky

1939. 125th Birth Anniv of Lermontov (poet and novelist).

884	**251**	15k. brown and blue	1·10	30
885	–	30k. black and green	2·75	55
886	–	45k. blue and red	3·00	95

1939. 50th Death Anniv of N. G. Chernyshevsky (writer and politician).

887b	**252**	15k. green	50	30
888		30k. violet	90	40
889b		60k. green	2·00	70

253 A. P. Chekhov

254 Welcoming Soviet Troops

1940. 80th Birth Anniv of Chekhov (writer).

890	**253**	10k. green	40	15
891		15k. blue	40	15

892 – 20k. violet 80 30
893 – 30k. brown . . . . 2·00 55
DESIGN: 20, 30k. Chekhov with hat on.

1940. Occupation of Eastern Poland.
893a **254** 10k. red . . . . 1·00 35
894 – 30k. green . . . . 1·00 35
895 – 50k. black . . . . 1·50 55
896 – 60k. blue . . . . 2·00 1·00
897 – 1r. red . . . . 4·50 1·75
DESIGNS: 30k. Villagers welcoming tank crew; 50, 60k. Soldier distributing newspapers to crowd; 1r. People waving to column of tanks.

255 Ice-breaker "Georgy Sedov" and Badigin and Trofimov

1940. Polar Research.
898 – 15k. green . . . . 2·25 40
899 **255** 30k. violet . . . . 3·00 70
900 – 50k. brown . . . . 5·00 1·75
901 – 1r. blue . . . . 9·00 2·25
DESIGNS: 15k. Ice-breaker "Iosif Stalin" and portraits of Papanin and Belousov; 50k. Badgin and Papanin meeting. LARGER. (46 × 26 mm): 1r. Route of drift of "Georgy Sedov".

256 V. Mayakovsky

1940. 10th Death Anniv of Mayakovsky (poet).
902 **256** 15k. red 30 15
903 30k. brown 55 20
904 – 60k. violet . . . . 1·00 45
905 – 80k. blue 80 45
DESIGN—VERT: 60, 80k. Mayakovsky in profile wearing a cap.

257 Timiryazev

1940. 20th Death Anniv of K. A. Timiryazev (scientist).
906 – 10k. blue 50 20
907 – 15k. violet 50 25
908 **257** 30k. brown 80 30
909 – 60k. green . . . . 2·50 1·10
DESIGNS—HORIZ: 10k. Miniature of Timiryazev and Academy of Agricultural Sciences, Moscow; 15k. Timiryazev in laboratory. VERT: 60k. Timiryazev's statue (by S. Merkurov), Moscow.

258 Relay Runner

259 Tchaikovsky and Passage from his "Fourth Symphony"

1940. 2nd All Union Physical Culture Festival.
910 **258** 15k. red . . . . 1·10 35
911a – 30k. purple . . . . . . 2·00 30
912a – 50k. blue . . . . 3·00 55
913 – 60k. blue . . . . 4·50 60
914 – 1r. green . . . . 6·00 1·40
DESIGNS—HORIZ: 30k. Girls parade; 60k. Skiing; 1r. Grenade throwing. VERT: 50k. Children and sports badges.

1940. Birth Cent of Tchaikovsky (composer).
915 – 15k. green . . . . 1·50 20
916 **259** 20k. brown . . . . 1·50 20
917 30k. blue . . . . 1·75 35
918 – 50k. red . . . . 2·50 60
919 – 60k. red . . . . 2·75 85
DESIGNS: 15, 50k. Tchaikovsky's house at Klin; 60k. Tchaikovsky and excerpt from "Eugene Onegin".

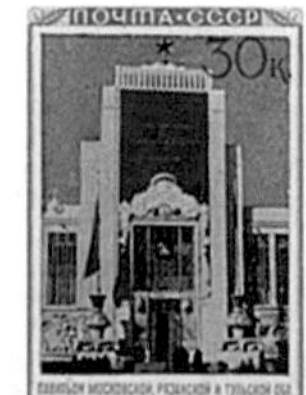
260 Central Regions Pavilion

ПАВИЛЬОН «ПОВОЛЖЬЕ»
No. 920

ПАВИЛЬОН «ДАЛЬНИЙ ВОСТОК»
No. 921

ВОРОТА ПАВИЛЬОНА „ЛЕНИНГРАД И СЕВЕРО-ВОСТОК РСФСР"
No. 922

ПАВИЛЬОН МОСКОВСКОЙ, РЯЗАНСКОЙ И ТУЛЬСКОЙ ОБЛ.
No. 923

ПАВИЛЬОН УКРАИНСКОЙ ССР
No. 924

ПАВИЛЬОН БЕЛОРУССКОЙ ССР
No. 925

ПАВИЛЬОН АЗЕРБАЙДЖАНСКОЙ ССР
No. 926

ПАВИЛЬОН ГРУЗИНСКОЙ ССР
No. 927

ПАВИЛЬОН АРМЯНСКОЙ ССР
No. 928

У ВХОДА В ПАВИЛЬОН УЗБЕКСКОЙ ССР
No. 929

ПАВИЛЬОН ТУРКМЕНСКОЙ ССР
No. 930

ПАВИЛЬОН ТАДЖИКСКОЙ ССР
No. 931

ПАВИЛЬОН КИРГИЗСКОЙ ССР
No. 932

ПАВИЛЬОН КАРЕЛО-ФИНСКОЙ ССР
No. 933

ПАВИЛЬОН КАЗАХСКОЙ ССР
No. 934

ГЛАВНЫЙ ПАВИЛЬОН
No. 935

ПАВИЛЬОН МЕХАНИЗАЦИИ
No. 936

1940. All Union Agricultural Fair. Coloured reproductions of Soviet Pavilions in green frames as T **260**. Inscriptions at foot as illustrated.
920 10k. Volga provinces (RSFSR) (horiz) . . . . . 2·50 90
921 15k. Far East . . . . . . 1·75 90
922 30k. Leningrad and North East RSFSR . . . . . . 1·90 90
923 30k. Three Central Regions (RSFSR) . . . . 1·90 90
924 30k. Ukrainian SSR . . . . 1·90 90
925 30k. Byelorussian SSR . . . 1·90 90
926 30k. Azerbaijan SSR . . . . 1·90 90
927 30k. Georgian SSR (horiz) . 1·90 90
928 30k. Armenian SSR . . . . 1·90 90
929 30k. Uzbek SSR . . . . . . 1·90 90
930 30k. Turkmen SSR (horiz) . 1·90 90
931 30k. Tadzhik SSR . . . . . 1·90 90
932 30k. Kirgiz SSR . . . . . . 1·90 90
933 30k. Karelo-Finnish SSR . . 3·25 90
934 30k. Kazakh SSR . . . . . 1·90 90
935 50k. Main Pavilion . . . . . 3·00 2·00
936 60k. Mechanization Pavilion and the statue of Stalin . . 4·00 2·25

261 Grenade Thrower

262 Railway Bridge and Moscow–Volga Canal, Khimka

1940. 20th Anniv of Wrangel's Defeat at Perekop (Crimea). Perf or imperf.
937b – 10k. green . . . . . . 1·40 30
938 **261** 15k. red 50 15
939 – 30k. brown and red . . 75 20
940b – 50k. purple 70 50
941 – 60k. blue . . . . 1·75 55
942 – 1r. black . . . . 4·00 1·40

DESIGNS—VERT: 10k. Red Army Heroes Monument; 30k. Map of Perekop and portrait of M. V. Frunze; 1r. Victorious soldier. HORIZ: 50k. Soldiers crossing R. Sivash; 60k. Army H.Q. at Stroganovka.

1941. Industrial and Agricultural Records.
943 – 10k. blue 30 15
944 – 15k. mauve 30 15
945 **262** 20k. blue . . . . 2·25 1·00
946 – 30k. brown . . . . 2·75 1·00
947 – 50k. brown 60 15
948 – 60k. brown . . . . 1·25 55
949 – 1r. green . . . . 1·60 80
DESIGNS—VERT: 10k. Coal-miners and pithead; 15k. Blast furnace; 1r. Derricks and petroleum refinery. HORIZ: 30k. Steam locomotives; 50k. Harvesting; 60k. Ball-bearing vehicles.

263 Red Army Ski Corps

264 N. E. Zhukovsky and Air Force Academy

1941. 23rd Anniv of Red Army. Designs with Hammer, Sickle and Star Symbol.
950a **263** 5k. violet . . . . 1·60 15
951 – 10k. blue . . . . 1·25 15
952 – 15k. green 45 15
953a – 20k. red 45 15
954a – 30k. brown 45 15
955a – 45k. green . . . . . . 1·90 70
956 – 50k. blue 70 75
957 – 1r. green . . . . 1·00 80
957b – 3r. green . . . . 6·50 3·00
DESIGNS—VERT: 10k. Sailor; 20k. Cavalry; 30k. Automatic Rifle Squad; 50k. Airman; 1, 3r. Marshal's star. HORIZ: 15k. Artillery; 45k. Clearing a hurdle.

1941. 20th Death Anniv of Zhukovsky (scientist).
958 – 15k. blue 65 20
959 **264** 30k. red . . . . 1·50 30
960 – 50k. red . . . . 2·00 55
DESIGNS—VERT: 15k. Zhukovsky; 50k. Zhukovsky lecturing.

265 Thoroughbred Horses

266 Arms of Karelo-Finnish S.S.R.

1941. 15th Anniv of Kirghiz S.S.R.
961 **265** 15k. brown . . . . . . 3·00 85
962a – 30k. violet . . . . . 4·00 1·25
DESIGN: 30k. Coal miner and colliery.

1941. 1st Anniv of Karelo-Finnish Republic.
963 **266** 30k. red . . . . 1·00 45
964 45k. green . . . . 1·00 75

267 Marshal Suvorov

268 Spassky Tower, Kremlin

1941. 150th Anniv of Battle of Izmail.
965 – 10k. green 80 35
966 – 15k. red 80 45
967 **267** 30k. blue . . . . 1·90 40
968 1r. brown . . . . 2·75 1·25
DESIGN: 10, 15k. Storming of Izmail.

1941.
970 **268** 1r. red . . . . 2·00 55
971 – 2r. brown . . . . 4·50 1·10
DESIGN—HORIZ: 2r. Kremlin Palace.

269 "Razin on the Volga"

1941. 25th Death Anniv of Surikov (artist).
972 – 20k. black . . . . 1·50 1·00
973 **269** 30k. red . . . . 3·50 1·00
974 – 50k. purple . . . . 6·00 2·75
975 **269** 1r. green . . . . 9·00 4·00
976 – 2r. brown . . . . 16·00 5·00

DESIGNS—VERT: 20, 50k. "Suvorov's march through Alps, 1799"; 2r. Surikov.

270 Lenin Museum (interior)

271 M. Yu. Lermontov

1941. 5th Anniv of Lenin Museum.
977 **270** 15k. red . . . . 2·75 1·50
978 – 30k. violet on mauve . . 22·00 16·00
979 **270** 45k. green . . . . 3·50 2·50
980 – 1r. red on rose . . . . . 16·00 12·00
DESIGN: 30k., 1r. Exterior of Lenin Museum.

1941. Death Centenary of M. Yu. Lermontov (poet and novelist).
981 **271** 15k. grey . . . . 4·50 3·75
982 30k. violet . . . . 8·00 6·00

272 Poster by L. Lisitsky

273 Mass Enlistment

1941. Mobilization.
983a **272** 30k. red . . . . . . 18·00 20·00

1941. National Defence.
984 **273** 30k. blue . . . . 55·00 50·00

274 Alishir Navoi

275 Lt. Talalikhin ramming Enemy Bomber

289a Five Heroes

1942. 5th Centenary of Uzbek poet Mir Ali Shir (Alishir Navoi).
985 **274** 30k. brown . . . . 14·00 8·50
986 1r. purple . . . . 16·00 18·00

1942. Russian Heroes (1st issue).
987 **275** 20k. blue 50 25
988 A 30k. grey 60 35
989 B 30k. black 60 30
990 C 30k. black 60 35
991 D 30k. black 60 40
1048c **275** 30k. green . . . . . 1·00 30
1048d A 30k. blue . . . . . 1·00 30
1048e C 30k. green . . . . . 1·00 30
1048f D 30k. purple . . . . 1·00 30
1048g **289a** 30k. blue . . . . . 1·00 30
992 C 1r. green . . . . . . 5·00 3·25
993 D 2r. green . . . . . . 9·00 5·00
DESIGNS: A, Capt. Gastello and burning fighter plane diving into enemy petrol tanks; B, Maj-Gen. Dovator and Cossack cavalry in action; C, Shura Chekalin guerrilla fighting; D, Zoya Kosmodemyanskaya being led to death.
See also Nos. 1072/6.

276 Anti-tank Gun

1942. War Episodes (1st series).
994 **276** 20k. brown . . . . 1·75 75
995 – 30k. blue . . . . 1·75 75
996 – 30k. green . . . . 1·75 75
997 – 30k. red . . . . 1·75 75
998 – 60k. grey . . . . 2·50 1·75
999 – 1r. brown . . . . 5·00 4·50
DESIGNS—HORIZ: 30k. (No. 996), Guerrillas attacking train; 30k. (No. 997), Munition worker; 1r. Machine gunners. VERT: 30k. (No. 995), Signallers; 60k. Defenders of Leningrad.

277 Distributing Gifts to Soldiers

1942. War Episodes (2nd series).
1000 **277** 20k. blue . . . . 1·75 75
1001 – 20k. purple . . . . . . 1·75 75
1002 – 30k. purple . . . . . . 2·25 1·40
1003 – 45k. red . . . . 4·00 2·75
1004 – 45k. blue . . . . 5·00 3·75
DESIGNS—VERT: No. 1001, Bomber destroying tank; No. 1002, Food packers; No. 1003, Woman sewing; No. 1004, Anti-aircraft gun.
See also Nos. 1013/17.

278 Munition Worker

1943. 25th Anniv of Russian Revolution.
1005 **278** 5k. brown 55 25
1006 – 10k. brown 80 15
1007 – 15k. blue 65 20
1008 – 20k. blue 65 20
1009 – 30k. brown 85 20
1010 – 60k. brown . . . . . . 1·50 45
1011 – 1r. red . . . . 2·25 1·25
1012 – 2r. brown . . . . 4·00 1·50
DESIGNS: 10k. Lorry convoy; 15k. Troops supporting Lenin's banner; 20k. Leningrad seen through an archway; 30k. Spassky Tower, Lenin and Stalin; 60k. Tank parade; 1r. Lenin speaking; 2r. Star of Order of Lenin.

279 Nurses and Wounded Soldier

1943. War Episodes (3rd series).
1013 **279** 30k. green . . . . 1·50 1·00
1014 – 30k. green (Scouts) . . . 1·50 1·00
1015 – 30k. brown (Mine-thrower) . . . . . . 1·50 1·00
1016 – 60k. green (Anti-tank troops) . . . . . . 2·50 1·00
1017 – 60k. blue (Sniper) . . . 2·50 1·00

280 Routes of Bering's Voyages

1943. Death Bicent of Vitus Bering (explorer).
1018 – 30k. blue . . . . 1·60 30
1019 **280** 60k. grey . . . . 3·00 60
1020 – 1r. green . . . . 4·25 90
1021 **280** 2r. brown . . . . 7·75 1·75
DESIGN: 30k., 1r. Mt. St. Ilya.

281 Gorky

1943. 75th Birth Anniv of Maksim Gorky (novelist).
1022 **281** 30k. green . . . . 1·00 25
1023 60k. blue . . . . 1·50 25

282 Order of the Great Patriotic War

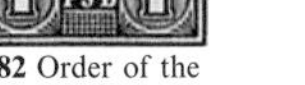
(**a**) Order of Suvorov

1943. War Orders and Medals (1st series), Medals with ribbon attached.
1024 **282** 1r. black . . . . 2·75 2·00
1025 a 10r. olive . . . . 9·00 7·50
See also Nos. 1051/8, 1089/94, 1097/99a, 1172/86, 1197/1204 and 1776/80a.

283 Karl Marx

284 Naval Landing Party

1943. 125th Birth Anniv of Marx.
1026 **283** 30k. blue . . . . 1·50 40
1027 60k. green . . . . 2·50 60

1943. 25th Anniv of Red Army and Navy.
1028 **284** 20k. brown 30 20
1029 – 30k. green 40 15
1030 – 60k. green . . . . 1·25 40
1031 **284** 3r. blue . . . . 3·00 90
DESIGNS: 30k. Sailors and anti-aircraft gun; 60k. Tanks and infantry.

285 Ivan Turgenev

286 Loading a Gun

1943. 125th Birth Anniv of Ivan Turgenev (novelist).
1032 **285** 30k. green . . . . . . 12·00 10·00
1032a 60k. violet . . . . . . 18·00 16·00

1943. 25th Anniv of Young Communist League.
1033 **286** 15k. blue 60 15
1034 – 20k. orange 60 15
1035 – 30k. brown and red . . 75 15
1036a – 1r. green . . . . 1·25 35
1037 – 2r. green . . . . 2·50 75
DESIGNS—As T **286**: 20k. Tank and banner; 1r. Infantrymen; 2r. Grenade thrower. 22½ × 28½ mm: 30k. Bayonet fighter and flag.

287 V. V. Mayakovsky

288 Memorial Tablet and Allied Flags

1943. 50th Birth Anniv of Mayakovsky (poet).
1038 **287** 30k. orange 65 20
1039 60k. blue . . . . 1·00 40

1943. Teheran Three Power Conference and 26th Anniv of Revolution.
1040 **288** 30k. black . . . . 1·10 50
1041 3r. blue . . . . 4·00 1·25

289 Defence of Odessa

1944. Liberation of Russian Towns.
1045 – 30k. brown and red . . 65 25
1046 – 30k. blue 65 25
1047 – 30k. green 65 25
1048 **289** 30k. green 65 25
DESIGNS: No. 1045, Stalingrad; No. 1046, Sevastopol; No. 1047, Leningrad.

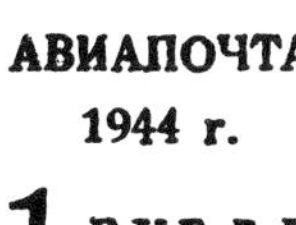

(**290**)

291 Order of Kutusov

(**b**) Order of Patriotic War

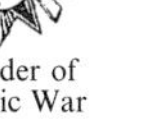
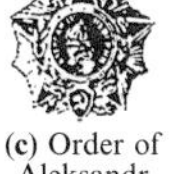
(**c**) Order of Aleksandr Nevsky

(**d**) Order of Suvorov

(**e**) Order of Kutusov

1944. Air. Surch with T **290**.
1049 **275** 1r. on 30k. grey . . . . 2·00 50
1050 A 1r. on 30k. blue (No. 1048d) . . . . . 2·00 50

1944. War Orders and Medals (2nd series). Various Stars without ribbons showing as Types **b** to **e**. Perf or imperf. (a) Frames as T **291**.
1051 b 15k. red 50 15
1052 c 20k. blue 50 15
1053 d 30k. green . . . . 1·00 25
1054 e 60k. red . . . . 1·50 40

(b) Frames as T **282**.
1055 b 1r. black 80 30
1056 c 3r. blue . . . . 3·25 60
1057 e 5r. green . . . . 4·00 1·00
1058 d 10r. red . . . . 4·00 1·50

293 Lenin Mausoleum and Red Square, Moscow

1944. "Twenty Years without Lenin". As Nos. 667/72, but inscr "1924–1944", and T **293**.
1059 – 30k. black and blue . . 50 20
1060 **199** 30k. red and orange . . 50 20
1061 – 45k. black and blue . . 65 25
1062 – 50k. black and blue . . 80 25
1063 – 60k. black and blue . . 1·75 50
1064 **293** 1r. brown and blue . . . 2·00 60
1065 **199** 3r. black and orange . . 4·00 1·75
DESIGNS—VERT: Lenin at 3 years of age (No. 1059): at school (45k.); as man (50k.); as orator (60k.).

294 Allied Flags

295 Rimsky-Korsakov and Bolshoi Theatre

1944. 14 June (Allied Nations' Day).
1066 **294** 60k. black, red and blue 1·50 45
1067 3r. blue and red . . . . 6·00 1·75

1944. Birth Centenary of Rimsky-Korsakov (composer). Imperf or perf.
1068 **295** 30k. grey 40 10
1069 60k. green 60 10
1070 1r. green . . . . 1·25 25
1071 3r. violet . . . . 2·50 50

296 Nuradilov and Machine-gun

297 Polivanova and Kovshova

298 S. A. Chaplygin

1944. War Heroes (3rd issue).
1072 **296** 30k. green 45 15
1073 – 60k. violet 85 15
1074 – 60k. blue 85 15
1075 **297** 60k. green . . . . 1·50 45
1076 – 60k. black . . . . 1·75 45
DESIGNS—HORIZ: No. 1073, Matrosov defending a snow-trench; 1074, Luzak hurling a hand grenade. VERT: No. 1076, B. Safonev, medals and aerial battle over the sea.

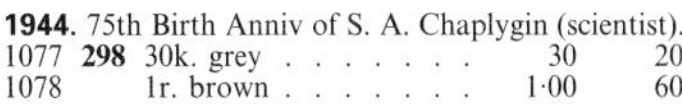
1944. 75th Birth Anniv of S. A. Chaplygin (scientist).
1077 **298** 30k. grey 30 20
1078 1r. brown . . . . 1·00 60

299 V. I. Chapaev

300 Repin (self-portrait)

301 "Reply of the Cossacks to Sultan Mahmoud IV"

302 I. A. Krylov

1944. Heroes of 1918 Civil War.
1079 **299** 30k. green . . . . 1·00 25
1080 – 30k. black (N. Shchors) 1·00 25
1081 – 30k. green (S. Lazo) . . 1·00 25
For 40k. stamp as Type **299**, see No. 1531.
See also Nos. 1349/51.

1944. Birth Centenary of Ilya Refimovich Repin (artist). Imperf or perf.
1082 **300** 30k. green 85 25
1083 **301** 50k. green 85 25
1084 60k. blue 85 25
1085 **300** 1r. brown . . . . 1·25 50
1086 **301** 2r. violet . . . . 2·75 1·00

1944. Death Centenary of Krylov (fabulist).
1087 **302** 30k. brown 60 15
1088 1r. blue . . . . 1·25 40

(**f**) Partisans' Medal

(**g**) Medal for Bravery

(**h**) Order of Bogdan Chmielnitsky

(**j**) Order of Victory

(**k**) Order of Ushakov

(**l**) Order of Nakhimov

1945. War Orders and Medals (3rd series). Frame as T **291** with various centres as Types **f** to **l**. Perf or imperf.
1089 f 15k. black 45 15
1090 g 30k. blue 85 20
1091 h 45k. blue . . . . 1·50 40
1092 j 60k. red . . . . 2·40 45
1093 k 1r. blue . . . . 3·25 1·00
1094 l 1r. green . . . . 3·25 1·00

303 Griboedov (after P. Karatygin)

305 Soldier

1945. 150th Birth Anniv of Aleksander S. Griboedov (author).
1095 **303** 30k. green . . . . 1·50 20
1096 60k. brown . . . . . . 2·00 35

1945. War Orders and Medals (4th series). Frames as T **282**. Various centres.
1097 g 1r. black . . . . 1·60 65
1098 h 2r. black . . . . 7·50 1·75
1098a 2r. purple . . . . 42·00 14·00
1098b 2r. olive . . . . 6·00 2·00
1099 j 3r. red . . . . 4·25 1·25
1099a 3r. purple . . . . 6·25 3·00

1945. Relief of Stalingrad.
1100 **305** 60k. black and red . . . 1·40 85
1101 3r. black and red . . . 3·50 1·60

306 Standard Bearer

308 Attack

1945. Red Army Victories.
1102 **306** 20k. green, red and black . . . 40 15
1103 – 30k. black and red . . . 40 15
1104 – 1r. green and red . . . . 2·25 1·40
DESIGN—HORIZ: 30k. Infantry v. Tank; 1r. Infantry charge.

1945. Liberation of Russian Soil.
1105 **308** 30k. blue 40 15
1106 – 60k. red . . . . 1·00 55
1107 – 1r. green . . . . 2·40 1·25
DESIGNS: 60k. Welcoming troops; 1r. Grenade thrower.

309 Badge and Guns

310 Barricade

1945. Red Guards Commemoration.
1108 **309** 60k. red . . . . 2·75 1·00

1945. Battle of Moscow.
1109 – 30k. blue 40 20
1110 **310** 60k. black 80 45
1111 – 1r. black . . . . 1·50 60
DESIGNS: 30k. Tanks in Red Square, Moscow. 1r. Aerial battle and searchlights.

311 Prof. Lomonosov and Academy of Sciences, Leningrad

312 Popov

1945. 220th Anniv of Academy of Sciences.
1112 – 30k. blue . . . . 1·00 35
1113 **311** 2r. black . . . . 3·25 80
DESIGN—VERT: 30k. Moscow Academy, inscr "1725–1945".

1945. 50th Anniv of Popov's Radio Discoveries.
1114 **312** 30k. blue 70 30
1115 60k. red . . . . 1·25 40
1116 – 1r. brown (Popov) . . . 1·90 65

314 Motherhood Medal

315 Motherhood Medal

1945. Orders and Medals of Motherhood. Imperf or perf.
1117b **314** 20k. brown on blue . . 35 20
1118b – 30k. brown on green . . 60 20
1119b – 60k. red . . . . 1·40 20
1120 **315** 1r. black on green . . . 1·75 20
1121 – 2r. blue . . . . 2·75 50
1122 – 3r. red on blue . . . . 4·00 90
DESIGNS: 30k., 2r. Order of Motherhood Glory; 60k., 3r. Order of Heroine-Mother.

316 Petlyakov Pe-2 Dive Bombers

317 Ilyushin Il-2M3 Stormovik Fighters

318 Petlyakov Pe-8 TB-7 Bomber

1945. Air. Aviation Day.
1123 **316** 1r. brown . . . . 3·50 1·00
1124 **317** 1r. brown . . . . 3·50 1·00
1125 – 1r. red . . . . 3·50 1·00
1126 – 1r. black . . . . 3·50 1·00
1127 – 1r. blue . . . . 3·50 1·00
1128 – 1r. green . . . . 3·50 1·00
1129 **318** 1r. grey . . . . 3·50 1·00
1130 – 1r. brown . . . . 3·50 1·00
1131 – 1r. red . . . . 3·50 1·00
DESIGNS—As Type **317**: No. 1125, Lavochkin La-7 fighter shooting tail off enemy plane; 1126, Ilyushin Il-4 DB-3 bombers dropping bombs; 1127, Tupolev ANT-60 Tu-2 bombers in flight; 1128, Polikarpov Po-2 biplane. As Type **318**: No. 1130, Yakovlev Yak-3 fighter destroying Messerschmitt BF 109 fighter; 1131, Yakovlev Yak-9 fighter destroying Henschel Hs 129B fighter.
See also Nos. 1163/71.

ПРАЗДНИК
ПОБЕДЫ

9 мая
1945 года
(319)

1945. VE Day. No. 1099 optd with T **319**.
1132 j 3r. red . . . . 4·00 1·50

320 Lenin

321 Lenin

1945. 75th Birth Anniv of Lenin.
1133 **320** 30k. blue 40 20
1134 – 50k. brown . . . . 1·00 20
1135 – 60k. red . . . . 1·00 30
1136 **321** 1r. black . . . . 1·90 35
1137 – 3r. brown . . . . 3·75 1·75
DESIGNS—VERT: (inscr "1870–1945") 50k. Lenin at desk; 60k. Lenin making a speech; 3r. Portrait of Lenin.

322 Kutuzov (after R. Volkov)

323 A. I. Herzen

1945. Birth Bicentenary of Mikhail Kutuzov (military leader).
1138 **322** 30k. blue . . . . 1·00 25
1139 60k. brown . . . . 1·60 50

1945. 75th Death Anniv of Herzen (author and critic).
1140 **323** 30k. brown 85 20
1141 2r. black . . . . 1·90 55

324 I. I. Mechnikov

325 Friedrich Engels

1945. Birth Centenary of Mechnikov (biologist).
1142 **324** 30k. brown 70 15
1143 1r. black . . . . 1·40 35

1945. 125th Birth Anniv of Engels.
1144 **325** 30k. brown 80 20
1145 60k. green . . . . 1·25 45

326 Observer and Guns

327 Heavy Guns

1945. Artillery Day.
1146 **326** 30k. brown . . . . 1·75 1·40
1147 **327** 60k. black . . . . 4·00 2·75

328 Tank Production

1945. Home Front.
1148 **328** 20k. blue and brown . . 2·25 50
1149 – 30k. black and brown . . 2·00 75
1150 – 60k. brown and green . . 3·25 1·40
1151 – 1r. blue and brown . . . 4·75 1·50
DESIGNS: 30k. Harvesting; 60k. Designing aircraft; 1r. Firework display.

329 Victory Medal

330 Soldier with Victory Flag

1946. Victory Issue.
1152 **329** 30k. violet 30 15
1153 30k. brown 30 15
1154 60k. black 55 20
1155 60k. brown 55 20
1156 **330** 60k. black and red . . . 1·75 85

331 Arms of U.S.S.R.

332 Kremlin, Moscow

1946. Supreme Soviet Elections.
1157 **331** 30k. red 30 10
1158 **332** 45k. red 50 30
1159 **331** 60k. green . . . . 2·00 80

333 Tank Parade

334 Infantry Parade

1946. 28th Anniv of Red Army and Navy.
1160 **333** 60k. brown . . . . . . 1·00 15
1161 2r. violet . . . . . . 2·00 50
1162 **334** 3r. black and red . . . . 5·00 1·40

1946. Air. As Nos. 1123/31.
1163 – 5k. violet (as No. 1130) 65 60
1164 **316** 10k. red 65 60
1165 **317** 15k. red 70 65
1166 **318** 15k. green 70 65
1167 – 20k. black (as No. 1127) 70 65
1168 – 30k. violet (as No. 1127) 1·40 95
1169 – 30k. brown (as No. 1128) . . . . . . 1·40 95
1170 – 50k. blue (as No. 1125) 2·00 1·50
1171 – 60k. blue (as No. 1131) 4·00 1·75

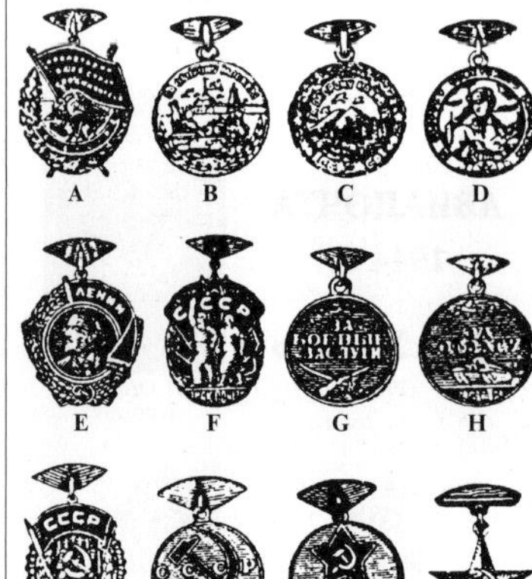
A B C D E F G H J K L M

N O P

1946. War Orders with Medals (5th series). Frames as T **291** with various centres as Types A to P.
1172 A 60k. red . . . . 1·60 1·25
1173 B 60k. red . . . . 1·60 1·25
1174 C 60k. green . . . . 1·60 1·25
1175 D 60k. green . . . . 1·60 1·25
1176 E 60k. green . . . . 1·60 1·25
1177 F 60k. blue . . . . 1·60 1·25
1178 G 60k. blue . . . . 1·60 1·25
1179 H 60k. violet . . . . 1·60 1·25
1180 J 60k. purple . . . . 1·60 1·25
1181 K 60k. brown . . . . 1·60 1·25
1182 L 60k. brown . . . . 1·60 1·25
1183 M 60k. purple . . . . 1·60 1·25
1184 N 60k. red . . . . 1·60 1·25
1185 O 60k. blue . . . . 1·60 1·25
1186 P 60k. purple . . . . 1·60 1·25

336 P. L. Chebyshev

337 Gorky

1946. 125th Birth Anniv of Chebyshev (mathematician).
1187 **336** 30k. brown 50 20
1188 60k. black 90 45

1946. Death of President Kalinin. As T **211**, but inscr "3-VI-1946".
1189 20k. black . . . . 1·90 75

1946. 10th Death Anniv of Maksim Gorky (novelist).
1190 **337** 30k. brown 55 15
1191 – 60k. green 80 20
DESIGN: 60k. Gorky and laurel leaves.

338 Gagry

340 Partisan Medal

339 Stalin and Parade of Athletes

1946. Health Resorts.
1192 – 15k. brown 40 15
1193 **338** 30k. green 60 25
1194 – 30k. green 70 25
1195 – 45k. brown . . . . 1·00 40
DESIGNS—HORIZ: 15k. Sukumi; 45k. Novy Afon. VERT: 30k. (No. 1194) Sochi.

1946. Sports Festival.
1196 **339** 30k. green . . . . 7·25 4·00

1946. War Medals (6th series). Frames as T **282** with various centres.
1197 **340** 1r. red . . . . 1·90 95
1198 B 1r. green . . . . 1·90 95
1199 C 1r. brown . . . . 1·90 95
1200 D 1r. blue . . . . 1·90 95
1201 G 1r. grey . . . . 1·90 95
1202 H 1r. red . . . . 1·90 95
1203 K 1r. purple . . . . 1·90 95
1204 L 1r. red . . . . 1·90 95

341 Moscow Opera House

342 Tanks in Red Square

1946. Moscow Buildings.
1205 – 5k. brown 40 15
1206 **341** 10k. grey 50 15
1207 – 15k. brown 40 15
1208 – 20k. brown 70 20
1209 – 45k. green 85 50
1210 – 50k. brown 95 75
1211 – 60k. violet 1·50 1·10
1212 – 1r. brown 2·25 1·75
DESIGNS—VERT: 5k. Church of Ivan the Great and Kremlin; 1r. Spassky Tower (larger). HORIZ: 15k. Hotel Moscow; 20k. Theatre and Sverdlov Square; 45k. As 5k. but horiz; 50k. Lenin Museum; 60k. St. Basil's Cathedral and Spassky Tower (larger).

1946. Heroes of Tank Engagements.
1213 **342** 30k. green 2·25 1·75
1214 60k. brown 3·50 2·25

343 "Iron" **345** Lenin and Stalin

344 Soviet Postage Stamps

1946. 4th Stalin "Five-Year Reconstruction Plan". Agriculture and Industry.
1215 – 5k. olive 30 10
1216 – 10k. green 40 10
1217 – 15k. brown 50 15
1218 – 20k. violet 80 20
1219 **343** 30k. brown 1·10 30
DESIGNS—HORIZ: 5k. "Agriculture"; 15k. "Coal". VERT: 10k. "Oil"; 20k. "Steel".

1946. 25th Anniv of Soviet Postal Services.
1220 – 15k. black and red 1·75 40
1221 – 30k. brown and green 2·50 1·00
1222 **344** 60k. black and green 4·25 1·60
DESIGNS: 15k. (48½ × 23 mm). Stamps on map of U.S.S.R.; 30k. (33 × 22½ mm). Reproduction of Type **47**.

1946. 29th Anniv of Russian Revolution. Imperf or Perf.
1223b **345** 30k. orange 3·00 2·75
1224b 30k. green 3·00 2·75

346 N. A. Nekrasov **347** Stalin Prize Medal

1946. 125th Birth Anniv of Nekrasov (poet).
1225 **346** 30k. black 1·10 25
1226 60k. brown 1·60 55

1946. Stalin Prize.
1227 **347** 30k. green 2·75 1·00

348 Dnieperprostroi Dam

1946. Restoration of Dnieperprostroi Hydro-electric Power Station.
1228 **348** 30k. black 1·75 65
1229 60k. blue 3·00 1·00

349 A. Karpinsky **350** N. E. Zhukovsky

1947. Birth Centenary of Karpinsky (geologist).
1230 **349** 30k. green 1·25 65
1231 50k. black 2·75 90

1947. Birth Centenary of Zhukovsky (scientist).
1232 **350** 30k. black 1·75 55
1233 60k. blue 2·50 85

351 Lenin Mausoleum **352** Lenin

1947. 23rd Death Anniv of Lenin.
1234 **351** 30k. green 90 50
1235 30k. blue 90 50
1236 **352** 50k. brown 3·25 1·00
For similar designs inscr "1924/1948" see Nos. 1334/6.

353 Nikolai M. Przhevalsky **354** Arms of R.S.F.S.R.

356 Arms of U.S.S.R.

1947. Centenary of Soviet Geographical Society.
1237 – 20k. brown 2·00 50
1238 – 20k. blue 2·00 50
1239 **353** 60k. olive 3·50 1·40
1240 – 60k. brown 3·50 1·40
DESIGN: 20k. Miniature portrait of F. P. Litke and full-rigged ship "Senyavin".

1947. Supreme Soviet Elections. Arms of Constituent Republics. As T **354**.
1241 **354** 30k. red (Russian Federation) 70 50
1242 – 30k. brown (Armenia) 70 50
1243 – 30k. bistre (Azerbaijan) 70 50
1244 – 30k. green (Byelorussia) 70 50
1245 – 30k. grey (Estonia) 70 50
1246 – 30k. brown (Georgia) 70 50
1247 – 30k. purple (Karelo-Finnish S.S.R.) 70 50
1248 – 30k. orange (Kazakhstan) 70 50
1249 – 30k. purple (Kirgizia) 70 50
1250 – 30k. brown (Latvia) 70 50
1251 – 30k. green (Lithuania) 70 50
1252 – 30k. purple (Moldavia) 70 50
1253 – 30k. green (Tadzhikistan) 70 50
1254 – 30k. black (Turkmenistan) 70 50
1255 – 30k. blue (Ukraine) 70 50
1256 – 30k. brown (Uzbekistan) 70 50
1257 **356** 1r. multicoloured 2·75 85
A hammer and sickle in the centre of No. 1247 and at the base of No. 1249 should assist identification.

357 Russian Soldier **359** A. S. Pushkin

1947. 29th Anniv of Soviet Army. Perf or imperf.
1258b **357** 20k. black 60 20
1259b – 30k. blue 55 15
1260b – 30k. brown 65 20
DESIGNS—VERT: No. 1259, Military cadet. HORIZ: No. 1260, Soldier, sailor and airman.

1947. 110th Death Anniv of Pushkin (poet).
1261 **359** 30k. black 90 45
1262 50k. green 1·50 1·00

360 Schoolroom

1947. International Women's Day.
1263 **360** 15k. blue 3·50 2·25
1264 – 30k. red 6·00 2·75
DESIGN—26½ × 39½ mm: 30k. Women students and banner.

362 Moscow Council Building **364** Yakovlev Yak-9 Fighter and Flag

363 May Day Procession

1947. 30th Anniv of Moscow Soviet. Perf or imperf.
1265b **362** 30k. red, blue and black 2·25 1·50

1947. May Day.
1266 **363** 30k. red 1·50 1·25
1267 1r. green 3·75 2·50

1947. Air Force Day.
1268 **364** 30k. violet 80 20
1269 1r. blue 2·25 55

365 Yakhromsky Lock

1947. 10th Anniv of Volga–Moscow Canal.
1270 – 30k. black 70 10
1271 **365** 30k. lake 70 10
1272 – 45k. red 90 25
1273 – 50k. blue 1·25 30
1274 – 60k. red 1·25 30
1275 – 1r. violet 2·50 60
DESIGNS—HORIZ: 30k. (No. 1270), Karamyshevsky Dam; 45k. Yakhromsky Pumping Station; 50k. Khimki Pier; 1r. Lock No. 8. VERT: 60k. Map of Volga–Moscow Canal.

800 лет Москвы
1147—1947 гг.
(**366**)

367 Izmailovskaya Station

1947. 800th Anniv of Moscow (1st issue). Optd as T **366**.
1276 20k. brown (No. 1208) 55 15
1277 50k. brown (No. 1210) 90 35
1278 60k. violet (No. 1211) 1·50 60
1279 1r. brown (No. 1212) 3·75 1·90
See also Nos. 1286/1300.

1947. Opening of New Moscow Underground Stations. Inscr "M".
1280 **367** 30k. blue 70 20
1281 – 30k. brown 70 20
1282 – 45k. brown 1·25 40
1283 – 45k. violet 1·25 40
1284 – 60k. green 2·50 65
1285 – 60k. red 2·50 65
DESIGNS—HORIZ: No. 1281, Power plant; No. 1282, Sokol underground station; No. 1283, Stalinskaya underground station; No. 1284, Kievskaya underground station. VERT: No. 1285, Maya Kovskaya underground station.

368 Crimea Bridge, Moscow

1947. 800th Anniv of Moscow (2nd issue).
1286 **368** 5k. brown and blue 50 10
1287 – 10k. black and brown 30 10
1288 – 30k. grey 1·50 25
1289 – 30k. blue 1·50 25
1290 – 30k. brown 55 25
1291 – 30k. green 55 25
1292 – 30k. green 55 25
1293 – 50k. green 1·40 70
1294 – 60k. blue 2·00 55
1295 – 60k. black and brown 2·00 55
1296 – 1r. purple 3·25 80
Centre in yellow, red and blue.
1297 – 1r. blue 5·50 1·75
1298 – 2r. red 8·50 2·50
1299 – 3r. blue 13·50 3·50
1300 – 5r. blue 25·00 7·50
DESIGNS—VERT: 10k. Gorky Street, Moscow; 30k. (No. 1292), Pushkin Place; 60k. (No. 1294), 2r. Kremlin; 1r. (No. 1296), "Old Moscow" after A. M. Vasnetsov; 1r. (No. 1279), St. Basil Cathedral. HORIZ: 30k. (No. 1288), Kiev railway station; 30k. (No. 1289), Kazan railway station; 30k. (No. 1290), Central Telegraph Offices; 30k. (No. 1291), Kaluga Street; 50k. Kremlin; 3r. Kremlin; 5r. Government Buildings. (54½ × 24½ mm): 60k. (No. 1295), Bridge and Kremlin.

369 "Ritz", Gagry **370** "Zapadugol", Sochi

1947. U.S.S.R. Health Resorts. (a) Vertical.
1301 **369** 30k. green 75 20
1302 – 30k. green (Sukhumi) 75 20
(b) Horizontal.
1303 **370** 30k. black 75 20
1304 – 30k. brown ("New Riviera", Sochi) 75 20
1305 – 30k. purple ("Voroshilov", Sochi) 75 20
1306 – 30k. violet ("Gulripsh", Sukhumi) 75 20
1307 – 30k. blue ("Kemeri", Riga) 75 20
1308 – 30k. brown ("Abkhazia", Novyi Afon) 75 20
1309 – 30k. bistre ("Krestyansky", Livadia) 75 20
1310 – 30k. blue ("Kirov", Kislovodsk) 75 20

371 1917 Revolution

1947. 30th Anniv of Revolution. Perf or imperf.
1311b **371** 30k. black and red 30 15
1312b – 50k. blue and red 1·60 20
1313b **371** 60k. black and red 1·00 30
1314b – 60k. brown and red 1·00 30
1315b – 1r. black and red 2·75 50
1316b – 2r. green and red 3·00 1·00
DESIGNS: 50k., 1r. "Industry"; 60k. (No. 1314), 2r. "Agriculture".

372 Metallurgical Works **373** Spassky Tower, Kremlin

1947. Post-War Five Year Plan. Horiz industrial designs. All dated "1947" except No. 1324. Perf or imperf.
1317 **372** 15k. brown 40 20
1318 – 20k. brown (Foundry) 50 30
1319 **372** 30k. purple 1·00 30
1320 – 30k. green (Harvesting machines) 75 50
1321 – 30k. brown (Tractor) 1·00 30
1322 – 30k. brown (Tractors) 75 30
1323 – 60k. bistre (Harvesting machines) 1·10 60
1324 – 60k. purple (Builders) 1·10 60
1325 – 1r. orange (Foundry) 2·25 1·25

1326	–	1r. red (Tractor)	3·75	1·75
1327	–	1r. violet (Tractors)	2·50	1·25

1947.

1328	373	60k. red	10·00	5·50
1329a		1r. red	1·75	35

374 Peter I Monument

376 Government Building, Kiev

1948. 4th Anniv of Relief of Leningrad.

1330	–	30k. violet	50	15
1331	374	50k. green	80	30
1332	–	60k. black	1·60	55
1333	–	1r. violet	2·10	1·10

DESIGNS—HORIZ: 30k. Winter Palace; 60k. Peter and Paul Fortress; 1r. Smolny Institute.

1948. 24th Death Anniv of Lenin. As issue of 1947, but dated "1924 1928".

1334	351	30k. red	85	50
1355		60k. blue	1·40	70
1336	352	60k. green	2·75	1·10

1948. 30th Anniv of Ukrainian S.S.R. Various designs inscr "XXX" and "1917–1947".

1337	376	30k. blue	55	15
1338	–	50k. violet	1·00	50
1339	–	60k. brown	1·25	75
1340	–	1r. brown	3·00	1·90

DESIGNS: 50k. Dnieper hydro-electric power station; 60k. Wheatfield and granary; 1r. Metallurgical works and colliery.

377 Vasily I. Surikov

378 Skiing

1948. Birth Centenary of Surikov (artist).

1341	377	30k. brown	1·60	65
1342		60k. green	2·40	1·40

1948. R.S.F.S.R. Games.

1343	378	15k. blue	2·25	25
1344	–	20k. blue	3·25	50

DESIGN—VERT: 20k. Motor cyclist crossing stream.

379 Artillery

381 Karl Marx and Friedrich Engels

380 Bulganin and Military School

1948. 30th Anniv of Founding of Soviet Defence Forces and of Civil War. (a) Various designs with arms and inscr "1918 XXX 1948".

1345	379	30k. brown	1·00	35
1346	–	30k. grey	1·25	35
1347	–	30k. blue	1·60	35
1348	380	60k. brown	2·50	70

DESIGNS—VERT: No. 1346, Navy. HORIZ: No. 1347, Air Force.

(b) Portraits of Civil War Heroes as Nos. 1079/81.

1349	299	60k. brown (Chapaev)	1·50	1·10
1350	–	60k. green (Shchors)	1·50	1·10
1351	–	60k. blue (Lazo)	1·50	1·10

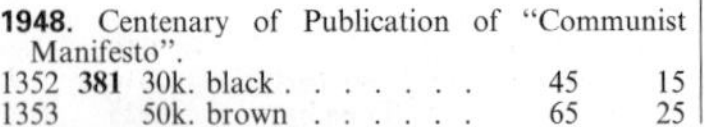

1948. Centenary of Publication of "Communist Manifesto".

1352	381	30k. black	45	15
1353		50k. brown	65	25

382 Miner

384b Arms of U.S.S.R.

384d Spassky Tower, Kremlin

1948.

1354	382	5k. black	1·75	90
1355	–	10k. violet (Sailor)	1·75	90
1356	–	15k. blue (Airman)	5·50	2·50
1361i	382	15k. black	20	10
1357	–	20k. brown (Farm girl)	5·50	2·50
1361j	–	20k. green (Farm girl)	30	10
1361ka	–	25k. blue (Airman)	50	10
1358	384b	30k. brown	7·00	3·75
1361l	–	30k. brown (Scientist)	60	10
1361n	384b	40k. red	2·50	10
1359	–	45k. violet (Scientist)	11·00	5·50
1361f	384d	50k. blue	14·50	5·00
1361	–	60k. green (Soldier)	26·00	13·00

385 Parade of Workers

1948. May Day.

1362	385	30k. red	1·10	55
1363		60k. blue	1·90	1·10

386 Belinsky (after K. Gorbunov)

1948. Death Centenary of Vissarion Grigorievich Belinsky (literary critic and journalist).

1364	386	30k. brown	1·10	35
1365		50k. green	2·75	1·00
1366		60k. violet	2·25	1·10

387 Ostrovsky

388 Ostrovsky (after V. Perov)

1948. 125th Birth Anniv of Aleksandr Ostrovsky (dramatist).

1367	387	30k. green	1·25	50
1368	388	60k. brown	1·60	1·00
1369		1r. violet	3·25	1·75

389 I. I. Shishkin (after I. Kramskoi)

391 Factories

390 "Rye Field"

1948. 50th Death Anniv of Shishkin (landscape painter).

1370	389	30k. brown and green	1·40	30
1371	390	50k. yellow, red and blue	3·00	55
1372	–	60k. multicoloured	4·50	75
1373	389	1r. blue and brown	5·00	1·75

DESIGN—HORIZ: 60k. "Morning in the Forest".

1948. Leningrad Workers' Four-Year Plan.

1374	391	15k. brown and red	2·50	1·00
1375	–	30k. black and red	2·25	1·50
1376	391	60k. brown and red	6·50	3·00

DESIGN—HORIZ (40 × 22 mm): 30k. Proclamation to Leningrad workers.

392 Arms and People of the U.S.S.R.

393 Caterpillar drawing Seed Drills

1948. 25th Anniv of U.S.S.R.

1377	392	30k. black and red	1·60	65
1378		60k. olive and red	2·75	1·40

1948. Five Year Agricultural Plan.

1379	393	30k. red	65	25
1380		30k. green	75	25
1381	–	45k. brown	1·40	60
1382	393	50k. black	2·10	1·00
1383	–	60k. green	1·60	40
1384	–	60k. green	1·60	40
1385	–	1r. violet	5·25	2·25

DESIGNS: 30k. (No. 1380), 1r. Harvesting sugar beet; 45, 60k. (No. 1383), Gathering cotton; 60k. (No. 1384), Harvesting machine.

НЮЛЬ 1948 года (394)

395 Miners

396 A. Zhdanov

1948. Air Force Day. Optd with T **394**.

1386	364	30k. violet	4·50	2·50
1387		1r. blue	4·50	2·50

1948. Miners' Day.

1388	395	30k. blue	80	40
1389	–	60k. violet	1·50	65
1390	–	1r. green	3·50	1·00

DESIGNS: 60k. Inside a coal mine; 1r. Miner's emblem.

1948. Death of A. A. Zhdanov (statesman).

1391	396	40k. blue	2·75	1·10

397 Sailor

398 Football

1948. Navy Day.

1392	397	30k. green	2·25	1·10
1393		60k. blue	3·25	1·60

1948. Sports.

1394	–	15k. violet	1·25	15
1395a	398	30k. brown	2·50	15
1396	–	45k. brown	2·75	35
1397a	–	50k. blue	3·75	35

DESIGNS—VERT: 15k. Running; 50k. Diving. HORIZ: 45k. Power boat racing.

399 Tank and Drivers

1948. Tank Drivers' Day.

1398	399	30k. black	2·00	1·40
1399	–	1r. red	4·75	2·00

DESIGN: 1r. Parade of tanks.

400 Horses and Groom

1948. Five Year Livestock Development Plan.

1400	400	30k. black	2·00	1·40
1401	–	60k. green	3·25	1·90
1402	400	1r. brown	6·00	2·75

DESIGN: 60k. Dairy farming.

401 Steam and Electric Locomotives

1948. Five Year Transport Plan.

1403	401	30k. brown	4·00	1·25
1404		50k. green	6·75	4·00
1405	–	60k. blue	5·75	4·00
1406	–	1r. violet	9·00	5·00

DESIGNS: 60k. Road traffic; 1r. Liner "Vyacheslav Molotov".

402 Iron Pipe Manufacture

1948. Five Year Rolled Iron, Steel and Machine-building Plan.

1407	–	30k. violet	1·75	90
1408	–	30k. purple	1·75	90
1409	–	50k. brown	2·75	1·40
1410	–	50k. black	2·75	1·40
1411	–	60k. brown	3·75	2·50
1412	402	60k. red	3·75	2·50
1413		1r. blue	5·75	3·25

DESIGNS—HORIZ: Nos. 1407, 1410, Foundry; No. 1408/9, Pouring molten metal; No. 1411, Group of machines.

403 Abovyan

404 Miner

1948. Death Centenary of Khachatur Abovyan (writer).

1414	403	40k. purple	2·25	1·60
1415		50k. green	3·25	2·25

1948. Five Year Coal Mining and Oil Extraction Plan.

1416	404	30k. black	1·50	70
1417		60k. brown	3·00	1·60
1418	–	60k. brown	4·25	1·75
1419	–	1r. green	6·25	4·00

DESIGN: Nos. 1418/19, Oil wells and tanker train.

405 Farkhadsk Power Station

406 Flying Model Aircraft

1948. Five Year Electrification Plan.

1420	405	30k. green	1·40	1·10
1421	–	60k. red	3·00	2·25
1422	405	1r. red	5·00	2·50

DESIGN: 60k. Zuevsk Power Station.

1948. Government Care of School Children's Summer Vacation.

1423	406	30k. green	3·25	95
1424	–	45k. red	6·50	5·00
1425	–	45k. violet	3·25	2·00
1426	–	60k. blue	9·00	5·00
1427	–	1r. blue	17·00	6·00

DESIGNS—VERT: No. 1424, Boy and girl saluting; 60k. Boy trumpeter. HORIZ: No. 1425, Children marching; 1r. Children round camp fire.

407 Children in School **408** Flag of U.S.S.R.

1948. 30th Anniv of Lenin's Young Communist League.
1428 – 20k. purple . . . . . . 3·00 1·10
1429 – 25k. red . . . . 2·00 1·10
1430 – 40k. brown and red . . 4·75 2·00
1431 **407** 50k. green . . . . 4·75 2·50
1432 **408** 1r. multicoloured . . . . 15·00 10·00
1433 – 2r. violet . . . . 15·00 10·00
DESIGNS—HORIZ: 20k. Youth parade. VERT: 25k. Peasant girl; 40k. Young people and flag; 2r. Industrial worker.

409 Interior of Theatre **410** Searchlights over Moscow

1948. 50th Anniv of Moscow Arts Theatre.
1434 **409** 50k. blue . . . . 2·75 2·25
1435 – 1r. purple . . . . 5·00 4·00
DESIGN: 1r. Stanislavsky and Dantchenko.

1948. 31st Anniv of October Revolution.
1436 **410** 40k. red . . . . 2·25 1·60
1437 1r. green . . . . 5·00 3·25

411 Artillery Barrage

1948. Artillery Day.
1438 **411** 30k. blue . . . . 2·75 2·25
1439 1r. red . . . . 4·50 3·25

412 Trade Union Building (venue)

1948. 16th World Chess Championship, Moscow.
1440 **412** 30k. blue . . . . 4·00 65
1441 – 40k. violet . . . . . . 9·00 1·00
1442 **412** 50k. brown . . . . . . 9·00 1·75
DESIGN—VERT: 40k. Players' badge showing chessboard and rook.

413 Stasov and Building

1948. Death Centenary of Stasov (architect).
1443 – 40k. brown . . . . . . 1·40 1·25
1444 **413** 1r. black . . . . 3·25 3·00
DESIGN—VERT: 40k. Portrait of Stasov.

414 Yakovlev Yak-9 Fighters and Flag **415** Statue of Ya. M. Sverdlov

1948. Air Force Day.
1445a **414** 1r. blue . . . . 7·25 1·90

1948. 225th Anniv of Sverdlovsk City. Imperf or perf.
1446b **415** 30k. blue 65 15
1447b – 40k. purple . . . . . . 1·60 50
1448b **415** 1r. green . . . . 1·90 60
DESIGN: 40k. View of Sverdlovsk.

416 Sukhumi **417** State Emblem

1948. Views of Crimea and Caucasus.
1449 **416** 40k. green . . . . 1·00 30
1450 – 40k. violet . . . . . . 1·00 30
1451 – 40k. mauve . . . . . . 1·00 30
1452 – 40k. brown . . . . . . 1·00 30
1453 – 40k. purple . . . . . . 1·00 30
1454 – 40k. green . . . . 1·00 30
1455 – 40k. blue . . . . 1·00 30
1456 – 40k. green . . . . 1·00 30
DESIGNS—VERT: No. 1450, Gardens, Sochi; 1451, Eagle-topped monument, Pyatigorsk; 1452, Cliffs, Crimea. HORIZ: No. 1453, Terraced gardens, Sochi; 1454, Roadside garden, Sochi; 1455, Colonnade, Kislovodsk; 1456, Seascape, Gagry.

1949. 30th Anniv of Byelorussian Soviet Republic.
1457 **417** 40k. red . . . . 1·90 1·60
1458 1r. green . . . . 3·50 2·25

418 M. V. Lomonosov **419** Lenin Mausoleum

1949. Establishment of Lomonosov Museum of Academy of Sciences.
1459 **418** 40k. brown . . . . . . 1·60 1·10
1460 50k. green . . . . 1·90 1·10
1461 – 1r. blue . . . . 4·25 2·75
DESIGN—HORIZ: 1r. Museum.

1949. 25th Death Anniv of Lenin.
1462 **419** 40k. brown and green . . 5·50 5·00
1463 1r. brown & deep brown 10·50 9·50

420 Dezhnev's Ship

1949. 300th Anniv of Dezhnev's Exploration of Bering Strait.
1464 – 40k. green . . . . 10·00 8·50
1465 **420** 1r. grey . . . . 20·00 12·50
DESIGN: 40k. Cape Dezhnev.

421 "Women in Industry" **422** Admiral S. O. Makarov

1949. International Women's Day.
1466 **421** 20k. violet 35 10
1467 – 25k. blue 40 10
1468 – 40k. red 55 15
1469 – 50k. grey . . . . 1·10 30
1470 – 50k. brown . . . . . . 1·10 30
1471 – 1r. green . . . . 3·50 50
1472 – 2r. red . . . . 5·25 80
DESIGNS—HORIZ: 25k. Kindergarten; 50k. grey, Woman teacher; 50k. brown, Women in field; 1r. Women sports champions. VERT: 40k., 2r. Woman broadcasting.

1949. Birth Centenary of Admiral S. O. Makarov (naval scientist).
1473 **422** 40k. blue . . . . 1·60 1·00
1474 1r. red . . . . 3·50 3·00

423 Soldier

1949. 31st Anniv of Soviet Army.
1475 **423** 40k. red . . . . 12·50 10·00

424 Kirov Military Medical Academy

1949. 150th Anniv of Kirov Military Medical Academy.
1476 **424** 40k. red . . . . 1·25 1·10
1477 – 50k. blue . . . . 1·75 1·60
1478 **424** 1r. green . . . . 4·25 3·00
DESIGN: 50k. Professors Botkin, Pirogov and Sechenov and Kirov Academy.

425 V. R. Williams **425a** Three Russians with Flag

1949. Agricultural Reform.
1479 **425** 25k. green . . . . 3·25 2·25
1480 50k. brown . . . . . . 5·50 4·50

1949. Labour Day.
1481 **425a** 40k. red . . . . 1·75 1·25
1482 1r. green . . . . 3·25 2·00

426 Newspapers and Books **427** A. S. Popov and Radio Equipment

1949. Press Day. Inscr "5 MAR 1949".
1483 **426** 40k. red . . . . 3·00 4·75
1484 – 1r. violet . . . . 6·25 8·25
DESIGN: 1r. Man and boy reading newspaper.

1949. Radio Day.
1485 **427** 40k. violet . . . . . . 1·75 1·40
1486 – 50k. brown . . . . . . 3·25 2·50
1487 **427** 1r. green . . . . 5·50 4·25
DESIGN—HORIZ: 50k. Popov demonstrating receiver to Admiral Makarov.

428 A. S. Pushkin **429** "Pushkin reading Poems to Southern Society" (Dmitry Kardovsky)

1949. 150th Birth Anniv of Pushkin (poet).
1488 **428** 25k. black and grey . . 1·10 50
1489 – 40k. black and brown . . 1·75 1·50
1490 **429** 40k. purple and red . . . 4·00 1·50
1491 – 1r. grey and brown . . . 5·25 5·00
1492 **429** 2r. blue and brown . . . 8·00 7·00
DESIGNS—VERT: No. 1489, Pushkin portrait after Kiprensky. HORIZ: 1r. Pushkin museum, Boldino.

430 "Boksimi Typlokod" (tug) **431** I. V. Michurin

1949. Centenary of Krasnoe Sormovo Machine-building and Ship-building Plant, Gorky.
1493 **430** 40k. blue . . . . 6·75 5·25
1494 – 1r. brown . . . . 10·00 8·25
DESIGN: 1r. Freighter "Bolshaya Volga".

1949. Agricultural Reform.
1495 **431** 40k. blue . . . . 1·75 1·10
1496 1r. green . . . . 2·75 1·90

432 Yachting

1949. National Sports.
1497 **432** 20k. blue . . . . 1·25 10
1498 – 25k. green . . . . 1·25 15
1499 – 30k. violet . . . . . . 1·75 20
1500 – 40k. brown . . . . . . 2·25 40
1501 – 40k. green . . . . 2·25 40
1502 – 50k. grey . . . . 2·25 50
1503 – 1r. red . . . . 5·00 1·00
1504 – 2r. black . . . . 8·50 2·25
DESIGNS: 25k. Canoeing; 30k. Swimming; 40k. (No. 1500), Cycling; 40k. (No. 1501), Football; 50k. Mountaineering; 1r. Parachuting; 2r. High jumping.

433 V. V. Dokuchaev

1949. Soil Research.
1505 **433** 40k. brown . . . . . . 1·25 30
1506 1r. green . . . . 2·50 50

434 V. I. Bazhenov **435** A. N. Radischev

1949. 150th Death Anniv of V. I. Bazhenov (architect).
1507 **434** 40k. violet . . . . . . 1·40 45
1508 1r. brown . . . . 3·25 90

1949. Birth Bicent of A. N. Radischev (writer).
1509 **435** 40k. green . . . . 1·60 1·40
1510 1r. grey . . . . 2·75 2·25

436 Green Cape Sanatorium, Makhindzhauri

1949. State Sanatoria. Designs showing various buildings.
1511 **436** 40k. green 75 20
1512 – 40k. green 75 20
1513 – 40k. blue 75 20
1514 – 40k. violet 75 20
1515 – 40k. red 75 20
1516 – 40k. orange 75 20
1517 – 40k. brown 75 20
1518 – 40k. brown 75 20
1519 – 40k. black 75 20
1520 – 40k. black 75 20
DESIGNS—HORIZ: No. 1512, VTsSPS No. 41, Zheleznovodsk; No. 1513, Energetics, Hosta; No. 1514, VTsSPS No. 3, Kislovodsk; No. 1515, VTsSPS No. 3, Hosta; No. 1516, State Theatre, Sochi; No. 1517, Clinical, Tskhaltubo; No. 1518, Frunze, Sochi; No. 1519, VTsSPS No. 1, Kislovodsk; No. 1520, Communication, Hosta.

437 I. P. Pavlov

1949. Birth Centenary of I. P. Pavlov (scientist).
1521 **437** 40k. brown . . . . . . 1·00 20
1522 1r. black . . . . 2·25 60

438 Globe and Letters

1949. 75th Anniv of U.P.U. Perf or imperf.
1523b **438** 40k. blue and brown . . 2·25 25
1524b 50k. violet and blue . . 2·25 25

439 Tree Planting Machines

440 Map of S. W. Russia

1949. Forestry and Field Conservancy.
1525 **439** 25k. green 75 30
1526 – 40k. violet 90 30
1527 **440** 40k. green and black . . 90 60
1528 – 50k. blue . . . . 1·40 1·00
1529 **439** 1r. black . . . . 4·50 2·40
1530 – 2r. brown . . . . 7·25 4·75
DESIGNS—33 × 22½ mm: 40k. violet, Harvesters; 50k. River scene. 33 × 19½ mm: 2r. Old man and children.

1949. 30th Death Anniv of V. I. Chapaev (military strategist).
1531 **299** 40k. orange . . . . . . 10·50 10·00

442 I. S. Nikitin (after P. Borel)

443 Malyi Theatre, Moscow

1949. 125th Birth Anniv of Nikitin (poet).
1532 **442** 40k. brown . . . . . . 1·10 35
1533 1r. blue . . . . 2·25 60

1949. 125th Anniv of Malyi Theatre, Moscow.
1534 **443** 40k. green . . . . 1·25 25
1535 50k. orange . . . . . . 1·75 30
1536 – 1r. brown . . . . 4·00 80
DESIGN: 1r. Five portraits and theatre.

444 Crowd with Banner

1949. 32nd Anniv of October Revolution.
1537 **444** 40k. red . . . . 2·50 2·25
1538 1r. green . . . . 4·50 4·00

445 Sheep and Cows

1949. Cattle-breeding Collective Farm.
1539 **445** 40k. brown . . . . . . 1·25 40
1540 1r. violet . . . . 2·50 80

446 Lenin Hydro-electric Station, Caucasus

448 Ski Jumping

447 Ilyushin Il-12 Airliners and Map

1949. Air. Aerial views and map.
1541 **446** 50k. brown on yellow . . 1·90 1·00
1542 – 60k. brown on buff . . . 2·00 1·50
1543 – 1r. orange on yellow . . 6·00 1·90
1544 – 1r. brown on buff . . . 5·50 1·90
1545 – 1r. blue on blue . . . . 5·50 1·90
1546 **447** 1r. blue, red and grey . . 10·00 5·50
1547 – 2r. red on blue . . . . . 12·00 5·50
1548 – 3r. green on blue . . . . 23·00 13·50
DESIGNS—Ilyushin Il-12 airplane over: HORIZ: No. 1542, Farm; 1543, Sochi. VERT: 1544, Leningrad; 1545, Aleppo; 1547, Moscow; 1548, Arctic.

1949. National Sports.
1549 **448** 20k. green . . . . 1·00 15
1550 – 40k. orange . . . . . . 3·00 75
1551 – 50k. blue . . . . 2·75 60
1552 – 1r. red . . . . 5·25 60
1553 – 2r. violet . . . . 9·00 1·50
DESIGNS: 40k. Girl gymnast; 50k. Ice hockey; 1r. Weightlifting; 2r. Shooting wolves.

449 Diesel-electric Train

450 Arms of U.S.S.R.

1949. Modern Railway Development.
1554 – 25k. red . . . . 2·00 35
1555 **449** 40k. violet . . . . . . 2·50 45
1556 – 50k. brown . . . . . . 3·50 60
1557 **449** 1r. green . . . . 9·00 1·40
DESIGNS: 25k. Electric tram; 50k. Steam train.

1949. Constitution Day.
1558 **450** 40k. red . . . . 7·00 5·00

451 Government Buildings, Dushanbe

452 People with Flag

1949. 20th Anniv of Republic of Tadzhikstan.
1559 – 20k. blue 70 10
1560 – 25k. green 80 10
1561 **451** 40k. red 90 30
1562 – 50k. violet . . . . . . 1·40 30
1563 **451** 1r. black . . . . 2·25 85
DESIGNS: 20k. Textile mills; 25k. Irrigation canal; 50k. Medical University.

1949. 10th Anniv of Incorporation of West Ukraine and West Byelorussia in U.S.S.R.
1564 **452** 40k. red . . . . 9·00 9·00
1565 – 40k. orange . . . . . . 9·00 9·00
DESIGN—VERT: No. 1565, Ukrainians and flag.

453 Worker and Globe

454 Government Buildings, Tashkent

1949. Peace Propaganda.
1566 **453** 40k. red 85 25
1567 50k. blue . . . . 1·10 35

1950. 25th Anniv of Uzbek S.S.R.
1568 – 20k. blue 45 20
1569 – 25k. black 45 20
1570 **454** 40k. red . . . . 1·00 20
1571 – 40k. violet . . . . . . 1·40 40
1572 – 1r. green . . . . 2·75 75
1573 – 2r. brown . . . . 5·00 1·60
DESIGNS: 20k. Teachers' College; 25k. Opera and Ballet House, Tashkent; 40k. (violet) Navots Street, Tashkent; 1r. Map of Fergana Canal; 2r. Lock, Fergana Canal.

455 Dam

456 "Lenin at Rozliv" (sculpture, V. Pinchuk)

1950. 25th Anniv of Turkmen S.S.R.
1574 – 25k. black . . . . 3·25 3·25
1575 **455** 40k. brown . . . . . . 1·75 1·50
1576 – 50k. green . . . . 4·00 3·75
1577 **455** 1r. violet . . . . 8·75 6·00
DESIGNS: 25k. Textile factory, Ashkhabad; 50k. Carpet-making.

1950. 26th Death Anniv of Lenin.
1578 **456** 40k. brown and grey . . 85 25
1579 – 50k. red, brown and green . . . . 1·40 60
1580 – 1r. buff, green and brown . . . . 3·25 85
DESIGNS—HORIZ: 50k. Lenin's Office, Kremlin; 1r. Lenin Museum, Gorky.

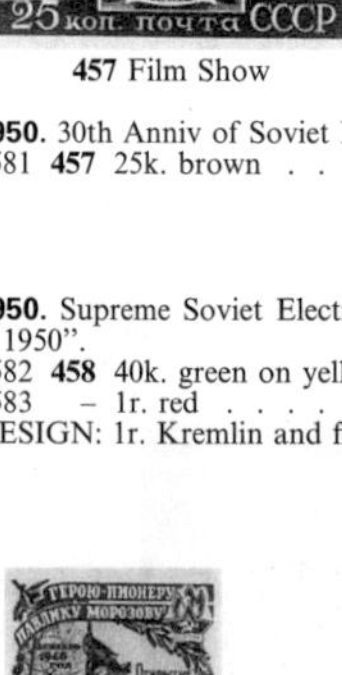
457 Film Show

458 Voter

1950. 30th Anniv of Soviet Film Industry.
1581 **457** 25k. brown . . . . . . 16·00 13·50

1950. Supreme Soviet Elections. Inscr "12 MAPTA 1950".
1582 **458** 40k. green on yellow . . 3·75 2·75
1583 – 1r. red . . . . 5·50 4·50
DESIGN: 1r. Kremlin and flags.

459 Monument (I. Rabinovich)

460 Lenin Central Museum

1950. Unveiling of Monument in Moscow to Pavlik Morozov (model Soviet youth).
1584 **459** 40k. black and red . . . 4·00 3·25
1585 1r. green and red . . . . 6·50 5·00

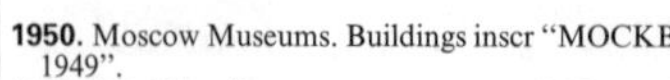

1950. Moscow Museums. Buildings inscr "MOCKBA 1949".
1586 **460** 40k. olive . . . . 1·25 25
1587 – 40k. red . . . . 1·25 25
1588 – 40k. turquoise . . . . . 1·25 25
1589 – 40k. brown . . . . . . 1·25 25
1590 – 40k. mauve . . . . . . 1·25 25
1591 – 40k. blue (no tree) . . . 1·25 25
1592 – 40k. brown . . . . . . 1·25 25
1593 – 40k. blue (with tree) . . 1·25 25
1594 – 40k. red . . . . 1·25 25
DESIGNS—HORIZ: (33½ × 23½ mm): No. 1587, Revolution Museum; 1588, Tretyakov Gallery; 1589, Timiryazev Biological Museum; No. 1591, Polytechnic Museum; 1593, Oriental Museum. (39½ × 26½ mm): No. 1590, Pushkin Pictorial Arts Museum. VERT: (22½ × 33½ mm): No. 1592, Historical Museum; 1594, Zoological Museum.

461 Hemispheres and Wireless Mast

1950. International Congress of P.T.T. and Radio Trade Unions, London.
1595 **461** 40k. green on blue . . . 3·25 2·75
1596 50k. blue on blue . . . 4·75 4·25

462 Three Workers

463 A. S. Shcherbakov

1950. Labour Day.
1597 **462** 40k. red and black . . . 3·25 2·75
1598 – 1r. red and black . . . . 6·00 5·25
DESIGN—HORIZ: 1r. Four Russians and banner.

1950. 5th Death Anniv of Shcherbakov (statesman).
1599 **463** 40k. black . . . . 1·40 1·10
1600 1r. green on pink . . . . 3·00 2·75

464 Suvorov (after N. Utkin)

465 Statue

1950. 150th Death Anniv of Suvorov.
1601 **464** 40k. blue on pink . . . 3·50 1·90
1602 – 50k. brown on pink . . 4·75 3·25
1603 – 60k. black on blue . . . 4·75 3·25
1604 **464** 1r. brown on yellow . . 6·00 4·50
1605 – 2r. green . . . . 11·00 7·00
DESIGNS—32½ × 47 mm: 50k. "Suvorov crossing the Alps" (V. I. Surikov). 24½ × 39½ mm—60k. Order of Suvorov and military parade (after portrait by N. Smdyak). 19½ × 33½ mm—2r. "Suvorov in the Alps" (N. Abbakumov).

1950. 5th Anniv of Victory over Germany.
1606 **465** 40k. red and brown . . 4·00 2·75
1607 – 1r. red . . . . 6·50 4·00
DESIGN—22½ × 33 mm: 1r. Medal for the Victory over Germany (profile of Stalin and Order of Victory).

466 Sowing on Collective Farm

1950. Agricultural Workers.
1608 – 40k. green on blue . . . 3·00 1·75
1609 **466** 40k. brown on pink . . . 3·00 1·75
1610 1r. blue on yellow . . . 4·75 3·75
DESIGNS: No. 1608, Collective farmers studying.

467 G. M. Dimitrov

468 State Opera and Ballet House, Baku

1950. 1st Death Anniv of Bulgarian Premier, Dimitrov.
1611 **467** 40k. black on yellow . . 1·75 1·40
1612 1r. black on orange . . . 4·25 2·75

1950. 30th Anniv of Azerbaijan S.S.R.
1613 **468** 25k. green on yellow . . 1·60 1·40
1614 – 40k. brown on red . . . 3·25 2·50
1615 – 1r. black on orange . . . 5·50 4·50
DESIGNS: 40k. Science Academy; 1r. Stalin Avenue, Baku.

469 Lenin Street, Stalingrad

1950. Stalingrad Reconstruction.
1616 – 20k. blue . . . . 1·00 90
1617 **469** 40k. green . . . . 2·00 1·25
1618 – 50k. orange . . . . . . 4·25 3·25
1619 – 1r. black . . . . 5·00 4·00
DESIGNS—VERT: 20k. Pobeda Cinema. HORIZ: 50k. Gorky Theatre; 1r. Pavlov House and Tank Memorial.

470 Kaluzhskaya Station

472 Trade Union Building

471 National Flags and Civilians

1950. Underground Railway Stations.
1620 **470** 40k. green on buff . . . 1·00 35
1621 A 40k. red . . . . 1·00 35
1622 B 40k. blue on buff . . . . 1·00 35
1623 C 1r. brown on yellow . . 3·00 1·10
1624 D 1r. violet on blue . . . . 3·00 1·10
1625 A 1r. green on yellow . . . 3·00 1·10
1626 E 1r. black on orange . . . 3·00 1·10
DESIGNS—HORIZ: (34 × 22½ mm): A, Culture Park; B, Taganskaya; C, Kurskaya; D, Paveletskaya. (34 × 18½ mm): E, Taganskaya.

1950. Unconquerable Democracy. Flags in red, blue and yellow.
1627 **471** 40k. black . . . . 1·10 20
1628 50k. brown . . . . . . 2·25 30
1629 1r. green . . . . 2·50 45

1950. 10th Anniv of Latvian S.S.R.
1630 **472** 25k. brown 90 60
1631 – 40k. red . . . . 1·40 90
1632 – 50k. green . . . . 2·10 1·40
1633 – 60k. blue . . . . 2·50 1·90
1634 – 1r. violet . . . . 4·50 3·00
1635 – 2r. brown . . . . 7·50 5·00
DESIGNS—VERT: 40k. Cabinet Council Offices; 50k. Monument to Jan Rainis (poet); 2r. Academy of Sciences. HORIZ: 60k. Theatre, Riga; 1r. State University, Riga.

473 Marite Melnikaite

474 Stalingrad Square, Tallinn

1950. 10th Anniv of Lithuanian S.S.R.
1636 – 25k. blue . . . . 1·25 70
1637 **473** 40k. brown . . . . . . 2·40 1·40
1638 – 1r. red . . . . 6·50 3·50
DESIGNS—HORIZ: 25k. Academy of Sciences; 1r. Cabinet Council Offices.

1950. 10th Anniv of Estonian S.S.R.
1639 **474** 25k. green . . . . 1·00 60
1640 – 40k. red . . . . 1·40 90
1641 – 50k. blue on yellow . . . 2·25 1·60
1642 – 1r. brown on blue . . . 7·00 5·50
DESIGNS—HORIZ: 40k. Government building; 50k. Opera and Ballet Theatre, Tallin. VERT: 1r. Viktor Kingisepp (revolutionary).

475 Signing Peace Appeal

1950. Peace Conference.
1643 **475** 40k. red on pink . . . . 1·60 1·10
1644 – 40k. black . . . . 1·60 1·10
1645 – 50k. red . . . . 3·50 3·00
1646 **475** 1r. brown on pink . . . 5·50 4·75
DESIGNS—VERT: 40k. black, Children and teacher; 50k. Young people with banner.

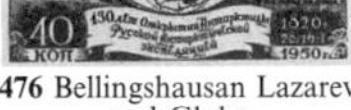
476 Bellingshausan Lazarev and Globe

477 Frunze (after I. Brodsky)

1950. 130th Anniv of 1st Antarctic Expedition.
1647 **476** 40k. red on blue . . . . 18·00 11·00
1648 – 1r. violet on blue . . . . 32·00 15·00
DESIGN—VERT: 1r. "Mirnyi" and "Vostok" (ships) and map of Antarctica.

1950. 25th Death Anniv of M.V. Frunze (military strategist).
1649 **477** 40k. blue on pink . . . 3·50 2·75
1650 1r. brown on blue . . . 8·25 6·00

478 M. I. Kalinin

479 Picking Grapes

1950. 75th Birth Anniv of Kalinin (statesman).
1651 **478** 40k. green . . . . 1·25 85
1652 1r. brown . . . . 2·75 1·60
1653 5r. violet . . . . 7·25 6·50

1950. 30th Anniv of Armenian S.S.R.
1654 **479** 20k. blue on pink . . . 1·50 1·10
1655 – 40k. orange on blue . . 2·75 1·60
1656 – 1r. black on yellow . . . 5·75 3·75
DESIGNS—HORIZ: (33 × 16 mm): 40k. Government Offices. VERT: (21½ × 33 mm): 1r. G. M. Sundukian (dramatist).

480 Kotelnicheskaya Quay

481 Spassky Tower, Kremlin

1950. Moscow Building Projects.
1657 **480** 1r. brown on pink . . . 35·00 25·00
1658 – 1r. black on pink . . . . 35·00 25·00
1659 – 1r. brown on blue . . . 35·00 25·00
1660 – 1r. green on yellow . . . 35·00 25·00
1661 – 1r. blue on pink . . . . 35·00 25·00
1662 – 1r. black . . . . 35·00 25·00
1663 – 1r. orange . . . . 35·00 25·00
1664 – 1r. green on blue . . . . 35·00 25·00
DESIGNS—HORIZ: No. 1659, Vosstaniya Square; 1660, Smolenskaya Square; 1662, Krasnye Vorota; 1664, Moscow University. VERT: No. 1658, Hotel Ukraine, Dorogomilovskaya Quay; 1661, Hotel Leningrad; 1663, Zaryade.

1950. 33rd Anniv of October Revolution.
1665 **481** 1r. red, yellow and green 16·00 9·00

482 "Golden Autumn"

1950. 50th Death Anniv of Levitan (painter).
1666 **482** 40k. multicoloured . . . 4·00 85
1667 – 50k. brown . . . . . . 5·00 85
DESIGN: 50k. Portrait of Levitan by V. Serov.

483 Aivazovsky (after A. Tyranov)

484 Newspapers "Iskra" and "Pravda"

1950. 50th Death Anniv of Aivazovsky (painter). Multicoloured centres.
1668 – 40k. brown . . . . . . 3·00 40
1669 – 50k. brown . . . . . . 4·00 65
1670 **483** 1r. blue . . . . 7·75 1·40
PAINTINGS—HORIZ: 40k. "Black Sea"; 50k. "Ninth Wave".

1950. 50th Anniv of Newspaper "Iskra".
1671 – 40k. red and black . . . 12·00 10·50
1672 **484** 1r. red and black . . . . 16·00 13·00
DESIGN: 40k. Newspapers and banners.

485 Government Offices

1950. 30th Anniv of Kazakh S.S.R.
1673 **485** 40k. black on blue . . . 4·75 2·50
1674 – 1r. brown on yellow . . 6·25 3·50
DESIGN: 1r. Opera House, Alma-Ata.

486 Decembrists and "Decembrist Rising in Senate Square, St. Petersburg, 14 December 1825" (K. Kolman)

1950. 125th Anniv of Decembrist Rising.
1675 **486** 1r. brown on yellow . . 7·25 5·50

487 Govt Offices, Tirana

1951. Friendship with Albania.
1676 **487** 40k. green on blue . . . 20·00 15·00

488 Greeting Soviet Troops

1951. Friendship with Bulgaria.
1677 **488** 25k. black on blue . . . 2·25 1·90
1678 – 40k. orange on pink . . 6·00 3·25
1679 – 60k. brown on orange . 6·75 4·25
DESIGNS: 40k. Lenin Square, Sofia; 60k. Monument to Soviet fighters, Kolarovgrad.

489 Lenin at Razliv

1951. 27th Death Anniv of Lenin. Multicoloured centres.
1680 **489** 40k. green . . . . 2·75 65
1681 – 1r. blue . . . . 5·50 1·00
DESIGN: 1r. Lenin talking to young Communists.

490 Horses

1951. 25th Anniv of Kirghiz S.S.R.
1682 **490** 25k. brown on blue . . . 5·00 4·50
1683 – 40k. green on blue . . . 7·25 6·75
DESIGN—33 × 22½ mm: 40k. Government Offices, Frunze.

490a Gathering Lemons

1951. 30th Anniv of Georgia S.S.R.
1683a – 20k. green on yellow 1·75 1·25
1683b **490a** 25k. orange and violet 2·75 2·00
1683c – 40k. brown on blue 4·50 3·00
1683d – 1r. green and brown 11·00 6·00
DESIGNS—VERT: 20k. State Opera and Ballet Theatre, Tbilisi. HORIZ: 40k. Rustaveli Avenue, Tbilisi; 1r. Plucking tea.

491 University, Ulan Bator

1951. Friendship with Mongolia.
1684 **491** 25k. violet on orange . . 1·75 75
1685 – 40k. orange on yellow 2·50 1·10
1686 – 1r. multicoloured . . . . 7·25 4·00
DESIGNS—HORIZ: (37 × 25 mm): 40k. State Theatre, Ulan Bator. VERT: (22 × 33 mm): 1r. State Emblem and Mongolian Flag.

492 D. A. Furmanov

493 Soviet Soldiers Memorial, Berlin (E. Buchetich)

1951. 25th Death Anniv of D. A. Furmanov (writer).
1687 **492** 40k. brown on blue . . . 1·90 1·40
1688 – 1r. black on orange . . . 4·25 3·25
DESIGN—HORIZ: 1r. Furmanov writing.

1951. Stockholm Peace Appeal.
1689 **493** 40k. green and red . . . 4·25 3·25
1690 1r. black and red . . . . 9·00 7·50

494 Factories

1951. 150th Anniv of Kirov Machine-building Factory, Leningrad.
1691 **494** 40k. brown on yellow . . 6·75 5·00

495 Bolshoi State Theatre

1951. 175th Anniv of State Theatre.
1692 **495** 40k. multicoloured . . . 5·00 55
1693 – 1r. multicoloured . . . . 7·25 1·40
DESIGN: 1r. Theatre and medallions of Glinka, Tchaikovsky, Moussorgsky, Rimsky-Korsakov, Borodin and theatre.

496 National Museum, Budapest

1951. Hungarian Peoples' Republic. Buildings in Budapest.
1694 – 25k. green . . . . 1·40 1·10
1695 – 40k. blue . . . . 1·50 90
1696 **496** 60k. black . . . . 2·50 1·25
1697 – 1r. black on pink . . . . 5·75 3·50
DESIGNS—HORIZ: 25k. Liberty Bridge; 40k. Parliament buildings. VERT: 1r. Liberation Monument.

497 Harvesting

1951. Agricultural Scenes.
1698 **497** 25k. green 90 50
1699 – 40k. green on blue . . . 1·75 60
1700 – 1r. brown on yellow . . 3·00 2·75
1701 – 2r. green on pink . . . . 5·25 4·75
DESIGNS: 40k. Apiary; 1r. Gathering citrus fruit; 2r. Harvesting cotton.

498 M. I. Kalinin **499** F. E. Dzerzhinsky

1951. 5th Death Anniv of Pres. Kalinin.
1702 – 20k. black, sepia & brown 75 35
1703 **498** 40k. brown, dp grn & grn . . . . 1·60 50
1704 – 1r. black, bl & ultram 3·25 90
DESIGNS—HORIZ: 20k. Kalinin Museum. VERT: 1r. Statue of Kalinin (G. Alekseev).

1951. 25th Death Anniv of Dzerzhinsky (founder of Cheka).
1705 **499** 40k. red . . . . 2·40 60
1706 – 1r. black (Portrait in uniform) . . . . . . 4·50 1·60

500 P. K. Kozlov **501** Kalinnikov

1951. Russian Scientists.
1707 **500** 40k. orange . . . . . . 1·50 25
1708 – 40k. orange on pink . . 1·50 25
1709 – 40k. orange on blue . . 4·50 1·10
1710 – 40k. brown . . . . . . 1·50 25
1711 – 40k. brown on pink (facing left) . . . . . 1·50 25
1712 – 40k. brown on pink (facing right) . . . . 1·50 25
1713 – 40k. grey . . . . 1·50 25
1714 – 40k. grey on pink . . . 1·50 25
1715 – 40k. grey on blue . . . 4·50 1·10
1716 – 40k. green . . . . . . 1·50 25
1717 – 40k. green on pink . . . 1·50 25
1718 – 40k. blue . . . . 1·50 25
1719 – 40k. blue on pink . . . 1·50 25
1720 – 40k. blue on blue . . . 1·50 25
1721 – 40k. violet . . . . . . 1·50 25
1722 – 40k. violet on pink . . . 1·50 25
PORTRAITS: No. 1708, N. N. Miklukho-Makai; 1709, A. M. Butlerov; 1710, N. I. Lobachevsky; 1711, K. A. Timiryazev; 1712, N. S. Kurnakov; 1713, P. N. Yablochkov; 1714, A. N. Severtsov; No. 1715, K. E. Tsiolkovsky; 1716, A. N. Lodygin; 1717, A. G. Stoletov; 1718, P. N. Lebedev; 1719, A. O. Kovalesky; 1720, D. I. Mendeleev; 1721, S. P. Krasheninnikov; 1722, S. V. Kovalevskaya.

1951. Russian Composers.
1723 **501** 40k. grey on pink . . . 10·00 8·25
1724 – 40k. brown on pink . . 10·00 8·25
PORTRAIT: No. 1724, A. Alyabev (after N. Andreev).

502 Aviation Society Badge **503** Vasnetsov (after I. Kramskoi)

1951. Aviation Developement.
1725 **502** 40k. multicoloured . . . 1·25 15
1726 – 60k. multicoloured . . . 2·00 20
1727 – 1r. multicoloured . . . . 3·25 85
1728 – 2r. multicoloured . . . . 6·25 1·50
DESIGNS—VERT: 60k. Boys and model gliders; 1r. Parachutists descending. HORIZ: (45 × 25 mm): 2r. Flight of Yakovlev Yak-18U trainers.

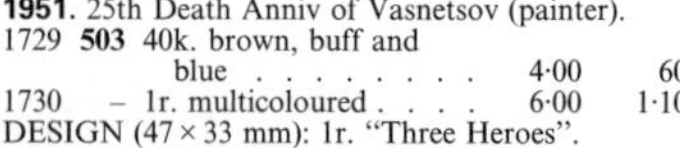

1951. 25th Death Anniv of Vasnetsov (painter).
1729 **503** 40k. brown, buff and blue . . . . 4·00 60
1730 – 1r. multicoloured . . . . 6·00 1·10
DESIGN (47 × 33 mm): 1r. "Three Heroes".

504 Lenin, Stalin and Dnieperprostroi Dam

1951. 34th Anniv of October Revolution.
1731 **504** 40k. blue and red . . . 6·00 3·25
1732 – 1r. brown and red . . . 8·00 5·50
DESIGN: 1r. Lenin, Stalin and Spassky Tower.

505 Volga–Don Canal

1951. Construction of Hydro-electric Power Stations.
1733 – 20k. multicoloured . . . 4·00 2·00
1734 **505** 30k. multicoloured . . . 4·50 3·50
1735 – 40k. multicoloured . . . 5·50 4·00
1736 – 60k. multicoloured . . . 8·50 4·50
1737 – 1r. multicoloured . . . . 13·00 8·00
DESIGNS—VERT: (32 × 47 mm): 20k. Khakhovsky power station. HORIZ: (47 × 32 mm); 40k. Stalingrad dam; 60k. Excavator and map of Turkmen canal; 1r. Kuibyshev power station.

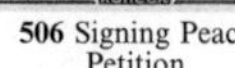

506 Signing Peace Petition **507** M. V. Ostrogradsky

1951. 3rd U.S.S.R. Peace Conference.
1738 **506** 40k. red and brown . . 9·25 7·25

1951. 150th Birth Anniv of Ostrogradsky (mathematician).
1739 **507** 40k. brown on pink . . 7·25 4·50

508 Zhizka Monument, Prague (B. Kafka) **509** Volkhovsky Hydro-electric Station and Lenin Monument

1951. Friendship with Czechoslovakia.
1740 **508** 20k. blue on pink . . . 2·00 1·25
1741 – 25k. red on yellow . . . 4·50 1·75
1742 – 40k. orange on orange 2·25 1·50
1743 – 60k. grey on pink . . . 5·25 2·75
1744 – 1r. grey on cream . . . 8·00 5·00
DESIGNS—VERT: 25k. Soviet Army Monument, Ostrava; 40k. J. Fucik by M. Shvabinsky; 60k. Smetana Museum, Prague. HORIZ: 1r. Soviet Soldiers Monument, Prague.

1951. 25th Anniv of Lenin Volkhovsky Hydro-electric Station.
1745a **509** 40k. yellow, indigo and blue . . . . 1·10 35
1746 1r. yellow, indigo and violet . . . . 2·25 50

510 Lenin when a Student (after V. Prager) **511** P. P. Semenov-Tian-Shansky

1952. 28th Death Anniv of Lenin. Multicoloured centres.
1747 **510** 40k. green . . . . 2·25 75
1748 – 60k. blue . . . . 2·75 90
1749 – 1r. brown . . . . 3·25 1·40
DESIGNS—HORIZ: 60k. Lenin and children (after A. Varlamov); 1r. Lenin talking to peasants (after V. Serov).

1952. 125th Birth Anniv of Semenov-Tian-Shansky (scientist).
1750 **511** 1r. brown on blue . . . 3·75 2·50

512 Skaters **513** V. O. Kovalevsky

1952. Winter Sports.
1751 **512** 40k. multicoloured . . . 3·25 45
1752 – 60k. multicoloured (Skiers) . . . . 4·00 75

1952. Birth Centenary of Kovalevsky (scientist).
1753 **513** 40k. brown on yellow . . 6·25 5·00

514 Gogol (after F. Möller) and Character from "Taras Bulba"

1952. Death Centenary of Nikolai Gogol (writer).
1754 **514** 40k. black on blue . . . 1·00 20
1755 – 60k. orange and black 1·40 30
1756 – 1r. multicoloured . . . 2·75 1·40
DESIGNS: 60k. Gogol and Belinsky (after B. Lebedev); 1r. Gogol and Ukrainian peasants.

515 G. K. Ordzhonikidze **516** Workers and Flag

1952. 15th Death Anniv of Ordzhonikidze (statesman).
1757 **515** 40k. green on pink . . . 5·50 3·25
1758 1r. black on blue . . . . 7·25 5·00

1952. 15th Anniv of Stalin Constitution.
1759 **516** 40k. red and black on cream . . . . 5·50 3·75
1760 – 40k. red and green on green . . . . 5·50 3·75
1761 – 40k. red and brown on blue . . . . 5·50 3·75
1762 – 40k. red and black . . . 5·50 3·75
DESIGNS—HORIZ: No. 1760, Chess players at recreation centre; 1761, Old people and banners. VERT: No. 1762, Schoolgirl and Spassky Tower, Kremlin.

517 Novikov-Priboy and Battleship "Orel"

1952. 75th Birth Anniv of Novikov-Priboy (writer).
1763 **517** 40k. grey, yellow & green . . . . 3·25 1·10

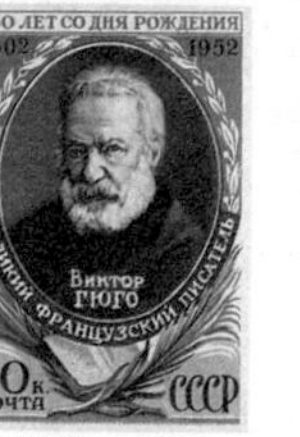

518 Victor Hugo **519** Yulaev (after T. Nechaevoi)

1952. 150th Birth Anniv of Victor Hugo (French writer).
1764 **518** 40k. black, blue & brown . . . . 1·75 50

1952. Birth Bicent of Yulaev (Bashkirian hero).
1765 **519** 40k. red on pink . . . . 1·75 55

520 G. Ya. Sedov **521** Arms and Flag of Rumania

1952. 75th Birth Anniv of Sedov (Arctic explorer).
1766 **520** 40k. brown, blue & green . . . . 10·50 8·00

1952. Friendship with Rumania.
1767 **521** 40k. multicoloured . . . 1·40 65
1768 – 60k. green on pink . . . 2·50 1·50
1769 – 1r. blue . . . . 3·00 2·25
DESIGNS—VERT: 60k. Soviet Soldiers' Monument, Bucharest. HORIZ: 1r. University Square, Bucharest.

522 Zhukovsky (after K. Bryullov) **523** Bryullov (after V. Tropilin)

1952. Death Centenary of V. Zhukovsky (poet).
1770 **522** 40k. black on blue . . . 1·10 55

1952. Death Centenary of K. Bryullov (artist).
1771 **523** 40k. green on blue . . . 1·10 55

524 Ogarev (after M. Lemmel) **525** Uspensky (after N. Yaroshenko)

1952. 75th Death Anniv of Ogarev (revolutionary writer).
1772 **524** 40k. green 65 35

1952. 50th Death Anniv of Uspensky (writer).
1773 **525** 40k. brown and blue . . 1·75 75

526 Nakhimov (after V. Timm) **527** Tartu University

1952. 150th Birth Anniv of Admiral Nakhimov.
1774 **526** 40k. multicoloured . . . 3·75 1·60

1952. 150th Anniv of Extension of Tartu University.
1775 **527** 40k. black on salmon . . 2·75 1·60

1952. War Orders and Medals (7th series). Frame as T **282** with various centres.
1776 F 1r. brown . . . . 12·00 9·00
1777 P 2r. red . . . . 1·90 1·00
1778 J 3r. violet 90 70
1779a A 5r. lake . . . . 1·25 85
1780 E 10r. red . . . . 1·75 1·00

528 Kayum Nasyri

529 A. N. Radishchev

1952. 50th Death Anniv of Nasyri (educationist).
1781 **528** 40k. brown on yellow . . 2·75 1·60

1952. 150th Death Anniv of Radishchev (writer).
1782 **529** 40k. black and red . . . 2·25 75

530 Entrance to Volga–Don Canal

531 P. A. Fedotov

1952. 35th Anniv of Russian Revolution.
1783 **530** 40k. multicoloured . . . 5·00 3·25
1784 – 1r. yellow, red and brown . . . . . . 7·25 5·00
DESIGN: 1r. Lenin, Stalin, Spassky Tower and flags.

1952. Death Centenary of Fedotov (painter).
1785 **531** 40k. brown and lake . . 2·25 65

532 Polenov (after I. Repin)

534 Odoevsky (after N. Bestuzhev)

533 "Moscow Courtyard" (painting)

1952. 25th Death Anniv of Polenov (painter).
1786 **532** 40k. lake and buff . . . 1·60 55
1787 **533** 1r. blue and grey . . . . 3·75 1·25

1952. 150th Birth Anniv of A. I. Odoevsky (poet).
1788 **534** 40k. black and red . . . 1·75 50

535 Mamin-Sibiryak

536 V. M. Bekhterev

1952. Birth Centenary of D. N. Mamin-Sibiryak (writer).
1789 **535** 40k. green on yellow . . 1·10 25

1952. 25th Death Anniv of Bekhterev (psychiatrist).
1790 **536** 40k. black, grey and blue 1·40 55

537 Komsomolskaya Koltsevaya Station

1952. Underground Stations. Multicoloured centres.
1791 – 40k. violet . . . . . . 2·00 40
1792 – 40k. blue . . . . 2·00 40
1793 – 40k. grey . . . . 2·00 40
1794 **537** 40k. green . . . . 2·00 40
STATIONS: No. 1791, Belorussia Koltsevaya; 1792, Botanical Gardens; 1793, Novoslo-bodskaya.

538 U.S.S.R. Arms and Flags

1952. 30th Anniv of U.S.S.R.
1795 **538** 1r. brown, red and green 4·50 3·25

539 Lenin and Flags (after A. Gerasimov)

1953. 29th Death Anniv of Lenin.
1796 **539** 40k. multicoloured . . . 5·00 4·25

540 Peace Prize Medal

541 V. V. Kuibyshev

1953. Stalin Peace Prize.
1797 **540** 40k. yellow, blue & brown . . . . 5·50 5·00

1953. 65th Birth Anniv of Kuibyshev (statesman).
1798 **541** 40k. black and lake . . . 1·90 1·25

542 V. V. Mayakovsky

543 N. G. Chernyshevsky

1953. 60th Birth Anniv of Mayakovsky (poet).
1799 **542** 40k. black and red . . . 2·75 2·25

1953. 125th Birth Anniv of Chernyshevsky (writer).
1800 **543** 40k. brown and buff . . 2·75 2·25

544 R. Volga Lighthouse

1953. Volga–Don Canal. Multicoloured.
1801 40k. Type **544** . . . . . . 1·60 60
1802 40k. Lock No. 9 . . . . . 1·60 60
1803 40k. Lock No. 13 . . . . . 1·60 60
1804 40k. Lock No. 15 . . . . . 1·90 60
1805 40k. Tsimlyanskaya hydro-electric station . . . . . 1·60 60
1806 1r. "Iosif Stalin" (river vessel) . . . . 3·00 1·40

545 V. G. Korolenko

546 Tolstoi (after N. Ge)

1953. Birth Centenary of Korolenko (writer).
1807 **545** 40k. brown . . . . . . 1·10 25

1953. 125th Birth Anniv of Leo Tolstoi (writer).
1808 **546** 1r. brown . . . . 6·50 3·25

547 Lomonosov University and Students

548 Peoples of the U.S.S.R.

1953. 35th Anniv of "Komsomol" (Russian Youth Organization). Multicoloured.
1809 40k. Type **547** . . . . . . 2·25 1·40
1810 1r. Four medals and "Komsomol" badge . . . 4·50 2·75

1953. 36th Anniv of Russian Revolution. Mult.
1811 40k. Type **548** . . . . . . 7·25 5·50
1812 60k. Lenin and Stalin in Smolny Institute, 1917 . . 12·50 9·50

549 Lenin Medallion

550 Lenin Statue

551 Peter I Monument

1953. 50th Anniv of Communist Party.
1813 **549** 40k. multicoloured . . . 3·50 2·75

1953. Views of Leningrad as T **550/1**.
1814 **550** 40k. black on yellow . . 2·00 1·00
1815 40k. brown on pink . . 2·00 1·00
1816 – 40k. brown on yellow . . 1·25 45
1817 – 40k. black on buff . . . 1·75 85
1818 **551** 1r. brown on blue . . . 3·00 1·10
1819 1r. violet on yellow . . . 3·00 1·40
1820 – 1r. green on pink . . . . 3·00 2·25
1821 – 1r. brown on blue . . . 3·50 2·40
DESIGNS: As Type **550**: Nos. 1816/17, Admiralty. As Type **551**: 1820/1, Smolny Institute.

552 Lenin and Book "What is to be Done?"

553 Pioneers and Moscow University Model

1953. 50th Anniv of 2nd Social Democratic Workers' Party Congress.
1822 **552** 1r. brown and red . . . 7·75 6·50

1953. Peace Propaganda.
1823 **553** 40k. black, olive and grey . . . . 3·75 2·75

554 Griboedov (after I. Kramskoi)

555 Kremlin

1954. 125th Death Anniv of A. S. Griboedov (author).
1824 **554** 40k. purple on buff . . 1·60 50
1825a 1r. black on green . . . 2·25 1·00

1954. General Election.
1826 **555** 40k. grey and red . . . 2·75 2·00

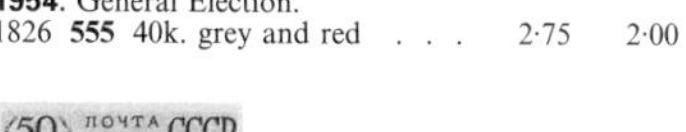

556 V. P. Chkalov

557 "Lenin in Smolny Institute" (after I. Brodsky)

1954. 50th Birthday of Chkalov (aviator).
1827 **556** 1r. multicoloured . . . . 4·00 1·60

1954. 30th Death Anniv of Lenin. Multicoloured.
1828 40k. Lenin (after M. Rundaltsov) (26 × 38 mm) . . . . . . 2·50 1·40
1829 40k. Type **557** . . . . . 2·50 1·40
1830 40k. Cottage Museum, Ulyanovsk (after I. Sokolov) . . . . 2·50 1·40
1831 40k. "Lenin proclaims Soviet Regime" (V. Serov) (48 × 35 mm) . . . . . . 2·50 1·40
1832 40k. "Lenin at Kazan University" (A. Pushnin) (48 × 35 mm) . . . . . . 2·50 1·40

558 Stalin

559 Supreme Soviet Buildings in Kiev and Moscow

1954. 1st Death Anniv of Stalin.
1833 **558** 40k. brown . . . . . . 3·50 2·25

1954. Tercentenary of Reunion of Ukraine with Russia. Multicoloured. (a) Designs as T **559** inscr "1654–1954".
1834 40k. Type **559** . . . . . . 1·10 40
1835 40k. Shevchenko Memorial, Kharkhov (vert) . . . . 1·10 25
1836 40k. State Opera House, Kiev . . . . 1·10 25
1837 40k. Shevchenko University, Kiev . . . . 1·10 25
1838 40k. Academy of Sciences, Kiev . . . . 1·50 25
1839 60k. Bogdan Chmielnitsky Memorial, Kiev (vert) . . 1·60 25
1840 1r. Flags of R.S.F.S.R. and Ukrainian S.S.R. (vert) 3·50 55
1841 1r. Shevchenko Monument, Kanev (vert) . . . . . . 2·50 35
1842 1r. Pereyaslavskaya Rada 3·50 45

(b) No. 1098b optd with five lines of Cyrillic characters as inscr at top of T **559**.
1843 h 2r. green . . . . 7·50 1·75

561 Running

1954. Sports. Frames in brown.
1844 **561** 40k. black and stone . . 1·00 20
1845 – 40k. black and blue . . 1·25 20
1846 – 40k. brown and buff . . 1·00 20
1847 – 40k. black and blue . . 1·00 20
1848 – 40k. black . . . . 1·00 20
1849 – 1r. grey and blue . . . . 5·00 1·50
1850 – 1r. black and blue . . . 5·00 1·50
1851 – 1r. brown and drab . . 5·00 1·50
DESIGNS—HORIZ: No. 1845, "Soling" yachts; 1846, Cycling; 1847, Swimming; 1848, Hurdling; 1849, Mountaineering; 1850, Skiing. VERT: No. 1851, Basketball.

562 Cattle **563** A. P. Chekhov

1954. Agriculture.
1852 **562** 40k. blue, brown & cream . . . . 2·40 50
1853 – 40k. green, brown & buff 2·40 50
1854 – 40k. black, blue and green . . . . 2·40 50
DESIGNS: No. 1853, Potato cultivation; 1854, Collective farm hydro-electric station.

1954. 50th Death Anniv of Chekhov (writer).
1855 **563** 40k. brown and green . . 1·10 40

564 Bredikhin, Struve, Belopolsky and Observatory **565** M. I. Glinka

1954. Rebuilding of Pulkov Observatory.
1856 **564** 40k. black, blue and violet . . . . 8·00 1·60

1954. 150th Birth Anniv of Glinka (composer).
1857 **565** 40k. brown, pink and red . . . . 2·25 35
1858 – 60k. multicoloured . . . 3·25 65
DESIGN—HORIZ: (38 × 25½ mm): 60k. "Glinka playing piano for Pushkin and Zhukovsky" (V. Artamonov).

566 Exhibition Emblem **567** N. A. Ostrovsky

1954. Agricultural Exhibition. Multicoloured.
1859 40k. Type **566** 85 35
1860 40k. Agricultural Pavilion 85 35
1861 40k. Cattle breeding Pavilion 85 35
1862 40k. Mechanization Pavilion 85 35
1863 1r. Exhibition Entrance . . 3·00 1·40
1864 1r. Main Pavilion . . . . . 3·00 1·40
Nos. 1860/3 are horiz, 1860/1 being 41 × 30½ mm, 1862, 40 × 30 mm and 1863 41 × 33 mm. No. 1864 is vert, 29 × 41 mm.

1954. 50th Birth Anniv of Ostrovsky (writer).
1865 **567** 40k. multicoloured . . . 1·75 45

568 Monument **569** Marx, Engels, Lenin and Stalin

1954. Centenary of Defence of Sevastopol.
1866 **568** 40k. black, brown & grn 1·40 40
1867 – 60k. black, brown & buff 1·60 60
1868 – 1r. multicoloured . . . . 3·50 1·00
DESIGNS—HORIZ: 60k. Heroes of Sevastopol (after V. Timm). VERT: 1r. Admiral Nakhimov (after V. Timm).

1954. 37th Anniv of October Revolution.
1869 **569** 1r. brown, red and orange . . . . 5·50 3·50

570 Kazan University

1954. 150th Anniv of Kazan University.
1870 **570** 40k. blue on blue . . . 1·00 45
1871 60k. red . . . . 1·75 55

571 Salomea Neris

1954. 50th Birth Anniv of Salomea Neris (poetess).
1872 **571** 40k. multicoloured . . . 1·25 35

572 Cultivating Vegetables **573** Stalin

1954. Agriculture. Multicoloured.
1873 40k. Type **572** . . . . . . 1·50 30
1874 40k. Tractor and plough . . 1·50 30
1875 40k. Harvesting flax (49 × 25½ mm) . . . . . 1·50 30
1876 60k. Harvesting sunflowers (49 × 25½ mm) . . . . . 3·00 65

1954. 75th Birth Anniv of Stalin.
1877 **573** 40k. purple . . . . . . 1·50 50
1878 1r. blue . . . . 3·50 1·40

574 Rubinstein (after I. Repin)

1954. 125th Birth Anniv of Rubinstein (composer).
1879 **574** 40k. black and purple . . 2·00 40

575 V. M. Garshin **576** Ilyushin Il-12 over Landscape

1955. Birth Centenary of Garshin (writer).
1880 **575** 40k. black, brown & grn 1·10 35

1955. Air.
1881 – 1r. multicoloured . . . . 1·75 40
1882 **576** 2r. black and green . . . 3·75 60
DESIGN: 1r. Ilyushin Il-12 over coastline.

577 Savitsky (after N. Frandkovsky) and "Construction of Railway"

1955. 50th Death Anniv of Savitsky (painter).
1883 **577** 40k. brown . . . . 1·75 30

578 Clasped Hands **579** Pushkin and Mickiewicz

1955. International Conference of Postal and Municipal Workers, Vienna.
1884 **578** 50k. multicoloured . . . 1·10 30

1955. 10th Anniv of Russo–Polish Friendship Agreement.
1885 **579** 40k. multicoloured . . . 2·25 30
1886 – 40k. black . . . . 2·25 30
1887 – 1r. multicoloured . . . . 4·00 85
1888 – 1r. multicoloured . . . . 6·00 1·25
DESIGNS: No. 1886, "Brotherhood in Arms" Monument, Warsaw (26½ × 39 mm); No. 1887, Palace of Science, Warsaw (37½ × 25½ mm); No. 1888, Copernicus and Matejko (39 × 26½ mm).

580 Lenin at Shushenskoe (after V. Basov)

1955. 85th Birth Anniv of Lenin. Multicoloured centres.
1889 **580** 60k. red . . . . 2·00 30
1890 – 1r. red . . . . 4·00 60
1891 – 1r. red . . . . 4·00 60
DESIGNS: No. 1890, Lenin in secret printing house (after F. Golubkov) (26½ × 39 mm). As Type **580**: No. 1891, Lenin and Krupskaya at Gorky (after N. Sysoev).

581 Schiller **582** Ilyushin Il-12 over Globe

1955. 150th Death Anniv of Schiller (poet).
1892 **581** 40k. brown . . . . . . 1·50 65

1955. Air.
1893 **582** 2r. brown . . . . 6·75 1·25
1894 2r. blue . . . . 3·50 55

583 V. Mayakovsky

1955. 25th Death Anniv of Mayakovsky (poet).
1895 **583** 40k. multicoloured . . . 1·10 30

584 Tadzhik S.S.R. Pavilion

1955. Agricultural Exhibition. Soviet Pavilion. Multicoloured designs with green frames.
1896 40k. R.S.F.S.R. 80 25
1897 40k. Byelorussian S.S.R. . . 80 25
1898 40k. Type **584** 80 25
1899 40k. Azerbaijan S.S.R. . . . 80 25
1900 40k. Latvian S.S.R. 80 25
1901 40k. Lithuanian S.S.R. . . . 80 25
1902 40k. Karelo Finnish S.S.R. 80 25
1903 40k. Estonian S.S.R. 80 25
1904 40k. Armenian S.S.R. . . . 80 25
1905 40k. Ukrainian S.S.R. . . . 80 25
1906 40k. Georgian S.S.R. . . . 80 25
1907 40k. Kazakh S.S.R. 80 25
1908 40k. Turkmen S.S.R. . . . 80 25
1909 40k. Kirgiz S.S.R. 80 25
1910 40k. Uzbek S.S.R. 80 25
1911 40k. Moldavian S.S.R. . . . 80 25

585 M. V. Lomonosov and University

1955. Bicentenary of Lomonosov University. Multicoloured.
1912 40k. Type **585** . . . . . . 1·10 30
1913 1r. Lomonosov University 1·90 55

586 A. G. Venetsianov (self-portrait) and "The Labours of Spring"

1955. 175th Birth Anniv of Venetsianov (painter). Multicoloured centre.
1914 **586** 1r. black . . . . 2·75 55

587 A. Lyadov

1955. Birth Centenary of Lyadov (composer).
1915 **587** 40k. multicoloured . . . 1·60 55

588 A. S. Popov **589** Lenin

590 "Capture of Winter Palace" (detail, P. Sokolov-Skalya)

1955. 60th Anniv of Popov's Radio Discoveries. Multicoloured centres.
1916 **588** 40k. blue . . . . 1·50 20
1917 1r. brown . . . . 2·75 50

1955. 38th Anniv of Russian Revolution.
1918 **589** 40k. multicoloured . . . 2·25 1·10
1919 **590** 40k. multicoloured . . . 2·25 1·10
1920 – 1r. multicoloured . . . . 5·00 2·25
DESIGN: As T **590**: 1r. Lenin speaking to revolutionaries (after D. Nalbandyan).

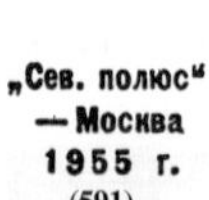
„Сев. полюс"
— Москва
1955 г.

(**591**)

592 Magnitogorsk

1955. Air. Opening of North Pole Scientific Stations. Nos. 1881/2 optd with T **591**.
1921 – 1r. multicoloured . . . . 9·00 6·00
1922 **576** 2r. black and green . . . 13·50 6·50

1955. 25th Anniv of Magnitogorsk.
1923 **592** 40k. multicoloured . . . 1·60 35

593 Mil Mi-4 Helicopter over Station **594** Shubin (self-portrait)

1955. North Pole Scientific Stations.
1924 **593** 40k. multicoloured . . . 3·25 30
1925 60k. multicoloured . . . 3·50 65
1926 – 1r. multicoloured . . . . 5·50 1·00
DESIGN: 1r. Meteorologist taking observations.

1955. 150th Death Anniv of Shubin (sculptor).
1927 **594** 40k. multicoloured . . . 90 20
1928 1r. multicoloured . . . . 1·50 40

595 A. N. Krylov

596 Racing

1956. 10th Death Anniv of Krylov (scientist).
1929 **595** 40k. multicoloured . . . 1·10 20

1956. International Horse Racing.
1930 **596** 40k. sepia and brown . . 1·25 25
1931 60k. blue and green . . 1·50 30
1932 – 1r. purple and blue . . . 2·75 55
DESIGN—HORIZ: 1r. Trotting.

597 Badge and Stadium

1956. 5th Spartacist Games.
1933 **597** 1r. purple and green . . 1·75 45

598 Atomic Power Station

1956. Foundation of Atomic Power Station of Russian Academy of Sciences.
1934 **598** 25k. multicoloured . . . 85 20
1935 – 60k. yellow, turq & brn 2·00 35
1936 **598** 1r. yellow, red and blue 2·75 70
DESIGN: 60k. Top of atomic reactor.

599 Statue of Lenin (E. Buchetich)

600 Kh. Abovyan

1956. 20th Communist Party Congress.
1937 **599** 40k. multicoloured . . . 90 35
1938 1r. multicoloured . . . . 1·75 55

1956. 150th Birth Anniv of Khatchatur Abovyan (Armenian writer).
1939 **600** 40k. black on blue . . . 1·10 20

601 Revolutionaries (after N. Tereshchenko)

602

1956. 50th Anniv of 1905 Revolution.
1940 **601** 40k. multicoloured . . . 4·25 1·60

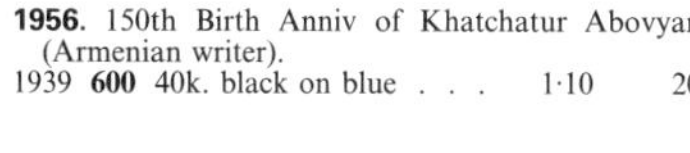

ПАВИЛЬОН «УРАЛ»
No. 1941

ПАВИЛЬОН СЕВЕРО-ВОСТОЧНЫХ ОБЛАСТЕЙ
No. 1942

ПАВИЛЬОН ЦЕНТРАЛЬНЫХ ЧЕРНОЗЕМНЫХ ОБЛАСТЕЙ
No. 1943

ПАВИЛЬОН «ЛЕНИНГРАД» СЕВЕРО-ЗАПАД»
No. 1944

ПАВИЛЬОН МОСКОВСКОЙ, ТУЛЬСКОЙ, КАЛУЖСКОЙ, РЯЗАНСКОЙ И БРЯНСКОЙ ОБЛАСТЕЙ
No. 1945

ПАВИЛЬОН БАШКИРСКОЙ АССР
No. 1946

ПАВИЛЬОН ДАЛЬНЕГО ВОСТОКА
No. 1947

ПАВИЛЬОН ТАТАРСКОЙ АССР
No. 1948

ПАВИЛЬОН ЦЕНТРАЛЬНЫХ ОБЛАСТЕЙ
No. 1949

ПАВИЛЬОН ЮНЫХ НАТУРАЛИСТОВ
No. 1950

ПАВИЛЬОН СЕВЕРНОГО КАВКАЗА
No. 1951

ПАВИЛЬОН «СИБИРЬ»
No. 1952

ПАВИЛЬОН «ПОВОЛЖЬЕ»
No. 1953

Inscr at foot as shown above.

1956. Agricultural Exhibition. Multicoloured. Views of Pavilions of U.S.S.R. regions as T **602**. Inscr "ВСХВ".
1941 1r. Ural . . . . 1·50 40
1942 1r. North East . . . . . . 1·50 40
1943 1r. Central Black Soil Region . . . . 1·50 40
1944 1r. Leningrad . . . . 1·50 40
1945 1r. Moscow-Tula-Kaluga-Ryazan-Bryansk . . . . 1·50 40
1946 1r. Bashkir . . . . 1·50 40
1947 1r. Far East . . . . 1·50 40
1948 1r. Tatar . . . . 1·50 40
1949 1r. Central Regions . . . . 1·50 40
1950 1r. Young Naturalists . . . 1·50 40
1951 1r. North Caucasus . . . . 1·50 40
1952 1r. Siberia . . . . 1·50 40
1953 1r. Volga . . . . 1·50 40

603 N. A. Kasatkin (painter)

1956. Kasatkin Commemoration.
1954 **603** 40k. red 85 25

604 A. E. Arkhipov and Painting "On the Oka River"

1956. Arkhipov Commemoration.
1955 **604** 40k. multicoloured . . . 1·50 20
1956 1r. multicoloured . . . . 2·75 45

605 I. P. Kulibin

1956. 220th Birth Anniv of Kulibin (inventor).
1957 **605** 40k. multicoloured . . . 1·25 35

606 "Fowler" (after Perov)

1956. Perov Commemoration. Inscr "1956". Multicoloured centres.
1958 – 40k. green . . . . 1·75 25
1959 **606** 1r. brown . . . . 3·50 70
1960 – 1r. brown . . . . 3·50 70
DESIGNS—VERT: No. 1958, Self-portrait. HORIZ: No. 1960, "Hunters Resting".

607 Lenin (after P. Vasilev)

608 N. I. Lobachevsky (after L. Kryukov)

1956. 86th Birth Anniv of Lenin.
1961 **607** 40k. multicoloured . . . 9·25 5·25

1956. Death Cent of Lobachevsky (mathematician).
1962 **608** 40k. brown 80 15

609 Student Nurses

1956. Red Cross.
1963 **609** 40k. red, blue and brown 1·00 30
1964 – 40k. red, olive & turquoise . . . . . . 1·00 30
DESIGN—37½ × 25½ mm: No. 1964, Nurse and textile factory.

610 Scientific Station

1956. Air. Opening of North Pole Scientific Station No. 6.
1965 **610** 1r. multicoloured . . . . 4·25 1·40

611 Sechenov (after I. Repin)

1956. 50th Death Anniv (1995) of I. Sechenov (naturalist).
1966 **611** 40k. multicoloured . . . 1·60 35

612 Arsenev

1956. V. K. Arsenev (writer).
1967 **612** 40k. black, violet & pink 2·00 70

613 I. V. Michurin

1956. Birth Centenary of Michurin (naturalist). Multicoloured centres.
1968 **613** 25k. brown 45 15
1969 – 60k. green . . . . 1·10 25
1970 **613** 1r. blue . . . . 2·00 45
DESIGN—47½ × 26½ mm: 60k. Michurin and children.

614 Savrasov (after V. Perov)

615 N. K. Krupskaya (Lenin's wife)

1956. 125th Birth Anniv (1955) of A. K. Savrasov (painter).
1971 **614** 1r. brown and yellow . . 1·50 60

1956. Krupskaya Commemoration.
1972 **615** 40k. brown, black & blue . . . . 1·50 30

616 S. M. Kirov

617 A. A. Blok

1956. 70th Birth Anniv of Kirov (statesman).
1973 **616** 40k. multicoloured . . . 65 15

1956. Blok (poet) Commemoration.
1974 **617** 40k. brown, black & olive 95 15

618 N. S. Leskov

1956. 125th Birth Anniv of Leskov (writer).
1975 **618** 40k. multicoloured . . . 65 15
1976 1r. multicoloured . . . . 1·75 40

619 Factory Building

1956. 25th Anniv of Rostov Agricultural Machinery Works.
1977 **619** 40k. multicoloured . . . 90 25

620 G. N. Fedotova (actress)

1956. Fedotova Commemoration.
1978 **620** 40k. multicoloured . . . 80 25
For similar stamp see No. 2159.

621 P. M. Tretyakov (after I. Repin) and Art Gallery

1956. Centenary of Tretyakov Art Gallery, Moscow.
1979 **621** 40k. multicoloured . . . 2·25 60
1980 – 40k. multicoloured . . . 1·50 50
DESIGN—VERT: No. 1980, "Rooks have arrived" (painting by Savrasov).

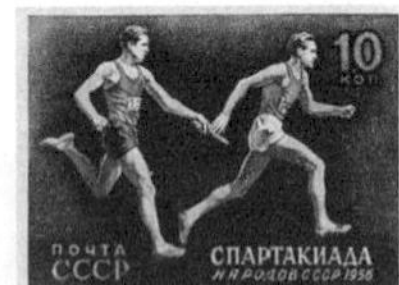

622 Relay-race

1956. Spartacist Games.
1981 **622** 10k. red 30 10
1982 – 25k. brown 40 15
1983 – 25k. multicoloured . . . 40 15
1984 – 25k. blue 40 15
1985 – 40k. blue 65 15
1986 – 40k. green 65 15
1987 – 40k. brown and green . . 65 15
1988 – 40k. deep brown, brown and green 65 15
1989 – 40k. red, green and light green 65 15
1990 – 40k. brown 65 15
1991 – 40k. multicoloured . . . 65 15
1992 – 60k. violet . . . . . . 1·75 25
1993 – 60k. violet . . . . . . 1·75 25
1994 – 1r. brown . . . . 3·25 55
DESIGNS—VERT: No. 1982, Volleyball; 1983, Swimming; 1984, Rowing; 1985, Diving; 1989, Flag and stadium; 1990, Tennis; 1991, Medal; 1993, Boxing. HORIZ: No. 1986, Cycle racing; 1987, Fencing; 1988, Football; 1992, Gymnastics; 1994, Netball.

623 Parachutist Landing **624** Construction Work

1956. 3rd World Parachute-jumping Competition.
1995 **623** 40k. multicoloured . . . 1·00 25

1956. Builders' Day.
1996a **624** 40k. orange 65 25
1997 – 60k. brown 80 30
1998 – 1r. blue . . . . 2·50 50
DESIGNS: 60k. Plant construction; 1r. Dam construction.

625 Self-portrait and "Volga River Boatmen"

626 "Reply of the Cossacks to Sultan Mahmoud IV"

1956. 26th Death Anniv of I. E. Repin (artist).
1999 **625** 40k. multicoloured . . . 3·75 60
2000 **626** 1r. multicoloured . . . . 7·25 1·00

627 Robert Burns **628** Ivan Franko

1956. 160th Death Anniv of Burns (Scots poet).
2001 **627** 40k. brown . . . . . . 7·50 5·25
2002 40k. brown and blue . . 5·25 3·25

1956. Birth Cent of Franko (writer) (1st issue).
2003 **628** 40k. purple 85 40
2004 1r. blue . . . . 1·40 50
See also No. 2037.

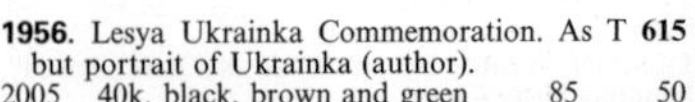

1956. Lesya Ukrainka Commemoration. As T **615** but portrait of Ukrainka (author).
2005 40k. black, brown and green 85 50

629 M. Aivazov (farmer) **630** Statue of Nestor (M. Antokol)

1956. 148th Birthday of Aivazov. (a) Wrongly inscr "Muhamed" (7 characters).
2006 **629** 40k. green . . . . 23·00 21·00
(b) Corrected to "Makmud" (6 characters).
2006a **629** 40k. green . . . . . . 11·50 8·25

1956. 900th Birth Anniv of Nestor (historian).
2007 **630** 40k. multicoloured . . . 1·10 30
2008 1r. multicoloured . . . . 2·10 50

631 Ivanov (after S. Postnikov)

1956. 150th Birth Anniv of A. A. Ivanov (painter).
2009 **631** 40k. brown and grey . . 85 25

632 Feeding Poultry

1956. Agriculture. Multicoloured.
2010 10k. Type **632** 35 10
2011 10k. Harvesting 35 10
2012 25k. Gathering maize . . . 65 20
2013 40k. Maize field . . . . . 1·25 20
2014 40k. Tractor station . . . . 1·25 20
2015 40k. Cattle grazing . . . . 1·25 20
2016 40k. "Agriculture and Industry" . . . . . . 1·25 20
SIZES: Nos. 2010, 2014/15, 37 × 25½ mm. Nos. 2011/13, 37 × 28 mm. No. 2016, 37 × 21 mm.

633 Mozart **634** Mirnyi Base and Supply Ship "Lena"

1956. Cultural Anniversaries.
2017 40k. blue (Type **633**) . . . . 3·50 60
2018 40k. green (Curie) . . . . . 3·50 60
2019 40k. lilac (Heine) . . . . . 1·50 40
2020 40k. brown (Ibsen) . . . . 1·50 40
2021 40k. green (Dostoevsky) . . 1·50 40
2022 40k. brown (Franklin) . . . 1·50 40
2023 40k. black (Shaw) . . . . . 3·00 60
2024 40k. orange (Sessku-Toyo Oda) . . . . 1·50 40
2025 40k. black (Rembrandt) . . 1·50 40
Nos. 2022/5 are larger, 25 × 38 mm.

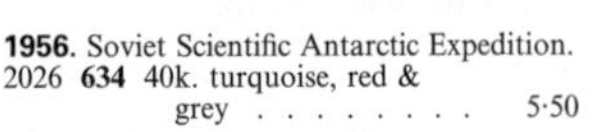

1956. Soviet Scientific Antarctic Expedition.
2026 **634** 40k. turquoise, red & grey . . . . 5·50 80

1956. Julia Zhemaite Commemoration. As T **615** but portrait of Zhemaite (author).
2027 40k. green, brown and sepia 1·00 35

635 F. A. Bredikhin **636** G. I. Kotovsky

1956. 125th Birth Anniv of Bredikhin (astronomer).
2028 **635** 40k. multicoloured . . . 5·00 1·25

1956. 75th Birth Anniv of Kotovsky (military leader).
2029a **636** 40k. mauve . . . . . . 1·60 65

637 Shatura Electric Power Station **638** Marshal Suvorov (after Utkin)

1956. 30th Anniv of Shatura Electric Power Station.
2030 **637** 40k. multicoloured . . . 90 35

1956. 225th Birth Anniv of Marshal Suvorov.
2031 **638** 40k. lake and orange . . 85 35
2032 1r. brown and olive . . 1·60 50
2033 3r. black and brown . . 4·25 1·10

639 Kryakutni's Ascent (after G. Savitsky)

1956. 225th Anniv of First Balloon Flight by Kryakutni.
2034 **639** 40k. multicoloured . . . 2·00 55

640 Vasnetsov (after S. Malyutin) and "Dawn at the Voskresenski Gate"

1956. 30th Death Anniv of A. M. Vasnetsov (artist).
2035 **640** 40k. multicoloured . . . 1·60 55

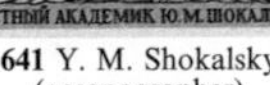

641 Y. M. Shokalsky (oceanographer) **642** Franko (after I. Trush)

1956. Birth Cent of Shokalsky.
2036 **641** 40k. brown and blue . . 2·25 50

1956. Birth Centenary of Franko (writer) (2nd issue).
2037 **642** 40k. green 75 25

643 Indian Temple and Books **644** F. G. Vokov (actor) (after A. Losenko) and State Theatre

1956. Kalidasa (Indian poet) Commemoration.
2038 **643** 40k. red 75 25

1956. Bicentenary of Leningrad State Theatre.
2039 **644** 40k. black, red and yellow 60 20

645 Lomonosov (after L. Miropolsky) at St. Petersburg University

1956. Russian Writers.
2040 **645** 40k. multicoloured . . . 1·00 25
2041 – 40k. multicoloured . . . 1·00 25
2042 – 40k. brown and blue . . 1·00 25
2043 – 40k. olive, brown & black . . . . 1·00 25
2044 – 40k. brown and turquoise . . . . . . 1·00 25
2045 – 40k. purple and brown 1·00 25
2046 – 40k. olive and blue . . . 1·00 25
DESIGNS: No. 2041, Gorky (after V. Efanov) and scene from "Mother" (novel); 2042, Pushkin and statue of Peter the Great, Leningrad (illustrating poem "Bronze Horseman"); 2043, Rustavely and episode from "The Knight in the Tiger Skin" (poem); 2044, Tolstoy and scene from "War and Peace" (novel); 2045, V. G. Belinsky and titles of literary works; 2046, M. Y. Lermontov and Daryal Pass.
See also Nos. 2076, 2089/90, 2256, 2316/22 and 2458.

646 Vitus Bering and Routes of his Voyages **647** Mendeleev

1956. 275th Birth Anniv of Bering (explorer).
2047 **646** 40k. multicoloured . . . 3·00 50

1957. 50th Death Anniv of Dmitri Mendeleev (chemist).
2048 **647** 40k. brown, grey & black . . . . 2·25 65

648 M. I. Glinka **649** Youth Festival Emblem

1957. Death Centenary of Glinka (composer). Mult.
2049a 40k. Type **648** . . . . . . 1·40 25
2050a 1r. Scene from "Ivan Susanin" . . . . 2·50 55

1957. All Union Festival of Soviet Youth.
2051 **649** 40k. multicoloured . . . 50 20

650 Ice Hockey Player **651** Youth Festival Emblem and Pigeon

1957. 23rd World and 35th European Ice Hockey Championships, Moscow.
2052a – 25k. violet 75 15
2053a **650** 40k. blue 90 15
2054a – 60k. green . . . . . . 1·00 30
DESIGNS: 25k. Championship emblem; 60k. Goalkeeper.

1957. 6th World Youth Festival, Moscow (1st issue). Perf or imperf.
2055 **651** 40k. multicoloured . . . 85 15
2056 60k. multicoloured . . . 1·40 30
See also Nos. 2084/7 and 2108/11.

652 Factory Plant **653** Sika Deer

1957. Cent of "Red Proletariat" Plant. Moscow.
2057 **652** 40k. multicoloured . . . 1·00 30

1957. Russian Wildlife. Multicoloured.
2057a 10k. Grey partridge . . . 80 25
2058 15k. Black grouse . . . . 1·00 10
2058a 15k. Polar bear 70 15

2059 20k. Type **653** 75 15
2059a 20k. Brown hare 60 25
2059b 25k. Tiger 75 25
2059c 25k. Wild horse 75 25
2060 30k. Mallard . . . . . . 1·25 25
2061 30k. European bison . . . 75 20
2062 40k. Elk . . . . 1·90 35
2063 40k. Sable . . . . 1·90 35
2063a 40k. Eurasian red squirrel 80 30
2063b 40k. Yellow-throated marten 80 30
2063c 60k. Hazel grouse . . . . 2·00 90
2063d 1r. Mute swan . . . . . . 2·50 1·75

Nos. 2058/a, 2059a/62, 2063a/b and 2063d are horiz.

See also Nos. 2534/6.

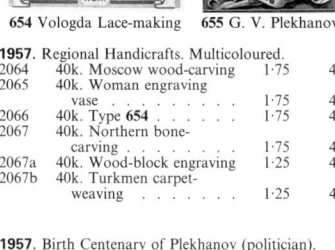

654 Vologda Lace-making **655** G. V. Plekhanov

1957. Regional Handicrafts. Multicoloured.
2064 40k. Moscow wood-carving 1·75 40
2065 40k. Woman engraving vase . . . . 1·75 40
2066 40k. Type **654** . . . . . . 1·75 40
2067 40k. Northern bone-carving . . . . 1·75 40
2067a 40k. Wood-block engraving 1·25 45
2067b 40k. Turkmen carpet-weaving . . . . 1·25 45

1957. Birth Centenary of Plekhanov (politician).
2068 **655** 40k. plum . . . . 1·00 35

656 A. N. Bakh **657** L. Euler

1957. Birth Centenary of Bakh (biochemist).
2069a **656** 40k. multicoloured . . 1·10 25

1957. 250th Birth Anniv of Euler (mathematician).
2070a **657** 40k. black and purple 1·50 35

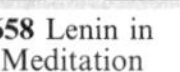

658 Lenin in Meditation **659** Dr. William Harvey

1957. 87th Birth Anniv of Lenin. Multicoloured.
2071 40k. Type **658** . . . . . . 1·00 20
2072 40k. Lenin carrying pole . . 1·00 20
2073 40k. Talking with soldier and sailor . . . . 1·00 20

1957. 300th Death Anniv of Dr. William Harvey (discoverer of circulation of blood).
2074 **659** 40k. brown 75 15

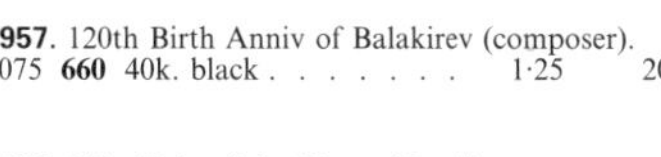

660 M. A. Balakirev **661** 12th-century Narrator

1957. 120th Birth Anniv of Balakirev (composer).
2075 **660** 40k. black . . . . 1·25 20

1957. "The Tale of the Host of Igor".
2076 **661** 40k. multicoloured . . . 80 20

662 Agricultural Medal **663** A. I. Herzen (after N. Ge) and N. P. Ogarev (after M. Lemmel) (founders)

1957. Cultivation of Virgin Soil.
2077 **662** 40k. multicoloured . . . 1·10 30

1957. Centenary of Publication of Magazine "Kolokol".
2078 **663** 40k. brown, black & blue . . . . 1·00 30

664 Monument

250 лет Ленинграда
(**665**)

1957. 250th Anniv of Leningrad. Vert designs as T **664** and stamps as Nos. 1818 and 1820 optd as T **665**.
2079 **664** 40k. green 50 15
2080 – 40k. violet 50 15
2081 – 40k. brown 65 15
2082 **551** 1r. brown on green . . . 1·40 25
2083 – 1r. green on salmon . . 1·40 25

DESIGNS: No. 2080, Nevsky Prospect, Leningrad; No. 2081, Lenin Statue.

666 Youths with Banner

1957. 6th World Youth Festival, Moscow (2nd issue). Multicoloured. Perf or imperf.
2084 10k. Type **666** 30 10
2084c 20k. Sculptor with statue 50 15
2085 25k. Type **666** 80 25
2086 40k. Dancers 85 25
2087 1r. Festival emblem and fireworks over Moscow State University . . . . 1·10 50

667 A. M. Lyapunov **668** T. G. Shevchenko (after I. Repin) and Scene from "Katharina"

1957. Birth Centenary of Lyapunov (mathematician).
2088 **667** 40k. brown . . . . . . 5·50 2·75

1957. 19th-Century Writers. Multicoloured.
2089 40k. Type **668** 85 20
2090 40k. N. G. Chernyshevsky and scene from "What is to be Done?" 85 20

669 Henry Fielding **670** Racing Cyclists

1957. 250th Birth Anniv of Fielding (novelist).
2091 **669** 40k. multicoloured . . . 50 20

1957. 10th International Cycle Race.
2092 **670** 40k. multicoloured . . . 1·25 25

671 Interior of Observatory

1957. International Geophysical Year (1st issue).
2093 **671** 40k. brown, yellow and blue . . . . 1·75 45
2094 – 40k. indigo, yellow and blue . . . . 2·50 45
2095 – 40k. violet and lavender 2·25 45
2095a – 40k. blue . . . . . . 2·25 30
2095b – 40k. green . . . . . . 2·50 40
2095c – 40k. yellow and blue 2·25 30

DESIGNS—As T **671**: No. 2094, Meteor in sky; 2095a, Malakhit radar scanner and balloon (meteorology); 2095b, "Zarya" (non-magnetic research schooner) (geo-magnetism); 2095c, Northern Lights and C-180 camera. 15 × 21 mm: No. 2095, Rocket.

See also Nos. 2371/3a.

672 Gymnast

1957. 3rd International Youth Games.
2096 **672** 20k. brown and blue . . 30 15
2097 – 25k. red and green . . . 35 15
2098 – 40k. violet and red . . . 70 30
2099 – 40k. olive, red and green 70 30
2100 – 60k. brown and blue . . 1·60 50

DESIGNS—As Type **672**: No. 2097, Wrestlers; 2098, Young athletes; 2099, Moscow Stadium; 2100, Throwing the javelin.

673 Football **674** Yanka Kupala

1957. Russian Successes at Olympic Games, Melbourne.
2101 – 20k. brown, blue & black 35 15
2102 – 20k. red and green . . . 35 15
2103 – 25k. blue and orange . . 40 20
2104 **673** 40k. multicoloured . . . 75 20
2105 – 40k. brown and purple 75 20
2106 – 60k. brown and violet 1·00 50

DESIGNS—VERT: No. 2101, Throwing the javelin; 2102, Running; 2103, Gymnastics; 2105, Boxing; 2106, Weightlifting.

1957. 75th Birth Anniv of Kupala (poet).
2107 **674** 40k. brown . . . . . . 4·00 1·75

675 Moscow State University

1957. 6th World Youth Festival (3rd issue). Moscow Views.
2108 – 40k. black and brown . . 55 15
2109 – 40k. black and purple . . 55 15
2110 – 1r. black and blue . . . 1·25 30
2111 **675** 1r. black and red . . . . 1·25 30

DESIGNS—HORIZ: No. 2108, Kremlin; 2109, Stadium; 2110, Bolshoi State Theatre.

676 Lenin Library

1957. Int Philatelic Exn, Moscow. Perf or imperf.
2112 **676** 40k. turquoise 75 20

677 Dove of Peace encircling Globe **678** P. Beranger

1957. "Defence of Peace".
2113 **677** 40k. multicoloured . . . 1·10 40
2114 1r. multicoloured . . . . 2·25 95

1957. Birth Centenary of Clara Zetkin (German revolutionary). As T **615** but portrait of Zetkin.
2115 40k. multicoloured . . . . 1·10 35

1957. Death Centenary of Beranger (French poet).
2116 **678** 40k. green . . . . 1·10 30

679 Krengholm Factory, Narva **680** Factory Plant and Statue of Lenin (M. Kharlamev)

1957. Centenary of Krengholm Textile Factory, Narva, Estonia.
2117 **679** 40k. brown . . . . . . 1·10 30

1957. Centenary of Krasny Vyborzhetz Plant, Leningrad.
2118 **680** 40k. blue 50 25

681 Stasov (after I. Repin) **682** Pigeon with Letter

1957. 50th Death Anniv of Stasov (art critic).
2119 **681** 40k. brown 55 15
2120 1r. blue . . . . 1·40 20

1957. International Correspondence Week.
2121 **682** 40k. blue 35 20
2122 60k. purple 55 25

683 K. E. Tsiolkovsky

1957. Birth Centenary of Tsiolkovsky (scientist).
2123 **683** 40k. multicoloured . . . 4·00 70

684 Congress Emblem

1957. 4th World T.U.C., Leipzig.
2124 **684** 40k. blue on blue . . . 45 20

685 Students **686** Workers and Emblem (Ukraine)

1957. 40th Anniv of Russian Revolution. (a) 1st issue. As T **685**. Multicoloured. Perf or imperf.
2125 10k. Type **685** 20 10
2126 40k. Railway worker (horiz) 70 20
2127 40k. Portrait of Lenin on banner 45 10

2128 40k. Lenin and workers with banners 45 10
2129 60k. Harvester (horiz) . . . 1·25 60

1957. 40th Anniv of Russian Revolution (2nd issue). Multicoloured.
2130 40k. Type **686** 65 30
2131 40k. Estonia 65 30
2132 40k. Uzbekistan 65 30
2133 40k. R.S.F.S.R. (horiz) . . . 1·10 30
2134 40k. Belorussia (horiz) . . . 65 30
2135 40k. Lithuania (horiz) . . . 65 30
2136 40k. Armenia (horiz) . . . 65 30
2137 40k. Azerbaijan (horiz) . . . 65 30
2138 40k. Georgia (horiz) 65 30
2139 40k. Kirghizia (horiz) . . . 65 30
2140 40k. Turkmenistan (horiz) 65 30
2141 40k. Tadzhikistan (horiz) . . 65 30
2142 40k. Kazakhstan (horiz) . . 65 30
2143 40k. Latvia (horiz) 65 30
2144 40k. Moldavia (horiz) . . . 65 30

687 Lenin (after G. Goldstein)

688 Satellite encircling Globe

1957. 40th Anniv of Russian Revolution (3rd issue). As T **687**.
2145 **687** 40k. blue . . . . 1·50 65
2146 – 60k. red . . . . 2·25 95
DESIGN—HORIZ: 60k. Lenin at desk.

1957. Launching of 1st Artifical Satellite.
2147 **688** 40k. indigo on blue . . . 3·25 85
2148 40k. blue . . . . 3·25 85

689 Meteor Falling

690 Kuibyshev Power Station Turbine

1957. Sikhote-Alin Meteor.
2149 **689** 40k. multicoloured . . . 2·75 1·10

1957. All Union Industrial Exhibition (1st issue).
2150 **690** 40k. brown 75 20
See also Nos. 2168.

4/X-57 г. Первый в мире искусств. спутник Земли

(691)

692 Soviet War Memorial, Berlin (after Ye. Bunchetich)

1957. 1st Artificial Satellite of the World. Optd with T **691**.
2151 **683** 40k. multicoloured . . . 35·00 22·00

1957. Bicentenary of Academy of Arts, Moscow.
2152 – 40k. black on salmon . . 40 10
2153 **692** 60k. black 80 15
2154 – 1r. black on pink . . . 1·60 35
DESIGNS—25½ × 37½ mm: 40k. Academy and portraits of K. Bryullov, I. Repin and V. Surikov (after I. Repin). 21½ × 32 mm: 1r. "Worker and Collective Farmer", Moscow (sculpture, Vera Mukhina).

693 Arms of Ukraine

694 Garibaldi

1957. 40th Anniv of Ukraine S.S.R.
2155 **693** 40k. multicoloured . . . 85 15

1957. 150th Birth Anniv of Garibaldi.
2156 **694** 40k. purple, maroon and green 75 20

695 Edvard Grieg

696 Borovikovsky (after I. Bugaevsky-Blagodarny)

1957. 50th Death Anniv of Grieg (composer).
2157 **695** 40k. black on salmon . . 1·25 20

1957. Birth Bicent of Borovikovsky (painter).
2158 **696** 40k. brown 80 20

1967. M. N. Ermolova (actress) Commemoration. As T **620** but portrait of Ermolova.
2159 40k. brown and violet . . . 1·00 40

698 Kolas

699 M-itskyavichyus-Kapsukas

700 G. Z-. B-ashindzhagian

1957. 75th Birth Anniv of Yakyb Kolas (poet).
2160 **698** 40k. black . . . . 2·40 1·50

1957. 22nd Death Anniv of V. S. Mitskyavichyus-Kapsukas (Communist Party leader).
2161 **699** 40k. brown . . . . . . 2·25 1·10

1957. Bashindzhagian (artist) Commemoration.
2162 **700** 40k. brown . . . . . . 2·25 1·10

701 Kuibyshev Hydro-electric Station

702 "To the Stars" (Ye. Buchetich)

1957. 40th Anniv of Kuibyshev Hydro-electric Station.
2163 **701** 40k. blue on flesh . . . 1·10 25

1957. Launching of 2nd Artificial Satellite.
2164 **702** 20k. red and black . . . 1·00 10
2165 40k. green and black . . 1·50 15
2166 60k. brown and black . . 2·00 25
2167 1r. blue and black . . . 3·00 60

703 Allegory of Industry

704 Tsi Bai-shi

1958. All Union Industrial Exn (2nd issue).
2168 **703** 60k. red, black & lavender . . . . . . 1·00 30

1958. Rosa Luxemburg Commemoration. As T **615** but portrait of Luxemburg (German revolutionary).
2169 40k. brown and blue . . . 1·00 35

1958. Tsi Bai-shi (Chinese artist) Commem.
2170 **704** 40k. violet 55 20

705 Linnaeus (Carl von Linne)

706 Tolstoi

1958. 250th Birth Anniv of Linnaeus.
2171 **705** 40k. brown . . . . . . 3·25 1·10

1958. 75th Birth Anniv of A. N. Tolstoi (writer).
2172 **706** 40k. bistre 65 20

707 Soldier, Sailor and Airman

708 E. Charents

1958. 40th Anniv of Red Army. Multicoloured.
2173 25k. Battle of Narva, 1918 40 15
2174 40k. Type **707** 60 20
2175 40k. Soldier and blast-furnaceman (vert) 60 20
2176 40k. Soldier and sailor (vert) 60 20
2177 60k. Storming the Reichstag, 1945 . . . . 1·75 60

1958. Charents (Armenian poet) Commemoration.
2178 **708** 40k. brown . . . . . . 2·40 1·40

709 Henry W. Longfellow

710 Blake

1958. 150th Birth Anniv of Longfellow.
2179 **709** 40k. black . . . . 2·40 1·40

1958. Birth Bicentenary of William Blake (poet).
2180 **710** 40k. black . . . . 2·50 1·40

711 Tchaikovsky

712 Admiral Rudnev and Cruiser "Varyag"

1958. Tchaikovsky International Music Competition, Moscow.
2181 **711** 40k. multicoloured . . 1·25 30
2182 – 40k. multicoloured . . 1·25 30
2183a – 1r. purple and green . . 3·50 75
DESIGNS—HORIZ: No. 2182, Scene from "Swan Lake" ballet. VERT: No. 2183, Pianist, violinist and inset portrait of Tchaikovsky.

1958. 45th Death Anniv of Admiral Rudnev.
2184 **712** 40k. multicoloured . . . 1·90 45

713 Gorky (after I. Brodsky)

714 Congress Emblem and Spassky Tower, Kremlin

1958. 90th Death Anniv of Maksim Gorky (writer).
2185 **713** 40k. multicoloured . . . 1·00 20

1958. 13th Young Communists' League Congress, Moscow.
2186 **714** 40k. violet on pink . . . 65 15
2187 60k. red on flesh . . . . 1·00 25

715 Russian Pavilion

716 J. A. Komensky ("Comenius")

1958. Brussels Int Exhibition. Perf or imperf.
2188 **715** 10k. multicoloured . . . 20 10
2189 40k. multicoloured . . . 65 15

1958. Komensky Commem.
2190 **716** 40k. green . . . . 3·25 1·10

717 Lenin

200 лет Академии художеств СССР. 1957

(718)

1958. Lenin Commemoration.
2191 **717** 40k. blue 60 10
2192 60k. red 85 15
2193 1r. brown . . . . 1·60 40

1958. Bicentenary of Russian Academy of Artists. Optd with T **718**.
2194 **557** 40k. multicoloured . . . 6·00 1·75

719 C. Goldoni

720 Lenin Prize Medal

1958. 250th Birth Anniv of C. Goldoni (Italian dramatist).
2195 **719** 40k. brown and blue . . 1·00 15

1958. Lenin Prize Medal.
2196 **720** 40k. red, yellow & brown 80 15

721 Karl Marx

1958. Karl Marx Commemoration.
2197 **721** 40k. brown 85 15
2198 60k. blue . . . . 1·00 25
2199 1r. red . . . . 2·10 35

722 Federation Emblem

723 Radio Beacon, Airliner and Freighter

1958. 4th International Women's Federation Congress.
2200 **722** 40k. blue and black . . 65 15
2201 60k. blue and black . . 1·00 20

1958. Radio Day.
2202 **723** 40k. green and red . . . 2·25 30

724 Chavchavadze (after G. Gabashvili)

725 Flags of Communist Countries

1958. Chavchavadze (Georgian poet) Commem.
2203 **724** 40k. black and blue . . 75 25

1958. Socialist Countries' Postal Ministers Conference, Moscow.
2204 **725** 40k. multicoloured (A) 17·00 6·25
2205 40k. multicoloured (B) 11·00 5·50
Central flag to left of inscription is in red, white and mauve. (A) has red at top and white at foot, (B) is vice versa.

726 Camp Bugler

727 Negro, European and Chinese Children

1958. "Pioneers" Day. Inscr "1958".
2206 **726** 10k. multicoloured . . . 35 10
2207 – 25k. multicoloured . . . 50 20
DESIGN: 25k. Pioneer with model airplane.

1958. International Children's Day. Inscr "1958".
2208 **727** 40k. multicoloured . . . 65 20
2209 – 40k. multicoloured . . . 65 20
DESIGN: No. 2209, Child with toys, and atomic bomb.

728 Fooballers and Globe

729 Rimsky-Korsakov

1958. World Cup Football Championship, Sweden. Perf or imperf.
2210 **728** 40k. multicoloured . . . 85 20
2211 60k. multicoloured . . . 1·40 40

1958. Rimsky-Korsakov (composer) Commem.
2212 **729** 40k. brown and blue . . 1·50 20

730 Athlete

1958. 14th World Gymnastic Championships, Moscow. Inscr "XIV". Multicoloured.
2213 40k. Type **730** 60 15
2214 40k. Gymnast 60 15

731 Young Construction Workers

1958. Russian Youth Day.
2215 **731** 40k. orange and blue . . 50 15
2216 60k. orange and green 60 20

732 Atomic Bomb, Globe, Sputniks, Atomic Symbol and "Lenin" (atomic ice-breaker)

733 Kiev Arsenal Uprising, 1918

1958. International Disarmament Conf, Stockholm.
2217 **732** 60k. black, orange & blue . . . . 3·50 65

1958. 40th Anniv of Ukrainian Communist Party.
2218 **733** 40k. violet and red . . . 1·10 20

734 Silhouette of Moscow State University

1958. 5th Int Architects Union Congress, Moscow.
2219 **734** 40k. blue and red . . . 90 15
2220 – 60k. multicoloured . . . 1·40 25

DESIGN—VERT: 60k. "U.I.A. Moscow 1958" in square panel of bricks and "V" in background.

735 Sadruddin Aini

1958. 80th Birth Anniv of Sadruddin Aini (Tadzhik writer).
2221 **735** 40k. red, black and buff 55 15

736 Third Artificial Satellite

737 Conference Emblem

1958. Launching of 3rd Artificial Satellite.
2222a **736** 40k. red, blue and green 1·60 50

1958. 1st World T.U. Young Workers' Conf, Prague.
2223 **737** 40k. blue and purple . . 40 20

738 Tupolev Tu-110 Jetliner

1958. Civil Aviation. Perf or imperf.
2224 – 20k. black, red and blue 50 10
2225 – 40k. black, red and green 75 15
2226 – 40k. black, red and blue 75 15
2227 – 60k. red, buff and blue 80 20
2228 **738** 60k. black and red . . . 80 20
2229 – 1r. black, red and orange 2·00 30
2230 – 2r. black, red and purple 2·75 45
DESIGNS—Russian aircraft flying across globe: No. 2224, Ilyushin Il-14M; 2225, Tupolev Tu-104; 2226, Tupolev Tu-114 Rossiya; 2229, Antonov An-10 Ukraina; 2230, Ilyushin Il-18B; No. 2227, Global air routes.

739 L. A. Kulik (scientist)

1958. 50th Anniv of Tunguz Meteor.
2231 **739** 40k. multicoloured . . . 2·25 40

740 Crimea Observatory

741 15th-century Scribe

1958. 10th International Astronomical Union Congress, Moscow.
2232 **740** 40k. turquoise and brown . . . . 1·25 20
2233 – 60k. yellow, violet & blue . . . . 1·60 30
2234 – 1r. brown and blue . . . 2·25 50
DESIGNS—HORIZ: 60k. Moscow University. VERT: 1r. Telescope of Moscow Observatory.

1958. Centenary of 1st Russian Postage Stamp.
2235 **741** 10k. multicoloured . . . 15 10
2236 – 10k. multicoloured . . . 15 10
2237 – 25k. blue, black and green 30 10
2238 – 25k. black and blue . . 30 10
2239 – 40k. brown, purple & sep 50 15
2240 – 40k. lake and brown . . 50 15
2241 – 40k. black, orange and red 50 15
2242 – 60k. turquoise, blk & vio 1·75 40
2243 – 60k. black, turquoise and purple . . . . 1·25 35
2244 – 1r. multicoloured . . . . 1·75 50
2245 – 1r. purple, black and orange . . . . 2·25 65

DESIGNS—HORIZ: No. 2236, 16th-century courier; 2237, Ordin-Nashchokin (17th-century postal administrator) (after Kh. Gusikov) and postal sleigh coach; 2238, 18th-century mail coach; 2239, Reproduction of Lenin portrait stamp of 1947; 2240, 19th-century postal troika (three-horse sleigh); 2241, Tupolev Tu-104 jetliner; 2242, Parcel post train; 2243, V. N. Podbelsky (postal administrator, 1918–20) and postal scenes; 2244, Parcel post Tupolev Tu-104; 2245, Globe and modern forms of mail transport.

741a Facade of Exhibition Building

742 Vladimir Gateway

1958. Stamp Cent Philatelic Exhibition, Leningrad.
2246 **741a** 40k. brown & lt brown 55 20

1958. 850th Anniv of Town of Vladimir. Mult.
2247 40k. Type **742** 50 15
2248 60k. Street scene in Vladimir 90 20

743 Chigorin

745 Red Cross Nurse and Patient

1958. 50th Death Anniv of Mikhail Ivanovich Chigorin (chess player).
2249 **743** 40k. green and black . . 1·75 20

1958. 40th Anniv of Red Cross and Crescent Societies.
2254 **745** 40k. multicoloured . . . 85 20
2255 – 40k. red, yellow and brown 85 20
DESIGN: No. 2255, Convalescent home.

746 Saltykov-Shchedrin (after I. Kramskoi) and Scene from his Works

747 V. Kapnist (after A. Osipov)

1958. 69th Death Anniv of Mikhail Saltykov-Shchedrin (writer).
2256 **746** 40k. black and purple . . 70 20
For similar stamps see Nos. 2316/22 and 2458.

1958. Birth Bicentenary of V. Kapnist (poet).
2257 **747** 40k. black and blue . . 1·10 20

748 Yerevan, Armenia

1958. Republican Capitals.
2258 40k. brown (T **748**) 70 20
2259 40k. violet (Baku, Azerbaijan) 70 20
2260 40k. brown (Minsk, Byelorussia) 70 20
2261 40k. blue (Tbilisi, Georgia) 70 20
2262 40k. green (Tallin, Estonia) 70 20
2263 40k. green (Alma-Ata, Kazakhstan) 70 20
2264 40k. blue (Frunze, Kirgizia) 70 20
2265 40k. brown (Riga, Latvia) 70 20
2266 40k. red (Vilnius, Lithuania) 70 20
2267 40k. bistre (Kishinev, Moldavia) 70 20
2268 40k. violet (Moscow, R.S.F.S.R.) 70 20
2269 40k. blue (Stalinabad, Tadzhikistan) 70 20
2270 40k. green (Ashkhabad, Turkmenistan) 70 20
2271 40k. mauve (Kiev, Ukraine) 70 20
2272 40k. black (Tashkent, Uzbekistan) 70 20
See also No. 2940.

749 Open Book, Torch, Lyre and Flowers

750 Rudaki

1958. Asian-African Writers' Conference, Tashkent.
2273 **749** 40k. orange, black and olive . . . . 1·00 15

1958. 1100th Birth Anniv of Rudaki (Tadzhik poet and musician).
2274 **750** 40k. multicoloured . . . 60 15

751 Statue of Founder Vakhtang I Gorgasal (E. Amashukeli)

1958. 1500th Anniv of Founding of Tbilisi (Georgian capital).
2275 **751** 40k. multicoloured . . . 1·25 30

752 Chelyabinsk Tractor Plant

1958. 25th Anniv of Industrial Plants.
2276 **752** 40k. green and yellow . . 80 20
2277 – 40k. blue and light blue 55 20
2278 – 40k. lake and light orange 80 20
DESIGNS: No. 2277, Ural machine construction plant; No. 2278, Zaporozhe foundry plant.

753 Young Revolutionary

754 Marx and Lenin (bas-relief)

1958. 40th Anniv of Young Communists League. Multicoloured.
2279 10k. Type **753** 20 10
2280 20k. Riveters 30 10
2281 25k. Soldier 40 15
2282 40k. Harvester 60 15
2283 60k. Builder . . . . 1·00 20
2284 1r. Students . . . . 2·40 75

1958. 41st Anniv of October Revolution.
2285 **754** 40k. black, yellow and red 85 25
2286 – 1r. multicoloured . . . . 1·10 40
DESIGN—HORIZ: 1r. Lenin (after N. Andreev) with student, peasant and miner.

755 "Human Rights"

756 Yesenin

1958. 10th Anniv of Declaration of Human Rights.
2287 **755** 60k. blue, black and buff 70 20

1958. 30th Death Anniv of Sergei Yesenin (poet).
2288 **756** 40k. multicoloured . . . 55 20

757 Kuan Han-ching

758 Ordzhonikidze

1958. Kuan Han-ching (Chinese playwright) Commemoration.
2289 **757** 40k. black and blue . . 55 20

1958. 21st Death Anniv of G. K. Ordzhonikidze (statesman).
2290 **758** 40k. multicoloured . . . 70 15

759 John Milton

760 Lenin's Statue, Minsk (M. Manizes)

1958. 350th Birth Anniv of John Milton (poet).
2291 **759** 40k. brown . . . . . . 1·10 15

1958. 40th Anniv of Byelorussian Republic.
2292 **760** 40k. brown, grey and red 70 15

761 Fuzuli

762 Census Emblem

1958. Fuzuli (Azerbaijan poet). Commemoration.
2293 **761** 40k. bistre and turquoise 1·00 15

1958. All Union Census, 1959. Multicoloured.
2294 40k. Type **762** 35 15
2295 40k. Census official with worker's family 35 15

763 Eleonora Duse

764 Rule

1958. Birth Centenary of Eleonora Duse (Italian actress).
2296 **763** 40k. black, grey and green . . . . 1·00 20

1958. Death Centenary of K. F. Rule (naturalist).
2297 **764** 40k. black and blue . . 1·00 30

765 Atomic Ice-breaker "Lenin"

766 Moon Rocket and Sputniks

1958. All-Union Industrial Exhibition. Mult.
2298 40k. Type **765** . . . . . . 2·50 65
2299 60k. Class TE 3 diesel-electric frieght locomotive 4·75 75

1959. 21st Communist Party Congress, Moscow.
2300 – 40k. multicoloured . . . 55 25
2301 – 60k. multicoloured . . . 65 40
2302 **766** 1r. multicoloured . . . . 2·75 80
DESIGNS: 40k. Lenin (after N. Andreev), Red Banner and Kremlin view; 60k. Workers beside Lenin hydro-electric plant, Volga River.

767 E. Torricelli

768 Ice Skater

1959. 350th Birth Anniv of Torricelli (physicist).
2303 **767** 40k. black and green . . 1·00 20

1959. Women's World Ice Skating Championships, Sverdlovsk.
2304 **768** 25k. multicoloured . . . 50 10
2305 40k. black, blue and grey 85 20

769 Charles Darwin

770 N. Gamaleya

1959. 150th Birth Anniv of Charles Darwin (naturalist).
2306 **769** 40k. brown and blue . . 1·10 15

1959. Birth Centenary of Gamaleya (microbiologist).
2307 **770** 40k. black and red . . . 1·10 25

771 Sholem Aleichem

Победа
баскетбольной
команды СССР.
Чили 1959 г.
(772)

1959. Birth Centenary of Aleichem (Jewish writer).
2308 **771** 40k. brown 90 20

1959. Russian (Unofficial) Victory in World Basketball Championships, Chile. No. 1851 optd with T **772**.
2309 1r. brown and drab . . . . 9·50 8·00

1959. Birth Bicent of Robert Burns. Optd **1759 1959**.
2310 **627** 40k. brown and blue . . 17·00 15·00

774 Selma Lagerlof

775 P. Cvirka

1959. Birth Centenary of Selma Lagerlof (Swedish writer).
2311 **774** 40k. black, brown and cream 95 20

1959. 50th Birth Anniv of Cvirka (Lithuanian poet).
2312 **775** 40k. black and red on yellow 55 15

776 F. Joliot-Curie (scientist)

777 Popov and Polar Rescue by Ice-breaker "Ermak"

1959. Joliot-Curie Commemoration.
2313 **776** 40k. black and turquoise 1·25 30

1959. Birth Centenary of A. S. Popov (radio pioneer).
2314 **777** 40k. brown, black & blue . . . . 1·00 40
2315 – 60k. multicoloured . . . 1·50 55
DESIGN: 60k. Popov and radio tower.

1959. Writers as T **746**. Inscr "1959".
2316 40k. grey, black and red . . 1·10 20
2317 40k. brown, sepia and yellow . . . . 1·10 20
2318 40k. brown and violet . . . 1·10 20
2319 40k. multicoloured . . . . 1·10 20
2320 40k. black, olive and yellow 1·10 20
2321 40k. multicoloured 90 90
2322 40k. slate and violet . . . . 1·10 20
PORTRAITS (with scene from works): No. 2316, Anton Chekhov; 2317, Ivan Krylov (after K. Bryullov); 2318, Aleksandr Ostrovsky; 2319, Aleksandr Griboedov (after I. Kramskoi); 2320, Nikolai Gogol (after F. Moller); 2321, Sergei Aksakov (after I. Kramskoi); 2322, Aleksei Koltsov (after K. Gorbunov).

778 Saadi (Persian poet)

1959. Saadi Commemoration.
2323 **778** 40k. black and blue . . 55 15

779 Orbeliani (Georgian writer)

780 "Hero riding Dolphin"

1959. Orbeliani Commemoration.
2324 **779** 40k. black and red . . . 55 15

1959. Birth Tercentenary of Ogata Korin (Japanese artist).
2325 **780** 40k. multicoloured . . . 2·50 2·00

781 "Rossiya" on Odessa-Batum Service

1959. Russian Liners. Multicoloured.
2326 10k. "Sovetsky Soyuz" on Vladivostok–Kamchatka service 30 15
2327 20k. "Feliks Dzerzhinsky" on Odessa–Latakia service 50 15
2328 40k. Type **781** 80 15
2329 40k. "Kooperatsiya" on Murmansk–Tyksi service 80 15
2330 60k. "Mikhail Kalinin" leaving Leningrad . . . . 1·10 20
2331 1r. "Baltika" on Leningrad–London service . . . . . 1·50 40

782 Trajectory of Moon Rocket

783 Lenin

1959. Launching of Moon Rocket. Inscr "2-1-1959".
2332 **782** 40k. brown and pink . . 1·00 30
2333 – 40k. blue and light blue 1·00 30
DESIGN: No. 2333, Preliminary route of moon rocket after launching.

1959. 89th Birth Anniv of Lenin.
2334 **783** 40k. brown . . . . . . 1·00 35

784 M. Cachin

785 Youths with Banner

1959. 90th Birth Anniv of Marcel Cachin (French communist leader).
2335 **784** 60k. brown 90 30

1959. 10th Anniv of World Peace Movement.
2336 **785** 40k. multicoloured . . . 65 30

786 A. von Humboldt

1959. Death Centenary of Alexander von Humboldt (German naturalist).
2337 **786** 40k. brown and violet 1·00 20

787 Haydn

788 Mountain Climbing

1959. 150th Death Anniv of Haydn (Austrian composer).
2338 **787** 40k. brown and blue . . 1·25 20

1959. Tourist Publicity. Multicoloured.
2339 40k. Type **788** 75 25
2340 40k. Map reading 75 25
2341 40k. Cross country skiing 75 25
2342 40k. Canoeing (horiz) . . . 75 25

789 Exhibition Emblem and New York Coliseum

790 Statue of I. Repin (painter), Moscow (M. Manizer)

1959. Russian Scientific, Technological and Cultural Exhibition, New York.
2343 **789** 20k. multicoloured . . . 35 15
2344 40k. multicoloured . . . 70 20

1959. Cultural Celebrities. Inscr "1959". Statues in black.
2345 **790** 10k. ochre 15 10
2346 – 10k. red 15 10
2347 – 20k. lilac 40 10
2348 – 25k. turquoise 65 15
2349 – 60k. green 90 20
2350 – 1r. blue . . . . 1·40 50
STATUES: 10k. (No. 2346), Lenin, Ulanovsk (M. Manizer); 80k. V. Mayakosky (poet), Moscow (A. Kibalnikov); 25k Aleksandr Pushkin (writer), Leningrad, (M. Anikushin; 60k. Maksim Gorky (writer), Moscow (Vera Mukhina); Ir. Tchaikovsky (composer), Moscow (Vera Mukhina).

791 Russian Sturgeon

792 Louis Braille

1959. Fisheries Protection.
2350a – 20k. black and blue . . 40 10
2350b – 25k. brown and lilac . . 50 10
2351 **791** 40k. black and turquoise 70 20
2351a – 40k. purple and mauve 90 20
2352 – 60k. black and blue . . 1·40 40
DESIGNS: 20k. Zander; 25k. Northern fur seals; 40k. (No. 2351a), Common whitefish; 60k. Chum salmon and map.

1959. 150th Birth Anniv of Braille (inventor of Braille).
2353 **792** 60k. brown, yell & turq 70 25

793 Musa Djalil (Tatar poet)

794 Vaulting

1959. Djalil Commemoration.
2354 **793** 40k. black and violet . . 65 15

1959. 2nd Russian Spartakiad. Inscr "1959".
2355 **794** 15k. grey and purple . . 25 10
2356 – 25k. grey, brown & green 45 10
2357 – 30k. olive and red . . . 55 15
2358 – 60k. grey, blue and yellow 95 30
DESIGNS—HORIZ: 25k. Running; 60k. Water polo. VERT: 30k. Athletes supporting Spartakiad emblem.

795

796 Steel Worker

1959. 2nd International T.U. Conference, Leipzig.
2359 **795** 40k. red, blue and yellow . . . 65 15

1959. Seven Year Plan.
2360 – 10k. red, blue and violet 10 10
2361 – 10k. lt red, dp red & yell 10 10
2362 – 15k. red, yellow & brn 15 10
2363 – 15k. brown, green & bis 15 10
2364 – 20k. red, yellow & green 25 10
2365 – 20k. multicoloured . . 25 10
2366 – 30k. red, flesh & purple 40 10
2366a – 30k. multicoloured . . 40 10
2367 **796** 40k. orange, yellow & bl 50 15
2368 – 40k. red, pink and blue 50 15
2369 – 60k. red, blue and yellow 95 35
2370 – 60k. red, buff and blue 95 35
DESIGNS: 2360, Chemist; 2361, Spassky Tower, hammer and sickle; 2362, Builder's labourer; 2363, Farm girl; 2364, Machine minder; No. 2365, Tractor driver; 2366, Oil technician; 2366a, Cloth production; . 2368, Coal miner; 2369, Iron moulder; 2370, Power station.

797 Glaciologist **798** Novgorod

1959. International Geophysical Year (2nd issue).
2371 **797** 10k. turquoise 60 15
2372 – 25k. red and blue . . . 1·25 15
2373 – 40k. red and blue . . . 2·75 20
2373a – 1r. blue and yellow . . 2·50 75
DESIGNS: 25k. Oceanographic survey ship "Vityaz"; 40k. Antarctic map, camp and emperor penguin; 1r. Observatory and rocket.

1959. 11th Centenary of Novgorod.
2374 **798** 40k. red, brown and blue . . 55 15

799 Schoolboys in Workshop **800** Exhibition Emblem

1959. Industrial Training Scheme for School-leavers. Inscr "1959".
2375 **799** 40k. violet 40 15
2376 – 1r. blue . . . . 1·00 30
DESIGN: 1r. Children at night-school.

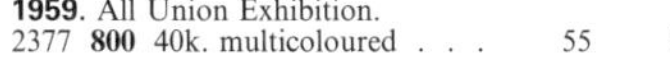
1959. All Union Exhibition.
2377 **800** 40k. multicoloured . . . 55 20

801 Russian and Chinese Students

1959. 10th Anniv of Chinese Peoples' Republic.
2378 **801** 20k. multicoloured . . . 20 15
2379 – 40k. multicoloured . . . 65 20
DESIGN: 40k. Russian miner and Chinese foundryman.

802 Postwoman **803** Mahtumkuli (after A. Khadzhiev)

1959. International Correspondence Week.
2380 **802** 40k. multicoloured . . . 50 15
2381 60k. multicoloured . . . 75 20

1959. 225th Birth Anniv of Mahtumkuli (Turkestan writer).
2382 **803** 40k. brown 65 15

804 Arms and Workers of the German Democratic Republic **805** Lunik 3's Trajectory around the Moon

1959. 10th Anniv of German Democratic Republic.
2383 **804** 40k. multicoloured . . . 45 15
2384 – 60k. purple and cream 65 20
DESIGN—VERT: 60k. Town Hall, East Berlin.

1959. Launching of "Lunik 3" Rocket.
2385 **805** 40k. violet . . . . . . 1·90 30

806 Republican Arms and Emblem **807** Red Square, Moscow

1959. 30th Anniv of Tadzhikistan Republic.
2386 **806** 40k. multicoloured . . . 1·25 25

1959. 42nd Anniv of October Revolution.
2387 **807** 40k. red 65 15

808 Capitol, Washington and Kremlin, Moscow

1959. Visit of Russian Prime Minister to U.S.A.
2388 **808** 60k. blue and yellow . . 1·00 30

809 Mil Mi-1 Helicopter

1959. Military Sports.
2389 **809** 10k. red and violet . . . 30 10
2390 – 25k. brown and blue . . 55 10
2391 – 40k. blue and brown . . 60 15
2392 – 60k. bistre and blue . . 90 25
DESIGNS: 25k. Skin diver; 40k. Racing motor cyclist; 60k. Parachutist.

810 Track of Moon Rocket **811** Liberty Monument (Zs. Kisfaludy-Strobl), Budapest

1959. Landing of Russian Rocket on Moon. Inscr "14.IX.1959". Multicoloured.
2393 40k. Type **810** . . . . . . 1·00 25
2394 40k. Diagram of flight trajectory . . . . 1·00 25

1959. 15th Anniv of Hungarian Republic. Mult.
2395 20k. Sandor Petofi (Hungarian poet) (horiz) 35 15
2396 40k. Type **811** 70 20

812 Manolis Glezos (Greek Communist)

1959. Glezos Commemoration.
2397 **812** 40k. brown and blue . . 15·00 11·50

813 A. Voskresensky (chemist) **814** River Chusovaya

1959. Voskresensky Commemoration.
2398 **813** 40k. brown and blue . . 75 20

1959. Tourist Publicity. Inscr "1959".
2399 **814** 10k. violet 15 10
2400 – 10k. mauve 15 10
2401 – 25k. blue 30 10
2402 – 25k. red 30 10
2403 – 25k. olive 30 10
2404 – 40k. red 50 10
2405 – 60k. turquoise 65 15
2406 – 1r. green . . . . 2·00 70
2407 – 1r. orange . . . . 1·25 60
DESIGNS: No. 2400, Riza Lake, Caucasus; 2401, River Lena; 2402, Iskanderkuly Lake; 2403, Coastal region; 2404, Lake Baikal; . 2405, Beluha Mountains, Altay; 2406, Khibinsky Mountains; 2407, Gursuff region, Crimea.

815 "The Trumpeters of the First Horse Army" (M. Grekov)

1959. 40th Anniv of Russian Cavalry.
2408 **815** 40k. multicoloured . . . 85 20

816 A. P. Chekhov and Moscow Residence **817** M. V. Frunze

1960. Birth Centenary of Chekhov (writer).
2409 **816** 20k. red, brown & vio 35 15
2410 – 40k. brown, blue & sepia 75 25
DESIGN: 40k. Chekhov and Yalta residence.

1960. 75th Birth Anniv of M. V. Frunze (military leader).
2411 **817** 40k. brown 65 15

818 G. N. Gabrichevsky **819** Vera Komissarzhevskaya

1960. Birth Centenary of G. N. Gabrichevsky (microbiologist).
2412 **818** 40k. brown and violet . . 1·00 25

1960. 50th Death Anniv of V. F. Komissarzhevskaya (actress).
2413 **819** 40k. brown 65 15

820 Free-skating

1960. Winter Olympic Games.
2414 – 10k. blue and orange . . 50 10
2415 – 25k. multicoloured . . . 75 10
2416 – 40k. orange, blue & pur 90 15
2417 **820** 60k. violet, brown & grn 1·40 20
2418 – 1r. blue, red and green 2·25 50
DESIGNS: 10k. Ice hockey; 25k. Ice skating; 40k. Skiing; 1r. Ski jumping.

821 Timur Frunze (fighter pilot) and Air Battle **822** Mil Mi-4 Helicopter over Kremlin

1960. War Heroes. Multicoloured.
2419 40k. Type **821** . . . . . . 1·75 55
2420 1r. Gen. Chernyakhovksy and battle scene . . . . . 1·40 40

1960. Air.
2421 **822** 60k. blue . . . . 1·25 25

823 Women of Various Races **824** "Swords into Ploughshares" (Ye. Buchetich)

1960. 50th Anniv of International Women's Day.
2422 **823** 40k. multicoloured . . . 85 25

1960. Presentation of Statue by Russia to U.N.
2423 **824** 40k. yellow, bistre and blue 65 15

15 лет освобождения Венгрии
(825)

826 Lenin when a Child

1960. 15th Anniv of Liberation of Hungary. Optd with T **825**.
2424 **811** 40k. multicoloured . . . 5·00 3·25

1960. 90th Birth Anniv of Lenin. Portraits of Lenin. Multicoloured.
2425 **826** 10k. multicoloured . . . 10 10
2426 – 20k. multicoloured . . . 20 10
2427 – 30k. multicoloured . . . 40 15
2428 – 40k. multicoloured . . . 50 20
2429 – 60k. multicoloured . . . 1·40 35
2430 – 1r. brown, blue and red 1·60 50
DESIGNS: Lenin: 20k. holding child (after N. Zhukov); 30k. and revolutionary scenes; 40k. with party banners; 60k. and industrial scenes; 1r. with globe and rejoicing people (after A. Seral).

827 "Lunik 3" photographing Moon

828 Government House, Baku

1960. Flight of "Lunik 3". Inscr "7.X.1959".
2431 **827** 40k. yellow and blue . . 1·10 35
2432 – 60k. yellow, blue & indigo . . . . 1·10 35
DESIGN: 60k. Lunar map.

1960. 40th Anniv of Azerbaijan Republic.
2433 **828** 40k. brown, bistre & yell 65 15

829 "Fraternization" (K. Pokorny)

830 Furnaceman

1960. 15th Anniv of Czechoslovak Republic.
2434 **829** 40k. black and blue . . 50 10
2435 – 60k. brown and yellow 85 15
DESIGN: 60k. Charles Bridge, Prague.

1960. Completion of First Year of Seven Year Plan.
2436 **830** 40k. brown and red . . 50 15

831 Popov Museum, Leningrad

1960. Radio Day.
2437 **831** 40k. multicoloured . . . 1·00 30

832 Robert Schumann 833 Sverdlov

1960. 150th Birth Anniv of Schumann (composer).
2438 **832** 40k. black and blue . . 1·00 20

1960. 75th Birth Anniv of Ya. M. Sverdlov (statesman).
2439 **833** 40k. sepia and brown . . 85 15

834 Magnifier and Stamp

1960. Philatelists' Day.
2440 **834** 60k. multicoloured . . . 1·10 30

835 Petrozavodsk (Karelian Republic)

1960. Capitals of Autonomous Republic (1st issue).
2441 **835** 40k. turquoise 80 20
2442 – 40k. blue 80 20
2443 – 40k. green 80 20
2444 – 40k. purple 80 20
2445 – 40k. red 80 20
2446 – 40k. blue 80 20
2447 – 40k. brown 80 20
2448 – 40k. brown 80 20
2449 – 40k. red 80 20
2450 – 40k. brown 80 20

CAPITALS: Nos. 2442, Batumi (Adzharian); 2443, Izhevsk (Udmurt); 2444, Grozny (Chechen-Ingush); 2445, Cheboksary (Chuvash); 2446, Yakutsk (Yakut); 2447, Ordzhonikidze (North Ossetian); 2448, Nukus (Kara-Kalpak); 2449, Makhachkala (Daghestan); 2450, Yoshkar-Ola (Mari).

See also Nos. 2586/92 and 2703/5.

836 Children of Different Races 838 Rocket

1960. International Children's Day. Multicoloured.
2451 10k. Type **836** 15 10
2452 20k. Children on farm (vert) 25 15
2453 25k. Children with snowman 40 15
2454 40k. Children in zoo gardens 65 20

1960. 40th Anniv of Karelian Autonomous Republic. Optd **40 лет КАССР 8.VI.1960**.
2455 **835** 40k. turquoise . . . . . 2·25 90

1960. Launching of Cosmic Rocket "Spacecraft 1" (first "Vostok" type spacecraft).
2456 **838** 40k. red and blue . . . 1·75 50

839 I.F.A.C. Emblem

1960. 1st International Automation Control Federation Congress, Moscow.
2457 **839** 60k. brown and yellow 1·90 40

1960. Birth Centenary (1959) of Kosta Khetagurov (poet). As T **746**. Inscr "1960".
2458 40k. brown and blue 80 15
DESIGN: 40k. Portrait of Khetagurov and scene from his works.

840 Cement Works, Belgorod

1960. 1st Plant Construction of Seven Year Plan.
2459 **840** 25k. black and blue . . 25 10
2460 – 40k. black and red . . 50 10
DESIGN. 40k. Metal works, Novokrivorog.

841 Capstans and Cogwheel

1960. Industrial Mass-Production Plant.
2461 **841** 40k. turquoise 70 10
2462 – 40k. purple (Factory plant) 70 10

842 Vilnius (Lithuania)

1960. 20th Anniv of Soviet Baltic Republics. Multicoloured.
2463 40k. Type **842** 65 10
2464 40k. Riga (Latvia) 65 10
2465 40k. Tallin (Estonia) 65 10

843 Running

Международная ярмарка в Риччоне

(844)

1960. Olympic Games. Inscr "1960". Multicoloured.
2466 5k. Type **843** 15 10
2467 10k. Wrestling 20 10
2468 15k. Basketball 35 10
2469 20k. Weightlifting 35 10
2470 25k. Boxing 35 10
2471 40k. High diving 50 15
2472 40k. Fencing 50 15
2473 40k. Gymnastics 50 20
2474 60k. Canoeing 80 25
2475 1r. Horse jumping . . . . . 2·25 55

1960. 20th Anniv of Moldavian Republic. As T **842**.
2476 40k. multicoloured 65 10
DESIGN: 40k. Kishinev (capital).

1960. International Exhibition, Riccione. No. 2471 optd with T **844**.
2477 40k. multicoloured . . . . 16·00 11·00

845 "Agriculture and Industry" 846 G. H. Minkh

1960. 15th Anniv of Vietnam Democratic Republic.
2478 40k. Type **845** 55 15
2479 60k. Book Museum, Hanoi (vert) 85 20

1960. 125th Birth Anniv of G. H. Minkh (epidemiologist).
2480 **846** 60k. brown and bistre 70 15

847 "March" (after I. Levitan)

1960. Birth Centenary of I. Levitan (painter).
2481 **847** 40k. black and olive . . 95 15

848 "Forest" (after Shishkin)

1960. 5th World Forestry Congress, Seattle.
2482 **848** 1r. brown . . . . 2·40 70

849 Addressing Letter

1960. International Correspondence Week.
2483 **849** 40k. multicoloured . . . 40 10
2484 60k. multicoloured . . . 70 20

850 Kremlin, Dogs "Belka" and "Strelka" and Rocket Trajectory

1960. 2nd Cosmic Rocket Flight.
2485 **850** 40k. purple and yellow 1·10 20
2486 1r. blue and orange . . . 1·75 30

851 Globes 852 People of Kazakhstan

1960. 15th Anniv of W.F.T.U.
2487 **851** 60k. blue, drab and lilac 80 15

1960. 40th Anniv of Kazakh Soviet Republic.
2488 **852** 40k. multicoloured . . . 65 15

853 "Karl Marx"

1960. River Boats. Multicoloured.
2489 25k. Type **853** 40 10
2490 40k. "Lenin" 70 15
2491 60k. "Raketa" (hydrofoil) 1·40 25

854 A. N. Voronikhin and Leningrad Cathedral

1960. Birth Bicentenary of A. N. Voronikhin (architect).
2492 **854** 40k. black and grey . . 65 15

855 Motor Coach

1960. Russian Motor Industry.
2493 – 25k. black and blue . . 40 10
2494 – 40k. blue and olive . . . 55 15
2495 – 60k. red and turquoise 1·10 20
2496 **855** 1r. multicoloured . . . 1·75 35
DESIGNS: 25k. Lorry; 40k. "Volga" car; 60k. "Moskvich" car.

856 J. S. Gogebashvily

1960. 120th Birth Anniv of J. S. Gogebashvily (Georgian teacher).
2497 **856** 40k. black and lake . . . 65 15

857 Industrial Plant and Power Plant 858 Federation Emblem

1960. 43rd Anniv of October Revolution.
2498 **857** 40k. multicoloured . . . 65 20

1960. 15th Anniv of International Federation of Democratic Women.
2499 **858** 60k. red and grey . . . 80 20

859 Youth of Three Races

40 лет Удмуртской АССР 4/XI 1960.

(860)

1960. 15th Anniv of World Democratic Youth Federation.
2500 **859** 60k. multicoloured . . . 80 20

1960. 40th Anniv of Udmurt Autonomous Republic. No. 2443 optd with T **860**.
2501 40k. green . . . . 2·75 1·10

861 Tolstoi and his Moscow Residence

1960. 50th Death Anniv of Leo Tolstoi (writer).
2502 **861** 20k. multicoloured . . . 30 15
2503 – 40k. brown, sepia & blue 55 15
2504 – 60k. multicoloured . . . 1·10 25
DESIGNS—HORIZ: 40k. Tolstoi and his country estate. VERT: 60k. Full face portrait.

862 Government House, Yerevan

1960. 40th Anniv of Armenian Republic.
2205 **862** 40k. multicoloured . . . 65 15

863 Students and University

864 Tulip

1960. Opening of Friendship University, Moscow.
2506 **863** 40k. purple 65 15

1960. Russian Flowers. Multicoloured.
2507 20k. Type **864** 30 10
2508 20k. Autumn crocus 30 10
2509 25k. Marsh marigold . . . 35 10
2510 40k. Tulip 45 10
2511 40k. Panax 45 10
2512 60k. Hypericum 90 25
2513 60k. Iris 90 25
2514 1r. Wild rose . . . . 1·60 45

865 Engels

867 N. Pirogov

866 Mark Twain

1960. 140th Birth Anniv of Engels.
2515 **865** 60k. grey . . . . 1·40 30

1960. 125th Birth Anniv of Mark Twain.
2516 **866** 40k. bistre and orange 2·75 1·75

1960. 150th Birth Anniv of N. Pirogov (surgeon).
2517 **867** 40k. brown and green . . 65 15

868 Chopin (after Eugene Delacroix)

869 North Korean Flag and Emblem

1960. 150th Birth Anniv of Chopin.
2518 **868** 40k. bistre and buff . . 1·50 20

1960. 15th Anniv of Korean Liberation.
2519 **869** 40k. multicoloured . . . 95 20

870 Lithuanian Costumes

871 A. Tseretely

1960. Provincial Costumes (1st issue). Inscr "1960". Multicoloured.
2520 10k. Type **870** 35 15
2521 60k. Uzbek costumes . . . 1·40 25
See also Nos. 2537/45, 2796 and 2835/8.

1960. 120th Birth Anniv of A. Tseretely (Georgian poet).
2522 **871** 40k. purple and lilac . . 1·00 20

Currency Revalued.
10 (old) Kopeks = 1 (new) Kopek.

872 Worker

873 "Ruslan and Lyudmila" (Pushkin)

1961. Inscr "1961".
2523 **872** 1k. bistre 70 10
2524 – 2k. green 25 10
2525 – 3k. violet . . . . . . 2·00 10
2526 – 4k. red 60 10
2526a – 4k. brown . . . . . . 3·00 1·40
2527 – 6k. red . . . . 4·50 45
2528 – 6k. claret . . . . . . 1·40 10
2529 – 10k. orange . . . . . 2·40 10
2533a – 12k. purple . . . . . 2·00 25
2530 – 16k. blue . . . . . . 3·50 70
DESIGNS: 2k. Combine harvester; 3k. Cosmic rocket; 4k. Soviet Arms and Flag; 6k. Spassky Tower and Kremlin; 10k. "Worker and Collective Farmer" (sculpture, Vera Mukhina); 12k. Monument to F. Minin and D. Pozharsky and Spassky Tower; 16k. Airliner over power station.

1961. Russian Wild Life. As T **653** but inscr "1961". Centres in natural colours. Frame colours given.
2534 1k. sepia (Brown bear) . . . 25 15
2535 6k. black (Eurasian beaver) 1·00 20
2536 10k. black (Roe deer) . . . 1·25 55
The 1k. is vert and the rest horiz.

1961. Provincial Costumes (2nd issue). As T **870** but inscr "1961".
2537 2k. red, brown and stone . . 25 10
2538 2k. multicoloured 25 10
2539 3k. multicoloured 50 10
2540 3k. multicoloured 50 10
2541 3k. multicoloured 50 10
2542 4k. multicoloured 60 15
2543 6k. multicoloured 70 20
2544 10k. multicoloured . . . . 1·40 30
2545 12k. multicoloured . . . . 2·25 35
COSTUMES: No. 2337, Moldavia; 2538, Georgia; 2539, Ukraine; 2540, Byelorussia; 2541, Kazakhs; 2542, Koryaks; 2543, Russia; 2544, Armenia; 2545, Estonia.

1961. Scenes from Russian Fairy Tales. Mult.
2546 1k. "Geese Swans" 25 10
2547 3k. "The Fox, the Hare and the Cock" 55 15
2548 4k. "The Little Humpbacked Horse" . . 75 15
2549 6k. "The Muzhik and the Bear" . . . . 1·10 20
2550 10k. Type **873** . . . . . . 1·60 40

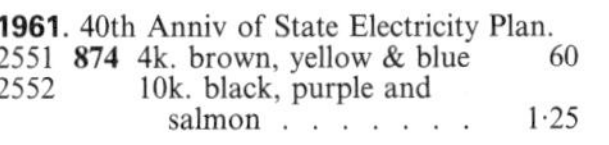

874 Lenin, Map and Power Station

1961. 40th Anniv of State Electricity Plan.
2551 **874** 4k. brown, yellow & blue 60 15
2552 10k. black, purple and salmon . . . . 1·25 25

875 Tractor

876 Dobrolyubov (after P. Borel)

1961. Soviet Agricultural Achievements. Inscr "1961".
2553 – 3k. mauve and blue . . 40 15
2554 **875** 4k. black and green . . 45 10
2555 – 6k. brown and blue . . . 55 25
2556 – 10k. purple and olive . . 1·10 15
DESIGNS: 3k. Dairy herd; 6k. Agricultural machinery; 10k. Fruit picking.

1961. 125th Birth Anniv of N. A. Dobrolyubov (writer).
2557 **876** 4k. buff, black and blue 55 20

877 N. D. Zelinsky

1961. Birth Centenary of N. D. Zelinsky (chemist).
2558 **877** 4k. purple and mauve . . 55 20

878 Georgian Republic Flag

1961. 40th Anniv of Georgian Republic.
2559 **878** 4k. multicoloured . . . 30 10

879 Sgt. Miroshnichenko and Battle

1961. War Hero.
2560 **879** 4k. blue and purple . . . 65 20
See also Nos. 2664/5.

880 Self-portrait and Birthplace

881 A. Rublev

1961. Death Centenary of T. G. Shevchenko (Ukrainian poet and painter).
2561 **880** 3k. brown and violet . . 35 10
2562 – 6k. purple and green . . 65 15
DESIGN: 6k. Shevchenko in old age (after I. Kramskoi), pen, book and candle.
See also Nos. 2956/62.

1961. 600th Birth Anniv of Rublev (painter).
2563 **881** 4k. multicoloured . . . 60 20

882 Statue of Shevchenko (poet), Kharkov (M. Manizer)

883 N. V. Sklifosovsky

1961. Cultural Celebrities.
2564 – 2k. brown and blue . . . 25 10
2565 **882** 4k. brown and black . . 30 15
2566 – 4k. brown and purple . . 35 15
DESIGNS: 2k. Shchors Monument, Kiev (M. Lysenko); 4k. (No. 2566), Kotovsky Monument, Kishinev (L. Dubinovsky).

1961. 125th Birth Anniv of N. Y. Sklifosovsky (surgeon).
2567 **883** 4k. black and blue . . . 40 10

884 Robert Koch

885 Zither-player and Folk Dancers

1961. 50th Death Anniv of Robert Koch (German microbiologist).
2568 **884** 6k. brown 60 20

1961. 50th Anniv of Russian National Choir.
2569 **885** 4k. multicoloured . . . 35 10

886 "Popular Science"

1961. Cent of "Vokrug Sveta" (science magazine).
2570 **886** 6k. brown, blue and deep blue . . . . . . 1·10 75

887 Venus Rocket

1961. Launching of Venus Rocket.
2571 **887** 6k. orange and blue . . 1·40 20
2572 – 10k. blue and yellow . . 1·90 40
DESIGN: 10k. Capsule and flight route.

(**888**)

1961. Patrice Lumumba (Congolese politician) Commemoration (1st issue). Surch with T **888**.
2573 **863** 4k. on 40k. purple . . . 1·25 85
See also No. 2593.

889 African breaking Chains

1961. Africa Freedom Day. Inscr "1961".
2574 **889** 4k. multicoloured . . . 20 10
2575 – 6k. purple, orange and blue 45 20
DESIGN: 6k. Hands clasping Torch of Freedom, and map.

891 Yuri Gagarin

892 Lenin

1961. World's First Manned Space Flight. Inscr "12-IV-1961". Perf or imperf.
2576 **891** 3k. blue 45 10
2577 – 6k. blue, violet and red 65 20
2578 – 10k. red, green & brown 1·25 30
DESIGNS—37 × 26 mm: 6k. Rocket and Spassky Tower; 10k. Rocket, Gagarin and Kremlin.

1961. 91st Birth Anniv of Lenin.
2579 **892** 4k. blk, salmon and red 30 10

893 Rabindranath Tagore

894 Garibaldi

1961. Birth Centenary of Tagore (Indian writer).
2580 **893** 6k. black, bistre and red 50 15

1961. International Labour Exhibition, Turin.
2581 – 4k. salmon and red . . . 40 10
2582 **894** 6k. salmon and lilac . . 45 10
DESIGN: 4k. "To the Stars" (statue, G. Postnikov).

895 Lenin

896 Patrice Lumumba

1961.
2583 **895** 20k. green and brown . . 1·40 85
2584 – 30k. blue and brown . . 2·50 1·10
2585 – 50k. red and brown . . 4·00 1·90
PORTRAITS (Lenin): 30k. In cap; 50k. Profile.

1961. Capitals of Autonomous Republics (2nd issue). As T **835**.
2586 4k. deep violet 40 15
2587 4k. blue 40 15
2588 4k. orange 40 15
2589 4k. black 40 15
2590 4k. lake 40 15
2591 4k. green 40 15
2592 4k. deep purple 40 15
CAPITALS: No. 2586, Nalchik (Kabardino-Balkar); 2587, Ulan-Ude (Buryat); 2588, Sukhumi (Abkhazia); 2589, Syktyvkar (Komi); 2590, Nakhichevan (Nakhichevan); 2591, Rodina Cinema, Elista (Kalmyk); 2592, Ufa (Bashkir).

1961. Lumumba Commemoration (2nd issue).
2593 **896** 2k. multicoloured . . . 30 10

897 Kindergarten

898 Chernushka and Rocket

1961. International Children's Day.
2594 **897** 2k. blue and orange . . 20 10
2595 – 3k. violet and ochre . . 30 10
2596 – 4k. drab and red 45 15
DESIGNS—HORIZ: 3k. Children in Pioneer camp. VERT: 4k. Children with toys and pets.

1961. 4th and 5th "Spacecraft" Flights.
2597 – 2k. black, blue and violet 35 15
2598 **898** 4k. turquoise and blue 65 15
DESIGN—HORIZ: 2k. Dog "Zvezdochka", rocket and controller (inscr "25.III.1961").

899 Belinsky (after I. Astafev)

900

1961. 150th Birth Anniv of Vissarion Grigorievich Belinsky (literary critic and journalist).
2599 **899** 4k. black and red . . . 30 15

1961. 40th Anniv of Soviet Hydro-meteorological Service.
2600 **900** 6k. multicoloured . . . 90 25

901 D. M. Karbyshev

902 Glider

1961. Lieut-Gen. Karbyshev (war hero).
2601 **901** 4k. black, red and yellow 30 10

1961. Soviet Spartakiad.
2602 **902** 4k. red and grey 30 10
2603 – 6k. red and grey 55 15
2604 – 10k. red and grey . . . 90 35
DESIGNS: 6k. Inflatable motor boat; 10k. Motor cyclists.

903 Sukhe Bator Monument and Govt. Buildings, Ulan Bator

904 S. I. Vavilov

1961. 40th Anniv of Revolution in Mongolia.
2605 **903** 4k. multicoloured . . . 65 20

1961. 70th Birthday of Vavilov (scientist).
2606 **904** 4k. brown, bistre & green 30 15

905 V. Pshavela

906 "Youth Activities"

1961. Birth Cent of Pshavela (Georgian poet).
2607 **905** 4k. brown and cream . . 30 10

1961. World Youth Forum.
2608 – 2k. brown and orange 30 10
2609 – 4k. green and lilac . . . 35 10
2610 **906** 6k. blue and ochre . . . 65 20
DESIGNS—HORIZ: 2k. Youths pushing tank into river. VERT: 4k. "Youths and progress".

907

908

1961. 5th Int Biochemical Congress, Moscow.
2611 **907** 6k. multicoloured . . . 65 15

1961. Centenary of "Kalevipoeg" (Estonian Saga).
2612 **908** 4k. yellow, turq & blk 30 15

909 Javelin Thrower

1961. 7th Soviet Trade Union Sports.
2613 **909** 6k. red 55 20

910 A.D. Zakharov (after S. Shchukin)

1961. Birth Bicentenary of Zakharov (architect).
2614 **910** buff, brown and blue . . 80 25

911 Counter-attack (after P. Krivonogov)

1961. War of 1941–45 (1st issue). Inscr "1961".
2615 **911** 4k. multicoloured . . . 55 15
2616 – 4k. multicoloured . . . 55 15
2617 – 4k. indigo and brown . . 65 15
DESIGNS: No. 2616, Sailor with bayonet; No. 2617, Soldier with tommy gun.
See also Nos. 2717 and 2851/5.

912 Union Emblem

1961. 15th Anniv of International Union of Students.
2617a **912** 6k. violet and red . . . 45 10

913 Stamps commemorating Industry

1961. 40th Anniv of First Soviet Stamp. Centres multicoloured.
2618 **913** 2k. ochre and brown . . 30 15
2619 – 4k. blue and indigo . . . 45 15
2620 – 6k. green and olive . . . 90 25
2621 – 10k. buff and brown . . 1·40 45
DESIGNS (stamps commemorating): 4k. Electrification; 8k. Peace; 10k. Atomic energy.

914 Titov and "Vostok 2"

1961. 2nd Manned Space Flight. Perf or imperf.
2622 – 4k. blue and purple . . . 70 20
2623 **914** 6k. orange, green & brn 1·00 30
DESIGN: 4k. Space pilot and globe.

915 Angara River Bridge

1961. Tercentenary of Irkutsk, Siberia.
2624 **915** 4k. black, lilac and bistre 55 15

916 Letters and Mail Transport

1961. International Correspondence Week.
2625 **916** 4k. black and mauve . . 55 10

917 Workers and Banners

1961. 22nd Communist Party Congress (1st issue).
2626 **917** 2k. brown, yellow and red 15 10
2627 – 3k. blue and orange . . 90 15
2628 – 4k. red, buff and purple 25 10
2629 – 4k. orange, black & mve 40 10
2630 – 4k. sepia, brown and red 25 10
DESIGNS: No. 2627, Moscow University and obelisk; 2628, Combine harvester; 2629, Workmen and machinery; 2630, Worker and slogan.
See also No. 2636.

918 Soviet Monument, Berlin

1961. 10th Anniv of International Federation of Resistance Fighters.
2631 **918** 4k. grey and red 35 10

919 Adult Education

1961. Communist Labour Teams.
2632 – 2k. purple & red on buff 20 10
2633 **919** 3k. brown & red on buff 20 10
2634 – 4k. blue and red on cream 35 15
DESIGNS: 2k. Worker at machine; 4k. Workers around piano.

920 Rocket and Globes

1961. Cosmic Flights. Aluminium-surfaced paper.
2635 **920** 1r. red and black on silver . . . . 22·00 22·00

XXII съезд
КПСС
(921)

1961. 22nd Communist Party Congress (2nd issue). Optd with T **921**.
2636 **920** 1r. red and black on silver . . . . 19·00 20·00

922 Imanov (after A. Kasteev)

923 Liszt, Piano and Music

1961. 42nd Death Anniv of Amangeldy Imanov (Kazakh Leader).
2637 **922** 4k. sepia, brown & green 35 10

1961. 150th Birth Anniv of Liszt.
2638 **923** 4k. brown, purple & yell 75 15

924 Flags, Rocket and Skyline

1961. 44th Anniv of October Revolution.
2639 **924** 4k. red, purple and yellow 70 15

925 Congress Emblem

926 Statue of Lomonosov (N. Tomsky) and Lomonosov University

1961. 5th W.F.T.U. Congress, Moscow. Inscr "МОСКВА 1961".
2640 **925** 2k. red and bistre . . . 25 10
2641 – 2k. violet and grey . . . 25 10
2642 – 4k. brown, purple & blue 50 15
2643 – 4k. red, blue and violet 50 15
2644 **925** 6k. red, bistre and green 75 20
2645 – 6k. blue, purple and bistre 75 20
DESIGNS—HORIZ: Nos. 2641, 2645, Negro breaking chains. VERT: No. 2642, Hand holding hammer; 2643, Hands holding globe.

1961. 250th Birth Anniv of Mikhail Lomonosov (scientist).
2646 **926** 4k. brown, green and blue 45 15
2647 – 6k. blue, buff and green 65 20
2648 – 10k. brown, blue & pur 1·40 40
DESIGNS—VERT: 6k. Lomonosov at desk (after M. Shreier). HORIZ: 10k. Lomonosov (after L. Miropolsky), his birthplace, and Leningrad Academy of Science.

927 Power Workers
928 Scene from "Romeo and Juliet" (Prokotiev)

1961. Young Builders of Seven Year Plan. Inscr "1961".
2649 **927** 3k. grey, brown and red 50 15
2650 – 4k. brown, blue and red 45 15
2651 – 6k. grey, brown and red 75 20
DESIGNS: 4k. Welders; 6k. Engineer with theodolite.

1961. Russian Ballet (1st issue). Multicoloured.
2652 6k. Type **928** . . . . 1·10 20
2653 10k. Scene from "Swan Lake" (Tchaikovsky) . . 1·50 45
See also Nos. 2666/7.

929 Hammer and Sickle
930 A. Pumpur

1961. 25th Anniv of Soviet Constitution.
2654 **929** 4k. lake, yellow and red 40 15

1961. 120th Birth Anniv of Pumpur (Lettish poet).
2655 **930** 4k. purple and grey . . . 25 10

1961. Air. Surch **1961 r. 6 kon.** and wavy lines.
2656 **822** 6k. on 60k. blue 90 20

932 "Bulgarian Achievements"

1961. 15th Anniv of Bulgarian Republic.
2657 **932** 4k. multicoloured . . . 35 10

933 Nansen and "Fram"

1961. Birth Centenary of Nansen (explorer).
2658 **933** 6k. brown, blue and black . . . . 1·75 15

934 M. Dolivo-Dobrovolsky
935 A. S. Pushkin (after O. Kiprensky)

1962. Birth Centenary of Dolivo-Dobrovolsky (electrical engineer).
2659 **934** 4k. blue and bistre . . . 35 10

1962. 125th Death Anniv of Pushkin (poet).
2660 **935** 4k. black, red and buff 30 10

936 Soviet Woman

1962. Soviet Women.
2661 **936** 4k. black, bistre & orange 35 10

937 People's Dancers

1962. 25th Anniv of Soviet People's Dance Ensemble.
2662 **937** 4k. brown and red . . . 35 10

938 Skaters

1962. Ice Skating Championships, Moscow.
2663 **938** 4k. blue and orange . . 40 10

1962. War Heroes. As T **879** but inscr "1962".
2664 4k. brown and blue 90 15
2665 6k. turquoise and brown . . 1·25 20
DESIGNS: 4k. Lieut. Shalandin, tanks and Yakovlev Yak-9T fighters; 6k. Capt. Gadzhiev, "K-3" submarine and sinking ship.

1962. Russian Ballet (2nd issue). As T **928** but inscr "1962".
2666 2k. multicoloured 60 15
2667 3k. multicoloured 65 15
DESIGNS: Scenes from—2k. "Red Flower" (Glier); 3k. "Paris Flame" (Asafev).

СОВЕТСКИЕ КОНЬКОБЕЖЦЫ— ЧЕМПИОНЫ МИРА
(939)

1962. Soviet Victory in Ice Skating Championships. Optd with T **939**.
2668 **938** 4k. blue and orange . . 2·75 1·50

940 Skiing

1962. 1st People's Winter Games, Sverdlovsk.
2669 **940** 4k. violet and red . . . 45 15
2670 – 6k. turquoise and purple 60 20
2671 – 10k. red, black and blue 1·25 30
DESIGN: 6k. Ice Hockey; 10k. Figure skating.

941 A. I. Herzen (after N. Ge)
942 Lenin on Banner

1962. 150th Birth Anniv of A. I. Herzen (writer).
2672 **941** 4k. flesh, black and blue 35 10

1962. 14th Leninist Young Communist League Congress. Inscr "1962".
2673 **942** 4k. red, yellow and purple 20 10
2674 – 6k. purple, orange & blue 35 10
DESIGN—HORIZ: 6k. Lenin (after A. Mylnikov) on flag.

943 Rocket and Globe
944 Tchaikovsky (after sculpture by Z. M. Vilensky)

1962. 1st Anniv of World's First Manned Space Flight. Perf or imperf.
2675 **943** 10k. multicoloured . . . 1·10 35

1962. 2nd Int Tchaikovsky Music Competition.
2676 **944** 4k. drab, black and blue 50 10

945 Youth of Three Races

1962. International Day of "Solidarity of Youth against Colonialism".
2677 **945** 6k. multicoloured . . . 45 10

946 The Ulyanov (Lenin's) Family

1962. 92nd Birth Anniv of Lenin.
2678 **946** 4k. brown, grey and red 40 15
2679 – 10k. purple, red and black . . . . 1·00 30
DESIGN: 10k. Bust of Lenin (N. Sokolov).

947 "Cosmos 3"

1962. Cosmic Research.
2680 **947** 6k. black, violet and blue 65 15

948 Charles Dickens

1962. 150th Birth Anniv of Charles Dickens.
2681 **948** 6k. purple, turq & brn 85 20

949 J. J. Rousseau
950 Karl Marx Monument, Moscow (L. Kerbel)

1962. 250th Birth Anniv of Rousseau.
2682 **949** 6k. bistre, purple and grey 70 20

1962. Karl Marx Commemoration.
2683 **950** 4k. grey and blue . . . 35 10

951 Lenin reading "Pravda"
952 Mosquito and Campaign Emblem

1962. 50th Anniv of "Pravda" Newspaper.
2684 **951** 4k. purple, red and buff 30 15
2685 – 4k. multicoloured . . . 30 15
2686 – 4k. multicoloured . . . 30 15
DESIGNS—25 × 38 mm: No. 2685, Statuary and front page of first issue of "Pravda"; No. 2686, Lenin (after A. Mylnikov) and modern front page of "Pravda".

1962. Malaria Eradication. Perf (6k. also imperf).
2687 **952** 4k. black, turquoise & red 40 10
2688 6k. black, green and red 70 10

953 Model Rocket Construction

1962. 40th Anniv of All Union Lenin Pioneer Organization. Designs embody Pioneer badge. Multicoloured.
2689 2k. Lenin and Pioneers giving Oath 25 10
2690 3k. Lenya Golikov and Valya Kotik (pioneer heroes) 25 10
2691 4k. Type **953** 35 10
2692 4k. Hygiene education . . . 40 15
2693 6k. Pioneers marching . . . 90 25

954 M. Mashtotz
955 Ski Jumping

1962. 1600th Birth Anniv of Mesrop Mashtotz (author of Armenian Alphabet).
2694 **954** 4k. brown and yellow . . 35 10

1962. F.I.S. International Ski Championships, Zakopane (Poland).
2695 **955** 2k. red, brown and blue 20 10
2696 – 10k. blue, black and red 90 35
DESIGN—VERT: 10k. Skier.

956 I. Goncharov (after I. Kramskoi)
957 Cycle Racing

1962. 150th Birth Anniv of I. Goncharov (writer).
2697 **956** 4k. brown and grey . . 35 10

1962. Summer Sports Championships.
2698 **957** 2k. black, red and brown 40 10
2699 – 4k. black, yellow & brn 75 20
2700 – 10k. black, lemon & blue 80 30
2701 – 12k. brown, yellow & bl 95 40
2702 – 16k. multicoloured . . . 1·50 50
DESIGN—VERT: 4k. Volleyball; 10k. Rowing; 16k. Horse jumping. HORIZ: 12k. Football (goal keeper).

1962. Capitals of Autonomous Republics. 3rd issue. As T **835**.
2703 4k. black 50 15
2704 4k. purple 50 15
2705 4k. green 50 15
CAPITALS: No. 2703, Kazan (Tatar); No. 2704, Kyzyl (Tuva); No.2705, Saransk (Mordovian).

958 Lenin Library, 1862

1962. Centenary of Lenin Library.
2706 **958** 4k. black and grey . . . 35 15
2707 – 4k. black and grey . . . 35 15
DESIGN: No. 2707, Modern library building.

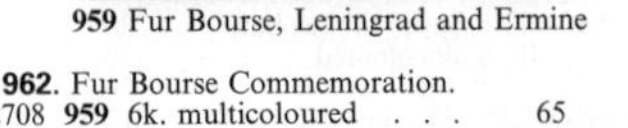

959 Fur Bourse, Leningrad and Ermine

1962. Fur Bourse Commemoration.
2708 **959** 6k. multicoloured . . . 65 30

960 Pasteur **961** Youth and Girl with Book

1982. Centenary of Pasteur's Sterilization Process.
2709 **960** 6k. brown and black . . 60 15

1962. Communist Party Programme. Mult.
2710 2k. Type **961** . . . 20 10
2711 4k. Workers of three races and dove 35 10

962 Hands breaking Bomb

1962. World Peace Congress, Moscow.
2712 **962** 6k. bistre, black and blue 30 15

963 Ya. Kupala and Ya. Kolas

1962. Byelorussian Poets Commemoration.
2713 **963** 4k. brown and yellow . . 30 10

964 Sabir **965** Congress Emblem

1962. Birth Centenary of Sabir (Azerbaijan poet).
2714 **964** 4k. brown, buff and blue 30 10

1962. 8th Anti-cancer Congress, Moscow.
2715 **965** 6k. red, black and blue 45 15

966 N. N. Zinin

1962. 150th Birth Anniv of N. N. Zinin (chemist).
2716 **966** 4k. brown and violet . . 30 10

1962. War of 1941–45 (2nd issue). As T **911** inscr "1962".
2717 4k. multicoloured 55 15
DESIGN: Sailor throwing petrol bomb (Defence of Sevastopol, after A. Deinekin).

967 M. V. Nesterov (painter) (after P. Korin)

1962. Russian Artists Commemoration.
2718 **967** 4k. multicoloured . . . 45 15
2719 – 4k. brown, purple & grey 45 15
2720 – 4k. black and brown . . 45 15
PORTRAITS—VERT: No. 2719, I. N. Kramskoi (painter) (after N. Yovoshenko). HORIZ: No. 2220, I. D. Shadr (sculptor).

968 "Vostok-2" **969** Nikolaev and "Vostok 3"

1962. 1st Anniv of Titov's Space Flight. Perf or imperf.
2721 **968** 10k. purple, black & blue . . . . 1·10 35
2722 10k. orange, black & blue . . . . 1·10 35

1962. 1st "Team" Manned Space Flight. Perf or imperf.
2723 **969** 4k. brown, red and blue 90 20
2724 – 4k. brown, red and blue 90 20
2725 – 6k. multicoloured . . . 1·50 25
DESIGNS: No. 2724, As Type **969** but with Popovich and "Vostok-4"; No. 2725 (47×28½ mm), Cosmonauts in flight.

970 House of Friendship

1962. People's House of Friendship, Moscow.
2726 **970** 6k. grey and blue . . . 30 10

971 Lomonosov University and Atomic Symbols

1962. "Atoms for Peace".
2727 **971** 4k. multicoloured . . . 35 10
2728 – 6k. multicoloured . . . 75 20
DESIGN: 6k. Map of Russia, Atomic symbol and "Peace" in ten languages.

972 Common Carp and Bream **973** F. E. Dzerzhinsky

1962. Fish Preservation Campaign.
2729 **972** 4k. yellow, violet and blue 50 10
2730 – 6k. blue, black and orange 75 20
DESIGN: 6k. Atlantic salmon.

1962. Birth Anniv of Feliks Dzerzhinsky (founder of Cheka).
2731 **973** 4k. blue and green . . . 25 10

974 O. Henry

1962. Birth Cent of O. Henry (American writer).
2732 **974** 6k. black, brown & yell 45 10

975 Field Marshals Barclay de Tolly, Kutuzov and Bagration

1962. 150th Anniv of Patriotic War of 1812.
2733 **975** 3k. brown 40 10
2734 – 4k. blue 55 15
2735 – 6k. slate 65 20
2736 – 10k. violet 90 25
DESIGNS: 4k. D. V. Davydov and partisans; 6k. Battle of Borodino; 10k. Partisan Vasilisa Kozhina escorting French prisoners of war.

976 Lenin Street, Vinnitsa

1962. 600th Anniv of Vinnitsa.
2737 **976** 4k. black and bistre . . 30 10

977 Transport, "Stamp" and "Postmark" **978** Cedar

1962. International Correspondence Week.
2738 **977** 4k. black, purple & turq 30 10

1962. 150th Anniv of Nikitsky Botanical Gardens. Multicoloured.
2739 3k. Type **978** 35 10
2740 4k. "Vostok-2" canna (plant) 55 10
2741 6k. Strawberry tree (arbutus) 70 15
2742 10k. "Road to the Stars" (chrysanthemum) 95 25

979 Builder **981** Akhundov (after N. Ismailov)

980 "Sputnik 1"

1962. "The Russian People". Multicoloured.
2743 4k. Type **979** 30 15
2744 4k. Textile worker 30 15
2745 4k. Surgeon 30 15
2746 4k. Farm girl 30 15
2747 4k. P. T. instructor 30 15
2748 4k. Housewife 30 15
2749 4k. Rambler 30 15

1962. 5th Anniv of Launching of "Sputnik 1".
2750 **980** 10k. multicoloured . . . 1·10 30

1962. 150th Birth Anniv of Mirza Akhundov (poet).
2751 **981** 4k. brown and green . . 35 10

982 Harvester **983** N. N. Burdenko

1962. "Settlers on Virgin Lands". Multicoloured.
2752 4k. Type **982** 55 20
2753 4k. Surveyors, tractors and map 55 20
2754 4k. Pioneers with flag . . . 55 20

1962. Soviet Scientists. Inscr "1962". Multicoloured.
2755 4k. Type **983** 30 10
2756 4k. V. P. Filatov (wearing beret) 35 10

984 Lenin Mausoleum

1962. 92nd Birth Anniv of Lenin.
2757 **984** 4k. multicoloured . . . 30 10

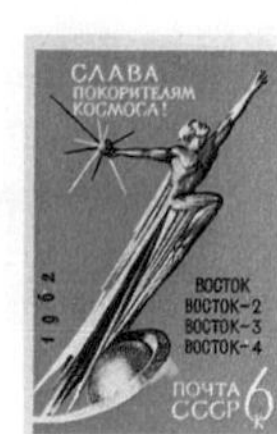
985 Worker with Banner **986** "Into Space" (sculpture, G. Postnikov)

1962. 45th Anniv of October Revolution.
2758 **985** 4k. multicoloured . . . 30 10

1962. Space Flights Commem. Perf or imperf.
2759 **986** 6k. black, brown and blue 60 15
2760 10k. ultram, bis & vio 1·00 20

ЗЕМЛЯ—МАРС
1.XI.

(**987**) **988** T. Moldo (Kirghiz poet)

1962. Launching of Rocket to Mars (1st issue). Optd with T **987**.
2761 **986** 10k. blue, bistre and violet . . . . 3·25 1·75
See also No. 2765.

1962. Poets' Anniversaries.
2762 **988** 4k. black and red . . . 40 10
2763 – 4k. black and blue . . . 40 10
DESIGN: No. 2763, Sayat-Nova (Armenian poet) with musical instrument (after G. Ruthkyan).

989 Hammer and Sickle

1962. 40th Anniv of U.S.S.R.
2764 **989** 4k. yellow, red and crimson 30 10

990 Mars Rocket in Space (⅔-size illustration)

1962. Launching of Rocket to Mars (2nd issue).
2765 **990** 10k. violet and red . . . 1·10 30

991 Chemical Industry and Statistics

1962. 22nd Communist Party Congress. "Achievements of the People". Multicoloured.
2766 4k. Type **991** 55 20
2767 4k. Engineering (machinery and atomic symbol) . . . 55 20
2768 4k. Hydro-electric power . . 55 20

2769 4k. Agriculture (harvester) 55 20
2770 4k. Engineering (surveyor and welder) 55 20
2771 4k. Communications (telephone installation) 55 20
2772 4k. Heavy industry (furnace) 55 20
2773 4k. Transport (signalman, etc) 65 20
2774 4k. Dairy farming (milkmaid, etc) 55 20

All the designs show production targets relating to 1980.

992 Chessmen 994 V. K. Blucher (military commander)

993 Four Soviet Cosmonauts (½-size illustration)

1962. 30th Soviet Chess Championships, Yerevan.
2775 **992** 4k. black and ochre 75 20

1962. Soviet Cosmonauts Commem. Perf or imperf.
2776 **993** 1r. black and blue 8·00 8·00

1962. V. K. Blucher Commemoration.
2777 **994** 4k. multicoloured 40 10

995 V. N. Podbelsky 996 A. Gaidar

1962. 75th Birth Anniv of V. N. Podbelsky (postal administrator, 1918–20).
2778 **995** 4k. violet and brown 25 10

1962. Soviet Writers.
2779 **996** 4k. buff, black and blue 30 10
2780 – 4k. multicoloured 30 10

DESIGN: No. 2780, A. S. Makharenko.

997 Dove and Christmas Tree

1962. New Year. Perf or imperf.
2781 **997** 4k. multicoloured 35 10

998 D. N. Pryanishnikov (agricultural chemist) 999 Rose-coloured Starlings

1962. D. N. Pryanishnikov Commemoration.
2782 **998** 4k. multicoloured 30 10

1962. Birds.
2783 **999** 3k. black, red and green 40 15
2784 – 4k. black, brown & orge 55 15
2785 – 6k. blue, black and red 65 20
2786 – 10k. blue, black and red 1·00 40
2787 – 16k. red, blue and black 1·50 65

BIRDS: 4k. Red-breasted geese; 6k. Snow geese; 10k. Great white cranes; 16k. Greater flamingos.

1000 F.I.R. Emblem and Handclasp 1001 Badge and Yakovlev Yak-9 Fighters

1962. 4th International Federation of Resistance Heroes Congress.
2788 **1000** 4k. violet and red 30 10
2789 6k. turquoise and red 45 15

1962. 20th Anniv of French Air Force "Normandy-Niemen" Unit.
2790 **1001** 6k. red, green and buff 65 15

1002 Map and Savings Book

1962. 40th Anniv of Soviet Banks.
2791 **1002** 4k. multicoloured 25 10
2792 – 6k. multicoloured 45 15

DESIGN: 6k. Savings book and map containing savers.

1003 Fertilizer Plant, Rustavi, Georgia

1962. Heavy Industries.
2793 **1003** 4k. black, lt blue & blue 40 15
2794 – 4k. black, turquoise & grn 40 15
2795 – 4k. black, blue and grey 40 15

DESIGNS: No. 2794, Construction of Bratsk hydro-electric station; 2795, Volzhskaya hydro-electric station, Volgograd.

1962. Provincial Costumes (3rd issue). As T **870**. Inscr "1962".
2796 3k. red, brown and drab 40 15

COSTUME: 3k. Latvia.

1004 K. S. Stanislavsky 1005 A. S. Serafimovich

1963. Russian Stage Celebrities.
2797 **1004** 4k. green on pale green 35 10
2798 – 4k. brown 35 10
2799 – 4k. brown 35 10

PORTRAITS AND ANNIVERSARIES: No. 2797, Type **1004** (actor, birth cent); 2798, M. S. Shchepkin (actor, death cent); 2799, V. D. Durov (animal trainer and circus artiste, birth cent).

1963. Russian Writers and Poets.
2800 **1005** 4k. brown, sepia & mve 35 10
2801 – 4k. brown and purple 35 10
2802 – 4k. brown, red and buff 35 10
2803 – 4k. brown and green 35 10
2804 – 4k. brown, sepia & mve 35 10
2805 – 4k. multicoloured 35 10

PORTRAITS AND ANNIVERSARIES: 2800, (birth cent); 2801, Demyan Bednyi (80th birth anniv); 2802, G. I. Uspensky (120th birth anniv); 2803, N. P. Ogarev (150th birth anniv); 2804, V. Ya. Bryusov (90th birth anniv); 2805, F. V. Gladkov (80th birth anniv).

1006 Children in Nursery 1007 Dolls and Toys

1963. Child Welfare.
2806 **1006** 4k. black and orange 30 10
2807 – 4k. purple, blue & orge 30 10
2808 – 4k. bistre, red and green 30 10
2809 – 4k. purple, red & orange 30 10

DESIGNS: No. 2807, Children with nurse; 2808, Young pioneers; 2809, Students at desk and trainee at lathe.

1963. Decorative Arts. Multicoloured.
2810 4k. Type **1007** 35 10
2811 6k. Pottery 45 15
2812 10k. Books 75 20
2813 12k. Porcelain 1·10 30

1008 Ilyushin Il-62 Jetliner

1962. 40th Anniv of "Aeroflot" Airline.
2814 **1008** 10k. black, brown & red 80 15
2815 – 12k. multicoloured 1·00 30
2816 – 16k. red, black and blue 1·40 60

DESIGNS: 12k. "Aeroflot" emblem; 16k. Tupolev Tu-124 airliner.

1009 M. N. Tukhachevsky 1010 M. A. Pavlov (scientist)

1963. 45th Anniv of Red Army and War Heroes.
2817 **1009** 4k. green and turquoise 30 10
2818 – 4k. black and brown 30 10
2819 – 4k. brown and blue 30 10
2820 – 4k. black and red 30 10
2821 – 4k. violet and mauve 30 10

DESIGNS (Army heroes and battle scenes): 2817, Type **1009** (70th birth anniv); 2818, U. M. Avetisyan; 2819, A. M. Matrosov; 2820, I. V. Panfilov; 2821, Ya. F. Fabricius.

1963. Academy of Sciences Members.
2822 **1010** 4k. blue, grey and brown 30 10
2823 – 4k. brown and green 30 10
2824 – 4k. multicoloured 30 10
2825 – 4k. brown, red and blue 30 10
2826 – 4k. multicoloured 30 10

PORTRAITS: No. 2823, I. V. Kurchatov; No. 2824, V. I. Vernadsky. LARGER (23½ × 30 mm): No. 2825, A. Krylov; No. 2826, V. Obruchev. All commemorate birth centenaries except No. 2823 (60th anniv of birth).

Советские хоккеисты-чемпионы мира и Европы. Стокгольм. 1963 г.

1011 Games Emblem (1012)

1963. 5th Soviet T.U. Winter Sports.
2827 **1011** 4k. orange, black & blue 30 10

1963. Soviet Victory in Swedish Ice Hockey Championships. No. 2670 optd with T **1012**.
2828 6k. turquoise and purple 1·60 60

1013 V. Kingisepp 1014 R. M. Blauman

1963. 75th Birth Anniv of Victor Kingisepp (Estonian Communist Party Leader).
2829 **1013** 4k. brown and blue 25 10

1963. Birth Centenary of Rudolf Blauman (Latvian writer).
2830 **1014** 4k. purple and blue 25 10

1015 Globe and Flowers 1016 Lenin (after I. Brodsky)

1963. "World without Arms and Wars". Perf or imperf.
2831 **1015** 4k. green, blue and red 35 10
2832 – 6k. lilac, green and red 55 10
2833 – 10k. violet, blue and red 1·10 25

DESIGNS: 6k. Atomic emblem and pylon; 10k. Sun and rocket.

1963. 93rd Birth Anniv of Lenin.
2834 **1016** 4k. brown and red 3·75 1·40

1963. Provincial Costumes (4th issue). As T **870**. Inscr "1963". Multicoloured.
2835 3k. Tadzhikistan 40 15
2836 4k. Azerbaijan 55 15
2837 4k. Kirgizia 55 15
2838 4k. Turkmenistan 55 15

1017 "Luna 4" Rocket

1963. Launching of "Luna 4" Space Rocket. Perf or imperf.
2839 **1017** 6k. red, black and blue 70 20

See also No. 3250.

1018 Woman and Lido

1963. 5th Anniv of World Health Day. Mult.
2840 2k. Type **1018** 20 10
2841 4k. Man and stadium 35 10
2842 10k. Child and school 85 20

1019 Sputniks and Globe

1963. Cosmonautics Day.
2843 **1019** 10k. blue, black and purple (white figures of value) 75 20
2843b 10k. blue, black and purple (blue figures) 75 20
2844 – 10k. purple, black and blue (white figures) 75 20
2844a 10k. purple, black and blue (purple figures) 75 20
2845 – 10k. red, black and yellow (white figures) 75 20
2845a 10k. red, black and yellow (yellow figures) 75 20

DESIGNS: Nos. 2844/a, "Vostok 1" and Moon; Nos. 2845/a, Space rocket and Sun.

1021 Cuban Horsemen with Flag

1963. Cuban-Soviet Friendship.
2846 **1021** 4k. black, red and blue 40 10
2847 – 6k. black, blue and red 50 10
2848 – 10k. blue, red and black 65 20
DESIGNS: 6k. Hands, weapon, book and flag; 10k. Crane, hoisting tractor and flags.

1022 J. Hasek **1023** Karl Marx

1963. 40th Death Anniv of Jaroslav Hasek (writer).
2849 **1022** 4k. black 65 15

1963. 80th Death Anniv of Karl Marx.
2850 **1023** 4k. black and brown . . 30 10

1963. War of 1941–45 (3rd issue). As T **911** inscr "1963".
2851 4k. multicoloured 45 15
2852 4k. multicoloured 45 15
2853 4k. multicoloured 45 15
2854 4k. sepia and red 45 15
2855 6k. olive, black and red . . 70 20
DESIGNS: No. 2851, Woman making shells (Defence of Leningrad, 1942); 2852, Soldier in winter kit with tommy gun (20th anniv of Battle of the Volga); 2853, Soldiers attacking (Liberation of Kiev, 1943); 2854, Tanks and map indicating Battle of Kursk, 1943; 2855, Tank commander and tanks.

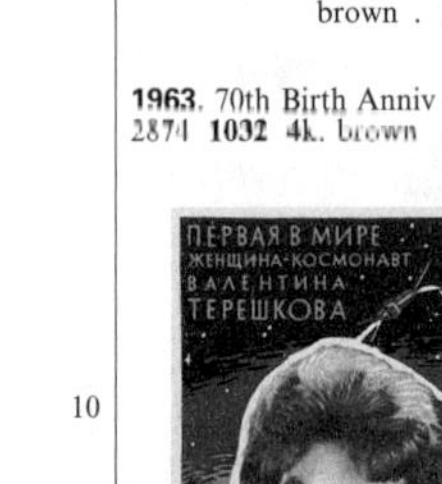

1024 International P.O. Building

1963. Opening of Int Post Office, Moscow.
2856 **1024** 6k. brown and blue . . 65 10

1025 Medal and Chessmen

1963. World Chess Championship, Moscow. Perf or imperf.
2857 **1025** 4k. multicoloured . . . 60 15
2858 – 6k. blue, mauve and ultramarine 70 20
2859 – 16k. black, mauve & pur . . . . 1·50 50
DESIGNS: 6k. Chessboard and pieces; 16k. Venue and pieces.

1026 Wagner

1027 Boxers on "Glove"

1963. 150th Birth Anniv of Wagner and Verdi (composers).
2860 **1026** 4k. black and red . . . 50 15
2861 – 4k. purple and red . . 50 15
DESIGN: No. 2861, Verdi.

1963. 15th European Boxing Championships, Moscow. Multicoloured.
2862 4k. Type **1027** 30 10
2863 6k. Referee and winning boxer on "glove" 55 15

1028 Bykovsky and "Vostok 5"

1963. Second "Team" Manned Space Flights (1st issue). Perf or imperf.
2864 **1028** 6k. brown and purple 55 20
2865 – 6k. red and green . . . 55 20
2866 – 10k. red and blue . . . 1·00 30
DESIGNS: No. 2865, Tereshkova and "Vostok 6"; No. 2866, Allegory—"Man and Woman in Space".
See also Nos. 2875/7.

Всемирный
конгресс
женщин.
(1029)

1030 Cycling

1963. International Women's Congress, Moscow. Optd with T **1029**.
2867 **1015** 4k. green, blue and red 55 30

1963. 3rd People's Spartakiad. Multicoloured. Perf or imperf.
2868b 3k. Type **1030** 25 10
2869b 4k. Athletics 30 15
2870b 6k. Swimming (horiz) . . . 45 15
2871b 12k. Basketball 85 35
2872b 16k. Football . . . . 1·25 50

1031 Globe, Film and Camera

1032 V. V. Mayakovsky

1963. International Film Festival, Moscow.
2873 **1031** 4k. blue, black & brown 30 10

1963. 70th Birth Anniv of Mayakovsky (poet).
2874 **1032** 4k. brown 40 15

1033 Tereshkova

1034 Ice Hockey Player

1963. 2nd "Team" Manned Space Flights (2nd issue). Multicoloured.
2875 4k. Bykovsky (horiz) . . . 40 20
2876 4k. Tereshkova (horiz) . . . 40 20
2877 10k. Type **1033** . . . . . . 1·60 35

1963. Russian Ice Hockey Championships.
2878 **1034** 6k. blue and red . . . 75 20

1035 Lenin

1037 Guibozo (polo)

1036 Freighter and Crate

1963. 60th Anniv of 2nd Socialist Party Congress.
2879 **1035** 4k. black and red . . . 30 10

1963. Red Cross Centenary.
2880 **1036** 6k. red and green . . . 60 15
2881 – 12k. red and blue . . . 1·25 30
DESIGN: 12k. Centenary emblem.

1963. Regional Sports.
2882 – 3k. multicoloured . . . 30 10
2883 **1037** 4k. black, red and ochre 40 10
2884 – 6k. red, brown & yellow 65 15
2885 – 10k. black, brn & olive 90 25
DESIGNS—HORIZ: 3k. Lapp reindeer racing; 6k. Buryat archery. VERT: 10k. Armenian wrestling.

1038 Aleksandr Mozhaisky and his Monoplane

1963. Aviation Celebrities.
2886 **1038** 6k. black and blue . . 60 10
2887 – 10k. black and blue . . 80 15
2888 – 16k. black and blue . . 1·25 35
DESIGNS: 10k. Pyotr Nesterov and "looping the loop"; 16k. N. E. Zhukovsky and "aerodynamics".

1039 S. S. Gulak-Artemovsky (composer, 150th birth anniv)

1040 Olga Kobilyanska (writer) (birth centenary)

1963. Celebrities.
2889 **1039** 4k. black and red . . . 40 15
2890 – 4k. brown and purple 40 15
2891 – 4k. brown and violet 40 15
2892 **1040** 4k. mauve and brown 40 15
2893 – 4k. mauve and green 40 15
DESIGNS AND ANNIVERSARIES: As Type **1039**: No. 2893, M. I. Petraskas (Lithuanian composer) and scene from one of his works (90th birth anniv). As Type **1040**: No. 2890, G. D. Eristavi (writer, death cent, 1964); No. 2891, A. S. Dargomizhsky (composer, 150th birth anniv).

1041 Antarctic Map and Supply Ship "Ob"

1043 E. O. Paton

1042 Letters and Transport

1963. Arctic and Antarctic Research. Mult.
2894 3k. Type **1041** . . . . . . 1·75 25
2895 4k. Convoy of snow tractors and map . . . . 1·00 30
2896 6k. Globe and aircraft at polar base . . . . 1·75 30
2897 12k. "Sovetskaya Ukraina" (whale factory ship), whale catcher and whale 4·00 50

1963. International Correspondence Week.
2898 **1042** 4k. violet, orange & blk 35 10

1963. 10th Death Anniv of Paton (engineer).
2899 **1043** 4k. black, red and blue 30 10

1045 D. Diderot

1046 "Peace"

1963. 250th Birth Anniv of Denis Diderot (French philosopher).
2900 **1045** 4k. brown, blue & bistre 30 10

1963. "Peace—Brotherhood—Liberty—Labour". All black, red and lake.
2901 4k. Type **1046** 35 15
2902 4k. Worker at desk and couple consulting plan ("Labour") 35 15
2903 4k. Artist and couple ("Liberty") 35 15
2904 4k. Voters ("Equality") . . 35 15
2905 4k. Man shaking hands with couple with banner ("Brotherhood") 35 15
2906 4k. Family group ("Happiness") 35 15

1047 Academy of Sciences, Frunze

1963. Centenary of Union of Kirgizia and Russia.
2907 **1047** 4k. blue, yellow and red 30 10

1049 Lenin and Congress Building

1050 Ilya Mechnikov

1963. 13th Soviet Trade Unions' Congress, Moscow.
2908 **1049** 4k. red and black . . . 25 10
2909 – 4k. red and black . . . 25 10
DESIGN: No. 2909, Lenin with man and woman workers.

1963. 75th Anniv of Pasteur Institute, Paris.
2910 **1050** 4k. green and bistre . . 35 10
2911 – 6k. violet and bistre . . 55 15
2912 – 12k. blue and bistre . . 1·25 30
PORTRAITS: 6k. Pasteur; 12k. Calmette.

1051 Cruiser "Aurora" and Rockets

1052 Gur Emi Mausoleum

1963. 46th Anniv of October Revolution.
2913 **1051** 4k. black, orange & lake 45 10
2914 4k. black, red and lake 65 30

1963. Ancient Samarkand Buildings. Mult.
2915 4k. Type **1052** 50 10
2916 4k. Shachi-Zinda Mosque 50 10
2917 6k. Registan Square (55 × 28½ mm) 65 20

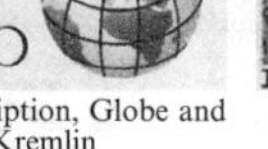

1053 Inscription, Globe and Kremlin

1054 Pushkin Monument, Kiev (A. Kovalev)

1963. Signing of Nuclear Test-ban Treaty, Moscow.
2918 **1053** 6k. violet and pale blue 60 15

1963.
2919 **1054** 4k. brown 30 10

1056 Shukhov and Radio Tower, Moscow

1057 Ya. Steklov and "Izvestia"

1963. 110th Birth Anniv of V. G. Shukhov (engineer).
2920 **1056** 4k. black and green . . 30 10

1963. 90th Birth Anniv of Ya. M. Steklov (first editor of "Izvestia").
2921 **1057** 4k. black and mauve 30 10

1058 Buildings and Emblems of Moscow (and U.S.S.R.) and Prague (and Czechoslovakia)

1963. 20th Anniv of Soviet-Czech Friendship Treaty.
2922 **1058** 6k. red, bistre and blue 45 10

1059 F. A. Poletaev (soldier) and Medals

1963. Poletaev Commemoration.
2923 **1059** 4k. multicoloured . . . 30 10

1062 J. Grimau (Spanish Communist)

1063 Rockets

1963. Grimau Commemoration.
2924 **1062** 6k. violet, red and cream 40 10

1963. New Year (1st issue).
2925 **1063** 6k. multicoloured . . . 50 10

1064 "Happy New Year"

1067 Topaz

1963. New Year (2nd issue).
2926 **1064** 4k. red, blue and green 40 10
2927 6k. red, blue and green 55 10

1963. "Precious Stones of the Urals". Multicoloured.
2928 2k. Type **1067** 25 10
2929 4k. Jasper 50 10
2030 6k. Amethyst 70 15
2931 10k. Emerald 75 25
2932 12k. Ruby . . . . 1·00 45
2933 16k. Malachite . . . . . . 1·25 55

1068 Sputnik 7

1071 Flame and Rainbow

1069 Dushanbe Putovsky Square

1963. "First in Space". Gold, vermilion and grey.
2934 10k. Type **1068** 90 30
2935 10k. Moon landing 90 30
2936 10k. Back of Moon 90 30
2937 10k. Vostok 7 . . . . . . 90 30
2938 10k. Twin flight 90 30
2939 10k. Seagull (first woman in space) 90 30

1963. Dushanbe, Capital of Tadzhikistan.
2940 **1069** 4k. blue 40 10

1963. 15th Anniv of Declaration of Human Rights.
2941 **1071** 6k. multicoloured . . . 45 10

1072 F. A, Sergeev ("Artem")

1963. 80th Birth Anniv of Sergeev (revolutionary).
2942 **1072** 4k. brown and red . . 30 10

1073 Sun and Globe

1074 K. Donelaitis

1964. International Quiet Sun Year.
2943 – 4k. black, orange & mve 30 10
2944 **1073** 6k. blue, yellow and red 45 10
2945 – 10k. violet, red and blue 60 20
DESIGNS—HORIZ: 4k. Giant telescope and sun; 10k. Globe and Sun.

1964. 250th Birth Anniv of K. Donelaitis (Lithuanian poet).
2946 **1074** 4k. black and myrtle . . 30 10

1075 Speed Skating

1964. Winter Olympic Games, Innsbruck.
2947b **1075** 2k. black, mauve & bl 25 10
2948b – 4k. black, blue & mve 40 15
2949b – 6k. red, black and blue 60 20
2950b – 10k. black, mve & grn 85 25
2951b – 12k. black, grn & mve 1·00 35
DESIGNS: 4k. Skiing; 6k. Games emblem; 10k. Rifle shooting (biathlon); 12k. Figure skating (pairs).
See also Nos. 2969/73.

1076 Golubkina (after N. Ulyanov) and Statue, Tolstoi

1077 "Agriculture"

1964. Birth Cent of A. S. Golubkina (sculptress).
2952 **1076** 4k. sepia and grey . . . 30 10

1964. Heavy Chemical Industries. Multicoloured.
2953 4k. Type **1077** 40 10
2954 4k. "Textiles" 40 10
2955 4k. "Tyre Production" . . . 40 10

150 років з дня народження. 1964 р.
(1078)

1079 Shevchenko's Statue, Kiev (M. Manizer)

1964. 150th Birth Anniv of T. G. Shevchenko (Ukrainian poet and painter). No. 2561 optd with T **1078** and designs as T **1079**.
2956 **880** 3k. brown and violet 1·50 75
2959 **1079** 4k. green 25 10
2960 4k. red 25 10
2961 – 6k. blue 40 10
2962 – 6k. brown 40 10
2957 – 10k. violet and brown 80 20
2958 – 10k. brown and bistre 80 20
DESIGNS: Nos. 2957/8, Portrait of Shevchenko by I. Repin; Nos. 2961/2, Self-portrait.

1080 K. S. Zaslonov

1964. War Heroes.
2963 **1080** 4k. sepia and brown . . 55 15
2964 – 4k. purple and blue . . 35 15
2965 – 4k. blue and red . . . 35 15
2966 – 4k. brown and blue . . 35 15
PORTRAITS: No. 2964, N. A. Vilkov; 2965, Yu. V. Smirnov; 2966, V. Z. Khoruzhaya.

1081 Fyodorov printing the first Russian book, "Apostle"

1964. 400th Anniv of First Russian Printed Book. Multicoloured.
2967 4k. Type **1081** 30 10
2968 6k. Statue of Ivan Fyodorov, Moscow (S. Volnukin), books and newspapers 45 20

Слава советским спортсменам— победителям IX зимней Олимпиады!
(1082)

1083 Ice Hockey Player

1964. Winter Olympic Games, Soviet Medal Winners.
(a) Nos. 2947/51 optd with T **1082** or similarly.
2969 2k. black, mauve and blue 25 10
2970 4k. black, blue and mauve 40 10
2971 6k. red, black and blue . . 40 15
2972 10k. black, mauve and green 80 25
2973 12k. black, green and mauve 1·00 30

(b) New designs.
2974 **1083** 3k. red, black & turquoise 45 10
2975 – 16k. orange and brown 1·40 40
DESIGN: 16k. Gold medal and inscr "Triumph of Soviet Sport–11 Gold, 8 Silver, 6 Bronze medals".

1084 Militiaman and Factory Guard

1964. "Public Security".
2976 **1084** 4k. blue, red and black 30 10

1085 Lighthouse, Odessa and Sailor

1964. 20th Anniv of Liberation of Odessa and Leningrad. Multicoloured.
2977 4k. Type **1085** 35 10
2978 4k. Lenin Statue, Leningrad 35 10

1086 Sputniks

1087 N. I. Kibalchich

1964. "The Way to the Stars". Imperf or perf.
(a) Cosmonautics. As T **1086**.
2979 4k. green, black and red . . 50 10
2980 6k. black, blue and red . . 70 20
2981 12k. turquoise, brown & black . . . . 1·40 30
DESIGNS: 6k. "Mars I" space station; 12k. Gagarin and space capsule.

(b) Rocket Construction Pioneers. As T **1087**.
2982b 10k. black, green and violet . . . . 1·10 30
2983b 10k. black, turquoise and red . . . . 1·10 30
2984b 10k. black, turquoise and red . . . . 1·10 30
2985b 10k. black and blue . . . 1·00 30
DESIGNS: No. 2982, Type **1087**; 2983, F. A. Zander; 2984, K. E. Tsiolkovsky; 2985, Pioneers' medallion and Saransk memorial.

1088 Lenin

1964. 94th Birth Anniv of Lenin.
2986a **1088** 4k. black, blue & mve 3·25 2·50

1089 Shakespeare (400th Birth Anniv)

1964. Cultural Anniversaries.
2987 – 6k. yellow, brn & sepia 90 15
2988 **1089** 10k. brown and olive 1·40 25
2989 – 12k. green and brown 1·60 35
DESIGNS AND ANNIVERSARIES: 6k. Michelangelo (400th death anniv); 12k. Galileo (400th birth anniv).

1090 Crop-watering Machine and Produce

1964. "Irrigation".
2990 **1090** 4k. multicoloured . . . 30 10

1091 Gamarnik

1964. 70th Birth Anniv of Ya. B. Gamarnik (Soviet Army commander).
2991 **1091** 4k. brown, blue & black 30 10

1092 D. I. Gulia (Abhazian poet)

1094 Indian Elephant

1093 A. Gaidar

1964. Cultural Anniversaries.
2992 **1092** 4k. black, green and light green 30 15
2993 – 4k. black, verm & red 30 15

2994 – 4k. black, brown & bis 30 15
2995 – 4k. black, yellow & brn 30 15
2996 – 4k. multicoloured . . . 30 15
2997 – 4k. black, yellow & brn 30 15
DESIGNS: No. 2993, Nijazi (Uzbek writer, composer and painter); 2994, S. Seifullin (Kazakh poet); 2995, M. M. Kotsyubinsky (writer); 2996, S. Nazaryan (Armenian writer); 2997, T. Satylganov (Kirghiz poet).

1964. 60th Birth Annivs of Writers A. P. Gaidar and N. A. Ostrovsky.
2998 **1093** 4k. red and blue . . . 30 10
2999 – 4k. green and red . . . 35 10
DESIGN: No. 2999, N. Ostrovsky and battle scene.

1964. Centenary of Moscow Zoo. Multicoloured. Imperf or perf.
3000 1k. Type **1094** 10 10
3001 2k. Giant panda 20 10
3002 4k. Polar bear 45 10
3003 6k. Elk 55 10
3004 10k. Eastern white pelican 1·25 25
3005 12k. Tiger . . . . 2·00 30
3006 16k. Lammergeier . . . . . 1·50 40
The 2k. and 12k. are horiz; the 4k. and 10k. are "square", approx $26\frac{1}{2} \times 28$ mm.

150 лет вхождения
в состав России
1964

4
коп.

(1095)

1964. 150th Anniv of Union of Azerbaijan and Russia. Surch with T **1095**.
3007 **328** 4k. on 40k. brown, bistre and yellow . . . . . 3·25 1·90

1096 Rumanian Woman and Emblems on Map
1097 Maize

1964. 20th. Anniv of Rumanian–Soviet Friendship Treaty.
3008 **1096** 6k. multicoloured . . . 50 15

1964. Agricultural Crops. Multicoloured. Imperf or perf.
3009b 2k. Type **1097** 15 10
3010b 3k. Wheat 20 10
3011b 4k. Potatoes 25 10
3012b 6k. Peas 35 20
3013b 10k. Sugar beet 70 25
3014b 12k. Cotton . . . . 1·00 30
3015b 16k. Flax . . . . 1·50 40

1098 Flag and Obelisk
1099 Leningrad G.P.O.

1964. 20th Anniv of Liberation of Byelorussia.
3016 **1098** 4k. multicoloured . . . 30 10

1964. 250th Anniv of Leningrad's Postal Service.
3017 **1099** 4k. black, bistre and red 30 10

1100 Map of Poland and Emblems

1964. 20th Anniv of Polish People's Republic.
3018 **1100** 6k. multicoloured . . . 45 10

1101 Horse-jumping
1102 M. Thorez (French Communist leader)

1964. Olympic Games, Tokyo. Imperf or perf.
3019b **1101** 3k. multicoloured . . 10 10
3020b – 4k. red, black & yellow 15 10
3021b – 6k. red, black and blue 25 15
3022b – 10k. red, black & turq 65 20
3023b – 12k. black and grey 80 25
3024b – 16k. violet, red and blue . . . . 1·40 30
DESIGNS: 4k. Weightlifting; 6k. Pole vaulting; 10k. Canoeing; 12k. Gymnastics; 16k. Fencing.

1964. Maurice Thorez Commemoration.
3025 **1102** 4k. black and red . . . 1·00 35

1103 Three Races
1104 Jawaharlal Nehru

1964. International Anthropologists and Ethnographers Congress, Moscow.
3026 **1103** 6k. black and yellow . . 40 15

1964. Nehru Commemoration.
3027 **1104** 4k. brown and grey . . 45 15

1105 Globe and Banner
1106 A. V. Vishnevsky (surgeon)

1964. Centenary of "First International".
3028 **1105** 4k. red, bistre and blue 30 10
3029 – 4k. red, olive and black 30 10
3030 – 4k. drab, red and lake 30 10
3031 – 4k. red, black and blue 30 10
3032 – 4k. multicoloured . . . 30 10
DESIGNS: No. 3029, Communist Party manifesto; 3030, Marx and Engels; 3031, Chain breaker; 3032, Lenin.

1964. "Outstanding Soviet Physicians".
3033 **1106** 4k. brown and purple 35 10
3034 – 4k. brown, red & yellow 35 10
3035 – 4k. brown, blue & bistre 35 10
DESIGNS: No. 3034, N. A. Semashko (public health pioneer). Both are 90th birth anniversaries. No. 3035, D. I. Ivanovsky and siphon (25 × 32 mm).

1107 Bulgarian Flag, Rose and Emblems
1108 P. Togliatti (Italian Communist leader)

1964. 20th Anniv of Bulgarian People's Republic.
3036 **1107** 6k. red, green and drab 45 15

1964. Togliatti Commemoration.
3037 **1108** 4k. black and red . . . 30 10

1110 Globe and Letters

1964. International Correspondence Week.
3038 **1110** 4k. mauve, blue & brn 30 10

1111 Soviet and Yugoslav Soldiers
1112 East German Arms, Industrial Plants, Freighter "Havel" and Electric Goods Train

1964. 20th Anniv of Liberation of Belgrade.
3039 **1111** 6k. multicoloured . . . 45 15

1964. 15th Anniv of German Democratic Republic.
3040 **1112** 6k. multicoloured . . . 45 15

1113 Woman holding Bowl of Produce (Moldavian Republic)

40 лет Советскому Таджикистану
1964 год

(1115)

1964. 40th Anniv of Soviet Republic. (a) As T **1113**.
3041 **1113** 4k. brown, green and red 30 10
3042 – 4k. multicoloured . . . 35 10
3043 – 4k. red, purple & yellow 35 10

(b) Optd with T **1115**.
3044 **1069** 4k. blue . . . . 1·10 60
DESIGNS—VERT: No. 3042, Woman holding Arms (Turkmenistan); 3043, Man and woman holding produce (Uzbekistan); 3044, commemorates the Tadzhikistan Republic.

1116 Yegorov

1964. Three-manned Space Flight. (a) Portraits in black, orange and turquoise.
3045 4k. Type **1116** 40 10
3046 4k. Feoktistov 40 10
3047 4k. Komarov 40 10
These can be identified by the close proximation of the Russian names on the stamps to the English versions.

(b) Designs $73\frac{1}{2} \times 22\frac{1}{2}$ mm.
3048 6k. purple and violet . . . 75 15
3049 10k. violet and blue . . . . 1·10 30
DESIGNS: 6k. The three cosmonauts; 10k. Space ship "Voskhod 1".

1117 Soldier and Flags

1964. 20th Anniv of Liberation of Ukraine.
3050 **1117** 4k. multicoloured . . . 25 10

1119 Lermontov's Birthplace
1121 N. K. Krupskaya (Lenin's wife)

1120 Hammer and Sickle

1964. 150th Birth Anniv of M. Lermontov (poet).
3051 **1119** 4k. violet 30 10
3052 – 6k. black 45 10
3053 – 10k. brown and flesh 85 25
DESIGNS: 6k. Lermontov (after K. Gorbunov); 10k. Lermontov talking with V. Belinsky.

1964. 47th Anniv of October Revolution.
3054 **1120** 4k. multicoloured . . . 25 10

1964. Birth Anniversaries.
3055 **1121** 4k. multicoloured . . . 30 10
3056 – 4k. multicoloured . . . 30 10
DESIGNS: 3055 (95th anniv); 3056, A. I. Yelizarova-Ulyanova (Lenin's sister) (cent).

1122 Mongolian Woman and Lamb
1124 Butter Mushroom

1964. 40th Anniv of Mongolian People's Republic.
3057 **1122** 4k. multicoloured . . . 45 15

1964. Mushrooms. Multicoloured.
3058 2k. Type **1124** 30 10
3059 4k. Chanterelle 50 10
3060 6k. Ceps 65 15
3061 10k. Red-capped sacker stalk . . . . 1·10 40
3062 12k. Saffron milk cap . . . 1·40 50

1125 A. P. Dovzhenko
1126 Christmas Tree, Star and Globe

1964. 70th Birth Anniv of Dovzhenko (film producer).
3063 **1125** 4k. blue and grey . . . 30 10

1964. New Year.
3064 **1126** 4k. multicoloured . . . 75 25

1127 Struve
1128 Ivanov (after O. Braz) and "March of the Moscovites. 16th Century"

1964. Death Centenary of V. Ya. Struve (scientist).
3065 **1127** 4k. brown and blue . . 60 15

1964. Birth Centenary of S. V. Ivanov (painter).
3066 **1128** 4k. brown and black . . 65 15

1129 Scene from Film

1964. 30th Anniv of Film "Chapaev".
3067 **1129** 6k. black and green . . 50 15

1130 Test-tubes, Jar and Agricultural Scenes

1964. Chemistry for the National Economy.
3068 **1130** 4k. purple and olive . . 25 15
3069 – 6k. black and blue . . 45 10
DESIGN: 6k. Chemical plant.

1131 Cranberries **1132** Library

1964. Woodland Fruits. Multicoloured.
3070 1k. Type **1131** 15 10
3071 3k. Bilberries 20 10
3072 4k. Rowanberries 30 10
3073 10k. Blackberries 70 20
3074 16k. Red bilberries . . . . 1·10 40

1964. 250th Anniv of Academy of Sciences Library, Leningrad.
3075 **1132** 4k. black, green and red 40 10

1133 Congress Palace and Spassky Tower **1134** Mt Khan-Tengri

1964.
3076 **1133** 1r. blue . . . . 7·00 1·60

1964. Mountaineering. Multicoloured.
3077 4k. Type **1134** 30 10
3078 6k. Mt Kazbek (horiz) . . . 45 15
3079 12k. Mt Ushba 90 30

1136 Bowl

1964. Kremlin Treasures. Multicoloured.
3080 4k. Helmet 45 15
3081 6k. Quiver 65 20
3082 10k. Coronation headgear 1·00 35
3083 12k. Ladle . . . . 1·40 45
3084 16k. Type **1136** . . . . . . 1·75 80

1137 I. M. Sivko **1138** Dante

1965. War Heroes.
3085 **1137** 4k. black and violet . . 40 15
3086 – 4k. brown and blue . . 40 15
DESIGN: No. 3086, General I. S. Polbin.

1965. 700th Birth Anniv of Dante.
3087 **1138** 4k. black, bistre and purple 60 15

1139 Blood Donor **1140** N. P. Kravkov

1965. Blood Donors. Multicoloured.
3088 4k. Type **1139** 35 15
3089 4k. Hand holding red carnation 35 15

1965. Birth Cent of N. Kravkov (pharmacologist).
3090 **1140** 4k. multicoloured . . . 35 10

1141 Figure Skaters **1142** Alsatian

1965. European Figure Skating Championships, Moscow.
3091 **1141** 6k. red, black and green 55 15
See also No. 3108.

1965. World Ice Hockey Championships, Moscow. Designs similar to T **1141** but depicting ice hockey players.
3092 4k. red, blue and bistre . . 40 15

1965. Hunting and Service Dogs.
3093 – 1k. black, yellow and red 15 10
3097 – 2k. brown, blue & black 20 10
3098 **1142** 3k. black, red and yellow 20 10
3099 – 4k. black, brown & grn 30 10
3100 – 4k. black, orange & grn 30 10
3101 – 6k. black, brown & blue 40 20
3102 – 6k. black, red and blue 40 20
3104 – 10k. multicoloured . . 75 25
3095 – 12k. black, brown & vio 90 35
3096 – 16k. multicoloured . . 1·40 45
DESIGNS—HORIZ: 1k. Hound; 2k. Setter; 4k. (3099) (value in green) Fox terrier; 4k. (3100) (value in orange) Pointer; 6k. (3101) Borzoi; 12k. Husky. VERT: 6k. (3102) Sheepdog; 10k. Collie; 16k. Caucasian sheepdog.

1143 R. Sorge

1965. Richard Sorge (Soviet secret agent) Commem.
3103 **1143** 4k. black and red . . . 55 15

1144 I.T.U. Emblem and Telecommunications Symbol

1965. Centenary of I.T.U.
3104 **1144** 6k. violet and blue . . 65 15

1145 Leonov in Space (½-size illustration)

1965. Space Flight of "Voskhod 2" (1st issue). Imperf or perf.
3105 **1145** 10k. orange, black & bl 1·25 30
See also Nos. 3138/9.

1965. Ice Hockey Championships. Optd **ТАМПЕРЕ 1965 г.**
3107 **1034** 6k. blue and red . . . 1·75 50

Советские фигуристы— чемпионы мира в парном катании

(1147)

1148 Soldier and Woman

1965. Soviet Victory in European Figure Skating Championships. Optd with T **1147**.
3108 **1141** 6k. red, black and green 1·75 50

1965. 20th Anniversaries.
3109 **1148** 6k. multicoloured . . . 40 15
3110 – 6k. multicoloured . . . 45 15
3111 – 6k. ochre and red . . . 40 15
3112 – 6k. multicoloured . . . 40 15
3113 – 6k. multicoloured . . . 40 15
DESIGNS: No. 3109, Type **1148** (Czech Liberation); 3110, Statue and emblems of development (Friendship with Hungary); 3111, Polish and Soviet arms (Polish–Soviet Friendship Treaty); 3112, Viennese buildings and Russian soldier (Freeing of Vienna); 3113, Liberation medal, Polish flag and building reconstruction (Freeing of Warsaw).
See also Nos. 3182 and 3232.

1149 Statue Rockets and Globe **1150** Rockets and Radio-telescope

1965. National Cosmonautics Day. Nos. 3117/18 on aluminium-surfaced paper.
3114 **1149** 4k. green, black and red 25 10
3115 – 12k. purple, red and blue 80 15
3116 – 16k. multicoloured . . 1·10 30
3117 **1150** 20k. red, black and green on silver . . . 7·00 5·00
3118 – 20k. red, black and blue on silver . . . . . . 7·00 5·00
DESIGNS: 12k. Statue and Globe; 16k. Rockets and Globe; No. 3118, Globe, satellite and cosomonauts.

1151 Lenin (after bas-relief by V. Sayapin)

1965. Lenin's 95th Birth Anniv.
3119 **1151** 10k. blue, black & brn 75 30

1152 Poppies **1153** Red Flag, Reichstag Building and Broken Swastika

1965. Flowers.
3120 **1152** 1k. red, lake and green 10 10
3121 – 3k. yellow, brown & grn 30 10
3122 – 4k. lilac, black and green 40 15
3123 – 6k. red, deep green and green 60 15
3124 – 10k. yellow, pur & grn 1·10 25
FLOWERS: 3k. Marguerite; 4k. Peony; 6k. Carnation; 10k. Tulips.

1965. 20th Anniv of Victory.
3125 **1153** 1k. black, gold and red 20 10
3126 – 2k. red, black and gold 25 15
3127 – 3k. blue and gold . . . 40 15
3128 – 4k. violet and gold . . 55 15
3129 – 4k. green and gold . . 60 15
3130 – 6k. purple, green & gold . . . . 1·25 20
3131 – 10k. purple, brn & gold 1·75 25
3132 – 12k. black, red and gold . . . . 2·25 30
3133 – 16k. red and gold . . . 2·50 40
3134 – 20k. black, red and gold . . . . 3·00 75
DESIGNS: 2k. Soviet mother holding manifesto (poster by I. Toidze); 3k. "The Battle for Moscow" (V. Bogatkin); 4k. (No. 3128), "Partisan Mother" (from S. Gerasimov's film); 4k. (No. 3129), "Red Army Soldiers and Partisans" (from Yu. Neprintsev's film); 6k. Soldiers and flag (poster by V. Ivanov); 10k. "Mourning the Fallen Hero" (from F. Bogorodsky's film); 12k. Soldier and worker holding bomb (poster by V. Korestsky); 16k. Victory celebrations, Red Square, Moscow (from K. Yuon's film); 20k. Soldier and machines of war.

1154 Marx and Lenin

1965. Marxism and Leninism.
3136 **1154** 6k. black and red . . . 40 10
No. 3136 is similar in design to those issued by China and Hungary for the Postal Ministers' Congress, Peking, but this event is not mentioned on the stamp or in the Soviet philatelic bulletins.

1155 Bolshoi Theatre

1965. International Theatre Day.
3137 **1155** 6k. ochre, black & turq 55 15

1156 Leonov **1157** Yakov Sverdlov (revolutionary)

1965. "Voskhod 2" Space Flight (2nd issue).
3138 **1156** 6k. violet and silver . . 45 15
3139 – 6k. purple and silver . . 45 15
DESIGN: No. 3139, Belyaev.

1965. 80th Birth Anniversaries.
3140 **1157** 4k. black and brown . . 35 10
3141 – 4k. black and violet . . 35 10
PORTRAIT: No. 3141, J. Akhunbabaev (statesman).

1158 Otto Grotewohl (1st death anniv) **1159** Telecommunications Satellite

1965. Annivs of Grotewohl and Thorez (Communist leaders).
3142 **1158** 4k. black and purple . . 35 10
3143 – 6k. brown and red . . 55 15
DESIGN: 6k. Maurice Thorez (65th birth anniv).

1965. International Co-operation Year. Mult.
3144 3k. Type **1159** 20 10
3145 6k. Star and sputnik 50 15
3146 6k. Foundry ladle, iron works and map of India 50 15
No. 3145 signifies peaceful uses of atomic energy and No. 3146 co-operation with India.

1160 Congress Emblem, Chemical Plant and Symbols

1965. 20th International Congress of Pure and Applied Chemistry, Moscow.
3147 **1160** 4k. red, black and blue 25 10

1161 V. A. Serov (after I. Repin)

1965. Birth Centenary of V. A. Serov (painter).
3148 **1161** 4k. black, brn & stone 95 20
3149 – 6k. black and drab . . 1·50 25
DESIGN: 6k. Full length portrait of Chaliapin (singer) by Serov.

1162 Vsevolod Ivanov and Armoured Train

1965. Famous Writers.
3150 **1162** 4k. black and purple . . 45 15
3151 – 4k. black and violet . . 40 15
3152 – 4k. black and blue . . 40 15
3153 – 4k. black and grey . . 40 15
3154 – 4k. black, red and green 40 15
3155 – 4k. black and brown . . 40 15
WRITERS AND ANNIVERSARIES: No. 3150, (70th birth anniv); 3151, A. Kunanbaev and military parade; 3152, J. Rainis (Lettish poet: 90th birth anniv); 3153, E. J. Vilde (Estonian author): 90th birth anniv); 3154, M. Ch. Abegjan (Armenian writer and critic: 90th birth anniv); 3155, M. L. Kropivnitsky and scene from play (Ukrainian playwright).

1163 Festival Emblem

1965. Film Festival, Moscow.
3156 **1163** 6k. black, gold and blue 50 15

1164 Concert Arena, Tallin **1165** Hand holding "Peace Flower"

1965. 25th Anniv of Incorporation of Estonia, Lithuania and Latvia in the U.S.S.R.
3157 **1164** 4k. multicoloured . . . 40 10
3158 – 4k. brown and red . . 40 10
3159 – 4k. brown, red and blue 40 10
DESIGNS—VERT: No. 3158, Lithuanian girl and Arms. HORIZ: No. 3159, Latvian Flag and Arms.

1965. Peace Issue.
3160 **1165** 6k. yellow, black & blue 45 10

1167 "Potemkin" Sailors Monument (V. Bogdanov), Odessa

1965. 60th Anniv of 1905 Rebellion.
3161 **1167** 4k. blue and red . . . 30 15
3162 – 4k. green, black and red 30 15
3163 – 4k. green, black and red 30 15
3164 – 4k. brown, black and red 30 15
DESIGNS: No. 3162, Demonstrator up lamp post; 3163, Defeated rebels; 3164, Troops at street barricade.

1168 G. Gheorgi-Dej (Rumanian Communist) **1169** Power Station

1965. G. Gheorgi-Dej Commemoration.
3165 **1168** 4k. black and red . . . 25 10

1965. Industrial Progress.
3166 **1169** 1k. multicoloured . . . 10 10
3167 – 2k. black, orange & yell 20 10
3168 – 3k. violet, yell & ochre 20 10
3169 – 4k. deep blue, blue and red 35 10
3170 – 6k. blue and bistre . . 45 10
3171 – 10k. brown, yellow and orange 70 20
3172 – 12k. turquoise and red 1·10 20
3173 – 16k. purple, blue & blk 1·40 40
DESIGNS: 2k. Steel works; 3k. Chemical works and formula; 4k. Machine tools production; 6k. Building construction; 10k. Agriculture; 12k. Communications and transport; 16k. Scientific research.

1170 Relay Racing **1171** Gymnastics

1965. Trade Unions Spartakiad. Multicoloured.
3174 4k. Type **1170** 35 15
3175 4k. Gymnastics 35 15
3176 4k. Cycling 35 15

1965. Schoolchildren's Spartakiad.
3177 **1171** 4k. red and blue . . . 30 10
3178 – 6k. red, brown & turq 50 15
DESIGN: 6k. Cycle racing.

1172 Throwing the Javelin and Running **1173** Star, Palms and Lotus

1965. American–Soviet Athletic Meeting, Kiev.
3179 **1172** 4k. red, brown and lilac 20 10
3180 – 6k. red, brown and green 45 10
3181 – 10k. red, brown and grey 60 15
DESIGNS: 6k. High jumping and putting the shot; 10k. Throwing the hammer and hurdling.

1965. 20th Anniv of North Vietnamese People's Republic.
3182 **1173** 6k. multicoloured . . . 40 15

1174 Worker with Hammer (World T.U. Federation) **1176** P. K. Sternberg (astonomer: birth cent)

1965. 20th Anniv of International Organizations.
3183 **1174** 6k. drab and plum . . 35 15
3184 – 6k. brown, red and blue 35 15
3185 – 6k. lt brown & turquoise 35 15
DESIGNS: No. 3184, Torch and heads of three races (World Democratic Youth Federation); No. 3185, Woman holding dove (International Democratic Women's Federation).

1965. Scientists' Anniversaries.
3186 **1176** 4k. brown and blue . . 50 15
3187 – 4k. black and purple . . 50 15
3188 – 4k. black, purple & yell 50 15
PORTRAITS: No. 3187, Ch. Valikhanov (scientific writer: death cent); 3188, V. A. Kistyakovsky (scientist: birth cent).

1177 "Battleship 'Potemkin'" (dir. Sergei Eisenshtein)

1965. Soviet Cinema Art. Designs showing scenes from films. Multicoloured.
3189 4k. Type **1177** 35 10
3190 6k. "Young Guard" (dir. S. Coesinov) 50 15
3191 12k. "A Soldier's Ballad" (dir. G. Chuthrai) . . . . 1·00 25

1178 Mounted Postman and Map

1965. History of the Russian Post Office.
3192 **1178** 1k. green, brown & vio 25 10
3193 – 1k. brown, ochre & grey 25 10
3194 – 2k. brown, blue and lilac 40 10
3195 – 4k. black, ochre & pur 45 10
3196 – 6k. black, green & brn 65 15
3197 – 12k. sepia, brown & blue . . . . 1·10 25
3198 – 16k. plum, red and grey 1·40 45
DESIGNS: No. 3193, Mail coach and map; 2k. Early steam train and medieval kogge; 4k. Mail lorry and map; 6k. Diesel-electric train and various transport; 12k. Moscow Post Office electronic facing sorting and cancelling machines; 16k. Airports and Lenin.

1179 "Vostok" and "Mirnyi" (Antarctic exploration vessels)

1965. Polar Research Annivs.
3199 – 4k. black, orange & blue 90 15
3200 – 4k. black, orange & blue 90 15
3201 – 6k. sepia and violet . . 75 25
3202 **1179** 10k. black, drab and red . . . . 1·75 35
3203 – 16k. black, violet & brn 1·25 65
DESIGNS—HORIZ: 37½ × 25½ mm: No. 3199, Ice breakers "Taimyr" and "Vaigach" in Arctic (50th anniv); 3200, Atomic ice breaker "Lenin"; 3201, Dikson settlement (50th anniv); 3203, Vostok Antarctic station. SQUARE. No. 3202, (145th anniv of Lazarev–Bellingshausen Expedition).

Nos. 3199/200 were issued together, se-tenant, forming a composite design.

1181 Agricultural Academy

1965. Centenary of Academy of Agricultural Sciences, Moscow.
3205 **1181** 4k. violet, red and drab 30 15

1183 N. Poussin (self-portrait) **1184** Kremlin

1965. 300th Death Anniv of Nicolas Poussin (French painter).
3207 **1183** 4k. multicoloured . . . 50 10

1965. New Year.
3208 **1184** 4k. red, silver and black 40 10

1185 M. I. Kalinin

1966. 90th Birth Anniv of Kalinin (statesman).
3209 **1185** 4k. lake and red . . . 30 10

1186 Klyuchevski Volcano

1965. Soviet Volcanoes. Multicoloured.
3210 4k. Type **1186** 40 15
3211 12k. Karumski Volcano (vert) . . . . 1·00 30
3212 16k. Koryaski Volcano . . 1·10 45

1187 Oktyabrskaya Station, Moscow

1965. Soviet Metro Stations.
3213 **1187** 6k. blue 40 10
3214 – 6k. brown 40 10
3215 – 6k. brown 40 10
3216 – 6k. green 40 10
STATIONS: No. 3214, Leninksy Prospekt, Moscow; 3215, Moscow Gate, Leningrad; 3216, Bolshevik Factory, Kiev.

1188 Common Buzzard **1189** "Red Star" (medal) and Scenes of Odessa

1965. Birds of Prey. Birds in black.
3217 **1188** 1k. grey 30 10
3218 – 2k. brown 40 15
3219 – 3k. olive 45 15
3220 – 4k. drab 55 15
3221 – 10k. brown . . . . . 1·10 30
3222 – 12k. blue . . . . . . 1·40 50
3223 – 14k. blue . . . . . . 1·50 65
3224 – 16k. purple . . . . . 2·00 75
BIRDS—VERT: 2k. Common kestrel; 3k. Tawny eagle; 4k. Red kite; 10k. Peregrine falcon; 16k. Gyr falcon. HORIZ: 12k. Golden eagle; 14k. Lammergeier.

1965. Heroic Soviet Towns. Multicoloured.
3225 10k. Type **1189** 55 25
3226 10k. Leningrad 55 25
3227 10k. Kiev 55 25
3228 10k. Moscow 55 25
3229 10k. Brest-Litovsk 55 25
3230 10k. Volgograd 55 25
3231 10k. Sevastopol 55 25

1190 Flag, Map and Parliament Building, Belgrade

1965. 20th Anniv of Yugoslavia Republic.
3232 **1190** 6k. multicoloured . . . 45 15

1191 Tupolev Tu-134 Jetliner

1965. Soviet Civil Aviation. Multicoloured.
3233 6k. Type **1191** 55 10
3234 10k. Antonov An-24 . . . . 80 15
3235 12k. Mil Mi-10 helicopter 95 25
3236 16k. Beriev Be-10 flying boat . . . . 1·40 40
3237 20k. Antonov An-22 Anteus 1·90 45

1192 "The Proposal of Marriage" (P. Fedotov, 150th birth anniv)

1965. Soviet Painters' Annivs.
3238 – 12k. black and red . . 1·50 25
3239 **1192** 16k. blue and red . . . 2·40 40
DESIGN—VERT: 12k. "A Collective Farm Watchman" (S. Gerasimov, 80th birth anniv).

1193 Crystallography Congress Emblem

1966. International Congresses, Moscow.
3240 **1193** 6k. black, blue and bistre 35 15
3241 – 6k. black, red and blue 35 15
3242 – 6k. purple, grey & black 35 15
3243 – 6k. black and blue . . 35 15
3244 – 6k. black, red and yellow 35 15
CONGRESS EMBLEMS: No. 3241, Microbiology; 3242, Poultry-raising; 3243, Oceanography; 3244, Mathematics.

1194 Postman and Milkmaid (19th-century statuettes, des A. Venetsianov)

1966. Bicentenary of Dmitrov Ceramic Works. Multicoloured.
3245 6k. Type **1194** 30 15
3246 10k. Modern tea set 65 25

1195 Rolland (after A. Yar-Kravchenko)

1966. Birth Centenary of Romain Rolland (French writer) and 150th Birth Anniv of Eugene Potier (French poet).
3247 **1195** 4k. brown and blue . . 30 15
3248 – 4k. brown, red and black 30 15
DESIGN: No. 3248, Potier and revolutionary scene.

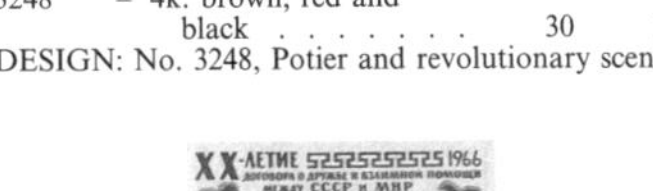

1196 Mongol Horseman

1966. 20th Anniv of Soviet–Mongolian Treaty.
3249 **1196** 4k. multicoloured . . . 30 10

„ЛУНА-9"—НА ЛУНЕ!
3.2.1966
(**1197**)

1966. Landing of "Luna 9" Rocket on Moon. Optd with T **1197**.
3250 **1017** 6k. red, black and blue 4·50 4·50

1198 Supply Ship "Ob"

1966. 10th Anniv of Soviet Antarctic Expedition.
3251 **1198** 10k. lake and silver . . 2·00 1·60
3252 – 10k. lake, silver and blue . . . . 2·25 50
3253 – 10k. lake, silver and blue . . . . 2·25 50
DESIGNS—TRIANGULAR: No. 3252, Snow vehicle. DIAMOND: No. 3253, Antarctic map. This stamp is partly perf across the centre.

1199 Mussa Dyalil and Scene from Poem

1966. Writers.
3254 **1199** 4k. black and brown . . 30 10
3255 – 4k. black and green . . 30 10
3256 – 4k. black and green . . 30 10
WRITERS: No. 3254 (Azerbaijan writer: 60th birth anniv); 3255, Akob Akopyan (Armenian poet: birth cent); 3256, Djalil Mamedkulizade (Azerbaijan writer: birth cent).

1200 Lenin (after bust by Kibalnikov)

1966. Lenin's 96th Birth Anniv
3257 **1200** 10k. gold and green . . 1·10 65
3258 10k. silver and red . . 1·10 25

1201 N. Ilin

1202 Scene from "Alive and Dead" (dir. A. Stolper)

1966. War Heroes.
3259 **1201** 4k. violet and red . . . 30 15
3260 – 4k. lilac and blue . . . 30 15
3261 – 4k. brown and green . . 30 15
PORTRAITS: No. 3260, G. P. Kravchenko; 3261, A. Uglovsky.

1966. Soviet Cinema Art.
3262 **1202** 4k. black, green and red 25 10
3263 – 10k. black and blue . . 60 20
DESIGN: 10k. Scene from "Hamlet" (dir. G. Kozintsev).

1203 Kremlin and Inscription

Учредительная конференция
Всесоюзного общества
филателистов. 1966
(**1204**)

1966. 23rd Soviet Comunist Party Congress, Moscow (1st issue).
3264 **1203** 4k. gold, red and blue 30 10
See also Nos. 3337/41.

1966. Philatelists All-Union Society Conference. No. 3198 optd with T **1204**.
3265 16k. plum, red and grey . . 2·75 1·75

1205 Ice Skating

1966. 2nd People's Winter Spartakiad.
3266 **1205** 4k. blue, red and olive 30 15
3267 – 6k. red, lake and lilac 50 20
3268 – 10k. lake, red and blue 75 30
DESIGNS: Inscription emblem and 6k. Ice hockey; 10k. Skiing.
Nos. 3266/8 are each perf across the centre.

1206 Liner "Aleksandr Pushkin"

1207 Government Building, Frunze

1966. Soviet Transport.
3269 – 4k. multicoloured . . . 55 10
3270 – 6k. multicoloured . . . 45 10
3271 – 10k. multicoloured . . 65 20
3272 **1206** 12k. multicoloured . . 1·00 20
3273 – 16k. multicoloured . . 1·00 25
DESIGNS—HORIZ: 4k. Electric train; 6k. Map of Lenin Volga–Baltic canal system; 16k. Silhouette of liner "Aleksandr Pushkin" on globe. VERT: 10k. Canal lock (Volga–Baltic canal).
Nos. 3271/3 commemorate the inauguration of Leningrad–Montreal Sea Service.

1966. 40th Anniv of Kirgizia.
3274 **1207** 4k. red 30 10

1208 S. M. Kirov (80th Birth Anniv)

1210 A. Fersman (mineralogist)

1966. Soviet Personalities.
3275 **1208** 4k. brown 30 10
3276 – 4k. green 30 10
3277 – 4k. violet 30 10
PORTRAITS: No. 3276, G. I. Ordzhonikidze (80th birth anniv); 3277, Ion Yakir (military commander, 70th birth anniv).

1966. Soviet Scientists. Multicoloured. Colours of name panels below.
3279 **1210** 4k. blue 60 15
3280 – 4k. brown 60 15
3281 – 4k. violet 60 15
3282 – 4k. brown and blue . . 60 15
PORTRAITS: No. 3280, D. K. Zabolotnyi (microbiologist); 3281, M. A. Shatelen (electrical engineer); 3282, O. Yu. Shmidt (arctic explorer).

„Луна-10"—XXIII съезду КПСС
(**1211**)

1966. Launching of "Luna 10". As No. 3284, but imperf, optd with T **1211**.
3283 **1212** 10k. multicoloured . . 3·75 3·00

1212 Arrowheads, "Luna 9" and Orbit

1966. Cosmonautics Day. Multicoloured.
3284 10k. Type **1212** 60 25
3285 12k. Rocket launching and different orbit 65 30

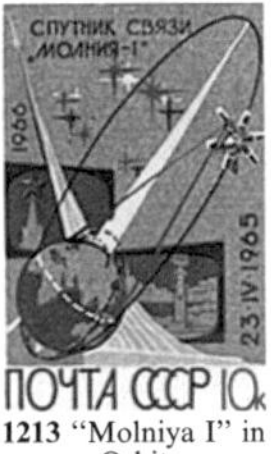

1213 "Molniya I" in Orbit

1214 Ernst Thalmann (80th birth anniv)

1966. Launching of "Molniya I" Telecommunications Satellite.
3286 **1213** 10k. multicoloured . . 55 20

1966. Prominent Leaders.
3287 **1214** 6k. red 45 10
3288 – 6k. violet 45 10
3289 – 6k. brown 45 10
PORTRAITS: No. 3288, Wilhelm Pieck (90th birth anniv); 3289, Sun Yat-sen (birth cent).

1216 Spaceman and Soldier

1966. 15th Young Communist League Congress.
3290 **1216** 4k. black and red . . . 30 10

1217 Ice Hockey Player

1966. Soviet Victory in World Ice Hockey Championships.
3291 **1217** 10k. multicoloured . . 60 25

1218 N. I. Kuznetsov

1219 Tchaikovsky

1966. War Heroes. Guerrilla Fighters.
3292 **1218** 4k. black and green . . 20 10
3293 – 4k. black and yellow . . 20 10
3294 – 4k. black and blue . . 20 10
3295 – 4k. black and purple . . 20 10
3296 – 4k. black and violet . . 20 10
PORTRAITS: No. 3293, I. Y. Sudmalis; 3294, A. A. Morozova; No. 3295, F. E. Strelets; 3296, T. P. Bumazhkov.

1966. 3rd International Tchaikovsky Music Competition, Moscow.
3297 – 4k. black, red and yellow 35 10
3298 **1219** 6k. black, red and yellow 55 10
3299 – 16k. black, red and blue 1·40 35
DESIGNS: 4k. Moscow State Conservatoire of Music; 16k. Tchaikovsky's house and museum, Klin.

1220 Running

1966. Sports Events.
3300 **1220** 4k. brown, olive & green 20 15
3301 – 6k. black, bistre & orge 45 15
3302 – 12k. black, bistre & blue 65 25
DESIGNS: 6k. Weightlifting; 12k. Wrestling.

1222 Gold Medal and Chess Pieces

1966. World Chess Championship, Moscow.
3303 **1222** 6k. multicoloured . . . 1·40 20

1223 Jules Rimet Cup and Football

1966. World Cup Football Championship (England) and World Fencing Championships (Moscow).
3304 **1223** 4k. black, gold and red . . 20 10
3305 – 6k. multicoloured . . . 35 10
3306 – 12k. multicoloured . . 70 20
3307 – 16k. multicoloured . . 1·10 40
DESIGNS: 6k. Footballers; 12k. Fencers; 16k. Fencer and fencing emblems.

1224 Sable, Lake Baikal and Animals (½-size illustration)

1966. Barguzin Nature Reserve.
3308 **1224** 4k. black and blue . . 60 15
3309 – 6k. black and purple . . 90 25
DESIGN: 6k. Map of reserve, and brown bear.

1225 Lotus Plants

1226 "Venus 3" Medal, Globe and Flight Trajectory

1966. 125th Anniv of Sukhumi Botanical Gardens.
3310 **1225** 3k. red, yellow and green 25 10
3311 – 6k. bistre, brown & blue 45 10
3312 – 12k. red, green & turq 70 30
DESIGNS: 6k. Palms and cypresses; 12k. Water lilies.

1966. Space Achievements.
3313 **1226** 6k. black, silver and red 50 20
3314 – 6k. deep blue, blue and brown 50 20
3315 – 6k. ochre and blue . . 50 20
3316 – 6k. multicoloured . . . 60 20
3317 – 6k. pink, mauve & black 60 20
DESIGNS: No. 3314, Spacedogs, Ugolek and Veterok; 3315, "Luna 10"; 3316, "Molniya I"; 3317, "Luna 2's" pennant, Earth and Moon.

1227 Itkol

1966. Tourist Resorts. Multicoloured.
3318 1k. Type **1227** 10 10
3319 4k. Cruise ship on the Volga 30 10
3320 6k. Archway, Leningrad (27½ × 28mm) 35 10
3321 10k. Castle, Kislovodsk . . 55 15
3322 12k. Ismail Samani Mausoleum, Bokhara . . 80 20
3323 16k. Kavkaz Hotel, Sochi (Black Sea) . . . . 1·25 30

1230 Congress Emblem

1231 Peace Dove and Japanese Crane

1966. 7th Consumers' Co-operative Societies Congress, Moscow.
3325 **1230** 4k. yellow and brown 40 10

1966. Soviet–Japanese Meeting, Khabarovsk.
3326 **1231** 6k. black and red . . . 50 20

1232 "Avtandil at a Mountain Spring", after engraving by S. Kabulazde

1966. 800th Birth Anniv of Shota Rustaveli (Georgian poet).
3327 – 3k. black on green . . 35 10
3328 – 4k. brown on yellow . . 45 10
3329 **1232** 6k. black on blue . . . 55 15
DESIGNS: 3k. Scene from poem "The Knight in the Tiger's Skin" (after I. Toidze); 4k. Rustaveli, (after bas-relief by Ya. Nikoladze).

1234 Arms, Moscow Skyline and Fireworks

1235 Trawler, Net and Map of Lake Baikal

1966. 49th Anniv of October Revolution.
3331 **1234** 4k. multicoloured . . . 30 10

1966. Fish Resources of Lake Baikal. Mult.
3332 2k. Baikal grayling (horiz) 25 10
3333 4k. Baikal sturgeon (horiz) 30 10
3334 6k. Type **1235** 35 10
3335 10k. Omul (horiz) 70 20
3336 12k. Baikal whitefish (horiz) 85 25

1236 "Agriculture and Industry"

1966. 23rd Soviet Communist Party Congress, Moscow (3rd issue).
3337 **1236** 4k. silver and brown . . 20 10
3338 – 4k. silver and blue . . . 20 10
3339 – 4k. silver and red . . . 20 10
3340 – 4k. silver and red . . . 20 10
3341 – 4k. silver and green . . 20 10
DESIGN (Map as Type **1236** with symbols of): No. 3338, "Communications and Transport"; 3339, "Education and Technology"; 3340, "Increased Productivity"; 3341, "Power Resources".

1237 Government Buildings, Kishinev

1966. 500th Anniv of Kishinev (Moldavian Republic).
3342 **1237** 4k. multicoloured . . . 30 10

1238 Clouds, Rain and Decade Emblem

1239 Nikitin Monument (S. Orlov and A. Zavalor), Kalinin

1966. International Hydrological Decade.
3343 **1238** 6k. multicoloured . . . 40 15

1966. 50th Anniv of Afanasy Nikitin's Voyage to India.
3344 **1239** 4k. black, green & yell 30 10

1240 Scene from "Nargiz" (Muslim Magomaev)

1966. Azerbaijan Operas.
3345 **1240** 4k. ochre and black . . 35 15
3346 – 4k. green and black . . 35 15
DESIGN: No. 3346, Scene from "Kehzoglu" (Uzeir Gadzhibekov).

1241 "Luna 9" and Moon

1242 Agricultural and Chemical Symbols

1966.
3347 1k. brown 10 10
3348 **1241** 2k. violet 10 10
3349 – 3k. purple 20 10
3350 – 4k. red 20 10
3351 – 6k. blue 60 10
3563 – 10k. olive 90 35
3353 – 12k. brown 70 10
3354 – 16k. blue 90 15
3355 – 20k. red, blue and drab 1·10 20
3566 – 20k. red . . . . 1·75 40
3356 **1242** 30k. green . . . . . . 1·75 40
3357 – 50k. ultram, blue & grey . . . . 3·00 50
3568 – 50k. blue . . . . 5·00 1·00
3358 – 1r. black and red . . . 5·25 1·50
3569 – 1r. brown and black . . 8·25 1·50
DESIGNS—As Type **1241**: 1k. Palace of Congresses, Kremlin; 3k. Youth, girl and Lenin emblem; 4k. Arms and hammer and sickle emblem; 6k. "Communications" (Antonov An-10A Ukrainia airplane and sputnik); 10k. Soldier and star emblem; 12k. Furnaceman; 16k. Girl with dove. As Type **1242**: 20k. Workers' demonstration and flower; 50k. "Postal communications"; 1r. Lenin and industrial emblems.

1243 "Presenting Arms"

1245 Campaign Meeting

1966. 25th Anniv of People's Voluntary Corps.
3359 **1243** 4k. brown and red . . 30 10

1966. "Hands off Vietnam".
3360 **1245** 6k. multicoloured . . . 30 10

1246 Servicemen

1966. 30th Anniv of Spanish Civil War.
3361 **1246** 6k. black, red and ochre 35 10

1247 Ostankino TV Tower, "Molniya I" (satellite) and "1967"

1249 Statue, Tank and Medal

1248 Flight Diagram

1966. New Year and "50th Year of October Revolution".
3362 **1247** 4k. multicoloured . . . 40 10

1966. Space Flight and Moon Landing of "Luna 9".
3363 **1248** 10k. black and silver . . 70 25
3364 – 10k. red and silver . . 70 25
3365 – 10k. black and silver . . 70 25
DESIGNS—SQUARE (25 × 25 mm): No. 3364, Arms of Russia and lunar pennant. HORIZ: No. 3365, "Lunar 9" on Moon's surface.

1966. 25th Anniv of Battle of Moscow.
3366 – 4k. brown 30 10
3367 **1249** 6k. ochre and sepia . . 30 15
3368 – 10k. yellow and brown 60 20
DESIGNS—HORIZ: (60 × 28 mm): 4k. Soviet troops advancing; 10k. "Moscow at peace"– Kremlin, Sun and "Defence of Moscow" medal.

1250 Cervantes and Don Quixote

1966. 350th Death Anniv of Cervantes.
3369 **1250** 6k. brown, green and deep green 40 15

1252 Bering's Ship "Sv. Pyotr" and Map of Komandor Islands

1966. Soviet Far Eastern Territories. Mult.
3370 1k. Type **1252** 40 10
3371 2k. Medny Island and map 45 10
3372 4k. Petropavlovsk Harbour, Kamchatka 65 10
3373 6k. Geyser, Kamchatka (vert) 80 10
3374 10k. Avatchinskaya Bay, Kamchatka . . . . 1·00 15
3375 12k. Northern fur seals, Bering Is . . . . 1·00 35
3376 16k. Common guillemot colony, Kurile Islands . . 1·50 75

1254 "The Lute Player" (Caravaggio)

1966. Art Treasures of the Hermitage Museum, Leningrad.
3377 – 4k. black on yellow . . 20 10
3378 – 6k. black on grey . . . 40 10
3379 – 10k. black on lilac . . . 65 15
3380 – 12k. black on green . . 85 20
3381 **1254** 16k. black on buff . . . 1·10 35
DESIGNS—HORIZ: 4k. "Golden Stag" (from Scythian battle shield (6th cent B.C.). VERT: 6k. Persian silver jug (5th cent A.D.; 10k. Statue of Voltaire (Houdon, 1781); 12k. Malachite vase (Urals, 1840).

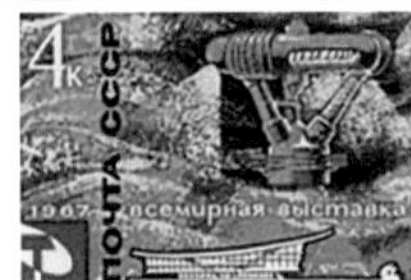

1255 Sea-water Distilling Apparatus

1967. World Fair, Montreal.
3382 **1255** 4k. black, silver & green 20 10
3383 – 6k. multicoloured . . . 35 15
3384 – 10k. multicoloured . . 60 20
DESIGNS—VERT: 6k. "Atomic Energy" (explosion and symbol). HORIZ: 10k. Space station "Proton 1".

1256 Lieut. B. I. Sizov

1967. War Heroes.
3386 **1256** 4k. brown on yellow . . 30 10
3387 – 4k. brown on drab . . 30 10
DESIGN: No. 3387, Private V. V. Khodyrev.

1257 Woman's Face and Pavlov Shawl

1967. International Women's Day.
3388 **1257** 4k. red, violet and green 30 10

1258 Cine-camera and Film "Flower"

1967. 5th International Film Festival, Moscow.
3389 **1258** 6k. multicoloured . . . 40 10

1259 Factory Ship "Cheryashevsky"

1967. Soviet Fishing Industry. Multicoloured.
3390 6k. Type **1259** 45 15
3391 6k. Refrigerated trawler . . 45 15
3392 6k. Crab canning ship . . . 45 15
3393 6k. Trawler 45 15
3394 6k. Seine-fishing boat, Black Sea 45 15

1260 Newspaper Cuttings, Hammer and Sickle

1261 I.S.O. Congress Emblem

1967. 50th Anniv of Newspaper "Izvestiya".
3395 **1260** 4k. multicoloured . . . 30 10

1967. Moscow Congresses.
3396 6k. turquoise, black and blue 30 10
3397 6k. red, black and blue . . 30 10
DESIGNS: No. 3396, Type **1261** (7th Congress of Int Standards Assn "I.S.O."; 3397, "V" emblem of 5th Int Mining Congress.

1262 I.T.Y. Emblem

1967. International Tourist Year.
3398 **1262** 4k. black, silver and blue 30 10

Вена - 1967
(1263)

1265 "Lenin as Schoolboy" (V. Tsigal)

1264 A. A. Leonov in Space

1967. Victory in World Ice Hockey Championship. No. 3291 optd with T **1263**.
3399 **1217** 10k. multicoloured . . 2·75 1·40

1967. Cosmonautics Day. Multicoloured.
3400 4k. Type **1264** 35 10
3401 10k. Rocket and Earth . . . 80 15
3402 16k. "Luna 10" over Moon 1·00 35

1967. Lenin's 97th Birth Anniv.
3403 **1265** 2k. brown, yellow & grn 25 10
3404 – 3k. brown and lake . . 45 10
3405 – 4k. green, yellow and olive 60 15
3406 – 6k. silver, black and blue 90 20
3407 – 10k. blue, black & silver . . . . 2·10 45
3408 – 10k. black and gold . . 70 30
SCULPTURES—VERT: 3k. Lenin's monument, Ulyanovsk; 6k. Bust of Lenin (G. and Yu. Neroda); 10k. (both) "Lenin as Leader" (N. Andreev). HORIZ: 4k. "Lenin at Razliv" (V. Pinchuk).

1266 M. F. Shmyrev

1967. War Heroes.
3409 **1266** 4k. sepia and brown . . 20 10
3410 – 4k. brown and blue . . 20 10
3411 – 4k. brown and violet 20 10
DESIGNS: No. 3410, Major-General S. V. Rudnev; 3411, First Lieut. M. S. Kharchenko.

1267 Transport crossing Ice on Lake Ladoga

1967. Siege of Leningrad, 1941–42.
3412 **1267** 4k. grey, red and cream 20 10

1268 Marshal Biryuzov

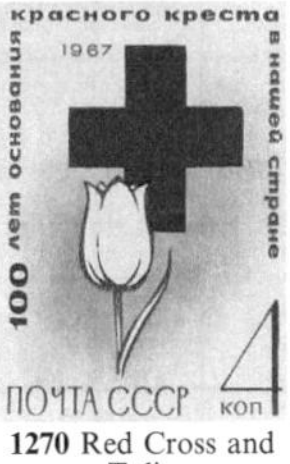

1270 Red Cross and Tulip

1269 Minsk Old and New

1967. Biryuzov Commemoration.
3413 **1268** 4k. green and yellow . . 20 10

1967. 900th Anniv of Minsk.
3414 **1269** 4k. green and black . . 30 10

1967. Centenary of Russian Red Cross.
3415 **1270** 4k. red and ochre . . . 30 10

1271 Russian Stamps of 1918 and 1967

1967. 50th Anniv of U.S.S.R. Philatelic Exn, Moscow.
3416 **1271** 20k. green and blue . . 1·50 65

1272 Komsomolsk-on-Amur and Map

1967. 35th Anniv of Komsomolsk-on-Amur.
3418 **1272** 4k. brown and red . . 50 10

1273 Motor Cyclist (International Motor Rally, Moscow)

1967. Sports and Pastimes. International Events.
3419 – 1k. brown, bistre & grn 20 10
3420 – 2k. brown 20 10
3421 – 3k. blue 20 10
3422 – 4k. turquoise 20 10
3423 – 6k. purple and bistre 30 10
3424 **1273** 10k. purple and lilac . . 75 30
DESIGNS AND EVENTS: 1k. Draughts board and players (World Draughts Championships); 2k. Throwing the javelin; 3k. Running; 4k. Long jumping (all preliminary events for Europa Cup Games); 6k. Gymnast (World Gymnastics Championships).

1275 G. D. Gai (soldier)

1276 Games Emblem and Cup

1967. Commander G. D. Gai Commemoration.
3426 **1275** 4k. black and red . . . 30 10

1967. All Union Schoolchildren's Spartakiad.
3427 **1276** 4k. red, black and silver 20 10

1277 Spartakiad Emblem and Cup

1967. 4th People's Spartakiad.
3428 4k. black, red and silver . . 25 10
3429 4k. black, red and silver . . 25 10
3430 4k. black, red and silver . . 25 10
3431 4k. black, red and silver . . 25 10
DESIGNS: Each with Cup. No. 3428, Type **1277**; No. 3429, Gymnastics; 3430, Diving; 3431, Cycling.

1278 V. G. Klochkov (Soviet hero)

1967. Klochkov Commemoration.
3432 **1278** 4k. black and red . . . 25 10

1279 Crest, Flag and Capital of Moldavia

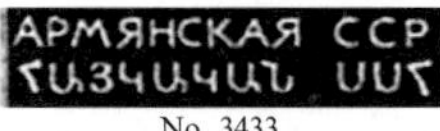

No. 3433

АЗЕРБАЙДЖАНСКАЯ ССР
АЗӘРБАЈҸАН ССР
No. 3434

БЕЛОРУССКАЯ ССР
БЕЛАРУСКАЯ ССР
No. 3435

No. 3436

No. 3437

No. 3438

КИРГИЗСКАЯ ССР
КЫРГЫЗ ССР
No. 3439

ЛАТВИЙСКАЯ ССР
LATVIJAS PSR
No. 3440

ЛИТОВСКАЯ ССР
LIETUVOS TSR
No. 3441

МОЛДАВСКАЯ ССР
РСС МОЛДОВЕНЯСКЭ
No. 3442

РОССИЙСКАЯ СОВЕТСКАЯ ФЕДЕРАТИВНАЯ СОЦИАЛИСТИЧЕСКАЯ РЕСПУБЛИКА
No. 3443

ТАДЖИКСКАЯ ССР
РСС ТОҶИКИСТОН
No. 3444

ТУРКМЕНСКАЯ ССР
ТҮРКМЕНИСТАН ССР
No. 3445

УКРАИНСКАЯ ССР
УКРАЇНСЬКА РСР
No. 3446

УЗБЕКСКАЯ ССР
ЎЗБЕКИСТОН ССР
No. 3447

Inscr at foot as shown above

1967. 50th Anniv of October Revolution (1st issue). Designs showing crests, flags and capitals of the Soviet Republics. Multicoloured.
3433 4k. Armenia 20 10
3434 4k. Azerbaijan 20 10

3435 4k. Belorussia 20 10
3436 4k. Estonia 20 10
3437 4k. Georgia 20 10
3438 4k. Kazakhstan 20 10
3439 4k. Kirgizia 20 10
3440 4k. Latvia 20 10
3441 4k. Lithuania 20 10
3442 4k. Type **1279** 20 10
3443 4k. Russia 20 10
3444 4k. Tadjikistan 20 10
3445 4k. Turkmenistan 20 10
3446 4k. Ukraine 20 10
3447 4k. Uzbekistan 20 10
3448 4k. Soviet Arms 20 10
No. 3448 is size 47 × 32 mm.
See also Nos. 3473/82.

1280 Telecommunications Symbols

1967. "Progress of Communism".
3449 **1280** 4k. red, purple and silver 3·25 1·40

1281 Manchurian Crane and Dove

1967. Soviet–Japanese Friendship.
3450 **1281** 16k. brown, black & red 90 35

1282 Karl Marx and Title Page

1967. Centenary of Karl Marx's "Das Kapital".
3451 **1282** 4k. brown and red 40 10

1283 Arctic Fox **1285** Krasnodon Memorial

1284 Ice Skating

1967. Fur-bearing Animals.
3452 **1283** 2k. blue, black & brown 20 10
3453 – 4k. blue, black and drab 30 10
3454 – 6k. ochre, black & green 45 10
3455 – 10k. brown, black & grn 60 15
3456 – 12k. black, ochre & vio 70 25
3457 – 16k. brown, black & yell 85 35
3458 – 20k. brown, black & turq 1·10 50
DESIGNS—VERT: 4k. Red fox; 12k. Stoat; 16k. Sable. HORIZ: 6k. Red fox; 10k. Muskrat; 20k. European mink.

1967. Winter Olympic Games, Grenoble (1968). Multicoloured.
3459 2k. Type **1284** 15 10
3460 3k. Ski jumping 25 10
3461 4k. Games emblem (vert) 30 10
3462 10k. Ice hockey 70 15
3463 12k. Skiing 90 30

1967. 25th Anniv of Krasnodon Defence.
3464 **1285** 4k. black, yellow & pur 20 10

1285a Map and Snow Leopard (½-size illustration)

1967. Cedar Valley Nature Reserve.
3465 **1285a** 10k. black and bistre 75 30

1286 Badge and Yakovlev Yak-9 Fighters **1288** Cosmonauts in Space

1287 Militiaman and Soviet Crest

1967. 25th Anniv of French "Normandie-Niemen" Fighter Squadron.
3466 **1286** 6k. red, blue and gold 40 15

1967. 50th Anniv of Soviet Militia.
3467 **1287** 4k. red and blue 30 10

1967. Space Fantasies. Multicoloured.
3468 4k. Type **1288** 25 10
3469 6k. Men on the Moon (horiz) 40 10
3470 10k. Cosmic vehicle 65 15
3471 12k. Planetary landscape (horiz) 80 20
3472 16k. Imaginary spacecraft 90 30

1289 Red Star and Soviet Crest (⅔-size illustration)

1967. 50th Anniv of October Revolution (2nd issue). "50 Heroic Years". Designs showing paintings and Soviet Arms. Multicoloured.
3473 4k. Type **1289** 25 15
3474 4k. "Lenin addressing Congress" (Serov—1955) 25 15
3475 4k. "Lenin explaining the GOELRO map" (Schmatko—1957) 25 15
3476 4k. "The First Cavalry" (Grekov—1924) 25 15
3477 4k. "Students" (Yoganson—1928) 25 15
3478 4k. "People's Friendship" (Karpov—1924) 25 15
3479 4k. "Dawn of the Five Year Plan" (construction work, Romas—1934) 60 15
3480 4k. "Farmers' Holiday" (Gerasimov—1937) 25 15
3481 4k. "Victory in World War II" (Korolev—1965) 25 15
3482 4k. "Builders of Communism" (Merpert and Skripkov—1965) 25 15

1290 S. Katayama **1293** Narva-Joesuu (Estonia)

1292 T.V. Tower, Moscow

1967. Katayama (founder of Japanese Communist Party) Commemoration.
3484 **1290** 6k. green 25 10

1967. Opening of Ostankino T.V. Tower, Moscow.
3486 **1292** 16k. black, silver & orge 1·00 20

1967. Baltic Health Resorts. Multicoloured.
3487 4k. Yurmala (Latvia) 20 10
3488 6k. Type **1293** 30 10
3489 10k. Druskininkai (Lithuania) 55 15
3490 12k. Zelenogradsk (Kaliningrad) (vert) 70 20
3491 16k. Svetlogorsk (Kaliningrad) (vert) 1·00 25

1294 K.G.B. Emblem **1295** Moscow View

1967. 50th Anniv of State Security Commission (K.G.B.).
3492 **1294** 4k. red, silver and blue 25 10

1967. New Year.
3493 **1295** 4k. brown, pink and silver 30 10

1296 Revolutionaries at Kharkov, and Monument

1967. 50th Anniv of Ukraine Republic.
3494 **1296** 4k. multicoloured 20 10
3495 – 6k. multicoloured 60 10
3496 – 10k. multicoloured 70 15
DESIGNS: 6k. Hammer and sickle and industrial and agricultural scenes; 10k. Unknown Soldier's monument, Kiev, and young Ukrainians with welcoming bread and salt.

1297 Armoury, Commandant and Trinity Towers **1299** Unknown Soldier's Tomb, Kremlin

1298 Moscow Badge, Lenin's Tomb and Rockets

1967. Kremlin Buildings.
3497 **1297** 4k. brown, purple & grn 20 10
3498 – 6k. brown, green & yell 30 10
3499 – 10k. brown and grey 55 15
3500 – 12k. green, violet and cream 80 30
3501 – 16k. brown, red and light brown 90 30

DESIGNS—HORIZ: 6k. Cathedral of the Annunciation. VERT: 10k. Konstantino-Yelenin, Alarm and Spassky Towers; 12k. Ivan the Great's bell tower; 16k. Kutafya and Trinity Towers.

1967. "50 Years of Communist Development".
3502 **1298** 4k. lake 25 10
3503 – 4k. brown 30 10
3504 – 4k. green 25 10
3505 – 4k. blue 25 10
3506 – 4k. blue 30 10
DESIGNS—HORIZ: No. 3503, Computer-tape cogwheel and industrial scene; 3504, Ear of wheat and grain silo; 3505, Microscope, radar antennae and Moscow University. VERT: No. 3506, T.V. Tower, "Aleksandr Pushkin" (liner), railway bridge and jet airliner.

1967. "Unknown Soldier" Commemoration.
3507 **1299** 4k. red 30 10

1300 "The Interrogation of Communists" (B. Ioganson)

1967. Paintings in the Tretyakov Gallery, Moscow. Multicoloured.
3508 3k. Type **1300** 20 10
3509 4k. "The Sea-shore" (I. Aivazovsky) 30 10
3510 4k. "The Lace Maker" (V. Tropinin) (vert) 30 10
3511 6k. "The Bakery" (T. Yablonskaya) (60 × 34 mm) 40 10
3512 6k. "Aleksandr Nevsky" (part of triptych by P. Korin) (34 × 60 mm) 40 10
3513 6k. "Boyarynya Morozova" (V. Surikov) (60 × 34 mm) 40 10
3514 10k. "The Swan Maiden" (M. Vrubel) (vert) 80 20
3515 10k. "The Arrest of a Propagandist" (I. Repin) 80 20
3516 16k. "Moscow Suburb in February" (G. Nissky) 2·25 45

1301 Congress Emblem

1968. 14th Soviet Trade Unions Congress, Moscow.
3517 **1301** 6k. red and green 30 10

1302 Lieut. S. G. Baikov

1968. War Heroes.
3518 **1302** 4k. black and blue 30 10
3519 – 4k. blue and green 20 10
3520 – 4k. black and red 20 10
PORTRAITS: No. 3519, Lieut. P. L. Guchenko; No. 3520, A. A. Pokaltchuk.

1303 Racehorses **1304** M. Ulyanova

1968. Soviet Horse Breeding.
3521 **1303** 4k. black, purple & blue 25 10
3522 – 6k. black, blue and red 35 10
3523 – 10k. black, brn & turq 60 15
3524 – 12k. black, green & brn 65 20
3525 – 16k. black, red and green 90 30
DESIGNS (each with horse's head and horses "in the field"). VERT: 6k. Show horses; 12k. Show jumpers. HORIZ: 10k. Trotters; 16k. Hunters.

1968. 90th Birth Anniv of M. I. Ulyanova (Lenin's sister).
3526 **1304** 4k. blue and green 25 10

1305 Red Star and Forces' Flags

1968. 50th Anniv of Soviet Armed Forces. Multicoloured.
3527 4k. Type **1305** 25 10
3528 4k. Lenin addressing recruits (horiz) 25 10
3529 4k. Recruiting poster (D. Moor) and volunteers (horiz) 25 10
3530 4k. Red Army entering Vladivostok, 1922, and monument (L. Shervud) (horiz) 25 10
3531 4k. Dnieper Dam and statue "On Guard" (horiz) . . . 25 10
3532 4k. "Liberators" poster (V. Ivanov) and tanks in the Ukraine (horiz) . . . 25 10
3533 4k. "To the East" poster and retreating Germans fording river (horiz) . . . 25 10
3534 4k. Stalingrad battle monument and German prisoners-of-war 25 10
3535 4k. Victory parade, Red Square, Moscow, and monument, Treptow (Berlin) (horiz) 25 10
3536 4k. Rockets, tank, warships and Red Flag 25 10

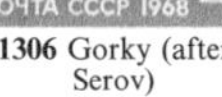

1306 Gorky (after Serov) **1307** Fireman and Appliances

1968. Birth Centenary of Maksim Gorky (writer).
3538 **1306** 4k. brown and drab . . 25 10

1968. 50th Anniv of Soviet Fire Services.
3539 **1307** 4k. black and red . . . 20 10

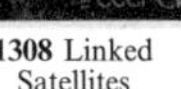

1308 Linked Satellites **1309** N. N. Popudrenko

1968. Space Link of "Cosmos" Satellites.
3540 **1308** 6k. black, gold & purple 30 10

1968. War Heroes.
3541 **1309** 4k. black and green . . 20 10
3542 – 4k. black and lilac . . . 20 10
DESIGN: No. 3542, P. P. Vershigora.

1310 Protective Hand

1968. "Solidarity with Vietnam".
3543 **1310** 6k. multicoloured . . . 25 10

1311 Leonov filming in Space

1968. Cosmonautics Day. Multicoloured.
3544 4k. Type **1311** 35 15
3545 6k. "Kosmos 186" and "Kosmos 188" linking in space 55 15
3546 10k. "Venera 4" space probe 1·00 15

1312 Lenin

1968. Lenin's 98th Birth Anniv.
3547 **1312** 4k. multicoloured . . . 85 15
3548 – 4k. black, red and gold 85 15
3549 – 4k. brown, red and gold 85 15
DESIGNS: No. 3548, Lenin speaking in Red Square; No. 3549, Lenin in peaked cap speaking from lorry during parade.

1313 Navoi (after V. Kaidalov) **1314** Karl Marx

1968. 525th Birth Anniv of Alisher Navoi (Uzbek poet).
3550 **1313** 4k. brown 25 10

1968. 150th Birth Anniv of Karl Marx.
3551 **1314** 4k. black and red . . . 30 10

1315 Frontier Guard **1316** Gem and Congress Emblem

1968. 50th Anniv of Soviet Frontier Guards. Multicoloured.
3552 4k. Type **1315** 25 10
3553 6k. Jubilee badge 40 10

1968. "International Congresses and Assemblies".
3554 **1316** 6k. deep blue, blue and green 25 15
3555 – 6k. gold, orange & brn 25 15
3556 – 6k. gold, black and red 25 15
3557 – 6k. orange, black & mve 25 15
DESIGNS: No. 3554, Type **1316** (8th Enriched Minerals Congress); 3555, Power stations, pylon and emblem (7th World Power Conference); 3556, "Carabus schaenherri" (ground beetle) and emblem (13th Entomological Congress); 3557, Roses and emblem (4th Congress on Volatile Oils).

1317 S. Aini **1319** "Kiev Uprising" (after V. Boroday)

1318 Congress Emblem and Postrider

1968. 90th Birth Anniv of Sadriddin Aini (Tadzhik writer).
3570 **1317** 4k. purple and bistre 30 10

1968. Meeting of U.P.U. Consultative Commission, Moscow.
3571 **1318** 6k. red and grey . . . 30 10
3572 – 6k. red and yellow . . 30 10
DESIGN: No. 3572, Emblem and transport.

1968. 50th Anniv of Ukraine Communist Party.
3573 **1319** 4k. red, purple and gold 20 10

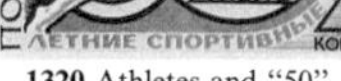

1320 Athletes and "50" **1321** Handball

1968. Young Communist League's 50th Anniv Games.
3574 **1320** 4k. red, drab and yellow 25 10

1968. Various Sports Events.
3575 **1321** 2k. multicoloured . . . 20 10
3576 – 4k. multicoloured . . . 30 10
3577 – 6k. multicoloured . . . 40 10
3578 – 10k. red, black & bistre 45 20
3579 – 12k. multicoloured . . 80 25
DESIGNS AND EVENTS—VERT: Type **1321** (World Handball Games, Moscow); 6k. Yachting (20th Baltic Regatta); 10k. Football (70th anniv of Russian soccer). HORIZ: 4k. Table tennis (All European Juvenile Competitions); 12k. Underwater swimming (European Underwater Sports Championships, Alushta, Ukraine).

1322 Girl Gymnasts **1323** Gediminas Tower, Vilnius (Vilna)

1968. Olympic Games, Mexico. Backgrounds in gold.
3580 **1322** 4k. turquoise and blue 20 10
3581 – 6k. violet and red . . . 30 10
3582 – 10k. green and turquoise 55 10
3583 – 12k. brown and orange 70 15
3584 – 16k. blue and pink . . 1·00 30
DESIGNS: 6k. Weightlifting; 10k. Rowing; 12k. Women's hurdles; 16k. Fencing match.

1968. 50th Anniv of Soviet Lithuania.
3586 **1323** 4k. red, drab and purple 30 10

1324 Tbilisi University **1325** "Death of Laocoon and his Sons" (from sculpture by Agesandre, Polidor and Asinodor)

1968. 50th Anniv of Tbilisi University.
3587 **1324** 4k. beige and green . . 25 10

1968. "Promote Solidarity with the Greek Democrats".
3588 **1325** 6k. drab, purple & brn 4·50 3·50

1326 Cavalryman

1968. 50th Anniv of Leninist Young Communist League (Komsomol) (1st issue). Multicoloured.
3589 2k. Type **1326** 10 10
3590 3k. Young workers 15 10
3591 4k. Army officer 20 10
3592 6k. Construction workers . . 25 10
3593 10k. Agricultural workers 40 20
See also No. 3654.

1327 Institute and Molecular Structure

1968. 50th Anniv of N. S. Kurnakov Institute of Chemistry.
3595 **1327** 4k. purple, black and blue 20 10

1328 Letter

1968. Int Correspondence Week and Stamp Day.
3596 **1328** 4k. brown, red and lake 20 10
3597 – 4k. blue, ochre and deep blue 20 10
DESIGN: No. 3597, Russian stamps.

1329 "The 26 Baku Commissars" (statue, S. Merkurov) **1330** T. Antikainen

1968. 50th Anniv of Execution of 26 Baku Commissars.
3598 **1329** 4k. multicoloured . . . 20 10

1968. 70th Birthday of Toivo Antikainen (Finnish Communist leader).
3599 **1330** 6k. brown and grey . . 25 10

1331 Liner "Ivan Franko" **1333** P. P. Postyshev (1887–1940)

1332 Order of the October Revolution

1968. Soviet Merchant Marine.
3600 **1331** 6k. red, dp blue & blue 35 10

1968. 51st Anniv of October Revolution.
3601 **1332** 4k. multicoloured . . . 20 10

1968. Soviet Personalities.
3602 **1333** 4k. black 15 10
3603 – 4k. black 15 10
3604 – 4k. black 15 10
DESIGNS: No. 3603, S. G. Shaumian (1878–1918); 3604, A. Ikramov (1898–1938).

1334 Statuette of Warrior and Ararat Mountains **1335** I. S. Turgenev

1968. 2,750th Anniv of Yerevan (Armenian capital).
3605 **1334** 4k. blk & brn on grey 25 10
3606 – 12k. brn & sepia on yell 60 25
DESIGN: 12k. David Sasunsky Monument (Ye. Kochar).

1968. 150th Birth Anniv of Ivan Turgenev (writer).
3607 **1335** 4k. green 25 10

1336 American Bison and Common Zebra

1968. Fauna. Soviet Wildlife Reservations. Mult.
3608 4k. Type **1336** 30 10
3609 4k. Purple swamphen and lotus 30 15
3610 6k. Great egrets (vert) . . . 35 15
3611 6k. Ostrich and golden pheasant (vert) 35 15
3612 10k. Eland and guanaco . . 55 25
3613 10k. Glossy ibis and white spoonbill 60 25

1337 Building and Equipment

1968. 50th Anniv of Lenin Radio-laboratory, Gorky.
3614 **1337** 4k. blue and ochre . . 20 10

1338 Prospecting for Minerals

1339 Djety-Oguz Kirgizia

1968. Geology Day. Multicoloured.
3615 4k. Type **1338** 30 10
3616 6k. "Tracking down" metals 30 20
3617 10k. Oil derrick 85 20

1968. Central Asian Spas. Multicoloured.
3618 4k. Type **1339** 20 10
3619 4k. Borovoe, Kazakhstan (horiz) 20 10
3620 6k. Issyk-kul, Kirgizia (horiz) 30 15
3621 6k. Borovoe, Kazakhstan . . 30 15

1340 Silver Medal, "Philatec", Paris 1964

1968. Awards to Soviet Post Office at Foreign Stamp Exhibitions.
3622 4k. black, silver and purple 20 10
3623 6k. black, gold and blue . . 25 10
3624 10k. black, gold and blue 55 15
3625 12k. black, silver & turquoise 45 15
3626 16k. black, gold and red . . 75 30
3627 20k. black, gold and blue 90 40
3628 30k. black, gold and brown 1·40 85
DESIGNS: 4k. Type **1340**; 6k. Plaque, "Debria", Berlin, 1959; 10k. Cup and medals, Riccione, 1952, 1968; 12k. Diploma and medal, "Thematic Biennale", Buenos Aires, 1965; 16k. Trophies and medals, Rome, 1952, 1954; 20k. Medals and plaques, "Wipa", Vienna, 1966; 30k. Glass trophies, Prague, 1950, 1955, 1962.

1341 V. K. Lebedinsky

1342 Soldier with Flag

1968. Birth Centenary of Lebedinsky (physicist).
3629 **1341** 4k. multicoloured . . . 30 10

1968. 50th Anniv of Estonian Workers' Commune.
3630 **1342** 4k. black and red . . . 20 10

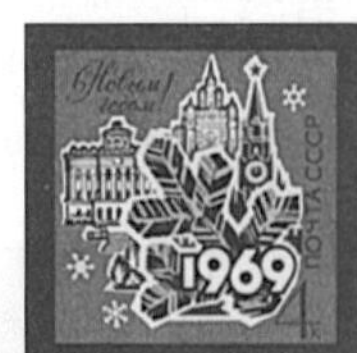

1344 Moscow Buildings and Fir Branch

1968. New Year.
3632 **1344** 4k. multicoloured . . . 35 10

1345 G. Beregovoi (cosmonaut)

1346 Electric Train, Map and Emblem

1968. Flight of "Soyuz 3".
3633 **1345** 10k. black, red and blue 55 20

1968. Soviet Railways.
3634 **1346** 4k. orange and mauve 25 15
3635 – 10k. brown and green 65 25
DESIGN: 10k. Track-laying train.

1347 Red Flag, Newspapers and Monument at Minsk

1348 "The Reapers" (A. Venetsianov)

1968. 50th Anniv of Byelorussian Communist Party.
3636 **1347** 4k. black, brown and red 20 10

1968. Paintings in State Museum, Leningrad. Mult.
3637 1k. Type **1348** 15 10
3638 2k. "The Last Days of Pompeii" (K. Bryullov) (61 × 28 mm) 35 10
3639 3k. "A Knight at the Crossroads" (V. Vasentsov) (61 × 28 mm) 40 10
3640 4k. "Conquering a Town in Winter" (V. Surikov) (61 × 28 mm) 50 10
3641 6k. "The Lake" (I. Levitan) (61 × 28 mm) 70 10
3642 10k. "The Year 1919: Alarm" (K. Petrov-Vodkin) 85 15
3643 16k. "The Defence of Sevastopol" (A. Deineka) (61 × 28 mm) . . . . . . 1·00 20
3644 20k. "Homer's Bust (G. Korzhev) . . . . . . 1·25 25
3645 30k. "The Celebration in Uritsky Square" (B. Kustodiev) (61 × 28 mm) . . . . . . 1·40 30
3646 50k. "The Duel between Peresvet and Chelumbei" (M. Avilov) (61 × 28 mm) 2·00 80

1349 House, Onega Region

1968. Soviet Architecture.
3647 **1349** 3k. brown on buff . . . 20 10
3648 – 4k. green on yellow . . 35 10
3649 – 6k. violet on grey . . . 65 15
3650 – 10k. blue on green . . 95 35
3651 – 12k. red on drab . . . 1·10 60
3652 – 16k. black on yellow . . 1·60 80
DESIGNS: 4k. Farmhouse door, Gorky region; 6k. Wooden church, Kishi; 10k. Citadel, Rostov-Yaroslavl; 12k. Entrance gate, Tsaritzino; 16k. Master-builder Rossi's Street, Leningrad.

1968. 50th Death Anniv of N. G. Markin (1893–1918) (revolutionary). As T **1333**.
3653 4k. black 20 10

1350 Flags and Order of October Revolution

1968. 50th Anniv of Leninist Young Communist League (Komsomol) (2nd issue).
3654 **1350** 12k. multicoloured . . 55 15

1351 "Declaration of Republic"

1969. 50th Anniv of Belorussian Republic. Mult.
3655 2k. Type **1351** 10 10
3656 4k. Partisans at war, 1941–45 . . . . 20 10
3657 6k. Reconstruction workers 30 10

1352 Red Guard in Riga (statue)

1354 University Buildings

1969. 50th Anniv of Soviet Revolution in Latvia.
3658 **1352** 4k. red and orange . . 20 10

1969. 150th Anniv of Leningrad University.
3660 **1354** 10k. black and lake . . 45 20

1355 Krylov (after K. Bryullov)

1356 N. D. Filchenkov

1969. Birth Bicent of Ivan Krylov (fabulist).
3661 **1355** 4k. multicoloured . . . 20 10

1969. War Heroes.
3662 **1356** 4k. brown and red . . 20 10
3663 – 4k. brown and green . . 20 10
DESIGN: No. 3663, A. A. Kosmodemiansky.

1357 "The Wheel Turns Round Again" (sculpture, Zs. Kisfaludi-Strobl)

1969. 50th Anniv of 1st Hungarian Soviet Republic.
3664 **1357** 6k. black, red and green 30 10

1358 Crest and Symbols of Petro-chemical Industry

1969. 50th Anniv of Bashkir Autonomous Soviet Socialist Republic.
3665 **1358** 4k. multicoloured . . . 20 10

1359 "Vostok 1" on Launching-pad

1969. Cosmonautics Day. Multicoloured.
3666 10k. Type **1359** 60 20
3667 10k. "Zond 5" in Lunar orbit (horiz) 60 20
3668 10k. Sergei Pavlovich Korolev (space scientist) (horiz) 60 20

1360 Lenin University, Kazan

1969. Buildings connected with Lenin. Mult.
3670 4k. Type **1360** 20 10
3671 4k. Lenin Museum, Kuibyshev 20 10
3672 4k. Lenin Museum, Pskov 20 10
3673 4k. Lenin Museum, Shushenskaya 20 10
3674 4k. "Hay Hut", Razliv . . . 20 10
3675 4k. Lenin Museum, Gorky Park, Leningrad 20 10
3676 4k. Smolny Institute, Leningrad 20 10
3677 4k. Lenin's Office, Kremlin 20 10
3678 4k. Library, Ulyanovsk (wrongly inscr "Lenin Museum") 20 10
3679 4k. Lenin Museum, Ulyanovsk 20 10

1361 Telephone and Radio Set

1969. 50th Anniv of VEF Electrical Works, Riga.
3680 **1361** 10k. brown and red . . 50 15

1362 I.L.O. Emblem

1969. 50th Anniv of Int Labour Organization.
3681 **1362** 6k. gold and red . . . 30 10

1363 Otakar Jaros

1364 P. E. Dybenko

1969. Otakar Jaros (Czech war hero) Commem.
3682 **1363** 4k. black and blue . . 25 10

1969. Soviet Personalities. 80th Birth Annivs.
3683 **1364** 4k. red 20 10
3684 – 4k. blue 20 10
DESIGN: No. 3684, S. V. Kosior (1889–1939).

1365 Suleiman Stalsky

1969. Birth Centenary of Suleiman Stalsky (Dagestan poet).
3685 **1365** 4k. green and brown . . 30 10

1366 Rose "Clear Glade"

1969. Academy of Sciences Botanical Gardens, Moscow. Multicoloured.
3686 2k. Type **1366** 15 10
3687 4k. Lily "Slender" 20 10
3688 10k. "Cattleya hybr" (orchid) 50 15
3689 12k. Dahlia "Leaves Fall" 60 25
3690 14k. Gladiolus "Ural Girl" 90 40

1367 Scientific Centre

1969. 50th Anniv of Ukraine Academy of Sciences, Kiev.
3691 **1367** 4k. purple and yellow 30 10

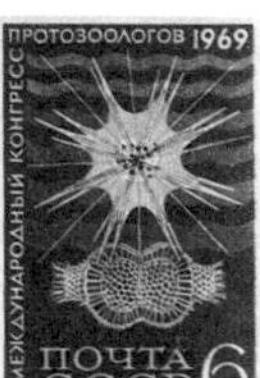

1368 Gold Medal within Film "Flower" **1369** Congress Emblem

1969. Cine and Ballet Events, Moscow. Mult.
3692 6k. Type **1368** (6th Int Cinema Festival) 30 15
3693 6k. Ballet dancers (1st Int Ballet Competitions) . . . 30 15

1969. 3rd Int Protozoologists Congress, Leningrad.
3694 **1369** 6k. multicoloured . . . 90 20

1370 Estonian Singer

1969. Centenary of Estonian Choir Festival.
3695 **1370** 4k. red and ochre . . . 35 10

1371 Mendeleev (after N. Yarashenko) and Formula

1969. Centenary of Mendeleev's Periodic Law of Elements.
3696 **1371** 6k. brown and red . . 50 20

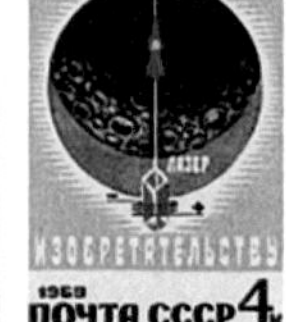

1372 Peace Banner and World Landmarks **1373** Rocket on Laser Beam, and Moon

1969. 20th Anniv of World Peace Movement.
3698 **1372** 10k. multicoloured . . 40 15

1969. "50 Years of Soviet Inventions".
3699 **1373** 4k. red, black and silver 20 10

1374 Kotlyarevsky (**1375**)

1969. Birth Bicentenary of Ivan Kotlyarevsky (Ukrainian writer).
3700 **1374** 4k. black, brown & grn 20 10

1969. Soviet Ice Hockey Victory in World Championships, Stockholm. No. 2828 further optd with **1375**.
3701 6k. turquoise and purple . . 3·25 2·00

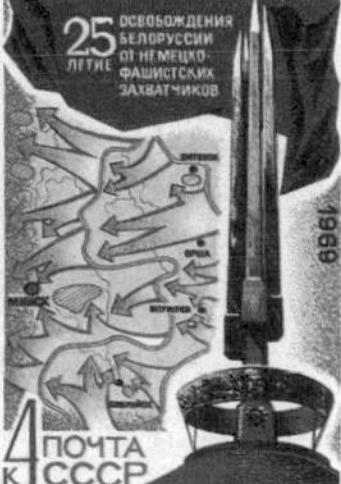

1376 War Memorial in Minsk (A. Bembel) and Campaign Map **1377** Hands holding Torch, and Bulgarian Arms

1969. 25th Anniv of Belorussian Liberation.
3702 **1376** 4k. red, purple and olive 20 10

1969. 25th Anniv of Bulgarian and Polish Peoples' Republics.
3703 **1377** 6k. multicoloured . . . 30 10
3704 – 6k. red and ochre . . . 30 10
DESIGN: No. 3704, Polish map, flag and arms.

1378 Registan Square, Samarkand

1969. 2,500th Anniv of Samarkand. Mult.
3705 4k. Type **1378** 25 10
3706 6k. Intourist Hotel, Samarkand 40 15

1379 Liberation Monument, Nikolaev **1380** Volleyball (European Junior Championships)

1969. 25th Anniv of Liberation of Nikolaev.
3707 **1379** 4k. red, violet and black 25 10

1969. International Sporting Events.
3708 **1380** 4k. red, brown & orange 20 10
3709 – 6k. multicoloured . . . 40 10
DESIGN: 6k. Canoeing (European Championships).

1381 M. Munkacsy and detail of painting, "Peasant Woman churning Butter" **1382** Miners' Statue, Donetsk

1969. 125th Birth Anniv of Mihaly Munkacsy (Hungarian painter).
3710 **1381** 6k. black, orange & brn 30 10

1969. Centenary of Donetsk.
3711 **1382** 4k. mauve and grey . . 20 10

1383 "Horse-drawn Machine-guns" (M. Grekov)

1969. 50th Anniv of 1st Cavalry Army.
3712 **1383** 4k. brown and red . . 40 15

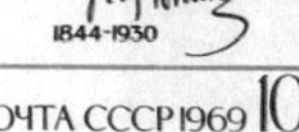

1384 Ilya Repin (self-portrait) **1385** Running

1969. 125th Birth Anniv of Ilya Repin (painter). Multicoloured.
3713 4k. "Barge-haulers on the Volga" 25 10
3714 6k. "Unexpected" 35 15
3715 10k. Type **1384** 40 15
3716 12k. "The Refusal of Confession" 55 20
3717 16k. "Dnieper Cossacks" . . 75 30

1969. 9th Trade Unions' Games, Moscow.
3718 **1385** 4k. black, green and red 15 10
3719 – 10k. black, blue & green 35 10
DESIGN: 10k. Gymnastics.

1386 V. L. Komarov **1387** O. Tumanyan and Landscape

1969. Birth Cent of V. L. Komarov (botanist).
3721 **1386** 4k. brown and olive . . 25 10

1969. Birth Cent of O. Tumanyan (Armenian poet).
3722 **1387** 10k. black and blue . . 50 15

1388 Turkoman Drinking- horn (2nd-cent B.C.) **1389** Mahatma Gandhi

1969. Oriental Art Treasures, State Museum of Oriental Art, Moscow. Multicoloured.
3723 4k. Type **1388** 25 10
3724 6k. Simurg vessel, Persia (13th-century) 35 10
3725 12k. Statuette, Korea (8th-century) 50 15
3726 16k. Bodhisatva statuette, Tibet (7th-century) . . . 70 20
3727 20k. Ebisu statuette, Japan (17th-century) . . . . . 1·00 50

1969. Birth Centenary of Mahatma Gandhi.
3728 **1389** 6k. brown 55 15

1390 Black Stork at Nest

1969. Belovezhaskaya Pushcha Nature Reserve. Multicoloured.
3729 4k. Type **1390** 30 15
3730 6k. Red deer and fawn . . . 45 15
3731 10k. European bison fighting 65 20
3732 12k. Lynx and cubs 75 20
3733 16k. Wild boar and young 90 35
No. 3731 is larger, 76 × 24 mm.

1391 "Komitas" and Rural Scene

1969. Birth Cent of "Komitas" (S. Sogomonyan, Armenian composer).
3734 **1391** 6k. black, flesh and grey 35 15

1392 Sergei Gritsevets (fighter-pilot) **1393** I. Pavlov (after portrait by A. Yar-Kravchenko)

1969. Soviet War Heroes.
3735 **1392** 4k. black and green . . 30 10
3736 – 4k. brown, red & yellow 20 10
3737 – 4k. brown and green . . 20 10
DESIGNS: As Type **1392**. No. 3737, Lisa Chaikina (partisan). (35½ × 24 mm); No. 3736, A. Cheponis, Y. Alexonis and G. Boris (Kaunas resistance fighters).

1969. 120th Birth Anniv of Ivan P. Pavlov (physiologist).
3738 **1393** 4k. multicoloured . . . 25 10

1394 D.D.R. Arms and Berlin Landmarks **1395** A. V. Koltsov (from portrait by A. Yar-Kravchenko)

1969. 20th Anniv of German Democratic Republic.
3739 **1394** 6k. multicoloured . . . 25 10

1969. 160th Birth Anniv of A. V. Koltsov (poet).
3740 **1395** 4k. brown and blue . . 25 10

1396 Arms of Ukraine and Memorial **1397** Kremlin, and Hammer and Sickle

1969. 25th Anniv of Ukraine Liberation.
3741 **1396** 4k. red and gold . . . 30 15

1969. 52nd Anniv of October Revolution.
3742 **1397** 4k. multicoloured . . . 25 10

1398 G. Shonin and V. Kubasov ("Soyuz 6")

1969. Triple Space Flights.
3744 **1398** 10k. green and gold . . 55 15
3745 – 10k. green and gold . . 55 15
3746 – 10k. green and gold . . 55 15
DESIGNS: No. 3745, A. Filipchenko, V. Volkov and V. Gorbatko ("Soyuz 7"); No. 3746, V. Shatalov and A. Yeliseev ("Soyuz 8").

1399 Lenin when a Youth (after V. Tsigal) and Emblems
1400 Corps Emblem on Red Star

1969. U.S.S.R. Youth Philatelic Exhibition to commemorate Lenin's Birth Centenary, Kiev.
3747 **1399** 4k. lake and pink . . . 25 15

1969. 50th Anniv of Red Army Communications Corps.
3748 **1400** 4k. red, brown & bistre 25 15

1401 "Worker and Collective Farmer" (sculpture, Vera Mukhina) and Title-page

1969. 3rd Soviet Collective Farmers' Congress, Moscow.
3749 **1401** 4k. brown and gold . . 20 10

1402 "Vasilisa, the Beauty" (folk tale)

1969. Russian Fairy Tales. Multicoloured.
3750 4k. Type **1402** 35 30
3751 10k. "Maria Morevna" (folk tale) 85 60
3752 16k. "The Golden Cockerel" (Pushkin) (horiz) . . . . 1·25 75
3753 20k. "Finist, the Fine Fellow" (folk tale) . . . . 1·50 1·00
3754 50k. "Tale of the Tsar Saltan" (Pushkin) . . . . 2·75 2·00

1403 Venus Plaque and Radio-telescope

1969. Space Exploration.
3755 **1403** 4k. red, brown and black 35 10
3756 – 6k. purple, grey & black 45 15
3757 – 10k. multicoloured . . 70 20
DESIGNS: 6k. Space station and capsule in orbit; 10k. Photograph of the Earth taken by "Zond 7".

1404 Soviet and Afghan Flags
1405 Red Star and Arms

1969. 50th Anniv of U.S.S.R.–Afghanistan Diplomatic Relations.
3759 **1404** 6k. red, black and green 35 10

1969. Coil Stamp.
3760 **1405** 4k. red . . . . 1·75 80

1406 Mikoyan Gurevich MiG-3 and MiG-23 Fighters

1969. "30 Years of MiG Aircraft".
3761 **1406** 6k. black, grey and red 70 15

1407 Lenin

1969. New Year.
3762 **1407** 4k. multicoloured . . . 25 10

1408 Tupolev ANT-2

1969. Development of Soviet Civil Aviation.
3763 **1408** 2k. multicoloured . . . 20 10
3764 – 3k. multicoloured . . . 25 10
3765 – 4k. multicoloured . . . 25 10
3766 – 6k. black, red and purple 25 10
3767 – 10k. multicoloured . . 55 15
3768 – 12k. multicoloured . . 60 20
3769 – 16k. multicoloured . . 80 25
3770 – 20k. multicoloured . . 95 35
AIRCRAFT: 3k. Polikarpov Po-2; 4k. Tupolev ANT-9; 6k. TsAGI 1-EA helicopter; 10k. Tupolev ANT-20 "Maksim Gorky"; 12k. Tupolev Tu-104; 16k. Mil Mi-10 helicopter; 20k. Ilyushin Il-62.

1409 Model Gliders

1969. Technical Sports.
3772 **1409** 3k. purple 15 10
3773 – 4k. green 20 10
3774 – 6k. brown 30 10
DESIGNS: 4k. Speed boat racing; 6k. Parachuting.

1410 Rumanian Arms and Soviet Memorial, Bucharest
1411 TV Tower, Ostankino

1969. 25th Anniv of Rumanian Liberation.
3775 **1410** 6k. red and brown . . 30 15

1969. Television Tower, Ostankino, Moscow.
3776 **1411** 10k. multicoloured . . 45 20

1412 "Lenin" (after N. Andreev)

1970. Birth Centenary of V. I. Lenin (1st issue). Multicoloured.
3777 4k. Type **1412** 25 10
3778 4k. "Marxist Meeting, Petrograd" (A. Moravov) 25 10
3779 4k. "Second RSDRP Congress" (Yu. Vinogradov) 25 10
3780 4k. "First Day of Soviet Power" (N. Babasyak) . . 25 10
3781 4k. "Visiting Lenin" (F. Modorov) 25 10
3782 4k. "Conversation with Ilich" (A. Shirokov) . . . 25 10
3783 4k. "May Day 1920" (I. Brodsky) 25 10
3784 4k. "With Lenin" (V. Serov) 25 10
3785 4k. "Conquerors of the Cosmos" (A. Deyineka) 25 10
3786 4k. "Communism Builders" (A. Korentsov, Ye. Merkulov, V. Burakov) 25 10
See also Nos. 3812/21.

1413 F. V. Sychkov and Painting "Tobogganing"

1970. Birth Centenary of F. V. Sychkov (artist).
3787 **1413** 4k. blue and brown . . 40 15

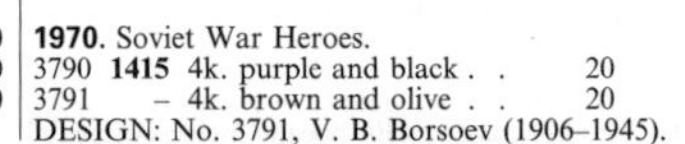

1414 "Vostok", "Mirnyi" and Antarctic Map
1415 V. I. Peshekhonov

1970. 150th Anniv of Antarctic Expedition by Bellinghausen and Lazarev.
3788 **1414** 4k. turquoise, mauve & bl . . . . 1·25 25
3789 – 16k. red, green & purple . . . . . . 2·50 55
DESIGN: 16k. Modern polar-station and map.

1970. Soviet War Heroes.
3790 **1415** 4k. purple and black . . 20 10
3791 – 4k. brown and olive . . 20 10
DESIGN: No. 3791, V. B. Borsoev (1906–1945).

1416 Geographical Society Emblem
1417 "The Torch of Peace" (A. Dumpe)

1970. 125th Anniv of Russian Geographical Society.
3792 **1416** 6k. multicoloured . . . 35 10

1970. 60th Anniv of Int Women's Solidarity Day.
3793 **1417** 6k. drab and turquoise 35 10

1418 Ivan Bazhov (folk hero) and Crafts
1419 Lenin

1970. World Fair "Expo 70", Osaka, Japan.
3794 **1418** 4k. black, red and green 15 10
3795 – 6k. silver, red and black 30 10
3796 – 10k. multicoloured . . 45 15
DESIGNS: 6k. U.S.S.R. Pavilion; 10k. Boy and model toys.

1970. Lenin Birth Centenary. All-Union Philatelic Exhibition, Moscow.
3798 **1419** 4k. black, gold and red 25 10

1420 Friendship Tree

1970. Friendship Tree, Sochi.
3800 **1420** 10k. multicoloured . . 45 20

1421 Ice Hockey Players

1970. World Ice Hockey Championships, Stockholm, Sweden.
3801 **1421** 6k. green and blue . . 60 15

1422 Hammer, Sickle and Azerbaijan Emblems

1970. 50th Anniv of Soviet Republics.
3802 **1422** 4k. red and gold . . . 20 10
3803 – 4k. brown and silver . . 20 10
3804 – 4k. purple and gold . . 20 10
DESIGNS: No. 3803, Woman and motifs of Armenia; 3804, Woman and emblem of Kazakh Republic.

1423 Worker and Book
1424 D. N. Medvedev

1970. U.N.E.S.C.O. "Lenin Centenary" Symposium.
3805 **1423** 6k. ochre and lake . . 20 10

1970. Partisan War Heroes.
3806 **1424** 4k. brown 20 10
3807 – 4k. brown 20 10
PORTRAIT: No. 3807, K. P. Orlovsky.

(1425) **1426** Hungarian Arms and Budapest View

1970. Russian Victory in World Ice Hockey Championships, Stockholm. No. 3801 optd with T **1425**.
3808 **1421** 6k. green and blue . . 70 20

1970. 25th Anniv of Hungarian and Czech Liberation. Multicoloured.
3809 6k. Type **1426** 20 10
3810 6k. Czech Arms and Prague view 20 10

1427 Cosmonauts' Emblem **1428** Lenin, 1891

1970. Cosmonautics Day.
3811 **1427** 6k. multicoloured . . . 20 10

1970. Birth Centenary of Lenin (2nd issue).
3812 **1428** 2k. green 10 10
3813 – 2k. olive 10 10
3814 – 4k. blue 15 10
3815 – 4k. lake 15 10
3816 – 6k. brown 35 10
3817 – 6k. lake 35 10
3818 – 10k. purple 50 15
3819 – 10k. brown 50 15
3820 – 12k. black and silver . . 55 20
3821 – 12k. red and gold . . . 55 20
PORTRAITS OF LENIN: No. 3813, In 1900; 3814, In 1914; 3815, In 1916; 3816, 3817, 3818, In 1918; 3819, In 1920; 3820, Sculptured head by Yu. Kolesnikov; 3821, Sculptured head by N. Andreev.

1429 Order of Victory **1431** Lenin (sculpture, Yu. Kolesnikov)

1430 Komsomol Badge

1970. 25th Anniv of Victory in Second World War.
3823 **1429** 1k. gold, grey and purple 10 10
3824 – 2k. purple, brn & gold 10 10
3825 – 3k. red, black and gold 15 10
3826 – 4k. red, brown and gold 20 10
3827 – 10k. gold, red & purple 55 30
DESIGNS: 2k. Eternal Flame; 3k. Treptow Monument, Berlin; 4k. Home Defence Order; 10k. Hero of the Soviet Union and Hero of Socialist Labour medals.

1970. 16th Congress of Leninist Young Communist League (Komsomol).
3829 **1430** 4k. multicoloured . . . 20 10

1970. World Youth Meeting for Lenin Birth Centenary.
3830 **1431** 6k. red 20 10

1432 "Young Workers" and Federation Emblem

1970. 25th Anniv of World Democratic Youth Federation.
3831 **1432** 6k. black and blue . . 35 10

1433 Arms and Government Building, Kazan

1970. 50th Anniv of Russian Federation Autonomous Soviet Socialist Republics.
3832 **1433** 4k. blue 30 10
3833 – 4k. green 30 10
3834 – 4k. red 30 10
3835 – 4k. brown 30 10
3836 – 4k. green 30 10
3837 – 4k. brown 30 10
DESIGNS: Arms and Government Buildings. No. 3832, (Tatar Republic); 3833, Petrozavodzk (Karelian Republic); 3834, Cheboksary (Chuvash Republic); 3835, Elista (Kalmyk Republic); 3836, Izhevsk (Udmurt Republic); 3837, Ioshkar-Ola (Mari Republic).
See also Nos. 3903/7, 4052/3, 4175, 4253, 4298, 4367 and 4955.

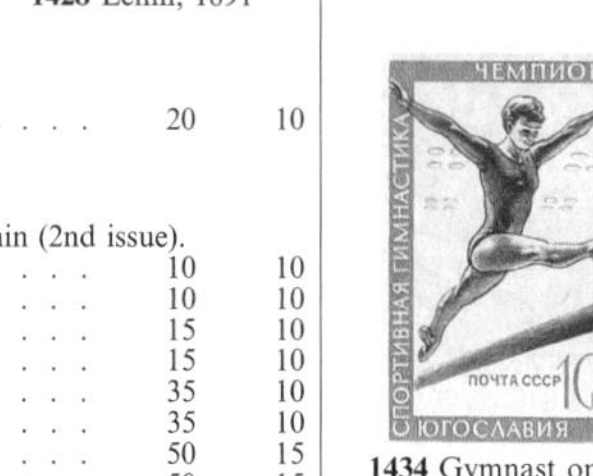

1434 Gymnast on Bar (World Championships, Yugoslavia) **1435** "Swords into Ploughshares" (sculpture by E. Vuchetich)

1970. International Sporting Events.
3838 **1434** 10k. red and drab . . . 50 15
3839 – 16k. brown and green 80 30
DESIGN: 16k. Three footballers (World Cup Championship, Mexico).

1970. 25th Anniv of United Nations.
3840 **1435** 12k. purple and green 50 10

1436 Cosmonauts and "Soyuz 9"

1970. Space Flight by "Soyuz 9".
3841 **1436** 10k. black, red & purple 50 10

1437 Engels

1970. 150th Birth Anniv of Friedrich Engels.
3842 **1437** 4k. brown and red . . 20 10

1438 Cruiser "Aurora"

1970. Soviet Warships.
3843 **1438** 3k. pink, lilac and black 30 10
3844 – 4k. black and yellow . . 35 10
3845 – 10k. blue and mauve 85 20
3846 – 12k. brown and buff . . 1·10 25
3847 – 20k. purple, blue & turq . . . . 1·60 40
DESIGNS: 4k. Missile cruiser "Groznyi"; 10k. Cruiser "Oktyabrskaya Revolyutsiya"; 12k. Missile cruiser "Varyag"; 20k. Nuclear submarine "Leninsky Komsomol".

1439 Soviet and Polish Workers **1440** Allegory of the Sciences

1970. 25th Anniv of Soviet-Polish Friendship Treaty.
3848 **1439** 6k. red and blue . . . 20 10

1970. 13th Int Historical Sciences Congress, Moscow.
3849 **1440** 4k. multicoloured . . . 20 10

1441 Mandarins **1442** Magnifying Glass, "Stamp" and Covers

1970. Fauna of Sikhote-Alin Nature Reserve. Multicoloured.
3850 4k. Type **1441** 30 15
3851 6k. Yellow-throated marten 45 15
3852 10k. Asiatic black bear (vert) 60 15
3853 16k. Red deer 70 25
3854 20k. Tiger . . . . 1·00 35

1970. 2nd U.S.S.R. Philatelic Society Congress, Moscow.
3855 **1442** 4k. silver and red . . . 25 10

1443 V. I. Kikvidze **1444** University Building

1970. 75th Birth Anniv of V. J. Kikvidze (Civil War hero).
3856 **1443** 4k. brown 20 10

1970. 50th Anniv of Yerevan University.
3857 **1444** 4k. red and blue . . . 20 10

1445 Pioneer Badge **1446** Library Book-plate (A. Kuchas)

1970. Pioneer Organization.
3858 **1445** 1k. gold, red and grey 10 10
3859 – 2k. grey and brown . . 10 10
3860 – 4k. multicoloured . . . 20 10

DESIGNS: 2k. "Lenin with Children" (sculpture, N. Scherbakov), 4k. Red Star and scarf.

1970. 400th Anniv of Vilnius (Vilna) University Library (Lithuania).
3861 **1446** 4k. black, grey and silver 20 10

1447 Woman with Bouquet

1970. 25th Anniv of International Democratic Women's Federation.
3862 **1447** 6k. brown and blue . . 20 10

1448 Milkmaid and Cows ("Livestock")

1970. Soviet Agriculture. Multicoloured.
3863 4k. Type **1448** 20 10
3864 4k. Driver, tractor and harvester ("Mechanization") . . . 20 10
3865 4k. Lock-operator and canal ("Irrigation and Chemical Research") 20 10

1449 Lenin addressing Meeting

1970. 53rd Anniv of October Revolution.
3866 **1449** 4k. gold and red . . . 20 10

50 лет
ленинскому плану
ГОЭЛРО • 1970
(1450)

1970. 50th Anniv of GOELRO Electrification Plan. No. 3475 optd with T **1450**.
3868 4k. multicoloured 85 40

1451 Spassky Tower, Kremlin **1452** A. A. Baikov

1970. New Year.
3869 **1451** 6k. multicoloured . . . 20 10

1970. Birth Centenary of A. A. Baikov (metallurgic scientist).
3870 **1452** 4k. black and brown . . 20 10

1453 Tsyurupa (after A. Yar-Kravchenkol) **1454** St. Basil's Cathedral, Red Square, Moscow

1970. Birth Centenary of A. D. Tsyurupa (Vice-Chairman of Soviet People's Commissars).
3871 **1453** 4k. brown and yellow 20 10

1970. Tourism.
3872 **1454** 4k. multicoloured . . . 20 10
3873 – 6k. blue, indigo & brown 35 10
3874 – 10k. brown and green 45 15
3875 – 12k. multicoloured . . 55 15
3876 – 14k. blue, red and brown 70 20
3877 – 16k. multicoloured . . 80 30
DESIGNS: 6k. Scene from ballet "Swan Lake" (Tchaikovsky); 10k. Sika deer; 12k. Souvenir handicrafts; 14k. "Swords into Ploughshares" (sculpture by Ye. Vuchetich); 16k. Tourist and camera.

1455 Camomile

1970. Flowers. Multicoloured.
3878 4k. Type **1455** 15 10
3879 6k. Dahlia 30 10
3880 10k. Phlox 45 10
3881 12k. Aster . . . . 1·00 20
3882 16k. Clematis 70 30

1456 African Woman and Child
1457 Beethoven

1970. 10th Anniv of U.N. Declaration on Colonial Independence.
3883 **1456** 10k. brown and blue . . 40 10

1970. Birth Bicentenary of Beethoven (composer).
3884 **1457** 10k. purple and pink 1·25 35

1458 "Luna 16" in Flight
1459 Speed Skating

1970. Flight of "Luna 16".
3885 **1458** 10k. green 50 15
3886 – 10k. purple 50 15
3887 – 10k. green 50 15
DESIGNS: No. 3886, "Luna 16" on Moon's surface; 3887, Parachute descent.

1970. Trade Unions' Winter Games (1971).
3889 **1459** 4k. blue, red and grey 20 10
3890 – 10k. green, brn & grey 60 15
DESIGN: 10k. Cross-country skiing.

1460 "The Conestabile Madonna" (Raphael)

1970. Foreign Paintings in Soviet Galleries. Mult.
3891 3k. Type **1460** 20 10
3892 4k. "Saints Peter and Paul" (El Greco) 30 10
3893 10k. "Perseus and Andromeda" (Rubens) (horiz) 60 15
3894 12k. "The Return of the Prodigal Son" (Rembrandt) 70 15
3895 16k. "Family Portrait" (Van Dyck) 95 25
3896 20k. "The Actress Jeanne Samary" (Renoir) . . . . 1·10 35
3897 30k. "Woman with Fruit" (Gauguin) . . . . 1·50 85

1461 Harry Pollitt and Freighter "Jolly George"

1970. 80th Birth Anniv of H. Pollitt (British Communist).
3899 **1461** 10k. brown and purple 40 15

1462 "75" Emblem
1464 "50", State Emblem and Flag

1463 Sculptured Head of Lenin (A. Belostotsky and E. Fridman)

1970. 75th Anniv of Int Co-operative Alliance.
3900 **1462** 12k. red and green . . 55 15

1971. 24th Soviet Union Communist Party Congress.
3901 **1463** 4k. red and gold . . . 20 10

1971. 50th Anniv of Georgian Soviet Republic.
3902 **1464** 4k. multicoloured . . . 20 10

1971. 50th Anniv of Autonomous Soviet Socialist Republics. Similar designs to T **1433**, but dated "1971".
3903 4k. turquoise 25 10
3904 4k. red 25 10
3905 4k. red 25 10
3906 4k. blue 25 10
3907 4k. green 25 10
DESIGNS: No. 3903, Russian Federation Arms and Supreme Soviet building (Dagestan Republic); 3904, National emblem and symbols of agriculture and industry (Abkhazian Republic); 3905, Arms, produce and industry (Adjarian Republic); 3906, Arms and State building (Kabardino-Balkar Republic); 3907, Arms, industrial products and Government building (Komi Republic).

1465 Genua Fortress and Cranes

1971. 2500th Anniv of Feodosia (Crimean city).
3908 **1465** 10k. multicoloured . . 50 15

1466 Palace of Culture, Kiev
1467 "Features of National Economy"

1971. 24th Ukraine Communist Party Congress, Kiev.
3909 **1466** 4k. multicoloured . . . 20 10

1971. 50th Anniv of Soviet State Planning Organization.
3910 **1467** 6k. red and brown . . 35 10

1468 N. Gubin, I. Chernykh and S. Kosinov (dive-bomber crew)

1971. Soviet Air Force Heroes.
3911 **1468** 4k. brown and green . . 20 10

1469 Gipsy Dance

1971. State Folk Dance Ensemble. Multicoloured.
3912 10k. Type **1469** 55 20
3913 10k. Russian "Summer" dance (women in circle) 55 20
3914 10k. Ukraine "Gopak" dance (dancer leaping) . . 55 20
3915 10k. Adjar "Khorumi" dance (with drummer) . . 55 20
3916 10k. "On the Ice" (ballet) 55 20

1470 L. Ukrainka
1472 Fighting at the Barricades

1471 "Luna 17" Module on Moon

1971. Birth Centenary of Lesya Ukrainka (Ukrainian writer).
3917 **1470** 4k. red and brown . . 20 10

1971. Soviet Moon Exploration.
3918 **1471** 10k. brown and violet 40 15
3919 – 12k. brown and blue . . 70 20
3920 – 12k. brown and blue . . 70 20
3921 – 16k. brown and violet 95 30
DESIGNS: No. 3919, Control room and radio telescope; 3920, Moon trench; 3921, "Lunokhod 1" Moon-vehicle.

1971. Centenary of Paris Commune.
3923 **1472** 6k. black, brown and red 20 10

1473 Hammer, Sickle and Development Emblems
1475 E. Birznieks-Upitis

1474 Gagarin Medal, Spaceships and Planets

1971. 24th Soviet Communist Party Congress, Moscow.
3924 **1473** 6k. red, bistre & brown 20 10

1971. 10th Anniv of First Manned Space Flight (1st issue) and Cosmonautics Day.
3925 **1474** 10k. olive, yellow & brn 45 15
3926 – 12k. purple, blue & grey 60 20
DESIGN: 12k. Spaceship over Globe and economic symbols.
See also No. 3974.

1971. Birth Centenary of E. Birznieks-Upitis (Lithuanian writer).
3927 **1475** 4k. red and green . . . 20 10

1476 Honey Bee on Flower

1971. 23rd Int Bee-keeping Congress, Moscow.
3928 **1476** 6k. multicoloured . . . 40 15

1478 Memorial Building

1971. Lenin Memorial Building, Ulyanovsk.
3930 **1478** 4k. olive and red . . . 20 10

1479 Lieut-Col. N. I. Vlasov
1480 Khafiz Shirazi

1971. 26th Anniv of Victory in 2nd World War.
3931 **1479** 4k. brown and green . . 20 10

1971. 650th Birth Anniv of Khafiz Shirazi (Tadzhik writer).
3932 **1480** 4k. multicoloured . . . 20 10

1481 "GAZ-66" Truck

1971. Soviet Motor Vehicles.
3933 **1481** 2k. multicoloured . . . 15 10
3934 – 3k. multicoloured . . . 15 10
3935 – 4k. blue, black and lilac 20 10
3936 – 4k. green, purple & drab 20 10
3937 – 10k. red, black and lilac 55 15
DESIGNS: 3k. "BelAZ-540" tipper truck; 4k. (3935) "Moskvitch-412" 4-door saloon; 4k. (3936) "Zaporozhets ZAZ-968" 2-door saloon; 10k. "Volga GAZ-24" saloon.

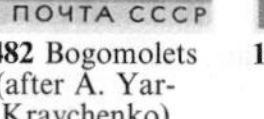

1482 Bogomolets (after A. Yar-Kravchenko)
1483 Commemorative Scroll

1971. 90th Birth Anniv of A. A. Bogomolets (medical scientist).
3938 **1482** 4k. black, pink & orange 20 10

1971. International Moscow Congresses.
3939 **1483** 6k. brown and green . . 35 10
3940 – 6k. multicoloured . . . 35 10
3941 – 6k. multicoloured . . . 25 10
DESIGNS AND EVENTS—HORIZ: No. 3939, (13th Science History Congress); 3940, Oil derrick and symbols (8th World Oil Congress). VERT: No. 3941, Satellite over globe (15th General Assembly of Geodesics and Geophysics Union).

1484 Sukhe Bator Statue, Ulan Bator

1971. 50th Anniv of Revolution in Mongolia.
3942 **1484** 6k. grey, gold and red 20 10

1485 Defence Monument (E. Guirbulis)

1486 Treaty Emblem

1971. 30th Anniv of Defence of Liepaja, Latvia.
3943 **1485** 4k. brown, black & grey 20 10

1971. 10th Anniv of Antarctic Treaty and 50th Anniv of Soviet Hydrometeorological Service.
3944 **1486** 6k. deep blue, black and blue 75 30
3945 – 10k. violet, black & red 1·00 35
DESIGN: 10k. Hydrometeorological map.

1487 "Motherland" (sculpture, Yu. Vuchetich)

1488 Throwing the Discus

1971. 20th Anniv of "Federation Internationale des Resistants".
3946 **1487** 6k. green and red . . . 20 10

1971. 5th Summer Spartakiad.
3947 **1488** 3k. blue on pink . . . 10 10
3948 – 4k. green on flesh . . . 15 10
3949 – 6k. brown on green . . 30 10
3950 – 10k. purple on blue . . 55 20
3951 – 12k. brown on yellow 60 20
DESIGNS: 4k. Archery; 6k. Horse-riding (dressage); 10k. Basketball; 12k. Wrestling.

1489 "Benois Madonna" (Leonardo da Vinci)

1971. Foreign Paintings in Russian Museums. Multicoloured.
3952 2k. Type **1489** 10 10
3953 4k. "Mary Magdalene confesses her Sins" (Titian) 20 10
3954 10k. "The Washerwoman" (Chardin) (horiz) 40 15
3955 12k. "Young Man with Glove" (Hals) 50 20
3956 14k. "Tancred and Erminia" (Poussin) (horiz) 65 20
3957 16k. "Girl Fruit-seller" (Murillo) 80 35
3958 20k. "Child on Ball" (Picasso) . . . . 1·25 50

1490 Lenin Badge and Kazakh Flag

1971. 50th Anniv of Kazakh Communist Youth Assn.
3959 **1490** 4k. brown, red and blue 20 10

1491 Posthorn within Star

1971. International Correspondence Week.
3960 **1491** 4k. black, blue and green 20 10

1492 A. Spendiarov (Armenian composer) (after M. Saryan)

1971. Birth Anniversaries. Multicoloured.
3961 4k. Type **1492** (cent) 20 10
3962 4k. Nikolai Nekrasov (after I. Kramskoi) (poet, 150th anniv) 20 10
3963 10k. Fyodor Dostoevsky (after V. Perov) (writer, 150th anniv) 60 25

1493 Z. Paliashvili

1494 Emblem, Gorky Kremlin and Hydrofoil

1971. Birth Centenary of Z. Paliashvili (Georgian composer).
3964 **1493** 4k. brown 20 10

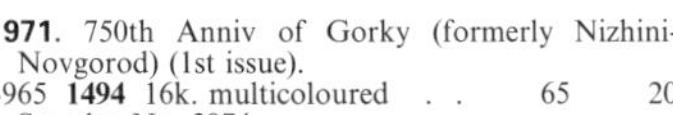

1971. 750th Anniv of Gorky (formerly Nizhni-Novgorod) (1st issue).
3965 **1494** 16k. multicoloured . . 65 20
See also No. 3974.

1495 Students and Globe

1971. 25th Anniv of Int Students Federation.
3966 **1495** 6k. blue, red and brown 20 10

1496 Atlantic White-sided Dolphins

1497 Star and Miners' Order

1971. Marine Fauna. Multicoloured.
3967 4k. Type **1496** 30 10
3968 6k. Sea otter 40 10
3969 10k. Narwhals 50 15
3970 12k. Walrus 75 20
3971 14k. Ribbon seals . . . . . 1·10 45

1971. 250th Anniv of Coal Discovery in Donetz Basin.
3972 **1497** 4k. red, brown and black 20 10

1498 Lord Rutherford and Atomic Formula

1499 Statue of Maksim Gorky (Vera Mukhina) and View

1971. Birth Cent of Lord Rutherford (physicist).
3973 **1498** 6k. brown and purple 35 15

1971. 750th Anniv of Gorky (formerly Nizhni-Novgorod) (2nd issue).
3974 **1499** 4k. multicoloured . . . 20 10

1500 Santa Claus in Troika

1971. New Year.
3975 **1500** 10k. red, gold and black 35 15

1501 Workers and Marx Books ("International Socialist Solidarity") (½-size illustration)

1971. 24th Soviet Union Communist Party Congress Resolutions.
3976 **1501** 4k. blue, ultram & red 25 10
3977 – 4k. red, yellow & brown 25 10
3978 – 4k. lilac, black and red 25 10
3979 – 4k. bistre, brown and red 25 10
3980 – 4k. red, green and yellow 25 10
DESIGNS: No. 3977, Farmworkers and wheatfield ("Agricultural Production"); 3978, Factory production line ("Increased Productivity"); 3979, Heavy industry ("Industrial Expansion"); 3980, Family in department store ("National Welfare").

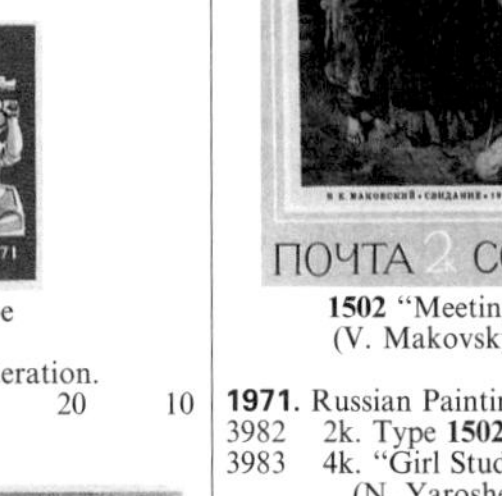

1502 "Meeting" (V. Makovsky)

1503 V. V. Vorovsky

1971. Russian Paintings. Multicoloured.
3982 2k. Type **1502** 20 10
3983 4k. "Girl Student" (N. Yaroshenko) 25 10
3984 6k. "Woman Miner" (N. Kasatkin) 85 10
3985 10k. "Harvesters" (G. Myasoedov) (horiz) 55 15
3986 16k. "Country Road" (A. Savrasov) 80 30
3987 20k. "Pine Forest" (I. Shishkin) (horiz) . . . 1·25 40
See also Nos. 4064/70.

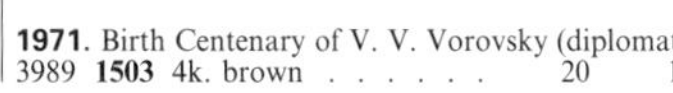

1971. Birth Centenary of V. V. Vorovsky (diplomat).
3989 **1503** 4k. brown 20 10

1504 Dobrovolsky, Volkov and Patsaev

1971. "Soyuz 11" Cosmonauts Commemoration.
3990 **1504** 4k. black, purple & orge 25 10

1505 Order of the Revolution and Building Construction

1971. 54th Anniv of October Revolution.
3991 **1505** 4k. multicoloured . . . 20 10

1506 E. Vakhtangov (founder) and characters from "Princess Turandot"

1507 "Dzhambul Dzhabaiev" (A. Yar-Kravchenko)

1971. 50th Anniv of Vakhtangov Theatre, Moscow.
3992 **1506** 10k. red and lake . . . 50 15
3993 – 10k. yellow and brown 50 15
3994 – 10k. orange and brown 50 15
DESIGNS—HORIZ: No. 3993, B. Shchukin (actor) and scene from "The Man with the Rifle"; 3994, R. Simonov (director) and scene from "Cyrano de Bergerac".

1971. 125th Anniv of Dzhambul Dzhabaiev (Kazakh poet).
3995 **1507** 4k. brown, yell & orge 20 10

1508 Pskov Kremlin

1971. Historical Buildings. Multicoloured.
3996 3k. Type **1508** 15 10
3997 4k. Novgorod kremlin . . . 20 10
3998 6k. Smolensk fortress and Liberation Monument . . 25 10
3999 10k. Kolomna kremlin . . . 40 15

1509 William Foster

1971. 90th Birth Anniv of Foster (American communist).
4001 **1509** 10k. black and brown 15·00 15·00
4002 10k. black and brown 50 15
No. 4001 shows the incorrect date of death "1964"; 4002 shows the correct date, "1961".

1510 Fadeev and Scene from "The Rout" (novel)

1971. 70th Birth Anniv of Aleksandr Fadeev (writer).
4003 **1510** 4k. orange and blue . . 20 10

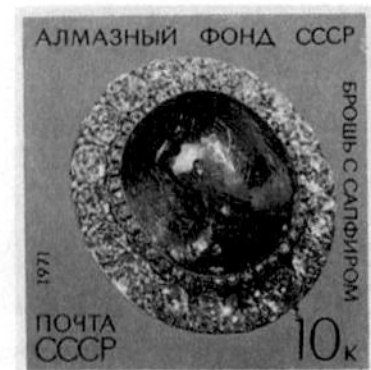

1511 Sapphire Brooch

1971. Diamonds and Jewels. Multicoloured.
4004 10k. Type **1511** 60 15
4005 10k. "Shah" diamond 60 15
4006 10k. "Narcissi" diamond brooch 60 15
4007 20k. Amethyst pendant 90 40
4008 20k. "Rose" platinum and diamond brooch 90 40
4009 30k. Pearl and diamond pendant 1·40 60

1512 Vanda Orchid **1514** Ice Hockey Players

1513 Peter the Great's Imperial Barge, 1723

1971. Tropical Flowers. Multicoloured.
4010 1k. Type **1512** 15 10
4011 2k. "Anthurium scherzerianum" 15 10
4012 4k. "Cactus epiphyllum" 30 10
4013 12k. Amaryllis 60 30
4014 14k. "Medinilla magnifica" 75 35

1971. History of the Russian Navy (1st series). Multicoloured.
4016 1k. Type **1513** 15 10
4017 4k. Galleon "Orel", 1668 (vert) 35 10
4018 10k. Ship of the line "Poltava", 1712 (vert) 75 15
4019 12k. Ship of the line "Ingermanland", 1715 (vert) 1·10 30
4020 16k. Steam frigate "Vladimir", 1848 1·40 50
See also Nos. 4117/21, 4209/13 and 4303/6.

1971. 25th Anniv of Soviet Ice Hockey.
4021 **1514** 6k. multicoloured 50 10

1515 Baku Oil Installations **1516** G. M. Krzhizhanovsky

1971. Baku Oil Industry.
4022 **1515** 4k. black, red and blue 30 10

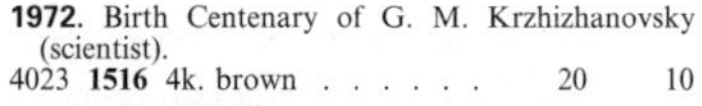
1972. Birth Centenary of G. M. Krzhizhanovsky (scientist).
4023 **1516** 4k. brown 20 10

1517 Scriabin **1518** Red-faced Cormorant

1972. Birth Centenary of Aleksandr Scriabin (composer).
4024 **1517** 4k. blue and green 30 10

1972. Sea Birds. Multicoloured.
4025 4k. Type **1518** 40 15
4026 6k. Ross's gull (horiz) 60 25
4027 10k. Pair of barnacle geese 75 35
4028 12k. Pair of spectacled eiders (horiz) 1·10 60
4029 16k. Mediterranean gull 1·25 75

1519 Speed Skating **1520** Heart Emblem

1972. Winter Olympic Games, Sapporo, Japan. Multicoloured.
4030 4k. Type **1519** 15 10
4031 6k. Figure skating 20 10
4032 10k. Ice hockey 50 15
4033 12k. Ski jumping 65 20
4034 16k. Cross-country skiing 75 30

1972. World Heart Month.
4036 **1520** 4k. red and green 20 10

1521 Fair Emblem **1522** Labour Emblems

1973. 50th Anniv of Soviet Participation in Leipzig Fair.
4037 **1521** 16k. gold and red 85 30

1972. 15th Soviet Trade Unions Congress, Moscow.
4038 **1522** 4k. brown, red and pink 20 10

1523 "Aloe arborescens" **1524** Alexandra Kollontai (diplomat) (birth cent)

1972. Medicinal Plants. Multicoloured.
4039 1k. Type **1523** 10 10
4040 2k. Yellow horned poppy 10 10
4041 4k. Groundsel 20 10
4042 6k. Nephrite tea 30 10
4043 10k. Kangaroo apple 55 15

1972. Birth Anniversaries.
4044 **1524** 4k. brown 20 10
4045 – 4k. lake 20 10
4046 – 4k. bistre 20 10
CELEBRITIES: No. 4045, G. Chicherin (Foreign Affairs Commissar) (birth cent); 4046, "Kamo" (S. A. Ter-Petrosyan—revolutionary) (90th birth anniv).

1526 "Salyut" Space-station and "Soyuz" Spacecraft

1972. Cosmonautics Day. Multicoloured.
4048 6k. Type **1526** 30 20
4049 6k. "Mars 2" approaching Mars 30 20
4050 16k. Capsule, "Mars 3" 75 30

1527 Factory and Products

1972. 250th Anniv of Izhora Factory.
4051 **1527** 4k. purple and silver 20 10

1972. 50th Anniv of Russian Federation Autonomous Soviet Socalist Republics. Designs similar to T **1433**, but dated "1972".
4052 4k. blue 35 10
4053 4k. mauve 25 10
DESIGNS: No. 4052, Arms, natural resources and industry (Yakut Republic); 4053, Arms, agriculture and industry (Checheno-Ingush Republic).

1528 L. Sobinov and scene from "Eugene Onegin"

1972. Birth Centenary of L. Sobinov (singer).
4054 **1528** 10k. brown 50 15

1529 Symbol of Knowledge and Children reading Books

1972. International Book Year.
4055 **1529** 6k. multicoloured 30 10

1530 Pavlik Morosov Monument (I. Rabinovich) and Pioneers Saluting

1972. 50th Anniv of Pioneer Organization.
4056 **1530** 1k. multicoloured 10 10
4057 – 2k. purple, red and green 10 10
4058 – 3k. blue, red and brown 20 10
4059 – 4k. red, blue and green 20 10
DESIGNS: 2k. Girl laboratory worker and Pioneers with book; 3k. Pioneer Place, Chukotka, and Pioneers at work; 4k. Pioneer parade.

1531 Pioneer Trumpeter

1972. "50th Anniv of Pioneer Organization" Youth Stamp Exhibition, Minsk.
4061 **1531** 4k. purple, red & yellow 20 10

1532 "World Security"

1972. European Security Conference, Brussels.
4062 **1532** 6k. blue, turquoise & gold 75 55

1533 M. S. Ordubady **1534** G. Dimitrov

1972. Birth Centenary of M. S. Ordubady (Azerbaijan writer).
4063 **1533** 4k. purple and orange 20 10

1972. Russian Paintings. As T **1502**, but dated "1972". Multicoloured.
4064 2k. "Cossack Hetman" (I. Nikitin) 10 10
4065 4k. "F. Volkov" (A. Lossenko) 20 10
4066 6k. "V. Majkov" (F. Rokotov) 25 10
4067 10k. "N. Novikov" (D. Levitsky) 40 10
4068 12k. "G. Derzhavin" (V. Borovikovsky) 55 15
4069 16k. "Peasants' Dinner" (M. Shibanov) (horiz) 75 25
4070 20k. "Moscow View" (F. Alexeiev) (horiz) 1·10 45

1972. 90th Birth Anniv of Georgi Dimitrov (Bulgarian statesman).
4071 **1534** 6k. brown and bistre 20 10

1535 Congress Building and Emblem

1972. 9th Int Gerontology Congress, Kiev.
4072 **1535** 6k. brown and blue 20 10

1536 Fencing

1972. Olympic Games, Munich.
4073 **1536** 4k. purple and gold 25 10
4074 – 6k. green and gold 35 10
4075 – 10k. blue and gold 50 10
4076 – 14k. blue and gold 70 20
4077 – 16k. red and gold 85 65
DESIGNS: 6k. Gymnastics; 10k. Canoeing; 14k. Boxing; 16k. Running.

1537 Amundsen, Airship N.1 "Norge" and Northern Lights **1538** Market-place, Lvov (Lemberg)

1972. Birth Centenary of Roald Amundsen (Polar explorer).
4079 **1537** 6k. blue and brown 1·50 30

1972. Ukraine's Architectural Monuments. Mult.
4080 4k. Type **1538** 15 10
4081 6k. 17th-century house, Chernigov (horiz) 30 15
4082 10k. Kovnirovsky building, Kiev (horiz) 45 20
4083 16k. Kamenetz-Podolsk Castle 75 30

1539 Indian Flag and Asokan Capital **1540** Liberation Monument, Vladivostok, and Cavalry

1972. 25th Anniv of India's Independence.
4084 **1539** 6k. red, blue and green 30 10

1972. 50th Anniv of Liberation of Far Eastern Territories.
4085 **1540** 3k. grey, orange and red 15 10
4086 – 4k. grey, yellow & ochre 20 10
4087 – 6k. grey, pink and red 30 15
DESIGNS: 4k. Labour Heroes Monument, Khabarovsk, and industrial scene; 6k. Naval statue, Vladivostok, "Vladivostok" (cruiser) and jet fighters.

1541 Miners' Day Emblem

1972. 25th Anniv of Miners' Day.
4088 **1541** 4k. red, black and violet 20 10

1542 "Boy with Dog" (Murillo)

1972. Paintings by Foreign Artists in Hermitage Gallery, Leningrad. Multicoloured.
4089 4k. "Breakfast" (Velazquez) (horiz) 20 10
4090 6k. "The Milk Seller's Family" (Le Nain) (horiz) 30 10
4091 10k. Type **1542** 55 20
4092 10k. "The Capricious Girl" (Watteau) 90 35
4093 20k. "Moroccan with Horse" (Delacroix) . . . 1·10 45

1543 "Sputnik I"

1972. 15th Anniv of "Cosmic Era". Multicoloured.
4095 6k. Type **1543** 35 15
4096 6k. Launch of "Vostok I" 35 15
4097 6k. "Lunokhod" vehicle on Moon 35 15
4098 6k. Man in space 35 15
4099 6k. "Mars 3" module on Mars 35 15
4100 6k. Touch down of "Venera 7" on Venus 35 15

1544 Konstantin Mardzhanishvili **1545** Museum Emblem

1972. Birth Centenary of K. Mardzhanishvili (Georgian actor).
4101 **1544** 4k. green 20 10

1972. Centenary of Popov Central Communications Museum.
4102 **1545** 4k. blue, purple & green 20 10

1546 Exhibition Labels

1972. "50th Anniv of U.S.S.R." Philatelic Exhibition.
4103 **1546** 4k. red & black on yell 20 10

1547 Lenin

1972. 55th Anniv of October Revolution.
4104 **1547** 4k. red and gold . . . 20 10

1548 Militia Badge and Soviet Flag **1549** Arms of U.S.S.R.

1972. 55th Anniv of Soviet Militia.
4105 **1548** 4k. gold, red and brown 20 10

1972. 50th Anniv of U.S.S.R.
4106 **1549** 4k. gold, purple and red 15 10
4107 – 4k. gold, red and brown 15 10
4108 – 4k. gold, purple & green 15 10
4109 – 4k. gold, purple and grey 15 10
4110 – 4k. gold, purple and grey 15 10
DESIGNS: No. 4107, Lenin and banner; No. 4108, Arms and Kremlin; No. 4109, Arms and industrial scenes; No. 4110, Arms, worker and open book "U.S.S.R. Constitutions".

1550 Emblem of U.S.S.R. **1552** Savings Book

1972. U.S.S.R. Victories in Olympic Games, Munich. Multicoloured.
4112 20k. Type **1550** . . . . . . 1·00 30
4113 30k. Olympic medals . . . 1·50 55

1972. "50 Years of Soviet Savings Bank".
4115 **1552** 4k. blue and purple . . 20 10

1553 Kremlin and Snowflakes **1555** Skovoroda (after P. Meshcheryakov)

1554 Battleship "Pyotr Veliky"

1972. New Year.
4116 **1553** 6k. multicoloured . . . 20 10

1972. History of the Russian Navy (2nd series). Multicoloured.
4117 2k. Type **1554** 25 10
4118 3k. Cruiser "Varyag" . . . 25 10
4119 4k. Battleship "Potemkin" 45 10
4120 6k. Cruiser "Ochakov" . . 55 15
4121 10k. Minelayer "Amur" . . 1·10 25

1972. 250th Birth Anniv of Grigory S. Skovoroda.
4122 **1555** 4k. blue 20 10

1556 "Pioneer Girl with Books" (N. A. Kasatkin)

1972. "History of Russian Painting". Mult.
4123 2k. "Meeting of Village Party Members" (E. M. Cheptsov) (horiz) 15 10
4124 4k. Type **1556** 20 15
4125 6k. "Party Delegate" (G. G. Ryazhsky) 25 15
4126 10k. "End of Winter—Midday" (K. F. Yuon) (horiz) 35 20
4127 16k. "Partisan Lunev" (N. I. Strunnikov) 70 35
4128 20k. "Self-portrait in Fur Coat" (I. E. Grabar) . . 1·10 50

1557 Child reading Safety Code **1558** Emblem of Technology

1972. Road Safety Campaign.
4130 **1557** 4k. black, blue and red 20 10

1972. Cent of Polytechnic Museum, Moscow.
4131 **1558** 4k. red, yellow and green 20 10

1559 "Venus 8" and Parachute

1972. Space Research.
4132 **1559** 6k. blue, black and purple 25 10

1560 Solidarity Emblem

1973. 15th Anniv of Asian and African People's Solidarity Organization.
4134 **1560** 10k. blue, red and brown 35 15

1561 Town and Gediminas Tower **1562** I. V. Babushkin

1973. 650th Anniv of Vilnius (Vilna).
4135 **1561** 10k. red, black and green 35 15

1973. Birth Cent of I. V. Babushkin (revolutionary).
4136 **1562** 4k. black 20 10

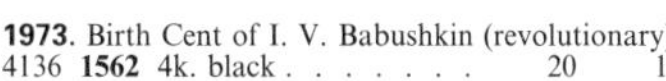

1563 Tupolev Tu-154 Jetliner

1973. 50th Anniv of Soviet Civil Aviation.
4137 **1563** 6k. multicoloured . . . 45 15

1564 "30" and Admiralty Spire, Leningrad **1565** Portrait and Masks (Mayakovsky Theatre)

1973. 30th Anniv of Relief of Leningrad.
4138 **1564** 4k. black, orange & brn 20 10

1973. 50th Anniv of Moscow Theatres.
4139 **1565** 10k. multicoloured . . 30 10
4140 – 10k. red and blue . . . 30 10
DESIGN: No. 4140, Commemorative panel (Mossoviet Theatre).

1566 Prishvin (after A. Kirillov)

1973. Birth Centenary of Mikhail Prishvin (writer).
4141 **1566** 4k. multicoloured . . . 30 10

1567 Heroes' Square, Volgograd

1973. 30th Anniv of Stalingrad Victory. Detail from Heroes' Memorial.
4142 – 3k. black, yellow & orge 20 10
4143 **1567** 4k. yellow and black . . 20 10
4144 – 10k. multicoloured . . 40 15
4145 – 12k. black, light red and red 60 20
DESIGNS—VERT: 3k. Soldier and Allegory; 12k. Hand with torch. HORIZ: 10k. Mother mourning for child.

1568 Copernicus and Planetary Chart

1973. 500th Birth Anniv of Copernicus (astronomer).
4147 **1568** 10k. brown and blue . . 55 15

1569 Chaliapin (after K. Korovin)

1973. Birth Centenary of Fyodor Chaliapin (opera singer).
4148 **1569** 10k. multicoloured . . 45 15

1570 Ice Hockey Players **1571** Athletes

1973. World Ice Hockey Championships, Moscow.
4149 **1570** 10k. brown, blue & gold 60 15

1973. 50th Anniv of Central Red Army Sports Club.
4151 **1571** 4k. multicoloured . . . 20 10

1572 Red Star, Tank, and Map

1573 N. E. Bauman

1973. 30th Anniv of Battle of Kursk.
4152 **1572** 4k. black, red and grey 20 10

1973. Birth Centenary of Nikolai Bauman (revolutionary).
4153 **1573** 4k. brown 25 10

1574 Red Cross and Red Crescent

1973. International Co-operation.
4154 **1574** 4k. red, black and green 15 10
4155 – 6k. light blue, red and blue 20 10
4156 – 16k. green, red and mauve 80 25

DESIGNS AND EVENTS: 4k. (50th anniv of Soviet Red Cross and Red Crescent Societies Union); 6k. Mask, emblem and theatre curtain (15th Int Theatre Institution Congress); 16k. Floral emblem (10th World Festival of Youth, Berlin).

1575 Ostrovsky (after V. Perov)

1576 Satellites

1973. 150th Birth Anniv of Aleksandr Ostrovsky (writer).
4157 **1575** 4k. multicoloured . . . 20 10

1973. Cosmonautics Day. Multicoloured.
4158 6k. Type **1576** 20 10
4159 6k. "Lunokhod 2" 20 10

1577 "Guitarist" (V. Tropinin)

1578 Athlete and Emblems

1973. "History of Russian Painting". Mult.
4162 2k. Type **1577** 15 10
4163 4k. "The Young Widow" (P. Fedotov) 20 10
4164 6k. "Self-portrait" (O. Kiprensky) 30 10
4165 10k. "An Afternoon in Italy" (K. Bryullov) . . . 45 20
4166 12k. "That's My Father's Dinner!" (boy with dog) (A. Venetsianov) 55 30
4167 16k. "Lower Gallery of Albano" (A. Ivanov) (horiz) 75 35
4168 20k. "Yermak conquering Siberia" (V. Surikov) (horiz) . . . . 1·00 50

1973. 50th Anniv of Dynamo Sports Club.
4169 **1578** 4k. multicoloured . . . 20 10

1580 Liner "Mikhail Lermontov"

1582 Sports

1581 E. T. Krenkel and Polar Scenes

1973. Inauguration of Leningrad–New York Trans-Atlantic Service.
4171 **1580** 16k. multicoloured . . 70 30

1973. 70th Birth Anniv of E. T. Krenkel (Polar explorer).
4172 **1581** 4k. brown and blue . . 75 20

1973. "Sport for Everyone".
4173 **1582** 4k. multicoloured . . . 20 10

1583 Girls' Choir

1973. Centenary of Latvian Singing Festival.
4174 **1583** 10k. multicoloured . . 35 10

1973. 50th Anniv of Russian Federation Autonomous Soviet Socialist Republics. Design similar to T **1433**, but dated "1973".
4175 4k. blue 20 10

DESIGN: No. 4175, Arms and industries of Buryat Republic.

1584 Throwing the Hammer

1973. Universiade Games, Moscow. Mult.
4176 2k. Type **1584** 10 10
4177 3k. Gymnastics 10 10
4178 4k. Swimming 15 10
4179 16k. Fencing 85 25

1586 European Bison

1973. Caucasus and Voronezh Nature Reserves. Multicoloured.
4182 1k. Type **1586** 10 10
4183 3k. Ibex 15 10
4184 4k. Caucasian snowcocks . . 1·25 20
4185 6k. Eurasian beaver with young 35 10
4186 10k. Red deer with fawns 55 20

1587 Lenin, Banner and Membership Card

1973. 70th Anniv of 2nd Soviet Social Democratic Workers Party Congress.
4187 **1587** 4k. multicoloured . . . 20 10

1588 A. R. al-Biruni (after M. Nabiev)

1590 "Portrait of the Sculptor S. T. Konenkov" (P. Korin)

1589 Schaumberg Palace, Bonn, and Spassky Tower, Moscow

1973. Millennium of Abu Reihan al-Biruni (astronomer and mathematician).
4188 **1588** 6k. brown 30 15

1973. General Secretary Leonid Brezhnev's Visits to West Germany, France and U.S.A. Multicoloured.
4189 **1589** 10k. mauve, brn & buff 40 15
4190 – 10k. brown, ochre and yellow 40 15
4191 – 10k. red, grey and brown 40 15

DESIGNS: No. 4190, Eiffel Tower, Paris, and Spassky Tower; 4191, White House, Washington, and Spassky Tower.

See also Nos. 4245 and 4257.

1973. "History of Russian Paintings". Mult.
4193 2k. Type **1590** 10 10
4194 4k. "Farm-workers' Supper" (A. Plastov) 15 10
4195 6k. "Letter from the Battle-front" (A. Laktionov) . . 25 15
4196 10k. "Mountain Landscape" (M. Saryan) 45 25
4197 16k. "Wedding on Tomorrow's Street" (Yu. Pimenov) 75 35
4198 20k. "Ice Hockey" (mosaic, A. Deineka) . . . . . . 1·10 45

1591 Lenin Museum

1592 Steklov

1973. Inaug of Lenin Museum, Tashkent.
4200 **1591** 4k. multicoloured . . . 20 10

1973. Birth Centenary of Y. Steklov (statesman).
4201 **1592** 4k. brown, red and pink 20 10

1593 "The Eternal Pen"

1594 "Oplopanax elatum"

1973. Afro-Asian Writers' Conference, Alma-Ata.
4202 **1593** 6k. multicoloured . . . 20 10

1973. Medicinal Plants. Multicoloured.
4203 1k. Type **1594** 10 10
4204 2k. Ginseng 15 10
4205 4k. Spotted orchid 20 10
4206 10k. Arnica 40 20
4207 12k. Lily of the valley . . . 55 25

1595 I. Nasimi (after M. Abdullaev)

1973. 600th Birth Anniv of Imadeddin Nasimi (Azerbaijan poet).
4208 **1595** 4k. brown 20 10

1596 Cruiser "Kirov"

1973. History of Russian Navy (3rd series). Multicoloured.
4209 3k. Type **1596** 20 10
4210 4k. Battleship "Oktyabrskaya Revolyutsiya" 25 10
4211 6k. Submarine "Krasnogvardeets" . . . 30 15
4212 10k. Destroyer "Soobrazitelnyi" 60 25
4213 16k. Cruiser "Krasnyi Kavkaz" . . . . 1·10 35

1597 Pugachev and Battle Scene

1973. Bicentenary of Peasant War.
4214 **1597** 4k. multicoloured . . . 20 10

1598 Red Flag encircling Globe

1973. 15th Anniv of Magazine "Problems of Peace and Socialism".
4215 **1598** 6k. red, gold and green 25 10

1599 Leningrad Mining Institute

1973. Bicentenary of Leningrad Mining Institute.
4216 **1599** 4k. multicoloured . . . 20 10

1600 Laurel and Hemispheres

1601 Elena Stasova

1973. World Congress of "Peaceful Forces", Moscow.
4217 **1600** 6k. multicoloured . . . 25 10

1973. Birth Centenary of Yelena Stasova (party official).
4218 **1601** 4k. mauve 20 10

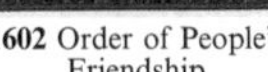

1602 Order of People's Friendship　　**1603** Marshal Malinovsky

1973. Foundation of Order of People's Friendship.
4219 **1602** 4k. multicoloured . . . 20 10

1973. 75th Birth Anniv of Marshal R. Malinovsky.
4220 **1603** 4k. grey 20 10

1604 Workers and Red Guard　　**1605** D. Cantemir

1973. 250th Anniv of Sverdlovsk.
4221 **1604** 4k. black, gold and red 20 10

1973. 300th Birth Anniv of Dmitri Cantemir (Moldavian scientist and encyclopaedist).
4222 **1605** 4k. red 20 10

1606 Pres. Allende of Chile

1973. Allende Commemoration.
4223 **1606** 6k. black and brown . . 30 10

1607 Kremlin　　**1608** N. Narimanov

1973. New Year.
4224 **1607** 6k. multicoloured . . . 20 10

1973. Birth Centenary (1970) of Nariman Narimanov (Azerbaijan politician).
4225 **1608** 4k. green 20 10

1609 "Russobalt" Touring Car (1909)

1973. History of Soviet Motor Industry (1st series). Multicoloured.
4226 2k. Type **1609** 15 10
4227 3k. "AMO-F15" lorry (1924) 15 10
4228 4k. Spartak "NAMI-1" tourer (1927) 20 10
4229 12k. Yaroslavsky "Ya-6" bus (1929) 55 20
4230 16k. Gorkovsky "GAZ-A" tourer (1932) 75 40
See also Nos. 4293/7, 4397/401 and 4512/16.

1610 "Game and Lobster" (Sneiders)

1973. Foreign Paintings in Soviet Galleries. Mult.
4231 4k. Type **1610** 20 10
4232 6k. "Young Woman with Ear-rings" (Rembrandt) (vert) 20 10
4233 10k. "Sick Woman and Physician" (Steen) (vert) 35 15
4234 12k. "Attributes of Art" (Chardin) 45 20
4235 14k. "Lady in a Garden" (Monet) 50 25
4236 16k. "Village Lovers" (Bastien-Lepage) (vert) . . 60 30
4237 20k. "Girl with Fan" (Renoir) (vert) 75 40

1611 Great Sea Gate, Tallin　　**1612** Picasso

1973. Historical Buildings of Estonia, Latvia and Lithuania.
4239 **1611** 4k. black, red and green 20 10
4240 – 4k. brown, red and green 20 10
4241 – 4k. multicoloured . . . 20 10
4242 – 10k. multicoloured . . 50 20
DESIGNS: No. 4240, Organ pipes and Dome Cathedral, Riga; 4241, Traku Castle, Lithuania; 4242, Town Hall and weather-vane, Tallin.

1973. Pablo Picasso Commemoration.
4243 **1612** 6k. green, red and gold 30 10

1613 Petrovsky

1973. I. G. Petrovsky (mathematician and Rector of Moscow University) Commemoration.
4244 **1613** 4k. multicoloured . . . 20 10

1973. Brezhnev's Visit to India. As T **1589**, but showing Kremlin, Red Fort, Delhi and flags.
4245 4k. multicoloured 20 10

1614 Soviet Soldier and Title Page　　**1616** Oil Workers

1617 "Comecon" Headquarters, Moscow　　**1618** Skaters and Stadium

1615 Siege Monument and Peter the Great Statue, Leningrad

1974. 50th Anniv of "Red Star" Newspaper.
4246 **1614** 4k. black, red and gold 20 10

1974. 30th Anniv of Soviet Victory in Battle for Leningrad.
4247 **1615** 4k. multicoloured . . . 30 10

1974. 10th Anniv of Tyumen Oil fields.
4248 **1616** 4k. black, red and blue 30 10

1974. 25th Anniv of Council for Mutual Economic Aid.
4249 **1617** 16k. green, red & brown 45 20

1974. European Women's Ice Skating Championships, Medeo, Alma-Ata.
4250 **1618** 6k. red, blue and slate 20 10

1619 Kunstkammer Museum, Leningrad, Text and Academy　　**1620** L. A. Artsimovich

1974. 250th Anniv of Russian Academy of Sciences.
4251 **1619** 10k. multicoloured . . 25 10

1974. 1st Death Anniv of Academician L. A. Artsimovich (physicist).
4252 **1620** 4k. brown and green . . 20 10

1974. 50th Anniv of Autonomous Soviet Socialist Republics. Design similar to T **1433**, but dated "1974".
4253 4k. brown 20 10
DESIGN: No. 4253, Arms and industries of Nakhichevan ASSR (Azerbaijan).

1621 K. D. Ushinsky　　**1622** M. D. Millionshchikov

1974. 150th Birth Anniv of K. D. Ushinsky (educationalist).
4254 **1621** 4k. brown and green . . 20 10

1974. 1st Death Anniv of M. D. Millionshchikov (scientist).
4255 **1622** 4k. brown, pink & green 20 10

1623 Spartakiad Emblem　　**1624** Young Workers and Emblem

1974. 3rd Winter Spartakiad Games.
4256 **1623** 10k. multicoloured . . 25 15

1974. General Secretary Leonid Brezhnev's Visit to Cuba. As T **1589** but showing Kremlin, Revolution Square, Havana and Flags.
4257 4k. multicoloured 20 10

1974. Scientific and Technical Youth Work Review.
4258 **1624** 4k. multicoloured . . . 20 10

1625 Theatre Facade　　**1626** Globe and Meteorological Activities

1974. Cent of Azerbaijan Drama Theatre, Baku.
4259 **1625** 6k. brown, red & orange 20 10

1974. Cosmonautics Day.
4260 **1626** 6k. blue, red and violet 20 10
4261 – 10k. brown, red and blue 40 15
4262 – 10k. black, red & yellow 40 15
DESIGNS: No. 4261, V. G. Lazarev and O. G. Makarov, and launch of "Soyuz 12"; 4262, P. I. Klimuk and V. V. Lebedev, and "Soyuz 13".

1627 "Odessa by Moonlight" (Aivazovsky)

1974. Marine Paintings by Ivan Aivazovsky. Mult.
4263 2k. Type **1627** 10 10
4264 4k. "Battle of Chesme" (vert) 15 10
4265 6k. "St. George's Monastery" 20 10
4266 10k. "Storm at Sea" 35 15
4267 12k. "Rainbow" 65 20
4268 16k. "Shipwreck" 80 30

1628 Young Communists

1974. 17th Leninist Young Communist League (Komsomol) Congress (4270) and 50th Anniv of Naming League after Lenin (4271). Multicoloured.
4270 4k. Type **1628** 20 10
4271 4k. "Lenin" (from sculpture by V. Tsigal) 20 10

1630 Swallow ("Atmosphere")　　**1631** "Cobble-stone, Proletarian Weapon" (sculpture, I. Shadr)

1974. "EXPO 74" World Fair, Spokane, U.S.A. "Preserve the Environment".
4273 **1630** 4k. black, red and lilac 15 10
4274 – 6k. yellow, black & blue 20 10
4275 – 10k. black, violet and red 45 15
4276 – 16k. blue, green & black 65 20
4277 – 20k. black, brn & orge 90 40
DESIGNS: 6k. Fish and globe ("The Sea"); 10k. Crystals ("The Earth"); 16k. Rose bush ("Flora"); 20k. Young red deer ("Fauna").

1974. 50th Anniv of Central Museum of the Revolution.
4279 **1631** 4k. green, red and gold 20 10

1632 Congress Emblem within Lucerne Grass　　**1634** Tchaikovsky and Competition Emblem

1633 Saiga

1974. 12th International Congress of Meadow Cultivation, Moscow.

4280 **1632** 4k. red, green & dp green 20 10

1974. 1st International Theriological Congress, Moscow. Fauna. Multicoloured.

4281 1k. Type **1633** 10 10

4282 3k. Asiatic wild ass 15 10

4283 4k. Russian desman 25 10

4284 6k. Northern fur seal . . . 35 15

4285 10k. Bowhead whale 75 25

1974. 5th Int Tchaikovsky Music Competition.

4286 **1634** 6k. black, violet & green 35 10

1636 Marshal F. I. Tolbukhin

1638 Runner and Emblem

1637 K. Stanislavsky, V. Nemirovich-Danchenko and Theatre Curtain

1974. 80th Birth Anniv of Marshal F. I. Tolbukhin.

4288 **1636** 4k. green 20 10

1974. 75th Anniv of Moscow Arts Festival.

4289 **1637** 10k. multicoloured . . 35 15

1974. 13th Soviet Schools Spartakiad, Alma Ata.

4290 **1638** 4k. multicoloured . . . 25 10

1639 Modern Passenger Coach

1640 Shield and Monument on Battle Map

1974. Centenary of Yegorov Railway Wagon Works, Leningrad.

4291 **1639** 4k. multicoloured . . . 30 10

1974. 30th Anniv of Liberation of Belorussia.

4292 **1640** 4k. multicoloured . . . 20 10

See also No. 4301.

1974. History of Soviet Motor Industry (2nd series). As T **1609**. Multicoloured.

4293 2k. Gorkovsky "GAZ-AA" lorry (1932) 15 10

4294 3k. Gorkovsky "GAZ-03-30" bus (1933) 15 10

4295 4k. Moscow Auto Works "ZIS-5" lorry (1933) . . . 20 10

4296 14k. Moscow Auto Works "ZIS-8" bus (1934) . . . 65 20

4297 16k. Moscow Auto Works "ZIS-101" saloon car (1936) 80 25

1974. 50th Anniv of Soviet Republics. As T **1433**, dated "1974".

4298 4k. red 20 10

DESIGN: 4k. Arms and industries of North Ossetian Republic.

No. 4298 also commemorates the 200th anniv of Ossetia's merger with Russia.

1641 Liberation Monument (E. Kuntsevich) and Skyline

1644 Admiral Isakov

1642 Flag and "Nike" Memorial, Warsaw

1974. 800th Anniv of Poltava.

4299 **1641** 4k. red and brown . . 20 10

1974. 30th Anniv of Polish People's Republic.

4300 **1642** 6k. brown and red . . 25 10

1974. 30th Anniv of Liberation of Ukraine. As T **1640**, but background details and colours changed.

4301 4k. multicoloured 20 10

1974. 80th Birth Anniv of Admiral I. S. Isakov.

4302 **1644** 4k. blue 20 10

1645 Minesweeper

1974. History of the Russian Navy (4th series). Modern Warships. Multicoloured.

4303 3k. Type **1645** 25 10

4304 4k. Aligator II tank landing ship 30 10

4305 6k. "Moskova" helicopter carrier 45 15

4306 16k. Destroyer "Otvazhny" 1·25 30

1646 Pentathlon Sports

1647 D. Ulyanov

1974. World Modern Pentathlon Championships, Moscow.

4307 **1646** 16k. brown, gold & blue 60 20

1974. Birth Centenary of D. Ulyanov (Lenin's brother).

4308 **1647** 4k. green 20 10

1648 V. Menzhinsky

1650 S. M. Budennyi

1649 "Lilac" (P. P. Konchalovsky)

1974. Birth Cent of V. Menzhinsky (statesman).

4309 **1648** 4k. maroon 20 10

1974. Soviet Paintings. Multicoloured.

4310 4k. Type **1649** 15 10

4311 6k. "Towards the Wind" (sailing) (E. Kalnins) . . . 25 15

4312 10k. "Spring" (young woman) (O. Zardaryan) 45 20

4313 16k. "Northern Harbour" (G. Nissky) 75 30

4314 20k. "Daughter of Soviet Kirgiz" (S. Chuikov) (vert) 90 35

1974. Marshal S. M. Budennyi Commemoration.

4315 **1650** 4k. green 20 10

1651 Page of First Russian Dictionary

1652 Flags and Soviet War Memorial, (K. Baraski), Bucharest

1974. 400th Anniv of First Russian Primer.

4316 **1651** 4k. red, black and gold 20 10

1974. 30th Anniv of Rumanian Liberation.

4317 **1652** 6k. blue, yellow and red 20 10

1653 Vitebsk

1974. Millenary of Vitebsk.

4318 **1653** 4k. red and green . . . 15 10

1654 Kirgizia

1655 Bulgarian Crest and Flags

1974. 50th Anniv of Soviet Republics. Flags, Agricultural and Industrial Emblems. Mult. Background colours given.

4319 **1654** 4k. blue 15 10

4320 – 4k. purple 15 10

4321 – 4k. blue 15 10

4322 – 4k. yellow 15 10

4323 – 4k. green 15 10

DESIGNS: No. 4320, Moldavia; 4321, Tadzhikistan; 4322, Turkmenistan; 4323, Uzbekistan.

1974. 30th Anniv of Bulgarian Revolution.

4324 **1655** 6k. multicoloured . . . 20 10

1656 G.D.R. Crest and Soviet War Memorial, Treptow, Berlin

1658 Theatre and Laurel Wreath

1974. 25th Anniv of German Democratic Republic.

4325 **1656** 6k. multicoloured . . . 20 10

1974. 150th Anniv of Maly State Theatre, Moscow.

4327 **1658** 4k. gold, red and black 20 10

1659 "Guests from Overseas"

1974. Birth Centenary of Nikolai K. Rorich (painter).

4328 **1659** 6k. multicoloured . . . 25 10

1660 Soviet Crest and U.P.U. Monument, Berne

1974. Centenary of U.P.U. Multicoloured.

4329 10k. Type **1660** 45 15

4330 10k. Ukraine crest, U.P.U. Emblem and U.P.U. H.Q., Berne 45 15

4331 10k. Byelorussia crest, U.P.U. emblem and mail transport 45 15

1661 Order of Labour Glory

1974. 57th Anniv of October Revolution. Mult.

4333 4k. Type **1661** 25 10

4334 4k. Kamaz truck (vert) . . . 15 10

4335 4k. Hydro-electric power station, Nurek (vert) . . . 15 10

1662 Soviet "Space Stations" over Mars

1974. Soviet Space Exploration. Multicoloured.

4336 6k. Type **1662** 25 10

4337 10k. P. R. Popovich and Yu. P. Artyukhin ("Soyuz 14" cosomonauts) 45 15

4338 10k. I. V. Sarafanov and L. S. Demin ("Soyuz 15" cosmonauts) 45 15

SIZES—VERT: No. 4337, 28 × 40 mm. HORIZ: No. 4338, 40 × 28 mm.

1663 Mongolian Crest Flag

1664 Commemorative Inscription

1974. 50th Anniv of Mongolian People's Republic.

4339 **1663** 6k. multicoloured . . . 20 10

1974. 30th Anniv of Estonian Liberation.

4340 **1664** 4k. multicoloured . . . 20 10

1665 Liner "Aleksandr Pushkin", Freighter and Tanker

1974. 50th Anniv of Soviet Merchant Navy.

4341 **1665** 4k. multicoloured . . . 30 10

1666 Spassky Clock-tower, Kremlin, Moscow

1974. New Year.
4342 **1666** 4k. multicoloured . . . 20 10

1667 "The Market Place" (Beuckelaar)

1974. Foreign Paintings in Soviet Galleries. Mult.
4343 4k. Type **1667** 15 10
4344 6k. "Woman selling Fish" (Pieters) (vert) 25 10
4345 10k. "A Goblet of Lemonade" (Terborsh) (vert) 35 15
4346 14k. "Girl at Work" (Metsu) (vert) 50 25
4347 16k. "Saying Grace" (Chardin) (vert) 55 30
4348 20k. "The Spoilt Child" (Greuze) (vert) 80 35

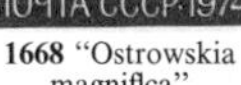

1668 "Ostrowskia magnifica" 1669 Nikitin (after P. Borel)

1974. Flowers. Multicoloured.
4350 1k. Type **1668** 10 10
4351 2k. "Paeonia intermedia" . . 10 10
4352 4k. "Roemeria refracta" . . 20 10
4353 10k. "Tulipia dasystemon" 45 20
4354 12k. "Dianthus versicolor" 55 25

1974. 150th Birth Anniv of I. S. Nikitin (poet).
4355 **1669** 4k. black, green & olive 20 10

1670 Leningrad Mint Building

1974. 250th Anniv of Leningrad Mint.
4356 **1670** 6k. multicoloured . . . 35 10

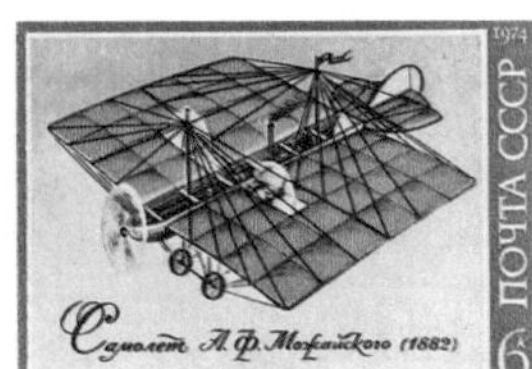

1671 Mozhaisky's Monoplane, 1884

1974. Early Russian Aircraft (1st series). Mult.
4357 6k. Type **1671** 30 15
4358 6k. Grizidubov No. 2 biplane, 1910 . . . . . . 30 15
4359 6k. Sikorsky "Russia A", 1910 . . . . 30 15
4360 6k. Sikorsky Russky Vityaz, 1913 . . . . 30 15
4361 6k. Grigorovich M-5 flying boat, 1914 . . . . 30 15
See also Nos. 4580/4, 4661/6 and 4791/6.

1673 Komsomol Emblem and Rotary Press ("Komsomolskaya Pravda")

1975. 50th Anniv of Children's Newspapers.
4363 **1673** 4k. red, black and blue 20 10
4364 – 4k. red, black and silver 20 10
DESIGN—VERT: No. 4364, Pioneer emblem and newspaper sheet ("Pioneerskaya Pravda").

1674 Emblem and Skiers (8th Trade Unions' Games)

1975. Winter Spartakiads.
4365 **1674** 4k. orange, black & blue 15 10
4366 – 16k. bistre, black & blue 55 20
DESIGN—HORIZ: 16k. Emblem, ice hockey player and skier (5th Friendly Forces Military Games).

1975. "50th Anniv of Automomous Soviet Socialist Republics. Designs similar to T **1433**, but dated "1975".
4367 4k. green 20 10
DESIGN: No. 4367, Arms, industries and produce of Karakalpak ASSR (Uzbekistan).

1675 "David"

1975. 500th Birth Anniv of Michelangelo.
4368 **1675** 4k. deep green and green 20 15
4369 – 6k. brown and ochre 25 15
4370 – 10k. deep green & green 35 15
4371 – 14k. brown and ochre 60 30
4372 – 20k. deep green & green 1·00 30
4373 – 30k. brown and ochre 1·50 30
DESIGNS: 6k. "Crouching Boy"; 10k. "Rebellious Slave"; 14k. "Creation of Adam" (detail, Sistine Chapel ceiling); 20k. Staircase of Laurentiana Library, Florence; 30k. Christ and the Virgins (detail of "The Last Judgement", Sistine Chapel).

1676 Mozhaisky, his Monoplane (1884) and Tupolev Tu-144 Jetliner

1975. 150th Birth Anniv of Aleksandr Mozhaisky (aircraft designer).
4375 **1676** 6k. brown and blue . . 40 10

1677 Convention Emblem

1975. Cent of International Metre Convention.
4376 **1677** 6k. multicoloured . . . 20 10

1678 Games Emblem

1975. 6th Summer Spartakiad.
4377 **1678** 6k. multicoloured . . . 20 10

1679 Towers of Charles Bridge, Prague (Czechoslovakia)

1975. 30th Anniv of Liberation. Multicoloured.
4378 6k. Type **1679** 15 10
4379 6k. Liberation Monument and Parliament Buildings, Budapest (Hungary) . . . 15 10

1680 French and Soviet Flags 1681 Yuri Gagarin (bust by L. Kerbel)

1975. 50th Anniv of Franco-Soviet Diplomatic Relations.
4380 **1680** 6k. multicoloured . . . 20 10

1975. Cosmonautics Day.
4381 **1681** 6k. red, silver and blue 20 10
4382 – 10k. red, black and blue 35 15
4383 – 16k. multicoloured . . 55 20
DESIGNS—HORIZ: 10k. A. A. Gubarev, G. M. Grechko ("Soyuz 17") and "Salyut 4"; 16k. A. V. Filipchenko, N. N. Rukavishnikov and "Soyuz 16".

1682 Treaty Emblem 1684 Lenin

1683 Emblem and Exhibition Hall, Sokolniki, Moscow

1975. 20th Anniv of Warsaw Treaty.
4384 **1682** 6k. multicoloured . . . 20 10

1975. "Communication 75" International Exhibition, Moscow.
4385 **1683** 6k. red, silver and blue 20 10

1975. 30th Anniv of Victory in Second World War. Multicoloured.
4386 4k. Type **1684** 15 10
4387 4k. Eternal flame and Guard of Honour 15 10
4388 4k. Woman in ammunition factory 15 10
4389 4k. Partisans 15 10
4390 4k. "Destruction of the enemy" 15 10
4391 4k. Soviet forces 15 10

1685 "Lenin" (V. G. Tsyplakov) 1686 Victory Emblems

1975. 105th Birth Anniv of Lenin.
4393 **1685** 4k. multicoloured . . . 20 10

1975. "Sozfilex 75" International Stamp Exhibition.
4394 **1686** 6k. multicoloured . . . 20 10

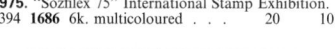

1687 "Apollo"–"Soyuz" Space Link

1975. "Apollo"–"Soyuz" Space Project.
4396 **1687** 20k. multicoloured . . 75 25

1975. History of Soviet Motor Industry (3rd series). As T **1609**.
4397 2k. black, orange and blue 15 10
4398 3k. black, brown and green 15 10
4399 4k. black, blue and green . . 15 10
4400 12k. black, buff and purple 45 20
4401 16k. black, green and olive 60 30
DESIGNS: 2k. Gorkovsky "GAZ-M1" saloon, 1936; 3k. Yaroslavsky "YAG-6" truck, 1936; 4k. Moscow Auto Works "ZIS-16" bus, 1938; 12k. Moscow KIM Works "KIM-10" saloon, 1940; 16k. Gorkovsky "GAZ-67B" field car, 1943.

1688 Irrigation Canal and Emblem 1689 Flags and Crests of Poland and Soviet Union

1975. 9th Int Irrigation Congress, Moscow.
4402 **1688** 6k. multicoloured . . . 20 10

1975. 30th Anniv of Soviet–Polish Friendship.
4403 **1689** 6k. multicoloured . . . 20 10

1690 A. A. Leonov in Space 1691 Ya. M. Sverdlov

1975. 10th Anniv of First Space Walk by A. A. Leonov.
4404 **1690** 6k. multicoloured . . . 25 10

1975. 90th Birth Anniv of Ya. M. Sverdlov (statesman).
4405 **1691** 4k. brown, buff & silver 15 10

1692 Congress Emblem

1975. 8th Int Plant Conservation Congress, Moscow.
4406 **1692** 6k. multicoloured . . . 20 10

1693 Emblem and Plants

1975. 12th Int Botanical Congress, Leningrad.
4407 **1693** 6k. multicoloured . . . 60 15

1695 Festival Emblem

1975. 9th International Film Festival, Moscow.
4409 **1695** 6k. multicoloured . . . 20 10

1696 Crews of "Apollo" and "Soyuz"

1975. "Apollo"–"Soyuz" Space Link. Mult.
4410 10k. Type **1696** 35 10
4411 12k. "Apollo" and "Soyuz 19" in docking procedure 55 20
4412 12k. "Apollo" and "Soyuz 19" linked together . . . 55 20
4413 16k. Launch of "Soyuz 19" (vert) 75 20

1697 Russian Sturgeon

1975. Int Exposition, Okinawa. Marine Life.
4415 **1697** 3k. bistre, black and blue 25 10
4416 – 4k. lilac, black and blue 30 10
4417 – 6k. purple, black & green 35 10
4418 – 10k. brown, black & bl 1·00 10
4419 – 16k. green, black & purple 70 25
4420 – 20k. blue, pur & stone 85 30
DESIGNS: 4k. Thomas rapa whelk; 6k. European eel; 10k. Long-tailed duck; 16k. Crab; 20k. Grey damselfish.

1698 "Parade in Red Square, Moscow" (K. F. Yuon)

1975. Birth Centenaries of Soviet Painters. Mult.
4422 1k. Type **1698** 10 10
4423 2k. "Winter Morning in Industrial Moscow" (K. P. Yuon) 15 10
4424 6k. "Soldiers with Captured Guns" (E. E. Lansere) . . 25 10
4425 10k. "Excavating the Metro Tunnel" (E. E. Lansere) 75 20
4426 16k. "A. A. Pushkin and N. N. Pushkina at Palace Ball" (N. P. Ulyanov) (vert) 60 30
4427 20k. "Lauriston at Kutuzov's Headquarters" (N. P. Ulyanov) 80 40

1699 Conference Emblem

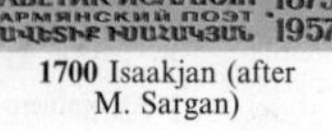

1700 Isaakjan (after M. Sargan)

1975. European Security and Co-operation Conf, Helsinki.
4428 **1699** 6k. black, gold and blue 30 10

1975. Birth Centenary of Avetic Isaakjan (Armenian poet).
4429 **1700** 4k. multicoloured . . . 20 10

1701 M. K. Ciurlionis

1702 J. Duclos

1975. Birth Centenary of M. K. Ciurlionis (Lithuanian composer).
4430 **1701** 4k. gold, green & yellow 20 10

1975. Jacques Duclos (French communist leader) Commemoration.
4431 **1702** 6k. purple and silver . . 20 10

1703 Al Farabi (after L. Leontev)

1704 Ruffs

1975. 1100th Birth Anniv of Al Farabi (Persian philosopher).
4432 **1703** 6k. multicoloured . . . 20 10

1975. 50th Anniv of Berezinsky and Stolby Nature Reserves. Multicoloured.
4433 1k. Type **1704** 20 10
4434 4k. Siberian musk deer . . . 30 10
4435 6k. Sable 30 10
4436 10k. Western capercaillie . . 60 30
4437 16k. Eurasian badger . . . 70 30

1705 Korean Crest with Soviet and Korean Flags

1707 Yesenin

1706 Cosmonauts, "Soyuz 18" and "Salyut 4" Linked

1975. 30th Anniversaries. Multicoloured.
4438 6k. Type **1705** (Korean liberation) 20 10
4439 6k. Vietnamese crest, Soviet and Vietnamese flags (Vietnam Democratic Republic) 20 10

1975. Space Flight of "Soyuz 18–Salyut 4" by Cosmonauts P. Klimuk and V. Sevastyanov.
4440 **1706** 10k. black, red and blue 30 10

1975. 80th Birth Anniv of Yesenin (poet).
4441 **1707** 6k. brown, yell & grey 20 10

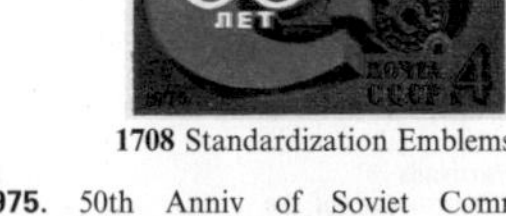

1708 Standardization Emblems

1975. 50th Anniv of Soviet Communications Standardization Committee.
4442 **1708** 4k. multicoloured . . . 15 10

1709 Astrakhan Lamb

1710 M. P. Konchalovsky

1975. 3rd International Astrakhan Lamb Breeding Symposium, Samarkand.
4443 **1709** 6k. black, green & stone 20 10

1975. Birth Centenary of M. P. Konchalovsky (therapeutist).
4444 **1710** 4k. brown and red . . 15 10

1711 Exhibition Emblem

1712 I.W.Y. Emblem and Rose

1975. 3rd All-Union Philatelic Exhibition, Yerevan.
4445 **1711** 4k. red, brown and blue 15 10

1975. International Women's Year.
4446 **1712** 6k. red, blue & turquoise 20 10

1713 Parliament Buildings, Belgrade

1714 Title-page of 1938 Edition

1975. 30th Anniv of Yugoslav Republic.
4447 **1713** 6k. blue, red and gold 20 10

1975. 175th Anniv of Publication of "Tale of the Host of Igor".
4448 **1714** 4k. red, grey and bistre 15 10

1715 M. I. Kalinin (statesman)

1975. Celebrities' Birth Centenaries.
4449 **1715** 4k. brown 15 10
4450 – 4k. brown 15 10
DESIGN: No. 4450, A. V. Lunacharsky (politician).

1716 Torch and Inscription

1975. 70th Anniv of Russian 1905 Revolution.
4451 **1716** 4k. red and brown . . 15 10

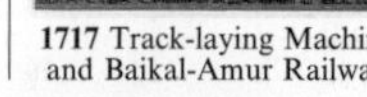

1717 Track-laying Machine and Baikal-Amur Railway

1719 Star of Spassky Tower

1718 "Decembrists in Senate Square" (D. N. Kardovsky) (⅔-size illustration)

1975. 58th Anniv of October Revolution. Mult.
4452 4k. Type **1717** 35 10
4453 4k. Rolling mill, Novolipetsk steel plant (vert) 20 10
4454 4k. Formula and ammonia plant, Nevynomyssk chemical works (vert) . . 20 10

1975. 150th Anniv of Decembrist Rising.
4455 **1718** 4k. multicoloured . . . 20 10

1975. New Year.
4456 **1719** 4k. multicoloured . . . 15 10

1720 "Village Street"

1975. 125th Birth Anniv of F. A. Vasilev (painter). Multicoloured.
4457 2k. Type **1720** 10 10
4458 5k. "Forest Path" 15 10
4459 6k. "After the Thunderstorm" 25 10
4460 10k. "Forest Marsh" (horiz) 45 15
4461 12k. "In the Crimean Mountains" 65 20
4462 16k. "Wet Meadow" (horiz) 1·00 30

1721 "Venus" Spacecraft

1975. Space Flights of "Venus 9" and "Venus 10".
4464 **1721** 10k. multicoloured . . 35 15

1722 G. Sundukyan

1975. 150th Birth Anniv of G. Sundukyan (Armenian playwright).
4465 **1722** 4k. multicoloured . . . 15 10

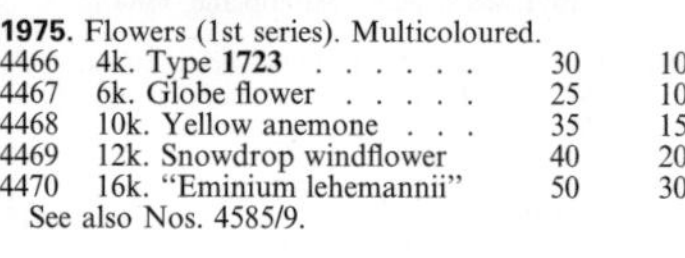

1723 Iceland Poppy

1724 A. L. Mints

1975. Flowers (1st series). Multicoloured.
4466 4k. Type **1723** 30 10
4467 6k. Globe flower 25 10
4468 10k. Yellow anemone . . . 35 15
4469 12k. Snowdrop windflower 40 20
4470 16k. "Eminium lehemannii" 50 30
See also Nos. 4585/9.

1975. A. L. Mints (scientist) Commemoration.
4471 **1724** 4k. brown and gold . . 15 10

1725 "Demon" (A. Kochupalov) **1726** Pieck

1975. Miniatures from Palekh Art Museum (1st series). Multicoloured.
4472 4k. Type **1725** 20 10
4473 6k. "Vasilisa the Beautiful" (I. Vakurov) 30 10
4474 10k. "The Snow Maiden" (T. Zubkova) 45 15
4475 16k. "Summer" (K. Kukulieva) 65 25
4476 20k. "Fisherman and Goldfish" (I. Vakurov) (horiz) 90 30
See also Nos. 4561/5.

1975. Birth Centenary of Wilhelm Pieck (President of German Democratic Republic).
4477 **1726** 6k. black 20 10

1727 Saltykov-Shchedrin (after I. Kramskoi) **1728** Congress Emblem

1976. 150th Birth Anniv of M. Saltykov-Shchedrin (writer).
4478 **1727** 4k. multicoloured . . . 15 10

1976. 25th Communist Party Congress, Moscow (1st issue).
4479 **1728** 4k. gold, brown and red 15 10
See also Nos. 4489 and 4556/60.

1729 Lenin (statue, S. Merkurov), Kiev

1976. 25th Ukraine Communist Party Congress, Kiev.
4481 **1729** 4k. black, red and blue 15 10

1730 Ice Hockey

1976. Winter Olympic Games, Innsbruck (1st series). Multicoloured.
4482 2k. Type **1730** 15 10
4483 4k. Skiing 20 10
4484 6k. Figure skating 25 10
4485 10k. Speed skating 35 15
4486 20k. Tobogganing 75 35

1731 Marshal C. E. Voroshilov **1732** Congress Hall and Red Banner

1976. 95th Birth Anniv of Marshal C. E. Voroshilov.
4488 **1731** 4k. green 15 10

1976. 25th Communist Party Congress, Moscow (2nd issue).
4489 **1732** 20k. orange, red & green . . . . 3·50 2·25

1733 "Lenin on Red Square" (P. Vasilev)

1976. 106th Birth Anniv of Lenin.
4490 **1733** 4k. multicoloured . . . 20 10

1734 Atomic Symbol and Institute Emblem

1976. 20th Anniv of Joint Institute of Nuclear Research, Dubna.
4491 **1734** 6k. multicoloured . . . 20 10

1736 Bolshoi Theatre

1976. Bicentenary of Bolshoi Theatre.
4493 **1736** 10k. blue, brn & ochre 30 15

1737 "Back from the Fair"

1976. Birth Centenary of P. P. Konchalovsky (painter). Multicoloured.
4494 1k. Type **1737** 10 10
4495 2k. "The Green Glass" . . 10 10
4496 6k. "Peaches" 25 10
4497 16k. "Meat, Game and Vegetables by the Window" 70 30
4498 20k. Self-portrait (vert) . . . 95 40

1738 "Vostok", "Salyut" and "Soyuz" Spacecraft

1976. 15th Anniv of First Manned Space Flight by Yuri Gagarin.
4499 4k. Type **1738** 15 10
4500 6k. "Meteor" and "Molniya" satellites . . . 25 10
4501 10k. Cosmonauts on board "Salyut" space-station . . 45 15
4502 12k. "Interkosmos" satellite and "Apollo"–"Soyuz" space link 55 20

1739 I. A. Dzhavakhishvili **1740** S. Vurgun

1976. Birth Centenary of I. A. Dzhavakhishvili (scientist).
4504 **1739** 4k. black, stone and green 15 10

1976. 70th Birth Anniv of Samed Vurgun (Azerbaijan poet).
4505 **1740** 4k. black, brown & green 15 10

1741 Festival Emblem **1742** F. I. P. Emblem

1976. 1st All-Union Amateur Art Festival.
4506 **1741** 4k. multicoloured . . . 15 10

1976. 50th Anniv of International Philatelic Federation.
4507 **1742** 6k. red and blue . . . 20 10

1744 Dnepropetrovsk Crest **1745** N. N. Burdenko

1976. Bicentenary of Dnepropetrovsk.
4509 **1744** 4k. multicoloured . . . 15 10

1976. Birth Centenary of N. N. Burdenko (neurologist).
4510 **1745** 4k. brown and red . . 15 10

1746 K. A. Trenev **1748** Electric Railway Train

1747 Canoeing

1976. Birth Centenary of K. A. Trenev (playwright).
4511 **1746** 4k. multicoloured . . . 15 10

1976. History of Soviet Motor Industry (4th series). As T **1609**.
4512 2k. black, red and green . . 10 10
4513 3k. black, orange and bistre 15 10
4514 4k. black, buff and blue . . 15 10
4515 12k. black, green and brown 45 20
4516 16k. black, red and yellow 65 30
DESIGNS: 2k. Moscow Auto Works "ZIS-110" saloon, 1945; 3k. Gorkovsky "GAZ-51" truck, 1946; 4k. Gorkovsky "GAZ-M20 (Pobeda)" saloon, 1946; 12k. Moscow Auto Works "ZIS-150" truck, 1947; 16k. Moscow Auto Works "ZIS-154" bus, 1947.

1976. Olympic Games, Montreal. Multicoloured.
4517 4k. Type **1747** 10 10
4518 6k. Basketball (vert) 20 10
4519 10k. Graeco-Roman wrestling 30 15
4520 14k. Discus throwing (vert) 45 15
4521 16k. Rifle-shooting 55 20

1976. 50th Anniv of Soviet Railway Electrification.
4523 **1748** 4k. black, red and green 30 10

1749 L. M. Pavlichenko **1750** L. E. Rekabarren

1976. 60th Birth Anniv of L. M. Pavlichenko (war heroine).
4524 **1749** 4k. brown, yellow and silver 15 10

1976. Birth Centenary of Luis Rekabarren (founder of Chilean Communist Party).
4525 **1750** 6k. black, red and gold 15 10

1751 "Fresh Partner"

1976. Russian Art. Paintings by P. A. Fedotov. Multicoloured.
4526 2k. Type **1751** 10 10
4527 4k. "Fastidious Fiancee" (horiz) 15 10
4528 6k. "Aristocrat's Breakfast" 20 10
4529 10k. "The Gamblers" (horiz) 50 20
4530 16k. "The Outing" 70 30

1752 S. S. Nemetkin **1753** Soviet Armed Forces Order

1754 Marx and Lenin (sculpture, Ye. Belostotsky and E. Fridman)

1976. Birth Centenary of Sergei S. Nemetkin (chemist).
4532 **1752** 4k. black, yellow & blue 15 10

1976. (a) As T **1753**.
4669 1k. olive 10 10
4670 2k. mauve 10 10
4671 3k. red 10 10
4672 4k. red 15 10
4673 6k. blue 20 10
4674 10k. green 35 10
4675 12k. blue 40 10
4676 15k. blue 70 10
4677 16k. green 50 15

(b) As T **1754**.
4678 20k. red 55 10
4679 30k. red 85 20
4680 32k. blue . . . . 1·60 45
4681 50k. brown . . . . 1·40 40
4682 1r. blue . . . . 3·00 1·00
DESIGNS: 2k. Gold Star (military) and Hammer and Sickle (labour) decorations; 3k. "Worker and Collective Farmer" (sculpture, Vera Mukhina); 4k. Soviet crest; 6k. Globe and Tupolev Tu-154 jetliner (Soviet postal communications); 10k. Soviet Reputation for Work Order; 23k. Yuri Gagarin and rocket (space exploration); 15k. Ostankino T.V. tower and globe; 16k. International Lenin Prize medal (international peace and security); 30k. Council for Mutual Economic Aid building; 32k. Ilyushin Il-76 airplane and compass rose; 50k. Lenin (after P. Zhukov); 1r. Satellites orbiting globe.

The 6 and 32k. are airmail stamps.

1755 Cattle Egret

1976. Water Birds. Multicoloured.
4545 1k. Type **1755** 15 15
4546 3k. Black-throated diver . . 20 20
4547 4k. Black coot 45 40
4548 6k. Atlantic puffin 85 40
4549 10k. Slender-billed gull . . . 1·40 45

1756 Peace Dove with Laurel

1976. 2nd Stockholm World Peace Appeal.
4550 **1756** 4k. blue, yellow and gold 15 10

1757 Federation Emblem

1976. 25th Anniv of International Resistance Movement Federation.
4551 **1757** 6k. black, gold and blue 15 10

1759 Soviet and Indian Flags
1761 UNESCO Emblem

1760 B. V. Volynov and V. M. Zholobov

1976. Soviet–Indian Friendship.
4553 **1759** 4k. multicoloured . . . 15 10

1976. Space Flight of "Soyuz 21".
4554 **1760** 10k. black, blue & brn 30 15

1976. 30th Anniv of UNESCO.
4555 **1761** 16k. brown, bistre & blue 45 20

1762 "Industry"

1976. 25th Communist Party Congress (3rd issue).
4556 **1762** 4k. brown, red & yellow 15 10
4557 – 4k. green, red & orange 15 10
4558 – 4k. violet, red and pink 15 10
4559 – 4k. deep red, red and grey 20 10
4560 – 4k. violet, red and blue 15 10
DESIGNS: No. 4557, "Agriculture"; 4558, "Science and Technology"; 4559, "Transport and Communications"; 4560, "International Co-operation".

1763 "The Ploughman" (I. Golikov)

1976. Minatures from Palekh Art Museum (2nd series). Multicoloured.
4561 2k. Type **1763** 10 10
4562 4k. "The Search" (I. Markichev) (vert) . . . 15 10
4563 12k. "The Firebird" (A. Kotukhin) 40 20
4564 14k. "Folk Festival" (A. Vatagin) (vert) . . . 55 25
4565 20k. "Victory" (I. Vakurov) (vert) 90 35

1764 Shostakovich and Part of 7th Symphony
1765 G. K. Zhukov

1976. 70th Birth Anniv of Dmitri Shostakovich (composer).
4566 **1764** 6k. blue 30 10

1976. 80th Birth Anniversaries of Soviet Marshals.
4567 **1765** 4k. green 15 10
4568 – 4k. brown 15 10
DESIGN: No. 4568, K. K. Rokossovsky.

1766 "Interkosmos 14" Satellite
1767 V. I. Dal

1976. International Co-operation in Space Research.
4569 **1766** 6k. blue, gold and black 20 10
4570 – 10k. violet, gold & black 25 10
4571 – 12k. purple, gold & black 40 15
4572 – 16k. green, gold & black 50 20
4573 – 20k. mauve, gold & black 90 25
DESIGNS: 10k. "Aryabhata" (Indian satellite); 12k. "Apollo"–"Soyuz" space link; 16k. "Aureole" (French satellite); 20k. Globe and spacecraft.

1976. 175th Birth Anniv of V. I. Dal (scholar).
4574 **1767** 4k. green 15 10

1768 Electric Power Station

1976. 59th Anniv of October Revolution. Mult.
4575 4k. Type **1768** 15 10
4576 4k. Balashovo fabrics factory 15 10
4577 4k. Irrigation ditch construction 15 10

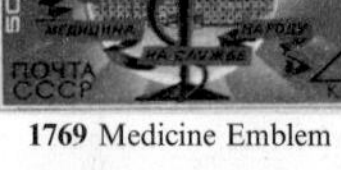

1769 Medicine Emblem
1770 M. A. Novinsky (oncologist)

1976. 50th Anniv of Petrov Institute of Cancer Research.
4578 **1769** 4k. lilac, gold and blue 20 10

1976. Centenary of Cancer Research.
4579 **1770** 4k. brown, blue and buff 20 10

1771 Hakkel VII Biplane, 1911

1976. Early Russian Aircraft (2nd series). Mult.
4580 3k. Type **1771** 10 10
4581 6k. Hakkel IX monoplane, 1912 . . . . 20 10
4582 12k. Steglau No. 2, 1912 . . 35 15
4583 14k. Dybovsky Dolphin, 1913 . . . . 50 15
4584 16k. Sikorsky Ilya Mourometz, 1914 . . . . 55 25
See also Nos. 4661/6 and 4791/6.

1976. Flowers (2nd series). As T **1723**. Mult.
4585 1k. Safflower 10 10
4586 2k. Anemone 10 10
4587 3k. Gentian 10 10
4588 4k. Columbine 15 10
4589 6k. Fitillaria 25 15

1772 New Year Greeting

1976. New Year.
4590 **1772** 4k. multicoloured . . . 15 10

1773 "Parable of the Vineyard"

1976. 370th Birth Anniv of Rembrandt. Mult.
4591 4k. Type **1773** 15 10
4592 6k. "Danae" 25 10
4593 10k. "David and Jonathan" (vert) 35 15
4594 14k. "The Holy Family" (vert) 55 20
4595 20k. "Andrian" (vert) . . . 85 30

1774 "Luna 24" and Emblem

1976. "Luna 24" Unmanned Space Flight to Moon.
4597 **1774** 10k. brown, yellow & blue 30 15

1775 "Pailot'

1976. Russian Ice-breakers (1st series). Mult.
4598 4k. Type **1775** 40 10
4599 6k. "Ermak" (vert) 50 10
4600 10k. "Fyodor Litke" . . . 70 15
4601 16k. "Vladmir Ilich" (vert) 95 25
4602 20k. "Krassin" . . . . . . 1·25 50
See also Nos. 4654/60, 4843/8 and 5147.

1776 "Raduga" Experiment and Cosmonauts

1976. "Soyuz 22" Space Flight by V. F. Bykovsky and V. V. Aksenov.
4603 **1776** 10k. green, blue and red 30 15

1777 Olympic Torch

1976. Olympic Games, Moscow (1980).
4604 **1777** 4k.+2k. black, red and blue 30 10
4605 – 10k.+5k. black, blue and red 65 25
4606 – 16k.+6k. black, mauve and yellow . . . . . 1·25 40
DESIGNS: 10, 16k. Games emblem.

1778 Society Emblem and "Red Star"
1779 S. P. Korolev Memorial Medallion

1977. 50th Anniv of Red Banner Forces Voluntary Society.
4608 **1778** 4k. multicoloured . . . 15 10

1977. 70th Birth Anniv of S. P. Korolev (scientist and rocket pioneer).
4609 **1779** 4k. gold, black and blue 15 10

1780 Congress Emblem

1977. World Peace Congress, Moscow.
4610 **1780** 4k. gold, ultramarine and blue 15 10

1781 Sedov and "Sv. Foka"

1977. Birth Cent of G. Y. Sedov (polar explorer).
4611 **1781** 4k. multicoloured . . . 1·10 20

1782 Working Class Monument, Red Flag and Newspaper Cover
1783 Ship on Globe

1977. 60th Anniv of Newspaper "Izvestiya".
4612 **1782** 4k. black, red and silver 15 10

1977. 24th International Navigation Congress, Leningrad.
4613 **1783** 6k. blue, black and gold 20 10

1784 Kremlin Palace of Congresses, Moscow
1785 L. A. Govorov

1977. 16th Soviet Trade Unions Congress.
4614 **1784** 4k. gold, black and red . . . 15 10

1977. 80th Birth Anniv of Marshal L. A. Govorov.
4615 **1785** 4k. brown 15 10

1786 Academy Emblem, Text and Building

1977. 150th Anniv of Grechko Naval Academy, Leningrad.
4616 **1786** 6k. multicoloured . . . 15 10

1787 J. Labourbe
1788 Chess Pieces

1977. Birth Centenary of Jeanne Labourbe (French communist).
4617 **1787** 4k. black, blue and red . . . 15 10

1977. 6th European Chess Team Championship, Moscow.
4618 **1788** 6k. multicoloured . . . 50 10

1789 "Soyuz 23" and Cosmonauts

1977. "Soyuz 23" Space Flight by V. D. Zudov and V. I. Rozhdestvensky.
4619 **1789** 10k. red, black & brown 35 15

1790 Novikov-Priboi
1791 "Welcome" (N. M. Soloninkin)

1977. Birth Centenary of Aleksei Novikov-Priboi (writer).
4620 **1790** 4k. black, orange & blue 15 10

1977. Folk Paintings from Fedoskino Village. Multicoloured.
4621 4k. Type **1791** 15 10
4622 6k. "Along the Street" (V. D. Antonov) (horiz) 20 10
4623 10k. "Northern Song" (J. V. Karapaev) 40 15
4624 12k. "Fairy Tale about Tzar Sultan" (A. I. Kozlov) . . 40 15
4625 14k. "Summer Troika" (V. A. Nalimov) (horiz) 50 20
4626 16k. "Red Flower" (V. D. Lipitsky) 60 25

1792 Congress Emblem

1977. World Electronics Congress, Moscow.
4627 **1792** 6k. red, grey and blue . . . 15 10

1793 "In Red Square" (K. V. Filatov)

1977. 107th Birth Anniv of Lenin.
4628 **1793** 4k. multicoloured . . . 15 10

1794 Yuri Gagarin and Spacecraft

1977. Cosmonautics Day.
4629 **1794** 6k. blue, lilac and purple 25 15

1795 N. I. Vavilov
1796 F. E. Dzerzhinsky

1977. 90th Birth Anniv of N. I. Vavilov (biologist).
4630 **1795** 4k. black and brown . . 15 10

1977. Birth Centenary of Feliks Dzerzhinsky (founder of Cheka).
4631 **1796** 4k. black 15 10

1797 Mountain Saxifrage
1798 V. V. Gorbatko and Yu. N. Glazkov (cosmonauts)

1977. Flowers. Multicoloured.
4632 2k. Type **1797** 10 10
4633 3k. Pinks 10 10
4634 4k. "Novosieversia glacialis" 15 10
4635 6k. "Cerastium maximum" 20 25
4636 16k. "Rhododendron aureum" 65 30

1977. "Soyuz 24–Salyut 5" Space Project.
4637 **1798** 10k. black, red and blue . . 40 15

1799 I. S. Konev
1800 Festival Emblem

1977. 80th Birth Anniv of Soviet Marshals.
4638 **1799** 4k. green 15 10
4639 – 4k. black 15 10
4640 – 4k. brown 15 10
DESIGNS: No. 4639, V. D. Sokolovsky; 4640, K. A. Meretskov.

1977. 10th International Film Festival, Moscow.
4641 **1800** 6k. gold, red and lake . . 15 10

1801 Greco-Roman Wrestling

1977. Olympic Sports (1st series).
4642 **1801** 4k.+2k. black, ochre and gold 20 10
4643 – 6k.+3k. black, green and gold 30 10
4644 – 10k.+5k. black, mauve and gold 45 20
4645 – 16k.+6k. black, blue and gold 70 30
4646 – 20k.+10k. black, brown and gold . . . . . . 1·75 65
DESIGNS: 6k. Free-style wrestling; 10k. Judo; 16k. Boxing; 29k. Weightlifting.
See also Nos. 4684/9, 4749/53, 4820/4, 4870/4, 4896/4900, 4962/6 and 4973/7.

1802 "Portrait of a Chambermaid"
1804 Stamps and Emblem

1977. 400th Birth Anniv of Rubens. Multicoloured.
4647 4k. Type **1802** 20 10
4648 6k. "The Lion Hunt" (horiz) 25 10
4649 10k. "Stone Carriers" (horiz) 35 10
4650 12k. "Water and Earth Alliance" 60 15
4651 20k. "Landscape with Rainbow" (horiz) 95 35

1977. Soviet Ice-breakers (2nd series). As T **1775**. Multicoloured.
4654 4k. "Aleksandr Sibiryakov" 25 10
4655 6k. "Georgy Sedov" 30 10
4656 10k. "Sadko" 55 15
4657 12k. "Dezhnev" 65 15
4658 14k. "Sibur" 75 20
4659 16k. "Lena" 90 30
4660 20k. "Amguema" . . . . . 1·10 40

1977. Air. Early Soviet Aircraft (3rd series). As T **1771** but dated 1977.
4661 4k. black, brown and blue 15 10
4662 6k. black, orange and green 25 10
4663 10k. black, mauve and blue 30 10
4664 12k. black, blue and red . . 35 15
4665 16k. multicoloured 50 15
4666 20k. black, green and blue 70 20
DESIGNS: 4k. Porokhovshchikov P-IV bis biplane trainer, 1917; 6k. Kalinin AK-1, 1924; 10k. Tupolev ANT-3 R-3, 1925; 12k. Tupolev ANT-4 TB-1 bomber, 1929; 16k. Polikarpov R-5 biplane, 1929; 20k. Shavrov Sh-2 flying boat, 1930.

1977. "60th Anniv of October Revolution" Philatelic Exhibition, Moscow.
4667 **1804** 4k. red, blue and brown . . 15 10

1805 Buildings and Arms, Stavropol
1807 Yuri Gagarin and "Vostok" Spacecraft

1977. Bicentenary of Stavropol.
4668 **1805** 6k. gold, red and green . . 20 10

1977. Olympic Sports (2nd series). As T **1801**.
4684 4k.+2k. black, gold and red 20 10
4685 6k.+3k. black, gold & blue 45 15
4686 10k.+5k. black, gold & grn 75 20
4687 16k.+6k. black, gold & olive 1·00 30
4688 20k.+10k. black, gold & pur 1·75 65
DESIGNS—HORIZ: 4k. Cycling; 10k. Rifle shooting; 16k. Horse-jumping; 20k. Fencing. VERT: 6k. Archery.

1977. 20th Anniv of Space Exploration.
4690 **1807** 10k. red, blue and brown 40 15
4691 – 10k. brown, blue & violet 40 15
4692 – 10k. red, purple & green 40 15
4693 – 20k. green, brown & red 70 25
4694 – 20k. purple, red and blue 70 25
4695 – 20k. red, blue and green 70 25
DESIGNS: No. 4691, Space walking; 4692, "Soyuz" spacecraft and "Salyut" space station linked; 4693, "Proton 4" satellite; 4694, "Luna Venus" and "Mars" space stations; 4695, "Intercosmos 10" satellite and "Apollo" and "Soyuz" spacecraft linked

1808 Carving from St. Dmitri's Cathedral, Vladimir (12th-cent)

1977. Russian Art. Multicoloured.
4697 4k. Type **1808** 15 10
4698 6k. Bracelet, Ryazan (12th cent) 20 15
4699 10k. Detail of Golden Gate from Nativity Cathedral, Suzdal (13th-cent) 30 15
4700 12k. Detail from "Arch-angel Michael" (icon) (A. Rublev) (15th-cent) 40 15
4701 16k. Gold and marble chalice made by I. Fomin (15th-cent) 55 20
4702 20k. St. Basil's Cathedral, Moscow (16th-cent) . . . 70 20

1809 "Snowflake and Fir Twig"
1810 Cruiser "Aurora"

1977. New Year.
4703 **1809** 4k. multicoloured . . . 15 10

1977. 60th Anniv of October Revolution.
4704 **1810** 4k. multicoloured . . . 15 10
4705 – 4k. black, red and gold 15 10
4706 – 4k. black, red and gold 15 10
4707 – 4k. multicoloured . . . 15 10
DESIGNS: No. 4705, Statue of Lenin; 4706, Page of "Izvestiya", book by Brezhnev and crowd; 4707, Kremlin spire, star and fireworks.

1811 First Clause of U.S.S.R. Constitution

1977. New Constitution.
4709 **1811** 4k. yellow, red & brown 15 10
4710 – 4k. multicoloured . . . 15 10
DESIGN: No. 4710, People of the U.S.S.R. welcoming new constitution.

1813 Postwoman and Post Code

1977. Postal Communications. Multicoloured.
4713 4k. Type **1813** 15 10
4714 4k. Letter collection 15 10
4715 4k. "Map-O" automatic sorting machine 15 10

4716 4k. Mail transport 15 10
4717 4k. Delivering the mail 15 10

1814 Red Fort, Delhi and Asokan Capital

1815 Monument, Kharkov

1977. 30th Anniv of Indian Independence.
4718 **1814** 6k. gold, purple and red 20 10

1977. 60th Anniv of Establishment of Soviet Power in the Ukraine.
4719 **1815** 6k. multicoloured 15 10

1816 Adder

1977. Snakes and Protected Animals. Mult.
4720 1k. Type **1816** 10 10
4721 4k. Levantine viper 15 10
4722 6k. Saw-scaled viper 20 10
4723 10k. Central Asian viper 30 15
4724 12k. Central Asian cobra 30 15
4725 16k. Polar bear and cub 40 25
4726 20k. Walrus and young 50 25
4727 30k. Tiger and cub 85 30

1817 Olympic Emblem and Arms of Vladimir

1977. 1980 Olympics. "Tourism around the Golden Ring" (1st issue). Multicoloured.
4728 1r.+50k. Type **1817** 4·50 2·25
4729 1r.+50k. Vladimir Hotel 4·50 2·25
4730 1r.+50k. Arms of Suzdal 4·50 2·25
4731 1r.+50k. Pozharsky monument 4·50 2·25
4732 1r.+50k. Arms of Ivanovo and Frunze monument 4·50 2·25
4733 1r.+50k. Monument to Revolutionary Fighters 4·50 2·25
See also Nos. 4828/31, 4850/3, 4914/17, 4928/9, 4968/9, 4981/2 and 4990/5.

1818 Combine Harvester

1819 Kremlin Palace of Congresses

1978. 50th Anniv of "Gigant" Collective Farm, Rostov.
4734 **1818** 4k. brown, red & yellow 15 10

1978. 18th Leninist Young Communist League (Komsomol) Congress.
4735 **1819** 4k. multicoloured 15 10

1820 Globe, Obelisk and Emblem

1978. 8th International Federation of Resistance Fighters Congress, Minsk.
4736 **1820** 6k. red, blue and black 15 10

1821 Red Army Detachment and Modern Sailor, Airman and Soldier

1978. 60th Anniv of Soviet Military Forces. Mult.
4737 4k. Type **1821** 15 10
4738 4k. Defenders of Moscow monument (detail), Lenin banner and Order of Patriotic War 15 10
4739 4k. Soviet soldier 15 10

1822 "Celebration in a Village" (½-size illustration)

1978. Birth Centenary of Boris M. Kustodiev (artist). Multicoloured.
4740 4k. Type **1822** 15 10
4741 6k. "Shrovetide" 20 10
4742 10k. "Morning" (50 × 36 mm) 30 15
4743 12k. "Merchant's Wife drinking Tea" (50 × 36 mm) 40 15
4744 20k. "Bolshevik" (50 × 36 mm) 55 25

1823 Gubarev and Remek at Launch Pad

1824 "Soyuz" Capsules linked to "Salyut" Space Station

1978. Soviet–Czech Space Flight. Multicoloured.
4746 6k. Type **1823** 15 10
4747 15k. "Soyuz-28" docking with "Salyut-6" space station 45 15
4748 32k. Splashdown 1·00 35

1978. Olympic Sports (3rd series). As T **1801**. Multicoloured.
4749 4k.+2k. Swimmer at start 20 10
4750 6k.+3k. Diving (vert) 35 10
4751 10k.+5k. Water polo 70 15
4752 10k.+6k. Canoeist 1·00 20
4753 20k.+10k. Single sculls 1·60 70

1978. Cosmonautics Day.
4755 **1824** 6k. gold, blue and deep blue 15 10

1825 Shield and Laurel Wreath

1826 E. A. and M. E. Cherepanov and their Locomotive, 1833

1978. 9th World Congress of Trade Unions.
4756 **1825** 6k. multicoloured 15 10

1978. Russian Locomotives (1st series). Mult.
4757 1k. Type **1826** 20 10
4758 2k. Series D locomotive, 1845 20 10
4759 3k. Series V locomotive (first passenger train, 1845) 20 10
4760 16k. Series Gv locomotive, 1863–67 95 25
4761 20k. Series Bv locomotive, 1863–67 1·25 30
Nos. 4758/61 are horizontal designs.
See also Nos. 4861/5.

1828 "XI" and Laurel Branch

1830 I.M.C.O. Emblem

1829 Tulip "Bolshoi Theatre"

1978. 11th World Youth and Students Festival, Havana.
4763 **1828** 4k. multicoloured 15 10

1978. Moscow Flowers. Multicoloured.
4764 1k. Type **1829** 10 10
4765 2k. Rose "Moscow Morning" 10 10
4766 4k. Dahlia "Red Star" 10 10
4767 10k. Gladiolus "Moscovite" 40 15
4768 12k. Iris "To Il'ich's Anniversary" 45 20

1978. 20th Anniv of Intergovernment Maritime Consultative Organization, and World Maritime Day.
4769 **1830** 6k. multicoloured 15 10

1831 "Salyut-6" Space Station performing Survey Work

1978. "Salyut-6" Space Station. Multicoloured.
4770 15k. Type **1831** 50 30
4771 15k. Yu. V. Romanenko and G. M. Grechko 50 30
Nos. 4770/1 were issued in se-tenant pairs forming a composite design.

1832 "Space Meteorology"

1978. Space Research. Multicoloured.
4772 10k. Type **1832** 30 15
4773 10k. "Soyuz" orbiting globe ("Natural resources") 30 15
4774 10k. Radio waves, ground station and "Molniya" satellite ("Communication") 30 15
4775 10k. Human figure, "Vostok" orbiting Earth ("Medicine and biology") 30 15

1833 Transporting Rocket to Launch Site

1978. Soviet–Polish Space Flight. Multicoloured.
4777 6k. Type **1833** 15 10
4778 15k. Crystal (Sirena experiment) 50 15
4779 32k. Space station, map and scientific research ship "Kosmonavt Vladimir Komarov" 1·10 35

1834 Komsomol Awards

1835 M. V. Zakharov

1978. 60th Anniv of Leninist Young Communist League (Komsomol). Multicoloured.
4780 4k. Type **1834** 10 10
4781 4k. Products of agriculture and industry 30 10

1978. 80th Birth Anniv of Marshal M. V. Zakharov.
4782 **1835** 4k. brown 10 10

1836 N. G. Chernyshevsky

1978. 150th Birth Anniv of Nikolai G. Chernyshevsky (revolutionary).
4783 **1836** 4k. brown and yellow 10 10

1837 Snow Petrel

1978. Antarctic Fauna. Multicoloured.
4784 1k. Snares Island penguin (horiz) 60 15
4785 3k. Type **1837** 75 15
4786 4k. Emperor penguin 95 15
4787 6k. Antarctic icefish 1·25 15
4788 10k. Southern elephant-seal (horiz) 1·25 15

1838 Torch and Flags

1839 William Harvey

1978. Construction of Orenburg–U.S.S.R. Western Frontier Gas Pipe-line.
4789 **1838** 4k. multicoloured 15 10

1978. 400th Birth Anniv of William Harvey (discoverer of blood circulation).
4790 **1839** 6k. green, black and blue 15 10

1978. Air. Early Russian Aircraft (3rd series). As T **1771**.
4791 4k. green, brown and black 15 10
4792 6k. multicoloured 25 10
4793 10k. yellow, blue and black 45 15
4794 12k. orange, blue and black 55 15
4795 16k. blue, deep blue and black 70 15
4796 20k. multicoloured 90 20

DESIGNS: 4k. Polikarpov Po-2 biplane, 1928; 6k. Kalinin K-5, 1929; 10k. Tupolev ANT-6 TB-3 bomber, 1930; 12k. Putilov Stal-2, 1931; 16k. Beriev Be-2 MBR-2 reconnaissance seaplane, 1932; 20k. Polikarpov I-16 fighter, 1934.

1840 "Bathing of Red Horse"

1978. Birth Centenary of K. S. Petrov-Vodkin (painter). Multicoloured.

4797 4k. Type **1840** 10 10
4798 6k. "Petrograd, 1918" . . . 15 10
4799 10k. "Commissar's Death" 30 15
4800 12k. "Rose Still Life" . . . 40 15
4801 16k. "Morning Still Life" 60 15

1841 Assembling "Soyuz 31"

1978. Soviet–East German Space Flight. Mult.

4803 6k. Type **1841** 15 10
4804 15k. Space photograph of Pamir mountains 55 15
4805 32k. Undocking from space station . . . . 1·10 35

1842 "Molniya 1" Satellite, "Orbita" Ground Station and Tupolev Tu-134 Jetliner

1978. "PRAGA 78" International Stamp Exhibition.

4806 **1842** 6k. multicoloured . . . 15 10

1843 Tolstoi

1978. 150th Birth Anniv of Leo Tolstoi (novelist).

4807 **1843** 4k. green . . . . 1·25 75

1844 Union Emblem

1845 Bronze Figure, Erebuni Fortress

1978. 14th General Assembly of International Union for the Protection of Nature and Natural Resources, Ashkhabad.

4808 **1844** 4k. multicoloured . . . 15 10

1978. Armenian Architecture. Multicoloured.

4809 4k. Type **1845** 10 10
4810 6k. Echmiadzin Cathedral 15 10
4811 10k. Khachkary (carved stones) 25 10
4812 12k. Matenadaran building (repository of manuscripts) (horiz) . . . 35 15
4813 16k. Lenin Square, Yerevan (horiz) 45 20

1846 Monument (P. Kufferge)

1847 Emblem, Ostankino TV Tower and Hammer and Sickle

1978. 70th Anniv of Russian Aid to Messina Earthquake Victims.

4814 **1846** 6k. multicoloured . . . 20 10

1978. 20th Anniv of Organization for Communications Co-operation.

4815 **1847** 4k. multicoloured . . . 10 10

(**1848**)

1978. "60th Anniv of Komsomol" Philatelic Exhibition. Optd with T **1848**.

4816 **1834** 4k. multicoloured . . . 1·00 50

1851 Shaumyan

1852 "Star" Yacht

1978. Birth Centenary of Stephan Georgievich Shaumyan (Commissar).

4819 **1851** 4k. green 10 10

1978. Olympic Sports (4th series). Sailing Regatta, Tallin. Multicoloured.

4820 4k.+2k. Type **1852** 20 10
4821 6k.+3k. "Soling" yacht . . 30 10
4822 10k.+5k. "470" dinghy . . . 50 15
4823 16k.+6k. "Finn" dinghy . . 80 25
4824 20k.+10k. "Flying Dutchman" dinghy . . . 1·25 55

1853 Industrial Structures and Flags

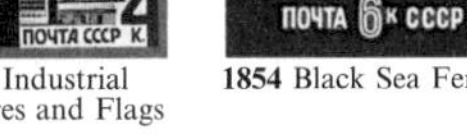

1854 Black Sea Ferry

1978. 61st Anniv of October Revolution.

4826 **1853** 4k. multicoloured . . . 10 10

1978. Inauguration of Ilichevsk–Varna, Bulgaria, Ferry Service.

4827 **1854** 6k. multicoloured . . . 15 10

1855 Zagorsk

1978. 1980 Olympics. "Tourism around the Golden Ring" (2nd issue). Multicoloured.

4828 1r.+50k. Type **1855** . . . . 4·75 2·75
4829 1r.+50k. Palace of Culture, Zagorsk . . . . 4·75 2·75
4830 1r.+50k. Kremlin, Rostov-Veliki . . . . 4·75 2·75
4831 1r.+50k. View of Rostov-Veliki . . . . 4·75 2·75

1856 Church of the Intercession on River Nerl

1978. "Masterpieces of Old Russian Culture". Mult.

4832 6k. Golden crater (horiz) . . 15 10
4833 10k. Type **1856** 25 15
4834 12k. "St. George and the Dragon" (15th-century icon) 35 15
4835 16k. Tsar Cannon (horiz) 45 20

1857 Cup with Snake and Institute

1859 Spassky Tower, Kremlin

1858 Nestor Pechersky and "Chronicle of Past Days"

1978. 75th Anniv of Herzen Oncology Research Institute, Moscow.

4836 **1857** 4k. gold, purple & black 15 10

1978. History of the Russian Posts. Multicoloured.

4837 4k. Type **1858** 10 10
4838 6k. Birch-bark letter 15 10
4839 10k. Messenger with trumpet 30 15
4840 12k. Mail sledges 35 15
4841 16k. Interior of Prikaz Post Office 45 20

1978. New Year.

4842 **1859** 4k. multicoloured . . . 15 10

1978. Soviet Ice breakers (3rd series). As T **1775**. Multicoloured.

4843 4k. "Vasily Pronchishchev" 20 10
4844 6k. "Kapitan Belousov" (vert) 25 10
4845 10k. "Moskva" 30 15
4846 12k. "Admiral Makarov" 45 15
4847 16k. "Lenin" atomic ice-breaker (vert) 65 20
4848 20k. "Arktika" atomic ice-breaker 80 35

1860 V. Kovalenok and A. Ivanchenkov

1978. "140 Days in Space".

4849 **1860** 10k. multicoloured . . 30 15

1978. 1980 Olympics "Tourism around the Golden Ring" (3rd issue). As T **1855**. Multicoloured.

4850 1r.+50k. Alexander Nevsky Monument, Pereslavl-Zalessky . . . . 4·00 2·50
4851 1r.+50k. Peter I Monument, Pereslavl-Zalessky . . . . 4·00 2·50
4852 1r.+50k. Monastery of the Transfiguration, Yaroslavl 4·00 2·50
4853 1r.+50k. Ferry terminal and Eternal Glory Monument, Yaroslavl . . . . 4·00 2·50

1862 Cuban Flags

1863 Government Building, Minsk

1979. 20th Anniv of Cuban Revolution.

4855 **1862** 6k. multicoloured . . . 15 10

1979. 60th Anniv of Byelorussian Soviet Socialist Republic and Communist Party.

4856 **1863** 4k. multicoloured . . . 15 10

1864 Flags and Reunion Monument

1865 Old and New University Buildings

1979. 325th Anniv of Reunion of Ukraine with Russia.

4857 **1864** 4k. multicoloured . . . 15 10

1979. 400th Anniv of Vilnius University.

4858 **1865** 4k. black and pink . . 15 10

1866 Exhibition Hall and First Bulgarian Stamp

1979. "Philaserdica 79" International Stamp Exhibition, Sofia.

4859 **1866** 15k. multicoloured . . 50 15

1867 Satellites "Radio 1" and "Radio 2"

1979. Launching of "Radio" Satellites.

4860 **1867** 4k. multicoloured . . . 35 10

1868 Series A Locomotive, 1878

1979. Railway Locomotives (2nd series). Mult.
4861 2k. Type **1868** 15 10
4862 3k. Class Shch steam locomotive, 1912 . . . . 15 10
4863 4k. Class Lp steam locomotive, 1915 . . . . 25 10
4864 6k. Class Su steam locomotive, 1925 . . . . 45 15
4865 15k. Class L steam locomotive, 1947 . . . . 1·10 40

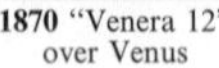

1870 "Venera 12" over Venus **1871** Albert Einstein

1979. "Venera" Flights to Venus.
4867 **1870** 10k. red, lilac and purple 35 10

1979. Birth Centenary of Albert Einstein (physicist).
4868 **1871** 6k. multicoloured . . . 20 10

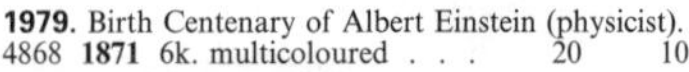

1872 Congress Emblem

1979. 21st World Veterinary Congress, Moscow.
4869 **1872** 6k. multicoloured . . . 15 10

1873 Free Exercise

1979. Olympic Sports (5th series). Gymnastics.
4870 **1873** 4k.+2k. brown, stone and orange 15 10
4871 – 6k.+3k. blue, grey and violet 20 10
4872 – 10k.+5k. red, stone and brown 30 15
4873 – 16k.+6k. mauve, grey and purple 75 40
4874 – 20k.+10k. red, stone and brown . . . . . 1·60 65
DESIGNS: 6k. Parallel bars; 10k. Horizontal bar; 16k. Beam; 20k. Asymmetric bars.

1874 "To Arms" (poster by R. Beren)

1979. 60th Anniv of First Hungarian Socialist Republic.
4876 **1874** 4k. multicoloured . . . 10 10

1875 Cosmonauts at Yuri Gagarin Training Centre

1979. Soviet–Bulgarian Space Flight. Mult.
4877 6k. Type **1875** 20 10
4878 32k. Landing of cosmonauts 90 35

1876 "Intercosmos"

1979. Cosmonautics Day.
4879 **1876** 15k. multicoloured . . 50 15

1878 Exhibition Emblem

1979. U.S.S.R. Exhibition, London.
4881 **1878** 15k. multicoloured . . 40 15

1880 Antonov An-28

1979. Air. Soviet Aircraft. Multicoloured.
4883 2k. Type **1880** 10 10
4884 3k. Yakovlev Yak-42 . . . 15 10
4885 10k. Tupolev Tu-154 . . . 40 15
4886 15k. Ilyushin Il-76 . . . . . 60 20
4887 32k. Ilyushin Il-86 . . . . . 1·00 40

1882 "Tent" Monument, Mining Institute, Pushkin Theatre and Blast Furnace **1883** Child and Apple Blossom

1979. 50th Anniv of Magnitogorsk City.
4889 **1882** 4k. multicoloured . . . 15 10

1979. International Year of the Child (1st issue).
4890 **1883** 4k. multicoloured . . . 15 10
See also Nos. 4918/21.

1884 Bogorodsk Wood-carvings

1979. Folk Crafts. Multicoloured.
4891 2k. Type **1884** 10 10
4892 3k. Khokhloma painted dish and jars 10 10
4893 4k. Zhostovo painted tray 15 10
4894 6k. Kholmogory bone-carvings 25 15
4895 15k. Vologda lace 50 35

1885 Football

1979. Olympic Sports (6th series). Multicoloured.
4896 **1885** 4k.+2k. blue, grey and orange 30 10
4897 – 6k.+3k. yellow, orange and blue 40 10
4898 – 10k.+5k. green, red and mauve 50 15
4899 – 16k.+6k. purple, blue and green 60 25
4900 – 20k.+10k. yellow, red and green . . . . . 1·25 60
DESIGNS—VERT: 6k. Basketball; 10k. Volleyball. HORIZ: 16k. Handball; 20k. Hockey.

1886 Lenin Square Underground Station

1979. Tashkent Underground Railway.
4901 **1886** 4k. multicoloured . . . 25 10

1887 V. A. Dzhanibekov and O. G. Makarov **1888** Council Building and Flags of Member Countries

1979. "Soyuz 27"–"Salyut 6"–"Soyuz 26" Orbital Complex.
4902 **1887** 4k. multicoloured . . . 20 10

1979. 30th Anniv of Council of Mutual Economic Aid.
4903 **1888** 16k. multicoloured . . 50 15

1889 Scene from "Battleship Potemkin" **1892** Exhibition Hall and Film Still

1979. 60th Anniv of Soviet Films (1st issue) and 11th International Film Festival, Moscow.
4904 **1889** 15k. multicoloured . . 50 15
See also No. 4907.

1979. 60th Anniv of Soviet Films (2nd issue).
4907 **1892** 4k. multicoloured . . . 15 10

1893 "Lilac" (K. A. Korovin) **1894** John McClean

1979. Flower Paintings. Multicoloured.
4908 1k. "Flowers and Fruits" (I. F. Khrutsky) (horiz) 10 10
4909 2k. "Phloxes" (I. N. Kramskoi) 15 10
4910 3k. Type **1893** 20 10
4911 15k. "Bluebells" (S. V. Gerasimov) 50 20
4912 32k. "Roses" (P. P. Konchalovsky) (horiz) . . 95 40

1979. Birth Centenary of John McClean (first Soviet consul for Scotland).
4913 **1894** 4k. black and red . . . 15 10

1979. 1980 Olympics. "Tourism around the Golden Ring" (4th issue). As T **1855**. Multicoloured.
4914 1r.+50k. Narikaly Fortress, Tbilisi . . . . 4·00 2·50
4915 1r.+50k. Georgian Philharmonic Society Concert Hall and "Muse" (sculpture), Tbilisi . . . . 4·00 2·50
4916 1r.+50k. Chir-Dor Mosque, Samarkand . . . . 4·00 2·50
4917 1r.+50k. People's Friendship Museum and "Courage" monument, Tashkent . . 4·00 2·50

1895 "Friendship" (Lena Liberda)

1979. International Year of the Child (2nd issue). Children's Paintings. Multicoloured.
4918 2k. Type **1895** 10 10
4919 3k. "After Rain" (Daniya Akhmetshina) 10 10
4920 4k. "Dance of Friendship" (Liliya Elistratova) . . . 20 10
4921 15k. "On the Excursion" (Vika Smalyuk) 45 20

1896 Golden Oriole

1979. Birds. Multicoloured.
4922 2k. Type **1896** 15 10
4923 3k. Lesser spotted woodpecker 20 10
4924 4k. Crested tit 20 10
4925 10k. Barn owl 60 15
4926 15k. European nightjar . . 80 35

1897 Soviet Circus Emblem **1898** Marx, Engels, Lenin and View of Berlin

1979. 60th Anniv of Soviet Circus.
4927 **1897** 4k. multicoloured . . . 15 10

1979. 1980 Olympics. "Tourism around the Golden Ring" (5th issue). As T **1855**. Multicoloured.
4928 1r.+50k. Relics of Yerevan's origin . . . . 4·00 2·00
4929 1r.+50k. Armenian State Opera and Ballet Theatre, Yerevan . . . . 4·00 2·00

1979. 30th Anniv of German Democratic Republic.
4930 **1898** 6k. multicoloured . . . 15 10

1899 V. A. Lyakhov, V. V. Ryumin and "Salyut 6"

1979. Lyakhov and Ryumin's 175 Days in Space. Multicoloured.
4931 15k. Type **1899** 40 20
4932 15k. Radio telescope mounted on "Salyut 6" 40 20
Nos. 4931/2 were issued together, se-tenant, forming a composite design.

1900 Hammer and Sickle **1901** Communications Equipment and Signal Corps Emblem

1979. 62nd Anniv of October Revolution.
4933 **1900** 4k. multicoloured . . . 15 10

1979. 60th Anniv of Signal Corps.
4934 **1901** 4k. multicoloured . . . 15 10

1902 "Katherine" (T. G. Shevchenko)
1903 Shabolovka Radio Mast, Moscow

1979. Ukrainian Paintings. Multicoloured.
4935 2k. Type **1902** 10 10
4936 3k. "Into Service" (K. K. Kostandi) 25 10
4937 4k. "To Petrograd" (A. M. Lopukhov) 55 10
4938 10k. "Return" (V. N. Kostetsky) 30 15
4939 15k. "Working Morning" (M. G. Belsky) 40 25

1979. 50th Anniv of Radio Moscow.
4940 **1903** 32k. multicoloured . . 1·00 35

1904 Misha (Olympic mascot)
1905 "Peace" and Hammer and Sickle

1979. New Year.
4941 **1904** 4k. multicoloured . . . 25 10

1979. "Peace Programme in Action". Mult.
4942 4k. Type **1905** 15 10
4943 4k. Hand holding demand for peace 15 10
4944 4k. Hands supporting emblem of peace 15 10

1906 Traffic Policeman
1909 Industrial Landscape

1907 "Vulkanolog"

1979. Road Safety. Multicoloured.
4945 3k. Type **1906** 10 10
4946 4k. Child playing in road . . 15 10
4947 6k. Speeding car out of control 25 10

1979. Soviet Scientific Research Ships. Mult.
4948 1k. Type **1907** 10 10
4949 2k. "Professor Bogorov" . . 10 10
4950 4k. "Ernst Krenkel" 15 10
4951 6k. "Kosmonavt Vladislav Volkov" 30 15
4952 10k. "Kosmonavt Yuri Gagarin" 60 25
4953 15k. "Akademik Kurchatov" 85 35

1980. 50th Anniv of Mordovian ASSR of Russian Federation.
4955 **1909** 4k. red 15 10

1910 Speed Skating
1912 N. I. Podvoisky

1911 Running

1980. Winter Olympic Games, Lake Placid.
4956 **1910** 4k. blue, lt blue & orange 15 10
4957 – 6k. violet, blue & orange 15 10
4958 – 10k. red, blue and gold 40 15
4959 – 15k. brown, blue & turquoise 50 15
4960 – 20k. turquoise, blue and red 60 25
DESIGNS—HORIZ: 6k. Figure skating (pairs); 10k. Ice hockey; 15k. Downhill skiing. VERT: 20k. Luge.

1980. Olympic Sports (7th series). Athletics. Mult.
4962 4k.+2k. Type **1911** 20 10
4963 6k.+3k. Hurdling 25 10
4964 10k.+5k. Walking (vert) . . 50 20
4965 16k.+6k. High jumping . . 75 20
4966 20k.+10k. Long jumping . . 1·10 60

1980. Birth Centenary of Nikolai Ilich Podvoisky (revolutionary).
4967 **1912** 4k. brown 10 10

1980. 1980 Olympics. "Tourism around the Golden Ring" (6th issue). Moscow. As T **1855**. Mult.
4968 1r.+50k. Kremlin . . . . . 4·50 2·75
4969 1r.+50k. Kalinin Prospect 4·50 2·75

1913 "Rainbow" (A. K. Savrasov) (½-size illustration)

1980. Birth Annivs of Soviet Artists. Mult.
4970 6k. "Harvest Summer" (A. G. Venetsianov (bicent)) (vert) 20 10
4971 6k. Type **1913** (150th anniv) 20 10
4972 6k. "Old Yerevan" (M. S. Saryan) (centenary) . . . 20 10

1980. Olympic Sports (8th series). Athletics. As T **1911**. Multicoloured.
4973 4k.+2k. Pole vaulting . . . 20 10
4974 6k.+3k. Discus throwing . . 25 10
4975 10k.+5k. Javelin throwing 50 20
4976 16k.+6k. Hammer throwing 75 20
4977 20k.+10k. Putting the shot 1·10 60

1915 Georg Ots
1916 Order of Lenin

1980. 60th Birth Anniv of Georg K. Ots (artist).
4980 **1915** 4k. blue 10 10

1980. 1980 Olympics. "Tourism around the Golden Ring" (7th issue). As T **1855**. Multicoloured.
4981 1r.+50k. St. Isaac's Cathedral, Leningrad . . 4·50 2·75
4982 1r.+50k. Monument to the Defenders of Leningrad 4·50 2·75

1980. 50th Anniv of Order of Lenin.
4983 **1916** 4k. multicoloured . . . 10 10

1919 "Motherland" (detail of Heroes Monument, Volgograd)
1920 Government House, Arms and Flag of Azerbaijan

1980. 35th Anniv of World War II Victory. Mult.
4986 4k. Type **1919** 15 10
4987 4k. Victory Monument, Treptow Park, Berlin . . 15 10
4988 4k. Victory Parade, Red Square, Moscow 15 10

1980. 60th Anniv of Azerbaijan Soviet Republic.
4989 **1920** 4k. multicoloured . . . 10 10

1980. 1980 Olympics. "Tourism around the Golden Ring" (8th issue). As T **1855**. Multicoloured.
4990 1r.+50k. Bogdan Khmelnitsky Monument and St. Sophia Monastery, Kiev . . . . 4·50 2·75
4991 1r.+50k. Underground bridge over River Dnieper, Kiev . . . . . 5·00 3·00
4992 1r.+50k. Sports Palace and War Memorial, Minsk . . 4·50 2·75
4993 1r.+50k. House of Cinematograhy, Minsk . . 4·50 2·75
4994 1r.+50k. Old City, Tallin . . 4·50 2·75
4995 1r.+50k. Hotel Viru, Tallin 4·50 2·75

1921 Monument, Ivanovo
1922 Shield and Industrial Complexes

1980. 75th Anniv of First Soviet of Workers Deputies, Ivanovo.
4996 **1921** 4k. multicoloured . . . 10 10

1980. 25th Anniv of Warsaw Treaty.
4997 **1922** 32k. multicoloured . . 1·25 65

1923 Yakovlev Yak-24 Helicopter, 1953

1980. Helicopters. Multicoloured.
4998 1k. Type **1923** 10 10
4999 2k. Mil Mi-8, 1962 . . . . 10 10
5000 3k. Kamov Ka-26, 1965 . . 20 10
5001 6k. Mil Mi-6, 1957 . . . . 30 15
5002 15k. Mil Mi-10K, 1965 . . 80 25
5003 32k. Mil Mi-V12, 1969 . . . 1·90 55

1924 Title Page of Book
1925 Medical Check-up of Cosmonauts

1980. 1500th Birth Anniv of David Anacht (Armenian philosopher).
5004 **1924** 4k. multicoloured . . . 10 10

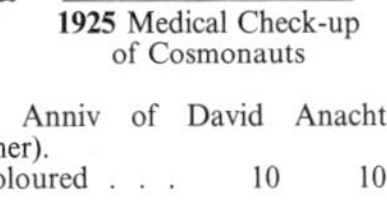

1980. Soviet–Hungarian Space Flight. Mult.
5005 6k. Type **1925** 15 10
5006 15k. Crew meeting on "Salyut-6" space station 45 15
5007 32k. Press conference . . . 1·00 50

1926 Red Fox
1927 Kazan

1980. Fur-bearing Animals. Multicoloured.
5008 2k. Type **1926** 10 10
5009 4k. Artic fox (horiz) 15 10
5010 6k. European mink 25 10
5011 10k. Coypu 45 20
5012 15k. Sable (horiz) 60 30

1980. 60th Anniv of Tatar Republic.
5013 **1927** 4k. multicoloured . . . 10 10

1928 College and Emblem
1929 Ho Chi Minh

1980. 150th Anniv of Bauman Technical College, Moscow.
5014 **1928** 4k. multicoloured . . . 10 10

1980. 90th Birth Anniv of Ho Chi Minh (Vietnamese leader).
5015 **1929** 6k. multicoloured . . . 20 10

1930 Arms, Monument and Modern Buildings

1980. 40th Anniv of Soviet Socialist Republics of Lithuania, Latvia and Estonia. Multicoloured.
5016 **1930** 4k. Lithuania 10 10
5017 – 4k. Latvia 10 10
5018 – 4k. Estonia 10 10

1933 Crew of "Soyuz 27" at Launching Site
1934 Avicenna (after E. Sokdov and M. Gerasimov)

1980. Soviet–Vietnamese Space Flight. Mult.
5019 6k. Type **1933** 15 10
5020 15k. Cosmonauts at work in space 45 20
5021 32k. Cosmonauts returning to Earth . . . . 1·75 70

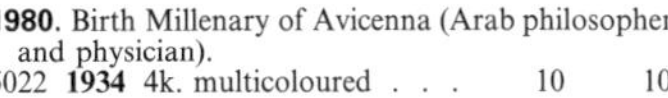

1980. Birth Millenary of Avicenna (Arab philosopher and physician).
5022 **1934** 4k. multicoloured . . . 10 10

1935 "Khadi-7" Gas turbine Car

1980. Racing cars designed by Kharkov Automobile and Road-building Institute. Mult.
5023 2k. Type **1935** 10 10
5024 6k. "Khadi-10" piston engined car 25 10
5025 15k. "Khadi-11 E" electric car 65 25
5026 32k. "Khadi-13 E" electric car . . . . 1·25 60

1936 Arms, Flags, Government House and Industrial Complex

1980. 60th Anniv of Kazakh Soviet Socialist Republic.
5027 **1936** 4k. multicoloured . . . 10 10

1937 "Self-portrait" and "The Spring"

1980. Birth Bicent of Jean Ingres (French painter).
5028 **1937** 32k. multicoloured . . 1·00 45

1938 "Morning on Kulikovo Field" (A. Bubnov)

1980. 600th Anniv of Battle of Kulikovo.
5029 **1938** 4k. multicoloured . . . 10 10

1939 Town Hall

1940 Yuri V. Malyshev and Valdimir V. Aksenov

1980. 950th Anniv of Tartu, Estonia.
5030 **1939** 4k. multicoloured . . . 10 10

1980. "Soyuz T-2" Space Flight.
5031 **1940** 10k. multicoloured . . 35 15

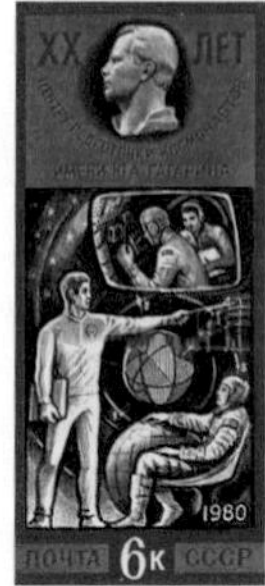

1941 Theoretical Training

1942 Crew Training

1980. 20th Anniv of Gagarin Cosmonaut Training Centre. Multicoloured.
5032 6k. Type **1941** 20 10
5033 15k. Practical training . . . 40 15
5034 32k. Physical endurance tests 95 50

1980. Soviet–Cuban Space Flight. Multicoloured.
5035 6k. Type **1942** 20 10
5036 15k. Physical exercise on board space complex . . 40 15
5037 32k. Returned cosmonauts and space capsule 95 50

1943 "Bargaining" (Nevrev) (⅔-size illustration)

1980. 150th Birth Anniv of N. V. Nevrev and K. D. Flavitsky (painters). Multicoloured.
5038 6k. Type **1943** 20 10
5039 6k. "Princess Tarakanova" (Flavitsky) 20 10

1944 Vasilevsky **1945** Banner

1980. 85th Birth Anniv of Marshal A. M. Vasilevsky.
5040 **1944** 4k. green 10 10

1980. 63rd Anniv of October Revolution.
5041 **1945** 4k. red, gold and purple 10 10

1946 Guramishvili **1947** Ioffe

1980. 275th Birth Anniv of David Guramishvili (Georgian poet).
5042 **1946** 4k. green, silver and black 10 10

1980. Birth Centenary of A. F. Ioffe (physicist).
5043 **1947** 4k. brown and buff . . 15 10

1948 Siberian Cedar

1980. Trees. Multicoloured.
5044 2k. Type **1948** 10 10
5045 4k. Pedunculate oak 10 10
5046 6k. Lime (vert) 20 10
5047 10k. Sea buckthorn 35 20
5048 15k. Ash 50 30

1950 Suvorov (after N. Utkin)

1980. 250th Birth Anniv of Field Marshal A. V. Suvorov.
5050 **1950** 4k. blue 15 10

1951 State Emblem and Republican Government House **1952** Blok (after K. Somov)

1980. 60th Anniv of Armenian Soviet Socialist Republic.
5051 **1951** 4k. multicoloured . . . 10 10

1980. Birth Cent of Aleksandr Aleksandrovich Blok (poet).
5052 **1952** 4k. multicoloured . . . 10 10

1980. Soviet Scientific Research Ships (2nd series). As T **1907**. Multicoloured.
5053 2k. "Ayu-Dag" 10 10
5054 3k. "Valerian Uryvaev" . . 10 10
5055 4k. "Mikhail Somov" . . . 20 10
5056 6k. "Akademik Sergei Korolev" 25 10
5057 10k. "Otto Schmidt" . . . 40 20
5058 15k. "Akademik Mstislav Keldysh" 65 30

1953 Spassky Tower and Kremlin Palace of Congresses **1955** Sable in Cedar

1980. New Year.
5059 **1953** 4k. multicoloured . . . 15 10

1980. Perf or imperf (2r.), perf (others).
5060 – 3k. orange 10 10
5061 – 5k. blue 15 10
5063 **1955** 35k. olive . . . . . . 1·00 35
5064 – 45k. brown . . . . . 1·40 40
5066 – 50k. green . . . . . . 1·60 10
5067a – 2r. black 25 10
5068 – 3r. black . . . . . . 8·00 4·00
5069 – 3r. green . . . . . . 2·00 1·00
5071 – 5r. blue . . . . . . 3·25 1·60

DESIGNS—14 × 22 mm: 3k. State flag; 5k. Forms of transport. 22 × 33 mm: 45k. Spassky Tower; 50k. Vodovzodny Tower and Grand Palace, Moscow Kremlin; 2r. "Arklika" atomic ice-breaker; 3r. Globe, child and olive branch; 5r. Globe and feather ("Peace").

1957 Institute Building

1980. 50th Anniv of Institute for Advanced Training of Doctors.
5075 **1957** 4k. multicoloured . . . 15 10

1958 Lenin Monument, Leningrad, and Dneproges Hydro-electric Station **1959** Nesmeyanov

1980. 60th Anniv of GOELRO (electrification plan).
5076 **1958** 4k. multicoloured . . . 10 10

1980. Academician A. N. Nesmeyanov (organic chemist) Commemoration.
5077 **1959** 4k. multicoloured . . . 10 10

1960 Nagatinsky Bridge

1980. Moscow Bridges. Multicoloured.
5078 4k. Type **1960** 15 10
5079 6k. Luzhniki underground railway bridge 35 10
5080 15k. Kalininsky bridge . . . 45 20

1961 Timoshenko **1962** Indian and Russian Flags with Government House, New Delhi

1980. 10th Death Anniv of Marshal S. K. Timoshenko.
5081 **1961** 4k. purple 10 10

1980. President Brezhnev's Visit to India.
5082 **1962** 4k. multicoloured . . . 25 10

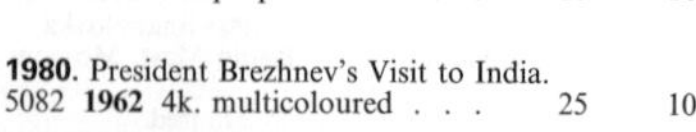

1963 Antarctic Research Station **1964** Arms and Symbols of Agriculture and Industry

1981. Antarctic Exploration. Multicoloured.
5083 4k. Type **1963** 15 10
5084 6k. Antennae, rocket, weather balloon and tracked vehicle (Meteorological research) 50 10
5085 15k. Map of Soviet bases and supply ship "Ob" . . 2·25 40

1981. 60th Anniv of Dagestan Autonomous Soviet Socialist Republic.
5086 **1964** 4k. multicoloured . . . 10 10

1965 Hockey Players and Emblem

1981. 12th World Hockey Championships, Khabarovsk.
5087 **1965** 6k. multicoloured . . . 20 10

1966 Banner and Star

1981. 26th Soviet Communist Party Congress. Multicoloured.
5088 4k. Type **1966** 10 10
5089 20k. Kremlin Palace of Congresses and Lenin (51 × 36 mm) . . . . . . 1·25 80

1967 Lenin and Congress Building **1968** Keldysh

1981. 26th Ukraine Communist Party Congress.
5090 **1967** 4k. multicoloured . . . 10 10

1981. 70th Birth Anniv of Academician Mstislav Vsevolodovich Keldysh (mathematician).
5091 **1968** 4k. multicoloured . . . 10 10

1970 Baikal–Amur Railway

1981. Construction Projects of the 10th Five Year Plan. Multicoloured.

5093	4k. Type **1970**	25	10
5094	4k. Urengoi gas field	15	10
5095	4k. Sayano-Shushenakaya hydro-electric dam	15	10
5096	4k. Atommash Volga–Don atomic reactor	15	10
5097	4k. Syktyvkar paper mill	15	10
5098	4k. Giant excavator, Ekibastuz	25	10

1971 Freighter and Russian and Indian Flags

1981. 25th Anniv of Soviet–Indian Shipping Line.
5099 **1971** 15k. multicoloured . . 55 20

1972 Arms, Monument and Building

1981. 60th Anniv of Georgian Soviet Socialist Republic.
5100 **1972** 4k. multicoloured . . . 10 10

1973 Arms and Abkhazian Scenes **1974** Institute Building

1981. 60th Anniv of Abkhazian Autonomous Soviet Socialist Republic.
5101 **1973** 4k. multicoloured . . . 10 10

1981. 60th Anniv of Moscow Electrotechnical Institute of Communications.
5102 **1974** 4k. multicoloured . . . 10 10

1975 Communications Equipment and Satellite **1976** L. I. Popov and V. V. Ryumin

1981. 30th All-Union Amateur Radio Exhibition.
5103 **1975** 4k. multicoloured . . . 20 10

1981. 185 Days in Space of Cosmonauts Popov and Ryumin. Multicoloured.

5104	15k. Type **1976**	45	20
5105	15k. "Salyut 6"–"Soyuz" complex	45	20

1977 O. G. Makarov, L. D. Kizim and G. M. Strekalov

1961. "Soyuz T-3" Space Flight.
5106 **1977** 10k. multicoloured . . 35 15

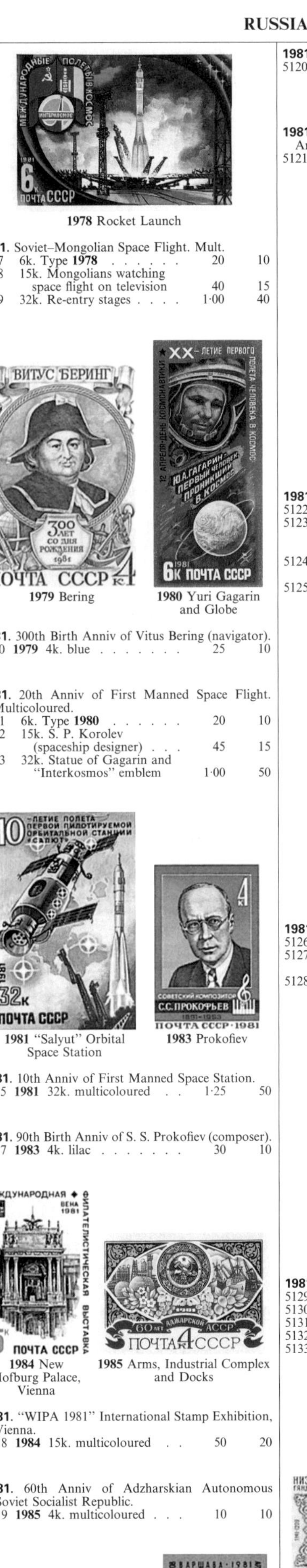

1978 Rocket Launch

1981. Soviet–Mongolian Space Flight. Mult.

5107	6k. Type **1978**	20	10
5108	15k. Mongolians watching space flight on television	40	15
5109	32k. Re-entry stages	1·00	40

1979 Bering **1980** Yuri Gagarin and Globe

1981. 300th Birth Anniv of Vitus Bering (navigator).
5110 **1979** 4k. blue 25 10

1981. 20th Anniv of First Manned Space Flight. Multicoloured.

5111	6k. Type **1980**	20	10
5112	15k. S. P. Korolev (spaceship designer)	45	15
5113	32k. Statue of Gagarin and "Interkosmos" emblem	1·00	50

1981 "Salyut" Orbital Space Station **1983** Prokofiev

1981. 10th Anniv of First Manned Space Station.
5115 **1981** 32k. multicoloured . . 1·25 50

1981. 90th Birth Anniv of S. S. Prokofiev (composer).
5117 **1983** 4k. lilac 30 10

1984 New Hofburg Palace, Vienna **1985** Arms, Industrial Complex and Docks

1981. "WIPA 1981" International Stamp Exhibition, Vienna.
5118 **1984** 15k. multicoloured . . 50 20

1981. 60th Anniv of Adzharskian Autonomous Soviet Socialist Republic.
5119 **1985** 4k. multicoloured . . . 10 10

1986 N. N. Benardos **1987** Congress Emblem

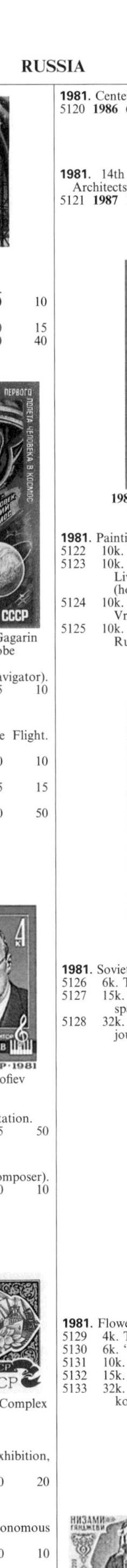

1981. Centenary of Invention of Welding.
5120 **1986** 6k. multicoloured . . . 15 10

1981. 14th Congress of International Union of Architects, Warsaw.
5121 **1987** 15k. multicoloured . . 50 20

1988 "Albanian Girl in Doorway" (A. A. Ivanov)

1981. Paintings. Multicoloured.

5122	10k. Type **1988**	40	15
5123	10k. "Sunset over Sea at Livorno" (N. N. Ge) (horiz)	40	15
5124	10k. "Demon" (M. A. Vrubel) (horiz)	40	15
5125	10k. "Horseman" (F. A. Rubo)	40	15

1989 Flight Simulator

1981. Soviet–Rumanian Space Flight. Mult.

5126	6k. Type **1989**	20	10
5127	15k. "Salyut"–"Soyuz" space complex	45	15
5128	32k. Cosmonauts greeting journalists after return	1·00	50

1990 "Primula minima"

1981. Flowers of the Carpathians. Multicoloured.

5129	4k. Type **1990**	15	10
5130	6k. "Carlina acaulis"	20	10
5131	10k. "Parageum montanum"	35	15
5132	15k. "Atragene alpina"	55	20
5133	32k. "Rhododendron kotschyi"	1·25	50

1991 Gyandzhevi **1992** Longo

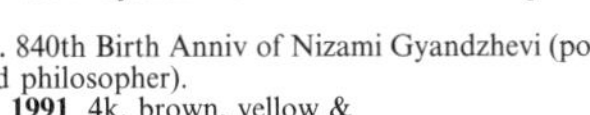

1981. 840th Birth Anniv of Nizami Gyandzhevi (poet and philosopher).
5134 **1991** 4k. brown, yellow & green 10 10

1981. Luigi Longo (Italian politician). Commem.
5135 **1992** 6k. multicoloured . . . 15 10

1993 Running **1994** Flag and Arms of Mongolia

1981. Sports. Multicoloured.

5136	4k. Type **1993**	15	10
5137	6k. Football	15	10
5138	10k. Throwing the discus	35	20
5139	15k. Boxing	60	25
5140	32k. Swimmer on block	1·25	60

1981. 60th Anniv of Revolution in Mongolia.
5141 **1994** 6k. multicoloured . . . 15 10

1995 Spassky Tower and Film encircling Globe **1996** "Lenin"

1981. 12th International Film Festival, Moscow.
5142 **1995** 15k. multicoloured . . 50 20

1981. River Ships. Multicoloured.

5143	4k. Type **1996**	20	10
5144	6k. "Kosmonavt Gagarin" (tourist ship)	25	10
5145	15k. "Valerian Kuibyshev" (tourist ship)	60	25
5146	32k. "Baltysky" (freighter)	1·40	55

1981. Russian Ice-breakers (4th issue). As T **1775**. Multicoloured.
5147 15k. "Malygin" 65 15

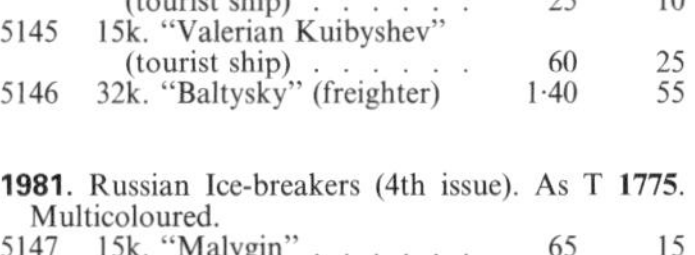

1997 Industry

1981. Resolutions of the 26th Party Congress. Multicoloured.

5148	4k. Type **1997**	20	10
5149	4k. Agriculture	15	10
5150	4k. Energy	15	10
5151	4k. Transport and communications	20	10
5152	4k. Arts and science	15	10
5153	4k. International co-operation	15	10

1998 Ulyanov **2000** Brushes, Palette and Gerasimov

1999 Facade of Theatre

1981. 150th Birth Anniv of I. N. Ulyanov (Lenin's father).
5154 **1998** 4k. brown, black & green 10 10

1981. 225th Anniv of Pushkin Drama Theatre, Leningrad.
5155 **1999** 6k. multicoloured . . . 15 10

1981. Birth Centenary of A. M. Gerasimov (artist).
5156 **2000** 4k. multicoloured . . . 10 10

2001 Institute Building

1981. 50th Anniv of Institute of Physical Chemistry, Academy of Sciences, Moscow.
5157 **2001** 4k. multicoloured . . . 10 10

2002 Severtzov's Tit Warbler

1981. Song Birds. Multicoloured.
5158 6k. Type **2002** 20 10
5159 10k. Asiatic paradise flycatcher (vert) 30 15
5160 15k. Jankowski's bunting . . 50 35
5161 20k. Vinous-throated parrotbill (vert) 65 45
5162 32k. Hodgson's bushchat (vert) . . . . 1·10 70

2003 Arms and Industrial Scenes

1981. 60th Anniv of Komi A.S.S.R.
5163 **2003** 4k. multicoloured . . . 30 10

2004 Orbiting Satellite and Exhibition Emblem

1981. "Svyaz 81" Communications Exhibition.
5164 **2004** 4k. multicoloured . . . 15 10

2005 Buildings, Arms and Monument

2006 Soviet Soldier (monument, Treptow Park, Berlin)

1981. 60th Anniv of Kabardino-Balkar A.S.S.R.
5165 **2005** 4k. multicoloured . . . 10 10

1981. 25th Anniv of Soviet War Veterans Committee.
5166 **2006** 4k. multicoloured . . . 10 10

2007 Four-masted Barque "Tovarishch"

1981. Cadet Sailing Ships. Multicoloured.
5167 4k. Type **2007** 15 10
5168 6k. Barquentine "Vega" . . 25 10
5169 10k. Schooner "Kodor" (vert) 35 15
5170 15k. Three-masted barque "Tovarishch" 55 20
5171 20k. Four-masted barque "Kruzenshtern" 85 40
5172 32k. Four-masted barque "Sedov" (vert) . . . . . 1·25 75

2008 Russian and Kazakh Citizens with Flags

2009 Lavrentev

1981. 250th Anniv of Unification of Russia and Kazakhstan.
5173 **2008** 4k. multicoloured . . . 10 10

1981. Academician Mikhail Alekseevich Lavrentev (mathematician) Commemoration.
5174 **2009** 4k. multicoloured . . . 10 10

2010 Kremlin Palace of Congresses, Moscow, and Arch of the General Staff, Leningrad

1981. 64th Anniv of October Revolution.
5175 **2010** 4k. multicoloured . . . 10 10

2011 Transmitter, Dish Aerial and "Ekran" Satellite

1981. "Ekran" Television Satellite.
5176 **2011** 4k. multicoloured . . . 10 10

2012 V. V. Kovalyonok and V. P. Savinykh

2014 Merkurov

1981. "Soyuz T-4"–"Salyut 6" Space Complex. Multicoloured.
5177 10k. Type **2012** 30 15
5178 10k. Microscope slide, crystal and text 30 15

1981. Birth Centenary of Sergei Dmitrievich Merkurov (sculpture).
5180 **2014** 4k. brown, green & bis 10 10

2015 "Autumn" (Nino A. Piromanashvili)

2016 Arms and Saviour Tower, Moscow

1981. Paintings by Georgian Artists. Multicoloured.
5181 4k. Type **2015** 15 10
5182 6k. "Gurian Woman" (Sh. G. Kikodze) 15 10
5183 10k. "Travelling Companions" (U. M. Dzhaparidze) (horiz) . . . 35 15

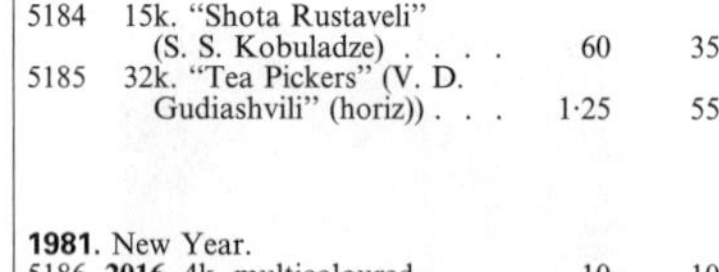
5184 15k. "Shota Rustaveli" (S. S. Kobuladze) 60 35
5185 32k. "Tea Pickers" (V. D. Gudiashvili" (horiz)) . . . 1·25 55

1981. New Year.
5186 **2016** 4k. multicoloured . . . 10 10

2017 Horse-drawn Sleigh (19th century)

1981. Moscow Municipal Transport.
5187 **2017** 4k. brown and silver . . 15 10
5188 – 6k. green and silver . . 35 10
5189 – 10k. lilac and silver . . 30 15
5190 – 15k. black and silver . . 45 25
5191 – 20k. brown and silver 60 30
5192 – 32k. red and silver . . 1·25 50
DESIGNS: 6k. Horse tram (19th century); 10k. Horse-drawn cab (19th century); 15k. Taxi, 1926; 20k. British Leyland bus, 1926; 32k. Electric tram, 1912.

2019 Modern Kiev

1982. 1500th Anniv of Kiev.
5194 **2019** 10k. multicoloured . . 35 15

2020 S. P. Korolev

2021 Arms and Industrial Complex

1982. 75th Birth Anniv of Academician S. P. Korolev (spaceship designer).
5195 **2020** 4k. multicoloured . . . 15 10

1982. 60th Anniv of Checheno-Ingush A.S.S.R.
5196 **2021** 4k. multicoloured . . . 15 10

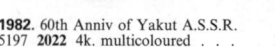

2022 Arms and Construction Sites

2023 Hikmet

1982. 60th Anniv of Yakut A.S.S.R.
5197 **2022** 4k. multicoloured . . . 15 10

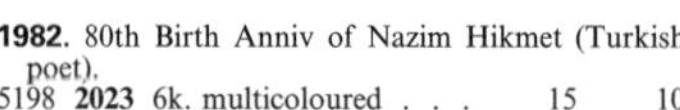
1982. 80th Birth Anniv of Nazim Hikmet (Turkish poet).
5198 **2023** 6k. multicoloured . . . 15 10

2024 "The Oaks"

1982. 150th Birth Anniv of I. I. Shishkin (artist).
5199 **2024** 6k. multicoloured . . . 20 10

2025 Trade Unionists and World Map

1982. 10th World Trade Unions Congress, Havana.
5200 **2025** 15k. multicoloured . . 45 20

2026 Kremlin Palace of Congresses and Flag

2027 "Self-portrait"

1982. 17th Soviet Trade Unions Congress.
5201 **2026** 4k. multicoloured . . . 10 10

1982. 150th Birth Anniv of Edouard Manet (artist).
5202 **2027** 32k. multicoloured . . 1·10 40

2028 Show Jumping

1982. Soviet Horse breeding. Multicoloured.
5203 4k. Type **2028** 30 10
5204 6k. Dressage 30 10
5205 15k. Racing 60 25

2029 Tito

2030 University, Book and Monument

1982. President Tito of Yugoslavia Commemoration.
5206 **2029** 6k. brown and black . . 15 10

1982. 350th Anniv of University of Tartu.
5207 **2030** 4k. multicoloured . . . 10 10

2031 Heart on Globe

1982. 9th Int Cardiologists Conference, Moscow.
5208 **2031** 15k. multicoloured . . 45 20

2033 Blackberry

1982. Wild Berries. Multicoloured.
5210 4k. Type **2033** 15 10
5211 6k. Blueberries 20 10
5212 10k. Cranberry 30 15
5213 15k. Cherry 60 25
5214 32k. Strawberry . . . . . . 1·25 55

2034 "Venera 13" and "14" **2035** "M. I. Lopukhina" (V. L. Borovikovsky)

1982. "Venera" Space Flights to Venus.
5215 **2034** 10k. multicoloured . . 30 15

1982. Paintings. Multicoloured.
5216 6k. Type **2035** 20 10
5217 6k. "E. V. Davydov" (O. A. Kiprensky) 20 10
5218 6k. "The Unequal Marriage" (V. V. Pukirev) 20 10

2036 Chukovsky **2039** Solovev-Sedoi

2037 Rocket, "Soyuz" Spaceship, Globe and Space Station

1982. Birth Cent of K. I. Chukovsky (author).
5219 **2036** 4k. black and grey . . 15 10

1982. Cosmonautics Day.
5220 **2037** 6k. multicoloured . . . 20 10

1982. 75th Birth Anniv of V. P. Solovev-Sedoi (composer).
5222 **2039** 4k. brown 15 10

2040 Dimitrov **2041** Masthead

1982. Birth Centenary of Georgi Dimitrov (Bulgarian statesman).
5223 **2040** 6k. green 15 10

1982. 70th Anniv of "Pravda" (Communist Party Newspaper).
5224 **2041** 4k. multicoloured . . . 15 10

2042 Congress Emblem and Ribbons **2043** Globe and Hands holding Seedling

1982. 19th Congress of Leninist Young Communist League (Komsomol).
5225 **2042** 4k. multicoloured . . . 15 10

1982. 10th Anniv of U.N. Environment Programme.
5226 **2043** 6k. multicoloured . . . 15 10

2044 Pioneers **2045** I.T.U. Emblem, Satellite and Receiving Station

1982. 60th Anniv of Pioneer Organization.
5227 **2044** 4k. multicoloured . . . 10 10

1982. I.T.U. Delegates' Conference, Nairobi.
5228 **2045** 15k. multicoloured . . 50 25

2046 Class VL-80t Electric Locomotive

1982. Locomotives. Multicoloured.
5229 4k. Type **2046** 25 10
5230 6k. Class TEP-75 diesel . . 30 10
5231 10k. Class TEM-7 diesel . . 60 20
5232 15k. Class VL-82m electric 90 30
5233 32k. Class EP-200 electric 1·90 60

2047 Players with Trophy and Football

1982. World Cup Football Championship, Spain.
5234 **2047** 20k. lilac, yellow and brown 65 30

2048 Hooded Crane

1982. 18th International Ornithological Congress, Moscow. Multicoloured.
5235 2k. Type **2048** 10 10
5236 4k. Steller's sea eagle . . . 20 15
5237 6k. Spoon-billed sandpiper 25 15
5238 10k. Bar-headed goose . . . 45 25
5239 15k. Sociable plover 65 30
5240 32k. White stork . . . . . 1·50 65

2049 Buildings and Workers with Picks **2051** U.N. Flag

2050 "The Cart"

1982. 50th Anniv of Komsomolsk-on-Amur.
5241 **2049** 4k. multicoloured . . . 15 10

1982. Birth Centenary of M. B. Grekov (artist).
5242 **2050** 6k. multicoloured . . . 40 10

1982. Second U.N. Conference on the Exploration and Peaceful Uses of Outer Space, Vienna.
5243 **2051** 15k. multicoloured . . 50 20

2052 Scientific Research in Space

1982. Soviet–French Space Flight. Multicoloured.
5244 6k. Type **2052** 15 10
5245 20k. Rocket and trajectory 60 30
5246 45k. Satellites and globe . . 1·40 75

2053 "Legend of the Golden Cockerel" (P. I. Sosin)

1982. Lacquerware Paintings. Multicoloured.
5248 6k. Type **2053** 20 10
5249 10k. "Minin's Appeal to Count Pozharsky" (I. A. Fomichev) 30 20
5250 15k. "Two Peasants" (A. F. Kotyagin) 45 25
5251 20k. "The Fisherman" (N. P. Klykov) 60 35
5252 32k. "Arrest of the Propagandists" (N. I. Shishakov) 95 55

2054 Early Telephone, Moscow, Leningrad, Odessa and Riga **2055** P. Schilling (inventor)

1982. Telephone Centenary.
5253 **2054** 4k. multicoloured . . . 15 10

1982. 150th Anniv of Electro-magnetic Telegraph in Russia.
5254 **2055** 6k. multicoloured . . . 15 10

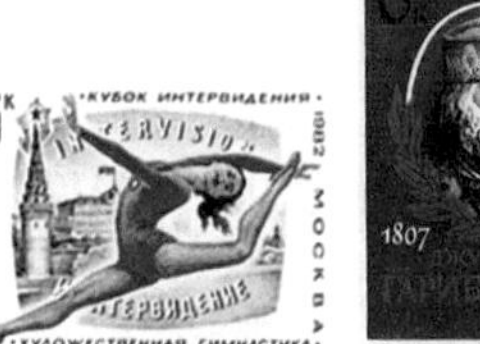

2056 Gymnast and Television Screen **2058** Garibaldi

2057 Mastyazhart Glider, 1923

1982. Intervision Cup Gymnastics Contest.
5255 **2056** 15k. multicoloured . . 40 20

1982. Gliders (1st series). Multicoloured.
5256 4k. Type **2057** 20 10
5257 6k. Red Star, 1930 . . . . 20 10
5258 10k. TsAGI-2, 1934 . . . . 40 15
5259 20k. Stakhanovets, 1939 (60 × 27 mm) 90 35
5260 32k. GR-29, 1941 (60 × 27 mm) . . . . . . 1·40 55
See also Nos. 5301/5.

1982. 175th Birth Anniv of Giuseppe Garibaldi.
5261 **2058** 6k. multicoloured . . . 15 10

2059 Emblem **2060** F.I.D.E. Emblem, Chess Symbol for Queen and Equestrian Statue

1982. 25th Anniv of International Atomic Energy Agency.
5262 **2059** 20k. multicoloured . . 55 30

1982. World Chess Championship Interzone Tournaments for Women (Tbilisi) and Men (Moscow). Multicoloured.
5263 6k. Type **2060** 35 15
5264 6k. F.I.D.E. emblem, chess symbol for King and Kremlin tower 35 15

2061 Shaposhnikov **2062** Clenched Fist

1982. Birth Cent of Marshal B. M. Shaposhnikov.
5265 **2061** 4k. brown 15 10

1982. 70th Anniv of African National Congress.
5266 **2062** 6k. multicoloured . . . 15 10

2063 Botkin

А. КАРПОВ — обладатель восьми „Шахматных Оскаров"

(2065)

1982. 150th Birth Anniv of S. P. Botkin (therapeutist).
5267 **2063** 4k. green 15 10

1982. Anatoly Karpov's Victory in World Chess Championship. No. 5264 optd with T **2065**.
5269 6k. multicoloured 50 35

2066 Submarine "S-56"

1982. Soviet Naval Ships. Multicoloured.
5270 4k. Type **2066** 20 10
5271 6k. Minelayer "Gremyashchy" 20 10
5272 15k. Minesweeper "Gafel" 65 25
5273 20k. Cruiser "Krasnyi Krim" 90 40
5274 45k. Battleship "Sevastopol" 1·90 85

2067 Flag and Arms

1982. 65th Anniv of October Revolution.
5275 **2067** 4k. multicoloured . . . 10 10

2068 House of the Soviets, Moscow

1982. 60th Anniv of U.S.S.R. Multicoloured.
5276 10k. Type **2068** 30 20
5277 10k. Dneiper Dam and statue 30 20
5278 10k. Soviet war memorial and resistance poster . . 30 20
5279 10k. Newspaper, worker holding peace text, and sun illuminating city . . . 30 20
5280 10k. Workers' Monument, Moscow, rocket, Ilyushin Il-86 jetliner and factories 30 20
5281 10k. Soviet arms and Kremlin tower 30 20

Всесоюзная филателистическая выставка
(2069)

1982. All-Union Stamp Exhibition, Moscow. No. 5280 optd with T **2069**.
5282 10k. multicoloured 60 30

2070 "Portrait of an Actor" (Domenico Fetti)
2072 Hammer and Sickle, Clock and Date

1982. Italian Paintings in the Hermitage Museum, Leningrad. Multicoloured.
5283 4k. Type **2070** 15 10
5284 10k. "St. Sebastian" (Pietro Perugino) 35 15
5285 20k. "Danae" (Titian) (horiz) 65 30
5286 45k. "Portrait of a Woman" (Correggio) . . . . 1·40 75
5287 50k. "Portrait of a Young Man" (Capriolo) . . . . 1·60 85

1982. New Year.
5289 **2072** 4k. multicoloured . . . 10 10

2075 Kherson Lighthouse, Black Sea
2076 F. P. Tolstoi

1982. Lighthouses (1st series). Multicoloured.
5292 6k. Type **2075** 40 15
5293 6k. Vorontsov lighthouse, Odessa, Black Sea 40 15
5294 6k. Temryuk lighthouse, Sea of Azov 40 15
5295 6k. Novorossiisk lighthouse, Black Sea 40 15
5296 6k. Dneiper harbour light 40 15
See also Nos. 5362/6 and 5449/53.

1983. Birth Bicentenary of Fyodor Petrovich Tolstoi (artist).
5297 **2076** 4k. multicoloured . . . 15 10

2077 Masthead of "Iskra"
2078 Army Star and Flag

1983. 80th Anniv of 2nd Social Democratic Workers' Congress.
5298 **2077** 4k. multicoloured . . . 10 10

1983. 65th Anniv of U.S.S.R. Armed Forces.
5299 **2078** 4k. multicoloured . . . 15 10

1983. Gliders (2nd series). As T **2057**. Mult.
5301 2k. Antonov A-9, 1948 . . . 10 10
5302 4k. Sumonov KAU-12, 1957 15 10
5303 6k. Antonov A-15, 1960 . . 25 10
5304 20k. SA-7, 1970 . . . . . . 80 35
5305 45k. LAK-12, 1979 . . . . 1·75 80

2080 "The Holy Family"
2081 B. N. Petrov

1983. 500th Birth Anniv of Raphael (artist).
5306 **2080** 50k. multicoloured . . 1·50 75

1983. 70th Birth Anniv of Academician B. N. Petrov (chairman of Interkosmos).
5307 **2081** 4k. multicoloured . . . 10 10

2082 Tashkent Buildings

1983. 2000th Anniv of Tashkent.
5308 **2082** 4k. multicoloured . . . 25 10

2083 Popov, Serebrov and Savitskaya

1983. "Soyuz T-7"–"Salyut 7"–"Soyuz T-5" Space Flight.
5309 **2083** 10k. multicoloured . . 45 15

2085 Aleksandrov and Bars of Music

1983. Birth Centenary of A. V. Aleksandrov (composer).
5311 **2085** 4k. multicoloured . . . 25 10

2086 "Portrait of an Old Woman"

1983. Rembrandt Paintings in Hermitage Museum, Leningrad. Multicoloured.
5312 4k. Type **2086** 20 10
5313 10k. "Portrait of a Learned Man" 40 15
5314 20k. "Old Warrior" 80 30
5315 45k. "Portrait of Mrs B. Martens Doomer" . . 1·50 75
5316 50k. "Sacrifice of Abraham" 1·75 1·00

2089 A. N. Berezovoi and V. V. Lebedev

1983. 211 Days in Space of Berezovoi and Lebedev. Multicoloured.
5320 10k. Type **2089** 40 20
5321 10k. "Salyut 7"–"Soyuz T" space complex 40 20

2090 Marx

1983. Death Centenary of Karl Marx.
5322 **2090** 4k. multicoloured . . . 15 10

2091 Memorial, Building and Hydrofoil

1983. Rostov-on-Don.
5323 **2091** 4k. multicoloured . . . 15 10

2092 Kirov Theatre

1983. Bicentenary of Kirov Opera and Ballet Theatre, Leningrad.
5324 **2092** 4k. black, blue and gold 20 10

2093 Arms, Communications and Industrial Complex

1983. 60th Anniv of Buryat A.S.S.R.
5325 **2093** 4k. multicoloured . . . 20 10

2094 Sports Vignettes

1983. 8th Summer Spartakiad.
5326 **2094** 6k. multicoloured . . . 15 10

2095 Khachaturyan

1983. 80th Birth Anniv of Aram I. Khachaturyan (composer).
5327 **2095** 4k. brown 30 10

2096 Tractor and Factory

1983. 50th Anniv of Lenin Tractor Factory, Chelyabinsk.
5328 **2096** 4k. multicoloured . . . 15 10

2097 Simon Bolivar

1983. Birth Bicentenary of Simon Bolivar.
5329 **2097** 6k. deep brown, brown and black 15 10

2098 18th-century Warship and modern Missile Cruiser "Groznyi"

1983. Bicentenary of Sevastopol.
5330 **2098** 5k. multicoloured . . . 40 15

2099 Snowdrops
2101 P. N. Pospelov

2100 "Vostok 6" and Tereshkova

1983. Spring Flowers. Multicoloured.
5331 4k. Type **2099** 15 10
5332 6k. Siberian squills 20 10
5333 10k. "Anemone hepatica" 45 15
5334 15k. Cyclamen 60 25
5335 20k. Yellow star of Bethlehem . . . . 1·10 45

1983. 20th Anniv of First Woman Cosmonaut Valentina V. Tereshkova's Space Flight.
5336 **2100** 10k. multicoloured . . 35 15

1983. 85th Birth Anniv of Pyotr Nicolaievich Pospelov (scientist).
5337 **2101** 4k. multicoloured . . . 10 10

2102 Congress Emblem
2103 Film around Globe and Festival Emblem

1983. 10th European Rheumatologists' Congress, Moscow.
5338 **2102** 4k. multicoloured . . . 20 10

1983. 13th International Film Festival, Moscow.
5339 **2103** 20k. multicoloured . . 55 25

2104 Vakhtangov

1983. Birth Centenary of Ye. B. Vakhtangov (producer and actor).
5340 **2104** 5k. multicoloured . . . 20 10

2105 Coastal Trawlers

1983. Fishing Vessels. Multicoloured.
5341 4k. Type **2105** 20 10
5342 6k. Refrigerated trawler . . 25 10
5343 10k. "Pulkovsky Meridian" (deep-sea trawler) 45 15
5344 15k. Refrigerated freighter 60 30
5345 20k. "50 Let SSR" (factory ship) . . . . 1·00 50

2106 "U.S.S.R.-1" **2107** Sockeye Salmon

1983. 50th Anniv of Stratosphere Balloon's Record Altitude Flight.
5346 **2106** 20k. multicoloured . . 85 30

1983. Fishes. Multicoloured.
5347 4k. Type **2107** 15 10
5348 6k. Zerro 25 10
5349 15k. Spotted wolffish . . . 60 20
5350 20k. Round goby 85 40
5351 45k. Starry flounder . . . . 1·75 90

2108 Exhibition Emblem **2110** S.W.A.P.O. Flag and Emblem

1983. "Sozphilex 83" Stamp Exhibition, Moscow.
5352 **2108** 6k. multicoloured . . . 15 10

1983. Namibia Day.
5355 **2110** 5k. multicoloured . . . 15 10

2111 Palestinian with Flag **2112** Emblem and Ostankino TV Tower, Moscow

1983. Palestinian Solidarity.
5356 **2111** 5k. multicoloured . . . 30 10

1983. 1st European Radio-telegraphy Championship, Moscow.
5357 **2112** 6k. multicoloured . . . 20 10

2113 Council Session Emblem **2114** Mohammed al-Khorezmi

1983. 4th UNESCO International Communications Development Programme Council Session, Tashkent.
5358 **2113** 10k. blue, mauve & black 30 15

1983. 1200th Birth Anniv of Mohammed al-Khorezmi (astonomer and mathematician).
5359 **2114** 4k. multicoloured . . . 10 10

2115 Yegorov **2116** Treaty

1983. Birth Centenary of Marshal A. I. Yegorov.
5360 **2115** 4k. purple 10 10

1983. Bicentenary of First Russian–Georgian Friendship Treaty.
5361 **2116** 6k. multicoloured . . . 10 10

1983. Lighthouses (2nd series). As Type **2075**. Multicoloured.
5362 1k. Kipu lighthouse, Baltic Sea 10 10
5363 5k. Keri lighthouse, Gulf of Finland 25 10
5364 10k. Stirsudden lighthouse, Gulf of Finland 40 25
5365 12k. Takhkun lighthouse, Baltic Sea 55 30
5366 20k. Tallin lighthouse, Gulf of Finland 75 45

2117 "Wife's Portrait with Flowers" (I. F. Khrutsky)

1983. Byelorussian Paintings. Multicoloured.
5367 4k. Type **2117** 15 10
5368 6k. "Early spring" (V. K. Byalynitsky-Birulya) . . . 20 10
5369 15k. "Young Partisan" (E. A. Zaitsev) (vert) . . 50 20
5370 20k. "Partisan Madonna" (M. A. Savitsky) (vert) . . 70 30
5371 45k. "Corn Harvest" (V. K. Tsvirko) . . . . 1·50 70

2118 Steel Mill

1983. Centenary of Hammer and Sickle Steel Mill.
5372 **2118** 4k. multicoloured . . . 10 10

2119 Grain Production **2120** Banner and Symbols of Economic Growth

1983. Food Programme. Multicoloured.
5373 5k. Type **2119** 15 10
5374 5k. Cattle breeding 15 10
5375 5k. Fruit and vegetable production 15 10

1983. 66th Anniv of October Revolution.
5376 **2120** 4k. multicoloured . . . 10 10

2121 Ivan Fyodorov

1983. 400th Death Anniv of Ivan Fyodorov (printer) and 420th Anniv of Publication of "The Apostle" (first Russian printed book).
5377 **2121** 4k. black 15 10

2122 Pipeline Construction

1983. Inaug of Urengoi–Uzhgorod Gas Pipeline.
5378 **2122** 5k. multicoloured . . . 15 10

2123 Sidorenko **2124** Marchers pushing Nuclear Weapons off Globe

1983. Academician A. V. Sidorenko (geologist) Commemoration.
5379 **2123** 4k. multicoloured . . . 15 10

1983. Nuclear Disarmament.
5380 **2124** 5k. multicoloured . . . 15 10

2125 Makhtumkuli **2126** "Madonna and Child under Apple Tree" (Cranach the Elder)

1983. 250th Birth Anniv of Makhtumkuli (Turkmen poet).
5381 **2125** 5k. multicoloured . . . 15 10

1983. German Paintings in the Hermitage Museum. Multicoloured.
5382 4k. Type **2126** 15 10
5383 10k. "Self-portrait" (Anton Raphael Mengs) 35 15
5384 20k. "Self-portrait" (Jurgens Ovens) 70 30
5385 45k. "On Board a Sailing Vessel" (Caspar David Friedrich) . . . . 1·40 60
5386 50k. "Rape of the Sabine Women" (Johann Schonfeld) (horiz) . . . . 1·60 80

2127 Sukhe Bator **2128** Globe and Hand holding Baby

1983. 90th Birth Anniv of Sukhe Bator (Mongolian statesman).
5388 **2127** 5k. multicoloured . . . 15 10

1983. International Association of Physicians against Nuclear War.
5389 **2128** 5k. multicoloured . . . 15 10

2129 Moscow Kremlin Tower Star

1983. New Year.
5390 **2129** 5k. multicoloured . . . 15 10

2130 Children's Music Theatre

1983. New Buildings in Moscow.
5391 **2130** 3k. green 10 10
5392 – 4k. blue 15 10
5393 – 6k. brown 15 10
5394 – 20k. green 60 30
5395 – 45k. green . . . . . . 1·40 70
DESIGNS—VERT: 4k. Hotel and Tourist Centre. HORIZ: 6k. Russian Federation Soviet (parliament building); 20k. Hotel Izmailovo; 45k. Novosti News and Press Agency.

2132 Cuban Flag **2133** Broadcasting Station

1984. 25th Anniv of Cuban Revolution.
5397 **2132** 5k. multicoloured . . . 15 10

1984. 50th Anniv of Moscow Broadcasting Network.
5398 **2133** 4k. multicoloured . . . 15 10

2134 Speed Skating

1984. Women's European Skating Championship, Alma-Ata.
5399 **2134** 5k. multicoloured . . . 20 10

2135 "T-34" Medium Tank

1984. World War II Armoured Vehicles. Mult.
5400 10k. Type **2135** 40 20
5401 10k. "KV" heavy tank . . . 40 20
5402 10k. "IS-2" heavy tank . . 40 20
5403 10k. "SU-100" self-propelled gun 40 20
5404 10k. "ISU-152" heavy self-propelled gun 40 20

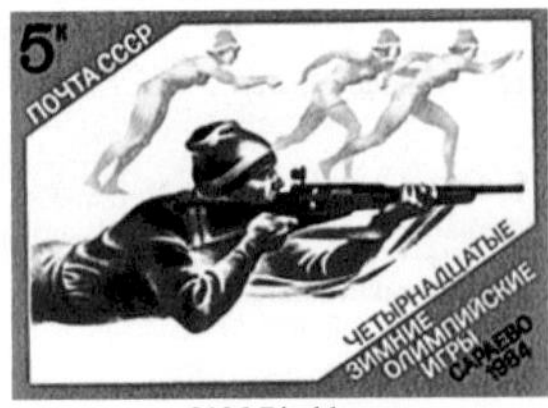

2136 Biathlon

1984. Winter Olympic Games, Sarajevo. Mult.
5405 5k. Type **2136** 15 10
5406 10k. Speed skating 35 15
5407 20k. Ice hockey 65 30
5408 45k. Figure skating . . . . 1·25 60

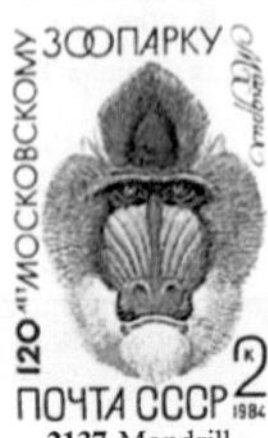

2137 Mandrill

1984. 120th Anniv of Moscow Zoo. Multicoloured.
5409 2k. Type **2137** 10 10
5410 3k. Blesbok 10 10
5411 4k. Snow leopard 15 10
5412 5k. South African crowned crane 20 15
5413 20k. Blue and yellow macaw 60 60

2138 Gagarin

1984. 50th Birth Anniv of Yuri Alekseevich Gagarin (first man in Space).
5414 **2138** 15k. blue 45 20

2140 "E. K. Vorontsova" (George Hayter)

2141 Ilyushin

1984. English Paintings in Hermitage Museum, Leningrad. Multicoloured.
5416 4k. Type **2140** 15 10
5417 10k. "Portrait of Mrs. Harriet Greer" (George Romney) 35 15
5418 20k. "Approaching Storm" (George Morland) (horiz) 70 25
5419 45k. "Portrait of an Unknown Man" (Marcus Gheeraerts, the younger) 1·50 85
5420 50k. "Cupid untying the Robe of Venus" (Joshua Reynolds) . . . . 1·75 1·00

1984. 90th Birth Anniv of Academician S. V. Ilyushin (aircraft designer).
5422 **2141** 5k. light brown, brown and black 15 10

2142 Bubnov

2143 Launching Site of "M-100" Meteorological Station

1984. Birth Centenary of Andrei Sergeevich Bubnov (Communist Party Leader).
5423 **2142** 5k. light brown, brown and black 15 10

1984. Soviet–Indian Space Co-operation. Mult.
5424 5k. Type **2143** 15 10
5425 20k. Satellite and observatory (space geodesy) 60 30
5426 45k. Rocket, satellites and dish aerials (Soviet–Indian space flight) . . . . . . 1·40 65

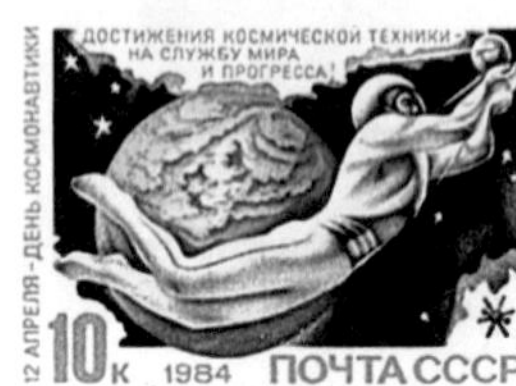

2144 Globe and Cosmonaut

1984. Cosmonautics Day.
5428 **2144** 10k. multicoloured . . 30 15

2145 "Chelyuskin" (ice-breaker) and Route Map

1984. 50th Anniv of Murmansk–Vladivostok Voyage of "Chelyuskin". Multicoloured.
5429 6k. Type **2145** 25 10
5430 15k. Evacuation of sinking ship 60 25
5431 45k. Air rescue of crew . . 1·75 75

2148 Lotus

2149 Globe and Peace March (left)

1984. Aquatic Flowers. Multicoloured.
5434 1k. Type **2148** 10 10
5435 2k. Euriala 10 10
5436 3k. Yellow water lilies (horiz) 15 10
5437 10k. White water lilies (horiz) 40 20
5438 20k. Marshflowers (horiz) 80 45

1984. Peace.
5439 **2149** 5k. multicoloured . . . 15 10
5440 – 5k. red, gold and black 15 10
5441 – 5k. multicoloured . . . 15 10
DESIGNS: No. 5440, Hammer and sickle and text; 5441, Globe and peace march (right).

2150 Welder

2151 Communications Emblem

1984. 50th Anniv of E. O. Paton Institute of Electric Welding, Kiev.
5442 **2150** 10k. multicoloured . . 25 15

1984. 25th Conference of Community for Mutual Economic Aid Electrical and Postal Communications Standing Committee, Cracow.
5443 **2151** 10k. multicoloured . . 25 15

2152 Emblem and Symbols of Match Venues **2153** Maurice Bishop

1984. European Youth Football Championship.
5444 **2152** 15k. multicoloured . . 50 20

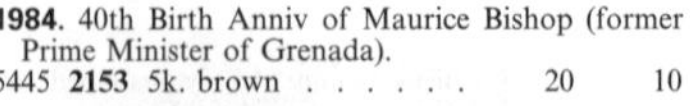

1984. 40th Birth Anniv of Maurice Bishop (former Prime Minister of Grenada).
5445 **2153** 5k. brown 20 10

2154 Lenin and Museum

2155 Freighter, Monument and Aurora Borealis

1984. 60th Anniv of Lenin Central Museum, Moscow.
5446 **2154** 5k. multicoloured . . . 15 10

1984. 400th Anniv of Archangel.
5447 **2155** 5k. multicoloured . . . 15 10

2156 Headquarters and Spassky Tower, Moscow

2158 Liner

2157 Vladimir A. Lyakhov and Aleksandr Aleksandrov

1984. Council of Mutual Economic Aid Conference, Moscow.
5448 **2156** 5k. blue, red and black 15 10

1984. Lighthouses (3rd series). As T **2075**. Mult.
5449 1k. Petropavlovsk lighthouse, Kamchatka . . 10 10
5450 2k. Tokarev lighthouse, Sea of Japan 10 10
5451 4k. Basargin lighthouse, Sea of Japan 20 10
5452 5k. Kronotsky lighthouse, Kamchatka 20 10
5443 10k. Marekan lighthouse, Sea of Okhotsk 35 15

1984. 150 Days in Space of "Salyut 7"–"Soyuz T-9" Cosmonauts.
5454 **2157** 15k. multicoloured . . 45 20

1984. 60th Anniv of Morflot (Soviet merchant fleet).
5455 **2158** 10k. multicoloured . . 35 15

2159 Komsomol Badge and Banner

1984. 60th Anniv of Naming of Young Communist League (Komsomol) after Lenin.
5456 **2159** 5k. multicoloured . . . 15 10

2160 Memorial, Minsk

1984. 40th Anniv of Byelorussian Liberation.
5457 **2160** 5k. multicoloured . . . 15 10

2161 Congress Emblem

2162 Polish Arms and Flag

1984. 27th International Geological Congress, Moscow.
5458 **2161** 5k. blue, gold and deep blue 20 10

1984. 40th Anniv of Republic of Poland.
5459 **2162** 5k. multicoloured . . . 15 10

2163 Asafev

1984. Birth Centenary of Boris Vladimirovich Asafev (composer).
5460 **2163** 5k. green 20 10

2164 Russian and Mexican Flags and Scroll

1984. 60th Anniv of U.S.S.R.–Mexico Diplomatic Relations.
5461 **2164** 5k. multicoloured . . . 15 10

2165 Title Page of "The Princess-Frog"

1984. Folk Tales. Illustration by I. Bilibin. Mult.
5462 5k. Type **2165** 20 15
5463 5k. Hunter and frog in marshland 20 15
5464 5k. Old man and hunter in forest 20 15
5465 5k. Crowd and mute swans 20 20
5466 5k. Title page of "Ivan the Tsarevich, the Fire-bird and the Grey Wolf" . . . 20 15
5467 5k. Ivan and the Fire-bird 20 15
5468 5k. Grave and Ivan on horse 40 15
5469 5k. Ivan and princess . . . 20 15
5470 5k. Title page of "Vasilisa the Beautiful" 20 15
5471 5k. Knight on horse . . . 20 15
5472 5k. Tree-man in forest . . . 40 15
5473 5k. Vasilisa and skulls . . . 40 15

2166 Basketball

1984. "Friendship 84" Sports Meetings. Mult.

5474 1k. Type **2166** 10 10
5475 5k. Gymnastics (vert) . . . 15 10
5476 10k. Weightlifting 30 10
5477 15k. Wrestling 50 20
5478 20k. High jumping 75 30

2167 Flag and Soviet Soldiers' Monument, Bucharest

2168 Emblem, Chess Symbol for Queen and Motherland Statue

1984. 40th Anniv of Rumania's Liberation.

5479 **2167** 5k. multicoloured . . . 15 10

1984. World Chess Championship Finals for Women (Volgograd) and Men (Moscow).

5480 **2168** 15k. gold, red and black 70 25
5481 – 15k. multicoloured . . 70 25

DESIGN: No. 5481, Emblem, chess symbol for king and Spassky tower, Moscow Kremlin

2169 Party House and Soviet Army Monument, Sofia, and State Emblem

1984. 40th Anniv of Bulgarian Revolution.

5482 **2169** 5k. multicoloured . . . 15 10

2170 Arms and Flag

1984. 10th Anniv of Ethiopian Revolution.

5483 **2170** 5k. multicoloured . . . 15 10

2171 Excavator

1984. 50th Anniv of Lenin Machine-building Plant, Novokramatorsk.

5484 **2171** 5k. multicoloured . . . 15 10

2172 Arms and Symbols of Industry and Agriculture

1984. 60th Anniv of Nakhichevan A.S.S.R.

5485 **2172** 5k. multicoloured . . . 15 10

2174 "Luna 3" photographing Moon

1984. 25th Anniv of Photography in Space. Mult.

5487 5k. Type **2174** 15 10
5488 20k. "Venera-9" and control centre 60 25
5489 45k. "Meteor" meteorological satellite and Earth . . . . 1·40 60

2175 Arms and Flag

1984. 35th Anniv of German Democratic Republic.

5491 **2175** 5k. multicoloured . . . 15 10

2176 Arms and Motherland Statue, Kiev

1984. 40th Anniv of Liberation of the Ukraine.

5492 **2176** 5k. multicoloured . . . 15 10

2177 Town, Arms and Countryside

1984. 60th Anniv of Moldavian Soviet Socialist Republic.

5493 **2177** 5k. multicoloured . . . 15 10

2178 Arms, Power Station and Mountains

1984. 60th Anniv of Kirgizia Soviet Socialist Republic.

5494 **2178** 5k. multicoloured . . . 15 10

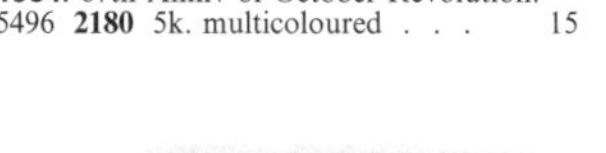

2179 Arms and Symbols of Industry and Agriculture

2180 Flags and Spassky Tower

1984. 60th Anniv of Tadzhikistan Soviet Socialist Republic.

5495 **2179** 5k. multicoloured . . . 15 10

1984. 67th Anniv of October Revolution.

5496 **2180** 5k. multicoloured . . . 15 10

2181 Arms, State Building and Dam

1984. 60th Anniv of Uzbekistan Soviet Socialist Republic.

5497 **2181** 5k. multicoloured . . . 15 10

2182 Arms, Flag and State Building

1984. 60th Anniv of Turkmenistan Soviet Socialist Republic.

5498 **2182** 5k. multicoloured . . . 15 10

2183 Medal, Workers, Diesel Train and Route Map

2184 Ilyushin Il-86 Jetliner, Rocket, "Soyuz"–"Salyut" Complex and Museum

1984. Completion of Baikal–Amur Railway.

5499 **2183** 5k. multicoloured . . . 30 10

1984. 60th Anniv of M. V. Frunze Central House of Aviation and Cosmonautics, Moscow.

5500 **2184** 5k. multicoloured . . . 15 10

2185 "Girl in Hat" (Jean-Louis Voile)

2186 Mongolian Arms and Flag

1984. French Paintings in Hermitage Museum, Leningrad. Multicoloured.

5501 4k. Type **2185** 15 10
5502 10k. "The Stolen Kiss" (Jean-Honore Fragonard) (horiz) 35 15
5503 20k. "Woman at her Toilette" (Edgar Degas) 70 30
5504 45k. "Pygmalion and Galatea" (Francois Boucher) (horiz) . . . . 1·50 60
5505 50k. "Landscape with Polyphemus" (Nicolas Poussin) (horiz) . . . . . 1·75 85

1984. 60th Anniv of Mongolian People's Republic.

5507 **2186** 5k. multicoloured . . . 15 10

2187 Spassky Tower and Snowflakes

1984. New Year.

5508 **2187** 5k. multicoloured . . . 15 10

2189 Horse-drawn Crew Wagon (19th-century)

1984. Fire Engines (1st series). Multicoloured.

5510 3k. Type **2189** 15 10
5511 5k. 19th-century horse-drawn steam pump . . . 25 10
5512 10k. "Freze" fire engine, 1904 . . . . 45 15
5513 15k. "Lessner" fire engine, 1904 . . . . 75 25
5514 20k. "Russo-Balt" fire engine, 1913 . . . . . . 1·00 35

See also Nos. 5608/12.

2190 Space Observatory and Flight Trajectory

1984. International Venus–Halley's Comet Space Project (1st issue).

5515 **2190** 15k. multicoloured . . 45 20

See also Nos. 5562 and 5630.

2191 Indira Gandhi

2192 Heroes of December Revolution Monument, Moscow

1984. Indira Gandhi (Indian Prime Minister) Commemoration.

5516 **2191** 5k. light brown & brown 30 10

1985. 80th Anniv of 1905 Revolution.

5517 **2192** 5k. multicoloured . . . 15 10

2193 Jubilee Emblem

2194 Frunze

1985. 25th Anniv of Patrice Lumumba University, Moscow.

5518 **2193** 5k. multicoloured . . . 15 10

1985. Birth Centenary of Mikhail Vasilievich Frunze (military strategist).

5519 **2194** 5k. stone, black and blue 15 10

2195 Arms and Industrial Landscape

2196 Ice Hockey Player

1985. 60th Anniv of Karakalpak A.S.S.R.

5520 **2195** 5k. multicoloured . . . 15 10

1985. 10th Friendly Armies Winter Spartakiad.

5521 **2196** 5k. multicoloured . . . 15 10

2197 Dulcimer Player and Title Page

2198 Pioneer Badge

1985. 150th Anniv of "Kalevala" (Karelian poems collected by Elino Lonnrot).

5522 **2197** 5k. brown, blue & black 20 10

1985. 60th Anniv of "Pionerskaya Pravda" (children's newspaper).

5523 **2198** 5k. multicoloured . . . 20 10

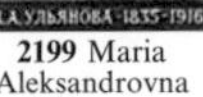
2199 Maria Aleksandrovna Ulyanova

2200 "Young Madonna Praying" (Francisco de Zurbaran)

1985. 150th Birth Anniv of Maria Aleksandrovna Ulyanova (Lenin's mother).
5524 **2199** 5k. black 20 10

1985. Spanish Paintings in Hermitage Museum, Leningrad. Multicoloured.
5525 4k. Type **2200** 15 10
5526 10k. "Still Life" (Antonio Pereda) (horiz) 30 15
5527 20k. "The Immaculate Conception" (Bartolome Esteban Murillo) 65 30
5528 45k. "The Grinder" (Antonio Puga) (horiz) . . 1·50 70
5529 50k. "Count Olivares" (Diego Velazquez) . . . . 1·75 85

2201 Cosmonauts and Globe

2203 Hungarian Arms and Budapest

1985. "Expo 85" World's Fair, Tsukuba, Japan. Multicoloured.
5531 5k. Type **2201** 15 10
5532 10k. "Molniya-I" communications satellite 30 15
5533 20k. Energy sources of the future 65 30
5534 45k. Futuristic city . . . . 1·40 60

1985. 40th Anniv of Hungary's Liberation.
5537 **2203** 5k. multicoloured . . . 20 10

2204 Emblem and Text

2206 Young People of Different Races

2205 Cosmonauts, "Soyuz T" Training Model and Gagarin

1985. 60th Anniv of Union of Soviet Societies of Friendship and Cultural Relations with Foreign Countries.
5538 **2204** 15k. multicoloured . . 45 20

1985. Cosmonautics Day. 25th Anniv of Yuri A. Gagarin Cosmonauts Training Centre.
5539 **2205** 15k. multicoloured . . 45 20

1985. 12th World Youth and Students' Festival, Moscow. Multicoloured.
5540 1k. Type **2206** 10 10
5541 3k. Girl with festival emblem in hair 10 10
5542 5k. Rainbow and girl . . . 15 10
5543 20k. Youth holding camera 65 30
5544 45k. Festival emblem . . . 1·50 65

Всесоюзная филателистическая выставка

„40 лет Великой Победы" (2209)

2207 Soviet Memorial, Berlin-Treptow

2208 Lenin and Paris Flat

1985. 40th Anniv of Victory in Second World War (1st issue). Multicoloured.
5545 5k. Type **2207** 20 15
5546 5k. Partisans 20 15
5547 5k. Lenin, soldier and Moscow Kremlin 20 15
5548 5k. Soldiers and military equipment 20 15
5549 5k. Woman worker, tank, tractor and assembly of Ilyushin Il-2M3 Stormovik fighter 20 15
See also No. 5555.

1985. 115th Birth Anniv of Lenin. Multicoloured.
5551 5k. Type **2208** 20 15
5552 5k. Lenin and Lenin Museum, Tampere, Finland 20 15

1985. "Second World War Victory" Philatelic Exhibition. No. 5545 optd with T **2209**.
5554 **2207** 5k. multicoloured . . . 25 20

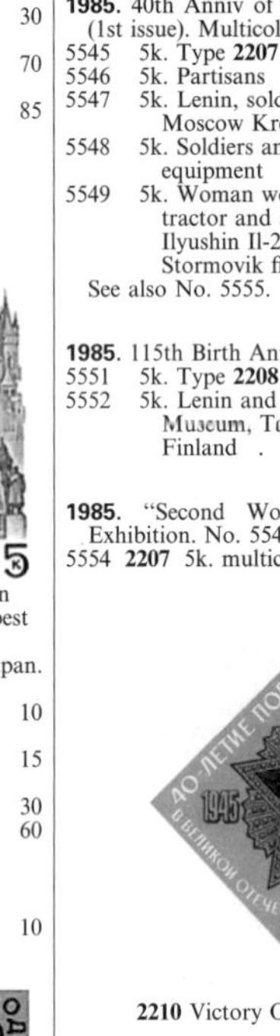
2210 Victory Order (½-size illustration)

1985. 40th Anniv of Victory in Second World War (2nd issue).
5555 **2210** 20k. multicoloured . . 65 35

2211 Czechoslovakian Arms and Prague Buildings

2212 Members' Flags on Shield

1985. 40th Anniv of Czechoslovakia's Liberation.
5556 **2211** 5k. multicoloured . . . 20 10

1985. 30th Anniv of Warsaw Pact Organization.
5557 **2212** 5k. multicoloured . . . 20 10

2213 Sholokhov and Books

2214 Sverdlov

1985. 80th Birth Anniv of Mikhail Aleksandrovich Sholokhov (writer).
5558 **2213** 5k. multicoloured . . . 20 10
5559 – 5k. multicoloured . . . 20 10
5560 – 5k. black, gold and brown 20 10

DESIGNS—As T **2213**. No. 5559, Sholokhov and books (different). 36 × 51 mm: No. 5560, Sholokhov.

1985. Birth Centenary of Ya. M. Sverdlov (Communist Party Leader).
5561 **2214** 5k. brown and red . . 15 10

1985. International Venus–Halley's Comet Space Project (2nd issue). As T **2190**. Multicoloured.
5562 15k. "Vega" space probe and Venus 55 30

2215 Battleship "Potemkin"

1985. 80th Anniv of Mutiny on Battleship "Potemkin".
5563 **2215** 5k. black, red and gold 20 10

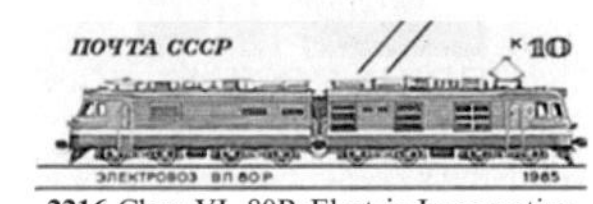
2216 Class VL-80R Electric Locomotive

1985. Locomotives and Rolling Stock.
5564 **2216** 10k. green 55 20
5565 – 10k. brown 55 20
5566 – 10k. blue 55 20
5567 – 10k. brown 55 20
5568 – 10k. blue 55 20
5569 – 10k. blue 55 20
5570 – 10k. brown 55 20
5571 – 10k. green 55 20

DESIGNS: No. 5565, Coal wagon; 5566, Oil tanker wagon; 5567, Goods wagon; 5568, Refrigerated wagon; 5569, Class TEM-2 diesel locomotive; 5570, Type SV passenger carriage; 5571, Mail van.

2217 Camp and Pioneer Badge

1985. 60th Anniv of Artek Pioneer Camp.
5572 **2217** 4k. multicoloured . . . 25 10

2218 Leonid Kizim, Vladimir Solovyov and Oleg Atkov

1985. "237 Days in Space".
5573 **2218** 15k. multicoloured . . 55 20

2219 Youths of different Races

2220 "Beating Swords into Ploughshares" (sculpture) and U.N. Emblem

1985. International Youth Year.
5574 **2219** 10k. multicoloured . . 30 15

1985. 40th Anniv of U.N.O. (1st issue).
5575 **2220** 45k. blue and gold . . 1·40 70
See also No. 5601.

2222 Larkspur

2224 Cecilienhof Palace and Flags

2223 V. A. Dzhanibekov, S. E. Savitskaya and I. P. Volk

1985. Plants of Siberia. Multicoloured.
5577 2k. Type **2222** 10 10
5578 3k. "Thermopsis lanceolata" 10 10
5579 5k. Rose 20 10
5580 20k. Cornflower 70 30
5581 45k. Bergenia . . . . 1·40 75

1985. 1st Anniv of First Space-walk by Woman Cosmonaut.
5582 **2223** 10k. multicoloured . . 35 15

1985. 40th Anniv of Potsdam Conference.
5583 **2224** 15k. multicoloured . . 40 20

2225 Finland Palace

2226 Russian and N. Korean Flags and Monument

1985. 10th Anniv of European Security and Co-operation Conference, Helsinki.
5584 **2225** 20k. multicoloured . . 75 25

1985. 40th Anniv of Liberation of Korea.
5585 **2226** 5k. multicoloured . . . 15 10

2227 Pamir Shrew

2228 A. G. Stakhanov and Industrial Scenes

1985. Protected Animals. Multicoloured.
5586 2k. Type **2227** 10 10
5587 3k. Satunin's jerboa (horiz) 10 10
5588 5k. Desert dormouse . . . 15 10
5589 20k. Caracal (47 × 32 mm) 65 30
5590 45k. Goitred gazelle (47 × 32 mm) . . . . . . 1·50 75

1985. 50th Anniv of Stakhanov Movement (for high labour productivity).
5592 **2228** 5k. yellow, red and black 15 10

2229 Cup, Football, F.I.F.A. Emblem and Kremlin Tower

2230 Chess Pieces

1985. World Junior Football Championship, Moscow.
5593 **2229** 5k. multicoloured . . . 20 10

1985. World Chess Championship Final between Anatoly Karpov and Gary Kasparov.
5594 **2230** 10k. multicoloured . . 55 20

2231 Vietnam State Emblem
2232 Immortality Monument and Buildings

1985. 40th Anniv of Vietnamese Independence.
5595 **2231** 5k. multicoloured . . . 15 10

1985. Millenary of Bryansk.
5596 **2232** 5k. multicoloured . . . 15 10

2233 Title Page

1985. 800th Anniv of "Song of Igor's Campaigns".
5597 **2233** 10k. multicoloured . . 35 15

2234 Lutsk Castle
2235 Gerasimov

1985. 900th Anniv of Lutsk.
5598 **2234** 5k. multicoloured . . . 15 10

1985. Birth Centenary of Sergei Vasilievich Gerasimov (artist).
5599 **2235** 5k. multicoloured . . . 15 10

2236 Globe, Cruiser "Aurora" and 1917
2237 Headquarters, New York, and Flag

1985. 68th Anniv of October Revolution.
5600 **2236** 5k. multicoloured . . . 20 10

1985. 40th Anniv of U.N.O. (2nd issue).
5601 **2237** 15k. green, blue and black 45 20

2238 Krisjanis Barons

1985. 150th Birth Anniv of Krisjanis Barons (writer).
5602 **2238** 5k. black and brown . . 15 10

2239 Lenin and Worker breaking Chains

1985. 90th Anniv of Petersburg Union of Struggle for Liberating the Working Class.
5603 **2239** 5k. multicoloured . . . 15 10

2240 Telescope

1985. 10th Anniv of World's Largest Telescope.
5604 **2240** 10k. blue 30 15

2241 Angolan Arms and Flag
2242 Yugoslav Arms, Flag and Parliament Building

1985. 10th Anniv of Independence of Angola.
5605 **2241** 5k. multicoloured . . . 15 10

1985. 40th Anniv of Federal People's Republic of Yugoslavia.
5606 **2242** 5k. multicoloured . . . 15 10

2243 Troitsky Tower and Palace of Congresses
2244 Samantha Smith

1985. New Year.
5607 **2243** 5k. multicoloured . . . 15 10

1985. Fire Engines (2nd series). As T **2189**. Mult.
5608 3k. "AMO-F15", 1926 . . . 15 10
5609 5k. "PMZ-1", 1933 . . . . 25 10
5610 10k. "ATs-40", 1977 . . . . 45 15
5611 20k. "AL-30" with automatic ladder, 1970 . . 80 30
5612 45k. "AA-60", 1978 . . . . 1·60 60

1985. Samantha Smith (American schoolgirl peace campaigner) Commemoration.
5613 **2244** 5k. brown, blue and red 35 10

2245 N. M. Emanuel
2246 Family and Places of Entertainment

1985. Academician N. M. Emanuel (chemist) Commemoration.
5614 **2245** 5k. multicoloured . . . 15 10

1985. Anti-alcoholism Campaign. Multicoloured.
5615 5k. Type **2246** 20 10
5616 5k. Sports centre and family 20 10

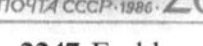

2247 Emblem
2248 Banners and Kremlin Palace of Congresses

1986. International Peace Year.
5617 **2247** 20k. blue, green & silver 55 25

1986. 27th Soviet Communist Party Congress.
5618 **2248** 5k. multicoloured . . . 15 10
5619 – 20k. multicoloured . . . 55 25

DESIGNS—36 × 51 mm: 20k. Palace of Congresses, Spassky Tower and Lenin.

2249 1896 Olympics Medal
2250 Tulips

1986. 90th Anniv of First Modern Olympic Games.
5621 **2249** 15k. multicoloured . . 45 20

1986. Plants of Russian Steppes. Multicoloured.
5622 4k. Type **2250** 15 10
5623 5k. Grass (horiz) 20 10
5624 10k. Iris 35 15
5625 15k. Violets 55 25
5626 20k. Cornflower 70 30

2251 Voronezh and Arms
2252 Bela Kun

1986. 400th Anniv of Voronezh.
5627 **2251** 5k. multicoloured . . . 15 10

1986. Birth Centenary of Bela Kun (Hungarian Communist Party leader).
5628 **2252** 10k. blue 25 15

2253 Pozela
2255 Crimson-spotted Moth

1986. 90th Birth Anniv of Karolis Pozela (founder of Lithuanian Communist Party).
5629 **2253** 5k. grey 15 10

1986. International Venus–Halley's Comet Space Project (3rd issue). As T **2190**. Multicoloured.
5630 15k. "Vega 1" and Halley's Comet 50 20

1986. Butterflies and Moths listed in U.S.S.R. Red Book (1st series). Multicoloured.
5632 4k. Type **2255** 15 10
5633 5k. Eastern festoon 20 10
5634 10k. Sooty orange-tip . . . 45 15
5635 15k. Dark crimson underwing 75 25
5636 20k. "Satyrus bischoffi" . . 95 40
See also Nos. 5726/30.

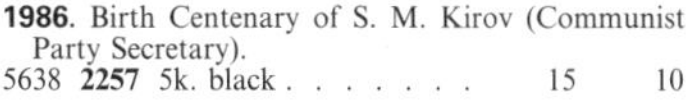
2256 Globe and Model of Space Complex
2257 Kirov

1986. "Expo '86" World's Fair, Vancouver.
5637 **2256** 20k. multicoloured . . 60 30

1986. Birth Centenary of S. M. Kirov (Communist Party Secretary).
5638 **2257** 5k. black 15 10

2258 Tsiolkovsky

1986. Cosmonautics Day. Multicoloured.
5639 5k. Type **2258** 15 10
5640 10k. Sergei Pavlovich Korolev (rocket designer) and "Vostok" rocket (vert) 30 15
5641 15k. Yuri Gagarin, "Vega", sputnik and globe (25th anniv of first man in space) 55 25

2259 Ice Hockey Player
2260 Thalmann

1986. World Ice Hockey Championship, Moscow.
5642 **2259** 15k. multicoloured . . 50 20

1986. Birth Centenary of Ernst Thalmann (German politician).
5643 **2260** 10k. brown 30 15

2261 Lenin Museum, Leipzig

1986. 116th Birth Anniv of Lenin.
5645 **2261** 5k. multicoloured . . . 15 10
5646 – 5k. olive, brown & black 15 10
5647 – 5k. multicoloured . . . 15 10
DESIGNS: No. 5646, Lenin (after P. Belousov) and Lenin Museum, Prague; 5647, Lenin Museum, Poronine, Poland.

2262 Tambov and Arms

1986. 350th Anniv of Tambov.
5648 **2262** 5k. multicoloured . . . 15 10

2263 Dove with Olive Branch and Globe
2264 Emblem and Cyclists

1986. 25th Anniv of Soviet Peace Fund.
5649 **2263** 10k. multicoloured . . 35 20

1986. 39th Peace Cycle Race.
5650 **2264** 10k. multicoloured . . 30 15

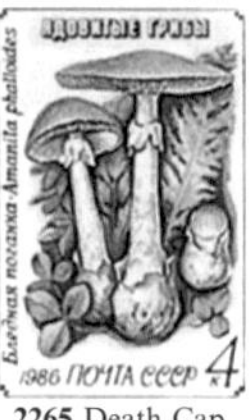
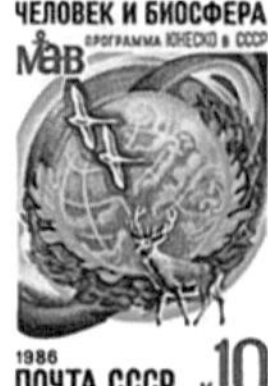

2265 Death Cap
2266 Globe and Wildlife

1986. Fungi. Multicoloured.
5651 4k. Type **2265** 15 10
5652 5k. Fly agaric 25 10

5653 10k. Panther cap 45 15
5654 15k. Bitter bolete 75 25
5655 20k. Clustered woodlover 95 45

1986. UNESCO Man and Biosphere Programme.
5656 **2266** 10k. multicoloured 35 15

2267 Torch and Runner **2268** Kuibyshev

1986. 9th People's Spartakiad.
5657 **2267** 10k. multicoloured 35 15

1986. 400th Anniv of Kuibyshev (formerly Samara).
5658 **2268** 5k. multicoloured 15 10
No. 5658 depicts the Lenin Museum, Eternal Glory and V. I. Chapaev monuments and Gorky State Theatre.

2269 Ostankino T.V. Tower **2270** Footballers

1986. "Communication 86" International Exhibition, Moscow.
5659 **2269** 5k. multicoloured 15 10

1986. World Cup Football Championship, Mexico. Multicoloured.
5660 5k. Type **2270** 20 10
5661 10k. Footballers (different) 40 15
5662 15k. Championship medal 50 20

2271 "Lane in Albano" (M. I. Lebedev) **2272** Arms and City

1986. Russian Paintings in Tretyakov Gallery, Moscow. Multicoloured.
5663 4k. Type **2271** 15 10
5664 5k. "View of the Kremlin in foul Weather" (A. K. Savrasov) (horiz) 20 10
5665 10k. "Sunlit Pine Trees" (I. I. Shishkin) 30 15
5666 15k. "Journey Back" (A. E. Arkhipov) (69 × 33 mm) 50 25
5667 45k. "Wedding Procession in Moscow" (A. P. Ryabushkin) (69 × 33 mm) 1·50 70

1986. 300th Anniv of Irkutsk City Status.
5668 **2272** 5k. multicoloured 15 10

2273 World Map, Stadium and Runners **2274** Globe, Punched Tape and Keyboard

1986. International Goodwill Games, Moscow.
5669 **2273** 10k. blue, brown & black 35 15

1986. UNESCO Programmes in U.S.S.R. Mult.
5671 5k. Type **2274** 20 10
5672 10k. Landscape and geological section (geological correlation) 35 15
5673 15k. Oceanographic research vessel, albatross and ocean (Inter-governmental Oceanographic Commission) 55 30
5674 35k. Fluvial drainage (International Hydrological Programme) 1·00 55

2275 Arms and Town Buildings

1986. 400th Anniv of Tyumen, Siberia.
5675 **2275** 5k. multicoloured 15 10

2276 Olof Palme **2277** Hands, Ball and Basket

1986. Olof Palme (Swedish Prime Minister) Commemoration.
5676 **2276** 10k. blue, black & brn 35 15

1986. 10th Women's Basketball Championship.
5677 **2277** 15k. brown, black & red 45 20

2278 "Ural-375D"

1986. Lorries. Multicoloured.
5678 4k. Type **2278** 15 10
5679 5k. "GAZ-53A" 20 10
5680 10k. "KrAZ-256B" 35 15
5681 15k. "MAZ-515B" 55 25
5682 20k. "ZIL-133GYa" 70 35

2279 Lenin Peak

1986. U.S.S.R. Sports Committee's International Mountaineers' Camps (1st series). Multicoloured.
5683 4k. Type **2279** 15 10
5684 5k. E. Korzhenevskaya Peak 20 10
5685 10k. Belukha Peak 30 15
5686 15k. Communism Peak 55 25
5687 30k. Elbrus Peak 95 55
See also Nos. 5732/5.

2281 Lenin Monument and Drama Theatre **2282** "Mukran", Maps and Flags

1986. 250th Anniv of Chelyabinsk City.
5689 **2281** 5k. multicoloured 15 10

1986. Opening of Mukran (East Germany)–Klaipeda (U.S.S.R.) Railway Ferry.
5690 **2282** 15k. multicoloured 75 25

2283 Victory Monument and Buildings **2284** Lenin Monument and Moscow Kremlin

1986. 750th Anniv of Siauliai, Lithuania.
5691 **2283** 5k. buff, brown and red 15 10

1986. 69th Anniv of October Revolution.
5692 **2284** 5k. multicoloured 30 15

2285 Ice-breaker "Vladivostok", Mil Mi-4 Helicopter, Satellite and Map

15.III—26.VII.1985
Дрейф во льдах Антарктики
(2286)

1986. Antarctic Drift of "Mikhail Somov" (research vessel). (a) As Type **2285**.
5693 5k. blue, black and red 25 10
5694 10k. multicoloured 30 20

(b) No. 5055 optd with T **2286**.
5696 4k. multicoloured 20 10
DESIGN—As T **2285**: 10k. Map and "Mikhail Somov".
Nos. 5693/4 were printed together, se-tenant, forming a composite design.

2287 Class Eu No. 684–37, Slavyansk

1986. Steam Locomotive as Monuments. Mult.
5697 4k. Type **2287** 20 10
5698 5k. Class FD No. 3000, Novosibirsk 20 10
5699 10k. Class Ov No. 5109, Volgograd 40 15
5700 20k. Class SO No. 17-1613, Dnepropetrovsk 75 30
5701 30k. Class FDp No. 20-578, Kiev 1·25 50

2288 G. K. Ordzhonikidze **2289** Novikov and Score

1986. Birth Centenary of Grigory Konstantinovich Ordzhonikidze (revolutionary).
5702 **2288** 5k. grey 15 10

1986. 90th Birth Anniv of Anatoli Novikov (composer).
5703 **2289** 5k. brown 20 10

2290 U.N. and UNESCO Emblem **2291** Sun Yat-sen

1986. 40th Anniv of UNESCO.
5704 **2290** 10k. silver and blue 35 15

1986. 120th Birth Anniv of Sun Yat-sen (first President of Chinese Republic).
5705 **2291** 5k. black and grey 15 10

2292 Lomonosov

1986. 275th Birth Anniv of Mikhail Vasilievich Lomonosov (scientist).
5706 **2292** 5k. brown 20 10

2293 Ya-1, 1927

1986. Sports Aircraft designed by Aleksandr Yakovlev. Multicoloured.
5707 4k. Type **2293** 15 10
5708 5k. VT-2 trainer, 1935 15 10
5709 10k. Yak-18, 1946 35 15
5710 20k. Yak-50, 1972 75 30
5711 30k. Yak-55, 1981 1·10 50

2294 Spassky, Senate and Nikolsky Towers, Kremlin **2295** Computer and Terminal

1986. New Year.
5712 **2294** 5k. multicoloured 15 10

1986. Resolutions of 27th Communist Party Congress. Multicoloured.
5713 5k. Type **2295** (scientific and technical progress) 20 10
5714 5k. Construction engineer and building project 20 10
5715 5k. City (welfare of people) 20 10
5716 5k. Peace demonstration at Council for Mutual Economic Aid building (peace) 20 10
5717 5k. Spassky Tower and Kremlin Palace, Moscow Kremlin (unity of party and people) 20 10

2296 Parkhomenko **2297** Machel

1986. Birth Centenary of Aleksandr Parkhomenko (revolutionary).
5718 **2296** 5k. black 15 10

1986. Samora Moizes Machel (President of Mozambique) Commemoration.
5719 **2297** 5k. brown and black 20 10

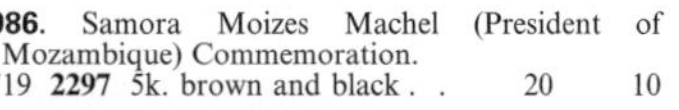

2298 Russian State Museum (Mikhailovsky Palace)

1986. Palace Museums of Leningrad.
5720 **2298** 5k. brown and green 20 15
5721 – 10k. green and blue 30 15
5722 – 15k. blue and green 50 20
5723 – 20k. green and brown 60 30
5724 – 50k. brown and blue 1·50 70

DESIGNS: 10k. Hermitage Museum (Winter Palace); 15k. Grand Palace Museum (Petrodvorets); 20k. Catherine Palace Museum (Pushkin); 50k. Palace Museum (Pavlovsk).

2299 Couple and Industrial Landscape

2300 Chinese Windmill

1987. 18th Soviet Trades Union Congress, Moscow.
5725 **2299** 5k. multicoloured . . . 15 10

1987. Butterflies listed in U.S.S.R. Red Book (2nd series). Multicoloured.
5726 4k. Type **2300** 20 10
5727 5k. Swallowtail 20 10
5728 10k. Southern swallowtail 35 15
5729 15k. "Papilio maackii" . . . 60 25
5730 30k. Scare swallowtail . . . 95 55

2301 Karlis Miesnieks

2302 Stasys Simkus

1987. Birth Centenary of Karlis Miesnieks (Latvian artist).
5731 **2301** 5k. multicoloured . . . 15 10

1987. U.S.S.R. Sports Committee's International Mountaineers' Camps (2nd series). As T **2279**. Multicoloured.
5732 4k. Chimbulak Gorge . . . 15 10
5733 10k. Shavla Gorge 30 15
5734 20k. Donguz-Orun and Nakra-Tau, Caucasus . . 70 30
5735 35k. Kazbek, Caucasus . . 1·25 60

1987. Birth Centenary of Stasys Simkus (Lithuanian composer).
5736 **2302** 5k. purple and yellow 20 10

2303 V. I. Chapaev

2304 Lenin

1987. Birth Cent of Vasily Ivanovich Chapaev (revolutionary).
5737 **2303** 5k. brown 15 10

1987. 20th Leninist Young Communist League (Komsomol) Congress, Moscow.
5738 **2304** 5k. multicoloured . . . 15 10

2305 Heino Eller

2306 Orbeli

1987. Birth Centenary of Heino Eller (Estonian composer).
5740 **2305** 5k. light brown & brown 20 10

1987. Birth Centenary of Academician Iosif Abgarovich Orbeli (first President of Armenian Academy of Sciences).
5741 **2306** 5k. brown and pink . . 15 10

2307 Bears in and out of Water

1987. Polar Bears. Multicoloured.
5742 5k. Type **2307** 20 10
5743 10k. Mother and cubs . . . 40 15
5744 20k. Mother and cubs (different) 75 30
5745 35k. Bears . . . . 1·25 55

2308 "Sputnik 1" and Globe

2309 Emblem and Headquarters, Bangkok

1987. Cosmonautics Day. Multicoloured.
5746 10k. Type **2308** (30th anniv of launching of first artificial satellite) 35 15
5747 10k. "Vostok-3", Vostok-4" and globe (25th anniv of first group space flight) 35 15
5748 10k. "Mars-1" and globe (25th anniv of launching of automatic interplanetary station) . . 35 15

1987. 40th Anniv of U.N. Economic and Social Commission for Asia and the Pacific Ocean.
5749 **2309** 10k. multicoloured . . 35 15

2310 "Birthday" (N. A. Sysoev)

1987. 117th Birth Anniv of Lenin. Multicoloured.
5750 5k. Type **2310** 15 10
5751 5k. "V. I. Lenin with Delegates to the Third Congress of the Young Communist League" (P. P. Belousov) 15 10

2311 Gymnast on Rings

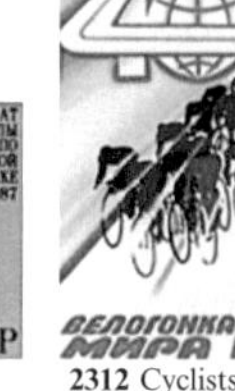

2312 Cyclists and "40"

1987. European Gymnastics Championships, Moscow.
5753 **2311** 10k. multicoloured . . 30 15

1987. 40th Peace Cycle Race.
5754 **2312** 10k. multicoloured . . 40 15

2313 Menzbir's Marmot

2315 "Portrait of a Woman" (Lucas Cranach the Elder)

2314 "Maksim Gorky"

1987. Mammals listed in U.S.S.R. Red Book. Multicoloured.
5755 5k. Type **2313** 20 10
5756 10k. Ratel (horiz) 35 15
5757 15k. Snow leopard (32 × 47 mm) 70 25

1987. River Tourist Ships. Multicoloured.
5758 5k. Type **2314** 25 10
5759 10k. "Aleksandr Pushkin" 40 15
5760 30k. "Sovetsky Soyuz" . . . 1·00 45

1987. West European Art in Hermitage Museum, Leningrad. Multicoloured.
5761 4k. Type **2315** 15 10
5762 5k. "St. Sebastian" (Titian) 15 10
5763 10k. "Justice" (drawing, Albrecht Durer) 30 15
5764 30k. "Adoration of the Magi" (Peter Breughel the younger) (horiz) . . . . . 1·00 45
5765 50k. "Statue of Ceres" (Peter Paul Rubens) . . . 1·75 80

2316 Car Production Line and Lenin Hydro-electric Power Station

2317 Pushkin (after T. Rait)

1987. 250th Anniv of Togliatti (formerly Stavropol).
5766 **2316** 5k. multicoloured . . . 15 10

1987. 150th Death Anniv of Aleksandr S. Pushkin (poet).
5767 **2317** 5k. deep brown, yellow and brown 15 10

2318 Kovpak

2319 Congress Emblem

1987. Birth Centenary of Major-General Sidor Artemevich Kovpak.
5768 **2318** 5k. black 15 10

1987. World Women's Congress, Moscow.
5769 **2319** 10k. multicoloured . . 35 15

2320 Arms, Kremlin, Docks, Drama Theatre and Yermak Monument

2321 Party Flag and Mozambican

1987. 400th Anniv of Tobolsk, Siberia.
5770 **2320** 5k. multicoloured . . . 15 10

1987. 25th Anniv of Mozambique Liberation Front (FRELIMO) (5771) and 10th Anniv of U.S.S.R.–Mozambique Friendship and Co-operation Treaty (5772). Multicoloured.
5771 5k. Type **2321** 15 10
5772 5k. Mozambique and U.S.S.R. flags 15 10

2322 "Scolopendrium vulgare"

2323 Moscow Kremlin and Indian Coin

1987. Ferns. Multicoloured.
5773 4k. Type **2322** 15 10
5774 5k. "Ceterach officinarum" 20 10
5775 10k. "Salvinia natans" (horiz) 35 15
5776 15k. "Matteuccia struthiopteris" 55 25
5777 50k. "Adiantum pedatum" 1·50 70

1987. Indian Festival in U.S.S.R. (5778) and U.S.S.R. Festival in India (5779). Multicoloured.
5778 5k. Type **2323** 15 10
5779 5k. Hammer, sickle, open book, satellite and Red Fort, Delhi 15 10

2324 Rossiya Hotel (venue), Globe and Film

2325 Cosmonauts training

1987. 15th International Film Festival, Moscow.
5780 **2324** 10k. multicoloured . . 35 15

1987. Soviet–Syrian Space Flight. Multicoloured.
5781 5k. Type **2325** 20 10
5782 10k. Moscow–Damascus satellite link and cosmonauts watching television screen 35 15
5783 15k. Cosmonauts at Gagarin monument, Zvezdny . . . 55 25

2326 Emblem and Vienna Headquarters

1987. 30th Anniv of Int Atomic Energy Agency.
5785 **2326** 20k. multicoloured . . 70 30

2327 14th–16th Century Messenger

1987. Russian Postal History.
5786 **2327** 4k. black and brown . . 15 10
5787 – 5k. black and brown . . 20 10
5788 – 10k. black and brown 35 15
5789 – 30k. black and brown 1·40 45
5790 – 35k. black and brown 3·00 50
DESIGNS: 5k. 17th–19th century horse-drawn sledge and 17th-century postman; 10k. 16th-century and 18th-century sailing packets; 30k. 19th-century railway mail vans; 35k. 1905 post car and 1926 "AMO-F-15" van.

2328 "V. I. Lenin" (P. V. Vasilev)

1987. 70th Anniv of October Revolution. Mult.
5792 5k. Type **2328** 20 10
5793 5k. "V. I. Lenin proclaims Soviet Power" (V. A. Serov) 20 10

5794 5k. "Long Live the Socialist Revolution!" (V. V. Kuznetsov) 20 10

5795 5k. "Storming the Winter Palace" (V. A. Serov) (69 × 32 mm) 20 10

5796 5k. "On the Eve of the Storm" (portraying Lenin, Sverdlov and Podvoisky) (V. V. Pimenov) (69 × 32 mm) 20 10

2330 Postyshev

2331 Yuri Dolgoruky (founder) Monument

1987. Birth Centenary of Pavel Petrovich Postyshev (revolutionary).

5799 **2330** 5k. blue 15 10

1987. 840th Anniv of Moscow.

5800 **2331** 5k. brown, yell & orge 15 10

2332 Ulugh Beg (astronomer and mathematician)

1987. Scientists.

5801 **2332** 5k. multicoloured . . . 20 15

5802 – 5k. black, green and blue 20 15

5803 – 5k. deep brown, brown and blue 20 15

DESIGNS: No. 5801, Type **2332** (550th anniv of "New Astronomical Tables"); 5802, Isaac Newton (300th anniv of "Principia Mathematica"); 5803, Marie Curie (120th birth anniv).

Всесоюзная
филателистическая выставка
„70 лет Великого Октября"

(2334)

1987. "70th Anniv of October Revolution" All-Union Stamp Exhibition. No. 5795 optd with T **2334**.

5805 5k. multicoloured 25 20

2335 "There will be Cities in the Taiga" (A. A. Yakovlev)

2336 Reed

1987. Soviet Paintings of the 1980s. Multicoloured.

5806 4k. Type **2335** 15 10

5807 5k. "Mother" (V. V. Shcherbakov) 15 10

5808 10k. "My Quiet Homeland" (V. M. Sidorov) (horiz) 30 15

5809 30k. "In Yakutsk, Land of Pyotr Alekseev" (A. N. Osipov) (horiz) 90 40

5810 35k. "Ivan's Return" (V. I. Yerofeev) (horiz) . . . . 1·00 50

1987. Birth Centenary of John Reed (American journalist and founder of U.S. Communist Party).

5812 **2336** 10k. brown, yell & blk 30 15

2337 Marshak

1987. Birth Centenary of Samuil Yakovlevich Marshak (poet).

5813 **2337** 5k. brown 15 10

2338 Chavchavadze

1987. 150th Anniv of Ilya Grigoryevich Chavchavadze (writer).

5814 **2338** 5k. blue 15 10

2339 Indira Gandhi

2340 Vadim N. Podbelsky (revolutionary)

1987. 70th Birth Anniv of Indira Gandhi (Indian Prime Minister, 1966–77 and 1980–84).

5815 **2339** 5k. brown and black . . 20 10

1987. Birth Centenaries.

5816 **2340** 5k. black 15 10

5817 – 5k. blue 15 10

DESIGN: No. 5817, Academician Nikolai Ivanovich Vavilov (geneticist).

2341 Tokamak Thermonuclear System

2342 Bagramyan

1987. Science.

5818 **2341** 5k. brown and grey . . 20 10

5819 – 10k. green, blue and black 35 15

5820 – 20k. black, stone and drab 60 30

DESIGNS: 10k. Kola borehole; 20k. "Ratan-600" radio telescope.

1987. 90th Birth Anniv of Marshal Ivan Khristoforovich Bagramyan.

5821 **2342** 5k. brown 15 10

2343 Moscow Kremlin

2344 Flags, Spassky Tower, Moscow, and Capitol, Washington

1987. New Year.

5822 **2343** 5k. multicoloured . . . 15 10

1987. Soviet–American Intermediate and Short-range Nuclear Weapons Treaty.

5823 **2344** 10k. multicoloured . . 30 15

2345 Grigori Andreevich Spiridov and "Tri Svyatitelya"

1987. Russian Naval Commanders (1st series).

5824 **2345** 4k. blue and deep blue 15 10

5825 – 5k. purple and blue . . 20 10

5826 – 10k. purple and blue . . 35 15

5827 – 25k. blue and deep blue 85 35

5828 – 30k. blue and deep blue 95 45

DESIGNS: 5k. Fyodor Fyodorovich Ushakov and "Sv. Pavel"; 10k. Dmitri Nikolaevich Senyavin, Battle of Afon and "Tverdyi" (battleship); 25k. Mikhail Petrovich Lazarev and "Azov"; 30k. Pavel Stepanovich Nakhimov and "Imperatritsa Maria".

See also Nos. 6091/6.

2346 Torch

2347 Biathlon

1987. 30th Anniv of Asia–Africa Solidarity Organization.

5829 **2346** 10k. multicoloured . . 25 15

1988. Winter Olympic Games, Calgary. Mult.

5830 5k. Type **2347** 20 10

5831 10k. Cross-country skiing 35 15

5832 15k. Slalom 45 25

5833 20k. Figure skating (pairs) 65 30

5834 30k. Ski jumping . . . . . 1·10 45

2348 1918 Stamps

2349 Emblem

1988. 70th Anniv of First Soviet Postage Stamps.

5836 **2348** 10k. blue, brown and gold 35 15

5837 10k. brown, blue and gold 35 15

On No. 5836 the lower stamp depicted is the 35k. in blue, on No. 5837 the lower stamp is the 70k. in brown.

1988. 40th Anniv of W.H.O.

5838 **2349** 35k. gold, blue and black . . . . 1·00 40

2350 Byron

1988. Birth Bicentenary of Lord Byron (English poet).

5839 **2350** 15k. black, green and blue 45 25

2351 Exchange Activities and National Flags

2352 Lomov-Oppokov

1988. 30th Anniv of Agreement on Cultural, Technical and Educational Exchanges with U.S.A.

5840 **2351** 20k. multicoloured . . 60 30

1988. Birth Centenary of Georgy Ippolitovich Lomov-Oppokov (Communist party official).

5841 **2352** 5k. black and brown . . 15 10

2353 "Little Humpbacked Horse" (dir. I. Ivanov-Vano, animated L. Milchin)

1988. Soviet Cartoon Films. Multicoloured.

5842 1k. Type **2353** 10 10

5843 3k. "Winnie the Pooh" (dir. F. Khitruk, animated V. Zuikov and E. Nazarov) 10 10

5844 4k. "Gena the Crocodile" (dir. R. Kachanov, animated L. Shartsmann) 15 10

5845 5k. "Just You Wait!" (dir. V. Kotyonochkin, animated S. Rusakov) . . 25 15

5846 10k. "Hedgehog in a Mist" (dir. Yu. Norshtein, animated F. Yarbusova) 45 25

2354 Bonch-Bruevich

2355 Nurse and Emblems

1988. Birth Centenary of Mikhail Alexandrovich Bonch-Bruevich (radio engineer).

5848 **2354** 10k. black and brown 30 15

1988. 125th Anniv of International Red Cross and Red Crescent.

5849 **2355** 15k. black, blue and red 45 25

2356 Skater

1988. World Speed Skating Championships, Alma-Ata.

5850 **2356** 15k. blue, violet and black 45 25

2357 Makarenko

1988. Birth Centenary of Anton Semenovich Makarenko (educationist and writer).

5851 **2357** 10k. green 30 15

2358 Skorina

2359 Banners and Globe

1988. 500th Birth Anniv of Frantsisk Skorina (printer).

5852 **2358** 5k. black 15 10

1988. Labour Day.

5853 **2359** 5k. multicoloured . . . 15 10

2360 Kingisepp

2361 Track and Athlete

1988. Birth Centenary of Victor Eduardovich Kingisepp (revolutionary).

5854 **2360** 5k. green 15 10

1988. Centenary of Russian Athletics.

5855 **2361** 15k. multicoloured . . 45 25

2362 M. S. Shaginyan

1988. Birth Centenary of Marietta Sergeevna Shaginyan (writer).
5856 **2362** 10k. brown 30 10

2363 Palace of Congresses, Moscow, Finlandia Hall, Helsinki, and National Flags

2364 "Mir"–"Soyuz TM" Space Complex and "Progress" Spacecraft

1988. 40th Anniv of U.S.S.R.–Finland Friendship Treaty.
5857 **2363** 15k. multicoloured . . 45 25

1988. Cosmonautics Day.
5858 **2364** 15k. multicoloured . . 45 25

2365 Sochi

1988. 150th Anniv of Sochi.
5859 **2365** 5k. multicoloured . . . 25 10

2366 "Victory" (P. A. Krivonogov)

1988. V. E. Day.
5860 **2366** 5k. multicoloured . . . 15 10

2367 Lenin Museum, Moscow

1988. 118th Birth Anniv of Lenin. Designs showing branches of Lenin Central Museum.
5861 **2367** 5k. brown, deep brown and gold 15 10
5862 – 5k. red, purple and gold 15 10
5863 – 5k. ochre, brown & gold 15 10
5864 – 5k. yellow, green & gold 15 10
DESIGNS: No. 5862, Kiev; 5863, Leningrad; 5864, Krasnoyarsk.
See also Nos. 5990/2 and 6131/3.

2368 Akulov

2369 Soviet Display Emblem

1988. Birth Centenary of Ivan Alekseevich Akulov (Communist Party official).
5865 **2368** 5k. blue 15 10

1988. "Expo 88" World's Fair, Brisbane.
5866 **2369** 20k. multicoloured . . 60 30

2370 Marx

2373 Shvernik

2371 Soldiers and Workers

1988. 170th Birth Anniv of Karl Marx.
5867 **2370** 5k. brown 15 10

1988. Perestroika (Reformation).
5868 **2371** 5k. multicoloured . . . 15 10
5869 – 5k. brown, red & orange 15 10
DESIGN: No. 5869, Banner, industrial scenes and worker.

1988. Birth Centenary of Nikolai Mikhailovich Shvernik (politician).
5871 **2373** 5k. black 15 10

2374 Russian Borzoi

1988. Hunting Dogs. Multicoloured.
5872 5k. Type **2374** 20 10
5873 10k. Kirgiz borzoi 30 25
5874 15k. Russian hound 45 25
5875 20k. Russian spaniel 60 30
5876 35k. East Siberian husky . . 1·25 50

2375 Flags, Spassky Tower and Handshake

2376 Kuibyshev

1988. Soviet–American Summit, Moscow.
5877 **2375** 5k. multicoloured . . . 15 10

1988. Birth Centenary of Valerian Vladimirovich Kuibyshev (politician).
5878 **2376** 5k. brown 15 10

2377 Flags, "Mir" Space Station and "Soyuz TM" Spacecraft

2378 Crowd and Peace Banners

1988. Soviet–Bulgarian Space Flight.
5879 **2377** 15k. multicoloured . . 50 25

1988. "For a Nuclear-free World".
5880 **2378** 5k. multicoloured . . . 15 10

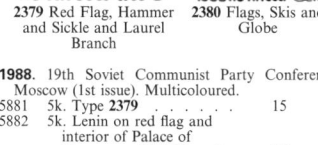

2379 Red Flag, Hammer and Sickle and Laurel Branch

2380 Flags, Skis and Globe

1988. 19th Soviet Communist Party Conference, Moscow (1st issue). Multicoloured.
5881 5k. Type **2379** 15 10
5882 5k. Lenin on red flag and interior of Palace of Congresses (35 × 23 mm) 15 10
See also Nos. 5960/2.

1988. Soviet–Canadian Transarctic Ski Expedition.
5884 **2380** 35k. multicoloured . . 1·25 50

2381 Hurdling

2382 Giant Bellflower

1988. Olympic Games, Seoul. Multicoloured.
5885 5k. Type **2381** 20 10
5886 10k. Long jumping 30 15
5887 15k. Basketball 45 25
5888 20k. Gymnastics 60 30
5889 30k. Swimming 95 45

1988. Deciduous Forest Flowers. Multicoloured.
5891 5k. Type **2382** 20 10
5892 10k. Spring pea (horiz) . . . 30 15
5893 15k. Lungwort 45 25
5894 20k. Turk's cap lily 60 30
5895 35k. "Ficaria verna" . . . . 1·40 50

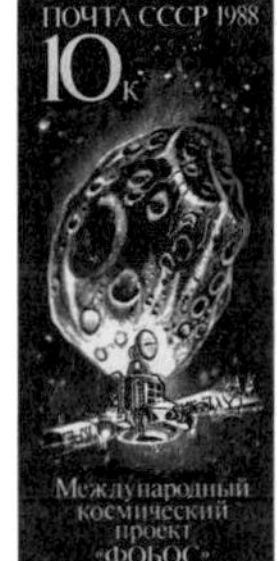

2383 Phobos and "Phobos" Space Probe

2384 Komsomol Badge

1988. Phobos (Mars Moon) International Space Project.
5896 **2383** 10k. multicoloured . . 30 15

1988. 70th Anniv of Leninist Young Communist League (Komsomol).
5897 **2384** 5k. multicoloured . . . 15 10

2385 Mandela

Филвыставка.
Москва
(2387)

2386 "Obeyan Serebryanyi, Light Grey Arab Stallion" (N. E. Sverchkov)

1988. 70th Birthday of Nelson Mandela (African nationalist).
5898 **2385** 10k. multicoloured . . 30 15

1988. Paintings in Moscow Horse Breeding Museum. Multicoloured.
5899 5k. Type **2386** 20 10
5900 10k. "Konvoets" (Kabardin breed) (M. A. Vrubel) (vert) 35 15
5901 15k. "Horsewoman on Orlov-Rastopchin Horse" (N. E. Sverchkov) 45 25
5902 20k. "Letuchy, Grey Stallion of Orlov Trotter Breed" (V. A. Serov) (vert) . . . 70 30
5903 30k. "Sardar, an Akhaltekin Stallion" (A. B. Villevalde) . . . . 1·10 45

1988. Stamp Exhibition, Moscow. No. 5897 optd with T **2387**.
5904 **2384** 5k. multicoloured . . . 20 10

2388 Voikov

2389 "Portrait of O. K. Lansere" (Z. E. Serebryakova)

1988. Birth Centenary of Pyotr Lazarevich Voikov (diplomat).
5905 **2388** 5k. black 15 10

1988. Soviet Culture Fund. Multicoloured.
5906 10k.+5k. Type **2389** 45 25
5907 15k.+7k. "Boyarynya (noblewoman) looking at Embroidery Design" (K. V. Lebedev) (horiz) 65 35
5908 30k.+15k. "Talent" (N. P. Bogdanov-Belsky) . . . . 1·40 70

2390 Envelopes and U.P.U. Emblem

2391 "Mir" Space Station and "Soyuz-TM" Spacecraft

1988. International Correspondence Week.
5910 **2390** 5k. turquoise, blue & black 15 10

1988. Soviet–Afghan Space Flight.
5911 **2391** 15k. green, red and black 55 25

2392 Emblem and Open Book

2393 Kviring

1988. 30th Anniv of "Problems of Peace and Socialism" (magazine).
5912 **2392** 10k. multicoloured . . 30 15

1988. Birth Centenary of Emmanuil Ionovich Kviring (politician).
5913 **2393** 5k. black 15 10

2394 "Ilya Muromets" (Russia) (R. Smirnov)

2395 "Appeal of the Leader" (detail, I. M. Toidze)

1988. Epic Poems of Soviet Union (1st series). Illustrations by artists named. Multicoloured.

5914 10k. Type **2394** 30 15
5915 10k. "Cossack Golota" (Ukraine) (M. Deregus) (horiz) 30 15
5916 10k. "Musician-Magician" (Byelorussia) (N. Poplavskaya) 30 15
5917 10k. "Koblandy Batyr" (Kazakhstan) (I. Isabaev) (horiz) 30 15
5918 10k. "Alpamysh" (Uzbekistan) (R. Khalilov) 30 15

See also Nos. 6017/21 and 6139/43.

1988. 71st Anniv of October Revolution.

5919 **2395** 5k. multicoloured . . . 15 10

2396 Bolotov

2397 Tupolev

1988. 250th Birth Anniv of Andrei Timofeevich Bolotov (agriculturalist).

5920 **2396** 10k. brown 30 15

1988. Birth Centenary of Academician Andrei Nikolaevich Tupolev (aircraft designer).

5921 **2397** 10k. blue 30 15

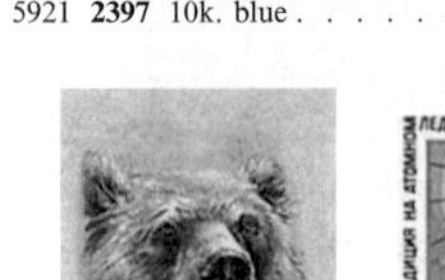

2398 Bear

2399 "Sibir" (atomic ice-breaker)

1988. Zoo Relief Fund. Multicoloured.

5922 10k.+5k. Type **2398** 45 25
5923 10k.+5k. Wolf 45 25
5924 10k.+10k. Fox 95 45
5925 20k.+10k. Wild boar . . . 95 45
5926 20k.+10k. Lynx 95 45

1988. Soviet Arctic Expedition.

5927 **2399** 20k. multicoloured . . 90 60

2400 Ustinov

2401 National Initials

1988. 80th Birth Anniv of Marshal Dmitri Fyodorovich Ustinov.

5928 **2400** 5k. brown 15 10

1988. 10th Anniv of U.S.S.R.–Vietnam Friendship Treaty.

5929 **2401** 10k. multicoloured . . 30 15

2402 Building Facade

1988. 50th Anniv of State House of Broadcasting and Sound Recording.

5930 **2402** 10k. multicoloured . . 30 15

2403 Emblem

1988. 40th Anniv of Declaration of Human Rights.

5931 **2403** 10k. multicoloured . . 30 15

2404 Life Guard of Preobrazhensky Regt. with Peter I's New Year Decree

1988. New Year.

5932 **2404** 5k. multicoloured . . . 15 10

2405 Flags and Cosmonauts

1988. Soviet–French Space Flight.

5933 **2405** 15k. multicoloured . . 55 25

2406 "Skating Rink" (Olya Krutova)

2407 Lacis

1988. Lenin Soviet Children's Fund. Children's Paintings. Multicoloured.

5934 5k.+2k. Type **2406** 25 15
5935 5k.+2k. "Cock" (Nasta Shcheglova) 25 15
5936 5k.+2k. "May is flying over the Meadows, May is flying over the Fields" (Larisa Gaidash) 25 15

1988. Birth Cent of Martins Lacis (revolutionary).

5937 **2407** 5k. green 15 10

(2408)

2410 Post Messenger

1988. "Space Post". No. 4682 optd with T **2408**.

5938 1r. blue . . . . 5·50 3·50

1988.

6072 **2410** 1k. brown 10 10
6073 – 2k. brown 10 10
6074 – 3k. green 10 10
6075 – 4k. blue 10 10
6076 – 5k. red 15 10
6077a – 7k. blue 20 10
6078 – 10k. brown 35 15
6079 – 12k. purple 40 20
6080 – 13k. violet 50 20
6081 – 15k. blue 50 25
6082 – 20k. brown 70 25
6083 – 25k. green 85 35
6084 – 30k. blue 80 60
6085 – 35k. brown . . . . . 1·00 50
6086 – 50k. blue . . . . . . 1·25 95
6087 – 1r. blue . . . . . . 3·50 1·40

DESIGNS: 2k. Old mail transport (sailing packet, steam train and mail coach); 3k. "Aurora" (cruiser); 4k. Spassky Tower and Lenin's Tomb, Red Square, Moscow; 5k. State emblem and flag; 7k. Modern mail transport (Ilyushin Il-86 jetliner, Mil Mi-2 helicopter, "Aleksandr Pushkin" (liner), train and mail van); 10k. "The Worker and the Collective Farmer" (statue, Vera Mukhina); 12k. Rocket on launch pad; 13k. Satellite; 15k. "Orbit" dish aerial; 20k. Symbols of art and literature; 25k. "The Discus-thrower" (5th-century Greek statue by Miron); 30k. Map of Antarctica and emperor penguins; 35k. "Mercury" (statue, Giovanni da Bologna); 50k. Great white cranes; 1r. Universal Postal Union emblem.

2411 Great Cascade and Samson Fountain

2412 1st-cent B.C. Gold Coin of Tigran the Great

1988. Petrodvorets Fountains. Each green and grey.

5952 5k. Type **2411** 20 10
5953 10k. Adam fountain (D. Bonazza) 30 15
5954 15k. Golden Mountain cascade (Niccolo Michetti and Mikhail Zemtsov) . . 50 25
5955 30k. Roman fountains (Bartolomeo Rastrelli) . . 1·00 45
5965 50k. Oaklet trick fountain (Rastrelli) . . . . 1·60 1·00

1988. Armenian Earthquake Relief. Armenian History. Multicoloured.

5957 20k.+10k. Type **2412** . . . 95 45
5958 30k.+15k. Rispsime Church 1·25 65
5959 50k.+25k. "Madonna and Child" (18th-century fresco, Ovnat Ovnatanyan) . . . . . . 2·25 1·25

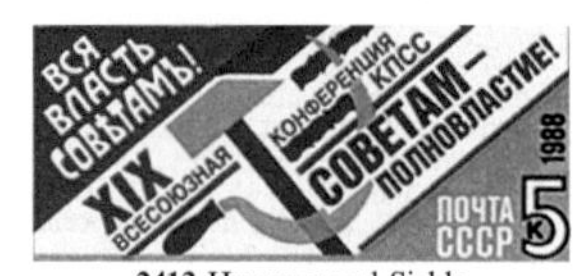

2413 Hammer and Sickle

1988. 19th Soviet Communist Party Conference, Moscow (2nd issue). Multicoloured.

5960 5k. Type **2413** 15 10
5961 5k. Hammer and sickle and building girders 15 10
5962 5k. Hammer and sickle and wheat 15 10

2415 "Vostok" Rocket, "Lunar 1", Earth and Moon

2416 Virtanen

1989. 30th Anniv of First Russian Moon Flight.

5964 **2415** 15k. multicoloured . . 35 25

1989. Birth Centenary of Jalmari Virtanen (poet).

5965 **2416** 5k. brown and bistre 15 10

2417 Headquarters Building, Moscow

1989. 40th Anniv of Council for Mutual Economic Aid.

5966 **2417** 10k. multicoloured . . 30 15

2418 Forest Protection

2419 18th-century Samovar

1989. Nature Conservation. Multicoloured.

5967 5k. Type **2418** 50 20
5968 10k. Arctic preservation . . 35 15
5969 15k. Anti-desertification campaign 50 20

1989. Russian Samovars in State Museum, Leningrad. Multicoloured.

5970 5k. Type **2419** 20 10
5971 10k. 19th-century barrel samovar by Ivan Lisitsin of Tula 30 15
5972 20k. 1830s Kabachok travelling samovar by Sokolov Brothers factory, Tula 55 30
5973 30k. 1840s samovar by Nikolai Malikov factory, Tula 85 45

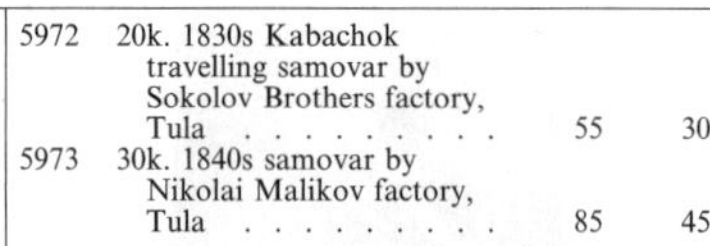

2420 Mussorgsky (after Repin) and Scene from "Boris Godunov"

2421 Dybenko

1989. 150th Birth Anniv of Modest Petrovich Mussorgsky (composer).

5974 **2420** 10k. purple and brown 30 15

1989. Birth Centenary of Pavel Dybenko (military leader).

5975 **2421** 5k. black 15 10

2422 Shevchenko

2423 "Lilium speciosum"

1989. 175th Birth Anniv of Taras Shevchenko (Ukrainian poet and painter).

5976 **2422** 5k. brown, green & black 15 10

1989. Lilies. Multicoloured.

5977 5k. Type **2423** 20 10
5978 10k. "African Queen" . . . 35 15
5979 15k. "Eclat du Soir" 45 20
5980 30k. "White Tiger" . . . . 1·10 45

2424 Marten

1989. Zoo Relief Fund. Multicoloured.

5981 10k.+5k. Type **2424** 45 20
5982 10k.+5k. Squirrel 45 20
5983 20k.+10k. Hare . . . . . . 1·00 45
5984 20k.+10k. Hedgehog . . . . 1·00 45
5985 20k.+10k. Badger . . . . . 1·00 45

2426 "Victory Banner" (P. Loginov and V. Pamfilov)

1989. Victory Day.

5987 **2426** 5k. multicoloured . . . 15 10

2427 "Mir" Space Station

1989. Cosmonautics Day.

5988 **2427** 15k. multicoloured . . 45 20

2428 Emblem and Flags **2430** Statue

1989. U.S.–Soviet Bering Bridge Expedition.
5989 **2428** 10k. multicoloured . . 35 15

1989. 119th Birth Anniv of Lenin. As T **2367**. Branches of Lenin Central Museum.
5990 5k. brown, ochre and gold 15 10
5991 5k. deep brown, brn & gold 15 10
5992 5k. multicoloured 15 10
DESIGNS: No. 5990, Frunze; 5991, Kazan; 5992, Kuibyshev.

1989. 70th Anniv of First Hungarian Soviet Republic.
5994 **2430** 5k. multicoloured . . . 15 10

2431 "Motherland Statue" **2432** Drone

1989. 400th Anniv of Volgograd (formerly Tsaritsyn).
5995 **2431** 5k. multicoloured . . . 15 10

1989. Honey Bees. Multicoloured.
5996 5k. Type **2432** 20 10
5997 10k. Bees, flowers and hive 30 15
5998 20k. Bee on flower 60 30
5999 35k. Feeding queen bee . . 1·25 45

2433 Negative and Positive Images **2434** Map above Dove as Galley

1989. 150th Anniv of Photography.
6000 **2433** 5k. multicoloured . . . 15 10

1989. "Europe—Our Common Home". Mult.
6001 5k. Type **2434** 20 10
6002 10k. Laying foundations of Peace 30 15
6003 15k. White storks' nest . . . 65 55

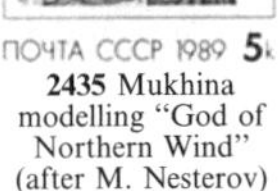

2435 Mukhina modelling "God of Northern Wind" (after M. Nesterov) **2436** Racine

1989. Birth Centenary of Vera Mukhina (sculptress).
6004 **2435** 5k. blue 15 10

1989. 150th Birth Anniv of Jean Racine (dramatist).
6005 **2436** 15k. multicoloured . . 45 20

2437 Rabbit

1989. Lenin Soviet Children's Fund. Children's Paintings. Multicoloured.
6006 5k.+2k. Type **2437** 20 10
6007 5k.+2k. Cat 20 10
6008 5k.+2k. Nurse 20 10
See also Nos. 6162/4.

2438 Kuratov

1989. 150th Birth Anniv of Ivan Kuratov (writer).
6009 **2438** 5k. deep brown & brown 15 10

2439 Emblem **2440** Common Shelduck

1989. 13th World Youth and Students' Festival, Pyongyang.
6010 **2439** 10k. multicoloured . . 30 15

1989. Ducks (1st series). Multicoloured.
6011 5k. Type **2440** 15 10
6012 15k. Green-winged teal . . . 40 30
6013 20k. Ruddy shelduck . . . 55 35
See also Nos. 6159/61 and 6264/6.

2441 "Storming of Bastille" (Gelman after Monnet)

1989. Bicentenary of French Revolution.
6014 **2441** 5k. multicoloured . . . 20 10
6015 – 15k. blue, black and red 45 20
6016 – 20k. blue, black and red 60 25
DESIGNS: 15k. Jean-Paul Marat, Georges Danton and Maximilien Robespierre; 20k. "Marseillaise" (relief by F. Rude from Arc de Triomphe).

1989. Epic Poems of Soviet Union (2nd series). Illustrations by named artists. As T **2394**. Mult.
6017 10k. "Amirani" (Georgia) (V. Oniani) 35 15
6018 10k. "Koroglu" (Azerbaijan) (A. Gadzhiev) 35 15
6019 10k. "Fir, Queen of Grass Snakes" (Lithuania) (A. Makunaite) 35 15
6020 10k. "Mioritsa" (Moldavia) (I. Bogdesko) 35 15
6021 10k. "Lachplesis" (Lettish) (G. Wilks) 35 15

2442 Observatory **2443** Hemispheres, Roses in Envelope and Posthorn

1989. 150th Anniv of Pulkovo Observatory.
6022 **2442** 10k. multicoloured . . 30 15

1989. International Letter Week.
6023 **2443** 5k. multicoloured . . . 15 10

2444 Lynx **2446** Buildings, Container Ship and Bicentenary Emblem

1989. 50th Anniv of Tallin Zoo.
6024 **2444** 10k. multicoloured . . 30 15

1989. Bicentenary of Nikolaev.
6026 **2446** 5k. multicoloured . . . 20 10

2447 Nkrumah **2448** 1921 40r. Stamp

1989. 80th Birth Anniv of Kwame Nkrumah (first Prime Minister and President of Ghana).
6027 **2447** 10k. multicoloured . . 30 15

1989. 6th All-Union Philatelic Society Congress, Moscow.
6028 **2448** 10k. multicoloured . . 35 15

2449 Cooper

1989. Birth Bicentenary of James Fenimore Cooper (writer) (1st issue).
6029 **2449** 15k. multicoloured . . 45 20
See also Nos. 6055/9.

2450 V. L. Durov (trainer) and Sealions

1989. 70th Anniv of Soviet Circus. Multicoloured.
6030 1k. Type **2450** 10 10
6031 3k. M. N. Rumyantsev (clown "Karandash") with donkey 10 10
6032 4k. V. I. Filatov (founder of Bear Circus) and bears on motor cycles 15 10
6033 5k. E. T. Kio (illusionist) and act 25 10
6034 10k. V. E. Lazarenko (clown and acrobat) and act . . 45 20

2451 Emblem on Glove **2452** Li Dazhao

1989. International Amateur Boxing Association Championship, Moscow.
6036 **2451** 15k. multicoloured . . 45 20

1989. Birth Centenary of Li Dazhao (co-founder of Chinese Communist Party).
6037 **2452** 5k. brown, stone & black 20 10

2453 Khetagurov

1989. 130th Birth Anniv of Kosta Khetagurov (Ossetian writer).
6038 **2453** 5k. brown 15 10

2454 "October Guardsmen" (M. M. Chepik)

1989. 72nd Anniv of October Revolution.
6039 **2454** 5k. multicoloured . . . 15 10

2455 Russian Spoons, Psaltery, Balalaika, Zhaleika and Accordion

1989. Traditional Musical Instruments (1st series). Multicoloured.
6040 10k. Type **2455** 35 15
6041 10k. Ukrainian bandura, trembita, drymba, svyril (pipes) and dulcimer . . . 35 15
6042 10k. Byelorussian tambourine, bastlya (fiddle), lera and dudka (pipe) 35 15
6043 10k. Uzbek nagors (drums), rubab, zang, karnai and gidzhak 35 15
See also Nos. 6183/6 and 6303/5.

2456 "Demonstration of First Radio Receiver, 1895" (N. A. Sysoev) **2457** National Flag and Provincial Arms

1989. 130th Birth Anniv of Aleksandr Stepanovich Popov (radio pioneer).
6044 **2456** 10k. multicoloured . . 30 15

1989. 40th Anniv of German Democratic Republic.
6045 **2457** 5k. multicoloured . . . 15 10

2458 Polish National Colours forming "45" **2459** Kosior

1989. 45th Anniv of Liberation of Poland.
6046 **2458** 5k. multicoloured . . . 15 10

1989. Birth Centenary of Stanislav Vikentievich Kosior (vice-chairman of Council of People's Commissars).
6047 **2459** 5k. black 15 10

2460 Nehru **2461** "Village Market" (A. V. Makovsky)

1989. Birth Centenary of Jawaharlal Nehru (Indian statesman).
6048 **2460** 15k. brown 45 20

1989. Soviet Culture Fund. Multicoloured.
6049 4k.+2k. Type **2461** 20 10
6050 5k.+2k. "Lady in Hat" (E. L. Zelenin) 25 15
6051 10k.+5k. "Portrait of the Actress Bazhenova" (A. F. Sofronova) 50 20
6052 20k.+10k. "Two Women" (Hugo Shaiber) 85 65
6053 30k.+15k. 19th-century teapot and plates from Popov porcelain works . . 1·50 85

2462 Berzin **2463** "The Hunter"

1989. Birth Centenary of Yan Karlovich Berzin (head of Red Army Intelligence).
6054 **2462** 5k. black 15 10

1989. Birth Bicentenary of James Fenimore Cooper (writer) (2nd issue). Illustrations of his novels. Multicoloured.
6055 20k. Type **2463** 60 30
6056 20k. "Last of the Mohicans" 60 30
6057 20k. "The Pathfinder" . . . 60 30
6058 20k. "The Pioneers" 60 30
6059 20k. "The Prairie" 60 30
Nos. 6055/9 were printed together, se-tenant, forming a composite design.

2464 St. Basil's Cathedral and Minin and Pozharsky Statue, Moscow **2465** Dymkovo Toy

1989. Historical Monuments (1st series). Mult.
6060 15k. Type **2464** 45 25
6061 15k. Sts. Peter and Paul Cathedral and statue of Peter I. Leningrad 45 25
6062 15k. St. Sophia's Cathedral and statue of Bogdan Chmielnitsky, Kiev . . . 45 25
6063 15k. Khodzha Ahmed Yasavi mausoleum, Turkestan 45 25
6064 15k. Khazret Khyzr Mosque, Samarkand . . . 45 25
See also Nos. 6165/72 and 6231/3.

1989. New Year.
6065 **2465** 5k. multicoloured . . . 15 10

2466 Soviet Lunar Vehicle **2468** Acid Rain destroying Rose

1989. "Expo 89" International Stamp Exhibition, Washington D.C. Multicoloured.
6066 25k. Type **2466** 90 45
6067 25k. Astronaut and landing module on Moon 90 45
6068 25k. Cosmonauts on Mars 90 45
6069 25k. Flag and shield on Mars 90 45

1989. Russian Naval Commanders (2nd series). As T **2345**.
6091 5k. blue and brown 10 15
6092 10k. blue and brown 25 15
6093 15k. blue and deep blue . . 40 20
6094 20k. blue and deep blue . . 55 25
6095 30k. blue and brown 90 60
6096 35k. blue and brown . . . . 1·40 65
DESIGNS: 5k. V. A. Kornilov and "Vladimer" (steam frigate) and "Pervaz-Bakhric" (Turkish) steam frigate); 10k. V. I. Istomin and "Parizh"; 15k. G. I. Nevelskoi and "Baikal"; 20k. G. I. Butakov and iron-clad squadron; 30k. A. A. Popov, "Pyotr Veliky" and "Vitze Admiral Popov"; 35k. S. O. Makarov, "Intibah" (Turkish warship) and "Veliky Khyaz Konstantin".

1990. Nature Conservation. Multicoloured.
6097 10k. Type **2468** 30 15
6098 15k. Oil-smeared great black-headed gull perching on globe 40 30
6099 20k. Blade sawing down tree 65 25

2469 Ladya Monument and Golden Gates, Kiev (Ukraine) **2470** Flag and Hanoi Monument

1990. Republic Capitals. Multicoloured.
6100 5k. Lenin Palace of Culture, Government House and Academy of Sciences, Alma-Ata (Kazakhstan) 15 10
6101 5k. Library, Mollanepes Theatre and War Heroes Monument, Ashkhabad (Turkmenistan) 15 10
6102 5k. Maiden's Tower and Divan-Khane Palace, Baku (Azerbaijan) 15 10
6103 5k. Sadriddin Aini Theatre and Avicenna Monument, Dushanbe (Tadzhikistan) 15 10
6104 5k. Spendyarov Theatre and David Sasunsky Monument, Yerevan (Armenia) 15 10
6105 5k. Satylganov Philharmonic Society building and Manas Memorial, Frunze (Kirgizia) 15 10
6106 5k. Type **2469** 15 10
6107 5k. Cathedral and Victory Arch, Kishinev (Moldavia) 15 10
6108 5k. Government House and Liberation Monument, Minsk (Byelorussia) . . . 15 10
6109 5k. Konstantino-Yeleninsky Tower and Ivan the Great Bell Tower, Moscow (Russian Federation) . . 15 10
6110 5k. Cathedral, "Three Brothers" building and Freedom Monument, Riga (Latvia) 15 10
6111 5k. Herman the Long, Oliviste Church, Cathedral and Town hall towers and wall turret, Tallin (Estonia) 15 10
6112 5k. Kukeldash Medrese and University, Tashkent (Uzbekistan) 15 10
6113 5k. Metekh Temple and Vakhtang Gorgasal Monument, Tbilisi (Georgia) 15 10
6114 5k. Gediminas Tower and St. Anne's Church, Vilnius (Lithuania) . . . 15 10

1990. 60th Anniv of Vietnamese Communist Party.
6115 **2470** 5k. multicoloured . . . 15 10

2471 Ho Chi Minh **2472** Snowy Owl

1990. Birth Cent of Ho Chi Minh (Vietnamese leader).
6116 **2471** 10k. brown and black 30 15

1990. Owls. Multicoloured.
6117 10k. Type **2472** 20 15
6118 20k. Eagle owl (vert) . . . 35 25
6119 55k. Long-eared owl . . . . 1·00 60

2473 Paddle-steamer, Posthorn and Penny Black

1990. 150th Anniv of the Penny Black.
6120 **2473** 10k. multicoloured . . 30 15
6121 – 20k. black and gold . . 55 25
6122 – 20k. black and gold . . 55 25
6123 – 35k. multicoloured . . 1·25 65
6124 – 35k. multicoloured . . 1·25 65
DESIGNS: No. 6121, Anniversary emblem and Penny Black (lettered "T P"); 6122, As No. 6121 but stamp lettered "T F"; 6123, "Stamp World London 90" International Stamp Exhibition emblem and Penny Black (lettered "V K"); 6124, As No. 6123 but stamp lettered "A H".

2474 Electric Cables

1990. 125th Anniv of I.T.U.
6126 **2474** 20k. multicoloured . . 55 30

2475 Flowers

1990. Labour Day.
6127 **2475** 5k. multicoloured . . . 15 10

2476 "Victory, 1945" (A. Lysenko)

1990. 45th Anniv of Victory in Second World War.
6128 **2476** 5k. multicoloured . . . 15 10

2477 "Mir" Space Complex and Cosmonaut **2478** Lenin

1990. Cosmonautics Day.
6129 **2477** 20k. multicoloured . . 45 25

1990. "Leniniana '90" All-Union Stamp Exhibition.
6130 **2478** 5k. brown 15 10

1990. 120th Birth Anniv of Lenin. Branches of Lenin Central Museum. As T **2367**.
6131 5k. red, lake and gold . . . 15 10
6132 5k. pink, purple and gold 15 10
6133 5k. multicoloured 15 10
DESIGNS: No. 6131, Ulyanovsk; 6132, Baku; 6133, Tashkent.

2479 Scene from "Iolanta" (opera) and Tchaikovsky

1990. 150th Birth Anniv of Pyotr Ilich Tchaikovsky (composer).
6134 **2479** 15k. black 60 30

2480 Golden Eagle

1990. Zoo Relief Fund. Multicoloured.
6135 10k.+5k. Type **2480** 35 25
6136 20k.+10k. Saker falcon ("Falco cherrug") 70 65
6137 20k.+10k. Common raven ("Corvus corax") 70 65

2481 Etching by G. A. Echeistov **2482** Goalkeeper and Players

1990. 550th Anniv of "Dzhangar" (Kalmuk folk epic).
6138 **2481** 10k. ochre, brown & black 30 15

1990. Epic Poems of Soviet Union (3rd series). Illustrations by named artists. As T **2394**. Mult.
6139 10k. "Manas" (Kirgizia) (T. Gertsen) (horiz) . . . 30 15
6140 10k. "Gurugli" (Tadzhikistan) (I. Martynov) (horiz) . . 30 15
6141 10k. "David Sasunsky" (Armenia) (M. Abegyan) 30 15
6142 10k. "Gerogly" (Turkmenistan) (I. Klychev) 30 15
6143 10k. "Kalevipoeg" (Estonia) (O. Kallis) 30 15

1990. World Cup Football Championship, Italy. Multicoloured.
6144 5k. Type **2482** 15 10
6145 10k. Players 35 15
6146 15k. Attempted tackle . . . 50 20
6147 25k. Referee and players . . 50 30
6148 35k. Goalkeeper saving ball 1·25 65

2483 Globe and Finlandia Hall, Helsinki **2484** Competitors and Target

1990. 15th Anniv of European Security and Co-operation Conference, Helsinki.
6149 **2483** 15k. multicoloured . .

1990. 45th World Shooting Championships, Moscow.
6150 **2484** 15k. multicoloured . . 45 20

2485 Glaciology Research

1990. Soviet–Australian Scientific Co-operation in Antarctica. Multicoloured.
6151 5k. Type **2485** 15 10
6152 50k. Krill (marine biology research) . . . . 1·50 90

2486 Emblem and Sports Pictograms

1990. Goodwill Games, Seattle.
6154 **2486** 10k. multicoloured . . 35 15

2488 Greylag Geese

1990. Poultry. Multicoloured.
6156 5k. Type **2488** 10 10
6157 10k. Adlers (chickens) . . . 35 15
6158 15k. Common turkeys . . . 40 40

2489 Mallards

1990. Ducks (2nd series). Multicoloured.
6159 5k. Type **2489** 10 10
6160 15k. Common goldeneyes 40 40
6161 20k. Red-crested pochards 50 50

1990. Lenin Soviet Children's Fund. Children's Paintings. As T **2437**. Multicoloured.
6162 5k.+2k. Clown 20 10
6163 5k.+2k. Ladies in crinolines 20 10
6164 5k.+2k. Children with banner 20 10

1990. Historical Monuments (2nd series). As T **2464**. Multicoloured.
6165 15k. St. Nshan's Church, Akhpat (Armenia) 45 20
6166 15k. Shirvanshah Palace, Baku (Azerbaijan) 45 20
6167 15k. Soroki Fortress and statue of Stefan III, Kishinev (Moldavia) . . . 45 20
6168 15k. Spaso-Efrosinevsky Cathedral, Polotsk (Byelorussia) 45 20
6169 15k. St. Peter's Church and 16th-century Riga (Latvia) 45 20
6170 15k. St. Nicholas's Church and carving of city arms, Tallin (Estonia) 45 20
6171 15k. Mtatsminda Pantheon and statue of Nikoloz Baratashvili, Tbilisi (Georgia) 45 20
6172 15k. Cathedral and bell tower, Vilnius (Lithuania) 45 20

2490 Sordes

1990. Prehistoric Animals. Multicoloured.
6173 1k. Type **2490** 10 10
6174 3k. Chalicotherium (vert) . . 10 10
6175 5k. Indricotherium (vert) . . 15 10
6176 10k. Saurolophus (vert) . . 25 15
6177 20k. Cephalaspid ostracoderm 65 30

2491 "St. Basil's Cathedral and Kremlin, Moscow" (Sanjay Adhikari)

2492 Pigeon Post

1990. Indo-Soviet Friendship. Children's Paintings. Multicoloured.
6178 10k. Type **2491** 30 10
6179 10k. "Life in India" (Tanya Vorontsova) 30 10

1990. Letter Writing Week.
6180 **2492** 5k. blue 15 10

2493 Traffic on Urban Roads

2495 Killer Whales

1990. Traffic Safety Week.
6181 **2493** 5k. multicoloured . . . 25 10

1990. Traditional Musical Instruments (2nd series). As T **2455**. Multicoloured.
6183 10k. Azerbaijani balalian, shar and caz (stringed instruments), zurna and drum 40 15
6184 10k. Georgian bagpipes, tambourine, flute, pipes and chonguri (stringed instrument) 40 15
6185 10k. Kazakh flute, rattle, daubra and kobyz (stringed instruments) . . 40 15
6186 10k. Lithuanian bagpipes, horns and kankles 40 15

1990. Marine Mammals.
6187 25k. Type **2495** 75 40
6188 25k. Northern sealions . . . 75 40
6189 25k. Sea otter 75 40
6190 25k. Common dolphin . . . 75 40

2496 "Lenin among Delegates to Second Congress of Soviets" (S. V. Gerasimov)

2497 Ivan Bunin (1933)

1990. 73rd Anniv of October Revolution.
6191 **2496** 5k. multicoloured . . . 15 10

1990. Nobel Prize Winners for Literature.
6192 **2497** 15k. brown 45 20
6193 – 15k. brown 45 20
6194 – 15k. black 45 20
DESIGNS: No. 6193, Mikhail Sholokhov (1965); 6194, Boris Pasternak.

2498 "Sever 2"

1990. Research Submarines. Multicoloured.
6195 5k. Type **2498** 15 10
6196 10k. "Tinro 2" 30 15
6197 15k. "Argus" 50 20
6198 25k. "Paisis" 75 30
6199 35k. "Mir" . . . . 1·10 65

2499 "Motherland" Statue (E. Kocher), Screen and Emblem

Филателистическая выставка „Армения-90" (**2500**)

Восстановление, милосердие, помощь (**2501**)

1990. "Armenia '90" Stamp Exhibition, Yerevan. (a) Type **2499**.
6200 **2499** 10k. multicoloured . . 30 15

(b) Nos. 5957/9 optd with T **2500** (20k.) or as T **2501**.
6201 **2412** 20k.+10k. mult 75 40
6202 – 30k.+15k. mult . . . . 1·10 70
6203 – 50k.+25k. mult . . . . 2·00 1·10

2502 S. A. Vaupshasov

2503 Soviet and Japanese Flags above Earth

1990. Intelligence Agents.
6204 **2502** 5k. dp grn, grn and blk 20 10
6205 – 5k. dp brn, brn and blk 20 10
6206 – 5k. deep blue, blue and black 20 10
6207 – 5k. brown, buff & black 20 10
6208 – 5k. brown, bistre and black 20 10
DESIGNS: No. 6205, R. I. Abel; 6206, Kim Philby; 6207, I. D. Kudrya; 6208, Konon Molodyi (alias Gordon Lonsdale).

1990. Soviet–Japanese Space Flight.
6209 **2503** 20k. multicoloured . . 55 25

2504 Grandfather Frost and Toys

1990. New Year.
6210 **2504** 5k. multicoloured . . . 10 10

2505 "Unkrada"

1990. Soviet Culture Fund. Paintings by N. K. Rerikh. Multicoloured.
6211 10k.+5k. Type **2505** 15 10
6212 20k.+10k. "Pskovo-Pechorsky Monastery" . . 30 20

2507 Globe, Eiffel Tower and Flags

1990. "Charter for New Europe". Signing of European Conventional Arms Treaty, Paris.
6214 **2507** 30k. multicoloured . . 35 15

2508 Jellyfish

1991. Marine Animals. Multicoloured.
6215 4k. Type **2508** 10 10
6216 5k. Anemone 10 10
6217 10k. Spurdog 30 15
6218 15k. European anchovy . . 40 20
6219 20k. Bottle-nosed dolphin 45 25

2509 Keres

1991. 75th Birth Anniv of Paul Keres (chess player).
6220 **2509** 15k. brown 35 20

2510 Radioactive Particles killing Vegetation

1991. 5th Anniv of Chernobyl Nuclear Power Station Disaster.
6221 **2510** 15k. multicoloured . . 15 10

2511 "Sorrento Coast with View of Capri" (Shchedrin)

1991. Birth Bicentenary of Silvestr Shchedrin and 150th Birth Anniv of Arkhip Kuindzhi (painters). Multicoloured.
6222 10k. Type **2511** 15 10
6223 10k. "New Rome. View of St. Angelo's Castle" (Shchedrin) 15 10
6224 10k. "Evening in the Ukraine" (Kuindzhi) . . 15 10
6225 10k. "Birch Grove" (Kuindzhi) 15 10

2512 White Stork

1991. Zoo Relief Fund.
6226 **2512** 10k.+5k. mult 50 50

2513 Sturgeon and Bell Tower, Volga

1991. Environmental Protection. Multicoloured.
6227 10k. Type **2513** 20 10
6228 15k. Sable and Lake Baikal 15 10
6229 20k. Saiga and dried bed of Aral Sea 20 15

1991. Historical Monuments (3rd series). As T **2464**. Multicoloured.
6231 15k. Minaret, Uzgen, Kirgizia 15 10
6232 15k. Mohammed Bashar Mausoleum, Tadzhikistan 15 10
6233 15k. Talkhatan-baba Mosque, Turkmenistan 15 10

2515 G. Shelikhov and Kodiak, 1784

1991. 500th Anniv of Discovery of America by Columbus. Russian Settlements.
6234 **2515** 20k. blue and black . . 20 10
6235 – 30k. bistre, brown & blk 35 15
6236 – 50k. orange, brown & blk 55 20
DESIGNS: 30k. Aleksandr Baranov and Sitka, 1804; 50k. I. Kuskov and Fort Ross, California, 1812.

2516 Satellite and Liner

2517 Yuri Gagarin in Uniform

1991. 10th Anniv of United Nations Transport and Communications in Asia and the Pacific Programme.
6237 **2516** 10k. multicoloured . . 20 10

1991. Cosmonautics Day. 30th Anniv of First Man in Space. Each brown.
6238 25k. Type **2517** 15 10
6239 25k. Gagarin wearing space suit 15 10
6240 25k. Gagarin in uniform with cap 15 10
6241 25k. Gagarin in civilian dress 15 10

2519 "May 1945" (A. and S. Tkachev)

1991. Victory Day.
6244 **2519** 5k. multicoloured . . . 10 10

2520 "Lenin working on Book 'Materialism and Empirical Criticism' in Geneva Library" (P. Belousov)

1991. 121st Birth Anniv of Lenin.
6245 **2520** 5k. multicoloured . . . 10 10

2521 Prokofiev

1991. Birth Centenary of Sergei Prokofiev (composer).

6246 **2521** 15k. brown 10 10

2522 Lady's Slipper

2523 Ilya I. Mechnikov (medicine, 1908)

1991. Orchids. Multicoloured.

6247	3k. Type **2522**	10	10
6248	5k. Lady orchid	10	10
6249	10k. Bee orchid	10	10
6250	20k. Calypso	15	10
6251	25k. Marsh helleborine	20	15

1991. Nobel Prize Winners. Each black.

6252	15k. Type **2523**	10	10
6253	15k. Ivan P. Pavlov (medicine, 1904)	10	10
6254	15k. A. D. Sakharov (peace, 1975)	10	10

2524 Soviet and British Flags in Space

1991. Soviet–British Space Flight.

6255 **2524** 20k. multicoloured . . 15 10

2525 Saroyan

1991. 10th Death Anniv of William Saroyan (writer).

6256 **2525** 1r. multicoloured . . . 60 30

2526 "The Universe"

1991. Lenin Soviet Children's Fund. Paintings by V. Lukyanets. Multicoloured.

6257	10k.+5k. Type **2526**	10	10
6258	10k.+5k. "Another Planet"	10	10

2527 Miniature from "Ostromirov Gospel" (first book written in Cyrillic), 1056–57

1991. Culture of Medieval Russia. Multicoloured.

6259	10k. Type **2527**	10	10
6260	15k. Page from "Russian Truth" (code of laws), 11th–13th century	15	10
6261	20k. Portrait of Sergy Radonezhsky (embroidered book cover), 1424	20	10
6262	25k. "The Trinity" (icon, Andrei Rublev), 1411	20	10
6263	30k. Illustration from "Book of the Apostles", 1564	20	15

2528 Pintails

2529 Emblem

1991. Ducks (3rd series). Multicoloured.

6264	5k. Type **2528**	10	10
6265	15k. Greater scaups	20	10
6266	20k. White-headed ducks	25	15

1991. European Conference on Security and Co-operation Session, Moscow.

6267 **2529** 10k. multicoloured . . 10 10

2530 Patroness

2531 Woman in Traditional Costume

1991. Soviet Charity and Health Fund.

6268 **2530** 20k.+10k. mult 25 15

1991. 1st Anniv of Declaration of Ukrainian Sovereignty.

6269 **2531** 30k. multicoloured . . 25 15

2532 "Albatros"

2534 Girl with Letter

2535 Bell and Bell Towers

2536 Kayak Race and "Santa Maria"

2533 "Sv. Pyotr" and Route Map

1991. Airships. Multicoloured.

6270	1k. Type **2532**	10	10
6271	3k. GA-42	15	10
6272	4k. "Norge" (horiz)	15	10
6273	5k. "Pobeda" (horiz)	15	10
6274	20k. LZ-127 "Graf Zeppelin" (horiz)	55	30

1991. 250th Anniv of Vitus Bering's and A. Chirkov's Expedition. Multicoloured.

6275	30k. Type **2533**	25	15
6276	30k. Sighting land	25	15

1991. Letter Writing Week.

6277 **2534** 7k. brown 10 10

1991. Soviet Culture Fund.

6278 **2535** 20k.+10k. mult 20 10

The belfries depicted are from Kuliga-Drakonovo, Church of the Assumption in Pskov, Ivan the Great in Moscow and Cathedral of the Assumption in Rostov.

1991. Olympic Games, Barcelona (1992) (1st issue). Multicoloured.

6279	10k. Type **2536**	20	10
6280	20k. Running and Church of the Holy Family	15	10
6281	30k. Football and stadium	25	15

See also Nos. 6362/4.

2537 Rainbow, Globe and Flags

2538 Ascension Day (Armenia)

1991. Soviet–Austrian Space Flight.

6282 **2537** 20k. multicoloured . . 15 10

1991. Folk Festivals. Multicoloured.

6283	15k. Type **2538**	15	10
6284	15k. Women carrying dishes of wheat (Novruz holiday, Azerbaijan)	15	10
6285	15k. Throwing garlands in water (Ivan Kupala summer holiday, Belorussia)	15	10
6286	15k. Stick wrestling and dancing round decorated tree (New Year, Estonia) (horiz)	15	10
6287	15k. Masked dancers (Berikaoba spring holiday, Georgia)	15	10
6288	15k. Riders with goat skin (Kazakhstan) (horiz)	15	10
6289	15k. Couple on horses (Kirgizia) (horiz)	15	10
6290	15k. Couple leaping over flames (Ligo (Ivan Kupala) holiday, Latvia) (horiz)	15	10
6291	15k. Family on way to church (Palm Sunday, Lithuania) (horiz)	15	10
6292	15k. Man in beribboned hat and musicians (Plugusorul (New Year) holiday, Moldova)	15	10
6293	15k. Sledge ride (Shrovetide, Russian Federation)	15	10
6294	15k. Musicians on carpet and stilt-walkers (Novruz holiday, Tajikistan)	15	10
6295	15k. Wrestlers (Harvest holiday, Turkmenistan) (horiz)	15	10
6296	15k. Dancers and couple with lute and tambourine (Christmas, Ukraine) (horiz)	15	10
6297	15k. Girls with tulips (Tulip holiday, Uzbekistan)	15	10

2539 Dimitry Komar

2540 Federation Government House and Flag

1991. Defeat of Attempted Coup. Multicoloured.

6298	7k. Type **2539**	10	10
6299	7k. Ilya Krichevsky	10	10
6300	7k. Vladimir Usov	10	10

Nos. 6298/6300 depict victims killed in opposing the attempted coup.

1991. Election of Boris Yeltsin as President of the Russian Federation.

6302 **2540** 7k. blue, gold and red 10 10

1991. Traditional Musical Instruments (3rd series). As T **2455**. Multicoloured.

6303	10k. Kirgiz flutes, komuzes and kyyak (string instruments)	10	10
6304	10k. Latvian ganurags and stabule (wind), tambourine, duga and kokle (string instruments)	10	10
6305	10k. Moldavian flute, bagpipes, nai (pipes), kobza and tsambal (string instruments)	10	10

2541 Decorations and Gifts

2542 Nikolai Mikhailovich Karamzin

1991. New Year.

6306 **2541** 7k. multicoloured . . . 10 10

1991. Historians' Birth Anniversaries. Mult.

6307	10k. Type **2542** (225th anniv)	10	10
6308	10k. V. O. Klyuchevsky (150th anniv)	10	10
6309	10k. Sergei M. Solovyov (171st anniv)	10	10
6310	10k. V. N. Tatishchev (after A. Osipov) (305th anniv)	10	10

RUSSIAN FEDERATION

2543 Cross-country Skiing and Ski Jumping

2546 Golden Gate, Vladimir

1992. Winter Olympic Games, Albertville, France. Multicoloured.

6311	14k. Type **2543**	10	10
6312	1r. Aerobatic skiing	20	10
6313	2r. Two and four-man bobsleighing	35	20

1992.

6316	**2546**	10k. orange	10	10
6317	–	15k. brown	10	10
6318	–	20k. red	10	10
6344	–	25k. red	10	10
6319	–	30k. black	10	10
6320	–	50k. blue	10	10
6321	–	55k. turquoise	10	10
6322	–	60k. green	10	10
6323	–	80k. purple	10	10
6324	–	1r. brown	10	10
6325	–	1r.50 green	10	10
6326	–	2r. blue	10	10
6327	–	3r. red	10	10
6328	–	4r. brown	10	10
6329	–	5r. brown	10	10
6330	–	6r. blue	10	10
6331	–	10r. blue	10	10
6332	–	15r. brown	10	10
6333	–	25r. purple	10	10
6334	–	45r. black	10	10
6335	–	50r. violet	10	10
6336	–	75r. brown	10	10
6337	–	100r. green	10	10
6338	**2546**	150r. blue	10	10
6339	–	250r. green	15	10
6340	–	300r. red	25	10
6341	–	500r. purple	30	10
6341a	–	750r. green	25	10
6341b	–	1000r. grey	35	15
6342	–	1500r. green	55	25
6342a	–	2500r. bistre	85	40
6342b	–	5000r. blue	1·75	80

DESIGNS: 15k. Pskov kremlin; 20, 50k. St. George killing dragon; 25, 55k. Victory Arch, Moscow; 30, 80k. "Millennium of Russia" monument (M. Mikeshin), Novgorod; 60k., 300r. Statue of K. Minin and D. Pozharsky, Moscow; 1, 4r. Church, Kizhky; 1r.50, 6r. Statue of Peter I, St. Petersburg; 2r. St. Basil's Cathedral, Moscow; 3r. Tretyakov Gallery, Moscow; 5r. Europe House, Moscow; 10r. St. Isaac's Cathedral, St. Petersburg; 15, 45r. "The Horse-tamer" (statue), St. Petersburg; 25, 75r. Statue of Yuri Dolgoruky, Moscow; 50r. Rostov Kremlin; 100r. Moscow Kremlin; 250r. Church, Bogulyubovo; 500r. Moscow University; 750r. State Library, Moscow; 1000r. Peter and Paul Fortress, St. Petersburg; 1500r. Pushkin Museum, Moscow; 2500r. Admiralty, St. Petersburg; 5000r. Bolshoi Theatre, Moscow.

2547 "Victory" (N. Baskakov)

2548 Western Capercaillie, Oak and Pine

1992. Victory Day.

6350 **2547** 5k. multicoloured . . . 10 10

1992. Prioksko–Terrasnyi Nature Reserve.

6351 **2548** 50k. multicoloured . . 15 15

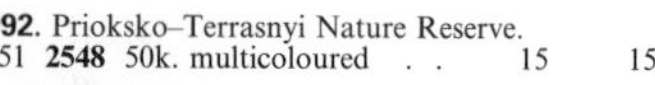

2549 "Mir" Space Station, Flags and Cosmonauts

2551 Pinocchio

1992. Russian–German Joint Space Flight.
6352 **2549** 5r. multicoloured . . . 40 30

1992. Characters from Children's Books (1st series). Multicoloured.
6354 25k. Type **2551** 10 10
6355 30k. Cipollino 10 10
6356 35k. Dunno 10 10
6357 50k. Karlson 15 10
See also Nos. 6391/5.

2552 Russian Cosmonaut and Space Shuttle
2553 Handball

1992. International Space Year. Multicoloured.
6358 25r. Type **2552** 15 10
6359 25r. American astronaut and "Mir" space station . . . 15 10
6360 25r. "Apollo" and "Vostok" spacecraft and sputnik . . 15 10
6361 25r. "Soyuz", "Mercury" and "Gemini" spacecraft 15 10
Nos. 6358/61 were issued together, se-tenant, forming a composite design.

1992. Olympic Games, Barcelona (2nd issue).
6362 **2553** 1r. multicoloured . . . 10 10
6363 – 2r. red, blue and black 10 10
6364 – 3r. red, green and black 15 10
DESIGNS—HORIZ: 2r. Fencing; 3r. Judo.

2554 L. A. Zagoskin and Yukon River, Alaska, 1842–44

1992. Expeditions. Multicoloured.
6365 55k. Type **2554** 10 10
6366 70k. N. N. Miklukho-Maklai in New Guinea, 1871–74 . . . . 10 10
6367 1r. G. I. Langsdorf and route map of expedition to Brazil, 1822–28 . . . . 10 10

2555 Garganeys

1992. Ducks. Multicoloured.
6368 1r. Type **2555** 15 10
6369 2r. Common pochards . . . 30 10
6370 3r. Falcated teals 40 20

2556 "Taj Mahal Mausoleum in Agra"

1992. 150th Birth Anniv of Vasily Vasilevich Vereshchagin (painter).
6371 1r.50 Type **2556** 15 10
6372 1r.50 "Don't Touch, Let Me Approach!" 15 10

2557 "The Saviour" (icon, Andrei Rublyov)
2558 Cathedral of the Assumption

1992.
6373 **2557** 1r. multicoloured . . . 10 10

1992. Moscow Kremlin Cathedrals. Multicoloured.
6374 1r. Type **2558** 10 10
6375 1r. Cathedral of the Annunciation (15th century) 10 10
6376 1r. Archangel Cathedral (16th century) 10 10
See also Nos. 6415/17 and 6440/2.

2559 Russian "Nutcracker" Puppets
2560 "Meeting of Joachim and Anna"

1992. Centenary of First Production of Tchaikovsky's Ballet "Nutcracker". Mult.
6377 10r. Type **2559** 10 10
6378 10r. German "Nutcracker" puppets 10 10
6379 25r. Pas de deux from ballet 30 20
6380 25r. Dance of the toys . . . 30 20

1992. Icons. Multicoloured.
6381 10r. Type **2560** 10 10
6382 10r. "Madonna and Child" 10 10
6383 10r. "Archangel Gabriel" (head) 10 10
6384 10r. "Saint Nicholas" (½-length portrait) 10 10

2561 Clockface and Festive Symbols
2562 "Discovery of America" Monument (Z. Tsereteli)

1992. New Year.
6385 **2561** 50k. multicoloured . . 10 10

1992. 500th Anniv of Discovery of America by Columbus.
6386 **2562** 15r. multicoloured . . . 20 10

2563 Petipa and Scene from "Paquita"
2564 Scrub 'n' Rub

1993. 175th Birth Anniv of Marius Petipa (choreographer). Multicoloured.
6387 25r. Type **2563** 10 10
6388 25r. "Sleeping Beauty", 1890 10 10
6389 25r. "Swan Lake", 1895 . . 10 10
6390 25r. "Raimunda", 1898 . . 10 10

1993. Characters from Children's Books (2nd series). Illustrations by Kornei Chukovsky. Mult.
6391 2r. Type **2564** 10 10
6392 3r. Big Cockroach 15 10
6393 10r. The Buzzer Fly 15 10
6394 15r. Doctor Doolittle . . . 15 10
6395 25r. Barmalei 20 10
Nos. 6391/5 were issued together, se-tenant, forming a composite design.

2565 Castle
2566 Part of Diorama in Belgorod Museum

1993. 700th Anniv of Vyborg.
6396 **2565** 10r. multicoloured . . . 10 10

1993. Victory Day. 50th Anniv of Battle of Kursk.
6397 **2566** 10r. multicoloured . . . 10 10

2567 African Violet
2568 "Molniya 3"

1993. Pot Plants. Multicoloured.
6398 10r. Type **2567** 10 10
6399 15r. "Hibiscus rosa-sinensis" 10 10
6400 25r. "Cyclamen persicum" 10 10
6401 50r. "Fuchsia hybrida" . . 15 10
6402 100r. "Begonia semperflorens" 35 25

1993. Communications Satellites. Multicoloured.
6403 25r. Type **2568** 10 10
6404 45r. "Ekran M" 10 10
6405 50r. "Gorizont" 10 10
6406 75r. "Luch" 15 10
6407 100r. "Ekspress" 20 15

2569 Snuff Box (Dmitry Kolesnikov) and Tankard
2570 Map

1993. Silverware. Multicoloured.
6409 15r. Type **2569** 10 10
6410 25r. Teapot 10 10
6411 45r. Vase 10 10
6412 75r. Tray and candlestick 20 10
6413 100r. Cream jug, coffee pot and sugar basin (Aleksandr Kordes) . . . 25 15

1993. Novgorod Kremlin. As T **2558**. Mult.
6415 25r. Kukui and Knyazhaya Towers (14th–17th century) 10 10
6416 25r. St. Sophia's Cathedral (11th century) 10 10
6417 25r. St. Sophia belfry (15th–18th century) 10 10

1993. Inauguration of Denmark–Russia Submarine Cable and 500th Anniv of Friendship Treaty.
6419 **2570** 90r. green & deep green 25 15

2571 Steller's Eider

1993. Ducks. Multicoloured.
6420 90r. Type **2571** 40 15
6421 100r. Eider 45 20
6422 250r. King eider . . . . . 1·10 55

2572 Ringed Seal

1993. Marine Animals. Multicoloured.
6423 50r. Type **2572** 20 10
6424 60r. "Paralithodes brevipes" (crab) 20 10
6425 90r. Japanese common squid 50 25
6426 100r. Cherry salmon 70 30
6427 250r. Fulmar . . . . 1·00 55

2573 Ceramic Candlestick, Skopino
2574 Banknotes and Coins

1993. Traditional Art. Multicoloured.
6428 50r. Type **2573** 10 10
6429 50r. Painted tray with picture "Summer Troika", Zhostovo (horiz) 10 10
6430 100r. Painted box, lid and distaff, Gorodets 15 10
6431 100r. Enamel icon of St. Dmitry of Solun, Rostov 15 10
6432 250r. "The Resurrection" (lacquer miniature), Fedoskino 35 20

1993. 175th Anniv of Goznak (State printing works and mint).
6433 **2574** 100r. multicoloured . . 15 10

2575 Peter I and "Goto Predestinatsiya"

1993. 300th Anniv of Russian Navy (1st issue). Multicoloured.
6434 100r. Type **2575** 15 10
6435 100r. K. A. Shilder and first all-metal submarine . . . 15 10
6436 100r. I. A. Amosov and "Arkhimed" (frigate) . . 15 10
6437 100r. I. G. Bubnov and "Bars" (submarine) . . . 15 10
6438 100r. B. M. Malinin and "Dekabrist" (submarine) 15 10
6439 100r. A. I. Maslov and "Kirov" (cruiser) 15 10
See also Nos. 6502/5, 6559/62 and 6612/18.

1993. Moscow Kremlin. As T **2558**. Mult.
6440 100r. Faceted Hall (15th century) 15 10
6441 100r. Church of the Deposition of the Virgin's Robe (15th century) . . . 15 10
6442 100r. Grand Palace (17th century) 15 10

2576 Tiger

1993. The Tiger. Multicoloured.
6443 50r. Type **2576** 10 10
6444 100r. Tiger in undergrowth 15 10
6445 250r. Two tiger cubs 30 15
6446 500r. Tiger in snow 60 30

2577 Splash of Blood on Figure
2579 Indian Elephant

2578 Seasonal Decorations

1993. Anti-AIDS Campaign.
6447 **2577** 90r. red, black and lilac 10 10

1993. New Year.
6448 **2578** 25r. multicoloured . . . 10 10

1993. Animals. Multicoloured.
6449 250r. Type **2579** 30 15
6450 250r. Japanese white-naped crane 40 20
6451 250r. Giant panda 30 15
6452 250r. American bald eagle 40 20
6453 250r. Dall's porpoise . . . 30 15
6454 250r. Koala 30 15
6455 250r. Hawaiian monk seal 30 15
6456 250r. Grey whale 30 15

2580 Rimsky-Korsakov and Scene from "Sadko"

1994. 150th Birth Anniv of Nikolai Rimsky-Korsakov (composer). Scenes from his operas. Multicoloured.
6457 250r. Type **2580** 25 15
6458 250r. "The Golden Cockerel" 25 15
6459 250r. "The Tsar's Bride" . . 25 15
6460 250r. "The Snow Maiden" 25 15

2581 "Epiphyllum peacockii"

2582 York Minster, Great Britain

1994. Cacti. Multicoloured.
6461 50r. Type **2581** 10 10
6462 100r. "Mammillaria swinglei" 10 10
6463 100r. "Lophophora williamsii" 10 10
6464 250r. "Opuntia basilaris" . . 30 15
6465 250r. "Selenicereus grandiflorus" 30 15

1994. Churches. Multicoloured.
6466 150r. Type **2582** 15 10
6467 150r. Small Metropolis church, Athens 15 10
6468 150r. Roskilde Cathedral, Denmark 15 10
6469 150r. Notre Dame Cathedral, Paris 15 10
6470 150r. St. Peter's, Vatican City 15 10
6471 150r. Cologne Cathedral, Germany 15 10
6472 150r. Seville Cathedral, Spain 15 10
6473 150r. St. Basil's Cathedral, Moscow 15 10
6474 150r. St. Patrick's Cathedral, New York 15 10

2583 "Soyuz" entering Earth's Atmosphere and "TsF-18" Centrifuge

1994. Yuri Gagarin Cosmonaut Training Centre. Multicoloured.
6475 100r. Type **2583** 10 10
6476 250r. "Soyuz"–"Mir" space complex and "Mir" simulator 15 10
6477 500r. Cosmonaut on space walk and hydrolaboratory 30 15

2584 Map and Rocket Launchers (Liberation of Russia)

1994. 50th Anniv of Liberation. Multicoloured.
6478 100r. Type **2584** 10 10
6479 100r. Map and airplanes (Ukraine) 10 10
6480 100r. Map, tank and soldiers (Belorussia) . . . 10 10

2585 Beautiful Gate, Moscow

1994. Architects' Birth Anniversaries.
6481 **2585** 50r. sepia, black and brown 10 10
6482 – 100r. brown, black and flesh 10 10
6483 – 150r. green, black and olive 15 10
6484 – 300r. violet, black and grey 35 15
DESIGNS: 50r. Type **2585** (D. V. Ukhtomsky, 250th anniv); 100r. Academy of Sciences, St. Petersburg (Giacomo Quarenghi, 250th anniv); 150r. Trinity Cathedral, St. Petersburg (V. P. Stasov, 225th anniv); 300r. Church of Christ the Saviour, Moscow (K. A. Ton, bicentenary).

2586 "Christ and the Sinner"

1994. 150th Birth Anniv of Vasily Dmitrievich Polenev (painter). Multicoloured.
6485 150r. Type **2586** 15 10
6486 150r. "Golden Autumn" . . 15 10

2587 European Wigeon

2588 Games Emblem and Runners

1994. Ducks. Multicoloured.
6487 150r. Type **2587** 15 10
6488 250r. Tufted duck 25 15
6489 300r. Baikal teal 50 30

1994. 3rd Goodwill Games, St. Petersburg.
6490 **2588** 100r. multicoloured . . 10 10

2589 Pyotr Leonidovich Kapitsa

2591 Design Motifs of First Russian Stamp

2590 Olympic Flag

1994 Physics Nobel Prize Winners. Each sepia.
6491 150r. Type **2589** (1978) . . . 15 10
6492 150r. Pavel Alekseevich Cherenkov (1958) 15 10

1994. Cent of International Olympic Committee.
6493 **2590** 250r. multicoloured . . 20 10

1994. Russian Stamp Day.
6494 **2591** 125r. multicoloured . . 10 10

2592 Snuff Box (D. Vinogradov)

2593 Centre of Asia Obelisk

1994. 250th Anniv of Imperial (now M. Lomonosov) Porcelain Factory, St. Petersburg. Multicoloured.
6495 50r. Type **2592** 10 10
6496 100r. Candlestick 10 10
6497 150r. "Water-Carrier" (statuette, after S. Pimenov) 10 10
6498 250r. Sphinx vase 25 15
6499 300r. "Lady with Mask" (statuette, after K. Somov) 30 15

1994. 50th Anniv of Incorporation of Tuva into Russian Socialist Federal Soviet Republic (R.S.F.S.R.).
6501 **2593** 125r. mulitcoloured . . 10 10

2594 Vice-Admiral V. M. Golovnin (Kurile Islands, 1811)

1994. 300th Anniv of Russian Navy (2nd issue). Explorations. Multicoloured.
6502 250r. Type **2594** 20 10
6503 250r. Admiral I. F. Kruzenshtern (first Russain round-the-world expedition, 1803–06) . . . 20 10
6504 250r. Admiral Ferdinand Petrovich Vrangel (Alaska, 1829–35) 20 10
6505 250r. Admiral F. P. Litke (Novaya Zemlya, 1821–24) 20 10

2595 Horses and Grandfather Frost

1994. New Year.
6506 **2595** 125r. blue, red and black 10 10

2596 Griboedov (after N. I. Utkin)

1995. Birth Bicentenary of Aleksandr Sergeevich Griboedov (dramatist and diplomat).
6507 **2596** 250r. brown, light brown and black . . 15 10

2597 "Sheherazade"

1995. 115th Birth Anniv of Mikhail Fokine (choreographer). Scenes from Ballets. Mult.
6508 500r. Type **2597** 25 15
6509 500r. "The Fire Bird" . . . 25 15
6510 500r. "Petrushka" 25 15

2598 Kutuzov (after J. Doe) and Sculptures from Monument, Moscow

1995. 250th Birth Anniv of Field-Marshal Mikhail Ilarionovich Kutuzov, Prince of Smolensk.
6511 **2598** 300r. multicoloured . . 15 10

2599 English Yard, Varvarka Street

2600 Syringes and Drugs around Addict

1995. 850th Anniv (1997) of Moscow (1st issue). Multicoloured.
6512 125r. Type **2599** 10 10
6513 250r. House of Averky Kirillov (scribe), Bersenevskaya Embankment 10 10
6514 300r. Volkov house, Bolshoi Kharitonevsky Lane . . . 15 10
See also Nos. 6600/2 and 6666/75.

1995. U.N. Anti-drugs Decade.
6515 **2600** 150r. multicoloured . . 10 10

2601 Shoreline

1995. Endangered Animals. Multicoloured.
6516 250r. Type **2601** 15 10
6517 250r. Ringed seal 15 10
6518 250r. Lynx 15 10
6519 250r. Landscape 15 10
Nos. 6516/19 were issued together, se-tenant, Nos. 6516/17 and 6518/19 respectively forming composite designs.

2602 Tomb of the Unknown Soldier, Moscow

1995. 50th Anniv of End of Second World War. Multicoloured.
6520 250r. Sir Winston Churchill, U.S. Pres. Franklin Roosevelt and Iosif Stalin (Yalta Conference) (horiz) 15 10
6521 250r. Storming of the Reichstag, Berlin (horiz) 15 10
6522 250r. Flags, map of Germany and German banners (Potsdam Conference) 15 10
6523 250r. Bombers (operation against Japanese in Manchuria (horiz)) . . . 15 10
6524 250r. Urn with victims' ashes, Auschwitz, and memorial, Sachsenhausen (liberation of concentration camps) (horiz) 15 10
6525 250r. Type **2602** 15 10
6526 500r. Victory Parade, Moscow (36 × 47 mm) . . 40 20

2603 Aleksandr Popov (radio pioneer) and Radio-telegraph Equipment

2604 Spreading Bellflower

1995. Centenary of Radio.
6528 **2603** 250r. multicoloured . . 10 10

1995. Meadow Flowers. Multicoloured.
6529 250r. Type **2604** 15 10
6530 250r. Ox-eye daisy ("Leucanthemum vulgare") 15 10
6531 300r. Red clover ("Trifolium pratense") 15 10
6532 300r. Brown knapweed ("Centaurea jacea") . . . 15 10
6533 500r. Meadow cranesbill . . 25 15

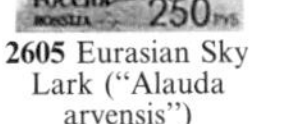

2605 Eurasian Sky Lark ("Alauda arvensis")

2606 U.S. Space Shuttle "Atlantis"

1995. Songbirds. Multicoloured.
6534 250r. Type **2605** 15 10
6535 250r. Song thrush ("Turdus philomelos") 15 10
6536 500r. Eurasian goldfinch ("Carduelis carduelis") . . 30 15
6537 500r. Bluethroat ("Cyanosylvia svecica") 30 15
6538 750r. Thrush nightingale ("Luscinia luscinia") . . . 45 25

1995. Russian–American Space Co-operation. Mult.
6539 1500r. Type **2606** 55 25
6540 1500r. "Mir" space station 55 25
6541 1500r. "Apollo" spacecraft 55 25
6542 1500r. "Soyuz" spacecraft 55 25
Nos. 6539/42 were issued together, se-tenant, forming a composite design of the spacecraft over Earth.

2607 Cathedral of the Trinity, Jerusalem

2608 Kremlin Cathedrals

1995. Russian Orthodox Churches Abroad. Mult.
6543 300r. Type **2607** 15 10
6544 300r. Apostles Saints Peter and Paul Cathedral, Karlovy Vary, Czechoslovakia 15 10
6545 500r. St. Nicholas's Cathedral, Vienna 30 15
6546 500r. St. Nicholas's Cathedral, New York . . 30 15
6547 750r. St. Aleksei's Cathedral, Leipzig 45 20

1995. 900th Anniv of Ryazan.
6548 **2608** 250r. multicoloured . . 10 10

2609 Easter Egg with Model of "Shtandart" (yacht)

1995. Faberge Exhibits in Moscow Kremlin Museum. Multicoloured.
6549 150r. Type **2609** 10 10
6550 250r. Goblet 15 10
6551 300r. Cross pendant 20 10
6552 500r. Ladle 30 15
6553 750r. Easter egg with model of Alexander III monument 45 25

2610 Harlequin Duck

1995. Ducks. Multicoloured.
6555 500r. Type **2610** 25 15
6556 750r. Baer's pochard 40 20
6557 1000r. Goosander 60 30

2612 "The Battle of Grengam, July 27, 1720" (F. Perrault)

1995. 300th Anniv of Russian Navy (3rd issue). Paintings. Multicoloured.
6559 250r. Type **2612** 15 10
6560 300r. "Preparations for Attacking the Turkish Fleet in the Bay of Cesme, Night of June 26, 1770" (P. Hackert) . . . 20 10
6561 500r. "The Battle at the Revel Roadstead, May 2, 1790" (A. Bogolyubov) 35 20
6562 750r. "The Kronstadt Roadstead" (I. Aivazovsky) 45 25

2613 State Flag and Arms

2614 Emblem and San Francisco Conference, 1945

1995. Constitution of the Russian Federation.
6563 **2613** 500r. multicoloured . . 25 10

1995. 50th Anniv of U.N.O.
6564 **2614** 500r. brown, blue and yellow 25 10

2615 White Storks in Nest

1995. Europa. Peace and Freedom. Multicoloured.
6565 1500r. Type **2615** 80 40
6566 1500r. Stork flying over landscape 80 40
Nos. 6565/6 were issued together, se-tenant, forming a composite design.

2616 "Birth of Christ" (icon, Assumption Cathedral, St. Cyril's Monastery, White Sea)

2618 Semyonov

2617 Yuri Dolgoruky (1090–1157), Kiev and Building of Moscow

1995. Christmas.
6567 **2616** 500r. multicoloured . . 20 10

1995. History of Russian State (1st series). Mult.
6568 1000r. Type **2617** 45 20
6569 1000r. Aleksandr Nevsky (1220–63), Battle of Lake Peipus and as Grand Duke of Vladimir 45 20
6570 1000r. Mikhail Yaroslavich (1271–1318), Tver and torture by the Golden Horde 45 20
6571 1000r. Dmitry Donskoi (1350–89), Moscow Kremlin and Battle of Kulikovo 45 20
6572 1000r. Ivan III (1440–1505), marriage to Sophia Paleologa and Battle of Ugra River 45 20
See also Nos. 6640/3.

1996. Birth Centenary of Nikolai Semyonov (Nobel Prize winner for chemistry, 1956).
6573 **2618** 750r. grey 30 15

2619 Pansies

2620 Tabbies

1996. Flowers. Multicoloured.
6574 500r. Type **2619** 20 10
6575 750r. Sweet-williams ("Dianthus barbatus") . . 35 15
6576 750r. Sweet peas ("Lathyrus odoratus") 35 15
6577 1000r. Crown imperial ("Fritillaria imperialis") 45 25
6578 1000r. Snapdragons ("Antirrhinum majus") . . 45 25

1996. Cats. Multicoloured.
6579 1000r. Type **2620** 40 20
6580 1000r. Russian blue 40 20
6581 1000r. White Persian . . . 40 20
6582 1000r. Sealpoint Siamese . . 40 20
6583 1000r. Siberian 40 20

2622 "Laying down of Banners" (A. Mikhailov)

1996. Victory Day.
6585 **2622** 1000r. multicoloured . . 40 20

2623 Tula Kremlin and Monument to Peter I

1996. 850th Anniv of Tula.
6586 **2623** 1500r. multicoloured . . 60 30

2624 Putilovsky Works Tramcar, 1896

1996. Centenary of First Russian Tramway, Nizhny Novgorod. Multicoloured.
6587 500r. Type **2624** 20 10
6588 750r. Sormovo tramcar, 1912 . . . . 35 15
6589 750r. 1928 Series X tramcar, 1928 . . . . 35 15
6590 1000r. 1931 Series KM tramcar, 1931 . . . . . . 40 20
6591 1000r. Type LM-57 tramcar, 1957 . . . . 40 20
6592 2500r. Model 71-608K tramcar, 1973 . . . . . . 75 45

2625 Ye. Dashkova (President of Academy of Sciences)

2626 Children walking Hand in Hand

1996. Europa. Famous Women.
6594 **2625** 1500r. green and black 60 30
6595 – 1500r. purple and black 60 30
DESIGN: No. 6594, S. Kovalevskaya (mathematician).

1996. 50th Anniv of UNICEF.
6596 **2626** 1000r. multicoloured . . 40 20

2627 "Post Troika in Snowstorm" (P. Sokolov)

1996. Post Troikas in Paintings. Mulicoloured.
6597 1500r. Type **2627** 60 30
6598 1500r. "Post Troika in Summer" (P. Sokolov) . . 60 30
6599 1500r. "Post Troika" (P. Gruzinsky) 60 30

2628 "View of Bridge over Yauza and of Shapkin House in Moscow" (J. Delabarte)

1996. 850th Anniv (1997) of Moscow (2nd issue). Paintings. Multicoloured.
6600 500r. Type **2628** 20 10
6601 500r. "View of Moscow from Balcony of Kremlin Palace" (detail, J. Delabarte) 20 10
6602 750r. "View of Voskresenskie and Nikolskie Gates and Kamenny Bridge" (F. Ya. Alekseev) 35 20
6603 750r. "Moscow Yard near Volkhonka" (anon) . . . 35 20
6604 1000r. "Varvarka Street" (anon) 40 20
6605 1000r. "Sledge Races in Petrovsky Park" 40 20

2630 Basketball

2632 Gorsky and Scenes from "Gudula's Daughter" and "Salambo"

2631 "Yevstafy" (ship of the line), 1762

1996. Olympic Games, Atlanta, U.S.A. Mult.
6607 500r. Type **2630** 20 10
6608 1000r. Boxing 40 20
6609 1000r. Swimming 40 20
6610 1500r. Gymnastics 60 30
6611 1500r. Hurdling 60 30

1996. 300th Anniv of Russian Navy (4th issue).
(a) As T **2631**.
6612 **2631** 750r. brown and yellow 35 20
6613 – 1000r. deep blue, cobalt and blue 40 20
6614 – 1000r. purple, pink and rose 40 20
6615 – 1500r. multicoloured . . 60 30
6616 – 1500r. black, grey and stone 60 30
DESIGNS: No. 6613, "Petropavlovsk" (battleship); 6614, "Novik" (destroyer); 6615, "Tashkent" (destroyer); 6616, "S-13" (submarine).

(b) Size 35 x 24 mm. Each blue and black.
6617 1000r. "Principium" (galley) 40 20
6618 1000r. "Admiral Kuznetsov" (aircraft carrier) 40 20

1996. 125th Birth Anniv of Aleksandr Gorsky (ballet choreographer). Multicoloured.
6620 750r. Type **2632** 35 20
6621 750r. Scene from "La Bayadere" 35 20
6622 1500r. Scene from "Don Quixote" 60 30
6623 1500r. Scene from "Giselle" 60 30

2633 National Flags

1996. Formation of Community of Sovereign Republics (union of Russian Federation and Belarus).
6624 **2633** 1500r. multicoloured . . 60 30

2634 Chalice

1996. Objets d'Art. Multicoloured.

6625	1000r. Type **2634**	40	20
6626	1000r. Perfume bottles . . .	40	20
6627	1000r. Double inkwell . . .	40	20
6628	1500r. Coffee pot	60	30
6629	1500r. Pendent scent containers (one ladybird-shaped)	60	30

2635 Symbols of Science and Culture on Open Book

1996. 50th Anniv of UNESCO.

6631	**2635** 1000r. black, gold and blue	40	20

2636 "Madonna and Child" (icon), Moscow

2637 Clockface of Spassky Tower, Moscow Kremlin

1996. Orthodox Religion. Multicoloured.

6632	1500r. Type **2636**	60	30
6633	1500r. Stavrovouni Monastery, Cyprus . . .	60	30
6634	1500r. "St. Nicholas" (icon), Cyprus	60	30
6635	1500r. Voskresenkie ("Resurrection") Gate, Moscow	60	30

1996. New Year.

6636	**2637** 1000r. multicoloured . .	35	15

2638 First Match between U.S.S.R. and Canada, 1972

1996. 50th Anniv of Ice Hockey in Russia. Mult.

6637	1500r. Type **2638**	60	30
6638	1500r. Goalkeeper and players (first match between Moscow and Prague, 1948)	60	30
6639	1500r. Players and referee (Russia versus Sweden)	60	30

1996. History of Russian State (2nd series). As T **2617**. Multicoloured.

6640	1500r. Basil III (1479–1533), removal of bell from Pskov and Siege of Smolensk, 1514	60	30
6641	1500r. Ivan IV the Terrible (1530–84), coronation in Cathedral of the Assumption (Moscow Kremlin) and executions by the Oprichnina	60	30
6642	1500r. Fyodor I Ivanovich (1557–98), with Cossacks and Siberian Kings, and election of Iove (first Russian Patriarch)	60	30
6643	1500r. Boris Godunov (1551–1605), as Tsar in 1598 and food distribution during famine, 1601–03	60	30

2639 Maule's Quince ("Chaenomeles japonica")

1997. Shrubs. Multicoloured.

6644	500r. Type **2639**	20	10
6645	500r. Ornamental almond ("Amygdalus triloba") . .	20	10
6646	1000r. Broom ("Cytisus scoparius")	40	20
6647	1000r. Burnet rose ("Rosa pimpinellifolia")	40	20
6648	1000r. Mock orange ("Philadelphus coronarius")	40	20

2641 Dmitri Shostakovich (composer) (from 90th birth anniv (1996) medal)

2643 Post Emblem

1997. "Shostakovich and World Musical Culture" International Music Festival.

6650	**2641** 1000r. multicoloured . .	35	15

1997.

6652	**2643** 100r. brown and black	10	10
6653	– 150r. mauve and black	10	10
6654	– 250r. green and black	10	10
6655	– 300r. green and black	10	10
6656	– 500r. blue and black . .	15	10
6657	– 750r. brown and black	20	10
6658	– 1000r. red and blue . .	30	15
6659	– 1500r. blue and black	45	20
6660	– 2000r. green and black	60	30
6661	– 2500r. red and black . .	75	35
6662	– 3000r. violet and black	90	45
6663	– 5000r. brown and black	1·50	75

DESIGNS: 100r. Combine harvesters in field; 150r. Oil rigs; 250r. White storks; 300r. Radio mast; 750r. St. George killing dragon; 1000r. State flag and arms; 1500r. Electric pylon inside generating machinery; 2000r. Class VL65 electric railway locomotive; 2500r. Moscow Kremlin; 3000r. Space satellite; 5000r. Pianist and theatre.

For these designs in revised currency, see Nos. 6718/35.

2644 Ioan Zlatoust Church, Sofiiski Cathedral and Admiral Barsh's House

2645 "Volga Svyatoslavovich" (I. Bilibin)

1997. 850th Anniv of Vologda.

6664	**2644** 1000r. multicoloured . .	35	15

1997. Europa. Tales and Legends.

6665	**2645** 1500r. multicoloured . .	55	30

2646 Jesus Christ the Saviour Cathedral

1997. 850th Anniv of Moscow (3rd issue). Mult.

6666	1000r. Type **2646**	40	20
6667	1000r. Towers and walls of Kremlin	40	20
6668	1000r. Grand Palace and cathedrals, Kremlin . . .	40	20
6669	1000r. St. Basil's Cathedral, Spassky Tower and Trinity Church	40	20
6670	1000r. "St. George killing Dragon" (16th-century icon)	40	20
6671	1000r. First reference to Moscow in Ipatevsky Chronicle, 1147	40	20
6672	1000r. Prince Daniil Alexandrovich and Danilov Monastery . . .	40	20
6673	1000r. "Building Moscow Kremlin, 1366" (16th-century miniature)	40	20
6674	1000r. Kazan cap and "Coronation of Ivan IV" (miniature)	40	20
6675	1000r. 16th-century plan of Moscow	40	20

Nos. 6666/75 were issued together, se-tenant, Nos. 6666/70 forming a composite design of Moscow in late 19th century.

2647 Mil Mi-14 (float)

1997. Helicopters. Multicoloured.

6676	500r. Type **2647**	20	10
6677	1000r. Mil Mi-24 (gunship)	35	15
6678	1500r. Mil Mi-26 (transport)	55	30
6679	2000r. Mil Mi-28 (gunship)	70	35
6680	2500r. Mil Mi-34 (patrol)	90	45

2648 "The Priest and Balda"

1997. Birth Bicentenary (1999) of Aleksandr Sergeevich Pushkin (poet) (1st issue). Mult.

6681	500r. Type **2648**	15	10
6682	1000r. "Tsar Saltan" . . .	30	15
6683	1500r. "The Fisherman and the Golden Fish"	50	25
6684	2000r. "The Dead Princess and the Seven Knights"	60	30
6685	3000r. "The Golden Cockerel"	90	45

See also Nos. 6762/6 and 6827/9.

2649 Petrodvorets (St. Petersburg) National Flags and Marble Temple, Bangkok

1997. Centenary of Russia–Thailand Diplomatic Relations and of Visit of King Rama V to St. Petersburg.

6686	**2649** 1500r. multicoloured . .	45	20

2650 Siberian Flying Squirrel

1997. Wildlife. Multicoloured.

6687	500r. Type **2650**	20	10
6688	750r. Lynx	25	10
6689	1000r. Western capercaillie	35	15
6690	2000r. European otter . . .	70	35
6691	3000r. Western curlew . . .	1·25	65

2651 Arkhangel Province

1997. Regions of the Russian Federation (1st series). Multicoloured.

6692	1500r. Type **2651**	50	25
6693	1500r. Kaliningrad Province (vert)	50	25
6694	1500r. Kamchatka Province	50	25
6695	1500r. Krasnodar Territory	50	25
6696	1500r. Sakha Republic (Yakutiya) (vert)	50	25

See also Nos. 6784/8, 6831/5, 6920/5, 6980/4, 7062/6 and 7153/8.

2652 Klyopa flying with Balloons

1997. Klyopa (cartoon character). Multicoloured.

6697	500r. Type **2652**	15	10
6698	1000r. Klyopa hang-gliding over Red Square	30	15
6699	1500r. Klyopa in troika (45 × 33 mm)	45	20

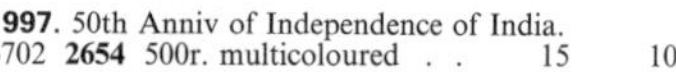

2653 Emblem, Mascot and Russian Federation 1992 and 20k. Stamp

2654 Indian Flag and Asokan Capital

1997. "Moscow 97" International Stamp Exhibition. Multicoloured.

6700	1500r. Russian Empire 1858 10k. and R.S.F.S.R. 1918 35k. stamps, and Spassky Tower, Moscow Kremlin	50	25
6701	1500r. Type **2653**	50	25

1997. 50th Anniv of Independence of India.

6702	**2654** 500r. multicoloured . .	15	10

2655 Presentation of Standard

1997. 325th Birth Anniv of Tsar Peter I. Mult.

6703	2000r. Type **2655** (creation of regular army and navy)	60	30
6704	2000r. Sea battle (access to Baltic Sea)	60	30
6705	2000r. Peter I reviewing plans (construction of St. Petersburg)	60	30
6706	2000r. Council (administrative reforms)	60	30
6707	2000r. Boy before tutor (cultural and educational reforms)	60	30

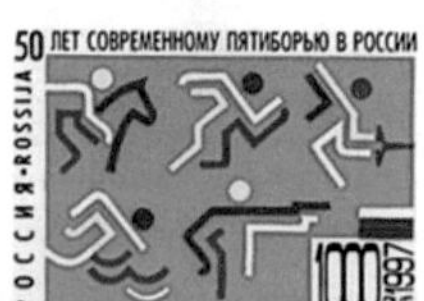

2656 Pictograms of Five Events

1997. 50th Anniv of Modern Pentathlon in Russia.

6709	**2656** 1000r. multicoloured . .	30	15

2657 Match Scenes

1997. Centenary of Football in Russia.

6710	**2657** 2000r. multicoloured . .	60	30

2658 Radiation and Earth

2659 National Flag and Palace of Europe, Strasbourg

1997. World Ozone Layer Day. 10th Anniv of Montreal Protocol (on reduction of use of chlorofluorocarbons).
6711 **2658** 1000r. multicoloured . . 30 15

1997. Admission of Russian Federation to European Council.
6712 **2659** 1000r. multicoloured . . 30 15

2660 "Boris and Gleb" (14th-century icon)

2663 Cross-country Skiing

2662 "Menshikov in Beresovo" (detail, Surikov)

1997. Centenary of Russian State Museum, St. Petersburg (1st issue). Multicoloured.
6713 500r. Type **2660** 15 10
6714 1000r. "Volga Boatmen" (I. Repin) (horiz) 30 15
6715 1500r. "Promenade" (Marc Chagall) 45 25
6716 2000r. "Merchant's Wife taking Tea" (B. Kustodiev) 60 30
See also Nos. 6753/6756.

1998. As Nos. 6652/63 but in reformed currency.
6718 10k. brown and black (as No. 6652) 10 10
6719 15k. mauve and black (as No. 6653) 10 10
6720 25k. green and black (as No. 6654) 10 10
6721 30k. green and black (as No. 6655) 10 10
6723 50k. blue and black (Type **2643**) 10 10
6726 1r. red and blue (as No. 6658) 15 10
6727 1r.50 blue and black (as No. 6659) 20 10
6728 2r. green and black (as No. 6660) 25 10
6729 2r.50 red and black (as No. 6661) 30 15
6730 3r. violet and black (as No. 6662) 35 20
6735 5r. brown and black (as No. 6663) 60 30

1998. 150th Birth Anniversaries of Vasily Ivanovich Surikov and V. M. Vasnetsov (artists). Multicoloured.
6741 1r.50 Type **2662** 20 10
6742 1r.50 "Morozov Boyar's Wife" (Surikov) 20 10
6743 1r.50 "Battle between Slavs and Nomads" (detail, Vasnetsov) (vert) 20 10
6744 1r.50 "Tsarevich Ivan on a Grey Wolf" (Vasnetsov) 20 10

1998. Winter Olympic Games, Nagano, Japan. Mult.
6745 50k. Type **2663** 10 10
6746 1r. Figure skating (pairs) . . 15 10
6747 1r.50 Biathlon 20 10

2664 Red-tailed Black Labeo "Epalzeorhynchus bicolor"

1998. Fishes. Multicoloured.
6748 50k. Type **2664** 10 10
6749 50k. Jewel tetra ("Hyphessobrycon callistus") 10 10
6750 1r. Galina's catfish ("Synodontis galinae") . . 15 10
6751 1r.50 "Botia kristinae" . . . 20 10
6752 1r.50 "Cichlasoma labiatum" 20 10

2665 "The Last Day of Pompeii" (K. P. Bryullov)

1998. Centenary of State Russian Museum, St. Petersburg (2nd issue). Multicoloured.
6753 1r.50 Type **2665** 20 10
6754 1r.50 "The Ninth Wave" (I. K. Aivazovsky) . . . 20 10
6755 1r.50 "Pines for Masts" (I. I. Shishkin) 20 10
6756 1r.50 "Our Lady of Tenderness for Sick Hearts" (K. S. Petrov-Vodkin) 20 10

2667 Theatre and Characters

1998. Centenary of Moscow Art Theatre.
6759 **2667** 1r.50 multicoloured . . 20 10

2668 "End of Winter" (Shrove-tide)

1998. Europa. National Festivals.
6760 **2668** 1r.50 multicoloured . . 20 10

2669 War Memorial, Venets Hotel, History Museum and Goncharovsky Pavilion

2670 "The Lyceum"

1998. 350th Anniv of Ulyanovsk (formerly Simbirsk).
6761 **2669** 1r. multicoloured . . . 15 10

1998. Birth Bicentenary (1999) of Aleksandr Sergeevich Pushkin (poet) (2nd issue). Drawings by Pushkin.
6762 **2670** 1r.50 black and blue . . 20 10
6763 – 1r.50 brown, stone & blk 20 10
6764 – 1r.50 brown, stone & blk 20 10
6765 – 1r.50 brown, stone & blk 20 10
6766 – 1r.50 black and blue . . 20 10
DESIGNS: No. 6763, "A.N. Wolf"; 6764, Self-portrait; 6765, "Tatyana" (from "Evgeny Onegin"); 6766, Knight in armour (manuscript cover from 1830).

2671 Local History Museum and Peter I Monument

1998. 300th Anniv of Taganrog.
6767 **2671** 1r. multicoloured . . . 15 10

2673 Tsar Nicholas II

2674 Grapes

1998. 80th Death Anniv of Tsar Nicholas II.
6769 **2673** 3r. multicoloured . . . 35 20

1998. Berries. Multicoloured.
6770 50k. Type **2674** 10 10
6771 75k. Raspberry 10 10
6772 1r. Magnolia vine 15 10
6773 1r.50 Cowberrry 20 10
6774 2r. Arctic bramble 25 15

2675 Landmarks

2676 Leontina Cohen

1998. 275th Anniv of Yekaterinburg.
6775 **2675** 1r. multicoloured . . . 15 10

1998. Intelligence Agents.
6776 **2676** 1r. blue, indigo & blk 15 10
6777 – 1r. brown, yellow & blk 15 10
6778 – 1r. green, dp green & blk 15 10
6779 – 1r. purple, brown & blk 15 10
DESIGNS: No. 6777, Morris Cohen; 6778, L. R. Kvasnikov; 6779, A. A. Yatskov.

2677 Order of St. Andrew

1998. Russian Orders (1st series). Multicoloured.
6780 1r. Type **2677** 15 10
6781 1r.50 Order of St. Catherine 20 10
6782 2r. Order of St. Aleksandr Nevsky 25 15
6783 2r.50 Order of St. George 30 15
See also Nos. 6807/11.

1998. Regions of the Russian Federation (2nd series). As T **2651**. Multicoloured.
6784 1r.50 Republic of Buryatiya (vert) 20 10
6785 1r.50 Republic of Kareliya (vert) 20 10
6786 1r.50 Khabarovsk Province 20 10
6787 1r.50 Murmansk Province 20 10
6788 1r.50 Primorsky Province . . 20 10

2678 Universal Postal Union Emblem

1998. World Post Day.
6789 **2678** 1r. multicoloured . . . 15 10

2679 Anniversary Emblem

1998. 50th Anniv of Universal Declaration of Human Rights.
6790 **2679** 1r.50 multicoloured . . 20 10

2680 Headquarters, Moscow

1998. 10th Anniv of Menatep Bank.
6791 **2680** 2r. multicoloured . . . 25 15

2681 Aviation

1998. Achievements of the Twentieth Century. Multicoloured.
6792 1r. Type **2681** 15 10
6793 1r. Computers 15 10
6794 1r. Genetics 15 10
6795 1r. Nuclear energy 15 10
6796 1r. Space exploration . . . 15 10
6797 1r. Television 15 10

2682 Koshkin

1998. Birth Centenary of Mikhail Ilich Koshkin (tank designer).
6798 **2682** 1r. multicoloured . . . 15 10

2683 Grandfather Frost

1998. New Year.
6799 **2683** 1r. multicoloured . . . 15 10

2684 Telephone and Switchboard Operators

1999. Centenary of First Long-distance Telephone Link in Russia (between Moscow and St. Petersburg).
6800 **2684** 1r. multicoloured . . . 15 10

2685 Western Capercaillie

1999. Hunting. Multicoloured.
6801 1r. Type **2685** 15 10
6802 1r.50 Shooting mallard ducks from rowing boat 20 10
6803 2r. Falconry (Gyr falcon) 25 15
6804 2r.50 Wolves 30 15
6805 3r. Bears 35 20

1999. Russian Orders (2nd series). As T **2677**. Multicoloured.
6807 1r. Order of St. Vladimir . . 15 10
6808 1r.50 Order of St. Anne . . 20 10
6809 2r. Order of St. John of Jerusalem 25 15
6810 2r.50 Order of the White Eagle 30 15
6811 3r. Order of St. Stanislas . . 35 20

2688 "Family at Tea" (Sofya Kondrashina)

1999. Russia in the 21st Century. Children's paintings. Multicoloured.
6813 1r.20 Type **2688** 15 10
6814 1r.20 "My Town" (Yuri Lapushkov) 15 10
6815 1r.20 "Fantasy City" (Aleksander Khudyshin) (vert) 15 10

2690 Albrecht Durer's House

1999. "iBRA '99" International Stamp Exhibition, Nuremberg, Germany.
6817 **2690** 3r. multicoloured . . . 30 15

2691 Setting Weighted Lines

1999. Fishing. Multicoloured.
6818 1r. Type **2691** 10 10
6819 2r. Fishing by rod and line from bank and boat . . . 20 10
6820 2r. Fishing by rod and line from kayak 20 10
6821 3r. Fishing through holes in ice 30 15
6822 3r. Underwater fishing . . . 30 15

2692 Council Flag and Headquarters, Strasbourg, and Spassky Tower, Moscow

1999. 50th Anniv of Council of Europe.
6823 **2692** 3r. multicoloured . . . 30 15

2693 Oksky State Natural Biosphere Preserve

1999. Europa. Parks and Gardens.
6824 **2693** 5r. multicoloured . . . 55 30

2694 Stag

1999. Red Deer. Multicoloured.
6825 2r.50 Type **2694** 25 15
6826 2r.50 Doe and fawns . . . 25 15

2695 Pushkin, 1815 (after S. G. Chirikov)

2696 Rose "Carina" ("Happy Birthday")

1999. Birth Bicentenary of Aleksandr Sergeevich Pushkin (poet) (3rd issue). Multicoloured.
6827 1r. Type **2695** 10 10
6828 3r. Pushkin, 1826 (after I.-E. Viven) 30 15
6829 5r. Pushkin, 1836 (after Karl Bryullov) 55 25

1999. Regions of the Russian Federation (3rd series). As T **2651**. Multicoloured.
6831 2r. Republic of North Osetia-Alaniya 20 10
6832 2r. Republic of Bashkortostan (vert) . . . 20 10
6833 2r. Kirov Province 20 10
6834 2r. Evenk Autonomous Region (vert) 20 10
6835 2r. Stavropol Region . . . 20 10

1999. Greetings stamps. Roses. Multicoloured.
6836 1r.20 Type **2696** 15 10
6837 1r.20 "Gloria Dei" ("From the bottom of my heart") 15 10
6838 2r. "Candia" ("Congratulations") . . . 20 10
6839 3r. "Confidence" ("Be happy") 30 15
6840 4r. "Ave Maria" ("With love") 40 20

1999. No. 6342b surch **1.20**.
6841 1r.20 on 5000r. blue 15 10

2698 River Station, City Arms and Nativity of the Virgin Cathedral

1999. 250th Anniv of Rostov-on-Don.
6842 **2698** 1r.20 multicoloured . . 15 10

2699 Automatic Post Sorting

1999. 125th Anniv of Universal Postal Union.
6843 **2699** 3r. multicoloured . . . 30 15

2700 "Horsewoman"

1999. Birth Bicentenary of Karl Bryullov (painter). Multicoloured.
6844 2r.50 Type **2700** 25 15
6845 2r.50 "Portrait of Yu. P. Samoilova and Amacilia Paccini" 25 15

2701 IZh-1 Motorcycle, 1929

1999. Russian Motor Cycles. Multicoloured.
6846 1r. Type **2701** 10 10
6847 1r.50 L-300, 1930 . . . . . 15 15
6848 2r. M-72, 1941 . . . . . . 20 10
6849 2r.50 M-1-A, 1945 . . . . 25 15
6850 5r. IZ-"Planeta-5", 1987 . . 55 25

2702 Suvorov's Vanguard passing Lake Klontal (after engraving by L. Hess)

1999. Bicentenary of General Aleksandr Suvorov's Crossing of the Alps. Multicoloured.
6851 2r.50 Type **2702** . . . . .
6852 2r.50 Schollenen Gorge Monument, Suvorov and soldiers . . . .

2703 Horse Racing

1999. Traditional Sports. Multicoloured.
6853 2r. Type **2703** 20 10
6854 2r. Wrestling 20 10
6855 2r. Gorodki (game with stick and blocks of wood) 20 10
6856 2r. Sleigh and deer team race 20 10
6857 2r. Weightlifting (vert) . . . 20 10

2704 Leonid Utesov

1999. Singers. Multicoloured.
6858 2r. Type **2704** 20 10
6859 2r. Lidiya Ruslanova (in costume) 20 10
6860 2r. Klavdiya Shulzhenko (with hands clasped) . . . 20 10
6861 2r. Mark Bernes (playing accordion) 20 10
6862 2r. Bulat Okudzhava (playing guitar in street scene) 20 10
6863 2r. Vladimir Vysotsky (with guitar and arms out wide) 20 10
6864 2r. Igor Talkov (with arm raised) 20 10
6865 2r. Victor Tsoi (playing guitar) 20 10

2705 Players chasing Ball and Club Badge

1999. Spartak-Alaniya, National Football Champions.
6877 **2705** 2r. multicoloured . . . 20 10

2706 Father Christmas and "2000"

1999. Christmas and New Year. Multicoloured.
6878 1r.20 Type **2706** 15 10
6879 1r.20 "2000", globe as pearl and shell 15 10

2707 "The Raising of the Daughter of Jairus" (V. D. Polenov)

2000. Bimillenary of Christianity. Religious Paintings. Multicoloured.
6880 3r. Type **2707** 30 15
6881 3r. "Christ in the Wilderness" (I. N. Kramskoy) 30 15
6882 3r. "Christ in the House of Mary and Martha" (G. I. Semiradsky) 30 15
6883 3r. "What is Truth?" (N. N. Ge) (vert) 30 15

2709 Psurtsev and Central Telegraph Office, Moscow

2000. Birth Centenary of Nikolai D. Psurtsev (statesman).
6886 **2709** 2r.50 multicoloured . . 25 15

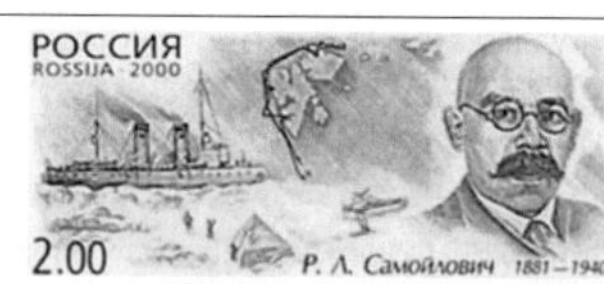

2711 R. L. Samoilovich

2000. Polar Explorers. Multicoloured.
6888 2r. Type **2711** 20 10
6889 2r. V. Yu Vize and polar station 20 10
6890 2r. M. M. Somov and ship 20 10
6891 2r. P. A. Gordienko and airplane 20 10
6892 2r. A. F. Treshnikov and tracked vehicles 20 10

2712 N. A. Panin-Kolomenkin (first Russian Olympic Ice-skating Champion, 1908)

2000. The Twentieth Century (1st issue). Sport. Multicoloured.
6893 25k. Type **2712** 10 10
6894 30k. Wrestlers (Olympic Games, Stockholm, 1912) 10 10
6895 50k. Athlete crossing finishing line (All-Russian Olympiad, 1913 and 1914) 10 10
6896 1r. Cyclists (All-Union Spartacist Games, 1928) 10 10
6897 1r.35 Emblem and parade of athletes (Sports Association for Labour and Defence, 1931) . . . 15 10
6898 1r.50 Emblem and athletes ("Honoured Master of Sports", 1934) 20 10
6899 2r. Gymnasts and shot-putter (Olympic Games, Helsinki, 1952) 20 10
6900 2r.50 V. P. Kutz and athletes (Olympic Games, Melbourne, 1956) 25 15
6901 3r. Gold Medal, goalkeeper and player (Olympic Football Champion, Melbourne Olympic Games) 30 15
6902 4r. Mikhail Botvinnik (World Chess Champion, 1948–57, 1958–60 and 1961–63) 45 25
6903 5r. Soviet Union–Canada ice hockey match, 1972 . . . 55 30
6904 6r. Stadium and emblem (Olympic Games, Moscow, 1980) 65 35

See also Nos. 6926/37, 6950/61 and 6964/76.

2714 Soldier (L. F. Golovanov)

2000. 55th Anniv of End of Second World War. Posters by named artists. Multicoloured.
6906 1r.50 Type **2714** 20 10
6907 1r.50 Mother and son (N. N. Vatolina) 20 10
6908 1r.50 Soldiers celebrating (V. V. Suryaninov) . . . 20 10
6909 1r.50 Soldier and woman (V. I. Ladyagin) 20 10
6910 5r. Soldier and emblem (V. S. Klimashin) 55 30

2715 "Apollo"–"Soyuz" Space Link, 1975

2000. International Space Co-operation. Mult.
6912 2r. Type **2715** 20 10
6913 3r. Projected international space station and flags (horiz) 30 15
6914 5r. Rocket taking off from launch pad at sea 55 30

2716 Mother and Child crossing Road and Emblem

2717 Star of David, Doves and "Holocaust"

2000. World Road Safety Week.

6915	**2716** 1r.75 multicoloured	20	10

2000. Holocaust Victims' Commemoration.

6916	**2717** 2r. multicoloured	20	10

2718 Spassky Tower and President's Flag

2719 "Building Europe"

2000. Election of President Vladimir Putin.

6917	**2718** 1r.75 multicoloured	20	10

2000. Europa.

6918	**2719** 7r. multicoloured	75	40

2000. Regions of the Russian Federation (4th issue). As T **2651**. Multicoloured.

6920	3r. Republic of Kalmyk (vert)	30	15
6921	3r. Mari El Republic (vert)	30	15
6922	3r. Tatarstan Republic (vert)	30	15
6923	3r. Udmurt Republic (vert)	30	15
6924	3r. Chuvash Republic	30	15
6925	3r. Autonomous Republic of Yamalo Nentsky	30	15

2721 V. K. Arkadjev (Observation of Ferromagnetic Resonance, 1913)

2000. The Twentieth Century (2nd issue). Science. Multicoloured.

6926	1r.30 Type **2721** (botanist and plant geneticist)	15	10
6927	1r.30 Nikolai Ivanovich Vavilov (botanist and plant geneticist) and ears of corn (theory on plant divergence)	15	10
6928	1r.30 N. N. Luzin (founder of Moscow Mathematical School, 1920–30)	15	10
6929	1r.75 I. E. Tamm and chemical model (Phenoms Theory, 1929)	20	10
6930	1r.75 P. L. Kapitsa and diagram of experiment (discovery of liquid helium superfluidity, 1938)	20	10
6931	1r.75 Nikolai Nikolayevich Semenov (physical chemist) (chemical chain reactions theory, 1934)	20	10
6932	2r. V. I. Veksler and charged particles in accelerators, 1944–45	20	10
6933	2r. Mayan text (decipherment of Mayan language by Yu V. Knorozov, 1950s)	20	10
6934	2r. A. V. Ivanov (discovery of pogonophora, 1955–57)	20	10
6935	3r. Globe, Moon and Luna 3 (first photograph of Moon's dark side, 1959)	30	15
6936	3r. Scientific equipment (development of quantum electronics, 1960s)	30	15
6937	3r. N. J. Tolstoi (ethnolinguistic dictionary, 1995)	30	15

2722 Chihuahua

2723 Fencing

2000. Dogs. Multicoloured.

6938	1r. Type **2722**	10	10
6939	1r.50 Terrier	20	10
6940	2r. Poodle	20	10
6941	2r.50 French bulldog	25	15
6942	3r. Japanese chin	30	15

2000. Olympic Games, Sydney. Multicoloured.

6943	2r. Type **2723**	20	10
6944	3r. Synchronized swimming	30	15
6945	5r. Volleyball	55	30

2724 Charoit

2000. Minerals. Multicoloured.

6946	1r. Type **2724**	10	10
6947	2r. Haematite	20	10
6948	3r. Rock crystal	30	15
6949	4r. Gold	45	25

2725 Ballerina and Actors

2000. The Twentieth Century (3rd series). Culture. Multicoloured.

6950	30k. Type **2725** (touring ballet and opera companies, 1908–14)	10	10
6951	50k. "Black Square" (K. S. Malevich)	10	10
6952	1r. Sergi Mikhailovich Eisenstein (director) and scene from *Battleship Potemkin* (film, 1925)	10	10
6953	1r.30 Book and Aleksei Maksimovich Gorky (writer)	15	10
6954	1r.50 Sculptures and red star	20	10
6955	1r.75 Vladimir Vladimirovich Mayakovsky (poet and playwright) and propaganda posters, 1920s	20	10
6956	2r. V. E. Meierkhold and K. S. Stanislavsky (theatre producers)	20	10
6957	2r.50 Dmitri Dmitriyevich Shostakovich (composer) and musicians	25	15
6958	3r. Galina Sergeyevna Ulanova (ballerina) and dancers	30	15
6959	4r. A. T. Tvardovsky (poet)	45	25
6960	5r. Fountain and Great Palace, Petrodvorets (restoration of historical monuments)	55	30
6961	6r. D. S. Likhachev (literary critic)	65	35

2726 Zander (*Stizostedion lucioperca*) and Common Whitefish (*Coregonus lavaretus manaenoides*)

2000. Fish of Chudsko-Pskovskoye Lake. Mult.

6962	2r.50 Type **2726**	25	15
6963	2r.50 European smelt (*Osmerus eperlanus spirinchus*) and European cisco (*Coregonus albula*)	25	15

2728 Moscow Kremlin, Pokrovsky Cathedral and Christmas Tree

2727 Doctors Operating and Medical Equipment

2000. The Twentieth Century (4th series). Technology. Multicoloured.

6964	1r.50 Type **2727**	10	10
6965	1r.50 City skyline (construction)	10	10
6966	1r.50 Bus, car and truck (transport)	10	10
6967	2r. Dam, electricity pylons and generator (engineering)	15	10
6968	2r. Telephones, televisions and rocket and satellite (communication)	15	10
6970	2r. Space stations and rocket (space technology)	15	10
6971	3r. Civil and military airplanes (aviation)	30	15
6972	3r. Steam, diesel and electric trains (rail transport)	30	15
6973	3r. Container ship, sailing ship and cruise liner (sea transport)	30	15
6974	4r. Furnace (metallurgy)	35	15
6975	4r. Oil refinery and truck (oil-refining industry)	35	15
6976	4r. Truck, conveyor and drill (mineral extraction)	35	15

2000. New Millennium.

6977	**2728** 2r. multicoloured	15	10

2729 Emblem

2731 White Tulip ("Happy Birthday")

2000. 80th Anniv of Foreign Intelligence Service.

6978	**2729** 2r.50 multicoloured	25	15

2001. Regions of the Russian Federation (5th issue). As T **2651**. Multicoloured.

6980	3r. Republic of Dagestan	30	15
6981	3r. Republic of Kabardino-Balkaskaya	30	15
6982	3r. Republic of Komi (vert)	30	15
6983	3r. Samara region	30	15
6984	3r. Chita region	30	15

2001. As Nos. 6718/35 but new designs and currency expressed as "P".

6985	10p. mauve and black	90	45
6986	25p. brown and black	2·25	1·10
6987	50p. blue and black	4·50	2·25
6988	100p. mauve and black	9·00	4·50

DESIGNS: 10p. Ballet dancer; 25p. Gymnast; 50p. Globe and computer; 100p. Universal Postal Union emblem.

2001. Greetings Stamps. Tulips. Multicoloured.

7000	2r. Type **2731**	15	10
7001	2r. Deep pink tulips ("With Love")	15	10
7002	2r. Orange tulip ("Good Luck")	15	10
7003	2r. Yellow tulip ("Congratulations")	15	10
7004	2r. Magenta and white tulip ("Be Happy")	15	10

2732 I. A. Galitsin

2001. 300th Birth Anniv of Andrei Matveeich Matveev (artist) (Nos. 7005/6) and 225th Birth Anniv of Vasily Andreevich Tropinin (artist) (Nos. 7007/8). Multicoloured.

7005	3r. Type **2732**	30	15
7006	3r. A. P. Galitsina	30	15
7007	3r. P. A. Bulakhov	30	15
7008	3r. E. I. Karzinkina	30	15

2733 "Senate Square and St. Peter the Great Monument" (B. Patersen)

2001. 300th Anniv of St. Petersburg. Paintings. Multicoloured.

7009	1r. Type **2733**	10	10
7010	2r. "English embankment near Senate" (B. Patersen)	15	10
7011	3r. "Mikhailovsky Castle from Fontanka Embankment" (B. Patersen)	30	15
7012	4r. "River Moika near Stable Department" (A. E. Martynov)	35	15
7013	5r. "Neva from Peter and Paul Fortress" (K. P. Beggrov)	45	20

2734 *Pyrrhosoma numphula* (damselfly)

2001. Damselflies and Dragonflies. Multicoloured.

7014	1r. Type **2734**	10	10
7015	1r.50 *Epitheca bimaculata* (dragonfly)	10	10
7016	2r. Brown aeshna (*Aeschna grandis*)	15	10
7017	3r. *Libellula depressa* (dragonfly)	30	15
7018	5r. *Coenagrion hastulatum* (damselfly)	45	20

2735 Yuri Gagarin, S. P. Korolev (spaceship designer) and Baikonur Launch Site

2001. 40th Anniv of First Manned Space Flight. Multicoloured.

7019	3r. Type **2735**	30	15
7020	3r. Gagarin in uniform	30	15

Nos. 7019/20 were issued together, se-tenant, forming a composite design.

2736 Baikal Lake

2001. Europa. Water Resources.

7021	**2736** 8r. multicoloured	70	35

2737 Emblem

2001. 75th Anniv of International Philatelic Federation.

7022	**2737** 2r.50 multicoloured	25	10

2738 Russian Flag

2001. State Emblems. Multicoloured.

7023	2r.50 Type **2738**	20	10
7024	2r.50 Russian Federation national anthem	20	10
7025	5r. State Arms	40	20

MS7026 Sheet 150 × 00 mm 2r.50 Type **2738**; 2r.50 As No. 7024; 100r. State Arms

The 100r. stamp in No. **MS**7026 has the arms embossed in gold foil.

2739 Map of Russian Federation and State Arms

2001. 11th Anniv of Declaration of State Sovereignty.
7027 **2739** 5r. multicoloured . . . 40 20

2740 Cathedral of the Assumption, Vladimir (1189)

2001. Religious Architecture. Multicoloured.
7028 2r.50 Type **2740** 20 10
7029 2r.50 Cathedral of the Nativity of the Virgin, Zvenigorod (1405) 20 10
7030 2r.50 Cathedral of the Intercession of the Virgin of the Old Belief Community of Rogozhsk, Moscow (1792) 20 10
7031 2r.50 Roman Catholic Church of the Immaculate Conception of the Blessed Virgin Mary, Moscow (1911) 20 10
7032 2r.50 Lutheran Church of St. Peter, St. Petersburg (1838) 20 10
7033 2r.50 Prayer House of the Evangelical Christians (Pentecostal), Lesosibirsk (1999) 20 10
7034 2r.50 Revival Church of Evangelical Christians (Baptist), Bezhitsk, Bryansk (1996) 20 10
7035 2r.50 Church of Seventh Day Adventists, Ryazan (1996) 20 10
7036 2r.50 Armenian Cathedral Surb Khach, Rostov-on-Don (1792) and Monastery of St. Daniel, Moscow (13th-century) . . 20 10
7037 2r.50 First Mosque, Ufa (1830) 20 10
7038 2r.50 Hay Market Mosque, Kazan (1849) 20 10
7039 2r.50 Choral Synagogue, Moscow (1891) 20 10
7040 2r.50 Large Choral Synagogue, St. Petersburg (1893) 20 10
7041 2r.50 Buddhist Soskshin-Dugan, Ivolginsk Datsan (1976) 20 10

2741 "Sokol" (high speed passenger train)

2001. 150th Anniv of St. Petersburg–Moscow Railway. Sheet 90 × 80 mm.
MS7042 **2741** 12r. multicoloured 1·00 50

2742 G. S. Titov (cosmonaut)

2001. 40th Anniv of First Manned Space Flight.
7043 **2742** 3r. multicoloured . . . 25 10

2743 Faina G. Ranevskaya in Cinderella

2001. Cinema Actors. Showing scenes from their films. Multicoloured.
7044 2r.50 Type **2743** 20 10
7045 2r.50 Mikhail I. Zharov in *Peter I* 20 10
7046 2r.50 Lubov P. Orlova in *Circus* 20 10
7047 2r.50 Nikolai A. Kryuchkov in *Tractor Drivers* 20 10
7048 2r.50 Yury V. Nikulin in *Diamond Arm* 20 10
7049 2r.50 Anatoly D. Papanov in *Alive and Dead* 20 10
7050 2r.50 Evgeny P. Leonov in *Stripy Voyage* 20 10
7051 2r.50 Nikolai N. Rybnikov in *Height* 20 10
7052 2r.50 Andrei A. Mironov in *Twelve Chairs* 20 10

2744 Lazarian and Institute

2001. Death Bicentenary of Horhannes Lazarian (founder of Oriental Languages Institute, Moscow).
7053 **2744** 2r.50 multicoloured . . 20 10
A stamp in a similar design was issued by Armenia.

2745 Arkadi Raikin

2746 Children encircling Globe

2001. 90th Birth Anniv of Arkadi I. Raikin (actor).
7054 **2745** 2r. agate and black . . 15 10

2001. United Nations Year of Dialogue among Civilizations.
7055 **2746** 5r. multicoloured . . . 45 25

2747 Vladimir Dal

2001. Birth Bicentenary of Vladimir I. Dal (writer and lexicographer). Sheet 70 × 100 mm.
MS7056 **2747** 10r. multicoloured 1·00 1·00

2748 Court Tower

2001. 10th Anniv of Russian Federation Constitutional Court.
7057 **2748** 3r. multicoloured . . . 30 15

2749 Tsar Nicholas I, St. Petersburg Winter Palace and Coin

2001. 160th Anniv of Savings Bank.
7058 **2749** 2r.20 multicoloured . . 25 15

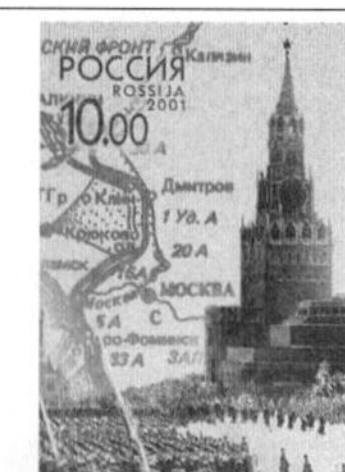

2750 Soldiers, Map and Red Square

2001. 60th Anniv of Battle for Moscow. Sheet 100 × 76 mm.
MS7059 **2750** 10r. multicoloured 1·00 1·00

2751 Union Emblem

2001. 10th Anniv of Union of Independent States.
7060 **2751** 2r. multicoloured . . . 25 10

2752 Father Christmas driving Troika with Three White Horses

2001. "Happy New Year".
7061 **2752** 2r.50 multicoloured . . 30 15

2002. Regions of the Russian Federation (6th issue). As T **2651**. Multicoloured.
7062 3r. Amur region 30 15
7063 3r. Republic of Karachaevo-Cherkeskaya 30 15
7064 3r. Republic of Altai (vert) 30 15
7065 3r. Sakhalin region 30 15
7066 3r. Republic of Khakassiya 30 15

2753 Skiing

2002. Winter Olympic Games, Salt Lake City. Multicoloured.
7067 3r. Type **2753** 30 15
7068 4r. Figure skating 45 20
7069 5r. Ski-jumping 50 25

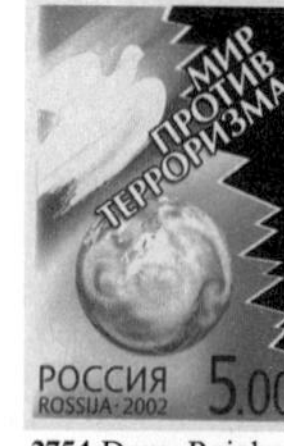

2754 Dove, Rainbow and Globe

2755 Locomotive emerging from Tunnel

2002. "World Unity against Terrorism".
7070 **2754** 5r. multicoloured . . . 55 30

2002. Centenary of Trans-Siberian Railway. Sheet 92 × 73 mm.
MS7071 **2755** 12r. multicoloured 1·30 1·30

2756 "Courtesan" (Hendrick Golzius)

2002. 150th Anniv of New Hermitage Museum, St. Petersburg. Multicoloured.
7072 2r.50 Type **2756** 25 15
7073 2r.50 "Ecco Homo" (Peter Paul Rubens) 25 15
7074 5r. 16th-century Italian Burgonet (helmet) 45 25
7075 5r. The Gonzaga Cameo . . 45 25
MS7076 76 × 106 mm. 12r. "New Hermitage" (Luigi Premazzi) (51 × 48 mm) (horiz) . . . . . 1·30 1·30

2757 Cinnabar Lily ("Congratulations")

2002. Greetings Stamps. Lilies. Multicoloured.
7077 2r.50 Type **2757** 25 15
7078 2r.50 Orange lily ("Happy Birthday") 25 15
7079 2r.50 Pink lily ("Happiness") 25 15
7080 2r.50 Gilded lily ("From our Hearts") 25 15
7081 2r.50 Regal lily ("Love and Joy") 25 15

2758 Cane-Corso

2002. Dogs. Multicoloured.
7082 1r. Type **2758** 15 10
7083 2r. Shar pei 20 10
7084 3r. Bull mastiff 30 15
7085 4r. Brazilian mastiff (*Fila Brasileiro*) 45 25
7086 5r. Neapolitan mastiff . . . 60 30
MS7087 151 × 152 mm. Nos. 7082 × 2, 7083 × 4 and 7085/6 1·60 1·60

2759 Cathedral of Our Lady of Kazan and Marshal Barclay de Tolli Monument

2002. 300th Anniv of St. Petersburg. Multicoloured.
7088 5r. Type **2759** 45 25
7089 5r. St. Isaak Cathedral . . . 45 25
7090 25r. River Neva, St. Peter and Paul Fortress and gilded angel (vert) . . . . 2·20 2·20
7091 25r. Griboedov Canal, Cathedral of the Resurrection and gilded griffin . . . . 2·20 2·20
7092 25r. Gilded ship and Admiralty building . . . 2·20 2·20

2760 Artur Artuzov

2002. Intelligence Agents. Sheet 141 × 91 mm containing T **2760** and similar horiz designs.
MS7093 2r. × 6, Type **2760**; Nikolai Demidenko; Jan Olsky; Sergei Putzitsky; Vladimir Styrne; Grigory Syroezhkin . . . . . 1·40 1·40

2761 Juggler, Trapeze Artist and Clown

2002. Europa. Circus.
7094 **2761** 8r. multicoloured . . . 90 45

2762 Pavel Nakhimov

2002. Birth Bicentenary of Pavel S. Nakhimov (naval commander).
7095 **2762** 2r. multicoloured . . . 25 15

2763 Congress Emblem

2002. 5th Eurosai (European Organization of Supreme Audit Institutions) Congress, Moscow.
7096 **2763** 2r. multicoloured . . . 25 15

2764 Geysers

2002. Volcanoes of Kamchatka Region. Multicoloured.
7097 1r. Type **2764** 10 10
7098 2r. Caldera, Uzon volcano 25 15
7099 3r. Karymsky volcano . . . 70 35
7100 5r. Troitsky acid lake, Maly Semyachic volcano . . . 45 25

2765 Russian Carriage (c. 1640)

2002. Horse-drawn Carriages. Multicoloured.
7101 2r.50 Type **2765** 25 15
7102 2r.50 Enclosed sleigh, Moscow (1732) 25 15
7103 5r. Coupe carriage, Berlin (1746) 45 25
7104 5r. English carriage (c. 1770) 45 25
7105 5r. St. Petersburg Berline type carriage (1769) . . . 45 25
MS7106 151 × 71 mm. 25r. × 3 Nos. 7103/5 . . . . 1·80 1·80

2766 Helicopter KA-10

2002. Birth Centenary of Nikolai Kamov (helicopter designer and manufacturer). Multicoloured.
7107 1r. Type **2766** 10 10
7108 1r.50 KA-22 . . . . 15 10
7109 2r. KA-26 . . . . 25 15
7110 2r.50 Navy helicopter KA-27 . . . . 25 15
7111 5r. Army helicopter KA-50 Black Shark 45 25

2767 Anatoli Sobchak

2768 Demoiselle Crane (*Anthropoides virgo*)

2002. 65th Birth Anniv of Anatoli Sobchak (reformer and mayor of St. Petersburg).
7112 **2767** 3r.25 multicoloured . . 30 15

2002. Endangered Species. Birds. Multicoloured.
7113 2r.50 Type **2768** 30 15
7114 2r.50 Great black-headed gull (Pallas' Gull) (*Larus ichthyaetus Pallas*) 30 15
Stamps of the same design were issued by Kazakhstan.

2769 City and Emblem

2002. 850th Anniv of Kostroma.
7115 **2769** 2r. multicoloured . . . 25 15

2770 Ministry of Internal Affairs

2002. Bicentenary of Government Ministries. Multicoloured.
7116 3r. Type **2770** 30 15
7117 3r. Palace Square, Alexander column, St. Petersburg and Ministry of Foreign Affairs building, Moscow 30 15
7118 3r. Church, Ministry of Defence building and state emblem (foreground) . . 30 15
7119 3r. Educational symbols and Moscow State University building 30 15
7120 3r. State emblem (centre) and Ministry of Finance building 30 15
7121 3r. Justice (statue), column, flag and state emblem (right) (Ministry of Justice) 30 15

2771 Census Emblem surrounded by People

2772 Russian Millenary Monument, Novgorod

2002. National Census. Multicoloured. (a) Self-adhesive.
7122 3r. Type **2771** 25 10

(b) Ordinary gum.
7123 4r. Census emblem 30 15

2002. 1140th Anniv of Russian State.
7124 **2772** 3r. multicoloured . . . 30 15

2773 Custom House, Archangelsk (19th-century engraving)

2002. Custom and Excise Service. Sheet 117 × 137 mm containing T **2773** and similar horiz designs. Multicoloured.
MS7125 2r. Type **2773**; 3r. Custom officers on horseback, St. Petersburg; 5r. Customs warehouse, Kalanchovsky Square 1·00 1·00

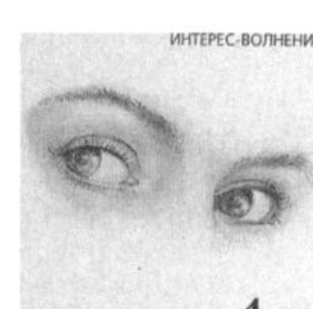

2774 The Motherland (statue)

2775 Eyes

2002. 60th Anniv of Battle for Stalingrad. Sheet 101 × 75 mm.
MS7126 **2774** 10r. multicoloured 95 95

2002. Eyes. Sheet 181 × 107 mm containing T **2775** and similar square designs. Multicoloured.
MS7127 1r.50 × 10 Ten different stamps showing eye . . . . . 1·50 1·50

2776 Emperor Alexander I, Neva River and St. Peter and Paul Cathedral

2778 Snowman on Skis

2777 Saint Daniel Monastery, Moscow (1282)

2002. History of Russian State. Alexander I. Multicoloured.
7128 4r. Type **2776** 40 20
7129 4r. N. M. Karamzin (author, History of State) and Alexander I 40 20
7130 7r. M. Speransky handing plan for Code of Law to Alexander I 70 35
7131 7r. Alexander I entering Paris, 1814 . . . . 70 35
MS7132 66 × 91 mm. 10r. Alexander I 95 95

2002. Monasteries (1st series). Multicoloured.
7133 5r. Type **2777** 55 25
7134 5r. Holy Trinity Monastery, Sergiev Posad (1337) . . . 55 25
7135 5r. Transfiguration of Our Saviour Monastery, Valaam (14th-century) . . 55 25
7136 5r. Rev. Savva of Storozha Monastery, Zvenigorod (1398) 55 25
7137 5r. Monastery of the Holy Assumption, Pechory (1470) 55 25
See also Nos. 7168/73.

2002. "Happy New Year".
7138 **2778** 3r.50 multicoloured . . 35 15

2779 *Artemis with Deer* (sculpture) and Palace, Arkhangelkoe

2002. Palaces and Parks. Multicoloured. Self-adhesive.
7139 2r. Type **2779** 25 10
7140 2r.50 *Omphala* (sculpture) Chinese Palace, Oranienbaum 35 15
7141 3r. *Gryphon* (sculpture) and mansion, Marfino 40 20
7142 4r. *Erminia* (sculpture) and palace, Pavlovsk 45 25
7143 5r. Scamander river (allegorical sculpture) and palace, Kuskovo 55 30

2780 I. V. Kurchatov and Nuclear Reactor

2003. Physicists' Birth Centenaries. Multicoloured.
7150 2r.50 Type **2780** 30 15
7151 2r.50 A. P. Alexandrov, reactor and *Arktica* (nuclear-powered ice-breaker) 30 15

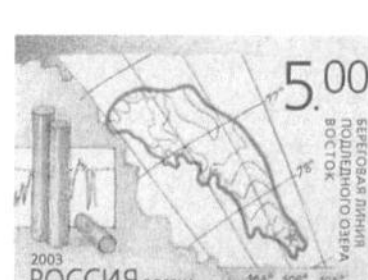

2781 Map, Lake Contours and Ice Cores

2003. International Antarctic Lake Survey. Sheet 90 × 65 mm containing T **2781** and similar horiz design. Multicoloured.
MS7152 5r. Type **2781**; 5r. Vostok polar station and drilling rig 1·00 1·00

2003. Regions of the Russian Federation (7th issue). As T **2651**. Multicoloured.
7153 3r. Kemerovo region . . . 30 15
7154 3r. Kurgan region 30 15
7155 3r. Astrakhan region (vert) 30 15
7156 3r. Magadan region 30 15
7157 3r. Perm region 30 15
7158 3r. Ulijanovsk region . . . 30 15

2782 Organization Emblem

2003. 10th Anniv of Intergovernmental Communications Courier Service.
7159 **2782** 3r. multicoloured . . . 25 10

2783 Russian Tennis Fans

2003. Russia, Winner of Davis Cup, 2002. Multicoloured.
7160 4r. Type **2783** 30 15
7161 8r. Flags, net and ball . . . 55 25
MS7162 125 × 91 mm. 50r. Davis Cup . . . . 3·50 3·50

2784 Building Yaroslavl Fortress, Yaroslav the Wise and Crowd

2003. History of Russian State. Princes. Multicoloured.
7163 8r. Type **2784** 75 40
7164 8r. Entering Kiev, Vladimir Monomach and Vladimir giving "Admonition" . . 75 40
7165 8r. Riding with army, Daniel of Moscow and founding St. Daniel monastery 75 40
7166 8r. Inauguration, Ivan Ivanovich of Moscow and Golden Horde 75 40

2785 Alexander Nevsky Cathedral, Peter I (statue) and Karelia Postal Building

2003. 300th Anniv of Petrozavodsk City.
7167 **2785** 3r. multicoloured . . . 35 25

2003. Monasteries (2nd series). As T **2777**. Multicoloured.
7168 5r. Yuriev Monastery, Novgorod (1030) 55 30
7169 5r. Tolgsky Nunnery (1314) 55 30
7170 5r. Kozelsk Optina Pustyn Monastery (14th–15th century) 55 30
7171 5r. Solovetsky Zosima and Savvatii Monastery, Zvenigorod (14th century) 55 30
7172 5r. Novodevichy Nunnery, Smolensk (1524) 55 30
7173 5r. Seraphim Nunnery, Diveeyevo, Nizhny Novgorod (1780) 55 30

2786 State Theatre, Youth Theatre, Statue and Novosibirsk Science Academy Emblem

2003. Centenary of Novosibirsk City.
7174 **2786** 3r. multicoloured . . . 35 25

2787 "Capture of Swedish Ships Gedan and Astrild, Neva Delta, May 7, 1703" (painting, L. Blinov)

2003. 300th Anniv of Baltic Fleet. Sheet 90 × 129 mm.
MS7175 **2787** 12r. multicoloured 1·20 1·20

2788 Aram Khachaturyan and *Spartacus* (ballet)

2003. Birth Centenary of Aram I. Katchaturyan (composer).
7176 **2788** 2r.50 multicoloured . . 25 15

2789 "My first Steps for Einem Biscuits"

2003. Europa. Poster Art.
7177 **2789** 8r. multicoloured . . . 75 35

2790 Bells of St. Rumbold's Cathedral, Maline

2003. 150th Anniv of Belgium–Russia Diplomatic Relations. Multicoloured.
7178 5r. Type **2790** 55 30
7179 5r. Bells of St. Peter and Paul's Cathedral, St. Petersburg 55 30
Nos. 7178/9 were issued together, se-tenant, forming a composite design.
Stamps of the same design were issued by Belgium.

2791 Anichkov Bridge over Fontanka River

2003. 300th Anniv of St. Petersburg. Multicoloured.
7180 5r. Type **2791** 55 30
7181 5r. Raised bridge on Neva river 55 30
7182 5r. Central Naval Museum, Vasilievsky Island 55 30
7183 5r. Palace Square 55 30
7184 5r. Winter Palace 55 30
7185 5r. Summer Gardens . . . 55 30
MS7186 3 sheets, each 165 × 70 mm. (a) 50r. The Bronze Horseman (statue, E. Falkonet) (38 × 51 mm); (b) 75r. As **MS**7186a (38 × 51 mm) (23.5); (c) 100r. As **MS**7186a (38 × 51 mm) . . . . 4·25 4·25

2792 Earth, Vostok Flight Paths and Valentina Tereshkova

2003. 40th Anniv of First Female Cosmonaut (Valentina V. Tereshkova).
7187 **2792** 3r. multicoloured . . . 35 25

2793 Globe and Emblem

2003. 2nd International "21st-century without Drugs" Conference, Moscow.
7188 **2793** 3r. multicoloured . . . 35 25

2794 Pskov Kremlin and Mirozhsky Monastery Cathedral

2003. 1100th Anniv of Pskov City.
7189 **2794** 3r. multicoloured . . . 35 25

2795 Town Arms and Andrey Dubensky Monument

2003. 375th Anniv of Krasnoyarsk City.
7190 **2795** 4r. multicoloured . . . 40 20

2796 5r. Coin and Industrial Scene

2003. Transparent Economy Legislation.
7191 **2796** 5r. multicoloured . . . 45 25

2797 Belfry, Prokhorovka and Triumphal Arch, Kursk

2003. 60th Anniv of Battle for Kursk. Sheet 100 × 75 mm.
MS7192 **2797** 10r. multicoloured 95 50

2798 Stone Pillars, Manpupuner Mountains

2003. UNESCO World Heritage Sites. Komi Virgin Forest. Multicoloured.
7193 2r. Type **2798** 25 15
7194 3r. Kozhim river 35 25
7195 5r. Pechora river 45 25

2799 Tsar Peter I receiving Letter from Count Aspraksin, Voronezh

2003. 300th Anniv of St. Petersburg Post. Sheet 103 × 95 mm.
MS7196 **2799** 12r. multicoloured 1·20 1·20

2800 Stag Beetle (*Lucanus cervus*)

2003. Beetles. Multicoloured.
7197 1r. Type **2800** 10 10
7198 2r. Caterpillar hunter (*Calosoma sycophanta*) . . 20 15
7199 3r. *Carabus lopatini* 35 25
7200 4r. *Carabus costricticollis* . . 35 25
7201 5r. *Carabus caucasicus* . . . 45 25

2801 Association Emblem

2003. 10th Anniv of International Association of Science Academies.
7202 **2801** 2r.50 multicoloured . . 20 15

2802 Archangel Mikhail Church, Transbaikalia Rail Building, Shumovs Palace and Post Building

2003. 350th Anniv of Chita, Eastern Siberia.
7203 **2802** 3r. multicoloured . . . 35 25

2803 Icebergs and Climate Zones Map

2003. World Climate Change Conference, Moscow.
7204 **2803** 4r. multicoloured . . . 40 20

2804 Satan's Bolete (*Boletus satanas*) (poisonous) and Oak Mushroom (*Boletus luridus*) (edible)

2003. Fungi. Edible and poisonous fungi. Multicoloured.
7205 2r. Type **2804** 20 15
7206 2r.50 Death cap (*Amanita phalloides*) (poisonous) and Field mushroom (*Agricus campestris*) (edible) 20 15
7207 3r. The panther (*Amanita pantherina*) (poisonous) and The blusher (*Amanita rubescens*) (edible) 35 25
7208 4r. *Amanita porphyria* (poisonous) and Grisette (*Amanita vaginata*) (edible) 40 20
7209 5r. Bitter bolete (*Tylopilus fellus*) (poisonous) and edible mushroom (*Boletus edulis*) (edible) 45 25

2805 Pineapple

2003. Fruits. Multicoloured.
7210 5r. Type **2805** 45 25
7211 5r. Strawberries 45 25
7212 5r. Apples 45 25
7213 5r. Pear 45 25
7214 5r. Melon 45 25
Nos. 7210/14 were each perforated in a circle within an outer perforated square and impregnated with the scent of the fruit pictured.

2806 Caspian Seal (*Phoca caspia*)

2003. Preservation of the Caspian Sea. Multicoloured.
7215 2r.50 Type **2806** 20 15
7216 2r.50 Beluga (*Huso huso*) . . 20 15
Stamps of a similar design were issued by Iran.

2807 18th-century Printing Works and *Vedomosti* (newspaper)

2003. 300th Anniv of Russian Journalism. Sheet 90 × 65 mm.
MS7217 **2807** 10r. multicoloured 95 50

2808 Russo-Balt K 12/20 (1911)

2003. Russian Cars. Multicoloured.
7218 3r. Type **2808** 35 25
7219 4r. Nami 1 (1929) 40 20
7220 4r. Gaz M1 (1939) 40 20
7221 5r. Gaz 67b (1946) 45 25
7222 5r. Gaz M20 "Pobeda" (1954) 45 25

EXPRESS STAMPS

E **171** Motor Cyclist

1932. Inscr "EXPRES".
E588 E **171** 5k. sepia . . . . . . 5·00 2·25
E589 – 10k. purple . . . . . 8·50 3·50
E590 – 80k. green . . . . . 35·00 14·00
DESIGNS—HORIZ: 10k. Express motor van; 80k. Class Ta steam locomotive.

E **173** Polar Region and Kalinin K-4 Airplane over Ice-breaker "Taimyr"

1932. Air Express. 2nd Int Polar Year and Franz Joseph's Land to Archangel Flight.
E591 E **173** 50k. red . . . . . . 42·00 18·00
E592 1r. green . . . . . . 60·00 20·00

POSTAGE DUE STAMPS

(D 96) (D 99)

1924. Surch as Type D **96**.

D401b	**45**	1k. on 35k. blue	20	30
D402b		3k. on 35k. blue	20	30
D403b		5k. on 35k. blue	20	30
D404		8k. on 35k. blue	50	50
D405b		10k. on 35k. blue	30	60
D406b		12k. on 70k. brown	20	40
D407c		14k. on 35k. blue	20	40
D408b		32k. on 35k. blue	90	90
D409c		40k. on 35k. blue	1·00	90

1924. Optd with Type D **99**.

D421	**48**	1k. on 100r. yellow	4·50	10·00

D 104

1925.

D464	D **104**	1k. red	25	30
D465		2k. mauve	25	30
D466		3k. blue	25	30
D467		7k. yellow	35	30
D468		8k. green	35	30
D469		10k. blue	40	50
D470		14k. brown	60	70

RUSSIAN POST OFFICES IN CHINA Pt. 17

Russian Post Offices were opened in various towns in Manchuria and China from 1870 onwards.

1899. 100 kopeks = 1 rouble.
1917. 100 cents = 1 dollar (Chinese).

КИТАЙ

(1)

1899. Arms types (with thunderbolts) of Russia optd with T **1**.

1	**9**	1k. orange	40	40
2		2k. green	50	40
3		3k. red	50	35
9	**14**	4k. red	3·00	1·50
4	**9**	5k. purple	65	50
5		7k. blue	70	50
6	**14**	10k. blue	75	50
30	**10**	14k. red and blue	75	1·75
31		15k. blue and brown	45	1·00
32	**14**	20k. red and blue	40	1·25
33	**10**	25k. violet and green	65	2·25
34		35k. green and purple	70	1·25
35	**14**	50k. green and purple	85	1·25
36	**10**	70k. orange and brown	60	1·50
37	**15**	1r. orange and brown	1·50	1·50
20	**11**	3r.50 grey and black	9·00	10·00
21	**20**	5r. blue and green on green	6·75	6·50
22	**11**	7r. yellow and black	12·00	11·00
23	**20**	10r. grey and red on yellow	55·00	55·00

1910. Arms types of Russia optd with T **1**.

24	**22**	1k. orange	35	60
25		2k. green	40	60
26		3k. red	30	35
27	**23**	4k. red	25	50
28	**22**	7k. blue	35	65
29	**23**	10k. blue	35	50

1917. Arms types of Russia surch in "cents" and "dollars" diagonally in one line.

42	**22**	1c. on 1k. orange	50	3·50
43		2c. on 2k. green	50	3·50
44		3c. on 3k. red	60	3·50
45	**23**	4c. on 4k. red	50	3·25
46	**22**	5c. on 5k. lilac	90	3·00
47	**23**	10c. on 10k. blue	60	3·00
48	**10**	14c. on 14k. red and blue	2·00	5·00
49		15c. on 15k. blue and purple	1·50	3·75
50	**14**	20c. on 20k. red and blue	1·75	3·50
51	**10**	25c. on 25k. violet and green	1·75	5·00
52		35c. on 35k. green & purple	1·75	6·50
53	**14**	50c. on 50k. green & purple	1·50	5·50
54	**10**	70c. on 70k. orange & brn	1·50	6·50
55	**15**	1d. on 1r. orge & brn on brn	1·50	7·00
39	**10**	3d.50 on 3r.50 grey & blk	10·00	14·00
40	**20**	5d. on 5r. bl & dp bl on grn	7·50	16·00
41	**11**	7d. on 7r. yellow and black	5·00	13·00
57	**20**	10d. on 10r. grey & red on yell	38·00	55·00

1920. Arms types of Russia surch in "cents" in two lines. Perf or imperf.

65	**22**	1c. on 1k. orange	16·00	25·00
59		2c. on 2k. green	6·00	15·00
60		3c. on 3k. red	6·00	15·00
61	**23**	4c. on 4k. red	16·00	22·00
62	**22**	5c. on 5k. lilac	18·00	28·00
63	**23**	10c. on 10k. blue	60·00	60·00
64	**22**	10c. on 10k. on 7k. blue	60·00	65·00

RUSSIAN POST OFFICES IN CRETE Pt. 3

(RETHYMNON PROVINCE)

The Russian Postal Service operated from 1 May to 29 July 1899.

4 metallik = 1 grosion (Turkish piastre).

These issues were optd with circular control marks as shown on Types R **3/4**. Prices are for stamps with these marks, but unused examples without them are known.

R 1

R 2

1899. Imperf.

R1	R **1**	1m. blue	45·00	12·00
R2	R **2**	1m. green	5·00	3·50
R3		2m. red	£150	£120
R4		2m. green	5·00	3·50

R 3

R 4

1899. Without stars in oval.

R 5	R **3**	1m. pink	55·00	35·00
R 6		2m. pink	55·00	35·00
R 7		1g. pink	55·00	35·00
R 8		1m. blue	55·00	35·00
R 9		2m. blue	55·00	35·00
R10		1g. blue	55·00	35·00
R11		1m. green	55·00	35·00
R12		2m. green	55·00	35·00
R13		1g. green	55·00	35·00
R14		1m. red	55·00	35·00
R15		2m. red	55·00	35·00
R16		1g. red	55·00	35·00
R17		1m. orange	55·00	35·00
R18		2m. orange	55·00	35·00
R19		1g. orange	55·00	35·00
R20		1m. yellow	55·00	35·00
R21		2m. yellow	55·00	35·00
R22		1g. yellow	55·00	35·00
R23		1m. black	£550	£550
R24		2m. black	£550	£550
R25		1g. black	£475	£475

1899. Starred at each side.

R26	R **4**	1m. pink	35·00	25·00
R27		2m. pink	11·00	3·25
R28		1g. pink	4·00	4·25
R29		1m. blue	18·00	10·00
R30		2m. blue	5·00	3·25
R31		1g. blue	4·00	4·25
R32		1m. green	14·00	10·00
R33		2m. green	5·00	3·25
R34		1g. green	4·00	4·25
R35		1m. red	14·00	10·00
R36		2m. red	5·00	3·25
R37		1g. red	4·00	2·25

RUSSIAN POST OFFICES IN TURKISH EMPIRE Pt. 16

General issues for Russian P.O.s in the Turkish Empire and stamps specially overprinted for use at particular offices.

1863. 100 kopeks = 1 rouble.
1900. 40 paras = 1 piastre.

1 Inscription = "Dispatch under Wrapper to the East"

1863. Imperf.

2a	**1**	6k. blue	£190	£1100

2

3

1865. Imperf.

4	**2**	(10pa.) brown and blue	£500	£400
5	**3**	(2pi.) blue and red	£700	£450

4

5

1865. Imperf.

6	**4**	(10pa.) red and blue	24·00	38·00
7	**5**	(2pi.) blue and red	35·00	45·00

The values of 4/7 were 10pa. (or 2k.) and 2pi. (or 20k.).

6 Inscription = "Eastern Correspondence"

12

1868. Perf.

14	**6**	1k. brown	8·00	4·50
11		3k. green	22·00	13·00
16		5k. blue	5·50	3·25
17a		10k. red and green	4·00	3·25

See also Nos. 26/35.

1876. Surch with large figures of value.

24	**6**	7k. on 10k. red and green	65·00	50·00
22		8k. on 10k. red and green	65·00	60·00

1879.

26	**6**	1k. black and yellow	2·25	1·25
32		1k. orange	50	35
27		2k. black and red	3·00	1·75
33		2k. green	50	35
34		5k. purple	1·25	1·00
28		7k. red and grey	4·50	1·10
35		7k. blue	85	35

1900. Arms types of Russia surch in "PARA" or "PIASTRES".

37	**9**	4pa. on 1k. orange	15	10
50	**22**	5pa. on 1k. orange	10	15
38	**9**	10pa. on 2k. green	40	25
51	**22**	10pa. on 2k. green	10	15
201		15pa. on 3k. red	20	5·00
41	**14**	20pa. on 4k. red	40	40
52	**23**	20pa. on 4k. red	10	15
42	**9**	20pa. on 5k. purple	40	40
181	**22**	20pa. on 5k. purple	10	15
43	**14**	1pi. on 10k. blue	20	20
53	**23**	1pi. on 10k. blue	10	15
182	**10**	1½pi. on 15k. blue & purple	15	20
183	**14**	2pi. on 20k. red and blue	15	20
184	**10**	2½pi. on 25k. violet & green	15	20
185		3½pi. on 35k. green & pur	20	30
54	**14**	5pi. on 50k. green and lilac	50	75
55	**10**	7pi. on 70k. orange & brn	70	90
56	**15**	10pi. on 1r. orange and brown on brown	80	1·10
48	**11**	35pi. on 3r.50 grey & blk	6·00	6·00
202	**20**	50pi. on 5r. blue on green	3·25	80·00
49	**11**	70pi. on 7r. yellow & black	9·00	9·00
203	**20**	100pi. on 10r. grey and red on yellow	14·00	£275

1909. As T **14**, **15**, and **11** of Russia, but ship and date in centre as T **12**, and surch in "paras" or "piastres".

57	**14**	5pa. on 1k. orange	20	30
58		10pa. on 2k. green	30	40
59		20pa. on 4k. red	60	75
60		1pi. on 10k. blue	70	1·10
61		5pi. on 50k. green & purple	1·25	2·50
62		7pi. on 70k. orange & brn	2·50	3·75
63	**15**	10pi. on 1r. orange & brown	3·75	6·50
64	**11**	35pi. on 3r.50 green & pur	9·00	35·00
65		70pi. on 7r. pink and green	26·00	55·00

The above stamps exist overprinted for Constantinople, Jaffa, Jerusalem, Kerassunde, Mount Athos, Salonika, Smyrna, Trebizonde, Beyrouth, Dardanelles, Mytilene and Rizeh. For full list see Part 10 (Russia) of the Stanley Gibbons Catalogue.

1913. Nos. 126/42 (Romanov types) of Russia surch.

186	5pa. on 1k. orange	40	40
187	10pa. on 3k. green	40	40
188	15pa. on 3k. red	40	40
189	20pa. on 4k. red	40	40
190	1pi. on 10k. blue	40	40
191	1½pi. on 15k. brown	60	60
192	2pi. on 20k. green	70	70
193	2½pi. on 25k. purple	1·00	1·00
194	3½pi. on 35k. green and violet	2·00	2·00
195	5pi. on 50k. grey and brown	2·25	2·25
196	7pi. on 70k. brown and green	7·00	17·00
197	10pi. on 1r. green	8·00	17·00
198	20pi. on 2r. brown	3·25	5·50
199	30pi. on 3r. violet	4·50	£170
200	50pi. on 5r. brown	90·00	£475

RWANDA Pt. 14

An independent republic established in July 1962, formerly part of Ruanda-Urundi.

100 centimes = 1 franc.

1 Pres. Kayibanda and Map

1962. Independence.

1	**1**	10c. sepia and green	10	10
2	–	40c. sepia and purple	10	10
3	**1**	1f. sepia and blue	70	35
4	–	1f.50 sepia and brown	10	10
5	**1**	3f.50 sepia and orange	10	10
6	–	6f.50 sepia and blue	15	10
7	**1**	10f. sepia and olive	30	15
8	–	20f. sepia and red	60	30

DESIGN: Nos. 2, 4, 6, 8 are as Type **1** but with halo around Rwanda on map in place of "R".

1963. Admission to U.N. No. 204 of Ruanda-Urundi with coloured frame obliterating old inscr (colours below), and surch **Admission a l'O.N.U. 18-9-1962 REPUBLIQUE RWANDAISE** and new value.

9	3f.50 on 3f. grey	10	10
10	6f.50 on 3f. pink	1·10	90
11	10f. on 3f. blue	25	25
12	20f. on 3f. silver	40	40

1963. Flowers issue of Ruanda-Urundi (Nos. 178 etc) optd **REPUBLIQUE RWANDAISE** or surch also in various coloured panels over old inscription and values. Flowers in natural colours.

13	25c. orange and green	20	20
14	40c. salmon and green	20	20
15	60c. purple and green	20	20
16	1f.25 blue and green	90	90
17	1f.50 green and violet	90	90
18	2f. on 1f.50 green and violet	1·40	1·10
19	4f. on 1f.50 green and violet	1·40	1·10
20	5f. green and purple	1·40	1·10
21	7f. brown and green	1·40	1·10
22	10f. olive and purple	1·75	1·50

The coloured panels are in various shades of silver except No. 19 which is in blue.

4 Ears of Wheat and Native Implements

1963. Freedom from Hunger.

23	**4**	2f. brown and green	10	10
24		4f. mauve and blue	10	10
25		7f. red and grey	20	10
26		10f. green and yellow	75	55

5 Coffee

6 Postal Services Emblem

5a "Post and Telecommunications"

1963. 1st Anniv of Independence.

27	**5**	10c. brown and blue	10	10
28	–	20c. yellow and blue	10	10
29	–	30c. green and orange	10	10
30	**5**	40c. brown and turquoise	10	10
31	–	1f. yellow and purple	10	10
32	–	2f. green and blue	80	45
33	**5**	4f. brown and red	10	10

34 – 7f. yellow and green 20 15
35 – 10f. green and violet 35 30
DESIGNS: 20c., 1, 7f. Bananas; 30c., 2, 10f. Tea.

1963. 2nd Anniv of African and Malagasy Posts and Telcommunications Union.
36 **5a** 14f. multicoloured . . . . . 1·10 90

1963. Admission of Rwanda to U.P.U.
37 **6** 50c. blue and pink 10 10
38 1f.50 brown and blue 65 45
39 3f. purple and grey 10 10
40 20f. green and yellow 45 20

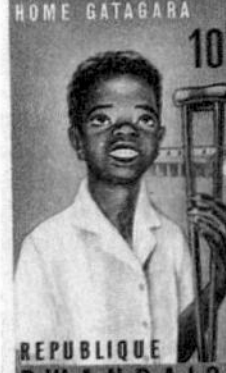

7 Emblem **8** Child Care

1963. 15th Anniv of Declaration of Human Rights.
41 **7** 5f. red 15 10
42 6f. violet 50 35
43 10f. blue 35 15

1963. Red Cross Centenary.
44 **8** 10c. multicoloured 10 10
45 – 20c. multicoloured 10 10
46 – 30c. multicoloured 10 10
47 – 40c. brown, red and violet . . 10 10
48 **8** 2f. multicoloured 80 60
49 – 7f. multicoloured 15 10
50 – 10f. brown, red and brown 20 15
51 – 20f. brown, red and orange 60 35
DESIGNS—HORIZ: 20c., 7f. Patient having blood test; 40, 20c. Stretcher party. VERT: 30c., 10f. Doctor examining child.

9 Map and Hydraulic Pump **10** Boy with Crutch

1964. World Meteorological Day.
52 **9** 3f. sepia, blue and green . . 10 10
53 7f. sepia, blue and red . . . 35 20
54 10f. sepia, blue and orange 50 35

1964. Stamps of Ruanda-Urundi optd **REPUBLIQUE RWANDAISE** or surch also in black over coloured metallic panels obliterating old inscription or value.
55 10c. on 20c. (No. 204) 10 10
56 20c. (No. 204) 10 10
57 30c. on 1f.50 (No. 208) . . . 10 10
58 40c. (No. 205) 10 10
59 50c. (No. 206) 10 10
60 1f. (No. 207) 10 10
61 2f. (No. 209) 10 10
62 3f. (No. 210) 10 10
63 4f. on 3f.50 on 3f. (No. 228) 20 10
64 5f. (No. 211) 20 10
65 7f.50 on 6f.50 (No. 212) . . . 45 15
66 8f. (No. 213) . . . . 4·50 2·25
67 10f. (No. 214) 65 20
68 20f. (No. 229) . . . . 1·10 45
69 50f. (No. 230) . . . . 2·10 85

1964. Gatagara Re-education Centre.
70 **10** 10c. sepia and violet 10 10
71 – 40c. sepia and blue 10 10
72 – 4f. sepia and brown 10 10
73 **10** 7f.50 sepia and green . . . 35 15
74 – 8f. sepia and bistre . . . . 1·40 95
75 – 10f. sepia and purple . . . 45 20
DESIGNS—HORIZ: 40c., 8f. Children operating sewing machines. VERT: 4, 10f. Crippled child on crutches.

11 Running

1964. Olympic Games, Tokyo. Sportsmen in slate.
76 **11** 10c. blue 10 10
77 – 20c. red 10 10
78 – 30c. turquoise 10 10
79 – 40c. brown 10 10
80 **11** 4f. blue 10 10
81 – 5f. green . . . . 1·40 1·25
82 – 20f. purple 35 35
83 – 50f. grey . . . . 1·10 90
DESIGNS—VERT: 20c., 5f. Basketball; 40c., 50f. Football. HORIZ: 20f. High-jumping.

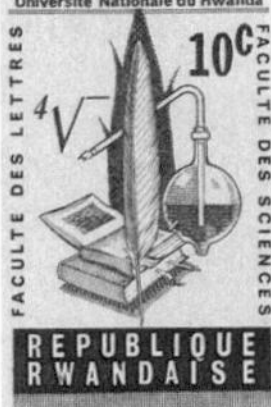

12 Faculties of "Letters" and "Sciences" **13** Abraham Lincoln

1965. National University. Multicoloured.
84 10c. Type **12** 10 10
85 20c. Student with microscope and building ("Medicine") (horiz) 10 10
86 30c. Scales of Justice, Hand of Law ("Social Sciences" and "Normal High School") 10 10
87 40c. University buildings (horiz) . . 10 10
88 5f. Type **12** 10 10
89 7f. As 20c. 15 10
90 10f. As 30c. . . . . . 1·00 85
91 12f. As 40c. 30 15

1965. Death Centenary of Abraham Lincoln.
92 **13** 10c. green and red 10 10
93 20c. brown and blue 10 10
94 30c. violet and red 10 10
95 40c. blue and brown 10 10
96 9f. brown and purple . . . 20 15
97 40f. purple and green . . . 1·90 70

14 Marabou Storks **15** "Telstar" Satellite

1965. Kagera National Park. Multicoloured.
98 10c. Type **14** 30 15
99 20c. Common zebras 10 10
100 30c. Impalas 10 10
101 40c. Crowned cranes, hippopotami and cattle egrets 30 15
102 1f. African buffaloes 10 10
103 3f. Hunting dogs 10 10
104 5f. Yellow baboons . . . . . 4·25 1·10
105 10f. African elephant and map 20 15
106 40f. Reed cormorants and African darters . . . . 1·75 50
107 100f. Lions . . . . 2·25 50
SIZES—As Type **14**: VERT: 30c., 2, 5f. HORIZ: 20, 40c., 3, 10f. LARGER (45 × 25½ mm); 40, 100f.

1965. Centenary of I.T.U. Multicoloured.
108 10c. Type **15** 10 10
109 40c. "Syncom" satellite . . . 10 10
110 4f.50 Type **15** . . . . 1·40 50
111 50f. "Syncom" satellite . . . 90 35

16 "Colotis aurigineus" **17** Cattle and I.C.Y. Emblem

1965. Rwanda Butterflies. Multicoloured.
112 10c. "Papilio bromius" . . . 15 20
113 15c. "Papilio hesperus" . . . 15 20
114 20c. Type **16** 15 20
115 30c. "Amphicallia pactolicus" 15 20
116 35c. "Lobobunaea phaedusa" 15 20
117 40c. "Papilio jacksoni ruandana" 15 20
118 1f.50 "Papilio dardanus" . . 15 20
119 3f. "Amaurina elliotti" . . . 4·25 1·25
120 4f. "Colias electo pseudohecate" . . . . . . 2·75 1·00
121 10f. "Bunaea alcinoe" . . . 55 30
122 50f. "Athletes gigas" . . . . 1·75 85
123 100f. "Charaxes ansorgei R" 3·50 1·25
The 10, 30, 35c., 3, 4 and 100f. are vert.

1965. International Co-operation Year.
124 **17** 10c. green and yellow . . . 10 10
125 – 40c. brown, blue and green 10 10
126 – 4f.50 green, brown & yell 1·10 50
127 – 45f. purple and brown . . 90 40
DESIGNS: 40c. Crater lake and giant plants; 4f.50, Gazelle and candelabra tree; 45f. Mt. Ruwenzori. Each with I.C.Y. emblem.

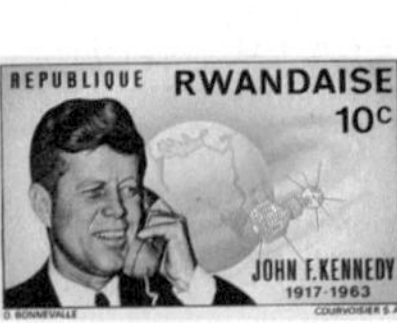

18 Pres. Kennedy, Globe and Satellites **19** Madonna and Child

1965. 2nd Anniv of Pres. Kennedy's Death.
128 **18** 10c. brown and green . . . 10 10
129 40c. brown and red 10 10
130 50c. brown and blue . . . 10 10
131 1f. brown and olive 10 10
132 8f. brown and violet . . . 1·75 1·10
133 50f. brown and grey . . . 1·10 90

1965. Christmas.
134 **19** 10c. green and gold 10 10
135 40c. brown and gold . . . 10 10
136 50c. blue and gold 10 10
137 4f. black and gold 70 65
138 6f. violet and gold 15 10
139 30f. brown and gold . . . 65 45

20 Father Damien

1966. World Leprosy Day.
140 **20** 10c. blue and brown . . . 10 10
141 – 40c. red and blue 10 10
142 **20** 4f.50 slate and green . . . 20 15
143 – 45f. brown and red . . . . 1·75 1·25
DESIGNS: 40c., 45f. Dr. Schweitzer.

21 Pope Paul, Rome and New York

1966. Pope Paul's Visit to U.N. Organization.
144 **21** 10c. blue and brown . . . 10 10
145 – 40c. indigo and blue . . . 10 10
146 **21** 4f.50 blue and purple . . . 1·60 1·00
147 – 50f. blue and green . . . . 1·00 55
DESIGN: 40c., 50f. Pope Paul, Arms and U.N. emblem.

22 "Echinops amplexicaulis" and "E. bequaertii"

1966. Flowers. Multicoloured.
148 10c. Type **22** 10 10
149 20c. "Haemanthus multiflorus" (vert) 10 10
150 30c. "Helichrysum erici-rosenii" 10 10
151 40c. "Carissa edulis" (vert) 10 10
152 1f. "Spathodea campanulata" (vert) 10 10
153 3f. "Habenaria praestans" (vert) 10 10
154 5f. "Aloe lateritia" (vert) . . 4·50 2·25
155 10f. "Ammocharis tinneana" (vert) 30 20
156 40f. "Erythrina abyssinica" 1·10 75
157 100f. "Capparis tomentosa" 2·75 1·40

23 W.H.O. Building

1966. Inaug of W.H.O. Headquarters, Geneva.
159 **23** 2f. olive 10 10
160 3f. red 20 20
161 5f. blue 10 10

24 Football **25** Mother and Child within Flames

1966. "Youth and Sports".
162 **24** 10c. black, blue and green 10 10
163 – 20c. black, green and red 10 10
164 – 30c. black, purple and blue 10 10
165 **24** 40c. black, green and bistre 10 10
166 – 9f. black, purple and grey 20 10
167 – 50f. black, blue and purple 1·10 1·00
DESIGNS: 20c., 9f. Basketball; 30c., 50f. Volleyball.

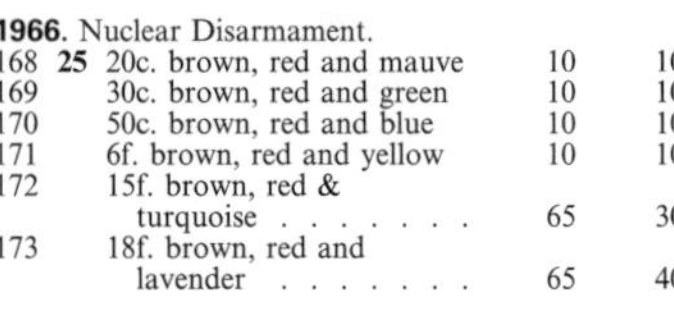

1966. Nuclear Disarmament.
168 **25** 20c. brown, red and mauve 10 10
169 30c. brown, red and green 10 10
170 50c. brown, red and blue 10 10
171 6f. brown, red and yellow 10 10
172 15f. brown, red & turquoise 65 30
173 18f. brown, red and lavender 65 40

26 Football **27** Yellow-crested Helmet Shrike and Mikeno Volcano

1966. World Cup Football Championship.
174 **26** 20c. blue and turquoise . . 10 10
175 30c. blue and violet 10 10
176 50c. blue and green 10 10
177 6f. blue and mauve 20 10
178 12f. blue and brown . . . 1·10 35
179 25f. indigo and blue . . . 2·25 60

1966. Rwanda Scenery.
180 **27** 10c. green 30 10
181 – 40c. lake 10 10
182 – 4f.50 blue 50 40
183 – 55f. purple 60 45
DESIGNS—VERT: 40c. Nyamiranga Falls (inscr "Nyamilanga"); 55f. Rusumo Falls (inscr "Rusumu"). HORIZ: 4f.50, Gahinga and Mahubura Volcanoes, and giant plants.

28 U.N.E.S.C.O. and Cultural Emblems

1966. 20th Anniv of U.N.E.S.C.O.
184 **28** 20c. mauve and blue . . . 10 10
185 – 30c. turquoise and black 10 10
186 – 50c. brown and black . . . 10 10
187 – 1f. violet and black 10 10
188 **28** 5f. green and brown . . . 10 10
189 – 10f. brown and black . . . 15 10
190 – 15f. purple and blue . . . 55 35
191 – 50f. blue and black 65 50
DESIGNS: 30c., 10f. "Animal" primer; 50c., 15f. Atomic symbol and drill operator; 1, 50f. Nubian monument partly submerged in the Nile.

29 "Bitis gabonica"

1967. Snakes. Multicoloured.
192 20c. Head of mamba 20 15
193 30c. Python (vert) 20 15
194 50c. Type **29** 20 15
195 1f. "Naja melanoleuca" (vert) 20 15
196 3f. Head of python 20 15
197 5f. "Psammophis sibilans" (vert) 45 15
198 20f. "Dendroaspis jamesoni kaimosae" . . . . 1·25 50
199 70f. "Dasypeltis scabra" (vert) . . . . 1·50 70

30 Girders and Tea Flower

1967. Ntaruka Hydro-electric Project.
200 **30** 20c. blue and purple 10 10
201 – 30c. brown and black 10 10
202 – 50c. violet and brown 10 10
203 **30** 4f. purple and green 10 10
204 – 25f. green and violet 50 50
205 – 50f. brown and blue 1·00 1·00
DESIGNS: 30c., 25f. Power conductors and pyrethrum flower; 50c., 50f. Barrage and coffee beans.

33 "St. Martin" (Van Dyck)

1967. Paintings.
208 **33** 20c. black, gold and violet 10 10
209 – 40c. black, gold and green 10 10
210 – 60c. black, gold and red 10 10
211 – 80c. black, gold and blue 10 10
212 **33** 9f. black, gold and brown 90 50
213 – 15f. black, gold and red 35 20
214 – 18f. black, gold and bronze 35 20
215 – 26f. black, gold and lake 45 45
PAINTINGS—HORIZ: 40c., 15f. "Rebecca and Eliezer" (Murillo); 80c., 26f. "Job and his Friends" (attributed to Il Calabrese). VERT: 60c., 18f. "St. Christopher" (D. Bouts).

34 Rwanda "Round Table" Emblem and Common Zebra's Head

1967. Rwanda "Round Table" Fund for Charitable Works. Each with "Round Table" Emblem. Mult.
216 20c. Type **34** 10 10
217 40c. African elephant's head 10 10
218 60c. African buffalo's head 10 10
219 80c. Impala's head 10 10
220 18f. Ear of wheat 35 15
221 100f. Palm 1·60 90

35 "Africa Place" and Dancers

1967. World Fair, Montreal.
222 **35** 20c. blue and sepia 10 10
223 – 30c. purple and sepia 10 10
224 – 50c. orange and sepia 10 10
225 – 1f. green and sepia 10 10
226 – 3f. violet and sepia 10 10
227 **35** 15f. green and sepia 15 15
228 – 34f. red and sepia 50 40
229 – 40f. turquoise and sepia 70 55
DESIGNS: "Africa Place" (two different views used alternately in order of value) and 30c., 3f. Drum and handicrafts; 50c., 40f. Dancers leaping; 1f., 34f. Spears, shields and weapons.

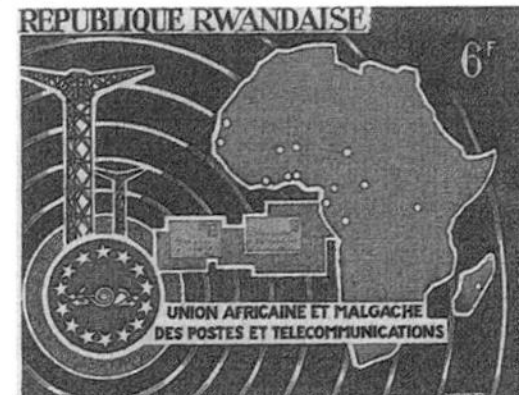

35a Map of Africa, Letters and Pylons

1967. Air. 5th Anniv of U.A.M.P.T.
230 **35a** 6f. slate, brown and lake 20 10
231 18f. purple and brown 65 35
232 30f. red, green and blue 1·10 65

36 Common Zebra's Head and Lion's Emblem
37 Red Bishop

1967. 50th Anniv of Lions International.
233 **36** 20c. black, blue and violet 10 10
234 80c. black, blue and green 10 10
235 1f. black, blue and red 10 10
236 8f. black, blue and brown 20 10
237 10f. black, blue and ultramarine 30 20
238 50f. black, blue and green 1·40 95

1967. Birds of Rwanda. Multicoloured.
239 20c. Type **37** 10 30
240 40c. Woodland kingfisher (horiz) 10 30
241 60c. Red-billed quelea 10 30
242 80c. Double-toothed barbet (horiz) 10 30
243 2f. Pin-tailed whydah 25 30
244 3f. Red-chested cuckoo (horiz) 35 30
245 18f. Green wood hoopoe 1·40 55
246 25f. Cinnamon-chested bee eater (horiz) 2·00 90
247 80f. Regal sunbird 4·50 2·50
248 100f. Fan-tailed whydah (horiz) 6·50 3·00

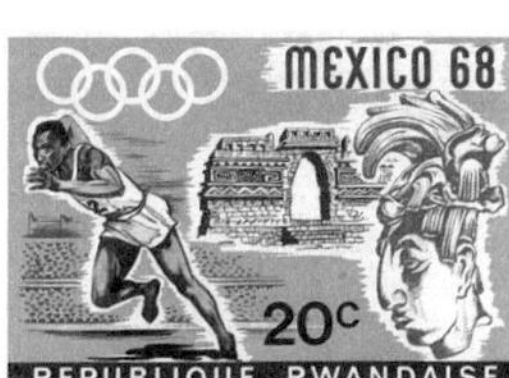

39 Running, and Mexican Antiquites

1968. Olympic Games, Mexico (1st issue). Mult.
250 20c. Type **39** 35 10
251 40c. Hammer-throwing 35 10
252 60c. Hurdling 35 10
253 80c. Javelin-throwing 35 10
254 8f. Football (vert) 45 10
255 10f. Mexican horseman and cacti (vert) 45 10
256 12f. Hockey (vert) 55 10
257 18f. Cathedral (vert) 70 15
258 20f. Boxing (vert) 90 55
259 30f. Mexico City (vert) 1·10 65
The 20c. to 80c. include Mexican antiquities in their designs.

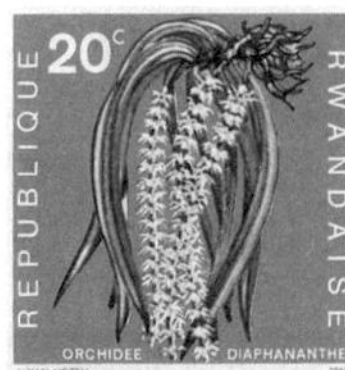

41 "Diaphananthe fragrantissima"

1968. Flowers. Multicoloured.
261 20c. Type **41** 10 10
262 40c. "Phaeomeria speciosa" 10 10
263 60c. "Ravenala madagascariensis" 10 10
264 80c. "Costus afer" 10 10
265 2f. Banana flowers 10 10
266 3f. Flowers and young fruit of pawpaw 10 10
267 18f. "Clerodendron sp." 35 15
268 25f. Sweet potato flowers 45 30
269 80f. Baobab flower 1·90 80
270 100f. Passion flower 2·25 1·25

42 Horse-jumping
43 Tuareg (Algeria)

1966. Olympic Games, Mexico (2nd issue).
271 **42** 20c. brown and orange 10 10
272 – 40c. brown and turquoise 10 10
273 – 60c. brown and purple 10 10
274 – 80c. brown and blue 10 10
275 – 38f. brown and red 50 40
276 – 60f. brown and green 1·10 65
SPORTS: 40c. Judo; 60c. Fencing; 80c. High-jumping; 38f. High-diving; 60f. Weightlifting. Each design also represents the location of previous Olympics as at left in Type **42**.

1968. African National Costumes (1st series). Mult.
277 30c. Type **43** 10 10
278 40c. Upper Volta 10 10
279 60c. Senegal 10 10
280 70c. Rwanda 10 10
281 8f. Morocco 10 10
282 20f. Nigeria 35 20
283 40f. Zambia 80 35
284 50f. Kenya 1·10 55
See also Nos. 345/52.

44a "Alexandre Lenoir" (J. L. David)

1968. Air. "Philexafrique" Stamp Exhibition, Abidjan (Ivory Coast, 1969) (1st issue).
286 **44a** 100f. multicoloured 2·50 1·60

45 Rwanda Scene and Stamp of Ruanda-Urundi (1953)

1969. Air. "Philexafrique" Stamp Exn (2nd issue).
287 **45** 50f. multicoloured 1·90 1·25

46 "The Musical Angels" (Van Eyck)
47 Tuareg Tribesmen

1969. "Paintings and Music". Multicoloured.
288 20c. Type **46** (postage) 10 10
289 40c. "The Angels' Concert" (M. Grunewald) 10 10
290 60c. "The Singing Boy" (Frans Hals) 10 10
291 80c. "The Lute player" (G. Terborch) 10 10
292 2f. "The Fifer" (Manet) 10 10
293 6f. "Young Girls at the Piano" (Renoir) 15 10
294 50f. "The Music Lesson" (Fragonard) (air) 1·40 85
295 100f. "Angels playing their Musical Instruments" (Memling) (horiz) 2·75 1·60

1969. African Headdresses (1st series). Mult.
297 20c. Type **47** 10 10
298 40c. Young Ovambo woman 10 10
299 60c. Ancient Guinean and Middle Congo festival headdresses 10 10

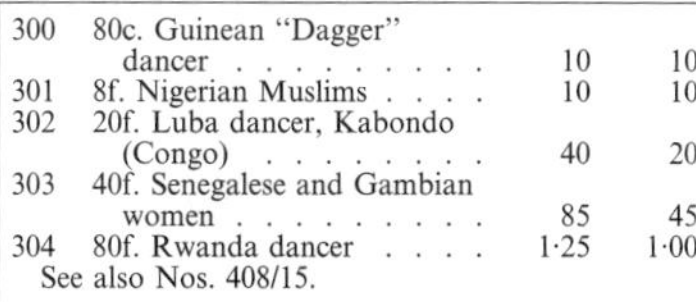
300 80c. Guinean "Dagger" dancer 10 10
301 8f. Nigerian Muslims 10 10
302 20f. Luba dancer, Kabondo (Congo) 40 20
303 40f. Senegalese and Gambian women 85 45
304 80f. Rwanda dancer 1·25 1·00
See also Nos. 408/15.

48 "The Moneylender and his Wife" (Quentin Metsys)

1969. 5th Anniv of African Development Bank.
305 **48** 30f. multicoloured on silver 55 50
306 – 70f. multicoloured on gold 1·60 1·40
DESIGN: 70f. "The Moneylender and his Wife" (Van Reymerswaele).

50 Pyrethrum
51 Revolutionary

1969. Medicinal Plants. Multicoloured.
308 20c. Type **50** 10 10
309 40c. Aloes 10 10
310 60c. Cola 10 10
311 80c. Coca 10 10
312 3f. Hagenia 10 10
313 75f. Cassia 1·40 80
314 80f. Cinchona 2·25 90
315 100f. Tephrosia 2·50 1·10

1969. 10th Anniv of Revolution.
316 **51** 6f. multicoloured 15 10
317 18f. multicoloured 50 45
318 40f. multicoloured 1·00 95

53 "Napoleon on Horseback" (David)

1969. Birth Bicent of Napoleon Bonaparte. Mult. Portraits of Napoleon. Artist's name given.
320 20c. Type **53** 10 10
321 40c. Debret 10 10
322 60c. Gautherot 10 10
323 80c. Ingres 10 10
324 8f. Pajou 20 15
325 20f. Gros 55 40
326 40f. Gros 1·00 55
327 80f. David 2·25 1·25

54 "The Quarryman" (O. Bonnevalle)

1969. 50th Anniv of I.L.O. Multicoloured.
328 20c. Type **54** 10 10
329 40c. "Ploughing" (detail Brueghel's "Descent of Icarus") 10 10
330 60c. "The Fisherman" (C. Meunier) 10 10
331 80c. "Ostend Slipway" (J. van Noten) 10 10
332 8f. "The Cook" (P. Aertsen) 20 10
333 10f. "Vulcan's Blacksmiths" (Velazquez) 35 15
334 50f. "Hiercheuse" (C. Meunier) 1·25 60
335 70f. "The Miner" (P. Paulus) 1·60 80
Nos. 330, 332 and 334/5 are vert.

55 "The Derby at Epsom" (Gericault)

1970. Paintings of Horses. Multicoloured.

336	20c. Type **55**	10	10
337	40c. "Horses leaving the Sea" (Delacroix)	10	10
338	60c. "Charles V at Muhlberg" (Titian) (vert)	10	10
339	80c. "To the Races, Amateur Jockeys" (Degas)	10	10
340	8f. "Horsemen at Rest" (Wouwermans)	20	10
341	20f. "Officer of the Imperial Guard" (Gericault) (vert)	60	30
342	40f. "Horse and Dromedary" (Bonnevalle)	1·50	45
343	80f. "The Prodigal Child" (Rubens)	2·00	80

1970. African National Costumes (2nd series). As T **43**. Multicoloured.

345	20c. Tharaka Meru woman	10	10
346	30c. Niger flautist	10	10
347	50c. Tunisian water-carrier	10	10
348	1f. Kano ceremonial (Nigeria)	10	10
349	3f. Mali troubador	10	10
350	5f. Quipongo, Angola women	10	10
351	50f. Mauritanian at prayer	95	55
352	90f. Sinehatiali dancers, Ivory Coast	2·00	1·00

58 Footballer attacking Goal

1970. World Cup Football Championship, Mexico.

353	**58**	20c. multicoloured	10	10
354	–	30c. multicoloured	10	10
355	–	50c. multicoloured	10	10
356	–	1f. multicoloured	10	10
357	–	6f. multicoloured	10	10
358	–	18f. multicoloured	45	30
359	–	30f. multicoloured	85	45
360	–	90f. multicoloured	2·00	95

Nos. 354/60 show footballers in various positions, similar to Type **58**.

59 Flowers and Green Peafowl

1970. "EXPO 70", World Fair, Osaka, Japan. Mult.

361	20c. Type **59**	60	10
362	30c. Torii gate and "Hibiscus" (Yashuda)	10	10
363	50c. Dancer and "Musician" (Katayama)	10	10
364	1f. Sun Tower and "Warrior"	10	10
365	3f. House and "Seated Buddha"	10	10
366	5f. Pagoda and "Head of Girl" (Yamakawa)	10	10
367	20f. Greeting and "Imperial Palace"	55	35
368	70f. Expo emblem and "Horseman"	1·60	90

60 Two Young Gorillas

1970. Gorillas of the Mountains.

369	**60**	20c. black and green	35	35
370	–	40c. black, brown & purple	35	35
371	–	60c. black, blue and brown	35	35
372	–	80c. black, orange & brown	35	35
373	–	1f. black and mauve	35	35
374	–	2f. multicoloured	35	35
375	–	15f. black and sepia	70	45
376	–	100f. black, brown and blue	3·75	2·25

GORILLA—VERT: 40c. Squatting; 80c. Beating chest; 2f. Eating banana; 100f. With young. HORIZ: 60c. Walking; 1f. With family; 15f. Heads.

61 Cinchona Bark

1970. 150th Anniv of Discovery of Quinine. Mult.

377	20c. Type **61**	10	10
378	80c. Pharmaceutical equipment	10	10
379	1f. Anopheles mosquito	10	10
380	3f. Malaria patient and nurse	10	10
381	25f. "Attack" on mosquito	55	35
382	70f. Pelletier and Caventou (discoverers of quinine)	1·50	80

62 Rocket in Flight

63 Pope Paul VI

63 F. D. Roosevelt and "Brasscattleya olympia alba"

1970. Moon Missions. Multicoloured.

383	20c. Type **62**	10	10
384	30c. Separation during orbit	10	10
385	50c. Spaceship above the moon	10	10
386	1f. Module and astonauts on moon	10	10
387	3f. Take-off from the moon	10	10
388	5f. Return journey to earth	15	10
389	10f. Final separation before landing	30	15
390	80f. Splashdown	2·25	1·40

1970. 25th Death Anniv of F. D. Roosevelt. Portraits and Orchids.

391	**63**	20c. brown, blue and black	10	10
392	–	30c. brown, red and black	10	10
393	–	50c. brown, orange & black	10	10
394	–	1f. brown, green and black	10	10
395	–	2f. green, brown and black	10	10
396	–	6f. green, purple and black	20	15
397	–	30f. green, blue and black	1·25	40
398	–	60f. green, red and black	2·00	70

ORCHIDS: 30c. "Laeliocattleya callistoglossa"; 50c. "Chondrorrhyncha chestertoni"; 1f. "Paphiopedilum"; 2f. "Cymbidium hybride"; 6f. "Cattleya labiata"; 30f. "Dendrobium nobile"; 60f. "Laelia gouldiana".

1970. Centenary of 1st Vatican Council.

400	**65**	10c. brown and gold	10	10
401	–	20c. green and gold	10	10
402	–	30c. lake and gold	10	10
403	–	40c. blue and gold	10	10
404	–	1f. violet and gold	10	10
405	–	18f. purple and gold	50	20
406	–	20f. orange and gold	60	20
407	–	60f. brown and gold	1·60	70

POPES: 20c. John XXIII; 30c. Pius XII; 40c. Pius XI; 1f. Benedict XV; 18f. Pius X; 20f. Leo XIII; 60f. Pius IX.

1971. African Headdresses (2nd series). Mult. As T **47**.

408	20c. Rendille woman	10	10
409	30c. Chad woman	10	10
410	50c. Bororo man (Niger)	10	10
411	1f. Masai man (Kenya)	10	10
412	5f. Air girl (Niger)	10	10
413	18f. Rwanda woman	35	20
414	25f. Mauritania man	65	35
415	50f. Rwanda girls	1·50	65

68 "Beethoven" (C. Horneman)

1971. Birth Cent (1970) of Beethoven. Portraits and funeral scene by various artists. Mult.

418	20c. Type **68**	10	10
419	30c. K. Stieler	10	10
420	50c. F. Schimon	10	10
421	3f. H. Best	10	10
422	6f. W. Fassbender	30	10
423	90f. "Beethoven's Burial" (Stober)	2·10	2·00

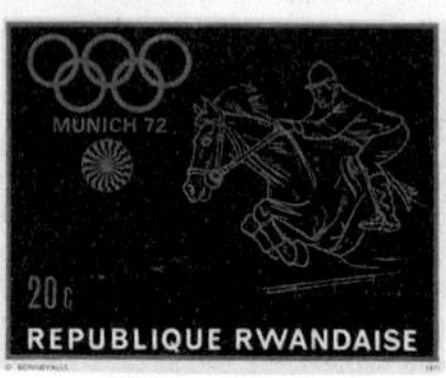

69 Horse-jumping

1971. Olympic Games, Munich (1972) (1st issue).

424	**69**	20c. gold and black	10	10
425	–	30c. gold and purple	10	10
426	–	50c. gold and violet	10	10
427	–	1f. gold and green	10	10
428	–	8f. gold and red	20	10
429	–	10f. gold and violet	30	15
430	–	20f. gold and brown	50	30
431	–	60f. gold and green	1·40	65

DESIGNS: 30c. Running (start); 50c. Basketball; 1f. High-jumping; 8f. Boxing; 10f. Pole-vaulting; 20f. Wrestling; 60f. Gymnastics.

See also Nos. 490/7.

70 U.A.M.P.T. H.Q. and Rwandaise Woman and Child

1971. Air. 10th Anniv of U.A.M.P.T.

432	**70**	100f. multicoloured	2·10	2·00

72 "Durer" (self-portrait)

1971. 500th Birth Anniv of Durer. Paintings. Multicoloured.

434	20c. "Adam"	10	10
435	30c. "Eve"	10	10
436	50c. "Portrait of H. Holzschuher"	10	10
437	1f. "Mourning the Dead Christ"	10	10
438	3f. "Madonna and Child"	10	10
439	5f. "St. Eustace"	10	10
440	20f. "St. Paul and St. Mark"	45	30
441	70f. Type **72**	1·60	1·00

73 Astronauts in Moon Rover

1972. Moon Mission of "Apollo 15".

442	**73**	600f. gold	95·00	

74 Participation in Sport

1972. National Guard. Multicoloured.

443	4f. Type **74**	10	10
444	6f. Transport of emergency supplies	15	10
445	15f. Helicopter transport for the sick	40	20
446	25f. Participation in health service	65	35
447	50f. Guard, map and emblem (vert)	1·25	1·10

75 Ice Hockey

1972. Winter Olympic Games, Sapporo, Japan. Multicoloured.

448	20c. Type **75**	10	10
449	30c. Speed-skating	10	10
450	50c. Ski-jumping	10	10
451	1f. Figure skating	10	10
452	6f. Cross-country skiing	10	10
453	12f. Slalom	15	15
454	20f. Tobogganing	45	20
455	60f. Downhill skiing	1·40	1·10

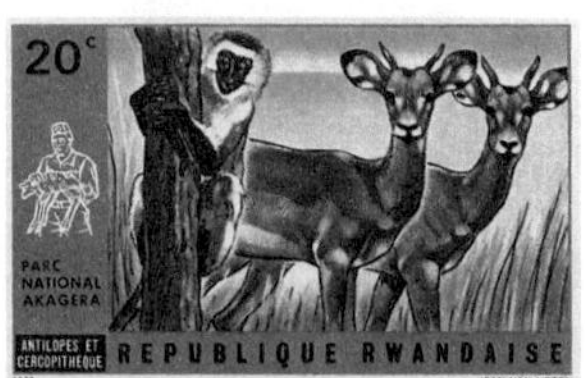

76 Savanna Monkey and Impala

1972. Akagera National Park. Multicoloured.

456	20c. Type **76**	15	10
457	30c. African buffalo	15	10
458	50c. Common zebra	15	10
459	1f. White rhinoceros	40	40
460	2f. Warthogs	15	10
461	6f. Hippopotamus	20	10
462	18f. Spotted hyenas	40	20
463	32f. Helmeted guineafowl	2·25	95
464	60f. Waterbucks	2·00	1·10
465	80f. Lion and lioness	2·75	1·75

77 Family supporting Flag

78 Variable Sunbirds

1972. 10th Anniv of Referendum.

466	**77**	6f. multicoloured	10	10
467		18f. multicoloured	45	35
468		60f. multicoloured	1·25	1·10

1972. Rwanda Birds. Multicoloured.

469	20c. Common waxbills	10	10
470	30c. Collared sunbird	15	10
471	50c. Type **78**	20	10
472	1f. Greater double-collared sunbird	30	10
473	4f. Ruwenzori puff-back flycatcher	35	15
474	6f. Red-billed fire finch	40	20
475	10f. Scarlet-chested sunbird	70	20
476	18f. Red-headed quelea	1·50	40
477	60f. Black-headed gonolek	4·75	1·50
478	100f. African golden oriole	8·00	2·40

79 King Baudouin and Queen Fabiola with President and Mrs. Kayibanda in Rwanda

1972. "Belgica 72" Stamp Exhibition, Brussels.
479 – 18f. multicoloured 70 70
480 – 22f. multicoloured 90 90
481 **79** 40f. blue, black and gold 1·75 1·75
DESIGNS: 18f. Rwanda village; 22f. View of Bruges. Nos. 479/80 are smaller, size 39 × 36 mm.

80 Announcement of Independence

1972. 10th Anniv of Independence.
482 **80** 20c. green and gold 10 10
483 – 30c. purple and gold . . . 10 10
484 – 50c. sepia and gold 10 10
485 – 6f. blue and gold 10 10
486 – 10f. purple and gold . . . 15 10
487 – 15f. blue and gold 35 20
488 – 18f. brown and gold . . . 45 30
489 – 50f. green and gold . . . . 1·10 70
DESIGNS—HORIZ: 30c. Promotion ceremony, officers of the National Guard; 50c. Pres. Kayibanda, wife and family; 6f. Pres. Kayibanda casting vote in legislative elections; 10f. Pres. and Mrs. Kayibanda at "Festival of Justice"; 15f. President and members of National Assembly; 18f. Investiture of Pres. Kayibanda. VERT: 50f. President Kayibanda.

81 Horse-jumping

1972. Olympic Games, Munich (2nd issue).
490 **81** 20c. green and gold 10 10
491 – 30c. violet and gold . . . 10 10
492 – 50c. green and gold 10 10
493 – 1f. purple and gold 10 10
494 – 6f. black and gold 10 10
495 – 18f. brown and gold . . . 35 30
496 – 30f. violet and gold 80 55
497 – 44f. blue and gold . . . . 1·10 65
DESIGNS: 30c. Hockey; 50c. Football; 1f. Long-jumping; 6f. Cycling; 18f. Yachting; 30f. Hurdling; 44f. Gymnastics.

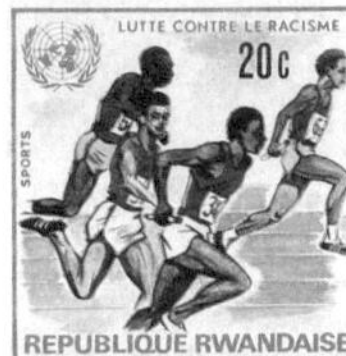

82 Runners

1972. Racial Equality Year. "Working Together". Multicoloured.
498 20c. Type **82** 10 10
499 30c. Musicians 10 10
500 50c. Ballet dancers 10 10
501 1f. Medical team in operating theatre 10 10
502 6f. Weaver and painter . . . 10 10
503 18f. Children in class 35 20
504 24f. Laboratory technicians 55 35
505 50f. U.N. emblem and hands of four races . . . . . . 1·00 65

84 "Phymateus brunneri"

1973. Rwanda Insects. Multicoloured.
507 20c. Type **84** 10 10
508 30c. "Diopsis fumipennis" (vert) 10 10
509 50c. "Kitoko alberti" 10 10
510 1f. "Archibracon fasciatus" (vert) 10 10
511 2f. "Ornithacris cyanea imperialis" 10 10
512 6f. "Clitodaca fenestralis" (vert) 15 10
513 18f. "Senaspis oesacus" . . . 40 20
514 22f. "Phonoctonus grandis" (vert) 55 35
515 70f. "Loba leopardina" . . . 2·25 2·40
516 100f. "Ceratocoris distortus" (vert) . . . . 4·00 3·10

85 "Emile Zola" (Manet) **86** Longombe

1973. International Book Year. "Readers and Writers". Paintings and portraits. Multicoloured.
518 20c. Type **85** 10 10
519 30c. "Rembrandt's Mother" (Rembrandt) 10 10
520 50c. "St. Jerome removing Thorn from Lion's paw" (Colantonio) 10 10
521 1f. "St. Peter and St. Paul" (El Greco) 10 10
522 2f. "Virgin and Child" (Van der Weyden) 10 10
523 6f. "St. Jerome in his Cell" (Antonella de Messina) . . 15 10
524 40f. "St. Barbara" (Master of Flemalle) . . . . 1·00 60
525 100f. "Don Quixote" (O. Bonnevalle) . . . . . 2·40 1·90

1973. Musical Instruments. Multicoloured.
527 20c. Type **86** 10 10
528 30c. Horn 10 10
529 50c. "Xylophone" 10 10
530 1f. "Harp" 10 10
531 4f. Alur horns 10 10
532 6f. Horn, bells and drum . . 10 10
533 18f. Drums 40 40
534 90f. Gourds . . . . 2·00 1·40

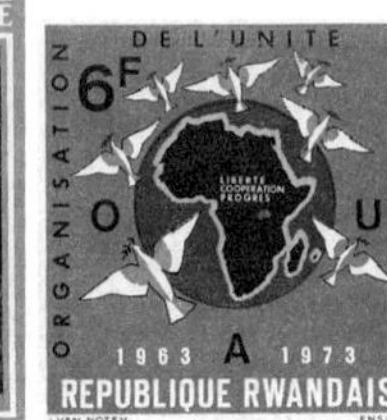

87 "Rubens and Isabelle Brandt" (Rubens) **88** Map of Africa and Doves

1973. "IBRA" Stamp Exhibition, Munich. Famous Paintings. Multicoloured.
535 20c. Type **87** 10 10
536 30c. "Portrait of a Lady" (Cranach the Younger) . . 10 10
537 50c. "Woman peeling Turnips" (Chardin) 10 10
538 1f. "Abduction of the Daughters of Leucippe" (Rubens) 10 10
539 2f. "Virgin and Child" (Lippi) 10 10
540 6f. "Boys eating Fruit" (Murillo) 20 10
541 40f. "The Sickness of Love" (Steen) 90 45
542 100f. "Jesus divested of His Garments" (El Greco) . . 2·25 1·40

1973. 10th Anniv of O.A.U. Multicoloured.
544 6f. Type **88** 20 10
545 94f. Map of Africa and hands 2·25 1·90

1973. Pan-African Drought Relief. Nos. 308/13 and 315 optd **SECHERESSE SOLIDARITE AFRICAINE** and No. 315 additionally surch.
546 **50** 20c. multicoloured 10 10
547 – 40c. multicoloured 10 10
548 – 60c. multicoloured 10 10
549 – 80c. multicoloured 10 10
550 – 3f. multicoloured 10 10
551 – 75f. multicoloured . . . . 1·60 1·40
552 – 100f.+50f. multicoloured 5·00 4·00

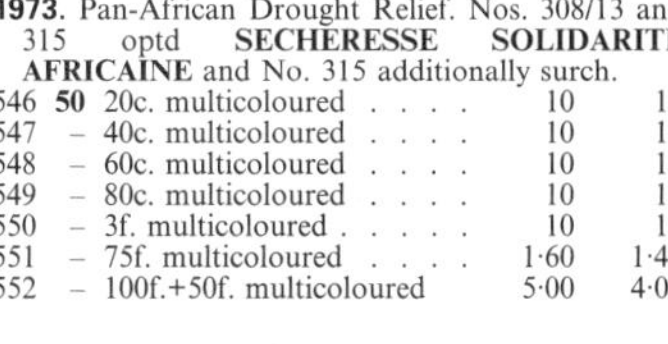

90 Six-banded Distichodus

1973. Fishes. Multicoloured.
553 20c. Type **90** 10 10
554 30c. Lesser tigerfish 10 10
555 50c. Angel squeaker 10 10
556 1f. Nile mouthbrooder . . . 10 10
557 2f. African lungfish 15 10
558 6f. Mandeville's catfish . . . 35 10
559 40f. Congo tetra . . . . . . 1·90 95
560 150f. Golden julie . . . . . 6·25 3·50

91 Crane with Letter and Telecommunications Emblem

1973. 12th Anniv of U.A.M.P.T.
562 **91** 100f. blue, brown and mauve . . . . 2·50 1·90

1973. African Fortnight, Brussels. Nos. 408/15 optd **QUINZAINE AFRICAINE BRUXELLES 15/30 SEPT. 1973** and globe.
563 20c. multicoloured 10 10
564 30c. multicoloured 10 10
565 50c. multicoloured 10 10
566 1f. multicoloured 10 10
567 5f. multicoloured 10 10
568 18f. multicoloured 40 20
569 25f. multicoloured 50 45
570 50f. multicoloured . . . . . 1·40 85

1973. Air. Congress of French-speaking Nations, Liege. No. 432 optd **LIEGE ACCUEILLE LES PAYS DE LANGUE FRANCAISE 1973** (No. 562) or congress emblem (No. 563).
571 100f. multicoloured . . . . . 4·00 2·75
572 100f. multicoloured . . . . . 4·00 2·75

1973. 25th Anniv of Declaration of Human Rights. Nos. 443/7 optd with Human Rights emblem.
574 **74** 4f. multicoloured 10 10
575 – 6f. multicoloured 10 10
576 – 15f. multicoloured 30 15
577 – 25f. multicoloured 60 40
578 – 50f. multicoloured . . . . 1·40 95

96 Copernicus and Astrolabe **97** Pres. Habyarimana

1973. 500th Birth Anniv of Copernicus. Mult.
580 20c. Type **96** 10 10
581 30c. Copernicus 10 10
582 50c. Copernicus and heliocentric system 10 10
583 1f. Type **96** 10 10
584 18f. As 30c. 65 60
585 80f. As 50c. . . . . 2·40 2·00

1974. "New Regime".
587 **97** 1f. brown, black and buff 10 10
588 2f. brown, black and blue 10 10
589 5f. brown, black and red 10 10
590 6f. brown, black and blue 10 10
591 26f. brown, black and lilac 55 45
592 60f. brown, black and green . . . . 1·25 1·00

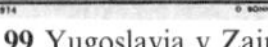

99 Yugoslavia v Zaire **101** "Diane de Poiters" (Fontainebleau School)

100 Marconi's Steam Yacht "Elettra"

1974. World Cup Football Championship, West Germany. Players represent specified teams. Mult.
594 20c. Type **99** 10 10
595 40c. Netherlands v Sweden 10 10
596 60c. West Germany v Australia 10 10
597 80c. Haiti v Argentina . . . 10 10
598 2f. Brazil v Scotland 10 10
599 6f. Bulgaria v Uruguay . . . 10 10
600 40f. Italy v Poland 80 65
601 50f. Chile v East Germany 1·40 1·00

1974. Birth Centenary of Guglielmo Marconi (radio pioneer). Multicoloured.
602 20c. Type **100** 20 10
603 30c. Cruiser "Carlo Alberto" 20 10
604 50c. Marconi's telegraph equipment 10 10
605 4f. "Global Telecommunications" . . . 10 10
606 35f. Early radio receiver . . . 85 45
607 60f. Marconi and Poldhu radio station . . . . 1·50 1·10

1974. International Stamp Exhibitions "Stockholmia" and "Internaba". Paintings from Stockholm and Basle. Multicoloured.
609 20c. Type **101** 10 10
610 30c. "The Flute-player" (J. Leyster) 10 10
611 50c. "Virgin Mary and Child" (G. David) 10 10
612 1f. "The Triumph of Venus" (F. Boucher) 10 10
613 10f. "Harlequin Seated" (P. Picasso) 15 10
614 18f. "Virgin and Child" (15th-century) 35 15
615 20f. "The Beheading of St. John" (H. Fries) . . . 45 35
616 50f. "The Daughter of Andersdotter" (J. Hockert) 1·40 1·00

102 Monastic Messenger **105** Head of Uganda Kob

1974. Centenary of U.P.U. Multicoloured.
619 20c. Type **102** 10 10
620 30c. Inca messenger 10 10
621 50c. Moroccan postman . . . 10 10
622 1f. Indian postman 10 10
623 18f. Polynesian postman . . 55 40
624 80f. Early Rwanda messenger with horn and drum . . . 2·00 1·40

1974. 15th Anniv of Revolution. Nos. 316/18 optd **1974 15e ANNIVERSAIRE**.
625 **51** 6f. multicoloured . . . .
626 18f. multicoloured . . . .
627 40f. multicoloured . . . .
Set of 3 . . . . 11·00 9·50

1974. 10th Anniv of African Development Bank. Nos. 305/6 optd **1974 10e ANNIVERSAIRE**.
629 **48** 30f. multicoloured 85 65
630 – 70f. multicoloured . . . . 1·90 1·40

1975. Antelopes. Multicoloured.
631 20c. Type **105** 15 10
632 30c. Bongo with calf (horiz) 15 10
633 50c. Roan antelope and sable antelope heads 15 10
634 1f. Young sitatungas (horiz) 15 10
635 4f. Great kudu 15 10
636 10f. Impala family (horiz) . . 80 10
637 34f. Waterbuck head . . . . 2·00 70
638 100f. Giant eland (horiz) . . 5·75 2·50

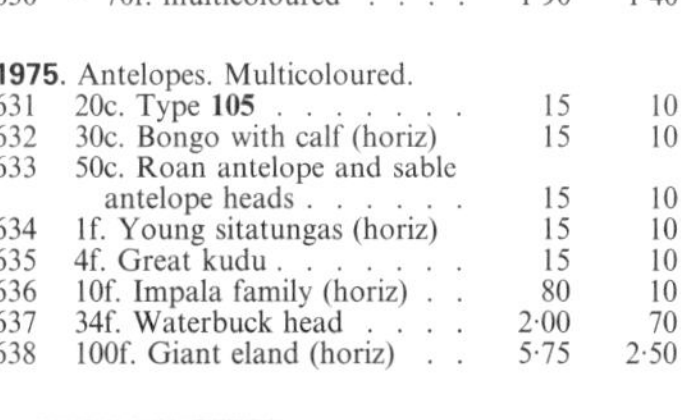

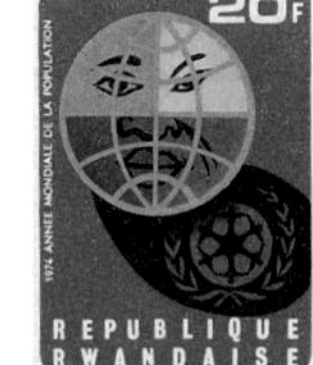

108 Pyrethrum Daisies **111** Globe and Emblem

110 Eastern White Pelicans

1975. Agricultural Labour Year. Multicoloured.
642 20c. Type **108** 10 10
643 30c. Tea plant 10 10
644 50c. Coffee berries 10 10
645 4f. Bananas 10 10
646 10f. Maize 20 10
647 12f. Sorghum 35 15

648 26f. Rice 80 45
649 47f. Coffee cultivation . . . 1·60 90

1975. Holy Year. Nos. 400/7 optd **1975 ANNEE SAINTE**.
652 **65** 10c. brown and gold . . . 10 10
653 – 20c. green and gold 10 10
654 – 30c. lake and gold 10 10
655 – 40c. blue and gold 10 10
656 – 1f. violet and gold 10 10
657 – 18f. purple and gold . . . 40 20
658 – 20f. orange and gold . . . 45 20
659 – 60f. brown and gold . . . 1·90 1·25

1975. Aquatic Birds. Multicoloured.
660 20c. Type **110** 10 10
661 30c. Malachite kingfisher . . 10 10
662 50c. Goliath herons 10 10
663 1f. Saddle-bill stork 10 10
664 4f. African jacana 40 15
665 10f. African darter 85 35
666 34f. Sacred ibis . . . . . . 2·40 1·00
667 80f. Hartlaub's duck . . . . 6·50 2·75

1975. World Population Year (1974). Mult.
669 20f. Type **111** 45 30
670 26f. Population graph 65 35
671 34f. Symbolic doorway . . . 95 50

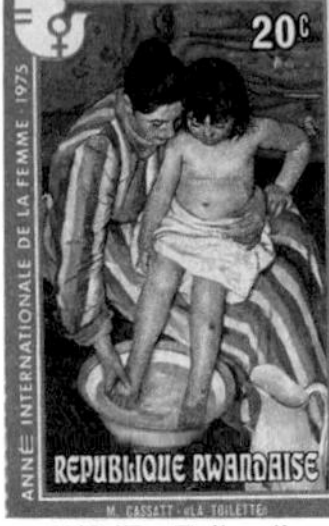

112 "La Toilette" (M. Cassatt)

113 "Arts"

1975. International Women's Year. Multicoloured.
672 20c. Type **112** 10 10
673 30c. "Mother and Child" (G. Melchers) 10 10
674 50c. "The Milk Jug" (Vermeer) 10 10
675 1f. "The Water-carrier" (Goya) 10 10
676 8f. Coffee picking 20 10
677 12f. Laboratory technician . . 35 20
678 18f. Rwandaise mother and child 55 20
679 60f. Woman carrying water jug . . . . 1·50 1·25

1975. 10th Anniv of National University. The Faculties. Multicoloured.
681 20c. Type **113** 10 10
682 30c. "Medicine" 10 10
683 1f.50 "Jurisprudence" 10 10
684 18f. "Science" 40 20
685 26f. "Commerce" 45 30
686 34f. University Building, Kigali 85 55

114 Cattle at Pool, and "Impatiens stuhlmannii"

1975. Protection of Nature. Multicoloured.
688 20c. Type **114** 10 10
689 30c. Euphorbis "candelabra" and savannah bush 10 10
690 50c. Bush fire and "Tapinanthus prunifolius" 10 10
691 5f. Lake Bulera and "Nymphaea lotus" 10 10
692 8f. Soil erosion and "Protea madiensis" 15 10
693 10f. Protected marshland and "Melanthera brownei" . . 20 15
694 26f. Giant lobelias and groundsel 55 40
695 100f. Sabyinyo volcano and "Polystachya kermesina" 2·50 2·25

1975. Pan-African Drought Relief. Nos. 345/52 optd or surch **SECHERESSE SOLIDARITE 1975** (both words share same initial letter).
696 20c. multicoloured 10 10
697 30c. multicoloured 10 10
698 50c. multicoloured 10 10
699 1f. multicoloured 10 10
700 3f. multicoloured 10 10
701 5f. multicoloured 15 10
702 50f.+25f. multicoloured . . . 1·60 1·25
703 90f.+25f. multicoloured . . . 2·40 2·00

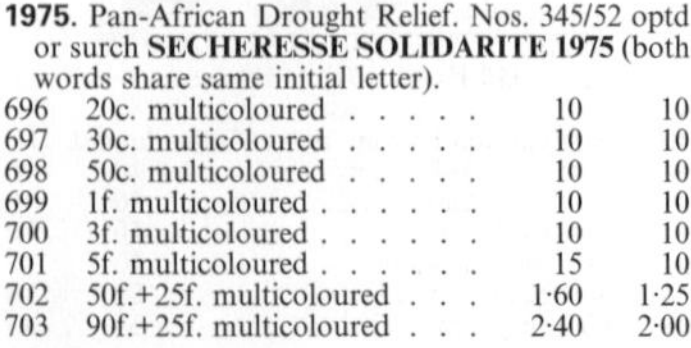

116 Loading Douglas DC-8F Jet Trader

1975. Year of Increased Production. Multicoloured.
704 20c. Type **116** 10 10
705 30c. Coffee-picking plant . . 10 10
706 50c. Lathe operator 10 10
707 10f. Farmer with hoe (vert) 15 10
708 35f. Coffee-picking (vert) . . 60 55
709 54f. Mechanical plough . . . 1·10 95

117 African Woman with Basket on Head

1975. "Themabelga" Stamp Exhibition, Brussels. African Costumes.
710 **117** 20c. multicoloured 10 10
711 – 30c. multicoloured 10 10
712 – 50c. multicoloured 10 10
713 – 1f. multicoloured 10 10
714 – 5f. multicoloured 10 10
715 – 7f. multicoloured 15 10
716 – 35f. multicoloured 70 60
717 – 51f. multicoloured . . . . 1·40 95
DESIGNS: 30c. to 51f. Various Rwanda costumes.

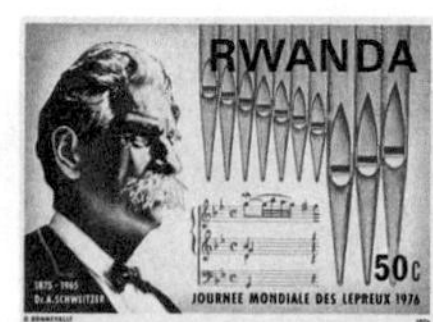

118 Dr. Schweitzer, Organ Pipes and Music Score

1976. World Leprosy Day.
719 – 20c. lilac, brown and black 10 10
720 – 30c. lilac, green and black 10 10
721 **118** 50c. lilac, brown and black 10 10
722 – 1f. lilac, purple and black 10 10
723 – 3f. lilac, blue and black 10 10
724 – 5f. lilac, brown and black 10 10
725 **118** 10f. lilac, blue and black 30 10
726 – 80f. lilac, red and black 1·90 1·40
DESIGNS: Dr. Schweitzer and: 20c. Piano keyboard and music; 30c. Lambarene Hospital; 1f. Lambarene residence; 3f. as 20c.; 5f. as 30 c; 80f. as 1f.

119 "Surrender at Yorktown"

1976. Bicentenary of American Revolution. Mult.
727 20c. Type **119** 10 10
728 30c. "The Sergeant-Instructor at Valley Forge" 10 10
729 50c. "Presentation of Captured Yorktown Flags to Congress" 10 10
730 1f. "Washington at Fort Lee" 10 10
731 18f. "Washington boarding a British warship" 45 30
732 26f. "Washington studying Battle plans" 55 40
733 34f. "Washington firing a Cannon" 90 55
734 40f. "Crossing the Delaware" 1·00 85

120 Sister Yohana

121 Yachting

1976. 75th Anniv of Catholic Church in Rwanda. Multicoloured.
736 20c. Type **120** 10 10
737 30c. Abdon Sabakati 10 10
738 50c. Father Alphonse Brard 10 10
739 4f. Abbe Balthazar Gafuku 10 10
740 10f. Monseigneur Bigirumwami 20 10
741 25f. Save Catholic Church (horiz) 60 45
742 60f. Kabgayi Catholic Cathedral (horiz) . . . . . 1·25 80

1976. Olympic Games, Montreal (1st issue).
743 **121** 20c. brown and green . . 10 10
744 – 30c. blue and green . . . 10 10
745 – 50c. black and green . . . 10 10
746 – 1f. violet and green . . . 10 10
747 – 10f. blue and green . . . 20 10
748 – 18f. brown and green . . . 35 30
749 – 29f. purple and green . . 80 60
750 – 51f. deep green and green 1·00 80
DESIGNS: 30c. Horse-jumping; 50c. Long jumping; 1f. Hockey; 10f. Swimming; 18f. Football; 29f. Boxing; 51f. Gymnastics.
See also Nos. 767/74.

122 Bell's Experimental Telephone and Manual Switchboard

1976. Telephone Centenary.
751 **122** 20c. brown and blue . . . 10 10
752 – 30c. blue and violet . . . 10 10
753 – 50c. brown and blue . . . 10 10
754 – 1f. orange and blue . . . 10 10
755 – 4f. mauve and blue . . . 10 10
756 – 8f. green and blue . . . . 2·50 35
757 – 26f. red and blue 70 55
758 – 60f. lilac and blue . . . . 1·40 1·00
DESIGNS: 30c. Early telephone and man making call; 50c. Early telephone and woman making call; 1f. Early telephone and exchange building; 4f. Alexander Graham Bell and "candlestick" telephone; 8f. Rwanda subscriber and dial telephone; 26f. Dish aerial, satellite and modern handset; 60f. Rwanda PTT building, operator and push-button telephone.

1976. Bicentenary of Declaration of American Independence. Nos. 727/34 optd **INDEPENDENCE DAY** and Bicentennial Emblem.
759 **119** 20c. multicoloured 10 10
760 – 30c. multicoloured 10 10
761 – 50c. multicoloured 10 10
762 – 1f. multicoloured 10 10
763 – 18f. multicoloured 35 20
764 – 26f. multicoloured 65 45
765 – 34f. multicoloured 80 55
766 – 40f. multicoloured . . . . 1·10 80

124 Football

1976. Olympic Games, Montreal (2nd issue). Mult.
767 20c. Type **124** 10 10
768 30c. Rifle-shooting 10 10
769 50c. Canoeing 10 10
770 1f. Gymnastics 10 10
771 10f. Weightlifting 15 10
772 12f. Diving 30 20
773 26f. Horse-riding 55 40
774 50f. Throwing the hammer 1·40 90

125 "Apollo" and "Soyuz" Launches and ASTP Badge

1976. "Apollo"–"Soyuz" Test Project. Mult.
776 20c. Type **125** 10 10
777 30c. "Soyuz" rocket 10 10
778 50c. "Apollo" rocket 10 10
779 1f. "Apollo" after separation 10 10
780 2f. Approach to link-up . . . 10 10
781 12f. Spacecraft docked . . . 35 15
782 30f. Sectional view of interiors . . . . 1·10 55
783 54f. "Apollo" splashdown . . 2·25 1·25

126 "Eulophia cucullata"
128 Hands embracing "Cultural Collaboration"

1976. Rwandaise Orchids. Multicoloured.
784 20c. Type **126** 10 10
785 30c. "Eulophia streptopetala" 10 10
786 50c. "Disa stairsii" 10 10
787 1f. "Aerangis kotschyana" . . 10 10
788 10f. "Eulophia abyssinica" 20 10
789 12f. "Bonatea steudneri" . . 30 15
790 26f. "Ansellia gigantea" . . . 1·10 45
791 50f. "Eulophia angolensis" 2·00 1·25

1977. World Leprosy Day. Nos. 719/26 optd with **JOURNEE MONDIALE 1977**.
793 – 20c. lilac, brown and black 10 10
794 – 30c. lilac, green and black 10 10
795 **118** 50c. lilac, brown and black 10 10
796 – 1f. lilac, purple and black 10 10
797 – 3f. lilac, blue and black 10 10
798 – 5f. lilac, brown and black 20 10
799 **118** 10f. lilac, brown and black 35 20
800 – 80f. lilac, red and black 1·60 1·60

1977. 10th OCAM Summit Meeting, Kigali. Mult.
801 10f. Type **128** 30 10
802 26f. Hands embracing "Technical Collaboration" 70 40
803 64f. Hands embracing "Economic Collaboration" 1·25 90

1977. World Water Conference. Nos. 688/95 optd **CONFERENCE MONDIALE DE L'EAU**.
805 **114** 20c. multicoloured 10 10
806 – 30c. multicoloured 10 10
807 – 50c. multicoloured 10 10
808 – 5f. multicoloured 15 10
809 – 8f. multicoloured 20 10
810 – 10f. multicoloured 40 15
811 – 26f. multicoloured . . . 1·40 75
812 – 100f. multicoloured . . . 3·50 3·25

131 Roman Signal Post and African Tam-Tam

1977. World Telecommunications Day. Mult.
813 20c. Type **131** 10 10
814 30c. Chappe's semaphore and post-rider 10 10
815 50c. Morse code 10 10
816 1f. "Goliath" laying Channel cable 10 10
817 4f. Telephone, radio and television 10 10
818 18f. "Kingsport" and maritime communications satellite 75 40
819 26f. Telecommunications satellite and aerial 50 40
820 50f. "Mariner 2" satellite . . 1·40 90

132 "The Ascent to Calvary" (detail)

135 Long-crested Eagle

133 Chateau Sassenage, Grenoble

1977. 400th Birth Anniv of Peter Paul Rubens. Multicoloured.
823 20c. Type **132** 10 10
824 30c. "The Judgement of Paris" (horiz) 10 10
825 50c. "Marie de Medici, Queen of France" 10 10
826 1f. "Heads of Negroes" (horiz) 10 10
827 4f. "St. Idelfonse Triptych" (detail) 10 10
828 8f. "Helene Fourment with her Children" (horiz) . . . 15 10
829 26f. "St. Idelfonse Triptych" (different detail) 80 65
830 60f. "Helene Fourment" . . 2·50 1·75

1977. Air. 10th Anniv of International French Language Council.
831 **133** 50f. multicoloured . . . . 1·60 1·10

1977. Birds of Prey. Multicoloured.
833 20c. Type **135** 10 10
834 30c. African harrier hawk . . 10 10
835 50c. African fish eagle . . . 15 10
836 1f. Hooded vulture 15 15
837 3f. Augur buzzard 20 15
838 5f. Black kite 30 15
839 20f. Black-shouldered kite . . 1·50 70
840 100f. Bateleur . . . . 5·75 3·25

1912. Dr. Wernher von Braun Commemoration. Nos. 776/83 optd with **in memoriam WERNHER VON BRAUN 1912 - 1977**.
841 20c. Type **125** 10 10
842 30c. "Soyuz" rocket 10 10
843 50c. "Apollo" rocket 10 10
844 1f. "Apollo" after separation 10 10
845 2f. Approach to link up . . . 10 10
846 12f. Spacecraft docked . . . 40 20
847 30f. Sectional view of interiors . . . . 1·40 50
848 54f. "Apollo" after splashdown . . . . 2·50 1·50

138 Scout playing Whistle

139 Chimpanzees

1978. 10th Anniv of Rwanda Scout Association. Multicoloured.
851 20c. Type **138** 10 10
852 30c. Camp fire 10 10
853 50c. Scouts constructing a platform 10 10
854 1f. Two scouts 10 10
855 10f. Scouts on look-out . . . 20 10
856 18f. Scouts in canoe 45 35
857 26f. Cooking at camp fire . . 80 60
858 44f. Lord Baden-Powell . . . 1·50 1·25

1978. Apes. Multicoloured.
859 20c. Type **139** 10 10
860 30c. Gorilla 10 10
861 50c. Eastern black-and-white colobus 10 10
862 3f. Eastern needle-clawed bushbaby 10 10
863 10f. Mona monkey 30 10
864 26f. Potto 65 65
865 60f. Savanna monkey . . . . 1·90 1·90
866 150f. Olive baboon . . . . . 3·75 3·75

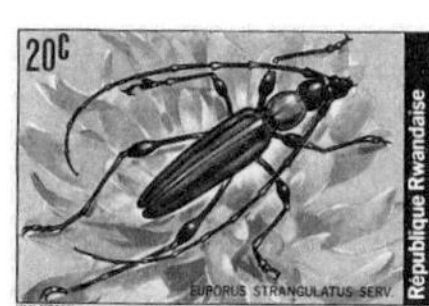

140 "Euporus strangulatus"

1978. Beetles. Multicoloured.
867 20c. Type **140** 10 10
868 30c. "Rhina afzelii" (vert) . . 10 10
869 50c. "Pentalobus palini" . . 10 10
870 3f. "Corynodes dejeani" (vert) 10 10
871 10f. "Mecynorhina torquata" 20 10
872 15f. "Mecocerus rhombeus" (vert) 55 10
873 20f. "Macrotoma serripes" 75 20
874 25f. "Neptunides stanleyi" (vert) 90 40
875 26f. "Petrognatha gigas" . . 90 40
876 100f. "Eudicella gralli" (vert) 3·25 2·50

141 Poling Boat across River of Poverty

1978. National Revolutionary Development Movement. Multicoloured.
877 4f. Type **141** 10 10
878 10f. Poling boat to right . . 15 10
879 26f. Type **141** 60 40
880 60f. As 10f. . . . . 1·10 85

142 Footballers, Cup and Flags of Netherlands and Peru

1978. World Cup Football Championship, Argentina. Multicoloured.
881 20c. Type **142** 10 10
882 30c. Flags of FIFA, Sweden and Spain 10 10
883 50c. Mascot and flags of Scotland and Iran 10 10
884 2f. Emblem and flags of West Germany and Tunisia . . . 10 10
885 3f. Cup and flags of Italy and Hungary 10 10
886 10f. Flags of FIFA, Brazil and Austria 20 10
887 34f. Mascot and flags of Poland and Mexico 85 70
888 100f. Emblem and flags of Argentina and France . . 2·50 2·00
No. 883 shows the Union Jack.

143 Wright Brothers and Wright Flyer I, 1903

1978. Aviation History. Multicoloured.
889 20c. Type **143** 10 10
890 30c. Alberto Santos-Dumont and biplane "14 bis", 1906 10 10
891 50c. Henri Farman and Farman Voisin No. 1 bis, 1908 . . . . 10 10
892 1f. Jan Olieslagers and Bleriot XI 10 10
893 3f. General Italo Balbo and Savoia S-17 flying boat, 1919 . . . . 10 10
894 10f. Charles Lindbergh and "Spirit of St. Louis", 1927 15 10
895 55f. Hugo Junkers and Junkers Ju 52/3m, 1932 . . 1·10 55
896 60f. Igor Sikorsky and Vought-Sikorsky VS-300 helicopter prototype . . . 1·60 85

143a Great Spotted Woodpecker and Oldenburg 1852 ⅓sgr. Stamp

1978. Air. "Philexafrique" Stamp Exhibition, Libreville, Gabon and Int Stamp Fair, Essen, West Germany. Multicoloured.
898 30f. Type **143a** . . . . 1·40 90
899 30f. Greater kudu and Rwanda 1967 20c. stamp 1·40 90

1978. 15th Anniv of Organization of African Unity. Nos. 544/5 optd **1963 1978**.
901 **88** 6f. multicoloured 30 10
902 – 94f. multicoloured . . . . 1·90 1·10

146 Spur-winged Goose and Mallard

147 "Papilio demodocus"

1978. Stock Rearing Year. Multicoloured.
903 20c. Type **146** 20 10
904 30c. Goats (horiz) 10 10
905 50c. Chickens 10 10
906 4f. Rabbits (horiz) 20 10
907 5f. Pigs 20 10
908 15f. Common turkey (horiz) 90 30
909 50f. Sheep and cattle . . . . 1·50 50
910 75f. Bull (horiz) . . . . . . 1·90 70

1979. Butterflies. Multicoloured.
911 20c. Type **147** 10 10
912 30c. "Precis octavia" 10 10
913 50c. "Charaxes smaragdalis caerulea" 10 10
914 4f. "Charaxes guderiana" . . 15 10
915 15f. "Colotis evippe" 20 10
916 30f. "Danaus limniace petiverana" 55 30
917 50f. "Byblia acheloia" . . . 1·50 55
918 150f. "Utetheisa pulchella" 3·75 1·40

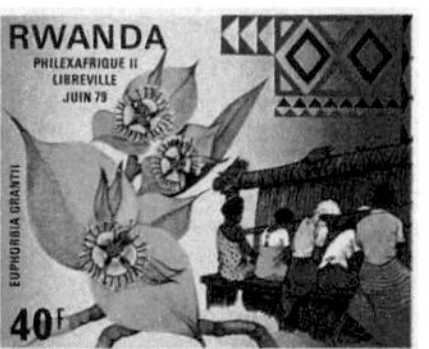

148 "Euphorbia grantii" and Women weaving

1979. "Philexafrique" Exhibition, Libreville. Mult.
919 40f. Type **148** . . . . 1·40 85
920 60f. Drummers and "Intelsat" satellite . . . . 2·25 1·10

149 "Polyscias fulva"

150 European Girl

1979. Trees. Multicoloured.
921 20c. Type **149** 10 10
922 30c. "Entandrophragma excelsum" (horiz) 10 10
923 50c. "Ilex mitis" 10 10
924 4f. "Kigelia africana" (horiz) 15 10
925 15f. "Ficus thonningi" . . . 35 10
926 20f. "Acacia senegal" (horiz) 50 20
927 50f. "Symphonia globulifera" 1·25 45
928 110f. "Acacia sieberana" (horiz) . . . . 2·50 1·25

1979. International Year of the Child. Each brown, gold and stone.
929 26f. Type **150** 65 60
930 26f. Asian 65 60
931 26f. Eskimo 65 60
932 26f. Asian boy 65 60
933 26f. African 65 60
934 26f. South American Indian 65 60
935 26f. Polynesian 65 60
936 26f. European girl (different) 65 60
937 42f. European and African (horiz) . . . . 2·00 65

151 Basket Weaving

1979. Handicrafts. Multicoloured.
939 50c. Type **151** 10 10
940 1f.50 Wood-carving (vert) . . 10 10
941 2f. Metal working 10 10
942 10f. Basket work (vert) . . . 35 10
943 20f. Basket weaving (different) 50 20
944 26f. Mural painting (vert) . . 65 55
945 40f. Pottery 95 65
946 100f. Smelting (vert) . . . . 2·50 1·75

153 Rowland Hill and 40c. Ruanda Stamp of 1916

1979. Death Centenary of Sir Rowland Hill. Multicoloured.
948 20c. Type **153** 10 10
949 30c. 1916 Occupation stamp 10 10
950 50c. 1918 "A.O." overprint 10 10
951 3f. 1925 overprinted 60c. stamp 10 10
952 10f. 1931 50c. African buffalo stamp 30 10
953 26f. 1942 20f. Common zebra stamp 65 15
954 60f. 1953 25f. Protea stamp 1·40 60
955 100f. 1960 Olympic stamp . . 2·75 1·10

154 Strange Weaver

156 Butare Rotary Club Banner, Globe and Chicago Club Emblem of 1905

155 Armstrong's first Step on Moon

1980. Birds. Multicoloured.
956 20c. Type **154** 15 10
957 30c. Regal sunbird (vert) . . 15 15
958 50c. White-spotted crake . . 15 15
959 3f. Black-casqued hornbill . . 30 15
960 10f. Ituri owl (vert) 70 25
961 26f. African emerald cuckoo 1·60 65
962 60f. Black-crowned waxbill (vert) . . . . 3·00 1·50
963 100f. Crowned eagle (vert) . . 5·50 2·50

1980. 10th Anniv of "Apollo 11" Moon Landing. Multicoloured.
964 50c. Type **155** 10 10
965 1f.50 Aldrin descending to Moon's surface 10 10
966 8f. Planting the American flag 55 10
967 30f. Placing seismometer . . . 95 60
968 50f. Taking samples . . . . 1·75 70
969 60f. Setting-up experiment . . 2·50 90

1980. 75th Anniv of Rotary International. Mult.
971 20c. Type **156** 10 10
972 30c. Kigali Rotary Club banner 10 10
973 50c. Type **156** 10 10
974 4f. As No. 972 . . . . 15 10
975 15f. Type **156** 35 10
976 20f. As No. 972 . . . . . . 45 20
977 50f. Type **156** 95 45
978 60f. As No. 972 . . . . . . 1·10 65

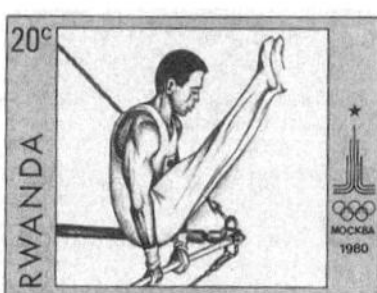

157 Gymnastics

1980. Olympic Games, Moscow.
979 **157** 20c. yellow and black . . 10 10
980 – 30c. green and black . . . 10 10
981 – 50c. red and black 10 10
982 – 3f. blue and black 15 10
983 – 20f. orange and black . . 45 20
984 – 26f. purple and black . . 50 25
985 – 50f. turquoise and black 1·10 45
986 – 100f. brown and black . . 2·50 1·10
DESIGNS: 30c. Basketball; 50c. Cycling; 3f. Boxing; 20f. Archery; 26f. Weightlifting; 50f. Javelin; 100f. Fencing.

159 "Geaster"

1980. Mushrooms. Multicoloured.
988 20c. Type **159** 10 10
989 30c. "Lentinus atrobrunneus" 10 10
990 50c. "Gomphus stereoides" . 10 10
991 4f. "Cantharellus cibarius" 30 10
992 10f. "Stilbothamnium dybowskii" 65 20
993 15f. "Xeromphalina tenuipes" 90 20
994 70f. "Podoscypha elegans" 3·75 80
995 100f. "Mycena" . . . . 7·50 1·60

160 "At the Theatre" (Toulouse-Lautrec)

1980. Impressionist Paintings. Multicoloured.

996	20c. "Still Life" (horiz) (Renoir)	10	10
997	30c. Type **160**	10	10
998	50c. "Seaside Garden" (Monet) (horiz)	10	10
999	4f. "Mother and Child" (Mary Cassatt)	10	10
1000	5f. "Starry Night" (Van Gogh) (horiz)	20	10
1001	10f. "Three Dancers at their Toilette" (Degas)	35	10
1002	50f. "The Card Players" (Cezanne) (horiz)	1·10	45
1003	70f. "Tahitian Girls" (Gauguin)	1·75	65
1004	100f. "La Grande Jatte" (Seurat) (horiz)	2·75	90

162 Revolutionary Scene

1980. 150th Anniv of Belgian Independence. Scenes of the Independence War from contemporary engravings.

1007	**162** 20c. green and brown	10	10
1008	– 30c. buff and brown	10	10
1009	– 50c. blue and brown	10	10
1010	– 9f. orange and brown	20	10
1011	– 10f. mauve and brown	30	10
1012	– 20f. green and brown	45	20
1013	– 70f. pink and brown	1·50	65
1014	– 90f. yellow and brown	1·90	1·00

163 Draining the Marshes

1980. Soil Protection and Conservation Year. Mult.

1015	20c. Type **163**	25	10
1016	30c. Bullock in pen (mixed farming and land fertilization)	10	10
1017	1f.50 Land irrigation and rice	10	10
1018	8f. Soil erosion and planting trees	20	10
1019	10f. Terrace	30	15
1020	40f. Crop fields	1·00	40
1021	90f. Bean crop	2·10	85
1022	100f. Picking tea	2·25	1·10

164 "Pavetta rwandensis"

1981. Flowers. Multicoloured.

1023	20c. Type **164**	10	10
1024	30c. "Cyrtorchis praetermissa"	10	10
1025	50c. "Pavonia urens"	10	10
1026	4f. "Cynorkis kassnerana"	10	10
1027	5f. "Gardenia ternifolia"	15	10
1028	10f. "Leptactina platyphylla"	20	10
1029	20f. "Lobelia petiolata"	50	15
1030	40f. "Tapinanthus brunneus"	1·25	50
1031	70f. "Impatiens niamniamensis"	1·60	95
1032	150f. "Dissotis rwandensis"	4·00	1·60

165 Mother and Child 166 Carol Singers

1981. SOS Children's Village. Multicoloured.

1033	20c. Type **165**	10	10
1034	30c. Child with pots	10	10
1035	50c. Children drawing	10	10
1036	1f. Girl sewing	10	10
1037	8f. Children playing	20	10
1038	10f. Girl knitting	20	10
1039	70f. Children making models	1·50	70
1040	150f. Mother and children	3·25	1·60

1981. Paintings by Norman Rockwell. Mult.

1041	20c. Type **166**	10	10
1042	30c. People of different races	10	10
1043	50c. Father Christmas	10	10
1044	1f. Coachman	10	10
1045	8f. Man at piano	15	10
1046	20f. "Springtime"	50	20
1047	50f. Man making donation to girl "nurse"	1·25	70
1048	70f. Clown	1·75	1·10

167 Serval

1981. Carnivorous Animals. Multicoloured.

1049	20c. Type **167**	10	10
1050	30c. Black-backed jackal	10	10
1051	2f. Servaline genet	10	10
1052	2f.50 Banded mongoose	10	10
1053	10f. Zorilla	20	10
1054	15f. Zaire clawless otter	55	10
1055	70f. African golden cat	1·75	1·25
1056	200f. Hunting dog (vert)	5·75	4·25

168 Drummer

1981. Telecommunications and Health. Mult.

1057	20c. Type **168**	10	10
1058	30c. Telephone receiver and world map	10	10
1059	2f. Airliner and radar screen	10	10
1060	2f.50 Satellite and computer tape	10	10
1061	10f. Satellite orbit and dish aerial	20	10
1062	15f. Tanker and radar equipment	35	25
1063	70f. Red Cross helicopter	1·90	70
1064	200f. Satellite	4·25	2·25

169 "St. Benedict leaving His Parents"

1981. 1500th Birth Anniv of St. Benedict. Mult.

1065	20c. Type **169**	10	10
1066	30c. Portrait (10th century) (vert)	10	10
1067	50c. Portrait (detail from "The Virgin of the Misericord" polyptich) (vert)	10	10
1068	4f. "St. Benedict presenting the Rules of His Order"	10	10
1069	5f. "St. Benedict and His Monks at their Meal"	15	10
1070	20f. Portrait (13th century) (vert)	45	40
1071	70f. St. Benedict at prayer (detail from "Our Lady in Glory with Sts. Gregory and Benedict") (vert)	1·75	1·40
1072	100f. "Priest bringing the Easter Meal to St. Benedict" (Jan van Coninxlo)	2·75	1·75

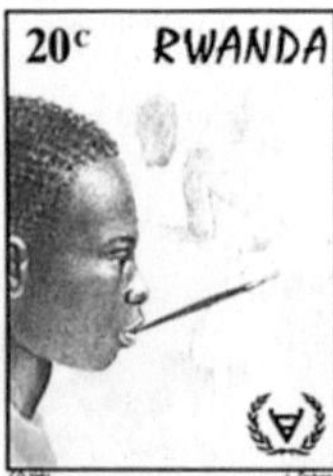

170 Disabled Child painting with Mouth

1981. International Year of Disabled Persons. Mult.

1073	20c. Type **170**	10	10
1074	30c. Boys on crutches playing football	10	10
1075	4f.50 Disabled girl knitting	10	10
1076	5f. Disabled child painting pot	15	10
1077	10f. Boy in wheelchair using saw	20	10
1078	60f. Child using sign language	1·25	60
1079	70f. Child in wheelchair playing with puzzle	1·60	70
1080	100f. Disabled child	2·00	1·10

172 Kob drinking at Pool

1981. Rural Water Supplies. Multicoloured.

1082	20c. Type **172**	10	10
1083	30c. Women collecting water (vert)	10	10
1084	50c. Constructing a pipeline	10	10
1085	10f. Woman collecting water from pipe (vert)	20	10
1086	10f. Man drinking	45	20
1087	70f. Woman collecting water (vert)	1·50	70
1088	100f. Floating pump (vert)	2·50	1·10

173 Cattle

1982. World Food Day. Multicoloured.

1089	20c. Type **173**	10	10
1090	30c. Bee keeping	10	10
1091	50c. Fishes	10	10
1092	1f. Avocado	10	10
1093	8f. Boy eating banana	10	10
1094	20f. Sorghum	45	15
1095	70f. Vegetables	1·50	65
1096	100f. Three generations and balanced diet	3·00	1·10

174 "Hibiscus berberidfolius"

1982. Flowers. Multicoloured.

1097	20c. Type **174**	10	10
1098	30c. "Hypericum lanceolatum" (vert)	10	10
1099	50c. "Canarina eminii"	10	10
1100	4f. "Polygala ruwenzoriensis"	10	10
1101	10f. "Kniphofia grantii" (vert)	15	10
1102	35f. "Euphorbia candelabrum" (vert)	90	60
1103	70f. "Disa erubescens" (vert)	1·75	80
1104	80f. "Gloriosa simplex"	2·40	1·10

175 Pres. Habyarimana and Flags

1982. 20th Anniv of Independence. Multicoloured.

1105	10f. Type **175**	20	10
1106	20f. Hands releasing doves (Peace)	35	20
1107	30f. Clasped hands and flag (Unity)	65	35
1108	50f. Building (Development)	1·00	50

176 Football

1982. World Cup Football Championship, Spain.

1109	**176** 20c. multicoloured	10	10
1110	– 30c. multicoloured	10	10
1111	– 1f.50 multicoloured	10	10
1112	– 8f. multicoloured	15	10
1113	– 10f. multicoloured	20	10
1114	– 20f. multicoloured	40	15
1115	– 70f. multicoloured	1·60	65
1116	– 90f. multicoloured	2·25	85

DESIGNS: 30c. to 90f. Designs show different players.

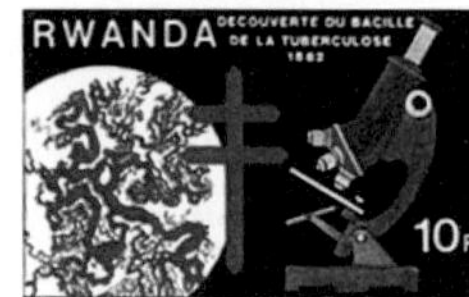

177 Microscope and Slide

1982. Centenary of Discovery of Tubercle Bacillus. Multicoloured.

1117	10f. Type **177**	15	10
1118	20f. Hand with test tube and slide	40	15
1119	70f. Lungs and slide	1·60	65
1120	100f. Dr. Robert Koch	2·25	95

180 African Elephants

1982. 10th Anniv of United Nations Environment Programme. Multicoloured.

1123	20c. Type **180**	10	10
1124	30c. Lion hunting impala	10	10
1125	50c. Flower	10	10
1126	4f. African buffalo	10	10
1127	5f. Impala	40	10
1128	10f. Flower (different)	20	10
1129	20f. Common zebra	45	15
1130	40f. Crowned cranes	1·50	35
1131	50f. African fish eagle	1·75	55
1132	70f. Woman with basket of fruit	1·60	80

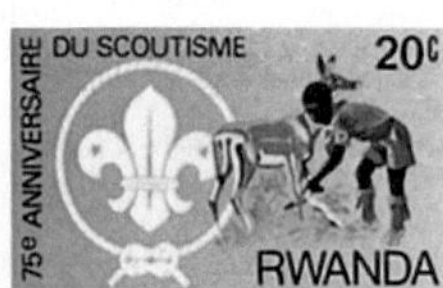

181 Scout tending Injured Kob

1982. 75th Anniv of Scout Movement. Mult.

1133	20c. Type **181**	10	10
1134	30c. Tents and northern doubled-collared sunbird	35	10
1135	1f.50 Campfire	10	10
1136	8f. Scout	15	10
1137	10f. Knot	20	10
1138	20f. Tent and campfire	40	15
1139	70f. Scout cutting stake	1·90	80
1140	90f. Scout salute	2·40	1·00

182 Northern Double-collared Sunbird 183 Driving Cattle

1983. Nectar-sucking Birds. Multicoloured.

1141	20c. Type **182**	10	10
1142	30c. Regal sunbird (horiz)	10	10
1143	50c. Red-tufted malachite sunbird	10	10
1144	4f. Bronze sunbird (horiz)	25	10
1145	5f. Collared sunbird	35	10
1146	10f. Blue-headed sunbird (horiz)	70	20

1147 20f. Purple-breasted sunbird 1·40 50
1148 40f. Coppery sunbird (horiz) 3·00 95
1149 50f. Olive-bellied sunbird 3·25 1·25
1150 70f. Red-chested sunbird (horiz) 4·50 2·00

1983. Campaign Against Soil Erosion. Mult.
1151 20c. Type **183** 10 10
1152 30c. Pineapple plantation 10 10
1153 50c. Interrupted ditches 10 10
1154 9f. Hedged terraces 20 10
1155 10f. Re-afforestation 20 10
1156 20f. Anti-erosion barriers 40 15
1157 30f. Contour planting 65 30
1158 50f. Terraces 1·00 40
1159 60f. River bank protection 1·40 60
1160 70f. Alternate fallow and planted strips 1·60 80

184 Feeding Ducks

1983. Birth Cent of Cardinal Cardijan (founder of Young Catholic Workers Movement). Mult.
1161 20c. Type **184** 10 10
1162 30c. Harvesting bananas 10 10
1163 50c. Carrying melons 10 10
1164 10f. Wood-carving 20 10
1165 19f. Making shoes 35 15
1166 20f. Children in field of millet 45 15
1167 70f. Embroidering 1·40 60
1168 80f. Cardinal Cardijan 1·60 65

185 Young Gorillas

1983. Mountain Gorillas. Multicoloured.
1169 20c. Type **185** 10 10
1170 30c. Gorilla family 10 10
1171 9f.50 Young and adult 45 30
1172 10f. Mother with young 45 30
1173 20f. Heads 65 45
1174 30f. Adult and head 90 50
1175 60f. Adult (vert) 2·00 1·40
1176 70f. Close-up of adult (vert) 2·40 1·50

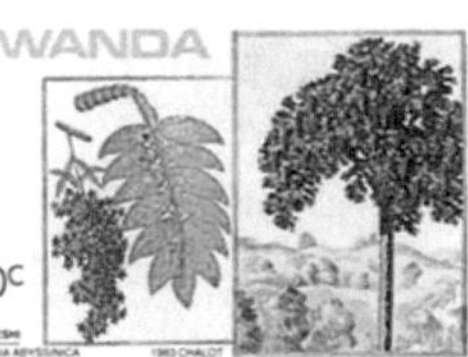

187 "Hagenia abyssinica"

1984. Trees. Multicoloured.
1178 20c. Type **187** 10 10
1179 30c. "Dracaena steudneri" 10 10
1180 50c. "Phoenix reclinata" 10 10
1181 10f. "Podocarpus milanjianus" 15 10
1182 19f. "Entada abyssinica" 40 15
1183 70f. "Parinari excelsa" 1·60 65
1184 100f. "Newtonia buchananii" 2·00 95
1185 200f. "Acacia gerrardi" (vert) 4·50 1·60

188 "Hikari" Express Train, Japan

189 "Le Martial", 1783

1984. World Communications Year. Multicoloured.
1186 20c. Type **188** 20 10
1187 30c. Liner and radar 15 10
1188 4f.50 Radio and transmitter 15 10
1189 10f. Telephone dial and cable 20 10
1190 15f. Letters and newspaper 35 10
1191 50f. Airliner and control tower 1·10 45
1192 70f. Television and antenna 1·60 65
1193 100f. Satellite and computer tape 2·50 90

1984. Bicentenary of Manned Flight. Mult.
1194 20c. Type **189** 10 10
1195 30c. De Rozier and Marquis d'Arlandes flight, 1783 10 10
1196 50c. Charles and Robert (1783) and Blanchard (1784) flights 10 10
1197 9f. M. and Mme. Blanchard 20 10
1198 10f. Blanchard and Jeffries, 1785 20 10
1199 50f. Demuyter (1937) and Piccard and Kipfer (1931) flights 1·10 40
1200 80f. Modern hot-air balloons 2·75 1·90
1201 200f. Trans-Atlantic flight, 1978 3·50 2·50

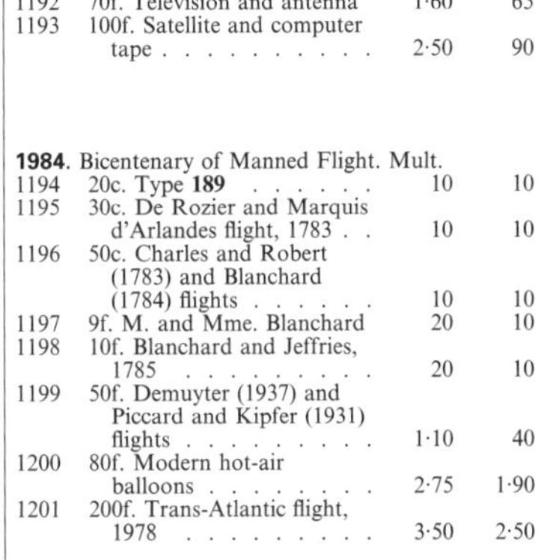
190 Equestrian

1984. Olympic Games, Los Angeles. Multicoloured.
1202 20c. Type **190** 10 10
1203 30c. Windsurfing 15 10
1204 50c. Football 10 10
1205 9f. Swimming 20 10
1206 10f. Hockey 20 10
1207 40f. Fencing 1·25 70
1208 80f. Running 2·00 1·75
1209 200f. Boxing 5·00 4·00

191 Mare and Foal

1984. Common Zebras and African Buffaloes. Mult.
1210 20c. Type **191** 10 10
1211 30c. Buffalo and calf (vert) 10 10
1212 50c. Pair of zebras (vert) 10 10
1213 9f. Zebras fighting 20 10
1214 10f. Close-up of buffalo (vert) 30 10
1215 80f. Herd of zebras 1·90 1·40
1216 100f. Close-up of zebras (vert) 2·50 1·75
1217 200f. Buffalo charging 4·75 3·50

193 Gorillas at Water-hole

1985. Gorillas. Multicoloured.
1219 10f. Type **193** 1·90 80
1220 15f. Two gorillas in tree 2·75 85
1221 25f. Gorilla family 3·75 2·10
1222 30f. Three adults 4·75 3·00

194 Man feeding Fowl

1985. Food Production Year. Multicoloured.
1224 20c. Type **194** 20 10
1225 30c. Men carrying pineapples 15 10
1226 50c. Farm animals 10 10
1227 9f. Men filling sacks with produce 20 10
1228 10f. Agricultural instruction 30 10
1229 50f. Sowing seeds 1·00 45
1230 80f. Storing produce 1·60 65
1231 100f. Working in banana plantation 2·10 80

195 Emblem

1985. 10th Anniv of National Revolutionary Redevelopment Movement.
1232 **195** 10f. multicoloured 20 10
1233 30f. multicoloured 65 30
1234 70f. multicoloured 1·60 70

196 U.N. Emblem within "40"

1985. 40th Anniv of U.N.O.
1235 **196** 50f. multicoloured 1·10 90
1236 100f. multicoloured 2·50 2·10

197 Barn Owls

1985. Birth Bicentenary of John J. Audubon (ornithologist). Multicoloured.
1237 10f. Type **197** 75 30
1238 20f. White-faced scops owls 1·60 60
1239 40f. Ruby-throated humming birds 3·00 1·10
1240 80f. Eastern meadowlarks 6·75 2·40

198 "Participation, Development and Peace"

1985. International Youth Year. Multicoloured.
1241 7f. Type **198** 15 10
1242 9f. Cycling 30 10
1243 44f. Youths carrying articles on head (teamwork) 1·10 45
1244 80f. Education 1·75 80

1985. 75th Anniv of Girl Guide Movement. Nos. 1133/40 optd **1910/1985** and guide emblem.
1245 20c. Type **181** 10 10
1246 30c. Tents 30 10
1247 1f.50 Campfire 10 10
1248 8f. Scout 20 10
1249 10f. Knot 20 10
1250 20f. Tent and campfire 45 10
1251 70f. Scout cutting stake 1·60 65
1252 90f. Scout salute 2·50 90

201 Container Lorry (Transport)

1986. Transport and Communications. Mult.
1254 10f. Type **201** 35 10
1255 30f. Handstamping cover (posts) 80 35
1256 40f. Kigali Earth Station (telecommunication) 1·10 45
1257 80f. Kigali airport (aviation) (48 × 31 mm) 1·75 1·25

1986. Intensified Agriculture Year. Nos. 1152/60 optd **ANNEE 1986 INTENSIFICATION AGRICOLE** or surch also.
1258 9f. Hedged terraces 20 10
1259 10f. Re-afforestation 20 10
1260 10f. on 30c. Pineapple plantation 20 10
1261 10f. on 50c. Interrupted ditches 20 10
1262 20f. Anti-erosion barriers 45 20
1263 30f. Contour planning 65 35
1264 50f. Terraces 1·10 50
1265 60f. River bank protection 1·40 55
1266 70f. Alternate fallow and planted strips 1·60 70

203 Morocco v England

1986. World Cup Football Championship, Mexico. Multicoloured.
1267 2f. Type **203** 10 10
1268 4f. Paraguay v Iraq 10 10
1269 5f. Brazil v Spain 10 10
1270 10f. Italy v Argentina 55 35
1271 40f. Mexico v Belgium 1·60 85
1272 45f. France v Russia 1·75 1·00

204 Roan Antelopes

1986. Akagera National Park. Multicoloured.
1273 4f. Type **204** 15 10
1274 7f. Whale-headed storks 45 20
1275 9f. Cape eland 20 10
1276 10f. Giraffe 40 10
1277 80f. African elephant 2·50 85
1278 90f. Crocodile 3·00 1·00
1279 100f. Heuglin's masked weavers 5·00 2·75
1280 100f. Zebras and eastern white pelican 5·00 2·75

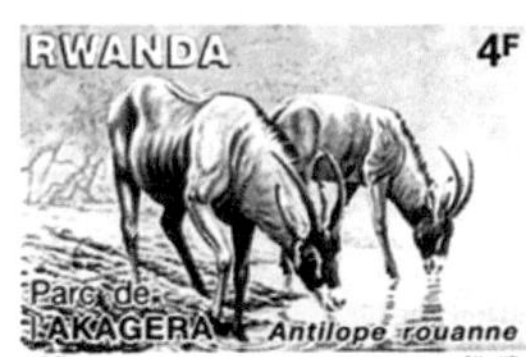

205 People of Different Races on Globe

1986. Christmas. International Peace Year. Mult.
1281 10f. Type **205** 35 15
1282 15f. Dove and globe 45 15
1283 30f. Type **205** 80 35
1284 70f. As No. 1282 1·75 1·00

206 Mother breast-feeding Baby

1987. U.N.I.C.E.F. Child Survival Campaign. Multicoloured.
1285 4f. Type **206** 15 15
1286 6f. Mother giving oral rehydration therapy to baby 20 15
1287 10f. Nurse immunizing baby 35 25
1288 70f. Nurse weighing baby and graph 1·75 1·60

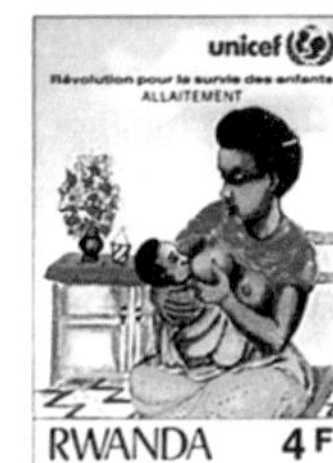

207 Couple packing Baskets with Food

1987. Food Self-sufficiency Year. Multicoloured.
1289 5f. Type **207** 10 10
1290 7f. Woman and baskets of food 15 10

1291 40f. Man with baskets of fish and fruits . . . . . 1·75 45
1292 60f. Fruits and vegetables 2·25 80

208 Pres. Habyarimana and Soldiers

1987. 25th Anniv of Independence. Multicoloured.
1293 10f. Type **208** 20 10
1294 40f. President at meeting . . 90 45
1295 70f. President with Pope John Paul II . . . . . . 2·50 85
1296 100f. Pres. Habyarimana (vert) . . . . 2·50 1·10

209 Bananas

1987. Fruits. Multicoloured.
1297 10f. Type **209** 20 10
1298 40f. Pineapples (horiz) . . . 90 45
1299 80f. Papaya (horiz) . . . . 2·25 90
1300 90f. Avocados (horiz) . . . 2·50 1·00
1301 100f. Strawberries . . . . . 2·50 1·10

210 Mother carrying cub

1987. The Leopard. Multicoloured.
1302 50f. Type **210** . . . . 2·00 1·10
1303 50f. Leopards fighting . . . 2·00 1·10
1304 50f. Leopards with prey . . 2·00 1·10
1305 50f. Leopard with prey in tree . . . . 2·00 1·10
1306 50f. Leopard leaping from tree . . . . 2·00 1·10

211 Village Activities

1987. International Volunteers Day. Mult.
1307 5f. Type **211** 10 10
1308 12f. Pupils in schoolroom 35 10
1309 20f. View of village 55 30
1310 60f. Woman tending oxen 1·75 85

213 Carpenter's Shop

1988. Rural Incomes Protection Year. Mult.
1312 10f. Type **213** 20 10
1313 40f. Dairy farm 95 95
1314 60f. Workers in field . . . 1·50 55
1315 80f. Selling baskets of eggs 2·10 1·50

214 Chimpanzees

1988. Primates of Nyungwe Forest. Multicoloured.
1316 2f. Type **214** 25 15
1317 3f. Black and white colobus 25 15
1318 10f. Lesser bushbabies . . . 85 50
1319 90f. Monkeys . . . . 6·00 3·00

215 Boxing

1988. Olympic Games, Seoul. Multicoloured.
1320 5f. Type **215** 10 10
1321 7f. Relay race 15 10
1322 8f. Table tennis 20 10
1323 10f. Running 35 15
1324 90f. Hurdling . . . . 2·25 1·00

216 "25" on Map of Africa

1988. 25th Anniv of Organization of African Unity. Multicoloured.
1325 5f. Type **216** 15 10
1326 7f. Hands clasped across map 20 10
1327 8f. Building on map 20 10
1328 90f. Words forming map . . 2·75 2·25

218 Newspaper Fragment and Refugees in Boat

1988. 125th Anniv of Red Cross Movement. Mult.
1330 10f. Type **218** 20 10
1331 30f. Red Cross workers and patient 80 35
1332 40f. Red Cross worker and elderly lady (vert) 95 40
1333 100f. Red Cross worker and family (vert) . . . . . . 2·75 1·25

219 "Plectranthus barbatus"

1989. Plants. Multicoloured.
1334 5f. Type **219** 15 20
1335 10f. "Tetradenia riparia" . . 50 20
1336 20f. "Hygrophila auriculata 1·00 45
1337 40f. "Datura stramonium 2·10 1·00
1338 50f. "Pavetta ternifolia" . . 2·75 1·40

220 Emblem, Dates and Sunburst

1989. Centenary of Interparliamentary Union. Mult.
1339 10f. Type **220** 30 10
1340 30f. Lake 85 65
1341 70f. River . . . . 1·60 1·40
1342 90f. Sun's rays . . . . . . 2·25 1·75

222 Throwing Clay and Finished Pots

1989. Rural Self-help Year. Multicoloured.
1344 10f. Type **222** 30 10
1345 70f. Carrying baskets of produce (vert) . . . . . 1·60 1·40
1346 90f. Firing clay pots . . . . 2·50 2·00
1347 200f. Clearing roadway . . 5·00 3·50

223 "Triumph of Marat" (Boilly)

1990. Bicentenary of French Revolution. Mult.
1348 10f. Type **223** 30 10
1349 60f. "Rouget de Lisle singing La Marseillaise" (Pils) . . . . 1·60 1·50
1350 70f. "Oath of the Tennis Court" (Jacques Louis David) . . . . 2·00 1·75
1351 100f. "Trial of Louis XVI" (Joseph Court) . . . . . 3·00 2·75

224 Old and New Lifestyles

1990. 30th Anniv of Revolution. Multicoloured.
1352 10f. Type **224** 30 10
1353 60f. Couple holding farming implements (vert) . . . . 1·60 1·40
1354 70f. Modernization . . . . 1·75 1·40
1355 100f. Flag, map and warrior 2·50 2·50

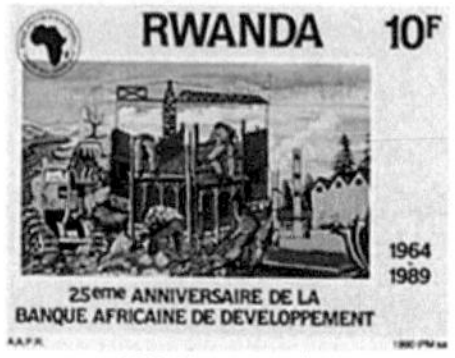

225 Construction

1990. 25th Anniv (1989) of African Development Bank. Multicoloured.
1356 10f. Type **225** 30 10
1357 20f. Tea picking 55 35
1358 40f. Road building . . . . 1·10 95
1359 90f. Tea pickers and modern housing . . . . 2·50 2·10

1990. World Cup Football Championship, Italy. Nos. 1267/72 optd **ITALIA 90**.
1361 **203** 2f. multicoloured 35 35
1362 – 4f. multicoloured 35 35
1363 – 5f. multicoloured 40 40
1364 – 10f. multicoloured . . . 65 65
1365 – 40f. multicoloured . . . 2·50 2·50
1366 – 45f. multicoloured . . . 2·75 2·75

228 Pope John Paul II

1990. Papal Visits. Multicoloured.
1367 10f. Type **228** 75 75
1368 70f. Pope giving blessing . . 8·25 8·25

229 Adults learning Alphabet at School

1991. International Literacy Year (1990). Mult.
1370 10f. Type **229** 15 10
1371 20f. Children reading at school 35 20
1372 50f. Lowland villagers learning alphabet in field 90 80
1373 90f. Highland villagers learning alphabet outdoors . . . . 1·40 1·10

230 Tool-making

1991. Self-help Organizations. Multicoloured.
1374 10f. Type **230** 15 10
1375 20f. Rearing livestock . . . 35 20
1376 50f. Textile manufacture . . 1·40 1·10
1377 90f. Construction . . . . . 2·00 1·50

231 Statue of Madonna

1992. Death Centenary of Cardinal Lavigerie (founder of Orders of White Fathers and Sisters).
1378 **231** 5f. multicoloured . . . . 95 1·00
1379 – 15f. multicoloured . . . 2·50 2·50
1380 – 70f. black and mauve . . 12·00 12·00
1381 – 110f. black and blue . . 18·00 20·00
DESIGNS—VERT: 15f. White Sister; 110f. Cardinal Lavigerie. HORIZ: 70f. White Fathers in Uganda, 1908.

232 Fisherman

1992. Int Nutrition Conference, Rome. Mult.
1382 15f. Type **232** 80 45
1383 50f. Market fruit stall . . . 1·60 1·40
1384 100f. Man milking cow . . 3·25 2·75
1385 500f. Woman breastfeeding 17·00 14·50

233 Running

1993. Olympic Games, Barcelona (1992). Mult.
1386 20f. Type **233** . . . . 2·50 2·50
1387 30f. Swimming . . . . . . 4·00 4·50
1388 90f. Football . . . . 12·00 10·00

234 Toad

1998. Animals. Multicoloured.
1390 15f. Type **234** 20 30
1391 100f. Snail 80 85
1392 150f. Porcupine . . . . . . 1·25 1·25
1393 300f. Chameleon . . . . . 2·50 2·75

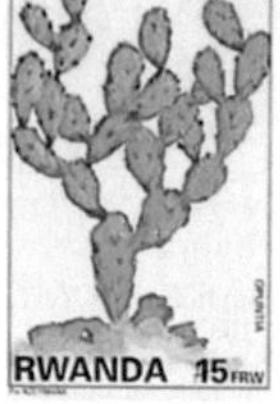

235 "Opuntia"

1998. Plants. Multicoloured.
1395 15f. Type **235** 20 30
1396 100f. "Gloriosa superba" . . 80 85

1397 150f. "Markhamia lutea" . . 1·25 1·25
1398 300f. "Hagenia abyssinica" (horiz) . . . . 2·50 2·75

RYUKYU ISLANDS Pt. 18

Group of islands between Japan and Taiwan, formerly Japanese until occupied by U.S. forces in 1945. After a period of military rule they became semi-autonomous under U.S. administration. The Amami Oshima group reverted to Japan in December 1953. The remaining islands were returned to Japan on 15 May 1972. Japanese stamps are now in use.

1948. 100 sen = 1 yen.
1958. 100 cents = 1 dollar (U.S.).

1 Cycad Palm — 3 Tribute Junk

1948.
1 **1** 5s. purple . . . . 3·00 1·75
2 – 10s. green . . . . 3·50 2·25
3 **1** 20s. green . . . . 3·50 2·25
4 **3** 30s. red . . . . 3·50 2·25
5 – 40s. purple . . . . 3·00 1·75
6 **3** 50s. blue . . . . 3·50 2·50
7 – 1y. blue . . . . 3·50 2·50
DESIGNS: 10s., 40s. Easter lily; 1y. Farmer with hoe.

6 Shi-Shi Roof Tiles — 12 Dove over Map of Ryukyus

1950.
8 **6** 50s. red 25 25
10 – 1y. blue . . . . 2·75 1·25
11 – 2y. purple . . . . 12·00 3·00
12 – 3y. pink . . . . 20·00 8·00
13 – 4y. grey . . . . 8·00 3·00
14 – 5y. green . . . . 10·00 4·50
DESIGNS: 1y. Shuri woman; 2y. Former Okinawa Palace, Shuri; 3y. Dragon's head; 4y. Okinawa women; 5y. Common spider and strawberry conches and radula scallop.

1950. Air.
15 **12** 8y. blue . . . . 65·00 20·00
16 12y. green . . . . 42·00 16·00
17 16y. red . . . . 18·00 12·00

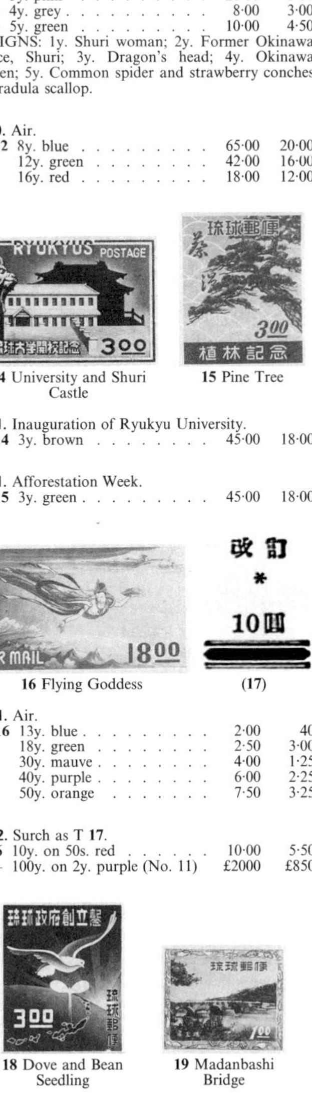

14 University and Shuri Castle — 15 Pine Tree

1951. Inauguration of Ryukyu University.
19 **14** 3y. brown . . . . 45·00 18·00

1951. Afforestation Week.
20 **15** 3y. green . . . . 45·00 18·00

16 Flying Goddess — (17)

1951. Air.
21 **16** 13y. blue . . . . 2·00 40
22 18y. green . . . . 2·50 3·00
23 30y. mauve . . . . 4·00 1·25
24 40y. purple . . . . 6·00 2·25
25 50y. orange . . . . 7·50 3·25

1952. Surch as T **17**.
27 **6** 10y. on 50s. red . . . . . . 10·00 5·50
29 – 100y. on 2y. purple (No. 11) £2000 £850

18 Dove and Bean Seedling — 19 Madanbashi Bridge

1952. Establishment of Ryukyuan Government.
30 **18** 3y. red . . . . £100 20·00

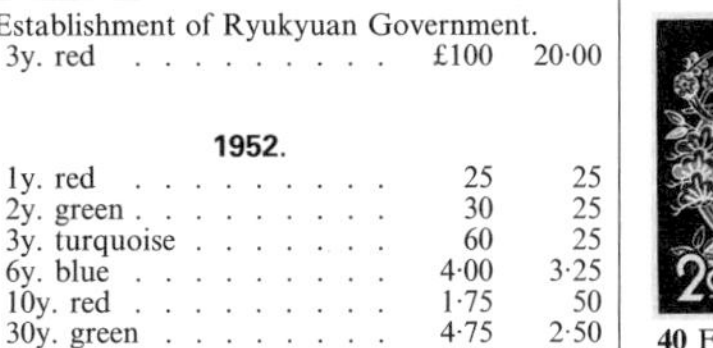

1952.
31 **19** 1y. red 25 25
32 – 2y. green 30 25
33 – 3y. turquoise 60 25
34 – 6y. blue . . . . 4·00 3·25
35 – 10y. red . . . . 1·75 50
36 – 30y. green . . . . 4·75 2·50
37 – 50y. purple . . . . 6·00 2·00
38 – 100y. purple . . . . 12·00 1·50
DESIGNS: 2y. Presence Chamber, Shuri Palace; 3y. Shuri Gate; 6y. Sogenji Temple Wall; 10y. Bensaitendo Temple; 30y. Sonohyamutake Gate; 50y. Tamaudum Mausoleum, Shuri; 100y. Hosho-chai Bridge.

27 Reception at Shuri Castle

28 Perry and American Fleet at Naha Harbour — 29 Chofu Ota and Matrix

1953. Centenary of Commodore Perry's Visit to Okinawa.
39 **27** 3y. purple . . . . 12·00 4·00
40 **28** 6y. blue . . . . 2·25 2·40

1953. 3rd Press Week.
41 **29** 4y. brown . . . . 12·00 5·00

30 Wine Flask to fit around Waist — 33 Shigo Toma and Pen-nib

1954.
42 **30** 4y. brown 50 35
43 – 15y. red . . . . 2·25 1·75
44 – 20y. orange . . . . 3·25 2·25
DESIGNS: 15y. Tung Dar Bon (lacquer bowl); 20y. Kasuri (textile pattern).

1954. 4th Press Week.
45 **33** 4y. blue . . . . 10·00 3·50

34 Noguni Shrine and Sweet Potatoes — 35 Stylized Trees

1955. 350th Anniv of Introduction of Sweet Potato Plant.
46 **34** 4y. blue . . . . 10·00 4·00

1956. Afforestation Week.
47 **35** 4y. green . . . . 8·00 3·00

38 Nidotekito Dance — 39 Telephone and Dial

1956. National Dances.
48 – 5y. purple . . . . 1·10 60
49 – 8y. violet . . . . 1·40 1·25
50 **38** 14y. brown . . . . 2·25 2·25
DESIGNS: 5y. Willow dance; 8y. Straw-hat dance.

1956. Inauguration of Telephone Dialling System.
51 **39** 4y. violet . . . . 12·00 8·00

40 Floral Garland — 41 Flying Goddess

1956. New Year.
52 **40** 2y. multicoloured . . . . . 2·00 1·40

1957. Air.
53 **41** 15y. green . . . . 2·00 40
54 20y. red . . . . 4·50 3·00
55 35y. green . . . . 10·00 4·00
56 45y. brown . . . . 16·00 6·00
57 60y. grey . . . . 22·00 8·50

42 "Rocket" Pencils — 43 Phoenix

1957. 7th Press Week.
58 **42** 4y. blue 55 55

1957. New Year.
59 **43** 2y. multicoloured 40 20

44 Various Ryukyuan Postage Stamps

1958. 10th Anniv of First Postage Stamps of Ryukyu Islands.
60 **44** 4y. multicoloured . . . . . 1·00 60

45 Stylized Dollar Sign over Yen Symbol

1958. With or without gum (Nos. 68/69), no gum (others).
61 **45** $\frac{1}{2}$c. yellow 25 20
62 1c. green 25 20
63 2c. blue 25 25
64 3c. red 20 15
65 4c. green 60 45
66 5c. brown . . . . 2·00 50
67 10c. blue . . . . 3·25 50
68 25c. blue . . . . 3·50 80
69 50c. grey . . . . 7·00 1·00
70 $1 purple . . . . 10·00 1·25

46 Gateway of Courtesy

1958. Restoration of Shuri Gateway.
71 **46** 3c. multicoloured . . . . . 1·25 50

47 Lion Dance — 48 Trees

1958. New Year.
72 **47** $1\frac{1}{2}$c. multicoloured 30 25

1959. Afforestation Week.
73 **48** 3c. multicoloured . . . . . 1·50 1·25

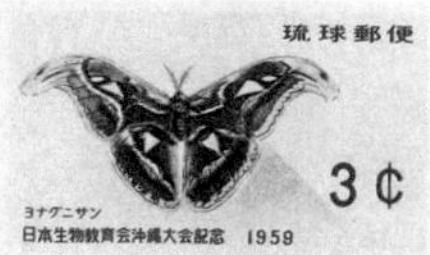

49 Atlas Moth — 50 Hibiscus

1959. Japanese Biological Teachers' Conference, Okinawa.
74 **49** 3c. multicoloured . . . . . 2·00 1·25

1959. Multicoloured. (a) Inscr as in T **50**.
75 $\frac{1}{2}$c. Type **50** 30 20
76 3c. Moorish idol . . . . . . 1·10 25
77 8c. Zebra moon, banded bonnet and textile cone (shells) . . . . 8·00 2·00
78 13c. Leaf butterfly (value at left) . . . . 2·00 1·50
79 17c. Jellyfish . . . . 22·00 5·50

(b) Inscr smaller and 13c. with value at right.
87 $\frac{1}{2}$c. Type **50** 30 15
88 3c. As No. 76 . . . . 2·00 20
89 8c. As No. 77 . . . . 2·50 1·00
90 13c. As No. 78 . . . . 1·75 1·00
91 17c. As No. 79 . . . . 8·00 3·25

55 Yakazi (Ryukyuan toy) — (56)

1959. New Year.
80 **55** $1\frac{1}{2}$c. multicoloured 80 40

1959. Air. Surch as T **56**.
81 **41** 9c. on 15y. green . . . . . 2·00 40
82 14c. on 20y. red . . . . . . 3·50 3·00
83 19c. on 35y. green . . . . . 5·00 4·00
84 27c. on 45y. brown . . . . . 10·00 6·00
85 35c. on 60y. grey . . . . . 14·00 8·00

57 University Badge — 60 "Munjuru"

1960. 10th Anniv of University of the Ryukyus.
86 **57** 3c. multicoloured . . . . . 1·25 60

1960. Air. Surch.
92 **30** 9c. on 4y. brown . . . . . 5·00 60
93 – 14c. on 5y. purple (No. 48) 3·00 2·00
94 – 19c. on 15y. red (No. 43) . . 5·00 2·75
95 **38** 27c. on 14y. brown . . . . 6·00 4·25
96 – 35c. on 20y. orange (No. 44) 7·00 5·25

1960. Ryukyuan Dances. Mult. (a) Inscr as in T **60**.
97 1c. Type **60** . . . . 2·00 1·00
98 $2\frac{1}{2}$c. "Inohabushi" . . . . . 1·75 1·00
99 5c. "Hatomabushi" . . . . . 1·00 1·00
100 10c. "Hanafu" . . . . 1·50 1·00

(b) As T **60** but additionally inscr "RYUKYUS".
107 1c. Type **60** 15 15
108 $2\frac{1}{2}$c. As No. 98 . . . . 15 15
109 4c. As No. 98 . . . . 20 15
110 5c. As No. 99 . . . . 30 25
111 10c. As No. 100 . . . . . . 50 15
112 20c. "Shudun" . . . . 1·25 35
113 25c. "Haodori" . . . . 1·25 60
114 50c. "Nobori Kuduchi" . . . 1·75 60
115 $1 "Koteibushi" . . . . 2·25 70

65 Start of Race

1960. 8th Kyushu Athletic Meeting.
101 – 3c. red, green and blue . . 5·00 1·50
102 **65** 8c. green and orange . . . 1·75 1·00
DESIGN: 3c. Torch and coastal scene.

66 Little Egret and Rising Sun

1960. National Census.
103 **66** 3c. brown . . . . 6·25 2·50

67 Bull Fight

1960. New Year.
104 **67** 1½c. brown, buff and blue . . . 1·00 60

68 Native Pine Tree

1961. Afforestation Week.
105 **68** 3c. deep green, red & green 1·75 90

69 Naha, Junk, Liner and City Seal

1961. 40th Anniv of Naha City.
106 **69** 3c. turquoise . . . . . . 2·50 1·25

74 Flying Goddess

79 White Silver Temple

1961. Air.
116 **74** 9c. multicoloured 50 15
117 – 14c. multicoloured 70 60
118 – 19c. multicoloured . . . . 1·25 75
119 – 27c. multicoloured . . . . 1·50 75
120 – 35c. multicoloured . . . . 2·00 75
DESIGNS: 14c. Flying goddess playing flute; 19c. Wind god; 27c. Wind god (different); 35c. Flying goddess over trees.

1961. Unification of Itoman District and Takamine, Kanegushiku and Miwa Villages.
121 **79** 3c. brown . . . . 1·25 75

80 Books and Bird

81 Sunrise and Eagles

1961. 10th Anniv of Ryukyu Book Week.
122 **80** 3c. multicoloured . . . . . 1·25 75

1961. New Year.
123 **81** 1½c. red, black and gold . . 3·25 1·00

82 Govt Building, Steps and Trees

85 Shuri Gate and Campaign Emblem

1962. 10th Anniv of Ryukyu Government. Mult.
124 1½c. Type **82** 60 60
125 3c. Government building . . 90 75

1962. Malaria Eradication. Multicoloured.
126 3c. "Anopheles hyrcanus sinensis" (mosquito) . . . 70 60
127 8c. Type **85** . . . . 1·25 1·75

86 Windmill, Dolls and Horse

87 "Hibiscus lilaceus"

1962. Children's Day.
128 **86** 3c. multicoloured . . . . . 2·00 1·25

1962. Ryukyu Flowers. Multicoloured.
129 ½c. Type **87** 20 15
142 1½c. "Etithyllum strictum" . . 30 20
130 2c. "Ixora chinensis" 20 25
131 3c. "Erythrina indica" . . . 50 20
132 3c. "Caesalpinia pulcherrima" 20 20
133 8c. "Schima mertensiana" . . 75 25
134 13c. "Impatiens balsamina" 1·00 50
135 15c. "Hamaomoto" (herb) . . 1·25 55
136 17c. "Alpinia speciosa" . . . 1·00 30
No. 142 is smaller, 18¾ × 22½ mm.

95 Akaeware Bowl

97 "Hare and Water" (textile design)

96 Kendo (Japanese Fencing)

1962. Philatelic Week.
137 **95** 3c. multicoloured . . . . . 5·00 2·25

1962. All-Japan Kendo Meeting.
138 **96** 3c. multicoloured . . . . . 5·00 2·50

1962. New Year.
139 **97** 1½c. multicoloured . . . . 2·50 1·00

98 Reaching Maturity (clay relief)

101 Okinawa Highway

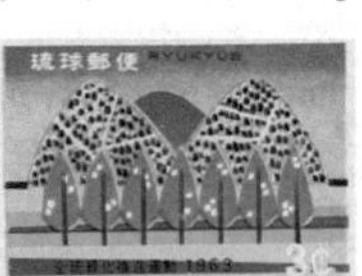
99 Trees and Wooded Hills

1963. Adults' Day.
140 **98** 3c. gold, black and blue . . 80 50

1963. Afforestation Week.
141 **99** 3c. multicoloured 80 50

1963. Opening of Okinawa Highway.
143 **101** 3c. multicoloured . . . . 1·00 60

102 Black Kites over Islands

1963. Bird Week.
144 **102** 3c. multicoloured . . . . 1·25 1·00

103 Shioya Bridge

1963. Opening of Shioya Bridge, Okinawa.
145 **103** 3c. multicoloured . . . . 1·00 60

104 Lacquerware Bowl

105 Convair 880 Jetliner and Shuri Gate

1963. Philatelic Week.
146 **104** 3c. multicoloured . . . . 3·25 1·50

1963. Air.
147 **105** 5½c. multicoloured 25 20
148 – 7c. black, red and blue . . 35 30
DESIGN: 7c. Convair 880 jetliner over sea.

107 Map and Emblem

1963. Meeting of Junior Int Chamber, Naha.
149 **107** 3c. multicoloured 60 50

108 Nakagusuku Castle Ruins

1963. Ancient Buildings Protection Week.
150 **108** 3c. multicoloured 90 50

109 Flame

110 Bingata "dragon" (textile design)

1963. 15th Anniv of Declaration of Human Rights.
151 **109** 3c. multicoloured 70 40

1963. New Year.
152 **110** 1½c. multicoloured 40 30

111 Carnation

112 Pineapples and Sugar-cane

1964. Mothers' Day.
153 **111** 3c. multicoloured 60 30

1964. Agricultural Census.
154 **112** 3c. multicoloured 45 30

113 Hand-woven Sash

114 Girl Scout and Emblem

1964. Philatelic Week.
155 **113** 3c. brown, blue and pink 60 30

1964. 10th Anniv of Ryukyu Girl Scouts.
156 **114** 3c. multicoloured 40 25

115 Transmitting Tower

117 Shuri Gate and Olympic Torch

1964. Inauguration of Ryukyu–Jap'an Microwave Link.
157 **115** 3c. green and black . . . 1·00 85
158 – 8c. blue and black . . . . 1·40 1·00
DESIGN: 8c. "Bowl" receiving aerial.
Both stamps have "1963" cancelled by bars and "1964" inserted in black.

1964. Passage of Olympic Torch through Okinawa.
159 **117** 3c. multicoloured 40 30

118 "Naihanchi" (Karate stance)

1964. Karate ("self-defence"). Multicoloured.
160 3c. Type **118** 65 40
161 3c. "Makiwara" (karate training) 60 50
162 3c. "Kumite" exercise 55 50

121 "Miyara Dunchi" (old Ryukyuan Residence)

1964. Ancient Buildings Protection Week.
163 **121** 3c. multicoloured 40 30

122 Bingata "snake" (textile design)

123 Boy Scouts, Badge and Shuri Gate

1964. New Year.
164 **122** 1½c. multicoloured 45 35

1965. 10th Anniv of Ryukyuan Boy Scouts.
165 **123** 3c. multicoloured 50 40

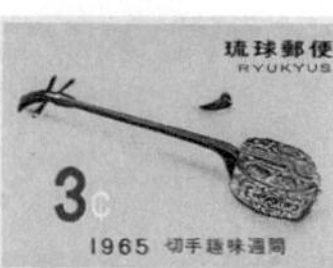
124 "Samisen" (musical instrument)

1965. Philatelic Week.
166 **124** 3c. multicoloured 50 40

125 Stadium

1965. Completion of Onoyama Sports Ground.
167 **125** 3c. multicoloured 30 25

126 Kin Power Station

127 I.C.Y. Emblem and "Globe"

1965. Completion of Kin Power Plant.
168 **126** 3c. multicoloured 30 25

1965. International Co-operation Year and 20th Anniv of United Nations.
169 **127** 3c. multicoloured 30 25

128 City Hall, Naha

1965. Completion of Naha City Hall.
170 **128** 3c. multicoloured 30 25

129 Semaruhakogame Turtle

1965. Ryukyuan Turtles. Multicoloured.
171 3c. Type **129** 80 35
172 3c. Taimai or hawksbill turtle 65 35
173 3c. Yamagame or hill tortoise 65 35

132 Bingata "horse" (textile design) **133** Pryer's Woodpecker

1965. New Year.
174 **132** 1½c. multicoloured 30 25

1966. "Natural Monument" (Wildlife). Mult.
175 3c. Type **133** 60 30
176 3c. Sika deer 50 25
177 3c. Dugong 50 25

136 Pacific Swallow **137** Lilies and Ruins

1966. Bird Week.
178 **136** 3c. multicoloured 45 25

1966. Memorial Day (Battle of Okinawa).
179 **137** 3c. multicoloured 30 25

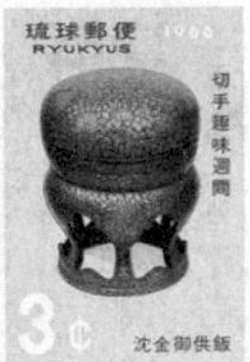

138 University of the Ryukyus **139** Lacquer Box

1966. Transfer of University of the Ryukyus to Government Administration.
180 **138** 3c. multicoloured 30 25

1966. Philatelic Week.
181 **139** 3c. multicoloured 30 25

140 Ryukyuan Tiled House **141** "GRI" Museum, Shuri

1966. 20th Anniv of U.N.E.S.C.O.
182 **140** 3c. multicoloured 30 25

1966. Completion of Government Museum, Shuri.
183 **141** 3c. multicoloured 30 25

142 Nakasone-Tuimya Tomb **143** Bingata "ram" (textile design)

1966. Ancient Buildings Protection Week.
184 **142** 3c. multicoloured 30 25

1966. New Year.
185 **143** 1½c. multicoloured 30 25

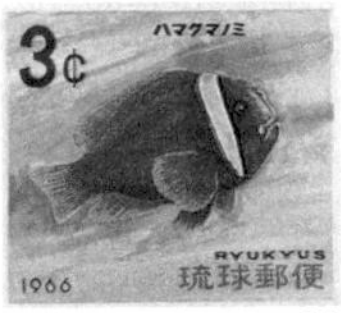

144 Tomato Anemonefish **149** Tsuboya Urn

1966. Tropical Fish. Multicoloured.
186 3c. Type **144** 50 30
187 3c. Blue-spotted boxfish . . . 50 30
188 3c. Long-nosed butterflyfish 50 30
189 3c. Clown triggerfish 50 30
190 3c. Saddle butterflyfish . . . 50 30

1967. Philatelic Week.
191 **149** 3c. multicoloured 40 25

150 Episcopal Mitre **155** Roof Tiles and Emblem

1967. Sea Shells. Multicoloured.
192 3c. Type **150** 40 25
193 3c. Venus comb murex ("Murex (Aranea) triremus") 40 25
194 3c. Chiragra spider conch ("Lambis (Harpago) chiragra") 60 40
195 3c. Great green turban ("Turbo (Olearia) marmoratus") 60 40
196 3c. Bubble conch ("Euprotomus bulla") . . 80 40

1967. International Tourist Year.
197 **155** 3c. multicoloured 30 25

156 Mobile Clinic

1967. 15th Anniv of Anti-T.B. Association.
198 **156** 3c. multicoloured 35 20

157 Hojo Bridge, Enkaku

1967. Ancient Buildings Protection Week.
199 **157** 3c. multicoloured 30 25

158 Bingata "monkey" (textile design) **159** T.V. Tower and Map

1967. New Year.
200 **158** 1½c. multicoloured 30 25

1967. Opening of T.V. Broadcasting Stations in Miyako and Yaeyama.
201 **159** 3c. multicoloured 30 25

160 Dr. Nakachi and Assistant **161** Medicine Case (after Sokei Dana)

1968. 120th Anniv of 1st Ryukyu Vaccination (by Dr. Kijin Nakachi).
202 **160** 3c. multicoloured 30 25

1968. Philatelic Week.
203 **161** 3c. multicoloured 50 30

162 Young Man, Book, Map and Library

1968. Library Week.
204 **162** 3c. multicoloured 45 30

163 Postmen with Ryukyu Stamp of 1948

1968. 20th Anniv of 1st Ryukyu Islands Stamps.
205 **163** 3c. multicoloured 40 30

164 Temple Gate **165** Old Man Dancing

1968. Restoration of Enkaku Temple Gate.
206 **164** 3c. multicoloured 40 30

1968. Old People's Day.
207 **165** 3c. multicoloured 40 30

166 "Mictyris longicarpus"

1968. Crabs. Multicoloured.
208 3c. Type **166** 80 60
209 3c. "Uca dubia" 80 60
210 3c. "Baptozius vinosus" . . . 80 60
211 3c. "Cardisoma carnifex" . . 80 60
212 3c. "Ocypode ceratophthalma" 80 60

171 Saraswati Pavilion **172** Player

1968. Ancient Buildings Protection Week.
213 **171** 3c. multicoloured 35 25

1968. 35th All-Japan East v West Men's Softball Tennis Tournament, Onoyama.
214 **172** 3c. multicoloured 40 25

173 Bingata "cock" (textile design) **174** Boxer

1968. New Year.
215 **173** 1½c. multicoloured 30 20

1969. 20th All-Japan Boxing Championships.
216 **174** 3c. multicoloured 30 25

175 Inkwell Screen **176** UHF Antennae and Map

1969. Philatelic Week.
217 **175** 3c. multicoloured 35 25

1969. Inauguration of Okinawa–Sakishima U.H.F. Radio Service.
218 **176** 3c. multicoloured 30 25

177 Gate of Courtesy **178** "Tug of War" Festival

1969. 22nd All-Japan Formative Education Study Conference, Naha.
219 **177** 3c. multicoloured 30 25

1969. Traditional Religious Ceremonies. Mult.
220 3c. Type **178** 60 40
221 3c. "Hari" canoe race 60 40
222 3c. "Izaiho" religious ceremony 60 40
223 3c. "Ushideiku" dance . . . 60 40
224 3c. "Sea God" dance 60 40

1969. No. 131 surch.
225 ½c. on 3c. multicoloured . . . 15 25

184 Nakamura-Ke

1969. Ancient Buildings Protection Week.
226 **184** 3c. multicoloured 25 20

185 Kyuzo Toyama and Map **186** Bingata "dog and flowers" (textile design)

1969. 70th Anniv of Toyama's Ryukyu–Hawaii Emigration Project.
227 **185** 3c. multicoloured 40 35
No. 227 has "1970" cancelled by bars and "1969" inserted in black.

1969. New Year.
228 **186** 1½c. multicoloured 20 20

187 Sake Flask

1970. Philatelic Week.
229 **187** 3c. multicoloured 35 20

188 "Shushin-Kaneiri"

189 "Chu-nusudu"

190 "Mekarushi"

191 "Nidotichiuchi"

192 "Kokonomaki"

1970. "Kumi-Odori" Ryukyu Theatre. Mult.
230 **188** 3c. multicoloured 70 55
231 **189** 3c. multicoloured 70 55
232 **190** 3c. multicoloured 70 55
233 **191** 3c. multicoloured 70 55
234 **192** 3c. multicoloured 70 55

193 Observatory

194 Noboru Jahana (politician)

1970. Completion of Underwater Observatory, Busena-Misaki, Nago.
240 **193** 3c. multicoloured 30 25

1970. Famous Ryukyuans.
241 **194** 3c. purple 60 60
242 – 3c. green 70 60
243 – 3c. black 60 60
PORTRAITS: No. 242, Saion Gushichan Bunjaku (statesman); 243, Choho Giwan (Regent).

197 "Population

198 "Great Cycad of Une"

1970. Population Census.
244 **197** 3c. multicoloured 25 25

1970. Ancient Buildings Protection Week.
245 **198** 3c. multicoloured 40 25

199 Ryukyu Islands, Flag and Japan Diet

200 "Wild Boar" (Bingata textile design)

1970. Election of Ryukyu Representatives to the Japanese Diet.
246 **199** 3c. multicoloured 85 60

1970. New Year.
247 **200** 1½c. multicoloured 30 25

201 "Jibata" (hand-loom)

202 "Filature" (spinning-wheel)

203 Farm-worker wearing "Shurunnu" Coat and "Kubagasa" Hat

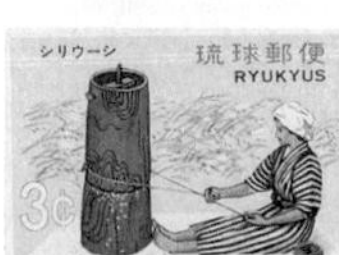

204 Woman using "Shiri-Ushi" (rice huller)

205 Fisherman's "Umi-Fujo" (box) and "Yutui" (bailer)

1971. Ryukyu Handicrafts.
248 **201** 3c. multicoloured 40 30
249 **202** 3c. multicoloured 40 30
250 **203** 3c. multicoloured 40 30
251 **204** 3c. multicoloured 40 30
252 **205** 3c. multicoloured 40 30

206 "Taku" (container)

208 Restored Battlefield, Okinawa

207 Civic Emblem with Old and New City Views

1971. Philatelic Week.
253 **206** 3c. multicoloured 35 25

1971. 50th Anniv of Naha's City Status.
254 **207** 3c. multicoloured 30 25

1971. Government Parks. Multicoloured.
255 3c. Type **208** 30 30
256 3c. Haneji Inland Sea 30 30
257 4c. Yabuchi Island 30 30

211 Deva King, Torinji Temple

212 "Rat" (Bingata textile pattern)

1971. Anicent Buildings Protection Week.
258 **211** 4c. multicoloured 25 25

1971. New Year.
259 **212** 2c. multicoloured 30 20

213 Student-nurse and Candle

214 Islands and Sunset

1971. 25th Anniv of Nurses' Training Scheme.
260 **213** 4c. multicoloured 25 25

1972. Maritime Scenery. Multicoloured.
261 5c. Type **214** 30 70
262 5c. Coral reef (horiz) 30 70
263 5c. Island and short-tailed albatrosses 95 45

217 Dove and Flags of Japan and U.S.A

218 "Yushibin" (ceremonial sake container)

1972. Ratification of Treaty for Return of Ryukyu Islands to Japan.
264 **217** 5c. multicoloured . . . . 40 1·00

1972. Philatelic Week.
265 **218** 5c. multicoloured . . . . 50 1·00

SPECIAL DELIVERY STAMP

E **13** Sea-horse

1951.
E18 E **13** 5y. blue . . . . 30·00 15·00

INDEX

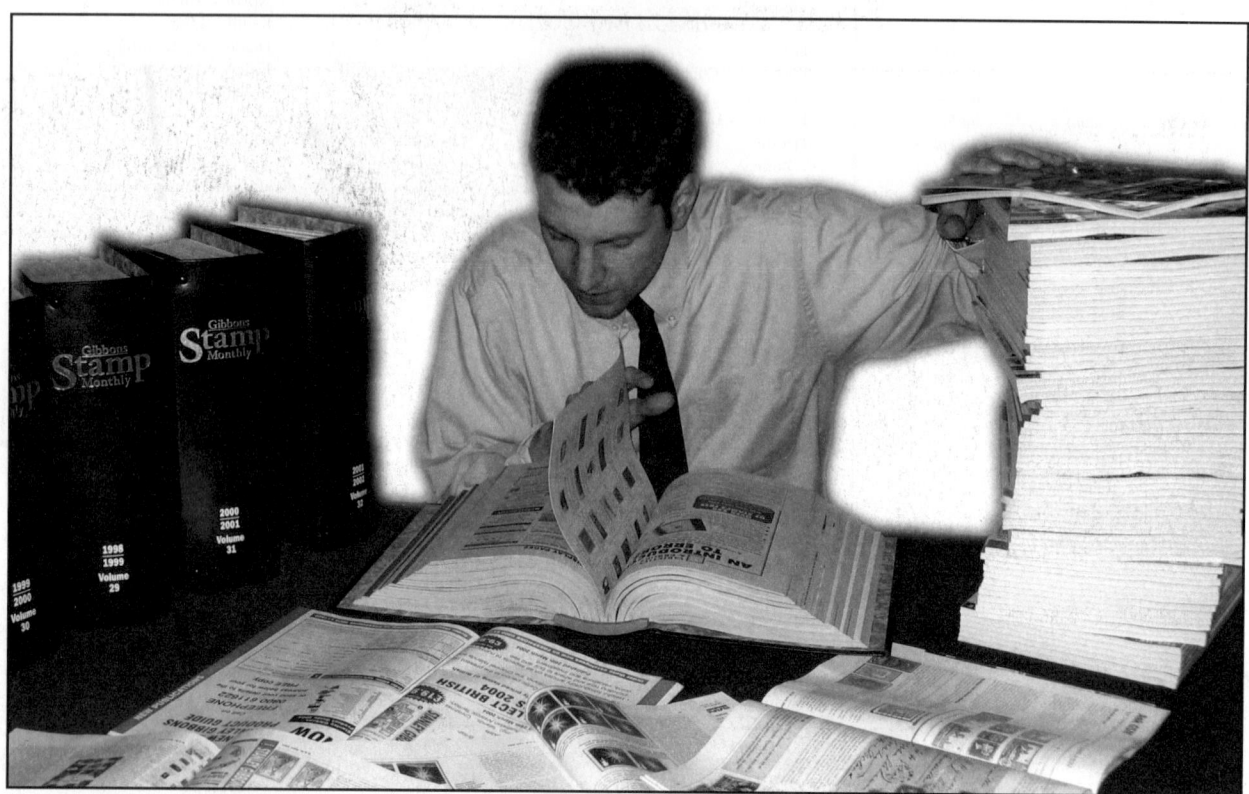